The College Blue Book®

34th Edition

Narrative Descriptions

The College Blue Book®

34th Edition

Narrative Descriptions

MACMILLAN REFERENCE USA

An imprint of Thomson Gale, a part of The Thomson Corporation

THOMSON

GALE

Detroit • New York • San Francisco • New Haven, Conn. • Waterville, Maine • London

The College Blue Book, 34th Edition
Volume 1

Project Editors
Bohdan Romaniuk, Verne Thompson

Editorial
Jessica Boguslawski, Kim Hunt-Lowrance, Amanda Sams, Kristy Swartout

Editorial Support Services
Wayne Fong

Imaging and Multimedia
Randy Bassett, Lezlie Light, Mike Logusz, Dan Newell

Rights and Acquisitions
Dean Dauphinais

Composition and Electronic Prepress
Gary Leach, Evi Seoud

Manufacturing
Rhonda Dover

Product Manager
Jennifer F. Bernardelli

ISBN-13:
978-0-02-866006-6 (set)
978-0-02-866007-3 (vol. 1)

ISBN-10:
0-02-866006-4 (set)
0-02-866007-2 (vol. 1)

ISSN 1082-7064

This book is also available as an e-book
ISBN 13: 978-0-02-866084-4 (set)   ISBN 10: 0-02-866084-6 (set)
Contact your Thomson Gale sales representative for ordering information.

Printed in the United States of America
10 9 8 7 6 5 4 3 2 1

Contents

Preface

The College Blue Book has been a standard, professional reference on higher education since it was first published in 1923. New features have been added during the intervening years to keep pace with the changing needs for information about our educational facilities. The information, especially in the areas of tuition, room and board, enrollment figures, library holdings, is constantly changing. It is difficult to maintain up-to-date figures in these areas, as many schools change tuition and related costs on an ongoing basis. We therefore urge our readers to check directly with the schools for the most current cost information.

Contents of Each Volume

Volume 1: Narrative Descriptions

More than 4,100 colleges in the United States and Canada are fully described. Entrance requirements are detailed and campus facilities and costs are described. A map of each U.S. state and Canadian province is included and each college has a grid index fore easy location. Web sites are also listed.

Volume 2: Tabular Data

Colleges are listed alphabetically by state or province. Information about costs, accreditation, enrollment figures, faculty, and names of the chief administrative officers are given for each school.

Volume 3: Degrees Offered by College and Subject

In Part I, the name of each college is listed alphabetically by state or province, with a list of the subject areas for which degrees are offered. Part II includes an alphabetical listing of subject areas for which degrees are granted by one or more institutions of higher education.

Volume 4: Occupational Education

More than 5,600 schools in the United States that provide occupational or technical training are fully described, offering such information as tuition costs, enrollment figures,

and entrance requirements. Two indexes are provided: an alphabetical listing of schools in the "Index of Occupational Education Schools," in addition to the "Curricula and Areas of Instruction" index.

Volume 5: Scholarships, Fellowships, Grants and Loans

This volume provides a listing of almost 3,500 different sources of financial aid for students wishing to further their education. Split alphabetically into eight broad subject areas (each containing several more specialized concentrations of study), as well as a general section, each listing provides basic information about a specific award, including eligibility requirements, amount of award, and application deadlines.

Volume 6: Distance Learning Programs

Responding to this rapidly growing trend in post-secondary education, this volume features comprehensive profiles of nearly 900 institutions offering distance learning programs within the United States and Canada, providing both basic information as well as in-depth descriptions of certain institutions.

FOR MORE INFORMATION

We are always open to suggestions and recommendations for improvement of The College Blue Book from our readers and from the educational professions. Please write or call:

Editor, The College Blue Book
Macmillan Reference USA
27500 Drake Rd.
Farmington Hills, MI 48331-3535
Phone: (248)699-4253
Toll-free: 800-347-GALE
Fax: (248)699-8075
Email: blue.book@thomson.com
Web site: www.gale.com

The decision to continue education beyond high school years, the selection of a collegiate institution, and the area of study to be pursued are some of the essential experiences necessary for students to determine their futures. Alternatives of choice institutions, work selection, job opportunities, professional training, or even discontinuing any further education are all selective decisions open to the students.

Nearly all students today have opportunities to continue education beyond high school. There are more schools accepting wider ranges of student ability and interest than ever before. This means more effort, more planning, and more personal study in making the college choice.

Self Appraisal

The best place to begin is with oneself. An appraisal with objective, honest answers is necessary. What are the personal potentials as a student? Where has the best performance been? What are the probabilities for improvement? What are the reasons for really wanting to go to college; is it for intellectual development, vocational preparation, or simply to satisfy a desire for status? What are the personal ideas of college? What is expected from the college experience? Have career plans been made? Where are the academic abilities? What subjects are preferred? What is the quality of performance in the preferred areas of study? What is the overall grade average? What is the class rank in high school? In what subject areas is there the greatest interest? What is the quality of work in these areas? Are interests and performance generally consistent? Are the expressed and recorded interests truly and accurately reflecting the inward wishes? What was liked best about the high school experience? Has the college preparatory program been followed in high school? What were the social and cultural experiences during high school years that were most meaningful? What was considered, if anything, to be lacking?

Well-thought-out answers to these and similar questions are helpful. Discussions of such topics with counselors, parents, and teachers increases the probability of success in college selection, attendance, and completion.

The counselor today is an extremely valued resource person available to assist the student. When an effective working team of counselor-student-parent actually exists, the probabilities for the student making selective choices that prove to be the "right" ones are unquestionably the greatest. The better the student and the counselor know one another, the more effective the guidance and counseling program will be. For this to occur, the opportunity for face-to-face student-counselor discussion needs to start in the latter elementary school years and continue through high school and college.

College Appraisals

Research is continuing in the areas of college admissions and student success. The identification and understanding of causes of success and failure need professional study. However, one thing is apparent: the more careful the preparations and planning by the student, the better the chances of college admission and success.

Systemized planning should begin early. The more self-understanding and knowledge about available colleges one has, the better one can plan with corresponding success. Certainly, early in the high school career, students should be reviewing detailed information on colleges and universities with the counselor, noting academic requirements such as scholastic performance, course requirements, costs and other particular qualities of individual collegiate institutions. There is no single one-and-only college for the student. Colleges have personalities just as the students do. There are always several colleges with academic and social climates compatible and acceptable to each student.

Entrance requirements, courses available, costs, size of student body, academic pressure, special programs, geographical location, and specialty schools are some of the considerations of every student in appraising available colleges.

The College Blue Book is dedicated to providing detailed information regarding collegiate institutions throughout the United States and Canada. Students and counselors should browse through *The College Blue Book* and become familiar with the colleges of our country and neighboring Canada. As interest sharpens and narrows, a more selective and in-depth study of institutions should be made.

Where feasible, students should plan visits to college campuses. Campus visiting may begin during the summer between the sophomore and junior years of high school. The best time to be on a college campus, however, is during the regular term with a carefully planned visit in the spring semester of the junior year. Preparatory plans should be made with the high school counselor, reviewing discussions of earlier personal conferences. Advance arrangements should be made with admission officers of the colleges the student expects to visit. The admission officer's name and telephone number will be found in most instances in *The College Blue Book* volume entitled *Tabular Data* . The admissions officer in many cases will want to know whether the student has actually applied for admission and probably the areas the student may plan to major in or other special interests the student has in the particular institution. The student should have prepared a summary of personal data. If possible, high school students should also talk to students of the colleges they wish to attend.

The growth of community colleges has opened up another avenue for students, especially those of limited finances or those who have not decided on their ultimate educational goals. Students will find many of these community colleges offer an excellent opportunity to gain a solid college background. Then one can choose a four-year institution to complete an undergraduate degree.

Any regular high school graduate can find a school that will accept him. Many students need to be encouraged to consider the smaller, private and public colleges of good standing.

Students entering professional training such as engineering or law might consider small schools that have cooperative programs with major universities. A knowledgeable student, through planning and guidance, can avoid unnecessary disappointment. A college career can be quite beneficial to the student who spends three to four years on a small campus and one, two, or three additional years of graduate work on another, larger campus.

Costs

Costs are continuing to rise. Tuition charges as listed herein should be only be used as a guide. It would be wise to check with the institution of interest to be sure of having the most up-to-date information available.

Should the need for financial aid be a factor in selecting a college, a college-bound student should be aware that the best single source of financial assistance and information is the financial aid officer or admission director at the college. It is most important for the student to contact the finance office as early as possible during the student's senior year in high school. A principal source of financial assistance is the major federal undergraduate aid programs. Applications can be obtained from the college. Most colleges and universities also offer financial assistance in several forms including academic and general scholarships, grants-in-aid, student

loans, and part-time work. For more information, see volume 5 of *The College Blue Book* : *Scholarships, Fellowships, Grants, and Loans.*

Two-Year Colleges

Two-year colleges, referred to as junior colleges or community colleges, both public and private, offer programs that prepare students for technical and semiprofessional careers in business and technology fields, and for transfer to senior colleges. There are hundreds of two-year colleges providing comprehensive programs meeting the lower division requirements of virtually all four-year colleges and universities.

There are decided advantages for some students to enroll in a two-year college. Some of these are: less cost, home residence, availability of highly specialized programs, opportunity for the student to mature, a smaller student body, and generally a closer relationship to the faculty. The development of two-year colleges across the nation is one of the most vital forces in education today. The two-year college is neither an extension of high school, nor a little senior college. It has its own identity, sphere of service, and contribution to make to American education. The comprehensive community college is considered one of the best means of accommodating the demands of higher education, embracing the increasing variety of abilities of students graduating from high schools, preparing students in the technological and semiprofessional occupations, and all in an economical manner.

One very important caution needs to be heeded by students enrolling in two- year colleges who are planning to continue their work through a bachelor's program. Students expecting to transfer should very carefully study the requirements of the institution they ultimately plan to attend. In conference with the junior college counselor, a careful review of the planned program should be made to be sure the contemplated courses at the junior college will satisfy the requirements of the senior institution. Students who depart from prescribed courses stated by the senior institution or fail in any of these courses may experience difficulty with admission or normal progress toward the bachelor degree.

Liberal Arts Colleges

The liberal arts colleges offer four years of college and award the Bachelor of Arts and the Bachelor of Science degrees. The curriculum for the first two years is usually broad with an emphasis in the humanities, natural sciences, and cultural history of our society. The last two years may provide a concentration of specific programs such as premedicine or pre-law leading to graduate professional training.

Students considering professional training at the graduate level should keep this in mind as they plan their work at the liberal arts college. Graduate schools in some cases have strict preparatory requirements. Familiarity with these requirements can greatly assist in making the transfer to graduate level without loss of credit or time.

Specialized Institutions

Four-year institutions of technology are examples of the more specialized schools where concentration in a specialty is intensively pursued throughout the college career. Most of these institutions are quite selective in admission practice and may require more high school mathematics and science than most other schools for entrance. These programs lead to engineering degrees in many fields emphasizing technology and science. Recently there has been a broadening of the program of the first two years, but, in general, such a program is not nearly as comprehensive and varied as the liberal arts college. The demand for engineers and scientists with specially developed skills creates great competition for entrance into schools of technology.

There are other specialized institutions such as conservatories of music, seminaries, medical and law schools, institutions specializing in teacher training, or schools of the fine arts, most of which require specialized preparation for entrance.

Universities

The university is generally composed of a number of degree-granting colleges and schools where both bachelor and graduate degrees are grouped under one administrative head. Bachelor degrees at the university may be earned in liberal arts or one of the professions such as engineering or the physical sciences. The university, to some extent, combines what is available at the liberal arts college with the specialized institution. Complete professional training in such areas as law, medicine, and science is available on the university campus.

As a rule, universities have much larger student bodies than colleges. In order to meet the demand, most state universities have established several campuses. Many state universities are very selective in admitting students. This is particularly true for a student who is applying for admission from out-of- state.

Entrance Examinations

There are more applicants than there is room for students on many campuses. As this demand increases, colleges and universities attempt to identify those applicants who are most likely to succeed on their campuses. A quality scholastic record has more influence on acceptance and admission than any other single factor. High school grades predict with better accuracy than any other single measurement what college grades and success will be. The more selective colleges and universities may choose students who come out highest on quantitative criteria, that is, high school scholastic averages combined with test scores. Some institutions have far more applicants (whose scholastic records and test scores are of a maximum quality) than they can accept. In such cases, applicants are sometimes screened and

accepted on the basis of categories according to residence in the state or region, special talents, minority groups, or relationship to alumni. Such procedures are used in an attempt to influence the makeup of the enrollment.

When investigating several schools, one of the most accurate ways for evaluation of an institution is to consider test scores and the high school rank order of the students actually on campus. In many instances this is more informative than the announced admission policies.

College testing is required by many colleges and universities for entering students; some have developed their own tests and over the years have established norms for such tests. Most institutions requiring tests for entrance, however, now use either the test of the American College Testing Program (ACT) or the examinations of the College Entrance Examination Board. The College Entrance Examination Board offers the Preliminary Scholastic Assessment Test/National Merit Scholarship Qualifying Test (PSAT/ NMSQT), the Scholastic Assessment Test I: Reasoning Test (Verbal and Math), and the SAT II: Subject Tests.

Coaching, tutoring, drill, and memorization of facts can do little to improve the scores of the standardized examinations. It is recommended that students not invest time and money in cramming in hopes of improving test scores. Students can do their best preparation in general reading, completing their school assignments, and arriving on the proper day of the test rested and refreshed.

American College testing Assessment (ACT)

The ACT Assessment provided by the American College Testing Program covers four subject areas: English, mathematics, reading, and science reasoning. The ACT test is scored on a range of 1 to 36. The ACT is administered at various test sites in the United States and other countries on specified dates throughout the year. Many colleges and universities recommend that prospective students take the examination early in the senior year.

The tests provide estimates of the students' current level of educational development in knowledge skill areas often required in college work. The ACT college testing program was founded in 1959. It is a nonprofit educational service offering programs in testing and financial need analysis.

Scholastic Assessment Tests (SAT)

The SAT I: Reasoning Test is an examination to measure the verbal and mathematics abilities students have developed both in and out of school. The SAT II: Subject Tests, which some colleges require for admission or placement purposes, consist of 22 separate tests that cover subjects such as literature, history, math, languages, chemistry, biology, and physics. Unlike the SAT I, which measures more general abilities, the SAT II tests measure the students' knowledge of a particular subject and their ability to apply that knowledge. Because of this, students should try to take a SAT II Test as soon as possible after completion of their last course in that subject.

The SAT I and II tests are given on certain dates throughout the year at various test centers in the United States and foreign countries. The combination of the student's academic record and the SAT scores, along with other pertinent secondary information enables admissions officers to estimate how well the student will perform on a particular college campus. The SAT is scored on a scale of 200 minimum to 800 maximum.

Admission Policies

One of the most important considerations in planning is to note when colleges and universities request applications, and to be sure that the applications are complete and forwarded during the appropriate periods. Failure in any way in this procedure will usually automatically disqualify a student from acceptance.

Counselors can provide students with freshman profiles on many of the institutions. Studying *The College Blue Book* , particularly the volume *Tabular Data,* provides a great amount of information on the kind of student bodies found on the campuses of American institutions. There are four general classifications of admission policies. An understanding of these provides valuable guidelines in identifying colleges for consideration.

Most Selective: Many more students apply who meet the announced admission requirements than the college could possibly accept. In addition to requiring outstanding academic records, personal recommendations are required from the high school, and identification of any special qualities of the student should be made known. In this regard, the high school recommendation made to the collegiate institution requires special attention.

Many times, particularly at selective institutions, the high school recommendation actually provides the necessary edge for admission. The recommendation should be on time, carefully providing all information called for, and finally, be precise and detailed in citing personal qualities of the applicant.

All these qualities, however, do not guarantee acceptance. It is strongly recommended that qualified students apply to more than one institution of this type, and that not all applicants should be made to the same type of institution.

Very Selective: Colleges having a very selective procedure in accepting students require ACT scores of 23 or over, or an SAT I score of 600 or more. Students should rank in the top 10 to 12 percent of their high school graduating classes. In addition, strong recommendations stressing particular talents and achievements are necessary. Applications should be made to several institutions of this type.

Selective: An ACT of 20 or over, or an SAT I score of 550 or more is generally necessary. Applications for admission to selective colleges and universities are usually called for in the spring prior to fall entry. In many situations, applications may be submitted in the fall of the senior year with final confirmation to be made after all grades are recorded and confirmed upon graduation from high school.

Least Selective: The fourth classification represents those institutions that will accept students with a C average on their high school work. In certain unusual instances, and under special situations, even the selective institutions may accept students who are in this category, particularly if the scores on the ACT are in the mid-20's or are in excess of 500 on the SAT I. Generally, for acceptance in the less selective schools, students should have an ACT composite score of 17 or a SAT I score of 450.

Entrance examinations may or may not be required. Occasionally, if examinations are required, the results are used for student placement rather than admission. Most high school graduates can meet the requirements for entry and will be accepted. It should be pointed out, however, that in some cases an institution may be liberal in acceptance but carefully screens candidates for graduation. In such an institution, a high attrition rate may occur.

Open Enrollment Policy: This is becoming more common, particularly with the public community colleges. Many students will find this privilege most helpful in continuing their formal education beyond high school. Such a policy enables those students to have a second chance who have failed to perform up to their ability during their high school years. Enrollment and attendance may enable the student to complete a most rewarding vocational program or to later transfer and complete the Bachelor degree, which otherwise might not have been possible because of the deficiency in the high school scholastic record.

A number of colleges and universities, particularly the publicly supported ones, have adopted the open enrollment policy. In response to a feeling of community responsibility, they accept any student who has a diploma (or G.E.D. equivalency certificate) from an accredited high school. This procedure allows students from disadvantaged and minority backgrounds, who might otherwise be denied such an opportunity, to acquire a college education and prepare for a meaningful occupation. These institutions have not lowered their graduation requirements; they have, instead, created opportunities for more students to satisfy these requirements.

Do not assume the erroneous generality that the tougher it is to get into an institution, the better the quality; or the easier to enter, the poorer the school. In fact, there is research evidence available indicating that it may be wise to re-examine some of our traditional notions and attitudes regarding admissions. Not all degree programs on any particular campus are equally outstanding. Every institution has its particular strengths in programs available. Certain institutions are excellent places for some kinds of students in some kinds of programs, but no institution is the one most suited for everyone.

More than 4,100 institutions of higher education, in the United States and Canada, are described in this volume of *The College Blue Book* including universities, senior colleges, two-year colleges, and specialized institutions. The data has been gathered by direct contact with all institutions as well as by inspection of the most current college catalogues available. The arrangement of information is alphabetical by state and by college within each state.

No judgments or evaluations have been made in these entries, but many applicable facts have been presented to assist the reader in making his own.

This edition includes state or regional maps, placing the appropriate map at the beginning of each state section; each college has the map coordinates listed in italics beside the college name.

To assist the user of this volume in making a valid evaluation and comparison of schools, information on each school has been standardized as follows: privately or publicly supported or church-related; level: university, college, graduate school; for whom: men, women, co-educational; type: liberal arts, technological, theological, teacher education, professional; names of degrees granted; fields of specialization, schools, or departments; term system: semester, quarter, trimester; enrollment; size of faculty and faculty-student ratio; regional accreditation; number of volumes in library; cooperative education (work-study) program availability; existence of a ROTC program; entrance requirements; costs per year; collegiate environment; community environment.

There are six regional accrediting commissions covering the United States that evaluate colleges and schools. Generally, these regional agencies grant accreditation to an entire institution of higher learning. They are as follows: Middle States Association of Colleges and Schools, New England Association of Schools and Colleges, North Central Association of Colleges and Schools, Northwest Association of Schools and Colleges, Southern Association of Colleges and Schools, and Western Association of Schools and Colleges.

An important consideration should be mentioned again, one which *The College Blue Book* stresses at several points; the "right" college for Student A may not be the "right" college for Student B. A large enrollment, a small teacher-student ratio, an enormous library and exacting entrance requirements do not necessarily mean that this is the best school. Consider all the factors available: is it in a small, rural college town or a huge, vibrating metropolis; does the student need readily available transportation; does this school have specific programs the student is interested in; if seeking a profession, does the school have professional accreditation; does it have on-campus dormitories, or must the student seek other housing arrangements; do expenses fall within the student's budget; can the entrance requirements be met; if accepted, what are the chances of graduating; if the student is not sure just exactly what is wanted in the way of a career, will this school provide opportunities to find out? This revised edition of *The College Blue Book* has been designed to assist in answering these questions and others that the college bound student may have.

Narrative Descriptions

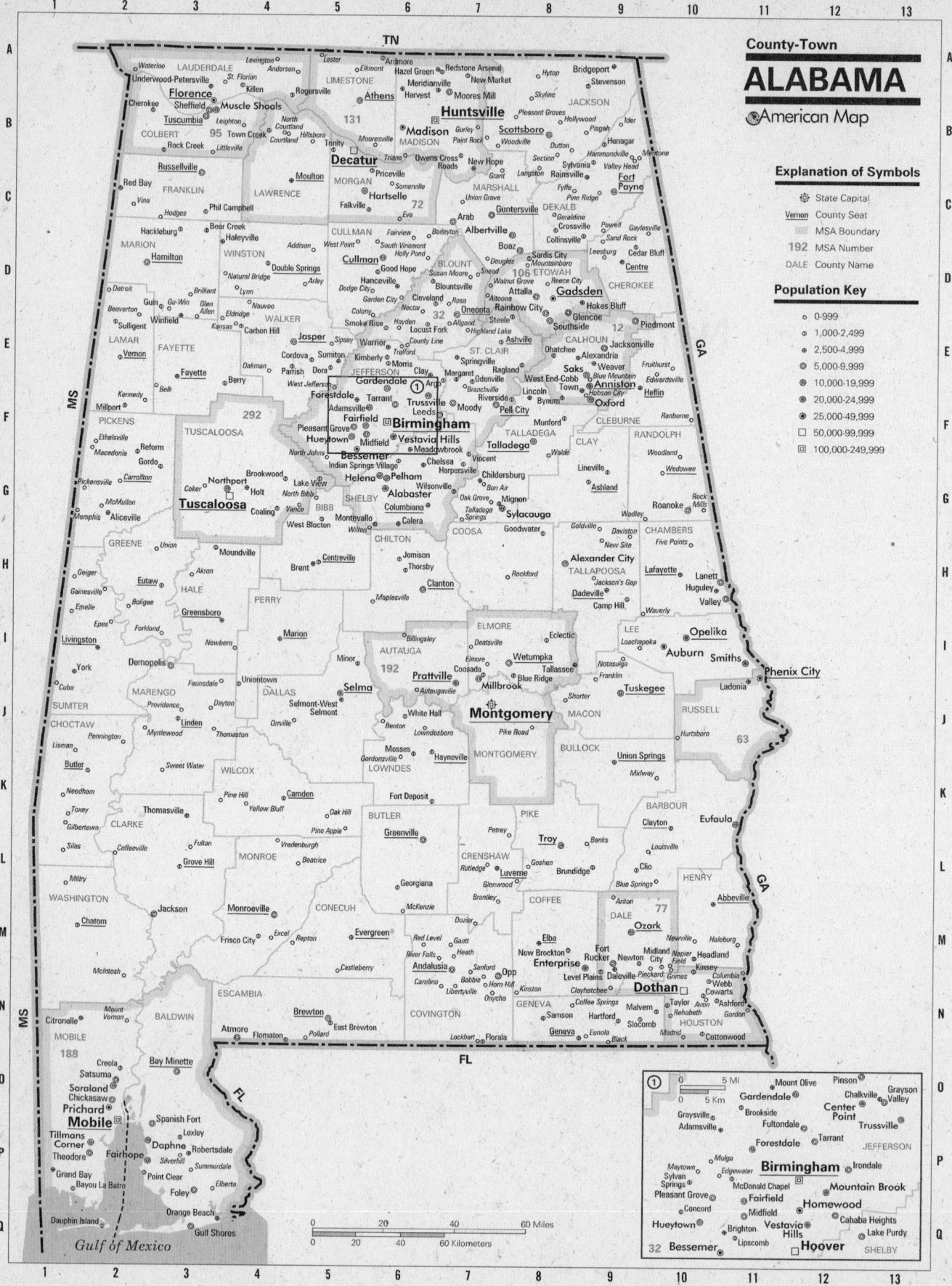

County-Town
ALABAMA
American Map

Explanation of Symbols

- ⊕ State Capital
- Vernon County Seat
- ▨ MSA Boundary
- 192 MSA Number
- DALE County Name

Population Key

- ∘ 0-999
- ⊙ 1,000-2,499
- ⦿ 2,500-4,999
- ⊚ 5,000-9,999
- ⦿ 10,000-19,999
- ● 20,000-24,999
- ◉ 25,000-49,999
- ▫ 50,000-99,999
- ▣ 100,000-249,999

■ **ALABAMA AGRICULTURAL AND MECHANICAL UNIVERSITY** *B-6*
4900 Meridian St.
Huntsville, AL 35811
Tel: (256)372-5000
Free: 800-553-0816
Admissions: (256)372-5245
Fax: (256)372-5881
E-mail: aboyle@asnaam.aamu.edu
Web Site: http://www.aamu.edu/
Description: State-supported, university, coed. Awards bachelor's, master's, and doctoral degrees. Founded 1875. Setting: 2,001-acre suburban campus. Endowment: $22.4 million. Research spending for 2004 fiscal year: $10.7 million. Educational spending for 2005 fiscal year: $3630 per student. Total enrollment: 6,323. 8,295 applied, 45% were admitted. 18% from top 10% of their high school class, 35% from top quarter, 61% from top half. 26 National Merit Scholars, 50 class presidents, 68 valedictorians, 400 student government officers. Full-time: 4,724 students, 52% women, 48% men. Part-time: 367 students, 53% women, 47% men. Students come from 48 states and territories, 45 other countries, 65% from out-of-state, 10% 25 or older, 45% live on campus, 4% transferred in. Retention: 74% of full-time freshmen returned the following year. Core. Calendar: semesters. Academic remediation for entering students, services for LD students, advanced placement, honors program, distance learning, double major, summer session for credit, part-time degree program, adult/continuing education programs, co-op programs, graduate courses open to undergrads. Off campus study at Georgia Institute of Technology, Oakwood College, University of Alabama in Huntsville, Calhoun Community College, Athens State College. ROTC: Army.
Entrance Requirements: Options: Common Application, electronic application, deferred admission. Required: high school transcript, minimum 2.0 high school GPA. Recommended: 1 recommendation, ACT. Entrance: minimally difficult. Application deadline: 7/15. Notification: continuous.
Costs Per Year: Application fee: $10. State resident tuition: $4420 full-time. Mandatory fees: $520 full-time.
Collegiate Environment: Orientation program. Drama-theater group, choral group, marching band, student-run newspaper, radio station. Social organizations: 85 open to all; national fraternities, national sororities, local fraternities, local sororities; 50% of eligible men and 50% of eligible women are members. Most popular organizations: University Voices Gospel Choir, University Choir and Band, Elementary/Early Childhood Club, National Alliance of Business Students. Major annual events: Homecoming, Annual All-Campus Convocation, Women's Week and Men's Week. Student services: health clinic, personal-psychological counseling. Campus security: 24-hour patrols, late night transport-escort service, controlled dormitory access. 2,683 college housing spaces available. On-campus residence required through sophomore year. Options: men-only, women-only housing available. J. F. Drake Learning Resources Center with 507,500 books, 712,000 microform titles, 2,500 serials, 33,000 audiovisual materials, and an OPAC. Operations spending for 2004 fiscal year: $2.6 million. 1,000 computers available on campus for general student use. A campuswide network can be accessed from student residence rooms and from off campus. Staffed computer lab on campus.
Community Environment: Population 180,000. Located in the northern part of the state, within the city limits of Huntsville, on U.S. Highways 231 and 431, which pass through the business section of the city. Huntsville may be reached by bus, and Northwest, American, and Delta airlines Taxi service is available to the community from all transportation centers. (See also University of Alabama Huntsville).

■ **ALABAMA SOUTHERN COMMUNITY COLLEGE** *M-4*
PO Box 2000
Monroeville, AL 36461
Tel: (251)575-3156
E-mail: jhorton@ascc.edu
Web Site: http://www.ascc.edu/
Description: State-supported, 2-year, coed. Part of Alabama College System. Awards certificates, transfer associate, and terminal associate degrees. Founded 1965. Setting: 80-acre rural campus. Educational spending for 2005 fiscal year: $1705 per student. Total enrollment: 1,500. Students come from 5 states and territories, 36% 25 or older. Core. Calendar: semesters. Academic remediation for entering students, advanced placement, honors program, summer session for credit, part-time degree program, adult/continuing education programs.
Entrance Requirements: Open admission. Option: early admission. Required: high school transcript. Placement: ACT COMPASS required; ACT recommended. Entrance: noncompetitive. Application deadline: 9/10. Preference given to district residents.
Collegiate Environment: Drama-theater group, choral group. Most popular organizations: Student Government Association, Ambassadors, Circle K, Phi Theta Kappa, Ethnic Student Society. Major annual events: Homecoming, Spring Fling, Spring theater production. Student services: personal-psychological counseling. Campus security: 24-hour patrols. College housing not available. Dennis Stone Forte Library plus 1 other with 43,000 books and 670 serials. 51 computers available on campus for general student use.
Community Environment: The campus is located in a rural area with a mild climate. The average temperature is 60 degrees. It is an excellent area for hunting and fishing. Part-time employment is available for students.

■ **ALABAMA STATE UNIVERSITY** *J-7*
915 South Jackson St.
Montgomery, AL 36101-0271
Tel: (334)229-4100
Free: 800-253-5037
Admissions: (334)229-4291
Fax: (334)229-4984
E-mail: mpettway@alasu.edu
Web Site: http://www.alasu.edu/
Description: State-supported, comprehensive, coed. Part of Alabama Commission on Higher Education. Awards associate, bachelor's, master's, and doctoral degrees and post-master's certificates. Founded 1867. Setting: 172-acre urban campus. Endowment: $20.5 million. Research spending for 2004 fiscal year: $2.4 million. Educational spending for 2005 fiscal year: $3844 per student. Total enrollment: 5,469. Faculty: 414 (234 full-time, 180 part-time). Student-undergrad faculty ratio is 15:1. 6,202 applied, 67% were admitted. Full-time: 3,958 students, 60% women, 40% men. Part-time: 527 students, 66% women, 34% men. Students come from 39 states and territories, 5 other countries, 35% from out-of-state, 0.04% Native American, 0.2% Hispanic, 97% black, 0.1% Asian American or Pacific Islander, 0.4% international, 17% 25 or older, 43% live on campus, 4% transferred in. Retention: 68% of full-time freshmen returned the following year. Academic

areas with the most degrees conferred: computer and information sciences; business/marketing; security and protective services. Core. Calendar: semesters. Academic remediation for entering students, advanced placement, honors program, double major, summer session for credit, part-time degree program, adult/continuing education programs, co-op programs and internships, graduate courses open to undergrads. Off campus study at National Student Exchange. Study abroad program. ROTC: Army (c), Naval.

Entrance Requirements: Options: Common Application, early admission, deferred admission. Required: high school transcript, minimum 2.0 high school GPA. Recommended: essay, interview, SAT or ACT. Entrance: minimally difficult. Application deadline: 7/30. Notification: continuous.

Costs Per Year: Application fee: $0. State resident tuition: $4008 full-time, $167 per credit hour part-time. Nonresident tuition: $8016 full-time, $334 per credit hour part-time. Full-time tuition varies according to course load. Part-time tuition varies according to course load. College room and board: $3700. College room only: $1980. Room and board charges vary according to board plan and housing facility.

Collegiate Environment: Orientation program. Drama-theater group, choral group, marching band, student-run newspaper. Social organizations: 50 open to all; national fraternities, national sororities; 2% of eligible men and 2% of eligible women are members. Most popular organizations: Student Orientation Services Leaders, Voices of Praise Gospel Choir, Student Government Association, University bands, Commuter Student Association. Major annual events: Founders' Day Convocation, Fall Convocation, Ms. ASU Coronation. Student services: health clinic, personal-psychological counseling. Campus security: 24-hour emergency response devices and patrols, late night transport-escort service, self-defense education, well-lit campus. 2,380 college housing spaces available; 2,369 were occupied in 2003-04. Options: men-only, women-only housing available. Levi Watkins Learning Center with 396,871 books, 2.6 million microform titles, 1,307 serials, 42,319 audiovisual materials, an OPAC, and a Web page. Operations spending for 2004 fiscal year: $1.7 million. 380 computers available on campus for general student use. Computer purchase/lease plans available. A campuswide network can be accessed from off-campus. Staffed computer lab on campus.

Community Environment: Population approximately 200,000. Capital of Alabama. A city known for its stately homes, many of which belong to the antebellum days. The city is also known for its magnolia trees, its southern traditions and culture, and its southern hospitality. Excellent air and highway connections. Montgomery is the home of the Alabama State Capitol Building, the first capital of the Confederacy, the Department of Archives and History, the Montgomery Public Library, Maxwell Air Force Base and Gunter Field, the Air University, and the very large Garrett Coliseum. The South Alabama State Fair, Southern Horse Show, an annual rodeo, an annual indoor track tournament, and other similar functions are held in the Garrett Coliseum. Located here is the First White House of the Confederacy, the home of the Jefferson Davis when Montgomery was the Confederate Capital.

■ **AMERICAN COLLEGE OF COMPUTER & INFORMATION SCIENCES** *F-6*

2101 Magnolia Ave., Ste. 200
Birmingham, AL 35205
Tel: (205)323-6191
Free: 800-767-2427
Fax: (205)328-2229
Web Site: http://www.accis.edu/

Description: Proprietary, comprehensive, coed. Awards bachelor's and master's degrees (offers only distance learning degree programs). Founded 1988. Total enrollment: 13,000. Faculty: 34 (5 full-time, 29 part-time). Students come from 52 states and territories, 120 other countries, 95% from out-of-state, 90% 25 or older. Core. Calendar: continuous. Academic remediation for entering students, advanced placement, accelerated degree program, honors program, distance learning, part-time degree program, external degree program, adult/continuing education programs, graduate courses open to undergrads.

Entrance Requirements: Open admission. Options: Common Application, electronic application. Required: high school transcript. Entrance: moderately difficult. Application deadline: Rolling.

Costs Per Year: Application fee: $40. Tuition: $155 per credit hour part-time. Mandatory fees: $60 per year part-time.

Collegiate Environment: Orientation program. College housing not available.

■ **ANDREW JACKSON UNIVERSITY** *F-6*

10 Old Montgomery Hwy.
Birmingham, AL 35209
Tel: (205)871-9288
Fax: (205)871-9294
E-mail: admissions@aju.edu
Web Site: http://www.aju.edu/

Description: Private, comprehensive, coed. Awards associate, bachelor's, and master's degrees (offers primarily external degree programs). Founded 1994. Total enrollment: 500. Faculty: 50 (all part-time). Student-undergrad faculty ratio is 11:1. Part-time: 200 students, 50% women, 50% men. 95% from out-of-state. Core. Accelerated degree program, independent study, distance learning, summer session for credit, part-time degree program, external degree program, adult/continuing education programs. Off campus study.

Entrance Requirements: Open admission. Required: essay. Required for some: high school transcript, recommendations. Entrance: noncompetitive.

Costs Per Year: Application fee: $75. Tuition: $3900 full-time, $375 per course part-time.

Collegiate Environment: College housing not available.

■ **ATHENS STATE UNIVERSITY** *B-5*

300 North Beaty St.
Athens, AL 35611
Tel: (256)233-8100
Free: 800-522-0272
Admissions: (256)233-8217
Fax: (256)233-8164
Web Site: http://www.athens.edu/

Description: State-supported, upper-level, coed. Part of The Alabama College System. Awards bachelor's degrees. Founded 1822. Setting: 45-acre small town campus. Endowment: $1.5 million. Total enrollment: 2,643. Student-undergrad faculty ratio is 23:1. Students come from 7 states and territories, 0.01% from out-of-state, 3% Native American, 1% Hispanic, 11% black, 1% Asian American or Pacific Islander, 0% international, 62% 25 or older. Academic areas with the most degrees conferred: engineering; business/marketing; library science. Core. Calendar: semesters. Advanced placement, independent study, distance learning, double major, summer session for credit, part-time degree program, adult/continuing education programs, co-op programs and internships. Off campus study at Oakwood College, Alabama Agricultural and Mechanical University, University of Alabama in Huntsville. Study abroad program.

Costs Per Year: Application fee: $30. State resident tuition: $3330 full-time, $111 per semester hour part-time. Nonresident tuition: $6660 full-time, $222 per semester hour part-time. Mandatory fees: $540 full-time, $18 per semester hour part-time. College room only: $900.

Collegiate Environment: Drama-theater group, student-run newspaper. Social organizations: national sororities, local sororities; 14% of eligible men and 19% of eligible women are members. Major annual event: homecoming. Student services: personal-psychological counseling. Campus security: 24-hour emergency response devices, controlled dormitory access. Option: coed housing available. Athens State University Library with 137,233 books, 250 serials, an OPAC, and a Web page. Operations spending for 2004 fiscal year: $128,240. 210 computers available on campus for general student use. A campuswide network can be accessed. Staffed computer lab on campus.

Community Environment: Located in the Tennessee Valley, Athens (population 16,901) is in Limestone County which has an overall population of 54,135. The town is noted for its fine antebellum homes, including the large Founders Hall, built in 1843. With an average temperature of 60 degrees and convenient to air (Huntsville), rail, and within two hours of Nashville and Birmingham, this is a rich, rapidly growing area for farming and industry. State Parks at Wheeler, Wilson Lakes, and Guntersville Reservoir provide for swimming, boating, fishing, and camping.

■ **AUBURN UNIVERSITY** *I-10*

Auburn University, AL 36849
Tel: (334)844-4000
Admissions: (334)844-6444
E-mail: bickecd@auburn.edu
Web Site: http://www.auburn.edu/

Description: State-supported, university, coed. Awards bachelor's, master's, doctoral, and first professional degrees and post-master's certificates. Founded 1856. Setting: 1,875-acre small town campus with easy access to Atlanta and Birmingham. Endowment: $316.1 million. Research spending for 2004 fiscal year: $101.2 million. Total enrollment: 23,333. Faculty: 1,331 (1,176 full-time, 155 part-time). Student-undergrad faculty ratio is 17:1. 14,249 applied, 82% were admitted. 31% from top 10% of their high school class, 55% from top quarter, 85% from top half. 26 National Merit Scholars, 98 valedictorians. Full-time: 17,778 students, 49% women, 51% men. Part-time: 1,476 students, 37% women, 63% men. Students come from 55 states and territories, 59 other countries, 34% from out-of-state, 1% Native American, 2% Hispanic, 8% black, 2% Asian American or Pacific Islander, 1% international, 5% 25 or older, 15% live on campus, 7% transferred in. Retention: 85% of full-time freshmen returned the following year. Academic areas with the most degrees conferred: business/marketing; engineering; education. Core. Calendar: semesters. ESL program, services for LD students, advanced placement, accelerated degree program, honors program, independent study, distance learning, double major, summer session for credit, part-time degree program, adult/continuing education programs, co-op programs and internships, graduate courses open to undergrads. Study abroad program. ROTC: Army, Naval, Air Force.

Entrance Requirements: Options: early admission, international baccalaureate accepted. Required: high school transcript, minimum 2.0 high school GPA, SAT and SAT Subject Tests or ACT. Required for some: minimum 3.0 high school GPA. Entrance: moderately difficult. Application deadlines: 8/1, 11/1 for early decision. Notification: continuous.

Costs Per Year: Application fee: $25. State resident tuition: $5278 full-time. Nonresident tuition: $14,878 full-time. Mandatory fees: $238 full-time. College room and board: $7232. College room only: $3060.

Collegiate Environment: Orientation program. Drama-theater group, choral group, marching band, student-run newspaper, radio station. Social organizations: 300 open to all; national fraternities, national sororities; 20% of eligible men and 32% of eligible women are members. Most popular organizations: Student Government Association, University Program Council, IMPACT (volunteer opportunities). Major annual events: Splash into Spring, Tigermania (Homecoming), Hey Day. Student services: health clinic, personal-psychological counseling. Campus security: 24-hour emergency response devices and patrols, late night transport-escort service, controlled dormitory access. 3,100 college housing spaces available; 3,027 were occupied in 2003-04. Options: coed, men-only, women-only housing available. R. B. Draughon Library plus 2 others with 2.6 million books, 2.5 million microform titles, 23,121 serials, 219,454 audiovisual materials, an OPAC, and a Web page. Operations spending for 2004 fiscal year: $12 million. 1,722 computers available on campus for general student use. A campus-wide network can be accessed from student residence rooms and from off campus. Staffed computer lab on campus.

Community Environment: Auburn (population 32,000) is located on U.S. 29 and Interstate 85, 55 miles east of Montgomery, 120 miles southeast of Birmingham, and 120 miles southwest of Atlanta, Georgia. Auburn University is the pride of the city. With the many churches in the area there is a cultural atmosphere which makes for pleasant living. Chewacla State Park is nearby for swimming and picnicking. The city has two well-equipped parks, a country club and 2 public courses for golf, a stadium for athletic games and many facilities for intramural sports including fields, swimming pools, racquetball and tennis courts, and a student activities building. Azaleas and camellias may be seen on the grounds of the university and many of the beautiful homes.

■ AUBURN UNIVERSITY MONTGOMERY *J-7*
PO Box 244023
Montgomery, AL 36124-4023
Tel: (334)244-3000
Admissions: (334)244-3667
Fax: (334)244-3795
Web Site: http://www.aum.edu/

Description: State-supported, comprehensive, coed. Part of Auburn University. Awards bachelor's, master's, and doctoral degrees and post-master's certificates. Founded 1967. Setting: 500-acre suburban campus. Endowment: $21.2 million. Research spending for 2004 fiscal year: $284,823. Educational spending for 2005 fiscal year: $5544 per student. Total enrollment: 5,128. Faculty: 305 (186 full-time, 119 part-time). Student-undergrad faculty ratio is 16:1. 814 applied, 98% were admitted. Full-time: 2,702 students, 64% women, 36% men. Part-time: 1,598 students, 66% women, 34% men. Students come from 35 states and territories, 21 other countries, 3% from out-of-state, 1% Native American, 1% Hispanic, 33% black, 2% Asian American or Pacific Islander, 0.5% international, 26% 25 or older, 12% live on campus. Academic areas with the most degrees conferred: business/marketing; personal and culinary services; health professions and related sciences. Core. Calendar: semesters. Academic remediation for entering students, ESL program, services for LD students, advanced placement, accelerated degree program, self-designed majors, honors program, independent study, distance learning, double major, summer session for credit, part-time degree program, adult/continuing education programs, co-op programs and internships, graduate courses open to undergrads. Off campus study at Huntingdon College, Alabama State University, Faulkner University. Study abroad program. ROTC: Army, Air Force (c).

Entrance Requirements: Options: Peterson's Universal Application, electronic application, deferred admission. Required: high school transcript, SAT or ACT. Entrance: moderately difficult. Application deadline: Rolling. Notification: continuous.

Costs Per Year: Application fee: $25. State resident tuition: $4410 full-time, $147 per semester hour part-time. Nonresident tuition: $13,230 full-time, $441 per semester hour part-time. Mandatory fees: $230 full-time, $5 per semester hour part-time, $40 per term part-time. Full-time tuition and fees vary according to course load. College room and board: $4890. College room only: $2400. Room and board charges vary according to housing facility.

Collegiate Environment: Orientation program. Drama-theater group, choral group, student-run newspaper. Social organizations: 66 open to all; national fraternities, national sororities; 5% of eligible men and 4% of eligible women are members. Most popular organizations: Student Government Association, Baptist campus ministries, International Student Association, African-American Student Alliance. Major annual events: homecoming, AUM Fest, Mardi Gras Parade. Student services: health clinic, personal-psychological counseling. Campus security: 24-hour emergency response devices and patrols, student patrols, late night transport-escort service, controlled dormitory access. 962 college housing spaces available; 665 were occupied in 2003-04. No special consideration for freshman housing applicants. Option: coed housing available. Auburn University Montgomery Library with 312,110 books, 2.4 million microform titles, 2,044 serials, 24,888 audiovisual materials, an OPAC, and a Web page. Operations spending for 2004 fiscal year: $1.9 million. 285 computers available on campus for general student use. A campuswide network can be accessed from student residence rooms and from off campus. Staffed computer lab on campus.

Community Environment: See Alabama State University.

■ BEVILL STATE COMMUNITY COLLEGE *E-5*
PO Box 800
Sumiton, AL 35148
Tel: (205)648-3271
Admissions: (205)932-3221
Web Site: http://www.bscc.edu/

Description: State-supported, 2-year, coed. Part of Alabama College System. Awards certificates, transfer associate, and terminal associate degrees. Founded 1969. Setting: 23-acre rural campus with easy access to Birmingham. Educational spending for 2005 fiscal year: $1344 per student. Total enrollment: 4,327. Full-time: 2,465 students, 62% women, 38% men. Part-time: 1,862 students, 66% women, 34% men. Students come from 4 states and territories, 0.2% Native American, 0.3% Hispanic, 12% black, 0.4% Asian American or Pacific Islander, 0% international, 33% 25 or older. Retention: 64% of full-time freshmen returned the following year. Core. Calendar: semesters. Academic remediation for entering students, services for LD students, advanced placement, honors program, summer session for credit, part-time degree program, adult/continuing education programs, co-op programs. Off campus study at University of Alabama at Birmingham, Wallace State Community College, Shelton State Community College, Northwest Alabama State Technical College.

Entrance Requirements: Open admission. Options: early admission, deferred admission. Required: high school transcript. Placement: ACT AS-SET required; ACT required for some. Entrance: noncompetitive. Application deadline: Rolling.

Collegiate Environment: Choral group. Most popular organizations: Student LPN Club, Phi Beta Lambda, campus ministries. Major annual events: Homecoming, Field Day, Christmas concert. Student services: personal-psychological counseling. 31,690 books and 192 serials. Operations spending for 2004 fiscal year: $799,871. 65 computers available on campus for general student use.

Community Environment: The Sumiton and Jasper Campuses are in urban areas. The Fayette and Hamilton Campuses are in small towns.

■ **BIRMINGHAM-SOUTHERN COLLEGE** *F-6*

900 Arkadelphia Rd.
Birmingham, AL 35254
Tel: (205)226-4600
Free: 800-523-5793
Admissions: (205)226-4696
Fax: (205)226-3074
E-mail: admissions@bsc.edu
Web Site: http://www.bsc.edu/

Description: Independent Methodist, comprehensive, coed. Awards bachelor's and master's degrees. Founded 1856. Setting: 196-acre urban campus. Endowment: $123.6 million. Educational spending for 2005 fiscal year: $8011 per student. Total enrollment: 1,411. Faculty: 137 (100 full-time, 37 part-time). Student-undergrad faculty ratio is 12:1. 2,217 applied, 63% were admitted. 30% from top 10% of their high school class, 59% from top quarter, 84% from top half. 7 National Merit Scholars, 28 valedictorians. Full-time: 1,294 students, 56% women, 44% men. Part-time: 30 students, 57% women, 43% men. Students come from 31 states and territories, 22 other countries, 25% from out-of-state, 0.2% Native American, 1% Hispanic, 7% black, 3% Asian American or Pacific Islander, 0.3% international, 1% 25 or older, 79% live on campus, 3% transferred in. Retention: 83% of full-time freshmen returned the following year. Academic areas with the most degrees conferred: business/marketing; English; visual and performing arts; interdisciplinary studies. Core. Calendar: 4-1-4. Advanced placement, self-designed majors, honors program, independent study, double major, summer session for credit, part-time degree program, internships, graduate courses open to undergrads. Off campus study at University of Alabama at Birmingham, Samford University, Miles College. Study abroad program. ROTC: Army (c), Air Force (c).

Entrance Requirements: Options: Peterson's Universal Application, Common Application, electronic application, early admission, early action, deferred admission, international baccalaureate accepted. Required: essay, high school transcript, minimum 2.0 high school GPA, 1 recommendation, SAT or ACT. Recommended: interview. Required for some: interview. Entrance: moderately difficult. Application deadline: Rolling. Notification: continuous.

Costs Per Year: Application fee: $25. Comprehensive fee: $28,135 includes full-time tuition ($20,425), mandatory fees ($630), and college room and board ($7080). College room only: $5000. Part-time tuition: $867 per credit hour.

Collegiate Environment: Orientation program. Drama-theater group, choral group, student-run newspaper, radio station. Social organizations: 70 open to all; national fraternities, national sororities; 44% of eligible men and 51% of eligible women are members. Most popular organizations: Southern Volunteer Services, Student Conservancy, Residence Hall Association. Major annual events: homecoming, Outreach Day, Entertainment Festival/Southern Comfort. Student services: health clinic, personal-psychological counseling. Campus security: 24-hour emergency response devices and patrols, late night transport-escort service, controlled dormitory access, vehicle safety inspection. 1,500 college housing spaces available; 1,122 were occupied in 2003-04. On-campus residence required through senior year. Options: men-only, women-only housing available. Charles Andrew Rush Learning Center/N. E. Miles Library with 232,330 books, 34,552 microform titles, 949 serials, 31,471 audiovisual materials, an OPAC, and a Web page. Operations spending for 2004 fiscal year: $853,400. 156 computers available on campus for general student use. A campuswide network can be accessed from student residence rooms and from off campus. Staffed computer lab on campus.

Community Environment: See Birmingham Southern College.

■ **BISHOP STATE COMMUNITY COLLEGE** *P-2*

351 North Broad St.
Mobile, AL 36603-5898
Tel: (251)690-6801
Admissions: (251)690-6419
Fax: (251)438-5403
Web Site: http://www.bscc.cc.al.us/

Description: State-supported, 2-year, coed. Part of Alabama College System. Awards certificates, transfer associate, and terminal associate degrees. Founded 1965. Setting: 9-acre urban campus. Total enrollment: 4,883. Student-undergrad faculty ratio is 14:1. 689 applied, 100% were admitted. Full-time: 2,381 students, 66% women, 34% men. Part-time: 2,502 students, 67% women, 33% men. Students come from 9 states and territories, 4% from out-of-state, 1% Native American, 1% Hispanic, 63% black, 1% Asian American or Pacific Islander, 0.02% international, 51% 25 or older, 12% transferred in. Core. Calendar: semesters. Academic remediation for entering students, services for LD students, summer session for credit, part-time degree program, adult/continuing education programs, co-op programs and internships.

Entrance Requirements: Open admission. Options: Common Application, early admission, deferred admission. Required: high school transcript. Entrance: noncompetitive. Application deadline: Rolling. Notification: continuous until 9/17.

Costs Per Year: Application fee: $0. State resident tuition: $1728 full-time, $72 per credit hour part-time. Nonresident tuition: $3456 full-time, $144 per credit hour part-time. Mandatory fees: $432 full-time, $18 per credit hour part-time.

Collegiate Environment: Drama-theater group, choral group, student-run radio station. Social organizations: 24 open to all. Most popular organizations: Student Government Association, Health Occupations Students of America, Phi Beta Lambda, Phi Theta Kappa, Vocational Industrial Clubs of America. Major annual event: Homecoming. Student services: health clinic. Campus security: 24-hour emergency response devices and patrols. College housing not available. Minnie Slade Bishop Library with 56,687 books, 5 microform titles, 265 serials, and 8,607 audiovisual materials. 96 computers available on campus for general student use. Staffed computer lab on campus.

Community Environment: See University of South Alabama.

■ **CALHOUN COMMUNITY COLLEGE** *B-5*

PO Box 2216
Decatur, AL 35609-2216
Tel: (256)306-2500
Admissions: (256)306-2595
Fax: (256)306-2877
Web Site: http://www.calhoun.edu/

Description: State-supported, 2-year, coed. Part of Alabama College System. Awards certificates, transfer associate, and terminal associate degrees. Founded 1965. Setting: suburban campus. Educational spending for 2005 fiscal year: $1088 per student. Total enrollment: 9,452. 5,088 applied, 78% were admitted. Students come from 9 states and territories, 16 other countries, 1% from out-of-state, 2% Native American, 2% Hispanic, 19% black, 1% Asian American or Pacific Islander, 0.2% international, 38% 25 or older. Core. Calendar: semesters. Academic remediation for entering students, ESL program, services for LD students, advanced placement, accelerated degree program, independent study, distance learning, summer session for credit, part-time degree program, adult/continuing education programs, co-op programs.

Entrance Requirements: Open admission except for nursing, dental services programs. Required for some: high school transcript, SAT or ACT. Entrance: noncompetitive. Application deadline: Rolling. Notification: continuous.

Costs Per Year: Application fee: $0. State resident tuition: $3040 full-time, $71 per semester hour part-time. Nonresident tuition: $5312 full-time, $142 per semester hour part-time. Mandatory fees: $768 full-time, $24 per semester hour part-time.

Collegiate Environment: Drama-theater group, choral group, student-run newspaper. Social organizations: 22 open to all. Most popular organizations: Student Government Association, Black Students Alliance, Phi Theta Kappa, BACCHUS/SADD, VICA. Major annual events: homecoming, Spring Fest, comedy club. Student services: personal-psychological counseling. Campus security: 24-hour patrols. College housing not available. Brewer Library plus 2 others with 36,699 books, 65,454 microform titles, 202 serials, 23,948 audiovisual materials, an OPAC, and a Web page. Operations spending for 2004 fiscal year: $495,698. 182 computers available on campus for general student use. A campuswide network can be accessed.

■ **CENTRAL ALABAMA COMMUNITY COLLEGE** *H-8*

PO Box 699
Alexander City, AL 35011-0699
Tel: (256)234-6346
Fax: (256)234-0384
Web Site: http://www.cacc.cc.al.us/

Description: State-supported, 2-year, coed. Part of Alabama College System. Awards certificates, transfer associate, and terminal associate degrees. Founded 1965. Setting: 100-acre small town campus. Research spending for 2004 fiscal year: $34,245. Total enrollment: 1,790. Students come from 6 states and territories, 0.2% Native American, 1% Hispanic, 25% black, 0.4% Asian American or Pacific Islander, 52% 25 or older. Core. Calendar: semesters. Academic remediation for entering students, services for LD students, advanced placement, distance learning, summer session for credit, part-time degree program, adult/continuing education programs, co-op programs and internships.

Entrance Requirements: Open admission. Options: Common Application, early admission. Required: high school transcript. Required for some: 3 recommendations, interview, SAT or ACT. Entrance: noncompetitive. Application deadline: 9/9.

Collegiate Environment: Orientation program. Drama-theater group, choral group, student-run radio station. Social organizations: 6 open to all. Most popular organizations: Cultural Unity, Baptist Campus Ministry, Student Government Association, Phi Theta Kappa. Major annual events: Fall Fest, Spring Fest. Student services: personal-psychological counseling. Campus security: evening security. College housing not available. Thomas D. Russell Library with 35,000 books and 455 serials. Operations spending for 2004 fiscal year: $235,461. 70 computers available on campus for general student use. A campuswide network can be accessed from off-campus. Staffed computer lab on campus.

Community Environment: Alexander City (population 13,145) is recognized as a city with great civic pride and a sound business climate. It is a pivotal point of transportation: 78 miles southeast of Birmingham, 55 miles northeast of Montgomery, 123 miles southwest of Atlanta, and 70 miles northwest of Columbus, GA. Childersburg is strategically located on Highway 280, 35 miles southeast of Birmingham, 76 miles north of Montgomery, and 42 miles southwest of Anniston. Both campuses are located in one of the South's principal industrial areas. Industries are diversified yet bolstered by the large payrolls of two leading textile corporations and a leading paper products company. Electrical energy, various foundries, emerging high tech companies, and many small businesses comprise the economic base of the College's service area. Both cities are favored with a mild climate year round, with outstanding recreational and sports facilities. In Alexander City, Lake Martin is the focus of boating, swimming, fishing, and camping. In Childersburg, Logan Martin Lake and Lay Lake allow for sports and recreational activities.

■ **CHATTAHOOCHEE VALLEY COMMUNITY COLLEGE** *I-11*
2602 College Dr.
Phenix City, AL 36869-7928
Tel: (334)291-4900
Fax: (334)291-4994
Web Site: http://www.cv.edu/
Description: State-supported, 2-year, coed. Awards certificates, transfer associate, and terminal associate degrees. Founded 1974. Setting: 103-acre small town campus. Endowment: $42,791. Educational spending for 2005 fiscal year: $2255 per student. Total enrollment: 2,034. Students come from 6 states and territories, 10 other countries, 0.05% Native American, 2% Hispanic, 43% black, 1% Asian American or Pacific Islander, 0% international, 45% 25 or older. Retention: 66% of full-time freshmen returned the following year. Core. Calendar: semesters. Academic remediation for entering students, services for LD students, advanced placement, self-designed majors, honors program, distance learning, summer session for credit, part-time degree program, adult/continuing education programs. Off campus study at Troy State University.
Entrance Requirements: Open admission. Options: Common Application, early admission. Required: high school transcript. Entrance: noncompetitive. Application deadline: Rolling. Notification: continuous. Preference given to state residents.
Collegiate Environment: Orientation program. Drama-theater group, choral group. Major annual events: multicultural activities, Blood Drive, Thanksgiving canned food drive. Student services: personal-psychological counseling. Campus security: 24-hour emergency response devices and patrols. College housing not available. Estelle Bain Owens Learning Resource Center and Library with 54,129 books, 4,024 microform titles, 90 serials, 853 audiovisual materials, and a Web page. Operations spending for 2004 fiscal year: $300,841. 55 computers available on campus for general student use. A campuswide network can be accessed from off-campus. Staffed computer lab on campus.

■ **COLUMBIA SOUTHERN UNIVERSITY** *Q-3*
24847 Commercial Ave.
PO Box 3110
Orange Beach, AL 36561
Tel: (251)981-3771
Free: 800-977-8449
Fax: (251)981-3815
Web Site: http://www.colsouth.edu/
Description: Proprietary, comprehensive, coed. Awards associate, bachelor's, and master's degrees (offers only distance learning degree programs). Total enrollment: 2,200. Students come from 54 states and territories, 42 other countries, 95% from out-of-state, 98% 25 or older. Core. Calendar: modular. Academic remediation for entering students, distance learning, part-time degree program, external degree program, adult/continuing education programs.
Entrance Requirements: Open admission. Options: Common Application, electronic application. Required for some: high school transcript. Entrance: noncompetitive. Application deadline: Rolling.
Collegiate Environment: College housing not available. CSU Online Library with a Web page.

■ **COMMUNITY COLLEGE OF THE AIR FORCE** *J-7*
130 West Maxwell Blvd.
Maxwell Air Force Base, AL 36112-6613
Tel: (334)953-2223
Admissions: (334)953-6436
Fax: (334)953-8211
E-mail: bobby.mcalexander@maxwell.af.mil
Web Site: http://www.au.af.mil/au/ccaf/
Description: Federally supported, 2-year, coed. Awards certificates and terminal associate degrees (courses conducted at 125 branch locations worldwide for members of the U.S. Air Force). Founded 1972. Setting: suburban campus. Total enrollment: 351,715. Student-undergrad faculty ratio is 28:1. 24,377 applied, 100% were admitted. Full-time: 351,715 students, 19% women, 81% men. 1% Native American, 0% Hispanic, 15% black, 4% Asian American or Pacific Islander, 0% international, 63% 25 or older. Core. Calendar: continuous. Academic remediation for entering students, advanced placement, independent study, distance learning, adult/continuing education programs, internships.
Entrance Requirements: Open admission. Option: electronic application. Required: high school transcript, recommendations, interview, pass military physical, be of good character, no criminal record, Armed Services Vocational Aptitude Battery. Entrance: noncompetitive. Application deadline: Rolling. Notification: continuous.
Costs Per Year: Application fee: $0.
Collegiate Environment: Major annual events: Armed Forces Day activities, Memorial Day activities, Veteran's Day activities. Student services: legal services, health clinic, personal-psychological counseling. Campus security: 24-hour emergency response devices and patrols. Freshmen given priority for college housing. On-campus residence required in freshman year. Option: coed housing available. Air Force Library Service with 5 million books, 56,654 serials, an OPAC, and a Web page.

■ **CONCORDIA COLLEGE** *J-5*
1804 Green St., PO Box 1329
Selma, AL 36701
Tel: (334)874-5700
Fax: (334)874-3728
Web Site: http://www.concordiaselma.edu/
Description: Independent Lutheran, 4-year, coed. Part of Concordia University System. Awards associate and bachelor's degrees. Founded 1922. Setting: 22-acre small town campus with easy access to Birmingham. Endowment: $3.8 million. Educational spending for 2005 fiscal year: $6243 per student. Total enrollment: 902. 307 applied, 80% were admitted. 4% from top 10% of their high school class, 15% from top quarter, 64% from top half. 6 valedictorians, 10 student government officers. Full-time: 731 students, 61% women, 39% men. Part-time: 171 students, 86% women, 14% men. Students come from 17 states and territories, 6 other countries, 0.1% from out-of-state, 0.1% Native American, 0% Hispanic, 93% black, 0.2% Asian American or Pacific Islander, 3% international, 0.03% 25 or older, 34% live on campus, 8% transferred in. Retention: 95% of full-time freshmen returned the following year. Core. Calendar: semesters. Academic remediation for entering students, services for LD students, advanced placement, honors program, part-time degree program, adult/continuing education programs, internships.
Entrance Requirements: Open admission. Option: deferred admission. Required: high school transcript, minimum 2.0 high school GPA. Recom-

mended: ACT. Placement: ACT recommended. Entrance: minimally difficult. Application deadline: 8/15. Notification: continuous.

Costs Per Year: Application fee: $10. Comprehensive fee: $9814 includes full-time tuition ($6000), mandatory fees ($214), and college room and board ($3600). College room only: $1600. Full-time tuition and fees vary according to course load. Room and board charges vary according to housing facility. Part-time tuition: $235 per credit hour. Part-time mandatory fees: $114 per term. Part-time tuition and fees vary according to course load.

Collegiate Environment: Orientation program. Drama-theater group, choral group, student-run newspaper. Social organizations: 5 open to all. Most popular organizations: Music Ensemble, Rotract Club, Phi Theta Kappa, Spiritual Life, Red Cross. Major annual events: Spiritual Life Extravaganza, Music Ensemble Annual Concert, Homecoming Coronation. Campus security: 24-hour patrols. College housing designed to accommodate 300 students; 306 undergraduates lived in college housing during 2003-04. Freshmen given priority for college housing. Option: coed housing available. Ellwinger-Hunt Learning Resource Center with 60,000 books, 4,585 microform titles, 183 serials, and 4,000 audiovisual materials. Operations spending for 2004 fiscal year: $65,000. 100 computers available on campus for general student use. A campuswide network can be accessed from off-campus. Staffed computer lab on campus.

■ **ENTERPRISE-OZARK COMMUNITY COLLEGE** *M-9*
PO Box 1300
Enterprise, AL 36331-1300
Tel: (334)347-2623
E-mail: gdeas@eocc.edu
Web Site: http://www.eocc.edu/

Description: State-supported, 2-year, coed. Part of Alabama College System. Awards certificates, transfer associate, and terminal associate degrees. Founded 1965. Setting: 100-acre small town campus. Total enrollment: 1,590. Full-time: 866 students, 63% women, 37% men. Part-time: 724 students, 66% women, 34% men. 1% Native American, 4% Hispanic, 21% black, 3% Asian American or Pacific Islander, 0% international, 21% 25 or older. Core. Calendar: semesters. Academic remediation for entering students, ESL program, services for LD students, advanced placement, honors program, summer session for credit, part-time degree program, adult/continuing education programs, internships.

Entrance Requirements: Open admission. Options: early admission, deferred admission. Required: high school transcript. Placement: SAT or ACT recommended. Entrance: noncompetitive. Application deadline: Rolling. Notification: continuous.

Collegiate Environment: Orientation program. Choral group, student-run newspaper. Student services: personal-psychological counseling, women's center. Campus security: security personnel. College housing not available. Snuggs Hall with 45,076 books and 349 serials. 100 computers available on campus for general student use. A campuswide network can be accessed. Staffed computer lab on campus.

Community Environment: Population 20,000, Enterprise has a cosmopolitan atmosphere. Due to its proximity to Fort Rucker, approximately 35% of its populace hail from all states in the union and many foreign countries. It enjoys a mild climate. Bus, railroad and a local airport serve the area. There is excellent shopping downtown, plus three shopping centers in the area. The college has a summer work program arranged with the city and local firms; part-time jobs are also available at Fort Rucker, six miles from Enterprise. The community contains many churches, a community center, and most major social, civic, and service groups as well as many city-sponsored programs for recreation.

■ **FAULKNER UNIVERSITY** *J-7*
5345 Atlanta Hwy.
Montgomery, AL 36109-3398
Tel: (334)386-7324
Free: 800-879-9816
Admissions: (334)386-7200
Fax: (334)386-7268
Web Site: http://www.faulkner.edu/

Description: Independent, comprehensive, coed, affiliated with Church of Christ. Awards associate, bachelor's, master's, and first professional degrees. Founded 1942. Setting: 75-acre urban campus. Endowment: $14 million. Total enrollment: 2,583. Faculty: 138 (88 full-time, 50 part-time). Student-undergrad faculty ratio is 19:1. 574 applied, 60% were admitted. 10% from top 10% of their high school class, 28% from top quarter, 58% from top half. 1 National Merit Scholar, 5 valedictorians. Full-time: 1,598

students, 63% women, 37% men. Part-time: 627 students, 73% women, 27% men. Students come from 25 states and territories, 3 other countries, 12% from out-of-state, 1% Native American, 1% Hispanic, 44% black, 0.4% Asian American or Pacific Islander, 0.2% international, 55% 25 or older, 59% live on campus, 75% transferred in. Retention: 55% of full-time freshmen returned the following year. Academic areas with the most degrees conferred: business/marketing; law/legal studies; education. Core. Calendar: semesters. Academic remediation for entering students, services for LD students, advanced placement, accelerated degree program, freshman honors college, honors program, independent study, distance learning, double major, summer session for credit, part-time degree program, adult/continuing education programs, internships. Off campus study at The University of Alabama at Birmingham, Huntingdon College, Auburn University Montgomery, Troy State University Montgomery. Study abroad program. ROTC: Army (c), Air Force (c).

Entrance Requirements: Options: Peterson's Universal Application, Common Application, electronic application, early admission, deferred admission. Required: high school transcript, minimum 2.0 high school GPA, 2 recommendations, SAT or ACT. Recommended: essay, interview. Entrance: minimally difficult. Application deadline: Rolling.

Costs Per Year: Application fee: $10. Comprehensive fee: $16,825 includes full-time tuition ($11,400), mandatory fees ($25), and college room and board ($5400). College room only: $2500. Part-time tuition: $395 per semester hour.

Collegiate Environment: Orientation program. Drama-theater group, choral group, student-run newspaper. Social organizations: 14 open to all; local fraternities, local sororities, social clubs; 50% of eligible men and 50% of eligible women are members. Most popular organizations: social clubs, student government, Senators, Christians In Action, a cappella chorus. Major annual events: Homecoming, Jamboree, College Bound. Student services: health clinic, personal-psychological counseling. Campus security: 24-hour patrols, late night transport-escort service. 416 college housing spaces available; 351 were occupied in 2003-04. Freshmen given priority for college housing. On-campus residence required through junior year. Options: coed, men-only, women-only housing available. Gus Nichols Library plus 1 other with 143,906 books, 166,390 microform titles, 3,233 serials, 87,120 audiovisual materials, an OPAC, and a Web page. Operations spending for 2004 fiscal year: $1.1 million. 185 computers available on campus for general student use. A campuswide network can be accessed from student residence rooms and from off campus. Staffed computer lab on campus.

Community Environment: See Alabama State University.

■ **GADSDEN STATE COMMUNITY COLLEGE** *D-8*
PO Box 227
Gadsden, AL 35902-0227
Tel: (256)549-8200
Free: 800-226-5563
Admissions: (256)549-8263
Fax: (256)549-8444
E-mail: info@gadsdenstate.edu
Web Site: http://www.gadsdenstate.edu/

Description: State-supported, 2-year, coed. Part of Alabama College System. Awards certificates, transfer associate, and terminal associate degrees. Founded 1965. Setting: 275-acre small town campus with easy access to Birmingham. Endowment: $1.3 million. Educational spending for 2005 fiscal year: $3240 per student. Total enrollment: 5,426. 1,680 applied, 100% were admitted. Full-time: 2,964 students, 55% women, 45% men. Part-time: 2,462 students, 69% women, 31% men. Students come from 4 states and territories, 32 other countries, 4% from out-of-state, 0.4% Native American, 2% Hispanic, 19% black, 2% Asian American or Pacific Islander, 0% international, 34% 25 or older. Core. Calendar: semesters. Academic remediation for entering students, ESL program, services for LD students, advanced placement, summer session for credit, part-time degree program, external degree program, adult/continuing education programs, co-op programs.

Entrance Requirements: Open admission. Options: early admission, deferred admission. Required: high school transcript. Entrance: noncompetitive. Application deadline: Rolling.

Costs Per Year: Application fee: $0. State resident tuition: $90 per credit hour part-time. Nonresident tuition: $161 per credit hour part-time.

Collegiate Environment: Orientation program. Drama-theater group, choral group, student-run newspaper, radio station. Social organizations: 18 open to all. Most popular organizations: Science, Math, and Engineering Club, Student Government Association, Circle K, Phi Beta Lambda, VICA. Major annual events: Get on Board days, G-Day, College Fest. Student services: women's center. Campus security: 24-hour patrols. Option: coed housing available. Meadows Library with 72,915 books and 303 serials. Operations spending for 2004 fiscal year: $551,825. 200 computers available on campus for general student use. A campuswide network can be accessed. Staffed computer lab on campus.

Community Environment: Gadsden (population 53,928) is the county seat, and is the 6th largest in Alabama. Buses and railroads serve the area. Noccalula Falls is located in the City. Industry includes steel, rubber, farm machinery, and cotton mills.

■ **GADSDEN STATE COMMUNITY COLLEGE-AYERS CAMPUS** *F-9*
PO Box 1647
Anniston, AL 36202-1647
Tel: (256)835-5400
Fax: (256)835-5479
Web Site: http://www.gadsdenstate.edu/
Description: State-supported, 2-year, coed. Awards certificates, transfer associate, and terminal associate degrees. Founded 1966. Setting: 25-acre small town campus with easy access to Birmingham. Total enrollment: 1,137. 15% from top 10% of their high school class, 25% from top quarter, 50% from top half. Full-time: 686 students, 63% women, 37% men. Part-time: 451 students, 47% women, 53% men. Students come from 2 states and territories, 0% from out-of-state, 1% Native American, 1% Hispanic, 31% black, 0% Asian American or Pacific Islander, 39% 25 or older. Calendar: semesters. Services for LD students, advanced placement, part-time degree program.
Entrance Requirements: Open admission. Option: deferred admission. Required: high school transcript. Placement: ACT ASSET required. Entrance: noncompetitive. Application deadline: Rolling. Notification: continuous.
Collegiate Environment: Student services: personal-psychological counseling. Campus security: late night transport-escort service. Cain Learning Resource Center with 4,645 books and 120 serials.

■ **GEORGE C. WALLACE COMMUNITY COLLEGE** *N-10*
1141 Wallace Dr.
Dothan, AL 36303-9234
Tel: (334)983-3521
Free: 800-543-2426
Fax: (334)983-3600
E-mail: bbarnes@wallace.edu
Web Site: http://www.wallace.edu/
Description: State-supported, 2-year, coed. Awards certificates, transfer associate, and terminal associate degrees. Founded 1949. Setting: 200-acre rural campus. Endowment: $446,000. Total enrollment: 3,500. Student-undergrad faculty ratio is 7:1. Full-time: 1,919 students, 60% women, 40% men. Part-time: 1,581 students, 69% women, 31% men. Students come from 31 states and territories, 4 other countries, 4% from out-of-state, 0.4% Native American, 1% Hispanic, 27% black, 2% Asian American or Pacific Islander, 0% international, 43% 25 or older. Core. Calendar: semesters. Academic remediation for entering students, advanced placement, summer session for credit, part-time degree program, adult/continuing education programs, co-op programs and internships. Off campus study at University of Alabama at Birmingham, Alabama Aviation and Technical College.
Entrance Requirements: Open admission. Option: early admission. Required: high school transcript. Entrance: noncompetitive. Application deadline: Rolling.
Costs Per Year: Application fee: $0. State resident tuition: $2160 full-time, $72 per credit hour part-time. Nonresident tuition: $4320 full-time, $144 per credit hour part-time. Mandatory fees: $540 full-time, $18 per credit hour part-time.
Collegiate Environment: Drama-theater group, student-run newspaper. Student services: personal-psychological counseling, veteran's counseling/advising. College housing not available. 45,353 books and 399 serials. 75 computers available on campus for general student use. Staffed computer lab on campus.

■ **GEORGE CORLEY WALLACE STATE COMMUNITY COLLEGE** *J-5*
PO Box 2530
Selma, AL 36702-2530
Tel: (334)876-9227
Admissions: (334)876-9305
Fax: (334)876-9250

Web Site: http://www.wccs.edu/
Description: State-supported, 2-year, coed. Part of Alabama College System. Awards certificates, diplomas, transfer associate, and terminal associate degrees. Founded 1966. Setting: small town campus. Total enrollment: 1,758. 650 applied, 100% were admitted. 5% from top 10% of their high school class, 15% from top quarter, 45% from top half. 35% 25 or older. Core. Calendar: semesters. Academic remediation for entering students, services for LD students, advanced placement, independent study, summer session for credit, part-time degree program, adult/continuing education programs.
Entrance Requirements: Open admission. Options: Common Application, early admission, deferred admission. Placement: ACT ASSET required. Entrance: noncompetitive. Application deadline: Rolling.
Costs Per Year: Application fee: $0. State resident tuition: $2160 full-time, $90 per credit hour part-time. Nonresident tuition: $4320 full-time, $180 per credit hour part-time.
Collegiate Environment: Orientation program. Choral group. Campus security: 24-hour patrols. College housing not available. George Corley Wallace Library with 16,598 books, 2,683 microform titles, 2,240 serials, 913 audiovisual materials, an OPAC, and a Web page. Operations spending for 2004 fiscal year: $176,324. 160 computers available on campus for general student use. Staffed computer lab on campus.
Community Environment: Selma, population 35,000 enjoys a temperate climate. Railroad, bus and air service is available for the area. There are many churches in the city, as well as hospitals, a library, and theaters. Gulf beaches are only 180 miles away. Part-time employment is available. Major civic, fraternal and veteran's organizations are represented. A traditional Market Day is held in October.

■ **H. COUNCILL TRENHOLM STATE TECHNICAL COLLEGE** *J-7*
1225 Air Base Blvd.
Montgomery, AL 36116-2699
Tel: (334)420-4200
Admissions: (334)420-4306
Fax: (334)420-4201
Web Site: http://www.trenholmtech.cc.al.us/
Description: State-supported, 2-year, coed. Part of Alabama Department of Post Secondary Education. Awards certificates, diplomas, and terminal associate degrees. Founded 1962. Setting: 78-acre urban campus. Educational spending for 2005 fiscal year: $6619 per student. Total enrollment: 1,403. Student-undergrad faculty ratio is 10:1. 1,204 applied, 42% were admitted. Full-time: 711 students, 50% women, 50% men. Part-time: 692 students, 51% women, 49% men. 0% from out-of-state, 0.1% Native American, 0.4% Hispanic, 60% black, 1% Asian American or Pacific Islander, 0% international, 55% 25 or older. Core. Calendar: semesters. Academic remediation for entering students, services for LD students, advanced placement, summer session for credit, part-time degree program, adult/continuing education programs, co-op programs and internships.
Entrance Requirements: Open admission except nursing program. Option: early admission. Required: high school transcript. Entrance: noncompetitive. Application deadline: Rolling.
Costs Per Year: Application fee: $0. One-time mandatory fee: $35. State resident tuition: $2160 full-time, $71 per hour part-time. Nonresident tuition: $4320 full-time, $142 per hour part-time. Mandatory fees: $540 full-time, $19 per hour part-time.
Collegiate Environment: Orientation program. Major annual events: Career Expo, Graduation, Honors Day. Campus security: 24-hour emergency response devices and patrols. College housing not available. Main library plus 1 other with 2,945 books, 80 serials, 206 audiovisual materials, an OPAC, and a Web page. Operations spending for 2004 fiscal year: $345,429. 443 computers available on campus for general student use. A campuswide network can be accessed. Staffed computer lab on campus.

■ **HERITAGE CHRISTIAN UNIVERSITY** *B-3*
PO Box HCU
Florence, AL 35630
Tel: (256)766-6610
Free: 800-367-3565
Fax: (256)760-0981
E-mail: tharmon@hcu.edu
Web Site: http://www.hcu.edu/
Description: Independent, comprehensive, coed, affiliated with Church of Christ. Awards associate, bachelor's, and master's degrees. Founded 1971. Setting: 43-acre small town campus. Endowment: $3.5 million. Total enroll-

ment: 123. Full-time: 46 students, 11% women, 89% men. Part-time: 63 students, 13% women, 87% men. Students come from 18 states and territories, 9 other countries, 63% from out-of-state, 57% 25 or older, 14% transferred in. Core. Calendar: semesters. Academic remediation for entering students, accelerated degree program, independent study, distance learning, summer session for credit, part-time degree program, external degree program, adult/continuing education programs, internships, graduate courses open to undergrads.

Entrance Requirements: Open admission. Options: electronic application, early admission, deferred admission, international baccalaureate accepted. Required: high school transcript, 3 recommendations. Recommended: interview. Entrance: noncompetitive. Application deadline: Rolling. Notification: continuous until 7/1. Preference given to applicants interested in preaching in Churches of Christ.

Costs Per Year: Application fee: $25. Tuition: $7784 full-time, $278 per hour part-time. Mandatory fees: $480 full-time, $20 per hour part-time. College room only: $1650.

Collegiate Environment: Most popular organizations: Missions Club, Preachers Club, Student Government Association, Christian Ladies Organization. Major annual events: Evangelism Seminar, Area-Wide Singing, Annual Theatre Production. Student services: personal-psychological counseling. 20 college housing spaces available; 18 were occupied in 2003-04. No special consideration for freshman housing applicants. Overton Memorial Library plus 1 other with 51,000 books, 675 microform titles, 309 serials, 12,342 audiovisual materials, and an OPAC. 12 computers available on campus for general student use. A campuswide network can be accessed. Staffed computer lab on campus.

■ **HERZING COLLEGE** *F-6*
280 West Valley Ave.
Birmingham, AL 35209
Tel: (205)916-2800
Fax: (205)916-2807
E-mail: admiss@bhm.herzing.edu
Web Site: http://www.herzing.edu/birmingham/
Description: Proprietary, primarily 2-year, coed. Part of Herzing Institutes, Inc. Awards diplomas, transfer associate, terminal associate, and bachelor's degrees. Founded 1965. Setting: 4-acre urban campus. Educational spending for 2005 fiscal year: $6000 per student. Total enrollment: 600. Full-time: 398 students, 23% women, 77% men. Part-time: 202 students, 39% women, 61% men. Students come from 3 states and territories, 1% from out-of-state, 0% Native American, 3% Hispanic, 41% black, 2% Asian American or Pacific Islander, 0% international, 70% 25 or older, 8% transferred in. Core. Calendar: semesters. Advanced placement, self-designed majors, summer session for credit, external degree program, adult/continuing education programs, co-op programs and internships.
Entrance Requirements: Options: Peterson's Universal Application, early admission, deferred admission. Entrance: minimally difficult. Application deadline: Rolling. Notification: continuous.
Collegiate Environment: Student services: personal-psychological counseling, women's center. Campus security: 24-hour emergency response devices, late night transport-escort service, security guard. College housing not available. 125 computers available on campus for general student use. Staffed computer lab on campus.

■ **HUNTINGDON COLLEGE** *J-7*
1500 East Fairview Ave.
Montgomery, AL 36106-2148
Tel: (334)833-4222
Free: 800-763-0313
Admissions: (334)833-4497
Fax: (334)833-4347
E-mail: admiss@huntingdon.edu
Web Site: http://www.huntingdon.edu/
Description: Independent United Methodist, 4-year, coed. Awards associate and bachelor's degrees. Founded 1854. Setting: 71-acre suburban campus with easy access to Birmingham. Endowment: $32.9 million. Educational spending for 2005 fiscal year: $7926 per student. Total enrollment: 731. 876 applied, 63% were admitted. 24% from top 10% of their high school class, 52% from top quarter, 76% from top half. 19 class presidents, 6 valedictorians, 148 student government officers. Full-time: 669 students, 49% women, 51% men. Part-time: 62 students, 61% women, 39% men. Students come from 19 states and territories, 20% from out-of-state, 1% Native American, 1% Hispanic, 12% black, 1% Asian American or Pacific Islander, 2%

international, 7% 25 or older, 72% live on campus, 5% transferred in. Retention: 66% of full-time freshmen returned the following year. Core. Calendar: semesters. Advanced placement, accelerated degree program, self-designed majors, honors program, independent study, double major, summer session for credit, part-time degree program, adult/continuing education programs, co-op programs and internships. Off campus study at Auburn University Montgomery, Faulkner University, Marine Environmental Sciences Consortium. Study abroad program. ROTC: Army (c), Air Force (c).
Entrance Requirements: Options: Peterson's Universal Application, Common Application, electronic application, early admission, deferred admission, international baccalaureate accepted. Required: high school transcript, minimum 2.25 high school GPA, SAT or ACT. Recommended: 3 recommendations. Required for some: essay, 2 recommendations, interview. Entrance: moderately difficult. Application deadline: Rolling.
Costs Per Year: Application fee: $25. Comprehensive fee: $22,050 includes full-time tuition ($15,250), mandatory fees ($700), and college room and board ($6100). Full-time tuition and fees vary according to class time, reciprocity agreements, and student level. Room and board charges vary according to housing facility. Tuition guaranteed not to increase for student's term of enrollment.
Collegiate Environment: Orientation program. Drama-theater group, choral group, student-run newspaper. Social organizations: 50 open to all; national fraternities, national sororities; 23% of eligible men and 25% of eligible women are members. Most popular organizations: Circle K, SGA, Civitan, International Student Association, BACCHUS. Major annual events: homecoming, Miss Huntingdon, Stallworth Lecture Series. Student services: health clinic, personal-psychological counseling. Campus security: 24-hour emergency response devices and patrols, late night transport-escort service, controlled dormitory access, electronic video surveillance. 488 college housing spaces available; 435 were occupied in 2003-04. Freshmen guaranteed college housing. On-campus residence required through junior year. Option: coed housing available. Houghton Memorial Library with 97,436 books, 50,214 microform titles, 443 serials, 1,811 audiovisual materials, and a Web page. Operations spending for 2004 fiscal year: $575,093. 75 computers available on campus for general student use. A campuswide network can be accessed from student residence rooms and from off campus. Staffed computer lab on campus.
Community Environment: Huntingdon's location in Montgomery gives students easy access to Gulf beaches (3 hours south), mountains (2 hours north), and major metropolitan areas (Birmingham, 90 miles; Atlanta, 180 miles; New Orleans 300 miles). Montgomery, Alabama's capital city, is an historic area rich in tradition and culture.

■ **ITT TECHNICAL INSTITUTE** *F-6*
500 Riverhills Business Park
Birmingham, AL 35242
Tel: (205)991-5410
Admissions: (205)497-5700
Fax: (205)991-5025
Web Site: http://www.itt-tech.edu/
Description: Proprietary, primarily 2-year, coed. Part of ITT Educational Services, Inc. Awards terminal associate and bachelor's degrees. Founded 1994. Setting: suburban campus. Core.
Entrance Requirements: Option: deferred admission. Required: high school transcript, interview, Wonderlic aptitude test. Recommended: recommendations. Entrance: minimally difficult. Application deadline: Rolling. Notification: continuous.
Costs Per Year: Application fee: $100.
Collegiate Environment: Orientation program. Student-run newspaper. Campus security: 24-hour emergency response devices. College housing not available.

■ **J. F. DRAKE STATE TECHNICAL COLLEGE** *B-6*
3421 Meridian St. North
Huntsville, AL 35811-1584
Tel: (256)539-8161; 888-413-7253
Admissions: (256)551-3109
E-mail: clemons@drakestate.edu
Web Site: http://www.drakestate.edu/
Description: State-supported, 2-year, coed. Part of State of Alabama Department of Postsecondary Education. Awards certificates, diplomas, and terminal associate degrees. Founded 1961. Setting: 6-acre urban campus with easy access to Huntsville. Educational spending for 2005 fiscal year: $4580 per student. Total enrollment: 764. Student-undergrad faculty ratio is

21:1. 628 applied, 60% were admitted. 33% from top 10% of their high school class, 48% from top quarter. Full-time: 454 students, 56% women, 44% men. Part-time: 310 students, 39% women, 61% men. 4% from out-of-state, 0.3% Native American, 2% Hispanic, 57% black, 1% Asian American or Pacific Islander, 55% 25 or older. Core. Calendar: semesters. Academic remediation for entering students, services for LD students, part-time degree program, co-op programs and internships.

Entrance Requirements: Open admission. Option: deferred admission. Required: high school transcript. Entrance: noncompetitive. Application deadline: Rolling.

Costs Per Year: Application fee: $0. State resident tuition: $2700 full-time, $72 per semester hour part-time. Nonresident tuition: $5400 full-time, $144 per semester hour part-time. Mandatory fees: $540 full-time, $18 per semester hour part-time.

Collegiate Environment: Orientation program. Student-run newspaper. Social organizations: 4 open to all. Most popular organizations: Phi Beta Lambda, Vocational Industrial Clubs of America. Major annual events: Student Government Election, Miss Drake Pageant. Campus security: 24-hour patrols. College housing not available. 380 computers available on campus for general student use. Staffed computer lab on campus.

■ **JACKSONVILLE STATE UNIVERSITY** *E-9*
700 Pelham Rd. North
Jacksonville, AL 36265-1602
Tel: (256)782-5781
Free: 800-231-5291
Admissions: (256)782-5363
Fax: (256)782-5291
E-mail: mmitchel@jsu.edu
Web Site: http://www.jsu.edu/

Description: State-supported, comprehensive, coed. Awards bachelor's and master's degrees and post-master's certificates. Founded 1883. Setting: 459-acre small town campus with easy access to Birmingham. Endowment: $8.7 million. Research spending for 2004 fiscal year: $1.3 million. Educational spending for 2005 fiscal year: $4302 per student. Total enrollment: 9,110. Faculty: 434 (305 full-time, 129 part-time). Student-undergrad faculty ratio is 21:1. 2,839 applied, 88% were admitted. 3% from top 10% of their high school class, 13% from top quarter, 34% from top half. Full-time: 5,813 students, 56% women, 44% men. Part-time: 1,472 students, 60% women, 40% men. Students come from 43 states and territories, 70 other countries, 17% from out-of-state, 1% Native American, 1% Hispanic, 22% black, 1% Asian American or Pacific Islander, 3% international, 26% 25 or older, 20% live on campus, 10% transferred in. Retention: 68% of full-time freshmen returned the following year. Academic areas with the most degrees conferred: education; business/marketing; security and protective services. Core. Calendar: semesters. Academic remediation for entering students, services for LD students, advanced placement, accelerated degree program, honors program, independent study, distance learning, double major, summer session for credit, part-time degree program, adult/continuing education programs, co-op programs and internships, graduate courses open to undergrads. ROTC: Army.

Entrance Requirements: Options: Peterson's Universal Application, early admission, deferred admission. Required: high school transcript, SAT or ACT. Entrance: minimally difficult. Application deadline: Rolling. Notification: continuous.

Costs Per Year: Application fee: $20. State resident tuition: $4040 full-time, $169 per credit hour part-time. Nonresident tuition: $8080 full-time, $338 per credit hour part-time. College room and board: $3258. College room only: $1680. Room and board charges vary according to board plan and housing facility.

Collegiate Environment: Orientation program. Drama-theater group, choral group, marching band, student-run newspaper, radio station. Social organizations: 97 open to all; national fraternities, national sororities, local fraternities, local sororities; 10% of eligible men and 10% of eligible women are members. Most popular organizations: Student Government Association, Archaeology Club, Campus Fellowship Clubs, Computer Science Club, Biology Club. Major annual events: Homecoming, Parents' Day, Jax Jamboree. Student services: health clinic, personal-psychological counseling. Campus security: 24-hour emergency response devices and patrols, student patrols, late night transport-escort service, night security officer in female residence halls. 1,511 college housing spaces available; 1,316 were occupied in 2003-04. No special consideration for freshman housing applicants. Options: coed, men-only, women-only housing available. Houston Cole Library with 685,991 books, 1.4 million microform titles, 14,376 serials, 35,636

audiovisual materials, an OPAC, and a Web page. Operations spending for 2004 fiscal year: $2.7 million. 330 computers available on campus for general student use. A campuswide network can be accessed from student residence rooms and from off campus. Staffed computer lab on campus.

Community Environment: Population 10,000, Jacksonville is relatively small and free from the many distractions of a large city. The community is easily accessible by good roads and is 6 miles from Fort McClellan (a military installation), 12 miles from Anniston, 22 miles from Gadsden, 75 miles from Birmingham, and 100 miles from Atlanta, GA. The climate is pleasant.

■ **JAMES H. FAULKNER STATE COMMUNITY COLLEGE** *O-3*
1900 Hwy. 31 South
Bay Minette, AL 36507
Tel: (251)580-2100
Free: 800-231-3752
Admissions: (251)580-2152
Fax: (251)580-2285
E-mail: pduck@faulknerstate.edu
Web Site: http://www.faulknerstate.edu/

Description: State-supported, 2-year, coed. Part of Alabama College System. Awards certificates, transfer associate, and terminal associate degrees. Founded 1965. Setting: 105-acre small town campus. Educational spending for 2005 fiscal year: $4278 per student. Total enrollment: 3,067. Student-undergrad faculty ratio is 15:1. Full-time: 1,925 students, 59% women, 41% men. Part-time: 1,142 students, 64% women, 36% men. 3% from out-of-state, 1% Native American, 1% Hispanic, 13% black, 0.5% Asian American or Pacific Islander, 0% international, 39% 25 or older, 9% live on campus. Calendar: semesters. Academic remediation for entering students, services for LD students, advanced placement, honors program, part-time degree program, adult/continuing education programs, co-op programs and internships.

Entrance Requirements: Open admission. Options: early admission, deferred admission. Required: high school transcript. Entrance: noncompetitive. Application deadline: Rolling. Notification: continuous until 8/18.

Costs Per Year: Application fee: $0. State resident tuition: $2790 full-time, $93 per credit hour part-time. Nonresident tuition: $4920 full-time, $164 per credit hour part-time. College room and board: $2931.

Collegiate Environment: Orientation program. Drama-theater group, choral group, student-run newspaper. Social organizations: national fraternities. Most popular organizations: Student Government Association, Pow-Wow Leadership Society, Phi Theta Kappa, Association of Computational Machinery, Phi Beta Lambda. Major annual events: Back-to-School Luau and Dance, Spring Fling, Homecoming Week activities. Student services: personal-psychological counseling. Campus security: 24-hour patrols, controlled dormitory access. Options: men-only, women-only housing available. Austin R. Meadows Library with 53,100 books, 1,949 microform titles, 200 serials, 2,513 audiovisual materials, and an OPAC. 208 computers available on campus for general student use. A campuswide network can be accessed. Staffed computer lab on campus.

■ **JEFFERSON DAVIS COMMUNITY COLLEGE** *N-5*
PO Box 958
Brewton, AL 36427-0958
Tel: (251)867-4832
Fax: (251)809-0178
Web Site: http://www.jdcc.edu/

Description: State-supported, 2-year, coed. Awards certificates, transfer associate, and terminal associate degrees. Founded 1965. Setting: 100-acre small town campus. Total enrollment: 1,442. Full-time: 908 students, 55% women, 45% men. Part-time: 534 students, 64% women, 36% men. Students come from 8 states and territories, 13% from out-of-state, 3% Native American, 1% Hispanic, 30% black, 0.5% Asian American or Pacific Islander, 0% international, 30% 25 or older. Calendar: semesters. Academic remediation for entering students, services for LD students, advanced placement, honors program, summer session for credit, part-time degree program, adult/continuing education programs.

Entrance Requirements: Open admission. Option: early admission. Required: high school transcript. Placement: ACT COMPASS required. Entrance: noncompetitive. Application deadline: Rolling.

Collegiate Environment: Orientation program. Drama-theater group. Student services: personal-psychological counseling. 926 books and 330 serials. 40 computers available on campus for general student use.

■ JEFFERSON STATE COMMUNITY COLLEGE *F-6*
2601 Carson Rd.
Birmingham, AL 35215-3098
Tel: (205)853-1200
Fax: (205)856-8547
Web Site: http://www.jeffstateonline.com
Description: State-supported, 2-year, coed. Part of Alabama College System. Awards certificates, transfer associate, and terminal associate degrees. Founded 1965. Setting: 234-acre suburban campus. Total enrollment: 7,173. Student-undergrad faculty ratio is 21:1. Full-time: 3,129 students, 57% women, 43% men. Part-time: 4,044 students, 65% women, 35% men. Students come from 28 states and territories, 61 other countries, 1% from out-of-state, 0.3% Native American, 1% Hispanic, 21% black, 2% Asian American or Pacific Islander, 2% international, 36% 25 or older, 8% transferred in. Core. Calendar: semesters: Academic remediation for entering students, services for LD students, advanced placement, honors program, independent study, distance learning, summer session for credit, part-time degree program, adult/continuing education programs, internships. ROTC: Army (c), Air Force (c).
Entrance Requirements: Open admission except for allied health programs. Options: electronic application, early admission, deferred admission. Required for some: high school transcript. Entrance: noncompetitive. Application deadline: Rolling. Notification: continuous.
Costs Per Year: Application fee: $0. State resident tuition: $2130 full-time, $71 per semester hour part-time. Nonresident tuition: $4260 full-time, $143 per semester hour part-time. Mandatory fees: $930 full-time, $31 per semester hour part-time.
Collegiate Environment: Drama-theater group, choral group, student-run newspaper, radio station. Social organizations: 23 open to all. Most popular organizations: Student Government Association, Phi Theta Kappa, Baptist Campus Ministries, Jefferson State Ambassadors, Students in Free Enterprise (SIFE). Major annual events: Black History Month Program, Spring Fling, Jeff Fest. Student services: women's center. Campus security: 24-hour patrols. College housing not available. James B. Allen Library plus 1 other with 77,015 books, 7,569 microform titles, 242 serials, 3,349 audiovisual materials, and an OPAC.
Community Environment: See University of Alabama Birmingham.

■ JUDSON COLLEGE *I-4*
302 Bibb St.
PO Box 120
Marion, AL 36756
Tel: (334)683-5100
Free: 800-447-9472
Admissions: (334)683-5110
Fax: (334)683-5158
E-mail: mscotto@judson.edu
Web Site: http://www.judson.edu/
Description: Independent Baptist, 4-year, women only. Awards bachelor's degrees. Founded 1838. Setting: 80-acre rural campus with easy access to Birmingham. Endowment: $13.5 million. Educational spending for 2005 fiscal year: $9138 per student. Total enrollment: 331. Student-undergrad faculty ratio is 9:1. 280 applied, 76% were admitted. 28% from top 10% of their high school class, 56% from top quarter, 72% from top half. Full-time: 257 students. Part-time: 74 students. Students come from 23 states and territories, 4 other countries, 29% from out-of-state, 0% Native American, 2% Hispanic, 15% black, 0.3% Asian American or Pacific Islander, 1% international, 26% 25 or older, 60% live on campus, 5% transferred in. Retention: 64% of full-time freshmen returned the following year. Academic areas with the most degrees conferred: biological/life sciences; psychology; history. Core. Calendar: semesters plus 2-month term. Academic remediation for entering students, advanced placement, accelerated degree program, self-designed majors, honors program, independent study, distance learning, double major, summer session for credit, part-time degree program, external degree program, adult/continuing education programs, internships. Off campus study. Study abroad program. ROTC: Army (c).
Entrance Requirements: Options: Peterson's Universal Application, Common Application, electronic application, early admission, deferred admission, international baccalaureate accepted. Required: high school transcript, minimum 2.0 high school GPA, 2 recommendations, interview, SAT or ACT. Recommended: essay. Entrance: moderately difficult. Application deadline: Rolling. Notification: continuous.
Costs Per Year: Application fee: $30. Comprehensive fee: $17,090 includes full-time tuition ($9900) and college room and board ($7190). Part-time tuition: $322 per semester hour.

Collegiate Environment: Orientation program. Drama-theater group, choral group, marching band, student-run newspaper. Social organizations: 29 open to all. Most popular organizations: Student Government Association, campus ministries, choir, Ambassadors, Science Club. Major annual events: Parents' Day, Christmas Tea, Rose Sunday. Student services: personal-psychological counseling. Campus security: 24-hour emergency response devices and patrols, late night transport-escort service, controlled dormitory access. 264 college housing spaces available; 215 were occupied in 2003-04. No special consideration for freshman housing applicants. On-campus residence required through senior year. Option: women-only housing available. Bowling Library with 57,783 books, 2,035 microform titles, 7,376 serials, 7,248 audiovisual materials, an OPAC, and a Web page. Operations spending for 2004 fiscal year: $266,356. 60 computers available on campus for general student use. A campuswide network can be accessed. Staffed computer lab on campus.

■ LAWSON STATE COMMUNITY COLLEGE *F-6*
3060 Wilson Rd., SW
Birmingham, AL 35221-1798
Tel: (205)925-2515
Admissions: (205)929-6361
Fax: (205)929-6316
Web Site: http://www.lawsonstate.edu/
Description: State-supported, 2-year, coed. Part of Alabama College System. Awards certificates, transfer associate, and terminal associate degrees. Founded 1949. Setting: 30-acre urban campus. Total enrollment: 3,371. Student-undergrad faculty ratio is 16:1. 1,738 applied, 50% were admitted. Full-time: 1,740 students, 67% women, 33% men. Part-time: 1,631 students, 62% women, 38% men. Students come from 2 states and territories, 1% from out-of-state, 0.1% Native American, 0.4% Hispanic, 83% black, 0.4% Asian American or Pacific Islander, 0% international, 33% 25 or older, 2% transferred in. Retention: 68% of full-time freshmen returned the following year. Core. Calendar: semesters. Academic remediation for entering students, freshman honors college, honors program, distance learning, summer session for credit, part-time degree program, adult/continuing education programs, co-op programs and internships.
Entrance Requirements: Open admission except for nursing, medical technology programs. Options: Common Application, early admission, deferred admission. Required: high school transcript. Entrance: noncompetitive. Application deadline: Rolling. Notification: continuous.
Costs Per Year: Application fee: $0. State resident tuition: $2160 full-time, $72 per credit part-time. Nonresident tuition: $4320 full-time, $144 per credit part-time. Mandatory fees: $540 full-time.
Collegiate Environment: Choral group. Campus security: 24-hour emergency response devices and patrols, student patrols. College housing not available. Lawson State Library with 31,998 books, 26,035 microform titles, 170 serials, 506 audiovisual materials, and an OPAC. 140 computers available on campus for general student use. A campuswide network can be accessed. Staffed computer lab on campus.
Community Environment: See University of Alabama - Birmingham.

■ LURLEEN B. WALLACE COMMUNITY COLLEGE *N-7*
PO Box 1418
Andalusia, AL 36420-1418
Tel: (334)222-6591
Web Site: http://www.lbwcc.edu/
Description: State-supported, 2-year, coed. Part of Alabama College System. Awards certificates, transfer associate, and terminal associate degrees. Founded 1969. Setting: 200-acre small town campus. Total enrollment: 1,490. Students come from 6 states and territories, 5% from out-of-state, 0.3% Native American, 1% Hispanic, 18% black, 0.5% Asian American or Pacific Islander, 27% 25 or older. Core. Calendar: semesters. Academic remediation for entering students, services for LD students, advanced placement, freshman honors college, summer session for credit, part-time degree program, co-op programs.
Entrance Requirements: Open admission. Options: early admission, deferred admission. Required: high school transcript. Placement: ACT recommended. Entrance: noncompetitive. Application deadline: Rolling. Notification: continuous until 9/15.
Collegiate Environment: Orientation program. Drama-theater group, student-run newspaper. Most popular organizations: Student Government Association, College Ambassadors, Phi Theta Kappa, Mu Alpha Theta, Christian Student Union. Major annual events: Blue and White Day, Miss LBW Pageant. Student services: personal-psychological counseling.

Campus security: 24-hour emergency response devices. College housing not available. Lurleen B. Wallace Library with 35,278 books and 133 serials. 45 computers available on campus for general student use. Staffed computer lab on campus.

■ **MARION MILITARY INSTITUTE** *I-4*
1101 Washington St.
Marion, AL 36756
Tel: (334)683-2306
Admissions: 800-664-1842
Fax: (334)683-2380
Web Site: http://www.marionmilitary.org/
Description: Independent, 2-year, coed. Awards transfer associate and terminal associate degrees. Founded 1842. Setting: 130-acre small town campus. Endowment: $1.2 million. Total enrollment: 213. 269 applied, 84% were admitted. 25% from top 10% of their high school class, 50% from top quarter, 96% from top half. Students come from 35 states and territories, 3 other countries, 8% from out-of-state, 0% 25 or older, 97% live on campus. Core. Calendar: semesters. Academic remediation for entering students, part-time degree program. Off campus study at Judson College. ROTC: Army, Air Force.
Entrance Requirements: Options: Common Application, deferred admission. Required: high school transcript, minimum 2.0 high school GPA, 2 recommendations, SAT or ACT. Recommended: interview, minimum SAT score of 920 or ACT score of 19. Entrance: moderately difficult. Application deadline: 8/30.
Collegiate Environment: Orientation program. Drama-theater group, choral group, marching band, student-run newspaper. Social organizations: 12 open to all. Most popular organizations: Swamp Foxes, White Knights, marching band, Drama Club, Scabbard and Blade. Major annual events: Military Ball, Gymkhana, Red Carpet Day. Student services: health clinic, personal-psychological counseling. Campus security: night patrols by trained security personnel. Options: men-only, women-only housing available. Baer Memorial Library with 36,000 books, 140 serials, and 8,471 audiovisual materials. 21 computers available on campus for general student use. A campuswide network can be accessed. Staffed computer lab on campus.
Community Environment: See Judson College.

■ **MILES COLLEGE** *F-6*
PO Box 3800
Birmingham, AL 35208
Tel: (205)929-1000
Free: 800-445-0708
Admissions: (205)929-1657
E-mail: admissions@miles.edu
Web Site: http://www.miles.edu/
Description: Independent Christian Methodist Episcopal, 4-year, coed. Awards bachelor's degrees. Founded 1905. Setting: 35-acre small town campus. Endowment: $10.7 million. Research spending for 2004 fiscal year: $1.2 million. Educational spending for 2005 fiscal year: $3900 per student. Total enrollment: 1,716. Student-undergrad faculty ratio is 20:1. 806 applied, 54% were admitted. Full-time: 1,628 students, 55% women, 45% men. Part-time: 88 students, 66% women, 34% men. Students come from 25 states and territories, 14% from out-of-state, 0% Native American, 0% Hispanic, 98% black, 0% Asian American or Pacific Islander, 0% international, 20% 25 or older, 36% live on campus, 6% transferred in. Retention: 78% of full-time freshmen returned the following year. Academic areas with the most degrees conferred: business/marketing; foreign languages and literature; public administration and social services. Core. Calendar: semesters. Academic remediation for entering students, services for LD students, accelerated degree program, honors program, summer session for credit, part-time degree program, adult/continuing education programs, co-op programs and internships. Off campus study at BACHE: UAB, Samford, Birmingham Southern. ROTC: Army (c), Air Force (c).
Entrance Requirements: Open admission. Recommended: ACT, ACT ASSET. Required for some: high school transcript. Placement: ACT, ACT ASSET recommended. Entrance: noncompetitive. Application deadline: 8/23. Notification: continuous.
Costs Per Year: Comprehensive fee: $10,962 includes full-time tuition ($5408), mandatory fees ($418), and college room and board ($5136). College room only: $3000. Full-time tuition and fees vary according to course load, location, and program. Room and board charges vary according to housing facility and location. Part-time tuition: $227 per credit. Part-time mandatory fees: $209 per term.

Collegiate Environment: Orientation program. Drama-theater group, choral group, marching band, student-run newspaper. Social organizations: 20 open to all; national fraternities, national sororities, local fraternities, local sororities; 18% of eligible men and 22% of eligible women are members. Most popular organizations: choir, Education Club, Student Government Association, Phi Beta Lambda Business Club, Communications Club. Major annual events: Founders' Day, Homecoming, M-Day. Student services: health clinic, personal-psychological counseling. Campus security: 24-hour emergency response devices and patrols. 624 college housing spaces available; all were occupied in 2003-04. No special consideration for freshman housing applicants. Options: coed, men-only, women-only housing available. C.A. Kirkeedoll Learning Resources Center with 180,000 books, 250 serials, 4,126 audiovisual materials, and an OPAC. Operations spending for 2004 fiscal year: $262,000. 50 computers available on campus for general student use. Staffed computer lab on campus.
Community Environment: See University of Alabama - Birmingham.

■ **NORTHEAST ALABAMA COMMUNITY COLLEGE** *C-9*
PO Box 159
Rainsville, AL 35986-0159
Tel: (256)228-6001
Web Site: http://www.nacc.edu/
Description: State-supported, 2-year, coed. Part of Alabama College System. Awards certificates, transfer associate, and terminal associate degrees. Founded 1963. Setting: 100-acre rural campus. Total enrollment: 2,015. 456 applied, 100% were admitted. Full-time: 978 students, 61% women, 39% men. Part-time: 1,037 students, 68% women, 32% men. Students come from 3 states and territories, 2% from out-of-state, 5% Native American, 1% Hispanic, 2% black, 0.2% Asian American or Pacific Islander, 0% international, 32% 25 or older. Retention: 62% of full-time freshmen returned the following year. Core. Academic remediation for entering students, services for LD students, advanced placement, accelerated degree program, honors program, summer session for credit, part-time degree program, adult/continuing education programs.
Entrance Requirements: Open admission. Options: early admission, deferred admission. Placement: ACT ASSET, ACT COMPASS required. Entrance: noncompetitive. Application deadline: Rolling. Notification: continuous.
Costs Per Year: Application fee: $0. State resident tuition: $2700 full-time, $90 per credit hour part-time. Nonresident tuition: $4860 full-time, $161 per credit hour part-time. Part-time tuition varies according to location.
Collegiate Environment: Orientation program. Drama-theater group, choral group. Social organizations: 7 open to all. Most popular organizations: Baptist Campus Ministry, theater, SGA, Spectrum Art Club, choral group. Major annual events: Spring Fling, Fall Dance, graduation. Student services: personal-psychological counseling. Campus security: 24-hour emergency response devices and patrols, late night transport-escort service. College housing not available. 45,000 books, 142 serials, and an OPAC. 50 computers available on campus for general student use. Staffed computer lab on campus.
Community Environment: Rainsville, population 5,000, is in a mountainous area with a very pleasant temperate climate. The town is 58 miles from commercial airline service, six miles from Interstate 59, and eight miles from rail service. Protestant churches, and hospitals in Fort Payne and Scottsboro service the community. Recreational activities include good fishing, boating, camping, and hiking at nearby state parks.

■ **NORTHWEST-SHOALS COMMUNITY COLLEGE** *B-3*
PO Box 2545
Muscle Shoals, AL 35662
Tel: (256)331-5200
Admissions: (256)331-5261
Fax: (256)331-5366
Web Site: http://www.nwscc.edu/
Description: State-supported, 2-year, coed. Part of State of Alabama Department of Postsecondary Education. Awards certificates, diplomas, and transfer associate degrees. Founded 1963. Setting: 205-acre small town campus. Educational spending for 2005 fiscal year: $1586 per student. Total enrollment: 3,380. Student-undergrad faculty ratio is 19:1. 1,576 applied, 69% were admitted. Full-time: 2,132 students, 57% women, 43% men. Part-time: 1,248 students, 67% women, 33% men. Students come from 8 states and territories, 5 other countries, 1% from out-of-state, 2% Native American, 1% Hispanic, 12% black, 0.1% Asian American or Pacific Islander, 0% international, 40% 25 or older, 2% live on campus. Core. Calendar:

semesters. Academic remediation for entering students, advanced placement, accelerated degree program, honors program, summer session for credit, part-time degree program, adult/continuing education programs, co-op programs and internships. ROTC: Army.

Entrance Requirements: Open admission except for nursing program. Option: Common Application. Required: high school transcript. Entrance: noncompetitive. Application deadline: Rolling.

Costs Per Year: Application fee: $0. State resident tuition: $2130 full-time, $71 per credit hour part-time. Nonresident tuition: $4260 full-time, $142 per credit hour part-time. Mandatory fees: $750 full-time, $25 per credit hour part-time. College room only: $1675.

Collegiate Environment: Choral group. Social organizations: 20 open to all. Most popular organizations: Student Government Association, Science Club, Phi Theta Kappa, Baptist Campus Ministry, Northwest-Shoals Singers. Major annual events: Homecoming and Dance, Spring Fling, Blood Drive. Student services: personal-psychological counseling. Campus security: 24-hour emergency response devices and patrols. 76 college housing spaces available; all were occupied in 2003-04. Option: coed housing available. Larry W. McCoy Learning Resource Center and James Glasgow Library with 57,827 books, 376 microform titles, 268 serials, and 1,428 audiovisual materials. Operations spending for 2004 fiscal year: $318,050. 620 computers available on campus for general student use. A campuswide network can be accessed from off-campus. Staffed computer lab on campus.

■ **OAKWOOD COLLEGE** *B-6*
7000 Adventist Blvd.
Huntsville, AL 35896
Tel: (256)726-7000
Admissions: (256)726-7354
Fax: (256)726-7404
E-mail: jmccracken@oakwood.edu
Web Site: http://www.oakwood.edu/

Description: Independent Seventh-day Adventist, 4-year, coed. Awards associate and bachelor's degrees. Founded 1896. Setting: 1,200-acre campus. Total enrollment: 1,751. Student-undergrad faculty ratio is 13:1. 1,155 applied, 60% were admitted. 6% from top 10% of their high school class, 21% from top quarter, 48% from top half. Full-time: 1,559 students, 58% women, 42% men. Part-time: 192 students, 53% women, 47% men. Students come from 39 states and territories, 22 other countries, 72% from out-of-state, 0.2% Native American, 0.3% Hispanic, 90% black, 0.1% Asian American or Pacific Islander, 7% international, 15% 25 or older, 68% live on campus, 5% transferred in. Retention: 70% of full-time freshmen returned the following year. Academic areas with the most degrees conferred: business/marketing; biological/life sciences; psychology. Core. Calendar: semesters. Academic remediation for entering students, advanced placement, honors program, double major, part-time degree program, internships. Off campus study at members of the Alabama Center for Higher Education, The University of Alabama in Huntsville. Study abroad program.

Entrance Requirements: Options: Common Application, early action, deferred admission. Required: high school transcript, minimum 2.00 high school GPA, recommendations, SAT or ACT. Required for some: essay. Entrance: minimally difficult. Application deadlines: Rolling, 3/30 for early action. Notification: 4/15 for early action.

Costs Per Year: Application fee: $20. Comprehensive fee: $18,894 includes full-time tuition ($11,374), mandatory fees ($692), and college room and board ($6828). College room only: $2884. Part-time tuition: $490 per hour.

Collegiate Environment: Orientation program. Choral group, student-run newspaper, radio station. Most popular organization: United Student Movement. Major annual events: homecoming, graduation, Youth Motivational Task Force Week. Student services: health clinic, personal-psychological counseling. Campus security: 24-hour patrols, student patrols, late night transport-escort service. On-campus residence required in freshman year. Options: men-only, women-only housing available. Eva B. Dykes Library with 128,000 books, 2,150 microform titles, 610 serials, and 5,135 audiovisual materials. 300 computers available on campus for general student use. A campuswide network can be accessed from student residence rooms and from off campus. Staffed computer lab on campus.

Community Environment: See University of Alabama Huntsville.

■ **PRINCE INSTITUTE OF PROFESSIONAL STUDIES** *J-7*
7735 Atlanta Hwy.
Montgomery, AL 36117-4231
Tel: (334)271-1670
Fax: (334)271-1671

E-mail: admissions@princeinstitute.edu
Web Site: http://www.princeinstitute.edu/

Description: Independent, 2-year, coed. Awards certificates and terminal associate degrees. Setting: suburban campus. Endowment: $6040. Educational spending for 2005 fiscal year: $9600 per student. Total enrollment: 94. Student-undergrad faculty ratio is 15:1. 9 applied, 100% were admitted. Full-time: 56 students, 100% women. Part-time: 38 students, 100% women. 1% from out-of-state, 0% Native American, 0% Hispanic, 17% black, 0% Asian American or Pacific Islander, 0% international, 50% 25 or older.

Entrance Requirements: Required: high school transcript, interview. Entrance: noncompetitive. Application deadline: 10/1.

Costs Per Year: Application fee: $90. Tuition: $8448 full-time. Mandatory fees: $340 full-time.

Collegiate Environment: Student services: personal-psychological counseling. College housing not available.

■ **REID STATE TECHNICAL COLLEGE** *M-5*
PO Box 588
Evergreen, AL 36401-0588
Tel: (251)578-1313
Fax: (251)578-5355
Web Site: http://www.rstc.cc.al.us/

Description: State-supported, 2-year, coed. Part of Alabama College System. Awards certificates, diplomas, and terminal associate degrees. Founded 1966. Setting: 26-acre rural campus. Research spending for 2004 fiscal year: $36,440. Educational spending for 2005 fiscal year: $4386 per student. Total enrollment: 620. 100 applied, 100% were admitted. Full-time: 390 students, 70% women, 30% men. Part-time: 230 students, 65% women, 35% men. Students come from 2 states and territories, 1% from out-of-state, 1% Native American, 1% Hispanic, 54% black, 0% Asian American or Pacific Islander, 55% 25 or older. Calendar: semesters. Academic remediation for entering students, services for LD students, independent study, double major, summer session for credit, part-time degree program, adult/continuing education programs, internships.

Entrance Requirements: Open admission. Options: Common Application, early admission. Required: high school transcript. Placement: ACT ASSET, Ability-To-Benefit Admissions Test required. Entrance: noncompetitive. Application deadline: Rolling.

Collegiate Environment: Orientation program. Student-run newspaper. Social organizations: 1 open to all. Most popular organization: Student Government Association. Major annual events: Challenge Cup Ambassadors, Talent Show. Student services: personal-psychological counseling. Campus security: 24-hour emergency response devices, day and evening security guard. College housing not available. 70 computers available on campus for general student use. A campuswide network can be accessed from off-campus. Staffed computer lab on campus.

■ **REMINGTON COLLEGE-MOBILE CAMPUS** *P-2*
828 Downtowner Loop West
Mobile, AL 36609-5404
Tel: (251)343-8200
Free: 800-866-0850
Fax: (251)343-0577
Web Site: http://www.remingtoncollege.edu/

Description: Proprietary, primarily 2-year, coed. Part of Education America. Awards diplomas, transfer associate, terminal associate, and bachelor's degrees. Setting: 5-acre suburban campus. Total enrollment: 433. Student-undergrad faculty ratio is 16:1. 119 applied, 96% were admitted. Students come from 3 states and territories, 4% from out-of-state, 1% Native American, 1% Hispanic, 47% black, 1% Asian American or Pacific Islander, 0% international, 49% 25 or older. Retention: 90% of full-time freshmen returned the following year. Services for LD students, adult/continuing education programs, co-op programs.

Entrance Requirements: Required: high school transcript, interview, Wonderlic aptitude test. Entrance: noncompetitive.

Costs Per Year: Application fee: $50. Tuition: $34,200 full-time. Mandatory fees: $50 full-time.

Collegiate Environment: Orientation program. Social organizations: 2 open to all. Most popular organizations: Association of Information Technology Professionals, Instrumentation Technology Association. Major annual event: Career Fair. College housing not available.

■ **SAMFORD UNIVERSITY** *F-6*
800 Lakeshore Dr.
Birmingham, AL 35229-0002

Tel: (205)726-2011
Free: 800-888-7218
Admissions: (205)726-3673
Fax: (205)726-2171
E-mail: ppkimrey@samford.edu
Web Site: http://www.samford.edu/
Description: Independent Baptist, university, coed. Awards associate, bachelor's, master's, doctoral, and first professional degrees and post-master's certificates. Founded 1841. Setting: 180-acre suburban campus. Endowment: $261.4 million. Educational spending for 2005 fiscal year: $11,095 per student. Total enrollment: 4,507. Faculty: 425 (278 full-time, 147 part-time). Student-undergrad faculty ratio is 12:1. 2,025 applied, 88% were admitted. 36% from top 10% of their high school class, 66% from top quarter, 86% from top half. 12 National Merit Scholars, 116 valedictorians, 124 student government officers. Full-time: 2,742 students, 64% women, 36% men. Part-time: 199 students, 73% women, 27% men. Students come from 44 states and territories, 17 other countries, 56% from out-of-state, 0.3% Native American, 1% Hispanic, 6% black, 1% Asian American or Pacific Islander, 1% international, 8% 25 or older, 65% live on campus, 4% transferred in. Retention: 85% of full-time freshmen returned the following year. Academic areas with the most degrees conferred: business/marketing; education; communications/journalism. Core. Calendar: 4-1-4. Services for LD students, advanced placement, accelerated degree program, honors program, independent study, distance learning, double major, summer session for credit, part-time degree program, adult/continuing education programs, co-op programs and internships, graduate courses open to undergrads. Off campus study at University of Alabama at Birmingham, Birmingham-Southern College, Miles College, University of Montevallo. Study abroad program. ROTC: Army (c), Air Force.
Entrance Requirements: Options: early admission, deferred admission, international baccalaureate accepted. Required: essay, 1 recommendation, leadership resume, SAT or ACT. Recommended: interview. Required for some: high school transcript. Entrance: moderately difficult. Application deadline: 12/15. Notification: continuous.
Costs Per Year: Application fee: $35. Comprehensive fee: $20,258 includes full-time tuition ($14,642) and college room and board ($5616). College room only: $2860. Full-time tuition varies according to course load. Room and board charges vary according to board plan and housing facility. Part-time tuition: $486 per semester hour. Part-time tuition varies according to course load.
Collegiate Environment: Orientation program. Drama-theater group, choral group, marching band, student-run newspaper, radio station. Social organizations: 102 open to all; national fraternities, national sororities; 24% of eligible men and 37% of eligible women are members. Most popular organizations: student ministries, student government. Major annual events: Step Sing, Homecoming, Spring Fling. Student services: health clinic, personal-psychological counseling, Amnesty International and Circle K. Campus security: 24-hour emergency response devices and patrols, student patrols, late night transport-escort service. 1,860 college housing spaces available; 1,831 were occupied in 2003-04. Freshmen guaranteed college housing. On-campus residence required through sophomore year. Options: men-only, women-only housing available. Samford University Library plus 3 others with 439,760 books, 1.3 million microform titles, 3,724 serials, 14,362 audiovisual materials, an OPAC, and a Web page. Operations spending for 2004 fiscal year: $4 million. 350 computers available on campus for general student use. Computer purchase/lease plans available. A campuswide network can be accessed from student residence rooms. Staffed computer lab on campus.
Community Environment: See University of Alabama Birmingham.

■ **SHELTON STATE COMMUNITY COLLEGE** *G-4*
9500 Old Greensboro Rd.
Tuscaloosa, AL 35405-8522
Tel: (205)391-2211
Admissions: (205)391-2236
Fax: (205)391-2426
Web Site: http://www.sheltonstate.edu/
Description: State-supported, 2-year, coed. Part of Alabama College System. Awards certificates, diplomas, transfer associate, and terminal associate degrees. Founded 1979. Setting: 30-acre small town campus with easy access to Birmingham. Educational spending for 2005 fiscal year: $2710 per student. Total enrollment: 5,754. Student-undergrad faculty ratio is 30:1. 2,201 applied, 100% were admitted. Full-time: 3,363 students, 55% women, 45% men. Part-time: 2,391 students, 51% women, 49% men.

Students come from 11 states and territories, 2% from out-of-state, 0.4% Native American, 1% Hispanic, 29% black, 1% Asian American or Pacific Islander, 0% international, 32% 25 or older, 35% transferred in. Core. Calendar: semesters. Academic remediation for entering students, services for LD students, advanced placement, accelerated degree program, honors program, distance learning, summer session for credit, part-time degree program, adult/continuing education programs. ROTC: Army (c), Air Force (c).
Entrance Requirements: Open admission except for practical nursing, registered nursing, respiratory technician and truck driving technology programs. Option: electronic application. Required: high school transcript. Entrance: noncompetitive. Application deadline: Rolling.
Costs Per Year: Application fee: $0. State resident tuition: $2130 full-time, $71 per credit hour part-time. Nonresident tuition: $4290 full-time, $143 per credit hour part-time. Mandatory fees: $570 full-time, $18 per credit hour part-time.
Collegiate Environment: Orientation program. Drama-theater group, choral group, student-run newspaper. Social organizations: 20 open to all. Most popular organizations: PTK, Student Government Association, African American Cultural Association. Campus security: 24-hour emergency response devices and patrols. College housing not available. Brooks-Cork Library plus 1 other with 50,123 books, 4,771 microform titles, 361 serials, 3,247 audiovisual materials, an OPAC, and a Web page. Operations spending for 2004 fiscal year: $651,801. 150 computers available on campus for general student use. A campuswide network can be accessed from off-campus. Staffed computer lab on campus.

■ **SNEAD STATE COMMUNITY COLLEGE** *D-8*
220 N Walnut St., PO Box 734
Boaz, AL 35957-0734
Tel: (256)593-5120
Fax: (256)593-7180
E-mail: mbucahanan@snead.edu
Web Site: http://www.snead.edu/
Description: State-supported, 2-year, coed. Part of Alabama College System. Awards certificates, transfer associate, and terminal associate degrees. Founded 1898. Setting: 42-acre small town campus with easy access to Birmingham. Endowment: $1.6 million. Students come from 6 states and territories, 1% from out-of-state, 26% 25 or older, 2% live on campus. Core. Calendar: semesters. Academic remediation for entering students, services for LD students, advanced placement, accelerated degree program, self-designed majors, independent study, distance learning, summer session for credit, part-time degree program, adult/continuing education programs, internships.
Entrance Requirements: Open admission. Options: early admission, deferred admission. Required: high school transcript. Required for some: interview. Entrance: noncompetitive. Application deadline: 8/24. Notification: 8/20.
Costs Per Year: Application fee: $0. State resident tuition: $2304 full-time, $72 per semester hour part-time. Nonresident tuition: $4608 full-time, $144 per semester hour part-time. Mandatory fees: $704 full-time, $22 per semester hour part-time.
Collegiate Environment: Choral group, student-run newspaper. Social organizations: 15 open to all. Most popular organizations: Phi Theta Kappa, Snead Agricultural Organization, North American Veterinary Technician Association, Ambassadors, Baptist Campus Ministry. Major annual events: Ham and Biscuit Day, Mocktail Party, Homecoming. Student services: personal-psychological counseling. Campus security: 24-hour patrols, student patrols. 75 college housing spaces available; 36 were occupied in 2003-04. No special consideration for freshman housing applicants. Option: coed housing available. McCain Learning Resource Center with 40,690 books, 19,689 microform titles, 223 serials, 1,699 audiovisual materials, an OPAC, and a Web page. Operations spending for 2004 fiscal year: $265,368. 250 computers available on campus for general student use. A campuswide network can be accessed from off-campus. Staffed computer lab on campus.
Community Environment: Boaz (population 7,500) is located 60 miles north of Birmingham, and has an average temperature of 65 degrees. Employment is available in industry and business. Churches, civic and social organizations are located in the city. Guntersville Lake is ten miles from Boaz. The town is a shopping outlet center, one of the largest in the U.S.

■ **SOUTH UNIVERSITY** *J-7*
5355 Vaughn Rd.
Montgomery, AL 36116-1120

Tel: (334)395-8800
Fax: (334)395-8859
Web Site: http://www.southuniversity.edu/
Description: Proprietary, comprehensive, coed. Awards associate, bachelor's, and master's degrees. Founded 1887. Setting: 4-acre urban campus. Educational spending for 2005 fiscal year: $2857 per student. Total enrollment: 420. Faculty: 37 (14 full-time, 23 part-time). Student-undergrad faculty ratio is 13:1. 5% from top 10% of their high school class, 10% from top quarter, 25% from top half. Full-time: 256 students, 76% women, 24% men. Part-time: 155 students, 75% women, 25% men. 0% from out-of-state, 0% Native American, 1% Hispanic, 67% black, 0.2% Asian American or Pacific Islander, 0.2% international, 51% 25 or older, 21% transferred in. Retention: 50% of full-time freshmen returned the following year. Academic areas with the most degrees conferred: business/marketing; computer and information sciences; law/legal studies. Core. Academic remediation for entering students, double major, summer session for credit, part-time degree program, internships.
Entrance Requirements: Required: high school transcript, interview. Required for some: 3 recommendations, SAT or ACT. Entrance: moderately difficult. Application deadline: Rolling. Notification: continuous.
Costs Per Year: Application fee: $25. Tuition: $11,475 full-time, $2995 per term part-time.
Collegiate Environment: Orientation program. Campus security: 24-hour emergency response devices, evening security guard. College housing not available. South University Library with 17,270 books, 82 serials, 499 audiovisual materials, and an OPAC. Operations spending for 2004 fiscal year: $234,930. 37 computers available on campus for general student use. Staffed computer lab on campus.

■ **SOUTHEASTERN BIBLE COLLEGE** *F-6*
2545 Valleydale Rd.
Birmingham, AL 35244-2083
Tel: (205)970-9200
Admissions: (205)970-9218
Fax: (205)970-9207
E-mail: jdunn@sebc.edu
Web Site: http://www.sebc.edu/
Description: Independent nondenominational, 4-year, coed. Awards bachelor's degrees (associate). Founded 1935. Setting: 10-acre suburban campus. Endowment: $1.1 million. Educational spending for 2005 fiscal year: $3946 per student. Total enrollment: 232. Student-undergrad faculty ratio is 7:1. Full-time: 174 students, 40% women, 60% men. Part-time: 58 students, 36% women, 64% men. Students come from 13 states and territories, 1 other country, 11% from out-of-state, 0.4% Hispanic, 19% black, 0.4% Asian American or Pacific Islander, 26% 25 or older, 19% live on campus, 23% transferred in. Retention: 62% of full-time freshmen returned the following year. Academic areas with the most degrees conferred: theology and religious vocations; education. Core. Calendar: semesters. Academic remediation for entering students, advanced placement, independent study, summer session for credit, part-time degree program, external degree program, adult/continuing education programs, internships.
Entrance Requirements: Options: Common Application, electronic application, early admission, deferred admission. Required: essay, high school transcript, minimum 2.0 high school GPA, 2 recommendations, SAT or ACT. Required for some: interview. Entrance: moderately difficult. Application deadline: 8/1. Notification: continuous until 9/1.
Costs Per Year: Application fee: $20. Tuition: $295 per semester hour part-time.
Collegiate Environment: Orientation program. Choral group. Most popular organizations: Student Council, Student Missions Fellowship, chorale. Major annual events: Missions Conference, Winter Banquet, Urban Emphasis Week. Student services: health clinic, personal-psychological counseling. Campus security: 24-hour emergency response devices, student patrols. 60 college housing spaces available; 39 were occupied in 2003-04. Freshmen given priority for college housing. On-campus residence required in freshman year. Options: men-only, women-only housing available. Gannett-Estes Library with 44,539 books, 2,071 microform titles, 1,022 serials, 2,242 audiovisual materials, an OPAC, and a Web page. Operations spending for 2004 fiscal year: $111,248. 30 computers available on campus for general student use.
Community Environment: See University of Alabama Birmingham.

■ **SOUTHERN CHRISTIAN UNIVERSITY** *J-7*
1200 Taylor Rd.
Montgomery, AL 36117

Tel: (334)387-3877
Free: 800-351-4040
Fax: (334)387-3878
E-mail: rickjohnson@southernchristian.edu
Web Site: http://www.southernchristian.edu/
Description: Independent, university, coed, affiliated with Church of Christ. Awards bachelor's, master's, doctoral, and first professional degrees. Founded 1967. Setting: 9-acre urban campus. Endowment: $750,000. Educational spending for 2005 fiscal year: $3600 per student. Total enrollment: 720. Faculty: 78 (63 full-time, 15 part-time). Student-undergrad faculty ratio is 11:1. Full-time: 310 students, 52% women, 48% men. Part-time: 61 students, 54% women, 46% men. Students come from 48 states and territories, 75% from out-of-state, 0.3% Native American, 4% Hispanic, 32% black, 0.3% Asian American or Pacific Islander, 0% international, 84% 25 or older. Retention: 85% of full-time freshmen returned the following year. Academic area with the most degrees conferred: liberal arts/general studies. Core. Calendar: semesters. Advanced placement, accelerated degree program, distance learning, double major, summer session for credit, part-time degree program, external degree program, adult/continuing education programs, internships.
Entrance Requirements: Open admission. Option: Common Application. Required: high school transcript, minimum 2.0 high school GPA. Entrance: minimally difficult. Application deadline: Rolling.
Costs Per Year: Application fee: $50. Tuition: $6000 full-time, $250 per semester hour part-time.
Collegiate Environment: Orientation program. Student services: personal-psychological counseling. College housing not available. Southern Christian University Library with 80,000 books, 300 microform titles, 1,200 serials, 800 audiovisual materials, an OPAC, and a Web page. Operations spending for 2004 fiscal year: $210,000. 5 computers available on campus for general student use. A campuswide network can be accessed from off-campus. Staffed computer lab on campus.
Community Environment: Southern Christian University is a 9-acre campus located in Montgomery, the capital city of Alabama adjacent to Interstate 85. This city is strategically located in the central part of the state. Montgomery is the fourth largest city in the state in terms of population, offering residential areas, parks and playgrounds, school and universities, museums, a zoo, and the capitol facilities. Montgomery has two major U.S. Air Force installations, as well as a number of historical sites. The city has an abundance of good housing and a variety of employment opportunities.

■ **SOUTHERN UNION STATE COMMUNITY COLLEGE** *G-10*
PO Box 1000, Roberts St.
Wadley, AL 36276
Tel: (256)395-2211
Fax: (256)395-2215
Web Site: http://www.suscc.cc.al.us/
Description: State-supported, 2-year, coed. Part of Alabama College System. Awards certificates, diplomas, transfer associate, and terminal associate degrees. Founded 1922. Setting: rural campus. Total enrollment: 4,500. 33% 25 or older, 6% live on campus. Core. Academic remediation for entering students, services for LD students, advanced placement, summer session for credit, part-time degree program, adult/continuing education programs, co-op programs and internships. ROTC: Air Force (c).
Entrance Requirements: Open admission. Options: Common Application, early admission, deferred admission. Required: high school transcript. Entrance: noncompetitive. Application deadline: Rolling. Notification: continuous.
Collegiate Environment: Drama-theater group, choral group, student-run newspaper. Social organizations: 12 open to all. Most popular organizations: Student Government Association, Phi Theta Kappa, Music Club, National Student Nurses Association, Global Environmental Organization of Students. Major annual events: Homecoming, Spring Fling, Miss Southern Union. Student services: personal-psychological counseling. Campus security: 24-hour patrols, controlled dormitory access. Option: coed housing available. McClintock-Ensminger Library plus 2 others with 90,791 books and 877 serials. 225 computers available on campus for general student use. Staffed computer lab on campus.
Community Environment: Population 746. Located in East Central Alabama approximately 90 miles southwest of Atlanta, and the same distance southeast of Birmingham. Wadley is on Alabama State Highways 22 and 77. Gently rolling farm and woodland, healthful country atmosphere. Easy access to neighboring cities for shopping and recreation. Hospital in Roanoke.

■ SPRING HILL COLLEGE *P-2*

4000 Dauphin St.
Mobile, AL 36608-1791
Tel: (251)380-4000
Free: 800-SHC-6704
Admissions: (251)380-3030
Fax: (251)460-2186
E-mail: admit@shc.edu
Web Site: http://www.shc.edu/

Description: Independent Roman Catholic (Jesuit), comprehensive, coed. Awards associate, bachelor's, and master's degrees. Founded 1830. Setting: 450-acre suburban campus. Endowment: $28.8 million. Educational spending for 2005 fiscal year: $5625 per student. Total enrollment: 1,497. Faculty: 138 (72 full-time, 66 part-time). Student-undergrad faculty ratio is 14:1. 1,190 applied, 80% were admitted. 28% from top 10% of their high school class, 50% from top quarter, 82% from top half. 5 valedictorians. Full-time: 1,174 students, 63% women, 37% men. Part-time: 125 students, 73% women, 27% men. Students come from 37 states and territories, 10 other countries, 54% from out-of-state, 1% Native American, 5% Hispanic, 15% black, 1% Asian American or Pacific Islander, 1% international, 13% 25 or older, 78% live on campus, 3% transferred in. Retention: 84% of full-time freshmen returned the following year. Academic areas with the most degrees conferred: business/marketing; biological/life sciences; communications/journalism. Core. Calendar: semesters. Academic remediation for entering students, services for LD students, advanced placement, accelerated degree program, self-designed majors, honors program, independent study, distance learning, double major, summer session for credit, part-time degree program, adult/continuing education programs, internships. Off campus study at Marine Environmental Sciences Consortium. Study abroad program. ROTC: Army (c), Air Force (c).

Entrance Requirements: Options: Common Application, electronic application, early admission, deferred admission, international baccalaureate accepted. Required: essay, high school transcript, 1 recommendation, SAT or ACT. Recommended: minimum 2.5 high school GPA, interview. Entrance: moderately difficult. Application deadline: 7/15. Notification: continuous.

Costs Per Year: Application fee: $25. Comprehensive fee: $28,678 includes full-time tuition ($19,658), mandatory fees ($1290), and college room and board ($7730). College room only: $4000. Room and board charges vary according to board plan and housing facility. Part-time tuition: $736 per semester hour. Part-time mandatory fees: $42 per semester hour.

Collegiate Environment: Orientation program. Drama-theater group, choral group, student-run newspaper. Social organizations: 30 open to all; national fraternities, national sororities; 14% of eligible men and 23% of eligible women are members. Most popular organizations: Student Government Association, Multicultural Student Union, Circle K, Campus Programming Board, Habitat for Humanity. Major annual events: Fall Formal, Christmas on the Hill, Campus Mardi Gras. Student services: health clinic, personal-psychological counseling. Campus security: 24-hour emergency response devices and patrols, late night transport-escort service, controlled dormitory access. 866 college housing spaces available; 835 were occupied in 2003-04. Freshmen guaranteed college housing. On-campus residence required through junior year. Options: coed, men-only, women-only housing available. Marnie and John Burke Memorial Library plus 1 other with 180,404 books, 305,470 microform titles, 2,195 serials, 1,494 audiovisual materials, an OPAC, and a Web page. Operations spending for 2004 fiscal year: $749,944. 194 computers available on campus for general student use. A campuswide network can be accessed from student residence rooms and from off campus. Staffed computer lab on campus.

Community Environment: See University of South Alabama.

■ STILLMAN COLLEGE *G-4*

PO Drawer 1430, 3600 Stillman Blvd.
Tuscaloosa, AL 35403-9990
Tel: (205)349-4240
Free: 800-841-5722
Admissions: (205)366-8817
Fax: (205)366-8996
E-mail: mbonner@stillman.edu
Web Site: http://www.stillman.edu/

Description: Independent, 4-year, coed, affiliated with Presbyterian Church (U.S.A.). Awards bachelor's degrees. Founded 1876. Setting: 100-acre urban campus with easy access to Birmingham. Endowment: $23.6 million. Total enrollment: 1,458. 2,591 applied, 50% were admitted. 18% from top 10% of their high school class, 48% from top quarter, 78% from top half.

Students come from 27 states and territories, 8 other countries, 19% from out-of-state, 0% Native American, 0% Hispanic, 96% black, 1% Asian American or Pacific Islander, 0.1% international, 19% 25 or older, 75% live on campus. Retention: 82% of full-time freshmen returned the following year. Core. Calendar: semesters. Academic remediation for entering students, advanced placement, honors program, independent study, distance learning, double major, summer session for credit, co-op programs and internships. ROTC: Army (c).

Entrance Requirements: Options: early admission, deferred admission. Required: high school transcript, SAT or ACT. Recommended: essay, interview. Required for some: recommendations. Entrance: minimally difficult. Application deadline: Rolling.

Collegiate Environment: Orientation program. Drama-theater group, choral group, marching band, student-run newspaper. Social organizations: 9 open to all; national fraternities, national sororities, local fraternities. Most popular organizations: Student Government Association, Pre-Alumni United Negro College Fund, Christian Student Association. Major annual events: Homecoming, Founders' Day, Christmas Concert. Student services: health clinic, personal-psychological counseling. Campus security: 24-hour patrols. Options: men-only, women-only housing available. Shepard's Library with 6,291 microform titles, 390 serials, and 3,534 audiovisual materials. 74 computers available on campus for general student use. Staffed computer lab on campus.

Community Environment: See University of Alabama.

■ TALLADEGA COLLEGE *F-8*

627 West Battle St.
Talladega, AL 35160-2354
Tel: (256)362-0206
Free: 800-633-2440
Admissions: (256)761-6219
Fax: (256)362-2268
E-mail: mthornton@talladega.edu
Web Site: http://www.talladega.edu/

Description: Independent, 4-year, coed. Awards bachelor's degrees. Founded 1867. Setting: 130-acre small town campus with easy access to Birmingham. Total enrollment: 368. Student-undergrad faculty ratio is 9:1. 1,960 applied, 38% were admitted. Full-time: 339 students, 64% women, 36% men. Part-time: 29 students, 28% women, 72% men. Students come from 24 states and territories, 2 other countries, 41% from out-of-state, 0% Native American, 0% Hispanic, 92% black, 0.3% Asian American or Pacific Islander, 0% international, 17% 25 or older, 76% live on campus, 0.3% transferred in. Retention: 43% of full-time freshmen returned the following year. Academic areas with the most degrees conferred: business/marketing; biological/life sciences; psychology. Core. Calendar: semesters. Academic remediation for entering students, independent study, double major, part-time degree program, adult/continuing education programs, co-op programs and internships. Off campus study at 7 members of the Alabama Center for Higher Education. ROTC: Army (c).

Entrance Requirements: Options: Common Application, electronic application, early admission, deferred admission, international baccalaureate accepted. Required: essay, high school transcript, minimum 2.0 high school GPA, 1 recommendation, SAT and SAT Subject Tests or ACT. Entrance: minimally difficult. Application deadline: Rolling. Notification: continuous.

Costs Per Year: Application fee: $25. One-time mandatory fee: $150. Comprehensive fee: $11,548 includes full-time tuition ($6720), mandatory fees ($408), and college room and board ($4420). College room only: $1600. Part-time tuition: $280 per credit hour. Part-time mandatory fees: $204 per term. Part-time tuition and fees vary according to course load.

Collegiate Environment: Orientation program. Choral group. Social organizations: 31 open to all; national fraternities, national sororities; 1% of eligible men and 3% of eligible women are members. Most popular organizations: Student Government Association, Crimson Ambassadors, academic major clubs, religion-based organizations. Major annual events: Dega Day, Founder's Weekend, Alumni Weekend. Student services: health clinic, personal-psychological counseling. Campus security: 24-hour patrols, late night transport-escort service, campus police. 660 college housing spaces available; 276 were occupied in 2003-04. Freshmen guaranteed college housing. Options: men-only, women-only housing available. Savery Library with 121,303 books, 105 microform titles, 87 serials, 330 audiovisual materials, and an OPAC. 105 computers available on campus for general student use. A campuswide network can be accessed from student residence rooms and from off campus. Staffed computer lab on campus.

Community Environment: Population 19,165, Talladega is at the heart of a fertile valley in the foothills of the Blue Ridge Mountains, 55 miles to

Birmingham. Bus service is available and the closest airline is in Anniston, 20 miles away. Its elevation gives it a healthy climate with an average temperature of 63.3 degrees, and annual rainfall of 54.3 inches. The highest point in Alabama, Cheaha Mountain, is 17 miles north in Talladega National Forest. Home of the Alabama School for Blind, and Alabama School for Deaf, the community has theatres, supervised playgrounds, and parks, with hunting, fishing, and hiking facilities.

■ **TROY UNIVERSITY** L-8

University Ave.
Troy, AL 36082
Tel: (334)670-3000
Free: 800-551-9716
Admissions: (334)670-3243
Fax: (334)670-3815
Web Site: http://www.troy.edu/

Description: State-supported, comprehensive, coed. Part of Troy University System. Awards associate, bachelor's, and master's degrees and post-master's certificates. Founded 1887. Setting: 577-acre small town campus. Endowment: $18.9 million. Research spending for 2004 fiscal year: $267,270. Educational spending for 2005 fiscal year: $3734 per student. Total enrollment: 26,880. Faculty: 1,405 (456 full-time, 949 part-time). Student-undergrad faculty ratio is 21:1. 46% from top quarter of their high school class, 84% from top half. Full-time: 8,395 students, 60% women, 40% men. Part-time: 10,383 students, 49% women, 51% men. Students come from 52 states and territories, 53 other countries, 15% from out-of-state, 1% Native American, 4% Hispanic, 36% black, 1% Asian American or Pacific Islander, 2% international, 24% 25 or older, 29% live on campus, 4% transferred in. Retention: 74% of full-time freshmen returned the following year. Academic areas with the most degrees conferred: business/marketing; security and protective services; education; psychology. Core. Calendar: semesters. Academic remediation for entering students, ESL program, services for LD students, advanced placement, accelerated degree program, honors program, independent study, distance learning, double major, summer session for credit, part-time degree program, adult/continuing education programs, internships, graduate courses open to undergrads. Study abroad program. ROTC: Army, Air Force.

Entrance Requirements: Options: Peterson's Universal Application, electronic application, deferred admission. Required: high school transcript. Recommended: interview. Entrance: moderately difficult. Application deadline: Rolling.

Costs Per Year: Application fee: $20. State resident tuition: $4004 full-time, $170 per credit hour part-time. Nonresident tuition: $8008 full-time, $340 per credit hour part-time. Mandatory fees: $674 full-time, $9 per credit hour part-time, $50 per term part-time. College room and board: $4964. College room only: $2300. Room and board charges vary according to board plan and housing facility.

Collegiate Environment: Orientation program. Drama-theater group, choral group, marching band, student-run newspaper. Social organizations: 110 open to all; national fraternities, national sororities; 20% of eligible men and 20% of eligible women are members. Most popular organizations: University band, University choir, yearbook, University Activities Council. Major annual events: homecoming, Honors Day. Student services: health clinic, personal-psychological counseling, women's center. Campus security: 24-hour patrols, student patrols, late night transport-escort service, controlled dormitory access. 1,573 college housing spaces available; all were occupied in 2003-04. Freshmen guaranteed college housing. On-campus residence required in freshman year. Options: coed, men-only, women-only housing available. Wallace Library with 443,415 books, 1.6 million microform titles, 1,397 serials, 5,938 audiovisual materials, an OPAC, and a Web page. Operations spending for 2004 fiscal year: $1.8 million. 557 computers available on campus for general student use. A campuswide network can be accessed from student residence rooms and from off campus. Staffed computer lab on campus.

Community Environment: Population 15,000, Troy is located at the junction of U.S. Highways 231 and 29 and is 50 miles from Montgomery, the state capital. There is regular bus service. The citizens take great interest in the University, and extend a cordial welcome to students. There are numerous social, church, civic and school organizations which provide cultural

enrichment for the citizens and for the students of the University. Recreational facilities include parks for swimming, tennis courts, a lake for fishing, and two golf courses.

■ **TUSKEGEE UNIVERSITY** J-9

Tuskegee, AL 36088
Tel: (334)727-8011
Free: 800-622-6531
Admissions: (334)727-8500
Web Site: http://www.tuskegee.edu/

Description: Independent, comprehensive, coed. Awards bachelor's, master's, doctoral, and first professional degrees. Founded 1881. Setting: 4,390-acre small town campus. Research spending for 2004 fiscal year: $13.7 million. Educational spending for 2005 fiscal year: $8250 per student. Total enrollment: 2,880. Faculty: 265 (223 full-time, 42 part-time). Student-undergrad faculty ratio is 12:1. 2,037 applied, 81% were admitted. 17% from top 10% of their high school class, 44% from top quarter, 82% from top half. Full-time: 2,391 students, 55% women, 45% men. Part-time: 119 students, 47% women, 53% men. Students come from 42 states and territories, 35 other countries, 57% from out-of-state, 0.1% Native American, 0.2% Hispanic, 72% black, 0.03% Asian American or Pacific Islander, 3% international, 5% 25 or older, 63% live on campus, 2% transferred in. Retention: 71% of full-time freshmen returned the following year. Academic areas with the most degrees conferred: engineering; social sciences; biological/life sciences. Core. Calendar: semesters. Academic remediation for entering students, ESL program, honors program, summer session for credit, part-time degree program, co-op programs and internships, graduate courses open to undergrads. Off campus study at Alabama Center for Higher Education. ROTC: Army, Air Force.

Entrance Requirements: Options: electronic application, early admission. Required: high school transcript, minimum 2.0 high school GPA, SAT or ACT. Entrance: moderately difficult. Application deadline: 4/15.

Costs Per Year: Application fee: $25. Comprehensive fee: $20,587 includes full-time tuition ($12,400), mandatory fees ($300), and college room and board ($7887). Part-time tuition: $490 per credit hour.

Collegiate Environment: Orientation program. Drama-theater group, choral group, marching band, student-run newspaper. Social organizations: national fraternities, national sororities; 7% of eligible men and 8% of eligible women are members. Major annual events: homecoming, Choir Christmas Concert, Scholarship Night. Student services: health clinic, personal-psychological counseling. Campus security: 24-hour emergency response devices and patrols, late night transport-escort service. Freshmen given priority for college housing. On-campus residence required through sophomore year. Hollis B. Frissell Library plus 3 others with 623,824 books, 287,500 microform titles, 81,157 serials, and an OPAC. Operations spending for 2004 fiscal year: $1.1 million. 1,000 computers available on campus for general student use. A campuswide network can be accessed from student residence rooms and from off campus. Staffed computer lab on campus.

Community Environment: Tuskegee, population 15,000, is approximately 40 miles east of Montgomery, AL, the state capital, and 120 miles south of Atlanta, GA. Travelers may fly to Montgomery's Dannelly Field and drive to Tuskegee via Interstate 85 north or fly to Atlanta and drive to Tuskegee via Interstate 85 south. Dannelly field is served by American, Delta, Northwest Airlink, and USA Express airlines. Commercial bus transportation is available to Tuskegee from Montgomery, Atlanta, and other nearby cities. Churches of all major denominations, a library and a museum contribute to the cultural atmosphere of the town. Motels and hotels are located in the area. The town also has various fraternal, civic, and veteran's organizations.

■ **THE UNIVERSITY OF ALABAMA** G-4

Tuscaloosa, AL 35487
Tel: (205)348-6010
Free: 800-933-BAMA
Admissions: (205)348-8197
Fax: (205)348-9046
E-mail: admissions@ua.edu
Web Site: http://www.ua.edu/

Description: State-supported, university, coed. Part of The University of Alabama System. Awards bachelor's, master's, doctoral, and first professional degrees and post-master's certificates. Founded 1831. Setting: 1,000-acre suburban campus with easy access to Birmingham. Endowment: $409.3 million. Research spending for 2004 fiscal year: $28.1 million. Educational spending for 2005 fiscal year: $6600 per student. Total enrollment: 21,835. Faculty: 1,148 (922 full-time, 226 part-time). Student-undergrad faculty ratio is 9:1. 10,451 applied, 74% were admitted. 32% from top 10% of their high school class, 51% from top quarter, 77% from top half. 35 National Merit Scholars. Full-time: 15,832 students, 53% women, 47% men. Part-time: 1,721 students, 54% women, 46% men. Students come from 52 states and territories, 92 other countries, 20% from out-of-state, 1% Native American, 2% Hispanic, 12% black, 1% Asian American or Pacific Islander, 1% international, 10% 25 or older, 22% live on campus, 8% transferred in. Retention: 86% of full-time freshmen returned the following year. Academic areas with the most degrees conferred: business/marketing; communications/journalism; family and consumer sciences. Core. Calendar: semesters. Academic remediation for entering students, ESL program, services for LD students, advanced placement, accelerated degree program, self-designed majors, freshman honors college, honors program, independent study, distance learning, double major, summer session for credit, part-time degree program, external degree program, adult/continuing education programs, co-op programs and internships, graduate courses open to undergrads. Off campus study at 95 members of the National Student Exchange, Stillman College. Study abroad program. ROTC: Army, Air Force.

Entrance Requirements: Options: Common Application, electronic application, early admission, deferred admission, international baccalaureate accepted. Required: high school transcript, minimum 3.0 high school GPA, SAT or ACT. Required for some: essay, interview. Entrance: moderately difficult.

Costs Per Year: Application fee: $30. State resident tuition: $4864 full-time. Nonresident tuition: $13,516 full-time. Full-time tuition varies according to course load. College room and board: $5024. College room only: $3120. Room and board charges vary according to board plan and housing facility.

Collegiate Environment: Orientation program. Drama-theater group, choral group, marching band, student-run newspaper, radio station. Social organizations: 318 open to all; national fraternities, national sororities, local fraternities, local sororities; 20% of eligible men and 26% of eligible women are members. Most popular organizations: Coordinating Council of Student Organizations, Residence Hall Association, International Student Association, Student Government Association, African-American Association. Major annual events: Homecoming/Football, University Program's Concerts, Honors Week. Student services: legal services, health clinic, personal-psychological counseling, women's center. Campus security: 24-hour emergency response devices and patrols, student patrols, late night transport-escort service, controlled dormitory access, crime prevention programs, community police protection. 4,509 college housing spaces available; 4,042 were occupied in 2003-04. Freshmen given priority for college housing. On-campus residence required in freshman year. Options: coed, men-only, women-only housing available. Amelia Gayle Gorgas Library plus 8 others with 2.5 million books, 4 million microform titles, 31,199 serials, 523,749 audiovisual materials, an OPAC, and a Web page. Operations spending for 2004 fiscal year: $14 million. 2,000 computers available on campus for general student use. A campuswide network can be accessed from student residence rooms and from off campus. Staffed computer lab on campus.

Community Environment: Tuscaloosa, with a population of approximately 85,000, is the fifth largest city in Alabama. The city is located 50 miles southwest of Birmingham, 100 miles northwest of Montgomery, the state capital, and 220 miles east of Atlanta, GA. The community is served by major bus, rail, and air services. Modern shopping and service facilities are accessible in the immediate area.

■ **THE UNIVERSITY OF ALABAMA AT BIRMINGHAM** *F-6*

1530 3rd Ave. South
Birmingham, AL 35294
Tel: (205)934-4011
Free: 800-421-8743
Admissions: (205)934-8221
Fax: (205)975-7114
E-mail: uabadmit@uabdpo.dpo.uab.edu
Web Site: http://main.uab.edu/

Description: State-supported, university, coed. Part of University of Alabama System. Awards bachelor's, master's, doctoral, and first professional degrees and post-master's certificates. Founded 1969. Setting: 265-acre urban campus. Endowment: $276.9 million. Research spending for 2004 fiscal year: $233.5 million. Educational spending for 2005 fiscal year: $15,864 per student. Total enrollment: 16,572. Faculty: 880 (777 full-time, 103 part-time). Student-undergrad faculty ratio is 18:1. 4,255 applied, 88% were admitted. 23% from top 10% of their high school class, 49% from top quarter, 77% from top half. 7 National Merit Scholars. Full-time: 8,059 students, 61% women, 39% men. Part-time: 3,411 students, 60% women,

40% men. Students come from 43 states and territories, 76 other countries, 6% from out-of-state, 0.4% Native American, 1% Hispanic, 32% black, 3% Asian American or Pacific Islander, 2% international, 28% 25 or older, 11% live on campus, 9% transferred in. Retention: 77% of full-time freshmen returned the following year. Core. Calendar: semesters. Academic remediation for entering students, services for LD students, advanced placement, self-designed majors, honors program, independent study, double major, summer session for credit, part-time degree program, adult/continuing education programs, co-op programs and internships, graduate courses open to undergrads. Off campus study at University of Alabama in Huntsville, University of Alabama, Birmingham Area Consortium for Higher Education. Study abroad program. ROTC: Army, Air Force (c).

Entrance Requirements: Options: early admission, deferred admission, international baccalaureate accepted. Required: high school transcript, minimum 2.0 high school GPA, SAT or ACT. Entrance: moderately difficult. Application deadline: 3/1. Notification: continuous.

Costs Per Year: Application fee: $30. State resident tuition: $3960 full-time, $132 per credit hour part-time. Nonresident tuition: $9900 full-time, $330 per credit hour part-time. Mandatory fees: $832 full-time. Full-time tuition and fees vary according to program. Part-time tuition varies according to program. College room only: $3390. Room charges vary according to housing facility and student level.

Collegiate Environment: Orientation program. Drama-theater group, choral group, marching band, student-run newspaper, radio station. Social organizations: 150 open to all; national fraternities, national sororities; 6% of eligible men and 6% of eligible women are members. Most popular organizations: campus ministries, service-oriented groups, sports-affiliated groups. Major annual events: Spring Fest, Homecoming, Madrigal Feaste. Student services: health clinic, personal-psychological counseling, women's center. Campus security: 24-hour emergency response devices and patrols, late night transport-escort service, controlled dormitory access. 1,700 college housing spaces available; 1,395 were occupied in 2003-04. No special consideration for freshman housing applicants. Options: coed, women-only housing available. Mervyn Sterne Library plus 1 other with 853,445 books, 1.3 million microform titles, 3,934 serials, 78,017 audiovisual materials, an OPAC, and a Web page. Operations spending for 2004 fiscal year: $11.4 million. 400 computers available on campus for general student use. A campuswide network can be accessed from student residence rooms and from off campus. Staffed computer lab on campus.

■ **THE UNIVERSITY OF ALABAMA IN HUNTSVILLE** *B-6*

301 Sparkman Dr.
Huntsville, AL 35899
Tel: (256)824-1000
Free: 800-UAH-CALL
Admissions: (256)824-6070
Fax: (256)824-6073
E-mail: admitme@email.uah.edu
Web Site: http://www.uah.edu/

Description: State-supported, university, coed. Part of University of Alabama System. Awards bachelor's, master's, and doctoral degrees and post-master's certificates. Founded 1950. Setting: 376-acre suburban campus. Endowment: $23.8 million. Research spending for 2004 fiscal year: $48.2 million. Educational spending for 2005 fiscal year: $6467 per student. Total enrollment: 7,084. Faculty: 468 (280 full-time, 188 part-time). Student-undergrad faculty ratio is 16:1. 1,698 applied, 87% were admitted. 31% from top 10% of their high school class, 57% from top quarter, 83% from top half. 2 National Merit Scholars, 10 valedictorians. Full-time: 4,101 students, 49% women, 51% men. Part-time: 1,589 students, 50% women, 50% men. Students come from 42 states and territories, 66 other countries, 13% from out-of-state, 1% Native American, 2% Hispanic, 14% black, 3% Asian American or Pacific Islander, 4% international, 25% 25 or older, 16% live on campus, 12% transferred in. Retention: 75% of full-time freshmen returned the following year. Academic areas with the most degrees conferred: business/marketing; engineering; health professions and related sciences. Core. Calendar: semesters. Academic remediation for entering students, ESL program, services for LD students, advanced placement, honors program, independent study, distance learning, double major, summer session for credit, part-time degree program, adult/continuing education programs, co-op programs and internships, graduate courses open to undergrads. Off campus study at Alabama Agricultural and Mechanical University, Oakwood College, Athens State College, John C. Calhoun State Community College. ROTC: Army (c).

Entrance Requirements: Options: Peterson's Universal Application, Common Application, electronic application, early admission, deferred admission, international baccalaureate accepted. Required: high school transcript, SAT or ACT. Entrance: moderately difficult. Application deadline: 8/15. Notification: continuous.

Costs Per Year: Application fee: $30. State resident tuition: $4688 full-time. Nonresident tuition: $9886 full-time. Full-time tuition varies according to course load. College room and board: $5320. College room only: $3720. Room and board charges vary according to board plan and housing facility.

Collegiate Environment: Orientation program. Drama-theater group, choral group, student-run newspaper. Social organizations: 111 open to all; national fraternities, national sororities; 5% of eligible men and 4% of eligible women are members. Most popular organizations: Student Government Association, Association for Campus Entertainment, Circle K International, Anointed Voices, Institute of Electrical and Electronic Engineers. Major annual events: homecoming, Fallfest, Springfest. Student services: health clinic, personal-psychological counseling. Campus security: 24-hour emergency response devices and patrols, late night transport-escort service, controlled dormitory access. 1,042 college housing spaces available; 871 were occupied in 2003-04. No special consideration for freshman housing applicants. Option: coed housing available. University of Alabama in Huntsville Library with 327,663 books, 584,267 microform titles, 1,051 serials, 2,677 audiovisual materials, an OPAC, and a Web page. Operations spending for 2004 fiscal year: $2.4 million. 1,091 computers available on campus for general student use. A campuswide network can be accessed from student residence rooms and from off campus. Staffed computer lab on campus.

■ **UNIVERSITY OF MOBILE** *P-2*

5735 College Parkway
Mobile, AL 36613
Tel: (251)442-2773
Free: 800-946-7267
Admissions: (251)442-2287
Fax: (251)442-2498
E-mail: adminfo@umobile.edu
Web Site: http://www.umobile.edu/

Description: Independent Southern Baptist, comprehensive, coed. Awards associate, bachelor's, and master's degrees. Founded 1961. Setting: 830-acre suburban campus. Endowment: $11.1 million. Educational spending for 2005 fiscal year: $4912 per student. Total enrollment: 1,758. Faculty: 156 (88 full-time, 68 part-time). Student-undergrad faculty ratio is 13:1. 504 applied. 20% from top 10% of their high school class, 42% from top quarter, 70% from top half. Full-time: 1,273 students, 63% women, 37% men. Part-time: 276 students, 78% women, 22% men. Students come from 21 states and territories, 19 other countries, 11% from out-of-state, 2% Native American, 1% Hispanic, 23% black, 1% Asian American or Pacific Islander, 4% international, 22% 25 or older, 20% live on campus, 11% transferred in. Retention: 68% of full-time freshmen returned the following year. Academic areas with the most degrees conferred: interdisciplinary studies; education; business/marketing; health professions and related sciences. Core. Calendar: semesters. Academic remediation for entering students, ESL program, advanced placement, accelerated degree program, honors program, independent study, double major, summer session for credit, part-time degree program, adult/continuing education programs, internships, graduate courses open to undergrads. ROTC: Army (c), Air Force (c).

Entrance Requirements: Options: Peterson's Universal Application, Common Application, early admission, deferred admission. Required: high school transcript, minimum 2.0 high school GPA, SAT or ACT. Required for some: interview. Entrance: moderately difficult. Application deadline: Rolling. Notification: continuous.

Costs Per Year: Application fee: $30. Comprehensive fee: $16,950 includes full-time tuition ($10,230), mandatory fees ($330), and college room and board ($6390). College room only: $2680. Full-time tuition and fees vary according to course load. Room and board charges vary according to housing facility. Part-time tuition: $341 per semester hour. Part-time tuition varies according to course load.

Collegiate Environment: Orientation program. Drama-theater group, choral group, student-run newspaper. Social organizations: 30 open to all. Most popular organizations: Campus Activity Board, Baptist Campus Ministry, Student Government Association, Fellowship of Christian Athletes. Major annual events: homecoming, Upper Room Dinner Theater, Starlight Pageant. Student services: health clinic, personal-psychological counseling. Campus security: 24-hour emergency response devices and patrols. 400 college housing spaces available; 386 were occupied in 2003-04. Freshmen guaranteed college housing. On-campus residence required in freshman year. Options: men-only, women-only housing available. J. L. Bedsole

Library plus 2 others with 100,250 books, 255 microform titles, 1,043 serials, 2,222 audiovisual materials, and an OPAC. Operations spending for 2004 fiscal year: $326,241. 110 computers available on campus for general student use. A campuswide network can be accessed from off-campus. Staffed computer lab on campus.

Community Environment: See University of South Alabama.

■ **UNIVERSITY OF MONTEVALLO** *G-6*

Station 6001
Montevallo, AL 35115
Tel: (205)665-6000
Free: 800-292-4349
Admissions: (205)665-6030
E-mail: admissions@um.montevallo.edu
Web Site: http://www.montevallo.edu/

Description: State-supported, comprehensive, coed. Awards bachelor's and master's degrees and post-master's certificates. Founded 1896. Setting: 106-acre small town campus with easy access to Birmingham. Endowment: $2 million. Research spending for 2004 fiscal year: $22,195. Educational spending for 2005 fiscal year: $4521 per student. Total enrollment: 2,999. Faculty: 200 (140 full-time, 60 part-time). Student-undergrad faculty ratio is 17:1. 1,386 applied, 76% were admitted. 68 valedictorians. Full-time: 2,357 students, 68% women, 32% men. Part-time: 259 students, 70% women, 30% men. Students come from 18 states and territories, 22 other countries, 3% from out-of-state, 1% Native American, 1% Hispanic, 13% black, 1% Asian American or Pacific Islander, 2% international, 27% 25 or older, 35% live on campus, 11% transferred in. Retention: 73% of full-time freshmen returned the following year. Academic areas with the most degrees conferred: business/marketing; visual and performing arts; education. Core. Calendar: semesters. Academic remediation for entering students, services for LD students, advanced placement, accelerated degree program, honors program, independent study, double major, summer session for credit, part-time degree program, internships, graduate courses open to undergrads. Study abroad program. ROTC: Army (c), Air Force (c).

Entrance Requirements: Options: Peterson's Universal Application, Common Application, electronic application, early admission, deferred admission, international baccalaureate accepted. Required: high school transcript, minimum 2.0 high school GPA, SAT or ACT. Recommended: interview, ACT. Entrance: moderately difficult. Application deadline: 8/1.

Costs Per Year: Application fee: $25. State resident tuition: $5460 full-time, $182 per credit hour part-time. Nonresident tuition: $10,920 full-time, $364 per credit hour part-time. Mandatory fees: $204 full-time. Full-time tuition and fees vary according to course load. Part-time tuition varies according to course load. College room and board: $3966. Room and board charges vary according to board plan and housing facility.

Collegiate Environment: Orientation program. Drama-theater group, choral group, student-run newspaper. Social organizations: 74 open to all; national fraternities, national sororities; 20% of eligible men and 16% of eligible women are members. Most popular organizations: Golden Key, Student Government Association, University Programming Council, campus ministries, African-American Association. Major annual events: College Night, Spring Fest, Honors Day. Student services: health clinic, personal-psychological counseling. Campus security: 24-hour emergency response devices and patrols, late night transport-escort service, controlled dormitory access. 1,212 college housing spaces available; 915 were occupied in 2003-04. Freshmen guaranteed college housing. On-campus residence required in freshman year. Options: coed, men-only, women-only housing available. Carmichael Library with 258,122 books, 810,909 microform titles, 813 serials, 4,030 audiovisual materials, an OPAC, and a Web page. Operations spending for 2004 fiscal year: $918,046. 250 computers available on campus for general student use. A campuswide network can be accessed from student residence rooms and from off campus. Staffed computer lab on campus.

Community Environment: Montevallo (population 5,000) is near the center of the state, and is accessible by automobile. Montevallo is 32 miles south of Birmingham and 68 miles north of Montgomery, and has a mild year-round climate. There are a library, golf course, municipal park, and many churches in the city. Recreational activities include hunting, lake and stream fishing, boating and water skiing on nearby lakes. Students belonging to church denominations that are not represented in Montevallo hold services in the Religious Association Room of the Student Union Building.

■ **UNIVERSITY OF NORTH ALABAMA** *B-3*

One Harrison Plaza
Florence, AL 35632-0001

Tel: (256)765-4100
Free: 800-TAL-KUNA
Admissions: (256)765-4316
Fax: (256)765-4329
E-mail: admissions@una.edu
Web Site: http://www.una.edu/

Description: State-supported, comprehensive, coed. Part of Alabama Commission on Higher Education. Awards bachelor's and master's degrees and post-master's certificates. Founded 1830. Setting: 125-acre urban campus. Endowment: $3.7 million. Research spending for 2004 fiscal year: $1.1 million. Educational spending for 2005 fiscal year: $4100 per student. Total enrollment: 6,415. Faculty: 322 (209 full-time, 113 part-time). Student-undergrad faculty ratio is 20:1. 2,125 applied, 80% were admitted. 44% from top quarter of their high school class, 76% from top half. Full-time: 4,444 students, 56% women, 44% men. Part-time: 973 students, 64% women, 36% men. Students come from 40 states and territories, 43 other countries, 20% from out-of-state, 1% Native American, 1% Hispanic, 10% black, 1% Asian American or Pacific Islander, 7% international, 19% 25 or older, 19% live on campus, 11% transferred in. Retention: 68% of full-time freshmen returned the following year. Academic areas with the most degrees conferred: business/marketing; education; health professions and related sciences. Core. Calendar: semesters. Academic remediation for entering students, ESL program, services for LD students, advanced placement, accelerated degree program, independent study, distance learning, double major, summer session for credit, part-time degree program, adult/continuing education programs, co-op programs and internships, graduate courses open to undergrads. ROTC: Army.

Entrance Requirements: Options: electronic application, early admission, deferred admission. Required: high school transcript, SAT or ACT. Entrance: minimally difficult. Application deadline: Rolling.

Costs Per Year: Application fee: $25. State resident tuition: $3648 full-time, $143 per credit hour part-time. Nonresident tuition: $7296 full-time, $286 per credit hour part-time. Mandatory fees: $718 full-time. Part-time tuition varies according to course load. College room and board: $4170. College room only: $1960. Room and board charges vary according to board plan and housing facility.

Collegiate Environment: Orientation program. Drama-theater group, choral group, marching band, student-run newspaper, radio station. Social organizations: 75 open to all; national fraternities, national sororities; 5% of eligible men and 6% of eligible women are members. Most popular organizations: Student Government Association, University Program Council, Baptist campus ministries, Physical Education Majors Club, Residence Hall Association. Major annual events: Homecoming, Spring Fling, Step Sing. Student services: health clinic, personal-psychological counseling, women's center. Campus security: 24-hour emergency response devices and patrols, student patrols, late night transport-escort service, controlled dormitory access. Options: coed, men-only, women-only housing available. Collier Library with 358,393 books, 1 million microform titles, 3,126 serials, 9,898 audiovisual materials, an OPAC, and a Web page. Operations spending for 2004 fiscal year: $2 million. 750 computers available on campus for general student use. A campuswide network can be accessed from student residence rooms and from off campus. Staffed computer lab on campus.

Community Environment: Population 38,000. Florence is contiguous to the towns of Sheffield, Tuscumbia, and Muscle Shoals City; it is part of an urban center with a population of 134,000. Area lakes and camping sites attract vacationists and sportsmen from all over the nation. Florence is served by buses and airlines; has excellent public schools, churches, libraries, recreation facilities, cultural centers; several radio stations and a television station.

■ **UNIVERSITY OF SOUTH ALABAMA** *P-2*

307 University Blvd.
Mobile, AL 36688-0002
Tel: (251)460-6101
Free: 800-872-5247
Admissions: (251)460-6141
Fax: (251)460-7025
Web Site: http://www.usouthal.edu/

Description: State-supported, university, coed. Awards bachelor's, master's, doctoral, and first professional degrees and post-master's certificates. Founded 1963. Setting: 1,225-acre suburban campus. Endowment: $270.3 million. Research spending for 2004 fiscal year: $16.5 million. Educational spending for 2005 fiscal year: $7704 per student. Total enrollment: 13,122. Faculty: 970 (720 full-time, 250 part-time). Student-undergrad faculty ratio is 18:1. 2,492 applied, 87% were admitted. 50% from top quarter of their high school class, 86% from top half. Full-time: 7,495 students, 60% women, 40% men. Part-time: 2,649 students, 61% women, 39% men. Students come from 48 states and territories, 102 other countries, 17% from out-of-state, 1% Native American, 1% Hispanic, 18% black, 3% Asian American or Pacific Islander, 5% international, 33% 25 or older, 19% live on campus, 10% transferred in. Retention: 71% of full-time freshmen returned the following year. Academic areas with the most degrees conferred: health professions and related sciences; business/marketing; education. Core. Calendar: semesters. Academic remediation for entering students, ESL program, services for LD students, advanced placement, accelerated degree program, self-designed majors, freshman honors college, independent study, distance learning, double major, summer session for credit, part-time degree program, external degree program, adult/continuing education programs, co-op programs and internships, graduate courses open to undergrads. Study abroad program. ROTC: Army, Air Force.

Entrance Requirements: Option: early admission. Required: high school transcript, SAT or ACT. Recommended: minimum 2.0 high school GPA. Entrance: moderately difficult. Application deadline: 7/15. Notification: continuous until 8/10. Preference given to state residents in certain allied health programs.

Costs Per Year: Application fee: $25. State resident tuition: $3810 full-time, $127 per credit hour part-time. Nonresident tuition: $7620 full-time, $254 per credit hour part-time. Mandatory fees: $692 full-time, $256 per term part-time. College room and board: $4428. College room only: $2468. Room and board charges vary according to board plan, housing facility, and location.

Collegiate Environment: Orientation program. Drama-theater group, choral group, student-run newspaper, radio station. Social organizations: 130 open to all; national fraternities, national sororities; 10% of eligible men and 7% of eligible women are members. Most popular organizations: Student Government Association, Black Student Union, Non-Traditional Student Committee. Major annual events: homecoming, Mayfest. Student services: legal services, health clinic, personal-psychological counseling. Campus security: 24-hour emergency response devices and patrols, late night transport-escort service. 2,000 college housing spaces available; all were occupied in 2003-04. Option: coed housing available. University Library plus 1 other with 1 million books, 581,629 microform titles, 5,296 serials, an OPAC, and a Web page. Operations spending for 2004 fiscal year: $4.9 million. 500 computers available on campus for general student use. A campuswide network can be accessed from student residence rooms and from off campus. Staffed computer lab on campus.

Community Environment: Mobile, with a population 526,000 in the greater metropolitan area, has a temperate climate. In July and August the average high temperature is 91 degrees, and the average low temperature is 73. Airlines, buses and railroads serve the area. The city has libraries, churches of all major denominations, theaters, and museums. Excellent facilities for boating, fishing, and swimming are available. Mobile hosts the annual Senior Bowl, Alabama Deep Sea Fishing Rodeo, Azalea Trail Run, and the oldest Mardi Gras celebration in the country. Part-time work is available.

■ **THE UNIVERSITY OF WEST ALABAMA** *I-2*

Livingston, AL 35470
Tel: (205)652-3400
Free: 800-621-8044
Web Site: http://www.uwa.edu/

Description: State-supported, comprehensive, coed. Awards associate, bachelor's, and master's degrees. Founded 1835. Setting: 595-acre small town campus. Endowment: $858,698. Research spending for 2004 fiscal year: $189,079. Total enrollment: 2,667. 691 applied, 74% were admitted. Full-time: 1,450 students, 53% women, 47% men. Part-time: 187 students, 63% women, 37% men. Students come from 24 states and territories, 7 other countries, 20% from out-of-state, 0.2% Native American, 1% Hispanic, 42% black, 0.4% Asian American or Pacific Islander, 1% international, 18% 25 or older, 35% live on campus, 12% transferred in. Retention: 80% of full-time freshmen returned the following year. Core. Calendar: semesters. Academic remediation for entering students, services for LD students, advanced placement, accelerated degree program, honors program, double major, summer session for credit, part-time degree program, internships. Off campus study at Wallace State Community College. ROTC: Army (c), Air Force (c).

Entrance Requirements: Options: Peterson's Universal Application, Common Application, electronic application, early admission, deferred admission. Required: high school transcript, minimum 2.0 high school GPA, SAT or ACT. Entrance: minimally difficult. Application deadline: Rolling. Notification: continuous.

Costs Per Year: Application fee: $20. State resident tuition: $3838 full-time, $162 per semester hour part-time. Nonresident tuition: $7676 full-time, $324 per semester hour part-time. Mandatory fees: $488 full-time, $235 per term part-time. Part-time tuition and fees vary according to course level. College room and board: $3285. College room only: $1746. Room and board charges vary according to board plan and housing facility.

Collegiate Environment: Orientation program. Drama-theater group, choral group, marching band, student-run newspaper. Social organizations: 30 open to all; national fraternities, national sororities; 10% of eligible men and 10% of eligible women are members. Most popular organization: Campus Outreach. Major annual events: Spring Fest, Homecoming, Parents' Day. Student services: health clinic, personal-psychological counseling. Campus security: 24-hour patrols. 833 college housing spaces available; 569 were occupied in 2003-04. No special consideration for freshman housing applicants. On-campus residence required through sophomore year. Options: coed, men-only, women-only housing available. Julia Tutwiler Library with 151,991 books, 473,473 microform titles, 5,257 serials, 3,072 audiovisual materials, an OPAC, and a Web page. Operations spending for 2004 fiscal year: $535,334. 400 computers available on campus for general student use. A campuswide network can be accessed from student residence rooms and from off campus. Staffed computer lab on campus.

Community Environment: Livingston (population 3,500) is the Sumter County Seat, and is located on Interstate 59/20 and Alabama Highway 28. It is 116 miles southwest of Birmingham, 130 miles west of Montgomery, and 37 miles east of Meridian, Mississippi. The climate is mild. Fishing and hunting are excellent.

■ **VC TECH** *G-6*
2790 Pelham Parkway
Pelham, AL 35124
Tel: (205)943-2100; 877-5-VCTECH
Web Site: http://www.vctechnical.com/
Description: Proprietary, 2-year, coed. Founded 2003.

■ **VIRGINIA COLLEGE AT BIRMINGHAM** *F-6*
65 Bagby Dr.
Birmingham, AL 35209
Tel: (205)802-1200
Fax: (205)802-1597
Web Site: http://www.vc.edu/
Description: Proprietary, comprehensive, coed. Awards associate and bachelor's degrees. Founded 1989. Setting: 1-acre urban campus. Total enrollment: 2,407. 600 applied, 86% were admitted. Full-time: 2,407 students, 66% women, 34% men. Students come from 7 states and territories, 0% from out-of-state, 1% Hispanic, 42% black, 1% Asian American or Pacific Islander, 75% 25 or older. Retention: 70% of full-time freshmen returned the following year. Core.

Entrance Requirements: Required: high school transcript. Placement: ACCUPLACER required. Entrance: moderately difficult. Application deadline: Rolling. Notification: continuous.

Costs Per Year: Tuition: $10,800 full-time, $300 per credit part-time. Mandatory fees: $150 full-time. Full-time tuition and fees vary according to program. Part-time tuition varies according to program. Tuition guaranteed not to increase for student's term of enrollment.

Collegiate Environment: Orientation program. Student services: personal-psychological counseling. College housing not available. Elma Bell Library plus 2 others with 3,900 books, 120 serials, 40 audiovisual materials, and an OPAC. 80 computers available on campus for general student use. A campuswide network can be accessed.

■ **VIRGINIA COLLEGE AT HUNTSVILLE** *B-6*
2800-A Bob Wallace Ave.
Huntsville, AL 35805
Tel: (256)533-7387
Admissions: (205)533-7387
Fax: (256)533-7785
Web Site: http://www.vc.edu/
Description: Proprietary, 2-year, coed. Awards diplomas and terminal associate degrees. Founded 1989. Total enrollment: 750.

Entrance Requirements: Required: high school transcript. Placement: CPAt required. Entrance: minimally difficult. Application deadline: Rolling. Notification: continuous.

Costs Per Year: Tuition: $9900 full-time, $255 per credit hour part-time. Full-time tuition varies according to course load, degree level, and program. Part-time tuition varies according to course load, degree level, and program.

Collegiate Environment: College housing not available.

■ **WALLACE STATE COMMUNITY COLLEGE** *D-6*
PO Box 2000
Hanceville, AL 35077-2000
Tel: (256)352-8000
Admissions: (256)352-8278
Fax: (256)352-8228
Web Site: http://www.wallacestate.edu/
Description: State-supported, 2-year, coed. Awards diplomas, transfer associate, and terminal associate degrees. Founded 1966. Setting: 216-acre rural campus with easy access to Birmingham. Educational spending for 2005 fiscal year: $3000 per student. Total enrollment: 6,028. 1,219 applied, 100% were admitted. 10% from top 10% of their high school class, 20% from top quarter, 40% from top half. Students come from 15 states and territories, 6% from out-of-state, 40% 25 or older, 3% live on campus. Calendar: semesters. Academic remediation for entering students, advanced placement, summer session for credit, part-time degree program, co-op programs.

Entrance Requirements: Open admission for technical, liberal arts programs. Options: Peterson's Universal Application, early admission, deferred admission. Required: high school transcript. Placement: ACT recommended; ACT, nursing exam required for some. Entrance: noncompetitive. Application deadline: Rolling. Notification: continuous.

Collegiate Environment: Orientation program. Choral group. Social organizations: 7 open to all. Most popular organizations: Student Government Association, Vocational Industrial Clubs of America. Major annual events: Homecoming, Women's Health Day. Student services: personal-psychological counseling. 200 college housing spaces available; all were occupied in 2003-04. Options: men-only, women-only housing available. Wallace State College Library with 41,500 books, 425 serials, and an OPAC. Operations spending for 2004 fiscal year: $412,784. 75 computers available on campus for general student use. Staffed computer lab on campus.

Community Environment: Hanceville is a rural community with a population of approximately 2,300, situated midway between Birmingham and Decatur. It is located on state highway 31 with easy access to I-65, both of which connect Decatur and Birmingham.

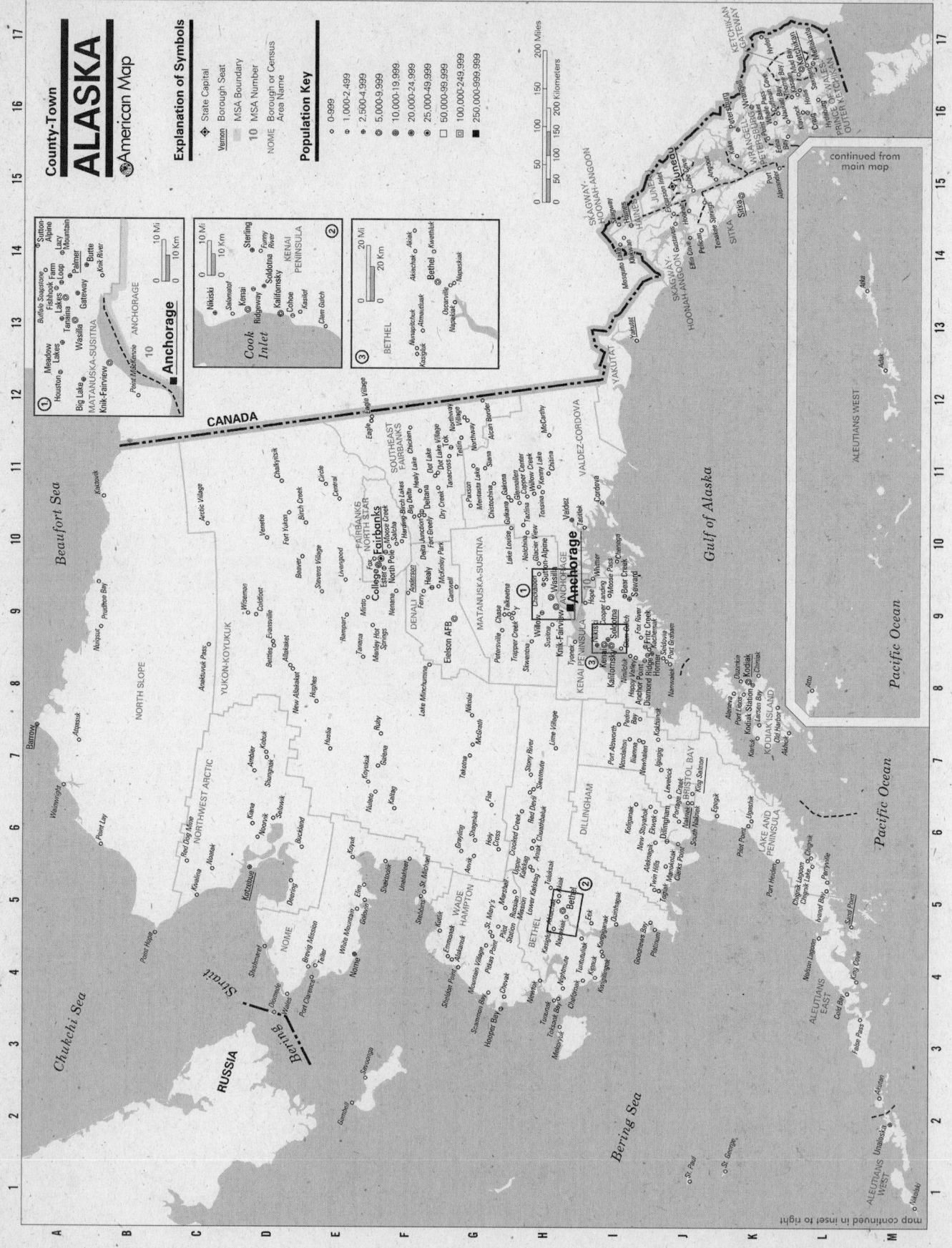

■ **ALASKA BIBLE COLLEGE**
Box 289
Glennallen, AK 99588-0289
Tel: (907)822-3201
Free: 800-478-7884
Fax: (907)822-5027
E-mail: info@akbible.edu
Web Site: http://www.akbible.edu/
Description: Independent nondenominational, 4-year, coed. Awards associate and bachelor's degrees. Founded 1966. Setting: 80-acre rural campus. Endowment: $45,000. Total enrollment: 48. Student-undergrad faculty ratio is 7:1. 13 applied, 92% were admitted. Full-time: 37 students, 19% women, 81% men. Part-time: 11 students, 64% women, 36% men. Students come from 18 states and territories, 62% from out-of-state, 2% Native American, 2% Hispanic, 2% black, 7% Asian American or Pacific Islander, 0% international, 30% 25 or older, 82% live on campus, 10% transferred in. Retention: 75% of full-time freshmen returned the following year. Academic area with the most degrees conferred: theology and religious vocations. Core. Calendar: semesters. Academic remediation for entering students, advanced placement, self-designed majors, double major, part-time degree program, internships.
Entrance Requirements: Option: deferred admission. Required: essay, high school transcript, minimum 2.0 high school GPA, 2 recommendations, interview, SAT or ACT. Entrance: minimally difficult. Application deadline: 7/1. Notification: 7/15.
Costs Per Year: Application fee: $35. Comprehensive fee: $10,700 includes full-time tuition ($5950) and college room and board ($4750). Part-time tuition: $260 per credit hour.
Collegiate Environment: Orientation program. Major annual events: Christmas Banquet, Graduation Banquet, Winter Retreat. Student services: health clinic. Campus security: 24-hour emergency response devices. 45 undergraduates lived in college housing during 2003-04. Freshmen guaranteed college housing. On-campus residence required through sophomore year. Options: men-only, women-only housing available. Alaska Bible College Library Center with 29,888 books, 116 serials, and 341 audiovisual materials. Operations spending for 2004 fiscal year: $18,040. 10 computers available on campus for general student use. A campuswide network can be accessed. Staffed computer lab on campus.
Community Environment: Glennallen is a rural community that has developed on the crossroads between Anchorage, Fairbanks, and Valdez. The original impetus for the community's growth was the construction of the Alcan Highway for communication during the war years. The climate of Glennallen area runs to extremes with the temperature falling to 50 degrees or more below zero for short periods in midwinter, and rising to 70 degrees or more above zero by the close of the school year in May. Sports such as hunting, fishing, hiking, rafting, and cross country skiing are common recreational activities.

■ **ALASKA PACIFIC UNIVERSITY** *H-9*
4101 University Dr.
Anchorage, AK 99508-4672
Tel: (907)561-1266
Free: 800-252-7528
Admissions: (907)564-8248
Fax: (907)564-8317
E-mail: mwarner@alaskapacific.edu

Web Site: http://www.alaskapacific.edu/
Description: Independent, comprehensive, coed. Awards associate, bachelor's, and master's degrees. Founded 1959. Setting: 170-acre suburban campus. Endowment: $32.5 million. Research spending for 2004 fiscal year: $55,440. Educational spending for 2005 fiscal year: $8735 per student. Total enrollment: 800. Faculty: 80 (40 full-time, 40 part-time). Student-undergrad faculty ratio is 8:1. 122 applied, 44% were admitted. 11% from top 10% of their high school class, 50% from top quarter, 68% from top half. Full-time: 336 students, 63% women, 38% men. Part-time: 244 students, 80% women, 20% men. Students come from 38 states and territories, 3 other countries, 31% from out-of-state, 16% Native American, 4% Hispanic, 6% black, 4% Asian American or Pacific Islander, 0.4% international, 55% 25 or older, 22% live on campus, 12% transferred in. Retention: 53% of full-time freshmen returned the following year. Academic areas with the most degrees conferred: parks and recreation; education; natural resources/environmental science. Core. Calendar: semesters. Academic remediation for entering students, services for LD students, advanced placement, accelerated degree program, self-designed majors, independent study, distance learning, double major, summer session for credit, part-time degree program, adult/continuing education programs, internships, graduate courses open to undergrads. Study abroad program.
Entrance Requirements: Options: Peterson's Universal Application, electronic application, early decision, deferred admission, international baccalaureate accepted. Required: essay, high school transcript, minimum 2.5 high school GPA, 2 recommendations, SAT or ACT. Required for some: interview. Entrance: moderately difficult. Application deadlines: 2/1, 1/1 for early decision. Notification: 3/15, 1/15 for early decision.
Costs Per Year: Application fee: $25. Comprehensive fee: $26,410 includes full-time tuition ($19,500), mandatory fees ($110), and college room and board ($6800). Part-time tuition: $812 per semester hour. Part-time mandatory fees: $55 per term.
Collegiate Environment: Orientation program. Drama-theater group, choral group, student-run newspaper. Social organizations: 20 open to all. Most popular organizations: Environmental Club, Student Government Association, Psychology Club, Student Organization of Native Americans, Students for Free Enterprise. Major annual events: Earth Day Celebration, Christmas dance, Honors Assembly. Student services: personal-psychological counseling. Campus security: 24-hour emergency response devices, controlled dormitory access. 120 college housing spaces available; 92 were occupied in 2003-04. Freshmen guaranteed college housing. On-campus residence required in freshman year. Option: coed housing available. Consortium Library with 788,708 books, 591,624 microform titles, 3,434 serials, an OPAC, and a Web page. Operations spending for 2004 fiscal year: $95,000. 40 computers available on campus for general student use. A campuswide network can be accessed from student residence rooms. Staffed computer lab on campus.
Community Environment: Alaska Pacific University is located in Anchorage, a modern, dynamic city with half the population of Alaska. To the west is Cook Inlet, named for the famous English explorer, while mountains rise to the south, east, and north, creating a mild climate. The drive south leads to the ski resort at Alyeska, the glacier at Portage and the famous fishing of the Kenai. To the north lie the Alaska Range and Mount McKinley. Anchorage is a young city on the move. Anchorage's per capita income is twice the national average. Anchorage is lively. Dog teams race down Fourth Avenue during the winter Fur Rendezvous while opera, symphony, theater and a steady stream of rock stars, dance troupes, and artists provide cultural

events for every taste. Winters are moderated by the warm Japanese current while summers are blessed with a sun that never sets. Daily intercontinental flights link Anchorage to Hawaii, Tokyo, Beijing, Moscow, Stockholm, London, and New York.

■ **CHARTER COLLEGE** *H-9*
2221 East Northern Lights Blvd., Ste. 120
Anchorage, AK 99508-4140
Tel: (907)277-1000
Fax: (907)274-3342
Web Site: http://www.chartercollege.org/

Description: Proprietary, primarily 2-year, coed. Awards certificates, transfer associate, terminal associate, and bachelor's degrees. Founded 1985. Setting: urban campus. Total enrollment: 416. Summer session for credit, part-time degree program, adult/continuing education programs, internships.

Entrance Requirements: Open admission. Required: high school transcript, interview. Entrance: noncompetitive. Application deadline: Rolling. Notification: continuous.

Collegiate Environment: Orientation program. Most popular organization: Student Support Committee. Major annual events: faculty/student/staff picnic, Quarterly Pizza Fest. Campus security: 24-hour emergency response devices. College housing not available. Charter College Library with 1,000 books, 50 serials, and a Web page. 85 computers available on campus for general student use. A campuswide network can be accessed. Staffed computer lab on campus.

■ **ILISAGVIK COLLEGE** *A-7*
UIC/Narl
Barrow, AK 99723
Tel: (907)852-3333
Admissions: (907)852-1820
Fax: (907)852-2729
Web Site: http://www.ilisagvik.cc/

Description: State-supported, 2-year, coed. Awards certificates, diplomas, and transfer associate degrees. Founded 1995. Endowment: $155,880. Educational spending for 2005 fiscal year: $9868 per student. Total enrollment: 263. Student-undergrad faculty ratio is 10:1. 214 applied, 100% were admitted. Full-time: 49 students, 61% women, 39% men. Part-time: 214 students, 43% women, 57% men. 0% from out-of-state, 90% Native American, 1% Hispanic, 0.4% black, 3% Asian American or Pacific Islander, 0% international. Calendar: semesters.

Entrance Requirements: Required: essay, high school transcript, minimum 2.0. high school GPA, ACT ASSET. Application deadline: 8/1.

Costs Per Year: Application fee: $0. Area resident tuition: $1440 full-time, $60 per credit hour part-time. State resident tuition: $2880 full-time, $120 per credit hour part-time. Nonresident tuition: $2880 full-time, $120 per credit hour part-time. Mandatory fees: $100 full-time, $50 per term part-time. College room only: $4000.

Collegiate Environment: Student services: women's center.

■ **SHELDON JACKSON COLLEGE** *K-15*
801 Lincoln St.
Sitka, AK 99835-7699
Tel: (907)747-5222
Free: 800-478-4556
Admissions: (907)747-5208
Fax: (907)747-5212
E-mail: admissions@sj-alaska.edu
Web Site: http://www.sj-alaska.edu

Description: Independent, 4-year, coed, affiliated with Presbyterian Church (U.S.A.). Awards associate and bachelor's degrees. Founded 1878. Setting: 320-acre small town campus. Endowment: $1.4 million. Educational spending for 2005 fiscal year: $7319 per student. Total enrollment: 274. 198 applied, 71% were admitted. Full-time: 135 students, 70% women, 30% men. Part-time: 139 students, 65% women, 35% men. Students come from 26 states and territories, 49% from out-of-state, 26% Native American, 5% Hispanic, 5% black, 0% Asian American or Pacific Islander, 0% international, 24% 25 or older, 80% live on campus, 8% transferred in. Retention: 60% of full-time freshmen returned the following year. Core. Calendar: semesters. Academic remediation for entering students, services for LD students, advanced placement, self-designed majors, independent study, double major, part-time degree program, co-op programs and internships. Study abroad program.

Entrance Requirements: Open admission. Options: Peterson's Universal Application, Common Application, electronic application, deferred admission. Required: high school transcript. Recommended: essay, minimum 2.0 high school GPA. Entrance: noncompetitive. Application deadline: Rolling. Notification: continuous. Preference given to Alaska natives.

Costs Per Year: Application fee: $25. Comprehensive fee: $18,500 includes full-time tuition ($10,600), mandatory fees ($600), and college room and board ($7300). College room only: $3700. Room and board charges vary according to board plan and housing facility. Part-time tuition: $355 per credit. Part-time mandatory fees: $355 per credit. Part-time tuition and fees vary according to course load and degree level.

Collegiate Environment: Orientation program. Choral group. Social organizations: 5 open to all. Most popular organizations: Fly Fishing Club, basketball, American Sign Language, American Fisheries Society, Student Ethnic Association. Major annual events: Fall Talent Show, Founders' Day, Spring Expo. Student services: personal-psychological counseling. Campus security: 24-hour patrols, controlled dormitory access. 180 college housing spaces available; 72 were occupied in 2003-04. No special consideration for freshman housing applicants. On-campus residence required through sophomore year. Options: coed, men-only, women-only housing available. Stratton Library with 46,000 books, 3 microform titles, 150 serials, an OPAC, and a Web page. Operations spending for 2004 fiscal year: $104,181. 60 computers available on campus for general student use. A campuswide network can be accessed from student residence rooms and from off campus. Staffed computer lab on campus.

Community Environment: Campus is located in Sitka on Baranof Island, Part of Tongass National Forest in Southeast Alaska. A mild marine climate keeps Sitka cool in summer and warm in the winter. Rainfall is slightly less than 100 inches per year. Sitka is Alaska's fifth largest city with a population of about 9,000 people. It supports a sizable business community including clothing stores, sporting goods, record stores, movie theater, convention center, museums, radio stations, local TV station, and a number of excellent restaurants. Access is by jet, plane, or ferry.

■ **UNIVERSITY OF ALASKA ANCHORAGE** *H-9*
3211 Providence Dr.
Anchorage, AK 99508-8060
Tel: (907)786-1800
Admissions: (907)786-1558
Fax: (907)786-4888
Web Site: http://www.uaa.alaska.edu/

Description: State-supported, comprehensive, coed. Part of University of Alaska System. Awards associate, bachelor's, and master's degrees. Founded 1954. Setting: 428-acre urban campus. Endowment: $7.3 million. Research spending for 2004 fiscal year: $4.5 million. Total enrollment: 16,261. 2,564 applied, 81% were admitted. 12% from top 10% of their high school class, 32% from top quarter, 60% from top half. Full-time: 6,906 students, 58% women, 42% men. Part-time: 8,575 students, 64% women, 36% men. Students come from 50 states and territories, 41 other countries, 6% from out-of-state, 10% Native American, 4% Hispanic, 4% black, 6% Asian American or Pacific Islander, 2% international, 46% 25 or older, 6% live on campus, 3% transferred in. Core. Calendar: semesters. Academic remediation for entering students, ESL program, services for LD students, advanced placement, accelerated degree program, self-designed majors, honors program, independent study, distance learning, double major, summer session for credit, part-time degree program, adult/continuing education programs, co-op programs and internships, graduate courses open to undergrads. Off campus study at members of the National Student Exchange, Western Interstate Commission for Higher Education, Western Undergraduate Exchange. Study abroad program. ROTC: Air Force.

Entrance Requirements: Option: deferred admission. Required: minimum 2.0 high school GPA, SAT or ACT. Required for some: high school transcript. Entrance: noncompetitive. Application deadline: 7/1.

Costs Per Year: Application fee: $40. State resident tuition: $2952 full-time, $116 per credit hour part-time. Nonresident tuition: $9048 full-time, $370 per credit hour part-time. Mandatory fees: $513 full-time. Full-time tuition and fees vary according to course level. Part-time tuition varies according to course level. College room and board: $7810. College room only: $4710. Room and board charges vary according to board plan and housing facility.

Collegiate Environment: Orientation program. Drama-theater group, choral group, student-run newspaper, radio station. Social organizations: 80 open to all. Most popular organizations: Accounting Club, African-American Students Association, Association of Latin-American Spanish Students, Inter-Varsity Christian Fellowship, Student Nurses Association. Major annual

events: UAA orientation programs, Great Alaska Shootout Basketball Tournament. Student services: health clinic, personal-psychological counseling, women's center. Campus security: 24-hour emergency response devices and patrols, student patrols, late night transport-escort service, controlled dormitory access. Option: coed housing available. Consortium Library with 894,080 books, 579,920 microform titles, 3,833 serials, and 9,006 audiovisual materials. 500 computers available on campus for general student use. A campuswide network can be accessed from student residence rooms and from off campus. Staffed computer lab on campus.

Community Environment: Anchorage, population 250,000, is a friendly, modern progressive city and the largest in Alaska. Summertime temperatures range between 60 and 70 degrees. The winters are less severe in Anchorage than in many U.S. cities. Anchorage is the major stopover point for most international transpolar flights. Living costs are higher than in the continental U.S., with an average living cost (plus tuition) of approximately $11,000 to $14,000 per year. The city bustles with growth and activity; cultural interests are wide range and include a symphony orchestra, museums, a theater group and a dance company. Recreation facilities include theaters, golf courses, bowling alleys, swimming pools, public beaches, skating rinks, ball parks, and several excellent ski areas. Hunting and fishing are easily accessible. There are several hospitals within the city which is near Ft. Richardson Army Post and Elmendorf AFB.

■ **UNIVERSITY OF ALASKA ANCHORAGE, KENAI PENINSULA COLLEGE** *I-9*
34820 College Dr.
Soldotna, AK 99669-9798
Tel: (907)262-0300
Fax: (907)262-0322
Web Site: http://www.kpc.alaska.edu/
Description: State-supported, 2-year, coed. Part of University of Alaska System. Awards certificates, transfer associate, and terminal associate degrees. Founded 1964. Setting: 360-acre rural campus. Endowment: $950,000. Educational spending for 2005 fiscal year: $4700 per student. Total enrollment: 1,923. 91 applied, 100% were admitted. 82% 25 or older. Core. Calendar: semesters. Academic remediation for entering students, ESL program, services for LD students, advanced placement, part-time degree program, adult/continuing education programs.
Entrance Requirements: Open admission. Option: Common Application. Required: high school transcript. Required for some: interview. Placement: ACT ASSET required. Entrance: noncompetitive. Application deadline: Rolling.
Collegiate Environment: Orientation program. Drama-theater group, student-run newspaper. Student services: personal-psychological counseling. Campus security: 24-hour emergency response devices. College housing not available. Kenai Peninsula College Library with 25,000 books and 95 serials. Operations spending for 2004 fiscal year: $130,200. 45 computers available on campus for general student use. A campuswide network can be accessed. Staffed computer lab on campus.
Community Environment: Soldotna, population 15,760, is located on the coast and enjoys a cool climate during the spring and summer months. Public transportation in and out of Kenai is mainly by air and highway with some bus service available. The city has a library, museum, many churches, and a full-service hospital. Recreation includes hunting, fishing, boating, water sports, and clam digging. Annual Kenai days around the middle of July is a traditional event. Part-time employment is available.

■ **UNIVERSITY OF ALASKA ANCHORAGE, KODIAK COLLEGE** *K-8*
117 Benny Benson Dr.
Kodiak, AK 99615-6643
Tel: (907)486-4161
Admissions: (907)486-1235
Fax: (907)486-1257
Web Site: http://www.koc.alaska.edu/
Description: State-supported, 2-year, coed. Part of University of Alaska System. Awards certificates, transfer associate, and terminal associate degrees. Founded 1968. Setting: 68-acre rural campus. Total enrollment: 786. 64 applied, 100% were admitted. 10% Native American, 4% Hispanic, 2% black, 6% Asian American or Pacific Islander, 0% international, 72% 25 or older. Core. Calendar: semesters. Academic remediation for entering students, advanced placement, double major, part-time degree program, adult/continuing education programs.
Entrance Requirements: Open admission. Recommended: high school transcript. Placement: ACT ASSET required. Entrance: noncompetitive. Application deadline: Rolling.

Collegiate Environment: College housing not available. Carolyn Floyd Library with 21,000 books, 30 microform titles, 39 serials, 2,400 audiovisual materials, an OPAC, and a Web page. 40 computers available on campus for general student use. A campuswide network can be accessed. Staffed computer lab on campus.
Community Environment: Population 8,200. Kodiak, located in the Gulf of Alaska on Kodiak Island, was once a Russian settlement. It has always looked to the sea for its livelihood and in 1968 became the largest fishing port in dollar volume in the United States. Transportation to Kodiak is an interesting trip by automobile. The Alaska Marine Highway ferry, Tustumena, serves Kodiak regularly. There is direct flight service from Anchorage. The city of Kodiak is the largest town in the Kodiak Island group and is the oldest permanent settlement in Alaska. The city is situated on the northeastern corner of Kodiak Island nestled at the foot of the 1,400 foot Pillar Mountain, overlooking the island-studded harbor of St. Paul. This northerly section of the City of Kodiak was rebuilt following the Good Friday earthquake and tidal wave of 1964. The average temperature in January is 30 degrees and in August, 55 degrees. The annual rainfall is 60 inches spread throughout the year. A number of churches, and service organizations are found in the city.

■ **UNIVERSITY OF ALASKA ANCHORAGE, MATANUSKA-SUSITNA COLLEGE** *A-14*
PO Box 2889
Palmer, AK 99645-2889
Tel: (907)745-9774
Admissions: (907)745-9712
Fax: (907)745-9747
Web Site: http://www.matsu.alaska.edu/
Description: State-supported, 2-year, coed. Part of University of Alaska System. Awards certificates, transfer associate, and terminal associate degrees. Founded 1958. Setting: 950-acre small town campus with easy access to Anchorage. Total enrollment: 1,326. Student-undergrad faculty ratio is 14:1. Full-time: 384 students, 57% women, 43% men. Part-time: 942 students, 73% women, 27% men. Students come from 51 states and territories, 18 other countries, 4% Native American, 3% Hispanic, 2% black, 1% Asian American or Pacific Islander, 0.2% international, 82% 25 or older. Retention: 67% of full-time freshmen returned the following year. Core. Calendar: semesters. Academic remediation for entering students, advanced placement, independent study, distance learning, double major, summer session for credit, part-time degree program, adult/continuing education programs, co-op programs and internships. Off campus study at Alaska Pacific University, University of Alaska Anchorage.
Entrance Requirements: Open admission. Required: high school transcript. Entrance: noncompetitive. Application deadline: 11/1. Notification: 12/1.
Costs Per Year: Application fee: $40. State resident tuition: $2880 full-time. Nonresident tuition: $9576 full-time. Mandatory fees: $250 full-time.
Collegiate Environment: Orientation program. Choral group, student-run newspaper. Most popular organizations: student government, Math Club. Major annual events: Christmas Ball, Spring BBQ. Campus security: 24-hour patrols. College housing not available. Al Okeson Library with 50,000 books, 292 microform titles, 280 serials, 1,840 audiovisual materials, an OPAC, and a Web page. 207 computers available on campus for general student use. Computer purchase/lease plans available. from off-campusStaffed computer lab on campus.
Community Environment: Population 47,000, Palmer is a rural town with subarctic climate. A branch of the Alaska Railroad and bus service to Anchorage serve this area. There are churches, a library, museum, hospital, and a health center in the town. Recreational activities include fishing, boating, ice skating and some swimming. There are good shopping facilities available. Palmer has the usual civic organizations found in most U.S. cities. The Alaska State Fair is the fourth weekend of August through Labor Day weekend each year.

■ **UNIVERSITY OF ALASKA FAIRBANKS** *F-10*
PO Box 757500
Fairbanks, AK 99775-7520
Tel: (907)474-7211
Free: 800-478-1823
Admissions: (907)474-7500
Fax: (907)474-5379
E-mail: fyapply@uaf.edu
Web Site: http://www.uaf.edu/
Description: State-supported, university, coed. Part of University of Alaska System. Awards associate, bachelor's, master's, and doctoral degrees.

Founded 1917. Setting: 2,250-acre small town campus. Research spending for 2004 fiscal year: $108.9 million. Educational spending for 2005 fiscal year: $10,462 per student. Total enrollment: 8,230. Faculty: 295 (288 full-time, 7 part-time). Student-undergrad faculty ratio is 16:1. 1,777 applied, 78% were admitted. 15% from top 10% of their high school class, 34% from top quarter, 61% from top half. Full-time: 3,462 students, 51% women, 49% men. Part-time: 3,674 students, 66% women, 34% men. Students come from 55 states and territories, 36 other countries, 13% from out-of-state, 19% Native American, 3% Hispanic, 3% black, 3% Asian American or Pacific Islander, 3% international, 35% 25 or older, 42% live on campus, 6% transferred in. Retention: 68% of full-time freshmen returned the following year. Academic areas with the most degrees conferred: engineering; business/marketing; biological/life sciences; communications/journalism. Core. Calendar: semesters. Academic remediation for entering students, ESL program, services for LD students, advanced placement, accelerated degree program, self-designed majors, honors program, independent study, distance learning, double major, summer session for credit, part-time degree program, external degree program, co-op programs and internships, graduate courses open to undergrads. Off campus study at National Student Exchange. Study abroad program. ROTC: Army.

Entrance Requirements: Options: electronic application, early admission, deferred admission, international baccalaureate accepted. Required: high school transcript, minimum 2.0 high school GPA, SAT or ACT. Placement: SAT or ACT required. Entrance: minimally difficult. Application deadline: 8/1.

Costs Per Year: Application fee: $40. State resident tuition: $3825 full-time, $128 per credit part-time. Nonresident tuition: $12,195 full-time, $407 per credit part-time. Mandatory fees: $693 full-time. College room and board: $5580. College room only: $2990.

Collegiate Environment: Orientation program. Drama-theater group, choral group, student-run newspaper, radio station. Social organizations: 78 open to all; national fraternities, national sororities; 1% of eligible men and 1% of eligible women are members. Most popular organizations: United Campus Ministry, Northern Star Chinese Student Association, Golden Key National Honor Society, UAF Good Time Swing Dance Club, University Women's Association. Major annual events: Starvation Gulch, Melt Down, Winter Carnival. Student services: legal services, health clinic, personal-psychological counseling, women's center. Campus security: 24-hour emergency response devices and patrols, student patrols, late night transport-escort service, controlled dormitory access, ID check at door of residence halls, crime prevention and safety workshops. 1,580 college housing spaces available; 1,310 were occupied in 2003-04. Freshmen given priority for college housing. Option: coed housing available. Rasmuson Library plus 2 others with 616,456 books, 1.2 million microform titles, 1,457 serials, 8,377 audiovisual materials, an OPAC, and a Web page. Operations spending for 2004 fiscal year: $7.8 million. 56 computers available on campus for general student use. Computer purchase/lease plans available. A campuswide network can be accessed from student residence rooms and from off campus. Staffed computer lab on campus.

Community Environment: The campus overlooks the Tanana Valley and the city of Fairbanks. Offering the amenities of larger communities, Fairbanks maintains the atmosphere of smaller, more personal towns. One hundred miles south is Denali National Park, home to North America's tallest mountain--Mt. McKinley. Closer lay the vast wilderness that makes up the Great Interior of Alaska. Adventure is unlimited here--hiking, biking, climbing, canoeing, skiing, dog mushing, and other recreational activities abound. Winters are cold, with an annual snowfall of 70 inches. Summers bring temperatures in the 80s and 24 hours of daylight, perfect weather for the activities Alaska has to offer.

■ **UNIVERSITY OF ALASKA, PRINCE WILLIAM SOUND COMMUNITY COLLEGE** *H-10*
PO Box 97
Valdez, AK 99686-0097
Tel: (907)834-1600
Admissions: (907)834-1632
Fax: (907)834-1661
E-mail: sfoster@pwscc.edu
Web Site: http://www.pwscc.edu/
Description: State-supported, 2-year, coed. Part of University of Alaska System. Awards certificates, diplomas, transfer associate, and terminal associate degrees. Founded 1978. Setting: small town campus. Endowment: $62,630. Research spending for 2004 fiscal year: $5000. Total enrollment: 2,308. 46 applied. Students come from 1 other country, 4% from out-of-state, 76% 25 or older, 2% live on campus. Core. Calendar: semesters. Academic

remediation for entering students, ESL program, advanced placement, independent study, distance learning, double major, summer session for credit, adult/continuing education programs, co-op programs and internships.

Entrance Requirements: Open admission. Option: early admission. Placement: ACT ASSET required. Entrance: noncompetitive. Application deadline: Rolling.

Collegiate Environment: Student services: personal-psychological counseling. Campus security: student patrols, housing manager supervision. Option: coed housing available. Valdez Consortium Library with 40,870 books, 137 serials, an OPAC, and a Web page. Operations spending for 2004 fiscal year: $40,000. 25 computers available on campus for general student use. Staffed computer lab on campus.

■ **UNIVERSITY OF ALASKA SOUTHEAST** *J-15*
11120 Glacier Hwy.
Juneau, AK 99801
Tel: (907)796-6457; 877-796-4827
Admissions: (907)796-6294
Fax: (907)796-6365
E-mail: admissions@uas.alaska.edu
Web Site: http://www.uas.alaska.edu/
Description: State-supported, comprehensive, coed. Part of University of Alaska System. Awards associate, bachelor's, and master's degrees. Founded 1972. Setting: 198-acre small town campus. Endowment: $3.3 million. Research spending for 2004 fiscal year: $892,900. Educational spending for 2005 fiscal year: $9339 per student. Total enrollment: 3,126. Faculty: 229 (101 full-time, 128 part-time). Student-undergrad faculty ratio is 12:1. 383 applied, 63% were admitted. 7% from top 10% of their high school class, 24% from top quarter, 51% from top half. Full-time: 866 students, 58% women, 42% men. Part-time: 2,048 students, 67% women, 33% men. Students come from 44 states and territories, 5 other countries, 16% from out-of-state, 18% Native American, 3% Hispanic, 1% black, 5% Asian American or Pacific Islander, 1% international, 47% 25 or older, 5% transferred in. Retention: 63% of full-time freshmen returned the following year. Academic areas with the most degrees conferred: business/marketing; liberal arts/general studies; biological/life sciences. Core. Calendar: semesters. Academic remediation for entering students, services for LD students, advanced placement, self-designed majors, independent study, distance learning, summer session for credit, part-time degree program, adult/continuing education programs, co-op programs and internships, graduate courses open to undergrads. Off campus study at National Student Exchange. Study abroad program.

Entrance Requirements: Open admission. Options: Peterson's Universal Application, early admission, deferred admission. Required: high school transcript, minimum 2.0 high school GPA, SAT or ACT. Required for some: essay. Entrance: noncompetitive. Application deadline: Rolling.

Costs Per Year: Application fee: $40. State resident tuition: $3060 full-time, $135 per credit hour part-time. Nonresident tuition: $9756 full-time, $414 per credit hour part-time. Mandatory fees: $796 full-time. College room and board: $6714. College room only: $4177.

Collegiate Environment: Orientation program. Student-run newspaper. Most popular organization: Native Student Club. Major annual events: Orientation Week, Winterfest. Student services: health clinic, personal-psychological counseling. Campus security: 24-hour emergency response devices and patrols, late night transport-escort service, controlled dormitory access. 213 college housing spaces available; 18 were occupied in 2003-04. Freshmen given priority for college housing. Option: coed housing available. Egan Memorial Library plus 1 other with 176,312 books, 501,202 microform titles, 438 serials, 4,181 audiovisual materials, an OPAC, and a Web page. Operations spending for 2004 fiscal year: $1.6 million. 75 computers available on campus for general student use. A campuswide network can be accessed from student residence rooms and from off campus. Staffed computer lab on campus.

Community Environment: Situated on the shores of scenic Auke Lake, with the famous Mendenhall Glacier in clear sight, the main campus is only a few miles from the heart of downtown Juneau, the capital of Alaska. Nestled between 4,000-foot snow-capped peaks on one side and the sparkling water of Gastineau Channel on the other, Juneau was the first Alaskan city founded after the American purchase of Alaska in 1867. The city is centrally located in the Tongass National Forest, the nation's largest. The combined city and borough encompass 3,108 square miles of land, ranging from tundra, to moss-draped forests, to wind-blown mountain peaks. Juneau's population is approximately 30,000 and provides numerous cultural, academic, and professional opportunities.

■ **UNIVERSITY OF ALASKA SOUTHEAST, KETCHIKAN CAMPUS**
L-17
2600 7th Ave.
Ketchikan, AK 99901-5798
Tel: (907)225-6177
Admissions: (907)228-4508
Fax: (907)225-3624
E-mail: knblj@acad1.alaska.edu
Web Site: http://www.ketch.alaska.edu/
Description: State and locally supported, 2-year, coed. Part of University of Alaska System. Awards transfer associate and terminal associate degrees. Founded 1954. Setting: 51-acre small town campus. Endowment: $2.6 million. Research spending for 2004 fiscal year: $92,750. Educational spending for 2005 fiscal year: $2800 per student. Total enrollment: 692. Students come from 5 states and territories, 2 other countries, 46% 25 or older. Core. Calendar: semesters. Academic remediation for entering students, ESL program, services for LD students, self-designed majors, independent study, distance learning, part-time degree program, adult/continuing education programs, internships. Off campus study at University of Alaska Southeast, Sheldon Jackson College.
Entrance Requirements: Open admission. Option: early admission. Required: high school transcript. Required for some: essay. Placement: SAT or ACT recommended; ACT ASSET required for some. Entrance: noncompetitive. Application deadline: Rolling.
Costs Per Year: Application fee: $35. State resident tuition: $2784 full-time. Mandatory fees: $796 full-time. Full-time tuition and fees vary according to course level and course load. College room and board: $6714. College room only: $4177.
Collegiate Environment: Orientation program. Most popular organization: student council. Student services: personal-psychological counseling. Campus security: 24-hour emergency response devices. Ketchikan Campus Library with 54,000 books, 175 serials, and an OPAC. Operations spending for 2004 fiscal year: $146,272. 40 computers available on campus for general student use. Staffed computer lab on campus.
Community Environment: Population 14,000. Located on the Revillagigedo Island 600 miles northwest of Seattle; climate is very wet - 13 feet of rain per year. Airlines and water transportation serves the area. Extensive access to the Tongass National Forest and intercoastal waterways.

■ **UNIVERSITY OF ALASKA SOUTHEAST, SITKA CAMPUS** *K-15*
1332 Seward Ave.
Sitka, AK 99835-9418

Tel: (907)747-6653
Admissions: (907)747-7703
Fax: (907)747-7747
Web Site: http://www.uas.alaska.edu/
Description: State-supported, 2-year, coed. Part of University of Alaska System. Awards certificates, diplomas, transfer associate, and terminal associate degrees. Founded 1962. Setting: small town campus. Total enrollment: 1,552. Students come from 10 states and territories, 2 other countries, 65% 25 or older. Core. Calendar: semesters. Academic remediation for entering students, ESL program, summer session for credit, part-time degree program, adult/continuing education programs, co-op programs and internships. Off campus study at Sheldon Jackson College, University of Alaska Southeast.
Entrance Requirements: Open admission. Options: Common Application, early admission. Required: high school transcript, minimum 2.0 high school GPA. Required for some: essay. Entrance: noncompetitive. Application deadline: Rolling. Notification: continuous.
Collegiate Environment: Social organizations: 2 open to all. Most popular organizations: Student Government Association, Tai Chi Club. Major annual events: campus-wide picnic, Christmas tree lighting, bi-annual stress fair. Campus security: 24-hour emergency response devices. College housing not available. Stratton Library with 80,050 books, 306 serials, an OPAC, and a Web page. Operations spending for 2004 fiscal year: $76,000. 45 computers available on campus for general student use. A campuswide network can be accessed from student residence rooms and from off campus. Staffed computer lab on campus.
Community Environment: Population 8,300. Sitka is the original capital of Russian-America and was the site of the transfer of Alaska from Russia to the United States in 1867. Many historic sites and museums convey these historic origins, as well as the strong Northwest Coast Native heritage of the region. The rainy climate is mild and comparable to that of Seattle or Portland. Located on Baranof Island, adjacent to the mainland coast of the Southeast Alaskan panhandle, Sitka is surrounded by the heavily forested mountains of the Tongass National Forest. It is served by daily jet service, as well as small regional air carriers. The Alaska Marine Highway System provides weekly passenger and vehicle transportation from the southern terminal of Bellingham, Washington, and the northern terminal of Haines, Alaska. A regional center for health services, business, and education, Sitka has two hospitals, several small but important museums, two colleges, and a State-operated boarding high school.

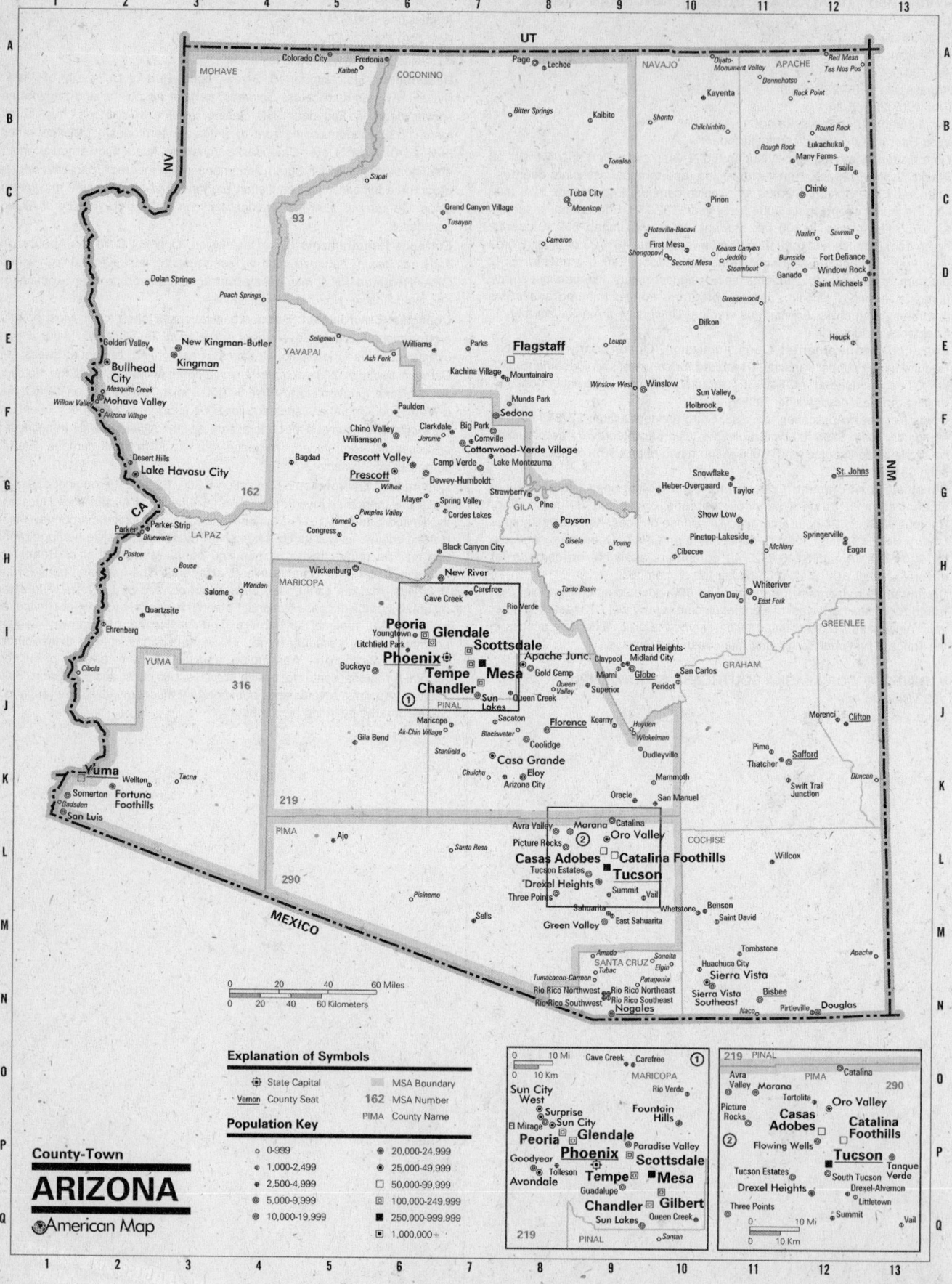

County-Town

ARIZONA

American Map

■ **AMERICAN INDIAN COLLEGE OF THE ASSEMBLIES OF GOD,
INC.** *P-9*
10020 North Fifteenth Ave.
Phoenix, AZ 85021-2199
Tel: (602)944-3335
Free: 800-933-3828
E-mail: sticeahkie@aicag.edu
Web Site: http://www.aicag.edu/
Description: Independent, 4-year, coed, affiliated with Assemblies of God.
Awards associate and bachelor's degrees. Founded 1957. Setting: 10-acre
urban campus. Total enrollment: 73. 18 applied, 44% were admitted. 60%
from top half of their high school class. Full-time: 60 students, 45% women,
55% men. Part-time: 13 students, 62% women, 38% men. Students come
from 10 states and territories, 29% from out-of-state, 67% Native American,
7% Hispanic, 3% black, 4% Asian American or Pacific Islander, 1%
international, 14% 25 or older, 7% transferred in. Retention: 88% of full-time
freshmen returned the following year. Core. Calendar: semesters. Academic
remediation for entering students, independent study, distance learning,
double major, internships.
Entrance Requirements: Required: essay, high school transcript, 1 recommendation, SAT or ACT. Entrance: minimally difficult. Application deadline:
8/15. Preference given to members of Assemblies of God and other
evangelical churches.
Collegiate Environment: Orientation program. Drama-theater group. Most
popular organizations: Missions Fellowship, Associated Student Body,
yearbook. Major annual events: homecoming, Student Benefit Festival, College Days. Student services: personal-psychological counseling. Campus
security: student patrols. On-campus residence required through senior year.
Cummings Memorial Library with 19,899 books, 120 serials, and an OPAC.
39 computers available on campus for general student use. A campuswide
network can be accessed. Staffed computer lab on campus.

■ **APOLLO COLLEGE-PHOENIX, INC.** *P-9*
8503 North 27th Ave.
Phoenix, AZ 85051
Tel: (602)864-1571
Fax: (602)864-8207
E-mail: rutley@apollocollege.com
Web Site: http://www.apollocollege.com/
Description: Proprietary, 2-year, coed. Part of Apollo Colleges, Inc. Awards
certificates, diplomas, transfer associate, and terminal associate degrees.
Founded 1976. Setting: urban campus. Educational spending for 2005 fiscal
year: $3204 per student. Total enrollment: 603. 366 applied, 97% were
admitted. Students come from 6 states and territories, 3 other countries, 6%
from out-of-state, 11% Native American, 30% Hispanic, 7% black, 2% Asian
American or Pacific Islander, 72% 25 or older. Calendar: continuous.
Academic remediation for entering students.
Entrance Requirements: Open admission. Option: Peterson's Universal
Application. Required: high school transcript. Required for some: essay,
interview. Entrance: noncompetitive.
Collegiate Environment: Orientation program. College housing not avail-
able.

■ **APOLLO COLLEGE-TRI-CITY, INC.** *I-7*
630 West Southern Ave.
Mesa, AZ 85210-5004

Tel: (480)831-6585
Free: 800-36-TRAIN
Fax: (480)827-0022
E-mail: jmiller@apollocollege.com
Web Site: http://www.apollocollege.com/
Description: Proprietary, 2-year, coed. Part of Apollo Colleges, Inc. Awards
diplomas, transfer associate, and terminal associate degrees. Founded
1977. Setting: suburban campus. Total enrollment: 244. 50% 25 or older.
Calendar: semesters.
Entrance Requirements: Open admission. Required: essay, high school
transcript, Wonderlic aptitude test. Required for some: recommendations,
interview. Entrance: noncompetitive. Application deadline: Rolling. Notification: continuous.
Collegiate Environment: Campus security: 24-hour emergency response
devices, late night transport-escort service. 25 computers available on
campus for general student use. Staffed computer lab on campus.

■ **APOLLO COLLEGE-TUCSON, INC.** *L-9*
3870 North Oracle Rd.
Tucson, AZ 85705-3227
Tel: (520)888-5885
Free: 800-36-TRAIN
E-mail: jmckinney@apollocollege.com
Web Site: http://www.apollocollege.com/
Description: Proprietary, 2-year, coed. Part of Apollo Colleges, Inc. Awards
diplomas, transfer associate, and terminal associate degrees. Founded
1984. Setting: suburban campus. Total enrollment: 202. Calendar:
semesters modular courses are offered.
Entrance Requirements: Required for some: essay, high school transcript,
recommendations, interview.
Collegiate Environment: 25 computers available on campus for general
student use.

■ **APOLLO COLLEGE-WESTSIDE, INC.** *P-9*
2701 West Bethany Home Rd.
Phoenix, AZ 85017
Tel: (602)433-1333
Free: 800-36-TRAIN
Admissions: (602)433-1222
E-mail: cnestor@apollocollege.com
Web Site: http://www.apollocollege.com/
Description: Proprietary, 2-year, coed. Part of Apollo Colleges, Inc. Awards
transfer associate and terminal associate degrees. Setting: urban campus.
Total enrollment: 136. 65% 25 or older. Calendar: semesters.
Entrance Requirements: Open admission. Required: essay, high school
transcript, Wonderlic aptitude test. Required for some: recommendations,
interview. Entrance: noncompetitive. Application deadline: Rolling. Notification: continuous.
Collegiate Environment: Campus security: 24-hour emergency response
devices, late night transport-escort service. 10 computers available on
campus for general student use. Staffed computer lab on campus.

■ **ARGOSY UNIVERSITY/PHOENIX** *P-9*
2301 West Dunlap Ave., Ste. 211
Phoenix, AZ 85021

Tel: (602)216-2600; (866)216-2777
Fax: (602)216-2601
E-mail: ahughes@argosyu.edu
Web Site: http://www.argosyu.edu/
Description: Proprietary, upper-level, coed. Part of Argosy University. Awards bachelor's, master's, and doctoral degrees. Founded 1997. Setting: 1-acre urban campus. Total enrollment: 394. 22 applied, 100% were admitted. Full-time: 36 students, 92% women, 8% men. Students come from 50 states and territories, 5 other countries, 80% from out-of-state. Calendar: semesters.
Costs Per Year: Tuition: $14,400 full-time. Mandatory fees: $25 full-time.
Collegiate Environment: Social organizations: 1 open to all; 20% of eligible men and 80% of eligible women are members. Most popular organization: Diversity Club. Campus security: 24-hour emergency response devices. College housing not available.

■ **ARIZONA AUTOMOTIVE INSTITUTE** *I-6*
6829 North 46th Ave.
Glendale, AZ 85301-3597
Tel: (602)934-7273
Admissions: (623)934-7273
Fax: (602)937-5000
Web Site: http://www.azautoinst.com/
Description: Proprietary, 2-year. Awards diplomas and terminal associate degrees. Educational spending for 2005 fiscal year: $4083 per student. Total enrollment: 600. 303 applied, 100% were admitted. Students come from 10 states and territories, 25% Native American, 24% Hispanic, 4% black, 5% Asian American or Pacific Islander, 1% international, 40% 25 or older.
Entrance Requirements: Required: high school transcript. Application deadline: Rolling.

■ **ARIZONA COLLEGE OF ALLIED HEALTH** *I-6*
4425 West Olive Ave., Ste. 300
Glendale, AZ 85302-3843
Tel: (602)222-9300
Fax: (602)200-8726
Web Site: http://www.arizonacollege.edu/
Description: Proprietary, 2-year, coed. Founded 1992.

■ **ARIZONA STATE UNIVERSITY** *I-7*
Tempe, AZ 85287
Tel: (480)965-9011
Admissions: (480)965-7788
E-mail: ugradadm@asuvm.inre.asu.edu
Web Site: http://www.asu.edu/
Description: State-supported, university, coed. Part of Arizona State University. Awards bachelor's, master's, doctoral, and first professional degrees and post-master's certificates. Founded 1885. Setting: 814-acre suburban campus with easy access to Phoenix. Endowment: $277.3 million. Research spending for 2004 fiscal year: $97.5 million. Total enrollment: 51,612. Faculty: 2,282 (1,878 full-time, 404 part-time). Student-undergrad faculty ratio is 22:1. 19,914 applied, 91% were admitted. 27% from top 10% of their high school class, 53% from top quarter, 83% from top half. 161 National Merit Scholars. Full-time: 32,865 students, 52% women, 48% men. Part-time: 8,391 students, 52% women, 48% men. Students come from 53 states and territories, 96 other countries, 24% from out-of-state, 2% Native American, 13% Hispanic, 4% black, 5% Asian American or Pacific Islander, 3% international, 17% 25 or older, 18% live on campus, 9% transferred in. Retention: 79% of full-time freshmen returned the following year. Academic areas with the most degrees conferred: business/marketing; communications/journalism; interdisciplinary studies. Core. Calendar: semesters. Academic remediation for entering students, services for LD students, advanced placement, accelerated degree program, honors program, independent study, distance learning, double major, summer session for credit, part-time degree program, adult/continuing education programs, co-op programs and internships, graduate courses open to undergrads. Off campus study at University of Arizona, Northern Arizona University. Study abroad program. ROTC: Army, Air Force.
Entrance Requirements: Options: early action, international baccalaureate accepted. Required: high school transcript, minimum 3.0 high school GPA, SAT or ACT. Entrance: moderately difficult. Application deadline: Rolling. Notification: continuous.
Costs Per Year: Application fee: $25, $50 for nonresidents. State resident tuition: $4311 full-time, $225 per credit part-time. Nonresident tuition:

$15,000 full-time, $625 per credit part-time. Mandatory fees: $95 full-time, $24 per term part-time. Full-time tuition and fees vary according to program. Part-time tuition and fees vary according to program. College room and board: $6768. College room only: $4275. Room and board charges vary according to board plan and housing facility.
Collegiate Environment: Orientation program. Drama-theater group, choral group, marching band, student-run newspaper, radio station. Social organizations: 515 open to all; national fraternities, national sororities, NPHC fraternities and sororities; 6% of eligible men and 6% of eligible women are members. Most popular organizations: Ski Club, Outing Club, Students Against Discrimination (SAD). Major annual events: World Festival, Blueprint Leadership Conference, Homecoming. Student services: legal services, health clinic, personal-psychological counseling, women's center. Campus security: 24-hour emergency response devices and patrols, late night transport-escort service. 6,342 undergraduates lived in college housing during 2003-04. Freshmen given priority for college housing. Option: coed housing available. Hayden Library plus 4 others with 2.4 million books, 5.7 million microform titles, 28,159 serials, 1.3 million audiovisual materials, an OPAC, and a Web page. 5,000 computers available on campus for general student use. Computer purchase/lease plans available. A campuswide network can be accessed from student residence rooms and from off campus. Staffed computer lab on campus.

■ **ARIZONA STATE UNIVERSITY AT THE POLYTECHNIC CAMPUS** *I-7*
7001 East Williams Field Rd.
Mesa, AZ 85212
Tel: (480)727-3278
Admissions: (480)727-1041
Fax: (480)727-1008
E-mail: gary.mcgrath@asu.edu
Web Site: http://www.poly.asu.edu/
Description: State-supported, comprehensive, coed. Part of Arizona State University. Awards bachelor's and master's degrees. Founded 1995. Setting: 600-acre suburban campus with easy access to Phoenix. Endowment: $5.1 million. Total enrollment: 4,865. Faculty: 139 (130 full-time, 9 part-time). Student-undergrad faculty ratio is 28:1. 762 applied, 86% were admitted. 30% from top 10% of their high school class, 67% from top quarter, 84% from top half. Full-time: 1,244 students, 49% women, 51% men. Part-time: 2,839 students, 51% women, 49% men. Students come from 42 states and territories, 27 other countries, 12% from out-of-state, 3% Native American, 11% Hispanic, 2% black, 3% Asian American or Pacific Islander, 2% international, 38% 25 or older, 10% transferred in. Retention: 0% of full-time freshmen returned the following year. Academic areas with the most degrees conferred: business/marketing; education; agriculture. Calendar: semesters. Services for LD students, advanced placement, accelerated degree program, self-designed majors, honors program, independent study, distance learning, double major, summer session for credit, part-time degree program, internships, graduate courses open to undergrads. Study abroad program. ROTC: Army (c), Air Force (c).
Entrance Requirements: Options: Common Application, electronic application, early action, international baccalaureate accepted. Required: high school transcript. Recommended: minimum 3.0 high school GPA, SAT or ACT. Required for some: essay, interview. Entrance: moderately difficult. Application deadlines: Rolling, 11/1 for early action. Notification: 12/1 for early action.
Costs Per Year: Application fee: $50. State resident tuition: $4301 full-time, $221 per credit hour part-time. Nonresident tuition: $13,918 full-time, $580 per credit hour part-time. Mandatory fees: $45 full-time. Full-time tuition and fees vary according to degree level, location, and program. Part-time tuition varies according to course load, degree level, location, and program. College room and board: $5155. College room only: $2655. Room and board charges vary according to board plan, housing facility, and student level.
Collegiate Environment: Orientation program. Student-run newspaper. Social organizations: 32 open to all; national fraternities, national sororities; 1% of eligible men and 1% of eligible women are members. Most popular organizations: Professional Golf Management Club, Aero Management Tech Student Advisory Committee, Graphic Information Technology Club, National Agri-Marketing Association, One Nation Club. Major annual events: Convocation, Dean's Feast and Fest, Dauntless Drumstix Dash. Student services: health clinic, personal-psychological counseling. Campus security: 24-hour emergency response devices and patrols, late night transport-escort service. 1,126 college housing spaces available. Freshmen given priority for college housing. Option: coed housing available. ASU East Library plus 1 other with 315 microform titles, 196 serials, 256 audiovisual materials, an

OPAC, and a Web page. 456 computers available on campus for general student use. Computer purchase/lease plans available. A campuswide network can be accessed from off-campus. Staffed computer lab on campus.

■ ARIZONA STATE UNIVERSITY WEST *P-9*

PO Box 37100, 4701 W Thunderbird Rd
Phoenix, AZ 85069-7100
Tel: (602)543-5500
Admissions: (602)543-8134
E-mail: cabot@asu.edu
Web Site: http://www.west.asu.edu/

Description: State-supported, comprehensive, coed. Part of Arizona State University. Awards bachelor's and master's degrees. Founded 1984. Setting: 300-acre urban campus. Educational spending for 2005 fiscal year: $4442 per student. Total enrollment: 7,734. Faculty: 388 (233 full-time, 155 part-time). Student-undergrad faculty ratio is 19:1. 1,403 applied, 63% were admitted. 31% from top 10% of their high school class, 60% from top quarter, 88% from top half. Full-time: 4,843 students, 66% women, 34% men. Part-time: 1,777 students, 62% women, 38% men. Students come from 31 states and territories, 23 other countries, 4% from out-of-state, 2% Native American, 19% Hispanic, 5% black, 4% Asian American or Pacific Islander, 1% international, 40% 25 or older, 2% live on campus, 18% transferred in. Retention: 73% of full-time freshmen returned the following year. Academic areas with the most degrees conferred: business/marketing; education; security and protective services; psychology. Core. Calendar: semesters. Services for LD students, self-designed majors, honors program, independent study, distance learning, double major, summer session for credit, part-time degree program, adult/continuing education programs, internships, graduate courses open to undergrads.

Entrance Requirements: Options: Common Application, electronic application. Required: high school transcript, SAT or ACT. Recommended: minimum 3.0 high school GPA. Entrance: moderately difficult. Application deadline: Rolling.

Costs Per Year: Application fee: $50. State resident tuition: $4251 full-time, $221 per credit hour part-time. Nonresident tuition: $15,000 full-time, $625 per credit hour part-time. Mandatory fees: $95 full-time. Part-time tuition varies according to course load. College room only: $5836.

Collegiate Environment: Orientation program. Student-run newspaper. Social organizations: 37 open to all. Most popular organizations: Justice Studies Club, American Marketing Association West, Beta Alpha Psi Accounting Honor Society, Communication Club, Outdoor Recreation Club. Major annual events: Martin Luther King Week, Cultural Fest, Student Activities Fair. Student services: health clinic, personal-psychological counseling, women's center. Campus security: 24-hour emergency response devices and patrols, student patrols, late night transport-escort service. Freshmen given priority for college housing. Option: coed housing available. ASU West Library with 397,987 books, 1.5 million microform titles, 2,481 serials, 27,535 audiovisual materials, an OPAC, and a Web page. 400 computers available on campus for general student use. A campuswide network can be accessed from off-campus. Staffed computer lab on campus.

■ ARIZONA WESTERN COLLEGE *K-1*

PO Box 929
Yuma, AZ 85366-0929
Tel: (928)317-6000; 888-293-0392
Admissions: (928)317-7617
Fax: (928)344-7730
E-mail: bryan.doak@azwestern.edu
Web Site: http://www.azwestern.edu/

Description: State and locally supported, 2-year, coed. Part of Arizona State Community College System. Awards certificates, transfer associate, and terminal associate degrees. Founded 1962. Setting: 640-acre rural campus. Total enrollment: 6,731. Student-undergrad faculty ratio is 16:1. Full-time: 1,849 students, 56% women, 44% men. Part-time: 4,882 students, 61% women, 39% men. Students come from 26 states and territories, 7% from out-of-state, 2% Native American, 53% Hispanic, 3% black, 2% Asian American or Pacific Islander, 10% international, 6% live on campus. Retention: 50% of full-time freshmen returned the following year. Core. Calendar: semesters. Academic remediation for entering students, ESL program, advanced placement, honors program, independent study, distance learning, summer session for credit, part-time degree program, adult/continuing education programs, co-op programs.

Entrance Requirements: Open admission except for nursing program. Op-

tions: Peterson's Universal Application, Common Application, early admission, deferred admission. Entrance: noncompetitive. Application deadline: Rolling.

Costs Per Year: Application fee: $0. State resident tuition: $1200 full-time, $40 per credit hour part-time. Nonresident tuition: $5760 full-time, $46 per credit hour part-time. College room and board: $4468. College room only: $1790.

Collegiate Environment: Drama-theater group, choral group, student-run newspaper, radio station. Social organizations: 15 open to all. Most popular organizations: Associated Students Governing Board, MECHA, Umoja, Honors Club, UVU. Major annual events: Career and Technology Fair, Spring Fling, Christmas Formal. Student services: health clinic, personal-psychological counseling. Campus security: 24-hour emergency response devices and patrols, student patrols, late night transport-escort service. 335 college housing spaces available. Option: coed housing available. Arizona Western College Library with 6,015 microform titles, 698 serials, 10,800 audiovisual materials, an OPAC, and a Web page. 500 computers available on campus for general student use. A campuswide network can be accessed from off-campus. Staffed computer lab on campus.

Community Environment: Yuma, population 770,000, is on the bank of the Colorado River, midway between Phoenix and San Diego. This is a metropolitan area with a warm, dry climate. Rail, air, and all other modes of transportation are available. There are over 50 churches of major denominations, a public library, historic Yuma Territorial Prison and Museum, Yuma Fine Arts Association, Community Concert Association, the St. Thomas Mission, and many civic, fraternal, and veteran's organizations. Recreational activities include boating, fishing, water skiing, and hunting. The Silver Spur Rodeo is in February; the County Fair is in April. Part-time employment is available.

■ THE ART CENTER DESIGN COLLEGE *L-9*

2525 North Country Club Rd.
Tucson, AZ 85716-2505
Tel: (520)325-0123
Free: 800-825-8753
Fax: (520)325-5535
E-mail: cgf@theartcenter.edu
Web Site: http://www.theartcenter.edu/

Description: Proprietary, 4-year, coed. Awards associate and bachelor's degrees. Founded 1983. Setting: suburban campus. Total enrollment: 330. Calendar: semester with a full summer program. Part-time degree program.

Entrance Requirements: Required for some: ACT ASSET. Entrance: moderately difficult. Application deadline: Rolling.

Costs Per Year: Application fee: $25. Tuition: $11,376 full-time, $474 per credit hour part-time.

Collegiate Environment: College housing not available.

■ THE ART INSTITUTE OF PHOENIX *P-9*

2233 West Dunlap Ave.
Phoenix, AZ 85021-2859
Tel: (602)331-7500
Free: 800-474-2479
Fax: (602)331-5301
Web Site: http://www.aipx.artinstitutes.edu/

Description: Proprietary, 4-year, coed. Part of Education Management Corporation. Awards associate and bachelor's degrees. Founded 1995. Setting: 3-acre suburban campus. Total enrollment: 1,114. Student-undergrad faculty ratio is 16:1. Full-time: 866 students, 45% women, 55% men. Part-time: 248 students, 42% women, 58% men. Students come from 33 states and territories, 7 other countries, 31% from out-of-state, 3% Native American, 23% Hispanic, 6% black, 3% Asian American or Pacific Islander, 1% international, 51% 25 or older, 10% live on campus. Core. Academic remediation for entering students, services for LD students, advanced placement, honors program, independent study, distance learning, co-op programs and internships.

Entrance Requirements: Option: Common Application. Required: essay, high school transcript, interview. Recommended: minimum 2.0 high school GPA. Entrance: minimally difficult. Application deadline: Rolling. Notification: continuous.

Costs Per Year: Application fee: $50. One-time mandatory fee: $100. Tuition: $18,144 full-time, $378 per credit hour part-time. Full-time tuition varies according to course load. Part-time tuition varies according to course load. College room only: $5217. Tuition guaranteed not to increase for student's term of enrollment.

Collegiate Environment: Orientation program. Student-run newspaper. Social organizations: 5 open to all. Most popular organizations: Computer Arts and Animation Club, Student Activities Council, Gay and Straight Student Alliance, American Institute of Graphic Arts, International Student Club. Major annual events: All-School Picnic, Halloween Costume Contest, Sexual Responsibility Week. Student services: personal-psychological counseling. Campus security: 24-hour emergency response devices, late night transport-escort service, security guard during open hours. 131 college housing spaces available; all were occupied in 2003-04. No special consideration for freshman housing applicants. Options: men-only, women-only housing available. Learning Resource Center with 13,463 books, 150 serials, and 2,724 audiovisual materials. Operations spending for 2004 fiscal year: $23,000. 258 computers available on campus for general student use. A campuswide network can be accessed. Staffed computer lab on campus.

■ **THE BRYMAN SCHOOL** *P-9*
2250 W. Peoria Ave.
Phoenix, AZ 85029
Tel: (602)274-4300
Free: 800-729-4819
Fax: (602)248-9087
Web Site: http://www.brymanschool.edu/
Description: Proprietary, 2-year, coed. Awards diplomas and terminal associate degrees. Founded 1964. Setting: urban campus. Total enrollment: 1,100. Students come from 20 states and territories, 20% from out-of-state, 30% 25 or older. Core. Calendar: continuous.
Entrance Requirements: Required: high school transcript, interview, The Health Occupations Basic Entrance Test. Entrance: minimally difficult. Application deadline: Rolling.
Collegiate Environment: Campus security: late night transport-escort service. College housing not available.

■ **CENTRAL ARIZONA COLLEGE** *J-8*
8470 North Overfield Rd.
Coolidge, AZ 85228-9779
Tel: (520)426-4444
Admissions: (520)426-4406
Fax: (520)426-4234
Web Site: http://www.cac.cc.az.us/
Description: County-supported, 2-year, coed. Awards certificates, transfer associate, and terminal associate degrees. Founded 1961. Setting: 709-acre rural campus with easy access to Phoenix. Total enrollment: 6,388. Student-undergrad faculty ratio is 17:1. 2,469 applied, 73% were admitted. Students come from 6 other countries, 6% Native American, 32% Hispanic, 5% black, 1% Asian American or Pacific Islander, 1% international, 71% 25 or older, 17% live on campus. Core. Calendar: semesters. Academic remediation for entering students, services for LD students, self-designed majors, honors program, independent study, distance learning, summer session for credit, part-time degree program, adult/continuing education programs.
Entrance Requirements: Open admission except for nursing program. Options: Common Application, early admission, deferred admission. Entrance: noncompetitive. Application deadline: Rolling. Notification: continuous.
Costs Per Year: State resident tuition: $1316 full-time, $47 per credit part-time. Nonresident tuition: $6356 full-time, $94 per credit part-time. Mandatory fees: $16 full-time, $8 per term part-time. Part-time tuition and fees vary according to course level. College room and board: $4160. Room and board charges vary according to housing facility.
Collegiate Environment: Drama-theater group, choral group, student-run newspaper. Student services: personal-psychological counseling. Campus security: 24-hour emergency response devices and patrols. 424 college housing spaces available; 380 were occupied in 2003-04. Learning Resource Center with 99,480 books and 494 serials.
Community Environment: Population 7,000. Coolidge is located in Pinal County near the intersection of two major interstate freeways that serve the areas of Southern California and Arizona's two principal cities, Phoenix and Tucson. One can be in the heart of either city within an hour. There are four Native American Reservations in the county. The area is rich in history of mining, cattle and agriculture. Few places on earth have more hours of sunshine a year than south-central Pinal County, which averages approximately 4,000 hours per year according to U.S. Weather Bureau records.

■ **CHANDLER-GILBERT COMMUNITY COLLEGE** *J-7*
2626 East Pecos Rd.
Chandler, AZ 85225-2479

Tel: (480)732-7000
Admissions: (480)732-7307
Web Site: http://www.cgc.maricopa.edu/
Description: State and locally supported, 2-year, coed. Part of Maricopa County Community College District System. Awards certificates, diplomas, transfer associate, and terminal associate degrees. Founded 1985. Setting: 80-acre rural campus with easy access to Phoenix. Endowment: $315,961. Research spending for 2004 fiscal year: $14.4 million. Total enrollment: 8,663. Students come from 38 states and territories, 5 other countries, 4% from out-of-state, 4% Native American, 16% Hispanic, 4% black, 3% Asian American or Pacific Islander, 1% international, 31% 25 or older. Core. Calendar: semesters. Academic remediation for entering students, ESL program, advanced placement, freshman honors college, honors program, summer session for credit, part-time degree program.
Entrance Requirements: Open admission except nursing and aviation programs. Options: Common Application, electronic application. Placement: ACT ASSET required for some. Entrance: noncompetitive.
Collegiate Environment: Orientation program. Choral group, student-run newspaper. Student services: personal-psychological counseling. Campus security: 24-hour emergency response devices and patrols, late night transport-escort service. Chandler-Gilbert Community College Library with 26,060 books, 90 microform titles, 170 serials, 990 audiovisual materials, and an OPAC. Operations spending for 2004 fiscal year: $580,807. 140 computers available on campus for general student use. A campuswide network can be accessed from off-campus. Staffed computer lab on campus.

■ **CHAPARRAL COLLEGE** *L-9*
4585 East Speedway, No 204
Tucson, AZ 85712
Tel: (520)327-6866
Fax: (520)325-0108
Web Site: http://www.chap-col.edu/
Description: Proprietary, primarily 2-year, coed. Awards diplomas, transfer associate, terminal associate, and bachelor's degrees (bachelor's degree in business administration only). Founded 1972. Setting: suburban campus with easy access to Phoenix. Total enrollment: 400. Students come from 3 other countries, 0% from out-of-state, 70% 25 or older. Core. Calendar: 5 five-week modules. Academic remediation for entering students, summer session for credit, internships.
Entrance Requirements: Open admission. Option: Common Application. Required: high school transcript, interview, CPAt. Required for some: recommendations, entrance test. Entrance: noncompetitive. Application deadline: Rolling.
Collegiate Environment: Student-run newspaper. Student services: personal-psychological counseling. Campus security: 24-hour emergency response devices. College housing not available. 6,000 books, 65 serials, 500 audiovisual materials, and a Web page. 150 computers available on campus for general student use. A campuswide network can be accessed. Staffed computer lab on campus.

■ **COCHISE COLLEGE (DOUGLAS)** *N-12*
4190 West Hwy. 80
Douglas, AZ 85607-9724
Tel: (520)364-7943
Free: 800-966-7946
Admissions: (520)417-4050
Fax: (520)364-0236
E-mail: info@tron.cochise.cc.az.us
Web Site: http://www.cochise.edu/
Description: State and locally supported, 2-year, coed. Part of Cochise College. Awards certificates, transfer associate, and terminal associate degrees. Founded 1962. Setting: 500-acre rural campus. Endowment: $1.3 million. Educational spending for 2005 fiscal year: $2702 per student. Total enrollment: 4,610. Student-undergrad faculty ratio is 13:1. 759 applied, 100% were admitted. Full-time: 1,440 students, 60% women, 40% men. Part-time: 3,170 students, 60% women, 40% men. Students come from 4 states and territories, 8 other countries, 5% from out-of-state, 1% Native American, 37% Hispanic, 7% black, 3% Asian American or Pacific Islander, 0.2% international, 33% 25 or older, 17% live on campus, 1% transferred in. Core. Calendar: semesters. Academic remediation for entering students, ESL program, services for LD students, accelerated degree program, independent study, distance learning, summer session for credit, part-time degree program, co-op programs and internships.

Entrance Requirements: Open admission except for nursing program. Options: early admission, deferred admission. Recommended: high school transcript. Entrance: noncompetitive. Application deadline: Rolling. Notification: continuous.

Costs Per Year: State resident tuition: $1350 full-time, $45 per credit hour part-time. Nonresident tuition: $6300 full-time, $65 per credit hour part-time. Mandatory fees: $60 full-time, $30 per term part-time. College room and board: $3562.

Collegiate Environment: Orientation program. Choral group. Social organizations: 6 open to all. Most popular organizations: student government, Phi Theta Kappa. Major annual events: Red and White Ball, Valentine Dance, Springfest. Student services: health clinic, personal-psychological counseling. Campus security: 24-hour emergency response devices and patrols, controlled dormitory access. 240 college housing spaces available; 120 were occupied in 2003-04. 42,876 books, 182 serials, and a Web page. 84 computers available on campus for general student use. Staffed computer lab on campus.

Community Environment: Douglas, population 17,000, located in Cochise County, has a dry climate with average yearly temperatures of 79.2 degrees high and 46.3 degrees low. The area is scenically beautiful and rich in historical lore. Hotels, motels, churches, a library, hospital, medical center, and civic and service organizations are available. There are recreational facilities for golf, tennis, football, baseball, basketball, and swimming. The Cochise County Fair is the last weekend in September. Part-time work is available for students.

■ **COCHISE COLLEGE (SIERRA VISTA)** *N-10*
901 North Columbo
Sierra Vista, AZ 85635-2317
Tel: (520)515-0500
Free: 800-593-9567
Admissions: (520)515-4770
Fax: (520)364-0206
Web Site: http://www.cochise.cc.az.us/

Description: State and locally supported, 2-year, coed. Part of Cochise College. Awards certificates, transfer associate, and terminal associate degrees. Founded 1977. Setting: 200-acre small town campus with easy access to Tucson. Educational spending for 2005 fiscal year: $7299 per student. Total enrollment: 4,446. 1,088 applied, 63% were admitted. 6% from top 10% of their high school class, 24% from top quarter, 74% from top half. Full-time: 1,257 students, 50% women, 50% men. Part-time: 3,189 students, 59% women, 41% men. Students come from 27 states and territories, 8 other countries, 5% from out-of-state, 1% Native American, 31% Hispanic, 7% black, 4% Asian American or Pacific Islander, 0.5% international, 50% 25 or older, 6% transferred in. Core. Calendar: semesters. Academic remediation for entering students, ESL program, services for LD students, accelerated degree program, honors program, independent study, distance learning, double major, summer session for credit, part-time degree program, external degree program, adult/continuing education programs, co-op programs and internships.

Entrance Requirements: Open admission except for nursing program. Options: Common Application, electronic application, early admission, deferred admission, international baccalaureate accepted. Recommended: high school transcript, SAT, ACT, SAT or ACT, SAT and SAT Subject Tests or ACT, SAT Subject Tests. Placement: SAT or ACT recommended; ACCUPLACER required for some. Entrance: noncompetitive. Application deadline: Rolling. Notification: continuous.

Collegiate Environment: Orientation program. Drama-theater group, choral group. Social organizations: 6 open to all. Most popular organizations: student government, Phi Theta Kappa. Major annual events: Red and White Ball, Halloween Dance. Student services: personal-psychological counseling. Campus security: 24-hour emergency response devices and patrols. 240 college housing spaces available; 161 were occupied in 2003-04. Freshmen guaranteed college housing. Charles DiPeso Main Library plus 1 other with 67,317 books, 5,662 microform titles, 305 serials, 3,124 audiovisual materials, an OPAC, and a Web page. 450 computers available on campus for general student use. A campuswide network can be accessed from off-campus. Staffed computer lab on campus.

■ **COCONINO COMMUNITY COLLEGE** *E-8*
2800 South Lonetree Rd.
Flagstaff, AZ 86001
Tel: (928)527-1222
Free: 800-350-7122

Fax: (928)526-1821
E-mail: smiller@coco.cc.az.us
Web Site: http://www.coconino.edu/

Description: State-supported, 2-year, coed. Awards certificates, transfer associate, and terminal associate degrees. Founded 1991. Setting: 5-acre small town campus. Endowment: $11,275. Total enrollment: 3,689. 38% 25 or older. Core. Calendar: semesters. Academic remediation for entering students, services for LD students, advanced placement, summer session for credit, part-time degree program, adult/continuing education programs.

Entrance Requirements: Open admission. Required for some: high school transcript. Entrance: noncompetitive. Application deadline: Rolling.

Costs Per Year: Application fee: $10. State resident tuition: $1344 full-time, $56 per credit hour part-time. Nonresident tuition: $5376 full-time, $224 per credit hour part-time.

Collegiate Environment: Orientation program. Choral group. Campus security: 24-hour patrols. College housing not available. 100 computers available on campus for general student use. Staffed computer lab on campus.

■ **COLLEGE OF THE HUMANITIES AND SCIENCES, HARRISON MIDDLETON UNIVERSITY** *I-7*
1105 East Broadway
Tempe, AZ 85282
Tel: (480)317-5955; 877-248-6724
Fax: (480)829-4999
Web Site: http://www.chumsci.edu/

Description: Independent, comprehensive, coed. Founded 1998. Calendar: continuous.

■ **COLLEGEAMERICA-FLAGSTAFF** *E-8*
5200 East Cortland Blvd., Ste. A-19
Flagstaff, AZ 86004
Tel: (928)526-0763
Admissions: 800-977-5455
Fax: (928)526-3468
E-mail: pberlioux@collegeamerica.edu
Web Site: http://www.collegeamerica.com/

Description: Proprietary, 2-year, coed. Total enrollment: 28,650.

■ **COLLINS COLLEGE: A SCHOOL OF DESIGN AND TECHNOLOGY** *I-7*
1140 South Priest Dr.
Tempe, AZ 85281-5206
Tel: (480)966-3000
Free: 800-876-7070
Fax: (480)966-2599
E-mail: toby@collinscollege.edu
Web Site: http://www.collinscollege.edu/

Description: Proprietary, 4-year, coed. Part of Career Education Corporation. Awards associate and bachelor's degrees. Founded 1978. Setting: 3-acre urban campus with easy access to Phoenix. Total enrollment: 1,828. Student-undergrad faculty ratio is 30:1. 4,304 applied, 37% were admitted. Students come from 49 states and territories, 75% from out-of-state, 2% Native American, 4% Hispanic, 3% black, 0.5% Asian American or Pacific Islander, 0% international, 26% 25 or older. Core. Calendar: trimesters.

Entrance Requirements: Open admission. Options: Common Application, early admission, deferred admission. Required: essay, high school transcript, interview. Recommended: SAT or ACT. Application deadline: Rolling. Notification: continuous.

Costs Per Year: Application fee: $50. Tuition: $13,875 full-time. Full-time tuition varies according to class time, course level, course load, degree level, location, program, reciprocity agreements, and student level. College room only: $2970. Tuition guaranteed not to increase for student's term of enrollment.

Collegiate Environment: Option: coed housing available. Al Collins Graphic Design School Library with 1,000 books and a Web page. Operations spending for 2004 fiscal year: $60,000. 402 computers available on campus for general student use.

■ **DEVRY UNIVERSITY (MESA)** *I-7*
1201 South Alma School Rd.
Mesa, AZ 85210-2011
Tel: (480)827-1511
Fax: (480)827-2552

Web Site: http://www.devry.edu/
Description: Proprietary, comprehensive, coed. Calendar: semesters.
Costs Per Year: One-time mandatory fee: $40. Tuition: $11,790 full-time, $440 per credit part-time. Mandatory fees: $60 full-time, $30 per year part-time.

■ DEVRY UNIVERSITY (PHOENIX) *P-9*
2149 West Dunlap Ave.
Phoenix, AZ 85021-2995
Tel: (602)870-9222; (866)338-7934
Web Site: http://www.devry.edu/
Description: Proprietary, comprehensive, coed. Part of DeVry University. Awards associate, bachelor's, and master's degrees. Founded 1967. Setting: 18-acre urban campus. Total enrollment: 1,380. Faculty: 87 (39 full-time, 48 part-time). Student-undergrad faculty ratio is 20:1. Full-time: 774 students, 22% women, 78% men. Part-time: 390 students, 26% women, 74% men. Students come from 41 states and territories, 4 other countries, 7% Native American, 18% Hispanic, 8% black, 6% Asian American or Pacific Islander, 1% international, 45% 25 or older. Retention: 49% of full-time freshmen returned the following year. Academic areas with the most degrees conferred: computer and information sciences; business/marketing; engineering technologies. Calendar: semesters. Academic remediation for entering students, services for LD students, advanced placement, accelerated degree program, distance learning, summer session for credit, part-time degree program, adult/continuing education programs, co-op programs. ROTC: Air Force.
Entrance Requirements: Options: electronic application, deferred admission, international baccalaureate accepted. Required: high school transcript, interview. Entrance: minimally difficult. Application deadline: Rolling. Notification: continuous.
Costs Per Year: Application fee: $50. One-time mandatory fee: $40. Tuition: $11,790 full-time, $440 per credit part-time. Mandatory fees: $270 full-time, $160 per year part-time. Full-time tuition and fees vary according to course load. Part-time tuition and fees vary according to course load.
Collegiate Environment: Orientation program. Social organizations: 13 open to all. Most popular organizations: Telecommunications Club, Board and Ski Club, Travel Club, SIFE, Institute of Electronic and Electrical Engineers. Major annual events: Thanksgiving dinner, Ethnic Day, Cinco de Mayo. Campus security: 24-hour emergency response devices, student patrols, late night transport-escort service, trained security personnel on duty, lighted pathways/sidewalks. College housing not available. Learning Resource Center with 22,500 books, 1 microform title, 7,230 serials, 11 audiovisual materials, an OPAC, and a Web page. 436 computers available on campus for general student use. Computer purchase/lease plans available. A campuswide network can be accessed from off-campus. Staffed computer lab on campus.

■ DINE COLLEGE *C-12*
PO Box 98
Tsaile, AZ 86556
Tel: (520)724-6600
Admissions: (928)724-6633
Fax: (520)724-3349
E-mail: louise@dinecollege.edu
Web Site: http://www.dinecollege.edu/
Description: Federally supported, 2-year, coed. Awards certificates, transfer associate, and terminal associate degrees. Founded 1968. Setting: 1,200-acre rural campus. Endowment: $3.5 million. Research spending for 2004 fiscal year: $383,607. Total enrollment: 1,825. Full-time: 843 students, 70% women, 30% men. Part-time: 982 students, 81% women, 19% men. Students come from 3 other countries, 98% Native American, 0% Hispanic, 0.2% black, 0.3% Asian American or Pacific Islander, 0% international, 63% 25 or older, 8% live on campus, 12% transferred in. Core. Calendar: semesters. Academic remediation for entering students, services for LD students, summer session for credit, part-time degree program, adult/continuing education programs. Off campus study at members of the American Indian Higher Education Consortium, Arizona State University.
Entrance Requirements: Open admission. Options: Common Application, early admission. Required: high school transcript, certificate of Indian Blood form for Native American Students. Entrance: noncompetitive. Application deadline: Rolling. Notification: continuous. Preference given to Native Americans.
Costs Per Year: Application fee: $0. State resident tuition: $720 full-time, $30 per hour part-time. Nonresident tuition: $720 full-time, $30 per hour part-time. College room and board: $3764. College room only: $1180.

Collegiate Environment: Orientation program. Social organizations: 7 open to all. Most popular organizations: Associate Students of Navajo Community College, Bar-N-Rodeo Club, Red Dawn Indian Club, Native American Church. Major annual events: Fall Bash, Spring Fling, Farewell Dance. Student services: health clinic, personal-psychological counseling. Campus security: 24-hour emergency response devices and patrols, student patrols, late night transport-escort service. Option: coed housing available. Tsaile-Navajo Community College Library plus 1 other with 50,000 books, 329 serials, and a Web page. 262 computers available on campus for general student use. A campuswide network can be accessed from off-campus. Staffed computer lab on campus.

■ EASTERN ARIZONA COLLEGE *K-11*
PO Box 769
Thatcher, AZ 85552-0769
Tel: (520)428-8322
Admissions: (928)428-8247
Fax: (520)428-8462
E-mail: admissions@eac.edu
Web Site: http://www.eac.edu/
Description: State and locally supported, 2-year, coed. Part of Arizona State Community College System. Awards certificates, transfer associate, and terminal associate degrees. Founded 1888. Setting: small town campus. Endowment: $1.6 million. Research spending for 2004 fiscal year: $110,090. Educational spending for 2005 fiscal year: $3326 per student. Total enrollment: 5,239. Student-undergrad faculty ratio is 17:1. 2,287 applied, 100% were admitted. Full-time: 1,413 students, 57% women, 43% men. Part-time: 3,826 students, 60% women, 40% men. Students come from 29 states and territories, 6% from out-of-state, 14% Native American, 28% Hispanic, 4% black, 2% Asian American or Pacific Islander, 1% international, 19% 25 or older, 5% live on campus. Retention: 43% of full-time freshmen returned the following year. Core. Calendar: semesters. Academic remediation for entering students, services for LD students, advanced placement, independent study, double major, summer session for credit, part-time degree program, adult/continuing education programs, co-op programs. Study abroad program.
Entrance Requirements: Open admission except for nursing program, some emergency medical technology programs. Options: electronic application, early admission, deferred admission. Recommended: high school transcript. Entrance: noncompetitive. Application deadline: Rolling. Notification: continuous.
Costs Per Year: Application fee: $0. State resident tuition: $1220 full-time, $50 per credit part-time. Nonresident tuition: $6460 full-time, $100 per credit part-time. College room and board: $4320.
Collegiate Environment: Orientation program. Drama-theater group, choral group, marching band. Social organizations: 20 open to all. Most popular organizations: Latter-Day Saints Student Association, Criminal Justice Student Association, Multicultural Council, Phi Theta Kappa, Mark Allen Dorm Club. Major annual events: Fall Homecoming, Fall Campus Picnic, Yearbook Party. Student services: personal-psychological counseling. Campus security: late night transport-escort service, controlled dormitory access, 20-hour patrols by trained security personnel. 370 college housing spaces available; 243 were occupied in 2003-04. No special consideration for freshman housing applicants. Options: men-only, women-only housing available. Alumni Library plus 1 other with an OPAC and a Web page. Operations spending for 2004 fiscal year: $496,767. 458 computers available on campus for general student use. A campuswide network can be accessed from student residence rooms and from off campus. Staffed computer lab on campus.
Community Environment: Population over 4,000. Thatcher is located in the broad valley of the Gila River. It is on Highway 70 about 75 miles east of the junction of Highways 60 and 70 at Globe, about 165 miles east of Phoenix, and 250 miles west of El Paso. Nearby Safford, with a population of over 9,000, is the county seat of government for Graham County. In addition, it serves as the hotel and shopping center for the upper Gila Valley. The area enjoys an invigorating climate with sunshine 90% of the year; rainfall is approximately nine inches during the year. The valley is flanked by the 10,000-foot Graham Mountains, Gila Mountain Range, Indian Hot Springs, Red Knolls Desert Theatre, Coolidge Dam, and the Great Surface copper mines. All are within easy driving distance. Elevation: 3,000.

■ EMBRY-RIDDLE AERONAUTICAL UNIVERSITY *G-6*
3700 Willow Creek Rd.
Prescott, AZ 86301-3720

Tel: (928)777-3728
Free: 800-888-3728
Admissions: (928)777-6600
Fax: (928)777-3740
E-mail: pradmit@erau.edu
Web Site: http://www.embryriddle.edu/

Description: Independent, comprehensive, coed. Awards bachelor's and master's degrees. Founded 1978. Setting: 547-acre small town campus. Endowment: $46.4 million. Research spending for 2004 fiscal year: $6.9 million. Educational spending for 2005 fiscal year: $10,687 per student. Total enrollment: 1,685. Faculty: 114 (96 full-time, 18 part-time). Student-undergrad faculty ratio is 15:1. 1,163 applied, 89% were admitted. 24% from top 10% of their high school class, 51% from top quarter, 83% from top half. Full-time: 1,466 students, 17% women, 83% men. Part-time: 187 students, 14% women, 86% men. Students come from 52 states and territories, 31 other countries, 77% from out-of-state, 1% Native American, 6% Hispanic, 2% black, 7% Asian American or Pacific Islander, 3% international, 9% 25 or older, 49% live on campus, 6% transferred in. Retention: 78% of full-time freshmen returned the following year. Academic areas with the most degrees conferred: transportation and materials moving; engineering; social sciences. Core. Calendar: semesters. Academic remediation for entering students, ESL program, services for LD students, advanced placement, independent study, distance learning, double major, summer session for credit, part-time degree program, adult/continuing education programs, co-op programs and internships. Study abroad program. ROTC: Army, Air Force.

Entrance Requirements: Options: Peterson's Universal Application, Common Application, electronic application, early admission, early decision, deferred admission, international baccalaureate accepted. Required: high school transcript, minimum 2.0 high school GPA, SAT or ACT. Recommended: essay, recommendations, interview. Required for some: minimum 3.0 high school GPA, medical examination for flight students. Entrance: moderately difficult. Application deadlines: 3/1, 12/1 for early decision plan 2. Notification: continuous, 12/31 for early decision plan 2.

Costs Per Year: Application fee: $50. Comprehensive fee: $30,006 includes full-time tuition ($22,820), mandatory fees ($670), and college room and board ($6516). College room only: $3580. Part-time tuition: $955 per credit hour.

Collegiate Environment: Orientation program. Student-run newspaper, radio station. Social organizations: 61 open to all; national fraternities, national sororities; 85% of eligible men and 93% of eligible women are members. Most popular organizations: Hawaii Club, Strike Eagles, Theta XI, American Institute of Aeronautics and Astronautics (AIAA), Arnold Air Society. Major annual events: October West/Homecoming, Spring Fling, Hawaii Club Luau. Student services: health clinic, personal-psychological counseling. Campus security: 24-hour emergency response devices and patrols, student patrols, late night transport-escort service. 849 college housing spaces available; 802 were occupied in 2003-04. Freshmen guaranteed college housing. On-campus residence required in freshman year. Option: coed housing available. ERAU - Prescott Campus Library with 28,264 books, 188,740 microform titles, 629 serials, 2,518 audiovisual materials, an OPAC, and a Web page. Operations spending for 2004 fiscal year: $3.1 million. 365 computers available on campus for general student use. A campuswide network can be accessed from student residence rooms and from off campus. Staffed computer lab on campus.

Community Environment: The Prescott area is one of the most colorful areas of the Bradshaw Mountains and has an approximate population of 60,000. The campus is surrounded by a national forest, rolling ranchlands, hiking trails, and wilderness areas. The city of Phoenix is approximately 90 miles away.

■ **ESTRELLA MOUNTAIN COMMUNITY COLLEGE** *P-8*
3000 North Dysart Rd.
Avondale, AZ 85323-1000
Tel: (623)935-8000
Admissions: (623)935-8808
Web Site: http://www.emc.maricopa.edu/

Description: State and locally supported, 2-year, coed. Part of Maricopa County Community College District System. Awards certificates, transfer associate, and terminal associate degrees. Setting: urban campus with easy access to Phoenix. Total enrollment: 5,947. 5,947 applied, 100% were admitted. Full-time: 1,372 students, 60% women, 40% men. Part-time: 4,575 students, 62% women, 38% men. 2% Native American, 31% Hispanic, 7% black, 3% Asian American or Pacific Islander, 1% international. Calendar: semesters.

Entrance Requirements: Open admission. Entrance: noncompetitive.

■ **EVEREST COLLEGE** *P-9*
10400 North 25th Ave.
Ste. 190
Phoenix, AZ 85021
Tel: (602)942-4141
Fax: (602)943-0960
E-mail: magee@cci.edu
Web Site: http://www.everest-college.com/

Description: Proprietary, primarily 2-year, coed. Awards diplomas, transfer associate, terminal associate, and bachelor's degrees. Founded 1982. Setting: urban campus. Educational spending for 2005 fiscal year: $3083 per student. Total enrollment: 804. Student-undergrad faculty ratio is 24:1. 526 applied, 73% were admitted. Full-time: 378 students, 84% women, 16% men. Part-time: 426 students, 77% women, 23% men. Students come from 2 states and territories, 25% from out-of-state, 4% Native American, 28% Hispanic, 11% black, 2% Asian American or Pacific Islander, 0% international, 95% 25 or older. Retention: 65% of full-time freshmen returned the following year. Core. Calendar: 6 or 12 week terms. Distance learning, double major, summer session for credit, adult/continuing education programs, internships.

Entrance Requirements: Option: deferred admission. Required: high school transcript, minimum 2.0 high school GPA, interview. Required for some: essay. Entrance: noncompetitive. Application deadline: Rolling. Notification: continuous.

Costs Per Year: Application fee: $0. Tuition: $13,111 full-time, $259 per quarter hour part-time. Mandatory fees: $100 full-time, $25 per term part-time.

Collegiate Environment: Orientation program. Social organizations: 2 open to all. Most popular organizations: Collegiate Secretaries International, Toastmasters. Major annual event: picnic. Student services: personal-psychological counseling. Campus security: 24-hour emergency response devices and patrols. College housing not available. Academy of Business College Library with 57 serials and a Web page. 50 computers available on campus for general student use. Staffed computer lab on campus.

■ **GATEWAY COMMUNITY COLLEGE** *P-9*
108 North 40th St.
Phoenix, AZ 85034-1795
Tel: (602)286-8000
Admissions: (602)286-8052
Fax: (602)286-8003
E-mail: cathy.gibson@gwmail.maricopa.edu
Web Site: http://www.gwc.maricopa.edu/

Description: State and locally supported, 2-year, coed. Part of Maricopa County Community College District System. Awards certificates, transfer associate, and terminal associate degrees. Founded 1968. Setting: 20-acre urban campus. Total enrollment: 9,377. Student-undergrad faculty ratio is 25:1. Full-time: 976 students, 64% women, 36% men. Part-time: 8,401 students, 46% women, 54% men. Students come from 50 states and territories, 26 other countries, 3% from out-of-state, 4% Native American, 21% Hispanic, 8% black, 2% Asian American or Pacific Islander, 31% 25 or older. Core. Calendar: semesters. Academic remediation for entering students, ESL program, services for LD students, advanced placement, accelerated degree program, honors program, independent study, distance learning, summer session for credit, part-time degree program, adult/continuing education programs, co-op programs and internships. ROTC: Army (c), Air Force (c).

Entrance Requirements: Open admission except for health science, nursing programs. Options: Peterson's Universal Application, Common Application, electronic application, early admission, deferred admission. Required for some: high school transcript. Entrance: noncompetitive. Application deadline: Rolling. Notification: continuous.

Costs Per Year: Application fee: $0. Area resident tuition: $1560 full-time, $65 per credit part-time. State resident tuition: $6720 full-time, $85 per credit part-time. Nonresident tuition: $6720 full-time, $85 per credit part-time. Mandatory fees: $30 full-time.

Collegiate Environment: Social organizations: 15 open to all. Most popular organizations: Associated Students, African-American Students Association, MECHA SAMO THRACE, Volunteer Committee, VA Club. Major annual events: Christmas Buffet, Annual Campus Celebration, Cultural Week. Student services: personal-psychological counseling, women's center. Campus security: 24-hour emergency response devices and patrols, student patrols, late night transport-escort service. College housing not available. Gateway Library with 50,000 books, 300 serials, and an OPAC. Operations spending for 2004 fiscal year: $339,763. 300 computers available on campus for general student use. Staffed computer lab on campus.

■ **GLENDALE COMMUNITY COLLEGE** *I-6*

6000 West Olive Ave.

Glendale, AZ 85302-3090

Tel: (623)845-3000

Admissions: (623)435-3305

Fax: (623)845-3329

E-mail: info@gc.maricopa.edu

Web Site: http://www.gc.maricopa.edu/

Description: State and locally supported, 2-year, coed. Part of Maricopa County Community College District System. Awards certificates, transfer associate, and terminal associate degrees. Founded 1965. Setting: 160-acre suburban campus with easy access to Phoenix. Endowment: $353,507. Educational spending for 2005 fiscal year: $4978 per student. Total enrollment: 20,070. Student-undergrad faculty ratio is 22:1. Full-time: 6,108 students, 53% women, 47% men. Part-time: 13,962 students, 58% women, 42% men. Students come from 50 states and territories, 3% from out-of-state, 2% Native American, 22% Hispanic, 7% black, 4% Asian American or Pacific Islander, 1% international, 44% 25 or older, 28% transferred in. Retention: 60% of full-time freshmen returned the following year. Core. Calendar: semesters. Academic remediation for entering students, ESL program, services for LD students, advanced placement, freshman honors college, honors program, distance learning, double major, summer session for credit, part-time degree program, adult/continuing education programs, co-op programs and internships. Off campus study. ROTC: Army (c), Air Force (c).

Entrance Requirements: Open admission. Options: Common Application, electronic application, international baccalaureate accepted. Required for some: high school transcript. Entrance: noncompetitive. Application deadline: 8/23. Notification: continuous until 8/23.

Costs Per Year: Application fee: $0. Area resident tuition: $1560 full-time, $65 per credit hour part-time. State resident tuition: $6720 full-time, $280 per credit hour part-time. Nonresident tuition: $6720 full-time, $280 per credit hour part-time. Mandatory fees: $30 full-time, $15 per term part-time.

Collegiate Environment: Orientation program. Drama-theater group, choral group, marching band, student-run newspaper. Social organizations: 28 open to all. Most popular organizations: LDS Student Association, Phi Theta Kappa International Honor Society, band, Glendale Association of Student Nurses, Inter-Varsity Christian Fellowship. Major annual events: Student Art Show, Multicultural Week, Read Fest. Student services: legal services, personal-psychological counseling. Campus security: 24-hour patrols, student patrols, late night transport-escort service. College housing not available. Library/Media Center plus 1 other with 79,006 books, 196,824 microform titles, 406 serials, 3,807 audiovisual materials, an OPAC, and a Web page. Operations spending for 2004 fiscal year: $1.3 million. 1,500 computers available on campus for general student use. A campuswide network can be accessed from off-campus. Staffed computer lab on campus.

■ **GRAND CANYON UNIVERSITY** *P-9*

3300 W Camelback Rd., PO Box 11097

Phoenix, AZ 85017-1097

Tel: (602)249-3300

Fax: (602)589-2580

Web Site: http://www.gcu.edu/

Description: Independent Southern Baptist, comprehensive, coed. Awards bachelor's and master's degrees. Founded 1949. Setting: 90-acre suburban campus. Endowment: $5.4 million. Research spending for 2004 fiscal year: $21,749. Total enrollment: 4,113. Faculty: 274 (97 full-time, 177 part-time). Student-undergrad faculty ratio is 16:1. 823 applied, 69% were admitted. 29% from top 10% of their high school class, 54% from top quarter, 78% from top half. 1 National Merit Scholar, 10 valedictorians. Full-time: 1,327 students, 66% women, 34% men. Part-time: 282 students, 55% women, 45% men. Students come from 40 states and territories, 14 other countries, 19% from out-of-state, 1% Native American, 7% Hispanic, 3% black, 2% Asian American or Pacific Islander, 3% international, 30% 25 or older, 30% live on campus, 19% transferred in. Retention: 76% of full-time freshmen returned the following year. Core. Calendar: semesters. Academic remediation for entering students, ESL program, advanced placement, accelerated degree program, freshman honors college, honors program, independent study, distance learning, double major, summer session for credit, part-time degree program, adult/continuing education programs, co-op programs and internships, graduate courses open to undergrads. Off campus study at Coalition for Christian Colleges and Universities. Study abroad program. ROTC: Army, Air Force (c).

Entrance Requirements: Required: high school transcript, minimum 3.0 high school GPA, SAT or ACT. Required for some: essay, 3 recommendations, interview. Entrance: moderately difficult. Application deadline: Rolling. Notification: continuous until 9/1.

Costs Per Year: Application fee: $50. State resident tuition: $4875 full-time. Nonresident tuition: $6000 full-time. College room and board: $7130.

Collegiate Environment: Orientation program. Drama-theater group, choral group, student-run newspaper. Student services: health clinic. Campus security: 24-hour emergency response devices and patrols, student patrols, late night transport-escort service, controlled dormitory access. On-campus residence required through sophomore year. Options: men-only, women-only housing available. Fleming Library with 75,905 books, 82,561 microform titles, 1,174 serials, 404 audiovisual materials, and an OPAC. Operations spending for 2004 fiscal year: $258,654. 119 computers available on campus for general student use. Staffed computer lab on campus.

Community Environment: See Phoenix College

■ **HIGH-TECH INSTITUTE** *P-9*

1515 East Indian School Rd.

Phoenix, AZ 85014-4901

Tel: (602)279-9700

Fax: (602)279-2999

E-mail: rcraven@hightechschools.com

Web Site: http://www.high-techinstitute.com/

Description: Proprietary, primarily 2-year, coed. Awards diplomas, terminal associate, and bachelor's degrees. Setting: 4-acre urban campus. Total enrollment: 1,544. Full-time: 1,544 students, 28% women, 72% men. 5% Native American, 35% Hispanic, 12% black, 2% Asian American or Pacific Islander. Calendar: semesters.

Entrance Requirements: Open admission. Required: high school transcript. Entrance: noncompetitive. Application deadline: Rolling.

Collegiate Environment: Most popular organizations: Alpha Beta Kappa, American Design Drafting Association, American Institute of Architects, American Institute of Building Designers, American Institute for Design and Drafting. College housing not available.

■ **INTERNATIONAL BAPTIST COLLEGE** *I-7*

2150 East Southern Ave.

Tempe, AZ 85282

Tel: (480)838-7070

Free: 800-422-4858

E-mail: registrar@ibconline.edu

Web Site: http://www.tri-citybaptist.org/ibc/

Description: Independent Baptist, comprehensive, coed. Awards associate, bachelor's, master's, and doctoral degrees. Founded 1980. Setting: 12-acre suburban campus with easy access to Phoenix. Educational spending for 2005 fiscal year: $5426 per student. Total enrollment: 76. Faculty: 13 (3 full-time, 10 part-time). Student-undergrad faculty ratio is 12:1. Full-time: 47 students, 55% women, 45% men. Part-time: 28 students, 39% women, 61% men. 32% from out-of-state, 4% Native American, 14% Hispanic, 4% black, 3% Asian American or Pacific Islander, 3% international. Academic areas with the most degrees conferred: theology and religious vocations; education. Core. Calendar: 4-1-4. Part-time degree program, graduate courses open to undergrads.

Entrance Requirements: Open admission. Options: Common Application, early admission. Required: essay, high school transcript, 3 recommendations. Application deadline: 8/20.

Costs Per Year: Application fee: $35. Comprehensive fee: $10,870 includes full-time tuition ($6000), mandatory fees ($570), and college room and board ($4300). Part-time tuition: $250 per credit. Part-time mandatory fees: $9 per credit.

Collegiate Environment: Choral group. Social organizations: local fraternities, local sororities; 100% of eligible men and 100% of eligible women are members. 6 computers available on campus for general student use. Staffed computer lab on campus.

■ **INTERNATIONAL IMPORT-EXPORT INSTITUTE** *P-9*

2432 West Peoria Ave., Ste. 1026

Phoenix, AZ 85029

Tel: (602)648-5750

Free: 800-474-8013
Fax: (602)648-5755
E-mail: director@expandglobal.com
Web Site: http://www.iiei.edu/
Description: Proprietary, upper-level, coed. Founded 1995. Student-undergrad faculty ratio is 15:1. 0% from out-of-state. Calendar: 4 semesters per year.
Costs Per Year: Application fee: $0.

■ INTERNATIONAL INSTITUTE OF THE AMERICAS (MESA) *I-7*
925 South Gilbert Rd., Ste. 201
Mesa, AZ 85204-4448
Tel: (480)545-8755; 888-886-2428
Fax: (480)926-1371
E-mail: mkiljan@iia.edu
Web Site: http://www.aibtonline.com/
Description: Independent, primarily 2-year, coed. Awards diplomas, terminal associate, and bachelor's degrees. Founded 1982. Total enrollment: 174. Student-undergrad faculty ratio is 13:1. 17% Native American, 29% Hispanic, 7% black, 0% Asian American or Pacific Islander, 0% international. Calendar: semesters.
Entrance Requirements: Required: interview. Entrance: noncompetitive. Application deadlines: Rolling, Rolling for nonresidents. Notification: continuous, continuous for nonresidents.
Costs Per Year: One-time mandatory fee: $200. Tuition: $9850 full-time. Mandatory fees: $350 full-time.

■ INTERNATIONAL INSTITUTE OF THE AMERICAS (PHOENIX) *P-9*
6049 North 43rd Ave.
Phoenix, AZ 85019-1600
Tel: (602)242-6265
Free: 800-793-2428
Fax: (602)973-2572
E-mail: lmcconnell@iia.edu
Web Site: http://www.aibtonline.com/
Description: Independent, primarily 2-year, coed. Awards diplomas, terminal associate, and bachelor's degrees. Founded 1979. Setting: urban campus. Total enrollment: 240. Student-undergrad faculty ratio is 13:1. Students come from 7 states and territories, 4% Native American, 30% Hispanic, 15% black, 0.4% Asian American or Pacific Islander, 0% international, 76% 25 or older. Core. Calendar: semesters. Accelerated degree program, distance learning, summer session for credit, adult/continuing education programs, co-op programs and internships.
Entrance Requirements: Open admission. Options: electronic application, early admission, deferred admission. Required: interview. Entrance: noncompetitive. Application deadlines: Rolling, Rolling for nonresidents. Notification: continuous, continuous for nonresidents.
Costs Per Year: One-time mandatory fee: $200. Tuition: $9850 full-time. Mandatory fees: $350 full-time.
Collegiate Environment: Orientation program. Major annual events: job fairs, holiday-themed student gatherings. Campus security: 24-hour emergency response devices. College housing not available. Learning Resource Center with 1,974 books, 1,750 serials, 120 audiovisual materials, an OPAC, and a Web page. Operations spending for 2004 fiscal year: $307,394. 421 computers available on campus for general student use. A campuswide network can be accessed. Staffed computer lab on campus.

■ INTERNATIONAL INSTITUTE OF THE AMERICAS (TUCSON) *L-9*
5441 East 22nd St., Ste. 125
Tucson, AZ 85711-5444
Tel: (520)748-9799; 888-292-2428
Fax: (520)748-9355
E-mail: lpechota@iia.edu
Web Site: http://www.aibtonline.com/
Description: Independent, primarily 2-year, coed. Awards diplomas, terminal associate, and bachelor's degrees. Founded 1979. Total enrollment: 298. Student-undergrad faculty ratio is 14:1. 6% Native American, 46% Hispanic, 12% black, 1% Asian American or Pacific Islander, 0% international. Calendar: semesters.
Entrance Requirements: Required: interview. Entrance: noncompetitive. Application deadlines: Rolling, Rolling for nonresidents. Notification: continuous, continuous for nonresidents.

■ INTERNATIONAL INSTITUTE OF THE AMERICAS (WEST VALLEY) *P-9*
4136 North 75th Ave., Ste. 211
Phoenix, AZ 85033-3196
Tel: (623)849-8208; 888-884-2428
Fax: (623)849-0110
E-mail: lebert@iia.edu
Web Site: http://www.aibtonline.com/
Description: Independent, primarily 2-year, coed. Awards diplomas, terminal associate, and bachelor's degrees. Founded 1979. Total enrollment: 205. Student-undergrad faculty ratio is 15:1. 5% Native American, 37% Hispanic, 15% black, 0.5% Asian American or Pacific Islander, 0% international. Calendar: semesters.
Entrance Requirements: Required: interview. Entrance: noncompetitive. Application deadlines: Rolling, Rolling for nonresidents. Notification: continuous, continuous for nonresidents.
Costs Per Year: One-time mandatory fee: $200. Tuition: $9850 full-time. Mandatory fees: $350 full-time.

■ ITT TECHNICAL INSTITUTE (PHOENIX) *P-9*
4837 East McDowell Rd.
Phoenix, AZ 85008-4292
Tel: (602)252-2331
Free: 800-879-4881
Fax: (602)267-8727
Web Site: http://www.itt-tech.edu/
Description: Proprietary, primarily 2-year, coed. Part of ITT Educational Services, Inc. Awards terminal associate and bachelor's degrees. Founded 1972. Setting: 2-acre urban campus. Total enrollment: 447. Core.
Entrance Requirements: Option: deferred admission. Required: high school transcript, interview, Wonderlic aptitude test. Recommended: recommendations. Entrance: minimally difficult. Application deadline: Rolling. Notification: continuous.
Collegiate Environment: Orientation program. Most popular organization: Student Activities Council. Major annual events: Very Special Arts Fair, APSA Sports Tournaments, St. Mary's Food Bank Annual Food Drive. Student services: personal-psychological counseling. College housing not available.

■ ITT TECHNICAL INSTITUTE (TEMPE) *I-7*
5005 S. Wendler Dr.
Tempe, AZ 85282
Tel: (602)437-7500
Free: 800-879-4881
Web Site: http://www.itt-tech.edu/
Description: Proprietary, 4-year. Awards associate and bachelor's degrees. Founded 1963.
Entrance Requirements: Required: high school transcript, interview, Wonderlic aptitude test. Recommended: recommendations. Application deadline: Rolling. Notification: continuous.
Costs Per Year: Application fee: $100.

■ ITT TECHNICAL INSTITUTE (TUCSON) *L-9*
1455 West River Rd.
Tucson, AZ 85704
Tel: (520)408-7488
Free: 800-870-9730
Fax: (520)292-9899
Web Site: http://www.itt-tech.edu/
Description: Proprietary, primarily 2-year, coed. Part of ITT Educational Services, Inc. Awards terminal associate and bachelor's degrees. Founded 1984. Setting: 3-acre urban campus. Core.
Entrance Requirements: Option: deferred admission. Required: high school transcript, interview, Wonderlic aptitude test. Recommended: recommendations. Entrance: minimally difficult. Application deadline: Rolling. Notification: continuous.
Costs Per Year: Application fee: $100.
Collegiate Environment: Orientation program. College housing not available.

■ LAMSON COLLEGE *I-7*
1126 North Scottsdale Rd., Ste. 17
Tempe, AZ 85281
Tel: (480)898-7000

Free: 800-898-7017
Fax: (480)967-6645
Web Site: http://www.lamsoncollege.com/
Description: Proprietary, 2-year, coed. Part of National Career Education, Inc. Awards transfer associate and terminal associate degrees. Founded 1889. Setting: urban campus with easy access to Phoenix. 1% from top 10% of their high school class, 5% from top quarter, 20% from top half. Students come from 4 states and territories, 5 other countries, 40% 25 or older. Academic remediation for entering students, ESL program, summer session for credit, adult/continuing education programs, internships.
Entrance Requirements: Required: high school transcript, interview, CPAt. Entrance: minimally difficult. Application deadline: Rolling. Notification: continuous.
Collegiate Environment: Campus security: 24-hour patrols. College housing not available. 4,400 books and 18 serials. 45 computers available on campus for general student use. Staffed computer lab on campus.

■ **LONG TECHNICAL COLLEGE** *P-9*
13450 North Black Canyon Hwy., Ste. 104
Phoenix, AZ 85029
Tel: (602)548-1955; 877-548-1955
Fax: (602)548-1956
E-mail: msavely@longtechnicalcollege.com
Web Site: http://www.longtechnicalcollege.com/
Description: Proprietary, 2-year, coed. Founded 1972. Calendar: continuous.

■ **MESA COMMUNITY COLLEGE** *I-7*
1833 West Southern Ave.
Mesa, AZ 85202-4866
Tel: (480)461-7000
Admissions: (480)461-7478
Fax: (480)461-7805
E-mail: admissions@mc.maricopa.edu
Web Site: http://www.mc.maricopa.edu/
Description: State and locally supported, 2-year, coed. Part of Maricopa County Community College District System. Awards certificates, transfer associate, and terminal associate degrees. Founded 1965. Setting: 160-acre urban campus with easy access to Phoenix. Research spending for 2004 fiscal year: $150,000. Total enrollment: 28,000. Students come from 18 states and territories, 4% from out-of-state, 3% Native American, 14% Hispanic, 3% black, 5% Asian American or Pacific Islander, 44% 25 or older. Core. Calendar: semesters. Academic remediation for entering students, ESL program, services for LD students, advanced placement, self-designed majors, freshman honors college, honors program, independent study, distance learning, summer session for credit, part-time degree program, adult/continuing education programs, co-op programs. Off campus study at Servicemembers Opportunity Colleges. Study abroad program. ROTC: Army (c), Air Force (c).
Entrance Requirements: Open admission. Options: electronic application, early admission, deferred admission. Placement: ACT ASSET required. Entrance: noncompetitive. Application deadline: 8/22. Notification: continuous.
Collegiate Environment: Orientation program. Drama-theater group, choral group, student-run newspaper, radio station. Social organizations: 25 open to all. Most popular organizations: MECHA, International Student Association, American Indian Association, Asian/Pacific Islander Club. Major annual events: Bash, Homecoming. Student services: legal services, personal-psychological counseling. Campus security: 24-hour emergency response devices and patrols, student patrols. College housing not available. Information Commons with 56,224 books, 794 serials, an OPAC, and a Web page. Operations spending for 2004 fiscal year: $500,000. 600 computers available on campus for general student use. A campuswide network can be accessed from off-campus. Staffed computer lab on campus.
Community Environment: Population 375,000, Arizona's third largest city, located 16 miles east of Phoenix, adjacent to Tempe, and near the Superstition Mountains. The average yearly temperature is 68.3 degrees, low humidity and 86 percent of the daylight hours are sunny. Mesa is a beautiful and friendly city; there are part-time jobs available for the college students. Most kinds of sports and recreation facilities available, plus many cultural activities.

■ **METROPOLITAN COLLEGE OF COURT REPORTING** *P-9*
4640 East Elwood St., Ste. 12
Phoenix, AZ 85040

Tel: (602)955-5900
Admissions: (480)955-5900
Fax: (480)894-8999
Web Site: http://www.metropolitancollege.edu/
Description: Proprietary, 4-year, coed. Awards associate and bachelor's degrees. Founded 1991. Setting: 1-acre suburban campus. Total enrollment: 118. 16 applied, 100% were admitted. 60% from top quarter of their high school class. Full-time: 118 students, 97% women, 3% men. Students come from 6 states and territories, 2 other countries, 15% from out-of-state, 85% 25 or older, 3% transferred in. Retention: 67% of full-time freshmen returned the following year. Core. Calendar: trimesters. Academic remediation for entering students, services for LD students, accelerated degree program, independent study, summer session for credit, adult/continuing education programs, internships.
Entrance Requirements: Open admission. Options: Common Application, electronic application, early admission, deferred admission. Required: high school transcript, interview, typing test.
Collegiate Environment: Student services: personal-psychological counseling. College housing not available. 20 computers available on campus for general student use. Staffed computer lab on campus.

■ **MIDWESTERN UNIVERSITY, GLENDALE CAMPUS** *I-6*
19555 North 59th Ave.
Glendale, AZ 85308
Tel: (623)572-3200; 888-247-9271
Admissions: (623)572-3340
Web Site: http://www.midwestern.edu/
Description: Independent, upper-level, coed. Awards bachelor's, master's, and doctoral degrees. Founded 1996. Total enrollment: 1,117. Student-undergrad faculty ratio is 20:1. 25 applied, 80% were admitted. Full-time: 20 students, 80% women, 20% men.
Costs Per Year: Application fee: $0. Comprehensive fee: $24,341 includes full-time tuition ($15,306), mandatory fees ($250), and college room and board ($8785). College room only: $5670.

■ **MOHAVE COMMUNITY COLLEGE** *E-3*
1971 Jagerson Ave.
Kingman, AZ 86401
Tel: (928)757-4331; 888-664-2832
Admissions: (928)757-0847
Fax: (928)757-0808
Web Site: http://www.mohave.edu/
Description: State-supported, 2-year, coed. Awards certificates, transfer associate, and terminal associate degrees. Founded 1971. Setting: 160-acre small town campus. Total enrollment: 6,187. 332 applied, 100% were admitted. Full-time: 1,208 students, 69% women, 31% men. Part-time: 4,979 students, 66% women, 34% men. Students come from 8 states and territories, 8% from out-of-state, 2% Native American, 13% Hispanic, 1% black, 2% Asian American or Pacific Islander, 0% international, 69% 25 or older. Core. Calendar: semesters. Academic remediation for entering students, ESL program, independent study, distance learning, summer session for credit, part-time degree program, adult/continuing education programs.
Entrance Requirements: Open admission except for nursing, paramedic programs. Options: early admission, deferred admission. Recommended: minimum 2.0 high school GPA. Required for some: high school transcript, interview. Entrance: noncompetitive. Application deadline: Rolling. Notification: continuous.
Costs Per Year: State resident tuition: $1104 full-time, $46 per credit hour part-time. Nonresident tuition: $3312 full-time, $138 per credit hour part-time. Part-time tuition varies according to course load.
Collegiate Environment: Orientation program. Drama-theater group, choral group, student-run newspaper. Social organizations: 10 open to all; national fraternities, national sororities. Most popular organizations: Art Club, Pottery Club, Astronomy Club, Phi Theta Kappa. Major annual events: Career Fair, Brighter Future Festival, New Student BBQ. Campus security: 24-hour emergency response devices, late night transport-escort service. College housing not available. Mohave Community College Library with 45,849 books and 476 serials. 120 computers available on campus for general student use. Staffed computer lab on campus.
Community Environment: The College campuses are accessible by all forms of transportation: bus, rail and air. The area is a rapidly expanding one, offering a variety of year-round activities due to its arid climate. Lake Havasu City boasts the famous London Bridge and English Village. The areas provide opportunities for hunting, fishing, camping and water sports.

■ **NORTHCENTRAL UNIVERSITY** *G-6*
505 West Whipple St.
Prescott, AZ 86301-1747
Tel: (928)541-7777; 888-327-2877
Admissions: (866)776-0331
Fax: (928)541-7817
E-mail: enrol@ncu.edu
Web Site: http://www.ncu.edu/
Description: Proprietary, comprehensive, coed. Awards bachelor's, master's, and doctoral degrees (offers only distance learning programs). Total enrollment: 1,401. Full-time: 10 students, 70% women, 30% men. Part-time: 156 students, 58% women, 42% men. Students come from 51 states and territories, 93% from out-of-state, 2% Native American, 2% Hispanic, 19% black, 3% Asian American or Pacific Islander, 92% 25 or older. Core. Calendar: continuous. Advanced placement, accelerated degree program, distance learning, summer session for credit, part-time degree program, external degree program, graduate courses open to undergrads.
Entrance Requirements: Options: electronic application, international baccalaureate accepted. Required: essay, high school transcript. Entrance: minimally difficult. Application deadline: Rolling. Notification: continuous.
Costs Per Year: Application fee: $100. Tuition: $9000 full-time, $375 per credit part-time.
Collegiate Environment: Major annual event: graduation. College housing not available. Electronic Learning Resources Center with a Web page.

■ **NORTHERN ARIZONA UNIVERSITY** *E-8*
South San Francisco St.
Flagstaff, AZ 86011
Tel: (928)523-9011; 888-MORE-NAU
Admissions: (928)523-6053
Fax: (928)523-0226
E-mail: Christopher.Lynch@nau.edu
Web Site: http://www.nau.edu/
Description: State-supported, university, coed. Part of Arizona University System. Awards bachelor's, master's, doctoral, and first professional degrees and post-master's certificates. Founded 1899. Setting: 730-acre small town campus. Endowment: $11.7 million. Research spending for 2004 fiscal year: $18.8 million. Educational spending for 2005 fiscal year: $7357 per student. Total enrollment: 18,779. Faculty: 1,374 (723 full-time, 651 part-time). Student-undergrad faculty ratio is 16:1. 7,304 applied, 86% were admitted. Full-time: 11,261 students, 60% women, 40% men. Part-time: 1,991 students, 63% women, 37% men. Students come from 50 states and territories, 66 other countries, 17% from out-of-state, 7% Native American, 12% Hispanic, 2% black, 2% Asian American or Pacific Islander, 2% international, 23% 25 or older, 38% live on campus, 11% transferred in. Retention: 69% of full-time freshmen returned the following year. Academic areas with the most degrees conferred: education; business/marketing; visual and performing arts. Core. Calendar: semesters. ESL program, services for LD students, advanced placement, accelerated degree program, freshman honors college, honors program, independent study, distance learning, double major, summer session for credit, part-time degree program, co-op programs and internships, graduate courses open to undergrads. Off campus study at National Student Exchange. Study abroad program. ROTC: Army, Air Force.
Entrance Requirements: Options: electronic application, deferred admission, international baccalaureate accepted. Required: high school transcript, SAT or ACT. Recommended: minimum 3.0 high school GPA. Required for some: recommendations. Entrance: moderately difficult. Application deadline: Rolling. Notification: continuous.
Costs Per Year: Application fee: $25. State resident tuition: $4223 full-time, $221 per credit part-time. Nonresident tuition: $12,853 full-time, $536 per credit part-time. Mandatory fees: $170 full-time, $85 per term part-time. Full-time tuition and fees vary according to program. Part-time tuition and fees vary according to program. College room and board: $5960. College room only: $3256. Room and board charges vary according to board plan and housing facility.
Collegiate Environment: Orientation program. Drama-theater group, choral group, marching band, student-run newspaper, radio station. Social organizations: 157 open to all; national fraternities, national sororities; 8% of eligible men and 6% of eligible women are members. Most popular organizations: ASNAU, Black Student Union, New Student Organization, Cardinal Key Society, Blue Key Society. Major annual events: Homecoming, Parents' Weekend, International Student Week. Student services: health clinic, personal-psychological counseling, women's center, tutoring. Campus security: 24-hour emergency response devices and patrols, late night transport-escort service, controlled dormitory access. 6,000 college housing spaces available; 5,500 were occupied in 2003-04. Freshmen guaranteed college housing. Options: coed, men-only, women-only housing available. Cline Library plus 1 other with 633,417 books, 547,729 microform titles, 2,595 serials, 31,746 audiovisual materials, an OPAC, and a Web page. Operations spending for 2004 fiscal year: $5.5 million. 903 computers available on campus for general student use. Computer purchase/lease plans available. A campuswide network can be accessed from student residence rooms and from off campus. Staffed computer lab on campus.
Community Environment: Flagstaff, population 58,000, is a city of Seven Wonders in the heart of the Coconino National Forest located at the foot of the San Francisco Peaks. Mountain slopes, canyons, buttes, Indian ruins, forests, and deserts mingle in a setting forever challenging in its appeal. The elevation, the protection provided by the forest, and the Arizona sunshine give Flagstaff unsurpassed year round climate. Recreational activities include hiking, bicycling, boating, fishing, and hunting. Skiing is nearby as are the Grand Canyon, the Petrified forest, numerous Indian villages, and national monuments.

■ **NORTHLAND PIONEER COLLEGE** *F-10*
PO Box 610
Holbrook, AZ 86025-0610
Tel: (928)524-7600
Free: 800-266-7845
Admissions: (928)536-6257
Fax: (928)524-7612
Web Site: http://www.npc.edu/
Description: State and locally supported, 2-year, coed. Part of Arizona State Community College System. Awards certificates, transfer associate, and terminal associate degrees. Founded 1974. Setting: 50-acre rural campus. Educational spending for 2005 fiscal year: $2802 per student. Total enrollment: 4,928. Full-time: 971 students, 67% women, 33% men. Part-time: 3,957 students, 67% women, 33% men. Students come from 13 states and territories, 5 other countries, 42% Native American, 7% Hispanic, 1% black, 1% Asian American or Pacific Islander, 0% international, 76% 25 or older, 1% live on campus, 9% transferred in. Retention: 2% of full-time freshmen returned the following year. Core. Calendar: semesters. Academic remediation for entering students, ESL program, services for LD students, advanced placement, freshman honors college, honors program, independent study, distance learning, double major, summer session for credit, part-time degree program, co-op programs and internships.
Entrance Requirements: Open admission. Option: early admission. Entrance: noncompetitive. Application deadline: Rolling.
Collegiate Environment: Orientation program. Drama-theater group, choral group. Most popular organization: Hiking/Skiing Club. Campus security: evening security. 24 college housing spaces available; 6 were occupied in 2003-04. No special consideration for freshman housing applicants. Option: coed housing available. Northland Pioneer College Library with 60,000 books, 240 serials, and an OPAC. Operations spending for 2004 fiscal year: $357,360. 200 computers available on campus for general student use. Staffed computer lab on campus.
Community Environment: The service area of 21,000 square miles has a population of approximately 154,000 people. The service area includes parts of three Indian reservations. The economy is based primarily on agriculture, tourism, and the lumber industry.

■ **PARADISE VALLEY COMMUNITY COLLEGE** *P-9*
18401 North 32nd St.
Phoenix, AZ 85032-1200
Tel: (602)787-6500
Admissions: (602)787-7020
Fax: (602)787-6625
Web Site: http://www.pvc.maricopa.edu/
Description: State and locally supported, 2-year, coed. Part of Maricopa County Community College District System. Awards certificates, transfer associate, and terminal associate degrees. Founded 1985. Setting: urban campus. Total enrollment: 8,237. 1% Native American, 10% Hispanic, 3% black, 3% Asian American or Pacific Islander. Core. Calendar: semesters. Academic remediation for entering students, services for LD students, advanced placement, honors program, distance learning, summer session for credit, adult/continuing education programs, co-op programs.
Entrance Requirements: Open admission. Option: early admission. Entrance: noncompetitive. Application deadline: Rolling.

Collegiate Environment: Drama-theater group, choral group, student-run newspaper. Social organizations: 16 open to all. Most popular organizations: Phi Theta Kappa, International Student Club, Recreational Outing Club, AWARE, Student Christian Association. Major annual events: International Education Week, Black American Month/Hispanic Week/Women's Week. Student services: personal-psychological counseling. Campus security: 24-hour emergency response devices, late night transport-escort service. College housing not available. Paradise Valley Community College Library plus 1 other with an OPAC and a Web page. 500 computers available on campus for general student use. Staffed computer lab on campus.

■ **THE PARALEGAL INSTITUTE, INC.** *P-9*
2933 West Indian School Rd.
Phoenix, AZ 85017
Tel: (602)212-0501
Free: 800-354-1254
Web Site: http://www.theparalegalinstitute.com/
Description: Proprietary, 2-year. Awards diplomas and terminal associate degrees. Founded 1974. Total enrollment: 400. 500 applied, 25% were admitted.

■ **PHOENIX COLLEGE** *P-9*
1202 West Thomas Rd.
Phoenix, AZ 85013-4234
Tel: (602)285-7500
Admissions: (602)285-7503
Fax: (602)285-7813
Web Site: http://www.pc.maricopa.edu/
Description: State and locally supported, 2-year, coed. Part of Maricopa County Community College District System. Awards certificates, diplomas, transfer associate, and terminal associate degrees. Founded 1920. Setting: 52-acre urban campus. Total enrollment: 12,549. Students come from 42 states and territories, 2% from out-of-state, 4% Native American, 32% Hispanic, 8% black, 2% Asian American or Pacific Islander, 0% international. Core. Calendar: semesters. Academic remediation for entering students, ESL program, services for LD students, advanced placement, freshman honors college, honors program, summer session for credit, part-time degree program, adult/continuing education programs, co-op programs and internships. Study abroad program. ROTC: Army (c), Air Force (c).
Entrance Requirements: Open admission. Options: Common Application, electronic application, early admission, deferred admission. Entrance: noncompetitive. Application deadline: Rolling. Notification: continuous.
Costs Per Year: Application fee: $0. State resident tuition: $1560 full-time, $65 per credit hour part-time. Nonresident tuition: $6720 full-time, $280 per credit hour part-time. Mandatory fees: $30 full-time, $15 per term part-time.
Collegiate Environment: Orientation program. Drama-theater group, choral group, student-run newspaper. Most popular organizations: Black Student Union, NASA (Native American Club), Asian American Club, MECHA (Mexican Club). Major annual event: Homecoming Week. Student services: legal services, personal-psychological counseling, women's center. Campus security: 24-hour emergency response devices, student patrols, late night transport-escort service. College housing not available. Fannin Library with 83,000 books and 394 serials. 250 computers available on campus for general student use. A campuswide network can be accessed from off-campus. Staffed computer lab on campus.
Community Environment: Phoenix, population over one million, is a thriving industrial and agricultural city. Easily accessible, served by railroads, buses and airlines, the city has many churches, libraries, museums, and theatres, as well as numerous fine restaurants, hotels, and motels. It is located in proximity to many scenic and historical places of interest including the Grand Canyon, the Petrified Forest, Montezuma Castle, and Oak Creek Canyon. It is one of the outstanding winter resorts of America with The Valley of the Sun nearby.

■ **PIMA COMMUNITY COLLEGE** *L-9*
4905 East Broadway
Tucson, AZ 85709-1010
Tel: (520)206-4666
Admissions: (520)206-4640
Fax: (520)884-6728
E-mail: wendy.kilgore@pima.edu
Web Site: http://www.pima.edu/
Description: State and locally supported, 2-year, coed. Awards certificates, transfer associate, and terminal associate degrees. Founded 1966. Setting:

483-acre urban campus. Endowment: $2.7 million. Educational spending for 2005 fiscal year: $5325 per student. Total enrollment: 30,884. Student-undergrad faculty ratio is 21:1. 5,456 applied, 100% were admitted. Full-time: 9,187 students, 54% women, 46% men. Part-time: 21,697 students, 58% women, 42% men. Students come from 40 states and territories, 64 other countries, 5% from out-of-state, 3% Native American, 31% Hispanic, 4% black, 3% Asian American or Pacific Islander, 1% international, 42% 25 or older, 9% transferred in. Core. Calendar: semesters. Academic remediation for entering students, ESL program, services for LD students, advanced placement, accelerated degree program, self-designed majors, freshman honors college, honors program, independent study, distance learning, double major, summer session for credit, part-time degree program, adult/continuing education programs, co-op programs and internships. ROTC: Army (c), Naval (c), Air Force (c).
Entrance Requirements: Open admission except for allied health programs. Options: Common Application, early admission. Entrance: noncompetitive. Application deadline: Rolling.
Costs Per Year: Application fee: $5. State resident tuition: $1104 full-time, $46 per credit part-time. Nonresident tuition: $5544 full-time, $78 per credit part-time. Mandatory fees: $80 full-time, $2.50 per credit part-time, $10 per term part-time.
Collegiate Environment: Orientation program. Drama-theater group, choral group, student-run newspaper. Student services: personal-psychological counseling, women's center. Campus security: 24-hour emergency response devices and patrols, late night transport-escort service. College housing not available. Pima College Library with 217,049 books, 14,419 microform titles, 984 serials, 24,005 audiovisual materials, an OPAC, and a Web page. Operations spending for 2004 fiscal year: $2.5 million. 2,500 computers available on campus for general student use. A campuswide network can be accessed from off-campus. Staffed computer lab on campus.
Community Environment: See University of Arizona.

■ **PIMA MEDICAL INSTITUTE (MESA)** *I-7*
957 South Dobson Rd.
Mesa, AZ 85202
Tel: (480)644-0267; 888-898-9048
Fax: (480)649-5249
E-mail: lipima@aol.com
Web Site: http://www.pimamedical.com/
Description: Proprietary, 2-year, coed. Part of Vocational Training Institutes, Inc. Awards certificates and terminal associate degrees. Founded 1985. Setting: urban campus. Total enrollment: 592. Calendar: modular.
Entrance Requirements: Required: interview, Wonderlic aptitude test. Required for some: high school transcript. Entrance: minimally difficult.
Collegiate Environment: College housing not available.

■ **PIMA MEDICAL INSTITUTE (TUCSON)** *L-9*
3350 East Grant Rd.
Tucson, AZ 85716-2800
Tel: (520)326-1600; 888-898-9048
Fax: (520)326-4125
Web Site: http://www.pmi.edu
Description: Proprietary, 2-year, coed. Part of Vocational Training Institutes, Inc. Awards certificates and terminal associate degrees. Founded 1972. Setting: urban campus. Total enrollment: 711. 120 applied, 97% were admitted. Full-time: 711 students, 81% women, 19% men. Calendar: modular. Academic remediation for entering students, accelerated degree program, adult/continuing education programs, co-op programs and internships.
Entrance Requirements: Options: Common Application, early admission. Required: interview, Wonderlic Scholastic Level Exam. Required for some: high school transcript. Entrance: minimally difficult.
Costs Per Year: Application fee: $150.
Collegiate Environment: Orientation program. College housing not available. Resource Center with an OPAC and a Web page. 30 computers available on campus for general student use. A campuswide network can be accessed. Staffed computer lab on campus.

■ **PRESCOTT COLLEGE** *G-6*
220 Grove Ave.
Prescott, AZ 86301
Tel: (928)778-2090
Free: 800-628-6364
Fax: (928)776-5157
Web Site: http://www.prescott.edu/

Description: Independent, comprehensive, coed. Awards bachelor's, master's, and doctoral degrees. Founded 1966. Setting: small town campus. Endowment: $150,000. Research spending for 2004 fiscal year: $35,000. Educational spending for 2005 fiscal year: $4358 per student. Total enrollment: 1,044. Faculty: 87 (50 full-time, 37 part-time). Student-undergrad faculty ratio is 7:1. 147 applied, 88% were admitted. 12% from top 10% of their high school class, 19% from top quarter, 50% from top half. Full-time: 723 students, 65% women, 35% men. Part-time: 70 students, 51% women, 49% men. Students come from 44 states and territories, 1 other country, 67% from out-of-state, 3% Native American, 6% Hispanic, 1% black, 1% Asian American or Pacific Islander, 0.1% international, 43% 25 or older, 23% transferred in. Retention: 68% of full-time freshmen returned the following year. Academic areas with the most degrees conferred: education; natural resources/environmental science; psychology. Core. Calendar: (4-week blocks followed by 10-week terms for each quarter). Services for LD students, advanced placement, self-designed majors, independent study, double major, summer session for credit, external degree program, adult/continuing education programs, internships. Off campus study at Four Corners School of Outdoor Education, Grand Canyon Field Institute.

Entrance Requirements: Options: deferred admission, international baccalaureate accepted. Required: essay, high school transcript, 2 recommendations, SAT or ACT. Required for some: interview. Entrance: moderately difficult. Application deadlines: 8/15, 12/1 for early decision. Notification: continuous, 12/15 for early decision.

Costs Per Year: Application fee: $25. Tuition: $18,576 full-time, $516 per credit hour part-time. Mandatory fees: $935 full-time.

Collegiate Environment: Orientation program. Drama-theater group, student-run newspaper. Social organizations: 10 open to all. Most popular organizations: Student Union, Amnesty International, Student Environmental Network. Major annual events: Student-Directed Days, PC Environmental Award. Student services: personal-psychological counseling. College housing not available. Prescott College Library with 23,899 books, 243 microform titles, 270 serials, 1,151 audiovisual materials, an OPAC, and a Web page. Operations spending for 2004 fiscal year: $237,000. 30 computers available on campus for general student use. A campuswide network can be accessed. Staffed computer lab on campus.

Community Environment: Located a mile high in the forested mountains of central Arizona, Prescott has a moderate climate and four seasons. Described by "Arizona Highways" magazine as "Everybody's Hometown," the community is known for its friendly atmosphere and small town charm. It was the capital of the Territory of Arizona back in the 1800s and the old governor's mansion still stands today. The town is rich in local history including gold-mining lore, cowboys, and the historic Roughriders. Classic Victorian homes line the streets. With clean air, abundant sunshine, and natural beauty in every direction, the Prescott area is truly an enjoyable place to live.

■ **THE REFRIGERATION SCHOOL** *P-9*
4210 East Washington St.
Phoenix, AZ 85034-1816
Tel: (602)275-7133
Web Site: http://www.refrigerationschool.com/
Description: Proprietary, 2-year, coed. Awards certificates, diplomas, and terminal associate degrees. Setting: urban campus. Total enrollment: 350. Calendar: continuous.
Collegiate Environment: College housing not available.

■ **REMINGTON COLLEGE-TEMPE CAMPUS** *I-7*
875 West Elliot Rd., Ste. 216
Tempe, AZ 85284
Tel: (480)834-1000
Free: 800-395-4322
Fax: (480)491-2970
E-mail: jdrennen@edamerica.com
Web Site: http://www.remingtoncollege.edu/
Description: Proprietary, 4-year, coed.

■ **RIO SALADO COLLEGE** *I-7*
2323 West 14th St.
Tempe, AZ 85281-6950
Tel: (480)517-8000
Free: 800-729-1197
Admissions: (480)517-8151
Fax: (480)517-8199

Web Site: http://www.rio.maricopa.edu/
Description: State and locally supported, 2-year, coed. Part of Maricopa County Community College District System. Awards certificates, transfer associate, and terminal associate degrees. Founded 1978. Setting: urban campus. Educational spending for 2005 fiscal year: $1807 per student. Total enrollment: 6,000. Students come from 44 states and territories, 38 other countries, 4% from out-of-state, 43% 25 or older. Core. Calendar: semesters. Academic remediation for entering students, ESL program, services for LD students, advanced placement, accelerated degree program, honors program, independent study, distance learning, double major, summer session for credit, part-time degree program, external degree program, adult/continuing education programs, co-op programs and internships.
Entrance Requirements: Open admission except for dental hygiene program. Options: electronic application, early admission, deferred admission. Placement: ACT ASSET required for some. Entrance: noncompetitive. Application deadline: Rolling.
Collegiate Environment: Student services: personal-psychological counseling. Campus security: 24-hour emergency response devices, late night transport-escort service. College housing not available. Rio Salado Library and Information Center with 16,000 books, 125 serials, 8,000 audiovisual materials, an OPAC, and a Web page. Operations spending for 2004 fiscal year: $197,853. 750 computers available on campus for general student use. A campuswide network can be accessed from off-campus. Staffed computer lab on campus.

■ **SCOTTSDALE COMMUNITY COLLEGE** *I-7*
9000 East Chaparral Rd.
Scottsdale, AZ 85256-2626
Tel: (480)423-6000
Admissions: (602)423-6133
Fax: (480)423-6200
E-mail: fran.watkins@sccmail.maricopa.edu
Web Site: http://www.sc.maricopa.edu/
Description: State and locally supported, 2-year, coed. Part of Maricopa County Community College District System. Awards certificates, diplomas, transfer associate, and terminal associate degrees. Founded 1969. Setting: 160-acre urban campus with easy access to Phoenix. Total enrollment: 11,261. Student-undergrad faculty ratio is 18:1. 517 applied, 100% were admitted. Full-time: 3,342 students, 46% women, 54% men. Part-time: 7,919 students, 58% women, 42% men. Students come from 49 other countries, 3% from out-of-state, 5% Native American, 11% Hispanic, 4% black, 2% Asian American or Pacific Islander, 1% international, 43% 25 or older. Core. Calendar: semesters. Academic remediation for entering students, ESL program, services for LD students, advanced placement, self-designed majors, honors program, summer session for credit, part-time degree program, adult/continuing education programs, co-op programs. Off campus study at Servicemembers Opportunity Colleges.
Entrance Requirements: Open admission. Option: early admission. Entrance: noncompetitive. Application deadline: Rolling. Notification: continuous.
Costs Per Year: Application fee: $0. Area resident tuition: $1980 full-time, $65 per credit hour part-time. State resident tuition: $8430 full-time, $90 per credit hour part-time. Nonresident tuition: $8430 full-time, $90 per credit hour part-time. Mandatory fees: $15 full-time.
Collegiate Environment: Orientation program. Drama-theater group, choral group, student-run newspaper, radio station. Student services: personal-psychological counseling. Campus security: 24-hour emergency response devices and patrols, student patrols, late night transport-escort service, 24-hour automatic surveillance cameras. College housing not available. 75 computers available on campus for general student use. A campuswide network can be accessed. Staffed computer lab on campus.
Community Environment: See Phoenix College.

■ **SCOTTSDALE CULINARY INSTITUTE** *I-7*
8100 East Camelback Rd., Ste. 1001
Scottsdale, AZ 85251-3940
Tel: (480)990-3773
Free: 800-848-2433
Fax: (480)990-0351
Web Site: http://www.scichefs.com/
Description: Proprietary, 2-year, coed. Awards certificates and terminal associate degrees. Founded 1986. Total enrollment: 1,200. Calendar: semesters.

■ **SOUTH MOUNTAIN COMMUNITY COLLEGE** *P-9*
7050 South Twenty-fourth St.
Phoenix, AZ 85040
Tel: (602)243-8000
Admissions: (602)243-8120
Fax: (602)243-8329
Web Site: http://www.smc.maricopa.edu/
Description: State and locally supported, 2-year, coed. Part of Maricopa County Community College District System. Awards certificates, transfer associate, and terminal associate degrees. Founded 1979. Setting: 108-acre suburban campus. Educational spending for 2005 fiscal year: $7803 per student. Total enrollment: 3,933. 2% from out-of-state, 4% Native American, 43% Hispanic, 14% black, 2% Asian American or Pacific Islander, 42% 25 or older. Core. Calendar: semesters. Academic remediation for entering students, ESL program, services for LD students, advanced placement, honors program, summer session for credit, part-time degree program, adult/continuing education programs, co-op programs. ROTC: Air Force (c).
Entrance Requirements: Open admission. Entrance: noncompetitive. Application deadline: 8/22. Notification: continuous until 8/22.
Costs Per Year: Application fee: $0. Area resident tuition: $1440 full-time. State resident tuition: $6192 full-time. Nonresident tuition: $6192 full-time. Mandatory fees: $10 full-time.
Collegiate Environment: Social organizations: 9 open to all. Major annual events: Festive Fall, Multicultural Week, Spring Fling. Student services: legal services. Campus security: late night transport-escort service, 18-hour patrols, campus lockdown. College housing not available. Learning Resource Center with 35,591 books, 475 serials, and an OPAC. 150 computers available on campus for general student use. Staffed computer lab on campus.
Community Environment: Located near both downtown Phoenix and Tempe, the college is just minutes from I-10 and Superstition freeways and Arizona State University. Ample parking is available. The college is served by the Phoenix Transit Bus System. Affordable housing, shopping, and services are within easy commuting distance. The campus is located in the shadow of South Mountain Park, the largest municipal park in the United States.

■ **SOUTHWEST INSTITUTE OF HEALING ARTS** *I-7*
1100 East Apache Blvd.
Tempe, AZ 85281
Tel: (480)994-9244; 888-504-9106
Fax: (480)994-3228
E-mail: joannl@swiha.net
Web Site: http://www.swiha.org/
Description: Proprietary, 2-year, coed. Founded 1992.

■ **SOUTHWESTERN COLLEGE** *P-9*
2625 East Cactus Rd.
Phoenix, AZ 85032-7042
Tel: (602)992-6101
Free: 800-247-2697
Web Site: http://www.swcaz.edu/
Description: Independent Conservative Baptist, 4-year, coed. Awards associate and bachelor's degrees. Founded 1960. Setting: 19-acre urban campus. Total enrollment: 267. 210 applied, 48% were admitted. Full-time: 237 students, 52% women, 48% men. Part-time: 30 students, 53% women, 47% men. Students come from 19 states and territories, 3 other countries, 16% from out-of-state, 1% Native American, 7% Hispanic, 2% black, 1% Asian American or Pacific Islander, 1% international, 16% 25 or older, 40% live on campus, 24% transferred in. Retention: 61% of full-time freshmen returned the following year. Core. Calendar: 4-4-1. Academic remediation for entering students, advanced placement, double major, summer session for credit, adult/continuing education programs, internships. ROTC: Air Force (c).
Entrance Requirements: Options: Common Application, electronic application, deferred admission. Required: essay, high school transcript, minimum 2.0 high school GPA, 1 recommendation, SAT and SAT Subject Tests or ACT. Entrance: minimally difficult. Application deadline: 8/1. Notification: continuous until 8/20.
Costs Per Year: Application fee: $25. Comprehensive fee: $15,930 includes full-time tuition ($11,130), mandatory fees ($440), and college room and board ($4360). College room only: $3360. Full-time tuition and fees vary according to course load and program. Room and board charges vary accord-

ing to housing facility. Part-time tuition: $464 per credit hour. Part-time mandatory fees: $220 per term. Part-time tuition and fees vary according to course load and program.
Collegiate Environment: Orientation program. Drama-theater group, choral group, student-run newspaper. Social organizations: 4 open to all. Most popular organizations: newspaper, drama, choral group, Student Leadership Council. Major annual events: Southwestern Days, Homecoming, Welcome Week. Campus security: controlled dormitory access. 176 college housing spaces available; 105 were occupied in 2003-04. Freshmen guaranteed college housing. On-campus residence required through sophomore year. Options: men-only, women-only housing available. R. S. Beal Library with 29,948 books, 20,446 microform titles, 808 serials, 2,866 audiovisual materials, and an OPAC. 44 computers available on campus for general student use. A campuswide network can be accessed from student residence rooms and from off campus. Staffed computer lab on campus.

■ **TOHONO O'ODHAM COMMUNITY COLLEGE** *M-7*
PO Box 3129
Sells, AZ 85634
Tel: (520)383-8401
Fax: (520)383-8403
Web Site: http://www.tocc.cc.az.us/
Description: Independent, 2-year, coed. Awards certificates, diplomas, transfer associate, and terminal associate degrees. Founded 1998. Total enrollment: 171. 97% Native American. Calendar: semesters.

■ **UNIVERSAL TECHNICAL INSTITUTE** *P-8*
10695 W. Pierce St.
Avondale, AZ 85323-7946
Tel: (602)264-4164
Free: 800-859-1202
Fax: (602)264-6412
Web Site: http://www.uticorp.com/
Description: Private, 2-year. Awards terminal associate degrees.
Entrance Requirements: Required: interview. Entrance: minimally difficult.

■ **UNIVERSITY OF ADVANCING TECHNOLOGY** *I-7*
2625 West Baseline Rd.
Tempe, AZ 85283-1042
Tel: (602)383-8228
Free: 800-658-5744
Fax: (602)383-8222
E-mail: admissions@uact.edu
Web Site: http://www.uat.edu/
Description: Proprietary, comprehensive, coed. Awards associate, bachelor's, and master's degrees. Founded 1983. Setting: urban campus. Total enrollment: 1,004. 834 applied, 93% were admitted. Full-time: 983 students, 9% women, 91% men. Students come from 39 states and territories, 61% from out-of-state, 1% Native American, 5% Hispanic, 4% black, 3% Asian American or Pacific Islander, 1% international, 28% 25 or older. Calendar: semesters. Advanced placement, accelerated degree program, independent study, distance learning, double major, summer session for credit, internships, graduate courses open to undergrads.
Entrance Requirements: Options: Peterson's Universal Application, electronic application. Required: high school transcript, SAT or ACT. Recommended: essay. Required for some: minimum 2.5 high school GPA, ACT, SAT Subject Tests. Application deadline: Rolling.
Costs Per Year: Application fee: $0. Tuition: $14,600 full-time.
Collegiate Environment: Orientation program. Student-run newspaper. Most popular organizations: Web Club, Gaming Club, Animation Club, Video Club, student government. Major annual events: technology forums, information nights, luncheons. Student services: personal-psychological counseling. Campus security: 24-hour patrols. College housing not available. University of Advancing Computer Technology Library with 19,211 books, 129 serials, 1,000 audiovisual materials, an OPAC, and a Web page. Operations spending for 2004 fiscal year: $178,000. 190 computers available on campus for general student use. A campuswide network can be accessed from off-campus. Staffed computer lab on campus.

■ **THE UNIVERSITY OF ARIZONA** *L-9*
Tucson, AZ 85721
Tel: (520)621-2211
Admissions: (520)621-3237
Fax: (520)621-9799

E-mail: appinfo@arizona.edu

Web Site: http://www.arizona.edu/

Description: State-supported, university, coed. Part of Arizona Board of Regents. Awards bachelor's, master's, doctoral, and first professional degrees. Founded 1885. Setting: 362-acre urban campus. Endowment: $348.3 million. Research spending for 2004 fiscal year: $328.5 million. Educational spending for 2005 fiscal year: $8281 per student. Total enrollment: 37,036. Faculty: 1,424 (1,378 full-time, 46 part-time). Student-undergrad faculty ratio is 19:1. 18,880 applied, 83% were admitted. 34% from top 10% of their high school class, 61% from top quarter, 88% from top half. 58 National Merit Scholars. Full-time: 24,725 students, 54% women, 46% men. Part-time: 3,737 students, 51% women, 49% men. Students come from 27 states and territories, 135 other countries, 27% from out-of-state, 2% Native American, 15% Hispanic, 3% black, 6% Asian American or Pacific Islander, 3% international, 9% 25 or older, 18% live on campus, 7% transferred in. Retention: 79% of full-time freshmen returned the following year. Academic areas with the most degrees conferred: business/marketing; communications/journalism; social sciences. Core. Calendar: semesters. ESL program, services for LD students, advanced placement, freshman honors college, honors program, independent study, distance learning, double major, summer session for credit, part-time degree program, adult/continuing education programs, internships, graduate courses open to undergrads. Study abroad program. ROTC: Army, Naval, Air Force.

Entrance Requirements: Options: electronic application, early admission, international baccalaureate accepted. Required: high school transcript. Recommended: SAT or ACT. Required for some: minimum 3.0 high school GPA, recommendations, interview. Entrance: moderately difficult. Application deadline: 4/1. Notification: continuous. Preference given to state residents.

Costs Per Year: Application fee: $25. State resident tuition: $4394 full-time, $246 per credit hour part-time. Nonresident tuition: $13,578 full-time, $582 per credit hour part-time. Mandatory fees: $104 full-time, $83 per year part-time. Full-time tuition and fees vary according to course load. Part-time tuition and fees vary according to course load. College room and board: $7460. College room only: $4100. Room and board charges vary according to board plan and housing facility.

Collegiate Environment: Orientation program. Drama-theater group, choral group, marching band, student-run newspaper, radio station. Social organizations: 280 open to all; national fraternities, national sororities, local fraternities, local sororities; 15% of eligible men and 15% of eligible women are members. Most popular organization: Student Government Association. Major annual events: Spring Fling, Homecoming, Family Weekend. Student services: legal services, health clinic, personal-psychological counseling, women's center. Campus security: 24-hour patrols, student patrols, late night transport-escort service, emergency telephones. 5,467 college housing spaces available; all were occupied in 2003-04. Freshmen given priority for college housing. Options: coed, men-only, women-only housing available. University of Arizona Main Library plus 5 others with 4.4 million books, 5.3 million microform titles, 23,790 serials, 51,136 audiovisual materials, an OPAC, and a Web page. Operations spending for 2004 fiscal year: $27 million. 1,950 computers available on campus for general student use. A campuswide network can be accessed from student residence rooms and from off campus. Staffed computer lab on campus.

Community Environment: Tucson is in a valley of the Sonoran Desert, and is surrounded by mountain ranges. Approximately 700,000 reside in the metropolitan area. Just north of the city are ski slopes and ponderosa pines as well as canyons and grassy meadows, which are popular with hikers and climbers. Yet Tucson has mild winters (average yearly temperature of 85 degrees) and attracts golf, tennis, and other sports enthusiasts year-round. The city has a professional symphony orchestra, opera company, theater company, and ballet, in addition to outstanding medical facilities. Located sixty miles north of Mexico, the community reflects the cultures of its Native American, Spanish, Mexican, and pioneer forefathers.

■ **UNIVERSITY OF PHOENIX ONLINE CAMPUS** *P-9*

3157 East Elwood St.

Phoenix, AZ 85034-7209

Tel: (602)387-7000

Free: 800-228-7240

Admissions: (480)557-1712

Web Site: http://www.uopxonline.com/

Description: Proprietary, comprehensive, coed. Awards associate, bachelor's, master's, and doctoral degrees and post-master's certificates. Founded 1989. Total enrollment: 117,259. Faculty: 5,974 (16 full-time, 5,958 part-time). Student-undergrad faculty ratio is 16:1. 505 applied. Full-time:

70,820 students, 59% women, 41% men. 0.4% Native American, 3% Hispanic, 5% black, 1% Asian American or Pacific Islander, 12% international, 91% 25 or older. Academic areas with the most degrees conferred: business/marketing; computer and information sciences; health professions and related sciences. Core. Calendar: continuous. Advanced placement, accelerated degree program, independent study, distance learning, external degree program, adult/continuing education programs, graduate courses open to undergrads.

Entrance Requirements: Open admission. Option: deferred admission. Required: 1 recommendation. Required for some: high school transcript. Entrance: noncompetitive. Application deadline: Rolling.

Costs Per Year: Application fee: $110. Tuition: $13,320 full-time, $444 per credit part-time. Mandatory fees: $560 full-time. Full-time tuition and fees vary according to program.

Collegiate Environment: College housing not available. University Library with 444 books, 666 serials, an OPAC, and a Web page. System-wide operations spending for 2004 fiscal year: $3.2 million.

■ **UNIVERSITY OF PHOENIX-PHOENIX CAMPUS** *P-9*

4635 East Elwood St.

Phoenix, AZ 85040-1958

Tel: (480)804-7600

Free: 800-228-7240

Admissions: (480)557-1712

E-mail: babarill@phoenix.edu

Web Site: http://www.phoenix.edu/

Description: Proprietary, comprehensive, coed. Awards bachelor's and master's degrees and post-master's certificates. Founded 1976. Setting: urban campus. Total enrollment: 9,408. Faculty: 784 (19 full-time, 765 part-time). Student-undergrad faculty ratio is 10:1. 175 applied. Full-time: 5,898 students, 57% women, 43% men. 0% from out-of-state, 1% Native American, 5% Hispanic, 3% black, 1% Asian American or Pacific Islander, 6% international, 89% 25 or older. Academic areas with the most degrees conferred: business/marketing; computer and information sciences; health professions and related sciences. Core. Calendar: continuous. Advanced placement, accelerated degree program, independent study, distance learning, external degree program, adult/continuing education programs, graduate courses open to undergrads.

Entrance Requirements: Open admission. Option: deferred admission. Required: 1 recommendation. Required for some: high school transcript. Entrance: noncompetitive. Application deadline: Rolling.

Costs Per Year: Application fee: $110. Tuition: $9765 full-time, $323 per credit part-time. Mandatory fees: $560 full-time, $70 per course part-time.

Collegiate Environment: Campus security: 24-hour patrols, late night transport-escort service. College housing not available. University Library with 442 books, 666 serials, an OPAC, and a Web page. System-wide operations spending for 2004 fiscal year: $3.2 million.

■ **UNIVERSITY OF PHOENIX-SOUTHERN ARIZONA CAMPUS** *L-9*

5099 East Grant Rd.

Tucson, AZ 85712-2732

Tel: (520)881-6512

Free: 800-228-7240

Admissions: (480)557-1712

Fax: (520)795-6177

Web Site: http://www.phoenix.edu/

Description: Proprietary, comprehensive, coed. Awards bachelor's and master's degrees and post-master's certificates. Founded 1979. Setting: urban campus. Total enrollment: 3,392. Faculty: 380 (4 full-time, 376 part-time). Student-undergrad faculty ratio is 8:1. 47 applied. Full-time: 2,431 students, 57% women, 43% men. 0% from out-of-state, 1% Native American, 11% Hispanic, 3% black, 1% Asian American or Pacific Islander, 15% international, 88% 25 or older. Academic areas with the most degrees conferred: business/marketing; computer and information sciences; health professions and related sciences. Core. Calendar: continuous. Advanced placement, accelerated degree program, independent study, distance learning, external degree program, adult/continuing education programs, graduate courses open to undergrads.

Entrance Requirements: Open admission. Option: deferred admission. Required: 1 recommendation. Required for some: high school transcript. Entrance: noncompetitive. Application deadline: Rolling.

Costs Per Year: Application fee: $110. Tuition: $9675 full-time, $322.50 per credit part-time. Mandatory fees: $560 full-time, $70 per course part-time.

Collegiate Environment: College housing not available. University Library with 444 books, 666 serials, an OPAC, and a Web page. System-wide operations spending for 2004 fiscal year: $3.2 million.

■ **WESTERN INTERNATIONAL UNIVERSITY** *P-9*
9215 North Black Canyon Hwy.
Phoenix, AZ 85021-2718
Tel: (602)943-2311
Web Site: http://www.wintu.edu/
Description: Proprietary, comprehensive, coed. Administratively affiliated with Apollo Group, Inc. Awards associate, bachelor's, and master's degrees. Founded 1978. Setting: 4-acre urban campus. Endowment: $20,000. Educational spending for 2005 fiscal year: $3351 per student. Total enrollment: 3,751. Full-time: 2,856 students, 56% women, 44% men. Students come from 40 other countries, 0.5% Native American, 5% Hispanic, 3% black, 2% Asian American or Pacific Islander, 2% international, 90% 25 or older. Core. Calendar: continuous. ESL program, advanced placement, accelerated degree program, honors program, independent study, double major, summer session for credit, part-time degree program, external degree program, adult/continuing education programs. Study abroad program.
Entrance Requirements: Option: deferred admission. Required: high school transcript, minimum 2.5 high school GPA, interview. Recommended: 3 recommendations. Required for some: 3 recommendations. Entrance: moderately difficult. Application deadline: Rolling.
Collegiate Environment: Social organizations: 3 open to all. Most popular organizations: Delta Mu Delta, Student Association, International Student Organization. Campus security: 24-hour emergency response devices and patrols, late night transport-escort service. College housing not available. Learning Resource Center with 7,500 books, 125 serials, and a Web page. Operations spending for 2004 fiscal year: $157,987. 30 computers available on campus for general student use. A campuswide network can be accessed. Staffed computer lab on campus.

■ **YAVAPAI COLLEGE** *G-6*
1100 East Sheldon St.
Prescott, AZ 86301-3297
Tel: (928)445-7300
Free: 800-922-6787
Admissions: (928)776-2188
Fax: (928)776-2151
Web Site: http://www2.yc.edu/
Description: State and locally supported, 2-year, coed. Part of Arizona State Community College System. Awards certificates, transfer associate, and terminal associate degrees. Founded 1966. Setting: 100-acre small town campus. Educational spending for 2005 fiscal year: $4339 per student. Total enrollment: 7,422. Student-undergrad faculty ratio is 15:1. Full-time: 1,322 students, 53% women, 47% men. Part-time: 6,100 students, 64% women, 36% men. Students come from 30 states and territories, 18% from out-of-state, 4% Native American, 7% Hispanic, 1% black, 1% Asian American or Pacific Islander, 0.02% international, 70% 25 or older, 5% live on campus. Core. Calendar: semesters. Academic remediation for entering students, ESL program, services for LD students, advanced placement, honors program, independent study, distance learning, summer session for credit, part-time degree program, adult/continuing education programs, co-op programs and internships. Off campus study at Northern Arizona University. ROTC: Army (c), Air Force (c).
Entrance Requirements: Open admission except for nursing, gunsmithing and independent filmmaking. Options: early admission, deferred admission. Required: high school transcript. Required for some: essay, recommendations. Entrance: noncompetitive. Application deadline: Rolling.
Costs Per Year: State resident tuition: $1080 full-time, $45 per credit part-time. Nonresident tuition: $6880 full-time, $56 per credit part-time.
Collegiate Environment: Orientation program. Drama-theater group, choral group, student-run newspaper. Social organizations: 20 open to all. Most popular organizations: Re-Entry Club, Student Nurses Association, Native American Club, International Club, VICA. Major annual events: Welcome Week, Homecoming/Parents' Weekend, Earth Day. Student services: health clinic, personal-psychological counseling, women's center. Campus security: 24-hour emergency response devices and patrols, student patrols, late night transport-escort service, controlled dormitory access. 371 college housing spaces available; 360 were occupied in 2003-04. No special consideration for freshman housing applicants. Option: coed housing available. Yavapai College Library with 81,144 books, 1,091 serials, an OPAC, and a Web page. Operations spending for 2004 fiscal year: $789,150. 677 computers available on campus for general student use. A campuswide network can be accessed from student residence rooms and from off campus. Staffed computer lab on campus.
Community Environment: Population 30,000. The city of Prescott is imbued with thoroughly Western informality. The city is easily reached from all parts of the United States by regularly scheduled airlines and bus service. Climate is ideal, embracing four seasons, but without the extremes of heat, cold, dryness, or dampness. Employment opportunities are average for a community of this size. Prescott has a community concert program, and an active interest in the arts provides cultural atmosphere. Prescott Frontier Days are held during the July Fourth weekend; this is the original cowboy rodeo of America. The Yavapai County Fair is held during September. There is horse racing at Prescott Downs on weekends from Memorial Day through Labor Day.

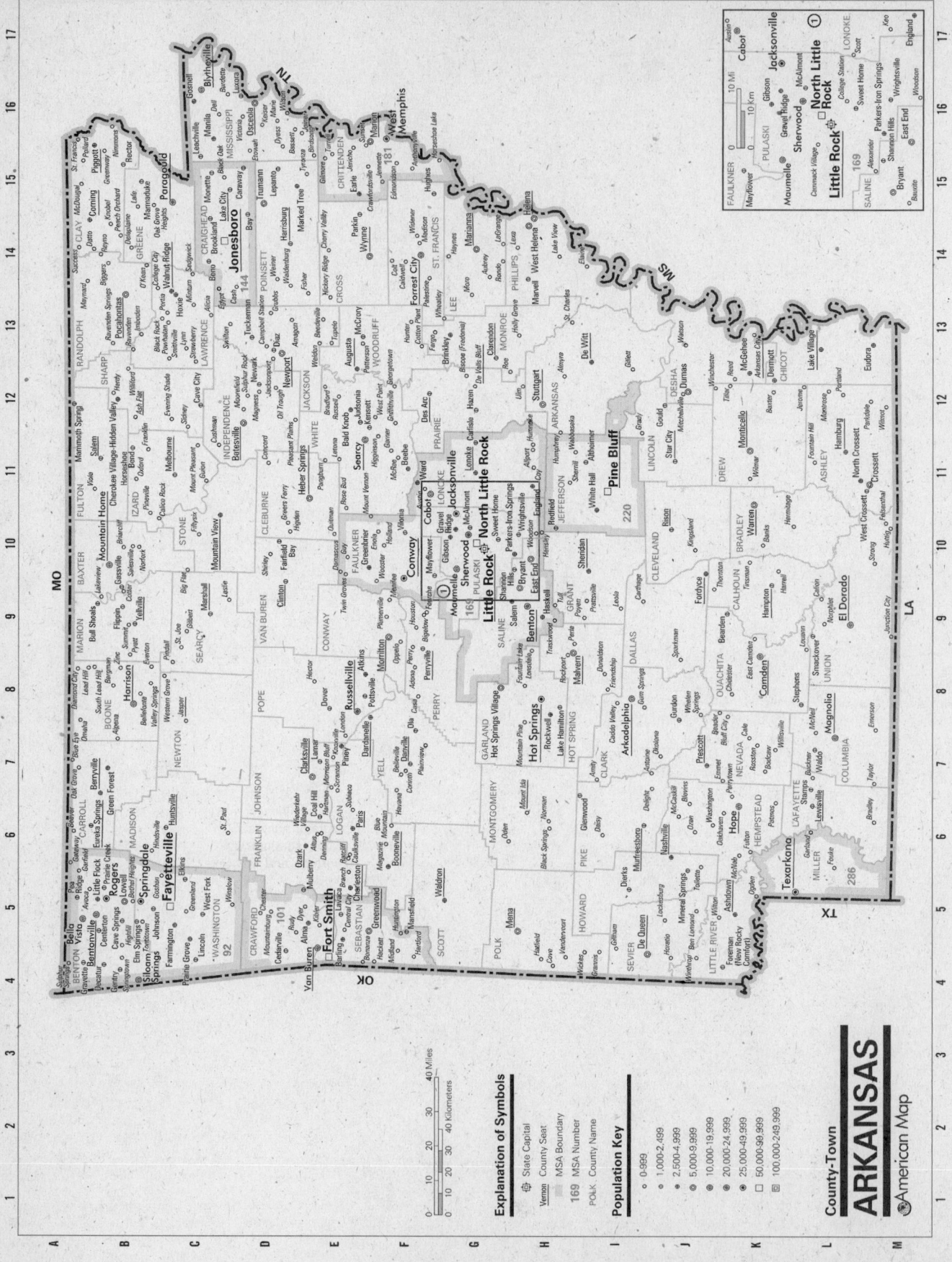

ARKANSAS

County-Town

American Map

Explanation of Symbols

✪ State Capital
Vernon ● County Seat
—·— MSA Boundary
169 MSA Number
POLK County Name

Population Key

○ 0-999
◦ 1,000-2,499
● 2,500-4,999
● 5,000-9,999
● 10,000-19,999
● 20,000-24,999
□ 25,000-49,999
□ 50,000-99,999
▣ 100,000-249,999

■ **ARKANSAS BAPTIST COLLEGE** *G-10*
1600 Bishop St.
Little Rock, AR 72202-6067
Tel: (501)374-7856
Web Site: http://www.arbaptcol.edu/
Description: Independent Baptist, 4-year, coed. Awards associate and bachelor's degrees. Founded 1884. Setting: urban campus. Endowment: $306,174. Total enrollment: 375. 3% from top 10% of their high school class, 20% from top quarter, 40% from top half. Full-time: 258 students, 52% women, 48% men. Part-time: 117 students, 65% women, 35% men. 99% black. Core. Calendar: semesters. Academic remediation for entering students, accelerated degree program, summer session for credit, part-time degree program, adult/continuing education programs.
Entrance Requirements: Open admission. Option: deferred admission. Required: high school transcript. Entrance: minimally difficult. Application deadline: Rolling.
Collegiate Environment: 175 college housing spaces available; all were occupied in 2003-04. 25 computers available on campus for general student use.

■ **ARKANSAS NORTHEASTERN COLLEGE** *C-16*
PO Box 1109
Blytheville, AR 72316-1109
Tel: (870)762-1020
Fax: (870)763-3704
Web Site: http://www.anc.edu/
Description: State-supported, 2-year, coed. Awards certificates, transfer associate, and terminal associate degrees. Founded 1975. Setting: 80-acre rural campus with easy access to Memphis. Endowment: $187,500. Educational spending for 2005 fiscal year: $4680 per student. Total enrollment: 1,830. Student-undergrad faculty ratio is 18:1. 513 applied, 100% were admitted. 17% from top 10% of their high school class. 3 valedictorians. Full-time: 962 students, 64% women, 36% men. Part-time: 868 students, 69% women, 31% men. Students come from 3 states and territories, 17% from out-of-state, 0.2% Native American, 1% Hispanic, 29% black, 1% Asian American or Pacific Islander, 0% international, 40% 25 or older, 5% transferred in. Retention: 50% of full-time freshmen returned the following year. Core. Calendar: semesters. Academic remediation for entering students, advanced placement, distance learning, double major, summer session for credit, part-time degree program, adult/continuing education programs.
Entrance Requirements: Open admission except for nursing program. Option: deferred admission. Recommended: high school transcript. Entrance: noncompetitive. Application deadline: Rolling. Notification: continuous.
Costs Per Year: Application fee: $0. Area resident tuition: $1410 full-time, $47 per semester hour part-time. State resident tuition: $1710 full-time, $57 per semester hour part-time. Nonresident tuition: $3210 full-time, $107 per semester hour part-time. Mandatory fees: $220 full-time, $6 per semester hour part-time, $20 per term part-time.
Collegiate Environment: Orientation program. Choral group. Social organizations: 10 open to all. Most popular organizations: Gamma Beta Phi, Association of Childhood Education International, Nursing Club, Cultural Diversity, Adult Student Association. Major annual events: Fall Funfest, Spring Funfest, Evening Student Appreciation Night. Campus security: 24-hour patrols. College housing not available. Adams/Vines Library with 15,493 books, 3,704 microform titles, 165 serials, 682 audiovisual materials,

and an OPAC. Operations spending for 2004 fiscal year: $371,306. 280 computers available on campus for general student use. A campuswide network can be accessed. Staffed computer lab on campus.
Community Environment: In a rural area with a population of 22,000.

■ **ARKANSAS STATE UNIVERSITY**
PO Box 10
State University, AR 72467
Tel: (870)972-2100
Admissions: (870)972-3024
Fax: (870)972-2090
E-mail: admissions@astate.edu
Web Site: http://www.astate.edu/
Description: State-supported, comprehensive, coed. Part of Arkansas State University System. Awards associate, bachelor's, master's, and doctoral degrees and post-master's certificates (specialist). Founded 1909. Setting: 942-acre small town campus with easy access to Memphis. Endowment: $36.5 million. Research spending for 2004 fiscal year: $6.5 million. Educational spending for 2005 fiscal year: $3700 per student. Total enrollment: 10,414. Faculty: 606 (447 full-time, 159 part-time). Student-undergrad faculty ratio is 17:1. 3,488 applied, 65% were admitted. Full-time: 7,194 students, 58% women, 42% men. Part-time: 1,944 students, 63% women, 37% men. Students come from 42 states and territories, 49 other countries, 10% from out-of-state, 0.4% Native American, 1% Hispanic, 17% black, 1% Asian American or Pacific Islander, 1% international, 28% 25 or older, 18% live on campus, 10% transferred in. Retention: 65% of full-time freshmen returned the following year. Academic areas with the most degrees conferred: business/marketing; education; health professions and related sciences. Core. Calendar: semesters. Academic remediation for entering students, ESL program, services for LD students, advanced placement, accelerated degree program, honors program, independent study, distance learning, double major, summer session for credit, part-time degree program, co-op programs and internships, graduate courses open to undergrads. Off campus study at Arkansas State University-Beebe, East Arkansas Community College, Mid-South Community College, ASU-Regional Programs, ASU-Mountain Home, ASU-Paragould, Arkansas Northeastern College. Study abroad program. ROTC: Army.
Entrance Requirements: Options: electronic application, early admission, deferred admission, international baccalaureate accepted. Required: high school transcript, minimum 2.0 high school GPA, proof of immunization, proof of enrollment in selective service for men over 18, SAT or ACT. Recommended: ACT. Required for some: ACT ASSET or ACT COMPASS. Entrance: minimally difficult. Application deadline: Rolling. Notification: continuous.
Costs Per Year: Application fee: $15. State resident tuition: $4260 full-time, $142 per credit hour part-time. Nonresident tuition: $10,965 full-time, $365.50 per credit hour part-time. Mandatory fees: $1180 full-time, $37 per credit hour part-time, $25 per term part-time. Full-time tuition and fees vary according to course load, location, and program. Part-time tuition and fees vary according to course load, location, and program. College room and board: $4190. Room and board charges vary according to board plan and housing facility.
Collegiate Environment: Orientation program. Drama-theater group, choral group, marching band, student-run newspaper, radio station. Social organizations: 192 open to all; national fraternities, national sororities; 15% of eligible men and 7% of eligible women are members. Most popular

organizations: Student Government Association, intramurals, academic clubs, minority/international organizations. Major annual events: Homecoming, International Night, Springfest. Student services: health clinic, personal-psychological counseling. Campus security: 24-hour emergency response devices and patrols. 2,315 college housing spaces available; 1,722 were occupied in 2003-04. No special consideration for freshman housing applicants. On-campus residence required in freshman year. Options: men-only, women-only housing available. Dean B. Ellis Library with 586,176 books, 578,473 microform titles, 1,675 serials, 15,649 audiovisual materials, an OPAC, and a Web page. Operations spending for 2004 fiscal year: $2.8 million. 510 computers available on campus for general student use. A campuswide network can be accessed from student residence rooms and from off campus. Staffed computer lab on campus.

Community Environment: Jonesboro is located on Crowley's Ridge, bordering the rich Mississippi Delta Agricultural and Industrial Center. Buses, railroads and airlines service the area. Jonesboro is 65 miles from Memphis, 133 miles from Little Rock, and 261 miles from St. Louis. The mean temperature is 60 degrees, and the average annual rainfall is 50 inches. There are more than 102 active clubs, and organizations, theaters, a Community Center, and several city parks in the city. Lake Frierson State Park and Craighead Forest Park and lake are nearby.

■ ARKANSAS STATE UNIVERSITY-BEEBE *F-11*
PO Box 1000
Beebe, AR 72012-1000
Tel: (501)882-3600
Admissions: (501)882-8280
Fax: (501)882-8370
Web Site: http://www.asub.edu/
Description: State-supported, 2-year, coed. Part of Arkansas State University System. Awards certificates, transfer associate, and terminal associate degrees. Founded 1927. Setting: 320-acre small town campus with easy access to Memphis. Educational spending for 2005 fiscal year: $11,374 per student. Total enrollment: 3,976. Student-undergrad faculty ratio is 30:1. 2 class presidents, 1 valedictorian, 20 student government officers. Full-time: 2,124 students, 57% women, 43% men. Part-time: 1,852 students, 57% women, 43% men. Students come from 25 states and territories, 1% Native American, 2% Hispanic, 5% black, 1% Asian American or Pacific Islander, 0.1% international, 38% 25 or older, 12% live on campus, 2% transferred in. Core. Calendar: semesters. Academic remediation for entering students, advanced placement, honors program, distance learning, summer session for credit, part-time degree program, adult/continuing education programs.
Entrance Requirements: Open admission. Options: Common Application, deferred admission. Required: high school transcript. Placement: ACT recommended. Entrance: noncompetitive. Application deadline: Rolling. Notification: continuous.
Costs Per Year: Application fee: $0. State resident tuition: $1824 full-time. Nonresident tuition: $3000 full-time. College room and board: $2480.
Collegiate Environment: Drama-theater group, choral group. Social organizations: 19 open to all. Most popular organizations: Student Arkansas Education Association, Art Club, Agri Club, Social Science Club, Leadership Council. Major annual events: Organizational Fair, Harvestfest/Spring Dance, Leadership Council activities. Student services: personal-psychological counseling. Campus security: 24-hour emergency response devices and patrols. 160 college housing spaces available; 126 were occupied in 2003-04. Options: men-only, women-only housing available. Abington Library with 90,000 books, 500 serials, and 10 audiovisual materials. 375 computers available on campus for general student use. A campuswide network can be accessed from off-campus. Staffed computer lab on campus.

■ ARKANSAS STATE UNIVERSITY-MOUNTAIN HOME *B-10*
1600 South College St.
Mountain Home, AR 72653
Tel: (870)508-6100
Admissions: (870)508-6104
E-mail: rblagg@asumh.edu
Web Site: http://www.asumh.edu/
Description: State-supported, 2-year, coed. Part of Arkansas State University. Awards certificates and terminal associate degrees. Setting: 136-acre small town campus. Total enrollment: 1,031. Student-undergrad faculty ratio is 20:1. 735 applied, 52% were admitted. Full-time: 625 students, 64% women, 36% men. Part-time: 406 students, 72% women, 28% men. Students come from 11 states and territories, 3 other countries, 0.1% from

out-of-state, 44% 25 or older, 15% transferred in. Retention: 46% of full-time freshmen returned the following year. Core. Calendar: semesters. Academic remediation for entering students, services for LD students, advanced placement, independent study, distance learning, summer session for credit, part-time degree program, co-op programs.
Entrance Requirements: Open admission. Required: high school transcript. Recommended: placement scores, ACT, SAT Subject Tests, COMPASS, ASSET. Entrance: noncompetitive. Notification: continuous.
Costs Per Year: Application fee: $0. State resident tuition: $2130 full-time, $71 per credit part-time. Nonresident tuition: $3660 full-time, $122 per credit part-time. Mandatory fees: $240 full-time, $8 per credit part-time.
Collegiate Environment: Choral group. Social organizations: 13 open to all. Most popular organizations: Phi Theta Kappa, Circle K, Criminal Justice Club, Mortuary Science Club, Student Ambassadors. Major annual events: Gaston Lecture Club events, Jingle-on-the-Green. College housing not available. Norma Wood Library with 30,682 books, 1,439 microform titles, 6,634 serials, 2,150 audiovisual materials, an OPAC, and a Web page. Operations spending for 2004 fiscal year: $319,675. 60 computers available on campus for general student use. A campuswide network can be accessed from off-campus. Staffed computer lab on campus.

■ ARKANSAS STATE UNIVERSITY-NEWPORT *D-13*
7648 Victory Blvd.
Newport, AR 72112
Tel: (870)512-7800
Free: 800-976-1676
Web Site: http://www.asun.edu/
Description: State-supported, 2-year, coed. Part of Arkansas State University. Awards certificates, diplomas, and transfer associate degrees. Total enrollment: 896. 1% Native American, 2% Hispanic, 16% black, 2% Asian American or Pacific Islander, 1% international, 38% 25 or older. Core. Calendar: semesters. Academic remediation for entering students, ESL program, services for LD students, independent study, external degree program, adult/continuing education programs, internships. Off campus study.
Entrance Requirements: Open admission. Option: Common Application. Required: interview, ACT. Entrance: noncompetitive.
Collegiate Environment: Orientation program.

■ ARKANSAS TECH UNIVERSITY *E-8*
Russellville, AR 72801
Tel: (479)968-0389
Free: 800-582-6953
Admissions: (479)968-0343
Fax: (479)964-0522
E-mail: shauna.donnell@atu.edu
Web Site: http://www.atu.edu/
Description: State-supported, comprehensive, coed. Awards associate, bachelor's, and master's degrees (Educational Specialist's). Founded 1909. Setting: 516-acre small town campus. Endowment: $12.4 million. Research spending for 2004 fiscal year: $790,945. Educational spending for 2005 fiscal year: $3641 per student. Total enrollment: 6,842. Faculty: 398 (252 full-time, 146 part-time). Student-undergrad faculty ratio is 19:1. 3,459 applied, 48% were admitted. 17% from top 10% of their high school class, 43% from top quarter, 70% from top half. Full-time: 5,365 students, 52% women, 48% men. Part-time: 963 students, 61% women, 39% men. Students come from 37 states and territories, 34 other countries, 4% from out-of-state, 1% Native American, 2% Hispanic, 5% black, 1% Asian American or Pacific Islander, 2% international, 21% 25 or older, 30% live on campus, 5% transferred in. Retention: 66% of full-time freshmen returned the following year. Academic areas with the most degrees conferred: education; business/marketing; health professions and related sciences. Core. Calendar: semesters. Academic remediation for entering students, services for LD students, advanced placement, honors program, independent study, distance learning, double major, summer session for credit, part-time degree program, external degree program, adult/continuing education programs, internships, graduate courses open to undergrads. ROTC: Army (c).
Entrance Requirements: Options: electronic application, deferred admission, international baccalaureate accepted. Required: high school transcript, minimum 2.0 high school GPA, SAT or ACT. Entrance: moderately difficult. Notification: continuous.
Costs Per Year: Application fee: $0. State resident tuition: $4290 full-time, $143 per credit hour part-time. Nonresident tuition: $8580 full-time, $286 per credit hour part-time. Mandatory fees: $410 full-time, $4 per credit hour part-

time, $145 per term part-time. Full-time tuition and fees vary according to course load and location. Part-time tuition and fees vary according to course load and location. College room and board: $4290. College room only: $2290. Room and board charges vary according to board plan and housing facility.

Collegiate Environment: Drama-theater group, choral group, marching band, student-run newspaper, radio station. Social organizations: 97 open to all; national fraternities, national sororities, local fraternities, local sororities; 5% of eligible men and 4% of eligible women are members. Most popular organizations: Student Government Association, Student Activities Board, Wesley Foundation, Chi Alpha, Baptist Student Union. Major annual events: SAB Bingo Night, Homecoming, Timeout for Tech. Student services: health clinic, personal-psychological counseling. Campus security: 24-hour patrols, late night transport-escort service, controlled dormitory access. College housing designed to accommodate 1,579 students; 1,813 undergraduates lived in college housing during 2003-04. Freshmen guaranteed college housing. On-campus residence required through sophomore year. Options: coed, men-only, women-only housing available. Ross Pendergraft Library and Technology Center with 259,372 books, 880,006 microform titles, 1,054 serials, 6,975 audiovisual materials, an OPAC, and a Web page. Operations spending for 2004 fiscal year: $1.1 million. 700 computers available on campus for general student use. A campuswide network can be accessed from student residence rooms and from off campus. Staffed computer lab on campus.

Community Environment: Russellville, the crossroads for State Highways 7, 22, 124, and 64, is located equidistant from Little Rock, Hot Springs, Harrison, and Fort Smith. Interstate 40 passes just north of Russellville, a city of 25,000. A 36,600 acre lake, formed by a lock and dam on the navigable Arkansas River, lies southwest of the city. The area, served by airplane, rail, and bus lines, is experiencing vigorous industrial development, which includes the construction of the first nuclear power plant in the Southwest. Recreational facilities in the area include lakes, picnic areas, city parks, swimming pools, tennis courts, and private country clubs. There are the usual civic organizations of a city. Part-time employment is available in stores and on campus.

■ **BLACK RIVER TECHNICAL COLLEGE** *B-13*
1410 Hwy. 304 East
Pocahontas, AR 72455
Tel: (870)248-4000
Free: 800-919-3086
Admissions: (870)892-4565
Fax: (870)248-4100
Web Site: http://www.blackrivertech.edu/
Description: State-supported, 2-year, coed. Awards transfer associate and terminal associate degrees. Founded 1972. Setting: 55-acre small town campus. Total enrollment: 1,243. Full-time: 652 students, 57% women, 43% men. Part-time: 591 students, 55% women, 45% men. Students come from 2 states and territories, 53% 25 or older. Calendar: semesters. Academic remediation for entering students, services for LD students, self-designed majors, honors program, summer session for credit, part-time degree program, co-op programs and internships.
Entrance Requirements: Open admission except for nursing program. Option: Common Application. Required for some: high school transcript, interview, ACT, ACT ASSET, or SAT. Entrance: noncompetitive. Application deadline: Rolling.
Collegiate Environment: Orientation program. Campus security: night patrol. College housing not available. Black River Technical College Library with 10,000 books, 200 serials, and an OPAC. 100 computers available on campus for general student use. Staffed computer lab on campus.

■ **CENTRAL BAPTIST COLLEGE** *F-9*
1501 College Ave.
Conway, AR 72034-6470
Tel: (501)329-6872
Free: 800-205-6872
E-mail: ccalhoun@cbc.edu
Web Site: http://www.cbc.edu/
Description: Independent Baptist, 4-year, coed. Awards associate and bachelor's degrees. Founded 1952. Setting: 11-acre small town campus. Endowment: $974,667. Educational spending for 2005 fiscal year: $3614 per student. Total enrollment: 395. Student-undergrad faculty ratio is 11:1. 154 applied, 68% were admitted. 6% from top 10% of their high school class, 31% from top quarter, 63% from top half. Full-time: 328 students, 45%

women, 55% men. Part-time: 67 students, 45% women, 55% men. Students come from 14 states and territories, 1 other country, 10% from out-of-state, 1% Native American, 2% Hispanic, 15% black, 1% Asian American or Pacific Islander, 0.3% international, 27% 25 or older, 40% live on campus, 19% transferred in. Academic areas with the most degrees conferred: business/marketing; theology and religious vocations; psychology. Core. Calendar: semesters. Academic remediation for entering students, advanced placement, summer session for credit, part-time degree program, adult/continuing education programs, internships. ROTC: Army (c).
Entrance Requirements: Options: Peterson's Universal Application, Common Application, electronic application, early admission. Required: essay, high school transcript, minimum 2.5 high school GPA, 2 recommendations, ACT. Entrance: minimally difficult. Application deadline: 8/15.
Costs Per Year: Application fee: $25. Comprehensive fee: $13,110 includes full-time tuition ($7950), mandatory fees ($500), and college room and board ($4660).
Collegiate Environment: Orientation program. Drama-theater group, choral group. Major annual events: Harvest Party, Discovery Day, Spring Fling. Student services: personal-psychological counseling. On-campus residence required through senior year. J. E. Cobb Library with 50,448 books, 27,268 microform titles, 330 serials, and 4,827 audiovisual materials. Operations spending for 2004 fiscal year: $78,269. 38 computers available on campus for general student use. A campuswide network can be accessed. Staffed computer lab on campus.
Community Environment: See University of Central Arkansas.

■ **COSSATOT COMMUNITY COLLEGE OF THE UNIVERSITY OF ARKANSAS** *J-4*
PO Box 960
De Queen, AR 71832
Tel: (870)584-4471
Free: 800-844-4471
Web Site: http://www.cccua.edu/
Description: State-supported, 2-year, coed. Part of University of Arkansas System. Awards certificates, transfer associate, and terminal associate degrees. Founded 1991. Setting: rural campus. Endowment: $110,096. Total enrollment: 1,020. Student-undergrad faculty ratio is 12:1. 361 applied, 83% were admitted. Students come from 6 states and territories, 2% from out-of-state, 2% Native American, 10% Hispanic, 10% black, 1% Asian American or Pacific Islander, 0% international. Calendar: semesters. Academic remediation for entering students, ESL program, services for LD students, advanced placement, independent study, distance learning, double major, summer session for credit, part-time degree program, external degree program, adult/continuing education programs, co-op programs and internships. Off campus study.
Entrance Requirements: Open admission. Options: Common Application, electronic application. Recommended: high school transcript. Entrance: noncompetitive.
Costs Per Year: Area resident tuition: $1350 full-time, $45 per credit hour part-time. State resident tuition: $1650 full-time, $55 per credit hour part-time. Nonresident tuition: $4950 full-time, $165 per credit hour part-time. Mandatory fees: $250 full-time, $15 per course part-time, $53 per term part-time. Full-time tuition and fees vary according to course load and program. Part-time tuition and fees vary according to course load and program.
Collegiate Environment: Orientation program. College housing not available.

■ **CROWLEY'S RIDGE COLLEGE** *C-15*
100 College Dr.
Paragould, AR 72450-9731
Tel: (870)236-6901
Free: 800-264-1096
Fax: (870)236-7748
E-mail: njoneshi@crowleysridgecollege.edu
Web Site: http://www.crowleysridgecollege.edu/
Description: Independent, 2-year, coed, affiliated with Church of Christ. Awards transfer associate and terminal associate degrees. Setting: 112-acre small town campus. Endowment: $1 million. Total enrollment: 183. 2% black, 1% Asian American or Pacific Islander, 1% international. Calendar: semesters. Academic remediation for entering students, honors program, independent study, double major, summer session for credit, part-time degree program.
Entrance Requirements: Open admission. Options: Common Application, electronic application. Required: high school transcript, recommendation

form filled out by high school. Required for some: interview. Placement: ACT, ACT ASSET required. Entrance: noncompetitive. Application deadline: Rolling.

Collegiate Environment: Orientation program. Drama-theater group, choral group, student-run newspaper. 112 college housing spaces available; 80 were occupied in 2003-04. On-campus residence required through sophomore year. Options: men-only, women-only housing available. Learning Center with an OPAC and a Web page. 9 computers available on campus for general student use. A campuswide network can be accessed from student residence rooms. Staffed computer lab on campus.

■ **EAST ARKANSAS COMMUNITY COLLEGE** *F-14*
1700 Newcastle Rd.
Forrest City, AR 72335-2204
Tel: (870)633-4480; 877-797-3222
Fax: (870)633-7222
E-mail: dadams@eacc.edu
Web Site: http://www.eacc.edu/

Description: State-supported, 2-year, coed. Awards certificates, transfer associate, and terminal associate degrees. Founded 1974. Setting: 40-acre small town campus with easy access to Memphis. Endowment: $217,500. Educational spending for 2005 fiscal year: $3666 per student. Total enrollment: 1,477. Student-undergrad faculty ratio is 17:1. Full-time: 745 students, 70% women, 30% men. Part-time: 732 students, 64% women, 36% men. Students come from 4 states and territories, 1% from out-of-state, 0.2% Native American, 1% Hispanic, 41% black, 1% Asian American or Pacific Islander, 0.1% international, 47% 25 or older. Core. Calendar: semesters. Academic remediation for entering students, services for LD students, advanced placement, honors program, summer session for credit, part-time degree program, adult/continuing education programs.

Entrance Requirements: Open admission. Options: early admission, deferred admission. Required: high school transcript. Entrance: minimally difficult. Application deadline: Rolling. Notification: continuous.

Costs Per Year: Application fee: $0. Area resident tuition: $1470 full-time, $49 per credit hour part-time. State resident tuition: $1710 full-time, $57 per credit hour part-time. Nonresident tuition: $2070 full-time, $69 per credit hour part-time. Mandatory fees: $150 full-time, $5 per credit hour part-time.

Collegiate Environment: Drama-theater group, choral group. Social organizations: 4 open to all. Most popular organizations: Gamma Beta Phi, Baptist Student Union, Student Activities Committee, Lambda Alpha Epsilon. Major annual events: Spring Barbecue, Homecoming. Student services: personal-psychological counseling. Campus security: 24-hour emergency response devices, 16-hour patrols by trained security personnel. College housing not available. Learning Resource Center plus 1 other with 21,908 books and 109 serials. 26 computers available on campus for general student use. Staffed computer lab on campus.

Community Environment: Forrest City, with a population of 13,803, is the county seat of St. Francis County.

■ **HARDING UNIVERSITY** *F-11*
900 East Center
Searcy, AR 72149-0001
Tel: (501)279-4000
Free: 800-477-4407
Admissions: (501)279-4407
Fax: (501)279-4865
E-mail: admissions@harding.edu
Web Site: http://www.harding.edu/

Description: Independent, comprehensive, coed, affiliated with Church of Christ. Awards bachelor's and master's degrees. Founded 1924. Setting: 200-acre small town campus with easy access to Little Rock. Endowment: $78.4 million. Research spending for 2004 fiscal year: $64,685. Educational spending for 2005 fiscal year: $6559 per student. Total enrollment: 5,744. Faculty: 332 (226 full-time, 106 part-time). Student-undergrad faculty ratio is 18:1. 1,658 applied, 62% were admitted. 27% from top 10% of their high school class, 52% from top quarter, 76% from top half. 16 National Merit Scholars. Full-time: 3,879 students, 54% women, 46% men. Part-time: 213 students, 53% women, 47% men. Students come from 50 states and territories, 70% from out-of-state, 1% Native American, 1% Hispanic, 4% black, 1% Asian American or Pacific Islander, 4% international, 5% 25 or older, 73% live on campus, 5% transferred in. Retention: 83% of full-time freshmen returned the following year. Academic areas with the most degrees conferred: business/marketing; education; health professions and related sciences. Core. Calendar: semesters. Academic remediation for entering

students, ESL program, services for LD students, advanced placement, accelerated degree program, self-designed majors, freshman honors college, honors program, independent study, distance learning, double major, summer session for credit, part-time degree program, adult/continuing education programs, co-op programs and internships, graduate courses open to undergrads. Study abroad program. ROTC: Army (c).

Entrance Requirements: Options: Peterson's Universal Application, Common Application, electronic application, early admission, deferred admission, international baccalaureate accepted. Required: high school transcript, 2 recommendations, interview, SAT or ACT. Entrance: moderately difficult. Application deadline: 6/1. Notification: continuous.

Costs Per Year: Application fee: $35. Comprehensive fee: $16,512 includes full-time tuition ($10,800), mandatory fees ($400), and college room and board ($5312). College room only: $2636. Full-time tuition and fees vary according to course load. Room and board charges vary according to board plan and housing facility. Part-time tuition: $360 per semester hour. Part-time mandatory fees: $20 per semester hour. Part-time tuition and fees vary according to course load.

Collegiate Environment: Orientation program. Drama-theater group, choral group, marching band, student-run newspaper, radio station. Social organizations: 52 open to all; local fraternities, local sororities; 50% of eligible men and 39% of eligible women are members. Most popular organizations: University Singers, RENEW (environmental group), JOY, concert choir, Omicron Delta Kappa. Major annual events: Spring Sing Festival, Homecoming Musical, Club Induction Week. Student services: health clinic, personal-psychological counseling. Campus security: 24-hour emergency response devices and patrols. 2,990 college housing spaces available; 2,952 were occupied in 2003-04. Freshmen guaranteed college housing. On-campus residence required through senior year. Options: men-only, women-only housing available. Brackett Library plus 1 other with 253,436 books, 251,230 microform titles, 16,879 serials, 8,281 audiovisual materials, an OPAC, and a Web page. Operations spending for 2004 fiscal year: $1.3 million. 327 computers available on campus for general student use. A campuswide network can be accessed from student residence rooms and from off campus. Staffed computer lab on campus.

Community Environment: Searcy is a small town located approximately 50 miles from Little Rock. The climate is temperate. A public library, two large hospitals, many churches, and a variety of shops serve the city of 20,000. Greer's Ferry Lake, with approximately 400 miles of shoreline, is located within 30 miles of campus. The Little Red River, which is famous for its rainbow trout, runs through the edge of Searcy. About 45 minutes from Harding, the University owns a 1,200 acre camp consisting of many log buildings, bluffs, and horse stables.

■ **HENDERSON STATE UNIVERSITY** *I-8*
1100 Henderson St.
Arkadelphia, AR 71999-0001
Tel: (870)230-5000
Free: 800-228-7333
Admissions: (870)230-5028
Fax: (870)230-5144
E-mail: hardwrv@hsu.edu
Web Site: http://www.hsu.edu

Description: State-supported, comprehensive, coed. Awards associate, bachelor's, and master's degrees. Founded 1890. Setting: 139-acre small town campus with easy access to Little Rock. Research spending for 2004 fiscal year: $367,540. Total enrollment: 3,584. Faculty: 229 (161 full-time, 68 part-time). Student-undergrad faculty ratio is 14:1. 2,020 applied, 58% were admitted. 18% from top 10% of their high school class, 43% from top quarter, 75% from top half. Full-time: 2,713 students, 56% women, 44% men. Part-time: 376 students, 64% women, 36% men. Students come from 24 states and territories, 27 other countries, 14% from out-of-state, 1% Native American, 2% Hispanic, 17% black, 0.4% Asian American or Pacific Islander, 2% international, 20% 25 or older, 9% transferred in. Retention: 63% of full-time freshmen returned the following year. Academic areas with the most degrees conferred: education; business/marketing; social sciences. Core. Calendar: semesters. Academic remediation for entering students, services for LD students, advanced placement, honors program, distance learning, summer session for credit, part-time degree program, internships, graduate courses open to undergrads. Off campus study at Ouachita Baptist University.

Entrance Requirements: Options: electronic application, deferred admission. Required: high school transcript, SAT or ACT. Recommended:

minimum 2.5 high school GPA, ACT. Required for some: essay, 3 recommendations. Entrance: moderately difficult. Application deadline: 7/15. Notification: continuous.

Costs Per Year: Application fee: $0. State resident tuition: $4050 full-time, $135 per credit hour part-time. Nonresident tuition: $8100 full-time, $270 per credit hour part-time. Mandatory fees: $575 full-time. Full-time tuition and fees vary according to course load and program. Part-time tuition varies according to course load and program. College room and board: $3888. Room and board charges vary according to board plan and housing facility.

Collegiate Environment: Orientation program. Drama-theater group, choral group, marching band, student-run newspaper, radio station. Social organizations: 85 open to all; national fraternities, national sororities; 11% of eligible men and 13% of eligible women are members. Most popular organizations: Heart and Key, Student Government Association, Residence Hall Association. Major annual events: homecoming, Spring Fling, Parents' Weekend. Student services: health clinic, personal-psychological counseling. Campus security: 24-hour emergency response devices and patrols, controlled dormitory access. 950 college housing spaces available; 876 were occupied in 2003-04. Freshmen given priority for college housing. On-campus residence required in freshman year. Options: coed, men-only, women-only housing available. Huie Library with 262,572 books, 212,722 microform titles, 1,516 serials, 18,717 audiovisual materials, an OPAC, and a Web page. Operations spending for 2004 fiscal year: $756,161. 125 computers available on campus for general student use. A campuswide network can be accessed from student residence rooms and from off campus. Staffed computer lab on campus.

Community Environment: Arkadelphia is 55 miles southwest of Little Rock, and 35 miles south of Hot Springs, America's oldest national park. Arkadelphia is a modern, progressive city, and a well-known educational center. The Missouri Pacific Railroad, U.S. Interstate 30, U.S. Highway 67, and state highways make this city easily accessible from all parts of the state.

■ **HENDRIX COLLEGE** *F-9*
1600 Washington Ave.
Conway, AR 72032-3080
Tel: (501)329-6811
Free: 800-277-9017
Admissions: (501)450-1362
Fax: (501)450-3843
E-mail: foust@hendrix.edu
Web Site: http://www.hendrix.edu/

Description: Independent United Methodist, comprehensive, coed. Awards bachelor's and master's degrees. Founded 1876. Setting: 158-acre suburban campus with easy access to Little Rock. Endowment: $149.4 million. Research spending for 2004 fiscal year: $639,278. Educational spending for 2005 fiscal year: $12,354 per student. Total enrollment: 1,031. Faculty: 107 (85 full-time, 22 part-time). Student-undergrad faculty ratio is 11:1. 1,086 applied, 83% were admitted. 37% from top 10% of their high school class, 73% from top quarter, 91% from top half. 7 National Merit Scholars, 12 valedictorians, 8 student government officers. Full-time: 1,001 students, 56% women, 44% men. Part-time: 21 students, 52% women, 48% men. Students come from 36 states and territories, 10 other countries, 45% from out-of-state, 1% Native American, 3% Hispanic, 4% black, 3% Asian American or Pacific Islander, 0.5% international, 1% 25 or older, 97% live on campus, 2% transferred in. Retention: 81% of full-time freshmen returned the following year. Academic areas with the most degrees conferred: social sciences; psychology; biological/life sciences. Core. Calendar: semesters. Services for LD students, advanced placement, self-designed majors, honors program, independent study, double major, co-op programs and internships, graduate courses open to undergrads. Off campus study at American University, Associated Colleges of the South. Study abroad program. ROTC: Army (c).

Entrance Requirements: Options: Peterson's Universal Application, Common Application, electronic application, early admission, deferred admission, international baccalaureate accepted. Required: essay, high school transcript, SAT or ACT. Recommended: 1 recommendation. Required for some: interview. Entrance: very difficult. Application deadline: 8/1. Notification: continuous.

Costs Per Year: Application fee: $40. Comprehensive fee: $27,946 includes full-time tuition ($21,336), mandatory fees ($300), and college room and board ($6310). College room only: $2760. Full-time tuition and fees vary according to course load. Room and board charges vary according to board

plan and housing facility. Part-time tuition: $2248 per course. Part-time mandatory fees: $40 per year. Part-time tuition and fees vary according to course load.

Collegiate Environment: Orientation program. Drama-theater group, choral group, student-run newspaper, radio station. Social organizations: 53 open to all. Most popular organizations: Volunteer Action Center, student government, music ensembles, Multicultural Development Committee, Social Committee. Major annual events: Coffee House, Spring Music Festival, Campus Kitty Week. Student services: health clinic, personal-psychological counseling. Campus security: 24-hour emergency response devices and patrols, late night transport-escort service, controlled dormitory access. 917 college housing spaces available; 846 were occupied in 2003-04. Freshmen guaranteed college housing. On-campus residence required through senior year. Options: coed, men-only, women-only housing available. Olin C. and Marjorie H. Bailey Library with 216,172 books, 184,127 microform titles, 799 serials, 2,151 audiovisual materials, an OPAC, and a Web page. Operations spending for 2004 fiscal year: $839,394. 75 computers available on campus for general student use. A campuswide network can be accessed from student residence rooms and from off campus. Staffed computer lab on campus.

Community Environment: See University of Central Arkansas.

■ **ITT TECHNICAL INSTITUTE** *G-10*
4520 South University
Little Rock, AR 72204
Tel: (501)565-5550
Web Site: http://www.itt-tech.edu/

Description: Proprietary, primarily 2-year, coed. Part of ITT Educational Services, Inc. Awards terminal associate and bachelor's degrees. Founded 1993. Setting: urban campus. Core.

Entrance Requirements: Option: deferred admission. Required: high school transcript, interview, Wonderlic aptitude test. Recommended: recommendations. Entrance: minimally difficult. Application deadline: Rolling. Notification: continuous.

Costs Per Year: Application fee: $100.

Collegiate Environment: Orientation program. College housing not available.

■ **JOHN BROWN UNIVERSITY** *B-4*
2000 West University St.
Siloam Springs, AR 72761-2121
Tel: (479)524-9500; 877-JBU-INFO
Admissions: (479)524-7150
Fax: (479)524-9548
E-mail: jbuinfo@acc.jbu.edu
Web Site: http://www.jbu.edu/

Description: Independent interdenominational, comprehensive, coed. Awards bachelor's and master's degrees. Founded 1919. Setting: 200-acre small town campus. Endowment: $49.2 million. Total enrollment: 1,904. Faculty: 148 (83 full-time, 65 part-time). Student-undergrad faculty ratio is 12:1. 874 applied, 62% were admitted. 29% from top 10% of their high school class, 59% from top quarter, 87% from top half. 2 National Merit Scholars, 17 valedictorians. Full-time: 1,581 students, 51% women, 49% men. Part-time: 78 students, 56% women, 44% men. Students come from 44 states and territories, 37 other countries, 72% from out-of-state, 2% Native American, 3% Hispanic, 3% black, 1% Asian American or Pacific Islander, 6% international, 4% 25 or older, 76% live on campus, 4% transferred in. Retention: 75% of full-time freshmen returned the following year. Academic areas with the most degrees conferred: business/marketing; communications/journalism; visual and performing arts. Core. Calendar: semesters. Academic remediation for entering students, ESL program, services for LD students, advanced placement, freshman honors college, honors program, independent study, distance learning, double major, external degree program, adult/continuing education programs, internships, graduate courses open to undergrads. Study abroad program. ROTC: Army (c), Air Force (c).

Entrance Requirements: Options: Peterson's Universal Application, Common Application, deferred admission. Required: essay, high school transcript, minimum 2.5 high school GPA, 2 recommendations, SAT or ACT. Recommended: interview. Entrance: moderately difficult. Application deadline: Rolling. Notification: continuous.

Costs Per Year: Application fee: $25. Comprehensive fee: $20,910 includes full-time tuition ($14,544), mandatory fees ($736), and college room and board ($5630). Full-time tuition and fees vary according to program. Room and board charges vary according to board plan and housing facility. Part-time tuition: $600 per semester hour. Part-time tuition varies according to course load and program.

Collegiate Environment: Orientation program. Drama-theater group, choral group, student-run newspaper, radio station. Social organizations: 20 open to all. Most popular organizations: Student Government Association, Student Ministries Organization, Student Missionary Fellowship, African Heritage Fellowship. Major annual events: homecoming, Christmas Candlelight Service, Parents' Weekend. Student services: health clinic, personal-psychological counseling. Campus security: 24-hour emergency response devices and patrols, late night transport-escort service. On-campus residence required through junior year. Options: coed, men-only, women-only housing available. Arutunoff Learning Resource Center plus 4 others with 114,799 books, 52,215 microform titles, 3,775 serials, 10,697 audiovisual materials, an OPAC, and a Web page. Operations spending for 2004 fiscal year: $446,451. 100 computers available on campus for general student use. A campuswide network can be accessed from student residence rooms and from off campus. Staffed computer lab on campus.

Community Environment: Located in the Benton County foothills of the beautiful Ozarks. The town is easily accessible from all parts of the state. The seasons are delightfully mild. Siloam Springs is far enough south to insure mild winters, and the summer nights are pleasantly cool. Northwest Arkansas is considered a very healthful location, and is noted as a summer retreat for many tourists from all sections of the United States.

■ **LYON COLLEGE** *D-12*
PO Box 2317
Batesville, AR 72503-2317
Tel: (870)793-9813
Free: 800-423-2542
Admissions: (870)698-4250
Fax: (870)698-4622
E-mail: admissions@lyon.edu
Web Site: http://www.lyon.edu/

Description: Independent Presbyterian, 4-year, coed. Awards bachelor's degrees. Founded 1872. Setting: 136-acre small town campus. Endowment: $42.9 million. Educational spending for 2005 fiscal year: $12,239 per student. Total enrollment: 488. Student-undergrad faculty ratio is 10:1. 470 applied, 72% were admitted. 29% from top 10% of their high school class, 69% from top quarter, 93% from top half. 1 National Merit Scholar, 11 valedictorians, 20 student government officers. Full-time: 458 students, 50% women, 50% men. Part-time: 30 students, 70% women, 30% men. Students come from 20 states and territories, 17 other countries, 17% from out-of-state, 1% Native American, 2% Hispanic, 5% black, 1% Asian American or Pacific Islander, 3% international, 10% 25 or older, 75% live on campus, 11% transferred in. Retention: 75% of full-time freshmen returned the following year. Academic areas with the most degrees conferred: business/marketing; biological/life sciences; social sciences. Core. Calendar: semesters. Academic remediation for entering students, advanced placement, accelerated degree program, self-designed majors, independent study, double major, summer session for credit, part-time degree program, internships. Study abroad program.

Entrance Requirements: Options: Peterson's Universal Application, Common Application, electronic application, early admission, deferred admission, international baccalaureate accepted. Required: high school transcript, minimum 2.5 high school GPA, SAT or ACT. Required for some: essay, 2 recommendations. Entrance: moderately difficult. Application deadline: Rolling. Notification: continuous.

Costs Per Year: Application fee: $25. Comprehensive fee: $21,130 includes full-time tuition ($14,420), mandatory fees ($440), and college room and board ($6270). College room only: $2580. Part-time tuition: $600 per credit hour.

Collegiate Environment: Orientation program. Drama-theater group, choral group, student-run newspaper. Social organizations: 48 open to all; national fraternities, national sororities, local sororities; 10% of eligible men and 13% of eligible women are members. Most popular organizations: Baptist Christian Ministry, Student Activities Council, Pre-Med Club. Major annual events: Arkansas Scottish Festival, Service Day, Lyonfest Weekend. Student services: health clinic, personal-psychological counseling. Campus security: 24-hour patrols, late night transport-escort service. 421 college housing spaces available; 363 were occupied in 2003-04. Freshmen guaranteed college housing. On-campus residence required through senior year. Options: men-only, women-only housing available. Mabee-Simpson Library with 181,789 books, 2,928 microform titles, 646 serials, 6,744 audiovisual materi-

als, an OPAC, and a Web page. Operations spending for 2004 fiscal year: $467,046. 81 computers available on campus for general student use. A campuswide network can be accessed from student residence rooms and from off campus. Staffed computer lab on campus.

Community Environment: Batesville is located on the banks of the White River, in the foothills of the Ozarks 90 miles north of Little Rock, and 120 miles northwest of Memphis. The climate is mild, summer mean is 78 degrees and the winter mean is 40 degrees. Average annual rainfall is 48 inches. There are many churches in the area, a fine city library, hospitals, and 4 radio stations and cable TV.

■ **MID-SOUTH COMMUNITY COLLEGE** *F-16*
2000 West Broadway
West Memphis, AR 72301
Tel: (870)733-6722
Admissions: (870)733-6732
Fax: (870)733-6719
Web Site: http://www.midsouthcc.edu/

Description: State-supported, 2-year, coed. Awards certificates, transfer associate, and terminal associate degrees. Founded 1993. Setting: 80-acre suburban campus with easy access to Memphis. Endowment: $894,155. Educational spending for 2005 fiscal year: $3581 per student. Total enrollment: 1,467. Student-undergrad faculty ratio is 15:1. 214 applied, 100% were admitted. Full-time: 457 students, 70% women, 30% men. Part-time: 1,010 students, 62% women, 38% men. Students come from 2 other countries, 5% from out-of-state, 0.2% Native American, 1% Hispanic, 49% black, 1% Asian American or Pacific Islander, 0.4% international, 48% 25 or older, 5% transferred in. Retention: 41% of full-time freshmen returned the following year. Core. Calendar: semesters. Academic remediation for entering students, independent study, distance learning, summer session for credit, part-time degree program, adult/continuing education programs, internships.

Entrance Requirements: Open admission. Options: Common Application, electronic application, early admission. Required: high school transcript. Required for some: ACT, ASSET, COMPASS. Entrance: noncompetitive. Application deadline: Rolling. Notification: continuous.

Costs Per Year: Application fee: $0. Area resident tuition: $1410 full-time, $47 per credit part-time. State resident tuition: $1740 full-time, $58 per credit part-time. Nonresident tuition: $3150 full-time, $105 per credit part-time. Mandatory fees: $210 full-time, $7 per credit part-time. Full-time tuition and fees vary according to course load and reciprocity agreements. Part-time tuition and fees vary according to course load and reciprocity agreements.

Collegiate Environment: Orientation program. Choral group. Social organizations: 6 open to all. Most popular organizations: Phi Theta Kappa, Baptist Collegiate Ministry, Campus Ministry International, Student Ambassador, Skills-USA-Vica. Major annual events: Student Appreciation Day, Stress Free Zone, Job Fair. Campus security: 24-hour emergency response devices, security during class hours. College housing not available. Mid-South Community College Library/Media Center with 14,672 books, 88 serials, 2,151 audiovisual materials, an OPAC, and a Web page. Operations spending for 2004 fiscal year: $135,643. 280 computers available on campus for general student use. A campuswide network can be accessed from off-campus. Staffed computer lab on campus.

■ **NATIONAL PARK COMMUNITY COLLEGE** *H-8*
101 College Dr.
Hot Springs, AR 71913
Tel: (501)760-4222
Fax: (501)760-4100
E-mail: bmoody@npcc.edu
Web Site: http://www.npcc.edu/

Description: State and locally supported, 2-year, coed. Part of Arkansas Department of Higher Education. Awards certificates, diplomas, transfer associate, and terminal associate degrees. Founded 1973. Setting: 50-acre suburban campus with easy access to Little Rock. Endowment: $11.3 million. Total enrollment: 2,996. 4,969 applied, 100% were admitted. Full-time: 1,237 students, 59% women, 41% men. Part-time: 1,759 students, 61% women, 39% men. 2% from out-of-state, 1% Native American, 1% Hispanic, 6% black, 1% Asian American or Pacific Islander, 0.03% international, 63% 25 or older, 17% transferred in. Retention: 100% of full-time freshmen returned the following year. Core. Calendar: semesters. Academic remediation for entering students, services for LD students, advanced placement, self-designed majors, honors program, independent study, distance learning, double major, summer session for credit, part-time degree program, external degree program, adult/continuing education programs, co-op programs and internships. Study abroad program.

Entrance Requirements: Open admission except for nursing, allied health programs. Options: Common Application, early admission, deferred admission. Required: high school transcript, SAT and SAT Subject Tests or ACT. Recommended: ACT ASSET. Entrance: noncompetitive. Application deadline: Rolling.

Collegiate Environment: Orientation program. Choral group, student-run newspaper. Most popular organizations: student newspaper, choral group. Student services: health clinic, personal-psychological counseling, women's center. Campus security: 24-hour emergency response devices and patrols. College housing not available. Garland County Community College Library with 17,800 books, 290 serials, and an OPAC. Operations spending for 2004 fiscal year: $280,000. 270 computers available on campus for general student use. A campuswide network can be accessed from off-campus. Staffed computer lab on campus.

■ NORTH ARKANSAS COLLEGE *B-8*
1515 Pioneer Dr.
Harrison, AR 72601
Tel: (870)743-3000
Free: 800-679-6622
Admissions: (870)391-3221
Fax: (870)391-3339
E-mail: charlam@northark.edu
Web Site: http://www.northark.edu/

Description: State and locally supported, 2-year, coed. Awards certificates, transfer associate, and terminal associate degrees. Founded 1974. Setting: 40-acre small town campus. Endowment: $333,030. Educational spending for 2005 fiscal year: $4218 per student. Total enrollment: 2,187. Student-undergrad faculty ratio is 16:1. 737 applied, 100% were admitted. Full-time: 1,138 students, 62% women, 38% men. Part-time: 1,049 students, 62% women, 38% men. Students come from 14 states and territories, 2% from out-of-state, 1% Native American, 2% Hispanic, 1% black, 1% Asian American or Pacific Islander, 0% international, 40% 25 or older, 5% transferred in. Retention: 48% of full-time freshmen returned the following year. Core. Calendar: semesters. Academic remediation for entering students, services for LD students, advanced placement, freshman honors college, honors program, independent study, distance learning, summer session for credit, part-time degree program, adult/continuing education programs.

Entrance Requirements: Open admission. Option: deferred admission. Required for some: high school transcript. Entrance: noncompetitive. Application deadline: Rolling. Notification: continuous.

Costs Per Year: Application fee: $0. Area resident tuition: $1590 full-time, $53 per credit hour part-time. State resident tuition: $2130 full-time, $71 per credit hour part-time. Nonresident tuition: $4110 full-time, $137 per credit hour part-time. Mandatory fees: $150 full-time.

Collegiate Environment: Drama-theater group, choral group. Social organizations: 8 open to all. Most popular organizations: Phi Beta Lambda, Phi Theta Kappa, Student Nurses Association, Vocational Industrial Clubs, Baptist Student Union. Major annual events: cookouts, Homecoming, plays. Student services: personal-psychological counseling. Campus security: 24-hour patrols. College housing not available. North Arkansas College Library plus 1 other with 29,969 books, 5,671 microform titles, 340 serials, 2,879 audiovisual materials, an OPAC, and a Web page. Operations spending for 2004 fiscal year: $356,001. 200 computers available on campus for general student use. A campuswide network can be accessed from off-campus. Staffed computer lab on campus.

■ NORTHWEST ARKANSAS COMMUNITY COLLEGE *B-5*
One College Dr.
Bentonville, AR 72712
Tel: (479)636-9222
Free: 800-995-6922
Fax: (479)619-4116
Web Site: http://www.nwacc.edu/

Description: State and locally supported, 2-year, coed. Awards certificates, transfer associate, and terminal associate degrees. Founded 1989. Setting: 77-acre urban campus. Educational spending for 2005 fiscal year: $2292 per student. Total enrollment: 4,915. 893 applied, 100% were admitted. Students come from 4 states and territories, 31% 25 or older. Core. Calendar: semesters. Academic remediation for entering students, services for LD students, advanced placement, honors program, independent study,

distance learning, summer session for credit, part-time degree program, adult/continuing education programs, co-op programs and internships.

Entrance Requirements: Open admission. Recommended: high school transcript. Placement: SAT or ACT, ACT ASSET, ACT COMPASS required. Entrance: noncompetitive. Application deadline: Rolling. Notification: continuous.

Collegiate Environment: Orientation program. Drama-theater group, choral group. Social organizations: 9 open to all. Most popular organizations: Student Advisory Activity Council, Gamma Beta Phi, Phi Beta Lambda, Student Nurses Association, Students in Free Enterprise. Major annual events: Red Ribbon Week, Student Organization Fair, Fall Festival. Campus security: 24-hour emergency response devices and patrols. College housing not available. Library Resource Center plus 1 other with 15,500 books, 159 serials, and an OPAC. 97 computers available on campus for general student use. Staffed computer lab on campus.

■ OUACHITA BAPTIST UNIVERSITY *I-8*
410 Ouachita St.
Arkadelphia, AR 71998-0001
Tel: (870)245-5000
Admissions: (870)245-5578
Fax: (870)245-5500
E-mail: jonesj@sigma.obu.edu
Web Site: http://www.obu.edu/

Description: Independent Baptist, 4-year, coed. Awards associate and bachelor's degrees. Founded 1886. Setting: 84-acre small town campus with easy access to Little Rock. Endowment: $58.7 million. Research spending for 2004 fiscal year: $54,895. Educational spending for 2005 fiscal year: $7503 per student. Total enrollment: 1,499. Student-undergrad faculty ratio is 12:1. 1,058 applied, 58% were admitted. 33% from top 10% of their high school class, 60% from top quarter, 82% from top half. 6 National Merit Scholars, 10 valedictorians. Full-time: 1,399 students, 55% women, 45% men. Part-time: 100 students, 53% women, 47% men. 44% from out-of-state, 0.1% Native American, 2% Hispanic, 6% black, 1% Asian American or Pacific Islander, 4% international, 3% 25 or older, 86% live on campus, 4% transferred in. Retention: 75% of full-time freshmen returned the following year. Academic areas with the most degrees conferred: business/marketing; theology and religious vocations; communications/journalism. Core. Calendar: semesters. Academic remediation for entering students, ESL program, advanced placement, accelerated degree program, honors program, double major, summer session for credit, part-time degree program, co-op programs and internships. Off campus study at Henderson State University. Study abroad program. ROTC: Army.

Entrance Requirements: Options: early admission, deferred admission. Required: high school transcript, minimum 2.75 high school GPA, SAT or ACT. Recommended: interview. Entrance: moderately difficult. Application deadlines: 8/15, 12/1 for early action. Notification: continuous, 12/1 for early action.

Costs Per Year: Application fee: $50. Comprehensive fee: $21,990 includes full-time tuition ($16,650), mandatory fees ($340), and college room and board ($5000). Part-time tuition: $460 per semester hour.

Collegiate Environment: Orientation program. Drama-theater group, choral group, marching band, student-run newspaper. Social organizations: 60 open to all; local fraternities, local sororities; 20% of eligible men and 30% of eligible women are members. Most popular organizations: Phi Beta Lambda, Campus Activities Board, Student Education Association, Student Foundation, International Club. Major annual events: Tiger Tunes, Tiger Traks, Homecoming. Student services: health clinic, personal-psychological counseling, career services, multi-cultural services, student support services. Campus security: 24-hour emergency response devices and patrols, controlled dormitory access. 1,487 college housing spaces available; 1,274 were occupied in 2003-04. Freshmen guaranteed college housing. On-campus residence required through senior year. Options: men-only, women-only housing available. Riley-Hickinbotham Library plus 1 other with 139,278 books, 263,171 microform titles, 1,931 serials, 8,306 audiovisual materials, and an OPAC. Operations spending for 2004 fiscal year: $559,221. 189 computers available on campus for general student use. A campuswide network can be accessed from student residence rooms and from off campus. Staffed computer lab on campus.

Community Environment: Ouachita Baptist University is located in Arkadelphia, Arkansas, about 70 miles southwest of Little Rock on I-30 and 35 miles south of Hot Springs. There is frequent Amtrak service to and from the city. Facilities for air transportation are available both in Hot Springs and Little Rock. Arkadelphia has a population of more than 10,000, including the students of Ouachita and Henderson State University.

■ **OUACHITA TECHNICAL COLLEGE** *H-8*
One College Circle
Malvern, AR 72104
Tel: (501)337-5000
Fax: (501)337-9382
E-mail: lindaj@otcweb.edu
Web Site: http://www.otcweb.edu/
Description: State-supported, 2-year, coed. Awards certificates, transfer associate, and terminal associate degrees. Founded 1972. Setting: 11-acre small town campus. Educational spending for 2005 fiscal year: $2800 per student. Total enrollment: 1,590. Student-undergrad faculty ratio is 16:1. 325 applied, 100% were admitted. Full-time: 556 students, 64% women, 36% men. Part-time: 1,034 students, 45% women, 55% men. Students come from 2 states and territories, 2 other countries, 0.1% from out-of-state, 1% Native American, 1% Hispanic, 12% black, 1% Asian American or Pacific Islander, 0.3% international, 45% 25 or older, 6% transferred in. Retention: 50% of full-time freshmen returned the following year. Core. Calendar: semesters. Academic remediation for entering students, services for LD students, advanced placement, accelerated degree program, independent study, distance learning, double major, summer session for credit, part-time degree program, co-op programs and internships.
Entrance Requirements: Open admission except for nursing program. Options: electronic application, early admission, deferred admission. Required: high school transcript. Recommended: SAT or ACT, ACT COMPASS or ACT ASSET. Entrance: noncompetitive. Application deadline: Rolling.
Costs Per Year: One-time mandatory fee: $35. State resident tuition: $1560 full-time, $52 per credit hour part-time. Nonresident tuition: $3120 full-time, $104 per credit hour part-time. Mandatory fees: $420 full-time, $14 per credit hour part-time.
Collegiate Environment: Orientation program. Major annual event: awards ceremony. Student services: personal-psychological counseling. Campus security: 24-hour patrols. College housing not available. Ouachita Technical College Library/Learning Resource Center with 8,000 books, 6,151 microform titles, 100 serials, 1,200 audiovisual materials, an OPAC, and a Web page. Operations spending for 2004 fiscal year: $118,492. 125 computers available on campus for general student use. A campuswide network can be accessed from off-campus. Staffed computer lab on campus.

■ **OZARKA COLLEGE** *C-11*
PO Box 10
Melbourne, AR 72556
Tel: (870)368-7371
Free: 800-821-4335
Fax: (870)368-4733
Web Site: http://www.ozarka.edu/
Description: State-supported, 2-year, coed. Awards certificates, transfer associate, and terminal associate degrees. Founded 1973. Setting: 40-acre rural campus. Educational spending for 2005 fiscal year: $1507 per student. Total enrollment: 756. 157 applied, 100% were admitted. Full-time: 569 students, 70% women, 30% men. Part-time: 187 students, 74% women, 26% men. 1% from out-of-state, 1% Native American, 1% Hispanic, 0.3% black, 43% 25 or older. Core. Calendar: semesters. Academic remediation for entering students, services for LD students, advanced placement, distance learning, summer session for credit, part-time degree program, external degree program, internships.
Entrance Requirements: Open admission except for nursing and information science technology programs. Option: deferred admission. Required: high school transcript. Recommended: minimum 2.0 high school GPA. Required for some: essay, recommendations, interview. Placement: ACT, ACT ASSET required. Entrance: noncompetitive. Application deadline: 8/19.
Costs Per Year: Application fee: $0. State resident tuition: $1950 full-time, $65 per credit hour part-time. Nonresident tuition: $5040 full-time, $168 per credit hour part-time. Mandatory fees: $330 full-time, $10 per credit hour part-time, $30 per term part-time. Full-time tuition and fees vary according to course load. Part-time tuition and fees vary according to course load.
Collegiate Environment: Orientation program. Drama-theater group. Social organizations: 7 open to all. Most popular organizations: VICA, Phi Beta Lambda, Drama Club, HOSA, Phi Theta Kappa. Major annual events: Community Service Day, Career Day. Student services: personal-psychological counseling. Campus security: security patrols 7 a.m. to 11 p.m. College housing not available. Ozarka College Library with 10,500 books, 4,000 serials, 1,500 audiovisual materials, and an OPAC. Operations spending for 2004 fiscal year: $171,858. 114 computers available on campus for general student use. A campuswide network can be accessed from off-campus. Staffed computer lab on campus.

■ **PHILANDER SMITH COLLEGE** *G-10*
812 West 13th St.
Little Rock, AR 72202-3799
Tel: (501)375-9845
Free: 800-446-6772
Admissions: (501)370-5310
Fax: (501)370-5225
Web Site: http://www.philander.edu/
Description: Independent United Methodist, 4-year, coed. Awards bachelor's degrees. Founded 1877. Setting: 25-acre urban campus. Endowment: $9.6 million. Research spending for 2004 fiscal year: $86,500. Educational spending for 2005 fiscal year: $2280 per student. Total enrollment: 949. 224 applied, 100% were admitted. 3% from top 10% of their high school class, 15% from top quarter, 31% from top half. Full-time: 781 students, 66% women, 34% men. Part-time: 168 students, 62% women, 38% men. Students come from 14 states and territories, 19 other countries, 9% from out-of-state, 0% Native American, 0.4% Hispanic, 97% black, 0% Asian American or Pacific Islander, 1% international, 32% 25 or older, 26% live on campus, 8% transferred in. Retention: 60% of full-time freshmen returned the following year. Core. Calendar: semesters. Academic remediation for entering students, services for LD students, independent study, summer session for credit, adult/continuing education programs, co-op programs and internships. ROTC: Army (c).
Entrance Requirements: Open admission. Options: Peterson's Universal Application, Common Application, electronic application, deferred admission. Required: high school transcript. Placement: SAT or ACT required. Entrance: noncompetitive. Application deadline: Rolling. Notification: continuous.
Costs Per Year: Application fee: $10. Comprehensive fee: $13,515 includes full-time tuition ($6950), mandatory fees ($1415), and college room and board ($5150). College room only: $3330. Full-time tuition and fees vary according to class time, course load, and program. Room and board charges vary according to housing facility. Part-time tuition: $290 per credit hour. Part-time mandatory fees: $21 per credit hour, $200 per term. Part-time tuition and fees vary according to class time, course load, and program.
Collegiate Environment: Orientation program. Drama-theater group, choral group, student-run newspaper. Social organizations: 10 open to all; national fraternities, national sororities; 8% of eligible men and 9% of eligible women are members. Most popular organizations: Student Government Association, Pre-Alumni Council, Student Christian Fellowship. Major annual events: Senior Day, Homecoming, Founders' Day. Student services: health clinic, personal-psychological counseling. Campus security: 24-hour patrols. 419 college housing spaces available; 249 were occupied in 2003-04. On-campus residence required in freshman year. Options: men-only, women-only housing available. M. L. Harris Library with 60,000 books, 3,816 microform titles, 280 serials, 196 audiovisual materials, an OPAC, and a Web page. Operations spending for 2004 fiscal year: $96,000. 95 computers available on campus for general student use. A campuswide network can be accessed from off-campus. Staffed computer lab on campus.
Community Environment: See University of Arkansas - Little Rock.

■ **PHILLIPS COMMUNITY COLLEGE OF THE UNIVERSITY OF ARKANSAS** *H-14*
PO Box 785
Helena, AR 72342-0785
Tel: (870)338-6474
Fax: (870)338-7542
Web Site: http://www.pccua.edu/
Description: State and locally supported, 2-year, coed. Part of University of Arkansas System. Awards certificates, transfer associate, and terminal associate degrees. Founded 1965. Setting: 80-acre small town campus with easy access to Memphis. Total enrollment: 2,322. 45% 25 or older. Core. Calendar: semesters. Academic remediation for entering students, services for LD students, advanced placement, summer session for credit, part-time degree program, adult/continuing education programs.
Entrance Requirements: Open admission except for nursing, medical laboratory technician programs. Options: Peterson's Universal Application, early admission. Placement: ACT, ACT ASSET required. Entrance: noncompetitive. Application deadline: 8/25. Notification: continuous until 8/25.
Costs Per Year: Area resident tuition: $750 full-time, $50 per semester hour part-time. State resident tuition: $885 full-time, $59 per semester hour part-time. Nonresident tuition: $1455 full-time, $97 per semester hour part-time.
Collegiate Environment: Drama-theater group, choral group, student-run newspaper. Student services: personal-psychological counseling. Campus

security: 24-hour patrols. College housing not available. 39,000 books and 352 serials. 200 computers available on campus for general student use.
Community Environment: Helena is in a suburban area, and blessed with a mild, warm climate. There are churches of major denominations, libraries, a museum, an accredited general hospital, and major civic and service organizations.

■ PULASKI TECHNICAL COLLEGE G-10
3000 West Scenic Dr.
North Little Rock, AR 72118
Tel: (501)812-2200
Admissions: (501)812-2734
Fax: (501)812-2316
E-mail: catkins@pulaskitech.edu
Web Site: http://www.pulaskitech.edu/
Description: State-supported, 2-year, coed. Awards certificates, transfer associate, and terminal associate degrees. Founded 1945. Setting: 40-acre urban campus with easy access to Little Rock. Educational spending for 2005 fiscal year: $1765 per student. Total enrollment: 7,685. Student-undergrad faculty ratio is 25:1. 2,268 applied, 100% were admitted. Full-time: 3,953 students, 66% women, 34% men. Part-time: 3,732 students, 69% women, 31% men. Students come from 3 states and territories, 1% from out-of-state, 0.5% Native American, 1% Hispanic, 46% black, 1% Asian American or Pacific Islander, 0.3% international, 54% 25 or older. Retention: 46% of full-time freshmen returned the following year. Core. Calendar: semesters. Academic remediation for entering students, services for LD students, advanced placement, distance learning, summer session for credit, part-time degree program.
Entrance Requirements: Open admission. Options: Common Application, electronic application. Required: high school transcript. Entrance: noncompetitive. Application deadline: Rolling.
Costs Per Year: Application fee: $0. State resident tuition: $2161 full-time, $72 per credit hour part-time. Nonresident tuition: $3570 full-time, $119 per credit hour part-time. Mandatory fees: $255 full-time, $8 per credit hour part-time, $15.
Collegiate Environment: Orientation program. Drama-theater group. Campus security: security personnel 7 a.m. to 11 p.m. College housing not available. Ottenheimer Library with 16,378 books, 234 serials, 1,520 audiovisual materials, an OPAC, and a Web page. Operations spending for 2004 fiscal year: $324,647. 75 computers available on campus for general student use. A campuswide network can be accessed. Staffed computer lab on campus.

■ REMINGTON COLLEGE-LITTLE ROCK CAMPUS G-10
8901 Kanis Rd.
Little Rock, AR 72205
Tel: (501)312-0007
Fax: (501)225-3819
E-mail: david.caldwell@remingtoncollege.edu
Web Site: http://www.remingtoncollege.edu/
Description: Proprietary, 2-year, coed.

■ RICH MOUNTAIN COMMUNITY COLLEGE H-5
1100 College Dr.
Mena, AR 71953
Tel: (479)394-7622
Fax: (479)394-2628
Web Site: http://www.rmcc.edu/
Description: State and locally supported, 2-year, coed. Awards certificates, transfer associate, and terminal associate degrees. Founded 1983. Setting: 40-acre small town campus. Endowment: $301,360. Total enrollment: 973. Students come from 2 states and territories, 2 other countries, 2% from out-of-state, 2% Native American, 1% Hispanic, 0% black, 1% Asian American or Pacific Islander, 0% international. Core. Calendar: semesters. Academic remediation for entering students, ESL program, services for LD students, advanced placement, distance learning, double major, summer session for credit, part-time degree program, adult/continuing education programs.
Entrance Requirements: Open admission. Options: Common Application, early admission. Required: high school transcript. Entrance: noncompetitive. Application deadline: 8/25. Notification: continuous until 8/25.
Costs Per Year: Application fee: $0. Area resident tuition: $960 full-time, $40 per semester hour part-time. State resident tuition: $1200 full-time, $50 per

semester hour part-time. Nonresident tuition: $3600 full-time, $150 per semester hour part-time. Mandatory fees: $72 full-time, $3 per semester hour part-time.
Collegiate Environment: Most popular organizations: SGA, Baptist Student Union, Phi Theta Kappa, Golf Club, TV and Video Club. Major annual events: SGA Spring Cookout, fall welcome back activities, Honors Ceremony. Student services: personal-psychological counseling. Campus security: administrator on night duty. College housing not available. St. John Library with 13,299 books, 417 microform titles, 81 serials, 674 audiovisual materials, and an OPAC. Operations spending for 2004 fiscal year: $103,418. 88 computers available on campus for general student use. A campuswide network can be accessed from off-campus. Staffed computer lab on campus.

■ SOUTH ARKANSAS COMMUNITY COLLEGE L-9
PO Box 7010
El Dorado, AR 71731-7010
Tel: (870)862-8131
Free: 800-955-2289
Admissions: (870)864-7142
Fax: (870)864-7122
E-mail: dinman@southark.edu
Web Site: http://www.southark.edu/
Description: State-supported, 2-year, coed. Part of Arkansas Department of Higher Education. Awards certificates, transfer associate, and terminal associate degrees. Founded 1975. Setting: 4-acre small town campus. Educational spending for 2005 fiscal year: $2511 per student. Total enrollment: 1,368. Student-undergrad faculty ratio is 13:1. Full-time: 612 students, 75% women, 25% men. Part-time: 756 students, 67% women, 33% men. Students come from 2 states and territories, 6% from out-of-state, 1% Native American, 1% Hispanic, 32% black, 0.3% Asian American or Pacific Islander, 43% 25 or older. Retention: 46% of full-time freshmen returned the following year. Core. Calendar: semesters. Academic remediation for entering students, services for LD students, advanced placement, summer session for credit, part-time degree program, adult/continuing education programs, internships.
Entrance Requirements: Open admission. Options: early admission, deferred admission. Required: high school transcript. Recommended: SAT or ACT. Required for some: ACT COMPASS. Entrance: noncompetitive. Application deadline: 8/25.
Costs Per Year: Area resident tuition: $1710 full-time. State resident tuition: $1950 full-time. Nonresident tuition: $3600 full-time.
Collegiate Environment: Orientation program. Choral group. Student services: personal-psychological counseling. Campus security: security guard. College housing not available. South Arkansas Community College Library with 22,652 books and 223 serials. 75 computers available on campus for general student use. A campuswide network can be accessed. Staffed computer lab on campus.
Community Environment: El Dorado is the seat of Union County, lying 117 miles south of Little Rock. Important industries are timber, poultry, oil, and chemicals. Bus and air service is available. Community services include a public library, two hospitals, several churches, an arts center, and good shopping facilities. There is good hunting and fishing in the general area, and water sports on nearby lakes and rivers.

■ SOUTHEAST ARKANSAS COLLEGE I-11
1900 Hazel St.
Pine Bluff, AR 71603
Tel: (870)543-5900
Admissions: (870)543-5957
E-mail: main@seark.edu
Web Site: http://www.seark.edu/
Description: State-supported, 2-year, coed. Awards certificates, transfer associate, and terminal associate degrees. Founded 1991. Total enrollment: 2,197. Full-time: 1,017 students, 72% women, 28% men. Part-time: 1,180 students, 68% women, 32% men. Students come from 3 states and territories, 0% from out-of-state, 0.5% Native American, 1% Hispanic, 48% black, 1% Asian American or Pacific Islander, 0.1% international, 58% 25 or older, 0% transferred in. Calendar: semesters. Academic remediation for entering students, services for LD students, advanced placement, accelerated degree program, honors program, independent study, distance learning, double major, summer session for credit, part-time degree program, co-op programs and internships.

Entrance Requirements: Open admission. Options: Peterson's Universal Application, Common Application, early admission. Required: high school transcript. Placement: SAT or ACT, ACT ASSET required. Entrance: noncompetitive. Notification: continuous.

Collegiate Environment: Orientation program. Choral group. Most popular organizations: Phi Beta Lambda, HOSA, Phi Theta Kappa, Student Senate. Major annual event: Spring Fling. Student services: personal-psychological counseling. Campus security: student patrols. College housing not available. Southeast Arkansas Technical College Library with 5,000 books and 75 serials. 62 computers available on campus for general student use. Staffed computer lab on campus.

■ **SOUTHERN ARKANSAS UNIVERSITY-MAGNOLIA** *L-7*

100 East University
Magnolia, AR 71753
Tel: (870)235-4000
Admissions: (870)235-4040
Fax: (870)235-5005
E-mail: addanna@saumag.edu
Web Site: http://www.saumag.edu/

Description: State-supported, comprehensive, coed. Part of Southern Arkansas University System. Awards associate, bachelor's, and master's degrees. Founded 1909. Setting: 781-acre small town campus. Endowment: $17.2 million. Research spending for 2004 fiscal year: $188,891. Educational spending for 2005 fiscal year: $1837 per student. Total enrollment: 3,057. 1,492 applied, 81% were admitted. 41% from top quarter of their high school class, 72% from top half. Full-time: 2,398 students, 54% women, 46% men. Part-time: 405 students, 72% women, 28% men. Students come from 31 states and territories, 37 other countries, 20% from out-of-state, 1% Native American, 1% Hispanic, 26% black, 1% Asian American or Pacific Islander, 5% international, 18% 25 or older, 36% live on campus, 6% transferred in. Retention: 65% of full-time freshmen returned the following year. Core. Calendar: semesters. Academic remediation for entering students, services for LD students, advanced placement, accelerated degree program, freshman honors college, honors program, independent study, distance learning, double major, summer session for credit, part-time degree program, adult/continuing education programs, internships, graduate courses open to undergrads. Study abroad program.

Entrance Requirements: Options: Peterson's Universal Application, electronic application, early admission, deferred admission, international baccalaureate accepted. Required: high school transcript, SAT or ACT. Recommended: ACT. Required for some: interview. Entrance: moderately difficult. Application deadline: 8/27.

Costs Per Year: State resident tuition: $3900 full-time, $130 per credit hour part-time. Nonresident tuition: $5910 full-time, $197 per credit hour part-time. Mandatory fees: $390 full-time, $390 per year part-time. Full-time tuition and fees vary according to course load. Part-time tuition and fees vary according to course load. College room and board: $3790. College room only: $1960.

Collegiate Environment: Orientation program. Drama-theater group, choral group, marching band, student-run newspaper, radio station. Social organizations: national fraternities, national sororities; 10% of eligible men and 10% of eligible women are members. Most popular organizations: Student Government Association, IMPACT. Major annual events: homecoming, Parents' Day, Spring Fling. Student services: health clinic, personal-psychological counseling. Campus security: 24-hour emergency response devices, student patrols, late night transport-escort service, controlled dormitory access. College housing designed to accommodate 1,399 students; 1,460 undergraduates lived in college housing during 2003-04. Freshmen guaranteed college housing. On-campus residence required through sophomore year. Options: men-only, women-only housing available. Magale Library with 151,166 books, 1 million microform titles, 1,065 serials, 12,130 audiovisual materials, an OPAC, and a Web page. Operations spending for 2004 fiscal year: $853,529. 175 computers available on campus for general student use. A campuswide network can be accessed from off-campus. Staffed computer lab on campus.

■ **SOUTHERN ARKANSAS UNIVERSITY TECH** *K-8*

100 Carr Rd.
PO Box 3499
Camden, AR 71711
Tel: (870)574-4500
Admissions: (870)574-4492
E-mail: psindle@sautech.edu
Web Site: http://www.sautech.edu/

Description: State-supported, 2-year, coed. Part of Arkansas Department of Higher Education. Awards certificates, transfer associate, and terminal associate degrees. Founded 1967. Setting: 96-acre rural campus. Educational spending for 2005 fiscal year: $5250 per student. Total enrollment: 1,767. Student-undergrad faculty ratio is 21:1. 555 applied, 100% were admitted. 4% from top 10% of their high school class, 50% from top quarter, 84% from top half. Full-time: 554 students, 41% women, 59% men. Part-time: 1,213 students, 43% women, 57% men. Students come from 6 states and territories, 1% from out-of-state, 1% Native American, 1% Hispanic, 25% black, 0.3% Asian American or Pacific Islander, 0% international, 54% 25 or older, 2% transferred in. Core. Calendar: semesters. Academic remediation for entering students, advanced placement, honors program, independent study, distance learning, double major, summer session for credit, part-time degree program, adult/continuing education programs, internships. Off campus study at Arkansas Fire Training Academy, Environmental Academy.

Entrance Requirements: Open admission. Option: deferred admission. Required for some: high school transcript. Entrance: noncompetitive. Application deadline: 8/15. Notification: continuous.

Costs Per Year: Application fee: $0. State resident tuition: $1638 full-time, $63 per hour part-time. Nonresident tuition: $2184 full-time, $84 per hour part-time. Mandatory fees: $574 full-time, $21 per credit hour part-time. College room and board: $3413. College room only: $2100.

Collegiate Environment: Orientation program. Student-run radio station. Social organizations: 11 open to all. Most popular organizations: Phi Beta Lambda, SAU Tech Ambassadors, Allied Health Student Club, Computer Club, Phi Theta Kappa. Major annual events: Fall Convocation, Red Ribbon Week, High Tech EXPO 2002. Student services: personal-psychological counseling. Campus security: 24-hour emergency response devices, patrols by trained security personnel. 42 college housing spaces available; 17 were occupied in 2003-04. No special consideration for freshman housing applicants. Southern Arkansas University Tech Learning Resource Center with 17,389 books, 250 microform titles, 115 serials, 960 audiovisual materials, and an OPAC. Operations spending for 2004 fiscal year: $149,793. 200 computers available on campus for general student use. A campuswide network can be accessed. Staffed computer lab on campus.

■ **UNIVERSITY OF ARKANSAS** *C-5*

800 Hotz Hall
Fayetteville, AR 72701-1201
Tel: (479)575-2000
Free: 800-377-8632
Admissions: (479)575-5346
Fax: (479)575-7515
E-mail: uafadmis@comp.uark.edu
Web Site: http://www.uark.edu/

Description: State-supported, university, coed. Part of University of Arkansas System. Awards bachelor's, master's, doctoral, and first professional degrees and post-master's certificates. Founded 1871. Setting: 357-acre suburban campus. Endowment: $692 million. Research spending for 2004 fiscal year: $88.3 million. Educational spending for 2005 fiscal year: $6244 per student. Total enrollment: 17,821. Faculty: 824 (787 full-time, 37 part-time). Student-undergrad faculty ratio is 18:1. 6,040 applied, 87% were admitted. 32% from top 10% of their high school class, 61% from top quarter, 86% from top half. 45 National Merit Scholars, 160 valedictorians. Full-time: 11,743 students, 50% women, 50% men. Part-time: 2,538 students, 47% women, 53% men. Students come from 50 states and territories, 103 other countries, 19% from out-of-state, 2% Native American, 2% Hispanic, 5% black, 3% Asian American or Pacific Islander, 2% international, 13% 25 or older, 29% live on campus, 8% transferred in. Retention: 81% of full-time freshmen returned the following year. Core. Calendar: semesters. ESL program, services for LD students, advanced placement, accelerated degree program, freshman honors college, honors program, independent study, distance learning, double major, summer session for credit, part-time degree program, co-op programs and internships, graduate courses open to undergrads. Study abroad program. ROTC: Army, Air Force.

Entrance Requirements: Options: Common Application, electronic application, early admission, early action, deferred admission, international baccalaureate accepted. Required: high school transcript, SAT or ACT. Recommended: minimum 3.0 high school GPA. Entrance: moderately difficult. Application deadlines: 8/15, 11/15 for early action. Notification: 10/1, 12/15 for early action.

Costs Per Year: Application fee: $40. State resident tuition: $4361 full-time, $145.38 per credit hour part-time. Nonresident tuition: $12,089 full-time, $402.96 per credit hour part-time. Mandatory fees: $1133 full-time. College room and board: $6365. College room only: $3782. Room and board charges vary according to board plan and housing facility.

Collegiate Environment: Orientation program. Drama-theater group, choral group, marching band, student-run newspaper, radio station. Social organizations: 273 open to all; national fraternities, national sororities; 11% of eligible men and 19% of eligible women are members. Most popular organizations: University programs, Booster Club, Associated Student Government, Black Students Association, Alpha Phi Omega. Major annual events: Welcome Week, Redeye, Homecoming. Student services: legal services, health clinic, personal-psychological counseling, women's center. Campus security: 24-hour emergency response devices and patrols, student patrols, late night transport-escort service, controlled dormitory access, RAD (Rape Aggression Defense program). College housing designed to accommodate 3,704 students; 3,741 undergraduates lived in college housing during 2003-04. Freshmen guaranteed college housing. On-campus residence required in freshman year. Options: coed, men-only, women-only housing available. David W. Mullins Library plus 4 others with 1.7 million books, 4.6 million microform titles, 22,485 serials, 25,291 audiovisual materials, an OPAC, and a Web page. Operations spending for 2004 fiscal year: $11.7 million. 1,252 computers available on campus for general student use. Computer purchase/lease plans available. A campuswide network can be accessed from student residence rooms and from off campus. Staffed computer lab on campus.

■ **UNIVERSITY OF ARKANSAS COMMUNITY COLLEGE AT BATESVILLE** *D-12*
PO Box 3350
Batesville, AR 72503
Tel: (870)793-7581
Admissions: (870)612-2010
Fax: (870)793-4988
Web Site: http://www.uaccb.edu/
Description: State-supported, 2-year, coed. Part of University of Arkansas System. Awards certificates, transfer associate, and terminal associate degrees. Setting: small town campus. Total enrollment: 1,317. Full-time: 784 students, 71% women, 29% men. Part-time: 533 students, 66% women, 34% men. 0% from out-of-state, 1% Native American, 1% Hispanic, 3% black, 0.5% Asian American or Pacific Islander, 0.1% international, 40% 25 or older, 9% transferred in. Retention: 57% of full-time freshmen returned the following year. Core. Calendar: semesters. Academic remediation for entering students, ESL program, services for LD students, advanced placement, self-designed majors, independent study, distance learning, double major, summer session for credit, part-time degree program, external degree program, adult/continuing education programs, co-op programs and internships. Off campus study.
Entrance Requirements: Open admission. Option: Common Application. Entrance: noncompetitive. Application deadline: Rolling. Notification: continuous.
Collegiate Environment: Orientation program. Student services: personal-psychological counseling. Campus security: security cameras. University of Arkansas Community College at Batesville Library with 8,000 books, 149 serials, 1,500 audiovisual materials, and an OPAC. 25 computers available on campus for general student use. A campuswide network can be accessed. Staffed computer lab on campus.

■ **UNIVERSITY OF ARKANSAS COMMUNITY COLLEGE AT HOPE** *K-6*
PO Box 140
Hope, AR 71802-0140
Tel: (870)777-5722
Fax: (870)722-5957
Web Site: http://www.uacch.edu/
Description: State-supported, 2-year, coed. Part of University of Arkansas System. Awards certificates, diplomas, transfer associate, and terminal associate degrees. Founded 1966. Setting: 60-acre rural campus. Total enrollment: 1,213. 463 applied, 100% were admitted. Full-time: 676 students, 67% women, 33% men. Part-time: 537 students, 74% women, 26% men. Students come from 4 states and territories, 1% Native American, 1% Hispanic, 30% black, 1% Asian American or Pacific Islander, 0.2% international, 38% 25 or older. Calendar: semesters. Academic remediation for entering students, ESL program, accelerated degree program, independent study, distance learning, summer session for credit, part-time degree program, internships.

Entrance Requirements: Open admission. Option: early admission. Required: high school transcript. Placement: ACT, ACT ASSET recommended; ACT ASSET required for some. Entrance: noncompetitive. Application deadline: Rolling.
Collegiate Environment: Orientation program. Social organizations: 4 open to all. Most popular organizations: Student Government Association, Phi Theta Kappa, Phi Beta Lambda, Circle K. Major annual events: Thanksgiving cookout/can drive, Fish Fry, Halloween Festival. Campus security: on-campus security during class hours. College housing not available. University of Arkansas Community College at Hope Library with 8,023 books, 111 serials, 614 audiovisual materials, an OPAC, and a Web page. Operations spending for 2004 fiscal year: $160,919.

■ **UNIVERSITY OF ARKANSAS COMMUNITY COLLEGE AT MORRILTON** *F-9*
One Bruce St.
Morrilton, AR 72110
Tel: (501)354-2465
Admissions: (501)977-2014
Fax: (501)354-9948
Web Site: http://www.uaccm.edu/
Description: State-supported, 2-year, coed. Part of University of Arkansas System. Awards certificates, transfer associate, and terminal associate degrees. Founded 1961. Setting: 63-acre rural campus. Educational spending for 2005 fiscal year: $2690 per student. Total enrollment: 1,514. 595 applied, 100% were admitted. 5% from top 10% of their high school class, 20% from top quarter, 50% from top half. 0% from out-of-state, 0.4% Native American, 2% Hispanic, 8% black, 1% Asian American or Pacific Islander, 0% international, 44% 25 or older. Core. Calendar: semesters. Academic remediation for entering students, services for LD students, advanced placement, self-designed majors, distance learning, double major, summer session for credit, part-time degree program, internships. Off campus study.
Entrance Requirements: Open admission. Options: early admission, deferred admission. Required: high school transcript. Required for some: immunization records. Placement: ACT, ACT ASSET or ACT COMPASS required. Entrance: noncompetitive. Application deadline: Rolling. Notification: continuous.
Costs Per Year: Application fee: $0. Area resident tuition: $1920 full-time, $64 per credit hour part-time. State resident tuition: $2100 full-time, $70 per credit hour part-time. Nonresident tuition: $3060 full-time, $102 per credit hour part-time. Mandatory fees: $210 full-time, $7. Full-time tuition and fees vary according to course load. Part-time tuition and fees vary according to course load.
Collegiate Environment: Orientation program. Social organizations: 10 open to all. Most popular organizations: Business Students' Organization, Student Activity Board, Early Childhood Development Organization, Graphic Design Club, Student Practical Nurses Organization. Major annual event: Spring Fling. Student services: personal-psychological counseling. Campus security: 24-hour emergency response devices. College housing not available. Gordon Library with 6,600 books and 76 serials. Operations spending for 2004 fiscal year: $109,433. 200 computers available on campus for general student use. Staffed computer lab on campus.

■ **UNIVERSITY OF ARKANSAS AT FORT SMITH** *E-4*
PO Box 3649
Fort Smith, AR 72913-3649
Tel: (479)788-7000; 888-512-5466
Admissions: (479)788-7038
Fax: (479)788-7003
E-mail: information@uafortsmith.edu
Web Site: http://www.uafortsmith.edu/
Description: State and locally supported, 4-year, coed. Part of University of Arkansas System. Awards associate and bachelor's degrees. Founded 1928. Setting: 120-acre suburban campus. Endowment: $34.2 million. Educational spending for 2005 fiscal year: $3216 per student. Total enrollment: 6,787. Student-undergrad faculty ratio is 23:1. 2,691 applied, 63% were admitted. 9% from top 10% of their high school class, 32% from top quarter, 65% from top half. Full-time: 3,838 students, 61% women, 39% men. Part-time: 2,949 students, 57% women, 43% men. Students come from 30 states and territories, 10 other countries, 14% from out-of-state, 4% Native American, 3% Hispanic, 4% black, 4% Asian American or Pacific Islander, 0.1% international, 38% 25 or older, 5% transferred in. Retention: 68% of full-time freshmen returned the following year. Academic areas with the most degrees conferred: education; business/marketing; computer and

information sciences. Core. Calendar: semesters. Academic remediation for entering students, ESL program, services for LD students, advanced placement, accelerated degree program, honors program, distance learning, double major, summer session for credit, part-time degree program, external degree program, adult/continuing education programs, co-op programs and internships. Off campus study. ROTC: Air Force (c).

Entrance Requirements: Open admission except for health-related programs. Options: electronic application, early admission, deferred admission. Required: high school transcript. Entrance: minimally difficult. Application deadline: Rolling.

Costs Per Year: Application fee: $0. State resident tuition: $2160 full-time, $72 per credit hour part-time. Nonresident tuition: $7050 full-time, $235 per credit hour part-time. Mandatory fees: $670 full-time, $21 per credit hour part-time, $20 per term part-time. College room and board: $5400.

Collegiate Environment: Orientation program. Choral group. Social organizations: 43 open to all. Most popular organizations: Student Activities Council, Phi Beta Lambda, Alpha Lambda Delta, College Republicans, Baptist Collegiate Ministry. Major annual events: Back to School Bash, Season of Entertainment, Student/Staff Picnic. Campus security: 24-hour emergency response devices and patrols, late night transport-escort service. College housing not available. Boreham Library with 82,000 books, 82,596 microform titles, 527 serials, 3,037 audiovisual materials, an OPAC, and a Web page. Operations spending for 2004 fiscal year: $1.2 million. 866 computers available on campus for general student use. A campuswide network can be accessed from off-campus. Staffed computer lab on campus.

■ **UNIVERSITY OF ARKANSAS AT LITTLE ROCK** *G-10*
2801 South University Ave.
Little Rock, AR 72204-1099
Tel: (501)569-3000
Admissions: (501)569-3127
Fax: (501)569-8915
Web Site: http://www.ualr.edu/
Description: State-supported, university, coed. Part of University of Arkansas System. Awards associate, bachelor's, master's, doctoral, and first professional degrees and post-master's certificates. Founded 1927. Setting: 150-acre urban campus. Endowment: $7.6 million. Research spending for 2004 fiscal year: $1.8 million. Total enrollment: 11,757. 2,531 applied, 99% were admitted. Full-time: 5,733 students, 61% women, 39% men. Part-time: 3,597 students, 64% women, 36% men. Students come from 45 states and territories, 43 other countries, 4% from out-of-state, 1% Native American, 2% Hispanic, 32% black, 2% Asian American or Pacific Islander, 2% international, 35% 25 or older, 3% live on campus, 8% transferred in. Retention: 64% of full-time freshmen returned the following year. Core. Calendar: semesters. Academic remediation for entering students, ESL program, services for LD students, advanced placement, accelerated degree program, self-designed majors, freshman honors college, honors program, independent study, summer session for credit, part-time degree program, adult/continuing education programs, co-op programs and internships, graduate courses open to undergrads. Off campus study at University of Arkansas for Medical Sciences. Study abroad program. ROTC: Army.
Entrance Requirements: Options: Peterson's Universal Application, early admission, deferred admission. Required: high school transcript, minimum 2.5 high school GPA, proof of immunization. Placement: SAT or ACT required. Entrance: minimally difficult. Application deadline: Rolling. Notification: continuous.
Costs Per Year: Application fee: $0. State resident tuition: $4230 full-time, $141 per credit hour part-time. Nonresident tuition: $11,100 full-time, $370 per credit hour part-time. Mandatory fees: $982 full-time, $32.75 per credit hour part-time. College room only: $2950.
Collegiate Environment: Orientation program. Choral group, student-run newspaper. Social organizations: 104 open to all; national fraternities, national sororities; 2% of eligible men and 2% of eligible women are members. Student services: health clinic, personal-psychological counseling, women's center. Campus security: 24-hour emergency response devices, student patrols, late night transport-escort service. Option: coed housing available. Ottenheimer Library plus 1 other with 3,998 serials and an OPAC. Operations spending for 2004 fiscal year: $2.7 million. 500 computers available on campus for general student use. A campuswide network can be accessed from off-campus. Staffed computer lab on campus.

■ **UNIVERSITY OF ARKANSAS FOR MEDICAL SCIENCES** *G-10*
4301 West Markham
Little Rock, AR 72205-7199

Tel: (501)686-5000
Admissions: (501)686-5730
Web Site: http://www.uams.edu/
Description: State-supported, upper-level, coed. Part of University of Arkansas System. Awards associate, bachelor's, master's, doctoral, and first professional degrees (bachelor's degree is upper-level). Founded 1879. Setting: 5-acre urban campus. Endowment: $22.1 million. Research spending for 2004 fiscal year: $28.1 million. Total enrollment: 2,016. 5% Native American, 2% Hispanic, 14% black, 0.4% Asian American or Pacific Islander, 0% international, 42% 25 or older. Calendar: semesters. Services for LD students, part-time degree program, graduate courses open to undergrads. ROTC: Army (c).
Collegiate Environment: Campus security: 24-hour emergency response devices and patrols, late night transport-escort service, controlled dormitory access. Option: coed housing available. Medical Sciences Library with 183,975 books, 1,567 serials, an OPAC, and a Web page. Operations spending for 2004 fiscal year: $2.6 million.

■ **UNIVERSITY OF ARKANSAS AT MONTICELLO** *K-11*
Monticello, AR 71656
Tel: (870)367-6811
Admissions: (870)460-1026
Fax: (870)460-1321
Web Site: http://www.uamont.edu/
Description: State-supported, comprehensive, coed. Part of University of Arkansas System. Awards associate, bachelor's, and master's degrees. Founded 1909. Setting: 400-acre small town campus. Total enrollment: 2,875. 1,208 applied, 73% were admitted. Full-time: 2,253 students, 57% women, 43% men. Part-time: 441 students, 73% women, 27% men. Students come from 20 states and territories, 2 other countries, 9% from out-of-state, 1% Native American, 2% Hispanic, 28% black, 0.4% Asian American or Pacific Islander, 0.4% international, 22% 25 or older, 25% live on campus, 6% transferred in. Retention: 54% of full-time freshmen returned the following year. Core. Calendar: semesters. Academic remediation for entering students, advanced placement, accelerated degree program, freshman honors college, independent study, summer session for credit, part-time degree program. Off campus study at University of Arkansas at Pine Bluff.
Entrance Requirements: Open admission except for nursing program. Options: Peterson's Universal Application, early admission, deferred admission. Required: high school transcript, proof of immunization. Placement: SAT or ACT required; ACT recommended. Entrance: noncompetitive. Application deadline: 8/1.
Collegiate Environment: Choral group, marching band, student-run newspaper. Social organizations: national fraternities, national sororities; 20% of eligible men and 22% of eligible women are members. Student services: health clinic, personal-psychological counseling. Campus security: 24-hour emergency response devices and patrols. 634 college housing spaces available; 477 were occupied in 2003-04. Options: men-only, women-only housing available. 126,229 books and 862 serials. 140 computers available on campus for general student use. Staffed computer lab on campus.

■ **UNIVERSITY OF ARKANSAS AT PINE BLUFF** *I-11*
1200 North University Dr.
Pine Bluff, AR 71601-2799
Tel: (870)543-8000
Free: 800-264-6585
Admissions: (870)575-8487
Fax: (870)543-2021
Web Site: http://www.uapb.edu/
Description: State-supported, comprehensive, coed. Part of University of Arkansas System. Awards associate, bachelor's, and master's degrees. Founded 1873. Setting: 327-acre urban campus. Total enrollment: 3,303. 1,701 applied, 89% were admitted. Full-time: 2,897 students, 57% women, 43% men. Part-time: 303 students, 67% women, 33% men. Students come from 30 states and territories, 17 other countries, 30% from out-of-state, 0.1% Native American, 0.2% Hispanic, 95% black, 0.2% Asian American or Pacific Islander, 1% international, 15% 25 or older, 43% live on campus, 5% transferred in. Retention: 64% of full-time freshmen returned the following year. Core. Calendar: semesters. Academic remediation for entering students, services for LD students, advanced placement, accelerated degree program, honors program, independent study, distance learning, double major, summer session for credit, part-time degree program, external degree program, adult/continuing education programs, co-op programs and intern-

ships, graduate courses open to undergrads. Off campus study at University of Arkansas, University of Arkansas at Little Rock, University of Arkansas at Monticello, University of Arkansas Community College at Hope. ROTC: Army.

Entrance Requirements: Options: early admission, deferred admission, international baccalaureate accepted. Required: high school transcript, minimum 2.0 high school GPA. Placement: SAT or ACT required. Entrance: minimally difficult. Application deadline: Rolling. Notification: continuous.

Collegiate Environment: Orientation program. Drama-theater group, choral group, marching band, student-run newspaper, radio station. Social organizations: national fraternities, national sororities, local fraternities, local sororities; 6% of eligible men and 6% of eligible women are members. Most popular organizations: Pre-Alumni Club, Honors College. Major annual events: Unity Fest, Homecoming. Student services: health clinic, personal-psychological counseling. Campus security: 24-hour emergency response devices. 1,489 college housing spaces available; 1,140 were occupied in 2003-04. Options: men-only, women-only housing available. Watson Memorial Library with 287,857 books, 136,742 microform titles, 3,041 serials, and an OPAC. 1,000 computers available on campus for general student use. A campuswide network can be accessed from student residence rooms. Staffed computer lab on campus.

■ **UNIVERSITY OF CENTRAL ARKANSAS** *F-9*

201 Donaghey Ave.
Conway, AR 72035-0001
Tel: (501)450-5000
Admissions: (501)450-5145
Fax: (501)450-5228
E-mail: admissons@uca.edu
Web Site: http://www.uca.edu/

Description: State-supported, comprehensive, coed. Awards associate, bachelor's, master's, and doctoral degrees. Founded 1907. Setting: 365-acre small town campus. Endowment: $32.1 million. Research spending for 2004 fiscal year: $643,985. Total enrollment: 11,375. Faculty: 607 (478 full-time, 129 part-time). Student-undergrad faculty ratio is 20:1. 5,830 applied, 68% were admitted. 24% from top 10% of their high school class, 48% from top quarter, 84% from top half. Full-time: 9,127 students, 58% women, 42% men. Part-time: 842 students, 62% women, 38% men. Students come from 38 states and territories, 55 other countries, 5% from out-of-state, 1% Native American, 1% Hispanic, 17% black, 2% Asian American or Pacific Islander, 2% international, 11% 25 or older, 42% live on campus, 6% transferred in. Retention: 73% of full-time freshmen returned the following year. Academic areas with the most degrees conferred: business/marketing; health professions and related sciences; education. Core. Calendar: semesters. Academic remediation for entering students, ESL program, advanced placement, accelerated degree program, freshman honors college, honors program, independent study, distance learning, double major, summer session for credit, part-time degree program, co-op programs and internships, graduate courses open to undergrads. Study abroad program. ROTC: Army.

Entrance Requirements: Options: electronic application, early admission, deferred admission. Required: high school transcript, SAT or ACT. Required for some: minimum 2.75 high school GPA. Entrance: moderately difficult. Application deadline: Rolling. Notification: continuous.

Costs Per Year: Application fee: $0. State resident tuition: $4500 full-time, $150 per credit hour part-time. Nonresident tuition: $9000 full-time, $300 per credit hour part-time. Mandatory fees: $1164 full-time, $35 per credit hour part-time, $61 per term part-time. Part-time tuition and fees vary according to course load. College room and board: $4320. College room only: $1940. Room and board charges vary according to board plan and housing facility.

Collegiate Environment: Orientation program. Drama-theater group, choral group, marching band, student-run newspaper, radio station. Social organizations: 32 open to all; national fraternities, national sororities; 10% of eligible men and 10% of eligible women are members. Most popular organizations: Student Government Association, Royal Rooters, student orientation staff, Ambassadors. Major annual events: Bearfacts Days, Homecoming, Parents' Day. Student services: health clinic, personal-psychological counseling. Campus security: 24-hour emergency response devices and patrols, student patrols, late night transport-escort service, controlled dormitory access, security personnel at entrances during evening hours. College housing designed to accommodate 3,600 students; 3,797 undergraduates lived in college housing during 2003-04. Freshmen guaranteed college housing. On-campus residence required in freshman year. Options: coed, men-only, women-only housing available. Torreyson Library with 505,000 books, 850,000 microform titles, 2,000 serials, an

OPAC, and a Web page. Operations spending for 2004 fiscal year: $2.4 million. 1,500 computers available on campus for general student use. Computer purchase/lease plans available. A campuswide network can be accessed from student residence rooms and from off campus. Staffed computer lab on campus.

Community Environment: Conway, population 45,000, is a growing center served by major highways, the Union Pacific Railway, and Little Rock National Airport which is 35 miles away. It is within a few miles of the geographic center of the state. Lake Conway, which covers approximately 6,500 acres, between Conway and Little Rock, is one of the principal resorts of the state. The Arkansas River, the largest to cross the state, is less than ten miles from Conway. Conway is a city with three colleges and is the government seat of Faulkner County. It has a diverse economic background, which includes manufacturers, education, government and service industries. Several major manufacturing firms including Kimberly Clark, Nucor Steel, Touksen and AmTran have facilities here. Axiom, a data processing center, has its corporation headquarters located in Conway and employs approximately 2,000 people. The city has many beautiful residences, churches, businesses, and public buildings.

■ **UNIVERSITY OF THE OZARKS** *E-7*

415 North College Ave.
Clarksville, AR 72830-2880
Tel: (479)979-1000
Free: 800-264-8636
Admissions: (479)979-1421
Fax: (479)979-1355
E-mail: admiss@ozarks.edu
Web Site: http://www.ozarks.edu/

Description: Independent Presbyterian, 4-year, coed. Awards bachelor's degrees. Founded 1834. Setting: 56-acre small town campus with easy access to Little Rock. Endowment: $58.7 million. Educational spending for 2005 fiscal year: $6063 per student. Total enrollment: 628. Student-undergrad faculty ratio is 12:1. 665 applied, 93% were admitted. 20% from top 10% of their high school class, 40% from top quarter, 78% from top half. 15 valedictorians. Full-time: 588 students, 52% women, 48% men. Part-time: 40 students, 68% women, 33% men. Students come from 22 states and territories, 22 other countries, 36% from out-of-state, 4% Native American, 4% Hispanic, 5% black, 2% Asian American or Pacific Islander, 17% international, 6% 25 or older, 66% live on campus; 5% transferred in. Retention: 67% of full-time freshmen returned the following year. Academic areas with the most degrees conferred: business/marketing; education; social sciences. Core. Calendar: semesters. Academic remediation for entering students, ESL program, services for LD students, advanced placement, independent study, double major, summer session for credit, part-time degree program, co-op programs and internships. Off campus study. Study abroad program.

Entrance Requirements: Options: Peterson's Universal Application, Common Application, electronic application, deferred admission, international baccalaureate accepted. Required: minimum 2.0 high school GPA, SAT or ACT. Required for some: essay, high school transcript, recommendations, interview. Entrance: moderately difficult. Application deadline: Rolling. Notification: continuous.

Costs Per Year: Comprehensive fee: $20,210 includes full-time tuition ($14,470), mandatory fees ($480), and college room and board ($5260). Part-time tuition: $605 per credit hour.

Collegiate Environment: Orientation program. Drama-theater group, choral group, student-run radio station. Social organizations: 27 open to all. Most popular organizations: Phi Beta Lambda, Planet Club, SGA, Student Foundation Board, Baptist Campus Ministries. Major annual events: Study Night Breakfast, Christmas Formal, Back to School Dance. Student services: health clinic. Campus security: 24-hour emergency response devices, late night transport-escort service. 475 college housing spaces available; 393 were occupied in 2003-04. On-campus residence required through sophomore year. Options: coed, men-only, women-only housing available. Robson Library with 105,000 books, 9,900 microform titles, 16,000 serials, 4,000 audiovisual materials, an OPAC, and a Web page. Operations spending for 2004 fiscal year: $419,216. 145 computers available on campus for general student use. A campuswide network can be accessed from student residence rooms and from off campus. Staffed computer lab on campus.

Community Environment: Clarksville is the county seat of Johnson County. The town lies 105 miles northwest of Little Rock on Interstate 40, & is 65 miles east of Fort Smith. The Continental bus line serves this area. Primarily an agricultural community, it also has some manufacturing. There are motel accommodations, and a hospital. A swimming pool, athletic fields, baseball park, football field, tennis courts, and all the outdoor sports are available. Annual events include the Peach Festival.

■ **UNIVERSITY OF PHOENIX-LITTLE ROCK CAMPUS** *G-10*
10800 Financial Center Parkway
Little Rock, AR 72211
Tel: (501)225-9337
Free: 800-228-7240
Admissions: (480)557-1712
Web Site: http://www.phoenix.edu/
Description: Proprietary, comprehensive, coed. Awards bachelor's and master's degrees. Founded 2003. Total enrollment: 499. Faculty: 69 (2 full-time, 67 part-time). Student-undergrad faculty ratio is 7:1. 31 applied. Full-time: 327 students, 69% women, 31% men. 0.3% Native American, 0% Hispanic, 7% black, 1% Asian American or Pacific Islander, 2% transferred in. Core. Calendar: continuous. Advanced placement, accelerated degree program, independent study, distance learning, external degree program, adult/continuing education programs, graduate courses open to undergrads.
Entrance Requirements: Open admission. Option: deferred admission. Required: 1 recommendation. Required for some: high school transcript. Entrance: noncompetitive. Application deadline: Rolling.
Costs Per Year: Application fee: $110. Tuition: $9540 full-time, $318 per credit part-time. Mandatory fees: $560 full-time, $70 per course part-time.
Collegiate Environment: College housing not available. University Library with 442 books, 666 serials, an OPAC, and a Web page. System-wide operations spending for 2004 fiscal year: $3.2 million.

■ **WILLIAMS BAPTIST COLLEGE** *C-13*
60 West Fulbright Ave.
Walnut Ridge, AR 72476
Tel: (870)886-6741
Free: 800-722-4434
Admissions: (870)759-4117
E-mail: admissions@wbclab.wbcoll.edu

Web Site: http://www.wbcoll.edu/
Description: Independent Southern Baptist, 4-year, coed. Awards associate and bachelor's degrees. Founded 1941. Setting: 180-acre rural campus. Endowment: $5.4 million. Total enrollment: 653. 407 applied, 69% were admitted. Full-time: 511 students, 57% women, 43% men. Part-time: 142 students, 51% women, 49% men. Students come from 13 states and territories, 5 other countries, 20% from out-of-state, 0.4% Native American, 1% Hispanic, 3% black, 1% Asian American or Pacific Islander, 0.4% international, 13% 25 or older, 62% live on campus, 7% transferred in. Retention: 61% of full-time freshmen returned the following year. Core. Calendar: semesters. Academic remediation for entering students, advanced placement, self-designed majors, honors program, independent study, double major, summer session for credit, part-time degree program, adult/continuing education programs, internships. Off campus study at Coalition for Christian Colleges and Universities. Study abroad program. ROTC: Army (c).
Entrance Requirements: Options: Peterson's Universal Application, electronic application. Required: high school transcript, minimum 2.5 high school GPA, SAT or ACT. Recommended: essay, interview. Entrance: minimally difficult. Application deadline: Rolling.
Collegiate Environment: Orientation program. Drama-theater group, choral group. Social organizations: 26 open to all. Most popular organizations: campus ministries, Fellowship of Christian Athletes, International Club, Alpha Psi Omega. Major annual events: Homecoming, Spring Fling, First Week. Student services: personal-psychological counseling. Campus security: 24-hour emergency response devices, student patrols. On-campus residence required through senior year. Options: men-only, women-only housing available. Felix Goodson Library with 57,321 books, 284 serials, and an OPAC. 71 computers available on campus for general student use. A campuswide network can be accessed. Staffed computer lab on campus.
Community Environment: Walnut Ridge is a rural area with a temperate climate. Railroads serve the area as well as a city airport. There are churches of major denominations, a public library, and a hospital. Recreational activities include boating and water sports. The city has Lions and Kiwanis organizations. An annual county fair is held. Part-time employment opportunities are limited.

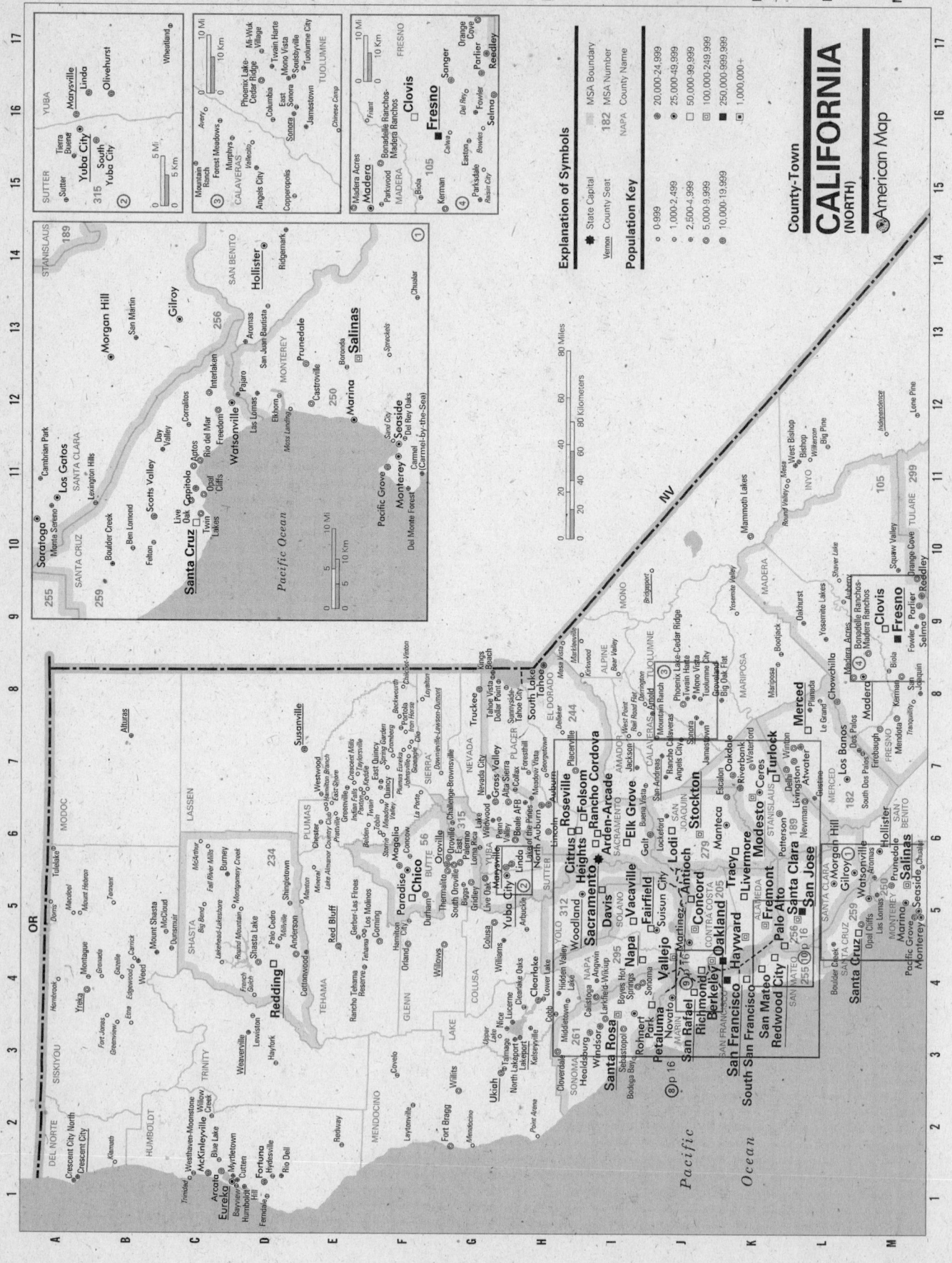

CALIFORNIA
(NORTH)

County-Town

American Map

Explanation of Symbols

★ State Capital
Vernon ◉ County Seat
▦ MSA Boundary
182 MSA Number
NAPA County Name

Population Key

○ 0-999
◉ 1,000-2,499
○ 2,500-4,999
◉ 5,000-9,999
◉ 10,000-19,999
● 20,000-24,999
□ 25,000-49,999
□ 50,000-99,999
▣ 100,000-249,999
■ 250,000-999,999
■ 1,000,000+

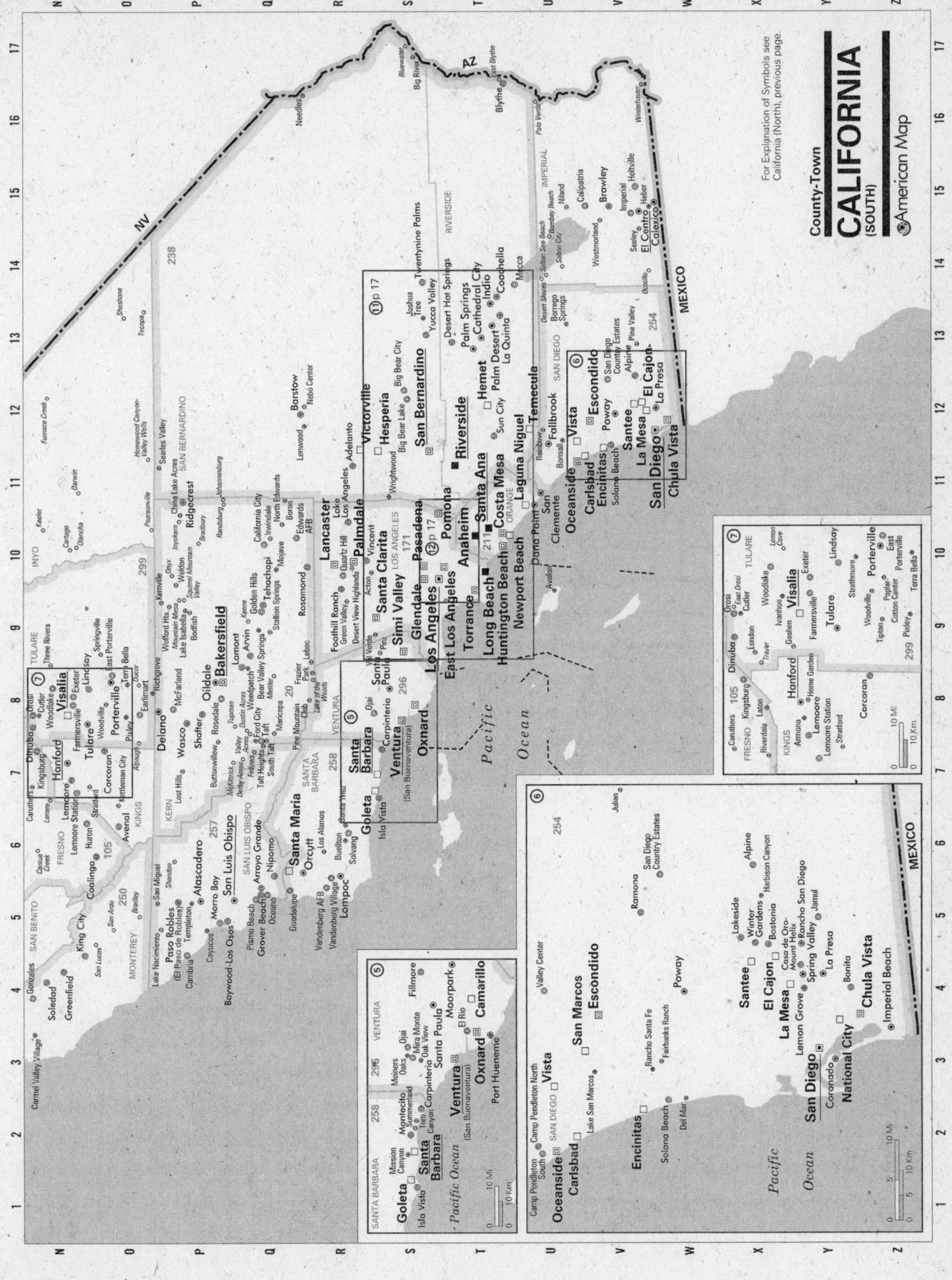

County-Town
CALIFORNIA
(SOUTH)
American Map

For Explanation of Symbols see California (North), previous page.

■ **ACADEMY OF ART UNIVERSITY** *K-4*
79 New Montgomery St.
San Francisco, CA 94105-3410
Tel: (415)274-2200
Free: 800-544-ARTS
Admissions: (415)263-5518
Fax: (415)263-4130
Web Site: http://www.academyart.edu/
Description: Proprietary, comprehensive, coed. Awards associate, bachelor's, and master's degrees. Founded 1929. Setting: 3-acre urban campus. Total enrollment: 8,270. Faculty: 675 (135 full-time, 540 part-time). Student-undergrad faculty ratio is 15:1. 80% from top half of their high school class. Full-time: 4,111 students, 48% women, 52% men. Part-time: 2,575 students, 53% women, 47% men. Students come from 53 states and territories, 39% from out-of-state, 1% Native American, 8% Hispanic, 4% black, 15% Asian American or Pacific Islander, 10% international, 39% 25 or older, 10% live on campus, 9% transferred in. Retention: 58% of full-time freshmen returned the following year. Academic area with the most degrees conferred: visual and performing arts. Core. Calendar: semesters. Academic remediation for entering students, ESL program, independent study, summer session for credit, part-time degree program, adult/continuing education programs, internships.
Entrance Requirements: Open admission. Options: Peterson's Universal Application, Common Application, early admission, deferred admission, international baccalaureate accepted. Required: high school transcript. Recommended: minimum 2.0 high school GPA, interview, portfolio. Entrance: noncompetitive. Application deadline: Rolling.
Costs Per Year: Application fee: $100. Comprehensive fee: $26,480 includes full-time tuition ($14,400), mandatory fees ($80), and college room and board ($12,000). College room only: $8400.
Collegiate Environment: Orientation program. Social organizations: 25 open to all. Most popular organizations: Circle of Nations, Advertising Club, Western Art Directors Club, Pinoy and Pinay Artists Club, Taiwanese Student Association. Major annual events: Spring Show, Lily Bunka Academy Exchange, Fine Art Faculty and Alumni Art Auction. Campus security: late night transport-escort service, ID check at all buildings. 725 college housing spaces available; 666 were occupied in 2003-04. Freshmen guaranteed college housing. Option: coed housing available. Academy of Art University Library with 37,342 books, 565 serials, 120,000 audiovisual materials, an OPAC, and a Web page. Operations spending for 2004 fiscal year: $718,000. 600 computers available on campus for general student use. Computer purchase/lease plans available. Staffed computer lab on campus.
Community Environment: Lining the street between the Powell and Sutter buildings are several of San Francisco's finest art galleries. The area provides an ideal environment for studying and developing as an artist.

■ **ALLAN HANCOCK COLLEGE** *Q-6*
800 South College Dr.
Santa Maria, CA 93454-6399
Tel: (805)922-6966; (866)342-5242
Fax: (805)922-3477
Web Site: http://www.hancockcollege.edu/
Description: State and locally supported, 2-year, coed. Awards certificates, transfer associate, and terminal associate degrees. Founded 1920. Setting: 120-acre small town campus. Endowment: $1.1 million. Research spending for 2004 fiscal year: $78,392. Educational spending for 2005 fiscal year:

$1690 per student. Total enrollment: 10,387. Student-undergrad faculty ratio is 17:1. Full-time: 2,996 students, 54% women, 46% men. Part-time: 7,391 students, 56% women, 44% men. Students come from 27 states and territories, 12 other countries, 1% Native American, 33% Hispanic, 4% black, 3% Asian American or Pacific Islander, 0.1% international. Core. Calendar: semesters. ESL program, services for LD students, advanced placement, distance learning, summer session for credit, part-time degree program, adult/continuing education programs, co-op programs. Study abroad program.
Entrance Requirements: Open admission except for nursing, drama, fire technology programs. Option: early admission. Required: high school transcript. Entrance: noncompetitive. Application deadline: Rolling. Notification: continuous.
Costs Per Year: Application fee: $0. State resident tuition: $0 full-time. Nonresident tuition: $4956 full-time, $177 per unit part-time. Mandatory fees: $792 full-time, $27 per unit part-time.
Collegiate Environment: Orientation program. Drama-theater group, choral group, student-run newspaper. Social organizations: 10 open to all. Most popular organizations: MECHA, AHC Student Club, Club Med (medical), Hancock Christian Fellowship, Vocational Industrial Clubs of America. Major annual events: Chili Cook-Off, Blood Drive, Spring Fest. Student services: legal services, health clinic, personal-psychological counseling. Campus security: 24-hour emergency response devices and patrols, student patrols, late night transport-escort service. College housing not available. Learning Resources Center with 47,370 books, 51,225 microform titles, 397 serials, 2,463 audiovisual materials, an OPAC, and a Web page. Operations spending for 2004 fiscal year: $252,771. 200 computers available on campus for general student use. Staffed computer lab on campus.
Community Environment: Santa Maria is located in the Central Coast region on United States Highway 101, 175 miles north of Los Angeles and 262 miles south of San Francisco. Average temperature ranges from 45 degrees minimum to 68.2 degrees maximum. Greyhound Bus and United Airlines serve the area. Santa Maria has a hospital, churches, a library, and a number of manufacturing firms. A municipal swimming pool, golf courses, parks and playgrounds provide facilities for sports. Hunting and fishing opportunities are good.

■ **ALLIANT INTERNATIONAL UNIVERSITY** *W-12*
10455 Pomerado Rd.
San Diego, CA 92131-1799
Tel: (858)271-4300; (866)825-5426
Admissions: (858)635-4772
Fax: (858)635-4739
E-mail: stopham@alliant.edu
Web Site: http://www.alliant.edu/
Description: Independent, university, coed. Part of Alliant International University. Awards bachelor's, master's, and doctoral degrees. Founded 1952. Setting: 60-acre suburban campus. Endowment: $1.7 million. Research spending for 2004 fiscal year: $9550. Total enrollment: 3,487. Faculty: 288 (131 full-time, 157 part-time). Student-undergrad faculty ratio is 15:1. Full-time: 226 students, 52% women, 48% men. Part-time: 28 students, 54% women, 46% men. Students come from 17 states and territories, 52 other countries, 10% from out-of-state, 1% Native American, 19% Hispanic, 8% black, 7% Asian American or Pacific Islander, 28% international, 15% 25 or older, 41% live on campus, 30% transferred in. Academic areas with the most degrees conferred: business/marketing; psychology;

public administration and social services. Core. Calendar: semesters. Academic remediation for entering students, ESL program, services for LD students, advanced placement, honors program, independent study, distance learning, summer session for credit, part-time degree program, adult/continuing education programs, internships, graduate courses open to undergrads. Study abroad program. ROTC: Army (c).

Entrance Requirements: Options: Peterson's Universal Application, Common Application, electronic application, deferred admission, international baccalaureate accepted. Required: high school transcript. Application deadline: Rolling.

Costs Per Year: Application fee: $45. Comprehensive fee: $22,170 includes full-time tuition ($14,000), mandatory fees ($370), and college room and board ($7800). Part-time tuition: $515 per unit.

Collegiate Environment: Orientation program. Student-run newspaper. Social organizations: 12 open to all. Most popular organizations: Residence Hall Association, Latino Students Association, Finance Club, Student Government, Sigma Iota Epsilon. Major annual events: International Friendship Festival, Winter Ball, Snow Day in Big Bear. Student services: health clinic, personal-psychological counseling. Campus security: 24-hour emergency response devices and patrols, student patrols, late night transport-escort service. 250 college housing spaces available; 138 were occupied in 2003-04. No special consideration for freshman housing applicants. On-campus residence required in freshman year. Option: coed housing available. Walter Library with 212,394 books, 344,518 microform titles, 674 serials, 4,688 audiovisual materials, an OPAC, and a Web page. Operations spending for 2004 fiscal year: $1.2 million. 80 computers available on campus for general student use. A campuswide network can be accessed from student residence rooms and from off campus. Staffed computer lab on campus.

■ AMERICAN ACADEMY OF DRAMATIC ARTS/HOLLYWOOD *S-10*
1336 North La Brea Ave.
Hollywood, CA 90028
Tel: (323)464-2777
Free: 800-222-2867
Fax: (323)464-1250
Web Site: http://www.aada.org/
Description: Independent, 2-year, coed. Awards certificates, diplomas, and transfer associate degrees. Founded 1974. Setting: 4-acre suburban campus with easy access to Los Angeles. Total enrollment: 308. Full-time: 308 students, 54% women, 46% men. Students come from 21 states and territories, 3 other countries, 40% from out-of-state, 1% Native American, 7% Hispanic, 6% black, 1% Asian American or Pacific Islander, 10% international, 15% 25 or older, 0% transferred in. Core. Calendar: continuous.
Entrance Requirements: Option: deferred admission. Required: essay, high school transcript, 2 recommendations, interview, audition. Recommended: minimum 2.0 high school GPA. Entrance: moderately difficult. Application deadline: Rolling. Notification: continuous.
Costs Per Year: Application fee: $50. Tuition: $16,000 full-time. Mandatory fees: $500 full-time.
Collegiate Environment: Major annual events: graduation, student performances, seminars by guest lecturers. Campus security: 24-hour emergency response devices, 8-hour patrols by trained security personnel. College housing not available. Bryn Morgan Library with 7,700 books, 24 serials, and 320 audiovisual materials. Operations spending for 2004 fiscal year: $48,825.

■ AMERICAN INTERCONTINENTAL UNIVERSITY *S-10*
12655 West Jefferson Blvd.
Los Angeles, CA 90066
Tel: (310)302-2000
Free: 800-333-2652
Fax: (310)302-2001
Web Site: http://www.aiuniv.edu/
Description: Proprietary, comprehensive, coed. Awards associate, bachelor's, and master's degrees. Founded 1982. Setting: urban campus. Total enrollment: 1,405. 720 applied, 38% were admitted. 0% from top 10% of their high school class, 0% from top quarter, 50% from top half. Students come from 50 states and territories, 21 other countries, 27% from out-of-state, 1% Native American, 3% Hispanic, 3% black, 2% Asian American or Pacific Islander, 2% international, 47% 25 or older, 10% live on campus. Retention: 63% of full-time freshmen returned the following year. Core. Calendar: five 10-week terms. Academic remediation for entering students,

accelerated degree program, distance learning, double major, summer session for credit, part-time degree program, internships. Study abroad program.

Entrance Requirements: Open admission. Options: electronic application, early admission, deferred admission, international baccalaureate accepted. Required: essay, high school transcript, interview. Entrance: noncompetitive. Application deadline: Rolling.

Collegiate Environment: Orientation program. Drama-theater group, student-run newspaper. Major annual events: Yacht Party, International Dinner, Graduation Ball. Student services: personal-psychological counseling. Campus security: 24-hour emergency response devices, late night transport-escort service. 175 college housing spaces available; 169 were occupied in 2003-04. Freshmen guaranteed college housing. Options: coed, men-only, women-only housing available. Library plus 1 other with 20,000 books, 50 microform titles, and 228 serials. Operations spending for 2004 fiscal year: $175,000. 40 computers available on campus for general student use. Computer purchase/lease plans available. A campuswide network can be accessed from off-campus. Staffed computer lab on campus.

■ AMERICAN RIVER COLLEGE *I-6*
4700 College Oak Dr.
Sacramento, CA 95841-4286
Tel: (916)484-8011
Admissions: (916)484-8171
E-mail: esposic@arc.losrios.cc.ca.us
Web Site: http://www.arc.losrios.edu/
Description: District-supported, 2-year, coed. Part of Los Rios Community College District System. Awards certificates, transfer associate, and terminal associate degrees. Founded 1955. Setting: 153-acre suburban campus. Total enrollment: 30,000. 2,471 applied, 100% were admitted. 0.2% from out-of-state, 19% 25 or older. Core. Calendar: semesters. Academic remediation for entering students, ESL program, services for LD students, advanced placement, summer session for credit, part-time degree program, adult/continuing education programs, co-op programs.
Entrance Requirements: Open admission except for nursing, respiratory therapy programs. Options: Common Application, early admission, deferred admission. Placement: SAT or ACT recommended; nursing exam required for some. Entrance: noncompetitive. Application deadline: Rolling.
Costs Per Year: Application fee: $0. Nonresident tuition: $4248 full-time, $177 per unit part-time. Mandatory fees: $639 full-time, $26 per unit part-time.
Collegiate Environment: Drama-theater group, student-run newspaper. Student services: health clinic, personal-psychological counseling, women's center. Campus security: 24-hour emergency response devices and patrols, student patrols, late night transport-escort service. College housing not available. 78,400 books and 75 serials.
Community Environment: See California State University - Sacramento.

■ ANTELOPE VALLEY COLLEGE *R-10*
3041 West Ave. K
Lancaster, CA 93536-5426
Tel: (661)722-6300
Fax: (661)943-5573
Web Site: http://www.avc.edu/
Description: State and locally supported, 2-year, coed. Part of California Community College System. Awards certificates, transfer associate, and terminal associate degrees. Founded 1929. Setting: 160-acre suburban campus with easy access to Los Angeles. Endowment: $299,569. Research spending for 2004 fiscal year: $69,540. Educational spending for 2005 fiscal year: $3146 per student. Total enrollment: 12,073. 1,947 applied, 100% were admitted. Students come from 7 states and territories, 1% from out-of-state, 44% 25 or older. Core. Calendar: semesters. Academic remediation for entering students, ESL program, services for LD students, advanced placement, honors program, summer session for credit, part-time degree program, adult/continuing education programs, co-op programs. Study abroad program. ROTC: Air Force (c).
Entrance Requirements: Open admission. Options: Common Application, early admission. Required: high school transcript. Entrance: noncompetitive. Application deadline: Rolling. Notification: continuous.
Collegiate Environment: Drama-theater group, choral group, student-run newspaper. Major annual events: Cinco de Mayo, Women's Workshop, Transfer Colleges Day. Student services: personal-psychological counseling. Campus security: 24-hour emergency response devices and patrols, late

night transport-escort service. College housing not available. Antelope Valley College Library with 43,000 books and 175 serials. Operations spending for 2004 fiscal year: $946,564.

Community Environment: Population 400,000 in Qutelope Valley. Lancaster is located in the center of the Antelope Valley in a semidesert region. Lancaster has over 350 days of sunshine a year and the climate is the reason that the United States Air Force and almost every manufacturer of aircraft build and maintain establishments in this area. There has been a great increase in population and excellent employment opportunities have developed in proportion to the growth.

■ **ANTIOCH UNIVERSITY LOS ANGELES** *W-1*
400 Corporate Pointe
Culver City, CA 90230
Tel: (310)578-1080
Free: 800-7ANTIOCH
Fax: (310)827-4742
Web Site: http://www.antiochla.edu/
Description: Independent, upper-level, coed. Part of Antioch University. Awards bachelor's and master's degrees and post-master's certificates. Founded 1972. Setting: 1-acre urban campus with easy access to Los Angeles. Educational spending for 2005 fiscal year: $2100 per student. Total enrollment: 650. Faculty: 172 (21 full-time, 151 part-time). Student-undergrad faculty ratio is 14:1. 65 applied, 88% were admitted. Full-time: 81 students, 75% women, 25% men. Part-time: 107 students, 75% women, 25% men. 0% from out-of-state, 2% Native American, 10% Hispanic, 17% black, 4% Asian American or Pacific Islander, 0% international, 97% 25 or older, 100% transferred in. Core. Academic remediation for entering students, services for LD students, advanced placement, accelerated degree program, self-designed majors, independent study, distance learning, double major, summer session for credit, part-time degree program, external degree program, adult/continuing education programs, co-op programs and internships, graduate courses open to undergrads.
Costs Per Year: Application fee: $60. Tuition: $13,500 full-time, $2700 per term part-time.
Collegiate Environment: Orientation program. Student services: personal-psychological counseling. Campus security: 24-hour emergency response devices, late night transport-escort service. College housing not available. Operations spending for 2004 fiscal year: $20,000. 12 computers available on campus for general student use. A campuswide network can be accessed from off-campus. Staffed computer lab on campus.

■ **ANTIOCH UNIVERSITY SANTA BARBARA** *S-7*
801 Garden St.
Santa Barbara, CA 93101-1581
Tel: (805)962-8179
Fax: (805)962-4786
E-mail: amcpherson@antiochsb.edu
Web Site: http://www.antiochsb.edu/
Description: Independent, upper-level, coed. Part of Antioch University. Awards bachelor's and master's degrees. Founded 1977. Setting: small town campus with easy access to Los Angeles. Total enrollment: 305. Faculty: 66 (14 full-time, 52 part-time). Student-undergrad faculty ratio is 15:1. Full-time: 39 students, 59% women, 41% men. Part-time: 56 students, 82% women, 18% men. 0% from out-of-state, 2% Native American, 15% Hispanic, 3% black, 3% Asian American or Pacific Islander, 0% international, 74% 25 or older, 100% transferred in. Academic area with the most degrees conferred: liberal arts/general studies. Core. Academic remediation for entering students, accelerated degree program, self-designed majors, independent study, summer session for credit, part-time degree program, adult/continuing education programs, internships, graduate courses open to undergrads.
Costs Per Year: Application fee: $60. Tuition: $13,140 full-time, $440 per unit part-time. Mandatory fees: $16 full-time.
Collegiate Environment: Campus security: late night transport-escort service. College housing not available. 14 computers available on campus for general student use. A campuswide network can be accessed from off-campus. Staffed computer lab on campus.

■ **ARGOSY UNIVERSITY/ORANGE COUNTY** *T-10*
3501 West Sunflower Ave., Ste. 110
Santa Ana, CA 92704
Tel: (714)338-6200
Free: 800-716-9598

Web Site: http://www.argosyu.edu/
Description: Proprietary, primarily 2-year, coed. Awards terminal associate, bachelor's, master's, and doctoral degrees. Setting: urban campus with easy access to Los Angeles and San Diego. Total enrollment: 646. Faculty: 81 (11 full-time, 70 part-time). Student-undergrad faculty ratio is 22:1. Full-time: 66 students, 59% women, 41% men. Part-time: 15 students, 60% women, 40% men. 62% transferred in. Core. Calendar: semesters. Academic remediation for entering students, services for LD students, distance learning, part-time degree program, graduate courses open to undergrads.
Entrance Requirements: Options: Common Application, electronic application, early admission, deferred admission, international baccalaureate accepted. Entrance: moderately difficult.
Collegiate Environment: College housing not available. Carrie Lixey with 1,200 books, 50 serials, and an OPAC. 12 computers available on campus for general student use. Staffed computer lab on campus.

■ **ARGOSY UNIVERSITY/SAN DIEGO** *W-12*
7650 Mission Valley Rd.
San Diego, CA 92108
; (866)505-0333
Web Site: http://www.argosyu.edu/sandiego/
Description: Proprietary, 2-year, coed. Awards terminal associate degrees.

■ **ARGOSY UNIVERSITY/SAN FRANCISCO BAY AREA** *J-4*
999A Canal Blvd.
Point Richmond, CA 94804-3547
Tel: (510)215-0277; (866)215-2777
Admissions: (510)837-3709
Fax: (510)215-0299
E-mail: jstofan@argosyu.edu
Web Site: http://www.argosyu.edu/
Description: Proprietary, upper-level, coed. Administratively affiliated with Education Management Corporation. Awards bachelor's, master's, and doctoral degrees. Founded 1998. Setting: urban campus with easy access to Oakland and San Francisco. Total enrollment: 71. Faculty: 11 (1 full-time, 10 part-time). Student-undergrad faculty ratio is 10:1. 24 applied, 92% were admitted. Full-time: 22 students, 86% women, 14% men. Part-time: 26 students, 85% women, 15% men. Students come from 2 other countries, 0% Native American, 13% Hispanic, 29% black, 15% Asian American or Pacific Islander, 90% 25 or older, 31% transferred in. Retention: 93% of full-time entering class returned the following year. Academic area with the most degrees conferred: psychology. Calendar: semesters.
Costs Per Year: Application fee: $50. Tuition: $400 full-time, $400 per credit part-time. Mandatory fees: $10 per credit part-time, $50 per year part-time.
Collegiate Environment: College housing not available.

■ **ARGOSY UNIVERSITY/SANTA MONICA** *Q-3*
2950 31st St.
Santa Monica, CA 90405
; (866)505-0332
Web Site: http://www.argosyu.edu/santamonica/
Description: Proprietary, comprehensive, coed. Awards associate degrees.

■ **ART CENTER COLLEGE OF DESIGN** *S-10*
1700 Lida St.
Pasadena, CA 91103-1999
Tel: (626)396-2200
Admissions: (626)396-2373
Fax: (626)795-0578
E-mail: admissions@artcenter.edu
Web Site: http://www.artcenter.edu/
Description: Independent, comprehensive, coed. Awards bachelor's and master's degrees. Founded 1930. Setting: 175-acre suburban campus with easy access to Los Angeles. Endowment: $21.3 million. Educational spending for 2005 fiscal year: $27,800 per student. Total enrollment: 1,642. Faculty: 407 (66 full-time, 341 part-time). Student-undergrad faculty ratio is 12:1. 1,079 applied, 74% were admitted. Full-time: 1,304 students, 40% women, 60% men. Part-time: 208 students, 41% women, 59% men. Students come from 31 states and territories, 28 other countries, 33% from out-of-state, 0.5% Native American, 12% Hispanic, 2% black, 37% Asian American or Pacific Islander, 16% international, 47% 25 or older, 2% transferred in. Retention: 94% of full-time freshmen returned the following

year. Core. Calendar: trimesters. Advanced placement, accelerated degree program, independent study, summer session for credit, adult/continuing education programs, internships.

Entrance Requirements: Options: deferred admission, international baccalaureate accepted. Required: essay, high school transcript, portfolio. Recommended: minimum 3.0 high school GPA, interview. Required for some: SAT or ACT. Entrance: very difficult. Application deadline: Rolling. Notification: continuous.

Costs Per Year: Application fee: $45. Tuition: $27,800 full-time. Mandatory fees: $200 full-time.

Collegiate Environment: Orientation program. Social organizations: 12 open to all. Most popular organizations: Contraste, Chroma, Women's Alliance, Korean Student Alliance, Industrial Design Society Student Chapter. Major annual event: School-Wide Party. Student services: personal-psychological counseling. Campus security: 24-hour emergency response devices and patrols. College housing not available. James LeMont Fogg Library with 93,038 books, 450 serials, and 10,000 audiovisual materials. Operations spending for 2004 fiscal year: $984,867. 225 computers available on campus for general student use. A campuswide network can be accessed from off-campus. Staffed computer lab on campus.

Community Environment: See California Institute of Technology.

■ **THE ART INSTITUTE OF CALIFORNIA-INLAND EMPIRE** *S-11*
630 East Brier Dr.
San Bernardino, CA 92408
Tel: (909)915-2100
Free: 800-353-0812
E-mail: mjeffs@aii.edu
Web Site: http://www.artinstitutes.edu/inlandempire/
Description: Proprietary, 4-year, coed. Awards bachelor's degrees. 0% from top 10% of their high school class, 4% from top quarter, 10% from top half. 2% from out-of-state. Retention: 0% of full-time freshmen returned the following year.

Entrance Requirements: Required: essay, high school transcript, interview. Required for some: recommendations. Entrance: noncompetitive.

Costs Per Year: Application fee: $150. Tuition: $18,911 full-time, $392 per credit part-time. Mandatory fees: $1200 full-time.

■ **THE ART INSTITUTE OF CALIFORNIA-LOS ANGELES** *Q-3*
2900 31st St.
Santa Monica, CA 90405-3035
Tel: (310)752-4700; 888-646-4610
Fax: (310)752-4708
E-mail: ailaadm@aii.edu
Web Site: http://www.aicala.artinstitutes.edu/
Description: Proprietary, 4-year, coed. Part of Education Management Corporation. Awards associate and bachelor's degrees. Total enrollment: 2,102. Student-undergrad faculty ratio is 20:1. 889 applied, 77% were admitted. 0% from top 10% of their high school class, 0% from top quarter, 0% from top half. Full-time: 2,102 students, 33% women, 67% men. Students come from 51 states and territories, 22 other countries, 0% from out-of-state, 1% Native American, 20% Hispanic, 6% black, 10% Asian American or Pacific Islander, 3% international, 15% 25 or older, 15% live on campus. Academic areas with the most degrees conferred: visual and performing arts; personal and culinary services. Core. Academic remediation for entering students, services for LD students, advanced placement, distance learning, adult/continuing education programs, internships.

Entrance Requirements: Open admission. Options: Common Application, electronic application, deferred admission, international baccalaureate accepted. Required: essay, high school transcript, interview. Required for some: recommendations, artwork. Application deadline: Rolling. Notification: continuous.

Costs Per Year: Application fee: $50. Tuition: $19,824 full-time. College room only: $7920.

Collegiate Environment: Orientation program. Student services: personal-psychological counseling. 300 college housing spaces available; 275 were occupied in 2003-04. The Library with 20,000 books, 300 serials, 500 audiovisual materials, an OPAC, and a Web page. 400 computers available on campus for general student use. A campuswide network can be accessed. Staffed computer lab on campus.

■ **THE ART INSTITUTE OF CALIFORNIA-ORANGE COUNTY** *T-10*
3601 West Sunflower Ave.
Santa Ana, CA 92704-9888

Tel: (714)830-0200; 888-549-3055
E-mail: vdavid@aii.edu
Web Site: http://www.aicaoc.artinstitutes.edu/
Description: Proprietary, 4-year, coed. Part of Education Management Corporation. Awards associate and bachelor's degrees. Founded 2000. Setting: urban campus with easy access to Orange County, Los Angeles. Total enrollment: 1,757. Student-undergrad faculty ratio is 20:1. 1,756 applied, 68% were admitted. Full-time: 1,485 students, 39% women, 61% men. Part-time: 272 students, 36% women, 64% men. Students come from 17 states and territories, 1% Native American, 15% Hispanic, 2% black, 10% Asian American or Pacific Islander, 0% international, 28% 25 or older, 9% live on campus. Core. Academic remediation for entering students, services for LD students, advanced placement, independent study, distance learning, co-op programs and internships. Study abroad program.

Entrance Requirements: Options: electronic application, early admission, early decision, deferred admission. Required: essay, high school transcript, minimum 2.0 high school GPA, interview. Recommended: recommendations, SAT and SAT Subject Tests or ACT. Required for some: recommendations, portfolio. Application deadline: Rolling. Notification: continuous.

Costs Per Year: Tuition: $403 per quarter hour part-time. Mandatory fees: $15 per quarter hour part-time. College room only: $9800. Tuition guaranteed not to increase for student's term of enrollment.

Collegiate Environment: Orientation program. Student-run newspaper. Social organizations: 9 open to all. Most popular organizations: Pastry Club, GDSA (Game Developers Student Association), Women in Animation, Classic Game Club, AIGA (American Institute of Graphic Arts). Major annual events: Up All Night, Welcome Week, Stress Relief Week. Student services: personal-psychological counseling. 155 undergraduates lived in college housing during 2003-04. Freshmen guaranteed college housing. Option: coed housing available. 312 computers available on campus for general student use. A campuswide network can be accessed from off-campus. Staffed computer lab on campus.

■ **THE ART INSTITUTE OF CALIFORNIA-SAN DIEGO** *W-12*
10025 Mesa Rim Rd.
San Diego, CA 92121
Tel: (858)546-0602
Admissions: (858)598-1399
Web Site: http://www.aica.artinstitutes.edu/
Description: Proprietary, 4-year, coed. Part of Education Management Corporation. Awards associate and bachelor's degrees. Founded 1981. Setting: urban campus. Total enrollment: 1,912. Student-undergrad faculty ratio is 22:1. Students come from 23 states and territories, 36% from out-of-state, 1% Native American, 22% Hispanic, 5% black, 12% Asian American or Pacific Islander, 1% international, 30% 25 or older, 12% live on campus. Retention: 85% of full-time freshmen returned the following year. Academic areas with the most degrees conferred: visual and performing arts; business/marketing. Core. Services for LD students, double major, summer session for credit, co-op programs and internships.

Entrance Requirements: Options: Peterson's Universal Application, Common Application, electronic application, early admission, deferred admission. Required: essay, high school transcript, interview. Recommended: minimum 2.0 high school GPA. Required for some: recommendations. Entrance: minimally difficult. Application deadline: Rolling. Notification: continuous.

Costs Per Year: Application fee: $50. Tuition: $19,344 full-time, $403 per credit part-time. Mandatory fees: $784 full-time. Full-time tuition and fees vary according to program. College room only: $9480.

Collegiate Environment: Orientation program. Student-run newspaper. Social organizations: 2 open to all. Most popular organizations: Advertising Club-AAF, Communicating Art Club, 3-D Club, ASB, AIGA. Major annual events: Bestival, Spring Social, Fall Open House. Student services: personal-psychological counseling. Campus security: 24-hour emergency response devices. 230 college housing spaces available; 200 were occupied in 2003-04. Freshmen given priority for college housing. Options: men-only, women-only housing available. The Art Institute of California Library plus 1 other with 7,197 books, 108 serials, 500 audiovisual materials, and a Web page. 300 computers available on campus for general student use. A campuswide network can be accessed. Staffed computer lab on campus.

■ **THE ART INSTITUTE OF CALIFORNIA-SAN FRANCISCO** *K-4*
1170 Market St.
San Francisco, CA 94102-4908
Tel: (415)865-0198; 888-493-3261
Fax: (415)863-6344

Web Site: http://www.aicasf.artinstitutes.edu/

Description: Proprietary, 4-year, coed. Part of Education Management Corporation. Awards associate and bachelor's degrees. Founded 1939. Setting: urban campus. Total enrollment: 1,347. Core. Services for LD students, accelerated degree program, distance learning, summer session for credit, part-time degree program, internships. Off campus study.

Entrance Requirements: Options: Common Application, electronic application, deferred admission. Required: essay, high school transcript. Recommended: minimum 2.0 high school GPA, 2 recommendations, interview. Entrance: moderately difficult. Application deadline: Rolling.

Collegiate Environment: Orientation program. Student-run newspaper. Social organizations: 5 open to all. Most popular organizations: Animation club, Game Art and Design Club, Fashion Salon, Society of Web Architects and Programmers, Student Federation. Major annual event: Annual Fashion Show. Campus security: 24-hour emergency response devices. Learning Resource Center plus 1 other with a Web page.

■ **AVIATION & ELECTRONIC SCHOOLS OF AMERICA** *H-7*
210 South Railroad St.
PO Box 1810
Colfax, CA 95713-1810
Tel: (530)346-6792
Free: 800-345-2742
Fax: (530)346-8466
Web Site: http://www.aesa.com/
Description: Proprietary, 2-year, coed. Founded 1988. Calendar: continuous.

■ **AZUSA PACIFIC UNIVERSITY** *U-7*
901 East Alosta Ave., PO Box 7000
Azusa, CA 91702-7000
Tel: (626)969-3434
Free: 800-TALK-APU
Admissions: (626)812-3016
E-mail: admissions@apu.edu
Web Site: http://www.apu.edu/
Description: Independent nondenominational, comprehensive, coed. Awards bachelor's, master's, doctoral, and first professional degrees. Founded 1899. Setting: 60-acre small town campus with easy access to Los Angeles. Endowment: $26.8 million. Total enrollment: 8,162. Faculty: 356 (344 full-time, 12 part-time). Student-undergrad faculty ratio is 15:1. 2,824 applied, 73% were admitted. 29% from top 10% of their high school class, 60% from top quarter, 86% from top half. Full-time: 3,770 students, 65% women, 35% men. Part-time: 671 students, 70% women, 30% men. Students come from 44 states and territories, 52 other countries, 21% from out-of-state, 0.3% Native American, 12% Hispanic, 3% black, 5% Asian American or Pacific Islander, 2% international, 16% 25 or older, 69% live on campus, 10% transferred in. Retention: 83% of full-time freshmen returned the following year. Core. Calendar: semesters. Academic remediation for entering students, ESL program, services for LD students, advanced placement, accelerated degree program, freshman honors college, honors program, independent study, distance learning, double major, summer session for credit, part-time degree program, adult/continuing education programs, co-op programs and internships, graduate courses open to undergrads. Off campus study. Study abroad program. ROTC: Army (c).

Entrance Requirements: Options: Peterson's Universal Application, early admission, early action, deferred admission. Required: essay, high school transcript, minimum 2.8 high school GPA, 2 recommendations, SAT or ACT. Required for some: interview. Entrance: moderately difficult. Application deadlines: 6/1, 12/1 for early action. Notification: continuous, 1/15 for early action.

Costs Per Year: Application fee: $45. Comprehensive fee: $28,526 includes full-time tuition ($21,500), mandatory fees ($660), and college room and board ($6366). College room only: $3510. Full-time tuition and fees vary according to course load. Room and board charges vary according to board plan, housing facility, and student level. Part-time tuition: $900 per unit. Part-time tuition varies according to course load.

Collegiate Environment: Orientation program. Drama-theater group, choral group, marching band, student-run newspaper. Social organizations: 32 open to all. Most popular organizations: community service groups, choir, outreach ministries groups, Habitat for Humanity, Multi-Ethnic Student Alliance (MESA). Major annual events: Mega Weekend (Homecoming/dinner rally), Mexicali Outreach, Night of Champions. Student services: health clinic, personal-psychological counseling. Campus security: 24-hour

emergency response devices and patrols, student patrols, late night transport-escort service, controlled dormitory access. 2,807 college housing spaces available; 2,322 were occupied in 2003-04. Freshmen given priority for college housing. Options: coed, men-only, women-only housing available. Marshburn Memorial Library plus 2 others with 185,708 books, 691,829 microform titles, 14,031 serials, 17,706 audiovisual materials, an OPAC, and a Web page. 300 computers available on campus for general student use. Computer purchase/lease plans available. A campuswide network can be accessed from off-campus. Staffed computer lab on campus.

Community Environment: Azusa is in a suburban area 26 miles east of Los Angeles with a temperate climate. Bus, air, and rail services are nearby. The city has a public library, churches of major denominations, hospitals, and clinics within a 10-mile radius. Mountains and beaches are within easy driving distance and Azusa is close to the cultural and recreational advantages of Los Angeles County.

■ **BAKERSFIELD COLLEGE** *P-8*
1801 Panorama Dr.
Bakersfield, CA 93305-1299
Tel: (661)395-4011
Admissions: (661)395-4301
Fax: (661)395-4230
E-mail: svaughn@bc.cc.ca.us
Web Site: http://www.bakersfieldcollege.edu/
Description: State and locally supported, 2-year, coed. Part of California Community College System. Awards transfer associate and terminal associate degrees. Founded 1913. Setting: 175-acre urban campus. Total enrollment: 15,001. 50% 25 or older. Core. Calendar: semesters. Academic remediation for entering students, ESL program, services for LD students, advanced placement, accelerated degree program, summer session for credit, part-time degree program, adult/continuing education programs, co-op programs and internships.

Entrance Requirements: Open admission except for registered nursing, radiological technology programs. Entrance: noncompetitive. Application deadline: Rolling. Preference given to district residents for nursing, radiological technology programs.

Collegiate Environment: Orientation program. Drama-theater group, choral group, student-run newspaper, radio station. Student services: health clinic, women's center. Campus security: 24-hour patrols, late night transport-escort service. College housing not available. Grace Van Dyke Bird Library with 93,500 books, 298 serials, an OPAC, and a Web page. 650 computers available on campus for general student use. A campuswide network can be accessed. Staffed computer lab on campus.

Community Environment: See California State University Bakersfield.

■ **BARSTOW COLLEGE** *Q-12*
2700 Barstow Rd.
Barstow, CA 92311-6699
Tel: (760)252-2411
Fax: (760)252-1875
Web Site: http://www.barstow.edu/
Description: State and locally supported, 2-year, coed. Part of California Community College System. Awards transfer associate and terminal associate degrees. Founded 1959. Setting: 50-acre small town campus. Total enrollment: 3,000. Students come from 43 states and territories, 8 other countries, 60% 25 or older. Core. Calendar: semesters. Academic remediation for entering students, ESL program, services for LD students, self-designed majors, summer session for credit, part-time degree program, external degree program, adult/continuing education programs, co-op programs.

Entrance Requirements: Open admission except for allied health programs. Options: Common Application, early admission, deferred admission. Recommended: high school transcript. Placement: assessment test approved by the Chancellor's office required. Entrance: noncompetitive. Application deadline: Rolling.

Collegiate Environment: Drama-theater group, student-run newspaper. Student services: personal-psychological counseling. Campus security: evening security personnel. College housing not available. Thomas Kimball Library with 38,000 books, 110 serials, an OPAC, and a Web page. 85 computers available on campus for general student use. A campuswide network can be accessed. Staffed computer lab on campus.

Community Environment: This is a desert community with a dry, warm climate. The Santa Fe and Union Pacific Railroads meet here. Greyhound and Orange Belt bus service is also available. The city has a county library, hospital, many churches, including numerous Protestant Churches, an Episcopal Church, a Roman Catholic Church, a Jewish Synagogue. There is a Community Players Association, which presents locally produced programs. Lectures and concerts are presented throughout the year. Part-time employment is available. Barstow has 4 parks and swimming pools for recreation. There are 82 civic, fraternal, and veterans organizations.

■ **BERKELEY CITY COLLEGE** *J-4*
2050 Center St.
Berkeley, CA 94704-5102
Tel: (510)981-2800
Admissions: (510)466-7363
Fax: (510)841-7333
E-mail: hperdue@peralta.edu
Web Site: http://www.peralta.cc.ca.us/
Description: State and locally supported, 2-year, coed. Awards certificates, transfer associate, and terminal associate degrees. Founded 1974. Setting: urban campus with easy access to San Francisco. Research spending for 2004 fiscal year: $23,297. Educational spending for 2005 fiscal year: $485 per student. Total enrollment: 4,500. Student-undergrad faculty ratio is 25:1. 1% from out-of-state, 1% Native American, 11% Hispanic, 23% black, 12% Asian American or Pacific Islander, 5% international, 65% 25 or older. Core. Calendar: semesters. Academic remediation for entering students, ESL program, services for LD students, self-designed majors, independent study, summer session for credit, part-time degree program, adult/continuing education programs, internships. Off campus study at members of the Downtown Oakland Business Education Consortium; University of California, Berkeley. Study abroad program.
Entrance Requirements: Open admission. Options: Common Application, electronic application, early admission, deferred admission. Recommended: high school transcript. Entrance: noncompetitive. Application deadline: Rolling. Notification: continuous. Preference given to state residents.
Costs Per Year: Application fee: $0. Nonresident tuition: $172 per unit part-time. Mandatory fees: $26 per unit part-time.
Collegiate Environment: Orientation program. Drama-theater group, student-run newspaper. Student services: personal-psychological counseling. College housing not available. Vista Community College Library with a Web page. 50 computers available on campus for general student use. A campuswide network can be accessed. Staffed computer lab on campus.

■ **BETHANY UNIVERSITY** *B-10*
800 Bethany Dr.
Scotts Valley, CA 95066-2820
Tel: (831)438-3800
Free: 800-843-9410
Fax: (831)438-4517
E-mail: info@bethany.edu
Web Site: http://www.bethany.edu/
Description: Independent Assemblies of God, comprehensive, coed. Awards associate, bachelor's, and master's degrees. Founded 1919. Setting: 40-acre small town campus with easy access to San Francisco and San Jose. Endowment: $1.2 million. Research spending for 2004 fiscal year: $60,000. Total enrollment: 549. Faculty: 72 (27 full-time, 45 part-time). Student-undergrad faculty ratio is 11:1. 245 applied, 56% were admitted. 7% from top 10% of their high school class, 36% from top quarter, 69% from top half. Full-time: 391 students, 56% women, 44% men. Part-time: 78 students, 73% women, 27% men. Students come from 21 states and territories, 14% from out-of-state, 0.4% Native American, 14% Hispanic, 5% black, 4% Asian American or Pacific Islander, 2% international, 48% 25 or older, 80% live on campus, 23% transferred in. Retention: 65% of full-time freshmen returned the following year. Core. Calendar: semesters. Academic remediation for entering students, services for LD students, advanced placement, accelerated degree program, independent study, distance learning, summer session for credit, part-time degree program, external degree program, adult/continuing education programs, internships, graduate courses open to undergrads.
Entrance Requirements: Options: early admission, deferred admission. Required: essay, high school transcript, minimum 2.0 high school GPA, 2 recommendations, Christian commitment, SAT or ACT. Entrance: minimally difficult. Application deadline: 7/1. Notification: continuous until 7/31. Preference given to members of Assemblies of God and other evangelical churches.
Costs Per Year: Application fee: $35. One-time mandatory fee: $135. Comprehensive fee: $22,765 includes full-time tuition ($15,500), mandatory

fees ($765), and college room and board ($6500). College room only: $3300. Part-time tuition: $650 per unit. Part-time mandatory fees: $245 per term.
Collegiate Environment: Orientation program. Drama-theater group, choral group, student-run newspaper. Social organizations: 25 open to all. Major annual events: homecoming, New Student Orientation, Open Dorms. Student services: personal-psychological counseling. Campus security: 24-hour emergency response devices, student patrols, controlled dormitory access. 375 college housing spaces available; 350 were occupied in 2003-04. On-campus residence required through junior year. Wilson Library with 59,453 books and 858 serials. 17 computers available on campus for general student use. A campuswide network can be accessed from off-campus. Staffed computer lab on campus.

■ **BETHESDA CHRISTIAN UNIVERSITY** *T-10*
730 North Euclid St.
Anaheim, CA 92801
Tel: (714)517-1945
Fax: (714)517-1948
E-mail: admission@bcu.edu
Web Site: http://www.bcu.edu/
Description: Independent, comprehensive, coed, affiliated with Full Gospel World Mission. Awards bachelor's, master's, and first professional degrees. Founded 1978. Setting: suburban campus with easy access to Los Angeles. Endowment: $7 million. Educational spending for 2005 fiscal year: $2268 per student. Total enrollment: 206. Full-time: 129 students, 47% women, 53% men. Part-time: 35 students, 80% women, 20% men. Students come from 3 states and territories, 3 other countries, 0.01% from out-of-state, 0% Native American, 0% Hispanic, 0% black, 30% Asian American or Pacific Islander, 70% international, 70% 25 or older, 0% live on campus, 13% transferred in. Retention: 36% of full-time freshmen returned the following year. Core. Calendar: semesters. ESL program, accelerated degree program, independent study, double major, summer session for credit, part-time degree program, adult/continuing education programs, internships. Study abroad program.
Entrance Requirements: Open admission. Options: Common Application, early admission, international baccalaureate accepted. Required: essay, high school transcript, minimum 2.0 high school GPA, 2 recommendations, interview, 2 photographs. Entrance: minimally difficult. Application deadline: 8/11. Notification: continuous until 8/25.
Costs Per Year: Application fee: $35. Tuition: $6300 full-time. Mandatory fees: $120 full-time.
Collegiate Environment: Orientation program. Social organizations: 1 open to all. Most popular organizations: Student Council, Ping Pong Team. Major annual events: Homecoming Day, Orientation for new students, Athletic Meeting. Student services: personal-psychological counseling. Campus security: student patrols, late night transport-escort service, 24-hour security monitor. Library plus 1 other with 27,763 books, 99 serials, and 3,042 audiovisual materials. Operations spending for 2004 fiscal year: $74,000. 30 computers available on campus for general student use. Staffed computer lab on campus.

■ **BIOLA UNIVERSITY** *Y-6*
13800 Biola Ave.
La Mirada, CA 90639-0001
Tel: (562)903-6000
Free: 800-652-4652
Admissions: (562)903-4752
Fax: (562)903-4709
E-mail: admissions@biola.edu
Web Site: http://www.biola.edu/
Description: Independent interdenominational, university, coed. Awards bachelor's, master's, doctoral, and first professional degrees. Founded 1908. Setting: 95-acre suburban campus with easy access to Los Angeles. Endowment: $37.5 million. Educational spending for 2005 fiscal year: $29,372 per student. Total enrollment: 5,455. Faculty: 395 (191 full-time, 204 part-time). Student-undergrad faculty ratio is 16:1. 2,077 applied, 82% were admitted. 36% from top 10% of their high school class, 69% from top quarter, 91% from top half. Full-time: 3,138 students, 62% women, 38% men. Part-time: 108 students, 47% women, 53% men. Students come from 47 states and territories, 40 other countries, 25% from out-of-state, 1% Native American, 10% Hispanic, 2% black, 9% Asian American or Pacific Islander, 3% international, 19% 25 or older, 65% live on campus, 7% transferred in. Retention: 83% of full-time freshmen returned the following year. Academic

areas with the most degrees conferred: physical sciences; business/ marketing; psychology. Core. Calendar: 4-1-4. Academic remediation for entering students, ESL program, services for LD students, advanced placement, accelerated degree program, freshman honors college, honors program, independent study, double major, summer session for credit, part-time degree program, adult/continuing education programs, co-op programs and internships, graduate courses open to undergrads. Off campus study at Council for Christian Colleges and Universities. Study abroad program. ROTC: Army (c), Air Force (c).

Entrance Requirements: Options: Peterson's Universal Application, Common Application, electronic application, early admission, early action, deferred admission, international baccalaureate accepted. Required: essay, high school transcript, 2 recommendations, SAT or ACT. Recommended: minimum 3.0 high school GPA, interview. Required for some: interview. Entrance: moderately difficult. Application deadlines: 3/1, 12/1 for early action. Notification: 4/1, 1/15 for early action.

Costs Per Year: Application fee: $45. Comprehensive fee: $30,998 includes full-time tuition ($23,782), mandatory fees ($100), and college room and board ($7116). College room only: $3756. Part-time tuition: $942 per unit.

Collegiate Environment: Orientation program. Drama-theater group, choral group, student-run newspaper, radio station. Social organizations: 33 open to all. Most popular organizations: Korean Student Association, Brothers and Sisters in Christ, Accounting Society, Maharlika (Filipino Club), SOUL (Seeking Out Unity and Love). Major annual events: BAB Week (Betty Asks Bob), Celebrate the Son, Missions Conference. Student services: legal services, health clinic, personal-psychological counseling. Campus security: 24-hour emergency response devices and patrols, student patrols, late night transport-escort service, controlled dormitory access, access gates to roads through the middle of campus. 2,285 college housing spaces available; 2,140 were occupied in 2003-04. Freshmen guaranteed college housing. On-campus residence required through sophomore year. Options: men-only, women-only housing available. The Biola University Library with 279,560 books, 570,437 microform titles, 13,123 serials, 15,350 audiovisual materials, an OPAC, and a Web page. Operations spending for 2004 fiscal year: $1.6 million. 165 computers available on campus for general student use. Computer purchase/lease plans available. A campuswide network can be accessed from student residence rooms and from off campus. Staffed computer lab on campus.

Community Environment: Population 50,000. La Mirada is a suburban area less than one hour from the Los Angeles International Airport. The Santa Fe Railroad and buses serve the area as does the Santa Ana Freeway. There are libraries, churches, and a hospital. Part-time employment is available. The beaches are 20 miles away and the mountains are an hour and half drive with Knott's Berry Farm and Disneyland a few minutes from campus.

■ **BROOKS COLLEGE (LONG BEACH)** *T-10*
4825 East Pacific Coast Hwy.
Long Beach, CA 90804-3291
Tel: (562)498-2441
Free: 800-421-3775
Fax: (562)597-7412
Web Site: http://www.brookscollege.edu/
Description: Proprietary, 2-year, coed. Awards diplomas and terminal associate degrees. Founded 1971. Setting: 7-acre suburban campus with easy access to Los Angeles. Total enrollment: 826. 10% from top 10% of their high school class, 30% from top quarter, 80% from top half. Full-time: 757 students, 66% women, 34% men. Part-time: 69 students, 64% women, 36% men. Students come from 17 other countries, 39% from out-of-state, 0.5% Native American, 18% Hispanic, 6% black, 5% Asian American or Pacific Islander, 0% international, 3% 25 or older, 60% live on campus. Academic remediation for entering students, services for LD students, summer session for credit, co-op programs and internships.

Entrance Requirements: Options: Peterson's Universal Application, deferred admission. Required: essay, high school transcript, minimum 2.0 high school GPA, recommendations, interview. Recommended: portfolio. Entrance: moderately difficult. Application deadline: Rolling. Notification: continuous.

Collegiate Environment: Student services: personal-psychological counseling, free tutoring. Campus security: 24-hour emergency response devices and patrols, controlled dormitory access. 15,000 books and 80 serials. 50 computers available on campus for general student use. Staffed computer lab on campus.

Community Environment: See California State University Long Beach.

■ **BROOKS COLLEGE (SUNNYVALE)** *J-6*
1120 Kifer Rd.
Sunnyvale, CA 94086
Tel: (408)719-9209
Fax: (408)719-0722
Web Site: http://www.brookssv.com/
Description: Proprietary, 2-year, coed.

■ **BROOKS INSTITUTE OF PHOTOGRAPHY** *S-7*
801 Alston Rd.
Santa Barbara, CA 93108-2399
Tel: (805)966-3888; 888-304-3456
Fax: (805)564-1475
E-mail: admissions@brooks.edu
Web Site: http://www.brooks.edu/
Description: Proprietary, comprehensive, coed. Awards bachelor's and master's degrees. Founded 1945. Setting: 25-acre suburban campus. Total enrollment: 1,507. Full-time: 1,425 students, 48% women, 52% men. Students come from 27 states and territories, 22 other countries, 0.1% Native American, 3% Hispanic, 0.3% black, 3% Asian American or Pacific Islander, 2% international, 36% 25 or older, 4% transferred in. Retention: 97% of full-time freshmen returned the following year. Core. Calendar: trimesters. Services for LD students, advanced placement, accelerated degree program, adult/continuing education programs, internships. Off campus study at University of Pittsburgh (Semester at Sea). Study abroad program.

Entrance Requirements: Options: Peterson's Universal Application, deferred admission. Required: essay, high school transcript, minimum 3.0 high school GPA, 15 semester hours of college credit. Recommended: interview. Entrance: moderately difficult. Application deadline: Rolling. Notification: continuous.

Collegiate Environment: Major annual events: Annual Barbecue, All Student Show. Campus security: campus closed after 11:30 p.m. College housing not available. Brooks Institute of Photography Library with 6,500 books and 128 serials. 15 computers available on campus for general student use. Staffed computer lab on campus.

■ **BROWN MACKIE COLLEGE-ORANGE COUNTY** *T-10*
3601 West Sunflower Ave.
Santa Ana, CA 92704
; (866)505-0334
Web Site: http://www.brownmackie.edu/locations.asp?locid=15
Description: Proprietary, 2-year, coed.

■ **BRYMAN COLLEGE (CITY OF INDUSTRY)** *T-10*
12801 Crossroads Parkway South
City of Industry, CA 91746
Tel: (562)908-2500
Fax: (562)908-7656
Web Site: http://bryman-college.com/
Description: Proprietary, 2-year, coed. Founded 1969.

■ **BRYMAN COLLEGE (ONTARIO)** *Q-8*
1460 South Milliken Ave.
Ontario, CA 91761
Tel: (909)984-5027
Fax: (909)988-9339
Web Site: http://bryman-college.com/
Description: Proprietary, 2-year, coed.

■ **BUTTE COLLEGE** *G-6*
3536 Butte Campus Dr.
Oroville, CA 95965-8399
Tel: (530)895-2511
Admissions: (530)895-2366
Fax: (530)895-2345
Web Site: http://www.butte.edu/
Description: District-supported, 2-year, coed. Part of California Community College System. Awards certificates, transfer associate, and terminal associate degrees. Founded 1966. Setting: 900-acre rural campus. Total enrollment: 14,251. 1,102 applied, 100% were admitted. 5% from top 10% of their high school class, 60% from top half. Students come from 19 states and territories, 25 other countries, 2% Native American, 11% Hispanic, 2% black, 5% Asian American or Pacific Islander, 1% international, 53% 25 or older.

Core. Calendar: semesters. Academic remediation for entering students, ESL program, services for LD students, advanced placement, accelerated degree program, honors program, summer session for credit, part-time degree program, adult/continuing education programs, co-op programs and internships. Study abroad program.

Entrance Requirements: Open admission except for allied health, criminal justice, fire science programs. Options: early admission, deferred admission. Required for some: high school transcript. Entrance: noncompetitive. Application deadline: Rolling.

Collegiate Environment: Drama-theater group, student-run newspaper. Student services: legal services, health clinic, personal-psychological counseling. Campus security: 24-hour emergency response devices and patrols, student patrols. College housing not available. 50,000 books, 300 serials, and an OPAC. 65 computers available on campus for general student use. A campuswide network can be accessed from off-campus. Staffed computer lab on campus.

Community Environment: Butte College is located in the geographical center of Butte County, population 121,400, at the edge of the Sierra Foothills. The county's amenities include a clean environment, moderate climate, ready access to necessities and luxuries and proximity to recreational areas, including the huge Lake Oroville.

■ **CABRILLO COLLEGE** *C-11*
6500 Soquel Dr.
Aptos, CA 95003-3194
Tel: (831)479-6100
Admissions: (831)479-6201
Fax: (831)479-6425
Web Site: http://www.cabrillo.edu/
Description: District-supported, 2-year, coed. Part of California Community College System. Awards certificates, transfer associate, and terminal associate degrees. Founded 1959. Setting: 120-acre small town campus with easy access to San Jose. Educational spending for 2005 fiscal year: $2511 per student. Total enrollment: 13,905. Students come from 21 states and territories, 63 other countries, 3% from out-of-state, 1% Native American, 23% Hispanic, 2% black, 5% Asian American or Pacific Islander, 2% international, 50% 25 or older. Core. Calendar: semesters. Academic remediation for entering students, ESL program, services for LD students, advanced placement, honors program, independent study, distance learning, double major, summer session for credit, part-time degree program, adult/continuing education programs, co-op programs and internships. Study abroad program.

Entrance Requirements: Open admission except for international applicants. Option: early admission. Required for some: high school transcript. Entrance: noncompetitive. Application deadline: Rolling.

Collegiate Environment: Drama-theater group, student-run newspaper. Student services: health clinic, personal-psychological counseling, women's center. College housing not available. 60,000 books, 300 serials, an OPAC, and a Web page. Operations spending for 2004 fiscal year: $1.2 million. 500 computers available on campus for general student use. A campuswide network can be accessed. Staffed computer lab on campus.

Community Environment: Aptos is a suburban area nine miles from Santa Cruz, with a temperate climate. There is a municipal library, churches of major denominations within a ten mile area, and 2 hospitals in the county. Excellent water sports area for swimming, surfing and deep sea fishing. Fine shopping facilities are available. The University of California at Santa Cruz is nearby.

■ **CALIFORNIA BAPTIST UNIVERSITY** *T-11*
8432 Magnolia Ave.
Riverside, CA 92504-3206
Tel: (909)689-5771; 877-228-8866
Admissions: (951)343-5037
Fax: (909)351-1808
E-mail: admissions@calbaptist.edu
Web Site: http://www.calbaptist.edu/
Description: Independent Southern Baptist, comprehensive, coed. Awards bachelor's and master's degrees. Founded 1950. Setting: 82-acre suburban campus with easy access to Los Angeles. Endowment: $8 million. Educational spending for 2005 fiscal year: $5042 per student. Total enrollment: 3,105. Faculty: 226 (96 full-time, 130 part-time). Student-undergrad faculty ratio is 16:1. 1,072 applied, 71% were admitted. 12% from top 10% of their high school class, 42% from top quarter, 44% from top half. Full-time: 1,976 students, 65% women, 35% men. Part-time: 439 students, 65%

women, 35% men. Students come from 31 states and territories, 15 other countries, 5% from out-of-state, 1% Native American, 17% Hispanic, 9% black, 2% Asian American or Pacific Islander, 1% international, 27% 25 or older, 57% live on campus, 8% transferred in. Retention: 86% of full-time freshmen returned the following year. Academic areas with the most degrees conferred: liberal arts/general studies; psychology; business/marketing. Core. Calendar: 2-4-4-2. ESL program, advanced placement, accelerated degree program, honors program, independent study, distance learning, double major, summer session for credit, part-time degree program, adult/continuing education programs, internships, graduate courses open to undergrads. Off campus study at Council for Christian Colleges and Universities. Study abroad program. ROTC: Army (c), Air Force (c).

Entrance Requirements: Options: Peterson's Universal Application, Common Application, early admission, early action, deferred admission, international baccalaureate accepted. Required: essay, high school transcript, minimum 2.5 high school GPA, 2 recommendations, SAT or ACT. Recommended: interview. Entrance: minimally difficult. Application deadlines: Rolling, Rolling for nonresidents, 11/19 for early action. Notification: continuous until 9/6, continuous until 9/6 for nonresidents, 12/20 for early action.

Costs Per Year: Application fee: $45. Comprehensive fee: $23,780 includes full-time tuition ($16,250), mandatory fees ($1220), and college room and board ($6310). College room only: $2640. Full-time tuition and fees vary according to class time and program. Room and board charges vary according to board plan and housing facility. Part-time tuition: $625 per semester hour. Part-time tuition varies according to class time and program.

Collegiate Environment: Orientation program. Drama-theater group, choral group, student-run newspaper. Social organizations: 16 open to all. Most popular organizations: Student Senate, Fellowship of Christian Athletes, Blue Crew, Christian student organizations, Community Life Committees. Major annual events: Campus Day, Octoberfest, Yule Christmas Celebration. Student services: personal-psychological counseling. Campus security: 24-hour emergency response devices and patrols, student patrols, late night transport-escort service, controlled dormitory access. 1,035 college housing spaces available; 872 were occupied in 2003-04. Freshmen given priority for college housing. Options: men-only, women-only housing available. Annie Gabriel Library with 100,230 books, 50,949 microform titles, 349 serials, 4,992 audiovisual materials, an OPAC, and a Web page. Operations spending for 2004 fiscal year: $664,968. 154 computers available on campus for general student use. A campuswide network can be accessed from student residence rooms and from off campus. Staffed computer lab on campus.

Community Environment: See University of California Riverside.

■ **CALIFORNIA CHRISTIAN COLLEGE** *M-9*
4881 East University Ave.
Fresno, CA 93703-3533
Tel: (559)251-4215
Web Site: http://www.calchristiancollege.org/
Description: Independent religious, 4-year, coed. Awards associate and bachelor's degrees. Setting: 5-acre urban campus with easy access to Fresno. Endowment: $60,000. Educational spending for 2005 fiscal year: $1700 per student. Total enrollment: 52. 5 applied, 100% were admitted. Full-time: 45 students, 29% women, 71% men. Part-time: 7 students, 43% women, 57% men. Students come from 4 states and territories, 2 other countries, 4% from out-of-state, 2% Native American, 13% Hispanic, 15% black, 0% Asian American or Pacific Islander, 4% international, 62% 25 or older, 21% live on campus, 17% transferred in. Retention: 22% of full-time freshmen returned the following year. Core. Calendar: semesters. Academic remediation for entering students, accelerated degree program, independent study, summer session for credit, part-time degree program, co-op programs.

Entrance Requirements: Open admission. Option: international baccalaureate accepted. Required: essay, high school transcript, minimum 2.0 high school GPA, 3 recommendations, statement of faith, moral/ethical statement, standardized Bible content tests. Recommended: interview, SAT or ACT. Entrance: noncompetitive. Application deadline: Rolling. Notification: continuous.

Collegiate Environment: Orientation program. Drama-theater group, choral group, student-run newspaper. Major annual events: Hospitality Days, CCC Banquet, Missions Conference. Student services: personal-psychological counseling. 60 college housing spaces available; 11 were occupied in 2003-04. No special consideration for freshman housing applicants. On-campus residence required through sophomore year. Option: coed housing available. Cortese Library with 13,154 books, 7 serials, and 430 audiovisual materials.

Operations spending for 2004 fiscal year: $8700. 6 computers available on campus for general student use. Staffed computer lab on campus.

■ **CALIFORNIA COAST UNIVERSITY** *T-10*
700 North Main St.
Santa Ana, CA 92701
Tel: (714)547-9625; 888-CCU-UNIV
Web Site: http://www.calcoast.edu/
Description: Proprietary, comprehensive, coed. Awards associate, bachelor's, and master's degrees (distance learning only). Founded 1973.
Costs Per Year: Tuition: $85 per unit part-time.

■ **CALIFORNIA COLLEGE OF THE ARTS** *K-4*
1111 Eighth St.
San Francisco, CA 94107
Tel: (415)703-9500
Free: 800-447-1ART
Admissions: (415)703-9523
Fax: (415)703-9539
E-mail: enroll@cca.edu
Web Site: http://www.cca.edu/
Description: Independent, comprehensive, coed. Awards bachelor's and master's degrees. Founded 1907. Setting: 4-acre urban campus. Endowment: $18.2 million. Educational spending for 2005 fiscal year: $9486 per student. Total enrollment: 1,616. Faculty: 370 (42 full-time, 328 part-time). Student-undergrad faculty ratio is 14:1. 785 applied, 78% were admitted. 9% from top 10% of their high school class, 36% from top quarter, 86% from top half. Full-time: 1,227 students, 59% women, 41% men. Part-time: 85 students, 56% women, 44% men. Students come from 39 states and territories, 26 other countries, 35% from out-of-state, 1% Native American, 9% Hispanic, 2% black, 12% Asian American or Pacific Islander, 7% international, 69% 25 or older, 12% live on campus, 19% transferred in. Retention: 79% of full-time freshmen returned the following year. Core. Calendar: semesters. Academic remediation for entering students, services for LD students, advanced placement, self-designed majors, independent study, double major, summer session for credit, internships. Off campus study at Mills College, Holy Names College, AICAD Mobility Program, University of San Francisco. Study abroad program.
Entrance Requirements: Options: Peterson's Universal Application, Common Application, electronic application, deferred admission, international baccalaureate accepted. Required: essay, high school transcript, minimum 2.0 high school GPA, 2 recommendations, portfolio. Recommended: SAT or ACT. Required for some: interview. Entrance: moderately difficult. Application deadline: 2/1. Notification: continuous.
Costs Per Year: Application fee: $50. Comprehensive fee: $34,530 includes full-time tuition ($25,810), mandatory fees ($290), and college room and board ($8430). Full-time tuition and fees vary according to course load. Room and board charges vary according to housing facility. Part-time tuition: $1075 per unit. Part-time tuition varies according to course load.
Collegiate Environment: Orientation program. Social organizations: 11 open to all. Most popular organizations: American Institute of Architecture Student Chapter, American Institute of Graphic Arts Student Chapter, Women's Caucus for the Arts, International Student Club, Artists that are Queer. Major annual events: Winter and Spring Fairs, Founders' Day, All-College Honors. Student services: personal-psychological counseling. Campus security: 24-hour emergency response devices and patrols, late night transport-escort service. 231 college housing spaces available; 193 were occupied in 2003-04. Option: coed housing available. Meyer Library plus 1 other with 39,000 books, 50 microform titles, 340 serials, 520 audiovisual materials, an OPAC, and a Web page. Operations spending for 2004 fiscal year: $457,514. 180 computers available on campus for general student use. A campuswide network can be accessed from student residence rooms and from off campus. Staffed computer lab on campus.
Community Environment: See Laney College.

■ **CALIFORNIA CULINARY ACADEMY** *K-4*
625 Polk St.
San Francisco, CA 94102-3368
Tel: (415)771-3500
Free: 800-BAY-CHEF
Admissions: 800-229-2433
Fax: (415)771-2194
Web Site: http://www.baychef.com/

Description: Proprietary, 2-year, coed. Awards certificates and terminal associate degrees. Founded 1977. Setting: urban campus. Total enrollment: 822. Full-time: 822 students, 45% women, 55% men. Students come from 40 states and territories, 12 other countries, 30% from out-of-state, 1% Native American, 13% Hispanic, 7% black, 12% Asian American or Pacific Islander, 7% international, 62% 25 or older, 39% live on campus. Core. Calendar: continuous. Services for LD students, co-op programs.
Entrance Requirements: Options: Common Application, electronic application. Required: high school transcript, interview. Entrance: minimally difficult. Application deadline: Rolling. Notification: continuous.
Collegiate Environment: Orientation program. Social organizations: dining club. Most popular organization: Student Council. Major annual event: Career Fair. Campus security: 24-hour emergency response devices and patrols, controlled dormitory access. 246 college housing spaces available; all were occupied in 2003-04. Option: coed housing available. Academy Library plus 1 other with 3,000 books and 70 serials. 50 computers available on campus for general student use. Staffed computer lab on campus.

■ **CALIFORNIA DESIGN COLLEGE** *S-10*
3440 Wilshire Blvd., Tenth Floor
Los Angeles, CA 90010
Tel: (213)251-3636; 877-468-6232
Fax: (213)385-3545
Web Site: http://www.cdc.edu/
Description: Proprietary, 4-year, coed. Part of Education Management Corporation. Administratively affiliated with Education Management Corporation, The Art Institutes. Awards associate and bachelor's degrees. Founded 1992. Setting: urban campus. Educational spending for 2005 fiscal year: $22,191 per student. Total enrollment: 353. 214 applied, 99% were admitted. Full-time: 338 students, 86% women, 14% men. Part-time: 15 students, 100% women. Students come from 21 states and territories, 6 other countries, 8% from out-of-state, 1% Native American, 34% Hispanic, 13% black, 15% Asian American or Pacific Islander, 2% international, 24% 25 or older, 0.3% transferred in. Core. Academic remediation for entering students, advanced placement, distance learning, part-time degree program, adult/continuing education programs.
Entrance Requirements: Options: Common Application, electronic application, deferred admission. Required: essay, high school transcript, interview. Required for some: portfolio. Application deadline: Rolling. Notification: continuous.
Collegiate Environment: Orientation program. Campus security: 24-hour emergency response devices and patrols, late night transport-escort service. College housing not available. CDC Library with 3,200 books, 124 serials, 2,068 audiovisual materials, and a Web page. Operations spending for 2004 fiscal year: $102,991. 106 computers available on campus for general student use. A campuswide network can be accessed. Staffed computer lab on campus.

■ **CALIFORNIA INSTITUTE OF THE ARTS** *S-9*
24700 McBean Parkway
Valencia, CA 91355-2340
Tel: (661)255-1050
Free: 800-545-2787
E-mail: admiss@muse.calarts.edu
Web Site: http://www.calarts.edu/
Description: Independent, comprehensive, coed. Awards bachelor's and master's degrees. Founded 1961. Setting: 60-acre suburban campus with easy access to Los Angeles. Endowment: $81.8 million. Educational spending for 2005 fiscal year: $18,633 per student. Total enrollment: 1,327. Faculty: 287 (147 full-time, 140 part-time). Student-undergrad faculty ratio is 7:1. 2,975 applied, 31% were admitted. Full-time: 812 students, 44% women, 56% men. Part-time: 9 students, 33% women, 67% men. Students come from 46 states and territories, 34 other countries, 53% from out-of-state, 1% Native American, 12% Hispanic, 7% black, 10% Asian American or Pacific Islander, 8% international, 18% 25 or older, 40% live on campus, 5% transferred in. Retention: 78% of full-time freshmen returned the following year. Academic area with the most degrees conferred: visual and performing arts. Core. Calendar: semesters. Services for LD students, advanced placement, self-designed majors, independent study, co-op programs and internships, graduate courses open to undergrads. Study abroad program.
Entrance Requirements: Option: international baccalaureate accepted. Required: essay, high school transcript, 2 recommendations, portfolio or audition. Required for some: interview. Entrance: very difficult. Application deadline: 1/5. Notification: continuous.

Costs Per Year: Application fee: $65. Comprehensive fee: $35,422 includes full-time tuition ($27,260), mandatory fees ($465), and college room and board ($7697). College room only: $4095. Full-time tuition and fees vary according to course load. Room and board charges vary according to board plan, housing facility, and location.

Collegiate Environment: Orientation program. Drama-theater group, choral group, student-run radio station. Major annual events: President's Picnic, Halloween Party, Graduation. Student services: health clinic, personal-psychological counseling. Campus security: 24-hour emergency response devices and patrols, late night transport-escort service, controlled dormitory access. 350 college housing spaces available; 334 were occupied in 2003-04. Freshmen given priority for college housing. Option: coed housing available. California Institute of the Arts Library plus 1 other with 98,415 books, 5,712 microform titles, 324 serials, 25,487 audiovisual materials, an OPAC, and a Web page. Operations spending for 2004 fiscal year: $1.3 million. 40 computers available on campus for general student use. A campuswide network can be accessed from student residence rooms and from off campus. Staffed computer lab on campus.

Community Environment: Valencia is located on the Golden State Freeway (Interstate 5) 35 miles north of Los Angeles, and historically has been devoted to agriculture and cattle ranching. The area, encompassing the towns of Newhall, Saugus, Valencia and Castaic, is surrounded by the Tehachapi Mountains to the North, the San Gabriel to the east and the Santa Susana to the west. In the last 10 years light industry and numerous housing developments have contributed to the city's growth.

■ **CALIFORNIA INSTITUTE OF INTEGRAL STUDIES** *K-4*
1453 Mission St.
San Francisco, CA 94103
Tel: (415)575-6100
Admissions: (415)575-6156
Fax: (415)575-1264
E-mail: admissions@ciis.edu
Web Site: http://www.ciis.edu/

Description: Independent, upper-level, coed. Awards bachelor's, master's, and doctoral degrees. Founded 1968. Total enrollment: 1,005. Faculty: 61. Student-undergrad faculty ratio is 19:1. Core. Calendar: semesters. External degree program, adult/continuing education programs, graduate courses open to undergrads.

Costs Per Year: Application fee: $65. Tuition: $610 per unit part-time.

Collegiate Environment: Orientation program. Drama-theater group. Most popular organization: Student Alliance. The Laurance S. Rockefeller with 4,000 books.

Community Environment: See San Francisco State University.

■ **CALIFORNIA INSTITUTE OF TECHNOLOGY** *S-10*
1200 East California Blvd.
Pasadena, CA 91125-0001
Tel: (626)395-6811
Admissions: (626)395-6341
Fax: (626)683-3026
E-mail: ugadmissions@caltech.edu
Web Site: http://www.caltech.edu/

Description: Independent, university, coed. Awards bachelor's, master's, and doctoral degrees. Founded 1891. Setting: 124-acre suburban campus with easy access to Los Angeles. Endowment: $1.2 billion. Research spending for 2004 fiscal year: $179 million. Educational spending for 2005 fiscal year: $69,879 per student. Total enrollment: 2,172. 3,071 applied, 17% were admitted. 94% from top 10% of their high school class, 100% from top quarter. 56 National Merit Scholars, 76 valedictorians. Full-time: 891 students, 33% women, 67% men. Students come from 46 states and territories, 28 other countries, 59% from out-of-state, 1% Native American, 7% Hispanic, 1% black, 31% Asian American or Pacific Islander, 8% international, 1% 25 or older, 90% live on campus, 3% transferred in. Retention: 95% of full-time freshmen returned the following year. Core. Calendar: 3 ten-week terms. ESL program, services for LD students, self-designed majors, independent study, double major, internships, graduate courses open to undergrads. Off campus study at Occidental College, Scripps College, Art Center College of Design. Study abroad program. ROTC: Army (c), Air Force (c).

Entrance Requirements: Options: electronic application, early admission, early action, deferred admission. Required: essay, high school transcript, 2 recommendations, SAT or ACT, SAT Subject Test in Math Level II C and either physics, chemistry, or biology. Entrance: most difficult. Application deadlines: 1/1, 11/1 for early action. Notification: 4/1, 12/30 for early action.

Costs Per Year: Application fee: $50. Comprehensive fee: $36,123 includes full-time tuition ($27,309) and college room and board ($8814).

Collegiate Environment: Orientation program. Drama-theater group, choral group, student-run newspaper. Social organizations: 85 open to all. Most popular organizations: ASCIT, Entrepreneur's Club, instrumental music groups, Glee Club, Theater Arts. Major annual events: Ditch Day, International Day, Pre-Frosh Weekend. Student services: health clinic, personal-psychological counseling, women's center. Campus security: 24-hour emergency response devices and patrols, late night transport-escort service. 876 college housing spaces available; all were occupied in 2003-04. Freshmen guaranteed college housing. On-campus residence required in freshman year. Option: coed housing available. Millikan Library plus 10 others with 3.2 million books, 3,500 serials, an OPAC, and a Web page. Operations spending for 2004 fiscal year: $6.9 million. 600 computers available on campus for general student use. Computer purchase/lease plans available. A campuswide network can be accessed from student residence rooms and from off campus. Staffed computer lab on campus.

Community Environment: Population 135,000, Pasadena is located at the foot of the San Gabriel Mountains, the center of a large metropolitan area with ideal climate throughout the year. The famous Huntington Library, located in nearby San Marino, is open to the public and makes available its rich resources for scholarly research work in numerous fields. Pasadena has many cultural activities in the fields of art, music, and literature. The finest talent in America can be seen and heard in Pasadena and Los Angeles. Exhibits of famous artists and art instruction are provided by the community. The annual New Year's Day Tournament of Roses is held in the winter, and nearby is the Rose Bowl that seats 104,000 people.

■ **CALIFORNIA LUTHERAN UNIVERSITY** *P-1*
60 West Olsen Rd.
Thousand Oaks, CA 91360-2787
Tel: (805)492-2411; 877-258-3678
Admissions: (805)493-3135
Fax: (805)493-3114
E-mail: cluadm@clunet.edu
Web Site: http://www.clunet.edu/

Description: Independent Lutheran, comprehensive, coed. Awards bachelor's, master's, and doctoral degrees and post-master's certificates. Founded 1959. Setting: 290-acre suburban campus with easy access to Los Angeles. Endowment: $44.3 million. Educational spending for 2005 fiscal year: $6415 per student. Total enrollment: 3,212. Faculty: 260 (130 full-time, 130 part-time). Student-undergrad faculty ratio is 15:1. 1,977 applied, 69% were admitted. 23% from top 10% of their high school class, 80% from top quarter, 88% from top half. Full-time: 1,884 students, 56% women, 44% men. Part-time: 211 students, 56% women, 44% men. Students come from 37 states and territories, 25 other countries, 24% from out-of-state, 2% Native American, 17% Hispanic, 3% black, 5% Asian American or Pacific Islander, 2% international, 5% 25 or older, 65% live on campus, 7% transferred in. Retention: 84% of full-time freshmen returned the following year. Academic areas with the most degrees conferred: business/marketing; communications/journalism; social sciences. Core. Calendar: semesters. Advanced placement, accelerated degree program, self-designed majors, honors program, independent study, double major, summer session for credit, part-time degree program, adult/continuing education programs, co-op programs and internships, graduate courses open to undergrads. Off campus study at Wagner College, American University (Washington Semester). Study abroad program. ROTC: Army (c), Air Force (c).

Entrance Requirements: Options: Peterson's Universal Application, Common Application, electronic application, deferred admission, international baccalaureate accepted. Required: essay, high school transcript, minimum 2.8 high school GPA, 1 recommendation, SAT or ACT. Recommended: minimum 3.0 high school GPA, interview. Entrance: moderately difficult. Notification: 12/1.

Costs Per Year: Application fee: $45. Comprehensive fee: $31,690 includes full-time tuition ($23,170), mandatory fees ($200), and college room and board ($8320). College room only: $4330. Room and board charges vary according to board plan. Part-time tuition: $750 per unit. Part-time mandatory fees: $200 per year.

Collegiate Environment: Orientation program. Drama-theater group, choral group, student-run newspaper, radio station. Social organizations: 60 open to all. Most popular organizations: student government, music and drama clubs, service organizations, campus ministry organizations, multicultural organizations. Major annual events: Club Lu, The Need (student run coffeehouse), Midnight Madness. Student services: health clinic, personal-psychological counseling, women's center. Campus security: 24-hour emergency response devices and patrols, late night transport-escort service, controlled dormitory access, escort service; shuttle service. 1,130 college housing spaces available; 1,121 were occupied in 2003-04. Freshmen guaranteed college housing. On-campus residence required through junior year. Option: coed housing available. Pearson Library with 132,744 books, 22,200 microform titles, 1,497 serials, 1,852 audiovisual materials, an OPAC, and a Web page. Operations spending for 2004 fiscal year: $809,833. 267 computers available on campus for general student use. A campuswide network can be accessed from student residence rooms and from off campus. Staffed computer lab on campus.

Community Environment: Located in the Conejo Valley, Thousand Oaks has a mild pleasant climate with temperatures ranging from a mean low of 57 degrees in winter to a mean high of 77 degrees in summer. Average rainfall is 14 inches, the rainy season being between October and April. Buses, trains and airlines serve the area. Principal industries are electronics, aerospace, research, insurance and manufacturing. There are numerous shopping areas in Thousand Oaks. Recreational facilities include the community center, theatres, championship golf courses, Lake Sherwood, and the marinas in Oxnard and Ventura. Pacific Ocean Beaches are thirty minutes from The Campus.

■ **CALIFORNIA MARITIME ACADEMY** *J-4*
200 Maritime Academy Dr.
Vallejo, CA 94590
Tel: (707)654-1000
Free: 800-561-1945
Admissions: (707)654-1331
Fax: (707)648-4204
Web Site: http://www.csum.edu/
Description: State-supported, 4-year, coed. Part of California State University System. Awards bachelor's degrees. Founded 1929. Setting: 64-acre suburban campus with easy access to San Francisco. Total enrollment: 702. Student-undergrad faculty ratio is 22:1. 1,032 applied, 56% were admitted. Students come from 18 states and territories, 16 other countries, 14% from out-of-state, 16% 25 or older, 65% live on campus. Retention: 89% of full-time freshmen returned the following year. Core. Calendar: semesters. Academic remediation for entering students, advanced placement, distance learning, summer session for credit, internships.
Entrance Requirements: Option: electronic application. Required: high school transcript, minimum 2.0 high school GPA, health form, SAT or ACT. Entrance: moderately difficult. Notification: continuous. Preference given to California residents who meet the admissions resident index.
Costs Per Year: Application fee: $55. State resident tuition: $0 full-time. Nonresident tuition: $12,690 full-time. Mandatory fees: $5884 full-time. Full-time tuition and fees vary according to program and student level. College room and board: $7270. College room only: $3390. Room and board charges vary according to board plan and housing facility.
Collegiate Environment: Orientation program. Student-run newspaper. Social organizations: 12 open to all. Most popular organizations: Sailing Club, Dive Club, drill team. Major annual events: Changeover Dance, Homecoming, open house. Student services: health clinic, personal-psychological counseling. Campus security: 24-hour patrols, student patrols. On-campus residence required through junior year. Option: coed housing available. Main library plus 1 other with 28,377 books, 20,677 microform titles, 273 serials, 241 audiovisual materials, an OPAC, and a Web page. 50 computers available on campus for general student use. A campuswide network can be accessed from student residence rooms and from off campus. Staffed computer lab on campus.
Community Environment: Vallejo has a population of 103,000 and is located on the north shore of the Carquinez Strait, adjacent to San Pablo Bay.

■ **CALIFORNIA NATIONAL UNIVERSITY FOR ADVANCED STUDIES** *S-9*
8550 Balboa Blvd., Ste. 210
Northridge, CA 91325-3576
Tel: (818)830-2411
Free: 800-782-2422
Fax: (818)830-2418
E-mail: smmith@mail.cauas.edu
Web Site: http://www.cnuas.edu/

Description: Proprietary, comprehensive, coed. Awards bachelor's and master's degrees. Founded 1993. Setting: urban campus. Total enrollment: 500. Faculty: 98 (all part-time). Student-undergrad faculty ratio is 10:1. Students come from 25 other countries, 0% from out-of-state. Core. Calendar: trimesters. Advanced placement, accelerated degree program, independent study, distance learning, double major, part-time degree program, external degree program, adult/continuing education programs, internships. Off campus study.
Entrance Requirements: Open admission. Options: Common Application, electronic application, deferred admission, international baccalaureate accepted. Required: essay, high school transcript. Required for some: interview. Application deadline: Rolling. Notification: continuous.
Costs Per Year: Application fee: $75. Tuition: $4860 full-time, $270 per unit part-time.

■ **CALIFORNIA POLYTECHNIC STATE UNIVERSITY, SAN LUIS OBISPO** *Q-5*
1 Grand Ave.
San Luis Obispo, CA 93407
Tel: (805)756-1111
Admissions: (805)756-2311
E-mail: dp141@oasis.calpoly.edu
Web Site: http://www.calpoly.edu/
Description: State-supported, comprehensive, coed. Part of California State University System. Awards bachelor's and master's degrees. Founded 1901. Setting: 6,000-acre small town campus. Endowment: $2.7 million. Research spending for 2004 fiscal year: $4.8 million. Educational spending for 2005 fiscal year: $11,355 per student. Total enrollment: 18,475. Faculty: 1,246 (726 full-time, 520 part-time). Student-undergrad faculty ratio is 20:1. 23,691 applied, 45% were admitted. 37% from top 10% of their high school class, 76% from top quarter, 96% from top half. Full-time: 16,591 students, 44% women, 56% men. Part-time: 897 students, 41% women, 59% men. Students come from 48 states and territories, 41 other countries, 6% from out-of-state, 1% Native American, 10% Hispanic, 1% black, 11% Asian American or Pacific Islander, 1% international, 6% 25 or older, 22% live on campus, 4% transferred in. Retention: 91% of full-time freshmen returned the following year. Academic areas with the most degrees conferred: engineering; business/marketing; agriculture. Core. Academic remediation for entering students, ESL program, services for LD students, advanced placement, honors program, independent study, distance learning, double major, summer session for credit, part-time degree program, external degree program, co-op programs and internships, graduate courses open to undergrads. Off campus study at other units of the California State University System. Study abroad program. ROTC: Army.
Entrance Requirements: Options: electronic application, early admission, early decision. Required: high school transcript, SAT or ACT. Entrance: moderately difficult. Application deadlines: 11/30, 10/31 for early decision. Notification: continuous, 12/15 for early decision.
Costs Per Year: Application fee: $55. State resident tuition: $0 full-time. Nonresident tuition: $10,170 full-time, $226 per unit part-time. Mandatory fees: $4245 full-time, $2853 per year part-time. Full-time tuition and fees vary according to course load and program. Part-time tuition and fees vary according to course load and program. College room and board: $8145. College room only: $4583. Room and board charges vary according to board plan and housing facility.
Collegiate Environment: Orientation program. Drama-theater group, choral group, marching band, student-run newspaper, radio station. Social organizations: 360 open to all; national fraternities, national sororities, local fraternities, local sororities; 10% of eligible men and 11% of eligible women are members. Most popular organizations: Ski Club, American Marketing Association, Rose Float Club, MECHA, Society of Women Engineers. Major annual events: Homecoming, Fall and Spring Commencement, open house. Student services: legal services, health clinic, personal-psychological counseling, women's center. Campus security: 24-hour emergency response devices and patrols, student patrols, late night transport-escort service, controlled dormitory access. Options: coed, men-only, women-only housing available. Kennedy Library with 763,651 books, 2.1 million microform titles, 5,529 serials, 5,204 audiovisual materials, an OPAC, and a Web page. Operations spending for 2004 fiscal year: $4.6 million. 1,880 computers available on campus for general student use. A campuswide network can be accessed from student residence rooms and from off campus. Staffed computer lab on campus.
Community Environment: San Luis Obispo, located midway between San Francisco and Los Angeles, is 12 miles from the Pacific Ocean. The average

high winter temperature is in the 60s, and the summer high average is in the 70s. Buses, trains and airlines serve the area. There are 3 hospitals and a student health center. Student housing is available in campus dormitories and college approved housing in the city. Part time work is available in the community. Recreation includes surfing, fishing, clamming, golfing, hunting, boating and swimming. The Mission San Luis Obispo de Tolosa was founded in 1772, named for the Bishop of Toulouse, an Italian saint of the 13th century.

■ **CALIFORNIA SCHOOL OF CULINARY ARTS** *S-10*
521 East Green St.
Pasadena, CA 91101
Web Site: http://calchef.com
Description: Proprietary, 2-year, coed.

■ **CALIFORNIA STATE POLYTECHNIC UNIVERSITY, POMONA** *S-11*
3801 West Temple Ave.
Pomona, CA 91768-2557
Tel: (909)869-7659
Admissions: (909)869-3427
Fax: (909)869-4529
Web Site: http://www.csupomona.edu/
Description: State-supported, comprehensive, coed. Part of California State University System. Awards bachelor's and master's degrees. Founded 1938. Setting: 1,400-acre urban campus with easy access to Los Angeles. Endowment: $25.6 million. Educational spending for 2005 fiscal year: $5237 per student. Total enrollment: 19,885. Faculty: 1,281 (659 full-time, 622 part-time). Student-undergrad faculty ratio is 23:1. 17,252 applied, 24% were admitted. Full-time: 14,982 students, 43% women, 57% men. Part-time: 2,992 students, 40% women, 60% men. Students come from 52 states and territories, 116 other countries, 2% from out-of-state, 0.3% Native American, 27% Hispanic, 4% black, 31% Asian American or Pacific Islander, 3% international, 18% 25 or older, 9% live on campus, 9% transferred in. Retention: 85% of full-time freshmen returned the following year. Academic areas with the most degrees conferred: business/marketing; engineering; liberal arts/general studies. Core. Academic remediation for entering students, ESL program, services for LD students, advanced placement, honors program, double major, summer session for credit, part-time degree program, adult/ continuing education programs, co-op programs and internships, graduate courses open to undergrads. Off campus study at other units of the California State University System, Desert Studies Consortium, Southern California Ocean Studies Consortium. Study abroad program. ROTC: Army, Air Force (c).
Entrance Requirements: Option: electronic application. Required: high school transcript, minimum 2.0 high school GPA, SAT or ACT. Entrance: moderately difficult. Application deadline: 11/30. Notification: 11/1.
Costs Per Year: Application fee: $55. State resident tuition: $0 full-time. Nonresident tuition: $10,170 full-time, $226 per unit part-time. Mandatory fees: $3015 full-time. College room and board: $7908.
Collegiate Environment: Orientation program. Drama-theater group, choral group, student-run newspaper. Social organizations: 220 open to all; national fraternities, national sororities, local fraternities, local sororities; 1% of eligible men and 1% of eligible women are members. Most popular organizations: Rose Float Club, Ridge Runners Ski Club, Barkada (Asian club), American Marketing Association, Cal Poly Society of Accountants. Major annual events: Rose Float, Founder's Day, Bronco Days. Student services: health clinic, personal-psychological counseling, women's center. Campus security: 24-hour emergency response devices and patrols, student patrols, late night transport-escort service, video camera surveillance. 1,800 college housing spaces available; 1,769 were occupied in 2003-04. Freshmen given priority for college housing. Option: coed housing available. University Library with 758,700 books, 1.8 million microform titles, 5,153 serials, 11,288 audiovisual materials, an OPAC, and a Web page. Operations spending for 2004 fiscal year: $4.2 million. 1,864 computers available on campus for general student use. A campuswide network can be accessed from student residence rooms and from off campus. Staffed computer lab on campus.
Community Environment: Cal Poly Pomona is located just 35 miles southeast of downtown Los Angeles in the heart of Southern California. Near business and industry, the university's location is ideal for internships and/or employment. Cal Poly Pomona is also suitable for recreation; the beach, the desert, ski slopes, museums, Disneyland, and much more are just a short drive away.

■ **CALIFORNIA STATE UNIVERSITY, BAKERSFIELD** *P-8*
9001 Stockdale Hwy.
Bakersfield, CA 93311-1022

Tel: (661)664-2011
Admissions: (661)654-3036
Fax: (661)664-3188
E-mail: kmagnuson@csub.edu
Web Site: http://www.csubak.edu/
Description: State-supported, comprehensive, coed. Part of California State University System. Awards bachelor's and master's degrees. Founded 1970. Setting: 575-acre urban campus. Educational spending for 2005 fiscal year: $5200 per student. Total enrollment: 7,549. Faculty: 515 (332 full-time, 183 part-time). Student-undergrad faculty ratio is 17:1. Full-time: 4,881 students, 66% women, 34% men. Part-time: 1,079 students, 65% women, 35% men. Students come from 16 states and territories, 48 other countries, 1% Native American, 35% Hispanic, 7% black, 7% Asian American or Pacific Islander, 2% international, 34% 25 or older, 4% live on campus, 14% transferred in. Academic areas with the most degrees conferred: liberal arts/general studies; social sciences; business/marketing. Core. Academic remediation for entering students, ESL program, services for LD students, advanced placement, accelerated degree program, self-designed majors, freshman honors college, honors program, independent study, distance learning, double major, summer session for credit, part-time degree program, external degree program, adult/continuing education programs, co-op programs and internships, graduate courses open to undergrads. Off campus study at National Student Exchange. Study abroad program.
Entrance Requirements: Options: electronic application, early admission, deferred admission. Required: high school transcript, SAT or ACT. Recommended: SAT Subject Tests. Entrance: moderately difficult. Application deadline: 9/23. Notification: continuous. Preference given to state residents.
Costs Per Year: Application fee: $55. State resident tuition: $0 full-time. Nonresident tuition: $6780 full-time, $226 per unit part-time. Mandatory fees: $2959 full-time, $579 per term part-time. College room and board: $5946.
Collegiate Environment: Orientation program. Drama-theater group, choral group, student-run newspaper. Social organizations: 74 open to all; national fraternities, national sororities; 2% of eligible men and 2% of eligible women are members. Most popular organizations: MECHA, LUPE, STAAR, Psi Chi, Art Club. Major annual events: Cinco de Mayo, Earth Day. Student services: health clinic, personal-psychological counseling, women's center. Campus security: 24-hour emergency response devices and patrols, late night transport-escort service. Option: coed housing available. Walter W. Stiern Library with 354,016 books, 2,260 serials, and a Web page. Operations spending for 2004 fiscal year: $2.4 million. 600 computers available on campus for general student use. A campuswide network can be accessed from student residence rooms and from off campus. Staffed computer lab on campus.
Community Environment: Bakersfield is the county seat of Kern County which is noted for its rich agriculture, petroleum, and light industries. The city is located 112 miles north of Los Angeles and 295 miles south of San Francisco. Airline, bus, transcontinental railroad, and Amtrak services are available in the area. Bakersfield is considered the trading center of the Southern San Joaquin Valley. Central California beaches are located approximately 100 miles west of the campus. Shirley Meadow ski area is 51 miles northeast of Bakersfield, 20 minutes from Lake Isabella. The county is home to world-famous Edwards Air Force Base. Part-time employment is available.

■ **CALIFORNIA STATE UNIVERSITY CHANNEL ISLANDS** *T-4*
One University Dr.
Camarillo, CA 93012
Tel: (805)437-8979
Admissions: (805)437-8500
Fax: (805)437-8951
E-mail: admissionsandrecords@csuci.edu
Web Site: http://www.csuci.edu/
Description: State-supported, 4-year, coed. Awards bachelor's and master's degrees. Founded 2002. Endowment: $7.9 million. Educational spending for 2005 fiscal year: $7969 per student. Total enrollment: 2,575. Faculty: 227 (84 full-time, 143 part-time). Student-undergrad faculty ratio is 16:1. 4,853 applied, 43% were admitted. Full-time: 1,805 students, 62% women, 38% men. Part-time: 555 students, 64% women, 36% men. 0% from out-of-state, 1% Native American, 24% Hispanic, 2% black, 6% Asian American or Pacific Islander, 0% international. Retention: 80% of full-time freshmen returned the following year. Academic areas with the most degrees conferred: liberal arts/ general studies; business/marketing; psychology.
Entrance Requirements: Required: high school transcript, minimum 2.0 high school GPA, SAT or ACT. Recommended: minimum 3.0 high school

GPA, SAT and SAT Subject Tests or ACT. Required for some: SAT and SAT Subject Tests or ACT. Entrance: noncompetitive.

Costs Per Year: Application fee: $50. Nonresident tuition: $10,170 full-time, $339 per unit part-time. Mandatory fees: $2980 full-time. College room and board: $8800.

Collegiate Environment: Student-run newspaper. Social organizations: local fraternities, local sororities. Student services: health clinic, personal-psychological counseling, women's center, advising center, career center, math & writing center.

■ **CALIFORNIA STATE UNIVERSITY, CHICO** *F-5*
400 West First St.
Chico, CA 95929-0722
Tel: (530)898-6116
Free: 800-542-4426
Admissions: (530)898-4428
Fax: (530)898-6456
E-mail: info@csuchico.edu
Web Site: http://www.csuchico.edu/
Description: State-supported, comprehensive, coed. Part of California State University System. Awards bachelor's and master's degrees and post-master's certificates. Founded 1887. Setting: 119-acre small town campus. Endowment: $28.3 million. Research spending for 2004 fiscal year: $2.8 million. Educational spending for 2005 fiscal year: $5429 per student. Total enrollment: 15,919. Faculty: 913 (499 full-time, 414 part-time). Student-undergrad faculty ratio is 21:1. 12,853 applied, 85% were admitted. 35% from top 10% of their high school class, 76% from top quarter, 100% from top half. Full-time: 13,079 students, 53% women, 47% men. Part-time: 1,447 students, 56% women, 44% men. Students come from 37 states and territories, 45 other countries, 1% from out-of-state, 1% Native American, 11% Hispanic, 2% black, 5% Asian American or Pacific Islander, 2% international, 15% 25 or older, 12% live on campus, 11% transferred in. Retention: 85% of full-time freshmen returned the following year. Academic areas with the most degrees conferred: business/marketing; liberal arts/general studies; social sciences. Core. Calendar: semesters. Academic remediation for entering students, ESL program, services for LD students, advanced placement, self-designed majors, honors program, independent study, distance learning, double major, summer session for credit, part-time degree program, external degree program, adult/continuing education programs, co-op programs and internships, graduate courses open to undergrads. Off campus study at other units of the California State University System, National Student Exchange. Study abroad program.
Entrance Requirements: Options: electronic application, deferred admission, international baccalaureate accepted. Required: high school transcript, GPA of 10th and 11th grade college prep courses only, SAT or ACT. Required for some: minimum 2.0 high school GPA. Entrance: moderately difficult. Application deadline: 11/30. Notification: 3/1.
Costs Per Year: Application fee: $55. State resident tuition: $0 full-time. Nonresident tuition: $12,690 full-time, $339 per unit part-time. Mandatory fees: $3370 full-time, $425 per term part-time. Part-time tuition and fees vary according to course load. College room and board: $7993. College room only: $5550. Room and board charges vary according to board plan and housing facility.
Collegiate Environment: Orientation program. Drama-theater group, choral group, student-run newspaper, radio station. Social organizations: 226 open to all; national fraternities, national sororities, local fraternities, local sororities; 7% of eligible men and 6% of eligible women are members. Most popular organizations: Golden Key International Honor Society, Newman Catholic Campus Ministry, The Edge. Major annual events: Community Challenge, Multicultural Night, Scour and Devour. Student services: legal services, health clinic, personal-psychological counseling, women's center. Campus security: 24-hour emergency response devices and patrols, student patrols, late night transport-escort service, controlled dormitory access, crime prevention workshops, RAD self-defense program, Chico Safe Rides, blue light emergency phones. 1,765 college housing spaces available; all were occupied in 2003-04. Freshmen given priority for college housing. Option: coed housing available. Meriam Library with 957,181 books, 1.2 million microform titles, 24,244 serials, 27,156 audiovisual materials, an OPAC, and a Web page. Operations spending for 2004 fiscal year: $4.6 million. 840 computers available on campus for general student use. A campuswide network can be accessed from student residence rooms and from off campus. Staffed computer lab on campus.
Community Environment: Chico is located close to the northern end of the Sacramento Valley and is one of the oldest communities in the state. Today

Chico has a population of 46,750 (87,000 in the Greater Chico area) and Butte county has a population of 201,000. It is considered the business center for a large agricultural area, which produces an abundance of rice, grains, nuts, and fruits. Winters are mild and summers are hot, averaging 95-105 degrees. Regional airlines connect Chico with adjacent cities, including San Francisco and Sacramento. Greyhound Bus service is available. Chico is the home of Bidwell Park, one of the largest and most beautiful municipal parks in the nation. Lower Bidwell Park starts near the campus and extends 10 miles east along the Big Chico creek. The park offers swimming, hiking, a municipal golf course, horseback riding, a children's park, picnic areas, and softball fields among its recreational facilities. Biking is a favorite (and practical) means of transportation. Local Public Bus transportation is free to university students and personnel. Skiing facilities are only two hours away. Bidwell Mansion, located on campus, is now a historical site maintained by the Department of Parks and Recreation. Part-time employment is available but scarce.

■ **CALIFORNIA STATE UNIVERSITY, DOMINGUEZ HILLS** *Z-3*
1000 East Victoria St.
Carson, CA 90747-0001
Tel: (310)243-3300
Admissions: (310)243-3600
Web Site: http://www.csudh.edu/
Description: State-supported, comprehensive, coed. Part of California State University System. Awards bachelor's and master's degrees. Founded 1960. Setting: 350-acre urban campus with easy access to Los Angeles. Total enrollment: 12,357. Faculty: 678 (252 full-time, 426 part-time). Student-undergrad faculty ratio is 22:1. 2,323 applied, 45% were admitted. Full-time: 5,322 students, 67% women, 33% men. Part-time: 3,621 students, 71% women, 29% men. Students come from 29 states and territories, 42 other countries, 2% from out-of-state, 0.5% Native American, 36% Hispanic, 27% black, 9% Asian American or Pacific Islander, 2% international, 56% 25 or older, 14% transferred in. Retention: 73% of full-time freshmen returned the following year. Academic areas with the most degrees conferred: liberal arts/general studies; business/marketing; health professions and related sciences. Core. Calendar: semesters. Academic remediation for entering students, ESL program, advanced placement, self-designed majors, honors program, summer session for credit, part-time degree program, external degree program, adult/continuing education programs, co-op programs and internships, graduate courses open to undergrads. Off campus study at other institutions of the California State University System, National Student Exchange. Study abroad program. ROTC: Army (c), Air Force (c).
Entrance Requirements: Options: electronic application, early admission. Required: high school transcript, SAT or ACT. Entrance: moderately difficult. Application deadline: Rolling. Notification: continuous. Preference given to state residents.
Costs Per Year: Application fee: $55. State resident tuition: $0 full-time. Nonresident tuition: $339 per unit part-time. Mandatory fees: $3618 full-time. College room only: $5850.
Collegiate Environment: Orientation program. Drama-theater group, choral group, student-run newspaper. Social organizations: national fraternities, national sororities. Student services: legal services, health clinic, personal-psychological counseling, women's center. Campus security: student patrols, late night transport-escort service. Option: coed housing available. Leo F. Cain Educational Resource Center with 440,181 books, 687,888 microform titles, an OPAC, and a Web page. 200 computers available on campus for general student use. Staffed computer lab on campus.
Community Environment: This is a metropolitan area in Los Angeles County with a Mediterranean climate. Trains, buses and airlines serve the area. Carson is surrounded by freeways, which makes the larger nearby cities easy to reach. The city has churches, hospitals, a YMCA building and library. The State Department of Employment, which is located in Torrance, has established a program designed to aid students in finding employment.

■ **CALIFORNIA STATE UNIVERSITY, EAST BAY** *K-5*
25800 Carlos Bee Blvd.
Hayward, CA 94542-3000
Tel: (510)885-3000
Admissions: (510)885-7002
Fax: (510)885-3816
E-mail: adminfo@csuhayward.edu
Web Site: http://www.csueastbay.edu/
Description: State-supported, comprehensive, coed. Part of California State University System. Awards bachelor's and master's degrees. Founded 1957.

Setting: 343-acre suburban campus with easy access to San Francisco. Research spending for 2004 fiscal year: $8.7 million. Educational spending for 2005 fiscal year: $7868 per student. Total enrollment: 12,535. Faculty: 741 (324 full-time, 417 part-time). Student-undergrad faculty ratio is 17:1. 7,110 applied, 10% were admitted. Full-time: 7,262 students, 62% women, 38% men. Part-time: 1,867 students, 60% women, 40% men. Students come from 50 states and territories, 86 other countries, 3% from out-of-state, 1% Native American, 14% Hispanic, 12% black, 29% Asian American or Pacific Islander, 5% international, 37% 25 or older, 4% live on campus, 17% transferred in. Retention: 81% of full-time freshmen returned the following year. Academic areas with the most degrees conferred: liberal arts/general studies; social sciences; business/marketing. Core. Academic remediation for entering students, ESL program, services for LD students, advanced placement, accelerated degree program, self-designed majors, honors program, independent study, distance learning, double major, summer session for credit, part-time degree program, adult/continuing education programs, co-op programs and internships, graduate courses open to undergrads. Off campus study at Regional Association of East Bay Colleges and Universities, National Student Exchange. Study abroad program.

Entrance Requirements: Options: electronic application, deferred admission, international baccalaureate accepted. Required: high school transcript, minimum 2.00 high school GPA, CSU eligibility index. Required for some: SAT or ACT. Entrance: moderately difficult. Application deadline: 8/31. Notification: continuous.

Costs Per Year: Application fee: $55. State resident tuition: $0 full-time. Nonresident tuition: $10,170 full-time. Mandatory fees: $2916 full-time. College room only: $6759.

Collegiate Environment: Orientation program. Drama-theater group, choral group, student-run newspaper, radio station. Social organizations: 90 open to all; national fraternities, national sororities, local sororities. Most popular organizations: Vietnamese Student Association, Accounting Association, Filipino-American Students Association, Movimiento Estudiantil Chicano, Hayward Orientation Team. Major annual events: Al Fresco, Pioneer Days, Club Days. Student services: legal services, health clinic, personal-psychological counseling. Campus security: 24-hour emergency response devices and patrols, late night transport-escort service. Option: coed housing available. California State University, East Bay Library plus 1 other with 908,577 books, 803,844 microform titles, 2,210 serials, 28,416 audiovisual materials, an OPAC, and a Web page. Operations spending for 2004 fiscal year: $3.5 million. 700 computers available on campus for general student use. A campuswide network can be accessed from student residence rooms and from off campus. Staffed computer lab on campus.

Community Environment: Population 110,000 in a metropolitan area of 5 1/2 million. Hayward is a suburban area near Oakland, Berkeley, San Francisco and San Jose. The climate is mild. All modes of transportation serve the area. The university's proximity to all major Bay Area cities provides access to museums, art galleries, plays, concerts, and libraries as well as to the recreational opportunities of the bay. The climate makes outdoor recreation a year-round activity. Its nearness to ocean and mountain areas offer recreational diversity.

■ **CALIFORNIA STATE UNIVERSITY, FRESNO** *M-9*
5241 North Maple Ave.
Fresno, CA 93740-8027
Tel: (559)278-4240
Admissions: (559)278-2261
Fax: (559)278-4715
E-mail: vivian_franco@csufresno.edu
Web Site: http://www.csufresno.edu/
Description: State-supported, comprehensive, coed. Part of California State University System. Awards bachelor's, master's, and doctoral degrees. Founded 1911. Setting: 1,410-acre urban campus. Endowment: $86.6 million. Research spending for 2004 fiscal year: $5 million. Educational spending for 2005 fiscal year: $10,450 per student. Total enrollment: 20,371. Faculty: 1,267 (754 full-time, 513 part-time). Student-undergrad faculty ratio is 20:1. 13,252 applied, 65% were admitted. Full-time: 14,786 students, 59% women, 41% men. Part-time: 2,642 students, 56% women, 44% men. Students come from 50 states and territories, 69 other countries, 1% from out-of-state, 1% Native American, 30% Hispanic, 5% black, 14% Asian American or Pacific Islander, 2% international, 18% 25 or older, 5% live on campus, 10% transferred in. Retention: 85% of full-time freshmen returned the following year. Core. Calendar: semesters. Academic remediation for entering students, ESL program, services for LD students, advanced placement, accelerated degree program, self-designed majors, freshman honors

college, honors program, independent study, distance learning, double major, summer session for credit, part-time degree program, adult/continuing education programs, co-op programs and internships, graduate courses open to undergrads. Off campus study at other units of the California State University System. Study abroad program. ROTC: Army, Air Force.

Entrance Requirements: Options: Common Application, electronic application. Required: high school transcript, minimum 2.00 high school GPA, SAT or ACT. Entrance: minimally difficult. Application deadline: 4/1. Preference given to state residents.

Costs Per Year: Application fee: $55. State resident tuition: $0 full-time. Nonresident tuition: $13,207 full-time, $339 per unit part-time. Mandatory fees: $3037 full-time, $990 per term part-time. College room and board: $7344.

Collegiate Environment: Orientation program. Drama-theater group, choral group, marching band, student-run newspaper, radio station. Social organizations: 250 open to all; national fraternities, national sororities, local fraternities, local sororities; 3% of eligible men and 3% of eligible women are members. Major annual events: Vintage Day, Welcome Week, Commencement. Student services: health clinic, personal-psychological counseling, women's center. Campus security: 24-hour emergency response devices and patrols, late night transport-escort service, controlled dormitory access. 1,035 college housing spaces available. No special consideration for freshman housing applicants. Option: coed housing available. Henry Madden Library with 1.2 million microform titles, 2,617 serials, 77,125 audiovisual materials, an OPAC, and a Web page. Operations spending for 2004 fiscal year: $6.3 million. 853 computers available on campus for general student use. A campuswide network can be accessed from off-campus. Staffed computer lab on campus.

Community Environment: Fresno (population 510,00) is located in the heart of the San Joaquin Valley, at the center of the state. The climate is mild all year. All modes of transportation serve the area. Fresno is in an agricultural area producing figs, grapes and cotton. Roma Winery and several other wineries are located here; other industries include processing and packing of fruit, the manufacture of cottonseed oil, livestock and poultry feed, agricultural equipment and aircraft parts. There are facilities in the area for swimming, fishing, sailing, water skiing, horseback riding, hiking, rock climbing and all the winter sports. Three national parks and two national forests are nearby.

■ **CALIFORNIA STATE UNIVERSITY, FULLERTON** *R-6*
PO Box 34080
Fullerton, CA 92834-9480
Tel: (714)278-2011
Admissions: (714)278-2350
Web Site: http://www.fullerton.edu/
Description: State-supported, comprehensive, coed. Part of California State University System. Awards bachelor's and master's degrees. Founded 1957. Setting: 225-acre urban campus with easy access to Los Angeles. Total enrollment: 35,040. Faculty: 1,935 (719 full-time, 1,216 part-time). Student-undergrad faculty ratio is 23:1. 29,692 applied, 69% were admitted. 18% from top 10% of their high school class, 50% from top quarter, 86% from top half. Full-time: 21,187 students, 58% women, 42% men. Part-time: 8,275 students, 58% women, 42% men. Students come from 36 states and territories, 64 other countries, 2% from out-of-state, 0.5% Native American, 28% Hispanic, 4% black, 22% Asian American or Pacific Islander, 4% international, 22% 25 or older, 2% live on campus, 13% transferred in. Retention: 82% of full-time freshmen returned the following year. Academic areas with the most degrees conferred: business/marketing; communications/journalism; education. Core. Calendar: semesters. Academic remediation for entering students, ESL program, services for LD students, advanced placement, self-designed majors, honors program, independent study, distance learning, double major, summer session for credit, part-time degree program, adult/continuing education programs, co-op programs and internships. Off campus study at other institutions of the California State University System. Study abroad program. ROTC: Army.

Entrance Requirements: Options: electronic application, international baccalaureate accepted. Required: high school transcript, minimum 2.0 high school GPA, SAT or ACT. Entrance: moderately difficult. Application deadline: 11/30. Notification: continuous. Preference given to state residents.

Costs Per Year: Application fee: $55. State resident tuition: $0 full-time. Nonresident tuition: $10,170 full-time, $339 per unit part-time. Mandatory fees: $2990 full-time, $967 per term part-time. Full-time tuition and fees vary according to course load. Part-time tuition and fees vary according to course load. College room only: $4504.

Collegiate Environment: Orientation program. Drama-theater group, choral group, student-run newspaper, radio station. Social organizations: 225 open to all; national fraternities, national sororities, local fraternities, local sororities; 9% of eligible men and 8% of eligible women are members. Student services: legal services, health clinic, personal-psychological counseling, women's center. Campus security: 24-hour emergency response devices and patrols, student patrols, late night transport-escort service, controlled dormitory access. 836 college housing spaces available; all were occupied in 2003-04. No special consideration for freshman housing applicants. Option: coed housing available. California State University, Fullerton Pollak Library with 1.2 million books, 1.1 million microform titles, 10,827 serials, 15,220 audiovisual materials, an OPAC, and a Web page. 1,993 computers available on campus for general student use. A campuswide network can be accessed from student residence rooms and from off campus. Staffed computer lab on campus.

Community Environment: Fullerton is in a metropolitan area with a temperate climate. Airlines, buses and trains serve the area. Freeways make all neighboring cities easily accessible. Fullerton is an area of many cultural interests, in art, music and theatre. The city is near Disneyland and the California Angel Stadium; 35 miles from Hollywood and Los Angeles. Recreational facilities include the beaches and the mountains which are both within easy driving distance. Part-time work is available. The major service clubs are represented in the city.

■ **CALIFORNIA STATE UNIVERSITY, LONG BEACH** *T-10*
1250 Bellflower Blvd.
Long Beach, CA 90840
Tel: (562)985-4111
Admissions: (562)985-4641
Web Site: http://www.csulb.edu/
Description: State-supported, comprehensive, coed. Part of California State University System. Awards bachelor's and master's degrees. Founded 1949. Setting: 320-acre suburban campus with easy access to Los Angeles. Endowment: $27.9 million. Research spending for 2004 fiscal year: $9.3 million. Educational spending for 2005 fiscal year: $5673 per student. Total university enrollment: 1,344. Total unit enrollment: 34,547. Faculty: 2,074 (966 full-time, 1,108 part-time). Student-undergrad faculty ratio is 20:1. 38,579 applied, 55% were admitted. 84% from top quarter of their high school class, 100% from top half. Full-time: 22,525 students, 61% women, 39% men. Part-time: 5,989 students, 57% women, 43% men. Students come from 45 states and territories, 89 other countries, 1% from out-of-state, 1% Native American, 25% Hispanic, 6% black, 22% Asian American or Pacific Islander, 5% international, 21% 25 or older, 7% live on campus, 16% transferred in. Retention: 85% of full-time freshmen returned the following year. Academic areas with the most degrees conferred: business/marketing; liberal arts/general studies; visual and performing arts. Core. Calendar: semesters. Academic remediation for entering students, ESL program, services for LD students, advanced placement, accelerated degree program, self-designed majors, honors program, independent study, distance learning, double major, summer session for credit, part-time degree program, adult/continuing education programs, internships, graduate courses open to undergrads. Off campus study at other institutions of the California State University System. Study abroad program. ROTC: Army.
Entrance Requirements: Option: electronic application. Required: high school transcript, SAT or ACT. Required for some: minimum 2.0 high school GPA, minimum GPA of 2.4 for nonresidents. Entrance: moderately difficult. Application deadline: 11/30. Notification: continuous. Preference given to local residents.
Costs Per Year: Application fee: $55. State resident tuition: $0 full-time. Nonresident tuition: $10,170 full-time. Mandatory fees: $2864 full-time. College room and board: $6648.
Collegiate Environment: Orientation program. Drama-theater group, choral group, student-run newspaper, radio station. Social organizations: 300 open to all; national fraternities, national sororities, local fraternities, local sororities; 7% of eligible men and 5% of eligible women are members. Major annual events: Kaleidoscope Spring Festival, Odyssey Theme Year. Student services: legal services, health clinic, personal-psychological counseling, women's center. Campus security: 24-hour emergency response devices and patrols, student patrols, late night transport-escort service. 1,962 college housing spaces available; all were occupied in 2003-04. No special consideration for freshman housing applicants. Option: coed housing available. University Library with 1.5 million books, 1.5 million microform titles, 18,749 serials, 28,060 audiovisual materials, an OPAC, and a Web page. Operations spending for 2004 fiscal year: $6.3 million. 2,000 computers

available on campus for general student use. A campuswide network can be accessed from off-campus. Staffed computer lab on campus.
Community Environment: Long Beach is approximately 20 miles south of Los Angeles and has a Mediterranean climate. The eight mile beach area provides the finest and safest public bathing on the Pacific Coast, having the largest protected harbor in North America. All modes of transportation serve the area. There are 25 city parks which provide facilities for golf, tennis, baseball, swimming, shuffleboard, and lawn bowling, as well as a sports arena and a municipal auditorium.

■ **CALIFORNIA STATE UNIVERSITY, LOS ANGELES** *S-10*
5151 State University Dr.
Los Angeles, CA 90032-8530
Tel: (323)343-3000
Admissions: (323)343-3940
Fax: (323)343-2670
E-mail: jwoosley@csianet.calstatela.edu
Web Site: http://www.calstatela.edu/
Description: State-supported, comprehensive, coed. Part of California State University System. Awards bachelor's, master's, and doctoral degrees. Founded 1947. Setting: 173-acre urban campus. Endowment: $13.6 million. Total enrollment: 20,014. Faculty: 1,141 (581 full-time, 560 part-time). Student-undergrad faculty ratio is 16:1. 17,150 applied, 62% were admitted. Full-time: 10,872 students, 62% women, 38% men. Part-time: 4,083 students, 59% women, 41% men. 4% from out-of-state, 0.4% Native American, 46% Hispanic, 8% black, 21% Asian American or Pacific Islander, 4% international, 34% 25 or older, 11% transferred in. Retention: 75% of full-time freshmen returned the following year. Academic areas with the most degrees conferred: business/marketing; security and protective services; education. Core. Academic remediation for entering students, ESL program, services for LD students, advanced placement, accelerated degree program, self-designed majors, honors program, summer session for credit, part-time degree program, adult/continuing education programs, co-op programs and internships, graduate courses open to undergrads. Off campus study at other units of the California State University System. Study abroad program. ROTC: Army (c), Air Force (c).
Entrance Requirements: Options: Common Application, electronic application, early admission. Required: high school transcript. Required for some: SAT or ACT. Entrance: moderately difficult. Application deadline: 6/15.
Costs Per Year: Application fee: $55. State resident tuition: $0 full-time. Nonresident tuition: $11,171 full-time, $226 per unit part-time. Mandatory fees: $3035 full-time, $658.75 per term part-time. Full-time tuition and fees vary according to course level. Part-time tuition and fees vary according to course level. College room and board: $7353.
Collegiate Environment: Orientation program. Drama-theater group, choral group, student-run newspaper. Social organizations: 130 open to all; national fraternities, national sororities, local fraternities, local sororities; 2% of eligible men and 2% of eligible women are members. Most popular organizations: Society of Hispanic, Engineering and Science Students, Institute of Electrical and Electronics Engineer, Sigma Delta PI, Asian Unified, Society of Automotive Engineers. Major annual events: Haunted Union, Mardi Gras, Spring Student Fest. Student services: legal services, health clinic, personal-psychological counseling, women's center. Campus security: 24-hour emergency response devices, student patrols, late night transport-escort service. 996 college housing spaces available; 850 were occupied in 2003-04. Option: coed housing available. John F. Kennedy Memorial Library with 1.7 million books, 1.1 million microform titles, 2,724 serials, 1,163 audiovisual materials, an OPAC, and a Web page. 1,500 computers available on campus for general student use. A campuswide network can be accessed from off-campus. Staffed computer lab on campus.
Community Environment: See University of California - Los Angeles.

■ **CALIFORNIA STATE UNIVERSITY, MONTEREY BAY** *M-5*
100 Campus Center
Seaside, CA 93955-8001
Tel: (831)582-3000
Admissions: (831)582-3544
Fax: (831)582-3540
Web Site: http://csumb.edu/
Description: State-supported, comprehensive, coed. Part of California State University. Awards bachelor's and master's degrees. Founded 1994. Setting: 1,500-acre campus with easy access to San Jose. Endowment: $520,445. Research spending for 2004 fiscal year: $11 million. Educational spending for 2005 fiscal year: $10,191 per student. Total enrollment: 3,020. 3,023 ap-

plied, 83% were admitted. Full-time: 2,673 students, 58% women, 42% men. Part-time: 80 students, 53% women, 48% men. Students come from 34 states and territories, 5% from out-of-state, 1% Native American, 27% Hispanic, 4% black, 6% Asian American or Pacific Islander, 0% international, 29% 25 or older, 65% live on campus, 52% transferred in. Retention: 76% of full-time freshmen returned the following year. Calendar: semesters. Academic remediation for entering students, services for LD students, self-designed majors, independent study, distance learning, double major, part-time degree program, external degree program, co-op programs and internships.

Entrance Requirements: Options: deferred admission, international baccalaureate accepted. Required: high school transcript, minimum 2.0 high school GPA, SAT or ACT. Entrance: minimally difficult. Application deadline: Rolling. Notification: continuous.

Costs Per Year: Application fee: $55. State resident tuition: $0 full-time. Nonresident tuition: $10,848 full-time, $339 per credit part-time. Mandatory fees: $2947 full-time, $945.50 per term part-time. College room and board: $6900. College room only: $4400.

Collegiate Environment: Drama-theater group, choral group, student-run newspaper, radio station. Social organizations: 20 open to all. Most popular organization: MECHA. Major annual events: Graduation, On-Campus Admission Day. Student services: health clinic, personal-psychological counseling. Campus security: 24-hour emergency response devices and patrols, student patrols, late night transport-escort service, controlled dormitory access. On-campus residence required through sophomore year. Options: men-only, women-only housing available.

■ **CALIFORNIA STATE UNIVERSITY, NORTHRIDGE** *S-9*
18111 Nordhoff St.
Northridge, CA 91330
Tel: (818)677-1200
Admissions: (818)677-3700
Fax: (818)677-3766
Web Site: http://www.csun.edu/
Description: State-supported, comprehensive, coed. Part of California State University System. Awards bachelor's and master's degrees. Founded 1958. Setting: 353-acre urban campus with easy access to Los Angeles. Endowment: $2.4 million. Research spending for 2004 fiscal year: $66,989. Educational spending for 2005 fiscal year: $4989 per student. Total enrollment: 33,243. Faculty: 1,822 (803 full-time, 1,019 part-time). Student-undergrad faculty ratio is 23:1. 18,178 applied, 75% were admitted. Full-time: 20,638 students, 59% women, 41% men. Part-time: 6,216 students, 57% women, 43% men. Students come from 40 states and territories, 7 other countries, 1% from out-of-state, 0.4% Native American, 28% Hispanic, 9% black, 12% Asian American or Pacific Islander, 5% international, 13% transferred in. Retention: 77% of full-time freshmen returned the following year. Academic areas with the most degrees conferred: business/marketing; social sciences; psychology. Core. Calendar: semesters. Academic remediation for entering students, ESL program, services for LD students, advanced placement, accelerated degree program, self-designed majors, honors program, summer session for credit, part-time degree program, adult/continuing education programs, graduate courses open to undergrads. Off campus study at other units of the California State University System, National Student Exchange. Study abroad program. ROTC: Army (c), Air Force (c).

Entrance Requirements: Options: electronic application, early admission, early action. Required: high school transcript. Recommended: SAT or ACT. Entrance: moderately difficult. Application deadlines: 11/30, 8/30 for early action. Notification: continuous, 9/30 for early action. Preference given to state residents for business administration, engineering, computer science, economics programs.

Costs Per Year: Application fee: $55. State resident tuition: $0 full-time. Nonresident tuition: $10,170 full-time, $339 per unit part-time. Mandatory fees: $3036 full-time, $1464 per term part-time. College room and board: $7616. College room only: $4766. Room and board charges vary according to housing facility.

Collegiate Environment: Orientation program. Drama-theater group, choral group, marching band, student-run newspaper, radio station. Social organizations: national fraternities, national sororities; 6% of eligible men and 4% of eligible women are members. Student services: health clinic, personal-psychological counseling, women's center. Campus security: 24-hour emergency response devices, late night transport-escort service. Option: coed housing available. Oviatt Library with 1.2 million books, 3 million microform titles, 2,754 serials, and an OPAC. Operations spending for 2004 fiscal year: $7.1 million.

Community Environment: Located north of Los Angeles and part of the Los Angeles metropolitan area. Climate is mild; all modes of transportation available in the Los Angeles area. The community facilities include churches, library, hospitals and all the service organizations are represented. Part-time employment available in this center for electronic and space research and development; about three-quarters of the students work. Northridge enjoys the cultural and recreational advantages of Los Angeles and is 20 miles from the Pacific Ocean and near the mountain areas for winter sports.

■ **CALIFORNIA STATE UNIVERSITY, SACRAMENTO** *I-6*
6000 J St.
Sacramento, CA 95819-6048
Tel: (916)278-6011
Admissions: (916)278-7362
Web Site: http://www.csus.edu/
Description: State-supported, comprehensive, coed. Part of California State University System. Awards bachelor's, master's, and doctoral degrees. Founded 1947. Setting: 300-acre urban campus. Total enrollment: 27,932. Faculty: 1,530 (812 full-time, 718 part-time). Student-undergrad faculty ratio is 22:1. 15,980 applied, 47% were admitted. Full-time: 17,864 students, 58% women, 42% men. Part-time: 5,164 students, 55% women, 45% men. Students come from 36 states and territories, 122 other countries, 1% from out-of-state, 1% Native American, 15% Hispanic, 7% black, 19% Asian American or Pacific Islander, 1% international, 25% 25 or older, 5% live on campus, 13% transferred in. Retention: 81% of full-time freshmen returned the following year. Academic areas with the most degrees conferred: business/marketing; social sciences; public administration and social services. Core. Calendar: semesters. Academic remediation for entering students, ESL program, services for LD students, advanced placement, accelerated degree program, self-designed majors, independent study, distance learning, double major, summer session for credit, part-time degree program, external degree program, co-op programs and internships, graduate courses open to undergrads. Off campus study at other units of the California State University System. Study abroad program. ROTC: Army (c), Air Force.

Entrance Requirements: Options: electronic application, early action, deferred admission, international baccalaureate accepted. Required: minimum 2.0 high school GPA. Required for some: high school transcript, SAT or ACT. Entrance: moderately difficult. Application deadlines: 8/1, 11/30 for early action. Notification: 11/1, 11/1 for early action.

Costs Per Year: Application fee: $55. Nonresident tuition: $13,242 full-time, $339 per unit part-time. Mandatory fees: $3624 full-time, $276 per term part-time. College room and board: $7458.

Collegiate Environment: Orientation program. Drama-theater group, choral group, marching band, student-run newspaper, radio station. Social organizations: 250 open to all; national fraternities, national sororities, local fraternities, local sororities; 7% of eligible men and 5% of eligible women are members. Most popular organizations: Ski Club, American Marketing Association, Society for Advancement of Management, Accounting Society, Human Resources Management Association. Major annual events: River City Days, Student Orientation Program. Student services: legal services, health clinic, personal-psychological counseling, women's center. Campus security: 24-hour emergency response devices and patrols, student patrols, late night transport-escort service, controlled dormitory access. 1,100 college housing spaces available; all were occupied in 2003-04. No special consideration for freshman housing applicants. Option: coed housing available. California State University, Sacramento Library with 1.3 million books, 2.4 million microform titles, 3,761 serials, 50,722 audiovisual materials, an OPAC, and a Web page. 700 computers available on campus for general student use. A campuswide network can be accessed from student residence rooms and from off campus. Staffed computer lab on campus.

Community Environment: Sacramento, the capital of California, is the gateway to historic Gold Rush country and the High Sierra vacation regions. All modes of transportation serve the area; San Francisco is a two-hour drive on the freeway. The cultural center of Northern California, Sacramento has the historic Crocker Art Gallery, symphony orchestra, summer theater series, state library, a state museum, a state railroad museum and the Sacramento History Center. Numerous part time jobs on campus and in the city are available through the Student Placement Office and the California Department of Employment. There are many post-college vocational opportunities with defense industries, two air bases, state and local government and other growing industrial and high-tech firms. Off campus housing is available to students. There are many points of interest and a great number of recreational facilities in the Sacramento area; parks, zoo, golf courses, boating and fishing on the American and Sacramento Rivers. Squaw Valley, 100 miles away, was the home of the 1960 Olympics for winter sports. There are good health facilities and a wide range of fraternal and civic organizations.

■ **CALIFORNIA STATE UNIVERSITY, SAN BERNARDINO** S-11
5500 University Parkway
San Bernardino, CA 92407-2397
Tel: (909)537-5000
Admissions: (909)537-5188
E-mail: orosas@csusb.edu
Web Site: http://www.csusb.edu/
Description: State-supported, comprehensive, coed. Part of California State University System. Awards bachelor's and master's degrees. Founded 1965. Setting: 430-acre suburban campus with easy access to Los Angeles. Total enrollment: 16,431. Faculty: 447 (363 full-time, 84 part-time). Student-undergrad faculty ratio is 22:1. 9,629 applied, 25% were admitted. 18% from top 10% of their high school class, 35% from top quarter, 90% from top half. Full-time: 10,375 students, 66% women, 34% men. Part-time: 2,089 students, 64% women, 36% men. Students come from 37 states and territories, 43 other countries, 1% from out-of-state, 1% Native American, 34% Hispanic, 12% black, 8% Asian American or Pacific Islander, 3% international, 21% 25 or older, 11% live on campus, 13% transferred in. Retention: 81% of full-time freshmen returned the following year. Academic areas with the most degrees conferred: business/marketing; liberal arts/general studies; social sciences. Core. Services for LD students, accelerated degree program, self-designed majors, honors program, independent study, distance learning, double major, summer session for credit, part-time degree program, adult/continuing education programs, co-op programs and internships. Off campus study at National Student Exchange. Study abroad program. ROTC: Army, Air Force.
Entrance Requirements: Option: early admission. Required: high school transcript, minimum 2.0 high school GPA, SAT or ACT. Entrance: moderately difficult. Application deadline: Rolling. Notification: continuous.
Costs Per Year: Application fee: $55. State resident tuition: $0 full-time. Nonresident tuition: $8136 full-time, $226 per unit part-time. Mandatory fees: $3398 full-time. Part-time tuition varies according to course load. College room and board: $5886. College room only: $4376. Room and board charges vary according to board plan and housing facility.
Collegiate Environment: Orientation program. Drama-theater group, choral group, student-run newspaper, radio station. Social organizations: 80 open to all; national fraternities, national sororities, local fraternities, local sororities; 3% of eligible men and 6% of eligible women are members. Major annual events: Earth Day, Annual University Picnic, International Day. Student services: legal services, health clinic, personal-psychological counseling, women's center. Campus security: 24-hour emergency response devices and patrols, student patrols, late night transport-escort service, residence staff on call 24-hours. 1,500 college housing spaces available; 1,431 were occupied in 2003-04. Freshmen given priority for college housing. Options: coed, women-only housing available. Pfau Library with 731,259 books, 643,292 microform titles, 2,028 serials, 15,252 audiovisual materials, an OPAC, and a Web page. 1,300 computers available on campus for general student use. A campuswide network can be accessed from student residence rooms and from off campus. Staffed computer lab on campus.
Community Environment: Population 104,000. San Bernardino is located 58 miles east of Los Angeles at the foot of the San Bernardino Mountains. Climate is ideal with 312 days of sunshine a year. Citrus groves surround the city. Greyhound and Trailways bus lines and Santa Fe Railroad serve the area. The nearest airport is Ontario International. San Bernardino has art galleries, Swing Auditorium, theaters, many churches, and a library. Pacific Ocean beaches provide water sports. Resort areas of Lake Arrowhead and Big Bear Lake in the mountains have facilities for water sports and winter sports. Cajon Pass offers a scenic drive through the mountains into the Mojave Desert; City Creek Highway connects with the Rim of the World Drive at Running Springs.

■ **CALIFORNIA STATE UNIVERSITY, SAN MARCOS** V-3
333 South Twin Oaks Valley Rd.
San Marcos, CA 92096-0001
Tel: (760)750-4000
Admissions: (760)750-4848
Fax: (760)750-4030
E-mail: apply@csusm.edu
Web Site: http://www.csusm.edu/

Description: State-supported, comprehensive, coed. Part of California State University System. Awards bachelor's and master's degrees. Founded 1990. Setting: 304-acre suburban campus with easy access to San Diego. Endowment: $5.9 million. Research spending for 2004 fiscal year: $1.8 million. Educational spending for 2005 fiscal year: $5150 per student. Total enrollment: 6,956. Faculty: 402. 6,586 applied, 44% were admitted. Full-time: 4,658 students, 63% women, 37% men. Part-time: 1,669 students, 58% women, 42% men. 1% from out-of-state, 1% Native American, 21% Hispanic, 3% black, 11% Asian American or Pacific Islander, 3% international, 30% 25 or older, 7% live on campus, 17% transferred in. Retention: 73% of full-time freshmen returned the following year. Core. Calendar: semesters. Academic remediation for entering students, ESL program, services for LD students, advanced placement, self-designed majors, independent study, distance learning, double major, summer session for credit, part-time degree program, adult/continuing education programs, internships. Off campus study at San Diego State University, Palomar College, Mira Costa College. Study abroad program. ROTC: Army (c), Naval (c), Air Force (c).
Entrance Requirements: Options: electronic application, international baccalaureate accepted. Required: high school transcript, minimum 3.0 high school GPA. Required for some: SAT or ACT. Entrance: moderately difficult. Application deadline: 11/30. Notification: continuous.
Costs Per Year: Application fee: $55. State resident tuition: $0 full-time. Nonresident tuition: $8136 full-time, $339 per credit hour part-time. Mandatory fees: $3062 full-time. Part-time tuition varies according to course load. College room only: $7470. Room charges vary according to housing facility.
Collegiate Environment: Orientation program. Drama-theater group, choral group, student-run newspaper. Social organizations: 30 open to all; national fraternities, national sororities. Most popular organizations: Accounting Club, Liberal Studies Club, MECHA, Sigma IOTA Epsilon. Major annual events: Pow-Wow, Welcome Week, Awards Dinner. Student services: health clinic, personal-psychological counseling, women's center. Campus security: 24-hour patrols, student patrols, late night transport-escort service. Options: men-only, women-only housing available. Kellogg Library with 233,445 books, 941,482 microform titles, 2,043 serials, 8,528 audiovisual materials, an OPAC, and a Web page. Operations spending for 2004 fiscal year: $2.7 million. 1,300 computers available on campus for general student use. A campuswide network can be accessed from student residence rooms and from off campus. Staffed computer lab on campus.

■ **CALIFORNIA STATE UNIVERSITY, STANISLAUS** K-7
801 West Monte Vista Ave.
Turlock, CA 95382
Tel: (209)667-3122
Admissions: (209)667-3152
Fax: (209)667-3333
E-mail: outreach_help_desk@csustan.edu
Web Site: http://www.csustan.edu/
Description: State-supported, comprehensive, coed. Part of California State University System. Awards bachelor's and master's degrees. Founded 1957. Setting: 220-acre small town campus. Research spending for 2004 fiscal year: $397,203. Total enrollment: 8,137. Faculty: 495 (285 full-time, 210 part-time). Student-undergrad faculty ratio is 17:1. 4,292 applied, 65% were admitted. Full-time: 4,500 students, 66% women, 34% men. Part-time: 1,983 students, 67% women, 33% men. Students come from 29 states and territories, 58 other countries, 1% from out-of-state, 1% Native American, 28% Hispanic, 4% black, 12% Asian American or Pacific Islander, 1% international, 31% 25 or older, 9% live on campus. Retention: 82% of full-time freshmen returned the following year. Academic areas with the most degrees conferred: liberal arts/general studies; business/marketing; social sciences. Core. Calendar: 4-1-4. Academic remediation for entering students, ESL program, services for LD students, advanced placement, accelerated degree program, self-designed majors, honors program, independent study, distance learning, double major, summer session for credit, part-time degree program, external degree program, adult/continuing education programs, co-op programs and internships, graduate courses open to undergrads. Off campus study at other units of the California State University System. Study abroad program.
Entrance Requirements: Options: electronic application, early decision. Required: high school transcript. Recommended: minimum 3.0 high school GPA. Required for some: interview, ELM/EPT, TOEFL, SAT or ACT, ELM/EPT, TOEFL. Entrance: moderately difficult. Application deadlines: 7/1, 10/1 for early action. Notification: 1/1, 10/1 for early action.
Costs Per Year: Application fee: $55. State resident tuition: $0 full-time. Nonresident tuition: $10,170 full-time, $339 per unit part-time. Mandatory

fees: $3030 full-time, $855.50 per term part-time. College room and board: $8253. College room only: $5612. Room and board charges vary according to board plan and housing facility.

Collegiate Environment: Orientation program. Drama-theater group, choral group, marching band, student-run newspaper, radio station. Social organizations: 57 open to all; national fraternities, national sororities, local fraternities, local sororities; 3% of eligible men and 3% of eligible women are members. Most popular organization: MECHA. Major annual events: Warrior Day, Homecoming. Student services: health clinic, personal-psychological counseling, women's center, Remedial services, academic/career counseling, placement service, day care. Campus security: 24-hour emergency response devices and patrols, student patrols, late night transport-escort service, controlled dormitory access. 548 college housing spaces available; 533 were occupied in 2003-04. No special consideration for freshman housing applicants. Option: coed housing available. University Library with 365,870 books, 1.3 million microform titles, 1,693 serials, 5,435 audiovisual materials, an OPAC, and a Web page. Operations spending for 2004 fiscal year: $3 million. 150 computers available on campus for general student use. A campuswide network can be accessed from student residence rooms and from off campus. Staffed computer lab on campus.

Community Environment: Population 5,200. This is a growing and prosperous residential community in a rural area of central California. Dairying is of major importance; turkeys, melons, grapes and peaches are the chief products. The area is served by bus and railroad. One general hospital, one clinic, many churches, three libraries and most all of the major fraternal and civic organizations are represented in Turlock. Part-time employment opportunities are average. Special events are the Stanislaus County Fair and the Annual Chamber of Commerce Roundup Week in the fall. A summer concert series is held at the university.

■ **CAÑADA COLLEGE** *K-4*
4200 Farm Hill Blvd.
Redwood City, CA 94061-1099
Tel: (650)306-3100
Admissions: (650)306-3125
Fax: (650)306-3457
Web Site: http://www.canadacollege.net/
Description: State and locally supported, 2-year, coed. Part of San Mateo County Community College District System. Awards certificates, transfer associate, and terminal associate degrees. Founded 1968. Setting: 131-acre suburban campus with easy access to San Francisco and San Jose. Total enrollment: 6,421. 1,020 applied, 100% were admitted. Students come from 32 other countries, 0.4% Native American, 42% Hispanic, 4% black, 8% Asian American or Pacific Islander, 65% 25 or older. Retention: 65% of full-time freshmen returned the following year. Core. Calendar: semesters. Academic remediation for entering students, ESL program, services for LD students, advanced placement, accelerated degree program, summer session for credit, part-time degree program, adult/continuing education programs, co-op programs and internships. Study abroad program.
Entrance Requirements: Open admission except for radiological technology programs. Option: early admission. Entrance: noncompetitive. Application deadline: Rolling.
Collegiate Environment: Drama-theater group, choral group. Social organizations: 15 open to all. Most popular organizations: Latin-American Club, student government, Environmental Club, athletics, Interior Design Club. Major annual event: Spring Fair. Student services: health clinic, personal-psychological counseling. Campus security: 12-hour patrols by trained security personnel. College housing not available. 53,417 books, 414 serials, and an OPAC. 55 computers available on campus for general student use. Staffed computer lab on campus.

■ **CERRITOS COLLEGE** *R-5*
11110 Alondra Blvd.
Norwalk, CA 90650-6298
Tel: (562)860-2451
E-mail: smurguia@cerritos.edu
Web Site: http://www.cerritos.edu/
Description: State and locally supported, 2-year, coed. Part of California Community College System. Awards transfer associate and terminal associate degrees. Founded 1956. Setting: 140-acre suburban campus with easy access to Los Angeles. Total enrollment: 24,000. Students come from 32 other countries, 46% 25 or older. Core. Calendar: semesters. Academic remediation for entering students, ESL program, services for LD students,

advanced placement, summer session for credit, part-time degree program, adult/continuing education programs. Study abroad program.
Entrance Requirements: Open admission. Options: early admission, deferred admission. Placement: CEPT, Nelson Denny Reading Test recommended. Entrance: noncompetitive. Application deadline: Rolling.
Collegiate Environment: Drama-theater group, student-run newspaper, radio station. Social organizations: local fraternities, local sororities. Student services: legal services, health clinic, personal-psychological counseling, women's center. College housing not available. Wilford Michael Library with 74,502 books and 396 serials. 400 computers available on campus for general student use. A campuswide network can be accessed from off-campus.
Community Environment: Norwalk is an urban area 17 miles from Los Angeles. The climate is subtropical. There is bus and rail service to Los Angeles, where other major transportation facilities are located. The city has many community facilities, industrial firms and retail outlets. Part-time work is available.

■ **CERRO COSO COMMUNITY COLLEGE** *P-11*
3000 College Heights Blvd.
Ridgecrest, CA 93555-9571
Tel: (760)384-6100
Admissions: (760)384-6291
Fax: (760)375-4776
Web Site: http://www.cerrocoso.edu/
Description: State-supported, 2-year, coed. Part of Kern Community College District System. Awards certificates, transfer associate, and terminal associate degrees. Founded 1973. Setting: 320-acre small town campus. Research spending for 2004 fiscal year: $25,000. Educational spending for 2005 fiscal year: $3000 per student. Total enrollment: 5,020. 375 applied, 100% were admitted. Full-time: 1,218 students, 60% women, 40% men. Part-time: 3,802 students, 62% women, 38% men. Students come from 30 states and territories, 2% from out-of-state, 3% Native American, 12% Hispanic, 6% black, 6% Asian American or Pacific Islander, 0.4% international, 55% 25 or older, 4% transferred in. Retention: 51% of full-time freshmen returned the following year. Core. Calendar: semesters. Academic remediation for entering students, ESL program, services for LD students, honors program, distance learning, summer session for credit, part-time degree program, adult/continuing education programs, co-op programs.
Entrance Requirements: Open admission except for nursing program. Option: early admission. Recommended: high school transcript. Placement: ACT ASSET required for some. Entrance: noncompetitive. Application deadline: Rolling.
Costs Per Year: Application fee: $0. State resident tuition: $0 full-time. Nonresident tuition: $5010 full-time, $162 per unit part-time. Mandatory fees: $780 full-time, $26 per unit part-time.
Collegiate Environment: Orientation program. Most popular organizations: Special Services Club, Art Club, LVN Club, Athletic Club, Drama Club. Student services: personal-psychological counseling. Campus security: patrols by trained security personnel. College housing not available. Walter Stiern Memorial Library with 25,000 books, 800 serials, an OPAC, and a Web page. Operations spending for 2004 fiscal year: $400,000. 100 computers available on campus for general student use. A campuswide network can be accessed from off-campus. Staffed computer lab on campus.

■ **CHABOT COLLEGE** *K-5*
25555 Hesperian Blvd.
Hayward, CA 94545-5001
Tel: (510)723-6600
Admissions: (510)723-6700
Web Site: http://www.chabotcollege.edu/
Description: State-supported, 2-year, coed. Part of California Community College System. Awards certificates, transfer associate, and terminal associate degrees. Founded 1961. Setting: 245-acre suburban campus with easy access to San Francisco. Total enrollment: 15,075. 1,248 applied, 100% were admitted. Students come from 78 other countries, 2% from out-of-state, 1% Native American, 22% Hispanic, 13% black, 30% Asian American or Pacific Islander, 47% 25 or older. Retention: 66% of full-time freshmen returned the following year. Core. Calendar: semesters. Academic remediation for entering students, ESL program, services for LD students, advanced placement, self-designed majors, distance learning, double major, summer session for credit, part-time degree program, adult/continuing education programs, internships. Off campus study at Mills College; California State University, Hayward. Study abroad program. ROTC: Army (c), Air Force (c).

Entrance Requirements: Open admission except for dental hygiene, nursing, emergency medical technician programs. Option: electronic application. Required: high school transcript. Entrance: noncompetitive. Notification: continuous. Preference given to state residents.

Collegiate Environment: Orientation program. Drama-theater group, choral group, student-run newspaper, radio station. Social organizations: 21 open to all. Most popular organizations: Chinese Club, International Club, MECHA, ASCC, SCTA (Student California Teachers Association). Major annual events: Homecoming, Health Fair, International Night. Student services: legal services, personal-psychological counseling. Campus security: 24-hour emergency response devices, late night transport-escort service. College housing not available. Chabot Library with 100,000 books and 160 serials. 100 computers available on campus for general student use. A campuswide network can be accessed from off-campus. Staffed computer lab on campus.

Community Environment: See California State University - Hayward.

■ **CHAFFEY COLLEGE** *S-11*
5885 Haven Ave.
Rancho Cucamonga, CA 91737-3002
Tel: (909)987-1737
Admissions: (909)941-2631
Fax: (909)941-2783
Web Site: http://www.chaffey.edu/

Description: District-supported, 2-year, coed. Part of California Community College System. Awards certificates, transfer associate, and terminal associate degrees. Founded 1883. Setting: 200-acre suburban campus with easy access to Los Angeles. Total enrollment: 17,930. 2% from out-of-state, 40% 25 or older. Core. Calendar: semesters. Academic remediation for entering students, ESL program, services for LD students, advanced placement, honors program, summer session for credit, part-time degree program, adult/continuing education programs, co-op programs and internships. Study abroad program. ROTC: Army (c).

Entrance Requirements: Open admission. Option: early admission. Entrance: noncompetitive. Application deadline: Rolling. Notification: continuous.

Collegiate Environment: Drama-theater group, choral group, student-run newspaper, radio station. Social organizations: 30 open to all. Most popular organizations: The Associated Students of Chaffey College, Multicultural Club, Style Club. Major annual events: Club Rush, Toy and Food Drive, ICC sponsored events. Student services: health clinic, personal-psychological counseling. Campus security: 24-hour emergency response devices, late night transport-escort service. College housing not available. Chaffey College Library with 72,000 books and 232 serials. 150 computers available on campus for general student use.

Community Environment: Rancho Cucamonga is a suburban community 44 miles east of Los Angeles. With the west end of San Bernadino County the area has a population of 475,000. It has dry climate conditions, with temperatures ranging from 25 to 112 degrees during the year. Farming, namely citrus and grapes, is the main economy. Rail, bus, and air (Ontario International Airport) serve the area. There are four hospitals nearby.

■ **CHAPMAN UNIVERSITY** *S-7*
One University Dr.
Orange, CA 92866
Tel: (714)997-6815; 888-CUAPPLY
Admissions: (714)997-6711
Fax: (714)997-6713
E-mail: low@chapman.edu
Web Site: http://www.chapman.edu/

Description: Independent, comprehensive, coed, affiliated with Christian Church (Disciples of Christ). Awards bachelor's, master's, and first professional degrees. Founded 1861. Setting: 45-acre suburban campus with easy access to Los Angeles. Endowment: $175 million. Educational spending for 2005 fiscal year: $19,969 per student. Total enrollment: 5,732. Faculty: 581 (264 full-time, 317 part-time). Student-undergrad faculty ratio is 14:1. 3,862 applied, 53% were admitted. 9 National Merit Scholars, 10 class presidents, 8 valedictorians. Full-time: 3,661 students, 59% women, 41% men. Part-time: 203 students, 55% women, 45% men. Students come from 48 states and territories, 37 other countries, 20% from out-of-state, 1% Native American, 11% Hispanic, 2% black, 8% Asian American or Pacific Islander, 2% international, 6% 25 or older, 38% live on campus, 9% transferred in. Retention: 85% of full-time freshmen returned the following year. Academic areas with the most degrees conferred: visual and performing arts; business/marketing; communications/journalism. Core. Calendar: 4-1-4. Academic

remediation for entering students, ESL program, services for LD students, advanced placement, accelerated degree program, honors program, independent study, distance learning, double major, summer session for credit, part-time degree program, adult/continuing education programs, co-op programs and internships, graduate courses open to undergrads. Study abroad program. ROTC: Army (c), Air Force (c).

Entrance Requirements: Options: Common Application, electronic application, early admission, early action, international baccalaureate accepted. Required: essay, high school transcript, minimum 2.75 high school GPA, 1 recommendation, SAT or ACT. Recommended: minimum 3.5 high school GPA, interview, SAT Subject Tests. Entrance: moderately difficult. Application deadlines: 1/31, 11/30 for early action. Notification: continuous, 1/15 for early action.

Costs Per Year: Application fee: $55. Comprehensive fee: $41,248 includes full-time tuition ($29,900), mandatory fees ($848), and college room and board ($10,500). Part-time tuition: $920 per credit.

Collegiate Environment: Orientation program. Drama-theater group, choral group, student-run newspaper, radio station. Social organizations: 60 open to all; national fraternities, national sororities. Most popular organizations: Associated Students, Disciples on Campus, Gamma Beta Phi honor society. Major annual events: homecoming, Spring Sizzle, Orientation. Student services: health clinic, personal-psychological counseling. Campus security: 24-hour emergency response devices and patrols, late night transport-escort service, controlled dormitory access, full safety education program. 1,450 college housing spaces available; 1,411 were occupied in 2003-04. On-campus residence required in freshman year. Option: coed housing available. Leatherby Libraries plus 1 other with 182,169 books, 430,100 microform titles, 1,802 serials, 18,099 audiovisual materials, an OPAC, and a Web page. Operations spending for 2004 fiscal year: $1.9 million. 453 computers available on campus for general student use. Computer purchase/lease plans available. A campuswide network can be accessed from student residence rooms and from off campus. Staffed computer lab on campus.

Community Environment: Orange is located 32 miles southeast of Los Angeles and 94 miles north of San Diego. Its climate is mild with a very low rainfall. It is accessible by car, bus or train and plane. Orange County Airport is a short distance away, and Los Angeles International Airport is a 45-minute drive away. As the name implies, Orange lies in a vast citrus belt; avocados are also grown here. All the necessary facilities of a city are available as well as many recreational facilities for swimming, golf, surfing, skiing, fishing, hunting, and boating. Beaches and mountain resorts are nearby.

■ **CHARLES R. DREW UNIVERSITY OF MEDICINE AND SCIENCE** *S-10*
1731 East 120th St.
Los Angeles, CA 90059
Tel: (323)563-4800
Admissions: (323)563-5849
E-mail: mavalero@cdrewu.edu
Web Site: http://www.cdrewu.edu/

Description: Independent, comprehensive, coed. Awards associate, bachelor's, master's, and doctoral degrees. Founded 1966. Total enrollment: 250. Faculty: 35. Student-undergrad faculty ratio is 7:1. 364 applied, 55% were admitted. 0.4% Native American, 22% Hispanic, 49% black, 16% Asian American or Pacific Islander. Academic area with the most degrees conferred: health professions and related sciences. Calendar: trimesters. Academic remediation for entering students, services for LD students, independent study, part-time degree program, internships.

Entrance Requirements: Required: essay, high school transcript, minimum 2.0 high school GPA, 3 recommendations, interview. Recommended: SAT or ACT. Required for some: preadmission assessment exams. Entrance: moderately difficult. Application deadline: 4/30. Notification: continuous.

Costs Per Year: Application fee: $35. Tuition: $10,000 full-time, $250 per unit part-time. Mandatory fees: $100 full-time, $100 per year part-time.

Collegiate Environment: Student services: health clinic, personal-psychological counseling. College housing not available.

■ **CITRUS COLLEGE** *P-6*
1000 West Foothill Blvd.
Glendora, CA 91741-1899
Tel: (626)963-0323
Web Site: http://www.citruscollege.edu/

Description: State and locally supported, 2-year, coed. Part of California Community College System. Awards certificates, diplomas, transfer associate, and terminal associate degrees. Founded 1915. Setting: 104-acre small town campus with easy access to Los Angeles. Total enrollment: 12,393. Student-undergrad faculty ratio is 29:1. 25% 25 or older. Core. Calendar: semesters. Academic remediation for entering students, ESL program, services for LD students, advanced placement, honors program, distance learning, summer session for credit, part-time degree program, co-op programs. Study abroad program.

Entrance Requirements: Open admission. Required: high school transcript. Entrance: noncompetitive.

Costs Per Year: Application fee: $0. State resident tuition: $0 full-time. Nonresident tuition: $4954 full-time, $150 per unit part-time. Mandatory fees: $754 full-time, $26 per unit part-time. Full-time tuition and fees vary according to course load. Part-time tuition and fees vary according to course load.

Collegiate Environment: Orientation program. Drama-theater group, choral group, student-run newspaper. Social organizations: 40 open to all. Most popular organizations: Student Government, AGS Honor Society, International Student Association, Cosmetology Club. Major annual events: Fall Fest, Spring Fest, Club Rush. Student services: legal services, health clinic, personal-psychological counseling. Campus security: 24-hour patrols, student patrols, late night transport-escort service. College housing not available. Hayden Library with 45,091 books, 133 serials, 4,752 audiovisual materials, an OPAC, and a Web page. 1,100 computers available on campus for general student use. A campuswide network can be accessed. Staffed computer lab on campus.

Community Environment: See Azusa Pacific University

■ **CITY COLLEGE OF SAN FRANCISCO** *K-4*
50 Phelan Ave.
San Francisco, CA 94112-1821
Tel: (415)239-3000
Admissions: (415)239-3291
Fax: (415)239-3936
Web Site: http://www.ccsf.edu/

Description: State and locally supported, 2-year, coed. Part of California Community College System. Awards certificates, diplomas, transfer associate, and terminal associate degrees. Founded 1935. Setting: 56-acre urban campus. Total enrollment: 106,480. Students come from 51 states and territories, 1% Native American, 16% Hispanic, 9% black, 38% Asian American or Pacific Islander, 62% 25 or older. Core. Calendar: semesters. Academic remediation for entering students, ESL program, services for LD students, advanced placement, summer session for credit, part-time degree program, adult/continuing education programs, internships. Off campus study at members of The San Francisco Consortium. Study abroad program. ROTC: Army (c).

Entrance Requirements: Open admission. Option: early admission. Entrance: noncompetitive. Application deadline: Rolling. Notification: continuous.

Collegiate Environment: Orientation program. Drama-theater group, student-run newspaper. Student services: health clinic, personal-psychological counseling, women's center. Campus security: 24-hour patrols. College housing not available. Louise and Claude Rosenberg, Jr. Library with 93,518 books, 774 serials, and a Web page.

Community Environment: See San Francisco State University

■ **CLAREMONT MCKENNA COLLEGE** *V-10*
500 East 9th St.
Claremont, CA 91711
Tel: (909)621-8000
Admissions: (909)621-8088
E-mail: admission@claremontmckenna.edu
Web Site: http://www.claremontmckenna.edu/

Description: Independent, 4-year, coed. Part of The Claremont Colleges Consortium. Awards bachelor's degrees. Founded 1946. Setting: 50-acre small town campus with easy access to Los Angeles. Endowment: $316 million. Research spending for 2004 fiscal year: $2.4 million. Total enrollment: 1,139. Student-undergrad faculty ratio is 9:1. 3,734 applied, 21% were admitted. 83% from top 10% of their high school class, 97% from top quarter, 100% from top half. 11 National Merit Scholars, 12 class presidents, 7 valedictorians, 36 student government officers. Full-time: 1,139 students, 46% women, 54% men. Students come from 46 states and territories, 21 other countries, 53% from out-of-state, 0.4% Native American, 12% Hispanic, 4% black, 15% Asian American or Pacific Islander, 4% international, 0.1% 25 or older, 96% live on campus, 3% transferred in. Retention: 97% of full-time freshmen returned the following year. Core. Calendar:

semesters. Services for LD students, advanced placement, accelerated degree program, self-designed majors, honors program, independent study, double major, internships. Off campus study at 5 members of The Claremont Colleges, Haverford College, Colby College, Spelman College, Morehouse College. Study abroad program. ROTC: Army, Air Force (c).

Entrance Requirements: Options: Peterson's Universal Application, Common Application, electronic application, early admission, early decision, deferred admission, international baccalaureate accepted. Required: essay, high school transcript, minimum 3.0 high school GPA, 3 recommendations, SAT or ACT. Recommended: interview, SAT Subject Tests. Entrance: very difficult. Application deadlines: 1/2, 11/15 for early decision plan 1, 1/2 for early decision plan 2. Notification: 4/1, 12/15 for early decision plan 1, 2/15 for early decision plan 2.

Costs Per Year: Application fee: $60. Comprehensive fee: $42,920 includes full-time tuition ($30,800), mandatory fees ($1850), and college room and board ($10,270). College room only: $5160. Full-time tuition and fees vary according to reciprocity agreements. Room and board charges vary according to board plan and housing facility. Part-time tuition: $5100 per course.

Collegiate Environment: Orientation program. Drama-theater group, choral group, student-run newspaper, radio station. Social organizations: 280 open to all. Most popular organizations: student government, Debate/Forensics Club, newspaper, Volunteer Student Admission Committee, Civitas (community service club). Major annual events: Athenaeum Lectures, Winter Madrigal, Monte Carlo Night. Student services: health clinic, personal-psychological counseling, women's center. Campus security: 24-hour emergency response devices and patrols, student patrols, late night transport-escort service, controlled dormitory access. College housing designed to accommodate 972 students; 1,008 undergraduates lived in college housing during 2003-04. Freshmen guaranteed college housing. On-campus residence required in freshman year. Option: coed housing available. Honnold Library plus 3 others with 2 million books, 1.4 million microform titles, 6,028 serials, 606 audiovisual materials, an OPAC, and a Web page. Operations spending for 2004 fiscal year: $2.3 million. 120 computers available on campus for general student use. A campuswide network can be accessed from student residence rooms and from off campus. Staffed computer lab on campus.

■ **CLEVELAND CHIROPRACTIC COLLEGE-LOS ANGELES CAMPUS** *S-10*
590 North Vermont Ave.
Los Angeles, CA 90004-2196
Tel: (323)660-6166
Free: 800-446-CCLA
Admissions: (323)906-2031
Fax: (323)660-5387
Web Site: http://www.clevelandchiropractic.edu/

Description: Independent, upper-level, coed. Administratively affiliated with Cleveland Chiropractic College-Kansas City. Awards associate, bachelor's, and first professional degrees. Founded 1911. Total enrollment: 435. Faculty: 39 (22 full-time, 17 part-time). Student-undergrad faculty ratio is 6:1. Full-time: 92 students, 33% women, 67% men. Part-time: 31 students, 29% women, 71% men. Students come from 15 states and territories, 8 other countries, 3% from out-of-state, 0% Native American, 18% Hispanic, 7% black, 11% Asian American or Pacific Islander, 2% international, 47% 25 or older, 92% transferred in. Retention: 53% of full-time entering class returned the following year. Academic area with the most degrees conferred: health professions and related sciences. Core. Calendar: trimesters. ESL program, advanced placement, accelerated degree program, freshman honors college, distance learning, double major, summer session for credit, part-time degree program, adult/continuing education programs, co-op programs.

Costs Per Year: Application fee: $35. Tuition: $5242 full-time, $219 per credit part-time. Mandatory fees: $200 full-time, $200 per year part-time.

Collegiate Environment: Orientation program. College housing not available. Carl Cleveland Jr. with 23,618 books, 1,671 microform titles, 152 serials, 11,341 audiovisual materials, an OPAC, and a Web page.

■ **COASTLINE COMMUNITY COLLEGE** *T-6*
11460 Warner Ave.
Fountain Valley, CA 92708-2597
Tel: (714)546-7600
Admissions: (714)241-6160
Fax: (714)241-6288
Web Site: http://coastline.cccd.edu/

Description: State and locally supported, 2-year, coed. Part of Coast Community College District System. Awards certificates and transfer associate degrees. Founded 1976. Setting: urban campus with easy access to Los Angeles. Research spending for 2004 fiscal year: $90,000. Educational spending for 2005 fiscal year: $330 per student. Total enrollment: 8,559. Full-time: 493 students, 57% women, 43% men. Part-time: 8,066 students, 60% women, 40% men. 1% Native American, 14% Hispanic, 6% black, 29% Asian American or Pacific Islander, 1% international, 75% 25 or older, 48% transferred in. Core. Calendar: semesters. Academic remediation for entering students, ESL program, services for LD students, advanced placement, distance learning, summer session for credit, part-time degree program, external degree program, adult/continuing education programs, co-op programs and internships.

Entrance Requirements: Open admission. Options: Common Application, early admission. Recommended: high school transcript. Entrance: noncompetitive. Application deadline: Rolling.

Collegiate Environment: Student services: health clinic. Campus security: 24-hour emergency response devices. College housing not available.

■ **COGSWELL POLYTECHNICAL COLLEGE** *J-6*

1175 Bordeaux Dr.
Sunnyvale, CA 94089-1299
Tel: (408)541-0100
Free: 800-264-7955
Fax: (408)747-0764
E-mail: info@cogswell.edu
Web Site: http://www.cogswell.edu/

Description: Independent, 4-year, coed. Part of Foundation for Educational Achievement, San Diego. Awards bachelor's degrees. Founded 1887. Setting: 2-acre suburban campus with easy access to San Francisco and San Jose. Endowment: $9 million. Educational spending for 2005 fiscal year: $3348 per student. Total enrollment: 282. Student-undergrad faculty ratio is 8:1. 61 applied, 98% were admitted. Full-time: 133 students, 15% women, 85% men. Part-time: 149 students, 10% women, 90% men. Students come from 20 states and territories, 5 other countries, 10% from out-of-state, 0.4% Native American, 9% Hispanic, 2% black, 11% Asian American or Pacific Islander, 0% international, 50% 25 or older, 9% live on campus, 24% transferred in. Retention: 70% of full-time freshmen returned the following year. Core. Calendar: semesters. Advanced placement, distance learning, summer session for credit, part-time degree program, external degree program, adult/continuing education programs, internships.

Entrance Requirements: Options: Peterson's Universal Application, Common Application, deferred admission. Required: essay, high school transcript, minimum 2.5 high school GPA. Required for some: recommendations, interview, portfolio. Entrance: moderately difficult. Application deadline: 6/1. Notification: continuous.

Costs Per Year: Application fee: $55. Tuition: $13,680 full-time, $570 per credit part-time. Full-time tuition varies according to course load. Part-time tuition varies according to course load. College room only: $3000. Room charges vary according to housing facility.

Collegiate Environment: Orientation program. Student-run newspaper. Social organizations: 1 open to all. Most popular organization: ASB. Major annual events: Founders' Day, dance, movie nights. Student services: personal-psychological counseling. Campus security: 24-hour emergency response devices. 30 undergraduates lived in college housing during 2003-04. No special consideration for freshman housing applicants. Options: men-only, women-only housing available. Cogswell College Library with 11,257 books, 43 microform titles, 102 serials, 359 audiovisual materials, and an OPAC. Operations spending for 2004 fiscal year: $77,625. 125 computers available on campus for general student use. A campuswide network can be accessed from off-campus. Staffed computer lab on campus.

■ **THE COLBURN SCHOOL CONSERVATORY OF MUSIC** *S-10*

200 South Grand Ave.
Los Angeles, CA 90012
Tel: (213)621-2200
Fax: (213)621-2110
E-mail: ktesar@colburnschool.edu
Web Site: http://www.colburnschool.edu/

Description: Independent, 4-year, coed. Awards bachelor's degrees. Founded 1980. Setting: urban campus with easy access to Los Angeles. Total enrollment: 17. 39 applied, 31% were admitted. Students come from 4 states and territories, 4 other countries, 0% Native American, 0% Hispanic,

0% black, 24% Asian American or Pacific Islander, 47% international, 100% live on campus. Calendar: semesters.

Entrance Requirements: Required: essay, high school transcript, 2 recommendations, interview. Recommended: SAT or ACT. Application deadline: 1/15.

Costs Per Year: Application fee: $100. Tuition: $0 full-time. Mandatory fees: $1200 full-time.

Collegiate Environment: Student services: personal-psychological counseling. Campus security: trained security personnel during open building hours. College housing not available.

■ **COLEMAN COLLEGE (LA MESA)** *V-12*

7380 Parkway Dr.
La Mesa, CA 91942-1532
Tel: (619)465-3990
Fax: (619)465-0162
Web Site: http://www.coleman.edu/

Description: Independent, comprehensive, coed. Awards associate, bachelor's, and master's degrees. Founded 1963. Setting: 3-acre suburban campus with easy access to San Diego. Educational spending for 2005 fiscal year: $1700 per student. Total enrollment: 468. Full-time: 444 students, 23% women, 77% men. Students come from 19 states and territories, 5% from out-of-state, 0% Native American, 15% Hispanic, 10% black, 11% Asian American or Pacific Islander, 2% international, 68% 25 or older. Core. Services for LD students, accelerated degree program, distance learning, summer session for credit, part-time degree program.

Entrance Requirements: Options: Common Application, deferred admission. Required: high school transcript, interview. Entrance: moderately difficult. Application deadline: 8/1. Notification: continuous.

Costs Per Year: Application fee: $100. Tuition: $20,580 full-time, $245 per unit part-time. Mandatory fees: $100 full-time. Tuition guaranteed not to increase for student's term of enrollment.

Collegiate Environment: Student services: personal-psychological counseling. Campus security: 24-hour emergency response devices and patrols, late night transport-escort service. College housing not available. Coleman College LaMesa Library with 66,800 books and 69 serials. Operations spending for 2004 fiscal year: $6000. 420 computers available on campus for general student use. A campuswide network can be accessed.

■ **COLEMAN COLLEGE (SAN MARCOS)** *V-3*

1284 West San Marcos Blvd.
San Marcos, CA 92069
Tel: (760)747-3990
Fax: (760)752-9808
Web Site: http://www.coleman.edu/

Description: Independent, 2-year, coed. Awards certificates and terminal associate degrees. Founded 1967. Setting: suburban campus. Total enrollment: 203. Full-time: 203 students, 27% women, 73% men. 16% Hispanic, 8% black, 9% Asian American or Pacific Islander.

■ **COLLEGE OF ALAMEDA** *H-5*

555 Atlantic Ave.
Alameda, CA 94501-2109
Tel: (510)522-7221
Admissions: (510)466-7365
E-mail: hperdue@peralta.cc.ca.us
Web Site: http://www.peralta.cc.ca.us/

Description: State and locally supported, 2-year, coed. Part of Peralta Community College District System. Awards certificates, transfer associate, and terminal associate degrees. Founded 1970. Setting: 62-acre urban campus with easy access to San Francisco. Research spending for 2004 fiscal year: $37,247. Educational spending for 2005 fiscal year: $953 per student. Total enrollment: 5,500. Students come from 18 states and territories, 9 other countries, 44% 25 or older. Calendar: semesters. Academic remediation for entering students, services for LD students, summer session for credit, part-time degree program, adult/continuing education programs, co-op programs. Off campus study at other units of the Peralta Community College District System.

Entrance Requirements: Open admission. Placement: SAT or ACT recommended. Entrance: noncompetitive. Application deadline: Rolling.

Collegiate Environment: Student-run newspaper. Student services: women's center. College housing not available. Learning Resources Center with 40,000 books and 200 serials. 20 computers available on campus for general student use.

Community Environment: See Laney College.

■ **COLLEGE OF THE CANYONS** *S-9*
26455 Rockwell Canyon Rd.
Santa Clarita, CA 91355-1803
Tel: (661)259-7800; 888-206-7827
Admissions: (661)362-3280
Fax: (661)362-5300
Web Site: http://www.canyons.edu/
Description: State and locally supported, 2-year, coed. Part of California Community College System. Awards certificates, transfer associate, and terminal associate degrees. Founded 1969. Setting: 158-acre suburban campus with easy access to Los Angeles. Research spending for 2004 fiscal year: $282,253. Educational spending for 2005 fiscal year: $2060 per student. Total enrollment: 16,504. Student-undergrad faculty ratio is 27:1. Full-time: 12,679 students, 40% women, 60% men. Part-time: 3,825 students, 49% women, 51% men. Students come from 15 states and territories, 3% from out-of-state, 1% Native American, 23% Hispanic, 4% black, 9% Asian American or Pacific Islander, 1% international, 35% 25 or older, 3% transferred in. Retention: 51% of full-time freshmen returned the following year. Core. Calendar: semesters. Academic remediation for entering students, ESL program, services for LD students, advanced placement, honors program, independent study, distance learning, double major, summer session for credit, part-time degree program, adult/continuing education programs, co-op programs and internships. Off campus study. Study abroad program.
Entrance Requirements: Open admission. Options: electronic application, early admission. Recommended: high school transcript. Entrance: noncompetitive. Application deadline: 8/22. Notification: continuous until 8/22.
Costs Per Year: Application fee: $0. State resident tuition: $0 full-time. Nonresident tuition: $5168 full-time, $171 per unit part-time. Mandatory fees: $818 full-time, $26 per unit part-time.
Collegiate Environment: Orientation program. Drama-theater group, choral group, student-run newspaper. Social organizations: 12 open to all. Most popular organizations: HITE, Phi Theta Kappa, Alpha Gamma Sigma, MECHA, Biology Club. Student services: health clinic, personal-psychological counseling. Campus security: student patrols, late night transport-escort service. College housing not available. College of the Canyons Library with 40,646 books, 84,510 microform titles, 233 serials, 29,955 audiovisual materials, an OPAC, and a Web page. Operations spending for 2004 fiscal year: $831,649. 650 computers available on campus for general student use. A campuswide network can be accessed. Staffed computer lab on campus.
Community Environment: The Valencia-Newhall-Saugus-Canyon Country communities comprise the city of Santa Clarita located 32 miles northwest of Los Angeles near the San Fernando Valley. The average mean temperature is 65 degrees. Community facilities include hospitals, churches, a library, newspapers and banks. Recreational facilities include theaters, parks, a riding stable and golf courses. Desert area and many secluded canyons are nearby. The Castaic Reservoir water recreation area opened in 1970.

■ **COLLEGE OF THE DESERT** *T-13*
43-500 Monterey Ave.
Palm Desert, CA 92260-9305
Tel: (760)346-8041
Admissions: (760)773-7516
Web Site: http://desert.cc.ca.us/
Description: State and locally supported, 2-year, coed. Part of California Community College System. Awards certificates, diplomas, transfer associate, and terminal associate degrees. Founded 1959. Setting: 160-acre small town campus. Total enrollment: 9,946. Students come from 23 states and territories, 1% from out-of-state, 1% Native American, 52% Hispanic, 3% black, 6% Asian American or Pacific Islander, 40% 25 or older. Core. Calendar: semesters. Academic remediation for entering students, ESL program, services for LD students, honors program, summer session for credit, part-time degree program, adult/continuing education programs.
Entrance Requirements: Open admission except for international applicants or nursing program. Option: early admission. Entrance: noncompetitive. Application deadline: Rolling. Notification: continuous. Preference given to district residents.
Collegiate Environment: Drama-theater group, choral group, student-run newspaper. Most popular organizations: student association, International Club, African-Americans for College Education. Major annual events:

Homecoming, Mayor's Forum, Rotary Awards. Student services: health clinic, personal-psychological counseling. Campus security: 24-hour emergency response devices, late night transport-escort service. College housing not available. College of the Desert Library with 58,000 books and 260 serials. 43 computers available on campus for general student use. A campuswide network can be accessed from off-campus. Staffed computer lab on campus.
Community Environment: Palm Desert is a resort area with a population of 12,000, where the climate is temperate. Buses and planes serve the area; Highway 111 goes through town. There are churches of major denominations, civic and service groups, and hospitals are nearby. Indio and Palm Springs have such recreational activities as boating, fishing, water skiing, and hiking. There are nearby mountains for winter sports. The area is a major center for golf and tennis tournaments.

■ **COLLEGE OF MARIN** *F-3*
835 College Ave.
Kentfield, CA 94904
Tel: (415)457-8811
Admissions: (415)485-9417
Fax: (415)883-2632
Web Site: http://www.marin.cc.ca.us/
Description: State and locally supported, 2-year, coed. Part of California Community College System. Awards transfer associate and terminal associate degrees. Founded 1926. Setting: 410-acre small town campus with easy access to San Francisco. Total enrollment: 6,516. 50% 25 or older. Core. Calendar: semesters. Academic remediation for entering students, ESL program, services for LD students, summer session for credit, part-time degree program, adult/continuing education programs, co-op programs.
Entrance Requirements: Open admission. Option: early admission. Entrance: noncompetitive. Application deadline: Rolling. Notification: continuous.
Collegiate Environment: Drama-theater group, student-run newspaper. Student services: health clinic, personal-psychological counseling. Campus security: 24-hour patrols. College housing not available. 85,000 books and 500 serials. 25 computers available on campus for general student use. Staffed computer lab on campus.
Community Environment: Kentfield is suburban community in a beautiful countryside across the Golden Gate from San Francisco. Located on a peninsula with the Pacific Ocean on one side and San Francisco Bay on the other. A mild climate averaging 70 degrees; average rainfall 36 inches per year. The Golden Gate bus line serves the area. Entertainment and recreational facilities are close by and shopping facilities are good. Good opportunities for part-time employment.

■ **COLLEGE OF THE REDWOODS** *D-1*
7351 Tompkins Hill Rd.
Eureka, CA 95501-9300
Tel: (707)476-4100
Admissions: (707)476-4177
Web Site: http://www.redwoods.edu/
Description: State and locally supported, 2-year, coed. Part of California Community College System. Awards certificates, transfer associate, and terminal associate degrees. Founded 1964. Setting: 322-acre small town campus. Endowment: $1.8 million. Educational spending for 2005 fiscal year: $3058 per student. Total enrollment: 7,708. 717 applied, 100% were admitted. Students come from 52 states and territories, 51% 25 or older, 2% live on campus. Core. Calendar: semesters. Academic remediation for entering students, ESL program, services for LD students, advanced placement, honors program, distance learning, summer session for credit, part-time degree program, adult/continuing education programs, co-op programs. Off campus study at Oregon Institute of Technology, Rogue Community College, Southern Oregon University.
Entrance Requirements: Open admission except for nursing program or international students. Options: Peterson's Universal Application, Common Application, early admission. Entrance: noncompetitive. Application deadline: Rolling.
Collegiate Environment: Social organizations: 15 open to all. Most popular organizations: Associated Students College of the Redwoods, Spanish Club, Computer Information Systems Club, Math/Science Club, International Student Club. Major annual events: Wood Fair, Music and Arts Fair, Multicultural Week. Student services: health clinic, personal-psychological counseling. Campus security: 24-hour emergency response devices and patrols, late night transport-escort service. 160 college housing spaces avail-

able; all were occupied in 2003-04. No special consideration for freshman housing applicants. Option: coed housing available. College of the Redwoods Library with 50,266 books, 969 serials, an OPAC, and a Web page. Operations spending for 2004 fiscal year: $335,024. 550 computers available on campus for general student use. A campuswide network can be accessed from student residence rooms and from off campus. Staffed computer lab on campus.

Community Environment: Eureka is located on the north coast of Humboldt Bay, 283 miles north of San Francisco; the climate is cool and humid. Buses and railroads serve the area, airlines to connecting flights in San Francisco, Oakland, Sacramento and Portland are available. Community facilities include two hospitals, a medical center, churches, libraries, and a good downtown shopping area. The city provides a park, a community recreation building and a 18 hole golf course. Fishing and hunting are excellent; mountain area very near. In Summer, salmon fishing is good in Humboldt and Trinidad Bay north of the city; in early fall, steelhead and salmon are caught in the Eel Mud, and Trinity Rivers nearby. Eureka sponsors an annual Rhododendron Festival and two fairs each year.

■ **COLLEGE OF SAN MATEO** *K-4*

1700 West Hillsdale Blvd.
San Mateo, CA 94402-3784
Tel: (650)574-6161
Admissions: (650)574-6594
E-mail: csmadmission@smcccd.cc.ca.us
Web Site: http://www.collegeofsanmateo.edu/

Description: State and locally supported, 2-year, coed. Part of California Community College System. Awards certificates, transfer associate, and terminal associate degrees. Founded 1922. Setting: 150-acre suburban campus. Total enrollment: 10,872. Students come from 35 other countries, 51% 25 or older. Core. Calendar: semesters. Academic remediation for entering students, ESL program, services for LD students, advanced placement, accelerated degree program, honors program, summer session for credit, part-time degree program, adult/continuing education programs, co-op programs and internships. Study abroad program. ROTC: Army (c), Naval (c), Air Force (c).

Entrance Requirements: Open admission except for nursing program. Option: early admission. Entrance: noncompetitive. Application deadline: Rolling.

Collegiate Environment: Orientation program. Student-run newspaper. Student services: health clinic, personal-psychological counseling. Campus security: 24-hour emergency response devices and patrols. College housing not available. College of San Mateo Library with 85,085 books, 300 serials, an OPAC, and a Web page. 150 computers available on campus for general student use. A campuswide network can be accessed from off-campus. Staffed computer lab on campus.

Community Environment: San Mateo, located on picturesque El Camino Real, is an attractive residential suburb, 19 miles south of San Francisco. Climate is moderate and the city claims to have an average of 258 days of sunshine each year. San Mateo has access to all major forms of transportation and has a municipal transit system. There are many churches, hospitals, and libraries. An outstanding retail shopping center is found on the Peninsula. Recreational facilities include golf courses, yacht harbor, public beach, public parks and the Bay Meadows Race Track.

■ **COLLEGE OF THE SEQUOIAS** *N-8*

915 South Mooney Blvd.
Visalia, CA 93277-2234
Tel: (559)730-3700
Admissions: (559)737-4844
Web Site: http://www.cos.edu/

Description: State and locally supported, 2-year, coed. Part of California Community College System. Awards certificates, transfer associate, and terminal associate degrees. Founded 1925. Setting: 215-acre suburban campus. Endowment: $1.2 million. Educational spending for 2005 fiscal year: $1805 per student. Total enrollment: 11,169. 2,171 applied, 100% were admitted. Full-time: 4,427 students, 59% women, 41% men. Part-time: 6,742 students, 60% women, 40% men. Students come from 23 states and territories, 1% Native American, 44% Hispanic, 4% black, 5% Asian American or Pacific Islander, 0.2% international, 46% 25 or older, 45% transferred in. Core. Calendar: semesters. Academic remediation for entering students, ESL program, services for LD students, advanced placement, accelerated degree program, freshman honors college, honors program, summer ses-

sion for credit, part-time degree program, adult/continuing education programs, co-op programs and internships. Study abroad program. ROTC: Air Force (c).

Entrance Requirements: Open admission except for nursing, engineering, chemistry, math, English programs. Option: early admission. Required: high school transcript. Entrance: noncompetitive. Application deadline: 8/15. Notification: continuous.

Collegiate Environment: Orientation program. Drama-theater group, choral group, student-run newspaper. Social organizations: 35 open to all. Most popular organizations: MECHA, Ag Club, Alpha Gamma Sigma, Paralegal Association, Sports Medicine Club. Major annual events: Homecoming, Multicultural Fair, Tech Prep Expo. Student services: health clinic, personal-psychological counseling, women's center. Campus security: 24-hour emergency response devices and patrols, student patrols, late night transport-escort service, 18 hour patrols by trained security personnel. College housing not available. College of the Sequoias Library with 73,557 books, 430 serials, an OPAC, and a Web page. Operations spending for 2004 fiscal year: $513,224. 190 computers available on campus for general student use. A campuswide network can be accessed from off-campus. Staffed computer lab on campus.

Community Environment: Visalia is 42 miles southeast of Fresno. It is the Tulare County seat and is situated in the fertile San Joaquin Valley. It ranks highest in the world in agricultural production of citrus fruits, dairy products, olives, cotton, and walnuts. A number of manufacturers and industrial plants are located here. Bus, rail, and air lines serve the area. The community has churches, hospitals, a symphony orchestra, ballet, theatres, 20 city parks, and 5 golf courses. Tulare County Park provides recreational facilities for picnicking and water sports. Nearby is the High Sierra mountain wonderland in the Sierra National Forest.

■ **COLLEGE OF THE SISKIYOUS** *B-4*

800 College Ave.
Weed, CA 96094-2899
Tel: (530)938-5555
Admissions: (530)938-5374
Fax: (530)938-5227
E-mail: richards@siskiyous.edu
Web Site: http://www.siskiyous.edu/

Description: State and locally supported, 2-year, coed. Part of California Community College System. Awards certificates, transfer associate, and terminal associate degrees. Founded 1957. Setting: 260-acre rural campus. Educational spending for 2005 fiscal year: $2631 per student. Total enrollment: 2,998. Student-undergrad faculty ratio is 21:1. 389 applied, 100% were admitted. Students come from 18 states and territories, 6 other countries, 27% from out-of-state, 4% Native American, 7% Hispanic, 3% black, 3% Asian American or Pacific Islander, 1% international, 39% 25 or older, 10% live on campus. Core. Calendar: semesters. Academic remediation for entering students, ESL program, services for LD students, advanced placement, self-designed majors, honors program, independent study, distance learning, double major, summer session for credit, part-time degree program, adult/continuing education programs, co-op programs and internships.

Entrance Requirements: Open admission. Options: early admission, deferred admission. Entrance: noncompetitive. Application deadline: Rolling. Notification: continuous.

Costs Per Year: Nonresident tuition: $174 per unit part-time. Mandatory fees: $26 per unit part-time, $12 per term part-time.

Collegiate Environment: Orientation program. Drama-theater group, choral group, student-run newspaper. Social organizations: 71 open to all. Most popular organizations: Associated Student Body, Latino Student Union, Phi Theta Kappa, Black Student Union, American Indian Alliance. Major annual events: Cinco de Mayo, Transfer Schools and Career Day. Student services: legal services, health clinic, personal-psychological counseling, women's center. Campus security: 24-hour emergency response devices, controlled dormitory access. 135 college housing spaces available; 120 were occupied in 2003-04. No special consideration for freshman housing applicants. Options: coed, men-only housing available. College of the Siskiyous Library with 34,708 books, 19,646 microform titles, 148 serials, 9,433 audiovisual materials, an OPAC, and a Web page. Operations spending for 2004 fiscal year: $379,177. 260 computers available on campus for general student use. A campuswide network can be accessed from off-campus. Staffed computer lab on campus.

Community Environment: Centrally located in Siskiyou County, just off Interstate 5, the historic lumber town of Weed lies nestled at the base of majestic 14,162-foot Mt. Shasta. At the midpoint between two major population centers - Medford, Oregon, to the north and Redding to the south - Weed is easily accessible by airline, train and bus services. The climate features four distinct seasons with an average snowfall of 24 inches. Outdoor enthusiasts will delight in the spectacular alpine environment of this rural northern California region, which provides for a wide variety of recreational activities including downhill and cross-country skiing, snowboarding, hunting, fishing, hiking, rock climbing, wind surfing, and more.

■ COLUMBIA COLLEGE *J-8*

11600 Columbia College Dr.
Sonora, CA 95370
Tel: (209)588-5100
Admissions: (209)588-5107
E-mail: gervind@yosemite.edu
Web Site: http://www.gocolumbia.org/
Description: State and locally supported, 2-year, coed. Part of Yosemite Community College District System. Awards certificates, transfer associate, and terminal associate degrees. Founded 1968. Setting: 200-acre rural campus. Total enrollment: 2,691. Student-undergrad faculty ratio is 16:1. 242 applied, 100% were admitted. Full-time: 940 students, 52% women, 48% men. Part-time: 1,751 students, 56% women, 44% men. Students come from 7 states and territories, 5% from out-of-state, 3% Native American, 7% Hispanic, 1% black, 2% Asian American or Pacific Islander, 0.1% international, 68% 25 or older. Core. Calendar: semesters. Academic remediation for entering students, ESL program, services for LD students, advanced placement, independent study, distance learning, double major, summer session for credit, part-time degree program, adult/continuing education programs, co-op programs and internships.
Entrance Requirements: Open admission. Options: Common Application, electronic application, early admission. Required for some: high school transcript. Entrance: noncompetitive. Application deadline: Rolling. Notification: continuous. Preference given to EOPS, disabled.
Costs Per Year: Application fee: $0. State resident tuition: $0 full-time. Nonresident tuition: $4286 full-time, $177 per unit part-time. Mandatory fees: $662 full-time, $26 per unit part-time, $24 per term part-time. College room and board: $6115.
Collegiate Environment: Orientation program. Drama-theater group, choral group, student-run newspaper. Social organizations: 7 open to all. Most popular organizations: International Club, Jazz Club, Ecology Action Club, Christian Club. Student services: health clinic, personal-psychological counseling. Campus security: 24-hour emergency response devices and patrols, late night transport-escort service. 200 college housing spaces available; 41 were occupied in 2003-04. Columbia College Library with 34,892 books, 67,497 microform titles, 320 serials, 4,852 audiovisual materials, an OPAC, and a Web page. 85 computers available on campus for general student use. Staffed computer lab on campus.

■ COLUMBIA COLLEGE HOLLYWOOD *S-9*

18618 Oxnard St.
Tarzana, CA 91356
Tel: (818)345-8414
Fax: (818)345-9053
Web Site: http://www.columbiacollege.edu/
Description: Independent, 4-year, coed. Awards associate and bachelor's degrees. Founded 1952. Setting: 1-acre urban campus. Total enrollment: 177. 83 applied, 39% were admitted. 8% from top 10% of their high school class, 23% from top quarter, 44% from top half. 2 class presidents, 20 student government officers. Students come from 30 other countries, 50% from out-of-state, 0% Native American, 12% Hispanic, 15% black, 5% Asian American or Pacific Islander, 18% international, 28% 25 or older. Retention: 83% of full-time freshmen returned the following year. Core. Accelerated degree program, summer session for credit, part-time degree program, adult/continuing education programs.
Entrance Requirements: Option: deferred admission. Required: essay, high school transcript, minimum 2.0 high school GPA, 2 recommendations, interview. Recommended: SAT. Entrance: minimally difficult. Application deadline: Rolling. Notification: continuous until 9/1.
Costs Per Year: Application fee: $50. Comprehensive fee: $18,350 includes full-time tuition ($11,400), mandatory fees ($1100), and college room and board ($5850). Part-time tuition: $325 per unit.
Collegiate Environment: Major annual event: Alumni Weekend. Student services: personal-psychological counseling. College housing not available.

Joseph E. Blath Memorial Library with 5,500 books, 23 serials, 220 audiovisual materials, and an OPAC. 12 computers available on campus for general student use. Staffed computer lab on campus.
Community Environment: The college is located close to freeways, public transportation, housing, and major recreational areas in Southern California.

■ COMPTON COMMUNITY COLLEGE *Y-3*

1111 East Artesia Blvd.
Compton, CA 90221-5393
Tel: (310)900-1600
Fax: (310)900-1692
Web Site: http://www.compton.edu/.
Description: State and locally supported, 2-year, coed. Part of California Community College System. Awards transfer associate and terminal associate degrees. Founded 1927. Setting: 83-acre urban campus with easy access to Los Angeles. Total enrollment: 7,900. 1,650 applied, 100% were admitted. Students come from 4 states and territories, 25 other countries, 69% 25 or older. Core. Calendar: semesters. Academic remediation for entering students, ESL program, services for LD students, advanced placement, honors program, summer session for credit, part-time degree program, adult/continuing education programs.
Entrance Requirements: Open admission. Option: early admission. Entrance: noncompetitive. Application deadline: Rolling. Notification: continuous.
Collegiate Environment: Drama-theater group. Student services: personal-psychological counseling. Campus security: 24-hour patrols. College housing not available. Compton Community College Library with 45,000 books and 400 serials. 30 computers available on campus for general student use.
Community Environment: Located between the cities of Los Angeles and Long Beach in the center of a large residential area. The population of the general area surrounding the city is now about 200,000, and is increasing each year. The city offers a mild climate and many days of sun. Mountains and the beaches are both nearby which provide a wealth of recreational activities. Work for room and board in private homes may be secured, part-time employment is also available.

■ CONCORDE CAREER INSTITUTE *S-10*

12412 Victory Blvd.
North Hollywood, CA 91606
Tel: (818)766-8151
Fax: (818)766-1587
Web Site: http://www.concordecareercolleges.com/
Description: Proprietary, 2-year, coed. Founded 1955.

■ CONCORDIA UNIVERSITY *T-7*

1530 Concordia West
Irvine, CA 92612-3299
Tel: (949)854-8002
Free: 800-229-1200
Fax: (949)854-6894
E-mail: admission@cui.edu
Web Site: http://www.cui.edu/
Description: Independent, comprehensive, coed, affiliated with Lutheran Church-Missouri Synod. Part of The Ten-campus Concordia University System. Awards bachelor's and master's degrees (associate's degree for international students only). Founded 1972. Setting: 70-acre suburban campus with easy access to Los Angeles. Endowment: $8.6 million. Educational spending for 2005 fiscal year: $4419 per student. Total enrollment: 2,092. Faculty: 208 (77 full-time, 131 part-time). Student-undergrad faculty ratio is 15:1. 998 applied, 68% were admitted. 15% from top 10% of their high school class, 53% from top quarter, 93% from top half. Full-time: 1,370 students, 63% women, 37% men. Part-time: 75 students, 64% women, 36% men. Students come from 28 states and territories, 10 other countries, 18% from out-of-state, 1% Native American, 13% Hispanic, 4% black, 4% Asian American or Pacific Islander, 2% international, 10% 25 or older, 73% live on campus, 8% transferred in. Retention: 75% of full-time freshmen returned the following year. Academic areas with the most degrees conferred: business/marketing; liberal arts/general studies; education. Core. Calendar: semesters. ESL program, advanced placement, accelerated degree program, self-designed majors, honors program, independent study, distance learning, double major, summer session for credit, part-time degree program, external degree program, adult/continuing education programs, internships, graduate courses open to undergrads. Off campus study at San Diego and Temecula Degree Completion Satellite Campuses.

Entrance Requirements: Options: Peterson's Universal Application, Common Application, electronic application, deferred admission, international baccalaureate accepted. Required: high school transcript, 2 recommendations, SAT or ACT. Recommended: minimum 2.8 high school GPA, interview. Application deadline: Rolling. Notification: continuous.

Costs Per Year: Application fee: $50. Comprehensive fee: $28,190 includes full-time tuition ($21,130) and college room and board ($7060). College room only: $4380. Part-time tuition: $600 per unit.

Collegiate Environment: Orientation program. Drama-theater group, choral group, student-run newspaper, radio station. Social organizations: 14 open to all. Most popular organizations: Student Senate, Spiritual Life Board, Student Activities Committee, intramurals, Outreach. Major annual events: homecoming, Closing Banquet, Midnight Madness. Student services: health clinic, personal-psychological counseling. Campus security: 24-hour patrols, student patrols, late night transport-escort service, lighted walkways. 1,024 college housing spaces available; 945 were occupied in 2003-04. Freshmen guaranteed college housing. On-campus residence required in freshman year. Options: men-only, women-only housing available. Concordia University Library with 85,432 books, 53,175 microform titles, 9,768 serials, 3,693 audiovisual materials, an OPAC, and a Web page. Operations spending for 2004 fiscal year: $349,066. 42 computers available on campus for general student use. A campuswide network can be accessed from student residence rooms and from off campus. Staffed computer lab on campus.

■ **CONTRA COSTA COLLEGE** *J-4*
2600 Mission Bell Dr.
San Pablo, CA 94806-3195
Tel: (510)235-7800
Web Site: http://www.contracosta.edu/
Description: State and locally supported, 2-year, coed. Part of Contra Costa Community College District and California Community College System. Awards certificates, transfer associate, and terminal associate degrees. Founded 1948. Setting: 83-acre small town campus with easy access to San Francisco. Total enrollment: 8,834. 5,794 applied. Full-time: 3,973 students, 60% women, 40% men. Part-time: 4,861 students, 64% women, 36% men. Students come from 5 states and territories, 16 other countries, 1% Native American, 28% Hispanic, 28% black, 15% Asian American or Pacific Islander, 2% international, 54% 25 or older. Core. Calendar: semesters. Academic remediation for entering students, ESL program, services for LD students, honors program, summer session for credit, part-time degree program, adult/continuing education programs, co-op programs. Off campus study at University of California, Berkeley; members of the Regional Association of East Bay Colleges and Universities. Study abroad program. ROTC: Army (c), Air Force (c).
Entrance Requirements: Open admission. Options: Common Application, early admission. Placement: SAT or ACT recommended. Entrance: noncompetitive. Application deadline: Rolling.
Collegiate Environment: Drama-theater group, student-run newspaper. Student services: personal-psychological counseling, women's center. Campus security: 24-hour patrols. College housing not available. Contra Costa College Library with 57,017 books, 333 serials, 1,860 audiovisual materials, and a Web page. 180 computers available on campus for general student use. Staffed computer lab on campus.
Community Environment: San Pablo is located on San Francisco Bay north of Richmond and Oakland on Highway 40. Buses and railroads serve the area. The city has 70 major industries; skilled and unskilled labor opportunities are available. San Pablo community facilities include churches, library and hospitals. Recreational facilities are provided by the beaches nearby and the mountain resort area for winter sports, which are approximately a three hour drive.

■ **COPPER MOUNTAIN COLLEGE** *S-13*
6162 Rotary Way
Joshua Tree, CA 92252
Tel: (760)366-3791
Admissions: (760)366-5290
Web Site: http://www.cmccd.cc.ca.us/
Description: State-supported, 2-year, coed. Awards certificates, transfer associate, and terminal associate degrees. Founded 1966. Total enrollment: 1,800. 1,800 applied, 100% were admitted. 1% Native American, 13% Hispanic, 7% black, 4% Asian American or Pacific Islander. Calendar: semesters.
Collegiate Environment: College housing not available.

■ **COSUMNES RIVER COLLEGE (SACRAMENTO)** *I-6*
8401 Center Parkway
Sacramento, CA 95823-5799
Tel: (916)691-7451
Admissions: (916)688-7410
Fax: (916)691-7375
Web Site: http://www.crc.losrios.edu/
Description: District-supported, 2-year, coed. Part of Los Rios Community College District System. Awards certificates, transfer associate, and terminal associate degrees. Founded 1970. Setting: 180-acre rural campus. Total enrollment: 19,284. Students come from 15 states and territories, 30 other countries, 52% 25 or older. Calendar: semesters. Academic remediation for entering students, ESL program, services for LD students, advanced placement, honors program, summer session for credit, part-time degree program, adult/continuing education programs, co-op programs. Study abroad program.
Entrance Requirements: Open admission except for international applicants. Options: Peterson's Universal Application, early admission. Placement: SAT or ACT recommended. Entrance: noncompetitive. Application deadline: 8/1. Notification: continuous until 8/15.
Collegiate Environment: Drama-theater group, choral group, student-run newspaper, radio station. Social organizations: 16 open to all. Most popular organizations: Latino/Hispanic Scholars Club, Animal Health Technology Club, Christian Club, Club Mesa, Writers' Workshop. Student services: health clinic, personal-psychological counseling, women's center. Campus security: 24-hour emergency response devices and patrols, student patrols, late night transport-escort service. College housing not available. Cosumnes River College Library with 55,447 books and 375 serials. 190 computers available on campus for general student use. Staffed computer lab on campus.
Community Environment: See California State University - Sacramento.

■ **CRAFTON HILLS COLLEGE** *Q-11*
11711 Sand Canyon Rd.
Yucaipa, CA 92399-1799
Tel: (909)794-2161
Admissions: (909)389-3355
Fax: (909)389-9141
Web Site: http://www.craftonhills.edu/
Description: State and locally supported, 2-year, coed. Part of California Community College System. Awards certificates, transfer associate, and terminal associate degrees. Founded 1972. Setting: 526-acre small town campus with easy access to Los Angeles. Educational spending for 2005 fiscal year: $500 per student. Total enrollment: 5,300. Students come from 19 states and territories, 12 other countries, 47% 25 or older. Core. Calendar: semesters. Academic remediation for entering students, services for LD students, advanced placement, self-designed majors, distance learning, summer session for credit, part-time degree program, adult/continuing education programs, co-op programs.
Entrance Requirements: Open admission. Options: Common Application, early admission, deferred admission. Required for some: high school transcript. Placement: ACT, SAT, SCAT, CGP, ACT ASSET, Nelson Denny Reading Test, or ACCUPLACER required for some. Entrance: noncompetitive. Application deadline: Rolling. Notification: continuous. Preference given to district residents.
Collegiate Environment: Drama-theater group. Social organizations: 9 open to all. Major annual events: College Night, Career and College Fair, Native American Pow Wow. Student services: health clinic, personal-psychological counseling, women's center. Campus security: 24-hour patrols, late night transport-escort service. College housing not available. Crafton Hills College Library with 65,731 books and 425 serials. 52 computers available on campus for general student use. A campuswide network can be accessed from off-campus. Staffed computer lab on campus.
Community Environment: See California State University - San Bernardino

■ **CUESTA COLLEGE** *Q-5*
PO Box 8106
San Luis Obispo, CA 93403-8106
Tel: (805)546-3100
Admissions: (805)546-3130
Web Site: http://www.cuesta.edu/
Description: District-supported, 2-year, coed. Awards certificates, transfer associate, and terminal associate degrees. Founded 1964. Setting: 129-acre rural campus. Research spending for 2004 fiscal year: $44,374. Educational

spending for 2005 fiscal year: $1550 per student. Total enrollment: 10,771. Students come from 19 other countries, 10% from out-of-state, 1% Native American, 15% Hispanic, 1% black, 4% Asian American or Pacific Islander, 33% 25 or older. Core. Calendar: semesters. Academic remediation for entering students, ESL program, services for LD students, advanced placement, honors program, independent study, distance learning, double major, summer session for credit, part-time degree program, adult/continuing education programs, co-op programs and internships. Off campus study. Study abroad program. ROTC: Army (c).

Entrance Requirements: Open admission. Options: Common Application, electronic application, early admission, deferred admission. Required: high school transcript. Recommended: essay. Placement: Assessment and Placement Services for Community Colleges recommended. Entrance: noncompetitive. Application deadline: Rolling. Notification: continuous. Preference given to district residents.

Collegiate Environment: Orientation program. Drama-theater group, choral group, student-run newspaper, radio station. Social organizations: 16 open to all. Most popular organizations: Associated Students of Cuesta College, Alpha Gamma Sigma, Student Nurses Association, Latina Leadership Network, MECHA. Major annual events: Student Life Orientation Days, Jazz Festival, Welcome Open House. Student services: legal services, health clinic, personal-psychological counseling. Campus security: 24-hour emergency response devices and patrols, late night transport-escort service. College housing not available. Cuesta College Library with 64,814 books, 584 serials, an OPAC, and a Web page. Operations spending for 2004 fiscal year: $975,000. 400 computers available on campus for general student use. A campuswide network can be accessed from off-campus. Staffed computer lab on campus.

Community Environment: See California Polytechnic State University - San Luis Obispo.

■ CUYAMACA COLLEGE *V-12*
900 Rancho San Diego Parkway
El Cajon, CA 92019-4304
Tel: (619)660-4000
Admissions: (619)660-4302
Web Site: http://www.cuyamaca.net/
Description: State-supported, 2-year, coed. Part of Grossmont-Cuyamaca Community College District. Awards certificates, diplomas, transfer associate, and terminal associate degrees. Founded 1978. Setting: 165-acre suburban campus with easy access to San Diego. Total enrollment: 7,690. Students come from 8 other countries, 1% from out-of-state, 2% Native American, 20% Hispanic, 8% black, 6% Asian American or Pacific Islander, 2% international, 37% 25 or older. Core. Calendar: semesters. Academic remediation for entering students, ESL program, services for LD students, advanced placement, self-designed majors, distance learning, summer session for credit, part-time degree program, adult/continuing education programs, co-op programs. Study abroad program. ROTC: Army (c), Air Force (c).

Entrance Requirements: Open admission. Options: Common Application, electronic application, early admission. Placement: ACT ASSET required. Entrance: noncompetitive. Application deadline: Rolling.

Collegiate Environment: Orientation program. Student-run newspaper. Student services: health clinic, personal-psychological counseling. College housing not available. Library plus 1 other with 32,129 books, 712 microform titles, 130 serials, 2,588 audiovisual materials, an OPAC, and a Web page. Operations spending for 2004 fiscal year: $1.2 million. 396 computers available on campus for general student use. A campuswide network can be accessed from off-campus. Staffed computer lab on campus.

■ CYPRESS COLLEGE *Z-6*
9200 Valley View
Cypress, CA 90630-5897
Tel: (714)484-7000
Admissions: (714)484-7435
Fax: (714)761-3934
E-mail: dwassenaar@cypresscollege.edu
Web Site: http://www.cypress.cc.ca.us/
Description: State and locally supported, 2-year, coed. Part of California Community College System. Awards certificates, transfer associate, and terminal associate degrees. Founded 1966. Setting: 108-acre suburban campus with easy access to Los Angeles. Total enrollment: 15,347. Students come from 41 states and territories, 22 other countries, 1% from out-of-state, 45% 25 or older. Core. Calendar: semesters. Academic remediation for

entering students, ESL program, services for LD students, advanced placement, freshman honors college, honors program, independent study, distance learning, double major, summer session for credit, part-time degree program, adult/continuing education programs, co-op programs and internships. Off campus study. Study abroad program.

Entrance Requirements: Open admission. Recommended: high school transcript. Entrance: noncompetitive. Application deadline: 8/25.

Collegiate Environment: Orientation program. Drama-theater group, choral group, student-run newspaper. Social organizations: 63 open to all. Most popular organizations: Alpha Gamma Sigma, California Student Nurses Association, Court Reporting Club, MECHA. Major annual events: Senior Day, Scare Fair, club information days. Student services: legal services, health clinic, personal-psychological counseling, women's center. Campus security: 24-hour emergency response devices. College housing not available. Cypress College Library plus 1 other with 76,696 books, 4,203 microform titles, 255 serials, 1,113 audiovisual materials, an OPAC, and a Web page. Operations spending for 2004 fiscal year: $483,959. 500 computers available on campus for general student use. A campuswide network can be accessed from off-campus. Staffed computer lab on campus.

Community Environment: Cypress is a rapidly growing suburban city, 20 miles east of Los Angeles. The climate is dry and mild. Buses, trains, freeway system and the Los Angeles International Airport 20 miles away all serve the area. The city has three private hospitals, twelve churches, a library, and an amphitheater. There are city parks, a golf course, swimming pool and a gymnasium for those interested in sports. Anaheim Stadium is seven miles away, Disneyland five and one-half miles, Knotts Berry Farm and Movieland Wax Museum two and one-half miles. Beaches and mountain areas provide additional recreational facilities and are within easy driving distance. Many universities and colleges are nearby.

■ DE ANZA COLLEGE *K-6*
21250 Stevens Creek Blvd.
Cupertino, CA 95014-5793
Tel: (408)864-5678
Admissions: (408)864-8292
Fax: (408)864-8329
E-mail: webregda@mercury.fhda.edu
Web Site: http://www.deanza.fhda.edu/
Description: State and locally supported, 2-year, coed. Part of California Community College System. Awards certificates, diplomas, transfer associate, and terminal associate degrees. Founded 1967. Setting: 112-acre small town campus with easy access to San Francisco and San Jose. Total enrollment: 23,344. Full-time: 8,860 students, 48% women, 52% men. Part-time: 14,484 students, 55% women, 45% men. Students come from 48 states and territories, 79 other countries, 1% Native American, 15% Hispanic, 6% black, 33% Asian American or Pacific Islander, 6% international, 52% 25 or older. Core. Academic remediation for entering students, ESL program, services for LD students, advanced placement, honors program, summer session for credit, part-time degree program, external degree program, adult/continuing education programs, co-op programs and internships. Study abroad program. ROTC: Army (c), Air Force (c).

Entrance Requirements: Open admission except for nursing program. Options: Common Application, early admission. Placement: SAT, CPT, DTLS, DTMS required for some. Entrance: noncompetitive. Application deadline: Rolling. Notification: continuous.

Costs Per Year: Application fee: $22. State resident tuition: $0 full-time. Nonresident tuition: $3636 full-time, $101 per unit part-time. Mandatory fees: $818 full-time, $17 per unit part-time.

Collegiate Environment: Orientation program. Drama-theater group, choral group, student-run newspaper. Social organizations: 45 open to all. Most popular organizations: Student Nurses Association, Phi Theta Kappa, Automotive Club, Vietnamese Club, Filipino Club. Major annual events: Graduation, Orientation, Club Day. Student services: legal services, health clinic, personal-psychological counseling. Campus security: 24-hour emergency response devices, student patrols, late night transport-escort service. College housing not available. A. Robert DeHart Learning Center with 80,000 books and 927 serials. 800 computers available on campus for general student use. A campuswide network can be accessed from off-campus. Staffed computer lab on campus.

Community Environment: The district, population 174,000, is within an hour's drive from San Francisco. Buses and trains serve the area and the San Jose International Airport is nearby for air transportation. There are parks, playgrounds and nearby beaches for recreational activities as well as the cultural advantages of the San Francisco Bay Area.

■ **DESIGN INSTITUTE OF SAN DIEGO** *W-12*

8555 Commerce Ave.

San Diego, CA 92121-2685

Tel: (858)566-1200

Free: 800-619-4337

Fax: (858)566-2711

E-mail: admisssions@disd.edu

Web Site: http://www.disd.edu/

Description: Proprietary, 4-year, coed. Awards bachelor's degrees. Founded 1977. Setting: urban campus. Total enrollment: 450. Students come from 10 states and territories, 15 other countries, 70% 25 or older. Retention: 87% of full-time freshmen returned the following year. Core. Calendar: semesters. Part-time degree program, internships. Study abroad program.

Entrance Requirements: Option: Peterson's Universal Application. Required: high school transcript, minimum 2.0 high school GPA. Recommended: interview. Entrance: noncompetitive. Application deadline: Rolling.

Collegiate Environment: Most popular organizations: American Society of Interior Designers, International Interior Designers Association, Illuminating Electrical Society. Major annual events: West Week at Pacific Design Center, Showcase House. College housing not available. 5,000 books, 90 serials, and an OPAC. 50 computers available on campus for general student use. Staffed computer lab on campus.

■ **DEVRY UNIVERSITY (ELK GROVE)** *I-6*

Sacramento Center

2218 Kausen Dr.

Elk Grove, CA 95758

Tel: (916)478-2847; (866)573-3879

Fax: (916)478-2849

Web Site: http://www.devry.edu/

Description: Proprietary, comprehensive, coed. Calendar: semesters.

Costs Per Year: One-time mandatory fee: $40. Tuition: $11,790 full-time, $440 per credit part-time. Mandatory fees: $60 full-time, $30 per year part-time. Full-time tuition and fees vary according to course load. Part-time tuition and fees vary according to course load.

■ **DEVRY UNIVERSITY (FREMONT)** *K-5*

6600 Dumbarton Circle

Fremont, CA 94555

Tel: (510)574-1100; 888-393-3879

Fax: (510)742-0868

Web Site: http://www.devry.edu/

Description: Proprietary, comprehensive, coed. Part of DeVry University. Awards associate, bachelor's, and master's degrees. Founded 1998. Setting: 17-acre suburban campus with easy access to San Francisco. Total enrollment: 1,580. Faculty: 78 (46 full-time, 32 part-time). Student-undergrad faculty ratio is 21:1. Full-time: 942 students, 28% women, 72% men. Part-time: 506 students, 33% women, 67% men. Students come from 25 states and territories, 9 other countries, 1% Native American, 22% Hispanic, 8% black, 32% Asian American or Pacific Islander, 1% international, 34% 25 or older. Academic areas with the most degrees conferred: business/marketing; engineering technologies; computer and information sciences. Core. Calendar: semesters. Academic remediation for entering students, services for LD students, advanced placement, accelerated degree program, distance learning, summer session for credit, part-time degree program, adult/continuing education programs, co-op programs.

Entrance Requirements: Options: electronic application, deferred admission, international baccalaureate accepted. Required: high school transcript, interview. Entrance: minimally difficult. Application deadline: Rolling. Notification: continuous.

Costs Per Year: Application fee: $50. One-time mandatory fee: $40. Tuition: $13,060 full-time, $475 per credit part-time. Mandatory fees: $270 full-time, $160 per year part-time. Full-time tuition and fees vary according to course load. Part-time tuition and fees vary according to course load.

Collegiate Environment: Orientation program. Social organizations: 6 open to all. Most popular organizations: Latino-American Student Organization, Telecommunications Club, Chess Club. Major annual events: Thanksgiving dinner, summer barbecue, book fair. Campus security: 24-hour emergency response devices and patrols, late night transport-escort service, lighted pathways/sidewalks. College housing not available. Learning Resource Center with 40,000 books, 3,060 serials, 2,000 audiovisual materials, an OPAC, and a Web page. 350 computers available on campus for general student use. Computer purchase/lease plans available. A campuswide network can be accessed from off-campus. Staffed computer lab on campus.

■ **DEVRY UNIVERSITY (IRVINE)** *T-7*

3333 Michelson Dr., Ste. 420

Irvine, CA 92612-1682

Tel: (949)752-5631

Fax: (949)752-5637

Web Site: http://www.devry.edu/

Description: Proprietary, comprehensive, coed. Calendar: semesters.

Costs Per Year: One-time mandatory fee: $40. Tuition: $12,450 full-time, $460 per credit part-time. Mandatory fees: $60 full-time, $30 per year part-time.

■ **DEVRY UNIVERSITY (LONG BEACH)** *T-10*

3880 Kilroy Airport Way

Long Beach, CA 90806

Tel: (562)427-0861

Free: 800-597-0444

Web Site: http://www.devry.edu/

Description: Proprietary, comprehensive, coed. Part of DeVry University. Awards associate, bachelor's, and master's degrees. Founded 1984. Setting: 23-acre urban campus with easy access to Los Angeles. Total enrollment: 1,201. Faculty: 151 (27 full-time, 124 part-time). Student-undergrad faculty ratio is 12:1. Full-time: 614 students, 30% women, 70% men. Part-time: 409 students, 40% women, 60% men. Students come from 23 states and territories, 11 other countries, 2% from out-of-state, 0.5% Native American, 39% Hispanic, 16% black, 22% Asian American or Pacific Islander, 2% international, 44% 25 or older. Academic areas with the most degrees conferred: computer and information sciences; business/marketing; engineering technologies. Calendar: semesters. Academic remediation for entering students, services for LD students, advanced placement, accelerated degree program, distance learning, summer session for credit, part-time degree program, adult/continuing education programs, co-op programs.

Entrance Requirements: Options: electronic application, deferred admission, international baccalaureate accepted. Required: high school transcript, interview. Entrance: minimally difficult. Application deadline: Rolling. Notification: continuous.

Costs Per Year: Application fee: $50. One-time mandatory fee: $40. Tuition: $12,450 full-time, $460 per credit part-time. Mandatory fees: $270 full-time, $160 per year part-time. Full-time tuition and fees vary according to course load. Part-time tuition and fees vary according to course load.

Collegiate Environment: Orientation program. Social organizations: 13 open to all. Most popular organizations: Teamnet, Society of Hispanic Professional Engineers, National Society of Black Engineers, Institute of Electronics and Electrical Engineers, United Islands. Major annual events: Welcome Back, New Horizons Retreat, Winter Formal. Campus security: 24-hour emergency response devices and patrols, late night transport-escort service, motion detectors, closed hours. College housing not available. Learning Resource Center with 15,500 books, 85 serials, 2,000 audiovisual materials, an OPAC, and a Web page. 458 computers available on campus for general student use. Computer purchase/lease plans available. A campuswide network can be accessed from off-campus. Staffed computer lab on campus.

■ **DEVRY UNIVERSITY (POMONA)** *S-11*

901 Corporate Center Dr.

Pomona, CA 91768-2642

Tel: (909)622-8866; (866)338-7934

Fax: (909)623-5666

Web Site: http://www.devry.edu/

Description: Proprietary, comprehensive, coed. Part of DeVry University. Awards associate, bachelor's, and master's degrees. Founded 1983. Setting: 15-acre urban campus with easy access to Los Angeles. Total enrollment: 1,899. Faculty: 80 (38 full-time, 42 part-time). Student-undergrad faculty ratio is 25:1. Full-time: 956 students, 27% women, 73% men. Part-time: 765 students, 33% women, 67% men. Students come from 25 states and territories, 19 other countries, 1% Native American, 44% Hispanic, 8% black, 19% Asian American or Pacific Islander, 2% international, 42% 25 or older. Retention: 53% of full-time freshmen returned the following year. Academic areas with the most degrees conferred: computer and information sciences; business/marketing; engineering technologies. Calendar: semesters. Academic remediation for entering students, services for LD students, advanced placement, accelerated degree program, distance learning, summer session for credit, part-time degree program, adult/continuing education programs, co-op programs.

Entrance Requirements: Options: electronic application, deferred admission, international baccalaureate accepted. Required: high school transcript, interview. Entrance: minimally difficult. Application deadline: Rolling. Notification: continuous.

Costs Per Year: Application fee: $50. One-time mandatory fee: $40. Tuition: $12,450 full-time, $460 per credit part-time. Mandatory fees: $270 full-time, $160 per year part-time. Full-time tuition and fees vary according to course load. Part-time tuition and fees vary according to course load.

Collegiate Environment: Orientation program. Social organizations: 14 open to all. Most popular organizations: Phi Beta Lambda, Society of Hispanic Professional Engineers, National Society of Black Engineers, International Telecommunications Management Association, United Islands Student Association. Major annual events: The Welcome Barbecue, Winter Formal, Part-Time Jobs Fair. Campus security: 24-hour emergency response devices, late night transport-escort service. College housing not available. Learning Resource Center with 17,000 books, 77 serials, 1,234 audiovisual materials, an OPAC, and a Web page. 513 computers available on campus for general student use. Computer purchase/lease plans available. A campuswide network can be accessed from off-campus. Staffed computer lab on campus.

■ **DEVRY UNIVERSITY (SAN DIEGO)** *W-12*
2655 Camino Del Rio North, Ste. 201
San Diego, CA 92108-1633
Tel: (619)683-2446
Fax: (619)683-2448
Web Site: http://www.devry.edu/
Description: Proprietary, comprehensive, coed. Calendar: semesters.
Costs Per Year: One-time mandatory fee: $40. Tuition: $12,450 full-time, $460 per credit part-time. Mandatory fees: $60 full-time, $30 per year part-time. Full-time tuition and fees vary according to course load. Part-time tuition and fees vary according to course load.

■ **DEVRY UNIVERSITY (SAN FRANCISCO)** *K-4*
455 Market St., Ste. 1650
San Francisco, CA 94105-2472
Tel: (415)243-8787
Fax: (415)243-8686
Web Site: http://www.devry.edu/
Description: Proprietary, comprehensive, coed. Calendar: semesters.
Costs Per Year: One-time mandatory fee: $40. Tuition: $13,060 full-time, $475 per credit part-time. Mandatory fees: $60 full-time, $30 per year part-time. Full-time tuition and fees vary according to course load. Part-time tuition and fees vary according to course load.

■ **DEVRY UNIVERSITY (WEST HILLS)** *S-8*
22801 West Roscoe Blvd.
West Hills, CA 91304
Tel: (818)932-3001; 888-610-0800
Fax: (818)932-3091
Web Site: http://www.devry.edu/
Description: Proprietary, comprehensive, coed. Part of DeVry University. Awards associate, bachelor's, and master's degrees. Founded 1999. Setting: 20-acre suburban campus. Total enrollment: 769. Faculty: 61 (17 full-time, 44 part-time). Student-undergrad faculty ratio is 16:1. Full-time: 329 students, 26% women, 74% men. Part-time: 342 students, 26% women, 74% men. Students come from 10 states and territories, 13 other countries, 3% Native American, 30% Hispanic, 5% black, 20% Asian American or Pacific Islander, 3% international, 42% 25 or older. Retention: 53% of full-time freshmen returned the following year. Academic areas with the most degrees conferred: computer and information sciences; business/marketing; engineering technologies. Calendar: semesters. Academic remediation for entering students, services for LD students, advanced placement, accelerated degree program, distance learning, summer session for credit, part-time degree program, adult/continuing education programs, co-op programs.
Entrance Requirements: Options: electronic application, deferred admission, international baccalaureate accepted. Required: high school transcript, interview. Entrance: minimally difficult. Application deadline: Rolling. Notification: continuous.
Costs Per Year: Application fee: $50. One-time mandatory fee: $40. Tuition: $12,450 full-time, $460 per credit part-time. Mandatory fees: $270 full-time,

$160 per year part-time. Full-time tuition and fees vary according to course load. Part-time tuition and fees vary according to course load.
Collegiate Environment: Orientation program. Social organizations: 10 open to all. Most popular organizations: Associated Student Body, Computer Information Systems/Telecommunication Association, Women's Caucus, United Island Student Association, Institute of Electronics and Electrical Engineers. Major annual events: Welcome BBQ, Winter Formal, Cosmic Bowling. Campus security: 24-hour emergency response devices, late night transport-escort service, lighted pathways/sidewalks. College housing not available. Learning Resource Center with 16,177 books, 130 serials, 597 audiovisual materials, an OPAC, and a Web page. 390 computers available on campus for general student use. Computer purchase/lease plans available. A campuswide network can be accessed from off-campus. Staffed computer lab on campus.

■ **DIABLO VALLEY COLLEGE** *G-6*
321 Golf Club Rd.
Pleasant Hill, CA 94523-1544
Tel: (925)685-1230
Fax: (925)685-1551
Web Site: http://www.dvc.edu/
Description: State and locally supported, 2-year, coed. Part of Contra Costa Community College District, part of California Community Colleges. Awards certificates, transfer associate, and terminal associate degrees. Founded 1949. Setting: 100-acre suburban campus with easy access to San Francisco. Total enrollment: 20,688. Student-undergrad faculty ratio is 15:1. Students come from 16 states and territories, 0.2% from out-of-state, 1% Native American, 13% Hispanic, 6% black, 18% Asian American or Pacific Islander, 0% international, 38% 25 or older. Core. Calendar: semesters. Academic remediation for entering students, services for LD students, advanced placement, self-designed majors, summer session for credit, part-time degree program, adult/continuing education programs, co-op programs. Study abroad program. ROTC: Air Force (c).
Entrance Requirements: Open admission. Option: early admission. Recommended: high school transcript. Entrance: noncompetitive. Application deadline: 8/15.
Costs Per Year: Application fee: $0. State resident tuition: $0 full-time. Nonresident tuition: $5190 full-time, $173 per unit part-time. Mandatory fees: $799 full-time, $26 per unit part-time, $19 per term part-time.
Collegiate Environment: Drama-theater group, choral group, student-run newspaper. Student services: women's center. Campus security: 24-hour emergency response devices and patrols, student patrols. College housing not available. 88,286 books and 298 serials. 450 computers available on campus for general student use. A campuswide network can be accessed from off-campus. Staffed computer lab on campus.
Community Environment: Population 31,000. Pleasant Hill is a suburban residential community that has an average winter temperature of 46.4 degrees and summer temperature of 71.8 degrees. It is located 22 miles from San Francisco. All transportation facilities are available nearby. Churches representing 14 denominations, a hospital and excellent shopping facilities comprise the town. Employment opportunities are available. Pleasant Hill enjoys the cultural atmosphere of the San Francisco Bay Area. A nearby beach area provides recreational facilities; the mountain area for winter sports is accessible for a weekend trip.

■ **DOMINICAN SCHOOL OF PHILOSOPHY AND THEOLOGY** *J-4*
2301 Vine St.
Berkeley, CA 94708
Tel: (510)849-2030
Admissions: (510)883-2073
Web Site: http://www.dspt.edu/
Description: Independent Roman Catholic, upper-level, coed. Awards bachelor's, master's, and first professional degrees. Founded 1932. Setting: urban campus with easy access to San Francisco. Endowment: $2 million. Research spending for 2004 fiscal year: $37,000. Educational spending for 2005 fiscal year: $9000 per student. Total enrollment: 123. Full-time: 11 students, 18% women, 82% men. Part-time: 4 students, 50% women, 50% men. Students come from 5 other countries, 50% from out-of-state, 0% Native American, 33% Hispanic, 0% black, 27% Asian American or Pacific Islander, 0% international, 73% 25 or older, 17% live on campus, 20% transferred in. Retention: 75% of full-time entering class returned the following year. Core. Calendar: semesters. Independent study, double major, part-time degree program, graduate courses open to undergrads. Off campus

study at University of California, Berkeley, Graduate Theological Union, Mills College, Holy Names College. Study abroad program.

Costs Per Year: Application fee: $30. Tuition: $10,560 full-time, $440 per credit part-time. Mandatory fees: $50 full-time, $50 per year part-time.

Collegiate Environment: Orientation program. Social organizations: 1 open to all; 2% of men are members. Most popular organization: DSPT Associated Students. Major annual events: Christmas Party, Tri-School Liturgies, End of the Year Party. Student services: personal-psychological counseling, women's center. Campus security: late night transport-escort service. 12 college housing spaces available; 3 were occupied in 2003-04. Option: coed housing available. Flora Lamson Hewlett Library plus 1 other with 409,592 books, 279,143 microform titles, 1,466 serials, 21,735 audiovisual materials, an OPAC, and a Web page. Operations spending for 2004 fiscal year: $125,614. 5 computers available on campus for general student use. Computer purchase/lease plans available. A campuswide network can be accessed from off-campus.

Community Environment: See University of California - Berkeley.

■ **DOMINICAN UNIVERSITY OF CALIFORNIA** *J-4*
50 Acacia Ave.
San Rafael, CA 94901-2298
Tel: (415)457-4440; 888-323-6763
Admissions: (415)485-3204
Fax: (415)485-3214
E-mail: enroll@dominican.edu
Web Site: http://www.dominican.edu/

Description: Independent, comprehensive, coed, affiliated with Roman Catholic Church. Awards bachelor's and master's degrees. Founded 1890. Setting: 80-acre suburban campus with easy access to San Francisco. Endowment: $10.6 million. Educational spending for 2005 fiscal year: $6676 per student. Total enrollment: 1,631. Faculty: 287 (71 full-time, 216 part-time). Student-undergrad faculty ratio is 10:1. 2,564 applied, 53% were admitted. 25% from top 10% of their high school class, 47% from top quarter, 79% from top half. Full-time: 1,058 students, 77% women, 23% men. Part-time: 119 students, 78% women, 22% men. Students come from 20 states and territories, 22 other countries, 8% from out-of-state, 1% Native American, 15% Hispanic, 8% black, 20% Asian American or Pacific Islander, 3% international, 30% 25 or older, 42% live on campus, 24% transferred in. Retention: 74% of full-time freshmen returned the following year. Academic areas with the most degrees conferred: health professions and related sciences; social sciences; liberal arts/general studies. Core. Calendar: semesters. Academic remediation for entering students, ESL program, services for LD students, advanced placement, self-designed majors, honors program, independent study, double major, summer session for credit, part-time degree program, external degree program, adult/continuing education programs, internships, graduate courses open to undergrads. Off campus study at University of California, Berkeley, Aquinas College, St. Thomas Aquinas College, Barry University. Study abroad program.

Entrance Requirements: Options: Peterson's Universal Application, Common Application, electronic application, early admission, deferred admission, international baccalaureate accepted. Required: essay, high school transcript, minimum 2.5 high school GPA, 1 recommendation, SAT or ACT. Recommended: SAT Subject Tests. Required for some: interview. Entrance: moderately difficult. Application deadline: 8/1. Notification: continuous until 9/1.

Costs Per Year: Application fee: $40. Comprehensive fee: $39,370 includes full-time tuition ($27,770), mandatory fees ($300), and college room and board ($11,300). College room only: $6580. Part-time tuition: $1160 per unit. Part-time mandatory fees: $150 per term.

Collegiate Environment: Orientation program. Drama-theater group, choral group, student-run newspaper, radio station. Social organizations: 19 open to all. Most popular organizations: Students Promoting Dominican Islands, Perceptions, Science Club, Filipino Club, Scripture Union. Major annual events: Shield Day, Boat Dance, Ecumenical Thanksgiving Dinner. Student services: health clinic, personal-psychological counseling, Teaching and Learning Center. Campus security: 24-hour emergency response devices and patrols, late night transport-escort service, controlled dormitory access. 600 college housing spaces available; 544 were occupied in 2003-04. Freshmen given priority for college housing. Option: coed housing available. Archbishop Alemany Library plus 1 other with 95,000 books, 3,200 microform titles, 508 serials, 1,507 audiovisual materials, an OPAC, and a Web page. Operations spending for 2004 fiscal year: $868,394. 45 computers available on campus for general student use. A campuswide network can be accessed from student residence rooms and from off campus. Staffed computer lab on campus.

Community Environment: Located in the hills of Marin County 25 minutes from San Francisco across the Golden Gate Bridge, Dominican is close enough to permit easy access to the city's diverse cultural attractions - the opera, symphony, theaters and playhouses. The campus adjoins San Rafael (pop. 52,000), with a climate rated as one of the six most ideal in the world, in addition to a wide variety of libraries, museums and churches. The nearby cities of Mill Valley, Bolinas, and Sausalito harbor a large community of writers, painters and other artists, and a diverse collection of shops, restaurants and galleries. Five state parks and beaches lie within easy reach, including Muir Woods, the Golden Gate National Recreational Area, and the Point Reyes National Seashore.

■ **DON BOSCO TECHNICAL INSTITUTE** *V-5*
1151 San Gabriel Blvd.
Rosemead, CA 91770-4299
Tel: (626)940-2000
Fax: (626)940-2001
Web Site: http://www.boscotech.edu/

Description: Independent, 2-year, coed, affiliated with Roman Catholic Church. Awards transfer associate and terminal associate degrees. Founded 1955. Setting: 30-acre suburban campus with easy access to Los Angeles. Total enrollment: 1,208. 2% from top 10% of their high school class, 13% from top quarter, 36% from top half. 0% 25 or older. Core. Calendar: semesters. Advanced placement, independent study, co-op programs.

Entrance Requirements: Option: Common Application. Required: high school transcript, minimum 2.0 high school GPA, 2 recommendations. Required for some: SAT or ACT. Entrance: noncompetitive. Application deadline: 2/15.

Collegiate Environment: Marching band. Student services: personal-psychological counseling. Campus security: 24-hour emergency response devices. College housing not available. 16,400 books and 70 serials. 100 computers available on campus for general student use. A campuswide network can be accessed. Staffed computer lab on campus.

■ **EAST LOS ANGELES COLLEGE** *W-5*
1301 Avenida Cesar Chavez
Monterey Park, CA 91754-6099
Tel: (323)265-8650
Admissions: (323)265-8801
Fax: (323)265-8763
Web Site: http://www.elac.edu/

Description: State and locally supported, 2-year, coed. Part of Los Angeles Community College District. Awards certificates, transfer associate, and terminal associate degrees. Founded 1945. Setting: 84-acre urban campus with easy access to Los Angeles. Research spending for 2004 fiscal year: $120,000. Educational spending for 2005 fiscal year: $4050 per student. Total enrollment: 24,015. 5,348 applied, 100% were admitted. Full-time: 5,773 students, 60% women, 40% men. Part-time: 18,242 students, 60% women, 40% men. 0.2% Native American, 70% Hispanic, 3% black, 19% Asian American or Pacific Islander, 51% 25 or older. Core. Calendar: semesters. Academic remediation for entering students, ESL program, services for LD students, advanced placement, self-designed majors, honors program, independent study, distance learning, part-time degree program, adult/continuing education programs, co-op programs.

Entrance Requirements: Options: Common Application, early admission. Recommended: high school transcript, English and mathematics placement test. Entrance: noncompetitive. Application deadline: 9/12. Notification: continuous until 9/12.

Collegiate Environment: Drama-theater group, choral group, marching band, student-run newspaper, radio station. Most popular organizations: Asian Club, Spanish Club, Chicanos for Creative Medicine. Major annual events: Cinco de Mayo, Black Week, Asian Week. Student services: health clinic, personal-psychological counseling. Campus security: 24-hour emergency response devices and patrols, late night transport-escort service. College housing not available. ELAC Helen Miller Bailey Library plus 2 others with 102,000 books, 3,370 microform titles, 228 serials, an OPAC, and a Web page. Operations spending for 2004 fiscal year: $806,000. 350 computers available on campus for general student use. A campuswide network can be accessed from off-campus. Staffed computer lab on campus.

■ **EL CAMINO COLLEGE** *T-10*
16007 Crenshaw Blvd.
Torrance, CA 90506-0001
Tel: (310)532-3670; (866)ELCAMINO

Admissions: (310)660-3418
Fax: (310)660-3818
Web Site: http://www.elcamino.edu/
Description: State-supported, 2-year, coed. Part of California Community College System. Awards certificates, diplomas, and transfer associate degrees. Founded 1947. Setting: 115-acre urban campus with easy access to Los Angeles. Total enrollment: 27,039. 0.4% Native American, 29% Hispanic, 18% black, 19% Asian American or Pacific Islander, 42% 25 or older. Retention: 81% of full-time freshmen returned the following year. Core. Calendar: semesters. Academic remediation for entering students, ESL program, services for LD students, advanced placement, self-designed majors, honors program, summer session for credit, part-time degree program, co-op programs.
Entrance Requirements: Open admission. Option: early admission. Required: high school transcript. Entrance: noncompetitive. Application deadline: Rolling. Notification: continuous.
Collegiate Environment: Orientation program. Drama-theater group, student-run newspaper. Student services: health clinic, personal-psychological counseling, women's center. College housing not available. 116,051 books and 864 serials. 151 computers available on campus for general student use.
Community Environment: Torrance, situated in southwest Los Angeles County, is a suburb of Los Angeles and does enjoy the advantages of the city's cultural and recreational facilities. All forms of commercial transportation are convenient. Outstanding shopping centers are in the city as well as all the other usual community facilities. Climate is normally sunny and mild. Beaches and mountains are within easy driving distance for recreation.

■ **EMMANUEL BIBLE COLLEGE** *S-10*
1605 East Elizabeth St.
Pasadena, CA 91104
Tel: (626)791-2575
Fax: (626)398-2424
Web Site: http://www.emmanuelbiblecollege.edu/
Description: Independent, 4-year, affiliated with Church of the Nazarene. Awards associate and bachelor's degrees. Endowment: $51,000. Total enrollment: 20. 10 applied, 100% were admitted. Full-time: 6 students, 17% women, 83% men. Part-time: 14 students, 21% women, 79% men. Students come from 2 other countries, 10% from out-of-state, 35% Hispanic, 5% Asian American or Pacific Islander, 100% 25 or older, 10% transferred in. Retention: 90% of full-time freshmen returned the following year. Core. Independent study, distance learning, part-time degree program, adult/continuing education programs, internships. Off campus study.
Entrance Requirements: Open admission. Options: Common Application, early admission, international baccalaureate accepted. Required: essay, high school transcript, interview, Christian commitment. Recommended: recommendations. Required for some: recommendations. Application deadline: 9/15. Notification: continuous until 8/31.
Collegiate Environment: Drama-theater group, student-run newspaper. Most popular organizations: Student Council, drama. Major annual events: Evangelism activities, drama performances, banquets. Student services: personal-psychological counseling. Campus security: 24-hour emergency response devices and patrols. Immanuel Bible College Library plus 1 other with 15,000 books and 20 serials. Operations spending for 2004 fiscal year: $800. 3 computers available on campus for general student use. A campuswide network can be accessed from student residence rooms and from off campus. Staffed computer lab on campus.

■ **EMPIRE COLLEGE** *I-4*
3035 Cleveland Ave.
Santa Rosa, CA 95403
Tel: (707)546-4000
Fax: (707)546-4058
Web Site: http://www.empcol.com/
Description: Proprietary, 2-year, coed. Awards certificates, diplomas, and terminal associate degrees. Founded 1961. Setting: suburban campus with easy access to San Francisco. Educational spending for 2005 fiscal year: $7350 per student. Total enrollment: 834. 0% from out-of-state, 2% Native American, 16% Hispanic, 3% black, 6% Asian American or Pacific Islander, 0% international, 75% 25 or older. Retention: 90% of full-time freshmen returned the following year. Calendar: continuous. Double major.
Entrance Requirements: Option: international baccalaureate accepted. Required: high school transcript, interview, Wonderlic aptitude test. Required for some: essay. Entrance: minimally difficult. Application deadline: Rolling.

Collegiate Environment: Orientation program. Campus security: 24-hour emergency response devices. 450 computers available on campus for general student use. Computer purchase/lease plans available. A campuswide network can be accessed. Staffed computer lab on campus.

■ **EVEREST COLLEGE** *S-11*
9616 Archibald Ave., Ste. 100
Rancho Cucamonga, CA 91730
Tel: (909)484-4311
Web Site: http://www.everest-college.com/
Description: Proprietary, 2-year, coed. Founded 2000. Calendar: 6 or 12 week terms.

■ **EVERGREEN VALLEY COLLEGE** *L-5*
3095 Yerba Buena Rd.
San Jose, CA 95135-1598
Tel: (408)274-7900
Admissions: (408)270-6423
Fax: (408)223-9351
Web Site: http://www.evc.edu/
Description: State and locally supported, 2-year, coed. Part of California Community College System. Awards certificates, transfer associate, and terminal associate degrees. Founded 1975. Setting: 175-acre urban campus. Educational spending for 2005 fiscal year: $624 per student. Total enrollment: 11,751. 2,186 applied, 100% were admitted. Students come from 23 states and territories, 11 other countries, 1% from out-of-state, 1% Native American, 29% Hispanic, 5% black, 40% Asian American or Pacific Islander, 1% international, 52% 25 or older. Core. Calendar: semesters. Academic remediation for entering students, ESL program, services for LD students, advanced placement, accelerated degree program, freshman honors college, honors program, independent study, distance learning, summer session for credit, part-time degree program, adult/continuing education programs, co-op programs. Off campus study at other community colleges in the area. ROTC: Army (c).
Entrance Requirements: Open admission except for nursing program. Option: early admission. Entrance: noncompetitive. Application deadline: Rolling. Notification: continuous.
Costs Per Year: State resident tuition: $0 full-time. Nonresident tuition: $4872 full-time, $177 per unit part-time. Mandatory fees: $664 full-time, $26 per unit part-time.
Collegiate Environment: Drama-theater group, choral group. Most popular organizations: Affirm, Edlace, Phi Theta Kappa, Vietnamese Student Association. Major annual events: Cinco de Mayo, St. Andrews Day. Student services: health clinic, personal-psychological counseling, special programs for ethnic populations. Campus security: 24-hour emergency response devices, late night transport-escort service, patrols by trained security personnel. College housing not available. Evergreen Valley College Library with 42,782 books and 368 serials. 415 computers available on campus for general student use. Staffed computer lab on campus.

■ **FASHION CAREERS COLLEGE** *W-12*
1923 Morena Blvd.
San Diego, CA 92110
Tel: (619)275-4700; 888-FCCC999
Fax: (619)275-0635
E-mail: judy@fashioncareerscollege.com
Web Site: http://www.fashioncollege.com/
Description: Proprietary, 2-year, coed. Awards certificates, transfer associate, and terminal associate degrees. Founded 1979. Setting: urban campus. Educational spending for 2005 fiscal year: $2551 per student. Total enrollment: 101. Student-undergrad faculty ratio is 32:1. 27 applied, 100% were admitted. Full-time: 101 students, 88% women, 12% men. Students come from 18 states and territories, 3 other countries, 27% from out-of-state, 0% Native American, 31% Hispanic, 7% black, 4% Asian American or Pacific Islander, 2% international, 9% 25 or older, 0% transferred in. Retention: 75% of full-time freshmen returned the following year. Core. Double major, adult/continuing education programs, co-op programs and internships.
Entrance Requirements: Options: Common Application, electronic application. Required: essay, high school transcript, interview, Wonderlic aptitude test. Entrance: minimally difficult. Application deadline: Rolling. Notification: continuous.
Costs Per Year: Application fee: $25. Tuition: $15,900 full-time, $400 per credit part-time. Mandatory fees: $325 full-time.

Collegiate Environment: Orientation program. Major annual events: Golden Hanger Fashion Award Gala, holiday party, community charity events. Campus security: 24-hour emergency response devices. College housing not available. Fashion Careers of California Library with 800 books, 14 serials, and 175 audiovisual materials. Operations spending for 2004 fiscal year: $9420. 36 computers available on campus for general student use. Staffed computer lab on campus.

■ **FEATHER RIVER COLLEGE** *F-7*
570 Golden Eagle Ave.
Quincy, CA 95971-9124
Tel: (530)283-0202
Free: 800-442-9799
Fax: (530)283-3757
E-mail: info@frc.edu
Web Site: http://www.frc.edu/
Description: State and locally supported, 2-year, coed. Part of California Community College System. Awards certificates, diplomas, transfer associate, and terminal associate degrees. Founded 1968. Setting: 150-acre rural campus. Educational spending for 2005 fiscal year: $2521 per student. Total enrollment: 1,714. Student-undergrad faculty ratio is 18:1. Full-time: 732 students, 46% women, 54% men. Part-time: 982 students, 63% women, 37% men. Students come from 24 states and territories, 6 other countries, 23% from out-of-state, 3% Native American, 9% Hispanic, 7% black, 3% Asian American or Pacific Islander, 1% international, 31% 25 or older, 24% live on campus, 4% transferred in. Retention: 62% of full-time freshmen returned the following year. Core. Calendar: semesters. Academic remediation for entering students, services for LD students, advanced placement, honors program, independent study, distance learning, double major, summer session for credit, part-time degree program, adult/continuing education programs, co-op programs.
Entrance Requirements: Open admission. Option: electronic application. Entrance: noncompetitive.
Costs Per Year: Application fee: $0. State resident tuition: $0 full-time. Nonresident tuition: $5250 full-time, $175 per unit part-time. Mandatory fees: $806 full-time, $27 per unit part-time, $13 per term part-time. College room only: $3865. Room charges vary according to housing facility.
Collegiate Environment: Orientation program. Drama-theater group, choral group. Social organizations: 10 open to all. Most popular organizations: Mountain Ultimate Disc (MUD), Varsity Club, Feather River Outings Group, SIFE, Chess Club. Major annual events: Thanksgiving Luncheon, MUD Classic, Earth Day/Day on the Green. Campus security: student patrols. 150 college housing spaces available; all were occupied in 2003-04. No special consideration for freshman housing applicants. Option: coed housing available. Feather River Library with 20,782 books, 197 microform titles, 4,122 serials, 1,762 audiovisual materials, and an OPAC. Operations spending for 2004 fiscal year: $177,859. 146 computers available on campus for general student use. A campuswide network can be accessed. Staffed computer lab on campus.

■ **FIDM/THE FASHION INSTITUTE OF DESIGN & MERCHANDISING, LOS ANGELES CAMPUS** *S-10*
919 South Grand Ave.
Los Angeles, CA 90015-1421
Tel: (213)624-1200
Free: 800-624-1200
Fax: (213)624-4799
E-mail: info@fidm.com
Web Site: http://www.fidm.edu/
Description: Proprietary, primarily 2-year, coed. Part of Fashion Institute of Design and Merchandising. Awards transfer associate, terminal associate, and bachelor's degrees (also includes Orange County Campus). Founded 1969. Setting: urban campus. Total enrollment: 3,522. Student-undergrad faculty ratio is 26:1. Full-time: 2,778 students, 91% women, 9% men. Part-time: 744 students, 88% women, 12% men. Students come from 40 states and territories, 30 other countries, 29% from out-of-state, 0.3% Native American, 20% Hispanic, 5% black, 16% Asian American or Pacific Islander, 7% international, 18% 25 or older. Core. Academic remediation for entering students, ESL program, services for LD students, advanced placement, independent study, distance learning, summer session for credit, part-time degree program, adult/continuing education programs, co-op programs and internships. Study abroad program.
Entrance Requirements: Options: Common Application, electronic application, deferred admission. Required: essay, high school transcript, 3 recom-

mendations, interview, major-determined project, Wonderlic Aptitude Test. Required for some: 3 recommendations, interview, major-determined project. Entrance: moderately difficult. Application deadline: Rolling.
Costs Per Year: Application fee: $225. Tuition: $17,415 full-time, $387 per unit part-time. Mandatory fees: $500 full-time.
Collegiate Environment: Orientation program. Student-run newspaper. Most popular organizations: ASID (student chapter), International Club, DECA, Association of Manufacturing Students, Honor Society. Major annual events: Debut Fashion Show, International Food Fair, Career Connection. Student services: personal-psychological counseling, learning services design studios. Campus security: 24-hour emergency response devices and patrols, late night transport-escort service. College housing not available. Resource and Research Center with 19,099 books, 369 serials, 3,607 audiovisual materials, and an OPAC. 322 computers available on campus for general student use. A campuswide network can be accessed from student residence rooms and from off campus. Staffed computer lab on campus.

■ **FIDM/THE FASHION INSTITUTE OF DESIGN & MERCHANDISING, ORANGE COUNTY CAMPUS** *T-7*
17590 Gillette Ave.
Irvine, CA 92614-5610
Tel: (949)851-6200
Fax: (949)851-6808
Web Site: http://www.fidm.com/
Description: Proprietary, 2-year, coed. Awards transfer associate degrees. Founded 1981. Total enrollment: 320. 10% from out-of-state.
Entrance Requirements: Required: essay, high school transcript, minimum 2.0 high school GPA, 3 recommendations, entrance requirement project. Required for some: interview. Application deadlines: Rolling, Rolling for nonresidents. Notification: continuous, continuous for nonresidents.
Collegiate Environment: Student-run newspaper. Most popular organizations: ASID Student Chapter, DECA, Association of Manufacturing Students. Student services: personal-psychological counseling. Campus security: 24-hour emergency response devices and patrols, late night transport-escort service. College housing not available.

■ **FIDM/THE FASHION INSTITUTE OF DESIGN & MERCHANDISING, SAN DIEGO CAMPUS** *W-12*
1010 Second Ave., Ste. 200
San Diego, CA 92101-4903
Tel: (619)235-2049
Free: 800-243-3436
Fax: (619)232-4322
E-mail: dbaca@fidm.com
Web Site: http://www.fidm.com/
Description: Proprietary, 2-year, coed. Part of Fashion Institute of Design and Merchandising. Awards transfer associate and terminal associate degrees. Founded 1985. Setting: urban campus. Total enrollment: 272. Student-undergrad faculty ratio is 20:1. Full-time: 235 students, 96% women, 4% men. Part-time: 37 students, 89% women, 11% men. Students come from 15 states and territories, 1 other country, 19% from out-of-state, 0.4% Native American, 23% Hispanic, 4% black, 11% Asian American or Pacific Islander, 1% international, 10% 25 or older. Core. Academic remediation for entering students, ESL program, services for LD students, advanced placement, independent study, distance learning, summer session for credit, part-time degree program, adult/continuing education programs, co-op programs and internships. Study abroad program.
Entrance Requirements: Options: Common Application, electronic application, deferred admission. Required: essay, 3 recommendations, interview, major-determined project. Recommended: minimum 2.5 high school GPA. Required for some: 3 recommendations, interview, major-determined project. Entrance: moderately difficult. Application deadline: Rolling.
Costs Per Year: Application fee: $225. Tuition: $17,415 full-time, $387 per unit part-time. Mandatory fees: $500 full-time.
Collegiate Environment: Orientation program. Most popular organizations: ASID (student chapter), DECA, Honor Society, Phi Theta Kappa. Major annual events: Debut Fashion Show, International Food Fair, Career Connection. Student services: personal-psychological counseling, learning support, design studios. Campus security: 24-hour emergency response devices and patrols. College housing not available. Resource and Research Center with 2,642 books, 100 serials, 915 audiovisual materials, and an OPAC. 32 computers available on campus for general student use. A campuswide

network can be accessed from student residence rooms and from off campus. Staffed computer lab on campus.

■ **FIDM/THE FASHION INSTITUTE OF DESIGN & MERCHANDISING, SAN FRANCISCO CAMPUS** *K-4*

55 Stockton St.
San Francisco, CA 94108-5829
Tel: (415)675-5200
Free: 800-711-7175
Admissions: (415)433-6691
Fax: (415)296-7299
E-mail: info@fidm.com
Web Site: http://www.fidm.edu/

Description: Proprietary, 2-year, coed. Part of Fashion Institute of Design and Merchandising. Awards transfer associate and terminal associate degrees. Founded 1973. Setting: urban campus. Total enrollment: 936. Full-time: 747 students, 92% women, 8% men. Part-time: 189 students, 93% women, 7% men. Students come from 15 states and territories, 20 other countries, 6% from out-of-state, 1% Native American, 17% Hispanic, 5% black, 18% Asian American or Pacific Islander, 2% international, 25% 25 or older. Core. Academic remediation for entering students, ESL program, services for LD students, advanced placement, honors program, independent study, distance learning, summer session for credit, part-time degree program, adult/continuing education programs, co-op programs and internships. Off campus study at Fashion Institute of Design and Merchandising, Los Angeles Campus. Study abroad program.
Entrance Requirements: Options: Common Application, electronic application, deferred admission. Required: essay, high school transcript, 3 recommendations, interview, major-determined project, Wonderlic aptitude test. Recommended: minimum 2.0 high school GPA. Required for some: 3 recommendations, interview, major-determined project. Entrance: moderately difficult. Application deadline: Rolling.
Costs Per Year: Application fee: $225. Tuition: $17,415 full-time, $387 per unit part-time.
Collegiate Environment: Orientation program. Most popular organizations: ASID (student chapter), DECA, Visual Design Form, Honor Society. Major annual events: Career Connection, Industry Lunch Connections. Student services: personal-psychological counseling, learning center and design studio. Campus security: 24-hour emergency response devices and patrols. College housing not available. Resource and Research Center with 5,073 books, 173 serials, 616 audiovisual materials, and an OPAC. 81 computers available on campus for general student use. A campuswide network can be accessed from student residence rooms and from off campus. Staffed computer lab on campus.

■ **FOLSOM LAKE COLLEGE** *I-6*

100 Scholar Way
Folsom, CA 95630
Tel: (916)608-6500
Web Site: http://www.flc.losrios.edu/

Description: County-supported, 2-year, coed. Part of Los Rios Community College District. Awards transfer associate and terminal associate degrees. Total enrollment: 12,000. 1% Native American, 9% Hispanic, 2% black, 8% Asian American or Pacific Islander, 47% 25 or older.

■ **FOOTHILL COLLEGE** *F-15*

12345 El Monte Rd.
Los Altos Hills, CA 94022-4599
Tel: (650)949-7777
Admissions: (650)949-7326
Web Site: http://www.foothill.edu/

Description: State and locally supported, 2-year, coed. Part of Foothill-DeAnza Community College District. Awards certificates, transfer associate, and terminal associate degrees. Founded 1958. Setting: 122-acre suburban campus with easy access to San Jose. Educational spending for 2005 fiscal year: $4026 per student. Total enrollment: 17,488. Student-undergrad faculty ratio is 28:1. 5,284 applied, 100% were admitted. 10% from top 10% of their high school class, 35% from top quarter, 50% from top half. Students come from 51 states and territories, 101 other countries, 2% from out-of-state, 0.4% Native American, 12% Hispanic, 3% black, 24% Asian American or Pacific Islander, 5% international, 57% 25 or older. Core. Academic remediation for entering students, ESL program, services for LD students, advanced placement, accelerated degree program, self-designed majors, honors program, independent study, distance learning, summer session for

credit, part-time degree program, adult/continuing education programs, co-op programs and internships. Off campus study at DeAnza College. Study abroad program. ROTC: Army (c), Air Force (c).
Entrance Requirements: Open admission except for dental hygiene, allied health programs. Option: electronic application. Recommended: high school transcript. Entrance: noncompetitive. Application deadline: 9/15. Notification: continuous.
Costs Per Year: Nonresident tuition: $4500 full-time, $100 per unit part-time. Mandatory fees: $780 full-time, $17 per unit part-time, $28.50 per term part-time.
Collegiate Environment: Orientation program. Drama-theater group, choral group, student-run newspaper, radio station. Most popular organizations: Alpha Gamma Sigma, student government. Major annual events: Career Day, Club Day, Transfer Day. Student services: legal services, health clinic, personal-psychological counseling. Campus security: 24-hour emergency response devices and patrols, late night transport-escort service. College housing not available. Hubert H. Semans Library with 70,000 books, 450 serials, an OPAC, and a Web page. 400 computers available on campus for general student use. A campuswide network can be accessed from off-campus. Staffed computer lab on campus.
Community Environment: This is a suburban area with temperate climate averaging 50 to 80 degrees. Los Altos Hills is strictly residential but all recreational and commercial facilities and services may be found in the neighboring cities of Palo Alto, Los Altos, Mountain View and Sunnyvale.

■ **FOUNDATION COLLEGE** *W-12*

5353 Mission Center Rd., Ste. 100
San Diego, CA 92108-1306
Tel: (619)683-3273; 888-707-3273
Fax: (619)683-3224
Web Site: http://www.foundationcollege.org/

Description: Independent, 2-year, coed. Awards certificates, transfer associate, and terminal associate degrees. Setting: urban campus. Total enrollment: 106. 221 applied, 49% were admitted. Full-time: 106 students, 22% women, 78% men. 3% Native American, 20% Hispanic, 18% black, 18% Asian American or Pacific Islander, 0% international. Calendar: continuous.
Entrance Requirements: Entrance: minimally difficult. Application deadline: Rolling. Notification: continuous.
Costs Per Year: Tuition: $17,940 full-time, $260 per credit part-time. Mandatory fees: $1200 full-time, $120 per course part-time.
Collegiate Environment: College housing not available.

■ **FRESNO CITY COLLEGE** *M-9*

1101 East University Ave.
Fresno, CA 93741-0002
Tel: (559)442-4600
Admissions: (559)442-8217
Web Site: http://www.fresnocitycollege.com/

Description: District-supported, 2-year, coed. Part of California Community College System. Awards certificates, transfer associate, and terminal associate degrees. Founded 1910. Setting: 103-acre urban campus. Endowment: $853,060. Total enrollment: 22,812. 2,996 applied, 100% were admitted. 0% from out-of-state, 1% Native American, 32% Hispanic, 8% black, 14% Asian American or Pacific Islander, 1% international, 7% 25 or older. Retention: 85% of full-time freshmen returned the following year. Core. Calendar: semesters. Academic remediation for entering students, ESL program, services for LD students, advanced placement, freshman honors college, honors program, summer session for credit, part-time degree program, co-op programs. Off campus study at Reedley College; California State University, Fresno. Study abroad program. ROTC: Army (c), Air Force (c).
Entrance Requirements: Open admission. Options: Common Application, early admission, deferred admission. Required: high school transcript. Placement: ACCUPLACER required. Entrance: noncompetitive. Application deadline: Rolling. Notification: continuous.
Collegiate Environment: Orientation program. Drama-theater group, choral group, marching band, student-run newspaper. Most popular organizations: MECHA, HMONG Club, Rotaract, Students in Free Enterprise, Latter Day Saints Student Association. Major annual events: Showcase, Club Awareness Day, Homecoming. Student services: health clinic, personal-psychological counseling. Campus security: 24-hour emergency response devices and patrols, late night transport-escort service. College housing not available. Fresno City College Library with 67,500 books, an OPAC, and a Web page. Operations spending for 2004 fiscal year: $1.5 million. 600 computers available on campus for general student use. Staffed computer lab on campus.

Community Environment: See California State University - Fresno.

■ **FRESNO PACIFIC UNIVERSITY** *M-9*
1717 South Chestnut Ave.
Fresno, CA 93702-4709
Tel: (559)453-2000
Admissions: (559)453-2030
Fax: (559)453-2007
E-mail: cwtemple@fresno.edu
Web Site: http://www.fresno.edu/
Description: Independent, comprehensive, coed, affiliated with Mennonite Brethren Church. Awards associate, bachelor's, and master's degrees. Founded 1944. Setting: 42-acre suburban campus. Endowment: $4.5 million. Educational spending for 2005 fiscal year: $6208 per student. Total enrollment: 2,371. Faculty: 198 (81 full-time, 117 part-time). Student-undergrad faculty ratio is 16:1. 608 applied, 68% were admitted. Full-time: 1,319 students, 67% women, 33% men. Part-time: 173 students, 57% women, 43% men. Students come from 18 states and territories, 36 other countries, 3% from out-of-state, 1% Native American, 26% Hispanic, 4% black, 4% Asian American or Pacific Islander, 3% international, 31% 25 or older, 53% live on campus, 18% transferred in. Retention: 76% of full-time freshmen returned the following year. Academic areas with the most degrees conferred: education; business/marketing; theology and religious vocations. Core. Calendar: semesters. ESL program, services for LD students, advanced placement, accelerated degree program, self-designed majors, independent study, distance learning, double major, summer session for credit, part-time degree program, adult/continuing education programs, co-op programs and internships, graduate courses open to undergrads. Off campus study at California State University, Fresno; Mennonite Brethren Biblical Seminary; San Joaquin College of Law. Study abroad program.
Entrance Requirements: Options: electronic application, early admission, deferred admission. Required: essay, high school transcript, 1 recommendation, SAT and SAT Subject Tests or ACT. Recommended: minimum 3.10 high school GPA. Entrance: moderately difficult. Application deadline: Rolling. Notification: continuous until 7/31.
Costs Per Year: Application fee: $40. Comprehensive fee: $26,780 includes full-time tuition ($20,550), mandatory fees ($240), and college room and board ($5990). Part-time tuition: $735 per unit.
Collegiate Environment: Orientation program. Drama-theater group, choral group, student-run newspaper. Social organizations: 20 open to all. Most popular organizations: International Club, Kid's Klub, Amigos Unidos, Slavic Club, Women's Soccer Club. Major annual events: Homecoming, M.C.C. Sale. Student services: health clinic, personal-psychological counseling. Campus security: 24-hour emergency response devices and patrols, student patrols, late night transport-escort service, controlled dormitory access, 24-hour monitored closed-circuit security cameras. 595 college housing spaces available; 514 were occupied in 2003-04. Freshmen guaranteed college housing. On-campus residence required through sophomore year. Options: men-only, women-only housing available. Hiebert Library with 181,020 books, 315,000 microform titles, 14,400 serials, 10,530 audiovisual materials, an OPAC, and a Web page. Operations spending for 2004 fiscal year: $694,934. 72 computers available on campus for general student use. A campuswide network can be accessed from student residence rooms and from off campus. Staffed computer lab on campus.
Community Environment: See California State University Fresno.

■ **FULLERTON COLLEGE** *R-6*
321 East Chapman Ave.
Fullerton, CA 92832-2095
Tel: (714)992-7000
Admissions: (714)992-7582
Web Site: http://www.fullcoll.edu/
Description: State and locally supported, 2-year, coed. Part of California Community College System. Awards certificates, transfer associate, and terminal associate degrees. Founded 1913. Setting: 79-acre suburban campus with easy access to Los Angeles. Total enrollment: 19,862. Students come from 21 other countries, 40% 25 or older. Retention: 50% of full-time freshmen returned the following year. Core. Calendar: semesters. Academic remediation for entering students, ESL program, services for LD students, advanced placement, honors program, summer session for credit, part-time degree program, adult/continuing education programs, co-op programs. Study abroad program. ROTC: Army (c), Naval (c), Air Force (c).
Entrance Requirements: Open admission. Option: early admission. Entrance: noncompetitive. Application deadline: Rolling.

Collegiate Environment: Drama-theater group, student-run newspaper, radio station. Student services: legal services, health clinic, personal-psychological counseling, women's center. College housing not available. William T. Boyce Library with 113,236 books and 600 serials. 600 computers available on campus for general student use. Staffed computer lab on campus.
Community Environment: See California State University - Fullerton

■ **GAVILAN COLLEGE** *L-6*
5055 Santa Teresa Blvd.
Gilroy, CA 95020-9599
Tel: (408)847-1400
Admissions: (408)848-4735
Fax: (408)848-4801
E-mail: jparker@gavilan.edu
Web Site: http://www.gavilan.edu/
Description: State and locally supported, 2-year, coed. Part of California Community College System. Awards certificates, diplomas, transfer associate, and terminal associate degrees. Founded 1919. Setting: 150-acre rural campus with easy access to San Jose. Total enrollment: 6,064. Students come from 6 states and territories, 11 other countries, 4% from out-of-state, 1% Native American, 41% Hispanic, 2% black, 6% Asian American or Pacific Islander, 0.1% international, 58% 25 or older. Core. Calendar: semesters. Academic remediation for entering students, ESL program, services for LD students, advanced placement, honors program, independent study, distance learning, summer session for credit, part-time degree program, adult/continuing education programs, co-op programs and internships. Study abroad program.
Entrance Requirements: Open admission. Option: international baccalaureate accepted. Entrance: noncompetitive. Application deadline: Rolling. Notification: continuous.
Costs Per Year: Application fee: $0. State resident tuition: $0 full-time. Nonresident tuition: $4800 full-time. Mandatory fees: $676 full-time, $26.
Collegiate Environment: Orientation program. Drama-theater group, marching band, student-run newspaper. Most popular organization: Student Government. Major annual events: Cinco de Maio, Black History Month, Career Transfer Day. Student services: health clinic, personal-psychological counseling. Campus security: 24-hour emergency response devices and patrols, late night transport-escort service. College housing not available. 55,440 books and 205 serials. 31 computers available on campus for general student use. A campuswide network can be accessed. Staffed computer lab on campus.
Community Environment: Gilroy has a population of 35,000 and is located 77 miles south of San Francisco; served by buses and railroads. There are churches, a hospital, a library, and radio station. Gilroy has theatres, parks, civic organizations, and a public swimming pool for recreational activities; nearby are beaches and five state parks.

■ **GLENDALE COMMUNITY COLLEGE** *S-10*
1500 North Verdugo Rd.
Glendale, CA 91208-2894
Tel: (818)240-1000
Admissions: (818)551-5115
Fax: (818)549-9436
Web Site: http://www.glendale.edu/
Description: State and locally supported, 2-year, coed. Part of California Community College System. Awards certificates, transfer associate, and terminal associate degrees. Founded 1927. Setting: 119-acre urban campus with easy access to Los Angeles. Endowment: $5.3 million. Research spending for 2004 fiscal year: $226,457. Educational spending for 2005 fiscal year: $2158 per student. Total enrollment: 14,265. 5,313 applied, 52% were admitted. Full-time: 4,730 students, 57% women, 43% men. Part-time: 9,535 students, 58% women, 42% men. Students come from 56 states and territories, 121 other countries, 1% from out-of-state, 0.4% Native American, 22% Hispanic, 3% black, 10% Asian American or Pacific Islander, 26% international, 42% 25 or older, 6% transferred in. Core. Calendar: semesters. Academic remediation for entering students, ESL program, services for LD students, advanced placement, honors program, independent study, distance learning, summer session for credit, part-time degree program, adult/continuing education programs, co-op programs and internships. Study abroad program.
Entrance Requirements: Open admission. Options: Common Application, electronic application, early admission, deferred admission. Recommended: high school transcript. Placement: CPT recommended. Entrance: noncompetitive. Application deadline: Rolling.

Costs Per Year: Application fee: $0. State resident tuition: $0 full-time. Nonresident tuition: $4280 full-time, $150 per unit part-time. Mandatory fees: $680 full-time, $26 per unit part-time, $170 per term part-time.

Collegiate Environment: Orientation program. Drama-theater group, choral group, student-run newspaper. Social organizations: 30 open to all. Most popular organizations: Alpha Gamma Sigma, Armenian Student Association, Korean Christian Fellowship, Theatre Guild, International Student Association. Major annual events: ASGCC Honors and Awards Banquet, Transfer Day, graduation. Student services: health clinic, personal-psychological counseling. Campus security: student patrols, late night transport-escort service. College housing not available. Glendale Community College Library with 91,371 books, 41,808 microform titles, 312 serials, 1,893 audiovisual materials, an OPAC, and a Web page. Operations spending for 2004 fiscal year: $1.7 million. 534 computers available on campus for general student use. A campuswide network can be accessed from off-campus. Staffed computer lab on campus.

■ **GOLDEN GATE UNIVERSITY** *K-4*
536 Mission St.
San Francisco, CA 94105-2968
Tel: (415)442-7000
Free: 800-448-4968
Admissions: (415)442-7800
Fax: (415)442-7807
E-mail: info@ggu.edu
Web Site: http://www.ggu.edu/
Description: Independent, university, coed. Awards bachelor's, master's, doctoral, and first professional degrees. Founded 1901. Setting: urban campus. Endowment: $16.6 million. Educational spending for 2005 fiscal year: $4423 per student. Total enrollment: 3,891. Faculty: 489 (30 full-time, 459 part-time). Student-undergrad faculty ratio is 16:1. Students come from 50 other countries, 5% from out-of-state, 1% Native American, 11% Hispanic, 9% black, 17% Asian American or Pacific Islander, 8% international, 76% 25 or older. Retention: 80% of full-time freshmen returned the following year. Academic areas with the most degrees conferred: business/marketing; computer and information sciences; liberal arts/general studies. Core. Calendar: trimesters. Academic remediation for entering students, ESL program, advanced placement, accelerated degree program, distance learning, summer session for credit, part-time degree program, adult/continuing education programs, internships, graduate courses open to undergrads. Off campus study at The San Francisco Consortium.
Entrance Requirements: Options: Peterson's Universal Application, Common Application, electronic application, deferred admission, international baccalaureate accepted. Required: high school transcript, minimum 2.0 high school GPA. Recommended: essay, minimum 3.0 high school GPA. Required for some: minimum 3.2 high school GPA, interview. Entrance: moderately difficult. Application deadline: Rolling. Notification: continuous.
Costs Per Year: Application fee: $55. Tuition: $11,520 full-time, $1440 per course part-time.
Collegiate Environment: Student-run newspaper. Social organizations: 16 open to all. Most popular organizations: American Marketing Association, Korean Student Association, Japanese Student Association, Thai Student Association, Computing Society. Major annual events: International Cultural Celebration Day, welcome party, farewell party. Student services: personal-psychological counseling. Campus security: late night transport-escort service. College housing not available. Golden Gate University Library plus 1 other with 79,204 books, 442,800 microform titles, 3,335 serials, and an OPAC. Operations spending for 2004 fiscal year: $1.3 million. 52 computers available on campus for general student use. Computer purchase/lease plans available. A campuswide network can be accessed. Staffed computer lab on campus.
Community Environment: See San Francisco State University.

■ **GOLDEN WEST COLLEGE** *T-10*
PO Box 2748, 15744 Golden West St.
Huntington Beach, CA 92647-2748
Tel: (714)892-7711
Web Site: http://www.gwc.cccd.edu/
Description: State and locally supported, 2-year, coed. Part of Coast Community College District System. Awards certificates, transfer associate, and terminal associate degrees. Founded 1966. Setting: 122-acre suburban campus with easy access to Los Angeles. Endowment: $880,684. Research spending for 2004 fiscal year: $119,377. Educational spending for 2005 fiscal year: $1831 per student. Total enrollment: 13,091. Students come from

28 other countries, 44% 25 or older. Core. Calendar: semesters (summer session). Academic remediation for entering students, ESL program, advanced placement, self-designed majors, summer session for credit, part-time degree program, external degree program, adult/continuing education programs, co-op programs and internships. Study abroad program. ROTC: Air Force (c).
Entrance Requirements: Open admission except for nursing program. Option: early admission. Recommended: high school transcript. Required for some: essay. Placement: ACT COMPASS recommended; ACT COMPASS required for some. Entrance: noncompetitive. Application deadline: Rolling. Notification: continuous.
Costs Per Year: Application fee: $0. State resident tuition: $0 full-time. Nonresident tuition: $5034 full-time, $152 per unit part-time. Mandatory fees: $778 full-time, $26 per unit part-time.
Collegiate Environment: Drama-theater group, choral group, student-run newspaper, radio station. Major annual events: College Transfer Day, Gold Rush Days. Student services: legal services, health clinic, personal-psychological counseling. Campus security: 24-hour emergency response devices and patrols, late night transport-escort service. College housing not available. Golden West College Library plus 1 other with 95,000 books, 410 serials, an OPAC, and a Web page. Operations spending for 2004 fiscal year: $750,639. 680 computers available on campus for general student use. A campuswide network can be accessed from off-campus. Staffed computer lab on campus.
Community Environment: Huntington Beach is located in the northern coastal region of Orange County, which is 35 miles southeast of Los Angeles. The climate is moderate with a mean yearly temperature of 70 degrees. All major transportation facilities available. Eight miles of the finest, safest beach in California is located here. The city has three public golf courses and parks for recreational activities. This is one of the fastest growing cities in the west.

■ **GROSSMONT COLLEGE** *V-12*
8800 Grossmont College Dr.
El Cajon, CA 92020-1799
Tel: (619)644-7000
Admissions: (619)644-7188
Fax: (619)644-7922
Web Site: http://www.grossmont.edu/
Description: State and locally supported, 2-year, coed. Part of California Community College System. Awards certificates, transfer associate, and terminal associate degrees. Founded 1961. Setting: 135-acre suburban campus with easy access to San Diego. Total enrollment: 16,829. Students come from 52 other countries, 38% 25 or older. Core. Calendar: semesters. Academic remediation for entering students, ESL program, services for LD students, advanced placement, self-designed majors, honors program, summer session for credit, part-time degree program, adult/continuing education programs, co-op programs and internships. ROTC: Army (c), Air Force (c).
Entrance Requirements: Open admission. Options: Common Application, early admission. Placement: Assessment and Placement Services for Community Colleges recommended. Entrance: noncompetitive. Application deadline: 8/12. Notification: continuous until 8/12.
Collegiate Environment: Drama-theater group, choral group, student-run newspaper, radio station. Social organizations: 23 open to all. Student services: legal services, health clinic, personal-psychological counseling. Campus security: 24-hour emergency response devices, student patrols, late night transport-escort service. College housing not available. Lewis F. Smith Learning Resource Center with 105,000 books, 759 serials, an OPAC, and a Web page. 300 computers available on campus for general student use. Staffed computer lab on campus.
Community Environment: El Cajon is situated east of San Diego in a suburban community with a Mediterranean climate. Gillespie Airport and buses serve the area. The County Branch Library is located here; there are churches of all denominations. Employment is available through the California Department of Employment which is located on the Grossmont college campus. There are recreational facilities at both the beaches and in the nearby mountain area. Annual festivities include the "Mother Goose Parade."

■ **HARTNELL COLLEGE** *M-5*
156 Homestead Ave.
Salinas, CA 93901-1697
Tel: (831)755-6700
Admissions: (831)755-6711

Web Site: http://www.hartnell.edu/

Description: District-supported, 2-year, coed. Part of California Community College System. Awards certificates, transfer associate, and terminal associate degrees. Founded 1920. Setting: 50-acre small town campus with easy access to San Jose. Total enrollment: 10,074. Students come from 16 states and territories, 14 other countries. Core. Calendar: semesters. Academic remediation for entering students, ESL program, services for LD students, self-designed majors, honors program, summer session for credit, part-time degree program, adult/continuing education programs, co-op programs. Study abroad program.

Entrance Requirements: Open admission except for allied health programs. Options: early admission, deferred admission. Required for some: high school transcript. Entrance: noncompetitive. Application deadline: Rolling. Notification: continuous.

Collegiate Environment: Drama-theater group, choral group, student-run newspaper. Social organizations: 20 open to all. Most popular organizations: Chicano Students Club, Alpha Gamma Sigma. Major annual events: College Night, Western Stage, Spring Conference Day. Student services: women's center. Campus security: 24-hour emergency response devices, student patrols, late night transport-escort service. College housing not available. Hartnell College Library plus 1 other with 70,000 books and 480 serials. Operations spending for 2004 fiscal year: $646,064. 100 computers available on campus for general student use. Staffed computer lab on campus.

Community Environment: Population 78,000. Salinas is the county seat of Monterey County, 106 miles south of San Francisco on Highway 101. Southern Pacific Railroad, Greyhound bus and United Airlines serve the area. The Santa Lucia Mountains are to the west of Salinas and the Gabilan foothills to the east. Agriculture is the chief factor of economy in Salinas with new industries designed to take advantage of the abundant harvest. The climate is comfortable, the average temperature being 57 degrees. Salinas has a great number of churches, YMCA, theatres, community concert association, Monterey County symphony, a variety of civic, fraternal and veteran's organizations. John Steinbeck was born here. Part-time employment opportunities for students available in nearby recreational areas, agriculture, industrial and commercial firms. The recreational facilities include nine municipal recreation centers, a municipal golf course, private country clubs, the Monterey Peninsula playland area, the famous white sandy beaches of Carmel, a 20-minute drive away, flying clubs, a ski club, and many hobby clubs. This is the location of the oldest and largest four-day California Rodeo.

■ **HARVEY MUDD COLLEGE** *V-10*

301 East 12th St.
Claremont, CA 91711-5994
Tel: (909)621-8000
Admissions: (909)621-8011
Fax: (909)621-8360
E-mail: admission@hmc.edu
Web Site: http://www.hmc.edu/

Description: Independent, 4-year, coed. Part of The Claremont Colleges Consortium. Awards bachelor's and master's degrees. Founded 1955. Setting: 33-acre suburban campus with easy access to Los Angeles. Endowment: $179.1 million. Research spending for 2004 fiscal year: $2.1 million. Educational spending for 2005 fiscal year: $21,095 per student. Total enrollment: 743. Faculty: 93 (79 full-time, 14 part-time). Student-undergrad faculty ratio is 8:1. 1,899 applied, 36% were admitted. 91% from top 10% of their high school class, 100% from top quarter. 38 National Merit Scholars, 27 valedictorians. Students come from 47 states and territories, 14 other countries, 57% from out-of-state, 1% Native American, 7% Hispanic, 2% black, 18% Asian American or Pacific Islander, 4% international, 1% 25 or older, 97% live on campus. Retention: 95% of full-time freshmen returned the following year. Academic areas with the most degrees conferred: engineering; physical sciences; computer and information sciences. Core. Calendar: semesters. Services for LD students, advanced placement, self-designed majors, double major, internships. Off campus study at other members of The Claremont Colleges, Swarthmore College, Rensselaer Polytechnic Institute. Study abroad program. ROTC: Army (c), Air Force.

Entrance Requirements: Options: Peterson's Universal Application, Common Application, electronic application, early decision, deferred admission, international baccalaureate accepted. Required: essay, high school transcript, 3 recommendations, SAT Subject Test in Math 2C and second exam of choice (Math 1C is not accepted). Recommended: interview. Entrance: most difficult. Application deadlines: 1/15, 11/15 for early decision. Notification: 4/1, 12/15 for early decision.

Costs Per Year: Application fee: $50. Comprehensive fee: $42,352 includes full-time tuition ($31,738), mandatory fees ($202), and college room and board ($10,412). College room only: $5282. Room and board charges vary according to board plan.

Collegiate Environment: Orientation program. Drama-theater group, choral group, student-run newspaper, radio station. Social organizations: 80 open to all. Most popular organizations: Delta 'H' Outdoor Club, Etc. Players - Drama Club, club sports, Jazz Orchestra, Society of Women Engineers. Major annual events: 5-Class Competition, Mudd Occasional Ball, Presentations and Projects Week. Student services: health clinic, personal-psychological counseling, women's center. Campus security: 24-hour emergency response devices and patrols, late night transport-escort service. 712 college housing spaces available; 695 were occupied in 2003-04. Freshmen guaranteed college housing. On-campus residence required in freshman year. Option: coed housing available. Honnold Library plus 1 other with 3.2 million books, 1.5 million microform titles, 16,308 serials, 10,040 audiovisual materials, an OPAC, and a Web page. Operations spending for 2004 fiscal year: $645,035. 360 computers available on campus for general student use. Computer purchase/lease plans available. A campuswide network can be accessed from student residence rooms and from off campus. Staffed computer lab on campus.

■ **HEALD COLLEGE-CONCORD** *J-5*

5130 Commercial Circle
Concord, CA 94520
Tel: (925)288-5800
Fax: (925)288-5896
Web Site: http://www.heald.edu/

Description: Independent, 2-year, coed. Awards certificates, diplomas, transfer associate, and terminal associate degrees. Founded 1863. Setting: 5-acre small town campus with easy access to San Francisco. Total enrollment: 639. Student-undergrad faculty ratio is 18:1. Full-time: 524 students, 67% women, 33% men. Part-time: 115 students, 65% women, 35% men. 0% from out-of-state, 0% Native American, 5% Hispanic, 5% black, 3% Asian American or Pacific Islander, 0% international. Academic remediation for entering students, advanced placement, summer session for credit, part-time degree program, internships.

Entrance Requirements: Open admission. Options: electronic application, early admission, deferred admission. Required: high school transcript, interview, COMPASS. Entrance: minimally difficult. Application deadline: Rolling. Notification: continuous.

Collegiate Environment: Orientation program. Campus security: 24-hour emergency response devices. College housing not available. Learning Resource Center with an OPAC.

■ **HEALD COLLEGE-FRESNO** *M-9*

255 West Bullard Ave.
Fresno, CA 93704-1706
Tel: (559)438-4222
Web Site: http://www.heald.edu/

Description: Independent, 2-year, coed. Awards certificates, diplomas, transfer associate, and terminal associate degrees. Founded 1863. Setting: 3-acre suburban campus. Total enrollment: 729. Student-undergrad faculty ratio is 20:1. Full-time: 547 students, 63% women, 37% men. Part-time: 182 students, 61% women, 39% men. 0% from out-of-state, 0.1% Native American, 11% Hispanic, 2% black, 3% Asian American or Pacific Islander, 0% international. Academic remediation for entering students, advanced placement, summer session for credit, part-time degree program, internships.

Entrance Requirements: Open admission. Options: electronic application, early admission, deferred admission. Required: high school transcript, interview, COMPASS. Entrance: minimally difficult. Application deadline: Rolling. Notification: continuous.

Collegiate Environment: Orientation program. College housing not available. Learning Resource Center with an OPAC.

■ **HEALD COLLEGE-HAYWARD** *K-5*

25500 Industrial Blvd.
Hayward, CA 94545
Tel: (510)783-2100
Fax: (510)783-3287
Web Site: http://www.heald.edu/

Description: Independent, 2-year, coed. Awards certificates, diplomas, transfer associate, and terminal associate degrees. Founded 1863. Setting:

urban campus with easy access to San Francisco. Total enrollment: 864. Student-undergrad faculty ratio is 26:1. Full-time: 637 students, 62% women, 38% men. Part-time: 227 students, 72% women, 28% men. 0% from out-of-state, 0.3% Native American, 9% Hispanic, 6% black, 6% Asian American or Pacific Islander, 0% international. Academic remediation for entering students, advanced placement, summer session for credit, part-time degree program, internships.

Entrance Requirements: Open admission. Options: electronic application, early admission, deferred admission. Required: high school transcript, interview, COMPASS. Entrance: minimally difficult. Application deadline: Rolling. Notification: continuous.

Collegiate Environment: Orientation program. Campus security: 24-hour emergency response devices and patrols. College housing not available. Learning Resource Center (LRC) with an OPAC.

■ **HEALD COLLEGE-RANCHO CORDOVA** *I-6*
2910 Prospect Park Dr.
Rancho Cordova, CA 95670-6005
Tel: (916)638-1616
Fax: (916)853-8282
Web Site: http://www.heald.edu/

Description: Independent, 2-year, coed. Awards certificates, diplomas, transfer associate, and terminal associate degrees. Founded 1863. Setting: 1-acre suburban campus with easy access to Sacramento. Total enrollment: 471. Student-undergrad faculty ratio is 20:1. Full-time: 349 students, 65% women, 35% men. Part-time: 122 students, 70% women, 30% men. 0% from out-of-state, 0.2% Native American, 13% Hispanic, 12% black, 9% Asian American or Pacific Islander, 0% international. Academic remediation for entering students, advanced placement, summer session for credit, part-time degree program, internships.

Entrance Requirements: Open admission. Options: electronic application, early admission, deferred admission. Required: high school transcript, interview, COMPASS. Entrance: minimally difficult. Application deadline: Rolling. Notification: continuous.

Collegiate Environment: Orientation program. Campus security: late night transport-escort service. College housing not available. Learning Resource Center with an OPAC.

■ **HEALD COLLEGE-ROSEVILLE** *H-6*
Seven Sierra Gate Plaza
Roseville, CA 95678
Tel: (916)789-8600
Web Site: http://www.heald.edu/

Description: Independent, 2-year, coed. Awards certificates, diplomas, transfer associate, and terminal associate degrees. Founded 1863. Setting: 5-acre urban campus. Total enrollment: 528. Student-undergrad faculty ratio is 19:1. Full-time: 376 students, 60% women, 40% men. Part-time: 152 students, 61% women, 39% men. 0% from out-of-state, 1% Native American, 7% Hispanic, 1% black, 2% Asian American or Pacific Islander, 0% international. Academic remediation for entering students, advanced placement, summer session for credit, part-time degree program, internships.

Entrance Requirements: Options: electronic application, early admission, deferred admission. Required: high school transcript, interview, COMPASS. Entrance: minimally difficult.

Collegiate Environment: Orientation program. Campus security: 24-hour emergency response devices, evening security guard. College housing not available. Learning Resource Center with an OPAC.

■ **HEALD COLLEGE-SALINAS** *M-5*
1450 North Main St.
Salinas, CA 93906
Tel: (831)443-1700
Fax: (831)443-1050
Web Site: http://www.heald.edu/

Description: Independent, 2-year, coed. Awards certificates, diplomas, transfer associate, and terminal associate degrees. Founded 1863. Setting: small town campus with easy access to San Jose. Total enrollment: 414. Student-undergrad faculty ratio is 24:1. Full-time: 329 students, 66% women, 34% men. Part-time: 85 students, 71% women, 29% men. 0% from out-of-state, 0% Native American, 18% Hispanic, 3% black, 0.5% Asian American or Pacific Islander, 0% international. Academic remediation for entering students, advanced placement, summer session for credit, part-time degree program, internships.

Entrance Requirements: Open admission. Options: electronic application, early admission, deferred admission. Required: high school transcript, interview, COMPASS. Entrance: minimally difficult. Application deadline: Rolling. Notification: continuous.

Collegiate Environment: Orientation program. Campus security: 24-hour emergency response devices, evening security personnel. College housing not available. Learning Resource Center with an OPAC.

■ **HEALD COLLEGE-SAN FRANCISCO** *K-4*
350 Mission St.
San Francisco, CA 94105-2206
Tel: (415)808-3000
Fax: (415)808-3003
Web Site: http://www.heald.edu/

Description: Independent, 2-year, coed. Awards certificates, diplomas, transfer associate, and terminal associate degrees. Founded 1863. Setting: urban campus. Total enrollment: 389. Student-undergrad faculty ratio is 16:1. Full-time: 273 students, 57% women, 43% men. Part-time: 116 students, 51% women, 49% men. 0% from out-of-state, 0.3% Native American, 5% Hispanic, 5% black, 5% Asian American or Pacific Islander, 0% international. Academic remediation for entering students, advanced placement, summer session for credit, part-time degree program, internships.

Entrance Requirements: Open admission. Options: electronic application, early admission, deferred admission. Required: high school transcript, interview, COMPASS. Entrance: minimally difficult. Application deadline: Rolling. Notification: continuous.

Collegiate Environment: Orientation program. College housing not available. Learning Resource Center with an OPAC.

■ **HEALD COLLEGE-SAN JOSE** *J-6*
341 Great Mall Parkway
Milpitas, CA 95035
Tel: (408)934-4900
Fax: (408)934-7777
Web Site: http://www.heald.edu/

Description: Independent, 2-year, coed. Awards certificates, diplomas, transfer associate, and terminal associate degrees. Founded 1863. Setting: 5-acre small town campus with easy access to San Jose. Total enrollment: 639. Student-undergrad faculty ratio is 20:1. Full-time: 502 students, 63% women, 37% men. Part-time: 137 students, 66% women, 34% men. 0% from out-of-state, 0.3% Native American, 39% Hispanic, 11% black, 19% Asian American or Pacific Islander, 0% international. Academic remediation for entering students, advanced placement, summer session for credit, part-time degree program, internships.

Entrance Requirements: Open admission. Options: electronic application, early admission, deferred admission. Required: high school transcript, interview, COMPASS. Entrance: minimally difficult. Application deadline: Rolling. Notification: continuous.

Collegiate Environment: Orientation program. College housing not available. Learning Resource Center with an OPAC.

■ **HEALD COLLEGE-STOCKTON** *J-6*
1605 East March Ln.
Stockton, CA 95210
Tel: (209)473-5200
Fax: (209)477-2739
Web Site: http://www.heald.edu/

Description: Independent, 2-year, coed. Awards certificates, diplomas, transfer associate, and terminal associate degrees. Founded 1863. Total enrollment: 530. Student-undergrad faculty ratio is 17:1. Full-time: 398 students, 74% women, 26% men. Part-time: 132 students, 73% women, 27% men. 0% from out-of-state, 0.2% Native American, 17% Hispanic, 4% black, 8% Asian American or Pacific Islander, 0% international. Academic remediation for entering students, advanced placement, summer session for credit, part-time degree program, internships.

Entrance Requirements: Open admission. Options: electronic application, early admission, deferred admission. Required: high school transcript, interview, COMPASS. Entrance: minimally difficult. Application deadline: Rolling. Notification: continuous.

Collegiate Environment: Orientation program. College housing not available. Learning Resource Center with an OPAC.

■ **HIGH-TECH INSTITUTE** *I-6*
1111 Howe Ave., No. 250
Sacramento, CA 95825

Tel: (916)929-9700
Free: 800-987-0110
Fax: (916)929-9703
E-mail: rdyer@hightechschools.com
Web Site: http://www.high-techinstitute.com/
Description: Proprietary, 2-year, coed. Founded 1992.

■ **HOLY NAMES UNIVERSITY** *K-4*
3500 Mountain Blvd.
Oakland, CA 94619-1699
Tel: (510)436-1000
Free: 800-430-1321
Admissions: (510)436-1351
Fax: (510)436-1325
E-mail: admissions@hnu.edu
Web Site: http://www.hnu.edu/
Description: Independent Roman Catholic, comprehensive, coed. Awards bachelor's and master's degrees. Founded 1868. Setting: 60-acre urban campus with easy access to San Francisco. Endowment: $7.5 million. Educational spending for 2005 fiscal year: $4336 per student. Total enrollment: 1,093. Faculty: 140 (34 full-time, 106 part-time). Student-undergrad faculty ratio is 13:1. 278 applied, 64% were admitted. 21% from top 10% of their high school class, 41% from top quarter, 74% from top half. Full-time: 465 students, 67% women, 33% men. Part-time: 221 students, 85% women, 15% men. Students come from 17 states and territories, 14 other countries, 5% from out-of-state, 1% Native American, 18% Hispanic, 26% black, 9% Asian American or Pacific Islander, 6% international, 51% 25 or older, 30% live on campus, 20% transferred in. Retention: 64% of full-time freshmen returned the following year. Academic areas with the most degrees conferred: health professions and related sciences; business/marketing; psychology. Core. Calendar: semesters. Academic remediation for entering students, ESL program, services for LD students, advanced placement, accelerated degree program, self-designed majors, independent study, distance learning, double major, summer session for credit, part-time degree program, adult/continuing education programs, internships, graduate courses open to undergrads. Study abroad program. ROTC: Army (c), Air Force (c).
Entrance Requirements: Options: Peterson's Universal Application, Common Application, electronic application, deferred admission, international baccalaureate accepted. Required: essay, high school transcript, SAT or ACT. Recommended: 1 recommendation. Required for some: interview. Entrance: moderately difficult. Application deadline: 8/1. Notification: continuous.
Costs Per Year: Application fee: $50. Tuition: $22,470 full-time. Mandatory fees: $240 full-time.
Collegiate Environment: Orientation program. Drama-theater group, choral group. Social organizations: 10 open to all. Most popular organizations: Drama Club, Latinos Unidos, Black Student Union, Biology Club, Hiking Club. Major annual events: CORE Festival, Founders' Day, Convocation. Student services: personal-psychological counseling. Campus security: 24-hour emergency response devices, late night transport-escort service, controlled dormitory access, electronically operated main gate. 326 college housing spaces available; 190 were occupied in 2003-04. Freshmen guaranteed college housing. Option: coed housing available. Cushing Library with 111,243 books, 50,931 microform titles, 8,003 serials, 4,378 audiovisual materials, and a Web page. Operations spending for 2004 fiscal year: $289,097. 86 computers available on campus for general student use. A campuswide network can be accessed from student residence rooms and from off campus. Staffed computer lab on campus.
Community Environment: The College is located in the Oakland hills, overlooking San Francisco Bay and San Francisco itself. The campus is within 15-45 minutes of all the rich cultural, recreational, and sports activities of San Francisco, Berkeley and Oakland. Easy day trips can be made to the wine country, beaches, ski areas and National Parks.

■ **HOPE INTERNATIONAL UNIVERSITY** *R-6*
2500 East Nutwood Ave.
Fullerton, CA 92831-3138
Tel: (714)879-3901
Free: 800-762-1294
Fax: (714)526-0231
Web Site: http://www.hiu.edu/
Description: Independent, comprehensive, coed, affiliated with Christian Churches and Churches of Christ. Awards associate, bachelor's, and master's degrees. Founded 1928. Setting: 16-acre suburban campus with easy access to Los Angeles. Endowment: $3.3 million. Educational spending for 2005 fiscal year: $5045 per student. Total enrollment: 1,136. Faculty: 211 (27 full-time, 184 part-time). Student-undergrad faculty ratio is 10:1. Full-time: 646 students, 63% women, 37% men. Part-time: 211 students, 57% women, 43% men. Students come from 33 states and territories, 25 other countries, 26% from out-of-state, 1% Native American, 18% Hispanic, 8% black, 6% Asian American or Pacific Islander, 6% international, 50% 25 or older, 75% live on campus, 7% transferred in. Retention: 62% of full-time freshmen returned the following year. Academic areas with the most degrees conferred: family and consumer sciences; theology and religious vocations; business/marketing. Core. Calendar: 4-1-4. Academic remediation for entering students, ESL program, advanced placement, accelerated degree program, independent study, distance learning, double major, summer session for credit, part-time degree program, adult/continuing education programs, internships, graduate courses open to undergrads. Off campus study at California State University, Fullerton. Study abroad program.
Entrance Requirements: Options: electronic application, early admission, deferred admission, international baccalaureate accepted. Required: essay, high school transcript, minimum 2.5 high school GPA, 2 recommendations, rank in upper 50% of high school class, SAT or ACT. Recommended: SAT. Required for some: interview. Entrance: moderately difficult. Application deadline: 6/1. Notification: continuous until 7/1.
Costs Per Year: Application fee: $40. Comprehensive fee: $24,000 includes full-time tuition ($17,700), mandatory fees ($300), and college room and board ($6000). College room only: $3300. Full-time tuition and fees vary according to program. Room and board charges vary according to board plan. Part-time tuition: $655 per unit. Part-time tuition varies according to program.
Collegiate Environment: Orientation program. Drama-theater group, choral group, student-run newspaper. Major annual events: Spring Banquet, Sadie Hawkins Day, Happy House. Student services: health clinic, personal-psychological counseling. Campus security: 24-hour emergency response devices, student patrols. 400 college housing spaces available; 357 were occupied in 2003-04. No special consideration for freshman housing applicants. On-campus residence required through sophomore year. Options: men-only, women-only housing available. Darling Library with 100,000 books, 500 serials, 600 audiovisual materials, and an OPAC. Operations spending for 2004 fiscal year: $217,865. 44 computers available on campus for general student use. A campuswide network can be accessed from off-campus. Staffed computer lab on campus.
Community Environment: See California State University - Fullerton.

■ **HUMBOLDT STATE UNIVERSITY** *C-1*
1 Harpst St.
Arcata, CA 95521-8299
Tel: (707)826-3011
Admissions: (707)826-6220
Fax: (707)826-6194
E-mail: hsuinfo@humboldt.edu
Web Site: http://www.humboldt.edu/
Description: State-supported, comprehensive, coed. Part of California State University System. Awards bachelor's and master's degrees. Founded 1913. Setting: 161-acre rural campus. Endowment: $10.2 million. Research spending for 2004 fiscal year: $8.5 million. Educational spending for 2005 fiscal year: $5531 per student. Total enrollment: 7,550. 6,319 applied, 58% were admitted. 10% from top 10% of their high school class, 36% from top quarter, 75% from top half. Full-time: 5,899 students, 55% women, 45% men. Part-time: 630 students, 52% women, 48% men. Students come from 50 states and territories, 24 other countries, 4% from out-of-state, 2% Native American, 8% Hispanic, 3% black, 4% Asian American or Pacific Islander, 1% international, 26% 25 or older, 20% live on campus, 13% transferred in. Retention: 72% of full-time freshmen returned the following year. Core. Calendar: semesters. Academic remediation for entering students, ESL program, services for LD students, advanced placement, self-designed majors, honors program, independent study, distance learning, double major, summer session for credit, part-time degree program, adult/continuing education programs, co-op programs and internships, graduate courses open to undergrads. Off campus study at members of the National Student Exchange, California State University System. Study abroad program.
Entrance Requirements: Option: electronic application. Required: high school transcript, minimum 2.0 high school GPA. Required for some: SAT or ACT. Entrance: moderately difficult. Application deadline: 11/30. Notification: continuous. Preference given to state residents.
Collegiate Environment: Orientation program. Drama-theater group, choral group, marching band, student-run newspaper, radio station. Social

organizations: 140 open to all; national fraternities, national sororities, local sororities; 1% of eligible men and 1% of eligible women are members. Most popular organizations: student radio station, Student Environmental Action Coalition, youth educational services, Ballet Folklorico, International Student Union. Major annual events: homecoming, Arts and Music Festival, Film Festival. Student services: legal services, health clinic, personal-psychological counseling, women's center. Campus security: 24-hour emergency response devices and patrols, late night transport-escort service, controlled dormitory access. 1,350 college housing spaces available; 1,300 were occupied in 2003-04. No special consideration for freshman housing applicants. Option: coed housing available. 585,386 books, 602,973 microform titles, 2,629 serials, 4,947 audiovisual materials, an OPAC, and a Web page. Operations spending for 2004 fiscal year: $2.9 million. 778 computers available on campus for general student use. A campuswide network can be accessed from student residence rooms and from off campus. Staffed computer lab on campus.

Community Environment: Arcata, population 19,300, is located on the north shore of Humboldt Bay in northwestern California with an unrestricted panorama of mountains, bay, dairy and farm lands, sand dunes, and the Pacific Ocean. It is eight miles north of Eureka, and 275 miles north of San Francisco. Industry includes lumbering, manufacturing of wood products, tourism and dairy products. Humboldt Bay region climate is moist, but stimulating, with no extremes of heat or cold. Summer and fall are considered particularly delightful seasons. Buses and airlines serve the area. The city has a library, churches and the usual service clubs. Recreational opportunities include river rafting, kayaking, backpacking, hunting, trout fishing in mountain streams, salmon fishing in Humboldt and Trinidad Bays, and deep sea fishing. There is an Azalea Reserve, three miles north.

■ **HUMPHREYS COLLEGE** *J-6*
6650 Inglewood Ave.
Stockton, CA 95207-3896
Tel: (209)478-0800
Fax: (209)478-8721
Web Site: http://www.humphreys.edu/
Description: Independent, comprehensive, coed. Awards associate, bachelor's, and first professional degrees. Founded 1896. Setting: 10-acre suburban campus with easy access to San Francisco. Total enrollment: 721. Students come from 3 states and territories, 4 other countries, 70% 25 or older, 6% live on campus. Retention: 50% of full-time freshmen returned the following year. Core. Academic remediation for entering students, advanced placement, accelerated degree program, self-designed majors, summer session for credit, part-time degree program, adult/continuing education programs, co-op programs and internships.
Entrance Requirements: Open admission. Options: early admission, deferred admission. Required: high school transcript, minimum 2.0 high school GPA. Recommended: interview. Required for some: recommendations. Entrance: noncompetitive. Application deadline: Rolling.
Collegiate Environment: Most popular organizations: Business Club, Paralegal Club, Student Council, Collegiate Secretaries International. Major annual events: Hot Dog Day (quarterly BBQ), Annual Christmas Dinner, Students Versus Staff Softball. Campus security: 24-hour patrols, late night transport-escort service. Option: coed housing available. Humphreys College Library plus 1 other with 20,500 books and 115 serials. Operations spending for 2004 fiscal year: $66,952. 40 computers available on campus for general student use. Staffed computer lab on campus.
Community Environment: See University of the Pacific.

■ **IMPERIAL VALLEY COLLEGE** *V-15*
380 East Aten Rd.
PO Box 158
Imperial, CA 92251-0158
Tel: (760)352-8320
Web Site: http://www.imperial.cc.ca.us/
Description: State and locally supported, 2-year, coed. Part of California Community College System. Awards certificates, transfer associate, and terminal associate degrees. Founded 1922. Setting: 160-acre rural campus. Endowment: $832,061. Educational spending for 2005 fiscal year: $2672 per student. Total enrollment: 7,413. Students come from 12 states and territories, 3% from out-of-state, 0.4% Native American, 86% Hispanic, 1% black, 1% Asian American or Pacific Islander. Calendar: semesters. Academic remediation for entering students, ESL program, services for LD students, advanced placement, accelerated degree program, self-designed majors, double major, summer session for credit, part-time degree program, adult/continuing education programs.

Entrance Requirements: Open admission. Recommended: high school transcript. Required for some: high school transcript. Entrance: noncompetitive. Application deadline: Rolling. Notification: continuous.
Collegiate Environment: Orientation program. Drama-theater group, choral group, student-run newspaper. Social organizations: 12 open to all. Most popular organizations: Student Support Services Club, Pre-School Mothers, Care Club, Christian Club, Nursing Club. Major annual events: College and University Day, Career Fair, Life's a Beach. Student services: personal-psychological counseling, women's center. Campus security: student patrols. College housing not available. Spencer Library with 55,875 books, 13,324 microform titles, 425 serials, 3,383 audiovisual materials, an OPAC, and a Web page. Operations spending for 2004 fiscal year: $743,156. 235 computers available on campus for general student use. A campuswide network can be accessed from off-campus. Staffed computer lab on campus.
Community Environment: Imperial is in the southern desert area of California known as the Imperial Valley. It has a very dry climate. The Chocolate Mountains are separated from Imperial by a ribbon of sand dunes. Buses and airlines serve the area. The surrounding Imperial Valley is a large and abundant agricultural area. There are six small cities in surrounding area that provide additional employment opportunities. The annual midwinter fair and the Christmas Parade are here at Imperial.

■ **INSTITUTE OF COMPUTER TECHNOLOGY** *S-10*
3200 Wilshire Blvd., No. 400
Los Angeles, CA 90010-1308
Tel: (213)381-3333
Fax: (213)383-9369
Web Site: http://www.ictcollege.edu/
Description: Proprietary, 4-year, coed. Awards associate and bachelor's degrees. Founded 1981. Setting: urban campus. Total enrollment: 286. 121 applied, 30% were admitted. Full-time: 286 students, 27% women, 73% men. Students come from 4 other countries, 0% from out-of-state, 0% Native American, 23% Hispanic, 11% black, 36% Asian American or Pacific Islander, 15% international, 94% 25 or older, 2% transferred in. Advanced placement, independent study, internships.
Entrance Requirements: Open admission. Option: Common Application. Required: high school transcript, interview, CPAt. Entrance: noncompetitive.
Collegiate Environment: Orientation program. Campus security: 24-hour patrols. College housing not available. Main library plus 1 other with 2,000 books. 100 computers available on campus for general student use. Staffed computer lab on campus.

■ **INTERIOR DESIGNERS INSTITUTE** *T-10*
1061 Camelback Rd.
Newport Beach, CA 92660
Tel: (949)675-4451
Fax: (949)759-0667
Web Site: http://www.idi.edu/
Description: Proprietary, 4-year. Awards associate and bachelor's degrees.

■ **INTERNATIONAL TECHNOLOGICAL UNIVERSITY** *L-5*
1650 Warburton Ave.
Santa Clara, CA 95050
Tel: (408)556-9010
Admissions: (408)556-9027
Fax: (408)556-9016
Web Site: http://www.itu.edu/
Description: Independent, upper-level, coed. Awards bachelor's and master's degrees. Total enrollment: 160. Full-time: 28 students, 57% women, 43% men. Part-time: 12 students, 50% women, 50% men. Students come from 4 states and territories, 5% black, 73% Asian American or Pacific Islander, 15% international, 66% 25 or older, 28% transferred in. Core. Calendar: trimesters. Academic remediation for entering students, ESL program, part-time degree program, external degree program, adult/continuing education programs, internships, graduate courses open to undergrads.
Collegiate Environment: Orientation program. College housing not available. ITU - Library plus 1 other with 1,200 books, 57 serials, and 25 audiovisual materials. 20 computers available on campus for general student use. Computer purchase/lease plans available. A campuswide network can be accessed. Staffed computer lab on campus.

■ **IRVINE VALLEY COLLEGE** *T-7*
5500 Irvine Center Dr.
Irvine, CA 92618

Tel: (949)451-5100
Admissions: (949)451-5416
Fax: (949)559-3443
Web Site: http://www.ivc.edu/
Description: State and locally supported, 2-year, coed. Part of Saddleback Community College District. Awards certificates and transfer associate degrees. Founded 1979. Setting: 20-acre suburban campus with easy access to Los Angeles. Total enrollment: 10,511. 55% 25 or older. Core. Calendar: semesters. Academic remediation for entering students, ESL program, services for LD students, advanced placement, summer session for credit, part-time degree program, adult/continuing education programs, co-op programs.
Entrance Requirements: Open admission. Options: Common Application, early admission. Entrance: noncompetitive. Application deadline: Rolling. Notification: continuous.
Collegiate Environment: Drama-theater group, student-run newspaper. Student services: health clinic, personal-psychological counseling, women's center. Campus security: late night transport-escort service. College housing not available. Irvine Valley College Library with 24,000 books and 250 serials. 125 computers available on campus for general student use. Staffed computer lab on campus.

■ ITT TECHNICAL INSTITUTE (ANAHEIM) T-10
525 North Muller St.
Anaheim, CA 92801-9938
Tel: (714)535-3700
Web Site: http://www.itt-tech.edu/
Description: Proprietary, primarily 2-year, coed. Part of ITT Educational Services, Inc. Awards terminal associate and bachelor's degrees. Founded 1982. Setting: 5-acre suburban campus with easy access to Los Angeles. Core.
Entrance Requirements: Option: deferred admission. Required: high school transcript, interview, Wonderlic aptitude test. Recommended: recommendations. Entrance: minimally difficult. Application deadline: Rolling. Notification: continuous.
Costs Per Year: Application fee: $100.
Collegiate Environment: Orientation program. Student-run newspaper. College housing not available.

■ ITT TECHNICAL INSTITUTE (LATHROP) G-9
16916 South Harlan Rd.
Lathrop, CA 95330
Tel: (209)858-0077
Web Site: http://www.itt-tech.edu/
Description: Proprietary, primarily 2-year, coed. Part of ITT Educational Services. Awards terminal associate and bachelor's degrees. Core.
Entrance Requirements: Option: deferred admission. Required: high school transcript, interview, Wonderlic aptitude test. Recommended: recommendations. Entrance: minimally difficult. Application deadline: Rolling. Notification: continuous.
Costs Per Year: Application fee: $100.
Collegiate Environment: Orientation program. College housing not available.

■ ITT TECHNICAL INSTITUTE (OXNARD) S-8
2051 Solar Dr., Ste. 150
Oxnard, CA 93036
Tel: (805)988-0143
Fax: (805)988-1813
Web Site: http://www.itt-tech.edu/
Description: Proprietary, primarily 2-year, coed. Part of ITT Educational Services, Inc. Awards transfer associate, terminal associate, and bachelor's degrees. Founded 1993. Setting: urban campus with easy access to Los Angeles. Core.
Entrance Requirements: Option: deferred admission. Required: high school transcript, interview, Wonderlic aptitude test. Recommended: recommendations. Entrance: minimally difficult. Application deadline: Rolling. Notification: continuous.
Costs Per Year: Application fee: $100.
Collegiate Environment: Orientation program. Campus security: 24-hour emergency response devices and patrols. College housing not available.

■ ITT TECHNICAL INSTITUTE (RANCHO CORDOVA) I-6
10863 Gold Center Dr.
Rancho Cordova, CA 95670-6034

Tel: (916)851-3900
Free: 800-488-8466
Fax: (916)366-9225
Web Site: http://www.itt-tech.edu/
Description: Proprietary, primarily 2-year, coed. Part of ITT Educational Services, Inc. Awards terminal associate and bachelor's degrees. Founded 1954. Setting: 5-acre urban campus. Core.
Entrance Requirements: Option: deferred admission. Required: high school transcript, interview, Wonderlic aptitude test. Recommended: recommendations. Entrance: minimally difficult. Application deadline: Rolling. Notification: continuous.
Costs Per Year: Application fee: $100.
Collegiate Environment: Orientation program. College housing not available.

■ ITT TECHNICAL INSTITUTE (SAN BERNARDINO) S-11
630 East Brier Dr., Ste. 150
San Bernardino, CA 92408-2800
Tel: (909)889-3800
Admissions: (909)806-4600
Fax: (909)888-6970
Web Site: http://www.itt-tech.edu/
Description: Proprietary, primarily 2-year, coed. Part of ITT Educational Services, Inc. Awards terminal associate and bachelor's degrees. Founded 1987. Setting: urban campus with easy access to Los Angeles. Core.
Entrance Requirements: Option: deferred admission. Required: high school transcript, interview, Wonderlic aptitude test. Recommended: recommendations. Entrance: minimally difficult. Application deadline: Rolling. Notification: continuous.
Costs Per Year: Application fee: $100.
Collegiate Environment: Orientation program. College housing not available.

■ ITT TECHNICAL INSTITUTE (SAN DIEGO) W-12
9680 Granite Ridge Dr., Ste. 100
San Diego, CA 92123
Tel: (858)571-8500
Fax: (858)571-1277
Web Site: http://www.itt-tech.edu/
Description: Proprietary, primarily 2-year, coed. Part of ITT Educational Services, Inc. Awards terminal associate and bachelor's degrees. Founded 1981. Setting: suburban campus. Core.
Entrance Requirements: Option: deferred admission. Required: high school transcript, interview, Wonderlic aptitude test. Recommended: recommendations. Entrance: minimally difficult. Application deadline: Rolling. Notification: continuous.
Costs Per Year: Application fee: $100.
Collegiate Environment: Orientation program. College housing not available.

■ ITT TECHNICAL INSTITUTE (SYLMAR) S-9
12669 Encinitas Ave.
Sylmar, CA 91342-3664
Tel: (818)364-5151
Web Site: http://www.itt-tech.edu/
Description: Proprietary, primarily 2-year, coed. Part of ITT Educational Services, Inc. Awards terminal associate and bachelor's degrees. Founded 1982. Setting: urban campus with easy access to Los Angeles. Core.
Entrance Requirements: Option: deferred admission. Required: high school transcript, interview, Wonderlic aptitude test. Recommended: recommendations. Entrance: minimally difficult. Application deadline: Rolling. Notification: continuous.
Costs Per Year: Application fee: $100.
Collegiate Environment: Orientation program. College housing not available.

■ ITT TECHNICAL INSTITUTE (TORRANCE) T-10
20050 South Vermont Ave.
Torrance, CA 90502
Tel: (310)380-1555
Fax: (310)380-1557
Web Site: http://www.itt-tech.edu/

Description: Proprietary, primarily 2-year, coed. Part of ITT Educational Services, Inc. Awards terminal associate and bachelor's degrees. Founded 1987. Setting: urban campus with easy access to Los Angeles. Core.

Entrance Requirements: Option: deferred admission. Required: high school transcript, interview, Wonderlic aptitude test. Recommended: recommendations. Entrance: minimally difficult. Application deadline: Rolling. Notification: continuous.

Costs Per Year: Application fee: $100.

Collegiate Environment: Orientation program. College housing not available.

■ **ITT TECHNICAL INSTITUTE (WEST COVINA)** *Q-6*
1530 West Cameron Ave.
West Covina, CA 91790-2711
Tel: (626)960-8681
Fax: (626)960-8681
Web Site: http://www.itt-tech.edu/

Description: Proprietary, primarily 2-year, coed. Part of ITT Educational Services, Inc. Awards terminal associate and bachelor's degrees. Founded 1982. Setting: 4-acre suburban campus with easy access to Los Angeles. Core.

Entrance Requirements: Option: deferred admission. Required: high school transcript, interview, Wonderlic aptitude test. Recommended: recommendations. Entrance: minimally difficult. Application deadline: Rolling. Notification: continuous.

Costs Per Year: Application fee: $100.

Collegiate Environment: Orientation program. College housing not available.

■ **JOHN F. KENNEDY UNIVERSITY** *G-6*
100 Ellinwood Way
Pleasant Hill, CA 94523-4817
Tel: (925)969-3300
Free: 800-696-JFKU
Admissions: (925)969-3330
Fax: (925)254-6964
Web Site: http://www.jfku.edu/

Description: Independent, comprehensive, coed. Awards bachelor's, master's, doctoral, and first professional degrees. Founded 1964. Setting: 5-acre suburban campus with easy access to San Francisco. Endowment: $1.4 million. Educational spending for 2005 fiscal year: $3887 per student. Total enrollment: 1,653. 0% from out-of-state, 2% Native American, 11% Hispanic, 9% black, 7% Asian American or Pacific Islander, 86% 25 or older. Core. Calendar: semesters for law school. Services for LD students, advanced placement, self-designed majors, independent study, summer session for credit, part-time degree program, adult/continuing education programs, graduate courses open to undergrads. Off campus study at University of California, Berkeley, California State University, Hayward, Contra Costa College, Laney College.

Entrance Requirements: Open admission. Options: Common Application, deferred admission. Entrance: noncompetitive.

Collegiate Environment: Student-run newspaper. Student services: personal-psychological counseling. Campus security: late night transport-escort service. College housing not available. Robert M. Fisher Library plus 1 other with 96,366 books, 7,845 microform titles, 823 serials, 2,147 audiovisual materials, an OPAC, and a Web page. Operations spending for 2004 fiscal year: $1.2 million. 50 computers available on campus for general student use. Staffed computer lab on campus.

Community Environment: Orinda, population 15,000, is located just east of the Oakland-Berkeley Hills. Oakland, 10 miles away, and San Francisco, 20 miles, are easily accessed. Climate is mild the year round, with the average temperature 65-70 degrees.

■ **THE KING'S COLLEGE AND SEMINARY** *S-9*
14800 Sherman Way
Van Nuys, CA 91405-8040
Tel: (818)779-8040
Fax: (818)779-8241
Web Site: http://www.kingscollege.edu/

Description: Independent, 4-year, coed, affiliated with International Church of the Foursquare Gospel.

Costs Per Year: Tuition: $7200 full-time, $160 per quarter hour part-time. Mandatory fees: $285 full-time, $35.

■ **LA SIERRA UNIVERSITY** *T-11*
45 Riverwalk Parkway
Riverside, CA 92515
Tel: (951)785-2000
Free: 800-874-5587
Admissions: (909)785-2176
Fax: (951)785-2901
E-mail: ivy@lasierra.edu
Web Site: http://www.lasierra.edu/

Description: Independent Seventh-day Adventist, comprehensive, coed. Awards bachelor's, master's, and doctoral degrees and post-master's certificates. Founded 1922. Setting: 630-acre suburban campus with easy access to Los Angeles. Endowment: $11.6 million. Research spending for 2004 fiscal year: $1.2 million. Total enrollment: 1,941. Faculty: 164 (88 full-time, 76 part-time). Student-undergrad faculty ratio is 15:1. 1,389 applied, 38% were admitted. 14% from top 10% of their high school class, 38% from top quarter, 72% from top half. Full-time: 1,454 students, 59% women, 41% men. Part-time: 184 students, 56% women, 44% men. Students come from 34 states and territories, 51 other countries, 13% from out-of-state, 1% Native American, 28% Hispanic, 9% black, 22% Asian American or Pacific Islander, 10% international, 14% 25 or older, 11% transferred in. Retention: 61% of full-time freshmen returned the following year. Academic areas with the most degrees conferred: business/marketing; biological/life sciences; liberal arts/general studies. Core. Academic remediation for entering students, ESL program, services for LD students, advanced placement, accelerated degree program, self-designed majors, honors program, independent study, double major, summer session for credit, part-time degree program, adult/continuing education programs, internships, graduate courses open to undergrads. Off campus study at Loma Linda University. Study abroad program.

Entrance Requirements: Required: essay, high school transcript, minimum 2.5 high school GPA, 1 recommendation, SAT or ACT. Required for some: interview. Entrance: moderately difficult. Application deadline: Rolling. Notification: continuous. Preference given to Seventh-day Adventists.

Costs Per Year: Application fee: $30. Comprehensive fee: $26,507 includes full-time tuition ($19,908), mandatory fees ($726), and college room and board ($5873). Part-time tuition: $553 per unit.

Collegiate Environment: Orientation program. Drama-theater group, choral group, student-run newspaper. Social organizations: 23 open to all. Most popular organizations: Student Association of LSU, Korean Student Association, Students In Free Enterprise (SIFE), Ole Club, Black Student Association. Major annual events: Christmas Candlelight Concert, Festival of Nations, La Sierra Live Weekends. Student services: health clinic, personal-psychological counseling, women's center. Campus security: 24-hour emergency response devices and patrols, student patrols, late night transport-escort service. 850 college housing spaces available; 771 were occupied in 2003-04. On-campus residence required through senior year. Options: men-only, women-only housing available. University Library plus 1 other with 251,632 books, 353,000 microform titles, an OPAC, and a Web page. Operations spending for 2004 fiscal year: $968,236. 125 computers available on campus for general student use. A campuswide network can be accessed from student residence rooms and from off campus. Staffed computer lab on campus.

Community Environment: See University of California Riverside.

■ **LAGUNA COLLEGE OF ART & DESIGN** *U-7*
2222 Laguna Canyon Rd.
Laguna Beach, CA 92651-1136
Tel: (949)376-6000
Free: 800-255-0762
Fax: (949)376-6009
Web Site: http://www.lagunacollege.edu/

Description: Independent, 4-year, coed. Awards bachelor's degrees. Founded 1962. Setting: 9-acre small town campus with easy access to Los Angeles. Endowment: $411,000. Educational spending for 2005 fiscal year: $6512 per student. Total enrollment: 310. 245 applied, 88% were admitted. 15 National Merit Scholars, 5 class presidents, 12 valedictorians, 31 student government officers. Full-time: 310 students, 47% women, 53% men. Students come from 32 states and territories, 42% from out-of-state, 1% Native American, 9% Hispanic, 2% black, 15% Asian American or Pacific Islander, 6% international, 22% 25 or older. Retention: 83% of full-time freshmen returned the following year. Core. Calendar: semesters. Academic remediation for entering students, ESL program, advanced placement, independent study, summer session for credit, part-time degree program, adult/continuing education programs, internships. Off campus study at Art College Exchange, Association of Independent Colleges of Art and Design.

Entrance Requirements: Options: Peterson's Universal Application, Common Application, electronic application, deferred admission, international baccalaureate accepted. Required: essay, high school transcript, minimum 3.0 high school GPA, 1 recommendation, interview, portfolio, SAT or ACT. Recommended: minimum 3.5 high school GPA. Entrance: very difficult. Application deadline: 2/2. Notification: 5/1.

Collegiate Environment: Orientation program. Student-run newspaper. Major annual event: Student Juried Art Exhibition. Student services: personal-psychological counseling. Campus security: 24-hour emergency response devices. College housing not available. Ruth Salyer Library plus 1 other with 16,000 books, 30 microform titles, 100 serials, 8 audiovisual materials, and an OPAC. Operations spending for 2004 fiscal year: $85,000. 85 computers available on campus for general student use. Computer purchase/lease plans available. A campuswide network can be accessed from off-campus. Staffed computer lab on campus.

■ **LAKE TAHOE COMMUNITY COLLEGE** *H-8*
One College Dr.
South Lake Tahoe, CA 96150-4524
Tel: (530)541-4660
Fax: (530)541-7852
Web Site: http://www.ltcc.edu/

Description: State and locally supported, 2-year, coed. Part of California Community College System. Awards transfer associate and terminal associate degrees. Founded 1975. Setting: 164-acre small town campus. Educational spending for 2005 fiscal year: $4350 per student. Total enrollment: 3,700. 71% 25 or older. Core. Academic remediation for entering students, ESL program, services for LD students, double major, summer session for credit, part-time degree program, co-op programs and internships.

Entrance Requirements: Open admission. Option: early admission. Required for some: high school transcript. Entrance: noncompetitive. Application deadline: Rolling. Notification: continuous.

Collegiate Environment: Drama-theater group, choral group. Social organizations: 8 open to all. Most popular organizations: Associated Student Council, Alpha Gamma Sigma, Foreign Language Club, Art Club, Performing Arts League. Major annual events: AIDS Awareness Day, Club Day, Multicultural Day. Student services: personal-psychological counseling. Campus security: 24-hour emergency response devices, late night transport-escort service. College housing not available. Lake Tahoe Community College Library with 38,950 books, 382 serials, and an OPAC. Operations spending for 2004 fiscal year: $307,421. 135 computers available on campus for general student use. A campuswide network can be accessed. Staffed computer lab on campus.

■ **LANEY COLLEGE** *K-4*
900 Fallon St.
Oakland, CA 94607-4893
Tel: (510)834-5740
Admissions: (510)466-7365
Web Site: http://www.peralta.cc.ca.us/

Description: State and locally supported, 2-year, coed. Part of Peralta Community College District System. Awards certificates, transfer associate, and terminal associate degrees. Founded 1953. Setting: urban campus with easy access to San Francisco. Research spending for 2004 fiscal year: $68,724. Total enrollment: 13,463. Full-time: 2,424 students, 57% women, 43% men. Part-time: 11,039 students, 58% women, 42% men. 57% 25 or older. Core. Calendar: semesters. Academic remediation for entering students, services for LD students, summer session for credit, part-time degree program, adult/continuing education programs.

Entrance Requirements: Open admission. Option: early admission. Entrance: noncompetitive. Application deadline: Rolling.

Collegiate Environment: Drama-theater group, student-run newspaper. Most popular organizations: La Raza Club, African Student Union, Vision Christian Society, Asian/Pacific Islander Club, Vietnamese Student Club. Major annual events: Cinco de Mayo, Black History Month, Multicultural Day. College housing not available. Laney Library with 78,054 books and 209 serials. 30 computers available on campus for general student use.

Community Environment: Oakland is the fourth largest city in the state. Located on the mainland side of San Francisco Bay; adjoined on the north by Berkeley; on the south by Alameda and San Leandro. Climate is mild and the average temperature is 65.9 degrees. All modes of transportation are available; the Oakland Airport is a 12-minute drive. Oakland has all the advantages of a large metropolitan area, being a part of the San Francisco Bay Area. Numerous churches, museums, libraries, hospitals, service groups, and organizations are in the city. Oakland has many tourist attractions and recreational facilities. Lake Merritt, a 160-acre body of salt water, is the only tidal lake in the heart of any American city. There are parks, golf courses, swimming pools within a short distance.

■ **LAS POSITAS COLLEGE** *K-5*
3033 Collier Canyon Rd.
Livermore, CA 94551-7650
Tel: (925)373-5800
Admissions: (925)373-4942
Fax: (925)443-0742
Web Site: http://www.clpccd.cc.ca.us/lpc/

Description: State-supported, 2-year, coed. Part of California Community College System. Awards certificates, diplomas, transfer associate, and terminal associate degrees. Founded 1988. Setting: 150-acre suburban campus with easy access to Oakland and San Francisco. Total enrollment: 8,044. 50% 25 or older. Core. Calendar: semesters. Academic remediation for entering students, ESL program, services for LD students, advanced placement, self-designed majors, summer session for credit, part-time degree program, internships.

Entrance Requirements: Open admission. Recommended: high school transcript. Entrance: noncompetitive.

Collegiate Environment: Drama-theater group, choral group, student-run newspaper. Social organizations: 23 open to all. Student services: health clinic, personal-psychological counseling. Campus security: 24-hour emergency response devices, late night transport-escort service. College housing not available.

■ **LASSEN COMMUNITY COLLEGE DISTRICT** *E-7*
Hwy. 139
PO Box 3000
Susanville, CA 96130
Tel: (530)257-6181
Fax: (530)257-8964
Web Site: http://www.lassencollege.edu/

Description: State and locally supported, 2-year, coed. Part of California Community College System. Awards certificates, transfer associate, and terminal associate degrees. Founded 1925. Setting: 100-acre rural campus. Students come from 12 states and territories, 3 other countries, 58% 25 or older. Core. Calendar: semesters. Academic remediation for entering students, ESL program, services for LD students, advanced placement, summer session for credit, part-time degree program, adult/continuing education programs, co-op programs and internships. Off campus study at members of the Northeastern California Higher Education Council.

Entrance Requirements: Open admission. Option: early admission. Recommended: high school transcript. Placement: ACT recommended. Entrance: noncompetitive. Application deadline: Rolling. Notification: continuous.

Collegiate Environment: Drama-theater group, student-run newspaper. Most popular organization: Lassen Student Union. Major annual events: Career Day, Vocational Olympics, Skunk Days. Student services: legal services, health clinic. Option: coed housing available. Lassen College Library with 15,000 books and 100 serials. 30 computers available on campus for general student use. Staffed computer lab on campus.

■ **LIFE PACIFIC COLLEGE** *V-9*
1100 Covina Blvd.
San Dimas, CA 91773-3298
Tel: (909)599-5433; 877-886-5433
Fax: (909)599-6690
E-mail: adm@lifepacific.edu
Web Site: http://www.lifepacific.edu/

Description: Independent, 4-year, coed, affiliated with International Church of the Foursquare Gospel. Awards associate and bachelor's degrees. Founded 1923. Setting: 9-acre suburban campus with easy access to Los Angeles. Endowment: $2.3 million. Educational spending for 2005 fiscal year: $4654 per student. Total enrollment: 528. Student-undergrad faculty ratio is 18:1. 102 applied, 87% were admitted. 5% from top 10% of their high school class, 21% from top quarter, 38% from top half. Full-time: 403 students, 49% women, 51% men. Part-time: 125 students, 35% women, 65% men. Students come from 36 states and territories, 2 other countries,

48% from out-of-state, 0.4% Native American, 14% Hispanic, 6% black, 6% Asian American or Pacific Islander, 1% international, 17% 25 or older, 50% live on campus, 12% transferred in. Retention: 69% of full-time freshmen returned the following year. Academic area with the most degrees conferred: theology and religious vocations. Core. Calendar: semesters. Services for LD students, advanced placement, independent study, distance learning, summer session for credit, part-time degree program, external degree program, adult/continuing education programs, co-op programs and internships. Study abroad program.

Entrance Requirements: Options: Peterson's Universal Application, Common Application, electronic application, deferred admission, international baccalaureate accepted. Required: essay, high school transcript, minimum 2.0 high school GPA, 1 recommendation, Christian testimony, SAT or ACT. Entrance: minimally difficult. Application deadline: 6/1. Notification: continuous.

Costs Per Year: Application fee: $35. Comprehensive fee: $15,100 includes full-time tuition ($9750), mandatory fees ($350), and college room and board ($5000). Part-time tuition: $325 per credit hour. Part-time tuition varies according to course load.

Collegiate Environment: Orientation program. Drama-theater group, choral group, student-run newspaper. Social organizations: 1 open to all. Most popular organizations: tutoring, chorale. Major annual events: Spring/Fall Retreats, Honors Banquet, Junior/Senior Banquet. Student services: personal-psychological counseling. Campus security: 24-hour emergency response devices, student patrols, part-time security personnel. 320 college housing spaces available; 248 were occupied in 2003-04. Freshmen guaranteed college housing. On-campus residence required in freshman year. Options: men-only, women-only housing available. Life Pacific College Alumni Library with 40,022 books, 513 microform titles, 1,954 serials, 1,563 audiovisual materials, an OPAC, and a Web page. Operations spending for 2004 fiscal year: $203,806. 46 computers available on campus for general student use. A campuswide network can be accessed from student residence rooms. Staffed computer lab on campus.

Community Environment: San Dimas is a suburban community approximately 45 minutes from Los Angeles, located at the foothills of the San Gabriel Mountains.

■ LINCOLN UNIVERSITY *K-4*

401 15th St.
Oakland, CA 94612
Tel: (510)628-8010
Fax: (510)628-8026
E-mail: admissions@lincolnuca.edu
Web Site: http://www.lincolnuca.edu/

Description: Independent, comprehensive, coed. Awards bachelor's and master's degrees. Founded 1919. Setting: 2-acre urban campus. Total enrollment: 147. Full-time: 30 students, 63% women, 37% men. Part-time: 21 students, 57% women, 43% men. Students come from 2 states and territories, 10 other countries, 52% 25 or older. Core. Calendar: semesters. ESL program, advanced placement, summer session for credit, internships.

Entrance Requirements: Options: Common Application, electronic application, deferred admission. Required: high school transcript, minimum 2.0 high school GPA. Required for some: essay, recommendations, interview. Entrance: minimally difficult. Application deadline: 8/31.

Costs Per Year: Application fee: $75. Tuition: $7320 full-time, $305 per unit part-time. Mandatory fees: $400 full-time. Full-time tuition and fees vary according to program.

Collegiate Environment: Student-run newspaper. Student services: personal-psychological counseling. Campus security: 24-hour emergency response devices. College housing not available. Lincoln Library with 17,532 books and 642 serials. 20 computers available on campus for general student use. Staffed computer lab on campus.

■ LOMA LINDA UNIVERSITY *Q-10*

Loma Linda, CA 92350
Tel: (909)558-1000
Fax: (909)558-4577
Web Site: http://www.llu.edu/

Description: Independent Seventh-day Adventist, upper-level, coed. Awards associate, bachelor's, master's, doctoral, and first professional degrees (associate degree and nursing students may enter at the sophomore level). Founded 1905. Setting: small town campus with easy access to Los Angeles. Endowment: $176 million. Research spending for 2004 fiscal year: $31.8 million. Educational spending for 2005 fiscal year: $27,243 per

student. Total enrollment: 3,906. Faculty: 150 (106 full-time, 44 part-time). Student-undergrad faculty ratio is 8:1. Full-time: 798 students, 76% women, 24% men. Part-time: 321 students, 74% women, 26% men. Students come from 29 states and territories, 28 other countries, 13% from out-of-state, 1% Native American, 21% Hispanic, 6% black, 21% Asian American or Pacific Islander, 5% international, 52% 25 or older, 25% live on campus, 22% transferred in. Academic area with the most degrees conferred: health professions and related sciences. ESL program, independent study, distance learning, internships. Off campus study.

Costs Per Year: Application fee: $60. Tuition: $23,280 full-time, $485 per unit part-time. Mandatory fees: $1290 full-time, $430 per term part-time. College room only: $2370.

Collegiate Environment: Most popular organizations: Students for International Mission Services, Students Computing Organization. Student services: health clinic, personal-psychological counseling. Campus security: 24-hour emergency response devices and patrols, late night transport-escort service. On-campus residence required through senior year. Options: men-only, women-only housing available. Del E. Webb Memorial Library with 322,657 books, 1,394 serials, an OPAC, and a Web page. Operations spending for 2004 fiscal year: $1 million.

Community Environment: Loma Linda is located 56 miles east of Los Angeles, between Redlands, San Bernardino, and Riverside. The climate is pleasant and mild. Loma Linda is a medical center that has three hospitals, including the 515-bed University Medical Center and the 500-bed Jerry L. Pettis Memorial Veterans Hospital. Pacific ocean beaches, ski slopes, and lakes for boating and water skiing are all within a one-hour drive. Part-time and full-time work is available.

■ LONG BEACH CITY COLLEGE *T-10*

4901 East Carson St.
Long Beach, CA 90808-1780
Tel: (562)938-4353
Admissions: (562)938-4130
Web Site: http://www.lbcc.edu/

Description: State-supported, 2-year, coed. Part of California Community College System. Awards certificates, transfer associate, and terminal associate degrees. Founded 1927. Setting: 40-acre urban campus with easy access to Los Angeles. Research spending for 2004 fiscal year: $266,890. Educational spending for 2005 fiscal year: $2154 per student. Total enrollment: 26,296. Student-undergrad faculty ratio is 24:1. Full-time: 9,580 students, 55% women, 45% men. Part-time: 16,716 students, 56% women, 44% men. 1% from out-of-state, 1% Native American, 37% Hispanic, 14% black, 15% Asian American or Pacific Islander, 54% 25 or older, 3% transferred in. Core. Calendar: semesters. Academic remediation for entering students, ESL program, services for LD students, advanced placement, honors program, distance learning, summer session for credit, part-time degree program, adult/continuing education programs, internships.

Entrance Requirements: Open admission except for nursing program. Option: early admission. Recommended: high school transcript. Entrance: noncompetitive. Application deadline: Rolling.

Costs Per Year: Application fee: $0. State resident tuition: $0 full-time. Nonresident tuition: $3840 full-time, $160 per unit part-time. Mandatory fees: $692 full-time, $26 per unit part-time, $34 per term part-time.

Collegiate Environment: Drama-theater group, choral group, student-run newspaper, radio station. Social organizations: 70 open to all; local fraternities, local sororities; 5% of eligible men and 5% of eligible women are members. Most popular organizations: American Criminal Justice Association, AGS Scholarship Organization, American Association of Future Firefighters, Vietnamese Club, Network Christian Fellowship. Major annual events: Homecoming, Spring Sing, Mini-Grand Prix. Student services: legal services, health clinic, personal-psychological counseling, women's center. Campus security: 24-hour emergency response devices and patrols, student patrols, late night transport-escort service. College housing not available. Long Beach City College Library plus 1 other with 151,367 books, 176,896 microform titles, 471 serials, 3,150 audiovisual materials, an OPAC, and a Web page. Operations spending for 2004 fiscal year: $1.3 million. 200 computers available on campus for general student use. Staffed computer lab on campus.

■ LOS ANGELES CITY COLLEGE *S-10*

855 North Vermont Ave.
Los Angeles, CA 90029-3590
Tel: (323)953-4000
Fax: (323)953-4294

Web Site: http://www.lacc.cc.ca.us/
Description: District-supported, 2-year, coed. Part of Los Angeles Community College District System. Awards certificates, diplomas, transfer associate, and terminal associate degrees. Founded 1929. Setting: 42-acre urban campus. Total enrollment: 25,000. Students come from 52 states and territories, 43% Hispanic, 12% black, 19% Asian American or Pacific Islander, 62% 25 or older. Core. Calendar: semesters. Academic remediation for entering students, ESL program, services for LD students, advanced placement, honors program, summer session for credit, part-time degree program, adult/continuing education programs. Study abroad program. ROTC: Army (c), Air Force (c).
Entrance Requirements: Open admission except for international applicants or optics, radiological technology programs. Option: Peterson's Universal Application. Entrance: noncompetitive. Application deadline: 9/5. Notification: continuous until 9/5.
Collegiate Environment: Drama-theater group, choral group, marching band, student-run newspaper. Student services: health clinic, personal-psychological counseling. Campus security: 24-hour emergency response devices and patrols, student patrols, late night transport-escort service. College housing not available. 150,000 books and 150 serials. 200 computers available on campus for general student use. A campuswide network can be accessed from off-campus. Staffed computer lab on campus.
Community Environment: See University of California - Los Angeles

■ **LOS ANGELES COUNTY COLLEGE OF NURSING AND ALLIED HEALTH** *S-10*
1237 North Mission Rd.
Los Angeles, CA 90033
Tel: (323)226-4911
Fax: (323)226-6427
Web Site: http://www.ladhs.org/lacusc/lacnah/
Description: County-supported, 2-year, coed. Awards terminal associate degrees. Founded 1895. Total enrollment: 281. Calendar: semesters.
Collegiate Environment: College housing not available.

■ **LOS ANGELES HARBOR COLLEGE** *T-9*
1111 Figueroa Place
Wilmington, CA 90744-2397
Tel: (310)233-4000
Admissions: (310)233-4091
Fax: (310)233-4223
Web Site: http://www.lahc.edu/
Description: State and locally supported, 2-year, coed. Part of Los Angeles Community College District System. Awards certificates, transfer associate, and terminal associate degrees. Founded 1949. Setting: 80-acre suburban campus. Total enrollment: 9,469. 1,970 applied, 100% were admitted. Full-time: 2,311 students, 61% women, 39% men. Part-time: 7,158 students, 61% women, 39% men. Students come from 14 states and territories, 43% Hispanic, 15% black, 17% Asian American or Pacific Islander, 49% 25 or older. Core. Calendar: semesters. Academic remediation for entering students, ESL program, services for LD students, advanced placement, freshman honors college, honors program, independent study, distance learning, double major, summer session for credit, part-time degree program, external degree program, adult/continuing education programs, co-op programs. Off campus study at California State University, Dominguez Hills. Study abroad program.
Entrance Requirements: Open admission except for nursing program. Options: early admission, deferred admission. Required for some: essay, high school transcript. Entrance: noncompetitive. Application deadline: 9/3.
Collegiate Environment: Orientation program. Drama-theater group, choral group, student-run radio station. Social organizations: 7 open to all. Most popular organizations: Alpha Gamma Sigma, Abilities Unlimited, Students in Free Enterprise, Association of Future Firefighters. Major annual events: graduation, Christmas Show, homecoming. Student services: legal services, health clinic, personal-psychological counseling. Campus security: 24-hour emergency response devices and patrols. College housing not available. Harbor College Library with 82,790 books, 302 serials, an OPAC, and a Web page. 250 computers available on campus for general student use. A campuswide network can be accessed from off-campus. Staffed computer lab on campus.
Community Environment: The Harbor College service area encompasses a multicultural population of 369,907 persons who live in the communities of San Pedro, Wilmington, Carson, Gardena, Lomita, Harbor City, and on the Palos Verdes Peninsula and parts of South Los Angeles. A business,

industrial, shipping and civic center of the Port of Los Angeles, Wilmington is located in the heart of the Southern California oil refining district. Points of interest are Marineland, the Queen Mary, Ports O' Call Village, and a Korean Liberty Bell, all within easy driving distance.

■ **LOS ANGELES MISSION COLLEGE** *S-9*
13356 Eldridge Ave.
Sylmar, CA 91342-3245
Tel: (818)364-7600
Admissions: (818)364-7766
Web Site: http://www.lamission.cc.ca.us/
Description: State and locally supported, 2-year, coed. Part of Los Angeles Community College District System. Awards transfer associate and terminal associate degrees. Founded 1974. Setting: 22-acre small town campus with easy access to Los Angeles. Educational spending for 2005 fiscal year: $890 per student. Total enrollment: 7,617. Students come from 8 other countries, 55% 25 or older. Core. Calendar: semesters. Academic remediation for entering students, ESL program, services for LD students, advanced placement, summer session for credit, part-time degree program, external degree program, adult/continuing education programs, co-op programs.
Entrance Requirements: Open admission. Option: early admission. Entrance: noncompetitive. Notification: continuous until 9/25.
Collegiate Environment: Orientation program. Drama-theater group, student-run newspaper. Student services: personal-psychological counseling, women's center. Campus security: 24-hour emergency response devices and patrols, student patrols. College housing not available. Los Angeles Mission College with 40,000 books, 450 serials, an OPAC, and a Web page. Operations spending for 2004 fiscal year: $70,000. 103 computers available on campus for general student use. A campuswide network can be accessed. Staffed computer lab on campus.

■ **LOS ANGELES PIERCE COLLEGE** *S-8*
6201 Winnetka Ave.
Woodland Hills, CA 91371-0001
Tel: (818)710-4123
Admissions: (818)719-6448
Fax: (818)710-9844
Web Site: http://www.lapc.cc.ca.us/
Description: State and locally supported, 2-year, coed. Part of Los Angeles Community College District System. Awards certificates, transfer associate, and terminal associate degrees. Founded 1947. Setting: 425-acre suburban campus with easy access to Los Angeles. Total enrollment: 16,255. 26,070 applied, 100% were admitted. Students come from 2 states and territories, 48 other countries, 48% 25 or older. Core. Calendar: semesters. Academic remediation for entering students, ESL program, services for LD students, advanced placement, honors program, independent study, distance learning, summer session for credit, part-time degree program, adult/continuing education programs, co-op programs and internships. Study abroad program.
Entrance Requirements: Open admission except for nursing, honors programs. Options: Common Application, electronic application, early admission. Entrance: noncompetitive. Application deadline: 8/20.
Collegiate Environment: Orientation program. Drama-theater group, choral group, student-run newspaper. Social organizations: 28 open to all. Most popular organizations: Alpha Gamma Sigma, Club Latino United for Education, United African-American Student Association, Hillel Club, Filipino Club. Major annual events: Club Day, Job Fair, University Day. Student services: health clinic, personal-psychological counseling, women's center. Campus security: 24-hour patrols, late night transport-escort service. College housing not available. Pierce College Library plus 1 other with 106,122 books and 395 serials. 60 computers available on campus for general student use. A campuswide network can be accessed. Staffed computer lab on campus.
Community Environment: Woodland Hills is a suburban area of Los Angeles with a subtropical climate, and known as a beautiful residential area. Buses serve the area. The community has a library, hospital, churches, and civic and service organizations. Nearby are shopping centers, theatres, and a public park with a swimming pool. The Pacific Ocean is within easy driving distance. Part-time employment is available.

■ **LOS ANGELES SOUTHWEST COLLEGE** *S-10*
1600 West Imperial Hwy.
Los Angeles, CA 90047-4810
Tel: (323)241-5225
Admissions: (323)241-5279

Web Site: http://www.lasc.cc.ca.us/

Description: State and locally supported, 2-year, coed. Part of Los Angeles Community College District System. Awards certificates, diplomas, and transfer associate degrees. Founded 1967. Setting: 69-acre urban campus. Research spending for 2004 fiscal year: $321,616. Total enrollment: 6,000. Students come from 20 states and territories, 4 other countries, 63% 25 or older. Core. Calendar: semesters. Academic remediation for entering students, ESL program, services for LD students, accelerated degree program, freshman honors college, honors program, summer session for credit, part-time degree program, adult/continuing education programs, co-op programs and internships.

Entrance Requirements: Open admission except for nursing program. Option: early admission. Recommended: essay, minimum 2.0 high school GPA. Required for some: high school transcript. Entrance: noncompetitive. Application deadline: 9/9. Notification: continuous until 9/9.

Collegiate Environment: Choral group, student-run newspaper. Social organizations: 8 open to all. Campus security: 24-hour emergency response devices and patrols, student patrols, late night transport-escort service. College housing not available. Main library plus 1 other with 60,000 books, 600 serials, an OPAC, and a Web page. Operations spending for 2004 fiscal year: $329,727. 40 computers available on campus for general student use. A campuswide network can be accessed from off-campus. Staffed computer lab on campus.

Community Environment: See University of California - Los Angeles.

■ LOS ANGELES TRADE-TECHNICAL COLLEGE S-10

400 West Washington Blvd.
Los Angeles, CA 90015-4108
Tel: (213)744-9500
Admissions: (213)763-5301
Fax: (213)748-7334
Web Site: http://www.lattc.edu/

Description: State and locally supported, 2-year, coed. Part of Los Angeles Community College District System. Awards certificates, diplomas, transfer associate, and terminal associate degrees. Founded 1925. Setting: 25-acre urban campus. Total enrollment: 13,194. Full-time: 4,160 students, 56% women, 44% men. Part-time: 9,034 students, 49% women, 51% men. Students come from 25 states and territories, 20 other countries, 0.3% Native American, 47% Hispanic, 35% black, 9% Asian American or Pacific Islander, 1% international, 47% 25 or older. Core. Calendar: semesters. Academic remediation for entering students, ESL program, services for LD students, advanced placement, summer session for credit, part-time degree program, adult/continuing education programs, co-op programs.

Entrance Requirements: Open admission. Options: early admission, deferred admission. Recommended: high school transcript. Entrance: noncompetitive. Application deadline: 9/7.

Collegiate Environment: Orientation program. Choral group. Student services: health clinic, personal-psychological counseling, women's center. Campus security: 24-hour patrols, student patrols, late night transport-escort service. College housing not available. 98,000 books and 367 serials. 200 computers available on campus for general student use. A campuswide network can be accessed. Staffed computer lab on campus.

Community Environment: See University of California - Los Angeles.

■ LOS ANGELES VALLEY COLLEGE S-9

5800 Fulton Ave.
Van Nuys, CA 91401-4096
Tel: (818)947-2600
Admissions: (818)947-2353
Fax: (818)947-2610
E-mail: manzanf@lavc.edu
Web Site: http://www.lavc.cc.ca.us/

Description: State and locally supported, 2-year, coed. Part of Los Angeles Community College District System. Awards certificates, transfer associate, and terminal associate degrees. Founded 1949. Setting: 105-acre suburban campus. Endowment: $120,000. Research spending for 2004 fiscal year: $583,057. Educational spending for 2005 fiscal year: $3177 per student. Total enrollment: 18,761. Full-time: 5,021 students, 59% women, 41% men. Part-time: 13,740 students, 60% women, 40% men. Students come from 43 other countries, 4% from out-of-state, 43% 25 or older, 27% transferred in. Core. Calendar: semesters. Academic remediation for entering students, ESL program, services for LD students, self-designed majors, honors program, independent study, distance learning, double major, summer ses-

sion for credit, part-time degree program, adult/continuing education programs, co-op programs and internships.

Entrance Requirements: Open admission except for allied health programs. Options: Common Application, electronic application, early admission. Recommended: high school transcript. Placement: ACT required. Entrance: noncompetitive. Application deadline: Rolling.

Collegiate Environment: Orientation program. Drama-theater group, choral group, student-run newspaper, radio station. Major annual events: graduation, Dean's Reception. Student services: legal services, health clinic, personal-psychological counseling, women's center. Campus security: 24-hour emergency response devices and patrols, student patrols, late night transport-escort service. College housing not available. Los Angeles Valley Library with 124,000 books, 7,300 microform titles, 400 serials, an OPAC, and a Web page. Operations spending for 2004 fiscal year: $777,729. 200 computers available on campus for general student use. A campuswide network can be accessed from off-campus. Staffed computer lab on campus.

■ LOS MEDANOS COLLEGE F-6

2700 East Leland Rd.
Pittsburg, CA 94565-5197
Tel: (925)439-2181
Fax: (925)439-8797
Web Site: http://www.losmedanos.net/

Description: District-supported, 2-year, coed. Part of California Community College System. Awards certificates, transfer associate, and terminal associate degrees. Founded 1974. Setting: 120-acre suburban campus with easy access to San Francisco. Research spending for 2004 fiscal year: $70,348. Educational spending for 2005 fiscal year: $1873 per student. Total enrollment: 7,152. Students come from 3 states and territories, 15 other countries, 0.2% from out-of-state, 56% 25 or older. Core. Calendar: semesters. Academic remediation for entering students, ESL program, services for LD students, advanced placement, honors program, independent study, double major, summer session for credit, part-time degree program, co-op programs. Study abroad program.

Entrance Requirements: Open admission. Option: Common Application. Required for some: high school transcript. Placement: Assessment and Placement Services for Community Colleges required for some. Entrance: noncompetitive. Application deadline: 8/29. Notification: continuous until 8/29.

Collegiate Environment: Orientation program. Choral group, student-run newspaper. Social organizations: 16 open to all. Most popular organizations: Alpha Gamma Sigma, Christian Fellowship Club, Student Nurses Association, La Raza Club. Student services: women's center. Campus security: 24-hour patrols, student patrols, late night transport-escort service. College housing not available. Learning Resource Center with 15,439 books and 205 serials. Operations spending for 2004 fiscal year: $926,689. 200 computers available on campus for general student use. Staffed computer lab on campus.

■ LOYOLA MARYMOUNT UNIVERSITY S-10

One LMU Dr.
Los Angeles, CA 90045-2659
Tel: (310)338-2700
Free: 800-LMU-INFO
Admissions: (310)338-2750
Fax: (310)338-2797
E-mail: admissions@lmu.edu
Web Site: http://www.lmu.edu/

Description: Independent Roman Catholic, comprehensive, coed. Awards bachelor's, master's, doctoral, and first professional degrees. Founded 1911. Setting: 128-acre suburban campus. Endowment: $252.6 million. Total enrollment: 8,855. 7,075 applied, 60% were admitted. 50% from top 10% of their high school class, 66% from top quarter, 99% from top half. Full-time: 5,375 students, 61% women, 39% men. Part-time: 346 students, 45% women, 55% men. Students come from 51 states and territories, 32 other countries, 23% from out-of-state, 1% Native American, 18% Hispanic, 7% black, 13% Asian American or Pacific Islander, 2% international, 5% 25 or older, 50% live on campus, 1% transferred in. Retention: 88% of full-time freshmen returned the following year. Core. Calendar: semesters. Services for LD students, advanced placement, accelerated degree program, self-designed majors, honors program, independent study, double major, summer session for credit, part-time degree program, adult/continuing education programs, co-op programs and internships, graduate courses open to undergrads. Study abroad program. ROTC: Army (c), Air Force.

Entrance Requirements: Options: Peterson's Universal Application, electronic application, early admission, deferred admission, international baccalaureate accepted. Required: essay, high school transcript, 2 recommendations, SAT or ACT. Recommended: interview. Entrance: very difficult. Application deadline: 1/15. Notification: continuous.

Costs Per Year: Application fee: $50. Comprehensive fee: $38,212 includes full-time tuition ($27,710) and college room and board ($10,502). Room and board charges vary according to board plan and housing facility.

Collegiate Environment: Orientation program. Drama-theater group, choral group, student-run newspaper, radio station. Social organizations: 120 open to all; national fraternities, national sororities; 56% of eligible men and 48% of eligible women are members. Most popular organizations: service clubs, Student Government and Activity Board, community service opportunities, student media opportunities, clubs and organizations. Major annual events: special games for handicapped children, Cinco de Mayo, ASLMU Formal Dance. Student services: health clinic, personal-psychological counseling. Campus security: 24-hour emergency response devices and patrols, late night transport-escort service, controlled dormitory access. 2,897 college housing spaces available; 2,670 were occupied in 2003-04. Freshmen guaranteed college housing. Options: coed, men-only, women-only housing available. Charles von der Ahe Library plus 1 other with 495,920 books, 1.6 million microform titles, 10,057 serials, 40,234 audiovisual materials, an OPAC, and a Web page. Operations spending for 2004 fiscal year: $9.8 million. 300 computers available on campus for general student use. Computer purchase/lease plans available. A campuswide network can be accessed from student residence rooms and from off campus. Staffed computer lab on campus.

Community Environment: See University of California - Los Angeles.

■ **MARIC COLLEGE (ANAHEIM)** *T-10*
1360 South Anaheim Blvd.
Anaheim, CA 92805
Tel: (714)758-1500
Free: 800-206-0095
Fax: (714)758-1220
Web Site: http://www.mariccollege.edu/
Description: Proprietary, 2-year, coed. Founded 1989.

■ **MARIC COLLEGE (NORTH HOLLYWOOD)** *S-10*
6180 Laurel Canyon Blvd., Ste. 101
North Hollywood, CA 91606
Tel: (818)763-2563
Free: 800-404-9729
Fax: (818)763-1623
E-mail: mark@moderntec.com
Web Site: http://www.mariccollege.edu/
Description: Proprietary, 2-year, coed. Founded 1982.

■ **MARIC COLLEGE (PANORAMA CITY)** *S-9*
14355 Roscoe Blvd.
Panorama City, CA 91402
Tel: (818)672-8907
Free: 800-206-0095
Fax: (818)672-8919
Web Site: http://www.mariccollege.edu/
Description: Proprietary, 2-year, coed. Founded 1996.

■ **MARIC COLLEGE (SACRAMENTO)** *I-6*
4330 Watt Ave.,Ste. 400
Sacramento, CA 95821
Tel: (916)649-8168
Free: 800-955-8168
Fax: (916)649-8344
Web Site: http://www.californiacollege.com/
Description: Proprietary, 2-year. Awards transfer associate and terminal associate degrees. Total enrollment: 360. Calendar: semesters.
Entrance Requirements: Required: CPAt. Entrance: minimally difficult.
Collegiate Environment: College housing not available.

■ **MARIC COLLEGE (SALIDA)** *H-10*
5172 Kiernan Ct.
Salida, CA 95368
Tel: (209)571-8777
Admissions: (209)543-7000

Fax: (209)571-9836
Web Site: http://www.mariccollege.edu/
Description: Proprietary, 2-year, coed. Awards diplomas and terminal associate degrees. Total enrollment: 289. 16 applied, 100% were admitted. Full-time: 289 students, 94% women, 6% men. 0% Native American, 38% Hispanic, 13% black, 13% Asian American or Pacific Islander, 0% international. Calendar: semesters.
Entrance Requirements: Entrance: moderately difficult.
Collegiate Environment: College housing not available.

■ **MARIC COLLEGE (SAN DIEGO)** *W-12*
3666 Kearny Villa Rd., Ste. 100
San Diego, CA 92123-1995
Tel: (858)279-4000
Free: 800-400-8232
Admissions: (858)654-3624
Fax: (858)279-4885
Web Site: http://www.mariccollege.edu/
Description: Proprietary, 2-year, coed. Awards certificates, transfer associate, and terminal associate degrees (also includes Vista campus). Founded 1976. Setting: 4-acre urban campus. Total enrollment: 298. Full-time: 298 students, 90% women, 10% men. 4% Native American, 40% Hispanic, 9% black, 3% Asian American or Pacific Islander, 0% international, 60% 25 or older. Core. Calendar: semesters. Academic remediation for entering students, summer session for credit, adult/continuing education programs, internships.
Entrance Requirements: Options: Peterson's Universal Application, Common Application. Required: essay, high school transcript, interview. Entrance: minimally difficult. Notification: continuous.
Collegiate Environment: Campus security: 24-hour patrols. College housing not available. 100 computers available on campus for general student use. Staffed computer lab on campus.

■ **MARYMOUNT COLLEGE, PALOS VERDES, CALIFORNIA** *S-3*
30800 Palos Verdes Dr. East
Rancho Palos Verdes, CA 90275-6299
Tel: (310)377-5501
Fax: (310)377-6223
E-mail: admission@marymountpv.edu
Web Site: http://www.marymountpv.edu/
Description: Independent Roman Catholic, 2-year, coed. Awards transfer associate and terminal associate degrees. Founded 1932. Setting: 26-acre suburban campus with easy access to Los Angeles. Total enrollment: 790. 1,051 applied, 75% were admitted. 6 class presidents, 42 student government officers. Full-time: 683 students, 47% women, 53% men. Part-time: 107 students, 62% women, 38% men. Students come from 26 states and territories, 40 other countries, 20% 25 or older, 48% live on campus. Retention: 53% of full-time freshmen returned the following year. Core. Calendar: semesters. Academic remediation for entering students, ESL program, services for LD students, advanced placement, honors program, independent study, summer session for credit, part-time degree program, adult/continuing education programs, internships. Study abroad program.
Entrance Requirements: Options: Peterson's Universal Application, Common Application, electronic application, early admission, international baccalaureate accepted. Required: high school transcript. Recommended: minimum 2.0 high school GPA, SAT or ACT. Required for some: essay, recommendations, interview. Entrance: minimally difficult. Application deadline: 7/1. Notification: continuous until 9/1.
Collegiate Environment: Orientation program. Drama-theater group, choral group, student-run newspaper. Social organizations: 20 open to all. Most popular organizations: Socratic Circle, Hawaii Club, Ski Club, African-American Student Union, MOVE (Marymount Opportunities for Volunteer Experiences). Major annual events: Spring Formal, Art Attack, Fun Flicks. Student services: health clinic, personal-psychological counseling. Campus security: 24-hour patrols, late night transport-escort service, controlled dormitory access. Option: coed housing available. College Library plus 1 other with 42,104 books, 150,000 microform titles, 328 serials, 400 audiovisual materials, and an OPAC. 60 computers available on campus for general student use. A campuswide network can be accessed. Staffed computer lab on campus.

■ **THE MASTER'S COLLEGE AND SEMINARY** *S-9*
21726 Placerita Canyon Rd.
Santa Clarita, CA 91321-1200

Tel: (661)259-3540

Free: 800-568-6248

E-mail: admissions@masters.edu

Web Site: http://www.masters.edu/

Description: Independent nondenominational, comprehensive, coed. Awards bachelor's, master's, doctoral, and first professional degrees and first professional certificates. Founded 1927. Setting: 110-acre suburban campus with easy access to Los Angeles. Endowment: $5.9 million. Educational spending for 2005 fiscal year: $6741 per student. Total enrollment: 1,537. Faculty: 159 (76 full-time, 83 part-time). Student-undergrad faculty ratio is 12:1. 654 applied, 29% were admitted. 33% from top 10% of their high school class, 53% from top quarter, 78% from top half. 9 valedictorians. Full-time: 957 students, 53% women, 47% men. Part-time: 182 students, 40% women, 60% men. Students come from 42 states and territories, 19 other countries, 33% from out-of-state, 1% Native American, 7% Hispanic, 3% black, 4% Asian American or Pacific Islander, 3% international, 16% 25 or older, 75% live on campus, 9% transferred in. Retention: 77% of full-time freshmen returned the following year. Academic areas with the most degrees conferred: business/marketing; education; history. Core. Calendar: semesters. Academic remediation for entering students, services for LD students, advanced placement, accelerated degree program, independent study, double major, summer session for credit, part-time degree program, external degree program, adult/continuing education programs, co-op programs and internships. Study abroad program.

Entrance Requirements: Options: electronic application, early admission, early action, deferred admission, international baccalaureate accepted. Required: essay, high school transcript, minimum 2.50 high school GPA, 2 recommendations, interview, SAT or ACT. Entrance: moderately difficult. Application deadline: 11/1 for early action. Notification: 3/15, 12/22 for early action.

Costs Per Year: Application fee: $55. Comprehensive fee: $25,850 includes full-time tuition ($19,230) and college room and board ($6620). College room only: $3660. Full-time tuition varies according to course load, degree level, and program. Room and board charges vary according to board plan. Part-time tuition: $805 per credit hour. Part-time tuition varies according to course load, degree level, and program.

Collegiate Environment: Orientation program. Choral group. Social organizations: 15 open to all. Most popular organizations: college chorale, Summer Missions, intramurals, church ministries, Drama Club. Major annual events: Missions Conference, College View Weekend, Homecoming. Student services: health clinic, personal-psychological counseling. Campus security: 24-hour patrols. College housing designed to accommodate 805 students; 868 undergraduates lived in college housing during 2003-04. Freshmen guaranteed college housing. On-campus residence required through sophomore year. Options: men-only, women-only housing available. Powell Library plus 1 other with 215,649 books, 30,689 microform titles, 10,652 serials, 7,271 audiovisual materials, an OPAC, and a Web page. Operations spending for 2004 fiscal year: $1.1 million. 57 computers available on campus for general student use. Computer purchase/lease plans available. A campuswide network can be accessed from student residence rooms and from off campus. Staffed computer lab on campus.

■ **MENDOCINO COLLEGE** *G-3*

1000 Hensley Creek Rd.

Ukiah, CA 95482-0300

Tel: (707)468-3000

Admissions: (707)468-3103

Fax: (707)468-3430

E-mail: ktaylor@mendocino.cc.ca.us

Web Site: http://www.mendocino.cc.ca.us/

Description: State and locally supported, 2-year, coed. Part of California Community College System. Awards certificates, transfer associate, and terminal associate degrees. Founded 1973. Setting: 127-acre rural campus. Total enrollment: 5,400. 459 applied, 100% were admitted. Students come from 16 states and territories, 4% Native American, 12% Hispanic, 1% black, 2% Asian American or Pacific Islander, 0% international, 65% 25 or older. Core. Calendar: semesters. Academic remediation for entering students, ESL program, services for LD students, advanced placement, honors program, summer session for credit, part-time degree program, adult/continuing education programs, co-op programs and internships.

Entrance Requirements: Open admission. Options: early admission, deferred admission. Placement: SAT or ACT recommended; CPT required for some. Entrance: noncompetitive. Application deadline: Rolling. Notification: continuous. Preference given to state residents.

Collegiate Environment: Drama-theater group, student-run newspaper. Social organizations: 14 open to all. Student services: personal-psychological counseling. Campus security: late night transport-escort service, security patrols 6 p.m. to 10 p.m. College housing not available. Lowery Library with 27,441 books and 275 serials. 90 computers available on campus for general student use. A campuswide network can be accessed from off-campus. Staffed computer lab on campus.

■ **MENLO COLLEGE** *E-15*

1000 El Camino Real

Atherton, CA 94027-4301

Tel: (650)688-3753

Free: 800-556-3656

Admissions: (650)543-3910

Fax: (650)617-2395

E-mail: admissions@menlo.edu

Web Site: http://www.menlo.edu/

Description: Independent, 4-year, coed. Awards bachelor's degrees. Founded 1927. Setting: 45-acre small town campus with easy access to San Francisco. Endowment: $7.2 million. Research spending for 2004 fiscal year: $3196. Educational spending for 2005 fiscal year: $3421 per student. Total enrollment: 769. Student-undergrad faculty ratio is 18:1. 753 applied, 69% were admitted. 6% from top 10% of their high school class, 26% from top quarter, 67% from top half. Full-time: 669 students, 39% women, 61% men. Part-time: 100 students, 60% women, 40% men. Students come from 24 states and territories, 34 other countries, 18% from out-of-state, 1% Native American, 15% Hispanic, 9% black, 12% Asian American or Pacific Islander, 10% international, 17% 25 or older, 66% live on campus, 14% transferred in. Retention: 64% of full-time freshmen returned the following year. Academic areas with the most degrees conferred: business/marketing; communications/journalism; liberal arts/general studies. Core. Calendar: semesters. Academic remediation for entering students, services for LD students, advanced placement, accelerated degree program, self-designed majors, honors program, independent study, double major, summer session for credit, part-time degree program, adult/continuing education programs, co-op programs and internships. Study abroad program. ROTC: Army (c).

Entrance Requirements: Options: Peterson's Universal Application, Common Application, electronic application, early admission, early action, deferred admission, international baccalaureate accepted. Required: essay, high school transcript, 1 recommendation, SAT or ACT. Recommended: minimum 3.0 high school GPA, interview. Entrance: moderately difficult. Application deadlines: Rolling, 12/1 for early action. Notification: continuous, continuous for nonresidents, 1/1 for early action.

Costs Per Year: Application fee: $40. Comprehensive fee: $34,050 includes full-time tuition ($24,300), mandatory fees ($150), and college room and board ($9600). Full-time tuition and fees vary according to program. Room and board charges vary according to housing facility. Part-time tuition: $1000 per unit. Part-time mandatory fees: $75. Part-time tuition and fees vary according to course load and program.

Collegiate Environment: Orientation program. Drama-theater group, student-run newspaper, radio station. Social organizations: 20 open to all. Most popular organizations: International Club, Residence Hall Association, French Club, media network, Hawaiian Club. Major annual events: Homecoming, Luau, Spring Festival. Student services: personal-psychological counseling. Campus security: 24-hour emergency response devices and patrols. 423 college housing spaces available; 360 were occupied in 2003-04. Freshmen given priority for college housing. On-campus residence required through sophomore year. Options: coed, men-only, women-only housing available. Bowman Library with 64,700 books, 295 microform titles, 175 serials, 785 audiovisual materials, an OPAC, and a Web page. Operations spending for 2004 fiscal year: $427,864. 130 computers available on campus for general student use. A campuswide network can be accessed from student residence rooms and from off campus. Staffed computer lab on campus.

Community Environment: This is a residential community 30 miles south of San Francisco and 20 miles north of San Jose. The climate is moderate. The Southern Pacific Railroad, and Pacific Greyhound Bus serve the area with San Francisco International Airport 16 miles north. Activities are planned for all ages at the recreation center and many parks and playgrounds.

■ **MERCED COLLEGE** *L-8*

3600 M St.

Merced, CA 95348-2898

Tel: (209)384-6000

Admissions: (209)384-6188

Fax: (209)384-6339

Web Site: http://www.mccd.edu/

Description: State and locally supported, 2-year, coed. Part of California Community College System. Awards certificates, transfer associate, and terminal associate degrees. Founded 1962. Setting: 168-acre small town campus. Endowment: $1 million. Research spending for 2004 fiscal year: $65,602. Educational spending for 2005 fiscal year: $2065 per student. Total enrollment: 8,200. 421 applied. Students come from 30 states and territories, 51% 25 or older. Core. Calendar: semesters. Academic remediation for entering students, ESL program, services for LD students, advanced placement, honors program, summer session for credit, part-time degree program, adult/continuing education programs, co-op programs. Off campus study at several local community colleges. Study abroad program. ROTC: Army (c).

Entrance Requirements: Open admission except for allied health programs or international students. Options: Common Application, early admission. Placement: SAT or ACT recommended. Entrance: noncompetitive. Application deadline: Rolling. Notification: continuous.

Collegiate Environment: Drama-theater group, choral group, student-run newspaper. Social organizations: 30 open to all. Student services: legal services, health clinic, personal-psychological counseling, women's center. Campus security: 24-hour patrols, late night transport-escort service. College housing not available. Lesher Library with 35,000 books and 400 serials. Operations spending for 2004 fiscal year: $666,963. 400 computers available on campus for general student use.

Community Environment: Merced is a rural, suburban area with a dry temperate climate. All forms of transportation serve the area. The community has a library, churches, theatres, a symphony, two general hospitals and all national service clubs. Merced is located at the foot of the Sierra Nevada Mountains and near Yosemite National Park, which provides recreational facilities for camping, hiking, fishing, and skiing, the major winter sport. Job opportunities are good during the summer.

■ **MERRITT COLLEGE** *K-4*

12500 Campus Dr.

Oakland, CA 94619-3196

Tel: (510)531-4911

Admissions: (510)466-7365

E-mail: hperdue@peralta.cc.ca.us

Web Site: http://www.merritt.edu/

Description: State and locally supported, 2-year, coed. Part of Peralta Community College District System. Awards certificates, transfer associate, and terminal associate degrees. Founded 1953. Setting: 130-acre urban campus with easy access to San Francisco. Research spending for 2004 fiscal year: $34,939. Educational spending for 2005 fiscal year: $1076 per student. Total enrollment: 7,984. 40% from top half of their high school class. Full-time: 1,195 students, 70% women, 30% men. Part-time: 6,789 students, 69% women, 31% men. Students come from 12 other countries, 1% Native American, 13% Hispanic, 47% black, 19% Asian American or Pacific Islander, 55% 25 or older. Core. Calendar: semesters. Academic remediation for entering students, ESL program, services for LD students, summer session for credit, part-time degree program, adult/continuing education programs, co-op programs. Off campus study at Holy Names College; Mills College; University of California, Berkeley.

Entrance Requirements: Open admission. Options: early admission, deferred admission. Placement: SAT or ACT recommended. Entrance: noncompetitive. Application deadline: 8/28. Notification: continuous.

Collegiate Environment: Student-run newspaper. Student services: women's center. College housing not available. Merritt College Library with 80,000 books and 200 serials. 20 computers available on campus for general student use. Staffed computer lab on campus.

Community Environment: See Laney College.

■ **MILLS COLLEGE** *K-4*

5000 MacArthur Blvd.

Oakland, CA 94613-1000

Tel: (510)430-2255

Free: 800-87-MILLS

Admissions: (510)430-2135

Fax: (510)430-3314

E-mail: admission@mills.edu

Web Site: http://www.mills.edu/

Description: Independent, comprehensive. Awards bachelor's, master's, and doctoral degrees. Founded 1852. Setting: 135-acre urban campus with easy access to San Francisco. Endowment: $177.8 million. Research spending for 2004 fiscal year: $1.1 million. Educational spending for 2005 fiscal year: $12,862 per student. Total enrollment: 1,372. Faculty: 184 (90 full-time, 94 part-time). Student-undergrad faculty ratio is 11:1. 783 applied, 77% were admitted. 37% from top 10% of their high school class, 61% from top quarter, 92% from top half. Full-time: 849 students, 100% women. Part-time: 32 students, 100% women. Students come from 35 states and territories, 6 other countries, 21% from out-of-state, 1% Native American, 9% Hispanic, 8% black, 8% Asian American or Pacific Islander, 6% international, 25% 25 or older, 54% live on campus, 13% transferred in. Retention: 75% of full-time freshmen returned the following year. Academic areas with the most degrees conferred: social sciences; English; visual and performing arts. Core. Calendar: semesters. Services for LD students, advanced placement, self-designed majors, honors program, independent study, double major, adult/continuing education programs, internships, graduate courses open to undergrads. Off campus study at University of California, Berkeley, California State University, Hayward, Sonoma State University, 9 other California colleges, American University, Agnes Scott College, Barnard College, Fisk University, Hollins College, Howard University, Manhattanville College, Mount Holyoke College, Simmons College, Spelman College, Swarthmore College, Wellesley College, Wheaton College. Study abroad program.

Entrance Requirements: Options: Peterson's Universal Application, Common Application, early action, deferred admission, international baccalaureate accepted. Required: high school transcript, 3 recommendations, essay or graded paper, SAT or ACT. Recommended: interview, SAT Subject Tests. Entrance: moderately difficult. Application deadlines: 2/1, 11/15 for early action. Notification: 3/30, 12/15 for early action.

Costs Per Year: Application fee: $40. Comprehensive fee: $39,870 includes full-time tuition ($27,750), mandatory fees ($2240), and college room and board ($9880). College room only: $5150. Room and board charges vary according to board plan and housing facility. Part-time tuition: $4630 per course. Part-time tuition varies according to course load.

Collegiate Environment: Orientation program. Drama-theater group, choral group, student-run newspaper. Social organizations: 30 open to all. Most popular organizations: class organizations, MECHA, ASA (Asian Sisterhood Alliance), Mills Environmental Organization, BWC (Black Women's Collective). Major annual events: Commencement, Colloquium, Health Fair. Student services: health clinic, personal-psychological counseling, women's center. Campus security: 24-hour emergency response devices and patrols, late night transport-escort service, controlled dormitory access. 409 undergraduates lived in college housing during 2003-04. Freshmen guaranteed college housing. Options: coed, women-only housing available. F. W. Olin Library plus 1 other with 254,351 books, 28,324 microform titles, 13,211 serials, 7,640 audiovisual materials, an OPAC, and a Web page. Operations spending for 2004 fiscal year: $1.1 million. 267 computers available on campus for general student use. Computer purchase/lease plans available. A campuswide network can be accessed from student residence rooms and from off campus. Staffed computer lab on campus.

Community Environment: See Laney College.

■ **MIRACOSTA COLLEGE** *U-11*

One Barnard Dr.

Oceanside, CA 92056-3899

Tel: (760)757-2121; 888-201-8480

Admissions: (760)795-6627

Fax: (760)795-6609

Web Site: http://www.miracosta.edu/

Description: State-supported, 2-year, coed. Part of California Community College System. Awards certificates, diplomas, transfer associate, and terminal associate degrees. Founded 1934. Setting: 131-acre suburban campus with easy access to San Diego. Endowment: $894,495. Research spending for 2004 fiscal year: $189,200. Educational spending for 2005 fiscal year: $2451 per student. Total enrollment: 10,252. Student-undergrad faculty ratio is 23:1. Students come from 37 states and territories, 44 other countries, 2% from out-of-state, 33% 25 or older. Core. Calendar: semesters. Academic remediation for entering students, ESL program, services for LD students, advanced placement, accelerated degree program, self-designed majors, freshman honors college, honors program, independent study, distance learning, double major, summer session for credit, part-time degree program, adult/continuing education programs, co-op programs and internships. Study abroad program.

Entrance Requirements: Open admission except for nursing program. Options: early admission, deferred admission, international baccalaureate accepted. Entrance: noncompetitive. Application deadline: Rolling.

Costs Per Year: Application fee: $0. State resident tuition: $0 full-time. Nonresident tuition: $4800 full-time, $160 per unit part-time. Mandatory fees: $804 full-time, $26 per unit part-time.

Collegiate Environment: Orientation program. Drama-theater group, choral group, student-run newspaper. Social organizations: 37 open to all. Most popular organizations: African-American Student Alliance, Spanish Club, Cultural Exchange Program, Phi Theta Kappa, Friends of EOPS. Major annual events: Career Day Fair, Christmas Angel Exchange, Cinco de Mayo. Student services: health clinic, personal-psychological counseling, women's center. Campus security: 24-hour emergency response devices, student patrols, late night transport-escort service, trained security personnel during class hours. College housing not available. MiraCosta College Library with 113,810 books, 128,890 microform titles, 272 serials, 5,340 audiovisual materials, an OPAC, and a Web page. Operations spending for 2004 fiscal year: $942,502. 753 computers available on campus for general student use. A campuswide network can be accessed from off-campus. Staffed computer lab on campus.

■ MISSION COLLEGE *L-5*
3000 Mission College Blvd.
Santa Clara, CA 95054-1897
Tel: (408)988-2200
Admissions: (408)855-5195
Web Site: http://www.missioncollege.org/

Description: State and locally supported, 2-year, coed. Part of California Community College System. Awards certificates, diplomas, transfer associate, and terminal associate degrees. Founded 1977. Setting: 167-acre urban campus with easy access to San Francisco and San Jose. Total enrollment: 10,500. Full-time: 4,000 students, 52% women, 48% men. Part-time: 6,500 students, 52% women, 48% men. Students come from 18 other countries, 0.3% from out-of-state, 0.2% Native American, 14% Hispanic, 8% black, 52% Asian American or Pacific Islander, 3% international, 60% 25 or older, 0.5% transferred in. Core. Calendar: semesters. Academic remediation for entering students, ESL program, services for LD students, independent study, distance learning, double major, summer session for credit, part-time degree program, adult/continuing education programs, co-op programs and internships. ROTC: Army (c), Air Force (c).

Entrance Requirements: Open admission except for nursing program. Options: Common Application, electronic application, early admission. Placement: SAT recommended. Entrance: noncompetitive. Application deadline: Rolling. Notification: continuous. Preference given to district residents.

Collegiate Environment: Orientation program. Student services: personal-psychological counseling. Campus security: 24-hour emergency response devices, late night transport-escort service. College housing not available. 43,456 books and 323 serials. Operations spending for 2004 fiscal year: $900,000. 120 computers available on campus for general student use. A campuswide network can be accessed from off-campus. Staffed computer lab on campus.

■ MODESTO JUNIOR COLLEGE *K-7*
435 College Ave.
Modesto, CA 95350-5800
Tel: (209)575-6498
Admissions: (209)575-6470
Web Site: http://www.mjc.edu/

Description: State and locally supported, 2-year, coed. Part of Yosemite Community College District System. Awards certificates, transfer associate, and terminal associate degrees. Founded 1921. Setting: 229-acre urban campus. Endowment: $817,811. Research spending for 2004 fiscal year: $134,554. Educational spending for 2005 fiscal year: $2373 per student. Total enrollment: 18,240. Student-undergrad faculty ratio is 40:1. 11,385 applied, 100% were admitted. 53% 25 or older. Core. Calendar: semesters. Academic remediation for entering students, ESL program, services for LD students, advanced placement, honors program, independent study, distance learning, summer session for credit, part-time degree program, adult/continuing education programs, co-op programs. Study abroad program.

Entrance Requirements: Open admission. Option: electronic application. Recommended: high school transcript. Entrance: noncompetitive. Application deadline: Rolling. Notification: continuous.

Costs Per Year: Application fee: $0. State resident tuition: $0 full-time. Nonresident tuition: $3840 full-time, $160 per unit part-time. Mandatory fees: $664 full-time, $26 per unit part-time, $40 per year part-time.

Collegiate Environment: Orientation program. Drama-theater group, choral group, student-run newspaper, radio station. Social organizations: 24 open to all. Most popular organizations: Young Farmers, Red Nations, Psychology Club, Alpha Gamma Sigma, MECHA. Major annual events: Transfer Day/ College Night, Job Fair, Club Fair. Student services: health clinic, personal-psychological counseling. Campus security: 24-hour emergency response devices and patrols, late night transport-escort service. College housing not available. Modesto Junior College Library with 69,865 books, 5,600 microform titles, 4,161 audiovisual materials, an OPAC, and a Web page. Operations spending for 2004 fiscal year: $1.1 million. 95 computers available on campus for general student use. A campuswide network can be accessed from off-campus. Staffed computer lab on campus.

Community Environment: Modesto is located in the heart of the San Joaquin Valley and is the access point for the Sonora Pass vacationland in the Stanislaus National Forest, Mother Lode Country and the Big Oak Flat route to Yosemite. Modesto is the county seat of Stanislaus County. Churches of all denominations, a library, hospitals, plus the usual businesses make up the City of Modesto. There are 20 parks, playgrounds, golf courses, tennis courts, swimming pools for recreational facilities plus areas where there is boating, fishing, hunting and skiing. Part-time employment is available.

■ MONTEREY PENINSULA COLLEGE *M-5*
980 Fremont St.
Monterey, CA 93940-4799
Tel: (831)646-4000
Admissions: (831)646-4007
Fax: (831)655-2627
E-mail: vcoleman@mpc.edu
Web Site: http://www.mpc.edu/

Description: State-supported, 2-year, coed. Part of California Community College System. Awards certificates, transfer associate, and terminal associate degrees. Founded 1947. Setting: 87-acre small town campus. Total enrollment: 14,074. Students come from 29 states and territories, 47 other countries. Core. Calendar: semesters. Academic remediation for entering students, ESL program, services for LD students, advanced placement, summer session for credit, part-time degree program, adult/continuing education programs, co-op programs.

Entrance Requirements: Open admission except for nonresident aliens. Option: early admission. Entrance: noncompetitive. Application deadline: Rolling. Notification: continuous.

Collegiate Environment: Drama-theater group, choral group, student-run newspaper. Student services: health clinic, personal-psychological counseling, women's center. Campus security: 24-hour emergency response devices, late night transport-escort service. College housing not available. Monterey Peninsula College Library with 52,000 books, 137,300 microform titles, 281 serials, 2,623 audiovisual materials, an OPAC, and a Web page. 120 computers available on campus for general student use. A campuswide network can be accessed from off-campus. Staffed computer lab on campus.

Community Environment: Monterey Peninsula's population is approximately 150,000 including the cities of Carmel, Carmel Valley, Marina, Monterey, Pacific Grove, Pebble Beach, and Seaside. Monterey is a good two hour drive south of San Francisco on Highway 1. Airlines and buses serve the area. The climate is pleasing; average summer temperature is 60 and winter average is 51 degrees. This is the home of the Bach Festival, Golf Tournaments, Sports Car Races, the Monterey Jazz and Blues Festivals, and the County Fair. Artists, photographers, and writers enjoy Monterey for its beautiful scenery and good weather. Little theatre groups, music groups, art council and symphony guilds make up the cultural atmosphere of the city. Monterey Peninsula is a popular playground with several golf courses, facilities for fishing, boating, hunting and tennis. There are twelve championship golf courses in the area.

■ MOORPARK COLLEGE *T-4*
7075 Campus Rd.
Moorpark, CA 93021-1695
Tel: (805)378-1400
Admissions: (805)378-1406
Web Site: http://www.moorpark.cc.ca.us/

Description: County-supported, 2-year, coed. Part of Ventura County Community College District System. Awards certificates, transfer associate, and terminal associate degrees. Founded 1967. Setting: 121-acre small town campus with easy access to Los Angeles. Total enrollment: 15,266. 2,000 applied, 100% were admitted. Students come from 45 states and territories,

50 other countries, 1% Native American, 15% Hispanic, 2% black, 11% Asian American or Pacific Islander, 42% 25 or older. Core. Calendar: semesters. Academic remediation for entering students, ESL program, services for LD students, advanced placement, honors program, independent study, distance learning, summer session for credit, part-time degree program, adult/continuing education programs, co-op programs and internships.

Entrance Requirements: Open admission except for nursing, exotic animal training programs. Options: electronic application, early admission, deferred admission. Recommended: high school transcript. Required for some: high school transcript. Entrance: noncompetitive. Application deadline: Rolling. Notification: continuous.

Collegiate Environment: Student-run newspaper. Major annual event: Multicultural Day. Student services: health clinic, personal-psychological counseling, women's center. Campus security: 24-hour patrols. College housing not available. 50,000 books and 100 serials. 80 computers available on campus for general student use. Staffed computer lab on campus.

Community Environment: See California Lutheran University.

■ **MOUNT ST. MARY'S COLLEGE** *S-10*
12001 Chalon Rd.
Los Angeles, CA 90049-1599
Tel: (310)954-4000
Free: 800-999-9893
Admissions: (310)954-4252
E-mail: admissions@msmc.la.edu
Web Site: http://www.msmc.la.edu/
Description: Independent Roman Catholic, comprehensive, coed. Awards associate, bachelor's, and master's degrees. Founded 1925. Setting: 71-acre suburban campus. Endowment: $49.5 million. Educational spending for 2005 fiscal year: $3097 per student. Total enrollment: 2,480. Faculty: 299 (74 full-time, 225 part-time). Student-undergrad faculty ratio is 13:1. 1,035 applied, 85% were admitted. Full-time: 1,470 students, 97% women, 3% men. Part-time: 510 students, 87% women, 13% men. Students come from 17 states and territories, 7% from out-of-state, 1% Native American, 44% Hispanic, 10% black, 21% Asian American or Pacific Islander, 0.3% international, 28% 25 or older, 59% live on campus, 4% transferred in. Retention: 72% of full-time freshmen returned the following year. Academic areas with the most degrees conferred: health professions and related sciences; social sciences; business/marketing. Core. Calendar: semesters. Academic remediation for entering students, ESL program, services for LD students, advanced placement, accelerated degree program, self-designed majors, freshman honors college, honors program, independent study, double major, summer session for credit, part-time degree program, adult/continuing education programs, internships, graduate courses open to undergrads. Off campus study at University of Southern California, University of California, Los Angeles, Sisters of Saint Joseph College Consortium. Study abroad program.

Entrance Requirements: Options: electronic application, early action, deferred admission, international baccalaureate accepted. Required: essay, high school transcript, minimum 2.0 high school GPA, 1 recommendation, SAT or ACT. Recommended: minimum 3.0 high school GPA, interview, SAT. Entrance: moderately difficult. Application deadlines: 2/15, 12/1 for early action. Notification: continuous, 1/1 for early action.

Costs Per Year: Application fee: $40. Comprehensive fee: $32,897 includes full-time tuition ($23,380), mandatory fees ($770), and college room and board ($8747). Part-time tuition: $900 per unit.

Collegiate Environment: Orientation program. Drama-theater group, choral group, student-run newspaper. Social organizations: 29 open to all; national sororities, local sororities; 6% of women are members. Most popular organizations: Latinas Unidas, student government, Pi Theta Mu, Kappa Delta Chi, Student Ambassadors. Major annual event: Mary's Day. Student services: health clinic, personal-psychological counseling, women's center. Campus security: 24-hour patrols, controlled dormitory access. 728 college housing spaces available; 682 were occupied in 2003-04. Freshmen given priority for college housing. Charles Williard Coe Memorial Library with 140,000 books, 4,760 microform titles, 750 serials, an OPAC, and a Web page. Operations spending for 2004 fiscal year: $1 million. 85 computers available on campus for general student use. A campuswide network can be accessed from student residence rooms and from off campus. Staffed computer lab on campus.

■ **MT. SAN ANTONIO COLLEGE** *W-8*
1100 North Grand Ave.
Walnut, CA 91789-1399

Tel: (909)594-5611
Free: 800-672-2463
Web Site: http://www.mtsac.edu/
Description: District-supported, 2-year, coed. Part of California Community College System. Awards certificates, diplomas, transfer associate, and terminal associate degrees. Founded 1946. Setting: 421-acre suburban campus with easy access to Los Angeles. Total enrollment: 27,195. Full-time: 8,567 students, 51% women, 49% men. Part-time: 18,628 students, 57% women, 43% men. Students come from 51 states and territories, 0.5% Native American, 44% Hispanic, 6% black, 24% Asian American or Pacific Islander, 1% international. Core. Calendar: semesters. Academic remediation for entering students, ESL program, services for LD students, honors program, distance learning, summer session for credit, part-time degree program, adult/continuing education programs, co-op programs. Study abroad program.

Entrance Requirements: Open admission. Options: early admission, deferred admission. Required for some: high school transcript. Entrance: noncompetitive. Notification: continuous.

Costs Per Year: State resident tuition: $0 full-time. Nonresident tuition: $4248 full-time, $177 per term part-time. Mandatory fees: $672 full-time, $26 per unit part-time, $24 per term part-time.

Collegiate Environment: Orientation program. Drama-theater group, choral group, student-run radio station. Most popular organizations: Alpha Gamma Sigma, Muslim Student Association, student government, Asian Student Association, Kasama-Filipino Student Organization. Major annual events: Cinco de Mayo, Asian Awareness Week, Join-a-Club. Student services: legal services, health clinic, personal-psychological counseling, women's center. Campus security: 24-hour emergency response devices and patrols, late night transport-escort service. Learning Resources Center with 64,291 books, 20,857 microform titles, 753 serials, 6,494 audiovisual materials, an OPAC, and a Web page. 1,200 computers available on campus for general student use. A campuswide network can be accessed from off-campus. Staffed computer lab on campus.

■ **MT. SAN JACINTO COLLEGE** *S-12*
1499 North State St.
San Jacinto, CA 92583-2399
Tel: (909)487-6752
Fax: (909)654-6738
E-mail: egonzale@msjc.edu
Web Site: http://www.msjc.edu/
Description: State and locally supported, 2-year, coed. Part of California Community College System. Awards certificates, diplomas, transfer associate, and terminal associate degrees. Founded 1963. Setting: 180-acre suburban campus with easy access to San Diego. Endowment: $2 million. Total enrollment: 12,592. Students come from 11 states and territories, 1% from out-of-state, 60% 25 or older. Core. Calendar: semesters. Academic remediation for entering students, ESL program, services for LD students, advanced placement, honors program, distance learning, double major, summer session for credit, part-time degree program, adult/continuing education programs. Off campus study at Citrus College. Study abroad program.

Entrance Requirements: Open admission except for nursing program. Option: early admission. Recommended: high school transcript. Placement: Assessment and Placement Services for Community Colleges required. Entrance: noncompetitive. Application deadline: Rolling.

Collegiate Environment: Drama-theater group. Student services: personal-psychological counseling. Campus security: part-time trained security personnel. College housing not available. Milo P. Johnson Library plus 1 other with 28,000 books and 330 serials. 35 computers available on campus for general student use. Staffed computer lab on campus.

■ **MT. SIERRA COLLEGE** *P-6*
101 East Huntington Dr.
Monrovia, CA 91016
Tel: (626)873-2144; 888-828-8800.
Admissions: (626)873-2100
Fax: (626)359-5528
Web Site: http://www.mtsierra.edu/
Description: Proprietary, 4-year, coed. Awards bachelor's degrees. Founded 1990. Setting: 5-acre suburban campus. Educational spending for 2005 fiscal year: $9000 per student. Total enrollment: 1,100. 380 applied, 73% were admitted. 2 class presidents, 15 student government officers. Full-time: 1,085 students, 30% women, 70% men. Part-time: 15 students, 33%

women, 67% men. Students come from 7 states and territories, 5% from out-of-state, 4% Native American, 26% Hispanic, 5% black, 26% Asian American or Pacific Islander, 0% international, 60% 25 or older, 5% transferred in. Retention: 70% of full-time freshmen returned the following year. Core. Accelerated degree program, independent study, distance learning, summer session for credit, adult/continuing education programs, internships.

Entrance Requirements: Open admission. Options: electronic application, international baccalaureate accepted. Required: essay, high school transcript, interview. Entrance: moderately difficult. Notification: 10/1.

Collegiate Environment: Orientation program. Campus security: 24-hour emergency response devices, student patrols, late night transport-escort service. College housing not available. Mt. Sierra College Learning Resource Center with 6,000 books, 5,000 serials, and 100 audiovisual materials. Operations spending for 2004 fiscal year: $50,000. 300 computers available on campus for general student use. Computer purchase/lease plans available. A campuswide network can be accessed from off-campus. Staffed computer lab on campus.

■ **MTI COLLEGE OF BUSINESS AND TECHNOLOGY** *I-6*
5221 Madison Ave.
Sacramento, CA 95841
Tel: (916)339-1500
Fax: (916)339-0305
E-mail: mmiller@mticollege.edu
Web Site: http://www.mticollege.com/
Description: Proprietary, 2-year, coed. Awards diplomas, transfer associate, and terminal associate degrees. Founded 1965. Total enrollment: 600. Calendar: continuous.
Entrance Requirements: Required: MTI Assessment.

■ **MUSICIANS INSTITUTE** *S-10*
1655 North McCadden Place
Hollywood, CA 90028
Tel: (323)462-1384
Free: 800-255-PLAY
Fax: (323)462-6978
E-mail: admissions@mi.edu
Web Site: http://www.mi.edu/
Description: Proprietary, 4-year, coed. Awards associate and bachelor's degrees. Founded 1976. Total enrollment: 650.
Entrance Requirements: Entrance: minimally difficult. Application deadline: Rolling. Notification: continuous.
Costs Per Year: Application fee: $100. Tuition: $16,800 full-time, $280 per credit part-time. Mandatory fees: $400 full-time, $100 per term part-time. Full-time tuition and fees vary according to degree level and program. Part-time tuition and fees vary according to course load.
Collegiate Environment: College housing not available.

■ **NAPA VALLEY COLLEGE** *I-4*
2277 Napa-Vallejo Hwy.
Napa, CA 94558-6236
Tel: (707)253-3000
Fax: (707)253-3064
E-mail: eshenk@napavalley.edu
Web Site: http://www.napavalley.edu/
Description: State and locally supported, 2-year, coed. Part of California Community College System. Awards certificates, transfer associate, and terminal associate degrees. Founded 1942. Setting: 188-acre suburban campus with easy access to San Francisco. Total enrollment: 6,908. 2,000 applied, 100% were admitted. Full-time: 1,909 students, 57% women, 43% men. Part-time: 4,999 students, 62% women, 38% men. 1% Native American, 20% Hispanic, 8% black, 18% Asian American or Pacific Islander. Retention: 66% of full-time freshmen returned the following year. Core. Calendar: semesters. Academic remediation for entering students, ESL program, services for LD students, advanced placement, distance learning, summer session for credit, part-time degree program, co-op programs. Study abroad program.
Entrance Requirements: Open admission except for allied health programs. Required for some: high school transcript. Placement: SAT or ACT required for some. Entrance: noncompetitive. Application deadlines: Rolling, Rolling for nonresidents.
Costs Per Year: Application fee: $0. State resident tuition: $0 full-time. Nonresident tuition: $3624 full-time, $151 per unit part-time. Mandatory fees:

$648 full-time, $26 per unit part-time, $12 per term part-time. Full-time tuition and fees vary according to course load. Part-time tuition and fees vary according to course load.
Collegiate Environment: Drama-theater group, choral group, student-run newspaper. Most popular organizations: Hispano-Americano Club, African-American Club, Environmental Action Coalition, International Student Club, Phi Theta Kappa. Major annual events: Black History Month, Cinco de Mayo, Native American Pow Wow. Student services: personal-psychological counseling, women's center. Campus security: late night transport-escort service. College housing not available. Napa Valley College Library plus 1 other with 42,000 books, 250 serials, and an OPAC. 90 computers available on campus for general student use. Staffed computer lab on campus.
Community Environment: Population 63,000. The town of Napa, in the southern wine district, is the center of a fruit and nut raising region as well as the southeastern entrance to the Redwood Empire. Located in the Napa Valley area, there are numerous wineries, most of which are open to the public for tours. The climate is delightful. Buses and trains serve the area. Napa has churches of all denominations, hospitals, clinics, and libraries. Recreation includes parks, picnic grounds, swimming pools, and golf courses.

■ **THE NATIONAL HISPANIC UNIVERSITY** *L-5*
14271 Story Rd.
San Jose, CA 95127-3823
Tel: (408)254-6900
Web Site: http://www.nhu.edu/
Description: Independent, 4-year, coed. Awards associate and bachelor's degrees. Founded 1981. Setting: 1-acre urban campus. Endowment: $1 million. Research spending for 2004 fiscal year: $88,901. Total enrollment: 469. 179 applied, 82% were admitted. 3% from top 10% of their high school class, 15% from top quarter, 82% from top half. Full-time: 176 students, 32% women, 68% men. Part-time: 117 students, 64% women, 36% men. Students come from 4 states and territories, 6 other countries, 0.4% Native American, 84% Hispanic, 1% black, 6% Asian American or Pacific Islander, 5% international, 40% 25 or older. Retention: 86% of full-time freshmen returned the following year. Core. Calendar: semesters. Academic remediation for entering students, ESL program, advanced placement, accelerated degree program, summer session for credit, part-time degree program, adult/continuing education programs, co-op programs and internships. Off campus study at California State University, Hayward, San Jose City College, Lincoln University, San Jose State University. Study abroad program.
Entrance Requirements: Options: Common Application, electronic application. Required: essay, high school transcript, minimum 2.0 high school GPA, recommendations, interview. Recommended: SAT and SAT Subject Tests or ACT. Entrance: minimally difficult. Application deadline: 8/15. Notification: continuous.
Collegiate Environment: Orientation program. Social organizations: 1 open to all. Most popular organizations: Teatro De Los Pobres, Student Government Association. Major annual events: Christmas Party, Las Posadas, Summer Family Festival. Student services: personal-psychological counseling. Campus security: 24-hour emergency response devices and patrols. College housing not available. University Library with 10,000 books and 40 serials. Operations spending for 2004 fiscal year: $85,845. 40 computers available on campus for general student use. A campuswide network can be accessed. Staffed computer lab on campus.

■ **NATIONAL POLYTECHNIC COLLEGE OF ENGINEERING AND OCEANEERING** *T-9*
272 South Fries Ave.
Wilmington, CA 90744-6399
Tel: (310)834-2501
Free: 800-432-DIVE
Fax: (310)834-7132
Web Site: http://www.coo.edu/
Description: Proprietary, 2-year, coed. Awards certificates and transfer associate degrees. Setting: 5-acre suburban campus with easy access to Los Angeles. Educational spending for 2005 fiscal year: $16,000 per student. Total enrollment: 272. 598 applied, 59% were admitted. Students come from 52 states and territories, 5 other countries, 50% from out-of-state, 40% 25 or older. Core. Calendar: continuous. Advanced placement, double major, co-op programs and internships. Off campus study at San Pedro/Wilmington Skills Center.

Entrance Requirements: Options: Peterson's Universal Application, Common Application, electronic application, deferred admission. Required: essay, high school transcript, interview, physical examination. Entrance: moderately difficult. Application deadline: Rolling. Notification: continuous.

Collegiate Environment: Orientation program. Major annual events: Graduation, cook-outs, Thanksgiving Dinner. Student services: personal-psychological counseling. Campus security: 24-hour emergency response devices. College housing not available. 3 computers available on campus for general student use. A campuswide network can be accessed.

■ **NATIONAL UNIVERSITY** *W-12*
11255 North Torrey Pines Rd.
La Jolla, CA 92037-1011
Tel: (619)563-7100
Free: 800-NAT-UNIV
Admissions: (858)628-8648
Fax: (619)563-7299
E-mail: mmagee@nu.edu
Web Site: http://www.nu.edu/
Description: Independent, comprehensive, coed. Awards associate, bachelor's, and master's degrees. Founded 1971. Setting: urban campus. Endowment: $243.2 million. Research spending for 2004 fiscal year: $889,600. Educational spending for 2005 fiscal year: $2948 per student. Total enrollment: 26,035. Faculty: 2,701 (199 full-time, 2,502 part-time). Student-undergrad faculty ratio is 14:1. Full-time: 1,631 students, 60% women, 40% men. Part-time: 4,890 students, 55% women, 45% men. Students come from 64 other countries, 5% from out-of-state, 1% Native American, 18% Hispanic, 12% black, 9% Asian American or Pacific Islander, 1% international, 82% 25 or older, 6% transferred in. Retention: 100% of full-time freshmen returned the following year. Academic areas with the most degrees conferred: business/marketing; interdisciplinary studies; psychology. Core. ESL program, services for LD students, advanced placement, accelerated degree program, independent study, distance learning, double major, summer session for credit, part-time degree program, adult/continuing education programs, internships. Off campus study at Servicemembers Opportunity Colleges. ROTC: Army (c), Air Force (c).
Entrance Requirements: Open admission. Option: deferred admission. Required: high school transcript, minimum 2.0 high school GPA, interview. Required for some: essay. Entrance: moderately difficult. Application deadline: Rolling. Notification: continuous.
Costs Per Year: Application fee: $60. Tuition: $8352 full-time, $1044 per course part-time. Full-time tuition varies according to course load. Part-time tuition varies according to course load.
Collegiate Environment: Campus security: 24-hour emergency response devices and patrols, late night transport-escort service. College housing not available. Central Library with 226,049 books, 253,052 microform titles, 2,794 serials, 5,539 audiovisual materials, an OPAC, and a Web page. Operations spending for 2004 fiscal year: $3.1 million. 2,253 computers available on campus for general student use. A campuswide network can be accessed from off-campus. Staffed computer lab on campus.

■ **NEW COLLEGE OF CALIFORNIA** *K-4*
50 Fell St.
San Francisco, CA 94102-5206
Tel: (415)437-3460; 888-437-3460
Fax: (415)626-5171
Web Site: http://www.newcollege.edu/
Description: Independent, comprehensive, coed. Awards bachelor's and master's degrees. Founded 1971. Setting: urban campus. Total enrollment: 1,133. Full-time: 611 students, 49% women, 51% men. Part-time: 7 students, 57% women, 43% men. Students come from 5 other countries, 0.5% Native American, 5% Hispanic, 3% black, 1% Asian American or Pacific Islander, 0.5% international, 50% 25 or older, 19% transferred in. Retention: 87% of full-time freshmen returned the following year. Core. Calendar: semesters. Academic remediation for entering students, accelerated degree program, self-designed majors, independent study, part-time degree program, co-op programs and internships, graduate courses open to undergrads. Study abroad program.
Entrance Requirements: Open admission. Option: deferred admission. Required: essay, high school transcript. Recommended: interview. Required for some: 2 recommendations. Entrance: noncompetitive. Application deadline: Rolling. Notification: continuous.
Costs Per Year: Application fee: $50. Tuition: $12,642 full-time, $550 per unit part-time. Mandatory fees: $200 full-time, $100 per term part-time.

Collegiate Environment: Drama-theater group, student-run newspaper. Student services: legal services, personal-psychological counseling. Campus security: trained security personnel. College housing not available. New College Library plus 2 others with 24,000 books and 50 serials. 10 computers available on campus for general student use. A campuswide network can be accessed from off-campus. Staffed computer lab on campus.

■ **NEWSCHOOL OF ARCHITECTURE & DESIGN** *W-12*
1249 F St.
San Diego, CA 92101-6634
Tel: (619)235-4100
E-mail: nsa1249@aol.com
Web Site: http://www.newschoolarch.edu/
Description: Proprietary, comprehensive, coed. Awards associate, bachelor's, master's, and first professional degrees. Founded 1980. Setting: 1-acre urban campus. Research spending for 2004 fiscal year: $20,000. Educational spending for 2005 fiscal year: $10,620 per student. Total enrollment: 198. 2 applied, 100% were admitted. Full-time: 4 students, 100% men. Students come from 4 states and territories, 15% from out-of-state, 0% Native American, 25% Hispanic, 0% black, 0% Asian American or Pacific Islander, 0% international, 65% 25 or older, 10% live on campus, 25% transferred in. Core. Academic remediation for entering students, ESL program, advanced placement, summer session for credit, part-time degree program, adult/continuing education programs, co-op programs and internships, graduate courses open to undergrads. Off campus study. Study abroad program.
Entrance Requirements: Options: Peterson's Universal Application, early decision, international baccalaureate accepted. Required: essay, high school transcript, minimum 2.5 high school GPA, interview. Recommended: recommendations. Required for some: portfolio. Entrance: moderately difficult. Application deadlines: Rolling, 8/30 for nonresidents, 7/1 for early decision. Notification: continuous, continuous for nonresidents.
Collegiate Environment: Orientation program. Student-run newspaper. Social organizations: 1 open to all; 10% of eligible men and 10% of eligible women are members. Most popular organization: American Institute of Architects Student Chapter. Major annual events: National American Institute of Architects Convention, Sweatshirt Design Competition, Catalog Design Competition. Student services: personal-psychological counseling. Campus security: 24-hour emergency response devices, controlled dormitory access. Option: coed housing available. Newschool of Arts Foundation Library with 7,500 books, 50 serials, and 250 audiovisual materials. Operations spending for 2004 fiscal year: $40,000. 14 computers available on campus for general student use. A campuswide network can be accessed. Staffed computer lab on campus.

■ **NORTHROP RICE AVIATION INSTITUTE OF TECHNOLOGY** *R-4*
1155 West Arbor Vitae St., Ste. 115
Inglewood, CA 90301-2904
Tel: (310)568-8541
Fax: (310)568-8542
E-mail: info@nrait.edu
Web Site: http://www.nrait.edu/
Description: Proprietary, 2-year, coed. Founded 1942.

■ **NORTHWESTERN POLYTECHNIC UNIVERSITY** *K-5*
117 Fourier Ave.
Fremont, CA 94539-7482
Tel: (510)657-5913
Admissions: (510)657-0256
Fax: (510)657-8975
Web Site: http://www.npu.edu/
Description: Independent, comprehensive, coed. Awards bachelor's, master's, and doctoral degrees. Founded 1984. Setting: 2-acre urban campus with easy access to San Francisco and San Jose. Total enrollment: 351. 7 applied, 100% were admitted. Full-time: 62 students, 35% women, 65% men. Part-time: 55 students, 38% women, 62% men. Students come from 7 states and territories, 10 other countries, 7% from out-of-state, 0% Native American, 0% Hispanic, 0% black, 33% Asian American or Pacific Islander, 61% international, 63% 25 or older, 12% live on campus, 8% transferred in. Retention: 89% of full-time freshmen returned the following year. Core. Calendar: trimesters. ESL program, advanced placement, distance learning, summer session for credit, part-time degree program, adult/continuing education programs, internships, graduate courses open to undergrads.

Entrance Requirements: Options: Common Application, electronic application, international baccalaureate accepted. Required: high school transcript, minimum 2.0 high school GPA. Recommended: interview. Required for some: essay. Application deadline: 9/20. Notification: continuous.

Costs Per Year: Application fee: $75. Tuition: $6600 full-time, $275 per unit part-time. Mandatory fees: $140 full-time, $70 per term part-time. Full-time tuition and fees vary according to course load. Part-time tuition and fees vary according to course load.

Collegiate Environment: Orientation program. Most popular organizations: NPU Student Association, Table Tennis Club, IEEE Student Chapter, Softball Club. Major annual events: Halloween party, dance party, picnic. Campus security: late night transport-escort service. 35 college housing spaces available; 8 were occupied in 2003-04. No special consideration for freshman housing applicants. Options: coed, men-only, women-only housing available. NPU Library plus 1 other with 12,000 books, 100 microform titles, 200 serials, 200 audiovisual materials, an OPAC, and a Web page. Operations spending for 2004 fiscal year: $750,000. 200 computers available on campus for general student use. A campuswide network can be accessed from student residence rooms and from off campus. Staffed computer lab on campus.

■ **NORTHWESTERN TECHNICAL COLLEGE** *I-6*

1825 Bell St., No. 100
Sacramento, CA 95825
Tel: (916)649-2400; (866)649-2400
Fax: (916)649-8649
E-mail: rnaylor@ntcollege.com
Web Site: http://www.ntcollege.com/
Description: Proprietary, 2-year, coed. Founded 1995.

■ **NOTRE DAME DE NAMUR UNIVERSITY** *I-4*

1500 Ralston Ave.
Belmont, CA 94002-1908
Tel: (650)508-3500
Free: 800-263-0545
Admissions: (650)508-3600
Fax: (650)508-3660
E-mail: admissions@ndnu.edu
Web Site: http://www.ndnu.edu
Description: Independent Roman Catholic, comprehensive, coed. Awards bachelor's and master's degrees. Founded 1851. Setting: 80-acre suburban campus with easy access to San Francisco. Endowment: $10.8 million. Educational spending for 2005 fiscal year: $11,545 per student. Total enrollment: 1,588. Faculty: 143 (50 full-time, 93 part-time). Student-undergrad faculty ratio is 13:1. 642 applied, 96% were admitted. 17% from top 10% of their high school class, 40% from top quarter, 66% from top half. Full-time: 631 students, 61% women, 39% men. Part-time: 259 students, 67% women, 33% men. Students come from 24 states and territories, 17 other countries, 28% from out-of-state, 1% Native American, 22% Hispanic, 5% black, 15% Asian American or Pacific Islander, 4% international, 41% 25 or older, 36% live on campus, 62% transferred in. Retention: 69% of full-time freshmen returned the following year. Academic areas with the most degrees conferred: business/marketing; public administration and social services; liberal arts/general studies; psychology. Core. Calendar: semesters. Academic remediation for entering students, ESL program, services for LD students, advanced placement, accelerated degree program, independent study, double major, summer session for credit, part-time degree program, adult/continuing education programs, co-op programs and internships. Off campus study at Trinity College (DC), Emmanuel College (MA). Study abroad program. ROTC: Air Force (c).

Entrance Requirements: Options: Peterson's Universal Application, early action, deferred admission, international baccalaureate accepted. Required: essay, high school transcript, recommendations, audition is required for music programs, SAT or ACT. Required for some: interview. Entrance: moderately difficult. Application deadline: Rolling. Notification: continuous.

Costs Per Year: Application fee: $40. Comprehensive fee: $34,230 includes full-time tuition ($23,650), mandatory fees ($200), and college room and board ($10,380). College room only: $7000. Part-time tuition: $545 per unit. Part-time mandatory fees: $30 per term.

Collegiate Environment: Orientation program. Drama-theater group, choral group, student-run newspaper. Social organizations: 29 open to all. Most popular organizations: Associated Students of Notre Dame de Namur University, BizCom, Social Action Club, Alianza Latina, Hawaiian Club. Major annual events: International Reception, Hawaiian Luau, Spring Formal.

Student services: health clinic, personal-psychological counseling. Campus security: 24-hour emergency response devices and patrols, late night transport-escort service, controlled dormitory access. 520 college housing spaces available; 440 were occupied in 2003-04. Options: coed, men-only, women-only housing available. College of Notre Dame Library with 24,169 microform titles, 726 serials, 8,314 audiovisual materials, and an OPAC. Operations spending for 2004 fiscal year: $568,320. 50 computers available on campus for general student use. A campuswide network can be accessed from off-campus. Staffed computer lab on campus.

Community Environment: Population 27,000, Belmont is located 25 miles south of San Francisco, and has the advantages of a suburban location. The climate is ideal. The average high is 69.5 degrees, the low 47 degrees and the average rainfall is 19.8 inches. It is on the main line of Southern Pacific Railroad and San Francisco International Airport is 12 miles away. Students attending Notre Dame are close enough to San Francisco to enjoy all the cultural and recreational benefits such as major drama, music, and opera productions, films, rock group performances, and professional and collegiate sports. The beaches of the Pacific Ocean are 12 miles away. Two hours to the north is the wine country, and a few hours' drive east are the historic gold country, Lake Tahoe, and the Sierra Nevada Range with famous facilities for skiing and other winter sports.

■ **OCCIDENTAL COLLEGE** *S-10*

1600 Campus Rd.
Los Angeles, CA 90041-3314
Tel: (323)259-2500
Free: 800-825-5262
Admissions: (323)259-2700
Fax: (323)341-4875
E-mail: admission@oxy.edu
Web Site: http://www.oxy.edu/
Description: Independent, comprehensive, coed. Awards bachelor's and master's degrees. Founded 1887. Setting: 120-acre urban campus. Endowment: $279.8 million. Total enrollment: 1,839. Faculty: 215 (148 full-time, 67 part-time). Student-undergrad faculty ratio is 10:1. 5,114 applied, 41% were admitted. 60% from top 10% of their high school class, 86% from top quarter, 100% from top half. 27 class presidents, 23 valedictorians, 92 student government officers. Full-time: 1,794 students, 57% women, 43% men. Part-time: 25 students, 52% women, 48% men. Students come from 47 states and territories, 25 other countries, 50% from out-of-state, 1% Native American, 14% Hispanic, 6% black, 13% Asian American or Pacific Islander, 3% international, 1% 25 or older, 70% live on campus, 3% transferred in. Retention: 92% of full-time freshmen returned the following year. Academic areas with the most degrees conferred: social sciences; visual and performing arts; psychology. Core. Calendar: semesters. Services for LD students, advanced placement, self-designed majors, honors program, independent study, double major, summer session for credit, internships. Off campus study at California Institute of Technology, Art Center College of Design, Morehouse College, Spelman College. Study abroad program. ROTC: Army (c), Naval (c), Air Force (c).

Entrance Requirements: Options: Peterson's Universal Application, Common Application, early admission, early decision, deferred admission, international baccalaureate accepted. Required: essay, high school transcript, 2 recommendations, SAT or ACT. Recommended: interview, SAT Subject Tests. Entrance: very difficult. Application deadlines: 1/10, 11/15 for early decision. Notification: 4/1, 12/15 for early decision.

Costs Per Year: Application fee: $50. Comprehensive fee: $42,686 includes full-time tuition ($32,800), mandatory fees ($844), and college room and board ($9042). College room only: $4972. Part-time tuition: $1387 per credit.

Collegiate Environment: Orientation program. Drama-theater group, choral group, student-run newspaper, radio station. Social organizations: 104 open to all; national fraternities, national sororities, local sororities; 6% of eligible men and 13% of eligible women are members. Most popular organizations: Asian-Pacific Islander Alliance, community service, Inter-Faith Student Council, Black Student Alliance, MECHA/ALAS. Major annual events: spring concert, Da Getaway, homecoming. Student services: legal services, health clinic, personal-psychological counseling, women's center. Campus security: 24-hour emergency response devices and patrols, late night transport-escort service, controlled dormitory access, lighted pathways and sidewalks; whistle alert program. College housing designed to accommodate 1,300 students; 1,350 undergraduates lived in college housing during 2003-04. Freshmen guaranteed college housing. On-campus residence required in freshman year. Options: coed, women-only housing available. Mary Norton Clapp Library plus 2 others with 497,161 books, 413,190 microform titles,

903 serials, 17,408 audiovisual materials, an OPAC, and a Web page. 300 computers available on campus for general student use. A campuswide network can be accessed from student residence rooms and from off campus. Staffed computer lab on campus.

Community Environment: See University of California - Los Angeles

■ **OHLONE COLLEGE** *K-5*
43600 Mission Blvd.
Fremont, CA 94539-5884
Tel: (510)659-6000
Admissions: (510)659-6108
Web Site: http://www.ohlone.edu/

Description: State and locally supported, 2-year, coed. Part of California Community College System. Awards transfer associate and terminal associate degrees. Founded 1967. Setting: 530-acre suburban campus with easy access to San Francisco. Total enrollment: 11,500. Students come from 54 states and territories, 49% 25 or older. Calendar: semesters. Academic remediation for entering students, ESL program, services for LD students, self-designed majors, honors program, summer session for credit, part-time degree program, adult/continuing education programs, co-op programs. Off campus study at Contra Costa Community College District, Chabot College, members of the California State University System. Study abroad program. ROTC: Army (c), Air Force (c).

Entrance Requirements: Open admission except for nursing, respiratory therapy, physical therapy assistant, interpreter preparation programs. Option: early admission. Required: high school transcript. Placement: ACT ASSET required for some. Entrance: noncompetitive. Application deadline: Rolling. Notification: continuous.

Collegiate Environment: Orientation program. Drama-theater group, choral group, student-run newspaper. Campus security: 24-hour emergency response devices and patrols, late night transport-escort service. College housing not available. Ohlone College Library with 65,000 books and 410 serials. 250 computers available on campus for general student use. Staffed computer lab on campus.

Community Environment: The Fremont area is one of the faster growing areas of California. Mild climate is enjoyed in this city located on the San Francisco Bay. Fremont is within easy driving distance of San Francisco, Berkeley, Oakland and Palo Alto, and enjoys the cultural advantages of those cities. Beaches are nearby for swimming, boating and fishing. There are numerous golf courses and parks for recreational facilities. Shopping facilities are good.

■ **ORANGE COAST COLLEGE** *T-10*
2701 Fairview Rd., PO Box 5005
Costa Mesa, CA 92628-5005
Tel: (714)432-0202
Admissions: (714)432-5788
Fax: (714)432-5072
Web Site: http://www.orangecoastcollege.com/

Description: State and locally supported, 2-year, coed. Part of Coast Community College District System. Awards certificates, transfer associate, and terminal associate degrees. Founded 1947. Setting: 200-acre suburban campus with easy access to Los Angeles. Endowment: $5.1 million. Research spending for 2004 fiscal year: $104,225. Educational spending for 2005 fiscal year: $1752 per student. Total enrollment: 24,350. Student-undergrad faculty ratio is 20:1. Full-time: 10,671 students, 48% women, 52% men. Part-time: 13,679 students, 52% women, 48% men. Students come from 52 states and territories, 76 other countries; 2% from out-of-state, 1% Native American, 18% Hispanic, 2% black, 24% Asian American or Pacific Islander, 2% international, 34% 25 or older, 8% transferred in. Retention: 79% of full-time freshmen returned the following year. Core. Calendar: semesters plus summer session. Academic remediation for entering students, ESL program, services for LD students, advanced placement, self-designed majors, freshman honors college, honors program, distance learning, double major, summer session for credit, part-time degree program, external degree program, adult/continuing education programs, co-op programs and internships. Off campus study at Golden West College, Coastline Community College. Study abroad program. ROTC: Army (c), Air Force (c).

Entrance Requirements: Open admission. Option: Common Application. Entrance: noncompetitive. Application deadline: Rolling. Notification: continuous.

Costs Per Year: Application fee: $0. Nonresident tuition: $152 per unit part-time. Mandatory fees: $26 per unit part-time, $28 per term part-time.

Collegiate Environment: Orientation program. Drama-theater group, choral group, student-run newspaper. Social organizations: 55 open to all. Most popular organizations: Vietnamese Student Association, International Club, Adventurist Souls, Muslim Student Association. Major annual events: Club Rush, Senior Day, Coast Days. Student services: legal services, health clinic, personal-psychological counseling. Campus security: 24-hour emergency response devices and patrols, student patrols, late night transport-escort service. College housing not available. Norman E. Watson Library with 84,447 books, 8,276 microform titles, 420 serials, 2,510 audiovisual materials, an OPAC, and a Web page. Operations spending for 2004 fiscal year: $702,946. 1,515 computers available on campus for general student use. A campuswide network can be accessed from off-campus. Staffed computer lab on campus.

Community Environment: Costa Mesa, three miles inland from the Pacific Ocean and Highway 101-A, is at the edge of Newport Beach. The city has a moderate climate - mild winters, and cool summer breezes from the ocean. Orange County's economy is derived from defense manufacture, electronics, light industry, housing, business, agriculture, and tourism. The campus is located within 15 minutes of the Orange County Performing Arts Center; Irvine Industrial Center (home of many high-tech industries); South Coast Plaza (one of the nation's largest shopping malls); and the University of California at Irvine (a major educational and research institution). The Los Angeles Museum, Pasadena Art Gallery, and the Griffith Park Observatory and planetarium are 50 miles away. The mountains and the desert are an easy two-hour drive. Recreational activities locally are boating, fishing, and all forms of water sports to be found on its beaches, canals, and waterways. Part-time employment is available.

■ **OTIS COLLEGE OF ART AND DESIGN** *S-10*
9045 Lincoln Blvd.
Los Angeles, CA 90045-9785
Tel: (310)665-6800
Free: 800-527-OTIS
Admissions: (310)665-6820
Fax: (310)665-6805
E-mail: otisinfo@otisart.edu
Web Site: http://www.otis.edu/

Description: Independent, comprehensive, coed. Awards bachelor's and master's degrees. Founded 1918. Setting: 5-acre urban campus. Total enrollment: 1,098. Faculty: 277 (51 full-time, 226 part-time). Student-undergrad faculty ratio is 9:1. 829 applied, 62% were admitted. Full-time: 1,020 students, 65% women, 35% men. Part-time: 20 students, 50% women, 50% men. 30% from out-of-state, 1% Native American, 13% Hispanic, 3% black, 28% Asian American or Pacific Islander, 11% international, 18% 25 or older, 16% transferred in. Retention: 76% of full-time freshmen returned the following year. Academic areas with the most degrees conferred: visual and performing arts; architecture. Core. Calendar: semesters. Academic remediation for entering students, ESL program, advanced placement, freshman honors college, honors program, independent study, summer session for credit, adult/continuing education programs, co-op programs and internships. Off campus study at The Consortium of East Coast Art Schools. Study abroad program.

Entrance Requirements: Options: Peterson's Universal Application, early admission. Required: essay, high school transcript, minimum 2.5 high school GPA, portfolio, SAT or ACT. Recommended: 1 recommendation, interview. Entrance: moderately difficult. Application deadline: Rolling. Notification: continuous.

Costs Per Year: Application fee: $50. Tuition: $26,996 full-time, $900 per credit part-time. Mandatory fees: $550 full-time.

Collegiate Environment: Orientation program. Student-run newspaper. Social organizations: 5 open to all. Most popular organizations: Student Government Association, international students organization, Otis Students in Service (OASIS), Literary Magazine Club, Campus Crusade. Major annual events: Otis Scholarship Benefit Fashion Show, senior exhibitions, Orientation. Student services: personal-psychological counseling. Campus security: 24-hour patrols. Milliard Sheets Library with 42,000 books, 150 serials, 2,500 audiovisual materials, an OPAC, and a Web page. 220 computers available on campus for general student use. A campuswide network can be accessed. Staffed computer lab on campus.

■ **OXNARD COLLEGE** *S-8*
4000 South Rose Ave.
Oxnard, CA 93033-6699
Tel: (805)986-5800

Admissions: (805)986-5843
Fax: (805)986-5806
Web Site: http://www.oxnard.cc.ca.us/
Description: State-supported, 2-year, coed. Part of Ventura County Community College District System. Awards certificates, diplomas, and transfer associate degrees. Founded 1975. Setting: 119-acre urban campus. Total enrollment: 7,233. 1,367 applied, 100% were admitted. Students come from 10 states and territories, 30 other countries, 1% Native American, 61% Hispanic, 5% black, 10% Asian American or Pacific Islander, 44% 25 or older. Core. Calendar: semesters. Academic remediation for entering students, ESL program, services for LD students, advanced placement, accelerated degree program, honors program, independent study, distance learning, double major, summer session for credit, part-time degree program, adult/continuing education programs.
Entrance Requirements: Open admission. Options: Common Application, electronic application, early admission. Entrance: noncompetitive. Application deadline: Rolling. Notification: continuous.
Collegiate Environment: Orientation program. Drama-theater group, choral group, student-run newspaper. Student services: health clinic, personal-psychological counseling, women's center. Campus security: 24-hour patrols. College housing not available. Oxnard College Library with 31,500 books, 107 serials, an OPAC, and a Web page. 116 computers available on campus for general student use. Computer purchase/lease plans available. A campuswide network can be accessed. Staffed computer lab on campus.
Community Environment: The city of Oxnard has a population of approximately 128,000 people, and is located on the Gold Coast of California, situated about 45 miles south of Santa Barbara and 60 miles north of Los Angeles. The climate has been described as Mediterranean. Oxnard has seven miles of shoreline with wide, uncrowded beaches. It is a paradise for people who love to boat, surf and sport-fish. There are many museums and points of historical interest. Some of the major annual events include the California Strawberry Festival in May, Fiestas Patrias Celebration in September, and the Parade of Lights in December.

■ **PACIFIC OAKS COLLEGE** *S-10*
5 Westmoreland Place
Pasadena, CA 91103
Tel: (626)397-1300
Free: 800-684-0900
Admissions: (626)397-4945
Fax: (626)397-1317
Web Site: http://www.pacificoaks.edu/
Description: Independent, upper-level, coed. Awards bachelor's and master's degrees and post-master's certificates. Founded 1945. Setting: 2-acre small town campus with easy access to Los Angeles. Endowment: $7.3 million. Research spending for 2004 fiscal year: $236,517. Educational spending for 2005 fiscal year: $9523 per student. Total enrollment: 863. Full-time: 14 students, 93% women, 7% men. Part-time: 194 students, 95% women, 5% men. Students come from 34 states and territories, 19% from out-of-state, 2% Native American, 35% Hispanic, 13% black, 6% Asian American or Pacific Islander, 0.5% international, 91% 25 or older, 21% transferred in. Core. Calendar: semesters summer sessions and 2 intensive sessions. Independent study, distance learning, summer session for credit, part-time degree program, adult/continuing education programs, internships, graduate courses open to undergrads. Off campus study at Four College Consortium.
Costs Per Year: Application fee: $55. Tuition: $16,320 full-time, $680 per unit part-time. Mandatory fees: $60 full-time, $30 per term part-time.
Collegiate Environment: Orientation program. Social organizations: 4 open to all. Most popular organizations: Latina/o Support Group, Student Empowerment Group, Teacher Education Student Association, Marriage, Family Therapy Student Association. College housing not available. Andrew Norman Library with 32,580 books, 87 serials, 184 audiovisual materials, an OPAC, and a Web page. Operations spending for 2004 fiscal year: $188,124. 25 computers available on campus for general student use. A campuswide network can be accessed from off-campus. Staffed computer lab on campus.
Community Environment: See California Institute of Technology.

■ **PACIFIC STATES UNIVERSITY** *S-10*
1516 South Western Ave.
Los Angeles, CA 90006
Tel: (323)731-2383; 888-200-0383
Fax: (323)731-7276

Web Site: http://www.psuca.edu/
Description: Independent, comprehensive, coed. Awards bachelor's and master's degrees. Founded 1928. Setting: 1-acre urban campus. Total enrollment: 68. Faculty: 16 (4 full-time, 12 part-time). Student-undergrad faculty ratio is 20:1. 50 applied, 100% were admitted. Full-time: 44 students, 18% women, 82% men. 10% from out-of-state, 0% Native American, 0% Hispanic, 0% black, 100% Asian American or Pacific Islander, 0% international, 100% 25 or older. Retention: 75% of full-time freshmen returned the following year. ESL program, accelerated degree program, self-designed majors, independent study, summer session for credit, adult/continuing education programs, graduate courses open to undergrads. Study abroad program.
Entrance Requirements: Open admission. Options: Common Application, electronic application, early admission, deferred admission, international baccalaureate accepted. Required: essay, high school transcript, minimum 2.5 high school GPA. Entrance: minimally difficult. Application deadline: 9/21. Notification: continuous.
Costs Per Year: Application fee: $100. Tuition: $8400 full-time, $195 per unit part-time. Mandatory fees: $480 full-time. Full-time tuition and fees vary according to course load. Part-time tuition varies according to course load.
Collegiate Environment: Campus security: patrols by trained security personnel during campus hours. College housing not available. University Library plus 1 other with 15,000 books, 108 serials, and an OPAC. Operations spending for 2004 fiscal year: $15,000. 25 computers available on campus for general student use. Staffed computer lab on campus.

■ **PACIFIC UNION COLLEGE** *I-4*
One Angwin Ave.
Angwin, CA 94508-9707
Tel: (707)965-6311
Free: 800-862-7080
Admissions: (707)965-6425
Fax: (707)965-6390
E-mail: enroll@puc.edu
Web Site: http://www.puc.edu/
Description: Independent Seventh-day Adventist, comprehensive, coed. Awards associate, bachelor's, and master's degrees. Founded 1882. Setting: 200-acre rural campus with easy access to San Francisco. Endowment: $15.4 million. Educational spending for 2005 fiscal year: $6833 per student. Total enrollment: 1,518. Faculty: 99 (80 full-time, 19 part-time). Student-undergrad faculty ratio is 15:1. 2,174 applied, 29% were admitted. Full-time: 1,370 students, 53% women, 47% men. Part-time: 146 students, 62% women, 38% men. Students come from 44 states and territories, 18 other countries, 19% from out-of-state, 1% Native American, 12% Hispanic, 3% black, 23% Asian American or Pacific Islander, 6% international, 12% 25 or older, 70% live on campus, 10% transferred in. Retention: 73% of full-time freshmen returned the following year. Academic areas with the most degrees conferred: health professions and related sciences; education; mathematics. Core. Academic remediation for entering students, ESL program, services for LD students, advanced placement, self-designed majors, honors program, independent study, distance learning, double major, summer session for credit, part-time degree program, adult/continuing education programs, co-op programs and internships, graduate courses open to undergrads. Study abroad program.
Entrance Requirements: Options: Peterson's Universal Application, electronic application, deferred admission, international baccalaureate accepted. Required: high school transcript, minimum 2.3 high school GPA, 3 recommendations, SAT and SAT Subject Tests or ACT. Recommended: ACT, SAT or ACT. Entrance: moderately difficult. Application deadline: Rolling.
Costs Per Year: Application fee: $30. Comprehensive fee: $24,555 includes full-time tuition ($18,990), mandatory fees ($135), and college room and board ($5430). College room only: $3312. Full-time tuition and fees vary according to course load. Part-time tuition: $550 per quarter hour. Part-time mandatory fees: $45 per term. Part-time tuition and fees vary according to course load. Tuition guaranteed not to increase for student's term of enrollment.
Collegiate Environment: Orientation program. Drama-theater group, choral group, student-run newspaper, radio station. Social organizations: 22 open to all. Most popular organizations: Student Association, Business Club, Asian Student Association, Korean Adventist Student Association, Black Student Forum. Major annual events: Fall Festival, All College Get Acquainted Party, talent show. Student services: health clinic, personal-psychological counseling. Campus security: 24-hour emergency response devices and patrols, late night transport-escort service. 1,130 college housing spaces available;

1,088 were occupied in 2003-04. No special consideration for freshman housing applicants. On-campus residence required through senior year. Options: men-only, women-only housing available. W. E. Nelson Memorial Library with 173,839 books, 124,432 microform titles, 812 serials, 56,323 audiovisual materials, an OPAC, and a Web page. Operations spending for 2004 fiscal year: $827,224. 150 computers available on campus for general student use. A campuswide network can be accessed from student residence rooms and from off campus. Staffed computer lab on campus.

Community Environment: This is a rural un-incorporated area on Howell Mountain, an extinct volcano, 80 miles from San Francisco. The climate is not extreme, although it is not unusual to have as much as 60 inches of rain in the winter. Bus service is available in St. Helena; railroads and airlines serve the San Francisco Bay area. Freeways are nearby. A hospital is located five miles from Angwin. Employment is available for students.

■ **PALO VERDE COLLEGE** *T-17*
One College Dr.
Blythe, CA 92225-9561
Tel: (760)921-5500
Admissions: (760)921-5409
Fax: (760)921-5590
Web Site: http://www.paloverde.edu/

Description: State and locally supported, 2-year, coed. Part of California Community College System. Awards transfer associate and terminal associate degrees. Founded 1947. Setting: 10-acre small town campus. Total enrollment: 3,648. 300 applied, 100% were admitted. Students come from 4 states and territories, 3 other countries, 2% Native American, 30% Hispanic, 9% black, 4% Asian American or Pacific Islander, 88% 25 or older. Core. Calendar: semesters. Academic remediation for entering students, ESL program, services for LD students, advanced placement, summer session for credit, part-time degree program, adult/continuing education programs, internships.

Entrance Requirements: Open admission. Option: early admission. Recommended: high school transcript. Entrance: noncompetitive. Application deadline: Rolling. Notification: continuous.

Costs Per Year: Application fee: $0. Nonresident tuition: $4248 full-time, $177 per unit part-time. Mandatory fees: $624 full-time, $26 per unit part-time.

Collegiate Environment: Drama-theater group, student-run newspaper. Most popular organizations: Extended Opportunity Program and Services Club, Associated Student Body. Major annual events: 5th of May Celebration, Thanksgiving Lunch, Graduation. Student services: personal-psychological counseling. Campus security: student patrols, security personnel during open hours. College housing not available. Palo Verde College Library with 21,457 books and 165 serials. 25 computers available on campus for general student use. Staffed computer lab on campus.

Community Environment: Blythe, in the Palo Verde Valley, is on Interstate 10, 225 miles east of Los Angeles and 165 miles west of Phoenix. The climate is dry and temperate. It is an agricultural region with year-round farming. Greyhound Bus serves the area. There is a public library, 30 churches, a hospital, 2 clinics and the usual civic organizations. Recreation includes hunting, boating, and fishing on the Colorado River. There are good part-time employment opportunities.

■ **PALOMAR COLLEGE** *V-3*
1140 West Mission Rd.
San Marcos, CA 92069-1487
Tel: (760)744-1150
Fax: (760)744-2932
E-mail: hlee@palomar.edu
Web Site: http://www.palomar.edu/

Description: State and locally supported, 2-year, coed. Part of California Community College System. Awards certificates and transfer associate degrees. Founded 1946. Setting: 156-acre suburban campus with easy access to San Diego. Total enrollment: 28,597. 5,569 applied, 100% were admitted. 1% Native American, 24% Hispanic, 3% black, 8% Asian American or Pacific Islander, 3% 25 or older. Core. Calendar: semesters. Academic remediation for entering students, ESL program, services for LD students, advanced placement, distance learning, summer session for credit, part-time degree program, co-op programs and internships. Study abroad program.

Entrance Requirements: Open admission. Option: electronic application. Placement: ACT ASSET required for some. Entrance: noncompetitive. Application deadline: Rolling. Notification: continuous.

Collegiate Environment: Orientation program. Drama-theater group, choral group, student-run newspaper, radio station. Most popular organization: Bible clubs. Student services: health clinic, personal-psychological counseling. Campus security: 24-hour patrols, student patrols, late night transport-escort service. College housing not available. Palomar Library with 108,000 books, an OPAC, and a Web page. 922 computers available on campus for general student use. A campuswide network can be accessed. Staffed computer lab on campus.

■ **PASADENA CITY COLLEGE** *S-10*
1570 East Colorado Blvd.
Pasadena, CA 91106-2041
Tel: (626)585-7123
Admissions: (626)585-7805
Fax: (626)585-7915
E-mail: mbramey@pasadena.edu
Web Site: http://www.pasadena.edu/

Description: State and locally supported, 2-year, coed. Part of California Community College System. Awards certificates, transfer associate, and terminal associate degrees. Founded 1924. Setting: 55-acre urban campus with easy access to Los Angeles. Educational spending for 2005 fiscal year: $2040 per student. Total enrollment: 29,189. Student-undergrad faculty ratio is 20:1. Students come from 15 states and territories, 1% Native American, 34% Hispanic, 6% black, 30% Asian American or Pacific Islander, 0% international, 42% 25 or older. Core. Calendar: semesters. Academic remediation for entering students, ESL program, services for LD students, advanced placement, self-designed majors, honors program, summer session for credit, part-time degree program, adult/continuing education programs. Study abroad program.

Entrance Requirements: Open admission except for some nonresident aliens. Options: early admission, deferred admission. Entrance: noncompetitive. Application deadline: Rolling. Notification: continuous.

Costs Per Year: State resident tuition: $0 full-time. Nonresident tuition: $5000 full-time, $160 per unit part-time. Mandatory fees: $780 full-time, $26 per unit part-time.

Collegiate Environment: Orientation program. Drama-theater group, choral group, marching band, student-run newspaper, radio station. Student services: health clinic, personal-psychological counseling, women's center. Campus security: 24-hour emergency response devices and patrols, late night transport-escort service, cadet patrols. College housing not available. Pasadena City College Library plus 1 other with 120,000 books, 350 serials, and an OPAC. Operations spending for 2004 fiscal year: $1.5 million. 300 computers available on campus for general student use. Staffed computer lab on campus.

Community Environment: See California Institute of Technology.

■ **PATTEN UNIVERSITY** *K-4*
2433 Coolidge Ave.
Oakland, CA 94601-2699
Tel: (510)261-8500
Fax: (510)534-8564
Web Site: http://www.patten.edu/

Description: Independent interdenominational, comprehensive, coed. Awards associate, bachelor's, and master's degrees. Founded 1944. Setting: 5-acre urban campus with easy access to San Francisco. Endowment: $274,588. Educational spending for 2005 fiscal year: $3304 per student. Total enrollment: 559. 67 applied, 58% were admitted. 13% from top 10% of their high school class, 35% from top quarter, 52% from top half. 7 National Merit Scholars, 5 class presidents, 1 valedictorian, 6 student government officers. Full-time: 207 students, 65% women, 35% men. Part-time: 239 students, 18% women, 82% men. Students come from 12 states and territories, 5% from out-of-state, 59% 25 or older, 15% live on campus. Retention: 65% of full-time freshmen returned the following year. Core. Calendar: semesters. Services for LD students, advanced placement, accelerated degree program, honors program, distance learning, double major, summer session for credit, part-time degree program, adult/continuing education programs, internships.

Entrance Requirements: Open admission. Options: early admission, deferred admission. Required: essay, high school transcript, minimum 2.5 high school GPA, 2 recommendations, SAT or ACT. Recommended: interview. Entrance: noncompetitive. Application deadline: 7/31. Notification: continuous.

Collegiate Environment: Orientation program. Drama-theater group, choral group, student-run newspaper. Social organizations: 5 open to all. Most

popular organizations: Student Council, Patten College Chorus, Patten Symphonette. Major annual events: Patten Christmas Party, Campus Day, Graduation Banquet. Student services: personal-psychological counseling. Campus security: 24-hour emergency response devices, student patrols, late night transport-escort service. Option: coed housing available. Patten Library with 35,000 books, 250 serials, and an OPAC. Operations spending for 2004 fiscal year: $124,610. 25 computers available on campus for general student use. Staffed computer lab on campus.

Community Environment: The Oakland Bay Area is beautiful and there is easy access to San Francisco, Berkeley, and the Regional Park System. There is a variety of cultural, sporting, religious, and recreational activities available.

■ **PEPPERDINE UNIVERSITY** *Q-2*
24255 Pacific Coast Hwy.
Malibu, CA 90263
Tel: (310)506-4000
Admissions: (310)506-4392
Fax: (310)506-4861
E-mail: admission-seaver@pepperdine.edu
Web Site: http://www.pepperdine.edu/
Description: Independent, university, coed, affiliated with Church of Christ. Awards bachelor's, master's, doctoral, and first professional degrees and post-master's certificates. Founded 1937. Setting: 830-acre small town campus with easy access to Los Angeles. Endowment: $475.8 million. Total enrollment: 7,685. Faculty: 726 (400 full-time, 326 part-time). Student-undergrad faculty ratio is 12:1. 7,307 applied, 28% were admitted. 43% from top 10% of their high school class, 76% from top quarter, 96% from top half. Full-time: 2,740 students, 59% women, 41% men. Part-time: 458 students, 50% women, 50% men. Students come from 50 states and territories, 61 other countries, 50% from out-of-state, 2% Native American, 11% Hispanic, 8% black, 11% Asian American or Pacific Islander, 6% international, 2% 25 or older, 62% live on campus, 2% transferred in. Retention: 91% of full-time freshmen returned the following year. Academic areas with the most degrees conferred: business/marketing; communications/journalism; social sciences. Core. Calendar: semesters. Advanced placement, self-designed majors, honors program, independent study, double major, summer session for credit, part-time degree program, internships, graduate courses open to undergrads. Study abroad program. ROTC: Army (c), Air Force (c).
Entrance Requirements: Options: electronic application, international baccalaureate accepted. Required: essay, high school transcript, 2 recommendations, SAT or ACT. Recommended: interview. Entrance: very difficult. Application deadline: 1/15. Notification: 4/1.
Costs Per Year: Application fee: $65. Comprehensive fee: $42,240 includes full-time tuition ($32,620), mandatory fees ($120), and college room and board ($9500). Part-time tuition: $1010 per unit.
Collegiate Environment: Orientation program. Drama-theater group, choral group, student-run newspaper, radio station. Social organizations: 50 open to all; national fraternities, national sororities; 25% of eligible men and 25% of eligible women are members. Most popular organizations: Student Government Association, Black Student Union, International Club, Alpha Chi Honor Society, Golden Key Honor Society. Major annual events: Homecoming, Songfest, Family Weekend. Student services: health clinic, personal-psychological counseling. Campus security: 24-hour emergency response devices and patrols, student patrols, late night transport-escort service, front gate security, 24-hour security in residence halls, controlled access, crime prevention programs. Freshmen guaranteed college housing. On-campus residence required through sophomore year. Options: men-only, women-only housing available. Payson Library plus 2 others with 315,078 books, 258,343 microform titles, 3,182 serials, 5,044 audiovisual materials, an OPAC, and a Web page. 292 computers available on campus for general student use. Computer purchase/lease plans available. A campuswide network can be accessed from student residence rooms. Staffed computer lab on campus.
Community Environment: See University of California - Los Angeles.

■ **PIMA MEDICAL INSTITUTE** *W-12*
780 Bay Blvd., Ste. 101
Chula Vista, CA 91910
Tel: (619)425-3200; 888-898-9048
Fax: (619)425-3450
Web Site: http://www.pmi.edu
Description: Proprietary, 2-year, coed. Administratively affiliated with Vocational Training Institutes, Inc. Awards certificates and terminal associate

degrees. Setting: urban campus. Total enrollment: 447. 53 applied, 85% were admitted. Full-time: 447 students, 79% women, 21% men. 0% from out-of-state, 0% transferred in. Core. Calendar: modular. Co-op programs and internships.
Entrance Requirements: Option: Common Application. Required: high school transcript, interview, Wonderlic Scholastic Level Exam. Entrance: minimally difficult.
Costs Per Year: Application fee: $100. Tuition guaranteed not to increase for student's term of enrollment.
Collegiate Environment: Orientation program. College housing not available.

■ **PITZER COLLEGE** *V-10*
1050 North Mills Ave.
Claremont, CA 91711-6101
Tel: (909)621-8000
Free: 800-748-9371
Admissions: (909)621-8129
Fax: (909)621-8770
E-mail: admission@email.pitzer.edu
Web Site: http://www.pitzer.edu/
Description: Independent, 4-year, coed. Part of The Claremont Colleges Consortium. Awards bachelor's degrees. Founded 1963. Setting: 35-acre suburban campus with easy access to Los Angeles. Endowment: $52.7 million. Research spending for 2004 fiscal year: $319,673. Educational spending for 2005 fiscal year: $19,158 per student. Total enrollment: 963. Student-undergrad faculty ratio is 11:1. 3,251 applied, 39% were admitted. 45% from top 10% of their high school class, 75% from top quarter, 92% from top half. Full-time: 911 students, 59% women, 41% men. Part-time: 52 students, 67% women, 33% men. Students come from 43 states and territories, 10 other countries, 43% from out-of-state, 1% Native American, 15% Hispanic, 5% black, 10% Asian American or Pacific Islander, 2% international, 7% 25 or older, 73% live on campus. Retention: 88% of full-time freshmen returned the following year. Academic areas with the most degrees conferred: social sciences; psychology; visual and performing arts. Core. Calendar: semesters. ESL program, services for LD students, advanced placement, self-designed majors, honors program, independent study, double major, summer session for credit, part-time degree program, adult/continuing education programs, co-op programs and internships. Off campus study at The Claremont Colleges, Colby College, Haverford College, Spelman College, Morehouse College. Study abroad program. ROTC: Army (c), Air Force (c).
Entrance Requirements: Options: Peterson's Universal Application, Common Application, electronic application, early admission, early action, deferred admission, international baccalaureate accepted. Required: essay, high school transcript, 3 recommendations. Recommended: interview. Required for some: SAT or ACT. Entrance: moderately difficult. Application deadlines: 1/1, 11/15 for early action. Notification: 4/1, 1/1 for early action.
Costs Per Year: Application fee: $50. Comprehensive fee: $41,644 includes full-time tuition ($29,520), mandatory fees ($3492), and college room and board ($8632). College room only: $5402. Full-time tuition and fees vary according to course load. Room and board charges vary according to board plan. Part-time tuition: $3690 per course. Part-time tuition varies according to course load.
Collegiate Environment: Orientation program. Drama-theater group, choral group, student-run radio station. Social organizations: 75 open to all. Most popular organizations: Student Senate, The Other Side, Without A Box, Residence Hall Association. Major annual events: Kohoutek Festival, Senior Celebration, Groove at the Grove. Student services: health clinic, personal-psychological counseling, women's center. Campus security: 24-hour emergency response devices and patrols, late night transport-escort service, controlled dormitory access. 634 college housing spaces available; all were occupied in 2003-04. Freshmen guaranteed college housing. On-campus residence required through junior year. Options: coed, women-only housing available. Honnold Library plus 3 others with 2 million books, 1.1 million microform titles, 6,000 serials, an OPAC, and a Web page. Operations spending for 2004 fiscal year: $1.1 million. 100 computers available on campus for general student use. A campuswide network can be accessed from student residence rooms and from off campus. Staffed computer lab on campus.

■ **PLATT COLLEGE (CERRITOS)** *Z-5*
10900 East 183rd St., Ste. 290
Cerritos, CA 90703-5342

Tel: (562)809-5100
Free: 800-807-5288
Fax: (562)809-7100
Web Site: http://www.platt.edu/
Description: Proprietary, 2-year, coed. Awards certificates, diplomas, transfer associate, and terminal associate degrees. Founded 1879. Setting: urban campus with easy access to Los Angeles. Total enrollment: 320. Calendar: continuous.
Entrance Requirements: Required: Wonderlic aptitude test. Entrance: minimally difficult.
Collegiate Environment: College housing not available.

■ **PLATT COLLEGE-LOS ANGELES, INC** *Q-5*
1000 South Fremont A9W
Alhambra, CA 91803
Tel: (323)258-8050
Fax: (323)258-8532
Web Site: http://www.plattcollege.edu/
Description: Proprietary, 2-year, coed. Awards certificates, diplomas, transfer associate, and terminal associate degrees. Founded 1987. Setting: suburban campus. Educational spending for 2005 fiscal year: $4044 per student. Total enrollment: 179. 122 applied, 73% were admitted. Students come from 18 states and territories, 2% from out-of-state, 0% Native American, 46% Hispanic, 9% black, 11% Asian American or Pacific Islander, 1% international, 53% 25 or older. Core. Calendar: continuous. Academic remediation for entering students, accelerated degree program, summer session for credit, internships.
Entrance Requirements: Option: Common Application. Required: interview, CPAt. Required for some: essay. Entrance: minimally difficult. Application deadline: Rolling. Notification: continuous.
Collegiate Environment: Orientation program. Social organizations: 3 open to all. Most popular organizations: Latin American Designers, Graphic Designers Mobilized for the Environment, Multimedia Club. Major annual events: Career Day, Symposium, graduation. Campus security: parking lot security. College housing not available. Platt College Library with 808 books, 20 serials, and 70 audiovisual materials. Operations spending for 2004 fiscal year: $27,000. 80 computers available on campus for general student use. A campuswide network can be accessed. Staffed computer lab on campus.

■ **PLATT COLLEGE (NEWPORT BEACH)** *T-10*
3901 MacArthur Blvd.
Newport Beach, CA 92660
Tel: (949)833-2300; 888-866-6697
Web Site: http://www.plattcollege.edu/
Description: Independent, primarily 2-year, coed. Awards certificates, diplomas, transfer associate, and bachelor's degrees. Founded 1985. Setting: urban campus. Educational spending for 2005 fiscal year: $4419 per student. Total enrollment: 270. 50 applied, 80% were admitted. Full-time: 270 students, 33% women, 67% men. Students come from 12 states and territories, 5 other countries. Core. Calendar: continuous. Accelerated degree program, summer session for credit, adult/continuing education programs.
Entrance Requirements: Required: essay, high school transcript, interview, CPAt. Entrance: moderately difficult. Application deadline: Rolling. Notification: continuous.
Collegiate Environment: Major annual events: Career Day, Career Symposium, student art exhibit. Campus security: 24-hour emergency response devices. College housing not available. Platt Library with 1,100 books, 15 serials, and 100 audiovisual materials. Operations spending for 2004 fiscal year: $35,525. 10 computers available on campus for general student use. Staffed computer lab on campus.

■ **PLATT COLLEGE (ONTARIO)** *Q-8*
3700 Inland Empire Blvd., Ste. 400
Ontario, CA 91764
Tel: (909)941-9410; 888-866-6697
Fax: (909)989-8974
Web Site: http://www.plattcollege.edu/
Description: Independent, 2-year, coed. Awards certificates, diplomas, transfer associate, and terminal associate degrees. Total enrollment: 385. Full-time: 385 students, 46% women, 54% men. 1% Native American, 34% Hispanic, 15% black, 5% Asian American or Pacific Islander, 1% international, 49% 25 or older. Calendar: continuous. Academic remediation for

entering students, accelerated degree program, honors program, independent study, summer session for credit, internships.
Entrance Requirements: Required: essay, interview, CPAt. Entrance: minimally difficult. Application deadline: Rolling. Notification: continuous.
Collegiate Environment: Orientation program. College housing not available. Main Library-Platt College with 2,800 books, 12 serials, and 35 audiovisual materials. 125 computers available on campus for general student use. A campuswide network can be accessed. Staffed computer lab on campus.

■ **PLATT COLLEGE SAN DIEGO** *W-12*
6250 El Cajon Blvd.
San Diego, CA 92115-3919
Tel: (619)265-0107; (866)752-8826
Fax: (619)265-8655
E-mail: mleiker@platt.edu
Web Site: http://www.platt.edu/
Description: Proprietary, primarily 2-year, coed. Awards certificates, diplomas, transfer associate, terminal associate, and bachelor's degrees. Founded 1879. Setting: suburban campus with easy access to San Diego. Educational spending for 2005 fiscal year: $4220 per student. Total enrollment: 253. Student-undergrad faculty ratio is 20:1. Full-time: 253 students, 24% women, 76% men. Students come from 4 states and territories, 2 other countries, 5% from out-of-state, 0% Native American, 20% Hispanic, 6% black, 8% Asian American or Pacific Islander, 0% international, 70% 25 or older. Retention: 72% of full-time freshmen returned the following year. Academic area with the most degrees conferred: visual and performing arts. Calendar: continuous.
Entrance Requirements: Required: high school transcript, interview, Wonderlic aptitude test.
Costs Per Year: Application fee: $110. Tuition: $17,226 full-time. Mandatory fees: $110 full-time.
Collegiate Environment: Student services: personal-psychological counseling. Campus security: 24-hour emergency response devices, video camera. College housing not available.

■ **POINT LOMA NAZARENE UNIVERSITY** *W-12*
3900 Lomaland Dr.
San Diego, CA 92106-2899
Tel: (619)849-2200
Free: 800-733-7770
Admissions: (619)849-2273
Fax: (619)849-2579
Web Site: http://www.ptloma.edu/
Description: Independent Nazarene, comprehensive, coed. Awards bachelor's and master's degrees. Founded 1902. Setting: 88-acre suburban campus. Research spending for 2004 fiscal year: $472,971. Educational spending for 2005 fiscal year: $6883 per student. Total enrollment: 3,445. Faculty: 338 (139 full-time, 199 part-time). Student-undergrad faculty ratio is 11:1. 1,857 applied, 65% were admitted. 39% from top 10% of their high school class, 75% from top quarter, 95% from top half. 21 valedictorians. Full-time: 2,282 students, 60% women, 40% men. Part-time: 78 students, 58% women, 42% men. Students come from 40 states and territories, 15 other countries, 21% from out-of-state, 1% Native American, 10% Hispanic, 2% black, 5% Asian American or Pacific Islander, 1% international, 3% 25 or older, 68% live on campus, 6% transferred in. Retention: 85% of full-time freshmen returned the following year. Academic areas with the most degrees conferred: business/marketing; liberal arts/general studies; psychology. Core. Calendar: semesters. Academic remediation for entering students, services for LD students, advanced placement, honors program, independent study, double major, summer session for credit, part-time degree program, internships, graduate courses open to undergrads. Off campus study at American University, Coalition for Christian Colleges and Universities. Study abroad program. ROTC: Army (c), Naval (c), Air Force (c).
Entrance Requirements: Options: electronic application, early action, deferred admission. Required: essay, high school transcript, minimum 2.8 high school GPA, 2 recommendations, SAT or ACT. Recommended: SAT. Required for some: interview. Entrance: moderately difficult. Application deadlines: 3/1, 12/1 for early action. Notification: continuous, 1/15 for early action.
Costs Per Year: Application fee: $50. Comprehensive fee: $29,310 includes full-time tuition ($21,620), mandatory fees ($530), and college room and board ($7160).

Collegiate Environment: Orientation program. Drama-theater group, choral group, student-run newspaper, radio station. Social organizations: 30 open to all; national sororities, local fraternities, local sororities. Most popular organizations: Chi Delta Psi, Psi Omega Theta, SNAPL (nurses association), Chi Beta Sigma. Major annual events: homecoming, Christmas Messiah Concert. Student services: health clinic, personal-psychological counseling, women's center. Campus security: 24-hour patrols, student patrols, late night transport-escort service. 1,637 college housing spaces available; 1,613 were occupied in 2003-04. Freshmen guaranteed college housing. On-campus residence required through junior year. Options: men-only, women-only housing available. Ryan Library with 152,377 books, 125,582 microform titles, 25,505 serials, 15,198 audiovisual materials, an OPAC, and a Web page. Operations spending for 2004 fiscal year: $937,147. 196 computers available on campus for general student use. A campuswide network can be accessed from student residence rooms and from off campus. Staffed computer lab on campus.

Community Environment: San Diego is an area of matchless climate and spectacular scenery. Resident institutions provide ample resources in research, culture, entertainment, and recreation. They involve the University of California, San Diego; San Diego State University; University of San Diego; San Diego Symphony; San Diego Opera; Scripps Institute of Oceanography; Palomar Observatory; and Balboa Park with its world famous Zoo, Natural History Museum, Fine Arts Gallery, Old Globe Theatre, Museum of Man, Photographic Arts Museum, Aerospace Museum, Starlight Opera, and Reuben H. Fleet Space Theatre and Museum. Los Angeles is two and one-half hours driving time to the north and Mexico thirty minutes to the south. The Laguna Mountains are to the east.

■ **POMONA COLLEGE** *V-10*
333 North College Way
Claremont, CA 91711
Tel: (909)621-8000
Admissions: (909)621-8134
Fax: (909)621-8403
E-mail: admissions@pomona.edu
Web Site: http://www.pomona.edu/
Description: Independent, 4-year, coed. Part of The Claremont Colleges Consortium. Awards bachelor's degrees. Founded 1887. Setting: 140-acre suburban campus with easy access to Los Angeles. Endowment: $1.3 billion. Total enrollment: 1,532. Student-undergrad faculty ratio is 8:1. 5,054 applied, 19% were admitted. 88% from top 10% of their high school class, 98% from top quarter, 100% from top half. 72 National Merit Scholars, 12 class presidents, 32 valedictorians, 59 student government officers. Full-time: 1,532 students, 50% women, 50% men. Students come from 48 states and territories, 31 other countries, 63% from out-of-state, 0.5% Native American, 11% Hispanic, 6% black, 14% Asian American or Pacific Islander, 2% international, 1% 25 or older, 97% live on campus, 1% transferred in. Core. Calendar: semesters. Advanced placement, self-designed majors, independent study, double major, internships. Off campus study at other members of The Claremont Colleges, Swarthmore College, Colby College, Smith College, Spelman College. Study abroad program.
Entrance Requirements: Options: Peterson's Universal Application, Common Application, electronic application, early admission, early decision, deferred admission, international baccalaureate accepted. Required: essay, high school transcript, 2 recommendations, SAT Subject Tests. Recommended: minimum 3.0 high school GPA, interview, portfolio or tapes for art and performing arts programs. Entrance: most difficult. Application deadlines: 1/2, 11/1 for early decision plan 1, 12/28 for early decision plan 2. Notification: 4/10, 12/15 for early decision plan 1, 2/15 for early decision plan 2.
Costs Per Year: Application fee: $60. Comprehensive fee: $40,774 includes full-time tuition ($29,650), mandatory fees ($273), and college room and board ($10,851). Room and board charges vary according to board plan.
Collegiate Environment: Orientation program. Drama-theater group, choral group, student-run newspaper, radio station. Social organizations: 280 open to all; local fraternities; 3% of men are members. Most popular organizations: student government, music/choral organizations, service organizations, intramural sports. Major annual events: Harwood Halloween Costume Party, Ski/Beach Day, Semester-End 'Death by Chocolate' Party. Student services: health clinic, personal-psychological counseling, women's center. Campus security: 24-hour emergency response devices and patrols, late night transport-escort service, controlled dormitory access. 1,387 college housing spaces available. Freshmen guaranteed college housing. On-campus residence required in freshman year. Option: coed housing avail-

able. Honnold Library plus 3 others with an OPAC and a Web page. 180 computers available on campus for general student use. Computer purchase/lease plans available. A campuswide network can be accessed from student residence rooms and from off campus. Staffed computer lab on campus.

■ **PORTERVILLE COLLEGE** *O-8*
100 East College Ave.
Porterville, CA 93257-6058
Tel: (559)791-2200
Admissions: (559)791-2222
Fax: (559)791-2349
Web Site: http://www.pc.cc.ca.us/
Description: State-supported, 2-year, coed. Part of Kern Community College District System. Awards certificates, transfer associate, and terminal associate degrees. Founded 1927. Setting: 60-acre rural campus. Endowment: $1.3 million. Total enrollment: 5,024. 3,586 applied, 100% were admitted. Students come from 4 other countries, 48% 25 or older. Core. Calendar: semesters. Academic remediation for entering students, services for LD students, advanced placement, distance learning, summer session for credit, part-time degree program, adult/continuing education programs.
Entrance Requirements: Open admission. Options: electronic application, early admission. Required: high school transcript. Entrance: noncompetitive. Application deadline: Rolling.
Collegiate Environment: Orientation program. Drama-theater group, choral group. Student services: health clinic, personal-psychological counseling. Campus security: 24-hour emergency response devices, student patrols. College housing not available. Porterville College Library/Media Center with 31,557 books, 297 serials, and an OPAC. Operations spending for 2004 fiscal year: $404,219. 350 computers available on campus for general student use. A campuswide network can be accessed. Staffed computer lab on campus.
Community Environment: Population 30,000, Porterville is located in southeastern Tulare County and is in a vast olive, grape, peach, walnut, cotton, and citrus growing area. The annual rainfall is 11.47 inches with an annual mean temperature of 62.8 degrees. Bus transportation is available to the airports and rail stations. The community has many churches, a library, auditorium, a community concert and theatre series each year, and an excellent shopping center with several new shopping centers in outlying areas. Recreational activities include fishing, camping, hunting in season, golf, boating, tennis, and skiing. Porterville is a 1 1/2 hour drive from Sequoia National Park; 2 1/2 hours from Kings Canyon National Park; and 3 hours from Yosemite National Park. Employment opportunities are good.

■ **PROFESSIONAL GOLFERS CAREER COLLEGE** *U-12*
PO Box 892319
Temecula, CA 92589
Tel: (909)693-2963
Free: 800-877-4380
Admissions: (951)693-2963
Fax: (909)693-2863
Web Site: http://www.golfcollege.edu/
Description: Independent, 2-year, coed. Awards terminal associate degrees. Total enrollment: 318. 40 applied, 100% were admitted. Students come from 50 states and territories, 13 other countries, 75% from out-of-state, 2% Native American, 4% Hispanic, 1% black, 26% Asian American or Pacific Islander, 50% 25 or older. Core. Calendar: semesters. ESL program.
Entrance Requirements: Options: early admission, deferred admission. Required: high school transcript, 4 recommendations.
Costs Per Year: Application fee: $75. Tuition: $14,370 full-time. Mandatory fees: $475 full-time. Full-time tuition and fees vary according to student level. College room only: $2525. Room charges vary according to location.
Collegiate Environment: Orientation program. 78 college housing spaces available; all were occupied in 2003-04. Option: coed housing available. Professional Golfers Career College with 2,291 books, 45 serials, 115 audiovisual materials, and a Web page. Operations spending for 2004 fiscal year: $24,325. 20 computers available on campus for general student use. Staffed computer lab on campus.

■ **QUEEN OF THE HOLY ROSARY COLLEGE** *K-5*
PO Box 3908
Mission San Jose, CA 94539-0391
Tel: (510)657-2468
Fax: (510)657-1734

Web Site: http://www.msjdominicans.org/college.html

Description: Independent Roman Catholic, 2-year, coed. Awards transfer associate degrees. Founded 1930. Setting: 37-acre suburban campus with easy access to San Jose. Educational spending for 2005 fiscal year: $3600 per student. Total enrollment: 195. 2 applied, 100% were admitted. 100% 25 or older. Core. Calendar: semesters. Academic remediation for entering students, ESL program, summer session for credit, part-time degree program, adult/continuing education programs.

Entrance Requirements: Open admission. Required: essay, high school transcript, minimum 2.0 high school GPA. Recommended: minimum 3.0 high school GPA, interview, SAT. Entrance: noncompetitive. Application deadline: 7/1.

Collegiate Environment: Choral group. Major annual events: Christmas Boutique, Dominican Sisters Assemblies, Retreat. Student services: health clinic, personal-psychological counseling. Campus security: 24-hour emergency response devices. College housing not available. Karcher Library with 24,937 books, 150 serials, 502 audiovisual materials, and an OPAC. Operations spending for 2004 fiscal year: $18,731. 7 computers available on campus for general student use. Staffed computer lab on campus.

■ **REEDLEY COLLEGE** *M-9*
995 North Reed Ave.
Reedley, CA 93654-2099
Tel: (559)638-3641
Admissions: (559)638-0323
Web Site: http://www.reedleycollege.com/

Description: State and locally supported, 2-year, coed. Part of State Center Community College District System. Awards certificates, diplomas, transfer associate, and terminal associate degrees. Founded 1926. Setting: 350-acre rural campus. Total enrollment: 11,305. 1,224 applied, 100% were admitted. Full-time: 4,556 students, 57% women, 43% men. Part-time: 6,749 students, 64% women, 36% men. Students come from 15 states and territories, 2% from out-of-state, 2% Native American, 42% Hispanic, 3% black, 5% Asian American or Pacific Islander, 0.3% international, 39% 25 or older. Retention: 62% of full-time freshmen returned the following year. Core. Calendar: semesters. Academic remediation for entering students, ESL program, services for LD students, advanced placement, freshman honors college, honors program, independent study, distance learning, summer session for credit, part-time degree program, adult/continuing education programs, co-op programs. Study abroad program. ROTC: Air Force (c).

Entrance Requirements: Open admission. Option: international baccalaureate accepted. Required: high school transcript. Placement: CPT recommended; CPT required for some. Entrance: noncompetitive. Application deadline: Rolling. Notification: continuous until 8/1.

Collegiate Environment: Orientation program. Drama-theater group, choral group, student-run newspaper. Student services: personal-psychological counseling. Campus security: on-campus police department. Option: coed housing available. Reedley College Library with 36,000 books, 8,400 microform titles, 217 serials, 50 audiovisual materials, and an OPAC. 303 computers available on campus for general student use. A campuswide network can be accessed from student residence rooms and from off-campus. Staffed computer lab on campus.

Community Environment: Population 15,200. Reedley is in a rural area southeast of Fresno with a temperate climate. The rich farmlands around Reedley produce a diversity of crops, including citrus fruits, plums, peaches, grapes, tomatoes, celery and walnuts. The community has 19 packing houses, two wineries, and a sawmill. There are a number of churches, a public library and a hospital. Part-time employment is available. Reedley is near Kings Canyon and Sequoia National Parks which provide recreational activities. Major civic, fraternal and veteran's organizations are part of the town.

■ **REMINGTON COLLEGE-SAN DIEGO CAMPUS** *W-12*
123 Camino de la Reina
North Bldg., Ste. 100
San Diego, CA 92108
Tel: (619)686-8600
Free: 800-214-7001
Fax: (619)686-8684
E-mail: jose.cisneros@remingtoncollege.edu
Web Site: http://www.remingtoncollege.edu/

Description: Proprietary, comprehensive, coed. Founded 1995. Setting: 2-acre campus. Total enrollment: 250. 114 applied, 53% were admitted.

■ **RIO HONDO COLLEGE** *R-5*
3600 Workman Mill Rd.
Whittier, CA 90601-1699
Tel: (562)692-0921
Fax: (562)692-9318
Web Site: http://www.rh.cc.ca.us/

Description: State and locally supported, 2-year, coed. Part of California Community College System. Awards certificates, transfer associate, and terminal associate degrees. Founded 1960. Setting: 128-acre suburban campus with easy access to Los Angeles. Total enrollment: 15,000. Students come from 5 states and territories, 40 other countries, 40% 25 or older. Core. Calendar: semesters. Academic remediation for entering students, ESL program, services for LD students, advanced placement, honors program, summer session for credit, part-time degree program, adult/continuing education programs. Study abroad program. ROTC: Army (c), Naval (c), Air Force (c).

Entrance Requirements: Open admission. Option: early admission. Entrance: noncompetitive. Application deadline: 7/10. Notification: continuous.

Collegiate Environment: Drama-theater group, choral group, student-run newspaper, radio station. Social organizations: 15 open to all. Student services: legal services, health clinic, personal-psychological counseling, women's center. Campus security: 24-hour patrols, late night transport-escort service. College housing not available. Main library plus 1 other with 94,143 books, 479 serials, and a Web page. 150 computers available on campus for general student use.

Community Environment: Small ex-urban community, 23 miles from downtown Los Angeles. District population of approximately 350,000. Small business and manufacturing predominate.

■ **RIVERSIDE COMMUNITY COLLEGE DISTRICT** *T-11*
4800 Magnolia Ave.
Riverside, CA 92506-1299
Tel: (909)222-8000
Admissions: (951)222-8600
Fax: (909)222-8037
E-mail: admissions@rcc.edu
Web Site: http://www.rcc.edu/

Description: State and locally supported, 2-year, coed. Part of California Community College System. Awards certificates and terminal associate degrees. Founded 1916. Setting: 108-acre suburban campus with easy access to Los Angeles. Total enrollment: 30,390. Student-undergrad faculty ratio is 22:1. 1,081 applied, 100% were admitted. Full-time: 8,701 students, 56% women, 44% men. Part-time: 21,689 students, 58% women, 42% men. Students come from 23 states and territories, 60 other countries, 1% Native American, 35% Hispanic, 14% black, 11% Asian American or Pacific Islander, 40% 25 or older, 2% transferred in. Core. Calendar: semesters. Academic remediation for entering students, ESL program, services for LD students, advanced placement, distance learning, double major, summer session for credit, part-time degree program, adult/continuing education programs, internships. Study abroad program. ROTC: Army (c), Air Force (c).

Entrance Requirements: Open admission except for some programs. Required: high school transcript. Entrance: noncompetitive. Application deadline: Rolling. Notification: continuous.

Costs Per Year: Application fee: $0. State resident tuition: $0 full-time. Nonresident tuition: $6090 full-time, $203 per unit part-time. Mandatory fees: $820 full-time, $26 per unit part-time, $20 per term part-time.

Collegiate Environment: Drama-theater group, choral group, marching band, student-run newspaper, radio station. Social organizations: 30 open to all. Most popular organizations: Marching Tigers Band, Wind Ensemble, Student Nurses Organization, Gospel Singers, Alpha Gamma Sigma. Major annual events: Homecoming, graduation, Job Fair. Student services: health clinic, personal-psychological counseling. Campus security: 24-hour patrols, late night transport-escort service. College housing not available. Digital Library Learning Resource Center with 101,243 books, 15,317 microform titles, 911 serials, 5,417 audiovisual materials, an OPAC, and a Web page. Operations spending for 2004 fiscal year: $3.2 million. 200 computers available on campus for general student use. A campuswide network can be accessed from off-campus. Staffed computer lab on campus.

Community Environment: See University of California Riverside.

■ **SACRAMENTO CITY COLLEGE** *I-6*
3835 Freeport Blvd.
Sacramento, CA 95822-1386

Tel: (916)558-2111
Admissions: (916)558-2438
Fax: (916)558-2190
Web Site: http://www.scc.losrios.edu/

Description: State and locally supported, 2-year, coed. Part of California Community College System. Awards certificates, diplomas, transfer associate, and terminal associate degrees. Founded 1916. Setting: 60-acre urban campus. Total enrollment: 21,890. 5% from top 10% of their high school class, 10% from top quarter, 25% from top half. Students come from 35 states and territories, 2% Native American, 14% Hispanic, 13% black, 24% Asian American or Pacific Islander, 50% 25 or older. Core. Calendar: semesters. Academic remediation for entering students, ESL program, services for LD students, advanced placement, self-designed majors, honors program, summer session for credit, part-time degree program, adult/continuing education programs, co-op programs. Off campus study at University of California, Davis; California State University, Sacramento. Study abroad program.

Entrance Requirements: Open admission. Entrance: noncompetitive. Application deadline: Rolling. Notification: continuous.

Collegiate Environment: Orientation program. Drama-theater group, choral group, student-run newspaper. Most popular organizations: BOSS, African Student Alliance, Asian Pacific Club, MECHA, SMEC. Major annual events: Welcome Back Day, Peoples' Day. Student services: personal-psychological counseling, women's center. Campus security: 24-hour emergency response devices and patrols, student patrols, late night transport-escort service. College housing not available. Sacramento City College Library with 68,462 books, 415 serials, an OPAC, and a Web page. Operations spending for 2004 fiscal year: $995,408. 450 computers available on campus for general student use. A campuswide network can be accessed from off-campus. Staffed computer lab on campus.

■ **SADDLEBACK COLLEGE** *T-8*
28000 Marguerite Parkway
Mission Viejo, CA 92692-3635
Tel: (949)582-4500
Admissions: (949)582-4340
Fax: (949)347-8315
E-mail: jrosenkrans@saddleback.edu
Web Site: http://www.saddleback.cc.ca.us/

Description: State and locally supported, 2-year, coed. Awards certificates and transfer associate degrees. Founded 1967. Setting: 200-acre suburban campus with easy access to Los Angeles and San Diego. Total enrollment: 18,351. Students come from 37 states and territories, 23 other countries, 1% Native American, 14% Hispanic, 2% black, 11% Asian American or Pacific Islander, 1% international, 52% 25 or older. Core. Calendar: semesters. Academic remediation for entering students, ESL program, services for LD students, advanced placement, honors program, distance learning, summer session for credit, part-time degree program, adult/continuing education programs, co-op programs. Off campus study at Irvine Valley College. Study abroad program.

Entrance Requirements: Open admission. Option: early admission. Entrance: noncompetitive. Application deadline: Rolling.

Costs Per Year: Nonresident tuition: $178 per unit part-time. Mandatory fees: $26 per unit part-time, $14 per term part-time.

Collegiate Environment: Drama-theater group, choral group, student-run newspaper, radio station. Social organizations: 19 open to all. Student services: legal services, health clinic, personal-psychological counseling, women's center. Campus security: 24-hour emergency response devices and patrols, late night transport-escort service. College housing not available. James B. Utt Memorial Library with 109,000 books and 132 serials. 200 computers available on campus for general student use. A campuswide network can be accessed. Staffed computer lab on campus.

Community Environment: Mission Viejo is largely a residential community located in the rolling hills midway between Los Angeles and San Diego. This is one of Orange County's fast growing areas, with a dry temperate climate. Good shopping facilities are available with most major department stores represented. Buses serve the area and Orange County Airport is only a short drive away. Beach resorts are located nearby for all water sports. The mountains are approximately a two-hour drive and ski slopes abound in the Big Bear area.

■ **SAGE COLLEGE** *R-10*
12125 Day St., Bldg. L
Moreno Valley, CA 92557-6720

Tel: (951)781-2727
Fax: (951)781-0570
Web Site: http://www.sagecollege.edu/
Description: Proprietary, 2-year, coed. Founded 1973.

■ **SAINT MARY'S COLLEGE OF CALIFORNIA** *G-5*
1928 Saint Mary's Rd.
Moraga, CA 94575
Tel: (925)631-4000
Free: 800-800-4SMC
Admissions: (925)631-4224
Fax: (925)376-7193
E-mail: smcadmit@stmarys-ca.edu
Web Site: http://www.stmarys-ca.edu/

Description: Independent Roman Catholic, comprehensive, coed. Awards bachelor's, master's, and doctoral degrees. Founded 1863. Setting: 420-acre suburban campus with easy access to San Francisco. Endowment: $135.4 million. Educational spending for 2005 fiscal year: $19,885 per student. Total enrollment: 4,432. Faculty: 547 (213 full-time, 334 part-time). Student-undergrad faculty ratio is 12:1. 3,381 applied, 85% were admitted. Full-time: 2,514 students, 61% women, 39% men. Part-time: 777 students, 68% women, 32% men. Students come from 26 states and territories, 29 other countries, 11% from out-of-state, 1% Native American, 18% Hispanic, 7% black, 9% Asian American or Pacific Islander, 2% international, 3% 25 or older, 63% live on campus, 5% transferred in. Retention: 88% of full-time freshmen returned the following year. Academic areas with the most degrees conferred: business/marketing; communications/journalism; social sciences. Core. Calendar: 4-1-4. Advanced placement, self-designed majors, honors program, independent study, double major, part-time degree program, external degree program, adult/continuing education programs, internships, graduate courses open to undergrads. Off campus study at members of the January Interim Program. Study abroad program. ROTC: Army (c), Air Force (c).

Entrance Requirements: Options: Peterson's Universal Application, Common Application, electronic application, early action, deferred admission, international baccalaureate accepted. Required: essay, high school transcript, minimum 2.0 high school GPA, 1 recommendation, SAT or ACT. Recommended: minimum 3.0 high school GPA. Required for some: minimum 3.0 high school GPA, interview. Entrance: moderately difficult. Application deadlines: 2/1, 11/30 for early action. Notification: continuous until 3/15, 1/15 for early action.

Costs Per Year: Application fee: $55. Comprehensive fee: $37,290 includes full-time tuition ($27,130), mandatory fees ($150), and college room and board ($10,010). College room only: $5590. Full-time tuition and fees vary according to course load. Room and board charges vary according to board plan and housing facility. Part-time tuition: $3392 per course. Part-time tuition varies according to course load.

Collegiate Environment: Orientation program. Drama-theater group, choral group, student-run newspaper, radio station. Social organizations: 42 open to all. Most popular organizations: LASA-Latin American Student Association, Student Alumni Association, Black Student Union, Inter-Varsity Christian Fellowship, Asian Pacific America Student Association. Major annual events: Saint Mary's Day Off, Welcome Back Dance, Oasis. Student services: health clinic, personal-psychological counseling, women's center. Campus security: 24-hour emergency response devices and patrols, late night transport-escort service. 1,557 college housing spaces available; 1,554 were occupied in 2003-04. Freshmen guaranteed college housing. Options: coed, women-only housing available. St. Albert Hall with 111,068 books, 484,760 microform titles, 13,012 serials, 5,377 audiovisual materials, an OPAC, and a Web page. Operations spending for 2004 fiscal year: $1.8 million. 250 computers available on campus for general student use. A campuswide network can be accessed from student residence rooms and from off campus. Staffed computer lab on campus.

■ **THE SALVATION ARMY COLLEGE FOR OFFICER TRAINING AT CRESTMONT** *S-3*
30840 Hawthorne Blvd.
Rancho Palos Verdes, CA 90275
Tel: (310)377-0481
Admissions: (310)544-6442
Fax: (310)265-6565
E-mail: kevin_jackson@usw.salvationarmy.org
Web Site: http://www.crestmont.edu/

Description: Independent religious, 2-year, coed. Administratively affiliated with The Salvation Army. Awards transfer associate and terminal associate degrees. Founded 1878. Setting: 44-acre suburban campus with easy access to Los Angeles. Endowment: $85.5 million. Total enrollment: 27. Student-undergrad faculty ratio is 1:1. 21 applied, 67% were admitted. Full-time: 27 students, 52% women, 48% men. Students come from 14 states and territories, 1 other country, 67% from out-of-state, 0% Native American, 30% Hispanic, 7% black, 15% Asian American or Pacific Islander, 7% international, 100% 25 or older, 100% live on campus. Retention: 98% of full-time freshmen returned the following year. Core. Academic remediation for entering students, ESL program, accelerated degree program, self-designed majors, independent study, distance learning, external degree program, co-op programs and internships. Off campus study.

Entrance Requirements: Required: essay, high school transcript, 2 recommendations, interview. Entrance: noncompetitive. Application deadline: 6/1. Notification: 8/20. Preference given to members of the Salvation Army.

Costs Per Year: Application fee: $15. Comprehensive fee: $10,600 includes full-time tuition ($1500), mandatory fees ($850), and college room and board ($8250).

Collegiate Environment: Orientation program. Drama-theater group, choral group. Major annual event: performing arts production. Student services: health clinic, personal-psychological counseling. Campus security: 24-hour emergency response devices and patrols. 60 college housing spaces available; 33 were occupied in 2003-04. On-campus residence required through sophomore year. The Salvation Army Elfman Memorial Library with 35,700 books, 125 serials, and an OPAC. Operations spending for 2004 fiscal year: $194,700. 65 computers available on campus for general student use. Computer purchase/lease plans available. A campuswide network can be accessed from student residence rooms and from off campus. Staffed computer lab on campus.

■ **SAMUEL MERRITT COLLEGE** *K-4*
370 Hawthorne Ave.
Oakland, CA 94609-3108
Tel: (510)869-6511
Free: 800-607-MERRITT
Admissions: (510)869-6610
Fax: (510)869-6525
E-mail: admission@samuelmerritt.edu
Web Site: http://www.samuelmerritt.edu/

Description: Independent, comprehensive, coed. Awards bachelor's, master's, doctoral, and first professional degrees (bachelor's degree offered jointly with Saint Mary's College of California). Founded 1909. Setting: 1-acre urban campus with easy access to San Francisco. Endowment: $22.5 million. Educational spending for 2005 fiscal year: $11,249 per student. Total enrollment: 1,080. Faculty: 157 (64 full-time, 93 part-time). Student-undergrad faculty ratio is 10:1. Full-time: 304 students, 91% women, 9% men. Part-time: 59 students, 86% women, 14% men. Students come from 5 states and territories, 1 other country, 1% Native American, 11% Hispanic, 5% black, 30% Asian American or Pacific Islander, 1% international, 43% 25 or older, 6% live on campus, 12% transferred in. Retention: 100% of full-time freshmen returned the following year. Academic area with the most degrees conferred: health professions and related sciences. Core. Calendar: 4-1-4. Academic remediation for entering students, services for LD students, advanced placement, independent study, distance learning, summer session for credit, part-time degree program, co-op programs and internships. Off campus study at Saint Mary's College of California. ROTC: Army (c), Air Force (c).

Entrance Requirements: Options: Peterson's Universal Application, Common Application, deferred admission, international baccalaureate accepted. Required for some: interview. Entrance: moderately difficult. Notification: continuous.

Costs Per Year: Application fee: $35. Tuition: $29,220 full-time, $1214 per unit part-time. Mandatory fees: $356 full-time, $356 per year part-time. College room only: $5903.

Collegiate Environment: Orientation program. Student-run newspaper. Most popular organizations: Multicultural Group, California Nursing Students Association, Student Body Association. Major annual events: Convocation, Opening Barbecue, Diversity Day. Student services: health clinic, personal-psychological counseling. Campus security: 24-hour emergency response devices and patrols, late night transport-escort service, controlled dormitory access, 24-hour controlled access. 91 college housing spaces available; 18 were occupied in 2003-04. No special consideration for freshman housing applicants. Option: coed housing available. John A. Graziano Memorial

Library plus 1 other with 33,000 books, 60 serials, and 1,522 audiovisual materials. Operations spending for 2004 fiscal year: $540,592. 48 computers available on campus for general student use. Computer purchase/lease plans available. A campuswide network can be accessed from student residence rooms. Staffed computer lab on campus.

■ **SAN BERNARDINO VALLEY COLLEGE** *S-11*
701 South Mt Vernon Ave.
San Bernardino, CA 92410-2748
Tel: (909)384-4400
Admissions: (909)384-4401
Web Site: http://www.valleycollege.edu/

Description: State and locally supported, 2-year, coed. Part of San Bernardino Community College District System. Awards certificates, diplomas, transfer associate, and terminal associate degrees. Founded 1926. Setting: 82-acre campus with easy access to Los Angeles. Total enrollment: 1,540. Students come from 2 states and territories, 55% 25 or older. Core. Calendar: semesters. Academic remediation for entering students, services for LD students, summer session for credit, part-time degree program, co-op programs.

Entrance Requirements: Open admission. Placement: CGP required. Entrance: noncompetitive. Application deadline: 8/29.

Collegiate Environment: Drama-theater group, student-run newspaper, radio station. Student services: health clinic, personal-psychological counseling, women's center. College housing not available. 122,802 books and 657 serials. 180 computers available on campus for general student use. Staffed computer lab on campus.

Community Environment: See California State University - San Bernardino.

■ **SAN DIEGO CHRISTIAN COLLEGE** *V-12*
2100 Greenfield Dr.
El Cajon, CA 92019-1157
Tel: (619)441-2200
Free: 800-676-2242
Fax: (619)440-0209
Web Site: http://www.sdcc.edu/

Description: Independent nondenominational, 4-year, coed. Awards bachelor's degrees. Founded 1970. Setting: 55-acre suburban campus with easy access to San Diego. Endowment: $398,365. Educational spending for 2005 fiscal year: $5348 per student. Total enrollment: 553. Student-undergrad faculty ratio is 12:1. 493 applied, 72% were admitted. 9% from top 10% of their high school class, 33% from top quarter, 67% from top half. 1 valedictorian. Full-time: 457 students, 58% women, 42% men. Part-time: 54 students, 65% women, 35% men. Students come from 15 states and territories, 7 other countries, 10% from out-of-state, 1% Native American, 17% Hispanic, 7% black, 3% Asian American or Pacific Islander, 24% 25 or older, 43% live on campus, 15% transferred in. Retention: 75% of full-time freshmen returned the following year. Academic areas with the most degrees conferred: interdisciplinary studies; family and consumer sciences; psychology. Core. Calendar: semesters. Academic remediation for entering students, ESL program, advanced placement, self-designed majors, honors program, independent study, double major, summer session for credit, part-time degree program, adult/continuing education programs, internships. Study abroad program. ROTC: Army (c), Air Force (c).

Entrance Requirements: Options: electronic application, deferred admission. Required: essay, high school transcript, 2 recommendations, SAT or ACT. Recommended: minimum 2.75 high school GPA, interview. Entrance: moderately difficult. Application deadline: 7/1. Notification: continuous.

Costs Per Year: Application fee: $25. Comprehensive fee: $24,522 includes full-time tuition ($16,476), mandatory fees ($866), and college room and board ($7180). Part-time tuition: $570 per credit.

Collegiate Environment: Orientation program. Drama-theater group, choral group, student-run newspaper. Social organizations: 12 open to all. Most popular organizations: Senate, Missions Club, Aviators Club, Women of Influence, Hope Ministries. Major annual events: Homecoming, Bible Conference, International Festival. Student services: health clinic, personal-psychological counseling. Campus security: 24-hour emergency response devices and patrols. 206 college housing spaces available; 195 were occupied in 2003-04. No special consideration for freshman housing applicants. Options: men-only, women-only housing available. Christian Heritage College Library with 75,001 books, 7,400 serials, 918 audiovisual materials, and an OPAC. Operations spending for 2004 fiscal year: $213,115. 50 computers available on campus for general student use. A

campuswide network can be accessed from student residence rooms and from off campus. Staffed computer lab on campus.

Community Environment: The campus is two miles from the center of El Cajon, a suburb of San Diego. The location of the college affords short travel distances to nearby mountain, desert and beach resorts.

■ SAN DIEGO CITY COLLEGE *W-12*
1313 Park Blvd.
San Diego, CA 92101-4787
Tel: (619)388-3400
Admissions: (619)388-3474
Fax: (619)388-3063
E-mail: lhumphri@sdccd.edu
Web Site: http://www.sdcity.edu/

Description: State and locally supported, 2-year, coed. Part of San Diego Community College District System. Awards certificates and transfer associate degrees. Founded 1914. Setting: 56-acre urban campus. Total enrollment: 14,591. Student-undergrad faculty ratio is 35:1. 1% Native American, 30% Hispanic, 14% black, 12% Asian American or Pacific Islander, 0% international, 63% 25 or older. Core. Calendar: semesters. Academic remediation for entering students, ESL program, services for LD students, self-designed majors, honors program, independent study, distance learning, summer session for credit, part-time degree program, external degree program, adult/continuing education programs, co-op programs. Off campus study at San Diego State University. ROTC: Air Force (c).

Entrance Requirements: Open admission. Option: electronic application. Required for some: high school transcript. Entrance: noncompetitive. Application deadline: Rolling.

Costs Per Year: Application fee: $0. State resident tuition: $0 full-time. Nonresident tuition: $4800 full-time, $186 per unit part-time. Mandatory fees: $806 full-time, $26 per unit part-time, $13 per term part-time.

Collegiate Environment: Orientation program. Drama-theater group, choral group, student-run newspaper, radio station. Most popular organizations: Alpha Gamma Sigma, Association of United Latin American Students, MECHA, Afrikan Student Union, Student Nurses Association. Major annual events: World Cultures Day I, World Cultures Day II, Entrepreneurs' Day. Student services: health clinic, personal-psychological counseling. Campus security: 24-hour emergency response devices and patrols, late night transport-escort service. College housing not available. San Diego City College Library with 73,000 books, 337 serials, and an OPAC. Operations spending for 2004 fiscal year: $428,270. 121 computers available on campus for general student use. A campuswide network can be accessed from student residence rooms and from off campus. Staffed computer lab on campus.

Community Environment: See San Diego State University.

■ SAN DIEGO GOLF ACADEMY *U-12*
1910 Shadowridge Dr., Ste. 111
Vista, CA 92083
Tel: (760)734-1208
Free: 800-342-7342
Admissions: (760)414-1501
Fax: (760)734-1642
E-mail: sdga@sdgagolf.com
Web Site: http://www.sdgagolf.com/

Description: Proprietary, 2-year. Awards transfer associate and terminal associate degrees. Founded 1974. Total enrollment: 600. Calendar: semesters.

Entrance Requirements: Entrance: moderately difficult. Application deadline: Rolling.

Collegiate Environment: College housing not available.

■ SAN DIEGO MESA COLLEGE *W-12*
7250 Mesa College Dr.
San Diego, CA 92111-4998
Tel: (619)388-2600
Admissions: (619)388-2689
Fax: (619)388-2968
E-mail: ialvarez@sdccd.edu
Web Site: http://www.sandiegomesacollege.net/

Description: State and locally supported, 2-year, coed. Part of San Diego Community College District System. Awards certificates, diplomas, and transfer associate degrees. Founded 1964. Setting: 104-acre suburban campus. Total enrollment: 21,198. 1,678 applied, 100% were admitted. 1% Native American, 17% Hispanic, 6% black, 16% Asian American or Pacific

Islander, 51% 25 or older. Core. Calendar: semesters. Academic remediation for entering students, ESL program, services for LD students, honors program, independent study, summer session for credit, part-time degree program, external degree program, adult/continuing education programs.

Entrance Requirements: Open admission. Option: early admission. Entrance: noncompetitive. Application deadline: Rolling. Notification: continuous.

Collegiate Environment: Drama-theater group, choral group, student-run newspaper. Social organizations: 39 open to all. Most popular organizations: Alpha Gamma Sigma, Black Students Association, MECHA, Gay and Lesbian Student Group, Vietnamese Student Association. Major annual events: Festival of Colors, Job Fair, Club Rush/Back to School Reception. Student services: health clinic, personal-psychological counseling. Campus security: 24-hour emergency response devices and patrols, late night transport-escort service. College housing not available. 84,353 books and 657 serials. 350 computers available on campus for general student use. Staffed computer lab on campus.

Community Environment: San Diego lies along and around one of the world's ten most beautiful, protected, natural harbors. Known as a winter playground, it has 19 miles of beautiful beaches and a very special "sea-washed, air-conditioned" climate, with the average maximum temperature of 70.8 degrees and a minimum of 55.4 degrees. The population is 1,200,900, with a greater metropolitan area population of 2,166,200. The Santa Fe Railroad, and numerous bus and airlines serve the area. The city is a manufacturing and shipping center with its main industries being fishing, fish packing, and the construction of aircraft parts, missiles, and boats. The county is also the country's largest producer of avocados. San Diego has a public library with 30 branches, nine general hospitals, churches, museums, and galleries. There are numerous golf courses, all aquatic sports, hiking, mountain climbing, horseback riding, fishing, hunting, skiing and other snow sports. This is the home of the San Diego Chargers, the professional football team, and also the San Diego Padres, the professional baseball team.

■ SAN DIEGO MIRAMAR COLLEGE *W-12*
10440 Black Mountain Rd.
San Diego, CA 92126-2999
Tel: (619)388-7800
Admissions: (619)388-7844
Fax: (619)388-7801
E-mail: dandras@sdccd.net
Web Site: http://www.miramar.sdccd.cc.ca.us/

Description: State and locally supported, 2-year, coed. Part of San Diego Community College District System. Awards transfer associate degrees. Founded 1969. Setting: 120-acre suburban campus. Total enrollment: 8,080. 1% Native American, 16% Hispanic, 6% black, 20% Asian American or Pacific Islander, 47% 25 or older. Calendar: semesters. Academic remediation for entering students, ESL program, services for LD students, advanced placement, accelerated degree program, self-designed majors, honors program, independent study, distance learning, double major, summer session for credit, part-time degree program, adult/continuing education programs, co-op programs. Study abroad program.

Entrance Requirements: Open admission. Option: electronic application. Entrance: noncompetitive.

Costs Per Year: Application fee: $0. State resident tuition: $0 full-time. Nonresident tuition: $4492 full-time, $186 per unit part-time. Mandatory fees: $652 full-time, $26 per unit part-time.

Collegiate Environment: Student-run newspaper. Social organizations: 9 open to all. Most popular organizations: Science Club, International Club, Parent Student Advisory Board, Filipino-American Student Union, Miramar-U. S. Tennis Association. Major annual events: Majors Fair, Health Fair. Student services: health clinic, personal-psychological counseling. Campus security: 24-hour emergency response devices and patrols. College housing not available. Miramar College Library with 19,301 books, 95,586 microform titles, 135 serials, 901 audiovisual materials, and an OPAC. Operations spending for 2004 fiscal year: $317,458. 130 computers available on campus for general student use. A campuswide network can be accessed. Staffed computer lab on campus.

■ SAN DIEGO STATE UNIVERSITY *W-12*
5500 Campanile Dr.
San Diego, CA 92182
Tel: (619)594-5200
Admissions: (619)594-6336
Web Site: http://www.sdsu.edu/

Description: State-supported, university, coed. Part of California State University System. Awards bachelor's, master's, and doctoral degrees and post-master's certificates. Founded 1897. Setting: 300-acre urban campus. Endowment: $86.5 million. Research spending for 2004 fiscal year: $39.6 million. Educational spending for 2005 fiscal year: $6994 per student. Total enrollment: 32,936. Faculty: 1,618 (915 full-time, 703 part-time). Student-undergrad faculty ratio is 24:1. 33,334 applied, 47% were admitted. Full-time: 21,630 students, 58% women, 42% men. Part-time: 5,223 students, 58% women, 42% men. Students come from 50 states and territories, 125 other countries, 5% from out-of-state, 1% Native American, 22% Hispanic, 4% black, 15% Asian American or Pacific Islander, 3% international, 17% 25 or older, 11% live on campus, 13% transferred in. Retention: 82% of full-time freshmen returned the following year. Core. Calendar: semesters. Academic remediation for entering students, ESL program, services for LD students, advanced placement, self-designed majors, honors program, independent study, distance learning, double major, summer session for credit, part-time degree program, internships, graduate courses open to undergrads. Off campus study at other units of the California State University System. Study abroad program. ROTC: Army, Naval, Air Force.

Entrance Requirements: Options: electronic application, international baccalaureate accepted. Required: high school transcript, minimum 2.0 high school GPA, 2.5 GPA for non-California residents, SAT or ACT. Entrance: moderately difficult. Application deadline: 11/30. Notification: 3/1.

Costs Per Year: Application fee: $55. State resident tuition: $0 full-time. Nonresident tuition: $10,170 full-time, $339 per unit part-time. Mandatory fees: $3155 full-time, $1033 per term part-time. Full-time tuition and fees vary according to degree level. Part-time tuition and fees vary according to course load and degree level. College room and board: $9849. Room and board charges vary according to board plan and housing facility.

Collegiate Environment: Orientation program. Drama-theater group, choral group, marching band, student-run newspaper, radio station. Social organizations: 190 open to all; national fraternities, national sororities, local fraternities, local sororities; 7% of eligible men and 6% of eligible women are members. Most popular organizations: American Marketing Association, Associated Students, Student Accounting Society, Residence Hall Association, MECHA. Major annual events: Associated Students Fiesta, Homecoming, Chocolate Fest. Student services: health clinic, personal-psychological counseling, women's center. Campus security: 24-hour emergency response devices and patrols, student patrols, late night transport-escort service. 3,059 college housing spaces available; 3,048 were occupied in 2003-04. Freshmen given priority for college housing. Option: coed housing available. Malcolm A. Love Library with 1.3 million books, 4.3 million microform titles, 8,245 serials, 12,616 audiovisual materials, an OPAC, and a Web page. Operations spending for 2004 fiscal year: $11.7 million. 400 computers available on campus for general student use. A campuswide network can be accessed from student residence rooms and from off campus. Staffed computer lab on campus.

Community Environment: San Diego lies along and around one of the world's ten most beautiful protected natural harbors and has a very special "sea-washed, air-conditioned climate." The maximum average temperature of 70.8 degrees and a minimum of 55.4 degrees make the climate very special. The population of San Diego is 1,200,900 with a greater metropolitan area population of 2,166,200. The Santa Fe Railroad, buses, and a number of major airlines serve the area. The city is a manufacturing and shipping center, with its main industries being tourism, agriculture, and defense. The county is the country's largest producer of avocados. It has a public library with 30 branches, nine general hospitals, numerous museums, galleries, and churches. Residents and visitors will find many golf courses, all aquatic sports, hiking, mountain climbing, horseback riding, fishing and hunting, and skiing and other snow sports nearby. This area is home of the San Diego Chargers professional football team, and the San Diego Padres professional baseball team. Known as a winter playground, it has 19 miles of Pacific Ocean shores with beautiful beaches.

■ **SAN FRANCISCO ART INSTITUTE** *K-4*
800 Chestnut St.
San Francisco, CA 94133
Tel: (415)771-7020
Free: 800-345-SFAI
Admissions: (415)749-4580
Web Site: http://www.sfai.edu/

Description: Independent, comprehensive, coed. Awards bachelor's and master's degrees. Founded 1871. Setting: 3-acre urban campus. Endowment: $8.2 million. Educational spending for 2005 fiscal year: $13,955 per student. Total enrollment: 595. Faculty: 146 (14 full-time, 132 part-time). Student-undergrad faculty ratio is 4:1. 196 applied, 88% were admitted. Full-time: 319 students, 51% women, 49% men. Part-time: 65 students, 48% women, 52% men. Students come from 38 states and territories, 16 other countries, 43% from out-of-state, 2% Native American, 9% Hispanic, 2% black, 8% Asian American or Pacific Islander, 9% international, 35% 25 or older, 23% transferred in. Retention: 78% of full-time freshmen returned the following year. Academic area with the most degrees conferred: visual and performing arts. Core. Calendar: semesters. Academic remediation for entering students, ESL program, services for LD students, advanced placement, independent study, double major, summer session for credit, part-time degree program, adult/continuing education programs, co-op programs and internships. Off campus study at Association of Independent Colleges of Art and Design; Akademic Vytvarnych Umenr, Prague, Czech Republic; Bezalel Academy of Arts and Design, Jerusalem, Israel; Chelsea College of Art and Design, London, England; Ecole Nationale Supericure des Beaux-Arts, Paris, France; Glasgow School of Art, Glasgow, Scotland; Gerritt-Rietveld Academie, Amsterdam, Holland; Valand School of Fine Arts, Goteborg, Sweden. Study abroad program.

Entrance Requirements: Options: early admission, deferred admission. Required: essay, high school transcript, recommendations, portfolio, SAT or ACT. Recommended: interview. Entrance: moderately difficult. Application deadline: Rolling. Notification: continuous.

Costs Per Year: Application fee: $65. Tuition: $27,400 full-time, $1175 per unit part-time. Mandatory fees: $15. College room only: $6540.

Collegiate Environment: Orientation program. Most popular organization: Student Senate. Major annual events: Commencement, Spring Art Exhibition, Roy G. Biv Ball. Student services: personal-psychological counseling. Campus security: 24-hour patrols, security cameras. 41 college housing spaces available; all were occupied in 2003-04. Freshmen given priority for college housing. Option: coed housing available. Anne Bremer Memorial Library with 35,500 books, 210 serials, 121,000 audiovisual materials, an OPAC, and a Web page. 30 computers available on campus for general student use. A campuswide network can be accessed. Staffed computer lab on campus.

Community Environment: See San Francisco State University.

■ **SAN FRANCISCO CONSERVATORY OF MUSIC** *K-4*
1201 Ortega St.
San Francisco, CA 94122-4411
Tel: (415)564-8086
Admissions: (415)759-3431
Fax: (415)759-3499
Web Site: http://www.sfcm.edu/

Description: Independent, comprehensive, coed. Awards bachelor's and master's degrees. Founded 1917. Setting: 2-acre urban campus. Endowment: $30.3 million. Educational spending for 2005 fiscal year: $16,150 per student. Total enrollment: 287. 116 applied, 63% were admitted. 43% from top quarter of their high school class, 71% from top half. Students come from 28 states and territories, 16 other countries, 49% from out-of-state, 1% Native American, 7% Hispanic, 3% black, 12% Asian American or Pacific Islander, 20% international, 11% 25 or older. Retention: 86% of full-time freshmen returned the following year. Core. Calendar: semesters. Academic remediation for entering students, advanced placement, independent study, part-time degree program.

Entrance Requirements: Option: early admission. Required: high school transcript, 2 recommendations, audition, SAT or ACT. Recommended: SAT. Entrance: moderately difficult. Application deadline: 2/1. Notification: 4/1.

Collegiate Environment: Choral group. Major annual events: Sing It Yourself Messiah, End of Year Picnic, Fall Convocation. Student services: health clinic, personal-psychological counseling. Campus security: late night transport-escort service. College housing not available. Conservatory Library with 36,821 books, 80 serials, 14,614 audiovisual materials, and an OPAC. Operations spending for 2004 fiscal year: $205,900. 7 computers available on campus for general student use.

Community Environment: See San Francisco State University.

■ **SAN FRANCISCO STATE UNIVERSITY** *K-4*
1600 Holloway Ave.
San Francisco, CA 94132-1722
Tel: (415)338-1100
Web Site: http://www.sfsu.edu/

Description: State-supported, comprehensive, coed. Part of California State University System. Awards bachelor's, master's, and doctoral degrees.

Founded 1899. Setting: 90-acre urban campus. Endowment: $3.6 million. Educational spending for 2005 fiscal year: $4582 per student. Total enrollment: 28,950. Faculty: 1,725 (865 full-time, 860 part-time). Student-undergrad faculty ratio is 21:1. 22,219 applied, 67% were admitted. Full-time: 17,917 students, 60% women, 40% men. Part-time: 5,157 students, 57% women, 43% men. Students come from 48 states and territories, 113 other countries, 1% from out-of-state, 1% Native American, 14% Hispanic, 6% black, 31% Asian American or Pacific Islander, 5% international, 22% 25 or older, 10% live on campus, 14% transferred in. Retention: 81% of full-time freshmen returned the following year. Academic areas with the most degrees conferred: business/marketing; visual and performing arts; social sciences; psychology. Core. Calendar: semesters. Academic remediation for entering students, ESL program, services for LD students, advanced placement, accelerated degree program, self-designed majors, honors program, independent study, distance learning, double major, summer session for credit, part-time degree program, adult/continuing education programs, co-op programs and internships, graduate courses open to undergrads. Off campus study at The San Francisco Consortium, 18 other institutions of the California State University System. Study abroad program. ROTC: Army (c), Naval (c), Air Force (c).

Entrance Requirements: Option: international baccalaureate accepted. Required: high school transcript. Required for some: SAT or ACT. Entrance: moderately difficult. Application deadline: Rolling. Notification: continuous.

Costs Per Year: Application fee: $55. State resident tuition: $0 full-time. Nonresident tuition: $13,540 full-time, $339 per unit part-time. Mandatory fees: $3370 full-time. College room and board: $9124. College room only: $5900.

Collegiate Environment: Orientation program. Drama-theater group, choral group, marching band, student-run newspaper, radio station. Social organizations: 200 open to all; national fraternities, national sororities, local fraternities, local sororities; 1% of eligible men and 1% of eligible women are members. Most popular organizations: African Student Union, Asian Student Union, Laraza Student Organization, Filipino Collegial Endeavor, Sigma Sigma Sigma. Major annual events: Activities Fair, Crafts Fair, Healthy Lifestyles Fair. Student services: legal services, health clinic, personal-psychological counseling, women's center. Campus security: 24-hour emergency response devices and patrols, student patrols, late night transport-escort service, controlled dormitory access. Option: coed housing available. J. Paul Leonard Library plus 2 others with 780,230 books, 2.2 million microform titles, 5,679 serials, 72,245 audiovisual materials, an OPAC, and a Web page. Operations spending for 2004 fiscal year: $8.2 million. 1,474 computers available on campus for general student use. A campuswide network can be accessed from student residence rooms and from off campus. Staffed computer lab on campus.

Community Environment: San Francisco is one of the most cosmopolitan cities in the United States. It is the financial center of the west, and an important industrial city. A great port, it serves as the terminus for Trans-Pacific and coastwise steamship lines and airlines. The city is located on hills at the end of a narrow peninsula with the Pacific Ocean on one side and the San Francisco Bay on the other. The annual temperature averages 57 degrees. San Francisco Bay is the largest landlocked harbor in the world, and is the home of the beautiful Golden Gate Bridge. All modes of transportation serve the area. A large civic center includes the city hall, public library, civic auditorium, state building, federal office building, health center, opera house and war memorial building. The opera house is the only municipally owned opera house in America. Job opportunities vary considerably but are available. San Francisco has 438 churches, 52 public parks, and 100 theaters. Recreational facilities are numerous for all water sports, hiking, and fishing. Mountain resort areas are approximately a three hour drive. Famous Chinatown is located here, as is the picturesque Fisherman's Wharf.

■ **SAN JOAQUIN DELTA COLLEGE** *J-6*
5151 Pacific Ave.
Stockton, CA 95207-6370
Tel: (209)954-5151
Admissions: (209)954-5635
Fax: (209)954-5600
Web Site: http://www.deltacollege.edu/
Description: District-supported, 2-year, coed. Part of California Community College System. Awards certificates, transfer associate, and terminal associate degrees. Founded 1935. Setting: 165-acre urban campus with easy access to Sacramento. Educational spending for 2005 fiscal year: $3500 per student. Total enrollment: 18,525. Student-undergrad faculty ratio is 33:1.

20,530 applied, 100% were admitted. Students come from 15 states and territories, 1% Native American, 27% Hispanic, 9% black, 20% Asian American or Pacific Islander, 40% 25 or older. Retention: 25% of full-time freshmen returned the following year. Core. Calendar: semesters. Academic remediation for entering students, ESL program, services for LD students, advanced placement, honors program, independent study, distance learning, summer session for credit, part-time degree program, adult/continuing education programs, co-op programs.

Entrance Requirements: Open admission except special admit programs, i.e., nursing. Options: Common Application, electronic application, early admission, international baccalaureate accepted. Entrance: noncompetitive. Application deadline: Rolling. Notification: continuous.

Costs Per Year: Application fee: $0. State resident tuition: $0 full-time. Nonresident tuition: $5250 full-time, $175 per unit part-time. Mandatory fees: $780 full-time, $26 per unit part-time.

Collegiate Environment: Orientation program. Drama-theater group, choral group, student-run newspaper, radio station. Social organizations: 25 open to all. Most popular organizations: Alpha Gamma Sigma, Fashion Club, International Club, Badminton Club. Major annual events: Diversity Events, Fashion Show, Cinco de Mayo. Student services: legal services, personal-psychological counseling. Campus security: 24-hour emergency response devices and patrols, late night transport-escort service. College housing not available. Goleman Library plus 1 other with 92,398 books, 605 serials, an OPAC, and a Web page. Operations spending for 2004 fiscal year: $1.4 million. 400 computers available on campus for general student use. A campuswide network can be accessed from off-campus. Staffed computer lab on campus.

Community Environment: See University of the Pacific.

■ **SAN JOAQUIN VALLEY COLLEGE** *N-8*
8400 West Mineral King Ave.
Visalia, CA 93291
Tel: (559)651-2500
E-mail: josephh@sjvc.edu
Web Site: http://www.sjvc.edu
Description: Independent, 2-year, coed. Awards certificates, transfer associate, and terminal associate degrees. Founded 1977. Setting: small town campus. Total enrollment: 3,352. Student-undergrad faculty ratio is 10:1. 3,471 applied, 97% were admitted. Full-time: 3,351 students, 75% women, 25% men. Part-time: 1 student, 100% men. 6% from out-of-state, 1% Native American, 42% Hispanic, 8% black, 6% Asian American or Pacific Islander, 0% international. Core. Calendar: semesters. Academic remediation for entering students.

Entrance Requirements: Open admission. Required: high school transcript. Required for some: essay, minimum X high school GPA, recommendations, interview. Entrance: noncompetitive. Application deadline: Rolling. Notification: continuous.

Costs Per Year: Tuition: $11,475 full-time, $348 per unit part-time.

Collegiate Environment: Orientation program. Social organizations: 5 open to all. Most popular organizations: Associated Student Body, Students in Free Enterprise, American Medical Technologists. Major annual events: Student Appreciation Day, March of Dimes Fundraiser, graduation. Student services: health clinic, personal-psychological counseling, women's center. Campus security: late night transport-escort service, full-time security personnel. College housing not available. SJVC Visalia Campus Library with 4,720 books, 53 serials, and 125 audiovisual materials. 740 computers available on campus for general student use. A campuswide network can be accessed. Staffed computer lab on campus.

■ **SAN JOSE CITY COLLEGE** *L-5*
2100 Moorpark Ave.
San Jose, CA 95128-2799
Tel: (408)298-2181
Admissions: (408)288-3707
Web Site: http://www.sjcc.edu/
Description: District-supported, 2-year, coed. Part of San Jose/Evergreen Community College District System. Awards transfer associate and terminal associate degrees. Founded 1921. Setting: 58-acre urban campus. Total enrollment: 9,819. Students come from 33 other countries, 1% Native American, 30% Hispanic, 7% black, 34% Asian American or Pacific Islander, 56% 25 or older. Core. Calendar: semesters. Academic remediation for entering students, ESL program, services for LD students, advanced placement, self-designed majors, summer session for credit, part-time degree program, adult/continuing education programs, co-op programs. ROTC: Army (c), Air Force (c).

Entrance Requirements: Open admission. Options: early admission, deferred admission. Entrance: noncompetitive. Application deadline: Rolling. Preference given to district residents.

Collegiate Environment: Drama-theater group, student-run newspaper, radio station. Student services: health clinic. College housing not available. San Jose City College Library with 54,075 books and 345 serials. 48 computers available on campus for general student use. Staffed computer lab on campus.

Community Environment: See San Jose State University.

■ **SAN JOSE STATE UNIVERSITY** *L-5*
One Washington Square
San Jose, CA 95192-0001
Tel: (408)924-1000
Admissions: (408)283-7500
Fax: (408)924-2050
E-mail: contact@sjsu.edu
Web Site: http://www.sjsu.edu/

Description: State-supported, comprehensive, coed. Part of California State University System. Awards bachelor's and master's degrees. Founded 1857. Setting: 104-acre urban campus. Total enrollment: 29,975. 16,893 applied, 65% were admitted. Full-time: 16,950 students, 50% women, 50% men. Part-time: 5,783 students, 52% women, 48% men. 0% from out-of-state, 0.4% Native American, 16% Hispanic, 5% black, 38% Asian American or Pacific Islander, 3% international, 27% 25 or older, 9% transferred in. Academic areas with the most degrees conferred: business/marketing; engineering; visual and performing arts. Core. Calendar: semesters. Academic remediation for entering students, ESL program, services for LD students, advanced placement, accelerated degree program, self-designed majors, honors program, independent study, distance learning, double major, summer session for credit, part-time degree program, adult/continuing education programs, co-op programs and internships, graduate courses open to undergrads. Off campus study at other institutions of the California State University System. Study abroad program. ROTC: Army, Air Force.

Entrance Requirements: Option: electronic application. Required: high school transcript. Required for some: SAT or ACT. Application deadline: 11/30. Notification: continuous. Preference given to state residents.

Costs Per Year: Application fee: $55. Nonresident tuition: $10,170 full-time, $339 per unit part-time. Mandatory fees: $3292 full-time. Full-time tuition and fees vary according to course load. Part-time tuition varies according to course load. College room and board: $8718. College room only: $5412. Room and board charges vary according to board plan and housing facility.

Collegiate Environment: Orientation program. Drama-theater group, choral group, marching band, student-run newspaper, radio station. Social organizations: 175 open to all; national fraternities, national sororities, local fraternities, local sororities. Major annual events: International Food Bazaar, Welcome Day. Student services: health clinic, personal-psychological counseling, women's center. Campus security: 24-hour emergency response devices and patrols, student patrols, late night transport-escort service. No special consideration for freshman housing applicants. Option: coed housing available. Dr. Martin Luther King Jr. Library plus 1 other with an OPAC and a Web page.

Community Environment: Population 686,178. 15th largest city in U.S. Located in the Santa Clara Valley, known worldwide as "Silicon Valley". 50 miles south of San Francisco, and 30 miles from the Pacific Ocean. The Mount Hamilton Range rises to 4,209 feet on the east, and the Santa Cruz Range provides the western view. San Jose was the first capital of California. Recreational facilities are numerous, including Alum Rock Park, six miles away which includes a museum, picnic grounds, active mineral springs, a large swimming pool, mineral baths, and several miles of marked trails. Mountain resort areas are within easy driving distance for the major winter sports. Points of interest are Lick Observatory on the summit of Mount Hamilton, Rosicrucian Egyptian Temple, Oriental Museum, Winchester Mystery House.

■ **SANTA ANA COLLEGE** *T-10*
1530 West 17th St.
Santa Ana, CA 92706-3398
Tel: (714)564-6000
Web Site: http://www.sac.edu/

Description: State-supported, 2-year, coed. Part of California Community College System. Awards certificates, transfer associate, and terminal associate degrees. Founded 1915. Setting: 58-acre urban campus with easy access to Los Angeles. Total enrollment: 22,189. Students come from 50 states and territories, 4% from out-of-state, 63% 25 or older. Core. Calendar: semesters. Academic remediation for entering students, ESL program, services for LD students, advanced placement, accelerated degree program, freshman honors college, honors program, distance learning, summer session for credit, part-time degree program, external degree program, adult/continuing education programs, co-op programs. Study abroad program. ROTC: Air Force (c).

Entrance Requirements: Open admission. Option: early admission. Entrance: noncompetitive. Application deadline: 8/21.

Collegiate Environment: Drama-theater group, choral group, student-run newspaper. Social organizations: 23 open to all. Most popular organizations: Students of Diverse Cultures, Students United for Better Education, Phi Beta Kappa, Alpha Gamma Sigma, Puente. Major annual events: International Festival, Club Rush, Cinco de Mayo. Student services: legal services, health clinic, personal-psychological counseling, women's center. Campus security: late night transport-escort service. College housing not available. McNeally Library with 99,473 books, 99,473 microform titles, and 7,690 audiovisual materials. 100 computers available on campus for general student use. A campuswide network can be accessed. Staffed computer lab on campus.

■ **SANTA BARBARA CITY COLLEGE** *S-7*
721 Cliff Dr.
Santa Barbara, CA 93109-2394
Tel: (805)965-0581
Fax: (805)963-SBCC
E-mail: admissions@sbcc.edu
Web Site: http://www.sbcc.edu/

Description: State and locally supported, 2-year, coed. Part of California Community College System. Awards certificates and terminal associate degrees. Founded 1908. Setting: 65-acre small town campus. Educational spending for 2005 fiscal year: $2689 per student. Total enrollment: 15,740. Student-undergrad faculty ratio is 29:1. 2,768 applied, 100% were admitted. Full-time: 6,488 students, 51% women, 49% men. Part-time: 9,252 students, 54% women, 46% men. Students come from 49 states and territories, 59 other countries, 6% from out-of-state, 1% Native American, 23% Hispanic, 3% black, 5% Asian American or Pacific Islander, 6% international, 25% 25 or older, 5% transferred in. Core. Calendar: semesters. Academic remediation for entering students, ESL program, services for LD students, advanced placement, honors program, independent study, distance learning, double major, summer session for credit, part-time degree program, adult/continuing education programs, co-op programs and internships. Study abroad program. ROTC: Army (c).

Entrance Requirements: Open admission. Option: early admission. Recommended: high school transcript. Entrance: noncompetitive. Application deadline: 8/26. Notification: continuous.

Costs Per Year: Application fee: $0. State resident tuition: $0 full-time. Nonresident tuition: $5310 full-time, $151 per unit part-time. Mandatory fees: $831 full-time, $26 per unit part-time, $51 per year part-time. Full-time tuition and fees vary according to course load. Part-time tuition and fees vary according to course load.

Collegiate Environment: Orientation program. Drama-theater group, choral group, student-run newspaper. Social organizations: 24 open to all. Most popular organizations: MECHA, International-Cultural Exchange Club, Geology Club, Computer Club, Future Teachers Club. Major annual events: Cinco de Mayo, Arts and Crafts Fair, College Fair. Student services: health clinic, personal-psychological counseling. Campus security: 24-hour emergency response devices and patrols, late night transport-escort service. College housing not available. Eli Luria Library with 121,622 books, 82,962 microform titles, 3,325 serials, 9,230 audiovisual materials, an OPAC, and a Web page. Operations spending for 2004 fiscal year: $909,121. 1,465 computers available on campus for general student use. A campuswide network can be accessed from off-campus. Staffed computer lab on campus.

Community Environment: See University of California Santa Barbara.

■ **SANTA CLARA UNIVERSITY** *L-5*
500 El Camino Real
Santa Clara, CA 95053
Tel: (408)554-4000
Admissions: (408)554-4700
Fax: (408)554-5255
E-mail: ugadmissions@scu.edu
Web Site: http://www.scu.edu/

Description: Independent Roman Catholic (Jesuit), university, coed. Awards bachelor's, master's, doctoral, and first professional degrees and post-master's and first professional certificates. Founded 1851. Setting: 104-acre suburban campus with easy access to San Francisco and San Jose. Endowment: $509.1 million. Research spending for 2004 fiscal year: $1.4 million. Educational spending for 2005 fiscal year: $10,987 per student. Total enrollment: 8,097. Faculty: 746 (447 full-time, 299 part-time). Student-undergrad faculty ratio is 12:1. 8,904 applied, 61% were admitted. 40% from top 10% of their high school class, 72% from top quarter, 95% from top half. 2 National Merit Scholars, 40 valedictorians, 149 student government officers. Full-time: 4,525 students, 56% women, 44% men. Part-time: 113 students, 50% women, 50% men. Students come from 35 states and territories, 11 other countries, 33% from out-of-state, 1% Native American, 13% Hispanic, 3% black, 18% Asian American or Pacific Islander, 3% international, 3% 25 or older, 44% live on campus, 5% transferred in. Retention: 94% of full-time freshmen returned the following year. Academic areas with the most degrees conferred: business/marketing; social sciences; engineering. Core. Advanced placement, self-designed majors, honors program, independent study, double major, summer session for credit, co-op programs and internships, graduate courses open to undergrads. Study abroad program. ROTC: Army, Air Force (c).

Entrance Requirements: Options: Common Application, electronic application, early action, deferred admission. Required: essay, high school transcript, 1 recommendation, SAT or ACT. Recommended: interview. Entrance: moderately difficult. Application deadlines: 1/15, 11/1 for early action. Notification: continuous until 4/1, 12/31 for early action.

Costs Per Year: Application fee: $55. Comprehensive fee: $38,931 includes full-time tuition ($28,899) and college room and board ($10,032). Room and board charges vary according to board plan, housing facility, and student level. Part-time tuition: $925 per unit. Part-time tuition varies according to course load.

Collegiate Environment: Orientation program. Drama-theater group, choral group, student-run newspaper, radio station. Social organizations: 86 open to all. Most popular organizations: Community Action Program, Associated Students, Activities Programming Board, Multicultural Programming Board, Residence Hall Association. Major annual events: Bronco Blowout, Global Village, Star Search. Student services: legal services, health clinic, personal-psychological counseling. Campus security: 24-hour emergency response devices and patrols, late night transport-escort service, controlled dormitory access. 2,159 college housing spaces available; 2,075 were occupied in 2003-04. Freshmen given priority for college housing. Option: coed housing available. Orradre Library plus 1 other with 1.2 million books, 1.7 million microform titles, 8,795 serials, 14,605 audiovisual materials, an OPAC, and a Web page. Operations spending for 2004 fiscal year: $4.9 million. 800 computers available on campus for general student use. Computer purchase/lease plans available. A campuswide network can be accessed from student residence rooms and from off campus. Staffed computer lab on campus.

Community Environment: Santa Clara is known as the "Mission City." It has an ideal climate, with a mean temperature of 71 degrees. Buses, trains and airlines serve the area. Community facilities include churches, a community symphony orchestra and an art gallery. Santa Clara is in the heart of "Silicon Valley," a dynamic center of high technology and progressive businesses. There are numerous part-time work opportunities. Recreational facilities include miles of beaches within a 30-minute drive of the university. San Francisco is 50 miles to the north.

■ **SANTA MONICA COLLEGE** *Q-3*
1900 Pico Blvd.
Santa Monica, CA 90405-1628
Tel: (310)434-4000
Admissions: (310)434-4880
Web Site: http://www.smc.edu/

Description: State and locally supported, 2-year, coed. Part of California Community College System. Awards certificates, transfer associate, and terminal associate degrees. Founded 1929. Setting: 40-acre urban campus with easy access to Los Angeles. Endowment: $4.6 million. Total enrollment: 24,497. 6,393 applied. Full-time: 8,902 students, 47% women, 53% men. Part-time: 15,595 students, 58% women, 42% men. Students come from 50 states and territories, 101 other countries, 4% from out-of-state, 1% Native American, 29% Hispanic, 10% black, 16% Asian American or Pacific Islander, 14% international, 25% 25 or older, 56% transferred in. Core. Calendar: semester plus optional winter and summer terms. Academic remediation for entering students, ESL program, services for LD students, advanced placement, honors program, independent study, distance learning,

summer session for credit, part-time degree program, adult/continuing education programs, co-op programs and internships. Study abroad program. ROTC: Army (c).

Entrance Requirements: Open admission. Option: early admission. Required: high school transcript. Placement: ACT, ACT COMPASS, ACCUPLACER required for some. Entrance: noncompetitive. Application deadline: 8/30. Notification: continuous until 8/30.

Costs Per Year: Application fee: $0. Nonresident tuition: $171 per unit part-time. Mandatory fees: $26 per unit part-time, $27 per term part-time.

Collegiate Environment: Orientation program. Drama-theater group, choral group, student-run newspaper. Social organizations: 50 open to all. Most popular organizations: Club Latino United for Education, African Student Union, Gay and Lesbian Union, Alpha Gamma Sigma, International Speakers Club. Major annual events: Transfer College Fair, Club Row, International Festival. Student services: legal services, health clinic, personal-psychological counseling, women's center. Campus security: 24-hour emergency response devices and patrols, student patrols, late night transport-escort service. College housing not available. Santa Monica College Library with 101,317 books, 77,458 microform titles, 389 serials, an OPAC, and a Web page. Operations spending for 2004 fiscal year: $1.3 million. 600 computers available on campus for general student use. A campuswide network can be accessed from off-campus. Staffed computer lab on campus.

Community Environment: A residential city and beach resort, Santa Monica is part of the Los Angeles metropolitan area. The temperature averages 64.2 degrees. All forms of major transportation serve the area. Excellent shopping facilities are in the city. Part-time employment is available. Beach area includes Ocean Park, Malibu Beach, and Will Rogers State Beach, providing recreational activities in addition to the city facilities for outdoor sports.

■ **SANTA ROSA JUNIOR COLLEGE** *I-4*
1501 Mendocino Ave.
Santa Rosa, CA 95401-4395
Tel: (707)527-4011
Admissions: (707)527-4510
E-mail: rlopilato@santarosa.edu
Web Site: http://www.santarosa.edu/

Description: State and locally supported, 2-year, coed. Part of California Community College System. Awards certificates, transfer associate, and terminal associate degrees. Founded 1918. Setting: 93-acre urban campus with easy access to San Francisco. Endowment: $15.7 million. Educational spending for 2005 fiscal year: $2080 per student. Total enrollment: 29,867. Student-undergrad faculty ratio is 19:1. 4,434 applied, 100% were admitted. Students come from 29 states and territories, 39 other countries, 2% from out-of-state, 56% 25 or older. Core. Calendar: semesters. Academic remediation for entering students, ESL program, services for LD students, advanced placement, independent study, distance learning, summer session for credit, part-time degree program, adult/continuing education programs, co-op programs and internships. Off campus study. Study abroad program. ROTC: Army (c).

Entrance Requirements: Open admission except for allied health programs. Options: electronic application, early admission. Entrance: noncompetitive. Application deadline: Rolling. Notification: continuous.

Costs Per Year: Application fee: $0. State resident tuition: $0 full-time. Nonresident tuition: $5630 full-time. Mandatory fees: $746 full-time, $26 per unit part-time.

Collegiate Environment: Drama-theater group, choral group, student-run newspaper. Social organizations: 31 open to all. Most popular organizations: International Club, MECHA, Alpha Gamma Sigma, Asian/Pacific Island Association, Phi Theta Kappa. Major annual events: Day Under the Oaks, Flea Market, Club Days. Student services: health clinic, personal-psychological counseling. Campus security: 24-hour emergency response devices and patrols. College housing not available. Plover Library plus 1 other with 119,803 books, 184,306 microform titles, 393 serials, 9,430 audiovisual materials, an OPAC, and a Web page. Operations spending for 2004 fiscal year: $2 million. 1,325 computers available on campus for general student use. A campuswide network can be accessed from off-campus. Staffed computer lab on campus.

Community Environment: Sonama County, located 50 miles north of San Francisco, is well known for its rolling hills, grassy valleys, vineyards and spectacular coast. The county's moderate climate is characterized by average afternoon temperatures in the lower 80's during the summer and mid-50's in the winter. Average annual rainfall is approximately 30 inches. Santa

Rosa is the county seat and commercial center for the north coast's Redwood Empire. The city enjoys an abundance of urban amenities including schools and colleges, business centers, three general hospitals and a family residency program as well as local theatres, the Santa Rosa Symphony, and the Luther Burbank Center for the Performing Arts. Nearby parks offer miles of hiking and riding trails as well as facilities for sailing, swimming, fishing, picnicking and camping.

■ **SANTIAGO CANYON COLLEGE** *S-7*

8045 East Chapman Ave.
Orange, CA 92869
Tel: (714)564-4000
Fax: (714)564-4379
Web Site: http://www.sccollege.edu/
Description: State-supported, 2-year, coed. Part of California Community College System. Awards certificates, transfer associate, and terminal associate degrees. Founded 2000. Total enrollment: 10,214. 50% 25 or older. Core. Calendar: semesters. Academic remediation for entering students, ESL program, services for LD students, advanced placement, freshman honors college, honors program, distance learning, summer session for credit, part-time degree program, external degree program, adult/continuing education programs, co-op programs.
Entrance Requirements: Open admission. Option: early admission. Entrance: noncompetitive. Application deadline: 8/21.
Collegiate Environment: College housing not available. Santiago Canyon College Library with 31,000 books, 135 microform titles, 2,260 serials, 4,082 audiovisual materials, an OPAC, and a Web page. 45 computers available on campus for general student use.

■ **SCRIPPS COLLEGE** *V-10*

1030 Columbia Ave.
Claremont, CA 91711-3948
Tel: (909)621-8000
Free: 800-770-1333
Admissions: (909)621-8149
Fax: (909)621-8323
E-mail: admission@scrippscollege.edu
Web Site: http://www.scrippscollege.edu
Description: Independent, 4-year, women only. Part of The Claremont Colleges Consortium. Awards bachelor's degrees. Founded 1926. Setting: 30-acre suburban campus with easy access to Los Angeles. Endowment: $199.9 million. Research spending for 2004 fiscal year: $407,300. Educational spending for 2005 fiscal year: $22,707 per student. Total enrollment: 908. Student-undergrad faculty ratio is 11:1. 1,836 applied, 46% were admitted. 69% from top 10% of their high school class, 93% from top quarter, 98% from top half. 17 National Merit Scholars, 7 valedictorians. Full-time: 879 students. Part-time: 8 students. Students come from 45 states and territories, 58% from out-of-state, 0.3% Native American, 5% Hispanic, 3% black, 13% Asian American or Pacific Islander, 2% international, 1% 25 or older, 92% live on campus, 2% transferred in. Retention: 88% of full-time freshmen returned the following year. Academic areas with the most degrees conferred: area and ethnic studies; visual and performing arts; social sciences. Core. Calendar: semesters. Advanced placement, accelerated degree program, self-designed majors, honors program, independent study, double major, part-time degree program, internships. Off campus study at 5 members of The Claremont Colleges, Colby College, Haverford College, Spelman College, California Institute of Technology, American University (Washington Semester), Drew University, George Washington University. Study abroad program. ROTC: Army (c), Air Force (c).
Entrance Requirements: Options: Peterson's Universal Application, Common Application, electronic application, early decision, deferred admission, international baccalaureate accepted. Required: essay, high school transcript, 3 recommendations, graded writing sample, SAT or ACT. Recommended: minimum 3.0 high school GPA, interview. Entrance: very difficult. Application deadlines: 1/15, 11/1 for early decision plan 1, 1/1 for early decision plan 2. Notification: 4/1, 12/15 for early decision plan 1, 2/15 for early decision plan 2.
Costs Per Year: Application fee: $50. Comprehensive fee: $41,000 includes full-time tuition ($31,332), mandatory fees ($168), and college room and board ($9500). College room only: $5100. Full-time tuition and fees vary according to program. Room and board charges vary according to board plan.
Collegiate Environment: Orientation program. Drama-theater group, choral group, student-run newspaper, radio station. Social organizations: 200 open to all. Most popular organizations: College Council, Asian/Black/Latina clubs,

National Organization for Women, Sexual Assault Task Force. Major annual events: Spring Formal, holiday dinners, 5-College Carnival. Student services: health clinic, personal-psychological counseling, women's center. Campus security: 24-hour emergency response devices and patrols, late night transport-escort service, controlled dormitory access. 738 college housing spaces available; all were occupied in 2003-04. Freshmen guaranteed college housing. On-campus residence required in freshman year. Option: women-only housing available. Honnold Library plus 4 others with 998,823 books, 1.4 million microform titles, 5,733 serials, 4,361 audiovisual materials, an OPAC, and a Web page. Operations spending for 2004 fiscal year: $1.1 million. 72 computers available on campus for general student use. A campuswide network can be accessed from student residence rooms and from off campus. Staffed computer lab on campus.
Community Environment: The Claremont consortium consists of five undergraduate institutions and the Claremont Graduate University -- all located in an area approximately one square mile in size.

■ **SHASTA BIBLE COLLEGE** *D-4*

2951 Goodwater Ave.
Redding, CA 96002
Tel: (530)221-4275
Free: 800-800-6929
Web Site: http://www.shasta.edu/
Description: Independent nondenominational, comprehensive, coed. Awards associate, bachelor's, and master's degrees. Founded 1971. Setting: 25-acre small town campus. Endowment: $1.1 million. Research spending for 2004 fiscal year: $51,642. Educational spending for 2005 fiscal year: $577 per student. Total enrollment: 123. 9 applied, 100% were admitted. Full-time: 57 students, 44% women, 56% men. Part-time: 33 students, 45% women, 55% men. Students come from 13 states and territories, 41% from out-of-state, 2% Native American, 0% Hispanic, 0% black, 0% Asian American or Pacific Islander, 0% international, 51% 25 or older, 39% live on campus, 19% transferred in. Retention: 90% of full-time freshmen returned the following year. Core. Calendar: semesters. Academic remediation for entering students, ESL program, accelerated degree program, independent study, distance learning, double major, summer session for credit, part-time degree program, adult/continuing education programs, co-op programs, graduate courses open to undergrads.
Entrance Requirements: Open admission. Options: Peterson's Universal Application, Common Application, early admission, international baccalaureate accepted. Required: essay, high school transcript, minimum 2.0 high school GPA, 4 recommendations. Required for some: interview. Entrance: noncompetitive. Application deadline: 8/28. Notification: continuous until 9/10.
Costs Per Year: Application fee: $35. Tuition: $6400 full-time, $200 per unit part-time. Mandatory fees: $350 full-time, $350 per year part-time. College room only: $1650.
Collegiate Environment: Choral group, student-run newspaper. Major annual events: Fall Round-Up-Barbecue at the Lake, Christmas Banquet, Graduation Banquet. Student services: personal-psychological counseling, women's center. Campus security: 24-hour emergency response devices. 60 college housing spaces available; 35 were occupied in 2003-04. Freshmen given priority for college housing. Options: men-only, women-only housing available. The Library plus 1 other with 30,321 books and 103 serials. Operations spending for 2004 fiscal year: $25,000. 15 computers available on campus for general student use. A campuswide network can be accessed. Staffed computer lab on campus.

■ **SHASTA COLLEGE** *D-4*

PO Box 496006
Redding, CA 96049-6006
Tel: (530)225-4600
Admissions: (530)225-4841
Web Site: http://www.shastacollege.edu/
Description: State and locally supported, 2-year, coed. Part of California Community College System. Awards certificates, transfer associate, and terminal associate degrees. Founded 1948. Setting: 336-acre rural campus. Endowment: $1.3 million. Research spending for 2004 fiscal year: $175,040. Educational spending for 2005 fiscal year: $1944 per student. Total enrollment: 10,240. 3,586 applied, 100% were admitted. Full-time: 4,336 students, 59% women, 41% men. Part-time: 5,904 students, 62% women, 38% men. 2% from out-of-state, 4% Native American, 6% Hispanic, 1% black, 3% Asian American or Pacific Islander, 0.3% international, 56% 25 or older. Core. Calendar: semesters. Academic remediation for entering students,

ESL program, services for LD students, advanced placement, honors program, distance learning, double major, summer session for credit, part-time degree program, adult/continuing education programs, co-op programs and internships.

Entrance Requirements: Open admission. Options: Common Application, early admission. Required: high school transcript. Placement: Assessment and Placement Services for Community Colleges required; SAT or ACT recommended. Entrance: noncompetitive. Application deadline: Rolling. Notification: continuous.

Collegiate Environment: Orientation program. Drama-theater group, choral group, student-run newspaper. Social organizations: 8 open to all. Most popular organizations: Associated Student Body, Environmental Resource Leadership Club, Intercultural Club, Inter-Varsity Christian Fellowship, Music Education National Conference. Major annual events: Cinco De Mayo, 'Tis The Season, Halloween Festivities. Student services: health clinic, personal-psychological counseling. Campus security: 24-hour emergency response devices, student patrols, late night transport-escort service, 16-hour patrols by trained security personnel. Option: coed housing available. Shasta College Learning Resource Center with 67,500 books, 55,486 microform titles, 1,700 serials, 4,859 audiovisual materials, an OPAC, and a Web page. Operations spending for 2004 fiscal year: $885,790. 154 computers available on campus for general student use. A campuswide network can be accessed from off-campus. Staffed computer lab on campus.

Community Environment: Redding is located at the northern end of the Sacramento Valley and is served by buses, railroads and airlines. The city provides unlimited recreational opportunities; Shasta National Forest, Sacramento Canyon, Mount Shasta, Shasta Dam which is the second largest concrete dam in the world and Shasta Lake which encompasses 30,000 acres. Excellent fishing, camping, picnicking and swimming in the area. Redding is a trade center with good shopping facilities.

■ **SIERRA COLLEGE** *AA-10*
5000 Rocklin Rd.
Rocklin, CA 95677-3397
Tel: (916)624-3333
Admissions: (916)789-2939
Web Site: http://www.sierracollege.edu/
Description: State-supported, 2-year, coed. Part of California Community College System. Awards certificates, transfer associate, and terminal associate degrees. Founded 1936. Setting: 327-acre suburban campus with easy access to Sacramento. Research spending for 2004 fiscal year: $192,586. Total enrollment: 19,416. 24,000 applied, 100% were admitted. Full-time: 5,355 students, 54% women, 46% men. Part-time: 14,061 students, 57% women, 43% men. 1% from out-of-state, 2% Native American, 8% Hispanic, 2% black, 2% Asian American or Pacific Islander, 1% international, 32% 25 or older, 1% live on campus, 4% transferred in. Core. Calendar: semesters. Academic remediation for entering students, ESL program, services for LD students, advanced placement, accelerated degree program, independent study, distance learning, double major, summer session for credit, part-time degree program, internships. Off campus study. Study abroad program.
Entrance Requirements: Open admission. Options: Peterson's Universal Application, Common Application, electronic application, early admission. Placement: APS required; ACT recommended. Entrance: noncompetitive. Application deadline: Rolling. Notification: continuous.
Costs Per Year: Application fee: $0. State resident tuition: $0 full-time. Nonresident tuition: $4470 full-time, $149 per unit part-time. Mandatory fees: $780 full-time, $26 per unit part-time.
Collegiate Environment: Orientation program. Drama-theater group, choral group, student-run newspaper. Social organizations: 32 open to all. Most popular organizations: Drama Club, student government, Art Club, band, Aggie Club. Major annual events: Scholarship Awards Banquet, Kids' Day, Sierra Daze. Student services: health clinic, personal-psychological counseling. Campus security: 24-hour emergency response devices and patrols, late night transport-escort service. 148 college housing spaces available; 135 were occupied in 2003-04. No special consideration for freshman housing applicants. Option: coed housing available. Leary Resource Center plus 1 other with 69,879 books, 189 serials, and an OPAC. Operations spending for 2004 fiscal year: $865,210. 430 computers available on campus for general student use. A campuswide network can be accessed from off-campus. Staffed computer lab on campus.
Community Environment: Population 9,820. Rocklin is located on Interstate 80 in the Loomis Basin, 23 miles northeast of Sacramento; the center of a large deciduous fruit-raising area. All forms of transportation available at nearby cities of Auburn and Roseville. Rocklin has libraries,

hospitals, clinics, a health department, churches, and civic, fraternal, and veteran's organizations. Industry includes three lumber mills and a granite quarry. Recreational activities include swimming, picnicking, skiing, fishing and hunting. Seasonal and part-time employment is available.

■ **SILICON VALLEY UNIVERSITY** *L-5*
3590 North First St., Ste. 320
San Jose, CA 95134
Tel: (408)435-8989
Fax: (408)435-8989
Web Site: http://www.svuca.edu/
Description: Proprietary, comprehensive, coed. Awards bachelor's and master's degrees. Calendar: trimesters.

■ **SIMPSON UNIVERSITY** *D-4*
2211 College View Dr.
Redding, CA 96003-8606
Tel: (530)226-4606
Free: 800-598-2493
Admissions: (530)226-5600
Fax: (530)226-4861
E-mail: admissions@simpsonuniversity.edu
Web Site: http://www.simpsonuniversity.edu/
Description: Independent, comprehensive, coed, affiliated with The Christian and Missionary Alliance. Awards associate, bachelor's, and master's degrees. Founded 1921. Setting: 92-acre suburban campus. Endowment: $3.2 million. Educational spending for 2005 fiscal year: $5315 per student. Total enrollment: 1,087. Faculty: 107 (40 full-time, 67 part-time). Student-undergrad faculty ratio is 17:1. 929 applied, 54% were admitted. 19% from top 10% of their high school class, 40% from top quarter, 67% from top half. Full-time: 899 students, 64% women, 36% men. Part-time: 24 students, 83% women, 17% men. Students come from 28 states and territories, 6 other countries, 20% from out-of-state, 1% Native American, 4% Hispanic, 1% black, 5% Asian American or Pacific Islander, 1% international, 20% 25 or older, 67% live on campus, 11% transferred in. Retention: 58% of full-time freshmen returned the following year. Academic areas with the most degrees conferred: liberal arts/general studies; psychology; theology and religious vocations. Core. Calendar: semesters. Services for LD students, advanced placement, accelerated degree program, self-designed majors, honors program, independent study, distance learning, double major, summer session for credit, part-time degree program, adult/continuing education programs, internships, graduate courses open to undergrads. Off campus study at Coalition for Christian Colleges and Universities. Study abroad program.
Entrance Requirements: Options: electronic application, deferred admission. Required: essay, high school transcript, 2 recommendations, Christian commitment, SAT or ACT. Required for some: interview. Entrance: moderately difficult. Application deadline: Rolling. Notification: continuous.
Costs Per Year: Application fee: $20. Comprehensive fee: $24,000 includes full-time tuition ($17,800) and college room and board ($6200). Part-time tuition: $750 per credit hour.
Collegiate Environment: Orientation program. Drama-theater group, choral group, student-run newspaper. Social organizations: 17 open to all. Most popular organizations: Summer Missions Trips, Worship Team (chapel), Student Senate, Spiritual Action Committee, Psychology Club. Major annual events: Homecoming and Genesis 'Nite Life' Events, Winter and Spring Banquets, International Street Festival. Student services: health clinic, personal-psychological counseling. Campus security: 24-hour emergency response devices and patrols, student patrols, late night transport-escort service, controlled dormitory access, emergency whistle program and monthly campus safety meetings. 590 college housing spaces available; 495 were occupied in 2003-04. Freshmen guaranteed college housing. On-campus residence required through junior year. Options: men-only, women-only housing available. Start-Kilgour Memorial Library with 87,203 books, 242,577 microform titles, 292 serials, 2,770 audiovisual materials, an OPAC, and a Web page. Operations spending for 2004 fiscal year: $396,095. 42 computers available on campus for general student use. A campuswide network can be accessed from student residence rooms and from off campus. Staffed computer lab on campus.

■ **SKYLINE COLLEGE** *I-4*
3300 College Dr.
San Bruno, CA 94066-1698
Tel: (650)738-4100

Web Site: http://skylinecollege.net/

Description: State and locally supported, 2-year, coed. Part of San Mateo County Community College District System. Awards certificates, transfer associate, and terminal associate degrees. Founded 1969. Setting: 125-acre suburban campus with easy access to San Francisco. Total enrollment: 8,147. Student-undergrad faculty ratio is 27:1. Students come from 9 other countries, 2% from out-of-state, 9% 25 or older. Core. Calendar: semesters. Academic remediation for entering students, ESL program, services for LD students, advanced placement, honors program, distance learning, summer session for credit, part-time degree program, adult/continuing education programs, co-op programs. Study abroad program.

Entrance Requirements: Open admission except for international students or auto technology, respiratory therapy, cosmetology, concurrent high school, emergency medical, surgical technician programs. Required for some: high school transcript. Entrance: noncompetitive. Application deadline: Rolling.

Costs Per Year: Application fee: $0.

Collegiate Environment: Choral group, student-run newspaper. Social organizations: 15 open to all. Student services: health clinic, personal-psychological counseling. Campus security: security guards during open hours. College housing not available. Skyline College Library with 50,000 books, 230 serials, and an OPAC. 220 computers available on campus for general student use. A campuswide network can be accessed from off-campus. Staffed computer lab on campus.

Community Environment: Population 38,000. San Bruno, located 12 miles south of San Francisco, is known as "The Airport City." The climate is temperate all year long, with cool, often foggy summers. All modes of transportation serve the area. This is a residential community with regional shopping centers, churches, library, and hospitals in nearby cities. Cultural advantages of San Francisco are appreciated by the people in San Bruno since it is so near.

■ **SOKA UNIVERSITY OF AMERICA** *T-7*
1 University Dr.
Aliso Viejo, CA 92656
Tel: (949)480-4000; 888-600-SOKA
Admissions: (949)480-4007
Fax: (949)480-4001
E-mail: hauber@soka.edu
Web Site: http://www.soka.edu/

Description: Independent, 4-year, coed. Awards bachelor's and master's degrees. Founded 2001. Endowment: $445 million. Total enrollment: 380. Faculty: 70 (37 full-time, 33 part-time). Student-undergrad faculty ratio is 8:1. 278 applied, 42% were admitted. 44% from top 10% of their high school class, 81% from top quarter, 98% from top half. Full-time: 360 students, 62% women, 38% men. Students come from 17 states and territories, 32 other countries, 81% from out-of-state, 0% Native American, 3% Hispanic, 3% black, 28% Asian American or Pacific Islander, 54% international, 3% 25 or older, 99% live on campus, 0% transferred in. Retention: 94% of full-time freshmen returned the following year. Academic area with the most degrees conferred: liberal arts/general studies. Core. Calendar: semesters. Academic remediation for entering students, services for LD students, independent study, internships. Study abroad program.

Entrance Requirements: Options: electronic application, early admission, deferred admission, international baccalaureate accepted. Required: essay, high school transcript, 2 recommendations, SAT or ACT, ACT Writing Test. Recommended: SAT Subject Tests. Entrance: moderately difficult. Application deadlines: 1/6, 10/15 for early action. Notification: 3/15, 12/1 for early action.

Costs Per Year: Application fee: $45. Comprehensive fee: $29,256 includes full-time tuition ($20,856) and college room and board ($8400).

Collegiate Environment: Choral group, student-run newspaper. Student services: health clinic, personal-psychological counseling, career paslnning and placement, volunteer and internship placement. 486 college housing spaces available; 372 were occupied in 2003-04. Freshmen guaranteed college housing. On-campus residence required through senior year. Option: coed housing available. Daisaku and Kaneko Ikeda Library with 63,806 books, 3,780 microform titles, 11,141 serials, 658 audiovisual materials, an OPAC, and a Web page.

■ **SOLANO COMMUNITY COLLEGE** *J-5*
4000 Suisun Valley Rd.
Suisun City, CA 94534-3197
Tel: (707)864-7000
Admissions: (707)864-7113

Fax: (707)864-7175
E-mail: admissions@solano.cc.ca.us
Web Site: http://www.solano.edu/

Description: State and locally supported, 2-year, coed. Part of California Community College System. Awards certificates, diplomas, transfer associate, and terminal associate degrees. Founded 1945. Setting: 192-acre rural campus with easy access to Sacramento and San Francisco. Total enrollment: 12,027. Students come from 43 states and territories, 6 other countries, 1% from out-of-state, 1% Native American, 14% Hispanic, 15% black, 18% Asian American or Pacific Islander, 0.2% international, 46% 25 or older. Core. Calendar: semesters. Academic remediation for entering students, ESL program, services for LD students, advanced placement, honors program, independent study, distance learning, double major, summer session for credit, part-time degree program, adult/continuing education programs, co-op programs. Off campus study at California State University, Hayward; University of California, Davis; University of California, Berkeley. Study abroad program.

Entrance Requirements: Open admission. Options: electronic application, early admission, deferred admission. Entrance: noncompetitive. Application deadline: Rolling.

Collegiate Environment: Orientation program. Drama-theater group, choral group, student-run newspaper. Social organizations: national fraternities. Student services: personal-psychological counseling. Campus security: 24-hour patrols, student patrols, late night transport-escort service. College housing not available. Solano Community College Library with 32,000 books. 300 computers available on campus for general student use. A campuswide network can be accessed from off-campus. Staffed computer lab on campus.

■ **SONOMA COLLEGE (PETALUMA)** *J-4*
1304 South Point Blvd., Ste. 280
Petaluma, CA 94954
Tel: (707)283-0800
Free: 800-437-9474
Admissions: (707)664-9267
Web Site: http://www.sonomacollege.com/

Description: Proprietary, 2-year, coed. Awards certificates and terminal associate degrees. Founded 1993. Setting: suburban campus with easy access to San Francisco. Total enrollment: 118. 22 applied, 100% were admitted. Students come from 3 states and territories, 1 other country, 5% from out-of-state, 60% 25 or older. Calendar: semesters. Distance learning, internships.

Entrance Requirements: Open admission. Required: essay, high school transcript, minimum 2.0 high school GPA, 2 recommendations, interview. Entrance: noncompetitive.

Collegiate Environment: Campus security: 24-hour emergency response devices and patrols. College housing not available. 15 computers available on campus for general student use.

■ **SONOMA COLLEGE (SAN FRANCISCO)** *K-4*
78 First St.
San Francisco, CA 94105
Tel: (415)543-1833; 888-649-7801
Fax: (415)543-1833
Web Site: http://www.sonomacollege.com/

Description: Proprietary, 2-year, coed. Founded 1992. Calendar: semesters.

■ **SONOMA STATE UNIVERSITY** *I-4*
1801 East Cotati Ave.
Rohnert Park, CA 94928-3609
Tel: (707)664-2880
Admissions: (707)664-2846
Web Site: http://www.sonoma.edu/

Description: State-supported, comprehensive, coed. Part of California State University System. Awards bachelor's and master's degrees. Founded 1960. Setting: 280-acre small town campus with easy access to San Francisco. Endowment: $21.1 million. Educational spending for 2005 fiscal year: $5431 per student. Total enrollment: 7,749. Faculty: 542. Student-undergrad faculty ratio is 23:1. 9,787 applied, 66% were admitted. Full-time: 5,653 students, 63% women, 37% men. Part-time: 946 students, 60% women, 40% men. Students come from 40 states and territories, 29 other countries, 2% from out-of-state, 1% Native American, 11% Hispanic, 2% black, 5% Asian American or Pacific Islander, 1% international, 20% 25 or older, 35% live on campus, 11% transferred in. Retention: 82% of full-time freshmen returned the following year. Core. Calendar: semesters. Academic remediation for entering students, ESL program, services for LD students, advanced placement, accelerated degree program, self-designed majors, honors program, independent study, distance learning, double major, summer session for credit, part-time degree program, adult/continuing education programs, co-op programs and internships, graduate courses open to undergrads. Off campus study at other units of the California State University System, National Student Exchange, Mills College. Study abroad program. ROTC: Army (c), Air Force (c).

Entrance Requirements: Options: electronic application, early admission. Required: high school transcript, SAT or ACT. Entrance: moderately difficult. Application deadline: Rolling. Notification: continuous.

Costs Per Year: Application fee: $55. State resident tuition: $0 full-time. Nonresident tuition: $10,170 full-time. Mandatory fees: $3616 full-time. Full-time tuition and fees vary according to course load. College room and board: $8890. College room only: $6052. Room and board charges vary according to board plan and housing facility.

Collegiate Environment: Orientation program. Drama-theater group, choral group, student-run newspaper, radio station. Social organizations: 100 open to all; national fraternities, national sororities. Most popular organizations: Accounting Forum, Sonoma Earth Action, Re-Entry Student Association, Lacrosse Club, Inter-Varsity Christian Fellowship. Major annual events: Welcome Week, Student Orientation, Science Night. Student services: legal services, health clinic, personal-psychological counseling, women's center. Campus security: 24-hour emergency response devices and patrols, student patrols, late night transport-escort service. 2,480 college housing spaces available; 2,353 were occupied in 2003-04. Freshmen given priority for college housing. Options: coed, women-only housing available. Jean and Charles Schultz Information Center with 636,613 books, 1.7 million microform titles, 21,115 serials, 29,529 audiovisual materials, an OPAC, and a Web page. Operations spending for 2004 fiscal year: $3 million. 400 computers available on campus for general student use. A campuswide network can be accessed from student residence rooms and from off campus. Staffed computer lab on campus.

Community Environment: Population 40,000. Rohnert Park is a rapidly growing suburban community with temperate climate. Located near Santa Rosa (pop. 180,000) in Sonoma County. Buses and airlines serve the area. Community facilities include many shopping centers, civic and sports clubs. Recreational facilities include swimming pools, baseball parks, a community park, golf courses and others within a 20 mile radius. Rohnert Park has the annual Founders Day Parade. There are five hospitals within a 10 mile radius. The Valley of the Moon, San Francisco, the Russian River recreation areas, Redwood National Park and Lake Tahoe are all within driving distance from an hour to a half day. Sonoma county produces premium wine and is the location of many famous wineries.

■ **SOUTH COAST COLLEGE** *S-7*
2011 West Chapman Ave.
Orange, CA 92868
Tel: (714)867-5009
Free: 800-337-8366
Fax: (714)867-5026
Web Site: http://www.southcoastcollege.com/
Description: Proprietary, 2-year, coed. Founded 1961.

■ **SOUTHERN CALIFORNIA INSTITUTE OF ARCHITECTURE** *S-10*
960 East Third St.
Los Angeles, CA 90013
Tel: (213)613-2200
Free: 800-774-7242
Fax: (213)613-0524
E-mail: admissions@sciarc.edu
Web Site: http://www.sciarc.edu/
Description: Independent, comprehensive, coed. Awards bachelor's, master's, and first professional degrees. Founded 1972. Setting: urban campus. Total enrollment: 447. 66% from top half of their high school class. Full-time: 183 students, 27% women, 73% men. Students come from 35 states and territories, 17 other countries, 1% Native American, 22% Hispanic, 2% black, 17% Asian American or Pacific Islander, 12% international, 42% 25 or older. Retention: 40% of full-time freshmen returned the following year. Core. Calendar: semesters. Academic remediation for entering students, ESL program, advanced placement, summer session for credit, co-op programs and internships, graduate courses open to undergrads. Study abroad program.

Entrance Requirements: Option: deferred admission. Required: essay, high school transcript, minimum 2.0 high school GPA, 3 recommendations, portfolio, SAT or ACT. Recommended: interview. Entrance: moderately difficult. Application deadline: 2/1. Notification: continuous until 7/1.
Collegiate Environment: Orientation program. Student-run newspaper. Most popular organizations: Student Council, Academic Council. Campus security: 24-hour emergency response devices and patrols. College housing not available. Kappe Library with 10,000 books and 70 serials. 30 computers available on campus for general student use. A campuswide network can be accessed. Staffed computer lab on campus.

■ **SOUTHERN CALIFORNIA INSTITUTE OF TECHNOLOGY** *T-10*
1900 West Crescent Ave., Bldg. B
Anaheim, CA 92801
Tel: (714)520-5552
Web Site: http://www.scitcollege.com/
Description: Proprietary, primarily 2-year. Awards terminal associate, bachelor's, and master's degrees. Total enrollment: 678. Full-time: 664 students, 39% women, 61% men. 1% Native American, 28% Hispanic, 2% black, 57% Asian American or Pacific Islander, 0.3% international.

■ **SOUTHERN CALIFORNIA SEMINARY** *V-12*
2075 East Madison Ave.
El Cajon, CA 92019
Tel: (619)442-9841
Fax: (619)442-4510
E-mail: coombsd@scbs.edu
Web Site: http://www.socalsem.edu/
Description: Independent interdenominational, comprehensive. Founded 1946.

■ **SOUTHWESTERN COLLEGE** *W-12*
900 Otay Lakes Rd.
Chula Vista, CA 91910-7299
Tel: (619)421-6700
Admissions: (619)482-6550
Web Site: http://www.swc.cc.ca.us/
Description: State and locally supported, 2-year, coed. Part of California Community College System. Awards certificates, transfer associate, and terminal associate degrees. Founded 1961. Setting: 158-acre suburban campus with easy access to San Diego. Endowment: $320,596. Research spending for 2004 fiscal year: $320,000. Educational spending for 2005 fiscal year: $3390 per student. Total enrollment: 18,799. Full-time: 5,609 students, 56% women, 44% men. Part-time: 13,190 students, 56% women, 44% men. 2% from out-of-state, 0.5% Native American, 58% Hispanic, 5% black, 17% Asian American or Pacific Islander, 26% 25 or older, 56% transferred in. Core. Calendar: semesters. Academic remediation for entering students, ESL program, services for LD students, advanced placement, freshman honors college, honors program, independent study, summer session for credit, part-time degree program, external degree program, adult/continuing education programs, co-op programs and internships.

Entrance Requirements: Open admission. Option: early admission. Required for some: high school transcript. Entrance: noncompetitive. Application deadline: Rolling. Notification: continuous.
Collegiate Environment: Drama-theater group, choral group, student-run newspaper. Social organizations: 20 open to all; national fraternities. Most popular organizations: MECHA, Business Club, Alpha Phi Epsilon, ABLE (disabled club), Society of Hispanic Engineers. Major annual events: Earth Day, Heritage Awareness Day, Human Services Day. Student services: health clinic, personal-psychological counseling, women's center. Campus security: 24-hour emergency response devices, student patrols, late night transport-escort service. College housing not available. Southwestern College Library with 85,003 books, 79,488 microform titles, 6,983 audiovisual materials, an OPAC, and a Web page. Operations spending for 2004 fiscal year: $848,734. 1,300 computers available on campus for general student use. A campuswide network can be accessed from off-campus. Staffed computer lab on campus.

■ **STANFORD UNIVERSITY** *F-15*
Stanford, CA 94305-9991
Tel: (650)723-2300
Admissions: (650)723-2091
Fax: (650)725-2846
E-mail: admission@stanford.edu

Web Site: http://www.stanford.edu/

Description: Independent, university, coed. Awards bachelor's, master's, doctoral, and first professional degrees. Founded 1891. Setting: 8,180-acre suburban campus with easy access to San Francisco. Endowment: $12.2 billion. Research spending for 2004 fiscal year: $930.2 million. Total enrollment: 19,042. Faculty: 1,031 (1,010 full-time, 21 part-time). Student-undergrad faculty ratio is 6:1. 20,192 applied, 12% were admitted. 89% from top 10% of their high school class, 97% from top quarter, 99% from top half. Full-time: 6,515 students, 47% women, 53% men. Part-time: 61 students, 56% women, 44% men. Students come from 52 states and territories, 62 other countries, 56% from out-of-state, 2% Native American, 11% Hispanic, 10% black, 24% Asian American or Pacific Islander, 6% international, 8% 25 or older, 94% live on campus, 1% transferred in. Retention: 98% of full-time freshmen returned the following year. Academic areas with the most degrees conferred: social sciences; interdisciplinary studies; engineering. Core. Services for LD students, advanced placement, self-designed majors, honors program, independent study, double major, summer session for credit, internships, graduate courses open to undergrads. Off campus study at Howard University; Hopkins Marine Station; Spelman College; Morehouse College, Dartmouth College. Study abroad program. ROTC: Army (c), Naval (c), Air Force (c).

Entrance Requirements: Options: early action, deferred admission, international baccalaureate accepted. Required: essay, high school transcript, 2 recommendations, SAT or ACT. Recommended: SAT Subject Tests. Entrance: most difficult. Application deadlines: 12/15, 11/1 for early action. Notification: 4/1, 12/15 for early action.

Costs Per Year: Application fee: $75. One-time mandatory fee: $425. Comprehensive fee: $41,132 includes full-time tuition ($31,200) and college room and board ($9932). College room only: $5275. Room and board charges vary according to board plan.

Collegiate Environment: Orientation program. Drama-theater group, choral group, marching band, student-run newspaper, radio station. Social organizations: 600 open to all; national fraternities, national sororities. Most popular organizations: Ram's Head (theatre club), Axe Committee (athletic support), Business Association of Engineering Students, Asian-American Student Association, Stanford Daily. Major annual events: Big Game, Gaities, Full Moon on the Quad. Student services: legal services, health clinic, personal-psychological counseling, women's center. Campus security: 24-hour emergency response devices and patrols, late night transport-escort service, controlled dormitory access. 6,130 college housing spaces available; all were occupied in 2003-04. Freshmen guaranteed college housing. On-campus residence required in freshman year. Options: coed, women-only housing available. Green Library plus 18 others with 8 million books, 5.8 million microform titles, 50,056 serials, 1.3 million audiovisual materials, an OPAC, and a Web page. Operations spending for 2004 fiscal year: $36.2 million. 1,000 computers available on campus for general student use. A campuswide network can be accessed from student residence rooms and from off campus. Staffed computer lab on campus.

Community Environment: Stanford is an unincorporated campus adjacent to Palo Alto. Palo Alto with a population of 60,000 is located 30 miles south of San Francisco with an ideal climate, the summer average being 70 degrees and the winter average 55 degrees. The average rainfall is 15.5 inches. The city is served by all modes of transportation, the San Francisco Airport being 18 miles north. Palo Alto has three libraries, a museum, art gallery, hotels, hospitals, and churches. The Silicon Valley, in large part an offspring of Stanford, begins at campus edge. The cultural and recreation opportunities of San Francisco and San Jose are added to the many of the Stanford campus and the surrounding area. The Pacific Ocean is 32 miles to the west; the Monterey peninsula is 75 miles to the south. The Sierra Nevada, 160 miles away and the site of several national parks, are a popular resort area for camping, hiking, and skiing.

■ **TAFT COLLEGE** Q-7

29 Emmons Park Dr.
Taft, CA 93268-2317
Tel: (661)763-7700
Admissions: (661)763-7763
Fax: (661)763-7705
Web Site: http://www.taftcollege.edu/

Description: State and locally supported, 2-year, coed. Part of California Community College System. Awards certificates and transfer associate degrees. Founded 1922. Setting: 15-acre small town campus. Endowment: $14,405. Total enrollment: 7,024. 1,249 applied, 100% were admitted. Full-time: 561 students, 61% women, 39% men. Part-time: 6,463 students, 23%

women, 77% men. Students come from 16 states and territories, 5% from out-of-state, 2% Native American, 24% Hispanic, 14% black, 4% Asian American or Pacific Islander, 55% 25 or older, 6% live on campus, 11% transferred in. Core. Calendar: semesters. Academic remediation for entering students, ESL program, services for LD students, advanced placement, honors program, independent study, distance learning, summer session for credit, part-time degree program, adult/continuing education programs.

Entrance Requirements: Open admission. Option: electronic application. Required for some: high school transcript. Entrance: noncompetitive. Application deadline: Rolling.

Costs Per Year: Application fee: $0. State resident tuition: $0 full-time. Nonresident tuition: $4530 full-time, $151 per unit part-time. Mandatory fees: $780 full-time, $26 per unit part-time. Full-time tuition and fees vary according to course load. Part-time tuition and fees vary according to course load. College room and board: $3146. College room only: $1294.

Collegiate Environment: Orientation program. Student-run newspaper. Social organizations: 3 open to all. Most popular organizations: International Club, Alpha Gamma Sigma, Rotoract Club, ASB Club. Student services: personal-psychological counseling. Campus security: controlled dormitory access, parking lot security. 160 college housing spaces available; 93 were occupied in 2003-04. No special consideration for freshman housing applicants. Option: coed housing available. Taft College Library with 28,500 books, 13,000 microform titles, 150 serials, 25 audiovisual materials, an OPAC, and a Web page. Operations spending for 2004 fiscal year: $263,133. 91 computers available on campus for general student use. A campuswide network can be accessed. Staffed computer lab on campus.

Community Environment: The population of the Taft area is 18,500. Centrally located two and one-half hours north of Los Angeles, Taft has a mild climate with hot summers. The city, surrounded by oilfields, is an important supply point for field equipment. Churches of all denominations, hospital, library, and shopping facilities make up the town. Part-time employment is available. Recreational facilities include a theatre, golf course, and more. Apartments are available.

■ **THOMAS AQUINAS COLLEGE** S-8

10000 North Ojai Rd.
Santa Paula, CA 93060-9980
Tel: (805)525-4417
Free: 800-634-9797
Fax: (805)525-9342
E-mail: jpdaly@thomasaquinas.edu
Web Site: http://www.thomasaquinas.edu/

Description: Independent Roman Catholic, 4-year, coed. Awards bachelor's degrees. Founded 1971. Setting: 170-acre rural campus with easy access to Los Angeles. Endowment: $10.1 million. Educational spending for 2005 fiscal year: $10,697 per student. Total enrollment: 359. Student-undergrad faculty ratio is 12:1. 196 applied, 81% were admitted. 75% from top 10% of their high school class, 75% from top quarter, 100% from top half. 1 National Merit Scholar, 3 valedictorians. Full-time: 359 students, 51% women, 49% men. Students come from 42 states and territories, 6 other countries, 61% from out-of-state, 1% Native American, 7% Hispanic, 0.3% black, 3% Asian American or Pacific Islander, 7% international, 4% 25 or older, 99% live on campus, 0% transferred in. Retention: 91% of full-time freshmen returned the following year. Academic area with the most degrees conferred: liberal arts/general studies. Core. Calendar: semesters.

Entrance Requirements: Options: early admission, deferred admission, international baccalaureate accepted. Required: essay, high school transcript, 3 recommendations, SAT or ACT. Recommended: minimum 3.0 high school GPA. Required for some: interview. Entrance: very difficult. Application deadline: Rolling. Notification: continuous.

Costs Per Year: Application fee: $0. Comprehensive fee: $25,300 includes full-time tuition ($19,300) and college room and board ($6000).

Collegiate Environment: Orientation program. Drama-theater group, choral group. Social organizations: 5 open to all. Most popular organizations: choir, Drama Club, Legion of Mary, language clubs, Pro-Life Ministry. Major annual events: St. Thomas Aquinas Day, Presidents Day, Alumni Day. Student services: health clinic, personal-psychological counseling. Campus security: 24-hour emergency response devices, student patrols, daily security daytime patrol. 398 college housing spaces available; 329 were occupied in 2003-04. Freshmen guaranteed college housing. On-campus residence required through senior year. Options: men-only, women-only housing available. St. Bernardine Library with 58,000 books, 3,100 microform titles, 84 serials, and 2,200 audiovisual materials. Operations spending for 2004 fiscal year: $117,795. 15 computers available on campus for general student use. A campuswide network can be accessed. Staffed computer lab on campus.

Community Environment: The college is located in a rural setting 60 miles from Los Angeles and 45 miles from Santa Barbara. It is bordered on three sides by Los Padres National Forest.

■ **TOURO UNIVERSITY INTERNATIONAL** *Z-6*
5665 Plaza Dr., 3rd Floor
Cypress, CA 90630
Tel: (714)816-0366
Fax: (714)816-0367
Web Site: http://www.tourou.edu/

Description: Independent, university, coed. Administratively affiliated with Touro College. Awards bachelor's, master's, and doctoral degrees (offers only online degree programs). Educational spending for 2005 fiscal year: $8000 per student. Total enrollment: 2,507. Faculty: 194 (41 full-time, 153 part-time). Student-undergrad faculty ratio is 18:1. 592 applied, 71% were admitted. Full-time: 1,795 students, 34% women, 66% men. Part-time: 712 students, 36% women, 64% men. Students come from 50 states and territories, 9 other countries, 90% from out-of-state, 85% 25 or older, 45% transferred in. Retention: 95% of full-time freshmen returned the following year. Core. Calendar: four 12 week sessions per year. Distance learning, summer session for credit, part-time degree program, adult/continuing education programs.

Entrance Requirements: Open admission. Options: Common Application, electronic application, international baccalaureate accepted. Required: high school transcript, minimum 3.0 high school GPA. Recommended: interview. Required for some: essay. Entrance: minimally difficult. Application deadline: Rolling. Notification: continuous.

Costs Per Year: Application fee: $75. Tuition: $8000 full-time, $250 per credit part-time. Part-time tuition varies according to degree level.

Collegiate Environment: College housing not available. Touro Cyber Library with 30,692 books, 1,500 serials, and a Web page. Operations spending for 2004 fiscal year: $300,000.

■ **TRINITY LIFE BIBLE COLLEGE** *I-6*
5225 Hillsdale Blvd.
Sacramento, CA 95842
Tel: (916)348-4689
Fax: (916)334-2315
E-mail: kathyc@tlbc.org
Web Site: http://www.tlbc.edu/

Description: Independent nondenominational, 4-year, coed. Founded 1974.

■ **UNIVERSITY OF CALIFORNIA, BERKELEY** *J-4*
Berkeley, CA 94720-1500
Tel: (510)642-6000
Admissions: (510)642-2316
Fax: (510)642-7333
E-mail: ouars@uclink.berkeley.edu
Web Site: http://www.berkeley.edu/

Description: State-supported, university, coed. Part of University of California System. Awards bachelor's, master's, doctoral, and first professional degrees. Founded 1868. Setting: 1,232-acre urban campus with easy access to San Francisco. Endowment: $2 billion. Research spending for 2004 fiscal year: $392.7 million. Educational spending for 2005 fiscal year: $13,663 per student. Total enrollment: 33,558. Faculty: 2,026 (1,543 full-time, 483 part-time). Student-undergrad faculty ratio is 15:1. 36,829 applied, 27% were admitted. 99% from top 10% of their high school class, 100% from top quarter. Full-time: 22,295 students, 54% women, 46% men. Part-time: 1,187 students, 52% women, 48% men. Students come from 53 states and territories, 63 other countries, 10% from out-of-state, 1% Native American, 11% Hispanic, 4% black, 41% Asian American or Pacific Islander, 3% international, 6% 25 or older, 35% live on campus, 7% transferred in. Academic areas with the most degrees conferred: social sciences; biological/life sciences; engineering. Core. Calendar: semesters. ESL program, services for LD students, advanced placement, accelerated degree program, self-designed majors, honors program, independent study, distance learning, double major, summer session for credit, adult/continuing education programs, internships, graduate courses open to undergrads. Off campus study at Holy Names College, Mills College, Dominican College, John F. Kennedy University, San Francisco State University, Sonoma State University, California State University, Hayward. Study abroad program. ROTC: Army, Naval, Air Force.

Entrance Requirements: Options: electronic application, international baccalaureate accepted. Required: essay, high school transcript, SAT or ACT,

SAT Subject Tests. Entrance: very difficult. Application deadline: 11/30. Notification: 3/31. Preference given to state residents.

Costs Per Year: Application fee: $60. State resident tuition: $0 full-time. Nonresident tuition: $18,684 full-time. Mandatory fees $6558 full-time. College room and board: $13,074.

Collegiate Environment: Orientation program. Drama-theater group, choral group, marching band, student-run newspaper, radio station. Social organizations: 400 open to all; national fraternities, national sororities, local fraternities, local sororities; 11% of eligible men and 10% of eligible women are members. Major annual events: Calapolooza, Big Game Week, Student Activities Fair. Student services: legal services, health clinic, personal-psychological counseling, women's center. Campus security: 24-hour emergency response devices and patrols, late night transport-escort service, controlled dormitory access, Office of Emergency Preparedness. 10,000 college housing spaces available. Freshmen guaranteed college housing. On-campus residence required in freshman year. Options: coed, men-only, women-only housing available. Doe Library plus 30 others with 13.9 million books, 6.4 million microform titles, 181,071 serials, 100,560 audiovisual materials, an OPAC, and a Web page. Operations spending for 2004 fiscal year: $46.4 million. 700 computers available on campus for general student use. Computer purchase/lease plans available. A campuswide network can be accessed from student residence rooms and from off campus. Staffed computer lab on campus.

Community Environment: The City of Berkeley (population 104,000) has a long history as one of America's most lively, culturally diverse, and politically adventurous cities. The surrounding San Francisco Bay Area offers culture, entertainment, and natural beauty without rival, much of it within easy reach by BART (Bay Area Rapid Transit).

■ **UNIVERSITY OF CALIFORNIA, DAVIS** *I-5*
One Shields Ave.
Davis, CA 95616
Tel: (530)752-1011
Admissions: (530)752-3018
Fax: (530)752-6363
E-mail: plburnett@ucdavis.edu
Web Site: http://www.ucdavis.edu/

Description: State-supported, university, coed. Part of University of California System. Awards bachelor's, master's, doctoral, and first professional degrees and post-master's certificates. Founded 1905. Setting: 5,993-acre suburban campus with easy access to San Francisco. Endowment: $95.9 million. Educational spending for 2005 fiscal year: $14,179 per student. Total enrollment: 28,815. Faculty: 1,883 (1,610 full-time, 273 part-time). Student-undergrad faculty ratio is 19:1. 30,079 applied, 61% were admitted. 95% from top 10% of their high school class, 100% from top quarter. Full-time: 22,445 students, 55% women, 45% men. Part-time: 290 students, 58% women, 42% men. Students come from 48 states and territories, 101 other countries, 2% from out-of-state, 1% Native American, 11% Hispanic, 3% black, 40% Asian American or Pacific Islander, 2% international, 6% 25 or older, 25% live on campus, 8% transferred in. Retention: 91% of full-time freshmen returned the following year. Academic areas with the most degrees conferred: social sciences; biological/life sciences; engineering. Core. Academic remediation for entering students, ESL program, services for LD students, advanced placement, self-designed majors, freshman honors college, honors program, independent study, double major, summer session for credit, part-time degree program, adult/continuing education programs, internships, graduate courses open to undergrads. Study abroad program. ROTC: Army, Naval (c), Air Force (c).

Entrance Requirements: Option: electronic application. Required: essay, high school transcript, minimum 2.8 high school GPA, high school subject requirements, SAT or ACT, SAT Subject Tests. Entrance: moderately difficult. Application deadline: 11/30. Notification: continuous until 3/15. Preference given to state residents for certain programs.

Costs Per Year: Application fee: $60. State resident tuition: $0 full-time. Nonresident tuition: $18,168 full-time. Mandatory fees $7593 full-time. College room and board: $11,239.

Collegiate Environment: Orientation program. Drama-theater group, choral group, marching band, student-run newspaper, radio station. Social organizations: 320 open to all; national fraternities, national sororities, state fraternities and sororities; 9% of eligible men and 8% of eligible women are members. Most popular organizations: Filipino Student Organization, Vietnamese Student Association, Jewish Student Union, Alpha Phi Omega. Major annual events: Picnic Day, Whole Earth Festival, Cultural Days. Student services: legal services, health clinic, personal-psychological counseling, women's center. Campus security: 24-hour emergency response devices and patrols, student patrols, late night transport-escort service, controlled dormitory access, rape prevention programs. 4,761 college housing spaces available; 4,334 were occupied in 2003-04. Freshmen guaranteed college housing. Options: coed, men-only, women-only housing available. Peter J. Shields Library plus 5 others with 4.4 million books, 3.4 million microform titles, 44,020 serials, 14,944 audiovisual materials, an OPAC, and a Web page. 600 computers available on campus for general student use. Computer purchase/lease plans available. A campuswide network can be accessed from student residence rooms and from off campus. Staffed computer lab on campus.

Community Environment: Population 50,000. Located in the center of the Sacramento Valley, the climate is typical of the Great Central Valley of California - cool in the winter and warm in the long dry summer season. January average temperatures range from a low of 37 to a high of 54 degrees; July average temperatures range 57 to 97 degrees. The average annual rainfall is 17 inches. The agricultural region surrounding Davis produces numerous crops including tomatoes, alfalfa, wheat and corn. Berkeley and San Francisco are within one hour by train, bus or car. Part-time employment is available either on or off campus. Davis is only 2-3 hours from the Lake Tahoe vacation area in the Sierra Nevada Mountains.

■ UNIVERSITY OF CALIFORNIA, IRVINE *T-7*

Irvine, CA 92697
Tel: (949)824-5011
Admissions: (949)824-6703
Web Site: http://www.uci.edu/

Description: State-supported, university, coed. Part of University of California System. Awards bachelor's, master's, doctoral, and first professional degrees. Founded 1965. Setting: 1,477-acre suburban campus with easy access to Los Angeles. Endowment: $169.2 million. Research spending for 2004 fiscal year: $175.6 million. Total enrollment: 24,362. Faculty: 1,290 (992 full-time, 298 part-time). Student-undergrad faculty ratio is 19:1. 34,531 applied, 60% were admitted. 96% from top 10% of their high school class, 100% from top quarter. Full-time: 19,333 students, 51% women, 49% men. Part-time: 597 students, 47% women, 53% men. Students come from 43 states and territories, 36 other countries, 3% from out-of-state, 0.4% Native American, 12% Hispanic, 2% black, 49% Asian American or Pacific Islander, 2% international, 5% 25 or older, 26% live on campus, 8% transferred in. Retention: 93% of full-time freshmen returned the following year. Academic areas with the most degrees conferred: social sciences; biological/life sciences; psychology. Core. Academic remediation for entering students, ESL program, services for LD students, advanced placement, honors program, independent study, distance learning, double major, summer session for credit, part-time degree program, adult/continuing education programs, internships, graduate courses open to undergrads. Off campus study at other campuses of University of California System. Study abroad program. ROTC: Army (c), Air Force (c).

Entrance Requirements: Options: electronic application, international baccalaureate accepted. Required: essay, high school transcript, minimum 2.8 high school GPA, SAT and SAT Subject Tests or ACT, SAT Subject Tests. Entrance: moderately difficult. Application deadline: 11/30. Notification: continuous until 3/31.

Costs Per Year: Application fee: $60. State resident tuition: $0 full-time. Nonresident tuition: $17,820 full-time. Mandatory fees: $6141 full-time. College room and board: $9875.

Collegiate Environment: Orientation program. Drama-theater group, choral group, student-run newspaper, radio station. Social organizations: 275 open to all; national fraternities, national sororities, local fraternities, local sororities; 8% of eligible men and 8% of eligible women are members. Most popular organizations: ASUCI, Kababayan. Major annual event: Celebrate UCI (open house). Student services: legal services, health clinic, personal-psychological counseling, women's center. Campus security: 24-hour emergency response devices and patrols, late night transport-escort service. Freshmen guaranteed college housing. Options: coed, women-only housing available. Langson Library plus 1 other with 2.6 million books, 2.9 million microform titles, 25,464 serials, 92,117 audiovisual materials, an OPAC, and a Web page. Operations spending for 2004 fiscal year: $20.5 million. 1,732 computers available on campus for general student use. A campuswide network can be accessed from student residence rooms and from off campus. Staffed computer lab on campus.

Community Environment: UCI's location combines the cultural and economic resources of an urban area along with access to the scenic, recreational areas of Southern California. Located 50 miles south of Los

Angeles, five miles from the Pacific Ocean, and nestled in 1,477 acres of coastal foothills near Newport Beach, UCI lies amid rapidly growing residential communities and a dynamic international business environment of Orange County and the surrounding region. The sailing and surfing beaches of Newport, Laguna, and Huntington are a 10-minute bike ride from campus, while hiking trails, desert camping, or mountain resorts for snow boarding and skiing are within two-hour's travel distance from Irvine. The campus itself is a natural arboretum of native species, as well as trees and shrubs from all over the world. Adjacent to the campus, the San Joaquin Freshwater Marsh serves as a natural classroom or peaceful refuge, with trails for viewing the rich diversity of wildlife. Within walking distance of the University are shops and restaurants, bookstores, markets, a post office, and a theatre. Complementing UCI cultural events throughout the academic year is the Orange County arts and entertainment environment. It offers everything from small venues for bands and performers to galleries, museums, the Irvine Barclay Theater, the Orange County Performing Arts Center, and the Pacific Symphony. Within a one- to two-hour drive are the metropolitan attractions of Los Angeles and San Diego, as well as desert and mountain recreational opportunities.

■ UNIVERSITY OF CALIFORNIA, LOS ANGELES *S-10*

405 Hilgard Ave.
Los Angeles, CA 90095
Tel: (310)825-4321
Admissions: (310)825-3101
E-mail: ugadm@saonet.ucla.edu
Web Site: http://www.ucla.edu/

Description: State-supported, university, coed. Part of University of California System. Awards bachelor's, master's, doctoral, and first professional degrees. Founded 1919. Setting: 419-acre urban campus. Total enrollment: 37,221. Faculty: 2,460 (1,859 full-time, 601 part-time). Student-undergrad faculty ratio is 18:1. 42,227 applied, 27% were admitted. 97% from top 10% of their high school class. Full-time: 23,850 students, 57% women, 43% men. Part-time: 961 students, 51% women, 49% men. Students come from 51 states and territories, 114 other countries, 3% from out-of-state, 0.5% Native American, 15% Hispanic, 3% black, 38% Asian American or Pacific Islander, 4% international, 7% 25 or older, 35% live on campus, 12% transferred in. Retention: 97% of full-time freshmen returned the following year. Academic areas with the most degrees conferred: social sciences; psychology; biological/life sciences. Core. ESL program, services for LD students, advanced placement, self-designed majors, freshman honors college, honors program, independent study, distance learning, double major, summer session for credit, adult/continuing education programs, internships, graduate courses open to undergrads. Off campus study. Study abroad program. ROTC: Army, Naval, Air Force.

Entrance Requirements: Options: electronic application, international baccalaureate accepted. Required: essay, SAT or ACT, SAT Subject Tests. Entrance: very difficult. Application deadline: 11/30. Notification: 3/15.

Costs Per Year: Application fee: $60. State resident tuition: $0 full-time. Nonresident tuition: $17,457 full-time. Mandatory fees: $6504 full-time. College room and board: $11,928. Room and board charges vary according to board plan and housing facility.

Collegiate Environment: Orientation program. Drama-theater group, choral group, marching band, student-run newspaper, radio station. Social organizations: national fraternities, national sororities, local fraternities, local sororities; 15% of eligible men and 11% of eligible women are members. Most popular organizations: Student Alumni Association, student government, Rally Committee. Major annual events: homecoming, Spring Sing. Student services: legal services, health clinic, personal-psychological counseling, women's center. Campus security: 24-hour emergency response devices, student patrols, late night transport-escort service. Option: coed housing available. Charles E. Young Research Library plus 13 others with 7.6 million books, 6 million microform titles, 94,801 serials, 4.6 million audiovisual materials, an OPAC, and a Web page.

Community Environment: Los Angeles is a major metropolitan center with a semiarid climate. There are very fine museums and libraries in the city, and a music center, which contribute to the cultural atmosphere of the city. Los Angeles has many points of interest, and is near enough to the beaches and to the mountains for all sports. There are excellent metropolitan shopping centers.

■ UNIVERSITY OF CALIFORNIA, RIVERSIDE *T-11*

900 University Ave.
Riverside, CA 92521-0102

Tel: (951)827-1012
Admissions: (951)827-3411
Fax: (951)827-6344
E-mail: discover@ucr.edu
Web Site: http://www.ucr.edu/

Description: State-supported, university, coed. Part of University of California System. Awards bachelor's, master's, and doctoral degrees. Founded 1954. Setting: 1,200-acre urban campus with easy access to Los Angeles. Endowment: $81.5 million. Research spending for 2004 fiscal year: $81.5 million. Educational spending for 2005 fiscal year: $7389 per student. Total enrollment: 16,622. Faculty: 849 (709 full-time, 140 part-time). Student-undergrad faculty ratio is 18:1. 19,060 applied, 76% were admitted. 94% from top 10% of their high school class, 100% from top half. Full-time: 14,128 students, 53% women, 47% men. Part-time: 443 students, 44% women, 56% men. Students come from 40 states and territories, 21 other countries, 1% from out-of-state, 0.3% Native American, 24% Hispanic, 7% black, 42% Asian American or Pacific Islander, 2% international, 5% 25 or older, 28% live on campus, 9% transferred in. Retention: 86% of full-time freshmen returned the following year. Academic areas with the most degrees conferred: business/marketing; social sciences; biological/life sciences. Academic remediation for entering students, ESL program, services for LD students, advanced placement, accelerated degree program, self-designed majors, freshman honors college, independent study, double major, summer session for credit, part-time degree program, adult/continuing education programs, co-op programs and internships, graduate courses open to undergrads. Off campus study at University of California, Santa Barbara, University of California, Davis, University of California, Los Angeles. Study abroad program. ROTC: Army (c), Air Force (c).

Entrance Requirements: Options: electronic application, early admission, international baccalaureate accepted. Required: essay, high school transcript, minimum 2.8 high school GPA, SAT or ACT. Entrance: very difficult. Application deadline: 11/30. Notification: continuous.

Costs Per Year: Application fee: $60. State resident tuition: $0 full-time. Nonresident tuition: $17,820 full-time. Mandatory fees: $7250 full-time. College room and board: $10,200. Room and board charges vary according to board plan and housing facility.

Collegiate Environment: Orientation program. Drama-theater group, choral group, student-run newspaper, radio station. Social organizations: 280 open to all; national fraternities, national sororities, local fraternities, local sororities, coed fraternities; 4% of eligible men and 4% of eligible women are members. Most popular organizations: Associated Students, Student Alumni Association, Health Careers Organization. Major annual events: Oktoberfest, Scots' Week, Annual Block Party. Student services: legal services, health clinic, personal-psychological counseling, women's center. Campus security: 24-hour emergency response devices and patrols, student patrols, late night transport-escort service, controlled dormitory access. College housing designed to accommodate 4,258 students; 4,471 undergraduates lived in college housing during 2003-04. Freshmen guaranteed college housing. Option: coed housing available. Tomas Rivera Library plus 6 others with 2.1 million books, 1.7 million microform titles, 21,323 serials, 141,663 audiovisual materials, an OPAC, and a Web page. Operations spending for 2004 fiscal year: $12.5 million. 793 computers available on campus for general student use. Computer purchase/lease plans available. A campuswide network can be accessed from student residence rooms and from off campus. Staffed computer lab on campus.

Community Environment: Population 250,000. A suburban area 60 miles east of Los Angeles with a temperate climate, Riverside is an important residential and commercial center in Riverside County. This city launched the navel orange industry in southern California. Major transportation facilities are available. Riverside has churches of the major denominations, a library, hospitals and all public health services. Recreational activities include all water sports. Beaches, desert and mountain/ski resort areas are nearby.

■ **UNIVERSITY OF CALIFORNIA, SAN DIEGO** *W-12*
9500 Gilman Dr.
La Jolla, CA 92093
Tel: (858)534-2230
Admissions: (858)534-4831
E-mail: admissionsinfo@ucsd.edu
Web Site: http://www.ucsd.edu/

Description: State-supported, university, coed. Part of University of California System. Awards bachelor's, master's, doctoral, and first professional degrees. Founded 1959. Setting: 1,976-acre suburban campus with easy access to San Diego. Endowment: $1.2 billion. Research spending for 2004 fiscal year: $387.9 million. Educational spending for 2005 fiscal year: $13,253 per student. Total enrollment: 24,645. Faculty: 1,149 (965 full-time, 184 part-time). Student-undergrad faculty ratio is 19:1. 41,330 applied, 42% were admitted. 99% from top 10% of their high school class, 100% from top quarter. 49 National Merit Scholars. Full-time: 20,048 students, 52% women, 48% men. Part-time: 291 students, 46% women, 54% men. 2% from out-of-state, 0.4% Native American, 10% Hispanic, 1% black, 38% Asian American or Pacific Islander, 3% international, 4% 25 or older, 33% live on campus, 7% transferred in. Retention: 93% of full-time freshmen returned the following year. Academic areas with the most degrees conferred: social sciences; engineering; psychology. Core. ESL program, services for LD students, advanced placement, accelerated degree program, self-designed majors, freshman honors college, honors program, independent study, double major, summer session for credit, co-op programs and internships, graduate courses open to undergrads. Off campus study at Dartmouth College, Spelman College, Morehouse College. Study abroad program. ROTC: Army (c).

Entrance Requirements: Options: electronic application, international baccalaureate accepted. Required: essay, high school transcript, minimum 2.8 high school GPA, SAT or ACT, SAT Subject Tests, 3 SAT Subject Tests (including SAT Writing Test). Required for some: minimum 3.4 high school GPA. Entrance: very difficult. Application deadline: 11/30. Notification: 3/31. Preference given to state residents.

Costs Per Year: Application fee: $60. State resident tuition: $0 full-time. Nonresident tuition: $17,820 full-time. Mandatory fees: $6,681 full-time. Full-time tuition and fees vary according to location. College room and board: $9421. Room and board charges vary according to board plan and location.

Collegiate Environment: Orientation program. Drama-theater group, choral group, student-run newspaper, radio station. Social organizations: 450 open to all; national fraternities, national sororities; 10% of eligible men and 10% of eligible women are members. Most popular organizations: cultural organizations, recreational clubs, service organizations, spiritual/religious organizations. Major annual events: Sun God Festival, Winterfest, Fall Festival on the Green. Student services: legal services, health clinic, personal-psychological counseling, women's center. Campus security: 24-hour emergency response devices and patrols, student patrols, late night transport-escort service, crime prevention programs. 6,534 college housing spaces available; all were occupied in 2003-04. Freshmen guaranteed college housing. Option: coed housing available. Geisel Library plus 9 others with 3.1 million books, 3 million microform titles, 28,104 serials, 405,266 audiovisual materials, an OPAC, and a Web page. Operations spending for 2004 fiscal year: $20.4 million. 1,500 computers available on campus for general student use. Computer purchase/lease plans available. A campuswide network can be accessed from student residence rooms and from off campus. Staffed computer lab on campus.

Community Environment: La Jolla is within the corporate limits of San Diego and is a popular resort with a rocky coast and fine beaches. San Diego lies along and around one of the world's ten most beautiful protected natural harbors, and has a very special seawashed, air-conditioned climate. The maximum average temperature of 70.8 degrees and a minimum of 55.4 degrees makes the climate very special. Amtrak, buses, a trolley system, and major airlines all serve the area. The city is a major center for biomedical, high technology electronics and wireless communication industries. Other industries include shipbuilding, shipping, and fishing. San Diego County is the country's largest producer of avocados. San Diego has a large public library system, hospitals, museums, galleries, and churches. Within San Diego County are numerous golf courses, all aquatic sports, hiking, camping, mountain climbing, horseback riding, snow sports, fishing and hunting. Sea World, the world-famous San Diego Zoo and Wild Animal Park, Balboa Park, and the Anza Borrego Desert State Park also provide recreational opportunities. This is the home of the 1994 AFC Champion San Diego Chargers, the professional football team, and the 1998 National League Champion San Diego Padres professional baseball team. Known as a winter playground, it has 70 miles of beautiful beaches. Population of San Diego is 1,254,000, with a greater metropolitan area population of 2,853,00.

■ **UNIVERSITY OF CALIFORNIA, SANTA BARBARA** *S-7*
Santa Barbara, CA 93106
Tel: (805)893-8000
Admissions: (805)893-2485
Web Site: http://www.ucsb.edu/

Description: State-supported, university, coed. Part of University of California System. Awards bachelor's, master's, and doctoral degrees and first professional certificates. Founded 1909. Setting: 989-acre suburban campus. Endowment: $109.9 million. Research spending for 2004 fiscal year: $105.2 million. Educational spending for 2005 fiscal year: $23,144 per student. Total enrollment: 21,016. Faculty: 1,054 (919 full-time, 135 part-time). Student-undergrad faculty ratio is 17:1. 37,451 applied, 53% were admitted. Full-time: 17,432 students, 56% women, 44% men. Part-time: 645 students, 47% women, 53% men. Students come from 51 states and territories, 110 other countries, 1% Native American, 18% Hispanic, 3% black, 16% Asian American or Pacific Islander, 1% international, 3% 25 or older, 26% live on campus, 9% transferred in. Retention: 90% of full-time freshmen returned the following year. Core. Calendar: plus 6-week summer term. ESL program, services for LD students, advanced placement, accelerated degree program, self-designed majors, honors program, independent study, distance learning, double major, summer session for credit, co-op programs and internships, graduate courses open to undergrads. Off campus study at other campuses of the University of California System. Study abroad program. ROTC: Army.

Entrance Requirements: Options: electronic application, international baccalaureate accepted. Required: essay, high school transcript, SAT or ACT, SAT Subject Tests. Required for some: interview. Entrance: very difficult. Application deadline: 11/30. Notification: 3/15.

Costs Per Year: Application fee: $40. State resident tuition: $0 full-time. Nonresident tuition: $17,820 full-time. Mandatory fees: $6993 full-time. College room and board: $10,577. College room only: $8110.

Collegiate Environment: Orientation program. Drama-theater group, choral group, student-run newspaper, radio station. Social organizations: 241 open to all; national fraternities, national sororities, local fraternities, local sororities; 4% of eligible men and 7% of eligible women are members. Student services: legal services, health clinic, personal-psychological counseling, women's center. Campus security: 24-hour emergency response devices, late night transport-escort service. 4,000 college housing spaces available. Freshmen given priority for college housing. Option: coed housing available. Davidson Library with 3.2 million books, 3.8 million microform titles, 23,218 serials, 311,863 audiovisual materials, an OPAC, and a Web page. Operations spending for 2004 fiscal year: $18.2 million. 3,000 computers available on campus for general student use. A campuswide network can be accessed from off-campus. Staffed computer lab on campus.

Community Environment: The University is located in Goleta, a suburb of Santa Barbara. Santa Barbara is a county seat, the largest city between Los Angeles and San Francisco, and is known as the "Riviera of the Pacific." The city lies at the foot of the Santa Ynez Mountains, facing the Pacific Ocean. The climate is moderate, and the temperature varies only 7 degrees in summer and winter. All modes of transportation serve the area, and hotel and motel accommodations are numerous. Santa Barbara has all the community facilities plus many points of interest, a planetarium, botanic garden, natural history, art, historical museums, and more. The annual horse show, Old Spanish Days, August Fiesta, Semana Nautica (Marine sports week), and flower shows are the highlights of the year. Active music organizations and the Symphony Orchestra are an important part of the cultural life of the city. Recreational facilities include golf courses, tennis courts, water sports at the beach, and many other activities.

■ **UNIVERSITY OF CALIFORNIA, SANTA CRUZ** *M-5*
1156 High St.
Santa Cruz, CA 95064
Tel: (831)459-0111
Admissions: (831)459-5779
Fax: (831)459-4452
E-mail: admissions@ucsc.edu
Web Site: http://www.ucsc.edu/

Description: State-supported, university, coed. Part of University of California System. Awards bachelor's, master's, and doctoral degrees. Founded 1965. Setting: 2,000-acre small town campus with easy access to San Francisco and San Jose. Endowment: $85.3 million. Total enrollment: 15,012. Faculty: 742 (537 full-time, 205 part-time). Student-undergrad faculty ratio is 19:1. 23,003 applied, 75% were admitted. 90% from top 10% of their high school class, 100% from top quarter. Full-time: 13,139 students, 54% women, 46% men. Part-time: 486 students, 51% women, 49% men. 4% from out-of-state, 1% Native American, 15% Hispanic, 3% black, 19% Asian American or Pacific Islander, 1% international, 45% live on campus, 6% transferred in. Retention: 89% of full-time freshmen returned the following year. Academic areas with the most degrees conferred: social sciences; biological/life sciences; visual and performing arts. Core. Academic remediation for entering students, ESL program, services for LD students, advanced placement, self-designed majors, freshman honors college,

independent study, double major, summer session for credit, part-time degree program, adult/continuing education programs, co-op programs and internships, graduate courses open to undergrads. Off campus study at other campuses of the University of California System, University of New Hampshire, University of New Mexico. Study abroad program. ROTC: Army (c), Naval (c), Air Force (c).

Entrance Requirements: Options: electronic application, international baccalaureate accepted. Required: essay, high school transcript, SAT or ACT, SAT Subject Tests required in two different areas: history/social science, English literature, mathematics, laboratory science, or language other than English. Entrance: very difficult. Application deadline: 11/30. Notification: 3/15. Preference given to qualified state residents.

Costs Per Year: Application fee: $65. State resident tuition: $0 full-time. Nonresident tuition: $17,820 full-time. Mandatory fees: $7603 full-time. College room and board: $11,571. Room and board charges vary according to board plan and housing facility.

Collegiate Environment: Orientation program. Drama-theater group, choral group, student-run newspaper, radio station. Social organizations: 100 open to all; national fraternities, national sororities, local fraternities, local sororities; 1% of eligible men and 1% of eligible women are members. Most popular organizations: Asian Pacific Islander Student Alliance, African/Black Student Alliance, Movimiento Estudiantil Chicano de Aztlan, Students Alliance of North American Indians, Estudiantes Para Salud del Pueblo. Major annual events: Martin Luther King Jr. Convocation, Multicultural Festival, Banana Slug Spring Fair. Student services: health clinic, personal-psychological counseling, women's center. Campus security: 24-hour emergency response devices and patrols, late night transport-escort service, controlled dormitory access, evening main gate security, campus police force and fire station. 6,158 undergraduates lived in college housing during 2003-04. Freshmen guaranteed college housing. Options: coed, men-only, women-only housing available. McHenry Library plus 9 others with 1.5 million books, 845,646 microform titles, 21,924 serials, 378,444 audiovisual materials, an OPAC, and a Web page. 200 computers available on campus for general student use. A campuswide network can be accessed from student residence rooms and from off campus. Staffed computer lab on campus.

Community Environment: The City of Santa Cruz, population 54,000, and other nearby communities are easily accessible via the local bus system. The area has long been a popular resort because of its recreational offerings, which include 10 miles of beaches, a widely varied coastal zone, and the densely wooded Santa Cruz Mountains. The temperate climate is characterized by sunny summer days with foggy mornings and rain in the winter. Many of the city's Victorian houses have been restored in recent years, and its main shopping street has been revitalized. For its size, Santa Cruz has a remarkable variety of outstanding restaurants in all price ranges. Numerous cultural activities are sponsored by the University, the local junior college, and community organizations.

■ **UNIVERSITY OF JUDAISM** *S-10*
15600 Mulholland Dr.
Bel Air, CA 90077-1599
Tel: (310)476-9777; 888-853-6763
Fax: (310)471-3657
E-mail: bpisetsky@uj.edu
Web Site: http://www.uj.edu/

Description: Independent Jewish, comprehensive, coed. Awards bachelor's and master's degrees. Founded 1947. Setting: 28-acre suburban campus with easy access to Los Angeles. Research spending for 2004 fiscal year: $9795. Educational spending for 2005 fiscal year: $30,000 per student. Total enrollment: 114. Faculty: 91 (19 full-time, 72 part-time). Student-undergrad faculty ratio is 7:1. 87 applied, 79% were admitted. 22% from top 10% of their high school class, 28% from top quarter, 50% from top half. Students come from 4 other countries, 31% from out-of-state, 4% black, 6% international, 14% 25 or older, 60% live on campus. Retention: 58% of full-time freshmen returned the following year. Core. Calendar: semesters. Academic remediation for entering students, services for LD students, advanced placement, accelerated degree program, self-designed majors, honors program, independent study, part-time degree program, adult/continuing education programs, internships, graduate courses open to undergrads. Off campus study at Mount Saint Mary's College, Cedars-Sinai Medical Center, University of California, Los Angeles. Study abroad program.

Entrance Requirements: Options: early admission, early decision, deferred admission, international baccalaureate accepted. Required: essay, high school transcript, 2 recommendations, SAT or ACT. Recommended: minimum 3.2 high school GPA, interview. Required for some: interview. Entrance: moderately difficult. Application deadlines: 1/31, 11/15 for early decision. Notification: continuous, 12/15 for early decision.

Costs Per Year: Application fee: $35. Comprehensive fee: $32,376 includes full-time tuition ($18,480), mandatory fees ($850), and college room and board ($13,046). College room only: $7964. Room and board charges vary according to board plan. Part-time tuition: $770 per credit.

Collegiate Environment: Orientation program. Drama-theater group, choral group, student-run newspaper, radio station. Social organizations: 5 open to all. Most popular organizations: ASUJC, Graduate Student Association, Resident Life Council, College Urban Fellows, UJ Chorale. Major annual events: City-Wide Purim Dance, Casino Casiano, Arabian Nights Dance. Student services: health clinic, personal-psychological counseling. Campus security: 24-hour emergency response devices and patrols, controlled dormitory access. 250 college housing spaces available; 80 were occupied in 2003-04. Freshmen guaranteed college housing. On-campus residence required through junior year. Option: coed housing available. Ostrow Library with 105,000 books, 400 serials, and a Web page. Operations spending for 2004 fiscal year: $320,700. 16 computers available on campus for general student use. Staffed computer lab on campus.

Community Environment: A suburb of Los Angeles, Bel Air enjoys a mild and delightful climate. The city is served by all modes of transportation and freeways. The Hollywood Bowl has special summer-long programs of music and the lively arts. There are many theaters, both movie and stage, the Griffith Park Zoo, Planetarium, the Getty Museum and Skirball Cultural Center, all offering broad cultural and recreational activities. Within the city are excellent world-famous restaurants, night clubs and fine hotels providing outstanding accommodations and service. Employment is usually available on full- or part-time basis.

■ **UNIVERSITY OF LA VERNE** *V-9*
1950 Third St.
La Verne, CA 91750-4443
Tel: (909)593-3511
Free: 800-876-4858
Fax: (909)593-0965
E-mail: laup@ulavacs.ulaverne.edu
Web Site: http://www.ulv.edu/

Description: Independent, university, coed. Awards associate, bachelor's, master's, doctoral, and first professional degrees and post-master's certificates (also offers continuing education program with significant enrollment not reflected in profile). Founded 1891. Setting: 26-acre suburban campus with easy access to Los Angeles. Total enrollment: 4,000. Faculty: 398 (187 full-time, 211 part-time). Student-undergrad faculty ratio is 12:1. 1,638 applied, 62% were admitted. 33% from top 10% of their high school class, 68% from top quarter, 93% from top half. Full-time: 1,583 students, 65% women, 35% men. Part-time: 102 students, 58% women, 42% men. Students come from 25 states and territories, 7 other countries, 5% from out-of-state, 1% Native American, 38% Hispanic, 9% black, 5% Asian American or Pacific Islander, 1% international, 3% 25 or older, 32% live on campus, 10% transferred in. Retention: 89% of full-time freshmen returned the following year. Academic areas with the most degrees conferred: business/marketing; social sciences; liberal arts/general studies. Core. Calendar: 4-1-4. Academic remediation for entering students, ESL program, services for LD students, advanced placement, accelerated degree program, self-designed majors, freshman honors college, honors program, independent study, distance learning, double major, summer session for credit, part-time degree program, external degree program, adult/continuing education programs, internships, graduate courses open to undergrads. Off campus study at Elizabethtown College, Juniata College, McPherson College, Bridgewater College, Manchester College. Study abroad program.

Entrance Requirements: Options: Common Application, electronic application, deferred admission, international baccalaureate accepted. Required: essay, high school transcript, 2 recommendations, SAT or ACT. Recommended: interview, SAT or ACT. Entrance: moderately difficult. Application deadline: 2/1. Notification: continuous.

Costs Per Year: Application fee: $50. Comprehensive fee: $33,470 includes full-time tuition ($24,260) and college room and board ($9210). College room only: $4780. Part-time tuition: $685 per unit.

Collegiate Environment: Orientation program. Drama-theater group, choral group, student-run newspaper, radio station. Social organizations: 31 open to all; national fraternities, national sororities, local sororities; 9% of eligible men and 16% of eligible women are members. Most popular organizations:

Latino Student Forum, African-American Student Association, Associated Students Federation, Alpha Kappa Psi. Major annual events: Homecoming, International Fair, Spring Formal. Student services: health clinic, personal-psychological counseling. Campus security: 24-hour emergency response devices and patrols, late night transport-escort service, controlled dormitory access, whistle program. 536 college housing spaces available; 501 were occupied in 2003-04. No special consideration for freshman housing applicants. Options: coed, women-only housing available. Wilson Library with 215,000 books, 4,500 serials, an OPAC, and a Web page. 150 computers available on campus for general student use. A campuswide network can be accessed from student residence rooms and from off campus. Staffed computer lab on campus.

Community Environment: La Verne is a suburban area approximately 35 miles east of Los Angeles, Pasadena, Beverly Hills and Hollywood. MetroLink railroad system and the Metropolitan Bus Lines provide access in and out of Los Angeles. La Verne is overshadowed on the north by the snowcapped San Gabriel Mountains, which rise to a height of 10,000 feet. La Verne is within easy driving distance of the beaches and mountains which provide both summer and winter recreational activities.

■ **UNIVERSITY OF THE PACIFIC** *J-6*
3601 Pacific Ave.
Stockton, CA 95211-0197
Tel: (209)946-2344
Free: 800-959-2867
Admissions: (209)946-2211
Fax: (209)946-2413
E-mail: admissions@pacific.edu
Web Site: http://www.pacific.edu/

Description: Independent, university, coed. Awards bachelor's, master's, doctoral, and first professional degrees. Founded 1851. Setting: 175-acre suburban campus with easy access to Sacramento. Endowment: $178.3 million. Research spending for 2004 fiscal year: $12.5 million. Total enrollment: 6,196. Faculty: 656 (401 full-time, 255 part-time). Student-undergrad faculty ratio is 14:1. 5,869 applied, 56% were admitted. 43% from top 10% of their high school class, 73% from top quarter, 92% from top half. 14 student government officers. Full-time: 3,357 students, 56% women, 44% men. Part-time: 100 students, 65% women, 35% men. Students come from 30 states and territories, 8 other countries, 19% from out-of-state, 1% Native American, 10% Hispanic, 3% black, 29% Asian American or Pacific Islander, 2% international, 6% 25 or older, 58% live on campus, 7% transferred in. Retention: 85% of full-time freshmen returned the following year. Academic areas with the most degrees conferred: business/marketing; biological/life sciences; engineering. Core. Calendar: semesters. Academic remediation for entering students, ESL program, services for LD students, advanced placement, accelerated degree program, self-designed majors, honors program, independent study, double major, summer session for credit, part-time degree program, adult/continuing education programs, co-op programs and internships. Study abroad program.

Entrance Requirements: Options: Peterson's Universal Application, Common Application, electronic application, early action, international baccalaureate accepted. Required: essay, high school transcript, minimum 2.5 high school GPA, 1 recommendation, SAT or ACT. Recommended: minimum 3.0 high school GPA. Required for some: audition for music program. Entrance: moderately difficult. Application deadlines: 1/15, 11/15 for early action. Notification: continuous, 1/15 for early action.

Costs Per Year: Application fee: $60. Comprehensive fee: $34,566 includes full-time tuition ($25,658), mandatory fees ($430), and college room and board ($8478). College room only: $5760. Room and board charges vary according to board plan and housing facility. Part-time tuition: $886 per unit. Part-time tuition varies according to course load.

Collegiate Environment: Orientation program. Drama-theater group, choral group, student-run newspaper, radio station. Social organizations: 100 open to all; national fraternities, national sororities, local fraternities; 19% of eligible men and 18% of eligible women are members. Most popular organizations: student government, cultural organizations, Marketing Club, Model United Nations. Major annual events: Fall Festival, Pacific Days, Cultural Diversity Week. Student services: legal services, health clinic, personal-psychological counseling. Campus security: 24-hour emergency response devices and patrols, late night transport-escort service, controlled dormitory access. 2,200 college housing spaces available. On-campus residence required through sophomore year. Option: coed housing available. Holt Memorial Library plus 1 other with 282,313 books, 701,525 microform titles, 1,356 serials, 10,894 audiovisual materials, an OPAC, and a Web page. 350 computers available on campus for general student use. Computer purchase/lease plans available. A campuswide network can be accessed from student residence rooms and from off campus. Staffed computer lab on campus.

Community Environment: Stockton, population 230,000, is located 80 miles east of San Francisco and 40 miles south of Sacramento. The city is located in a rich agricultural region. All major forms of transportation serve the area. Stockton has 110 churches, general hospitals, a library, museum, and fine shopping facilities. Recreational facilities include theaters, parks, playgrounds, stadiums, a large events center, and a baseball stadium. The city is only a short drive away from facilities for water skiing, sailing, and golf, and the Sierra Nevada mountain range is also nearby.

■ UNIVERSITY OF PHOENIX-BAY AREA CAMPUS *H-6*

7901 Stoneridge Dr., Ste. 100
Pleasanton, CA 94588-3677
Tel: (925)416-4100; 877-4-STUDENT
Admissions: (480)557-1712
Web Site: http://www.phoenix.edu/

Description: Proprietary, comprehensive, coed. Awards associate, bachelor's, and master's degrees. Setting: urban campus. Total enrollment: 3,681. Faculty: 747 (8 full-time, 739 part-time). Student-undergrad faculty ratio is 7:1. 45 applied. Full-time: 2,581 students, 60% women, 40% men. 0.2% Native American, 6% Hispanic, 6% black, 6% Asian American or Pacific Islander, 16% international, 91% 25 or older. Academic areas with the most degrees conferred: business/marketing; computer and information sciences; public administration and social services. Core. Calendar: continuous. Advanced placement, accelerated degree program, independent study, distance learning, external degree program, adult/continuing education programs, graduate courses open to undergrads.

Entrance Requirements: Open admission. Option: deferred admission. Required: 1 recommendation. Required for some: high school transcript. Entrance: noncompetitive. Application deadline: Rolling.

Costs Per Year: Application fee: $110. Tuition: $12,990 full-time, $444 per credit part-time. Mandatory fees: $560 full-time, $70 per course part-time.

Collegiate Environment: College housing not available. University Library with 444 books, 666 serials, an OPAC, and a Web page. System-wide operations spending for 2004 fiscal year: $3.2 million.

■ UNIVERSITY OF PHOENIX-CENTRAL VALLEY CAMPUS *M-9*

8355 N. Fresno St., Ste. 200
Fresno, CA 93720
; 888-228-7240
Admissions: (480)557-1712
Web Site: http://phoenix.edu/

Description: Proprietary, comprehensive, coed. Awards bachelor's and master's degrees. Founded 2004. Total enrollment: 1,887. Faculty: 658 (11 full-time, 647 part-time). Student-undergrad faculty ratio is 9:1. 20 applied. Full-time: 1,606 students, 66% women, 34% men. 0.4% Native American, 13% Hispanic, 4% black, 1% Asian American or Pacific Islander, 6% international, 89% 25 or older. Academic areas with the most degrees conferred: business/marketing; public administration and social services; computer and information sciences. Core. Advanced placement, accelerated degree program, independent study, distance learning, external degree program, adult/continuing education programs, graduate courses open to undergrads.

Entrance Requirements: Open admission. Option: deferred admission. Required: 1 recommendation. Required for some: high school transcript. Entrance: noncompetitive. Application deadline: Rolling.

Costs Per Year: Application fee: $110. Tuition: $11,775 full-time, $392.50 per credit part-time. Mandatory fees: $560 full-time, $70 per course part-time. Full-time tuition and fees vary according to program.

Collegiate Environment: College housing not available. University Library with 444 books, 666 serials, an OPAC, and a Web page. System-wide operations spending for 2004 fiscal year: $3.2 million.

■ UNIVERSITY OF PHOENIX-SACRAMENTO VALLEY CAMPUS *I-6*

1760 Creekside Oaks Dr., Ste. 100
Sacramento, CA 95833-3632
Tel: (916)923-2107
Free: 800-228-7240
Admissions: (480)557-1712
Fax: (916)923-3914
Web Site: http://www.phoenix.edu/

Description: Proprietary, comprehensive, coed. Awards bachelor's and master's degrees. Founded 1993. Setting: urban campus. Total enrollment: 4,629. Faculty: 547 (12 full-time, 535 part-time). Student-undergrad faculty ratio is 8:1. 61 applied. Full-time: 3,506 students, 65% women, 35% men. 0% from out-of-state, 0.5% Native American, 3% Hispanic, 5% black, 2% Asian American or Pacific Islander, 24% international, 89% 25 or older. Academic areas with the most degrees conferred: business/marketing; computer and information sciences; health professions and related sciences. Core. Calendar: continuous. Advanced placement, accelerated degree program, independent study, distance learning, external degree program, adult/continuing education programs, graduate courses open to undergrads.

Entrance Requirements: Open admission. Option: deferred admission. Required: 1 recommendation. Required for some: high school transcript. Entrance: noncompetitive. Application deadline: Rolling.

Costs Per Year: Application fee: $110. Tuition: $12,225 full-time, $407.50 per credit part-time. Mandatory fees: $560 full-time, $70 per course part-time.

Collegiate Environment: College housing not available. University Library with 444 books, 666 serials, an OPAC, and a Web page. System-wide operations spending for 2004 fiscal year: $3.2 million.

■ UNIVERSITY OF PHOENIX-SAN DIEGO CAMPUS *W-12*

3870 Murphy Canyon Rd., Ste. 210
San Diego, CA 92123
Tel: 800-473-4346; 888-228-7240
Admissions: (480)557-1712
Fax: (858)576-0032
Web Site: http://www.phoenix.edu/

Description: Proprietary, comprehensive, coed. Awards bachelor's and master's degrees. Founded 1988. Setting: urban campus. Total enrollment: 4,563. Faculty: 476 (15 full-time, 461 part-time). Student-undergrad faculty ratio is 9:1. 87 applied. Full-time: 3,459 students, 53% women, 47% men. 0% from out-of-state, 1% Native American, 6% Hispanic, 4% black, 3% Asian American or Pacific Islander, 15% international, 89% 25 or older. Academic areas with the most degrees conferred: business/marketing; computer and information sciences; health professions and related sciences. Core. Calendar: continuous. Advanced placement, accelerated degree program, independent study, distance learning, external degree program, adult/continuing education programs, graduate courses open to undergrads.

Entrance Requirements: Open admission. Option: deferred admission. Required: 1 recommendation. Required for some: high school transcript. Entrance: noncompetitive. Application deadline: Rolling.

Costs Per Year: Application fee: $110. Tuition: $11,940 full-time, $398 per credit part-time. Mandatory fees: $560 full-time, $70 per course part-time.

Collegiate Environment: College housing not available. University Library with 444 books, 666 serials, an OPAC, and a Web page. System-wide operations spending for 2004 fiscal year: $3.2 million.

■ UNIVERSITY OF PHOENIX-SOUTHERN CALIFORNIA CAMPUS *T-10*

3150 Bristol St., Ste. 340
Costa Mesa, CA 92626
Tel: 800-GO-TO-UOP
Free: 800-228-7240
Admissions: (480)557-1712
Web Site: http://www.phoenix.edu/

Description: Proprietary, comprehensive, coed. Awards bachelor's and master's degrees. Founded 1980. Setting: urban campus. Total enrollment: 16,134. Faculty: 1,297 (14 full-time, 1,283 part-time). Student-undergrad faculty ratio is 12:1. 257 applied. Full-time: 12,476 students, 62% women, 38% men. 0% from out-of-state, 0.3% Native American, 10% Hispanic, 7% black, 2% Asian American or Pacific Islander, 10% international, 91% 25 or older. Academic areas with the most degrees conferred: business/marketing; public administration and social services; computer and information sciences. Core. Calendar: continuous. Advanced placement, accelerated degree program, independent study, distance learning, external degree program, adult/continuing education programs, graduate courses open to undergrads.

Entrance Requirements: Open admission. Option: deferred admission. Required: 1 recommendation. Required for some: high school transcript. Entrance: noncompetitive. Application deadline: Rolling.

Costs Per Year: Application fee: $110. Tuition: $13,125 full-time, $437.50 per credit part-time. Mandatory fees: $560 full-time, $70 per course part-time.

Collegiate Environment: College housing not available. University Library with 444 books, 666 serials, an OPAC, and a Web page. System-wide operations spending for 2004 fiscal year: $3.2 million.

■ **UNIVERSITY OF REDLANDS** *Q-10*
1200 East Colton Ave.
PO Box 3080
Redlands, CA 92373-0999
Tel: (909)793-2121
Free: 800-455-5064
Admissions: (909)335-4074
Fax: (909)335-4089
Web Site: http://www.redlands.edu/
Description: Independent, comprehensive, coed. Awards bachelor's and master's degrees and post-master's certificates. Founded 1907. Setting: 140-acre small town campus with easy access to Los Angeles. Endowment: $95.9 million. Research spending for 2004 fiscal year: $2.6 million. Educational spending for 2005 fiscal year: $8120 per student. Total enrollment: 2,454. Faculty: 316 (165 full-time, 151 part-time). Student-undergrad faculty ratio is 12:1. 3,395 applied, 66% were admitted. 32% from top 10% of their high school class, 69% from top quarter, 93% from top half. 4 National Merit Scholars. Full-time: 2,338 students, 59% women, 41% men. Part-time: 24 students, 58% women, 42% men. Students come from 42 states and territories, 16 other countries, 29% from out-of-state, 0.4% Native American, 11% Hispanic, 2% black, 5% Asian American or Pacific Islander, 1% international, 2% 25 or older, 73% live on campus, 4% transferred in. Retention: 83% of full-time freshmen returned the following year. Academic areas with the most degrees conferred: liberal arts/general studies; business/marketing; social sciences. Core. Calendar: 4-4-1. Academic remediation for entering students, services for LD students, advanced placement, self-designed majors, freshman honors college, honors program, independent study, double major, adult/continuing education programs, internships, graduate courses open to undergrads. Off campus study at members of the Association for Innovation in Higher Education, American University. Study abroad program.
Entrance Requirements: Options: Common Application, electronic application, deferred admission, international baccalaureate accepted. Required: essay, high school transcript, 2 recommendations, SAT or ACT. Recommended: interview. Entrance: moderately difficult. Application deadline: 3/1. Notification: continuous.
Costs Per Year: Application fee: $45. Comprehensive fee: $36,164 includes full-time tuition ($26,864), mandatory fees ($300), and college room and board ($9000). College room only: $5020. Room and board charges vary according to board plan and housing facility. Part-time tuition: $840 per credit. Part-time mandatory fees: $150 per term. Part-time tuition and fees vary according to course load.
Collegiate Environment: Orientation program. Drama-theater group, choral group, student-run newspaper, radio station. Social organizations: 105 open to all; local fraternities, local sororities; 10% of eligible men and 13% of eligible women are members. Most popular organizations: Associated Students, service organizations, cultural organizations, social awareness groups. Major annual events: homecoming, Living on Common Ground Multicultural Festival, Convocation Lecture Series. Student services: health clinic, personal-psychological counseling, women's center. Campus security: 24-hour emergency response devices and patrols, student patrols, late night transport-escort service, controlled dormitory access, safety whistles. 1,568 college housing spaces available. Freshmen guaranteed college housing. On-campus residence required through senior year. Options: coed, men-only, women-only housing available. Armacost Library with 262,893 books, 310,863 microform titles, 9,800 serials, 10,995 audiovisual materials, an OPAC, and a Web page. Operations spending for 2004 fiscal year: $1.5 million. 655 computers available on campus for general student use. A campuswide network can be accessed from student residence rooms and from off campus. Staffed computer lab on campus.
Community Environment: Redlands is located halfway between Los Angeles and Palm Springs. It has a mild climate. The average yearly temperature is 65 degrees, and the average rainfall 14.45 inches. Once a principal center for navel oranges, the city has developed a more diversified economy in recent years. There are 60 churches, a community hospital and satellite clinics, a city library, fraternal and social service organizations, and museums. Buses serve the area, and the Ontario International Airport is 30 minutes from the campus. Through the Office of Community Service Learning and other organizations, students at the university have many opportunities to interact with community members.

■ **UNIVERSITY OF SAN DIEGO** *W-12*
5998 Alcala Park
San Diego, CA 92110-2492
Tel: (619)260-4600
Free: 800-248-4873
Admissions: (619)260-4506
E-mail: admissions@sandiego.edu
Web Site: http://www.sandiego.edu/
Description: Independent Roman Catholic, university, coed. Awards bachelor's, master's, doctoral, and first professional degrees and post-master's and first professional certificates. Founded 1949. Setting: 180-acre urban campus. Endowment: $172.1 million. Research spending for 2004 fiscal year: $1.6 million. Educational spending for 2005 fiscal year: $28,760 per student. Total enrollment: 7,548. Faculty: 722 (359 full-time, 363 part-time). Student-undergrad faculty ratio is 15:1. 7,862 applied, 60% were admitted. 41% from top 10% of their high school class, 79% from top quarter, 96% from top half. Full-time: 4,801 students, 61% women, 39% men. Part-time: 169 students, 53% women, 47% men. Students come from 50 states and territories, 64 other countries, 35% from out-of-state, 1% Native American, 13% Hispanic, 2% black, 7% Asian American or Pacific Islander, 2% international, 5% 25 or older, 50% live on campus, 7% transferred in. Retention: 83% of full-time freshmen returned the following year. Academic areas with the most degrees conferred: business/marketing; social sciences; communications/journalism. Core. Calendar: 4-1-4. ESL program, services for LD students, advanced placement, honors program, independent study, double major, summer session for credit, part-time degree program, internships. Study abroad program. ROTC: Army (c), Naval, Air Force (c).
Entrance Requirements: Options: Common Application, electronic application, early admission, early action, deferred admission, international baccalaureate accepted. Required: essay, high school transcript, 1 recommendation, SAT or ACT. Entrance: very difficult. Application deadlines: 1/5, 11/15 for early action. Notification: 4/15, 1/31 for early action.
Costs Per Year: Application fee: $55. Comprehensive fee: $41,664 includes full-time tuition ($30,480), mandatory fees ($224), and college room and board ($10,960). Part-time tuition: $1050 per unit. Part-time mandatory fees: $38.
Collegiate Environment: Orientation program. Drama-theater group, choral group, student-run newspaper. Social organizations: 75 open to all; national fraternities, national sororities; 25% of eligible men and 25% of eligible women are members. Most popular organizations: International Student Organization, Student Alumni Association, United Front/Multicultural Center, Associated Student Government. Major annual events: Orientation Week, Homecoming, Multicultural Week. Student services: legal services, health clinic, personal-psychological counseling, women's center. Campus security: 24-hour emergency response devices and patrols, student patrols, late night transport-escort service, controlled dormitory access. 2,400 college housing spaces available; 2,280 were occupied in 2003-04. Freshmen guaranteed college housing. On-campus residence required in freshman year. Options: coed, women-only housing available. Helen K. and James S. Copley Library plus 1 other with 714,082 books, 839,992 microform titles, 10,451 serials, 8,624 audiovisual materials, and an OPAC. Operations spending for 2004 fiscal year: $6.1 million. 260 computers available on campus for general student use. A campuswide network can be accessed from student residence rooms and from off campus. Staffed computer lab on campus.
Community Environment: Known for many reasons as "America's Finest City," San Diego has an almost perfect climate with warm, sunny days and cool evenings. Throughout the year, students can take advantage of San Diego's many outdoor recreational and cultural opportunities. The museums of Balboa Park, the Old Globe Theatre, the Zoo, Sea World, the beaches, the opera, and downtown San Diego and La Jolla are only minutes away. The rapidly developing economy of Greater San Diego provides varied employment opportunities for the USD graduate.

■ **UNIVERSITY OF SAN FRANCISCO** *K-4*
2130 Fulton St.
San Francisco, CA 94117-1080
Tel: (415)422-6886
Free: 800-CALL USF
Admissions: (415)422-6563
Fax: (415)422-2217
E-mail: admissions@usfca.edu
Web Site: http://www.usfca.edu/
Description: Independent Roman Catholic (Jesuit), university, coed. Awards bachelor's, master's, doctoral, and first professional degrees and post-

master's certificates. Founded 1855. Setting: 55-acre urban campus with easy access to in San Francisco. Research spending for 2004 fiscal year: $889,000. Total enrollment: 8,457. Faculty: 861 (348 full-time, 513 part-time). Student-undergrad faculty ratio is 14:1. 6,090 applied, 72% were admitted. 25% from top 10% of their high school class, 57% from top quarter, 90% from top half. Full-time: 4,981 students, 64% women, 36% men. Part-time: 231 students, 46% women, 54% men. Students come from 51 states and territories, 70 other countries, 24% from out-of-state, 1% Native American, 14% Hispanic, 5% black, 24% Asian American or Pacific Islander, 7% international, 5% 25 or older, 48% live on campus, 7% transferred in. Retention: 86% of full-time freshmen returned the following year. Core. Calendar: 4-1-4. Academic remediation for entering students, ESL program, services for LD students, advanced placement, self-designed majors, honors program, distance learning, double major, summer session for credit, part-time degree program, external degree program, adult/continuing education programs, co-op programs and internships, graduate courses open to undergrads. Off campus study at American University, Jackson State University. Study abroad program. ROTC: Army, Air Force (c).

Entrance Requirements: Options: Peterson's Universal Application, Common Application, electronic application, early action, deferred admission, international baccalaureate accepted. Required: essay, high school transcript, minimum 2.8 high school GPA, 1 recommendation, SAT or ACT. Recommended: minimum 3.0 high school GPA. Required for some: interview. Entrance: moderately difficult. Application deadlines: 2/1, 11/15 for early action. Notification: continuous until 8/15, 1/16 for early action.

Costs Per Year: Application fee: $55. Comprehensive fee: $39,160 includes full-time tuition ($28,420), mandatory fees ($160), and college room and board ($10,580). College room only: $7230. Part-time tuition: $1015 per credit. Part-time mandatory fees: $160 per year.

Collegiate Environment: Orientation program. Drama-theater group, choral group, student-run newspaper, radio station. Social organizations: 70 open to all; national fraternities, national sororities, local fraternities, local sororities; 2% of eligible men and 2% of eligible women are members. Most popular organizations: student leadership, student media, College Players. Major annual events: homecoming, Founders' Week, Welcome Week. Student services: health clinic, personal-psychological counseling. Campus security: 24-hour emergency response devices and patrols, late night transport-escort service, controlled dormitory access. 2,400 college housing spaces available; 1,948 were occupied in 2003-04. Freshmen guaranteed college housing. On-campus residence required through sophomore year. Options: coed, women-only housing available. Gleeson Library plus 2 others with 1.1 million books, 788,402 microform titles, 5,560 serials, 4,591 audiovisual materials, an OPAC, and a Web page. Operations spending for 2004 fiscal year: $3.3 million. 350 computers available on campus for general student use. A campuswide network can be accessed from student residence rooms and from off campus. Staffed computer lab on campus.

Community Environment: The University of San Francisco is located in the heart of one the world's most dynamic cities. San Francisco's diversity and geographical compactness afford opportunities for community involvement and employment experiences that few other cities can match.

■ **UNIVERSITY OF SOUTHERN CALIFORNIA** S-10
University Park Campus
Los Angeles, CA 90089
Tel: (213)740-2311
Admissions: (213)740-1111
Fax: (213)740-6364
E-mail: admitusc@usc.edu
Web Site: http://www.usc.edu/

Description: Independent, university, coed. Awards bachelor's, master's, doctoral, and first professional degrees and post-master's and first professional certificates. Founded 1880. Setting: 155-acre urban campus. Endowment: $2.7 billion. Research spending for 2004 fiscal year: $386 million. Total enrollment: 32,836. Faculty: 2,479 (1,495 full-time, 984 part-time). Student-undergrad faculty ratio is 10:1. 31,634 applied, 27% were admitted. 85% from top 10% of their high school class, 95% from top quarter, 100% from top half. 179 National Merit Scholars. Full-time: 16,072 students, 51% women, 49% men. Part-time: 825 students, 49% women, 51% men. Students come from 52 states and territories, 134 other countries, 37% from out-of-state, 1% Native American, 13% Hispanic, 6% black, 21% Asian American or Pacific Islander, 8% international, 6% 25 or older, 36% live on campus, 8% transferred in. Retention: 95% of full-time freshmen returned the following year. Academic areas with the most degrees conferred: business/marketing; visual and performing arts; social sciences. Core.

Calendar: semesters. ESL program, services for LD students, advanced placement, accelerated degree program, self-designed majors, freshman honors college, honors program, independent study, distance learning, double major, summer session for credit, part-time degree program, co-op programs and internships, graduate courses open to undergrads. Off campus study at Hebrew Union College-Jewish Institute of Religion, Howard University, American University. Study abroad program. ROTC: Army, Air Force.

Entrance Requirements: Options: electronic application, international baccalaureate accepted. Required: essay, high school transcript, SAT. Recommended: recommendations, interview. Required for some: recommendations. Entrance: most difficult. Application deadline: 1/10. Notification: 4/1.

Costs Per Year: Application fee: $65. Comprehensive fee: $41,618 includes full-time tuition ($31,458), mandatory fees ($550), and college room and board ($9610). College room only: $5260. Full-time tuition and fees vary according to program. Room and board charges vary according to board plan and housing facility. Part-time tuition: $1059 per credit hour. Part-time mandatory fees: $685 per year. Part-time tuition and fees vary according to course load and program.

Collegiate Environment: Orientation program. Drama-theater group, choral group, marching band, student-run newspaper, radio station. Social organizations: 450 open to all; national fraternities, national sororities, local fraternities, local sororities; 16% of eligible men and 20% of eligible women are members. Most popular organizations: Troy Camp, USC Helenes, Program Board, Student Senate, Alpha Phi Omega. Major annual events: Springfest, Troy Week, homecoming. Student services: health clinic, personal-psychological counseling, women's center. Campus security: 24-hour emergency response devices and patrols, student patrols, late night transport-escort service, controlled dormitory access. 6,100 college housing spaces available; all were occupied in 2003-04. Freshmen guaranteed college housing. Option: coed housing available. Doheny Memorial Library plus 20 others with 3.9 million books, 6.2 million microform titles, 52,569 serials, 3.3 million audiovisual materials, an OPAC, and a Web page. Operations spending for 2004 fiscal year: $28.8 million. 2,500 computers available on campus for general student use. Computer purchase/lease plans available. A campuswide network can be accessed from student residence rooms and from off campus. Staffed computer lab on campus.

Community Environment: Located in the heart of Los Angeles, USC exposes undergraduates to one of the world's great cosmopolitan centers. Students take advantage of this setting through internships with major corporations, new technology ventures, the entertainment industry, museums and galleries, non-profit organizations, and government agencies. Across the street from the campus in Exposition Park are museums, gardens, and the Memorial Coliseum. The nearby Figueroa Boulevard "Sports and Entertainment Corridor" includes the Shrine Auditorium, frequent host to the Grammy and Oscar events; the enormous Los Angeles Convention Center; the Staples Arena, which hosts the Lakers, Kings, and Clippers, and the 2000 Democratic Convention; and the Los Angeles Music Center, which offers world-class theatre, concerts, and opera. The campus is minutes away from the beaches of Santa Monica and Venice and also offers easy access to the hiking and bike trails of the Santa Monica Mountains. Local ski resorts are about a 90-minute drive from the campus.

■ **UNIVERSITY OF THE WEST** V-5
1409 North Walnut Grove Ave.
Rosemead, CA 91770
Tel: (626)571-8811
Fax: (626)571-1413
Web Site: http://www.uwest.edu/

Description: Independent, comprehensive, coed. Awards bachelor's, master's, doctoral, and first professional degrees and post-master's certificates. Founded 1991. Calendar: semesters.

Entrance Requirements: Application deadlines: 8/15, 7/31 for nonresidents.

Collegiate Environment: 200 college housing spaces available.

■ **UNIVERSITY OF WEST LOS ANGELES** R-4
1155 West Arbor Vitae St.
Inglewood, CA 90301-2902
Tel: (310)342-5200
Admissions: (310)342-5287
Fax: (310)313-2124
Web Site: http://www.uwla.edu/

Description: Independent, upper-level, coed. Awards bachelor's and first professional degrees. Founded 1966. Setting: 2-acre suburban campus with easy access to Los Angeles. Total enrollment: 63. Full-time: 19 students, 84% women, 16% men. Part-time: 44 students, 66% women, 34% men. 0% from out-of-state, 3% Native American, 7% Hispanic, 30% black, 13% Asian American or Pacific Islander, 13% international, 75% 25 or older, 11% transferred in. Retention: 50% of full-time entering class returned the following year. Core. Calendar: trimesters. Academic remediation for entering students, independent study, part-time degree program, adult/continuing education programs, internships.

Costs Per Year: Application fee: $55. Tuition: $9150 full-time, $305 per unit part-time. Mandatory fees: $360 full-time, $120 per term part-time.

Collegiate Environment: Student-run newspaper. Social organizations: 4 open to all. Most popular organizations: Black Law Students Association, American Trial Lawyers Association, Asian Pacific American Law Students Association, Toastmasters. Campus security: late night transport-escort service. College housing not available. Kelton Library with 33,000 books and 250 serials. 20 computers available on campus for general student use. Staffed computer lab on campus.

Community Environment: See West Los Angeles College.

■ **VANGUARD UNIVERSITY OF SOUTHERN CALIFORNIA** *T-10*
55 Fair Dr.
Costa Mesa, CA 92626-9601
Tel: (714)556-3610
Free: 800-722-6279
Fax: (714)966-5460
E-mail: admissions@vanguard.edu
Web Site: http://www.vanguard.edu/

Description: Independent, comprehensive, coed, affiliated with Assemblies of God. Awards bachelor's and master's degrees. Founded 1920. Setting: 38-acre suburban campus with easy access to Los Angeles. Endowment: $2.1 million. Educational spending for 2005 fiscal year: $5684 per student. Total enrollment: 2,246. Faculty: 197 (66 full-time, 131 part-time). Student-undergrad faculty ratio is 14:1. 903 applied, 86% were admitted. 26% from top 10% of their high school class, 53% from top quarter, 85% from top half. 2 National Merit Scholars, 16 class presidents, 14 valedictorians, 163 student government officers. Full-time: 1,493 students, 66% women, 34% men. Part-time: 407 students, 66% women, 34% men. Students come from 37 states and territories, 12 other countries, 20% from out-of-state, 1% Native American, 17% Hispanic, 4% black, 4% Asian American or Pacific Islander, 1% international, 19% 25 or older, 70% live on campus, 11% transferred in. Retention: 76% of full-time freshmen returned the following year. Academic areas with the most degrees conferred: business/marketing; psychology; education. Core. Calendar: semesters. Services for LD students, advanced placement, accelerated degree program, independent study, double major, summer session for credit, part-time degree program, external degree program, adult/continuing education programs, internships, graduate courses open to undergrads. Off campus study at Council for Christian Colleges and Universities, Los Angeles Film Studies Center. Study abroad program. ROTC: Air Force (c).

Entrance Requirements: Options: Common Application, electronic application, early admission, deferred admission, international baccalaureate accepted. Required: essay, high school transcript, minimum 2.8 high school GPA, 2 recommendations, SAT or ACT. Required for some: interview. Entrance: moderately difficult. Application deadline: 12/1. Notification: 1/15. Preference given to Christians.

Costs Per Year: Application fee: $45. Comprehensive fee: $27,071 includes full-time tuition ($19,900), mandatory fees ($415), and college room and board ($6756). College room only: $3366. Room and board charges vary according to board plan and housing facility. Part-time tuition: $829 per credit hour. Part-time mandatory fees: $25 per term.

Collegiate Environment: Orientation program. Drama-theater group, choral group, student-run newspaper. Social organizations: 50 open to all. Most popular organizations: student ministries, choral groups, orchestral bands. Major annual events: Harvest Party, Homecoming, Welcome Week. Student services: personal-psychological counseling, women's center. Campus security: 24-hour emergency response devices and patrols, late night transport-escort service. 1,028 college housing spaces available; 1,000 were occupied in 2003-04. Freshmen given priority for college housing. Options: coed, men-only, women-only housing available. O. Cope Budge Library with 142,893 books, 19,342 microform titles, 10,482 serials, 6,138 audiovisual materials, an OPAC, and a Web page. Operations spending for 2004 fiscal year: $533,119. 150 computers available on campus for general student use. A campuswide network can be accessed from student residence rooms and from off campus. Staffed computer lab on campus.

Community Environment: The college is adjacent to Newport Beach, the pleasure boat harbor of the West. See Orange Coast College.

■ **VENTURA COLLEGE** *S-9*
4667 Telegraph Rd.
Ventura, CA 93003-3899
Tel: (805)654-6400
Admissions: (805)654-6456
Fax: (805)654-6466
E-mail: sbricker@vcccd.net
Web Site: http://www.venturacollege.edu/

Description: State and locally supported, 2-year, coed. Part of California Community College System. Awards certificates, diplomas, transfer associate, and terminal associate degrees. Founded 1925. Setting: 103-acre suburban campus with easy access to Los Angeles. Educational spending for 2005 fiscal year: $800 per student. Total enrollment: 12,096. Student-undergrad faculty ratio is 22:1. 2,652 applied. Full-time: 4,112 students, 55% women, 45% men. Part-time: 7,984 students, 59% women, 41% men. Students come from 25 states and territories, 11% from out-of-state, 1% Native American, 38% Hispanic, 2% black, 7% Asian American or Pacific Islander, 47% 25 or older, 20% transferred in. Core. Calendar: semesters. Academic remediation for entering students, ESL program, services for LD students, advanced placement, independent study, summer session for credit, part-time degree program, adult/continuing education programs, internships.

Entrance Requirements: Open admission. Required: high school transcript. Entrance: noncompetitive.

Costs Per Year: Application fee: $0. State resident tuition: $0 full-time. Nonresident tuition: $4650 full-time. Mandatory fees: $850 full-time.

Collegiate Environment: Orientation program. Drama-theater group, choral group, student-run newspaper. Most popular organizations: Pan American Student Union, MECHA, Automotive Technology Club, Campus Christian Fellowship, Asian-American Club. Major annual events: ASB Welcome Barbecue, Cinco de Mayo, Native American International Pow Wow. Student services: health clinic, personal-psychological counseling, women's center. Campus security: 24-hour emergency response devices and patrols, student patrols. College housing not available. Ventura College Library with 63,529 books, 341 serials, an OPAC, and a Web page. 40 computers available on campus for general student use. Staffed computer lab on campus.

Community Environment: Ventura is the county seat of Ventura County as well as one of the oldest settlements on the coast. The climate is pleasant and smog-free all year with rain during a few months in the winter and spring. The city is located in the South Central Coast Region, 63 miles northwest of Los Angeles and is served by the Southern Pacific Railroad, Greyhound Bus Lines, and various airlines. Community facilities include hospitals, libraries, churches, and many civic and service organizations. Other facilities include recreation centers, a golf course, and the county fair grounds. An extensive ocean coastline, forest reserves, and mountains all combine to make the area ideal for outdoor recreation.

■ **VICTOR VALLEY COLLEGE** *R-11*
18422 Bear Valley Rd.
Victorville, CA 92392-5849
Tel: (760)245-4271
Fax: (760)245-9745
Web Site: http://www.vvc.edu/

Description: State-supported, 2-year, coed. Part of California Community College System. Awards certificates, transfer associate, and terminal associate degrees. Founded 1961. Setting: 253-acre small town campus with easy access to Los Angeles. Total enrollment: 10,580. Full-time: 3,663 students, 62% women, 38% men. Part-time: 6,917 students, 61% women, 39% men. 1% Native American, 24% Hispanic, 10% black, 4% Asian American or Pacific Islander, 0% international. Core. Calendar: semesters. Academic remediation for entering students, ESL program, services for LD students, advanced placement, honors program, distance learning, summer session for credit, part-time degree program, co-op programs. Off campus study. Study abroad program.

Entrance Requirements: Open admission except for allied health programs. Option: early admission. Placement: ACCUPLACER recommended. Entrance: noncompetitive. Application deadline: Rolling. Notification: continuous.

Costs Per Year: Application fee: $0. State resident tuition: $0 full-time. Nonresident tuition: $3768 full-time, $157 per unit part-time. Mandatory fees: $624 full-time, $26 per unit part-time.

Collegiate Environment: Orientation program. Drama-theater group, choral group, student-run newspaper. Most popular organizations: Black Student Union, Drama Club, rugby, Phi Theta Kappa. Major annual events: Back to School BBQ, MLK Day, Cinco de Mayo. Student services: health clinic, personal-psychological counseling. Campus security: 24-hour emergency response devices and patrols, late night transport-escort service, part-time trained security personnel. College housing not available. Learning Resource Center with 41,789 books, 534 serials, an OPAC, and a Web page. 260 computers available on campus for general student use. A campuswide network can be accessed. Staffed computer lab on campus.

Community Environment: Victorville is a suburban area with a dry temperate climate. Amtrak, Santa Fe and Union Pacific Railroads, and Greyhound bus lines serve the area. The town has a library, churches of major denominations, hospitals, major civic organizations, and shopping facilities. Part-time employment opportunities are good. Victorville is the distributing point for an irrigated agricultural area. The San Bernardino County Fair is held here each year around Labor Day.

■ **WEST HILLS COMMUNITY COLLEGE** *O-6*

300 Cherry Ln.
Coalinga, CA 93210-1399
Tel: (559)934-2000
Free: 800-266-1114
Admissions: (559)934-3204
Fax: (559)934-1511
E-mail: darlenegeorgatos@westhillcollege.com
Web Site: http://www.westhillscollege.com/

Description: State-supported, 2-year, coed. Part of California Community College System. Awards certificates, diplomas, transfer associate, and terminal associate degrees. Founded 1932. Setting: 193-acre small town campus. Total enrollment: 4,344. 2,034 applied, 100% were admitted. Full-time: 1,828 students, 61% women, 39% men. Part-time: 2,516 students, 65% women, 35% men. Students come from 25 states and territories, 5 other countries, 1% Native American, 45% Hispanic, 6% black, 6% Asian American or Pacific Islander, 1% international, 48% 25 or older. Core. Calendar: semesters. Academic remediation for entering students, ESL program, services for LD students, advanced placement, independent study, distance learning, summer session for credit, part-time degree program, adult/continuing education programs, co-op programs. Off campus study at Central California Consortium. Study abroad program.

Entrance Requirements: Open admission. Option: early admission. Recommended: high school transcript. Placement: SAT or ACT recommended. Entrance: noncompetitive. Application deadline: Rolling. Notification: continuous. Preference given to district residents.

Collegiate Environment: Orientation program. Drama-theater group. Student services: personal-psychological counseling. Options: men-only, women-only housing available. West Hills Community College Library with 32,000 books and 210 serials. 82 computers available on campus for general student use. A campuswide network can be accessed from student residence rooms and from off campus. Staffed computer lab on campus.

■ **WEST LOS ANGELES COLLEGE** *W-1*

4800 Freshman Dr.
Culver City, CA 90230-3519
Tel: (310)287-4200
Admissions: (310)287-4255
Fax: (310)841-0396
Web Site: http://www.wlac.cc.ca.us/

Description: State and locally supported, 2-year, coed. Part of Los Angeles Community College District System. Awards transfer associate and terminal associate degrees. Founded 1969. Setting: 69-acre urban campus with easy access to Los Angeles. Total enrollment: 9,800. Students come from 20 states and territories, 76% 25 or older. Core. Calendar: semesters. Academic remediation for entering students, ESL program, services for LD students, advanced placement, honors program, summer session for credit, part-time degree program, adult/continuing education programs, co-op programs. ROTC: Army (c), Air Force (c).

Entrance Requirements: Open admission. Option: early admission. Recommended: high school transcript. Entrance: noncompetitive. Application deadline: 8/16.

Collegiate Environment: Choral group. Student services: health clinic, personal-psychological counseling. Campus security: 24-hour patrols. College housing not available. 51,000 books and 400 serials.

Community Environment: Culver City is an industrial and residential city located near Los Angeles. The world's largest motion picture studio, Metro-Goldwyn-Mayer, was located here, as well as the Desilu Studios. All forms of transportation serve the area; Los Angeles International Airport is near. Churches of all major denominations are in the area; there are excellent shopping facilities available.

■ **WEST VALLEY COLLEGE** *A-10*

14000 Fruitvale Ave.
Saratoga, CA 95070-5698
Tel: (408)867-2200
Admissions: (408)741-2454
Fax: (408)867-5033
Web Site: http://www.westvalley.edu/

Description: State and locally supported, 2-year, coed. Part of California Community College System. Awards certificates, transfer associate, and terminal associate degrees. Founded 1963. Setting: 143-acre small town campus with easy access to San Francisco and San Jose. Total enrollment: 11,000. Students come from 2 states and territories, 20 other countries, 58% 25 or older. Core. Calendar: semesters. Academic remediation for entering students, ESL program, services for LD students, honors program, summer session for credit, part-time degree program, adult/continuing education programs, co-op programs and internships. ROTC: Army (c), Air Force (c).

Entrance Requirements: Open admission. Options: Common Application, early admission. Entrance: noncompetitive. Application deadline: Rolling. Notification: continuous. Preference given to district residents.

Collegiate Environment: Orientation program. Drama-theater group, student-run newspaper. Student services: health clinic, personal-psychological counseling. College housing not available. West Valley College Library with 82,959 books and 491 serials. 200 computers available on campus for general student use.

Community Environment: See San Jose State University.

■ **WESTERN CAREER COLLEGE (EMERYVILLE)** *G-4*

1400 65th St., Ste. 200
Emeryville, CA 94608
Tel: (510)601-0133
Fax: (510)601-0793
Web Site: http://www.westerncollege.edu/

Description: Proprietary, primarily 2-year, coed. Awards certificates, diplomas, transfer associate, and bachelor's degrees. Founded 2001. Educational spending for 2005 fiscal year: $3500 per student. Total enrollment: 375. Full-time: 375 students, 61% women, 39% men. 0% from out-of-state, 0.3% Native American, 7% Hispanic, 50% black, 14% Asian American or Pacific Islander. Calendar: semesters. Accelerated degree program, co-op programs and internships.

Entrance Requirements: Open admission. Option: Common Application. Required: interview, ACT. Required for some: high school transcript.

Collegiate Environment: Silicon Valley College Library plus 1 other with 1,000 books and 50 audiovisual materials.

■ **WESTERN CAREER COLLEGE (FREMONT)** *K-5*

41350 Christy St.
Fremont, CA 94538
Tel: (510)623-9966
Fax: (510)623-9822
Web Site: http://www.westerncollege.edu/

Description: Proprietary, primarily 2-year, coed. Awards certificates, diplomas, terminal associate, and bachelor's degrees. Founded 1989. Educational spending for 2005 fiscal year: $3500 per student. Total enrollment: 460. Full-time: 460 students, 58% women, 42% men. 0% from out-of-state, 1% Native American, 24% Hispanic, 9% black, 40% Asian American or Pacific Islander, 57% 25 or older. Calendar: semesters. Accelerated degree program, co-op programs and internships.

Entrance Requirements: Open admission. Option: Common Application. Required: interview, ACT. Required for some: high school transcript.

Collegiate Environment: Silicon Valley College plus 1 other with 1,000 books and 50 audiovisual materials. Operations spending for 2004 fiscal year: $3000.

■ **WESTERN CAREER COLLEGE (PLEASANT HILL)** *G-6*

380 Civic Dr.
Pleasant Hill, CA 94523
Tel: (925)609-6650

Free: 800-584-4520
Fax: (925)609-6666
Web Site: http://www.westerncollege.edu/
Description: Proprietary, 2-year, coed. Founded 1997. Calendar: semesters.

■ **WESTERN CAREER COLLEGE (SACRAMENTO)** *I-6*
8909 Folsom Blvd.
Sacramento, CA 95826
Tel: (916)361-1660
Free: 800-321-2386
Fax: (916)361-6666
Web Site: http://www.westerncollege.edu/
Description: Proprietary, 2-year, coed. Founded 1967. Calendar: semesters.

■ **WESTERN CAREER COLLEGE (SAN JOSE)** *L-5*
6201 San Ignacio Blvd.
San Jose, CA 95119
Tel: (408)360-0840
Fax: (408)360-0840
Web Site: http://www.westerncollege.edu/
Description: Proprietary, primarily 2-year, coed. Awards certificates, diplomas, terminal associate, and bachelor's degrees. Founded 1999. Educational spending for 2005 fiscal year: $3500 per student. Total enrollment: 478. Full-time: 478 students, 48% women, 52% men. 0% from out-of-state, 1% Native American, 32% Hispanic, 5% black, 21% Asian American or Pacific Islander, 70% 25 or older. Calendar: semesters. Accelerated degree program, co-op programs and internships.
Entrance Requirements: Open admission. Option: Common Application. Required: interview, ACT. Required for some: high school transcript.
Collegiate Environment: Silicon Valley College plus 1 other with 1,000 books and 50 audiovisual materials. Operations spending for 2004 fiscal year: $3000.

■ **WESTERN CAREER COLLEGE (SAN LEANDRO)** *H-5*
170 Bay Fair Mall
San Leandro, CA 94578
Tel: (510)276-3888
Free: 800-584-4553
Fax: (510)276-3854
Web Site: http://www.westerncollege.edu/
Description: Proprietary, 2-year, coed. Founded 1986. Calendar: semesters.

■ **WESTERN CAREER COLLEGE (WALNUT CREEK)** *G-5*
2800 Mitchell Dr.
Walnut Creek, CA 94598
Tel: (925)280-0235
Web Site: http://www.westerncollege.edu/campus_locations/
antioch_campus.html
Description: Proprietary, primarily 2-year, coed. Awards certificates, diplomas, terminal associate, and bachelor's degrees. Founded 1997. Total enrollment: 472. Students come from 4 states and territories, 0% from out-of-state, 4% Native American, 9% Hispanic, 16% black, 10% Asian American or Pacific Islander, 0.4% international, 49% 25 or older. Calendar: continuous. Accelerated degree program, co-op programs.
Entrance Requirements: Required: high school transcript, interview, entrance exam, CPAt. Required for some: essay. Notification: continuous.
Collegiate Environment: Major annual events: Annual Barbeque, Student Appreciation Days, Potluck (Monday, etc.). Campus security: 24-hour emergency response devices. College housing not available. Silicon Valley College plus 1 other with 1,000 books and 50 audiovisual materials.

■ **WESTMONT COLLEGE** *S-7*
955 La Paz Rd.
Santa Barbara, CA 93108-1099
Tel: (805)565-6000
Free: 800-777-9011
Admissions: (805)565-6200
Fax: (805)565-6234
E-mail: admissions@westmont.edu
Web Site: http://www.westmont.edu/
Description: Independent nondenominational, 4-year, coed. Awards bachelor's degrees. Founded 1937. Setting: 133-acre suburban campus with easy access to Los Angeles. Endowment: $61 million. Research spending for 2004 fiscal year: $248,363. Educational spending for 2005 fiscal year:

$9768 per student. Total enrollment: 1,379. Student-undergrad faculty ratio is 12:1. 1,813 applied, 68% were admitted. 44% from top 10% of their high school class, 75% from top quarter, 96% from top half. 10 National Merit Scholars, 81 class presidents, 37 valedictorians, 160 student government officers. Students come from 38 states and territories, 10 other countries, 32% from out-of-state, 2% Native American, 10% Hispanic, 2% black, 8% Asian American or Pacific Islander, 0.2% international, 0% 25 or older, 80% live on campus. Retention: 87% of full-time freshmen returned the following year. Academic areas with the most degrees conferred: English; communications/journalism; biological/life sciences. Core. Calendar: semesters. Services for LD students, advanced placement, accelerated degree program, self-designed majors, honors program, independent study, double major, summer session for credit, co-op programs and internships. Off campus study at 13 members of the Christian College Consortium, 90 members of the Christian Colleges and Universities, American University (Washington Semester). Study abroad program. ROTC: Army (c), Air Force (c).
Entrance Requirements: Options: Common Application, electronic application, early action, international baccalaureate accepted. Required: essay, high school transcript, 1 recommendation, SAT or ACT. Recommended: minimum 3.0 high school GPA, interview. Required for some: interview. Entrance: moderately difficult. Application deadlines: 2/15, 11/1 for early action. Notification: 4/1, 12/20 for early action.
Costs Per Year: Application fee: $50. Comprehensive fee: $36,672 includes full-time tuition ($27,076), mandatory fees ($730), and college room and board ($8866). College room only: $5376. Room and board charges vary according to board plan.
Collegiate Environment: Orientation program. Drama-theater group, choral group, student-run newspaper, radio station. Most popular organizations: Christian Concerns, student government, Leadership Development, music and theater ensembles, intramural athletics. Major annual events: Potter's Clay, Spring Sing, fall/spring formals. Student services: health clinic, personal-psychological counseling, women's center. Campus security: 24-hour emergency response devices and patrols, late night transport-escort service, controlled dormitory access. 1,148 college housing spaces available; 1,006 were occupied in 2003-04. Freshmen guaranteed college housing. On-campus residence required in freshman year. Option: coed housing available. Roger John Voskuyl Library with 150,385 books, 17,180 microform titles, 465 serials, 8,032 audiovisual materials, and an OPAC. Operations spending for 2004 fiscal year: $811,434. 100 computers available on campus for general student use. A campuswide network can be accessed from student residence rooms and from off campus. Staffed computer lab on campus.
Community Environment: See University of California - Santa Barbara.

■ **WESTWOOD COLLEGE-ANAHEIM** *T-10*
2461 West La Palma Ave.
Anaheim, CA 92801
Tel: (714)226-9990
Fax: (714)826-7398
Web Site: http://www.westwood.edu/
Description: Proprietary, primarily 2-year, coed. Awards terminal associate and bachelor's degrees. Setting: suburban campus with easy access to Los Angeles. Total enrollment: 674. 811 applied, 37% were admitted. Full-time: 570 students, 25% women, 75% men. Part-time: 104 students, 13% women, 87% men. 0.4% Native American, 41% Hispanic, 2% black, 11% Asian American or Pacific Islander, 0.1% international, 23% 25 or older. Calendar: continuous.
Entrance Requirements: Required: interview, high school diploma or GED and passing scores on SAT/ACT or Accuplacer test.

■ **WESTWOOD COLLEGE-INLAND EMPIRE** *Q-8*
20 West 7th St.
Upland, CA 91786
Tel: (909)931-7550
Fax: (909)931-9195
Web Site: http://www.westwood.edu/
Description: Proprietary, primarily 2-year, coed. Awards terminal associate and bachelor's degrees. Setting: suburban campus with easy access to Los Angeles. Total enrollment: 803. Full-time: 647 students, 28% women, 72% men. Part-time: 156 students, 19% women, 81% men. 1% Native American, 50% Hispanic, 7% black, 4% Asian American or Pacific Islander, 0% international, 31% 25 or older. Calendar: continuous.

Entrance Requirements: Required: interview, high school diploma or GED, pass entrance exam (or provide acceptable SAT/ACT scores).

■ WESTWOOD COLLEGE-LONG BEACH *T-10*

3901 Via Oro Ave.
Long Beach, CA 90801
Tel: (310)522-2088; 888-403-3308
Fax: (310)522-4318
Web Site: http://www.westwood.edu

Description: Proprietary, primarily 2-year, coed. Part of AITU Colleges. Awards terminal associate and bachelor's degrees. Founded 2002. Setting: 1-acre urban campus with easy access to Los Angeles. Educational spending for 2005 fiscal year: $2500 per student. Total enrollment: 265. Student-undergrad faculty ratio is 15:1. 204 applied, 50% were admitted. Full-time: 265 students, 34% women, 66% men. Students come from 4 states and territories, 2% from out-of-state, 0.4% Native American, 48% Hispanic, 14% black, 8% Asian American or Pacific Islander, 0.4% international, 50% 25 or older, 0% transferred in. Core. Calendar: continuous. Services for LD students, advanced placement, accelerated degree program, self-designed majors, freshman honors college, honors program, independent study, part-time degree program, external degree program, adult/continuing education programs, co-op programs and internships. Off campus study.

Entrance Requirements: Open admission. Options: Common Application, electronic application, international baccalaureate accepted. Required: high school transcript, interview, ACCUPLACER. Recommended: SAT or ACT. Entrance: moderately difficult. Application deadline: 8/2. Notification: continuous.

Collegiate Environment: Social organizations: 4 open to all. Most popular organizations: Westwood Expo, Mentorship Program, Director's Advisory Board. Major annual events: Westwood Expo, Back 2 School Jam, Westwood Family Day. Student services: personal-psychological counseling. Campus security: 24-hour emergency response devices and patrols, late night transport-escort service. College housing not available. Westwood College Library plus 1 other with an OPAC. Operations spending for 2004 fiscal year: $20,000.

■ WESTWOOD COLLEGE-LOS ANGELES *S-10*

3460 Wilshire Blvd., Ste. 700
Los Angeles, CA 90010
Tel: (213)739-9999
Fax: (213)382-2468
Web Site: http://www.westwood.edu/

Description: Proprietary, primarily 2-year, coed. Awards terminal associate and bachelor's degrees. Setting: urban campus with easy access to Los Angeles. Total enrollment: 679. 630 applied. Full-time: 577 students, 26% women, 74% men. Part-time: 102 students, 25% women, 75% men. 0% Native American, 66% Hispanic, 13% black, 10% Asian American or Pacific Islander, 0% international, 25% 25 or older. Calendar: continuous.

Entrance Requirements: Required: interview, high school diploma/GED and passing scores on ACT/SAT or Accuplacer.

■ WHITTIER COLLEGE *R-5*

13406 E Philadelphia St.
Whittier, CA 90608-0634
Tel: (562)907-4200
Admissions: (562)907-4238
Fax: (562)907-4870
E-mail: admission@whittier.edu
Web Site: http://www.whittier.edu/

Description: Independent, comprehensive, coed. Awards bachelor's, master's, and first professional degrees. Founded 1887. Setting: 95-acre suburban campus with easy access to Los Angeles. Endowment: $55 million. Research spending for 2004 fiscal year: $520,206. Educational spending for 2005 fiscal year: $11,932 per student. Total enrollment: 1,307. 1,987 applied, 78% were admitted. 25% from top 10% of their high school class, 59% from top quarter, 84% from top half. Full-time: 1,293 students, 56% women, 44% men. Part-time: 14 students, 71% women, 29% men. Students come from 33 states and territories, 20 other countries, 33% from out-of-state, 1% Native American, 25% Hispanic, 3% black, 9% Asian American or Pacific Islander, 4% international, 4% 25 or older, 68% live on campus, 5% transferred in. Retention: 74% of full-time freshmen returned the following year. Core. Calendar: 4-1-4. Academic remediation for entering students, services for LD students, advanced placement, accelerated degree program, self-designed majors, independent study, double major, summer session for

credit, adult/continuing education programs, internships, graduate courses open to undergrads. Off campus study at University of Miami. Study abroad program. ROTC: Army (c), Air Force (c).

Entrance Requirements: Options: Common Application, electronic application, early action, deferred admission, international baccalaureate accepted. Required: essay, high school transcript, minimum 2.0 high school GPA, 2 recommendations, SAT or ACT. Recommended: minimum 2.5 high school GPA, interview, SAT Subject Tests. Required for some: minimum 3.5 high school GPA. Entrance: moderately difficult. Application deadlines: Rolling, 12/1 for early action. Notification: continuous, 12/31 for early action.

Costs Per Year: Application fee: $50. Comprehensive fee: $34,066 includes full-time tuition ($25,838), mandatory fees ($300), and college room and board ($7928).

Collegiate Environment: Orientation program. Drama-theater group, choral group, student-run newspaper, radio station. Social organizations: 56 open to all; local fraternities, local sororities; 15% of eligible men and 15% of eligible women are members. Most popular organizations: Hispanic Students Association, Hawaiian Islander Club, choir, Asian Students Association, Students Organized for Multicultural Awareness. Major annual events: Spring Sing, Sportsfest, Homecoming. Student services: health clinic, personal-psychological counseling. Campus security: 24-hour emergency response devices and patrols, late night transport-escort service, controlled dormitory access. On-campus residence required through junior year. Options: coed, women-only housing available. Bonnie Bell Wardman Library plus 1 other with 225,337 books, 1,357 serials, an OPAC, and a Web page. Operations spending for 2004 fiscal year: $3.2 million. 150 computers available on campus for general student use. A campuswide network can be accessed from student residence rooms and from off campus. Staffed computer lab on campus.

Community Environment: Whittier enjoys a beautiful setting at the foot of the Puente Hills, in a suburban area in southeast Los Angeles County. The climate is pleasant with a minimum temperature of 53 degrees, a maximum temperature of 73 degrees, and an average rainfall of 15 inches. Buses and railroads serve the area with connection to the Los Angeles International Airport via helicopter, and to the metropolitan area via the freeway system. Modern shopping facilities are available in addition to many manufacturing plants. Recreational facilities include parks, theaters, nearby Disneyland, beaches, and mountains less than one hour away. The Whittier College School of Law is the only ABA accredited Law School in Orange County, California.

■ WILLIAM JESSUP UNIVERSITY *A-10*

333 Sunset Blvd.
Rocklin, CA 95765
Tel: (916)577-1800
Free: 800-355-7522
Admissions: (916)577-2222
Fax: (916)577-1813
E-mail: vpascua@jessup.edu
Web Site: http://www.jessup.edu/

Description: Independent nondenominational, 4-year, coed. Awards associate and bachelor's degrees. Founded 1939. Setting: 156-acre suburban campus with easy access to Sacramento. Total enrollment: 532. Student-undergrad faculty ratio is 11:1. 131 applied, 66% were admitted. 17% from top 10% of their high school class, 45% from top quarter, 72% from top half. Full-time: 388 students, 57% women, 43% men. Part-time: 133 students, 53% women, 47% men. Students come from 10 states and territories, 1 other country, 3% from out-of-state, 1% Native American, 9% Hispanic, 7% black, 6% Asian American or Pacific Islander, 0.2% international, 38% 25 or older, 36% live on campus, 30% transferred in. Retention: 58% of full-time freshmen returned the following year. Academic areas with the most degrees conferred: theology and religious vocations; business/marketing; psychology. Core. Calendar: semesters. Academic remediation for entering students, services for LD students, advanced placement, accelerated degree program, independent study, double major, summer session for credit, part-time degree program, adult/continuing education programs, internships.

Entrance Requirements: Options: electronic application, early action, deferred admission. Required: essay, high school transcript, minimum 2.0 high school GPA, 2 recommendations, letter of introduction, minimum SAT score of 830 or ACT score of 17, SAT or ACT. Entrance: noncompetitive. Application deadline: 8/1. Notification: continuous.

Costs Per Year: Application fee: $35. Comprehensive fee: $22,174 includes full-time tuition ($15,814) and college room and board ($6360). Part-time tuition: $670 per semester hour.

Collegiate Environment: Orientation program. Choral group. Social organizations: 10 open to all. Most popular organizations: Missions Club, student leadership, drama team, music ensemble. Major annual events: International Banquet, Christmas Banquet, All-School Barbecue. Student services: personal-psychological counseling. Campus security: student patrols, late night transport-escort service, day and evening patrols by trained security personnel. 186 college housing spaces available; 157 were occupied in 2003-04. Freshmen guaranteed college housing. On-campus residence required through sophomore year. Options: men-only, women-only housing available. William Jessup University Library with 58,114 books, 90 microform titles, 198 serials, 1,725 audiovisual materials, an OPAC, and a Web page. 26 computers available on campus for general student use. A campuswide network can be accessed from student residence rooms and from off campus. Staffed computer lab on campus.

Community Environment: See San Jose State University.

■ **WOODBURY UNIVERSITY** *S-10*
7500 Glenoaks Blvd.
Burbank, CA 91504-1099
Tel: (818)767-0888
Free: 800-784-WOOD
Fax: (818)504-9320
E-mail: mauro.diaz@woodbury.edu
Web Site: http://www.woodbury.edu/
Description: Independent, comprehensive, coed. Awards bachelor's and master's degrees. Founded 1884. Setting: 22-acre suburban campus with easy access to Los Angeles. Endowment: $9.8 million. Educational spending for 2005 fiscal year: $6068 per student. Total enrollment: 1,436. Faculty: 230 (44 full-time, 186 part-time). Student-undergrad faculty ratio is 12:1. 390 applied, 80% were admitted. 10% from top 10% of their high school class, 40% from top quarter, 80% from top half. Full-time: 1,027 students, 58% women, 42% men. Part-time: 240 students, 68% women, 32% men. Students come from 29 states and territories, 29 other countries, 0.1% Native American, 34% Hispanic, 6% black, 11% Asian American or Pacific Islander, 6% international, 37% 25 or older, 16% live on campus, 16% transferred in. Retention: 72% of full-time freshmen returned the following year. Academic areas with the most degrees conferred: business/marketing; architecture; visual and performing arts. Core. Calendar: semesters. Academic remediation for entering students, services for LD students, advanced placement, accelerated degree program, independent study, double major, summer session for credit, part-time degree program, adult/continuing education programs, internships. Study abroad program.
Entrance Requirements: Options: Common Application, electronic application, deferred admission, international baccalaureate accepted. Required: high school transcript, minimum 2.0 high school GPA, SAT or ACT. Recommended: essay, minimum 3.0 high school GPA, 2 recommendations, interview. Required for some: portfolio. Entrance: moderately difficult. Application deadline: Rolling.
Costs Per Year: Application fee: $35. Comprehensive fee: $31,672 includes full-time tuition ($23,234), mandatory fees ($240), and college room and board ($8198). College room only: $5000. Part-time tuition: $758 per unit.
Collegiate Environment: Orientation program. Student-run newspaper. Social organizations: 18 open to all; national fraternities, national sororities, local fraternities, local sororities; 5% of eligible men and 6% of eligible women are members. Most popular organizations: Associated Student Government, Fashion Guild, American Institute of Architecture Students, Delta Sigma Phi, Reliving Intercultural Experiences (RICE). Major annual events: Winter Formal, International Festival, Beaux Arts Ball. Student services: health clinic, personal-psychological counseling. Campus security: 24-hour patrols, late night transport-escort service, controlled dormitory access. 210 college housing spaces available; all were occupied in 2003-04. Freshmen given priority for college housing. Option: coed housing available. Los Angeles Times Library with 66,157 books, 93,815 microform titles, 9,621 serials, 11,140 audiovisual materials, an OPAC, and a Web page. Operations spending for 2004 fiscal year: $906,072. 135 computers available on campus for general student use. A campuswide network can be accessed from off-campus. Staffed computer lab on campus.
Community Environment: Southern California is famous for the variety of terrain it offers and the array of activities available to its residents. Valleys, mountains, beaches, and deserts enable Woodbury students to escape to practically any climate they wish. Woodbury is surrounded by a residential neighborhood in a city known as the heart of the entertainment industry. Students are just minutes away from the many benefits of southern California: historical and cultural events and museums, world-class

entertainment, professional sporting events, and vast beaches, deserts, mountains, and valleys for recreational leisure.

■ **WYOTECH (FREMONT)** *K-5*
200 Whitney Place
Fremont, CA 94539-7663
Tel: (510)490-6900
Free: 800-248-8585
Admissions: (510)580-3507
Fax: (510)490-8599
Web Site: http://www.wyotech.com/
Description: Proprietary, 2-year, coed. Awards certificates, diplomas, and terminal associate degrees. Founded 1966. Total enrollment: 1,364. Student-undergrad faculty ratio is 23:1. 307 applied, 81% were admitted. 1% Native American, 34% Hispanic, 8% black, 27% Asian American or Pacific Islander, 0% international. Calendar: continuous.
Entrance Requirements: Required: CPAt or ATB Entrance Exam.
Costs Per Year: Tuition: $24,525 full-time. Mandatory fees: $50 full-time.
Collegiate Environment: College housing not available.

■ **WYOTECH (WEST SACRAMENTO)** *I-5*
980 Riverside Parkway
West Sacramento, CA 95605-1507
Tel: (916)376-8888
Web Site: http://www.wyotech.com/
Description: Proprietary, 2-year, coed. Founded 2003. Calendar: 9-month program.

■ **YESHIVA OHR ELCHONON CHABAD/WEST COAST TALMUDICAL SEMINARY** *S-10*
7215 Waring Ave.
Los Angeles, CA 90046-7660
Tel: (213)937-3763
Description: Independent Jewish, 4-year, men only. Awards bachelor's degrees. Founded 1953. Setting: 4-acre urban campus. Research spending for 2004 fiscal year: $15,000. Total enrollment: 62. 20% from top 10% of their high school class, 30% from top quarter, 50% from top half. 1 class president, 2 valedictorians, 4 student government officers. Students come from 9 states and territories, 3 other countries, 0% Native American, 0% Hispanic, 0% black, 3% Asian American or Pacific Islander, 5% international, 0% 25 or older, 100% live on campus. Core. Calendar: semesters. Academic remediation for entering students, honors program, summer session for credit, adult/continuing education programs, internships. Off campus study at Central Yeshiva Tomchei Tmimim-Lubavitch, Rabbinical College of America, Talmudical Seminary Oholei Torah.
Entrance Requirements: Options: Common Application, early admission, deferred admission. Required: high school transcript, minimum 2.0 high school GPA, interview, oral examination. Recommended: recommendations. Required for some: recommendations. Entrance: moderately difficult. Application deadline: Rolling. Notification: continuous. Preference given to applicants with religious commitment.
Collegiate Environment: Major annual events: Yud-Tes Kislev Farbrengen, Annual Chassidic Purim Celebration. Student services: personal-psychological counseling. Campus security: 24-hour emergency response devices, student patrols. On-campus residence required through senior year. Yeshiva Ohr Elchonon Chabad Library plus 3 others with 12,000 books and 200 serials. 18 computers available on campus for general student use. Staffed computer lab on campus.

■ **YUBA COLLEGE** *G-6*
2088 North Beale Rd.
Marysville, CA 95901-7699
Tel: (530)741-6700
Admissions: (530)741-6705
Fax: (530)741-3541
Web Site: http://www.yccd.edu/
Description: State and locally supported, 2-year, coed. Part of California Community College System. Awards certificates and transfer associate degrees. Founded 1927. Setting: 160-acre rural campus with easy access to Sacramento. Endowment: $3.7 million. Total enrollment: 10,457. 2,021 applied, 100% were admitted. 2% Native American, 28% Hispanic, 3% black, 11% Asian American or Pacific Islander, 48% 25 or older. Core. Calendar: semesters. Academic remediation for entering students, ESL program,

services for LD students, advanced placement, distance learning, double major, summer session for credit, part-time degree program.

Entrance Requirements: Open admission. Options: Common Application, electronic application. Required: high school transcript. Entrance: noncompetitive. Application deadline: Rolling.

Costs Per Year: Application fee: $0. State resident tuition: $0 full-time. Mandatory fees: $780 full-time, $26 per unit part-time.

Collegiate Environment: Orientation program. Drama-theater group, choral group. Social organizations: 18 open to all. Student services: health clinic, personal-psychological counseling, women's center. Campus security: 24-hour patrols, student patrols. Learning Resource Center and Library plus 1 other with 65,000 books, 2,800 microform titles, 1,300 serials, 9,419 audiovisual materials, and an OPAC. Operations spending for 2004 fiscal year: $91,272. 200 computers available on campus for general student use. A campuswide network can be accessed from student residence rooms and from off campus. Staffed computer lab on campus.

Community Environment: Marysville is 50 miles north of Sacramento, has a moderate climate, and is the center of a rich agricultural area. Amtrak serves the area. The city has a hospital, churches, shopping center, and civic organizations. Excellent boating, hunting and fishing facilities are available.

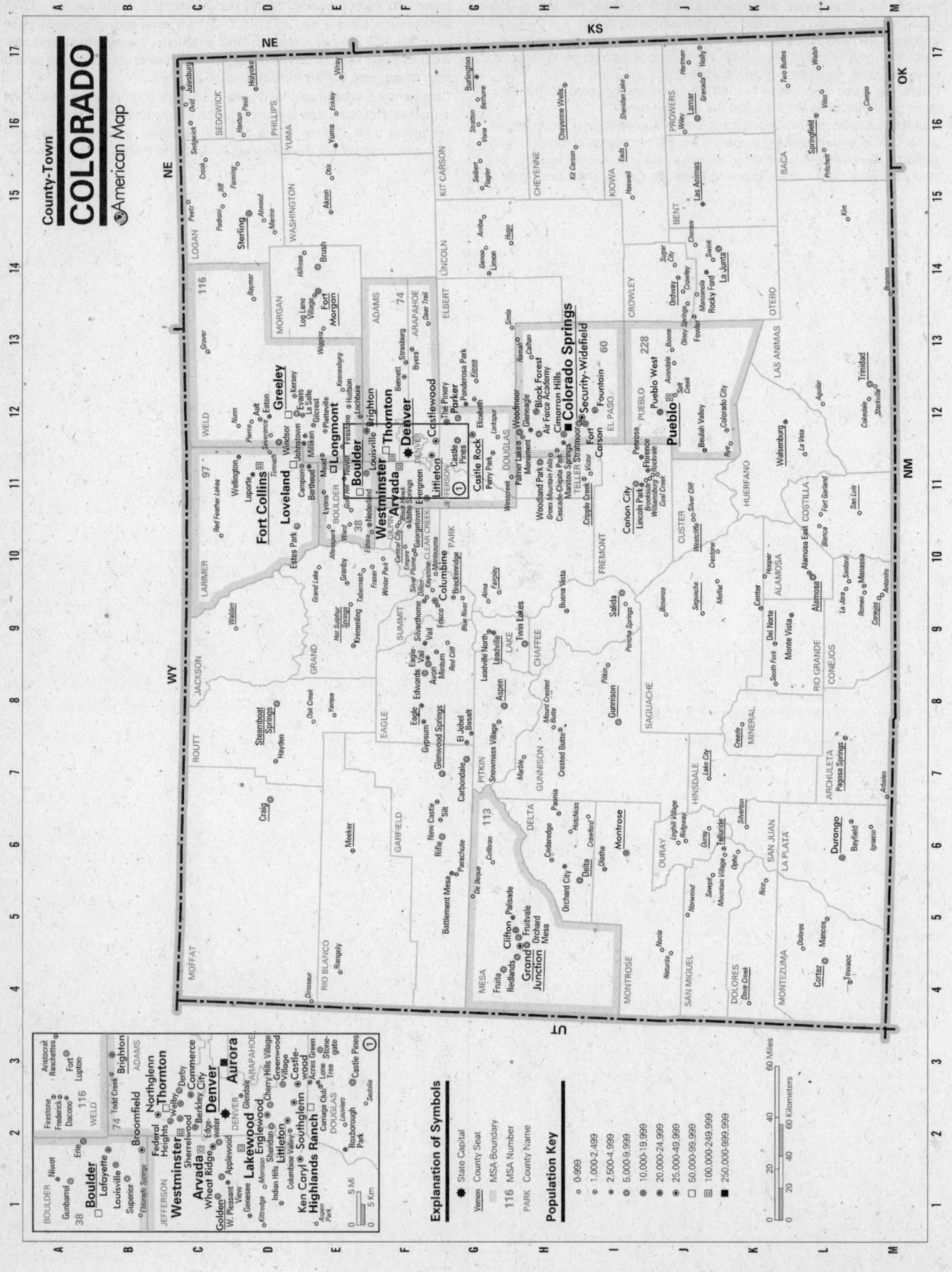

COLORADO

County-Town

American Map

■ **ADAMS STATE COLLEGE** *L-10*
208 Edgemont Blvd.
Alamosa, CO 81102
Tel: (719)587-7011
Free: 800-824-6494
Admissions: (719)587-7712
Fax: (719)587-7522
E-mail: ecarpio@adams.edu
Web Site: http://www.adams.edu/
Description: State-supported, comprehensive, coed. Awards associate, bachelor's, and master's degrees. Founded 1921. Setting: 90-acre small town campus. Endowment: $62,512. Educational spending for 2005 fiscal year: $5602 per student. Total enrollment: 5,578. Faculty: 185 (104 full-time, 81 part-time). Student-undergrad faculty ratio is 18:1. 1,765 applied, 60% were admitted. 7% from top 10% of their high school class, 24% from top quarter, 52% from top half. Full-time: 1,876 students, 55% women, 45% men. Part-time: 562 students, 68% women, 32% men. Students come from 56 states and territories, 6 other countries, 11% from out-of-state, 2% Native American, 29% Hispanic, 5% black, 1% Asian American or Pacific Islander, 0.1% international, 20% 25 or older, 40% live on campus, 9% transferred in. Retention: 57% of full-time freshmen returned the following year. Academic areas with the most degrees conferred: liberal arts/general studies; business/marketing; social sciences. Core. Calendar: semesters. Academic remediation for entering students, services for LD students, advanced placement, accelerated degree program, self-designed majors, independent study, distance learning, double major, summer session for credit, part-time degree program, adult/continuing education programs, internships, graduate courses open to undergrads. Off campus study at members of the Consortium of State Colleges in Colorado.
Entrance Requirements: Options: Peterson's Universal Application, Common Application, electronic application, early admission, deferred admission, international baccalaureate accepted. Required: high school transcript, minimum 2.0 high school GPA, audition for music majors, SAT or ACT. Required for some: essay, high school transcript, recommendations, interview. Entrance: moderately difficult. Application deadline: 8/1.
Costs Per Year: Application fee: $20. Area resident tuition: $90 per credit hour part-time. State resident tuition: $1980 full-time. Nonresident tuition: $8250 full-time, $344 per credit hour part-time. Mandatory fees: $874 full-time. College room and board: $5760.
Collegiate Environment: Orientation program. Drama-theater group, choral group, marching band, student-run newspaper, radio station. Social organizations: 40 open to all. Most popular organizations: student government, Student Ambassadors, Program Council, Circle K, Tri Beta. Major annual events: homecoming, Snow Daze, Spring Fest. Student services: health clinic, personal-psychological counseling. Campus security: 24-hour emergency response devices and patrols, student patrols, late night transport-escort service, controlled dormitory access. 1,126 college housing spaces available; 898 were occupied in 2003-04. Freshmen guaranteed college housing. On-campus residence required through sophomore year. Options: coed, women-only housing available. Nielsen Library with 493,581 books, 842,498 microform titles, 614 serials, 3,796 audiovisual materials, an OPAC, and a Web page. Operations spending for 2004 fiscal year: $305,019. 353 computers available on campus for general student use. A campuswide network can be accessed from student residence rooms and from off campus. Staffed computer lab on campus.

Community Environment: Located in the center of San Luis Valley, an extensive grazing and farming area larger than the state of Connecticut, Alamosa is completely surrounded by mountain ranges. It has an ideal climate, with an average yearly temperature of 65 degrees. A commuter airline and a bus line serve the area. Alamosa has churches, radio stations, libraries, hotels and motels, a hospital and a number of civic, social, cultural, fraternal and veterans organizations.

■ **AIMS COMMUNITY COLLEGE** *D-12*
Box 69
Greeley, CO 80632-0069
Tel: (970)330-8008
E-mail: stuart.thomas@aims.edu
Web Site: http://www.aims.edu/
Description: District-supported, 2-year, coed. Awards certificates, diplomas, transfer associate, and terminal associate degrees. Founded 1967. Setting: 185-acre urban campus with easy access to Denver. Endowment: $71,813. Total enrollment: 5,098. Full-time: 2,252 students, 51% women, 49% men. Part-time: 2,846 students, 57% women, 43% men. Students come from 8 states and territories, 60% 25 or older. Retention: 45% of full-time freshmen returned the following year. Core. Calendar: semesters. Academic remediation for entering students, ESL program, advanced placement, self-designed majors, freshman honors college, honors program, summer session for credit, part-time degree program, external degree program, adult/continuing education programs, co-op programs. ROTC: Air Force (c).
Entrance Requirements: Open admission. Options: early admission, deferred admission. Placement: CPT required. Entrance: noncompetitive. Application deadline: Rolling.
Collegiate Environment: Drama-theater group, choral group, student-run newspaper, radio station. Social organizations: 3 open to all. Major annual events: Fall-In Activity, Winter Fest, Spring-Fest/Blowout Activity. Student services: personal-psychological counseling, women's center. Campus security: 24-hour emergency response devices, day and evening patrols by trained security personnel. College housing not available. Aims Community College Library with 39,129 books, 258 serials, and an OPAC. Operations spending for 2004 fiscal year: $247,345. 700 computers available on campus for general student use. A campuswide network can be accessed from off-campus. Staffed computer lab on campus.
Community Environment: See University of Northern Colorado.

■ **ARAPAHOE COMMUNITY COLLEGE** *F-11*
5900 South Santa Fe Dr., PO Box 9002
Littleton, CO 80160-9002
Tel: (303)797-4222
Admissions: (303)797-5623
Fax: (303)797-5970
Web Site: http://www.arapahoe.edu/
Description: State-supported, 2-year, coed. Part of Community Colleges of Colorado. Awards certificates, diplomas, transfer associate, and terminal associate degrees. Founded 1965. Setting: 52-acre suburban campus with easy access to Denver. Total enrollment: 7,560. Student-undergrad faculty ratio is 19:1. 2,017 applied, 100% were admitted. Full-time: 2,312 students, 56% women, 44% men. Part-time: 5,248 students, 66% women, 34% men. Students come from 35 other countries, 1% Native American, 9% Hispanic, 3% black, 3% Asian American or Pacific Islander, 1% international. Core.

Calendar: semesters. Academic remediation for entering students, ESL program, services for LD students, advanced placement, accelerated degree program, self-designed majors, honors program, independent study, distance learning, double major, summer session for credit, part-time degree program, adult/continuing education programs, co-op programs and internships. Off campus study at Metropolitan State College. Study abroad program. ROTC: Army (c), Air Force (c).

Entrance Requirements: Open admission. Options: Common Application, electronic application, early admission, deferred admission. Entrance: noncompetitive. Application deadline: Rolling.

Costs Per Year: Application fee: $0. State resident tuition: $1619 full-time, $89.90 per credit hour part-time. Nonresident tuition: $8000 full-time, $369.30 per credit hour part-time. Mandatory fees: $81 full-time.

Collegiate Environment: Orientation program. Drama-theater group, choral group, student-run newspaper. Major annual events: International Day, Martin Luther King Day events, Veterans' Day events. Student services: personal-psychological counseling. Campus security: 24-hour emergency response devices and patrols, late night transport-escort service. College housing not available. Weber Center for Learning Resources plus 1 other with 45,000 books, 3 microform titles, 441 serials, an OPAC, and a Web page. 200 computers available on campus for general student use. A campuswide network can be accessed from off-campus. Staffed computer lab on campus.

Community Environment: Littleton is a suburban area 10 miles from Denver with seasonal variations in temperature. There are churches of all denominations, shopping centers, and medical clinics, with all forms of transportation available. Community facilities include parks with playground equipment, public swimming pools, indoor tennis courts, fairgrounds, golf courses and an ice rink. Skiing in the nearby mountains is excellent. Part-time employment is available.

■ **ARGOSY UNIVERSITY/DENVER** *F-12*
1200 Lincoln St.
Denver, CO 80203
Tel: (303)248-2700; (866)431-5981
Web Site: http://www.argosyu.edu/
Description: Proprietary, 2-year, coed. Awards terminal associate degrees.

■ **THE ART INSTITUTE OF COLORADO** *F-12*
1200 Lincoln St.
Denver, CO 80203
Tel: (303)837-0825
Free: 800-275-2420
Fax: (303)860-8520
E-mail: baparker@aii.edu
Web Site: http://www.aic.artinstitutes.edu/
Description: Proprietary, 4-year, coed. Part of Education Management Corporation. Awards associate and bachelor's degrees. Founded 1952. Setting: urban campus. Educational spending for 2005 fiscal year: $8465 per student. Total enrollment: 2,886. Student-undergrad faculty ratio is 18:1. 748 applied. 0% from top 10% of their high school class, 0% from top quarter, 0% from top half. Full-time: 2,137 students, 49% women, 51% men. Part-time: 749 students, 50% women, 50% men. Students come from 49 states and territories, 22 other countries, 50% from out-of-state, 1% Native American, 8% Hispanic, 4% black, 3% Asian American or Pacific Islander, 0% international, 41% 25 or older, 9% live on campus, 0.4% transferred in. Retention: 65% of full-time freshmen returned the following year. Academic areas with the most degrees conferred: personal and culinary services; education. Core. Academic remediation for entering students, services for LD students, advanced placement, independent study, distance learning, part-time degree program, external degree program, adult/continuing education programs, internships. Study abroad program.

Entrance Requirements: Options: early admission, deferred admission. Required: essay, high school transcript, interview. Entrance: minimally difficult. Application deadline: Rolling. Notification: continuous.

Costs Per Year: Application fee: $0. Tuition: $25,088 full-time, $392 per credit part-time. College room only: $7980.

Collegiate Environment: Orientation program. Student-run newspaper. Social organizations: 3 open to all; 50% of eligible men and 50% of eligible women are members. Most popular organizations: Culinary Student Forum, Computer Animation Club, American Society of Interior Designers Student Chapter. Major annual events: quarterly portfolio review, student picnic. Student services: personal-psychological counseling. Campus security: 24-hour emergency response devices. 254 college housing spaces available;

191 were occupied in 2003-04. Option: coed housing available. Art Institute of Colorado Learning Resource Center with 13,100 books, 200 serials, and an OPAC. Operations spending for 2004 fiscal year: $130,394. 400 computers available on campus for general student use. Staffed computer lab on campus.

■ **ASPEN UNIVERSITY** *F-12*
501 South Cherry St., Ste. 350
Denver, CO 80246
Tel: (303)333-4224
Fax: (303)336-1144
Web Site: http://www.aspen.edu/
Description: Independent, upper-level, coed. Awards bachelor's and master's degrees. Founded 1987. Calendar: 5 terms per year.

■ **BEL-REA INSTITUTE OF ANIMAL TECHNOLOGY** *F-12*
1681 South Dayton St.
Denver, CO 80247
Tel: (303)751-8700
Free: 800-950-8001
Fax: (303)751-9969
Web Site: http://www.bel-rea.com/
Description: Proprietary, 2-year, coed. Awards terminal associate degrees. Founded 1971. Setting: 4-acre suburban campus. Endowment: $17,500. Total enrollment: 615. 865 applied, 69% were admitted. 16% from top 10% of their high school class, 33% from top quarter, 62% from top half. Students come from 35 states and territories, 3 other countries, 45% 25 or older. Core. Academic remediation for entering students, internships.

Entrance Requirements: Options: Peterson's Universal Application, Common Application. Required: high school transcript, minimum 2.5 high school GPA. Recommended: interview. Entrance: moderately difficult. Application deadline: Rolling.

Collegiate Environment: Most popular organization: National Association of Veterinary Technicians. Student services: personal-psychological counseling. 1,800 books and 57 serials. 4 computers available on campus for general student use. Staffed computer lab on campus.

■ **BLAIR COLLEGE** *H-12*
1815 Jet Wing Dr.
Colorado Springs, CO 80916
Tel: (719)638-6580; 888-741-4271
Admissions: (719)630-6580
Fax: (719)638-6818
E-mail: dcollins@cci.edu
Web Site: http://blair-college.com/
Description: Proprietary, 2-year, coed. Part of Corinthian Colleges, Inc. Awards diplomas, transfer associate, and terminal associate degrees. Founded 1897. Setting: 5-acre suburban campus with easy access to Denver. Total enrollment: 600. Core. Academic remediation for entering students, services for LD students, co-op programs and internships.

Entrance Requirements: Open admission. Required: high school transcript, CPAt. Entrance: minimally difficult. Application deadline: Rolling. Notification: continuous.

Collegiate Environment: Campus security: 24-hour emergency response devices. College housing not available. Blair College Library with 45 serials. 45 computers available on campus for general student use.

Community Environment: See The Colorado College.

■ **BOULDER COLLEGE OF MASSAGE THERAPY** *E-11*
6255 Longbow Dr.
Boulder, CO 80301
Tel: (303)530-2100
Free: 800-442-5131
Fax: (303)530-2204
Web Site: http://www.bcmt.org/
Description: Independent, 2-year, coed. Founded 1975.

■ **CAMBRIDGE COLLEGE** *F-12*
12500 East Iliff Ave., No. 100
Aurora, CO 80014
Tel: (303)338-9700
Fax: (303)338-9701
Web Site: http://www.cambridgecollege.com/

Description: Independent, 2-year.

■ **COLLEGEAMERICA-COLORADO SPRINGS** *H-12*
3645 Citadel Dr. South
Colorado Springs, CO 80909
Tel: (719)637-0600
Fax: (719)637-0806
Web Site: http://www.collegeamerica.com/
Description: Proprietary, 2-year, coed.

■ **COLLEGEAMERICA-DENVER** *F-12*
1385 South Colorado Blvd.
Denver, CO 80222-1912
Tel: (303)691-9756
Fax: (303)692-9156
E-mail: collegeamerica@aol.com
Web Site: http://www.collegeamerica.com/
Description: Proprietary, 2-year, coed. Founded 1962. Setting: urban campus.

■ **COLLEGEAMERICA-FORT COLLINS** *D-11*
4601 South Mason St.
Fort Collins, CO 80525-3740
Tel: (970)223-6060
Fax: (970)223-6060
Web Site: http://www.collegeamerica.edu/
Description: Proprietary, primarily 2-year, coed. Awards terminal associate and bachelor's degrees. Founded 1962. Setting: suburban campus. Total enrollment: 232. 1 valedictorian. Students come from 3 states and territories, 0% from out-of-state, 70% 25 or older. Core. Calendar: continuous. Independent study, internships.
Entrance Requirements: Open admission. Option: international baccalaureate accepted. Required: essay, high school transcript, interview. Recommended: minimum 2.0 high school GPA. Required for some: recommendations. Entrance: noncompetitive. Notification: continuous.
Collegiate Environment: Orientation program. College housing not available. Library with 12 serials and 30 audiovisual materials. 86 computers available on campus for general student use. A campuswide network can be accessed. Staffed computer lab on campus.

■ **COLORADO CHRISTIAN UNIVERSITY** *C-2*
8787 West Alameda
Lakewood, CO 80226
Tel: (303)202-0100
Free: 800-44-FAITH
Admissions: (303)963-3163
Fax: (303)238-2191
E-mail: admission@ccu.edu
Web Site: http://www.ccu.edu/
Description: Independent interdenominational, comprehensive, coed. Awards associate, bachelor's, and master's degrees. Founded 1914. Setting: 26-acre suburban campus with easy access to Denver. Endowment: $18.8 million. Educational spending for 2005 fiscal year: $5255 per student. Total enrollment: 2,142. Faculty: 46 (43 full-time, 3 part-time). Student-undergrad faculty ratio is 21:1. 946 applied, 77% were admitted. 22% from top 10% of their high school class, 46% from top quarter, 79% from top half. Full-time: 1,075 students, 63% women, 37% men. Part-time: 751 students, 58% women, 42% men. Students come from 45 states and territories, 9 other countries, 56% from out-of-state, 1% Native American, 8% Hispanic, 4% black, 1% Asian American or Pacific Islander, 0.5% international, 65% live on campus, 3% transferred in. Retention: 72% of full-time freshmen returned the following year. Academic areas with the most degrees conferred: business/marketing; computer and information sciences; education. Core. Calendar: semesters. Academic remediation for entering students, services for LD students, advanced placement, accelerated degree program, self-designed majors, honors program, independent study, distance learning, double major, summer session for credit, part-time degree program, adult/continuing education programs, co-op programs and internships, graduate courses open to undergrads. Off campus study at Colorado Institute of Art, Metropolitan State College, University of Colorado at Denver, Red Rocks Community College. Study abroad program. ROTC: Army (c).
Entrance Requirements: Options: Common Application, electronic application, deferred admission, international baccalaureate accepted. Required: essay, high school transcript, 2 recommendations, SAT or ACT. Required for

some: minimum 2.8 high school GPA, 3 recommendations, interview. Entrance: moderately difficult. Application deadline: 8/21. Notification: 11/1.
Costs Per Year: Application fee: $50. Comprehensive fee: $23,422 includes full-time tuition ($16,590), mandatory fees ($150), and college room and board ($6682). College room only: $3930. Part-time tuition: $700 per credit hour.
Collegiate Environment: Orientation program. Drama-theater group, choral group, student-run newspaper. Social organizations: 26 open to all. Most popular organizations: FAT Boys (inner city ministry to homeless), SALT (Snowboarding as a Living Testimony), Freedom, In His Service Honor Society, Trash Club. Major annual events: Homecoming, O'Malley's Alley, Spring School Retreat. Student services: health clinic, personal-psychological counseling, women's center. Campus security: 24-hour emergency response devices and patrols, student patrols. 722 college housing spaces available; 570 were occupied in 2003-04. Freshmen guaranteed college housing. On-campus residence required through sophomore year. Options: coed, men-only, women-only housing available. Clifton Fowler Library plus 1 other with 71,565 books, 300,000 microform titles, 1,192 serials, 4,200 audiovisual materials, an OPAC, and a Web page. Operations spending for 2004 fiscal year: $390,375. 141 computers available on campus for general student use. A campuswide network can be accessed from student residence rooms and from off campus. Staffed computer lab on campus.
Community Environment: See University of Denver.

■ **THE COLORADO COLLEGE** *H-12*
14 East Cache La Poudre
Colorado Springs, CO 80903-3294
Tel: (719)389-6000
Free: 800-542-7214
Admissions: (719)389-6344
Fax: (719)389-6282
E-mail: admission@cc.colorado.edu
Web Site: http://www.coloradocollege.edu/
Description: Independent, comprehensive, coed. Awards bachelor's and master's degrees (master's degree in education only). Founded 1874. Setting: 90-acre urban campus with easy access to Denver. Endowment: $407.9 million. Research spending for 2004 fiscal year: $728,836. Educational spending for 2005 fiscal year: $18,389 per student. Total enrollment: 2,016. Faculty: 206 (176 full-time, 30 part-time). Student-undergrad faculty ratio is 9:1. 4,089 applied, 38% were admitted. 66% from top 10% of their high school class, 90% from top quarter, 99% from top half. Full-time: 1,928 students, 54% women, 46% men. Part-time: 49 students, 67% women, 33% men. Students come from 51 states and territories, 98% from out-of-state, 1% Native American, 7% Hispanic, 2% black, 4% Asian American or Pacific Islander, 2% international, 1% 25 or older, 73% live on campus, 1% transferred in. Retention: 92% of full-time freshmen returned the following year. Academic areas with the most degrees conferred: social sciences; biological/life sciences; visual and performing arts. Core. Calendar: modular. ESL program, services for LD students, advanced placement, self-designed majors, independent study, double major, summer session for credit, internships. Off campus study at American University, Associated Colleges of the Midwest Programs. Study abroad program. ROTC: Army (c).
Entrance Requirements: Options: Common Application, electronic application, early action, deferred admission, international baccalaureate accepted. Required: essay, high school transcript, 3 recommendations, SAT or ACT. Recommended: interview. Entrance: very difficult. Application deadlines: 1/15, 11/15 for early action. Notification: 4/1, 12/20 for early action.
Costs Per Year: Application fee: $50. Comprehensive fee: $37,668 includes full-time tuition ($30,048) and college room and board ($7620). College room only: $4116. Room and board charges vary according to board plan. Part-time tuition: $948.38 per credit hour.
Collegiate Environment: Orientation program. Drama-theater group, choral group, student-run newspaper, radio station. Social organizations: 80 open to all; national fraternities, national sororities. Most popular organizations: Community Service Center, student government, arts and crafts organizations, Outdoor Recreation Committee, theater workshop. Major annual events: homecoming, Llamapalooza (concert), arts and crafts annual sale. Student services: health clinic, personal-psychological counseling, women's center. Campus security: 24-hour emergency response devices and patrols, late night transport-escort service, controlled dormitory access, whistle program, student escort service. 1,470 college housing spaces available; 1,413 were occupied in 2003-04. Freshmen guaranteed college housing.

On-campus residence required through junior year. Options: coed, men-only, women-only housing available. Tutt Library plus 2 others with an OPAC and a Web page. 208 computers available on campus for general student use. Computer purchase/lease plans available. A campuswide network can be accessed from student residence rooms and from off campus. Staffed computer lab on campus.

Community Environment: Colorado Springs, metropolitan population of 500,000, is located 70 miles south of Denver at the foot of Pikes Peak. It is known for its healthful climate and spectacular scenery. the area averages more than 310 days of sunshine each year, has clean air, low humidity, cool summer nights, and mild winters. Bus, air, and good highways serve the area. The city has a fine arts center, opera, symphony, theatre, museums, art galleries, and numerous fine hotels, and motels. Areas for skiing, hunting, fishing, backpacking, and camping are nearby.

■ **COLORADO MOUNTAIN COLLEGE** *G-7*
831 Grand Ave.
Glenwood Springs, CO 81601
Tel: (970)945-7481
Free: 800-621-8559
Admissions: (970)947-8328
E-mail: joinus@coloradomtn.edu
Web Site: http://www.coloradomtn.edu/
Description: District-supported, 2-year, coed. Part of Colorado Mountain College District System. Awards certificates, transfer associate, and terminal associate degrees. Founded 1965. Setting: 680-acre rural campus. Educational spending for 2005 fiscal year: $9000 per student. Total enrollment: 867. Student-undergrad faculty ratio is 17:1. 579 applied, 100% were admitted. Students come from 38 states and territories, 20% from out-of-state, 1% Native American, 11% Hispanic, 0.3% black, 1% Asian American or Pacific Islander, 0.1% international, 23% 25 or older, 44% live on campus. Core. Calendar: semesters. Academic remediation for entering students, services for LD students, advanced placement, honors program, independent study, distance learning, summer session for credit, part-time degree program, adult/continuing education programs, co-op programs and internships. Study abroad program.
Entrance Requirements: Open admission. Options: early admission, deferred admission. Required: high school transcript. Recommended: SAT or ACT. Entrance: noncompetitive. Application deadline: Rolling.
Costs Per Year: Application fee: $0. Area resident tuition: $1290 full-time, $43 per credit part-time. State resident tuition: $2160 full-time, $72 per credit part-time. Nonresident tuition: $6930 full-time, $231 per credit part-time. Mandatory fees: $180 full-time. College room and board: $6600. College room only: $3400.
Collegiate Environment: Orientation program. Drama-theater group, student-run newspaper. Most popular organizations: student government, outdoor activities, World Awareness Society, Peer Mentors, Student Activities Board. Major annual events: Spring Fest, outdoor activities, residence hall activities. Student services: health clinic, personal-psychological counseling. Campus security: 24-hour emergency response devices, controlled dormitory access. 237 college housing spaces available; 200 were occupied in 2003-04. Freshmen given priority for college housing. On-campus residence required in freshman year. Option: coed housing available. Quigley Library with 36,000 books, 186 serials, an OPAC, and a Web page. 65 computers available on campus for general student use. A campuswide network can be accessed from student residence rooms. Staffed computer lab on campus.
Community Environment: Glenwood Springs is an urban area with a moderate climate; a beautiful place to live. Railroads and buses serve the area and charter air service is available. Glenwood Springs is the county seat of Garfield County, and has the best shopping facilities in the county. The city has churches of all major denominations, library, museum, theatres, hospital and many of the civic clubs. Hot mineral springs have made Glenwood Springs a popular resort. Seven miles above the town is the Shoshone Hydroelectric Plant. The Colorado employment office is located here; several businesses hire part-time workers. Over 1,000 miles of fishing streams and more than 100 lakes are accessible from Glenwood Springs. The Sunlight Ski area is located nine miles south of the town; it has a 7,000 foot double chair lift. Aspen and Snowmass are 45 miles away. Other recreational activities include fishing, hiking, hunting and tennis. Strawberry day is an annual event in June.

■ **COLORADO MOUNTAIN COLLEGE, ALPINE CAMPUS** *D-8*
1330 Bob Adams Dr.
Steamboat Springs, CO 80487

Tel: (970)870-4444
Free: 800-621-8559
Admissions: (970)945-8691
E-mail: joinus@coloradomtn.edu
Web Site: http://www.coloradomtn.edu/
Description: District-supported, 2-year, coed. Part of Colorado Mountain College District System. Awards certificates, transfer associate, and terminal associate degrees. Founded 1965. Setting: 10-acre rural campus. Educational spending for 2005 fiscal year: $9000 per student. Total enrollment: 1,104. 579 applied, 100% were admitted. Students come from 49 states and territories, 15% from out-of-state, 1% Native American, 11% Hispanic, 1% black, 2% Asian American or Pacific Islander, 1% international, 21% 25 or older, 44% live on campus. Core. Calendar: semesters. Academic remediation for entering students, services for LD students, advanced placement, honors program, independent study, distance learning, summer session for credit, part-time degree program, adult/continuing education programs, co-op programs and internships. Study abroad program.
Entrance Requirements: Open admission. Options: early admission, deferred admission. Required: high school transcript. Recommended: SAT or ACT. Entrance: noncompetitive. Application deadline: Rolling.
Costs Per Year: Application fee: $0. Area resident tuition: $1290 full-time, $43 per credit part-time. State resident tuition: $2160 full-time, $72 per credit part-time. Nonresident tuition: $6930 full-time, $231 per credit part-time. Mandatory fees: $180 full-time. College room and board: $6600. College room only: $3400.
Collegiate Environment: Orientation program. Student-run newspaper. Social organizations: 8 open to all. Most popular organizations: student government, Forensics Team, Ski Club, International Club, Phi Theta Kappa. Major annual events: Spring Fling, Winter Carnival. Student services: health clinic, personal-psychological counseling. Campus security: 24-hour emergency response devices, controlled dormitory access. College housing designed to accommodate 225 students; 230 undergraduates lived in college housing during 2003-04. On-campus residence required in freshman year. Option: coed housing available. 17,000 books, 192 serials, an OPAC, and a Web page. 60 computers available on campus for general student use. A campuswide network can be accessed from student residence rooms. Staffed computer lab on campus.
Community Environment: Steamboat Springs is 175 miles northwest of Denver. A permanent population of 6,000 swells to over 25,000 on Christmas Eve, largely due to the attraction of the town's famous champagne powder. The town flourishes with the contrasting influences of working cattle ranches and a world-class ski resort. The surrounding area offers unlimited opportunities for downhill and cross-country skiing, and hunting. Students learn additional outdoor skills through college-sponsored activities such as winter survival, desert camping, and orienteering.

■ **COLORADO MOUNTAIN COLLEGE, TIMBERLINE CAMPUS** *G-9*
901 South Hwy. 24
Leadville, CO 80461
Tel: (719)486-2015
Free: 800-621-8559
Admissions: (970)945-8691
E-mail: joinus@coloradomtn.edu
Web Site: http://www.coloradomtn.edu/
Description: District-supported, 2-year, coed. Part of Colorado Mountain College District System. Awards certificates, transfer associate, and terminal associate degrees. Founded 1965. Setting: 200-acre rural campus. Educational spending for 2005 fiscal year: $9000 per student. Total enrollment: 1,305. 242 applied, 100% were admitted. Students come from 48 states and territories, 20% from out-of-state, 0.2% Native American, 17% Hispanic, 0.1% black, 0.4% Asian American or Pacific Islander, 0% international, 33% 25 or older, 30% live on campus. Core. Calendar: semesters. Academic remediation for entering students, ESL program, services for LD students, advanced placement, honors program, independent study, distance learning, summer session for credit, part-time degree program, adult/continuing education programs, co-op programs and internships. Study abroad program.
Entrance Requirements: Open admission except for outdoor recreational leadership program. Options: early admission, deferred admission. Required: high school transcript. Entrance: noncompetitive. Application deadline: Rolling.
Costs Per Year: Application fee: $0. Area resident tuition: $1290 full-time, $43 per credit part-time. State resident tuition: $2160 full-time, $72 per credit

part-time. Nonresident tuition: $6930 full-time, $231 per credit part-time. Mandatory fees: $180 full-time. College room and board: $6600. College room only: $3400.

Collegiate Environment: Orientation program. Most popular organizations: Environmental Club, Outdoor Club, Student Activities Board. Student services: health clinic, personal-psychological counseling. Campus security: 24-hour emergency response devices, controlled dormitory access. 130 college housing spaces available; 90 were occupied in 2003-04. Freshmen given priority for college housing. On-campus residence required in freshman year. Option: coed housing available. 25,000 books and 185 serials. 30 computers available on campus for general student use. A campuswide network can be accessed from student residence rooms. Staffed computer lab on campus.

Community Environment: Leadville, situated at an altitude of 10,000 feet, is a rural community with a dry climate. Leadville has been the center of a famous mining district since the Placer Mines were opened in 1860. It became the silver capital and one of Colorado's greatest mining camps. Mining and tourism are major industries at the present. The city has a library, branch museum of the Colorado State Historical Society, churches, medical clinic and a hospital. Part-time work opportunities are available nearby. Recreation activities are numerous and include ice skating, golfing, tennis, fishing, soccer, bowling, swimming. There is skiing at Ski Cooper on the top of Tennessee Pass 12 miles north of Leadville and at nearby Copper Mountain, Vail, Keystone, Breckenridge and A-Basin. The World's Championship Pack Burro Race is an annual event the first weekend in August.

■ **COLORADO NORTHWESTERN COMMUNITY COLLEGE** *E-4*
500 Kennedy Dr.
Rangely, CO 81648-3598
Tel: (970)675-2261
Free: 800-562-1105
Admissions: (970)824-1103
Fax: (970)675-3343
E-mail: gene.bilodeau@cncc.edu
Web Site: http://www.cncc.edu/

Description: State-supported, 2-year, coed. Part of Colorado Community College and Occupational Education System. Awards certificates, transfer associate, and terminal associate degrees. Founded 1962. Setting: 150-acre rural campus. Endowment: $27,000. Educational spending for 2005 fiscal year: $4240 per student. Total enrollment: 2,242. 171 applied, 100% were admitted. Full-time: 499 students, 55% women, 45% men. Part-time: 1,743 students, 50% women, 50% men. Students come from 28 states and territories, 3 other countries, 5% from out-of-state, 1% Native American, 5% Hispanic, 1% black, 1% Asian American or Pacific Islander, 0.3% international, 12% 25 or older, 62% live on campus, 7% transferred in. Retention: 55% of full-time freshmen returned the following year. Core. Calendar: semesters. Academic remediation for entering students, services for LD students, advanced placement, self-designed majors, independent study, distance learning, double major, summer session for credit, part-time degree program, adult/continuing education programs, internships.

Entrance Requirements: Open admission except for dental hygiene programs. Options: Peterson's Universal Application, early admission, deferred admission. Required: high school transcript. Required for some: essay, 3 recommendations, interview. Entrance: noncompetitive. Application deadline: Rolling.

Collegiate Environment: Orientation program. Drama-theater group, choral group, student-run newspaper. Most popular organizations: Campus Activities Board, SADHA, Aero Club, Criminal Justice Club, Spartan Times Newspaper Club. Major annual events: All-Nighter Weekend, Crazy Daze, Christmas Dinner. Student services: personal-psychological counseling. Campus security: student patrols, late night transport-escort service. 356 college housing spaces available; 170 were occupied in 2003-04. Freshmen given priority for college housing. On-campus residence required in freshman year. Option: coed housing available. Colorado Northwestern Community College Library plus 1 other with 20,063 books, 5,525 microform titles, 230 serials, 3,559 audiovisual materials, and an OPAC. Operations spending for 2004 fiscal year: $126,399. 83 computers available on campus for general student use. A campuswide network can be accessed from student residence rooms and from off campus. Staffed computer lab on campus.

Community Environment: Rangely is a rural community (population 2,500) located on the western slope of Colorado, 300 miles northwest of Denver and 130 miles west of Steamboat Springs. It is a friendly community that offers a sharp change of pace from the urban areas. Excellent area for cross-country skiing, backpacking, river rafting, fishing and hunting. Close to Dinosaur National Monument and Flaming Gorge Dam and Reservoir. The area is two hours from downhill skiing at Steamboat Springs, Powder Horn and Sunlight Mountain. Community recreation facilities include: The Taylor Draw Dam Reservoir, a nine-hole golf course, tennis courts, a fitness trail, an ice skating rink, an indoor Olympic-size swimming pool, racquetball courts, and a dance and aerobics room. Bus and airport facilities are nearby.

■ **COLORADO SCHOOL OF HEALING ARTS** *C-2*
7655 West Mississippi Ave., Ste. 100
Lakewood, CO 80226
Tel: (303)986-2320
Free: 800-233-7114
Fax: (303)980-6594
Web Site: http://www.csha.net/

Description: Proprietary, 2-year, coed. Awards certificates and terminal associate degrees. Founded 1986. Educational spending for 2005 fiscal year: $1688 per student. Total enrollment: 240. Student-undergrad faculty ratio is 13:1. 26 applied, 100% were admitted. Full-time: 149 students, 88% women, 12% men. Part-time: 91 students, 84% women, 16% men. 2% Native American, 9% Hispanic, 3% black, 1% Asian American or Pacific Islander, 1% international.

Entrance Requirements: Required: high school transcript, interview. Entrance: noncompetitive. Application deadline: 10/1.

Costs Per Year: Application fee: $50. Tuition: $8925 full-time. Mandatory fees: $1236 full-time.

Collegiate Environment: Student services: personal-psychological counseling.

■ **COLORADO SCHOOL OF MINES** *C-1*
1500 Illinois St.
Golden, CO 80401-1887
Tel: (303)273-3000
Free: 800-446-9488
Admissions: (303)273-3227
Fax: (303)273-3509
E-mail: admit@mines.edu
Web Site: http://www.mines.edu/

Description: State-supported, university, coed. Awards bachelor's, master's, doctoral, and first professional degrees. Founded 1874. Setting: 373-acre small town campus with easy access to Denver. Endowment: $125 million. Research spending for 2004 fiscal year: $27.5 million. Educational spending for 2005 fiscal year: $17,000 per student. Total enrollment: 3,921. Faculty: 299 (193 full-time, 106 part-time). Student-undergrad faculty ratio is 14:1. 3,215 applied, 80% were admitted. 48% from top 10% of their high school class, 81% from top quarter, 100% from top half. 72 class presidents, 80 valedictorians, 220 student government officers. Full-time: 2,909 students, 21% women, 79% men. Part-time: 189 students, 24% women, 76% men. Students come from 51 states and territories, 62 other countries, 18% from out-of-state, 1% Native American, 7% Hispanic, 1% black, 5% Asian American or Pacific Islander, 3% international, 5% 25 or older, 25% live on campus, 4% transferred in. Retention: 84% of full-time freshmen returned the following year. Academic areas with the most degrees conferred: engineering; computer and information sciences; physical sciences. Core. Calendar: semesters. Academic remediation for entering students, ESL program, services for LD students, advanced placement, accelerated degree program, honors program, independent study, double major, summer session for credit, co-op programs and internships, graduate courses open to undergrads. Study abroad program. ROTC: Army.

Entrance Requirements: Options: Peterson's Universal Application, electronic application, deferred admission. Required: high school transcript, SAT or ACT. Recommended: rank in upper one-third of high school class. Required for some: essay, recommendations, interview. Entrance: very difficult. Application deadline: 6/1. Notification: continuous.

Costs Per Year: Application fee: $45. State resident tuition: $7248 full-time, $382 per semester hour part-time. Nonresident tuition: $19,830 full-time, $661 per semester hour part-time. Mandatory fees: $895 full-time, $60 per semester hour part-time. Part-time tuition and fees vary according to course load. College room and board: $6750. College room only: $3550. Room and board charges vary according to board plan and housing facility.

Collegiate Environment: Orientation program. Drama-theater group, choral group, marching band, student-run newspaper, radio station. Social organizations: 95 open to all; national fraternities, national sororities; 19% of eligible men and 19% of eligible women are members. Most popular organizations: Residence Hall Association, Society of Women Engineers, American Institute of Chemical Engineers. Major annual events: Greek Casino Night, Celebration of Mines, Engineers' Days. Student services: health clinic, personal-psychological counseling. Campus security: 24-hour emergency response devices and patrols, late night transport-escort service. 800 college housing spaces available; all were occupied in 2003-04. Freshmen guaranteed college housing. Option: coed housing available. Arthur Lakes Library with 150,000 books, 250,000 microform titles, 4,883 serials, 20 audiovisual materials, an OPAC, and a Web page. Operations spending for 2004 fiscal year: $2.4 million. 400 computers available on campus for general student use. A campuswide network can be accessed from student residence rooms and from off campus. Staffed computer lab on campus.

Community Environment: CSM is located in Golden, only 15 miles west of Denver's downtown business district. Golden is a community of 15,000 people nestled in the foothills of the Rocky Mountains. Maintaining a distinct identity from the other Denver suburbs, Golden is also home to the National Earthquake Center and the National Renewable Energy Laboratory. Many CSM students enjoy the outdoors, and favorite summer activities include hiking, jogging, camping, and bicycling. During the winter months, skiing is the major activity with some of the world's best slopes virtually in CSM's backyard. With a population of over two million people, nearby Denver offers all the attractions of a major metropolitan area. As a commercial, transportation, and financial center for the Rocky Mountain region, Denver is home to many government agencies, colleges and universities, and business involved in natural resources, computers, and biotechnology.

■ **COLORADO SCHOOL OF TRADES** *C-2*

1575 Hoyt St.
Lakewood, CO 80215-2996
Tel: (303)233-4697
Free: 800-234-4594
Fax: (303)233-4723
Web Site: http://www.schooloftrades.com/

Description: Proprietary, 2-year, coed. Awards terminal associate degrees. Total enrollment: 125. Student-undergrad faculty ratio is 12:1. 174 applied, 87% were admitted. Full-time: 125 students, 2% women, 98% men. 88% from out-of-state.

Entrance Requirements: Required: essay, high school transcript, interview.

Costs Per Year: Application fee: $25. Tuition: $16,200 full-time. Mandatory fees: $154 full-time.

■ **COLORADO STATE UNIVERSITY** *D-11*

Fort Collins, CO 80523-0015
Tel: (970)491-1101
Admissions: (970)491-6909
Fax: (970)491-7799
E-mail: admissions@vines.colostate.edu
Web Site: http://www.colostate.edu/

Description: State-supported, university, coed. Part of Colorado State University System. Awards bachelor's, master's, doctoral, and first professional degrees. Founded 1870. Setting: 666-acre urban campus with easy access to Denver. Endowment: $178.8 million. Research spending for 2004 fiscal year: $224.2 million. Educational spending for 2005 fiscal year: $8700 per student. Total enrollment: 27,133. Faculty: 881 (851 full-time, 30 part-time). Student-undergrad faculty ratio is 18:1. 10,770 applied, 88% were admitted. 17% from top 10% of their high school class, 46% from top quarter, 84% from top half. 14 National Merit Scholars. Full-time: 18,995 students, 52% women, 48% men. Part-time: 2,511 students, 48% women, 52% men. Students come from 50 other countries, 18% from out-of-state, 1% Native American, 6% Hispanic, 2% black, 3% Asian American or Pacific Islander, 1% international, 7% 25 or older, 23% live on campus, 7% transferred in. Retention: 82% of full-time freshmen returned the following year. Academic areas with the most degrees conferred: business/marketing; family and consumer sciences; social sciences. Core. Calendar: semesters. ESL program, services for LD students, advanced placement, accelerated degree program, self-designed majors, honors program, independent study, distance learning, double major, summer session for credit, part-time degree program, adult/continuing education programs, co-op programs and internships, graduate courses open to undergrads. Off campus study at Aims Community College. Study abroad program. ROTC: Army, Air Force.

Entrance Requirements: Options: electronic application, deferred admission, international baccalaureate accepted. Required: high school transcript,

SAT or ACT. Recommended: essay, recommendations. Entrance: moderately difficult. Application deadline: 7/1. Notification: continuous.

Costs Per Year: Application fee: $50. State resident tuition: $3381 full-time, $188 per credit part-time. Nonresident tuition: $14,343 full-time, $797 per credit part-time. Mandatory fees: $1181 full-time. Part-time tuition varies according to course load. College room and board: $6316. College room only: $2852. Room and board charges vary according to board plan and housing facility.

Collegiate Environment: Orientation program. Drama-theater group, choral group, marching band, student-run newspaper, radio station. Social organizations: 300 open to all; national fraternities, national sororities, local fraternities, local sororities; 8% of eligible men and 8% of eligible women are members. Most popular organizations: Club Sports Association, Associated Students (student government), Office of Community Services, Colorado Public Interest Research Group. Major annual events: Homecoming/Family Weekend, International Week, Earth Day/Spring Fest. Student services: legal services, health clinic, personal-psychological counseling, women's center. Campus security: 24-hour emergency response devices and patrols, student patrols, late night transport-escort service, controlled dormitory access. 5,031 college housing spaces available; 4,922 were occupied in 2003-04. Freshmen guaranteed college housing. On-campus residence required in freshman year. Option: coed housing available. William E. Morgan Library plus 3 others with 1.9 million books, 2.5 million microform titles, 20,935 serials, 9,428 audiovisual materials, an OPAC, and a Web page. Operations spending for 2004 fiscal year: $12.7 million. 2,095 computers available on campus for general student use. A campuswide network can be accessed from student residence rooms and from off campus. Staffed computer lab on campus.

Community Environment: Fort Collins, a community of 110,000 is situated at the foot of the Rocky Mountains. The excellent climate and beautiful mountains create an ideal college setting about 65 miles north of Denver. The city has many churches, a local airport, hospital, hotels, motels, and is the shopping center of Northern Colorado. Part-time employment is available for students and some full-time employment is available for graduates.

■ **COLORADO STATE UNIVERSITY-PUEBLO** *J-12*

2200 Bonforte Blvd.
Pueblo, CO 81001-4901
Tel: (719)549-2100
Admissions: (719)549-2461
Fax: (719)549-2419
Web Site: http://www.colostate-pueblo.edu/

Description: State-supported, comprehensive, coed. Part of Colorado State University System. Awards bachelor's and master's degrees. Founded 1933. Setting: 275-acre suburban campus with easy access to Colorado Springs. Endowment: $3.5 million. Research spending for 2004 fiscal year: $626,706. Educational spending for 2005 fiscal year: $4169 per student. Total enrollment: 5,835. 1,850 applied, 94% were admitted. 2% from top 10% of their high school class, 10% from top quarter, 41% from top half. Full-time: 3,367 students, 56% women, 44% men. Part-time: 2,050 students, 66% women, 34% men. Students come from 44 states and territories, 37 other countries, 8% from out-of-state, 2% Native American, 27% Hispanic, 5% black, 2% Asian American or Pacific Islander, 3% international, 35% 25 or older, 18% live on campus, 5% transferred in. Retention: 64% of full-time freshmen returned the following year. Core. Calendar: semesters. Academic remediation for entering students, ESL program, services for LD students, advanced placement, accelerated degree program, honors program, independent study, distance learning, double major, summer session for credit, part-time degree program, external degree program, adult/continuing education programs, co-op programs and internships, graduate courses open to undergrads. Off campus study at Adams State College, Colorado State University, University of Colorado at Denver. Study abroad program. ROTC: Army.

Entrance Requirements: Options: Peterson's Universal Application, Common Application, electronic application, deferred admission, international baccalaureate accepted. Required: high school transcript, minimum 2.0 high school GPA, SAT or ACT. Required for some: essay, recommendations. Placement: SAT or ACT required. Entrance: moderately difficult. Application deadline: 8/1. Notification: continuous until 8/1.

Costs Per Year: Application fee: $25. State resident tuition: $2902 full-time, $120.92 per credit part-time. Nonresident tuition: $13,542 full-time, $564.25 per credit part-time. Mandatory fees: $964 full-time, $40.17 per credit part-time. Full-time tuition and fees vary according to course load and reciprocity agreements. Part-time tuition and fees vary according to reciprocity agreements. College room and board: $6088. College room only: $2960. Room and board charges vary according to board plan and housing facility.

Collegiate Environment: Orientation program. Choral group, student-run newspaper, radio station. Social organizations: 49 open to all; national fraternities, national sororities, local fraternities, local sororities; 2% of eligible men and 1% of eligible women are members. Most popular organizations: Belmont Residence Hall Association, Associated Student Government, Hawaii Club, Medical Science Society, Student Social Worker's Association. Major annual events: Colorado Music Fest, Parti Gras, Winter Formal. Student services: health clinic, personal-psychological counseling. Campus security: 24-hour emergency response devices and patrols, late night transport-escort service, controlled dormitory access. 650 college housing spaces available; all were occupied in 2003-04. Freshmen guaranteed college housing. On-campus residence required in freshman year. Option: coed housing available. Colorado State University-Pueblo Library with 270,761 books, 10,000 microform titles, 1,327 serials, 16,862 audiovisual materials, an OPAC, and a Web page. Operations spending for 2004 fiscal year: $1.1 million. 521 computers available on campus for general student use. A campuswide network can be accessed from student residence rooms and from off campus. Staffed computer lab on campus.

Community Environment: Pueblo is a city of approximately 100,000 people located on the Arkansas River on the eastern slope of the Rocky Mountains. The city is a manufacturing and retail center for southeastern Colorado with a mild and semiarid climate. Recreational activities including skiing, hiking, camping, boating, fishing, and swimming are available in Pueblo and its immediate vicinity. The city and the university cooperate to provide cultural activities including a symphony orchestra and theatrical productions.

■ **COLORADO TECHNICAL UNIVERSITY** *H-12*
4435 North Chestnut St.
Colorado Springs, CO 80907-3896
Tel: (719)598-0200
E-mail: tjohnson@cos.coloradotech.edu
Web Site: http://www.coloradotech.edu

Description: Proprietary, comprehensive, coed. Part of Whitman Education Group. Awards associate, bachelor's, master's, and doctoral degrees. Founded 1965. Setting: 14-acre suburban campus with easy access to Denver. Educational spending for 2005 fiscal year: $6200 per student. Total enrollment: 1,684. 180 applied, 93% were admitted. Full-time: 305 students, 21% women, 79% men. Part-time: 910 students, 28% women, 72% men. Students come from 10 states and territories, 2% from out-of-state, 1% Native American, 6% Hispanic, 10% black, 3% Asian American or Pacific Islander, 0.5% international, 82% 25 or older, 10% transferred in. Core. Academic remediation for entering students, services for LD students, advanced placement, accelerated degree program, independent study, distance learning, double major, summer session for credit, part-time degree program, adult/continuing education programs, co-op programs and internships, graduate courses open to undergrads. ROTC: Army (c).

Entrance Requirements: Options: electronic application, deferred admission, international baccalaureate accepted. Recommended: high school transcript, minimum 3.0 high school GPA, interview, SAT or ACT. Required for some: essay, ACT COMPASS. Entrance: minimally difficult. Application deadline: Rolling. Notification: continuous.

Collegiate Environment: Orientation program. Social organizations: 7 open to all. Most popular organizations: Institute of Electrical and Electronics Engineers, Society of Logistic Engineers, Association of Computing Machinery, Society of Women Engineers, Phi Beta Lambda. Major annual events: Artsfest, Career Fair. Campus security: 24-hour emergency response devices, late night transport-escort service. College housing not available. Colorado Technical University Library with 29,819 books, 3,000 microform titles, 10,098 serials, 620 audiovisual materials, an OPAC, and a Web page. Operations spending for 2004 fiscal year: $345,000. 130 computers available on campus for general student use. A campuswide network can be accessed from off-campus. Staffed computer lab on campus.

Community Environment: Colorado Tech is located at the foot of beautiful Pikes Peak. This ideal location provides convenient access to Colorado's magnificent outdoor recreational facilities: skiing, camping, hunting, fishing, and backpacking. Beautiful Colorado Springs and its environs constitute a progressive, growing city of approximately 400,000.

■ **COLORADO TECHNICAL UNIVERSITY DENVER CAMPUS** *D-3*
5775 Denver Tech Center Blvd.
Greenwood Village, CO 80111

Tel: (303)694-6600
Fax: (303)694-6673
Web Site: http://www.coloradotech.edu/

Description: Proprietary, comprehensive, coed. Part of Whitman Education Group. Awards associate, bachelor's, and master's degrees. Founded 1965. Setting: 1-acre urban campus with easy access to Denver. Educational spending for 2005 fiscal year: $8200 per student. Total enrollment: 298. 23 applied, 65% were admitted. Full-time: 41 students, 24% women, 76% men. Part-time: 151 students, 19% women, 81% men. Students come from 12 states and territories, 7 other countries, 2% from out-of-state, 1% Native American, 5% Hispanic, 7% black, 5% Asian American or Pacific Islander, 5% international, 79% 25 or older, 8% transferred in. Core. Academic remediation for entering students, services for LD students, advanced placement, independent study, distance learning, double major, summer session for credit, part-time degree program, adult/continuing education programs, co-op programs, graduate courses open to undergrads.

Entrance Requirements: Options: electronic application, deferred admission, international baccalaureate accepted. Recommended: high school transcript, minimum 3.0 high school GPA, interview, SAT or ACT. Required for some: essay, ACT COMPASS. Entrance: minimally difficult. Application deadline: Rolling. Notification: continuous.

Collegiate Environment: Social organizations: 1 open to all. Most popular organization: Association of Information Technology Professionals. Campus security: 24-hour emergency response devices and patrols, late night transport-escort service. College housing not available. Colorado Technical University Resource Center with 12,715 books, 9,869 serials, and 15 audiovisual materials. Operations spending for 2004 fiscal year: $35,000. 112 computers available on campus for general student use. A campuswide network can be accessed. Staffed computer lab on campus.

■ **COMMUNITY COLLEGE OF AURORA** *F-12*
16000 East Centre Tech Parkway
Aurora, CO 80011-9036
Tel: (303)360-4700
E-mail: kristen.cusak@ccaurora.edu
Web Site: http://www.ccaurora.edu/

Description: State-supported, 2-year, coed. Awards certificates, transfer associate, and terminal associate degrees. Founded 1983. Setting: suburban campus with easy access to Denver. Endowment: $3.3 million. Educational spending for 2005 fiscal year: $1590 per student. Total enrollment: 5,477. Student-undergrad faculty ratio is 21:1. 3,568 applied, 100% were admitted. Full-time: 1,412 students, 52% women, 48% men. Part-time: 4,065 students, 64% women, 36% men. 0.1% from out-of-state, 1% Native American, 13% Hispanic, 24% black, 6% Asian American or Pacific Islander, 2% international, 59% 25 or older, 1% transferred in. Core. Calendar: semesters. Academic remediation for entering students, ESL program, services for LD students, independent study, distance learning, summer session for credit, part-time degree program, external degree program, adult/continuing education programs, internships. Off campus study at T. H. Pickens Technical Vocational Center.

Entrance Requirements: Open admission. Option: early admission. Required for some: high school transcript. Entrance: noncompetitive. Application deadline: Rolling. Notification: continuous.

Costs Per Year: Application fee: $0. State resident tuition: $2236 full-time, $74.55 per credit hour part-time. Nonresident tuition: $10,354 full-time, $345.15 per credit hour part-time. Mandatory fees: $126 full-time, $3 per credit hour part-time, $20.75.

Collegiate Environment: Drama-theater group. Student services: women's center. Campus security: late night transport-escort service. 120 college housing spaces available; 90 were occupied in 2003-04. 7,440 books, 126 serials, an OPAC, and a Web page. Operations spending for 2004 fiscal year: $12,924. 160 computers available on campus for general student use. A campuswide network can be accessed. Staffed computer lab on campus.

■ **COMMUNITY COLLEGE OF DENVER** *F-12*
PO Box 173363
Denver, CO 80217-3363
Tel: (303)556-2600
Admissions: (303)556-6325
Web Site: http://www.ccd.edu/

Description: State-supported, 2-year, coed. Part of Community Colleges of Colorado. Awards certificates, transfer associate, and terminal associate degrees. Founded 1970. Setting: 171-acre urban campus. Total enrollment: 8,909. Student-undergrad faculty ratio is 23:1. Full-time: 2,041 students,

64% women, 36% men. Part-time: 6,868 students, 63% women, 37% men. Students come from 35 states and territories, 0.4% from out-of-state, 2% Native American, 26% Hispanic, 17% black, 6% Asian American or Pacific Islander, 6% international, 47% 25 or older, 2% transferred in. Core. Calendar: semesters. Academic remediation for entering students, ESL program, services for LD students, advanced placement, accelerated degree program, freshman honors college, honors program, independent study, distance learning, double major, summer session for credit, part-time degree program, adult/continuing education programs, co-op programs and internships. Off campus study at Metropolitan State College, University of Colorado at Denver. Study abroad program. ROTC: Army (c).

Entrance Requirements: Open admission except for health occupation and computer information systems programs. Options: Common Application, electronic application, early admission, deferred admission. Entrance: noncompetitive. Application deadline: Rolling.

Costs Per Year: Application fee: $0. State resident tuition: $2237 full-time, $74.55 per credit part-time. Nonresident tuition: $10,355 full-time, $345.15 per credit part-time. Mandatory fees: $612 full-time.

Collegiate Environment: Orientation program. Student-run newspaper. Social organizations: 10 open to all. Most popular organizations: Trio Advocates for Multicultural Students, Student Alliance for Human Services, Ad Hoc Nursing, Black Men on Campus, Auraria Fine Arts. Major annual events: Halloween Scene, Cinco de Mayo, Black Community Leaders Luncheon. Student services: health clinic, personal-psychological counseling. Campus security: 24-hour emergency response devices and patrols, late night transport-escort service. College housing not available. Auraria Library plus 1 other with 683,045 books, 1.1 million microform titles, 3,233 serials, 16,821 audiovisual materials, an OPAC, and a Web page. 1,142 computers available on campus for general student use. A campuswide network can be accessed from off-campus. Staffed computer lab on campus.

Community Environment: See University of Denver.

■ DENVER ACADEMY OF COURT REPORTING *F-11*

9051 Harlan St., Unit 20
Westminster, CO 80030
Tel: (303)427-5292
Free: 800-574-2087
Fax: (303)427-5383
Web Site: http://www.dacr.org/

Description: Proprietary, 2-year, coed. Awards terminal associate degrees. Founded 1975. Setting: urban campus. Total enrollment: 225. Students come from 12 states and territories, 8% from out-of-state, 56% 25 or older. Core. Double major, part-time degree program, external degree program, adult/continuing education programs, internships.

Entrance Requirements: Open admission. Option: Common Application. Required: high school transcript. Recommended: interview. Entrance: noncompetitive. Application deadline: Rolling.

Collegiate Environment: Orientation program. Campus security: 24-hour emergency response devices, late night transport-escort service. College housing not available. 75 computers available on campus for general student use. Staffed computer lab on campus.

■ DENVER AUTOMOTIVE AND DIESEL COLLEGE *F-12*

460 South Lipan St.
Denver, CO 80223-2025
Tel: (303)722-5724
Free: 800-347-3232
Fax: (303)778-8264
Web Site: http://www.dadc.com/

Description: Proprietary, 2-year, coed. Awards diplomas and terminal associate degrees. Founded 1963. Setting: urban campus. Total enrollment: 368. Full-time: 368 students, 5% women, 95% men. Students come from 34 states and territories, 56% from out-of-state, 2% Native American, 11% Hispanic, 7% black, 4% Asian American or Pacific Islander, 0.3% international, 31% 25 or older, 1% transferred in. Core. Calendar: 8 six-week terms. Services for LD students, summer session for credit.

Entrance Requirements: Option: Common Application. Entrance: moderately difficult. Application deadline: Rolling.

Collegiate Environment: Orientation program. Most popular organization: student council. Student services: personal-psychological counseling. Campus security: 24-hour emergency response devices and patrols. College housing not available. Denver Automotive and Diesel College Library plus 1 other with 1,050 books, 8 serials, and a Web page. 4 computers available on campus for general student use. Staffed computer lab on campus.

■ DENVER CAREER COLLEGE *F-11*

500 East 84th Ave., Ste. W-200
Thornton, CO 80229
Tel: (303)295-0550
Web Site: http://www.denvercareercollege.com/

Description: Proprietary, 2-year, coed. Awards certificates and terminal associate degrees. Founded 1977. Calendar: continuous.

■ DEVRY UNIVERSITY (BROOMFIELD) *B-2*

12202 Airport Way, Ste. 190
Broomfield, CO 80021-2588
Tel: (303)469-9220
Admissions: (303)329-3340
Fax: (303)469-9224
Web Site: http://www.devry.edu/

Description: Proprietary, comprehensive, coed. Part of DeVry University. Awards associate and bachelor's degrees. Founded 2001. Total enrollment: 460. 329 applied, 66% were admitted. Full-time: 307 students, 18% women, 82% men. Part-time: 153 students, 33% women, 67% men. Students come from 16 states and territories, 4 other countries, 14% from out-of-state, 1% Native American, 6% Hispanic, 11% black, 4% Asian American or Pacific Islander, 2% international, 51% 25 or older, 0% transferred in. Calendar: semesters. Academic remediation for entering students, advanced placement, accelerated degree program, distance learning, part-time degree program, co-op programs.

Entrance Requirements: Options: electronic application, deferred admission, international baccalaureate accepted. Required: high school transcript, interview, CPT. Recommended: SAT or ACT. Entrance: minimally difficult.

Collegiate Environment: Orientation program. Learning Resource Center with 5,037 books, 46,172 serials, 446 audiovisual materials, an OPAC, and a Web page. 435 computers available on campus for general student use. Computer purchase/lease plans available. A campuswide network can be accessed from off-campus.

■ DEVRY UNIVERSITY (COLORADO SPRINGS) *H-12*

225 South Union Blvd.
Colorado Springs, CO 80910
Tel: (719)632-3000; (866)338-7934
Web Site: http://www.devry.edu/

Description: Proprietary, comprehensive, coed. Part of DeVry University. Awards associate, bachelor's, and master's degrees. Founded 2001. Setting: 9-acre urban campus. Total enrollment: 275. Faculty: 42 (1 full-time, 41 part-time). Student-undergrad faculty ratio is 9:1. Full-time: 89 students, 39% women, 61% men. Part-time: 127 students, 31% women, 69% men. Students come from 12 states and territories, 1 other country, 1% Native American, 11% Hispanic, 18% black, 5% Asian American or Pacific Islander, 0.5% international, 63% 25 or older. Retention: 36% of full-time freshmen returned the following year. Academic areas with the most degrees conferred: business/marketing; computer and information sciences. Calendar: semesters. Academic remediation for entering students, services for LD students, advanced placement, accelerated degree program, distance learning, summer session for credit, part-time degree program, adult/continuing education programs, co-op programs.

Entrance Requirements: Options: electronic application, deferred admission, international baccalaureate accepted. Required: high school transcript, interview. Entrance: minimally difficult. Application deadline: Rolling. Notification: continuous.

Costs Per Year: Application fee: $50. One-time mandatory fee: $40. Tuition: $12,450 full-time, $460 per credit part-time. Mandatory fees: $270 full-time, $30 per year part-time. Full-time tuition and fees vary according to course load. Part-time tuition and fees vary according to course load.

Collegiate Environment: Orientation program. Social organizations: 1 open to all. Most popular organization: Association for Information Technology Professionals. Major annual event: various food events. Campus security: 24-hour emergency response devices and patrols, late night transport-escort service, safety pamphlets, lighted sidewalks/pathways. College housing not available. Learning Resource Center with an OPAC and a Web page.

■ DEVRY UNIVERSITY (WESTMINSTER) *F-11*

1870 West 122nd Ave.
Westminster, CO 80234-2010
Tel: (303)280-7400; (866)338-7934
Web Site: http://www.devry.edu/

Description: Proprietary, 4-year, coed. Administratively affiliated with DeVry, Inc. Awards associate, bachelor's, and master's degrees. Founded 1945. Setting: 3-acre urban campus with easy access to Denver. Total enrollment: 745. Faculty: 73 (14 full-time, 59 part-time). Student-undergrad faculty ratio is 17:1. Full-time: 407 students, 39% women, 61% men. Part-time: 216 students, 43% women, 57% men. 1% Native American, 12% Hispanic, 6% black, 3% Asian American or Pacific Islander, 0.3% international, 74% 25 or older, 6% transferred in. Retention: 48% of full-time freshmen returned the following year. Academic areas with the most degrees conferred: business/marketing; computer and information sciences; engineering technologies. Calendar: semesters. Academic remediation for entering students, double major, summer session for credit, adult/continuing *education programs, co-op programs and internships.

Entrance Requirements: Open admission. Required: high school transcript. Required for some: essay, interview. Entrance: noncompetitive. Application deadline: Rolling.

Costs Per Year: Application fee: $50. One-time mandatory fee: $40. Tuition: $12,450 full-time, $460 per term part-time. Mandatory fees: $270 full-time, $160 per year part-time. Full-time tuition and fees vary according to course load. Part-time tuition and fees vary according to course load.

Collegiate Environment: Orientation program. Major annual events: Pancake Breakfast and Western Day, Campus Family Picnic. Student services: personal-psychological counseling. Campus security: 24-hour patrols, late night transport-escort service. College housing not available. 500,000 books, 27 serials, and an OPAC. Operations spending for 2004 fiscal year: $15,000. 83 computers available on campus for general student use. A campuswide network can be accessed. Staffed computer lab on campus.

■ FORT LEWIS COLLEGE *L-6*
1000 Rim Dr.
Durango, CO 81301-3999
Tel: (970)247-7010
Admissions: (970)247-7184
Fax: (970)247-7179
Web Site: http://www.fortlewis.edu/
Description: State-supported, 4-year, coed. Awards bachelor's degrees. Founded 1911. Setting: 350-acre small town campus. Endowment: $3.8 million. Research spending for 2004 fiscal year: $194,011. Educational spending for 2005 fiscal year: $3545 per student. Total enrollment: 3,946. Student-undergrad faculty ratio is 18:1. 2,765 applied, 74% were admitted. 4% from top 10% of their high school class, 20% from top quarter, 53% from top half. Full-time: 3,637 students, 48% women, 52% men. Part-time: 309 students, 49% women, 51% men. Students come from 49 states and territories, 15 other countries, 29% from out-of-state, 19% Native American, 6% Hispanic, 1% black, 1% Asian American or Pacific Islander, 1% international, 15% 25 or older, 32% live on campus, 7% transferred in. Retention: 58% of full-time freshmen returned the following year. Academic areas with the most degrees conferred: business/marketing; liberal arts/general studies; social sciences. Core. Calendar: modified trimesters. Academic remediation for entering students, ESL program, services for LD students, advanced placement, accelerated degree program, self-designed majors, honors program, independent study, distance learning, double major, summer session for credit, part-time degree program, adult/continuing education programs, co-op programs and internships. Study abroad program.
Entrance Requirements: Option: electronic application. Required: high school transcript, minimum 2.0 high school GPA, SAT or ACT. Recommended: essay, recommendations, interview. Entrance: moderately difficult. Application deadline: 8/1. Notification: continuous.
Costs Per Year: Application fee: $30. State resident tuition: $4862 full-time, $121 per credit hour part-time. Nonresident tuition: $12,870 full-time, $643 per credit hour part-time. Mandatory fees: $830 full-time, $45.75 per credit hour part-time. Full-time tuition and fees vary according to reciprocity agreements. Part-time tuition and fees vary according to course load and reciprocity agreements. College room and board: $6160. College room only: $3258. Room and board charges vary according to board plan and housing facility.
Collegiate Environment: Orientation program. Drama-theater group, choral group, marching band, student-run newspaper, radio station. Social organizations: 56 open to all. Most popular organizations: Business Club, AISES (American Indian Science and Engineering Club), Circle K, Cycling Sport Club, Dance Team. Major annual events: Weekend Wipeout, Homecoming, Hozhoni Days. Student services: legal services, health clinic, personal-psychological counseling. Campus security: 24-hour emergency response devices and patrols, late night transport-escort service, controlled dormitory access. 1,460 college housing spaces available; 1,357 were occupied in 2003-04. Freshmen given priority for college housing. On-campus residence required in freshman year. Option: coed housing available. John F. Reed Library plus 1 other with 184,860 books, 339,467 microform titles, 5,800 serials, 4,334 audiovisual materials, an OPAC, and a Web page. Operations spending for 2004 fiscal year: $1.1 million. 607 computers available on campus for general student use. Computer purchase/lease plans available. A campuswide network can be accessed from student residence rooms and from off campus. Staffed computer lab on campus.
Community Environment: Durango is located in the Four-Corners region where the states of Colorado, Utah, Arizona, and New Mexico come to a common point. Durango has magnificent mountain landscapes and glistening sunshine at an elevation of 6,700 feet. A modern jet port serves the area. Near Durango nestled in the spruce of the high country gleam thousands of mountain lakes, including two of the larger, Lemon and Vallecito. A few miles south is Navajo Lake, which extends into New Mexico. Agriculture and tourism are an integral part of the economy, as is retailing education, medicine, and law. La Plata County is home to over 27,000 people, and Durango has a population of over 13,000. Purgatory ski area offers complete ski resort facilities.

■ FRONT RANGE COMMUNITY COLLEGE *F-11*
3645 West 112th Ave.
Westminster, CO 80031-2105
Tel: (303)466-8811
Admissions: (303)404-5000
Web Site: http://frcc.cc.co.us/
Description: State-supported, 2-year, coed. Part of Community Colleges of Colorado System. Awards certificates, transfer associate, and terminal associate degrees. Founded 1968. Setting: 90-acre suburban campus with easy access to Denver. Educational spending for 2005 fiscal year: $4404 per student. Total enrollment: 14,957. Student-undergrad faculty ratio is 16:1. 6,269 applied, 100% were admitted. Full-time: 5,149 students, 54% women, 46% men. Part-time: 9,808 students, 62% women, 38% men. Students come from 40 states and territories, 104 other countries, 2% from out-of-state, 1% Native American, 11% Hispanic, 1% black, 3% Asian American or Pacific Islander, 1% international, 19% 25 or older. Core. Calendar: semesters. Academic remediation for entering students, ESL program, services for LD students, advanced placement, self-designed majors, freshman honors college, honors program, distance learning, double major, summer session for credit, part-time degree program, external degree program, adult/continuing education programs, co-op programs and internships. Off campus study at Metropolitan State College, University of Colorado at Denver, Colorado State University. Study abroad program. ROTC: Army (c), Air Force (c).
Entrance Requirements: Open admission. Options: Common Application, electronic application, early admission, deferred admission. Entrance: noncompetitive. Application deadline: Rolling.
Costs Per Year: Application fee: $0. State resident tuition: $1746 full-time, $72 per credit part-time. Nonresident tuition: $8284 full-time, $345 per credit part-time. Mandatory fees: $223 full-time, $4.05 per credit part-time, $40.40 per term part-time.
Collegiate Environment: Orientation program. Drama-theater group, student-run newspaper. Social organizations: 15 open to all. Most popular organizations: Student Government Association, Student Colorado Registry of Interpreters for the Deaf, Alpha Mu Psi, Alpha Tau Kappa, Hispanic Club. Major annual events: Spring Fling, Chili Cook-Off, culture days. Student services: personal-psychological counseling. Campus security: 24-hour patrols, late night transport-escort service. College housing not available. College Hill Library with an OPAC and a Web page. Operations spending for 2004 fiscal year: $498,927. 62 computers available on campus for general student use. A campuswide network can be accessed from off-campus. Staffed computer lab on campus.
Community Environment: See University of Denver.

■ HERITAGE COLLEGE *F-12*
12 Lakeside Ln.
Denver, CO 80212-7413
Tel: (303)477-7240
Fax: (303)477-7276
Web Site: http://www.heritage-education.com/
Description: Proprietary, 2-year, coed. Founded 1986.

■ INSTITUTE OF BUSINESS & MEDICAL CAREERS *D-11*
1609 Oakridge Dr., Ste. 102
Fort Collins, CO 80525

Tel: (970)223-2669

Web Site: http://www.ibmcedu.com/

Description: Private, 2-year, coed. Awards certificates, diplomas, and terminal associate degrees. Founded 1987. Setting: suburban campus with easy access to Denver. Total enrollment: 302. 366 applied, 100% were admitted. Full-time: 302 students, 89% women, 11% men. 2% from out-of-state, 0.3% Native American, 22% Hispanic, 1% black, 6% Asian American or Pacific Islander, 0% international, 20% 25 or older, 0% live on campus. Retention: 69% of full-time freshmen returned the following year. Calendar: continuous.

Entrance Requirements: Required: high school transcript. Application deadline: Rolling.

Costs Per Year: Application fee: $75. Tuition: $13,800 full-time. Mandatory fees: $75 full-time. Tuition guaranteed not to increase for student's term of enrollment.

Collegiate Environment: Student-run newspaper. Most popular organization: Alpha Beta Kappa. Major annual events: Nine News Health Fair, New West Festival.

■ **INTELLITEC COLLEGE (COLORADO SPRINGS)** *H-12*

2315 East Pikes Peak Ave.

Colorado Springs, CO 80909-6030

Tel: (719)632-7626

Free: 800-748-2282

Fax: (719)632-7451

Web Site: http://www.intelliteccollege.edu/

Description: Proprietary, 2-year, coed. Part of Technical Trades Institute, Inc. Awards certificates, diplomas, and terminal associate degrees. Founded 1965. Setting: 2-acre urban campus with easy access to Denver. Total enrollment: 427. Students come from 3 states and territories, 5% from out-of-state, 1% Native American, 15% Hispanic, 19% black, 2% Asian American or Pacific Islander, 0% international. Core. Calendar: 6-week terms. Advanced placement, double major.

Entrance Requirements: Open admission. Option: Common Application. Required: high school transcript, interview. Entrance: noncompetitive. Application deadline: Rolling.

Collegiate Environment: Orientation program. Major annual events: Summer Spree Day, student appreciation days. Campus security: 24-hour emergency response devices. College housing not available. 274 books and 28 serials. 45 computers available on campus for general student use. Staffed computer lab on campus.

■ **INTELLITEC COLLEGE (GRAND JUNCTION)** *H-5*

772 Horizon Dr.

Grand Junction, CO 81506

Tel: (970)245-8101

Fax: (970)243-8074

Web Site: http://www.intelliteccollege.edu/

Description: Proprietary, 2-year, coed. Awards certificates, diplomas, and transfer associate degrees. Setting: small town campus. Total enrollment: 486. 256 applied, 100% were admitted. Full-time: 486 students, 83% women, 17% men. 1% Native American, 28% Hispanic, 2% black, 0% Asian American or Pacific Islander, 0% international. Calendar: continuous.

Entrance Requirements: Required: high school transcript, interview. Entrance: noncompetitive.

Costs Per Year: Application fee: $0. Tuition: $5940 full-time.

■ **INTELLITEC MEDICAL INSTITUTE** *H-12*

2345 North Academy Blvd.

Colorado Springs, CO 80909

Tel: (719)596-7400

Fax: (719)596-2464

Web Site: http://www.intelliteccollege.edu/

Description: Proprietary, 2-year, coed. Awards diplomas and terminal associate degrees. Founded 1966. Setting: suburban campus. Total enrollment: 361. 191 applied, 100% were admitted. Full-time: 361 students, 92% women, 8% men. 2% from out-of-state, 1% Native American, 12% Hispanic, 25% black, 0% Asian American or Pacific Islander, 2% international, 1% transferred in. Retention: 70% of full-time freshmen returned the following year. Calendar: clock hours. Services for LD students, advanced placement, independent study, part-time degree program, co-op programs and internships.

Entrance Requirements: Open admission. Options: Common Application, electronic application. Required: high school transcript, interview. Entrance: noncompetitive. Application deadline: Rolling.

Collegiate Environment: Social organizations: 1 open to all. Most popular organization: AMT. Major annual event: Student Appreciation Day. College housing not available. 40 computers available on campus for general student use. Staffed computer lab on campus.

■ **ITT TECHNICAL INSTITUTE** *F-11*

500 East 84th Ave., Ste. B12

Thornton, CO 80229

Tel: (303)288-4488

Free: 800-395-4488

Fax: (303)288-8166

Web Site: http://www.itt-tech.edu/

Description: Proprietary, primarily 2-year, coed. Part of ITT Educational Services, Inc. Awards terminal associate and bachelor's degrees. Founded 1984. Setting: 2-acre suburban campus with easy access to Denver. Core.

Entrance Requirements: Options: Peterson's Universal Application, deferred admission. Required: high school transcript, interview, Wonderlic aptitude test. Recommended: recommendations. Entrance: minimally difficult. Application deadline: Rolling. Notification: continuous.

Costs Per Year: Application fee: $100.

Collegiate Environment: Orientation program. Student-run newspaper. College housing not available.

■ **JOHNSON & WALES UNIVERSITY** *F-12*

7150 Montview Blvd.

Denver, CO 80220

Tel: (303)256-9300; 877-598-3368

Fax: (303)256-9333

E-mail: den.admissions@jwu.edu

Web Site: http://www.jwu.edu/

Description: Independent, 4-year, coed. Administratively affiliated with Johnson & Wales University (RI). Awards associate and bachelor's degrees. Founded 1993. Setting: small town campus. Endowment: $168.3 million. Total enrollment: 1,544. Student-undergrad faculty ratio is 27:1. 3,252 applied, 84% were admitted. Full-time: 1,521 students, 50% women, 50% men. Part-time: 23 students, 39% women, 61% men. Students come from 50 states and territories, 20 other countries, 55% from out-of-state, 1% Native American, 11% Hispanic, 6% black, 3% Asian American or Pacific Islander, 3% international, 12% 25 or older. Academic areas with the most degrees conferred: history; family and consumer sciences; parks and recreation. Core. Calendar: modular. Academic remediation for entering students, services for LD students, advanced placement, accelerated degree program, honors program, summer session for credit, part-time degree program, adult/continuing education programs, co-op programs and internships.

Entrance Requirements: Options: Common Application, electronic application, early admission, deferred admission, international baccalaureate accepted. Required: high school transcript. Recommended: minimum 2.0 high school GPA, SAT or ACT. Required for some: essay, minimum 2.75 high school GPA, interview, SAT or ACT. Entrance: minimally difficult. Application deadline: Rolling. Notification: continuous.

Costs Per Year: Application fee: $0. Comprehensive fee: $29,326 includes full-time tuition ($19,875), mandatory fees ($951), and college room and board ($8500). Part-time tuition: $368 per quarter hour.

Collegiate Environment: Orientation program. Drama-theater group. Campus security: 24-hour emergency response devices and patrols, student patrols, late-night transport-escort service. 786 college housing spaces available. Freshmen guaranteed college housing. On-campus residence required in freshman year. Option: coed housing available. Johnson & Wales University Library with 26,000 books, 165 serials, 800 audiovisual materials, an OPAC, and a Web page. 184 computers available on campus for general student use. A campuswide network can be accessed from student residence rooms and from off campus. Staffed computer lab on campus.

■ **JONES INTERNATIONAL UNIVERSITY**

9697 East Mineral Ave.

Centennial, CO 80112

Tel: (303)784-8904

Free: 800-811-5663

Fax: (303)784-8547

Web Site: http://www.jonesinternational.edu/

Description: Proprietary, comprehensive, coed. Awards bachelor's and master's degrees (offers only online degree programs). Founded 1995. Total enrollment: 1,411. Faculty: 60 (all part-time). Student-undergrad faculty ratio is 23:1. 70 applied, 57% were admitted. Part-time: 255 students, 60% women, 40% men. Students come from 38 states and territories, 90% from out-of-state, 0.4% Native American, 2% Hispanic, 13% black, 4% Asian American or Pacific Islander, 87% 25 or older. Retention: 65% of full-time freshmen returned the following year. Academic areas with the most degrees conferred: communications/journalism; computer and information sciences; business/marketing. Core. Calendar: semesters. Academic remediation for entering students, advanced placement, accelerated degree program, self-designed majors, independent study, distance learning, double major, summer session for credit, part-time degree program, external degree program, adult/continuing education programs, graduate courses open to undergrads.
Entrance Requirements: Open admission. Options: electronic application, deferred admission, international baccalaureate accepted. Required: essay, high school transcript, minimum 2.0 high school GPA. Entrance: noncompetitive. Application deadline: Rolling. Notification: continuous.
Costs Per Year: Application fee: $50. Tuition: $9720 full-time, $1215 per course part-time. Mandatory fees: $480 full-time, $60 per course part-time.
Collegiate Environment: Orientation program. College housing not available. Jones e-global Library with a Web page.

■ **LAMAR COMMUNITY COLLEGE** *J-16*
2401 South Main St.
Lamar, CO 81052-3999
Tel: (719)336-2248
Free: 800-968-6920
Fax: (719)336-2448
E-mail: a_woodward@mash.colorado.edu
Web Site: http://www.lamarcc.edu/
Description: State-supported, 2-year, coed. Part of Colorado Community College and Occupational Education System. Awards certificates, diplomas, transfer associate, and terminal associate degrees. Founded 1937. Setting: 125-acre small town campus. Endowment: $200,000. Total enrollment: 1,021. 414 applied, 100% were admitted. Students come from 25 states and territories, 12 other countries, 43% 25 or older. Core. Calendar: semesters. Academic remediation for entering students, ESL program, services for LD students, advanced placement, self-designed majors, summer session for credit, part-time degree program, adult/continuing education programs, co-op programs and internships.
Entrance Requirements: Open admission. Options: Common Application, early admission. Placement: SAT or ACT recommended. Entrance: noncompetitive. Application deadline: 9/16. Preference given to state residents.
Collegiate Environment: Orientation program. Drama-theater group, choral group, student-run newspaper. Major annual events: Homecoming, Earth Day, Antelope Night. Student services: health clinic, personal-psychological counseling. Campus security: 24-hour emergency response devices and patrols, student patrols, late night transport-escort service, controlled dormitory access. On-campus residence required in freshman year. Option: coed housing available. Learning Resources Center with 27,729 books and 172 serials. Operations spending for 2004 fiscal year: $127,718. 60 computers available on campus for general student use. A campuswide network can be accessed. Staffed computer lab on campus.
Community Environment: Lamar is an All-America City located at the junction of U.S. Highways 50, 287, and 385 with a dry climate and a population of 9,000. Livestock and poultry are primary concerns in this extensively irrigated area for which Lamar is a trading center. Airlines, railroads and buses serve the area. The community facilities include churches, a hospital and clinics, a library and various civic clubs. Part-time employment is available. The recreational activities include hunting, fishing, boating, golfing, swimming, and baseball.

■ **MESA STATE COLLEGE** *H-5*
1100 North Ave.
Grand Junction, CO 81501-3122
Tel: (970)248-1020
Free: 800-982-MESA
Admissions: (970)248-1875
Fax: (970)248-1973
E-mail: tbush@mesastate.edu
Web Site: http://www.mesastate.edu/

Description: State-supported, comprehensive, coed. Part of State Colleges in Colorado. Awards associate, bachelor's, and master's degrees. Founded 1925. Setting: 42-acre small town campus. Research spending for 2004 fiscal year: $3500. Educational spending for 2005 fiscal year: $2988 per student. Total enrollment: 6,062. Faculty: 396 (206 full-time, 190 part-time). Student-undergrad faculty ratio is 19:1. 4,628 applied, 82% were admitted. 6% from top 10% of their high school class, 20% from top quarter, 47% from top half. Full-time: 4,521 students, 58% women, 42% men. Part-time: 1,513 students, 63% women, 37% men. Students come from 46 states and territories, 8% from out-of-state, 2% Native American, 8% Hispanic, 2% black, 2% Asian American or Pacific Islander, 1% international, 38% 25 or older, 18% live on campus, 7% transferred in. Retention: 57% of full-time freshmen returned the following year. Academic areas with the most degrees conferred: business/marketing; visual and performing arts; social sciences. Core. Calendar: semesters. Academic remediation for entering students, services for LD students, advanced placement, accelerated degree program, self-designed majors, honors program, independent study, distance learning, double major, summer session for credit, part-time degree program, adult/continuing education programs, co-op programs and internships, graduate courses open to undergrads. Off campus study at members of the Consortium of State Colleges in Colorado, National Student Exchange Program. Study abroad program.
Entrance Requirements: Open admission for Associate degree programs. Options: Peterson's Universal Application, Common Application, early admission, deferred admission. Required: high school transcript, minimum 2.0 high school GPA, SAT or ACT. Required for some: 1 recommendation, interview. Entrance: minimally difficult. Application deadline: Rolling. Notification: continuous.
Costs Per Year: Application fee: $30. State resident tuition: $3442 full-time, $132.40 per hour part-time. Nonresident tuition: $10,660 full-time, $410 per hour part-time.
Collegiate Environment: Orientation program. Drama-theater group, choral group, student-run newspaper, radio station. Social organizations: 50 open to all. Most popular organizations: Environmental Club, Student Body Association, KMSA radio station, Rodeo Club, Campus Residents Association. Major annual events: Homecoming, Spring Fling, Unityfest. Student services: legal services, health clinic, personal-psychological counseling. Campus security: 24-hour emergency response devices and patrols, late night transport-escort service, controlled dormitory access. 959 college housing spaces available; 909 were occupied in 2003-04. Freshmen given priority for college housing. On-campus residence required through sophomore year. Option: coed housing available. John U. Tomlinson Library with 247,338 books, 935,100 microform titles, 31,992 serials, 9,787 audiovisual materials, an OPAC, and a Web page. Operations spending for 2004 fiscal year: $1.3 million. 350 computers available on campus for general student use. A campuswide network can be accessed from off-campus. Staffed computer lab on campus.
Community Environment: Grand Junction is located in an irrigated valley in the heart of a vast vacationland that is also rich in energy-related natural resources. The climate is invigorating, sunny, and mild. The community has churches of many denominations, excellent public schools, library facilities, cultural programs, city parks, golf courses, tennis courts, 4 hospitals, and good transportation services including three major airlines. Recreational activities in the nearby mountains and deserts include hiking, camping, boating, river rafting, fishing, hunting, cross-country and downhill skiing, and more.

■ **METROPOLITAN STATE COLLEGE OF DENVER** *F-12*
PO Box 173362
Denver, CO 80217-3362
Tel: (303)556-2400
Admissions: (303)556-3058
Fax: (303)556-6345
Web Site: http://www.mscd.edu/
Description: State-supported, 4-year, coed. Awards bachelor's degrees. Founded 1963. Setting: 175-acre urban campus. Total enrollment: 20,761. 4,407 applied, 85% were admitted. 4% from top 10% of their high school class, 16% from top quarter, 44% from top half. Full-time: 12,397 students, 55% women, 45% men. Part-time: 8,364 students, 58% women, 42% men. Students come from 40 states and territories, 58 other countries, 2% from out-of-state, 1% Native American, 14% Hispanic, 6% black, 4% Asian American or Pacific Islander, 1% international, 41% 25 or older, 11% transferred in. Retention: 62% of full-time freshmen returned the following year. Core. Calendar: semesters. Services for LD students, advanced place-

ment, accelerated degree program, self-designed majors, honors program, independent study, distance learning, double major, summer session for credit, part-time degree program, external degree program, adult/continuing education programs, co-op programs and internships. Off campus study at 3 members of the Consortium of State Colleges in Colorado, University of Colorado at Denver, Community College of Denver. Study abroad program. ROTC: Army (c), Air Force (c).

Entrance Requirements: Options: Common Application, electronic application, deferred admission, international baccalaureate accepted. Required: high school transcript. Recommended: minimum 2.0 high school GPA. Required for some: essay, recommendations, SAT or ACT. Entrance: minimally difficult. Application deadline: 8/7. Notification: continuous.

Costs Per Year: Application fee: $25. State resident tuition: $2283 full-time. Nonresident tuition: $9366 full-time. Mandatory fees: $576 full-time. Full-time tuition and fees vary according to course load and location.

Collegiate Environment: Orientation program. Drama-theater group, choral group, student-run newspaper. Social organizations: 90 open to all. Most popular organizations: Political Science Association, Accounting Students Organization, Christian Students Organization, LGBTA, Golden Key National Honor Society. Major annual events: Into the Streets, Campus Involvement Week, Earth Day. Student services: legal services, health clinic, personal-psychological counseling, women's center. Campus security: 24-hour emergency response devices and patrols, late night transport-escort service. College housing not available. Auraria Library with 607,971 books, 1 million microform titles, 2,380 serials, 16,309 audiovisual materials, an OPAC, and a Web page. 800 computers available on campus for general student use. A campuswide network can be accessed from off-campus. Staffed computer lab on campus.

Community Environment: See University of Denver.

■ **MORGAN COMMUNITY COLLEGE** *E-14*

17800 County Rd. 20
Fort Morgan, CO 80701-4399
Tel: (970)542-3100
Free: 800-622-0216
Admissions: (970)542-3156
Web Site: http://www.morgancc.edu/

Description: State-supported, 2-year, coed. Part of Colorado Community College and Occupational Education System. Awards certificates, transfer associate, and terminal associate degrees. Founded 1967. Setting: 20-acre rural campus with easy access to Denver. Total enrollment: 1,564. 177 applied, 100% were admitted. Full-time: 351 students, 68% women, 32% men. Part-time: 1,213 students, 64% women, 36% men. Students come from 3 states and territories, 2% from out-of-state, 1% Native American, 11% Hispanic, 0.2% black, 1% Asian American or Pacific Islander, 0.2% international, 52% 25 or older, 3% transferred in. Core. Calendar: semesters. Academic remediation for entering students, services for LD students, advanced placement, summer session for credit, part-time degree program, adult/continuing education programs, internships.

Entrance Requirements: Open admission. Options: early admission, deferred admission. Required: high school transcript. Placement: ACT required for some. Entrance: noncompetitive. Application deadline: Rolling.

Collegiate Environment: Student-run newspaper. College housing not available. Learning Resource Center with 13,800 books, 80 serials, 1,096 audiovisual materials, an OPAC, and a Web page. 60 computers available on campus for general student use. A campuswide network can be accessed from off-campus. Staffed computer lab on campus.

Community Environment: Morgan County has an abundant supply of facilities for recreational enjoyment. In addition to the athletic activities close at hand, the students have access to the metropolitan offerings in Denver, one hour away, and the beautiful Rocky Mountains, a two hour drive on Interstate highways.

■ **NAROPA UNIVERSITY** *E-11*

2130 Arapahoe Ave.
Boulder, CO 80302-6697
Tel: (303)444-0202
Free: 800-772-0410
Admissions: (303)546-3572
Fax: (303)444-0410
E-mail: admissions@naropa.edu
Web Site: http://www.naropa.edu/

Description: Independent, comprehensive, coed. Awards bachelor's, master's, and first professional degrees. Founded 1974. Setting: 12-acre urban campus with easy access to Denver. Endowment: $2.9 million. Research spending for 2004 fiscal year: $3000. Educational spending for 2005 fiscal year: $10,556 per student. Total enrollment: 1,221. Faculty: 224 (55 full-time, 169 part-time). Student-undergrad faculty ratio is 10:1. 122 applied, 84% were admitted. 1 valedictorian. Full-time: 404 students, 58% women, 42% men. Part-time: 75 students, 63% women, 37% men. Students come from 43 states and territories, 12 other countries, 76% from out-of-state, 1% Native American, 7% Hispanic, 1% black, 2% Asian American or Pacific Islander, 3% international, 36% 25 or older, 6% live on campus, 17% transferred in. Retention: 82% of full-time freshmen returned the following year. Academic areas with the most degrees conferred: psychology; interdisciplinary studies; visual and performing arts. Core. Calendar: semesters. Services for LD students, advanced placement, self-designed majors, independent study, distance learning, double major, summer session for credit, part-time degree program, adult/continuing education programs, co-op programs and internships, graduate courses open to undergrads. Study abroad program.

Entrance Requirements: Options: electronic application, deferred admission, international baccalaureate accepted. Required: essay, high school transcript, 2 recommendations, interview. Recommended: SAT or ACT. Entrance: moderately difficult. Application deadlines: 1/15, 1/15 for nonresidents.

Costs Per Year: Application fee: $50. Comprehensive fee: $25,736 includes full-time tuition ($18,500) and college room and board ($7236). College room only: $4437. Full-time tuition varies according to course load. Room and board charges vary according to board plan. Part-time tuition: $600 per semester hour. Part-time mandatory fees: $250 per term. Part-time tuition and fees vary according to course load.

Collegiate Environment: Orientation program. Drama-theater group, choral group, student-run newspaper. Social organizations: 20 open to all. Most popular organizations: Student Union of Naropa (SUN), GLBT Group, International Students' Group, Root Outdoor Organization, Greenworks Environmental Group. Major annual events: Practice Day, Shambhala Day, Convocation. Student services: personal-psychological counseling. Campus security: late night transport-escort service, controlled dormitory access, foot and vehicle patrol 4:30 pm - midnight. 26 college housing spaces available; all were occupied in 2003-04. Freshmen given priority for college housing. Option: coed housing available. Allen Ginsberg Library with 27,500 books, 75 serials, 10,150 audiovisual materials, an OPAC, and a Web page. Operations spending for 2004 fiscal year: $200,942. 48 computers available on campus for general student use. A campuswide network can be accessed. Staffed computer lab on campus.

■ **NATIONAL AMERICAN UNIVERSITY (COLORADO SPRINGS)** *H-12*

5125 North Academy Blvd.
Colorado Springs, CO 80918
Tel: (719)277-0588
Fax: (719)277-0589
Web Site: http://www.national.edu/

Description: Proprietary, 4-year, coed. Awards associate, bachelor's, and master's degrees. Founded 1941. Setting: 1-acre suburban campus with easy access to Denver. Total enrollment: 250. Students come from 25 states and territories, 16% Hispanic, 15% black, 6% Asian American or Pacific Islander, 75% 25 or older. Retention: 73% of full-time freshmen returned the following year. Core. Academic remediation for entering students, ESL program, accelerated degree program, independent study, distance learning, double major, summer session for credit, part-time degree program, external degree program, adult/continuing education programs, internships. Off campus study.

Entrance Requirements: Open admission. Options: Common Application, deferred admission. Required: high school transcript, interview. Entrance: noncompetitive. Application deadline: Rolling.

Costs Per Year: Application fee: $25. Tuition: $11,650 full-time, $235 per credit hour part-time. Mandatory fees: $200 full-time.

Collegiate Environment: Orientation program. Campus security: late night transport-escort service. College housing not available. National American University Library with 15,000 books and 100 serials. 60 computers available on campus for general student use. A campuswide network can be accessed. Staffed computer lab on campus.

■ **NATIONAL AMERICAN UNIVERSITY (DENVER)** *F-12*

1325 South Colorado Blvd, Ste. 100
Denver, CO 80222
Tel: (303)758-6700

Fax: (303)758-6810

Web Site: http://www.national.edu/

Description: Proprietary, 4-year, coed. Awards associate, bachelor's, and master's degrees. Founded 1974. Setting: urban campus. Total enrollment: 250. 85% 25 or older. Retention: 60% of full-time freshmen returned the following year. Core. Academic remediation for entering students, ESL program, advanced placement, accelerated degree program, independent study, distance learning, double major, summer session for credit, part-time degree program, adult/continuing education programs, internships.

Entrance Requirements: Open admission. Options: Peterson's Universal Application, Common Application, electronic application, early admission, deferred admission. Required: high school transcript. Placement: SAT or ACT recommended. Entrance: noncompetitive. Application deadline: Rolling.

Costs Per Year: Application fee: $25. Tuition: $8820 full-time. Full-time tuition varies according to course load, location, and program.

Collegiate Environment: Orientation program. College housing not available. NAU Library with 400 books and 33 serials. 47 computers available on campus for general student use. A campuswide network can be accessed from off-campus. Staffed computer lab on campus.

■ **NAZARENE BIBLE COLLEGE** *H-12*

1111 Academy Park Loop

Colorado Springs, CO 80910-3704

Tel: (719)884-5000

Free: 800-873-3873

Admissions: (719)884-5061

Fax: (719)884-5199

Web Site: http://www.nbc.edu/

Description: Independent, 4-year, coed, affiliated with Church of the Nazarene. Awards associate and bachelor's degrees. Founded 1967. Setting: 64-acre urban campus with easy access to Denver. Endowment: $2.4 million. Educational spending for 2005 fiscal year: $2942 per student. Total enrollment: 532. Student-undergrad faculty ratio is 13:1. 356 applied, 44% were admitted. Full-time: 181 students, 35% women, 65% men. Part-time: 351 students, 32% women, 68% men. Students come from 48 states and territories, 55% from out-of-state, 2% Native American, 3% Hispanic, 3% black, 1% Asian American or Pacific Islander, 1% international, 89% 25 or older, 6% transferred in. Retention: 60% of full-time freshmen returned the following year. Academic area with the most degrees conferred: theology and religious vocations. Core. Academic remediation for entering students, independent study, distance learning, double major, summer session for credit, part-time degree program, internships.

Entrance Requirements: Open admission. Options: Common Application, electronic application, deferred admission. Required: essay, high school transcript, 2 recommendations. Entrance: noncompetitive. Application deadline: 8/31.

Costs Per Year: Application fee: $35. Tuition: $8460 full-time, $235 per semester hour part-time. Mandatory fees: $225 full-time.

Collegiate Environment: Orientation program. Choral group, student-run newspaper. Student services: personal-psychological counseling. Campus security: student patrols. College housing not available. Trimble Library with 75,842 books, 7,000 microform titles, 320 serials, 8,667 audiovisual materials, and an OPAC. Operations spending for 2004 fiscal year: $164,477. 10 computers available on campus for general student use. A campuswide network can be accessed from off-campus. Staffed computer lab on campus.

Community Environment: See The Colorado College.

■ **NORTHEASTERN JUNIOR COLLEGE** *D-15*

100 College Ave.

Sterling, CO 80751-2399

Tel: (970)521-6600

Admissions: (970)521-7000

Fax: (970)522-4945

Web Site: http://www.njc.edu/

Description: State-supported, 2-year, coed. Part of Colorado Community College and Occupational Education System. Awards certificates, transfer associate, and terminal associate degrees. Founded 1941. Setting: 65-acre small town campus. Endowment: $800,000. Educational spending for 2005 fiscal year: $2589 per student. Total enrollment: 3,633. 941 applied, 100% were admitted. 6% from top 10% of their high school class, 47% from top half. Full-time: 910 students, 52% women, 48% men. Part-time: 2,723 students, 59% women, 41% men. Students come from 21 states and territories, 10% from out-of-state, 3% 25 or older, 1% transferred in. Core. Calendar: semesters. Academic remediation for entering students, ESL

program, services for LD students, advanced placement, accelerated degree program, honors program, independent study, distance learning, double major, summer session for credit, part-time degree program, adult/continuing education programs, co-op programs and internships.

Entrance Requirements: Open admission. Options: Peterson's Universal Application, Common Application, electronic application, early admission, deferred admission. Required: high school transcript. Placement: ACT recommended; SAT or ACT required for some. Entrance: noncompetitive. Application deadline: 8/1. Notification: continuous until 8/1. Preference given to state residents.

Collegiate Environment: Orientation program. Drama-theater group, choral group, student-run newspaper, radio station. Social organizations: 27 open to all. Most popular organizations: Associated Student Government, Post Secondary Agriculture (PAS), Rodeo Team and Club, Students in Free Enterprise (SIFE), Campus Christian Fellowship. Major annual events: Midnight Barbecue and Dance, Spring Formal, Associated Student Government elections. Student services: health clinic, personal-psychological counseling, women's center. Campus security: 24-hour emergency response devices, controlled dormitory access, night patrols by trained security personnel. On-campus residence required in freshman year. Option: coed housing available. Monahan Library with 45,260 books, 414 serials, an OPAC, and a Web page. Operations spending for 2004 fiscal year: $303,723. 150 computers available on campus for general student use. A campuswide network can be accessed. Staffed computer lab on campus.

Community Environment: Sterling, population 15,000, in northeastern Colorado on the South Platte River, has a mild climate. Trains and buses serve the area. Community facilities include churches, hospitals, libraries, a health center, and museum. Recreational activities include golf, tennis, swimming, bowling, roller skating, and boating. Rooming houses and private homes are available for student housing. The County Fair and Overland Trail Roundup are annual events. Part-time work is available.

■ **OTERO JUNIOR COLLEGE** *K-14*

1802 Colorado Ave.

La Junta, CO 81050-3415

Tel: (719)384-6831

Admissions: (719)384-6833

Fax: (719)384-6880

E-mail: j_schiro@ojc.axp.cccoes.edu

Web Site: http://www.ojc.edu/

Description: State-supported, 2-year, coed. Part of Colorado Community College and Occupational Education System. Awards certificates, transfer associate, and terminal associate degrees. Founded 1941. Setting: 50-acre rural campus. Total enrollment: 1,636. 6% from top 10% of their high school class, 28% from top quarter, 65% from top half. Full-time: 771 students, 57% women, 43% men. Part-time: 865 students, 66% women, 34% men. Students come from 12 states and territories, 2% from out-of-state, 2% Native American, 30% Hispanic, 2% black, 1% Asian American or Pacific Islander, 0.4% international, 49% 25 or older, 14% live on campus, 15% transferred in. Core. Calendar: semesters. Academic remediation for entering students, advanced placement, distance learning, summer session for credit, part-time degree program, external degree program, adult/continuing education programs, internships.

Entrance Requirements: Open admission except for nursing program. Options: electronic application, early admission. Recommended: high school transcript. Entrance: noncompetitive. Application deadline: 8/30. Notification: continuous.

Costs Per Year: Application fee: $0. State resident tuition: $1788 full-time, $74.50 per credit part-time. Nonresident tuition: $6626 full-time, $276.10 per credit part-time. Mandatory fees: $184 full-time. College room and board: $4512.

Collegiate Environment: Orientation program. Drama-theater group, choral group, student-run newspaper. Social organizations: 6 open to all. Student services: personal-psychological counseling. Campus security: 24-hour patrols, late night transport-escort service. 220 college housing spaces available; all were occupied in 2003-04. On-campus residence required in freshman year. Option: coed housing available. Wheeler Library with 36,701 books, 183 serials, and an OPAC. 100 computers available on campus for general student use. A campuswide network can be accessed from student residence rooms. Staffed computer lab on campus.

Community Environment: La Junta is located in the rich agricultural and stock-raising territory of the Arkansas River Valley with a mild year-round climate; the average mean temperature being 54.1 degrees, and the average yearly precipitation, 13.61 inches. The community facilities include a library, churches, many shopping facilities, hotels, motels, hospital and a community sponsored concert association. La Junta has many civic and service organizations. Industries include canning, manufacture of copper tubings and the renovation of railroad cars. The Kid's Rodeo is held here each year in August.

■ PARKS COLLEGE (AURORA) *F-12*
14280 East Jewell Ave., Ste. 100
Aurora, CO 80014
Tel: (303)745-6244
E-mail: rharding@cci.edu
Web Site: http://www.parks-college.com/
Description: Proprietary, 2-year, coed. Founded 1989.

■ PARKS COLLEGE (DENVER) *F-12*
9065 Grant St.
Denver, CO 80229-4339
Tel: (303)457-2757
E-mail: jqnira@cci.edu
Web Site: http://www.parks-college.com/
Description: Proprietary, 2-year, coed. Awards terminal associate degrees. Founded 1895. Setting: 11-acre campus. Total enrollment: 425. 1% from top 10% of their high school class, 9% from top quarter, 56% from top half. Students come from 3 states and territories, 30% 25 or older. Core. Summer session for credit, part-time degree program, internships.
Entrance Requirements: Option: deferred admission. Required: CPAt. Entrance: moderately difficult. Application deadline: Rolling.
Collegiate Environment: Student-run newspaper. Student services: health clinic, personal-psychological counseling. College housing not available. 2,000 books and 58 serials. 66 computers available on campus for general student use. Staffed computer lab on campus.

■ PIKES PEAK COMMUNITY COLLEGE *H-12*
5675 South Academy Blvd.
Colorado Springs, CO 80906-5498
Tel: (719)576-7711; (866)411-7722
Admissions: (719)540-7041
Fax: (719)540-7614
Web Site: http://www.ppcc.edu/
Description: State-supported, 2-year, coed. Part of Colorado Community College System. Awards certificates, transfer associate, and terminal associate degrees. Founded 1968. Setting: 287-acre urban campus with easy access to Denver. Endowment: $1.4 million. Educational spending for 2005 fiscal year: $3014 per student. Total enrollment: 10,917. Full-time: 3,944 students, 57% women, 43% men. Part-time: 6,973 students, 58% women, 42% men. Students come from 48 states and territories, 90 other countries, 12% from out-of-state, 2% Native American, 11% Hispanic, 8% black, 4% Asian American or Pacific Islander, 1% international, 50% 25 or older, 7% transferred in. Core. Calendar: semesters. Academic remediation for entering students, ESL program, services for LD students, advanced placement, independent study, distance learning, double major, summer session for credit, part-time degree program, adult/continuing education programs, co-op programs and internships. ROTC: Army (c).
Entrance Requirements: Open admission. Option: international baccalaureate accepted. Required for some: high school transcript. Entrance: noncompetitive. Application deadline: Rolling.
Costs Per Year: State resident tuition: $2183 full-time, $72.75 per credit hour part-time. Nonresident tuition: $10,355 full-time, $345.15 per credit hour part-time. Mandatory fees: $156 full-time. Full-time tuition and fees vary according to course load and reciprocity agreements. Part-time tuition varies according to course load and reciprocity agreements.
Collegiate Environment: Orientation program. Drama-theater group, student-run newspaper. Student services: women's center. Campus security: 24-hour emergency response devices and patrols, late night transport-escort service. College housing not available. PPCC Library plus 1 other with 34,332 books, 4,505 microform titles, 311 serials, 3,832 audiovisual materials, and an OPAC. Operations spending for 2004 fiscal year: $690,702. 180 computers available on campus for general student use. A campuswide network can be accessed from off-campus. Staffed computer lab on campus.
Community Environment: Colorado Springs, a community of approximately 278,000 people, is situated 70 miles south of Denver. The dry, temperate climate and 310 days of sunshine annually make it a highly desirable place to live year-round. Many high technology industries are located in Colorado Springs. Housing is readily available and buses serve all parts of the city. Skiing, hiking, fishing, hunting, backpacking, and camping can be enjoyed within a one-half hour to one hour drive from Colorado Springs.

■ PIMA MEDICAL INSTITUTE *F-12*
1701 West 72nd Ave., Ste. 130
Denver, CO 80221
Tel: (303)426-1800; 888-898-9048
Fax: (303)412-8752
E-mail: denverpima@aol.com
Web Site: http://www.pmi.edu
Description: Proprietary, 2-year, coed. Part of Vocational Training Institutes, Inc. Awards certificates and terminal associate degrees. Founded 1988. Setting: urban campus. Total enrollment: 724. Calendar: modular. Academic remediation for entering students, co-op programs and internships.
Entrance Requirements: Required: interview, Wonderlic Scholastic Level Exam. Required for some: high school transcript. Entrance: minimally difficult.
Collegiate Environment: College housing not available.

■ PLATT COLLEGE *F-12*
3100 South Parker Rd., Ste. 200
Aurora, CO 80014-3141
Tel: (303)369-5151
Web Site: http://www.plattcolorado.edu/
Description: Proprietary, primarily 2-year, coed. Awards diplomas, terminal associate, and bachelor's degrees. Founded 1986. Setting: suburban campus. Total enrollment: 215. 47 applied, 100% were admitted. Calendar: continuous. Academic remediation for entering students, advanced placement.
Entrance Requirements: Open admission. Required: high school transcript, interview. Entrance: noncompetitive. Application deadline: Rolling.
Collegiate Environment: Orientation program. College housing not available.

■ PUEBLO COMMUNITY COLLEGE *J-12*
900 West Orman Ave.
Pueblo, CO 81004-1499
Tel: (719)549-3200
Admissions: (719)549-3010
Fax: (719)549-3012
Web Site: http://www.pueblocc.edu/
Description: State-supported, 2-year, coed. Part of Colorado Community College and Occupational Education System. Awards certificates, transfer associate, and terminal associate degrees. Founded 1933. Setting: 35-acre urban campus. Endowment: $5.4 million. Educational spending for 2005 fiscal year: $3061 per student. Total enrollment: 5,747. 1,230 applied, 100% were admitted. Full-time: 2,208 students, 62% women, 38% men. Part-time: 3,539 students, 66% women, 34% men. 1% from out-of-state, 3% Native American, 31% Hispanic, 2% black, 1% Asian American or Pacific Islander, 0.2% international, 38% 25 or older, 2% transferred in. Core. Calendar: semesters. Academic remediation for entering students, services for LD students, advanced placement, accelerated degree program, independent study, distance learning, double major, summer session for credit, part-time degree program, co-op programs and internships.
Entrance Requirements: Open admission except for allied health programs. Options: electronic application, early admission, deferred admission. Placement: ACT required for some. Entrance: noncompetitive. Application deadline: Rolling.
Collegiate Environment: Orientation program. Drama-theater group, choral group, student-run radio station. Social organizations: 20 open to all. Most popular organizations: Criminal Justice Club, Phi Beta Lambda, Automotive Society, Nursing Club, Business and Office Technology Club. Major annual events: Spring Fling, Fall Festival, Christmas Party. Student services: personal-psychological counseling. Campus security: 24-hour emergency response devices, late night transport-escort service. College housing not available. Pueblo Community College Learning Resources Center with 23,755 books, 2,980 microform titles, 286 serials, 14,626 audiovisual materials, and an OPAC. Operations spending for 2004 fiscal year: $262,034. 365 computers available on campus for general student use. A campuswide network can be accessed. Staffed computer lab on campus.
Community Environment: Pueblo, population 126,000, is 42 miles south of Colorado Springs and 112 miles south of Denver on I-25. The original site of Pueblo was a crossroad for Indians, Spanish troops, friars, fur trappers, and explorers. A trading post was built in 1842 and served travelers on their way

to California. Pueblo's location as the focal point for travel to the Rocky Mountain Empire continues to serve business and industry in the area. Puebloans enjoy clean air, uncrowded highways, and nearby water and mountain recreation set in the warm pleasant atmosphere of the Southwest. Pueblo boasts a fine community college, a university, symphony orchestra, chorale, ballet, theatrical groups, and a beautiful arts center.

■ **RED ROCKS COMMUNITY COLLEGE** *C-2*
13300 West 6th Ave.
Lakewood, CO 80228-1255
Tel: (303)914-6600
Fax: (303)914-6666
Web Site: http://www.rrcc.edu/
Description: State-supported, 2-year, coed. Part of Colorado Community College and Occupational Education System. Awards certificates, transfer associate, and terminal associate degrees. Founded 1969. Setting: 120-acre urban campus with easy access to Denver. Educational spending for 2005 fiscal year: $5674 per student. Total enrollment: 7,693. 4,499 applied, 100% were admitted. Full-time: 2,264 students, 46% women, 54% men. Part-time: 5,429 students, 49% women, 51% men. Students come from 27 states and territories, 2% Native American, 11% Hispanic, 1% black, 2% Asian American or Pacific Islander, 2% international, 53% 25 or older. Core. Calendar: semesters. Academic remediation for entering students, ESL program, summer session for credit, part-time degree program, adult/continuing education programs, co-op programs. Off campus study at Metropolitan State College, University of Colorado at Denver, Colorado School of Mines. Study abroad program. ROTC: Army (c).
Entrance Requirements: Open admission. Option: early admission. Entrance: noncompetitive. Application deadline: Rolling. Notification: continuous.
Collegiate Environment: Orientation program. Drama-theater group, student-run newspaper. Student services: personal-psychological counseling, women's center. Campus security: 24-hour emergency response devices and patrols. College housing not available. Marvin Buckels Library with 55,188 books, 9,958 microform titles, 350 serials, 4,497 audiovisual materials, an OPAC, and a Web page. Operations spending for 2004 fiscal year: $357,270. 580 computers available on campus for general student use. Staffed computer lab on campus.
Community Environment: See Colorado School of Mines.

■ **REGIS UNIVERSITY** *F-12*
3333 Regis Blvd.
Denver, CO 80221-1099
Tel: (303)458-4100
Free: 800-388-2366
Admissions: (303)458-4905
Fax: (303)964-5534
E-mail: regisadm@regis.edu
Web Site: http://www.regis.edu/
Description: Independent Roman Catholic (Jesuit), comprehensive, coed. Awards bachelor's, master's, and doctoral degrees. Founded 1877. Setting: 90-acre suburban campus. Endowment: $29.3 million. Educational spending for 2005 fiscal year: $4992 per student. Total enrollment: 16,335. 40,275 applied, 25% were admitted. 21% from top 10% of their high school class, 47% from top quarter, 79% from top half. Full-time: 2,261 students, 62% women, 38% men. Part-time: 5,898 students, 61% women, 39% men. Students come from 40 states and territories, 24% from out-of-state, 1% Native American, 9% Hispanic, 5% black, 3% Asian American or Pacific Islander, 1% international, 77% 25 or older, 8% live on campus, 84% transferred in. Retention: 79% of full-time freshmen returned the following year. Core. Calendar: semesters. Academic remediation for entering students, services for LD students, advanced placement, accelerated degree program, self-designed majors, freshman honors college, honors program, independent study, distance learning, double major, summer session for credit, part-time degree program, external degree program, adult/continuing education programs, co-op programs and internships, graduate courses open to undergrads. Off campus study at other Jesuit colleges and universities. Study abroad program. ROTC: Army (c), Air Force (c).
Entrance Requirements: Options: Peterson's Universal Application, Common Application, international baccalaureate accepted. Required: essay, high school transcript, minimum 2.5 high school GPA, 1 recommendation, SAT or ACT. Recommended: SAT Subject Tests. Required for some: 2 recommendations, interview. Entrance: moderately difficult. Application deadlines: Rolling, Rolling for nonresidents. Notification: continuous, continuous for nonresidents.

Costs Per Year: Application fee: $40. Comprehensive fee: $31,890 includes full-time tuition ($23,500), mandatory fees ($200), and college room and board ($8190). College room only: $4700. Full-time tuition and fees vary according to program. Room and board charges vary according to board plan and housing facility. Part-time tuition: $734 per hour. Part-time mandatory fees: $140 per year. Part-time tuition and fees vary according to program.
Collegiate Environment: Orientation program. Drama-theater group, choral group, student-run newspaper, radio station. Social organizations: 30 open to all. Most popular organizations: Programming Activities Council, hall governing boards, Student Executive Board, Outdoor Club, Rugby Club. Major annual events: Mistletoe Madness, Ranger Day and Week, Thursday Thrills. Student services: health clinic, personal-psychological counseling. Campus security: 24-hour emergency response devices and patrols, student patrols, late night transport-escort service, controlled dormitory access. 780 college housing spaces available; 657 were occupied in 2003-04. Freshmen guaranteed college housing. On-campus residence required in freshman year. Option: coed housing available. Dayton Memorial Library with 350,000 books, 70,000 microform titles, 20,800 serials, 110,000 audiovisual materials, an OPAC, and a Web page. Operations spending for 2004 fiscal year: $2.6 million. 300 computers available on campus for general student use. A campuswide network can be accessed from student residence rooms and from off campus. Staffed computer lab on campus.
Community Environment: See University of Denver.

■ **REMINGTON COLLEGE-COLORADO SPRINGS CAMPUS** *H-12*
6050 Erin Park Dr., No. 250
Colorado Springs, CO 80918
Tel: (719)532-1234
Admissions: (719)532-1234
Fax: (719)264-1234
Web Site: http://www.remingtoncollege.edu/
Description: Proprietary, 4-year, coed. Awards associate and bachelor's degrees. Setting: 3-acre urban campus. Total enrollment: 282. 71 applied, 100% were admitted. Full-time: 282 students, 51% women, 49% men. 1% Native American, 17% Hispanic, 16% black, 4% Asian American or Pacific Islander, 0% international.
Entrance Requirements: Entrance: noncompetitive.
Costs Per Year: Tuition: $15,745 full-time. Tuition guaranteed not to increase for student's term of enrollment.
Collegiate Environment: College housing not available.

■ **REMINGTON COLLEGE-DENVER CAMPUS** *C-2*
11011 West 6th Ave.
Lakewood, CO 80215-0090
Tel: (303)445-0500
Free: 800-999-5181
Fax: (303)445-0090
E-mail: jim.ploskonka@remingtoncollege.edu
Web Site: http://www.remingtoncollege.edu/
Description: Proprietary, 4-year, coed. Part of Education America Inc. Awards associate and bachelor's degrees. Setting: 1-acre suburban campus. Total enrollment: 500. Students come from 3 other countries, 0% from out-of-state, 90% 25 or older. Core. Accelerated degree program, double major, summer session for credit, external degree program, adult/continuing education programs.
Entrance Requirements: Open admission. Options: Common Application, early admission, deferred admission. Entrance: noncompetitive.
Collegiate Environment: Orientation program. College housing not available. Education American Denver Campus Library plus 1 other with 5,000 books, 23 serials, 60 audiovisual materials, an OPAC, and a Web page. 30 computers available on campus for general student use. Staffed computer lab on campus.

■ **ROCKY MOUNTAIN COLLEGE OF ART & DESIGN** *C-2*
1600 Pierce St.
Lakewood, CO 80214
Tel: (303)753-6046
Free: 800-888-ARTS
Fax: (303)759-4970
Web Site: http://www.rmcad.edu/
Description: Proprietary, 4-year, coed. Awards bachelor's degrees. Founded 1963. Setting: 23-acre suburban campus. Total enrollment: 448. Student-undergrad faculty ratio is 10:1. 216 applied, 100% were admitted. 2% from top 10% of their high school class, 8% from top quarter, 36% from

top half. Full-time: 365 students, 53% women, 47% men. Part-time: 83 students, 69% women, 31% men. Students come from 36 states and territories, 4 other countries, 31% from out-of-state, 1% Native American, 8% Hispanic, 2% black, 2% Asian American or Pacific Islander, 1% international, 22% 25 or older, 18% live on campus, 17% transferred in. Retention: 64% of full-time freshmen returned the following year. Academic areas with the most degrees conferred: visual and performing arts; communication technologies; education. Core. Calendar: trimesters. Academic remediation for entering students, advanced placement, accelerated degree program, independent study, double major, summer session for credit, part-time degree program, co-op programs and internships. Study abroad program.

Entrance Requirements: Options: Common Application, deferred admission. Required: high school transcript, minimum 2.0 high school GPA, interview, portfolio. Entrance: moderately difficult. Application deadline: Rolling.

Costs Per Year: Application fee: $35. Tuition: $17,880 full-time, $745 per credit part-time. College room only: $3840.

Collegiate Environment: Orientation program. Social organizations: 5 open to all. Most popular organizations: Artists Representative Team, The American Society of Interior Designers, The American Institute of Graphic Arts, Art Directors Club of Denver, International Animated Film Association. Major annual events: Annual Student Exhibition, Annual Faculty Exhibition, art and design forums. Student services: personal-psychological counseling. Campus security: 24-hour emergency response devices, late night transport-escort service. 88 college housing spaces available; all were occupied in 2003-04. Freshmen given priority for college housing. On-campus residence required in freshman year. Option: coed housing available. Rocky Mountain College of Art and Design Library with 6,287 books and 65 serials. 47 computers available on campus for general student use. A campuswide network can be accessed. Staffed computer lab on campus.

■ **TEIKYO LORETTO HEIGHTS UNIVERSITY** *F-12*
3001 South Federal Blvd.
Denver, CO 80236-2711
Tel: (303)937-4200
Web Site: http://www.tlhu.edu/
Description: Independent, 4-year. Part of Teikyo University Group.

■ **TRINIDAD STATE JUNIOR COLLEGE** *M-12*
600 Prospect
Trinidad, CO 81082-2396
Tel: (719)846-5011
Free: 800-621-8752
Admissions: (719)846-5545
Fax: (719)846-5667
E-mail: alex.borja@trinidadstate.edu
Web Site: http://www.trinidadstate.edu/
Description: State-supported, 2-year, coed. Part of Colorado Community College and Occupational Education System. Awards certificates, diplomas, transfer associate, and terminal associate degrees. Founded 1925. Setting: 17-acre small town campus. Endowment: $4.7 million. Educational spending for 2005 fiscal year: $2346 per student. Total enrollment: 1,831. Student-undergrad faculty ratio is 16:1. 841 applied, 100% were admitted. Full-time: 775 students, 55% women, 45% men. Part-time: 1,056 students, 64% women, 36% men. Students come from 33 states and territories, 5 other countries, 8% from out-of-state, 59% 25 or older, 30% live on campus, 2% transferred in. Retention: 50% of full-time freshmen returned the following year. Core. Calendar: semesters. Academic remediation for entering students, ESL program, services for LD students, advanced placement, accelerated degree program, self-designed majors, honors program, independent study, distance learning, double major, summer session for credit, part-time degree program, adult/continuing education programs, co-op programs and internships.

Entrance Requirements: Open admission except for practical nursing program. Options: Common Application, electronic application, deferred admission. Required: high school transcript. Entrance: noncompetitive. Application deadline: Rolling. Notification: continuous.

Costs Per Year: Application fee: $0. State resident tuition: $2,182 full-time, $72.75 per credit part-time. Nonresident tuition: $8280 full-time, $276 per credit part-time. Mandatory fees: $528 full-time, $14.35 per credit part-time. College room and board: $4298. College room only: $1048. Room and board charges vary according to board plan.

Collegiate Environment: Orientation program. Drama-theater group, choral group, student-run newspaper. Social organizations: 15 open to all. Most

popular organizations: student association, International Club, Gunsmithing Club, Nursing Club, Cosmetology Club. Major annual events: Winter Formal, Trinidad State Junior College Basketball Tourney, Job Fair. Campus security: 24-hour emergency response devices and patrols, late night transport-escort service. 350 college housing spaces available; 182 were occupied in 2003-04. Options: coed, men-only, women-only housing available. Frendenthal Library plus 1 other with 54,255 books, 17,076 microform titles, 105 serials, 1,574 audiovisual materials, and an OPAC. Operations spending for 2004 fiscal year: $92,000. 125 computers available on campus for general student use. A campuswide network can be accessed from student residence rooms and from off campus. Staffed computer lab on campus.

Community Environment: Located in South Central Colorado, Trinidad is the County Seat of Las Animas County and was a trading post on the Old Santa Fe Trail. Good highways, busses, and the railroad serve the area. Leading industries are coal production, farming, and ranching. The area offers Monument Lake, a 1,200-acre city owned park with fishing, boating and camping; Trinidad Lake, located 36 miles west of Trinidad in scenic Stonewall Valley, with water skiing, fishing, boating, camping, hiking and a recreation area; Cuchara Ski Area, located 50 miles west of Trinidad in scenic Cuchara valley.

■ **UNITED STATES AIR FORCE ACADEMY**
HQ USAFA/XPR
2304 Cadet Dr., Ste. 200
USAF Academy, CO 80840-5025
Tel: (719)333-1818
Free: 800-443-9266
Admissions: (719)333-2520
Fax: (719)333-3012
E-mail: wilsoncm.rr@usafa.af.mil
Web Site: http://www.usafa.edu/
Description: Federally supported, 4-year, coed. Awards bachelor's degrees. Founded 1954. Setting: 18,000-acre suburban campus with easy access to Denver. Total enrollment: 4,365. Student-undergrad faculty ratio is 8:1. 9,601 applied, 15% were admitted. 57% from top 10% of their high school class, 85% from top quarter, 98% from top half. Full-time: 4,365 students, 18% women, 82% men. Students come from 54 states and territories, 21 other countries, 94% from out-of-state, 2% Native American, 6% Hispanic, 4% black, 7% Asian American or Pacific Islander, 1% international, 0.4% 25 or older, 100% live on campus, 0% transferred in. Retention: 89% of full-time freshmen returned the following year. Core. Calendar: semesters. Academic remediation for entering students, ESL program, advanced placement, self-designed majors, independent study, double major, summer session for credit, internships. Off campus study at other United States service academies. Study abroad program.

Entrance Requirements: Option: international baccalaureate accepted. Required: essay, high school transcript, minimum 2.0 high school GPA, interview, authorized nomination, SAT or ACT. Entrance: most difficult. Application deadline: 1/31. Notification: continuous until 5/15.

Costs Per Year: Application fee: $0.

Collegiate Environment: Orientation program. Drama-theater group, choral group, marching band, student-run newspaper, radio station. Social organizations: 100 open to all. Most popular organizations: Cadet Ski Club, choir, Scuba Club, Aviation Club, Drum and Bugle Corps. Major annual events: Ring Dance, Doolie Day Out, Graduation. Student services: legal services, health clinic, personal-psychological counseling. Campus security: 24-hour emergency response devices and patrols, late night transport-escort service, self-defense education, well-lit campus. College housing designed to accommodate 4,000 students; 4,219 undergraduates lived in college housing during 2003-04. Freshmen guaranteed college housing. On-campus residence required through senior year. Option: coed housing available. United States Air Force Academy Library plus 2 others with 445,379 books, 635,244 microform titles, 1,693 serials, 4,458 audiovisual materials, an OPAC, and a Web page. Operations spending for 2004 fiscal year: $3 million.

■ **UNIVERSITY OF COLORADO AT BOULDER** *E-11*
Boulder, CO 80309
Tel: (303)492-1411
Admissions: (303)492-6301
Fax: (303)492-7115
Web Site: http://www.colorado.edu/
Description: State-supported, university, coed. Part of University of Colorado System. Awards bachelor's, master's, doctoral, and first profes-

sional degrees. Founded 1876. Setting: 600-acre small town campus with easy access to Denver. Endowment: $247.5 million. Research spending for 2004 fiscal year: $246.3 million. Educational spending for 2005 fiscal year: $8353 per student. Total enrollment: 31,068. Faculty: 1,786 (1,227 full-time, 559 part-time). Student-undergrad faculty ratio is 16:1. 17,111 applied, 88% were admitted. 22% from top 10% of their high school class, 54% from top quarter, 89% from top half. 8 National Merit Scholars, 192 valedictorians. Full-time: 23,539 students, 47% women, 53% men. Part-time: 2,303 students, 45% women, 55% men. Students come from 52 states and territories, 100 other countries, 30% from out-of-state, 1% Native American, 6% Hispanic, 2% black, 6% Asian American or Pacific Islander, 1% international, 7% 25 or older, 22% live on campus, 5% transferred in. Retention: 83% of full-time freshmen returned the following year. Academic areas with the most degrees conferred: social sciences; business/marketing; communications/journalism. Core. Calendar: semesters. ESL program, services for LD students, advanced placement, accelerated degree program, self-designed majors, freshman honors college, honors program, independent study, distance learning, double major, summer session for credit, part-time degree program, adult/continuing education programs, co-op programs and internships, graduate courses open to undergrads. Off campus study at other units of the University of Colorado System. Study abroad program. ROTC: Army, Naval, Air Force.

Entrance Requirements: Options: electronic application, deferred admission, international baccalaureate accepted. Required: high school transcript, minimum 2.0 high school GPA, SAT or ACT. Recommended: essay, minimum 3.0 high school GPA, recommendations. Required for some: audition for music program. Entrance: moderately difficult. Application deadline: 1/15. Notification: continuous. Preference given to state residents.

Costs Per Year: Application fee: $50. One-time mandatory fee: $108. State resident tuition: $4446 full-time. Nonresident tuition: $21,900 full-time. Mandatory fees: $926 full-time. Full-time tuition and fees vary according to program. College room and board: $7980. Room and board charges vary according to board plan, location, and student level.

Collegiate Environment: Orientation program. Drama-theater group, choral group, marching band, student-run newspaper, radio station. Social organizations: 200 open to all; national fraternities, national sororities, local sororities; 7% of eligible men and 9% of eligible women are members. Most popular organizations: student government, Ski and Snowboard Club, Environmental Center, AIESEC, Program Council. Major annual events: Homecoming, Parents' Weekend, Global Jam. Student services: legal services, health clinic, personal-psychological counseling, women's center. Campus security: 24-hour emergency response devices and patrols, student patrols, late night transport-escort service, University police department. 7,100 college housing spaces available. Freshmen given priority for college housing. On-campus residence required in freshman year. Option: coed housing available. Norlin Library plus 5 others with 3.5 million books, 6.8 million microform titles, 20,677 serials, 444,169 audiovisual materials, an OPAC, and a Web page. Operations spending for 2004 fiscal year: $18.4 million. 1,525 computers available on campus for general student use. A campuswide network can be accessed from student residence rooms and from off campus. Staffed computer lab on campus.

■ **UNIVERSITY OF COLORADO AT COLORADO SPRINGS** *H-12*
1420 Austin Bluffs Parkway
PO Box 7150
Colorado Springs, CO 80933-7150
Tel: (719)262-3000
Free: 800-990-8227
Admissions: (719)262-3375
E-mail: admrec@mail.uccs.edu
Web Site: http://www.uccs.edu/

Description: State-supported, comprehensive, coed. Awards bachelor's, master's, and doctoral degrees. Founded 1965. Setting: 400-acre suburban campus with easy access to Denver. Endowment: $14.7 million. Research spending for 2004 fiscal year: $2.2 million. Educational spending for 2005 fiscal year: $4512 per student. Total enrollment: 8,437. Faculty: 556 (200 full-time, 356 part-time). Student-undergrad faculty ratio is 18:1. 1,899 applied, 76% were admitted. 15% from top 10% of their high school class, 42% from top quarter, 78% from top half. Full-time: 4,827 students, 61% women, 39% men. Part-time: 1,444 students, 58% women, 42% men. Students come from 44 states and territories, 26 other countries, 20% from out-of-state, 1% Native American, 9% Hispanic, 4% black, 5% Asian American or Pacific Islander, 0.4% international, 10% live on campus. Retention: 67% of full-time freshmen returned the following year. Academic areas with the most

degrees conferred: business/marketing; social sciences; communications/journalism; health professions and related sciences. Core. Calendar: semesters. Services for LD students, advanced placement, accelerated degree program, independent study, distance learning, double major, summer session for credit, part-time degree program, co-op programs and internships, graduate courses open to undergrads. ROTC: Army.

Entrance Requirements: Options: Peterson's Universal Application, electronic application, deferred admission. Required: high school transcript, SAT or ACT. Entrance: moderately difficult. Application deadline: 7/1. Notification: continuous. Preference given to state residents.

Costs Per Year: Application fee: $50. State resident tuition: $3966 full-time, $178 per credit hour part-time. Nonresident tuition: $15,260 full-time, $763 per credit hour part-time. Mandatory fees: $922 full-time. College room and board: $6418. College room only: $4878.

Collegiate Environment: Orientation program. Drama-theater group, choral group, student-run newspaper, radio station. Social organizations: 55 open to all; local fraternities, local sororities. Most popular organizations: Business Club, Ski Club, United Students of Color, Psychology Club. Major annual events: Welcome Back Week, Casino Night, Comedy Night. Student services: health clinic, personal-psychological counseling, women's center. Campus security: 24-hour emergency response devices and patrols, student patrols, late night transport-escort service, controlled dormitory access. 600 college housing spaces available; all were occupied in 2003-04. No special consideration for freshman housing applicants. Options: coed, men-only, women-only housing available. University of Colorado at Colorado Springs Kraemer Family Library with 391,638 books, 642,082 microform titles, 2,201 serials, 5,229 audiovisual materials, an OPAC, and a Web page. Operations spending for 2004 fiscal year: $2 million. 250 computers available on campus for general student use. A campuswide network can be accessed from student residence rooms and from off campus. Staffed computer lab on campus.

■ **UNIVERSITY OF COLORADO AT DENVER AND HEALTH SCIENCES CENTER - DOWNTOWN DENVER CAMPUS** *F-12*
PO Box 173364
Denver, CO 80217-3364
Tel: (303)556-2400
Admissions: (303)556-3287
Fax: (303)556-2398
E-mail: admissions@cudenver.edu
Web Site: http://www.cudenver.edu/

Description: State-supported, university, coed. Part of University of Colorado System. Awards bachelor's, master's, doctoral, and first professional degrees and post-master's certificates. Founded 1912. Setting: 171-acre urban campus. Endowment: $181.5 million. Research spending for 2004 fiscal year: $6.4 million. Educational spending for 2005 fiscal year: $5427 per student. Total enrollment: 19,755. Faculty: 1,362 (579 full-time, 783 part-time). Student-undergrad faculty ratio is 15:1. 2,681 applied, 69% were admitted. 13% from top 10% of their high school class, 37% from top quarter, 74% from top half. Full-time: 5,763 students, 56% women, 44% men. Part-time: 4,479 students, 58% women, 42% men. Students come from 51 states and territories, 121 other countries, 4% from out-of-state, 1% Native American, 11% Hispanic, 4% black, 9% Asian American or Pacific Islander, 1% international, 32% 25 or older, 10% transferred in. Retention: 72% of full-time freshmen returned the following year. Academic areas with the most degrees conferred: business/marketing; social sciences; health professions and related sciences. Core. Calendar: semesters. ESL program, services for LD students, advanced placement, accelerated degree program, self-designed majors, honors program, independent study, distance learning, double major, summer session for credit, part-time degree program, adult/continuing education programs, co-op programs and internships, graduate courses open to undergrads. Off campus study at Metropolitan State College, Community College of Denver. Study abroad program. ROTC: Army, Air Force (c).

Entrance Requirements: Options: electronic application, deferred admission. Required: high school transcript, minimum 2.5 high school GPA, SAT or ACT. Entrance: moderately difficult. Application deadlines: 7/22, 7/22 for nonresidents. Notification: continuous, continuous for nonresidents.

Costs Per Year: Application fee: $50. State resident tuition: $4224 full-time, $210 per semester hour part-time. Nonresident tuition: $15,394 full-time, $924 per semester hour part-time. Mandatory fees: $797 full-time, $14 per semester hour part-time, $377.

Collegiate Environment: Orientation program. Drama-theater group, choral group, student-run newspaper. Social organizations: 65 open to all. Most

popular organizations: Gold Key National Honor Society, Muslim Student Association, Model United Nations (International Forum Club), Psi Chi Honor Society, Associated Engineering Students. Major annual events: Fall Festival, Spring Fling, Auraria Blood Drive. Student services: legal services, health clinic, personal-psychological counseling. Campus security: 24-hour emergency response devices and patrols, student patrols, late night transport-escort service. College housing not available. Auraria Library with 588,582 books, 1 million microform titles, 4,364 serials, 15,720 audiovisual materials, an OPAC, and a Web page. Operations spending for 2004 fiscal year: $6.6 million. 750 computers available on campus for general student use. A campuswide network can be accessed from student residence rooms and from off campus. Staffed computer lab on campus.

■ UNIVERSITY OF DENVER *F-12*

University Park
2199 South University Park
Denver, CO 80208
Tel: (303)871-2000
Free: 800-525-9495
Admissions: (303)871-3383
Fax: (303)871-3301
E-mail: admission@du.edu
Web Site: http://www.du.edu/

Description: Independent, university, coed. Awards bachelor's, master's, doctoral, and first professional degrees. Founded 1864. Setting: 125-acre suburban campus. Endowment: $194.4 million. Research spending for 2004 fiscal year: $21.8 million. Educational spending for 2005 fiscal year: $11,225 per student. Total enrollment: 10,374. Faculty: 1,050 (484 full-time, 566 part-time). Student-undergrad faculty ratio is 11:1. 4,038 applied, 82% were admitted. 36% from top 10% of their high school class, 69% from top quarter, 90% from top half. Full-time: 4,431 students, 53% women, 47% men. Part-time: 446 students, 82% women, 18% men. Students come from 52 states and territories, 54 other countries, 50% from out-of-state, 1% Native American, 7% Hispanic, 3% black, 5% Asian American or Pacific Islander, 4% international, 16% 25 or older, 49% live on campus, 4% transferred in. Retention: 88% of full-time freshmen returned the following year. Academic areas with the most degrees conferred: business/marketing; communications/journalism; social sciences. Core. Calendar: ; semesters for law school. ESL program, services for LD students, advanced placement, accelerated degree program, self-designed majors, freshman honors college, honors program, independent study, double major, summer session for credit, part-time degree program, adult/continuing education programs, co-op programs and internships, graduate courses open to undergrads. Study abroad program. ROTC: Army (c), Air Force (c).

Entrance Requirements: Options: Peterson's Universal Application, Common Application, electronic application, early admission, early action, deferred admission, international baccalaureate accepted. Required: essay, high school transcript, 2 recommendations, interview, SAT or ACT. Required for some: minimum 2.0 high school GPA. Entrance: moderately difficult. Application deadlines: 1/15, 11/1 for early action. Notification: 3/15, 1/15 for early action.

Costs Per Year: Application fee: $50. Comprehensive fee: $37,159 includes full-time tuition ($27,756), mandatory fees ($654), and college room and board ($8749). College room only: $5355. Full-time tuition and fees vary according to class time, course load, and program. Room and board charges vary according to board plan and housing facility. Part-time tuition: $771 per quarter hour. Part-time tuition varies according to class time, course load, and program.

Collegiate Environment: Orientation program. Drama-theater group, choral group, student-run newspaper. Social organizations: 82 open to all; national fraternities, national sororities; 20% of eligible men and 19% of eligible women are members. Most popular organizations: student government, Club Sports Council, Programming Board, International Student Organization, Residence Hall Association. Major annual events: Winter Carnival, Homecoming/Family Weekend, Festival of Nations. Student services: health clinic, personal-psychological counseling, women's center. Campus security: 24-hour emergency response devices and patrols, late night transport-escort service, controlled dormitory access, 24-hour locked residence hall entrances. College housing designed to accommodate 1,933 students; 1,978 undergraduates lived in college housing during 2003-04. Freshmen guaranteed college housing. On-campus residence required through sophomore year. Options: coed, men-only, women-only housing available. Penrose Library with 1.2 million books, 1 million microform titles, 6,283 serials, 6,293 audiovisual materials, an OPAC, and a Web page. Operations

spending for 2004 fiscal year: $9 million. 150 computers available on campus for general student use. A campuswide network can be accessed from student residence rooms and from off campus. Staffed computer lab on campus.

Community Environment: Denver is a metropolitan area, capital of Colorado, situated at the foot of the Rocky Mountains. The climate is temperate and considered healthful. The State Museum, Art Museum, Museum of Natural History, many public and private hospitals, churches, and the fine shopping areas make up the city. Part-time employment opportunities are good. Denver is the gateway to the playgrounds of the mountains; the city's mountain parks of 20,000 acres include the Genesee Mountain with its game preserve. There are lakes in the area for water sports and fishing. Denver has become a great center for snow sports activities, with several of the best known ski areas located 55 to 85 miles from Denver in the Arapaho National Forest. The annual National Western Stock Show is in January.

■ UNIVERSITY OF NORTHERN COLORADO *D-12*

Greeley, CO 80639
Tel: (970)351-1890
Admissions: (970)351-2881
E-mail: admissions.help@unco.edu
Web Site: http://www.unco.edu/

Description: State-supported, university, coed. Awards bachelor's, master's, and doctoral degrees (specialist). Founded 1890. Setting: 240-acre suburban campus with easy access to Denver. Endowment: $72.2 million. Research spending for 2004 fiscal year: $2.7 million. Educational spending for 2005 fiscal year: $4291 per student. Total enrollment: 13,156. Faculty: 601 (400 full-time, 201 part-time). Student-undergrad faculty ratio is 24:1. 7,318 applied, 82% were admitted. 12% from top 10% of their high school class, 32% from top quarter, 68% from top half. 25 valedictorians. Full-time: 9,685 students, 61% women, 39% men. Part-time: 1,126 students, 62% women, 38% men. Students come from 48 states and territories, 9% from out-of-state, 1% Native American, 8% Hispanic, 2% black, 3% Asian American or Pacific Islander, 0.3% international, 8% 25 or older, 31% live on campus, 8% transferred in. Retention: 71% of full-time freshmen returned the following year. Academic areas with the most degrees conferred: interdisciplinary studies; business/marketing; social sciences. Core. Calendar: semesters. Academic remediation for entering students, ESL program, services for LD students, advanced placement, self-designed majors, honors program, independent study, distance learning, double major, summer session for credit, part-time degree program, external degree program, adult/continuing education programs, co-op programs and internships, graduate courses open to undergrads. Off campus study at National Student Exchange. Study abroad program. ROTC: Army, Air Force.

Entrance Requirements: Options: electronic application, deferred admission. Required: high school transcript, minimum 2.9 high school GPA, SAT or ACT. Required for some: interview. Entrance: moderately difficult. Application deadline: 8/1. Notification: continuous.

Costs Per Year: Application fee: $40. State resident tuition: $3192 full-time, $133 per credit hour part-time. Nonresident tuition: $11,736 full-time, $489 per credit hour part-time. Mandatory fees: $645 full-time, $32.25 per credit hour part-time. College room and board: $6412. College room only: $3150. Room and board charges vary according to board plan and housing facility.

Collegiate Environment: Orientation program. Drama-theater group, choral group, marching band, student-run newspaper, radio station. Social organizations: 93 open to all; national fraternities, national sororities; 6% of eligible men and 4% of eligible women are members. Major annual events: homecoming, The Main Event, UPC Bazaar. Student services: legal services, health clinic, personal-psychological counseling, women's center. Campus security: 24-hour emergency response devices and patrols, student patrols, late night transport-escort service, controlled dormitory access. College housing designed to accommodate 3,101 students; 3,162 undergraduates lived in college housing during 2003-04. Freshmen guaranteed college housing. On-campus residence required in freshman year. Options: coed, women-only housing available. James A. Michener Library plus 2 others with 1 million books, 2 million microform titles, 3,417 serials, 30,450 audiovisual materials, an OPAC, and a Web page. Operations spending for 2004 fiscal year: $4.8 million. 1,100 computers available on campus for general student use. Computer purchase/lease plans available. A campuswide network can be accessed from student residence rooms and from off campus. Staffed computer lab on campus.

Community Environment: Located one hour north of Denver and one hour east of Rocky Mountain National Park, the city of Greeley has a population of more than 75,000. It has a symphony, rock and jazz concerts, community theatre, and the largest 4th of July rodeo in the country. The dry, desert climate produces sunny days and cool nights. There is some snow and very little rain.

■ UNIVERSITY OF PHOENIX-DENVER CAMPUS *D-3*

10004 Park Meadows Dr.
Lone Tree, CO 80124-5453
Tel: (303)694-9093
Free: 800-228-7240
Admissions: (480)557-1712
Web Site: http://www.phoenix.edu/
Description: Proprietary, comprehensive, coed. Awards bachelor's and master's degrees and post-master's certificates. Setting: urban campus. Total enrollment: 3,420. Faculty: 378 (5 full-time, 373 part-time). Student-undergrad faculty ratio is 9:1. 57 applied. Full-time: 2,010 students, 60% women, 40% men. 0.2% Native American, 5% Hispanic, 3% black, 1% Asian American or Pacific Islander, 9% international, 92% 25 or older. Academic areas with the most degrees conferred: business/marketing; computer and information sciences; health professions and related sciences. Core. Calendar: continuous. Advanced placement, accelerated degree program, independent study, distance learning, external degree program, adult/continuing education programs, graduate courses open to undergrads.
Entrance Requirements: Open admission. Option: deferred admission. Required: 1 recommendation. Required for some: high school transcript. Entrance: noncompetitive. Application deadline: Rolling.
Costs Per Year: Application fee: $110. Tuition: $9480 full-time, $316 per credit part-time. Mandatory fees: $560 full-time, $70 per course part-time.
Collegiate Environment: College housing not available. University Library with 444 books, 666 serials, an OPAC, and a Web page. System-wide operations spending for 2004 fiscal year: $3.2 million.

■ UNIVERSITY OF PHOENIX-SOUTHERN COLORADO CAMPUS *H-12*

5475 Tech Center, Ste. 130
Colorado Springs, CO 80919-2335
Tel: (719)599-5282
Free: 800-228-7240
Admissions: (480)557-1712
Web Site: http://www.phoenix.edu/
Description: Proprietary, comprehensive, coed. Awards bachelor's and master's degrees. Founded 1999. Setting: urban campus. Total enrollment: 1,294. Faculty: 175 (2 full-time, 173 part-time). Student-undergrad faculty ratio is 7:1. 17 applied. Full-time: 775 students, 52% women, 48% men. 0% from out-of-state, 0.3% Native American, 4% Hispanic, 4% black, 1% Asian American or Pacific Islander, 27% international, 94% 25 or older. Academic areas with the most degrees conferred: business/marketing; computer and information sciences; security and protective services. Core. Calendar: continuous. Advanced placement, accelerated degree program, independent study, distance learning, external degree program, adult/continuing education programs, graduate courses open to undergrads.
Entrance Requirements: Open admission. Option: deferred admission. Required: 1 recommendation. Required for some: high school transcript. Entrance: noncompetitive. Application deadline: Rolling.
Costs Per Year: Application fee: $110. Tuition: $9489 full-time, $316 per credit part-time. Mandatory fees: $560 full-time, $70 per course part-time.
Collegiate Environment: College housing not available. University Library with 444 books, 666 serials, an OPAC, and a Web page. System-wide operations spending for 2004 fiscal year: $3.2 million.

■ WESTERN STATE COLLEGE OF COLORADO *I-8*

600 North Adams St.
Gunnison, CO 81231
Tel: (970)943-0120
Free: 800-876-5309
Admissions: (970)943-2119
Fax: (970)943-7069
E-mail: talbers@western.edu
Web Site: http://www.western.edu/
Description: State-supported, 4-year, coed. Awards bachelor's degrees. Founded 1901. Setting: 381-acre small town campus. Research spending for 2004 fiscal year: $92,860. Educational spending for 2005 fiscal year: $4097 per student. Total enrollment: 2,177. Student-undergrad faculty ratio is 18:1. 1,308 applied, 83% were admitted. 7% from top 10% of their high school class, 20% from top quarter, 50% from top half. 3 valedictorians. Full-

time: 2,034 students, 40% women, 60% men. Part-time: 143 students, 45% women, 55% men. Students come from 50 states and territories, 27% from out-of-state, 1% Native American, 5% Hispanic, 2% black, 1% Asian American or Pacific Islander, 0.1% international, 13% 25 or older, 41% live on campus, 7% transferred in. Retention: 61% of full-time freshmen returned the following year. Academic areas with the most degrees conferred: business/marketing; visual and performing arts; parks and recreation. Core. Calendar: semesters. Services for LD students, advanced placement, accelerated degree program, self-designed majors, honors program, double major, summer session for credit, part-time degree program, adult/continuing education programs, co-op programs and internships. Off campus study at State Colleges of Colorado, National Student Exchange. Study abroad program.
Entrance Requirements: Options: Common Application, deferred admission. Required: high school transcript, SAT or ACT. Recommended: minimum 2.5 high school GPA. Required for some: essay, 2 recommendations, interview. Entrance: moderately difficult. Application deadline: 8/1. Notification: 11/1.
Costs Per Year: Application fee: $30. State resident tuition: $2,411 full-time, $100.45 per credit hour part-time. Nonresident tuition: $10,968 full-time, $457 per credit hour part-time. Mandatory fees: $796 full-time, $26.05 per credit hour part-time. College room and board: $6976. College room only: $3794.
Collegiate Environment: Orientation program. Drama-theater group, choral group, student-run newspaper, radio station. Social organizations: 110 open to all; national fraternities, local fraternities, local sororities. Most popular organizations: Mountain Search and Rescue Team, Student Government Association, Rodeo Club, wilderness pursuits, Peak Productions. Major annual events: Earth Day, Homecoming, Family Weekend. Student services: health clinic, personal-psychological counseling. Campus security: 24-hour emergency response devices and patrols, student patrols, late night transport-escort service, controlled dormitory access. 1,200 college housing spaces available; 1,000 were occupied in 2003-04. Freshmen given priority for college housing. On-campus residence required in freshman year. Options: coed, men-only, women-only housing available. Savage Library with 158,698 books, 1.2 million microform titles, 719 serials, 1,539 audiovisual materials, an OPAC, and a Web page. Operations spending for 2004 fiscal year: $572,911. 175 computers available on campus for general student use. A campuswide network can be accessed from student residence rooms and from off campus. Staffed computer lab on campus.
Community Environment: Gunnison is a community with a population of about 7,000. Western State students are welcome to participate in all kinds of cultural, political, recreational, and religious activities offered by the community. The summer climate and the natural beauties of the region annually attract millions of tourists. Winter sports enthusiasts enjoy excellent skiing at Crested Butte Mountain Resort and Monarch Ski Area and ice fishing on Colorado's Blue Mesa Reservoir, which is located just 9 miles from the campus.

■ WESTWOOD COLLEGE-DENVER NORTH *F-12*

7350 North Broadway
Denver, CO 80221-3653
Tel: (303)650-5050
Free: 800-992-5050
Fax: (303)426-0702
Web Site: http://www.westwood.edu/
Description: Proprietary, primarily 2-year, coed. Awards diplomas, terminal associate, and bachelor's degrees. Founded 1953. Setting: 11-acre suburban campus. Educational spending for 2005 fiscal year: $4301 per student. Total enrollment: 1,423. Student-undergrad faculty ratio is 13:1. 2,332 applied, 45% were admitted. Full-time: 1,086 students, 32% women, 68% men. Part-time: 337 students, 33% women, 67% men. Students come from 38 states and territories, 2 other countries, 16% from out-of-state, 2% Native American, 16% Hispanic, 3% black, 3% Asian American or Pacific Islander, 0.1% international, 32% 25 or older, 0.2% transferred in. Retention: 28% of full-time freshmen returned the following year. Calendar: 5 terms. Academic remediation for entering students, services for LD students, advanced placement, accelerated degree program, independent study, distance learning, summer session for credit, part-time degree program, internships.
Entrance Requirements: Options: Common Application, deferred admission, international baccalaureate accepted. Required: high school transcript, interview. Recommended: SAT or ACT, SAT and SAT Subject Tests or ACT. Required for some: ACCUPLACER, ACCUPLACER. Entrance: moderately difficult. Application deadline: Rolling. Notification: continuous.

Costs Per Year: Application fee: $100. Tuition: $2796 per term part-time. Mandatory fees: $425 per credit part-time, $120 per term part-time. Part-time tuition and fees vary according to course load and program.

Collegiate Environment: Orientation program. Social organizations: 3 open to all. Most popular organizations: American Institute of Graphic Arts, Social Club, Gaming Club. Major annual events: Summer BBQ, sports events. Campus security: 24-hour emergency response devices. College housing not available. Westwood DNN Library with 2,000 books, 90 serials, 120 audiovisual materials, an OPAC, and a Web page. Operations spending for 2004 fiscal year: $63,465. 30 computers available on campus for general student use. A campuswide network can be accessed.

■ **WESTWOOD COLLEGE-DENVER SOUTH** *F-12*
3150 South Sheridan Blvd.
Denver, CO 80227
Tel: (303)934-2790
Free: 800-281-2978
Fax: (303)934-2583
Web Site: http://www.westwood.edu/

Description: Proprietary, primarily 2-year, coed. Awards terminal associate and bachelor's degrees. Setting: urban campus with easy access to Denver, CO. Total enrollment: 429. 303 applied, 58% were admitted. Full-time: 294 students, 33% women, 67% men. Part-time: 135 students, 27% women, 73% men. 0% Native American, 17% Hispanic, 4% black, 4% Asian American or Pacific Islander, 0% international, 49% 25 or older. Calendar: continuous.

Entrance Requirements: Required: interview, high school diploma or GED and entrance exam (SAT/ACT or Accuplacer).

■ **YESHIVA TORAS CHAIM TALMUDICAL SEMINARY** *F-12*
1400 Quitman St.
Denver, CO 80204-1415
Tel: (303)629-8200
Fax: (303)623-5949

Description: Independent Jewish, comprehensive, men only. Awards bachelor's and master's degrees. Founded 1967. Setting: urban campus. Total enrollment: 20. Students come from 6 states and territories, 2 other countries. Core. Calendar: trimesters. Academic remediation for entering students, services for LD students, honors program, adult/continuing education programs, graduate courses open to undergrads.

Entrance Requirements: Option: early admission. Entrance: moderately difficult.

Collegiate Environment: On-campus residence required through senior year. 5 computers available on campus for general student use.

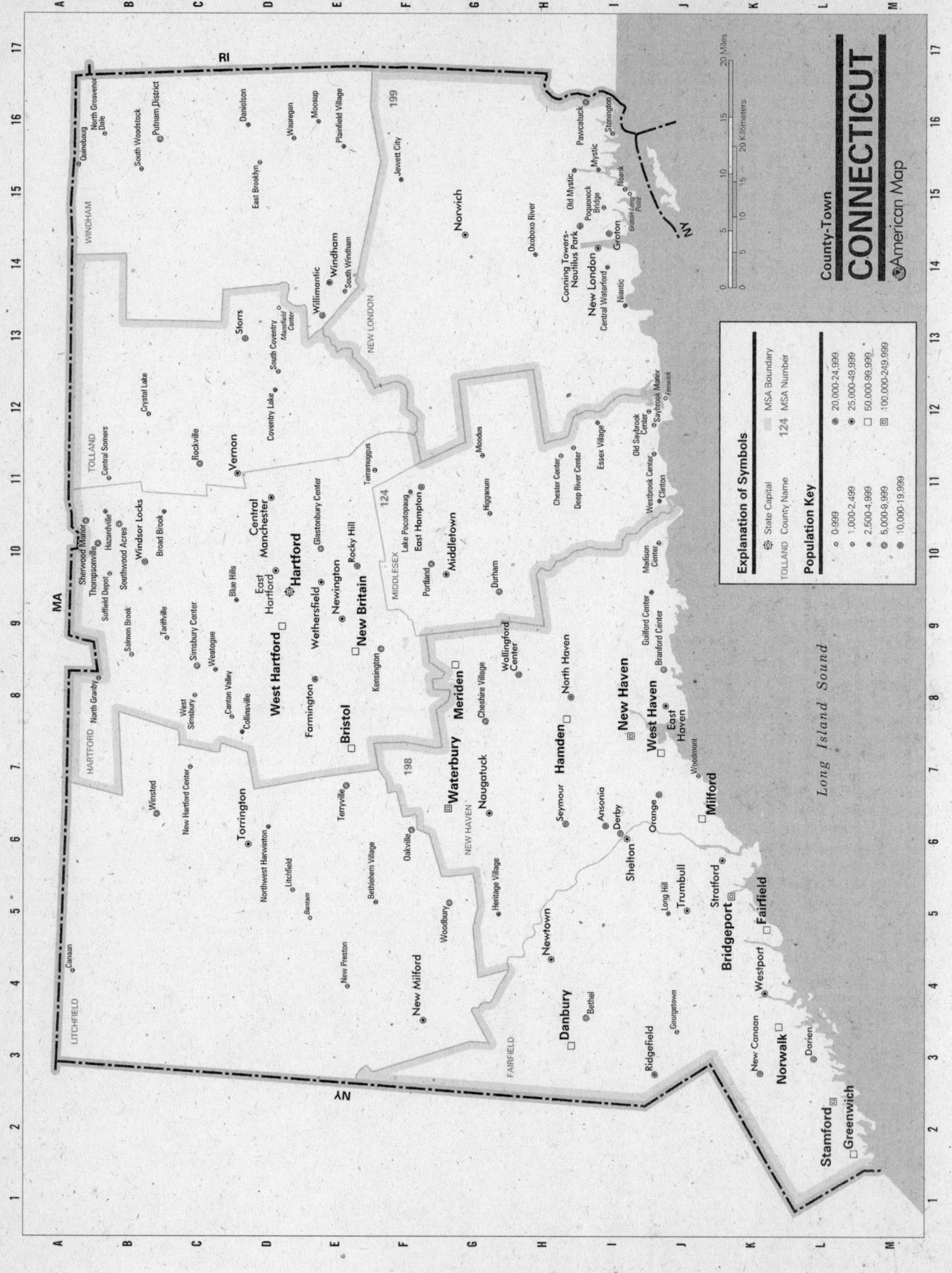

CONNECTICUT
County-Town
American Map

Explanation of Symbols

⊕ State Capital
TOLLAND County Name
■ MSA Boundary
124 MSA Number

Population Key
- ∘ 0-999
- ⊙ 1,000-2,499
- ⊚ 2,500-4,999
- ⊛ 5,000-9,999
- ⊜ 10,000-19,999
- ⊕ 20,000-24,999
- ⊛ 25,000-49,999
- □ 50,000-99,999
- ⊡ 100,000-249,999

Long Island Sound

■ **ALBERTUS MAGNUS COLLEGE** *I-8*

700 Prospect St.
New Haven, CT 06511-1189
Tel: (203)773-8550
Free: 800-578-9160
Admissions: (203)773-8501
Fax: (203)785-8652

Web Site: http://www.albertus.edu/

Description: Independent Roman Catholic, comprehensive, coed. Awards associate, bachelor's, and master's degrees. Founded 1925. Setting: 55-acre suburban campus with easy access to New York City and Hartford. Endowment: $7.8 million. Educational spending for 2005 fiscal year: $2951 per student. Total enrollment: 2,230. Faculty: 167 (34 full-time, 133 part-time). Student-undergrad faculty ratio is 15:1. 534 applied, 36% were admitted. 16% from top 10% of their high school class, 31% from top quarter, 63% from top half. Full-time: 1,695 students, 71% women, 29% men. Part-time: 87 students, 74% women, 26% men. Students come from 9 states and territories, 4 other countries, 24% from out-of-state, 0.3% Native American, 11% Hispanic, 27% black, 1% Asian American or Pacific Islander, 0.3% international, 64% 25 or older, 60% live on campus, 2% transferred in. Retention: 77% of full-time freshmen returned the following year. Academic areas with the most degrees conferred: business/marketing; social sciences; psychology. Core. Calendar: semesters. Academic remediation for entering students, ESL program, services for LD students, advanced placement, accelerated degree program, self-designed majors, freshman honors college, honors program, independent study, distance learning, double major, summer session for credit, part-time degree program, adult/continuing education programs, internships, graduate courses open to undergrads.

Entrance Requirements: Options: Peterson's Universal Application, deferred admission. Required: high school transcript, 1 recommendation, SAT or ACT. Recommended: minimum 2.5 high school GPA, interview, SAT Subject Tests. Required for some: minimum 2.5 high school GPA. Entrance: moderately difficult. Application deadline: 8/20. Notification: continuous.

Costs Per Year: Application fee: $35. Comprehensive fee: $24,860 includes full-time tuition ($16,600), mandatory fees ($710), and college room and board ($7550). Full-time tuition and fees vary according to class time and program. Part-time tuition: $1726 per course. Part-time tuition varies according to class time and program.

Collegiate Environment: Orientation program. Drama-theater group, student-run newspaper. Social organizations: 20 open to all. Most popular organizations: Student Government Association, College Drama, Minority Student Union. Major annual events: Candlelight Ceremony, Fall Festival, Spring Semi-Formal/Winter Wonderland. Student services: health clinic, personal-psychological counseling. Campus security: 24-hour emergency response devices and patrols, late night transport-escort service, controlled dormitory access. 350 college housing spaces available; 298 were occupied in 2003-04. Freshmen guaranteed college housing. Options: coed, women-only housing available. Rosary Hall with 5,638 microform titles, 538 serials, 817 audiovisual materials, an OPAC, and a Web page. Operations spending for 2004 fiscal year: $540,000. 150 computers available on campus for general student use. A campuswide network can be accessed from student residence rooms and from off campus. Staffed computer lab on campus.

Community Environment: See Yale University.

■ **ASNUNTUCK COMMUNITY COLLEGE** *B-10*

170 Elm St.
Enfield, CT 06082-3800
Tel: (860)253-3000
Free: 800-501-3967
Admissions: (860)253-3018
Fax: (860)253-9310
E-mail: dshaw@acc.commnet.edu
Web Site: http://www.acc.commnet.edu/

Description: State-supported, 2-year, coed. Part of Connecticut Community College System. Awards certificates, transfer associate, and terminal associate degrees. Founded 1972. Setting: 4-acre suburban campus. Total enrollment: 1,483. Student-undergrad faculty ratio is 16:1. 303 applied, 100% were admitted. Full-time: 526 students, 56% women, 44% men. Part-time: 957 students, 61% women, 39% men. Students come from 3 states and territories, 4% from out-of-state, 0.3% Native American, 3% Hispanic, 5% black, 2% Asian American or Pacific Islander, 0.1% international, 50% 25 or older, 3% transferred in. Core. Calendar: semesters. Academic remediation for entering students, ESL program, services for LD students, advanced placement, self-designed majors, independent study, distance learning, double major, summer session for credit, part-time degree program, adult/continuing education programs, internships. Study abroad program.

Entrance Requirements: Open admission. Option: deferred admission. Required: high school transcript. Entrance: noncompetitive. Application deadline: Rolling. Notification: continuous.

Costs Per Year: Application fee: $20. State resident tuition: $2352 full-time, $98 per credit part-time. Nonresident tuition: $7976 full-time, $294 per credit part-time. Mandatory fees: $320 full-time, $58 per credit part-time.

Collegiate Environment: Orientation program. Drama-theater group, student-run newspaper, radio station. Social organizations: 9 open to all. Most popular organizations: Phi Theta Kappa, Drama Club, Outdoor Club, Poetry Club, Ski Club. Student services: women's center. Campus security: 24-hour patrols, late night transport-escort service. College housing not available. ACTC Learning Resource Center with 31,700 books, 48,600 microform titles, 257 serials, 2,570 audiovisual materials, and an OPAC. 90 computers available on campus for general student use. A campuswide network can be accessed from off-campus. Staffed computer lab on campus.

■ **BETH BENJAMIN ACADEMY OF CONNECTICUT** *L-2*

132 Prospect St.
Stamford, CT 06901-1202
Tel: (203)325-4351

Description: Independent Jewish, comprehensive, men only. Awards bachelor's and master's degrees. Founded 1976. Calendar: trimesters.

■ **BRIARWOOD COLLEGE** *F-8*

2279 Mount Vernon Rd.
Southington, CT 06489-1057
Tel: (860)628-4751
Fax: (860)628-6444
E-mail: yamanisd@briarwood.edu
Web Site: http://www.briarwood.edu/

Description: Proprietary, primarily 2-year, coed. Awards certificates, diplomas, transfer associate, terminal associate, and bachelor's degrees. Founded 1966. Setting: 32-acre small town campus with easy access to Boston and Hartford. Endowment: $27,595. Total enrollment: 647. Student-undergrad faculty ratio is 10:1. 607 applied, 73% were admitted. 4% from top 10% of their high school class, 7% from top quarter, 24% from top half. Full-time: 389 students, 70% women, 30% men. Part-time: 258 students, 81% women, 19% men. Students come from 11 states and territories, 2 other countries, 7% from out-of-state, 0.2% Native American, 11% Hispanic, 22% black, 1% Asian American or Pacific Islander, 1% international, 38% 25 or older, 21% live on campus, 13% transferred in. Core. Calendar: semesters. Academic remediation for entering students, ESL program, services for LD students, advanced placement, accelerated degree program, independent study, double major, summer session for credit, part-time degree program, adult/continuing education programs, internships.
Entrance Requirements: Options: Peterson's Universal Application, Common Application, electronic application. Required: high school transcript. Required for some: essay, recommendations, interview. Entrance: minimally difficult. Application deadline: Rolling.
Costs Per Year: Application fee: $25. Tuition: $15,200 full-time, $500 per credit part-time. Mandatory fees: $220 full-time, $125 per term part-time. Full-time tuition and fees vary according to program. Part-time tuition and fees vary according to course load and program. College room only: $3320. Tuition guaranteed not to increase for student's term of enrollment.
Collegiate Environment: Orientation program. Student-run radio station. Most popular organizations: student government, Yearbook Committee, Student Ambassador Club, F.A.M.E. (Fashion Merchandising Club). Major annual events: Spring Prom, Class Night, holiday parties. Student services: personal-psychological counseling. Campus security: 24-hour patrols, late night transport-escort service. 174 college housing spaces available; 154 were occupied in 2003-04. Freshmen given priority for college housing. Option: coed housing available. Pupillo Library with 11,500 books, 154 serials, 130 audiovisual materials, and a Web page. Operations spending for 2004 fiscal year: $70,283. 54 computers available on campus for general student use. Staffed computer lab on campus.

■ **CAPITAL COMMUNITY COLLEGE** *D-10*
950 Main St.
Hartford, CT 06103
Tel: (860)906-5000
Admissions: (860)906-5127
E-mail: mbell-davis@ccc.commnet.edu
Web Site: http://www.ccc.commnet.edu/
Description: State-supported, 2-year, coed. Part of Connecticut Community College System. Awards certificates, transfer associate, and terminal associate degrees. Founded 1946. Setting: 10-acre urban campus. Total enrollment: 3,573. Full-time: 927 students, 65% women, 35% men. Part-time: 2,646 students, 75% women, 25% men. Students come from 3 states and territories, 0.3% Native American, 27% Hispanic, 39% black, 4% Asian American or Pacific Islander, 1% international, 56% 25 or older. Calendar: semesters. Academic remediation for entering students, ESL program, services for LD students, advanced placement, accelerated degree program, independent study, distance learning, double major, summer session for credit, part-time degree program, adult/continuing education programs, internships.
Entrance Requirements: Open admission except for nursing, emergency medical technology, radiological technology programs. Recommended: high school transcript. Entrance: noncompetitive. Application deadline: Rolling. Notification: continuous until 9/1.
Costs Per Year: Application fee: $20. State resident tuition: $2352 full-time, $98 per credit hour part-time. Nonresident tuition: $7056 full-time, $294 per credit hour part-time. Mandatory fees: $320 full-time.
Collegiate Environment: Drama-theater group, choral group. Social organizations: 20 open to all. Most popular organizations: Latin American Student Association, Student Senate, Senior Renewal Club, Early Childhood Club, Pre-Professional Club. Major annual events: Holiday Dinner Dance, ambassador ceremonies, Spring Outing. Student services: personal-psychological counseling. Campus security: late night transport-escort service, security staff during hours of operation, emergency telephones 7 a.m. - 11 p.m. College housing not available. Arthur C. Banks, Jr. Library plus 1 other with 46,760 books, 3,946 microform titles, 359 serials, 2,409 audiovisual materials, an OPAC, and a Web page. 180 computers available on campus for general student use. A campuswide network can be accessed from off-campus. Staffed computer lab on campus.

■ **CENTRAL CONNECTICUT STATE UNIVERSITY** *E-9*
1615 Stanley St.
New Britain, CT 06050-4010
Tel: (860)832-3200
Admissions: (860)832-2285
Fax: (860)832-2522
E-mail: admissions@ccsu.edu
Web Site: http://www.ccsu.edu/
Description: State-supported, comprehensive, coed. Part of Connecticut State University System. Awards bachelor's, master's, and doctoral degrees and post-master's certificates. Founded 1849. Setting: 294-acre suburban campus. Endowment: $17.6 million. Research spending for 2004 fiscal year: $643,696. Educational spending for 2005 fiscal year: $4740 per student. Total enrollment: 12,315. Faculty: 850 (416 full-time, 434 part-time). Student-undergrad faculty ratio is 19:1. 5,549 applied, 62% were admitted. 7% from top 10% of their high school class, 27% from top quarter, 68% from top half. Full-time: 7,445 students, 51% women, 49% men. Part-time: 2,233 students, 50% women, 50% men. Students come from 27 states and territories, 64 other countries, 4% from out-of-state, 1% Native American, 6% Hispanic, 8% black, 3% Asian American or Pacific Islander, 1% international, 20% 25 or older, 21% live on campus, 7% transferred in. Retention: 79% of full-time freshmen returned the following year. Academic areas with the most degrees conferred: business/marketing; social sciences; education. Core. Calendar: semesters. Academic remediation for entering students, ESL program, services for LD students, advanced placement, self-designed majors, honors program, summer session for credit, part-time degree program, adult/continuing education programs, co-op programs and internships, graduate courses open to undergrads. Off campus study at members of the Inter-Institutional Student Exchange Program. Study abroad program. ROTC: Army (c), Air Force (c).
Entrance Requirements: Options: Common Application, electronic application. Required: high school transcript, minimum 2.0 high school GPA, SAT. Recommended: minimum 3.0 high school GPA, 1 recommendation. Required for some: interview. Entrance: moderately difficult. Application deadline: 6/1. Notification: continuous until 7/1.
Costs Per Year: Application fee: $50. State resident tuition: $3034 full-time, $290 per credit part-time. Nonresident tuition: $9820 full-time, $290 per credit part-time. Mandatory fees: $3130 full-time, $55 per term part-time. Full-time tuition and fees vary according to course level, course load, and reciprocity agreements. Part-time tuition and fees vary according to course level and course load. College room and board: $7456. College room only: $4250. Room and board charges vary according to board plan.
Collegiate Environment: Orientation program. Drama-theater group, choral group, student-run newspaper, radio station. Social organizations: 100 open to all; national fraternities, national sororities, local fraternities, local sororities; 1% of eligible men and 1% of eligible women are members. Most popular organizations: Inter-Residence Council, student radio station, Program Council, Outing Club, NAACP. Major annual events: Homecoming, Film Series, Spring Weekend. Student services: health clinic, personal-psychological counseling, women's center. Campus security: 24-hour emergency response devices and patrols, student patrols, late night transport-escort service. 2,200 college housing spaces available; 1,901 were occupied in 2003-04. No special consideration for freshman housing applicants. Option: coed housing available. Burritt Library plus 1 other with 639,257 books, 552,591 microform titles, 2,762 serials, 5,669 audiovisual materials, and an OPAC. Operations spending for 2004 fiscal year: $4.6 million. 880 computers available on campus for general student use. A campuswide network can be accessed from student residence rooms and from off campus. Staffed computer lab on campus.
Community Environment: Population 75,000. Known as the "Hardware City of the World," New Britain is located nine miles southwest of Hartford. Sleigh bells were the first items manufactured here. Now there are 250 manufacturing establishments and over 600 retail outlets. Access to New York City is by train, and there is commercial air service nearby. New Britain has 44 churches of major denominations, outstanding hospital facilities and is now undertaking urban renewal projects. Points of interest are the New Britain Institute and Art Museum, memorial monuments, municipal golf course and the parks.

■ **CHARTER OAK STATE COLLEGE** *E-9*
55 Paul Manafort Dr.
New Britain, CT 06053-2142
Tel: (860)832-3800
Admissions: (860)832-3858

Fax: (860)832-3999
E-mail: pmorganti@commnet.edu
Web Site: http://www.charteroak.edu/
Description: State-supported, 4-year, coed. Awards associate and bachelor's degrees (offers only external degree programs). Founded 1973. Setting: small town campus. Endowment: $811,102. Total enrollment: 1,902. Student-undergrad faculty ratio is 12:1. Part-time: 1,902 students, 60% women, 40% men. Students come from 51 states and territories, 56% from out-of-state, 1% Native American, 6% Hispanic, 10% black, 2% Asian American or Pacific Islander, 0.1% international, 92% 25 or older. Academic area with the most degrees conferred: liberal arts/general studies. Core. Calendar: continuous. Services for LD students, advanced placement, accelerated degree program, self-designed majors, independent study, distance learning, summer session for credit, part-time degree program, external degree program, adult/continuing education programs.
Entrance Requirements: Open admission. Options: electronic application, deferred admission. Entrance: noncompetitive.
Costs Per Year: Application fee: $60. State resident tuition: $165 per credit part-time. Nonresident tuition: $235 per credit part-time.
Collegiate Environment: College housing not available.

■ **CONNECTICUT COLLEGE** *I-14*
270 Mohegan Ave.
New London, CT 06320-4196
Tel: (860)447-1911
Admissions: (860)439-2200
Fax: (860)439-4301
E-mail: admissions@conncoll.edu
Web Site: http://www.connecticutcollege.edu/
Description: Independent, comprehensive, coed. Awards bachelor's and master's degrees. Founded 1911. Setting: 702-acre suburban campus. Endowment: $164.8 million. Research spending for 2004 fiscal year: $1.4 million. Educational spending for 2005 fiscal year: $14,472 per student. Total enrollment: 1,898. Faculty: 242 (162 full-time, 80 part-time). Student-undergrad faculty ratio is 10:1. 4,183 applied, 35% were admitted. 54% from top 10% of their high school class, 83% from top quarter, 99% from top half. Full-time: 1,808 students, 60% women, 40% men. Part-time: 79 students, 72% women, 28% men. Students come from 46 states and territories, 40 other countries, 80% from out-of-state, 0.2% Native American, 5% Hispanic, 4% black, 5% Asian American or Pacific Islander, 4% international, 2% 25 or older, 99% live on campus, 2% transferred in. Retention: 92% of full-time freshmen returned the following year. Academic areas with the most degrees conferred: social sciences; biological/life sciences; visual and performing arts. Core. Calendar: semesters. Advanced placement, accelerated degree program, self-designed majors, honors program, independent study, double major, summer session for credit, part-time degree program, adult/continuing education programs, internships, graduate courses open to undergrads. Off campus study at members of the Twelve College Exchange Program, United States Coast Guard Academy, American University, Trinity College, Wesleyan University, National Theater Institute, Williams College. Study abroad program.
Entrance Requirements: Options: Peterson's Universal Application, Common Application, early decision, deferred admission, international baccalaureate accepted. Required: essay, high school transcript, minimum 2.0 high school GPA, 2 recommendations, ACT or any 3 SAT II Subject Tests. Recommended: interview, SAT. Entrance: very difficult. Application deadlines: 1/1, 11/15 for early decision plan 1, 1/1 for early decision plan 2. Notification: 3/31, 12/15 for early decision plan 1, 2/15 for early decision plan 2.
Costs Per Year: Application fee: $60. Comprehensive fee: $41,975. Part-time tuition: $975 per credit hour. Part-time tuition varies according to program. Tuition: $975 per credit hour part-time. Part-time tuition varies according to program.
Collegiate Environment: Orientation program. Drama-theater group, choral group, student-run newspaper, radio station. Social organizations: 60 open to all. Most popular organizations: Student Government Association, Student Activity Council, unity clubs, sports clubs, student radio station. Major annual events: Floralia, Harvestfest, Winter Formal. Student services: health clinic, personal-psychological counseling. Campus security: 24-hour emergency response devices and patrols, late night transport-escort service, controlled dormitory access. 1,716 college housing spaces available; 1,670 were occupied in 2003-04. Freshmen guaranteed college housing. Option: coed housing available. Charles Shain Library plus 1 other with 496,817 books, 153,545 microform titles, 2,279 serials, 155,884 audiovisual materials, an

OPAC, and a Web page. Operations spending for 2004 fiscal year: $3 million. 461 computers available on campus for general student use. A campuswide network can be accessed from student residence rooms and from off campus. Staffed computer lab on campus.
Community Environment: On the west bank of the Thames River, three miles from Long Island Sound, known historically as "The Whaling City." New London is a maritime center located midway between Boston and New York. It is a popular summer resort. Ocean Beach Park, a fifty-acre tract, borders a half-mile-long beach and provides recreational facilities. New London is the location of the annual Yale-Harvard Crew Races held each June.

■ **EASTERN CONNECTICUT STATE UNIVERSITY** *E-13*
83 Windham St.
Willimantic, CT 06226-2295
Tel: (860)465-5000; 877-353-3278
Admissions: (860)465-5286
E-mail: admissions@ecsu.ctstateu.edu
Web Site: http://www.easternct.edu
Description: State-supported, comprehensive, coed. Part of Connecticut State University System. Awards associate, bachelor's, and master's degrees. Founded 1889. Setting: 179-acre small town campus. Endowment: $60,000. Research spending for 2004 fiscal year: $140,742. Educational spending for 2005 fiscal year: $5579 per student. Total enrollment: 5,113. Faculty: 397 (188 full-time, 209 part-time). 3,066 applied, 69% were admitted. 5% from top 10% of their high school class, 21% from top quarter, 68% from top half. Full-time: 3,751 students, 55% women, 45% men. Part-time: 994 students, 59% women, 41% men. Students come from 24 states and territories, 21 other countries, 7% from out-of-state, 1% Native American, 5% Hispanic, 7% black, 2% Asian American or Pacific Islander, 1% international, 17% 25 or older, 10% transferred in. Retention: 78% of full-time freshmen returned the following year. Academic areas with the most degrees conferred: business/marketing; psychology; social sciences. Core. Calendar: semesters. Academic remediation for entering students, services for LD students, advanced placement, self-designed majors, freshman honors college, honors program, independent study, distance learning, double major, summer session for credit, part-time degree program, adult/continuing education programs, co-op programs and internships, graduate courses open to undergrads. Off campus study at University of Connecticut, Southern Connecticut State University, Central Connecticut State University, Western Connecticut State University. Study abroad program. ROTC: Army (c), Air Force (c).
Entrance Requirements: Options: Peterson's Universal Application, Common Application, electronic application, early admission, deferred admission. Required: high school transcript, SAT or ACT. Recommended: essay, recommendations, rank in upper 50% of high school class. Required for some: interview. Entrance: moderately difficult. Application deadline: 5/1. Notification: continuous.
Costs Per Year: Application fee: $50. State resident tuition: $3034 full-time, $277 per credit part-time. Nonresident tuition: $9820 full-time, $277 per credit part-time. Mandatory fees: $2930 full-time, $35 per term part-time. Full-time tuition and fees vary according to degree level. Part-time tuition and fees vary according to course load, degree level, and reciprocity agreements. College room and board: $7300. College room only: $4230. Room and board charges vary according to board plan and housing facility.
Collegiate Environment: Orientation program. Drama-theater group, choral group, student-run newspaper, radio station. Social organizations: 53 open to all. Most popular organizations: M.A.L.E.S, Organization of Latin American Students, 180 Christian Fellowship, A.L.A.Y.A.. Major annual events: Fall Fest, Spring Fest, Family Day. Student services: health clinic, personal-psychological counseling, women's center. Campus security: 24-hour emergency response devices and patrols, student patrols, late night transport-escort service, controlled dormitory access. 2,236 college housing spaces available; 2,168 were occupied in 2003-04. Freshmen guaranteed college housing. Options: coed, women-only housing available. J. Eugene Smith Library with 239,218 books, 1 million microform titles, 1,729 serials, 3,396 audiovisual materials, an OPAC, and a Web page. Operations spending for 2004 fiscal year: $3 million. 637 computers available on campus for general student use. A campuswide network can be accessed from student residence rooms and from off campus. Staffed computer lab on campus.
Community Environment: Located 28 miles from Hartford and New London and halfway between Boston and New York, Willimantic, with a population of approximately 22,000, is primarily a retail and service center for eastern Connecticut. Bus service connects the city with major transportation facilities in Hartford, Providence, and New York. Willimantic has excel-

lent health and hospital services and recreational facilities include the Willimantic Golf Course and nearby lakes and state parks.

■ FAIRFIELD UNIVERSITY *K-5*
1073 North Benson Rd.
Fairfield, CT 06824-5195
Tel: (203)254-4000
Admissions: (203)254-4100
Fax: (203)254-4199
E-mail: admis@mail.fairfield.edu
Web Site: http://www.fairfield.edu/

Description: Independent Roman Catholic (Jesuit), comprehensive, coed. Awards bachelor's and master's degrees and post-master's certificates. Founded 1942. Setting: 200-acre suburban campus with easy access to New York City. Endowment: $178.4 million. Research spending for 2004 fiscal year: $4.7 million. Educational spending for 2005 fiscal year: $9750 per student. Total enrollment: 5,173. Faculty: 423 (226 full-time, 197 part-time). Student-undergrad faculty ratio is 13:1. 6,895 applied, 74% were admitted. 31% from top 10% of their high school class, 69% from top quarter, 93% from top half. 16 National Merit Scholars, 20 class presidents, 6 valedictorians, 23 student government officers. Full-time: 3,485 students, 57% women, 43% men. Part-time: 588 students, 59% women, 41% men. Students come from 34 states and territories, 23 other countries, 74% from out-of-state, 0.2% Native American, 5% Hispanic, 2% black, 3% Asian American or Pacific Islander, 1% international, 0% 25 or older, 80% live on campus, 1% transferred in. Retention: 91% of full-time freshmen returned the following year. Academic areas with the most degrees conferred: business/marketing; social sciences; communications/journalism. Core. Calendar: semesters. Services for LD students, advanced placement, self-designed majors, honors program, independent study, double major, summer session for credit, part-time degree program, adult/continuing education programs, internships, graduate courses open to undergrads. Study abroad program. ROTC: Army (c).

Entrance Requirements: Options: Common Application, early admission, early decision, deferred admission. Required: essay, high school transcript, minimum 3.0 high school GPA, 1 recommendation, rank in upper 20% of high school class, SAT or ACT. Recommended: interview. Entrance: moderately difficult. Application deadlines: 1/15, 11/15 for early action. Notification: 4/1, 12/15 for early action.

Costs Per Year: Application fee: $55. Comprehensive fee: $39,855 includes full-time tuition ($29,750), mandatory fees ($505), and college room and board ($9600). College room only: $5560. Full-time tuition and fees vary according to student level. Room and board charges vary according to board plan and housing facility. Part-time tuition: $395 per credit. Part-time mandatory fees: $60 per term. Part-time tuition and fees vary according to course load and program.

Collegiate Environment: Orientation program. Drama-theater group, choral group, student-run newspaper, radio station. Social organizations: 100 open to all. Most popular organizations: student government, Glee Club, Drama Club, multicultural organizations, Mission Volunteers. Major annual events: Dogwood Festival, Harvest Weekend, Homecoming. Student services: health clinic, personal-psychological counseling, women's center. Campus security: 24-hour emergency response devices and patrols, late night transport-escort service, controlled dormitory access, bicycle patrols. 2,590 college housing spaces available; 2,585 were occupied in 2003-04. Freshmen guaranteed college housing. On-campus residence required through senior year. Option: coed housing available. Dimenna-Nyselius Library with 325,166 books, 888,554 microform titles, 1,793 serials, 9,615 audiovisual materials, an OPAC, and a Web page. Operations spending for 2004 fiscal year: $2.1 million. 150 computers available on campus for general student use. Computer purchase/lease plans available. A campuswide network can be accessed from student residence rooms and from off campus. Staffed computer lab on campus.

Community Environment: Population 60,000. Fairfield is a suburban area one hour north of New York City on the Long Island Sound. The climate is temperate. The Metro-North New Haven branch railroad serves the area, as well as the Connecticut Turnpike and Merritt Parkway. Community facilities include libraries, churches and shopping areas. Part-time employment opportunities are available. Beaches are nearby for water sports; other sports include golf and tennis. A special annual event is the Dogwood Festival.

■ GATEWAY COMMUNITY COLLEGE *I-8*
60 Sargent Dr.
New Haven, CT 06511-5918

Tel: (203)285-2000
Free: 800-390-7723
Admissions: (203)789-7043
Fax: (203)285-2018
Web Site: http://www.gwcc.commnet.edu/

Description: State-supported, 2-year, coed. Part of Connecticut Community College System. Awards certificates, transfer associate, and terminal associate degrees. Founded 1992. Setting: 5-acre urban campus with easy access to New York City. Educational spending for 2005 fiscal year: $3801 per student. Total enrollment: 5,739. Student-undergrad faculty ratio is 21:1. 3,381 applied, 94% were admitted. Full-time: 1,809 students, 57% women, 43% men. Part-time: 3,930 students, 67% women, 33% men. Students come from 8 states and territories, 60 other countries, 0.1% from out-of-state, 1% Native American, 13% Hispanic, 26% black, 3% Asian American or Pacific Islander, 1% international, 53% 25 or older, 7% transferred in. Core. Calendar: semesters. Academic remediation for entering students, ESL program, services for LD students, advanced placement, independent study, distance learning, summer session for credit, part-time degree program, external degree program, adult/continuing education programs, internships. Off campus study at Southern Connecticut State University.

Entrance Requirements: Open admission except for radiological technology, pharmacy technology, engineering technologies programs. Options: early admission, deferred admission. Required: high school transcript. Required for some: essay, interview. Entrance: noncompetitive. Application deadline: 9/1. Notification: continuous until 9/1.

Costs Per Year: Application fee: $20. State resident tuition: $2352 full-time, $98 per credit part-time. Nonresident tuition: $7056 full-time, $294 per credit part-time. Mandatory fees: $320 full-time.

Collegiate Environment: Campus security: late night transport-escort service. College housing not available. 54,802 books, 108,163 microform titles, 532 serials, 9,902 audiovisual materials, and an OPAC. Operations spending for 2004 fiscal year: $623,294. 385 computers available on campus for general student use. A campuswide network can be accessed from off-campus. Staffed computer lab on campus.

■ GIBBS COLLEGE *K-3*
142 East Ave.
Norwalk, CT 06851-5754
Tel: (203)838-4173
Free: 800-845-5333
Admissions: (203)633-2311
Fax: (203)853-6402
Web Site: http://www.gibbscollege.com/

Description: Proprietary, 2-year, coed. Part of Career Education Corporation. Awards certificates and terminal associate degrees. Founded 1975. Setting: 2-acre suburban campus with easy access to New York City. Total enrollment: 770. 1,460 applied, 61% were admitted. Full-time: 770 students, 52% women, 48% men. Students come from 15 states and territories, 1 other country, 2% from out-of-state, 0.3% Native American, 29% Hispanic, 32% black, 2% Asian American or Pacific Islander, 0.1% international, 45% 25 or older, 19% transferred in. Core. Academic remediation for entering students, accelerated degree program, adult/continuing education programs, co-op programs and internships.

Entrance Requirements: Options: Peterson's Universal Application, Common Application, electronic application, deferred admission. Required: high school transcript, interview. Recommended: essay. Entrance: minimally difficult. Application deadline: Rolling. Notification: continuous.

Collegiate Environment: Orientation program. Student services: personal-psychological counseling. Campus security: 24-hour emergency response devices. College housing not available. Sister Barbara Dewey Library with 10,000 books, 250 serials, 150 audiovisual materials, and an OPAC. 220 computers available on campus for general student use. A campuswide network can be accessed. Staffed computer lab on campus.

■ GOODWIN COLLEGE *D-10*
745 Burnside Ave.
East Hartford, CT 06108
Tel: (860)528-4111
Fax: (860)291-9550
E-mail: dnoonan@goodwincollege.edu
Web Site: http://www.goodwin.edu/

Description: Proprietary, 2-year, coed. Awards certificates, diplomas, transfer associate, and terminal associate degrees. Setting: urban campus with easy access to Hartford. Endowment: $1 million. Educational spending for 2005 fiscal year: $13,570 per student. Total enrollment: 1,219. Student-undergrad faculty ratio is 10:1. 360 applied, 90% were admitted. Full-time: 132 students, 86% women, 14% men. Part-time: 1,087 students, 90% women, 10% men. 1% from out-of-state, 0.4% Native American, 14% Hispanic, 30% black, 1% Asian American or Pacific Islander, 0% international, 59% 25 or older, 10% transferred in. Calendar: semesters. Academic remediation for entering students, ESL program, services for LD students, advanced placement, accelerated degree program, honors program, independent study, distance learning, double major, summer session for credit, part-time degree program, external degree program, adult/continuing education programs, co-op programs and internships. Off campus study.

Entrance Requirements: Open admission. Options: Common Application, electronic application, deferred admission, international baccalaureate accepted. Required: essay, high school transcript, minimum 2.0 high school GPA, medical exam. Recommended: 2 recommendations, interview. Entrance: minimally difficult. Notification: continuous until 8/1.

Costs Per Year: Application fee: $50. Tuition: $13,570 full-time, $425 per credit part-time. Mandatory fees: $300 full-time.

Collegiate Environment: Orientation program. Campus security: evening security patrolman. College housing not available. Goodwin College Library with 6,000 books, 1,300 serials, 506 audiovisual materials, and an OPAC. Operations spending for 2004 fiscal year: $320,000. 220 computers available on campus for general student use. A campuswide network can be accessed from off-campus. Staffed computer lab on campus.

■ **HOLY APOSTLES COLLEGE AND SEMINARY** *F-10*
33 Prospect Hill Rd.
Cromwell, CT 06416-2005
Tel: (860)632-3010
Free: 800-330-7272
Fax: (860)632-3030
Web Site: http://www.holyapostles.edu/
Description: Independent Roman Catholic, comprehensive, coed. Awards associate, bachelor's, master's, and first professional degrees and post-master's certificates. Founded 1956. Setting: 17-acre suburban campus with easy access to Hartford, CT New Haven, CT. Total enrollment: 294. Faculty: 24 (14 full-time, 10 part-time). Student-undergrad faculty ratio is 7:1. 1 applied, 100% were admitted. Full-time: 9 students, 33% women, 67% men. Part-time: 32 students, 25% women, 75% men. Students come from 3 states and territories, 2 other countries, 90% from out-of-state, 0% Native American, 9% Hispanic, 0% black, 9% Asian American or Pacific Islander, 9% international, 90% 25 or older, 80% live on campus, 12% transferred in. Retention: 50% of full-time freshmen returned the following year. Academic area with the most degrees conferred: social sciences. Core. Calendar: semesters. Academic remediation for entering students, ESL program, accelerated degree program, distance learning, part-time degree program, adult/continuing education programs, internships, graduate courses open to undergrads.

Entrance Requirements: Open admission. Options: Common Application, deferred admission. Required: high school transcript, interview, SAT. Required for some: recommendations. Entrance: noncompetitive. Application deadline: Rolling.

Costs Per Year: Application fee: $25. Tuition: $5520 full-time, $230 per credit part-time. Mandatory fees: $25 full-time.

Collegiate Environment: Orientation program. Student-run newspaper. Most popular organizations: Toastmasters, Pro-Life Organization, Student Council, Schola Choir. Major annual events: Christmas Party, Graduation, Spring Party. Student services: personal-psychological counseling. Campus security: 24-hour emergency response devices and patrols. 82 college housing spaces available; 6 were occupied in 2003-04. On-campus residence required through senior year. Option: men-only housing available. Holy Apostles College and Seminary Library with 84,584 books, 210 microform titles, 250 serials, 200 audiovisual materials, and an OPAC. 6 computers available on campus for general student use. Staffed computer lab on campus.

■ **HOUSATONIC COMMUNITY COLLEGE** *K-5*
900 Lafayette Blvd.
Bridgeport, CT 06604-4704
Tel: (203)332-5000
Admissions: (203)332-5102
Web Site: http://www.hctc.commnet.edu/
Description: State-supported, 2-year, coed. Part of Connecticut Community-Technical College System. Awards certificates, transfer associate, and

terminal associate degrees. Founded 1965. Setting: 4-acre urban campus with easy access to New York City. Total enrollment: 4,343. 2,252 applied, 89% were admitted. 0.2% Native American, 21% Hispanic, 30% black, 3% Asian American or Pacific Islander, 0% international, 46% 25 or older. Retention: 55% of full-time freshmen returned the following year. Core. Calendar: semesters. Academic remediation for entering students, ESL program, services for LD students, advanced placement, honors program, independent study, double major, summer session for credit, part-time degree program, adult/continuing education programs, co-op programs and internships. ROTC: Army (c).

Entrance Requirements: Open admission except for drug and alcohol rehabilitation counseling, medical laboratory technician, allied health, phlebotomy, nursing, physical therapy programs. Options: Common Application, deferred admission. Required: high school transcript. Required for some: recommendations, interview. Placement: ACCUPLACER required for some. Entrance: noncompetitive. Application deadline: Rolling.

Collegiate Environment: Student-run newspaper. Most popular organizations: Student Senate, Association of Latin American Students, African-American Cultural Society, Art Club. Major annual events: Spring Outing, Christmas Dinner, cultural jazz concerts. Student services: personal-psychological counseling. Campus security: 24-hour emergency response devices, late night transport-escort service. College housing not available. 30,000 books, 280 serials, an OPAC, and a Web page. 200 computers available on campus for general student use. A campuswide network can be accessed. Staffed computer lab on campus.

Community Environment: See University of Bridgeport.

■ **INTERNATIONAL COLLEGE OF HOSPITALITY MANAGEMENT** *B-10*
101 Wykeham Rd.
Suffield, CT 06078
Tel: (860)868-9555
Free: 800-955-0809
Admissions: (860)668-3515
Fax: (860)868-2114
E-mail: admissions@ichm.edu
Web Site: http://www.ichm.edu/
Description: Proprietary, 2-year, coed. Awards certificates, transfer associate, and terminal associate degrees. Founded 1992. Setting: 56-acre small town campus with easy access to New York City or Boston, MA. Educational spending for 2005 fiscal year: $2857 per student. Total enrollment: 116. 35 applied, 77% were admitted. Full-time: 116 students, 59% women, 41% men. Students come from 6 states and territories, 34 other countries, 50% from out-of-state, 0% Native American, 7% Hispanic, 6% black, 16% Asian American or Pacific Islander, 51% international, 14% 25 or older, 90% live on campus, 16% transferred in. Core. Calendar: continuous. Academic remediation for entering students, ESL program, services for LD students, advanced placement, accelerated degree program, independent study, distance learning, part-time degree program, adult/continuing education programs, co-op programs and internships. Study abroad program.

Entrance Requirements: Options: Common Application, electronic application, deferred admission. Required: high school transcript, 2 recommendations. Recommended: interview, SAT. Required for some: essay, interview. Entrance: minimally difficult. Application deadline: Rolling. Notification: continuous.

Costs Per Year: Application fee: $100. Comprehensive fee: $20,878 includes full-time tuition ($15,900) and college room and board ($4978). Room and board charges vary according to board plan.

Collegiate Environment: Orientation program. Student-run newspaper. Social organizations: 7 open to all; 100% of eligible men and 100% of eligible women are members. Most popular organizations: student committee, student newsletter, yearbook committee, Ritz Guild, Student Ambassadors. Major annual events: Career Day/Job Fair, formal theme banquets, college open houses. Student services: health clinic, personal-psychological counseling. Campus security: 24-hour emergency response devices, student patrols, late night transport-escort service, controlled dormitory access, weekend patrols by trained security personnel. Option: coed housing available. International College of Hospitality Management Library with 10,000 books, 50 serials, and an OPAC. Operations spending for 2004 fiscal year:

$44,000. 23 computers available on campus for general student use. A campuswide network can be accessed from off-campus. Staffed computer lab on campus.

■ LYME ACADEMY COLLEGE OF FINE ARTS *I-12*
84 Lyme St.
Old Lyme, CT 06371
Tel: (860)434-5232
Fax: (860)434-8725
Web Site: http://www.lymeacademy.edu/
Description: Independent, 4-year, coed. Awards bachelor's degrees. Founded 1976. Setting: 3-acre small town campus. Endowment: $2.4 million. Educational spending for 2005 fiscal year: $11,066 per student. Total enrollment: 160. 32 applied, 47% were admitted. Full-time: 71 students, 56% women, 44% men. Part-time: 89 students, 74% women, 26% men. Students come from 18 states and territories, 20% from out-of-state, 0% Native American, 5% Hispanic, 0% black, 0% Asian American or Pacific Islander, 0% international, 55% 25 or older, 35% transferred in. Retention: 48% of full-time freshmen returned the following year. Core. Calendar: semesters. Summer session for credit, part-time degree program. Off campus study.
Entrance Requirements: Options: electronic application, deferred admission. Required: essay, high school transcript, 2 recommendations, portfolio, SAT or ACT. Recommended: minimum 2.0 high school GPA, interview. Required for some: interview. Entrance: moderately difficult. Application deadline: Rolling.
Costs Per Year: Application fee: $35. Tuition: $16,416 full-time. Mandatory fees: $500 full-time.
Collegiate Environment: Orientation program. Student-run newspaper. Social organizations: 1 open to all. Most popular organization: Student Association. Major annual events: Small Wonders Art Show, Thanksgiving Feast, graduation. Student services: personal-psychological counseling. College housing not available. Krieble Library with 8,686 books, 60 serials, 14,232 audiovisual materials, an OPAC, and a Web page. Operations spending for 2004 fiscal year: $139,133. 6 computers available on campus for general student use. A campuswide network can be accessed.

■ MANCHESTER COMMUNITY COLLEGE *D-11*
PO Box 1046
Manchester, CT 06045-1046
Tel: (860)512-3000
Admissions: (860)512-3210
Fax: (860)647-6238
Web Site: http://www.mcc.commnet.edu/
Description: State-supported, 2-year, coed. Part of Connecticut Community College System. Awards certificates, transfer associate, and terminal associate degrees. Founded 1963. Setting: 160-acre small town campus with easy access to Hartford. Total enrollment: 6,135. Student-undergrad faculty ratio is 21:1. 2,016 applied, 100% were admitted. Full-time: 2,713 students, 51% women, 49% men. Part-time: 3,422 students, 60% women, 40% men. Students come from 5 states and territories, 0% from out-of-state, 0.2% Native American, 10% Hispanic, 12% black, 4% Asian American or Pacific Islander, 1% international, 35% 25 or older, 11% transferred in. Retention: 60% of full-time freshmen returned the following year. Core. Calendar: semesters. Academic remediation for entering students, ESL program, services for LD students, self-designed majors, independent study, distance learning, double major, summer session for credit, part-time degree program, adult/continuing education programs, co-op programs and internships. Off campus study at other institutions in the Connecticut Public Higher Education System.
Entrance Requirements: Open admission except for allied health programs. Options: electronic application, deferred admission. Required: high school transcript. Entrance: noncompetitive. Application deadline: Rolling. Notification: continuous.
Costs Per Year: Application fee: $20. State resident tuition: $2232 full-time, $93 per credit hour part-time. Nonresident tuition: $6696 full-time, $279 per credit hour part-time.
Collegiate Environment: Orientation program. Drama-theater group, choral group, student-run newspaper. Student services: women's center. College housing not available. 45,265 books, 188,155 microform titles, 493 serials, and 2,481 audiovisual materials.

■ MIDDLESEX COMMUNITY COLLEGE *G-10*
100 Training Hill Rd.
Middletown, CT 06457-4889

Tel: (860)343-5800
Admissions: (860)343-5742
Fax: (860)344-7488
E-mail: mshabazz@mxcc.commnet.edu
Web Site: http://www.mxcc.commnet.edu/
Description: State-supported, 2-year, coed. Part of Connecticut Community College System. Awards certificates, transfer associate, and terminal associate degrees. Founded 1966. Setting: 38-acre suburban campus with easy access to Hartford. Total enrollment: 2,286. Student-undergrad faculty ratio is 18:1. 671 applied, 100% were admitted. Full-time: 876 students, 57% women, 43% men. Part-time: 1,410 students, 71% women, 29% men. Students come from 4 states and territories, 1% from out-of-state, 0.1% Native American, 8% Hispanic, 7% black, 3% Asian American or Pacific Islander, 0.4% international, 64% 25 or older. Retention: 44% of full-time freshmen returned the following year. Core. Calendar: semesters. Academic remediation for entering students, ESL program, services for LD students, advanced placement, honors program, independent study, distance learning, double major, summer session for credit, part-time degree program, co-op programs and internships. Off campus study at other units of the Connecticut Community College System. ROTC: Army.
Entrance Requirements: Open admission except for radiological technology, human services, drug and alcohol counseling, broadcast journalism, ophthalmic design and dispensing programs. Options: early admission, deferred admission. Required: high school transcript, CPT. Entrance: noncompetitive. Application deadline: Rolling.
Costs Per Year: Application fee: $20. State resident tuition: $2232 full-time, $93 per credit part-time. Nonresident tuition: $6696 full-time, $279 per credit part-time. Mandatory fees: $304 full-time, $2.50 per credit part-time, $53 per term part-time.
Collegiate Environment: Orientation program. Social organizations: 8 open to all. Most popular organizations: Collegiate Secretaries International, Minority Opportunities in Education, Radio Club. Major annual events: International Day, bus trips, Senior Art Exhibit. Student services: personal-psychological counseling. Campus security: 24-hour patrols. College housing not available. Jean Burr Smith Library with 45,000 books, 180 serials, an OPAC, and a Web page. 50 computers available on campus for general student use. A campuswide network can be accessed from off-campus. Staffed computer lab on campus.

■ MITCHELL COLLEGE *I-14*
437 Pequot Ave.
New London, CT 06320-4498
Tel: (860)701-5000
Free: 800-443-2811
Admissions: (860)701-5038
Fax: (860)444-1209
Web Site: http://www.mitchell.edu/
Description: Independent, 4-year, coed. Awards associate and bachelor's degrees. Founded 1938. Setting: 67-acre suburban campus with easy access to Hartford and Providence. Endowment: $6 million. Educational spending for 2005 fiscal year: $3500 per student. Total enrollment: 727. Student-undergrad faculty ratio is 12:1. 1,158 applied, 58% were admitted. 3% from top 10% of their high school class, 9% from top quarter, 35% from top half. Full-time: 644 students, 49% women, 51% men. Part-time: 83 students, 64% women, 36% men. Students come from 22 states and territories, 5 other countries, 33% from out-of-state, 5% Native American, 7% Hispanic, 11% black, 0.3% Asian American or Pacific Islander, 1% international, 4% 25 or older, 80% live on campus, 5% transferred in. Academic areas with the most degrees conferred: business/marketing; psychology; liberal arts/general studies. Core. Calendar: semesters. ESL program, services for LD students, advanced placement, double major, summer session for credit, part-time degree program, adult/continuing education programs, co-op programs and internships.
Entrance Requirements: Options: Peterson's Universal Application, Common Application, electronic application, early admission, early decision, deferred admission. Required: essay, high school transcript, minimum 2.0 high school GPA, recommendations, SAT or ACT. Recommended: interview. Entrance: minimally difficult. Application deadlines: Rolling, 11/15 for early decision. Notification: continuous until 8/30, 12/15 for early decision.
Costs Per Year: Application fee: $30. Comprehensive fee: $28,735 includes full-time tuition ($19,405) and college room and board ($9330). College room only: $4850. Part-time tuition: $275 per credit hour. Part-time mandatory fees: $35 per term.
Collegiate Environment: Orientation program. Drama-theater group, choral group, student-run newspaper. Social organizations: 30 open to all. Most

popular organizations: Multicultural Club, Business Club, student government, student newspaper, Outdoor Adventure Club. Major annual events: Moving Up Ceremony, Homecoming/Parents' Weekend, Wellness Week. Student services: health clinic, personal-psychological counseling. Campus security: 24-hour emergency response devices and patrols, student patrols, late night transport-escort service, controlled dormitory access. 425 college housing spaces available; 372 were occupied in 2003-04. Freshmen guaranteed college housing. Options: coed, men-only, women-only housing available. Mitchell College Library plus 1 other with 80,000 books, 120 serials, 300 audiovisual materials, an OPAC, and a Web page. Operations spending for 2004 fiscal year: $950,000. 155 computers available on campus for general student use. Computer purchase/lease plans available. A campuswide network can be accessed from student residence rooms and from off campus. Staffed computer lab on campus.

Community Environment: Small city of 30,000. Southern Connecticut is one of the country's fastest-growing tourist attractions. Campus is located at the confluence of the Thames River and Long Island Sound. The college maintains its own beach and 26-acre wooded park.

■ **NAUGATUCK VALLEY COMMUNITY COLLEGE** *G-6*
750 Chase Parkway
Waterbury, CT 06708-3000
Tel: (203)575-8040
Admissions: (203)575-8016
Fax: (203)596-8766
E-mail: lsveda@nvcc.commnet.edu
Web Site: http://www.nvcc.commnet.edu/

Description: State-supported, 2-year, coed. Part of Connecticut Community-Technical College System. Awards certificates, transfer associate, and terminal associate degrees. Founded 1992. Setting: 110-acre urban campus. Total enrollment: 5,671. Student-undergrad faculty ratio is 5:1. 3,358 applied, 42% were admitted. Full-time: 2,215 students, 51% women, 49% men. Part-time: 3,456 students, 65% women, 35% men. 7% from out-of-state, 0.4% Native American, 11% Hispanic, 8% black, 3% Asian American or Pacific Islander, 0.4% international, 51% 25 or older, 0.1% transferred in. Core. Calendar: semesters. Academic remediation for entering students, ESL program, services for LD students, advanced placement, accelerated degree program, self-designed majors, independent study, summer session for credit, part-time degree program, external degree program, adult/continuing education programs, co-op programs and internships. Off campus study at other institutions in the Connecticut Public Higher Education System. Study abroad program.

Entrance Requirements: Open admission except for nursing, allied health, technician programs. Option: deferred admission. Required: high school transcript, ACCUPLACER. Required for some: interview. Entrance: noncompetitive. Application deadline: Rolling. Notification: continuous.

Costs Per Year: Application fee: $20. State resident tuition: $2672 full-time. Nonresident tuition: $7976 full-time.

Collegiate Environment: Orientation program. Drama-theater group, choral group, student-run newspaper. Social organizations: 35 open to all. Most popular organizations: Student Senate, Choral Society, Automotive Technician Club, Human Service Club, Legal Assistant Club. Major annual events: Awards Ceremony, Spring Picnic, Club Expo. Student services: health clinic, personal-psychological counseling. Campus security: 24-hour emergency response devices and patrols, late night transport-escort service, security escort service. College housing not available. Max R. Traurig Learning Resource Center with 35,000 books, 520 serials, an OPAC, and a Web page. Operations spending for 2004 fiscal year: $618,484. 450 computers available on campus for general student use. A campuswide network can be accessed. Staffed computer lab on campus.

Community Environment: See Teikyo Post University.

■ **NORTHWESTERN CONNECTICUT COMMUNITY COLLEGE** *B-6*
Park Place East
Winsted, CT 06098-1798
Tel: (860)738-6300
Admissions: (860)738-6329
Fax: (860)379-4465
Web Site: http://www.nwctc.commnet.edu/

Description: State-supported, 2-year, coed. Part of Connecticut Community-Technical College System. Awards certificates, transfer associate, and terminal associate degrees. Founded 1965. Setting: 5-acre small town campus with easy access to Hartford. Total enrollment: 1,569. Student-undergrad faculty ratio is 16:1. 390 applied, 100% were admitted. Full-time:

527 students, 60% women, 40% men. Part-time: 1,042 students, 72% women, 28% men. Students come from 6 states and territories, 1% from out-of-state, 0.3% Native American, 3% Hispanic, 2% black, 2% Asian American or Pacific Islander, 0.1% international, 36% 25 or older, 6% transferred in. Retention: 56% of full-time freshmen returned the following year. Core. Calendar: semesters. Academic remediation for entering students, ESL program, services for LD students, advanced placement, independent study, distance learning, double major, summer session for credit, part-time degree program, adult/continuing education programs, co-op programs and internships.

Entrance Requirements: Open admission except for physical therapy assistant, drug and alcohol counseling programs. Option: deferred admission. Entrance: noncompetitive. Application deadline: Rolling. Notification: continuous.

Costs Per Year: Application fee: $20. State resident tuition: $2672 full-time, $156 per semester hour part-time. Nonresident tuition: $7976 full-time, $458 per semester hour part-time.

Collegiate Environment: Student-run newspaper. Social organizations: 10 open to all. Most popular organizations: Ski Club, Student Senate, Deaf Club, Recreation Club, Early Childhood Educational Club. Campus security: evening security patrols. College housing not available. Northwestern Connecticut Community-Technical College Learning Center with 37,666 books, 2,848 microform titles, 267 serials, 1,599 audiovisual materials, and an OPAC. 90 computers available on campus for general student use. A campuswide network can be accessed from off-campus. Staffed computer lab on campus.

Community Environment: Population 11,500. Winsted is a suburban community with a temperate climate. It has shopping areas, library, churches, and a YMCA. Airport facilities are 30 miles away, but easy to reach. Recreational facilities are good, including excellent fishing in surrounding areas, boating on Highland Lake, and winter sports at Sundown ski area about three miles southeast.

■ **NORWALK COMMUNITY COLLEGE** *K-3*
188 Richards Ave.
Norwalk, CT 06854-1655
Tel: (203)857-7000
Admissions: (203)857-7060
Fax: (203)857-3335
Web Site: http://www.ncc.commnet.edu/

Description: State-supported, 2-year, coed. Part of Connecticut Community College System. Awards certificates, transfer associate, and terminal associate degrees. Founded 1961. Setting: 30-acre suburban campus with easy access to New York City. Endowment: $11 million. Educational spending for 2005 fiscal year: $5650 per student. Total enrollment: 6,036. Student-undergrad faculty ratio is 20:1. 3,391 applied. Students come from 4 states and territories, 30 other countries, 1% from out-of-state, 0.2% Native American, 19% Hispanic, 19% black, 5% Asian American or Pacific Islander, 0% international, 51% 25 or older. Core. Calendar: semesters. Academic remediation for entering students, ESL program, services for LD students, advanced placement, freshman honors college, honors program, independent study, distance learning, summer session for credit, part-time degree program, adult/continuing education programs, co-op programs and internships.

Entrance Requirements: Open admission except for allied health programs. Option: deferred admission. Required: high school transcript. Entrance: noncompetitive. Application deadline: Rolling. Notification: continuous.

Costs Per Year: Application fee: $20. State resident tuition: $2352 full-time, $98 per credit part-time. Nonresident tuition: $7056 full-time, $294 per credit part-time. Mandatory fees: $320 full-time, $20 per credit part-time, $160 per term part-time.

Collegiate Environment: Orientation program. Drama-theater group, choral group, student-run newspaper. Social organizations: 27 open to all; coed fraternity; 1% of eligible men and 1% of eligible women are members. Most popular organizations: African Culture Club, Archaeology Club, Hay Motivo Club, Art Club, Phi Theta Kappa. Major annual events: Awards Ceremony, Dean's Tea, Welcome Picnic. Student services: women's center. Campus security: 24-hour emergency response devices and patrols, student patrols, late night transport-escort service, patrols by security. College housing not available. Everett I. L. Baker Library with 66,080 books, 73,135 microform titles, 221 serials, 2,988 audiovisual materials, an OPAC, and a Web page. Operations spending for 2004 fiscal year: $742,222. 500 computers available on campus for general student use. A campuswide network can be accessed from off-campus. Staffed computer lab on campus.

Community Environment: Norwalk is a urban community located on Long Island Sound and is 50 minutes by rail from Grand Central Station in New York City. Community facilities include major shopping areas, libraries, churches, a symphony orchestra, and the Silvermine Guild Artists.

■ **PAIER COLLEGE OF ART, INC.** *H-8*

20 Gorham Ave.

Hamden, CT 06514-3902

Tel: (203)287-3030

Admissions: (203)287-3031

Web Site: http://www.paiercollegeofart.edu/

Description: Proprietary, 4-year, coed. Awards associate and bachelor's degrees. Founded 1946. Setting: 3-acre suburban campus with easy access to New York City. Total enrollment: 277. Student-undergrad faculty ratio is 7:1. 86 applied, 91% were admitted. 5% from top 10% of their high school class, 18% from top quarter, 24% from top half. Students come from 4 states and territories, 1 other country, 1% from out-of-state, 0% Native American, 1% Hispanic, 2% black, 0.4% Asian American or Pacific Islander, 0.4% international, 18% 25 or older. Retention: 79% of full-time freshmen returned the following year. Core. Calendar: semesters plus 1 summer session. Academic remediation for entering students, services for LD students, advanced placement, independent study, summer session for credit, part-time degree program. Study abroad program.

Entrance Requirements: Options: Peterson's Universal Application, deferred admission, international baccalaureate accepted. Required: high school transcript, minimum 2.0 high school GPA, 2 recommendations, interview, portfolio, SAT or ACT. Recommended: essay. Entrance: minimally difficult. Application deadline: Rolling. Notification: continuous.

Costs Per Year: Application fee: $25. Tuition: $12,000 full-time, $380 per credit part-time. Mandatory fees: $320 full-time.

Collegiate Environment: Orientation program. Social organizations: 1 open to all. Most popular organization: Student Council. Major annual events: Winter Art Show and Sale, Spring Art Show and Sale, Spring Paier Picnic. Student services: personal-psychological counseling. Campus security: evening patrols by security. College housing not available. Adele K. Paier Memorial Library with 11,515 books, 69 serials, and 66,136 audiovisual materials. Operations spending for 2004 fiscal year: $52,330. 30 computers available on campus for general student use. Staffed computer lab on campus.

■ **POST UNIVERSITY** *G-6*

800 Country Club Rd.

Waterbury, CT 06723-2540

Tel: (203)596-4500

Free: 800-345-2562

Admissions: (203)596-4630

Fax: (203)756-5810

E-mail: _dmiciotta@post.edu

Web Site: http://www.post.edu

Description: Independent, 4-year, coed. Awards associate and bachelor's degrees. Founded 1890. Setting: 70-acre suburban campus with easy access to Hartford. Educational spending for 2005 fiscal year: $4356 per student. Total enrollment: 1,101. Student-undergrad faculty ratio is 13:1. 1,254 applied, 62% were admitted. Full-time: 664 students, 55% women, 45% men. Part-time: 437 students, 69% women, 31% men. Students come from 13 states and territories, 15 other countries, 21% from out-of-state, 0.3% Native American, 10% Hispanic, 22% black, 2% Asian American or Pacific Islander, 3% international, 43% 25 or older, 54% live on campus, 7% transferred in. Retention: 74% of full-time freshmen returned the following year. Academic areas with the most degrees conferred: business/marketing; liberal arts/general studies; biological/life sciences. Core. Calendar: semesters (modular courses offered in the evening). Academic remediation for entering students, ESL program, services for LD students, advanced placement, accelerated degree program, independent study, distance learning, double major, summer session for credit, part-time degree program, adult/continuing education programs, co-op programs and internships. Study abroad program.

Entrance Requirements: Options: Peterson's Universal Application, Common Application, electronic application, deferred admission, international baccalaureate accepted. Required: high school transcript, 1 recommendation. Recommended: essay, minimum 2.0 high school GPA, interview, SAT or ACT. Entrance: minimally difficult. Application deadline: Rolling. Notification: continuous.

Costs Per Year: Application fee: $40. Comprehensive fee: $29,900 includes full-time tuition ($20,750), mandatory fees ($750), and college room and board ($8400). Part-time tuition: $690 per credit.

Collegiate Environment: Orientation program. Choral group. Social organizations: 30 open to all. Most popular organizations: Post Theatrical Players, Resident Hall Council, Student Government Association, Program Board. Major annual events: homecoming, Sepring Semi-Formal, Winterfest. Student services: health clinic, personal-psychological counseling. Campus security: 24-hour emergency response devices and patrols, late night transport-escort service, controlled dormitory access. 410 college housing spaces available; 372 were occupied in 2003-04. Freshmen guaranteed college housing. On-campus residence required in freshman year. Option: coed housing available. Trauriq Library and Resource Center with 85,000 books, 75,158 microform titles, 500 serials, 1,027 audiovisual materials, and an OPAC. Operations spending for 2004 fiscal year: $208,143. 70 computers available on campus for general student use. A campuswide network can be accessed from student residence rooms and from off campus. Staffed computer lab on campus.

Community Environment: Waterbury is a city of approximately 110,000, located in the northwest part of the state. There are three other colleges in the area and 15 other institutions of higher learning within a 30-minute drive. The Greater Waterbury area offers ample opportunities for cultural, athletic, and recreational activities.

■ **QUINEBAUG VALLEY COMMUNITY COLLEGE** *D-16*

742 Upper Maple St.

Danielson, CT 06239-1440

Tel: (860)774-1130

Fax: (860)774-7768

E-mail: tmoumouris@qvcc.commnet.edu

Web Site: http://www.qvcc.commnet.edu/

Description: State-supported, 2-year, coed. Part of Connecticut Community College System. Awards certificates, transfer associate, and terminal associate degrees. Founded 1971. Setting: 60-acre rural campus. Total enrollment: 1,714. Student-undergrad faculty ratio is 18:1. 586 applied, 98% were admitted. Full-time: 643 students, 60% women, 40% men. Part-time: 1,071 students, 72% women, 28% men. Students come from 3 states and territories, 1% from out-of-state, 1% Native American, 10% Hispanic, 2% black, 1% Asian American or Pacific Islander, 0% international, 60% 25 or older, 9% transferred in. Core. Calendar: semesters. Academic remediation for entering students, ESL program, services for LD students, advanced placement, distance learning, summer session for credit, part-time degree program, external degree program, adult/continuing education programs, internships.

Entrance Requirements: Open admission. Options: Common Application, electronic application, early admission, deferred admission. Recommended: high school transcript. Required for some: high school transcript. Entrance: noncompetitive. Application deadline: 9/1. Notification: continuous until 9/1.

Costs Per Year: Application fee: $20. State resident tuition: $2112 full-time. Nonresident tuition: $6336 full-time. Mandatory fees: $294 full-time. Full-time tuition and fees vary according to reciprocity agreements.

Collegiate Environment: Orientation program. Campus security: evening security guard. College housing not available. Audrey Beck Library with 31,000 books, 130 serials, and an OPAC. 80 computers available on campus for general student use. A campuswide network can be accessed. Staffed computer lab on campus.

Community Environment: Population, 4,580. Located in Northeastern Connecticut, Danielson is in the midst of a semi-rural area which is supported by poultry and dairy industries. Outdoor recreational possibilities abound. The Connecticut turnpike provides easy access to New London, Old Mystic, Massachusetts and Rhode Island.

■ **QUINNIPIAC UNIVERSITY** *H-8*

275 Mount Carmel Ave.

Hamden, CT 06518-1940

Tel: (203)582-8200

Free: 800-462-1944

Admissions: (203)582-8600

Fax: (203)582-6347

E-mail: admissions@quinnipiac.edu

Web Site: http://www.quinnipiac.edu/

Description: Independent, comprehensive, coed. Awards bachelor's, master's, doctoral, and first professional degrees. Founded 1929. Setting: 400-acre suburban campus with easy access to Hartford. Endowment:

$150.2 million. Research spending for 2004 fiscal year: $524,194. Educational spending for 2005 fiscal year: $8474 per student. Total enrollment: 7,293. Faculty: 780 (280 full-time, 500 part-time). Student-undergrad faculty ratio is 15:1. 11,397 applied, 53% were admitted. 21% from top 10% of their high school class, 56% from top quarter, 90% from top half. Full-time: 5,286 students, 61% women, 39% men. Part-time: 420 students, 62% women, 38% men. Students come from 28 states and territories, 20 other countries, 72% from out-of-state, 0.1% Native American, 4% Hispanic, 2% black, 2% Asian American or Pacific Islander, 1% international, 5% 25 or older, 70% live on campus, 3% transferred in. Retention: 87% of full-time freshmen returned the following year. Academic areas with the most degrees conferred: business/marketing; health professions and related sciences; communications/journalism. Core. Calendar: semesters. Services for LD students, advanced placement, self-designed majors, honors program, independent study, distance learning, double major, summer session for credit, part-time degree program, adult/continuing education programs, internships, graduate courses open to undergrads. Study abroad program. ROTC: Army (c), Air Force (c).

Entrance Requirements: Options: Peterson's Universal Application, Common Application, electronic application, deferred admission, international baccalaureate accepted. Required: essay, high school transcript, 1 recommendation, SAT or ACT. Recommended: interview. Required for some: minimum 3.0 high school GPA. Entrance: moderately difficult. Application deadline: 2/1. Notification: continuous until 3/1.

Costs Per Year: Application fee: $45. Comprehensive fee: $36,980 includes full-time tuition ($25,240), mandatory fees ($1040), and college room and board ($10,700). Part-time tuition: $625 per credit. Part-time mandatory fees: $30 per credit.

Collegiate Environment: Orientation program. Drama-theater group, choral group, student-run newspaper, radio station. Social organizations: 75 open to all; national fraternities, national sororities, local sororities; 5% of eligible men and 7% of eligible women are members. Most popular organizations: student government, Social Programming Board, Drama Club, student newspaper, dance company. Major annual events: May Weekend, Student/Faculty Holiday Dinner, Midnight Madness (basketball). Student services: health clinic, personal-psychological counseling. Campus security: 24-hour emergency response devices and patrols, late night transport-escort service, controlled dormitory access. 3,250 college housing spaces available; all were occupied in 2003-04. Freshmen guaranteed college housing. Option: coed housing available. Arnold Bernhard Library plus 1 other with 285,000 books, 4,400 serials, an OPAC, and a Web page. Operations spending for 2004 fiscal year: $4.3 million. 600 computers available on campus for general student use. Computer purchase/lease plans available. A campuswide network can be accessed from student residence rooms and from off campus. Staffed computer lab on campus.

Community Environment: Hamden, population 55,000. Sleeping Giant Mountain State Park is adjacent to the campus and has 1700 acres for walking and hiking.

■ **SACRED HEART UNIVERSITY** *K-5*
5151 Park Ave.
Fairfield, CT 06825-1000
Tel: (203)371-7999
Admissions: (203)365-4763
Fax: (203)371-7889
E-mail: enroll@sacredheart.edu
Web Site: http://www.sacredheart.edu/

Description: Independent Roman Catholic, comprehensive, coed. Awards associate, bachelor's, master's, and doctoral degrees and post-master's certificates (also offers part-time program with significant enrollment not reflected in profile). Founded 1963. Setting: 56-acre suburban campus with easy access to New York City. Endowment: $42.3 million. Educational spending for 2005 fiscal year: $6786 per student. Total enrollment: 5,560. Faculty: 472 (186 full-time, 286 part-time). Student-undergrad faculty ratio is 13:1. 5,856 applied, 64% were admitted. 8% from top 10% of their high school class, 37% from top quarter, 91% from top half. 11 valedictorians. Full-time: 3,244 students, 60% women, 40% men. Part-time: 860 students, 68% women, 32% men. Students come from 37 other countries, 56% from out-of-state, 0.2% Native American, 6% Hispanic, 5% black, 1% Asian American or Pacific Islander, 1% international, 19% 25 or older, 68% live on campus, 2% transferred in. Retention: 85% of full-time freshmen returned the following year. Academic areas with the most degrees conferred: business/marketing; psychology; health professions and related sciences. Core. Calendar: semesters. Academic remediation for entering students,

ESL program, services for LD students, advanced placement, accelerated degree program, self-designed majors, honors program, independent study, distance learning, double major, summer session for credit, part-time degree program, adult/continuing education programs, co-op programs and internships, graduate courses open to undergrads. Off campus study. Study abroad program. ROTC: Army.

Entrance Requirements: Options: Peterson's Universal Application, Common Application, electronic application, early admission, early decision, deferred admission, international baccalaureate accepted. Required: essay, high school transcript, minimum 3.0 high school GPA, 1 recommendation, SAT or ACT. Recommended: minimum 3.2 high school GPA. Required for some: interview. Entrance: moderately difficult. Application deadlines: 10/1 for early decision plan 1, 12/1 for early decision plan 2. Notification: continuous, 10/15 for early decision plan 1, 12/15 for early decision plan 2.

Costs Per Year: Application fee: $50. Comprehensive fee: $33,404 includes full-time tuition ($23,750) and college room and board ($9654). College room only: $7078. Full-time tuition varies according to program. Room and board charges vary according to board plan and housing facility. Part-time tuition: $390 per credit. Part-time mandatory fees: $76 per term. Part-time tuition and fees vary according to program.

Collegiate Environment: Orientation program. Drama-theater group, choral group, marching band, student-run newspaper, radio station. Social organizations: 60 open to all; local fraternities, local sororities; 5% of eligible men and 7% of eligible women are members. Most popular organizations: Student Government Association, marching/pep band, Campus Ministry, Multicultural/International Club. Major annual events: Midnight Breakfast, SHU-Vivor, SHU-Idol. Student services: health clinic, personal-psychological counseling, women's center. Campus security: 24-hour emergency response devices and patrols, late night transport-escort service, controlled dormitory access, campus housing has sprinklers and fire alarms. 2,228 college housing spaces available; 2,115 were occupied in 2003-04. Freshmen guaranteed college housing. Option: coed housing available. Ryan-Matura Library with 46,985 microform titles, 4,100 serials, 1,063 audiovisual materials, an OPAC, and a Web page. Operations spending for 2004 fiscal year: $1.2 million. 330 computers available on campus for general student use. Computer purchase/lease plans available. A campuswide network can be accessed from student residence rooms and from off campus. Staffed computer lab on campus.

Community Environment: Sacred Heart University is located in coastal Fairfield, Connecticut, one hour northeast of New York City. Numerous Fortune 500 companies are headquartered in Fairfield County providing students with unique opportunities for outside learning and hands-on experience. Transportation, restaurants, shopping malls, movies, theaters, and beaches are all easily accessible.

■ **SAINT JOSEPH COLLEGE** *D-9*
1678 Asylum Ave.
West Hartford, CT 06117-2700
Tel: (860)232-4571; (866)442-8752
Admissions: (860)231-5216
Fax: (860)233-5695
E-mail: admissions@sjc.edu
Web Site: http://www.sjc.edu/

Description: Independent Roman Catholic, comprehensive. Awards bachelor's and master's degrees. Founded 1932. Setting: 84-acre suburban campus with easy access to Hartford. Endowment: $14.8 million. Research spending for 2004 fiscal year: $125,000. Educational spending for 2005 fiscal year: $8027 per student. Total enrollment: 1,858. Faculty: 88 (77 full-time, 11 part-time). Student-undergrad faculty ratio is 11:1. 1,051 applied, 72% were admitted. 15% from top 10% of their high school class, 43% from top quarter, 78% from top half. Full-time: 871 students, 99% women, 0.2% men. Part-time: 288 students, 97% women, 3% men. Students come from 6 states and territories, 1 other country, 20% from out-of-state, 0.2% Native American, 8% Hispanic, 14% black, 2% Asian American or Pacific Islander, 0.1% international, 32% 25 or older, 21% transferred in. Retention: 68% of full-time freshmen returned the following year. Academic areas with the most degrees conferred: health professions and related sciences; social sciences; public administration and social services. Core. Calendar: semesters. Academic remediation for entering students, ESL program, services for LD students, advanced placement, accelerated degree program, self-designed majors, honors program, distance learning, double major, summer session for credit, part-time degree program, adult/continuing education programs, internships, graduate courses open to undergrads. Off campus study at members of the Hartford Consortium for Higher Education, Wesleyan University. Study abroad program.

Entrance Requirements: Options: Peterson's Universal Application, electronic application, early admission, early action, deferred admission. Required: essay, high school transcript, SAT or ACT. Recommended: interview. Entrance: moderately difficult. Application deadlines: Rolling, 11/15 for early action. Notification: continuous, 12/15 for early action.

Costs Per Year: Application fee: $35. Comprehensive fee: $33,250 includes full-time tuition ($22,890), mandatory fees ($600), and college room and board ($9760). College room only: $4780. Part-time tuition: $530 per credit. Part-time mandatory fees: $25 per credit.

Collegiate Environment: Orientation program. Drama-theater group, choral group. Social organizations: 24 open to all; 30% of women are members. Most popular organizations: Student Government Association, Student Nurse Association, Psychology Club, SJC choir, Business Society. Major annual events: Convocation, Diversity Day, Student Symposium. Student services: health clinic, personal-psychological counseling. Campus security: 24-hour emergency response devices and patrols, late night transport-escort service, controlled dormitory access. 428 college housing spaces available; 391 were occupied in 2003-04. Freshmen guaranteed college housing. Option: women-only housing available. Pope Pius XII Library plus 1 other with 120,094 books, 77,096 microform titles, 479 serials, 3,627 audiovisual materials, an OPAC, and a Web page. Operations spending for 2004 fiscal year: $686,672. 150 computers available on campus for general student use. A campuswide network can be accessed from student residence rooms and from off campus. Staffed computer lab on campus.

Community Environment: The campus is located in a suburban community within 5 miles of Hartford, the capital of Connecticut. Known as the Insurance City, Hartford offers multiple internship and employment possibilities and diverse attractions such as ballet, opera, theater, symphony, museums, historic landmarks, sporting events, shopping, churches, and hospitals. Many volunteer opportunities are also available.

■ **ST. VINCENT'S COLLEGE** *K-5*
2800 Main St.
Bridgeport, CT 06606-4292
Tel: (203)576-5235
Admissions: (203)576-5515
E-mail: jmarrone@stvincentscollege.edu
Web Site: http://www.stvincentscollege.edu/

Description: Independent, 2-year, coed, affiliated with Roman Catholic Church. Awards certificates and transfer associate degrees. Founded 1991. Setting: urban campus with easy access to New York City. Total enrollment: 413. 661 applied, 28% were admitted. 64% 25 or older. Core. Calendar: semesters. Academic remediation for entering students, advanced placement, summer session for credit, part-time degree program.

Entrance Requirements: Option: deferred admission. Required: essay, high school transcript, recommendations. Recommended: minimum 3.0 high school GPA. Required for some: interview. Placement: SAT or ACT required for some. Entrance: moderately difficult. Application deadline: Rolling.

Collegiate Environment: Orientation program. Choral group, student-run newspaper. Social organizations: 6 open to all. Most popular organizations: community service, Student Congress, Mentors, yearbook, Heartbeat. Major annual events: beginning of the year Liturgy, Day of Reflection, Awards Banquet. Student services: health clinic, personal-psychological counseling. Campus security: 24-hour patrols, late night transport-escort service. College housing not available. Daniel T. Banks Health Science Library with 9,428 books and 332 serials. 17 computers available on campus for general student use. Staffed computer lab on campus.

■ **SOUTHERN CONNECTICUT STATE UNIVERSITY** *I-8*
501 Crescent St.
New Haven, CT 06515-1355
Tel: (203)392-5200
Admissions: (203)392-5656
Fax: (203)392-5727
Web Site: http://www.southernct.edu/

Description: State-supported, comprehensive, coed. Part of Connecticut State University System. Awards bachelor's, master's, and doctoral degrees and post-master's certificates. Founded 1893. Setting: 168-acre urban campus with easy access to New York City. Endowment: $6.9 million. Research spending for 2004 fiscal year: $1.9 million. Educational spending for 2005 fiscal year: $5809 per student. Total enrollment: 12,158. Faculty: 958 (403 full-time, 555 part-time). Student-undergrad faculty ratio is 17:1. 5,037 applied, 54% were admitted. 6% from top 10% of their high school class, 22% from top quarter, 64% from top half. Full-time: 6,697 students,

63% women, 37% men. Part-time: 1,612 students, 59% women, 41% men. Students come from 34 states and territories, 46 other countries, 6% from out-of-state, 0.4% Native American, 7% Hispanic, 12% black, 2% Asian American or Pacific Islander, 1% international, 17% 25 or older, 33% live on campus, 11% transferred in. Retention: 75% of full-time freshmen returned the following year. Academic areas with the most degrees conferred: psychology; business/marketing; education. Core. Calendar: semesters. Academic remediation for entering students, services for LD students, advanced placement, accelerated degree program, self-designed majors, freshman honors college, honors program, independent study, distance learning, double major, summer session for credit, part-time degree program, adult/continuing education programs, co-op programs and internships, graduate courses open to undergrads. Off campus study at New England Board of Higher Education. Study abroad program. ROTC: Army (c), Air Force (c).

Entrance Requirements: Options: Peterson's Universal Application, Common Application, electronic application, deferred admission, international baccalaureate accepted. Required: essay, high school transcript, SAT or ACT. Recommended: recommendations. Entrance: moderately difficult. Application deadline: 7/1. Notification: continuous.

Costs Per Year: Application fee: $50. State resident tuition: $3187 full-time, $322 per credit part-time. Nonresident tuition: $10,315 full-time, $322 per credit part-time. Mandatory fees: $3255 full-time, $8 per credit part-time, $55 per term part-time. College room and board: $8031. College room only: $4446.

Collegiate Environment: Orientation program. Drama-theater group, choral group, marching band, student-run newspaper, radio station. Social organizations: 63 open to all; national fraternities, national sororities, local sororities; 1% of eligible men and 1% of eligible women are members. Most popular organizations: People to People, Pre-Law Society, Accounting Society, Crescent Players, Black Student Union. Major annual events: Spring Weekend, Homecoming, Convocation. Student services: health clinic, personal-psychological counseling, women's center. Campus security: 24-hour emergency response devices and patrols, late night transport-escort service, controlled dormitory access. 2,605 college housing spaces available; all were occupied in 2003-04. Freshmen guaranteed college housing. Option: coed housing available. Hilton C. Buley Library with 495,660 books, 3,549 serials, an OPAC, and a Web page. Operations spending for 2004 fiscal year: $5 million. 750 computers available on campus for general student use. Computer purchase/lease plans available. A campuswide network can be accessed from student residence rooms and from off campus. Staffed computer lab on campus.

Community Environment: Metropolitan.

■ **THREE RIVERS COMMUNITY COLLEGE** *G-14*
7 Mahan Dr.
Norwich, CT 06360
Tel: (860)886-0177
Admissions: (860)892-5762
Fax: (860)886-0691
E-mail: info3rivers@trcc.commnet.edu
Web Site: http://www.trcc.commnet.edu/

Description: State-supported, 2-year, coed. Part of Connecticut Community-Technical College System. Awards certificates, transfer associate, and terminal associate degrees (engineering technology programs are offered on the Thames Valley Campus; liberal arts, transfer and career programs are offered on the Mohegan Campus). Founded 1963. Setting: 40-acre small town campus with easy access to Hartford. Educational spending for 2005 fiscal year: $4382 per student. Total enrollment: 3,624. Students come from 6 states and territories, 1% from out-of-state, 2% Native American, 5% Hispanic, 7% black, 2% Asian American or Pacific Islander, 0.4% international, 63% 25 or older. Core. Calendar: semesters. Academic remediation for entering students, ESL program, services for LD students, advanced placement, self-designed majors, independent study, double major, summer session for credit, part-time degree program, external degree program, adult/continuing education programs, co-op programs and internships. Study abroad program.

Entrance Requirements: Open admission except for nursing, drug and alcohol rehabilitation counseling, paramedic programs. Options: early admission, deferred admission. Recommended: high school transcript. Required for some: minimum 3.0 high school GPA. Placement: ACCUPLACER required. Entrance: noncompetitive. Application deadline: Rolling. Notification: continuous.

Costs Per Year: Application fee: $20. State resident tuition: $2232 full-time,

$93 per semester hour part-time. Nonresident tuition: $7264 full-time, $279 per semester hour part-time. Mandatory fees: $304 full-time.

Collegiate Environment: Orientation program. Drama-theater group, student-run newspaper. Social organizations: 20 open to all; national fraternities. Most popular organizations: Student Senate/Student Government Association, Theater Guild, Phi Theta Kappa, Student Nurses Association, African-American Organization. Major annual events: Student Picnic, Awards Ceremony, Commencement. Student services: personal-psychological counseling. Campus security: late night transport-escort service, 14 hour patrols by trained security personnel. College housing not available. Three Rivers Community College Learning Resource Center plus 2 others with 53,768 books, 549 serials, and an OPAC. Operations spending for 2004 fiscal year: $513,909. 350 computers available on campus for general student use. A campuswide network can be accessed. Staffed computer lab on campus.

■ **TRINITY COLLEGE** *D-10*
300 Summit St.
Hartford, CT 06106-3100
Tel: (860)297-2000
Admissions: (860)297-2180
Fax: (860)297-2287
E-mail: admissions.office@mail.trincoll.edu
Web Site: http://www.trincoll.edu/

Description: Independent, comprehensive, coed. Awards bachelor's and master's degrees. Founded 1823. Setting: 100-acre urban campus. Endowment: $340.4 million. Research spending for 2004 fiscal year: $1.2 million. Educational spending for 2005 fiscal year: $20,783 per student. Total enrollment: 2,526. Faculty: 258 (183 full-time, 75 part-time). Student-undergrad faculty ratio is 10:1. 5,744 applied, 39% were admitted. 53% from top 10% of their high school class, 89% from top quarter, 99% from top half. Full-time: 2,165 students, 50% women, 50% men. Part-time: 178 students, 59% women, 41% men. Students come from 44 states and territories, 28 other countries, 80% from out-of-state, 0.1% Native American, 5% Hispanic, 5% black, 6% Asian American or Pacific Islander, 2% international, 0% 25 or older, 96% live on campus, 0.3% transferred in. Retention: 92% of full-time freshmen returned the following year. Academic areas with the most degrees conferred: social sciences; English; visual and performing arts. Calendar: semesters. Advanced placement, accelerated degree program, self-designed majors, honors program, independent study, double major, summer session for credit, adult/continuing education programs, internships, graduate courses open to undergrads. Off campus study at members of the Twelve College Exchange Program, Hartford Consortium for Higher Education. Study abroad program. ROTC: Army (c).

Entrance Requirements: Options: Peterson's Universal Application, Common Application, electronic application, early admission, early decision, deferred admission, international baccalaureate accepted. Required: essay, high school transcript, 3 recommendations, ACT or SAT and SAT Writing Test or three SAT subject tests. Recommended: interview. Entrance: very difficult. Application deadlines: 1/1, 11/15 for early decision plan 1, 1/1 for early decision plan 2. Notification: 4/1, 12/15 for early decision plan 1, 2/15 for early decision plan 2.

Costs Per Year: Application fee: $60. Comprehensive fee: $42,220 includes full-time tuition ($32,000), mandatory fees ($1630), and college room and board ($8590). College room only: $5550. Full-time tuition and fees vary according to program. Room and board charges vary according to board plan. Part-time tuition: $1185 per credit hour. Part-time tuition varies according to program.

Collegiate Environment: Orientation program. Drama-theater group, choral group, student-run newspaper, radio station. Social organizations: 112 open to all; national fraternities, national sororities, local fraternities, local sororities, coed fraternities; 20% of eligible men and 16% of eligible women are members. Most popular organizations: Community Outreach, Habitat for Humanity, Activities Council, student government, Multi-Cultural Affairs Committee. Major annual events: Spring Weekend, Homecoming. Student services: health clinic, personal-psychological counseling, women's center. Campus security: 24-hour emergency response devices and patrols, late night transport-escort service, controlled dormitory access. 1,861 college housing spaces available; 1,832 were occupied in 2003-04. Freshmen guaranteed college housing. Option: coed housing available. Trinity College Library plus 2 others with 988,536 books, 432,790 microform titles, 2,434 serials, 226,532 audiovisual materials, an OPAC, and a Web page. Operations spending for 2004 fiscal year: $3.4 million. 315 computers available on campus for general student use. A campuswide network can be accessed from student residence rooms and from off campus. Staffed computer lab on campus.

■ **TUNXIS COMMUNITY COLLEGE** *E-8*
271 Scott Swamp Rd.
Farmington, CT 06032-3026
Tel: (860)677-7701
Admissions: (860)255-3350
E-mail: pmccluskey@txcc.commnet.edu
Web Site: http://www.tunxis.commnet.edu/

Description: State-supported, 2-year, coed. Part of Connecticut Community College System. Awards certificates, transfer associate, and terminal associate degrees. Founded 1969. Setting: 12-acre suburban campus with easy access to Hartford. Educational spending for 2005 fiscal year: $2536 per student. Total enrollment: 3,894. Student-undergrad faculty ratio is 19:1. Full-time: 1,488 students, 54% women, 46% men. Part-time: 2,406 students, 66% women, 34% men. Students come from 6 states and territories, 2% from out-of-state, 0.4% Native American, 10% Hispanic, 6% black, 3% Asian American or Pacific Islander, 1% international, 47% 25 or older. Retention: 56% of full-time freshmen returned the following year. Calendar: semesters. Academic remediation for entering students, ESL program, summer session for credit, part-time degree program, adult/continuing education programs.

Entrance Requirements: Open admission except for dental hygiene, drug and alcohol rehabilitation counseling, physical therapist assistant, Command Institute Supervisory Leadership programs. Options: Common Application, deferred admission. Required: high school transcript. Entrance: noncompetitive. Application deadline: Rolling. Preference given to state residents.

Costs Per Year: Application fee: $20. Area resident tuition: $98 per credit hour part-time. State resident tuition: $2352 full-time. Nonresident tuition: $7056 full-time, $294 per credit hour part-time. Mandatory fees: $320 full-time, $178 per term part-time.

Collegiate Environment: Orientation program. Student-run newspaper. Social organizations: 14 open to all. Most popular organizations: Phi Theta Kappa, Student American Dental Hygiene Association (SADHA), Human Services Club, student newspaper, Bible Club. Major annual events: Art Show, Campus Barbecue, International Students' Day. Student services: health clinic. Campus security: 24-hour patrols. College housing not available. Tunxis Community College Library with 33,866 books, 106,400 microform titles, 285 serials, 3,571 audiovisual materials, and an OPAC. 274 computers available on campus for general student use. A campuswide network can be accessed from off-campus. Staffed computer lab on campus.

Community Environment: Farmington was settled in 1640 and incorporated in 1645. It is a suburban, residential town with a population of 25,000.

■ **UNITED STATES COAST GUARD ACADEMY** *I-14*
15 Mohegan Ave.
New London, CT 06320-8100
Tel: (860)444-8444
Free: 800-883-8724
Admissions: (860)444-8500
Fax: (860)444-8289
E-mail: admissions@cga.uscg.mil
Web Site: http://www.cga.edu/

Description: Federally supported, 4-year, coed. Awards bachelor's degrees. Founded 1876. Setting: 110-acre suburban campus with easy access to Providence and Hartford. Total enrollment: 1,012. Student-undergrad faculty ratio is 9:1. 1,597 applied, 26% were admitted. 47% from top 10% of their high school class, 86% from top quarter, 99% from top half. 20 class presidents, 13 valedictorians, 93 student government officers. Full-time: 1,012 students, 28% women, 72% men. Students come from 49 states and territories, 10 other countries, 94% from out-of-state, 1% Native American, 4% Hispanic, 3% black, 5% Asian American or Pacific Islander, 1% international, 0% 25 or older, 100% live on campus, 0% transferred in. Retention: 94% of full-time freshmen returned the following year. Academic areas with the most degrees conferred: engineering; biological/life sciences; social sciences. Core. Calendar: semesters. Academic remediation for entering students, honors program, independent study, double major, summer session for credit, internships. Off campus study at Connecticut College.

Entrance Requirements: Options: electronic application, early action. Required: essay, high school transcript, 3 recommendations, medical exam, physical fitness exam, SAT or ACT. Recommended: interview. Entrance: very difficult. Application deadlines: 3/1, 11/1 for early action. Notification: continuous, 12/15 for early action.

Costs Per Year: Application fee: $0.

Collegiate Environment: Orientation program. Drama-theater group, choral group, marching band. Major annual events: homecoming, Parents' Weekend, Community Service Day. Student services: legal services, health clinic, personal-psychological counseling. Campus security: 24-hour patrols, student patrols. 1,030 college housing spaces available; 994 were occupied in 2003-04. Freshmen guaranteed college housing. On-campus residence required through senior year. Option: coed housing available. Waesche Hall Library with an OPAC and a Web page. 325 computers available on campus for general student use. Computer purchase/lease plans available. A campuswide network can be accessed from student residence rooms and from off campus. Staffed computer lab on campus.

■ **UNIVERSITY OF BRIDGEPORT** *K-5*

126 Park Ave.
Bridgeport, CT 06604
Tel: (203)576-4000
Free: 800-243-9496
Admissions: (203)576-4552
Fax: (203)576-4941
E-mail: admit@bridgeport.edu
Web Site: http://www.bridgeport.edu/

Description: Independent, comprehensive, coed. Awards associate, bachelor's, master's, doctoral, and first professional degrees and post-master's certificates. Founded 1927. Setting: 86-acre urban campus with easy access to New York City. Educational spending for 2005 fiscal year: $6155 per student. Total enrollment: 3,626. Faculty: 349 (89 full-time, 260 part-time). Student-undergrad faculty ratio is 12:1. 2,327 applied, 74% were admitted. 1% from top 10% of their high school class, 25% from top quarter, 52% from top half. Full-time: 1,247 students, 60% women, 40% men. Part-time: 429 students, 76% women, 24% men. Students come from 39 states and territories, 54 other countries, 40% from out-of-state, 0.2% Native American, 14% Hispanic, 33% black, 4% Asian American or Pacific Islander, 13% international, 29% 25 or older; 45% live on campus, 11% transferred in. Retention: 62% of full-time freshmen returned the following year. Academic areas with the most degrees conferred: liberal arts/general studies; business/marketing; visual and performing arts. Core. Calendar: semesters. Academic remediation for entering students, ESL program, services for LD students, advanced placement, accelerated degree program, self-designed majors, honors program, independent study, distance learning, double major, summer session for credit, part-time degree program, adult/continuing education programs, co-op programs and internships, graduate courses open to undergrads. Off campus study at Fairfield University, Sacred Heart University. ROTC: Army.

Entrance Requirements: Options: Peterson's Universal Application, electronic application, early admission, early action, deferred admission. Required: essay, high school transcript, minimum 2.0 high school GPA, SAT or ACT. Recommended: 1 recommendation, interview. Required for some: interview, portfolio, audition, SAT Subject Tests. Entrance: moderately difficult. Application deadlines: Rolling, 1/1 for early action. Notification: continuous until 8/1, 1/15 for early action.

Costs Per Year: Application fee: $25. Comprehensive fee: $29,595 includes full-time tuition ($19,200), mandatory fees ($1395), and college room and board ($9000). College room only: $4600. Full-time tuition and fees vary according to program. Room and board charges vary according to board plan and student level. Part-time tuition: $640 per credit. Part-time mandatory fees: $60 per term. Part-time tuition and fees vary according to program.

Collegiate Environment: Orientation program. Choral group, student-run newspaper, radio station. Social organizations: 35 open to all; national fraternities, national sororities, local fraternities, local sororities; 1% of eligible men and 2% of eligible women are members. Most popular organizations: Student Congress, International Relations Club, Black Students Alliance, Scuba Club, Japanese Student Association. Major annual events: International Festival, spring week events, Halloween Bash. Student services: health clinic, personal-psychological counseling, women's center. Campus security: 24-hour emergency response devices and patrols, student patrols, late night transport-escort service. 976 college housing spaces available; 622 were occupied in 2003-04. Freshmen guaranteed college housing. On-campus residence required through sophomore year. Option: coed housing available. Wahlstrom Library with 272,430 books, 1.1 million microform titles, 2,117 serials, 5,485 audiovisual materials, an OPAC, and a Web page. Operations spending for 2004 fiscal year: $940,128. 500 computers available on campus for general student use. A campuswide network can be accessed from student residence rooms and from off campus. Staffed computer lab on campus.

Community Environment: Bridgeport is named for the first drawbridge erected over the Pequonock River and is easily accessible by auto, bus and train, automobiles using the Merrit Parkway and the Connecticut Thruway. Bridgeport is the home of P.T. Barnum. Barnum Institute of Science and History and the Museum of Art, Science and Industry is located in Bridgeport. Seaside Park, a 225-acre park stretching two and one half miles along Long Island Sound, offers opportunities for swimming and field sports. Beardsley Park has woodland walks and drives, a large lake and a zoo. Sixty-five percent of Connecticut's largest corporations are located in Fairfield County. These companies provide students with excellent opportunities for employment, before and after graduation.

■ **UNIVERSITY OF CONNECTICUT** *D-13*

Storrs, CT 06269
Tel: (860)486-2000
Admissions: (860)486-3137
Fax: (860)486-1476
E-mail: beahusky@uconn.edu
Web Site: http://www.uconn.edu/

Description: State-supported, university, coed. Awards associate, bachelor's, master's, doctoral, and first professional degrees and post-master's certificates. Founded 1881. Setting: 4,104-acre rural campus. Endowment: $343 million. Research spending for 2004 fiscal year: $62 million. Total enrollment: 23,185. Faculty: 1,265 (975 full-time, 290 part-time). Student-undergrad faculty ratio is 17:1. 18,608 applied, 51% were admitted. 37% from top 10% of their high school class, 80% from top quarter, 98% from top half. 38 valedictorians. Full-time: 15,296 students, 53% women, 47% men. Part-time: 816 students, 45% women, 55% men. Students come from 50 states and territories, 65 other countries, 23% from out-of-state, 0.4% Native American, 5% Hispanic, 5% black, 7% Asian American or Pacific Islander, 1% international, 3% 25 or older, 72% live on campus, 4% transferred in. Retention: 92% of full-time freshmen returned the following year. Academic areas with the most degrees conferred: social sciences; business/marketing; liberal arts/general studies. Core. Calendar: semesters. Academic remediation for entering students, ESL program, services for LD students, advanced placement, accelerated degree program, self-designed majors, honors program, independent study, distance learning, double major, summer session for credit, part-time degree program, adult/continuing education programs, co-op programs and internships, graduate courses open to undergrads. Off campus study at other public institutions in Connecticut. Study abroad program. ROTC: Army, Air Force.

Entrance Requirements: Options: electronic application, early admission, early action, deferred admission. Required: essay, high school transcript, SAT or ACT. Recommended: 1 recommendation. Entrance: moderately difficult. Application deadlines: 2/1, 12/1 for early action. Notification: continuous until 1/1, 1/1 for early action.

Costs Per Year: Application fee: $70. State resident tuition: $6456 full-time, $269 per credit part-time. Nonresident tuition: $19,656 full-time, $819 per credit part-time. Mandatory fees: $1906 full-time, $635 per term part-time. College room and board: $8266. College room only: $4350.

Collegiate Environment: Orientation program. Drama-theater group, choral group, marching band, student-run newspaper, radio station. Social organizations: 238 open to all; national fraternities, national sororities, local fraternities, local sororities; 8% of eligible men and 7% of eligible women are members. Major annual events: homecoming, Spring Weekend, UConn Do It Day. Student services: health clinic, personal-psychological counseling, women's center. Campus security: 24-hour emergency response devices, late night transport-escort service. 10,757 college housing spaces available; 10,629 were occupied in 2003-04. Freshmen guaranteed college housing. Options: coed, men-only, women-only housing available. Homer Babbidge Library plus 3 others with 3 million books, 4.3 million microform titles, 17,378 serials, 61,417 audiovisual materials, an OPAC, and a Web page. Operations spending for 2004 fiscal year: $12.7 million. 1,318 computers available on campus for general student use. Computer purchase/lease plans available. A campuswide network can be accessed from student residence rooms and from off campus. Staffed computer lab on campus.

Community Environment: Storrs, population 12,100, is in a rural area 25 miles east of Hartford and 70 miles south of Boston. The climate is temperate. Buses serve the area with other modes of transportation available in Hartford. Community facilities include various houses of worship and a small shopping area. Willimantic, nine miles away, has a hospital and additional shopping facilities. There are recreational activities at nearby lakes and State Parks. Part-time employment opportunities are limited.

■ **UNIVERSITY OF HARTFORD** *D-9*
200 Bloomfield Ave.
West Hartford, CT 06117-1599
Tel: (860)768-4100
Free: 800-947-4303
Admissions: (860)768-4296
Fax: (860)768-4961
E-mail: admission@hartford.edu
Web Site: http://www.hartford.edu/
Description: Independent, comprehensive, coed. Awards associate, bachelor's, master's, and doctoral degrees and post-master's certificates. Founded 1877. Setting: 320-acre suburban campus with easy access to Hartford. Endowment: $92 million. Research spending for 2004 fiscal year: $3.5 million. Educational spending for 2005 fiscal year: $12,689 per student. Total enrollment: 7,260. Faculty: 753 (325 full-time, 428 part-time). Student-undergrad faculty ratio is 14:1. 12,065 applied, 66% were admitted. Full-time: 4,657 students, 50% women, 50% men. Part-time: 935 students, 61% women, 39% men. Students come from 46 states and territories, 53 other countries, 60% from out-of-state, 0.3% Native American, 5% Hispanic, 10% black, 3% Asian American or Pacific Islander, 3% international, 14% 25 or older, 74% live on campus, 5% transferred in. Retention: 78% of full-time freshmen returned the following year. Academic areas with the most degrees conferred: visual and performing arts; business/marketing; communications/journalism; health professions and related sciences. Core. Calendar: semesters. Academic remediation for entering students, ESL program, services for LD students, advanced placement, self-designed majors, honors program, independent study, distance learning, double major, summer session for credit, part-time degree program, adult/continuing education programs, co-op programs and internships, graduate courses open to undergrads. Off campus study at members of the Hartford Consortium for Higher Education. Study abroad program. ROTC: Army (c), Air Force (c).
Entrance Requirements: Options: Peterson's Universal Application, Common Application, electronic application, early admission, deferred admission. Required: high school transcript, SAT or ACT. Recommended: essay, 2 recommendations, interview. Entrance: moderately difficult. Application deadline: Rolling. Notification: continuous.
Costs Per Year: Application fee: $35. Comprehensive fee: $35,688 includes full-time tuition ($24,576), mandatory fees ($1190), and college room and board ($9922). College room only: $6118. Part-time tuition: $360 per credit.
Collegiate Environment: Orientation program. Drama-theater group, choral group, student-run newspaper, radio station. Social organizations: 54 open to all; national fraternities, national sororities; 17% of eligible men and 21% of eligible women are members. Most popular organizations: Program Council, Brothers and Sisters United, Hillel, Student Government Association, Residence Hall Association. Major annual events: Hawks Fest, Lacrosse Under the Light, Midnight Mania. Student services: legal services, health clinic, personal-psychological counseling, women's center. Campus security: 24-hour emergency response devices and patrols, late night transport-escort service, controlled dormitory access, bicycle patrols. 3,400 college housing spaces available; all were occupied in 2003-04. Options: coed, women-only housing available. Mortenson Library plus 1 other with 468,780 books, 383,367 microform titles, 2,425 serials, an OPAC, and a Web page. Operations spending for 2004 fiscal year: $2.6 million. 400 computers available on campus for general student use. Computer purchase/lease plans available. A campuswide network can be accessed from student residence rooms and from off campus. Staffed computer lab on campus.
Community Environment: The University is located in a suburban area of West Hartford, four miles from the center of Hartford. In addition to the many activities available on campus, the proximity to a metropolitan area affords a multitude of cultural, educational and recreational opportunities.

■ **UNIVERSITY OF NEW HAVEN** *J-7*
300 Orange Ave.
West Haven, CT 06516-1916
Tel: (203)932-7000
Free: 800-DIAL-UNH
Admissions: (203)932-7319
Fax: (203)937-0756
Web Site: http://www.newhaven.edu/

Description: Independent, comprehensive, coed. Awards associate, bachelor's, and master's degrees and post-master's certificates. Founded 1920. Setting: 78-acre suburban campus with easy access to Hartford, New Haven. Total enrollment: 4,466. Faculty: 471 (162 full-time, 309 part-time). Student-undergrad faculty ratio is 14:1. 3,051 applied, 73% were admitted. 16% from top 10% of their high school class, 41% from top quarter, 77% from top half. 10 class presidents, 5 valedictorians, 57 student government officers. Full-time: 2,301 students, 50% women, 50% men. Part-time: 487 students, 44% women, 56% men. Students come from 33 states and territories, 33 other countries, 41% from out-of-state, 0.5% Native American, 6% Hispanic, 8% black, 2% Asian American or Pacific Islander, 2% international, 20% 25 or older, 64% live on campus, 8% transferred in. Retention: 77% of full-time freshmen returned the following year. Academic areas with the most degrees conferred: security and protective services; business/marketing; engineering. Core. Calendar: 4-1-4. Academic remediation for entering students, services for LD students, advanced placement, accelerated degree program, honors program, independent study, double major, summer session for credit, part-time degree program, adult/continuing education programs, co-op programs and internships, graduate courses open to undergrads.
Entrance Requirements: Options: Peterson's Universal Application, Common Application. Required: essay, high school transcript, 1 recommendation, SAT or ACT. Recommended: interview, SAT. Entrance: moderately difficult. Application deadline: Rolling. Notification: continuous.
Costs Per Year: Application fee: $50. Comprehensive fee: $32,532 includes full-time tuition ($22,380), mandatory fees ($602), and college room and board ($9550). College room only: $5796. Full-time tuition and fees vary according to course load and program. Room and board charges vary according to board plan and housing facility. Part-time tuition: $746 per credit hour. Part-time tuition varies according to class time, course load, location, and program.
Collegiate Environment: Orientation program. Drama-theater group, choral group, student-run newspaper, radio station. Social organizations: 50 open to all; national fraternities, local fraternities, local sororities; 3% of eligible men and 4% of eligible women are members. Major annual events: homecoming, Spring Weekend, Snowball Formal Dance. Student services: health clinic, personal-psychological counseling. Campus security: 24-hour emergency response devices and patrols, late night transport-escort service, escort service, vehicle, bicycle and foot patrols, crime prevention programs. 1,335 college housing spaces available; 1,321 were occupied in 2003-04. Option: coed housing available. 300 computers available on campus for general student use. Computer purchase/lease plans available. A campuswide network can be accessed from student residence rooms and from off campus. Staffed computer lab on campus.
Community Environment: Located in West Haven, a town with a population of 54,000; ten minutes from downtown New Haven. Cultural attractions include the Shubert Theater, The Palace, Long Wharf Theater, Yale Repertory Theater. The university is accessible to many shopping malls and the beaches of Long Island Sound.

■ **WESLEYAN UNIVERSITY** *G-10*
Middletown, CT 06459-0260
Tel: (860)685-2000
Admissions: (860)685-3000
Fax: (860)685-3001
E-mail: admissions@wesleyan.edu
Web Site: http://www.wesleyan.edu/
Description: Independent, university, coed. Awards bachelor's, master's, and doctoral degrees and post-master's certificates. Founded 1831. Setting: 120-acre small town campus. Endowment: $564.9 million. Research spending for 2004 fiscal year: $7.8 million. Educational spending for 2005 fiscal year: $17,100 per student. Total enrollment: 3,207. Faculty: 368 (325 full-time, 43 part-time). Student-undergrad faculty ratio is 9:1. 6,879 applied, 28% were admitted. 66% from top 10% of their high school class, 95% from top quarter, 99% from top half. Full-time: 2,750 students, 52% women, 48% men. Part-time: 14 students, 36% women, 64% men. Students come from 50 states and territories, 45 other countries, 85% from out-of-state, 0.4% Native American, 7% Hispanic, 7% black, 10% Asian American or Pacific Islander, 6% international, 0% 25 or older, 94% live on campus, 2% transferred in. Retention: 95% of full-time freshmen returned the following year. Academic areas with the most degrees conferred: social sciences; interdisciplinary studies; visual and performing arts. Calendar: semesters. ESL program, services for LD students, advanced placement, accelerated degree program, self-designed majors, honors program, independent study,

double major, summer session for credit, adult/continuing education programs, internships, graduate courses open to undergrads. Off campus study at members of the Twelve College Exchange Program, American University. Study abroad program. ROTC: Air Force (c).

Entrance Requirements: Options: Peterson's Universal Application, Common Application, electronic application, early admission, early decision, deferred admission, international baccalaureate accepted. Required: essay, high school transcript, 2 recommendations, SAT and SAT Subject Tests or ACT. Recommended: interview. Entrance: most difficult. Application deadlines: 1/1, 11/15 for early decision plan 1, 1/1 for early decision plan 2. Notification: 4/1, 12/15 for early decision plan 1, 2/15 for early decision plan 2.

Costs Per Year: Application fee: $55. Comprehensive fee: $44,770 includes full-time tuition ($34,930), mandatory fees ($300), and college room and board ($9540). College room only: $5808.

Collegiate Environment: Orientation program. Drama-theater group, choral group, student-run newspaper, radio station. Social organizations: 231 open to all; national fraternities, national sororities, local fraternities; 4% of eligible men and 3% of eligible women are members. Most popular organizations: community service, Students of Color groups, theater (student and faculty productions), campus publications, intramurals. Major annual events: Spring Fling, Fall Ball, homecoming. Student services: health clinic, personal-psychological counseling, women's center. Campus security: 24-hour emergency response devices and patrols, student patrols, late night transport-escort service, controlled dormitory access. 2,627 college housing spaces available; 2,549 were occupied in 2003-04. Freshmen guaranteed college housing. On-campus residence required in freshman year. Option: coed housing available. Olin Memorial Library plus 3 others with 1.3 million books, 292,223 microform titles, 6,789 serials, 46,589 audiovisual materials, an OPAC, and a Web page. Operations spending for 2004 fiscal year: $6.6 million. 190 computers available on campus for general student use. Computer purchase/lease plans available. A campuswide network can be accessed from student residence rooms and from off campus. Staffed computer lab on campus.

Community Environment: Population 45,000. In central Connecticut, 15 miles south of Hartford and 20 miles north of New Haven, Middletown is an important research and manufacturing center. Buses and railroads serve the area with an airline service nearby. Middletown has 21 churches of all denominations, hospital, three libraries with branches, several inns, motels, theatres and a shopping area. The various civic, fraternal and veterans organizations are active within the city. Parks, tennis courts, basketball courts, ball fields, picnic grounds and swimming pool provide facilities for recreation.

■ **WESTERN CONNECTICUT STATE UNIVERSITY** *H-3*
181 White St.
Danbury, CT 06810-6885
Tel: (203)837-8200; 877-837-9278
Admissions: (203)837-9000
Fax: (203)837-8320
E-mail: _hawkinsw@wcsu.edu
Web Site: http://www.wcsu.edu/

Description: State-supported, comprehensive, coed. Part of Connecticut State University System. Awards associate, bachelor's, master's, and doctoral degrees. Founded 1903. Setting: 340-acre urban campus with easy access to New York City. Endowment: $6.8 million. Research spending for 2004 fiscal year: $234,872. Total enrollment: 5,907. Faculty: 485 (197 full-time, 288 part-time). Student-undergrad faculty ratio is 16:1. 3,469 applied, 58% were admitted. 7% from top 10% of their high school class, 26% from top quarter, 62% from top half. Full-time: 4,002 students, 54% women, 46% men. Part-time: 1,193 students, 60% women, 40% men. Students come from 21 states and territories, 19 other countries, 12% from out-of-state, 0.1% Native American, 6% Hispanic, 6% black, 3% Asian American or Pacific Islander, 1% international, 6% 25 or older, 33% live on campus, 7% transferred in. Retention: 72% of full-time freshmen returned the following year. Academic areas with the most degrees conferred: business/marketing; education; security and protective services. Core. Calendar: semesters. Academic remediation for entering students, ESL program, services for LD students, advanced placement, accelerated degree program, self-designed majors, honors program, independent study, distance learning, double major, summer session for credit, part-time degree program, adult/continuing education programs, co-op programs and internships, graduate courses open to undergrads. Off campus study at other units of the Connecticut State University System. Study abroad program. ROTC: Army (c), Air Force (c).

Entrance Requirements: Options: Common Application, electronic application, early admission, deferred admission. Required: high school transcript, SAT or ACT. Recommended: essay, recommendations, interview. Entrance: moderately difficult. Application deadline: 5/1. Notification: continuous. Preference given to state residents.

Costs Per Year: Application fee: $40. State resident tuition: $3187 full-time, $304 per semester hour part-time. Nonresident tuition: $10,315 full-time, $304 per semester hour part-time. Mandatory fees: $2919 full-time, $60 per term part-time. College room and board: $7784. College room only: $4516.

Collegiate Environment: Orientation program. Drama-theater group, choral group, student-run newspaper, radio station. Social organizations: 40 open to all; national fraternities, national sororities, local sororities; 3% of eligible men and 2% of eligible women are members. Most popular organizations: Justice and Law Club, Black Student Alliance, Student Government Association, Music Education National Conference, WXCI. Major annual events: Spring Fest, Homecoming, Midnight Breakfast. Student services: health clinic, personal-psychological counseling. Campus security: 24-hour emergency response devices and patrols, student patrols, late night transport-escort service, controlled dormitory access. College housing designed to accommodate 1,258 students; 1,591 undergraduates lived in college housing during 2003-04. Freshmen guaranteed college housing. Options: coed, women-only housing available. Ruth Haas Library plus 1 other with 182,915 books, 471,099 microform titles, 1,273 serials, 8,654 audiovisual materials, an OPAC, and a Web page. Operations spending for 2004 fiscal year: $2.1 million. 400 computers available on campus for general student use. A campuswide network can be accessed from student residence rooms and from off campus. Staffed computer lab on campus.

Community Environment: Population 66,000, Danbury is within easy commuting distance of Stamford, Waterbury, Bridgeport, New Haven, and Torrington. Cultural centers in Danbury and in the surrounding cities are within easy reach. Trains and buses serve the area. Recreational facilities include nearby Candlewood Lake for swimming, boating, and fishing. Part time work is available in the community.

■ **YALE UNIVERSITY** *I-8*
New Haven, CT 06520
Tel: (203)432-4771
Admissions: (203)432-9316
Fax: (203)432-9392
E-mail: undergraduate.admissions@yale.edu
Web Site: http://www.yale.edu/

Description: Independent, university, coed. Awards bachelor's, master's, doctoral, and first professional degrees and post-master's certificates. Founded 1701. Setting: 200-acre urban campus with easy access to New York City. Endowment: $15.2 billion. Research spending for 2004 fiscal year: $276.7 million. Total enrollment: 11,483. Faculty: 1,430 (1,054 full-time, 376 part-time). Student-undergrad faculty ratio is 6:1. 19,451 applied, 10% were admitted. 95% from top 10% of their high school class. Full-time: 5,350 students, 49% women, 51% men. Part-time: 59 students, 47% women, 53% men. Students come from 50 states and territories, 74 other countries, 92% from out-of-state, 1% Native American, 7% Hispanic, 8% black, 14% Asian American or Pacific Islander, 8% international, 1% 25 or older, 87% live on campus, 0.1% transferred in. Retention: 98% of full-time freshmen returned the following year. Academic areas with the most degrees conferred: social sciences; history; English. Core. Calendar: semesters. ESL program, advanced placement, accelerated degree program, self-designed majors, honors program, independent study, double major, summer session for credit, part-time degree program, graduate courses open to undergrads. Study abroad program. ROTC: Army (c), Air Force (c).

Entrance Requirements: Options: electronic application, early admission, early action, deferred admission. Required: essay, high school transcript, 3 recommendations, SAT and SAT Subject Tests or ACT. Recommended: interview. Entrance: most difficult. Application deadlines: 12/31, 11/1 for early action. Notification: 4/1, 12/15 for early action.

Costs Per Year: Application fee: $75. Comprehensive fee: $41,000 includes full-time tuition ($31,460) and college room and board ($9540).

Collegiate Environment: Orientation program. Drama-theater group, choral group, marching band, student-run newspaper, radio station. Social organizations: 300 open to all; national fraternities, national sororities. Most popular organizations: community service, intramural sports, theater productions, music groups, campus publications. Major annual events: Spring Fling Weekend, Harvard Football Weekend, winter balls. Student services: health clinic, personal-psychological counseling, women's center. Campus security: 24-hour emergency response devices and patrols, late night transport-escort service, controlled dormitory access. 4,628 undergraduates lived in college housing during 2003-04. Freshmen guaranteed college housing. On-campus residence required through sophomore year. Option: coed housing available. Sterling Memorial Library plus 20 others with 11.1 million books, 8.1 million microform titles, 61,649 serials, 227,989 audiovisual materials, an OPAC, and a Web page. Operations spending for 2004 fiscal year: $16.4 million. 350 computers available on campus for general student use. A campuswide network can be accessed from student residence rooms and from off campus. Staffed computer lab on campus.

Community Environment: Southern Connecticut's major city, New Haven is in many respects a college town. The average temperature is 50.7 degrees. Buses, railroads, and airlines serve the area. New Haven is engaged in one of the most successful urban renewal projects in the country, restoring and rebuilding housing, community facilities and commercial redevelopment. Points of interest are the museums and libraries. New Haven also has the usual civic organizations, hospitals, shopping centers, hotels and motels. Employment is available. The recreational facilities include theaters, swimming areas, tennis courts, archery ranges, indoor swimming pool, bowling alleys, riding stables, roller skating rinks, municipal golf course and many parks. Important manufacturing establishments are located here.

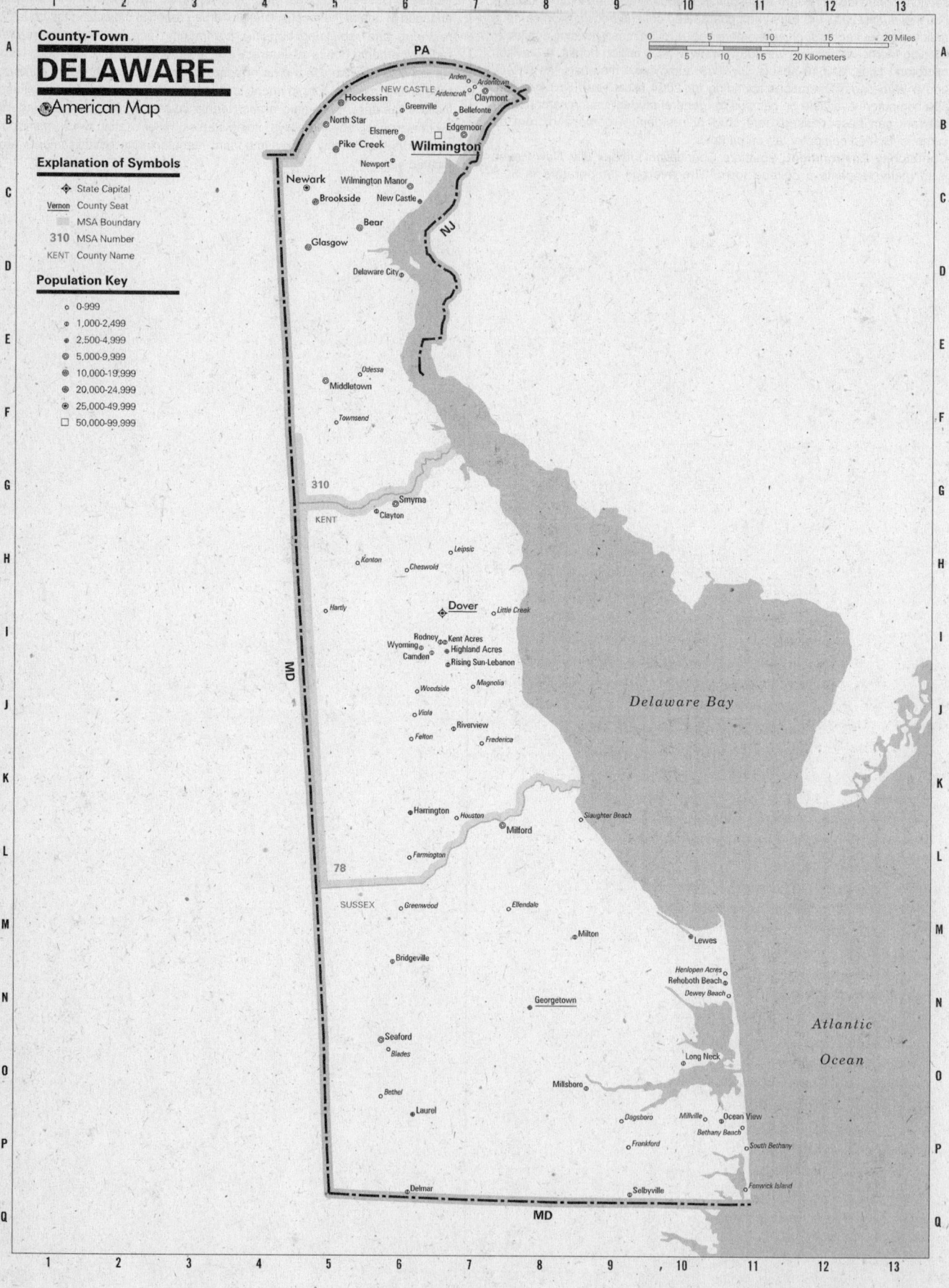

County-Town

DELAWARE

American Map

Explanation of Symbols

◈	State Capital
Vernon	County Seat
	MSA Boundary
310	MSA Number
KENT	County Name

Population Key

○	0-999
◔	1,000-2,499
●	2,500-4,999
◉	5,000-9,999
◉	10,000-19,999
●	20,000-24,999
◉	25,000-49,999
□	50,000-99,999

PA

NEW CASTLE

Arden
Ardentown
Ardencroft
Claymont
Hockessin
Greenville
Bellefonte
North Star
Edgemoor
Elsmere
Pike Creek
Wilmington
Newport
Newark
Wilmington Manor
Brookside
New Castle
NJ
Bear
Glasgow
Delaware City

Odessa
Middletown
Townsend

310

KENT

Smyrna
Clayton

Leipsic
Kenton
Cheswold

Hartly
Dover
Little Creek

Rodney Kent Acres
Wyoming Highland Acres
Camden Rising Sun-Lebanon

Woodside Magnolia

Viola
Riverview
Felton Frederica

Delaware Bay

Harrington Houston
Milford Slaughter Beach

Farmington

78

SUSSEX

Greenwood Ellendale

Milton
Lewes

Bridgeville

Henlopen Acres
Rehoboth Beach
Georgetown Dewey Beach

Atlantic

Ocean

Seaford
Blades
Long Neck

Bethel Millsboro

Laurel Dagsboro Millville Ocean View
Bethany Beach
Frankford South Bethany

Delmar Selbyville Fenwick Island

MD

MD

0   5   10   15   20 Miles
0   5   10   15   20 Kilometers

■ DELAWARE COLLEGE OF ART AND DESIGN *B-6*
600 North Market St.
Wilmington, DE 19801
Tel: (302)622-8000
Fax: (302)622-8870
E-mail: thaman@dcad.edu
Web Site: http://www.dcad.edu/
Description: Independent, 2-year, coed. Administratively affiliated with Corcoran College of Art and Design. Awards transfer associate and terminal associate degrees. Founded 1997. Setting: 1-acre urban campus. Endowment: $65,295. Educational spending for 2005 fiscal year: $4884 per student. Total enrollment: 194. Student-undergrad faculty ratio is 5:1. 322 applied, 58% were admitted. Full-time: 148 students, 54% women, 46% men. Part-time: 46 students, 41% women, 59% men. Students come from 9 states and territories, 45% from out-of-state, 1% Native American, 4% Hispanic, 9% black, 1% Asian American or Pacific Islander, 1% international, 13% 25 or older, 50% live on campus, 11% transferred in. Core. Calendar: semesters. Academic remediation for entering students, services for LD students, advanced placement, double major, summer session for credit, part-time degree program, adult/continuing education programs. Off campus study at regional galleries and museums. Study abroad program.
Entrance Requirements: Options: Common Application, electronic application, deferred admission. Required: essay, high school transcript, minimum 2 high school GPA, interview, portfolio. Required for some: recommendations. Entrance: moderately difficult. Application deadline: Rolling. Notification: continuous until 8/15.
Costs Per Year: Application fee: $25. Tuition: $14,070 full-time, $595 per credit part-time. Mandatory fees: $200 per term part-time. College room only: $5490.
Collegiate Environment: Orientation program. College housing designed to accommodate 75 students; 78 undergraduates lived in college housing during 2003-04. Freshmen given priority for college housing. Option: coed housing available. Information Resource Center plus 1 other with 8,000 books, 76 serials, 500 audiovisual materials, and an OPAC. Operations spending for 2004 fiscal year: $33,247. 68 computers available on campus for general student use. Computer purchase/lease plans available. A campuswide network can be accessed from student residence rooms and from off campus. Staffed computer lab on campus.

■ DELAWARE STATE UNIVERSITY *I-7*
1200 North DuPont Hwy.
Dover, DE 19901-2277
Tel: (302)857-6290
Free: 800-845-2544
Admissions: (302)857-6103
Fax: (302)857-6352
E-mail: cheatha@desu.edu
Web Site: http://www.desu.edu/
Description: State-supported, comprehensive, coed. Part of Delaware Higher Education Commission. Awards bachelor's, master's, and doctoral degrees. Founded 1891. Setting: 400-acre small town campus. Endowment: $13.8 million. Research spending for 2004 fiscal year: $3.2 million. Total enrollment: 3,722. Faculty: (182 full-time). 4,372 applied, 63% were admitted. 5% from top 10% of their high school class, 12% from top quarter, 48% from top half. Full-time: 2,946 students, 59% women, 41% men. Part-time: 494 students, 50% women, 50% men. Students come from 31 states and

territories, 49% from out-of-state, 0.2% Native American, 1% Hispanic, 81% black, 1% Asian American or Pacific Islander, 0.1% international, 17% 25 or older, 46% live on campus, 5% transferred in. Retention: 67% of full-time freshmen returned the following year. Academic areas with the most degrees conferred: business/marketing; social sciences; public administration and social services. Core. Calendar: semesters. Academic remediation for entering students, ESL program, services for LD students, advanced placement, accelerated degree program, self-designed majors, honors program, independent study, distance learning, double major, summer session for credit, part-time degree program, adult/continuing education programs, co-op programs and internships. Off campus study at University of Delaware. ROTC: Army, Air Force.
Entrance Requirements: Options: Common Application, electronic application, early admission. Required: high school transcript, minimum 2.0 high school GPA, 2 recommendations, SAT or ACT. Required for some: interview. Entrance: moderately difficult. Application deadline: 4/1. Preference given to state residents.
Costs Per Year: Application fee: $25. State resident tuition: $5480 full-time, $213 per credit hour part-time. Nonresident tuition: $11,704 full-time, $472 per credit hour part-time. Mandatory fees: $370 full-time, $105 per term part-time. College room and board: $8298. College room only: $5502.
Collegiate Environment: Orientation program. Drama-theater group, choral group, marching band, student-run newspaper, radio station. Social organizations: national fraternities, national sororities. Most popular organizations: NAACP, Women's Senate, Men's Council. Major annual events: homecoming, Parents' Day, Pride Day. Student services: health clinic, personal-psychological counseling, women's center. Campus security: 24-hour emergency response devices and patrols, student patrols, late night transport-escort service, controlled dormitory access. William C. Jason Library with 204,127 books, 77,918 microform titles, 3,094 serials, 13,775 audiovisual materials, and an OPAC. Operations spending for 2004 fiscal year: $1.4 million. 641 computers available on campus for general student use. A campuswide network can be accessed from student residence rooms and from off campus. Staffed computer lab on campus.
Community Environment: Dover, the capital of Delaware, is 75 miles from Philadelphia, 85 miles from Baltimore, 90 miles from Washington, DC, and 160 miles from New York City. Railway and bus are available in the area. Dover is an agricultural section noted for fruit, produce, grains and poultry. Many fine old colonial homes steeped in the traditions of the activity of the old town are found in the area."The Green" is the center of activity of the old town and still the hub from which radiate many of the political and government activities of both the city and the state. Located 10 miles south of"The Green" is Barratt's Chapel, often called the"Cradle of Methodism in America." Each year on Dover Days, the first Saturday and Sunday in May, many historic homes are open to the public for a small fee. Dover is the home of the largest air freight terminal in the world. General Food's multimillion-dollar Jell-O plant and Playtex Corporation are also located here.

■ DELAWARE TECHNICAL & COMMUNITY COLLEGE, JACK F. OWENS CAMPUS *N-8*
PO Box 610
Georgetown, DE 19947
Tel: (302)856-5400
Fax: (302)856-9461
Web Site: http://www.dtcc.edu/
Description: State-supported, 2-year, coed. Part of Delaware Technical and

Community College System. Awards certificates, diplomas, and terminal associate degrees. Founded 1967. Setting: 120-acre small town campus. Total enrollment: 3,936. Student-undergrad faculty ratio is 15:1. 1,122 applied, 73% were admitted. Full-time: 1,600 students, 61% women, 39% men. Part-time: 2,336 students, 71% women, 29% men. Students come from 3 states and territories, 9 other countries, 6% from out-of-state, 0.3% Native American, 3% Hispanic, 15% black, 1% Asian American or Pacific Islander, 6% international, 48% 25 or older. Core. Calendar: semesters. Academic remediation for entering students, ESL program, services for LD students, self-designed majors, distance learning, summer session for credit, part-time degree program, external degree program, adult/continuing education programs, co-op programs and internships.

Entrance Requirements: Open admission except for nursing, engineering technology, veterinary technology programs. Option: early admission. Required: high school transcript. Entrance: noncompetitive. Application deadline: Rolling. Notification: continuous. Preference given to state residents.

Costs Per Year: Application fee: $10. State resident tuition: $1956 full-time, $81.50 per credit hour part-time. Nonresident tuition: $4890 full-time, $203.75 per credit hour part-time. Mandatory fees: $204 full-time, $6 per credit hour part-time, $21 per term part-time.

Collegiate Environment: Student-run radio station. Social organizations: 7 open to all. Most popular organizations: Student Government Association, Student Nursing Association, Phi Beta Kappa, Occupational Therapy Assistant Club, Physical Therapy Assistant Club. Campus security: 24-hour patrols, late night transport-escort service. College housing not available. Stephen J. Betze Library plus 1 other with 72,657 books, 514 serials, and an OPAC. 400 computers available on campus for general student use. A campuswide network can be accessed. Staffed computer lab on campus.

■ **DELAWARE TECHNICAL & COMMUNITY COLLEGE, STANTON/ WILMINGTON CAMPUS** *C-5*
400 Stanton-Christiana Rd.
Newark, DE 19713
Tel: (302)454-3900
Admissions: (302)571-5366
Fax: (302)577-2548
Web Site: http://www.dtcc.edu/

Description: State-supported, 2-year, coed. Part of Delaware Technical and Community College System. Awards certificates, diplomas, and terminal associate degrees. Founded 1968. Educational spending for 2005 fiscal year: $5290 per student. Total enrollment: 7,473. Student-undergrad faculty ratio is 15:1. 1,965 applied, 74% were admitted. Full-time: 2,767 students, 56% women, 44% men. Part-time: 4,706 students, 68% women, 32% men. Students come from 13 states and territories, 45 other countries, 8% from out-of-state, 0.4% Native American, 5% Hispanic, 23% black, 3% Asian American or Pacific Islander, 2% international, 49% 25 or older. Core. Calendar: semesters. Academic remediation for entering students, ESL program, services for LD students, summer session for credit, part-time degree program, external degree program, adult/continuing education programs, co-op programs.

Entrance Requirements: Open admission except for nursing, dental hygiene, engineering technology programs. Option: early admission. Required: high school transcript. Entrance: noncompetitive. Application deadline: Rolling. Notification: continuous. Preference given to state residents.

Costs Per Year: Application fee: $10. State resident tuition: $1956 full-time, $81.50 per credit hour part-time. Nonresident tuition: $4890 full-time, $203.75 per credit hour part-time. Mandatory fees: $204 full-time, $6 per credit hour part-time, $21 per term part-time.

Collegiate Environment: Campus security: 24-hour patrols, late night transport-escort service. College housing not available. 60,066 books, 3,345 microform titles, 793 serials, and an OPAC. Operations spending for 2004 fiscal year: $196,688. 200 computers available on campus for general student use. A campuswide network can be accessed. Staffed computer lab on campus.

■ **DELAWARE TECHNICAL & COMMUNITY COLLEGE, TERRY CAMPUS** *I-7*
100 Campus Dr.
Dover, DE 19904-1383
Tel: (302)857-1000
Admissions: (302)857-1020
Fax: (302)857-1296

E-mail: mharris@outland.dtcc.edu
Web Site: http://www.dtcc.edu/terry/

Description: State-supported, 2-year, coed. Part of Delaware Technical and Community College System. Awards certificates, diplomas, and terminal associate degrees. Founded 1972. Setting: 70-acre small town campus with easy access to Philadelphia. Educational spending for 2005 fiscal year: $6658 per student. Total enrollment: 2,569. Student-undergrad faculty ratio is 14:1. 691 applied, 80% were admitted. Full-time: 875 students, 67% women, 33% men. Part-time: 1,694 students, 72% women, 28% men. Students come from 10 states and territories, 10 other countries, 3% from out-of-state, 0.4% Native American, 3% Hispanic, 24% black, 2% Asian American or Pacific Islander, 1% international, 57% 25 or older, 10% transferred in. Core. Calendar: semesters. Academic remediation for entering students, ESL program, services for LD students, summer session for credit, part-time degree program, adult/continuing education programs, co-op programs and internships.

Entrance Requirements: Open admission except for nursing program. Option: early admission. Required: high school transcript. Entrance: noncompetitive. Application deadline: Rolling. Notification: continuous. Preference given to state residents.

Costs Per Year: Application fee: $10. State resident tuition: $1956 full-time, $81.50 per credit hour part-time. Nonresident tuition: $4890 full-time, $203.75 per credit hour part-time. Mandatory fees: $204 full-time, $6 per credit hour part-time, $21 per term part-time.

Collegiate Environment: Social organizations: 15 open to all. Most popular organizations: Students of Kolor, Human Services Organization, Phi Theta Kappa, Alpha Beta Gamma. Campus security: late night transport-escort service. College housing not available. 9,663 books, 245 serials, and an OPAC. Operations spending for 2004 fiscal year: $307,239. 125 computers available on campus for general student use. A campuswide network can be accessed. Staffed computer lab on campus.

Community Environment: See Delaware State University.

■ **GOLDEY-BEACOM COLLEGE** *B-6*
4701 Limestone Rd.
Wilmington, DE 19808-1999
Tel: (302)998-8814
Free: 800-833-4877
Fax: (302)996-5408
Web Site: http://goldey.gbc.edu/

Description: Independent, comprehensive, coed. Awards associate, bachelor's, and master's degrees. Founded 1886. Setting: 27-acre suburban campus with easy access to Philadelphia. Endowment: $1.7 million. Educational spending for 2005 fiscal year: $2546 per student. Total enrollment: 1,324. 408 applied, 78% were admitted. 67% from top half of their high school class. Students come from 28 states and territories, 50% from out-of-state, 0% Native American, 5% Hispanic, 24% black, 10% Asian American or Pacific Islander, 0% international, 43% 25 or older, 16% live on campus. Retention: 82% of full-time freshmen returned the following year. Core. Calendar: semesters. Academic remediation for entering students, advanced placement, accelerated degree program, honors program, summer session for credit, part-time degree program, co-op programs and internships, graduate courses open to undergrads. Study abroad program.

Entrance Requirements: Options: Peterson's Universal Application, Common Application, electronic application, early admission, deferred admission. Required: high school transcript, minimum 2.0 high school GPA, SAT. Required for some: 1 recommendation, interview, DTLS, DTMS. Entrance: moderately difficult. Application deadline: Rolling. Notification: continuous until 8/15.

Costs Per Year: Application fee: $30. Tuition: $13,430 full-time. Mandatory fees: $306 full-time. College room only: $4240.

Collegiate Environment: Orientation program. Drama-theater group, choral group, student-run newspaper. Social organizations: 20 open to all; national fraternities, national sororities; 10% of eligible men and 10% of eligible women are members. Most popular organizations: Marketing/Management Association, Circle K International, Data Processing Management Association, GBC singers. Major annual events: Follies, Miss GBC Pageant, Spirit Day. Student services: health clinic. Campus security: 24-hour emergency response devices. Option: coed housing available. J. Wilbur Hirons Library with 29,700 books, 817 serials, and a Web page. Operations spending for 2004 fiscal year: $120,352. 136 computers available on campus for general student use. A campuswide network can be accessed from student residence rooms and from off campus. Staffed computer lab on campus.

Community Environment: Known as the "Chemical Capital of the World," Wilmington (pop. 71,529) lies on the west bank of the Delaware River in northern Delaware. Railroads and airlines serve the area. Almost 300 industries are located in the area. A great variety of items are shipped from Wilmington, including such products as automobiles, airplanes, steel, clothing, hosiery, machinery, paper and paper products. Points of interest include Holy Trinity Church (Old Swedes), Wilmington Institute, Free Library, Brandywine Park, Fort Christian State Park, Delaware Art Center, Hagley Museum, Old Town Hall, and the Henry Francis du Pont Winterthur Museum. Nearby are Longwood Gardens and the Brandywine Museum.

■ UNIVERSITY OF DELAWARE C-5

Newark, DE 19716
Tel: (302)831-2000
Admissions: (302)831-8123
Fax: (302)831-6905
E-mail: admissions@udel.edu
Web Site: http://www.udel.edu/

Description: State-related, university, coed. Awards associate, bachelor's, master's, and doctoral degrees. Founded 1743. Setting: 1,000-acre small town campus with easy access to Philadelphia and Baltimore. Total enrollment: 20,373. Faculty: 1,370 (1,126 full-time, 244 part-time). Student-undergrad faculty ratio is 13:1. 21,617 applied, 47% were admitted. 37% from top 10% of their high school class, 76% from top quarter, 96% from top half. Full-time: 14,899 students, 58% women, 42% men. Part-time: 2,040 students, 55% women, 45% men. Students come from 52 states and territories, 100 other countries, 59% from out-of-state, 0.3% Native American, 4% Hispanic, 6% black, 3% Asian American or Pacific Islander, 1% international, 5% 25 or older, 45% live on campus, 3% transferred in. Retention: 89% of full-time freshmen returned the following year. Academic areas with the most degrees conferred: business/marketing; social sciences; education. Core. Calendar: 4-1-4. Academic remediation for entering students, ESL program, services for LD students, advanced placement, accelerated degree program, self-designed majors, honors program, independent study, distance learning, double major, summer session for credit, part-time degree program, adult/continuing education programs, co-op programs and internships, graduate courses open to undergrads. Study abroad program. ROTC: Army, Air Force.
Entrance Requirements: Options: Common Application, electronic application, early decision, deferred admission, international baccalaureate accepted. Required: essay, high school transcript, 1 recommendation, SAT or ACT. Recommended: SAT Subject Tests. Entrance: moderately difficult. Application deadlines: 1/15, 11/1 for early decision. Notification: 3/15, 12/15 for early decision. Preference given to state residents.
Costs Per Year: Application fee: $60. State resident tuition: $6614 full-time, $276 per credit part-time. Nonresident tuition: $16,770 full-time, $699 per credit part-time. Mandatory fees: $704 full-time, $25 per term part-time. College room and board: $6824. College room only: $3924. Room and board charges vary according to housing facility.
Collegiate Environment: Orientation program. Drama-theater group, choral group, marching band, student-run newspaper, radio station. Social organizations: 200 open to all; national fraternities, national sororities, local fraternities, local sororities; 13% of eligible men and 13% of eligible women are members. Most popular organizations: Undergraduate Student Congress, Resident Student Association, Black Student Union, HOLA (Hispanic Student Association). Major annual events: homecoming, Greek Weekend, Step Show. Student services: health clinic, personal-psychological counseling, women's center. Campus security: 24-hour emergency response devices and patrols, student patrols, late night transport-escort service, controlled dormitory access. College housing designed to accommodate 7,115 students; 7,207 undergraduates lived in college housing during 2003-04. Freshmen guaranteed college housing. On-campus residence required in freshman year. Options: coed, women-only housing available. Hugh Morris Library plus 4 others with 2.6 million books, 3.4 million microform titles, 12,476 serials, 18,047 audiovisual materials, an OPAC, and a Web page. Operations spending for 2004 fiscal year: $14.8 million. 908 computers available on campus for general student use. A campuswide network can be accessed from student residence rooms and from off campus. Staffed computer lab on campus.
Community Environment: The campus is located in Newark, Delaware, a city of 24,000, which is situated halfway between Philadelphia and Baltimore on I-95. The location is ideal for students who want the advantages of a small community and easy access to the educational, cultural, and social opportunities offered in nearby metropolitan area.

■ WESLEY COLLEGE I-7

120 North State St.
Dover, DE 19901-3875
Tel: (302)736-2300
Free: 800-937-5398
Admissions: (302)736-2400
Fax: (302)736-2301
E-mail: admissions@wesley.edu
Web Site: http://www.wesley.edu/

Description: Independent United Methodist, comprehensive, coed. Awards associate, bachelor's, and master's degrees and post-master's certificates. Founded 1873. Setting: 40-acre small town campus. Endowment: $4.8 million. Educational spending for 2005 fiscal year: $1517 per student. Total enrollment: 2,282. Faculty: 137 (63 full-time, 74 part-time). Student-undergrad faculty ratio is 20:1. 2,175 applied, 60% were admitted. 17% from top 10% of their high school class, 42% from top quarter, 68% from top half. Full-time: 1,745 students, 55% women, 45% men. Part-time: 371 students, 44% women, 56% men. Students come from 13 states and territories, 5 other countries, 75% from out-of-state, 0.2% Native American, 2% Hispanic, 26% black, 2% Asian American or Pacific Islander, 1% international, 6% 25 or older, 65% live on campus, 3% transferred in. Retention: 88% of full-time freshmen returned the following year. Academic areas with the most degrees conferred: business/marketing; education; psychology. Core. Calendar: semesters. Academic remediation for entering students, ESL program, advanced placement, accelerated degree program, independent study, double major, summer session for credit, part-time degree program, external degree program, adult/continuing education programs, internships, graduate courses open to undergrads. Study abroad program. ROTC: Army (c).
Entrance Requirements: Options: Common Application, electronic application, early admission, early decision, deferred admission. Required: essay, high school transcript, minimum 2.2 high school GPA, 1 recommendation. Recommended: interview. Entrance: moderately difficult. Application deadlines: Rolling, 11/15 for early decision. Notification: 12/1 for early decision.
Costs Per Year: Application fee: $25. Comprehensive fee: $21,560 includes full-time tuition ($14,600) and college room and board ($6960). Full-time tuition varies according to class time. Room and board charges vary according to board plan and housing facility.
Collegiate Environment: Orientation program. Drama-theater group, choral group, student-run newspaper. Social organizations: 20 open to all; national fraternities, national sororities, local fraternities, local sororities; 3% of eligible men and 3% of eligible women are members. Most popular organizations: Student Activity Board, Student Government Association, National Coeducation Community Service Organization. Major annual events: homecoming, Families' Day, reunion. Student services: health clinic, personal-psychological counseling. Campus security: 24-hour patrols, controlled dormitory access. 846 college housing spaces available; all were occupied in 2003-04. Freshmen guaranteed college housing. On-campus residence required in freshman year. Options: coed, men-only, women-only housing available. Robert H. Parker Library with 102,528 books, 178,073 microform titles, 270 serials, 940 audiovisual materials, an OPAC, and a Web page. Operations spending for 2004 fiscal year: $352,849. 225 computers available on campus for general student use. Computer purchase/lease plans available. A campuswide network can be accessed from student residence rooms and from off campus. Staffed computer lab on campus.

■ WILMINGTON COLLEGE C-6

320 North DuPont Hwy.
New Castle, DE 19720-6491
Tel: (302)328-9401; 877-967-5464
Admissions: (302)328-9407
Fax: (302)328-5902
Web Site: http://www.wilmcoll.edu/

Description: Independent, comprehensive, coed. Awards associate, bachelor's, master's, and doctoral degrees and post-master's certificates. Founded 1967. Setting: 17-acre suburban campus with easy access to Philadelphia. Endowment: $12.2 million. Total enrollment: 7,511. Faculty: 642 (90 full-time, 552 part-time). Student-undergrad faculty ratio is 17:1. 746 applied, 100% were admitted. Full-time: 2,148 students, 65% women, 35% men. Part-time: 2,422 students, 67% women, 33% men. Students come from 12 states and territories, 29 other countries, 13% from out-of-state,

0.3% Native American, 2% Hispanic, 15% black, 1% Asian American or Pacific Islander, 0% international, 54% 25 or older, 11% transferred in. Retention: 69% of full-time freshmen returned the following year. Academic areas with the most degrees conferred: business/marketing; social sciences; liberal arts/general studies. Core. Calendar: semesters. Academic remediation for entering students, accelerated degree program, independent study, distance learning, double major, summer session for credit, part-time degree program, external degree program, adult/continuing education programs, co-op programs and internships. ROTC: Army (c), Air Force (c).

Entrance Requirements: Open admission. Options: early admission, deferred admission. Required: high school transcript. Recommended: recommendations, interview. Entrance: noncompetitive. Application deadline: Rolling. Notification: continuous.

Costs Per Year: Application fee: $25. Tuition: $7620 full-time, $254 per credit part-time. Mandatory fees: $50 full-time, $25 per term part-time. Full-time tuition and fees vary according to course load, degree level, and location. Part-time tuition and fees vary according to course load, degree level, and location.

Collegiate Environment: Orientation program. Major annual event: Commencement. Campus security: 24-hour emergency response devices and patrols, late night transport-escort service. College housing not available. Robert C. and Dorothy M. Peoples Library plus 1 other with 98,713 books, 99,418 microform titles, 425 serials, 3,070 audiovisual materials, and an OPAC. Operations spending for 2004 fiscal year: $657,504. 516 computers available on campus for general student use. Computer purchase/lease plans available. A campuswide network can be accessed. Staffed computer lab on campus.

■ **AMERICAN UNIVERSITY** *F-8*
4400 Massachusetts Ave., NW
Washington, DC 20016-8001
Tel: (202)885-1000
Admissions: (202)885-6000
Fax: (202)885-6014
E-mail: afa@american.edu
Web Site: http://www.american.edu/
Description: Independent Methodist, university, coed. Awards associate, bachelor's, master's, doctoral, and first professional degrees. Founded 1893. Setting: 84-acre suburban campus. Endowment: $318 million. Research spending for 2004 fiscal year: $11.4 million. Educational spending for 2005 fiscal year: $33,569 per student. Total enrollment: 11,279. Faculty: 941 (513 full-time, 428 part-time). Student-undergrad faculty ratio is 15:1. 13,583 applied, 51% were admitted. 47% from top 10% of their high school class, 82% from top quarter, 98% from top half. 14 National Merit Scholars, 26 valedictorians. Full-time: 5,624 students, 62% women, 38% men. Part-time: 297 students, 55% women, 45% men. Students come from 54 states and territories, 117 other countries, 99% from out-of-district, 0.4% Native American, 5% Hispanic, 6% black, 5% Asian American or Pacific Islander, 6% international, 2% 25 or older, 68% live on campus, 7% transferred in. Retention: 89% of full-time freshmen returned the following year. Academic areas with the most degrees conferred: social sciences; business/marketing; communication technologies. Core. Calendar: semesters. Services for LD students, advanced placement, accelerated degree program, self-designed majors, honors program, independent study, double major, summer session for credit, part-time degree program, adult/continuing education programs, co-op programs and internships, graduate courses open to undergrads. Off campus study at Consortium of Universities of the Washington Metropolitan Area. Study abroad program. ROTC: Army (c), Air Force (c).
Entrance Requirements: Options: Peterson's Universal Application, Common Application, electronic application, early decision, deferred admission, international baccalaureate accepted. Required: essay, high school transcript, minimum 2.0 high school GPA, 2 recommendations, SAT or ACT. Recommended: minimum 3.0 high school GPA, interview, SAT Subject Tests. Entrance: very difficult. Application deadlines: 1/15, 11/15 for early decision. Notification: 4/1, 12/31 for early decision.
Costs Per Year: Application fee: $45. Comprehensive fee: $41,043 includes full-time tuition ($29,205), mandatory fees ($496), and college room and board ($11,342). College room only: $7197. Part-time tuition: $973 per semester hour. Part-time mandatory fees: $159 per year.
Collegiate Environment: Orientation program. Drama-theater group, choral group, student-run newspaper, radio station. Social organizations: 128 open to all; national fraternities, national sororities; 14% of eligible men and 16% of eligible women are members. Most popular organizations: Kennedy Political Union, Student Confederation, Freshman Service Experience, Student Union Board, DC Reads. Major annual events: Homecoming, Family Weekend, Eagle Nights. Student services: health clinic, personal-psychological counseling. Campus security: 24-hour emergency response devices and patrols, late night transport-escort service, controlled dormitory access. 3,847 college housing spaces available; 3,500 were occupied in 2003-04. Freshmen guaranteed college housing. Option: coed housing available. American University Bender Library plus 1 other with 796,000 books, 1.1 million microform titles, 4,466 serials, 46,000 audiovisual materials, an OPAC, and a Web page. Operations spending for 2004 fiscal year: $11.1 million. 760 computers available on campus for general student use.

Computer purchase/lease plans available. A campuswide network can be accessed from student residence rooms and from off campus. Staffed computer lab on campus.
Community Environment: Washington, D.C., is located on the Potomac River between Maryland and Virginia. It is a beautiful and historic city of impressive buildings and residential neighborhoods, with a vibrant, diverse international character. All major forms of transportation are available: the Metro bus and subway system, historic Union Railroad Station, and three major airports serve Washington. The National Zoo, Rock Creek Park, and the C&O Canal are some of the city's finest recreation areas. Shopping facilities are excellent. Points of interest for students include government sites such as the U.S. Capitol, Senate and House office buildings, U.S. Treasury, Supreme Court, Federal Bureau of Investigation, and the White House; cultural institutions such as the Folger Shakespeare Library, Library of Congress, Smithsonian Institute, U.S. Holocaust Memorial Museum, Frederick Douglass Museum, National Gallery of Art, National Archives, Islamic Center, Washington Cathedral, and John F. Kennedy Center for the Performing Arts; scientific institutions such as the National Bureau of Standards, Naval Observatory, and the nearby National Institutes of Health; and international organizations such as the World Bank, Pan American Union, and the embassies and legations of many nations.

■ **THE CATHOLIC UNIVERSITY OF AMERICA** *F-8*
Cardinal Station
Washington, DC 20064
Tel: (202)319-5000
Free: 800-673-2772
Admissions: (202)319-5305
Fax: (202)319-6533
E-mail: cua-admissions@cua.edu
Web Site: http://www.cua.edu/
Description: Independent, university, coed, affiliated with Roman Catholic Church. Awards bachelor's, master's, doctoral, and first professional degrees and post-master's certificates. Founded 1887. Setting: 144-acre urban campus. Endowment: $169.8 million. Research spending for 2004 fiscal year: $20 million. Total enrollment: 6,130. Faculty: 714 (344 full-time, 370 part-time). Student-undergrad faculty ratio is 9:1. 3,152 applied, 81% were admitted. 23% from top 10% of their high school class, 54% from top quarter, 84% from top half. Full-time: 2,802 students, 55% women, 45% men. Part-time: 251 students, 67% women, 33% men. Students come from 52 states and territories, 36 other countries, 93% from out-of-district, 0.1% Native American, 5% Hispanic, 7% black, 3% Asian American or Pacific Islander, 2% international, 11% 25 or older, 66% live on campus, 3% transferred in. Retention: 82% of full-time freshmen returned the following year. Academic areas with the most degrees conferred: architecture; mechanic and repair technologies; visual and performing arts. Core. Calendar: semesters. ESL program, services for LD students, advanced placement, accelerated degree program, freshman honors college, honors program, independent study, double major, summer session for credit, part-time degree program, adult/continuing education programs, internships, graduate courses open to undergrads. Off campus study at members of the Consortium of Universities of the Washington Metropolitan Area. Study abroad program. ROTC: Army (c), Naval (c), Air Force (c).
Entrance Requirements: Options: Peterson's Universal Application, Common Application, electronic application, early admission, early decision, deferred admission, international baccalaureate accepted. Required: essay,

high school transcript, 1 recommendation, SAT or ACT. Recommended: minimum 3 high school GPA, interview, SAT Subject Tests. Entrance: moderately difficult. Application deadlines: 2/1, 11/15 for early action. Notification: continuous until 3/1, 11/15 for early action.

Costs Per Year: Application fee: $55. One-time mandatory fee: $365. Comprehensive fee: $35,838 includes full-time tuition ($24,800), mandatory fees ($1200), and college room and board ($9838). College room only: $5646. Full-time tuition and fees vary according to program. Room and board charges vary according to board plan and housing facility. Part-time tuition: $940 per credit. Part-time mandatory fees: $605 per year. Part-time tuition and fees vary according to course load.

Collegiate Environment: Orientation program. Drama-theater group, choral group, student-run newspaper, radio station. Social organizations: 100 open to all; national fraternities, national sororities; 1% of eligible men and 1% of eligible women are members. Most popular organizations: Knights of Columbus, Students for Life, College Republicans, Habitat for Humanity, College Democrats. Major annual events: homecoming, Family Weekend, Movies on the Mall. Student services: legal services, health clinic, personal-psychological counseling, women's center. Campus security: 24-hour emergency response devices and patrols, late night transport-escort service, controlled dormitory access, controlled access of academic buildings. 2,101 college housing spaces available; 1,961 were occupied in 2003-04. Freshmen guaranteed college housing. On-campus residence required through sophomore year. Options: coed, men-only, women-only housing available. Mullen Library plus 7 others with 1.6 million books, 1.1 million microform titles, 5,907 serials, 39,136 audiovisual materials, an OPAC, and a Web page. Operations spending for 2004 fiscal year: $7.5 million. 450 computers available on campus for general student use. Computer purchase/lease plans available. A campuswide network can be accessed from student residence rooms and from off campus. Staffed computer lab on campus.

Community Environment: See American University.

■ **CORCORAN COLLEGE OF ART AND DESIGN** *F-8*
500 17th St. NW
Washington, DC 20006-4804
Tel: (202)639-1800; 888-CORCORAN
Admissions: (202)639-1814
E-mail: admissions@corcoran.org
Web Site: http://www.corcoran.edu/

Description: Independent, comprehensive, coed. Awards associate, bachelor's, and master's degrees. Founded 1890. Setting: 7-acre urban campus. Endowment: $27.7 million. Educational spending for 2005 fiscal year: $6919 per student. Total enrollment: 590. Faculty: 221 (34 full-time, 187 part-time). Student-undergrad faculty ratio is 4:1. 233 applied, 61% were admitted. 20% from top 10% of their high school class, 35% from top quarter, 75% from top half. Full-time: 348 students, 65% women, 35% men. Part-time: 172 students, 72% women, 28% men. Students come from 25 states and territories, 38 other countries, 73% from out-of-district, 0% Native American, 8% Hispanic, 8% black, 10% Asian American or Pacific Islander, 29% 25 or older, 17% live on campus, 13% transferred in. Retention: 69% of full-time freshmen returned the following year. Academic area with the most degrees conferred: visual and performing arts. Core. Calendar: semesters. Academic remediation for entering students, ESL program, advanced placement, independent study, summer session for credit, adult/continuing education programs, internships, graduate courses open to undergrads. Off campus study at Alliance of Independent Colleges of Art and Design.

Entrance Requirements: Options: early admission, deferred admission, international baccalaureate accepted. Required: high school transcript, minimum 2.5 high school GPA, portfolio, SAT or ACT. Recommended: essay, minimum 3.0 high school GPA, 2 recommendations, interview. Required for some: essay, 2 recommendations, interview. Entrance: moderately difficult. Application deadline: Rolling. Notification: continuous.

Costs Per Year: Application fee: $40. Comprehensive fee: $32,850 includes full-time tuition ($22,700), mandatory fees ($100), and college room and board ($10,050). College room only: $8150. Full-time tuition and fees vary according to degree level. Part-time tuition: $630 per credit. Part-time mandatory fees: $100. Part-time tuition and fees vary according to degree level.

Collegiate Environment: Orientation program. Social organizations: 1 open to all. Most popular organization: Student Government Association. Major annual events: Bizarre, Off the Wall Art Sale. Student services: personal-psychological counseling. Campus security: 24-hour patrols, ID check at all entrances. 108 college housing spaces available; all were occupied in 2003-04. Freshmen given priority for college housing. Option: coed housing avail-

able. Corcoran School of Art Library plus 1 other with 29,413 books, 167 serials, 46,013 audiovisual materials, and an OPAC. Operations spending for 2004 fiscal year: $258,269. 117 computers available on campus for general student use. Staffed computer lab on campus.

■ **GALLAUDET UNIVERSITY** *F-8*
800 Florida Ave., NE
Washington, DC 20002-3625
Tel: (202)651-5000
Free: 800-995-0550
Admissions: (202)651-5750
Fax: (202)651-5774
E-mail: admissions@gallua.gallaudet.edu
Web Site: http://www.gallaudet.edu/

Description: Independent, university, coed. Awards bachelor's, master's, and doctoral degrees (undergraduate programs open primarily to the hearing-impaired). Founded 1864. Setting: 99-acre urban campus. Endowment: $144.3 million. Research spending for 2004 fiscal year: $5.1 million. Educational spending for 2005 fiscal year: $25,623 per student. Total enrollment: 1,834. 423 applied, 75% were admitted. Full-time: 1,098 students, 53% women, 47% men. Part-time: 109 students, 51% women, 49% men. Students come from 49 states and territories, 28 other countries, 96% from out-of-district, 4% Native American, 7% Hispanic, 12% black, 5% Asian American or Pacific Islander, 11% international, 31% 25 or older, 70% live on campus, 6% transferred in. Retention: 65% of full-time freshmen returned the following year. Core. Calendar: semesters. Academic remediation for entering students, ESL program, services for LD students, advanced placement, accelerated degree program, self-designed majors, honors program, independent study, distance learning, double major, summer session for credit, part-time degree program, adult/continuing education programs, co-op programs and internships, graduate courses open to undergrads. Off campus study at Oberlin College, McDaniel College, members of the Consortium of Universities of the Washington Metropolitan Area. Study abroad program.

Entrance Requirements: Options: electronic application, early admission, deferred admission. Required: essay, high school transcript, 2 recommendations, audiogram, SAT or ACT. Required for some: interview. Entrance: moderately difficult. Notification: continuous.

Costs Per Year: Application fee: $50. Comprehensive fee: $18,750 includes full-time tuition ($9920), mandatory fees ($330), and college room and board ($8500). College room only: $4850. Room and board charges vary according to board plan. Part-time tuition: $481.50 per credit.

Collegiate Environment: Orientation program. Drama-theater group, student-run newspaper. Social organizations: 30 open to all; national fraternities, national sororities, local fraternities, local sororities; 39% of eligible men and 34% of eligible women are members. Most popular organizations: Student Body Government, Delta Epsilon, Rainbow Society, Black Deaf Student Union. Major annual events: homecoming, RIT/Gallaudet Weekend. Student services: health clinic, personal-psychological counseling. Campus security: 24-hour emergency response devices and patrols, late night transport-escort service, controlled dormitory access. 1,220 college housing spaces available; 797 were occupied in 2003-04. Option: coed housing available. Merrill Learning Center with 242,543 books, 651,909 microform titles, 1,667 serials, 7,174 audiovisual materials, an OPAC, and a Web page. Operations spending for 2004 fiscal year: $2.3 million. 240 computers available on campus for general student use. A campuswide network can be accessed from student residence rooms and from off campus. Staffed computer lab on campus.

Community Environment: See American University.

■ **THE GEORGE WASHINGTON UNIVERSITY** *F-8*
2121 Eye St., NW
Washington, DC 20052
Tel: (202)994-1000
Free: 800-447-3765
Admissions: (202)994-6040
E-mail: gwadm@gwis2.circ.gwu.edu
Web Site: http://www.gwu.edu/

Description: Independent, university, coed. Awards associate, bachelor's, master's, doctoral, and first professional degrees and post-master's certificates. Founded 1821. Setting: 36-acre urban campus. Endowment: $621.1 million. Educational spending for 2005 fiscal year: $14,320 per student. Total enrollment: 24,099. Faculty: 2,036 (826 full-time, 1,210 part-time). Student-undergrad faculty ratio is 14:1. 19,406 applied, 37% were admitted. 63% from top 10% of their high school class, 88% from top quarter, 99% from top half. 36 National Merit Scholars. Full-time: 9,741 students, 57% women, 43% men. Part-time: 1,020 students, 51% women, 49% men. Students come from 55 states and territories, 101 other countries, 98% from out-of-district, 0.3% Native American, 5% Hispanic, 6% black, 9% Asian American or Pacific Islander, 4% international, 3% 25 or older, 62% live on campus, 4% transferred in. Retention: 92% of full-time freshmen returned the following year. Academic areas with the most degrees conferred: social sciences; business/marketing; psychology. Core. Calendar: semesters. ESL program, services for LD students, advanced placement, accelerated degree program, self-designed majors, honors program, independent study, distance learning, double major, summer session for credit, part-time degree program, adult/continuing education programs, co-op programs and internships, graduate courses open to undergrads. Off campus study at members of the Consortium of Universities of the Washington Metropolitan Area. Study abroad program. ROTC: Army (c), Naval, Air Force (c).

Entrance Requirements: Options: Peterson's Universal Application, Common Application, electronic application, early admission, early decision, deferred admission. Required: essay, high school transcript, 2 recommendations, SAT or ACT. Recommended: interview. Entrance: very difficult. Application deadlines: 1/15, 12/1 for early decision plan 1, 1/15 for early decision plan 2. Notification: continuous until 3/15, 12/15 for early decision plan 1, 2/1 for early decision plan 2.

Costs Per Year: Application fee: $70. Comprehensive fee: $48,820 includes full-time tuition ($37,790), mandatory fees ($30), and college room and board ($11,000). College room only: $8000. Part-time tuition: $1050 per credit hour.

Collegiate Environment: Orientation program. Drama-theater group, choral group, marching band, student-run newspaper, radio station. Social organizations: 208 open to all; national fraternities, national sororities; 16% of eligible men and 13% of eligible women are members. Most popular organizations: Program Board, Student Association, Residence Hall Association, College Democrats, College Republicans. Major annual events: homecoming, Welcome Week, Colonial Inauguration. Student services: legal services, health clinic, personal-psychological counseling. Campus security: 24-hour emergency response devices and patrols, late night transport-escort service, controlled dormitory access. 6,200 college housing spaces available; 6,172 were occupied in 2003-04. Freshmen guaranteed college housing. Options: coed, women-only housing available. Gelman Library plus 2 others with 2 million books, 2.6 million microform titles, 15,365 serials, 171,397 audiovisual materials, an OPAC, and a Web page. 550 computers available on campus for general student use. A campuswide network can be accessed from student residence rooms and from off campus. Staffed computer lab on campus.

Community Environment: See American University.

■ **GEORGETOWN UNIVERSITY** *F-8*

37th and O Sts., NW
Washington, DC 20057
Tel: (202)687-5055
Admissions: (202)687-3600
Fax: (202)687-6660
Web Site: http://www.georgetown.edu/

Description: Independent Roman Catholic (Jesuit), university, coed. Awards bachelor's, master's, doctoral, and first professional degrees. Founded 1789. Setting: 110-acre urban campus. Endowment: $755.2 million. Research spending for 2004 fiscal year: $125.4 million. Educational spending for 2005 fiscal year: $18,015 per student. Total enrollment: 13,652. Faculty: 1,258 (752 full-time, 506 part-time). Student-undergrad faculty ratio is 11:1. 15,285 applied, 21% were admitted. 86% from top 10% of their high school class, 97% from top quarter, 100% from top half. 43 National Merit Scholars, 47 class presidents, 199 valedictorians, 202 student government officers. Full-time: 6,504 students, 54% women, 46% men. Part-time: 215 students, 57% women, 43% men. Students come from 52 states and territories, 82 other countries, 98% from out-of-district, 0.1% Native American, 6% Hispanic, 7% black, 9% Asian American or Pacific Islander, 4% international, 2% 25 or older, 78% live on campus, 3% transferred in. Retention: 98% of full-time freshmen returned the following year. Academic areas with the most degrees conferred: social sciences; business/marketing; liberal arts/general studies. Core. Calendar: semesters. Academic remediation for entering students, ESL program, services for LD students, advanced placement, self-designed majors, honors program, independent study, double major, summer session for credit, adult/continuing education programs, internships, graduate courses open to undergrads. Off campus study at members of the

Consortium of Universities of the Washington Metropolitan Area. Study abroad program. ROTC: Army, Naval (c), Air Force (c).

Entrance Requirements: Options: electronic application, early action, deferred admission, international baccalaureate accepted. Required: essay, high school transcript, 2 recommendations, interview, SAT or ACT. Recommended: SAT Subject Tests. Entrance: most difficult. Application deadlines: 1/10, 11/1 for early action. Notification: 4/1, 12/15 for early action.

Costs Per Year: Application fee: $60. Comprehensive fee: $43,183 includes full-time tuition ($31,656), mandatory fees ($368), and college room and board ($11,159). College room only: $7410. Room and board charges vary according to board plan and housing facility. Part-time tuition: $1319 per credit hour. Part-time tuition varies according to course level.

Collegiate Environment: Orientation program. Drama-theater group, choral group, student-run newspaper, radio station. Social organizations: 129 open to all. Most popular organizations: University Choir, Mask and Bauble, The Hoya (student newspaper), International Relations Club, The Voice (weekly news magazine). Major annual events: Homecoming Block Party, GU Day, Student Activities Fair. Student services: health clinic, personal-psychological counseling, women's center. Campus security: 24-hour emergency response devices and patrols, late night transport-escort service, controlled dormitory access, student guards at residence halls and academic facilities. 5,053 college housing spaces available; 4,818 were occupied in 2003-04. Freshmen guaranteed college housing. On-campus residence required through sophomore year. Option: coed housing available. Lauinger Library plus 6 others with 2.4 million books, 3.8 million microform titles, 23,241 serials, 16,415 audiovisual materials, an OPAC, and a Web page. Operations spending for 2004 fiscal year: $23.3 million. 400 computers available on campus for general student use. Computer purchase/lease plans available. A campuswide network can be accessed from student residence rooms and from off campus. Staffed computer lab on campus.

Community Environment: See American University.

■ **HOWARD UNIVERSITY** *F-8*

2400 Sixth St., NW
Washington, DC 20059-0002
Tel: (202)806-6100
Free: 800-HOWARD-U
Web Site: http://www.howard.edu/

Description: Independent, university, coed. Awards bachelor's, master's, doctoral, and first professional degrees and post-master's and first professional certificates. Founded 1867. Setting: 256-acre urban campus. Endowment: $371.2 million. Research spending for 2004 fiscal year: $37 million. Total enrollment: 10,623. 8,860 applied, 47% were admitted. 23% from top 10% of their high school class, 49% from top quarter, 81% from top half. 9 class presidents, 8 valedictorians, 30 student government officers. Full-time: 6,730 students, 67% women, 33% men. Part-time: 382 students, 63% women, 37% men. Students come from 50 states and territories, 61 other countries, 90% from out-of-district, 0.1% Native American, 0.3% Hispanic, 84% black, 0.5% Asian American or Pacific Islander, 7% international, 17% 25 or older, 57% live on campus, 5% transferred in. Retention: 89% of full-time freshmen returned the following year. Core. Calendar: semesters. Academic remediation for entering students, services for LD students, advanced placement, accelerated degree program, self-designed majors, freshman honors college, honors program, independent study, distance learning, double major, summer session for credit, part-time degree program, adult/continuing education programs, co-op programs and internships, graduate courses open to undergrads. Off campus study at 9 members of the Consortium of Universities of the Washington Metropolitan Area; over 21 colleges and universities including Duke University; University of California, Berkeley; Smith College; Vassar College; Williams College. Study abroad program. ROTC: Army, Air Force.

Entrance Requirements: Options: early admission, early action, deferred admission. Required: high school transcript, SAT or ACT. Required for some: 2 recommendations. Entrance: moderately difficult. Application deadlines: 2/15, 11/1 for early action. Notification: continuous, 12/24 for early action.

Costs Per Year: Application fee: $45. Comprehensive fee: $18,481 includes full-time tuition ($11,490), mandatory fees ($805), and college room and board ($6186). College room only: $3736. Room and board charges vary according to board plan and housing facility. Part-time tuition: $479 per credit hour.

Collegiate Environment: Orientation program. Drama-theater group, choral group, marching band, student-run newspaper, radio station. Social organizations: 150 open to all; national fraternities, national sororities, local fraternities; 2% of eligible men and 1% of eligible women are members. Most popular organizations: Howard University Student Association, Undergraduate Student Assembly, Campus Pals. Major annual events: homecoming, Spring Black Arts Festival, Residence Hall Week. Student services: health clinic, personal-psychological counseling. Campus security: 24-hour emergency response devices and patrols, student patrols, late night transport-escort service, controlled dormitory access, security lighting. 9,000 college housing spaces available; 3,999 were occupied in 2003-04. Freshmen given priority for college housing. On-campus residence required through sophomore year. Option: coed housing available. Founders Library plus 8 others with 2.5 million books, 3.5 million microform titles, 12,795 serials, 40,872 audiovisual materials, an OPAC, and a Web page. 6,343 computers available on campus for general student use. Computer purchase/lease plans available. A campuswide network can be accessed from student residence rooms and from off campus. Staffed computer lab on campus.

Community Environment: See American University.

■ **POTOMAC COLLEGE** *F-8*
4000 Chesapeake St., NW
Washington, DC 20016
Tel: (202)686-0876; 888-686-0876
Admissions: (202)274-2305
Fax: (202)686-0818
E-mail: cparker@potomac.edu
Web Site: http://www.potomac.edu/

Description: Proprietary, 4-year, coed. Awards associate and bachelor's degrees. Founded 1991. Setting: urban campus. Total enrollment: 398. Student-undergrad faculty ratio is 15:1. 71 applied, 76% were admitted. Full-time: 87 students, 52% women, 48% men. Part-time: 311 students, 64% women, 36% men. 92% from out-of-district, 0% Native American, 3% Hispanic, 76% black, 1% Asian American or Pacific Islander, 0% international, 98% 25 or older. Retention: 76% of full-time freshmen returned the following year. Core. Calendar: 6-week modules. Academic remediation for entering students, services for LD students, advanced placement, accelerated degree program, independent study, double major, summer session for credit, part-time degree program, external degree program, adult/continuing education programs, internships.

Entrance Requirements: Open admission for undeclared majors and declared majors with 45 college credits. Option: international baccalaureate accepted. Required: high school transcript, interview. Entrance: noncompetitive. Application deadline: Rolling. Notification: continuous.

Costs Per Year: Application fee: $15. Tuition: $17,220 full-time. Mandatory fees: $90 full-time. Full-time tuition and fees vary according to course load and program.

Collegiate Environment: Orientation program. Social organizations: 1 open to all. Most popular organization: Student Government Association. Major annual events: Graduate School Brown Bag Lunches, Moving Up Day, Half-Way Ceremony. Student services: personal-psychological counseling. Campus security: 24-hour emergency response devices. College housing not available. Potomac College Library with 5,565 books, 40 serials, 100 audiovisual materials, and an OPAC. Operations spending for 2004 fiscal year: $16,250. 20 computers available on campus for general student use. A campuswide network can be accessed from off-campus. Staffed computer lab on campus.

■ **SOUTHEASTERN UNIVERSITY** *F-8*
501 I St., SW
Washington, DC 20024-2788
Tel: (202)478-8200
Fax: (202)488-8162
Web Site: http://www.seu.edu/

Description: Independent, comprehensive, coed. Awards associate, bachelor's, and master's degrees. Founded 1879. Setting: 1-acre urban campus. Endowment: $27,450. Educational spending for 2005 fiscal year: $3057 per student. Total enrollment: 935. 611 applied, 66% were admitted. Full-time: 212 students, 64% women, 36% men. Part-time: 453 students, 79% women, 21% men. Students come from 7 states and territories, 40 other countries, 25% from out-of-district, 0% Native American, 1% Hispanic, 83% black, 1% Asian American or Pacific Islander, 9% international, 60% 25 or older, 3% transferred in. Core. Calendar: quadmester (four 12-week semesters). Academic remediation for entering students, ESL program, advanced placement, accelerated degree program, honors program, independent study, double major, summer session for credit, part-time

degree program, external degree program, adult/continuing education programs, co-op programs and internships, graduate courses open to undergrads. Study abroad program.

Entrance Requirements: Open admission. Options: deferred admission, international baccalaureate accepted. Required: high school transcript. Recommended: essay, interview. Entrance: noncompetitive. Application deadline: Rolling.

Collegiate Environment: Orientation program. Social organizations: national fraternities, national sororities; 2% of eligible men and 2% of eligible women are members. Most popular organization: SGA. Major annual events: International Festival, Ramadan activities, Multicultural Holidays. Student services: personal-psychological counseling. Campus security: late night transport-escort service. College housing not available. The Learning Resources Center plus 1 other with 32,000 books, 2,000 microform titles, 200 serials, and 250 audiovisual materials. Operations spending for 2004 fiscal year: $259,594. 137 computers available on campus for general student use. A campuswide network can be accessed from off-campus. Staffed computer lab on campus.

Community Environment: See American University.

■ **STRAYER UNIVERSITY** *F-8*
1025 15th St., NW
Washington, DC 20005-2603
Tel: (202)408-2400; 888-4-STRAYER
Admissions: (202)419-4190
Fax: (202)289-1831
Web Site: http://www.strayer.edu/

Description: Proprietary, comprehensive, coed. Part of Strayer Education, Inc.. Awards associate, bachelor's, and master's degrees. Founded 1892. Setting: urban campus. Total enrollment: 20,138. 5% from out-of-district, 78% 25 or older. Core. Academic remediation for entering students, services for LD students, advanced placement, accelerated degree program, distance learning, double major, summer session for credit, part-time degree program, adult/continuing education programs, co-op programs and internships, graduate courses open to undergrads. Off.campus study at Servicemembers Opportunity Colleges.

Entrance Requirements: Open admission. Options: electronic application, early admission, deferred admission. Required: high school transcript. Recommended: essay, 1 recommendation, interview. Required for some: 1 recommendation. Entrance: noncompetitive. Application deadline: Rolling. Notification: continuous.

Collegiate Environment: Social organizations: 13 open to all. Most popular organizations: honor society, International Club, Association of Information Technology Professionals, Business Administration Club, Human Resource Management Club. Major annual event: International Day. Campus security: patrols by trained personnel during operating hours. College housing not available. Wilkes Library plus 20 others with 34,000 books, 600 serials, 1,687 audiovisual materials, an OPAC, and a Web page. 1,500 computers available on campus for general student use. A campuswide network can be accessed. Staffed computer lab on campus.

Community Environment: See American University.

■ **TRINITY (WASHINGTON) UNIVERSITY** *F-8*
125 Michigan Ave., NE
Washington, DC 20017-1094
Tel: (202)884-9000
Free: 800-IWA-NTTC
Admissions: 800-492-6882
Fax: (202)884-9229
E-mail: admissions@trinitydc.edu
Web Site: http://www.trinitydc.edu/

Description: Independent Roman Catholic, comprehensive. Awards bachelor's and master's degrees. Founded 1897. Setting: 26-acre urban campus. Endowment: $10 million. Educational spending for 2005 fiscal year: $4400 per student. Total enrollment: 1,672. 441 applied, 86% were admitted. 20 student government officers. Full-time: 549 students, 99% women, 1% men. Part-time: 419 students, 96% women, 4% men. Students come from 17 states and territories, 50% from out-of-district, 1% Native American, 11% Hispanic, 68% black, 2% Asian American or Pacific Islander, 1% international, 46% 25 or older, 30% live on campus, 3% transferred in. Retention: 69% of full-time freshmen returned the following year. Core. Calendar: semesters. Academic remediation for entering students, ESL program, services for LD students, advanced placement, accelerated degree program, self-designed majors, honors program, independent study, double major, summer session for credit, part-time degree program, external degree program, adult/continuing education programs, co-op programs and internships, graduate courses open to undergrads. Off campus study at Georgetown University; George Washington University; American University; Catholic University of America; University of Maryland, College Park; University of the District of Columbia; Marymount University. Study abroad program. ROTC: Army (c).

Entrance Requirements: Options: Peterson's Universal Application, Common Application, electronic application, early action, deferred admission, international baccalaureate accepted. Required: essay, high school transcript, minimum 2.0 high school GPA, 1 recommendation. Recommended: interview, SAT or ACT. Entrance: moderately difficult. Application deadlines: 3/1, 12/1 for early action. Notification: 1/1 for early action.

Costs Per Year: Application fee: $35. Comprehensive fee: $24,934 includes full-time tuition ($17,200), mandatory fees ($160), and college room and board ($7574). College room only: $3350. Full-time tuition and fees vary according to class time. Room and board charges vary according to board plan and housing facility. Part-time tuition: $555 per credit hour. Part-time tuition varies according to class time.

Collegiate Environment: Orientation program. Drama-theater group, choral group, student-run newspaper. Social organizations: 28 open to all. Most popular organizations: Campus Ministry, Athletic Association, International Club, Black Student Alliance, Young Democrats/Republicans. Major annual events: Founders' Day, Cap and Gown Sunday, Holly Hop. Student services: health clinic, personal-psychological counseling. Campus security: 24-hour emergency response devices and patrols, late night transport-escort service, controlled dormitory access. 230 college housing spaces available; 180 were occupied in 2003-04. On-campus residence required through junior year. Option: women-only housing available. Sister Helen Sheehan Library plus 1 other with 207,000 books, 6,754 microform titles, 498 serials, 13,760 audiovisual materials, an OPAC, and a Web page. Operations spending for 2004 fiscal year: $500,000. 80 computers available on campus for general student use. A campuswide network can be accessed from student residence rooms and from off campus. Staffed computer lab on campus.

■ **UNIVERSITY OF THE DISTRICT OF COLUMBIA** *F-8*
4200 Connecticut Ave., NW
Washington, DC 20008-1175
Tel: (202)274-5000
Admissions: (202)274-6110
Web Site: http://www.udc.edu/

Description: District-supported, comprehensive, coed. Awards associate, bachelor's, and master's degrees. Founded 1976. Setting: 28-acre urban campus. Endowment: $32.6 million. Research spending for 2004 fiscal year: $2.9 million. Educational spending for 2005 fiscal year: $9507 per student. Total enrollment: 5,364. Faculty: 478 (242 full-time, 236 part-time). Student-undergrad faculty ratio is 13:1. 4,190 applied, 82% were admitted. Full-time: 1,966 students, 60% women, 40% men. Part-time: 3,204 students, 68% women, 32% men. Students come from 54 states and territories, 125 other countries, 27% from out-of-district, 63% 25 or older, 11% transferred in. Retention: 60% of full-time freshmen returned the following year. Academic areas with the most degrees conferred: business/marketing; health professions and related sciences; security and protective services. Core. Calendar: semesters. Academic remediation for entering students, ESL program, services for LD students, accelerated degree program, honors program, summer session for credit, part-time degree program, external degree program, adult/continuing education programs, co-op programs and internships, graduate courses open to undergrads. Off campus study at members of the Consortium of Universities of the Washington Metropolitan Area. ROTC: Army (c), Air Force (c).

Entrance Requirements: Open admission. Options: Common Application, deferred admission. Required: high school transcript. Recommended: SAT. Required for some: GED. Entrance: noncompetitive. Application deadline: 8/1. Notification: continuous until 8/15. Preference given to district residents.

Costs Per Year: Application fee: $20. Area resident tuition: $1800 full-time, $75 per credit part-time. Nonresident tuition: $4440 full-time, $185 per credit part-time. Mandatory fees: $270 full-time, $135 per term part-time. Part-time tuition and fees vary according to course load.

Collegiate Environment: Drama-theater group, choral group, marching band, student-run newspaper. Social organizations: 61 open to all; national fraternities, national sororities; 2% of eligible men and 3% of eligible women are members. Most popular organizations: Caribbean Student Association, Theater Arts Ensemble, National Association for the Advancement of Colored People. Major annual events: homecoming, basketball games, Miss UDC Pageant. Student services: health clinic, personal-psychological counseling. Campus security: 24-hour patrols. College housing not available. Learning Resources Division Library plus 1 other with 544,412 books, 607,162 microform titles, 594 serials, 19,635 audiovisual materials, an OPAC, and a Web page. Operations spending for 2004 fiscal year: $2.6 million. 1,500 computers available on campus for general student use. A campuswide network can be accessed. Staffed computer lab on campus.

Community Environment: See American University.

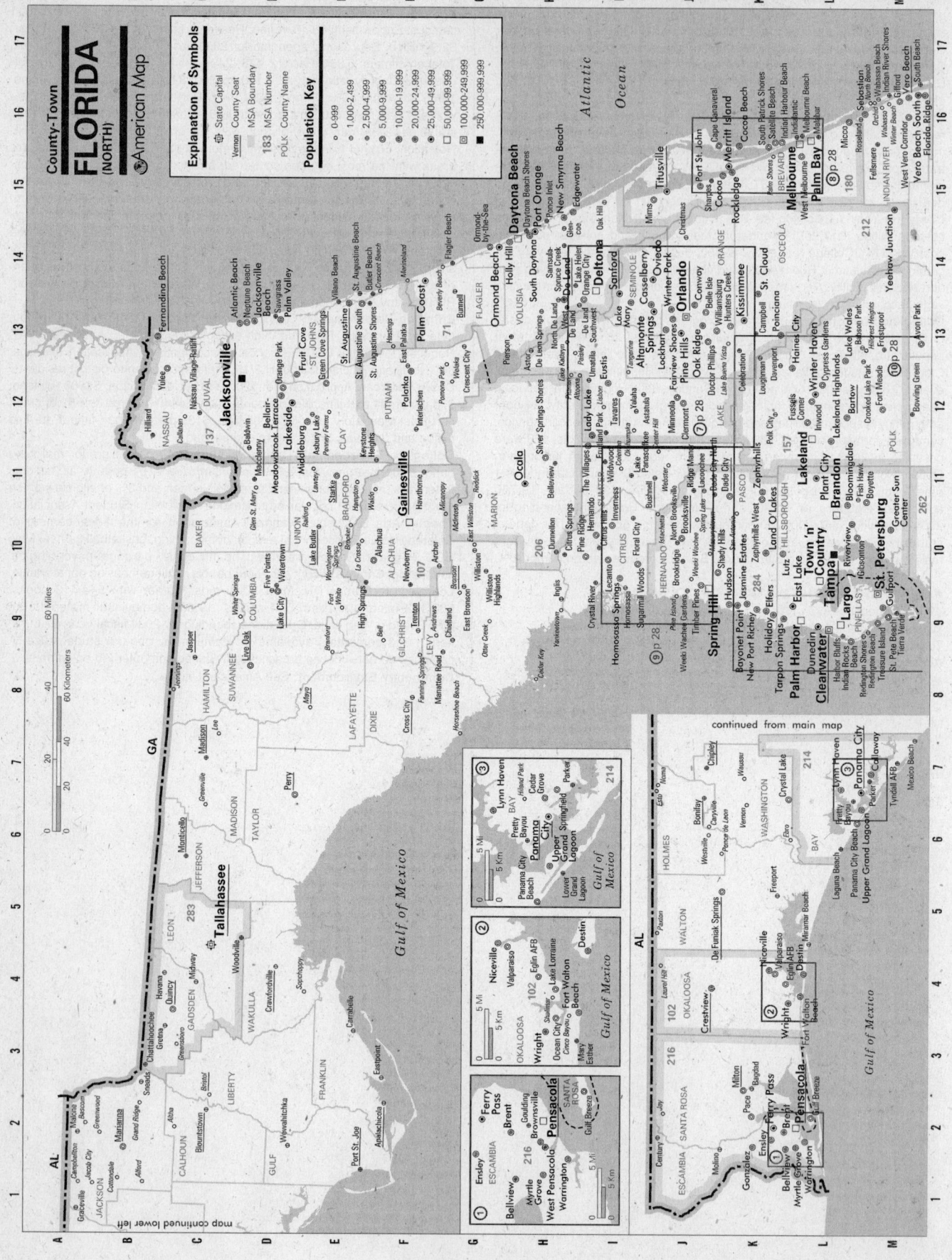

County-Town
FLORIDA
(NORTH)
⊕American Map

Explanation of Symbols
Vernon   ◉ State Capital
Vernon   ⊚ County Seat
     —— MSA Boundary
183   MSA Number
POLK   County Name

Population Key
• 0-999
○ 1,000-2,499
⊙ 2,500-4,999
⊙ 5,000-9,999
⊚ 10,000-19,999
⊚ 20,000-24,999
◉ 25,000-49,999
□ 50,000-99,999
■ 100,000-249,999
■ 250,000-999,999

Atlantic Ocean

Gulf of Mexico

GA

AL

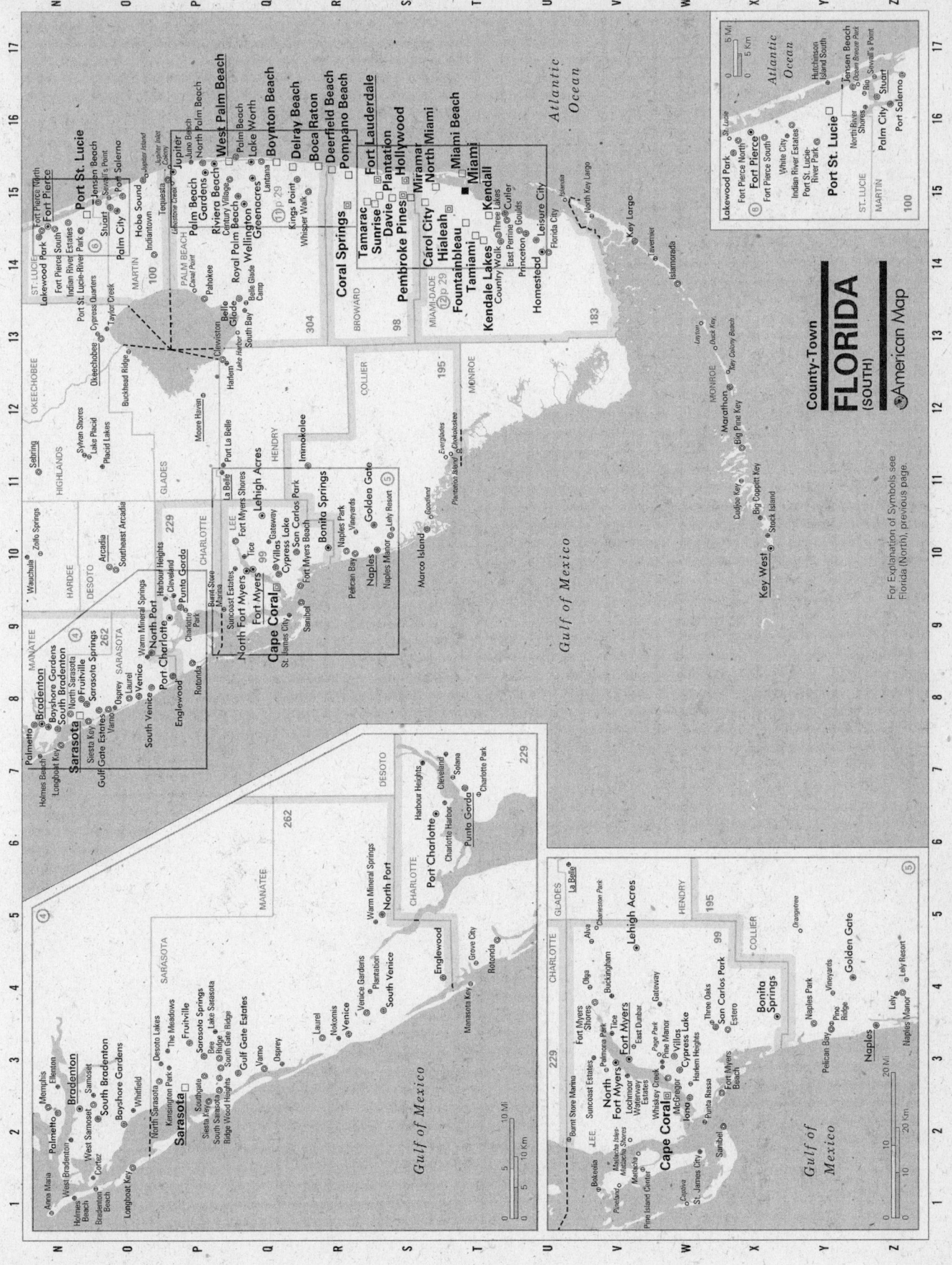

County-Town
FLORIDA
(SOUTH)
⊛ American Map

For Explanation of Symbols see
Florida (North), previous page.

■ **AMERICAN INTERCONTINENTAL UNIVERSITY** *O-12*
2250 North Commerce Parkway, Ste. 100
Weston, FL 33326
Tel: (954)446-6100; (866)248-4723
Fax: (954)835-1020
Web Site: http://www.aiufl.edu/
Description: Proprietary, comprehensive, coed. Administratively affiliated with Career Education Corporation. Awards associate, bachelor's, and master's degrees. Setting: 3-acre suburban campus. Total enrollment: 1,318. Faculty: 79 (38 full-time, 41 part-time). Student-undergrad faculty ratio is 22:1. Full-time: 1,114 students, 53% women, 47% men. Part-time: 91 students, 54% women, 46% men. Students come from 5 states and territories, 11 other countries, 3% from out-of-state, 0.2% Native American, 16% Hispanic, 24% black, 1% Asian American or Pacific Islander, 42% 25 or older, 5% live on campus, 0.2% transferred in. Academic areas with the most degrees conferred: computer and information sciences; business/marketing; visual and performing arts. Core. Calendar: five 10-week terms. Academic remediation for entering students, advanced placement, independent study, distance learning, part-time degree program, adult/continuing education programs. Off campus study at Cecore.
Entrance Requirements: Open admission. Options: Common Application, electronic application, international baccalaureate accepted. Required: high school transcript, high school diploma or GED, ACCUPLACER; completion of freshman English and math. Entrance: noncompetitive. Application deadline: Rolling. Notification: continuous.
Costs Per Year: Application fee: $50. Tuition: $55,000 full-time, $398 per credit part-time. Mandatory fees: $3500 full-time, $3500 per year part-time. Full-time tuition and fees vary according to course load and program. Part-time tuition and fees vary according to course load and program.
Collegiate Environment: Orientation program. College housing not available. AIU Fort Lauderdale Library with 3,256 books, 100 serials, and an OPAC. Operations spending for 2004 fiscal year: $100,000. 35 computers available on campus for general student use. Computer purchase/lease plans available. A campuswide network can be accessed from off-campus. Staffed computer lab on campus.

■ **ANGLEY COLLEGE** *H-13*
230 N. Woodland Blvd., Ste. 310
Deland, FL 32720
Tel: (386)740-1215
Web Site: http://www.angley.edu
Description: Proprietary, 2-year. Calendar: continuous.

■ **ARGOSY UNIVERSITY/SARASOTA** *N-8*
5250 17th St.
Sarasota, FL 34235-8246
Tel: (941)379-0404
Free: 800-331-5995
Fax: (941)379-9464
Web Site: http://www.sarasota.edu/
Description: Proprietary, upper-level, coed. Part of Education Management Corporation. Awards bachelor's, master's, and doctoral degrees. Founded 1974. Total enrollment: 40. Full-time: 14 students, 86% women, 14% men. Part-time: 26 students, 65% women, 35% men. 0% from out-of-state, 0% Native American, 8% Hispanic, 13% black, 0% Asian American or Pacific

Islander, 3% international, 85% 25 or older, 25% transferred in. Core. Calendar: semesters. Part-time degree program, adult/continuing education programs.
Collegiate Environment: College housing not available. Doris Pickett Library with 10,000 books, 18,000 serials, 300 audiovisual materials, an OPAC, and a Web page. 80 computers available on campus for general student use. A campuswide network can be accessed. Staffed computer lab on campus.

■ **ARGOSY UNIVERSITY/TAMPA** *L-10*
4401 North Himes Ave., Ste. 150
Tampa, FL 33614
Tel: (813)246-4419
Free: 800-850-6488
Admissions: (813)393-5260
Fax: (813)246-4045
Web Site: http://www.argosyu.edu/
Description: Proprietary, upper-level, coed. Administratively affiliated with Education Management Corporation. Awards bachelor's and master's degrees. Setting: urban campus. Total enrollment: 409. 0% from out-of-state, 0% Native American, 6% Hispanic, 20% black, 4% Asian American or Pacific Islander, 90% 25 or older. Calendar: semesters.
Collegiate Environment: Social organizations: 1 open to all; 1% of eligible men and 3% of eligible women are members. Most popular organization: Student Senate.

■ **THE ART INSTITUTE OF FORT LAUDERDALE** *S-15*
1799 Southeast 17th St. Causeway
Fort Lauderdale, FL 33316-3000
Tel: (954)527-1799
Free: 800-275-7603
Fax: (954)728-8637
Web Site: http://www.aifl.edu/
Description: Proprietary, 4-year, coed. Part of Education Management Corporation. Administratively affiliated with The Art Institutes. Awards associate and bachelor's degrees. Founded 1968. Setting: urban campus with easy access to Miami. Total enrollment: 3,500. 1% from top half of their high school class. Students come from 52 states and territories, 55 other countries, 40% 25 or older, 13% live on campus. Core. Academic remediation for entering students, ESL program, services for LD students, advanced placement, accelerated degree program, honors program, independent study, summer session for credit, adult/continuing education programs, co-op programs and internships. Off campus study. Study abroad program.
Entrance Requirements: Options: Common Application, electronic application. Required: essay, high school transcript, interview. Entrance: noncompetitive. Application deadline: Rolling.
Collegiate Environment: Orientation program. Student services: personal-psychological counseling. 500 college housing spaces available; 453 were occupied in 2003-04. Freshmen guaranteed college housing. Option: coed housing available. Nevin C. Meinhardt Memorial Library with 19,614 books, 339 serials, 2,679 audiovisual materials, an OPAC, and a Web page. Operations spending for 2004 fiscal year: $200,000. 600 computers available on campus for general student use. A campuswide network can be accessed from student residence rooms and from off campus. Staffed computer lab on campus.

Community Environment: AIFL is located in Broward County, Fort Lauderdale, pop. 150,000. It has a diverse mix of culture and lifestyles with a stimulating, creative learning environment nestled between 23 miles of beaches and 3,000 annual hours of sunshine.

■ THE ART INSTITUTE OF TAMPA *L-10*

4401 North Himes Ave., Ste. 150
Tampa, FL 33614
Tel: (866)703-3277; (866)703-3277
Admissions: (813)873-2112
Fax: (813)873-2171
E-mail: johanneg@aii.edu
Web Site: http://www.aita.artinstitutes.edu/

Description: Proprietary, 4-year, coed. Part of Education Management Corporation. Awards bachelor's degrees. Total enrollment: 490. Student-undergrad faculty ratio is 10:1. 450 applied, 65% were admitted. 14% from out-of-state, 18% live on campus. Core. Services for LD students, advanced placement, summer session for credit, co-op programs and internships.

Entrance Requirements: Options: Common Application, electronic application. Required: essay, high school transcript, minimum 2.0 high school GPA, interview. Recommended: SAT and SAT Subject Tests or ACT. Required for some: minimum 2.5 high school GPA, portfolio. Entrance: moderately difficult. Application deadline: 10/11. Notification: continuous.

Costs Per Year: Application fee: $50. Tuition: $15,405 full-time. College room only: $3500.

Collegiate Environment: Orientation program. Student services: personal-psychological counseling. 42 undergraduates lived in college housing during 2003-04. Freshmen given priority for college housing. Option: coed housing available. The Art Institute of Tampa Library with 2,039 books, 69 serials, 192 audiovisual materials, an OPAC, and a Web page. 85 computers available on campus for general student use. A campuswide network can be accessed. Staffed computer lab on campus.

■ ATI CAREER TRAINING CENTER (FORT LAUDERDALE) *S-15*

2880 NW 62nd St.
Fort Lauderdale, FL 33309-9731
Tel: (954)973-4760
Fax: (954)973-6422
Web Site: http://www.aticareertraining.com/

Description: Proprietary, 2-year, coed. Awards terminal associate degrees. Setting: suburban campus. Total enrollment: 350.

■ ATI CAREER TRAINING CENTER (MIAMI) *T-15*

1 NE 19th St.
Miami, FL 33132
Tel: (305)573-1600
Web Site: http://www.aticareertraining.com/

Description: Proprietary, 2-year. Total enrollment: 325.

■ ATI CAREER TRAINING CENTER (OAKLAND PARK) *N-16*

3501 NW 9th Ave.
Oakland Park, FL 33309-9612
Tel: (954)563-5899
Web Site: http://www.aticareertraining.com/

Description: Proprietary, 2-year.

■ ATI HEALTH EDUCATION CENTER *T-15*

1395 NW 167th St., Ste. 200
Miami, FL 33169-5742
Tel: (305)628-1000
E-mail: bwoolsey@atienterprises.edu
Web Site: http://www.aticareertraining.com/

Description: Proprietary, 2-year, coed. Part of ATI Enterprises Inc. of Florida. Awards transfer associate and terminal associate degrees. Founded 1976. Setting: 1-acre urban campus. Total enrollment: 275. Students come from 2 states and territories, 5 other countries, 50% 25 or older. Calendar: semesters. Academic remediation for entering students.

Entrance Requirements: Required: high school transcript, interview. Placement: Wonderlic aptitude test required. Entrance: minimally difficult. Application deadline: Rolling. Notification: continuous.

Collegiate Environment: Student services: health clinic, personal-psychological counseling. College housing not available. 20 serials.

■ AVE MARIA UNIVERSITY *S-10*

1025 Commons Circle
Naples, FL 34119

Tel: (239)280-2554; 877-AVE-UNIV
Fax: (239)352-2392
E-mail: dan.murphy@avemaria.edu
Web Site: http://www.avemaria.edu/

Description: Independent Roman Catholic, comprehensive, coed. Awards bachelor's and master's degrees. Founded 2002. Setting: suburban campus. Total enrollment: 316. 597 applied, 71% were admitted. Full-time: 307 students, 57% women, 43% men. Part-time: 9 students, 67% women, 33% men. Students come from 40 states and territories, 81% from out-of-state, 0% Native American, 10% Hispanic, 0.3% black, 3% Asian American or Pacific Islander, 5% international, 6% 25 or older, 98% live on campus, 52% transferred in. Core. Calendar: semesters. Double major, summer session for credit. Study abroad program.

Entrance Requirements: Option: electronic application. Required: essay, high school transcript, minimum 2.8 high school GPA, recommendations, interview, ACT. Recommended: interview. Entrance: moderately difficult. Application deadline: 3/1.

Collegiate Environment: Orientation program. Choral group, student-run newspaper. Most popular organizations: Pro-Life Club, Student Government, Soccer Club, Hall Council, Ultimate Frisbee Club. Major annual events: semi-formal dance, Parents' Weekend, Open House. Campus security: 24-hour patrols, controlled dormitory access. 300 college housing spaces available. Freshmen guaranteed college housing. On-campus residence required through senior year. Options: men-only, women-only housing available.

■ THE BAPTIST COLLEGE OF FLORIDA *A-1*

5400 College Dr.
Graceville, FL 32440-1898
Tel: (850)263-3261
Free: 800-328-2660
Fax: (850)263-7506
E-mail: cmbishop@baptistcollege.edu
Web Site: http://www.baptistcollege.edu/

Description: Independent Southern Baptist, 4-year, coed. Awards associate and bachelor's degrees. Founded 1943. Setting: 165-acre small town campus. Endowment: $3.8 million. Educational spending for 2005 fiscal year: $3700 per student. Total enrollment: 623. Student-undergrad faculty ratio is 12:1. 72 applied, 78% were admitted. 10% from top 10% of their high school class, 27% from top quarter, 53% from top half. Full-time: 429 students, 41% women, 59% men. Part-time: 194 students, 23% women, 77% men. Students come from 20 states and territories, 9 other countries, 26% from out-of-state, 1% Native American, 4% Hispanic, 5% black, 1% Asian American or Pacific Islander, 0% international, 42% 25 or older, 34% live on campus, 11% transferred in. Retention: 60% of full-time freshmen returned the following year. Academic area with the most degrees conferred: education. Core. Calendar: 4-4-2. Academic remediation for entering students, services for LD students, advanced placement, independent study, distance learning, double major, summer session for credit, part-time degree program, internships.

Entrance Requirements: Open admission. Options: electronic application, early admission, deferred admission. Required: essay, high school transcript, 3 recommendations, ACT. Recommended: interview. Entrance: noncompetitive. Application deadline: Rolling. Notification: continuous. Preference given to professing Christians who are members of an evangelical church.

Costs Per Year: Application fee: $20. Comprehensive fee: $10,820 includes full-time tuition ($6900), mandatory fees ($350), and college room and board ($3570). Full-time tuition and fees vary according to course load. Room and board charges vary according to board plan and housing facility. Part-time tuition: $230 per semester hour. Part-time mandatory fees: $175 per term. Part-time tuition and fees vary according to course load.

Collegiate Environment: Orientation program. Drama-theater group, choral group. Social organizations: 3 open to all. Most popular organizations: Baptist Collegiate Ministry, student government, AACC. Major annual events: Fall Campus Picnic, Spring Cookout, Spring/Christmas Concert. Student services: personal-psychological counseling. Campus security: student patrols, patrols by police officers 11 p.m. to 7 a.m. College housing designed to accommodate 209 students; 220 undergraduates lived in college housing during 2003-04. Freshmen given priority for college housing. On-campus residence required through sophomore year. Options: men-only, women-only housing available. Ida J. MacMillan Library plus 1 other with 72,211 books, 4,700 microform titles, 5,143 serials, 12,316 audiovisual materials, an OPAC, and a Web page. Operations spending for 2004 fiscal year:

$234,927. 25 computers available on campus for general student use. A campuswide network can be accessed from student residence rooms. Staffed computer lab on campus.

Community Environment: Graceville is in northwest Florida near the borders of Alabama, Florida and Georgia. 23 miles north is Dothan, Alabama, and 20 miles southeast is Marianna, Florida. Railroads and buses serve the area. One excellent shopping center is available.

■ **BARRY UNIVERSITY** *T-15*
11300 Northeast Second Ave.
Miami Shores, FL 33161-6695
Tel: (305)899-3000
Free: 800-695-2279
Admissions: (305)899-3138
Fax: (305)899-2971
E-mail: admissions@mail.barry.edu
Web Site: http://www.barry.edu/
Description: Independent Roman Catholic, university, coed. Awards bachelor's, master's, doctoral, and first professional degrees. Founded 1940. Setting: 122-acre suburban campus with easy access to Miami. Endowment: $24.1 million. Total enrollment: 9,207. 3,186 applied, 70% were admitted. Full-time: 4,427 students, 69% women, 31% men. Part-time: 1,515 students, 68% women, 32% men. Students come from 43 states and territories, 89 other countries, 15% from out-of-state, 0.1% Native American, 34% Hispanic, 22% black, 1% Asian American or Pacific Islander, 4% international, 59% 25 or older, 17% live on campus, 9% transferred in. Retention: 65% of full-time freshmen returned the following year. Core. Calendar: semesters. Academic remediation for entering students, ESL program, services for LD students, advanced placement, accelerated degree program, honors program, independent study, distance learning, double major, summer session for credit, part-time degree program, adult/continuing education programs, internships, graduate courses open to undergrads. Off campus study at St. Thomas Aquinas College, Dominican College of San Rafael. Study abroad program. ROTC: Air Force (c).
Entrance Requirements: Options: Peterson's Universal Application, Common Application, electronic application, early admission, deferred admission. Required: high school transcript, minimum 2.0 high school GPA, SAT or ACT. Recommended: interview. Required for some: essay. Entrance: moderately difficult. Application deadline: Rolling. Notification: continuous.
Costs Per Year: Application fee: $30. Comprehensive fee: $30,050 includes full-time tuition ($22,430) and college room and board ($7620). Room and board charges vary according to board plan.
Collegiate Environment: Orientation program. Drama-theater group, choral group, student-run newspaper, radio station. Social organizations: 24 open to all; national fraternities, national sororities; 13% of eligible men and 4% of eligible women are members. Most popular organizations: Student Government Association, Campus Activities Board, Scuba Society, Caribbean Students Association, Jamaican Association. Major annual events: Founders' Day, Spring and Winter formals, Festival of Nations. Student services: health clinic, personal-psychological counseling. Campus security: 24-hour emergency response devices and patrols, late night transport-escort service. 1,010 college housing spaces available; all were occupied in 2003-04. On-campus residence required in freshman year. Options: coed, men-only, women-only housing available. Monsignor William Barry Memorial Library plus 1 other with 233,938 books, 541,560 microform titles, 2,880 serials, 4,247 audiovisual materials, an OPAC, and a Web page. 368 computers available on campus for general student use. Computer purchase/lease plans available. A campuswide network can be accessed from student residence rooms and from off campus. Staffed computer lab on campus.
Community Environment: Located only minutes from the cities of Miami and Ft. Lauderdale, Barry University offers easy access to the recreational facilities and cultural opportunities of Florida's Gold Coast area. Golf, tennis, swimming, skin and scuba diving, sailing and waterskiing are available all year long. Professional football, basketball, soccer, and hockey teams play in South Florida. The Miami Beach Theater of the Performing Arts, Coconut Grove Playhouse and the New World Symphony provide a full season of highly acclaimed performances. Well known personalities entertain regularly in the area. The Miami/Ft. Lauderdale area provides ready access to beaches, recreational, and ecological features including the Florida Keys, the Everglades, and National, State and Marine parks.

■ **BEACON COLLEGE** *I-12*
105 East Main St.
Leesburg, FL 34748

Tel: (352)787-7660
Admissions: (352)315-9269
Fax: (352)787-0721
E-mail: cscott@beaconcollege.edu
Web Site: http://www.beaconcollege.edu/
Description: Independent, 4-year, coed. Awards associate and bachelor's degrees. Setting: 12-acre small town campus with easy access to Orlando. Endowment: $16,587. Educational spending for 2005 fiscal year: $5830 per student. Total enrollment: 101. Student-undergrad faculty ratio is 7:1. 60 applied, 55% were admitted. Full-time: 101 students, 45% women, 55% men. Students come from 25 states and territories, 75% from out-of-state, 0% Native American, 6% Hispanic, 12% black, 3% Asian American or Pacific Islander, 0% international, 3% 25 or older, 99% live on campus, 11% transferred in. Retention: 71% of full-time freshmen returned the following year. Core. Calendar: semesters. Academic remediation for entering students, services for LD students. Study abroad program.
Entrance Requirements: Options: early admission, deferred admission. Required: essay, high school transcript, 3 recommendations, interview, Psycho-Educational Evaluation. Entrance: minimally difficult. Notification: 8/16.
Costs Per Year: Application fee: $50. Comprehensive fee: $31,100 includes full-time tuition ($23,900) and college room and board ($7200). College room only: $4400.
Collegiate Environment: Orientation program. Student-run newspaper. Social organizations: 20 open to all. Most popular organizations: student government, yearbook, basketball, Book Club, Poets and Writers Association. Major annual events: Parents' Weekend, Alumni Weekend, Move-In and New Student Orientation. Student services: personal-psychological counseling. 140 college housing spaces available; 96 were occupied in 2003-04. Freshmen guaranteed college housing. Options: men-only, women-only housing available. Beacon College Library with 56,979 books, 96 serials, 584 audiovisual materials, an OPAC, and a Web page. Operations spending for 2004 fiscal year: $103,497.

■ **BETHUNE-COOKMAN COLLEGE** *H-14*
640 Dr Mary McLeod Bethune Blvd
Daytona Beach, FL 32114-3099
Tel: (386)481-2000
Free: 800-448-0228
Admissions: (386)481-2600
Fax: (386)481-2010
Web Site: http://www.bethune.cookman.edu/
Description: Independent Methodist, 4-year, coed. Awards bachelor's degrees. Founded 1904. Setting: 60-acre urban campus with easy access to Orlando. Endowment: $29 million. Research spending for 2004 fiscal year: $723,704. Educational spending for 2005 fiscal year: $5063 per student. Total enrollment: 3,090. Student-undergrad faculty ratio is 17:1. 3,974 applied, 74% were admitted. 6% from top 10% of their high school class, 22% from top quarter, 54% from top half. Full-time: 2,795 students, 59% women, 41% men. Part-time: 295 students, 58% women, 42% men. Students come from 42 states and territories, 35 other countries, 32% from out-of-state, 0.3% Native American, 1% Hispanic, 91% black, 0.2% Asian American or Pacific Islander, 3% international, 8% 25 or older, 57% live on campus, 4% transferred in. Retention: 71% of full-time freshmen returned the following year. Academic areas with the most degrees conferred: business/marketing; education; security and protective services. Core. Calendar: semesters. Academic remediation for entering students, advanced placement, accelerated degree program, honors program, independent study, distance learning, double major, summer session for credit, part-time degree program, adult/continuing education programs, co-op programs and internships. Study abroad program. ROTC: Army (c), Air Force (c).
Entrance Requirements: Options: Peterson's Universal Application, early admission, deferred admission, international baccalaureate accepted. Required: high school transcript, minimum 2.25 high school GPA, 1 recommendation, medical history, SAT or ACT. Recommended: essay. Required for some: interview. Entrance: minimally difficult. Application deadline: 6/30. Notification: continuous.
Costs Per Year: Application fee: $25. Comprehensive fee: $17,922 includes full-time tuition ($11,140), mandatory fees ($90), and college room and board ($6692). Part-time tuition: $464 per credit hour.
Collegiate Environment: Orientation program. Drama-theater group, choral group, marching band, student-run newspaper, radio station. Social organizations: 40 open to all; national fraternities, national sororities, local fraternities, local sororities; 3% of eligible men and 5% of eligible women are

members. Most popular organizations: concert chorale, marching band, Inspirational Gospel Choir, SGA. Major annual events: Homecoming, Founders' Day, Career Day. Student services: health clinic, personal-psychological counseling. Campus security: 24-hour emergency response devices and patrols, student patrols, late night transport-escort service. 1,772 college housing spaces available; 1,658 were occupied in 2003-04. Freshmen guaranteed college housing. On-campus residence required in freshman year. Options: men-only, women-only housing available. Carl S. Swisher Library plus 1 other with 173,193 books, 60,150 microform titles, 770 serials, 7,825 audiovisual materials, an OPAC, and a Web page. Operations spending for 2004 fiscal year: $553,165. 300 computers available on campus for general student use. A campuswide network can be accessed from student residence rooms and from off campus. Staffed computer lab on campus.

Community Environment: Daytona Beach is a resort area located on the Atlantic Ocean with a subtropical climate. All modes of transportation serve the area. The community facilities include two libraries, two museums, many churches, a hospital and major civic organizations. Part-time employment opportunities are available. Recreational activities include water sports, stock car racing, motor bike racing, and archery. Beach drivers almost outnumber swimmers. Spring vacation brings an influx of college students. Special events include the Antique Car Meet and car racing known as the Speed Week.

■ **BREVARD COMMUNITY COLLEGE** *K-15*
1519 Clearlake Rd.
Cocoa, FL 32922-6597
Tel: (321)632-1111
Admissions: (321)433-7056
Fax: (321)633-4565
E-mail: cocoaadmissions@brevardcc.edu
Web Site: http://www.brevardcc.edu/
Description: State-supported, 2-year, coed. Part of Florida Community College System. Awards certificates, transfer associate, and terminal associate degrees. Founded 1960. Setting: 100-acre suburban campus with easy access to Orlando. Total enrollment: 14,039. Student-undergrad faculty ratio is 18:1. 5,350 applied, 100% were admitted. Full-time: 5,129 students, 57% women, 43% men. Part-time: 8,910 students, 62% women, 38% men. Students come from 34 states and territories, 72 other countries, 1% Native American, 7% Hispanic, 9% black, 3% Asian American or Pacific Islander, 1% international, 38% 25 or older. Core. Calendar: semesters. Academic remediation for entering students, ESL program, services for LD students, advanced placement, accelerated degree program, honors program, independent study, distance learning, double major, summer session for credit, part-time degree program, external degree program, adult/continuing education programs, co-op programs and internships. Study abroad program. ROTC: Army, Air Force.
Entrance Requirements: Open admission. Options: Common Application, electronic application. Required: high school transcript. Entrance: noncompetitive. Application deadline: Rolling. Notification: continuous.
Costs Per Year: Application fee: $30. State resident tuition: $1542 full-time, $64.25 per credit hour part-time. Nonresident tuition: $5664 full-time, $236 per credit hour part-time.
Collegiate Environment: Orientation program. Drama-theater group, choral group, student-run newspaper. Most popular organizations: Phi Theta Kappa, ROTORACT, African-American Student Union, Student Government Association, Psi Beta. Major annual events: Spring Festival, Black Heritage Week, Student Welcome Days. Student services: women's center. Campus security: 24-hour emergency response devices and patrols, late night transport-escort service. College housing not available. UCF Library with 213,873 books, 216,720 microform titles, 904 serials, 17,904 audiovisual materials, an OPAC, and a Web page. Operations spending for 2004 fiscal year: $2.3 million. 125 computers available on campus for general student use. A campuswide network can be accessed from off-campus. Staffed computer lab on campus.
Community Environment: Cocoa, a suburban area with a subtropical climate, is the leading shipping point for the famous Indian River citrus fruits, and a resort town. Airline and bus service provide transportation for the area. Community facilities include four hospitals, two clinics and many churches. Recreational activities are water sports, golf, bowling and fishing. Part-time employment is limited.

■ **BROWARD COMMUNITY COLLEGE** *S-15*
225 East Las Olas Blvd.
Fort Lauderdale, FL 33301-2298

Tel: (954)761-7450
Admissions: (954)761-7465
Fax: (954)761-7484
E-mail: bbryan@broward.edu
Web Site: http://www.broward.edu/
Description: State-supported, 2-year, coed. Part of Florida Community College System. Awards certificates, diplomas, transfer associate, and terminal associate degrees. Founded 1960. Setting: urban campus with easy access to Miami. Total enrollment: 32,041. 4,630 applied, 100% were admitted. Full-time: 10,044 students, 58% women, 42% men. Part-time: 21,997 students, 64% women, 36% men. Students come from 100 other countries, 5% from out-of-state, 0.3% Native American, 24% Hispanic, 27% black, 3% Asian American or Pacific Islander, 9% international, 29% 25 or older. Core. Calendar: trimesters. Academic remediation for entering students, ESL program, services for LD students, advanced placement, self-designed majors, honors program, summer session for credit, part-time degree program, adult/continuing education programs, co-op programs. Study abroad program. ROTC: Army.
Entrance Requirements: Open admission. Options: Common Application, early admission, deferred admission. Required for some: high school transcript, minimum 2.75 high school GPA, SAT and SAT Subject Tests or ACT. Entrance: noncompetitive. Preference given to state residents.
Costs Per Year: Application fee: $35. State resident tuition: $1,574 full-time, $63.05 per credit hour part-time. Nonresident tuition: $6294 full-time, $228.55 per credit hour part-time. Mandatory fees: $318 full-time.
Collegiate Environment: Drama-theater group, choral group, student-run newspaper. Social organizations: local fraternities, local sororities. Student services: personal-psychological counseling, women's center. Campus security: 24-hour emergency response devices and patrols, late night transport-escort service. College housing not available. South Regional/Broward Community College Library with 200,000 books, 600 serials, and an OPAC.
Community Environment: Fort Lauderdale, population 150,000, is located on the Atlantic Ocean coastline, 25 miles north of Miami. The climate is subtropical and the average year-round temperature is 75 degrees.

■ **BROWN MACKIE COLLEGE-MIAMI** *T-15*
1501 Biscayne Blvd.
Miami, FL 33132
Tel: (305)341-6600; (866)505-0335
Admissions: (305)341-6601
Web Site: http://www.brownmackie.edu/locations.asp?locid=25
Description: Proprietary, 2-year, coed. Awards diplomas and terminal associate degrees. Total enrollment: 136. 325 applied, 53% were admitted. Full-time: 136 students, 71% women, 29% men. 0% from out-of-state, 0% Native American, 27% Hispanic, 65% black, 3% Asian American or Pacific Islander, 0% international.
Entrance Requirements: Required: high school transcript, interview. Application deadline: Rolling. Notification: continuous.
Costs Per Year: Application fee: $0. Comprehensive fee: $19,272 includes full-time tuition ($10,992), mandatory fees ($480), and college room and board ($7800).
Collegiate Environment: Social organizations: national sororities; 2% of women are members. Student services: personal-psychological counseling.

■ **CARLOS ALBIZU UNIVERSITY, MIAMI CAMPUS** *T-15*
2173 NW 99th Ave.
Miami, FL 33172-2209
Tel: (305)593-1223
Free: 800-672-3246
Fax: (305)592-7930
E-mail: galvarado@albizu.edu
Web Site: http://www.mia.albizu.edu/
Description: Independent, comprehensive, coed. Part of Carlos Albizu University. Awards bachelor's, master's, and doctoral degrees. Founded 1980. Setting: 2-acre urban campus. Educational spending for 2005 fiscal year: $2890 per student. Total enrollment: 1,076. Faculty: 50 (8 full-time, 42 part-time). Student-undergrad faculty ratio is 13:1. 176 applied, 73% were admitted. Full-time: 202 students, 81% women, 19% men. Part-time: 251 students, 80% women, 20% men. 0% from out-of-state, 0% Native American, 83% Hispanic, 11% black, 1% Asian American or Pacific Islander, 0% international, 57% 25 or older, 14% transferred in. Retention: 67% of full-time freshmen returned the following year. Academic areas with the most degrees conferred: psychology; business/marketing; education. Core.

Calendar: trimesters. Academic remediation for entering students, ESL program, services for LD students, advanced placement, accelerated degree program, independent study, summer session for credit, part-time degree program, external degree program, adult/continuing education programs, co-op programs and internships.

Entrance Requirements: Open admission. Options: Peterson's Universal Application, Common Application, international baccalaureate accepted. Required: high school transcript, minimum 2.0 high school GPA. Entrance: minimally difficult. Application deadline: 9/10. Notification: continuous.

Costs Per Year: Application fee: $25. Tuition: $10,440 full-time, $290 per credit part-time. Mandatory fees: $669 full-time, $223 per term part-time.

Collegiate Environment: Orientation program. Student-run newspaper. Social organizations: 6 open to all. Most popular organizations: Student Council, Psi Chi, Students for Cross-Cultural Advancement, Black Student Association, P.R.I.D.E. Gay/Lesbian/Bisexual Student Association. Major annual events: Albizu Student Excellence Awards Banquet, Student Council Elections, Town Hall Meetings. Campus security: 24-hour emergency response devices and patrols, late night transport-escort service. College housing not available. Albizu Library with 26,027 books, 398 serials, 1,137 audiovisual materials, and an OPAC. Operations spending for 2004 fiscal year: $265,136. 65 computers available on campus for general student use. Computer purchase/lease plans available. A campuswide network can be accessed. Staffed computer lab on campus.

■ **CENTRAL FLORIDA COLLEGE** *J-13*
1573 West Fairbanks Ave., Ste. 1-A
Winter Park, FL 32789
Tel: (407)843-3984
Fax: (407)843-9828
Description: Proprietary, 2-year, coed. Founded 1984.

■ **CENTRAL FLORIDA COMMUNITY COLLEGE** *H-11*
PO Box 1388
Ocala, FL 34478-1388
Tel: (352)854-2322
Admissions: (352)237-2111
Fax: (352)237-3747
E-mail: jonesch@cf.edu
Web Site: http://www.cf.edu/
Description: State and locally supported, 2-year, coed. Part of Florida Community College System. Awards certificates, transfer associate, and terminal associate degrees. Founded 1957. Setting: 139-acre small town campus. Endowment: $14.8 million. Educational spending for 2005 fiscal year: $3600 per student. Total enrollment: 5,978. Student-undergrad faculty ratio is 13:1. Full-time: 2,476 students, 61% women, 39% men. Part-time: 3,502 students, 69% women, 31% men. Students come from 20 states and territories, 1% Native American, 7% Hispanic, 11% black, 2% Asian American or Pacific Islander, 1% international, 41% 25 or older. Core. Calendar: semesters. Academic remediation for entering students, ESL program, services for LD students, advanced placement, freshman honors college, honors program, independent study, distance learning, summer session for credit, part-time degree program, adult/continuing education programs, co-op programs and internships.

Entrance Requirements: Open admission. Options: Common Application, early admission. Required: high school transcript. Entrance: noncompetitive. Application deadline: Rolling. Notification: continuous.

Costs Per Year: Application fee: $20. State resident tuition: $1961 full-time, $65.37 per credit hour part-time. Nonresident tuition: $7177 full-time, $239.24 per credit hour part-time. College room and board: $5562.

Collegiate Environment: Orientation program. Drama-theater group, choral group, student-run newspaper. Social organizations: 31 open to all. Most popular organizations: Student Activities Board, African-American Student Union, ROC (Realizing Our Cause), Gay Straight Alliance, Musagettas. Major annual events: homecoming, Student Activities Week, Student Activities Banquet. Student services: personal-psychological counseling. Campus security: 24-hour emergency response devices and patrols, student patrols, late night transport-escort service. College housing not available. Learning Resources Center plus 1 other with 54,491 books, 367 serials, and an OPAC. Operations spending for 2004 fiscal year: $606,772. 737 computers available on campus for general student use. A campuswide network can be accessed from off-campus. Staffed computer lab on campus.

Community Environment: Ocala, the county seat, is the largest city in Marion County, and the hub of local economic and cultural activity. Service and light manufacturing industries provide the majority of employment op-

portunities, although agriculture is also important to the area. The 450 horse farms in the Ocala area rival Kentucky as the home of the best American thoroughbreds. Ocala boasts a mild climate, beautiful countryside, and is in close proximity to major tourist and recreational facilities. Numerous lakes provide fishing and other water sports. Ocala has 16 parks and playgrounds, two municipal swimming pools, and an 18-hole public golf course. The Sunshine Christmas Parade is an annual event.

■ **CENTRAL FLORIDA INSTITUTE** *L-9*
60522 US Hwy. 19 North, Ste. 200
Palm Harbor, FL 34684
Tel: (727)786-4707
Fax: (727)781-9421
Web Site: http://www.cfinstitute.com/
Description: Proprietary, 2-year, coed. Awards certificates, diplomas, and terminal associate degrees. Setting: urban campus. Total enrollment: 346. Full-time: 346 students, 83% women, 17% men. 1% Native American, 10% Hispanic, 12% black, 2% Asian American or Pacific Islander, 0% international. Calendar: continuous.

■ **CHIPOLA COLLEGE** *B-2*
3094 Indian Circle
Marianna, FL 32446-3065
Tel: (850)526-2761
Admissions: (850)718-2209
Fax: (850)718-2388
E-mail: robertsj@chipola.edu
Web Site: http://www.chipola.edu/
Description: State-supported, primarily 2-year, coed. Awards certificates, transfer associate, terminal associate, and bachelor's degrees. Founded 1947. Setting: 105-acre rural campus. Total enrollment: 2,249. 798 applied, 95% were admitted. Full-time: 1,030 students, 60% women, 40% men. Part-time: 1,219 students, 63% women, 37% men. Students come from 13 states and territories, 7 other countries, 3% from out-of-state, 1% Native American, 2% Hispanic, 19% black, 1% Asian American or Pacific Islander, 0% international, 27% 25 or older, 4% transferred in. Core. Calendar: semesters. Academic remediation for entering students, services for LD students, advanced placement, honors program, independent study, distance learning, summer session for credit, part-time degree program, adult/continuing education programs.

Entrance Requirements: Open admission. Option: early admission. Required: high school transcript. Placement: SAT or ACT required. Entrance: noncompetitive. Application deadline: Rolling. Notification: continuous.

Collegiate Environment: Drama-theater group, choral group, student-run newspaper. Most popular organization: Drama/Theater Group. Major annual events: Fall Festival, Homecoming, Spring Frolics. Campus security: night security personnel. College housing not available. Chipola Library with 37,740 books and 226 serials. 80 computers available on campus for general student use. A campuswide network can be accessed from off-campus. Staffed computer lab on campus.

Community Environment: Marianna, located in northwest Florida, has an annual average temperature of 68.1 degrees and an average rainfall of 54.51 inches. Buses serve the area along the U.S. Highway 90. Community facilities include a hospital, several motels, a library, churches, and two radio stations. The Florida Caverns State Park, three miles north, has extensive limestone caverns with guided trips available. Picnic areas, campsites, rock gardens, a museum, and golf course are located here. There are fine beaches for all water sports, and excellent hunting in the area.

■ **CITY COLLEGE (CASSELBERRY)** *J-13*
853 Semoran Blvd., Ste. 200
Casselberry, FL 32707-5342
Tel: (407)831-8466
Admissions: (407)831-9816
Fax: (407)831-1147
E-mail: yhunter@citycollege.edu
Web Site: http://www.citycollege.edu/
Description: Independent, 2-year, coed. Calendar: semesters.

■ **CITY COLLEGE (FORT LAUDERDALE)** *S-15*
1401 West Cypress Creek Rd.
Fort Lauderdale, FL 33309
Tel: (954)492-5353
Fax: (954)491-1965

Web Site: http://www.citycollege.edu/
Description: Independent, 2-year, coed. Founded 1984. Total enrollment: 712. Calendar: semesters.

■ **CITY COLLEGE (GAINESVILLE)** *F-10*
2400 Southwest 13th St.
Gainesville, FL 32608
Tel: (352)335-4000
Fax: (352)335-4303
Web Site: http://www.citycollege.edu/
Description: Independent, 2-year, coed. Founded 1986. Calendar: semesters.

■ **CITY COLLEGE (MIAMI)** *T-15*
9300 South Dadeland Blvd.
Miami, FL 33156
Tel: (305)666-9242
Fax: (305)666-9243
Web Site: http://www.citycollege.edu/
Description: Independent, 2-year, coed. Calendar: semesters.

■ **CLEARWATER CHRISTIAN COLLEGE** *L-9*
3400 Gulf-to-Bay Blvd.
Clearwater, FL 33759-4595
Tel: (727)726-1153
Free: 800-348-4463
Fax: (727)726-8597
Web Site: http://www.clearwater.edu/
Description: Independent nondenominational, 4-year, coed. Awards associate and bachelor's degrees. Founded 1966. Setting: 130-acre suburban campus with easy access to Tampa-St. Petersburg. Endowment: $358,876. Educational spending for 2005 fiscal year: $3000 per student. Total enrollment: 582. Student-undergrad faculty ratio is 15:1. 526 applied, 86% were admitted. 11% from top 10% of their high school class, 22% from top quarter, 72% from top half. Full-time: 548 students, 50% women, 50% men. Part-time: 34 students, 38% women, 62% men. Students come from 40 states and territories, 15 other countries, 53% from out-of-state, 0% Native American, 5% Hispanic, 2% black, 1% Asian American or Pacific Islander, 0% international, 70% live on campus, 16% transferred in. Retention: 54% of full-time freshmen returned the following year. Academic areas with the most degrees conferred: business/marketing; biological/life sciences; education. Core. Calendar: semesters. Academic remediation for entering students, services for LD students, advanced placement, double major, summer session for credit, part-time degree program, internships. ROTC: Army (c), Air Force (c).
Entrance Requirements: Options: early admission, deferred admission. Required: essay, high school transcript, minimum 2.0 high school GPA, 2 recommendations, Christian testimony, SAT or ACT. Recommended: interview. Entrance: minimally difficult. Application deadline: Rolling. Notification: continuous.
Costs Per Year: Application fee: $35. Comprehensive fee: $17,830 includes full-time tuition ($11,860), mandatory fees ($640), and college room and board ($5330). Part-time tuition: $460 per hour.
Collegiate Environment: Orientation program. Drama-theater group, choral group, student-run newspaper. Social organizations: 13 open to all. Most popular organizations: Drama Club, Alpha Chi, College Republicans, Science Club, Student Missionary Fellowship. Student services: personal-psychological counseling. Campus security: 24-hour emergency response devices and patrols. On-campus residence required through senior year. Options: men-only, women-only housing available. Easter Library with 106,000 books, 700 serials, and an OPAC. Operations spending for 2004 fiscal year: $405,000. 25 computers available on campus for general student use. A campuswide network can be accessed from student residence rooms and from off campus. Staffed computer lab on campus.
Community Environment: Clearwater is located on Pinellas Peninsula, between Clearwater and Old Tampa Bays, 20 miles west of Tampa. The area is an all-year resort and citrus center. Amtrak, all major airlines, and buses serve the area. Airports are in St. Petersburg and Tampa. Community facilities include churches of all denominations, a library, museums, hotels, motels, two hospitals, a health center, city parks, floral gardens, a civic center, a maritime center and the usual fraternal civic and veterans organizations. Employment is available in the citrus packing and canning industries. The broad white sand beach on the gulf is the main attraction in the city. This beautiful beach provides for water sports, deep sea fishing, boating, etc. The

Philadelphia Phillies baseball team comes here for spring training. The Clearwater Yacht Club and four golf courses including the Professional Golfers Association Club provide additional recreational facilities.

■ **COLLEGE OF BUSINESS AND TECHNOLOGY** *T-15*
8991 SW 107th Ave., Ste. 200
Miami, FL 33176
Tel: (305)273-4499
Fax: (305)273-5216
E-mail: carlos@cbt.edu
Web Site: http://www.cbt.edu/
Description: Proprietary, 2-year, coed. Awards certificates, diplomas, and transfer associate degrees. Founded 1988. Endowment: $3.5 million. Total enrollment: 250. Student-undergrad faculty ratio is 10:1. 350 applied, 71% were admitted. 4 National Merit Scholars, 4 valedictorians, 2 student government officers. Students come from 7 states and territories, 0% from out-of-state, 90% Hispanic, 70% 25 or older. Core. Calendar: semesters. Academic remediation for entering students, ESL program, services for LD students, advanced placement, accelerated degree program, honors program, independent study, distance learning, double major, summer session for credit, part-time degree program, adult/continuing education programs, co-op programs and internships. Off campus study.
Entrance Requirements: Open admission. Options: Common Application, electronic application, international baccalaureate accepted. Required: essay, high school transcript, minimum 2.6 high school GPA, 2 recommendations, interview. Entrance: minimally difficult. Application deadline: 6/15.
Costs Per Year: Application fee: $100. Tuition: $10,500 full-time, $278 per semester hour part-time. Mandatory fees: $200 full-time. College room only: $6000.
Collegiate Environment: Orientation program. Student-run newspaper. The Bill Clinton Library plus 1 other with 700,000 books, 200,000 serials, 1,200 audiovisual materials, an OPAC, and a Web page. 560 computers available on campus for general student use. Computer purchase/lease plans available. A campuswide network can be accessed from student residence rooms and from off campus. Staffed computer lab on campus.

■ **DAYTONA BEACH COMMUNITY COLLEGE** *H-14*
PO Box 2811
Daytona Beach, FL 32120-2811
Tel: (386)255-8131
Admissions: (386)506-3732
Fax: (386)254-4458
Web Site: http://www.dbcc.edu/
Description: State-supported, 2-year, coed. Part of Florida Community College System. Awards certificates, transfer associate, and terminal associate degrees. Founded 1958. Setting: 100-acre suburban campus with easy access to Orlando. Endowment: $3.1 million. Educational spending for 2005 fiscal year: $4035 per student. Total enrollment: 11,945. 3,235 applied, 100% were admitted. Full-time: 4,776 students, 56% women, 44% men. Part-time: 7,169 students, 66% women, 34% men. Students come from 51 states and territories, 52 other countries, 5% from out-of-state, 1% Native American, 7% Hispanic, 12% black, 2% Asian American or Pacific Islander, 1% international, 42% 25 or older, 6% transferred in. Core. Calendar: semesters. Academic remediation for entering students, ESL program, services for LD students, advanced placement, honors program, summer session for credit, part-time degree program, adult/continuing education programs, co-op programs and internships. Study abroad program. ROTC: Army (c), Air Force (c).
Entrance Requirements: Open admission except for nursing, allied health, public services programs. Options: Common Application, early admission, deferred admission. Required: high school transcript. Placement: ACT ASSET, CPT required. Entrance: noncompetitive. Application deadline: Rolling.
Collegiate Environment: Orientation program. Drama-theater group, choral group, student-run newspaper. Social organizations: 20 open to all. Most popular organizations: Florida Student Nursing Association, International Club, SGA, History Club, Drama Club. Major annual events: Cultural Festival, Earth Day, Handicap Awareness Day. Student services: personal-psychological counseling, women's center. Campus security: 24-hour patrols, late night transport-escort service. College housing not available. Mary Karl Memorial Library with 66,312 books, 20,700 microform titles, 745 serials, 4,503 audiovisual materials, an OPAC, and a Web page. Operations spending for 2004 fiscal year: $2.5 million. 752 computers available on campus for general student use. Computer purchase/lease plans available. A campuswide network can be accessed. Staffed computer lab on campus.

Community Environment: See Bethune-Cookman College.

■ **DEVRY UNIVERSITY (MIAMI)** *T-15*
200 South Biscayne Blvd., Ste. 500
Miami, FL 33131-5351
Tel: (786)425-1113
Fax: (786)425-1136
Web Site: http://www.devry.edu/
Description: Proprietary, comprehensive, coed. Calendar: semesters.
Costs Per Year: One-time mandatory fee: $40. Tuition: $12,450 full-time.
Mandatory fees: $60 full-time.

■ **DEVRY UNIVERSITY (MIRAMAR)** *S-15*
2300 Southwest 145th Ave.
Miramar, FL 33027-4150
Tel: (954)499-9700; (866)338-7934
Web Site: http://www.devry.edu/
Description: Proprietary, comprehensive, coed. Part of DeVry University. Awards associate, bachelor's, and master's degrees. Founded 2002. Total enrollment: 1,068. Faculty: 56 (34 full-time, 22 part-time). Student-undergrad faculty ratio is 20:1. Full-time: 647 students, 57% women, 43% men. Part-time: 322 students, 59% women, 41% men. Students come from 9 states and territories, 5 other countries, 0.3% Native American, 41% Hispanic, 36% black, 1% Asian American or Pacific Islander, 6% international, 34% 25 or older. Retention: 43% of full-time freshmen returned the following year. Academic areas with the most degrees conferred: business/marketing; computer and information sciences; engineering technologies. Calendar: semesters. Academic remediation for entering students, services for LD students, advanced placement, accelerated degree program, distance learning, part-time degree program, co-op programs.
Entrance Requirements: Option: international baccalaureate accepted. Required: high school transcript, interview. Entrance: minimally difficult. Application deadline: Rolling.
Costs Per Year: Application fee: $50. One-time mandatory fee: $40. Tuition: $12,450 full-time, $460 per credit part-time. Mandatory fees: $270 full-time, $160 per year part-time. Full-time tuition and fees vary according to course load. Part-time tuition and fees vary according to course load.
Collegiate Environment: Orientation program. College housing not available. Learning Resource Center with 1,700 books, 75 serials, an OPAC, and a Web page. 124 computers available on campus for general student use. Computer purchase/lease plans available.

■ **DEVRY UNIVERSITY (ORLANDO)** *J-13*
4000 Millenia Blvd.
Orlando, FL 32839
Tel: (407)370-3131; (866)338-7934
Web Site: http://www.devry.edu/
Description: Proprietary, comprehensive, coed. Part of DeVry University. Awards associate, bachelor's, and master's degrees. Founded 2000. Setting: 10-acre urban campus. Total enrollment: 1,181. Faculty: 91 (37 full-time, 54 part-time). Student-undergrad faculty ratio is 16:1. Full-time: 703 students, 50% women, 50% men. Part-time: 345 students, 53% women, 47% men. 0.3% Native American, 22% Hispanic, 31% black, 3% Asian American or Pacific Islander, 2% international. Retention: 43% of full-time freshmen returned the following year. Academic areas with the most degrees conferred: computer and information sciences; business/marketing; engineering technologies. Calendar: semesters. Academic remediation for entering students, services for LD students, advanced placement, accelerated degree program, distance learning, summer session for credit, part-time degree program, adult/continuing education programs, co-op programs.
Entrance Requirements: Options: electronic application, deferred admission, international baccalaureate accepted. Required: high school transcript, interview. Entrance: minimally difficult. Application deadline: Rolling.
Costs Per Year: Application fee: $50. One-time mandatory fee: $40. Tuition: $12,450 full-time. Mandatory fees: $270 full-time. Full-time tuition and fees vary according to course load.
Collegiate Environment: Orientation program. Social organizations: 8 open to all. Most popular organizations: Association for Information Technology Professionals, DeVry Orlando Auto Club, Millenia Engineering Students Association, PBL, The Student Journal. Major annual events: Model Car Competition, Fun Flicks, Welcome Picnic. Campus security: 24-hour emergency response devices and patrols, late night transport-escort service, lighted pathways/sidewalks. College housing not available. Learning Resource Center with 11,000 books, 60 serials, 130 audiovisual materials,

an OPAC, and a Web page. 310 computers available on campus for general student use. Computer purchase/lease plans available. A campuswide network can be accessed from off-campus. Staffed computer lab on campus.

■ **DEVRY UNIVERSITY (TAMPA)** *L-10*
3030 North Rocky Point Dr. West, Ste. 100
Tampa, FL 33607-5901
Tel: (813)288-8994
Fax: (813)288-8980
Web Site: http://www.devry.edu/
Description: Proprietary, comprehensive, coed. Calendar: semesters.
Costs Per Year: One-time mandatory fee: $40. Tuition: $12,450 full-time.
Mandatory fees: $60 full-time.

■ **ECKERD COLLEGE** *M-9*
4200 54th Ave. South
St. Petersburg, FL 33711
Tel: (727)867-1166
Free: 800-456-9009
Admissions: (727)864-8331
Fax: (727)866-2304
E-mail: admissions@eckerd.edu
Web Site: http://www.eckerd.edu/
Description: Independent Presbyterian, 4-year, coed. Awards bachelor's degrees. Founded 1958. Setting: 267-acre suburban campus with easy access to Tampa. Endowment: $18.3 million. Research spending for 2004 fiscal year: $370,056. Total enrollment: 1,779. Student-undergrad faculty ratio is 13:1. 2,739 applied, 72% were admitted. 19% from top 10% of their high school class, 46% from top quarter, 83% from top half. 5 National Merit Scholars, 24 class presidents, 18 valedictorians, 125 student government officers. Students come from 50 states and territories, 44 other countries, 71% from out-of-state, 0.5% Native American, 4% Hispanic, 3% black, 2% Asian American or Pacific Islander, 5% international, 2% 25 or older, 79% live on campus. Retention: 88% of full-time freshmen returned the following year. Academic areas with the most degrees conferred: business/marketing; biological/life sciences; social sciences. Core. Calendar: 4-1-4. ESL program, services for LD students, advanced placement, accelerated degree program, self-designed majors, honors program, independent study, double major, summer session for credit, part-time degree program, external degree program, adult/continuing education programs, co-op programs and internships. Off campus study at other colleges having a 4-1-4 calendar. Study abroad program. ROTC: Army (c), Air Force (c).
Entrance Requirements: Options: Peterson's Universal Application, Common Application, electronic application, early admission, deferred admission, international baccalaureate accepted. Required: essay, high school transcript, 1 recommendation, SAT or ACT. Recommended: minimum 3.0 high school GPA, interview, SAT Subject Tests. Entrance: moderately difficult. Application deadline: Rolling. Notification: continuous.
Costs Per Year: Application fee: $35. Comprehensive fee: $35,486 includes full-time tuition ($27,352), mandatory fees ($266), and college room and board ($7868). College room only: $4072. Part-time tuition: $3300 per course.
Collegiate Environment: Orientation program. Drama-theater group, choral group, student-run newspaper, radio station. Social organizations: 50 open to all. Most popular organizations: Earth Society, Water Search and Rescue Team, Triton Tribune, College Choir, Organization of Students. Major annual events: Midnight Madness, Festival of Hope, Convocation. Student services: health clinic, personal-psychological counseling, women's center. Campus security: 24-hour emergency response devices and patrols, student patrols, late night transport-escort service, controlled dormitory access. 1,325 college housing spaces available; 1,296 were occupied in 2003-04. Freshmen guaranteed college housing. On-campus residence required in freshman year. Options: coed, men-only, women-only housing available. Peter Armacost Library with 165,085 books, 14,414 microform titles, 1,738 serials, 2,139 audiovisual materials, an OPAC, and a Web page. Operations spending for 2004 fiscal year: $1.2 million. 191 computers available on campus for general student use. Computer purchase/lease plans available. A campuswide network can be accessed from student residence rooms and from off campus. Staffed computer lab on campus.
Community Environment: St. Petersburg, known as the "Sunshine City," has a wonderful semitropical climate. The city is the state's fourth largest, and is the most important tourist center on the west coast of Florida. The city has 33 miles of shoreline on the Gulf of Mexico and several fresh water lakes: an excellent location for all water sports. Other sports are baseball,

basketball, soccer, cross country, volleyball, softball, golf, and tennis. This is the spring training area for several major league baseball teams. The Tampa Bay area also is home to football's Buccaneers, baseball's Devil Rays, hockey's Lightning, and the international headquarters of the Women's Tennis Association. Numerous points of interest include the Florida International Museum, Fort DeSoto Park, Sunshine Skyway, the St. Petersburg Museum of Fine Arts, the Dali Museum, and Tropicana Field.

■ **EDISON COLLEGE** *Q-10*
PO Box 60210
Fort Myers, FL 33906-6210
Tel: (239)489-9300
Free: 800-749-2ECC
Admissions: (941)489-9349
Fax: (239)489-9399
E-mail: llugo@edison.edu
Web Site: http://www.edison.edu/

Description: State and locally supported, 2-year, coed. Part of Florida Community College System. Awards certificates, transfer associate, and terminal associate degrees. Founded 1962. Setting: 80-acre urban campus. Total enrollment: 10,642. Students come from 21 states and territories, 45 other countries, 3% from out-of-state, 0.3% Native American, 10% Hispanic, 9% black, 2% Asian American or Pacific Islander, 3% international, 70% 25 or older. Core. Calendar: semesters. Academic remediation for entering students, ESL program, services for LD students, advanced placement, accelerated degree program, honors program, independent study, distance learning, summer session for credit, part-time degree program, adult/continuing education programs, co-op programs and internships.

Entrance Requirements: Open admission. Options: early admission, deferred admission, international baccalaureate accepted. Required: high school transcript. Placement: SAT, ACT, or CPT required. Entrance: noncompetitive. Application deadline: 8/18. Notification: continuous.

Collegiate Environment: Drama-theater group, choral group. Social organizations: 20 open to all; national fraternities, national sororities; 5% of eligible men and 5% of eligible women are members. Most popular organizations: Student Government Association, Phi Theta Kappa, African-American Student Association, Latin-American Student Association. Campus security: 24-hour emergency response devices and patrols, student patrols, late night transport-escort service. College housing not available. Learning Resources Center with 181,085 books and 10,297 audiovisual materials. 160 computers available on campus for general student use. A campuswide network can be accessed from off-campus. Staffed computer lab on campus.

Community Environment: Edison Community College campuses are located on the sunny coast of southwest Florida, between Naples and Tampa. The climate is semitropical. The offshore islands have many attractive beaches, and majestic Royal Palms line the streets. All modes of transportation serve the area. Tourism, commercial fishing, shrimping and livestock production are important industries. The community facilities include churches of all denominations, hospitals, little theater groups, dances, and lecture halls. The saltwater bays and freshwater lakes nearby are among the finest fishing grounds anywhere. Other sports include boating, hunting, horseback riding, golf, bowling, tennis, shuffleboard and greyhound racing in Bonita Springs. TECO Arena is home to minor league hockey and basketball teams. A minor league baseball team also plays in Fort Myers. The Boston Red Sox and Minnesota Twins have their spring training camps in Fort Myers.

■ **EDWARD WATERS COLLEGE**
1658 Kings Rd.
Jacksonville, FL 32209-6199
Tel: (904)470-8000; 888-898-3191
Admissions: (904)366-2715
Fax: (904)470-8039
Web Site: http://www.ewc.edu/

Description: Independent African Methodist Episcopal, 4-year, coed. Awards bachelor's degrees. Founded 1866. Setting: 20-acre urban campus. Total enrollment: 1,320. Full-time: 1,284 students, 49% women, 51% men. Part-time: 36 students, 53% women, 47% men. Students come from 15 states and territories, 1% Hispanic, 91% black, 2% international. Retention: 70% of full-time freshmen returned the following year. Core. Calendar: semesters. Academic remediation for entering students, self-designed majors, honors program, summer session for credit, part-time degree program, adult/continuing education programs, co-op programs and internships. Off campus study at University of North Florida. ROTC: Army (c).

Entrance Requirements: Open admission. Option: Common Application. Required: high school transcript, medical forms. Placement: CAT required; SAT or ACT recommended. Entrance: noncompetitive. Application deadline: Rolling. Notification: continuous.

Collegiate Environment: Student-run newspaper, radio station. Campus security: 24-hour emergency response devices and patrols, student patrols, late night transport-escort service, controlled dormitory access. Option: coed housing available. Centennial Library with 120,000 books and 7,300 serials. 125 computers available on campus for general student use.

Community Environment: See Jacksonville University.

■ **EMBRY-RIDDLE AERONAUTICAL UNIVERSITY** *H-14*
600 South Clyde Morris Blvd.
Daytona Beach, FL 32114-3900
Tel: (386)226-6000
Free: 800-862-2416
Admissions: (386)226-6100
Fax: (386)226-7070
E-mail: dbadmit@erau.edu
Web Site: http://www.embryriddle.edu/

Description: Independent, comprehensive, coed. Awards bachelor's and master's degrees. Founded 1926. Setting: 178-acre urban campus with easy access to Orlando. Endowment: $46.4 million. Research spending for 2004 fiscal year: $6.9 million. Educational spending for 2005 fiscal year: $10,687 per student. Total enrollment: 4,776. Faculty: 314 (227 full-time, 87 part-time). Student-undergrad faculty ratio is 16:1. 3,527 applied, 84% were admitted. 20% from top 10% of their high school class, 48% from top quarter, 77% from top half. Full-time: 4,093 students, 17% women, 83% men. Part-time: 289 students, 21% women, 79% men. Students come from 53 states and territories, 99 other countries, 68% from out-of-state, 0.3% Native American, 7% Hispanic, 5% black, 5% Asian American or Pacific Islander, 8% international, 9% 25 or older, 41% live on campus, 6% transferred in. Retention: 75% of full-time freshmen returned the following year. Academic areas with the most degrees conferred: transportation and materials moving; engineering; health professions and related sciences. Core. Calendar: semesters. Academic remediation for entering students, ESL program, services for LD students, advanced placement, independent study, distance learning, double major, summer session for credit, part-time degree program, adult/continuing education programs, co-op programs and internships, graduate courses open to undergrads. Study abroad program. ROTC: Army, Naval, Air Force.

Entrance Requirements: Options: Peterson's Universal Application, Common Application, electronic application, early admission, early decision, deferred admission, international baccalaureate accepted. Required: high school transcript, minimum 2.0 high school GPA, SAT or ACT. Recommended: essay, recommendations, interview. Required for some: minimum 3.0 high school GPA, medical examination for flight students. Entrance: moderately difficult. Application deadline: Rolling. Notification: continuous.

Costs Per Year: Application fee: $50. Comprehensive fee: $30,436 includes full-time tuition ($22,820), mandatory fees ($680), and college room and board ($6936). College room only: $2800. Part-time tuition: $855 per credit hour.

Collegiate Environment: Orientation program. Drama-theater group, choral group, student-run newspaper, radio station. Social organizations: 102 open to all; national fraternities, national sororities; 10% of eligible men and 14% of eligible women are members. Most popular organizations: Eagle Wing, Future Professional Pilots Association, African Student Association, Caribbean Student Association, Sigma Gamma Tau. Major annual events: homecoming, spring concert, hypnotist performance. Student services: health clinic, personal-psychological counseling. Campus security: 24-hour emergency response devices and patrols, student patrols, late night transport-escort service, controlled dormitory access. 1,889 college housing spaces available; 1,832 were occupied in 2003-04. Freshmen guaranteed college housing. On-campus residence required through sophomore year. Option: coed housing available. Jack R. Hunt Memorial Library with 138,327 books, 295,619 microform titles, 741 serials, 7,030 audiovisual materials, an OPAC, and a Web page. Operations spending for 2004 fiscal year: $3.1 million. 884 computers available on campus for general student use. A campuswide network can be accessed from student residence rooms and from off campus. Staffed computer lab on campus.

Community Environment: Daytona Beach has a population of approximately 300,000 in the immediate vicinity, and the campus itself has approximately 4,500 students. Boasting one of the finest recreational beaches in the world, it is also home to the Daytona International Speedway. Other major attractions include Walt Disney World and Sea World near Orlando (approximately 80 miles away). The area provides ample housing and excellent opportunities for part-time employment for ERAU students. The Prescott area is one of the more colorful areas of the old "Wild West," with a population in the immediate area approaching 100,000. The Prescott Campus of approximately 1,500 students is surrounded by a national forest and is close to mountains and excellent outdoor recreational areas. The city of Phoenix is about 90 miles away.

■ EMBRY-RIDDLE AERONAUTICAL UNIVERSITY, EXTENDED CAMPUS *H-14*

600 South Clyde Morris Blvd.
Daytona Beach, FL 32114-3900
Tel: (386)226-6910
Free: 800-522-6787
Admissions: (386)226-7610
Fax: (386)226-6984
E-mail: ecinfo@erau.edu
Web Site: http://www.embryriddle.edu/

Description: Independent, comprehensive, coed. Awards associate, bachelor's, and master's degrees (programs offered at 100 military bases worldwide). Founded 1970. Endowment: $46.4 million. Research spending for 2004 fiscal year: $6.9 million. Educational spending for 2005 fiscal year: $10,687 per student. Total enrollment: 16,255. Faculty: 2,104 (137 full-time, 1,967 part-time). Student-undergrad faculty ratio is 28:1. Full-time: 2,192 students, 11% women, 89% men. Part-time: 10,368 students, 12% women, 88% men. 1% Native American, 8% Hispanic, 8% black, 3% Asian American or Pacific Islander, 1% international, 0% transferred in. Academic areas with the most degrees conferred: transportation and materials moving; business/marketing. Core. Calendar: 5 9-week terms. Services for LD students, advanced placement, independent study, part-time degree program, external degree program, adult/continuing education programs, co-op programs, graduate courses open to undergrads. Off campus study at Servicemembers Opportunity Colleges.

Entrance Requirements: Option: deferred admission. Required for some: essay. Entrance: minimally difficult. Application deadline: Rolling. Notification: continuous.

Costs Per Year: Application fee: $50. Tuition: $4224 full-time.

Collegiate Environment: Jack R. Hunt Memorial Library with 138,237 books, 295,619 microform titles, 741 serials, 7,030 audiovisual materials, an OPAC, and a Web page. Operations spending for 2004 fiscal year: $3.1 million.

■ EVERGLADES UNIVERSITY (BOCA RATON) *R-15*

T-Rex Corporate Center
5002 T-Rex Ave., Ste. 100
Boca Raton, FL 33431
Tel: (561)912-1211; 888-772-6077
Fax: (561)912-1191
E-mail: jgraham@evergladesuniversity.edu
Web Site: http://www.evergladesuniversity.edu/

Description: Proprietary, comprehensive, coed. Awards bachelor's and master's degrees. Founded 1989. Setting: urban campus. Total enrollment: 433. Faculty: 117 (24 full-time, 93 part-time). 0.3% Native American, 10% Hispanic, 16% black, 2% Asian American or Pacific Islander, 2% international. Core. Calendar: continuous. Accelerated degree program, distance learning, summer session for credit, external degree program, adult/continuing education programs, co-op programs.

Entrance Requirements: Open admission. Options: Common Application, electronic application. Required: high school transcript. Required for some: SAT or ACT, Otis-Lennon School Ability Test. Entrance: noncompetitive. Notification: continuous.

Costs Per Year: Application fee: $50. Tuition: $9744 full-time. Mandatory fees: $400 full-time.

Collegiate Environment: Orientation program. College housing not available. 30 computers available on campus for general student use. Staffed computer lab on campus.

■ EVERGLADES UNIVERSITY (SARASOTA) *N-8*

6151 Lake Osprey Dr.
Sarasota, FL 34240
Tel: (941)907-2262; (866)907-2262
Fax: (941)907-6634
E-mail: bbrewer@evergladesuniversity.edu

Web Site: http://www.evergladesuniversity.edu/

Description: Proprietary, 4-year, coed. Awards bachelor's degrees. Founded 2003. Total enrollment: 152. Calendar: continuous.

Costs Per Year: Tuition: $406 per credit hour part-time.

■ FLAGLER COLLEGE *E-13*

74 King St.
PO Box 1027
St. Augustine, FL 32085-1027
Tel: (904)829-6481
Free: 800-304-4208
Admissions: (904)819-6220
Fax: (904)826-0094
E-mail: admiss@flagler.edu
Web Site: http://www.flagler.edu/

Description: Independent, 4-year, coed. Awards bachelor's degrees. Founded 1968. Setting: 36-acre small town campus with easy access to Jacksonville. Endowment: $37.7 million. Educational spending for 2005 fiscal year: $3211 per student. Total enrollment: 2,157. Student-undergrad faculty ratio is 20:1. 2,248 applied, 25% were admitted. 16% from top 10% of their high school class, 51% from top quarter, 88% from top half. Full-time: 2,089 students, 62% women, 38% men. Part-time: 68 students, 57% women, 43% men. Students come from 48 states and territories, 43 other countries, 32% from out-of-state, 0.3% Native American, 4% Hispanic, 2% black, 1% Asian American or Pacific Islander, 1% international, 1% 25 or older, 36% live on campus, 4% transferred in. Retention: 69% of full-time freshmen returned the following year. Academic areas with the most degrees conferred: business/marketing; communications/journalism; visual and performing arts. Core. Calendar: semesters. Academic remediation for entering students, services for LD students, advanced placement, independent study, double major, summer session for credit, internships. Off campus study at Northeast Florida Consortium for the Hearing Impaired, University of North Florida, Florida School for the Deaf and Blind, Fashion Institute of Technology. Study abroad program.

Entrance Requirements: Options: electronic application, early admission, early decision, international baccalaureate accepted. Required: essay, high school transcript, 1 recommendation, SAT or ACT. Recommended: minimum 2.75 high school GPA, recommendations, interview, rank in upper 50% of high school class. Entrance: moderately difficult. Application deadlines: 3/1, 12/1 for early decision plan 1, 1/15 for early decision plan 2. Notification: 3/30, 12/15 for early decision plan 1, 2/1 for early decision plan 2.

Costs Per Year: Application fee: $30. Comprehensive fee: $13,790 includes full-time tuition ($8600) and college room and board ($5190). College room only: $2130. Part-time tuition: $295 per credit hour.

Collegiate Environment: Orientation program. Drama-theater group, choral group, student-run newspaper, radio station. Social organizations: 26 open to all. Most popular organizations: Inter-Varsity, Student Government, Society for the Advancement of Management, Students in Free Enterprise, Deaf Awareness Club. Major annual events: Spirit Week, Special Olympics, Flagler Forums. Student services: health clinic, personal-psychological counseling. Campus security: 24-hour emergency response devices and patrols, late night transport-escort service, controlled dormitory access. College housing designed to accommodate 670 students; 713 undergraduates lived in college housing during 2003-04. Freshmen guaranteed college housing. On-campus residence required in freshman year. Options: men-only, women-only housing available. Proctor Library with 130,201 books, 69,158 microform titles, 549 serials, 3,884 audiovisual materials, an OPAC, and a Web page. Operations spending for 2004 fiscal year: $442,265. 210 computers available on campus for general student use. Computer purchase/lease plans available. A campuswide network can be accessed from student residence rooms and from off campus. Staffed computer lab on campus.

Community Environment: St. Augustine, the nation's oldest city, has a very mild climate; average high temperature is 79.9 degrees and the average low is 58.3 degrees. The city is located approximately 40 miles south of Jacksonville, near the Atlantic coast. St. Augustine is undergoing a restoration program to extend over a twenty-year period that will return the entire area to an authentic likeness of its colonial days. The leading industries are tourist trade, airplane rebuilding, aluminum extrusion, boat-building, food processing, and shrimp fishing. Recreation facilities include championship golf courses, beaches, tennis courts, and the ocean for deep sea fishing. The Matanzas River affords miles of protected waters for boating and fishing. The city has churches of all denominations, numerous hotels and motels, 2 hospitals, and a library. All major civic and fraternal organizations are represented. Sightseeing tours are available by trains and horse-drawn carriages. There are many points of interest, some of which are the Cathedral of St. Augustine, Lightner Museum, Marineland, Alligator Farm, Casa Del Hidalgo, the World Golf Village, Fountain of Youth, Mission of Nombre De Dios, Oldest Schoolhouse, the Zimenes House, Memorial Presbyterian Church, and the Castillo de San Marcos.

■ **FLORIDA AGRICULTURAL AND MECHANICAL UNIVERSITY** *C-5*
Tallahassee, FL 32307-3200
Tel: (850)599-3000
Admissions: (850)599-3796
Fax: (850)561-2428
Web Site: http://www.famu.edu/
Description: State-supported, university, coed. Part of State University System of Florida. Awards associate, bachelor's, master's, doctoral, and first professional degrees. Founded 1887. Setting: 419-acre urban campus. Research spending for 2004 fiscal year: $20 million. Total enrollment: 13,064. 5,709 applied, 71% were admitted. Full-time: 9,349 students, 57% women, 43% men. Part-time: 1,227 students, 51% women, 49% men. Students come from 47 states and territories, 73 other countries, 20% from out-of-state, 0.02% Native American, 1% Hispanic, 97% black, 0.3% Asian American or Pacific Islander, 5%. 25 or older, 3% transferred in. Retention: 80% of full-time freshmen returned the following year. Core. Calendar: semesters. Academic remediation for entering students, services for LD students, advanced placement, accelerated degree program, honors program, summer session for credit, part-time degree program, adult/continuing education programs, co-op programs and internships, graduate courses open to undergrads. Off campus study at Florida State University. ROTC: Army, Naval, Air Force (c).
Entrance Requirements: Options: Peterson's Universal Application, Common Application, electronic application, early admission, deferred admission, international baccalaureate accepted. Required: high school transcript, minimum 2.0 high school GPA, SAT or ACT. Recommended: minimum 3.2 high school GPA. Required for some: essay, recommendations. Entrance: moderately difficult. Application deadline: 5/9. Notification: continuous until 8/1. Preference given to state residents.
Costs Per Year: Application fee: $20. State resident tuition: $3318 full-time, $110.60 per credit hour part-time. Nonresident tuition: $16,662 full-time, $555.40 per credit hour part-time. Full-time tuition varies according to course load. Part-time tuition varies according to course load. College room and board: $5766. College room only: $3476. Room and board charges vary according to board plan and housing facility.
Collegiate Environment: Orientation program. Drama-theater group, choral group, marching band, student-run newspaper, radio station. Social organizations: 125 open to all; national fraternities, national sororities; 16% of eligible men and 19% of eligible women are members. Most popular organizations: Gospel Choir, University Marching Band, Alpha Kappa Alpha, Alpha Phi Alpha, SBJ. Major annual events: Homecoming Convocation, Business Expo, Black College Day. Student services: health clinic, personal-psychological counseling, women's center. Campus security: 24-hour emergency response devices and patrols, late night transport-escort service. 3,146 college housing spaces available; all were occupied in 2003-04. On-campus residence required in freshman year. Options: men-only, women-only housing available. Coleman Memorial Library plus 5 others with 484,801 books, 156,018 microform titles, 7,672 serials, 73,957 audiovisual materials, and an OPAC. Operations spending for 2004 fiscal year: $3.7 million.
Community Environment: Tallahassee, a community of varied interests, provides an ideal setting for a thriving comprehensive university. The community abounds in a broad range of programs and activities, including three institutions of higher education; city, county, and state government; civic and community organizations; art galleries; theater and music archives; libraries and museums; state parks and recreational facilities; tree-shaded streets and highways; and a 13,500-seat Civic Center.

■ **FLORIDA ATLANTIC UNIVERSITY** *R-15*
777 Glades Rd., PO Box 3091
Boca Raton, FL 33431-0991
Tel: (561)297-3000
Free: 800-299-4FAU
Admissions: (561)297-3040
E-mail: pletcher!@fau.edu
Web Site: http://www.fau.edu/
Description: State-supported, university, coed. Part of State University System of Florida. Awards associate, bachelor's, master's, and doctoral

degrees and post-master's certificates. Founded 1961. Setting: 850-acre suburban campus with easy access to Miami. Endowment: $132.6 million. Total enrollment: 25,704. Faculty: 1,386 (767 full-time, 619 part-time). Student-undergrad faculty ratio is 18:1. 13,033 applied, 56% were admitted. 3 National Merit Scholars. Full-time: 11,810 students, 58% women, 42% men. Part-time: 9,695 students, 63% women, 37% men. Students come from 50 states and territories, 175 other countries, 9% from out-of-state, 0.3% Native American, 17% Hispanic, 18% black, 4% Asian American or Pacific Islander, 4% international, 33% 25 or older, 9% live on campus, 14% transferred in. Retention: 71% of full-time freshmen returned the following year. Academic areas with the most degrees conferred: business/marketing; education; health professions and related sciences; social sciences. Core. Calendar: semesters. ESL program, services for LD students, advanced placement, accelerated degree program, freshman honors college, honors program, independent study, distance learning, double major, summer session for credit, part-time degree program, adult/continuing education programs, co-op programs and internships, graduate courses open to undergrads. Off campus study at other members of the State University System of Florida. Study abroad program. ROTC: Army (c), Air Force (c).
Entrance Requirements: Options: Common Application, electronic application, early admission, deferred admission, international baccalaureate accepted. Required: high school transcript, minimum 2.0 high school GPA, SAT and SAT Subject Tests or ACT. Required for some: 1 recommendation. Entrance: moderately difficult. Application deadline: 6/1. Notification: continuous.
Costs Per Year: Application fee: $30. State resident tuition: $2147 full-time, $108.64 per credit hour part-time. Nonresident tuition: $14,653 full-time, $546.36 per credit hour part-time. Mandatory fees: $1112 full-time. Full-time tuition and fees vary according to course load. Part-time tuition varies according to course load. College room and board: $7962. Room and board charges vary according to board plan and housing facility.
Collegiate Environment: Orientation program. Drama-theater group, choral group, marching band, student-run newspaper, radio station. Social organizations: 192 open to all; national fraternities, national sororities, local fraternities, local sororities; 2% of eligible men and 2% of eligible women are members. Most popular organizations: Latin American Student Organization, Alpha Tau Omega, Konbit Kreyol, Program Board, Owl Corral. Major annual events: homecoming, Freakers Ball, Student Affairs Day. Student services: legal services, health clinic, personal-psychological counseling, women's center. Campus security: 24-hour emergency response devices and patrols, student patrols, late night transport-escort service, controlled dormitory access. 2,200 college housing spaces available; 2,174 were occupied in 2003-04. Freshmen guaranteed college housing. On-campus residence required in freshman year. Options: coed, women-only housing available. S. E. Wimberly Library plus 2 others with 1.4 million books, 2.2 million microform titles, 10,572 serials, 19,685 audiovisual materials, an OPAC, and a Web page. 822 computers available on campus for general student use. A campuswide network can be accessed from student residence rooms and from off campus. Staffed computer lab on campus.
Community Environment: A resort and suburban area located on Florida's east coast, Boca Raton is 40 miles north of Miami and 25 miles from Ft. Lauderdale and Palm Beach airports. The area enjoys a subtropical climate. Local industry includes large regional centers for Sensormatic, Siemens, Motorola and other high tech multinational corporations. Several shopping centers, a library, many houses of worship, and two hospitals are some of the community facilities. Cultural activities are many. Recreational activities include swimming, tennis, golf, surf casting, and deep-sea fishing. There are three public beaches and numerous superior golf courses nearby. Everglades National Park lies to the west and south.

■ **FLORIDA ATLANTIC UNIVERSITY, JUPITER CAMPUS** *P-15*
5353 Parkside Dr.
Jupiter, FL 33458
Tel: (561)799-8500
Web Site: http://www.fau.edu/jupiter/
Description: State-supported, comprehensive, coed. Calendar: semesters.

■ **FLORIDA CAREER COLLEGE** *T-15*
1321 Southwest 107 Ave., Ste. 201B
Miami, FL 33174
Tel: (305)553-6065
Fax: (305)225-0128
Web Site: http://www.careercollege.edu/
Description: Proprietary, 2-year, coed. Awards certificates, diplomas, and terminal associate degrees. Founded 1982. Setting: urban campus.

Educational spending for 2005 fiscal year: $2500 per student. Total enrollment: 2,131. Full-time: 1,717 students, 43% women, 57% men. Part-time: 414 students, 34% women, 66% men. Students come from 2 states and territories, 3 other countries, 0% from out-of-state, 0.1% Native American, 49% Hispanic, 32% black, 2% Asian American or Pacific Islander, 1% international, 75% 25 or older, 0% transferred in. Core. Academic remediation for entering students, independent study, summer session for credit, part-time degree program.

Entrance Requirements: Open admission. Options: Common Application, deferred admission. Required: high school transcript, interview. Entrance: noncompetitive. Application deadline: Rolling. Notification: continuous.

Collegiate Environment: Orientation program. Campus security: 24-hour emergency response devices. College housing not available. Resource Center plus 1 other with 1,200 books and 200 serials. Operations spending for 2004 fiscal year: $24,000. 288 computers available on campus for general student use. A campuswide network can be accessed from off-campus. Staffed computer lab on campus.

■ **FLORIDA CHRISTIAN COLLEGE** *K-13*
1011 Bill Beck Blvd.
Kissimmee, FL 34744-5301
Tel: (407)847-8966
Fax: (407)847-3925
Web Site: http://www.fcc.edu/

Description: Independent, 4-year, coed, affiliated with Christian Churches and Churches of Christ. Awards associate and bachelor's degrees. Founded 1976. Setting: 40-acre small town campus with easy access to Orlando. Endowment: $1.5 million. Educational spending for 2005 fiscal year: $2855 per student. Total enrollment: 259. 120 applied, 71% were admitted. Students come from 23 states and territories, 1 other country, 18% from out-of-state, 0% Native American, 5% Hispanic, 3% black, 2% Asian American or Pacific Islander, 0.4% international, 31% 25 or older, 65% live on campus. Retention: 81% of full-time freshmen returned the following year. Core. Calendar: semesters. Academic remediation for entering students, advanced placement, summer session for credit, part-time degree program, adult/continuing education programs, internships. Study abroad program.

Entrance Requirements: Options: Peterson's Universal Application, early admission, deferred admission. Required: high school transcript, 3 recommendations. Placement: ACT required. Entrance: minimally difficult. Application deadline: 7/15. Notification: continuous until 8/25.

Costs Per Year: Application fee: $25. Tuition: $9280 full-time, $290 per credit part-time. Mandatory fees: $440 full-time. Full-time tuition and fees vary according to course load. Part-time tuition varies according to course load. College room only: $2200. Tuition guaranteed not to increase for student's term of enrollment.

Collegiate Environment: Orientation program. Drama-theater group, choral group, student-run newspaper. Most popular organizations: Student Council, Camera Club, Timothy Club. Major annual events: Homecoming, Christmas Banquet, Hearts Banquet. On-campus residence required in freshman year. 31,000 books, 285 serials, an OPAC, and a Web page. Operations spending for 2004 fiscal year: $117,112. 11 computers available on campus for general student use. A campuswide network can be accessed from off-campus. Staffed computer lab on campus.

■ **FLORIDA COLLEGE** *J-5*
119 North Glen Arven Ave.
Temple Terrace, FL 33617
Tel: (813)988-5131
Free: 800-326-7655
Fax: (813)899-6772
E-mail: admissions@flcoll.edu
Web Site: http://www.floridacollege.edu/

Description: Independent, 4-year, coed. Awards associate and bachelor's degrees. Founded 1944. Setting: 95-acre small town campus with easy access to Tampa. Educational spending for 2005 fiscal year: $6835 per student. Total enrollment: 456. Student-undergrad faculty ratio is 15:1. 299 applied, 72% were admitted. 1 National Merit Scholar, 2 valedictorians. Full-time: 438 students, 50% women, 50% men. Part-time: 18 students, 50% women, 50% men. Students come from 40 states and territories, 5 other countries, 71% from out-of-state, 0.4% Native American, 2% Hispanic, 3% black, 0% Asian American or Pacific Islander, 2% international, 83% live on campus, 5% transferred in. Academic areas with the most degrees conferred: liberal arts/general studies; education. Core. Calendar:

semesters. Academic remediation for entering students, advanced placement, independent study. ROTC: Army (c), Air Force (c).

Entrance Requirements: Options: electronic application, international baccalaureate accepted. Required: high school transcript, minimum 2.0 high school GPA, recommendations, SAT or ACT. Required for some: essay. Entrance: moderately difficult. Application deadline: 8/1. Notification: continuous.

Costs Per Year: Application fee: $25. Comprehensive fee: $15,930 includes full-time tuition ($10,180), mandatory fees ($550), and college room and board ($5200). Room and board charges vary according to board plan and housing facility. Part-time tuition: $410 per semester hour. Part-time mandatory fees: $200 per term.

Collegiate Environment: Orientation program. Drama-theater group, choral group. Social organizations: 16 open to all; 72% of eligible men and 80% of eligible women are members. Most popular organizations: Drama Workshop, concert band, chorus, SBGA, YWTO. Major annual events: Fall Banquet, Spring Banquet, Annual Alumni Basketball Game. Student services: health clinic, personal-psychological counseling. Campus security: controlled dormitory access, evening patrols by trained security personnel. 518 college housing spaces available; 416 were occupied in 2003-04. Freshmen guaranteed college housing. On-campus residence required through sophomore year. Options: men-only, women-only housing available. Chatlos Library with 114,938 books, 9,224 microform titles, 400 serials, 6,097 audiovisual materials, an OPAC, and a Web page. Operations spending for 2004 fiscal year: $165,090. 76 computers available on campus for general student use. A campuswide network can be accessed from student residence rooms and from off campus. Staffed computer lab on campus.

Community Environment: Located near Tampa, Temple Terrace has a subtropical climate. Buses serve the area. Community facilities include a library, churches, and one community college and two universities. Part-time employment is limited. Sport activities include boating, fishing, golf, professional baseball, football and soccer. Cultural and recreational facilities, broad and varied, are also available in Tampa.

■ **FLORIDA COLLEGE OF NATURAL HEALTH (BRADENTON)** *N-8*
616 67th St. Circle East
Bradenton, FL 34208
Tel: (941)954-8999
Free: 800-966-7117
Fax: (941)954-8991
E-mail: sarasota@fcnh.com
Web Site: http://www.fcnh.com/
Description: Proprietary, 2-year, coed. Founded 1998.

■ **FLORIDA COLLEGE OF NATURAL HEALTH (MAITLAND)** *D-5*
2600 Lake Lucien Dr., Ste. 140
Maitland, FL 32751
Tel: (407)261-0319
Free: 800-393-7337
Fax: (407)261-0342
E-mail: orlando@fcnh.com
Web Site: http://www.fcnh.com/
Description: Proprietary, 2-year, coed. Founded 1995.

■ **FLORIDA COLLEGE OF NATURAL HEALTH (MIAMI)** *T-15*
7925 Northwest 12th St.
Ste. 201
Miami, FL 33126
Tel: (305)597-9599
Free: 800-599-9599
Fax: (305)597-9110
E-mail: miami@fcnh.com
Web Site: http://www.fcnh.com/
Description: Proprietary, 2-year, coed. Founded 1993.

■ **FLORIDA COLLEGE OF NATURAL HEALTH (POMPANO BEACH)** *R-15*
2001 West Sample Rd., Ste. 100
Pompano Beach, FL 33064
Tel: (954)975-6400
Free: 800-541-9299
Fax: (954)975-9633
E-mail: adrener@fcnh.com
Web Site: http://www.fcnh.com/

Description: Proprietary, 2-year, coed. Founded 1986.

■ **FLORIDA COMMUNITY COLLEGE AT JACKSONVILLE** *D-12*
501 West State St.
Jacksonville, FL 32202-4030
Tel: (904)632-3000
Admissions: (904)632-3131
Fax: (904)632-3393
Web Site: http://www.fccj.edu/
Description: State-supported, 2-year, coed. Part of Florida Community College System. Awards certificates, diplomas, transfer associate, and terminal associate degrees. Founded 1963. Setting: 656-acre urban campus. Endowment: $3.9 million. Educational spending for 2005 fiscal year: $3243 per student. Total enrollment: 29,831. Student-undergrad faculty ratio is 21:1. 700 applied, 100% were admitted. Full-time: 7,462 students, 45% women, 55% men. Part-time: 22,369 students, 41% women, 59% men. Students come from 19 states and territories, 108 other countries, 23% from out-of-state, 0.3% Native American, 6% Hispanic, 28% black, 4% Asian American or Pacific Islander, 47% 25 or older, 20% transferred in. Core. Calendar: semesters. Academic remediation for entering students, ESL program, services for LD students, advanced placement, accelerated degree program, honors program, independent study, distance learning, double major, summer session for credit, part-time degree program, adult/continuing education programs, co-op programs and internships. Off campus study at Jacksonville Naval Station, Mayport Naval Air Station, Cecil Field Naval Air Station. Study abroad program. ROTC: Naval (c).
Entrance Requirements: Open admission. Options: Common Application, early admission, deferred admission. Required: high school transcript. Entrance: noncompetitive. Application deadline: Rolling.
Costs Per Year: Application fee: $15. State resident tuition: $1518 full-time, $63.25 per credit part-time. Nonresident tuition: $5742 full-time, $239.25 per credit part-time.
Collegiate Environment: Orientation program. Drama-theater group, choral group, student-run newspaper, radio station. Most popular organizations: Phi Theta Kappa, Troupe de Kent, Forensic Team, Brain Bowl Team, International Student Association. Major annual events: Miss FCCJ Scholarship Pageant, FCCJ Talent/Variety Show, FCCJ Spring Dance. Student services: personal-psychological counseling, women's center. Campus security: 24-hour emergency response devices and patrols, student patrols, late night transport-escort service. College housing not available. Main library plus 6 others with 412,856 books, 282,482 microform titles, 4,137 serials, 15,286 audiovisual materials, an OPAC, and a Web page. Operations spending for 2004 fiscal year: $2.9 million. 2,500 computers available on campus for general student use. A campuswide network can be accessed from off-campus. Staffed computer lab on campus.

■ **FLORIDA CULINARY INSTITUTE** *Q-15*
2400 Metrocenter Blvd.
West Palm Beach, FL 33407
Tel: (561)688-2001
Admissions: (561)842-8324
E-mail: info@floridaculinary.com
Web Site: http://www.floridaculinary.com/
Description: Proprietary, 2-year. Awards terminal associate degrees (degree in science only (18 or 24 month program)). Total enrollment: 600.

■ **FLORIDA GULF COAST UNIVERSITY** *Q-10*
10501 FGCU Blvd. South
Fort Myers, FL 33965-6565
Tel: (239)590-1000; 888-889-1095
Admissions: (239)590-7878
Fax: (239)590-7894
Web Site: http://www.fgcu.edu/
Description: State-supported, comprehensive, coed. Part of State University System of Florida. Awards associate, bachelor's, and master's degrees. Founded 1991. Setting: 760-acre suburban campus. Endowment: $25.7 million. Research spending for 2004 fiscal year: $1 million. Educational spending for 2005 fiscal year: $5816 per student. Total enrollment: 7,249. Faculty: 441 (253 full-time, 188 part-time). Student-undergrad faculty ratio is 18:1. 3,449 applied, 76% were admitted. 20% from top 10% of their high school class, 49% from top quarter, 84% from top half. Full-time: 4,601 students, 62% women, 38% men. Part-time: 1,537 students, 64% women, 36% men. Students come from 46 states and territories, 25 other countries, 9% from out-of-state, 0.3% Native American, 9% Hispanic, 6%

black, 2% Asian American or Pacific Islander, 1% international, 21% 25 or older, 32% live on campus. Retention: 73% of full-time freshmen returned the following year. Academic areas with the most degrees conferred: liberal arts/general studies; business/marketing; health professions and related sciences. Core. Calendar: semesters. Academic remediation for entering students, services for LD students, advanced placement, accelerated degree program, honors program, independent study, distance learning, double major, summer session for credit, part-time degree program, co-op programs and internships, graduate courses open to undergrads. Off campus study. Study abroad program.
Entrance Requirements: Options: electronic application, deferred admission, international baccalaureate accepted. Required: high school transcript, minimum 2.0 high school GPA, SAT or ACT. Required for some: essay, recommendations, interview. Entrance: moderately difficult. Application deadline: 8/1. Notification: continuous.
Costs Per Year: Application fee: $30. State resident tuition: $3260 full-time, $108.67 per credit part-time. Nonresident tuition: $15,249 full-time, $508.31 per credit part-time. Mandatory fees: $160 full-time, $2 per credit part-time, $100 per year part-time. Full-time tuition and fees vary according to course load. Part-time tuition and fees vary according to course load. College room and board: $7460. College room only: $3620. Room and board charges vary according to board plan.
Collegiate Environment: Orientation program. Drama-theater group, student-run newspaper. Social organizations: 42 open to all; national fraternities, national sororities; 1% of eligible men and 1% of eligible women are members. Most popular organizations: Golden Key National Honor Society, student government, Student Nurses Association, Student Council for Exceptional Children, Physical Therapy Association. Major annual events: SGA DAY, Eagle Blast, 5K Scholarship Run. Student services: health clinic, personal-psychological counseling. Campus security: 24-hour emergency response devices and patrols, late night transport-escort service. 1,662 college housing spaces available; 1,511 were occupied in 2003-04. No special consideration for freshman housing applicants. Option: coed housing available. Library Services with 282,557 books, 327,657 microform titles, 1,429 serials, 2,491 audiovisual materials, an OPAC, and a Web page. Operations spending for 2004 fiscal year: $2.7 million. 323 computers available on campus for general student use. A campuswide network can be accessed from student residence rooms and from off campus. Staffed computer lab on campus.

■ **FLORIDA HOSPITAL COLLEGE OF HEALTH SCIENCES** *J-13*
800 Lake Estelle Dr.
Orlando, FL 32803
Tel: (407)303-7747
Free: 800-500-7747
Admissions: (407)303-9798
Web Site: http://www.fhchs.edu/
Description: Independent, primarily 2-year, coed. Awards certificates, terminal associate, and bachelor's degrees. Setting: 9-acre urban campus. Endowment: $1 million. Research spending for 2004 fiscal year: $9082. Educational spending for 2005 fiscal year: $4589 per student. Total enrollment: 1,403. 463 applied, 96% were admitted. Full-time: 609 students, 78% women, 22% men. Part-time: 794 students, 73% women, 27% men. Students come from 8 states and territories, 23 other countries, 1% Native American, 15% Hispanic, 14% black, 9% Asian American or Pacific Islander, 0% international, 8% live on campus. Core. Calendar: semesters. Academic remediation for entering students, services for LD students, advanced placement, independent study, distance learning. ROTC: Air Force (c).
Entrance Requirements: Open admission. Options: Common Application, electronic application. Required: minimum 2.7 high school GPA. Required for some: essay, high school transcript, 3 recommendations, SAT or ACT. Entrance: minimally difficult. Application deadlines: 7/18, 7/18 for nonresidents. Notification: continuous until 8/30, continuous until 8/30 for nonresidents.
Costs Per Year: Application fee: $20. Tuition: $8060 full-time, $230 per credit part-time. Mandatory fees: $570 full-time. College room only: $1760.
Collegiate Environment: Orientation program. Drama-theater group, student-run newspaper. Major annual events: International Food Fair, Annual Picnic, Fall Festival. Student services: personal-psychological counseling. Campus security: 24-hour emergency response devices and patrols, late night transport-escort service, controlled dormitory access. 120 college housing spaces available; all were occupied in 2003-04. No special consideration for freshman housing applicants. Option: coed housing available. Robert Arthur Williams Library with 74,581 books, 158 serials, 1,627

audiovisual materials, and an OPAC. Operations spending for 2004 fiscal year: $510,809. 45 computers available on campus for general student use. Computer purchase/lease plans available. A campuswide network can be accessed. Staffed computer lab on campus.

■ FLORIDA INSTITUTE OF TECHNOLOGY *L-16*

150 West University Blvd.
Melbourne, FL 32901-6975
Tel: (321)674-8000
Free: 800-888-4348
Admissions: (321)674-8030
Fax: (321)723-9468
E-mail: admissions@fit.edu
Web Site: http://www.fit.edu/

Description: Independent, university, coed. Awards bachelor's, master's, and doctoral degrees and post-master's certificates. Founded 1958. Setting: 130-acre small town campus with easy access to Orlando. Endowment: $36.8 million. Research spending for 2004 fiscal year: $8.2 million. Educational spending for 2005 fiscal year: $10,269 per student. Total enrollment: 4,745. Faculty: 408 (215 full-time, 193 part-time). Student-undergrad faculty ratio is 13:1. 2,463 applied, 83% were admitted. 32% from top 10% of their high school class, 66% from top quarter, 92% from top half. 2 National Merit Scholars, 7 valedictorians. Full-time: 2,264 students, 31% women, 69% men. Part-time: 94 students, 27% women, 73% men. Students come from 50 states and territories, 84 other countries, 64% from out-of-state, 0.4% Native American, 7% Hispanic, 4% black, 3% Asian American or Pacific Islander, 14% international, 5% 25 or older, 52% live on campus, 6% transferred in. Retention: 78% of full-time freshmen returned the following year. Academic areas with the most degrees conferred: engineering; transportation and materials moving; biological/life sciences. Core. Calendar: semesters. Academic remediation for entering students, ESL program, services for LD students, advanced placement, accelerated degree program, double major, summer session for credit, part-time degree program, adult/continuing education programs, co-op programs and internships, graduate courses open to undergrads. Study abroad program. ROTC: Army.

Entrance Requirements: Options: Peterson's Universal Application, Common Application, electronic application, early admission, deferred admission, international baccalaureate accepted. Required: high school transcript, minimum 2.5 high school GPA, SAT or ACT. Recommended: essay, minimum 2.8 high school GPA, interview. Required for some: minimum 3.0 high school GPA. Entrance: moderately difficult. Application deadline: Rolling. Notification: continuous.

Costs Per Year: Application fee: $50. Comprehensive fee: $31,950 includes full-time tuition ($25,150) and college room and board ($6800). College room only: $4000. Full-time tuition varies according to course load and program. Room and board charges vary according to board plan and housing facility. Part-time tuition: $765 per credit hour. Part-time tuition varies according to course load and program.

Collegiate Environment: Orientation program. Drama-theater group, choral group, student-run newspaper, radio station. Social organizations: 110 open to all; national fraternities, national sororities, local sororities; 15% of eligible men and 15% of eligible women are members. Most popular organizations: Squamish, Muslim Student Association, Phi Eta Sigma, Chinese Student Scholars Association. Major annual events: Homecoming, Halloween celebration. Student services: legal services, health clinic, personal-psychological counseling. Campus security: 24-hour emergency response devices and patrols, late night transport-escort service, self-defense education. 1,347 college housing spaces available; 1,163 were occupied in 2003-04. Freshmen guaranteed college housing. On-campus residence required in freshman year. Options: coed, men-only, women-only housing available. Evans Library with 281,809 books, 309,613 microform titles, 6,079 serials, 5,546 audiovisual materials, an OPAC, and a Web page. Operations spending for 2004 fiscal year: $1.9 million. 400 computers available on campus for general student use. A campuswide network can be accessed from student residence rooms and from off campus. Staffed computer lab on campus.

Community Environment: Florida Tech is located in the city of Melbourne, Brevard County, on Florida's space coast, approximately 30 miles south of Spaceport, 60 miles east of Orlando and 170 miles north of Miami. It is 5 minutes from the Melbourne International Airport, which is host to 2 major

airlines. Recreation includes public swimming pools, golf courses, a tourist club with facilities for a number of sports, a harbor, and a yacht basin. Fresh and salt water fishing are available.

■ FLORIDA INTERNATIONAL UNIVERSITY *T-15*

11200 S.W. 8th St.
Miami, FL 33199
Tel: (305)348-2000
Admissions: (305)348-3675
Fax: (305)348-3648
E-mail: admiss@servms.fiu.edu
Web Site: http://www.fiu.edu/

Description: State-supported, university, coed. Part of State University System of Florida. Awards bachelor's, master's, doctoral, and first professional degrees. Founded 1965. Setting: 573-acre urban campus. Endowment: $79.3 million. Research spending for 2004 fiscal year: $24 million. Educational spending for 2005 fiscal year: $5009 per student. Total enrollment: 36,904. Faculty: 1,429 (757 full-time, 672 part-time). Student-undergrad faculty ratio is 17:1. 10,223 applied, 47% were admitted. 42% from top 10% of their high school class, 89% from top quarter, 99% from top half. 1 National Merit Scholar, 6 valedictorians. Full-time: 18,697 students, 57% women, 43% men. Part-time: 11,987 students, 55% women, 45% men. Students come from 52 states and territories, 115 other countries, 2% from out-of-state, 0.2% Native American, 60% Hispanic, 13% black, 4% Asian American or Pacific Islander, 7% international, 50% 25 or older, 7% live on campus, 8% transferred in. Retention: 83% of full-time freshmen returned the following year. Academic areas with the most degrees conferred: business/marketing; health professions and related sciences; psychology. Core. Calendar: semesters. ESL program, services for LD students, advanced placement, accelerated degree program, freshman honors college, honors program, independent study, distance learning, double major, summer session for credit, part-time degree program, adult/continuing education programs, co-op programs and internships, graduate courses open to undergrads. Off campus study at other members of the State University System of Florida. Study abroad program. ROTC: Army, Air Force.

Entrance Requirements: Options: Common Application, electronic application, early admission, deferred admission, international baccalaureate accepted. Required: high school transcript, minimum 3.0 high school GPA, SAT or ACT. Required for some: 1 recommendation. Entrance: moderately difficult. Application deadline: Rolling. Notification: continuous until 8/1.

Costs Per Year: Application fee: $25. State resident tuition: $3062 full-time, $102.08 per credit hour part-time. Nonresident tuition: $15,461 full-time, $515.38 per credit hour part-time. Mandatory fees: $252 full-time, $126 per term part-time. Full-time tuition and fees vary according to course load. Part-time tuition and fees vary according to course load. College room and board: $9102. College room only: $5518. Room and board charges vary according to housing facility.

Collegiate Environment: Orientation program. Drama-theater group, choral group, marching band, student-run newspaper, radio station. Social organizations: 190 open to all; national fraternities, national sororities; 8% of eligible men and 9% of eligible women are members. Most popular organizations: Students for Community Service, Black Student Leadership Council, Hospitality Management Student Club, Hispanic Students Association, Haitian Students Organization. Major annual events: comedy shows, lecture series, International Week. Student services: legal services, health clinic, personal-psychological counseling, women's center. Campus security: 24-hour emergency response devices and patrols, late night transport-escort service, controlled dormitory access. 5,500 college housing spaces available; 2,000 were occupied in 2003-04. No special consideration for freshman housing applicants. Option: coed housing available. University Park Library plus 2 others with 1.8 million books, 4.5 million microform titles, 16,920 serials, 46,917 audiovisual materials, an OPAC, and a Web page. Operations spending for 2004 fiscal year: $5.3 million. 600 computers available on campus for general student use. A campuswide network can be accessed from student residence rooms and from off campus. Staffed computer lab on campus.

Community Environment: The Greater Miami area offers cultural diversity and a dynamic economic and aesthetic climate. South Florida is a major center of higher education and stands at the forefront of international trading, finance and banking, as well as tourism and a developing high technology industry. Miami International Airport is served by more airlines than any other airport in the country. One of the most culturally diverse cities in America, Miami has many distinctive neighborhoods. Both visual and performing arts thrive in Miami. The Metro-Dade Cultural Complex in downtown Miami houses the Metropolitan Library, the Museum of South Florida, and the Center for the Fine Arts. The city also maintains both an opera and three ballet companies. A wealth of galleries, libraries, and theaters are valuable resources. The greater Miami area also hosts many professional sports events and offers year round recreation activities such as fishing, boating, scuba diving, wind surfing, snorkeling, swimming, and deep-sea fishing.

■ FLORIDA KEYS COMMUNITY COLLEGE *X-10*

5901 College Rd.
Key West, FL 33040-4397
Tel: (305)296-9081
Web Site: http://www.fkcc.edu/

Description: State-supported, 2-year, coed. Part of Florida Community College System. Awards certificates, transfer associate, and terminal associate degrees. Founded 1965. Setting: 20-acre small town campus. Endowment: $658,235. Educational spending for 2005 fiscal year: $4416 per student. Total enrollment: 1,551. 717 applied, 77% were admitted. 1% from out-of-state, 55% 25 or older. Core. Calendar: trimesters. Academic remediation for entering students, ESL program, services for LD students, advanced placement, self-designed majors, independent study, distance learning, double major, summer session for credit, part-time degree program, adult/continuing education programs, co-op programs and internships.

Entrance Requirements: Open admission except for nursing program. Options: early admission, deferred admission. Required for some: high school transcript. Placement: SAT or ACT required for some. Entrance: noncompetitive. Application deadline: Rolling. Notification: continuous.

Collegiate Environment: Orientation program. Choral group. Social organizations: 12 open to all. Most popular organizations: Florida Student Nursing Association, Nurses Pinning Club, Phi Theta Kappa, Keys Chorale, Ceramics Club. Major annual events: State University System Representatives Visit, Graduation Dance, Fall Ice Cream Social. Student services: personal-psychological counseling. Campus security: 24-hour patrols. College housing not available. Florida Keys Community College Library with 29,402 books, 81,675 microform titles, 330 serials, 1,001 audiovisual materials, and an OPAC. Operations spending for 2004 fiscal year: $312,420.

Community Environment: Key West is the southernmost city in the continental United States. It is a tropical island 157 miles southwest of Miami with an Old-World atmosphere. The setting is a blend of Cuban, West Indian, and Bahamian. The climate is warm and the air is almost pollen free. A rich and colorful history is retained in a thriving modern city. All forms of transportation serve the area. Searstown and four shopping centers are among the nation's most unique, all having a tropical flair. Year-round outdoor recreation includes a coral reef several miles offshore and provides some of the world's finest fishing and diving. Numerous points of interest are the Audubon house, Ernest Hemingway Home and Museum, Martello Gallery and Museum, the Lighthouse and the Military Museum.

■ FLORIDA MEMORIAL COLLEGE *Q-15*

15800 NW 42nd Ave.
Miami, FL 33054
Tel: (305)626-3600
Free: 800-822-1362
Admissions: (305)626-3147
Web Site: http://www.fmuniv.edu/

Description: Independent, 4-year, coed, affiliated with Baptist Church. Awards bachelor's degrees. Founded 1879. Setting: 77-acre suburban campus. Endowment: $6.7 million. Total enrollment: 2,161. Students come from 37 states and territories, 12% from out-of-state, 30% 25 or older. Core. Calendar: semesters. Academic remediation for entering students, ESL program, freshman honors college, honors program, summer session for credit, part-time degree program, external degree program, co-op programs and internships. Off campus study. ROTC: Army, Air Force (c).

Entrance Requirements: Open admission. Option: Common Application. Required: essay, high school transcript, minimum 2.2 high school GPA, 2 recommendations. Placement: SAT or ACT required. Entrance: noncompetitive. Application deadline: 7/1. Notification: continuous.

Collegiate Environment: Orientation program. Drama-theater group, student-run newspaper. Social organizations: national fraternities, national sororities, eating clubs. Student services: health clinic. Option: coed housing available. Florida Memorial College Library with 122,919 books and 405 serials. 30 computers available on campus for general student use. Staffed computer lab on campus.

■ FLORIDA METROPOLITAN UNIVERSITY-BRANDON CAMPUS *L-10*

3924 Coconut Palm Dr.
Tampa, FL 33619

Tel: (813)621-0041; 877-338-0068
E-mail: spointer@cci.edu
Web Site: http://www.fmu.edu/

Description: Proprietary, comprehensive, coed. Part of Corinthian Colleges, Inc. Awards associate, bachelor's, and master's degrees. Founded 1890. Setting: 5-acre urban campus. Faculty: 68 (12 full-time, 56 part-time). Student-undergrad faculty ratio is 17:1. 68% 25 or older. Core. Academic remediation for entering students, services for LD students, accelerated degree program, honors program, double major, summer session for credit, part-time degree program, external degree program, adult/continuing education programs, co-op programs and internships.

Entrance Requirements: Options: Common Application, early admission, deferred admission, international baccalaureate accepted. Required: high school transcript, interview, minimum CPAt score of 120, CPAt. Recommended: SAT or ACT. Entrance: minimally difficult. Application deadline: Rolling. Notification: continuous.

Costs Per Year: Application fee: $25. Tuition: $13,200 full-time, $275 per quarter hour part-time. Mandatory fees: $240 full-time, $60 per term part-time. Full-time tuition and fees vary according to program. Part-time tuition and fees vary according to program.

Collegiate Environment: Orientation program. Social organizations: 12 open to all. Most popular organizations: Accounting Club, Medical Assistants Club, Paralegal Club. Major annual events: Special Olympics Fundraiser, Student Appreciation Days, Thanksgiving and Christmas food drives. Campus security: 24-hour emergency response devices. College housing not available. Tampa College Library with 1,000 books, 50 serials, an OPAC, and a Web page. 81 computers available on campus for general student use. A campuswide network can be accessed. Staffed computer lab on campus.

■ FLORIDA METROPOLITAN UNIVERSITY-JACKSONVILLE CAMPUS *D-12*

8226 Phillips Hwy.
Jacksonville, FL 32256
Tel: (904)731-4949; 888-741-4271
Fax: (904)731-0599
Web Site: http://www.fmu.edu/

Description: Proprietary, comprehensive, coed. Awards associate, bachelor's, and master's degrees. Founded 2000. Total enrollment: 954.

Entrance Requirements: Entrance: minimally difficult.

■ FLORIDA METROPOLITAN UNIVERSITY-LAKELAND CAMPUS *L-12*

995 East Memorial Blvd., Ste. 110
Lakeland, FL 33801
Tel: (863)686-1444
Fax: (863)688-9881
Web Site: http://www.fmu.edu/

Description: Proprietary, comprehensive, coed. Part of Corinthian Colleges, Inc. Awards associate, bachelor's, and master's degrees (bachelor's degree in business administration only). Founded 1890. Setting: 3-acre suburban campus with easy access to Orlando and Tampa-St. Petersburg. Total enrollment: 752. Full-time: 506 students, 78% women, 22% men. Part-time: 206 students, 73% women, 27% men. Students come from 5 states and territories, 5 other countries, 5% from out-of-state, 0.4% Native American, 7% Hispanic, 18% black, 2% Asian American or Pacific Islander, 1% international, 62% 25 or older, 1% transferred in. Retention: 70% of full-time freshmen returned the following year. Core. Academic remediation for entering students, advanced placement, summer session for credit, part-time degree program, adult/continuing education programs, internships.

Entrance Requirements: Options: Common Application, early admission, international baccalaureate accepted. Required: high school transcript, interview, CPAt. Recommended: essay, recommendations, SAT, ACT. Entrance: minimally difficult.

Collegiate Environment: Student-run newspaper. Social organizations: 4 open to all. Most popular organizations: C. J. Association, Paralegal Society, Club Med, Phi Beta Lambda. Major annual events: Student Appreciation Week, Academic Event Weeks. Campus security: 24-hour patrols. College housing not available. Tampa College Library with 5,000 books and 30 serials. 50 computers available on campus for general student use. Staffed computer lab on campus.

■ FLORIDA METROPOLITAN UNIVERSITY-MELBOURNE CAMPUS *L-16*

2401 North Harbor City Blvd.
Melbourne, FL 32935-6657

Tel: (321)253-2929
Fax: (321)255-2017
Web Site: http://www.fmu.edu/
Description: Proprietary, comprehensive, coed. Part of Corinthian Colleges, Inc. Awards associate, bachelor's, and master's degrees. Founded 1953. Setting: 5-acre small town campus with easy access to Orlando. Total enrollment: 880. 339 applied, 68% were admitted. Students come from 3 other countries, 0% from out-of-state, 5% Native American, 4% Hispanic, 26% black, 4% Asian American or Pacific Islander, 1% international, 80% 25 or older. Retention: 68% of full-time freshmen returned the following year. Core. Academic remediation for entering students, advanced placement, accelerated degree program, summer session for credit, part-time degree program, internships, graduate courses open to undergrads.
Entrance Requirements: Options: Common Application, deferred admission. Required: high school transcript, interview, CPAt. Entrance: minimally difficult. Application deadline: Rolling.
Collegiate Environment: Student services: personal-psychological counseling. Campus security: 24-hour emergency response devices. College housing not available. 5,000 books and 51 serials. 37 computers available on campus for general student use.

■ **FLORIDA METROPOLITAN UNIVERSITY-NORTH ORLANDO CAMPUS** *J-13*
5421 Diplomat Circle
Orlando, FL 32810-5674
Tel: (407)628-5870
Free: 800-628-5870
Fax: (407)628-2616
Web Site: http://www.cci.edu/
Description: Proprietary, comprehensive, coed. Part of Corinthian Colleges, Inc. Awards associate, bachelor's, and master's degrees. Founded 1953. Setting: 1-acre urban campus. Total enrollment: 1,498. 2,842 applied, 53% were admitted. Full-time: 790 students, 72% women, 28% men. Part-time: 601 students, 66% women, 34% men. Students come from 33 other countries, 0.3% Native American, 19% Hispanic, 33% black, 2% Asian American or Pacific Islander, 3% international, 32% 25 or older. Core. Advanced placement, independent study, double major, summer session for credit, part-time degree program, external degree program, internships.
Entrance Requirements: Options: Common Application, deferred admission. Required: high school transcript, interview, entrance evaluation. Entrance: minimally difficult. Application deadline: Rolling. Notification: continuous.
Costs Per Year: Application fee: $0. Tuition: $9720 full-time, $270 per quarter hour part-time. Mandatory fees: $180 full-time, $60 per term part-time. Full-time tuition and fees vary according to program. Part-time tuition and fees vary according to program.
Collegiate Environment: Orientation program. Campus security: door alarms. College housing not available. FMU North Orlando Library with 18,000 books, 78 serials, 337 audiovisual materials, an OPAC, and a Web page. 70 computers available on campus for general student use. A campuswide network can be accessed. Staffed computer lab on campus.

■ **FLORIDA METROPOLITAN UNIVERSITY-ORANGE PARK CAMPUS** *D-12*
805 Wells Rd.
Orange Park, FL 32073
Tel: (904)264-9122
Fax: (904)264-9952
Web Site: http://www.fmu.edu/
Description: Proprietary, 2-year, coed. Founded 2003.

■ **FLORIDA METROPOLITAN UNIVERSITY-PINELLAS CAMPUS** *L-9*
2471 McMullen Booth Rd.
Clearwater, FL 33759
Tel: (727)725-2688
Free: 800-353-FMUS
Fax: (727)796-3722
E-mail: tcpinellas2@juno.com
Web Site: http://www.fmu.edu/
Description: Proprietary, comprehensive, coed. Part of Corinthian Colleges, Inc. Awards associate, bachelor's, and master's degrees. Founded 1890. Setting: 3-acre urban campus with easy access to Tampa-St. Petersburg. Total enrollment: 1,201. 622 applied, 70% were admitted. 6% from top 10% of their high school class, 15% from top quarter, 28% from top half. Students

come from 11 states and territories, 6% from out-of-state, 1% Native American, 7% Hispanic, 18% black, 4% Asian American or Pacific Islander, 88% 25 or older. Retention: 72% of full-time freshmen returned the following year. Core. Academic remediation for entering students, services for LD students, advanced placement, accelerated degree program, honors program, double major, summer session for credit, part-time degree program, adult/continuing education programs, co-op programs and internships.
Entrance Requirements: Options: Common Application, early admission, deferred admission, international baccalaureate accepted. Required: high school transcript, interview, CPAt. Recommended: minimum 2.0 high school GPA, SAT or ACT. Entrance: minimally difficult. Application deadline: Rolling.
Collegiate Environment: Orientation program. Student-run newspaper. Social organizations: 3 open to all. Most popular organizations: Human Resource Management Association, American Marketing Association, Criminal Justice Professional Fraternity. Major annual events: Student Appreciation Day, Commencement, Homecoming. Campus security: 24-hour emergency response devices, late night transport-escort service, evening patrols by security. College housing not available. Laurel Raffel Memorial Library with 6,721 books and 51 serials. 42 computers available on campus for general student use. A campuswide network can be accessed. Staffed computer lab on campus.

■ **FLORIDA METROPOLITAN UNIVERSITY-POMPANO BEACH CAMPUS** *R-15*
225 North Federal Hwy.
Pompano Beach, FL 33062
Tel: (954)783-7339
Free: 800-468-0168
Fax: (954)568-2008
Web Site: http://www.fmu.edu/
Description: Proprietary, comprehensive, coed. Part of Corinthian Colleges, Inc. Awards associate, bachelor's, and master's degrees. Founded 1940. Setting: urban campus with easy access to Miami. Total enrollment: 1,612. Students come from 25 states and territories, 0% Native American, 2% Hispanic, 8% black, 0.1% Asian American or Pacific Islander, 0.1% international, 55% 25 or older. Core. Academic remediation for entering students, ESL program, advanced placement, accelerated degree program, distance learning, summer session for credit, part-time degree program, adult/continuing education programs, internships.
Entrance Requirements: Options: Common Application, electronic application, deferred admission. Required: essay, high school transcript, CPAt. Recommended: interview, SAT or ACT. Required for some: recommendations. Entrance: minimally difficult. Application deadline: Rolling. Notification: continuous.
Collegiate Environment: Orientation program, Student-run newspaper. Social organizations: 2 open to all. Most popular organizations: American Marketing Association, International Business Club. Major annual events: Christmas Party, Halloween Party, Spring Dance. Student services: personal-psychological counseling. Campus security: late night transport-escort service, building security. College housing not available. Florida Metropolitan University Library plus 1 other with 14,500 books, 61 serials, and an OPAC. Operations spending for 2004 fiscal year: $131,425. 86 computers available on campus for general student use. Computer purchase/lease plans available. Staffed computer lab on campus.

■ **FLORIDA METROPOLITAN UNIVERSITY-SOUTH ORLANDO CAMPUS** *J-13*
9200 South Park Center Loop
Orlando, FL 32819
Tel: (407)851-2525; 888-471-4270
Fax: (407)851-1477
Web Site: http://www.fmu.edu/
Description: Proprietary, comprehensive, coed. Awards associate, bachelor's, and master's degrees. Total enrollment: 1,964. 205 applied, 45% were admitted. Full-time: 1,142 students, 75% women, 25% men. Part-time: 746 students, 72% women, 28% men. Students come from 50 states and territories, 10 other countries, 15% from out-of-state, 1% Native American, 33% Hispanic, 34% black, 3% Asian American or Pacific Islander, 2% international, 30% 25 or older, 2% transferred in. Core. Academic remediation for entering students, services for LD students, accelerated degree program, distance learning, double major, part-time degree program, adult/continuing education programs, co-op programs and internships.

Entrance Requirements: Option: Common Application. Required: high school transcript, interview, ACT, SAT Subject Tests. Entrance: minimally difficult. Application deadline: Rolling. Notification: continuous.

Costs Per Year: Application fee: $50. Tuition: $9900 full-time. Full-time tuition varies according to program.

Collegiate Environment: Orientation program. College housing not available. 5,113 books, 79 serials, 441 audiovisual materials, and a Web page.

■ **FLORIDA METROPOLITAN UNIVERSITY-TAMPA CAMPUS** *L-10*
3319 West Hillsborough Ave.
Tampa, FL 33614-5899
Tel: (813)879-6000
Fax: (813)871-2483
Web Site: http://fmu.edu/

Description: Proprietary, comprehensive, coed. Part of Corinthian Colleges, Inc. Awards associate, bachelor's, and master's degrees. Founded 1890. Setting: 4-acre urban campus. Total enrollment: 1,390. 320 applied, 53% were admitted. Full-time: 798 students, 59% women, 41% men. Part-time: 483 students, 63% women, 37% men. Students come from 15 states and territories, 3 other countries, 51% 25 or older, 3% transferred in. Core. ESL program, advanced placement, accelerated degree program, self-designed majors, independent study, distance learning, double major, summer session for credit, part-time degree program, external degree program, adult/continuing education programs, co-op programs and internships.

Entrance Requirements: Options: Common Application, deferred admission, international baccalaureate accepted. Required: high school transcript, CPAt. Required for some: SAT, ACT. Entrance: minimally difficult. Application deadline: Rolling. Notification: continuous.

Costs Per Year: Application fee: $25. Tuition: $9720 full-time, $270 per quarter hour part-time. Mandatory fees: $180 full-time, $60 per term part-time. Full-time tuition and fees vary according to program. Part-time tuition and fees vary according to program.

Collegiate Environment: Social organizations: 6 open to all; coed fraternity; 7% of eligible men and 13% of eligible women are members. Most popular organizations: Legal Network, Phi Beta Lambda, PC-MAC Users Group, International Club, Art League. Major annual events: Network Night (career planning), Health Fair. Campus security: 24-hour emergency response devices, evening and Saturday afternoon patrols by trained security personnel. College housing not available. Tampa College Library with 4,000 books, 95 microform titles, 130 serials, 260 audiovisual materials, an OPAC, and a Web page. Operations spending for 2004 fiscal year: $90,000. 113 computers available on campus for general student use. Staffed computer lab on campus.

■ **FLORIDA NATIONAL COLLEGE** *T-15*
4425 West 20th Ave.
Hialeah, FL 33012
Tel: (305)821-3333
Fax: (305)362-0595
Web Site: http://www.fnc.edu/

Description: Proprietary, 2-year, coed. Awards certificates, diplomas, transfer associate, and terminal associate degrees. Founded 1982. Setting: urban campus with easy access to Miami. Total enrollment: 1,871. Student-undergrad faculty ratio is 24:1. 591 applied, 72% were admitted. Full-time: 1,723 students, 67% women, 33% men. Part-time: 148 students, 67% women, 33% men. 0.3% Native American, 91% Hispanic, 4% black, 1% Asian American or Pacific Islander, 2% international, 60% 25 or older. Calendar: semesters. Academic remediation for entering students, ESL program, services for LD students, self-designed majors, summer session for credit, adult/continuing education programs, co-op programs.

Entrance Requirements: Open admission. Options: Peterson's Universal Application, Common Application, deferred admission. Required: high school transcript. Entrance: noncompetitive. Application deadline: Rolling. Notification: continuous.

Costs Per Year: Tuition: $10,200 full-time, $340 per credit part-time. Mandatory fees: $760 full-time.

Collegiate Environment: Student-run newspaper. Most popular organization: Student Government Association. Major annual event: annual picnic. Campus security: 24-hour emergency response devices. College housing not available. Hialeah Campus Library with 23,507 books, 87 serials, 3,337 audiovisual materials, an OPAC, and a Web page. Operations spending for 2004 fiscal year: $257,000. 152 computers available on campus for general student use. A campuswide network can be accessed from off-campus.

■ **THE FLORIDA SCHOOL OF MIDWIFERY** *F-10*
PO Box 5505
Gainesville, FL 32601
Tel: (352)338-0766
Fax: (352)338-2013
Web Site: http://www.midwiferyschool.org/

Description: Independent, 2-year, women only. Awards terminal associate degrees. Founded 1993. Total enrollment: 25.

■ **FLORIDA SOUTHERN COLLEGE** *L-12*
111 Lake Hollingsworth Dr.
Lakeland, FL 33801-5698
Tel: (863)680-4111
Free: 800-274-4131
Admissions: (863)680-3905
Fax: (863)680-4120
E-mail: fscadm@flsouthern.edu
Web Site: http://www.flsouthern.edu/

Description: Independent, comprehensive, coed, affiliated with United Methodist Church. Awards bachelor's and master's degrees. Founded 1885. Setting: 100-acre suburban campus with easy access to Tampa and Orlando. Endowment: $64 million. Educational spending for 2005 fiscal year: $5153 per student. Total enrollment: 1,921. Faculty: 166 (107 full-time, 59 part-time). Student-undergrad faculty ratio is 14:1. 1,829 applied, 73% were admitted. 23% from top 10% of their high school class, 47% from top quarter, 77% from top half. 5 valedictorians. Full-time: 1,759 students, 61% women, 39% men. Part-time: 57 students, 47% women, 53% men. Students come from 41 states and territories, 46 other countries, 28% from out-of-state, 0.3% Native American, 6% Hispanic, 6% black, 1% Asian American or Pacific Islander, 4% international, 5% 25 or older, 67% live on campus, 5% transferred in. Retention: 67% of full-time freshmen returned the following year. Academic areas with the most degrees conferred: business/marketing; education; communications/journalism. Core. Calendar: semesters. Academic remediation for entering students, advanced placement, honors program, independent study, double major, summer session for credit, part-time degree program, adult/continuing education programs, internships. Off campus study at American University, Drew University. Study abroad program. ROTC: Army, Air Force (c).

Entrance Requirements: Options: Common Application, electronic application, early admission, early decision, deferred admission, international baccalaureate accepted. Required: essay, high school transcript, recommendations, SAT or ACT. Recommended: minimum 2.5 high school GPA, interview. Entrance: moderately difficult. Application deadlines: 4/1, 12/1 for early decision. Notification: continuous, 12/15 for early decision.

Costs Per Year: Application fee: $30. Comprehensive fee: $25,965 includes full-time tuition ($18,765), mandatory fees ($400), and college room and board ($6800). College room only: $3750. Full-time tuition and fees vary according to student level. Room and board charges vary according to board plan and housing facility. Part-time tuition: $500 per credit hour. Part-time mandatory fees: $400 per year.

Collegiate Environment: Orientation program. Drama-theater group, choral group, student-run newspaper, radio station. Social organizations: 66 open to all; national fraternities, national sororities; 16% of eligible men and 15% of eligible women are members. Most popular organizations: Fellowship of Christian Athletes, Student Government Association, Student Union Board, Shades of Color, International Student Association. Major annual events: Annual Concert, Christmas tree lighting, O-Week Welcome Back Dance. Student services: health clinic, personal-psychological counseling. Campus security: 24-hour emergency response devices and patrols, student patrols, late night transport-escort service, controlled dormitory access. 1,242 college housing spaces available; 1,228 were occupied in 2003-04. Freshmen guaranteed college housing. On-campus residence required through junior year. Options: coed, men-only, women-only housing available. E. T. Roux Library with 172,803 books, 448,221 microform titles, 939 serials, 11,490 audiovisual materials, an OPAC, and a Web page. Operations spending for 2004 fiscal year: $803,039. 250 computers available on campus for general student use. Computer purchase/lease plans available. A campuswide network can be accessed from student residence rooms and from off campus. Staffed computer lab on campus.

Community Environment: Lakeland is located in the geographical center of Florida, 35 miles East of Tampa, 50 miles west of Orlando, 100 miles from the Atlantic Ocean, 35 miles from Disney World and 60 miles from the Gulf of Mexico. The Seaboard Coast Line Railroad serves the area. The"World's Citrus Center" is the permanent spring training headquarters of the Detroit

Tigers. Excellent shopping facilities in the city; a civic center, concert association, and community theatre are part of the lively community. Recreational facilities include 12 lakes within the city for excellent fishing, golf courses, boating, hiking, and waterskiing. The annual Orange Cup Regatta Hydroplane Race is held the weekend closest to February 1st.

■ FLORIDA STATE UNIVERSITY *C-5*
Tallahassee, FL 32306
Tel: (850)644-2525
Admissions: (850)644-6200
Fax: (850)644-0197
E-mail: admissions@admin.fsu.edu
Web Site: http://www.fsu.edu/

Description: State-supported, university, coed. Part of State University System of Florida. Awards associate, bachelor's, master's, doctoral, and first professional degrees and post-master's certificates. Founded 1851. Setting: 448-acre suburban campus. Endowment: $441.3 million. Research spending for 2004 fiscal year: $94.4 million. Educational spending for 2005 fiscal year: $7786 per student. Total enrollment: 39,146. Faculty: 1,592 (1,265 full-time, 327 part-time). Student-undergrad faculty ratio is 22:1. 22,450 applied, 62% were admitted. 26% from top 10% of their high school class, 61% from top quarter, 94% from top half. 15 National Merit Scholars. Full-time: 27,203 students, 57% women, 43% men. Part-time: 3,582 students, 55% women, 45% men. Students come from 51 states and territories, 126 other countries, 13% from out-of-state, 0.4% Native American, 11% Hispanic, 12% black, 3% Asian American or Pacific Islander, 1% international, 8% 25 or older, 14% live on campus, 7% transferred in. Retention: 89% of full-time freshmen returned the following year. Academic areas with the most degrees conferred: business/marketing; social sciences; family and consumer sciences. Core. Calendar: semesters. ESL program, services for LD students, advanced placement, accelerated degree program, honors program, independent study, distance learning, double major, summer session for credit, part-time degree program, adult/continuing education programs, co-op programs and internships, graduate courses open to undergrads. Off campus study at Florida Agricultural and Mechanical University, Tallahassee Community College. Study abroad program. ROTC: Army, Naval (c), Air Force.

Entrance Requirements: Options: Peterson's Universal Application, Common Application, electronic application, early admission, international baccalaureate accepted. Required: high school transcript, SAT or ACT. Recommended: essay, minimum 3.0 high school GPA. Required for some: audition. Entrance: very difficult. Application deadline: 3/1. Notification: continuous until 4/1.

Costs Per Year: Application fee: $30. State resident tuition: $3208 full-time, $106.93 per credit hour part-time. Nonresident tuition: $16,340 full-time, $544.67 per credit hour part-time. Full-time tuition varies according to location. Part-time tuition varies according to location. College room and board: $6778. College room only: $3600. Room and board charges vary according to board plan and housing facility.

Collegiate Environment: Orientation program. Drama-theater group, choral group, marching band, student-run newspaper, radio station. Social organizations: 266 open to all; national fraternities, national sororities, local fraternities, local sororities; 13% of eligible men and 15% of eligible women are members. Most popular organizations: student government, honors program, Gold Key Society, Marching Chiefs, intramural sports. Major annual events: Parents' Weekend, Homecoming, Dance Marathon. Student services: legal services, health clinic, personal-psychological counseling, women's center. Campus security: 24-hour emergency response devices and patrols, late night transport-escort service, controlled dormitory access. College housing designed to accommodate 4,296 students; 4,436 undergraduates lived in college housing during 2003-04. Freshmen given priority for college housing. Options: coed, women-only housing available. Robert Manning Strozier Library plus 6 others with 2.7 million books, 9.1 million microform titles, 38,271 serials, 75,304 audiovisual materials, an OPAC, and a Web page. Operations spending for 2004 fiscal year: $12.6 million. 3,771 computers available on campus for general student use. Computer purchase/lease plans available. A campuswide network can be accessed from student residence rooms and from off campus. Staffed computer lab on campus.

Community Environment: Situated in north Florida, FSU is nestled in the heart of Tallahassee, the state's capital city. A classic college town, Tallahassee is not only one of Florida's oldest and fastest growing cities, it is also part of the "other Florida" with its rolling hills, canopy roads, mild climate, and southern hospitality. More than 100 state and federal agencies furnish

students with opportunities for internships, research, and work-study programs that match all areas of academic interest. Part-time jobs are plentiful. In addition, Tallahassee affords a rich offering of social, cultural, and recreational activities, making it an excellent place to live, study, and grow.

■ FLORIDA TECHNICAL COLLEGE (AUBURNDALE) *I-9*
298 Havendale Blvd.
Auburndale, FL 33823
Tel: (863)967-8822
Fax: (863)967-4972
Web Site: http://www.flatech.edu/

Description: Proprietary, 2-year, coed. Awards certificates, diplomas, transfer associate, and terminal associate degrees. Total enrollment: 185. 175 applied, 100% were admitted. 0% Native American, 12% Hispanic, 15% black, 0% Asian American or Pacific Islander, 0% international.

Entrance Requirements: Entrance: moderately difficult.

■ FLORIDA TECHNICAL COLLEGE (DELAND) *H-13*
1450 South Woodland Blvd., 3rd Floor
DeLand, FL 32720
Tel: (904)734-3303
Admissions: (386)734-3303
Fax: (904)734-5150
E-mail: batkinson@flatech.edu
Web Site: http://www.flatech.edu/

Description: Proprietary, 2-year, coed. Awards transfer associate and terminal associate degrees. Total enrollment: 260. Student-undergrad faculty ratio is 22:1. Full-time: 260 students, 58% women, 42% men.

■ FLORIDA TECHNICAL COLLEGE (JACKSONVILLE) *D-12*
8711 Lone Star Rd.
Jacksonville, FL 32211
Tel: (904)724-2229
Admissions: (407)678-5600
Fax: (904)720-0920
Web Site: http://www.flatech.edu/

Description: Proprietary, 2-year, coed. Awards diplomas and terminal associate degrees. Total enrollment: 225. 117 applied, 91% were admitted.

Entrance Requirements: Open admission. Entrance: noncompetitive. Application deadline: Rolling. Notification: continuous.

■ FLORIDA TECHNICAL COLLEGE (ORLANDO) *J-13*
1819 North Semoran Blvd.
Orlando, FL 32807-3546
Tel: (407)678-5600
Fax: (407)678-1149
Web Site: http://www.flatech.edu/

Description: Proprietary, 2-year, coed. Part of Forefront Education. Awards certificates, diplomas, and terminal associate degrees. Founded 1982. Setting: 1-acre urban campus. Endowment: $14,000. Educational spending for 2005 fiscal year: $22,000 per student. Total enrollment: 231. 123 applied, 91% were admitted. Students come from 1 other country, 63% 25 or older. Core. Advanced placement, accelerated degree program, independent study, distance learning, double major, external degree program.

Entrance Requirements: Options: Common Application, international baccalaureate accepted. Required: high school transcript, interview. Recommended: essay. Entrance: minimally difficult.

Collegiate Environment: Orientation program. Student-run newspaper. College housing not available. 35 computers available on campus for general student use. Staffed computer lab on campus.

■ FULL SAIL REAL WORLD EDUCATION *J-13*
3300 University Blvd.
Winter Park, FL 32792-7437
Tel: (407)679-6333
Free: 800-226-7625
Admissions: (407)679-0100
Fax: (407)678-0070
E-mail: admissions@fullsail.com
Web Site: http://www.fullsail.com/

Description: Proprietary, primarily 2-year, coed. Awards terminal associate and bachelor's degrees. Founded 1979. Setting: suburban campus with easy access to Orlando. Research spending for 2004 fiscal year: $350,000. Total enrollment: 5,219. Student-undergrad faculty ratio is 10:1. 2,954 applied, 69% were admitted. Full-time: 5,219 students, 11% women, 89% men. Students come from 47 states and territories, 6 other countries, 70% from out-of-state, 1% Native American, 10% Hispanic, 11% black, 3% Asian American or Pacific Islander, 1% international, 12% 25 or older. Core. Calendar: modular. Academic remediation for entering students, services for LD students, summer session for credit, co-op programs and internships.

Entrance Requirements: Open admission. Options: Common Application, electronic application, international baccalaureate accepted. Required: high school transcript. Required for some: minimum 'A' average in Algebra II. Entrance: noncompetitive. Application deadline: Rolling.

Collegiate Environment: Orientation program. Most popular organization: Student Chapter of Audio Engineering Society. Major annual events: Annual Speech Tournament, Success Seminar, Entertainment Business. Student services: personal-psychological counseling. Campus security: 24-hour patrols. College housing not available. Full Sail Library plus 1 other with 2,531 books, 84 serials, 784 audiovisual materials, and an OPAC.

■ **GULF COAST COLLEGE** *L-10*
3910 US Hwy. 301 North, Ste. 200
Tampa, FL 33619-1259
Tel: (813)620-1446; 888-729-7247
Web Site: http://gulfcoastcollege.com/
Description: Private, 2-year, coed. Awards diplomas and terminal associate degrees. Founded 1978. Setting: 2-acre urban campus. Total enrollment: 152. 0% from out-of-state, 21% Hispanic, 21% black, 35% 25 or older. Core. Advanced placement, accelerated degree program, internships.
Entrance Requirements: Open admission. Option: electronic application. Required: interview.
Collegiate Environment: Orientation program. Major annual events: quarterly barbecues, Christmas Party, Halloween costume party. Student services: personal-psychological counseling. Campus security: 24-hour emergency response devices, evening security guard. College housing not available. Webster Tech Library with 2,063 books, 14 serials, and 65 audiovisual materials. 70 computers available on campus for general student use. Staffed computer lab on campus.

■ **GULF COAST COMMUNITY COLLEGE** *L-7*
5230 West Hwy. 98
Panama City, FL 32401-1058
Tel: (850)769-1551
Free: 800-311-3628
Admissions: (850)872-3891
Fax: (850)913-3308
Web Site: http://www.gulfcoast.edu/
Description: State-supported, 2-year, coed. Awards certificates, transfer associate, and terminal associate degrees. Founded 1957. Setting: 80-acre suburban campus. Endowment: $13.9 million. Educational spending for 2005 fiscal year: $4387 per student. Total enrollment: 6,058. Full-time: 2,248 students, 60% women, 40% men. Part-time: 3,810 students, 59% women, 41% men. Students come from 28 states and territories, 8 other countries, 1% Native American, 3% Hispanic, 12% black, 2% Asian American or Pacific Islander, 1% international, 41% 25 or older. Core. Calendar: semesters. Academic remediation for entering students, ESL program, services for LD students, advanced placement, accelerated degree program, honors program, independent study, distance learning, double major, summer session for credit, part-time degree program, external degree program, adult/continuing education programs, co-op programs. Off campus study.
Entrance Requirements: Open admission. Options: electronic application, early admission, deferred admission, international baccalaureate accepted. Required: high school transcript. Placement: CPT required. Entrance: noncompetitive. Application deadline: Rolling. Notification: continuous.
Costs Per Year: Application fee: $0. State resident tuition: $1446 full-time, $48.20 per credit part-time. Nonresident tuition: $6232 full-time, $207.74 per credit part-time. Mandatory fees: $309 full-time, $10.30 per credit part-time. Full-time tuition and fees vary according to course load. Part-time tuition and fees vary according to course load.
Collegiate Environment: Orientation program. Drama-theater group, choral group, student-run newspaper, radio station. Social organizations: 14 open to all. Most popular organizations: Student Activities Board, Baptist Campus Ministry, Theater Club, Phi Theta Kappa, Muslim Student Association. Major annual events: homecoming, Spring Luau, Alcohol Awareness Week. Student services: personal-psychological counseling. Campus security: patrols by trained security personnel during campus hours. College housing not available. Gulf Coast Community College Library with 80,000 books,

435,487 microform titles, 521 serials, 32,041 audiovisual materials, an OPAC, and a Web page. Operations spending for 2004 fiscal year: $672,655. 850 computers available on campus for general student use. A campuswide network can be accessed from off-campus. Staffed computer lab on campus.

Community Environment: Panama City is an urban area with a temperate climate and is recognized as one of the most progressive industrial and resort cities in the state. A municipal marina includes a city hall, an auditorium, a library, and berths for about 400 boats. Community facilities include libraries, churches of major denominations, two hospitals and several clinics; shopping facilities are excellent. Some part-time employment is available. The city's industries include tourism, oil companies, wholesale fisheries, chemical production, boat manufacturing. Outdoor sports include golfing, yachting, sailing, water skiing and swimming. Panama City is a noted sport fishing center for both fresh and salt water fish.

■ **HERZING COLLEGE** *J-13*
1595 South Semoran Blvd., Ste. 1501
Winter Park, FL 32792-5509
Tel: (407)380-6315
Admissions: (407)478-0500
Fax: (407)380-0269
Web Site: http://www.herzing.edu/
Description: Proprietary, 2-year, coed. Awards certificates, diplomas, and terminal associate degrees. Founded 1989. Total enrollment: 307. Full-time: 243 students, 27% women, 73% men. Part-time: 64 students, 33% women, 67% men. Calendar: semesters.

■ **HIGH-TECH INSTITUTE** *J-13*
1000 Woodcock Rd.
Orlando, FL 32803
Tel: (407)895-1985
Free: 800-987-0110
Fax: (407)657-9778
Web Site: http://www.high-techinstitute.com/
Description: Proprietary, 2-year, coed. Founded 1998.

■ **HILLSBOROUGH COMMUNITY COLLEGE** *L-10*
PO Box 31127
Tampa, FL 33631-3127
Tel: (813)253-7000
Admissions: (813)253-7027
Fax: (813)253-7196
Web Site: http://www.hccfl.edu/
Description: State-supported, 2-year, coed. Part of Florida Community College System. Awards certificates, transfer associate, and terminal associate degrees. Founded 1968. Setting: urban campus. Endowment: $1.6 million. Educational spending for 2005 fiscal year: $4410 per student. Total enrollment: 22,149. 4,223 applied, 100% were admitted. Full-time: 7,009 students, 58% women, 42% men. Part-time: 15,140 students, 60% women, 40% men. Students come from 40 states and territories, 100 other countries, 4% from out-of-state, 0.4% Native American, 19% Hispanic, 19% black, 4% Asian American or Pacific Islander, 1% international, 37% 25 or older, 19% transferred in. Retention: 57% of full-time freshmen returned the following year. Core. Calendar: semesters. Academic remediation for entering students, ESL program, services for LD students, advanced placement, honors program, distance learning, summer session for credit, part-time degree program, adult/continuing education programs, co-op programs. Off campus study at University of South Florida, Linkage Program institutions. ROTC: Army (c), Air Force (c).
Entrance Requirements: Open admission. Options: Common Application, early admission. Required: high school transcript. Placement: CPT required for some. Entrance: noncompetitive. Application deadline: Rolling.
Collegiate Environment: Orientation program. Drama-theater group, student-run newspaper, radio station. Social organizations: 40 open to all; national fraternities; 1% of eligible men and 1% of eligible women are members. Most popular organizations: Student Government Association, Student Nursing Association, Phi Theta Kappa, Disabled Students Association, Radiography Club. Major annual events: Halloween Fest, Spring Fling, Valentine's Day events. Student services: personal-psychological counseling. Campus security: 24-hour emergency response devices and patrols. College housing not available. Main library plus 4 others with 170,615 books, 88,182 microform titles, 1,283 serials, 50,000 audiovisual materials, an

OPAC, and a Web page. Operations spending for 2004 fiscal year: $1.8 million. 600 computers available on campus for general student use. Staffed computer lab on campus.

Community Environment: See University of South Florida.

■ HOBE SOUND BIBLE COLLEGE O-15

PO Box 1065
Hobe Sound, FL 33475-1065
Tel: (561)546-5534
Free: 800-881-5534
Admissions: (772)546-5534
Fax: (561)545-1422
E-mail: hsbcuwin@aol.com
Web Site: http://www.hsbc.edu/

Description: Independent nondenominational, 4-year, coed. Awards associate and bachelor's degrees. Founded 1960. Setting: 84-acre small town campus. Endowment: $433,096. Educational spending for 2005 fiscal year: $2829 per student. Total enrollment: 143. Student-undergrad faculty ratio is 7:1. 24 applied, 92% were admitted. 17% from top 10% of their high school class, 30% from top quarter, 53% from top half. 1 valedictorian. Students come from 23 states and territories, 8 other countries, 45% from out-of-state, 0% Native American, 1% Hispanic, 11% black, 1% Asian American or Pacific Islander, 11% international, 19% 25 or older, 75% live on campus. Retention: 65% of full-time freshmen returned the following year. Academic area with the most degrees conferred: education. Core. Calendar: semesters. Academic remediation for entering students, ESL program, advanced placement, independent study, distance learning, double major, summer session for credit, external degree program, internships.

Entrance Requirements: Open admission. Options: Common Application, early admission. Required: high school transcript, 3 recommendations, photograph, medical report. Required for some: SAT or ACT. Entrance: noncompetitive. Application deadline: Rolling. Notification: continuous until 8/30. Preference given to applicants committed to Wesleyan-Armenian theological position.

Costs Per Year: Application fee: $25. Comprehensive fee: $7360 includes full-time tuition ($4020), mandatory fees ($100), and college room and board ($3240).

Collegiate Environment: Orientation program. Choral group. Major annual events: Leadership Conference, Welcome Week. Campus security: student patrols, late night transport-escort service, controlled dormitory access. On-campus residence required through senior year. Options: men-only, women-only housing available. College Library with 35,468 books, 11,745 microform titles, 119 serials, 2,646 audiovisual materials, and a Web page. Operations spending for 2004 fiscal year: $32,112. 10 computers available on campus for general student use. Staffed computer lab on campus.

■ INDIAN RIVER COMMUNITY COLLEGE N-15

3209 Virginia Ave.
Fort Pierce, FL 34981-5596
Tel: (772)462-4700
Admissions: (772)462-4740
Fax: (772)462-4796
Web Site: http://www.ircc.edu/

Description: State-supported, 2-year, coed. Part of Florida Community College System. Awards certificates, diplomas, transfer associate, and terminal associate degrees. Founded 1960. Setting: 133-acre small town campus. Total enrollment: 38,464. Students come from 33 states and territories, 2% from out-of-state, 0.4% Native American, 12% Hispanic, 17% black, 1% Asian American or Pacific Islander, 48% 25 or older. Core. Calendar: semesters. Academic remediation for entering students, ESL program, services for LD students, advanced placement, independent study, distance learning, summer session for credit, part-time degree program, adult/continuing education programs.

Entrance Requirements: Open admission. Options: early admission, deferred admission. Required: high school transcript. Placement: SAT, ACT, or CPT required. Entrance: noncompetitive. Application deadline: Rolling. Notification: continuous.

Collegiate Environment: Orientation program. Drama-theater group, choral group. Social organizations: 31 open to all; local fraternities, local sororities; 50% of eligible men and 50% of eligible women are members. Most popular organizations: Phi Beta Lambda, Distributive Education Club of America, International Club, Cultural Exchange, Human Services Club. Major annual events: United Way Day, Welcome Back Cookout, Valentine's Day Celebration. Student services: health clinic, personal-psychological counseling,

women's center. Campus security: 24-hour patrols. College housing not available. Charles S. Miley Learning Resource Center with 58,657 books, 554 serials, and an OPAC. 500 computers available on campus for general student use. A campuswide network can be accessed. Staffed computer lab on campus.

Community Environment: A midsize city on the east coast of Florida with a subtropical climate, the area is known for citrus fruits and winter vegetables. Florida's Turnpike, I-95, the Florida East Coast Railroad and the Greyhound bus line serve the area. Community facilities include public libraries, YMCA, churches, hospitals, mental health centers, beaches and recreational activities. Part-time employment opportunities are moderate. Swimming from two ocean beaches, golf and sports fishing are the principal outdoor sports.

■ INTERNATIONAL ACADEMY OF DESIGN & TECHNOLOGY L-10

5225 Memorial Hwy.
Tampa, FL 33634-7350
Tel: (813)881-0007
Free: 800-ACA-DEMY
Fax: (813)881-0008
E-mail: admissions@academy.edu
Web Site: http://www.academy.edu/

Description: Proprietary, 4-year, coed. Part of Career Education Corporation. Founded 1984. Setting: 1-acre urban campus. Total enrollment: 2,405. Student-undergrad faculty ratio is 16:1. 962 applied, 46% were admitted. Full-time: 1,702 students, 63% women, 37% men. Part-time: 703 students, 68% women, 32% men. Students come from 56 states and territories, 9 other countries, 22% from out-of-state, 0.5% international, 37% 25 or older, 8% transferred in. Retention: 62% of full-time freshmen returned the following year. Core. Academic remediation for entering students, advanced placement, accelerated degree program, distance learning, summer session for credit, internships. Study abroad program.

Entrance Requirements: Options: Peterson's Universal Application, Common Application, electronic application, early admission, deferred admission, international baccalaureate accepted. Required: interview, high school diploma or equivalent. Recommended: essay. Entrance: noncompetitive. Application deadline: Rolling.

Costs Per Year: Application fee: $50. Tuition: $385 per credit hour part-time. Mandatory fees: $100 per term part-time.

Collegiate Environment: Orientation program. Social organizations: 5 open to all. Most popular organizations: Student Chapter ASID, Fashion Design International, Computer Animation Club, Marketing Club. Major annual events: Annual Fashion Show/Portfolio Review, Mardi Gras at the Academy. Campus security: 24-hour emergency response devices, late night patrols by trained security personnel. International Academy Learning Resource Center with 6,000 books, 150 serials, 50 audiovisual materials, and an OPAC. 310 computers available on campus for general student use. A campuswide network can be accessed. Staffed computer lab on campus.

■ INTERNATIONAL COLLEGE S-10

2655 Northbrooke Dr.
Naples, FL 34119
Tel: (239)513-1122
Free: 800-466-8017
Fax: (239)513-9071
E-mail: admit@international.edu
Web Site: http://www.internationalcollege.edu/

Description: Independent, comprehensive, coed. Awards associate, bachelor's, and master's degrees. Founded 1990. Setting: suburban campus with easy access to Miami. Endowment: $342,357. Educational spending for 2005 fiscal year: $4733 per student. Total enrollment: 1,544. Full-time: 947 students, 69% women, 31% men. Part-time: 395 students, 66% women, 34% men. Students come from 8 states and territories, 1% from out-of-state, 0.3% Native American, 14% Hispanic, 12% black, 1% Asian American or Pacific Islander, 8% international, 72% 25 or older, 19% transferred in. Core. Calendar: trimesters. Academic remediation for entering students, ESL program, services for LD students, advanced placement, accelerated degree program, distance learning, double major, summer session for credit, part-time degree program, external degree program, adult/continuing education programs, co-op programs and internships.

Entrance Requirements: Options: Common Application, electronic application, deferred admission, international baccalaureate accepted. Required: essay, high school transcript, interview, CPAt. Recommended: SAT, ACT. Required for some: 2 recommendations. Entrance: minimally difficult. Application deadline: Rolling. Notification: continuous.

Costs Per Year: Application fee: $20. Tuition: $9120 full-time, $380 per credit part-time. Mandatory fees: $380 full-time, $190 per term part-time.

Collegiate Environment: Orientation program. Most popular organizations: Ambassadors, Paralegal Club, Institute of Managerial Accountants, Running Club, Entrepreneurial Club. Major annual events: Student Recognition Banquet, Salvation Army food drive, seasonal socials. Student services: personal-psychological counseling. Campus security: late night transport-escort service, building security. College housing not available. Information Resource Center plus 1 other with 29,711 books, 230 serials, 356 audiovisual materials, an OPAC, and a Web page. Operations spending for 2004 fiscal year: $621,323. 500 computers available on campus for general student use. A campuswide network can be accessed. Staffed computer lab on campus.

■ **ITT TECHNICAL INSTITUTE (FORT LAUDERDALE)** *S-15*
3401 South University Dr.
Fort Lauderdale, FL 33328-2021
Tel: (954)476-9300
Fax: (954)476-6889
Web Site: http://www.itt-tech.edu/

Description: Proprietary, primarily 2-year, coed. Part of ITT Educational Services, Inc. Awards terminal associate and bachelor's degrees. Founded 1991. Setting: suburban campus with easy access to Miami. Core.

Entrance Requirements: Option: deferred admission. Required: high school transcript, interview, Wonderlic aptitude test. Recommended: recommendations. Entrance: minimally difficult. Application deadline: Rolling. Notification: continuous.

Costs Per Year: Application fee: $100.

Collegiate Environment: Orientation program. College housing not available.

■ **ITT TECHNICAL INSTITUTE (JACKSONVILLE)** *D-12*
6600-10 Youngerman Circle
Jacksonville, FL 32244-6630
Tel: (904)573-9100
Web Site: http://www.itt-tech.edu/

Description: Proprietary, primarily 2-year, coed. Part of ITT Educational Services, Inc. Awards terminal associate and bachelor's degrees. Founded 1991. Setting: 1-acre urban campus. Core.

Entrance Requirements: Option: deferred admission. Required: high school transcript, interview, Wonderlic aptitude test. Recommended: recommendations. Entrance: minimally difficult. Application deadline: Rolling. Notification: continuous.

Costs Per Year: Application fee: $100.

Collegiate Environment: Orientation program. College housing not available.

■ **ITT TECHNICAL INSTITUTE (LAKE MARY)** *I-13*
1400 South International Parkway
Lake Mary, FL 32746
Tel: (407)660-2900
Web Site: http://www.itt-tech.edu/

Description: Proprietary, primarily 2-year, coed. Part of ITT Educational Services, Inc. Awards terminal associate and bachelor's degrees. Founded 1989. Setting: 1-acre suburban campus with easy access to Orlando. Core.

Entrance Requirements: Option: deferred admission. Required: high school transcript, interview, Wonderlic aptitude test. Recommended: recommendations. Entrance: minimally difficult. Application deadline: Rolling. Notification: continuous.

Costs Per Year: Application fee: $100.

Collegiate Environment: Orientation program. Student-run newspaper. College housing not available.

■ **ITT TECHNICAL INSTITUTE (MIAMI)** *T-15*
7955 NW 12th St.
Miami, FL 33126
Tel: (305)477-3080
Web Site: http://www.itt-tech.edu/

Description: Proprietary, primarily 2-year, coed. Part of ITT Educational Services, Inc. Awards terminal associate and bachelor's degrees. Founded 1996. Core.

Entrance Requirements: Option: deferred admission. Required: high school transcript, interview, Wonderlic aptitude test. Recommended: recommendations. Entrance: minimally difficult. Application deadline: Rolling. Notification: continuous.

Costs Per Year: Application fee: $100.

Collegiate Environment: Orientation program. College housing not available.

■ **ITT TECHNICAL INSTITUTE (TAMPA)** *L-10*
4809 Memorial Hwy.
Tampa, FL 33634-7151
Tel: (813)885-2244
Fax: (813)888-6078
Web Site: http://www.itt-tech.edu/

Description: Proprietary, primarily 2-year, coed. Part of ITT Educational Services, Inc. Awards terminal associate and bachelor's degrees. Founded 1981. Setting: suburban campus with easy access to St. Petersburg. Core.

Entrance Requirements: Option: deferred admission. Required: high school transcript, interview, Wonderlic aptitude test. Recommended: recommendations. Entrance: minimally difficult. Application deadline: Rolling. Notification: continuous.

Costs Per Year: Application fee: $100.

Collegiate Environment: Orientation program. College housing not available.

■ **JACKSONVILLE UNIVERSITY** *D-12*
2800 University Blvd. North
Jacksonville, FL 32211-3394
Tel: (904)256-8000
Free: 800-225-2027
Admissions: (904)256-7000
Fax: (904)256-7086
E-mail: admissions@junix.ju.edu
Web Site: http://www.ju.edu/

Description: Independent, comprehensive, coed. Awards bachelor's and master's degrees and first professional certificates. Founded 1934. Setting: 260-acre suburban campus. Endowment: $24 million. Total enrollment: 2,948. Faculty: 162 (121 full-time, 41 part-time). Student-undergrad faculty ratio is 15:1. 1,902 applied, 72% were admitted. Full-time: 1,877 students, 49% women, 51% men. Part-time: 684 students, 81% women, 19% men. Students come from 46 states and territories, 61 other countries, 37% from out-of-state, 1% Native American, 5% Hispanic, 16% black, 2% Asian American or Pacific Islander, 3% international, 15% 25 or older, 59% live on campus, 8% transferred in. Retention: 66% of full-time freshmen returned the following year. Core. Calendar: semesters. Academic remediation for entering students, services for LD students, advanced placement, accelerated degree program, self-designed majors, honors program, independent study, distance learning, double major, summer session for credit, part-time degree program, adult/continuing education programs, co-op programs and internships, graduate courses open to undergrads. Off campus study at Art Institute of Fort Lauderdale, Art Institute of Dallas, Art Institute of Houston. Study abroad program. ROTC: Naval.

Entrance Requirements: Options: Peterson's Universal Application, Common Application, electronic application, early admission, deferred admission, international baccalaureate accepted. Required: essay, high school transcript, minimum 2.0 high school GPA, SAT or ACT. Recommended: recommendations, interview. Entrance: moderately difficult. Application deadline: Rolling.

Costs Per Year: Application fee: $30. Comprehensive fee: $26,430 includes full-time tuition ($19,970) and college room and board ($6460). College room only: $3030. Part-time tuition: $666 per credit hour.

Collegiate Environment: Orientation program. Drama-theater group, choral group, student-run newspaper, radio station. Social organizations: 50 open to all; national fraternities, national sororities; 18% of eligible men and 15% of eligible women are members. Most popular organizations: Student Government Association, Baptist Campus Ministry. Major annual events: Homecoming, Senior Week. Student services: health clinic, personal-psychological counseling. Campus security: 24-hour emergency response devices and patrols, student patrols, late night transport-escort service, controlled dormitory access, code lock doors in residence halls, trained security patrols during evening hours. 1,085 college housing spaces available; all were occupied in 2003-04. Freshmen guaranteed college housing. On-campus residence required through junior year. Options: coed, men-only, women-only housing available. Carl S. Swisher Library with 374,016 books, 312,297 microform titles, 686 serials, 32,887 audiovisual materials, and a Web page. 450 computers available on campus for general student use. A campuswide network can be accessed from student residence rooms and from off campus. Staffed computer lab on campus.

Community Environment: Jacksonville is located on the St. John's River near the Atlantic Ocean and has a temperate climate characterized by short mild winters and long relatively warm summers with the average temperature being 67.8 degrees. The city functions as the financial, industrial, transportation, and commercial center of Florida. Along with the usual community facilities, there are seven hospitals, churches of almost all denominations, excellent shopping facilities, a civic performing arts center which features the finest of concerts, plays, and ballet, and many little theatre groups. Jacksonville and the surrounding area provide ample beaches and facilities for yachting, swimming, fishing, and golfing. The Friendship Park on the south side of the St. Johns River contains the spectacular Friendship Fountain and marina. A sports complex consists of the Coliseum, Alltell, Stadium, home of the NFL Jacksonville Jaguars; and Wolfson Park, home of the minor league baseball Jacksonville Suns. Part-time employment is available.

■ **JOHNSON & WALES UNIVERSITY** *T-15*
1701 Northeast 127th St.
North Miami, FL 33181
Tel: (305)892-7000
Free: 800-232-2433
Admissions: (305)892-7002
Fax: (305)892-7030
E-mail: admissions.mia@jwu.edu
Web Site: http://www.jwu.edu/
Description: Independent, 4-year, coed. Administratively affiliated with Johnson & Wales University (RI). Awards associate and bachelor's degrees. Founded 1992. Setting: 8-acre suburban campus with easy access to Miami. Endowment: $168.3 million. Total enrollment: 2,452. Student-undergrad faculty ratio is 36:1. 7,628 applied, 73% were admitted. Full-time: 2,317 students, 54% women, 46% men. Part-time: 135 students, 51% women, 49% men. Students come from 44 states and territories, 52 other countries, 45% from out-of-state, 0.3% Native American, 20% Hispanic, 31% black, 2% Asian American or Pacific Islander, 7% international. Academic areas with the most degrees conferred: business/marketing; family and consumer sciences; parks and recreation; personal and culinary services. Core. Academic remediation for entering students, ESL program, services for LD students, advanced placement, accelerated degree program, honors program, independent study, summer session for credit, part-time degree program, co-op programs and internships. Study abroad program.
Entrance Requirements: Options: Common Application, early admission, deferred admission, international baccalaureate accepted. Required: high school transcript. Recommended: minimum 2.0 high school GPA, SAT or ACT. Required for some: essay, recommendations, interview, SAT or ACT. Entrance: minimally difficult. Application deadline: Rolling. Notification: continuous.
Costs Per Year: Application fee: $0. Comprehensive fee: $30,126 includes full-time tuition ($19,875), mandatory fees ($951), and college room and board ($9300). Part-time tuition: $368 per quarter hour.
Collegiate Environment: Orientation program. Drama-theater group, student-run newspaper. Social organizations: 26 open to all; national fraternities, national sororities, local fraternities, local sororities. Most popular organizations: Vocational Industrial Clubs of America, American Culinary Federation, Collegiate Ambassador Team, New Frontiers, Tasters of the Vine. Major annual events: Family Day, New Frontiers, December Dance. Student services: personal-psychological counseling. Campus security: 24-hour emergency response devices and patrols, video camera surveillance throughout campus. 1,040 college housing spaces available. Freshmen guaranteed college housing. On-campus residence required in freshman year. Option: coed housing available. Florida Campus Library with 11,642 books, 200 serials, 1,987 audiovisual materials, and an OPAC. 100 computers available on campus for general student use. A campuswide network can be accessed from off-campus. Staffed computer lab on campus.

■ **JONES COLLEGE (JACKSONVILLE)** *D-12*
5353 Arlington Expressway
Jacksonville, FL 32211
Tel: (904)743-1122
E-mail: jmccaffe@jones.edu
Web Site: http://www.jones.edu/
Description: Independent, 4-year, coed. Awards associate and bachelor's degrees. Founded 1918. Setting: 5-acre urban campus. Total enrollment: 623. Student-undergrad faculty ratio is 14:1. 290 applied, 72% were admitted. Full-time: 183 students, 80% women, 20% men. Part-time: 440

students, 79% women, 21% men. Students come from 36 states and territories, 29% from out-of-state, 0.5% Native American, 6% Hispanic, 56% black, 1% Asian American or Pacific Islander, 0% international, 79% 25 or older. Retention: 68% of full-time freshmen returned the following year. Academic areas with the most degrees conferred: business/marketing; computer and information sciences; health professions and related sciences; law/legal studies. Core. Calendar: trimesters. Academic remediation for entering students, advanced placement, accelerated degree program, self-designed majors, distance learning, double major, summer session for credit, part-time degree program, adult/continuing education programs, co-op programs and internships.
Entrance Requirements: Open admission. Options: early admission, deferred admission. Required: high school transcript, interview. Entrance: noncompetitive. Application deadline: Rolling.
Costs Per Year: Application fee: $0. Tuition: $6600 full-time, $275 per credit hour part-time. Mandatory fees: $90 full-time.
Collegiate Environment: Most popular organization: PBL. Student services: personal-psychological counseling. Campus security: late night transport-escort service. College housing not available. James V. Forrestal Library plus 2 others with 34,000 books, 161 serials, and a Web page. 80 computers available on campus for general student use. A campuswide network can be accessed. Staffed computer lab on campus.
Community Environment: See Jacksonville University.

■ **JONES COLLEGE (MIAMI)** *T-15*
11430 North Kendall Dr., Ste. 200
Miami, FL 33176
Tel: (305)275-9996
Admissions: (904)743-1122
Fax: (305)275-9571
Web Site: http://www.jones.edu/
Description: Independent, 4-year, coed. Awards associate and bachelor's degrees. Founded 1987. Setting: suburban campus. Total enrollment: 837. 0.5% Native American, 16% Hispanic, 49% black, 1% Asian American or Pacific Islander, 1% international. Calendar: trimesters.

■ **KEISER COLLEGE (DAYTONA BEACH)** *H-14*
1800 Business Park Blvd.
Daytona Beach, FL 32114
Tel: (904)274-5060
Free: 800-749-4456
Admissions: (386)274-5060
Fax: (904)274-2725
Web Site: http://www.keisercollege.edu/
Description: Proprietary, 2-year, coed. Awards transfer associate and terminal associate degrees (enrollment data reflects all campuses). Founded 1995. Setting: 1-acre suburban campus with easy access to Orlando. Total enrollment: 2,434. Calendar: 3 semesters per year.
Entrance Requirements: Required: high school transcript, SAT, ACT, or Otis-Lennon School Ability Test. Entrance: minimally difficult. Application deadline: Rolling. Notification: continuous.
Collegiate Environment: Orientation program. Social organizations: national fraternities. Most popular organization: Phi Beta Lambda. Major annual events: March of Dimes, Strides for Life, Earth Day. Student services: personal-psychological counseling. Campus security: 24-hour emergency response devices. College housing not available. Jim Bishop Memorial Library with 5,000 books and 30 serials.

■ **KEISER COLLEGE (FORT LAUDERDALE)** *S-15*
1500 Northwest 49th St.
Fort Lauderdale, FL 33309
Tel: (954)776-4456
Free: 800-749-4456
Admissions: (954)776-4476
E-mail: admissions@keisercollege.edu
Web Site: http://www.keisercollege.edu
Description: Proprietary, primarily 2-year, coed. Awards diplomas, transfer associate, terminal associate, and bachelor's degrees (profile includes data from Daytona Beach, Melbourne, Sarasota, Tallahassee, and Lakeland campuses). Founded 1977. Setting: 4-acre suburban campus with easy access to Miami. Total enrollment: 6,121. Full-time: 5,043 students, 72% women, 28% men. Part-time: 1,078 students, 67% women, 33% men. Students come from 25 other countries, 0.5% Native American, 17% Hispanic, 26% black, 1% Asian American or Pacific Islander, 1% interna-

tional, 70% 25 or older. Core. Calendar: 3 semesters per year. Independent study, distance learning, adult/continuing education programs, internships.
Entrance Requirements: Options: Peterson's Universal Application, deferred admission. Required: high school transcript, minimum 2.0 high school GPA, interview, SAT, ACT, or Otis-Lennon School Ability Test. Entrance: minimally difficult. Application deadline: Rolling. Notification: continuous.
Costs Per Year: Application fee: $55.
Collegiate Environment: Orientation program. Major annual events: March of Dimes, Strides for Life, Earth Day. Campus security: security guard after 8 p.m. College housing not available. Jim Bishop Memorial Library with an OPAC and a Web page.

■ **KEISER COLLEGE (LAKELAND)** *L-12*
3515 Aviation Dr.
Lakeland, FL 33811
Tel: (863)701-7789
Fax: (863)701-8758
Web Site: http://www.keisercollege.edu/
Description: Proprietary, primarily 2-year, coed. Awards transfer associate, terminal associate, and bachelor's degrees. Setting: suburban campus. Calendar: 3 semesters per year.

■ **KEISER COLLEGE (MELBOURNE)** *L-16*
900 South Babcock St.
Melbourne, FL 32901-1461
Tel: (321)255-2255
Admissions: (954)776-4456
Web Site: http://www.keisercollege.edu/
Description: Proprietary, 2-year. Awards transfer associate and terminal associate degrees (enrollment data reflects all campuses). Founded 1989. Total enrollment: 3,041. Calendar: 3 semesters per year.
Entrance Requirements: Required: high school transcript. Entrance: minimally difficult. Application deadline: Rolling. Notification: continuous.
Collegiate Environment: Orientation program. College housing not available.

■ **KEISER COLLEGE (MIAMI)** *T-15*
8505 Mills Dr.
Miami, FL 33183
Tel: (305)596-2226
Fax: (305)596-7077
Web Site: http://www.keisercollege.edu/
Description: Proprietary, primarily 2-year, coed. Awards transfer associate, terminal associate, and bachelor's degrees. Total enrollment: 739. Student-undergrad faculty ratio is 18:1. Full-time: 739 students, 58% women, 42% men. Students come from 3 states and territories, 0% from out-of-state, 0% Native American, 78% Hispanic, 10% black, 0% Asian American or Pacific Islander, 1% international, 55% 25 or older. Calendar: 3 semesters per year.
Entrance Requirements: Required: high school transcript, interview. Recommended: SAT or ACT.
Costs Per Year: Application fee: $55. Tuition: $11,032 full-time. Mandatory fees: $400 full-time.
Collegiate Environment: Social organizations: 1 open to all. Most popular organization: Student Ambassador Program. Major annual events: Annual Picnic, Student Appreciation Days, Career Fair. Campus security: 24-hour patrols. College housing not available.

■ **KEISER COLLEGE (ORLANDO)** *J-13*
5600 Lake Underhill Rd.
Orlando, FL 32807
Tel: (407)273-5800
Web Site: http://www.keisercollege.edu/
Description: Proprietary, 2-year, coed. Calendar: 3 semesters per year.

■ **KEISER COLLEGE (PEMBROKE PINES)** *S-15*
12520 Pines Blvd.
Pembroke Pines, FL 33027
Tel: (954)431-4300
Fax: (954)431-2929
Web Site: http://www.keisercollege.edu

Description: Proprietary, primarily 2-year, coed. Awards diplomas, transfer associate, terminal associate, and bachelor's degrees. Founded 1998. Calendar: semesters.

■ **KEISER COLLEGE (PORT ST. LUCIE)** *N-15*
9468 South US Hwy. 1
Port St. Lucie, FL 34952
Tel: (772)398-9990
Fax: (772)335-9619
Web Site: http://www.keisercollege.edu
Description: Proprietary, 2-year, coed. Awards diplomas, transfer associate, and terminal associate degrees. Founded 1999. Calendar: semesters.

■ **KEISER COLLEGE (SARASOTA)** *N-8*
6151 Lake Osprey Dr.
Sarasota, FL 34240
Tel: (941)954-0954; (866)KEI-SER2
Admissions: (941)907-3900
Web Site: http://www.keisercollege.edu/
Description: Proprietary, 2-year, coed. Awards terminal associate degrees (enrollment data reflects all campuses). Founded 1995. Setting: small town campus with easy access to Tampa. Total enrollment: 2,434. Core. Calendar: 3 semesters per year. Internships.
Entrance Requirements: Required: high school transcript, interview, SAT, ACT, or Otis-Lennon School Ability Test. Entrance: minimally difficult. Application deadline: Rolling. Notification: continuous.
Collegiate Environment: Orientation program. Major annual events: March of Dimes, Strides for Life, Earth Day. Campus security: 24-hour patrols, late night transport-escort service. College housing not available. Jim Bishop Memorial Library with a Web page. 38 computers available on campus for general student use. A campuswide network can be accessed. Staffed computer lab on campus.

■ **KEISER COLLEGE (TALLAHASSEE)** *C-5*
1700 Halstead Blvd.
Tallahassee, FL 32308
Tel: (850)906-9494
Fax: (850)906-9497
Web Site: http://www.keisercollege.edu/
Description: Proprietary, 2-year, coed. Awards transfer associate and terminal associate degrees. Founded 1992. Setting: small town campus. Total enrollment: 240. Calendar: 3 semesters per year.
Entrance Requirements: Required: high school transcript, interview, SAT, ACT, or Otis-Lennon School Ability Test. Entrance: minimally difficult. Application deadline: Rolling. Notification: continuous.
Collegiate Environment: Orientation program. Major annual events: March of Dimes, Strides for Life, Earth Day. College housing not available.

■ **KEISER COLLEGE (WEST PALM BEACH)** *Q-15*
2085 Vista Parkway
West Palm Beach, FL 33411
Tel: (561)471-6000
Fax: (561)547-6609
Web Site: http://www.keisercollege.edu
Description: Proprietary, primarily 2-year, coed. Awards diplomas, transfer associate, terminal associate, and bachelor's degrees. Founded 1988. Calendar: semesters.

■ **KEY COLLEGE** *S-15*
5225 West Broward Blvd.
Fort Lauderdale, FL 33317
Tel: (954)581-2223
Free: 800-581-8292
Fax: (954)583-9458
Web Site: http://www.keycollege.edu/
Description: Proprietary, 2-year, coed. Awards certificates, diplomas, transfer associate, and terminal associate degrees. Founded 1881. Setting: suburban campus with easy access to Miami. Educational spending for 2005 fiscal year: $3714 per student. Total enrollment: 147. 54 applied, 72% were admitted. Full-time: 147 students, 92% women, 8% men. Students come from 2 states and territories, 0% from out-of-state, 1% Native American, 12% Hispanic, 34% black, 1% Asian American or Pacific Islander, 0% interna-

tional, 64% 25 or older, 4% transferred in. Core. Advanced placement, honors program, double major, external degree program, adult/continuing education programs, internships.

Entrance Requirements: Options: Common Application, electronic application, deferred admission. Required: high school transcript, interview. Required for some: CPAt, SAT, or ACT. Entrance: minimally difficult. Application deadline: Rolling. Notification: continuous.

Collegiate Environment: Orientation program. Campus security: 24-hour emergency response devices. College housing not available. Law Library with 3 serials and a Web page. Operations spending for 2004 fiscal year: $2200. 45 computers available on campus for general student use. Staffed computer lab on campus.

■ LAKE CITY COMMUNITY COLLEGE *D-9*

Route 19, Box 1030
Lake City, FL 32025-8703
Tel: (386)752-1822
Admissions: (386)754-4288
Fax: (386)755-1521
E-mail: admissions@mail.lakecity.cc.fl.us
Web Site: http://www.lakecity.cc.fl.us/

Description: State-supported, 2-year, coed. Part of Florida Community College System. Awards certificates, diplomas, transfer associate, and terminal associate degrees. Founded 1962. Setting: 132-acre small town campus with easy access to Jacksonville. Endowment: $3.3 million. Total enrollment: 2,736. Student-undergrad faculty ratio is 18:1. 1,162 applied, 57% were admitted. 10% from top 10% of their high school class. Full-time: 1,084 students, 53% women, 47% men. Part-time: 1,652 students, 71% women, 29% men. Students come from 18 states and territories, 7 other countries, 0.2% Native American, 2% Hispanic, 11% black, 2% Asian American or Pacific Islander, 1% international, 52% 25 or older, 2% live on campus. Core. Calendar: semesters. Academic remediation for entering students, ESL program, services for LD students, advanced placement, independent study, distance learning, summer session for credit, part-time degree program, adult/continuing education programs, co-op programs and internships. Study abroad program.

Entrance Requirements: Open admission except for nursing, golf course operations, allied health programs. Options: early admission, deferred admission. Required for some: high school transcript. Entrance: noncompetitive. Application deadline: Rolling. Notification: continuous.

Costs Per Year: Application fee: $15. State resident tuition: $2037 full-time. Nonresident tuition: $7290 full-time. College room and board: $4535.

Collegiate Environment: Orientation program. Drama-theater group, choral group. Social organizations: 22 open to all. Most popular organizations: student government, Florida Turf Grass Association, Florida Student Nurses Association, Phi Theta Kappa, Multicultural Student Union. Major annual events: Fall Fest, Student Government Awards Banquet, Persons with Disabilities Awareness Week. Campus security: 24-hour patrols. 90 college housing spaces available; all were occupied in 2003-04. Option: coed housing available. Learning Resources Center with 42,000 books, 180 serials, and an OPAC. 150 computers available on campus for general student use. A campuswide network can be accessed. Staffed computer lab on campus.

Community Environment: Lake City is the county seat of Columbia County, located midway between Atlanta and Miami. It has a temperate climate. Community facilities include excellent hospital and health facilities and fine motel accommodations. Annual deer and bear hunting is staged in nearby Osceola National Forest. Numerous lakes and streams are well stocked with bass, bream, and speckled perch. Tubing on the nearby Ichetucknee River is popular with students.

■ LAKE-SUMTER COMMUNITY COLLEGE *I-12*

9501 US Hwy. 441
Leesburg, FL 34788-8751
Tel: (352)787-3747
Admissions: (352)323-3677
Web Site: http://www.lscc.edu/

Description: State and locally supported, 2-year, coed. Part of Florida Department of Education. Awards certificates, diplomas, transfer associate, and terminal associate degrees. Founded 1962. Setting: 110-acre suburban campus with easy access to Orlando. Endowment: $3.3 million. Total enrollment: 3,409. Student-undergrad faculty ratio is 20:1. 1,088 applied, 100% were admitted. Full-time: 1,208 students, 62% women, 38% men. Part-time: 2,201 students, 68% women, 32% men. Students come from 8 states and territories, 6 other countries, 1% from out-of-state, 0.4% Native American,

9% Hispanic, 10% black, 2% Asian American or Pacific Islander, 1% international, 39% 25 or older, 28% transferred in. Core. Calendar: semesters. Academic remediation for entering students, services for LD students, advanced placement, independent study, distance learning, double major, summer session for credit, part-time degree program, adult/continuing education programs, co-op programs. Off campus study.

Entrance Requirements: Open admission except for nursing program. Required: high school transcript. Entrance: noncompetitive. Application deadline: Rolling. Notification: continuous.

Costs Per Year: Application fee: $25. State resident tuition: $1932 full-time, $64.40 per credit hour part-time. Nonresident tuition: $7108 full-time, $236.95 per credit hour part-time. Mandatory fees: $30 full-time, $1 per credit hour part-time. Full-time tuition and fees vary according to course load. Part-time tuition and fees vary according to course load.

Collegiate Environment: Orientation program. Drama-theater group, choral group, student-run newspaper. Social organizations: 14 open to all. Most popular organizations: Phi Theta Kappa, Baptist Collegiate Ministry, Environmental Society, Nursing Students' Association. Student services: women's center. Campus security: 24-hour emergency response devices. College housing not available. Lake-Sumter Community College Library with 69,465 books, 2,822 microform titles, 528 serials, 1,262 audiovisual materials, an OPAC, and a Web page. Operations spending for 2004 fiscal year: $489,165. 537 computers available on campus for general student use. A campuswide network can be accessed from off-campus. Staffed computer lab on campus.

Community Environment: Leesburg is a rapidly growing rural area with a temperate climate, located in central Florida near the shores of Lakes Griffin and Harris, within easy driving distance of metropolitan areas. Community facilities include numerous libraries, churches, general hospitals, active major civic and service groups. Part-time and full-time employment are available. Many forms of recreation are found, including fishing, swimming, golf, tennis, shuffleboard, water skiing and hunting. Lake Griffin State Park nearby provides additional recreational facilities.

■ LYNN UNIVERSITY *R-15*

3601 North Military Trail
Boca Raton, FL 33431-5598
Tel: (561)237-7000
Free: 800-888-5966
Admissions: (561)237-7900
Fax: (561)241-3552
E-mail: admission@lynn.edu
Web Site: http://www.lynn.edu/

Description: Independent, comprehensive, coed. Administratively affiliated with American College Dublin. Awards bachelor's, master's, and doctoral degrees and post-master's certificates. Founded 1962. Setting: 123-acre suburban campus with easy access to Fort Lauderdale. Endowment: $5 million. Total enrollment: 2,747. Faculty: 271 (93 full-time, 178 part-time). Student-undergrad faculty ratio is 17:1. 2,939 applied, 80% were admitted. 8% from top 10% of their high school class, 33% from top quarter, 65% from top half. 21 National Merit Scholars. Full-time: 1,951 students, 49% women, 51% men. Part-time: 332 students, 61% women, 39% men. Students come from 44 states and territories, 89 other countries, 56% from out-of-state, 0.4% Native American, 7% Hispanic, 5% black, 1% Asian American or Pacific Islander, 13% international, 14% 25 or older, 45% live on campus, 8% transferred in. Retention: 63% of full-time freshmen returned the following year. Academic areas with the most degrees conferred: business/marketing; security and protective services; communications/journalism. Core. Calendar: semesters plus 3 summer sessions. Academic remediation for entering students, ESL program, services for LD students, advanced placement, accelerated degree program, freshman honors college, honors program, independent study, distance learning, double major, summer session for credit, part-time degree program, adult/continuing education programs, co-op programs and internships, graduate courses open to undergrads. Study abroad program. ROTC: Air Force (c).

Entrance Requirements: Options: Peterson's Universal Application, Common Application, electronic application, early admission, deferred admission, international baccalaureate accepted. Required: essay, high school transcript, minimum 2.5 high school GPA, 1 recommendation, SAT or ACT. Recommended: essay, minimum 3.0 high school GPA, interview. Entrance: minimally difficult. Application deadline: Rolling. Notification: continuous.

Costs Per Year: Application fee: $35. Comprehensive fee: $37,000 includes full-time tuition ($26,200), mandatory fees ($1150), and college room and board ($9650). Part-time tuition: $760 per credit hour.

Collegiate Environment: Orientation program. Drama-theater group, choral group, student-run newspaper, radio station. Social organizations: 25 open to all; national fraternities, national sororities. Most popular organizations: Knights of the Round Table, intramural groups, student newspaper, Residence Hall Council, Activities Board. Major annual events: Fall Fest, Homecoming, Spring Fling. Student services: health clinic, personal-psychological counseling. Campus security: 24-hour patrols, late night transport-escort service, video monitor at residence entrances. 933 college housing spaces available. Freshmen guaranteed college housing. On-campus residence required through sophomore year. Option: coed housing available. Eugene M. and Christine E. Lynn Library with 235,000 books, 32,000 microform titles, 10,450 serials, 2,000 audiovisual materials, and an OPAC. Operations spending for 2004 fiscal year: $592,836. 150 computers available on campus for general student use. A campuswide network can be accessed from student residence rooms and from off campus. Staffed computer lab on campus.

Community Environment: See Florida Atlantic University.

■ **MANATEE COMMUNITY COLLEGE** *N-8*

5840 26th St. West, PO Box 1849
Bradenton, FL 34206-7046
Tel: (941)752-5000
Admissions: (941)752-5031
Fax: (941)727-6177
Web Site: http://www.mccfl.edu/

Description: State-supported, 2-year, coed. Part of Florida Community College System. Awards certificates, transfer associate, and terminal associate degrees. Founded 1957. Setting: 100-acre suburban campus with easy access to Tampa-St. Petersburg. Research spending for 2004 fiscal year: $92,312. Educational spending for 2005 fiscal year: $4800 per student. Total enrollment: 9,767. Student-undergrad faculty ratio is 23:1. Full-time: 3,855 students, 59% women, 41% men. Part-time: 5,912 students, 65% women, 35% men. Students come from 47 states and territories, 86 other countries, 4% from out-of-state, 0.3% Native American, 7% Hispanic, 10% black, 2% Asian American or Pacific Islander, 2% international, 41% 25 or older, 6% transferred in. Retention: 64% of full-time freshmen returned the following year. Core. Calendar: semesters. Academic remediation for entering students, ESL program, services for LD students, advanced placement, honors program, independent study, distance learning, summer session for credit, part-time degree program, co-op programs.

Entrance Requirements: Open admission except for allied health programs. Option: early admission. Required: high school transcript. Entrance: noncompetitive. Application deadline: 8/20. Notification: continuous.

Costs Per Year: Application fee: $40. State resident tuition: $1,983 full-time, $66.11 per credit part-time. Nonresident tuition: $7,352 full-time, $245.05 per credit part-time.

Collegiate Environment: Orientation program. Drama-theater group, choral group, student-run newspaper. Social organizations: 36 open to all. Most popular organizations: Student Government Association, Phi Theta Kappa, American Chemical Society Student Affiliate, Campus Ministry, Medical Community Club. Major annual events: Fall Frolic, Spring Fling, Great Safe Holiday Break Campaign. Campus security: 24-hour emergency response devices and patrols, late night transport-escort service. College housing not available. Sara Harlee Library plus 1 other with 65,386 books, 125,726 microform titles, 378 serials, 14,617 audiovisual materials, an OPAC, and a Web page. Operations spending for 2004 fiscal year: $1.1 million. 1,000 computers available on campus for general student use. A campuswide network can be accessed from off-campus. Staffed computer lab on campus.

Community Environment: A suburban area with a subtropical climate, Bradenton is located on the west coast and is known as "The Friendly City;" the hub of activities are in Manatee County. Air service at the Bradenton-Sarasota airport are available. Shopping centers, hospital, city parks, theaters and a modern municipal auditorium are part of the community facilities. The city is a rich agricultural area, producing, processing and shipping citrus fruits, winter vegetables and gladiola. Recreational facilities include beaches, a municipal pier, yacht basin, boat launching, and fishing. Points of interest are the South Florida Museum and Planetarium, and the De Soto National Memorial. The Pittsburgh Pirates baseball team trains here. A De Soto celebration is an annual event in March. Venice, Florida, is located approximately 42 miles south of the Bradenton campus. Some part-time employment is available.

■ **MEDVANCE INSTITUTE** *T-7*

170 JFK Dr.
Atlantis, FL 33462
Tel: (561)304-3466; 888-86-GO-MED
Fax: (561)304-3471
E-mail: bcortez@medvance.org
Web Site: http://www.medvance.org/

Description: Proprietary, 2-year, coed. Founded 1970.

■ **MIAMI DADE COLLEGE** *T-15*

300 Northeast Second Ave.
Miami, FL 33132-2296
Tel: (305)237-3131
Admissions: (305)237-0633
Fax: (305)237-3761
E-mail: skelly@mdc.edu
Web Site: http://www.mdc.edu/

Description: State and locally supported, primarily 2-year, coed. Part of Florida Community College System. Awards certificates, transfer associate, terminal associate, and bachelor's degrees. Founded 1960. Setting: urban campus. Endowment: $109.2 million. Educational spending for 2005 fiscal year: $4315 per student. Total enrollment: 54,169. Student-undergrad faculty ratio is 26:1. 20,445 applied, 100% were admitted. Full-time: 18,836 students, 60% women, 40% men. Part-time: 35,333 students, 62% women, 38% men. Students come from 43 states and territories, 160 other countries, 1% from out-of-state, 0.1% Native American, 64% Hispanic, 21% black, 1% Asian American or Pacific Islander, 3% international, 41% 25 or older, 2% transferred in. Academic area with the most degrees conferred: education. Core. Calendar: 16-16-6-6. Academic remediation for entering students, ESL program, services for LD students, advanced placement, freshman honors college, honors program, independent study, distance learning, summer session for credit, part-time degree program, adult/continuing education programs, co-op programs and internships. Study abroad program. ROTC: Army (c), Air Force (c).

Entrance Requirements: Open admission. Options: electronic application, early admission, international baccalaureate accepted. Required: high school transcript. Entrance: noncompetitive. Application deadline: Rolling. Notification: continuous.

Costs Per Year: Application fee: $20. State resident tuition: $1620 full-time, $54 per credit part-time. Nonresident tuition: $5997 full-time, $199.90 per credit part-time. Mandatory fees: $302 full-time.

Collegiate Environment: Drama-theater group, choral group, student-run newspaper, radio station. Social organizations: 40 open to all. Most popular organizations: Welcome Back, Hispanic Heritage Month, Black History Month, Paella Festival. Major annual events: Spooky Nights, Graduation. Student services: personal-psychological counseling. Campus security: 24-hour patrols. College housing not available. Main library plus 8 others with 327,417 books, 624,384 microform titles, 4,916 serials, 17,186 audiovisual materials, an OPAC, and a Web page. Operations spending for 2004 fiscal year: $10 million. 6,750 computers available on campus for general student use. Computer purchase/lease plans available. A campuswide network can be accessed from off-campus. Staffed computer lab on campus.

Community Environment: See Florida International University.

■ **MIAMI INTERNATIONAL UNIVERSITY OF ART & DESIGN** *T-15*

1501 Biscayne Blvd., Ste. 100
Miami, FL 33132-1418
Tel: (305)428-5700
Free: 800-225-9023
Fax: (305)374-7946
Web Site: http://www.aimiu.aii.edu/

Description: Proprietary, comprehensive, coed. Part of Education Management Corporation. Awards associate, bachelor's, and master's degrees. Founded 1965. Setting: 4-acre urban campus. Educational spending for 2005 fiscal year: $2956 per student. Total enrollment: 1,406. Faculty: 110 (45 full-time, 65 part-time). Student-undergrad faculty ratio is 20:1. 958 applied, 32% were admitted. Full-time: 1,328 students, 64% women, 36% men. Students come from 51 states and territories, 60 other countries, 32% from out-of-state, 0.4% Native American, 50% Hispanic, 12% black, 2% Asian American or Pacific Islander, 1% international, 22% 25 or older, 40% live on campus. Retention: 87% of full-time freshmen returned the following year. Academic area with the most degrees conferred: visual and performing arts. Core. Academic remediation for entering students, ESL program, services for LD students, distance learning, summer session for credit, internships.

Entrance Requirements: Options: Peterson's Universal Application, Common Application, electronic application, deferred admission. Required: essay, high school transcript, minimum 2.0 high school GPA, interview, 2 photographs, art portfolio. Recommended: 2 recommendations, SAT and SAT Subject Tests or ACT. Entrance: moderately difficult. Application deadline: Rolling. Notification: continuous.

Costs Per Year: Application fee: $50. Tuition: $18,960 full-time. College room only: $6150.

Collegiate Environment: Social organizations: local fraternities, local sororities. Most popular organizations: Caribbean Students Association, student government, DECA. Major annual events: Halloween Party, trip to Disney World, Luau Party. Student services: personal-psychological counseling. Campus security: 24-hour emergency response devices, student patrols, late night transport-escort service, controlled dormitory access, security service. 200 college housing spaces available. Freshmen guaranteed college housing. Option: coed housing available. 22,000 books and 158 serials. Operations spending for 2004 fiscal year: $98,135. 350 computers available on campus for general student use. Staffed computer lab on campus.

Community Environment: See Barry University.

■ **NATIONAL SCHOOL OF TECHNOLOGY, INC. (FORT LAUDERDALE)** *S-15*
1040 Bayview Dr.
Fort Lauderdale, FL 33304
Tel: (954)630-0066
Fax: (954)630-0076
E-mail: amiller@cci.edu
Web Site: http://www.nst.cc/
Description: Proprietary, 2-year, coed. Founded 2003. Calendar: continuous.

■ **NATIONAL SCHOOL OF TECHNOLOGY, INC. (HIALEAH)** *T-15*
4410 West 16th Ave., Ste. 52
Hialeah, FL 33012
Tel: (305)558-9500
Fax: (305)558-4419
E-mail: dalonso@cci.edu
Web Site: http://www.nst.cc/
Description: Proprietary, 2-year, coed. Total enrollment: 675. Calendar: continuous.

■ **NATIONAL SCHOOL OF TECHNOLOGY, INC. (MIAMI)** *T-15*
111 Northwest 183rd St., 2nd Floor
Miami, FL 33169
Tel: (305)386-9900
Fax: (305)388-1740
Web Site: http://www.nst.cc/
Description: Proprietary, 2-year, coed. Awards diplomas and terminal associate degrees. Total enrollment: 700. Calendar: continuous.

■ **NATIONAL SCHOOL OF TECHNOLOGY, INC. (NORTH MIAMI BEACH)** *R-15*
16150 Northeast 17th Ave.
North Miami Beach, FL 33162-4744
Tel: (305)949-9500
Fax: (305)956-5758
Web Site: http://www.nst.cc/
Description: Proprietary, 2-year, coed. Awards diplomas and terminal associate degrees. Founded 1977. Setting: urban campus. Total enrollment: 608. Full-time: 608 students, 67% women, 33% men. 0.3% Native American, 13% Hispanic, 70% black, 0% Asian American or Pacific Islander, 0% international. Calendar: continuous.
Entrance Requirements: Entrance: minimally difficult.

■ **NEW COLLEGE OF FLORIDA** *N-8*
5700 North Tamiami Trail
Sarasota, FL 34243-2197
Tel: (941)359-4700
Admissions: (941)359-4269

Fax: (941)359-4435
E-mail: ncadmissions@virtu.sar.usf.edu
Web Site: http://www.ncf.edu/
Description: State-supported, 4-year, coed. Part of State University System of Florida. Awards bachelor's degrees. Founded 1960. Setting: 144-acre suburban campus with easy access to Tampa-St. Petersburg. Endowment: $32.7 million. Research spending for 2004 fiscal year: $2.4 million. Total enrollment: 761. Student-undergrad faculty ratio is 10:1. 684 applied, 60% were admitted. 44% from top 10% of their high school class, 80% from top quarter, 97% from top half. 14 National Merit Scholars, 2 valedictorians. Full-time: 761 students, 61% women, 39% men. Students come from 38 states and territories, 28 other countries, 20% from out-of-state, 0.4% Native American, 9% Hispanic, 2% black, 3% Asian American or Pacific Islander, 2% international, 4% 25 or older, 68% live on campus, 6% transferred in. Retention: 75% of full-time freshmen returned the following year. Academic areas with the most degrees conferred: interdisciplinary studies; psychology; area and ethnic studies; physical sciences. Core. Calendar: 4-1-4. Services for LD students, accelerated degree program, self-designed majors, honors program, independent study, double major, internships. Off campus study at National Student Exchange. Study abroad program.

Entrance Requirements: Options: Peterson's Universal Application, Common Application, electronic application, early admission, deferred admission, international baccalaureate accepted. Required: essay, high school transcript, 1 recommendation, SAT or ACT. Recommended: minimum 3.0 high school GPA, interview, analytical paper. Entrance: very difficult. Application deadline: 5/1. Notification: continuous until 5/1.

Costs Per Year: Application fee: $30. State resident tuition: $3797 full-time. Nonresident tuition: $20,345 full-time. College room and board: $6750. College room only: $4170.

Collegiate Environment: Orientation program. Drama-theater group, choral group, student-run newspaper, radio station. Social organizations: 43 open to all. Most popular organizations: Nice Random Acts of Kindness, Interfaith groups, New College Student Alliance, Feminist Majority Leadership Alliance, Sailing Club. Major annual events: Halloween Palm Court Party, Towne Meetings, Dance Tutorial Perfomances. Student services: health clinic, personal-psychological counseling, women's center. Campus security: 24-hour emergency response devices and patrols, late night transport-escort service. College housing designed to accommodate 460 students; 470 undergraduates lived in college housing during 2003-04. Freshmen guaranteed college housing. On-campus residence required through sophomore year. Option: coed housing available. Jane Bancroft Cook Library with 256,581 books, 539,038 microform titles, 1,925 serials, 4,246 audiovisual materials, an OPAC, and a Web page. Operations spending for 2004 fiscal year: $1.1 million. 41 computers available on campus for general student use. Computer purchase/lease plans available. A campuswide network can be accessed from student residence rooms and from off campus. Staffed computer lab on campus.

■ **NEW ENGLAND INSTITUTE OF TECHNOLOGY AT PALM BEACH** *Q-15*
2410 Metro Centre Blvd.
West Palm Beach, FL 33407
Tel: (561)842-8324
Free: 800-826-9986
Fax: (561)842-9503
Web Site: http://newenglandtech.com/
Description: Proprietary, 2-year, coed. Awards certificates, diplomas, transfer associate, and terminal associate degrees. Founded 1983. Setting: 7-acre urban campus with easy access to Miami. Total enrollment: 1,200. 450 applied, 100% were admitted. 40% 25 or older. Academic remediation for entering students, internships.
Entrance Requirements: Open admission. Option: early admission. Required: high school transcript. Entrance: noncompetitive. Application deadline: Rolling. Notification: continuous.
Collegiate Environment: Student services: personal-psychological counseling. College housing not available. 58 computers available on campus for general student use.

■ **NEW WORLD SCHOOL OF THE ARTS** *T-15*
300 NE 2nd Ave.
Miami, FL 33132
Tel: (305)237-3135
Admissions: (305)237-3472
Fax: (305)237-3794

E-mail: nwsaadm@mdc.edu

Web Site: http://www.mdc.edu/nwsa

Description: State-supported, 4-year, coed. Administratively affiliated with Miami Dade College and University of Florida. Awards associate and bachelor's degrees. Founded 1984. Setting: 5-acre urban campus. Endowment: $4 million. Total enrollment: 371. Student-undergrad faculty ratio is 5:1. 296 applied, 47% were admitted. Full-time: 371 students, 59% women, 41% men. Students come from 34 states and territories, 19 other countries, 22% from out-of-state, 0% Native American, 50% Hispanic, 11% black, 2% Asian American or Pacific Islander, 5% international, 10% 25 or older, 5% transferred in. Retention: 80% of full-time freshmen returned the following year. Academic area with the most degrees conferred: visual and performing arts. Core. Calendar: semesters. Academic remediation for entering students, ESL program, services for LD students, advanced placement, freshman honors college, honors program, independent study, distance learning, summer session for credit, co-op programs and internships.

Entrance Requirements: Required: essay, high school transcript, 2 recommendations, interview, audition. Entrance: noncompetitive. Application deadline: Rolling. Notification: continuous until 8/1.

Costs Per Year: Application fee: $0. State resident tuition: $12,000 full-time, $65.05 per credit part-time. Nonresident tuition: $17,000 full-time, $216.15 per credit part-time.

Collegiate Environment: Orientation program. Most popular organization: student government. Major annual event: Rising Stars. Student services: personal-psychological counseling. Campus security: 24-hour patrols. College housing not available. Miami Dade Community College library (Wolfson Campus) plus 1 other with an OPAC and a Web page. 100 computers available on campus for general student use. A campuswide network can be accessed from student residence rooms and from off campus. Staffed computer lab on campus.

■ **NORTH FLORIDA COMMUNITY COLLEGE** *C-7*

1000 Turner Davis Dr.

Madison, FL 32340-1602

Tel: (850)973-2288

Admissions: (850)973-1622

Fax: (850)973-1696

Web Site: http://www.nfcc.edu/

Description: State-supported, 2-year, coed. Awards certificates, transfer associate, and terminal associate degrees. Founded 1958. Setting: 109-acre small town campus. Total enrollment: 1,297. 10% from top 10% of their high school class, 30% from top quarter, 80% from top half. Full-time: 593 students, 64% women, 36% men. Part-time: 704 students, 65% women, 35% men. 0% from out-of-state, 0% Native American, 1% Hispanic, 24% black, 1% Asian American or Pacific Islander, 0% international, 31% 25 or older. Core. Calendar: semesters. Academic remediation for entering students, services for LD students, advanced placement, accelerated degree program, honors program, distance learning, summer session for credit, part-time degree program, adult/continuing education programs.

Entrance Requirements: Open admission. Options: Common Application, early admission. Required: high school transcript, minimum 2.0 high school GPA. Placement: SAT or ACT required for some. Entrance: noncompetitive. Application deadline: Rolling.

Collegiate Environment: Drama-theater group, choral group, student-run newspaper. Social organizations: 7 open to all. Most popular organizations: Student Government Association, Sentinel Ambassadors, Phi Theta Kappa, African-American Student Union, Fellowship of Christian Athletes. Major annual event: Octoberfest. Student services: women's center. Campus security: 24-hour emergency response devices. College housing not available. Dr. Marshall Hamilton Library with 30,137 books, 125 serials, an OPAC, and a Web page. Operations spending for 2004 fiscal year: $300,000. 60 computers available on campus for general student use. A campuswide network can be accessed. Staffed computer lab on campus.

Community Environment: Madison is located in a rural area with a temperate climate. Railroads and buses serve the area along with three highways. Community facilities include a public library, hospital, ten churches, and major civic and fraternal organizations. Within easy reach are large shopping and cultural centers. Recreational facilities include a golf course, recreation center, and many facilities for all water sports. Part-time employment opportunities are limited.

■ **NORTHWOOD UNIVERSITY, FLORIDA CAMPUS** *Q-15*

2600 North Military Trail

West Palm Beach, FL 33409-2911

Tel: (561)478-5500

Free: 800-458-8325

Admissions: (989)837-4367

Fax: (561)640-3328

E-mail: admissions@northwood.edu

Web Site: http://www.northwood.edu/

Description: Independent, 4-year, coed. Awards associate and bachelor's degrees. Founded 1982. Setting: 90-acre suburban campus with easy access to Miami. System endowment: $58.2 million. Educational spending for 2005 fiscal year: $3292 per student. Total enrollment: 923. Student-undergrad faculty ratio is 25:1. 913 applied, 60% were admitted. 4% from top 10% of their high school class, 13% from top quarter, 58% from top half. Full-time: 794 students, 41% women, 59% men. Part-time: 129 students, 57% women, 43% men. Students come from 35 states and territories, 40 other countries, 43% from out-of-state, 0.1% Native American, 8% Hispanic, 10% black, 2% Asian American or Pacific Islander, 25% international, 6% 25 or older, 46% live on campus, 11% transferred in. Retention: 59% of full-time freshmen returned the following year. Academic areas with the most degrees conferred: business/marketing; parks and recreation; communications/journalism. Core. Academic remediation for entering students, ESL program, advanced placement, accelerated degree program, honors program, independent study, distance learning, double major, summer session for credit, part-time degree program, external degree program, adult/continuing education programs, internships. Off campus study. Study abroad program.

Entrance Requirements: Options: Peterson's Universal Application, Common Application, electronic application, early admission, deferred admission, international baccalaureate accepted. Required: essay, high school transcript, SAT or ACT. Recommended: minimum 2.0 high school GPA, 1 recommendation, interview. Entrance: moderately difficult. Application deadline: Rolling. Notification: continuous.

Costs Per Year: Application fee: $25. Comprehensive fee: $23,316 includes full-time tuition ($15,216), mandatory fees ($585), and college room and board ($7515). College room only: $3870. Part-time tuition: $317 per credit hour.

Collegiate Environment: Orientation program. Social organizations: 24 open to all. Most popular organizations: Student Government Association, International Club, Auto Show. Major annual events: Homecoming, Auto Show, Spring Fling. Student services: health clinic, personal-psychological counseling. Campus security: 24-hour emergency response devices and patrols, student patrols. 400 college housing spaces available; 337 were occupied in 2003-04. Freshmen guaranteed college housing. On-campus residence required through sophomore year. Options: men-only, women-only housing available. Peter C. Cook Library with 25,362 books, 152 serials, 525 audiovisual materials, an OPAC, and a Web page. Operations spending for 2004 fiscal year: $267,895. 89 computers available on campus for general student use. A campuswide network can be accessed from student residence rooms and from off campus. Staffed computer lab on campus.

■ **NOVA SOUTHEASTERN UNIVERSITY** *S-15*

3301 College Ave.

Fort Lauderdale, FL 33314-7796

Tel: (954)262-7300

Free: 800-541-NOVA

Admissions: (954)262-8000

Fax: (954)262-3967

E-mail: nsuinfo@nova.edu

Web Site: http://www.nova.edu/

Description: Independent, university, coed. Awards associate, bachelor's, master's, doctoral, and first professional degrees and post-master's and first professional certificates. Founded 1964. Setting: 300-acre suburban campus. Total enrollment: 26,334. Faculty: 1,615 (582 full-time, 1,033 part-time). Student-undergrad faculty ratio is 18:1. 2,429 applied, 54% were admitted. 17% from top 10% of their high school class, 43% from top quarter, 82% from top half. Full-time: 3,379 students, 72% women, 28% men. Part-time: 2,074 students, 74% women, 26% men. Students come from 53 states and territories, 42 other countries, 20% from out-of-state, 0.3% Native American, 25% Hispanic, 26% black, 5% Asian American or Pacific Islander, 6% international, 60% 25 or older, 9% live on campus, 5% transferred in. Retention: 63% of full-time freshmen returned the following year. Academic areas with the most degrees conferred: business/marketing; health professions and related sciences; education; psychology. Core. Calendar: trimesters. Academic remediation for entering students, services for LD students, advanced placement, accelerated degree program, honors program, distance learning, double major, summer session for credit, part-time degree program, adult/continuing education programs, co-op programs and internships. Study abroad program.

Entrance Requirements: Options: Peterson's Universal Application, Common Application, electronic application, early admission, deferred admission, international baccalaureate accepted. Required: high school transcript, SAT or ACT. Recommended: minimum 2.5 high school GPA, recommendations, interview. Entrance: moderately difficult. Application deadline: Rolling. Notification: continuous.

Costs Per Year: Application fee: $50. Comprehensive fee: $24,320 includes full-time tuition ($17,250), mandatory fees ($550), and college room and board ($6520). College room only: $4120. Full-time tuition and fees vary according to class time and program. Room and board charges vary according to board plan and housing facility. Part-time tuition: $575 per credit hour. Part-time tuition varies according to class time, course load, and program.

Collegiate Environment: Orientation program. Drama-theater group, choral group, student-run newspaper, radio station. Social organizations: 34 open to all; national fraternities, national sororities. Most popular organizations: Pre-Pharmacy Society, Pre-Med Society, Beta Theta Pi, Delta Phi Epsilon, Nova International Muslim Association. Major annual events: Orientation, Homecoming, Got Wood bonfire. Student services: health clinic, personal-psychological counseling, women's center. Campus security: 24-hour emergency response devices and patrols, late night transport-escort service, controlled dormitory access, shuttle bus service. 464 college housing spaces available; all were occupied in 2003-04. Freshmen guaranteed college housing. On-campus residence required through sophomore year. Option: coed housing available. Alvin Sherman Library, Research, and Information Technology Center plus 4 others with 668,738 books, 601,505 microform titles, 22,837 serials, 5,600 audiovisual materials, an OPAC, and a Web page. 2,000 computers available on campus for general student use. A campuswide network can be accessed from student residence rooms and from off campus. Staffed computer lab on campus.

Community Environment: Nova Southeastern University is located on a 227-acre site west of Fort Lauderdale in the town of Davie, 10 miles inland from the Atlantic Ocean and easily accessible from major U.S. and state highways including the Sunshine State Parkway. The climate is subtropical and the average year-round temperature is 75 degrees. Nova Southeastern University is situated in close proximity to Broward Community College and to the Nova complex of elementary, middle and high schools.

■ **OKALOOSA-WALTON COLLEGE** *K-4*
100 College Blvd.
Niceville, FL 32578-1295
Tel: (850)678-5111
Admissions: (850)729-5373
E-mail: registrar@owc.edu
Web Site: http://www.owc.edu/
Description: State and locally supported, primarily 2-year, coed. Part of Florida Community College System. Awards certificates, transfer associate, terminal associate, and bachelor's degrees. Founded 1963. Setting: 264-acre small town campus. Endowment: $21 million. Educational spending for 2005 fiscal year: $5003 per student. Total enrollment: 8,728. Student-undergrad faculty ratio is 20:1. Students come from 18 states and territories, 10% black, 49% 25 or older. Core. Calendar: semesters plus summer sessions. Academic remediation for entering students, ESL program, services for LD students, advanced placement, independent study, distance learning, summer session for credit, part-time degree program, adult/continuing education programs. ROTC: Army (c).

Entrance Requirements: Open admission. Options: early admission, deferred admission. Required: high school transcript, ACT, SAT I, ACT ASSET, MAPS, or Florida College Entry Placement Test. Entrance: noncompetitive. Application deadline: Rolling. Notification: continuous. Preference given to state residents.

Costs Per Year: Application fee: $0. State resident tuition: $1774 full-time, $55.45 per credit part-time. Nonresident tuition: $6661 full-time, $208.15 per credit part-time.

Collegiate Environment: Drama-theater group, choral group. Social organizations: 24 open to all. Major annual events: College Night, Drug Prevention Campaign, Student Government Association Picnic. Student services: health clinic. Campus security: 24-hour patrols. College housing not available. Okaloosa-Walton Community College Learning Resource Center with 84,991 books, 139,142 microform titles, 365 serials, 10,800 audiovisual materials, an OPAC, and a Web page. Operations spending for 2004 fiscal year: $928,500. 643 computers available on campus for general student use. A campuswide network can be accessed. Staffed computer lab on campus.

Community Environment: Twin cities with temperate climate, largely residential in nature. Many residents are military retirees or civil service personnel. Airlines and Greyhound and AmTrak buses serve the area. Large shopping centers are within easy driving distance. Part-time job opportunities for students are limited.

■ **ORLANDO CULINARY ACADEMY** *J-13*
8511 Commodity Circle, Ste. 100
Orlando, FL 32819
Tel: (407)888-4000; (866)OCA-CHEF
Fax: (407)888-4019
Web Site: http://www.orlandoculinary.com/
Description: Proprietary, 2-year, coed. Founded 2002.

■ **PALM BEACH ATLANTIC UNIVERSITY** *Q-15*
901 South Flagler Dr, PO Box 24708
West Palm Beach, FL 33416-4708
Tel: (561)803-2000
Free: 800-238-3998
E-mail: admit@pbac.edu
Web Site: http://www.pba.edu/
Description: Independent nondenominational, comprehensive, coed. Awards associate, bachelor's, master's, and first professional degrees. Founded 1968. Setting: 25-acre urban campus with easy access to Miami. Endowment: $53.9 million. Research spending for 2004 fiscal year: $31,777. Educational spending for 2005 fiscal year: $15,780 per student. Total enrollment: 3,171. Faculty: 268 (138 full-time, 130 part-time). Student-undergrad faculty ratio is 13:1. 2,224 applied, 44% were admitted. 21% from top 10% of their high school class, 47% from top quarter, 82% from top half. Full-time: 2,285 students, 64% women, 36% men. Part-time: 201 students, 56% women, 44% men. Students come from 46 states and territories, 17 other countries, 27% from out-of-state, 0.4% Native American, 8% Hispanic, 15% black, 2% Asian American or Pacific Islander, 2% international, 23% 25 or older, 45% live on campus, 11% transferred in. Retention: 71% of full-time freshmen returned the following year. Academic areas with the most degrees conferred: business/marketing; communications/journalism; education. Core. Calendar: semesters. Academic remediation for entering students, ESL program, advanced placement, accelerated degree program, freshman honors college, honors program, independent study, double major, summer session for credit, part-time degree program, adult/continuing education programs, co-op programs and internships. Study abroad program.

Entrance Requirements: Options: Peterson's Universal Application, Common Application, electronic application, early admission, early action, deferred admission, international baccalaureate accepted. Required: essay, high school transcript, minimum 2.0 high school GPA, 2 recommendations, interview, SAT or ACT. Recommended: minimum 3.0 high school GPA. Entrance: moderately difficult. Application deadlines: Rolling, 12/1 for early action. Notification: continuous, 12/15 for early action.

Costs Per Year: Application fee: $25. Comprehensive fee: $24,030 includes full-time tuition ($17,130), mandatory fees ($220), and college room and board ($6680). College room only: $3350. Full-time tuition and fees vary according to course load, degree level, program, and reciprocity agreements. Room and board charges vary according to board plan and housing facility. Part-time tuition: $420 per credit. Part-time mandatory fees: $85 per term. Part-time tuition and fees vary according to course load, degree level, program, and reciprocity agreements.

Collegiate Environment: Orientation program. Drama-theater group, choral group, student-run newspaper. Major annual events: homecoming, Welcome Week, Blitz Week. Student services: health clinic, personal-psychological counseling. Campus security: 24-hour emergency response devices and patrols, late night transport-escort service, controlled dormitory access. 1,100 college housing spaces available; 1,025 were occupied in 2003-04. Freshmen given priority for college housing. On-campus residence required through sophomore year. Options: men-only, women-only housing available. E. C. Blomeyer Library with 140,714 books, 256,205 microform titles, 27,696 serials, 5,213 audiovisual materials, an OPAC, and a Web page. Operations spending for 2004 fiscal year: $822,523. 147 computers available on campus for general student use. A campuswide network can be accessed from student residence rooms and from off campus. Staffed computer lab on campus.

Community Environment: West Palm Beach is the county seat of Palm Beach County, one of the fastest-growing areas in Florida. The campus is minutes away from the Atlantic Ocean and just across the Intracoastal

Waterway from Palm Beach. Cultural, athletic and recreational events abound, and a railway system offers easy access to Fort Lauderdale and Miami.

■ **PALM BEACH COMMUNITY COLLEGE** *Q-15*
4200 Congress Ave.
Lake Worth, FL 33461-4796
Tel: (561)967-7222
Admissions: (561)868-3032
Web Site: http://www.pbcc.edu/
Description: State-supported, 2-year, coed. Part of Florida Community College System. Awards certificates, transfer associate, and terminal associate degrees. Founded 1933. Setting: 150-acre urban campus with easy access to West Palm Beach. Endowment: $14.4 million. Educational spending for 2005 fiscal year: $3140 per student. Total enrollment: 22,666. Student-undergrad faculty ratio is 22:1. 27,824 applied, 100% were admitted. 5% from top 10% of their high school class, 60% from top half. Full-time: 6,917 students, 57% women, 43% men. Part-time: 15,749 students, 64% women, 36% men. Students come from 49 states and territories, 138 other countries, 5% from out-of-state, 0.3% Native American, 15% Hispanic, 22% black, 3% Asian American or Pacific Islander, 3% international, 37% 25 or older, 10% transferred in. Core. Calendar: semesters. Academic remediation for entering students, ESL program, services for LD students, advanced placement, self-designed majors, freshman honors college, honors program, independent study, distance learning, double major, summer session for credit, part-time degree program, adult/continuing education programs, co-op programs and internships. Off campus study. Study abroad program.
Entrance Requirements: Open admission except for nursing, dental hygiene programs, radiography, respiratory therapy, firefighter, police and corrections. Options: electronic application, early admission, deferred admission. Entrance: noncompetitive. Application deadline: 8/20. Notification: continuous until 8/20. Preference given to state residents.
Costs Per Year: Application fee: $20. Area resident tuition: $63 per hour part-time. State resident tuition: $1890 full-time, $63 per hour part-time. Nonresident tuition: $6892 full-time, $229.75 per hour part-time. Mandatory fees: $10 full-time.
Collegiate Environment: Orientation program. Drama-theater group, choral group, student-run newspaper. Social organizations: 27 open to all; national fraternities; 3% of eligible men and 3% of eligible women are members. Most popular organizations: student government, Phi Theta Kappa, Students for International Understanding, Black Student Union, Drama Club. Major annual event: Graduation. Student services: health clinic, women's center. Campus security: 24-hour emergency response devices and patrols. Harold C. Manor Library plus 3 others with 151,000 books, 685,608 microform titles, 1,474 serials, 9,700 audiovisual materials, an OPAC, and a Web page. Operations spending for 2004 fiscal year: $1.9 million. 2,300 computers available on campus for general student use. A campuswide network can be accessed from off-campus. Staffed computer lab on campus.
Community Environment: Located south of West Palm Beach, Lake Worth has an annual average temperature of 75 degrees and an average rainfall of 61.72 inches. All modes of transportation serve the area. Recreational activities are golfing, shuffleboard, polo, tennis, swimming, water skiing, jai alai, deep sea and fresh water fishing. Deep sea fishing for sailfish, surf fishing for pompano and blue fish are excellent; fresh water fishing at Lake Osborne. Points of interest are the Palm Beach Speedway, Kennel Club Race Track, and art galleries.

■ **PASCO-HERNANDO COMMUNITY COLLEGE** *K-9*
10230 Ridge Rd.
New Port Richey, FL 34654-5199
Tel: (727)847-2727
Admissions: (727)816-3261
Fax: (727)816-3450
E-mail: bullard@phcc.edu
Web Site: http://www.phcc.edu/
Description: State-supported, 2-year, coed. Part of Florida Community College System. Awards certificates, diplomas, transfer associate, and terminal associate degrees. Founded 1972. Setting: 142-acre small town campus with easy access to Tampa. Endowment: $20.3 million. Total enrollment: 7,346. Student-undergrad faculty ratio is 25:1. Full-time: 2,670 students, 62% women, 38% men. Part-time: 4,676 students, 69% women, 31% men. Students come from 11 states and territories, 10 other countries, 1% from out-of-state, 1% Native American, 8% Hispanic, 4% black, 2% Asian American or Pacific Islander, 1% international, 42% 25 or older, 5%

transferred in. Core. Calendar: semesters. Academic remediation for entering students, services for LD students, advanced placement, accelerated degree program, honors program, independent study, distance learning, double major, summer session for credit, part-time degree program, adult/continuing education programs, co-op programs and internships. Off campus study at other members of the Florida Community College System and the State University System of Florida. ROTC: Army (c).
Entrance Requirements: Open admission. Options: electronic application, international baccalaureate accepted. Required: high school transcript. Entrance: noncompetitive. Application deadline: Rolling. Notification: continuous.
Costs Per Year: Application fee: $20. State resident tuition: $1872 full-time, $62 per credit part-time. Nonresident tuition: $7222 full-time, $241 per credit part-time.
Collegiate Environment: Orientation program. Drama-theater group, choral group. Social organizations: 26 open to all. Most popular organizations: Student Government Association, Phi Theta Kappa, Phi Beta Lambda, Human Services, PHCC Cares. Major annual events: fall club carnivals, Welcome Back activities, Spring Fling. Campus security: 24-hour patrols. College housing not available. Pottberg Library plus 2 others with 67,852 books, 193,442 microform titles, 351 serials, 4,357 audiovisual materials, an OPAC, and a Web page. Operations spending for 2004 fiscal year: $697,419. 974 computers available on campus for general student use. Computer purchase/lease plans available. A campuswide network can be accessed. Staffed computer lab on campus.
Community Environment: See Saint Leo University.

■ **PENSACOLA JUNIOR COLLEGE** *L-2*
1000 College Blvd.
Pensacola, FL 32504-8998
Tel: (850)484-1000
Admissions: (850)484-1600
Fax: (850)484-1826
Web Site: http://www.pjc.edu/
Description: State-supported, 2-year, coed. Part of Florida Community College System. Awards certificates, diplomas, transfer associate, and terminal associate degrees. Founded 1948. Setting: 160-acre urban campus. Educational spending for 2005 fiscal year: $3766 per student. Total enrollment: 11,000. Students come from 37 states and territories, 21 other countries, 2% from out-of-state, 50% 25 or older. Core. Calendar: semesters. Academic remediation for entering students, services for LD students, advanced placement, honors program, independent study, distance learning, double major, summer session for credit, part-time degree program, external degree program, adult/continuing education programs, co-op programs. ROTC: Army.
Entrance Requirements: Open admission except for some health-related programs. Option: early admission. Required: high school transcript. Entrance: noncompetitive. Application deadline: 8/30. Notification: continuous until 8/30.
Costs Per Year: Application fee: $30. State resident tuition: $1755 full-time. Nonresident tuition: $6540 full-time. Mandatory fees: $300 full-time.
Collegiate Environment: Orientation program. Drama-theater group, choral group, student-run newspaper. Social organizations: 16 open to all. Most popular organizations: Baptist Student Union, Campus Activities Board, Students for a Multicultural Society, International Council, Engineering Club. Major annual events: spring and fall cookouts, Fall End of Term Party, Spring End of Term Party. Student services: health clinic, personal-psychological counseling. Campus security: 24-hour emergency response devices and patrols, student patrols, late night transport-escort service. College housing not available. Operations spending for 2004 fiscal year: $1.6 million. 1,200 computers available on campus for general student use. A campuswide network can be accessed. Staffed computer lab on campus.
Community Environment: Pensacola Junior College offers courses at five locations in Escambia and Santa Rosa counties in northwest Florida. Famous for the white sand beaches of the Emerald Coast, Pensacola is the center of a growing metropolitan area of a third of a million residents. Pensacola is the "Cradle of Naval Aviation" and several Navy bases are located in the area, including the Pensacola Naval Air Station, Whiting Field, Corry Field, and Saufley Field. The white beaches of the Gulf of Mexico are a mecca for tourists. The area is served by the University of West Florida as well as Pensacola Junior College. In addition, the city has numerous museums, galleries, and historical areas, including Seville Quarter, a part of Pensacola dating back to the mid 1700s. Florida's First Place City continues to grow and expand.

■ **POLK COMMUNITY COLLEGE** *L-12*
999 Ave. H, NE
Winter Haven, FL 33881-4299
Tel: (863)297-1000
Admissions: (863)297-1010
Fax: (863)297-1060
E-mail: clyle@polk.edu and rwebb@polk.edu
Web Site: http://www.polk.edu/
Description: State-supported, 2-year, coed. Part of Florida Community College System. Awards certificates, transfer associate, and terminal associate degrees. Founded 1964. Setting: 98-acre suburban campus with easy access to Orlando and Tampa. Endowment: $11.1 million. Total enrollment: 7,082. Student-undergrad faculty ratio is 16:1. 1,125 applied, 100% were admitted. Full-time: 2,037 students, 58% women, 42% men. Part-time: 5,045 students, 70% women, 30% men. Students come from 25 states and territories, 73 other countries, 10% from out-of-state, 0.3% Native American, 8% Hispanic, 13% black, 2% Asian American or Pacific Islander, 4% international, 38% 25 or older. Core. Calendar: semesters 16-16-6-6. Academic remediation for entering students, ESL program, services for LD students, advanced placement, accelerated degree program, self-designed majors, independent study, distance learning, double major, summer session for credit, part-time degree program, adult/continuing education programs, co-op programs. ROTC: Army (c).
Entrance Requirements: Open admission. Options: early admission, deferred admission, international baccalaureate accepted. Required: high school transcript. Entrance: noncompetitive. Application deadline: Rolling. Notification: continuous.
Costs Per Year: Application fee: $20. State resident tuition: $1901 full-time, $63.38 per credit hour part-time. Nonresident tuition: $7044 full-time, $234.79 per credit hour part-time.
Collegiate Environment: Orientation program. Drama-theater group, choral group, student-run newspaper. Social organizations: 2 open to all. Campus security: 24-hour emergency response devices and patrols. College housing not available. Polk Community College Library with 181,000 books, 40,208 microform titles, 325 serials, 4,527 audiovisual materials, an OPAC, and a Web page. Operations spending for 2004 fiscal year: $1.8 million. 171 computers available on campus for general student use. A campuswide network can be accessed. Staffed computer lab on campus.

■ **REMINGTON COLLEGE-JACKSONVILLE CAMPUS** *D-12*
7011 A.C. Skinner Parkway
Jacksonville, FL 32256
Tel: (904)296-3435
Fax: (904)296-9097
E-mail: tony.galang@remingtoncollege.edu
Web Site: http://www.remingtoncollege.edu/
Description: Proprietary, primarily 2-year, coed. Awards diplomas, terminal associate, and bachelor's degrees. Total enrollment: 368. 122 applied, 100% were admitted. 0% Native American, 10% Hispanic, 40% black, 7% Asian American or Pacific Islander, 0% international.
Entrance Requirements: Entrance: noncompetitive.

■ **REMINGTON COLLEGE-PINELLAS CAMPUS** *L-9*
8550 Ulmerton Rd.
Largo, FL 33771
Tel: (727)532-1999; 888-900-2343
Fax: (727)530-7710
Web Site: http://www.remingtoncollege.edu/
Description: Proprietary, primarily 2-year, coed. Awards diplomas, transfer associate, terminal associate, and bachelor's degrees. Setting: suburban campus. Calendar: continuous.

■ **REMINGTON COLLEGE-TAMPA CAMPUS** *L-10*
2410 East Busch Blvd.
Tampa, FL 33612-8410
Tel: (813)932-0701
Admissions: (813)935-5700
Fax: (813)935-7415
Web Site: http://www.remingtoncollege.edu/
Description: Proprietary, primarily 2-year, coed. Awards diplomas, transfer associate, and bachelor's degrees. Founded 1948. Setting: 10-acre urban campus. Total enrollment: 685. Student-undergrad faculty ratio is 15:1. 1% Native American, 18% Hispanic, 36% black, 1% Asian American or Pacific

Islander, 3% international, 32% 25 or older. Core. Academic remediation for entering students, accelerated degree program, internships.
Entrance Requirements: Open admission. Options: Peterson's Universal Application, Common Application, deferred admission. Required: high school transcript, interview, Wonderlic aptitude test. Entrance: noncompetitive. Application deadline: Rolling.
Costs Per Year: Application fee: $50.
Collegiate Environment: Orientation program. Social organizations: national fraternities; 20% of eligible men and 20% of eligible women are members. Campus security: late night transport-escort service. College housing not available. Tampa Technical Institute Library with 4,100 books, 124 serials, 340 audiovisual materials, and an OPAC. 200 computers available on campus for general student use. A campuswide network can be accessed. Staffed computer lab on campus.

■ **RINGLING SCHOOL OF ART AND DESIGN** *N-8*
2700 North Tamiami Trail
Sarasota, FL 34234-5895
Tel: (941)351-5100
Free: 800-255-7695
Fax: (941)359-7517
E-mail: admissions@rsad.edu
Web Site: http://www.ringling.edu/
Description: Independent, 4-year, coed. Awards bachelor's degrees. Founded 1931. Setting: 37-acre small town campus with easy access to Tampa-St. Petersburg. Endowment: $13.1 million. Educational spending for 2005 fiscal year: $9357 per student. Total enrollment: 1,088. Student-undergrad faculty ratio is 13:1. 958 applied, 27% were admitted. Full-time: 1,050 students, 49% women, 51% men. Part-time: 38 students, 42% women, 58% men. Students come from 46 states and territories, 33 other countries, 45% from out-of-state, 1% Native American, 11% Hispanic, 3% black, 4% Asian American or Pacific Islander, 5% international, 11% 25 or older, 47% live on campus, 10% transferred in. Retention: 86% of full-time freshmen returned the following year. Academic area with the most degrees conferred: visual and performing arts. Core. Calendar: semesters. Academic remediation for entering students, services for LD students, advanced placement, independent study, part-time degree program, internships. Off campus study at Association of Independent Colleges of Art and Design, New York Studio Program. Study abroad program.
Entrance Requirements: Options: Peterson's Universal Application, electronic application, deferred admission, international baccalaureate accepted. Required: essay, high school transcript, minimum 2.0 high school GPA, 2 recommendations, portfolio, resume. Recommended: interview. Entrance: moderately difficult. Application deadline: Rolling. Notification: continuous.
Costs Per Year: Application fee: $35. Comprehensive fee: $30,565 includes full-time tuition ($21,200), mandatory fees ($200), and college room and board ($9165). College room only: $4917. Full-time tuition and fees vary according to course load, program, and student level. Room and board charges vary according to board plan and housing facility. Part-time tuition: $1000 per credit hour. Part-time tuition varies according to course load, program, and student level.
Collegiate Environment: Orientation program. Drama-theater group. Social organizations: 22 open to all; national fraternities, national sororities; 3% of eligible men and 2% of eligible women are members. Most popular organizations: FEWS, Nontraditional Student Group, Phi Delta Theta, Sigma Sigma Sigma, Ringling Ambassadors. Major annual events: Welcome Back Beach Party, Activities Fair, coffeehouses. Student services: personal-psychological counseling. Campus security: 24-hour emergency response devices and patrols, late night transport-escort service, controlled dormitory access, lighted campus. 483 college housing spaces available; 476 were occupied in 2003-04. Freshmen given priority for college housing. Options: coed, men-only, women-only housing available. Verman Kimbrough Memorial Library with 46,802 books, 340 serials, 123,891 audiovisual materials, an OPAC, and a Web page. Operations spending for 2004 fiscal year: $546,540. 640 computers available on campus for general student use. Computer purchase/lease plans available. A campuswide network can be accessed from student residence rooms and from off campus. Staffed computer lab on campus.

■ **ROLLINS COLLEGE** *J-13*
1000 Holt Ave.
Winter Park, FL 32789-4499
Tel: (407)646-2000

Admissions: (407)646-2161
Fax: (407)646-2600
E-mail: admission@rollins.edu
Web Site: http://www.rollins.edu/
Description: Independent, comprehensive, coed. Awards bachelor's and master's degrees. Founded 1885. Setting: 70-acre suburban campus with easy access to Orlando. Endowment: $264.5 million. Educational spending for 2005 fiscal year: $8692 per student. Total enrollment: 2,493. Faculty: 217 (185 full-time, 32 part-time). Student-undergrad faculty ratio is 11:1. 2,958 applied, 53% were admitted. 34% from top 10% of their high school class, 67% from top quarter, 94% from top half. Full-time: 1,719 students, 60% women, 40% men. Students come from 46 states and territories, 43 other countries, 46% from out-of-state, 1% Native American, 8% Hispanic, 5% black, 4% Asian American or Pacific Islander, 2% international, 1% 25 or older, 66% live on campus, 3% transferred in. Retention: 84% of full-time freshmen returned the following year. Academic areas with the most degrees conferred: social sciences; psychology; visual and performing arts. Core. Calendar: semesters. Academic remediation for entering students, services for LD students, advanced placement, accelerated degree program, self-designed majors, honors program, independent study, double major, part-time degree program, adult/continuing education programs, internships. Off campus study at American University. Study abroad program.
Entrance Requirements: Options: Peterson's Universal Application, Common Application, electronic application, early admission, early decision, deferred admission, international baccalaureate accepted. Required: essay, high school transcript, 1 recommendation, SAT or ACT. Recommended: minimum X high school GPA, interview. Entrance: very difficult. Application deadlines: 2/15, 11/15 for early decision plan 1, 1/15 for early decision plan 2. Notification: 4/1, 12/15 for early decision plan 1, 2/1 for early decision plan 2.
Costs Per Year: Application fee: $40. Comprehensive fee: $38,366 includes full-time tuition ($28,390), mandatory fees ($834), and college room and board ($9142). College room only: $5376.
Collegiate Environment: Orientation program. Drama-theater group, choral group, student-run newspaper, radio station. Social organizations: 122 open to all; national fraternities, national sororities, local fraternities, local sororities; 75% of eligible men and 75% of eligible women are members. Student services: health clinic, personal-psychological counseling. Campus security: 24-hour emergency response devices and patrols, late night transport-escort service, controlled dormitory access. 1,250 college housing spaces available; 1,117 were occupied in 2003-04. Freshmen guaranteed college housing. Options: coed, men-only, women-only housing available. Olin Library with 288,323 books, 86,595 microform titles, 15,749 serials, 5,501 audiovisual materials, an OPAC, and a Web page. Operations spending for 2004 fiscal year: $2.1 million. 195 computers available on campus for general student use. A campuswide network can be accessed from student residence rooms and from off campus. Staffed computer lab on campus.
Community Environment: Within the metropolitan area of which Orlando is the center, Winter Park is a residential area of great beauty. This area of Florida is popularly known as"The Lake Region." Orange groves, subtropical forest, flowering shrubs and trees are the dominant features of the landscape. Scenic boat trips may be taken through a chain of four lakes. Annual events are the Sidewalk Arts Festival and a Bach festival held on the campus of Rollins College.

■ **ST. JOHN VIANNEY COLLEGE SEMINARY** *T-15*
2900 Southwest 87th Ave.
Miami, FL 33165-3244
Tel: (305)223-4561
E-mail: noonan@sjvcs.edu
Web Site: http://www.sjvcs.edu/
Description: Independent Roman Catholic, 4-year, coed. Awards bachelor's degrees. Founded 1959. Setting: 33-acre urban campus. Research spending for 2004 fiscal year: $5200. Total enrollment: 47. 11 applied, 100% were admitted. 17% from top 10% of their high school class, 33% from top half. Full-time: 47 students, 9% women, 91% men. Students come from 5 states and territories, 11 other countries, 17% from out-of-state, 0% Native American, 45% Hispanic, 9% black, 4% Asian American or Pacific Islander, 23% international, 45% 25 or older, 98% live on campus. Retention: 83% of full-time freshmen returned the following year. Core. Calendar: semesters. Academic remediation for entering students, ESL program, advanced placement, internships.
Entrance Requirements: Required: high school transcript, minimum 2.0 high school GPA, 1 recommendation, psychological examination. Recom-

mended: interview, SAT or ACT. Entrance: moderately difficult. Application deadline: Rolling. Preference given to candidates for the priesthood.
Collegiate Environment: Orientation program. Choral group. Major annual events: Parents' Weekend, Vocation Awareness, special topics workshops. Student services: legal services, personal-psychological counseling. Campus security: 24-hour emergency response devices, student patrols. On-campus residence required through senior year. Option: men-only housing available. Maytag Memorial Library with 54,000 books, 150 serials, and an OPAC. Operations spending for 2004 fiscal year: $114,934. 16 computers available on campus for general student use. A campuswide network can be accessed. Staffed computer lab on campus.

■ **ST. JOHNS RIVER COMMUNITY COLLEGE** *F-12*
5001 Saint Johns Ave.
Palatka, FL 32177-3897
Tel: (386)312-4200
Admissions: (386)312-4032
Fax: (386)312-4292
Web Site: http://www.sjrcc.cc.fl.us/
Description: State-supported, 2-year, coed. Awards certificates, diplomas, transfer associate, and terminal associate degrees. Founded 1958. Setting: 105-acre small town campus with easy access to Jacksonville. Total enrollment: 3,459. 1,200 applied, 100% were admitted. 43% 25 or older. Core. Calendar: semesters. Academic remediation for entering students, services for LD students, advanced placement, accelerated degree program, distance learning, summer session for credit, part-time degree program, adult/continuing education programs.
Entrance Requirements: Open admission. Options: Common Application, early admission. Required: high school transcript. Entrance: noncompetitive. Application deadline: Rolling. Notification: continuous.
Costs Per Year: State resident tuition: $1732 full-time, $66.88 per semester hour part-time. Nonresident tuition: $6348 full-time, $251.14 per semester hour part-time.
Collegiate Environment: Choral group, student-run newspaper. Social organizations: 12 open to all. Campus security: 24-hour patrols. College housing not available. 56,925 books, 90,725 microform titles, 7,015 audiovisual materials, an OPAC, and a Web page. 203 computers available on campus for general student use. Staffed computer lab on campus.

■ **SAINT LEO UNIVERSITY** *K-10*
PO Box 6665
St. Leo, FL 33574-6665
Tel: (352)588-8200
Free: 800-334-5532
Admissions: (352)588-8283
Fax: (352)588-8257
E-mail: admissions@saintleo.edu
Web Site: http://www.saintleo.edu/
Description: Independent Roman Catholic, comprehensive, coed. Awards associate, bachelor's, and master's degrees. Founded 1889. Setting: 186-acre rural campus with easy access to Tampa and Orlando. Endowment: $10.8 million. Total enrollment: 2,263. Faculty: 122 (66 full-time, 56 part-time). Student-undergrad faculty ratio is 16:1. 3,248 applied, 43% were admitted. 8% from top 10% of their high school class, 30% from top quarter, 67% from top half. Full-time: 1,335 students, 55% women, 45% men. Part-time: 49 students, 57% women, 43% men. Students come from 35 states and territories, 42 other countries, 33% from out-of-state, 1% Native American, 9% Hispanic, 8% black, 1% Asian American or Pacific Islander, 8% international, 9% 25 or older, 68% live on campus, 8% transferred in. Retention: 71% of full-time freshmen returned the following year. Academic areas with the most degrees conferred: business/marketing; education; social sciences. Core. Calendar: semesters. Academic remediation for entering students, ESL program, services for LD students, advanced placement, honors program, independent study, distance learning, double major, summer session for credit, part-time degree program, adult/continuing education programs, internships. Study abroad program. ROTC: Army, Air Force (c).
Entrance Requirements: Options: Peterson's Universal Application, Common Application, electronic application, early admission, deferred admission, international baccalaureate accepted. Required: essay, high school transcript, minimum 2.3 high school GPA, 1 recommendation, SAT or ACT. Recommended: minimum 3.0 high school GPA, interview. Required for some: interview. Entrance: moderately difficult. Application deadline: 8/15. Notification: continuous.

Costs Per Year: Application fee: $35. Comprehensive fee: $22,140 includes full-time tuition ($14,250), mandatory fees ($430), and college room and board ($7460). College room only: $3920. Full-time tuition and fees vary according to location. Room and board charges vary according to board plan and housing facility.

Collegiate Environment: Orientation program. Drama-theater group, choral group, student-run newspaper, radio station. Social organizations: 43 open to all; national fraternities, national sororities, local fraternities, local sororities; 26% of eligible men and 14% of eligible women are members. Most popular organizations: Student Government Union, Circle K, Samaritans, American Marketing Association, Campus Activities Board. Major annual events: Fall Festival, Spring Fling, Community Service Day. Student services: health clinic, personal-psychological counseling. Campus security: 24-hour emergency response devices and patrols, late night transport-escort service, controlled dormitory access. 887 college housing spaces available; 844 were occupied in 2003-04. Freshmen given priority for college housing. On-campus residence required through junior year. Options: coed, men-only, women-only housing available. Cannon Memorial Library with 141,521 books, 28,290 microform titles, 700 serials, 6,437 audiovisual materials, an OPAC, and a Web page. Operations spending for 2004 fiscal year: $1.1 million. 750 computers available on campus for general student use. A campuswide network can be accessed from student residence rooms and from off campus. Staffed computer lab on campus.

Community Environment: Saint Leo is located 25 miles north of Tampa, and 38 miles from Tampa International Airport. Semitropical climate. Orlando and Disney World are 65 miles to the east.

■ **ST. PETERSBURG COLLEGE** *M-9*
PO Box 13489
St. Petersburg, FL 33733-3489
Tel: (727)341-3600
Admissions: (727)712-5892
Fax: (727)341-3150
Web Site: http://www.spjc.edu/

Description: State and locally supported, primarily 2-year, coed. Awards certificates, diplomas, transfer associate, terminal associate, and bachelor's degrees. Founded 1927. Setting: suburban campus. Endowment: $13.4 million. Educational spending for 2005 fiscal year: $5165 per student. Total enrollment: 24,102. 3,919 applied, 100% were admitted. Full-time: 8,012 students, 59% women, 41% men. Part-time: 16,090 students, 64% women, 36% men. Students come from 45 states and territories, 30 other countries, 4% from out-of-state, 1% Native American, 6% Hispanic, 11% black, 3% Asian American or Pacific Islander, 1% international, 46% 25 or older. Academic areas with the most degrees conferred: education; business/marketing; health professions and related sciences. Core. Calendar: semesters. Academic remediation for entering students, ESL program, services for LD students, advanced placement, freshman honors college, honors program, distance learning, summer session for credit, part-time degree program, adult/continuing education programs, co-op programs and internships.

Entrance Requirements: Open admission. Options: Common Application, electronic application, early admission, deferred admission. Required: high school transcript. Entrance: noncompetitive. Application deadline: Rolling. Notification: continuous.

Costs Per Year: Application fee: $35. State resident tuition: $1646 full-time, $54.88 per credit part-time. Nonresident tuition: $6587 full-time, $219.11 per credit part-time. Mandatory fees: $337 full-time, $25.17 per credit part-time. Full-time tuition and fees vary according to degree level and program. Part-time tuition and fees vary according to degree level and program.

Collegiate Environment: Orientation program. Drama-theater group, student-run newspaper. Student services: women's center. Campus security: late night transport-escort service. College housing not available. M. M. Bennett Library plus 5 others with 222,990 books, 79,591 microform titles, 1,393 serials, 16,543 audiovisual materials, an OPAC, and a Web page. Operations spending for 2004 fiscal year: $2.4 million. 2,951 computers available on campus for general student use. Computer purchase/lease plans available. A campuswide network can be accessed from off-campus. Staffed computer lab on campus.

■ **ST. PETERSBURG THEOLOGICAL SEMINARY** *M-9*
10830 Navajo Dr.
St. Petersburg, FL 33708
Tel: (727)399-0276
Fax: (727)347-3695

E-mail: sptseminary@tampabay.rr.com
Web Site: http://www.sptseminary.edu/

Description: Independent interdenominational, upper-level, coed. Awards bachelor's, master's, and doctoral degrees. Founded 1983. Educational spending for 2005 fiscal year: $550 per student. Total enrollment: 70. 0% Native American, 3% Hispanic, 17% black, 0% Asian American or Pacific Islander, 0% international. Core. Calendar: semesters. Advanced placement, independent study, distance learning, double major, summer session for credit, external degree program, adult/continuing education programs, co-op programs and internships, graduate courses open to undergrads.

Costs Per Year: Tuition: $3600 full-time, $120 per credit hour part-time. Mandatory fees: $30 full-time, $15 per term part-time. Full-time tuition and fees vary according to course level and degree level. Part-time tuition and fees vary according to course level and degree level.

Collegiate Environment: Orientation program. College housing not available. Vern-Roberta Donzero with 25,146 books, 22 serials, 125 audiovisual materials, and an OPAC. Operations spending for 2004 fiscal year: $10,772. 3 computers available on campus for general student use.

■ **ST. THOMAS UNIVERSITY** *Q-15*
16401 Northwest 37th Ave.
Miami Gardens, FL 33054-6459
Tel: (305)625-6000
Free: 800-367-9010
Admissions: (305)628-6546
Fax: (305)628-6591
Web Site: http://www.stu.edu/

Description: Independent Roman Catholic, comprehensive, coed. Awards bachelor's, master's, and first professional degrees and post-master's certificates. Founded 1961. Setting: 140-acre suburban campus. Endowment: $9.1 million. Total enrollment: 2,692. Faculty: 250 (95 full-time, 155 part-time). Student-undergrad faculty ratio is 17:1. 551 applied, 91% were admitted. Full-time: 1,096 students, 58% women, 42% men. Part-time: 62 students, 52% women, 48% men. Students come from 25 states and territories, 58 other countries, 9% from out-of-state, 0.2% Native American, 44% Hispanic, 27% black, 1% Asian American or Pacific Islander, 10% international, 36% 25 or older, 10% live on campus, 10% transferred in. Retention: 69% of full-time freshmen returned the following year. Academic areas with the most degrees conferred: business/marketing; health professions and related sciences; communications/journalism. Core. Calendar: semesters. Academic remediation for entering students, services for LD students, advanced placement, freshman honors college, honors program, independent study, distance learning, double major, summer session for credit, part-time degree program, adult/continuing education programs, graduate courses open to undergrads. ROTC: Army (c), Air Force (c).

Entrance Requirements: Options: Common Application, electronic application, early admission, deferred admission, international baccalaureate accepted. Required: high school transcript, minimum 2.0 high school GPA, SAT or ACT. Recommended: essay, 1 recommendation, interview. Entrance: moderately difficult. Application deadline: Rolling. Notification: continuous.

Costs Per Year: Application fee: $40. Comprehensive fee: $23,490 includes full-time tuition ($17,860) and college room and board ($5630). Room and board charges vary according to board plan and housing facility. Part-time tuition: $595 per credit.

Collegiate Environment: Orientation program. Choral group. Social organizations: 29 open to all. Most popular organizations: International Student Organization, Pre-Med Club, Hispanic Heritage Club, Inter-Dorm Council, Communicators Club. Major annual events: Homecoming, St. Thomas of Villanova Annual Picnic, Land and Water Olympics. Student services: health clinic, personal-psychological counseling. Campus security: 24-hour emergency response devices and patrols, late night transport-escort service, controlled dormitory access. Options: men-only, women-only housing available. St. Thomas University Library plus 1 other with 154,017 books, 319,889 microform titles, 898 serials, 7,894 audiovisual materials, and a Web page. Operations spending for 2004 fiscal year: $1.6 million. 60 computers available on campus for general student use. A campuswide network can be accessed. Staffed computer lab on campus.

■ **SANFORD-BROWN INSTITUTE (JACKSONVILLE)** *D-12*
10255 Fortune Parkway, Ste. 501
Jacksonville, FL 32256
Tel: (904)363-6221
Fax: (904)363-6824
Web Site: http://www.sbjacksonville.com/

Description: Proprietary, 2-year, coed. Founded 1992.

■ **SANFORD-BROWN INSTITUTE (LAUDERDALE LAKES)** *N-15*
4780 N. State Rd., 7 Bldg. E, Ste. 100
Lauderdale Lakes, FL 33309
Tel: (954)733-8900
Fax: (954)733-8994
Web Site: http://www.sbftlauderdale.com/
Description: Proprietary, 2-year, coed.

■ **SANFORD-BROWN INSTITUTE (TAMPA)** *L-10*
5701 E. Hillsborough Ave.
Tampa, FL 33610
Tel: (813)621-0072
Fax: (813)626-0392
Web Site: http://www.sbtampa.com/
Description: Proprietary, 2-year, coed.

■ **SANTA FE COMMUNITY COLLEGE** *F-10*
3000 Northwest 83rd St.
Gainesville, FL 32606-6200
Tel: (352)395-5000
Admissions: (352)395-5857
Fax: (352)395-5581
E-mail: information@santafe.cc.fl.us
Web Site: http://www.sfcc.edu/
Description: State and locally supported, 2-year, coed. Part of Florida Community College System. Awards certificates, transfer associate, and terminal associate degrees (offers bachelor's degrees in conjunction with Saint Leo College). Founded 1966. Setting: 175-acre suburban campus with easy access to Jacksonville. Total enrollment: 13,806. 1,796 applied, 100% were admitted. Full-time: 6,560 students, 50% women, 50% men. Part-time: 7,246 students, 56% women, 44% men. Students come from 46 states and territories, 80 other countries, 3% from out-of-state, 1% Native American, 8% Hispanic, 12% black, 3% Asian American or Pacific Islander, 3% international, 28% 25 or older, 11% transferred in. Retention: 61% of full-time freshmen returned the following year. Core. Calendar: semesters. Academic remediation for entering students, ESL program, services for LD students, advanced placement, self-designed majors, honors program, independent study, distance learning, summer session for credit, part-time degree program, adult/continuing education programs, co-op programs. ROTC: Army (c), Air Force (c).
Entrance Requirements: Open admission. Option: early admission. Required: high school transcript. Placement: SAT, ACT, or CPT required. Entrance: noncompetitive. Application deadline: Rolling. Notification: continuous.
Costs Per Year: Application fee: $30. State resident tuition: $1755 full-time, $58.50 per credit hour part-time. Nonresident tuition: $6540 full-time, $218 per credit hour part-time.
Collegiate Environment: Drama-theater group, choral group. Most popular organizations: Black Student Union, student government. Major annual events: Student Orientation, College Night, Homecoming. Student services: personal-psychological counseling. Campus security: 24-hour emergency response devices and patrols. College housing not available. Lawrence W. Tyree Library with 81,832 books, 624 serials, an OPAC, and a Web page. 400 computers available on campus for general student use. A campuswide network can be accessed from off-campus. Staffed computer lab on campus.
Community Environment: See University of Florida.

■ **SCHILLER INTERNATIONAL UNIVERSITY** *L-9*
453 Edgewater Dr.
Dunedin, FL 34698-7532
Tel: (727)736-5082
Free: 800-336-4133
Fax: (727)734-0359
E-mail: admissions@schiller.edu
Web Site: http://www.schiller.edu/
Description: Independent, comprehensive, coed. Part of Schiller International University. Awards associate, bachelor's, and master's degrees. Founded 1991. Setting: suburban campus with easy access to Tampa. Total enrollment: 177. Faculty: 34 (4 full-time, 30 part-time). Student-undergrad faculty ratio is 5:1. Full-time: 103 students, 41% women, 59% men. Part-time: 5 students, 20% women, 80% men. Students come from 60 other countries, 68% from out-of-state, 32% international, 13% 25 or older. Reten-

tion: 22% of full-time freshmen returned the following year. Core. Calendar: semesters. ESL program, advanced placement, accelerated degree program, self-designed majors, summer session for credit, part-time degree program, adult/continuing education programs, internships. Study abroad program.
Entrance Requirements: Options: Peterson's Universal Application, Common Application, deferred admission, international baccalaureate accepted. Required: essay, high school transcript. Recommended: minimum 2.0 high school GPA. Entrance: noncompetitive. Application deadline: Rolling.
Costs Per Year: Application fee: $35. Comprehensive fee: $24,480 includes full-time tuition ($16,880) and college room and board ($7600). Part-time tuition: $470 per credit.
Collegiate Environment: Orientation program. Student-run newspaper. Most popular organizations: student government, student newspaper, yearbook staff, Model United Nations. Major annual event: Formal Dance. Student services: personal-psychological counseling. Campus security: night patrols. 70 college housing spaces available. Option: coed housing available. SIU Library with 1,918 books and 30 serials. 17 computers available on campus for general student use. Staffed computer lab on campus.

■ **SEMINOLE COMMUNITY COLLEGE** *I-14*
100 Weldon Blvd.
Sanford, FL 32773-6199
Tel: (407)328-4722
Admissions: (407)708-2380
Fax: (407)328-2395
Web Site: http://www.scc-fl.edu/
Description: State and locally supported, 2-year, coed. Awards certificates, diplomas, transfer associate, and terminal associate degrees. Founded 1966. Setting: 200-acre small town campus with easy access to Orlando. Endowment: $5.3 million. Total enrollment: 11,682. Student-undergrad faculty ratio is 11:1. Full-time: 4,079 students, 56% women, 44% men. Part-time: 7,603 students, 63% women, 37% men. Students come from 18 states and territories, 123 other countries, 0.4% Native American, 13% Hispanic, 13% black, 3% Asian American or Pacific Islander, 5% international, 45% 25 or older, 20% transferred in. Core. Calendar: semesters. Academic remediation for entering students, ESL program, services for LD students, advanced placement, accelerated degree program, honors program, independent study, distance learning, double major, summer session for credit, part-time degree program, external degree program, adult/continuing education programs, co-op programs and internships. Study abroad program. ROTC: Army.
Entrance Requirements: Open admission except for physical therapy, respiratory therapy, nursing programs. Options: early admission, deferred admission, international baccalaureate accepted. Required: high school transcript, minimum 2.0 high school GPA. Entrance: noncompetitive. Application deadline: Rolling. Notification: continuous.
Costs Per Year: Application fee: $0. State resident tuition: $1592 full-time, $53.08 per credit hour part-time. Nonresident tuition: $6125 full-time, $214.18 per credit hour part-time. Mandatory fees: $488 full-time, $16.28 per credit hour part-time.
Collegiate Environment: Orientation program. Drama-theater group, choral group, student-run newspaper. Social organizations: 17 open to all. Most popular organizations: Phi Beta Lambda, Phi Theta Kappa, Student Government Association, International Student Organization. Major annual events: Welcome Back, Career Fair. Student services: personal-psychological counseling. Campus security: 24-hour emergency response devices and patrols. College housing not available. Seminole Community College Library plus 2 others with 102,744 books, 84,200 microform titles, 353 serials, 8,913 audiovisual materials, an OPAC, and a Web page. Operations spending for 2004 fiscal year: $1.7 million. 56 computers available on campus for general student use. A campuswide network can be accessed from off-campus. Staffed computer lab on campus.
Community Environment: A residential city with subtropical climate. Sanford is located 20 miles northeast of Orlando. Air service is available through Orlando International Airport, and Amtrak serves the area. Part-time employment for students is available in the metropolitan Orlando Area. Lake Monroe is a recreation area nearby with a municipal zoo, picnic facilities and playground. Other sports include boating, fishing, tennis, and more. The close proximity to Orlando offers many convenient cultural and recreational activities.

■ **SOUTH FLORIDA COMMUNITY COLLEGE** *M-13*
600 West College Dr.
Avon Park, FL 33825-9356

Tel: (863)453-6661
Fax: (863)453-0165
Web Site: http://www.sfcc.cc.fl.us/

Description: State-supported, 2-year, coed. Part of Florida Community College System. Awards certificates, diplomas, transfer associate, and terminal associate degrees. Founded 1965. Setting: 80-acre rural campus with easy access to Tampa-St. Petersburg and Orlando. Endowment: $3.3 million. Educational spending for 2005 fiscal year: $1929 per student. Total enrollment: 2,076. Full-time: 813 students, 52% women, 48% men. Part-time: 1,263 students, 64% women, 36% men. Students come from 12 states and territories, 4 other countries, 33% 25 or older. Core. Calendar: semesters. Academic remediation for entering students, ESL program, services for LD students, advanced placement, accelerated degree program, summer session for credit, part-time degree program, adult/continuing education programs, co-op programs and internships.

Entrance Requirements: Open admission. Options: early admission, deferred admission. Required: high school transcript. Placement: SAT, ACT or Florida College Entry-Level Placement Test, CPT required. Entrance: noncompetitive. Application deadline: Rolling. Notification: continuous.

Collegiate Environment: Choral group, student-run newspaper. Social organizations: 12 open to all. Most popular organizations: Phi Theta Kappa, Student Activities Board, Cheerleaders Club, African-American Association, Future Educators. Major annual events: International Jamboree, Back to School Pool Party, Community College Week. Student services: personal-psychological counseling, women's center. Campus security: 24-hour patrols. Learning Resource Center with 42,000 books, 237 serials, and an OPAC. Operations spending for 2004 fiscal year: $376,594. 284 computers available on campus for general student use. A campuswide network can be accessed. Staffed computer lab on campus.

Community Environment: An urban area in south central Florida; semitropical climate and a tourist center. Trains and buses serve the area. Citrus production is the main source of income. Part time employment is limited to eating establishments and grocery stores. Recreational activities are numerous; they include golfing, bowling, tennis, shuffleboard, water sports, hunting, fishing and camping. Avon Park has many active civic organizations. The annual International Jamboree and Cultural Series is a special event.

■ **SOUTH UNIVERSITY (TAMPA)** *L-10*
4401 N. Himes Ave.
Tampa, FL 33614
Tel: (813)393-3800
Web Site: http://www.southuniversity.edu

Description: Proprietary, 4-year, coed. Awards bachelor's degrees. Educational spending for 2005 fiscal year: $2857 per student.

Entrance Requirements: Required for some: SAT or ACT.

Costs Per Year: Tuition: $11,475 full-time, $2995 per term part-time.

■ **SOUTH UNIVERSITY (WEST PALM BEACH)** *Q-15*
1760 North Congress Ave.
West Palm Beach, FL 33409
Tel: (561)697-9200; (866)629-9200
Admissions: (866)629-2902
Fax: (561)697-9944
E-mail: jrogalski@southuniversity.edu
Web Site: http://www.southuniversity.edu/

Description: Proprietary, primarily 2-year, coed. Part of Education Management Corporation. Awards terminal associate, bachelor's, and master's degrees. Founded 1899. Setting: 1-acre suburban campus with easy access to Miami. Educational spending for 2005 fiscal year: $2719 per student. Total enrollment: 502. Faculty: 58 (18 full-time, 40 part-time). Student-undergrad faculty ratio is 13:1. Full-time: 347 students, 84% women, 16% men. Part-time: 155 students, 89% women, 11% men. Students come from 4 other countries, 0% from out-of-state, 0.2% Native American, 9% Hispanic, 51% black, 1% Asian American or Pacific Islander, 1% international, 38% 25 or older. Retention: 60% of full-time freshmen returned the following year. Academic areas with the most degrees conferred: health professions and related sciences; law/legal studies; business/marketing. Core. Academic remediation for entering students, advanced placement, double major, part-time degree program, adult/continuing education programs, internships.

Entrance Requirements: Options: Peterson's Universal Application, Common Application, electronic application, early admission, deferred admission, international baccalaureate accepted. Required: high school transcript.

Recommended: SAT or ACT. Required for some: recommendations, interview. Entrance: minimally difficult. Application deadline: Rolling. Notification: continuous.

Costs Per Year: Application fee: $25. Tuition: $11,475 full-time, $2995 per term part-time.

Collegiate Environment: Orientation program. Social organizations: 3 open to all. Most popular organization: Pro Bono Club. Major annual events: Food Drive, Blood Drive, Clothing Drive. Student services: personal-psychological counseling. Campus security: evening security personnel. College housing not available. South University Library plus 3 others with 8,400 books and 67 serials. Operations spending for 2004 fiscal year: $116,440. 53 computers available on campus for general student use. A campuswide network can be accessed. Staffed computer lab on campus.

■ **SOUTHEASTERN UNIVERSITY** *L-12*
1000 Longfellow Blvd.
Lakeland, FL 33801-6099
Tel: (863)667-5000
Free: 800-500-8760
Fax: (863)667-5200
Web Site: http://www.seuniversity.edu/

Description: Independent, 4-year, coed, affiliated with Assemblies of God. Awards bachelor's degrees. Founded 1935. Setting: 62-acre suburban campus with easy access to Tampa and Orlando. Endowment: $1.8 million. Total enrollment: 1,964. 509 applied, 86% were admitted. Students come from 44 states and territories, 40% from out-of-state, 0.4% Native American, 11% Hispanic, 6% black, 2% Asian American or Pacific Islander, 0.4% international, 10% 25 or older, 60% live on campus. Retention: 70% of full-time freshmen returned the following year. Core. Calendar: semesters. Advanced placement, accelerated degree program, summer session for credit, part-time degree program, adult/continuing education programs, internships. ROTC: Army (c), Air Force (c).

Entrance Requirements: Options: Peterson's Universal Application, electronic application, early admission, deferred admission, international baccalaureate accepted. Required: high school transcript, 2 recommendations. Required for some: essay, interview. Placement: SAT or ACT required. Entrance: minimally difficult. Application deadline: 8/1. Notification: continuous until 8/1.

Costs Per Year: Application fee: $40. Comprehensive fee: $17,178 includes full-time tuition ($11,040), mandatory fees ($460), and college room and board ($5678). Full-time tuition and fees vary according to degree level, program, and reciprocity agreements. Room and board charges vary according to board plan and housing facility. Part-time tuition: $460 per credit. Part-time tuition varies according to course load, degree level, program, and reciprocity agreements.

Collegiate Environment: Orientation program. Drama-theater group, choral group, student-run newspaper, radio station. Social organizations: 21 open to all. Most popular organizations: Spanish Club, travel music groups, Impact (cross-cultural awareness), Psyche, Student Broadcast Organization. Major annual events: Homecoming, College Days. Student services: health clinic, personal-psychological counseling. Campus security: 24-hour emergency response devices and patrols, late night transport-escort service. 1,200 college housing spaces available; all were occupied in 2003-04. Freshmen guaranteed college housing. On-campus residence required through senior year. Options: men-only, women-only housing available. Steelman Library plus 3 others with 96,000 books, 490 serials, and an OPAC. 40 computers available on campus for general student use. A campuswide network can be accessed from student residence rooms and from off campus. Staffed computer lab on campus.

■ **SOUTHWEST FLORIDA COLLEGE (FORT MYERS)** *Q-10*
1685 Medical Ln.
Fort Myers, FL 33907
Tel: (239)939-4766; (866)SWFC-NOW
Fax: (239)936-4040
Web Site: http://www.swfc.edu/

Description: Independent, primarily 2-year, coed. Awards diplomas, terminal associate, and bachelor's degrees. Founded 1940. Setting: urban campus. Total enrollment: 1,263. Academic remediation for entering students, co-op programs and internships.

Entrance Requirements: Open admission. Option: Common Application. Recommended: high school transcript. Entrance: noncompetitive. Application deadline: Rolling. Notification: continuous.

Collegiate Environment: Orientation program. Campus security: day and evening security guards. College housing not available. Learning Resource Center with 1,000 books, 20 serials, and a Web page. 80 computers available on campus for general student use. A campuswide network can be accessed from off-campus. Staffed computer lab on campus.

■ **SOUTHWEST FLORIDA COLLEGE (TAMPA)** *L-10*
3910 Riga Blvd.
Tampa, FL 33619
Tel: (813)630-4401; 877-907-2456
Web Site: http://www.swfc.edu/
Description: Independent, 2-year, coed.

■ **STETSON UNIVERSITY** *H-13*
421 North Woodland Blvd.
DeLand, FL 32723
Tel: (386)822-7000
Free: 800-688-0101
Admissions: (386)822-7100
Fax: (386)822-8832
E-mail: admissions@stetson.edu
Web Site: http://www.stetson.edu/
Description: Independent, comprehensive, coed. Awards bachelor's, master's, and first professional degrees and post-master's and first professional certificates. Founded 1883. Setting: 170-acre small town campus with easy access to Orlando. Endowment: $114.8 million. Total enrollment: 3,665. Faculty: 268 (186 full-time, 82 part-time). Student-undergrad faculty ratio is 10:1. 2,777 applied, 69% were admitted. 14 valedictorians. Full-time: 2,160 students, 58% women, 42% men. Part-time: 74 students, 47% women, 53% men. Students come from 41 states and territories, 41 other countries, 21% from out-of-state, 0.5% Native American, 7% Hispanic, 4% black, 2% Asian American or Pacific Islander, 3% international, 5% 25 or older, 67% live on campus, 4% transferred in. Retention: 77% of full-time freshmen returned the following year. Academic areas with the most degrees conferred: business/marketing; visual and performing arts; biological/life sciences; social sciences. Core. Calendar: semesters. Advanced placement, accelerated degree program, self-designed majors, honors program, independent study, double major, summer session for credit, part-time degree program, adult/continuing education programs, internships, graduate courses open to undergrads. Off campus study at American University. Study abroad program. ROTC: Army (c).
Entrance Requirements: Options: Peterson's Universal Application, Common Application, electronic application, early admission, early decision, deferred admission, international baccalaureate accepted. Required: essay, high school transcript, recommendations, SAT or ACT. Recommended: interview. Entrance: moderately difficult. Application deadlines: 3/15, 11/1 for early decision. Notification: 11/15 for early decision.
Costs Per Year: Application fee: $40. Comprehensive fee: $32,725 includes full-time tuition ($23,975), mandatory fees ($1475), and college room and board ($7275). College room only: $4075. Full-time tuition and fees vary according to course load and student level. Room and board charges vary according to board plan and housing facility. Part-time tuition: $760 per credit hour. Part-time tuition varies according to course load.
Collegiate Environment: Orientation program. Drama-theater group, choral group, student-run newspaper, radio station. Social organizations: 93 open to all; national fraternities, national sororities; 23% of eligible men and 22% of eligible women are members. Most popular organizations: Into the Streets, Multi-Cultural Student Council, Black Student Association, Best Buddies, Habitat For Humanity. Major annual events: Stetson Weekend, Greenfeather, Family Weekend. Student services: health clinic, personal-psychological counseling. Campus security: 24-hour emergency response devices and patrols, late night transport-escort service. 1,547 college housing spaces available; 1,478 were occupied in 2003-04. Freshmen guaranteed college housing. On-campus residence required through junior year. Options: coed, men-only, women-only housing available. DuPont-Ball Library plus 2 others with 382,154 books, 404,979 microform titles, 11,833 serials, 17,879 audiovisual materials, an OPAC, and a Web page. 400 computers available on campus for general student use. A campuswide network can be accessed from student residence rooms and from off campus. Staffed computer lab on campus.

■ **TALLAHASSEE COMMUNITY COLLEGE** *C-5*
444 Appleyard Dr.
Tallahassee, FL 32304-2895

Tel: (850)201-6200
Web Site: http://www.tcc.fl.edu/
Description: State and locally supported, 2-year, coed. Part of Florida Community College System. Awards certificates, transfer associate, and terminal associate degrees. Founded 1966. Setting: 191-acre suburban campus. Educational spending for 2005 fiscal year: $2027 per student. Total enrollment: 11,966. Full-time: 5,533 students, 48% women, 52% men. Part-time: 6,433 students, 59% women, 41% men. Students come from 32 states and territories, 75 other countries, 10% from out-of-state, 1% Native American, 5% Hispanic, 31% black, 1% Asian American or Pacific Islander, 1% international, 26% 25 or older, 30% transferred in. Core. Calendar: semesters. Academic remediation for entering students, ESL program, services for LD students, advanced placement, accelerated degree program, honors program, independent study, distance learning, summer session for credit, part-time degree program, external degree program, adult/continuing education programs. Off campus study at Florida Agricultural and Mechanical University, Florida State University. Study abroad program. ROTC: Army (c), Air Force (c).
Entrance Requirements: Open admission except for allied health programs. Options: electronic application, early admission, deferred admission. Required: high school transcript. Placement: Florida College Entry-Level Placement Test required; SAT or ACT recommended. Entrance: noncompetitive. Application deadline: 8/1.
Collegiate Environment: Orientation program. Drama-theater group, choral group, student-run newspaper. Social organizations: 20 open to all. Most popular organizations: Phi Theta Kappa, student government, International Student Organization, Black Student Union, Returning Adults Valuing Education. Major annual events: student/faculty days, Turkey Shoot, Eagle Fest. Student services: personal-psychological counseling. Campus security: 24-hour emergency response devices, late night transport-escort service. College housing not available. Tallahassee Community College Library with 84,415 books, 1,073 serials, and an OPAC. Operations spending for 2004 fiscal year: $1.5 million. 170 computers available on campus for general student use. A campuswide network can be accessed from off-campus. Staffed computer lab on campus.
Community Environment: See Florida State University.

■ **TALMUDIC COLLEGE OF FLORIDA** *T-15*
1910 Alton Rd.
Miami Beach, FL 33139
Tel: (305)534-7050; 888-825-6834
Fax: (305)534-8444
Web Site: http://www.talmudicu.edu/
Description: Independent Jewish, comprehensive, men only. Awards bachelor's, master's, and doctoral degrees. Founded 1974. Setting: urban campus with easy access to Miami. Educational spending for 2005 fiscal year: $10,000 per student. Total enrollment: 30. 12 applied, 67% were admitted. Full-time: 15 students. Students come from 4 states and territories, 5 other countries, 95% from out-of-state, 7% Hispanic, 67% international, 0.3% 25 or older, 99% live on campus, 53% transferred in. Retention: 50% of full-time freshmen returned the following year. Core. Calendar: semesters. Academic remediation for entering students, ESL program, honors program, independent study, summer session for credit, part-time degree program, adult/continuing education programs, graduate courses open to undergrads. Study abroad program.
Entrance Requirements: Options: early admission, deferred admission, international baccalaureate accepted. Required: interview, placement exam. Recommended: essay, 2 recommendations. Required for some: high school transcript. Entrance: moderately difficult. Application deadline: Rolling.
Costs Per Year: Application fee: $250. Comprehensive fee: $12,500 includes full-time tuition ($7250), mandatory fees ($250), and college room and board ($5000). College room only: $2500. Tuition guaranteed not to increase for student's term of enrollment.
Collegiate Environment: Student services: personal-psychological counseling. 55 college housing spaces available; 29 were occupied in 2003-04. Freshmen guaranteed college housing. On-campus residence required through senior year. Option: men-only housing available. Beis Medrash plus 1 other with 25,000 books and a Web page.

■ **TRINITY BAPTIST COLLEGE** *D-12*
800 Hammond Blvd.
Jacksonville, FL 32221
Tel: (904)596-2400
Free: 800-786-2206

Admissions: (904)596-2538
Fax: (904)596-2531
E-mail: trinity@tbc.edu
Web Site: http://www.tbc.edu/
Description: Independent Baptist, comprehensive, coed. Awards associate, bachelor's, and master's degrees. Founded 1974. Setting: 148-acre urban campus. Total enrollment: 465. Faculty: 50 (12 full-time, 38 part-time). Student-undergrad faculty ratio is 15:1. 159 applied, 100% were admitted. Full-time: 294 students, 49% women, 51% men. Part-time: 128 students, 40% women, 60% men. Students come from 30 states and territories, 4 other countries, 32% from out-of-state, 0% Native American, 3% Hispanic, 5% black, 1% Asian American or Pacific Islander, 1% international, 13% 25 or older, 57% live on campus, 7% transferred in. Retention: 65% of full-time freshmen returned the following year. Academic areas with the most degrees conferred: theology and religious vocations; education. Core. Calendar: semesters. Academic remediation for entering students, services for LD students, advanced placement, accelerated degree program, independent study, summer session for credit, part-time degree program, adult/continuing education programs, internships, graduate courses open to undergrads.
Entrance Requirements: Option: Common Application. Required: essay, high school transcript, minimum 2.0 high school GPA, 3 recommendations, SAT or ACT. Entrance: moderately difficult. Application deadline: Rolling. Notification: continuous until 8/15.
Costs Per Year: Application fee: $30. Comprehensive fee: $10,600. Part-time tuition: $245 per semester hour. Tuition: $245 per semester hour part-time.
Collegiate Environment: Orientation program. Drama-theater group, choral group. Major annual events: Missions Conference, Bible Conference, Youth Conference. Student services: health clinic, personal-psychological counseling. Campus security: 24-hour emergency response devices, student patrols, controlled dormitory access, evening security. 230 college housing spaces available; 224 were occupied in 2003-04. Freshmen guaranteed college housing. On-campus residence required through junior year. Options: men-only, women-only housing available. Travis Hudson Library with 35,070 books and 191 serials. 35 computers available on campus for general student use. A campuswide network can be accessed from student residence rooms and from off campus. Staffed computer lab on campus.

■ **TRINITY COLLEGE OF FLORIDA** *K-9*
2430 Welbilt Blvd.
New Port Richey, FL 34655
Tel: (727)376-6911
Free: 800-388-0869
Fax: (727)376-0781
Web Site: http://www.trinitycollege.edu/
Description: Independent nondenominational, 4-year, coed. Awards associate and bachelor's degrees. Founded 1932. Setting: 40-acre small town campus with easy access to Tampa. Endowment: $1.3 million. Educational spending for 2005 fiscal year: $4196 per student. Total enrollment: 203. 61 applied, 100% were admitted. 7% from top 10% of their high school class, 25% from top quarter, 59% from top half. Full-time: 138 students, 42% women, 58% men. Part-time: 65 students, 48% women, 52% men. Students come from 15 states and territories, 6 other countries, 9% from out-of-state, 0% Native American, 3% Hispanic, 4% black, 0.5% Asian American or Pacific Islander, 4% international, 37% 25 or older, 54% live on campus, 28% transferred in. Retention: 60% of full-time freshmen returned the following year. Core. Calendar: semesters. Academic remediation for entering students, services for LD students, advanced placement, independent study, double major, summer session for credit, part-time degree program, external degree program, adult/continuing education programs, internships.
Entrance Requirements: Options: Peterson's Universal Application, Common Application, electronic application, early admission, deferred admission. Required: essay, high school transcript, 3 recommendations, interview. Recommended: minimum 2.75 high school GPA, SAT or ACT. Entrance: minimally difficult. Application deadlines: 7/15, 7/1 for nonresidents. Notification: continuous until 7/31, continuous until 7/15 for nonresidents.
Collegiate Environment: Orientation program. Drama-theater group, choral group. Social organizations: 5 open to all. Most popular organizations: Great Commission Missionary Fellowship, Men's Basketball/Soccer Leagues, Music Club, Bible and Theology Club, Student Government. Major annual events: Trinityfest, Missions Conference, Breakaway. Student services: personal-psychological counseling. Campus security: controlled dormitory access, on-campus security personnel. 74 college housing spaces available; all were occupied in 2003-04. Freshmen guaranteed college housing. On-

campus residence required in freshman year. Options: men-only, women-only housing available. Raymond H. Center, M.D. Library with 40,523 books, 275 serials, 2,300 audiovisual materials, and an OPAC. Operations spending for 2004 fiscal year: $93,172. 16 computers available on campus for general student use. A campuswide network can be accessed from student residence rooms and from off campus. Staffed computer lab on campus.
Community Environment: See Clearwater Christian College.

■ **UNIVERSIDAD FLET** *T-15*
14540 SW 136th St., Ste. 200
Miami, FL 33186
Tel: (305)232-5880; 888-376-3538
Admissions: (305)378-8700
Fax: (305)232-3592
Web Site: http://www.flet.edu/
Description: Independent religious, comprehensive, coed. Awards associate, bachelor's, and master's degrees. Founded 1977. Total enrollment: 866. 212 applied, 100% were admitted. Full-time: 75 students, 35% women, 65% men. Part-time: 707 students, 38% women, 62% men. 0% Native American, 99% Hispanic, 0.1% black, 0% Asian American or Pacific Islander, 0% international.
Costs Per Year: Tuition: $30 per credit part-time. Mandatory fees: $700 full-time.
Collegiate Environment: College housing not available.

■ **UNIVERSITY OF CENTRAL FLORIDA** *J-13*
4000 Central Florida Blvd.
Orlando, FL 32816
Tel: (407)823-2000
Admissions: (407)823-3000
Fax: (407)823-3419
E-mail: admission@mail.ucf.edu
Web Site: http://www.ucf.edu/
Description: State-supported, university, coed. Part of State University System of Florida. Awards associate, bachelor's, master's, and doctoral degrees. Founded 1963. Setting: 1,415-acre suburban campus. Endowment: $78.8 million. Research spending for 2004 fiscal year: $91.4 million. Total enrollment: 44,953. Faculty: 1,637 (1,192 full-time, 445 part-time). Student-undergrad faculty ratio is 27:1. 20,265 applied, 62% were admitted. 35% from top 10% of their high school class, 75% from top quarter, 91% from top half. 34 National Merit Scholars, 55 valedictorians. Full-time: 28,584 students, 55% women, 45% men. Part-time: 9,212 students, 54% women, 46% men. Students come from 52 states and territories, 131 other countries, 5% from out-of-state, 0.4% Native American, 13% Hispanic, 9% black, 5% Asian American or Pacific Islander, 1% international, 18% 25 or older, 20% live on campus, 8% transferred in. Retention: 83% of full-time freshmen returned the following year. Academic areas with the most degrees conferred: business/marketing; psychology; education. Core. Calendar: semesters. ESL program, services for LD students, advanced placement, freshman honors college, honors program, distance learning, double major, summer session for credit, part-time degree program, external degree program, adult/continuing education programs, co-op programs and internships, graduate courses open to undergrads. Off campus study. Study abroad program. ROTC: Army, Air Force.
Entrance Requirements: Options: Common Application, electronic application, early admission, international baccalaureate accepted. Required: high school transcript, minimum 2.0 high school GPA, SAT or ACT. Recommended: essay. Entrance: moderately difficult. Application deadline: 3/1. Notification: continuous. Preference given to state residents who are designated as Talented 20.
Costs Per Year: Application fee: $30. State resident tuition: $3141 full-time, $105 per credit part-time. Nonresident tuition: $16,272 full-time, $542 per credit part-time. Mandatory fees: $198 full-time, $6.60 per credit part-time. Full-time tuition and fees vary according to course load. Part-time tuition and fees vary according to course load. College room and board: $7400. College room only: $4300. Room and board charges vary according to board plan and housing facility.
Collegiate Environment: Orientation program. Drama-theater group, choral group, marching band, student-run newspaper, radio station. Social organizations: 329 open to all; national fraternities, national sororities; 11% of eligible men and 9% of eligible women are members. Most popular organizations: student government, Hispanic American Student Association, Volunteer UCF, Pre-Professional Medical Society and Student Nurses Association, African-American Student Union. Major annual events: homecom-

ing, Spirit Splash, Homecoming Carnival and Job Fair. Student services: legal services, health clinic, personal-psychological counseling, women's center. Campus security: 24-hour emergency response devices and patrols, late night transport-escort service, controlled dormitory access. 7,940 college housing spaces available; 6,793 were occupied in 2003-04. Freshmen given priority for college housing. Options: coed, men-only, women-only housing available. University Library with 1.2 million books, 2.4 million microform titles, 9,866 serials, 35,233 audiovisual materials, an OPAC, and a Web page. Operations spending for 2004 fiscal year: $11.1 million. 2,420 computers available on campus for general student use. Computer purchase/lease plans available. A campuswide network can be accessed from student residence rooms and from off campus. Staffed computer lab on campus.

Community Environment: Orlando has become a focal point for business and major industry, easily accessible by major forms of public transportation, and serves as a regional retail market for eight counties and over a million people. The area's reputation as a tourism mecca has brought a resultant surge in the hospitality industry as well. It also is an important agricultural center, noted for citrus and truck gardening. The temperate climate year-round provides ideal conditions for numerous recreational opportunities: fishing, boating, dog and horse racing, Jai-Alai, golf, tennis, and other outdoor activities. Points of interest include Walt Disney World, Epcot Center, MGM Studios, Universal Studios, Sea World, plus such seasonal attractions as the Church Street Station, Citrus Open Golf Tournament, Walt Disney World Golf Classic, Orlando Horse Show, Central Florida Fair, Orlando Magic Pro-Basketball, and Citrus Bowl. Cultural activities are widespread in the Orlando-Winter Park area, and include annual Sidewalk Art Festivals, Orlando Shakespeare Festival, the Florida Symphony Orchestra, Central Florida Civic Theatre, and the John Young Museum and Planetarium, located adjacent to the Loch Haven Art Center.

■ **UNIVERSITY OF FLORIDA** *F-10*

Gainesville, FL 32611
Tel: (352)392-3261
Admissions: (352)392-1365
Web Site: http://www.ufl.edu/

Description: State-supported, university, coed. Part of Board of Trustees. Awards bachelor's, master's, doctoral, and first professional degrees. Founded 1853. Setting: 2,000-acre suburban campus with easy access to Jacksonville. Endowment: $670.4 million. Total enrollment: 49,693. Faculty: 2,311 (2,229 full-time, 82 part-time). Student-undergrad faculty ratio is 21:1. 22,973 applied, 52% were admitted. 85% from top 10% of their high school class, 90% from top quarter, 97% from top half. 130 National Merit Scholars. Full-time: 32,006 students, 54% women, 46% men. Part-time: 2,662 students, 49% women, 51% men. Students come from 52 states and territories, 114 other countries, 5% from out-of-state, 0.3% Native American, 13% Hispanic, 9% black, 7% Asian American or Pacific Islander, 1% international, 7% 25 or older, 21% live on campus, 5% transferred in. Retention: 94% of full-time freshmen returned the following year. Academic areas with the most degrees conferred: business/marketing; social sciences; engineering. Core. Calendar: semesters. ESL program, services for LD students, advanced placement, accelerated degree program, self-designed majors, honors program, independent study, distance learning, double major, summer session for credit, part-time degree program, external degree program, adult/continuing education programs, co-op programs and internships, graduate courses open to undergrads. Off campus study at Miami New World School of the Arts, Miami-Dade Community College. Study abroad program. ROTC: Army, Air Force.

Entrance Requirements: Options: Common Application, electronic application, early admission, early decision, international baccalaureate accepted. Required: essay, high school transcript, SAT or ACT. Entrance: very difficult. Application deadlines: 1/17, 10/1 for early decision. Notification: continuous, 12/1 for early decision. Preference given to state residents.

Costs Per Year: Application fee: $30. State resident tuition: $3,094 full-time, $103.12 per credit hour part-time. Nonresident tuition: $17,222 full-time, $574.08 per credit hour part-time. College room and board: $6260. College room only: $3940. Room and board charges vary according to board plan and housing facility.

Collegiate Environment: Orientation program. Drama-theater group, choral group, marching band, student-run newspaper, radio station. Social organizations: 525 open to all; national fraternities, national sororities, local fraternities, local sororities; 15% of eligible men and 15% of eligible women are members. Most popular organizations: Blue Key Society, student government, Black Student Union, Hispanic Student Association, Reitz

Union Program Council. Major annual events: Gator Growl, Celebration, People Awareness Week. Student services: legal services, health clinic, personal-psychological counseling, women's center. Campus security: 24-hour emergency response devices and patrols, student patrols, late night transport-escort service, controlled dormitory access, crime and rape prevention programs. 7,346 college housing spaces available; 7,308 were occupied in 2003-04. Freshmen given priority for college housing. Options: coed, women-only housing available. George A. Smathers Library plus 8 others with 5 million books, 6.7 million microform titles, 28,103 serials, 36,078 audiovisual materials, an OPAC, and a Web page. 472 computers available on campus for general student use. Computer purchase/lease plans available. A campuswide network can be accessed from student residence rooms and from off campus. Staffed computer lab on campus.

Community Environment: Gainesville is the county seat of Alachua County located on the rolling highlands of north-central Florida midway between the Gulf of Mexico and the Atlantic Ocean. The climate is subtropical with an average mean temperature of 70 degrees. Railroads, buses and airlines serve the area. Gainesville is the focal point of diversified industrial and agricultural activities. The city facilities include churches of many denominations, center for science, education and medicine, medical center with hospital, museum and numerous civic organizations. Recreational facilities include golf courses, swimming at nearby springs, boating and freshwater fishing in surrounding lakes and rivers. Both the Atlantic Ocean and the Gulf of Mexico are within a two-hour drive. Off-campus housing is available for over 20,000 students in addition to university housing.

■ **UNIVERSITY OF MIAMI** *U-14*

University of Miami Branch
Coral Gables, FL 33124
Tel: (305)284-2211
Admissions: (305)284-4323
Fax: (305)284-2507
Web Site: http://www.miami.edu/

Description: Independent, university, coed. Awards bachelor's, master's, doctoral, and first professional degrees and post-master's certificates. Founded 1925. Setting: 260-acre suburban campus with easy access to Miami. Endowment: $526.1 million. Research spending for 2004 fiscal year: $11.9 million. Educational spending for 2005 fiscal year: $20,778 per student. Total enrollment: 15,674. Faculty: 1,275 (892 full-time, 383 part-time). Student-undergrad faculty ratio is 13:1. 18,807 applied, 46% were admitted. 62% from top 10% of their high school class, 89% from top quarter, 98% from top half. Full-time: 9,766 students, 56% women, 44% men. Part-time: 771 students, 64% women, 36% men. Students come from 53 states and territories, 89 other countries, 46% from out-of-state, 0.3% Native American, 23% Hispanic, 9% black, 5% Asian American or Pacific Islander, 6% international, 7% 25 or older, 42% live on campus, 7% transferred in. Retention: 89% of full-time freshmen returned the following year. Academic areas with the most degrees conferred: business/marketing; visual and performing arts; biological/life sciences; communications/journalism. Core. Calendar: semesters. Academic remediation for entering students, ESL program, services for LD students, advanced placement, accelerated degree program, self-designed majors, honors program, independent study, distance learning, double major, summer session for credit, part-time degree program, adult/continuing education programs, internships, graduate courses open to undergrads. Study abroad program. ROTC: Army, Air Force.

Entrance Requirements: Options: Peterson's Universal Application, Common Application, electronic application, early admission, early decision, early action, deferred admission, international baccalaureate accepted. Required: essay, high school transcript, recommendations, counselor evaluation, SAT or ACT. Required for some: interview, SAT Subject Tests. Entrance: very difficult. Application deadlines: 2/1, 11/1 for early decision, 11/1 for early action. Notification: 4/15, 12/15 for early decision, 2/1 for early action.

Costs Per Year: Application fee: $65. Comprehensive fee: $37,926 includes full-time tuition ($29,020) and college room and board ($8906). College room only: $5224. Full-time tuition varies according to course load, location, and program. Room and board charges vary according to board plan and housing facility. Part-time tuition: $1208 per credit. Part-time tuition varies according to course load, location, and program. Tuition guaranteed not to increase for student's term of enrollment.

Collegiate Environment: Orientation program. Drama-theater group, choral group, marching band, student-run newspaper, radio station. Social organizations: 175 open to all; national fraternities, national sororities; 12% of eligible men and 14% of eligible women are members. Most popular organizations: student government, international student organizations, sports and recreation clubs, Association of Commuter Students, United Black Students. Major annual events: Sports Fest, Homecoming, International Week. Student services: health clinic, personal-psychological counseling, women's center. Campus security: 24-hour emergency response devices and patrols, student patrols, late night transport-escort service, controlled dormitory access, crime prevention and safety workshops, residential college crime watch. College housing designed to accommodate 4,228 students; 4,356 undergraduates lived in college housing during 2003-04. Freshmen guaranteed college housing. On-campus residence required in freshman year. Option: coed housing available. Otto G. Richter Library plus 7 others with 1.4 million books, 3.5 million microform titles, 16,305 serials, 109,900 audiovisual materials, an OPAC, and a Web page. Operations spending for 2004 fiscal year: $11.7 million. 1,800 computers available on campus for general student use. Computer purchase/lease plans available. A campuswide network can be accessed from student residence rooms and from off campus. Staffed computer lab on campus.

Community Environment: A part of the metropolitan Miami area, Coral Gables is known as "City Beautiful" with the mildest climate in the United States. The Miami International Airport is nearby. The city offers a distinguished retail shopping district, the opera, theatre, ballet, concerts, the Vizcaya Museum, and Lowe Art Gallery. Recreational activities are numerous including swimming, golf, tennis, boating, sport fishing, and snorkeling and scuba diving among the only coral reefs in the continental United States, in the Florida Keys. The Everglades National Park is 1 hour away.

■ **UNIVERSITY OF NORTH FLORIDA** *D-12*
4567 St. Johns Bluff Rd. South
Jacksonville, FL 32224-2645
Tel: (904)620-1000
Admissions: (904)620-2624
Fax: (904)620-1040
E-mail: osprey@unfivm.unf.edu
Web Site: http://www.unf.edu/
Description: State-supported, comprehensive, coed. Part of State University System of Florida. Awards associate, bachelor's, master's, and doctoral degrees and post-master's certificates (doctoral degree in education only). Founded 1965. Setting: 1,300-acre urban campus. Endowment: $63.8 million. Research spending for 2004 fiscal year: $4.7 million. Educational spending for 2005 fiscal year: $4992 per student. Total enrollment: 15,234. Faculty: 700 (448 full-time, 252 part-time). Student-undergrad faculty ratio is 22:1. 9,147 applied, 62% were admitted. 23% from top 10% of their high school class, 55% from top quarter, 87% from top half. Full-time: 9,540 students, 58% women, 42% men. Part-time: 3,870 students, 59% women, 41% men. Students come from 49 states and territories, 54 other countries, 3% from out-of-state, 0.5% Native American, 6% Hispanic, 10% black, 5% Asian American or Pacific Islander, 1% international, 22% 25 or older, 17% live on campus, 7% transferred in. Retention: 75% of full-time freshmen returned the following year. Academic areas with the most degrees conferred: business/marketing; health professions and related sciences; education. Core. Calendar: semesters. ESL program, services for LD students, advanced placement, accelerated degree program, self-designed majors, freshman honors college, honors program, independent study, distance learning, double major, summer session for credit, part-time degree program, adult/continuing education programs, co-op programs and internships, graduate courses open to undergrads. Off campus study at State University System of Florida. Study abroad program. ROTC: Naval (c).
Entrance Requirements: Options: Common Application, electronic application, early admission, early action, deferred admission, international baccalaureate accepted. Required: high school transcript, minimum 2.0 high school GPA, SAT or ACT. Recommended: minimum 3.0 high school GPA. Required for some: essay, recommendations. Entrance: very difficult. Application deadlines: 7/2, 11/15 for early action. Notification: continuous, 12/2 for early action.
Costs Per Year: Application fee: $30. State resident tuition: $3269 full-time, $108.95 per semester hour part-time. Nonresident tuition: $14,911 full-time, $497.02 per semester hour part-time. College room and board: $6640. College room only: $3810. Room and board charges vary according to board plan and housing facility.
Collegiate Environment: Orientation program. Drama-theater group, choral group, student-run newspaper, radio station. Social organizations: 149 open to all; national fraternities, national sororities; 8% of eligible men and 6% of eligible women are members. Most popular organizations: International Student Association, Filipino Student Association, Student Physical Therapy Association, National Education Association, Student Government Associa-

tion. Major annual events: Earth Music Fest, Toga Party, homecoming. Student services: health clinic, personal-psychological counseling, women's center. Campus security: 24-hour emergency response devices and patrols, student patrols, late night transport-escort service, controlled dormitory access, electronic parking lot security. College housing designed to accommodate 2,000 students; 2,252 undergraduates lived in college housing during 2003-04. Freshmen given priority for college housing. Option: coed housing available. Thomas G. Carpenter Library with 746,604 books, 1.3 million microform titles, 3,466 serials, 67,208 audiovisual materials, an OPAC, and a Web page. Operations spending for 2004 fiscal year: $3.3 million. 750 computers available on campus for general student use. A campuswide network can be accessed from student residence rooms and from off campus. Staffed computer lab on campus.
Community Environment: See Jacksonville University.

■ **UNIVERSITY OF PHOENIX-CENTRAL FLORIDA CAMPUS** *D-5*
2290 Lucien Way, Ste. 400
Maitland, FL 32751-7057
Tel: (407)667-0555
Free: 800-228-7240
Admissions: (480)557-1712
Web Site: http://www.phoenix.edu/
Description: Proprietary, comprehensive, coed. Awards bachelor's and master's degrees. Founded 1996. Setting: urban campus. Total enrollment: 2,267. Faculty: 243 (17 full-time, 226 part-time). Student-undergrad faculty ratio is 10:1. 32 applied. Full-time: 1,654 students, 61% women, 39% men. 0.3% Native American, 5% Hispanic, 6% black, 1% Asian American or Pacific Islander, 26% international, 92% 25 or older. Academic areas with the most degrees conferred: business/marketing; computer and information sciences; health professions and related sciences. Core. Calendar: continuous. Advanced placement, accelerated degree program, independent study, distance learning, external degree program, adult/continuing education programs, graduate courses open to undergrads.
Entrance Requirements: Open admission. Option: deferred admission. Required: 1 recommendation. Required for some: high school transcript. Entrance: noncompetitive. Application deadline: Rolling.
Costs Per Year: Application fee: $110. Tuition: $9960 full-time, $332 per credit part-time. Mandatory fees: $560 full-time, $70 per course part-time. Full-time tuition and fees vary according to program.
Collegiate Environment: College housing not available. University Library with 444 books, 666 serials, an OPAC, and a Web page. System-wide operations spending for 2004 fiscal year: $3.2 million.

■ **UNIVERSITY OF PHOENIX-NORTH FLORIDA CAMPUS** *D-12*
4500 Salisbury Rd.
Jacksonville, FL 32216-0959
Tel: (904)636-6645
Free: 800-894-1758
Admissions: (480)557-1712
Web Site: http://www.phoenix.edu/
Description: Proprietary, comprehensive, coed. Awards bachelor's and master's degrees. Founded 1976. Setting: urban campus. Total enrollment: 2,380. Faculty: 255 (9 full-time, 246 part-time). Student-undergrad faculty ratio is 10:1. 42 applied. Full-time: 1,784 students, 59% women, 41% men. 0.4% Native American, 2% Hispanic, 12% black, 1% Asian American or Pacific Islander, 9% international, 94% 25 or older. Academic areas with the most degrees conferred: business/marketing; computer and information sciences; health professions and related sciences. Core. Calendar: continuous. Advanced placement, accelerated degree program, independent study, distance learning, external degree program, adult/continuing education programs, graduate courses open to undergrads.
Entrance Requirements: Open admission. Option: deferred admission. Required: 1 recommendation. Required for some: high school transcript. Entrance: noncompetitive. Application deadline: Rolling.
Costs Per Year: Application fee: $110. Tuition: $9960 full-time, $332 per credit part-time. Mandatory fees: $560 full-time, $70 per course part-time.
Collegiate Environment: College housing not available. University Library with 444 books, 666 serials, an OPAC, and a Web page. System-wide operations spending for 2004 fiscal year: $3.2 million.

■ **UNIVERSITY OF PHOENIX-SOUTH FLORIDA CAMPUS** *S-15*
600 North Pine Island Rd., Ste. 500
Fort Lauderdale, FL 33324-1393
Tel: (954)382-5303

Free: 800-228-7240
Admissions: (480)557-1712
Web Site: http://www.phoenix.edu/
Description: Proprietary, comprehensive, coed. Awards bachelor's and master's degrees. Setting: urban campus. Total enrollment: 2,791. Faculty: 264 (10 full-time, 254 part-time). Student-undergrad faculty ratio is 10:1. 40 applied. Full-time: 2,043 students, 69% women, 31% men. 0% from out-of-state, 0.1% Native American, 8% Hispanic, 12% black, 0.3% Asian American or Pacific Islander, 26% international, 94% 25 or older. Academic areas with the most degrees conferred: business/marketing; computer and information sciences; health professions and related sciences. Core. Calendar: continuous. Advanced placement, accelerated degree program, independent study, distance learning, external degree program, adult/continuing education programs, graduate courses open to undergrads.
Entrance Requirements: Open admission. Option: deferred admission. Required: 1 recommendation. Required for some: high school transcript. Entrance: noncompetitive. Application deadline: Rolling.
Costs Per Year: Application fee: $110. Tuition: $9960 full-time, $332 per credit part-time. Mandatory fees: $560 full-time, $70 per course part-time.
Collegiate Environment: College housing not available. University Library with an OPAC and a Web page. System-wide operations spending for 2004 fiscal year: $3.2 million.

■ **UNIVERSITY OF PHOENIX-WEST FLORIDA CAMPUS** *J-5*
12802 Tampa Oaks Blvd., Ste. 200
Temple Terrace, FL 33637
Tel: (813)626-7911
Free: 800-228-7240
Admissions: (480)557-1712
Fax: (813)977-1449
Web Site: http://www.phoenix.edu/
Description: Proprietary, comprehensive, coed. Awards bachelor's and master's degrees. Total enrollment: 2,755. Faculty: 234 (18 full-time, 216 part-time). Student-undergrad faculty ratio is 10:1. 54 applied. Full-time: 2,064 students, 60% women, 40% men. 0% from out-of-state, 0.5% Native American, 5% Hispanic, 7% black, 1% Asian American or Pacific Islander, 8% international, 92% 25 or older. Academic areas with the most degrees conferred: business/marketing; computer and information sciences; health professions and related sciences. Core. Calendar: continuous. Advanced placement, accelerated degree program, independent study, distance learning, external degree program, adult/continuing education programs, graduate courses open to undergrads.
Entrance Requirements: Open admission. Option: deferred admission. Required: 1 recommendation. Required for some: high school transcript. Entrance: noncompetitive. Application deadline: Rolling.
Costs Per Year: Application fee: $110. Tuition: $9960 full-time, $332 per credit part-time. Mandatory fees: $560 full-time, $70 per course part-time.
Collegiate Environment: College housing not available. University Library with 444 books, 666 serials, an OPAC, and a Web page. System-wide operations spending for 2004 fiscal year: $3.2 million.

■ **UNIVERSITY OF SOUTH FLORIDA** *L-10*
4202 East Fowler Ave.
Tampa, FL 33620-9951
Tel: (813)974-2011; 877-USF-BULLS
Admissions: (813)974-3350
Fax: (813)974-9689
E-mail: bullseye@admin.usf.edu
Web Site: http://www.usf.edu
Description: State-supported, university, coed. Part of State University System of Florida. Awards associate, bachelor's, master's, doctoral, and first professional degrees. Founded 1956. Setting: 1,913-acre urban campus. Endowment: $298.2 million. Research spending for 2004 fiscal year: $135 million. Total enrollment: 42,660. Faculty: 2,429 (1,727 full-time, 702 part-time). 18,307 applied, 58% were admitted. 35% from top 10% of their high school class, 59% from top quarter, 90% from top half. 3 National Merit Scholars, 44 valedictorians, 460 student government officers. Full-time: 23,945 students, 59% women, 41% men. Part-time: 9,758 students, 60% women, 40% men. Students come from 52 states and territories, 133 other countries, 4% from out-of-state, 0.4% Native American, 11% Hispanic, 13% black, 6% Asian American or Pacific Islander, 3% international, 22% 25 or older, 13% live on campus, 13% transferred in. Retention: 82% of full-time freshmen returned the following year. Academic areas with the most degrees conferred: business/marketing; social sciences; education. Core. Calendar:

semesters. Academic remediation for entering students, services for LD students, advanced placement, accelerated degree program, self-designed majors, freshman honors college, honors program, independent study, distance learning, double major, summer session for credit, part-time degree program, external degree program, adult/continuing education programs, co-op programs and internships, graduate courses open to undergrads. Off campus study at members of the National Student Exchange, State University System of Florida. Study abroad program. ROTC: Army, Naval, Air Force.
Entrance Requirements: Options: Common Application, electronic application, early admission, international baccalaureate accepted. Required: minimum 2.0 high school GPA, SAT or ACT. Required for some: high school transcript, recommendations. Entrance: moderately difficult. Application deadline: 4/15. Notification: continuous.
Costs Per Year: Application fee: $30. State resident tuition: $3310 full-time, $108 per credit hour part-time. Nonresident tuition: $16,076 full-time, $533 per credit hour part-time. Mandatory fees: $74 full-time, $37 per term part-time. Full-time tuition and fees vary according to course level, course load, and location. Part-time tuition and fees vary according to course level, course load, and location. College room and board: $6900. College room only: $3563. Room and board charges vary according to board plan, housing facility, and location.
Collegiate Environment: Orientation program. Drama-theater group, choral group, marching band, student-run newspaper, radio station. Social organizations: 200 open to all; national fraternities, national sororities. Most popular organizations: student government, Campus Activities Board, USF Ambassadors, student admissions representatives. Major annual events: homecoming, Welcome Week, University lecture series. Student services: legal services, health clinic, personal-psychological counseling, women's center. Campus security: 24-hour emergency response devices and patrols, student patrols, late night transport-escort service, controlled dormitory access, residence hall lobby personnel 8 p.m. to 6 a.m. 4,176 college housing spaces available; all were occupied in 2003-04. No special consideration for freshman housing applicants. Options: coed, men-only, women-only housing available. Tampa Campus Library plus 2 others with 2 million books, 4.3 million microform titles, 20,571 serials, 154,199 audiovisual materials, an OPAC, and a Web page. Operations spending for 2004 fiscal year: $14.1 million. 593 computers available on campus for general student use. A campuswide network can be accessed from student residence rooms and from off campus. Staffed computer lab on campus.
Community Environment: Tampa, located on the west coast of Florida, is the seventh largest port in the nation. It is a significant industrial and commercial center; the second largest city in the state. A fine harbor with a 34 foot channel to the Gulf of Mexico is located here. It is important in trade and travel to and from Central and South America. Annual mean temperature is 72.3 degrees, the average rainfall is 49 inches. All modes of travel serve the area. Industries include cigar manufacturing, phosphate, beer, cement, cans, wire and cable, and canned citrus fruits and vegetables. Tampa is a tourist city with many recreational facilities; yacht basin, golf courses, tennis clubs, saddle clubs, swimming pools, bowling alleys, baseball diamonds, and basketball courts. Salt water fishing is excellent. Swimming is excellent all year in Tampa Bay, and at the municipal beach on Courtney Campell Causeway. The Tampa Bay Buccaneers is the local NFL team and the Cincinnati Reds make Tampa their spring training quarters. Points of interest are the Busch Gardens, Lowry Park, Tampa Art Institute, and the Tampa Museum.

■ **THE UNIVERSITY OF TAMPA** *L-10*
401 West Kennedy Blvd.
Tampa, FL 33606-1490
Tel: (813)253-3333; 888-MINARET
Admissions: (813)253-6211
Fax: (813)254-4955
E-mail: bstrickler@alpha.utampa.edu
Web Site: http://www.utampa.edu/
Description: Independent, comprehensive, coed. Awards associate, bachelor's, and master's degrees. Founded 1931. Setting: 90-acre urban campus. Research spending for 2004 fiscal year: $49,738. Total enrollment: 5,202. Faculty: 425 (208 full-time, 217 part-time). Student-undergrad faculty ratio is 17:1. 6,365 applied, 50% were admitted. 20% from top 10% of their high school class, 50% from top quarter, 84% from top half. Full-time: 4,169 students, 61% women, 39% men. Part-time: 467 students, 66% women, 34% men. Students come from 50 states and territories, 100 other countries, 54% from out-of-state, 0.5% Native American, 9% Hispanic, 6% black, 2%

Asian American or Pacific Islander, 5% international, 10% 25 or older, 59% live on campus, 7% transferred in. Retention: 77% of full-time freshmen returned the following year. Academic areas with the most degrees conferred: business/marketing; social sciences; communications/journalism. Core. Calendar: semesters. Academic remediation for entering students, ESL program, services for LD students, advanced placement, self-designed majors, honors program, independent study, double major, summer session for credit, part-time degree program, adult/continuing education programs, co-op programs and internships. Off campus study at Gulf Coast Research Laboratory. Study abroad program. ROTC: Army, Air Force (c).

Entrance Requirements: Options: Peterson's Universal Application, Common Application, electronic application, early admission, deferred admission, international baccalaureate accepted. Required: essay, high school transcript, minimum 2.0 high school GPA, SAT or ACT. Recommended: interview. Entrance: moderately difficult. Application deadline: Rolling.

Costs Per Year: Application fee: $35. Comprehensive fee: $25,784 includes full-time tuition ($17,906), mandatory fees ($942), and college room and board ($6936). College room only: $3710. Full-time tuition and fees vary according to class time. Room and board charges vary according to board plan and housing facility. Part-time tuition: $380 per hour. Part-time mandatory fees: $35 per term. Part-time tuition and fees vary according to class time.

Collegiate Environment: Orientation program. Drama-theater group, choral group, student-run newspaper, radio station. Social organizations: 104 open to all; national fraternities, national sororities; 12% of eligible men and 14% of eligible women are members. Most popular organizations: PEACE, Kappa Delta Pi, student productions, Minaret. Major annual events: Into the Streets, Homecoming, Leadership Awards Night. Student services: health clinic, personal-psychological counseling, women's center. Campus security: 24-hour emergency response devices and patrols, late night transport-escort service, controlled dormitory access. 2,504 college housing spaces available; all were occupied in 2003-04. Freshmen given priority for college housing. Options: coed, women-only housing available. Macdonald Keloe Library with 252,147 books, 16,661 microform titles, 10,854 serials, 4,181 audiovisual materials, an OPAC, and a Web page. Operations spending for 2004 fiscal year: $1.4 million. 493 computers available on campus for general student use. Computer purchase/lease plans available. A campuswide network can be accessed from student residence rooms and from off campus. Staffed computer lab on campus.

Community Environment: The university is situated along the Hillsborough River adjacent to the downtown area of Tampa, Florida. The city of Tampa (population 300,000) is part of the Tampa Bay metropolitan area of over 2 million. This rapidly growing area is a business and resort center featuring year-round sunshine with school year temperatures averaging 60-80 degrees Fahrenheit and excellent job prospects. Tampa's ultramodern international airport is just 15 minutes from campus. The city is easily accessible by interstate highway, bus or rail. Tampa is 30 minutes from the beaches of the Gulf of Mexico and 60 minutes from Central Florida's parks and amusement areas such as Walt Disney World.

■ **UNIVERSITY OF WEST FLORIDA** *L-2*
11000 University Parkway
Pensacola, FL 32514-5750
Tel: (850)474-2000
Free: 800-263-1074
Admissions: (850)474-2230
Fax: (850)474-2096
E-mail: admissions@uwf.edu
Web Site: http://uwf.edu/

Description: State-supported, comprehensive, coed. Part of State University System of Florida. Awards associate, bachelor's, master's, and doctoral degrees (specialists). Founded 1963. Setting: 1,600-acre suburban campus. Endowment: $53.4 million. Research spending for 2004 fiscal year: $22.4 million. Educational spending for 2005 fiscal year: $6135 per student. Total enrollment: 9,632. Faculty: 527 (308 full-time, 219 part-time). Student-undergrad faculty ratio is 19:1. 3,401 applied, 68% were admitted. Full-time: 5,771 students, 60% women, 40% men. Part-time: 2,397 students, 59% women, 41% men. Students come from 49 states and territories, 13% from out-of-state, 1% Native American, 5% Hispanic, 9% black, 4% Asian American or Pacific Islander, 1% international, 30% 25 or older, 18% live on campus, 16% transferred in. Retention: 73% of full-time freshmen returned the following year. Academic areas with the most degrees conferred: business/marketing; education; communications/journalism. Core. Calendar: semesters. ESL program, services for LD students, advanced placement, honors program, independent study, distance learning, summer session for

credit, part-time degree program, co-op programs and internships, graduate courses open to undergrads. Off campus study at other members of the State University System of Florida. Study abroad program. ROTC: Army, Air Force.

Entrance Requirements: Options: electronic application, early admission, deferred admission, international baccalaureate accepted. Required: high school transcript, minimum 2.0 high school GPA, SAT or ACT. Entrance: moderately difficult. Application deadline: 6/30. Notification: continuous. Preference given to applicants with associate degrees from Florida public junior colleges.

Costs Per Year: Application fee: $30. State resident tuition: $2147 full-time, $106.59 per semester hour part-time. Nonresident tuition: $14,654 full-time, $523.48 per semester hour part-time. Mandatory fees: $1050 full-time. Full-time tuition and fees vary according to location. Part-time tuition varies according to location. College room and board: $6600. Room and board charges vary according to housing facility.

Collegiate Environment: Orientation program. Drama-theater group, choral group, student-run newspaper. Social organizations: 109 open to all; national fraternities, national sororities, local sororities; 5% of eligible men and 5% of eligible women are members. Most popular organizations: Marketing Association, Student Council for Exceptional Children, Inter-Varsity Christian Fellowship, Baptist Student Ministry, Golden Key Honor Society. Major annual events: Homecoming, Exam Jam, Love Fest (Valentine's celebration). Student services: health clinic, personal-psychological counseling. Campus security: 24-hour emergency response devices and patrols, student patrols, late night transport-escort service, controlled dormitory access. 1,340 undergraduates lived in college housing during 2003-04. Option: coed housing available. Pace Library with 414,418 books, 1.6 million microform titles, 3,236 serials, 4,303 audiovisual materials, an OPAC, and a Web page. Operations spending for 2004 fiscal year: $2.1 million. 900 computers available on campus for general student use. A campuswide network can be accessed from student residence rooms and from off campus. Staffed computer lab on campus.

Community Environment: Pensacola is Florida's westernmost metropolitan area, situated approximately 50 miles east of Mobile, Alabama. A mild climate and more than 200 miles of Gulf and bay shoreline combine to produce an environment perfect for outdoor recreation. Pensacola is the home of the largest naval air training facility in the United States and of Florida's largest industrial plant. Boating, skin diving, swimming, surfing, and sailing are among the numerous water-related sports enjoyed practically year-round. More than 20 miles of Pensacola Beach are within the confines of the National Seashore, including historic Fort Pickens. Numerous museums and related facilities provide amateur historians with a wealth of exploring. The U.S. Naval Air Training museum provides a historical compendium of naval aviation in the United States. Such annual events as the Fiesta of Five Flags, the Gulf Coast Fine Arts Festival and the West Florida Music Festival draw thousands of people annually.

■ **VALENCIA COMMUNITY COLLEGE** *J-13*
PO Box 3028
Orlando, FL 32802-3028
Tel: (407)299-5000
Admissions: (407)582-1511
Web Site: http://www.valencia.cc.fl.us/

Description: State-supported, 2-year, coed. Part of Florida Community College System. Awards certificates, diplomas, transfer associate, and terminal associate degrees. Founded 1967. Setting: urban campus. Endowment: $14.4 million. Educational spending for 2005 fiscal year: $2228 per student. Total enrollment: 29,342. Student-undergrad faculty ratio is 21:1. 11,409 applied. Students come from 40 states and territories, 92 other countries, 4% from out-of-state, 0.5% Native American, 23% Hispanic, 15% black, 6% Asian American or Pacific Islander, 31% 25 or older. Core. Calendar: semesters. Academic remediation for entering students, ESL program, services for LD students, advanced placement, accelerated degree program, self-designed majors, honors program, independent study, distance learning, double major, summer session for credit, part-time degree program, adult/continuing education programs, co-op programs and internships. ROTC: Army (c).

Entrance Requirements: Open admission except for health-related programs. Option: early admission. Required: high school transcript. Entrance: noncompetitive. Application deadlines: 8/12, 8/12 for nonresidents. Preference given to local residents for health-related programs.

Costs Per Year: Application fee: $25. State resident tuition: $1673 full-time, $66.11 per credit hour part-time. Nonresident tuition: $6287 full-time, $248.05 per credit hour part-time.

Collegiate Environment: Orientation program. Drama-theater group, choral group, student-run newspaper. Social organizations: 55 open to all. Most popular organizations: Phi Theta Kappa, Valencia Intercultural Student Association, Student Government Association, Latin American Student Association, Valencia Student Nurses Association. Major annual events: Matador Day, Student Activity Awards Ceremonies, Commencement. Student services: personal-psychological counseling. Campus security: 24-hour emergency response devices and patrols, student patrols, late night transport-escort service. College housing not available. Learning Resources Center plus 3 others with 101,000 books, 138,000 microform titles, 650 serials, 15,500 audiovisual materials, an OPAC, and a Web page. Operations spending for 2004 fiscal year: $3 million. 1,927 computers available on campus for general student use. A campuswide network can be accessed. Staffed computer lab on campus.

Community Environment: See University of Central Florida.

■ **WARNER SOUTHERN COLLEGE** *L-13*

13895 US Hwy. 27

Lake Wales, FL 33859

Tel: (863)638-1426

Admissions: (863)638-7212

Web Site: http://www.warner.edu/

Description: Independent, comprehensive, coed, affiliated with Church of God. Awards associate, bachelor's, and master's degrees. Founded 1968. Setting: 320-acre rural campus with easy access to Tampa and Orlando. Endowment: $3 million. Educational spending for 2005 fiscal year: $3468 per student. Total enrollment: 970. Faculty: 99 (35 full-time, 64 part-time). Student-undergrad faculty ratio is 16:1. 391 applied, 58% were admitted. 10% from top 10% of their high school class, 30% from top quarter, 66% from top half. 1 National Merit Scholar. Full-time: 778 students, 57% women, 43% men. Part-time: 143 students, 62% women, 38% men. Students come from 27 states and territories, 17 other countries, 13% from out-of-state, 0.3% Native American, 10% Hispanic, 21% black, 1% Asian American or Pacific Islander, 2% international, 46% 25 or older, 41% live on campus, 8% transferred in. Retention: 57% of full-time freshmen returned the following year. Academic areas with the most degrees conferred: business/marketing; education; theology and religious vocations. Core. Calendar: semesters. Academic remediation for entering students, ESL program, advanced placement, accelerated degree program, independent study, distance learning, double major, summer session for credit, part-time degree program, adult/continuing education programs, internships. Study abroad program.

Entrance Requirements: Options: Peterson's Universal Application, Common Application, electronic application, deferred admission. Required: high school transcript, minimum 2.25 high school GPA, 1 recommendation, SAT or ACT. Recommended: essay. Required for some: interview. Entrance: minimally difficult. Application deadline: Rolling. Notification: continuous.

Costs Per Year: Application fee: $20. Comprehensive fee: $18,466 includes full-time tuition ($12,440), mandatory fees ($150), and college room and board ($5876). College room only: $2890. Full-time tuition and fees vary according to program. Room and board charges vary according to board plan. Part-time tuition: $320 per hour. Part-time mandatory fees: $25 per term. Part-time tuition and fees vary according to program.

Collegiate Environment: Orientation program. Choral group, student-run newspaper. Social organizations: 4 open to all. Most popular organizations: concert choir, Fellowship of Christian Athletes, Young Americans, Student Government Association. Major annual events: Spring Banquet, Warner Weekend. Student services: health clinic, personal-psychological counseling. Campus security: 24-hour emergency response devices and patrols, late night transport-escort service, controlled dormitory access. 233 college housing spaces available; all were occupied in 2003-04. Freshmen guaranteed college housing. On-campus residence required through sophomore year. Options: men-only, women-only housing available. Pontious Learning Resource Center with 56,419 books, 8,140 microform titles, 224 serials, 14,935 audiovisual materials, an OPAC, and a Web page. Operations spending for 2004 fiscal year: $336,106. 75 computers available on campus for general student use. A campuswide network can be accessed. Staffed computer lab on campus.

Community Environment: See Webber College.

■ **WEBBER INTERNATIONAL UNIVERSITY** *M-13*

PO Box 96, 1200 North Scenic Hwy.

Babson Park, FL 33827-0096

Tel: (863)638-1431

Free: 800-741-1844

Admissions: (863)638-2910

Fax: (863)638-2823

E-mail: admissions@webber.edu

Web Site: http://www.webber.edu/

Description: Independent, comprehensive, coed. Awards associate, bachelor's, and master's degrees. Founded 1927. Setting: 110-acre small town campus with easy access to Orlando. Endowment: $4.9 million. Educational spending for 2005 fiscal year: $2263 per student. Total enrollment: 616. Faculty: 45 (25 full-time, 20 part-time). Student-undergrad faculty ratio is 17:1. 396 applied, 66% were admitted. 5 student government officers. Full-time: 506 students, 36% women, 64% men. Part-time: 51 students, 45% women, 55% men. Students come from 19 states and territories, 25 other countries, 4% from out-of-state, 0% Native American, 6% Hispanic, 23% black, 0.4% Asian American or Pacific Islander, 15% international, 18% 25 or older, 37% live on campus, 13% transferred in. Retention: 56% of full-time freshmen returned the following year. Academic area with the most degrees conferred: business/marketing. Core. Calendar: semesters. Academic remediation for entering students, services for LD students, advanced placement, accelerated degree program, double major, summer session for credit, part-time degree program, adult/continuing education programs, co-op programs and internships. Study abroad program.

Entrance Requirements: Options: Peterson's Universal Application, electronic application, early action, international baccalaureate accepted. Required: high school transcript, minimum 2.0 high school GPA, SAT or ACT. Recommended: essay. Required for some: recommendations, interview. Entrance: moderately difficult. Application deadlines: 8/1, 4/1 for early action.

Costs Per Year: Application fee: $35. Comprehensive fee: $19,090 includes full-time tuition ($14,390) and college room and board ($4700).

Collegiate Environment: Orientation program. Student-run newspaper. Social organizations: 12 open to all; 1% of eligible men and 4% of eligible women are members. Most popular organizations: Fellowship of Christian Athletes, PBL, student government, Society of Hosteleurs, Webber Ambassadors. Major annual events: homecoming, beach party, Christmas Party. Student services: health clinic. Campus security: 24-hour emergency response devices and patrols, late night transport-escort service, controlled dormitory access. 250 college housing spaces available; 217 were occupied in 2003-04. Freshmen guaranteed college housing. On-campus residence required in freshman year. Options: men-only, women-only housing available. Grace and Roger Babson Library plus 1 other with 25,000 books, 300 serials, and 210 audiovisual materials. Operations spending for 2004 fiscal year: $105,960. 110 computers available on campus for general student use. A campuswide network can be accessed from off-campus. Staffed computer lab on campus.

■ **WEBSTER COLLEGE (HOLIDAY)** *K-9*

2127 Grand Blvd.

Holiday, FL 34690

Tel: (727)942-0069; 888-729-7247

Fax: (727)938-5709

Web Site: http://www.webstercollege.com/

Description: Proprietary, primarily 2-year. Awards diplomas, terminal associate, and bachelor's degrees. Total enrollment: 220. 58 applied, 100% were admitted.

Entrance Requirements: Required: high school transcript, minimum 2.0 high school GPA, interview, Wonderlic aptitude test. Required for some: essay. Application deadline: Rolling.

Collegiate Environment: 60 computers available on campus for general student use. Staffed computer lab on campus.

■ **WEBSTER COLLEGE (OCALA)** *H-11*

1530 SW Third Ave.

Ocala, FL 34474

Tel: (352)629-1941

Fax: (352)629-0926

Web Site: http://www.webstercollege.com/

Description: Proprietary, 2-year, coed. Awards diplomas and terminal associate degrees. Founded 1984. Setting: 3-acre suburban campus with easy access to Orlando. Total enrollment: 375. 2% from top 10% of their high school class, 28% from top quarter, 70% from top half. Students come from 5 states and territories, 70% 25 or older. Retention: 65% of full-time freshmen returned the following year. Core. Academic remediation for entering students, summer session for credit, part-time degree program, adult/continuing education programs.

Entrance Requirements: Open admission. Option: deferred admission.

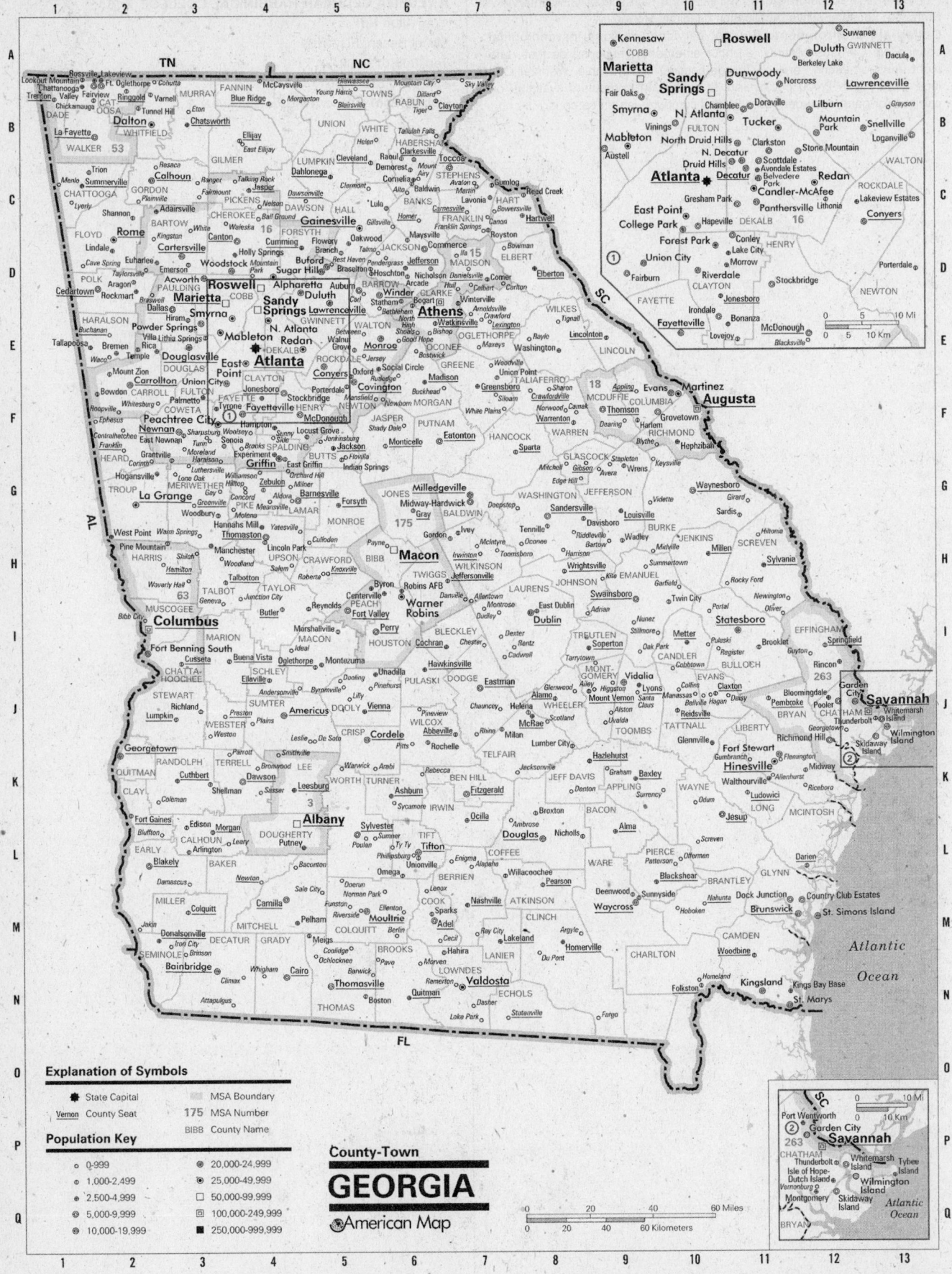

County-Town

GEORGIA

American Map

Explanation of Symbols

★ State Capital
Vernon County Seat
▨ MSA Boundary
175 MSA Number
BIBB County Name

Population Key

○ 0-999
⊙ 1,000-2,499
⊙ 2,500-4,999
⊙ 5,000-9,999
⊙ 10,000-19,999
⊛ 20,000-24,999
⊛ 25,000-49,999
□ 50,000-99,999
▣ 100,000-249,999
■ 250,000-999,999

Required: high school transcript, minimum 2.0 high school GPA, interview. Entrance: noncompetitive. Application deadline: Rolling.

Collegiate Environment: Student services: personal-psychological counseling. Campus security: 24-hour emergency response devices, late night transport-escort service. College housing not available. Webster College Library with 2,400 books and 32 serials. 31 computers available on campus for general student use. Staffed computer lab on campus.

■ **YESHIVA GEDOLAH RABBINICAL COLLEGE** *T-15*
1140 Alton Rd.
Miami Beach, FL 33139
Tel: (305)673-5664
Fax: (305)532-9820
Description: Independent Jewish, 4-year.

■ **ABRAHAM BALDWIN AGRICULTURAL COLLEGE** *L-6*
2802 Moore Hwy.
Tifton, GA 31793
Tel: (229)386-3236
Free: 800-733-3653
Admissions: (229)391-5001
Fax: (229)386-7006
E-mail: esaxon@abac.edu
Web Site: http://www.abac.edu/
Description: State-supported, 2-year, coed. Part of University System of Georgia. Awards certificates, transfer associate, and terminal associate degrees. Founded 1933. Setting: 390-acre small town campus. Endowment: $4.3 million. Educational spending for 2005 fiscal year: $1968 per student. Total enrollment: 3,423. Student-undergrad faculty ratio is 22:1. 2,114 applied, 60% were admitted. Full-time: 2,237 students, 51% women, 49% men. Part-time: 1,186 students, 71% women, 29% men. Students come from 10 states and territories, 0.1% Native American, 3% Hispanic, 17% black, 1% Asian American or Pacific Islander, 1% international, 29% 25 or older, 28% live on campus. Core. Calendar: semesters. Academic remediation for entering students, ESL program, services for LD students, advanced placement, honors program, summer session for credit, part-time degree program, adult/continuing education programs, internships. Off campus study at Ben Hill Irwin Technical Institute, Moultrie Technical Institute.
Entrance Requirements: Open admission. Options: Common Application, early admission, deferred admission. Required: high school transcript, minimum 2.0 high school GPA, college prep curriculum. Required for some: minimum 2.2 high school GPA. Entrance: noncompetitive. Application deadline: 9/24.
Costs Per Year: Application fee: $20. State resident tuition: $1542 full-time, $65 per credit hour part-time. Nonresident tuition: $6166 full-time, $257 per credit hour part-time. Mandatory fees: $232 full-time, $52 per term part-time. College room and board: $5040.
Collegiate Environment: Orientation program. Drama-theater group, choral group, student-run newspaper, radio station. Most popular organizations: Rodeo Club, Baptist Student Union, Forestry/Wildlife Club. Major annual events: Spring Fling, concerts, dances. Student services: health clinic, personal-psychological counseling. Campus security: 24-hour emergency response devices and patrols, late night transport-escort service. On-campus residence required in freshman year. Option: coed housing available. Baldwin Library with 69,986 books and 431 serials. 158 computers available on campus for general student use. Staffed computer lab on campus.
Community Environment: A rural area between Macon and Valdosta having a temperate climate. All modes of transportation serve the area. Scheduled airlines are nearby at Moultrie and Albany. Tifton is an agricultural area; plants are grown here and then sent north for transplanting. Other products are tobacco, cotton, peanuts, melons, commercial grasses and livestock. Part and full-time employment is good. Recreational activities include hunting, tennis, golf, swimming and other water sports.

■ **AGNES SCOTT COLLEGE** *C-11*
141 East College Ave.
Decatur, GA 30030-3797
Tel: (404)471-6000
Free: 800-868-8602
Admissions: (404)471-6285

Fax: (404)471-6414
E-mail: admission@agnesscott.edu
Web Site: http://www.agnesscott.edu/
Description: Independent, comprehensive, affiliated with Presbyterian Church (U.S.A.). Awards bachelor's and master's degrees. Founded 1889. Setting: 100-acre urban campus with easy access to Atlanta. Endowment: $274.7 million. Educational spending for 2005 fiscal year: $14,489 per student. Total enrollment: 1,016. Faculty: 110 (81 full-time, 29 part-time). Student-undergrad faculty ratio is 10:1. 1,526 applied, 53% were admitted. 48% from top 10% of their high school class, 75% from top quarter, 96% from top half. 4 National Merit Scholars, 32 student government officers. Full-time: 879 students, 99% women, 0.3% men. Part-time: 124 students, 94% women, 6% men. Students come from 39 states and territories, 29 other countries, 54% from out-of-state, 0.2% Native American, 3% Hispanic, 20% black, 5% Asian American or Pacific Islander, 8% international, 7% 25 or older, 87% live on campus, 1% transferred in. Retention: 84% of full-time freshmen returned the following year. Academic areas with the most degrees conferred: social sciences; psychology; visual and performing arts. Core. Calendar: semesters. Services for LD students, advanced placement, accelerated degree program, self-designed majors, independent study, double major, summer session for credit, part-time degree program, adult/continuing education programs, internships, graduate courses open to undergrads. Off campus study at Mills College, American University, members of Atlanta Regional Consortium for Higher Education and Public Leadership Education Network. Study abroad program. ROTC: Air Force (c).
Entrance Requirements: Options: Peterson's Universal Application, Common Application, electronic application, early admission, early decision, deferred admission, international baccalaureate accepted. Required: essay, high school transcript, 2 recommendations, SAT or ACT. Recommended: minimum 3.0 high school GPA, interview. Required for some: SAT Subject Tests. Entrance: very difficult. Application deadlines: 3/1, 11/15 for early decision. Notification: continuous until 5/1, 12/15 for early decision.
Costs Per Year: Application fee: $35. Comprehensive fee: $32,070 includes full-time tuition ($23,260), mandatory fees ($310), and college room and board ($8500). College room only: $4250. Room and board charges vary according to board plan and housing facility. Part-time tuition: $970 per credit hour. Part-time mandatory fees: $310 per year. Part-time tuition and fees vary according to course load.
Collegiate Environment: Orientation program. Drama-theater group, choral group, student-run newspaper. Social organizations: 77 open to all. Most popular organizations: Student Government Association, Blackfriars, Joyful Noise, Witkaze (African-American Student organization), Volunteer Board. Major annual events: Black Cat, Senior Investiture, Sophomore Family Weekend. Student services: health clinic, personal-psychological counseling. Campus security: 24-hour emergency response devices and patrols, late night transport-escort service, security systems in apartments, public safety facility, surveillance equipment. 775 college housing spaces available; 755 were occupied in 2003-04. Freshmen guaranteed college housing. On-campus residence required through senior year. Option: women-only housing available. McCain Library with 220,041 books, 32,677 microform titles, 1,264 serials, 15,505 audiovisual materials, an OPAC, and a Web page. Operations spending for 2004 fiscal year: $905,954. 558 computers available on campus for general student use. A campuswide network can be accessed from student residence rooms and from off campus. Staffed computer lab on campus.
Community Environment: See Clark Atlanta University.

■ **ALBANY STATE UNIVERSITY** *L-4*
504 College Dr.
Albany, GA 31705-2717
Tel: (229)430-4600
Admissions: (229)430-4646
Fax: (229)430-3936
Web Site: http://www.asurams.edu/
Description: State-supported, comprehensive, coed. Part of University System of Georgia. Awards associate, bachelor's, and master's degrees. Founded 1903. Setting: 144-acre urban campus. Endowment: $2 million. Educational spending for 2005 fiscal year: $6843 per student. Total enrollment: 3,668. 1,777 applied, 91% were admitted. Full-time: 2,658 students, 65% women, 35% men. Part-time: 554 students, 79% women, 21% men. 35% live on campus. Retention: 82% of full-time freshmen returned the following year. Core. Calendar: semesters. Academic remediation for entering students, services for LD students, advanced placement, honors program, independent study, distance learning, double major, summer session for credit, part-time degree program, adult/continuing education programs, co-op programs and internships. Off campus study at Abraham Baldwin Agricultural College, Bainbridge College, Waycross College. Study abroad program. ROTC: Army.
Entrance Requirements: Options: early admission, deferred admission. Required: high school transcript, minimum 2.0 high school GPA, SAT or ACT. Required for some: interview. Entrance: minimally difficult. Application deadline: 7/1.
Collegiate Environment: Orientation program. Drama-theater group, choral group, marching band, student-run newspaper. Social organizations: 47 open to all; national fraternities, national sororities. Most popular organizations: Gospel Choir, Religious Life Organization, Business Professionals of America, Concert Chorale, NAACP ASU Chapter. Major annual events: Homecoming Week, Honors Day, Founders' Day. Student services: health clinic, personal-psychological counseling, women's center. Campus security: 24-hour emergency response devices and patrols, late night transport-escort service, controlled dormitory access. 1,070 college housing spaces available; 1,040 were occupied in 2003-04. Options: coed, men-only, women-only housing available. James Pendergrast Memorial Library with 338,744 books, 691,524 microform titles, 1,066 serials, 3,301 audiovisual materials, an OPAC, and a Web page. Operations spending for 2004 fiscal year: $891,081. 1,000 computers available on campus for general student use. A campuswide network can be accessed from student residence rooms and from off campus. Staffed computer lab on campus.
Community Environment: The campus is situated in a progressive community that affords a variety of advantages. Albany is located on the Flint River. Air transportation is accessible at the Southwest Georgia Regional Airport. The Marine Corps Supply Center is located here. Albany's economy is broadly based on agriculture, manufacturing, and business from the nearby military bases. The most notable industry is the production of papershell pecans; more than 700,000 pecan trees cover 60,000 acres in the vicinity. The Spanish peanut industry and other diversified businesses and farming contribute to the city's high rating in retail sales. Part-time employment is available. Radium Springs, four miles south, has the largest natural spring in the state.

■ **ALBANY TECHNICAL COLLEGE** *L-4*
1704 South Slappey Blvd.
Albany, GA 31701-3514
Tel: (229)430-3500
Admissions: (229)430-3520
Fax: (229)430-5155
E-mail: lcheevers@albanytech.edu
Web Site: http://www.albanytech.edu/
Description: State-supported, 2-year, coed. Awards certificates, diplomas, and terminal associate degrees. Founded 1961. Total enrollment: 2,787. Full-time: 1,390 students, 61% women, 39% men. Part-time: 1,397 students, 66% women, 34% men. 0.2% Native American, 1% Hispanic, 66% black, 0.3% Asian American or Pacific Islander, 0% international. Core. Academic remediation for entering students, services for LD students, advanced placement, distance learning, part-time degree program, adult/continuing education programs, internships.
Entrance Requirements: Open admission. Options: Common Application, electronic application, deferred admission. Required: high school transcript, ACT COMPASS or ASSET. Entrance: noncompetitive.
Costs Per Year: Application fee: $15. State resident tuition: $1116 full-time, $31 per credit hour part-time. Nonresident tuition: $2232 full-time, $62 per credit hour part-time.

Collegiate Environment: Orientation program. College housing not available. Albany Technical College Library and Media Center plus 1 other with 42,000 books, 20 microform titles, 40 serials, 520 audiovisual materials, an OPAC, and a Web page. 500 computers available on campus for general student use. Computer purchase/lease plans available. A campuswide network can be accessed from off-campus. Staffed computer lab on campus.

■ **ALTAMAHA TECHNICAL COLLEGE** *L-10*
1777 West Cherry St.
Jesup, GA 31545
Tel: (912)427-5800
Admissions: (912)427-5817
Fax: (912)427-5823
E-mail: lburns@altamahatech.edu
Web Site: http://www.altamahatech.edu/
Description: State-supported, 2-year, coed. Awards certificates, diplomas, and terminal associate degrees. Total enrollment: 859. Full-time: 342 students, 56% women, 44% men. Part-time: 517 students, 59% women, 41% men. 0.1% Native American, 2% Hispanic, 27% black, 0.2% Asian American or Pacific Islander, 0% international. Academic remediation for entering students, services for LD students, advanced placement, distance learning, internships.
Entrance Requirements: Open admission. Option: deferred admission. Required: high school transcript. Placement: ACT COMPASS or ASSET required. Entrance: noncompetitive.
Costs Per Year: Application fee: $15. State resident tuition: $1116 full-time, $31 per credit hour part-time. Nonresident tuition: $2232 full-time, $62 per credit hour part-time.
Collegiate Environment: College housing not available. 4,435 books, 90 serials, and 292 audiovisual materials.

■ **AMERICAN INTERCONTINENTAL UNIVERSITY (ATLANTA)** *E-4*
3330 Peachtree Rd., NE
Atlanta, GA 30326-1016
Tel: (404)231-9000; 888-999-4248
Admissions: (404)965-5772
Fax: (404)231-1062
E-mail: david.naylor@buckhead.aiuniv.edu
Web Site: http://www.aiuniv.edu/
Description: Proprietary, 4-year, coed. Administratively affiliated with Career Education Corporation. Awards associate, bachelor's, and master's degrees. Founded 1977. Setting: 3-acre urban campus. Educational spending for 2005 fiscal year: $3000 per student. Total enrollment: 1,732. 1,305 applied, 93% were admitted. Full-time: 1,319 students, 65% women, 35% men. Part-time: 378 students, 67% women, 33% men. Students come from 31 states and territories, 39 other countries, 39% from out-of-state, 0.2% Native American, 1% Hispanic, 16% black, 0.4% Asian American or Pacific Islander, 4% international, 30% 25 or older, 14% live on campus, 40% transferred in. Retention: 44% of full-time freshmen returned the following year. Core. Calendar: five 10-week terms. Academic remediation for entering students, accelerated degree program, independent study, distance learning, double major, summer session for credit, part-time degree program, adult/continuing education programs, co-op programs and internships. Study abroad program.
Entrance Requirements: Open admission. Options: early admission, deferred admission. Required: high school transcript. Recommended: essay, minimum 2.0 high school GPA, 2 recommendations, interview, SAT or ACT, SAT Subject Tests. Entrance: noncompetitive. Application deadline: 10/15. Notification: continuous.
Costs Per Year: Application fee: $50. Tuition: $16,386 full-time, $430 per credit part-time. Full-time tuition varies according to course load and program. Part-time tuition varies according to course load and program. College room only: $5400. Tuition guaranteed not to increase for student's term of enrollment.
Collegiate Environment: Orientation program. Student-run newspaper. Most popular organizations: Student Government Association, Positive Image (Black History), International Student Association, Ministries in Action, Fashion Association. Major annual events: Beginning of Quarter Welcome Party, Professional Week, graduation. Student services: personal-psychological counseling. Campus security: 24-hour patrols. 237 undergraduates lived in college housing during 2003-04. No special consideration for freshman housing applicants. American Intercontinental University Library-Buckhead Campus with 29,672 books, 245 serials, 2,296 audiovisual materials, and an OPAC. Operations spending for 2004 fiscal year:

$222,648. 86 computers available on campus for general student use. A campuswide network can be accessed from off-campus. Staffed computer lab on campus.

■ AMERICAN INTERCONTINENTAL UNIVERSITY (DUNWOODY CAMPUS) *E-4*

6600 Peachtree-Dunwoody Rd.
500 Embassy Row
Atlanta, GA 30328
Tel: (404)965-6500
Free: 800-255-6839
Admissions: (404)965-8050
Fax: (404)965-6501
Web Site: http://www.aiudunwoody.com/

Description: Proprietary, comprehensive, coed. Part of AIU is owned by Career Education Corporation. Awards associate, bachelor's, and master's degrees. Founded 1970. Setting: 2-acre urban campus. Total enrollment: 1,150. 367 applied, 80% were admitted. Full-time: 924 students, 53% women, 47% men. Part-time: 183 students, 63% women, 37% men. 0.2% Native American, 1% Hispanic, 11% black, 0.4% Asian American or Pacific Islander, 1% international, 13% live on campus. Calendar: five 10-week terms.

Entrance Requirements: Required: high school transcript, minimum 2.0 high school GPA, interview. Recommended: SAT or ACT. Required for some: TOEFL or equivalent, ACCUPLACER/PLATO.

Collegiate Environment: Major annual event: Student Forum. Student services: personal-psychological counseling. College housing not available.

■ ANDREW COLLEGE *K-3*

413 College St.
Cuthbert, GA 39840-1313
Tel: (229)732-2171
Free: 800-664-9250
Admissions: (229)732-5934
Fax: (229)732-2176
E-mail: admissions@andrewcollege.edu
Web Site: http://www.andrewcollege.edu/

Description: Independent United Methodist, 2-year, coed. Awards certificates and transfer associate degrees. Founded 1854. Setting: 40-acre small town campus. Endowment: $7 million. Educational spending for 2005 fiscal year: $3926 per student. Total enrollment: 331. 578 applied, 96% were admitted. Full-time: 328 students, 48% women, 52% men. Part-time: 3 students, 33% women, 67% men. Students come from 11 states and territories, 10 other countries, 16% from out-of-state, 4% Hispanic, 45% black, 1% Asian American or Pacific Islander, 6% international, 2% 25 or older, 90% live on campus, 6% transferred in. Core. Calendar: semesters. Academic remediation for entering students, ESL program, services for LD students, advanced placement, honors program, summer session for credit, part-time degree program.

Entrance Requirements: Options: Peterson's Universal Application, electronic application, early admission, deferred admission. Required: high school transcript, SAT or ACT. Recommended: minimum 2.0 high school GPA. Required for some: essay, 1 recommendation, interview. Entrance: moderately difficult. Application deadline: 8/6.

Costs Per Year: Application fee: $20. Comprehensive fee: $15,980 includes full-time tuition ($9814) and college room and board ($6166).

Collegiate Environment: Orientation program. Drama-theater group, choral group, student-run newspaper. Social organizations: 10 open to all. Most popular organizations: Drama Club, Outdoor Club, International Club, BSU. Major annual events: Homecoming, Christmas Dance, Spring Semi-Formal. Student services: health clinic, personal-psychological counseling. Campus security: 24-hour patrols, controlled dormitory access, night patrols by trained security personnel. 360 college housing spaces available; 321 were occupied in 2003-04. Freshmen guaranteed college housing. On-campus residence required through sophomore year. Options: coed, men-only, women-only housing available. Pitts Library with 40,000 books and 100 serials. 50 computers available on campus for general student use. A campuswide network can be accessed from student residence rooms and from off campus. Staffed computer lab on campus.

Community Environment: Cuthbert is a rural community 40 miles from Albany, and 55 miles from Columbus. Its climate is ideal. Airline services are available one hour away. Part-time employment exists for students. Community facilities include a library, churches, and good shopping. A public

recreation center, two swimming pools, golf course and nearby lakes provide facilities for fishing, boating and water skiing.

■ APPALACHIAN TECHNICAL COLLEGE *C-4*

100 Campus Dr.
Jasper, GA 30143
Tel: (706)253-4500
Admissions: (706)253-4537
Fax: (706)253-4510
E-mail: nfaix@appalachiantech.edu
Web Site: http://www.appalachiantech.edu/

Description: State-supported, 2-year, coed. Awards certificates, diplomas, and terminal associate degrees. Founded 1965. Total enrollment: 1,047. Full-time: 414 students, 70% women, 30% men. Part-time: 633 students, 67% women, 33% men. 0.3% Native American, 1% Hispanic, 2% black, 0.5% Asian American or Pacific Islander, 0% international. Academic remediation for entering students, services for LD students, advanced placement, distance learning, internships.

Entrance Requirements: Open admission. Option: deferred admission. Required: high school transcript, ACT COMPASS or ASSET. Entrance: noncompetitive.

Costs Per Year: Application fee: $15. State resident tuition: $1116 full-time, $31 per credit hour part-time. Nonresident tuition: $2232 full-time, $62 per credit hour part-time.

Collegiate Environment: College housing not available.

■ ARGOSY UNIVERSITY/ATLANTA *E-4*

990 Hammond Dr., 11th Floor
Atlanta, GA 30328-5505
Tel: (770)671-1200; 888-671-4777
Fax: (770)671-0476
Web Site: http://www.argosyu.edu/

Description: Proprietary, upper-level, coed. Administratively affiliated with Education Management Corporation. Awards bachelor's, master's, and doctoral degrees and post-master's certificates. Founded 1990. Setting: suburban campus. Total enrollment: 13. 18 applied, 72% were admitted. Full-time: 4 students, 75% women, 25% men. Part-time: 9 students, 89% women, 11% men. 0% Native American, 0% Hispanic, 38% black, 0% Asian American or Pacific Islander, 0% international, 60% 25 or older. Calendar: semesters.

Collegiate Environment: Student-run newspaper. Social organizations: 4 open to all; 10% of eligible men and 30% of eligible women are members. Most popular organizations: SGA, Student Senate. College housing not available.

■ ARMSTRONG ATLANTIC STATE UNIVERSITY *J-13*

11935 Abercorn St.
Savannah, GA 31419-1997
Tel: (912)927-5211
Free: 800-633-2349
Admissions: (912)927-5275
Fax: (912)921-5462
E-mail: westkim@mail.armstrong.edu
Web Site: http://www.armstrong.edu/

Description: State-supported, comprehensive, coed. Part of University System of Georgia. Awards associate, bachelor's, and master's degrees. Founded 1935. Setting: 250-acre suburban campus. Endowment: $2.2 million. Research spending for 2004 fiscal year: $13,680. Educational spending for 2005 fiscal year: $2779 per student. Total enrollment: 6,710. Faculty: 424 (224 full-time, 200 part-time). Student-undergrad faculty ratio is 17:1. 804 applied, 99% were admitted. Full-time: 3,677 students, 66% women, 34% men. Part-time: 2,238 students, 72% women, 28% men. Students come from 46 states and territories, 71 other countries, 11% from out-of-state, 0.4% Native American, 3% Hispanic, 21% black, 3% Asian American or Pacific Islander, 2% international, 39% 25 or older, 10% live on campus, 10% transferred in. Retention: 67% of full-time freshmen returned the following year. Academic areas with the most degrees conferred: health professions and related sciences; education; liberal arts/general studies. Core. Calendar: semesters. Academic remediation for entering students, services for LD students, advanced placement, honors program, independent study, distance learning, double major, summer session for credit, part-time degree program, adult/continuing education programs, co-op programs and internships, graduate courses open to undergrads. Off campus study at Georgia Southern University, Savannah State University. Study abroad program. ROTC: Army, Naval (c).

Entrance Requirements: Options: Peterson's Universal Application, early admission, deferred admission. Required: high school transcript, proof of immunization, SAT or ACT. Required for some: SAT Subject Tests. Entrance: minimally difficult. Application deadline: 7/1. Notification: continuous.

Costs Per Year: Application fee: $20. State resident tuition: $2894 full-time, $102 per hour part-time. Nonresident tuition: $10,210 full-time, $407 per hour part-time. Mandatory fees: $456 full-time, $213 per term part-time. Full-time tuition and fees vary according to program. Part-time tuition and fees vary according to course load and program. College room only: $4980. Room charges vary according to housing facility.

Collegiate Environment: Orientation program. Drama-theater group, choral group, student-run newspaper. Social organizations: 57 open to all; national fraternities, national sororities, local fraternities, local sororities. Most popular organizations: Wesley Fellowship, Hispanic Student Society, Ebony Coalition, American Chemical Society, Phi Alpha Theta. Major annual events: AASU Day, Saint Patrick's Day, Beach Bash. Student services: health clinic, personal-psychological counseling. Campus security: 24-hour emergency response devices and patrols, student patrols, late night transport-escort service. 600 college housing spaces available; all were occupied in 2003-04. No special consideration for freshman housing applicants. Option: coed housing available. Lane Library with 223,412 books, 666,657 microform titles, 1,166 serials, 15,618 audiovisual materials, an OPAC, and a Web page. Operations spending for 2004 fiscal year: $1.8 million. 160 computers available on campus for general student use. A campuswide network can be accessed from student residence rooms and from off campus. Staffed computer lab on campus.

Community Environment: The college is located on the southside of Savannah, 30 miles from the Atlantic Ocean. All modes of transportation are available. Savannah is a highly industrialized metropolitan area with only minor agricultural activities. Industrial plants number over 350. This city is considered to be one of the first planned cities in North America. The charm of the city comes from the cobblestoned riverfront, and the many squares shaded by majestic oak trees. Points of interest include Factor's Walk, Savannah riverfront shopping, Johnson Square, Pink House, Owens-Thomas House, Cathedral of St. John the Baptist, Independent Presbyterian Church, Colonial Park, and many others.

■ **THE ART INSTITUTE OF ATLANTA** *E-4*
6600 Peachtree Dunwoody Rd., 100 Embassy Row
Atlanta, GA 30328
Tel: (770)394-8300
Free: 800-275-4242
Fax: (770)394-0008
Web Site: http://www.aia.artinstitutes.edu/

Description: Proprietary, 4-year, coed. Part of Education Management Corporation. Awards associate and bachelor's degrees. Founded 1949. Setting: 7-acre suburban campus. Educational spending for 2005 fiscal year: $3742 per student. Total enrollment: 2,651. Full-time: 2,322 students, 47% women, 53% men. Part-time: 329 students, 43% women, 57% men. Students come from 43 states and territories, 33 other countries, 38% from out-of-state, 0.4% Native American, 4% Hispanic, 32% black, 3% Asian American or Pacific Islander, 3% international, 31% 25 or older, 13% live on campus. Core. Academic remediation for entering students, services for LD students, advanced placement, honors program, independent study, distance learning, summer session for credit, part-time degree program, adult/continuing education programs, internships. Study abroad program.

Entrance Requirements: Options: Peterson's Universal Application, electronic application, deferred admission, international baccalaureate accepted. Required: essay, minimum 2.0 high school GPA, interview. Required for some: high school transcript. Entrance: minimally difficult. Notification: continuous.

Costs Per Year: Application fee: $50. Tuition: $18,000 full-time, $375 per credit part-time. Full-time tuition varies according to course load. Part-time tuition varies according to course load. College room only: $7311. Room charges vary according to housing facility. Tuition guaranteed not to increase for student's term of enrollment.

Collegiate Environment: Orientation program. Student-run newspaper. Social organizations: 16 open to all. Most popular organizations: AIGA (American Institute of Graphic Artists) Student Chapter, ASID (American Society of Interior Designers) Student Chapter, SGA - Student Government Association, Housing Council, Haven. Major annual events: Spring Party,

Fall Carnival. Student services: personal-psychological counseling. Campus security: 24-hour emergency response devices and patrols, late night transport-escort service, controlled dormitory access. 350 undergraduates lived in college housing during 2003-04. Freshmen guaranteed college housing. Option: coed housing available. Library with 40,799 books, 159 serials, 35,562 audiovisual materials, an OPAC, and a Web page. Operations spending for 2004 fiscal year: $1.3 million. 388 computers available on campus for general student use. A campuswide network can be accessed. Staffed computer lab on campus.

Community Environment: Just north of Atlanta's city limits, the campus is located in one of Atlanta's fastest growing business and residential districts and provides easy access to public transportation, shopping, housing, restaurants, and jobs for students.

■ **ASHWORTH COLLEGE** *B-11*
430 Technology Parkway
Norcross, GA 30092
Tel: (770)729-8400
Free: 800-223-4542
Fax: (770)729-9296
Web Site: http://www.ashworthcollege.com/

Description: Proprietary, 2-year, coed. Administratively affiliated with Professional Career Development, LLC. Awards transfer associate and terminal associate degrees. Students come from 50 states and territories. Core. Calendar: semesters. Services for LD students, advanced placement, accelerated degree program, independent study, distance learning, summer session for credit, part-time degree program, external degree program, adult/continuing education programs. Off campus study. Study abroad program.

Entrance Requirements: Options: Common Application, electronic application. Required: high school transcript. Entrance: noncompetitive.

■ **ATHENS TECHNICAL COLLEGE** *D-7*
800 US Hwy. 29 North
Athens, GA 30601-1500
Tel: (706)355-5000
Admissions: (706)355-5124
Fax: (706)369-5753
E-mail: lreid@athenstech.org
Web Site: http://www.athenstech.edu/

Description: State-supported, 2-year, coed. Part of Georgia Department of Technical and Adult Education. Awards certificates, diplomas, and terminal associate degrees. Founded 1958. Setting: 41-acre suburban campus with easy access to Atlanta. Total enrollment: 3,805. Full-time: 1,436 students, 65% women, 35% men. Part-time: 2,369 students, 70% women, 30% men. Students come from 2 states and territories, 0.1% Native American, 2% Hispanic, 23% black, 4% Asian American or Pacific Islander, 0.03% international, 40% 25 or older. Core. Academic remediation for entering students, services for LD students, advanced placement, distance learning, summer session for credit, part-time degree program, adult/continuing education programs, internships.

Entrance Requirements: Open admission. Option: deferred admission. Required: high school transcript, ACT COMPASS or ASSET. Entrance: noncompetitive.

Costs Per Year: Application fee: $15. State resident tuition: $1116 full-time, $31 per credit hour part-time. Nonresident tuition: $2232 full-time, $62 per credit hour part-time.

Collegiate Environment: Most popular organizations: Athens Technical Student Advisory Council, Phi Theta Kappa, Delta Epsilon Chi, Radiological Technology Society, Organized Black Students Encouraging Unity and Excellence. Major annual events: Blood Drives, Can-A-Thon, Smoke Out. Campus security: 24-hour patrols. College housing not available. 33,891 books, 15,608 microform titles, 538 serials, and 3,279 audiovisual materials. 277 computers available on campus for general student use. A campuswide network can be accessed. Staffed computer lab on campus.

■ **ATLANTA CHRISTIAN COLLEGE** *E-4*
2605 Ben Hill Rd.
East Point, GA 30344-1999
Tel: (404)761-8861
Free: 800-776-1ACC
Web Site: http://www.acc.edu/

Description: Independent Christian, 4-year, coed. Awards associate and bachelor's degrees. Founded 1937. Setting: 52-acre suburban campus with easy access to Atlanta. Endowment: $30 million. Total enrollment: 443. 827

applied, 37% were admitted. Students come from 13 states and territories, 10% from out-of-state, 2% Hispanic, 17% black, 1% Asian American or Pacific Islander, 30% 25 or older, 60% live on campus. Core. Calendar: semesters. Academic remediation for entering students, services for LD students, advanced placement, independent study, double major, summer session for credit, part-time degree program, internships.

Entrance Requirements: Options: Peterson's Universal Application, electronic application, early admission, early decision, deferred admission. Required: high school transcript, minimum 2.0 high school GPA, 2 recommendations, medical history, SAT or ACT. Entrance: moderately difficult. Application deadlines: 8/1, 11/15 for early decision.

Costs Per Year: Application fee: $25. Comprehensive fee: $17,180 includes full-time tuition ($11,800), mandatory fees ($580), and college room and board ($4800). Full-time tuition and fees vary according to course level. Part-time tuition: $495 per hour. Part-time tuition varies according to course level and student level.

Collegiate Environment: Orientation program. Drama-theater group, choral group, student-run radio station. Social organizations: local fraternities, local sororities; 15% of eligible men and 10% of eligible women are members. Major annual events: Spring Picnic, choir concerts, Junior/Senior Banquet. Student services: health clinic, personal-psychological counseling. Campus security: controlled dormitory access, 12-hour patrols by security personnel. 350 college housing spaces available; 250 were occupied in 2003-04. Freshmen guaranteed college housing. On-campus residence required in freshman year. Options: men-only, women-only housing available. Atlanta Christian College Library with 50,000 books, 187 serials, and an OPAC. 30 computers available on campus for general student use. A campuswide network can be accessed from student residence rooms and from off campus. Staffed computer lab on campus.

Community Environment: A suburban area with temperate climate, East Point is served by all major forms of transportation. Along with the usual community facilities, the opportunities are excellent for part-time employment.

■ **ATLANTA METROPOLITAN COLLEGE** *E-4*
1630 Metropolitan Parkway, SW
Atlanta, GA 30310-4498
Tel: (404)756-4000
Admissions: (404)756-4004
E-mail: admissions@atlm.edu
Web Site: http://www.atlm.edu/

Description: State-supported, 2-year, coed. Part of University System of Georgia. Awards certificates, transfer associate, and terminal associate degrees. Founded 1974. Setting: 68-acre urban campus. Research spending for 2004 fiscal year: $2260. Educational spending for 2005 fiscal year: $3121 per student. Total enrollment: 1,748. Student-undergrad faculty ratio is 23:1. 1,422 applied, 57% were admitted. Full-time: 860 students, 60% women, 40% men. Part-time: 888 students, 67% women, 33% men. Students come from 33 states and territories, 39 other countries, 8% from out-of-state, 0.1% Native American, 1% Hispanic, 94% black, 1% Asian American or Pacific Islander, 3% international, 43% 25 or older, 8% transferred in. Core. Calendar: semesters. Academic remediation for entering students, services for LD students, summer session for credit, part-time degree program, adult/continuing education programs, co-op programs. Study abroad program.

Entrance Requirements: Options: Common Application, electronic application. Required: high school transcript. Entrance: minimally difficult. Application deadline: 7/15. Notification: continuous until 8/12.

Costs Per Year: Application fee: $20. State resident tuition: $1560 full-time, $65 per credit hour part-time. Nonresident tuition: $6168 full-time, $257 per credit hour part-time. Mandatory fees: $230 full-time, $115 per term part-time.

Collegiate Environment: Orientation program. Drama-theater group, choral group, student-run newspaper. Social organizations: 16 open to all. Most popular organizations: International Students Organization, Drama Club, choir, Criminal Justice Club, Study Abroad Club. Major annual events: Fall Convocation, Spring Festival, Graduation Exercises. Student services: personal-psychological counseling. Campus security: 24-hour emergency response devices and patrols. College housing not available. Atlanta Metropolitan College Library plus 1 other with 48,719 books, 66,612 microform titles, 113 serials, 3,874 audiovisual materials, an OPAC, and a Web page. Operations spending for 2004 fiscal year: $253,706. 585 computers available on campus for general student use. A campuswide network can be accessed from off-campus. Staffed computer lab on campus.

Community Environment: The College, though within view of the city, is situated on a 83-acre wooded tract. It is located next to Atlanta Technical College, and is convenient to major bus lines and Hartsfield International Airport, and is adjacent to Interstate 75-85 South.

■ **ATLANTA TECHNICAL COLLEGE** *E-4*
1560 Metropolitan Parkway
Atlanta, GA 30310
Tel: (404)756-3700
Admissions: (404)225-4446
Fax: (404)752-0809
E-mail: jtriplet@atlantatech.edu
Web Site: http://www.atlantatech.org/

Description: State-supported, 2-year, coed. Awards certificates, diplomas, and terminal associate degrees. Founded 1945. Total enrollment: 3,523. Full-time: 1,535 students, 60% women, 40% men. Part-time: 1,988 students, 61% women, 39% men. 0.1% Native American, 1% Hispanic, 88% black, 2% Asian American or Pacific Islander, 0% international. Academic remediation for entering students, services for LD students, advanced placement, distance learning, internships.

Entrance Requirements: Open admission. Option: deferred admission. Required: high school transcript, ACT COMPASS or ASSET. Entrance: noncompetitive.

Costs Per Year: Application fee: $15. State resident tuition: $1116 full-time, $31 per credit hour part-time. Nonresident tuition: $2232 full-time, $62 per credit hour part-time.

Collegiate Environment: College housing not available.

■ **AUGUSTA STATE UNIVERSITY** *F-10*
2500 Walton Way
Augusta, GA 30904-2200
Tel: (706)737-1400
Free: 800-341-4373
Admissions: (706)737-1632
Fax: (706)737-1774
E-mail: admissions@ac.edu
Web Site: http://www.aug.edu/

Description: State-supported, comprehensive, coed. Part of University System of Georgia. Awards associate, bachelor's, and master's degrees and post-master's certificates. Founded 1925. Setting: 72-acre urban campus. Endowment: $307,215. Research spending for 2004 fiscal year: $101,239. Educational spending for 2005 fiscal year: $4543 per student. Total enrollment: 6,312. Faculty: 330 (215 full-time, 115 part-time). Student-undergrad faculty ratio is 19:1. 1,939 applied, 63% were admitted. Full-time: 3,686 students, 61% women, 39% men. Part-time: 1,775 students, 71% women, 29% men. Students come from 42 states and territories, 57 other countries, 12% from out-of-state, 0.3% Native American, 3% Hispanic, 26% black, 3% Asian American or Pacific Islander, 1% international, 34% 25 or older, 8% transferred in. Retention: 65% of full-time freshmen returned the following year. Academic areas with the most degrees conferred: business/marketing; education; social sciences. Core. Calendar: semesters. Academic remediation for entering students, ESL program, services for LD students, advanced placement, honors program, independent study, double major, summer session for credit, part-time degree program, adult/continuing education programs, co-op programs and internships. Off campus study at Medical College of Georgia, Paine College. Study abroad program. ROTC: Army.

Entrance Requirements: Options: Common Application, early admission, deferred admission. Required: high school transcript, minimum 2.0 high school GPA, SAT or ACT. Entrance: minimally difficult. Application deadline: 7/21. Notification: continuous.

Costs Per Year: Application fee: $20. State resident tuition: $2438 full-time, $102 per hour part-time. Nonresident tuition: $9754 full-time, $407 per hour part-time. Mandatory fees: $482 full-time, $241 per term part-time. College room only: $4920.

Collegiate Environment: Drama-theater group, choral group, student-run newspaper. Social organizations: 30 open to all; national fraternities, national sororities; 5% of eligible men and 5% of eligible women are members. Most popular organizations: Jazz Ensemble, Baptist Student Union, ASU Orchestra, Student Art Association, Black Student Union. Major annual events: homecoming, Pig-Out, Midnight Madness. Student services: personal-psychological counseling. Campus security: 24-hour patrols, late night transport-escort service. Reese Library plus 1 other with 454,590 books, 957,862 microform titles, 33,797 serials, 6,124 audiovisual materials, an OPAC, and a Web page. Operations spending for 2004 fiscal year: $1.5 million. 325 computers available on campus for general student use. A campuswide network can be accessed from off-campus. Staffed computer lab on campus.

Community Environment: Augusta, located on the Savannah River in east central Georgia, is the second largest MSA in the state, the third leading producer of clay products in the southeast, and a regional medical center. All forms of transportation are available. Recreational facilities are available for fishing, boating, golf, horseback riding, and tennis. The famous Augusta National Golf Club course, home of the Masters Golf Tournament, is located here. Points of interest include the Augusta River Walk, the Jessye Norman Amphitheatre, the Morris Museum of Art, the Lucy Laney Museum, Meadow Gardens, New Savannah Bluff Lock and Dam, Sacred Heart Cultural Center, and the National Science Center at Fort Gordon, Fort Discovery at River Walk.

■ **AUGUSTA TECHNICAL COLLEGE** *F-10*
3200 Augusta Tech Dr.
Augusta, GA 30906
Tel: (706)771-4000
Admissions: (706)771-4027
Fax: (706)771-4016
E-mail: bcrobert@augustatech.edu
Web Site: http://www.augustatech.edu/
Description: State-supported, 2-year, coed. Part of Georgia Department of Technical and Adult Education. Awards certificates, diplomas, and terminal associate degrees. Founded 1961. Setting: 70-acre urban campus. Total enrollment: 4,171. Full-time: 1,986 students, 64% women, 36% men. Part-time: 2,185 students, 59% women, 41% men. Students come from 2 states and territories, 0.5% Native American, 3% Hispanic, 50% black, 2% Asian American or Pacific Islander, 0.1% international, 49% 25 or older. Core. Academic remediation for entering students, services for LD students, advanced placement, distance learning, summer session for credit, part-time degree program, co-op programs and internships.
Entrance Requirements: Open admission. Option: deferred admission. Required: high school transcript, ACT COMPASS or ASSET. Entrance: noncompetitive. Preference given to state residents.
Costs Per Year: Application fee: $15. State resident tuition: $1116 full-time, $31 per credit hour part-time. Nonresident tuition: $2232 full-time, $62 per credit hour part-time.
Collegiate Environment: Orientation program. Most popular organizations: VICA, professional organizations. Major annual events: Field Day, Open House, Graduation. Campus security: 24-hour emergency response devices, 12-hour patrols by trained security personnel. College housing not available. Information Technology Center with 70,816 books, 445 serials, 7,733 audiovisual materials, an OPAC, and a Web page. 339 computers available on campus for general student use. A campuswide network can be accessed from off-campus. Staffed computer lab on campus.

■ **BAINBRIDGE COLLEGE** *N-3*
2500 East Shotwell St.
Bainbridge, GA 39819
Tel: (229)248-2500
Admissions: (229)248-2504
Fax: (229)248-2525
Web Site: http://www.bainbridge.edu/
Description: State-supported, 2-year, coed. Part of University System of Georgia. Awards certificates, transfer associate, and terminal associate degrees. Founded 1972. Setting: 160-acre small town campus. Total enrollment: 2,475. 1,330 applied, 78% were admitted. Students come from 5 states and territories, 1% from out-of-state, 0.2% Native American, 1% Hispanic, 51% black, 3% Asian American or Pacific Islander, 0% international, 47% 25 or older. Core. Calendar: semesters. Academic remediation for entering students, services for LD students, advanced placement, independent study, distance learning, double major, summer session for credit, part-time degree program, adult/continuing education programs. Study abroad program.
Entrance Requirements: Options: electronic application, early admission. Required for some: high school transcript, minimum 1.8 high school GPA, 3 recommendations, interview, immunizations, or waivers; medical records and criminal background checks, SAT or ACT, ACT COMPASS. Entrance: noncompetitive. Application deadline: 8/1. Notification: continuous.
Costs Per Year: Application fee: $0. State resident tuition: $1542 full-time, $65 per credit hour part-time. Nonresident tuition: $6166 full-time, $257 per credit hour part-time. Mandatory fees: $124 full-time.

Collegiate Environment: Orientation program. Drama-theater group. Social organizations: 5 open to all. Most popular organizations: Phi Theta Kappa, Alpha Beta Gamma, Drama Club, Delta Club, Sigma Kappa Delta. Campus security: 24-hour patrols. College housing not available. Bainbridge College Library with 37,387 books, 8,752 microform titles, 180 serials, 1,795 audiovisual materials, and an OPAC. 250 computers available on campus for general student use. A campuswide network can be accessed. Staffed computer lab on campus.

■ **BAUDER COLLEGE** *E-4*
Phipps Plaza, 3500 Peachtree Rd, NE
Atlanta, GA 30326
Tel: (404)237-7573
Free: 800-241-3797
Fax: (404)237-1642
Web Site: http://www.bauder.edu/
Description: Proprietary, 2-year, coed. Awards transfer associate degrees. Founded 1964. Setting: suburban campus. Total enrollment: 715. 600 applied, 50% were admitted. 100% from top half of their high school class. 0.4% Native American, 2% Hispanic, 56% black, 2% Asian American or Pacific Islander, 2% international. Core. Academic remediation for entering students, summer session for credit, internships.
Entrance Requirements: Option: electronic application. Required: essay, high school transcript, 2 recommendations, interview. Entrance: minimally difficult. Application deadline: Rolling. Notification: continuous.
Collegiate Environment: Drama-theater group, student-run newspaper. Student services: personal-psychological counseling. Campus security: 24-hour emergency response devices and patrols. 4,000 books and 65 serials. 50 computers available on campus for general student use. Staffed computer lab on campus.

■ **BEACON UNIVERSITY** *I-2*
6003 Veterans Parkway
Columbus, GA 31909
Tel: (706)323-5364
Fax: (706)323-3236
E-mail: registrar@beacon.edu
Web Site: http://www.beacon.edu/
Description: Independent religious, comprehensive, coed. Awards associate, bachelor's, master's, and doctoral degrees. Founded 1993. Setting: 12-acre urban campus. Total enrollment: 141. 49 applied, 88% were admitted. Students come from 4 states and territories, 2 other countries, 27% from out-of-state, 5% Hispanic, 43% black, 2% international, 55% 25 or older. Retention: 95% of full-time freshmen returned the following year. Core. Calendar: semesters. Academic remediation for entering students, advanced placement, accelerated degree program, independent study, distance learning, double major, summer session for credit, part-time degree program, external degree program, adult/continuing education programs, graduate courses open to undergrads. Off campus study.
Entrance Requirements: Options: Common Application, early admission, international baccalaureate accepted. Required: high school transcript, minimum 2.0 high school GPA, 3 recommendations, interview. Recommended: SAT or ACT. Required for some: ACT COMPASS. Application deadline: Rolling.
Collegiate Environment: Orientation program. Student-run newspaper. Social organizations: 2 open to all. Most popular organizations: Student Government Association, practical ministry. Major annual events: Harvest Festival, Missions Convention, Founders' Day. Student services: personal-psychological counseling. College housing not available. Beacon College Library plus 1 other with 25,000 books, 67 serials, and a Web page. 30 computers available on campus for general student use. A campuswide network can be accessed. Staffed computer lab on campus.

■ **BERRY COLLEGE**
PO Box 490159
Mount Berry, GA 30149-0159
Tel: (706)232-5374
Free: 800-237-7942
Admissions: (706)236-2215
Fax: (706)236-2248
E-mail: admissions@berry.edu
Web Site: http://www.berry.edu/
Description: Independent interdenominational, comprehensive, coed. Awards bachelor's and master's degrees and post-master's certificates.

Founded 1902. Setting: 28,000-acre suburban campus with easy access to Atlanta. Endowment: $525.4 million. Research spending for 2004 fiscal year: $439,963. Total enrollment: 1,970. Faculty: 196 (134 full-time, 62 part-time). Student-undergrad faculty ratio is 13:1. 1,827 applied, 83% were admitted. 28% from top 10% of their high school class, 59% from top quarter, 89% from top half. 7 valedictorians. Full-time: 1,829 students, 64% women, 36% men. Part-time: 34 students, 59% women, 41% men. Students come from 30 states and territories, 18 other countries, 15% from out-of-state, 0.1% Native American, 2% Hispanic, 3% black, 2% Asian American or Pacific Islander, 2% international, 0.02% 25 or older, 72% live on campus, 4% transferred in. Retention: 78% of full-time freshmen returned the following year. Academic areas with the most degrees conferred: business/marketing; education; psychology. Core. Calendar: semesters. Advanced placement, accelerated degree program, self-designed majors, honors program, independent study, double major, summer session for credit, part-time degree program, adult/continuing education programs, co-op programs and internships, graduate courses open to undergrads. Study abroad program.

Entrance Requirements: Options: Peterson's Universal Application, Common Application, electronic application, early admission, deferred admission, international baccalaureate accepted. Required: high school transcript, recommendations, SAT or ACT. Entrance: moderately difficult. Application deadline: 7/21. Notification: continuous.

Costs Per Year: Application fee: $50. Comprehensive fee: $26,114 includes full-time tuition ($18,950) and college room and board ($7164). College room only: $4024.

Collegiate Environment: Orientation program. Drama-theater group, choral group, student-run newspaper. Social organizations: 75 open to all. Most popular organizations: Student Government Association, Baptist Student Union, equestrian sports, Campus Outreach, Viking crew team. Major annual events: Mountain Day, fall outdoor movie, Welcome Back Dance. Student services: health clinic, personal-psychological counseling. Campus security: 24-hour emergency response devices and patrols, controlled dormitory access, lighted pathways. 1,414 college housing spaces available; 1,334 were occupied in 2003-04. Freshmen given priority for college housing. On-campus residence required through sophomore year. Options: coed, men-only, women-only housing available. Memorial Library plus 1 other with 321,335 books, 722,840 microform titles, 1,792 serials, 4,249 audiovisual materials, an OPAC, and a Web page. Operations spending for 2004 fiscal year: $1.6 million. 134 computers available on campus for general student use. A campuswide network can be accessed from student residence rooms and from off campus. Staffed computer lab on campus.

Community Environment: Located on Highway 27 between Chattanooga and Atlanta, Mount Berry is in the mountains of North Georgia in Floyd County, adjoining Rome. Recreation, cultural facilities and transportation are found in Rome.

■ **BEULAH HEIGHTS BIBLE COLLEGE** *E-4*
892 Berne St., SE, PO Box 18145
Atlanta, GA 30316
Tel: (404)627-2681; 888-777-BHBC
Fax: (404)627-0702
Web Site: http://www.beulah.org/
Description: Independent Pentecostal, 4-year, coed. Awards associate and bachelor's degrees. Founded 1918. Setting: 10-acre urban campus. Endowment: $19,881. Research spending for 2004 fiscal year: $56,000. Educational spending for 2005 fiscal year: $800 per student. Total enrollment: 620. Full-time: 256 students, 53% women, 47% men. Part-time: 364 students, 60% women, 40% men. Students come from 22 states and territories, 12 other countries, 30% from out-of-state, 0% Native American, 1% Hispanic, 77% black, 0.5% Asian American or Pacific Islander, 14% international, 90% 25 or older, 10% live on campus, 8% transferred in. Retention: 42% of full-time freshmen returned the following year. Core. Calendar: semesters. Academic remediation for entering students, advanced placement, accelerated degree program, distance learning, double major, summer session for credit, part-time degree program, adult/continuing education programs, co-op programs and internships.

Entrance Requirements: Open admission. Options: Peterson's Universal Application, Common Application, early admission. Required: high school transcript, minimum 2.0 high school GPA, 2 recommendations. Recommended: interview, SAT or ACT. Entrance: noncompetitive. Application deadline: Rolling. Notification: continuous.

Collegiate Environment: Orientation program. Choral group. Major annual events: Discovery Days, Annual College Banquet. Student services: personal-psychological counseling. Campus security: 24-hour emergency

response devices, student patrols. Options: men-only, women-only housing available. Barth Memorial Library with 40,000 books, 328 serials, 236 audiovisual materials, and a Web page. Operations spending for 2004 fiscal year: $203,807. 28 computers available on campus for general student use. Staffed computer lab on campus.

Community Environment: See Clark Atlanta University.

■ **BRENAU UNIVERSITY** *C-5*
500 Washington St. SE
Gainesville, GA 30501
Tel: (770)534-6299
Free: 800-252-5119
Admissions: (770)718-5320
Fax: (770)534-6114
Web Site: http://www.brenau.edu/
Description: Independent, comprehensive. Awards bachelor's and master's degrees and post-master's certificates (also offers coed evening and weekend programs with significant enrollment not reflected in profile). Founded 1878. Setting: 57-acre small town campus with easy access to Atlanta. Endowment: $44.3 million. Educational spending for 2005 fiscal year: $6302 per student. Total enrollment: 743. Faculty: 105 (72 full-time, 33 part-time). Student-undergrad faculty ratio is 9:1. 2,063 applied, 38% were admitted. Full-time: 670 students, 100% women. Part-time: 41 students, 100% women. Students come from 16 states and territories, 15 other countries, 12% from out-of-state, 4% Native American, 3% Hispanic, 16% black, 2% Asian American or Pacific Islander, 1% international, 17% 25 or older, 55% live on campus, 15% transferred in. Retention: 73% of full-time freshmen returned the following year. Academic areas with the most degrees conferred: health professions and related sciences; visual and performing arts; education. Core. Calendar: semesters. Academic remediation for entering students, services for LD students, advanced placement, honors program, independent study, distance learning, double major, summer session for credit, part-time degree program, co-op programs and internships, graduate courses open to undergrads. Off campus study. Study abroad program.

Entrance Requirements: Options: Peterson's Universal Application, Common Application, electronic application, early admission, deferred admission, international baccalaureate accepted. Required: essay, high school transcript, minimum 2.5 high school GPA, minimum SAT score of 900 or ACT score of 18, SAT or ACT. Recommended: recommendations. Required for some: interview. Entrance: moderately difficult. Application deadline: Rolling. Notification: continuous.

Costs Per Year: Application fee: $35. Comprehensive fee: $24,990 includes full-time tuition ($16,440) and college room and board ($8550). Full-time tuition varies according to class time, location, and program. Room and board charges vary according to housing facility. Part-time tuition: $548 per semester hour. Part-time mandatory fees: $75 per term. Part-time tuition and fees vary according to class time, location, and program.

Collegiate Environment: Orientation program. Drama-theater group, choral group, student-run newspaper, radio station. Social organizations: 53 open to all; national sororities; 33% of women are members. Most popular organizations: Student Government/Campus Activities Board, Silhouettes (diversity awareness), Recreation Association, DIVAS Peer Education, International Club. Major annual events: May Day, Family Weekend, Winter Weekend. Student services: health clinic, personal-psychological counseling. Campus security: 24-hour emergency response devices and patrols, late night transport-escort service. 448 college housing spaces available; 337 were occupied in 2003-04. Freshmen guaranteed college housing. On-campus residence required through junior year. Option: women-only housing available. Trustee Library with 61,059 books, 872 microform titles, 205 serials, 2,104 audiovisual materials, an OPAC, and a Web page. Operations spending for 2004 fiscal year: $696,436. 200 computers available on campus for general student use. A campuswide network can be accessed from student residence rooms and from off campus. Staffed computer lab on campus.

■ **BREWTON-PARKER COLLEGE**
Hwy. 280
Mt. Vernon, GA 30445-0197
Tel: (912)583-2241
Free: 800-342-1087
Admissions: (912)583-3265
Fax: (912)583-4498
Web Site: http://www.bpc.edu/

Description: Independent Southern Baptist, 4-year, coed. Awards associate and bachelor's degrees. Founded 1904. Setting: 280-acre rural campus. Endowment: $12.8 million. Educational spending for 2005 fiscal year: $4413 per student. Total enrollment: 1,094. Student-undergrad faculty ratio is 13:1. 435 applied, 97% were admitted. 12% from top 10% of their high school class, 26% from top quarter, 62% from top half. Full-time: 846 students, 62% women, 38% men. Part-time: 248 students, 71% women, 29% men. Students come from 21 states and territories, 12 other countries, 5% from out-of-state, 0% Native American, 2% Hispanic, 23% black, 0.5% Asian American or Pacific Islander, 1% international, 37% 25 or older, 34% live on campus, 8% transferred in. Retention: 52% of full-time freshmen returned the following year. Academic areas with the most degrees conferred: education; liberal arts/general studies; business/marketing. Core. Calendar: semesters. Academic remediation for entering students, services for LD students, advanced placement, honors program, summer session for credit, part-time degree program, adult/continuing education programs, co-op programs and internships.

Entrance Requirements: Options: Peterson's Universal Application, Common Application, early admission. Required: high school transcript, minimum 2.0 high school GPA, SAT or ACT. Recommended: interview. Entrance: minimally difficult. Application deadline: Rolling. Notification: continuous.

Costs Per Year: Application fee: $25. Comprehensive fee: $17,504 includes full-time tuition ($11,584), mandatory fees ($1100), and college room and board ($4820). College room only: $2150. Room and board charges vary according to board plan and housing facility. Part-time tuition: $362 per credit hour. Part-time mandatory fees: $275 per term.

Collegiate Environment: Orientation program. Drama-theater group, choral group, student-run newspaper. Social organizations: 26 open to all; local fraternities, local sororities; 5% of eligible men and 7% of eligible women are members. Most popular organizations: Council of Intramural Activities, Student Activities Council, Rotaract, Circle K, Baptist Student Union. Major annual events: Homecoming Weekend, Fall Festival, Black History Month. Student services: health clinic, personal-psychological counseling. Campus security: 24-hour emergency response devices and patrols, controlled dormitory access. 450 college housing spaces available; 385 were occupied in 2003-04. Freshmen guaranteed college housing. On-campus residence required through junior year. Options: men-only, women-only housing available. Fountain-New Library with 74,331 books, 3,098 microform titles, 393 serials, 5,510 audiovisual materials, an OPAC, and a Web page. Operations spending for 2004 fiscal year: $510,729. 87 computers available on campus for general student use. A campuswide network can be accessed from student residence rooms. Staffed computer lab on campus.

■ **BROWN MACKIE COLLEGE-ATLANTA** *B-11*
4975 Jimmy Carter Blvd., Ste. 600
Norcross, GA 30093
Tel: (770)638-0121
Admissions: (770)510-2312
Fax: (770)638-0479
E-mail: rlcampbell@brownmackie.edu
Web Site: http://www.brownmackie.edu/locations.asp?locid=3
Description: Proprietary, 2-year, coed. Awards diplomas and terminal associate degrees. Educational spending for 2005 fiscal year: $2350 per student. Total enrollment: 150. Student-undergrad faculty ratio is 19:1. Full-time: 150 students, 73% women, 27% men. 35% from out-of-state, 0% Native American, 2% Hispanic, 76% black, 0% Asian American or Pacific Islander, 0% international.

Entrance Requirements: Required: high school transcript, interview. Entrance: minimally difficult. Application deadline: Rolling. Notification: continuous.

Costs Per Year: Application fee: $0. Tuition: $6084 full-time, $169 per credit hour part-time. Mandatory fees: $360 full-time, $10 per credit hour part-time.

Collegiate Environment: Student-run newspaper. Student services: health clinic, personal-psychological counseling.

■ **CARVER BIBLE COLLEGE** *E-4*
437 Nelson St.
Atlanta, GA 30313
Tel: (404)527-4520
Fax: (404)527-4526
Web Site: http://www.carver.edu/
Description: Independent nondenominational, 4-year, coed. Awards bachelor's degrees. Founded 1943. Total enrollment: 150. 61 applied, 16% were admitted. 5 class presidents, 5 valedictorians, 10 student government

officers. Students come from 4 states and territories, 7 other countries, 10% from out-of-state, 0% Native American, 1% Hispanic, 91% black, 0% Asian American or Pacific Islander, 7% international, 45% 25 or older. Core. Calendar: semesters. Academic remediation for entering students, independent study, summer session for credit, part-time degree program, adult/continuing education programs, internships. Off campus study.

Entrance Requirements: Open admission. Option: Common Application. Required: essay, high school transcript, minimum 2.0 high school GPA, 4 recommendations. Required for some: interview. Entrance: noncompetitive.

Collegiate Environment: Orientation program. 30 college housing spaces available; all were occupied in 2003-04. No special consideration for freshman housing applicants. Carver Bible College Library plus 1 other with 150 serials and 1,000 audiovisual materials. 4 computers available on campus for general student use. Staffed computer lab on campus.

■ **CENTRAL GEORGIA TECHNICAL COLLEGE** *H-6*
3300 Macon Tech Dr.
Macon, GA 31206-3628
Tel: (478)757-3400
Admissions: (478)757-3408
Fax: (478)757-3454
E-mail: amymc@cgtcollege.edu
Web Site: http://www.cgtcollege.org/
Description: State-supported, 2-year, coed. Part of Georgia Department of Technical and Adult Education. Awards certificates, diplomas, and terminal associate degrees. Founded 1966. Setting: 152-acre suburban campus. Total enrollment: 6,047. Full-time: 3,057 students, 68% women, 32% men. Part-time: 2,990 students, 67% women, 33% men. Students come from 5 states and territories, 1 other country, 0.4% Native American, 1% Hispanic, 59% black, 1% Asian American or Pacific Islander, 0.03% international, 59% 25 or older, 21% transferred in. Core. Academic remediation for entering students, services for LD students, advanced placement, distance learning, part-time degree program, external degree program, internships. Off campus study at Northwestern Technical Institute, Augusta Technical Institute, Athens Area Technical Institute.

Entrance Requirements: Open admission. Option: deferred admission. Required: high school transcript, ACT COMPASS or ASSET. Entrance: noncompetitive.

Costs Per Year: Application fee: $15. State resident tuition: $1116 full-time, $61 per credit hour part-time. Nonresident tuition: $2232 full-time, $62 per credit hour part-time.

Collegiate Environment: Orientation program. Social organizations: 2 open to all. Most popular organizations: Skills USA-VICA, student government. Major annual events: Tobofest Fall Festival, Spring Fling, Student Appreciation Day. Campus security: 24-hour patrols. College housing not available. 16,500 books, 300 serials, 1,800 audiovisual materials, an OPAC, and a Web page.

■ **CHATTAHOOCHEE TECHNICAL COLLEGE** *D-3*
980 South Cobb Dr.
Marietta, GA 30060
Tel: (770)528-4500
Fax: (770)528-4578
Web Site: http://www.chattcollege.com
Description: State-supported, 2-year, coed. Part of Georgia Department of Technical and Adult Education. Awards certificates, diplomas, and terminal associate degrees. Founded 1961. Setting: suburban campus with easy access to Atlanta. Total enrollment: 6,243. Full-time: 2,260 students, 52% women, 48% men. Part-time: 3,983 students, 55% women, 45% men. 0.3% Native American, 4% Hispanic, 33% black, 2% Asian American or Pacific Islander, 2% international, 52% 25 or older. Core. Academic remediation for entering students, services for LD students, advanced placement, distance learning, part-time degree program, internships. Study abroad program.

Entrance Requirements: Open admission. Option: deferred admission. Required: high school transcript, ACT COMPASS or ASSET. Entrance: noncompetitive.

Costs Per Year: Application fee: $15. State resident tuition: $1116 full-time, $31 per credit hour part-time. Nonresident tuition: $2232 full-time, $62 per credit hour part-time.

Collegiate Environment: Social organizations: 5 open to all. Most popular organizations: student government, Vocational Industrial Clubs of America, Institute for Electrical and Electronic Engineers, National Technical-Vocational Honor Society, Phi Beta Lambda. Major annual events: Career Fair, Fall Festival. Campus security: full-time day and evening security. College housing not available. 22,127 books, 292 serials, 1,826 audiovisual materials, and a Web page. 200 computers available on campus for general student use. Staffed computer lab on campus.

■ **CLARK ATLANTA UNIVERSITY** *E-4*
223 James P. Brawley Dr., SW
Atlanta, GA 30314
Tel: (404)880-8000
Free: 800-688-3228
Fax: (404)880-6174
Web Site: http://www.cau.edu/

Description: Independent United Methodist, university, coed. Awards bachelor's, master's, and doctoral degrees and post-master's certificates. Founded 1865. Setting: 113-acre urban campus with easy access to Atlanta. Endowment: $33.6 million. Research spending for 2004 fiscal year: $12.5 million. Educational spending for 2005 fiscal year: $7820 per student. Total enrollment: 4,598. 5,181 applied, 60% were admitted. Full-time: 3,557 students, 71% women, 29% men. Part-time: 144 students, 72% women, 28% men. Students come from 46 states and territories, 61% from out-of-state, 0.1% Native American, 0.1% Hispanic, 93% black, 0.1% Asian American or Pacific Islander, 37% live on campus, 6% transferred in. Retention: 72% of full-time freshmen returned the following year. Core. Calendar: semesters. Academic remediation for entering students, ESL program, services for LD students, advanced placement, accelerated degree program, freshman honors college, honors program, distance learning, summer session for credit, part-time degree program, adult/continuing education programs, co-op programs and internships. Off campus study at University Center in Georgia, Atlanta University Center. Study abroad program. ROTC: Army, Air Force.

Entrance Requirements: Options: Common Application, electronic application, early admission, deferred admission, international baccalaureate accepted. Required: essay, high school transcript, minimum 2.0 high school GPA, 2 recommendations, SAT or ACT. Recommended: minimum 2.5 high school GPA, interview. Entrance: moderately difficult. Application deadline: 7/1. Notification: continuous.

Costs Per Year: Application fee: $35. Comprehensive fee: $21,338 includes full-time tuition ($14,522) and college room and board ($6816). Room and board charges vary according to board plan and housing facility.

Collegiate Environment: Orientation program. Drama-theater group, choral group, marching band, student-run newspaper, radio station. Social organizations: 105 open to all; national fraternities, national sororities; 3% of eligible men and 12% of eligible women are members. Most popular organizations: Spirit Boosters, Pre-Alumni Council, Campus Activities Board (CAB), Orientation Guides, National Association for the Advancement of Colored People (NAACP). Major annual events: Homecoming, Greek Symposium, Miss Clark Atlanta University (CAU) Pagents. Student services: health clinic, personal-psychological counseling. Campus security: 24-hour emergency response devices and patrols, late night transport-escort service, controlled dormitory access. 1,420 college housing spaces available; 1,330 were occupied in 2003-04. Freshmen given priority for college housing. Options: coed, men-only, women-only housing available. Robert W. Woodruff Library with 520,727 books, 867,237 microform titles, 17,536 serials, 10,827 audiovisual materials, an OPAC, and a Web page. Operations spending for 2004 fiscal year: $2.4 million. 640 computers available on campus for general student use. A campuswide network can be accessed from off-campus.

Community Environment: One mile east of the campus lie the mirrored skyscrapers and modern expressways of Atlanta. The World Congress Center, the Civic Center, the Arts Alliance Center (home of the Atlanta Symphony Orchestra and the Atlantic Ballet Company), the Martin Luther King, Jr. Center for Nonviolent Social Change, the Dome (home of the Atlanta Falcons football team), the Jimmy Carter Presidential Library, and outstanding entertainment features, such as Underground Atlanta, Stone Mountain Park, and Six Flags Over Georgia amusement park, mark Atlanta as the capital of the Sun Belt.

■ **CLAYTON STATE UNIVERSITY** *D-11*
5900 North Lee St.
Morrow, GA 30260-0285
Tel: (678)466-4000
Admissions: (678)466-4115
E-mail: csc-info@ce.clayton.peachnet.edu
Web Site: http://www.clayton.edu/

Description: State-supported, 4-year, coed. Part of University System of Georgia. Awards associate and bachelor's degrees. Founded 1969. Setting: 163-acre suburban campus with easy access to Atlanta. Educational spending for 2005 fiscal year: $10,412 per student. Total enrollment: 6,152. Student-undergrad faculty ratio is 20:1. 5,221 applied, 55% were admitted. Full-time: 3,291 students, 67% women, 33% men. Part-time: 2,861 students, 73% women, 27% men. Students come from 45 states and territories, 34 other countries, 3% from out-of-state, 0.4% Native American, 2% Hispanic, 48% black, 4% Asian American or Pacific Islander, 2% international, 45% 25 or older, 10% transferred in. Retention: 57% of full-time freshmen returned the following year. Academic areas with the most degrees conferred: business/marketing; health professions and related sciences; psychology. Core. Calendar: semesters. Academic remediation for entering students, services for LD students, advanced placement, self-designed majors, freshman honors college, honors program, independent study, distance learning, double major, summer session for credit, part-time degree program, adult/continuing education programs, co-op programs and internships. Off campus study at University Center in Georgia. Study abroad program. ROTC: Army (c), Naval (c), Air Force (c).

Entrance Requirements: Options: electronic application, early admission, deferred admission. Required: high school transcript, proof of immunization, SAT or ACT. Required for some: SAT Subject Tests. Entrance: minimally difficult. Application deadline: 7/17. Notification: continuous.

Costs Per Year: Application fee: $40. State resident tuition: $2802 full-time, $102 per credit hour part-time. Nonresident tuition: $9770 full-time, $407 per credit hour part-time. Mandatory fees: $488 full-time, $244 per term part-time.

Collegiate Environment: Orientation program. Drama-theater group, choral group, student-run newspaper. Social organizations: 26 open to all; national fraternities, national sororities; 10% of eligible men and 15% of eligible women are members. Most popular organizations: Accounting Club, International Awareness Club, Black Cultural Awareness Association, Student Government Association, Music Club. Major annual events: Homecoming, Spring Fling. Student services: health clinic, personal-psychological counseling. Campus security: 24-hour emergency response devices and patrols, late night transport-escort service, lighted pathways. College housing not available. Clayton College & State University Library plus 1 other with 77,043 books, 190,729 microform titles, 4,250 serials, 5,636 audiovisual materials, an OPAC, and a Web page. 3,500 computers available on campus for general student use. A campuswide network can be accessed from off-campus. Staffed computer lab on campus.

Community Environment: See Clark Atlanta University.

■ **COASTAL GEORGIA COMMUNITY COLLEGE** *M-12*
3700 Altama Ave.
Brunswick, GA 31520
Tel: (912)264-7235
Free: 800-675-7235
Admissions: (912)264-7253
Fax: (912)262-3072
Web Site: http://www.cgcc.edu/

Description: State-supported, 2-year, coed. Part of University System of Georgia. Awards certificates, transfer associate, and terminal associate degrees. Founded 1961. Setting: 193-acre small town campus with easy access to Jacksonville. Endowment: $88,674. Educational spending for 2005 fiscal year: $5770 per student. Total enrollment: 3,062. Student-undergrad faculty ratio is 18:1. 1,866 applied, 54% were admitted. Full-time: 1,002 students, 65% women, 35% men. Part-time: 2,060 students, 70% women, 30% men. Students come from 8 states and territories, 4% from out-of-state, 0.4% Native American, 2% Hispanic, 30% black, 1% Asian American or Pacific Islander, 0.4% international, 50% 25 or older, 5% transferred in. Core. Calendar: semesters. Academic remediation for entering students, services for LD students, advanced placement, distance learning, double major, summer session for credit, part-time degree program, adult/continuing education programs. Study abroad program.

Entrance Requirements: Options: Common Application, electronic application, deferred admission. Required: high school transcript, minimum 2.0 high school GPA, immunization records. Entrance: noncompetitive. Application deadline: 8/15. Notification: continuous.

Costs Per Year: Application fee: $20. State resident tuition: $1468 full-time, $62 per credit hour part-time. Nonresident tuition: $245 per credit hour part-time. Mandatory fees: $212 full-time, $52 per term part-time.

Collegiate Environment: Orientation program. Student-run newspaper. Social organizations: 14 open to all. Most popular organizations: Association of Nursing Students, Minority Advisement and Social Development Association, Student Government Association, Baptist Student Union, Phi Theta Kappa. Major annual events: Winter Semi-Formal, Turkey Trot, Welcome Back Cookout. Student services: personal-psychological counseling. Campus security: 24-hour patrols, late night transport-escort service. College housing not available. Clara Wood Gould Memorial Library with 535 serials, 1,151 audiovisual materials, and an OPAC. Operations spending for 2004 fiscal year: $430,802. 250 computers available on campus for general student use. A campuswide network can be accessed from off-campus. Staffed computer lab on campus.

Community Environment: Brunswick is the county seat of Glynn County, which includes the historic resort islands of St. Simons, Sea Island, and Jekyll Island. The climate is mild with a mean temperature of 68 degrees. Bus and rail serve the area. Besides being a tourist center, it is an industrial city. Recreational activities are unlimited including golf, bowling, fresh, salt water, and deep sea fishing, tennis, picnicking, surfing, and water skiing at excellent beaches. Numerous points of historical interest are in or near Brunswick. Kings Bay Naval Submarine Base and the Federal Law Enforcement Training Center are nearby.

■ COLUMBUS STATE UNIVERSITY *I-2*

4225 University Ave.
Columbus, GA 31907-5645
Tel: (706)568-2001; (866)264-2035
Admissions: (706)568-2035
Fax: (706)568-2123
Web Site: http://www.colstate.edu/

Description: State-supported, comprehensive, coed. Part of University System of Georgia. Awards associate, bachelor's, and master's degrees and post-master's certificates. Founded 1958. Setting: 132-acre suburban campus with easy access to Atlanta. Total enrollment: 7,475. Faculty: 411 (216 full-time, 195 part-time). Student-undergrad faculty ratio is 20:1. 3,005 applied, 64% were admitted. Full-time: 4,414 students, 63% women, 37% men. Part-time: 2,210 students, 60% women, 40% men. Students come from 35 states and territories, 40 other countries, 13% from out-of-state, 0.3% Native American, 3% Hispanic, 32% black, 2% Asian American or Pacific Islander, 1% international, 27% 25 or older, 14% live on campus, 8% transferred in. Retention: 72% of full-time freshmen returned the following year. Academic areas with the most degrees conferred: business/marketing; education; computer and information sciences. Core. Calendar: semesters. Academic remediation for entering students, services for LD students, advanced placement, freshman honors college, honors program, independent study, distance learning, summer session for credit, part-time degree program, adult/continuing education programs, co-op programs and internships, graduate courses open to undergrads. Study abroad program. ROTC: Army.

Entrance Requirements: Options: Common Application, electronic application, early admission, deferred admission, international baccalaureate accepted. Required: high school transcript, minimum 2.5 high school GPA, proof of immunization, SAT or ACT. Required for some: SAT Subject Tests. Entrance: minimally difficult. Application deadline: 7/1. Notification: continuous.

Costs Per Year: Application fee: $25. State resident tuition: $2438 full-time, $102 per semester hour part-time. Nonresident tuition: $9754 full-time, $407 per semester hour part-time. Mandatory fees: $506 full-time. College room and board: $5720. College room only: $3510. Room and board charges vary according to board plan and location.

Collegiate Environment: Orientation program. Drama-theater group, choral group, student-run newspaper. Social organizations: 50 open to all; national fraternities, national sororities, local sororities; 1% of eligible men and 1% of eligible women are members. Most popular organizations: Student Government Association, Student Programming Council, Baptist Student Union. Major annual events: homecoming, Greek Week. Student services: health clinic, personal-psychological counseling. Campus security: 24-hour emergency response devices and patrols, late night transport-escort service. Option: coed housing available. Simon Schwob Memorial Library with 250,000 books, 840,000 microform titles, 1,400 serials, 2,500 audiovisual materials, an OPAC, and a Web page. 300 computers available on campus for general student use. A campuswide network can be accessed from student residence rooms and from off campus. Staffed computer lab on campus.

Community Environment: Columbus, Georgia's second largest city, is located in the Chattahoochee Valley, 100 miles south of Atlanta on the Georgia-Alabama border, having an annual mean temperature of 65 degrees and annual rainfall of 37 inches. All forms of transportation serve the area. Columbus is one of the South's largest textile centers, a regional retail center, and manufacturers high-tech industrial products, iron and metal goods, hosiery, processed foods, soft drinks, candy and peanut products. Cultural facilities are the churches, libraries, symphony orchestra, Museum of Arts and Sciences, Fort Benning Little Theatre, and Springer Opera House which is the State Theatre. With the completion of the dam projects on the Chattahoochee River and the Apalachicola River in Florida, Columbus became a port city. A navigable waterway extends to the Gulf of Mexico and the Intracoastal Canal. Oliver Dam provides facilities for all water sports. There are recreational facilities at community centers, golf courses, bowling alleys, and swimming pools.

■ COLUMBUS TECHNICAL COLLEGE *I-2*

928 Manchester Expressway
Columbus, GA 31904-6572
Tel: (706)649-1800
Admissions: (706)649-1174
Fax: (706)649-1937
E-mail: nkennedy@columbustech.edu
Web Site: http://www.columbustech.edu

Description: State-supported, 2-year, coed. Part of Georgia Department of Technical and Adult Education. Awards certificates, diplomas, and terminal associate degrees. Founded 1961. Setting: urban campus with easy access to Atlanta. Total enrollment: 3,530. Full-time: 1,536 students, 66% women, 34% men. Part-time: 1,994 students, 62% women, 38% men. Students come from 9 states and territories, 1% Native American, 3% Hispanic, 48% black, 2% Asian American or Pacific Islander, 0% international. Core. Academic remediation for entering students, services for LD students, advanced placement, distance learning, part-time degree program, adult/continuing education programs, internships.

Entrance Requirements: Open admission. Options: Common Application, deferred admission. Required: high school transcript, ACT COMPASS or ASSET. Entrance: noncompetitive.

Costs Per Year: Application fee: $15. State resident tuition: $1116 full-time, $31 per credit hour part-time. Nonresident tuition: $2232 full-time, $62 per credit hour part-time.

Collegiate Environment: Orientation program. Major annual event: faculty/staff softball game. Campus security: security patrols during class hours. College housing not available. Columbus Technical College Library with 26,072 books, 2,429 microform titles, 49 serials, and 533 audiovisual materials. 50 computers available on campus for general student use. A campuswide network can be accessed from off-campus. Staffed computer lab on campus.

■ COOSA VALLEY TECHNICAL COLLEGE *D-2*

One Maurice Culberson Dr.
Rome, GA 30161
Tel: (706)295-6963
Admissions: (706)624-1117
Fax: (706)295-6944
E-mail: sphillip@coosavalleytech.edu
Web Site: http://www.coosavalleytech.edu/

Description: State-supported, 2-year, coed. Awards certificates, diplomas, and terminal associate degrees. Founded 1962. Total enrollment: 2,893. Full-time: 1,219 students, 66% women, 34% men. Part-time: 1,674 students, 62% women, 38% men. 1% Native American, 1% Hispanic, 11% black, 1% Asian American or Pacific Islander, 0.04% international. Academic remediation for entering students, services for LD students, advanced placement, distance learning, internships.

Entrance Requirements: Open admission. Option: deferred admission. Required: high school transcript, ACT COMPASS or ASSET. Entrance: noncompetitive.

Costs Per Year: Application fee: $15. State resident tuition: $1116 full-time, $31 per credit hour part-time. Nonresident tuition: $2232 full-time, $62 per credit hour part-time.

Collegiate Environment: College housing not available.

■ COVENANT COLLEGE *A-1*

14049 Scenic Hwy.
Lookout Mountain, GA 30750
Tel: (706)820-1560; 888-451-2683
Admissions: (706)419-1127
E-mail: admissions@covenant.edu

Web Site: http://www.covenant.edu/

Description: Independent, comprehensive, coed, affiliated with Presbyterian Church in America. Awards associate, bachelor's, and master's degrees (master's degree in education only). Founded 1955. Setting: 250-acre suburban campus. Endowment: $14.8 million. Educational spending for 2005 fiscal year: $5210 per student. Total enrollment: 898. Faculty: 77 (58 full-time, 19 part-time). Student-undergrad faculty ratio is 15:1. 934 applied, 33% were admitted. Full-time: 898 students, 57% women, 43% men. Students come from 47 states and territories, 37 other countries, 76% from out-of-state, 0.2% Native American, 2% Hispanic, 3% black, 2% Asian American or Pacific Islander, 1% 25 or older, 86% live on campus, 6% transferred in. Core. Calendar: semesters. Academic remediation for entering students, advanced placement, self-designed majors, independent study, double major, summer session for credit, part-time degree program, adult/continuing education programs, internships. Off campus study. Study abroad program.

Entrance Requirements: Options: electronic application, early admission, deferred admission. Required: essay, high school transcript, minimum 2.5 high school GPA, 2 recommendations, SAT or ACT. Recommended: ACT. Entrance: moderately difficult. Application deadline: Rolling. Notification: continuous.

Costs Per Year: Application fee: $35. Comprehensive fee: $28,030 includes full-time tuition ($21,100), mandatory fees ($750), and college room and board ($6180). Part-time tuition: $880 per credit hour.

Collegiate Environment: Orientation program. Drama-theater group, choral group, student-run newspaper, radio station. Social organizations: 48 open to all. Most popular organizations: Psychology Club, interpretive dance group, Drama Club, Backpacking Club, various ministries. Major annual events: Homecoming, Madrigal dinners, Spring Banquet. Student services: health clinic, personal-psychological counseling, women's center. Campus security: night security guards. 776 college housing spaces available; 740 were occupied in 2003-04. Freshmen guaranteed college housing. On-campus residence required through junior year. Options: men-only, women-only housing available. Kresge Memorial Library with 85,000 books, 5,000 microform titles, 12,000 serials, 4,500 audiovisual materials, an OPAC, and a Web page. Operations spending for 2004 fiscal year: $395,000. 135 computers available on campus for general student use. A campuswide network can be accessed from student residence rooms and from off campus. Staffed computer lab on campus.

Community Environment: Located 5 miles from Chattanooga, TN, and 120 miles from Atlanta, GA, Lookout Mountain is a suburban community that enjoys the cultural, recreational and social facilities of Chattanooga. The community has churches of all denominations, a library, various cultural opportunities, an aquarium, several hospitals, and health center at nearby Chattanooga. Part-time jobs are available.

■ **DALTON STATE COLLEGE** *B-2*
213 North College Dr.
Dalton, GA 30720-3797
Tel: (706)272-4436
Free: 800-829-4436
Fax: (706)272-2530
Web Site: http://www.daltonstate.edu/

Description: State-supported, 4-year, coed. Part of University System of Georgia. Awards associate and bachelor's degrees. Founded 1963. Setting: 141-acre small town campus. Endowment: $11.1 million. Educational spending for 2005 fiscal year: $6083 per student. Total enrollment: 4,267. Student-undergrad faculty ratio is 23:1. 1,941 applied, 69% were admitted. Students come from 4 states and territories, 1% from out-of-state, 0.2% Native American, 9% Hispanic, 2% black, 1% Asian American or Pacific Islander, 44% 25 or older. Core. Calendar: semesters. Academic remediation for entering students, ESL program, services for LD students, advanced placement, distance learning, summer session for credit, part-time degree program, adult/continuing education programs, internships. Off campus study. Study abroad program.

Entrance Requirements: Open admission. Options: Common Application, early admission. Required: high school transcript. Entrance: noncompetitive. Application deadline: Rolling. Notification: continuous.

Costs Per Year: Application fee: $25. Area resident tuition: $66.75 per credit hour part-time. State resident tuition: $1592 full-time. Nonresident tuition: $5996 full-time.

Collegiate Environment: Orientation program. Social organizations: 23 open to all. Most popular organizations: Baptist Student Union, Social Work Club, International Students Association, Medical Laboratory Technicians,

Phi Theta Kappa. Major annual events: Club Registration Day, Back to School Cookout, Spring Fling. Campus security: 24-hour emergency response devices and patrols. College housing not available. Derrell C. Roberts Library with 119,515 books, 207,614 microform titles, 777 serials, 8,450 audiovisual materials, an OPAC, and a Web page. Operations spending for 2004 fiscal year: $710,875. 559 computers available on campus for general student use. A campuswide network can be accessed. Staffed computer lab on campus.

Community Environment: Dalton is an urban area 20 miles south of the Tenhessee line. The climate is mild year-round. This is known as the"Carpet Capital of the World." Railroads and buses serve the area. Commercial air transportation is available at Chattanooga, 31 miles distant. Fishing is excellent in the many surrounding lakes. Nearby mountains offer opportunities for hunting, fishing, hiking, and other sports. Recreation within the city includes a supervised recreation program at the center with swimming, football, baseball, softball, tennis, and an indoor picnic area.

■ **DARTON COLLEGE** *L-4*
2400 Gillionville Rd.
Albany, GA 31707-3098
Tel: (229)430-6000
Admissions: (229)430-6740
Fax: (229)430-2926
E-mail: darton@cavalier.dartnet.peachnet.edu
Web Site: http://www.darton.edu/

Description: State-supported, 2-year, coed. Part of University System of Georgia. Awards certificates, transfer associate, and terminal associate degrees. Founded 1965. Setting: 185-acre suburban campus. Total enrollment: 4,126. 2,194 applied, 81% were admitted. 5% from top 10% of their high school class, 15% from top quarter, 40% from top half. Full-time: 1,904 students, 67% women, 33% men. Part-time: 2,222 students, 77% women, 23% men. Students come from 6 other countries, 4% from out-of-state, 0.1% Native American, 1% Hispanic, 43% black, 1% Asian American or Pacific Islander, 1% international, 38% 25 or older, 5% transferred in. Retention: 63% of full-time freshmen returned the following year. Core. Calendar: semesters. Academic remediation for entering students, ESL program, services for LD students, advanced placement, accelerated degree program, self-designed majors, honors program, independent study, distance learning, double major, summer session for credit, part-time degree program, adult/continuing education programs, co-op programs. Study abroad program. ROTC: Army (c).

Entrance Requirements: Options: Common Application, electronic application, early admission. Required: high school transcript, minimum 1.8 high school GPA, proof of immunization. Required for some: SAT or ACT, SAT Subject Tests. Entrance: minimally difficult. Application deadline: 7/20. Notification: continuous until 7/27.

Costs Per Year: Application fee: $20. State resident tuition: $1542 full-time, $65 per credit hour part-time. Nonresident tuition: $6166 full-time, $257 per credit hour part-time. Mandatory fees: $300 full-time, $150 per term part-time. Full-time tuition and fees vary according to course load. Part-time tuition and fees vary according to course load.

Collegiate Environment: Orientation program. Drama-theater group, choral group, student-run newspaper. Social organizations: 17 open to all. Most popular organizations: Students in Free Enterprise (SIFE), Darton Ambassadors, Alpha Beta Gamma, Darton Association of Nursing Students (DANS), Delta Psi Omega. Major annual events: Beach Day, Speakers Series, Fairly Renaissance. Student services: personal-psychological counseling, women's center. Campus security: 24-hour patrols, student patrols, late night transport-escort service. College housing not available. Weatherbee Learning Resources Center with 67,507 books, an OPAC, and a Web page.

■ **DEKALB TECHNICAL COLLEGE** *B-11*
495 North Indian Creek Dr.
Clarkston, GA 30021-2397
Tel: (404)297-9522
Fax: (404)294-4234
E-mail: richardt@dekalbtech.org
Web Site: http://www.dekalbtech.edu/

Description: State-supported, 2-year, coed. Part of Georgia Department of Technical and Adult Education. Awards certificates, diplomas, and terminal associate degrees. Founded 1961. Setting: 17-acre suburban campus with easy access to Atlanta. Total enrollment: 4,083. Student-undergrad faculty ratio is 15:1. Full-time: 1,535 students, 60% women, 40% men. Part-time:

2,548 students, 65% women, 35% men. Students come from 2 states and territories, 0.1% Native American, 2% Hispanic, 72% black, 4% Asian American or Pacific Islander, 0.02% international, 64% 25 or older. Core. Academic remediation for entering students, services for LD students, advanced placement, distance learning, summer session for credit, part-time degree program, adult/continuing education programs, internships.

Entrance Requirements: Open admission. Options: Common Application, deferred admission. Required: high school transcript, ACT COMPASS or AS-SET. Entrance: noncompetitive.

Costs Per Year: Application fee: $15. State resident tuition: $1116 full-time, $31 per credit hour part-time. Nonresident tuition: $2232 full-time, $62 per credit hour part-time.

Collegiate Environment: Orientation program. Social organizations: 13 open to all. Most popular organizations: Student Government Association, Phi Beta Lambda, National Vocational-Technical Honor Society, Collegiate Secretaries International, Epsilon Delta Phi. Major annual events: Fall Festival, Spring Fling, Honors Day. Campus security: security during class hours. College housing not available. 500 computers available on campus for general student use. A campuswide network can be accessed. Staffed computer lab on campus.

■ **DEVRY UNIVERSITY (ALPHARETTA)** *D-4*
2555 Northwinds Parkway
Alpharetta, GA 30004
Tel: (770)521-4900; (866)338-7934
Web Site: http://www.devry.edu/
Description: Proprietary, comprehensive, coed. Part of DeVry University. Awards associate, bachelor's, and master's degrees. Founded 1997. Setting: 9-acre suburban campus with easy access to Atlanta. Total enrollment: 1,044. Faculty: 76 (36 full-time, 40 part-time). Student-undergrad faculty ratio is 14:1. Full-time: 452 students, 40% women, 60% men. Part-time: 399 students, 43% women, 57% men. 0.5% Native American, 4% Hispanic, 46% black, 3% Asian American or Pacific Islander, 2% international. Academic areas with the most degrees conferred: computer and information sciences; business/marketing; engineering technologies. Calendar: semesters. Academic remediation for entering students, services for LD students, advanced placement, accelerated degree program, distance learning, summer session for credit, part-time degree program, adult/continuing education programs, co-op programs.
Entrance Requirements: Options: electronic application, deferred admission, international baccalaureate accepted. Required: high school transcript, interview. Entrance: minimally difficult. Application deadline: Rolling. Notification: continuous.
Costs Per Year: Application fee: $50. One-time mandatory fee: $40. Tuition: $11,790 full-time, $440 per credit part-time. Mandatory fees: $270 full-time, $160 per year part-time. Full-time tuition and fees vary according to course load. Part-time tuition and fees vary according to course load.
Collegiate Environment: Orientation program. Social organizations: 12 open to all. Most popular organizations: Epsilon Delta Pi, International Student Organization, Programming Club, Alpha Sigma Lambda, National Society of Black Engineers. Major annual events: Fall Festival, Spring Fling, Thanksgiving Dinner. Campus security: 24-hour emergency response devices, late night transport-escort service, lighted pathways, video recorder (CCTV). College housing not available. Learning Resource Center with 7,659 books, 73 serials, 301 audiovisual materials, an OPAC, and a Web page. 218 computers available on campus for general student use. Computer purchase/lease plans available. A campuswide network can be accessed from off-campus. Staffed computer lab on campus.

■ **DEVRY UNIVERSITY (ATLANTA)** *E-4*
Fifteen Piedmont Center, Plaza Level 100
Atlanta, GA 30305-1543
Tel: (404)296-7400
Fax: (404)240-0227
Web Site: http://www.devry.edu/
Description: Proprietary, comprehensive, coed. Calendar: semesters.
Costs Per Year: One-time mandatory fee: $40. Tuition: $11,790 full-time, $440 per credit part-time. Mandatory fees: $60 full-time, $60 per year part-time. Full-time tuition and fees vary according to course load. Part-time tuition and fees vary according to course load.

■ **DEVRY UNIVERSITY (DECATUR)** *C-11*
250 North Arcadia Ave.
Decatur, GA 30030-2198

Tel: (404)292-7900; (866)338-7934
Fax: (404)292-2321
Web Site: http://www.devry.edu/
Description: Proprietary, comprehensive, coed. Part of DeVry University. Awards associate, bachelor's, and master's degrees. Founded 1969. Setting: 21-acre suburban campus with easy access to Atlanta. Total enrollment: 2,197. Faculty: 133 (53 full-time, 80 part-time). Student-undergrad faculty ratio is 18:1. Full-time: 977 students, 34% women, 66% men. Part-time: 891 students, 35% women, 65% men. 0.3% Native American, 2% Hispanic, 78% black, 2% Asian American or Pacific Islander, 2% international, 49% 25 or older. Academic areas with the most degrees conferred: business/marketing; computer and information sciences; engineering technologies. Calendar: semesters. Academic remediation for entering students, services for LD students, advanced placement, accelerated degree program, distance learning, summer session for credit, part-time degree program, adult/continuing education programs, co-op programs.
Entrance Requirements: Options: electronic application, deferred admission, international baccalaureate accepted. Required: high school transcript, interview. Entrance: minimally difficult. Application deadline: Rolling. Notification: continuous.
Costs Per Year: Application fee: $50. One-time mandatory fee: $40. Tuition: $11,790 full-time, $440 per credit part-time. Mandatory fees: $270 full-time, $160 per year part-time. Full-time tuition and fees vary according to course load. Part-time tuition and fees according to course load.
Collegiate Environment: Orientation program. Social organizations: 12 open to all. Most popular organizations: Programming Club, Epsilon Delta Pi, Tau Alpha Pi, National Society of Black Engineers, International Student Organization. Major annual events: Fall Festival, Spring Fling, Thanksgiving Dinner. Campus security: 24-hour emergency response devices and patrols, late night transport-escort service, lighted pathways/sidewalks. College housing not available. Learning Resource Center with 18,849 books, 21,024 microform titles, 80 serials, 800 audiovisual materials, an OPAC, and a Web page.

■ **DEVRY UNIVERSITY (DULUTH)** *D-5*
3505 Koger Blvd., Ste. 170
Duluth, GA 30096-7671
Tel: (678)380-9780
Fax: (678)924-0958
Web Site: http://www.devry.edu/
Description: Proprietary, comprehensive, coed. Calendar: semesters.
Costs Per Year: One-time mandatory fee: $40. Tuition: $11,790 full-time, $440 per credit part-time. Mandatory fees: $60 full-time, $30 per year part-time. Full-time tuition and fees vary according to course load. Part-time tuition and fees vary according to course load.

■ **EAST CENTRAL TECHNICAL COLLEGE** *K-7*
667 Perry House Rd.
Fitzgerald, GA 31750
Tel: (229)468-2000
Admissions: (229)468-2033
Fax: (229)468-2110
E-mail: ccoffey@ectcollege.org
Web Site: http://www.eastcentraltech.edu/
Description: State-supported, 2-year, coed. Awards certificates, diplomas, and terminal associate degrees. Founded 1968. Setting: 30-acre rural campus. Total enrollment: 1,238. Full-time: 561 students, 71% women, 29% men. Part-time: 677 students, 70% women, 30% men. 0% Native American, 1% Hispanic, 37% black, 0.1% Asian American or Pacific Islander, 0% international. Academic remediation for entering students, services for LD students, distance learning, co-op programs and internships.
Entrance Requirements: Open admission. Option: deferred admission. Required: high school transcript, ACT COMPASS or ASSET. Entrance: noncompetitive.
Costs Per Year: Application fee: $15. State resident tuition: $1116 full-time, $31 per credit hour part-time. Nonresident tuition: $2232 full-time, $62 per credit hour part-time.
Collegiate Environment: College housing not available.

■ **EAST GEORGIA COLLEGE** *I-9*
131 College Circle
Swainsboro, GA 30401-2699
Tel: (478)289-2000
Admissions: (478)289-2009

Fax: (478)289-2038

Web Site: http://www.ega.edu/

Description: State-supported, 2-year, coed. Part of University System of Georgia. Awards certificates and transfer associate degrees. Founded 1973. Setting: 207-acre rural campus. Endowment: $32,500. Educational spending for 2005 fiscal year: $3293 per student. Total enrollment: 1,318. 758 applied, 65% were admitted. Full-time: 887 students, 59% women, 41% men. Part-time: 431 students, 62% women, 38% men. Students come from 12 states and territories, 3 other countries, 1% from out-of-state, 0.3% Native American, 1% Hispanic, 32% black, 1% Asian American or Pacific Islander, 0% international, 18% 25 or older, 1% transferred in. Core. Calendar: semesters. Academic remediation for entering students, services for LD students, advanced placement, honors program, independent study, distance learning, summer session for credit, part-time degree program, adult/continuing education programs. Off campus study. Study abroad program.

Entrance Requirements: Options: early admission, deferred admission. Required: high school transcript. Entrance: minimally difficult. Application deadline: Rolling. Notification: continuous.

Costs Per Year: Application fee: $20. State resident tuition: $1560 full-time, $65 per credit hour part-time. Nonresident tuition: $6168 full-time, $257 per credit hour part-time. Mandatory fees: $38 per term part-time. Full-time tuition varies according to course load and location. Part-time tuition and fees vary according to course load and location.

Collegiate Environment: Orientation program. Drama-theater group, choral group, student-run newspaper. Most popular organizations: Hoopee Bird, student government, yearbook, Gamma Beta Phi, Wiregrass. Major annual events: free food days, Honors Day, Convocation. Student services: personal-psychological counseling. Campus security: 24-hour patrols. College housing not available. East Georgia College Library with 43,780 books, 203 serials, an OPAC, and a Web page. Operations spending for 2004 fiscal year: $187,940. 90 computers available on campus for general student use. A campuswide network can be accessed from off-campus. Staffed computer lab on campus.

Community Environment: Swainsboro, the county seat of Emanuel County, is located in the southeast section of Georgia near the Center of the vast southern pine forest. The climate is mild with an annual mean temperature of 66 degrees; the average rainfall is 42 inches. Transportation is provided by the Georgia and Florida Railroad and Greyhound. Community facilities include one hospital, 24 churches, restaurants, hotels, motels, and shopping areas. Industry, agriculture, and forestry are important to the economy of the area. Agricultural products include cotton, tobacco, peanuts, soybeans, corn, and potatoes. Some of the industries manufacture sprinkler system valves, furniture, dressed lumber, seed processing, playground equipment, knitwear, molded plastics, screws, rivets, and component parts. A well-staffed and budgeted recreation department offers many recreational opportunities to youth. Fish ponds are in abundance in Emanuel County. Many fresh water streams are filled with trout and bream. Quail and wild turkeys abound and there are excellent reserves for hunting. The first week in May is set aside for the annual Emanuel County Pine Tree Festival.

■ **EMMANUEL COLLEGE**

PO Box 129

181 Springs St.

Franklin Springs, GA 30639-0129

Tel: (706)245-7226

E-mail: admissions@emmanuel-college.edu

Web Site: http://www.emmanuelcollege.edu/

Description: Independent, 4-year, coed, affiliated with Pentecostal Holiness Church. Awards associate and bachelor's degrees. Founded 1919. Setting: 90-acre rural campus with easy access to Atlanta. Endowment: $4.4 million. Educational spending for 2005 fiscal year: $3389 per student. Total enrollment: 707. Student-undergrad faculty ratio is 12:1. 1,039 applied, 38% were admitted. Full-time: 594 students, 57% women, 43% men. Part-time: 113 students, 57% women, 43% men. Students come from 22 states and territories, 3 other countries, 20% from out-of-state, 0.3% Native American, 1% Hispanic, 15% black, 1% Asian American or Pacific Islander, 1% international, 18% 25 or older, 44% live on campus, 11% transferred in. Retention: 71% of full-time freshmen returned the following year. Academic areas with the most degrees conferred: education; business/marketing; theology and religious vocations. Core. Calendar: semesters. Academic remediation for entering students, advanced placement, accelerated degree program, honors program, independent study, distance learning, summer session for credit, part-time degree program, internships.

Entrance Requirements: Options: Peterson's Universal Application, early admission, deferred admission. Required: high school transcript, SAT or ACT. Entrance: minimally difficult. Application deadline: 8/1. Notification: 8/1.

Costs Per Year: Application fee: $25. Comprehensive fee: $14,850 includes full-time tuition ($9800), mandatory fees ($350), and college room and board ($4700). College room only: $2150. Room and board charges vary according to board plan. Part-time tuition: $408 per hour.

Collegiate Environment: Orientation program. Drama-theater group, choral group, student-run newspaper. Social organizations: 15 open to all. Most popular organizations: SIFE, FCA, SOS, BSU, International Students Club. Major annual events: Feast of Ingathering, Homecoming Weekend, Spring Musical. Student services: health clinic, personal-psychological counseling. Campus security: 24-hour patrols, controlled dormitory access. 370 college housing spaces available; 328 were occupied in 2003-04. Freshmen guaranteed college housing. On-campus residence required through sophomore year. Options: men-only, women-only housing available. Shaw-Leslie Library with 74,735 books, 6,055 microform titles, 76 serials, 3,315 audiovisual materials, an OPAC, and a Web page. Operations spending for 2004 fiscal year: $92,417. 50 computers available on campus for general student use. A campuswide network can be accessed from student residence rooms and from off campus. Staffed computer lab on campus.

■ **EMORY UNIVERSITY** *E-4*

1380 South Oxford Rd.

Atlanta, GA 30322-1100

Tel: (404)727-6123

Free: 800-727-6036

Admissions: (404)727-6036

E-mail: admiss@unix.cc.emory.edu

Web Site: http://www.emory.edu/

Description: Independent Methodist, university, coed. Awards associate, bachelor's, master's, doctoral, and first professional degrees (enrollment figures include Emory University, Oxford College; application data for main campus only). Founded 1836. Setting: 631-acre suburban campus. Endowment: $4.4 billion. Research spending for 2004 fiscal year: $351 million. Educational spending for 2005 fiscal year: $37,233 per student. Total enrollment: 12,134. Faculty: 1,435 (1,236 full-time, 199 part-time). Student-undergrad faculty ratio is 7:1. 12,011 applied, 37% were admitted. 90% from top 10% of their high school class, 98% from top quarter, 100% from top half. 67 National Merit Scholars. Full-time: 6,421 students, 58% women, 42% men. Part-time: 89 students, 74% women, 26% men. Students come from 52 states and territories, 64 other countries, 80% from out-of-state, 0.3% Native American, 3% Hispanic, 9% black, 16% Asian American or Pacific Islander, 4% international, 2% 25 or older, 70% live on campus, 1% transferred in. Retention: 94% of full-time freshmen returned the following year. Academic areas with the most degrees conferred: social sciences; business/marketing; psychology. Core. Calendar: semesters. Services for LD students, advanced placement, accelerated degree program, honors program, double major, summer session for credit, internships, graduate courses open to undergrads. Off campus study at University Center in Georgia; Washington Semester, American University. Study abroad program. ROTC: Air Force (c).

Entrance Requirements: Options: Peterson's Universal Application, Common Application, electronic application, early admission, early decision, deferred admission, international baccalaureate accepted. Required: essay, high school transcript, 1 recommendation, SAT or ACT. Recommended: minimum 3.0 high school GPA, SAT Subject Tests. Entrance: most difficult. Application deadlines: 1/15, 11/1 for early decision plan 1, 1/1 for early decision plan 2. Notification: 4/1, 12/15 for early decision plan 1, 2/1 for early decision plan 2.

Costs Per Year: Application fee: $50. Comprehensive fee: $40,546 includes full-time tuition ($30,400), mandatory fees ($394), and college room and board ($9752). College room only: $6112. Room and board charges vary according to board plan, housing facility, and student level. Part-time tuition: $1267 per credit.

Collegiate Environment: Orientation program. Drama-theater group, choral group, student-run newspaper, radio station. Social organizations: 220 open to all; national fraternities, national sororities; 31% of eligible men and 33% of eligible women are members. Most popular organizations: Volunteer Emory, music/theater, student government, Outdoor Emory. Major annual events: Heritage/Homecoming Week, Halloween Ball, Dooley's Spring Fest. Student services: legal services, health clinic, personal-psychological counseling, women's center. Campus security: 24-hour emergency response devices and patrols, student patrols, late night transport-escort service.

4,014 college housing spaces available. Freshmen guaranteed college housing. On-campus residence required through sophomore year. Option: coed housing available. Robert W. Woodruff Library plus 7 others with 2.5 million books, 3.6 million microform titles, 51,500 serials, an OPAC, and a Web page. Operations spending for 2004 fiscal year: $29 million. 600 computers available on campus for general student use. Computer purchase/lease plans available. A campuswide network can be accessed from student residence rooms and from off campus. Staffed computer lab on campus.

Community Environment: Emory is located in a residential area of Atlanta, 6 miles from downtown. Atlanta, capital of Georgia, is the commercial, industrial and financial giant of the southeast. It is located in the foothills of the Blue Ridge Mountains. Atlanta was host to the 1996 Olympic Games. Atlanta's moderate climate permits year-round golf, fishing and outdoor living. All major forms of public transportation are available. Peachtree Street is experiencing one of the biggest building booms in the country. Peachtree Center includes the Atlanta Merchandise Mart, and the 22-story regency Hyatt Hotel. Bridges 22 stories above the street connect buildings on the Peachtree Center. The city is the cultural center of the South with a symphony, art center, and theaters. Atlanta is a major business and manufacturing center that produces more that 3,500 different commodities. Excellent part-time employment opportunities are available. Recreational activities include all major sports, swimming, golfing, boating, horseback riding, tennis, and fishing. Many spectator sports events take place in the Atlanta Stadium.

■ **EMORY UNIVERSITY, OXFORD COLLEGE** *E-5*

100 Hamill St., PO Box 1328
Oxford, GA 30054
Tel: (770)784-8888
Free: 800-723-8328
Admissions: (770)784-8328
Fax: (770)784-8359
Web Site: http://www.emory.edu/OXFORD/
Description: Independent Methodist, 2-year, coed. Part of Emory University. Awards transfer associate degrees. Founded 1836. Setting: 150-acre small town campus with easy access to Atlanta. Endowment: $26 million. Research spending for 2004 fiscal year: $50,000. Total enrollment: 554. 1,421 applied, 72% were admitted. Full-time: 554 students, 59% women, 41% men. Students come from 29 states and territories, 7 other countries, 45% from out-of-state, 0.4% Native American, 4% Hispanic, 12% black, 21% Asian American or Pacific Islander, 3% international, 0% 25 or older, 95% live on campus, 1% transferred in. Retention: 83% of full-time freshmen returned the following year. Core. Calendar: semesters. Services for LD students, advanced placement, independent study, distance learning, double major, summer session for credit, internships. Off campus study. Study abroad program.
Entrance Requirements: Options: Common Application, electronic application, early admission, early action, deferred admission, international baccalaureate accepted. Required: essay, high school transcript, 1 recommendation, level of interest, SAT or ACT. Recommended: minimum 3.0 high school GPA, 2 recommendations. Required for some: interview, SAT Subject Tests. Entrance: moderately difficult. Application deadlines: 2/1, 11/15 for early action. Notification: continuous, 1/3 for early action.
Collegiate Environment: Orientation program. Drama-theater group, choral group, student-run newspaper. Social organizations: 45 open to all; local coed social organizations; 8% of eligible men and 10% of eligible women are members. Most popular organizations: Residence Hall Association, intramurals/junior varsity sports, Student Government Association, Student Admissions Association, Volunteer Oxford. Major annual events: drama productions, Oxford Day, fall and spring formal dances. Student services: health clinic, personal-psychological counseling. Campus security: 24-hour emergency response devices and patrols, student patrols, late night transport-escort service, controlled dormitory access. 579 college housing spaces available; 521 were occupied in 2003-04. Freshmen guaranteed college housing. On-campus residence required through sophomore year. Options: coed, women-only housing available. Hoke O'Kelly Library with 80,099 books, 495 microform titles, 240 serials, 656 audiovisual materials, an OPAC, and a Web page. Operations spending for 2004 fiscal year: $250,000. 110 computers available on campus for general student use. A

campuswide network can be accessed from student residence rooms and from off campus. Staffed computer lab on campus.

■ **FLINT RIVER TECHNICAL COLLEGE** *H-4*

1533 US Hwy. 19 South
Thomaston, GA 30286
Tel: (706)646-6148
Free: 800-752-9681
Fax: (706)646-6163
E-mail: gwilliams@flintrivertech.edu
Web Site: http://www.flintrivertech.edu/
Description: State-supported, 2-year, coed. Awards certificates, diplomas, and terminal associate degrees. Founded 1961. Total enrollment: 805. Full-time: 425 students, 78% women, 22% men. Part-time: 380 students, 72% women, 28% men. 0.1% Native American, 0.5% Hispanic, 48% black, 0.1% Asian American or Pacific Islander, 0% international. Academic remediation for entering students, services for LD students, advanced placement, distance learning, co-op programs and internships.
Entrance Requirements: Open admission. Option: deferred admission. Required: high school transcript, ACT COMPASS or ASSET. Entrance: noncompetitive.
Costs Per Year: Application fee: $15. State resident tuition: $1116 full-time, $31 per credit hour part-time. Nonresident tuition: $2232 full-time, $62 per credit hour part-time.
Collegiate Environment: College housing not available. 2,653 books, 82 serials, and 202 audiovisual materials.

■ **FORT VALLEY STATE UNIVERSITY** *I-5*

1005 State University Dr.
Fort Valley, GA 31030-4313
Tel: (478)825-6211
Free: 800-248-7343
Admissions: (478)825-6307
Fax: (478)825-6394
Web Site: http://www.fvsu.edu/
Description: State-supported, comprehensive, coed. Part of University System of Georgia. Awards associate, bachelor's, master's, doctoral, and first professional degrees. Founded 1895. Setting: 1,365-acre small town campus. Endowment: $3.8 million. Research spending for 2004 fiscal year: $5.7 million. Educational spending for 2005 fiscal year: $5852 per student. Total enrollment: 2,174. Faculty: 121 (105 full-time, 16 part-time). Student-undergrad faculty ratio is 22:1. 2,190 applied, 36% were admitted. Full-time: 1,723 students, 53% women, 47% men. Part-time: 274 students, 62% women, 38% men. Students come from 15 states and territories, 21 other countries, 6% from out-of-state, 0.1% Native American, 0.3% Hispanic, 95% black, 0.3% Asian American or Pacific Islander, 1% international, 21% 25 or older, 59% live on campus, 5% transferred in. Retention: 72% of full-time freshmen returned the following year. Academic areas with the most degrees conferred: psychology; biological/life sciences; business/marketing. Core. Calendar: semesters. Academic remediation for entering students, services for LD students, advanced placement, freshman honors college, honors program, distance learning, double major, summer session for credit, part-time degree program, adult/continuing education programs, co-op programs and internships, graduate courses open to undergrads. Off campus study. Study abroad program. ROTC: Army.
Entrance Requirements: Options: Peterson's Universal Application, Common Application, electronic application, early admission, deferred admission. Required: high school transcript, SAT or ACT. Entrance: moderately difficult. Application deadline: 8/1. Notification: continuous until 8/10.
Costs Per Year: Application fee: $20. State resident tuition: $3044 full-time, $102 per credit part-time. Nonresident tuition: $10,360 full-time, $407 per credit part-time. Mandatory fees: $606 full-time, $303 per term part-time. Full-time tuition and fees vary according to course load. Part-time tuition and fees vary according to course load. College room and board: $4496. College room only: $2200. Room and board charges vary according to board plan.
Collegiate Environment: Orientation program. Drama-theater group, choral group, marching band, student-run newspaper, radio station. Social organizations: 45 open to all; national fraternities, national sororities. Most popular organizations: Drama Group, Christian Student Organization, Habitat for Humanity, Debate Club. Major annual events: Founders' Day, Black History Observance, Annual Fall Convocation. Student services: health clinic, personal-psychological counseling. Campus security: 24-hour emergency response devices and patrols, student patrols, late night transport-escort service. 2,000 college housing spaces available; 1,500 were

occupied in 2003-04. No special consideration for freshman housing applicants. Options: coed, men-only, women-only housing available. Henry A. Hunt Memorial Library plus 2 others with 186,365 books, 1,213 serials, and an OPAC. Operations spending for 2004 fiscal year: $1.5 million. 633 computers available on campus for general student use. A campuswide network can be accessed from off-campus. Staffed computer lab on campus.

Community Environment: Fort Valley is a small town with a temperate climate. It is the main peach-growing section of the state. Miles of blooming peach orchards adorn the roadways in the spring. Community facilities include churches of major denominations, a library, and hospital. The Blue Bird Body Company, manufacturers of school bus bodies, is also located here. Part-time employment opportunities are available in Peach and surrounding counties. The Massee Lane Farms located five miles southwest of the City has one of the finest collections of camellias in the country.

■ GAINESVILLE COLLEGE *C-5*

PO Box 1358
Gainesville, GA 30503-1358
Tel: (770)718-3639
Admissions: (770)718-3641
Fax: (770)718-3859
E-mail: mpalmour@gsc.edu
Web Site: http://www.gc.peachnet.edu/

Description: State-supported, primarily 2-year, coed. Part of University System of Georgia. Awards transfer associate, terminal associate, and bachelor's degrees. Founded 1964. Setting: 220-acre small town campus with easy access to Atlanta. Endowment: $9.2 million. Educational spending for 2005 fiscal year: $1700 per student. Total enrollment: 5,985. Student-undergrad faculty ratio is 24:1. 3,171 applied, 84% were admitted. Full-time: 3,550 students, 50% women, 50% men. Part-time: 2,435 students, 59% women, 41% men. Students come from 22 states and territories, 12 other countries, 4% from out-of-state, 0.4% Native American, 4% Hispanic, 4% black, 2% Asian American or Pacific Islander, 2% international, 11% 25 or older. Core. Calendar: semesters. Academic remediation for entering students, ESL program, services for LD students, advanced placement, honors program, distance learning, double major, summer session for credit, part-time degree program, adult/continuing education programs, internships. Off campus study.

Entrance Requirements: Option: early admission. Required: high school transcript. Recommended: SAT or ACT. Entrance: noncompetitive. Application deadline: 7/1.

Costs Per Year: Application fee: $35. State resident tuition: $1542 full-time, $65 per credit hour part-time. Nonresident tuition: $6166 full-time, $257 per credit hour part-time. Mandatory fees: $164 full-time.

Collegiate Environment: Orientation program. Drama-theater group, choral group, student-run newspaper. Social organizations: 26 open to all. Most popular organizations: student newspaper, Baptist Student Union, Student Government Association, Pre-Law/Political Science Club. Major annual events: Field Day, Jazz on the Green, Honors Day. Student services: personal-psychological counseling. Campus security: 24-hour patrols. College housing not available. John Harrison Hosch Library with 70,000 books, 398 serials, an OPAC, and a Web page. 500 computers available on campus for general student use. A campuswide network can be accessed from off-campus. Staffed computer lab on campus.

■ GEORGIA AVIATION & TECHNICAL COLLEGE *J-7*

71 Airport Rd., Heart of Georgia Regional Airport
Eastman, GA 31023
Tel: (478)374-6980
Fax: (478)374-6809
E-mail: tspires@gaaviationtech.edu
Web Site: http://www.gavtc.org/

Description: State-supported, 2-year, coed. Awards certificates, diplomas, and terminal associate degrees. Founded 1995. Total enrollment: 252. Full-time: 158 students, 12% women, 88% men. Part-time: 94 students, 18% women, 82% men. 1% Native American, 1% Hispanic, 6% black, 0.4% Asian American or Pacific Islander, 0% international. Academic remediation for entering students, services for LD students, advanced placement, co-op programs and internships.

Entrance Requirements: Open admission. Option: deferred admission. Required: high school transcript, ACT COMPASS or ASSET. Entrance: noncompetitive.

Costs Per Year: Application fee: $15. State resident tuition: $1116 full-time, $31 per credit hour part-time. Nonresident tuition: $2232 full-time, $62 per credit hour part-time.

Collegiate Environment: College housing not available.

■ GEORGIA COLLEGE & STATE UNIVERSITY *G-7*

Hancock St.
Milledgeville, GA 31061
Tel: (478)445-5004
Admissions: (478)445-1283
Fax: (478)445-6795
E-mail: paul.jones@gcsu.edu
Web Site: http://www.gcsu.edu/

Description: State-supported, comprehensive, coed. Part of University System of Georgia. Awards bachelor's and master's degrees and post-master's certificates. Founded 1889. Setting: 590-acre small town campus. Endowment: $12.6 million. Research spending for 2004 fiscal year: $184,782. Educational spending for 2005 fiscal year: $8972 per student. Total enrollment: 5,659. Faculty: 402 (268 full-time, 134 part-time). Student-undergrad faculty ratio is 15:1. 3,236 applied, 60% were admitted. 16% from top 10% of their high school class, 46% from top quarter, 86% from top half. Full-time: 4,243 students, 59% women, 41% men. Part-time: 555 students, 59% women, 41% men. Students come from 39 states and territories, 42 other countries, 1% from out-of-state, 0.2% Native American, 1% Hispanic, 8% black, 1% Asian American or Pacific Islander, 2% international, 11% 25 or older, 36% live on campus, 8% transferred in. Retention: 84% of full-time freshmen returned the following year. Academic areas with the most degrees conferred: business/marketing; education; health professions and related sciences. Core. Calendar: semesters. Academic remediation for entering students, ESL program, services for LD students, advanced placement, accelerated degree program, self-designed majors, freshman honors college, honors program, independent study, distance learning, double major, summer session for credit, part-time degree program, internships, graduate courses open to undergrads. Study abroad program. ROTC: Army (c).

Entrance Requirements: Options: electronic application, early admission, early action, deferred admission. Required: essay, high school transcript, proof of immunization, SAT or ACT. Recommended: interview. Required for some: SAT Subject Tests. Entrance: moderately difficult. Application deadlines: 4/1, 11/1 for early action. Notification: continuous, 12/1 for early action.

Costs Per Year: Application fee: $25. State resident tuition: $3404 full-time, $142 per semester hour part-time. Nonresident tuition: $13,616 full-time, $568 per semester hour part-time. Mandatory fees: $738 full-time, $369 per term part-time. Full-time tuition and fees vary according to location. Part-time tuition and fees vary according to course load and location. College room and board: $6878. College room only: $3690. Room and board charges vary according to board plan and housing facility.

Collegiate Environment: Orientation program. Drama-theater group, choral group, student-run newspaper, radio station. Social organizations: 100 open to all; national fraternities, national sororities; 9% of eligible men and 13% of eligible women are members. Most popular organization: Baptist Student Union. Major annual events: Fall Freshman Convocation/Week of Welcome, Midnight Breakfast, Progressive Dinner. Student services: health clinic, personal-psychological counseling, women's center. Campus security: 24-hour emergency response devices and patrols, student patrols, late night transport-escort service, controlled dormitory access. 1,777 college housing spaces available; 1,638 were occupied in 2003-04. Freshmen given priority for college housing. On-campus residence required in freshman year. Option: coed housing available. Ina Dillard Russell Library with 169,735 books, 654,476 microform titles, 13,165 serials, 4,650 audiovisual materials, an OPAC, and a Web page. Operations spending for 2004 fiscal year: $1.5 million. 500 computers available on campus for general student use. A campuswide network can be accessed from student residence rooms and from off campus. Staffed computer lab on campus.

■ GEORGIA HIGHLANDS COLLEGE *D-2*

3175 Cedartown Hwy., SE
PO Box 1864
Rome, GA 30162-1864
Tel: (706)802-5000
Free: 800-332-2406
Admissions: (706)295-6339
Fax: (706)295-6610
E-mail: tjones@highlands.edu
Web Site: http://www.highlands.edu/

Description: State-supported, 2-year, coed. Part of University System of Georgia. Awards certificates, diplomas, transfer associate, and terminal associate degrees. Founded 1970. Setting: 226-acre small town campus with easy access to Atlanta. Endowment: $443,000. Total enrollment: 3,817. Student-undergrad faculty ratio is 40:1. 2,079 applied, 84% were admitted. Full-time: 2,059 students, 58% women, 42% men. Part-time: 1,758 students, 72% women, 28% men. 14% from out-of-state. 0.2% Native American, 3% Hispanic, 11% black, 2% Asian American or Pacific Islander, 35% 25 or older. Core. Calendar: semesters. Academic remediation for entering students, services for LD students, advanced placement, honors program, independent study, distance learning, double major, summer session for credit, part-time degree program, co-op programs. Study abroad program.

Entrance Requirements: Options: Peterson's Universal Application, Common Application, electronic application, early admission, deferred admission. Required: high school transcript, minimum 2.0 high school GPA. Recommended: SAT or ACT. Required for some: minimum 2.2 high school GPA. Entrance: noncompetitive. Application deadline: Rolling. Notification: continuous, continuous for nonresidents.

Costs Per Year: Application fee: $20. State resident tuition: $1542 full-time, $65 per hour part-time. Nonresident tuition: $6168 full-time, $257 per hour part-time. Mandatory fees: $198 full-time, $99 per term part-time. Part-time tuition and fees vary according to course load.

Collegiate Environment: Orientation program. Student-run newspaper. Social organizations: 16 open to all. Most popular organizations: Floyd Association of Nursing Students, Health, Physical Education, and Recreation Club, Black Awareness Society, Political Science Association. Major annual events: Tower Hour, Welcome Back Cookout, Spring Fling. Student services: personal-psychological counseling. Campus security: 24-hour patrols. College housing not available. Georgia Highlands Library plus 1 other with 65,090 books, 19,204 microform titles, 267 serials, 9,207 audiovisual materials, an OPAC, and a Web page.

Community Environment: See Shorter College.

■ **GEORGIA INSTITUTE OF TECHNOLOGY** *E-4*
225 North Ave., NW
Atlanta, GA 30332-0001
Tel: (404)894-2000
Admissions: (404)894-4154
Fax: (404)853-9163
E-mail: admission@gatech.edu
Web Site: http://www.gatech.edu/
Description: State-supported, university, coed. Part of University System of Georgia. Awards bachelor's, master's, and doctoral degrees. Founded 1885. Setting: 400-acre urban campus. Endowment: $1.2 billion. Research spending for 2004 fiscal year: $431.4 million. Educational spending for 2005 fiscal year: $10,768 per student. Total enrollment: 17,135. Faculty: 837 (810 full-time, 27 part-time). Student-undergrad faculty ratio is 14:1. 9,172 applied, 67% were admitted. Full-time: 10,992 students, 28% women, 72% men. Part-time: 849 students, 28% women, 72% men. Students come from 54 states and territories, 121 other countries, 28% from out-of-state, 0.3% Native American, 4% Hispanic, 7% black, 15% Asian American or Pacific Islander, 5% international, 4% 25 or older, 53% live on campus, 4% transferred in. Retention: 92% of full-time freshmen returned the following year. Academic areas with the most degrees conferred: engineering; business/marketing; computer and information sciences. Core. Calendar: semesters. Academic remediation for entering students, ESL program, services for LD students, advanced placement, accelerated degree program, self-designed majors, honors program, independent study, distance learning, double major, summer session for credit, part-time degree program, co-op programs and internships, graduate courses open to undergrads. Off campus study at University Center in Georgia. Study abroad program. ROTC: Army, Naval, Air Force.

Entrance Requirements: Options: Peterson's Universal Application, Common Application, electronic application, early admission, international baccalaureate accepted. Required: essay, high school transcript, SAT or ACT. Entrance: very difficult. Application deadline: 1/15. Notification: 3/15. Preference given to state residents.

Costs Per Year: Application fee: $50. State resident tuition: $3638 full-time, $152 per hour part-time. Nonresident tuition: $17,980 full-time, $750 per hour part-time. Mandatory fees: $1010 full-time, $505 per term part-time. Part-time tuition and fees vary according to course load. College room and board: $6802. College room only: $3992. Room and board charges vary according to board plan and housing facility.

Collegiate Environment: Orientation program. Drama-theater group, choral group, marching band, student-run newspaper, radio station. Social organizations: 308 open to all; national fraternities, national sororities, local

sororities; 21% of eligible men and 24% of eligible women are members. Most popular organizations: Christian Campus Fellowship, IEEE, Mechanical Engineering Graduate Student Association, Gamma Beta Phi Society. Major annual events: homecoming, Greek Week. Student services: legal services, health clinic, personal-psychological counseling, women's center. Campus security: 24-hour emergency response devices and patrols, student patrols, late night transport-escort service, controlled dormitory access, self defense education, lighted pathways and walks, video cameras. 5,633 college housing spaces available; all were occupied in 2003-04. Freshmen guaranteed college housing. Options: coed, men-only, women-only housing available. Library and Information Center plus 1 other with 213,128 books, 4.4 million microform titles, 26,068 serials, 329,981 audiovisual materials, an OPAC, and a Web page. Operations spending for 2004 fiscal year: $11.6 million. 2,160 computers available on campus for general student use. A campus-wide network can be accessed from student residence rooms and from off campus. Staffed computer lab on campus.

Community Environment: See Clark Atlanta University.

■ **GEORGIA MEDICAL INSTITUTE-DEKALB** *E-4*
1706 Northeast Expressway
Atlanta, GA 30329
Tel: (404)327-8787
Fax: (404)327-8980
Web Site: http://www.georgia-med.com/
Description: Proprietary, 2-year, coed. Awards diplomas and terminal associate degrees. Founded 1977. Setting: 3-acre suburban campus. Total enrollment: 550. 782 applied, 70% were admitted. 0% Native American, 1% Hispanic, 84% black, 1% Asian American or Pacific Islander, 0.4% international. Calendar: continuous.

■ **GEORGIA MILITARY COLLEGE** *G-7*
201 East Greene St.
Milledgeville, GA 31061-3398
Tel: (478)445-2700
Free: 800-342-0413
Admissions: (478)445-2751
Fax: (478)445-2688
Web Site: http://www.gmc.cc.ga.us/
Description: State and locally supported, 2-year, coed. Awards transfer associate and terminal associate degrees. Founded 1879. Setting: 40-acre small town campus. Total enrollment: 4,062. 2,258 applied, 100% were admitted. Full-time: 2,471 students, 60% women, 40% men. Part-time: 1,591 students, 55% women, 45% men. Students come from 29 states and territories, 0.4% Native American, 3% Hispanic, 40% black, 2% Asian American or Pacific Islander, 0.02% international, 27% 25 or older. Core. Academic remediation for entering students, advanced placement, summer session for credit, part-time degree program, external degree program. Off campus study at Georgia College. ROTC: Army.

Entrance Requirements: Options: early admission, deferred admission. Required: high school transcript. Recommended: SAT or ACT. Required for some: SAT or ACT. Entrance: minimally difficult. Application deadline: Rolling.

Collegiate Environment: Marching band, student-run newspaper. Major annual event: parades. Student services: personal-psychological counseling. Campus security: 24-hour emergency response devices and patrols. 264 college housing spaces available; 20 were occupied in 2003-04. On-campus residence required through sophomore year. Option: coed housing available. Sibley-Cone Library with 20,000 books and 150 serials. 40 computers available on campus for general student use. Staffed computer lab on campus.

Community Environment: Milledgeville, an educational center, was the state capital from 1807 to 1867. Georgia Military College occupies the old state house. Railroads and buses serve the area. Some of the industries are spinning, canning, manufacture of clay products, and mobile homes. Job opportunities are numerous in textile plants. Nearby Lake Sinclair provides boating, fishing and water skiing. The early nineteenth-century homes add atmosphere and beauty to community life.

■ **GEORGIA PERIMETER COLLEGE** *C-11*
3251 Panthersville Rd.
Decatur, GA 30034-3897
Tel: (404)244-5090; 888-696-2780
Admissions: (404)299-4551
Fax: (404)244-2996
Web Site: http://www.gpc.edu/

Description: State-supported, 2-year, coed. Part of University System of Georgia. Awards certificates, transfer associate, and terminal associate degrees. Founded 1964. Setting: 100-acre suburban campus with easy access to Atlanta. Endowment: $136,686. Educational spending for 2005 fiscal year: $2419 per student. Total enrollment: 18,986. Full-time: 8,548 students, 58% women, 42% men. Part-time: 10,438 students, 67% women, 33% men. Students come from 40 states and territories, 125 other countries, 7% from out-of-state, 0.3% Native American, 4% Hispanic, 37% black, 9% Asian American or Pacific Islander, 5% international, 36% 25 or older, 5% transferred in. Core. Calendar: semesters. Academic remediation for entering students, ESL program, services for LD students, advanced placement, honors program, distance learning, summer session for credit, part-time degree program, adult/continuing education programs. Study abroad program. ROTC: Army (c).

Entrance Requirements: Option: early admission. Required: high school transcript, SAT or ACT. Entrance: minimally difficult. Application deadline: 7/1. Notification: continuous.

Collegiate Environment: Orientation program. Drama-theater group, choral group, student-run newspaper. Social organizations: 45 open to all. Student services: personal-psychological counseling. Campus security: 24-hour emergency response devices and patrols, late night transport-escort service. College housing not available. Georgia Perimeter College Library with 369,969 books, 36,511 microform titles, 2,032 serials, 15,500 audiovisual materials, and an OPAC. Operations spending for 2004 fiscal year: $429,889.

■ **GEORGIA SOUTHERN UNIVERSITY** *I-11*
PO Box 8055
Statesboro, GA 30460
Tel: (912)681-5611
Admissions: (912)681-5391
Fax: (912)681-5635
E-mail: admissions@gasou.edu
Web Site: http://www.georgiasouthern.edu/

Description: State-supported, comprehensive, coed. Part of University System of Georgia. Awards bachelor's, master's, and doctoral degrees and post-master's certificates. Founded 1906. Setting: 634-acre small town campus. Endowment: $27.8 million. Research spending for 2004 fiscal year: $2.2 million. Educational spending for 2005 fiscal year: $4785 per student. Total enrollment: 16,646. Faculty: 713 (660 full-time, 53 part-time). Student-undergrad faculty ratio is 20:1. 8,302 applied, 55% were admitted. Full-time: 13,119 students, 49% women, 51% men. Part-time: 1,531 students, 51% women, 49% men. Students come from 45 states and territories, 77 other countries, 4% from out-of-state, 0.2% Native American, 1% Hispanic, 22% black, 1% Asian American or Pacific Islander, 1% international, 9% 25 or older, 23% live on campus, 6% transferred in. Retention: 78% of full-time freshmen returned the following year. Academic areas with the most degrees conferred: business/marketing; education; health professions and related sciences; parks and recreation. Core. Calendar: semesters. Academic remediation for entering students, ESL program, services for LD students, advanced placement, accelerated degree program, honors program, independent study, distance learning, double major, summer session for credit, part-time degree program, external degree program, adult/continuing education programs, co-op programs and internships, graduate courses open to undergrads. Off campus study. Study abroad program. ROTC: Army.

Entrance Requirements: Options: Common Application, electronic application, early admission, deferred admission, international baccalaureate accepted. Required: minimum 2.0 high school GPA, proof of immunization prior to enrollment, SAT or ACT. Required for some: high school transcript. Entrance: moderately difficult. Application deadline: 5/1. Notification: continuous.

Costs Per Year: Application fee: $50. State resident tuition: $2438 full-time, $102 per semester hour part-time. Nonresident tuition: $9754 full-time, $407 per semester hour part-time. Mandatory fees: $1024 full-time, $512 per term part-time. Full-time tuition and fees vary according to degree level and location. Part-time tuition and fees vary according to course load, degree level, and location. College room and board: $6300. College room only: $3968. Room and board charges vary according to board plan and housing facility.

Collegiate Environment: Orientation program. Drama-theater group, choral group, marching band, student-run newspaper, radio station. Social organizations: 212 open to all; national fraternities, national sororities; 12% of eligible men and 12% of eligible women are members. Most popular organizations: Residence Hall Association, Campus Religious Ministries. Major annual events: Black History Month, Homecoming Week, Welcome

Week. Student services: health clinic, personal-psychological counseling. Campus security: 24-hour emergency response devices and patrols, student patrols, late night transport-escort service, residence hall security, locked residence hall entrances. 3,289 college housing spaces available; 3,236 were occupied in 2003-04. No special consideration for freshman housing applicants. Options: coed, men-only, women-only housing available. Henderson Library with 568,551 books, 884,997 microform titles, 2,697 serials, 28,913 audiovisual materials, an OPAC, and a Web page. Operations spending for 2004 fiscal year: $3.8 million. 1,675 computers available on campus for general student use. A campuswide network can be accessed from student residence rooms and from off campus. Staffed computer lab on campus.

Community Environment: Georgia Southern ranks among the safest college communities in the country. Its hometown of Statesboro is a neighborly college town and the seat of Bulloch County (50,000 residents). Because the campus and community have grown up together over the past century, shopping, services, and housing are tuned to student's needs. Just an hour down the road are the historic seaside city of Savannah and the beaches of Tybee Island.

■ **GEORGIA SOUTHWESTERN STATE UNIVERSITY** *J-4*
800 Wheatley St.
Americus, GA 31709-4693
Tel: (229)928-1273
Free: 800-338-0082
Fax: (229)931-2983
E-mail: ghayes@gsw.edu
Web Site: http://www.gsw.edu/

Description: State-supported, comprehensive, coed. Part of University System of Georgia. Awards associate, bachelor's, and master's degrees and post-master's certificates. Founded 1906. Setting: 255-acre small town campus. Endowment: $22.6 million. Research spending for 2004 fiscal year: $306,667. Educational spending for 2005 fiscal year: $2384 per student. Total enrollment: 2,427. Faculty: 151 (96 full-time, 55 part-time). Student-undergrad faculty ratio is 17:1. 1,083 applied, 74% were admitted. 14% from top 10% of their high school class, 40% from top quarter, 77% from top half. Full-time: 1,699 students, 63% women, 37% men. Part-time: 539 students, 72% women, 28% men. Students come from 18 states and territories, 35 other countries, 2% from out-of-state, 1% Native American, 1% Hispanic, 34% black, 1% Asian American or Pacific Islander, 2% international, 31% 25 or older, 27% live on campus, 11% transferred in. Retention: 70% of full-time freshmen returned the following year. Academic areas with the most degrees conferred: education; business/marketing; psychology. Core. Calendar: semesters. Academic remediation for entering students, ESL program, services for LD students, advanced placement, freshman honors college, honors program, distance learning, double major, summer session for credit, part-time degree program, adult/continuing education programs, co-op programs and internships, graduate courses open to undergrads. Off campus study at Abraham Baldwin Agricultural College, Middle Georgia College. Study abroad program.

Entrance Requirements: Options: Peterson's Universal Application, Common Application, electronic application, early admission, early decision. Required: high school transcript, minimum 2.0 high school GPA, proof of immunization, SAT or ACT. Recommended: interview. Entrance: moderately difficult. Application deadlines: 7/21, 12/15 for early decision. Notification: continuous, 1/15 for early decision.

Costs Per Year: Application fee: $25. State resident tuition: $2438 full-time, $102 per semester hour part-time. Nonresident tuition: $9754 full-time, $407 per semester hour part-time. Mandatory fees: $596 full-time, $289 per term part-time. Part-time tuition and fees vary according to course load. College room and board: $4810. College room only: $2620. Room and board charges vary according to board plan and housing facility.

Collegiate Environment: Orientation program. Drama-theater group, choral group, student-run newspaper. Social organizations: 60 open to all; national fraternities, national sororities; 13% of eligible men and 15% of eligible women are members. Most popular organizations: religious clubs and organizations, SABU (Black Student Organization), Biology Club, Gamma Beta Phi. Major annual events: Homecoming, Student Appreciation Day, Alumni Weekend. Student services: health clinic, personal-psychological counseling. Campus security: 24-hour emergency response devices and patrols, late night transport-escort service, controlled dormitory access. 567 college housing spaces available; 562 were occupied in 2003-04. Freshmen guaranteed college housing. On-campus residence required through sophomore year. Options: coed, men-only, women-only housing available.

James Earl Carter Library with 428,197 books, 480,606 microform titles, 516 serials, 9,356 audiovisual materials, an OPAC, and a Web page. Operations spending for 2004 fiscal year: $613,268. 550 computers available on campus for general student use. A campuswide network can be accessed from student residence rooms and from off campus. Staffed computer lab on campus.

Community Environment: Americus is located 135 miles south of Atlanta, the climate is mild with a yearly mean temperature of 65.7 degrees, and an annual rainfall of 49 inches. Airlines serve the area. The usual community facilities include a hospital, library, the newly restored Rylander Theatre, daily newspaper, radio stations, clinics, and shopping centers. Manufactured products include shirts, lumber, nails, auto parts, and paper products. Kaolin and Bauxite mines are nearby. Outdoor sports include tennis, baseball, golf and basketball. Historic sites in Americus include Plains, home of President Jimmy Carter, Andersonville National Cemetery and Civil War prison site, and Souther field where Charles Lindbergh made his first solo flight. Americus is also home to International Habitat for Humanity.

■ **GEORGIA STATE UNIVERSITY** *E-4*
Atlanta, GA 30303-3083
Tel: (404)651-2000
Admissions: (404)651-2365
E-mail: admdmw@langate.gsu.edu
Web Site: http://www.gsu.edu/
Description: State-supported, university, coed. Part of University System of Georgia. Awards bachelor's, master's, doctoral, and first professional degrees and post-master's and first professional certificates. Founded 1913. Setting: 44-acre urban campus. Endowment: $62 million. Research spending for 2004 fiscal year: $60.5 million. Educational spending for 2005 fiscal year: $6085 per student. Total enrollment: 25,945. Faculty: 1,430 (1,054 full-time, 376 part-time). Student-undergrad faculty ratio is 20:1. 8,313 applied, 50% were admitted. 3 National Merit Scholars. Full-time: 13,752 students, 60% women, 40% men. Part-time: 5,208 students, 61% women, 39% men. Students come from 52 states and territories, 142 other countries, 4% from out-of-state, 0.2% Native American, 3% Hispanic, 31% black, 10% Asian American or Pacific Islander, 3% international, 28% 25 or older, 10% live on campus, 8% transferred in. Retention: 80% of full-time freshmen returned the following year. Academic areas with the most degrees conferred: business/marketing; social sciences; psychology. Core. Calendar: semesters. Academic remediation for entering students, ESL program, services for LD students, advanced placement, accelerated degree program, honors program, independent study, distance learning, double major, summer session for credit, part-time degree program, co-op programs and internships, graduate courses open to undergrads. Off campus study. Study abroad program. ROTC: Army, Naval (c), Air Force (c).
Entrance Requirements: Options: Peterson's Universal Application, electronic application, deferred admission, international baccalaureate accepted. Required: high school transcript, minimum 2.8 high school GPA, college prep high school curriculum, SAT or ACT. Recommended: essay. Required for some: interview, SAT Subject Tests. Entrance: moderately difficult. Application deadline: 3/1. Notification: continuous until 10/1.
Costs Per Year: Application fee: $50. State resident tuition: $3638 full-time, $152 per semester hour part-time. Nonresident tuition: $14,552 full-time, $607 per semester hour part-time. Mandatory fees: $826 full-time, $413 per term part-time. Full-time tuition and fees vary according to course load, degree level, and program. Part-time tuition and fees vary according to course load, degree level, and program. College room and board: $6980. College room only: $5380. Room and board charges vary according to board plan and housing facility.
Collegiate Environment: Orientation program. Drama-theater group, choral group, student-run newspaper, radio station. Social organizations: 180 open to all; national fraternities, national sororities; 3% of eligible men and 4% of eligible women are members. Most popular organizations: Spotlight Programs Board, Sports Club Council, Student Government Association, Cinefest Movie Theatre, WRAS (radio station). Major annual events: Hurt Day in the Park, International Student Festival, homecoming. Student services: health clinic, personal-psychological counseling. Campus security: 24-hour emergency response devices and patrols, late night transport-escort service, controlled dormitory access. 2,435 college housing spaces available; 2,321 were occupied in 2003-04. Freshmen given priority for college housing. Option: coed housing available. Pullen Library plus 1 other with 2.2 million books, 80,051 microform titles, 7,989 serials, 22,000 audiovisual materials, an OPAC, and a Web page. Operations spending for 2004 fiscal year: $9.2 million. 775 computers available on campus for general student

use. Computer purchase/lease plans available. A campuswide network can be accessed from student residence rooms and from off campus. Staffed computer lab on campus.
Community Environment: See Clark Atlanta University.

■ **GORDON COLLEGE** *G-4*
419 College Dr.
Barnesville, GA 30204-1762
Tel: (770)358-5000
Admissions: (770)358-5354
Fax: (770)358-3031
Web Site: http://www.gdn.edu/
Description: State-supported, 2-year, coed. Part of University System of Georgia. Awards certificates, transfer associate, and terminal associate degrees. Founded 1852. Setting: 125-acre small town campus with easy access to Atlanta. Endowment: $4.5 million. Total enrollment: 3,449. 2,899 applied, 54% were admitted. Full-time: 2,297 students, 62% women, 38% men. Part-time: 1,152 students, 73% women, 27% men. Students come from 12 other countries, 1% from out-of-state, 0.1% Native American, 1% Hispanic, 27% black, 2% Asian American or Pacific Islander, 1% international, 20% live on campus. Core. Calendar: semesters. Academic remediation for entering students, services for LD students, advanced placement, accelerated degree program, honors program, summer session for credit, part-time degree program, adult/continuing education programs, co-op programs. Off campus study.
Entrance Requirements: Open admission. Options: electronic application, early admission, deferred admission. Required: high school transcript, minimum 1.8 high school GPA, minimum SAT score of 830 and 15 CPC credits, SAT or ACT. Entrance: minimally difficult. Application deadline: Rolling.
Collegiate Environment: Orientation program. Drama-theater group, choral group, student-run newspaper. Social organizations: 13 open to all. Most popular organizations: Explorers, Minority Advisement Program, Georgia Association of Nursing Students, Baptist Student Union, Phi Beta Lambda. Major annual events: Gordon Days, Homecoming, Spring Fling. Student services: personal-psychological counseling. Campus security: 24-hour patrols, late night transport-escort service. 550 college housing spaces available; all were occupied in 2003-04. No special consideration for freshman housing applicants. Options: coed, men-only, women-only housing available. Hightower Library with 118,000 books, 98 serials, an OPAC, and a Web page. 142 computers available on campus for general student use. A campuswide network can be accessed from student residence rooms and from off campus. Staffed computer lab on campus.

■ **GRIFFIN TECHNICAL COLLEGE** *G-4*
501 Varsity Rd.
Griffin, GA 30223
Tel: (770)228-7348
Admissions: (770)228-7371
Fax: (770)229-3227
E-mail: cbrown@griftec.org
Web Site: http://www.griffintech.edu
Description: State-supported, 2-year, coed. Part of Georgia Department of Technical and Adult Education. Awards certificates, diplomas, and terminal associate degrees. Founded 1965. Setting: 10-acre small town campus with easy access to Atlanta. Total enrollment: 3,407. Full-time: 1,494 students, 59% women, 41% men. Part-time: 1,913 students, 65% women, 35% men. 0.3% Native American, 1% Hispanic, 37% black, 1% Asian American or Pacific Islander, 0% international, 49% 25 or older. Core. Academic remediation for entering students, services for LD students, advanced placement, honors program, distance learning, part-time degree program, adult/continuing education programs, internships.
Entrance Requirements: Open admission. Option: deferred admission. Required: high school transcript, ACT COMPASS or ASSET. Entrance: noncompetitive.
Costs Per Year: Application fee: $15. State resident tuition: $1116 full-time, $31 per credit hour part-time. Nonresident tuition: $2232 full-time, $62 per credit hour part-time.
Collegiate Environment: Orientation program. Most popular organizations: Phi Beta Lambda, Vocational Industrial Clubs of America, student government. College housing not available. Griffin Technical College Library with 12,493 books, 188 serials, 1,326 audiovisual materials, an OPAC, and a Web page. 500 computers available on campus for general student use. A campuswide network can be accessed. Staffed computer lab on campus.

■ **GUPTON-JONES COLLEGE OF FUNERAL SERVICE** *C-11*

5141 Snapfinger Woods Dr.
Decatur, GA 30035-4022
Tel: (770)593-2257
Free: 800-848-5352
Fax: (770)593-1891
Web Site: http://www.gupton-jones.edu/

Description: Independent, 2-year, coed. Part of Pierce Mortuary Colleges, Inc. Awards terminal associate degrees. Founded 1920. Setting: 3-acre suburban campus with easy access to Atlanta. Total enrollment: 198. Full-time: 198 students, 49% women, 51% men. Students come from 12 states and territories, 30% from out-of-state, 74% black, 35% 25 or older. Core. Academic remediation for entering students, distance learning, summer session for credit.

Entrance Requirements: Open admission. Options: Common Application, electronic application. Required: high school transcript, health certificate. Recommended: minimum 3.0 high school GPA. Entrance: noncompetitive. Application deadline: Rolling.

Collegiate Environment: Social organizations: national fraternities; 10% of men are members. College housing not available. Russell Millison Library with 3,500 books, 15 serials, and an OPAC. 20 computers available on campus for general student use. Staffed computer lab on campus.

■ **GWINNETT TECHNICAL COLLEGE** *D-5*

PO Box 1505
Lawrenceville, GA 30046-1505
Tel: (770)962-7580
E-mail: mmcintire@gwinnett.tec.ga.us
Web Site: http://www.gwinnetttech.edu/

Description: State-supported, 2-year, coed. Awards certificates, diplomas, and terminal associate degrees. Founded 1984. Setting: 93-acre suburban campus with easy access to Atlanta. Total enrollment: 4,204. Full-time: 1,617 students, 57% women, 43% men. Part-time: 2,587 students, 54% women, 46% men. 0.1% Native American, 6% Hispanic, 26% black, 6% Asian American or Pacific Islander, 0.02% international, 80% 25 or older. Academic remediation for entering students, services for LD students, advanced placement, summer session for credit, part-time degree program, adult/continuing education programs, internships.

Entrance Requirements: Open admission. Option: deferred admission. Required: high school transcript, ACT COMPASS or ASSET. Placement: ACT COMPASS or ASSET required. Entrance: noncompetitive.

Costs Per Year: Application fee: $20. State resident tuition: $1116 full-time, $31 per credit hour part-time. Nonresident tuition: $2232 full-time, $62 per credit hour part-time.

Collegiate Environment: Major annual events: Fall Festival, Spring Fling, Awards Day. Campus security: patrols by campus police. College housing not available. Gwinnett Technical Institute Media Center with 19,547 books, 246 serials, and 2,289 audiovisual materials. 264 computers available on campus for general student use. Staffed computer lab on campus.

■ **HEART OF GEORGIA TECHNICAL COLLEGE** *I-8*

560 Pinehill Rd.
Dublin, GA 31021
Tel: (478)275-6589
Admissions: (478)274-7837
Fax: (478)275-6642
E-mail: lisak@hgtc.org
Web Site: http://www.hgtc.org/

Description: State-supported, 2-year, coed. Awards certificates, diplomas, and terminal associate degrees. Founded 1984. Setting: small town campus with easy access to Atlanta. Total enrollment: 1,755. Full-time: 576 students, 60% women, 40% men. Part-time: 1,179 students, 54% women, 46% men. 0.2% Native American, 2% Hispanic, 44% black, 1% Asian American or Pacific Islander, 0.1% international. Academic remediation for entering students, services for LD students, advanced placement, distance learning, co-op programs and internships.

Entrance Requirements: Open admission. Option: deferred admission. Required: high school transcript, ACT COMPASS or ASSET. Entrance: noncompetitive.

Costs Per Year: Application fee: $15. State resident tuition: $1116 full-time, $31 per credit hour part-time. Nonresident tuition: $2232 full-time, $62 per credit hour part-time.

Collegiate Environment: College housing not available.

■ **HERZING COLLEGE** *E-4*

3355 Lenox Rd., Ste. 100
Atlanta, GA 30326
Tel: (404)816-4533
Free: 800-573-4533
Fax: (404)816-5576
E-mail: rwhite@ath.lerzing.edu
Web Site: http://www.herzing.edu/atlanta/

Description: Proprietary, primarily 2-year, coed. Part of Herzing Institutes, Inc. Awards certificates, diplomas, terminal associate, and bachelor's degrees. Founded 1949. Setting: urban campus. Total enrollment: 276. Student-undergrad faculty ratio is 8:1. 279 applied, 75% were admitted. Students come from 5 states and territories, 1% Native American, 3% Hispanic, 73% black, 4% Asian American or Pacific Islander, 56% 25 or older. Calendar: semesters. Academic remediation for entering students, ESL program, honors program, internships.

Entrance Requirements: Option: Peterson's Universal Application. Required: high school transcript, interview, Wonderlic aptitude test. Entrance: moderately difficult. Application deadline: Rolling. Notification: continuous.

Costs Per Year: Application fee: $25. Tuition: $11,200 full-time, $350 per credit hour part-time. Mandatory fees: $125 full-time, $30 per credit hour part-time, $25 per term part-time.

Collegiate Environment: Social organizations: ; 2% of eligible men and 2% of eligible women are members. Student services: personal-psychological counseling, women's center. Campus security: 24-hour patrols. College housing not available. Loretta Herzing Library with 6,000 books, 25 serials, and a Web page. Operations spending for 2004 fiscal year: $40,000. 125 computers available on campus for general student use. A campuswide network can be accessed.

■ **HIGH-TECH INSTITUTE** *D-3*

1090 Northchase Parkway, Ste. 150
Marietta, GA 30067
Tel: (770)988-9877
Free: 800-987-0110
Fax: (770)988-8824
E-mail: ckusema@hightechschools.com
Web Site: http://www.high-techinstitute.com/

Description: Proprietary, 2-year, coed. Founded 2001. Calendar: semesters.

■ **INTERACTIVE COLLEGE OF TECHNOLOGY** *B-11*

5303 New Peachtree Rd.
Chamblee, GA 30341
Tel: (770)216-2960
Free: 800-550-3475
Fax: (770)216-2989
Web Site: http://www.ict-ils.edu/

Description: Proprietary, 2-year, coed. Part of Interactive Learning Systems. Awards certificates, diplomas, and terminal associate degrees. Research spending for 2004 fiscal year: $17,000. Educational spending for 2005 fiscal year: $1100 per student. Total enrollment: 1,069. Student-undergrad faculty ratio is 18:1. Full-time: 1,063 students, 49% women, 51% men. Part-time: 6 students, 67% women, 33% men. Students come from 3 states and territories, 80 other countries, 56% 25 or older, 0% transferred in. Core. Academic remediation for entering students, ESL program, advanced placement, accelerated degree program, independent study, double major, part-time degree program, adult/continuing education programs, internships.

Entrance Requirements: Open admission. Option: international baccalaureate accepted. Required: high school transcript. Recommended: high school transcript, interview. Application deadline: Rolling.

Costs Per Year: Application fee: $50. Tuition: $6480 full-time.

Collegiate Environment: Orientation program. 1,600 books, 43 serials, and an OPAC. Operations spending for 2004 fiscal year: $66,000. 164 computers available on campus for general student use. A campuswide network can be accessed from student residence rooms. Staffed computer lab on campus.

■ **ITT TECHNICAL INSTITUTE (DULUTH)** *D-5*

10700 Abbotts Bridge Rd., Ste. 190
Duluth, GA 30097
Tel: (678)957-8510; (866)489-8818

Web Site: http://www.itt-tech.edu/

Description: Proprietary, primarily 2-year, coed. Part of ITT Educational Services, Inc. Awards terminal associate and bachelor's degrees. Founded 2003. Core.

Entrance Requirements: Option: deferred admission. Required: high school transcript, interview, Wonderlic aptitude test. Recommended: recommendations. Entrance: minimally difficult. Application deadline: Rolling. Notification: continuous.

Costs Per Year: Application fee: $100.

Collegiate Environment: Orientation program. College housing not available.

■ **ITT TECHNICAL INSTITUTE (KENNESAW)** *A-9*
1000 Cobb Place Blvd., NW
Kennesaw, GA 30144-3605
Admissions: (770)426-2300
Web Site: http://www.itt-tech.edu/

Description: primarily 2-year, coed. Awards terminal associate and bachelor's degrees.

Entrance Requirements: Required: high school transcript, interview, Wonderlic aptitude test. Recommended: recommendations. Application deadline: Rolling. Notification: continuous.

Costs Per Year: Application fee: $100.

■ **KENNESAW STATE UNIVERSITY** *A-9*
1000 Chastain Rd.
Kennesaw, GA 30144-5591
Tel: (770)423-6000
Admissions: (770)423-6300
Fax: (770)423-6541
E-mail: ksuadmit@ksumail.kennesaw.edu
Web Site: http://www.kennesaw.edu/

Description: State-supported, comprehensive, coed. Part of University System of Georgia. Awards bachelor's and master's degrees. Founded 1963. Setting: 185-acre suburban campus with easy access to Atlanta. Endowment: $12 million. Educational spending for 2005 fiscal year: $3130 per student. Total enrollment: 18,556. Faculty: 915 (586 full-time, 329 part-time). Student-undergrad faculty ratio is 20:1. 6,658 applied, 62% were admitted. 21% from top 10% of their high school class, 53% from top quarter, 81% from top half. Full-time: 11,411 students, 61% women, 39% men. Part-time: 5,328 students, 63% women, 37% men. Students come from 40 states and territories, 132 other countries, 10% from out-of-state, 0.3% Native American, 2% Hispanic, 8% black, 2% Asian American or Pacific Islander, 8% international, 35% 25 or older, 9% live on campus, 9% transferred in. Retention: 74% of full-time freshmen returned the following year. Academic areas with the most degrees conferred: business/marketing; education; computer and information sciences. Core. Calendar: semesters. Academic remediation for entering students, services for LD students, advanced placement, freshman honors college, honors program, summer session for credit, part-time degree program, adult/continuing education programs, co-op programs and internships, graduate courses open to undergrads. Off campus study at University Center in Georgia, 19 colleges and universities in the Atlanta area. Study abroad program. ROTC: Army, Air Force.

Entrance Requirements: Options: electronic application, deferred admission. Required: high school transcript, minimum 2.5 high school GPA, proof of immunization, SAT or ACT. Required for some: SAT Subject Tests. Entrance: moderately difficult. Application deadline: 5/19. Notification: continuous.

Costs Per Year: Application fee: $40. State resident tuition: $2438 full-time, $102 per credit hour part-time. Nonresident tuition: $9754 full-time, $407 per credit hour part-time. Mandatory fees: $606 full-time, $303 per term part-time. Part-time tuition and fees vary according to course load. College room only: $5880. Room charges vary according to housing facility.

Collegiate Environment: Orientation program. Drama-theater group, choral group, student-run newspaper. Social organizations: 100 open to all; national fraternities, national sororities; 1% of eligible men and 1% of eligible women are members. Most popular organizations: Golden Key National Honor Society, Student Government Association, Campus Activities Board, African-American Student Alliance, International Student Association. Major annual events: KSU Day, Homecoming, Awards Ceremony. Student services: health clinic, personal-psychological counseling. Campus security: 24-hour emergency response devices and patrols, student patrols, late night transport-escort service. 2,067 college housing spaces available; 1,537 were occupied in 2003-04. Freshmen given priority for college housing. Option:

coed housing available. Horace W. Sturgis Library with 608,342 books, 1.6 million microform titles, 4,580 serials, 10,500 audiovisual materials, an OPAC, and a Web page. Operations spending for 2004 fiscal year: $2.4 million. 1,087 computers available on campus for general student use. A campuswide network can be accessed from student residence rooms and from off campus. Staffed computer lab on campus.

Community Environment: A suburban area of Marietta, the average winter temperature is 45 degrees, the average summer temperature is 80 degrees, with an average rainfall of 50 inches. Community facilities include churches, and civic organizations with hospitals and shopping areas in Marietta. In view is Kennesaw Mountain, site of Civil War battles and the"The Great Locomotive Chase."

■ **LAGRANGE COLLEGE**
601 Broad St.
LaGrange, GA 30240-2999
Tel: (706)880-8000
Free: 800-593-2885
Admissions: (706)880-8253
Fax: (706)880-8040
Web Site: http://www.lagrange.edu/

Description: Independent United Methodist, comprehensive, coed. Awards associate, bachelor's, and master's degrees. Founded 1831. Setting: 120-acre small town campus with easy access to Atlanta. Endowment: $62.8 million. Educational spending for 2005 fiscal year: $6669 per student. Total enrollment: 1,046. Faculty: 118 (65 full-time, 53 part-time). Student-undergrad faculty ratio is 10:1. 1,247 applied, 48% were admitted. 21% from top 10% of their high school class, 40% from top quarter, 76% from top half. Full-time: 898 students, 60% women, 40% men. Part-time: 88 students, 72% women, 28% men. Students come from 17 states and territories, 10% from out-of-state, 1% Native American, 1% Hispanic, 20% black, 1% Asian American or Pacific Islander, 3% international, 7% 25 or older, 61% live on campus, 9% transferred in. Retention: 78% of full-time freshmen returned the following year. Academic areas with the most degrees conferred: business/marketing; visual and performing arts; biological/life sciences; health professions and related sciences; psychology. Core. Calendar: 4-1-4. Advanced placement, independent study, double major, summer session for credit, part-time degree program, adult/continuing education programs, internships, graduate courses open to undergrads. Study abroad program.

Entrance Requirements: Options: Peterson's Universal Application, electronic application, early admission, deferred admission, international baccalaureate accepted. Required: essay, high school transcript, minimum 2.0 high school GPA, SAT or ACT. Required for some: 1 recommendation, interview. Entrance: moderately difficult. Application deadline: 8/30. Notification: continuous.

Costs Per Year: Application fee: $20. Comprehensive fee: $22,874 includes full-time tuition ($16,200) and college room and board ($6674). Full-time tuition varies according to class time, degree level, location, and program. Room and board charges vary according to housing facility. Part-time tuition: $668 per hour. Part-time tuition varies according to class time, degree level, location, and program.

Collegiate Environment: Orientation program. Drama-theater group, choral group, student-run newspaper. Social organizations: 31 open to all; national fraternities, national sororities; 37% of eligible men and 28% of eligible women are members. Most popular organizations: Student Government Association, drama/theater groups, Habitat for Humanity, BSU/Wesley Fellowship. Major annual events: Family Weekend, Greek Week, Homecoming. Student services: health clinic, personal-psychological counseling. Campus security: 24-hour patrols, controlled dormitory access. 646 college housing spaces available; 539 were occupied in 2003-04. Freshmen guaranteed college housing. On-campus residence required through senior year. Options: coed, men-only, women-only housing available. William and Evelyn Banks Library with 108,389 books, 119,000 microform titles, 512 serials, 3,451 audiovisual materials, an OPAC, and a Web page. Operations spending for 2004 fiscal year: $649,788. 175 computers available on campus for general student use. A campuswide network can be accessed from student residence rooms and from off campus. Staffed computer lab on campus.

■ **LANIER TECHNICAL COLLEGE** *D-5*
2990 Landrun Education Dr.
PO Box 58
Oakwood, GA 30566
Tel: (770)531-6300
Admissions: (770)531-6332

Fax: (770)531-6328
E-mail: mike@laniertech.edu
Web Site: http://www.laniertech.edu/
Description: State-supported, 2-year, coed. Awards certificates, diplomas, and terminal associate degrees. Founded 1964. Total enrollment: 3,196. Full-time: 1,248 students, 64% women, 36% men. Part-time: 1,948 students, 64% women, 36% men. 0.2% Native American, 4% Hispanic, 11% black, 2% Asian American or Pacific Islander, 0% international. Academic remediation for entering students, services for LD students, advanced placement, distance learning.
Entrance Requirements: Open admission. Option: deferred admission. Required: high school transcript, ACT COMPASS or ASSET. Entrance: noncompetitive.
Costs Per Year: Application fee: $15. State resident tuition: $1116 full-time, $31 per credit hour part-time. Nonresident tuition: $2232 full-time, $62 per credit hour part-time.
Collegiate Environment: College housing not available. 7,096 books, 154 serials, and 570 audiovisual materials.

■ **LE CORDON BLEU COLLEGE OF CULINARY ARTS, ATLANTA**
B-11
1957 Lakeside Parkway, Ste. 515
Tucker, GA 30084
Web Site: http://www.atlantaculinary.com/
Description: Proprietary, 2-year, coed.

■ **LIFE UNIVERSITY** *D-3*
1269 Barclay Circle
Marietta, GA 30060-2903
Tel: (770)426-2600
Admissions: (770)426-2884
E-mail: drdeb@life.edu
Web Site: http://www.life.edu/
Description: Independent, comprehensive, coed. Awards associate, bachelor's, master's, and first professional degrees. Founded 1974. Setting: 96-acre suburban campus. Endowment: $1.7 million. Research spending for 2004 fiscal year: $488,000. Total enrollment: 1,473. Faculty: 108 (93 full-time, 15 part-time). Student-undergrad faculty ratio is 12:1. 131 applied, 100% were admitted. Students come from 42 states and territories, 46 other countries, 23% from out-of-state, 0% Native American, 1% Hispanic, 6% black, 2% Asian American or Pacific Islander, 0% international, 53% 25 or older. Retention: 64% of full-time freshmen returned the following year. Academic areas with the most degrees conferred: biological/life sciences; business/marketing; health professions and related sciences. Core. Academic remediation for entering students, ESL program, services for LD students, advanced placement, accelerated degree program, independent study, double major, summer session for credit, part-time degree program, co-op programs and internships, graduate courses open to undergrads. Off campus study.
Entrance Requirements: Open admission. Options: Common Application, electronic application, international baccalaureate accepted. Required: high school transcript, minimum 2.0 high school GPA, SAT or ACT. Entrance: noncompetitive. Application deadline: 9/1. Notification: continuous.
Costs Per Year: Application fee: $50. Comprehensive fee: $18,045 includes full-time tuition ($6750), mandatory fees ($315), and college room and board ($10,980). Full-time tuition and fees vary according to course load. Part-time tuition: $148 per hour. Part-time mandatory fees: $105 per term. Part-time tuition and fees vary according to course load.
Collegiate Environment: Orientation program. Student services: health clinic. 270 college housing spaces available; 86 were occupied in 2003-04. No special consideration for freshman housing applicants. Nell K. Williams Learning Resource Center plus 1 other with 53,619 books, 45,000 microform titles, 3,000 serials, 9,601 audiovisual materials, an OPAC, and a Web page. Operations spending for 2004 fiscal year: $1.5 million. 118 computers available on campus for general student use. A campuswide network can be accessed from student residence rooms and from off campus. Staffed computer lab on campus.

■ **LUTHER RICE UNIVERSITY** *C-12*
3038 Evans Mill Rd.
Lithonia, GA 30038-2454
Tel: (770)484-1204
Free: 800-442-1577
Web Site: http://www.lrs.edu/

Description: Independent Baptist, comprehensive, coed. Awards bachelor's, master's, and doctoral degrees. Founded 1962. Setting: 5-acre urban campus with easy access to Atlanta. Endowment: $121,000. Educational spending for 2005 fiscal year: $955 per student. Total enrollment: 1,600. 72 applied, 100% were admitted. Full-time: 60 students, 38% women, 62% men. Part-time: 595 students, 17% women, 83% men. Students come from 23 other countries, 0.3% Native American, 5% Hispanic, 16% black, 10% Asian American or Pacific Islander, 1% international, 88% 25 or older. Retention: 60% of full-time freshmen returned the following year. Core. Calendar: semesters. Academic remediation for entering students, advanced placement, independent study, distance learning, part-time degree program, external degree program, adult/continuing education programs, co-op programs and internships, graduate courses open to undergrads. Study abroad program.
Entrance Requirements: Open admission. Options: Common Application, electronic application, early admission, international baccalaureate accepted. Required: high school transcript, recommendations, Bible examination. Entrance: noncompetitive. Application deadline: Rolling.
Costs Per Year: Application fee: $50. Tuition: $4128 full-time, $516 per course part-time. Mandatory fees: $100 full-time, $50 per term part-time.
Collegiate Environment: Student services: personal-psychological counseling. Campus security: 24-hour emergency response devices, late night transport-escort service. College housing not available. Bertha Smith Library with 45,200 books and 70 serials. Operations spending for 2004 fiscal year: $60,000. 8 computers available on campus for general student use.

■ **MACON STATE COLLEGE** *H-6*
100 College Station Dr.
Macon, GA 31206
Tel: (478)471-2800
Free: 800-272-7619
Fax: (478)471-2846
E-mail: mscinfo@mail.maconstate.edu
Web Site: http://www.maconstate.edu/
Description: State-supported, 4-year, coed. Part of University System of Georgia. Awards associate and bachelor's degrees. Founded 1968. Setting: 167-acre urban campus. Endowment: $8 million. Educational spending for 2005 fiscal year: $3271 per student. Total enrollment: 6,150. Student-undergrad faculty ratio is 21:1. 0% from out-of-state, 0.3% Native American, 2% Hispanic, 39% black, 2% Asian American or Pacific Islander, 0.5% international, 50% 25 or older. Retention: 60% of full-time freshmen returned the following year. Academic areas with the most degrees conferred: computer and information sciences; business/marketing; health professions and related sciences. Core. Calendar: semesters. Academic remediation for entering students, services for LD students, advanced placement, honors program, distance learning, summer session for credit, part-time degree program, adult/continuing education programs, co-op programs and internships. Study abroad program.
Entrance Requirements: Options: Common Application, electronic application, early admission. Required: high school transcript, minimum 1.8 high school GPA, SAT or ACT. Required for some: SAT Subject Tests. Entrance: minimally difficult. Application deadline: Rolling. Notification: continuous.
Costs Per Year: Application fee: $20. One-time mandatory fee: $25. State resident tuition: $1542 full-time, $65 per credit hour part-time. Nonresident tuition: $6166 full-time, $257 per credit hour part-time. Mandatory fees: $188 full-time, $94 per term part-time.
Collegiate Environment: Orientation program. Drama-theater group, choral group, student-run newspaper. Most popular organizations: student government, Macon College Association of Nursing Students, Macon State College Association for Respiratory Education (MSCARE), Phi Beta Lambda, Baptist Student Union. Student services: health clinic, personal-psychological counseling. Campus security: 24-hour emergency response devices and patrols, late night transport-escort service. College housing not available. Macon State College Library with 80,000 books, 513 serials, an OPAC, and a Web page. Operations spending for 2004 fiscal year: $577,426. 95 computers available on campus for general student use. A campuswide network can be accessed from off-campus. Staffed computer lab on campus.
Community Environment: See Mercer University - Macon.

■ **MEDICAL COLLEGE OF GEORGIA** *F-10*
1120 Fifteenth St.
Augusta, GA 30912
Tel: (706)721-0211
Admissions: (706)721-2725

Fax: (706)721-3461
E-mail: underadm@mail.mcg.edu
Web Site: http://www.mcg.edu/

Description: State-supported, upper-level, coed. Part of University System of Georgia. Awards bachelor's, master's, doctoral, and first professional degrees. Founded 1828. Setting: 100-acre urban campus. Total enrollment: 2,115. Full-time: 637 students, 86% women, 14% men. Part-time: 88 students, 90% women, 10% men. Students come from 18 states and territories, 14 other countries, 13% from out-of-state, 0.4% Native American, 1% Hispanic, 15% black, 3% Asian American or Pacific Islander, 0% international, 26% 25 or older, 9% live on campus, 53% transferred in. Core. Calendar: semesters. Distance learning, summer session for credit. Off campus study at Augusta State University, University of Georgia, Albany State University, Columbus State University, Gwinnett University Center.

Costs Per Year: State resident tuition: $3638 full-time, $152 per hour part-time. Nonresident tuition: $14,552 full-time, $607 per hour part-time. Mandatory fees: $418 full-time, $209 per term part-time. Full-time tuition and fees vary according to location. Part-time tuition and fees vary according to course load and location. College room only: $2334. Room charges vary according to housing facility.

Collegiate Environment: Orientation program. Choral group, student-run newspaper. Social organizations: 20 open to all. Most popular organizations: Student Government Association, Baptist Student Union, International Club, Campus Outreach, Medical Student Auxiliary. Major annual event: TGIF monthly events. Student services: health clinic, personal-psychological counseling. Campus security: 24-hour emergency response devices and patrols, late night transport-escort service. 220 college housing spaces available; 65 were occupied in 2003-04. Option: coed housing available. Robert B. Greenblatt MD Library with 164,154 books, 15,712 microform titles, 2,458 serials, 3,410 audiovisual materials, an OPAC, and a Web page. 322 computers available on campus for general student use. A campuswide network can be accessed. Staffed computer lab on campus.

Community Environment: Augusta is the second largest city in Georgia with a metropolitan-area population of around 400,000. The city offers a wide array of cultural and recreational activities, including a world-class Riverwalk, the site of many activities including the Augusta Invitation Regatta (a national collegiate rowing event) and the Augusta Southern Nationals, dubbed the World's Richest Drag Boat Race. The city also is a short drive from the huge Lake Thurmond Reservoir. Outdoor activities such as water-skiing, swimming, boating, and camping abound. Kid-friendly sites include the Funsville Amusement Park, Krystal River Water Park, and Augusta Iceforum, an ice-skating rink. Attractions that promise both fun and enlightenment include the National Science Center's Fort Discovery, the Morris Museum of Art, the Georgia Golf Hall of Fame, the Lucy Craft Laney Museum of Black History, the Augusta Cotton Exchange Welcome Center and Museum, and the Augusta Museum of History. Augusta has many association dedicated to the performing and visual arts, including the Fort Gordon Dinner Theater, Augusta Opera Association, the Augusta Ballet, the Augusta Players, the Augusta Symphony, and the Augusta Art Association. The Medical College of Georgia, Augusta State University, and Paine College often bring prestigious films, speakers, and special events to the city. Augusta is within an easy three-hour drive of Atlanta, the University of Georgia, the Atlantic Ocean, and the mountains. The sporting life is ubiquitous throughout Augusta, whether you consider yourself an athlete or spectator. The city is home to professional baseball and ice hockey teams. The city annually hosts the Augusta Futurity, the largest cutting-horse futurity in the eastern United States. And of course, Augusta is world-renowned as the home of the Masters Golf Tournament. Augusta is a leading health care center of the Southeast and has a rapidly developing and diversified industrial base. The area's nine hospitals serve the Southeast and beyond.

■ **MERCER UNIVERSITY** *H-6*
1400 Coleman Ave.
Macon, GA 31207-0003
Tel: (478)301-2700
Free: 800-840-8577
Admissions: (478)301-2650
Fax: (478)301-2828
E-mail: admissions@mercer.edu
Web Site: http://www.mercer.edu/

Description: Independent Baptist, comprehensive, coed. Awards bachelor's, master's, doctoral, and first professional degrees and post-master's and first professional certificates. Founded 1833. Setting: 150-acre suburban campus with easy access to Atlanta. Endowment: $171.6 million. Research spending

for 2004 fiscal year: $17.7 million. Total enrollment: 7,154. Faculty: 614 (345 full-time, 269 part-time). Student-undergrad faculty ratio is 13:1. 3,108 applied, 80% were admitted. 48% from top 10% of their high school class, 74% from top quarter, 94% from top half. Full-time: 3,796 students, 68% women, 32% men. Part-time: 702 students, 75% women, 25% men. Students come from 39 states and territories, 37 other countries, 24% from out-of-state, 0.1% Native American, 2% Hispanic, 27% black, 4% Asian American or Pacific Islander, 3% international, 5% 25 or older, 65% live on campus, 2% transferred in. Retention: 80% of full-time freshmen returned the following year. Academic areas with the most degrees conferred: business/marketing; education; public administration and social services. Core. Calendar: semesters. ESL program, services for LD students, advanced placement, accelerated degree program, self-designed majors, honors program, independent study, double major, summer session for credit, part-time degree program, adult/continuing education programs, co-op programs and internships, graduate courses open to undergrads. Off campus study at Wesleyan College (GA). Study abroad program. ROTC: Army.

Entrance Requirements: Options: Peterson's Universal Application, Common Application, electronic application, early admission, early action, deferred admission, international baccalaureate accepted. Required: high school transcript, minimum 3.0 high school GPA, SAT or ACT. Recommended: interview, counselor's evaluation. Required for some: 2 recommendations, interview. Entrance: moderately difficult. Application deadlines: 7/1, 11/1 for early action. Notification: continuous, 11/15 for early action.

Costs Per Year: Application fee: $50. Comprehensive fee: $30,873 includes full-time tuition ($23,460) and college room and board ($7413). College room only: $3570. Full-time tuition varies according to class time, course load, and location. Room and board charges vary according to board plan, housing facility, and location. Part-time tuition: $782 per credit hour. Part-time tuition varies according to class time, course load, and location.

Collegiate Environment: Orientation program. Drama-theater group, choral group, student-run newspaper. Social organizations: 120 open to all; national fraternities, national sororities, local sororities; 24% of eligible men and 25% of eligible women are members. Most popular organizations: AGAPE, Baptist Student Union, Student Government Association, Reformed University Worship, Organization of Black Students. Major annual events: Fall Orientation/Organizational Fair, Homecoming, Founders' Day. Student services: health clinic, personal-psychological counseling. Campus security: 24-hour emergency response devices and patrols, student patrols, late night transport-escort service, controlled dormitory access, patrols by police officers. 1,673 college housing spaces available; 1,529 were occupied in 2003-04. Freshmen guaranteed college housing. On-campus residence required through sophomore year. Options: coed, men-only, women-only housing available. Jack Tarver Library plus 3 others with 692,225 books, 2.2 million microform titles, 28,163 serials, 64,319 audiovisual materials, an OPAC, and a Web page. Operations spending for 2004 fiscal year: $7 million. 350 computers available on campus for general student use. A campuswide network can be accessed from student residence rooms and from off campus. Staffed computer lab on campus.

■ **MIDDLE GEORGIA COLLEGE** *I-7*
1100 Second St., SE
Cochran, GA 31014-1599
Tel: (478)934-6221
Admissions: (478)934-3138
Fax: (478)934-3199
Web Site: http://www.mgc.edu/

Description: State-supported, 2-year, coed. Part of University System of Georgia. Awards certificates, transfer associate, and terminal associate degrees. Founded 1884. Setting: 165-acre small town campus. Endowment: $1 million. Educational spending for 2005 fiscal year: $3673 per student. Total enrollment: 2,677. Student-undergrad faculty ratio is 22:1. 1,771 applied, 91% were admitted. Full-time: 1,808 students, 57% women, 43% men. Part-time: 869 students, 65% women, 35% men. Students come from 37 states and territories, 5% from out-of-state, 0.3% Native American, 1% Hispanic, 34% black, 1% Asian American or Pacific Islander, 0.4% international, 26% 25 or older, 32% live on campus, 15% transferred in. Core. Calendar: semesters. Academic remediation for entering students, services for LD students, advanced placement, accelerated degree program, honors program, distance learning, summer session for credit, part-time degree program, adult/continuing education programs, co-op programs. Study abroad program.

Entrance Requirements: Options: Common Application, electronic application, early admission, deferred admission. Required: high school transcript, minimum 2.0 high school GPA. Required for some: essay, minimum 3.5 high school GPA, recommendations, interview. Entrance: minimally difficult. Application deadline: Rolling. Notification: continuous.

Costs Per Year: Application fee: $20. State resident tuition: $1542 full-time, $65 per credit hour part-time. Nonresident tuition: $6166 full-time, $257 per credit hour part-time. Mandatory fees: $424 full-time. Full-time tuition and fees vary according to location. Part-time tuition varies according to location. College room and board: $4200. College room only: $1950. Room and board charges vary according to board plan and housing facility.

Collegiate Environment: Orientation program. Drama-theater group, choral group, marching band, student-run newspaper. Social organizations: 18 open to all. Most popular organizations: Baptist Student Union, Student Government Association, MGC Ambassadors, Encore Productions, United Voices of Praise. Major annual events: Movie Night, Homecoming, Spring Fling. Student services: health clinic, personal-psychological counseling. Campus security: 24-hour emergency response devices and patrols, student patrols, late night transport-escort service, controlled dormitory access, patrols by police officers. 832 college housing spaces available; 637 were occupied in 2003-04. Freshmen guaranteed college housing. On-campus residence required through sophomore year. Options: men-only, women-only housing available. Roberts Memorial Library with 110,000 books, 15,292 microform titles, 147 serials, 5,119 audiovisual materials, an OPAC, and a Web page. Operations spending for 2004 fiscal year: $44,523. 439 computers available on campus for general student use. A campuswide network can be accessed from student residence rooms and from off campus. Staffed computer lab on campus.

Community Environment: Cochran is 40 miles south of Macon, between interstate highways 75 and 16, almost squarely in the center of the state. Both mountain and beach resorts are about three hours away.

■ MIDDLE GEORGIA TECHNICAL COLLEGE J-6

80 Cohen Walker Dr.
Warner Robins, GA 31088
Tel: (912)988-6800
Free: 800-474-1031
Admissions: (478)988-6843
Fax: (912)988-6813
E-mail: cjackson@middlegatech.edu
Web Site: http://www.middlegatech.edu/

Description: State-supported, 2-year, coed. Awards certificates, diplomas, and terminal associate degrees. Founded 1973. Total enrollment: 2,351. Full-time: 1,078 students, 51% women, 49% men. Part-time: 1,273 students, 53% women, 47% men. 0.4% Native American, 2% Hispanic, 39% black, 1% Asian American or Pacific Islander, 0% international. Academic remediation for entering students, services for LD students, advanced placement, distance learning, co-op programs and internships.

Entrance Requirements: Open admission. Option: deferred admission. Required: high school transcript, ACT COMPASS or ASSET. Entrance: noncompetitive.

Costs Per Year: Application fee: $15. State resident tuition: $1116 full-time, $31 per credit hour part-time. Nonresident tuition: $2232 full-time, $62 per credit hour part-time.

Collegiate Environment: College housing not available. 2,124 books, 69 serials, and 211 audiovisual materials.

■ MOREHOUSE COLLEGE E-4

830 Westview Dr., SW
Atlanta, GA 30314
Tel: (404)681-2800
Free: 800-851-1254
Admissions: (404)215-2632
Fax: (404)659-6536
Web Site: http://www.morehouse.edu/

Description: Independent, 4-year, men only. Awards bachelor's degrees. Founded 1867. Setting: 61-acre urban campus. Endowment: $109.4 million. Research spending for 2004 fiscal year: $3 million. Educational spending for 2005 fiscal year: $9720 per student. Total enrollment: 3,029. Student-undergrad faculty ratio is 16:1. 2,520 applied, 53% were admitted. 18% from top 10% of their high school class, 41% from top quarter, 72% from top half. Full-time: 2,857 students. Part-time: 172 students. Students come from 49 states and territories, 15 other countries, 70% from out-of-state, 0.1% Native American, 0.1% Hispanic, 96% black, 0% Asian American or Pacific Islander, 1% international, 4% 25 or older, 40% live on campus, 2% transferred in. Retention: 84% of full-time freshmen returned the following year. Academic

areas with the most degrees conferred: business/marketing; social sciences; psychology. Core. Calendar: semesters. Academic remediation for entering students, services for LD students, advanced placement, honors program, double major, summer session for credit, part-time degree program, co-op programs and internships. Off campus study at members of the Atlanta University Center, University Center of Georgia. Study abroad program. ROTC: Army, Naval, Air Force.

Entrance Requirements: Options: Peterson's Universal Application, Common Application, electronic application, early admission, early decision, deferred admission. Required: essay, high school transcript, minimum 2.8 high school GPA, recommendations, SAT or ACT, SAT Subject Tests. Recommended: minimum 3.0 high school GPA, interview. Entrance: moderately difficult. Application deadlines: 2/15, 10/15 for early decision. Notification: continuous until 4/1, 12/15 for early decision.

Costs Per Year: Application fee: $45. Comprehensive fee: $26,284 includes full-time tuition ($15,284), mandatory fees ($1546), and college room and board ($9454). College room only: $5388.

Collegiate Environment: Orientation program. Drama-theater group, choral group, marching band, student-run newspaper. Social organizations: 34 open to all; national fraternities; 3% of eligible undergrads are members. Most popular organizations: Glee Club, Political Science Club, STRIPES. Major annual events: Homecoming, Founders' Week, Commencement/Reunion. Student services: health clinic, personal-psychological counseling. Campus security: 24-hour emergency response devices and patrols, late night transport-escort service. College housing designed to accommodate 1,325 students; 1,388 undergraduates lived in college housing during 2003-04. Freshmen guaranteed college housing. Option: men-only housing available. Woodruff Library plus 1 other with 560,000 books, 1,000 serials, and an OPAC. Operations spending for 2004 fiscal year: $1.4 million. 355 computers available on campus for general student use. A campuswide network can be accessed from student residence rooms and from off campus. Staffed computer lab on campus.

Community Environment: See Clark Atlanta University.

■ MOULTRIE TECHNICAL COLLEGE M-5

361 Industrial Dr.
Moultrie, GA 31768
Tel: (229)891-7000
Admissions: (229)891-4144
Fax: (229)891-7010
E-mail: lwallace@moultrietech.edu
Web Site: http://www.moultrietech.edu/

Description: State-supported, 2-year, coed. Awards certificates, diplomas, and terminal associate degrees. Founded 1964. Total enrollment: 1,951. Full-time: 831 students, 71% women, 29% men. Part-time: 1,120 students, 59% women, 41% men. 0.2% Native American, 2% Hispanic, 35% black, 0.2% Asian American or Pacific Islander, 0% international. Academic remediation for entering students, services for LD students, advanced placement, distance learning, internships.

Entrance Requirements: Open admission. Option: deferred admission. Required: high school transcript, ACT COMPASS or ASSET. Entrance: noncompetitive.

Costs Per Year: Application fee: $15. State resident tuition: $1116 full-time, $31 per credit hour part-time. Nonresident tuition: $2232 full-time, $62 per credit hour part-time.

Collegiate Environment: College housing not available.

■ NORTH GEORGIA COLLEGE & STATE UNIVERSITY C-5

82 College Circle
Dahlonega, GA 30597
Tel: (706)864-1400
Free: 800-498-9581
Admissions: (706)864-2885
Fax: (706)864-1478
Web Site: http://www.ngcsu.edu/

Description: State-supported, comprehensive, coed. Part of University System of Georgia. Awards associate, bachelor's, and master's degrees and post-master's certificates. Founded 1873. Setting: 140-acre small town campus with easy access to Atlanta. Endowment: $258.3 million. Educational spending for 2005 fiscal year: $5108 per student. Total enrollment: 4,765. Faculty: 314 (191 full-time, 123 part-time). Student-undergrad faculty ratio is 16:1. 2,081 applied, 68% were admitted. 24% from top 10% of their high school class, 57% from top quarter, 85% from top half. Full-time: 3,353 students, 61% women, 39% men. Part-time: 837 students, 68% women,

32% men. Students come from 40 states and territories, 4% from out-of-state, 0.4% Native American, 3% Hispanic, 3% black, 1% Asian American or Pacific Islander, 1% international, 20% 25 or older, 37% live on campus, 8% transferred in. Retention: 78% of full-time freshmen returned the following year. Academic areas with the most degrees conferred: business/marketing; education; social sciences. Core. Calendar: semesters. Academic remediation for entering students, services for LD students, advanced placement, freshman honors college, honors program, independent study, distance learning, double major, summer session for credit, part-time degree program, external degree program, adult/continuing education programs, co-op programs and internships. Study abroad program. ROTC: Army.

Entrance Requirements: Options: Peterson's Universal Application, electronic application, early admission, international baccalaureate accepted. Required: high school transcript, minimum 2.0 high school GPA, proof of immunization, SAT or ACT. Entrance: moderately difficult. Application deadline: 7/1. Notification: continuous.

Costs Per Year: Application fee: $25. State resident tuition: $2438 full-time, $102 per semester hour part-time. Nonresident tuition: $9754 full-time, $407 per semester hour part-time. Mandatory fees: $630 full-time. Part-time tuition varies according to course load. College room and board: $4596. College room only: $2292. Room and board charges vary according to board plan and housing facility.

Collegiate Environment: Orientation program. Drama-theater group, choral group, marching band, student-run newspaper. Social organizations: 106 open to all; national fraternities, national sororities; 1% of eligible men and 3% of eligible women are members. Most popular organizations: Student Government Association, College Union Board, Resident Student Affairs Board, Baptist Student Union. Major annual events: Parents'/Alumni Weekend, Homecoming, Honors' Day. Student services: health clinic, personal-psychological counseling. Campus security: 24-hour emergency response devices and patrols, late night transport-escort service, controlled dormitory access. 963 undergraduates lived in college housing during 2003-04. No special consideration for freshman housing applicants. On-campus residence required through sophomore year. Options: men-only, women-only housing available. Stewart Library with 146,888 books, 761,477 microform titles, 2,548 serials, 3,151 audiovisual materials, an OPAC, and a Web page. Operations spending for 2004 fiscal year: $1 million. 470 computers available on campus for general student use. A campuswide network can be accessed from student residence rooms and from off campus. Staffed computer lab on campus.

■ **NORTH GEORGIA TECHNICAL COLLEGE** *C-6*
Georgia Hwy. 197, North
PO Box 65
Clarkesville, GA 30523
Tel: (706)754-7700
Admissions: (706)754-7724
Fax: (706)754-7777
E-mail: gtaylor@northgatech.edu
Web Site: http://www.northgatech.edu/
Description: State-supported, 2-year, coed. Awards certificates, diplomas, and terminal associate degrees. Founded 1943. Total enrollment: 1,812. Full-time: 974 students, 58% women, 42% men. Part-time: 838 students, 67% women, 33% men. 0.2% Native American, 1% Hispanic, 6% black, 1% Asian American or Pacific Islander, 0% international. Academic remediation for entering students, services for LD students, advanced placement, distance learning, internships.
Entrance Requirements: Open admission. Option: deferred admission. Required: high school transcript, ACT COMPASS or ASSET. Entrance: noncompetitive.
Costs Per Year: Application fee: $15. State resident tuition: $1116 full-time, $31 per credit hour part-time. Nonresident tuition: $2232 full-time, $62 per credit hour part-time.
Collegiate Environment: 194 college housing spaces available. 15,684 books, 162 serials, and 990 audiovisual materials.

■ **NORTH METRO TECHNICAL COLLEGE** *D-3*
5198 Ross Rd.
Acworth, GA 30102
Tel: (770)975-4000
Admissions: (770)975-4079
Fax: (770)975-4044
E-mail: mcusack@northmetrotech.edu

Web Site: http://www.northmetrotech.edu/
Description: State-supported, 2-year, coed. Awards certificates, diplomas, and terminal associate degrees. Founded 1989. Total enrollment: 1,903. Full-time: 790 students, 55% women, 45% men. Part-time: 1,113 students, 63% women, 37% men. 0.5% Native American, 2% Hispanic, 15% black, 1% Asian American or Pacific Islander, 0% international. Academic remediation for entering students, services for LD students, advanced placement, distance learning, internships.
Entrance Requirements: Open admission. Option: deferred admission. Required: high school transcript, ACT COMPASS or ASSET. Entrance: noncompetitive.
Costs Per Year: Application fee: $15. State resident tuition: $1116 full-time, $31 per credit hour part-time. Nonresident tuition: $2232 full-time, $62 per credit hour part-time.
Collegiate Environment: College housing not available.

■ **NORTHWESTERN TECHNICAL COLLEGE**
PO Box 569, 265 Bicentennial Trail
Rock Spring, GA 30739
Tel: (706)764-3510
Free: 800-735-5726
Admissions: (706)764-3511
E-mail: csolmon@northwesterntech.edu
Web Site: http://www.northwesterntech.edu/
Description: State-supported, 2-year, coed. Part of Georgia Department of Technical and Adult Education. Awards certificates, diplomas, and terminal associate degrees. Founded 1966. Setting: rural campus. Total enrollment: 2,303. Full-time: 891 students, 69% women, 31% men. Part-time: 1,412 students, 70% women, 30% men. Students come from 3 states and territories, 0.5% Native American, 1% Hispanic, 4% black, 0.4% Asian American or Pacific Islander, 0% international, 60% 25 or older. Core. Academic remediation for entering students, services for LD students, advanced placement, distance learning, summer session for credit, part-time degree program, adult/continuing education programs, internships.
Entrance Requirements: Open admission. Option: deferred admission. Required: high school transcript, ACT COMPASS or ASSET. Entrance: noncompetitive.
Costs Per Year: Application fee: $15. State resident tuition: $1116 full-time, $31 per credit hour part-time. Nonresident tuition: $2232 full-time, $62 per credit hour part-time.
Collegiate Environment: Orientation program. College housing not available. Northwestern Technical Institute Library with 350,000 books, 180 serials, 20,000 audiovisual materials, an OPAC, and a Web page. 270 computers available on campus for general student use. A campuswide network can be accessed from off-campus. Staffed computer lab on campus.

■ **OGEECHEE TECHNICAL COLLEGE** *I-11*
One Joe Kennedy Blvd.
Statesboro, GA 30458
Tel: (912)681-5500
Free: 800-646-1316
Admissions: (912)871-1600
E-mail: rfoley@ogeecheetech.edu
Web Site: http://www.ogeecheetech.edu
Description: State-supported, 2-year, coed. Part of Georgia Department of Technical and Adult Education. Awards certificates, diplomas, and terminal associate degrees. Founded 1989. Setting: small town campus. Total enrollment: 1,950. Full-time: 1,008 students, 68% women, 32% men. Part-time: 942 students, 71% women, 29% men. 0.5% Native American, 1% Hispanic, 33% black, 0.5% Asian American or Pacific Islander, 0% international, 39% 25 or older. Academic remediation for entering students, services for LD students, advanced placement, distance learning, internships.
Entrance Requirements: Open admission. Option: deferred admission. Required: high school transcript, ACT COMPASS or ASSET. Entrance: noncompetitive.
Costs Per Year: Application fee: $15. State resident tuition: $31 per credit hour part-time. Nonresident tuition: $62 per credit hour part-time.
Collegiate Environment: College housing not available. 2,477 books, 109 serials, and 276 audiovisual materials.

■ **OGLETHORPE UNIVERSITY** *E-4*
4484 Peachtree Rd., NE
Atlanta, GA 30319-2797
Tel: (404)261-1441

Free: 800-428-4484
Admissions: (404)364-8307
Fax: (404)364-8500
E-mail: admission@oglethorpe.edu
Web Site: http://www.oglethorpe.edu/

Description: Independent, comprehensive, coed. Awards bachelor's and master's degrees. Founded 1835. Setting: 118-acre suburban campus. Endowment: $21.5 million. Educational spending for 2005 fiscal year: $22,797 per student. Total enrollment: 1,083. Faculty: 115 (56 full-time, 59 part-time). Student-undergrad faculty ratio is 13:1. 1,236 applied, 64% were admitted. 27% from top 10% of their high school class, 57% from top quarter, 84% from top half. Full-time: 886 students, 63% women, 37% men. Part-time: 132 students, 70% women, 30% men. Students come from 36 states and territories, 21 other countries, 29% from out-of-state, 0.1% Native American, 1% Hispanic, 21% black, 4% Asian American or Pacific Islander, 6% international, 5% 25 or older, 58% live on campus, 6% transferred in. Retention: 79% of full-time freshmen returned the following year. Academic areas with the most degrees conferred: business/marketing; English; psychology. Core. Calendar: semesters. Services for LD students, advanced placement, accelerated degree program, self-designed majors, honors program, independent study, double major, summer session for credit, part-time degree program, adult/continuing education programs, co-op programs and internships, graduate courses open to undergrads. Off campus study at University Center in Georgia, 19 colleges and universities in the Atlanta area. Study abroad program.

Entrance Requirements: Options: Peterson's Universal Application, Common Application, electronic application, early action, deferred admission, international baccalaureate accepted. Required: essay, high school transcript, 1 recommendation, SAT and SAT Subject Tests or ACT. Recommended: minimum 2.5 high school GPA, interview. Required for some: interview. Entrance: very difficult. Application deadlines: Rolling, 12/1 for early action. Notification: continuous, 1/1 for early action.

Costs Per Year: Application fee: $35. Comprehensive fee: $30,300 includes full-time tuition ($22,200), mandatory fees ($100), and college room and board ($8000). Room and board charges vary according to board plan and housing facility. Part-time tuition: $925 per credit hour. Part-time tuition varies according to program.

Collegiate Environment: Orientation program. Drama-theater group, choral group, student-run newspaper, radio station. Social organizations: 52 open to all; national fraternities, national sororities; 33% of eligible men and 28% of eligible women are members. Most popular organizations: Alpha Phi Omega, Christian Fellowship, International Club, Playmakers. Major annual events: Homecoming, Boar's Head Ceremony, Oglethorpe Day. Student services: health clinic, personal-psychological counseling. Campus security: 24-hour emergency response devices and patrols, student patrols, late night transport-escort service, controlled dormitory access. Options: coed, men-only, women-only housing available. Philip Weltner Library with 150,000 books, 710 serials, an OPAC, and a Web page. 60 computers available on campus for general student use. A campuswide network can be accessed from student residence rooms and from off campus. Staffed computer lab on campus.

Community Environment: Oglethorpe students enjoy the scenic setting of a suburban campus combined with the opportunities of a great international city. Atlanta offers professional and amateur art and entertainment, professional and amateur sports, renowned intellectual and research activities, and world-class dining and enjoyment opportunities. It also offers small town values of friendliness, courtesy, and respect. Students can find part-time employment, internships, cultural activities, and an active job placement program, all of which are enhanced by the Atlanta location.

■ **OKEFENOKEE TECHNICAL COLLEGE** *M-9*

1701 Carswell Ave.
Waycross, GA 31503
Tel: (912)287-6584
Admissions: (912)287-5806
Fax: (912)287-4865
E-mail: reba@okefenokeetech.org
Web Site: http://www.okefenokeetech.org/

Description: State-supported, 2-year, coed. Awards certificates, diplomas, and terminal associate degrees. Setting: small town campus. Total enrollment: 1,731. Full-time: 595 students, 71% women, 29% men. Part-time: 1,136 students, 66% women, 34% men. 1% Native American, 1% Hispanic, 25% black, 1% Asian American or Pacific Islander, 0% international. Academic remediation for entering students, services for LD students, advanced placement, distance learning, internships.

Entrance Requirements: Open admission. Option: deferred admission. Required: high school transcript, ACT COMPASS or ASSET. Entrance: noncompetitive.

Costs Per Year: Application fee: $15. State resident tuition: $1116 full-time, $31 per credit hour part-time. Nonresident tuition: $2232 full-time, $62 per credit hour part-time.

Collegiate Environment: College housing not available. 1,714 books.

■ **PAINE COLLEGE** *F-10*

1235 15th St.
Augusta, GA 30901-3182
Tel: (706)821-8200
Free: 800-476-7703
Admissions: (706)821-8320
Fax: (706)821-8293
E-mail: tinsleyi@mail.paine.edu
Web Site: http://www.paine.edu/

Description: Independent Methodist, 4-year, coed. Awards bachelor's degrees. Founded 1882. Setting: 55-acre urban campus with easy access to Atlanta. Endowment: $11.7 million. Total enrollment: 828. Student-undergrad faculty ratio is 10:1. 3,683 applied, 29% were admitted. Full-time: 760 students, 70% women, 30% men. Part-time: 68 students, 68% women, 32% men. Students come from 29 states and territories, 3 other countries, 16% from out-of-state, 0% Native American, 0.1% Hispanic, 98% black, 0% Asian American or Pacific Islander, 0.4% international, 13% 25 or older, 58% live on campus, 4% transferred in. Retention: 60% of full-time freshmen returned the following year. Academic areas with the most degrees conferred: social sciences; business/marketing; biological/life sciences. Core. Calendar: semesters. Academic remediation for entering students, advanced placement, accelerated degree program, honors program, independent study, summer session for credit, part-time degree program, co-op programs and internships. Off campus study at Augusta State University, Clark Atlanta University. Study abroad program. ROTC: Army (c).

Entrance Requirements: Options: early admission, deferred admission. Required: essay, high school transcript, minimum 2.0 high school GPA, 3 recommendations, medical history, SAT or ACT. Entrance: minimally difficult. Application deadline: 8/1. Notification: continuous.

Costs Per Year: Application fee: $20. Comprehensive fee: $14,418 includes full-time tuition ($8952), mandatory fees ($738), and college room and board ($4728). Full-time tuition and fees vary according to course load and reciprocity agreements. Room and board charges vary according to housing facility. Part-time tuition: $373 per credit hour. Part-time mandatory fees: $369 per term. Part-time tuition and fees vary according to course load, location, and reciprocity agreements.

Collegiate Environment: Orientation program. Drama-theater group, choral group, marching band, student-run newspaper. Social organizations: 20 open to all; national fraternities, national sororities; 10% of eligible men and 10% of eligible women are members. Major annual events: homecoming, Founders' Day, Conference on the Black Experience. Student services: health clinic, personal-psychological counseling. Campus security: 24-hour emergency response devices and patrols, late night transport-escort service. College housing designed to accommodate 506 students; 519 undergraduates lived in college housing during 2003-04. Freshmen given priority for college housing. Options: men-only, women-only housing available. Collins-Callaway Library with 88,809 books, 6,931 microform titles, 5,447 serials, 1,655 audiovisual materials, and an OPAC. Operations spending for 2004 fiscal year: $355,233. 100 computers available on campus for general student use. A campuswide network can be accessed from student residence rooms and from off campus. Staffed computer lab on campus.

Community Environment: Augusta, located on the Savannah River in east central Georgia, is a river port and industrial center, and is the third leading producer of clay products in the southeast. All forms of transportation are available. Recreational facilities include lakes for fishing, boating and hunting, golf courses, horseback riding, and polo. The famous Augusta National Golf Club course, home of the Masters Golf Tournament, is located here. Some of the points of interest are the Mackay Trading Post, Meadow Garden, Fort Augusta, Confederate Monument, New Savannah Bluff Lock and Dam System, churches of historic interest, and two large enclosed shopping malls, one of which is the largest in Georgia.

■ **PIEDMONT COLLEGE** *C-6*

PO Box 10
165 Central Ave.
Demorest, GA 30535-0010

Tel: (706)778-3000
Free: 800-277-7020
Admissions: (706)776-0103
Fax: (706)776-6635
E-mail: cpeterson@piedmont.edu
Web Site: http://www.piedmont.edu/

Description: Independent, comprehensive, coed, affiliated with United Church of Christ. Awards bachelor's and master's degrees and post-master's certificates. Founded 1897. Setting: 115-acre rural campus with easy access to Atlanta. Endowment: $48.1 million. Educational spending for 2005 fiscal year: $5059 per student. Total enrollment: 1,938. Faculty: 200 (98 full-time, 102 part-time). Student-undergrad faculty ratio is 13:1. 485 applied, 66% were admitted. 18% from top 10% of their high school class, 41% from top quarter, 79% from top half. Full-time: 845 students, 63% women, 37% men. Part-time: 94 students, 68% women, 32% men. Students come from 17 states and territories, 23 other countries, 5% from out-of-state, 0.3% Native American, 2% Hispanic, 6% black, 1% Asian American or Pacific Islander, 0.2% international, 47% 25 or older, 16% live on campus, 13% transferred in. Retention: 69% of full-time freshmen returned the following year. Academic areas with the most degrees conferred: education; business/marketing; social sciences. Core. Calendar: semesters. Services for LD students, advanced placement, accelerated degree program, self-designed majors, honors program, independent study, distance learning, double major, summer session for credit, part-time degree program, adult/continuing education programs, co-op programs and internships, graduate courses open to undergrads. Off campus study at Piedmont College, Athens, Georgia. Study abroad program.

Entrance Requirements: Options: Peterson's Universal Application, Common Application, electronic application, early admission, deferred admission, international baccalaureate accepted. Required: high school transcript, minimum 2.0 high school GPA, SAT or ACT. Recommended: essay, recommendations. Required for some: interview. Entrance: moderately difficult. Application deadline: 7/1.

Costs Per Year: Application fee: $0. Comprehensive fee: $20,500 includes full-time tuition ($15,500) and college room and board ($5000). College room only: $2600. Full-time tuition varies according to course load and program. Room and board charges vary according to housing facility. Part-time tuition: $646 per semester hour. Part-time tuition varies according to course load and program.

Collegiate Environment: Orientation program. Drama-theater group, choral group, student-run newspaper, radio station. Social organizations: 25 open to all. Most popular organizations: student government, Student Georgia Association of Educators, Students In Free Enterprise, Psychology Club, Alternatives. Major annual events: Homecoming, Welcome Back Blowout, Spring Formal. Student services: personal-psychological counseling. Campus security: 24-hour emergency response devices and patrols, late night transport-escort service. 410 college housing spaces available; 408 were occupied in 2003-04. Freshmen guaranteed college housing. On-campus residence required through junior year. Options: coed, men-only, women-only housing available. Arrendale Library with 118,750 books, 48,462 microform titles, 366 serials, 1,064 audiovisual materials, an OPAC, and a Web page. Operations spending for 2004 fiscal year: $245,000. 150 computers available on campus for general student use. A campuswide network can be accessed from student residence rooms and from off campus. Staffed computer lab on campus.

Community Environment: Demorest, located in Habersham County in the northeastern corner of Georgia, is in the foothills of the southern Blue Ridge Mountains. The climate is considered unusually healthful. Buses serve the area with rail service in Toccoa, eighteen miles away and Hartfield International Airport in Atlanta, 75 miles southwest by major highway.

■ **REINHARDT COLLEGE**
7300 Reinhardt College Circle
Waleska, GA 30183-2981
Tel: (770)720-5600; (87R)EINHARDT
Admissions: (770)720-5526
Fax: (770)720-5602
E-mail: admissions@reinhardt.edu
Web Site: http://www.reinhardt.edu/

Description: Independent, 4-year, coed, affiliated with United Methodist Church. Awards associate and bachelor's degrees. Founded 1883. Setting: 600-acre rural campus with easy access to Atlanta. Endowment: $38 million. Educational spending for 2005 fiscal year: $13,000 per student. Total enrollment: 1,010. Student-undergrad faculty ratio is 13:1. 958 applied, 52% were

admitted. 11% from top 10% of their high school class, 25% from top quarter, 63% from top half. Full-time: 881 students, 57% women, 43% men. Part-time: 129 students, 60% women, 40% men. Students come from 18 states and territories, 21 other countries, 2% from out-of-state, 0.3% Native American, 2% Hispanic, 7% black, 1% Asian American or Pacific Islander, 1% international, 24% 25 or older, 39% live on campus, 1% transferred in. Retention: 65% of full-time freshmen returned the following year. Academic areas with the most degrees conferred: business/marketing; education; communications/journalism. Core. Calendar: semesters. Academic remediation for entering students, services for LD students, advanced placement, honors program, independent study, double major, summer session for credit, part-time degree program, external degree program, adult/continuing education programs, co-op programs and internships. Study abroad program.

Entrance Requirements: Options: Peterson's Universal Application, Common Application, electronic application, early admission, deferred admission. Required: high school transcript, minimum 2.0 high school GPA, SAT or ACT. Recommended: essay, interview. Entrance: moderately difficult. Application deadline: Rolling. Notification: continuous.

Costs Per Year: Application fee: $25. Comprehensive fee: $20,020 includes full-time tuition ($13,020), mandatory fees ($200), and college room and board ($6800). Part-time tuition: $435 per hour.

Collegiate Environment: Orientation program. Choral group, student-run newspaper. Social organizations: 25 open to all. Most popular organizations: Real Deal, International & Historical Film Society, Student Government Association, SOAR (Student Orientation Leaders), Communication Club. Major annual events: Spring Formal, Homecoming, Spirit Week. Student services: health clinic, personal-psychological counseling. Campus security: 24-hour patrols, student patrols, late night transport-escort service. College housing designed to accommodate 410 students; 420 undergraduates lived in college housing during 2003-04. Freshmen guaranteed college housing. On-campus residence required through sophomore year. Options: men-only, women-only housing available. Hill Freeman Library with 48,614 books, 2,140 microform titles, 329 serials, 17,362 audiovisual materials, an OPAC, and a Web page. Operations spending for 2004 fiscal year: $411,181. 164 computers available on campus for general student use. A campuswide network can be accessed from student residence rooms and from off campus. Staffed computer lab on campus.

Community Environment: Waleska is located on the summit of a ridge, an hour's drive from metropolitan Atlanta. The high altitude assures a crisp, dry atmosphere and a year-round climate never excelled in its healthful and invigorating qualities. The picturesque southern foothills of the Blue Ridge Mountains surround Waleska.

■ **SANDERSVILLE TECHNICAL COLLEGE** *G-8*
1189 Deepstep Rd.
Sandersville, GA 31082
Tel: (478)553-2050
Admissions: (478)553-2065
Fax: (478)553-2118
E-mail: pwilson@sandervilletech.edu
Web Site: http://www.sandersvilletech.org/

Description: State-supported, 2-year, coed. Awards certificates, diplomas, and terminal associate degrees. Total enrollment: 765. Full-time: 237 students, 51% women, 49% men. Part-time: 528 students, 71% women, 29% men. 0.4% Native American, 0.1% Hispanic, 65% black, 0.3% Asian American or Pacific Islander, 0% international. Academic remediation for entering students, services for LD students, advanced placement, distance learning, internships.

Entrance Requirements: Open admission. Option: deferred admission. Required: high school transcript, ACT COMPASS or ASSET. Entrance: noncompetitive.

Costs Per Year: Application fee: $15. State resident tuition: $1116 full-time, $31 per credit hour part-time. Nonresident tuition: $2232 full-time, $62 per credit hour part-time.

Collegiate Environment: College housing not available.

■ **SAVANNAH COLLEGE OF ART AND DESIGN** *J-13*
342 Bull St., PO Box 3146
Savannah, GA 31402-3146
Tel: (912)525-5000
Free: 800-869-7223
Admissions: (912)525-5100
Fax: (912)238-2436
E-mail: admission@scad.edu

Web Site: http://www.scad.edu/

Description: Independent, comprehensive, coed. Awards bachelor's and master's degrees. Founded 1978. Setting: urban campus. Educational spending for 2005 fiscal year: $6200 per student. Total enrollment: 7,356. Faculty: 419 (366 full-time, 53 part-time). Student-undergrad faculty ratio is 18:1. 4,782 applied, 68% were admitted. 3 National Merit Scholars, 1 class president, 8 valedictorians, 4 student government officers. Full-time: 5,528 students, 52% women, 48% men. Part-time: 608 students, 49% women, 51% men. Students come from 54 states and territories, 82 other countries, 84% from out-of-state, 0.3% Native American, 4% Hispanic, 5% black, 2% Asian American or Pacific Islander, 4% international, 5% 25 or older, 33% live on campus, 7% transferred in. Academic areas with the most degrees conferred: visual and performing arts; computer and information sciences; communication technologies. Core. ESL program, services for LD students, advanced placement, independent study, distance learning, double major, summer session for credit, part-time degree program, internships. Off campus study at LaCoste School of the Arts, Savannah College of Art and Design-Atlanta. Study abroad program.

Entrance Requirements: Options: electronic application, early admission, international baccalaureate accepted. Required: high school transcript, 3 recommendations, SAT or ACT. Recommended: interview. Required for some: portfolio/audition. Entrance: moderately difficult. Application deadline: Rolling. Notification: continuous.

Costs Per Year: Application fee: $50. Comprehensive fee: $33,045 includes full-time tuition ($22,950), mandatory fees ($500), and college room and board ($9595). College room only: $6250. Part-time tuition: $2550 per course.

Collegiate Environment: Orientation program. Drama-theater group, choral group, student-run newspaper, radio station. Social organizations: 45 open to all. Most popular organizations: United Student Forum, Inter-Club Council, American Institute of Architecture Students, Inter-Cultural Council, American Society of Interior Designers. Major annual events: Sidewalk Arts Festival, Beaux Arts Ball, International Festival. Student services: health clinic, personal-psychological counseling. Campus security: 24-hour emergency response devices and patrols, late night transport-escort service, video camera surveillance. 2,300 college housing spaces available; 2,250 were occupied in 2003-04. Freshmen given priority for college housing. Options: coed, women-only housing available. Jen Library plus 1 other with 126,680 books, 6,080 microform titles, 926 serials, 4,451 audiovisual materials, an OPAC, and a Web page. Operations spending for 2004 fiscal year: $1.7 million. 2,220 computers available on campus for general student use. Computer purchase/lease plans available. A campuswide network can be accessed from student residence rooms and from off campus. Staffed computer lab on campus.

Community Environment: The college is located in the downtown historic district of Savannah, Georgia, only minutes from Georgia's golden coast. The metropolitan area population is 160,000. Savannah is a popular tourist area, creating activities available to students throughout the year. Students enjoy new-age technology in an old-world environment. A free campus bus service transports students to and from classes.

■ **SAVANNAH RIVER COLLEGE** *F-10*
2528 Center West Parkway
Augusta, GA 30909
Tel: (706)738-5046
Web Site: http://www.savannahrivercollege.edu/
Description: Proprietary, 2-year, coed. Founded 1983.

■ **SAVANNAH STATE UNIVERSITY** *J-13*
3219 College Ave.
Savannah, GA 31404
Tel: (912)356-2186
Free: 800-788-0478
Admissions: (912)356-2181
Fax: (912)356-2529
E-mail: mooreg@savstate.edu
Web Site: http://www.savstate.edu/
Description: State-supported, comprehensive, coed. Part of University System of Georgia. Awards bachelor's and master's degrees. Founded 1890. Setting: 165-acre suburban campus. Endowment: $1.3 million. Research spending for 2004 fiscal year: $688,897. Educational spending for 2005 fiscal year: $641 per student. Total enrollment: 3,055. Faculty: 167 (123 full-time, 44 part-time). Student-undergrad faculty ratio is 19:1. 2,824 applied, 50% were admitted. Full-time: 2,365 students, 57% women, 43% men.

Part-time: 574 students, 54% women, 46% men. Students come from 18 states and territories, 20 other countries, 11% from out-of-state, 0.03% Native American, 0.3% Hispanic, 96% black, 1% Asian American or Pacific Islander, 0% international, 45% live on campus, 3% transferred in. Retention: 71% of full-time freshmen returned the following year. Academic areas with the most degrees conferred: biological/life sciences; business/marketing; computer and information sciences. Core. Calendar: semesters. Academic remediation for entering students, services for LD students, advanced placement, accelerated degree program, summer session for credit, part-time degree program, adult/continuing education programs, co-op programs and internships. Off campus study at Armstrong Atlantic State University. ROTC: Army, Naval.

Entrance Requirements: Options: Common Application, electronic application, early admission, deferred admission. Required: high school transcript, minimum 2.0 high school GPA, SAT or ACT. Recommended: SAT. Required for some: SAT Subject Tests. Entrance: minimally difficult. Application deadline: 6/1. Notification: continuous. Preference given to state residents.

Costs Per Year: Application fee: $20. State resident tuition: $3056 full-time. Nonresident tuition: $10,372 full-time. College room and board: $4716. College room only: $2136.

Collegiate Environment: Orientation program. Drama-theater group, choral group, marching band, student-run newspaper, radio station. Social organizations: national fraternities, national sororities, local fraternities, local sororities; 35% of eligible men and 38% of eligible women are members. Most popular organizations: marching band, gospel choir, concert choir. Major annual events: homecoming, Icebreaker (Greek talent), Martin Luther King Observance Day. Student services: health clinic, personal-psychological counseling. Campus security: 24-hour patrols. On-campus residence required through junior year. Options: men-only, women-only housing available. Asa H. Gordon Library with 187,916 books, 547,522 microform titles, 812 serials, an OPAC, and a Web page. Operations spending for 2004 fiscal year: $689,322. 440 computers available on campus for general student use. A campuswide network can be accessed. Staffed computer lab on campus.

Community Environment: See Armstrong Atlantic State University.

■ **SAVANNAH TECHNICAL COLLEGE** *J-13*
5717 White Bluff Rd.
Savannah, GA 31405
Tel: (912)351-6362
Admissions: (912)303-1772
Fax: (912)352-4362
E-mail: asoutherland@savannahtech.edu
Web Site: http://www.savannahtech.edu/
Description: State-supported, 2-year, coed. Part of Georgia Department of Technical and Adult Education. Awards certificates, diplomas, and terminal associate degrees. Founded 1929. Setting: 15-acre urban campus. Total enrollment: 3,786. Full-time: 1,577 students, 65% women, 35% men. Part-time: 2,209 students, 72% women, 28% men. Students come from 4 states and territories, 0.4% Native American, 3% Hispanic, 57% black, 2% Asian American or Pacific Islander, 2% international, 59% 25 or older, 3% transferred in. Academic remediation for entering students, services for LD students, advanced placement, distance learning, summer session for credit, part-time degree program, internships.

Entrance Requirements: Open admission. Option: deferred admission. Required: high school transcript, ACT COMPASS or ASSET. Entrance: noncompetitive.

Costs Per Year: Application fee: $15. State resident tuition: $1116 full-time, $31 per credit hour part-time. Nonresident tuition: $2232 full-time, $62 per credit hour part-time.

Collegiate Environment: Orientation program. Social organizations: 10 open to all. Most popular organizations: Phi Beta Lambda, Vocational Industrial Clubs of America (VICA). College housing not available. 20,804 books, 35,000 microform titles, 160 serials, 3,150 audiovisual materials, an OPAC, and a Web page.

■ **SHORTER COLLEGE** *D-2*
315 Shorter Ave.
Rome, GA 30165
Tel: (706)291-2121
Free: 800-868-6980
Admissions: (706)233-7342
Fax: (706)236-1515
E-mail: admissions@shorter.edu

Web Site: http://www.shorter.edu/

Description: Independent Baptist, 4-year, coed. Awards bachelor's degrees. Founded 1873. Setting: 155-acre small town campus with easy access to Atlanta. Endowment: $21.2 million. Educational spending for 2005 fiscal year: $6414 per student. Total enrollment: 967. Student-undergrad faculty ratio is 11:1. 1,031 applied, 75% were admitted. 19% from top 10% of their high school class, 46% from top quarter, 75% from top half. Full-time: 929 students, 51% women, 49% men. Part-time: 38 students, 55% women, 45% men. Students come from 20 states and territories, 23 other countries, 9% from out-of-state, 0.2% Native American, 2% Hispanic, 9% black, 1% Asian American or Pacific Islander, 4% international, 8% 25 or older, 63% live on campus, 9% transferred in. Retention: 71% of full-time freshmen returned the following year. Academic areas with the most degrees conferred: business/marketing; education; biological/life sciences. Core. Calendar: semesters. Academic remediation for entering students, services for LD students, advanced placement, self-designed majors, honors program, independent study, double major, summer session for credit, part-time degree program, adult/continuing education programs, internships. Off campus study at Berry College. Study abroad program.

Entrance Requirements: Options: electronic application, early admission, deferred admission. Required: essay, high school transcript, SAT or ACT. Recommended: minimum 2.0 high school GPA, 1 recommendation, interview. Required for some: interview, audition for music and theater programs. Entrance: moderately difficult. Application deadline: 8/25. Notification: continuous.

Costs Per Year: Application fee: $25. Comprehensive fee: $19,700 includes full-time tuition ($13,200), mandatory fees ($300), and college room and board ($6200). College room only: $3400. Full-time tuition and fees vary according to course load. Room and board charges vary according to board plan and housing facility. Part-time tuition: $285 per semester hour.

Collegiate Environment: Orientation program. Drama-theater group, choral group, marching band, student-run newspaper, radio station. Social organizations: 9 open to all; local fraternities; 7% of eligible men and 32% of eligible women are members. Most popular organizations: Baptist Student Union, Student Government Association, Fellowship of Christian Athletes, Shorter Players, Habitat for Humanity. Major annual events: Midnight Breakfast, Shorter Fest, Parents' Weekend. Student services: health clinic, personal-psychological counseling. Campus security: 24-hour emergency response devices and patrols. 600 college housing spaces available; 534 were occupied in 2003-04. Freshmen given priority for college housing. On-campus residence required through senior year. Options: men-only, women-only housing available. Livingston Library with 134,201 books, 7,334 microform titles, 596 serials, 4,645 audiovisual materials, an OPAC, and a Web page. Operations spending for 2004 fiscal year: $502,324. 100 computers available on campus for general student use. A campuswide network can be accessed from student residence rooms. Staffed computer lab on campus.

■ **SOUTH GEORGIA COLLEGE** *L-8*
100 West College Park Dr.
Douglas, GA 31533-5098
Tel: (912)389-4510
Admissions: (912)389-4200
Fax: (912)389-4392
E-mail: rbraswell@sga.edu
Web Site: http://www.sga.edu/

Description: State-supported, 2-year, coed. Part of University System of Georgia. Awards certificates, transfer associate, and terminal associate degrees. Founded 1906. Setting: 250-acre small town campus. Endowment: $150,321. Total enrollment: 1,431. 554 applied, 99% were admitted. Students come from 3 states and territories, 2 other countries, 0.1% Native American, 2% Hispanic, 23% black, 1% Asian American or Pacific Islander, 0.3% international, 34% 25 or older, 11% live on campus. Core. Calendar: semesters. Academic remediation for entering students, services for LD students, advanced placement, summer session for credit, part-time degree program, adult/continuing education programs. Study abroad program.

Entrance Requirements: Options: electronic application, early admission, deferred admission. Required: high school transcript. Placement: SAT or ACT required; SAT Subject Tests required for some. Entrance: minimally difficult. Notification: continuous.

Collegiate Environment: Orientation program. Drama-theater group, student-run newspaper. Social organizations: 12 open to all. Most popular organizations: Georgia Association of Student Nurses, Baptist Student Union, Agricultural Club, Residents Assistants Club, Student Organization for

Black Unity. Student services: personal-psychological counseling. Campus security: 24-hour emergency response devices and patrols, controlled dormitory access. 150 college housing spaces available; 140 were occupied in 2003-04. On-campus residence required in freshman year. William S. Smith Library with 79,190 books, 327 serials, an OPAC, and a Web page. Operations spending for 2004 fiscal year: $444,906. 80 computers available on campus for general student use. A campuswide network can be accessed from off-campus. Staffed computer lab on campus.

Community Environment: Douglas is situated in the southern part of Georgia; having a delightful climate, winters are mild, and the summers pleasant. This community is one of the largest tobacco markets in the South. Livestock, poultry, naval stores, light industry, and the manufacture of mobile homes. Part-time employment is available for students. The community facilities include churches of all denominations, regional library, hospital, community concert association. Recreational facilities are the golf course, recreation center, tennis courts, pools, etc.

■ **SOUTH GEORGIA TECHNICAL COLLEGE** *J-4*
1583 Southerfield Rd.
Americus, GA 31709
Tel: (229)931-2394
Admissions: (229)931-2299
Fax: (229)931-2459
E-mail: kwerling@southgatech.edu
Web Site: http://www.southgatech.edu/

Description: State-supported, 2-year, coed. Awards certificates, diplomas, and terminal associate degrees. Founded 1948. Total enrollment: 1,669. Full-time: 886 students, 53% women, 47% men. Part-time: 783 students, 50% women, 50% men. 0.1% Native American, 1% Hispanic, 59% black, 0.4% Asian American or Pacific Islander, 0% international. Academic remediation for entering students, services for LD students, advanced placement, distance learning, co-op programs and internships.

Entrance Requirements: Open admission. Option: deferred admission. Required: high school transcript, ACT COMPASS or ASSET. Entrance: noncompetitive.

Costs Per Year: Application fee: $15. State resident tuition: $1116 full-time, $31 per credit hour part-time. Nonresident tuition: $2232 full-time, $62 per credit hour part-time.

Collegiate Environment: 200 college housing spaces available.

■ **SOUTH UNIVERSITY** *J-13*
709 Mall Blvd.
Savannah, GA 31406-4805
Tel: (912)201-8000; (866)629-2901
Fax: (912)201-8070
E-mail: mmills@southuniversity.edu
Web Site: http://www.southuniversity.edu/

Description: Proprietary, comprehensive, coed. Awards associate, bachelor's, master's, and doctoral degrees. Founded 1899. Setting: 9-acre urban campus. Educational spending for 2005 fiscal year: $2857 per student. Total enrollment: 1,037. Faculty: 91 (41 full-time, 50 part-time). Student-undergrad faculty ratio is 13:1. Students come from 31 states and territories, 3 other countries, 41% from out-of-state, 46% 25 or older. Core. Academic remediation for entering students, accelerated degree program, double major, summer session for credit, part-time degree program, adult/continuing education programs, internships.

Entrance Requirements: Options: Peterson's Universal Application, electronic application, deferred admission. Required: high school transcript, interview. Required for some: essay, 3 recommendations, SAT and SAT Subject Tests or ACT. Entrance: moderately difficult. Application deadline: Rolling. Notification: continuous.

Costs Per Year: Application fee: $25. Tuition: $11,475 full-time, $2995 per term part-time.

Collegiate Environment: Orientation program. Most popular organizations: Medical Assisting Club, Paralegal Club, Student Advisory Committee. Student services: personal-psychological counseling. Campus security: late night transport-escort service. College housing not available. South College Library with 22,240 books, 3,065 serials, 3,320 audiovisual materials, and an OPAC. Operations spending for 2004 fiscal year: $326,000. 83 computers available on campus for general student use. A campuswide network can be accessed from off-campus. Staffed computer lab on campus.

■ **SOUTHEASTERN TECHNICAL COLLEGE** *J-9*
3001 East First St.
Vidalia, GA 30474

Tel: (912)538-3100
Admissions: (912)538-3121
Fax: (912)538-3156
E-mail: ccarroll@southeasterntech.edu
Web Site: http://www.southeasterntech.edu/
Description: State-supported, 2-year, coed. Awards certificates, diplomas, and terminal associate degrees. Founded 1989. Total enrollment: 982. Full-time: 447 students, 77% women, 23% men. Part-time: 535 students, 69% women, 31% men. 0.3% Native American, 2% Hispanic, 29% black, 0.2% Asian American or Pacific Islander, 0% international. Academic remediation for entering students, services for LD students, advanced placement, distance learning, internships.
Entrance Requirements: Open admission. Option: deferred admission. Required: high school transcript, ACT COMPASS or ASSET. Entrance: noncompetitive.
Costs Per Year: Application fee: $15. State resident tuition: $1116 full-time, $31 per credit hour part-time. Nonresident tuition: $2232 full-time, $62 per credit hour part-time.
Collegiate Environment: College housing not available.

■ SOUTHERN POLYTECHNIC STATE UNIVERSITY *D-3*
1100 South Marietta Parkway
Marietta, GA 30060-2896
Tel: (678)915-7778
Free: 800-635-3204
Admissions: (678)915-4188
E-mail: vhead@sct.edu
Web Site: http://www.spsu.edu/
Description: State-supported, comprehensive, coed. Part of University System of Georgia. Awards associate, bachelor's, and master's degrees. Founded 1948. Setting: 200-acre suburban campus with easy access to Atlanta. Endowment: $3.4 million. Research spending for 2004 fiscal year: $328,431. Educational spending for 2005 fiscal year: $9147 per student. Total enrollment: 3,806. Faculty: 226 (135 full-time, 91 part-time). Student-undergrad faculty ratio is 17:1. 1,056 applied, 66% were admitted. Full-time: 2,193 students, 16% women, 84% men. Part-time: 1,137 students, 18% women, 82% men. Students come from 40 states and territories, 5% from out-of-state, 0.2% Native American, 3% Hispanic, 21% black, 6% Asian American or Pacific Islander, 6% international, 33% 25 or older, 12% live on campus, 12% transferred in. Retention: 68% of full-time freshmen returned the following year. Academic areas with the most degrees conferred: engineering technologies; computer and information sciences; business/marketing. Core. Calendar: semesters. Services for LD students, advanced placement, self-designed majors, honors program, independent study, distance learning, double major, summer session for credit, part-time degree program, adult/continuing education programs, co-op programs and internships. Study abroad program. ROTC: Army (c), Naval (c), Air Force (c).
Entrance Requirements: Options: early admission, international baccalaureate accepted. Required: high school transcript, minimum 2.5 high school GPA, proof of immunization, SAT or ACT. Entrance: moderately difficult. Application deadline: 8/1. Notification: continuous.
Costs Per Year: Application fee: $20. State resident tuition: $2622 full-time, $110 per credit hour part-time. Nonresident tuition: $10,486 full-time, $437 per credit hour part-time. Mandatory fees: $552 full-time. College room and board: $5490. College room only: $3210.
Collegiate Environment: Orientation program. Student-run newspaper, radio station. Social organizations: 24 open to all; national fraternities, national sororities, local fraternities; 4% of eligible men and 1% of eligible women are members. Most popular organizations: International Student Association, Campus Activities Board, National Society of Black Engineers, Aerial Robotics Team. Major annual events: Fall Party, movie nights, Spring Fling. Student services: health clinic, personal-psychological counseling. Campus security: 24-hour emergency response devices and patrols, late night transport-escort service, controlled dormitory access. 1,133 college housing spaces available; 680 were occupied in 2003-04. No special consideration for freshman housing applicants. Option: coed housing available. Lawrence V. Johnson Library with 117,963 books, 56,619 microform titles, 1,320 serials, 60 audiovisual materials, and an OPAC. Operations spending for 2004 fiscal year: $767,577. 1,500 computers available on campus for general student use. A campuswide network can be accessed from student residence rooms and from off campus. Staffed computer lab on campus.
Community Environment: Nestled between the Chattahoochee National Recreation Area and Kennesaw National Battlefield Park on the Piedmont

Plateau of north central Georgia lies historic Marietta, Georgia. Incorporated in 1834, Marietta is the heart of Cobb County, Georgia, and serves as the seat of Cobb County Government. Marietta, the "Gem City of the South," is the second largest municipality in the Atlantic area (15 miles from downtown Atlanta), but has the lowest tax rate. Cobb is one of the twenty-five fastest growing counties in the country with a population of 539,000. Lockheed Martin is the county's largest single employer. Cobb has one of the metro area's highest per family incomes at $46,119. College-educated residents make up 33 percent of the population. Five colleges and two technical institutes serve the area, as do two public school systems.

■ SOUTHWEST GEORGIA TECHNICAL COLLEGE *N-5*
15689 US 19 North
Thomasville, GA 31792
Tel: (229)225-4096
Admissions: (229)225-5077
Fax: (229)225-4330
E-mail: lhoover@southwestgatech.edu
Web Site: http://www.southwestgatech.edu/
Description: State-supported, 2-year, coed. Part of Georgia Department of Technical and Adult Education. Awards certificates, diplomas, and terminal associate degrees. Founded 1963. Total enrollment: 1,491. Full-time: 588 students, 74% women, 26% men. Part-time: 903 students, 71% women, 29% men. 1% Native American, 1% Hispanic, 41% black, 0.3% Asian American or Pacific Islander, 0.1% international, 74% 25 or older. Core. Academic remediation for entering students, services for LD students, advanced placement, distance learning, summer session for credit, part-time degree program, co-op programs and internships.
Entrance Requirements: Open admission. Options: electronic application, deferred admission. Required: high school transcript, ACT COMPASS or AS-SET. Entrance: noncompetitive.
Costs Per Year: Application fee: $20. State resident tuition: $1116 full-time, $31 per credit hour part-time. Nonresident tuition: $2232 full-time, $62 per credit hour part-time.
Collegiate Environment: Orientation program. College housing not available. 19,767 books, 113 serials, 920 audiovisual materials, an OPAC, and a Web page. 430 computers available on campus for general student use. A campuswide network can be accessed.

■ SPELMAN COLLEGE *E-4*
350 Spelman Ln., SW
Atlanta, GA 30314-4399
Tel: (404)681-3643
Free: 800-982-2411
Fax: (404)215-7788
E-mail: admiss@spelman.edu
Web Site: http://www.spelman.edu/
Description: Independent, 4-year, women only. Awards bachelor's degrees. Founded 1881. Setting: 32-acre urban campus. Endowment: $258.1 million. Research spending for 2004 fiscal year: $4.8 million. Educational spending for 2005 fiscal year: $27,856 per student. Total enrollment: 2,318. Student-undergrad faculty ratio is 12:1. 4,534 applied, 39% were admitted. 33% from top 10% of their high school class, 71% from top quarter, 91% from top half. 4 National Merit Scholars. Full-time: 2,226 students. Part-time: 92 students. Students come from 42 states and territories, 18 other countries, 74% from out-of-state, 0.1% Native American, 0.1% Hispanic, 95% black, 0.04% Asian American or Pacific Islander, 2% international, 3% 25 or older, 53% live on campus, 1% transferred in. Retention: 90% of full-time freshmen returned the following year. Academic areas with the most degrees conferred: social sciences; history; psychology. Core. Calendar: semesters. Academic remediation for entering students, services for LD students, advanced placement, self-designed majors, honors program, independent study, double major, part-time degree program, adult/continuing education programs, internships. Off campus study at Babson College; Bates College; Bryn Mawr College; Claremont McKenna College; Connecticut College; Rutgers, The State University of New Jersey, Douglass College; Dartmouth College; Grinnell College; Haverford College; Illinois Wesleyan University; Mount Holyoke College; Middlebury College; Mills College; New York University; Occidental College; Ohio Wesleyan University; Pitzer College; Pomona College; Scripps College; Simmons College; Stanford University; University of California, San Diego; Vassar College; Wellesley College. Study abroad program. ROTC: Army (c), Air Force (c).
Entrance Requirements: Options: Peterson's Universal Application, Common Application, electronic application, early admission, early action,

deferred admission, international baccalaureate accepted. Required: essay, high school transcript, minimum 2.0 high school GPA, 2 recommendations, SAT or ACT. Required for some: interview. Entrance: very difficult. Application deadlines: 2/1, 11/1 for nonresidents, 11/15 for early decision. Notification: 4/1, 12/15 for nonresidents, 12/31 for early decision.

Costs Per Year: Application fee: $35. Comprehensive fee: $24,250 includes full-time tuition ($13,525), mandatory fees ($2270), and college room and board ($8455). Part-time tuition: $565 per credit hour.

Collegiate Environment: Orientation program. Drama-theater group, choral group, student-run newspaper. Social organizations: national sororities; 15% of eligible undergrads are members. Most popular organizations: Student Government Association, Spotlight (newspaper), Health Careers Club, NAACP (campus organization), SHAPE (health organization). Major annual events: Founders' Day, Family Weekend, Blue and White Ball. Student services: health clinic, personal-psychological counseling, women's center. Campus security: 24-hour emergency response devices and patrols, late night transport-escort service, controlled dormitory access. 1,178 college housing spaces available; all were occupied in 2003-04. Freshmen given priority for college housing. Option: women-only housing available. Robert Woodruff Library with 727,767 books, 851,268 microform titles, 1,549 serials, 10,656 audiovisual materials, an OPAC, and a Web page. Operations spending for 2004 fiscal year: $1.2 million. 105 computers available on campus for general student use. A campuswide network can be accessed from off-campus. Staffed computer lab on campus.

Community Environment: See Clark Atlanta University.

■ **SWAINSBORO TECHNICAL COLLEGE** *I-9*

346 Kite Rd.
Swainsboro, GA 30401
Tel: (478)289-2200
Admissions: (478)289-2259
Fax: (478)289-2263
E-mail: mfagler@swainsborotech.edu
Web Site: http://www.swainsborotech.edu/

Description: State-supported, 2-year, coed. Awards certificates, diplomas, and terminal associate degrees. Founded 1963. Total enrollment: 684. Full-time: 286 students, 73% women, 27% men. Part-time: 398 students, 76% women, 24% men. 0.3% Native American, 0.3% Hispanic, 43% black, 0.4% Asian American or Pacific Islander, 0% international. Services for LD students, advanced placement, distance learning, co-op programs and internships.

Entrance Requirements: Open admission. Option: deferred admission. Required: high school transcript, ACT COMPASS or ASSET. Entrance: noncompetitive.

Costs Per Year: Application fee: $15. State resident tuition: $1116 full-time, $31 per credit hour part-time. Nonresident tuition: $2232 full-time, $62 per credit hour part-time.

Collegiate Environment: College housing not available.

■ **THOMAS UNIVERSITY** *N-5*

1501 Millpond Rd.
Thomasville, GA 31792-7499
Tel: (229)226-1621
Free: 800-538-9784
E-mail: hmueller@thomasu.edu
Web Site: http://www.thomasu.edu/

Description: Independent, comprehensive, coed. Awards associate, bachelor's, and master's degrees. Founded 1950. Setting: 24-acre small town campus. Endowment: $3.2 million. Educational spending for 2005 fiscal year: $8550 per student. Total enrollment: 739. Faculty: 79 (46 full-time, 33 part-time). Student-undergrad faculty ratio is 10:1. 329 applied, 68% were admitted. Full-time: 445 students, 70% women, 30% men. Part-time: 190 students, 76% women, 24% men. Students come from 8 states and territories, 12 other countries, 4% from out-of-state, 1% Native American, 1% Hispanic, 37% black, 1% Asian American or Pacific Islander, 4% international, 70% 25 or older, 9% live on campus, 13% transferred in. Retention: 49% of full-time freshmen returned the following year. Core. Calendar: semesters. Academic remediation for entering students, services for LD students, advanced placement, accelerated degree program, independent study, distance learning, double major, summer session for credit, part-time degree program, adult/continuing education programs, co-op programs and internships. Study abroad program.

Entrance Requirements: Open admission. Options: electronic application, early admission, deferred admission, international baccalaureate accepted.

Required: high school transcript. Entrance: noncompetitive. Application deadline: Rolling. Notification: continuous.

Costs Per Year: Application fee: $25. Tuition: $10,050 full-time, $395 per semester hour part-time. Mandatory fees: $520 full-time, $130 per term part-time. College room only: $2500.

Collegiate Environment: Orientation program. Drama-theater group, choral group, student-run newspaper. Social organizations: 20 open to all; 7% of eligible men and 7% of eligible women are members. Most popular organizations: Nursing Club, Psychology Club, Baptist Student Union. Major annual events: Homecoming, Valentine's Dance, Fall Fling. Student services: personal-psychological counseling. Campus security: late night transport-escort service, evening security guards. 64 college housing spaces available; all were occupied in 2003-04. Freshmen given priority for college housing. Option: coed housing available. Thomas University Library with 61,096 books, 408 serials, 943 audiovisual materials, and an OPAC. 50 computers available on campus for general student use. A campuswide network can be accessed from student residence rooms and from off campus. Staffed computer lab on campus.

■ **TOCCOA FALLS COLLEGE**

325 Chapel Dr.
Toccoa Falls, GA 30598
Tel: (706)886-6831
Fax: (706)282-6012
E-mail: admissions@tfc.edu
Web Site: http://www.tfc.edu/

Description: Independent interdenominational, 4-year, coed. Awards associate and bachelor's degrees. Founded 1907. Setting: 500-acre small town campus. Endowment: $2.5 million. Educational spending for 2005 fiscal year: $3940 per student. Total enrollment: 922. Student-undergrad faculty ratio is 16:1. 815 applied, 61% were admitted. 18% from top 10% of their high school class, 40% from top quarter, 69% from top half. Full-time: 863 students, 58% women, 42% men. Part-time: 59 students, 56% women, 44% men. Students come from 39 states and territories, 9 other countries, 46% from out-of-state, 0.1% Native American, 2% Hispanic, 3% black, 7% Asian American or Pacific Islander, 2% international, 11% 25 or older, 63% live on campus, 7% transferred in. Retention: 71% of full-time freshmen returned the following year. Academic areas with the most degrees conferred: theology and religious vocations; security and protective services; education. Core. Calendar: semesters. Services for LD students, advanced placement, accelerated degree program, independent study, double major, summer session for credit, part-time degree program, internships. Study abroad program.

Entrance Requirements: Options: Peterson's Universal Application, electronic application, early admission, deferred admission, international baccalaureate accepted. Required: essay, high school transcript, minimum 2.0 high school GPA, 1 recommendation, SAT or ACT. Required for some: interview. Entrance: moderately difficult. Application deadline: Rolling. Notification: continuous.

Costs Per Year: Application fee: $20. One-time mandatory fee: $475. Comprehensive fee: $16,650 includes full-time tuition ($12,050) and college room and board ($4600). Full-time tuition varies according to course load. Room and board charges vary according to board plan. Part-time tuition: $502 per credit hour. Part-time tuition varies according to course load.

Collegiate Environment: Orientation program. Drama-theater group, choral group, student-run newspaper, radio station. Social organizations: 10 open to all. Most popular organizations: Outdoor Club, Hmong Student Fellowship, Impact, Student Missionary Fellowship, Fellowship of Christian Athletes. Major annual events: Spiritual Emphasis Week, lecture series, World Outreach Conference. Student services: health clinic, personal-psychological counseling. Campus security: student patrols. 629 college housing spaces available; 504 were occupied in 2003-04. Freshmen guaranteed college housing. On-campus residence required through junior year. Options: men-only, women-only housing available. Seby Jones Library with 139,082 books, 22,309 microform titles, 18,134 serials, 4,418 audiovisual materials, an OPAC, and a Web page. Operations spending for 2004 fiscal year: $305,590. 60 computers available on campus for general student use. A campuswide network can be accessed from student residence rooms and from off campus. Staffed computer lab on campus.

Community Environment: Toccoa is in a rural area in the foothills of the Blue Ridge Mountains. The Southern Railway and Greyhound Bus provide public transportation. Industries located here are the manufacturing of machinery, garments, furniture and thread. Toccoa has a municipal recreation center and golf course. Mountain lakes and resorts are within a short distance, providing fishing, hunting, water sports, and picnicking.

■ TRUETT-McCONNELL COLLEGE C-6

100 Alumni Dr.
Cleveland, GA 30528
Tel: (706)865-2134
Fax: (706)219-3339
E-mail: ploggins@truett.edu
Web Site: http://www.truett.edu/

Description: Independent Baptist, primarily 2-year, coed. Awards transfer associate, terminal associate, and bachelor's degrees. Founded 1946. Setting: 310-acre rural campus with easy access to Atlanta. Total enrollment: 375. Student-undergrad faculty ratio is 11:1. 604 applied, 42% were admitted. Full-time: 340 students, 44% women, 56% men. Part-time: 35 students, 71% women, 29% men. Students come from 4 states and territories, 4 other countries, 3% from out-of-state, 0.3% Native American, 3% Hispanic, 11% black, 2% Asian American or Pacific Islander, 0% international, 4% 25 or older, 73% live on campus, 5% transferred in. Retention: 55% of full-time freshmen returned the following year. Core. Calendar: semesters. Academic remediation for entering students, services for LD students, advanced placement, accelerated degree program, honors program, double major, summer session for credit, part-time degree program. Study abroad program.

Entrance Requirements: Options: early admission, deferred admission. Required: high school transcript, minimum 2.0 high school GPA, minimum SAT score of 720 or ACT score of 15, SAT or ACT. Required for some: recommendations, interview. Entrance: minimally difficult. Application deadline: 8/1. Notification: continuous.

Costs Per Year: Application fee: $25. Comprehensive fee: $17,450 includes full-time tuition ($11,950), mandatory fees ($500), and college room and board ($5000). College room only: $2300. Part-time tuition: $398 per credit hour. Part-time mandatory fees: $250 per term.

Collegiate Environment: Orientation program. Choral group. Social organizations: 8 open to all. Most popular organizations: intramurals, Baptist Student Union, College Choir, Student Government Association, Fellowship of Christian Athletes (FCA). Major annual events: Welcome Week, Miss Reflections, Spring Fling. Campus security: 24-hour weekday patrols, 10-hour weekend patrols by trained security personnel. 408 college housing spaces available; 263 were occupied in 2003-04. No special consideration for freshman housing applicants. Options: men-only, women-only housing available. Cofer Library with 30,779 books, 38,800 microform titles, 155 serials, 2,522 audiovisual materials, and an OPAC. 38 computers available on campus for general student use. A campuswide network can be accessed from student residence rooms and from off campus. Staffed computer lab on campus.

Community Environment: Cleveland is in the mountains of north Georgia, a few miles south of the famous Vogel State Park. Bus service is available. The community, with its inspiring mountain scenery, provides a wholesome environment for young people. The Chattahoochee National Forest is 10 miles away.

■ UNIVERSITY OF GEORGIA D-7

Athens, GA 30602
Tel: (706)542-3000
Admissions: (706)542-8776
E-mail: adm-info@uga.edu
Web Site: http://www.uga.edu/

Description: State-supported, university, coed. Part of University System of Georgia. Awards associate, bachelor's, master's, doctoral, and first professional degrees. Founded 1785. Setting: 1,289-acre suburban campus with easy access to Atlanta. Endowment: $517 million. Research spending for 2004 fiscal year: $258 million. Educational spending for 2005 fiscal year: $6029 per student. Total enrollment: 33,660. Faculty: 2,111 (1,661 full-time, 450 part-time). Student-undergrad faculty ratio is 18:1. 12,329 applied, 65% were admitted. 52% from top 10% of their high school class, 84% from top quarter, 98% from top half. 44 National Merit Scholars. Full-time: 22,730 students, 57% women, 43% men. Part-time: 2,474 students, 57% women, 43% men. Students come from 54 states and territories, 120 other countries, 13% from out-of-state, 0.2% Native American, 2% Hispanic, 6% black, 5% Asian American or Pacific Islander, 1% international, 6% 25 or older, 27% live on campus, 3% transferred in. Retention: 93% of full-time freshmen returned the following year. Academic areas with the most degrees conferred: business/marketing; social sciences; education. Core. Calendar: semesters. Academic remediation for entering students, ESL program, services for LD students, advanced placement, accelerated degree program, self-designed majors, freshman honors college, honors program, independent study, distance learning, double major, summer session for credit, part-time degree program, adult/continuing education programs, co-op programs and internships, graduate courses open to undergrads. Off campus study at National Student Exchange. Study abroad program. ROTC: Army, Air Force.

Entrance Requirements: Options: Peterson's Universal Application, electronic application, early admission, early action, deferred admission, international baccalaureate accepted. Required: high school transcript, counselor evaluation, SAT or ACT, writing assessment portion of the SAT or ACT. Recommended: essay, SAT Subject Tests. Entrance: moderately difficult. Application deadlines: 1/15, 10/15 for early action. Notification: 2/15, 12/15 for early action.

Costs Per Year: Application fee: $50. State resident tuition: $3638 full-time, $152 per credit part-time. Nonresident tuition: $15,858 full-time, $661 per credit part-time. Mandatory fees: $990 full-time, $495 per term part-time. Full-time tuition and fees vary according to course load, location, program, and reciprocity agreements. Part-time tuition and fees vary according to course load, location, program, and reciprocity agreements. College room and board: $6376. College room only: $3436. Room and board charges vary according to board plan and housing facility.

Collegiate Environment: Orientation program. Drama-theater group, choral group, marching band, student-run newspaper, radio station. Social organizations: 430 open to all; national fraternities, national sororities, local fraternities, local sororities; 19% of eligible men and 24% of eligible women are members. Most popular organizations: intramurals, recreational sports program, Communiversity, University Union, Red Coat Band. Major annual events: Concerts at Legion Field, Homecoming, UGA Health Fair. Student services: legal services, health clinic, personal-psychological counseling, women's center. Campus security: 24-hour emergency response devices and patrols, late night transport-escort service, controlled dormitory access. College housing designed to accommodate 6,824 students; 6,844 undergraduates lived in college housing during 2003-04. Freshmen guaranteed college housing. On-campus residence required in freshman year. Options: coed, men-only, women-only housing available. Ilah Dunlap Little Memorial Library plus 2 others with 4 million books, 6.4 million microform titles, 51,599 serials, 108,612 audiovisual materials, an OPAC, and a Web page. Operations spending for 2004 fiscal year: $24.8 million. 2,500 computers available on campus for general student use. Computer purchase/lease plans available. A campuswide network can be accessed from student residence rooms and from off campus. Staffed computer lab on campus.

Community Environment: Athens, the largest city in the rolling Piedmont area of northeast Georgia, is 70 miles northeast of Atlanta. Many of its buildings exemplify Greek Revival architecture characteristic of the Old South. It enjoys a mild climate, with an annual mean temperature of 60 degrees. Recreational facilities include parks, golf courses, swimming pools, tennis courts, baseball parks, a bowling center, and skating rinks, as well as areas for hunting, fishing and boating. Athens, serviced by buses and an airline, has numerous lodging accommodations and restaurants both in town and on campus. Its manufactured products include textiles, plastics, metals, electrical equipment, dairy products, and paper goods.

■ UNIVERSITY OF PHOENIX-ATLANTA CAMPUS E-4

8200 Roberts Dr., Ste. 300
Atlanta, GA 30350-4153
Tel: (678)731-0555
Free: 800-228-7240
Admissions: (480)557-1712
Fax: (770)821-5399
Web Site: http://www.phoenix.edu/

Description: Proprietary, comprehensive, coed. Awards bachelor's and master's degrees. Setting: urban campus. Total enrollment: 2,495. Faculty: 217 (9 full-time, 208 part-time). Student-undergrad faculty ratio is 9:1. 87 applied. Full-time: 1,741 students, 67% women, 33% men. 0.4% Native American, 1% Hispanic, 18% black, 0.2% Asian American or Pacific Islander, 9% international, 93% 25 or older. Academic areas with the most degrees conferred: business/marketing; computer and information sciences; security and protective services. Core. Calendar: continuous. Advanced placement, accelerated degree program, independent study, distance learning, external degree program, adult/continuing education programs, graduate courses open to undergrads.

Entrance Requirements: Open admission. Option: deferred admission. Required: 1 recommendation. Required for some: high school transcript. Entrance: noncompetitive. Application deadline: Rolling.

Costs Per Year: Application fee: $110. Tuition: $10,590 full-time, $353 per credit part-time. Mandatory fees: $560 full-time, $70 per course part-time.

Collegiate Environment: College housing not available. University Library with 444 books, 666 serials, an OPAC, and a Web page. System-wide operations spending for 2004 fiscal year: $3.2 million.

■ UNIVERSITY OF PHOENIX-COLUMBUS GEORGIA CAMPUS *I-2*
4747 Hamilton Rd., Ste. E
Columbus, GA 31904
Tel: (706)320-1262
Free: 800-228-7240
Admissions: (480)557-1712
Web Site: http://www.phoenix.edu/
Description: Proprietary, comprehensive, coed. Awards bachelor's and master's degrees. Founded 2003. Total enrollment: 676. Faculty: 82 (9 full-time, 73 part-time). Student-undergrad faculty ratio is 8:1. 29 applied. Full-time: 581 students, 71% women, 29% men. 0.2% Native American, 1% Hispanic, 11% black, 0.3% Asian American or Pacific Islander, 4% international, 84% 25 or older. Academic area with the most degrees conferred: business/marketing. Core. Calendar: continuous. Advanced placement, accelerated degree program, independent study, distance learning, external degree program, adult/continuing education programs, graduate courses open to undergrads.
Entrance Requirements: Open admission. Option: deferred admission. Required: 1 recommendation. Required for some: high school transcript. Entrance: noncompetitive. Application deadline: Rolling.
Costs Per Year: Application fee: $110. Tuition: $10,320 full-time, $344 per credit part-time. Mandatory fees: $560 full-time, $70 per course part-time.
Collegiate Environment: College housing not available. University Library with 444 books, 666 serials, an OPAC, and a Web page.

■ UNIVERSITY OF WEST GEORGIA *F-2*
1601 Maple St.
Carrollton, GA 30118
Tel: (678)839-5000
Admissions: (678)839-4000
E-mail: admiss@westga.edu
Web Site: http://www.westga.edu/
Description: State-supported, comprehensive, coed. Part of University System of Georgia. Awards bachelor's, master's, and doctoral degrees and post-master's certificates. Founded 1933. Setting: 394-acre small town campus with easy access to Atlanta. Endowment: $13.3 million. Research spending for 2004 fiscal year: $239,778. Educational spending for 2005 fiscal year: $7962 per student. Total enrollment: 10,155. Faculty: 518 (383 full-time, 135 part-time). Student-undergrad faculty ratio is 19:1. 5,175 applied, 55% were admitted. Full-time: 6,921 students, 60% women, 40% men. Part-time: 1,425 students, 61% women, 39% men. Students come from 36 states and territories, 62 other countries, 1% from out-of-state, 0.2% Native American, 2% Hispanic, 23% black, 1% Asian American or Pacific Islander, 1% international, 15% 25 or older, 30% live on campus, 8% transferred in. Retention: 71% of full-time freshmen returned the following year. Academic areas with the most degrees conferred: business/marketing; education; social sciences. Core. Calendar: semesters. Academic remediation for entering students, services for LD students, advanced placement, accelerated degree program, honors program, independent study, distance learning, double major, summer session for credit, part-time degree program, external degree program, adult/continuing education programs, co-op programs and internships, graduate courses open to undergrads. Off campus study at Dalton College, State University of West Georgia/Newman Center. Study abroad program. ROTC: Army.
Entrance Requirements: Options: Peterson's Universal Application, electronic application, early admission. Required: high school transcript, proof of immunization, SAT or ACT. Required for some: 2 recommendations, interview. Entrance: minimally difficult. Application deadline: 7/1. Notification: continuous until 9/1.
Costs Per Year: Application fee: $20. State resident tuition: $2438 full-time, $102 per semester hour part-time. Nonresident tuition: $9754 full-time, $407 per semester hour part-time. Mandatory fees: $832 full-time, $25.17 per semester hour part-time, $114 per term part-time. Full-time tuition and fees vary according to course load. Part-time tuition and fees vary according to course load. College room and board: $5568. College room only: $3540. Room and board charges vary according to board plan and housing facility.
Collegiate Environment: Orientation program. Drama-theater group, choral group, marching band, student-run newspaper, radio station. Social organizations: 82 open to all; national fraternities, national sororities; 3% of eligible men and 3% of eligible women are members. Most popular organiza-

tions: Black Student Alliance, Student Activities Council, Baptist Student Union, Campus Outreach, United Voices Gospel Choir. Major annual events: Homecoming, Annual Campus Awards Program, Spring Fling. Student services: health clinic, personal-psychological counseling. Campus security: 24-hour emergency response devices and patrols, late night transport-escort service, controlled dormitory access. 2,740 college housing spaces available; 2,529 were occupied in 2003-04. Freshmen guaranteed college housing. On-campus residence required in freshman year. Options: coed, men-only, women-only housing available. Irvine Sullivan Ingram Library with 391,330 books, 1.1 million microform titles, 1,194 serials, 10,030 audiovisual materials, an OPAC, and a Web page. Operations spending for 2004 fiscal year: $2.2 million. 745 computers available on campus for general student use. A campuswide network can be accessed from student residence rooms and from off campus. Staffed computer lab on campus.
Community Environment: Located in northwest Georgia, 48 miles southwest of the state capital, Atlanta, Carrollton has a mild climate with an average temperature of 63 degrees. Part-time employment is available. The benefits of this unique area include a safe, peaceful small town atmosphere, offering educational excellence in a personal environment, within 45 minutes of the cultural and social diversities of Atlanta. Private housing is available.

■ VALDOSTA STATE UNIVERSITY *N-7*
1500 North Patterson St.
Valdosta, GA 31698
Tel: (229)333-5800
Free: 800-618-1878
Admissions: (229)333-5791
Fax: (229)333-5482
E-mail: wpeacock@valdosta.edu
Web Site: http://www.valdosta.edu/
Description: State-supported, university, coed. Part of University System of Georgia. Awards associate, bachelor's, master's, and doctoral degrees and post-master's certificates. Founded 1906. Setting: 200-acre small town campus with easy access to Jacksonville. Endowment: $6 million. Research spending for 2004 fiscal year: $118,951. Educational spending for 2005 fiscal year: $4080 per student. Total enrollment: 10,503. Faculty: 545 (435 full-time, 110 part-time). Student-undergrad faculty ratio is 20:1. 5,782 applied, 63% were admitted. Full-time: 7,557 students, 59% women, 41% men. Part-time: 1,536 students, 58% women, 42% men. Students come from 45 states and territories, 61 other countries, 6% from out-of-state, 0.3% Native American, 2% Hispanic, 22% black, 1% Asian American or Pacific Islander, 1% international, 21% 25 or older, 17% live on campus, 7% transferred in. Retention: 76% of full-time freshmen returned the following year. Academic areas with the most degrees conferred: education; business/marketing; health professions and related sciences. Core. Calendar: semesters. Academic remediation for entering students, ESL program, services for LD students, advanced placement, accelerated degree program, freshman honors college, honors program, independent study, distance learning, double major, summer session for credit, part-time degree program, co-op programs and internships, graduate courses open to undergrads. Off campus study at Abraham Baldwin Agricultural College, South Georgia College, Valdosta Technical Institution, Waycross College, Bainbridge College. Study abroad program. ROTC: Air Force.
Entrance Requirements: Options: Peterson's Universal Application, electronic application, early admission, international baccalaureate accepted. Required: high school transcript, minimum 2.0 high school GPA, proof of immunization, SAT or ACT. Required for some: SAT and SAT Subject Tests or ACT, SAT Subject Tests. Entrance: moderately difficult. Application deadline: 7/1. Notification: continuous.
Costs Per Year: Application fee: $20. State resident tuition: $2438 full-time, $102 per semester hour part-time. Nonresident tuition: $9754 full-time, $407 per semester hour part-time. Mandatory fees: $840 full-time, $38. Part-time tuition and fees vary according to course load. College room and board: $5524. College room only: $2904. Room and board charges vary according to board plan and housing facility.
Collegiate Environment: Orientation program. Drama-theater group, choral group, marching band, student-run newspaper, radio station. Social organizations: 108 open to all; national fraternities, national sororities; 10% of eligible men and 8% of eligible women are members. Most popular organizations: Blazing Brigade (marching band), Student Government Association, intramural athletics, Baptist Student Union. Major annual events: Homecoming, Family Day, beach trip. Student services: health clinic, personal-psychological counseling. Campus security: 24-hour emergency response devices and patrols, student patrols, late night transport-escort

service, controlled dormitory access, bicycle patrols, security cameras. 1,929 college housing spaces available; 1,713 were occupied in 2003-04. Freshmen given priority for college housing. On-campus residence required in freshman year. Options: coed, men-only, women-only housing available. Odum Library with 467,560 books, 1.1 million microform titles, 2,815 serials, 21,512 audiovisual materials, an OPAC, and a Web page. Operations spending for 2004 fiscal year: $3.5 million. 1,400 computers available on campus for general student use. A campuswide network can be accessed from student residence rooms and from off campus. Staffed computer lab on campus.

Community Environment: Valdosta, located in the south-central section of Georgia, is the largest city of the 16-county area that it serves. Buses and railroads serve the area, and airlines are available in Valdosta, Tallahassee, Jacksonville and Atlanta. Average temperature for the year is 67 degrees. Valdosta is the largest inland naval stores market in the world. Industries are tobacco, lumber, mobile homes, cotton, paper and metal goods. Valdosta Entertainment Association brings outstanding cultural events to the city. The Gulf of Mexico and the Atlantic Ocean are within 125 miles. Near the city are numerous freshwater lakes that provide fishing, boating, water skiing, beaches for swimming and picnic areas. Valdosta boasts a congenial atmosphere and friendly spirit. Newcomers and visitors are welcomed. Part-time employment is available.

■ **VALDOSTA TECHNICAL COLLEGE** *N-7*
4089 Val Tech Rd.
PO Box 928
Valdosta, GA 31603-0928
Tel: (229)333-2100
Admissions: (229)333-1394
Fax: (229)333-2129
E-mail: aleavy@valdostatech.edu
Web Site: http://www.valdostatech.edu/
Description: State-supported, 2-year, coed. Part of Georgia Department of Technical and Adult Education. Awards certificates, diplomas, and terminal associate degrees. Founded 1963. Setting: 18-acre suburban campus. Total enrollment: 2,444. Full-time: 992 students, 62% women, 38% men. Part-time: 1,452 students, 65% women, 35% men. Students come from 2 states and territories, 0.5% Native American, 1% Hispanic, 39% black, 1% Asian American or Pacific Islander, 0% international, 29% 25 or older, 4% transferred in. Core. Academic remediation for entering students, services for LD students, advanced placement, distance learning, external degree program, internships.
Entrance Requirements: Open admission. Options: Common Application, deferred admission. Required: high school transcript, ACT COMPASS or AS-SET. Entrance: noncompetitive.
Costs Per Year: Application fee: $15. State resident tuition: $1116 full-time, $31 per credit hour part-time. Nonresident tuition: $2232 full-time, $62 per credit hour part-time.
Collegiate Environment: College housing not available. Valdosta Technical College Library plus 1 other with 3,373 books, 109 serials, 225 audiovisual materials, and an OPAC. 564 computers available on campus for general student use. A campuswide network can be accessed from off-campus. Staffed computer lab on campus.

■ **WAYCROSS COLLEGE** *M-9*
2001 South Georgia Parkway
Waycross, GA 31503-9248
Tel: (912)285-6133
Fax: (912)287-4909
E-mail: jporter@mail.way.peachnet.edu
Web Site: http://www.waycross.edu/
Description: State-supported, 2-year, coed. Part of University System of Georgia. Awards certificates, transfer associate, and terminal associate degrees. Founded 1976. Setting: 150-acre small town campus. Endowment: $85,583. Total enrollment: 1,026. 231 applied, 100% were admitted. 14% from top 10% of their high school class, 43% from top quarter, 71% from top half. Full-time: 326 students, 68% women, 32% men. Part-time: 700 students, 68% women, 32% men. Students come from 9 states and territories, 1 other country, 1% from out-of-state, 0.2% Native American, 1% Hispanic, 20% black, 1% Asian American or Pacific Islander, 0.2% international, 43% 25 or older. Core. Calendar: semesters. Academic remediation for entering students, services for LD students, advanced placement, summer session for credit, part-time degree program, adult/continuing education programs. Off campus study at South Georgia College, Valdosta

State University, Albany State College, Okefenokee Technical Institute, Altamaha Technical Institute. Study abroad program.
Entrance Requirements: Options: electronic application, early admission, deferred admission. Required: high school transcript, SAT or ACT. Entrance: noncompetitive. Application deadline: Rolling. Notification: continuous.
Collegiate Environment: Orientation program. Drama-theater group, choral group, student-run newspaper. Social organizations: 9 open to all. Most popular organizations: Black Student Alliance, Georgia Association of Nursing Students, Baptist Student Union, Sigma Club, Student Government Association. Major annual events: Spring Fest, Breakfast with Santa. Student services: personal-psychological counseling. Campus security: late night transport-escort service, security guards. College housing not available. Waycross College Library with 32,461 books, 2 microform titles, and 251 serials. 56 computers available on campus for general student use. Staffed computer lab on campus.

■ **WESLEYAN COLLEGE** *H-6*
4760 Forsyth Rd.
Macon, GA 31210-4462
Tel: (478)477-1110
Free: 800-447-6610
Admissions: (478)757-5206
Fax: (478)757-4030
E-mail: admissions@wesleyancollege.edu
Web Site: http://www.wesleyancollege.edu/
Description: Independent United Methodist, comprehensive. Awards bachelor's and master's degrees. Founded 1836. Setting: 200-acre suburban campus with easy access to Atlanta. Endowment: $42.1 million. Research spending for 2004 fiscal year: $26,923. Educational spending for 2005 fiscal year: $10,611 per student. Total enrollment: 640. Faculty: 80 (47 full-time, 33 part-time). Student-undergrad faculty ratio is 8:1. 483 applied, 55% were admitted. 34% from top 10% of their high school class, 57% from top quarter, 85% from top half. 2 class presidents, 7 valedictorians, 11 student government officers. Full-time: 400 students, 99% women, 0.3% men. Part-time: 151 students, 99% women, 1% men. Students come from 27 states and territories, 31 other countries, 10% from out-of-state, 0% Native American, 2% Hispanic, 32% black, 2% Asian American or Pacific Islander, 13% international, 13% 25 or older, 63% live on campus, 6% transferred in. Retention: 63% of full-time freshmen returned the following year. Academic areas with the most degrees conferred: business/marketing; psychology; education. Core. Calendar: semesters. Services for LD students, advanced placement, self-designed majors, honors program, independent study, double major, summer session for credit, part-time degree program, adult/continuing education programs, co-op programs and internships. Off campus study at Mercer University, National Student Exchange. Study abroad program.
Entrance Requirements: Options: Peterson's Universal Application, Common Application, early admission, early decision, early action, deferred admission, international baccalaureate accepted. Required: essay, high school transcript, minimum 2 high school GPA, SAT or ACT. Recommended: 2 recommendations, interview. Entrance: moderately difficult. Application deadlines: 4/1, 11/15 for early decision plan 1, 1/15 for early decision plan 2, 2/1 for early action. Notification: continuous until 8/1, 12/15 for early decision plan 1, 2/15 for early decision plan 2, 3/1 for early action.
Costs Per Year: Application fee: $30. Comprehensive fee: $19,560 includes full-time tuition ($11,260), mandatory fees ($850), and college room and board ($7450). Full-time tuition and fees vary according to class time, course load, and program. Room and board charges vary according to board plan and housing facility. Part-time tuition: $355 per semester hour. Part-time tuition varies according to class time, course load, and program.
Collegiate Environment: Orientation program. Drama-theater group, choral group, student-run newspaper. Social organizations: 40 open to all. Most popular organizations: Student Recreation Council, Campus Activities Board, Student Government Association, Council on Religious Concerns, Christian Fellowship. Major annual events: homecoming, Stunt, Spring Bandfest. Student services: health clinic, personal-psychological counseling, women's center. Campus security: 24-hour emergency response devices and patrols, late night transport-escort service, controlled dormitory access. 622 college housing spaces available; 342 were occupied in 2003-04. Freshmen guaranteed college housing. On-campus residence required through senior year. Option: women-only housing available. Lucy Lester Willet Memorial Library with 141,818 books, 32,942 microform titles, 630 serials, 6,553 audiovisual materials, an OPAC, and a Web page. Operations spending for 2004 fiscal year: $398,625. 24 computers available on campus for

general student use. A campuswide network can be accessed from student residence rooms and from off campus. Staffed computer lab on campus.

Community Environment: The college is located in suburban Macon. There are 5 other coed colleges within a 60-mile radius of Macon.

■ **WEST CENTRAL TECHNICAL COLLEGE**

176 Murphy Campus Blvd.
Waco, GA 30182
Tel: (770)537-6000
Admissions: (770)537-5712
Fax: (770)836-4719
E-mail: malderhold@westcentral.edu
Web Site: http://www.westcentraltech.edu/

Description: State-supported, 2-year, coed. Part of Georgia Department of Technical and Adult Education. Awards certificates, diplomas, and terminal associate degrees. Founded 1968. Total enrollment: 2,888. Full-time: 877 students, 66% women, 34% men. Part-time: 2,011 students, 73% women, 27% men. 47% from out-of-state, 0.5% Native American, 1% Hispanic, 22% black, 1% Asian American or Pacific Islander, 0% international, 13% 25 or older. Core. Academic remediation for entering students, services for LD students, advanced placement, distance learning, part-time degree program, external degree program, adult/continuing education programs, internships.

Entrance Requirements: Open admission. Options: electronic application, deferred admission. Required: high school transcript, ACT COMPASS or ASSET. Entrance: noncompetitive.

Costs Per Year: Application fee: $25. State resident tuition: $1116 full-time, $31 per credit hour part-time. Nonresident tuition: $2232 full-time, $62 per credit hour part-time.

Collegiate Environment: Orientation program. College housing not available. 18,462 books and 1,635 audiovisual materials. 109 computers available on campus for general student use. Staffed computer lab on campus.

■ **WEST GEORGIA TECHNICAL COLLEGE**

303 Fort Dr.
LaGrange, GA 30240
Tel: (706)845-4323
Admissions: (706)837-4244
Fax: (706)845-4339
E-mail: lbasham@westgatech.edu
Web Site: http://www.westgatech.edu/

Description: State-supported, 2-year, coed. Part of Georgia Department of Technical and Adult Education. Awards certificates, diplomas, and terminal associate degrees. Founded 1966. Total enrollment: 1,858. Full-time: 843 students, 69% women, 31% men. Part-time: 1,015 students, 56% women, 44% men. Students come from 2 states and territories, 0.4% Native American, 1% Hispanic, 41% black, 1% Asian American or Pacific Islander, 0% international, 60% 25 or older, 7% transferred in. Academic remediation for entering students, services for LD students, advanced placement, distance learning, internships.

Entrance Requirements: Open admission. Option: deferred admission. Required: high school transcript, ACT COMPASS or ASSET. Entrance: noncompetitive.

Costs Per Year: Application fee: $15. State resident tuition: $1116 full-time, $31 per credit hour part-time. Nonresident tuition: $2232 full-time, $62 per credit hour part-time.

Collegiate Environment: Most popular organizations: Student Government Association, Vocational Industrial Clubs of America, Phi Beta Lambda. Major annual events: Metro-Crime Prevention/Fall Festival in October, Trick or Treat Festival, Holiday Open House. Campus security: 24-hour emergency response devices. College housing not available. 19,683 books, 218 serials, and 525 audiovisual materials.

■ **WESTWOOD COLLEGE-ATLANTA MIDTOWN** *E-4*

1100 Spring St.
Atlanta, GA 30309
Tel: (404)745-9096
Admissions: (404)870-8982
Fax: (404)892-7253
Web Site: http://www.westwood.edu/

Description: Proprietary, primarily 2-year, coed. Awards terminal associate and bachelor's degrees. Founded 2003. Total university enrollment: 90. Calendar: continuous.

Entrance Requirements: Required: interview, high school diploma or GED, and passing scores on ACT/SAT or Accuplacer exam. Application deadlines: Rolling, Rolling for nonresidents.

■ **WESTWOOD COLLEGE-ATLANTA NORTHLAKE** *E-4*

2220 Parklake Dr.
Ste. 175
Atlanta, GA 30345
Tel: (404)962-2999
Web Site: http://www.westwood.edu/

Description: Proprietary, 4-year, coed. Awards associate and bachelor's degrees. Educational spending for 2005 fiscal year: $3000 per student. Total enrollment: 220. Student-undergrad faculty ratio is 12:1. 1% from out-of-state, 0% Native American, 3% Hispanic, 60% black, 3% Asian American or Pacific Islander, 0% international.

Entrance Requirements: Required: high school transcript, entrance assessment.

■ **YOUNG HARRIS COLLEGE**

PO Box 98
Young Harris, GA 30582-0098
Tel: (706)379-3111
Fax: (706)379-4306
E-mail: admissions@yhc.edu
Web Site: http://www.yhc.edu/

Description: Independent United Methodist, 2-year, coed. Awards transfer associate degrees. Founded 1886. Setting: rural campus. Endowment: $110.4 million. Educational spending for 2005 fiscal year: $8548 per student. Total enrollment: 533. Student-undergrad faculty ratio is 14:1. 1,421 applied, 58% were admitted. Full-time: 508 students, 54% women, 46% men. Part-time: 25 students, 60% women, 40% men. Students come from 12 states and territories, 5 other countries, 6% from out-of-state, 0% Native American, 2% Hispanic, 2% black, 1% Asian American or Pacific Islander, 0.4% international, 1% 25 or older, 90% live on campus, 4% transferred in. Retention: 63% of full-time freshmen returned the following year. Core. Calendar: semesters. Academic remediation for entering students, advanced placement, accelerated degree program, double major, summer session for credit, part-time degree program, internships.

Entrance Requirements: Options: electronic application, early admission, deferred admission, international baccalaureate accepted. Required: high school transcript, minimum 2.5 high school GPA, SAT or ACT. Recommended: interview. Required for some: recommendations. Entrance: moderately difficult. Application deadline: Rolling. Notification: continuous.

Costs Per Year: Application fee: $30. Comprehensive fee: $19,510 includes full-time tuition ($14,730) and college room and board ($4780). College room only: $1970. Part-time tuition: $500 per hour.

Collegiate Environment: Orientation program. Drama-theater group, choral group, student-run newspaper. Social organizations: 36 open to all; local fraternities, local sororities; 30% of eligible men and 35% of eligible women are members. Most popular organizations: Wesley Fellowship, BSU, Quantrek (outdoor club), intramurals. Major annual events: Spring Formal, The Big Project, Springfest. Student services: health clinic, personal-psychological counseling. Campus security: 24-hour emergency response devices and patrols. 534 college housing spaces available; 85 were occupied in 2003-04. On-campus residence required through sophomore year. Options: coed, men-only, women-only housing available. J. Lon Duckworth Library with 55,201 books, 21,352 microform titles, 260 serials, 1,850 audiovisual materials, an OPAC, and a Web page. Operations spending for 2004 fiscal year: $463,874. 85 computers available on campus for general student use. A campuswide network can be accessed from student residence rooms and from off campus. Staffed computer lab on campus.

Community Environment: Young Harris is situated in the Blue Ridge Mountains of northeast Georgia where the climate is moderate. Atlanta, Asheville, Chattanooga, and Greenville, South Carolina, are all within one hundred miles. Various religious denominations, a Lions Club, a clinic, and two hospitals serve the community. As part of a resort area the recreational activities include fishing, boating, hiking, horseback riding, picnicking, swimming, tennis, and golf. The county fair is an annual event.

■ GUAM COMMUNITY COLLEGE

PO Box 23069 Guam Main Facility
Barrigada, GU 96921-3069
Tel: (671)735-4422
Admissions: (671)735-5531
Fax: (671)734-5238
Web Site: http://www.guamcc.net/
Description: Territory-supported, 2-year, coed. Awards certificates, diplomas, and terminal associate degrees. Founded 1977. Setting: 22-acre suburban campus. Endowment: $6.4 million. Total enrollment: 2,841. Full-time: 504 students, 62% women, 38% men. Part-time: 2,337 students, 65% women, 35% men. Students come from 10 other countries, 0.1% Native American, 1% Hispanic, 1% black, 90% Asian American or Pacific Islander, 2% international, 47% 25 or older. Core. Calendar: semesters. Academic remediation for entering students, ESL program, services for LD students, honors program, independent study, double major, summer session for credit, part-time degree program, adult/continuing education programs, co-op programs and internships. Off campus study at University of Guam. ROTC: Army (c).
Entrance Requirements: Open admission. Options: Common Application, early admission. Required: high school transcript. Entrance: noncompetitive. Application deadline: Rolling. Notification: continuous.
Costs Per Year: Application fee: $0. Area resident tuition: $2100 full-time. Nonresident tuition: $2850 full-time. Mandatory fees: $244 full-time.
Collegiate Environment: Most popular organizations: Council of Post Secondary Student Association (COPSA), Phi Theta Kappa. Major annual event: Diversity Day. Student services: health clinic, personal-psychological counseling. Campus security: 12-hour patrols by trained security personnel. College housing not available. 15,806 books, 11,000 microform titles, 375 serials, 1,567 audiovisual materials, and an OPAC. 220 computers available on campus for general student use. A campuswide network can be accessed. Staffed computer lab on campus.

■ PACIFIC ISLANDS BIBLE COLLEGE

PO Box 22619
Guam Main Facility, GU 96921-2619
Tel: (671)734-1812
Fax: (671)734-1813
E-mail: guamcampus@pibc.edu
Web Site: http://www.pibc-edu.org/
Description: Independent interdenominational, 4-year, coed. Founded 1976. Total enrollment: 188. Student-undergrad faculty ratio is 7:1. Full-time: 132 students, 58% women, 42% men. Part-time: 56 students, 54% women, 46% men. 0% from out-of-territory, 97% Asian American or Pacific Islander, 1% international. Calendar: semesters.

Entrance Requirements: Required: essay, high school transcript, 2 recommendations, interview. Required for some: TOEFL score. Application deadline: 8/25.
Costs Per Year: Application fee: $25. Comprehensive fee: $8530 includes full-time tuition ($5400), mandatory fees ($270), and college room and board ($2860). Part-time tuition: $675 per course. Part-time mandatory fees: $85.

■ UNIVERSITY OF GUAM

UOG Station
Mangilao, GU 96923
Tel: (671)735-2350
Admissions: (671)735-2207
Fax: (671)734-6005
E-mail: admitme@uog9.uog.edu
Web Site: http://www.uog.edu/
Description: Territory-supported, comprehensive, coed. Awards bachelor's and master's degrees. Founded 1952. Setting: 100-acre rural campus. Endowment: $6 million. Research spending for 2004 fiscal year: $6 million. Total enrollment: 3,034. Faculty: 254 (176 full-time, 78 part-time). Student-undergrad faculty ratio is 11:1. 654 applied, 99% were admitted. Full-time: 2,042 students, 60% women, 40% men. Part-time: 778 students, 64% women, 36% men. Students come from 52 states and territories, 30 other countries, 0.1% Native American, 1% Hispanic, 1% black, 89% Asian American or Pacific Islander, 1% international, 31% 25 or older. Retention: 61% of full-time freshmen returned the following year. Academic areas with the most degrees conferred: business/marketing; education; law/legal studies. Core. Calendar: semesters. Academic remediation for entering students, ESL program, accelerated degree program, summer session for credit, part-time degree program, external degree program, adult/continuing education programs, graduate courses open to undergrads. ROTC: Army.
Entrance Requirements: Open admission. Options: Common Application, early admission, deferred admission. Required: high school transcript. Entrance: noncompetitive. Application deadline: 6/1. Notification: continuous.
Costs Per Year: Application fee: $49. Territory resident tuition: $3900 full-time, $130 per credit part-time. Nonresident tuition: $11,580 full-time, $386 per credit part-time. Mandatory fees: $450 full-time, $225 per term part-time. College room and board: $6918. College room only: $1555.
Collegiate Environment: Drama-theater group, choral group, student-run newspaper. Student services: health clinic, personal-psychological counseling. Campus security: 24-hour emergency response devices and patrols, late night transport-escort service, controlled dormitory access. 182 college housing spaces available; 124 were occupied in 2003-04. Option: coed housing available. 327,925 books and 3,060 serials. 150 computers available on campus for general student use. Staffed computer lab on campus.

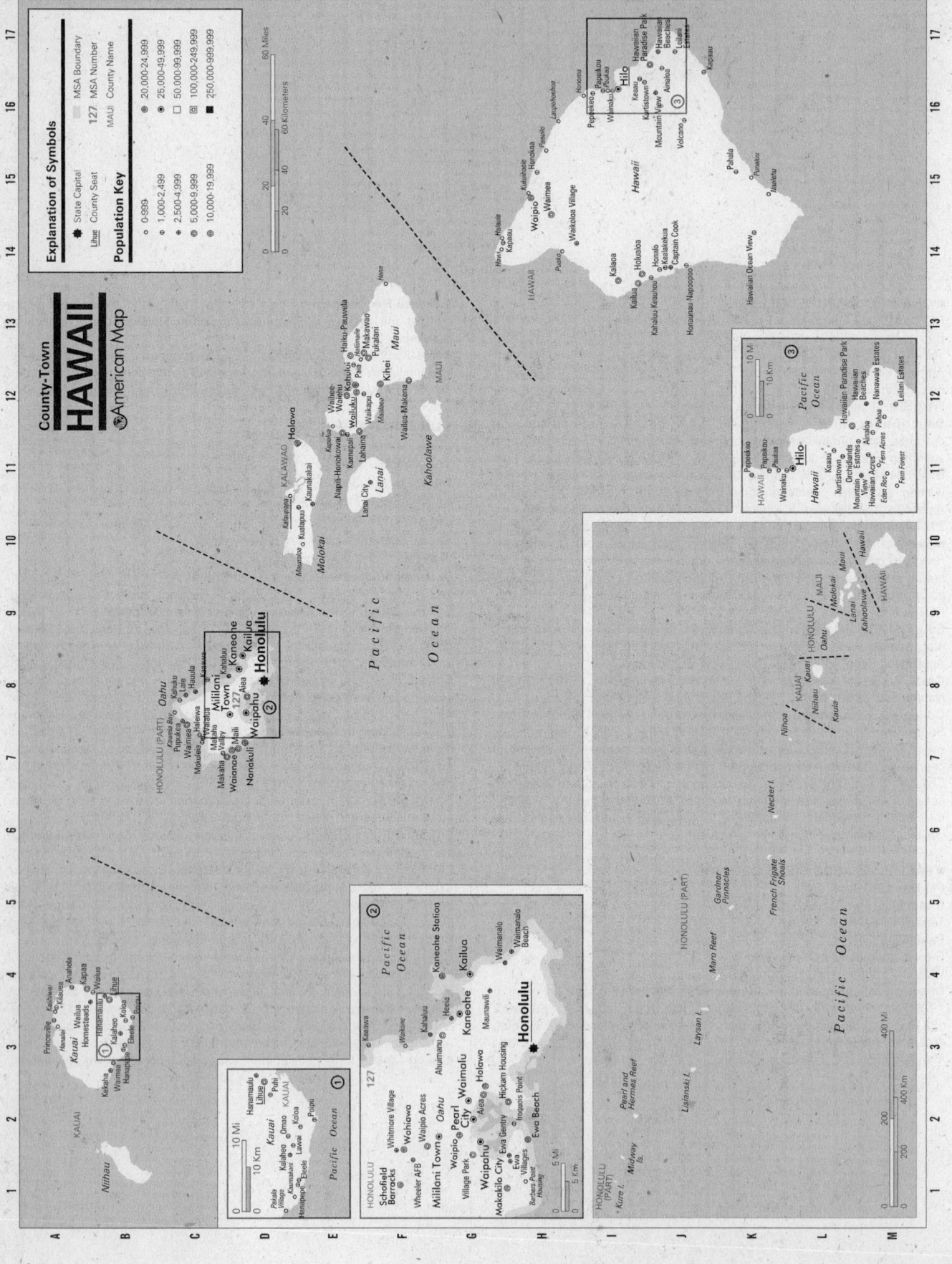

HAWAII

County-Town

American Map

Explanation of Symbols

★ State Capital	▨ MSA Boundary
Lihue County Seat	127 MSA Number
	MAUi County Name

Population Key

○ 0-999	⊙ 20,000-24,999
⊙ 1,000-2,499	⊙ 25,000-49,999
⊙ 2,500-4,999	☐ 50,000-99,999
⊙ 5,000-9,999	⊡ 100,000-249,999
⊙ 10,000-19,999	■ 250,000-999,999

60 Miles
60 Kilometers

Inset ① (Kauai)

Pacific Ocean

Princeville Kalihiwai
Hanalei   Kilauea
Anahola
Kauai Wailua Kapaa
Homesteads Wailua
Hanamaulu
Lihue
Kekaha Kalaheo Koloa
Waimea Eleele Poipu
Hanapepe

KAUAI

Niihau

Inset ② (Honolulu/Oahu)

Pacific Ocean

Kaaawa
Waikane
Kahaluu
Kaneohe Station
Heeia
Ahuimanu
Kaneohe
Kailua
Waimanalo
Maunawili
Waimanalo Beach
Honolulu ★
Halawa
Hickam Housing
Aiea
Waimalu
Iroquois Point

Inset ① (lower left — Oahu/Kauai)

Pacific Ocean

HONOLULU
Schofield Barracks
Whitmore Village
Wahiawa
Wheeler AFB
Waipio Acres
Mililani Town
Oahu
Waipio
Pearl City
Ewa Gentry
Village Park
Waipahu
Mokakilo City
Ewa
Ewa Villages
Barbers Point Housing
Ewa Beach

Hanamaulu
Lihue
Kauai
Kalaheo Omao Puhi
Kaumakani Lawai Koloa
Kekaha Eleele Poipu
Hanapepe
Pakala Village
Waimea
Menehune

KAUAI

Maui / Molokai / Lanai

Honolua
Haiku-Pauwela
Waihee Wailuku Kohului Paia
Waiehu Kapalua Kaanapali Pukalani
Napili-Honokowai Lahaina Waikapu Makawao
Kagelua Maalaea Maui
Kihei
Wailea-Makena

MAUI

Halawa
Kalaupapa Kualapuu
Maunaloa Kaunakakai
Molokai

Lana City
Lanai

Kahoolawe

Hana

Hawaii (Big Island)

Honomu
Papaikou
Pepeekeo Kaumana Hawaiian Paradise Park
Waimea Wainaku-Puueo Hilo
Kawaihae Kurtistown Hawaiian Beaches
Waikoloa Village Mountain View Ainaloa Leilani Estates
Waipio Volcano Kapaau
Honaunau Hawi
Puako Kapaau
Kalaoa Hawaii Pahala
Kailua Holualoa Naalehu
Kahaluu-Keauhou Honalo Kealakekua
Hawaiian Ocean View Captain Cook
Honaunau-Napoopoo
Pahala
HAWAII

Inset ③ (Hilo area)

Pacific Ocean

Papeekeo
Papaikou Hawaiian Paradise Park
Wainaku Hawaiian Beaches
Keaau Orchidlands Nanawale Estates
Kurtistown Estates Pahoa
Mountain View Ainaloa
Hawaiian Acres Eden Roc Leilani Estates
HAWAII Fern Forest
Hilo
Hawaii

10 Km

HONOLULU (PART) — lower right key map

KAUAI
Niihau
Nihoa Kauai
Niihau Oahu Molokai Maui
Kaula Lanai Hawaii
Kahoolawe
HONOLULU
MAUI

HONOLULU (PART)

Necker I.
French Frigate Shoals
Gardner Pinnacles
Maro Reef
Laysan I.
Lisianski I.
Pearl and Hermes Reef
Midway Is.
Kure I.
HONOLULU (PART)

400 Mi
400 Km

Pacific Ocean

Honolulu inset

Pacific Ocean
Honolulu ★

HONOLULU (PART)
Oahu
Laie
Kahuku
Pupukea Haleiwa
Waimea Wahiawa
Mokuleia Makaha Valley
Makaha Mililani Town
Waianae Waipahu Aiea
Nanakuli Honolulu ★
Kahaluu
Kaneohe
Kailua

Honolulu

■ **ARGOSY UNIVERSITY/HAWAII** *D-8*
400 ASBTower, 1001 Bishop St.
Honolulu, HI 96813
Tel: (808)536-5555
Fax: (808)536-5505
Web Site: http://www.argosyu.edu/honolulu/
Description: Proprietary, upper-level, coed. Founded 1994. Calendar: semesters.

■ **BRIGHAM YOUNG UNIVERSITY-HAWAII** *C-8*
55-220 Kulanui St.
Laie, HI 96762-1294
Tel: (808)293-3211
Admissions: (808)293-3731
Web Site: http://www.byuh.edu/
Description: Independent Latter-day Saints, 4-year, coed. Administratively affiliated with Brigham Young University. Awards associate and bachelor's degrees. Founded 1955. Setting: 60-acre small town campus with easy access to Honolulu. Endowment: $43.2 million. Research spending for 2004 fiscal year: $71,856. Educational spending for 2005 fiscal year: $10,600 per student. Total enrollment: 2,486. 2,106 applied, 12% were admitted. Full-time: 2,190 students, 56% women, 44% men. Part-time: 296 students, 65% women, 35% men. Students come from 47 states and territories, 67 other countries, 39% from out-of-state, 1% Native American, 2% Hispanic, 0.4% black, 22% Asian American or Pacific Islander, 45% international, 25% 25 or older, 52% live on campus, 9% transferred in. Retention: 60% of full-time freshmen returned the following year. Core. Calendar: 4-4-2-2. Academic remediation for entering students, ESL program, services for LD students, advanced placement, accelerated degree program, freshman honors college, honors program, double major, summer session for credit, part-time degree program, adult/continuing education programs, co-op programs and internships. Off campus study. ROTC: Army (c), Naval (c), Air Force (c).
Entrance Requirements: Options: electronic application, early admission, deferred admission, international baccalaureate accepted. Required: essay, high school transcript, minimum 3.0 high school GPA, resume of activities, ecclesiastical endorsement, SAT or ACT. Recommended: ACT. Required for some: recommendations. Entrance: moderately difficult. Application deadline: 2/15. Notification: continuous. Preference given to Latter Day Saints Church members.
Costs Per Year: Application fee: $30. Comprehensive fee: $7740 includes full-time tuition ($2760) and college room and board ($4980). Full-time tuition varies according to course load. Room and board charges vary according to board plan and housing facility. Part-time tuition: $187 per credit.
Collegiate Environment: Orientation program. Drama-theater group, choral group, student-run newspaper. Social organizations: 49 open to all. Most popular organizations: Tonga Club, Samoa Club, Hawaiian Club, Japanese Club. Major annual events: Culture Night, Foodfest, Songfest. Student services: health clinic, personal-psychological counseling. Campus security: 24-hour patrols, late night transport-escort service. 1,356 college housing spaces available; 1,300 were occupied in 2003-04. Freshmen given priority for college housing. On-campus residence required in freshman year. Options: men-only, women-only housing available. Joseph F. Smith Library plus 1 other with 321,400 books, 948,000 microform titles, 11,325 serials, 7,000 audiovisual materials, an OPAC, and a Web page. Operations spending for 2004 fiscal year: $2.7 million. 465 computers available on campus for

general student use. A campuswide network can be accessed from student residence rooms. Staffed computer lab on campus.

■ **CHAMINADE UNIVERSITY OF HONOLULU** *D-8*
3140 Waialae Ave.
Honolulu, HI 96816-1578
Tel: (808)735-4711
Free: 800-735-3733
Admissions: (808)735-4735
Fax: (808)739-4647
E-mail: admissions@chaminade.edu
Web Site: http://www.chaminade.edu/
Description: Independent Roman Catholic, comprehensive, coed. Awards associate, bachelor's, and master's degrees. Founded 1955. Setting: 62-acre urban campus. Endowment: $3.7 million. Educational spending for 2005 fiscal year: $3733 per student. Total enrollment: 1,810. Faculty: 131 (82 full-time, 49 part-time). Student-undergrad faculty ratio is 11:1. 904 applied, 96% were admitted. 11% from top 10% of their high school class, 35% from top quarter, 62% from top half. Full-time: 1,058 students, 69% women, 31% men. Part-time: 48 students, 79% women, 21% men. Students come from 41 states and territories, 11 other countries, 50% from out-of-state, 1% Native American, 7% Hispanic, 4% black, 64% Asian American or Pacific Islander, 2% international, 17% 25 or older, 10% transferred in. Retention: 69% of full-time freshmen returned the following year. Academic areas with the most degrees conferred: security and protective services; education; business/marketing; history; psychology. Core. Calendar: semesters. Academic remediation for entering students, advanced placement, accelerated degree program, self-designed majors, independent study, distance learning, double major, summer session for credit, part-time degree program, adult/continuing education programs, internships, graduate courses open to undergrads. Off campus study at University of Hawaii at Manoa, Brigham Young University, Hawaii Pacific University. ROTC: Army (c), Air Force (c).
Entrance Requirements: Options: Peterson's Universal Application, Common Application, electronic application, deferred admission, international baccalaureate accepted. Required: essay, high school transcript, SAT or ACT. Recommended: minimum 2.25 high school GPA. Required for some: interview. Entrance: minimally difficult. Application deadline: Rolling. Notification: continuous.
Costs Per Year: Application fee: $50. Comprehensive fee: $24,340 includes full-time tuition ($14,820), mandatory fees ($140), and college room and board ($9380). College room only: $4980. Part-time tuition: $494 per credit.
Collegiate Environment: Orientation program. Drama-theater group, choral group, student-run newspaper. Social organizations: 32 open to all. Most popular organizations: Lumana O Samoa (Samoan Club), Kaimi Lalakea (Hawaiian Club), Rotaract Club, Residence Hall Association, Chaminade Student Government Association. Major annual events: International Extravaganza, Campus Ministry Awakening Retreats, Club Fest. Student services: personal-psychological counseling. Campus security: 24-hour emergency response devices and patrols, late night transport-escort service, controlled dormitory access. 395 college housing spaces available; 346 were occupied in 2003-04. No special consideration for freshman housing applicants. Options: coed, women-only housing available. Sullivan Library with 78,000 books, 6,361 microform titles, 6,730 serials, 566 audiovisual materials, an OPAC, and a Web page. Operations spending for 2004 fiscal year: $377,150. 90 computers available on campus for general student use. A

campuswide network can be accessed from student residence rooms and from off campus. Staffed computer lab on campus.

Community Environment: See University of Hawaii - Manoa.

■ HAWAII BUSINESS COLLEGE *D-8*

33 South King St., Fourth Floor
Honolulu, HI 96813-4316
Tel: (808)524-4014
Fax: (808)524-0284
Web Site: http://www.hbc.edu/

Description: Independent, 2-year, coed. Awards certificates, diplomas, transfer associate, and terminal associate degrees. Founded 1973. Setting: urban campus. Total enrollment: 303. 1% Native American, 2% Hispanic, 7% black, 78% Asian American or Pacific Islander, 1% international. Core. Academic remediation for entering students, ESL program, advanced placement, independent study, double major, summer session for credit, part-time degree program, external degree program, adult/continuing education programs, co-op programs and internships.

Entrance Requirements: Open admission. Option: deferred admission. Required: high school transcript. Required for some: essay, interview. Placement: Wonderlic Basic Skills Test required. Entrance: noncompetitive. Application deadline: Rolling.

Collegiate Environment: Student-run newspaper. Most popular organizations: SCA (Student Council Association), Computer Club, Polynesian Club, SIFE. Major annual events: spring job fair, summer job fair. Student services: personal-psychological counseling. College housing not available. 1,000 books and 25 serials.

■ HAWAII COMMUNITY COLLEGE *I-16*

200 West Kawili St.
Hilo, HI 96720-4091
Tel: (808)974-7611
Admissions: (808)974-7661
Fax: (808)974-7692
Web Site: http://www.hawcc.hawaii.edu/

Description: State-supported, 2-year, coed. Part of University of Hawaii System. Awards certificates, diplomas, transfer associate, and terminal associate degrees. Founded 1954. Setting: small town campus. Total enrollment: 2,409. 1,163 applied, 99% were admitted. Full-time: 1,025 students, 56% women, 44% men. Part-time: 1,384 students, 70% women, 30% men. Students come from 12 states and territories, 32 other countries, 1% Native American, 2% Hispanic, 1% black, 57% Asian American or Pacific Islander, 3% international, 40% 25 or older. Calendar: semesters. ESL program, services for LD students, advanced placement, honors program, summer session for credit, part-time degree program, co-op programs.

Entrance Requirements: Open admission. Options: Common Application, early admission. Entrance: noncompetitive. Application deadline: 8/1.

Collegiate Environment: Orientation program. Campus security: 24-hour patrols. Option: coed housing available. 100 computers available on campus for general student use. A campuswide network can be accessed from off-campus. Staffed computer lab on campus.

■ HAWAII PACIFIC UNIVERSITY *D-8*

1166 Fort St.
Honolulu, HI 96813-2785
Tel: (808)544-0200; (866)225-5478
Admissions: (808)544-0238
Fax: (808)544-1136
E-mail: admissions@hpu.edu
Web Site: http://www.hpu.edu/

Description: Independent, comprehensive, coed. Awards associate, bachelor's, and master's degrees and post-master's certificates. Founded 1965. Setting: 140-acre urban campus. Endowment: $60.2 million. Research spending for 2004 fiscal year: $7.7 million. Educational spending for 2005 fiscal year: $4079 per student. Total enrollment: 8,046. Faculty: 612 (238 full-time, 374 part-time). Student-undergrad faculty ratio is 16:1. 3,094 applied, 82% were admitted. 22% from top 10% of their high school class, 50% from top quarter, 79% from top half. Full-time: 4,240 students, 63% women, 37% men. Part-time: 2,671 students, 54% women, 46% men. Students come from 52 states and territories, 90 other countries, 25% from out-of-state, 1% Native American, 7% Hispanic, 8% black, 34% Asian American or Pacific Islander, 11% international, 41% 25 or older, 10% live on campus, 14% transferred in. Retention: 66% of full-time freshmen returned the following year. Academic areas with the most degrees conferred: business/

marketing; health professions and related sciences; computer and information sciences. Core. Calendar: semesters. Academic remediation for entering students, ESL program, services for LD students, advanced placement, accelerated degree program, self-designed majors, freshman honors college, honors program, independent study, distance learning, double major, summer session for credit, part-time degree program, adult/continuing education programs, co-op programs and internships, graduate courses open to undergrads. Off campus study at Carroll College, Creighton University, Samuel Merritt College, Southern California University of Health Sciences. Study abroad program. ROTC: Army (c), Air Force (c).

Entrance Requirements: Options: Peterson's Universal Application, Common Application, electronic application, early admission, deferred admission, international baccalaureate accepted. Required: high school transcript, minimum 2.5 high school GPA, SAT or ACT. Recommended: essay, 2 recommendations. Required for some: interview. Entrance: moderately difficult. Application deadline: Rolling.

Costs Per Year: Application fee: $50. Comprehensive fee: $21,080 includes full-time tuition ($11,550), mandatory fees ($80), and college room and board ($9450). Full-time tuition and fees vary according to course load, program, and student level. Room and board charges vary according to housing facility. Part-time tuition: $225 per credit. Part-time tuition varies according to course load.

Collegiate Environment: Orientation program. Drama-theater group, choral group, student-run newspaper. Social organizations: 80 open to all. Most popular organizations: Association of Students of HPU, Swedish Student Association, President's Hosts, Akamai Advertising, Christian Fellowship. Major annual events: Intercultural Day, Club Carnival, The Monster Ball. Student services: health clinic, personal-psychological counseling. Campus security: 24-hour emergency response devices and patrols, student patrols, late night transport-escort service, controlled dormitory access. 210 college housing spaces available; all were occupied in 2003-04. Freshmen given priority for college housing. Option: coed housing available. Meader Library plus 2 others with 162,000 books, 325,863 microform titles, 12,000 serials, 8,700 audiovisual materials, an OPAC, and a Web page. Operations spending for 2004 fiscal year: $2.7 million. 590 computers available on campus for general student use. Computer purchase/lease plans available. A campuswide network can be accessed from student residence rooms and from off campus. Staffed computer lab on campus.

Community Environment: Honolulu, the travel capital of the world and nexus of the Pacific Basin, is a cosmopolitan city of some 800,000. Its leading industries are the travel industry, agriculture, and government-related services. Positions are available for HPU students in a wide variety of fields via the university's Cooperative Education and Internship Program. Such cultural institutions as the Bishop Museum, the Honolulu Academy of Arts, and the Honolulu Symphony are located within two to four miles of the campus. Recreation facilities, most of them free, are widely available throughout Hawaii and are among the finest in the world; also among the world's finest are Hawaii's many major restaurants and hotels.

■ HAWAII THEOLOGICAL SEMINARY *D-8*

20 Dowsett Ave.
Honolulu, HI 96817
Tel: (808)595-4247
Fax: (808)595-4779
E-mail: icgs@hawaii.rr.com
Web Site: http://www.icgshawaii.org/

Description: Independent interdenominational, upper-level, coed. Awards bachelor's, master's, and first professional degrees. Founded 1967. Setting: urban campus. Total enrollment: 58. Full-time: 8 students, 38% women, 63% men. Part-time: 14 students, 14% women, 86% men. Students come from 6 other countries, 0% from out-of-state, 0% Native American, 5% Hispanic, 0% black, 68% Asian American or Pacific Islander, 14% international, 23% 25 or older, 0% transferred in. Core. Calendar: semesters. ESL program, advanced placement, independent study, summer session for credit, part-time degree program, adult/continuing education programs, internships, graduate courses open to undergrads. Study abroad program.

Costs Per Year: Application fee: $50. Tuition: $6150 full-time, $615 per course part-time. Mandatory fees: $200 full-time, $100 per term part-time. Full-time tuition and fees vary according to course load. Part-time tuition and fees vary according to course load.

Collegiate Environment: College housing not available. J. W. Cook Memorial Library with 21,182 books, 453 microform titles, 52 serials, 1,094 audiovisual materials, an OPAC, and a Web page. 3 computers available on campus for general student use. A campuswide network can be accessed from off-campus.

■ HAWAII TOKAI INTERNATIONAL COLLEGE *D-8*

2241 Kapiolani Blvd.
Honolulu, HI 96826-4310
Tel: (808)983-4000
Admissions: (808)983-4154
Fax: (808)983-4107
E-mail: htic@tokai.edu
Web Site: http://www.tokai.edu/
Description: Independent, 2-year, coed. Part of Tokai University Educational System (Japan). Awards certificates, diplomas, and transfer associate degrees. Founded 1992. Setting: urban campus. Educational spending for 2005 fiscal year: $15,000 per student. Total enrollment: 54. Student-undergrad faculty ratio is 4:1. 2 applied, 100% were admitted. Full-time: 54 students, 46% women, 54% men. Students come from 3 other countries, 100% Asian American or Pacific Islander, 17% 25 or older, 60% live on campus, 0% transferred in. Retention: 83% of full-time freshmen returned the following year. Core. ESL program, summer session for credit.
Entrance Requirements: Option: deferred admission. Required: essay, high school transcript, interview. Entrance: noncompetitive. Application deadline: 9/1. Notification: continuous.
Costs Per Year: Application fee: $50. Tuition: $375 per credit part-time.
Collegiate Environment: Student-run newspaper. Social organizations: 5 open to all. Most popular organizations: Basketball Club, Hula Club, Martial Arts Club, Chinese and Japanese Culture Club, fishing. Major annual events: Opening Ceremony, Student Presentation Day, Graduation ceremony. Campus security: 24-hour patrols. On-campus residence required in freshman year. Option: coed housing available. The Learning Center with 7,000 books, 100 serials, 500 audiovisual materials, an OPAC, and a Web page. Operations spending for 2004 fiscal year: $15,000. 45 computers available on campus for general student use. A campuswide network can be accessed from student residence rooms and from off campus. Staffed computer lab on campus.

■ HEALD COLLEGE-HONOLULU *D-8*

1500 Kapiolani Blvd.
Honolulu, HI 96814-3797
Tel: (808)955-1500
Fax: (808)955-6964
Web Site: http://www.heald.edu/
Description: Independent, 2-year, coed. Awards certificates, diplomas, transfer associate, and terminal associate degrees. Founded 1863. Setting: urban campus. Total enrollment: 807. Student-undergrad faculty ratio is 17:1. Full-time: 591 students, 59% women, 41% men. Part-time: 216 students, 71% women, 29% men. 0% from out-of-state. 0.2% Native American, 2% Hispanic, 3% black, 80% Asian American or Pacific Islander, 0% international. Academic remediation for entering students, advanced placement, summer session for credit, part-time degree program, internships.
Entrance Requirements: Open admission. Options: electronic application, early admission, deferred admission. Required: high school transcript, interview, COMPASS. Entrance: minimally difficult. Application deadline: Rolling. Notification: continuous.
Collegiate Environment: Orientation program. College housing not available. Learning Resource Center with an OPAC.
Community Environment: Heald is conveniently located in the Ala Moana/Kapiolani Business District just one block from the huge Ala Moana shopping, hotel, and office complex. Its location offers favorable transportation factors: Kapiolani Boulevard is a primary traffic artery that provides a direct link with both downtown and Waikiki, freeway access is excellent, and Ala Moana is a focal point of the bus system providing public transportation to all parts of the island.

■ HONOLULU COMMUNITY COLLEGE *D-8*

874 Dillingham Blvd.
Honolulu, HI 96817-4598
Tel: (808)845-9211
Admissions: (808)845-9129
E-mail: admission@hccadb.hcc.hawaii.edu
Web Site: http://www.honolulu.hawaii.edu/
Description: State-supported, 2-year, coed. Part of University of Hawaii System. Awards certificates, transfer associate, and terminal associate degrees. Founded 1920. Setting: 20-acre urban campus. Endowment: $472,659. Educational spending for 2005 fiscal year: $1745 per student. Total enrollment: 4,238. 1,467 applied, 83% were admitted. Full-time: 1,672 students, 41% women, 59% men. Part-time: 2,566 students, 52% women,

48% men. Students come from 36 states and territories, 39 other countries, 0.2% Native American, 2% Hispanic, 2% black, 78% Asian American or Pacific Islander, 1% international, 41% 25 or older, 29% transferred in. Core. Calendar: semesters. Academic remediation for entering students, ESL program, services for LD students, advanced placement, accelerated degree program, self-designed majors, distance learning, summer session for credit, part-time degree program, co-op programs and internships. ROTC: Army (c), Air Force (c).
Entrance Requirements: Open admission except for international applicants. Options: Common Application, early admission. Entrance: noncompetitive. Application deadline: 8/15. Notification: continuous until 8/15. Preference given to state residents.
Collegiate Environment: Orientation program. Student-run newspaper. Major annual events: Campus Awareness Day, HCC Week. Student services: health clinic. Campus security: 24-hour emergency response devices. College housing not available. Honolulu Community College Library with 54,902 books, 65,679 microform titles, 1,280 serials, 858 audiovisual materials, an OPAC, and a Web page. Operations spending for 2004 fiscal year: $476,757. 120 computers available on campus for general student use. A campuswide network can be accessed from off-campus. Staffed computer lab on campus.
Community Environment: See University of Hawaii - Manoa.

■ KAPIOLANI COMMUNITY COLLEGE *D-8*

4303 Diamond Head Rd.
Honolulu, HI 96816-4421
Tel: (808)734-9111
Admissions: (808)734-9897
Web Site: http://www.kcc.hawaii.edu/
Description: State-supported, 2-year, coed. Part of University of Hawaii System. Awards certificates, transfer associate, and terminal associate degrees. Founded 1957. Setting: 52-acre urban campus. Educational spending for 2005 fiscal year: $1644 per student. Total enrollment: 7,174. 1,455 applied, 92% were admitted. Full-time: 2,833 students, 56% women, 44% men. Part-time: 4,341 students, 60% women, 40% men. Students come from 27 states and territories, 59 other countries, 0.2% Native American, 2% Hispanic, 1% black, 75% Asian American or Pacific Islander, 7% international, 40% 25 or older, 18% transferred in. Core. Calendar: semesters. Academic remediation for entering students, ESL program, services for LD students, advanced placement, self-designed majors, honors program, distance learning, summer session for credit, part-time degree program, adult/continuing education programs, co-op programs and internships. Off campus study at other units of the University of Hawaii System. ROTC: Army (c), Air Force (c).
Entrance Requirements: Open admission except for nursing, health sciences, paralegal programs. Option: early admission. Entrance: noncompetitive. Application deadline: 7/1. Notification: continuous until 8/15. Preference given to state residents.
Costs Per Year: State resident tuition: $1344 full-time, $56 per credit hour part-time. Nonresident tuition: $5976 full-time, $249 per credit hour part-time. Mandatory fees: $60 full-time, $2 per credit hour part-time, $10 per term part-time.
Collegiate Environment: Orientation program. Choral group, student-run newspaper. Social organizations: 19 open to all. Most popular organizations: Hawaiian Club, Phi Theta Kappa, Chinese Club, Hospitality Industry, Bayanihan. Major annual event: International Festival. Campus security: 24-hour patrols. College housing not available. Lama Library with 50,000 books and 600 serials. Operations spending for 2004 fiscal year: $741,632. 175 computers available on campus for general student use. A campuswide network can be accessed from off-campus. Staffed computer lab on campus.
Community Environment: See University of Hawaii - Manoa.

■ KAUAI COMMUNITY COLLEGE *B-4*

3-1901 Kaumualii Hwy.
Lihue, HI 96766
Tel: (808)245-8311
Admissions: (808)245-8225
Fax: (808)245-8297
E-mail: leighton@hawaii.edu
Web Site: http://kauai.hawaii.edu/
Description: State-supported, 2-year, coed. Part of University of Hawaii System. Awards certificates and transfer associate degrees. Founded 1965. Setting: 100-acre small town campus. Total enrollment: 1,210. Core. Calendar: semesters. ESL program, services for LD students, advanced

placement, accelerated degree program, distance learning, summer session for credit, part-time degree program, co-op programs and internships.

Entrance Requirements: Open admission except for nursing, electrical installation and maintenance, electronics technology, facilities engineering programs. Options: Common Application, early admission. Recommended: high school transcript. Required for some: high school transcript. Entrance: noncompetitive. Application deadline: 8/1. Notification: continuous until 8/1. Preference given to state residents.

Costs Per Year: Application fee: $0. State resident tuition: $1176 full-time, $49 per credit part-time. Nonresident tuition: $5808 full-time, $242 per credit part-time. Mandatory fees: $15 full-time, $1.25 per credit part-time. Full-time tuition and fees vary according to course load. Part-time tuition and fees vary according to course load.

Collegiate Environment: Choral group, student-run newspaper. Social organizations: 8 open to all. Most popular organizations: Food Service Club, Hui O Hana Po'okela (Hoper Club), Nursing Club, Phi Theta Kappa, Pamantasan Club. Student services: health clinic, personal-psychological counseling. Campus security: student patrols, 6-hour evening patrols by trained security personnel. College housing not available. S. W. Wilcox II Learning Resource Center plus 1 other with 51,875 books, 16,946 microform titles, 165 serials, 1,248 audiovisual materials, an OPAC, and a Web page. 173 computers available on campus for general student use. A campuswide network can be accessed. Staffed computer lab on campus.

Community Environment: Kauai is known as the"Garden Island," offering magnificent scenery and lush vegetation, beautiful waterfalls, the spectacular Waimea Canyon, the great"hidden" valley of Kalalau, and colorful tropical plants and flowers. Airlines and boats serve the area. Honolulu is 100 nautical miles away. Industries are sugar and tourism; oceanography research and development is conducted here. Community facilities include five public libraries and many churches of all denominations. Several county beach parks and one major state park provide recreation facilities for boating, swimming, scuba diving, deepsea and surf fishing. Wild boar, goat and pheasant hunting are favorite sports.

■ LEEWARD COMMUNITY COLLEGE *G-2*

96-045 Ala Ike
Pearl City, HI 96782-3393
Tel: (808)455-0011
Admissions: (808)455-0219
Fax: (808)455-0471
Web Site: http://www.lcc.hawaii.edu/

Description: State-supported, 2-year, coed. Part of University of Hawaii System. Awards transfer associate and terminal associate degrees. Founded 1968. Setting: 49-acre suburban campus with easy access to Honolulu. Total enrollment: 6,201. Students come from 25 states and territories, 35% 25 or older. Calendar: semesters. Academic remediation for entering students, ESL program, services for LD students, advanced placement, honors program, independent study, distance learning, summer session for credit, part-time degree program, adult/continuing education programs, co-op programs and internships. Off campus study at other units of the University of Hawaii System. ROTC: Army, Air Force (c).

Entrance Requirements: Open admission. Option: early admission. Required for some: high school transcript, recommendations. Entrance: noncompetitive. Application deadline: 8/15. Notification: continuous until 8/19. Preference given to state residents.

Collegiate Environment: Orientation program. Drama-theater group, choral group, student-run newspaper. Student services: health clinic, personal-psychological counseling. Campus security: 24-hour patrols, late night transport-escort service. College housing not available. 62,000 books, 49 microform titles, 358 serials, 1,009 audiovisual materials, an OPAC, and a Web page. 162 computers available on campus for general student use. A campuswide network can be accessed from off-campus. Staffed computer lab on campus.

Community Environment: See University of Hawaii - Manoa.

■ MAUI COMMUNITY COLLEGE *E-12*

310 Kaahumanu Ave.
Kahului, HI 96732
Tel: (808)984-3500
Free: 800-479-6692
Admissions: (808)984-3267
Fax: (808)242-9618
E-mail: kameda@hawaii.edu
Web Site: http://mauicc.hawaii.edu/

Description: State-supported, 2-year, coed. Part of University of Hawaii System. Awards certificates, transfer associate, and terminal associate degrees. Founded 1967. Setting: 77-acre rural campus. Total enrollment: 2,657. Full-time: 978 students, 56% women, 44% men. Part-time: 1,679 students, 65% women, 35% men. Students come from 15 other countries, 0.5% Native American, 2% Hispanic, 0.3% black, 60% Asian American or Pacific Islander, 4% international, 43% 25 or older, 75% live on campus. Core. Calendar: semesters. Academic remediation for entering students, ESL program, services for LD students, summer session for credit, part-time degree program, external degree program, adult/continuing education programs, co-op programs.

Entrance Requirements: Open admission. Options: Common Application, electronic application, early admission. Required for some: high school transcript. Placement: CTBS required. Entrance: noncompetitive. Application deadline: Rolling.

Collegiate Environment: Student-run newspaper. Student services: health clinic, personal-psychological counseling. Campus security: 24-hour emergency response devices and patrols. Option: coed housing available. Maui Community College Library plus 1 other with 49,812 books, 7,993 microform titles, 631 serials, 1,333 audiovisual materials, an OPAC, and a Web page. Operations spending for 2004 fiscal year: $412,000. 487 computers available on campus for general student use. A campuswide network can be accessed from off-campus. Staffed computer lab on campus.

Community Environment: Kahului is an urban community on the Island of Maui enjoying an average temperature of 74.9 degrees. Both airlines and boats serve the area. The community facilities include churches of most denominations, hospital, clinic and shopping center. The pineapple and sugar industries provide work during the summer. Recreational activities are mainly surfing and swimming. The Island of Maui has three golf courses; the Maui Country Club, Royal Kaanapali Golf Course and the Waiehu Golf Course.

■ REMINGTON COLLEGE-HONOLULU CAMPUS *D-8*

1111 Bishop St., Ste. 400
Honolulu, HI 96813
Tel: (808)942-1000
Fax: (808)533-3064
E-mail: ken.heinemann@remingtoncollege.edu
Web Site: http://www.remingtoncollege.edu/

Description: Proprietary, 4-year, coed.

■ TRANSPACIFIC HAWAII COLLEGE *D-8*

5257 Kalanianaole Hwy.
Honolulu, HI 96821-1884
Tel: (808)377-5402
Fax: (808)373-4754
E-mail: jnorris@transpacific.org
Web Site: http://www.transpacific.org/

Description: Independent, 2-year, coed. Awards transfer associate degrees (majority of students are from outside of U.S. and participate in intensive ESL program in preparation for transfer to a 4-year institution). Founded 1977. Setting: suburban campus. Endowment: $1 million. Educational spending for 2005 fiscal year: $10,000 per student. Total enrollment: 240. Student-undergrad faculty ratio is 5:1. 110 applied, 89% were admitted. Full-time: 240 students, 60% women, 40% men. Students come from 3 other countries, 0% from out-of-state, 100% international, 0% 25 or older, 2% transferred in. Core. Academic remediation for entering students, ESL program, accelerated degree program, independent study.

Entrance Requirements: Open admission. Options: Common Application, electronic application, early admission, deferred admission. Required: essay, high school transcript. Required for some: interview. Entrance: minimally difficult. Application deadline: 8/5. Preference given to students from Asia.

Costs Per Year: Application fee: $50. Tuition: $16,250 full-time.

Collegiate Environment: Orientation program. Student-run newspaper. Most popular organizations: Basketball Club, Volleyball Club, Hula Club, Swim Club, Surfing Club. Major annual events: Christmas party, Halloween Party, camping. Student services: personal-psychological counseling. Campus security: 24-hour emergency response devices. College housing not available. TransPacific Hawaii College Library with 606 books, 6 serials, 50 audiovisual materials, an OPAC, and a Web page. Operations spending for 2004 fiscal year: $15,000. 41 computers available on campus for general student use. A campuswide network can be accessed. Staffed computer lab on campus.

■ **UNIVERSITY OF HAWAII AT HILO** *I-16*
200 West Kawili St.
Hilo, HI 96720-4091
Tel: (808)974-7311
Free: 800-897-4456
Admissions: (808)974-7414
Fax: (808)933-0861
E-mail: uhhao@uhhadc.uhh.hawaii.edu
Web Site: http://www.uhh.hawaii.edu/
Description: State-supported, comprehensive, coed. Part of University of Hawaii System. Awards bachelor's and master's degrees. Founded 1970. Setting: 115-acre small town campus. Endowment: $1.5 million. Research spending for 2004 fiscal year: $7.9 million. Total enrollment: 3,288. 1,470 applied, 66% were admitted. 18% from top 10% of their high school class, 46% from top quarter, 84% from top half. Students come from 48 states and territories, 40 other countries, 21% from out-of-state, 1% Native American, 3% Hispanic, 1% black, 38% Asian American or Pacific Islander, 11% international, 32% 25 or older, 29% live on campus. Retention: 64% of full-time freshmen returned the following year. Core. Calendar: semesters. ESL program, services for LD students, advanced placement, self-designed majors, honors program, independent study, distance learning, double major, summer session for credit, part-time degree program, internships. Off campus study at members of the National Student Exchange. Study abroad program.
Entrance Requirements: Options: Peterson's Universal Application, Common Application, electronic application, deferred admission, international baccalaureate accepted. Required: high school transcript, SAT or ACT. Recommended: minimum 3.0 high school GPA. Required for some: recommendations. Entrance: moderately difficult. Application deadline: 7/1. Notification: 7/31.
Costs Per Year: Application fee: $40. State resident tuition: $2472 full-time, $103 per credit hour part-time. Nonresident tuition: $8040 full-time, $335 per credit hour part-time. Mandatory fees: $132 full-time. College room and board: $5374. College room only: $2774.
Collegiate Environment: Orientation program. Drama-theater group, choral group, student-run newspaper. Social organizations: 43 open to all. Most popular organizations: International Student Association, Hawaiian Leadership and Development, Delta Sigma Pi Business Fraternity, University Canoe Club, Samoan Club. Major annual events: International Night, Homecoming, Hilo Basketball Classic. Student services: health clinic, personal-psychological counseling, women's center. Campus security: 24-hour emergency response devices and patrols, controlled dormitory access. 620 college housing spaces available; 600 were occupied in 2003-04. No special consideration for freshman housing applicants. Option: coed housing available. Edwin H. Mookini Library with 250,000 books, 2,500 serials, an OPAC, and a Web page. Operations spending for 2004 fiscal year: $1.7 million. 600 computers available on campus for general student use. A campuswide network can be accessed from student residence rooms and from off campus. Staffed computer lab on campus.

■ **UNIVERSITY OF HAWAII AT MANOA** *D-8*
2500 Campus Rd.
Honolulu, HI 96822
Tel: (808)956-8111
Free: 800-823-9771
Admissions: (808)956-8975
E-mail: ar-info@hawaii.edu
Web Site: http://www.uhm.hawaii.edu/
Description: State-supported, university, coed. Awards bachelor's, master's, doctoral, and first professional degrees. Founded 1907. Setting: 300-acre urban campus. Endowment: $187 million. Research spending for 2004 fiscal year: $223.5 million. Educational spending for 2005 fiscal year: $13,248 per student. Total enrollment: 20,644. Faculty: 1,169 (1,086 full-time, 83 part-time). Student-undergrad faculty ratio is 12:1. 6,896 applied, 68% were admitted. 26% from top 10% of their high school class, 61% from top quarter, 91% from top half. Full-time: 11,857 students, 56% women, 44% men. Part-time: 2,494 students, 55% women, 45% men. Students come from 73 other countries, 20% from out-of-state, 0.4% Native American, 2% Hispanic, 1% black, 65% Asian American or Pacific Islander, 3% international, 17% 25 or older, 13% live on campus, 12% transferred in. Retention: 75% of full-time freshmen returned the following year. Academic areas with the most degrees conferred: business/marketing; social sciences; education. Core. Calendar: semesters. ESL program, services for LD students, advanced placement, accelerated degree program, self-designed majors, honors program, independent study, distance learning, double major, summer session for

credit, part-time degree program, adult/continuing education programs, co-op programs and internships, graduate courses open to undergrads. Off campus study at members of the National Student Exchange. Study abroad program. ROTC: Army, Air Force.
Entrance Requirements: Options: electronic application, international baccalaureate accepted. Required: high school transcript, minimum 2.8 high school GPA, minimum SAT score of 510 for verbal, math and writing sections, SAT or ACT. Entrance: moderately difficult. Application deadline: 5/1. Notification: continuous. Preference given to state residents.
Costs Per Year: Application fee: $50. State resident tuition: $4320 full-time, $180 per credit hour part-time. Nonresident tuition: $12,942 full-time, $508 per credit hour part-time. Mandatory fees: $193 full-time. Full-time tuition and fees vary according to class time, course load, program, and reciprocity agreements. Part-time tuition varies according to class time, course load, program, and reciprocity agreements. College room and board: $6690. College room only: $4232. Room and board charges vary according to board plan and housing facility.
Collegiate Environment: Orientation program. Drama-theater group, choral group, marching band, student-run newspaper, radio station. Social organizations: 150 open to all; national fraternities, national sororities, local fraternities, local sororities; 1% of men are members. Most popular organizations: Associated Students of University of Hawaii, Campus Center Board, Broadcast Communication Authority, Board of Publications, Student Activities and Program Fee Board. Major annual events: All Nighter, Manoa Jams, Hawaiian Music Concerts. Student services: health clinic, personal-psychological counseling, women's center. Campus security: 24-hour emergency response devices and patrols, student patrols, late night transport-escort service, controlled dormitory access. 2,986 college housing spaces available; 1,738 were occupied in 2003-04. Option: coed housing available. Hamilton Library plus 6 others with 3.2 million books, 6 million microform titles, 27,328 serials, 53,383 audiovisual materials, an OPAC, and a Web page. Operations spending for 2004 fiscal year: $21.6 million. 1,400 computers available on campus for general student use. Computer purchase/lease plans available. A campuswide network can be accessed from student residence rooms and from off campus. Staffed computer lab on campus.

■ **UNIVERSITY OF HAWAII-WEST OAHU** *G-2*
96-129 Ala Ike
Pearl City, HI 96782-3366
Tel: (808)454-4700
Admissions: (808)453-4700
E-mail: robyno@hawaii.edu
Web Site: http://www.uhwo.hawaii.edu/
Description: State-supported, upper-level, coed. Part of University of Hawaii System. Awards bachelor's degrees. Founded 1976. Setting: small town campus with easy access to Honolulu. Total enrollment: 852. Student-undergrad faculty ratio is 13:1. 436 applied, 86% were admitted. Full-time: 284 students, 67% women, 33% men. Part-time: 568 students, 71% women, 29% men. Students come from 3 other countries, 7% from out-of-state, 1% Native American, 3% Hispanic, 2% black, 59% Asian American or Pacific Islander, 76% 25 or older. Academic areas with the most degrees conferred: psychology; business/marketing; social sciences. Core. Calendar: semesters. Services for LD students, advanced placement, distance learning, double major, summer session for credit, part-time degree program, internships. Off campus study at Windwood Community College; University of Hawaii Centers at Maui, Kauai and West Hawaii. Study abroad program. ROTC: Army (c), Air Force (c).
Costs Per Year: Application fee: $50. State resident tuition: $2736 full-time, $114 per credit part-time. Nonresident tuition: $8784 full-time, $366 per credit part-time. Mandatory fees: $10 full-time, $5 per term part-time.
Collegiate Environment: Orientation program. Social organizations: 4 open to all. Student services: personal-psychological counseling. Campus security: 24-hour emergency response devices and patrols, late night transport-escort service. College housing not available. University of Hawaii-West Oahu Library with 25,000 books, 132 serials, an OPAC, and a Web page. Operations spending for 2004 fiscal year: $245,000. 18 computers available on campus for general student use. A campuswide network can be accessed from off-campus. Staffed computer lab on campus.

■ **UNIVERSITY OF PHOENIX-HAWAII CAMPUS** *D-8*
827 Fort St.
Honolulu, HI 96813-4317
Tel: (808)536-2686
Free: 800-228-7240

Admissions: (480)557-1712
Web Site: http://www.phoenix.edu/
Description: Proprietary, comprehensive, coed. Awards bachelor's and master's degrees (courses conducted at 121 campuses and learning centers in 25 states). Setting: urban campus. Total enrollment: 1,348. Faculty: 206 (4 full-time, 202 part-time). Student-undergrad faculty ratio is 6:1. 12 applied. Full-time: 907 students, 69% women, 31% men. 1% Native American, 2% Hispanic, 2% black, 23% Asian American or Pacific Islander, 23% international, 93% 25 or older. Academic areas with the most degrees conferred: business/marketing; computer and information sciences; public administration and social services. Core. Calendar: continuous. Advanced placement, accelerated degree program, independent study, distance learning, external degree program, adult/continuing education programs, graduate courses open to undergrads.
Entrance Requirements: Open admission. Option: deferred admission. Required: 1 recommendation. Required for some: high school transcript. Entrance: noncompetitive. Application deadline: Rolling.
Costs Per Year: Application fee: $110. Tuition: $11,550 full-time, $385 per credit part-time. Mandatory fees: $560 full-time, $70 per course part-time.
Collegiate Environment: College housing not available. University Library with an OPAC and a Web page. System-wide operations spending for 2004 fiscal year: $3.2 million.

■ **WINDWARD COMMUNITY COLLEGE** *D-8*
45-720 Keaahala Rd.
Kaneohe, HI 96744-3528

Tel: (808)235-7400
Web Site: http://www.wcc.hawaii.edu/
Description: State-supported, 2-year, coed. Part of University of Hawaii System. Awards certificates, transfer associate, and terminal associate degrees. Founded 1972. Setting: 78-acre small town campus with easy access to Honolulu. Total enrollment: 1,761. 6% from out-of-state, 32% 25 or older. Core. Calendar: semesters. Academic remediation for entering students, services for LD students, advanced placement, independent study, distance learning, summer session for credit, part-time degree program, adult/continuing education programs, co-op programs. ROTC: Army (c), Air Force (c).
Entrance Requirements: Open admission. Option: early admission. Entrance: noncompetitive. Application deadline: Rolling. Notification: continuous until 8/1. Preference given to state residents.
Costs Per Year: Application fee: $25. State resident tuition: $1176 full-time, $49 per credit part-time. Nonresident tuition: $5808 full-time, $242 per credit part-time. Mandatory fees: $40 full-time.
Collegiate Environment: Orientation program. Drama-theater group, student-run newspaper. Social organizations: 5 open to all. Student services: personal-psychological counseling. College housing not available. 70 computers available on campus for general student use. Staffed computer lab on campus.

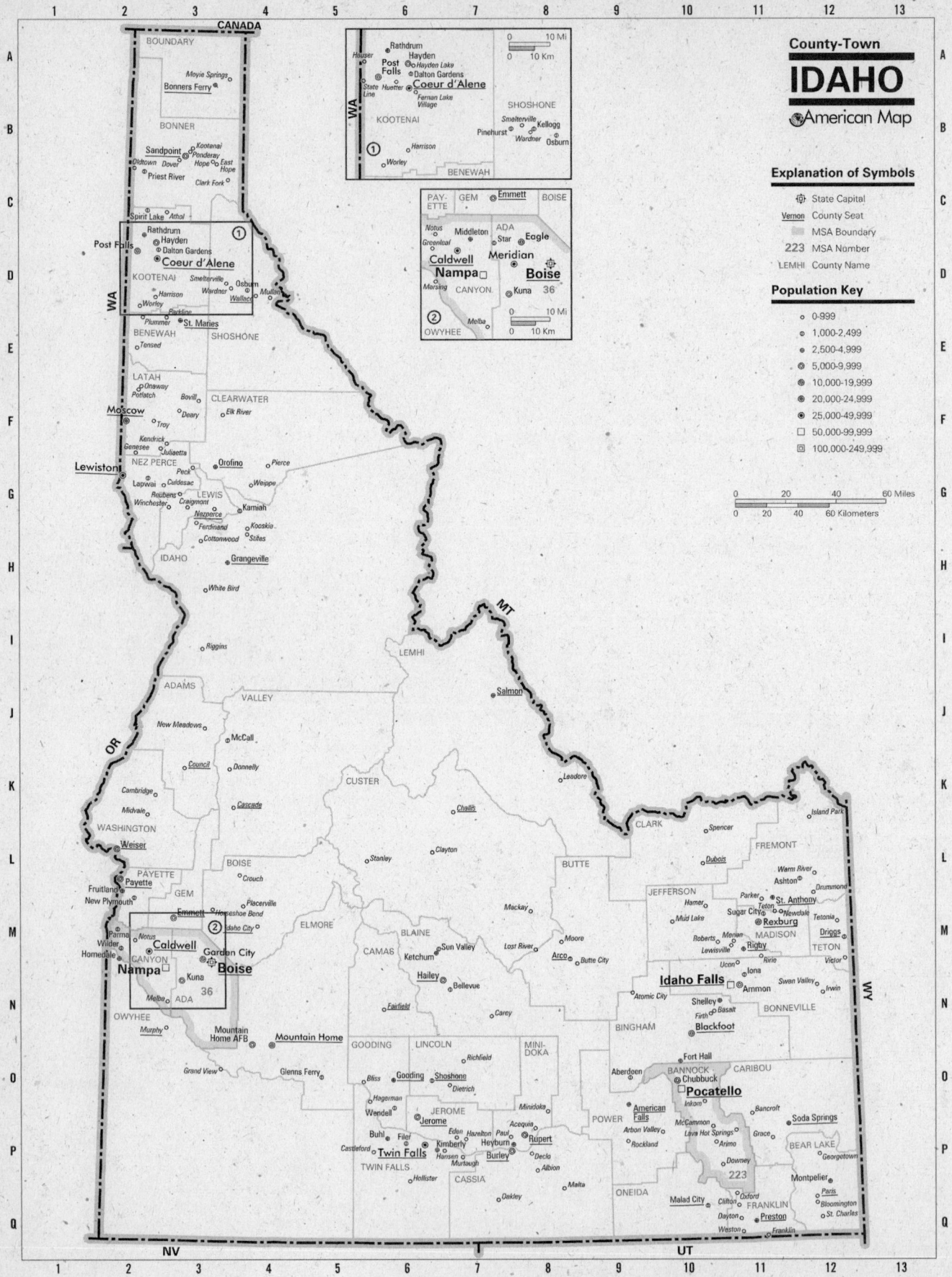

County-Town

IDAHO

🌐 American Map

Explanation of Symbols

⊕	State Capital
Vernon	County Seat
▨	MSA Boundary
223	MSA Number
LEMHI	County Name

Population Key

○	0-999
◎	1,000-2,499
◉	2,500-4,999
◉	5,000-9,999
◉	10,000-19,999
◉	20,000-24,999
◉	25,000-49,999
☐	50,000-99,999
▣	100,000-249,999

■ **ALBERTSON COLLEGE OF IDAHO** *M-2*

2112 Cleveland Blvd.

Caldwell, ID 83605-4494

Tel: (208)459-5011

Free: 800-244-3246

Admissions: (208)459-5689

Fax: (208)454-2077

E-mail: admission@albertson.edu

Web Site: http://www.albertson.edu/

Description: Independent, comprehensive, coed. Awards bachelor's and master's degrees. Founded 1891. Setting: 50-acre suburban campus. Endowment: $39 million. Educational spending for 2005 fiscal year: $6398 per student. Total enrollment: 818. Faculty: 71 (66 full-time, 5 part-time). Student-undergrad faculty ratio is 11:1. 924 applied, 84% were admitted. 34% from top 10% of their high school class, 70% from top quarter, 90% from top half. 1 National Merit Scholar. Full-time: 761 students, 58% women, 42% men. Part-time: 39 students, 51% women, 49% men. Students come from 21 states and territories, 28% from out-of-state, 1% Native American, 5% Hispanic, 1% black, 3% Asian American or Pacific Islander, 2% international, 3% 25 or older, 52% live on campus, 5% transferred in. Retention: 76% of full-time freshmen returned the following year. Academic areas with the most degrees conferred: business/marketing; history; social sciences. Core. Calendar: semesters plus 6-week Winter term. Services for LD students, advanced placement, self-designed majors, honors program, independent study, double major, part-time degree program, co-op programs and internships. Off campus study at Northwest Nazarene University. Study abroad program. ROTC: Army (c).

Entrance Requirements: Options: Peterson's Universal Application, Common Application, electronic application, early admission, early action, deferred admission, international baccalaureate accepted. Required: essay, high school transcript, 1 recommendation, SAT or ACT. Recommended: interview. Entrance: moderately difficult. Application deadlines: 6/1, 11/15 for early action. Notification: continuous.

Costs Per Year: Application fee: $50. Comprehensive fee: $22,191 includes full-time tuition ($16,000) and college room and board ($6191). College room only: $2700. Part-time tuition: $670 per credit.

Collegiate Environment: Orientation program. Drama-theater group, choral group, student-run newspaper, radio station. Social organizations: 55 open to all; national fraternities, national sororities, local fraternities, local sororities; 12% of eligible men and 13% of eligible women are members. Most popular organizations: Scarlet Masque Drama Group, Latino American Students, International Studies Association. Major annual events: Spring Fling, Midnight Finals Breakfast, Campus Ministry Late Nite Chapel. Student services: health clinic, personal-psychological counseling. Campus security: 24-hour emergency response devices and patrols, student patrols, late night transport-escort service, controlled dormitory access. 517 college housing spaces available; 431 were occupied in 2003-04. Freshmen guaranteed college housing. On-campus residence required through sophomore year. Option: coed housing available. Terteling Library with 183,308 books, 28,751 microform titles, 703 serials, an OPAC, and a Web page. Operations spending for 2004 fiscal year: $338,787. 240 computers available on campus for

general student use. A campuswide network can be accessed from student residence rooms and from off campus. Staffed computer lab on campus.

■ **APOLLO COLLEGE** *N-3*

1200 North Liberty Rd.

Boise, ID 83704

Tel: (208)377-8080

Free: 800-473-4365

Fax: (208)322-7658

Web Site: http://www.apolloboise.com/

Description: Proprietary, 2-year, coed. Administratively affiliated with U.S. Education Corporation. Awards certificates, diplomas, transfer associate, and terminal associate degrees. Founded 1980. Total enrollment: 469. Full-time: 444 students, 90% women, 10% men. Part-time: 25 students, 44% women, 56% men. Students come from 5 states and territories, 21% from out-of-state, 1% Native American, 9% Hispanic, 1% black, 2% Asian American or Pacific Islander, 0% international, 65% 25 or older, 1% transferred in. Calendar: semesters.

Entrance Requirements: Open admission. Required: high school transcript, 3 recommendations, interview, Wonderlic aptitude test. Required for some: essay. Entrance: minimally difficult. Application deadline: 3/1. Notification: continuous until 9/1.

Collegiate Environment: Orientation program. Major annual events: graduation reception, Christmas Dance, Plato's Place. Campus security: 24-hour patrols. College housing not available. Apollo College with 20,000 books, 10,000 serials, 109 audiovisual materials, and an OPAC. 55 computers available on campus for general student use. A campuswide network can be accessed. Staffed computer lab on campus.

■ **BOISE BIBLE COLLEGE** *N-3*

8695 West Marigold St.

Boise, ID 83714-1220

Tel: (208)376-7731

Free: 800-893-7755

Fax: (208)376-7743

Web Site: http://www.boisebible.edu/

Description: Independent nondenominational, 4-year, coed. Awards associate and bachelor's degrees. Founded 1945. Setting: 17-acre suburban campus. Endowment: $507,870. Educational spending for 2005 fiscal year: $4604 per student. Total enrollment: 134. 71 applied, 94% were admitted. 11% from top 10% of their high school class, 42% from top quarter, 63% from top half. Students come from 9 states and territories, 24% 25 or older. Retention: 56% of full-time freshmen returned the following year. Core. Calendar: semesters. Advanced placement, independent study, distance learning, double major, part-time degree program, adult/continuing education programs, co-op programs and internships.

Entrance Requirements: Option: deferred admission. Required: essay, high school transcript, minimum 2.0 high school GPA, 3 recommendations, SAT or ACT. Recommended: interview. Entrance: minimally difficult. Application deadline: 8/1. Notification: continuous.

Collegiate Environment: Orientation program. Choral group. Social organizations: 5 open to all. Most popular organizations: concert choir, Missions, Women's TLC, Spiritual Families, Drama Club. Major annual events: Spiritual Emphasis Week, High School Preview, Spring Conference. Student services: personal-psychological counseling. Campus security: patrols by police officers. On-campus residence required through sophomore year. Options: men-only, women-only housing available. Boise Bible College Library with 29,431 books and 115 serials. Operations spending for 2004 fiscal year: $35,153. 8 computers available on campus for general student use. Staffed computer lab on campus.

■ BOISE STATE UNIVERSITY *N-3*

1910 University Dr.
Boise, ID 83725-0399
Tel: (208)426-1011
Free: 800-824-7017
Admissions: (208)426-1177
E-mail: bfortin@boisestate.edu
Web Site: http://www.boisestate.edu/

Description: State-supported, comprehensive, coed. Part of Idaho System of Higher Education. Awards associate, bachelor's, master's, and doctoral degrees. Founded 1932. Setting: 130-acre urban campus. Endowment: $50.5 million. Research spending for 2004 fiscal year: $8.8 million. Educational spending for 2005 fiscal year: $5617 per student. Total enrollment: 18,586. Faculty: 1,127 (578 full-time, 549 part-time). Student-undergrad faculty ratio is 18:1. 3,340 applied, 90% were admitted. 9% from top 10% of their high school class, 28% from top quarter, 64% from top half. Full-time: 10,840 students, 53% women, 47% men. Part-time: 6,085 students, 55% women, 45% men. Students come from 35 states and territories, 47 other countries, 9% from out-of-state, 1% Native American, 6% Hispanic, 1% black, 3% Asian American or Pacific Islander, 1% international, 42% 25 or older, 8% live on campus, 6% transferred in. Retention: 63% of full-time freshmen returned the following year. Academic areas with the most degrees conferred: business/marketing; health professions and related sciences; education. Core. Calendar: semesters. Academic remediation for entering students, ESL program, services for LD students, advanced placement, self-designed majors, freshman honors college, honors program, independent study, distance learning, double major, summer session for credit, part-time degree program, adult/continuing education programs, co-op programs and internships, graduate courses open to undergrads. Off campus study at National Student Exchange. Study abroad program. ROTC: Army.

Entrance Requirements: Option: electronic application. Recommended: high school transcript. Required for some: high school transcript, minimum 2.0 high school GPA, SAT or ACT. Entrance: minimally difficult. Application deadline: 7/12. Notification: continuous.

Costs Per Year: Application fee: $30. State resident tuition: $2568 full-time, $138 per credit part-time. Nonresident tuition: $9976 full-time, $138 per credit part-time. Mandatory fees: $1304 full-time, $57 per credit part-time. Full-time tuition and fees vary according to reciprocity agreements. Part-time tuition and fees vary according to course load. College room and board: $5566. Room and board charges vary according to board plan and housing facility.

Collegiate Environment: Orientation program. Drama-theater group, choral group, marching band, student-run newspaper. Social organizations: 176 open to all; national fraternities, national sororities, local fraternities, local sororities; 1% of eligible men and 1% of eligible women are members. Most popular organizations: Latter-Day Saints Student Association, Residence Hall Association, Organization of Student Social Workers, Marching Band Association, Teacher Education Association. Major annual events: homecoming, Student Organizational Fair, Spring Fling. Student services: legal services, health clinic, personal-psychological counseling, women's center. Campus security: 24-hour emergency response devices and patrols. 1,200 college housing spaces available; 900 were occupied in 2003-04. Freshmen given priority for college housing. Option: coed housing available. Albertsons Library with 675,000 books, 1 million microform titles, 5,000 serials, 60,000 audiovisual materials, an OPAC, and a Web page. Operations spending for 2004 fiscal year: $6.2 million. 900 computers available on campus for general student use. A campuswide network can be accessed from student residence rooms and from off campus. Staffed computer lab on campus.

Community Environment: Boise, the capital of Idaho and its largest city, is located on the Boise River at the upper end of the Boise Valley. It enjoys mild winters with very little snow and temperate summers with cool nights. Community facilities include hospitals and libraries. The Idaho Concert and Artists Association features artists of national and international fame. Points of interest are the State Capitol, Ann Morrison and Julia Davis Parks, Platt Gardens, State Historical Museum, Pioneer Village, Urquides Village, Boise

Heights, Idaho City, and Silver City. The latter two are pioneer gold rush communities. Year-round recreational opportunities are available in and around Boise.

■ BRIGHAM YOUNG UNIVERSITY -IDAHO *M-11*

Rexburg, ID 83460-1650
Tel: (208)496-2011
Admissions: (208)496-1026
Fax: (208)496-1220
E-mail: westenskowg@byui.edu
Web Site: http://www.byui.edu/

Description: Independent, 2-year, coed, affiliated with The Church of Jesus Christ of Latter-day Saints. Awards transfer associate and terminal associate degrees. Founded 1888. Setting: 255-acre small town campus. Total enrollment: 10,100. 6,500 applied, 95% were admitted. Students come from 50 states and territories, 64% from out-of-state, 2% 25 or older, 20% live on campus. Core. Calendar: semesters. Academic remediation for entering students, services for LD students, advanced placement, accelerated degree program, honors program, summer session for credit, part-time degree program, adult/continuing education programs, internships. ROTC: Army.

Entrance Requirements: Option: electronic application. Required: essay, high school transcript, interview, SAT or ACT. Entrance: moderately difficult. Application deadline: 2/15. Notification: 4/1. Preference given to Latter-Day Saints Church members.

Collegiate Environment: Orientation program. Drama-theater group, choral group, student-run newspaper, radio station. Social organizations: 60 open to all; national fraternities, national sororities; 5% of eligible men and 10% of eligible women are members. Most popular organizations: R Friends, Dance Committee, Student Activities Committee. Major annual events: Homecoming, Men's Week, Women's Week. Student services: legal services, health clinic, personal-psychological counseling. Campus security: 24-hour emergency response devices and patrols, late night transport-escort service. Options: men-only, women-only housing available. David O. McKay Library with 134,423 books, 124,788 microform titles, 889 serials, 34,556 audiovisual materials, and an OPAC. 380 computers available on campus for general student use. A campuswide network can be accessed. Staffed computer lab on campus.

■ COLLEGE OF SOUTHERN IDAHO *P-6*

PO Box 1238
Twin Falls, ID 83303-1238
Tel: (208)733-9554
Admissions: (208)732-6232
Fax: (208)736-3014
Web Site: http://www.csi.edu/

Description: State and locally supported, 2-year, coed. Awards certificates, diplomas, transfer associate, and terminal associate degrees. Founded 1964. Setting: 287-acre small town campus. Endowment: $15 million. Educational spending for 2005 fiscal year: $6220 per student. Total enrollment: 7,105. Full-time: 3,175 students, 61% women, 39% men. Part-time: 3,930 students, 67% women, 33% men. Students come from 29 states and territories, 27 other countries, 3% from out-of-state, 1% Native American, 9% Hispanic, 1% black, 1% Asian American or Pacific Islander, 4% international, 49% 25 or older, 10% live on campus. Core. Calendar: semesters. Academic remediation for entering students, ESL program, services for LD students, advanced placement, honors program, independent study, distance learning, summer session for credit, part-time degree program, adult/continuing education programs, co-op programs and internships.

Entrance Requirements: Open admission except for nursing program. Option: Common Application. Required: high school transcript, ACT COMPASS. Required for some: recommendations, interview, ACT. Entrance: noncompetitive. Application deadline: Rolling.

Costs Per Year: State resident tuition: $1900 full-time, $95 per credit part-time. Nonresident tuition: $5300 full-time, $265 per credit part-time. College room and board: $3870. Room and board charges vary according to board plan.

Collegiate Environment: Drama-theater group, choral group, student-run newspaper, radio station. Social organizations: 60 open to all. Most popular organizations: BPA, Dex, Chi Alpha (Christian Group), Vet Tech Club, Equine Club. Major annual events: Lane of Trees, Halloween Carnival, Ski Day. Student services: legal services, health clinic, personal-psychological counseling, women's center. Campus security: 24-hour emergency response devices and patrols, controlled dormitory access. 246 college housing spaces available; all were occupied in 2003-04. No special consideration for freshman housing applicants. Option: coed housing available. College of Southern Idaho Library with 62,556 books, 374 serials, 4,216 audiovisual materials, an OPAC, and a Web page. Operations spending for 2004 fiscal year: $549,680. 750 computers available on campus for general student use. Computer purchase/lease plans available. A campuswide network can be accessed from student residence rooms and from off campus. Staffed computer lab on campus.

Community Environment: Twin Falls, a pleasant residential town with a population of 30,000, is the county seat of Twin Falls County, the cultural and trade center of South Central Idaho's Magic Valley. The city is located at the junction of Transcontinental Highway 30 and International Highway 93. Buses, railroads, and airlines serve the area. Due to the climate, location, and natural surroundings, there are an unlimited variety of outdoor recreational facilities and activities. The city serves as headquarters for the Sawtooth National Forest.

■ EASTERN IDAHO TECHNICAL COLLEGE *N-11*
1600 South 25th East
Idaho Falls, ID 83404-5788
Tel: (208)524-3000
Free: 800-662-0261
Fax: (208)524-3007
E-mail: salbisto@eite.edu
Web Site: http://www.eitc.edu/

Description: State-supported, 2-year, coed. Awards certificates and terminal associate degrees. Founded 1970. Setting: 40-acre small town campus. Endowment: $1.4 million. Educational spending for 2005 fiscal year: $7001 per student. Total enrollment: 755. Student-undergrad faculty ratio is 12:1. 631 applied, 42% were admitted. Full-time: 229 students, 54% women, 46% men. Part-time: 526 students, 79% women, 21% men. Students come from 5 states and territories, 0.01% from out-of-state, 0.5% Native American, 6% Hispanic, 1% black, 1% Asian American or Pacific Islander, 0% international, 47% 25 or older, 11% transferred in. Retention: 50% of full-time freshmen returned the following year. Calendar: semesters. Academic remediation for entering students, services for LD students, distance learning, summer session for credit, part-time degree program, adult/continuing education programs, co-op programs and internships.

Entrance Requirements: Open admission. Option: deferred admission. Required: high school transcript, interview, COMPASS. Required for some: essay. Entrance: noncompetitive. Application deadline: 8/21.

Costs Per Year: Application fee: $10. State resident tuition: $1578 full-time, $79 per credit part-time. Nonresident tuition: $5784 full-time, $158 per credit part-time. Mandatory fees: $124 full-time, $15 per term part-time.

Collegiate Environment: Orientation program. Major annual events: Fall BBQ, Spring Banquet, Halloween Party. Student services: personal-psychological counseling. Campus security: 24-hour patrols. College housing not available. Richard and Lila Jordan Library plus 1 other with 18,000 books, 64,350 microform titles, 125 serials, 150 audiovisual materials, an OPAC, and a Web page. Operations spending for 2004 fiscal year: $167,886. 105 computers available on campus for general student use. A campuswide network can be accessed. Staffed computer lab on campus.

■ IDAHO STATE UNIVERSITY *O-10*
921 South 8th Ave.
Pocatello, ID 83209
Tel: (208)282-0211
Admissions: (208)282-2578
Web Site: http://www.isu.edu/

Description: State-supported, university, coed. Awards bachelor's, master's, doctoral, and first professional degrees and post-master's and first professional certificates. Founded 1901. Setting: 972-acre small town campus. Endowment: $25.1 million. Research spending for 2004 fiscal year: $12.3 million. Educational spending for 2005 fiscal year: $7506 per student. Total enrollment: 13,977. Faculty: 908 (651 full-time, 257 part-time). Student-undergrad faculty ratio is 15:1. 3,566 applied, 77% were admitted. 13% from top 10% of their high school class, 32% from top quarter, 61% from top half. Full-time: 7,745 students, 54% women, 46% men. Part-time: 3,907 students, 62% women, 38% men. Students come from 37 states and territories, 49 other countries, 5% from out-of-state, 2% Native American, 5% Hispanic, 1% black, 1% Asian American or Pacific Islander, 2% international, 43% 25 or older, 4% live on campus, 10% transferred in. Retention: 57% of full-time freshmen returned the following year. Core. Calendar: semesters. Academic remediation for entering students, ESL program, services for LD students, advanced placement, self-designed majors, honors program, independent

study, distance learning, double major, summer session for credit, part-time degree program, external degree program, adult/continuing education programs, internships, graduate courses open to undergrads. Off campus study at University of Idaho, National Student Exchange. Study abroad program. ROTC: Army (c).

Entrance Requirements: Open admission. Options: Common Application, electronic application, early admission, deferred admission, international baccalaureate accepted. Required: high school transcript, minimum 2.0 high school GPA, SAT or ACT. Recommended: ACT. Entrance: minimally difficult. Application deadline: 8/1. Notification: 3/1.

Costs Per Year: Application fee: $40. One-time mandatory fee: $660. Nonresident tuition: $7700 full-time. Mandatory fees: $4000 full-time. College room and board: $5030. College room only: $2100.

Collegiate Environment: Orientation program. Drama-theater group, choral group, marching band, student-run newspaper, radio station. Social organizations: 127 open to all; national fraternities, national sororities, local fraternities, local sororities; 1% of eligible men and 1% of eligible women are members. Most popular organizations: International Students Association, Vocational Industrial Clubs of America, Latter Day Saints Student Association, Student American Dental Hygienists Association, Academy of Students of Pharmacy. Major annual events: homecoming, Springfest, Greek Olympiad. Student services: legal services, health clinic, personal-psychological counseling, women's center. Campus security: 24-hour emergency response devices and patrols, student patrols, late night transport-escort service, controlled dormitory access. 423 college housing spaces available; 65 were occupied in 2003-04. Freshmen guaranteed college housing. Options: coed, men-only, women-only housing available. Eli M. Oboler Library with 712,041 books, 2 million microform titles, 6,672 serials, 923 audiovisual materials, an OPAC, and a Web page. Operations spending for 2004 fiscal year: $2.3 million. 562 computers available on campus for general student use. A campuswide network can be accessed from student residence rooms and from off campus. Staffed computer lab on campus.

Community Environment: Pocatello is located in a farming and industrial area of southeastern Idaho where the climate is dry and sunny. Planes and buses provide transportation. The community facilities include many churches, two hospitals, the district health department, hotels, motels, etc. The municipal park has facilities for archery, baseball, field games, and includes a swimming pool and a zoo. Other facilities outside of Pocatello are in the intermountain region, which offers some of the best hunting and fishing in the United States. Camping, hiking, snowmobiling, swimming, boating, horseback riding and skiing available for the outdoor life. Rodeos and the Indian Sun Dances are special annual events.

■ ITT TECHNICAL INSTITUTE *N-3*
12302 West Explorer Dr.
Boise, ID 83713
Tel: (208)322-8844
Fax: (208)322-0173
Web Site: http://www.itt-tech.edu/

Description: Proprietary, primarily 2-year, coed. Part of ITT Educational Services, Inc. Awards terminal associate and bachelor's degrees. Founded 1906. Setting: 1-acre urban campus. Core.

Entrance Requirements: Option: deferred admission. Required: high school transcript, interview, Wonderlic aptitude test. Recommended: recommendations. Entrance: minimally difficult. Application deadline: Rolling. Notification: continuous.

Costs Per Year: Application fee: $100.

Collegiate Environment: Orientation program. College housing not available.

■ LEWIS-CLARK STATE COLLEGE *G-2*
500 Eighth Ave.
Lewiston, ID 83501-2698
Tel: (208)792-5272
Free: 800-933-LCSC
Admissions: (208)792-2210
Fax: (208)799-2063
E-mail: sbussoli@lcsc.edu
Web Site: http://www.lcsc.edu/

Description: State-supported, 4-year, coed. Awards associate and bachelor's degrees. Founded 1893. Setting: 44-acre small town campus. Endowment: $1.9 million. Research spending for 2004 fiscal year: $182,591. Educational spending for 2005 fiscal year: $6099 per student. Total enrollment: 3,451. Student-undergrad faculty ratio is 15:1. 1,108 applied. 9% from top 10% of their high school class, 26% from top quarter, 55% from top half. Full-time: 2,281 students, 59% women, 41% men. Part-time: 1,170 students, 65% women, 35% men. Students come from 28 states and territories, 33 other countries, 14% from out-of-state, 5% Native American, 5% Hispanic, 1% black, 1% Asian American or Pacific Islander, 3% international, 42% 25 or older, 8% live on campus, 8% transferred in. Retention: 57% of full-time freshmen returned the following year. Academic areas with the most degrees conferred: business/marketing; health professions and related sciences; education; public administration and social services. Core. Calendar: semesters. Academic remediation for entering students, ESL program, services for LD students, advanced placement, accelerated degree program, self-designed majors, honors program, independent study, distance learning, double major, summer session for credit, part-time degree program, external degree program, adult/continuing education programs, co-op programs and internships. Off campus study. Study abroad program. ROTC: Army, Air Force (c).

Entrance Requirements: Options: Peterson's Universal Application, electronic application, deferred admission, international baccalaureate accepted. Required: high school transcript, minimum 2.0 high school GPA. Required for some: interview, SAT or ACT, ACT COMPASS. Entrance: minimally difficult. Application deadline: Rolling. Notification: continuous.

Costs Per Year: Application fee: $35. Area resident tuition: $185 per credit part-time. State resident tuition: $3714 full-time, $185 per credit part-time. Nonresident tuition: $10,266 full-time. Mandatory fees: $11 per credit part-time. Full-time tuition varies according to course load and reciprocity agreements. College room and board: $4500. College room only: $1900. Room and board charges vary according to board plan and housing facility.

Collegiate Environment: Orientation program. Drama-theater group, choral group, student-run newspaper, radio station. Social organizations: 57 open to all. Most popular organizations: Business Students Organization, Ambassadors Club, International Club, honors society, Explorers. Major annual events: Welcome Back Faire, Dogwood Festival, Native American Week. Student services: health clinic, personal-psychological counseling. Campus security: 24-hour emergency response devices and patrols, student patrols, late night transport-escort service. 202 college housing spaces available; all were occupied in 2003-04. No special consideration for freshman housing applicants. Option: coed housing available. Lewis-Clark State College Library with 139,499 books, 155,600 microform titles, 1,612 serials, 6,957 audiovisual materials, an OPAC, and a Web page. Operations spending for 2004 fiscal year: $1.1 million. 88 computers available on campus for general student use. Computer purchase/lease plans available. A campuswide network can be accessed from student residence rooms and from off campus. Staffed computer lab on campus.

Community Environment: Lewiston is a small urban area that is a major community in the Nez Perce National Park area; climate is temperate. It is the center of a vast lumbering, mining, farming and ranching territory. Planes, buses and trains serve the area. Community facilities include libraries, museums, YWCA, hospital, clinics, community concert series and shopping areas. Part-time employment opportunities are good. Facilities are good for boating, fishing and big game hunting. Boat trips up Hell's Canyon of the Snake River are spectacular journeys; shorter trips are available. The Lewiston Roundup and Dogwood festival are special events.

■ **NEW SAINT ANDREWS COLLEGE** *F-2*
PO Box 9025
Moscow, ID 83843
Tel: (208)882-1566
Fax: (208)882-4293
Web Site: http://www.nsa.edu/
Description: Proprietary, 4-year, coed. Founded 1993. Calendar: 4 8-week terms.

■ **NORTH IDAHO COLLEGE** *D-3*
1000 West Garden Ave.
Coeur d'Alene, ID 83814-2199
Tel: (208)769-3300; 877-404-4536
Admissions: (208)769-3303
Fax: (208)769-3273
E-mail: maxine_gish@nic.edu
Web Site: http://www.nic.edu/
Description: State and locally supported, 2-year, coed. Awards certificates, transfer associate, and terminal associate degrees. Founded 1933. Setting: 42-acre small town campus. Endowment: $5.4 million. Educational spending

for 2005 fiscal year: $3874 per student. Total enrollment: 4,099. Student-undergrad faculty ratio is 14:1. 3,148 applied, 59% were admitted. 9% from top 10% of their high school class, 24% from top quarter, 52% from top half. Full-time: 2,492 students, 57% women, 43% men. Part-time: 1,607 students, 71% women, 29% men. Students come from 27 states and territories, 16 other countries, 2% Native American, 2% Hispanic, 0.4% black, 1% Asian American or Pacific Islander, 0% international, 36% 25 or older, 14% transferred in. Core. Calendar: semesters. Academic remediation for entering students, ESL program, services for LD students, advanced placement, independent study, distance learning, summer session for credit, part-time degree program, adult/continuing education programs, co-op programs and internships. Off campus study at Lewis-Clark State College, University of Idaho.

Entrance Requirements: Options: Peterson's Universal Application, electronic application, early admission, deferred admission. Required for some: essay, high school transcript, county residency certificate. Entrance: noncompetitive. Application deadline: 8/20.

Costs Per Year: Application fee: $25. Area resident tuition: $1068 full-time, $67 per credit part-time. State resident tuition: $2068 full-time, $129 per credit part-time. Nonresident tuition: $5620 full-time, $351 per credit part-time. Mandatory fees: $820 full-time, $60 per credit part-time. Full-time tuition and fees vary according to course load, program, and reciprocity agreements. College room and board: $5010. College room only: $3210. Room and board charges vary according to board plan and housing facility.

Collegiate Environment: Orientation program. Drama-theater group, choral group, student-run newspaper. Social organizations: 25 open to all. Most popular organizations: Ski Club, Fusion, Baptist student ministries, Journalism Club, Phi Theta Kappa. Student services: legal services, health clinic, personal-psychological counseling, women's center. Campus security: 24-hour emergency response devices and patrols, late night transport-escort service. 202 college housing spaces available; 180 were occupied in 2003-04. No special consideration for freshman housing applicants. Molstead Library Computer Center with 60,893 books, 751 serials, an OPAC, and a Web page. Operations spending for 2004 fiscal year: $771,133. 145 computers available on campus for general student use. A campuswide network can be accessed. Staffed computer lab on campus.

Community Environment: Coeur d'Alene is located on the north shore of Lake Coeur d'Alene, 33 miles east of Spokane, Washington. The area is a popular resort for summer and winter events. Two major ski areas are only minutes away from downtown and the lake offers many water sports activities. Average summer high temperature is 82 degrees and average summer lows are 51 degrees, average winter high temperature is 38 degrees and the average low is 26 degrees. There is an average of 50 inches of snow each year and total average precipitation is 26 inches. Transportation facilities for the Spokane/Coeur d'Alene area include bus, train and airline. Facilities of the community include library, hospital, county health unit and active civic clubs. The college hosts art and music programs for the community in its 1,200 seat Boswell Hall auditorium. Coeur d'Alene draws its industry from tourism, high tech, forestry products and agricultural. Outdoor sports are boating, biking, hunting, fishing, golfing, water and snow skiing, sailing, windsurfing, swimming, and mountain biking.

■ **NORTHWEST NAZARENE UNIVERSITY** *N-3*
623 Holly St.
Nampa, ID 83686-5897
Tel: (208)467-8011; 877-668-4968
Admissions: (208)467-8000
Fax: (208)467-8645
E-mail: slberggren@nnu.edu
Web Site: http://www.nnu.edu/
Description: Independent, comprehensive, coed, affiliated with Church of the Nazarene. Awards bachelor's and master's degrees. Founded 1913. Setting: 85-acre small town campus. Endowment: $14 million. Total enrollment: 1,625. Faculty: 100 (95 full-time, 5 part-time). Student-undergrad faculty ratio is 12:1. 923 applied, 52% were admitted. 24% from top 10% of their high school class, 49% from top quarter, 80% from top half. 3 National Merit Scholars. Full-time: 1,073 students, 61% women, 39% men. Part-time: 91 students, 57% women, 43% men. 60% from out-of-state, 1% Native American, 2% Hispanic, 1% black, 1% Asian American or Pacific Islander, 1% international, 70% live on campus, 8% transferred in. Retention: 71% of full-time freshmen returned the following year. Academic areas with the most degrees conferred: business/marketing; education; theology and religious vocations. Core. Calendar: semesters. Academic remediation for entering students, services for LD students, advanced placement, accelerated degree

program, self-designed majors, freshman honors college, honors program, independent study, summer session for credit, part-time degree program, adult/continuing education programs, co-op programs and internships, graduate courses open to undergrads. Off campus study at CCCU Exchange programs. Study abroad program. ROTC: Army.

Entrance Requirements: Options: electronic application, early action, deferred admission. Required: essay, high school transcript, minimum 2.5 high school GPA, 2 recommendations, SAT or ACT. Required for some: interview. Entrance: moderately difficult. Application deadlines: 8/8, 12/15 for early action. Notification: continuous, 1/15 for early action.

Costs Per Year: Application fee: $25. Comprehensive fee: $23,780 includes full-time tuition ($18,430), mandatory fees ($340), and college room and board ($5010). Part-time tuition: $798 per credit.

Collegiate Environment: Orientation program. Drama-theater group, choral group, student-run newspaper. Social organizations: 30 open to all. Most popular organizations: student government, Are You Serving Him (RUSH), ministry clubs, service clubs, science clubs. Major annual events: Malibu-A Spring Festival, RUSH Days, Intramural Snowball Game. Student services: health clinic, personal-psychological counseling. Campus security: 24-hour patrols, student patrols, late night transport-escort service, controlled dormitory access, residence hall check-in system, on-campus police hub. 776 college housing spaces available; 637 were occupied in 2003-04. Freshmen guaranteed college housing. On-campus residence required through sophomore year. Options: coed, men-only, women-only housing available. John E. Riley Library with 100,966 books, 821 serials, an OPAC, and a Web page. 400 computers available on campus for general student use. Computer purchase/lease plans available. A campuswide network can be accessed from student residence rooms and from off campus. Staffed computer lab on campus.

Community Environment: Nampa, located in southwestern Idaho, has a mild climate with an average mean temperature of 51 degrees and average rainfall of 13 inches. It is the agricultural, industrial and transportation center of southwest Idaho. Industries are processing and packing food, building mobile homes, feed mills, and seed houses; Zilog, a computer chip manufacturer is located here. Community facilities include excellent library, churches representing 22 denominations, hospitals, motels and hotels. One hundred fifty civic, fraternal, and veterans organizations are active. Part-time employment is available. Recreational facilities consist of a state-of-the-art recreation center, six parks, softball and baseball fields, horseshoe courts, tennis courts, roller skating rink and bowling alleys; other facilities are Lake Lowell for swimming, boating, fishing and hunting. A ski run is within 35 miles. Points of interest are the Deer Flat National Wildlife Refuge, Givens' Hot Springs, Lakeview Park and Silver City and De Lamar, old mining towns. The Snake River Stampede, a rodeo, is an annual event held in July.

■ **UNIVERSITY OF IDAHO** *F-2*
875 Perimeter Dr., PO Box 442282
Moscow, ID 83844-2282
Tel: (208)885-6111; 888-884-3246
Admissions: (208)885-6326
Fax: (208)885-6911
E-mail: admappl@uidaho.edu
Web Site: http://www.uidaho.edu/
Description: State-supported, university, coed. Awards bachelor's, master's, doctoral, and first professional degrees and post-master's certificates. Founded 1889. Setting: 1,450-acre small town campus. Endowment: $143.5 million. Research spending for 2004 fiscal year: $125.3 million. Educational spending for 2005 fiscal year: $10,514 per student. Total enrollment: 12,476. Faculty: 586 (564 full-time, 22 part-time). Student-undergrad faculty ratio is 20:1. 4,444 applied, 82% were admitted. 20% from top 10% of their high school class, 46% from top quarter, 77% from top half. 8 National Merit Scholars, 31 class presidents, 71 valedictorians, 30 student government officers. Full-time: 8,380 students, 45% women, 55% men. Part-time: 1,123 students, 49% women, 51% men. 28% from out-of-state, 1% Native American, 4% Hispanic, 1% black, 2% Asian American or Pacific Islander, 2% international, 18% 25 or older, 55% live on campus. Academic areas with the most degrees conferred: business/marketing; education; engineering. Core. Calendar: semesters. Academic remediation for entering students, services for LD students, advanced placement, accelerated degree program, self-designed majors, honors program, independent study, distance learning, double major, summer session for credit, part-time degree program, adult/

continuing education programs, co-op programs and internships, graduate courses open to undergrads. Off campus study at National Student Exchange. Study abroad program. ROTC: Army, Naval, Air Force (c).

Entrance Requirements: Options: Common Application, electronic application, deferred admission, international baccalaureate accepted. Required: high school transcript, minimum 2.2 high school GPA, SAT or ACT. Recommended: SAT. Required for some: essay. Entrance: moderately difficult. Application deadline: 8/1. Notification: continuous.

Costs Per Year: Application fee: $40. State resident tuition: $0 full-time. Nonresident tuition: $8770 full-time, $130 per credit part-time. Mandatory fees: $3968 full-time, $190 per credit part-time. Full-time tuition and fees vary according to degree level and program. Part-time tuition and fees vary according to course load, degree level, and program. College room and board: $5342. Room and board charges vary according to board plan and housing facility.

Collegiate Environment: Orientation program. Drama-theater group, choral group, marching band, student-run newspaper, radio station. Social organizations: 132 open to all; national fraternities, national sororities; 16% of eligible men and 13% of eligible women are members. Most popular organizations: Alpha Phi Omega, Campus Crusade for Christ, Student International Association, OELA, Students of Human Resource Management. Major annual events: Jazz Festival, Palouse-A-Fest, homecoming. Student services: legal services, health clinic, personal-psychological counseling, women's center, Career/Professional Planning, Academic Advising, Employment Program. Campus security: late night transport-escort service, controlled dormitory access. 1,950 college housing spaces available; 1,600 were occupied in 2003-04. Freshmen guaranteed college housing. Options: coed, men-only, women-only housing available. University of Idaho Library plus 1 other with 1.4 million books, 1.5 million microform titles, 14,230 serials, 8,717 audiovisual materials, an OPAC, and a Web page. Operations spending for 2004 fiscal year: $6.5 million. 670 computers available on campus for general student use. Computer purchase/lease plans available. A campuswide network can be accessed from student residence rooms and from off campus. Staffed computer lab on campus.

Community Environment: The location is rural, combining the peace, calm, and simplicity of the country with the intellectual atmosphere of a progressive college town. Moscow is in Idaho's Palouse Hill country and leads the nation in the production and processing of seed peas and lentils. Community facilities include a library, churches, clinics, hospital, hotels and motels and 2 shopping malls. Air, bus and railroads serve the area. Part-time work is available. Apartments and rooms may be rented. Eight miles away is Washington State University, the land grant institution for the state of Washington. There is an active faculty exchange, cross registration, and multiple library resources.

■ **UNIVERSITY OF PHOENIX-IDAHO CAMPUS** *D-8*
3080 Gentry Way, Ste. 150
Meridian, ID 83642-3014
Tel: (208)888-1505
Free: 800-228-7240
Admissions: (480)557-1712
Fax: (208)888-4775
Web Site: http://www.phoenix.edu/
Description: Proprietary, comprehensive, coed. Awards bachelor's and master's degrees. Setting: urban campus. Total enrollment: 767. Faculty: 116 (2 full-time, 114 part-time). Student-undergrad faculty ratio is 6:1. 14 applied. Full-time: 656 students, 51% women, 49% men. 0.2% Native American, 0.5% Hispanic, 0.3% black, 1% Asian American or Pacific Islander, 37% international, 91% 25 or older. Academic areas with the most degrees conferred: business/marketing; computer and information sciences; security and protective services. Core. Calendar: continuous. Advanced placement, accelerated degree program, independent study, distance learning, external degree program, adult/continuing education programs, graduate courses open to undergrads.

Entrance Requirements: Open admission. Option: deferred admission. Required: 1 recommendation. Required for some: high school transcript. Entrance: noncompetitive. Application deadline: Rolling.

Costs Per Year: Application fee: $110. Tuition $9900 full-time, $330 per credit part-time. Mandatory fees: $560 full-time, $70 per course part-time.

Collegiate Environment: College housing not available. University Library with an OPAC and a Web page. System-wide operations spending for 2004 fiscal year: $3.2 million.

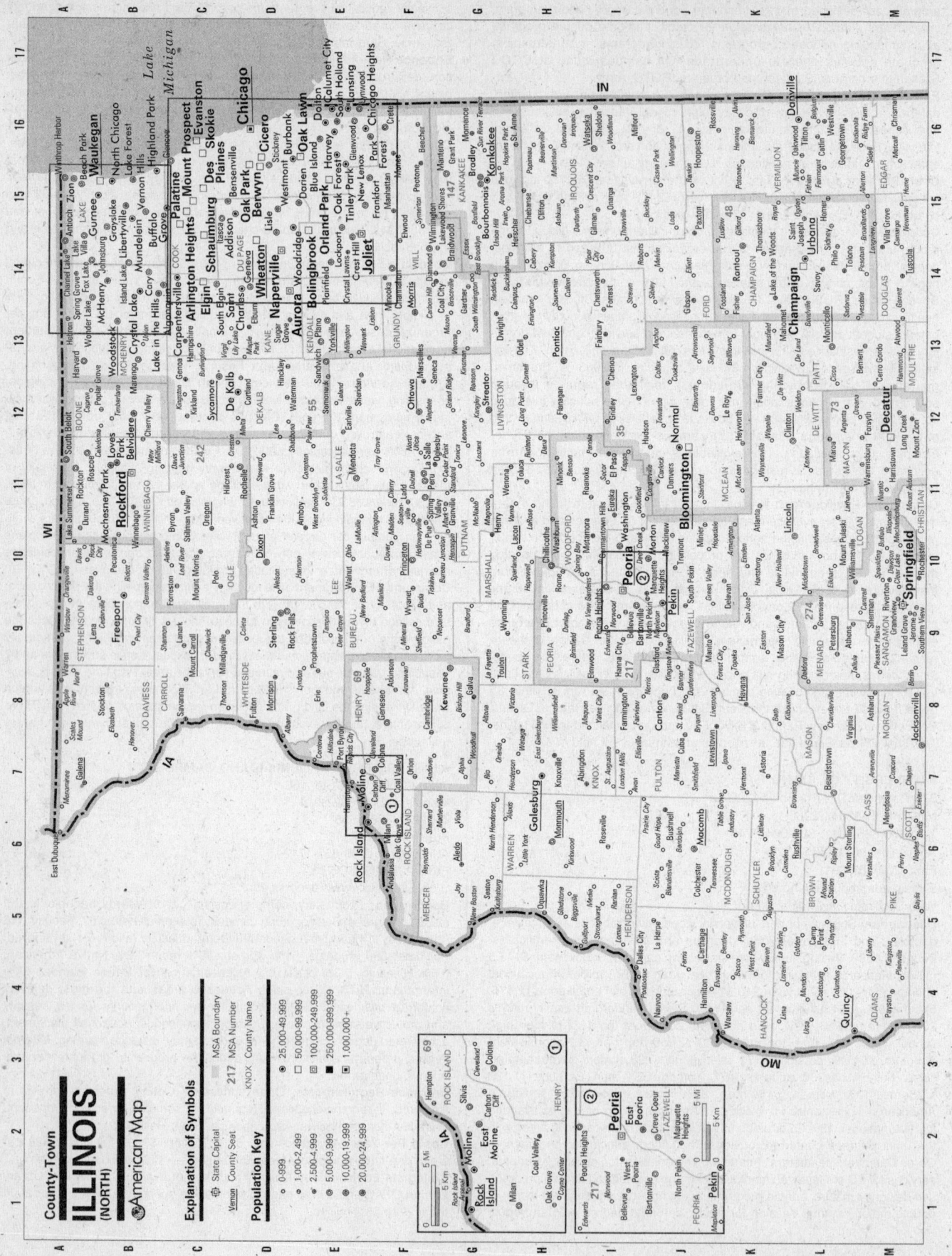

County-Town
ILLINOIS
(NORTH)

● American Map

Explanation of Symbols

⊕ State Capital	MSA Boundary
Vernon County Seat	217 MSA Number
	KNOX County Name

Population Key

○ 0-999	◉ 25,000-49,999
● 1,000-2,499	▣ 50,000-99,999
● 2,500-4,999	▢ 100,000-249,999
● 5,000-9,999	■ 250,000-999,999
◉ 10,000-19,999	▣ 1,000,000+
◉ 20,000-24,999	

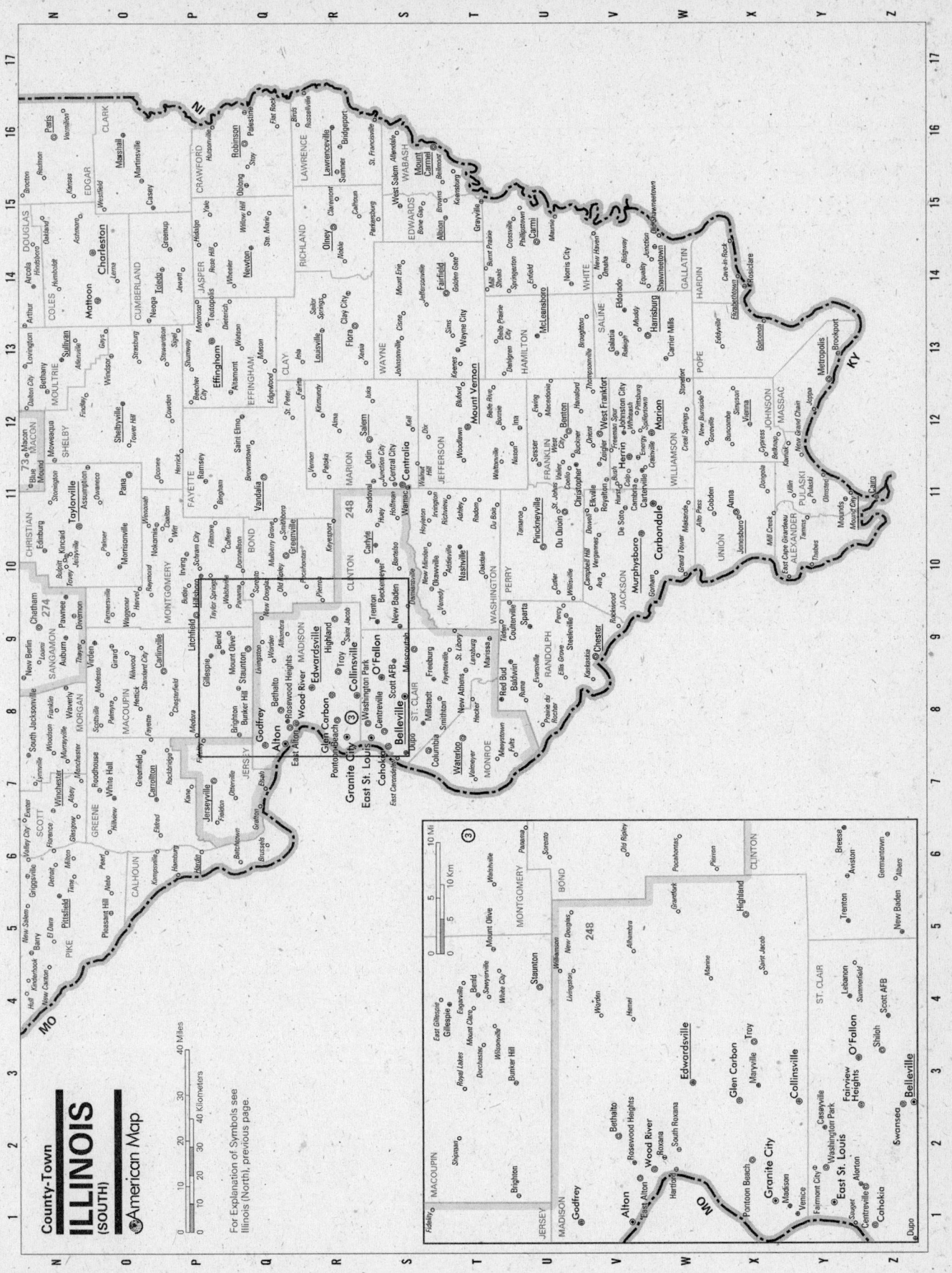

County-Town
ILLINOIS
(SOUTH)

American Map

For Explanation of Symbols see
Illinois (North), previous page.

■ **AMERICAN ACADEMY OF ART** *D-16*
332 South Michigan Ave, Ste. 300
Chicago, IL 60604-4302
Tel: (312)461-0600
E-mail: srosenbloom@aaart.edu
Web Site: http://www.aaart.edu/
Description: Proprietary, comprehensive, coed. Awards bachelor's and master's degrees. Founded 1923. Setting: urban campus. Total enrollment: 410. Faculty: 35 (25 full-time, 10 part-time). Student-undergrad faculty ratio is 10:1. Full-time: 338 students, 41% women, 59% men. Part-time: 58 students, 33% women, 67% men. Students come from 8 states and territories, 3 other countries, 10% from out-of-state, 0% Native American, 20% Hispanic, 11% black, 4% Asian American or Pacific Islander, 0.2% international, 13% 25 or older, 7% transferred in. Retention: 77% of full-time freshmen returned the following year. Academic area with the most degrees conferred: visual and performing arts. Core. Calendar: semesters. Academic remediation for entering students, accelerated degree program, independent study, summer session for credit, part-time degree program, adult/continuing education programs, internships. Study abroad program.
Entrance Requirements: Option: electronic application. Required: high school transcript, interview. Entrance: moderately difficult. Application deadline: Rolling.
Costs Per Year: Application fee: $25. Tuition: $20,680 full-time. Mandatory fees: $250 full-time.
Collegiate Environment: Major annual events: Student Art Show, Faculty Art Show, Visiting Artist Program. Campus security: 24-hour emergency response devices. College housing not available. Irving Shapiro Library with 1,730 books, 62 serials, and 101 audiovisual materials. 2 computers available on campus for general student use.
Community Environment: See University of Chicago.

■ **AMERICAN INTERCONTINENTAL UNIVERSITY ONLINE** *C-11*
5550 Prairie Stone Parkway, Ste. 400
Hoffman Estates, IL 60192
Tel: (847)851-5000; 877-701-3800
Fax: (847)851-6002
Web Site: http://www.aiuonline.edu/
Description: Proprietary, comprehensive, coed. Part of American InterContinental University. Awards associate, bachelor's, and master's degrees (offers online degree programs only). Founded 1970. Setting: 1-acre suburban campus. Calendar: five 10-week terms.
Entrance Requirements: Required: interview, documentation of high school graduation or its equivalency. Recommended: essay. Application deadline: Rolling. Notification: continuous.

■ **ARGOSY UNIVERSITY/CHICAGO** *D-16*
20 South Clark St., Ste. 300
Chicago, IL 60603
Tel: (312)201-0200
Admissions: 800-626-4123
Fax: (312)201-1907
E-mail: adelaney@argosyu.edu
Web Site: http://www.argosyu.edu/
Description: Proprietary, upper-level, coed. Awards bachelor's, master's, and doctoral degrees. Founded 1976. Setting: urban campus. Research

spending for 2004 fiscal year: $70,100. Educational spending for 2005 fiscal year: $5883 per student. Total enrollment: 890. 19 applied, 74% were admitted. Full-time: 8 students, 75% women, 25% men. Part-time: 29 students, 72% women, 28% men. Students come from 2 states and territories, 5% from out-of-state, 0% Native American, 14% Hispanic, 27% black, 3% Asian American or Pacific Islander, 0% international, 71% 25 or older, 95% transferred in. Core. Calendar: semesters. Services for LD students, advanced placement, accelerated degree program, independent study, distance learning, summer session for credit, part-time degree program.
Collegiate Environment: Orientation program. Student-run newspaper. Social organizations: 8 open to all. Major annual event: Diversity Day. Campus security: 24-hour patrols. College housing not available. Argosy University Chicago Library with 20,000 books, 2,400 microform titles, 150 serials, 550 audiovisual materials, and an OPAC. Operations spending for 2004 fiscal year: $108,617. 15 computers available on campus for general student use. A campuswide network can be accessed from off-campus. Staffed computer lab on campus.

■ **ARGOSY UNIVERSITY/SCHAUMBURG** *C-15*
1000 North Plaza Dr., Ste. 100
Schaumburg, IL 60173
Tel: (847)290-7400; (866)290-2777
Fax: (847)598-6191
Web Site: http://www.argosyu.edu/
Description: Proprietary, upper-level, coed. Awards bachelor's, master's, and doctoral degrees and post-master's certificates. Founded 1979. Setting: suburban campus with easy access to Chicago. Calendar: semesters.
Collegiate Environment: College housing not available.

■ **AUGUSTANA COLLEGE** *E-6*
639 38th St.
Rock Island, IL 61201-2296
Tel: (309)794-7000
Free: 800-798-8100
Admissions: (309)794-7341
Fax: (309)794-7431
E-mail: admissions@augustana.edu
Web Site: http://www.augustana.edu/
Description: Independent, 4-year, coed, affiliated with Evangelical Lutheran Church in America. Awards bachelor's degrees. Founded 1860. Setting: 115-acre suburban campus. Endowment: $93 million. Research spending for 2004 fiscal year: $274,253. Educational spending for 2005 fiscal year: $12,696 per student. Total enrollment: 2,386. Student-undergrad faculty ratio is 12:1. 2,921 applied, 84% were admitted. 29% from top 10% of their high school class, 63% from top quarter, 94% from top half. Full-time: 2,363 students, 58% women, 42% men. Part-time: 23 students, 52% women, 48% men. Students come from 31 states and territories, 23 other countries, 11% from out-of-state, 0.3% Native American, 3% Hispanic, 2% black, 2% Asian American or Pacific Islander, 1% international, 1% 25 or older, 72% live on campus, 3% transferred in. Retention: 85% of full-time freshmen returned the following year. Academic areas with the most degrees conferred: business/marketing; biological/life sciences; social sciences. Core. Services for LD students, advanced placement, accelerated degree program, honors program, independent study, double major, summer session for credit, part-time degree program, internships. Study abroad program.

Entrance Requirements: Options: Peterson's Universal Application, Common Application, deferred admission, international baccalaureate accepted. Required: high school transcript, SAT or ACT. Required for some: essay, interview. Entrance: moderately difficult. Application deadline: Rolling. Notification: continuous.

Costs Per Year: Application fee: $25. Comprehensive fee: $29,862 includes full-time tuition ($22,971), mandatory fees ($486), and college room and board ($6405). College room only: $3243. Full-time tuition and fees vary according to course load. Room and board charges vary according to board plan and housing facility. Part-time tuition: $960 per credit hour.

Collegiate Environment: Orientation program. Drama-theater group, choral group, student-run newspaper, radio station. Social organizations: 109 open to all; local fraternities, local sororities; 19% of eligible men and 26% of eligible women are members. Most popular organizations: College Union Board of Managers, Student Government Association, Literacy Council, student radio station. Major annual events: homecoming, All Campus Volunteer Day, Diversity Week. Student services: health clinic, personal-psychological counseling, women's center. Campus security: 24-hour emergency response devices and patrols, late night transport-escort service, controlled dormitory access. College housing designed to accommodate 1,600 students; 1,611 undergraduates lived in college housing during 2003-04. Freshmen guaranteed college housing. On-campus residence required through junior year. Options: coed, men-only, women-only housing available. Augustana College Library plus 3 others with 190,641 books, 100,794 microform titles, 1,705 serials, 2,019 audiovisual materials, an OPAC, and a Web page. Operations spending for 2004 fiscal year: $1.4 million. 600 computers available on campus for general student use. A campuswide network can be accessed from student residence rooms and from off campus. Staffed computer lab on campus.

■ **AURORA UNIVERSITY** *D-14*
347 South Gladstone Ave.
Aurora, IL 60506-4892
Tel: (630)892-6431
Free: 800-742-5281
Admissions: (630)844-5533
Fax: (630)844-5535
E-mail: admissions@aurora.edu
Web Site: http://www.aurora.edu/

Description: Independent, comprehensive, coed. Awards bachelor's, master's, and doctoral degrees and post-master's certificates. Founded 1893. Setting: 26-acre suburban campus with easy access to Chicago. Endowment: $26 million. Educational spending for 2005 fiscal year: $7965 per student. Total enrollment: 3,556. Faculty: 271 (95 full-time, 176 part-time). Student-undergrad faculty ratio is 17:1. 1,405 applied, 74% were admitted. 10% from top 10% of their high school class, 36% from top quarter, 70% from top half. Full-time: 1,686 students, 66% women, 34% men. Part-time: 221 students, 68% women, 32% men. Students come from 21 states and territories, 1 other country, 6% from out-of-state, 0.3% Native American, 12% Hispanic, 13% black, 2% Asian American or Pacific Islander, 0.1% international, 23% 25 or older, 30% live on campus, 15% transferred in. Retention: 71% of full-time freshmen returned the following year. Academic areas with the most degrees conferred: business/marketing; education; health professions and related sciences. Core. Calendar: trimesters. Academic remediation for entering students, services for LD students, advanced placement, self-designed majors, honors program, independent study, double major, summer session for credit, part-time degree program, adult/continuing education programs, internships, graduate courses open to undergrads. Off campus study at 3 members of the Council of West Suburban Colleges. Study abroad program.

Entrance Requirements: Options: Peterson's Universal Application, Common Application, electronic application, deferred admission. Required: high school transcript, minimum 2.0 high school GPA. Recommended: essay, interview. Required for some: essay, 2 recommendations, interview. Entrance: moderately difficult. Application deadline: Rolling. Notification: continuous.

Costs Per Year: Application fee: $25. Comprehensive fee: $22,770 includes full-time tuition ($16,080), mandatory fees ($100), and college room and board ($6590). College room only: $2994. Part-time tuition: $495 per semester hour.

Collegiate Environment: Orientation program. Drama-theater group, choral group, student-run newspaper. Social organizations: 20 open to all; national fraternities, national sororities, local fraternities, local sororities; 1% of eligible men and 3% of eligible women are members. Most popular organiza-

tions: Black Student Association, Aurora University Student Association, Student Nursing Association, Social Work Association. Major annual events: homecoming, Parents' Weekend, Wellness Fair. Student services: health clinic, personal-psychological counseling. Campus security: 24-hour patrols, late night transport-escort service, controlled dormitory access. Option: coed housing available. Charles B. Phillips Library plus 1 other with 115,642 books, 220,042 microform titles, 748 serials, 6,015 audiovisual materials, an OPAC, and a Web page. Operations spending for 2004 fiscal year: $743,772. 90 computers available on campus for general student use. A campuswide network can be accessed from student residence rooms and from off campus. Staffed computer lab on campus.

Community Environment: Aurora is a large suburb in the Chicago metropolitan area but retains its own distinctive community life and atmosphere. The city is located in the Fox River Valley, 40 miles west of Chicago. Aurora is a city of schools, churches, libraries, and beautiful homes. Phillips Park provides facilities for tennis, swimming and golf.

■ **BENEDICTINE UNIVERSITY** *D-15*
5700 College Rd.
Lisle, IL 60532-0900
Tel: (630)829-6000; 888-829-6363
Admissions: (630)829-6306
Fax: (630)960-1126
Web Site: http://www.ben.edu/

Description: Independent Roman Catholic, comprehensive, coed. Awards associate, bachelor's, master's, and doctoral degrees. Founded 1887. Setting: 108-acre suburban campus with easy access to Chicago. Endowment: $20.4 million. Educational spending for 2005 fiscal year: $5980 per student. Total enrollment: 3,400. Faculty: 353 (87 full-time, 266 part-time). Student-undergrad faculty ratio is 12:1. 972 applied, 82% were admitted. 20% from top 10% of their high school class, 45% from top quarter, 74% from top half. 4 valedictorians. Full-time: 1,518 students, 57% women, 43% men. Part-time: 802 students, 65% women, 35% men. Students come from 23 states and territories, 7 other countries, 2% from out-of-state, 0.3% Native American, 7% Hispanic, 10% black, 14% Asian American or Pacific Islander, 1% international, 29% 25 or older, 24% live on campus, 10% transferred in. Retention: 76% of full-time freshmen returned the following year. Academic areas with the most degrees conferred: business/marketing; health professions and related sciences; psychology. Core. Calendar: semesters. Academic remediation for entering students, services for LD students, advanced placement, accelerated degree program, honors program, independent study, distance learning, double major, summer session for credit, part-time degree program, adult/continuing education programs, internships, graduate courses open to undergrads. Off campus study at 3 members of the Council of West Suburban Colleges. Study abroad program. ROTC: Army (c).

Entrance Requirements: Options: Peterson's Universal Application, Common Application, electronic application, deferred admission. Required: essay, high school transcript, recommendations, ACT. Recommended: rank in upper 50% of high school class, ACT score of 21. Required for some: interview. Entrance: moderately difficult. Application deadline: Rolling. Notification: continuous.

Costs Per Year: Application fee: $40. Comprehensive fee: $25,810 includes full-time tuition ($18,700), mandatory fees ($510), and college room and board ($6600). Full-time tuition and fees vary according to class time, degree level, and location. Room and board charges vary according to board plan and housing facility. Part-time tuition: $630 per credit hour. Part-time mandatory fees: $15 per credit hour. Part-time tuition and fees vary according to class time and degree level.

Collegiate Environment: Orientation program. Choral group, student-run newspaper. Social organizations: 38 open to all. Most popular organizations: Student Government Association, campus ministry, choir/gospel choir. Major annual events: homecoming, Quad Day, Spring Fest. Student services: health clinic, personal-psychological counseling. Campus security: 24-hour emergency response devices and patrols, late night transport-escort service, controlled dormitory access. Freshmen guaranteed college housing. Options: coed, men-only, women-only housing available. Benedictine Library with an OPAC and a Web page.

Community Environment: Lisle (population 19,000) is a suburban city located in Greater Chicago between Downers Grove and Naperville; it enjoys a temperate climate. Trains and buses serve the area. Ten shopping centers are located within 10 miles of the campus. Part-time employment is available for students. Recreational activities include varsity and intramural sports. Lisle is the home of the world famous Morton Arboretum. Benedictine University is located in DuPage County, one of the fastest growing areas in the Midwest.

■ BLACK HAWK COLLEGE *E-7*
6600 34th Ave.
Moline, IL 61265-5899
Tel: (309)796-5000
Admissions: (309)796-5043
Web Site: http://www.bhc.edu/

Description: State and locally supported, 2-year, coed. Part of Black Hawk College District System. Awards certificates, transfer associate, and terminal associate degrees. Founded 1946. Setting: 161-acre urban campus. Educational spending for 2005 fiscal year: $2593 per student. Total enrollment: 6,600. 5% from top 10% of their high school class, 18% from top quarter, 49% from top half. Full-time: 3,138 students, 57% women, 43% men. Part-time: 3,462 students, 65% women, 35% men. Students come from 5 states and territories, 3% from out-of-state, 0.5% Native American, 7% Hispanic, 7% black, 1% Asian American or Pacific Islander, 0% international, 43% 25 or older, 0.1% transferred in. Retention: 62% of full-time freshmen returned the following year. Core. Calendar: semesters. Academic remediation for entering students, ESL program, services for LD students, advanced placement, accelerated degree program, independent study, distance learning, summer session for credit, part-time degree program, adult/continuing education programs, co-op programs and internships. Off campus study at Scott Community College, WEIC. Study abroad program.

Entrance Requirements: Open admission except for nursing and allied health programs. Options: early admission, deferred admission. Required: high school transcript. Placement: ACT, COMPASS required for some. Entrance: noncompetitive. Application deadline: Rolling. Notification: continuous.

Costs Per Year: Application fee: $0. Area resident tuition: $1860 full-time, $62 per credit hour part-time. State resident tuition: $4200 full-time, $140 per credit hour part-time. Nonresident tuition: $7770 full-time, $259 per credit hour part-time. Mandatory fees: $210 full-time, $7 per credit hour part-time. Full-time tuition and fees vary according to program and reciprocity agreements. Part-time tuition and fees vary according to program and reciprocity agreements.

Collegiate Environment: Orientation program. Drama-theater group, choral group, student-run newspaper. Student services: personal-psychological counseling. Campus security: 24-hour patrols. College housing not available. Quad City Campus Library plus 1 other with 59,840 books, 8,340 microform titles, 612 serials, 140 audiovisual materials, and an OPAC. Operations spending for 2004 fiscal year: $581,228. 822 computers available on campus for general student use. Computer purchase/lease plans available. A campuswide network can be accessed from off-campus. Staffed computer lab on campus.

■ BLACKBURN COLLEGE *P-9*
700 College Ave.
Carlinville, IL 62626-1498
Tel: (217)854-3231
Free: 800-233-3550
Fax: (217)854-3713
E-mail: jmali@mail.blackburn.edu
Web Site: http://www.blackburn.edu/

Description: Independent Presbyterian, 4-year, coed. Awards bachelor's degrees. Founded 1837. Setting: 80-acre small town campus with easy access to St. Louis. Endowment: $10.4 million. Educational spending for 2005 fiscal year: $3474 per student. Total enrollment: 590. 916 applied, 56% were admitted. 13% from top 10% of their high school class, 41% from top quarter, 81% from top half. 8 class presidents, 9 valedictorians, 14 student government officers. Full-time: 580 students, 55% women, 45% men. Part-time: 10 students, 80% women, 20% men. Students come from 12 states and territories, 8 other countries, 1% Native American, 1% Hispanic, 8% black, 1% Asian American or Pacific Islander, 3% international. Retention: 65% of full-time freshmen returned the following year. Core. Calendar: semesters. Advanced placement, self-designed majors, honors program, independent study, double major, part-time degree program, co-op programs and internships. Off campus study at American University. Study abroad program.

Entrance Requirements: Options: electronic application, deferred admission. Required: essay, high school transcript, minimum 2.0 high school GPA,

SAT or ACT. Required for some: 1 recommendation, interview. Entrance: moderately difficult. Application deadline: Rolling.

Costs Per Year: Application fee: $0. Comprehensive fee: $16,628 includes full-time tuition ($12,733) and college room and board ($3895). College room only: $1795. Full-time tuition varies according to program. Room and board charges vary according to board plan. Part-time tuition: $501 per semester hour.

Collegiate Environment: Orientation program. Drama-theater group, choral group, student-run newspaper. Social organizations: 31 open to all. Most popular organizations: Cultural Expressions, Residence Hall Association, New Student Orientation Committee, choral groups, student government. Major annual events: Academic Honors Banquet, Founder's Day Convocation, President's Convocation. Student services: personal-psychological counseling. Campus security: student patrols, late night transport-escort service. 475 college housing spaces available; 425 were occupied in 2003-04. Freshmen guaranteed college housing. On-campus residence required through junior year. Options: coed, men-only, women-only housing available. Lumpkin Library with 61,586 books, 10,844 microform titles, 79 serials, and 1,181 audiovisual materials. Operations spending for 2004 fiscal year: $148,304. 202 computers available on campus for general student use. A campuswide network can be accessed from student residence rooms and from off campus. Staffed computer lab on campus.

■ BLESSING-RIEMAN COLLEGE OF NURSING *M-4*
Broadway at 11th St., POB 7005
Quincy, IL 62305-7005
Tel: (217)228-5520
Free: 800-877-9140
Fax: (217)223-6400
E-mail: aosullivan@brcn.edu
Web Site: http://www.brcn.edu/

Description: Independent, 4-year, coed. Awards bachelor's degrees. Founded 1985. Setting: 1-acre small town campus. Endowment: $7 million. Educational spending for 2005 fiscal year: $3805 per student. Total enrollment: 211. Student-undergrad faculty ratio is 13:1. 46 applied, 63% were admitted. 23% from top 10% of their high school class, 72% from top quarter, 100% from top half. Full-time: 193 students, 93% women, 7% men. Part-time: 18 students, 94% women, 6% men. Students come from 7 states and territories, 34% from out-of-state, 0.5% Native American, 0.5% Hispanic, 2% black, 4% Asian American or Pacific Islander, 0% international, 29% 25 or older, 82% live on campus, 19% transferred in. Retention: 86% of full-time freshmen returned the following year. Academic area with the most degrees conferred: health professions and related sciences. Core. Calendar: semesters. Academic remediation for entering students, advanced placement, honors program, distance learning, double major, summer session for credit, part-time degree program, adult/continuing education programs, internships.

Entrance Requirements: Options: Peterson's Universal Application, electronic application, deferred admission. Required: high school transcript, minimum 3.0 high school GPA, SAT or ACT. Recommended: essay, interview. Entrance: moderately difficult. Application deadline: Rolling.

Costs Per Year: Application fee: $0. Comprehensive fee: $20,025 includes full-time tuition ($13,900), mandatory fees ($350), and college room and board ($5775). Full-time tuition and fees vary according to course load, location, and student level. Room and board charges vary according to location.

Collegiate Environment: Orientation program. Drama-theater group, choral group, student-run newspaper, radio station. Social organizations: national fraternities, national sororities; 30% of women are members. Most popular organization: Student Nurses Organization. Major annual events: Teddy Bear Clinic, Health Fair, Convocation. Student services: health clinic, personal-psychological counseling. Campus security: 24-hour patrols, late night transport-escort service, controlled dormitory access. 40 college housing spaces available; 26 were occupied in 2003-04. Freshmen guaranteed college housing. On-campus residence required through sophomore year. Option: coed housing available. Blessing Health Professions Library plus 1 other with 4,282 books, 123 serials, 656 audiovisual materials, an OPAC, and a Web page. Operations spending for 2004 fiscal year: $60,000. 23 computers available on campus for general student use. A campuswide network can be accessed. Staffed computer lab on campus.

■ BRADLEY UNIVERSITY *I-10*
1501 West Bradley Ave.
Peoria, IL 61625-0002
Tel: (309)676-7611

Free: 800-447-6460
Admissions: (309)677-3144
E-mail: admissions@bradley.edu
Web Site: http://www.bradley.edu/

Description: Independent, comprehensive, coed. Awards bachelor's, master's, and first professional degrees. Founded 1897. Setting: 75-acre urban campus with easy access to Chicago and St. Louis. Endowment: $193.5 million. Research spending for 2004 fiscal year: $5.3 million. Educational spending for 2005 fiscal year: $7550 per student. Total enrollment: 6,154. Faculty: 550 (326 full-time, 224 part-time). Student-undergrad faculty ratio is 14:1. 4,218 applied, 91% were admitted. 28% from top 10% of their high school class, 59% from top quarter, 91% from top half. 2 National Merit Scholars, 41 valedictorians. Full-time: 5,055 students, 55% women, 45% men. Part-time: 314 students, 59% women, 41% men. Students come from 44 states and territories, 31 other countries, 11% from out-of-state, 0.1% Native American, 2% Hispanic, 6% black, 3% Asian American or Pacific Islander, 1% international, 7% 25 or older, 42% live on campus, 7% transferred in. Retention: 87% of full-time freshmen returned the following year. Academic areas with the most degrees conferred: business/marketing; communications/journalism; engineering. Core. Calendar: semesters. Academic remediation for entering students, advanced placement, accelerated degree program, self-designed majors, honors program, independent study, distance learning, double major, summer session for credit, part-time degree program, adult/continuing education programs, co-op programs and internships, graduate courses open to undergrads. Off campus study at Georgetown University. Study abroad program. ROTC: Army.

Entrance Requirements: Options: Common Application, electronic application, early admission, deferred admission, international baccalaureate accepted. Required: essay, high school transcript, recommendations, SAT or ACT. Recommended: minimum 3.0 high school GPA, interview. Entrance: moderately difficult. Application deadline: Rolling. Notification: continuous.

Costs Per Year: Application fee: $35. Comprehensive fee: $25,280 includes full-time tuition ($18,700), mandatory fees ($130), and college room and board ($6450). College room only: $3700. Full-time tuition and fees vary according to program. Room and board charges vary according to board plan. Part-time tuition: $510 per credit. Part-time tuition varies according to course load.

Collegiate Environment: Orientation program. Drama-theater group, choral group, student-run newspaper, radio station. Social organizations: 220 open to all; national fraternities, national sororities; 28% of eligible men and 25% of eligible women are members. Most popular organizations: Alpha Phi Omega, Student Activities Council, Student Action for Environment, Investment Club, Student Senate. Major annual events: All School Picnic, International Night, Activities Fair. Student services: health clinic, personal-psychological counseling. Campus security: 24-hour emergency response devices and patrols, late night transport-escort service, controlled dormitory access, bicycle patrol. 3,395 college housing spaces available; 3,270 were occupied in 2003-04. Freshmen guaranteed college housing. On-campus residence required through sophomore year. Option: coed housing available. Cullom-Davis Library with 435,394 books, 809,009 microform titles, 1,724 serials, 9,889 audiovisual materials, an OPAC, and a Web page. Operations spending for 2004 fiscal year: $2.4 million. 2,000 computers available on campus for general student use. A campuswide network can be accessed from student residence rooms and from off campus. Staffed computer lab on campus.

Community Environment: Bradley benefits tremendously from its location in Peoria, the state's second largest metropolitan area. (350,000) Students find manifold opportunities in terms of professional internships, cooperative education programs, research opportunities, social and cultural life and employment, and they also benefit from adjunct professors employed in various professors employed in various Peoria area businesses, professions, and other organizations. Peoria is a mecca for the arts and medical sciences. The city's three major health care facilities and the University of Illinois School of Medicine are known collectively as the Downstate Medical Center of Illinois. Together they have built one of the most modern, comprehensive health systems in the Midwest. With a symphony orchestra, civic opera, ballet company and a rich theater and gallery life, Peoria is the center of arts activity in central Illinois. Peoria is blessed with natural beauty, clean air and water, numerous parks, an all-season sports arena and a wealth of recreational opportunities. Peoria is within easy driving distance of two great cities: Three hours from Chicago and from St. Louis.

■ **CAREER COLLEGES OF CHICAGO** *D-16*
11 East Adams St., 2nd Floor
Chicago, IL 60603-6301

Tel: (312)895-6300
Admissions: (312)895-6217
Fax: (312)895-6301
Web Site: http://www.careerchi.com/

Description: Proprietary, 2-year, coed. Awards certificates and terminal associate degrees. Founded 1950. Setting: urban campus. Total enrollment: 144. 26 applied, 100% were admitted. Full-time: 35 students, 80% women, 20% men. Part-time: 109 students, 88% women, 12% men. 0% from out-of-state, 71% 25 or older. Core. Advanced placement, summer session for credit, part-time degree program, internships.

Entrance Requirements: Open admission. Option: deferred admission. Required: high school transcript, interview. Recommended: ACT. Entrance: noncompetitive. Application deadline: Rolling.

Collegiate Environment: Major annual events: Holiday Party, Professional Day. Campus security: 24-hour emergency response devices, guard on duty during building hours. College housing not available. Main library plus 1 other with 1,000 books and 10 serials. 46 computers available on campus for general student use. Staffed computer lab on campus.

■ **CARL SANDBURG COLLEGE** *H-7*
2400 Tom L. Wilson Blvd.
Galesburg, IL 61401-9576
Tel: (309)344-2518
Admissions: (309)341-5234
Fax: (309)344-1395
Web Site: http://www.sandburg.edu/

Description: State and locally supported, 2-year, coed. Part of Illinois Community College Board. Awards certificates, transfer associate, and terminal associate degrees. Founded 1967. Setting: 105-acre small town campus with easy access to Peoria. Educational spending for 2005 fiscal year: $1150 per student. Total enrollment: 5,290. Students come from 5 states and territories, 2 other countries, 0.3% Native American, 2% Hispanic, 4% black, 0.5% Asian American or Pacific Islander, 0.4% international. Calendar: semesters. Academic remediation for entering students, ESL program, services for LD students, advanced placement, self-designed majors, summer session for credit, part-time degree program, adult/continuing education programs, co-op programs and internships. ROTC: Army (c).

Entrance Requirements: Open admission for district residents. Options: early admission, deferred admission. Required: high school transcript. Placement: ACT ASSET required. Entrance: noncompetitive. Application deadline: Rolling.

Collegiate Environment: Drama-theater group, choral group. Student services: personal-psychological counseling. Campus security: 24-hour emergency response devices and patrols. College housing not available. Learning Resource Center plus 1 other with 39,900 books and 290 serials. 110 computers available on campus for general student use. Staffed computer lab on campus.

Community Environment: Galesburg (population 36,290), once selected as one of the four ideal American cities by noted editor and author, Edward Bok, is located 180 miles southwest of Chicago on the main lines of the Burlington and Santa Fe Railroads. The Carl Sandburg birthplace preserves the early home of the poet and contains interesting Sandburg and Lincoln memoirs.

■ **CHICAGO STATE UNIVERSITY** *D-16*
9501 South King Dr.
Chicago, IL 60628
Tel: (773)995-2000
Admissions: (773)995-2513
Web Site: http://www.csu.edu/

Description: State-supported, comprehensive, coed. Awards bachelor's, master's, and doctoral degrees. Founded 1867. Setting: 161-acre urban campus. Endowment: $1.9 million. Research spending for 2005 fiscal year: $2.6 million. Educational spending for 2005 fiscal year: $2967 per student. Total enrollment: 7,131. Faculty: 462 (307 full-time, 155 part-time). Student-undergrad faculty ratio is 14:1. 2,997 applied, 51% were admitted. 11% from top 10% of their high school class, 32% from top quarter, 63% from top half. Full-time: 3,456 students, 70% women, 30% men. Part-time: 1,704 students, 76% women, 24% men. Students come from 32 states and territories, 9 other countries, 2% from out-of-state, 0.1% Native American, 6% Hispanic, 87% black, 1% Asian American or Pacific Islander, 1% international, 54% 25 or older, 7% live on campus, 12% transferred in. Retention: 53% of full-time freshmen returned the following year. Academic areas with the most degrees conferred: liberal arts/general studies; business/marketing; psychology.

Core. Calendar: semesters. Academic remediation for entering students, advanced placement, accelerated degree program, self-designed majors, honors program, distance learning, double major, summer session for credit, part-time degree program, external degree program, adult/continuing education programs, co-op programs and internships, graduate courses open to undergrads. Study abroad program. ROTC: Army, Naval (c), Air Force (c).

Entrance Requirements: Options: Peterson's Universal Application, electronic application. Required: high school transcript, minimum 2.0 high school GPA. Recommended: SAT or ACT. Required for some: essay, interview. Entrance: minimally difficult. Notification: continuous.

Costs Per Year: Application fee: $25. State resident tuition: $5670 full-time, $189 per credit hour part-time. Nonresident tuition: $11,280 full-time, $376 per credit hour part-time. Mandatory fees: $1468 full-time, $227 per term part-time. College room and board: $6492.

Collegiate Environment: Orientation program. Drama-theater group, student-run newspaper, radio station. Social organizations: 75 open to all; national fraternities, national sororities, local fraternities, local sororities. Most popular organizations: Math/Computer Science Club, Geographic Society Club, gospel choir, Movie Club. Student services: health clinic, personal-psychological counseling, women's center. Campus security: 24-hour emergency response devices and patrols, student patrols, controlled dormitory access. 328 college housing spaces available; 311 were occupied in 2003-04. Option: coed housing available. Paul and Emily Douglas Library with 320,000 books, 587,812 microform titles, 1,539 serials, 7,887 audiovisual materials, an OPAC, and a Web page. Operations spending for 2004 fiscal year: $3.2 million. 75 computers available on campus for general student use. A campuswide network can be accessed from student residence rooms and from off campus. Staffed computer lab on campus.

Community Environment: See University of Chicago.

■ **CHRISTIAN LIFE COLLEGE** *C-15*
400 East Gregory St.
Mount Prospect, IL 60056
Tel: (847)259-1840
E-mail: jspenner@christianlifecollege.edu
Web Site: http://www.christianlifecollege.edu/
Description: Independent religious, 4-year, coed. Awards associate and bachelor's degrees. Total enrollment: 80. 14 applied, 57% were admitted. Full-time: 47 students, 32% women, 68% men. Part-time: 33 students, 61% women, 39% men. 0% Native American, 8% Hispanic, 4% black, 4% Asian American or Pacific Islander, 9% international. Retention: 62% of full-time freshmen returned the following year.

■ **CITY COLLEGES OF CHICAGO, HAROLD WASHINGTON COLLEGE** *D-16*
30 East Lake St.
Chicago, IL 60601-2449
Tel: (312)553-5600
Admissions: (312)553-6006
Fax: (312)553-6077
Web Site: http://hwashington.ccc.edu/
Description: State and locally supported, 2-year, coed. Part of City Colleges of Chicago. Awards certificates, transfer associate, and terminal associate degrees. Founded 1962. Setting: 1-acre urban campus. Research spending for 2004 fiscal year: $85,131. Educational spending for 2005 fiscal year: $4080 per student. Total enrollment: 8,434. Full-time: 2,608 students, 56% women, 44% men. Part-time: 5,826 students, 59% women, 41% men. Students come from 3 states and territories, 1% Native American, 19% Hispanic, 47% black, 11% Asian American or Pacific Islander, 0% international, 57% 25 or older, 6% transferred in. Core. Calendar: semesters. Academic remediation for entering students, ESL program, services for LD students, advanced placement, accelerated degree program, independent study, distance learning, double major, summer session for credit, part-time degree program, adult/continuing education programs, co-op programs and internships. Off campus study at Governors State University, Roosevelt University.

Entrance Requirements: Open admission. Options: early admission, deferred admission. Placement: DTLS, DTMS required. Entrance: noncompetitive. Application deadline: Rolling. Notification: continuous.

Collegiate Environment: Orientation program. Drama-theater group, choral group, student-run newspaper. Social organizations: 22 open to all. Most popular organizations: Phi Theta Kappa, Organization of Latin American Students, Black Student Union, Student Government Association, Global Friendship. Major annual events: Black History Month activities, Hispanic-

American History Month, Women's History Month. Student services: personal-psychological counseling, women's center. Campus security: 24-hour emergency response devices and patrols. College housing not available. Harold Washington College Library plus 1 other with 65,926 books, 8,980 microform titles, 360 serials, and 2,695 audiovisual materials. Operations spending for 2004 fiscal year: $818,867. 360 computers available on campus for general student use. Staffed computer lab on campus.

Community Environment: See University of Chicago.

■ **CITY COLLEGES OF CHICAGO, HARRY S. TRUMAN COLLEGE** *D-16*
1145 West Wilson Ave.
Chicago, IL 60640-5616
Tel: (773)907-4000
Admissions: (773)907-4720
Fax: (773)907-4464
Web Site: http://www.trumancollege.cc/
Description: State and locally supported, 2-year, coed. Part of City Colleges of Chicago. Awards certificates, diplomas, transfer associate, and terminal associate degrees. Founded 1956. Setting: 5-acre urban campus. Total enrollment: 32,859. 0% from out-of-state, 70% 25 or older. Retention: 25% of full-time freshmen returned the following year. Core. Calendar: semesters. Academic remediation for entering students, ESL program, services for LD students, advanced placement, honors program, distance learning, summer session for credit, part-time degree program, adult/continuing education programs, co-op programs and internships.

Entrance Requirements: Open admission. Options: Common Application, early admission, deferred admission. Placement: ACT required. Entrance: noncompetitive. Application deadline: Rolling. Notification: continuous until 9/8.

Collegiate Environment: Orientation program. Drama-theater group. Social organizations: 40 open to all. Student services: personal-psychological counseling. Campus security: 24-hour patrols, late night transport-escort service. College housing not available. 59,750 books and 250 serials. 150 computers available on campus for general student use. Staffed computer lab on campus.

Community Environment: See University of Chicago.

■ **CITY COLLEGES OF CHICAGO, KENNEDY-KING COLLEGE** *D-16*
6800 South Wentworth Ave.
Chicago, IL 60621-3733
Tel: (773)602-5000
Admissions: (773)602-5080
Web Site: http://kennedyking.ccc.edu/
Description: State and locally supported, 2-year, coed. Part of City Colleges of Chicago. Awards certificates, transfer associate, and terminal associate degrees. Founded 1935. Setting: 18-acre urban campus. Endowment: $14.1 million. Educational spending for 2005 fiscal year: $2645 per student. Total enrollment: 3,054. Students come from 51 states and territories, 0% from out-of-state, 48% 25 or older. Core. Calendar: semesters. Academic remediation for entering students, ESL program, advanced placement, honors program, distance learning, summer session for credit, part-time degree program, adult/continuing education programs, co-op programs and internships.

Entrance Requirements: Open admission. Option: electronic application. Required: high school transcript. Placement: SAT or ACT recommended. Entrance: noncompetitive. Application deadline: Rolling. Preference given to city residents.

Collegiate Environment: Orientation program. Drama-theater group, choral group, student-run newspaper, radio station. Social organizations: 12 open to all; national fraternities; 1% of men are members. Most popular organizations: Phi Theta Kappa, Phi Beta Lambda, Herman Bryant Auto Club, Communication Art Guild, POP (print club). Major annual events: Freshmen Reception, Honors Convocation, Career Week. Student services: personal-psychological counseling. Campus security: late night transport-escort service. College housing not available. Harold Washington College Library with 45,000 books, 200 serials, 2,500 audiovisual materials, an OPAC, and a Web page. 700 computers available on campus for general student use. A campuswide network can be accessed. Staffed computer lab on campus.

Community Environment: See University of Chicago.

■ **CITY COLLEGES OF CHICAGO, MALCOLM X COLLEGE** *D-16*
1900 West Van Buren St.
Chicago, IL 60612-3145

Tel: (312)850-7000
Admissions: (312)850-7120
Fax: (312)850-7092
Web Site: http://malcolmx.ccc.edu/
Description: State and locally supported, 2-year, coed. Part of City Colleges of Chicago. Awards certificates, transfer associate, and terminal associate degrees. Founded 1911. Setting: 20-acre urban campus. Total enrollment: 8,024. 861 applied, 100% were admitted. Full-time: 4,069 students, 66% women, 34% men. Part-time: 3,955 students, 66% women, 34% men. 1% Native American, 12% Hispanic, 79% black, 4% Asian American or Pacific Islander, 0% international, 55% 25 or older. Core. Calendar: semesters. Academic remediation for entering students, ESL program, services for LD students, advanced placement, distance learning, summer session for credit, part-time degree program, adult/continuing education programs, co-op programs.
Entrance Requirements: Open admission except for allied health programs. Options: Common Application, early admission, deferred admission. Required: high school transcript, minimum 2.0 high school GPA. Required for some: essay, interview. Entrance: noncompetitive. Application deadline: Rolling. Notification: continuous. Preference given to state residents.
Collegiate Environment: Orientation program. Student-run newspaper. Social organizations: 11 open to all. Most popular organizations: Student Government Association, Phi Theta Kappa Honor Society, Phi Beta Lambda business organization, Chess Club, Latino Leadership Council. Major annual events: Homecoming Parade, African-American History Month, Hispanic Heritage Month. Student services: personal-psychological counseling. Campus security: 24-hour emergency response devices and patrols. College housing not available. The Carter G. Woodson Library with 50,000 books, 250 serials, 300 audiovisual materials, an OPAC, and a Web page. Operations spending for 2004 fiscal year: $69,081. 275 computers available on campus for general student use. A campuswide network can be accessed. Staffed computer lab on campus.
Community Environment: See University of Chicago.

■ **CITY COLLEGES OF CHICAGO, OLIVE-HARVEY COLLEGE** *D-16*
10001 South Woodlawn Ave.
Chicago, IL 60628-1645
Tel: (773)291-6100
Admissions: (773)291-6349
Fax: (773)291-6304
E-mail: madams@ccc.edu
Web Site: http://oliveharvey.ccc.edu/
Description: State and locally supported, 2-year, coed. Part of City Colleges of Chicago. Awards certificates, transfer associate, and terminal associate degrees. Founded 1970. Setting: 67-acre urban campus. Total enrollment: 1,697. 54% 25 or older. Core. Calendar: semesters. Academic remediation for entering students, services for LD students, advanced placement, accelerated degree program, honors program, summer session for credit, part-time degree program, adult/continuing education programs, co-op programs. Study abroad program. ROTC: Air Force (c).
Entrance Requirements: Open admission except for nursing, computer electronics, respiratory care programs. Options: Common Application, early admission, deferred admission. Required: high school transcript. Recommended: minimum 2.0 high school GPA. Entrance: noncompetitive. Application deadline: Rolling. Preference given to city residents.
Costs Per Year: Application fee: $0. Area resident tuition: $72 per credit part-time. State resident tuition: $180.83 per credit part-time. Nonresident tuition: $291.61 per credit part-time. Mandatory fees: $250 per year part-time.
Collegiate Environment: Drama-theater group. Social organizations: 9 open to all. Most popular organizations: Student Government Association, Club Tech, African-American Club, Phi Theta Kappa, Panther Dena. Major annual events: Oh What A Fair , awards banquet for faculty and SGA, Transfer Center College Fair. Student services: personal-psychological counseling, women's center. Campus security: 24-hour emergency response devices and patrols. College housing not available. Olga Haley Library with 56,318 books and 325 serials. Operations spending for 2004 fiscal year: $215,681.
Community Environment: See University of Chicago.

■ **CITY COLLEGES OF CHICAGO, RICHARD J. DALEY COLLEGE** *D-16*
7500 South Pulaski Rd.
Chicago, IL 60652-1242

Tel: (773)838-7500
Fax: (773)838-7524
Web Site: http://daley.ccc.edu/
Description: State and locally supported, 2-year, coed. Part of City Colleges of Chicago. Awards certificates, transfer associate, and terminal associate degrees. Founded 1960. Setting: 25-acre urban campus. Research spending for 2004 fiscal year: $50,000. Educational spending for 2005 fiscal year: $3469 per student. Total enrollment: 10,654. Full-time: 3,545 students, 64% women, 36% men. Part-time: 7,109 students, 62% women, 38% men. Students come from 29 states and territories, 71 other countries, 0.3% Native American, 42% Hispanic, 37% black, 2% Asian American or Pacific Islander, 0% international, 47% 25 or older. Core. Calendar: semesters. Academic remediation for entering students, ESL program, services for LD students, advanced placement, honors program, summer session for credit, part-time degree program, adult/continuing education programs. Off campus study at Governors State University, Chicago State University. ROTC: Air Force (c).
Entrance Requirements: Open admission except for nursing program. Options: Common Application, early admission, deferred admission. Required: high school transcript. Recommended: interview. Required for some: essay, recommendations. Placement: ACT recommended; ACT required for some. Entrance: noncompetitive. Application deadline: Rolling. Preference given to city residents.
Collegiate Environment: Drama-theater group, student-run newspaper. Most popular organizations: Latin Student Organization, Student Government Association, African-American Culture Club. Major annual event: Annual Ethnic Festival. Student services: personal-psychological counseling. Campus security: 24-hour patrols. College housing not available. Learning Resource Center plus 1 other with 53,201 books, 275 serials, and an OPAC. Operations spending for 2004 fiscal year: $550,000. 325 computers available on campus for general student use. A campuswide network can be accessed.
Community Environment: See University of Chicago.

■ **CITY COLLEGES OF CHICAGO, WILBUR WRIGHT COLLEGE** *D-16*
4300 North Narragansett Ave.
Chicago, IL 60634-1591
Tel: (773)777-7900
Admissions: (773)481-8207
Web Site: http://wright.ccc.edu/
Description: State and locally supported, 2-year, coed. Part of City Colleges of Chicago. Awards certificates, transfer associate, and terminal associate degrees. Founded 1934. Setting: 20-acre urban campus with easy access to Chicago, Illinois. Educational spending for 2005 fiscal year: $1700 per student. Total enrollment: 7,365. Student-undergrad faculty ratio is 22:1. 2,825 applied, 100% were admitted. 5% from top 10% of their high school class, 20% from top quarter, 41% from top half. 0% from out-of-state, 1% Native American, 40% Hispanic, 10% black, 10% Asian American or Pacific Islander, 43% 25 or older. Core. Calendar: semesters. Academic remediation for entering students, ESL program, accelerated degree program, distance learning, summer session for credit, part-time degree program, adult/continuing education programs.
Entrance Requirements: Open admission. Options: Common Application, early admission, deferred admission. Entrance: noncompetitive. Application deadline: Rolling. Notification: continuous. Preference given to city residents.
Costs Per Year: Application fee: $0. Area resident tuition: $2304 full-time, $72 per credit hour part-time. State resident tuition: $5787 full-time, $181 per credit hour part-time. Nonresident tuition: $9332 full-time, $292 per credit hour part-time. Mandatory fees: $250 full-time, $75 per term part-time.
Collegiate Environment: Orientation program. Drama-theater group, choral group, student-run newspaper. Social organizations: 23 open to all. Most popular organizations: student government, Circle K, Phi Theta Kappa, Black Student Union. Major annual events: Ethnic Food Fair, Hispanic-American History Month, Graduation. Student services: legal services. Campus security: 24-hour emergency response devices and patrols, student patrols, late night transport-escort service. College housing not available. Learning Resource Center plus 1 other with 60,000 books and 350 serials. Operations spending for 2004 fiscal year: $750,000. 700 computers available on campus for general student use. A campuswide network can be accessed. Staffed computer lab on campus.

■ **COLLEGE OF DUPAGE** *F-11*
425 Fawell Blvd.
Glen Ellyn, IL 60137-6599

Tel: (630)942-2800
Admissions: (630)942-2442
Fax: (630)790-2686
E-mail: protis@cdnet.cod.edu
Web Site: http://www.cod.edu/
Description: State and locally supported, 2-year, coed. Part of Illinois Community College Board. Awards certificates, transfer associate, and terminal associate degrees. Founded 1967. Setting: 297-acre suburban campus with easy access to Chicago. Endowment: $10.5 million. Educational spending for 2005 fiscal year: $3135 per student. Total enrollment: 27,117. Student-undergrad faculty ratio is 21:1. Full-time: 8,784 students, 48% women, 52% men. Part-time: 18,333 students, 58% women, 42% men. Students come from 19 states and territories, 0% from out-of-state, 0.3% Native American, 14% Hispanic, 6% black, 12% Asian American or Pacific Islander, 0% international, 34% 25 or older, 7% transferred in. Retention: 65% of full-time freshmen returned the following year. Core. Academic remediation for entering students, ESL program, services for LD students, advanced placement, accelerated degree program, self-designed majors, honors program, independent study, distance learning, double major, summer session for credit, part-time degree program, external degree program, adult/continuing education programs, co-op programs and internships. Off campus study at other colleges of the Illinois Community College System. Study abroad program.
Entrance Requirements: Open admission except for allied health programs. Options: early admission, deferred admission. Entrance: noncompetitive. Application deadline: Rolling. Notification: continuous.
Costs Per Year: Application fee: $10. Area resident tuition: $2850 full-time, $96 per semester hour part-time. State resident tuition: $6690 full-time, $223 per semester hour part-time. Nonresident tuition: $8400 full-time, $280 per semester hour part-time. Mandatory fees: $634 full-time.
Collegiate Environment: Orientation program. Drama-theater group, choral group, student-run newspaper. Social organizations: 37 open to all. Most popular organizations: Latino Ethnic Awareness Association, The Christian Group, Phi Theta Kappa, International Students Organization, Muslim Student Association. Major annual events: international students year-end cruise, Annual Pool Tournament, Street Fair. Student services: health clinic, personal-psychological counseling. Campus security: 24-hour emergency response devices and patrols, student patrols, late night transport-escort service. College housing not available. College of DuPage Library with 203,300 books, 312,000 microform titles, 6,005 serials, 33,600 audiovisual materials, an OPAC, and a Web page. Operations spending for 2004 fiscal year: $3.7 million. 2,403 computers available on campus for general student use. Computer purchase/lease plans available. A campuswide network can be accessed from off-campus. Staffed computer lab on campus.
Community Environment: Glen Ellyn is an attractive residential village with trees, rolling terrain, and well-landscaped dwellings; a suburban area near Wheaton, served by the regional commuter rail system, the shopping facilities are excellent. Glen Ellyn also has a library, YMCA, clinic in town, and hospitals nearby. Lake Ellyn is nearby for recreation, boating, swimming, etc.

■ **COLLEGE OF LAKE COUNTY** *B-15*
19351 West Washington St.
Grayslake, IL 60030-1198
Tel: (847)543-2000
Admissions: (847)543-2384
Fax: (847)223-1017
Web Site: http://www.clcillinois.edu/
Description: District-supported, 2-year, coed. Part of Illinois Community College Board. Awards certificates, transfer associate, and terminal associate degrees. Founded 1967. Setting: 226-acre suburban campus with easy access to Chicago and Milwaukee. Endowment: $2.6 million. Educational spending for 2005 fiscal year: $3301 per student. Total enrollment: 15,745. Student-undergrad faculty ratio is 20:1. 1,959 applied, 100% were admitted. 4% from top 10% of their high school class, 15% from top quarter, 41% from top half. Full-time: 4,514 students, 50% women, 50% men. Part-time: 11,231 students, 60% women, 40% men. Students come from 22 states and territories, 42 other countries, 1% from out-of-state, 0.3% Native American, 16% Hispanic, 9% black, 6% Asian American or Pacific Islander, 2% international, 41% 25 or older, 8% transferred in. Retention: 60% of full-time freshmen returned the following year. Core. Calendar: semesters. Academic remediation for entering students, ESL program, services for LD students, advanced placement, self-designed majors, honors program, independent study, distance learning, double major, summer session for credit, part-time degree program, adult/continuing education programs, co-op programs and

internships. Off campus study at McHenry County College, Gateway Technical College, Oakton Community College, William Rainey Harper College, Elgin Community College, College of DuPage. Study abroad program.
Entrance Requirements: Open admission except for health programs. Options: Common Application, electronic application, early admission, deferred admission. Required for some: high school transcript, interview. Entrance: noncompetitive. Application deadline: Rolling. Notification: continuous. Preference given to district residents.
Costs Per Year: Application fee: $0. Area resident tuition: $2130 full-time, $71 per credit hour part-time. State resident tuition: $5880 full-time, $196 per credit hour part-time. Nonresident tuition: $8010 full-time, $267 per credit hour part-time. Mandatory fees: $270 full-time, $9 per credit hour part-time.
Collegiate Environment: Orientation program. Drama-theater group, choral group, student-run newspaper, radio station. Social organizations: 31 open to all. Most popular organizations: Latino Alliance, Asian Student Alliance, Black Student Union, International Student Council, Phi Theta Kappa. Major annual events: Welcome Week activities, Spring Fling, Retro Week. Student services: health clinic, personal-psychological counseling, women's center. Campus security: 24-hour emergency response devices and patrols, late night transport-escort service. College housing not available. College of Lake County Library plus 1 other with 106,842 books, 766 serials, 7,433 audiovisual materials, an OPAC, and a Web page. Operations spending for 2004 fiscal year: $1.6 million. 1,500 computers available on campus for general student use. A campuswide network can be accessed from off-campus. Staffed computer lab on campus.
Community Environment: The college has 2 campuses. The main campus centrally located in Grayslake (population 6,400), and the second campus situated in Waukegan (population 67,600). Waukegan is situated in the northeast corner of Illinois on the scenic shores of Lake Michigan. Excellent transportation facilities are available. Waukegan is an industrial city and is part of the metropolitan area of Chicago. Two of the principal industrial products are pharmaceutical supplies and outboard motors. Community facilities include over 50 churches of various denominations and municipal libraries. Recreation and sports include fishing, swimming, skiing, and hunting in the forest preserves. There are more than 60 lakes located in the county.

■ **THE COLLEGE OF OFFICE TECHNOLOGY** *D-16*
1514-20 West Division St., Second Floor
Chicago, IL 60622
Tel: (773)278-0042
Fax: (773)278-0143
E-mail: bbolton@cotedu.com
Web Site: http://www.cotedu.com/
Description: Private, 2-year. Total enrollment: 1,010.

■ **COLUMBIA COLLEGE CHICAGO** *D-16*
600 South Michigan Ave.
Chicago, IL 60605-1996
Tel: (312)663-1600
Admissions: (312)344-7133
E-mail: admissions@colum.edu
Web Site: http://www.colum.edu/
Description: Independent, comprehensive, coed. Awards bachelor's and master's degrees. Founded 1890. Setting: urban campus. Endowment: $93.8 million. Research spending for 2004 fiscal year: $3.8 million. Total enrollment: 10,842. Faculty: 1,626 (299 full-time, 1,327 part-time). Student-undergrad faculty ratio is 14:1. 3,428 applied, 91% were admitted. 7% from top 10% of their high school class, 23% from top quarter, 50% from top half. Full-time: 8,728 students, 51% women, 49% men. Part-time: 1,416 students, 50% women, 50% men. Students come from 50 states and territories, 73 other countries, 22% from out-of-state, 1% Native American, 9% Hispanic, 14% black, 3% Asian American or Pacific Islander, 2% international, 17% 25 or older, 13% transferred in. Retention: 68% of full-time freshmen returned the following year. Academic areas with the most degrees conferred: visual and performing arts; liberal arts/general studies; communications/journalism. Core. Calendar: semesters. Academic remediation for entering students, ESL program, services for LD students, advanced placement, self-designed majors, independent study, summer session for credit, part-time degree program, internships, graduate courses open to undergrads. Off campus study at Adler Planetarium. Study abroad program.
Entrance Requirements: Open admission. Option: deferred admission. Required: high school transcript. Recommended: essay, minimum 2.0 high school GPA, interview, SAT or ACT. Entrance: noncompetitive. Application deadline: 6/15.

Costs Per Year: Application fee: $35. Comprehensive fee: $26,553 includes full-time tuition ($16,328), mandatory fees ($460), and college room and board ($9765). College room only: $8265. Part-time tuition: $565 per credit hour.

Collegiate Environment: Orientation program. Drama-theater group, choral group, student-run newspaper, radio station. Social organizations: 39 open to all. Most popular organizations: Columbia Urban Music Association, International Student Organization, Acianza Latina, Marketing Club. Major annual events: Student Organizations Day, Welcome Back Dance, CUMBA Annual Music Conference. Student services: health clinic, personal-psychological counseling. Campus security: 24-hour emergency response devices and patrols, late night transport-escort service, controlled dormitory access, escort upon request. 1,136 college housing spaces available; all were occupied in 2003-04. Freshmen given priority for college housing. On-campus residence required in freshman year. Option: coed housing available. Columbia College Library with 219,952 books, 1,150 serials, an OPAC, and a Web page. Operations spending for 2004 fiscal year: $9.8 million. 730 computers available on campus for general student use. A campuswide network can be accessed. Staffed computer lab on campus.

Community Environment: The college is located in the dynamic South Loop neighborhood. It is within walking distance of the Art Institute of Chicago, the Shedd Aquarium, major theaters, and the Orchestra Hall. Across the street from the campus are beautiful Grant Park and Lake Michigan.

■ CONCORDIA UNIVERSITY *E-14*

7400 Augusta St.
River Forest, IL 60305-1499
Tel: (708)771-8300
Free: 800-285-2668
Admissions: (708)209-3100
Fax: (708)209-3176
E-mail: crfadmis@curf.edu
Web Site: http://www.curf.edu/

Description: Independent, comprehensive, coed, affiliated with Lutheran Church-Missouri Synod. Part of Concordia University System. Awards bachelor's, master's, and doctoral degrees and post-master's certificates. Founded 1864. Setting: 40-acre suburban campus with easy access to Chicago. Endowment: $12.7 million. Research spending for 2004 fiscal year: $90,000. Educational spending for 2005 fiscal year: $5434 per student. Total enrollment: 2,783. Faculty: (80 full-time). Student-undergrad faculty ratio is 11:1. 1,005 applied, 62% were admitted. 25% from top 10% of their high school class, 50% from top quarter, 72% from top half. Full-time: 961 students, 63% women, 37% men. Part-time: 71 students, 70% women, 30% men. Students come from 22 states and territories, 1 other country, 35% from out-of-state, 7% Hispanic, 8% black, 1% Asian American or Pacific Islander, 16% 25 or older, 40% live on campus, 11% transferred in. Retention: 73% of full-time freshmen returned the following year. Academic areas with the most degrees conferred: education; business/marketing; theology and religious vocations. Core. Calendar: semesters. Academic remediation for entering students, services for LD students, advanced placement, accelerated degree program, honors program, independent study, distance learning, double major, summer session for credit, part-time degree program, adult/continuing education programs, internships, graduate courses open to undergrads. Off campus study at Chicago Consortium of Colleges and Universities, Dominican University. Study abroad program.

Entrance Requirements: Options: electronic application, deferred admission, international baccalaureate accepted. Required: high school transcript, minimum 2.0 high school GPA, 1 recommendation, minimum ACT score of 20 or SAT score of 930, SAT or ACT. Required for some: essay, interview. Entrance: moderately difficult. Application deadline: Rolling.

Costs Per Year: Comprehensive fee: $26,300 includes full-time tuition ($19,500), mandatory fees ($500), and college room and board ($6300). Full-time tuition and fees vary according to program. Part-time tuition: $585 per semester hour. Part-time mandatory fees: $10 per semester hour, $100 per year. Part-time tuition and fees vary according to program.

Collegiate Environment: Orientation program. Drama-theater group, choral group, student-run newspaper, radio station. Social organizations: 43 open to all. Most popular organizations: Concordia Youth Ministries, Kappelle Choir, Wind Symphony, student government, intramural sports. Major annual events: homecoming, Spring Formal, Chicago Experience. Student services: legal services, personal-psychological counseling. Campus security: 24-hour emergency response devices and patrols, student patrols, late night transport-escort service, emergency call boxes. 753 college housing spaces

available; 628 were occupied in 2003-04. No special consideration for freshman housing applicants. Options: coed, women-only housing available. Klinck Memorial Library with 163,711 books, 659,912 microform titles, 6,101 serials, 5,438 audiovisual materials, an OPAC, and a Web page. Operations spending for 2004 fiscal year: $432,950. 70 computers available on campus for general student use. A campuswide network can be accessed from student residence rooms and from off campus. Staffed computer lab on campus.

■ THE COOKING AND HOSPITALITY INSTITUTE OF CHICAGO *D-16*

361 West Chestnut
Chicago, IL 60610-3050
Tel: (312)944-0882
Admissions: (312)873-2064
Fax: (312)944-8557
Web Site: http://www.chicnet.org/

Description: Proprietary, 2-year, coed. Part of Career Education Corporation. Awards transfer associate and terminal associate degrees. Founded 1983. Setting: urban campus. Endowment: $35,000. Educational spending for 2005 fiscal year: $4850 per student. Total enrollment: 950. Students come from 25 states and territories, 15 other countries, 25% from out-of-state, 65% 25 or older. Core. Calendar: continuous. Academic remediation for entering students, services for LD students, advanced placement, accelerated degree program, double major, summer session for credit, adult/continuing education programs, co-op programs.

Entrance Requirements: Open admission. Options: Common Application, electronic application, deferred admission, international baccalaureate accepted. Recommended: essay, high school transcript, interview. Placement: SAT or ACT recommended. Entrance: minimally difficult.

Collegiate Environment: Student-run newspaper. Social organizations: 8 open to all. Most popular organizations: The Student Board, Culinary Competition Club, Recipe Development Association, The Cellar Club, Pastry Display Club. College housing not available. Learning Resource Center plus 1 other with 5,000 books, 100 serials, and 200 audiovisual materials. Operations spending for 2004 fiscal year: $75,000. 25 computers available on campus for general student use. A campuswide network can be accessed from off-campus. Staffed computer lab on campus.

■ DANVILLE AREA COMMUNITY COLLEGE *L-16*

2000 East Main St.
Danville, IL 61832-5199
Tel: (217)443-3222
Admissions: (217)443-8800
Fax: (217)443-8560
Web Site: http://www.dacc.cc.il.us/

Description: State and locally supported, 2-year, coed. Part of Illinois Community College Board. Awards certificates, transfer associate, and terminal associate degrees. Founded 1946. Setting: 50-acre small town campus. Endowment: $978,329. Total enrollment: 3,000. 7% from top 10% of their high school class, 25% from top quarter, 60% from top half. Students come from 4 states and territories, 1% from out-of-state, 0.1% Native American, 3% Hispanic, 10% black, 1% Asian American or Pacific Islander, 0% international, 41% 25 or older. Core. Calendar: semesters. Academic remediation for entering students, ESL program, services for LD students, advanced placement, independent study, distance learning, double major, summer session for credit, part-time degree program, adult/continuing education programs, co-op programs and internships.

Entrance Requirements: Open admission. Options: Peterson's Universal Application, early admission, deferred admission. Required: high school transcript. Placement: ACT ASSET required for some. Entrance: noncompetitive. Application deadline: Rolling.

Costs Per Year: Application fee: $0. State resident tuition: $1392 full-time, $58 per credit hour part-time. Nonresident tuition: $3600 full-time, $150 per credit hour part-time. Mandatory fees: $144 full-time, $6 per credit hour part-time.

Collegiate Environment: Choral group. Social organizations: 2 open to all. Most popular organization: choral group. Student services: personal-psychological counseling. Campus security: 24-hour patrols. College housing not available. Learning Resources Center with 50,000 books, 8,790 microform titles, 2,487 audiovisual materials, and an OPAC. 332 computers available on campus for general student use. A campuswide network can be accessed from off-campus. Staffed computer lab on campus.

Community Environment: Danville, population 39,000, is the county seat of Vermillion County situated in the eastern part of the state, four miles from the Indiana border, and 124 miles south of Chicago. Four railroads serve the area which is in the middle of the cornbelt. The city is the site of the large radio telescope used by the University of Illinois for studying signals a billion light years away. Community facilities include many churches, a newspaper, TV station, YMCA, YWCA, radio stations, and hospitals. Within the city are ten city parks. Nearby is Lake Vermillion for boating, swimming and fishing; Kickapoo State Park is also available for camping and fishing. Annual events are the All Breed Dog Show, boat races, and auto races.

■ DEPAUL UNIVERSITY *D-16*

1 East Jackson Blvd.
Chicago, IL 60604-2287
Tel: (312)362-8000
Admissions: (312)362-8650
Fax: (312)362-3322
E-mail: admitdpu@depaul.edu
Web Site: http://www.depaul.edu/

Description: Independent Roman Catholic, university, coed. Awards bachelor's, master's, doctoral, and first professional degrees and post-master's certificates. Founded 1898. Setting: 36-acre urban campus. Total enrollment: 23,148. Faculty: 1,477 (834 full-time, 643 part-time). Student-undergrad faculty ratio is 17:1. 9,779 applied, 71% were admitted. 19% from top 10% of their high school class, 43% from top quarter, 76% from top half. Full-time: 11,381 students, 57% women, 43% men. Part-time: 3,359 students, 59% women, 41% men. Students come from 50 states and territories, 74 other countries, 15% from out-of-state, 0.3% Native American, 13% Hispanic, 10% black, 9% Asian American or Pacific Islander, 1% international, 23% 25 or older, 18% live on campus, 9% transferred in. Retention: 85% of full-time freshmen returned the following year. Academic areas with the most degrees conferred: business/marketing; liberal arts/general studies; computer and information sciences. Core. Calendar: ; semesters for law school. Academic remediation for entering students, ESL program, services for LD students, advanced placement, accelerated degree program, freshman honors college, honors program, independent study, distance learning, double major, summer session for credit, part-time degree program, adult/continuing education programs, co-op programs and internships, graduate courses open to undergrads. Study abroad program. ROTC: Army (c).

Entrance Requirements: Options: Peterson's Universal Application, Common Application, electronic application, early admission, early decision, early action, deferred admission, international baccalaureate accepted. Required: high school transcript, minimum 2.0 high school GPA, 1 recommendation, SAT or ACT. Recommended: minimum 3.0 high school GPA. Required for some: minimum 3.0 high school GPA, interview, audition. Entrance: moderately difficult. Application deadlines: Rolling, 11/15 for early action. Notification: 10/15, 1/15 for early action.

Costs Per Year: Application fee: $40. Comprehensive fee: $29,905 includes full-time tuition ($20,900), mandatory fees ($140), and college room and board ($8865). College room only: $6507. Full-time tuition and fees vary according to program. Room and board charges vary according to board plan, housing facility, and location. Part-time tuition: $384 per quarter hour. Part-time tuition varies according to program.

Collegiate Environment: Orientation program. Drama-theater group, choral group, student-run newspaper. Social organizations: 120 open to all; national fraternities, national sororities; 1% of eligible men and 1% of eligible women are members. Most popular organizations: Student Ambassadors, DePaul Activities Board, DePaul Community Service Association. Major annual events: homecoming, Blues Fest, National Hunger and Homeless Awareness Week. Student services: legal services, health clinic, personal-psychological counseling, women's center. Campus security: 24-hour emergency response devices and patrols, late night transport-escort service, controlled dormitory access, security lighting, prevention/awareness programs, on-campus police officers, video cameras, smoke detectors in residence halls. 3,500 college housing spaces available; 3,000 were occupied in 2003-04. Freshmen given priority for college housing. Option: coed housing available. John T. Richardson Library plus 2 others with 896,864 books, 287,886 microform titles, 26,822 serials, 159,336 audiovisual materials, and a Web page. 1,361 computers available on campus for general student use. A campuswide network can be accessed from student residence rooms and from off campus. Staffed computer lab on campus.

Community Environment: DePaul is located in a culturally and academically rich urban environment. The downtown campus is minutes away from the Art Institute, Orchestra Hall, Lake Michigan, and the LaSalle Street business district. Because 75% of DePaul's students work to help finance their

education, they find that the downtown location provides many employment opportunities. Facilities of the Colleges of Law and Commerce have undergone extensive remodeling, and further renovations are in progress, thus ensuring DePaul's continuing commitment to the growth and development of downtown Chicago. At the Lincoln Park campus, restoration of the community has paralleled the expansion of University facilities. The potpourri of stores, theaters, musical groups, and events reflects the broad spectrum of interests of the people who live and work in the area. A short walk or local bus ride enables students to browse through neighborhoods of craft shops and fine old Victorian homes or visit the area's conservatory, zoo, and two museums.

■ DEVRY UNIVERSITY (ADDISON) *D-15*

1221 North Swift Rd.
Addison, IL 60101-6106
Tel: (630)953-1300
Free: 800-346-5420
Fax: (630)953-1236
Web Site: http://www.devry.edu/

Description: Proprietary, 4-year, coed. Part of DeVry University. Awards associate and bachelor's degrees. Founded 1982. Setting: 14-acre suburban campus with easy access to Chicago. Total enrollment: 1,577. Student-undergrad faculty ratio is 18:1. Full-time: 1,142 students, 39% women, 61% men. Part-time: 435 students, 44% women, 56% men. 0.3% Native American, 13% Hispanic, 12% black, 13% Asian American or Pacific Islander, 1% international. Academic areas with the most degrees conferred: computer and information sciences; business/marketing; engineering technologies. Calendar: semesters. Academic remediation for entering students, services for LD students, advanced placement, accelerated degree program, distance learning, summer session for credit, part-time degree program, adult/continuing education programs, co-op programs.

Entrance Requirements: Options: electronic application, deferred admission, international baccalaureate accepted. Required: high school transcript, interview. Entrance: minimally difficult. Application deadline: Rolling. Notification: continuous.

Costs Per Year: Application fee: $50. One-time mandatory fee: $40. Tuition: $11,890 full-time, $445 per credit part-time. Mandatory fees: $270 full-time, $160 per year part-time. Full-time tuition and fees vary according to course load. Part-time tuition and fees vary according to course load.

Collegiate Environment: Orientation program. Social organizations: 11 open to all. Most popular organizations: Epsilon Delta Phi (EDP), International Student Organizations (ISO), Muslim Student Association (MSA), Institute for Electric and Electronic Engineers. Major annual events: Summer Fest, Casino Night, Santa Day. Campus security: 24-hour emergency response devices, lighted pathways/sidewalks. College housing not available. Learning Resource Center with 18,500 books, 4,000 serials, 1,000 audiovisual materials, an OPAC, and a Web page. 574 computers available on campus for general student use. Computer purchase/lease plans available. A campuswide network can be accessed from off-campus. Staffed computer lab on campus.

■ DEVRY UNIVERSITY (CHICAGO) *D-16*

3300 North Campbell Ave.
Chicago, IL 60618-5994
Tel: (773)929-8500
Free: 800-383-3879
Web Site: http://www.devry.edu/

Description: Proprietary, comprehensive, coed. Part of DeVry University. Awards associate and bachelor's degrees. Founded 1931. Setting: 17-acre urban campus. Total enrollment: 2,166. Student-undergrad faculty ratio is 22:1. Full-time: 1,343 students, 39% women, 61% men. Part-time: 823 students, 46% women, 54% men. 0.2% Native American, 32% Hispanic, 37% black, 7% Asian American or Pacific Islander, 1% international. Retention: 48% of full-time freshmen returned the following year. Academic areas with the most degrees conferred: computer and information sciences; business/marketing; engineering technologies. Core. Calendar: semesters. Academic remediation for entering students, ESL program, services for LD students, advanced placement, accelerated degree program, distance learning, summer session for credit, part-time degree program, adult/continuing education programs, co-op programs.

Entrance Requirements: Options: electronic application, deferred admission, international baccalaureate accepted. Required: high school transcript, interview. Entrance: minimally difficult. Application deadline: Rolling. Notification: continuous.

Costs Per Year: Application fee: $50. One-time mandatory fee: $40. Tuition: $11,890 full-time, $445 per credit part-time. Mandatory fees: $270 full-time, $160 per year part-time. Full-time tuition and fees vary according to course load. Part-time tuition and fees vary according to course load.

Collegiate Environment: Orientation program. Social organizations: 16 open to all. Most popular organizations: DeVry Student Government Association (DSGA), DeVry Telecommunications Society, Filipinos of a Culturally-Unified Society (FOCUS), Institute of Electrical and Electronics Engineering (IEEE), Society of Mexican-American Engineers and Scientists (MAES). Major annual events: Megaflicks and Freaky Photos, Taste of Chicago, Welcome Week. Campus security: 24-hour emergency response devices and patrols, late night transport-escort service, lighted pathways/sidewalks. College housing not available. Learning Resource Center with 16,573 books, 79 serials, 1,047 audiovisual materials, an OPAC, and a Web page. 326 computers available on campus for general student use. Computer purchase/lease plans available. A campuswide network can be accessed from off-campus. Staffed computer lab on campus.

■ **DEVRY UNIVERSITY (ELGIN)** *C-14*
385 Airport Rd.
Elgin, IL 60123-9341
Tel: (847)622-1135
Fax: (847)622-1246
Web Site: http://www.devry.edu/
Description: Proprietary, comprehensive, coed. Calendar: semesters.

■ **DEVRY UNIVERSITY (GURNEE)** *B-15*
1075 Tri-State Parkway, Ste. 800
Gurnee, IL 60031-9126
Tel: (847)855-2649; (866)563-3879
Fax: (847)855-5932
Web Site: http://www.devry.edu/
Description: Proprietary, comprehensive, coed. Calendar: semesters.
Costs Per Year: One-time mandatory fee: $40. Tuition: $11,890 full-time, $445 per credit part-time. Mandatory fees: $60 full-time, $30 per year part-time. Full-time tuition and fees vary according to course load. Part-time tuition and fees vary according to course load.

■ **DEVRY UNIVERSITY (NAPERVILLE)** *D-14*
2056 Westings Ave., Ste. 40
Naperville, IL 60563-2361
Tel: (630)428-9086
Fax: (630)428-4721
Web Site: http://www.devry.edu/
Description: Proprietary, comprehensive, coed. Calendar: semesters.
Costs Per Year: One-time mandatory fee: $40. Tuition: $11,890 full-time, $445 per credit part-time. Mandatory fees: $60 full-time, $30 per year part-time. Full-time tuition and fees vary according to course load. Part-time tuition and fees vary according to course load.

■ **DEVRY UNIVERSITY (OAKBROOK TERRACE)** *F-12*
One Tower Ln.
Oakbrook Terrace, IL 60181
Tel: (630)574-1960
Web Site: http://www.devry.edu/
Description: Proprietary, comprehensive, coed. Founded 1973. Calendar: semesters.
Costs Per Year: One-time mandatory fee: $40. Tuition: $11,890 full-time, $445 per credit part-time. Mandatory fees: $60 full-time, $30 per year part-time. Full-time tuition and fees vary according to course load. Part-time tuition and fees vary according to course load.

■ **DEVRY UNIVERSITY ONLINE** *F-12*
One Tower Ln., Ste. 1000
Oakbrook Terrace, IL 60181
Tel: (630)574-1960; (866)338-7934
Fax: (630)574-1969
Web Site: http://online.devry.edu/
Description: Proprietary, comprehensive, coed. Awards associate, bachelor's, and master's degrees. Founded 2000. Total enrollment: 6,569. Faculty: 791 (all part-time). Student-undergrad faculty ratio is 16:1. Full-time: 2,146 students, 63% women, 37% men. Part-time: 2,281 students, 57% women, 43% men. 1% Native American, 7% Hispanic, 26% black, 3% Asian American or Pacific Islander, 0.3% international. Retention: 48% of full-time

freshmen returned the following year. Academic areas with the most degrees conferred: business/marketing; computer and information sciences. Calendar: semesters.
Entrance Requirements: Required: high school transcript, interview. Application deadline: Rolling. Notification: continuous.
Costs Per Year: Application fee: $50. One-time mandatory fee: $40. Tuition: $13,060 full-time. Mandatory fees: $30 full-time.

■ **DEVRY UNIVERSITY (TINLEY PARK)** *E-16*
18624 West Creek Dr.
Tinley Park, IL 60477
Tel: (708)342-3300; (866)338-7934
Web Site: http://www.devry.edu/
Description: Proprietary, comprehensive, coed. Part of DeVry University. Awards associate, bachelor's, and master's degrees. Founded 2000. Setting: 12-acre suburban campus. Total enrollment: 1,285. Faculty: 74 (33 full-time, 41 part-time). Student-undergrad faculty ratio is 20:1. Full-time: 701 students, 37% women, 63% men. Part-time: 348 students, 45% women, 55% men. 0.4% Native American, 9% Hispanic, 33% black, 3% Asian American or Pacific Islander, 1% international. Retention: 48% of full-time freshmen returned the following year. Academic areas with the most degrees conferred: computer and information sciences; business/marketing; engineering technologies. Calendar: semesters. Academic remediation for entering students, services for LD students, advanced placement, accelerated degree program, distance learning, summer session for credit, part-time degree program, adult/continuing education programs, co-op programs.
Entrance Requirements: Options: electronic application, deferred admission, international baccalaureate accepted. Required: high school transcript, interview. Entrance: minimally difficult. Application deadline: Rolling.
Costs Per Year: Application fee: $50. One-time mandatory fee: $40. Tuition: $11,890 full-time, $445 per credit part-time. Mandatory fees: $270 full-time, $160 per year part-time. Full-time tuition and fees vary according to course load. Part-time tuition and fees vary according to course load.
Collegiate Environment: Orientation program. Social organizations: 6 open to all. Most popular organizations: Institute of Electrical and Electronic Engineers (IEEE), Student Leadership, Hash Bang Slash, OGRE. Major annual event: Anniversary Celebration. Campus security: 24-hour emergency response devices, late night transport-escort service, lighted pathways/sidewalks, security patrols. College housing not available. Learning Resource Center with 17,500 books, 82 serials, 476 audiovisual materials, an OPAC, and a Web page. 504 computers available on campus for general student use. Computer purchase/lease plans available. A campuswide network can be accessed from off-campus. Staffed computer lab on campus.

■ **DOMINICAN UNIVERSITY** *E-14*
7900 West Division St.
River Forest, IL 60305-1099
Tel: (708)366-2490
Free: 800-828-8475
Admissions: (708)524-6800
Fax: (708)366-5360
E-mail: domadmis@dom.edu
Web Site: http://www.dom.edu/
Description: Independent Roman Catholic, comprehensive, coed. Awards bachelor's and master's degrees and post-master's certificates. Founded 1901. Setting: 30-acre suburban campus with easy access to Chicago. Endowment: $17.3 million. Research spending for 2004 fiscal year: $113,983. Educational spending for 2005 fiscal year: $6813 per student. Total enrollment: 3,250. Faculty: 309 (109 full-time, 200 part-time). Student-undergrad faculty ratio is 11:1. 993 applied, 81% were admitted. 24% from top 10% of their high school class, 52% from top quarter, 85% from top half. 3 valedictorians. Full-time: 1,146 students, 69% women, 31% men. Part-time: 191 students, 72% women, 28% men. Students come from 22 states and territories, 18 other countries, 11% from out-of-state, 0.1% Native American, 19% Hispanic, 7% black, 3% Asian American or Pacific Islander, 1% international, 13% 25 or older, 35% live on campus, 9% transferred in. Retention: 83% of full-time freshmen returned the following year. Academic areas with the most degrees conferred: business/marketing; social sciences; psychology. Core. Calendar: semesters. ESL program, services for LD students, advanced placement, accelerated degree program, self-designed majors, honors program, independent study, distance learning, double major, summer session for credit, part-time degree program, adult/continuing education programs, internships, graduate courses open to undergrads. Off campus study at Concordia University (IL), Illinois Institute of Technology. Study abroad program.

Entrance Requirements: Options: Common Application, deferred admission, international baccalaureate accepted. Required: essay, high school transcript, minimum 2.75 high school GPA, SAT or ACT. Recommended: recommendations, interview. Required for some: 2 recommendations, interview. Entrance: moderately difficult. Application deadline: Rolling. Notification: continuous.

Costs Per Year: Application fee: $25. Comprehensive fee: $26,370 includes full-time tuition ($19,950), mandatory fees ($100), and college room and board ($6320). Full-time tuition and fees vary according to program. Room and board charges vary according to board plan and housing facility. Part-time tuition: $665 per semester hour. Part-time mandatory fees: $10 per course. Part-time tuition and fees vary according to location and program.

Collegiate Environment: Orientation program. Drama-theater group, choral group, student-run newspaper. Social organizations: 30 open to all. Most popular organizations: student government, Torch, Center Stage, Resident Student Association, International Club. Major annual events: Candle and Rose, Spring Fling, Homecoming. Student services: health clinic, personal-psychological counseling. Campus security: 24-hour emergency response devices and patrols, student patrols, late night transport-escort service, controlled dormitory access, door alarms. 435 college housing spaces available; 425 were occupied in 2003-04. Freshmen given priority for college housing. Options: coed, men-only, women-only housing available. Rebecca Crown Library with 255,840 books, 49,610 microform titles, 14,089 serials, 4,635 audiovisual materials, an OPAC, and a Web page. Operations spending for 2004 fiscal year: $445,959. 212 computers available on campus for general student use. A campuswide network can be accessed from student residence rooms and from off campus. Staffed computer lab on campus.

Community Environment: The university is located in River Forest, a quiet, tree-lined residential suburb of Chicago; public transportation is easily accessible to downtown Chicago.

■ **EAST-WEST UNIVERSITY** *D-16*
816 South Michigan Ave.
Chicago, IL 60605-2103
Tel: (312)939-0111
Fax: (312)939-0083
Web Site: http://www.eastwest.edu/

Description: Independent, 4-year, coed. Awards associate and bachelor's degrees. Founded 1978. Setting: urban campus. Endowment: $15 million. Educational spending for 2005 fiscal year: $6092 per student. Total enrollment: 1,040. 947 applied, 90% were admitted. 8% from top 10% of their high school class, 21% from top quarter, 76% from top half. Students come from 6 states and territories, 10 other countries, 0.1% Native American, 12% Hispanic, 73% black, 1% Asian American or Pacific Islander, 11% international, 20% 25 or older. Retention: 80% of full-time freshmen returned the following year. Core. Academic remediation for entering students, independent study, double major, summer session for credit, part-time degree program, internships.

Entrance Requirements: Options: Common Application, electronic application, early decision. Required: essay, high school transcript, minimum 2.0 high school GPA, interview, ACT. Required for some: 1 recommendation. Entrance: minimally difficult. Application deadlines: Rolling, 7/1 for early decision.

Costs Per Year: Application fee: $50. Tuition: $10,950 full-time, $365 per credit hour part-time. Mandatory fees: $495 full-time. Full-time tuition and fees vary according to course level.

Collegiate Environment: Drama-theater group, choral group, student-run newspaper. College housing not available. East-West University Library with 32,000 books, 1,300 microform titles, 3,450 serials, 1,700 audiovisual materials, and an OPAC. Operations spending for 2004 fiscal year: $206,298. 130 computers available on campus for general student use. A campuswide network can be accessed from student residence rooms and from off campus. Staffed computer lab on campus.

Community Environment: Located in Chicago's South Loop (Burnham Park) District, East-West overlooks scenic Grant Park and is within walking distance of the Field Museum, Shedd Aquarium, Adler Planetarium, Art Institute and Buckingham Fountain. Also within walking distance of the University is the"Loop" (Chicago's main business and banking district) and the historic Printer's Row area. The accessibility of such cultural landmarks adds to the overall education of the students.

■ **EASTERN ILLINOIS UNIVERSITY** *O-14*
600 Lincoln Ave.
Charleston, IL 61920-3099

Tel: (217)581-5000
Free: 800-252-5711
Admissions: (217)581-2223
Fax: (217)581-7060
E-mail: bmajor@eiu.edu
Web Site: http://www.eiu.edu/

Description: State-supported, comprehensive, coed. Awards bachelor's and master's degrees and post-master's certificates. Founded 1895. Setting: 320-acre small town campus. Endowment: $33.3 million. Research spending for 2004 fiscal year: $811,115. Total enrollment: 12,129. Faculty: 755 (610 full-time, 145 part-time). Student-undergrad faculty ratio is 16:1. 7,682 applied, 78% were admitted. 8% from top 10% of their high school class, 24% from top quarter, 60% from top half. Full-time: 9,293 students, 57% women, 43% men. Part-time: 1,082 students, 67% women, 33% men. Students come from 32 states and territories, 44 other countries, 2% from out-of-state, 0.2% Native American, 2% Hispanic, 7% black, 1% Asian American or Pacific Islander, 0.5% international, 10% 25 or older, 44% live on campus, 10% transferred in. Retention: 81% of full-time freshmen returned the following year. Academic areas with the most degrees conferred: education; business/marketing; English. Core. Calendar: semesters. Academic remediation for entering students, services for LD students, advanced placement, honors program, independent study, double major, summer session for credit, part-time degree program, external degree program, adult/continuing education programs, internships, graduate courses open to undergrads. Off campus study at Olney Central College, Kaskaskia College, Parkland College, Danville Aea Community College, Richland Community College, Lakeland College. Study abroad program. ROTC: Army.

Entrance Requirements: Option: electronic application. Required: essay, high school transcript, minimum 2.25 high school GPA, audition for music program, SAT or ACT. Application deadline: Rolling. Notification: continuous.

Costs Per Year: Application fee: $30. State resident tuition: $4629 full-time, $154 per credit hour part-time. Nonresident tuition: $13,887 full-time, $463 per credit hour part-time. Mandatory fees: $1744 full-time, $63 per credit hour part-time. Full-time tuition and fees vary according to course load. Part-time tuition and fees vary according to course load. College room and board: $6196. Room and board charges vary according to board plan and housing facility.

Collegiate Environment: Orientation program. Drama-theater group, choral group, marching band, student-run newspaper, radio station. Social organizations: 137 open to all; national fraternities, national sororities; 16% of eligible men and 17% of eligible women are members. Most popular organization: Black Student Union. Major annual events: Homecoming, Arts Festival, Family Weekend. Student services: legal services, health clinic, personal-psychological counseling, women's center. Campus security: 24-hour emergency response devices and patrols, student patrols. 5,527 college housing spaces available; 4,330 were occupied in 2003-04. Freshmen guaranteed college housing. On-campus residence required in freshman year. Options: coed, men-only, women-only housing available. Booth Library with 1 million books, 1.4 million microform titles, 18,901 serials, 24,100 audiovisual materials, an OPAC, and a Web page. Operations spending for 2004 fiscal year: $4 million. 798 computers available on campus for general student use. Computer purchase/lease plans available. A campuswide network can be accessed from student residence rooms and from off campus. Staffed computer lab on campus.

Community Environment: Located in east central Illinois, 50 miles south of the University of Illinois at Urbana-Champaign, Charleston (population 20,000) is second only to Springfield in Lincoln Lore. Airline service is available at the county airport. Within the community are churches of all denominations, medical facilities, library, and motels. Part-time employment is available. Fox Ridge and Lincoln Log Cabin State Parks nearby are of historical, scenic, and recreational interest.

■ **ELGIN COMMUNITY COLLEGE** *C-14*
1700 Spartan Dr.
Elgin, IL 60123-7193
Tel: (847)697-1000
Admissions: (847)214-7414
Web Site: http://www.elgin.edu/

Description: State and locally supported, 2-year, coed. Part of Illinois Community College Board. Awards certificates, diplomas, transfer associate, and terminal associate degrees. Founded 1949. Setting: 145-acre suburban campus with easy access to Chicago. Research spending for 2004 fiscal year: $160,158. Educational spending for 2005 fiscal year: $8801 per student. Total enrollment: 10,851. Full-time: 3,348 students, 51% women,

49% men. Part-time: 7,503 students, 58% women, 42% men. Students come from 4 states and territories, 22 other countries, 1% from out-of-state, 0.2% Native American, 16% Hispanic, 5% black, 6% Asian American or Pacific Islander, 0.4% international, 51% 25 or older, 29% transferred in. Core. Calendar: semesters. Academic remediation for entering students, ESL program, services for LD students, advanced placement, accelerated degree program, self-designed majors, honors program, independent study, distance learning, double major, summer session for credit, part-time degree program, adult/continuing education programs, co-op programs and internships. Off campus study at McHenry County College, Waubonsee Community College, College of DuPage, William Rainey Harper College, Rock Valley College, Illinois Valley Community College, College of Lake County.

Entrance Requirements: Open admission except for nursing, selected health programs. Option: early admission. Required for some: high school transcript. Placement: ACT recommended. Entrance: noncompetitive. Application deadline: Rolling. Notification: continuous.

Costs Per Year: Application fee: $15. Area resident tuition: $2250 full-time, $75 per credit hour part-time. State resident tuition: $7666 full-time, $255.54 per credit hour part-time. Nonresident tuition: $9947 full-time, $331.59 per credit hour part-time. Mandatory fees: $10 full-time, $5 per term part-time.

Collegiate Environment: Orientation program. Drama-theater group, choral group, student-run newspaper. Social organizations: 29 open to all. Most popular organizations: Phi Theta Kappa, United Students of All Cultures, Organization of Latin American Students, Black Student Association, Office Administration Association. Major annual events: Welcome Week, International Week, Career Expo. Student services: legal services, personal-psychological counseling. Campus security: 24-hour patrols. College housing not available. Renner Learning Resource Center with 58,413 books, 56,000 microform titles, 458 serials, 7,394 audiovisual materials, an OPAC, and a Web page. Operations spending for 2004 fiscal year: $1 million. 1,011 computers available on campus for general student use. Computer purchase/lease plans available. A campuswide network can be accessed. Staffed computer lab on campus.

Community Environment: See Judson College.

■ **ELMHURST COLLEGE** *EE-12*
190 Prospect Ave.
Elmhurst, IL 60126-3296
Tel: (630)617-3500
Free: 800-697-1871
Admissions: (630)617-3400
Fax: (630)617-5501
E-mail: admit@elmhurst.edu
Web Site: http://www.elmhurst.edu/

Description: Independent, comprehensive, coed, affiliated with United Church of Christ. Awards bachelor's and master's degrees. Founded 1871. Setting: 38-acre suburban campus with easy access to Chicago. Endowment: $59.9 million. Educational spending for 2005 fiscal year: $7057 per student. Total enrollment: 2,670. 1,487 applied, 76% were admitted. 24% from top 10% of their high school class, 48% from top quarter, 79% from top half. Full-time: 2,129 students, 63% women, 37% men. Part-time: 355 students, 65% women, 35% men. Students come from 26 states and territories, 21 other countries, 8% from out-of-state, 0.4% Native American, 5% Hispanic, 5% black, 3% Asian American or Pacific Islander, 1% international, 22% 25 or older, 40% live on campus. Retention: 83% of full-time freshmen returned the following year. Core. Calendar: 4-1-4. Academic remediation for entering students, services for LD students, advanced placement, accelerated degree program, honors program, independent study, double major, summer session for credit, part-time degree program, adult/continuing education programs, co-op programs and internships. Off campus study. Study abroad program. ROTC: Army (c), Air Force (c).

Entrance Requirements: Options: Peterson's Universal Application, electronic application, deferred admission, international baccalaureate accepted. Required: high school transcript, SAT or ACT. Recommended: essay, interview. Required for some: essay, recommendations, interview. Entrance: moderately difficult. Application deadline: 7/15. Notification: continuous.

Costs Per Year: Application fee: $25. Comprehensive fee: $28,506 includes full-time tuition ($21,600) and college room and board ($6906). College room only: $3816. Room and board charges vary according to board plan and housing facility. Part-time tuition: $614 per semester hour.

Collegiate Environment: Orientation program. Drama-theater group, choral group, student-run newspaper, radio station. Social organizations: 100 open to all; national fraternities, national sororities, local sororities; 5% of eligible

men and 11% of eligible women are members. Most popular organizations: Programming Board and Student Government, theater and music groups, Black Student Union, residence life groups, Hablamos. Major annual events: homecoming, Orientation/Welcome Week, Spring Fling. Student services: health clinic, personal-psychological counseling. Campus security: 24-hour emergency response devices and patrols, late night transport-escort service, controlled dormitory access. 805 college housing spaces available; 796 were occupied in 2003-04. Freshmen given priority for college housing. Option: coed housing available. Buehler Library with 222,441 books, 50,605 microform titles, 2,010 serials, 7,537 audiovisual materials, an OPAC, and a Web page. Operations spending for 2004 fiscal year: $1.2 million. 345 computers available on campus for general student use. A campuswide network can be accessed from student residence rooms and from off campus. Staffed computer lab on campus.

Community Environment: A beautiful residential suburb of Chicago, 16 miles west of the Loop, Elmhurst has a population of approximately 40,000. Residents enjoy the advantages of life in a small city and the resources of a large city with its social and cultural facilities.

■ **EUREKA COLLEGE** *I-11*
300 East College Ave.
Eureka, IL 61530-1500
Tel: (309)467-3721; 888-4-EUREKA
Admissions: (309)467-6350
Fax: (309)467-6576
E-mail: admissions@eureka.edu
Web Site: http://www.eureka.edu/

Description: Independent, 4-year, coed, affiliated with Christian Church (Disciples of Christ). Awards bachelor's degrees. Founded 1855. Setting: 112-acre small town campus. Endowment: $10.7 million. Educational spending for 2005 fiscal year: $5861 per student. Total enrollment: 516. 635 applied, 75% were admitted. 17% from top 10% of their high school class, 44% from top quarter, 79% from top half. 5 class presidents, 9 valedictorians, 15 student government officers. Full-time: 505 students, 55% women, 45% men. Part-time: 11 students, 82% women, 18% men. Students come from 15 states and territories, 2 other countries, 0% Native American, 1% Hispanic, 9% black, 1% Asian American or Pacific Islander, 1% international, 5% 25 or older, 84% live on campus, 8% transferred in. Retention: 67% of full-time freshmen returned the following year. Core. Calendar: 4 8-week terms. Advanced placement, self-designed majors, honors program, independent study, double major, summer session for credit, part-time degree program, co-op programs and internships. Study abroad program.

Entrance Requirements: Options: Peterson's Universal Application, Common Application, electronic application, deferred admission. Required: high school transcript, minimum 2.3 high school GPA, 1 recommendation, minimum 17 ACT Composite, SAT or ACT. Recommended: essay, interview. Required for some: essay, 3 recommendations. Placement: SAT or ACT required. Entrance: moderately difficult. Application deadline: 8/1. Notification: continuous.

Costs Per Year: Application fee: $0. Comprehensive fee: $19,280 includes full-time tuition ($13,000), mandatory fees ($400), and college room and board ($5880). College room only: $2820. Full-time tuition and fees vary according to course load and program. Room and board charges vary according to board plan and housing facility. Part-time tuition: $375 per semester hour. Part-time tuition varies according to course load and program.

Collegiate Environment: Orientation program. Drama-theater group, choral group, student-run newspaper. Social organizations: 41 open to all; national fraternities, national sororities, local sororities; 45% of eligible men and 45% of eligible women are members. Most popular organizations: College Choral, theater, Campus Activities Board, intercollegiate athletics. Major annual events: homecoming, Greek Week. Student services: health clinic, personal-psychological counseling. Campus security: 24-hour emergency response devices, late night patrols. 534 college housing spaces available; 378 were occupied in 2003-04. Freshmen guaranteed college housing. On-campus residence required through senior year. Option: coed housing available. Melick Library with 75,000 books, 6,127 microform titles, 330 serials, 500 audiovisual materials, and an OPAC. Operations spending for 2004 fiscal year: $288,280. 95 computers available on campus for general student use. A campuswide network can be accessed from student residence rooms and from off campus. Staffed computer lab on campus.

Community Environment: A small community in central Illinois, between Bloomington and Peoria, Eureka, population 4,000, is 140 miles southwest of Chicago. The community provides a public library, churches, and a hospital. A lake more than a mile long offers boating and fishing. Part-time employment is available.

■ **FOX COLLEGE** *D-16*
4201 West 93rd St.
Oak Lawn, IL 60453
Tel: (708)636-7700; (866)636-7711
Fax: (708)636-8078
E-mail: sszala@foxcollege.edu
Web Site: http://www.foxcollege.com/
Description: Proprietary, 2-year, coed. Founded 1932. Total enrollment: 251. Full-time: 251 students, 92% women, 8% men. 0% Native American, 54% Hispanic, 8% black, 0.5% Asian American or Pacific Islander, 0% international.
Costs Per Year: Tuition: $12,720 full-time.

■ **GEM CITY COLLEGE** *M-4*
PO Box 179
Quincy, IL 62301
Tel: (217)222-0391
Fax: (217)222-1557
Web Site: http://www.gemcitycollege.com/
Description: Proprietary, 2-year, coed. Awards diplomas and terminal associate degrees. Founded 1870. Setting: small town campus. Total enrollment: 150. 65 applied, 100% were admitted. 10% from top 10% of their high school class, 20% from top quarter, 40% from top half. Students come from 10 states and territories, 1 other country, 40% 25 or older. Academic remediation for entering students, summer session for credit, part-time degree program, adult/continuing education programs, internships.
Entrance Requirements: Open admission. Options: early admission, deferred admission. Entrance: noncompetitive. Application deadline: Rolling.
Collegiate Environment: Student services: personal-psychological counseling. College housing not available. 2,700 books and 40 serials. 40 computers available on campus for general student use. Staffed computer lab on campus.

■ **GOVERNORS STATE UNIVERSITY** *J-15*
One University Parkway
University Park, IL 60466-0975
Tel: (708)534-5000
Admissions: (708)534-4490
Fax: (708)534-1640
Web Site: http://www.govst.edu/
Description: State-supported, upper-level, coed. Awards bachelor's and master's degrees. Founded 1969. Setting: 750-acre suburban campus with easy access to Chicago. Total enrollment: 5,405. Faculty: 212 (185 full-time, 27 part-time). Student-undergrad faculty ratio is 16:1. Students come from 8 states and territories, 20 other countries, 3% from out-of-state, 0.2% Native American, 7% Hispanic, 38% black, 2% Asian American or Pacific Islander, 1% international, 60% 25 or older. Academic areas with the most degrees conferred: liberal arts/general studies; education; business/marketing. Core. Calendar: trimesters. Services for LD students, advanced placement, self-designed majors, honors program, independent study, distance learning, summer session for credit, part-time degree program, external degree program, adult/continuing education programs, internships, graduate courses open to undergrads. Off campus study at Chicago State University, Northeastern Illinois University, Western Illinois University, Eastern Illinois University. Study abroad program. ROTC: Army (c), Air Force (c).
Costs Per Year: Application fee: $0. State resident tuition: $3720 full-time, $155 per credit part-time. Nonresident tuition: $11,160 full-time, $465 per credit part-time. Mandatory fees: $580 full-time, $170 per term part-time.
Collegiate Environment: Orientation program. Choral group, student-run newspaper. Social organizations: 30 open to all; 7% of eligible men and 12% of eligible women are members. Most popular organizations: Future Teachers of America, American College of Health Executives, Circle K, Counseling Club, African-American Student Association. Student services: personal-psychological counseling. Campus security: 24-hour emergency response devices and patrols, late night transport-escort service. College housing not available. University Library with 260,000 books, 86,000 microform titles, 2,200 serials, 2,700 audiovisual materials, an OPAC, and a Web page. 165 computers available on campus for general student use. A campuswide network can be accessed from off-campus. Staffed computer lab on campus.
Community Environment: Located in University Park, Illinois, on 750 acres, the University is in a suburban/rural setting. However, it is about 35 miles from downtown Chicago and thirty miles from Kankakee or Joliet, Illinois, in the Southern metropolitan area of Chicago. The campus is accessible via public transportation, from the city and most of the southern suburbs. Governors State University is a commuter institution. There is no student housing available.

■ **GREENVILLE COLLEGE** *Q-10*
315 East College, PO Box 159
Greenville, IL 62246-0159
Tel: (618)664-2800
Free: 800-345-4440
Admissions: (618)664-7100
Fax: (618)664-9841
E-mail: admissions@greenville.edu
Web Site: http://www.greenville.edu/
Description: Independent Free Methodist, comprehensive, coed. Awards bachelor's and master's degrees. Founded 1892. Setting: 12-acre small town campus with easy access to St. Louis. Endowment: $13.7 million. Educational spending for 2005 fiscal year: $4279 per student. Total enrollment: 1,350. Faculty: 124 (59 full-time, 65 part-time). Student-undergrad faculty ratio is 15:1. 633 applied, 90% were admitted. 16% from top 10% of their high school class, 37% from top quarter, 71% from top half. 2 National Merit Scholars, 13 valedictorians. Full-time: 1,175 students, 54% women, 46% men. Part-time: 40 students, 75% women, 25% men. Students come from 39 states and territories, 15 other countries, 32% from out-of-state, 1% Native American, 2% Hispanic, 8% black, 1% Asian American or Pacific Islander, 1% international, 24% 25 or older, 62% live on campus, 12% transferred in. Retention: 73% of full-time freshmen returned the following year. Academic areas with the most degrees conferred: business/marketing; education; visual and performing arts. Core. Calendar: 4-1-4. Academic remediation for entering students, advanced placement, accelerated degree program, self-designed majors, honors program, independent study, double major, summer session for credit, part-time degree program, adult/continuing education programs, co-op programs and internships. Off campus study at 13 members of the Christian College Consortium; 100 members of the Council for Christian Colleges and Universities. Study abroad program.
Entrance Requirements: Options: electronic application, early admission, deferred admission, international baccalaureate accepted. Required: essay, high school transcript, minimum 2.5 high school GPA, 2 recommendations, agreement to code of conduct, SAT or ACT. Required for some: interview. Entrance: moderately difficult. Application deadline: 8/1. Notification: continuous.
Costs Per Year: Application fee: $25. Comprehensive fee: $23,146 includes full-time tuition ($17,142), mandatory fees ($100), and college room and board ($5904). College room only: $2794. Room and board charges vary according to housing facility. Part-time tuition: $361 per credit hour. Part-time tuition varies according to course load.
Collegiate Environment: Orientation program. Drama-theater group, choral group, student-run newspaper, radio station. Social organizations: 25 open to all. Most popular organizations: Campus Activity Board, Intramurals, Greenville Student Outreach, Habitat for Humanity, Student Senate. Major annual events: Back to School Bash, Agape Music Festival, All-College Hike. Student services: personal-psychological counseling. Campus security: 24-hour emergency response devices, student patrols, late night transport-escort service, controlled dormitory access. 743 college housing spaces available; 709 were occupied in 2003-04. Freshmen guaranteed college housing. On-campus residence required through senior year. Options: men-only, women-only housing available. Ruby E. Dare Library with 126,210 books, 14,023 microform titles, 490 serials, 4,377 audiovisual materials, an OPAC, and a Web page. Operations spending for 2004 fiscal year: $297,024. 65 computers available on campus for general student use. A campuswide network can be accessed from student residence rooms and from off campus. Staffed computer lab on campus.

■ **HARRINGTON COLLEGE OF DESIGN** *D-16*
200 West Madison St.
Chicago, IL 60606
Tel: (312)939-4975; 877-939-4975
Fax: (312)939-8005
Web Site: http://www.interiordesign.edu/
Description: Proprietary, 4-year, coed. Part of Career Education Corporation. Awards associate and bachelor's degrees. Founded 1931. Setting: urban campus. Educational spending for 2005 fiscal year: $3100 per student. Total enrollment: 1,563. Student-undergrad faculty ratio is 12:1. Full-time: 747 students, 87% women, 13% men. Part-time: 816 students, 88% women, 12% men. Students come from 19 states and territories, 6% from

out-of-state, 0.4% Native American, 9% Hispanic, 6% black, 4% Asian American or Pacific Islander, 0% international, 46% 25 or older, 6% live on campus, 34% transferred in. Retention: 43% of full-time freshmen returned the following year. Academic area with the most degrees conferred: visual and performing arts. Core. Calendar: semesters. Part-time degree program, internships. Study abroad program.

Entrance Requirements: Options: Common Application, electronic application, deferred admission. Required: high school transcript, interview. Recommended: essay, 1 recommendation. Entrance: noncompetitive. Application deadline: Rolling. Notification: continuous.

Costs Per Year: Application fee: $60. Tuition: $6930 full-time, $550 per credit hour part-time. Mandatory fees: $580 full-time. Full-time tuition and fees vary according to course load and program. Part-time tuition varies according to course load and program. College room only: $5000. Room charges vary according to housing facility.

Collegiate Environment: Orientation program. Student-run newspaper. Social organizations: 4 open to all. Most popular organizations: American Society of Interior Designers, International Interior Design Association, Green Design Club, Student Government. Campus security: 24-hour patrols. 85 undergraduates lived in college housing during 2003-04. Freshmen given priority for college housing. Option: coed housing available. Harrington Institute Design Library with 19,672 books, 100 serials, 26,514 audiovisual materials, an OPAC, and a Web page. Operations spending for 2004 fiscal year: $262,983. 52 computers available on campus for general student use. A campuswide network can be accessed. Staffed computer lab on campus.

■ **HEARTLAND COMMUNITY COLLEGE** *J-12*
1500 West Raab Rd.
Normal, IL 61761
Tel: (309)268-8000
Fax: (309)268-7999
Web Site: http://www.heartland.edu/

Description: State and locally supported, 2-year, coed. Part of Illinois Community College Board. Awards certificates, transfer associate, and terminal associate degrees. Founded 1990. Setting: urban campus. Educational spending for 2005 fiscal year: $6193 per student. Total enrollment: 4,667. Student-undergrad faculty ratio is 19:1. Students come from 5 states and territories, 2 other countries, 1% from out-of-state, 38% 25 or older. Retention: 55% of full-time freshmen returned the following year. Core. Calendar: semesters. Academic remediation for entering students, ESL program, services for LD students, advanced placement, independent study, distance learning, double major, summer session for credit, part-time degree program, adult/continuing education programs, co-op programs and internships. Study abroad program. ROTC: Army (c).

Entrance Requirements: Open admission except for nursing program, network administration program. Recommended: high school transcript. Placement: SAT, ACT recommended; ACT COMPASS required for some. Entrance: noncompetitive. Application deadline: Rolling. Notification: continuous.

Costs Per Year: Application fee: $0. Area resident tuition: $2010 full-time, $67 per semester hour part-time. State resident tuition: $4020 full-time, $134 per semester hour part-time. Nonresident tuition: $6030 full-time, $201 per semester hour part-time. Mandatory fees: $90 full-time, $3 per semester hour part-time.

Collegiate Environment: Orientation program. Drama-theater group, choral group, student-run newspaper. Social organizations: 21 open to all. Most popular organizations: Environmental Club, Early Childhood Club, student government, Nursing Club, Phi Theta Kappa. Major annual events: Fall Fest, Spring Fest, Diversity Day. Student services: personal-psychological counseling. Campus security: 24-hour emergency response devices and patrols. College housing not available. Heartland Community College Library with 5,000 books, 188 serials, 4,000 audiovisual materials, an OPAC, and a Web page. 400 computers available on campus for general student use. A campuswide network can be accessed. Staffed computer lab on campus.

■ **HEBREW THEOLOGICAL COLLEGE** *C-16*
7135 North Carpenter Rd.
Skokie, IL 60077-3263
Tel: (847)982-2500
Web Site: http://www.htcnet.edu/

Description: Independent Jewish, comprehensive, men only, coordinate with Anne M. Blitstein Teachers Institute of the Hebrew Theological College. Awards bachelor's and first professional degrees. Founded 1922. Setting: 13-acre suburban campus with easy access to Chicago. Total enrollment:

155. Students come from 16 states and territories. Core. Calendar: semesters. Academic remediation for entering students, advanced placement, accelerated degree program, independent study, double major, summer session for credit, part-time degree program, internships. Study abroad program.

Entrance Requirements: Required: essay, high school transcript, 2 recommendations, interview, SAT or ACT. Entrance: moderately difficult. Application deadline: 8/15.

Collegiate Environment: Orientation program. Campus security: controlled dormitory access. Option: men-only housing available. Saul Silber Memorial Library plus 2 others with 63,000 books and 60 serials. 30 computers available on campus for general student use. A campuswide network can be accessed. Staffed computer lab on campus.

Community Environment: A suburb of Chicago and adjacent to Evanston, Skokie has all the usual community facilities as well as good shopping areas.

■ **HIGHLAND COMMUNITY COLLEGE** *B-10*
2998 West Pearl City Rd.
Freeport, IL 61032-9341
Tel: (815)235-6121
Fax: (815)235-6130
Web Site: http://www.highland.edu/

Description: State and locally supported, 2-year, coed. Part of Illinois Community College Board. Awards certificates, transfer associate, and terminal associate degrees. Founded 1962. Setting: 240-acre rural campus. Endowment: $5.6 million. Educational spending for 2005 fiscal year: $1340 per student. Total enrollment: 2,406. Student-undergrad faculty ratio is 16:1. 665 applied, 100% were admitted. 12% from top 10% of their high school class, 32% from top quarter, 41% from top half. Full-time: 1,134 students, 57% women, 43% men. Part-time: 1,272 students, 68% women, 32% men. Students come from 8 states and territories, 2% from out-of-state, 0.1% Native American, 2% Hispanic, 9% black, 1% Asian American or Pacific Islander, 0.2% international, 58% 25 or older. Retention: 65% of full-time freshmen returned the following year. Core. Calendar: semesters. Academic remediation for entering students, ESL program, services for LD students, advanced placement, self-designed majors, independent study, distance learning, summer session for credit, part-time degree program, external degree program, adult/continuing education programs, internships.

Entrance Requirements: Open admission except for nursing program. Options: early admission, deferred admission. Required for some: high school transcript. Entrance: noncompetitive. Application deadline: Rolling. Preference given to district residents.

Costs Per Year: Application fee: $0. Area resident tuition: $1608 full-time, $67 per credit part-time. State resident tuition: $2880 full-time, $120 per credit part-time. Nonresident tuition: $2880 full-time, $120 per credit part-time. Mandatory fees: $120 full-time, $5 per credit part-time.

Collegiate Environment: Drama-theater group, choral group, student-run newspaper. Social organizations: 21 open to all. Most popular organizations: Phi Theta Kappa, Royal Scots, Prairie Wind, intramurals, Collegiate Choir. Major annual events: Spring Fling, Welcome Back to Campus Day. Student services: personal-psychological counseling. Campus security: 24-hour patrols. College housing not available. Highland Library plus 1 other with 47,000 books, 295 microform titles, 3,980 serials, 2,776 audiovisual materials, an OPAC, and a Web page. Operations spending for 2004 fiscal year: $242,430. 200 computers available on campus for general student use. A campuswide network can be accessed. Staffed computer lab on campus.

■ **ILLINOIS CENTRAL COLLEGE** *I-2*
One College Dr.
East Peoria, IL 61635-0001
Tel: (309)694-5011
Admissions: (309)694-5784
Fax: (309)694-5450
Web Site: http://www.icc.edu/

Description: State and locally supported, 2-year, coed. Part of Illinois Community College Board. Awards certificates, transfer associate, and terminal associate degrees. Founded 1967. Setting: 430-acre suburban campus. Total enrollment: 12,343. Students come from 20 other countries, 0.4% Native American, 2% Hispanic, 10% black, 2% Asian American or Pacific Islander, 1% international, 55% 25 or older. Calendar: semesters. Academic remediation for entering students, ESL program, services for LD students, advanced placement, honors program, summer session for credit, part-time degree program, adult/continuing education programs, internships.

Entrance Requirements: Open admission except for college transfer associate degree, health applied science programs. Option: early admission. Required: high school transcript. Entrance: noncompetitive. Application deadline: Rolling. Notification: continuous.

Costs Per Year: Application fee: $0. Area resident tuition: $2240 full-time, $70 per semester hour part-time. State resident tuition: $4960 full-time, $155 per semester hour part-time. Nonresident tuition: $4960 full-time, $155 per semester hour part-time. College room only: $3978.

Collegiate Environment: Drama-theater group, choral group, student-run newspaper. Most popular organizations: Student Association for the Environment, Horticulture Club. Major annual events: Fine Arts Festival, Gaming Fair, Train Fair. Student services: health clinic, personal-psychological counseling. 82,492 books and 563 serials. 250 computers available on campus for general student use. A campuswide network can be accessed from off-campus. Staffed computer lab on campus.

Community Environment: Illinois Central College is located in rural Tazewell County on the outskirts of East Peoria, IL. Primarily a commuter college, adequate bus transportation is available from the city of Peoria. The large rolling campus of 434 acres provides an open feeling for attending students. With the surrounding wooded areas, the beautiful campus provides easy access to classrooms, laboratories, bookstore, cafeteria, and other student services. Illinois Central faculty and staff are committed to student learning and take pride in the large number of successful graduates. Over the 25-year history of the college, approximately 225,000 different individuals have taken classes, and more than 20,000 have received degrees and certificates. Illinois Central College offers a diverse curriculum including college transfer, career education, developmental assistance and continuing community education.

■ **ILLINOIS COLLEGE** *M-7*
1101 West College Ave.
Jacksonville, IL 62650-2299
Tel: (217)245-3000; (866)464-5265
Admissions: (217)245-3030
Fax: (217)245-3034
E-mail: admissions@ic.edu
Web Site: http://www.ic.edu/

Description: Independent interdenominational, 4-year, coed. Awards bachelor's degrees. Founded 1829. Setting: 62-acre small town campus with easy access to St. Louis. Endowment: $123 million. Total enrollment: 1,030. Student-undergrad faculty ratio is 12:1. 1,144 applied, 64% were admitted. 22% from top 10% of their high school class, 52% from top quarter, 82% from top half. 17 valedictorians. Full-time: 1,009 students, 53% women, 47% men. Part-time: 21 students, 86% women, 14% men. Students come from 19 states and territories, 7 other countries, 8% from out-of-state, 0.1% Native American, 1% Hispanic, 3% black, 1% Asian American or Pacific Islander, 2% international, 2% 25 or older, 75% live on campus, 4% transferred in. Retention: 75% of full-time freshmen returned the following year. Academic areas with the most degrees conferred: business/marketing; biological/life sciences; social sciences. Core. Calendar: semesters. Advanced placement, accelerated degree program, independent study, double major, summer session for credit, internships. Study abroad program.

Entrance Requirements: Options: Peterson's Universal Application, Common Application, electronic application, international baccalaureate accepted. Required: high school transcript, 1 recommendation, SAT or ACT. Recommended: essay, minimum 2.5 high school GPA, interview. Required for some: essay. Entrance: moderately difficult. Application deadline: 7/1. Notification: continuous until 8/15.

Costs Per Year: Application fee: $25. Comprehensive fee: $23,600 includes full-time tuition ($17,100) and college room and board ($6500). Part-time tuition: $712 per credit hour.

Collegiate Environment: Orientation program. Drama-theater group, choral group, student-run newspaper. Social organizations: 50 open to all; local fraternities, local sororities; 22% of eligible men and 18% of eligible women are members. Most popular organizations: Student Activity Board, Forum, Homecoming Committee, literary societies, B.A.S.I.C. (Brothers and Sisters in Christ). Major annual events: homecoming, Night of a Thousand Stars, All-College Christmas Dinner. Student services: health clinic, personal-psychological counseling. Campus security: 24-hour emergency response devices and patrols, late night transport-escort service, controlled dormitory access. 750 college housing spaces available; 730 were occupied in 2003-04. Freshmen guaranteed college housing. On-campus residence required through sophomore year. Options: coed, men-only, women-only housing available. Schewe Library plus 1 other with 163,810 books, 7,957 microform

titles, 10,234 serials, 4,011 audiovisual materials, an OPAC, and a Web page. Operations spending for 2004 fiscal year: $422,578. 110 computers available on campus for general student use. A campuswide network can be accessed from student residence rooms and from off campus. Staffed computer lab on campus.

Community Environment: Jacksonville, population 20,553, is located in the west-central part of Illinois. It is the home of the only ferris wheel factory in the United States. Within the community are a library, many churches, hospitals, movie theaters, golf courses, and lakes for boating and fishing. Part-time jobs are available.

■ **ILLINOIS EASTERN COMMUNITY COLLEGES, FRONTIER COMMUNITY COLLEGE** *T-14*
Frontier Dr.
Fairfield, IL 62837-2601
Tel: (618)842-3711
Fax: (618)842-6340
Web Site: http://www.iecc.edu/fcc/

Description: State and locally supported, 2-year, coed. Part of Illinois Eastern Community College System. Awards certificates, transfer associate, and terminal associate degrees. Founded 1976. Setting: 8-acre rural campus. Total enrollment: 2,164. Full-time: 249 students, 65% women, 35% men. Part-time: 1,915 students, 66% women, 34% men. 0.1% Native American, 0.3% Hispanic, 0.2% black, 1% Asian American or Pacific Islander, 0% international, 56% 25 or older. Core. Calendar: semesters. Academic remediation for entering students, ESL program, services for LD students, advanced placement, self-designed majors, independent study, distance learning, double major, summer session for credit, part-time degree program, external degree program, adult/continuing education programs, co-op programs.

Entrance Requirements: Open admission. Options: early admission, deferred admission. Required: high school transcript. Entrance: noncompetitive. Application deadline: Rolling. Notification: continuous. Preference given to district residents.

Costs Per Year: Application fee: $10. Area resident tuition: $1696 full-time, $53 per credit hour part-time. State resident tuition: $5908 full-time, $184.63 per credit hour part-time. Nonresident tuition: $7314 full-time, $228.55 per credit hour part-time. Mandatory fees: $106 full-time, $3 per credit hour part-time.

Collegiate Environment: College housing not available. 19,088 books, 25,656 microform titles, 7,664 serials, and 2,679 audiovisual materials. Operations spending for 2004 fiscal year: $17,786. 42 computers available on campus for general student use. Staffed computer lab on campus.

■ **ILLINOIS EASTERN COMMUNITY COLLEGES, LINCOLN TRAIL COLLEGE** *Q-16*
11220 State Hwy. 1
Robinson, IL 62454
Tel: (618)544-8657
Fax: (618)544-7423
Web Site: http://www.iecc.edu/ltc/

Description: State and locally supported, 2-year, coed. Part of Illinois Eastern Community College System. Awards certificates, transfer associate, and terminal associate degrees. Founded 1969. Setting: 120-acre rural campus. Total enrollment: 1,532. Full-time: 505 students, 52% women, 48% men. Part-time: 1,027 students, 47% women, 53% men. 0.2% Native American, 4% Hispanic, 15% black, 2% Asian American or Pacific Islander, 0.3% international, 54% 25 or older. Core. Calendar: semesters. Academic remediation for entering students, ESL program, services for LD students, advanced placement, self-designed majors, independent study, distance learning, double major, summer session for credit, part-time degree program, external degree program, adult/continuing education programs, co-op programs and internships.

Entrance Requirements: Open admission. Options: early admission, deferred admission. Required: high school transcript. Entrance: noncompetitive. Application deadline: Rolling. Notification: continuous. Preference given to district residents.

Costs Per Year: Application fee: $10. Area resident tuition: $1696 full-time, $53 per credit hour part-time. State resident tuition: $5908 full-time, $184.63 per credit hour part-time. Nonresident tuition: $7314 full-time, $228.55 per credit hour part-time. Mandatory fees: $106 full-time, $3 per credit hour part-time.

Collegiate Environment: Drama-theater group, choral group. Social organizations: national fraternities. Student services: personal-psychological counseling. College housing not available. Eagleton Learning Resource Center with 16,654 books, 7,654 microform titles, 7,391 serials, and 2,029 audiovisual materials. Operations spending for 2004 fiscal year: $9632. 96 computers available on campus for general student use. Staffed computer lab on campus.

■ ILLINOIS EASTERN COMMUNITY COLLEGES, OLNEY CENTRAL COLLEGE *R-15*

305 North West St.
Olney, IL 62450
Tel: (618)395-7777
Fax: (618)392-5212
Web Site: http://www.iecc.edu/occ/
Description: State and locally supported, 2-year, coed. Part of Illinois Eastern Community College System. Awards certificates, transfer associate, and terminal associate degrees. Founded 1962. Setting: 128-acre rural campus. Total enrollment: 1,701. Full-time: 758 students, 57% women, 43% men. Part-time: 943 students, 57% women, 43% men. 0.1% Native American, 1% Hispanic, 1% black, 1% Asian American or Pacific Islander, 0.1% international, 64% 25 or older. Core. Calendar: semesters. Academic remediation for entering students, ESL program, services for LD students, advanced placement, self-designed majors, independent study, distance learning, double major, summer session for credit, part-time degree program, external degree program, adult/continuing education programs, co-op programs and internships.
Entrance Requirements: Open admission. Options: early admission, deferred admission. Required: high school transcript. Entrance: noncompetitive. Application deadline: Rolling. Notification: continuous. Preference given to district residents.
Costs Per Year: Application fee: $10. Area resident tuition: $1696 full-time, $53 per credit hour part-time. State resident tuition: $5908 full-time, $184.63 per credit hour part-time. Nonresident tuition: $7314 full-time, $228.55 per credit hour part-time. Mandatory fees: $106 full-time, $3 per credit hour part-time.
Collegiate Environment: Drama-theater group, choral group, student-run newspaper. Student services: personal-psychological counseling, women's center. College housing not available. Anderson Learning Resources Center with 22,976 books, 81 serials, and 693 audiovisual materials. Operations spending for 2004 fiscal year: $15,047. 125 computers available on campus for general student use. Staffed computer lab on campus.

■ ILLINOIS EASTERN COMMUNITY COLLEGES, WABASH VALLEY COLLEGE *S-16*

2200 College Dr.
Mount Carmel, IL 62863-2657
Tel: (618)262-8641
Fax: (618)262-8641
Web Site: http://www.iecc.edu/wvc/
Description: State and locally supported, 2-year, coed. Part of Illinois Eastern Community College System. Awards certificates, transfer associate, and terminal associate degrees. Founded 1960. Setting: 40-acre rural campus. Total enrollment: 3,155. Full-time: 631 students, 48% women, 52% men. Part-time: 2,524 students, 37% women, 63% men. 0.2% Native American, 1% Hispanic, 3% black, 1% Asian American or Pacific Islander, 0.1% international, 53% 25 or older. Core. Calendar: semesters. Academic remediation for entering students, ESL program, services for LD students, advanced placement, self-designed majors, independent study, distance learning, double major, summer session for credit, part-time degree program, external degree program, adult/continuing education programs, co-op programs and internships.
Entrance Requirements: Open admission. Options: early admission, deferred admission. Required: high school transcript. Entrance: noncompetitive. Application deadline: Rolling. Notification: continuous. Preference given to district residents.
Costs Per Year: Application fee: $10. Area resident tuition: $1696 full-time, $53 per credit hour part-time. State resident tuition: $5908 full-time, $184.63 per credit hour part-time. Nonresident tuition: $7314 full-time, $228.55 per credit hour part-time. Mandatory fees: $106 full-time, $3 per credit hour part-time.
Collegiate Environment: Drama-theater group, choral group, student-run newspaper, radio station. College housing not available. Bauer Media Center with 34,589 books, 51,262 microform titles, 7,665 serials, and 1,629 audiovisual materials. Operations spending for 2004 fiscal year: $6704. 100 computers available on campus for general student use. Staffed computer lab on campus.

■ THE ILLINOIS INSTITUTE OF ART-CHICAGO *D-16*

350 North Orleans
Chicago, IL 60654
Tel: (312)280-3500
Free: 800-351-3450
Fax: (312)280-3528
Web Site: http://www.ilic.artinstitutes.edu/
Description: Proprietary, 4-year, coed. Part of Education Management Corporation. Awards associate and bachelor's degrees. Founded 1916. Setting: 2-acre urban campus. Educational spending for 2005 fiscal year: $2265 per student. Total enrollment: 2,588. Student-undergrad faculty ratio is 24:1. 2,177 applied, 48% were admitted. Full-time: 1,932 students, 62% women, 38% men. Part-time: 656 students, 54% women, 46% men. Students come from 42 states and territories, 26 other countries, 30% from out-of-state, 1% Native American, 8% Hispanic, 12% black, 3% Asian American or Pacific Islander, 0.04% international, 30% 25 or older, 6% transferred in. Retention: 70% of full-time freshmen returned the following year. Academic areas with the most degrees conferred: visual and performing arts; communication technologies; communications/journalism. Core. Academic remediation for entering students, services for LD students, advanced placement, accelerated degree program, independent study, summer session for credit, part-time degree program, adult/continuing education programs, co-op programs and internships. Off campus study at members of the International Council of Design Schools.
Entrance Requirements: Options: Common Application, electronic application, early admission, deferred admission, international baccalaureate accepted. Required: essay, high school transcript, interview. Recommended: minimum 2.0 high school GPA, ACT. Required for some: recommendations, portfolio, SAT and SAT Subject Tests or ACT, ACT ASSET. Entrance: minimally difficult. Application deadline: Rolling. Notification: continuous.
Costs Per Year: Application fee: $150. Tuition: $18,720 full-time, $390 per credit part-time. Mandatory fees: $300 full-time. College room only: $8070.
Collegiate Environment: Orientation program. Social organizations: 10 open to all. Most popular organizations: Student Activities Committee, American Society of Interior Designers Club, Commercial Art Club, Student Ambassador Program, Fashion Focus. Major annual events: Halloween Party, Fashion Show, Student Show. Student services: personal-psychological counseling. Campus security: 24-hour emergency response devices and patrols. 500 college housing spaces available; 350 were occupied in 2003-04. The Illinois Institute of Art Library plus 1 other with 11,324 books, 264 serials, 502 audiovisual materials, an OPAC, and a Web page. 150 computers available on campus for general student use. Staffed computer lab on campus.

■ THE ILLINOIS INSTITUTE OF ART-SCHAUMBURG *C-15*

1000 Plaza Dr.
Schaumburg, IL 60173
Tel: (847)619-3450
Free: 800-314-3450
Fax: (847)619-3064
Web Site: http://www.ilis.artinstitutes.edu/
Description: Proprietary, 4-year, coed. Part of Education Management Corporation. Awards associate and bachelor's degrees. Setting: suburban campus. Total enrollment: 1,187. Student-undergrad faculty ratio is 19:1. 562 applied, 74% were admitted. Full-time: 911 students, 45% women, 55% men. Part-time: 276 students, 42% women, 58% men. Students come from 11 states and territories, 6 other countries, 13% from out-of-state, 0.3% Native American, 8% Hispanic, 2% black, 6% Asian American or Pacific Islander, 0.4% international, 21% 25 or older, 8% transferred in. Retention: 8% of full-time freshmen returned the following year. Core. Services for LD students, advanced placement, accelerated degree program, self-designed majors, independent study, double major, summer session for credit, part-time degree program, internships. Off campus study.
Entrance Requirements: Options: Common Application, electronic application, international baccalaureate accepted. Required: essay, high school transcript, minimum 2.0 high school GPA. Required for some: recommendations, interview. Entrance: minimally difficult. Application deadline: Rolling. Notification: continuous.
Costs Per Year: Application fee: $0. Tuition: $16,605 full-time, $369 per credit hour part-time. Tuition guaranteed not to increase for student's term of enrollment.
Collegiate Environment: Orientation program. Student-run newspaper. Most popular organizations: Animation Club, ASID, newspaper, Music Club, A.I.G.A. (graphic design club). Major annual events: ASID job fair, Portfolio

Show, Artimation (video festival). Student services: personal-psychological counseling. Campus security: 24-hour emergency response devices and patrols, student patrols. 130 undergraduates lived in college housing during 2003-04. No special consideration for freshman housing applicants. 300 computers available on campus for general student use. A campuswide network can be accessed. Staffed computer lab on campus.

■ **ILLINOIS INSTITUTE OF TECHNOLOGY** *D-16*
3300 South Federal St.
Chicago, IL 60616-3793
Tel: (312)567-3000
Free: 800-448-2329
Admissions: (312)567-3025
Fax: (312)567-6939
E-mail: admission@vax1.ais.iit.edu
Web Site: http://www.iit.edu/
Description: Independent, university, coed. Awards bachelor's, master's, doctoral, and first professional degrees. Founded 1890. Setting: 120-acre urban campus. Endowment: $225.6 million. Research spending for 2004 fiscal year: $31.2 million. Educational spending for 2005 fiscal year: $9463 per student. Total enrollment: 6,378. 2,609 applied, 65% were admitted. 37% from top 10% of their high school class, 70% from top quarter, 92% from top half. 15 valedictorians. Full-time: 1,825 students, 25% women, 75% men. Part-time: 264 students, 19% women, 81% men. Students come from 50 states and territories, 61 other countries, 30% from out-of-state, 0.3% Native American, 7% Hispanic, 5% black, 14% Asian American or Pacific Islander, 16% international, 14% 25 or older, 56% live on campus, 7% transferred in. Retention: 81% of full-time freshmen returned the following year. Core. Calendar: semesters. ESL program, services for LD students, advanced placement, independent study, distance learning, double major, summer session for credit, part-time degree program, co-op programs and internships, graduate courses open to undergrads. Study abroad program. ROTC: Army, Naval, Air Force.
Entrance Requirements: Options: Peterson's Universal Application, electronic application, deferred admission, international baccalaureate accepted. Required: essay, high school transcript, minimum 3.0 high school GPA, 1 recommendation, minimum ACT score of 24 or SAT score of 1150, SAT or ACT. Required for some: interview. Entrance: very difficult. Application deadline: Rolling. Notification: continuous.
Costs Per Year: Application fee: $30. Comprehensive fee: $30,520 includes full-time tuition ($22,218), mandatory fees ($784), and college room and board ($7518). College room only: $3900. Room and board charges vary according to board plan and housing facility. Part-time tuition: $692 per credit hour. Part-time mandatory fees: $7 per credit hour. Part-time tuition and fees vary according to course load.
Collegiate Environment: Orientation program. Drama-theater group, choral group, student-run newspaper, radio station. Social organizations: 98 open to all; national fraternities, national sororities, local sororities; 13% of eligible men and 13% of eligible women are members. Most popular organizations: Union Board, Student Government Association, Residence Hall Association, Techmate Commuters, International Student Organization. Major annual events: International Fest, Greek Week, Union Board Spring Formal. Student services: health clinic, personal-psychological counseling, women's center. Campus security: 24-hour emergency response devices and patrols, late night transport-escort service, controlled dormitory access. 1,251 college housing spaces available; 1,170 were occupied in 2003-04. Freshmen guaranteed college housing. On-campus residence required in freshman year. Options: coed, men-only, women-only housing available. Paul V. Galvin Library plus 5 others with 877,581 books, 184,392 microform titles, 678 serials, 54,611 audiovisual materials, an OPAC, and a Web page. Operations spending for 2004 fiscal year: $4.5 million. 650 computers available on campus for general student use. Computer purchase/lease plans available. A campuswide network can be accessed from student residence rooms and from off campus. Staffed computer lab on campus.
Community Environment: See University of Chicago.

■ **ILLINOIS STATE UNIVERSITY** *J-12*
Normal, IL 61790-2200
Tel: (309)438-2111
Admissions: (309)438-2181
Fax: (309)438-3932
E-mail: pawutz@ilstu.edu
Web Site: http://www.ilstu.edu/

Description: State-supported, university, coed. Awards bachelor's, master's, and doctoral degrees and post-master's certificates. Founded 1857. Setting: 850-acre urban campus. Endowment: $32.7 million. Research spending for 2004 fiscal year: $14.9 million. Educational spending for 2005 fiscal year: $4901 per student. Total enrollment: 20,653. Faculty: 1,103 (829 full-time, 274 part-time). Student-undergrad faculty ratio is 19:1. 10,414 applied, 77% were admitted. 11% from top 10% of their high school class, 36% from top quarter, 79% from top half. 1 National Merit Scholar, 29 valedictorians. Full-time: 16,635 students, 58% women, 42% men. Part-time: 1,223 students, 54% women, 46% men. Students come from 43 states and territories, 46 other countries, 1% from out-of-state, 0.3% Native American, 3% Hispanic, 6% black, 2% Asian American or Pacific Islander, 1% international, 8% 25 or older, 35% live on campus, 10% transferred in. Retention: 85% of full-time freshmen returned the following year. Academic areas with the most degrees conferred: education; business/marketing; social sciences. Core. Calendar: semesters. Academic remediation for entering students, ESL program, services for LD students, advanced placement, accelerated degree program, self-designed majors, honors program, independent study, distance learning, double major, summer session for credit, part-time degree program, adult/continuing education programs, co-op programs and internships, graduate courses open to undergrads. Off campus study at National Student Exchange. Study abroad program. ROTC: Army.
Entrance Requirements: Options: electronic application, international baccalaureate accepted. Required: essay, high school transcript, SAT or ACT. Entrance: moderately difficult. Application deadline: 3/1. Notification: continuous.
Costs Per Year: Application fee: $30. State resident tuition: $5400 full-time, $180 per credit hour part-time. Nonresident tuition: $11,280 full-time, $376 per credit hour part-time. Mandatory fees: $1691 full-time, $46.70 per credit hour part-time, $700.50 per term part-time. Full-time tuition and fees vary according to course load. Part-time tuition and fees vary according to course load. College room and board: $5748. College room only: $3010. Room and board charges vary according to board plan. Tuition guaranteed not to increase for student's term of enrollment.
Collegiate Environment: Orientation program. Drama-theater group, choral group, marching band, student-run newspaper, radio station. Social organizations: 250 open to all; national fraternities, national sororities; 7% of eligible men and 8% of eligible women are members. Student services: legal services, health clinic, personal-psychological counseling, women's center. Campus security: 24-hour emergency response devices and patrols, late night transport-escort service, controlled dormitory access. 6,901 college housing spaces available; 6,865 were occupied in 2003-04. Freshmen guaranteed college housing. On-campus residence required through sophomore year. Options: coed, women-only housing available. Milner Library with 1.6 million books, 14,166 serials, an OPAC, and a Web page. Operations spending for 2004 fiscal year: $8 million. 1,869 computers available on campus for general student use. A campuswide network can be accessed from student residence rooms and from off campus. Staffed computer lab on campus.
Community Environment: Bloomington-Normal, with a combined population of 142,650, has a strong agricultural base with many business and industrial affiliations. Located at the intersection of Interstates 55 and 74, it is 132 miles from Chicago, 65 miles from Springfield, and 168 miles from St. Louis. Winters are moderately cold, summers are warm, and spring and fall are delightful. Both the twin-cities offer business districts for shopping, banking, and professional services, as well as year-round municipal recreational programs.

■ **ILLINOIS VALLEY COMMUNITY COLLEGE** *F-11*
815 North Orlando Smith Ave.
Oglesby, IL 61348-9692
Tel: (815)224-2720
Admissions: (815)224-0437
Fax: (815)224-3033
Web Site: http://www.ivcc.edu/
Description: District-supported, 2-year, coed. Part of Illinois Community College Board. Awards transfer associate and terminal associate degrees. Founded 1924. Setting: 410-acre rural campus with easy access to Chicago. Total enrollment: 4,315. 6% 25 or older. Core. Calendar: semesters. Academic remediation for entering students, ESL program, services for LD students, advanced placement, self-designed majors, honors program, independent study, distance learning, summer session for credit, part-time degree program, adult/continuing education programs, internships. Off campus study at Sauk Valley Community College, Kishwaukee College,

Kankakee Community College, Joliet Junior College, Rock Valley College, Elgin Community College, Waubonsee Community College. Study abroad program.

Entrance Requirements: Open admission except for nursing, dental assistant programs, therapeutic massage. Options: early admission, deferred admission. Required: high school transcript. Placement: ACT recommended. Entrance: noncompetitive. Application deadline: Rolling. Notification: continuous.

Costs Per Year: Area resident tuition: $63.25 per credit hour part-time. State resident tuition: $214.02 per credit hour part-time. Nonresident tuition: $246.71 per credit hour part-time.

Collegiate Environment: Orientation program. Drama-theater group, choral group, student-run newspaper. Social organizations: 3 open to all. Student services: personal-psychological counseling. Campus security: 24-hour patrols. College housing not available. Jacobs Library with 58,250 books and 504 serials. 420 computers available on campus for general student use.

Community Environment: Oglesby (population 4,175) is almost 75 miles southwest of Chicago, 50 miles northeast of Peoria.

■ **ILLINOIS WESLEYAN UNIVERSITY** *J-12*
PO Box 2900
Bloomington, IL 61702-2900
Tel: (309)556-1000
Free: 800-332-2498
Admissions: (309)556-3031
Fax: (309)556-3411
E-mail: iwuadmit@iwu.edu
Web Site: http://www.iwu.edu/

Description: Independent, 4-year, coed. Awards bachelor's degrees. Founded 1850. Setting: 79-acre suburban campus. Endowment: $158.7 million. Total enrollment: 2,146. Student-undergrad faculty ratio is 12:1. 2,770 applied, 57% were admitted. 47% from top 10% of their high school class, 81% from top quarter, 99% from top half. 13 National Merit Scholars, 32 valedictorians. Full-time: 2,140 students, 57% women, 43% men. Part-time: 6 students, 17% women, 83% men. Students come from 36 states and territories, 17 other countries, 14% from out-of-state, 0.2% Native American, 3% Hispanic, 4% black, 3% Asian American or Pacific Islander, 2% international, 0% 25 or older, 81% live on campus, 1% transferred in. Retention: 92% of full-time freshmen returned the following year. Academic areas with the most degrees conferred: business/marketing; social sciences; visual and performing arts. Core. Calendar: 4-4-1. Services for LD students, advanced placement, self-designed majors, honors program, independent study, double major, internships. Off campus study at Midwest College Arts program, Colleges of the Midwest Urban Education program, Washington semester, United Nations semester. Study abroad program. ROTC: Army (c).

Entrance Requirements: Options: Peterson's Universal Application, Common Application, electronic application, early admission, deferred admission, international baccalaureate accepted. Required: essay, high school transcript, minimum 2.0 high school GPA, 1 recommendation, SAT or ACT. Recommended: minimum 3.0 high school GPA, 2 recommendations, interview. Entrance: very difficult. Notification: continuous, continuous for nonresidents.

Costs Per Year: Application fee: $0. Comprehensive fee: $35,790 includes full-time tuition ($28,926), mandatory fees ($150), and college room and board ($6714). College room only: $4104. Part-time tuition: $3619 per course.

Collegiate Environment: Orientation program. Drama-theater group, choral group, student-run newspaper, radio station. Social organizations: 160 open to all; national fraternities, national sororities, local sororities; 33% of eligible men and 25% of eligible women are members. Most popular organizations: Alpha Phi Omega, Christian Fellowship, Students for a Just Society, Black Student Union, Habitat for Humanity. Major annual events: Soul Food Dinner, Homecoming, Undercover. Student services: health clinic, personal-psychological counseling. Campus security: 24-hour emergency response devices and patrols, late night transport-escort service, Emergency Response Team. 1,745 college housing spaces available; 1,640 were occupied in 2003-04. Freshmen guaranteed college housing. On-campus residence required through sophomore year. Option: coed housing available. The Ames Library with 314,894 books, 23,297 microform titles, 15,226 serials, 15,076 audiovisual materials, an OPAC, and a Web page. Operations spending for 2004 fiscal year: $2.4 million. 450 computers available on campus for general student use. A campuswide network can be accessed from student residence rooms and from off campus. Staffed computer lab on campus.

Community Environment: Illinois Wesleyan University is located in Bloomington, Illinois, which is known as a research, insurance, retail, education and business center. Situated in a corporate community of 100,000 people, Bloomington is now one of the fastest growing communities in the country and is listed among the most desirable places to live in the nation.

■ **INTERNATIONAL ACADEMY OF DESIGN & TECHNOLOGY** *D-16*
One North State St., Ste. 400
Chicago, IL 60602-9736
Tel: (312)980-9200; 877-ACADEMY
Fax: (312)828-9405
E-mail: dlochbaum@iadtchicago.com
Web Site: http://www.iadtchicago.edu/

Description: Proprietary, 4-year, coed. Part of Career Education Corporation. Awards associate and bachelor's degrees. Founded 1977. Setting: 1-acre urban campus. Total enrollment: 2,768. Student-undergrad faculty ratio is 15:1. 1,713 applied, 99% were admitted. 5% from top 10% of their high school class, 15% from top quarter, 45% from top half. Full-time: 2,409 students, 69% women, 31% men. Part-time: 359 students, 70% women, 30% men. Students come from 20 states and territories, 5% from out-of-state, 0.5% Native American, 20% Hispanic, 33% black, 3% Asian American or Pacific Islander, 2% international, 27% 25 or older, 13% transferred in. Retention: 34% of full-time freshmen returned the following year. Academic areas with the most degrees conferred: visual and performing arts; business/marketing; computer and information sciences. Core. Academic remediation for entering students, services for LD students, advanced placement, independent study, summer session for credit, part-time degree program, adult/continuing education programs, internships. Study abroad program.

Entrance Requirements: Options: Common Application, electronic application, early admission, international baccalaureate accepted. Required: high school transcript, interview. Recommended: essay, minimum 2.0 high school GPA. Required for some: GED. Entrance: minimally difficult. Application deadline: Rolling.

Costs Per Year: Application fee: $50. Tuition: $22,400 full-time, $2200 per course part-time. Mandatory fees: $600 full-time, $150 per term part-time.

Collegiate Environment: Orientation program. Student-run newspaper. Social organizations: 5 open to all. Most popular organizations: ASID/IDSA (Interior Design Student Organization), Byte-Me Club/AIGA (American Institute of Graphic Artists), International Club, Fashion Council, Adult Student Support Group. Major annual events: Windy City Starz Fashion Show, Senior Salute, Industry Speaks. Student services: personal-psychological counseling. Campus security: 24-hour emergency response devices, building security during hours of operation. College housing not available. International Academy of Design and Technology Library with 6,500 books, 80 serials, 750 audiovisual materials, an OPAC, and a Web page. Operations spending for 2004 fiscal year: $61,500. 360 computers available on campus for general student use. A campuswide network can be accessed. Staffed computer lab on campus.

■ **ITT TECHNICAL INSTITUTE (BURR RIDGE)** *H-12*
7040 High Grove Blvd.
Burr Ridge, IL 60527
Tel: (630)455-6470
Web Site: http://www.itt-tech.edu/

Description: Proprietary, primarily 2-year, coed. Part of ITT Educational Services, Inc. Awards terminal associate and bachelor's degrees. Core.

Entrance Requirements: Option: deferred admission. Required: high school transcript, interview, Wonderlic aptitude test. Recommended: recommendations. Entrance: minimally difficult. Application deadline: Rolling. Notification: continuous.

Costs Per Year: Application fee: $100.

Collegiate Environment: Orientation program. College housing not available.

■ **ITT TECHNICAL INSTITUTE (MATTESON)** *L-15*
600 Holiday Plaza Dr.
Matteson, IL 60443
Tel: (708)747-2571
Web Site: http://www.itt-tech.edu/

Description: Proprietary, primarily 2-year, coed. Part of ITT Educational Services, Inc. Awards terminal associate and bachelor's degrees. Founded 1993. Setting: suburban campus with easy access to Chicago. Core.

Entrance Requirements: Option: deferred admission. Required: high school transcript, interview, Wonderlic aptitude test. Recommended: recommendations. Entrance: minimally difficult. Application deadline: Rolling. Notification: continuous.

Costs Per Year: Application fee: $100.
Collegiate Environment: Orientation program. College housing not available.

■ **ITT TECHNICAL INSTITUTE (MOUNT PROSPECT)** *C-15*
1401 Feehanville Dr.
Mount Prospect, IL 60056
Tel: (847)375-8800
Web Site: http://www.itt-tech.edu/
Description: Proprietary, primarily 2-year, coed. Part of ITT Educational Services, Inc. Awards terminal associate and bachelor's degrees. Founded 1986. Setting: 1-acre suburban campus with easy access to Chicago. Core.
Entrance Requirements: Option: deferred admission. Required: high school transcript, interview, Wonderlic aptitude test. Recommended: recommendations. Entrance: minimally difficult. Application deadline: Rolling. Notification: continuous.
Costs Per Year: Application fee: $100.
Collegiate Environment: Orientation program. College housing not available.

■ **JOHN A. LOGAN COLLEGE** *V-11*
700 Logan College Rd.
Carterville, IL 62918-9900
Tel: (618)985-3741
Fax: (618)985-2248
E-mail: terry.crain@jalc.edu
Web Site: http://www.jalc.edu/
Description: State and locally supported, 2-year, coed. Part of Illinois Community College Board. Awards certificates and transfer associate degrees. Founded 1967. Setting: 160-acre rural campus. Endowment: $19,000. Educational spending for 2005 fiscal year: $4580 per student. Total enrollment: 5,501. 5% from top 10% of their high school class, 65% from top half. Students come from 41 states and territories, 20 other countries, 54% 25 or older. Core. Calendar: semesters. Academic remediation for entering students, services for LD students, advanced placement, distance learning, summer session for credit, part-time degree program, adult/continuing education programs, co-op programs and internships. Off campus study at Belleville Area College, Rend Lake College, Illinois Eastern Community Colleges, Shawnee Community College, Southern Illinois University Carbondale, Southeastern Illinois College. Study abroad program. ROTC: Army (c), Air Force (c).
Entrance Requirements: Open admission except for nursing program. Options: Peterson's Universal Application, electronic application, early admission. Required: high school transcript. Placement: ACT ASSET required; SAT or ACT recommended. Entrance: noncompetitive. Application deadline: 8/25. Notification: continuous.
Costs Per Year: Application fee: $0. Area resident tuition: $1900 full-time, $61 per credit hour part-time. State resident tuition: $6000 full-time, $169.24 per credit hour part-time. Nonresident tuition: $9000 full-time, $254.89 per credit hour part-time.
Collegiate Environment: Drama-theater group, choral group, student-run newspaper. Campus security: 24-hour emergency response devices and patrols. College housing not available. Learning Resource Center with 33,306 books, 298 serials, and a Web page. Operations spending for 2004 fiscal year: $16,687. 150 computers available on campus for general student use. Staffed computer lab on campus.

■ **JOHN WOOD COMMUNITY COLLEGE** *M-4*
1301 South 48th St.
Quincy, IL 62305-8736
Tel: (217)224-6500
Admissions: (217)641-4339
Fax: (217)224-4208
E-mail: admissions@jwcc.edu
Web Site: http://www.jwcc.edu/
Description: District-supported, 2-year, coed. Part of Illinois Community College Board. Awards certificates, transfer associate, and terminal associate degrees. Founded 1974. Setting: small town campus. Educational spending for 2005 fiscal year: $2730 per student. Total enrollment: 2,530. Student-undergrad faculty ratio is 15:1. 711 applied, 100% were admitted. 4% from top 10% of their high school class, 19% from top quarter, 53% from top half. Full-time: 1,197 students, 58% women, 42% men. Part-time: 1,333 students, 68% women, 32% men. Students come from 4 states and territories, 3 other countries, 9% from out-of-state, 0.3% Native American, 1%

Hispanic, 4% black, 1% Asian American or Pacific Islander, 0.2% international, 32% 25 or older, 6% transferred in. Core. Calendar: semesters. Academic remediation for entering students, ESL program, services for LD students, advanced placement, self-designed majors, independent study, distance learning, summer session for credit, part-time degree program, external degree program, adult/continuing education programs, co-op programs and internships. Off campus study at members of the Quincy Area Education Consortium, Southeastern Community College (IA), Blessing Hospital, Quincy Area Vocational Technical Center. Study abroad program.
Entrance Requirements: Open admission except for broadcast electronics program. Options: Peterson's Universal Application, Common Application, early admission. Required: high school transcript. Recommended: ACT. Entrance: noncompetitive. Application deadline: Rolling. Notification: continuous. Preference given to district residents.
Costs Per Year: Area resident tuition: $2280 full-time, $76 per credit hour part-time. State resident tuition: $5280 full-time, $176 per credit hour part-time. Mandatory fees: $150 full-time, $5 per credit hour part-time.
Collegiate Environment: Orientation program. Choral group. Campus security: 24-hour emergency response devices, late night transport-escort service. College housing not available. 18,000 books, 160 serials, 2,200 audiovisual materials, an OPAC, and a Web page. Operations spending for 2004 fiscal year: $195,684. 250 computers available on campus for general student use. A campuswide network can be accessed. Staffed computer lab on campus.
Community Environment: See Quincy University.

■ **JOLIET JUNIOR COLLEGE** *E-15*
1215 Houbolt Rd.
Joliet, IL 60431-8938
Tel: (815)729-9020
Admissions: (815)280-2493
E-mail: admission@jjc.edu
Web Site: http://www.jjc.edu/
Description: State and locally supported, 2-year, coed. Part of Illinois Community College Board. Awards certificates, diplomas, transfer associate, and terminal associate degrees. Founded 1901. Setting: suburban campus with easy access to Chicago. Endowment: $9.6 million. Educational spending for 2005 fiscal year: $6999 per student. Total enrollment: 13,022. Student-undergrad faculty ratio is 24:1. 4,484 applied, 100% were admitted. 6% from top 10% of their high school class, 22% from top quarter, 54% from top half. Full-time: 4,895 students, 52% women, 48% men. Part-time: 8,127 students, 64% women, 36% men. Students come from 12 states and territories, 0.3% from out-of-state, 0.3% Native American, 9% Hispanic, 10% black, 2% Asian American or Pacific Islander, 0.1% international, 44% 25 or older, 2% transferred in. Core. Calendar: semesters. Academic remediation for entering students, ESL program, services for LD students, advanced placement, honors program, independent study, distance learning, summer session for credit, part-time degree program, adult/continuing education programs, internships.
Entrance Requirements: Open admission except for nursing program. Options: Peterson's Universal Application, early admission, deferred admission. Required: high school transcript. Entrance: noncompetitive. Application deadline: Rolling. Preference given to district residents.
Costs Per Year: Application fee: $0. Area resident tuition: $1800 full-time, $60 per hour part-time. State resident tuition: $6248 full-time, $208 per hour part-time. Nonresident tuition: $7149 full-time, $238 per hour part-time. Mandatory fees: $390 full-time, $13 per hour part-time.
Collegiate Environment: Orientation program. Drama-theater group, choral group, student-run newspaper. Social organizations: 47 open to all; national fraternities; 8% of men are members. Most popular organizations: Phi Theta Kappa, JC Players, Nursing Student Association, Student Agricultural Association, Inter-Varsity Christian Fellowship. Student services: personal-psychological counseling, women's center. Campus security: 24-hour emergency response devices and patrols, student patrols, late night transport-escort service. 296 college housing spaces available; all were occupied in 2003-04. Learning Resource Center with 60,364 books, 1,516 microform titles, 360 serials, and an OPAC. Operations spending for 2004 fiscal year: $646,078.
Community Environment: Joliet is a leading industrial area 38 miles southwest of Chicago's Loop. Railroads and buses are accessible; Midway and O'Hare Airports serve the area. Industries are steel, petroleum products, chemicals, wallpaper, machinery, and greeting cards. Shipping is also a major industry. Community facilities include excellent libraries, churches of

almost every denomination, hospitals, YMCA, hotels and private rooming houses. Outdoor sports include hunting, boating, fishing, golf, and other sports.

■ JUDSON COLLEGE C-14
1151 North State St.
Elgin, IL 60123-1498
Tel: (847)628-2500
Free: 800-879-5376
Admissions: (847)695-2500
Fax: (847)695-0712
E-mail: pguth@judsoncollege.edu
Web Site: http://www.judsoncollege.edu/

Description: Independent Baptist, comprehensive, coed. Awards bachelor's and master's degrees. Founded 1963. Setting: 80-acre suburban campus with easy access to Chicago. Endowment: $6 million. Research spending for 2004 fiscal year: $2527. Educational spending for 2005 fiscal year: $5386 per student. Total enrollment: 1,241. Faculty: 111 (55 full-time, 56 part-time). Student-undergrad faculty ratio is 14:1. 457 applied, 76% were admitted. Full-time: 915 students, 57% women, 43% men. Part-time: 278 students, 63% women, 37% men. Students come from 21 states and territories, 18 other countries, 30% from out-of-state, 0.2% Native American, 5% Hispanic, 4% black, 1% Asian American or Pacific Islander, 3% international, 8% 25 or older, 64% live on campus, 5% transferred in. Retention: 78% of full-time freshmen returned the following year. Core. Calendar: semesters. Academic remediation for entering students, ESL program, advanced placement, accelerated degree program, honors program, independent study, distance learning, double major, part-time degree program, adult/continuing education programs, internships. Off campus study at Christian College Coalition. Study abroad program.

Entrance Requirements: Options: Peterson's Universal Application, Common Application, early admission, deferred admission. Required: high school transcript, minimum 2.0 high school GPA, Lifestyle statement, SAT and SAT Subject Tests or ACT. Required for some: essay, 2 recommendations, interview. Entrance: moderately difficult. Application deadline: Rolling. Notification: continuous.

Costs Per Year: Application fee: $35. Comprehensive fee: $26,350 includes full-time tuition ($19,150), mandatory fees ($300), and college room and board ($6900).

Collegiate Environment: Orientation program. Drama-theater group, choral group, student-run newspaper. Most popular organizations: Judson Choir, Nowhere Near Broadway, Philosophy and Religion Club, Phi Beta Lambda. Major annual events: Founders' Day, Homecoming, Spiritual Emphasis Week. Student services: health clinic, personal-psychological counseling. Campus security: 24-hour emergency response devices and patrols, controlled dormitory access. On-campus residence required through junior year. Options: coed, men-only, women-only housing available. Benjamin P. Browne Library plus 2 others with 104,331 books, 20,000 microform titles, 450 serials, 12,500 audiovisual materials, an OPAC, and a Web page. Operations spending for 2004 fiscal year: $414,446. 90 computers available on campus for general student use. A campuswide network can be accessed from student residence rooms. Staffed computer lab on campus.

■ KANKAKEE COMMUNITY COLLEGE G-15
PO Box 888
Kankakee, IL 60901-0888
Tel: (815)933-0345
Admissions: (815)802-8520
Fax: (815)933-0217
Web Site: http://www.kcc.cc.il.us/

Description: State and locally supported, 2-year, coed. Part of Illinois Community College Board. Awards certificates, diplomas, transfer associate, and terminal associate degrees (also offers continuing education program with significant enrollment not reflected in profile). Founded 1966. Setting: 178-acre small town campus with easy access to Chicago. Total enrollment: 3,475. 0.2% Native American, 3% Hispanic, 13% black, 1% Asian American or Pacific Islander, 0.1% international. Core. Calendar: semesters. Academic remediation for entering students, ESL program, services for LD students, advanced placement, self-designed majors, honors program, independent study, distance learning, summer session for credit, part-time degree program, adult/continuing education programs, co-op programs and internships. Off campus study at Olivet Nazarene University. Study abroad program.

Entrance Requirements: Open admission except for health occupations programs. Option: early admission. Required: high school transcript. Placement: ACT ASSET or ACT COMPASS recommended; ACT, ACT ASSET or ACT COMPASS required for some. Entrance: noncompetitive. Application deadline: Rolling. Notification: continuous. Preference given to district residents for health occupations programs.

Collegiate Environment: Orientation program. Campus security: 24-hour patrols. College housing not available. Kankakee Community College Learning Resource Center with 48,239 books, 19,761 microform titles, 245 serials, and 2,308 audiovisual materials. 250 computers available on campus for general student use. A campuswide network can be accessed from off-campus. Staffed computer lab on campus.

Community Environment: Kankakee (population 31,000), one of the fastest growing cities of Illinois and the U.S., has beautiful residential sections along the banks of the picturesque Kankakee River. Kankakee is located 60 miles southwest of Chicago and is the seat of Kankakee County. Some of the world's largest gladiolus fields are nearby. The manufacturing plants offer ample opportunity for employment. Nearby Chicago provides the cultural facilities for the outlying area. Kankakee County Fair and Championship Rodeo is an annual event in August.

■ KASKASKIA COLLEGE S-11
27210 College Rd.
Centralia, IL 62801-7878
Tel: (618)545-3000
Admissions: (618)545-3066
Fax: (618)532-1135
Web Site: http://www.kaskaskia.edu/

Description: State and locally supported, 2-year, coed. Part of Illinois Community College Board. Awards certificates, transfer associate, and terminal associate degrees. Founded 1966. Setting: 195-acre rural campus with easy access to St. Louis. Endowment: $606,505. Educational spending for 2005 fiscal year: $15,323 per student. Total enrollment: 4,742. Student-undergrad faculty ratio is 22:1. 514 applied, 100% were admitted. Full-time: 1,908 students, 62% women, 38% men. Part-time: 2,834 students, 56% women, 44% men. Students come from 23 states and territories, 2 other countries, 1% from out-of-state, 0.3% Native American, 2% Hispanic, 7% black, 0.4% Asian American or Pacific Islander, 0.2% international, 42% 25 or older, 21% transferred in. Core. Calendar: semesters. Academic remediation for entering students, ESL program, services for LD students, accelerated degree program, honors program, independent study, distance learning, double major, summer session for credit, part-time degree program, adult/continuing education programs, co-op programs and internships. Off campus study at Belleville Area College, Illinois Eastern Community Colleges, Lake Land College, Rend Lake College, Shawnee Community College, Lincoln Land Community College. Study abroad program.

Entrance Requirements: Open admission except for allied health programs. Options: Common Application, early admission, deferred admission. Required: high school transcript. Recommended: ACT, ASSET. Required for some: interview. Entrance: noncompetitive. Application deadline: Rolling. Notification: continuous. Preference given to district residents.

Costs Per Year: Application fee: $0. Area resident tuition: $1590 full-time, $53 per credit hour part-time. State resident tuition: $3030 full-time, $101 per credit hour part-time. Nonresident tuition: $7038 full-time, $234.60 per credit hour part-time. Mandatory fees: $210 full-time, $7 per credit hour part-time. Full-time tuition and fees vary according to location. Part-time tuition and fees vary according to location.

Collegiate Environment: Orientation program. Drama-theater group, choral group, student-run newspaper. Social organizations: 26 open to all. Most popular organizations: Phi Theta Kappa, Administration of Justice, Student Radiology Club, Cosmetology Club, Vocal Music Club. Major annual events: Student Picnic, Blood Drive, Chili Cook-Off. Student services: personal-psychological counseling. Campus security: 24-hour patrols, late night transport-escort service. College housing not available. Kaskaskia College Library with 23,685 books, 2,649 microform titles, 165 serials, 480 audiovisual materials, an OPAC, and a Web page. Operations spending for 2004 fiscal year: $241,956. 129 computers available on campus for general student use. A campuswide network can be accessed from off-campus. Staffed computer lab on campus.

Community Environment: Centralia, located 60 miles east of St. Louis, has mild winters and warm summers. Buses and planes serve the area. Community facilities include a hospital, library, hotels, motels, rooming houses, and a good shopping area. Three lakes are located nearby, for hunting and fishing, and there are three golf courses. The local merchants and civic organizations sponsor a Halloween Parade each year.

■ **KENDALL COLLEGE** *D-16*
900 North Branch St.
Chicago, IL 60622
Tel: (847)448-2000; 877-588-8860
Admissions: (312)752-2160
Fax: (847)448-2556
E-mail: tfitzgibbons@kendall.edu
Web Site: http://www.kendall.edu/

Description: Independent United Methodist, 4-year, coed. Awards associate and bachelor's degrees. Founded 1934. Setting: 1-acre urban campus. Total enrollment: 780. Student-undergrad faculty ratio is 19:1. 605 applied, 30% were admitted. 4 class presidents, 12 student government officers. Students come from 20 states and territories, 19 other countries, 12% from out-of-state, 0.3% Native American, 2% Hispanic, 1% black, 1% Asian American or Pacific Islander, 5% international, 38% 25 or older, 20% live on campus. Core. Academic remediation for entering students, ESL program, advanced placement, accelerated degree program, self-designed majors, independent study, summer session for credit, part-time degree program, adult/continuing education programs, co-op programs and internships. Study abroad program.

Entrance Requirements: Options: Common Application, deferred admission, international baccalaureate accepted. Required: essay, high school transcript, minimum ACT score of 18, SAT or ACT. Recommended: minimum 2.0 high school GPA. Required for some: recommendations, interview. Entrance: moderately difficult. Application deadline: Rolling. Notification: continuous.

Costs Per Year: Application fee: $75. Comprehensive fee: $30,750 includes full-time tuition ($20,100), mandatory fees ($450), and college room and board ($10,200).

Collegiate Environment: Orientation program. Most popular organizations: culinary competition group, student culinary board, ECHO (early childhood organization), Volunteer Club, student government. Major annual events: trip to Great America, Cubs Game Day, Lake Michigan Cruise. Student services: personal-psychological counseling. Campus security: student patrols, late night security in dorms. 300 college housing spaces available. Option: coed housing available. Kendall Library plus 1 other with 37,000 books, 215 serials, and 150 audiovisual materials. Operations spending for 2004 fiscal year: $120,000. 48 computers available on campus for general student use. A campuswide network can be accessed from student residence rooms and from off campus. Staffed computer lab on campus.

Community Environment: See Northwestern University.

■ **KISHWAUKEE COLLEGE** *C-12*
21193 Malta Rd.
Malta, IL 60150-9699
Tel: (815)825-2086
Fax: (815)825-2306
Web Site: http://www.kishwaukeecollege.edu/

Description: State and locally supported, 2-year, coed. Part of Illinois Community College Board. Awards certificates, transfer associate, and terminal associate degrees. Founded 1967. Setting: 120-acre rural campus with easy access to Chicago. Endowment: $1.3 million. Total enrollment: 4,076. Full-time: 577 students, 45% women, 55% men. Part-time: 3,499 students, 58% women, 42% men. Students come from 25 states and territories, 14 other countries, 0.03% from out-of-state, 0.2% Native American, 11% Hispanic, 11% black, 4% Asian American or Pacific Islander, 0.2% international, 33% 25 or older, 15% transferred in. Core. Calendar: semesters. Academic remediation for entering students, ESL program, services for LD students, advanced placement, independent study, distance learning, double major, summer session for credit, part-time degree program, external degree program, adult/continuing education programs, co-op programs and internships. Off campus study at 6 other Illinois community colleges. Study abroad program.

Entrance Requirements: Open admission except for nursing, radiological technology programs. Options: Common Application, early admission, deferred admission. Required: high school transcript, transcripts from all other colleges or universities previously attended. Recommended: minimum 2.0 high school GPA. Required for some: minimum 2.0 high school GPA. Placement: ACT, SAT, or in-house placement test required for some. Entrance: noncompetitive. Application deadline: Rolling. Notification: continuous.

Collegiate Environment: Orientation program. Drama-theater group, choral group, student-run newspaper. Social organizations: 14 open to all. Most popular organizations: student association, Black Student Union, Horticulture Club, Student Nurses Association, International Club. Major annual events: Awards and Recognition Ceremony, Black History Month/Soul Food Buffet, Women's History Month. Student services: health clinic, personal-psychological counseling. Campus security: 24-hour patrols. College housing not available. Learning Resource Center with 52,075 books, 13,003 microform titles, 248 serials, 3,500 audiovisual materials, an OPAC, and a Web page. Operations spending for 2004 fiscal year: $435,355. 565 computers available on campus for general student use. A campuswide network can be accessed. Staffed computer lab on campus.

Community Environment: See Northern Illinois University.

■ **KNOX COLLEGE** *H-7*
2 East South St.
Galesburg, IL 61401
Tel: (309)341-7000
Free: 800-678-KNOX
Admissions: (309)341-7100
Fax: (309)341-7070
E-mail: admission@knox.edu
Web Site: http://www.knox.edu/

Description: Independent, 4-year, coed. Awards bachelor's degrees. Founded 1837. Setting: 82-acre small town campus with easy access to Peoria. Endowment: $51.2 million. Educational spending for 2005 fiscal year: $10,867 per student. Total enrollment: 1,245. Student-undergrad faculty ratio is 12:1. 1,771 applied, 76% were admitted. 33% from top 10% of their high school class, 61% from top quarter, 97% from top half. 4 National Merit Scholars, 9 valedictorians. Full-time: 1,218 students, 55% women, 45% men. Part-time: 27 students, 52% women, 48% men. Students come from 46 states and territories, 41 other countries, 45% from out-of-state, 0.1% Native American, 4% Hispanic, 4% black, 5% Asian American or Pacific Islander, 7% international, 2% 25 or older, 95% live on campus, 3% transferred in. Retention: 85% of full-time freshmen returned the following year. Academic areas with the most degrees conferred: social sciences; English; visual and performing arts; psychology. Core. Calendar: three courses for each of three terms. Academic remediation for entering students, ESL program, services for LD students, advanced placement, self-designed majors, honors program, independent study, double major, part-time degree program, internships. Off campus study at Associated Colleges of the Midwest, Great Lakes College Association. Study abroad program.

Entrance Requirements: Options: Peterson's Universal Application, Common Application, electronic application, early admission, early action, deferred admission, international baccalaureate accepted. Required: essay, high school transcript, 2 recommendations. Recommended: interview. Required for some: SAT and SAT Subject Tests or ACT. Entrance: very difficult. Application deadlines: 2/1, 12/1 for early action. Notification: 3/31, 12/31 for early action.

Costs Per Year: Application fee: $40. Comprehensive fee: $32,385 includes full-time tuition ($25,815), mandatory fees ($285), and college room and board ($6285). College room only: $2784. Room and board charges vary according to board plan. Part-time tuition: $870 per credit. Part-time tuition varies according to course load.

Collegiate Environment: Orientation program. Drama-theater group, choral group, student-run newspaper, radio station. Social organizations: 102 open to all; national fraternities, national sororities; 24% of eligible men and 11% of eligible women are members. Most popular organizations: International Club, Allied Blacks for Liberty and Equality, Sexual Equality Awareness Coalition, Union Board, campus radio station. Major annual events: Pumphandle (welcome to all students), International Fair, Flunk Day. Student services: personal-psychological counseling. Campus security: 24-hour emergency response devices and patrols, late night transport-escort service. 1,113 college housing spaces available; 1,098 were occupied in 2003-04. Freshmen guaranteed college housing. On-campus residence required through senior year. Options: coed, men-only, women-only housing available. Seymour Library plus 2 others with 308,614 books, 98,696 microform titles, 927 serials, 7,159 audiovisual materials, an OPAC, and a Web page. Operations spending for 2004 fiscal year: $1.1 million. 338 computers available on campus for general student use. A campuswide network can be accessed from student residence rooms and from off campus. Staffed computer lab on campus.

Community Environment: Knox College is situated in the small city of Galesburg, Illinois, with a population of 33,500. It is 180 miles west of Chicago and easily accessible by Amtrak, Interstate Highway 74, and Greyhound bus lines.

■ **LAKE FOREST COLLEGE** *B-15*
555 North Sheridan Rd.
Lake Forest, IL 60045-2399
Tel: (847)234-3100
Free: 800-828-4751
Admissions: (847)735-5000
Fax: (847)735-6271
E-mail: motzer@lfc.edu
Web Site: http://www.lakeforest.edu/

Description: Independent, comprehensive, coed. Awards bachelor's and master's degrees. Founded 1857. Setting: 110-acre suburban campus with easy access to Chicago. Endowment: $60.2 million. Research spending for 2004 fiscal year: $862,043. Educational spending for 2005 fiscal year: $9287 per student. Total enrollment: 1,435. Faculty: 158 (89 full-time, 69 part-time). Student-undergrad faculty ratio is 12:1. 2,195 applied, 65% were admitted. 32% from top 10% of their high school class, 54% from top quarter, 90% from top half. 27 class presidents, 7 valedictorians, 164 student government officers. Full-time: 1,398 students, 58% women, 42% men. Part-time: 20 students, 50% women, 50% men. Students come from 47 states and territories, 47 other countries, 54% from out-of-state, 0.1% Native American, 6% Hispanic, 5% black, 3% Asian American or Pacific Islander, 8% international, 1% 25 or older, 80% live on campus, 4% transferred in. Retention: 82% of full-time freshmen returned the following year. Academic areas with the most degrees conferred: social sciences; communications/ journalism; business/marketing. Core. Calendar: semesters. Services for LD students, advanced placement, accelerated degree program, self-designed majors, freshman honors college, honors program, independent study, double major, summer session for credit, part-time degree program, adult/ continuing education programs, internships. Off campus study at 14 members of the Associated Colleges of the Midwest. Study abroad program.

Entrance Requirements: Options: Peterson's Universal Application, Common Application, electronic application, early admission, early decision, early action, deferred admission, international baccalaureate accepted. Required: essay, high school transcript, 2 recommendations, graded paper, SAT or ACT. Recommended: interview. Entrance: very difficult. Application deadlines: 2/15, 12/1 for early decision, 12/1 for early action. Notification: 3/15, 12/20 for early decision, 1/15 for early action.

Costs Per Year: Application fee: $40. Comprehensive fee: $33,860 includes full-time tuition ($27,000), mandatory fees ($334), and college room and board ($6526). College room only: $3456. Room and board charges vary according to housing facility. Part-time tuition: $3375 per course.

Collegiate Environment: Orientation program. Drama-theater group, choral group, student-run newspaper, radio station. Social organizations: 67 open to all; national fraternities, national sororities, local fraternities, local sororities; 18% of eligible men and 14% of eligible women are members. Most popular organizations: Garrick Players Drama Group, League for Environmental Awareness and Protection, International Student Organization, Ambassadors Host Organization. Major annual events: homecoming, Semana Latina, Winter Ball. Student services: health clinic, personal-psychological counseling, women's center. Campus security: 24-hour emergency response devices and patrols, student patrols, late night transport-escort service. 1,105 college housing spaces available; 1,078 were occupied in 2003-04. Freshmen guaranteed college housing. On-campus residence required in freshman year. Options: coed, women-only housing available. Donnelley and Lee Library plus 1 other with 259,977 books, 104,075 microform titles, 1,303 serials, 5,223 audiovisual materials, an OPAC, and a Web page. Operations spending for 2004 fiscal year: $1.4 million. 120 computers available on campus for general student use. Computer purchase/lease plans available. A campuswide network can be accessed from student residence rooms and from off campus. Staffed computer lab on campus.

■ **LAKE LAND COLLEGE** *O-14*
5001 Lake Land Blvd.
Mattoon, IL 61938-9366
Tel: (217)234-5253
Admissions: (217)234-5378
Web Site: http://www.lakelandcollege.edu/

Description: State and locally supported, 2-year, coed. Part of Illinois Community College Board. Awards certificates, transfer associate, and terminal associate degrees. Founded 1966. Setting: 304-acre rural campus. Endowment: $2.7 million. Total enrollment: 7,038. Student-undergrad faculty ratio is 21:1. 2,159 applied, 100% were admitted. Students come from 23 other countries, 5% from out-of-state, 0.2% Native American, 2% Hispanic, 9% black, 1% Asian American or Pacific Islander, 1% international, 36% 25 or older. Core. Calendar: semesters. Academic remediation for entering students, ESL program, services for LD students, accelerated degree program, honors program, distance learning, summer session for credit, part-time degree program, external degree program, adult/continuing education programs, co-op programs and internships.

Entrance Requirements: Open admission except for dental services, nursing, physical therapist assistant, civil engineering technology, John Deere agricultural technology programs. Options: Common Application, electronic application, early admission. Recommended: high school transcript. Required for some: recommendations. Entrance: noncompetitive. Application deadline: Rolling. Notification: continuous.

Costs Per Year: Application fee: $0. Area resident tuition: $1545 full-time, $51.50 per credit hour part-time. State resident tuition: $3595 full-time, $119.86 per credit hour part-time. Nonresident tuition: $7568 full-time, $252.27 per credit hour part-time. Mandatory fees: $358 full-time, $11.95 per credit hour part-time.

Collegiate Environment: Choral group, student-run newspaper, radio station. Social organizations: 18 open to all. Most popular organizations: Agriculture Production and Management Club, Cosmetology Club, Agriculture Transfer Club, Phi Theta Kappa, Civil Engineering Technology Club. Major annual events: Spring Carnival, Alcohol Awareness Week, Blood Drives. Student services: personal-psychological counseling. Campus security: 24-hour patrols. College housing not available. Virgil H. Judge Learning Resource Center with 36,912 books, 23,956 microform titles, 193 serials, 1,446 audiovisual materials, and an OPAC. Operations spending for 2004 fiscal year: $439,600. 100 computers available on campus for general student use. A campuswide network can be accessed. Staffed computer lab on campus.

Community Environment: Mattoon (population 20,000) is an agricultural, commercial, industrial, oil, and transportation center with an average temperature of 53 degrees and an annual rainfall of 39 inches. Bus, train, and air service is available. Community facilities include churches of all denominations, many civic, service, and fraternal organizations, a civic center, hospital, nursing center, clinic, and excellent shopping facilities. Recreational facilities include golf courses, swimming pools, bowling lanes, theatres, skating rinks, and Lakes Paradise and Mattoon with swimming, boating, fishing, and an amusement park. Mattoon is located in the heart of the Lincoln-Lore Lane with many historic points of interest in the area. Part-time employment is available.

■ **LAKEVIEW COLLEGE OF NURSING** *L-16*
903 North Logan Ave.
Danville, IL 61832
Tel: (217)443-5238
Fax: (217)431-4015
E-mail: kholden@lakeviewcol.edu
Web Site: http://www.lakeviewcol.edu/

Description: Independent, upper-level, coed. Part of Danville Area Community College. Awards bachelor's degrees. Founded 1987. Setting: 1-acre small town campus. Endowment: $6.2 million. Educational spending for 2005 fiscal year: $9994 per student. Total enrollment: 83. 45 applied, 87% were admitted. Full-time: 41 students, 98% women, 2% men. Part-time: 42 students, 90% women, 10% men. Students come from 3 states and territories, 5% from out-of-state, 0% Native American, 1% Hispanic, 7% black, 0% Asian American or Pacific Islander, 0% international, 70% 25 or older, 47% transferred in. Core. Calendar: semesters. Honors program, independent study, distance learning, summer session for credit, part-time degree program, external degree program. Off campus study at Eastern Illinois University-branch campus.

Collegiate Environment: Orientation program. Student-run newspaper. Social organizations: 2 open to all. Most popular organizations: Student Nurses Association, Nurses Christian Fellowship (NCF). Student services: personal-psychological counseling. Campus security: 24-hour emergency response devices. College housing not available. Lakeview College of Nursing Library with 1,500 books, 60 serials, 450 audiovisual materials, an OPAC, and a Web page. Operations spending for 2004 fiscal year: $19,990. 12 computers available on campus for general student use. Computer purchase/lease plans available. A campuswide network can be accessed from off-campus. Staffed computer lab on campus.

■ LEWIS AND CLARK COMMUNITY COLLEGE *Q-8*
5800 Godfrey Rd.
Godfrey, IL 62035-2466
Tel: (618)466-7000
Admissions: (618)468-5100
Fax: (618)466-2798
Web Site: http://www.lc.edu/
Description: District-supported, 2-year, coed. Part of Illinois Community College Board. Awards certificates, transfer associate, and terminal associate degrees. Founded 1970. Setting: 275-acre small town campus with easy access to St. Louis. Total enrollment: 7,446. Students come from 3 states and territories, 4 other countries, 1% from out-of-state, 0.2% Native American, 1% Hispanic, 6% black, 0.4% Asian American or Pacific Islander, 0.4% international, 30% 25 or older. Core. Calendar: semesters. Academic remediation for entering students, ESL program, services for LD students, advanced placement, independent study, distance learning, double major, summer session for credit, part-time degree program, adult/continuing education programs, co-op programs and internships. Off campus study at Blackburn College. ROTC: Army.
Entrance Requirements: Open admission except for nursing, dental assisting, dental hygiene, occupational therapy programs, paramedicine, and therapeutic massage. Options: early admission, deferred admission. Recommended: high school transcript. Required for some: interview. Entrance: noncompetitive. Application deadline: Rolling. Notification: continuous.
Collegiate Environment: Orientation program. Choral group, student-run newspaper, radio station. Social organizations: 25 open to all. Most popular organizations: Phi Beta Lambda, Data Processing Club, Nursing Club, Clinical Laboratory Technicians Club, Music Club. Major annual event: Springfest. Student services: health clinic, personal-psychological counseling. Campus security: 24-hour emergency response devices and patrols. College housing not available. Reid Memorial with 47,000 books, 2,500 microform titles, 3,500 serials, 1,700 audiovisual materials, an OPAC, and a Web page. 350 computers available on campus for general student use. Staffed computer lab on campus.
Community Environment: Godfrey (population 1,225) is near Alton (population 40,000), an industrial city just north of St. Louis. Industries include glass production, oil refineries, and manufacturing of steel products, brass, bronze, and copper goods. Railroads serve the area and air service is available at St. Louis airport, approximately 17 miles away. Alton has a community concert association, civic orchestra, little theater, and other similar facilities at nearby colleges. Recreational activities include golf, water sports, tennis, and spectator sports. Hunting and fishing opportunities are outstanding. Part-time work is available in industrial and commercial establishments.

■ LEWIS UNIVERSITY *J-10*
One University Parkway
Romeoville, IL 60446
Tel: (815)838-0500
Free: 800-897-9000
Fax: (815)838-9456
Web Site: http://www.lewisu.edu/
Description: Independent, comprehensive, coed, affiliated with Roman Catholic Church. Awards associate, bachelor's, master's, and doctoral degrees. Founded 1932. Setting: 375-acre small town campus with easy access to Chicago. Endowment: $19.9 million. Total enrollment: 5,065. Faculty: 472 (164 full-time, 308 part-time). Student-undergrad faculty ratio is 13:1. 2,014 applied, 69% were admitted. 15% from top 10% of their high school class, 40% from top quarter, 74% from top half. 1 valedictorian. Full-time: 2,662 students, 59% women, 41% men. Part-time: 931 students, 67% women, 33% men. Students come from 24 states and territories, 31 other countries, 5% from out-of-state, 0.2% Native American, 9% Hispanic, 12% black, 4% Asian American or Pacific Islander, 3% international, 40% 25 or older, 27% live on campus, 9% transferred in. Retention: 76% of full-time freshmen returned the following year. Academic areas with the most degrees conferred: business/marketing; health professions and related sciences; security and protective services. Core. Calendar: semesters. Academic remediation for entering students, ESL program, advanced placement, accelerated degree program, self-designed majors, honors program, independent study, distance learning, double major, summer session for credit, part-time degree program, adult/continuing education programs, internships, graduate courses open to undergrads. Study abroad program. ROTC: Army (c), Air Force (c).

Entrance Requirements: Options: Common Application, electronic application, deferred admission. Required: high school transcript, minimum 2.0 high school GPA, SAT or ACT. Required for some: interview. Entrance: moderately difficult. Application deadline: 8/1.
Costs Per Year: Application fee: $40. Comprehensive fee: $26,800 includes full-time tuition ($19,200) and college room and board ($7600). College room only: $5100. Part-time tuition: $605 per credit hour.
Collegiate Environment: Orientation program. Drama-theater group, choral group, student-run newspaper, radio station. Social organizations: 27 open to all; national fraternities, national sororities, local fraternities, local sororities; 12% of eligible men and 9% of eligible women are members. Most popular organizations: Phi Kappa Theta, Scholars Academy, Black Student Union, Fellowship of Justice, Latin American Student Organization. Major annual events: Greekstock, Spring Formal, International Student Food Festival. Student services: health clinic, personal-psychological counseling. Campus security: 24-hour emergency response devices and patrols, student patrols, late night transport-escort service, controlled dormitory access. 1,044 college housing spaces available; 998 were occupied in 2003-04. Freshmen guaranteed college housing. Option: coed housing available. Lewis University Library with 149,870 books, 147,132 microform titles, 1,990 serials, 2,281 audiovisual materials, an OPAC, and a Web page. Operations spending for 2004 fiscal year: $1.1 million. 310 computers available on campus for general student use. A campuswide network can be accessed from student residence rooms and from off campus. Staffed computer lab on campus.
Community Environment: Romeoville, located 35 miles southwest of Chicago, enjoys a seasonal climate. The Regional Transportation Authority between Chicago and Joliet serves the area, as well as Amtrak. Romeoville has the usual civic, fraternal, and veterans' organizations. Part-time employment is available.

■ LEXINGTON COLLEGE *D-16*
310 South Peoria St., Ste. 512
Chicago, IL 60607-3534
Tel: (312)226-6294
Fax: (312)226-6405
E-mail: pr@lexingtoncollege.edu
Web Site: http://lexingtoncollege.edu/general-education.htm
Description: Independent, 4-year, women only. Awards associate and bachelor's degrees. Founded 1977. Setting: urban campus. Endowment: $29,600. Research spending for 2004 fiscal year: $8500. Educational spending for 2005 fiscal year: $7702 per student. Total enrollment: 56. Student-undergrad faculty ratio is 6:1. 37 applied, 51% were admitted. 8% from top 10% of their high school class, 42% from top quarter, 58% from top half. Full-time: 45 students. Part-time: 11 students. Students come from 4 states and territories, 3 other countries, 13% from out-of-state, 0% Native American, 27% Hispanic, 45% black, 2% Asian American or Pacific Islander, 7% international, 33% 25 or older, 14% transferred in. Retention: 56% of full-time freshmen returned the following year. Core. Calendar: semesters. Academic remediation for entering students, independent study, part-time degree program, adult/continuing education programs, co-op programs and internships.
Entrance Requirements: Open admission. Required: essay, high school transcript, minimum 2.0 high school GPA, minimum ACT score of 18 or minimum SAT score of 1000. Recommended: interview. Required for some: 2 recommendations, SAT or ACT. Entrance: noncompetitive. Application deadline: Rolling.
Costs Per Year: Application fee: $30. Tuition: $16,100 full-time, $530 per credit hour part-time. Mandatory fees: $940 full-time, $200 per term part-time.
Collegiate Environment: Orientation program. Social organizations: 2 open to all. Major annual events: cultural appreciation events, Taste of Lexington, Christmas Party. Campus security: 24-hour emergency response devices and patrols, patrols by municipal security personnel. College housing not available. Lexington College Library with 3,000 books, 40 serials, and an OPAC. Operations spending for 2004 fiscal year: $83,845. 30 computers available on campus for general student use. A campuswide network can be accessed. Staffed computer lab on campus.

■ LINCOLN CHRISTIAN COLLEGE *L-10*
100 Campus View Dr.
Lincoln, IL 62656-2167
Tel: (217)732-3168; 888-522-5228
Fax: (217)732-5914

E-mail: coladmis@iccs.edu

Web Site: http://www.lccs.edu/

Description: Independent, 4-year, coed, affiliated with Christian Churches and Churches of Christ. Administratively affiliated with Lincoln Christian Seminary. Awards associate and bachelor's degrees. Founded 1944. Setting: 227-acre small town campus. Total enrollment: 708. Student-undergrad faculty ratio is 13:1. 269 applied, 78% were admitted. 15% from top 10% of their high school class, 32% from top quarter, 70% from top half. Full-time: 610 students, 47% women, 53% men. Part-time: 98 students, 52% women, 48% men. Students come from 27 states and territories, 6 other countries, 30% from out-of-state, 0% Native American, 1% Hispanic, 3% black, 0.3% Asian American or Pacific Islander, 1% international, 23% 25 or older, 50% live on campus, 5% transferred in. Retention: 69% of full-time freshmen returned the following year. Academic areas with the most degrees conferred: theology and religious vocations; business/marketing. Core. Calendar: semesters. Academic remediation for entering students, ESL program, services for LD students, advanced placement, honors program, independent study, distance learning, double major, summer session for credit, part-time degree program, external degree program, adult/continuing education programs, internships. Off campus study at University of Illinois at Springfield, Illinois State University, Greenville College.

Entrance Requirements: Option: deferred admission. Required: essay, high school transcript, 3 recommendations, SAT or ACT. Required for some: interview. Entrance: moderately difficult. Application deadline: Rolling. Preference given to applicants interested in religious studies.

Costs Per Year: Application fee: $20. Comprehensive fee: $15,100 includes full-time tuition ($10,200) and college room and board ($4900). Part-time tuition: $340 per semester hour.

Collegiate Environment: Orientation program. Drama-theater group, choral group. Student services: health clinic, personal-psychological counseling. Campus security: 24-hour emergency response devices, student patrols. 420 college housing spaces available; 390 were occupied in 2003-04. Freshmen guaranteed college housing. On-campus residence required through senior year. Options: men-only, women-only housing available. Jessie Eury Library with 127,000 books, 500 serials, 27,000 audiovisual materials, an OPAC, and a Web page. 45 computers available on campus for general student use. A campuswide network can be accessed from student residence rooms and from off campus. Staffed computer lab on campus.

Community Environment: See Lincoln College.

■ **LINCOLN COLLEGE** *L-10*

300 Keokuk St.

Lincoln, IL 62656-1699

Tel: (217)732-3155

Free: 800-569-0556

Fax: (217)732-8859

Web Site: http://www.lincolncollege.edu/

Description: Independent, 2-year, coed. Awards transfer associate degrees. Founded 1865. Setting: 42-acre small town campus. Endowment: $14 million. Total enrollment: 758. Student-undergrad faculty ratio is 16:1. 835 applied, 65% were admitted. 5% from top 10% of their high school class, 17% from top quarter, 43% from top half. 9 class presidents, 3 valedictorians, 41 student government officers. Full-time: 700 students, 45% women, 55% men. Part-time: 58 students, 67% women, 33% men. Students come from 15 states and territories, 9% from out-of-state, 3% 25 or older, 90% live on campus, 2% transferred in. Core. Calendar: semesters. Academic remediation for entering students, accelerated degree program, freshman honors college, honors program, independent study, summer session for credit, part-time degree program.

Entrance Requirements: Options: Peterson's Universal Application, early admission, deferred admission. Required: high school transcript, SAT or ACT. Recommended: interview. Required for some: 1 recommendation. Entrance: minimally difficult. Application deadline: Rolling.

Costs Per Year: Application fee: $25. Comprehensive fee: $21,370 includes full-time tuition ($15,000), mandatory fees ($570), and college room and board ($5800). College room only: $2200. Part-time tuition: $500 per credit. Part-time mandatory fees: $19 per credit.

Collegiate Environment: Orientation program. Drama-theater group, choral group, student-run newspaper, radio station. Social organizations: 22 open to all. Most popular organizations: Admissions Ambassadors, Phi Beta Kappa, Connections, SHOS, Spanish Club. Major annual events: Parents' Weekend, Spring Formal, Commencement. Student services: health clinic. Campus security: 24-hour emergency response devices and patrols, controlled dormitory access. 602 college housing spaces available; 600 were

occupied in 2003-04. On-campus residence required through sophomore year. Options: men-only, women-only housing available. McKinstry Library with 42,500 books, 380 serials, an OPAC, and a Web page. Operations spending for 2004 fiscal year: $116,773. 72 computers available on campus for general student use. Staffed computer lab on campus.

Community Environment: Lincoln (population 17,582) was founded in 1852, the only one of 24 similarly named cities of the United States that was named for Abraham Lincoln before he became famous. He assisted in planning the city and performed law work necessary for its incorporation. Lincoln christened the town with the juice of a watermelon when the first lots were sold in 1853. Lincoln is midway between Chicago and St. Louis on the main line of Alton route of GM & O Railroad. Churches of many denominations are located here.

■ **LINCOLN COLLEGE-NORMAL** *J-12*

715 West Raab Rd.

Normal, IL 61761

Tel: (309)452-0500

Free: 800-569-0558

Fax: (309)454-5652

E-mail: admissions@lincolncollege.edu

Web Site: http://www.lincolncollege.edu/normal/

Description: Independent, primarily 2-year, coed. Awards certificates, transfer associate, terminal associate, and bachelor's degrees. Founded 1865. Setting: 10-acre suburban campus. Endowment: $14 million. Total enrollment: 520. Student-undergrad faculty ratio is 14:1. 5% from top 10% of their high school class, 10% from top quarter, 35% from top half. Full-time: 350 students, 63% women, 37% men. Part-time: 170 students, 59% women, 41% men. Students come from 6 states and territories, 3 other countries, 6% from out-of-state, 0% Native American, 2% Hispanic, 17% black, 0% Asian American or Pacific Islander, 1% international, 8% 25 or older, 40% live on campus, 10% transferred in. Core. Calendar: semesters. Academic remediation for entering students, honors program, summer session for credit, part-time degree program, adult/continuing education programs, co-op programs and internships.

Entrance Requirements: Options: Common Application, electronic application, deferred admission. Required: high school transcript, interview. Required for some: 2 recommendations, SAT or ACT. Entrance: minimally difficult. Application deadline: Rolling.

Costs Per Year: Application fee: $25. Tuition: $1500 full-time, $413 per credit hour part-time. Mandatory fees: $810 full-time, $8 per credit hour part-time, $35 per term part-time. College room only: $3200.

Collegiate Environment: Orientation program. Social organizations: local fraternities, local sororities; 40% of eligible men and 60% of eligible women are members. Most popular organizations: Phi Theta Kappa, Student Ambassadors. Major annual events: concerts, trips. Student services: health clinic. Campus security: 24-hour emergency response devices and patrols, student patrols, late night transport-escort service, controlled dormitory access. 240 college housing spaces available; 210 were occupied in 2003-04. No special consideration for freshman housing applicants. On-campus residence required in freshman year. Option: coed housing available. Milner Library at Illinois State University plus 1 other with 1.8 million books, 2 million microform titles, 25,000 audiovisual materials, an OPAC, and a Web page. 50 computers available on campus for general student use. A campuswide network can be accessed from student residence rooms and from off campus. Staffed computer lab on campus.

■ **LINCOLN LAND COMMUNITY COLLEGE** *M-9*

5250 Shepherd Rd.

PO Box 19256

Springfield, IL 62794-9256

Tel: (217)786-2200

Admissions: (217)786-2243

Fax: (217)786-2492

Web Site: http://www.llcc.edu/

Description: District-supported, 2-year, coed. Part of Illinois Community College Board. Awards certificates, transfer associate, and terminal associate degrees. Founded 1967. Setting: 441-acre suburban campus with easy access to St. Louis. Endowment: $1.7 million. Educational spending for 2005 fiscal year: $3200 per student. Total enrollment: 6,847. Student-undergrad faculty ratio is 19:1. 765 applied, 100% were admitted. 5% from top 10% of their high school class, 27% from top quarter, 58% from top half. Full-time: 2,700 students, 54% women, 46% men. Part-time: 4,147 students, 63% women, 37% men. Students come from 4 states and territories, 3 other countries, 0.03% from out-of-state, 0.4% Native American, 2% Hispanic, 7% black, 1% Asian American or Pacific Islander, 0.2% international, 39% 25 or older, 3% transferred in. Retention: 46% of full-time freshmen returned the following year. Core. Calendar: semesters. Academic remediation for entering students, ESL program, services for LD students, advanced placement, accelerated degree program, honors program, independent study, distance learning, summer session for credit, part-time degree program, external degree program, adult/continuing education programs, internships. Off campus study at Foreign Language/International Studies Consortium. Study abroad program.

Entrance Requirements: Open admission except for allied health programs. Options: Peterson's Universal Application, Common Application, early admission, deferred admission. Recommended: high school transcript. Entrance: noncompetitive. Application deadline: Rolling. Notification: continuous.

Costs Per Year: Application fee: $0. Area resident tuition: $1890 full-time, $63 per credit hour part-time. State resident tuition: $7980 full-time, $266 per credit hour part-time. Nonresident tuition: $9510 full-time, $317 per credit hour part-time. Mandatory fees: $165 full-time, $5.50 per credit hour part-time. Full-time tuition and fees vary according to course load. Part-time tuition and fees vary according to course load.

Collegiate Environment: Orientation program. Drama-theater group, choral group, student-run newspaper. Social organizations: 26 open to all. Most popular organizations: Student Senate, Phi Theta Kappa, Model Illinois Government, student newspaper, Madrigals. Major annual event: graduation. Student services: health clinic, personal-psychological counseling, women's center. Campus security: 24-hour emergency response devices and patrols, late night transport-escort service. College housing not available. Learning Resource Center with 65,000 books, 3,638 microform titles, 10,000 serials, 3,300 audiovisual materials, an OPAC, and a Web page. Operations spending for 2004 fiscal year: $698,579. 130 computers available on campus for general student use. A campuswide network can be accessed from off-campus. Staffed computer lab on campus.

■ **LOYOLA UNIVERSITY CHICAGO** *D-16*
820 North Michigan Ave.
Chicago, IL 60611-2196
Tel: (773)274-3000
Free: 800-262-2373
Admissions: (773)508-3080
Fax: (773)915-6414
E-mail: admission@luc.edu
Web Site: http://www.luc.edu/
Description: Independent Roman Catholic (Jesuit), university, coed. Awards bachelor's, master's, doctoral, and first professional degrees and post-master's certificates (also offers adult part-time program with significant enrollment not reflected in profile). Founded 1870. Setting: 105-acre urban campus. Endowment: $259.1 million. Research spending for 2004 fiscal year: $47.3 million. Educational spending for 2005 fiscal year: $7057 per student. Total enrollment: 14,764. Faculty: 1,106 (523 full-time, 583 part-time). Student-undergrad faculty ratio is 14:1. 13,163 applied, 81% were admitted. 30% from top 10% of their high school class, 63% from top quarter, 94% from top half. 34 valedictorians. Full-time: 8,318 students, 65% women, 35% men. Part-time: 922 students, 61% women, 39% men. Students come from 50 states and territories, 60 other countries, 33% from out-of-state, 0.3% Native American, 10% Hispanic, 6% black, 11% Asian American or Pacific Islander, 2% international, 11% 25 or older, 29% live on campus, 6% transferred in. Retention: 83% of full-time freshmen returned the following year. Academic areas with the most degrees conferred: business/marketing; psychology; biological/life sciences. Core. Calendar: semesters. Academic remediation for entering students, ESL program, services for LD students, advanced placement, accelerated degree program, honors program, double major, summer session for credit, part-time degree program, adult/continuing education programs, internships, graduate courses open to undergrads. Off campus study at School of the Art Institute of Chicago. Study abroad program. ROTC: Army (c), Naval (c).
Entrance Requirements: Options: Common Application, electronic application, deferred admission. Required: essay, high school transcript, SAT or ACT. Recommended: interview. Entrance: moderately difficult. Application deadline: 4/1. Notification: continuous.
Costs Per Year: Application fee: $25. Comprehensive fee: $36,520 includes full-time tuition ($26,150), mandatory fees ($756), and college room and board ($9614). College room only: $6490. Part-time tuition: $530 per semester hour. Part-time mandatory fees: $75.

Collegiate Environment: Orientation program. Drama-theater group, choral group, student-run newspaper, radio station. Social organizations: 136 open to all; national fraternities, national sororities; 6% of eligible men and 5% of eligible women are members. Most popular organizations: Campus Life Union Board, Activities Programming Board, student government. Major annual events: President's Ball, Oktoberfest, Student Leadership Awards Program. Student services: health clinic, personal-psychological counseling, women's center. Campus security: 24-hour emergency response devices and patrols, late night transport-escort service, controlled dormitory access. 2,449 college housing spaces available; 2,346 were occupied in 2003-04. Freshmen guaranteed college housing. Options: coed, women-only housing available. Cudahy Library plus 4 others with 1.1 million books, 1.7 million microform titles, 68,886 serials, 35,090 audiovisual materials, an OPAC, and a Web page. Operations spending for 2004 fiscal year: $10.8 million. 318 computers available on campus for general student use. A campuswide network can be accessed from student residence rooms and from off campus. Staffed computer lab on campus.
Community Environment: See University of Chicago.

■ **MACCORMAC COLLEGE** *D-16*
506 South Wabash Ave.
Chicago, IL 60605-1667
Tel: (312)922-1884
Fax: (312)922-3196
Web Site: http://www.maccormac.edu/
Description: Independent, 2-year, coed. Awards certificates, diplomas, transfer associate, and terminal associate degrees. Founded 1904. Setting: urban campus. Total enrollment: 377. 72% from top half of their high school class. Full-time: 159 students, 86% women, 14% men. Part-time: 218 students, 89% women, 11% men. Students come from 7 states and territories, 8 other countries, 1% from out-of-state, 27% Hispanic, 42% black, 1% Asian American or Pacific Islander, 20% 25 or older. Core. Calendar: semesters. Academic remediation for entering students, ESL program, advanced placement, honors program, summer session for credit, part-time degree program, adult/continuing education programs, internships.
Entrance Requirements: Options: Peterson's Universal Application, Common Application, deferred admission. Required: high school transcript, ACT. Recommended: interview, SAT. Entrance: moderately difficult. Application deadline: Rolling. Notification: continuous.
Collegiate Environment: Orientation program. Social organizations: 2 open to all. Major annual events: Halloween Party, Christmas Dance, All-College Picnic. Campus security: late night transport-escort service. College housing not available. MacCormac College Library with 11,000 books and 140 serials. 180 computers available on campus for general student use. A campuswide network can be accessed.
Community Environment: See University of Chicago.

■ **MACMURRAY COLLEGE** *M-7*
447 East College Ave.
Jacksonville, IL 62650
Tel: (217)479-7000
Admissions: (217)479-7056
Fax: (217)245-0405
E-mail: admiss@mac.edu
Web Site: http://www.mac.edu/
Description: Independent United Methodist, 4-year, coed. Awards associate and bachelor's degrees. Founded 1846. Setting: 60-acre small town campus. Endowment: $12.1 million. Educational spending for 2005 fiscal year: $5745 per student. Total enrollment: 703. Student-undergrad faculty ratio is 13:1. 1,421 applied, 57% were admitted. 13% from top 10% of their high school class, 28% from top quarter, 86% from top half. 2 valedictorians. Full-time: 646 students, 59% women, 41% men. Part-time: 57 students, 74% women, 26% men. Students come from 21 states and territories, 7 other countries, 12% from out-of-state, 1% Native American, 3% Hispanic, 11% black, 0.4% Asian American or Pacific Islander, 1% international, 15% 25 or older, 50% live on campus, 11% transferred in. Retention: 56% of full-time freshmen returned the following year. Academic areas with the most degrees conferred: personal and culinary services; social sciences; psychology. Core. Calendar: 4-1-4. Academic remediation for entering students, services for LD students, advanced placement, honors program, independent study, double major, summer session for credit, part-time degree program, internships. Off campus study at 5 members of the Western Illinois Foreign Language Consortium.

Entrance Requirements: Options: Peterson's Universal Application, Common Application, electronic application, early admission, international baccalaureate accepted. Required: high school transcript, SAT or ACT. Required for some: essay, minimum 2.5 high school GPA, recommendations, interview. Entrance: moderately difficult. Application deadline: Rolling. Notification: continuous.

Costs Per Year: Application fee: $0. Comprehensive fee: $21,748 includes full-time tuition ($15,500), mandatory fees ($250), and college room and board ($5998). College room only: $2732. Part-time tuition: $250 per credit hour. Part-time mandatory fees: $35 per term.

Collegiate Environment: Orientation program. Drama-theater group, choral group, student-run newspaper. Social organizations: 35 open to all; national fraternities, local sororities; 12% of eligible men and 10% of eligible women are members. Most popular organizations: Campus Activity Board, MacMurray Student Association, Sigma Tau Gamma, Alpha Phi Omega, Circle K. Major annual events: homecoming, Sig Tau Days, Spring Fling Week. Student services: health clinic, personal-psychological counseling. Campus security: 24-hour emergency response devices, student patrols, late night transport-escort service, controlled dormitory access. 582 college housing spaces available; 335 were occupied in 2003-04. Freshmen guaranteed college housing. On-campus residence required through sophomore year. Options: coed, women-only housing available. Henry Pfeiffer Library with 1.8 million books, 25,855 microform titles, 185 serials, 1,021 audiovisual materials, an OPAC, and a Web page. Operations spending for 2004 fiscal year: $261,952. 100 computers available on campus for general student use. A campuswide network can be accessed from student residence rooms. Staffed computer lab on campus.

Community Environment: See Illinois College.

■ **MCHENRY COUNTY COLLEGE** *B-14*

8900 US Hwy. 14
Crystal Lake, IL 60012-2761
Tel: (815)455-3700
Admissions: (815)479-7620
Web Site: http://www.mchenry.edu/

Description: State and locally supported, 2-year, coed. Part of Illinois Community College Board. Awards certificates, transfer associate, and terminal associate degrees. Founded 1967. Setting: 109-acre suburban campus with easy access to Chicago. Total enrollment: 5,940. 3% from top 10% of their high school class, 12% from top quarter, 38% from top half. Full-time: 2,048 students, 51% women, 49% men. Part-time: 3,892 students; 61% women, 39% men. Students come from 6 states and territories, 17 other countries, 1% from out-of-state, 0.3% Native American, 5% Hispanic, 1% black, 2% Asian American or Pacific Islander, 0.5% international, 39% 25 or older, 6% transferred in. Core. Calendar: semesters. Academic remediation for entering students, ESL program, services for LD students, advanced placement, accelerated degree program, honors program, independent study, distance learning, summer session for credit, part-time degree program, adult/continuing education programs, co-op programs and internships. Study abroad program.

Entrance Requirements: Open admission. Options: early admission, deferred admission. Required: high school transcript. Placement: ACT recommended. Entrance: noncompetitive. Application deadline: Rolling. Notification: continuous.

Collegiate Environment: Orientation program. Drama-theater group, choral group, student-run newspaper. Social organizations: 13 open to all. Most popular organizations: Phi Theta Kappa, Tallywackers, Latinos Unidos, Campus Activities Board, Student Trustee. Major annual events: SOAR (orientation), open house. Student services: personal-psychological counseling. Campus security: 24-hour emergency response devices and patrols, late night transport-escort service. College housing not available. McHenry County College Library with 40,000 books, 13,500 microform titles, 330 serials, 6,000 audiovisual materials, an OPAC, and a Web page. 100 computers available on campus for general student use. A campuswide network can be accessed. Staffed computer lab on campus.

Community Environment: Crystal Lake, after which the city (population 25,500) was named, is the only natural spring-fed lake between Chicago and Wisconsin. Within the city are 27 large industrial firms and 45 smaller ones, churches, library, medical center, hospitals, and 350 apartment units ranging from small to luxury townhouses. Recreational facilities include the 400 acres of parks and beaches along the lake for all types of water sports and other recreation.

■ **MCKENDREE COLLEGE** *Y-4*

701 College Rd.
Lebanon, IL 62254-1299
Tel: (618)537-4481
Free: 800-232-7228
Fax: (618)537-6259
Web Site: http://www.mckendree.edu/

Description: Independent, comprehensive, coed, affiliated with United Methodist Church. Awards bachelor's and master's degrees. Founded 1828. Setting: 80-acre small town campus with easy access to St. Louis. Endowment: $20.3 million. Educational spending for 2005 fiscal year: $5188 per student. Total enrollment: 2,585. Faculty: 214 (74 full-time, 140 part-time). Student-undergrad faculty ratio is 21:1. 1,465 applied, 66% were admitted. 26% from top 10% of their high school class, 54% from top quarter, 90% from top half. 11 valedictorians. Full-time: 1,617 students, 53% women, 47% men. Part-time: 640 students, 63% women, 37% men. Students come from 23 states and territories, 22 other countries, 17% from out-of-state, 0.2% Native American, 2% Hispanic, 13% black, 1% Asian American or Pacific Islander, 2% international, 35% 25 or older, 54% live on campus, 14% transferred in. Retention: 80% of full-time freshmen returned the following year. Core. Calendar: semesters. Academic remediation for entering students, services for LD students, advanced placement, accelerated degree program, self-designed majors, honors program, independent study, double major, summer session for credit, part-time degree program, internships, graduate courses open to undergrads. Off campus study at University of Evansville. Study abroad program. ROTC: Army (c), Air Force (c).

Entrance Requirements: Options: Peterson's Universal Application, Common Application, electronic application, deferred admission. Required: essay, high school transcript, minimum 2.5 high school GPA, 1 recommendation, rank in upper 50% of high school class, minimum ACT score of 20, SAT or ACT. Required for some: interview. Entrance: moderately difficult. Application deadline: Rolling. Notification: continuous.

Costs Per Year: Application fee: $40. Comprehensive fee: $26,280 includes full-time tuition ($18,300), mandatory fees ($600), and college room and board ($7380). College room only: $3900. Part-time tuition: $615 per hour.

Collegiate Environment: Orientation program. Drama-theater group, choral group, marching band, student-run newspaper. Social organizations: 54 open to all; national fraternities, local fraternities, local sororities; 8% of eligible men and 6% of eligible women are members. Most popular organizations: Model United Nations, Campus Christian Fellowship, Team Bogey, Student Government Association, Students Against Social Injustice. Major annual events: homecoming, Stress Fest (finals week), Family Fest. Student services: health clinic, personal-psychological counseling. Campus security: 24-hour emergency response devices and patrols, student patrols, late night transport-escort service, controlled dormitory access. 710 college housing spaces available; 702 were occupied in 2003-04. Freshmen guaranteed college housing. On-campus residence required through junior year. Option: coed housing available. Holman Library with 105,000 books, 37,395 microform titles, 450 serials, 9,500 audiovisual materials, an OPAC, and a Web page. Operations spending for 2004 fiscal year: $459,312. 140 computers available on campus for general student use. A campuswide network can be accessed from student residence rooms and from off campus. Staffed computer lab on campus.

Community Environment: Lebanon, population 3,700, is 23 miles east of St. Louis. The city has the usual Mississippi Valley climate, neither too hot nor too cold but unpredictable. Scott Air Force Base is six miles from downtown. Employment is available in Belleville, 12 miles away, Fairview Heights, 12 miles away, and in St. Louis proper. Hospital facilities are in Belleville, Highland, Breese and St. Louis. Local recreational activities are tennis, hunting, fishing, golfing, picnicking, and community theater.

■ **MIDSTATE COLLEGE** *I-10*

411 West Northmoor Rd.
Peoria, IL 61614
Tel: (309)692-4092
Fax: (309)692-3893
Web Site: http://www.midstate.edu/

Description: Proprietary, 4-year, coed. Awards associate and bachelor's degrees. Founded 1888. Setting: 1-acre urban campus. Total enrollment: 478. 11% from top 10% of their high school class, 21% from top quarter,

76% from top half. Full-time: 244 students, 81% women, 19% men. Part-time: 234 students, 79% women, 21% men. Students come from 6 states and territories, 3% from out-of-state, 1% Hispanic, 17% black, 0.4% Asian American or Pacific Islander, 0.2% international, 56% 25 or older. Core. Academic remediation for entering students, freshman honors college, honors program, summer session for credit, part-time degree program, co-op programs and internships.

Entrance Requirements: Options: Common Application, early admission, deferred admission. Required: high school transcript, Wonderlic aptitude test. Recommended: interview. Entrance: moderately difficult. Application deadline: Rolling.

Collegiate Environment: Social organizations: 2 open to all; national sororities, local fraternities. Campus security: late night transport-escort service. College housing not available. Barbara Fields Library with 8,724 books, 104 serials, and an OPAC. 49 computers available on campus for general student use. Staffed computer lab on campus.

Community Environment: Peoria is the third largest city of downstate Illinois. All modes of transportation are available. It is the hub of the central area of the state for cultural, business and professional activities. Peoria is a manufacturing and shipping center located in the heart of the farm belt. Community facilities include good shopping areas and recreational opportunities. Job opportunities are good, particularly for summer work. Points of interest are Fort Creve Coer, Indian burial mounds, Peoria Historical Society Museum, Lakeview Center for Arts Sciences, the Planetarium, the Peoria Civic Center, and Wildlife Prairie Park.

■ **MILLIKIN UNIVERSITY** *M-12*
1184 West Main St.
Decatur, IL 62522-2084
Tel: (217)424-6211
Free: 800-373-7733
Admissions: (217)424-6210
Fax: (217)425-4669
E-mail: phughes@millikin.edu
Web Site: http://www.millikin.edu/

Description: Independent, comprehensive, coed, affiliated with Presbyterian Church (U.S.A.). Awards bachelor's and master's degrees. Founded 1901. Setting: 70-acre suburban campus. Endowment: $65,137. Educational spending for 2005 fiscal year: $16,374 per student. Total enrollment: 2,641. Faculty: 282 (145 full-time, 137 part-time). Student-undergrad faculty ratio is 13:1. 2,917 applied, 70% were admitted. 17% from top 10% of their high school class, 44% from top quarter, 79% from top half. 10 valedictorians. Full-time: 2,438 students, 58% women, 42% men. Part-time: 178 students, 71% women, 29% men. Students come from 30 states and territories, 4 other countries, 13% from out-of-state, 0.2% Native American, 2% Hispanic, 9% black, 1% Asian American or Pacific Islander, 0.3% international, 13% 25 or older, 70% live on campus, 5% transferred in. Retention: 75% of full-time freshmen returned the following year. Academic areas with the most degrees conferred: business/marketing; visual and performing arts; education. Core. Calendar: semesters. Services for LD students, advanced placement, self-designed majors, honors program, independent study, double major, summer session for credit, part-time degree program, internships. Off campus study at Drew University, American University, Urban Life Center. Study abroad program.

Entrance Requirements: Options: Common Application, electronic application, deferred admission, international baccalaureate accepted. Required: high school transcript, minimum 2.0 high school GPA, 2 recommendations, SAT or ACT. Recommended: interview. Required for some: audition for school of music; portfolio review for art program; audition for theatre and musical/theatre program. Entrance: moderately difficult. Application deadline: Rolling. Notification: continuous.

Costs Per Year: Application fee: $0. One-time mandatory fee: $75. Comprehensive fee: $27,834 includes full-time tuition ($20,696), mandatory fees ($425), and college room and board ($6713). College room only: $3763. Full-time tuition and fees vary according to course load. Room and board charges vary according to board plan and housing facility. Part-time tuition: $717 per credit hour.

Collegiate Environment: Orientation program. Drama-theater group, choral group, student-run newspaper, radio station. Social organizations: 91 open to all; national fraternities, national sororities; 15% of eligible men and 25% of eligible women are members. Most popular organizations: University Center Board, Millikin Marketing Association, Residence Hall Association. Major annual events: Homecoming, Fall Family Weekend, Performing Arts Series. Student services: health clinic, personal-psychological counseling.

Campus security: 24-hour emergency response devices and patrols, late night transport-escort service, controlled dormitory access. 1,553 college housing spaces available; 1,549 were occupied in 2003-04. Freshmen guaranteed college housing. On-campus residence required through junior year. Options: coed, men-only, women-only housing available. Staley Library with 199,660 books, 21,032 microform titles, 927 serials, 9,017 audiovisual materials, an OPAC, and a Web page. Operations spending for 2004 fiscal year: $660,801. 189 computers available on campus for general student use. Computer purchase/lease plans available. A campuswide network can be accessed from student residence rooms. Staffed computer lab on campus.

Community Environment: Decatur is a diversified industrial community. Bus and air service are available. Many part-time jobs are available. A well-developed park system provides varied recreational opportunities. South of Decatur is the Lincoln Trail Homestead State Park, which marks the first homestead site of the Lincoln family in Illinois.

■ **MONMOUTH COLLEGE** *H-6*
700 East Broadway
Monmouth, IL 61462-1998
Tel: (309)457-2311
Free: 800-747-2687
Admissions: (309)457-2131
Fax: (309)457-2141
Web Site: http://www.monm.edu/

Description: Independent, 4-year, coed, affiliated with Presbyterian Church. Awards bachelor's degrees. Founded 1853. Setting: 80-acre small town campus with easy access to Peoria. Endowment: $51.8 million. Total enrollment: 1,345. Student-undergrad faculty ratio is 15:1. 1,634 applied, 79% were admitted. 12% from top 10% of their high school class, 37% from top quarter, 79% from top half. Full-time: 1,329 students, 53% women, 47% men. Part-time: 16 students, 75% women, 25% men. Students come from 20 states and territories, 14 other countries, 7% from out-of-state, 0.3% Native American, 3% Hispanic, 3% black, 1% Asian American or Pacific Islander, 2% international, 1% 25 or older, 94% live on campus, 4% transferred in. Retention: 80% of full-time freshmen returned the following year. Academic areas with the most degrees conferred: business/marketing; education; social sciences. Core. Calendar: semesters. Advanced placement, self-designed majors, honors program, independent study, double major, part-time degree program, internships. Off campus study at members of the Associated Colleges of the Midwest, Great Lakes Colleges Association. Study abroad program. ROTC: Army (c).

Entrance Requirements: Options: Peterson's Universal Application, Common Application, electronic application, deferred admission, international baccalaureate accepted. Required: high school transcript, SAT or ACT. Recommended: interview. Required for some: essay, 2 recommendations, interview. Entrance: moderately difficult. Application deadline: Rolling. Notification: continuous.

Costs Per Year: Application fee: $0. Comprehensive fee: $25,950 includes full-time tuition ($20,200) and college room and board ($5750). College room only: $3240.

Collegiate Environment: Orientation program. Drama-theater group, choral group, marching band, student-run newspaper, radio station. Social organizations: 60 open to all; national fraternities, national sororities; 23% of eligible men and 24% of eligible women are members. Most popular organizations: Student Service Organization, Student Association, M-Club, Crimson Masque. Major annual events: Homecoming, SCOTS' Day, Family Weekend. Student services: personal-psychological counseling. Campus security: 24-hour emergency response devices, late night transport-escort service, night security. 1,196 college housing spaces available; 1,135 were occupied in 2003-04. On-campus residence required through senior year. Options: coed, men-only, women-only housing available. Hewes Library with 176,470 books, 228,943 microform titles, 514 serials, 3,975 audiovisual materials, an OPAC, and a Web page. Operations spending for 2004 fiscal year: $697,131. 300 computers available on campus for general student use. A campuswide network can be accessed from student residence rooms and from off campus. Staffed computer lab on campus.

Community Environment: Monmouth is located about 180 miles southwest of Chicago and 180 miles north of St. Louis in the heart of the rich corn belt of the Midwest. Although agriculture is the backbone of the economy in the area, numerous small businesses and light industry firms are located here. As a region noted for beef cattle feeding, Monmouth holds a three-day Prime Beef Festival in September. Monmouth Park, a natural forest at the outskirts of the city, has playground equipment, picnic facilities, and an 18-hole municipal golf course.

■ MOODY BIBLE INSTITUTE *D-16*

820 North LaSalle Blvd.
Chicago, IL 60610-3284
Tel: (312)329-4000
Free: 800-967-4MBI
Admissions: (312)329-4267
Fax: (312)329-8987
E-mail: admissions@moody.edu
Web Site: http://www.moody.edu/

Description: Independent nondenominational, comprehensive, coed. Awards bachelor's, master's, and first professional degrees. Founded 1886. Setting: 25-acre urban campus. Total enrollment: 2,687. 1,174 applied, 40% were admitted. 20% from top 10% of their high school class. Full-time: 1,458 students, 43% women, 57% men. Part-time: 944 students, 35% women, 65% men. Students come from 48 states and territories, 41 other countries, 69% from out-of-state, 0.2% Native American, 4% Hispanic, 4% black, 2% Asian American or Pacific Islander, 5% international, 7% 25 or older, 90% live on campus, 3% transferred in. Retention: 87% of full-time freshmen returned the following year. Core. Calendar: semesters. ESL program, advanced placement, independent study, distance learning, double major, summer session for credit, part-time degree program, external degree program, adult/continuing education programs, internships, graduate courses open to undergrads. Off campus study at Roosevelt University, University of Illinois at Chicago, City Colleges of Chicago, Harold Washington College. Study abroad program.

Entrance Requirements: Options: early admission, early decision, international baccalaureate accepted. Required: essay, high school transcript, minimum 2.3 high school GPA, 4 recommendations, Christian testimony, SAT and SAT Subject Tests or ACT. Required for some: interview. Entrance: moderately difficult. Application deadlines: 3/1, 12/1 for early decision. Notification: continuous until 8/1, 1/15 for early decision.

Costs Per Year: Application fee: $35. Comprehensive fee: $13,880 includes full-time tuition ($0), mandatory fees ($1400), and college room and board ($12,480). College room only: $4300. Room and board charges vary according to housing facility. All students are awarded full-tuition scholarships.

Collegiate Environment: Orientation program. Drama-theater group, choral group, student-run newspaper, radio station. Social organizations: ; 70% of eligible men and 80% of eligible women are members. Most popular organizations: Student Missionary Fellowship, Big Brother/Big Sister, music groups, Drama Group. Major annual events: Missions Conference, Founder's Week, Candelight Carols. Student services: health clinic, personal-psychological counseling. Campus security: 24-hour emergency response devices and patrols, student patrols, late night transport-escort service, controlled dormitory access. 1,280 college housing spaces available; 1,152 were occupied in 2003-04. On-campus residence required through senior year. Options: men-only, women-only housing available. Henry Crowell Learning Center plus 1 other with 135,000 books and 987 serials. 26 computers available on campus for general student use. A campuswide network can be accessed from student residence rooms and from off campus. Staffed computer lab on campus.

Community Environment: See University of Chicago.

■ MORAINE VALLEY COMMUNITY COLLEGE *I-14*

10900 South 88th Ave.
Palos Hills, IL 60465-0937
Tel: (708)974-4300
Admissions: (708)974-5346
Fax: (708)974-0681
E-mail: manser@morainevalley.edu
Web Site: http://www.morainevalley.edu/

Description: State and locally supported, 2-year, coed. Part of Illinois Community College Board. Awards certificates, transfer associate, and terminal associate degrees. Founded 1967. Setting: 294-acre suburban campus with easy access to Chicago. Endowment: $12.3 million. Educational spending for 2005 fiscal year: $2081 per student. Total enrollment: 15,929. Student-undergrad faculty ratio is 36:1. 3,961 applied, 100% were admitted. 5% from top 10% of their high school class, 17% from top quarter, 46% from top half. Full-time: 6,654 students, 52% women, 48% men. Part-time: 9,275 students, 63% women, 37% men. Students come from 10 states and territories, 34 other countries, 0% from out-of-state, 0.3% Native American, 10% Hispanic, 9% black, 2% Asian American or Pacific Islander, 2% international, 36% 25 or older, 1% transferred in. Retention: 65% of full-time freshmen returned the following year. Core. Calendar: semesters. Academic remediation for entering students, ESL program, services for LD students, advanced placement,

accelerated degree program, honors program, independent study, distance learning, double major, summer session for credit, part-time degree program, external degree program, adult/continuing education programs, co-op programs and internships. Off campus study. Study abroad program.

Entrance Requirements: Open admission except for allied health, nursing programs. Options: electronic application, early admission, deferred admission. Required: high school transcript. Entrance: noncompetitive. Application deadline: Rolling. Notification: continuous. Preference given to district residents for allied health, nursing programs.

Costs Per Year: Application fee: $0. Area resident tuition: $1920 full-time, $64 per credit hour part-time. State resident tuition: $5970 full-time, $199 per credit hour part-time. Nonresident tuition: $7260 full-time, $242 per credit hour part-time. Mandatory fees: $152 full-time, $5 per credit hour part-time, $1 per term part-time.

Collegiate Environment: Orientation program. Drama-theater group, choral group, student-run newspaper. Social organizations: 30 open to all. Most popular organizations: student newspaper, Speech Team, Alliance of Latin American Students, Phi Theta Kappa, Arab Student Union. Major annual events: Back to School Fest, Phi Theta Kappa initiation, Student Activities Awards Banquet. Student services: personal-psychological counseling, women's center. Campus security: 24-hour emergency response devices and patrols, late night transport-escort service, safety and security programs. College housing not available. Robert E. Turner Learning Resources Center/Library plus 1 other with 77,164 books, 236,210 microform titles, 399 serials, 22,092 audiovisual materials, an OPAC, and a Web page. Operations spending for 2004 fiscal year: $1.3 million. 1,200 computers available on campus for general student use. A campuswide network can be accessed from off-campus. Staffed computer lab on campus.

Community Environment: Palos Hills is located 20 miles south of downtown Chicago near Oak Lawn, a suburban area that has access to all the cultural, educational, and recreational opportunities of Chicago. All major forms of transportation are available. The climate is seasonal. Part-time employment is available.

■ MORRISON INSTITUTE OF TECHNOLOGY *D-8*

701 Portland Ave.
Morrison, IL 61270-0410
Tel: (815)772-7218
Fax: (815)772-7584
E-mail: mit@essexl.com
Web Site: http://www.morrison.tec.il.us/

Description: Independent, 2-year, coed. Awards transfer associate and terminal associate degrees. Founded 1973. Setting: 17-acre small town campus. Endowment: $76,000. Educational spending for 2005 fiscal year: $1535 per student. Total enrollment: 126. Student-undergrad faculty ratio is 12:1. 3% from top 10% of their high school class, 16% from top quarter, 38% from top half. 1 National Merit Scholar, 4 student government officers. Students come from 4 states and territories, 6% from out-of-state, 0% Native American, 3% Hispanic, 4% black, 8% 25 or older, 55% live on campus. Core. Calendar: semesters. Academic remediation for entering students, double major, part-time degree program, internships.

Entrance Requirements: Open admission. Options: Common Application, deferred admission. Required: high school transcript, proof of immunization. Recommended: SAT or ACT. Entrance: noncompetitive. Application deadline: Rolling. Notification: continuous until 9/1.

Costs Per Year: Application fee: $100. Tuition: $12,100 full-time, $504.60 per credit part-time. Mandatory fees: $560 full-time, $125 per term part-time. College room only: $2600.

Collegiate Environment: Major annual events: Turkey Day, Harvest Hammer. Campus security: late night transport-escort service, controlled dormitory access. 136 college housing spaces available; 85 were occupied in 2003-04. Freshmen given priority for college housing. On-campus residence required in freshman year. Option: coed housing available. Milikan Library with 7,946 books and 39 serials. Operations spending for 2004 fiscal year: $22,000. 60 computers available on campus for general student use. Computer purchase/lease plans available. A campuswide network can be accessed from student residence rooms. Staffed computer lab on campus.

Community Environment: Morrison is located 130 miles west of Chicago and 10 miles east of the Mississippi River. It is close to the Chestnut Lodge Winter Ski Area. Students are welcome in the local Theater Association and recreation leagues. Morrison also has two city parks and a state park with a lake. Community facilities include shopping areas, 16 churches, a public library, and two medical centers. A very safe campus environment.

■ **MORTON COLLEGE** *D-16*
3801 South Central Ave.
Cicero, IL 60804-4398
Tel: (708)656-8000
Fax: (708)656-9592
Web Site: http://www.morton.edu/
Description: State and locally supported, 2-year, coed. Part of Illinois Community College Board. Awards certificates, transfer associate, and terminal associate degrees. Founded 1924. Setting: 25-acre suburban campus with easy access to Chicago. Total enrollment: 5,244. Students come from 2 states and territories, 0.1% Native American, 68% Hispanic, 3% black, 2% Asian American or Pacific Islander, 53% 25 or older. Core. Calendar: semesters. Academic remediation for entering students, ESL program, services for LD students, advanced placement, self-designed majors, summer session for credit, part-time degree program, adult/continuing education programs, internships.
Entrance Requirements: Open admission except for nursing, physical therapy assistant programs. Required: high school transcript. Entrance: noncompetitive. Application deadline: Rolling. Preference given to district residents for nursing, physical therapy assistant programs.
Collegiate Environment: Drama-theater group, choral group, student-run newspaper. Social organizations: 20 open to all. Most popular organizations: Hispanic Heritage Club, Program Board, Student Senate, Law Enforcement Association, Nursing Club. Major annual events: Welcome Week, Health Week, comedy/variety series. Campus security: 24-hour patrols, security cameras. College housing not available. Learning Resource Center with 40,972 books and 327 serials. 150 computers available on campus for general student use. Staffed computer lab on campus.
Community Environment: Cicero, (population 62,000), is a residential and industrial suburb on the west side of the greater Chicago area.

■ **NATIONAL-LOUIS UNIVERSITY** *D-16*
122 South Michigan Ave.
Chicago, IL 60603
Tel: (312)621-9650
Free: 800-443-5522
Admissions: 888-NLU-TODAY
Fax: (312)261-3057
Web Site: http://www.nl.edu/
Description: Independent, university, coed. Awards bachelor's, master's, and doctoral degrees and post-master's certificates. Founded 1886. Setting: 12-acre urban campus. Endowment: $21.1 million. Research spending for 2004 fiscal year: $64,560. Total enrollment: 7,345. Faculty: 284 (all full-time). Student-undergrad faculty ratio is 16:1. Full-time: 1,588 students, 72% women, 28% men. Part-time: 572 students, 80% women, 20% men. Students come from 18 states and territories, 1% from out-of-state, 0.4% Native American, 8% Hispanic, 26% black, 2% Asian American or Pacific Islander, 0% international, 74% 25 or older, 5% live on campus, 26% transferred in. Retention: 100% of full-time freshmen returned the following year. Academic areas with the most degrees conferred: business/marketing; interdisciplinary studies; education. Core. Academic remediation for entering students, ESL program, services for LD students, advanced placement, accelerated degree program, honors program, independent study, summer session for credit, part-time degree program, external degree program, adult/continuing education programs, internships, graduate courses open to undergrads.
Entrance Requirements: Options: deferred admission, international baccalaureate accepted. Required: high school transcript, minimum 2.0 high school GPA. Recommended: interview. Required for some: 2 recommendations, SAT or ACT. Entrance: minimally difficult. Application deadline: Rolling. Notification: continuous.
Costs Per Year: Application fee: $25. Tuition: $17,640 full-time, $393 per quarter hour part-time. Mandatory fees: $120 full-time, $40 per term part-time.
Collegiate Environment: Orientation program. Drama-theater group, choral group. Social organizations: 14 open to all. Most popular organizations: Student Council, Nosotros Unidos, Accounting Club, African-American Club. Major annual events: Career Fair, holiday dances, Student-Alumni Dinner Dance. Student services: health clinic, personal-psychological counseling. Campus security: 24-hour emergency response devices and patrols. 170 college housing spaces available; 150 were occupied in 2003-04. Option:

coed housing available. NLU Library plus 5 others with 925,978 microform titles, 5,043 audiovisual materials, and an OPAC. Operations spending for 2004 fiscal year: $1.7 million.
Community Environment: See Northwestern University.

■ **NORTH CENTRAL COLLEGE** *D-14*
30 North Brainard St., PO Box 3063
Naperville, IL 60566-7063
Tel: (630)637-5100
Free: 800-411-1861
Admissions: (630)637-5802
E-mail: admissions@noctrl.edu
Web Site: http://www.noctrl.edu/
Description: Independent United Methodist, comprehensive, coed. Awards bachelor's and master's degrees. Founded 1861. Setting: 56-acre suburban campus with easy access to Chicago. Endowment: $61.6 million. Research spending for 2004 fiscal year: $196,029. Educational spending for 2005 fiscal year: $5909 per student. Total enrollment: 2,472. Faculty: 203 (111 full-time, 92 part-time). Student-undergrad faculty ratio is 15:1. 1,936 applied, 70% were admitted. 21% from top 10% of their high school class, 49% from top quarter, 81% from top half. 1 National Merit Scholar, 7 valedictorians. Full-time: 1,910 students, 59% women, 41% men. Part-time: 223 students, 51% women, 49% men. Students come from 26 states and territories, 24 other countries, 8% from out-of-state, 0.2% Native American, 5% Hispanic, 4% black, 3% Asian American or Pacific Islander, 2% international, 33% 25 or older, 58% live on campus, 11% transferred in. Retention: 79% of full-time freshmen returned the following year. Academic areas with the most degrees conferred: business/marketing; education; social sciences. Core. Academic remediation for entering students, ESL program, services for LD students, advanced placement, accelerated degree program, self-designed majors, honors program, independent study, double major, summer session for credit, part-time degree program, adult/continuing education programs, co-op programs and internships, graduate courses open to undergrads. Off campus study at Aurora University, Benedictine University. Study abroad program. ROTC: Army (c), Air Force (c).
Entrance Requirements: Options: Peterson's Universal Application, Common Application, early admission, deferred admission. Required: high school transcript, minimum 2.0 high school GPA, SAT or ACT. Recommended: essay, 1 recommendation, ACT. Required for some: interview. Entrance: moderately difficult. Application deadline: Rolling. Notification: continuous.
Costs Per Year: Application fee: $25. Comprehensive fee: $28,926 includes full-time tuition ($21,528), mandatory fees ($405), and college room and board ($6993). Room and board charges vary according to housing facility. Part-time tuition: $540 per semester hour. Part-time mandatory fees: $20 per term.
Collegiate Environment: Orientation program. Drama-theater group, choral group, student-run newspaper, radio station. Social organizations: 42 open to all. Most popular organizations: College Union Activities Board, student radio station, Cards in Action (service group), Black Student Organization, Residence Hall Association. Major annual events: homecoming, African-American History Month, Spring Formal. Student services: health clinic, personal-psychological counseling. Campus security: 24-hour emergency response devices and patrols, late night transport-escort service. 990 college housing spaces available; 984 were occupied in 2003-04. Freshmen given priority for college housing. Options: coed, men-only, women-only housing available. Oesterle Library with 149,181 books, 205,396 microform titles, 648 serials, 2,717 audiovisual materials, an OPAC, and a Web page. Operations spending for 2004 fiscal year: $988,367. 200 computers available on campus for general student use. Computer purchase/lease plans available. A campuswide network can be accessed from student residence rooms and from off campus. Staffed computer lab on campus.
Community Environment: Naperville, population 120,000, is a suburban community 29 miles west of Chicago on the Burlington Northern Railroad route. It has a moderate, temperate climate, is the site of many corporate and scientific research installations, and is in the "Research and Development Corridor of Illinois." The community facilities include public and college libraries, a YMCA, hospital, many churches, motels, restaurants, shopping, entertainment, and numerous civic organizations. Many parks and attractive natural surroundings provide for outdoor sports and recreation. Part-time employment for students is generally available.

■ **NORTH PARK UNIVERSITY** *D-16*
3225 West Foster Ave.
Chicago, IL 60625-4895

Tel: (773)244-6200
Free: 800-888-NPC8
Admissions: (773)244-5500
Fax: (773)583-0858
E-mail: afao@northpark.edu
Web Site: http://www.northpark.edu/

Description: Independent, comprehensive, coed, affiliated with Evangelical Covenant Church. Awards bachelor's, master's, doctoral, and first professional degrees. Founded 1891. Setting: 30-acre urban campus. Endowment: $36.4 million. Educational spending for 2005 fiscal year: $6835 per student. Total enrollment: 2,181. 1,068 applied, 74% were admitted. 20% from top 10% of their high school class, 41% from top quarter, 70% from top half. 5 National Merit Scholars. Full-time: 1,252 students, 60% women, 40% men. Part-time: 321 students, 67% women, 33% men. Students come from 38 states and territories, 32 other countries, 39% from out-of-state, 0.4% Native American, 10% Hispanic, 12% black, 5% Asian American or Pacific Islander, 5% international, 20% 25 or older, 12% transferred in. Retention: 70% of full-time freshmen returned the following year. Core. Calendar: semesters. Academic remediation for entering students, ESL program, advanced placement, accelerated degree program, self-designed majors, freshman honors college, honors program, summer session for credit, part-time degree program, adult/continuing education programs, internships. Off campus study at Christian College Coalition. Study abroad program.

Entrance Requirements: Options: Peterson's Universal Application, early admission. Required: essay, high school transcript, minimum 2.0 high school GPA, 2 recommendations, SAT or ACT. Recommended: minimum 3.0 high school GPA. Required for some: interview. Entrance: moderately difficult. Application deadline: Rolling. Notification: continuous.

Costs Per Year: Application fee: $20. Comprehensive fee: $21,240 includes full-time tuition ($13,900), mandatory fees ($60), and college room and board ($7280). College room only: $3800. Full-time tuition and fees vary according to program. Room and board charges vary according to board plan, housing facility, and student level. Part-time tuition: $650 per credit. Part-time tuition varies according to program.

Collegiate Environment: Orientation program. Drama-theater group, choral group, student-run newspaper. Social organizations: 10 open to all. Most popular organizations: Student Association, Urban Outreach, College Life, College Music. Major annual events: homecoming, Spring Event, New Student Orientation. Student services: health clinic, personal-psychological counseling. Campus security: 24-hour emergency response devices and patrols, late night transport-escort service. On-campus residence required through junior year. Options: men-only, women-only housing available. Consolidated Library plus 4 others with 260,685 books, 254,468 microform titles, 1,178 serials, an OPAC, and a Web page. Operations spending for 2004 fiscal year: $890,036. 105 computers available on campus for general student use. A campuswide network can be accessed from student residence rooms and from off campus. Staffed computer lab on campus.

Community Environment: See University of Chicago.

■ **NORTHEASTERN ILLINOIS UNIVERSITY** *D-16*
5500 North St Louis Ave.
Chicago, IL 60625-4699
Tel: (773)583-4050
Admissions: (773)442-4000
Fax: (773)794-6243
Web Site: http://www.neiu.edu/

Description: State-supported, comprehensive, coed. Awards bachelor's and master's degrees. Founded 1961. Setting: 67-acre urban campus. Endowment: $2.3 million. Research spending for 2004 fiscal year: $148,649. Educational spending for 2005 fiscal year: $4492 per student. Total enrollment: 12,227. Faculty: 680 (415 full-time, 265 part-time). Student-undergrad faculty ratio is 16:1. 3,071 applied, 75% were admitted. 7% from top 10% of their high school class, 16% from top quarter, 55% from top half. Full-time: 5,207 students, 62% women, 38% men. Part-time: 4,211 students, 63% women, 37% men. Students come from 18 states and territories, 45 other countries, 1% from out-of-state, 0.2% Native American, 29% Hispanic, 12% black, 11% Asian American or Pacific Islander, 2% international, 40% 25 or older, 13% transferred in. Retention: 69% of full-time freshmen returned the following year. Academic areas with the most degrees conferred: education; liberal arts/general studies; business/marketing. Core. Calendar: semesters. Academic remediation for entering students, ESL program, services for LD students, advanced placement, honors program, independent study, distance learning, double major, summer session for credit, part-time degree program, external degree program, adult/continuing education programs,

co-op programs and internships. Off campus study at National Student Exchange. Study abroad program. ROTC: Army (c), Air Force (c).

Entrance Requirements: Options: deferred admission, international baccalaureate accepted. Required: high school transcript, ACT. Required for some: SAT or ACT. Entrance: minimally difficult. Application deadline: 7/1. Notification: 9/1.

Costs Per Year: Application fee: $25. State resident tuition: $4800 full-time, $160 per credit hour part-time. Nonresident tuition: $9600 full-time, $320 per credit hour part-time. Mandatory fees: $846 full-time. Full-time tuition and fees vary according to student level.

Collegiate Environment: Orientation program. Drama-theater group, student-run newspaper, radio station. Social organizations: 42 open to all; national sororities; 5% of eligible men and 10% of eligible women are members. Most popular organizations: student government, Chimexla, WZRD Radio Club, Business and Management Club, Black Heritage Gospel Choir. Major annual events: International Day, Student Organization Fair, Fall Fest. Student services: health clinic, personal-psychological counseling, women's center. Campus security: 24-hour emergency response devices and patrols, late night transport-escort service. College housing not available. Ronald Williams Library with 713,076 books, 850,696 microform titles, 3,108 serials, 6,324 audiovisual materials, an OPAC, and a Web page. Operations spending for 2004 fiscal year: $3.8 million. 360 computers available on campus for general student use. A campuswide network can be accessed from off-campus. Staffed computer lab on campus.

Community Environment: See University of Chicago.

■ **NORTHERN ILLINOIS UNIVERSITY** *D-12*
DeKalb, IL 60115-2854
Tel: (815)753-1000
Admissions: (815)753-0446
E-mail: admission-info@niu.edu
Web Site: http://www.niu.edu/

Description: State-supported, university, coed. Awards bachelor's, master's, doctoral, and first professional degrees. Founded 1895. Setting: 589-acre small town campus with easy access to Chicago. Endowment: $1.8 million. Research spending for 2004 fiscal year: $13 million. Educational spending for 2005 fiscal year: $6319 per student. Total enrollment: 25,208. Faculty: 1,193 (894 full-time, 299 part-time). Student-undergrad faculty ratio is 17:1. 15,007 applied, 66% were admitted. 9% from top 10% of their high school class, 34% from top quarter, 75% from top half. 7 National Merit Scholars. Full-time: 16,609 students, 52% women, 48% men. Part-time: 1,858 students, 53% women, 47% men. Students come from 50 states and territories, 105 other countries, 3% from out-of-state, 0.3% Native American, 7% Hispanic, 12% black, 5% Asian American or Pacific Islander, 1% international, 13% 25 or older, 33% live on campus, 12% transferred in. Retention: 76% of full-time freshmen returned the following year. Core. Calendar: semesters. Services for LD students, advanced placement, accelerated degree program, self-designed majors, honors program, independent study, double major, summer session for credit, part-time degree program, adult/continuing education programs, co-op programs and internships, graduate courses open to undergrads. Off campus study at Rockford Regional Academic Center, Quad-Cities Graduate Study Center, Hoffman Estate. Study abroad program. ROTC: Army, Air Force (c).

Entrance Requirements: Options: Peterson's Universal Application, electronic application. Required: high school transcript, high school rank, SAT or ACT. Entrance: moderately difficult. Application deadline: 8/1. Notification: continuous.

Costs Per Year: State resident tuition: $5061 full-time, $169 per credit hour part-time. Nonresident tuition: $10,123 full-time, $338 per credit hour part-time. Mandatory fees: $1378 full-time, $58 per credit hour part-time. Full-time tuition and fees vary according to course load. Part-time tuition and fees vary according to course load. College room and board: $5950. Room and board charges vary according to board plan and housing facility.

Collegiate Environment: Orientation program. Drama-theater group, choral group, marching band, student-run newspaper, radio station. Social organizations: 200 open to all; national fraternities, national sororities; 19% of eligible men and 11% of eligible women are members. Most popular organizations: American Marketing Association, Delta Sigma Pi, Pi Sigma Epsilon, Black Choir, Student Volunteer Choir. Major annual event: homecoming. Student services: legal services, health clinic, personal-psychological counseling, women's center. Campus security: 24-hour emergency response devices and patrols, student patrols, late night transport-escort service, controlled dormitory access. 6,200 college housing spaces available; 6,000 were occupied in 2003-04. Freshmen given priority for college housing. On-campus residence required in freshman year. Option: coed housing available. Founders Memorial Library plus 8 others with 3.1 million books, 3.5 million microform titles, 24,696 serials, 52,123 audiovisual materials, an OPAC, and a Web page. Operations spending for 2004 fiscal year: $9.7 million. 1,200 computers available on campus for general student use. A campuswide network can be accessed from student residence rooms and from off campus. Staffed computer lab on campus.

■ NORTHWESTERN BUSINESS COLLEGE D-16
4829 North Lipps Ave.
Chicago, IL 60630-2298
Tel: (773)777-4220
Free: 800-396-5613
Admissions: (773)481-3730
Web Site: http://www.northwesternbc.edu/

Description: Proprietary, 2-year, coed. Awards certificates, transfer associate, and terminal associate degrees. Founded 1902. Setting: 3-acre urban campus. Total enrollment: 2,000. 900 applied, 63% were admitted. Students come from 4 other countries, 21% 25 or older. Core. Academic remediation for entering students, summer session for credit, part-time degree program, co-op programs and internships.

Entrance Requirements: Required: high school transcript, SAT or ACT. Entrance: minimally difficult. Application deadline: Rolling.

Collegiate Environment: College housing not available. Edward G. Schumacher Memorial Library with 2,000 books and 20 serials. 69 computers available on campus for general student use. Staffed computer lab on campus.

■ NORTHWESTERN UNIVERSITY C-16
Evanston, IL 60208
Tel: (847)491-3741
Admissions: (847)491-7271
E-mail: ug-admission@nwu.edu
Web Site: http://www.northwestern.edu/

Description: Independent, university, coed. Awards bachelor's, master's, doctoral, and first professional degrees and post-master's certificates. Founded 1851. Setting: 250-acre suburban campus with easy access to Chicago. Endowment: $4.2 billion. Total enrollment: 17,004. Faculty: 1,145 (938 full-time, 207 part-time). Student-undergrad faculty ratio is 7:1. 16,221 applied, 30% were admitted. 82% from top 10% of their high school class, 96% from top quarter, 100% from top half. 152 National Merit Scholars, 158 valedictorians. Full-time: 7,872 students, 53% women, 47% men. Part-time: 151 students, 51% women, 49% men. Students come from 51 states and territories, 48 other countries, 70% from out-of-state, 0.1% Native American, 5% Hispanic, 5% black, 17% Asian American or Pacific Islander, 5% international, 1% 25 or older, 65% live on campus, 2% transferred in. Retention: 97% of full-time freshmen returned the following year. Academic areas with the most degrees conferred: communications/journalism; social sciences; engineering. Core. Services for LD students, advanced placement, accelerated degree program, self-designed majors, honors program, independent study, double major, summer session for credit, part-time degree program, adult/continuing education programs, co-op programs and internships, graduate courses open to undergrads. Study abroad program. ROTC: Army (c), Naval, Air Force (c).

Entrance Requirements: Options: electronic application, early admission, early decision, deferred admission. Required: essay, high school transcript, 1 recommendation, SAT or ACT. Recommended: SAT Subject Tests. Required for some: audition for music program, SAT Subject Tests. Entrance: most difficult. Application deadlines: 1/1, 11/1 for early decision. Notification: 4/15, 12/15 for early decision.

Costs Per Year: Application fee: $65. Comprehensive fee: $43,825 includes full-time tuition ($33,408), mandatory fees ($151), and college room and board ($10,266). College room only: $5835. Part-time tuition: $3963 per course.

Collegiate Environment: Orientation program. Drama-theater group, choral group, marching band, student-run newspaper, radio station. Social organizations: 415 open to all; national fraternities, national sororities; 32% of eligible men and 38% of eligible women are members. Most popular organizations: Associated Student Government, Asian Christian Ministry, Activities and Organization Board, Dance Marathon, Arts Alliance. Major annual events: homecoming, dance marathon, Armadillo Day. Student services: health clinic, personal-psychological counseling, women's center. Campus security: 24-hour emergency response devices and patrols, late night transport-escort service, controlled dormitory access. 4,250 college

housing spaces available; 3,950 were occupied in 2003-04. Freshmen guaranteed college housing. Options: coed, men-only, women-only housing available. University Library plus 6 others with 4.4 million books, 4.3 million microform titles, 39,944 serials, 79,794 audiovisual materials, an OPAC, and a Web page. Operations spending for 2004 fiscal year: $25.6 million. 678 computers available on campus for general student use. Computer purchase/lease plans available. A campuswide network can be accessed from student residence rooms and from off campus. Staffed computer lab on campus.

Community Environment: Evanston is a residential city on Lake Michigan, adjoining the northern limits of the city of Chicago. With Lake Michigan forming an impressive backdrop, an abundance of oak, elm, and maple trees enhance the beauty of the community. Situated 12 miles from the center of Chicago, Evanston offers the advantages of a quiet, modern community close to a great thriving city. Excellent shopping facilities are available.

■ OAKTON COMMUNITY COLLEGE C-15
1600 East Golf Rd.
Des Plaines, IL 60016-1268
Tel: (847)635-1600
Admissions: (847)635-1629
Fax: (847)635-1706
E-mail: dcohen@oakton.edu
Web Site: http://www.oakton.edu/

Description: District-supported, 2-year, coed. Part of Illinois Community College Board. Awards certificates, transfer associate, and terminal associate degrees. Founded 1969. Setting: 193-acre suburban campus with easy access to Chicago. Educational spending for 2005 fiscal year: $5650 per student. Total enrollment: 9,893. Students come from 50 other countries, 7% from out-of-state, 0.2% Native American, 7% Hispanic, 5% black, 17% Asian American or Pacific Islander, 2% international, 45% 25 or older. Core. Calendar: semesters. Academic remediation for entering students, ESL program, services for LD students, advanced placement, honors program, independent study, distance learning, summer session for credit, part-time degree program, adult/continuing education programs. Study abroad program.

Entrance Requirements: Open admission except for health care programs. Recommended: high school transcript. Required for some: recommendations, interview. Entrance: noncompetitive. Application deadline: Rolling. Notification: continuous.

Collegiate Environment: Orientation program. Drama-theater group, choral group, student-run newspaper. Social organizations: 33 open to all. Most popular organizations: Board of Student Affairs, College Program Board, Phi Theta Kappa, honors student organization, Occurrence (student newspaper). Major annual events: Cultures Week, Spring Fling, Volunteer Day. Student services: health clinic, personal-psychological counseling. Campus security: 24-hour emergency response devices and patrols, student patrols, late night transport-escort service. College housing not available. Oakton Community College Library plus 1 other with 92,000 books, 7,800 microform titles, 586 serials, 10,500 audiovisual materials, an OPAC, and a Web page. Operations spending for 2004 fiscal year: $1.4 million. 750 computers available on campus for general student use. A campuswide network can be accessed from off-campus. Staffed computer lab on campus.

Community Environment: Des Plaines, population 53,568, is a suburban community situated about 12 miles from the center of Chicago, the third largest city in the nation. Cultural facilities of Chicago include museums which cover a wide variety of fields, art galleries, research libraries, theaters, opera, and symphony orchestra.

■ OLIVET NAZARENE UNIVERSITY G-15
One University Ave.
Bourbonnais, IL 60914-2271
Tel: (815)939-5011
Free: 800-648-1463
Admissions: (815)939-5203
E-mail: admissions@olivet.edu
Web Site: http://www.olivet.edu/

Description: Independent, comprehensive, coed, affiliated with Church of the Nazarene. Awards associate, bachelor's, and master's degrees. Founded 1907. Setting: 200-acre small town campus with easy access to Chicago. Endowment: $12.9 million. Research spending for 2004 fiscal year: $431,865. Educational spending for 2005 fiscal year: $5201 per student. Total enrollment: 4,364. 2,747 applied, 65% were admitted. 25% from top 10% of their high school class, 50% from top quarter, 75% from top half. 1

National Merit Scholar, 24 valedictorians. Full-time: 2,352 students, 60% women, 40% men. Part-time: 281 students, 62% women, 38% men. Students come from 41 states and territories, 15 other countries, 51% from out-of-state, 0.2% Native American, 3% Hispanic, 9% black, 1% Asian American or Pacific Islander, 1% international, 17% 25 or older, 79% live on campus, 7% transferred in. Retention: 71% of full-time freshmen returned the following year. Core. Calendar: semesters. Academic remediation for entering students, advanced placement, independent study, double major, summer session for credit, part-time degree program, adult/continuing education programs, internships, graduate courses open to undergrads. Study abroad program. ROTC: Army.

Entrance Requirements: Options: electronic application, deferred admission. Required: high school transcript, minimum 2.0 high school GPA, 2 recommendations, ACT. Recommended: essay, interview. Entrance: minimally difficult. Application deadline: Rolling. Notification: continuous.

Costs Per Year: Application fee: $0. Comprehensive fee: $22,590 includes full-time tuition ($15,650), mandatory fees ($840), and college room and board ($6100). College room only: $3050. Full-time tuition and fees vary according to course load. Room and board charges vary according to board plan. Part-time tuition: $652 per hour. Part-time mandatory fees: $10 per term. Part-time tuition and fees vary according to course load.

Collegiate Environment: Orientation program. Drama-theater group, choral group, student-run newspaper, radio station. Social organizations: 30 open to all. Most popular organizations: Fellowship of Christian Athletes, C.A.U.S.E. College and University Serving and Enabling, Diakonia, Student Education Association, Women's Residence Association. Major annual events: All-School Christmas Banquet, Junior/Senior Banquet, Homecoming Coronation. Student services: health clinic, personal-psychological counseling. Campus security: 24-hour patrols, late night transport-escort service. 1,900 college housing spaces available; 1,829 were occupied in 2003-04. Freshmen guaranteed college housing. On-campus residence required through senior year. Options: men-only, women-only housing available. Benner Library with 160,039 books, 240,846 microform titles, 925 serials, 6,818 audiovisual materials, an OPAC, and a Web page. Operations spending for 2004 fiscal year: $1.1 million. 339 computers available on campus for general student use. Computer purchase/lease plans available. A campuswide network can be accessed from student residence rooms and from off campus. Staffed computer lab on campus.

Community Environment: The campus is in the historic village of Bourbonnais (16,000) on the north edge of Kankakee, Illinois (100,000). This is the growing edge of the community, with excellent schools and small businesses. A shopping mall and numerous stores provide shopping convenience and employment opportunities. Major industries in the area include Armour Pharmaceutical, Armstrong Tile, Quaker Oats, General Foods, and a variety of metal working plants. The proximity to the Chicago metropolitan area is a definite asset.

■ **PARKLAND COLLEGE** *L-14*
2400 West Bradley Ave.
Champaign, IL 61821-1899
Tel: (217)351-2200
Admissions: (217)351-2558
Fax: (217)351-7640
Web Site: http://www.parkland.edu/
Description: District-supported, 2-year, coed. Part of Illinois Community College Board. Awards certificates, transfer associate, and terminal associate degrees. Founded 1967. Setting: 233-acre suburban campus. Research spending for 2004 fiscal year: $6499. Educational spending for 2005 fiscal year: $3487 per student. Total enrollment: 9,752. Student-undergrad faculty ratio is 17:1. 4,097 applied, 52% were admitted. 12% from top 10% of their high school class, 31% from top quarter, 66% from top half. Full-time: 4,536 students, 51% women, 49% men. Part-time: 5,216 students, 57% women, 43% men. Students come from 30 states and territories, 14 other countries, 1% from out-of-state, 1% Native American, 3% Hispanic, 13% black, 4% Asian American or Pacific Islander, 4% international, 31% 25 or older, 6% transferred in. Core. Calendar: semesters. Academic remediation for entering students, ESL program, services for LD students, advanced placement, accelerated degree program, self-designed majors, honors program, independent study, distance learning, double major, summer session for credit, part-time degree program, adult/continuing education programs, co-op programs and internships. Off campus study at University of Illinois at Urbana-Champaign. Study abroad program. ROTC: Army (c), Naval (c), Air Force (c).

Entrance Requirements: Open admission except for allied health, nursing programs. Option: deferred admission. Recommended: high school

transcript. Required for some: ACT. Entrance: noncompetitive. Application deadline: Rolling. Notification: continuous.

Costs Per Year: Application fee: $0. Area resident tuition: $2220 full-time, $72 per credit hour part-time. State resident tuition: $6360 full-time, $212 per credit hour part-time. Nonresident tuition: $9450 full-time, $315 per credit hour part-time.

Collegiate Environment: Orientation program. Drama-theater group, choral group, student-run newspaper, radio station. Student services: personal-psychological counseling. Campus security: 24-hour emergency response devices and patrols, late night transport-escort service. College housing not available. Parkland College Library with 122,676 books, 300 serials, 8,115 audiovisual materials, an OPAC, and a Web page. Operations spending for 2004 fiscal year: $135,263. 800 computers available on campus for general student use. A campuswide network can be accessed. Staffed computer lab on campus.

Community Environment: See University of Illinois at Urbana-Champaign.

■ **PRAIRIE STATE COLLEGE** *E-16*
202 South Halsted St.
Chicago Heights, IL 60411-8226
Tel: (708)709-3500; (708)709-3516
Admissions: (708)709-3542
Web Site: http://www.prairiestate.edu/
Description: State and locally supported, 2-year, coed. Part of Illinois Community College Board. Awards certificates, transfer associate, and terminal associate degrees. Founded 1958. Setting: 68-acre suburban campus with easy access to Chicago. Endowment: $573,000. Educational spending for 2005 fiscal year: $2638 per student. Total enrollment: 5,083. Student-undergrad faculty ratio is 16:1. 836 applied, 100% were admitted. Full-time: 1,714 students, 61% women, 39% men. Part-time: 3,369 students, 62% women, 38% men. Students come from 4 states and territories, 4% from out-of-state, 1% Native American, 10% Hispanic, 47% black, 1% Asian American or Pacific Islander, 0.2% international, 50% 25 or older, 0.4% transferred in. Retention: 48% of full-time freshmen returned the following year. Core. Calendar: semesters. Academic remediation for entering students, ESL program, services for LD students, advanced placement, self-designed majors, honors program, distance learning, summer session for credit, part-time degree program, adult/continuing education programs, internships.

Entrance Requirements: Open admission except for nursing, dental hygiene programs. Options: Common Application, deferred admission. Required: high school transcript. Entrance: noncompetitive. Application deadline: Rolling.

Costs Per Year: Application fee: $10. Area resident tuition: $1824 full-time, $67 per credit hour part-time. State resident tuition: $5280 full-time, $211 per credit hour part-time. Nonresident tuition: $7200 full-time, $291 per credit hour part-time. Mandatory fees: $236 full-time, $9 per credit hour part-time, $10 per term part-time. Full-time tuition and fees vary according to course load. Part-time tuition and fees vary according to course load. College room and board: $4500. Room and board charges vary according to location.

Collegiate Environment: Orientation program. Drama-theater group, choral group, student-run newspaper. Social organizations: 10 open to all. Most popular organizations: Phi Theta Kappa, Black Student Union, Student Government Association, student newspaper, Mental Health Club. Major annual event: Student Leadership Awards. Student services: personal-psychological counseling. Campus security: 24-hour emergency response devices and patrols, student patrols, late night transport-escort service. Learning Resource Center with 45,000 books, 80,000 microform titles, 515 serials, 4,000 audiovisual materials, and an OPAC. Operations spending for 2004 fiscal year: $632,000. 300 computers available on campus for general student use. A campuswide network can be accessed. Staffed computer lab on campus.

Community Environment: Chicago Heights is a metropolitan area located 25 miles south of the Chicago loop. Railroads and buses serve the area. Within the city are shopping centers, many churches, a library, and a hospital. For recreation, there are many parks, a community center with an educational, recreational and social service program, and a Forest Preserve of 1,350 acres.

■ **PRINCIPIA COLLEGE** *Q-7*
One Maybeck Place
Elsah, IL 62028-9799
Tel: (618)374-2131
Free: 800-277-4648 Ext. 2802

Admissions: (618)374-5180

Fax: (618)374-4000

E-mail: collegeadmissions@prin.edu

Web Site: http://www.prin.edu/college/

Description: Independent Christian Science, 4-year, coed. Awards bachelor's degrees. Founded 1910. Setting: 2,600-acre rural campus with easy access to St. Louis. Endowment: $493.7 million. Research spending for 2004 fiscal year: $111,201. Educational spending for 2005 fiscal year: $16,646 per student. Total enrollment: 542. Student-undergrad faculty ratio is 8:1. 242 applied, 89% were admitted. 38% from top 10% of their high school class, 63% from top quarter, 79% from top half. 1 National Merit Scholar, 2 class presidents, 2 valedictorians, 36 student government officers. Full-time: 536 students, 53% women, 47% men. Part-time: 6 students, 17% women, 83% men. Students come from 38 states and territories, 24 other countries, 92% from out-of-state, 0% Native American, 1% Hispanic, 1% black, 1% Asian American or Pacific Islander, 13% international, 2% 25 or older, 100% live on campus, 3% transferred in. Retention: 78% of full-time freshmen returned the following year. Academic areas with the most degrees conferred: social sciences; visual and performing arts; business/marketing. Core. ESL program, advanced placement, accelerated degree program, self-designed majors, honors program, independent study, double major, internships. Study abroad program.

Entrance Requirements: Options: electronic application, early action, deferred admission, international baccalaureate accepted. Required: essay, high school transcript, minimum 2.3 high school GPA, 4 recommendations, Christian Science commitment, SAT or ACT. Recommended: interview, SAT Subject Tests. Required for some: interview. Entrance: moderately difficult. Application deadlines: 3/1, 11/15 for early action. Notification: continuous, 12/1 for early action.

Costs Per Year: Application fee: $0. Comprehensive fee: $29,346 includes full-time tuition ($21,150), mandatory fees ($300), and college room and board ($7896). College room only: $3831. Part-time tuition: $470 per quarter hour.

Collegiate Environment: Orientation program. Drama-theater group, choral group, student-run newspaper, radio station. Social organizations: 36 open to all. Most popular organizations: Christian Science Organization, student newspaper, International Students Association, student radio station, student government. Major annual events: Whole World Festival, Public Affairs Conference, Speakers Series. Student services: health clinic. Campus security: 24-hour patrols. 600 college housing spaces available; 542 were occupied in 2003-04. Freshmen guaranteed college housing. On-campus residence required through senior year. Options: men-only, women-only housing available. Marshall Brooks Library plus 1 other with 211,460 books, 187,434 microform titles, 11,876 serials, 7,792 audiovisual materials, an OPAC, and a Web page. Operations spending for 2004 fiscal year: $770,741. 200 computers available on campus for general student use. A campuswide network can be accessed from student residence rooms and from off campus. Staffed computer lab on campus.

Community Environment: Principia College is located on 2,600 acres of the highest and loveliest section of the Piasa Bluffs above the Mississippi River. In a setting rich in beauty and historical significance, three great rivers may be seen from the bluffs: the Mississippi below, the Missouri to the southeast, and the Illinois, which joins the Mississippi to the west several miles upstream. Mean temperatures are 28-78 degrees, and rainfall averages 35 inches. Recreation, entertainment, and shopping are found in Alton and St. Louis. Part-time student employment is available at the college.

■ **QUINCY UNIVERSITY** *M-4*

1800 College Ave.

Quincy, IL 62301-2699

Tel: (217)222-8020

Free: 800-688-4295

Admissions: (217)228-5210

Fax: (217)228-5479

E-mail: clynes@quincy.edu

Web Site: http://www.quincy.edu/

Description: Independent Roman Catholic, comprehensive, coed. Awards associate, bachelor's, and master's degrees. Founded 1860. Setting: 75-acre small town campus. Educational spending for 2005 fiscal year: $4072 per student. Total enrollment: 1,359. Faculty: 127 (54 full-time, 73 part-time). Student-undergrad faculty ratio is 13:1. 986 applied, 94% were admitted. 9% from top 10% of their high school class, 30% from top quarter, 61% from top half. Full-time: 927 students, 56% women, 44% men. Part-time: 148 students, 61% women, 39% men. Students come from 24 states and ter-

ritories, 6 other countries, 29% from out-of-state, 0.1% Native American, 3% Hispanic, 6% black, 1% Asian American or Pacific Islander, 1% international, 15% 25 or older, 77% live on campus, 11% transferred in. Retention: 68% of full-time freshmen returned the following year. Academic areas with the most degrees conferred: business/marketing; education; health professions and related sciences. Core. Calendar: semesters. Academic remediation for entering students, ESL program, advanced placement, accelerated degree program, self-designed majors, honors program, independent study, distance learning, double major, summer session for credit, part-time degree program, adult/continuing education programs, internships, graduate courses open to undergrads. Study abroad program.

Entrance Requirements: Options: Common Application, electronic application, early admission, deferred admission. Required: essay, high school transcript, minimum 2.0 high school GPA, SAT or ACT. Recommended: interview. Entrance: moderately difficult. Application deadline: Rolling. Notification: continuous.

Costs Per Year: Application fee: $25. Comprehensive fee: $25,970 includes full-time tuition ($18,450), mandatory fees ($560), and college room and board ($6960). College room only: $3740. Part-time tuition: $465 per credit hour. Part-time mandatory fees: $15 per credit hour.

Collegiate Environment: Orientation program. Drama-theater group, choral group, student-run newspaper, radio station. Social organizations: 41 open to all; national fraternities, national sororities; 15% of eligible men and 28% of eligible women are members. Most popular organizations: Student Senate, campus ministry, Student Programming Board, BACCHUS, Students in Free Enterprise. Major annual events: Fall Festival, Hawk Pride Weekend, Mothers' Weekend. Student services: health clinic, personal-psychological counseling. Campus security: 24-hour emergency response devices and patrols, student patrols, late night transport-escort service, controlled dormitory access. 833 college housing spaces available; 614 were occupied in 2003-04. Freshmen guaranteed college housing. On-campus residence required through sophomore year. Options: coed, men-only, women-only housing available. Brenner Library with 239,983 books, 187,438 microform titles, 694 serials, 4,383 audiovisual materials, an OPAC, and a Web page. Operations spending for 2004 fiscal year: $397,828. 190 computers available on campus for general student use. A campuswide network can be accessed from student residence rooms and from off campus. Staffed computer lab on campus.

Community Environment: The University is located in a residential section of Quincy, a city of 50,000, located on the bluffs of the Mississippi River. It is within easy traveling distance of St. Louis (2 1/2 hours), Kansas City (4 hours), and Chicago (4 hours).

■ **REND LAKE COLLEGE** *U-12*

468 North Ken Gray Parkway

Ina, IL 62846-9801

Tel: (618)437-5321

Fax: (618)437-5677

E-mail: mitchelp@rlc.cc.il.us

Web Site: http://www.rlc.edu/

Description: State-supported, 2-year, coed. Part of Illinois Community College Board. Awards certificates, transfer associate, and terminal associate degrees. Founded 1967. Setting: 350-acre rural campus. Endowment: $1.7 million. Educational spending for 2005 fiscal year: $2375 per student. Total enrollment: 5,142. Students come from 2 states and territories, 2 other countries, 1% from out-of-state, 0.2% Native American, 1% Hispanic, 3% black, 1% Asian American or Pacific Islander, 0.1% international, 70% 25 or older. Core. Calendar: semesters. Academic remediation for entering students, services for LD students, advanced placement, honors program, independent study, distance learning, summer session for credit, part-time degree program, adult/continuing education programs, co-op programs and internships. Off campus study at SICCM, Murphy-Wall Pinckneyville Center, Reno Lake College Marketplace.

Entrance Requirements: Open admission except for allied health programs. Options: electronic application, deferred admission. Required: high school transcript. Placement: SAT or ACT, ACT ASSET, ACT COMPASS required. Entrance: noncompetitive. Application deadline: 8/18.

Collegiate Environment: Orientation program. Drama-theater group, choral group, student-run newspaper. Social organizations: 24 open to all. Most popular organizations: Student Senate, Psi Beta, Phi Theta Kappa, Student Ambassadors. Major annual events: Career Day, Homecoming, Fun Fest. Campus security: 24-hour emergency response devices and patrols, late night transport-escort service. College housing not available. Learning Resource Center with 35,426 books, 68,500 microform titles, 265 serials,

3,770 audiovisual materials, an OPAC, and a Web page. Operations spending for 2004 fiscal year: $286,412. 451 computers available on campus for general student use. Computer purchase/lease plans available. A campuswide network can be accessed from off-campus. Staffed computer lab on campus.

Community Environment: The college is located in a rural area with all forms of transportation available. Industries in nearby Mount Vernon, population 16,382, include the manufacture of electric equipment, radiators, women's wear, shoes, forest products, boats, automobile tires, and chemicals. Oil production and agriculture are important in the surrounding areas. Cultural opportunities offered by the State Law Library and Museum. Community facilities include 40 churches of major denominations, hospitals, a clinic, and major civic and service organizations. Recreational activities are boating, fishing, swimming, bowling, and golf. Du Quoin State Fair is an annual event.

■ **RICHLAND COMMUNITY COLLEGE** *M-12*
One College Park
Decatur, IL 62521-8513
Tel: (217)875-7200
Fax: (217)875-6991
E-mail: sblahnik@richland.edu
Web Site: http://www.richland.edu/

Description: District-supported, 2-year, coed. Part of Illinois Community College Board. Awards certificates, transfer associate, and terminal associate degrees. Founded 1971. Setting: 117-acre small town campus. Endowment: $4.8 million. Educational spending for 2005 fiscal year: $3742 per student. Total enrollment: 3,034. Student-undergrad faculty ratio is 14:1. 769 applied, 100% were admitted. 0% from top 10% of their high school class, 10% from top quarter, 61% from top half. 0% from out-of-state, 0.5% Native American, 1% Hispanic, 12% black, 1% Asian American or Pacific Islander, 0.1% international, 40% 25 or older. Retention: 53% of full-time freshmen returned the following year. Core. Calendar: semesters. Academic remediation for entering students, ESL program, services for LD students, advanced placement, self-designed majors, freshman honors college, honors program, distance learning, summer session for credit, part-time degree program, adult/continuing education programs.

Entrance Requirements: Open admission. Option: early admission. Required: high school transcript. Recommended: ACT. Entrance: noncompetitive. Application deadline: Rolling.

Costs Per Year: Application fee: $0. Area resident tuition: $1785 full-time, $59.50 per credit hour part-time. State resident tuition: $7566 full-time, $258.20 per credit hour part-time. Nonresident tuition: $11,490 full-time, $383 per credit hour part-time. Mandatory fees: $155 full-time, $4.50 per credit hour part-time, $10 per term part-time.

Collegiate Environment: Orientation program. Student-run newspaper. Social organizations: 35 open to all. Most popular organizations: Student Senate, Forensics Club, Drama Club, Black Student Association, Student Activities Board. Major annual events: Multicultural Fair, Career Fair. Student services: personal-psychological counseling. Campus security: 24-hour emergency response devices and patrols. College housing not available. Kitty Lindsay Library with 39,452 books, 2,635 microform titles, 275 serials, 2,910 audiovisual materials, an OPAC, and a Web page. Operations spending for 2004 fiscal year: $562,302. 150 computers available on campus for general student use. Staffed computer lab on campus.

Community Environment: See Millikin University.

■ **ROBERT MORRIS COLLEGE** *D-16*
401 South State St.
Chicago, IL 60605
Tel: (312)935-6800
Free: 800-RMC-5960
Admissions: (312)935-6640
Fax: (312)836-4599
E-mail: enroll@rmcil.edu
Web Site: http://www.robertmorris.edu/

Description: Independent, 4-year, coed. Awards associate, bachelor's, and master's degrees. Founded 1913. Setting: urban campus. Endowment: $36.4 million. Educational spending for 2005 fiscal year: $1916 per student. Total enrollment: 5,418. Faculty: 368 (134 full-time, 234 part-time). Student-undergrad faculty ratio is 26:1. 2,714 applied, 80% were admitted. 7% from top 10% of their high school class, 23% from top quarter, 50% from top half. Full-time: 4,706 students, 65% women, 35% men. Part-time: 712 students, 73% women, 27% men. Students come from 21 states and territories, 17

other countries, 1% from out-of-state, 0.4% Native American, 24% Hispanic, 37% black, 2% Asian American or Pacific Islander, 0.5% international, 37% 25 or older, 2% live on campus, 21% transferred in. Retention: 56% of full-time freshmen returned the following year. Academic areas with the most degrees conferred: business/marketing; computer and information sciences; visual and performing arts. Core. Calendar: 5 ten-week academic sessions per year. Academic remediation for entering students, advanced placement, accelerated degree program, freshman honors college, honors program, distance learning, summer session for credit, part-time degree program, adult/continuing education programs, co-op programs and internships. Study abroad program. ROTC: Army (c).

Entrance Requirements: Options: Peterson's Universal Application, Common Application, electronic application, deferred admission, international baccalaureate accepted. Required: high school transcript. Recommended: minimum 2.0 high school GPA, interview. Entrance: minimally difficult. Application deadline: Rolling. Notification: continuous.

Costs Per Year: Application fee: $30. Tuition: $15,900 full-time.

Collegiate Environment: Orientation program. Drama-theater group, choral group, student-run newspaper. Social organizations: 19 open to all. Most popular organizations: Fitness in Transition, Sigma Beta Delta (honor society), Eagle (newspaper), National Phlebotomy Society, Association for Medical Assistants. Major annual events: Ice Cream Social/Karaoke, African-American and Hispanic-American Heritage Month, St. Patrick's Day Parade. Student services: personal-psychological counseling. Campus security: 24-hour emergency response devices and patrols. 119 college housing spaces available; 109 were occupied in 2003-04. Freshmen guaranteed college housing. Option: coed housing available. Thomas Jefferson Library plus 6 others with 121,737 books, 193 serials, 21,011 audiovisual materials, an OPAC, and a Web page. Operations spending for 2004 fiscal year: $852,694. 1,879 computers available on campus for general student use. A campuswide network can be accessed from student residence rooms. Staffed computer lab on campus.

Community Environment: Located in Chicago's Loop, the main campus is in the heart of the downtown business and financial district.

■ **ROCK VALLEY COLLEGE** *B-11*
3301 North Mulford Rd.
Rockford, IL 61114-5699
Tel: (815)921-7821
Free: 800-973-7821
Admissions: (815)921-4088
Fax: (815)654-5568
Web Site: http://www.rockvalleycollege.edu/

Description: District-supported, 2-year, coed. Part of Illinois Community College Board. Awards certificates, transfer associate, and terminal associate degrees. Founded 1964. Setting: 217-acre suburban campus with easy access to Chicago. Total enrollment: 8,145. Student-undergrad faculty ratio is 21:1. Full-time: 3,508 students, 52% women, 48% men. Part-time: 4,637 students, 65% women, 35% men. Students come from 2 states and territories, 3 other countries, 1% from out-of-state, 0.4% Native American, 6% Hispanic, 9% black, 3% Asian American or Pacific Islander, 0.3% international, 43% 25 or older. Core. Calendar: semesters. Academic remediation for entering students, ESL program, services for LD students, advanced placement, self-designed majors, honors program, independent study, distance learning, summer session for credit, part-time degree program, adult/continuing education programs, co-op programs and internships. Study abroad program.

Entrance Requirements: Open admission. Required: high school transcript. Entrance: noncompetitive. Application deadline: 8/29. Notification: continuous.

Costs Per Year: Application fee: $0. Area resident tuition: $1830 full-time, $61 per credit part-time. State resident tuition: $7350 full-time, $245 per credit part-time. Nonresident tuition: $12,030 full-time, $401 per credit part-time.

Collegiate Environment: Orientation program. Drama-theater group, choral group, student-run newspaper. Social organizations: 12 open to all. Most popular organizations: Black Student Alliance, Phi Theta Kappa, Adults on Campus, Inter-Varsity Club, Christian Fellowship. Major annual events: New Student Week, Homecoming Week, May Fest. Student services: personal-psychological counseling. Campus security: 24-hour emergency response devices and patrols, late night transport-escort service. College housing not available. Educational Resource Center with 67,168 books, an OPAC, and a Web page. Operations spending for 2004 fiscal year: $880,000. 130 computers available on campus for general student use. A campuswide network can be accessed from off-campus. Staffed computer lab on campus.

Community Environment: See Rockford College.

■ **ROCKFORD BUSINESS COLLEGE** *B-11*

730 North Church St.
Rockford, IL 61103
Tel: (815)965-8616
Fax: (815)965-0360
Web Site: http://www.rbcsuccess.com/

Description: Independent, 2-year, coed. Awards certificates, diplomas, and terminal associate degrees. Founded 1862. Setting: urban campus with easy access to Chicago. Total enrollment: 428. 125 applied. Full-time: 243 students, 90% women, 10% men. Part-time: 185 students, 87% women, 13% men. Students come from 2 states and territories, 1% from out-of-state, 0.2% Native American, 7% Hispanic, 34% black, 0.2% Asian American or Pacific Islander, 65% 25 or older, 8% transferred in. Core. Academic remediation for entering students, services for LD students, advanced placement, honors program, independent study, summer session for credit, part-time degree program, adult/continuing education programs, co-op programs and internships.

Entrance Requirements: Open admission. Options: Common Application, electronic application, early admission. Required: high school transcript, interview. Required for some: essay. Entrance: minimally difficult. Application deadline: 9/4.

Collegiate Environment: Orientation program. Student-run newspaper. Most popular organization: International Students Club. Student services: personal-psychological counseling. Campus security: 24-hour patrols, late night transport-escort service. Rockford Business College Library plus 1 other with 1,823 books, 161 serials, and 50 audiovisual materials. 65 computers available on campus for general student use. A campuswide network can be accessed. Staffed computer lab on campus.

Community Environment: See Rockford College.

■ **ROCKFORD COLLEGE** *B-11*

5050 East State St.
Rockford, IL 61108-2393
Tel: (815)226-4000
Free: 800-892-2984
Admissions: (815)226-4050
Fax: (815)226-4119
E-mail: mplocinski@rockford.edu
Web Site: http://www.rockford.edu/

Description: Independent, comprehensive, coed. Awards bachelor's and master's degrees. Founded 1847. Setting: 130-acre suburban campus with easy access to Chicago. Endowment: $8.9 million. Educational spending for 2005 fiscal year: $5185 per student. Total enrollment: 1,376. Faculty: (68 full-time). Student-undergrad faculty ratio is 11:1. 762 applied, 59% were admitted. 16% from top 10% of their high school class, 35% from top quarter, 57% from top half. 4 valedictorians. Full-time: 731 students, 63% women, 37% men. Part-time: 141 students, 72% women, 28% men. Students come from 8 states and territories, 10 other countries, 6% from out-of-state, 0.5% Native American, 5% Hispanic, 7% black, 2% Asian American or Pacific Islander, 2% international, 16% 25 or older, 36% live on campus, 15% transferred in. Retention: 61% of full-time freshmen returned the following year. Academic areas with the most degrees conferred: education; business/marketing; social sciences. Core. Calendar: semesters. Academic remediation for entering students, ESL program, advanced placement, self-designed majors, honors program, double major, summer session for credit, part-time degree program, adult/continuing education programs, internships, graduate courses open to undergrads. Off campus study at American University, Central College (IA), Drew University. Study abroad program. ROTC: Army (c).

Entrance Requirements: Options: Peterson's Universal Application, Common Application, electronic application, early admission, deferred admission, international baccalaureate accepted. Required: high school transcript, SAT or ACT. Recommended: minimum 2.65 high school GPA, interview, campus visit. Required for some: essay, minimum 2.65 high school GPA, 2 recommendations. Entrance: moderately difficult. Application deadline: 8/1.

Costs Per Year: Application fee: $35. Comprehensive fee: $29,681 includes full-time tuition ($22,460) and college room and board ($7221). College room only: $4441. Part-time tuition: $595 per credit.

Collegiate Environment: Orientation program. Drama-theater group, choral group, student-run radio station. Social organizations: 25 open to all. Most popular organizations: student government, Intercultural Club, 4Ts (Tomorrow's Teachers Together Today), Psychology Society, Nursing Student

Organization. Major annual events: Homecoming, Flake Out Winter Carnival, Hunger and Homelessness Week Activities. Student services: health clinic, personal-psychological counseling. Campus security: 24-hour emergency response devices and patrols, late night transport-escort service, controlled dormitory access. 1,000 college housing spaces available; 650 were occupied in 2003-04. On-campus residence required through senior year. Options: coed, men-only, women-only housing available. Howard Colman Library with 140,000 books, 20 microform titles, 831 serials, 9,723 audiovisual materials, and an OPAC. Operations spending for 2004 fiscal year: $479,382. 65 computers available on campus for general student use. A campuswide network can be accessed from student residence rooms. Staffed computer lab on campus.

Community Environment: Rockford, population 147,370, is the second largest city in the state. It is 75 miles northwest of Chicago, and is situated in the historic and attractive Rock River Valley close to the Wisconsin border. Rockford is also an important industrial city that produces machine tools, furniture, hardware and automobile accessories.

■ **ROOSEVELT UNIVERSITY** *D-16*

430 South Michigan Ave.
Chicago, IL 60605-1394
Tel: (312)341-3500; 877-APPLYRU
E-mail: dessimm@admvsbk.roosevelt.edu
Web Site: http://www.roosevelt.edu/

Description: Independent, comprehensive, coed. Awards bachelor's, master's, and doctoral degrees and post-master's certificates. Founded 1945. Setting: urban campus. Endowment: $47.6 million. Research spending for 2004 fiscal year: $273,350. Educational spending for 2005 fiscal year: $7638 per student. Total enrollment: 7,234. Faculty: 644 (212 full-time, 432 part-time). Student-undergrad faculty ratio is 12:1. 1,390 applied, 60% were admitted. 3% from top 10% of their high school class, 11% from top quarter, 33% from top half. Full-time: 2,041 students, 66% women, 34% men. Part-time: 2,032 students, 69% women, 31% men. Students come from 44 states and territories, 65 other countries, 8% from out-of-state, 0.3% Native American, 11% Hispanic, 24% black, 5% Asian American or Pacific Islander, 2% international, 63% 25 or older, 9% live on campus, 15% transferred in. Retention: 70% of full-time freshmen returned the following year. Academic areas with the most degrees conferred: business/marketing; psychology; computer and information sciences. Calendar: semesters. Academic remediation for entering students, ESL program, services for LD students, advanced placement, accelerated degree program, self-designed majors, honors program, independent study, distance learning, double major, summer session for credit, part-time degree program, external degree program, adult/continuing education programs, internships, graduate courses open to undergrads. Off campus study at School of the Art Institute of Chicago. Study abroad program.

Entrance Requirements: Options: Peterson's Universal Application, Common Application, electronic application, deferred admission, international baccalaureate accepted. Required: essay, high school transcript, minimum 2.5 high school GPA, audition for music and theater programs, SAT or ACT. Required for some: recommendations, interview. Entrance: moderately difficult. Application deadline: 9/1. Notification: continuous.

Costs Per Year: Application fee: $25. Comprehensive fee: $22,420 includes full-time tuition ($14,180), mandatory fees ($250), and college room and board ($7990). College room only: $5800. Full-time tuition and fees vary according to course load and program. Room and board charges vary according to board plan, housing facility, and location. Part-time tuition: $575 per hour. Part-time mandatory fees: $125 per term. Part-time tuition and fees vary according to course load and program.

Collegiate Environment: Orientation program. Drama-theater group, choral group, student-run newspaper, radio station. Social organizations: 14 open to all; 1% of eligible men and 1% of eligible women are members. Most popular organizations: International Student Union, RU Proud, RU Latinos, Student Government, Residence Hall Council. Major annual events: International Day, semi-formal dances, Student Organization Fair. Student services: personal-psychological counseling. Campus security: 24-hour emergency response devices and patrols, controlled dormitory access. College housing designed to accommodate 300 students; 347 undergraduates lived in college housing during 2003-04. Freshmen guaranteed college housing. On-campus residence required through sophomore year. Option: coed housing available. Murray-Green Library plus 4 others with 186,944 books, 169,907 microform titles, 1,195 serials, 11,357 audiovisual materials, an OPAC, and a Web page. Operations spending for 2004 fiscal year: $2.1 million. 250 computers available on campus for general student use. A

campuswide network can be accessed from student residence rooms and from off campus. Staffed computer lab on campus.

Community Environment: Roosevelt University's downtown location places students only blocks away from such cultural and educational resources as the Art Institute, Orchestra Hall, the Opera House, the Field Museum of Natural History, the Grant Park Band Shell, the Shedd Aquarium and the Adler Planetarium. Roosevelt University is also located in the hub of the city's mercantile and financial districts - the Board of Trade, the State Street department stores, the LaSalle and Dearborn Streets banking houses, law offices, and government buildings all being within easy walking distance of the university. The Schauburg campus is located across from the Chicago area's largest shopping mall and only 15 minutes from O'Hare International Airport. The two campuses are linked by regularly scheduled van service and all academic programs are available at both locations except the Performing Arts (Chicago only).

■ **RUSH UNIVERSITY** *D-16*
600 South Paulina
Chicago, IL 60612-3832
Tel: (312)942-5000
Admissions: (312)942-7100
Fax: (312)942-2100
Web Site: http://www.rushu.rush.edu/
Description: Independent, upper-level, coed. Awards bachelor's, master's, doctoral, and first professional degrees and post-master's certificates. Founded 1969. Setting: 35-acre urban campus. Endowment: $340.2 million. Research spending for 2004 fiscal year: $41.6 million. Educational spending for 2005 fiscal year: $20,780 per student. Total enrollment: 1,362. 306 applied, 36% were admitted. Full-time: 195 students, 86% women, 14% men. Part-time: 17 students, 88% women, 12% men. Students come from 8 states and territories, 3 other countries, 12% from out-of-state, 0% Native American, 5% Hispanic, 7% black, 11% Asian American or Pacific Islander, 3% international, 27% live on campus, 40% transferred in. Accelerated degree program, distance learning, part-time degree program.
Costs Per Year: Application fee: $40. Tuition: $18,195 full-time, $475 per quarter hour part-time. Full-time tuition varies according to course load, degree level, and program. Part-time tuition varies according to course load, degree level, and program. College room only: $5715. Room charges vary according to housing facility.
Collegiate Environment: Major annual events: Octoberfest, TGIF's, Spring Formal. Student services: health clinic, personal-psychological counseling. Campus security: 24-hour emergency response devices and patrols, late night transport-escort service, controlled dormitory access. Option: coed housing available. Library of Rush University Medical Center with 120,042 books, 1,100 serials, 4,750 audiovisual materials, an OPAC, and a Web page. Operations spending for 2004 fiscal year: $2 million. 150 computers available on campus for general student use. Computer purchase/lease plans available. A campuswide network can be accessed from student residence rooms and from off campus. Staffed computer lab on campus.
Community Environment: See University of Chicago.

■ **SAINT ANTHONY COLLEGE OF NURSING** *B-11*
5658 East State St.
Rockford, IL 61108-2468
Tel: (815)395-5091
Admissions: (815)395-5100
Web Site: http://www.sacn.edu/
Description: Independent Roman Catholic, upper-level, coed. Awards bachelor's degrees. Founded 1915. Setting: 17-acre urban campus with easy access to Chicago. Endowment: $600,000. Educational spending for 2005 fiscal year: $13,656 per student. Total enrollment: 125. Student-undergrad faculty ratio is 9:1. Full-time: 108 students, 92% women, 8% men. Part-time: 17 students, 88% women, 12% men. Students come from 2 states and territories, 4% from out-of-state, 0% Native American, 3% Hispanic, 1% black, 5% Asian American or Pacific Islander, 0% international, 68% 25 or older, 22% transferred in. Academic area with the most degrees conferred: health professions and related sciences. Core. Calendar: semesters. Services for LD students, advanced placement, accelerated degree program, independent study, summer session for credit, part-time degree program, internships. Off campus study.
Costs Per Year: Application fee: $50. Tuition: $16,192 full-time, $506 per credit part-time. Mandatory fees: $116 full-time.
Collegiate Environment: Orientation program. Social organizations: 1 open to all; 8% of eligible men and 92% of eligible women are members. Most

popular organization: Student Organization. Major annual events: Opening Mass and Breakfast, Welcome Party for new students, Student Organization Activities. Student services: legal services, health clinic, personal-psychological counseling. Campus security: 24-hour emergency response devices and patrols, late night transport-escort service. College housing not available. Sister Mary Linus Learning Resource Center plus 1 other with 1,394 books, 3,136 serials, 163 audiovisual materials, an OPAC, and a Web page. Operations spending for 2004 fiscal year: $116,000. 17 computers available on campus for general student use. A campuswide network can be accessed from off-campus. Staffed computer lab on campus.

■ **ST. AUGUSTINE COLLEGE** *D-16*
1333-1345 West Argyle
Chicago, IL 60640-3501
Tel: (773)878-8756
Admissions: (773)878-3256
Web Site: http://www.staugustinecollege.edu/
Description: Independent, 4-year, coed. Awards associate and bachelor's degrees (offers bilingual Spanish/English degree programs). Founded 1980. Setting: 4-acre urban campus. Endowment: $503,322. Educational spending for 2005 fiscal year: $3007 per student. Total enrollment: 1,582. 1,085 applied, 78% were admitted. Full-time: 1,279 students, 79% women, 21% men. Part-time: 303 students, 76% women, 24% men. Students come from 2 states and territories, 0% from out-of-state, 0% Native American, 84% Hispanic, 7% black, 7% Asian American or Pacific Islander, 1% international, 68% 25 or older, 2% transferred in. Retention: 69% of full-time freshmen returned the following year. Core. Calendar: semesters. Academic remediation for entering students, ESL program, independent study, summer session for credit, part-time degree program, co-op programs and internships.
Entrance Requirements: Open admission. Option: deferred admission. Required: Ability-To-Benefit Admissions Test. Entrance: noncompetitive. Application deadline: Rolling.
Costs Per Year: Application fee: $0. Tuition: $7128 full-time, $297 per credit part-time.
Collegiate Environment: Orientation program. Choral group, student-run newspaper. Most popular organization: ENLACE. Major annual events: Student Alliance Week, Hispanic History Week, Mexican Fiesta. Student services: personal-psychological counseling. Campus security: 24-hour patrols, late night transport-escort service. College housing not available. St. Augustine College Library plus 1 other with 21,000 books, 48 serials, 931 audiovisual materials, an OPAC, and a Web page. Operations spending for 2004 fiscal year: $121,000. 292 computers available on campus for general student use. A campuswide network can be accessed. Staffed computer lab on campus.

■ **SAINT FRANCIS MEDICAL CENTER COLLEGE OF NURSING** *I-10*
511 NE Greenleaf St.
Peoria, IL 61603-3783
Tel: (309)655-2201
Admissions: (309)624-8980
Web Site: http://www.sfmccon.edu/
Description: Independent Roman Catholic, upper-level, coed. Awards bachelor's and master's degrees. Founded 1986. Setting: urban campus. Total enrollment: 272. Full-time: 182 students, 86% women, 14% men. Part-time: 38 students, 100% women. Students come from 2 states and territories, 0% Native American, 1% Hispanic, 2% black, 0% Asian American or Pacific Islander, 0% international, 56% 25 or older, 28% live on campus, 27% transferred in. Retention: 100% of full-time entering class returned the following year. Core. Calendar: semesters. Advanced placement, independent study, distance learning, summer session for credit, part-time degree program.
Costs Per Year: Application fee: $50. Tuition: $10,200 full-time, $425 per semester hour part-time. Mandatory fees: $450 full-time, $225 per term part-time. Full-time tuition and fees vary according to course load. Part-time tuition and fees vary according to course load. College room only: $1880.
Collegiate Environment: Orientation program. Choral group. Social organizations: 2 open to all. Most popular organizations: Student Senate, SNAI. Major annual events: Open House, Christmas Dinner, Spring Formal. Student services: health clinic, personal-psychological counseling. Campus security: 24-hour emergency response devices, controlled dormitory access. 118 college housing spaces available. Option: coed housing available. 6,215 books and 125 serials. 0 computers available on campus for general student use. Staffed computer lab on campus.

■ **ST. JOHN'S COLLEGE** *M-9*
421 North Ninth St.
Springfield, IL 62702-5317
Tel: (217)525-5628
Web Site: http://www.st-johns.org/education/schools/nursing/
Description: Independent Roman Catholic, upper-level, coed. Awards bachelor's degrees. Founded 1886. Setting: urban campus. Endowment: $546,206. Educational spending for 2005 fiscal year: $31,436 per student. Total enrollment: 82. 85 applied, 58% were admitted. Full-time: 79 students, 92% women, 8% men. Part-time: 3 students, 100% women. Students come from 3 states and territories, 1 other country, 2% from out-of-state, 1% Native American, 0% Hispanic, 1% black, 0% Asian American or Pacific Islander, 1% international, 20% 25 or older, 59% transferred in. Core. Calendar: semesters. Part-time degree program.
Costs Per Year: Application fee: $35. Tuition: $9980 full-time, $416 per credit hour part-time. Mandatory fees: $380 full-time. Full-time tuition and fees vary according to course load. Part-time tuition varies according to course load.
Collegiate Environment: Orientation program. Social organizations: 2 open to all. Most popular organizations: NSNA, class/student government. Major annual events: Christmas Gathering, community service projects. Student services: health clinic, personal-psychological counseling. Campus security: 24-hour emergency response devices and patrols, late night transport-escort service. College housing not available. St. John's Health Science Library with 7,715 books, 349 serials, 735 audiovisual materials, and an OPAC. 21 computers available on campus for general student use. A campuswide network can be accessed. Staffed computer lab on campus.

■ **SAINT XAVIER UNIVERSITY** *D-16*
3700 West 103rd St.
Chicago, IL 60655-3105
Tel: (773)298-3000
Free: 800-462-9288
Admissions: (773)298-3063
Fax: (773)298-3076
E-mail: admissions@sxu.edu
Web Site: http://www.sxu.edu/
Description: Independent Roman Catholic, comprehensive, coed. Awards bachelor's and master's degrees and post-master's certificates. Founded 1847. Setting: 70-acre urban campus. Endowment: $7.7 million. Total enrollment: 5,705. Faculty: 426 (168 full-time, 258 part-time). Student-undergrad faculty ratio is 15:1. 1,998 applied, 69% were admitted. 14% from top 10% of their high school class, 43% from top quarter, 73% from top half. Full-time: 2,391 students, 70% women, 30% men. Part-time: 791 students, 79% women, 21% men. Students come from 23 states and territories, 2 other countries, 4% from out-of-state, 0.3% Native American, 13% Hispanic, 18% black, 2% Asian American or Pacific Islander, 0.4% international, 28% 25 or older, 20% live on campus, 15% transferred in. Retention: 75% of full-time freshmen returned the following year. Academic areas with the most degrees conferred: business/marketing; education; health professions and related sciences. Core. Calendar: semesters. Academic remediation for entering students, ESL program, services for LD students, advanced placement, accelerated degree program, self-designed majors, honors program, independent study, double major, summer session for credit, part-time degree program, adult/continuing education programs, co-op programs and internships, graduate courses open to undergrads. Study abroad program. ROTC: Air Force (c).
Entrance Requirements: Options: Peterson's Universal Application, Common Application, electronic application, deferred admission, international baccalaureate accepted. Required: high school transcript, SAT or ACT. Recommended: essay, minimum 2.5 high school GPA, interview. Required for some: interview. Entrance: moderately difficult. Application deadline: Rolling. Notification: continuous.
Costs Per Year: Application fee: $25. Comprehensive fee: $25,598 includes full-time tuition ($18,350), mandatory fees ($170), and college room and board ($7078). College room only: $4428. Full-time tuition and fees vary according to course load. Room and board charges vary according to board plan and housing facility. Part-time tuition: $611 per credit hour. Part-time mandatory fees: $110 per year. Part-time tuition and fees vary according to course load.
Collegiate Environment: Orientation program. Drama-theater group, choral group, marching band, student-run newspaper, radio station. Social organizations: 37 open to all. Most popular organizations: Student Activities Board, Black Student Union, UNIDOS (Hispanic Organization), Student

Nurses Association, Business Students Association. Major annual events: Homecoming Celebrations, Boat Bash. Student services: health clinic, personal-psychological counseling, women's center. Campus security: 24-hour emergency response devices and patrols, late night transport-escort service. 630 college housing spaces available; 600 were occupied in 2003-04. No special consideration for freshman housing applicants. Option: coed housing available. Byrne Memorial Library with 170,753 books, 10,519 microform titles, 717 serials, 3,112 audiovisual materials, an OPAC, and a Web page. Operations spending for 2004 fiscal year: $1.2 million. 306 computers available on campus for general student use. A campuswide network can be accessed from student residence rooms and from off campus. Staffed computer lab on campus.
Community Environment: See University of Chicago.

■ **SAUK VALLEY COMMUNITY COLLEGE** *D-10*
173 Illinois Route 2
Dixon, IL 61021
Tel: (815)288-5511
E-mail: clodfep@svcc.edu
Web Site: http://www.svcc.edu/
Description: District-supported, 2-year, coed. Part of Illinois Community College Board. Awards certificates, transfer associate, and terminal associate degrees. Founded 1965. Setting: 165-acre rural campus. Total enrollment: 2,745. Student-undergrad faculty ratio is 19:1. 1,327 applied, 100% were admitted. 5% from top 10% of their high school class, 21% from top quarter, 53% from top half. Full-time: 1,154 students, 60% women, 40% men. Part-time: 1,591 students, 63% women, 37% men. 0% from out-of-state, 0.2% Native American, 7% Hispanic, 2% black, 1% Asian American or Pacific Islander, 0% international, 50% 25 or older. Core. Calendar: semesters. Academic remediation for entering students, ESL program, services for LD students, accelerated degree program, self-designed majors, honors program, independent study, distance learning, part-time degree program, adult/continuing education programs, co-op programs and internships. Off campus study at Highland Community College, Illinois Valley Community College, Rock Valley College, Kishwaukee College.
Entrance Requirements: Open admission except for health programs. Options: early admission, deferred admission. Recommended: high school transcript, ACT. Entrance: noncompetitive. Application deadline: Rolling. Notification: continuous.
Costs Per Year: Application fee: $0. Area resident tuition: $2418 full-time, $74 per credit hour part-time. State resident tuition: $9065 full-time, $259 per credit hour part-time. Nonresident tuition: $9375 full-time, $293 per credit hour part-time.
Collegiate Environment: Orientation program. Drama-theater group, choral group. Social organizations: 10 open to all. Student services: personal-psychological counseling. Campus security: 24-hour emergency response devices and patrols, late night transport-escort service. College housing not available. Learning Resource Center plus 1 other with 55,000 books and 268 serials. 100 computers available on campus for general student use. A campuswide network can be accessed. Staffed computer lab on campus.
Community Environment: Dixon has a population of 15,701; Sterling (population 16,281) is a small industrial city, enjoying a seasonal climate. Ozark Airlines and Greyhound buses serve the area. Community facilities include a public library, hospital, YMCA, YWCA, many churches, and all the major civic and service groups. Recreational opportunities abound in the many city parks providing swimming, tennis, picnic areas, boating and fishing, along with access to golf, bowling, roller skating, miniature golf and go-carting. Jobs are plentiful in this highly industrialized area.

■ **SCHOOL OF THE ART INSTITUTE OF CHICAGO** *D-16*
37 South Wabash
Chicago, IL 60603-3103
Tel: (312)899-5100
Free: 800-232-SAIC
Admissions: (312)899-5219
Fax: (312)263-0141
E-mail: admiss@artic.edu
Web Site: http://www.artic.edu/saic/
Description: Independent, comprehensive, coed. Awards bachelor's and master's degrees. Founded 1866. Setting: 1-acre urban campus. Endowment: $225 million. Educational spending for 2005 fiscal year: $13,923 per student. Total enrollment: 2,679. Faculty: 468 (124 full-time, 344 part-time). Student-undergrad faculty ratio is 11:1. 1,354 applied, 84% were admitted. Full-time: 1,889 students, 65% women, 35% men. Part-time: 210 students,

72% women, 28% men. Students come from 50 states and territories, 27 other countries, 64% from out-of-state, 1% Native American, 7% Hispanic, 3% black, 10% Asian American or Pacific Islander, 16% international, 17% 25 or older, 35% live on campus, 14% transferred in. Retention: 77% of full-time freshmen returned the following year. Academic area with the most degrees conferred: visual and performing arts. Core. Calendar: semesters. Academic remediation for entering students, ESL program, services for LD students, advanced placement, self-designed majors, independent study, double major, summer session for credit, part-time degree program, co-op programs and internships, graduate courses open to undergrads. Off campus study at Association of Independent Colleges of Art and Design. Study abroad program.

Entrance Requirements: Option: deferred admission. Required: essay, high school transcript, 1 recommendation, portfolio, SAT or ACT. Recommended: interview. Entrance: moderately difficult. Application deadlines: Rolling, 1/2 for early action. Notification: continuous, 2/15 for early action.

Costs Per Year: Application fee: $65. Tuition: $28,950 full-time, $965 per credit hour part-time. Mandatory fees: $250 full-time. College room only: $8600.

Collegiate Environment: Orientation program. Drama-theater group, student-run newspaper, radio station. Social organizations: 28 open to all. Most popular organizations: Student Government/Student Union Galleries, N.I.A. (black student union), L.A.S.O. (Latin Art Student organization), Soccer Group/Kickball League, Student Diversity Council. Major annual events: Day Without Art, Holiday Art Sale, Undergraduate Bachelor of Fine Arts Show. Student services: health clinic, personal-psychological counseling. Campus security: 24-hour emergency response devices and patrols, late night transport-escort service, controlled dormitory access. 718 college housing spaces available; 704 were occupied in 2003-04. No special consideration for freshman housing applicants. Option: coed housing available. Flaxman Memorial Library plus 1 other with 72,490 books, 157 microform titles, 334 serials, 4,067 audiovisual materials, an OPAC, and a Web page. Operations spending for 2004 fiscal year: $747,141. 450 computers available on campus for general student use. Computer purchase/lease plans available. A campuswide network can be accessed from student residence rooms and from off campus. Staffed computer lab on campus.

Community Environment: See University of Chicago.

■ **SHAWNEE COMMUNITY COLLEGE** *Y-11*

8364 Shawnee College Rd.
Ullin, IL 62992-2206
Tel: (618)634-3200
Fax: (618)634-3300
Web Site: http://www.shawneecc.edu/

Description: State and locally supported, 2-year, coed. Part of Illinois Community College Board. Awards certificates, transfer associate, and terminal associate degrees. Founded 1967. Setting: 163-acre rural campus. Total enrollment: 3,191. 5% from top 10% of their high school class, 20% from top quarter, 60% from top half. Full-time: 943 students, 65% women, 35% men. Part-time: 2,248 students, 52% women, 48% men. Students come from 3 states and territories, 1% Native American, 1% Hispanic, 22% black, 1% Asian American or Pacific Islander, 54% 25 or older. Core. Calendar: semesters. Academic remediation for entering students, ESL program, services for LD students, accelerated degree program, summer session for credit, part-time degree program, adult/continuing education programs, internships.

Entrance Requirements: Open admission except for health programs. Options: Peterson's Universal Application, Common Application, early admission, deferred admission. Required: high school transcript. Placement: ACT ASSET required; ACT recommended; ACT required for some. Entrance: noncompetitive. Application deadline: Rolling. Notification: continuous. Preference given to district residents.

Collegiate Environment: Orientation program. Drama-theater group, choral group, student-run newspaper. Major annual events: Homecoming, Fall Fest, Spring Fest. Campus security: student patrols. College housing not available. Shawnee Community College Library with 38,000 books, 245 serials, an OPAC, and a Web page. 40 computers available on campus for general student use. A campuswide network can be accessed from off-campus. Staffed computer lab on campus.

■ **SHIMER COLLEGE** *B-15*

PO Box 500
Waukegan, IL 60079-0500
Tel: (847)623-8400

Free: 800-215-7173
Admissions: (847)249-7174
Fax: (847)249-7171
Web Site: http://www.shimer.edu/

Description: Independent, 4-year, coed. Awards bachelor's degrees. Founded 1853. Setting: 3-acre suburban campus with easy access to Chicago and Milwaukee. Total enrollment: 138. 59 applied, 88% were admitted. 25% from top quarter of their high school class, 38% from top half. Full-time: 114 students, 33% women, 67% men. Part-time: 12 students, 33% women, 67% men. Students come from 20 states and territories, 4 other countries, 42% from out-of-state, 0% Native American, 0% Hispanic, 12% black, 1% Asian American or Pacific Islander, 4% international, 32% 25 or older, 50% live on campus, 12% transferred in. Retention: 66% of full-time freshmen returned the following year. Core. Calendar: semesters. Self-designed majors, independent study, distance learning, double major, summer session for credit, part-time degree program, adult/continuing education programs, co-op programs and internships. Off campus study at Barat College, Northwestern University. Study abroad program.

Entrance Requirements: Open admission. Options: Common Application, electronic application, early admission, deferred admission. Required: essay, high school transcript, 1 recommendation, interview. Recommended: SAT or ACT. Required for some: SAT or ACT. Entrance: moderately difficult. Application deadline: 8/30. Notification: continuous.

Collegiate Environment: Orientation program. Drama-theater group, choral group, student-run newspaper. Social organizations: 8 open to all. Most popular organizations: student government, Drama Group, Quality of Life Committee. Major annual events: Orange Horse, Solidarity Night, Commencement. Student services: personal-psychological counseling. Campus security: 24-hour emergency response devices, late night transport-escort service. 55 college housing spaces available; all were occupied in 2003-04. Freshmen guaranteed college housing. Option: coed housing available. 200,000 books and 200 serials. 9 computers available on campus for general student use. A campuswide network can be accessed from student residence rooms and from off campus. Staffed computer lab on campus.

Community Environment: Waukegan (population 70,000) is the county seat of Lake County on Lake Michigan. Excellent public transportation is available to Chicago. Students enjoy all the usual services of a small city, including a nearby state park.

■ **SOUTH SUBURBAN COLLEGE** *E-16*

15800 South State St.
South Holland, IL 60473-1270
Tel: (708)596-2000
Web Site: http://www.southsuburbancollege.edu/

Description: State and locally supported, 2-year, coed. Part of Illinois Community College Board. Awards certificates, transfer associate, and terminal associate degrees. Founded 1927. Setting: suburban campus with easy access to Chicago. Total enrollment: 6,672. 851 applied, 100% were admitted. 20% from top 10% of their high school class, 49% from top quarter. 4 National Merit Scholars, 3 student government officers. 0.4% Native American, 8% Hispanic, 60% black, 1% Asian American or Pacific Islander, 0.4% international, 49% 25 or older. Core. Calendar: semesters. Academic remediation for entering students, ESL program, services for LD students, advanced placement, honors program, independent study, double major, summer session for credit, part-time degree program, adult/continuing education programs, co-op programs and internships. Off campus study at other colleges of the Illinois Community College System. Study abroad program.

Entrance Requirements: Open admission except for nursing, occupational therapy, court reporting, practical nursing, radiological technology programs. Options: early admission, deferred admission. Required: high school transcript. Recommended: minimum 2.0 high school GPA. Required for some: essay, interview. Placement: ACT ASSET required. Entrance: noncompetitive. Application deadline: Rolling. Notification: continuous. Preference given to district residents for nursing program.

Collegiate Environment: Drama-theater group, choral group, student-run newspaper. Social organizations: 20 open to all. Most popular organizations: Returning Adult Organization, Business Professionals, Disabled Students Organization, O.T. Organization, PAC Rats. Major annual events: Welcome Back Week, Pre-Finals Celebration, Discovering Diversity. Student services: personal-psychological counseling. Campus security: 24-hour emergency response devices and patrols. College housing not available. South Suburban College Library plus 2 others with 38,845 books, 403 serials, an

OPAC, and a Web page. 250 computers available on campus for general student use. A campuswide network can be accessed from off-campus. Staffed computer lab on campus.

■ **SOUTHEASTERN ILLINOIS COLLEGE** *W-13*

3575 College Rd.
Harrisburg, IL 62946-4925
Tel: (618)252-5400; (866)338-2742
Web Site: http://www.sic.edu/

Description: State-supported, 2-year, coed. Part of Illinois Community College Board. Awards certificates, transfer associate, and terminal associate degrees. Founded 1960. Setting: 140-acre rural campus. Educational spending for 2005 fiscal year: $4188 per student. Total enrollment: 2,559. Student-undergrad faculty ratio is 12:1. 496 applied, 100% were admitted. Students come from 5 states and territories, 2 other countries, 17% from out-of-state, 1% Hispanic, 7% black, 0.3% international, 40% 25 or older. Core. Calendar: semesters. Academic remediation for entering students, services for LD students, advanced placement, self-designed majors, independent study, distance learning, summer session for credit, part-time degree program, adult/continuing education programs, internships. Off campus study at Southern Illinois Collegiate Common Market.

Entrance Requirements: Open admission except for nursing, medical records technology, medical lab technology, operating room technology, game management, occupational therapy programs, health information technology. Options: Peterson's Universal Application, electronic application, early admission, deferred admission. Required: high school transcript. Entrance: noncompetitive. Application deadline: 9/1. Notification: continuous. Preference given to district residents.

Costs Per Year: Application fee: $0. Area resident tuition: $1920 full-time, $64 per hour part-time. State resident tuition: $2790 full-time, $93 per hour part-time. Nonresident tuition: $3210 full-time, $107 per hour part-time. Mandatory fees: $60 full-time, $2 per hour part-time, $2. College room and board: $3655.

Collegiate Environment: Drama-theater group, choral group. Social organizations: 13 open to all. Most popular organizations: Math and Science Club, Phi Theta Kappa, Forestry Club, Phi Beta Lambda, BASIC. Student services: personal-psychological counseling. Campus security: student patrols, evening security guard. Melba Patton Library plus 2 others with 58,030 books, 2,939 microform titles, 300 serials, 1,059 audiovisual materials, an OPAC, and a Web page. Operations spending for 2004 fiscal year: $277,328. 250 computers available on campus for general student use. A campuswide network can be accessed. Staffed computer lab on campus.

Community Environment: Harrisburg is an important coal mining, dairying, agricultural, and commercial center. Community facilities include a library, hospital, churches, an historical museum, and TV and radio stations. Recreational facilities are unlimited with Shawnee National Forest and other federal and state recreation areas within five to ten miles, and many large lakes in the area. The Saline County Fair is an annual event each July. Some part-time work is available.

■ **SOUTHERN ILLINOIS UNIVERSITY CARBONDALE** *W-11*

Carbondale, IL 62901-4701
Tel: (618)453-2121
Admissions: (618)453-2908
Fax: (618)453-3250
E-mail: admrec@siu.edu
Web Site: http://www.siu.edu/siuc/

Description: State-supported, university, coed. Part of Southern Illinois University. Awards associate, bachelor's, master's, doctoral, and first professional degrees and first professional certificates. Founded 1869. Setting: 1,133-acre rural campus with easy access to St. Louis. Endowment: $64.4 million. Research spending for 2004 fiscal year: $44.6 million. Educational spending for 2005 fiscal year: $3567 per student. Total enrollment: 21,441. Faculty: 1,081 (901 full-time, 180 part-time). Student-undergrad faculty ratio is 17:1. 9,285 applied, 77% were admitted. 9% from top 10% of their high school class, 27% from top quarter, 60% from top half. 1 National Merit Scholar, 32 valedictorians. Full-time: 14,962 students, 43% women, 57% men. Part-time: 1,735 students, 42% women, 58% men. Students come from 56 states and territories, 120 other countries, 14% from out-of-state, 1% Native American, 4% Hispanic, 16% black, 2% Asian American or Pacific Islander, 2% international, 18% 25 or older, 27% live on campus, 12% transferred in. Academic areas with the most degrees conferred: education; engineering technologies; business/marketing. Core. Calendar: semesters plus 8-week summer session. Academic remediation for entering students,

ESL program, services for LD students, advanced placement, accelerated degree program, honors program, independent study, distance learning, double major, summer session for credit, part-time degree program, adult/continuing education programs, co-op programs and internships, graduate courses open to undergrads. Off campus study at Southern Illinois University School of Medicine; off campus courses offered at 34 Military bases across the U.S.. Study abroad program. ROTC: Army, Air Force.

Entrance Requirements: Options: electronic application, deferred admission. Required: high school transcript, SAT or ACT. Entrance: moderately difficult. Application deadline: 8/22. Notification: continuous.

Costs Per Year: Application fee: $30. State resident tuition: $5310 full-time, $177 per semester hour part-time. Nonresident tuition: $13,275 full-time, $442.50 per semester hour part-time. Mandatory fees: $1521 full-time, $654 per term part-time. Full-time tuition and fees vary according to course load and student level. Part-time tuition and fees vary according to course load and student level. College room and board: $5560. College room only: $3058. Room and board charges vary according to board plan and housing facility. Tuition guaranteed not to increase for student's term of enrollment.

Collegiate Environment: Orientation program. Drama-theater group, choral group, marching band, student-run newspaper, radio station. Social organizations: 386 open to all; national fraternities, national sororities, local fraternities, local sororities; 5% of eligible men and 5% of eligible women are members. Most popular organizations: Undergraduate Student Government, International Student Council, Black Togetherness Organization, Black Affairs Council, Hispanic Council. Major annual events: homecoming, Parents' Weekend, Cardboard Boat Regatta. Student services: legal services, health clinic, personal-psychological counseling, women's center. Campus security: 24-hour emergency response devices and patrols, student patrols, late night transport-escort service, well-lit pathways, night safety vans, student transit system. 4,884 college housing spaces available; 4,407 were occupied in 2003-04. Freshmen guaranteed college housing. On-campus residence required in freshman year. Options: coed, men-only, women-only housing available. Morris Library plus 1 other with 4.2 million books, 4.2 million microform titles, 18,271 serials, 371,180 audiovisual materials, an OPAC, and a Web page. Operations spending for 2004 fiscal year: $14.2 million. 1,827 computers available on campus for general student use. Computer purchase/lease plans available. A campuswide network can be accessed from student residence rooms and from off campus. Staffed computer lab on campus.

Community Environment: Carbondale, an economic center of Southern Illinois, is only a few hours from Chicago, St. Louis, and Memphis. It sits amid rolling hills, farmlands, and orchards just 60 miles above the confluence of the Mississippi and Ohio Rivers. The area from Carbondale south is ruggedly scenic and suitable for a wide range of year-round outdoor activities. Within minutes are four large recreational lakes, the two great rivers, and spectacular 270,000-acre Shawnee National Forest. A large number of smaller lakes, state parks, and recreational areas are within easy driving distance.

■ **SOUTHERN ILLINOIS UNIVERSITY EDWARDSVILLE** *R-8*

Edwardsville, IL 62026-0001
Tel: (618)650-2000
Free: 800-447-SIUE
Admissions: (618)650-2298
Fax: (618)692-2081
E-mail: admissions@siue.edu
Web Site: http://www.siue.edu/

Description: State-supported, comprehensive, coed. Part of Southern Illinois University. Awards bachelor's, master's, and first professional degrees and post-master's and first professional certificates. Founded 1957. Setting: 2,660-acre suburban campus with easy access to St. Louis. Endowment: $10.3 million. Research spending for 2004 fiscal year: $3.9 million. Educational spending for 2005 fiscal year: $5209 per student. Total enrollment: 13,460. Faculty: 819 (556 full-time, 263 part-time). Student-undergrad faculty ratio is 17:1. 5,879 applied, 71% were admitted. 16% from top 10% of their high school class, 43% from top quarter, 78% from top half. Full-time: 9,232 students, 55% women, 45% men. Part-time: 1,713 students, 53% women, 47% men. Students come from 46 states and territories, 48 other countries, 9% from out-of-state, 0.3% Native American, 2% Hispanic, 10% black, 2% Asian American or Pacific Islander, 1% international, 18% 25 or older, 28% live on campus, 12% transferred in. Retention: 76% of full-time freshmen returned the following year. Academic areas with the most degrees conferred: business/marketing; education; psychology. Core. Calendar: semesters. Academic remediation for entering students, ESL program, services for LD students, advanced placement, accelerated degree program, self-designed majors, honors program, independent study, distance learning, double major, summer session for credit, part-time degree program, adult/continuing education programs, co-op programs and internships, graduate courses open to undergrads. Off campus study at University of Missouri-St. Louis, International Student Exchange Program, MBA program at southwestern Illinois College. Study abroad program. ROTC: Army, Air Force.

Entrance Requirements: Options: electronic application, early admission, deferred admission, international baccalaureate accepted. Required: high school transcript, SAT or ACT. Recommended: minimum 2.5 high school GPA. Entrance: moderately difficult. Application deadline: 5/1. Notification: continuous.

Costs Per Year: Application fee: $50. State resident tuition: $4320 full-time, $144 per semester hour part-time. Nonresident tuition: $10,800 full-time, $360 per semester hour part-time. Mandatory fees: $859 full-time, $366.50 per term part-time. Full-time tuition and fees vary according to course load. Part-time tuition and fees vary according to course load. College room and board: $5819. College room only: $3389. Room and board charges vary according to board plan and housing facility.

Collegiate Environment: Orientation program. Drama-theater group, choral group, student-run newspaper, radio station. Social organizations: 140 open to all; national fraternities, national sororities. Most popular organizations: student government, campus newspaper, University Center Board, International Student Council. Major annual events: Welcome Week, Homecoming, Springfest. Student services: legal services, health clinic, personal-psychological counseling. Campus security: 24-hour emergency response devices and patrols, student patrols, late night transport-escort service, controlled dormitory access, 24-hour ID check at residence hall entrances, emergency call boxes located throughout campus. 3,000 college housing spaces available; 2,900 were occupied in 2003-04. Freshmen given priority for college housing. Option: coed housing available. Lovejoy Library with 788,003 books, 1.7 million microform titles, 14,371 serials, 29,495 audiovisual materials, an OPAC, and a Web page. Operations spending for 2004 fiscal year: $4.6 million. 600 computers available on campus for general student use. Computer purchase/lease plans available. A campuswide network can be accessed from student residence rooms and from off campus. Staffed computer lab on campus.

Community Environment: Edwardsville/Glen Carbon (population more than 24,000) is a suburban St. Louis community with a public library, many churches, museum, YMCA, and hospital facilities nearby. It is located only 30 minutes from Lambert St. Louis International Airport.

■ **SOUTHWESTERN ILLINOIS COLLEGE** *S-8*
2500 Carlyle Rd.
Belleville, IL 62221-5899
Tel: (618)235-2700
Fax: (618)235-1578
E-mail: michelle.birk@swic.edu
Web Site: http://www.southwestern.cc.il.us/

Description: District-supported, 2-year, coed. Part of Illinois Community College Board. Awards certificates, diplomas, transfer associate, and terminal associate degrees. Founded 1946. Setting: 150-acre suburban campus with easy access to St. Louis. Endowment: $3.1 million. Educational spending for 2005 fiscal year: $2640 per student. Total enrollment: 14,479. Student-undergrad faculty ratio is 17:1. Full-time: 5,296 students, 57% women, 43% men. Part-time: 9,183 students, 58% women, 42% men. Students come from 6 states and territories, 19 other countries, 1% Native American, 3% Hispanic, 18% black, 2% Asian American or Pacific Islander, 0.1% international, 45% 25 or older, 43% transferred in. Core. Calendar: semesters. Academic remediation for entering students, ESL program, services for LD students, advanced placement, accelerated degree program, distance learning, double major, summer session for credit, part-time degree program, adult/continuing education programs, co-op programs and internships. Off campus study at other colleges of the Illinois Community College System. Study abroad program. ROTC: Army (c), Air Force (c).

Entrance Requirements: Open admission. Options: early admission, deferred admission. Required: high school transcript. Required for some: ACT ASSET or ACT COMPASS. Placement: ACT ASSET or ACT COMPASS required for some. Entrance: noncompetitive. Application deadline: Rolling.

Costs Per Year: Application fee: $10. Area resident tuition: $1890 full-time, $63 per credit hour part-time. State resident tuition: $5220 full-time, $174 per credit hour part-time. Nonresident tuition: $8070 full-time, $269 per credit hour part-time.

Collegiate Environment: Drama-theater group, choral group, student-run newspaper. Social organizations: 35 open to all. Most popular organizations:

College Activities Board, Phi Theta Kappa, Student Nurses Association, Horticulture Club, Data Processing Management Association. Major annual events: Spring Blast, Fall Fest, Summer Picnic. Student services: personal-psychological counseling, women's center. Campus security: 24-hour emergency response devices and patrols, student patrols, late night transport-escort service. College housing not available. Belleville Area College Library with 82,537 books, 5,680 microform titles, 638 serials, 2,688 audiovisual materials, an OPAC, and a Web page. Operations spending for 2004 fiscal year: $1.6 million. 348 computers available on campus for general student use. A campuswide network can be accessed. Staffed computer lab on campus.

■ **SPOON RIVER COLLEGE** *J-8*
23235 North County 22
Canton, IL 61520-9801
Tel: (309)647-4645
Admissions: (309)649-6305
Fax: (309)649-6235
Web Site: http://www.spoonrivercollege.net/

Description: State-supported, 2-year, coed. Part of Illinois Community College Board. Awards certificates, transfer associate, and terminal associate degrees. Founded 1959. Setting: 160-acre rural campus. Endowment: $98,726. Educational spending for 2005 fiscal year: $2705 per student. Total enrollment: 2,333. Student-undergrad faculty ratio is 20:1. Students come from 6 states and territories, 0.5% from out-of-state, 1% Native American, 1% Hispanic, 5% black, 1% Asian American or Pacific Islander, 0.1% international, 36% 25 or older. Core. Calendar: semesters. ESL program, services for LD students, advanced placement, accelerated degree program, freshman honors college, honors program, distance learning, summer session for credit, part-time degree program, adult/continuing education programs, internships. ROTC: Army.

Entrance Requirements: Open admission except for nursing program. Option: early admission. Required: high school transcript. Entrance: noncompetitive. Application deadline: Rolling.

Costs Per Year: Application fee: $0. Area resident tuition: $1845 full-time, $61.50 per credit hour part-time. State resident tuition: $3465 full-time, $115.50 per credit hour part-time. Nonresident tuition: $4545 full-time, $151.50 per credit hour part-time. Mandatory fees: $255 full-time, $8.50 per credit hour part-time. Full-time tuition and fees vary according to course load. Part-time tuition and fees vary according to course load.

Collegiate Environment: Orientation program. Drama-theater group. Social organizations: 9 open to all. Most popular organizations: Student Senate, PEACE, Peer Ambassadors. Major annual events: Crusaders' Day, Homecoming, Spring Formal. Student services: personal-psychological counseling. Campus security: 24-hour emergency response devices. College housing not available. Learning Resource Center with 34,799 books, 121 serials, 3,213 audiovisual materials, and an OPAC. Operations spending for 2004 fiscal year: $171,085. 34 computers available on campus for general student use. A campuswide network can be accessed. Staffed computer lab on campus.

Community Environment: Canton is situated in an extremely fertile agricultural district with a seasonal climate. Planes and buses are available. Air service at Peoria some 30 miles distant. Industries are coal mining and the manufacture of farm implements. The city has a library, YMCA, YWCA, concert association, hospital, a downtown shopping area with over 100 retail outlets. Additional shopping facilities in Peoria. Recreational activities are boating, fishing, hunting, bowling, and golf. At least 12 retail and community-sponsored events are conducted each year.

■ **SPRINGFIELD COLLEGE IN ILLINOIS** *M-9*
1500 North Fifth St.
Springfield, IL 62702-2694
Tel: (217)525-1420
Free: 800-635-7289
Fax: (217)789-1698
Web Site: http://www.sci.edu/

Description: Independent, 2-year, coed, affiliated with Roman Catholic Church. Awards transfer associate degrees (the college partners with Benedictine University, which offers baccalaureate and master degree programs at Springfield College's campus). Founded 1929. Setting: 8-acre urban campus. Endowment: $694,388. Total enrollment: 552. Student-undergrad faculty ratio is 12:1. 243 applied, 86% were admitted. 3% from top 10% of their high school class, 12% from top quarter, 40% from top half. Full-time: 271 students, 59% women, 41% men. Part-time: 281 students,

77% women, 23% men. Students come from 13 states and territories, 8 other countries, 3% from out-of-state, 0.2% Native American, 1% Hispanic, 15% black, 0.2% Asian American or Pacific Islander, 1% international, 6% 25 or older, 6% transferred in. Core. Calendar: semesters. Academic remediation for entering students, advanced placement, self-designed majors, summer session for credit, part-time degree program, adult/continuing education programs. Off campus study at Illinois College, MacMurray College, Sangamon State University, Lincoln Land Community College.

Entrance Requirements: Options: Peterson's Universal Application, Common Application, international baccalaureate accepted. Required: high school transcript, SAT and SAT Subject Tests or ACT. Recommended: minimum 2.0 high school GPA. Required for some: interview. Entrance: moderately difficult. Application deadline: Rolling. Notification: continuous.

Costs Per Year: Application fee: $20. Comprehensive fee: $15,400 includes full-time tuition ($7490), mandatory fees ($1990), and college room and board ($5920). Part-time tuition: $312 per hour.

Collegiate Environment: Orientation program. Student-run newspaper. Social organizations: 12 open to all; national fraternities. Most popular organizations: Phi Theta Kappa, Student Ambassadors, Student Activity Council, Sculpture Club, Pep/Poms. Student services: personal-psychological counseling. Campus security: 24-hour emergency response devices. Option: coed housing available. Charles E. Becker Library plus 1 other with 19,951 books, 15,398 microform titles, 146 serials, 2,490 audiovisual materials, an OPAC, and a Web page. 25 computers available on campus for general student use. A campuswide network can be accessed. Staffed computer lab on campus.

■ **TAYLOR BUSINESS INSTITUTE** *D-16*
200 North Michigan Ave., Ste. 301
Chicago, IL 60601
Tel: (312)236-6400
Fax: (312)658-0867
Description: Proprietary, 2-year, coed. Founded 1964.

■ **TELSHE YESHIVA-CHICAGO** *D-16*
3535 West Foster Ave.
Chicago, IL 60625-5598
Tel: (773)463-7738
Description: Independent Jewish, comprehensive, men only. Awards bachelor's and master's degrees. Founded 1960. Total enrollment: 73. 15 applied, 100% were admitted. Core. Calendar: semesters. Summer session for credit, part-time degree program.
Entrance Requirements: Required: interview. Recommended: recommendations.
Collegiate Environment: Student services: health clinic, personal-psychological counseling. On-campus residence required through senior year.

■ **TRINITY CHRISTIAN COLLEGE** *I-14*
6601 West College Dr.
Palos Heights, IL 60463-0929
Tel: (708)597-3000
Free: 800-748-0085
Admissions: (708)239-4708
Fax: (708)239-3995
E-mail: admissions@trnty.edu
Web Site: http://www.trnty.edu/
Description: Independent Christian Reformed, 4-year, coed. Awards bachelor's degrees. Founded 1959. Setting: 53-acre suburban campus with easy access to Chicago. Endowment: $5.5 million. Research spending for 2004 fiscal year: $58,923. Educational spending for 2005 fiscal year: $6484 per student. Total enrollment: 1,280. Student-undergrad faculty ratio is 12:1. 600 applied, 89% were admitted. 14% from top 10% of their high school class, 33% from top quarter, 64% from top half. 1 valedictorian. Full-time: 1,049 students, 64% women, 36% men. Part-time: 231 students, 76% women, 24% men. Students come from 38 states and territories, 12 other countries, 37% from out-of-state, 0.3% Native American, 5% Hispanic, 8% black, 2% Asian American or Pacific Islander, 1% international, 17% 25 or older, 67% live on campus, 6% transferred in. Retention: 80% of full-time freshmen returned the following year. Academic areas with the most degrees conferred: education; business/marketing; theology and religious vocations. Core. Calendar: semesters plus 2 week interim term. Academic remediation for entering students, services for LD students, advanced placement, honors

program, independent study, double major, part-time degree program, adult/continuing education programs, co-op programs and internships. Off campus study at Saint Xavier College, Moraine Valley Community College. Study abroad program.

Entrance Requirements: Options: deferred admission, international baccalaureate accepted. Required: essay, high school transcript, minimum 2.0 high school GPA, interview, SAT or ACT. Recommended: ACT. Required for some: 1 recommendation. Entrance: moderately difficult. Application deadline: Rolling. Notification: continuous.

Costs Per Year: Application fee: $20. Comprehensive fee: $23,735 includes full-time tuition ($16,985), mandatory fees ($150), and college room and board ($6600). College room only: $3400. Room and board charges vary according to board plan. Part-time tuition: $570 per semester hour. Part-time tuition varies according to course load.

Collegiate Environment: Orientation program. Drama-theater group, choral group, student-run newspaper. Social organizations: 15 open to all. Most popular organizations: Student Association, student ministries, student-run campus newspaper, Pro-Life Task Force, PACE (prison tutoring program). Major annual events: OPUS, The Gathering, Convocation. Student services: personal-psychological counseling. Campus security: 24-hour emergency response devices, student patrols, late night transport-escort service. 768 college housing spaces available; 657 were occupied in 2003-04. Freshmen guaranteed college housing. On-campus residence required through senior year. Option: coed housing available. Jenny Huizenga Memorial Library with 77,833 books, 34,690 microform titles, 437 serials, 820 audiovisual materials, an OPAC, and a Web page. Operations spending for 2004 fiscal year: $286,278. 140 computers available on campus for general student use. A campuswide network can be accessed from student residence rooms and from off campus. Staffed computer lab on campus.

Community Environment: Palos Heights is residential area located 25 miles from downtown Chicago.

■ **TRINITY COLLEGE OF NURSING AND HEALTH SCIENCES** *E-6*
2122-25th Ave.
Rock Island, IL 91201
Tel: (309)779-7700
Admissions: (309)779-7812
Fax: (309)779-7796
Web Site: http://www.trinitycollegeqc.edu/
Description: Independent, 4-year, coed. Administratively affiliated with Trinity Medical Center. Awards associate and bachelor's degrees (general education requirements are taken off campus, usually at Black Hawk College, Eastern Iowa Community College District and Western Illinois University). Founded 1994. Setting: 2-acre urban campus. Endowment: $1 million. Educational spending for 2005 fiscal year: $4000 per student. Total enrollment: 165. 115 applied, 43% were admitted. 10% from top 10% of their high school class, 30% from top quarter, 50% from top half. Full-time: 109 students, 77% women, 23% men. Part-time: 56 students, 82% women, 18% men. Students come from 2 states and territories, 28% from out-of-state, 0% Native American, 4% Hispanic, 1% black, 1% Asian American or Pacific Islander, 0% international, 50% 25 or older, 30% transferred in. Core. Calendar: semesters. Academic remediation for entering students, services for LD students, honors program, independent study, distance learning, summer session for credit, part-time degree program, adult/continuing education programs. Off campus study at Black Hawk College, Western Illinois University.

Entrance Requirements: Option: Common Application. Required: high school transcript, minimum 2.75 high school GPA, minimum ACT score of 21, SAT or ACT. Entrance: most difficult. Application deadline: 6/1. Preference given to students from colleges with whom Trinity College of Nursing has an articulation agreement.

Collegiate Environment: Orientation program. Social organizations: 1 open to all. Most popular organizations: Student Nurses Association, student government, BSN Honor Society, Phi Theta Kappa, Alpha Beta Gamma Radiology Honor Society. Major annual events: Career Day, Quad City Visiting Artists, Alumni Weekend. Student services: personal-psychological counseling. Campus security: 24-hour emergency response devices, controlled dormitory access. College housing not available. Trinity Medical Center Library with a Web page. Operations spending for 2004 fiscal year: $30,000.

■ **TRINITY INTERNATIONAL UNIVERSITY** *M-6*
2065 Half Day Rd.
Deerfield, IL 60015-1284

Tel: (847)945-8800
Free: 800-822-3225
Admissions: (847)317-7000
Fax: (847)317-7081
E-mail: tcadmissions@tiu.edu
Web Site: http://www.tiu.edu/

Description: Independent, university, coed, affiliated with Evangelical Free Church of America. Administratively affiliated with Evangelical Free Church of America. Awards bachelor's, master's, doctoral, and first professional degrees. Founded 1897. Setting: 108-acre suburban campus with easy access to Chicago. Endowment: $10.1 million. Educational spending for 2005 fiscal year: $5619 per student. Total enrollment: 2,836. Faculty: 360 (86 full-time, 274 part-time). Student-undergrad faculty ratio is 13:1. 459 applied, 82% were admitted. 19% from top 10% of their high school class, 48% from top quarter, 88% from top half. 4 valedictorians. Full-time: 1,090 students, 58% women, 42% men. Part-time: 173 students, 68% women, 32% men. Students come from 33 states and territories, 6 other countries, 45% from out-of-state, 0.4% Native American, 4% Hispanic, 13% black, 4% Asian American or Pacific Islander, 1% international, 26% 25 or older, 80% live on campus, 7% transferred in. Retention: 71% of full-time freshmen returned the following year. Academic areas with the most degrees conferred: education; theology and religious vocations; business/marketing. Core. Calendar: semesters. Academic remediation for entering students, advanced placement, honors program, independent study, double major, part-time degree program, adult/continuing education programs, internships, graduate courses open to undergrads. Off campus study at 13 members of the Christian College Consortium. Study abroad program.

Entrance Requirements: Options: electronic application, early admission, deferred admission. Required: essay, high school transcript, minimum 2.5 high school GPA, 1 recommendation, SAT or ACT. Recommended: minimum 3.0 high school GPA. Required for some: interview. Entrance: moderately difficult. Application deadline: Rolling. Notification: continuous until 9/1.

Costs Per Year: Application fee: $25. Comprehensive fee: $25,686 includes full-time tuition ($19,080), mandatory fees ($286), and college room and board ($6320). College room only: $3430. Full-time tuition and fees vary according to location. Room and board charges vary according to board plan. Part-time tuition: $796 per hour. Part-time mandatory fees: $143 per term. Part-time tuition and fees vary according to location.

Collegiate Environment: Orientation program. Drama-theater group, choral group, student-run newspaper. Social organizations: 15 open to all. Most popular organizations: Student Senate, College Union, Trinity Summer Mission, student newspaper, yearbook. Major annual events: homecoming, Santa Lucia, Parents' Weekend. Student services: health clinic, personal-psychological counseling. Campus security: 24-hour patrols, controlled dormitory access. 760 college housing spaces available; all were occupied in 2003-04. Freshmen guaranteed college housing. On-campus residence required through junior year. Options: men-only, women-only housing available. Rolfing Memorial Library with 206,404 books, 110,350 microform titles, 1,342 serials, 7,273 audiovisual materials, an OPAC, and a Web page. Operations spending for 2004 fiscal year: $1.3 million. 130 computers available on campus for general student use. A campuswide network can be accessed from student residence rooms and from off campus. Staffed computer lab on campus.

Community Environment: Deerfield, population 20,000, is located 25 miles north of Chicago.

■ **TRITON COLLEGE** *E-13*
2000 5th Ave.
River Grove, IL 60171-1995
Tel: (708)456-0300
Free: 800-942-7404
Fax: (708)583-3121
E-mail: dolson@triton.edu
Web Site: http://www.triton.cc.il.us/

Description: State-supported, 2-year, coed. Part of Illinois Community College Board. Awards certificates, transfer associate, and terminal associate degrees. Founded 1964. Setting: 100-acre suburban campus with easy access to Chicago. Educational spending for 2005 fiscal year: $1585 per student. Total enrollment: 11,021. Student-undergrad faculty ratio is 22:1. 5,492 applied, 100% were admitted. Full-time: 3,831 students, 51% women, 49% men. Part-time: 7,190 students, 57% women, 43% men. Students come from 26 other countries, 2% from out-of-state, 0.3% Native American, 17% Hispanic, 21% black, 5% Asian American or Pacific Islander, 0.2% international, 45% 25 or older. Core. Calendar: semesters. Academic

remediation for entering students, ESL program, advanced placement, self-designed majors, freshman honors college, honors program, distance learning, summer session for credit, part-time degree program, adult/continuing education programs, co-op programs and internships.

Entrance Requirements: Open admission except for some allied health programs. Option: deferred admission. Required: high school transcript. Entrance: noncompetitive. Application deadline: Rolling. Preference given to district residents.

Costs Per Year: Application fee: $0. Area resident tuition: $1680 full-time, $56 per semester hour part-time. State resident tuition: $5244 full-time, $174.80 per semester hour part-time. Nonresident tuition: $6670 full-time, $222.32 per semester hour part-time. Mandatory fees: $250 full-time, $5 per credit hour part-time, $30 per term part-time.

Collegiate Environment: Orientation program. Drama-theater group, choral group, student-run newspaper, radio station. Social organizations: 34 open to all. Most popular organizations: student government, Program Board. Major annual events: Triton Spirit Week, World's Largest Sober Party. Student services: health clinic, personal-psychological counseling. Campus security: 24-hour emergency response devices and patrols. College housing not available. Learning Resource Center with 70,859 books, 11,297 microform titles, and 1,247 serials. 350 computers available on campus for general student use. Staffed computer lab on campus.

Community Environment: Triton college district is in the near west suburbs of Chicago. The college is approximately 15 miles from downtown Chicago.

■ **UNIVERSITY OF CHICAGO** *D-16*
5801 Ellis Ave.
Chicago, IL 60637-1513
Tel: (773)702-1234
Admissions: (773)702-8650
Fax: (773)702-4199
E-mail: toneill@uchicago.edu
Web Site: http://www.uchicago.edu/

Description: Independent, university, coed. Awards bachelor's, master's, doctoral, and first professional degrees. Founded 1891. Setting: 211-acre urban campus. Endowment: $4 billion. Educational spending for 2005 fiscal year: $12,846 per student. Total enrollment: 14,150. Faculty: 1,587 (1,057 full-time, 530 part-time). Student-undergrad faculty ratio is 4:1. 9,011 applied, 40% were admitted. 79% from top 10% of their high school class, 95% from top quarter, 98% from top half. 212 National Merit Scholars. Full-time: 4,614 students, 51% women, 49% men. Part-time: 57 students, 35% women, 65% men. Students come from 51 states and territories, 59 other countries, 85% from out-of-state, 0.4% Native American, 8% Hispanic, 4% black, 14% Asian American or Pacific Islander, 7% international, 1% 25 or older, 67% live on campus, 4% transferred in. Retention: 96% of full-time freshmen returned the following year. Academic areas with the most degrees conferred: social sciences; biological/life sciences; mathematics. Core. Advanced placement, accelerated degree program, self-designed majors, independent study, double major, summer session for credit, adult/continuing education programs, internships, graduate courses open to undergrads. Off campus study at Committee on Institutional Cooperation, Associated Colleges of the Midwest. Study abroad program. ROTC: Army (c), Air Force (c).

Entrance Requirements: Options: electronic application, early admission, early action, deferred admission, international baccalaureate accepted. Required: essay, high school transcript, 3 recommendations, SAT or ACT. Recommended: interview. Entrance: most difficult. Application deadlines: 1/1, 11/1 for early action. Notification: 4/1, 12/15 for early action.

Costs Per Year: Application fee: $60. Comprehensive fee: $42,369 includes full-time tuition ($31,629), mandatory fees ($636), and college room and board ($10,104). Room and board charges vary according to board plan and housing facility.

Collegiate Environment: Orientation program. Drama-theater group, choral group, student-run newspaper, radio station. Social organizations: 300 open to all; national fraternities, national sororities. Most popular organizations: Model United Nations, University Theater, Documentary Films Club, Major Activities Board, student radio station. Major annual events: Folk Festival, Blues 'N Ribs, Summer Breeze. Student services: health clinic, personal-psychological counseling, women's center. Campus security: 24-hour emergency response devices and patrols, student patrols, late night transport-escort service, controlled dormitory access. Freshmen guaranteed college housing. On-campus residence required in freshman year. Option: coed housing available. Joseph Regenstein Library plus 6 others with 7 million books, 47,000 serials, an OPAC, and a Web page. 1,000 computers available on campus for general student use. A campuswide network can be accessed from student residence rooms and from off campus. Staffed computer lab on campus.

Community Environment: Chicago, with a population of nearly 3 million and the third largest city in the nation, is a metropolitan area extending along the southern end of Lake Michigan. It is a leading industrial, medical, educational, and cultural center. The University's campus is located in a residential neighborhood along the lake shore fifteen minutes away from the central downtown area. Cultural facilities include museums that cover a wide variety of fields, art galleries, research libraries, public libraries, theaters, opera, and a symphony orchestra. Numerous recreational activities and points of interest exist.

■ **UNIVERSITY OF ILLINOIS AT CHICAGO** *D-16*

601 South Morgan St.
Chicago, IL 60607-7128
Tel: (312)996-7000
Admissions: (312)996-4350
E-mail: uic.admit@uic.edu
Web Site: http://www.uic.edu/

Description: State-supported, university, coed. Part of University of Illinois System. Awards bachelor's, master's, doctoral, and first professional degrees and first professional certificates. Founded 1946. Setting: 240-acre urban campus. Endowment: $148 million. Research spending for 2004 fiscal year: $228.1 million. Total enrollment: 24,812. Faculty: 1,456 (1,193 full-time, 263 part-time). Student-undergrad faculty ratio is 16:1. 12,692 applied, 58% were admitted. 25% from top 10% of their high school class, 57% from top quarter, 91% from top half. Full-time: 13,733 students, 54% women, 46% men. Part-time: 1,417 students, 50% women, 50% men. Students come from 52 states and territories, 48 other countries, 3% from out-of-state, 0.2% Native American, 17% Hispanic, 9% black, 25% Asian American or Pacific Islander, 1% international, 12% 25 or older, 11% live on campus, 9% transferred in. Retention: 78% of full-time freshmen returned the following year. Academic areas with the most degrees conferred: business/marketing; biological/life sciences; engineering. Core. Calendar: semesters. Academic remediation for entering students, ESL program, services for LD students, advanced placement, accelerated degree program, self-designed majors, honors program, independent study, distance learning, double major, summer session for credit, part-time degree program, co-op programs and internships, graduate courses open to undergrads. Off campus study at University Center of Lake County. Study abroad program. ROTC: Army, Naval (c), Air Force (c).

Entrance Requirements: Options: electronic application, international baccalaureate accepted. Required: high school transcript, SAT or ACT. Recommended: essay. Required for some: interview. Entrance: moderately difficult. Application deadline: 1/15. Notification: continuous.

Costs Per Year: Application fee: $40. State resident tuition: $6194 full-time. Nonresident tuition: $18,584 full-time. Mandatory fees: $2108 full-time. College room and board: $7954.

Collegiate Environment: Orientation program. Drama-theater group, choral group, student-run newspaper, radio station. Social organizations: 233 open to all; national fraternities, national sororities, local fraternities, local sororities; 1% of eligible men and 1% of eligible women are members. Most popular organizations: Golden Key National Honor Society, Chinese Students and Scholars Friendship Association, Muslim Student Association, MBA Association, Alternative Spring Break. Major annual events: Activities and Services Fair, Black History Month, UIC Fashion Show. Student services: legal services, health clinic, personal-psychological counseling, women's center. Campus security: 24-hour emergency response devices and patrols, student patrols, late night transport-escort service, controlled dormitory access, housing ID stickers, guest escort policy, 24-hour closed circuit videos for exits and entrances, security screen for first floor. 3,051 college housing spaces available; all were occupied in 2003-04. No special consideration for freshman housing applicants. Option: coed housing available. Richard J. Daley Library plus 5 others with 3 million books, 3.9 million microform titles, 31,236 serials, 28,168 audiovisual materials, an OPAC, and a Web page. Operations spending for 2004 fiscal year: $17.9 million. 1,100 computers available on campus for general student use. A campuswide network can be accessed from student residence rooms and from off campus. Staffed computer lab on campus.

■ **UNIVERSITY OF ILLINOIS AT SPRINGFIELD** *M-9*

One University Plaza
Springfield, IL 62703-5407

Tel: (217)206-6600; 888-977-4847
Fax: (217)206-7279
Web Site: http://www.uis.edu/

Description: State-supported, comprehensive, coed. Part of University of Illinois. Awards bachelor's, master's, and doctoral degrees and post-master's certificates. Founded 1969. Setting: 746-acre suburban campus. Endowment: $6.4 million. Research spending for 2004 fiscal year: $1.3 million. Educational spending for 2005 fiscal year: $6828 per student. Total enrollment: 4,517. Faculty: 331 (179 full-time, 152 part-time). Student-undergrad faculty ratio is 12:1. 493 applied, 63% were admitted. 20% from top 10% of their high school class, 52% from top quarter, 90% from top half. Full-time: 1,558 students, 59% women, 41% men. Part-time: 1,076 students, 62% women, 38% men. Students come from 35 states and territories, 8% from out-of-state, 0.4% Native American, 2% Hispanic, 9% black, 3% Asian American or Pacific Islander, 1% international, 48% 25 or older, 21% transferred in. Retention: 84% of full-time freshmen returned the following year. Academic areas with the most degrees conferred: business/marketing; psychology; liberal arts/general studies. Core. Calendar: semesters. Academic remediation for entering students, services for LD students, self-designed majors, independent study, distance learning, double major, summer session for credit, part-time degree program, external degree program, co-op programs and internships, graduate courses open to undergrads. Study abroad program.

Entrance Requirements: Option: electronic application. Required: essay, high school transcript, 3 recommendations, SAT or ACT. Required for some: interview. Entrance: moderately difficult. Application deadline: Rolling. Notification: continuous.

Costs Per Year: Application fee: $40. State resident tuition: $3953 full-time, $132 per credit hour part-time. Nonresident tuition: $11,858 full-time, $396 per credit hour part-time. Mandatory fees: $1382 full-time, $586 per term part-time. Full-time tuition and fees vary according to program. College room and board: $7110. College room only: $3270. Room and board charges vary according to housing facility. Tuition guaranteed not to increase for student's term of enrollment.

Collegiate Environment: Orientation program. Drama-theater group, choral group, student-run newspaper. Social organizations: 59 open to all. Most popular organizations: USAS - United Students Against Sweatshops, OLAS Organization of Latin American Students, Culturazzi, Christian Student Fellowship, Blue Crew. Major annual events: First Week, Homecoming, Spring Fest. Student services: health clinic, personal-psychological counseling, women's center. Campus security: 24-hour patrols, late night transport-escort service. 807 college housing spaces available. Option: coed housing available. Operations spending for 2004 fiscal year: $2.5 million. 132 computers available on campus for general student use. Computer purchase/lease plans available. A campuswide network can be accessed from student residence rooms and from off campus. Staffed computer lab on campus.

■ **UNIVERSITY OF ILLINOIS AT URBANA-CHAMPAIGN** *L-14*

601 East John St.
Champaign, IL 61820
Tel: (217)333-1000
Admissions: (217)333-0302
Fax: (217)244-7278
E-mail: admssion@uiuc.edu
Web Site: http://www.uiuc.edu/

Description: State-supported, university, coed. Part of University of Illinois System. Awards bachelor's, master's, doctoral, and first professional degrees and post-master's certificates. Founded 1867. Setting: 1,470-acre small town campus. Endowment: $800.1 million. Research spending for 2004 fiscal year: $361.9 million. Educational spending for 2005 fiscal year: $8960 per student. Total enrollment: 41,938. Faculty: 2,701 (2,271 full-time, 430 part-time). Student-undergrad faculty ratio is 14:1. 18,916 applied, 76% were admitted. 48% from top 10% of their high school class, 86% from top quarter, 99% from top half. Full-time: 29,912 students, 47% women, 53% men. Part-time: 997 students, 41% women, 59% men. Students come from 52 states and territories, 70 other countries, 13% from out-of-state, 0.3% Native American, 6% Hispanic, 7% black, 13% Asian American or Pacific Islander, 5% international, 2% 25 or older, 39% live on campus, 4% transferred in. Retention: 93% of full-time freshmen returned the following year. Academic areas with the most degrees conferred: business/marketing; engineering; social sciences. Core. Calendar: semesters. Academic remediation for entering students, ESL program, services for LD students, advanced placement, self-designed majors, honors program, independent study, distance learning, double major, summer session for credit, co-op programs and internships, graduate courses open to undergrads. Off campus study at members of the Committee on Institutional Cooperation, Midwest Universities Consortium for International Activities. Study abroad program. ROTC: Army, Naval, Air Force.

Entrance Requirements: Options: deferred admission, international baccalaureate accepted. Required: essay, high school transcript, SAT or ACT. Required for some: recommendations, interview, audition, statement of professional interest. Entrance: very difficult. Application deadline: 12/15. Notification: continuous.

Costs Per Year: Application fee: $40. State resident tuition: $7042 full-time. Nonresident tuition: $21,128 full-time. Mandatory fees: $1582 full-time. Full-time tuition and fees vary according to course load, program, and student level. College room and board: $7176. College room only: $2970. Room and board charges vary according to board plan and housing facility. Tuition guaranteed not to increase for student's term of enrollment.

Collegiate Environment: Orientation program. Drama-theater group, choral group, marching band, student-run newspaper, radio station. Social organizations: 1,000 open to all; national fraternities, national sororities, local fraternities, local sororities; 22% of eligible men and 22% of eligible women are members. Most popular organizations: Volunteer Illini Project, Alpha Phi Omega, Indian Student Organization, Residence Hall Association. Major annual events: Homecoming, Moms' Weekend/Dads' Weekend, Quad Day. Student services: legal services, health clinic, personal-psychological counseling, women's center. Campus security: 24-hour emergency response devices and patrols, student patrols, late night transport-escort service, controlled dormitory access, safety training classes, ID cards with safety numbers. 11,033 college housing spaces available; all were occupied in 2003-04. Freshmen guaranteed college housing. On-campus residence required in freshman year. Options: coed, men-only, women-only housing available. University Library plus 42 others with 10.2 million books, 9.2 million microform titles, 89,444 serials, 169,894 audiovisual materials, an OPAC, and a Web page. Operations spending for 2004 fiscal year: $33.8 million. 3,500 computers available on campus for general student use. Computer purchase/lease plans available. A campuswide network can be accessed from student residence rooms and from off campus. Staffed computer lab on campus.

■ **UNIVERSITY OF PHOENIX-CHICAGO CAMPUS** *C-15*
1500 McConner Parkway, Ste. 700
Schaumburg, IL 60173-4399
Tel: (847)413-1922
Free: 800-228-7240
Admissions: (480)557-1712
Fax: (847)413-8706
Web Site: http://www.phoenix.edu/
Description: Proprietary, comprehensive, coed. Awards bachelor's and master's degrees. Founded 2002. Total enrollment: 1,602. Faculty: 207 (12 full-time, 195 part-time). Student-undergrad faculty ratio is 8:1. 46 applied. Full-time: 1,279 students, 57% women, 43% men. 0.3% Native American, 3% Hispanic, 6% black, 2% Asian American or Pacific Islander, 10% international, 91% 25 or older. Academic areas with the most degrees conferred: business/marketing; computer and information sciences. Core. Calendar: continuous. Advanced placement, accelerated degree program, independent study, distance learning, external degree program, adult/continuing education programs, graduate courses open to undergrads.
Entrance Requirements: Open admission. Option: deferred admission. Required: 1 recommendation. Required for some: high school transcript. Entrance: noncompetitive. Application deadline: Rolling.
Costs Per Year: Application fee: $110. Tuition: $11,145 full-time, $371.50 per credit part-time. Mandatory fees: $560 full-time, $70 per course part-time.
Collegiate Environment: College housing not available. University Library with 444 books, 666 serials, an OPAC, and a Web page. System-wide operations spending for 2004 fiscal year: $3.2 million.

■ **UNIVERSITY OF ST. FRANCIS** *E-15*
500 Wilcox St.
Joliet, IL 60435-6169
Tel: (815)740-3400
Free: 800-735-3500
Admissions: 800-735-7500
Fax: (815)740-4285
E-mail: cbeutel@stfrancis.edu

Web Site: http://www.stfrancis.edu/
Description: Independent Roman Catholic, comprehensive, coed. Awards bachelor's and master's degrees. Founded 1920. Setting: 17-acre suburban campus with easy access to Chicago. Endowment: $14.1 million. Educational spending for 2005 fiscal year: $6237 per student. Total enrollment: 2,062. Faculty: 219 (74 full-time, 145 part-time). Student-undergrad faculty ratio is 12:1. 749 applied, 57% were admitted. 18% from top 10% of their high school class, 43% from top quarter, 84% from top half. Full-time: 1,138 students, 68% women, 32% men. Part-time: 138 students, 72% women, 28% men. Students come from 8 states and territories, 4 other countries, 2% from out-of-state, 0.3% Native American, 7% Hispanic, 9% black, 4% Asian American or Pacific Islander, 1% international, 21% 25 or older, 22% live on campus, 14% transferred in. Retention: 80% of full-time freshmen returned the following year. Academic areas with the most degrees conferred: education; business/marketing; health professions and related sciences. Core. Calendar: semesters. Academic remediation for entering students, services for LD students, advanced placement, accelerated degree program, self-designed majors, independent study, distance learning, double major, summer session for credit, part-time degree program, external degree program, adult/continuing education programs, internships. Off campus study. Study abroad program.
Entrance Requirements: Options: electronic application, deferred admission, international baccalaureate accepted. Required: high school transcript, minimum 2.0 high school GPA, SAT or ACT. Required for some: essay, 2 recommendations, interview. Entrance: moderately difficult. Application deadline: 8/1. Notification: continuous.
Costs Per Year: Application fee: $30. Comprehensive fee: $26,430 includes full-time tuition ($19,150) and college room and board ($7280). Part-time tuition: $625 per credit hour.
Collegiate Environment: Orientation program. Drama-theater group, choral group, student-run newspaper, radio station. Social organizations: 23 open to all. Most popular organizations: Ethnic Affairs Council, Student Activities Board, Student Government Association, Sometimes Thespians, Student Business Association. Major annual events: Homecoming, Family Celebration, Little Sibs Weekend. Student services: personal-psychological counseling. Campus security: 24-hour emergency response devices and patrols, late night transport-escort service, controlled dormitory access, First Response trained security personnel. 433 college housing spaces available; 270 were occupied in 2003-04. Freshmen guaranteed college housing. Option: coed housing available. University of St. Francis Library with 106,346 books, 1,308 microform titles, 776 serials, 1,177 audiovisual materials, an OPAC, and a Web page. Operations spending for 2004 fiscal year: $848,450. 250 computers available on campus for general student use. A campuswide network can be accessed from student residence rooms and from off campus. Staffed computer lab on campus.

■ **VANDERCOOK COLLEGE OF MUSIC** *D-16*
3140 South Federal St.
Chicago, IL 60616-3731
Tel: (312)225-6288
Free: 800-448-2655
Fax: (312)225-5211
E-mail: vcmusic@mcs.com
Web Site: http://www.vandercook.edu/
Description: Independent, comprehensive, coed. Awards bachelor's and master's degrees. Founded 1909. Setting: 1-acre urban campus. Endowment: $432,276. Total enrollment: 227. 44 applied, 95% were admitted. Full-time: 105 students, 50% women, 50% men. Part-time: 45 students, 44% women, 56% men. Students come from 12 states and territories, 2 other countries, 0% Native American, 13% Hispanic, 14% black, 2% Asian American or Pacific Islander, 2% international, 11% 25 or older, 5% transferred in. Retention: 89% of full-time freshmen returned the following year. Core. Calendar: semesters. Advanced placement, independent study, internships.
Entrance Requirements: Required: essay, high school transcript, 3 recommendations, interview, audition, SAT or ACT. Recommended: minimum 3.0 high school GPA. Required for some: minimum 3.0 high school GPA. Entrance: moderately difficult. Application deadline: Rolling.
Costs Per Year: Application fee: $35. Comprehensive fee: $25,940 includes full-time tuition ($17,120), mandatory fees ($770), and college room and board ($8050). Part-time tuition: $590 per credit hour.
Collegiate Environment: Orientation program. Choral group. Social organizations: 2 open to all; national fraternities, national sororities, local fraternities, local sororities. Most popular organizations: MENC (Music

Educators Natural Conference), ACDA (American Choral Directors Association). Major annual event: Mid-West International Band and Orchestra Clinic Concert. Campus security: 24-hour emergency response devices and patrols, late night transport-escort service, controlled dormitory access. No special consideration for freshman housing applicants. Option: coed housing available. Harry Ruppel Memorial Library with an OPAC and a Web page. Operations spending for 2004 fiscal year: $44,600. 20 computers available on campus for general student use. A campuswide network can be accessed from student residence rooms and from off campus. Staffed computer lab on campus.

Community Environment: Urban.

■ **WAUBONSEE COMMUNITY COLLEGE** *D-13*
Route 47 at Waubonsee Dr.
Sugar Grove, IL 60554-9799
Tel: (630)466-7900
Fax: (630)466-4964
E-mail: recruitment@waubonsee.edu
Web Site: http://www.waubonsee.edu/
Description: District-supported, 2-year, coed. Part of Illinois Community College Board. Awards certificates, transfer associate, and terminal associate degrees. Founded 1966. Setting: 243-acre rural campus with easy access to Chicago. Endowment: $1.6 million. Educational spending for 2005 fiscal year: $2299 per student. Total enrollment: 8,834. Student-undergrad faculty ratio is 17:1. 916 applied, 100% were admitted. Full-time: 2,624 students, 53% women, 47% men. Part-time: 6,210 students, 59% women, 41% men. Students come from 2 other countries, 0% from out-of-state, 0.4% Native American, 17% Hispanic, 7% black, 2% Asian American or Pacific Islander, 0.05% international, 21% 25 or older, 2% transferred in. Retention: 63% of full-time freshmen returned the following year. Core. Calendar: semesters. Academic remediation for entering students, services for LD students, advanced placement, accelerated degree program, honors program, independent study, distance learning, summer session for credit, part-time degree program, internships. Study abroad program. ROTC: Army (c).
Entrance Requirements: Open admission except for nursing, interpreter training, auto body, certified nurse assistant programs, medical assistant, health care interpreting, therapeutic massage, phlebotomy, translation.. Entrance: noncompetitive. Application deadline: Rolling. Preference given to in-district residents.
Costs Per Year: Application fee: $0. Area resident tuition: $2010 full-time, $67 per semester hour part-time. State resident tuition: $6300 full-time, $210 per semester hour part-time. Nonresident tuition: $7110 full-time, $237 per semester hour part-time. Mandatory fees: $90 full-time, $3 per semester hour part-time.
Collegiate Environment: Orientation program. Drama-theater group, choral group, student-run newspaper. Social organizations: 22 open to all. Most popular organizations: Phi Theta Kappa, VICA, Alpha Sigma Lamda, Latinos Unidos, Christian Fellowship. Major annual events: College Night, Club Fair, Cinco de Mayo Celebration. Campus security: 24-hour emergency response devices and patrols, late night transport-escort service. College housing not available. Todd Library with 53,679 books, 100,840 microform titles, 562 serials, 6,388 audiovisual materials, an OPAC, and a Web page. Operations spending for 2004 fiscal year: $682,516. 160 computers available on campus for general student use. A campuswide network can be accessed from off-campus. Staffed computer lab on campus.
Community Environment: See Aurora University.

■ **WEST SUBURBAN COLLEGE OF NURSING** *D-15*
3 Erie Ct.
Oak Park, IL 60302
Tel: (708)763-6530
Fax: (708)763-1531
Web Site: http://www.wscn.edu/
Description: Independent, upper-level, coed. Awards bachelor's degrees. Founded 1982. Setting: 10-acre suburban campus with easy access to Chicago. Total enrollment: 105. 40 applied, 35% were admitted. Full-time: 90 students, 98% women, 2% men. Part-time: 15 students, 93% women, 7% men. Students come from 8 states and territories, 8% from out-of-state, 0% Native American, 6% Hispanic, 17% black, 8% Asian American or Pacific Islander, 0% international, 39% 25 or older, 50% live on campus, 24% transferred in. Calendar: semesters. Advanced placement, accelerated degree program, independent study, summer session for credit, part-time degree program, adult/continuing education programs.

Collegiate Environment: Orientation program. Drama-theater group, choral group, student-run newspaper. Student services: personal-psychological counseling. Campus security: 24-hour emergency response devices and patrols, late night transport-escort service, controlled dormitory access. Options: coed, men-only, women-only housing available. 20 computers available on campus for general student use. A campuswide network can be accessed. Staffed computer lab on campus.

■ **WESTERN ILLINOIS UNIVERSITY** *J-6*
1 University Circle
Macomb, IL 61455-1390
Tel: (309)298-1414; 877-742-5948
Admissions: (309)298-3157
Fax: (309)298-3111
E-mail: karen_helmers@uniu.edu
Web Site: http://www.wiu.edu/
Description: State-supported, comprehensive, coed. Awards bachelor's, master's, and doctoral degrees and post-master's certificates. Founded 1899. Setting: 1,050-acre small town campus. Endowment: $21.9 million. Educational spending for 2005 fiscal year: $5872 per student. Total enrollment: 13,404. Faculty: 731 (649 full-time, 82 part-time). Student-undergrad faculty ratio is 17:1. 7,286 applied, 72% were admitted. 5% from top 10% of their high school class, 22% from top quarter, 55% from top half. Full-time: 10,317 students, 48% women, 52% men. Part-time: 967 students, 52% women, 48% men. Students come from 37 states and territories, 46 other countries, 5% from out-of-state, 0.3% Native American, 4% Hispanic, 7% black, 1% Asian American or Pacific Islander, 1% international, 14% 25 or older, 51% live on campus, 12% transferred in. Retention: 79% of full-time freshmen returned the following year. Academic areas with the most degrees conferred: liberal arts/general studies; education; security and protective services. Core. Calendar: semesters. Academic remediation for entering students, ESL program, services for LD students, advanced placement, self-designed majors, freshman honors college, honors program, independent study, distance learning, double major, summer session for credit, part-time degree program, external degree program, adult/continuing education programs, internships, graduate courses open to undergrads. Off campus study at Western Illinois Education Consortium. Study abroad program. ROTC: Army.
Entrance Requirements: Options: electronic application, deferred admission. Required: high school transcript, SAT or ACT. Entrance: moderately difficult. Application deadline: 5/15. Notification: continuous until 8/3.
Costs Per Year: Application fee: $30. State resident tuition: $4968 full-time, $213.69 per semester hour part-time. Nonresident tuition: $7452 full-time, $296.49 per semester hour part-time. Mandatory fees: $1931 full-time, $48.09 per semester hour part-time. Full-time tuition and fees vary according to location and student level. Part-time tuition and fees vary according to location and student level. College room and board: $6143. College room only: $3693. Room and board charges vary according to housing facility and student level. Tuition guaranteed not to increase for student's term of enrollment.
Collegiate Environment: Orientation program. Drama-theater group, choral group, marching band, student-run newspaper, radio station. Social organizations: 240 open to all; national fraternities, national sororities, local fraternities, local sororities; 9% of eligible men and 8% of eligible women are members. Most popular organizations: Student Government Association, Black Student Association, University Union Board, International Friendship Club, Bureau of Cultural Affairs. Major annual events: Family Weekend, Homecoming. Student services: legal services, health clinic, personal-psychological counseling, women's center. Campus security: 24-hour emergency response devices and patrols, student patrols, late night transport-escort service, controlled dormitory access. College housing designed to accommodate 5,200 students; 5,363 undergraduates lived in college housing during 2003-04. Freshmen guaranteed college housing. On-campus residence required through sophomore year. Options: coed, men-only, women-only housing available. Leslie Malpass Library plus 4 others with 998,041 books, 1.3 million microform titles, 3,200 serials, 3,445 audiovisual materials, an OPAC, and a Web page. Operations spending for 2004 fiscal year: $4.5 million. 1,000 computers available on campus for general student use. A campuswide network can be accessed from student residence rooms and from off campus. Staffed computer lab on campus.
Community Environment: Macomb is located 240 miles southwest of Chicago and 150 miles north of St. Louis on the main line of the Burlington Railroad. Besides agriculture, Macomb's industries produce ball bearings, plastic bags, porcelain insulators, and pottery. This is a friendly, Midwest

community balanced by the youthfulness and creativity of the rapidly expanding university. The community facilities include a hospital, library, hotels, motels, and many clubs and organizations in the city. Recreational facilities include a swimming pool, bowling alleys, parks, and movie theaters.

■ WESTWOOD COLLEGE-CHICAGO DU PAGE *D-15*

7155 Janes Ave.
Woodridge, IL 60517
Tel: (630)434-8244
Fax: (630)434-8255
Web Site: http://www.westwood.edu/

Description: Proprietary, primarily 2-year, coed. Awards terminal associate and bachelor's degrees. Setting: suburban campus with easy access to Chicago, IL. Total enrollment: 470. 881 applied, 40% were admitted. Full-time: 420 students, 22% women, 78% men. Part-time: 50 students, 44% women, 56% men. 10% from out-of-state, 0.2% Native American, 12% Hispanic, 12% black, 3% Asian American or Pacific Islander, 0.4% international, 21% 25 or older. Calendar: continuous.

Entrance Requirements: Required: interview, entrance exam (SAT, ACT or Accuplacer) and high school diploma or GED.

■ WESTWOOD COLLEGE-CHICAGO LOOP CAMPUS *D-16*

17 North State St., Ste. 1500
Chicago, IL 60602
Tel: (312)739-0850
Fax: (312)739-1004
Web Site: http://www.westwood.edu/

Description: Proprietary, primarily 2-year, coed. Awards terminal associate and bachelor's degrees. Founded 2002. Total enrollment: 106. 163 applied, 68% were admitted. Full-time: 105 students, 47% women, 53% men. Part-time: 1 student, 100% men. 0% Native American, 24% Hispanic, 66% black, 1% Asian American or Pacific Islander, 0% international, 21% 25 or older.

Entrance Requirements: Required: interview, high school diploma or GED, and passing SAT/ACT or Accuplacer scores.

■ WESTWOOD COLLEGE-CHICAGO O'HARE AIRPORT *E-13*

4825 North Scott St., Ste. 100
Schiller Park, IL 60176
Tel: (847)928-0200
Fax: (847)928-2120
Web Site: http://www.westwood.edu/

Description: Proprietary, primarily 2-year, coed. Awards terminal associate and bachelor's degrees. Setting: urban campus with easy access to Chicago. Total enrollment: 425. 399 applied. Full-time: 315 students, 27% women, 73% men. Part-time: 110 students, 32% women, 68% men. 10% from out-of-state, 0.5% Native American, 28% Hispanic, 12% black, 8% Asian American or Pacific Islander, 0% international, 24% 25 or older. Calendar: continuous.

Entrance Requirements: Required: essay, interview, entrance exam (SAT, ACT or ACCUPLACER) and high school diploma/GED.

■ WESTWOOD COLLEGE-CHICAGO RIVER OAKS *E-16*

80 River Oaks Dr., Ste. D-49
Calumet City, IL 60409
Tel: (708)832-1988
Fax: (708)832-9617
Web Site: http://www.westwood.edu/

Description: Proprietary, primarily 2-year, coed. Awards terminal associate and bachelor's degrees. Setting: suburban campus with easy access to Chicago. Total enrollment: 650. 574 applied, 55% were admitted. Full-time: 592 students, 37% women, 63% men. Part-time: 58 students, 50% women, 50% men. 0.2% Native American, 15% Hispanic, 62% black, 0% Asian American or Pacific Islander, 37% 25 or older. Calendar: continuous.

Entrance Requirements: Required: interview, high school diploma or GED and passing scores on entrance exam (ACT/SAT or Accuplacer).

■ WHEATON COLLEGE *D-14*

501 East College Ave.
Wheaton, IL 60187-5593
Tel: (630)752-5000
Free: 800-222-2419
Admissions: (630)752-5011
Fax: (630)752-5285
E-mail: admissions@wheaton.edu

Web Site: http://www.wheaton.edu/

Description: Independent nondenominational, comprehensive, coed. Awards bachelor's, master's, and doctoral degrees. Founded 1860. Setting: 80-acre suburban campus with easy access to Chicago. Endowment: $294 million. Research spending for 2004 fiscal year: $196,267. Educational spending for 2005 fiscal year: $14,224 per student. Total enrollment: 2,932. Faculty: 287 (191 full-time, 96 part-time). Student-undergrad faculty ratio is 12:1. 2,163 applied, 51% were admitted. 54% from top 10% of their high school class, 81% from top quarter, 97% from top half. 34 National Merit Scholars. Full-time: 2,342 students, 51% women, 49% men. Part-time: 75 students, 51% women, 49% men. Students come from 51 states and territories, 15 other countries, 72% from out-of-state, 0.4% Native American, 3% Hispanic, 2% black, 7% Asian American or Pacific Islander, 1% international, 1% 25 or older, 89% live on campus, 2% transferred in. Retention: 95% of full-time freshmen returned the following year. Academic areas with the most degrees conferred: social sciences; education; theology and religious vocations. Core. Calendar: semesters. Services for LD students, advanced placement, self-designed majors, independent study, double major, summer session for credit, internships, graduate courses open to undergrads. Off campus study at members of the Christian College Consortium, Council for Christian Colleges and Universities. Study abroad program. ROTC: Army, Air Force (c).

Entrance Requirements: Option: early action. Required: essay, high school transcript, 2 recommendations, SAT or ACT. Recommended: interview, SAT Subject Test in French, German, Latin, Spanish or Hebrew. Entrance: very difficult. Application deadlines: 1/15, 11/1 for early action. Notification: 4/10, 12/31 for early action. Preference given to Christians.

Costs Per Year: Application fee: $50. Comprehensive fee: $27,700 includes full-time tuition ($21,100) and college room and board ($6600). College room only: $3900. Room and board charges vary according to board plan and housing facility. Part-time tuition: $586 per credit hour. Part-time tuition varies according to course load.

Collegiate Environment: Orientation program. Drama-theater group, choral group, student-run newspaper, radio station. Social organizations: 60 open to all. Most popular organizations: intramurals, Discipleship small groups, Christian Service Council, Orientation Committee, Resident Assistant Staff. Major annual events: talent show, Class Films Festival, Air Jam. Student services: health clinic, personal-psychological counseling. Campus security: 24-hour emergency response devices and patrols, student patrols, late night transport-escort service, controlled dormitory access. 2,116 college housing spaces available; 2,089 were occupied in 2003-04. Freshmen guaranteed college housing. On-campus residence required through senior year. Options: men-only, women-only housing available. Buswell Memorial Library plus 1 other with 450,620 books, 674,552 microform titles, 3,556 serials, 33,738 audiovisual materials, an OPAC, and a Web page. Operations spending for 2004 fiscal year: $2.1 million. 238 computers available on campus for general student use. A campuswide network can be accessed from student residence rooms and from off campus. Staffed computer lab on campus.

■ WILLIAM RAINEY HARPER COLLEGE *C-15*

1200 West Algonquin Rd.
Palatine, IL 60067-7398
Tel: (847)925-6000
Fax: (847)925-6044
Web Site: http://www.harpercollege.edu/

Description: State and locally supported, 2-year, coed. Part of Illinois Community College Board. Awards certificates, transfer associate, and terminal associate degrees. Founded 1965. Setting: 200-acre suburban campus with easy access to Chicago. Research spending for 2004 fiscal year: $228,497. Total enrollment: 15,026. Student-undergrad faculty ratio is 22:1. 4,887 applied, 100% were admitted. 8% from top 10% of their high school class, 32% from top quarter, 69% from top half. Full-time: 6,174 students, 50% women, 50% men. Part-time: 8,852 students, 62% women, 38% men. Students come from 13 states and territories, 31 other countries, 1% from out-of-state, 0.3% Native American, 14% Hispanic, 4% black, 12% Asian American or Pacific Islander, 1% international, 32% 25 or older, 3% transferred in. Retention: 70% of full-time freshmen returned the following year. Core. Calendar: semesters. Academic remediation for entering students, ESL program, services for LD students, advanced placement, honors program, independent study, distance learning, summer session for credit, part-time degree program, adult/continuing education programs, co-op programs and internships. Study abroad program.

Entrance Requirements: Open admission. Options: electronic application, early admission, deferred admission. Required: high school transcript.

Entrance: noncompetitive. Application deadline: Rolling. Notification: continuous. Preference given to for district residents for nursing, dental hygienist and cardiac technology programs.

Costs Per Year: Application fee: $25. Area resident tuition: $1800 full-time, $75 per credit hour part-time. State resident tuition: $6600 full-time, $275 per credit hour part-time. Nonresident tuition: $8256 full-time, $344 per credit hour part-time. Mandatory fees: $450 full-time.

Collegiate Environment: Orientation program. Drama-theater group, choral group, student-run newspaper, radio station. Social organizations: 48 open to all. Most popular organizations: student radio station, Program Board, Student Senate, Nursing Club, Phi Theta Kappa. Major annual events: Transfer Information Week, Wellness Week, Career Expo. Student services: legal services, health clinic, personal-psychological counseling, women's center. Campus security: 24-hour emergency response devices and patrols, late night transport-escort service. College housing not available. Harper College Library with 143,817 books, 47,666 microform titles, 6,606 serials, 33,049 audiovisual materials, an OPAC, and a Web page. Operations spending for 2004 fiscal year: $1.5 million. 206 computers available on campus for general student use. A campuswide network can be accessed from off-campus. Staffed computer lab on campus.

Community Environment: Palatine, population 57,000, is a suburban community located 30 miles northwest of Chicago. It enjoys a temperate Midwestern climate. Rail and bus services are available. Community facilities include churches of major denominations, a public library, and hospitals nearby. Many active organizations provide social, recreational, and cultural programs and functions.

■ **WORSHAM COLLEGE OF MORTUARY SCIENCE** *A-12*
495 Northgate Parkway
Wheeling, IL 60090-2646
Tel: (847)808-8444
Fax: (847)808-8493
Web Site: http://www.worshamcollege.com/
Description: Independent, 2-year, coed. Awards terminal associate degrees. Total enrollment: 120. 70 applied, 100% were admitted. 0% Native American, 10% Hispanic, 20% black, 10% Asian American or Pacific Islander, 0% international.

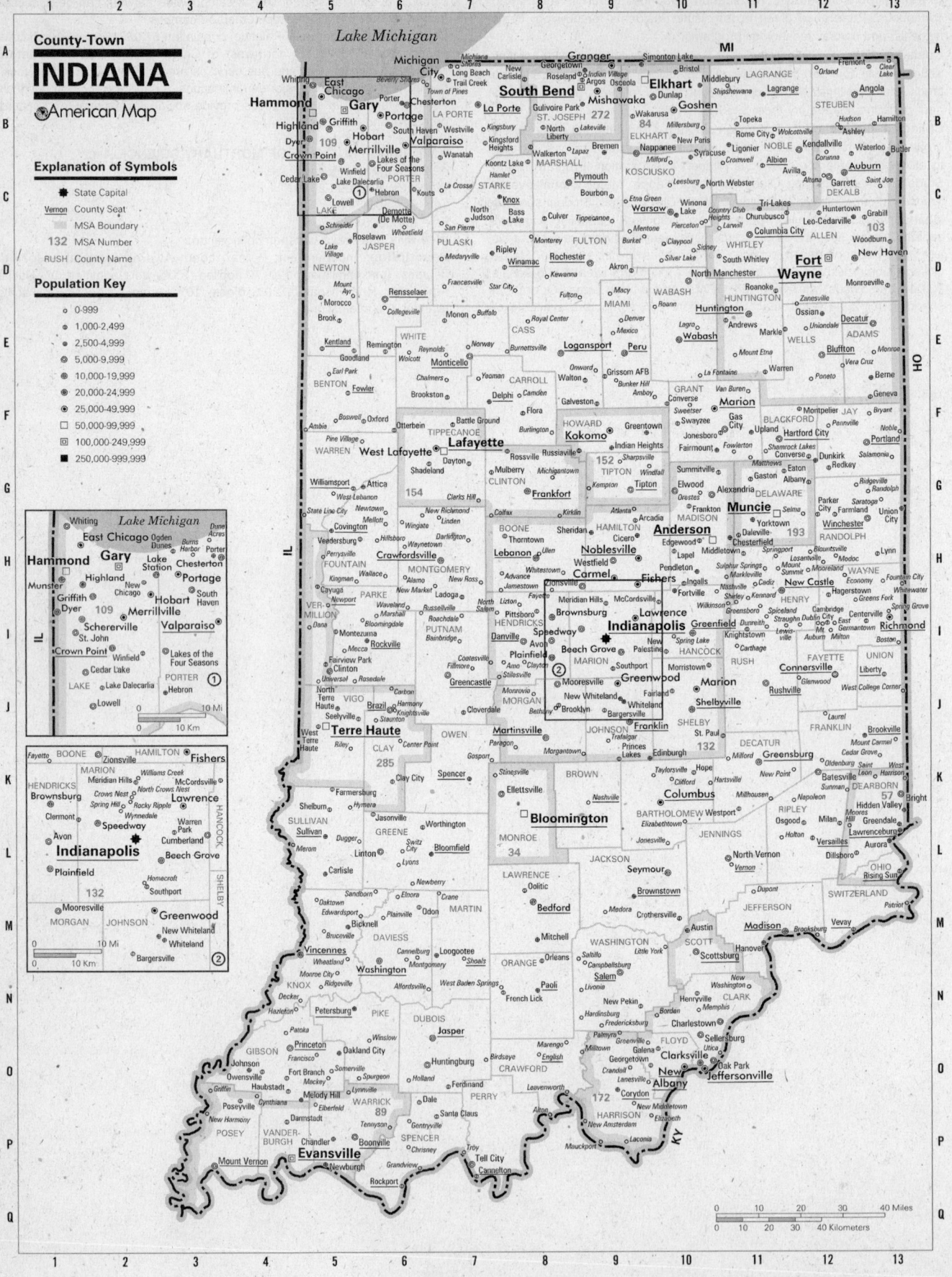

■ **AMERICAN TRANS AIR AVIATION TRAINING ACADEMY** *I-9*
7251 West McCarty St.
Indianapolis, IN 46241
Tel: (317)243-4519
Free: 800-241-9699
Fax: (317)243-4569
Web Site: http://www.aviationtraining.net/
Description: Proprietary, 2-year, coed. Founded 1992. Calendar: semesters.

■ **ANCILLA COLLEGE**
Union Rd., PO Box 1
Donaldson, IN 46513
Tel: (574)936-8898
Fax: (574)935-1773
Web Site: http://www.ancilla.edu/
Description: Independent Roman Catholic, 2-year, coed. Awards certificates, transfer associate, and terminal associate degrees. Founded 1937. Setting: 63-acre rural campus with easy access to Chicago. Endowment: $1.9 million. Educational spending for 2005 fiscal year: $8286 per student. Total enrollment: 624. Student-undergrad faculty ratio is 15:1. 574 applied, 95% were admitted. 3% from top 10% of their high school class, 10% from top quarter, 39% from top half. Full-time: 397 students, 68% women, 32% men. Part-time: 227 students, 82% women, 18% men. Students come from 10 states and territories, 1% from out-of-state, 1% Native American, 3% Hispanic, 6% black, 0.2% Asian American or Pacific Islander, 0.2% international, 40% 25 or older, 9% transferred in. Retention: 55% of full-time freshmen returned the following year. Core. Calendar: semesters. Academic remediation for entering students, services for LD students, advanced placement, accelerated degree program, self-designed majors, independent study, double major, summer session for credit, part-time degree program, adult/continuing education programs, co-op programs and internships.
Entrance Requirements: Open admission. Options: Common Application, electronic application. Required: high school transcript, SAT and SAT Subject Tests or ACT. Recommended: interview, SAT, SAT or ACT. Entrance: noncompetitive. Application deadline: Rolling.
Costs Per Year: Application fee: $25. Tuition: $10,800 full-time, $360 per credit hour part-time. Mandatory fees: $230 full-time, $55 per term part-time.
Collegiate Environment: Orientation program. Student-run newspaper. Social organizations: 3 open to all. Most popular organizations: Student Senate, Scripta Literary Magazine, Ancilla student ambassadors. Major annual events: homecoming, Community College Day. Student services: personal-psychological counseling. Campus security: 24-hour patrols, late night transport-escort service. College housing not available. Ball Library with 27,859 books, 152 serials, 1,499 audiovisual materials, an OPAC, and a Web page. Operations spending for 2004 fiscal year: $124,491. 82 computers available on campus for general student use. Computer purchase/lease plans available. A campuswide network can be accessed. Staffed computer lab on campus.
Community Environment: Situated in a rural area with a temperate climate.

■ **ANDERSON UNIVERSITY** *H-10*
1100 East Fifth St.
Anderson, IN 46012-3495
Tel: (765)649-9071

Free: 800-428-6414
Admissions: (765)641-4080
Fax: (765)641-3851
E-mail: info@anderson.edu
Web Site: http://www.anderson.edu/
Description: Independent, comprehensive, coed, affiliated with Church of God. Awards associate, bachelor's, master's, doctoral, and first professional degrees. Founded 1917. Setting: 100-acre suburban campus with easy access to Indianapolis. Endowment: $7.1 million. Total enrollment: 2,811. Faculty: 254 (137 full-time, 117 part-time). Student-undergrad faculty ratio is 14:1. 1,110 applied, 90% were admitted. 24% from top 10% of their high school class, 52% from top quarter, 80% from top half. Full-time: 2,149 students, 57% women, 43% men. Part-time: 188 students, 65% women, 35% men. Students come from 46 states and territories, 40% from out-of-state, 1% Native American, 1% Hispanic, 5% black, 0.1% Asian American or Pacific Islander, 2% international, 8% 25 or older, 60% live on campus, 4% transferred in. Retention: 74% of full-time freshmen returned the following year. Academic areas with the most degrees conferred: business/marketing; education; health professions and related sciences; visual and performing arts. Core. Calendar: semesters. Academic remediation for entering students, services for LD students, advanced placement, accelerated degree program, self-designed majors, honors program, independent study, double major, summer session for credit, part-time degree program, adult/continuing education programs, internships. Study abroad program.
Entrance Requirements: Options: deferred admission, international baccalaureate accepted. Required: high school transcript, minimum 2.0 high school GPA, 2 recommendations, lifestyle statement, SAT or ACT. Recommended: essay. Required for some: interview. Entrance: moderately difficult. Application deadline: 7/1. Notification: continuous until 9/1.
Costs Per Year: Application fee: $20. Comprehensive fee: $26,450 includes full-time tuition ($19,990) and college room and board ($6460). College room only: $3940. Part-time tuition: $850 per semester hour.
Collegiate Environment: Orientation program. Drama-theater group, choral group, student-run newspaper, radio station. Social organizations: 33 open to all. Most popular organizations: social clubs, Adult and Continuing Education Students Association, Multicultural Student Union, campus ministries, intramurals. Major annual events: homecoming, Vision/Revision, Rush Week. Student services: health clinic, personal-psychological counseling. Campus security: 24-hour emergency response devices and patrols, student patrols, late night transport-escort service, 24-hour crime line. 1,343 college housing spaces available; 1,320 were occupied in 2003-04. On-campus residence required through junior year. Options: men-only, women-only housing available. Robert A. Nicholson Library with 245,019 books, 117,370 microform titles, 937 serials, 372 audiovisual materials, an OPAC, and a Web page. 200 computers available on campus for general student use. A campuswide network can be accessed from student residence rooms and from off campus. Staffed computer lab on campus.
Community Environment: Anderson (population 62,000) is located 35 miles northeast of Indianapolis, and is known for the automotive electrical systems and lighting equipment produced by Delco-Remy Division America. Other industries located here manufacture recreation equipment, files, copper wire, corrugated paper boxes, dairy products and agricultural products. Railroads, buses and airports serve the area. The community has a library, churches, and hospitals. Recreational facilities include five 18-hole golf courses and 17 city parks. Mounds State Park is nearby. Employment opportunities are available.

■ **THE ART INSTITUTE OF INDIANAPOLIS** *I-9*
3500 Depauw Blvd.
Indianapolis, IN 46268
Tel: (866)441-9031
Web Site: http://www.artinstitutes.edu/indianapolis/
Description: Proprietary, 4-year, coed. Awards associate and bachelor's degrees.
Entrance Requirements: Application deadline: Rolling. Notification: continuous.

■ **AVIATION INSTITUTE OF MAINTENANCE-INDIANAPOLIS** *I-9*
7251 W. McCarty St.
Indianapolis, IN 46241
Tel: (317)243-4519; 888-349-5387
Fax: (317)243-4569
E-mail: directorami@aviationmaintenance.edu
Web Site: http://www.aviationmaintenance.edu/aviation-indianapolis.asp
Description: Proprietary, 2-year.
Entrance Requirements: Required: High school diploma or GED.
Costs Per Year: Application fee: $25.

■ **BALL STATE UNIVERSITY** *G-11*
2000 University Ave.
Muncie, IN 47306-1099
Tel: (765)289-1241
Free: 800-482-4BSU
Admissions: (765)285-8300
Fax: (765)285-1632
E-mail: askus@wp.bsu.edu
Web Site: http://www.bsu.edu/
Description: State-supported, university, coed. Awards associate, bachelor's, master's, and doctoral degrees and post-master's certificates. Founded 1918. Setting: 955-acre suburban campus with easy access to Indianapolis. Research spending for 2004 fiscal year: $4.7 million. Educational spending for 2005 fiscal year: $5473 per student. Total enrollment: 20,351. Faculty: 1,149 (910 full-time, 239 part-time). Student-undergrad faculty ratio is 17:1. 9,889 applied, 80% were admitted. 14% from top 10% of their high school class, 41% from top quarter, 79% from top half. 11 National Merit Scholars, 23 valedictorians. Full-time: 16,063 students, 51% women, 49% men. Part-time: 1,363 students, 57% women, 43% men. Students come from 49 states and territories, 7% from out-of-state, 0.3% Native American, 2% Hispanic, 7% black, 1% Asian American or Pacific Islander, 0.03% international, 8% 25 or older, 41% live on campus, 5% transferred in. Retention: 77% of full-time freshmen returned the following year. Academic areas with the most degrees conferred: education; business/marketing; liberal arts/general studies. Core. Calendar: semesters. Academic remediation for entering students, ESL program, advanced placement, freshman honors college, honors program, independent study, distance learning, double major, summer session for credit, part-time degree program, adult/continuing education programs, co-op programs and internships, graduate courses open to undergrads. Study abroad program. ROTC: Army.
Entrance Requirements: Options: Common Application, deferred admission, international baccalaureate accepted. Required: high school transcript, SAT or ACT. Required for some: essay, recommendations, interview. Entrance: moderately difficult. Application deadline: Rolling. Notification: continuous.
Costs Per Year: Application fee: $25. State resident tuition: $6030 full-time, $221 per credit hour part-time. Nonresident tuition: $15,790 full-time, $569 per credit hour part-time. Mandatory fees: $428 full-time. College room and board: $6680.
Collegiate Environment: Orientation program. Drama-theater group, choral group, marching band, student-run newspaper, radio station. Social organizations: 330 open to all; national fraternities, national sororities; 7% of eligible men and 10% of eligible women are members. Most popular organizations: Student Association, Excellence in Leadership, Black Student Association, student voluntary services. Major annual events: Homecoming, Unity Week, Quad Bash. Student services: legal services, health clinic, personal-psychological counseling, women's center. Campus security: 24-hour emergency response devices and patrols, late night transport-escort service, controlled dormitory access. 6,300 college housing spaces available. On-campus residence required in freshman year. Options: coed, men-only, women-only housing available. Bracken Library plus 3 others with 1.1 million books, 1 million microform titles, 2,937 serials, 506,303 audiovisual materials, an OPAC, and a Web page. Operations spending for 2004 fiscal year: $7.9 million. 1,500 computers available on campus for general student use. A campuswide network can be accessed from student residence rooms and from off campus. Staffed computer lab on campus.
Community Environment: Muncie is the county seat and the largest city in east-central Indiana. It is located on the White River, 66 miles northeast of Indianapolis. All forms of commercial transportation are available.

■ **BETHEL COLLEGE** *B-9*
1001 West McKinley Ave.
Mishawaka, IN 46545-5591
Tel: (574)259-8511
Free: 800-422-4101
Admissions: (574)257-3319
Fax: (574)257-3326
Web Site: http://www.bethelcollege.edu
Description: Independent, comprehensive, coed, affiliated with Missionary Church. Awards associate, bachelor's, and master's degrees. Founded 1947. Setting: 70-acre suburban campus. Endowment: $4.2 million. Research spending for 2004 fiscal year: $59,870. Educational spending for 2005 fiscal year: $5753 per student. Total enrollment: 2,093. Faculty: 184 (90 full-time, 94 part-time). Student-undergrad faculty ratio is 13:1. 713 applied, 75% were admitted. 23% from top 10% of their high school class, 48% from top quarter, 77% from top half. 2 class presidents, 4 valedictorians, 30 student government officers. Full-time: 1,338 students, 63% women, 37% men. Part-time: 596 students, 69% women, 31% men. Students come from 32 states and territories, 13 other countries, 26% from out-of-state, 0.4% Native American, 3% Hispanic, 10% black, 2% Asian American or Pacific Islander, 2% international, 61% 25 or older, 49% live on campus, 7% transferred in. Retention: 91% of full-time freshmen returned the following year. Academic areas with the most degrees conferred: business/marketing; education; liberal arts/general studies. Core. Calendar: semesters. Academic remediation for entering students, advanced placement, accelerated degree program, honors program, independent study, double major, summer session for credit, part-time degree program, adult/continuing education programs, internships. Off campus study at Northern Indiana Consortium for Education, Coalition for Christian Colleges and Universities. Study abroad program. ROTC: Army (c), Air Force (c).
Entrance Requirements: Options: Peterson's Universal Application, Common Application, electronic application, early admission, deferred admission. Required: essay, high school transcript, minimum 2.0 high school GPA, 1 recommendation, SAT or ACT. Recommended: minimum 2.5 high school GPA, interview. Entrance: minimally difficult. Application deadline: 8/6. Notification: continuous.
Costs Per Year: Application fee: $25. One-time mandatory fee: $600. Comprehensive fee: $22,830 includes full-time tuition ($17,450) and college room and board ($5380). Part-time tuition: $350 per hour.
Collegiate Environment: Orientation program. Drama-theater group, choral group, student-run newspaper, radio station. Social organizations: 18 open to all. Most popular organizations: 'Task Force' Mission Teams, Student Council, Center for Community Service, Fellowship of Christian Athletes. Major annual events: Community Service Day, Health Fair, Spiritual Emphasis Week. Student services: health clinic, personal-psychological counseling. Campus security: 24-hour emergency response devices and patrols, student patrols, late night transport-escort service, controlled dormitory access. 860 college housing spaces available; 855 were occupied in 2003-04. On-campus residence required through sophomore year. Options: men-only, women-only housing available. Otis and Elizabeth Bowen Library with 106,584 books, 4,298 microform titles, 450 serials, 3,926 audiovisual materials, an OPAC, and a Web page. Operations spending for 2004 fiscal year: $477,656. 110 computers available on campus for general student use. A campuswide network can be accessed from student residence rooms and from off campus. Staffed computer lab on campus.

■ **BROWN MACKIE COLLEGE-FORT WAYNE** *D-12*
4422 East State Blvd.
Fort Wayne, IN 46815
Tel: (219)484-4400
Admissions: (260)481-5038
Fax: (219)484-2678
E-mail: ktaboh@brownmackie.edu
Web Site: http://www.brownmackie.edu/locations.asp?locid=1
Description: Proprietary, 2-year, coed. Awards certificates, diplomas, and terminal associate degrees. Educational spending for 2005 fiscal year:

$8112 per student. Total enrollment: 706. Student-undergrad faculty ratio is 13:1. 933 applied, 65% were admitted. Full-time: 706 students, 86% women, 14% men. 3% from out-of-state, 0% Native American, 4% Hispanic, 30% black, 0.3% Asian American or Pacific Islander, 0% international. Retention: 0% of full-time freshmen returned the following year.

Entrance Requirements: Open admission. Required: high school transcript, interview, Verify High School Grad or Equivalent. Entrance: noncompetitive. Application deadline: Rolling. Notification: continuous.

Costs Per Year: Application fee: $0. Tuition: $8592 full-time, $179 per credit hour part-time. Mandatory fees: $480 full-time, $10 per credit hour part-time.

Collegiate Environment: Student services: personal-psychological counseling.

■ **BROWN MACKIE COLLEGE-MERRILLVILLE** *B-5*
1000 East 80th Place, Ste. 101, N
Merrillville, IN 46410
Tel: (219)769-3321
Fax: (219)258-3321
E-mail: admissions@brownmackie.edu
Web Site: http://www.brownmackie.edu/locations.asp?locid=19
Description: Proprietary, 2-year, coed. Part of American Education Centers. Awards certificates and terminal associate degrees. Founded 1890. Setting: 2-acre small town campus with easy access to Chicago. Educational spending for 2005 fiscal year: $4250 per student. Total enrollment: 585. Student-undergrad faculty ratio is 15:1. Full-time: 585 students, 80% women, 20% men. 4% from out-of-state, 0.2% Native American, 8% Hispanic, 42% black, 0.2% Asian American or Pacific Islander, 0% international, 40% 25 or older. Retention: 0% of full-time freshmen returned the following year. Core. Self-designed majors, summer session for credit, internships.
Entrance Requirements: Open admission. Options: Common Application, early admission, deferred admission. Required: high school transcript, interview. Entrance: noncompetitive. Application deadline: Rolling. Notification: continuous.
Costs Per Year: Application fee: $0. Tuition: $8592 full-time, $179 per credit hour part-time.
Collegiate Environment: Campus security: 24-hour emergency response devices. College housing not available. 150 computers available on campus for general student use. Staffed computer lab on campus.

■ **BROWN MACKIE COLLEGE-MICHIGAN CITY** *A-7*
325 East US Hwy. 20
Michigan City, IN 46360
Tel: (219)877-3100
Free: 800-519-2416
Fax: (219)877-3110
E-mail: selston@brownmackie.edu
Web Site: http://www.brownmackie.edu/locations.asp?locid=20
Description: Proprietary, 2-year, coed. Part of Commonwealth Business College, Inc. Awards diplomas, transfer associate, and terminal associate degrees. Founded 1890. Setting: 2-acre rural campus with easy access to Chicago. Total enrollment: 461. Student-undergrad faculty ratio is 13:1. 461 applied, 100% were admitted. 2% from top 10% of their high school class, 21% from top quarter, 77% from top half. Full-time: 461 students, 79% women, 21% men. Students come from 2 states and territories, 2% from out-of-state, 0% Native American, 3% Hispanic, 18% black, 0.4% Asian American or Pacific Islander, 0% international, 44% 25 or older. Core. Advanced placement, self-designed majors, summer session for credit, part-time degree program, adult/continuing education programs, internships.
Entrance Requirements: Options: early admission, deferred admission. Required: high school transcript. Entrance: minimally difficult. Application deadline: Rolling. Notification: continuous.
Costs Per Year: Application fee: $0. Tuition: $6444 full-time, $179 per credit hour part-time. Mandatory fees: $960 full-time.
Collegiate Environment: Student-run newspaper. Social organizations: local fraternities, local sororities. Campus security: 24-hour emergency response devices. College housing not available. 24 computers available on campus for general student use. Staffed computer lab on campus.

■ **BROWN MACKIE COLLEGE-SOUTH BEND** *B-9*
1030 East Jefferson Blvd.
South Bend, IN 46617-3123
Tel: (574)237-0774
Free: 800-743-2447
Fax: (219)237-3585

Web Site: http://www.brownmackie.edu/locations.asp?locid=2
Description: Proprietary, 2-year, coed. Part of American Education Centers. Awards certificates, transfer associate, and terminal associate degrees. Founded 1882. Setting: 5-acre urban campus with easy access to Chicago. Educational spending for 2005 fiscal year: $740 per student. Total enrollment: 619. Student-undergrad faculty ratio is 12:1. 29 applied, 100% were admitted. Full-time: 619 students, 87% women, 13% men. Students come from 2 states and territories, 10% from out-of-state, 0% Native American, 4% Hispanic, 29% black, 1% Asian American or Pacific Islander, 0% international, 65% 25 or older, 5% transferred in. Core. Academic remediation for entering students, accelerated degree program, double major, summer session for credit, adult/continuing education programs.
Entrance Requirements: Options: Peterson's Universal Application, Common Application, deferred admission. Required: essay, high school transcript, interview. Required for some: minimum 2.0 high school GPA, 2 recommendations. Entrance: minimally difficult. Application deadline: Rolling. Notification: continuous.
Costs Per Year: Application fee: $0. Comprehensive fee: $12,402 includes full-time tuition ($6444), mandatory fees ($360), and college room and board ($5598). College room only: $3618. Part-time tuition: $179 per credit hour. Part-time mandatory fees: $10 per credit hour.
Collegiate Environment: Orientation program. Social organizations: 5 open to all. Most popular organizations: Business Club, Medical Assisting Club, Legal Club, Physical Therapy Assistant Club, Occupational Therapy Assistant Club. Major annual event: graduation. Student services: personal-psychological counseling. Campus security: 24-hour emergency response devices. College housing not available. Michiana College Library with 1,409 books, 65 serials, and 65 audiovisual materials. 8 computers available on campus for general student use.

■ **BUTLER UNIVERSITY** *I-9*
4600 Sunset Ave.
Indianapolis, IN 46208-3485
Tel: (317)940-8000; 888-940-8100
Admissions: (317)940-8100
Fax: (317)940-8150
E-mail: admission@butler.edu
Web Site: http://www.butler.edu/
Description: Independent, comprehensive, coed. Awards bachelor's, master's, and first professional degrees. Founded 1855. Setting: 290-acre urban campus. Endowment: $119 million. Research spending for 2004 fiscal year: $1.5 million. Educational spending for 2005 fiscal year: $8460 per student. Total enrollment: 4,384. Faculty: 434 (279 full-time, 155 part-time). Student-undergrad faculty ratio is 12:1. 4,782 applied, 72% were admitted. 43% from top 10% of their high school class, 74% from top quarter, 93% from top half. 9 National Merit Scholars, 69 valedictorians. Full-time: 3,576 students, 62% women, 38% men. Part-time: 75 students, 45% women, 55% men. Students come from 47 states and territories, 44 other countries, 40% from out-of-state, 0.2% Native American, 2% Hispanic, 3% black, 2% Asian American or Pacific Islander, 3% international, 4% 25 or older, 57% live on campus, 3% transferred in. Retention: 87% of full-time freshmen returned the following year. Academic areas with the most degrees conferred: business/marketing; health professions and related sciences; communications/journalism. Core. Calendar: semesters. ESL program, advanced placement, self-designed majors, honors program, independent study, double major, summer session for credit, part-time degree program, adult/continuing education programs, co-op programs and internships, graduate courses open to undergrads. Off campus study at 6 members of the Consortium for Urban Education. Study abroad program. ROTC: Army, Air Force (c).
Entrance Requirements: Options: Peterson's Universal Application, Common Application, electronic application, early action, deferred admission. Required: essay, high school transcript, SAT or ACT. Required for some: interview, audition. Entrance: moderately difficult. Application deadlines: Rolling, 12/1 for early action. Notification: continuous, 12/20 for early action.
Costs Per Year: Application fee: $35. Comprehensive fee: $31,944 includes full-time tuition ($23,530), mandatory fees ($244), and college room and board ($8170). College room only: $3980. Full-time tuition and fees vary according to program. Room and board charges vary according to housing facility. Part-time tuition: $980 per credit. Part-time tuition varies according to program.
Collegiate Environment: Orientation program. Drama-theater group, choral group, marching band, student-run newspaper. Social organizations: 100 open to all; national fraternities, national sororities; 24% of eligible men and 29% of eligible women are members. Most popular organizations: University

YMCA, Student Government Association, Academic Service Honoraries, Alpha Phi Omega, Mortar Board. Major annual events: Geneva Stunts, Spring Sports Spectacular, Spring Sing. Student services: health clinic, personal-psychological counseling. Campus security: 24-hour emergency response devices and patrols, late night transport-escort service, controlled dormitory access. 2,400 college housing spaces available; 1,546 were occupied in 2003-04. Freshmen guaranteed college housing. On-campus residence required in freshman year. Options: coed, women-only housing available. Irwin Library System plus 1 other with 311,429 books, 94,225 microform titles, 1,898 serials, 13,492 audiovisual materials, an OPAC, and a Web page. Operations spending for 2004 fiscal year: $2.3 million. 430 computers available on campus for general student use. A campuswide network can be accessed from student residence rooms and from off campus. Staffed computer lab on campus.

Community Environment: Indianapolis is the capital city, located in the exact center of the state, enjoying a fine climate. All modes of transportation are available. Excellent city facilities include a library with 21 branches, a museum, churches of all denominations, and 17 hospitals. Recreational facilities consist of 32 parks and eight golf courses with additional facilities for auto races, boating, baseball, basketball, football, riding, swimming, roller skating, boxing, wrestling, and ice skating.

■ **CALUMET COLLEGE OF SAINT JOSEPH** *B-5*
2400 New York Ave.
Whiting, IN 46394-2195
Tel: (219)473-7770; 877-700-9100
Admissions: (219)473-4215
Fax: (219)473-4259
Web Site: http://www.ccsj.edu/
Description: Independent Roman Catholic, comprehensive, coed. Awards associate, bachelor's, and master's degrees. Founded 1951. Setting: 25-acre urban campus with easy access to Chicago. Endowment: $4 million. Research spending for 2004 fiscal year: $56,685. Educational spending for 2005 fiscal year: $4052 per student. Total enrollment: 1,265. Faculty: 131 (32 full-time, 99 part-time). Student-undergrad faculty ratio is 22:1. 221 applied, 27% were admitted. 10% from top 10% of their high school class, 26% from top quarter, 50% from top half. Full-time: 475 students, 62% women, 38% men. Part-time: 707 students, 54% women, 46% men. Students come from 2 states and territories, 29% from out-of-state, 0.1% Native American, 20% Hispanic, 29% black, 0.4% Asian American or Pacific Islander, 0.1% international, 65% 25 or older, 18% transferred in. Retention: 69% of full-time freshmen returned the following year. Academic areas with the most degrees conferred: security and protective services; business/marketing; education. Core. Calendar: semesters. Academic remediation for entering students, advanced placement, accelerated degree program, self-designed majors, independent study, double major, summer session for credit, part-time degree program, external degree program, adult/continuing education programs, co-op programs and internships.
Entrance Requirements: Options: Peterson's Universal Application, Common Application, electronic application, deferred admission, international baccalaureate accepted. Required: high school transcript. Recommended: minimum 2.0 high school GPA, interview, SAT or ACT. Required for some: essay, interview, ACT COMPASS. Entrance: noncompetitive. Application deadline: Rolling.
Costs Per Year: Application fee: $0. Tuition: $9900 full-time, $330 per credit hour part-time.
Collegiate Environment: Orientation program. Drama-theater group, choral group, student-run newspaper. Social organizations: 25 open to all. Most popular organizations: student government, Los Amigos Hispanic Club, Criminal Justice Club, Drama Club, Black Student Union. Student services: personal-psychological counseling. Campus security: late night transport-escort service, night security. College housing not available. Mary Gorman Specker Memorial Library plus 1 other with 93,067 books, 3,089 microform titles, 277 serials, 6,580 audiovisual materials, an OPAC, and a Web page. Operations spending for 2004 fiscal year: $362,771. 98 computers available on campus for general student use. Computer purchase/lease plans available. A campuswide network can be accessed from off-campus. Staffed computer lab on campus.
Community Environment: Hammond-Whiting, facing Lake Michigan, is one of the greatest industrial regions in the world. Industries produce pig iron,

rolled, forged and casted steel products, petroleum, lead and aluminum products, chemicals, railroad freight cars and building materials. Part-time employment is available.

■ **COLLEGE OF COURT REPORTING** *B-6*
111 West Tenth St., Ste. 111
Hobart, IN 46342
Tel: (219)942-1459
Fax: (219)942-1631
E-mail: sdrohoskie@ccvedu.com
Web Site: http://www.ccredu.com/
Description: Proprietary, 2-year, coed. Awards certificates, diplomas, transfer associate, and terminal associate degrees. Total enrollment: 156. 33 applied, 88% were admitted. Full-time: 89 students, 99% women, 1% men. Part-time: 67 students, 99% women, 1% men. Students come from 3 states and territories, 5% from out-of-state, 60% 25 or older, 2% transferred in.
Costs Per Year: Tuition: $8100 full-time, $225 per credit hour part-time. Mandatory fees: $50 full-time. Tuition guaranteed not to increase for student's term of enrollment.

■ **CROSSROADS BIBLE COLLEGE** *I-9*
601 North Shortridge Rd.
Indianapolis, IN 46219
Tel: (317)352-8736
Free: 800-273-2224
Fax: (317)352-9145
E-mail: bholdcroft@crossroads.edu
Web Site: http://www.crossroads.edu/
Description: Independent Baptist, 4-year, coed. Awards associate and bachelor's degrees. Founded 1980. Setting: 6-acre urban campus. Total enrollment: 244. 38 applied, 79% were admitted. 23% from top quarter of their high school class, 41% from top half. 2 National Merit Scholars. Full-time: 20 students, 55% women, 45% men. Part-time: 9 students, 33% women, 67% men. Students come from 12 states and territories, 8% from out-of-state, 0% Native American, 2% Hispanic, 30% black, 0% Asian American or Pacific Islander, 0% international, 41% 25 or older, 10% live on campus, 79% transferred in. Retention: 66% of full-time freshmen returned the following year. Core. Calendar: semesters. Services for LD students, accelerated degree program, independent study, distance learning, double major, summer session for credit, part-time degree program, external degree program, adult/continuing education programs, internships.
Entrance Requirements: Open admission. Options: Common Application, deferred admission. Required: essay, high school transcript, recommendations. Recommended: SAT and SAT Subject Tests or ACT. Required for some: interview. Entrance: noncompetitive. Application deadline: 8/8.
Costs Per Year: Application fee: $10. Tuition: $6600 full-time, $210 per credit hour part-time. Mandatory fees: $140 full-time, $140 per term part-time. College room only: $3000.
Collegiate Environment: Orientation program. 18 undergraduates lived in college housing during 2003-04. Freshmen guaranteed college housing. Options: men-only, women-only housing available. 20 computers available on campus for general student use. A campuswide network can be accessed. Staffed computer lab on campus.

■ **DAVENPORT UNIVERSITY (GRANGER)** *A-9*
7121 Grape Rd.
Granger, IN 46530
Tel: (574)277-8447
Free: 800-632-9569
Fax: (574)272-2967
Web Site: http://www.davenport.edu/
Description: Independent, primarily 2-year, coed. Part of Davenport Educational System. Awards diplomas, transfer associate, terminal associate, and bachelor's degrees. Founded 1977. Total university enrollment: 13,124. Calendar: semesters. ESL program, accelerated degree program, self-designed majors, independent study, distance learning, internships.
Entrance Requirements: Open admission. Option: deferred admission. Entrance: noncompetitive. Application deadline: Rolling. Notification: continuous.

■ **DAVENPORT UNIVERSITY (HAMMOND)** *B-5*
5727 Solh Ave.
Hammond, IN 46320
Tel: (219)937-6236

Free: 800-632-9569
Fax: (219)937-6265
Web Site: http://www.davenport.edu/
Description: Independent, 2-year, coed. Part of Davenport Educational System. Awards diplomas, transfer associate, and terminal associate degrees. Founded 1977. Total university enrollment: 13,124. Calendar: semesters. ESL program, accelerated degree program, self-designed majors, independent study, distance learning, internships.
Entrance Requirements: Open admission. Option: deferred admission. Entrance: noncompetitive. Application deadline: Rolling. Notification: continuous.
Costs Per Year: Application fee: $25. Tuition: $7080 full-time, $295 per credit hour part-time. Mandatory fees: $120 full-time.

■ **DAVENPORT UNIVERSITY (MERRILLVILLE)** *B-5*
8200 Georgia St.
Merrillville, IN 46410
Tel: (219)769-5556
Free: 800-632-9569
Fax: (219)756-8911
Web Site: http://www.davenport.edu/
Description: Independent, primarily 2-year, coed. Part of Davenport Educational System. Awards diplomas, transfer associate, terminal associate, and bachelor's degrees. Founded 1977. Total university enrollment: 13,124. Calendar: semesters. ESL program, accelerated degree program, self-designed majors, independent study, distance learning, internships.
Entrance Requirements: Open admission. Option: deferred admission. Entrance: noncompetitive. Application deadline: Rolling. Notification: continuous.
Costs Per Year: Application fee: $25. Tuition: $7080 full-time, $295 per credit hour part-time. Mandatory fees: $120 full-time.

■ **DEPAUW UNIVERSITY** *J-7*
313 South Locust St.
Greencastle, IN 46135-0037
Tel: (765)658-4800
Free: 800-447-2495
Admissions: (765)658-4006
Fax: (765)658-4007
E-mail: admission@depauw.edu
Web Site: http://www.depauw.edu/
Description: Independent, 4-year, coed, affiliated with United Methodist Church. Awards bachelor's degrees. Founded 1837. Setting: 655-acre small town campus with easy access to Indianapolis. Endowment: $452.8 million. Educational spending for 2005 fiscal year: $15,027 per student. Total enrollment: 2,397. Student-undergrad faculty ratio is 10:1. 3,440 applied, 66% were admitted. 55% from top 10% of their high school class, 87% from top quarter, 98% from top half. 14 National Merit Scholars, 30 valedictorians. Full-time: 2,351 students, 55% women, 45% men. Part-time: 46 students, 52% women, 48% men. Students come from 42 states and territories, 21 other countries, 53% from out-of-state, 0.3% Native American, 3% Hispanic, 6% black, 2% Asian American or Pacific Islander, 2% international, 0.1% 25 or older, 95% live on campus, 0.3% transferred in. Retention: 92% of full-time freshmen returned the following year. Academic areas with the most degrees conferred: social sciences; English; foreign languages and literature. Core. Calendar: 4-1-4. Advanced placement, self-designed majors, honors program, independent study, double major, part-time degree program, internships. Off campus study at Great Lakes Colleges Association. Study abroad program. ROTC: Army (c), Air Force (c).
Entrance Requirements: Options: Peterson's Universal Application, Common Application, electronic application, early admission, early decision, early action, deferred admission, international baccalaureate accepted. Required: essay, high school transcript, 1 recommendation, SAT or ACT. Recommended: interview. Entrance: moderately difficult. Application deadlines: 2/1, 11/1 for early decision, 12/1 for early action. Notification: 4/1, 1/1 for early decision, 2/15 for early action.
Costs Per Year: Application fee: $40. Comprehensive fee: $35,580 includes full-time tuition ($27,400), mandatory fees ($380), and college room and board ($7800). College room only: $4100. Part-time tuition: $856.25 per semester hour.
Collegiate Environment: Orientation program. Drama-theater group, choral group, student-run newspaper, radio station. Social organizations: 90 open to all; national fraternities, national sororities; 72% of eligible men and 68% of eligible women are members. Most popular organizations: Community

Service Program, Union Board, Student Congress, Resident Students Association, Independent Council. Major annual events: Fall Dance Marathon (to raise money for pediatric AIDS), Monon Bell Game, American Cancer Society Relay for Life. Student services: health clinic, personal-psychological counseling, women's center. Campus security: 24-hour emergency response devices and patrols, student patrols, late night transport-escort service, controlled dormitory access. 1,407 college housing spaces available; 1,323 were occupied in 2003-04. Freshmen guaranteed college housing. On-campus residence required through senior year. Options: coed, men-only, women-only housing available. Roy O. West Library plus 3 others with 545,736 books, 500,678 microform titles, 2,134 serials, 12,126 audiovisual materials, an OPAC, and a Web page. Operations spending for 2004 fiscal year: $5.9 million. 424 computers available on campus for general student use. Computer purchase/lease plans available. A campuswide network can be accessed from student residence rooms and from off campus. Staffed computer lab on campus.
Community Environment: Greencastle is located 40 miles west of Indianapolis, and within a 4-hour drive of Chicago, Cincinnati, Columbus, Louisville, and St. Louis. Community facilities include churches and a county hospital. The resort areas of Cataract Lake and Mansfield Lake are within 15 miles, and provide facilities for water sports and fishing.

■ **DEVRY UNIVERSITY (INDIANAPOLIS)** *I-9*
9100 Keystone Crossing, Ste. 350
Indianapolis, IN 46240-2158
Tel: (317)581-8854; (866)513-3879
Web Site: http://www.devry.edu/
Description: Proprietary, comprehensive, coed. Part of DeVry University. Awards associate, bachelor's, and master's degrees. Total enrollment: 143. Faculty: 27 (all part-time). Student-undergrad faculty ratio is 4:1. Full-time: 21 students, 57% women, 43% men. Part-time: 51 students, 49% women, 51% men. 0% Native American, 4% Hispanic, 33% black, 0% Asian American or Pacific Islander, 3% international. Calendar: semesters. Academic remediation for entering students, ESL program, services for LD students, advanced placement, accelerated degree program, distance learning, summer session for credit, part-time degree program, adult/continuing education programs, co-op programs.
Entrance Requirements: Options: electronic application, deferred admission, international baccalaureate accepted. Required: high school transcript, interview. Entrance: minimally difficult. Application deadline: Rolling.
Costs Per Year: Application fee: $50. One-time mandatory fee: $40. Tuition: $11,790 full-time, $440 per credit part-time. Mandatory fees: $30 full-time, $30 per year part-time. Full-time tuition and fees vary according to course load. Part-time tuition and fees vary according to course load.
Collegiate Environment: Orientation program. College housing not available.

■ **DEVRY UNIVERSITY (MERRILLVILLE)** *B-5*
Twin Towers
1000 East 80th Place, Ste. 222 Mall
Merrillville, IN 46410-5673
Tel: (219)736-7440
Fax: (219)736-7874
Web Site: http://www.devry.edu/
Description: Proprietary, comprehensive, coed. Calendar: semesters.
Costs Per Year: One-time mandatory fee: $40. Tuition: $11,890 full-time, $445 per credit part-time. Mandatory fees: $60 full-time, $30 per year part-time. Full-time tuition and fees vary according to course load. Part-time tuition and fees vary according to course load.

■ **EARLHAM COLLEGE** *I-13*
801 National Rd. West
Richmond, IN 47374-4095
Tel: (765)983-1200
Free: 800-327-5426
Admissions: (765)983-1600
Fax: (765)983-1560
E-mail: admission@earlham.edu
Web Site: http://www.earlham.edu/
Description: Independent, comprehensive, coed, affiliated with Society of Friends. Awards bachelor's, master's, and first professional degrees. Founded 1847. Setting: 800-acre small town campus with easy access to Cincinnati, Indianapolis, and Dayton. Endowment: $378.8 million. Research spending for 2004 fiscal year: $450,133. Educational spending for 2005 fis-

cal year: $12,502 per student. Total enrollment: 1,372. Faculty: 108 (93 full-time, 15 part-time). Student-undergrad faculty ratio is 12:1. 1,554 applied, 70% were admitted. 30% from top 10% of their high school class, 61% from top quarter, 87% from top half. 7 National Merit Scholars, 19 class presidents, 10 valedictorians, 136 student government officers. Full-time: 1,201 students, 58% women, 42% men. Part-time: 25 students, 56% women, 44% men. Students come from 49 states and territories, 53 other countries, 72% from out-of-state, 0.3% Native American, 3% Hispanic, 7% black, 2% Asian American or Pacific Islander, 7% international, 4% 25 or older, 88% live on campus, 1% transferred in. Retention: 83% of full-time freshmen returned the following year. Academic areas with the most degrees conferred: biological/life sciences; social sciences; visual and performing arts. Core. Calendar: semesters. Services for LD students, advanced placement, accelerated degree program, self-designed majors, independent study, double major, internships. Off campus study at members of the Great Lakes Colleges Association. Study abroad program.

Entrance Requirements: Options: Peterson's Universal Application, Common Application, electronic application, early admission, early decision, early action, deferred admission, international baccalaureate accepted. Required: essay, high school transcript, minimum 3.0 high school GPA, 2 recommendations, SAT or ACT. Recommended: interview. Entrance: moderately difficult. Application deadlines: 2/15, 12/1 for early decision, 1/1 for early action. Notification: 3/15, 12/15 for early decision, 2/1 for early action. Preference given to Quakers, children of alumni, state residents, minorities.

Costs Per Year: Application fee: $30. Comprehensive fee: $33,604 includes full-time tuition ($26,984), mandatory fees ($700), and college room and board ($5920). College room only: $2900. Room and board charges vary according to board plan. Part-time tuition: $899 per credit hour. Part-time mandatory fees: $700 per year.

Collegiate Environment: Orientation program. Drama-theater group, choral group, student-run newspaper, radio station. Social organizations: 70 open to all. Most popular organizations: Gospel Revelations Chorus, Dance Alloy, club sports, student government, Black Leadership Action Coalition. Major annual events: Homecoming, Air Guitar, Spring Fest. Student services: health clinic, personal-psychological counseling, women's center. Campus security: 24-hour emergency response devices and patrols, student patrols, late night transport-escort service, controlled dormitory access. 974 college housing spaces available; all were occupied in 2003-04. Freshmen guaranteed college housing. On-campus residence required through senior year. Options: coed, men-only, women-only housing available. Lilly Library plus 1 other with 392,100 books, 235,400 microform titles, 1,660 serials, 53,000 audiovisual materials, an OPAC, and a Web page. Operations spending for 2004 fiscal year: $657,001. 168 computers available on campus for general student use. Computer purchase/lease plans available. A campuswide network can be accessed from student residence rooms. Staffed computer lab on campus.

Community Environment: The campus lies at the southwest edge of Richmond, IN, a city of 40,000 people. Richmond is 70 miles from Cincinnati, OH, and Indianapolis, IN, and 40 miles from Dayton, OH. Local activities include auctions, the city's arboretum, the pedestrian shopping mall downtown, the symphony orchestra, civic theater and opera companies, a historical museum and the art association. The city is served by buses. Airline service is available in Dayton, OH.

■ **FRANKLIN COLLEGE** *J-9*
101 Branigin Blvd.
Franklin, IN 46131-2623
Tel: (317)738-8000
Free: 800-852-0232
Admissions: (317)738-8062
Fax: (317)738-8274
E-mail: admissions@franklincoll.edu
Web Site: http://www.franklincollege.edu/
Description: Independent, 4-year, coed, affiliated with American Baptist Churches in the U.S.A.. Awards bachelor's degrees. Founded 1834. Setting: 74-acre small town campus with easy access to Indianapolis. Endowment: $73.3 million. Educational spending for 2005 fiscal year: $7099 per student. Total enrollment: 1,003. Student-undergrad faculty ratio is 12:1. 1,009 applied, 80% were admitted. 20% from top 10% of their high school class, 54% from top quarter, 82% from top half. 5 valedictorians. Full-time: 946 students, 49% women, 51% men. Part-time: 57 students, 40% women, 60% men. Students come from 16 states and territories, 7 other countries, 6% from out-of-state, 0.3% Native American, 1% Hispanic, 4% black, 0.5% Asian American or Pacific Islander, 1% international, 2% 25 or older, 72% live on

campus, 2% transferred in. Retention: 76% of full-time freshmen returned the following year. Academic areas with the most degrees conferred: communications/journalism; education; social sciences. Core. Calendar: 4-1-4. Academic remediation for entering students, services for LD students, advanced placement, independent study, double major, summer session for credit, part-time degree program, co-op programs and internships. Off campus study at Marian College, University of Indianapolis, Indiana University-Purdue University at Indianapolis, Butler University, Martin University, Ivy Tech State College. Study abroad program. ROTC: Army (c).

Entrance Requirements: Options: electronic application, deferred admission. Required: essay, high school transcript, TOEFL for international students, SAT or ACT. Recommended: minimum X high school GPA, recommendations, interview. Entrance: moderately difficult.

Costs Per Year: Application fee: $30. Comprehensive fee: $25,005 includes full-time tuition ($19,100), mandatory fees ($175), and college room and board ($5730). College room only: $3340. Room and board charges vary according to board plan and housing facility. Part-time tuition: $265 per credit hour. Part-time tuition varies according to course load.

Collegiate Environment: Orientation program. Drama-theater group, choral group, student-run newspaper, radio station. Social organizations: 66 open to all; national fraternities, national sororities; 41% of eligible men and 41% of eligible women are members. Most popular organizations: FLOW, FC Volunteers, Student Entertainment Board, Student Congress. Major annual events: Homecoming, Grizzly Grand Prix Festival. Student services: health clinic, personal-psychological counseling. Campus security: 24-hour emergency response devices and patrols, late night transport-escort service. College housing designed to accommodate 671 students; 676 undergraduates lived in college housing during 2003-04. Freshmen guaranteed college housing. On-campus residence required through junior year. Option: coed housing available. Hamilton Library plus 1 other with 126,345 books, 299,715 microform titles, 334 serials, 7,665 audiovisual materials, an OPAC, and a Web page. Operations spending for 2004 fiscal year: $535,775. 150 computers available on campus for general student use. A campuswide network can be accessed from student residence rooms and from off campus. Staffed computer lab on campus.

Community Environment: Franklin (population 15,000) is situated 20 miles south of Indianapolis with facilities that include a library, hospital, 15 churches representing major denominations, and various service, fraternal, and veteran's organizations. Recreational activities are fishing, swimming, tennis, and bowling. Part-time job opportunities are available.

■ **GOSHEN COLLEGE** *B-10*
1700 South Main St.
Goshen, IN 46526-4794
Tel: (574)535-7000
Free: 800-348-7422
Admissions: (574)535-7535
Fax: (574)535-7060
E-mail: admissions@goshen.edu
Web Site: http://www.goshen.edu/
Description: Independent Mennonite, 4-year, coed. Awards bachelor's degrees. Founded 1894. Setting: 135-acre small town campus. Endowment: $95.9 million. Research spending for 2004 fiscal year: $61,654. Educational spending for 2005 fiscal year: $7210 per student. Total enrollment: 922. Student-undergrad faculty ratio is 10:1. 492 applied, 76% were admitted. 30% from top 10% of their high school class, 63% from top quarter, 90% from top half. 9 National Merit Scholars, 6 valedictorians. Full-time: 831 students, 59% women, 41% men. Part-time: 91 students, 70% women, 30% men. Students come from 36 states and territories, 30 other countries, 49% from out-of-state, 0.2% Native American, 4% Hispanic, 3% black, 1% Asian American or Pacific Islander, 8% international, 11% 25 or older, 67% live on campus, 6% transferred in. Retention: 80% of full-time freshmen returned the following year. Academic areas with the most degrees conferred: business/marketing; health professions and related sciences; computer and information sciences; visual and performing arts. Core. Calendar: semesters. Academic remediation for entering students, services for LD students, advanced placement, accelerated degree program, self-designed majors, freshman honors college, honors program, independent study, double major, summer session for credit, part-time degree program, adult/continuing education programs, internships. Off campus study at Northern Indiana Consortium for Education. Study abroad program.

Entrance Requirements: Options: Common Application, electronic application, early action, deferred admission, international baccalaureate accepted. Required: essay, high school transcript, minimum 2.5 high school GPA, 2 recommendations, rank in upper 50% of high school class, minimum SAT score of 1000 or ACT score of 22, SAT or ACT. Recommended: interview. Entrance: moderately difficult. Application deadlines: 8/15, 12/1 for early action. Notification: continuous, 12/15 for early action.

Costs Per Year: Application fee: $25. Comprehensive fee: $27,000 includes full-time tuition ($20,300) and college room and board ($6700). College room only: $3600. Part-time tuition: $800 per credit hour.

Collegiate Environment: Orientation program. Drama-theater group, choral group, student-run newspaper, radio station. Social organizations: 26 open to all; 50% of eligible men and 50% of eligible women are members. Most popular organizations: Business Club, Black Student Union, Non-Traditional Student Network, Goshen Student Women's Organization, International Student Club. Major annual events: February Fest, Ethnic Fair, Fall Festival. Student services: health clinic, personal-psychological counseling, women's center. Campus security: 24-hour emergency response devices and patrols, late night transport-escort service. 633 college housing spaces available; 467 were occupied in 2003-04. Freshmen guaranteed college housing. On-campus residence required through junior year. Options: coed, men-only, women-only housing available. Harold and Wilma Good Library plus 2 others with 127,028 books, 178,314 microform titles, 750 serials, 3,250 audiovisual materials, an OPAC, and a Web page. Operations spending for 2004 fiscal year: $597,946. 160 computers available on campus for general student use. A campuswide network can be accessed from student residence rooms and from off campus. Staffed computer lab on campus.

Community Environment: Goshen,"The Maple City" is a diversified small industry center, situated ten miles south of the Michigan state line. Annual mean temperature is 55 degrees, and the annual rainfall is 34 inches. All forms of transportation are available, and the airport is five miles southeast. Community facilities include a public library, hospital, 24 churches and many civic, service and social organizations. Goshen is noted for its large number of Amish farmers, and hundreds of lakes are within a 40-mile radius.

■ **GRACE COLLEGE** *C-10*
200 Seminary Dr.
Winona Lake, IN 46590-1294
Tel: (574)372-5100
Free: 800-54 GRACE
Fax: (574)372-5139
E-mail: millerar@grace.edu
Web Site: http://www.grace.edu/

Description: Independent, comprehensive, coed, affiliated with Fellowship of Grace Brethren Churches. Administratively affiliated with Grace Theological Seminary. Awards associate, bachelor's, master's, doctoral, and first professional degrees. Founded 1948. Setting: 160-acre small town campus. Endowment: $5.5 million. Educational spending for 2005 fiscal year: $5391 per student. Total enrollment: 1,275. Faculty: 121 (43 full-time, 78 part-time). Student-undergrad faculty ratio is 16:1. 837 applied, 73% were admitted. 24% from top 10% of their high school class, 53% from top quarter, 76% from top half. Full-time: 980 students, 47% women, 53% men. Part-time: 148 students, 41% women, 59% men. Students come from 30 states and territories, 5 other countries, 40% from out-of-state, 1% Native American, 2% Hispanic, 9% black, 1% Asian American or Pacific Islander, 1% international, 25% 25 or older, 36% live on campus, 4% transferred in. Academic areas with the most degrees conferred: education; business/marketing; psychology. Core. Calendar: semesters. Academic remediation for entering students, services for LD students, advanced placement, accelerated degree program, honors program, independent study, distance learning, double major, summer session for credit, part-time degree program, adult/continuing education programs, co-op programs and internships, graduate courses open to undergrads. Off campus study at Coalition for Christian Colleges and Universities. Study abroad program.

Entrance Requirements: Options: Peterson's Universal Application, electronic application, early admission, deferred admission, international baccalaureate accepted. Required: essay, high school transcript, minimum 2.3 high school GPA, 2 recommendations, personal statement of faith, SAT or ACT. Required for some: interview. Entrance: moderately difficult. Application deadline: 8/1. Notification: continuous until 8/15.

Costs Per Year: Application fee: $20. Comprehensive fee: $22,170 includes full-time tuition ($15,620), mandatory fees ($400), and college room and board ($6150). College room only: $3070. Room and board charges vary according to board plan and housing facility. Part-time tuition: $295 per credit. Part-time mandatory fees: $280 per year. Part-time tuition and fees vary according to course load.

Collegiate Environment: Orientation program. Drama-theater group, choral group, student-run newspaper. Social organizations: 30 open to all. Most

popular organizations: Grace Ministries in Action, Student Activities Board, Funfest, women's ministries, Breakout. Major annual events: homecoming, Heart of the Holidays, Halloween Fun Fest. Student services: health clinic, personal-psychological counseling. Campus security: student patrols, late night transport-escort service, controlled dormitory access, evening patrols by trained security personnel. 716 college housing spaces available; 400 were occupied in 2003-04. Freshmen guaranteed college housing. On-campus residence required through senior year. Options: men-only, women-only housing available. Morgan Library with 142,865 books, 22,995 microform titles, 12,500 serials, 3,583 audiovisual materials, an OPAC, and a Web page. Operations spending for 2004 fiscal year: $379,811. 62 computers available on campus for general student use. A campuswide network can be accessed from student residence rooms and from off campus. Staffed computer lab on campus.

Community Environment: One of the outstanding Christian summer resorts in America, Winona Lake, population 4,000, is situated two miles from Warsaw, Indiana, on the main line of Amtrack Railroad. This is a resort area for the entire family.

■ **HANOVER COLLEGE** *M-11*
PO Box 108
Hanover, IN 47243-0108
Tel: (812)866-7000
Free: 800-213-2178
Admissions: (812)866-7021
Fax: (812)866-7098
E-mail: admissions@hanover.edu
Web Site: http://www.hanover.edu/

Description: Independent Presbyterian, 4-year, coed. Awards bachelor's degrees. Founded 1827. Setting: 630-acre rural campus with easy access to Louisville. Endowment: $141.9 million. Research spending for 2004 fiscal year: $31,243. Educational spending for 2005 fiscal year: $12,628 per student. Total enrollment: 1,008. Student-undergrad faculty ratio is 10:1. 1,680 applied, 70% were admitted. 44% from top 10% of their high school class, 80% from top quarter, 96% from top half. 10 valedictorians. Full-time: 1,004 students, 56% women, 44% men. Part-time: 4 students, 75% women, 25% men. Students come from 28 states and territories, 17 other countries, 33% from out-of-state, 0.4% Native American, 1% Hispanic, 1% black, 3% Asian American or Pacific Islander, 5% international, 1% 25 or older, 96% live on campus, 1% transferred in. Retention: 77% of full-time freshmen returned the following year. Academic areas with the most degrees conferred: social sciences; business/marketing; psychology. Core. Calendar: 4-4-1. Advanced placement, self-designed majors, independent study, double major, internships. Off campus study at 8 members of the Spring Term Consortium. Study abroad program.

Entrance Requirements: Options: Peterson's Universal Application, Common Application, electronic application, early admission, early action, deferred admission, international baccalaureate accepted. Required: essay, high school transcript, 1 recommendation, SAT or ACT. Recommended: interview. Entrance: moderately difficult. Application deadlines: 3/1, 12/1 for early action. Notification: continuous, 12/20 for early action.

Costs Per Year: Application fee: $35. Comprehensive fee: $28,150 includes full-time tuition ($21,150), mandatory fees ($500), and college room and board ($6500). College room only: $3100. Full-time tuition and fees vary according to reciprocity agreements. Room and board charges vary according to housing facility and location. Part-time tuition: $2350 per unit. Part-time tuition varies according to course load and reciprocity agreements.

Collegiate Environment: Orientation program. Drama-theater group, choral group, student-run newspaper, radio station. Social organizations: 41 open to all; national fraternities, national sororities; 35% of eligible men and 38% of eligible women are members. Most popular organizations: Christian Life, Baptist Collegiate Ministries, Student Programming Board, Link, American Chemical Society. Major annual events: homecoming, Parents' Day, Alumni Day. Student services: health clinic, personal-psychological counseling. Campus security: 24-hour emergency response devices and patrols, late night transport-escort service, controlled dormitory access. 980 college housing spaces available; 974 were occupied in 2003-04. Freshmen guaranteed college housing. On-campus residence required through senior year. Options: coed, men-only, women-only housing available. Duggan Library with 224,478 books, 44,770 microform titles, 1,035 serials, 5,080 audiovisual materials, an OPAC, and a Web page. Operations spending for 2004 fiscal year: $1.3 million. 90 computers available on campus for general student use. A campuswide network can be accessed from student residence rooms and from off campus. Staffed computer lab on campus.

Community Environment: Hanover is located four and one-half miles from Madison, Indiana (population 15,000), overlooking the beautiful Ohio River valley from a hilltop nearly 400 feet above the river. Community facilities include a modern hospital. The Hanover/Madison area is rich in historic lore and antiques. Clifty Falls, a large State Park, well known for its rugged scenery, serves this community.

■ **HOLY CROSS COLLEGE**
PO Box 308, 54515 State Rd. 933 North
Notre Dame, IN 46556-0308
Tel: (574)239-8400
Fax: (574)239-8323
E-mail: vduke@hcc-nd.edu
Web Site: http://www.hcc-nd.edu/
Description: Independent Roman Catholic, primarily 2-year, coed. Awards transfer associate and bachelor's degrees. Founded 1966. Setting: 150-acre urban campus. Educational spending for 2005 fiscal year: $5342 per student. Total enrollment: 369. Student-undergrad faculty ratio is 12:1. 459 applied. Full-time: 328 students, 38% women, 62% men. Part-time: 41 students, 49% women, 51% men. Students come from 37 states and territories, 12 other countries, 42% from out-of-state, 0% Native American, 7% Hispanic, 3% black, 2% Asian American or Pacific Islander, 1% international, 2% 25 or older, 54% live on campus, 10% transferred in. Retention: 53% of full-time freshmen returned the following year. Academic area with the most degrees conferred: liberal arts/general studies. Core. Calendar: semesters. Academic remediation for entering students, ESL program, advanced placement, freshman honors college, summer session for credit, part-time degree program, internships. Off campus study at members of the Northern Indiana Consortium for Education. ROTC: Army (c), Air Force (c).
Entrance Requirements: Options: Common Application, electronic application, deferred admission. Required: essay, high school transcript, minimum 2.5 high school GPA, SAT or ACT. Recommended: interview. Required for some: recommendations. Entrance: minimally difficult. Application deadline: Rolling.
Costs Per Year: Application fee: $50. Comprehensive fee: $23,500 includes full-time tuition ($14,500), mandatory fees ($1000), and college room and board ($8000). Part-time tuition: $365 per semester hour.
Collegiate Environment: Orientation program. Drama-theater group, choral group, marching band, student-run newspaper. Most popular organizations: Student Advisory Committee, Campus Ministry, Volunteers in Support of Admissions, intramural athletics. Major annual events: Campus Open House, All College Picnic, Opening Mass. Student services: personal-psychological counseling. Campus security: 24-hour emergency response devices, 24-hour patrols by trained personnel on certain days. 300 college housing spaces available; 239 were occupied in 2003-04. Options: coed, men-only, women-only housing available. Holy Cross Library with 15,000 books, 23,000 microform titles, 160 serials, and an OPAC. Operations spending for 2004 fiscal year: $133,131. 60 computers available on campus for general student use. A campuswide network can be accessed from student residence rooms and from off campus. Staffed computer lab on campus.
Community Environment: See University of Notre Dame.

■ **HUNTINGTON UNIVERSITY** *E-11*
2303 College Ave.
Huntington, IN 46750-1299
Tel: (260)356-6000
Free: 800-642-6493
Fax: (260)356-9448
E-mail: jberggren@huntington.edu
Web Site: http://www.huntington.edu/
Description: Independent, comprehensive, coed, affiliated with Church of the United Brethren in Christ. Administratively affiliated with Church of the United Brethren in Christ. Awards associate, bachelor's, and master's degrees. Founded 1897. Setting: 200-acre small town campus with easy access to Fort Wayne. Endowment: $20.3 million. Total enrollment: 1,019. Faculty: 122 (59 full-time, 63 part-time). Student-undergrad faculty ratio is 11:1. 692 applied, 93% were admitted. 28% from top 10% of their high school class, 54% from top quarter, 87% from top half. Full-time: 830 students, 55% women, 45% men. Part-time: 119 students, 62% women, 38% men. Students come from 27 states and territories, 13 other countries, 18% from out-of-state, 0.1% Native American, 0.4% Hispanic, 1% black, 0.5% Asian American or Pacific Islander, 4% international, 1% 25 or older, 70% live on campus, 3% transferred in. Retention: 78% of full-time freshmen

returned the following year. Academic areas with the most degrees conferred: business/marketing; education; theology and religious vocations. Core. Calendar: 4-1-4. Academic remediation for entering students, advanced placement, independent study, double major, summer session for credit, part-time degree program, adult/continuing education programs, internships, graduate courses open to undergrads. Off campus study at Saint Francis College (IN). Study abroad program.
Entrance Requirements: Options: Peterson's Universal Application, Common Application, electronic application, deferred admission. Required: essay, high school transcript, minimum 2.3 high school GPA, SAT or ACT. Recommended: interview. Entrance: moderately difficult. Application deadline: 8/1. Notification: continuous until 7/1.
Costs Per Year: Application fee: $20. Comprehensive fee: $25,390 includes full-time tuition ($18,420), mandatory fees ($440), and college room and board ($6530). Part-time tuition: $530 per semester hour.
Collegiate Environment: Orientation program. Drama-theater group, choral group, student-run newspaper, radio station. Social organizations: 35 open to all; 7% of women are members. Most popular organizations: Joe Mertz Volunteer Center, Student Senate, Ministry groups, student publications, Chapel Worship Team. Major annual events: Huntington College Olympiad, Parents' Weekend/Homecoming, Powderpuff Football. Student services: health clinic, personal-psychological counseling. Campus security: 24-hour emergency response devices, late night transport-escort service, night patrols by trained security personnel. 639 college housing spaces available; 526 were occupied in 2003-04. Freshmen guaranteed college housing. On-campus residence required through junior year. Options: men-only, women-only housing available. RichLyn Library with 91,709 books, 2,221 microform titles, 553 serials, 4,323 audiovisual materials, and a Web page. 190 computers available on campus for general student use. A campuswide network can be accessed from student residence rooms and from off campus. Staffed computer lab on campus.
Community Environment: Huntington (population 18,217) is located 24 miles southwest of Fort Wayne and is 90 miles north of Indianapolis. It is in a grain and industrial region. City facilities include museums, library, many churches, YMCA, hospital and numerous civic organizations. The retail and industrial organizations and citizens of the community appreciate the importance of the college students in the overall well being of the community. Salamonie Reservoir, six miles southwest has facilities for camping, picnicking, fishing, and boating.

■ **INDIANA BUSINESS COLLEGE (ANDERSON)** *H-10*
140 East 53rd St.
Anderson, IN 46013
Tel: (765)644-7514
Web Site: http://www.ibcschools.edu/
Description: Proprietary, 2-year, coed. Awards certificates, diplomas, and terminal associate degrees. Founded 1902. Total enrollment: 235. Student-undergrad faculty ratio is 20:1. Distance learning, double major, part-time degree program, adult/continuing education programs, co-op programs and internships.
Entrance Requirements: Options: electronic application, early admission. Required: high school transcript, interview, Wonderlic Scholastic Level Exam (SLE). Entrance: moderately difficult. Application deadline: Rolling. Notification: continuous.
Costs Per Year: Application fee: $50.
Collegiate Environment: Orientation program.

■ **INDIANA BUSINESS COLLEGE (COLUMBUS)** *K-10*
2222 Poshard Dr.
Columbus, IN 47203-1843
Tel: (812)379-9000
Web Site: http://www.ibcschools.edu/
Description: Proprietary, 2-year, coed. Awards certificates, diplomas, and terminal associate degrees. Total enrollment: 273. Student-undergrad faculty ratio is 20:1. Distance learning, double major, part-time degree program, adult/continuing education programs, co-op programs and internships.
Entrance Requirements: Option: electronic application. Required: high school transcript, interview, Wonderlic Scholastic Level Exam (SLE). Entrance: moderately difficult. Application deadline: Rolling. Notification: continuous.
Costs Per Year: Application fee: $50.
Collegiate Environment: Orientation program.

■ **INDIANA BUSINESS COLLEGE (EVANSVILLE)** *P-4*
4601 Theatre Dr.
Evansville, IN 47715-4601

Tel: (812)476-6000
Web Site: http://www.ibcschools.edu/
Description: Proprietary, 2-year, coed. Awards certificates, diplomas, and terminal associate degrees. Total enrollment: 295. Student-undergrad faculty ratio is 20:1. Distance learning, double major, part-time degree program, adult/continuing education programs, co-op programs and internships.
Entrance Requirements: Option: electronic application. Required: high school transcript, interview, Wonderlic Scholastic Level Exam (SLE). Entrance: moderately difficult. Application deadline: Rolling. Notification: continuous.
Costs Per Year: Application fee: $50.
Collegiate Environment: Orientation program.

■ **INDIANA BUSINESS COLLEGE (FORT WAYNE)** *D-12*
6413 North Clinton St.
Fort Wayne, IN 46825
Tel: (260)471-7667
Web Site: http://www.ibcschools.edu/
Description: Proprietary, 2-year, coed. Awards certificates, diplomas, and terminal associate degrees. Total enrollment: 384. Student-undergrad faculty ratio is 20:1. Distance learning, double major, part-time degree program, adult/continuing education programs, co-op programs and internships.
Entrance Requirements: Option: electronic application. Required: high school transcript, interview, Wonderlic Scholastic Level Exam (SLE). Entrance: moderately difficult. Application deadline: Rolling. Notification: continuous.
Costs Per Year: Application fee: $50.
Collegiate Environment: Orientation program.

■ **INDIANA BUSINESS COLLEGE (INDIANAPOLIS)** *I-9*
6300 Technology Center Dr.
Indianapolis, IN 46278
Tel: (317)873-6500
Web Site: http://www.ibcschools.edu/Campuses/northwest.asp
Description: Proprietary, 2-year, coed. Awards certificates, diplomas, and terminal associate degrees. Total enrollment: 86.
Entrance Requirements: Required: high school transcript, interview, Wonderlic Scholastic Level Exam. Entrance: moderately difficult. Application deadline: Rolling. Notification: continuous.
Costs Per Year: Application fee: $50.

■ **INDIANA BUSINESS COLLEGE (INDIANAPOLIS)** *I-9*
550 East Washington St.
Indianapolis, IN 46204
Tel: (317)264-5656
Fax: (317)264-5650
Web Site: http://www.ibcschools.edu/
Description: Proprietary, 2-year, coed. Awards certificates, diplomas, and terminal associate degrees. Founded 1902. Setting: 1-acre urban campus. Total enrollment: 782. Student-undergrad faculty ratio is 20:1. Distance learning, double major, summer session for credit, part-time degree program, adult/continuing education programs, co-op programs and internships.
Entrance Requirements: Option: electronic application. Required: high school transcript, interview, Wonderlic Scholastic Level Exam (SLE). Entrance: moderately difficult. Application deadline: Rolling. Notification: continuous.
Costs Per Year: Application fee: $50.
Collegiate Environment: Orientation program. Most popular organizations: Student Advisory Board, Student Ambassadors, Phi Beta Lambda. Campus security: 24-hour patrols. College housing not available.

■ **INDIANA BUSINESS COLLEGE (INDIANAPOLIS-NORTHWEST CAMPUS)** *I-9*
6300 Technology Center Dr.
Indianapolis, IN 46278
Tel: (317)873-6500
Web Site: http://www.ibcschools.edu/campuses/northwest.asp
Description: Proprietary, 2-year, coed. Awards certificates, diplomas, and terminal associate degrees. Total enrollment: 584. Student-undergrad faculty ratio is 20:1.
Entrance Requirements: Required: high school transcript, interview, Wonderlic Scholastic Level Exam. Entrance: moderately difficult. Application deadline: Rolling. Notification: continuous.

Costs Per Year: Application fee: $50.

■ **INDIANA BUSINESS COLLEGE (LAFAYETTE)** *G-7*
2 Executive Dr.
Lafayette, IN 47905
Tel: (765)447-9550
Web Site: http://www.ibcschools.edu/
Description: Proprietary, 2-year, coed. Awards certificates, diplomas, and terminal associate degrees. Total enrollment: 215. Student-undergrad faculty ratio is 20:1. Distance learning, double major, part-time degree program, adult/continuing education programs, co-op programs and internships.
Entrance Requirements: Option: electronic application. Required: high school transcript, interview, Wonderlic Scholastic Level Exam (SLE). Entrance: moderately difficult. Application deadline: Rolling. Notification: continuous.
Costs Per Year: Application fee: $50.
Collegiate Environment: Orientation program.

■ **INDIANA BUSINESS COLLEGE (MARION)** *F-10*
830 North Miller Ave.
Marion, IN 46952-2338
Tel: (765)662-7497
Web Site: http://www.ibcschools.edu/
Description: Proprietary, 2-year, coed. Awards certificates, diplomas, and terminal associate degrees. Total enrollment: 120. Student-undergrad faculty ratio is 20:1. Distance learning, double major, part-time degree program, adult/continuing education programs, co-op programs and internships.
Entrance Requirements: Option: electronic application. Required: high school transcript, interview, Wonderlic Scholastic Level Exam (SLE). Entrance: moderately difficult. Application deadline: Rolling. Notification: continuous.
Costs Per Year: Application fee: $50.
Collegiate Environment: Orientation program.

■ **INDIANA BUSINESS COLLEGE-MEDICAL** *I-9*
8150 Brookville Rd.
Indianapolis, IN 46239
Tel: (317)375-8000
Fax: (317)351-1871
Web Site: http://www.ibcschools.edu/
Description: Proprietary, 2-year, coed. Awards certificates, diplomas, and terminal associate degrees. Total enrollment: 584. Student-undergrad faculty ratio is 20:1. Distance learning, double major, part-time degree program, adult/continuing education programs, co-op programs and internships.
Entrance Requirements: Option: electronic application. Required: high school transcript, interview, Wonderlic Scholastic Level Exam (SLE). Entrance: moderately difficult. Application deadline: Rolling. Notification: continuous.
Costs Per Year: Application fee: $50.
Collegiate Environment: Orientation program.

■ **INDIANA BUSINESS COLLEGE (MUNCIE)** *G-11*
411 West Riggin Rd.
Muncie, IN 47303
Tel: (765)288-8681
Fax: (765)288-8797
Web Site: http://www.ibcschools.edu/
Description: Proprietary, 2-year, coed. Awards certificates, diplomas, and terminal associate degrees. Total enrollment: 310. Student-undergrad faculty ratio is 20:1. Distance learning, double major, part-time degree program, co-op programs and internships.
Entrance Requirements: Option: electronic application. Required: high school transcript, interview, Wonderlic Scholastic Level Exam (SLE). Entrance: moderately difficult. Application deadline: Rolling. Notification: continuous.
Costs Per Year: Application fee: $50.
Collegiate Environment: Orientation program. Most popular organization: Phi Beta Lambda. College housing not available.

■ **INDIANA BUSINESS COLLEGE (TERRE HAUTE)** *J-5*
3175 South Third Place
Terre Haute, IN 47802
Tel: (812)232-4458
Web Site: http://www.ibcschools.edu/

Description: Proprietary, 2-year, coed. Awards certificates, diplomas, and terminal associate degrees. Founded 1902. Total enrollment: 220. Student-undergrad faculty ratio is 20:1. Distance learning, double major, part-time degree program, adult/continuing education programs, co-op programs and internships.

Entrance Requirements: Option: electronic application. Required: high school transcript, interview, Wonderlic Scholastic Level Exam, Wonderlic Scholastic Level Exam (SLE). Entrance: moderately difficult. Application deadline: Rolling. Notification: continuous.

Costs Per Year: Application fee: $50.

Collegiate Environment: Orientation program.

■ **INDIANA STATE UNIVERSITY** *J-5*
210 North Seventh St.
Terre Haute, IN 47809-1401
Tel: (812)237-6311
Free: 800-742-0891
Admissions: (812)237-2121
Fax: (812)237-8023
Web Site: http://web.indstate.edu/

Description: State-supported, university, coed. Awards associate, bachelor's, master's, and doctoral degrees and post-master's certificates. Founded 1865. Setting: 91-acre small town campus with easy access to Indianapolis. Endowment: $42.7 million. Research spending for 2004 fiscal year: $11.1 million. Educational spending for 2005 fiscal year: $6340 per student. Total enrollment: 10,679. Faculty: 662 (489 full-time, 173 part-time). Student-undergrad faculty ratio is 17:1. 5,351 applied, 80% were admitted. 10% from top 10% of their high school class, 28% from top quarter, 62% from top half. Full-time: 7,628 students, 51% women, 49% men. Part-time: 1,042 students, 58% women, 42% men. Students come from 44 states and territories, 44 other countries, 10% from out-of-state, 0.4% Native American, 1% Hispanic, 11% black, 1% Asian American or Pacific Islander, 2% international, 18% 25 or older, 36% live on campus, 8% transferred in. Retention: 67% of full-time freshmen returned the following year. Academic areas with the most degrees conferred: education; business/marketing; social sciences. Calendar: semesters. Academic remediation for entering students, ESL program, services for LD students, advanced placement, accelerated degree program, honors program, independent study, distance learning, double major, summer session for credit, part-time degree program, adult/continuing education programs, co-op programs and internships, graduate courses open to undergrads. Off campus study at Saint Mary-of-the-Woods College, Rose-Hulman Institute of Technology. Study abroad program. ROTC: Army, Air Force.

Entrance Requirements: Options: electronic application, deferred admission. Required: high school transcript, SAT or ACT. Required for some: recommendations, interview. Entrance: moderately difficult. Application deadline: 8/15. Notification: continuous.

Costs Per Year: Application fee: $25. State resident tuition: $5756 full-time, $208 per credit hour part-time. Nonresident tuition: $12,752 full-time, $450 per credit hour part-time. Mandatory fees: $108 full-time, $54 per term part-time. Full-time tuition and fees vary according to course load. College room and board: $5938. College room only: $3150. Room and board charges vary according to board plan, housing facility, and student level.

Collegiate Environment: Orientation program. Drama-theater group, choral group, marching band, student-run newspaper, radio station. Social organizations: 183 open to all; national fraternities, national sororities; 12% of eligible men and 11% of eligible women are members. Most popular organizations: Union Boards, Student Government Association, Black Student Union, Student Alumni Association. Major annual events: Homecoming, Donaghy Day, Tandemonia. Student services: legal services, health clinic, personal-psychological counseling, women's center. Campus security: 24-hour emergency response devices and patrols, student patrols, late night transport-escort service. 3,630 college housing spaces available; 3,251 were occupied in 2003-04. Freshmen guaranteed college housing. On-campus residence required in freshman year. Options: coed, men-only, women-only housing available. Cunningham Memorial Library plus 1 other with 2.5 million books, 2,827 serials, an OPAC, and a Web page. Operations spending for 2004 fiscal year: $4.8 million. 450 computers available on campus for general student use. A campuswide network can be accessed from student residence rooms and from off campus. Staffed computer lab on campus.

Community Environment: Indiana State is located in Terre Haute, a city of 60,000, on the banks of the Wabash River. Terre Haute is within a 500-mile radius of more than half the population of the United States. Chicago, St. Louis, Cincinnati, Louisville, and Nashville are within a half-day drive, and

Indianapolis is only an hour and a half away. Terre Haute's cultural attractions include the Terre Haute Symphony Orchestra, Community Theater, the Sheldon Swope Art Museum, the Eugene V. Debs Museum, and the Vigo County Historical Museum. The educational atmosphere of the city is enhanced by Saint Mary-of-the-Woods College, Rose-Hulman Institute of Technology, and Indiana Vocational-Tech College.

■ **INDIANA TECH** *D-12*
1600 East Washington Blvd.
Fort Wayne, IN 46803-1297
Tel: (260)422-5561; 888-666-TECH
Fax: (260)422-7696
E-mail: agcarnahan@indianatech.edu
Web Site: http://www.indianatech.edu

Description: Independent, comprehensive, coed. Awards associate, bachelor's, and master's degrees. Founded 1930. Setting: 25-acre urban campus. Endowment: $21.6 million. Educational spending for 2005 fiscal year: $4103 per student. Total enrollment: 3,229. Faculty: 245 (35 full-time, 210 part-time). Student-undergrad faculty ratio is 20:1. 2,251 applied, 54% were admitted. 8% from top 10% of their high school class, 27% from top quarter, 57% from top half. Full-time: 1,579 students, 53% women, 47% men. Part-time: 1,278 students, 59% women, 41% men. Students come from 29 states and territories, 4 other countries, 3% from out-of-state, 1% Native American, 2% Hispanic, 19% black, 1% Asian American or Pacific Islander, 0.4% international, 6% 25 or older, 49% live on campus, 2% transferred in. Retention: 96% of full-time freshmen returned the following year. Academic areas with the most degrees conferred: business/marketing; computer and information sciences; engineering. Core. Calendar: semesters. Academic remediation for entering students, ESL program, services for LD students, advanced placement, accelerated degree program, self-designed majors, independent study, distance learning, double major, summer session for credit, part-time degree program, external degree program, adult/continuing education programs, internships.

Entrance Requirements: Options: Peterson's Universal Application, electronic application, early admission, deferred admission. Required: high school transcript, SAT or ACT. Recommended: minimum 3.0 high school GPA, interview, 2 references. Entrance: moderately difficult. Notification: continuous until 10/15.

Costs Per Year: Application fee: $50. Comprehensive fee: $24,600 includes full-time tuition ($17,600), mandatory fees ($250), and college room and board ($6750). Part-time tuition: $586 per credit hour.

Collegiate Environment: Orientation program. Choral group, student-run newspaper. Social organizations: national fraternities, national sororities, local fraternities, local sororities; 15% of eligible men and 5% of eligible women are members. Major annual events: homecoming, graduation, Student Board Dance. Student services: health clinic, personal-psychological counseling. Campus security: 24-hour emergency response devices and patrols, controlled dormitory access. 317 college housing spaces available; 312 were occupied in 2003-04. On-campus residence required through sophomore year. Option: coed housing available. McMillen Library with 32,000 books, 150 serials, 92 audiovisual materials, and an OPAC. Operations spending for 2004 fiscal year: $190,600. 270 computers available on campus for general student use. A campuswide network can be accessed from student residence rooms and from off campus. Staffed computer lab on campus.

Community Environment: Fort Wayne is the hub of the great north central industrial and agricultural America and gateway to the northern Indiana lake region. Gasoline tank and pump manufacturing originated here, and industries now include a General Motors truck plant, electronics, automotive, and agriculture. The city has 147 churches, a civic theatre, and Philharmonic Symphony. Points of interest are the Allen County War Memorial Coliseum, Cathedral of the Immaculate Conception, Concordia Senior College, Fort Wayne Art School and Museum, Lincoln Museum, Lincoln Tower Building, Historical Fort Wayne, and many city parks.

■ **INDIANA UNIVERSITY BLOOMINGTON** *L-8*
107 S. Indiana Ave.
Bloomington, IN 47405-7000
Tel: (812)855-4848
Admissions: (812)855-0661
Fax: (812)855-1871
E-mail: iuadmit@indiana.edu
Web Site: http://www.iub.edu/

Description: State-supported, university, coed. Part of Indiana University System. Awards associate, bachelor's, master's, doctoral, and first professional degrees and post-master's certificates. Founded 1820. Setting: 1,931-acre small town campus with easy access to Indianapolis. Endowment: $660.2 million. Research spending for 2004 fiscal year: $67.9 million. Educational spending for 2005 fiscal year: $7475 per student. Total enrollment: 37,958. Faculty: (1,589 full-time). Student-undergrad faculty ratio is 18:1. 21,974 applied, 85% were admitted. 25% from top 10% of their high school class, 57% from top quarter, 94% from top half. Full-time: 27,974 students, 52% women, 48% men. Part-time: 1,588 students, 50% women, 50% men. Students come from 56 states and territories, 135 other countries, 30% from out-of-state, 0.2% Native American, 2% Hispanic, 5% black, 3% Asian American or Pacific Islander, 4% international, 5% 25 or older, 42% live on campus, 3% transferred in. Retention: 87% of full-time freshmen returned the following year. Academic areas with the most degrees conferred: business/marketing; education; communications/journalism. Core. Calendar: semesters plus 2 summer sessions. Academic remediation for entering students, ESL program, services for LD students, advanced placement, accelerated degree program, self-designed majors, freshman honors college, honors program, independent study, distance learning, double major, summer session for credit, part-time degree program, external degree program, adult/continuing education programs, co-op programs and internships, graduate courses open to undergrads. Off campus study. Study abroad program. ROTC: Army, Air Force.

Entrance Requirements: Options: electronic application, deferred admission. Required: high school transcript, SAT or ACT. Recommended: interview, SAT Subject Tests. Entrance: moderately difficult. Application deadline: Rolling. Notification: continuous. Preference given to state residents.

Costs Per Year: Application fee: $50. State resident tuition: $6291 full-time, $196.40 per credit hour part-time. Nonresident tuition: $18,687 full-time, $584.05 per credit hour part-time. Mandatory fees: $821 full-time. Full-time tuition and fees vary according to location, program, and student level. Part-time tuition varies according to course load, location, program, and student level. College room and board: $6240. College room only: $3760. Room and board charges vary according to board plan and housing facility.

Collegiate Environment: Orientation program. Drama-theater group, choral group, marching band, student-run newspaper, radio station. Social organizations: 500 open to all; national fraternities, national sororities; 16% of eligible men and 18% of eligible women are members. Most popular organizations: Union Board, Student Association, Student Foundation, Habitat for Humanity, Student Athletic Board. Major annual events: homecoming, Little 500 Bike Race, Founders' Day. Student services: legal services, health clinic, personal-psychological counseling, women's center. Campus security: 24-hour emergency response devices and patrols, late night transport-escort service, safety seminars, lighted pathways, escort service, shuttle bus service, emergency telephones. Freshmen given priority for college housing. On-campus residence required in freshman year. Options: coed, men-only, women-only housing available. Indiana University Library plus 32 others with 6.5 million books, 4.7 million microform titles, 60,019 serials, 252,801 audiovisual materials, an OPAC, and a Web page. Operations spending for 2004 fiscal year: $28.3 million. 2,262 computers available on campus for general student use. A campuswide network can be accessed from student residence rooms and from off campus. Staffed computer lab on campus.

Community Environment: The 1,900-acre main campus is located in a community of 66,000 in southern Indiana. Indianapolis, site of the I.U. Medical Center, is 50 miles away. Places of worship are located in the immediate community for all faiths. The city is served by air and bus.

■ **INDIANA UNIVERSITY EAST** *I-13*
2325 Chester Blvd.
Richmond, IN 47374-1289
Tel: (765)973-8200
Free: 800-959-EAST
Admissions: (765)973-8208
Fax: (765)973-8288
E-mail: musmith@indiana.edu
Web Site: http://www.iu.edu/

Description: State-supported, 4-year, coed. Part of Indiana University System. Awards associate and bachelor's degrees. Founded 1971. Setting: 194-acre small town campus with easy access to Indianapolis. Endowment: $4.9 million. Research spending for 2004 fiscal year: $235,586. Educational spending for 2005 fiscal year: $5176 per student. Total enrollment: 2,459.

Student-undergrad faculty ratio is 13:1. 491 applied, 88% were admitted. 8% from top 10% of their high school class, 26% from top quarter, 58% from top half. Full-time: 1,292 students, 69% women, 31% men. Part-time: 1,100 students, 66% women, 34% men. Students come from 7 states and territories, 13% from out-of-state, 0.5% Native American, 1% Hispanic, 4% black, 1% Asian American or Pacific Islander, 0.1% international, 48% 25 or older, 6% transferred in. Retention: 54% of full-time freshmen returned the following year. Academic areas with the most degrees conferred: education; health professions and related sciences; liberal arts/general studies. Core. Calendar: semesters. Academic remediation for entering students, services for LD students, advanced placement, independent study, distance learning, double major, summer session for credit, part-time degree program, external degree program, adult/continuing education programs, co-op programs and internships. Off campus study at Earlham College.

Entrance Requirements: Options: early admission, deferred admission. Required: high school transcript. Recommended: minimum 2.0 high school GPA, SAT or ACT. Entrance: moderately difficult. Application deadline: Rolling. Notification: continuous.

Costs Per Year: Application fee: $25. State resident tuition: $4475 full-time, $149.15 per credit hour part-time. Nonresident tuition: $11,153 full-time, $371.75 per credit hour part-time. Mandatory fees: $331 full-time. Full-time tuition and fees vary according to course load and reciprocity agreements. Part-time tuition varies according to course load and reciprocity agreements.

Collegiate Environment: Drama-theater group, student-run newspaper. Social organizations: 18 open to all. Most popular organizations: Student Government Association, Phi Beta Lambda, Multicultural Awareness Association, Psychology Club, Sociology Club. Major annual events: Spring Fling, Santa Party, Halloween Party. Student services: personal-psychological counseling. Campus security: 24-hour emergency response devices, late night transport-escort service, safety awareness, lighted pathways, 14-hour foot and vehicle patrol. College housing not available. Library and Media Services plus 1 other with 67,036 books, 53,013 microform titles, 435 serials, and 2,222 audiovisual materials. Operations spending for 2004 fiscal year: $540,452. 110 computers available on campus for general student use. A campuswide network can be accessed from off-campus. Staffed computer lab on campus.

Community Environment: The school is located in an outlying area of Richmond, which has a population of about 39,000.

■ **INDIANA UNIVERSITY KOKOMO** *F-9*
PO Box 9003
Kokomo, IN 46904-9003
Tel: (765)453-2000; 888-875-4485
Admissions: (765)455-9216
Fax: (765)455-9537
E-mail: iuadmis@iuk.edu
Web Site: http://www.iuk.edu/

Description: State-supported, comprehensive, coed. Part of Indiana University System. Awards associate, bachelor's, and master's degrees. Founded 1945. Setting: 51-acre small town campus with easy access to Indianapolis. Endowment: $4.4 million. Research spending for 2004 fiscal year: $260,146. Educational spending for 2005 fiscal year: $5248 per student. Total enrollment: 2,895. Faculty: (85 full-time). Student-undergrad faculty ratio is 16:1. 717 applied, 82% were admitted. 5% from top 10% of their high school class, 20% from top quarter, 57% from top half. Full-time: 1,423 students, 70% women, 30% men. Part-time: 1,314 students, 71% women, 29% men. Students come from 3 states and territories, 1% from out-of-state, 1% Native American, 1% Hispanic, 3% black, 1% Asian American or Pacific Islander, 0.3% international, 44% 25 or older, 9% transferred in. Retention: 56% of full-time freshmen returned the following year. Academic areas with the most degrees conferred: education; liberal arts/general studies; health professions and related sciences. Core. Calendar: semesters. Academic remediation for entering students, services for LD students, advanced placement, freshman honors college, honors program, independent study, distance learning, summer session for credit, part-time degree program, external degree program, adult/continuing education programs, internships, graduate courses open to undergrads. Study abroad program. ROTC: Army (c).

Entrance Requirements: Options: early admission, deferred admission. Required: high school transcript, SAT or ACT. Entrance: minimally difficult. Application deadline: Rolling. Notification: continuous.

Costs Per Year: Application fee: $30. State resident tuition: $4475 full-time, $149.15 per credit hour part-time. Nonresident tuition: $11,153 full-time,

$371.75 per credit hour part-time. Mandatory fees: $360 full-time. Full-time tuition and fees vary according to course load. Part-time tuition varies according to course load.

Collegiate Environment: Orientation program. Drama-theater group, choral group, student-run newspaper. Social organizations: 20 open to all. Student services: personal-psychological counseling. Campus security: 24-hour patrols, late night transport-escort service, campus police, lighted pathways. College housing not available. Main library plus 1 other with 132,424 books, 460,552 microform titles, 1,513 serials, and 1,466 audiovisual materials. Operations spending for 2004 fiscal year: $766,980. 120 computers available on campus for general student use. Staffed computer lab on campus.

Community Environment: Kokomo (population 44,042) is an urban area, enjoying a temperate climate, with excellent community facilities; shopping areas, library, museum, 71 churches and two hospitals. All forms of transportation are available. The General Motors Corp. and Chrysler Corp. plants in Kokomo manufacture car radios, transistors, transmissions, and aluminum die castings. Kokomo is the home of Elwood Haynes who invented one of the first American automobiles in 1893. Part-time employment is available.

■ **INDIANA UNIVERSITY NORTHWEST** *B-5*
3400 Broadway
Gary, IN 46408-1197
Tel: (219)980-6500
Free: 800-968-7486
Admissions: (219)980-6767
Fax: (219)981-4219
E-mail: wlee@unhaw1.iun.indiana.edu
Web Site: http://www.iun.edu/

Description: State-supported, comprehensive, coed. Part of Indiana University System. Awards associate, bachelor's, and master's degrees. Founded 1959. Setting: 38-acre urban campus with easy access to Chicago. Endowment: $6.6 million. Research spending for 2004 fiscal year: $341,762. Educational spending for 2005 fiscal year: $5741 per student. Total enrollment: 4,987. Faculty: (163 full-time). Student-undergrad faculty ratio is 13:1. 1,062 applied, 75% were admitted. 6% from top 10% of their high school class, 21% from top quarter, 49% from top half. Full-time: 2,469 students, 68% women, 32% men. Part-time: 1,918 students, 73% women, 27% men. Students come from 6 states and territories, 1% from out-of-state, 0.3% Native American, 12% Hispanic, 22% black, 1% Asian American or Pacific Islander, 0.2% international, 42% 25 or older, 7% transferred in. Retention: 58% of full-time freshmen returned the following year. Academic areas with the most degrees conferred: business/marketing; education; health professions and related sciences. Core. Calendar: semesters. Academic remediation for entering students, services for LD students, advanced placement, accelerated degree program, self-designed majors, honors program, independent study, distance learning, double major, summer session for credit, part-time degree program, external degree program, adult/continuing education programs, co-op programs and internships. Off campus study. Study abroad program. ROTC: Army.

Entrance Requirements: Options: early admission, deferred admission. Required: high school transcript, minimum 2.0 high school GPA, SAT or ACT. Entrance: minimally difficult. Application deadline: Rolling. Notification: continuous.

Costs Per Year: Application fee: $35. State resident tuition: $4475 full-time, $149.15 per credit hour part-time. Nonresident tuition: $11,153 full-time, $371.75 per credit hour part-time. Mandatory fees: $427 full-time. Full-time tuition and fees vary according to course load. Part-time tuition varies according to course load.

Collegiate Environment: Orientation program. Drama-theater group, choral group, student-run newspaper. Social organizations: 45 open to all; national fraternities, national sororities. Most popular organizations: Student Government Association, Student Guides Organization, Nursing Association, Dental Association, International Affairs Club. Major annual events: Welcome Back Week, Spring Fest, Black History Month activities. Student services: personal-psychological counseling. Campus security: 24-hour emergency response devices and patrols, late night transport-escort service, lighted pathways. College housing not available. IUN Library with 251,508 books, 350,045 microform titles, 1,541 serials, 331 audiovisual materials, an OPAC, and a Web page. Operations spending for 2004 fiscal year: $1.3 million. 250 computers available on campus for general student use. A campuswide network can be accessed from off-campus. Staffed computer lab on campus.

Community Environment: Gary (population 150,000) is the second largest city in Indiana, a metropolitan area, and is in one of the country's outstanding steel production areas. The United States Steel Corp. is located here on Lake Michigan. All forms of transportation are available. Community facilities include libraries, churches, hospitals, and shopping areas. Part-time employment is available. Marquette Park nearby has a four-mile beach, a pavilion, piers, and a picnic area.

■ **INDIANA UNIVERSITY-PURDUE UNIVERSITY FORT WAYNE** *D-12*
2101 East Coliseum Blvd.
Fort Wayne, IN 46805-1499
Tel: (260)481-6100
Admissions: (260)481-6812
E-mail: ipfwadmns@ppfw.edu
Web Site: http://www.ipfw.edu/

Description: State-supported, comprehensive, coed. Part of Indiana University System and Purdue University System. Awards associate, bachelor's, and master's degrees. Founded 1917. Setting: 565-acre urban campus. Endowment: $21.6 million. Research spending for 2004 fiscal year: $637,537. Educational spending for 2005 fiscal year: $4565 per student. Total enrollment: 11,795. Faculty: 766 (372 full-time, 394 part-time). Student-undergrad faculty ratio is 17:1. 2,786 applied, 96% were admitted. 9% from top 10% of their high school class, 28% from top quarter, 62% from top half. Full-time: 6,813 students, 56% women, 44% men. Part-time: 4,215 students, 59% women, 41% men. Students come from 47 states and territories, 66 other countries, 4% from out-of-state, 0.4% Native American, 3% Hispanic, 5% black, 2% Asian American or Pacific Islander, 1% international, 38% 25 or older, 6% live on campus, 6% transferred in. Retention: 64% of full-time freshmen returned the following year. Academic areas with the most degrees conferred: education; business/marketing; liberal arts/general studies. Core. Calendar: semesters. Academic remediation for entering students, ESL program, services for LD students, advanced placement, accelerated degree program, self-designed majors, honors program, independent study, distance learning, double major, summer session for credit, part-time degree program, adult/continuing education programs, co-op programs and internships, graduate courses open to undergrads. Off campus study at National Student Exchange. Study abroad program.

Entrance Requirements: Options: electronic application, early admission, deferred admission. Required: high school transcript, SAT or ACT. Recommended: rank in upper 50% of high school class. Entrance: minimally difficult. Application deadline: 8/1. Notification: continuous.

Costs Per Year: Application fee: $30. State resident tuition: $4523 full-time, $168 per semester hour part-time. Nonresident tuition: $11,142 full-time, $413 per semester hour part-time. Mandatory fees: $544 full-time, $20 per semester hour part-time. Full-time tuition and fees vary according to course load, location, and student level. Part-time tuition and fees vary according to course load, location, and student level. College room only: $4750. Room charges vary according to housing facility.

Collegiate Environment: Orientation program. Drama-theater group, choral group, student-run newspaper. Social organizations: 80 open to all; national fraternities; 1% of men are members. Most popular organizations: Campus Ministry, Hispanos Unidos, Sigma Phi Epsilon, Psi Chi, United Sexualities. Major annual events: PIT Theater Performances, Kids' Carnival, IPFW Health Fair. Student services: health clinic, personal-psychological counseling, women's center. Campus security: 24-hour emergency response devices and patrols, late night transport-escort service. 580 college housing spaces available; 492 were occupied in 2003-04. No special consideration for freshman housing applicants. Option: coed housing available. Helmke Library with 479,992 books, 536,519 microform titles, 10,964 serials, 1,000 audiovisual materials, an OPAC, and a Web page. Operations spending for 2004 fiscal year: $2.5 million. 285 computers available on campus for general student use. A campuswide network can be accessed from off-campus. Staffed computer lab on campus.

Community Environment: See Indiana Institute of Technology.

■ **INDIANA UNIVERSITY-PURDUE UNIVERSITY INDIANAPOLIS** *I-9*
355 North Lansing
Indianapolis, IN 46202-2896
Tel: (317)274-5555
Admissions: (317)274-4591
Fax: (317)278-1862
E-mail: apply@ses.iupui.edu
Web Site: http://www.iupui.edu/

Description: State-supported, university, coed. Part of Indiana University System. Awards associate, bachelor's, master's, doctoral, and first professional degrees. Founded 1969. Setting: 511-acre urban campus. Endowment: $376 million. Research spending for 2004 fiscal year: $131.5 million. Educational spending for 2005 fiscal year: $12,828 per student. Total enrollment: 29,933. Faculty: (875 full-time). Student-undergrad faculty ratio is 17:1. 6,136 applied, 74% were admitted. 9% from top 10% of their high school class, 33% from top quarter, 70% from top half. Full-time: 13,736 students, 59% women, 41% men. Part-time: 7,702 students, 58% women, 42% men. Students come from 49 states and territories, 122 other countries, 2% from out-of-state, 0.3% Native American, 2% Hispanic, 11% black, 2% Asian American or Pacific Islander, 2% international, 39% 25 or older, 2% live on campus, 9% transferred in. Retention: 65% of full-time freshmen returned the following year. Academic areas with the most degrees conferred: business/marketing; liberal arts/general studies; health professions and related sciences. Core. Calendar: semesters. Academic remediation for entering students, ESL program, services for LD students, advanced placement, honors program, independent study, distance learning, double major, summer session for credit, part-time degree program, external degree program, adult/continuing education programs, co-op programs and internships, graduate courses open to undergrads. Off campus study at 5 members of the Consortium for Urban Education. Study abroad program. ROTC: Army, Naval (c), Air Force (c).

Entrance Requirements: Options: electronic application, early admission, deferred admission, international baccalaureate accepted. Required: high school transcript, SAT or ACT. Recommended: portfolio for art program. Required for some: interview. Entrance: moderately difficult. Application deadline: 6/1. Notification: continuous.

Costs Per Year: Application fee: $50. State resident tuition: $5625 full-time, $188 per credit hour part-time. Nonresident tuition: $15,953 full-time, $532 per credit hour part-time. Mandatory fees: $594 full-time. Full-time tuition and fees vary according to course load and program. Part-time tuition varies according to course load and program. College room and board: $4740. College room only: $2340. Room and board charges vary according to board plan and housing facility.

Collegiate Environment: Orientation program. Drama-theater group, choral group, student-run newspaper. Social organizations: 191 open to all; national fraternities, national sororities; 1% of eligible men and 1% of eligible women are members. Most popular organizations: Undergraduate Student Assembly, Black Student Union, Student Activities Programming Board. Major annual events: Ice Cream Social and Activities Fair, Spring Dance, Career Day. Student services: health clinic, personal-psychological counseling, women's center. Campus security: 24-hour emergency response devices and patrols, late night transport-escort service, controlled dormitory access, lighted pathways, self-defense education. Option: coed housing available. University Library plus 5 others with 1.5 million books, 2.4 million microform titles, 14,673 serials, 1,663 audiovisual materials, an OPAC, and a Web page. Operations spending for 2004 fiscal year: $8.3 million. 500 computers available on campus for general student use. A campuswide network can be accessed from student residence rooms and from off campus. Staffed computer lab on campus.

Community Environment: See Butler University.

■ **INDIANA UNIVERSITY SOUTH BEND** *B-9*
1700 Mishawaka Ave., PO Box 7111
South Bend, IN 46634-7111
Tel: (574)520-4872; 877-GO-2-IUSB
Admissions: (574)237-4480
Fax: (574)520-4834
Web Site: http://www.iusb.edu/
Description: State-supported, comprehensive, coed. Part of Indiana University System. Awards associate, bachelor's, and master's degrees. Founded 1922. Setting: 73-acre suburban campus with easy access to Chicago. Endowment: $7.7 million. Research spending for 2004 fiscal year: $756,661. Educational spending for 2005 fiscal year: $5819 per student. Total enrollment: 7,459. Faculty: (232 full-time). Student-undergrad faculty ratio is 14:1. 1,560 applied, 88% were admitted. 7% from top 10% of their high school class, 24% from top quarter, 59% from top half. Full-time: 3,636 students, 62% women, 38% men. Part-time: 2,688 students, 62% women, 38% men. Students come from 13 states and territories, 3% from out-of-state, 0.5% Native American, 3% Hispanic, 7% black, 1% Asian American or Pacific Islander, 2% international, 38% 25 or older, 9% transferred in. Retention: 64% of full-time freshmen returned the following year. Academic areas with the most degrees conferred: education; business/marketing; liberal arts/general studies. Core. Calendar: semesters. ESL program, accelerated degree program, honors program, distance learning, double major, summer session for credit, part-time degree program, external degree program, adult/

continuing education programs, internships, graduate courses open to undergrads. Off campus study at Bethel College, Saint Mary's College (IN), Holy Cross College, Goshen College. Study abroad program. ROTC: Army (c), Naval (c), Air Force (c).

Entrance Requirements: Option: deferred admission. Required: high school transcript, minimum 2.0 high school GPA, SAT or ACT. Entrance: moderately difficult. Application deadline: Rolling. Notification: continuous.

Costs Per Year: Application fee: $43. State resident tuition: $4583 full-time, $152.75 per credit hour part-time. Nonresident tuition: $12,002 full-time, $400.05 per credit hour part-time. Mandatory fees: $406 full-time. Full-time tuition and fees vary according to course load. Part-time tuition varies according to course load.

Collegiate Environment: Drama-theater group, choral group, student-run newspaper. Social organizations: 30 open to all; national fraternities, local sororities. Major annual event: Student Welcome Day. Student services: personal-psychological counseling, women's center. Campus security: 24-hour emergency response devices and patrols, late night transport-escort service, safety seminars, lighted pathways. College housing not available. Franklin D. Schurz Library plus 1 other with 300,202 books, 445,960 microform titles, 1,937 serials, and 13,001 audiovisual materials. Operations spending for 2004 fiscal year: $2 million. 200 computers available on campus for general student use. Staffed computer lab on campus.

Community Environment: See University of Notre Dame.

■ **INDIANA UNIVERSITY SOUTHEAST** *O-10*
4201 Grant Line Rd.
New Albany, IN 47150-6405
Tel: (812)941-2000
Admissions: (812)941-2212
E-mail: admissions@ius.indiana.edu
Web Site: http://www.ius.edu/
Description: State-supported, comprehensive, coed. Part of Indiana University System. Awards associate, bachelor's, and master's degrees. Founded 1941. Setting: 177-acre suburban campus with easy access to Louisville. Endowment: $10.2 million. Research spending for 2004 fiscal year: $441,731. Educational spending for 2005 fiscal year: $5702 per student. Total enrollment: 6,164. Faculty: (172 full-time). Student-undergrad faculty ratio is 16:1. 1,194 applied, 89% were admitted. 8% from top 10% of their high school class, 28% from top quarter, 68% from top half. Full-time: 3,220 students, 63% women, 37% men. Part-time: 2,080 students, 64% women, 36% men. Students come from 3 states and territories, 22% from out-of-state, 0.4% Native American, 1% Hispanic, 4% black, 1% Asian American or Pacific Islander, 0.3% international, 35% 25 or older, 7% transferred in. Retention: 65% of full-time freshmen returned the following year. Academic areas with the most degrees conferred: business/marketing; education; liberal arts/general studies. Core. Calendar: semesters. Academic remediation for entering students, services for LD students, advanced placement, accelerated degree program, independent study, double major, summer session for credit, part-time degree program, external degree program, adult/continuing education programs, internships. Off campus study at 7 members of the Kentuckiana Metroversity. Study abroad program. ROTC: Army (c), Air Force (c).

Entrance Requirements: Options: early admission, deferred admission. Required: high school transcript, SAT or ACT. Required for some: interview. Entrance: minimally difficult. Application deadline: Rolling. Notification: continuous.

Costs Per Year: Application fee: $30. State resident tuition: $4475 full-time, $149.15 per credit hour part-time. Nonresident tuition: $11,153 full-time, $371.75 per credit hour part-time. Mandatory fees: $405 full-time. Full-time tuition and fees vary according to course load and reciprocity agreements. Part-time tuition varies according to course load and reciprocity agreements.

Collegiate Environment: Orientation program. Drama-theater group, choral group, student-run newspaper. Social organizations: 50 open to all; national fraternities, national sororities; 3% of eligible men and 3% of eligible women are members. Major annual events: Late Nighter, Diversity Week, Comedy Series. Student services: personal-psychological counseling. Campus security: 24-hour emergency response devices and patrols, self-defense education, lighted pathways, police department on campus. College housing not available. Main library plus 1 other with 215,429 books, 352,318 microform titles, 962 serials, and 9,360 audiovisual materials. Operations spending for 2004 fiscal year: $1.3 million. 200 computers available on campus for general student use. A campuswide network can be accessed from off-campus.

Community Environment: New Albany (population 38,000), a highly industrialized area, enjoys a temperate climate. It is one of the Falls Cities, the others being Louisville, Kentucky and Jeffersonville, Indiana. Buses and railroads serve the area with airlines available at Louisville, Kentucky, Airport. The American Commercial Barge Line, one of the largest, has a terminal there. Community facilities include many churches, Steamboat Museum, hospital and parks. Some part-time employment is available. Ohio River provides facilities for all water sports. Derby Week is an annual event.

■ **INDIANA WESLEYAN UNIVERSITY** *F-10*
4201 South Washington St.
Marion, IN 46953-4974
Tel: (765)674-6901
Free: 800-332-6901
Admissions: (765)677-2138
Fax: (765)677-2333
E-mail: daniel.solms@indwes.edu
Web Site: http://www.indwes.edu/

Description: Independent Wesleyan, comprehensive, coed. Awards associate, bachelor's, master's, and doctoral degrees and post-master's certificates (also offers adult program with significant enrollment not reflected in profile). Founded 1920. Setting: 132-acre small town campus with easy access to Indianapolis. Endowment: $20.3 million. Total enrollment: 11,020. 2,523 applied, 54% were admitted. 31% from top 10% of their high school class, 59% from top quarter, 83% from top half. Full-time: 6,908 students, 64% women, 36% men. Part-time: 701 students, 60% women, 40% men. Students come from 37 states and territories, 1 other country, 30% from out-of-state, 0.4% Native American, 2% Hispanic, 13% black, 1% Asian American or Pacific Islander, 0.3% international, 59% 25 or older. Retention: 89% of full-time freshmen returned the following year. Core. Calendar: 4-4-1. Academic remediation for entering students, services for LD students, advanced placement, accelerated degree program, self-designed majors, freshman honors college, honors program, independent study, distance learning, double major, summer session for credit, part-time degree program, adult/continuing education programs, internships, graduate courses open to undergrads. Off campus study at Taylor University, Council for Christian Colleges and Universities. Study abroad program.

Entrance Requirements: Options: Peterson's Universal Application, electronic application, deferred admission. Required: essay, high school transcript, minimum 2.0 high school GPA, 1 recommendation, SAT or ACT. Required for some: interview. Entrance: moderately difficult. Application deadline: Rolling. Notification: continuous.

Costs Per Year: Application fee: $25. Comprehensive fee: $22,074 includes full-time tuition ($16,184) and college room and board ($5890). College room only: $2800. Room and board charges vary according to board plan. Part-time tuition: $344 per credit hour. Part-time tuition varies according to course load.

Collegiate Environment: Orientation program. Drama-theater group, choral group, student-run newspaper, radio station. Social organizations: 35 open to all. Most popular organizations: Student Government Organization, Student Activities Council, University Players, World Christian Fellowship, International Student Association. Major annual events: Homecoming, Youth Conference, Resident Life Week. Student services: health clinic, personal-psychological counseling. Campus security: 24-hour emergency response devices and patrols, late night transport-escort service, controlled dormitory access. 2,200 college housing spaces available; all were occupied in 2003-04. On-campus residence required through junior year. Options: men-only, women-only housing available. Goodman Library with 110,000 books, 200,000 microform titles, an OPAC, and a Web page.

Community Environment: Marion is an industrial city in a farming and fruit raising region, located 70 miles northeast of Indianapolis and 50 miles southwest of Ft. Wayne in Grant County. Bus service is available. Major industries located here are Thompson Electronics, BICC Cahles, General Motors, Gencorp., Foster-Forbes Glass, and General Plastics. Part-time employment is abundant. Mississinewa Lake and Salamonie Reservoir and Dam are nearby, providing facilities for many outdoor sports; also the city has facilities for tennis, swimming, and picnics. The Easter Pageant and Christmas Walkway of Lights are an annual event.

■ **INTERNATIONAL BUSINESS COLLEGE (FORT WAYNE)** *D-12*
5699 Covington Ln.
Fort Wayne, IN 46804
Tel: (219)459-4500
Free: 800-589-6363
Admissions: (219)459-4513
Fax: (219)436-1896

Web Site: http://www.ibcfortwayne.edu/

Description: Proprietary, primarily 2-year, coed. Part of Bradford Schools, Inc. Awards diplomas, terminal associate, and bachelor's degrees. Founded 1889. Setting: 2-acre suburban campus. Total enrollment: 800. 879 applied, 97% were admitted. Full-time: 690 students, 73% women, 27% men. Part-time: 110 students, 71% women, 29% men. 0% transferred in. Core. Calendar: semesters. Independent study, part-time degree program, adult/continuing education programs; internships.

Entrance Requirements: Option: deferred admission. Required: high school transcript. Entrance: minimally difficult. Application deadline: 9/2.

Collegiate Environment: Social organizations: 3 open to all. Most popular organizations: Student Senate, Collegiate Secretarial Institute, Accounting Club. Campus security: controlled dormitory access. 144 college housing spaces available; all were occupied in 2003-04. Freshmen given priority for college housing. 2,100 books and 100 serials. 157 computers available on campus for general student use. Staffed computer lab on campus.

■ **INTERNATIONAL BUSINESS COLLEGE (INDIANAPOLIS)** *I-9*
7205 Shadeland Station
Indianapolis, IN 46256
Tel: (317)841-6400
Admissions: (317)213-2320
Fax: (317)841-6419
Web Site: http://www.intlbusinesscollege.com/

Description: Proprietary, 2-year, coed. Administratively affiliated with Bradford Schools, Charlotte, NC. Awards diplomas and terminal associate degrees. Total enrollment: 289. Student-undergrad faculty ratio is 20:1. 597 applied, 94% were admitted. Full-time: 289 students, 71% women, 29% men. 0% from out-of-state, 0% Native American, 3% Hispanic, 14% black, 1% Asian American or Pacific Islander, 0% international, 1% 25 or older. Calendar: semesters. Academic remediation for entering students, internships.

Entrance Requirements: Open admission. Options: Common Application, electronic application. Required: high school transcript. Required for some: paralegal test. Entrance: minimally difficult. Application deadline: Rolling. Notification: continuous.

Costs Per Year: Application fee: $50. Tuition: $11,960 full-time. College room only: $6100.

Collegiate Environment: 83 college housing spaces available; 48 were occupied in 2003-04. Freshmen given priority for college housing. 125 computers available on campus for general student use. Staffed computer lab on campus.

■ **ITT TECHNICAL INSTITUTE (FORT WAYNE)** *D-12*
4919 Coldwater Rd.
Fort Wayne, IN 46825-5532
Tel: (219)484-4107
Free: 800-866-4488
Admissions: (260)497-6200
Web Site: http://www.itt-tech.edu/

Description: Proprietary, primarily 2-year, coed. Part of ITT Educational Services, Inc. Awards terminal associate and bachelor's degrees. Founded 1967. Core.

Entrance Requirements: Option: deferred admission. Required: high school transcript, interview, Wonderlic aptitude test. Recommended: recommendations. Entrance: minimally difficult. Application deadline: Rolling. Notification: continuous.

Costs Per Year: Application fee: $100.

Collegiate Environment: Orientation program. College housing not available.

■ **ITT TECHNICAL INSTITUTE (INDIANAPOLIS)** *I-9*
9511 Angola Ct.
Indianapolis, IN 46268-1119
Tel: (317)875-8640
Free: 800-937-4488
Fax: (317)875-8641
Web Site: http://www.itt-tech.edu/

Description: Proprietary, primarily 2-year, coed. Part of ITT Educational Services, Inc. Awards diplomas, terminal associate, and bachelor's degrees. Founded 1966. Setting: 10-acre suburban campus. Core. Distance learning.

Entrance Requirements: Option: deferred admission. Required: high school transcript, interview, Wonderlic aptitude test. Recommended: recommendations. Entrance: minimally difficult. Application deadline: Rolling. Notification: continuous.

Costs Per Year: Application fee: $100.
Collegiate Environment: Orientation program. Student-run newspaper. College housing not available.

■ ITT TECHNICAL INSTITUTE (NEWBURGH) *P-5*

10999 Stahl Rd.
Newburgh, IN 47630-7430
Tel: (812)858-1600
Web Site: http://www.itt-tech.edu/

Description: Proprietary, primarily 2-year, coed. Part of ITT Educational Services, Inc. Awards terminal associate and bachelor's degrees. Founded 1966. Core.

Entrance Requirements: Option: deferred admission. Required: high school transcript, interview, Wonderlic aptitude test. Recommended: recommendations. Entrance: minimally difficult. Application deadline: Rolling. Notification: continuous.

Costs Per Year: Application fee: $100.

Collegiate Environment: Orientation program. College housing not available.

■ IVY TECH COMMUNITY COLLEGE-BLOOMINGTON *L-8*

3116 Canterbury Ct.
Bloomington, IN 47404
Tel: (812)332-1559
Admissions: (812)330-6026
Fax: (812)332-8147
E-mail: nfrederi@ivytech.edu
Web Site: http://www.ivytech.edu/

Description: State-supported, 2-year, coed. Part of Ivy Tech State College System. Awards certificates, transfer associate, and terminal associate degrees. Founded 2001. System endowment: $15.9 million. Total enrollment: 3,565. 899 applied, 100% were admitted. Full-time: 1,639 students, 57% women, 43% men. Part-time: 1,926 students, 64% women, 36% men. 0.3% Native American, 1% Hispanic, 3% black, 1% Asian American or Pacific Islander, 0.1% international, 47% 25 or older, 4% transferred in. Core. Calendar: semesters. Academic remediation for entering students, services for LD students, advanced placement, distance learning, summer session for credit, part-time degree program, external degree program, adult/continuing education programs, internships.

Entrance Requirements: Open admission. Option: deferred admission. Required: high school transcript. Required for some: interview. Entrance: noncompetitive. Application deadline: Rolling. Notification: continuous. Preference given to state residents.

Costs Per Year: Application fee: $0. State resident tuition: $2520 full-time, $83.95 per credit part-time. Nonresident tuition: $5108 full-time, $170.25 per credit part-time. Mandatory fees: $70 full-time, $35 per term part-time.

Collegiate Environment: Orientation program. Most popular organizations: Student Government, Phi Theta Kappa. Campus security: late night transport-escort service. 5,516 books, 97 serials, 1,281 audiovisual materials, an OPAC, and a Web page. 221 computers available on campus for general student use.

■ IVY TECH COMMUNITY COLLEGE-CENTRAL INDIANA *I-9*

50 W. Fall Creek Parkway North Dr.
Indianapolis, IN 46208
Tel: (317)921-4800; 888-IVYLINE
Admissions: (317)921-4371
E-mail: tfunk@ivytech.edu
Web Site: http://www.ivytech.edu/

Description: State-supported, 2-year, coed. Awards certificates, transfer associate, and terminal associate degrees. Founded 1963. Setting: 10-acre urban campus. System endowment: $15,900. Total enrollment: 11,590. 2,926 applied, 100% were admitted. Full-time: 3,581 students, 61% women, 39% men. Part-time: 8,009 students, 59% women, 41% men. 0% from out-of-state, 0.5% Native American, 2% Hispanic, 25% black, 1% Asian American or Pacific Islander, 0.2% international, 57% 25 or older, 6% transferred in. Core. Calendar: semesters. Academic remediation for entering students, ESL program, services for LD students, advanced placement, distance learning, summer session for credit, part-time degree program, adult/continuing education programs, co-op programs and internships. Off campus study at Indiana University-Purdue University at Indianapolis, Butler University, Marian College, University of Indianapolis, Martin University, Franklin College of Indiana.

Entrance Requirements: Open admission except for human services and health technology programs. Options: early admission, deferred admission. Required: high school transcript. Required for some: interview. Entrance: noncompetitive. Application deadline: Rolling. Notification: continuous. Preference given to state residents.

Costs Per Year: Application fee: $0. State resident tuition: $2520 full-time, $83.95 per credit part-time. Nonresident tuition: $5108 full-time, $170.25 per credit part-time. Mandatory fees: $70 full-time, $35 per term part-time.

Collegiate Environment: Orientation program. Student-run newspaper. Most popular organizations: Student Government, Phi Theta Kappa, Human Services Club, Administrative Office Assistants Club, Radiology Club. Student services: personal-psychological counseling. Campus security: 24-hour emergency response devices and patrols, late night transport-escort service. College housing not available. 20,247 books, 138 serials, 2,135 audiovisual materials, an OPAC, and a Web page. 407 computers available on campus for general student use. Staffed computer lab on campus.

■ IVY TECH COMMUNITY COLLEGE-COLUMBUS *K-10*

4475 Central Ave.
Columbus, IN 47203-1868
Tel: (812)372-9925
Free: 800-922-4838
Fax: (812)372-0311
E-mail: nbagadio@ivytech.edu
Web Site: http://www.ivytech.edu/

Description: State-supported, 2-year, coed. Part of Ivy Tech State College System. Awards certificates, transfer associate, and terminal associate degrees. Founded 1963. Setting: small town campus with easy access to Indianapolis. Endowment: $15.9 million. Total enrollment: 2,216. 506 applied, 100% were admitted. Full-time: 777 students, 72% women, 28% men. Part-time: 1,439 students, 70% women, 30% men. 0.2% Native American, 1% Hispanic, 2% black, 1% Asian American or Pacific Islander, 0.1% international, 58% 25 or older, 8% transferred in. Core. Calendar: semesters. Academic remediation for entering students, services for LD students, advanced placement, distance learning, summer session for credit, part-time degree program, adult/continuing education programs, internships.

Entrance Requirements: Open admission except for human services and health technology programs. Options: early admission, deferred admission. Required: high school transcript. Required for some: interview. Entrance: noncompetitive. Application deadline: Rolling. Notification: continuous. Preference given to state residents.

Costs Per Year: Application fee: $0. State resident tuition: $2520 full-time, $83.95 per credit part-time. Nonresident tuition: $5108 full-time, $170.25 per credit part-time. Mandatory fees: $70 full-time, $35 per term part-time.

Collegiate Environment: Orientation program. Most popular organizations: Student Government, Phi Theta Kappa, LPN Club. Campus security: late night transport-escort service, trained evening security personnel, escort service. College housing not available. 7,855 books, 13,382 serials, 989 audiovisual materials, an OPAC, and a Web page. 185 computers available on campus for general student use. Staffed computer lab on campus.

■ IVY TECH COMMUNITY COLLEGE-EAST CENTRAL *G-11*

4301 South Cowan Rd., PO Box 3100
Muncie, IN 47302-9448
Tel: (765)289-2291
E-mail: mlewelle@ivytech.edu
Web Site: http://www.ivytech.edu/

Description: State-supported, 2-year, coed. Part of Ivy Tech State College System. Awards certificates, transfer associate, and terminal associate degrees. Founded 1968. Setting: 15-acre suburban campus with easy access to Indianapolis. System endowment: $15.9 million. Total enrollment: 5,943. 1,146 applied, 100% were admitted. Full-time: 2,551 students, 61% women, 39% men. Part-time: 3,392 students, 68% women, 32% men. 0.3% Native American, 1% Hispanic, 8% black, 0.3% Asian American or Pacific Islander, 0.02% international, 57% 25 or older, 4% transferred in. Core. Calendar: semesters. Academic remediation for entering students, services for LD students, advanced placement, distance learning, part-time degree program, adult/continuing education programs, internships.

Entrance Requirements: Open admission except for allied health programs in human services and health technology. Options: early admission, deferred admission. Required: high school transcript. Required for some: interview. Entrance: noncompetitive. Application deadline: Rolling. Notification: continuous. Preference given to state residents.

Costs Per Year: Application fee: $0. State resident tuition: $2520 full-time, $83.95 per credit part-time. Nonresident tuition: $5108 full-time, $170.25 per credit part-time. Mandatory fees: $70 full-time, $35 per term part-time.

Collegiate Environment: Orientation program. Most popular organizations: Business Professionals of America, Skills USA-VICA, Student Government, Phi Theta Kappa, Human Services Club. College housing not available. 5,779 books, 145 serials, 6,266 audiovisual materials, an OPAC, and a Web page. 270 computers available on campus for general student use. A campuswide network can be accessed from off-campus. Staffed computer lab on campus.

■ IVY TECH COMMUNITY COLLEGE-KOKOMO *F-9*

1815 East Morgan St, PO Box 1373
Kokomo, IN 46903-1373
Tel: (765)459-0561
E-mail: acook@ivytech.edu
Web Site: http://www.ivytech.edu/

Description: State-supported, 2-year, coed. Part of Ivy Tech State College System. Awards certificates, transfer associate, and terminal associate degrees. Founded 1968. Setting: 20-acre small town campus with easy access to Indianapolis. System endowment: $15.9 million. Total enrollment: 3,248. 1,083 applied, 100% were admitted. Full-time: 1,031 students, 62% women, 38% men. Part-time: 2,217 students, 65% women, 35% men. 1% Native American, 2% Hispanic, 4% black, 0.4% Asian American or Pacific Islander, 0% international, 59% 25 or older, 0.2% transferred in. Core. Calendar: semesters. Academic remediation for entering students, services for LD students, advanced placement, distance learning, summer session for credit, part-time degree program, adult/continuing education programs, internships.

Entrance Requirements: Open admission except for allied health programs in human services and health technology. Option: early admission. Required: high school transcript. Required for some: interview. Entrance: noncompetitive. Application deadline: Rolling. Notification: continuous. Preference given to state residents.

Costs Per Year: Application fee: $0. State resident tuition: $2520 full-time, $83.95 per credit part-time. Nonresident tuition: $5108 full-time, $170.25 per credit part-time. Mandatory fees: $70 full-time, $35 per term part-time.

Collegiate Environment: Student-run newspaper. Most popular organizations: Student Government, Collegiate Secretaries International, Licensed Practical Nursing Club, Phi Theta Kappa. Student services: personal-psychological counseling. Campus security: 24-hour emergency response devices, late night transport-escort service. College housing not available. 5,177 books, 99 serials, 772 audiovisual materials, an OPAC, and a Web page. 320 computers available on campus for general student use. A campuswide network can be accessed from off-campus. Staffed computer lab on campus.

■ IVY TECH COMMUNITY COLLEGE-LAFAYETTE *G-7*

3101 South Creasy Ln.
Lafayette, IN 47905-5266
Tel: (765)772-9100
Admissions: (765)772-9116
E-mail: jdoppelf@ivytech.edu
Web Site: http://www.ivytech.edu/

Description: State-supported, 2-year, coed. Part of Ivy Tech State College System. Awards certificates, transfer associate, and terminal associate degrees. Founded 1968. Setting: suburban campus with easy access to Indianapolis. System endowment: $15.9 million. Total enrollment: 5,970. 1,326 applied, 100% were admitted. Full-time: 2,374 students, 56% women, 44% men. Part-time: 3,596 students, 48% women, 52% men. 0.3% Native American, 4% Hispanic, 3% black, 1% Asian American or Pacific Islander, 0.1% international, 50% 25 or older, 4% transferred in. Core. Calendar: semesters. Academic remediation for entering students, services for LD students, advanced placement, distance learning, summer session for credit, part-time degree program, internships.

Entrance Requirements: Open admission except for allied health programs in human services and health technology. Required: high school transcript. Required for some: interview. Entrance: noncompetitive. Application deadline: Rolling. Notification: continuous. Preference given to state residents.

Costs Per Year: Application fee: $0. State resident tuition: $2520 full-time, $83.95 per credit part-time. Nonresident tuition: $5108 full-time, $170.25 per credit part-time. Mandatory fees: $70 full-time, $35 per term part-time.

Collegiate Environment: Orientation program. Student-run newspaper. Most popular organizations: Student Government, Phi Theta Kappa, LPN Club, Accounting Club, Student Computer Technology Association. Student services: personal-psychological counseling. College housing not available. 8,043 books, 200 serials, 2,234 audiovisual materials, an OPAC, and a Web page. 267 computers available on campus for general student use. A campuswide network can be accessed. Staffed computer lab on campus.

■ IVY TECH COMMUNITY COLLEGE-NORTH CENTRAL *B-9*

220 Dean Johnson Blvd.
South Bend, IN 46601
Tel: (574)289-7001
Fax: (574)236-7181
E-mail: pdecker@ivytech.edu
Web Site: http://www.ivytech.edu/

Description: State-supported, 2-year, coed. Part of Ivy Tech State College System. Awards certificates, transfer associate, and terminal associate degrees. Founded 1968. Setting: 4-acre suburban campus. System endowment: $15.9 million. Total enrollment: 5,228. 1,113 applied, 100% were admitted. Full-time: 1,225 students, 65% women, 35% men. Part-time: 4,003 students, 55% women, 45% men. 2% from out-of-state, 0.5% Native American, 5% Hispanic, 14% black, 1% Asian American or Pacific Islander, 0.3% international, 61% 25 or older, 2% transferred in. Core. Calendar: semesters. Academic remediation for entering students, ESL program, services for LD students, advanced placement, distance learning, summer session for credit, part-time degree program, adult/continuing education programs, internships. Off campus study at other members of the Northern Indiana Consortium for Education.

Entrance Requirements: Open admission except for allied health programs, in human services and health technology. Options: early admission, deferred admission. Required: high school transcript. Required for some: interview. Entrance: noncompetitive. Application deadline: Rolling. Notification: continuous. Preference given to state residents.

Costs Per Year: Application fee: $0. State resident tuition: $2520 full-time, $83.95 per credit part-time. Nonresident tuition: $5108 full-time, $170.25 per credit part-time. Mandatory fees: $70 full-time, $35 per term part-time.

Collegiate Environment: Orientation program. Most popular organizations: Phi Theta Kappa, Student Government, LPN Club. Student services: personal-psychological counseling, women's center. Campus security: 24-hour emergency response devices and patrols, late night transport-escort service, security during open hours. College housing not available. 6,246 books, 90 serials, 689 audiovisual materials, an OPAC, and a Web page. 426 computers available on campus for general student use. Staffed computer lab on campus.

■ IVY TECH COMMUNITY COLLEGE-NORTHEAST *D-12*

3800 North Anthony Blvd.
Fort Wayne, IN 46805-1430
Tel: (260)482-9171
Free: 800-859-4882
Admissions: (260)480-4221
Fax: (260)480-4177
E-mail: sscheer@ivytech.edu
Web Site: http://www.ivytech.edu/

Description: State-supported, 2-year, coed. Part of Ivy Tech State College System. Awards certificates, transfer associate, and terminal associate degrees. Founded 1969. Setting: 22-acre urban campus. System endowment: $15.9 million. Total enrollment: 6,082. 841 applied, 100% were admitted. Full-time: 2,120 students, 63% women, 37% men. Part-time: 3,962 students, 60% women, 40% men. 1% from out-of-state, 1% Native American, 2% Hispanic, 15% black, 1% Asian American or Pacific Islander, 0.1% international, 60% 25 or older, 3% transferred in. Core. Calendar: semesters. ESL program, services for LD students, advanced placement, distance learning, summer session for credit, part-time degree program, adult/continuing education programs, internships.

Entrance Requirements: Open admission except for allied health programs in human services and health technology. Option: early admission. Required: high school transcript. Required for some: interview. Entrance: noncompetitive. Application deadline: Rolling. Notification: continuous. Preference given to state residents.

Costs Per Year: Application fee: $0. State resident tuition: $2520 full-time, $83.95 per credit part-time. Nonresident tuition: $5108 full-time, $170.25 per credit part-time. Mandatory fees: $70 full-time, $35 per term part-time.

Collegiate Environment: Orientation program. Student-run newspaper. Most popular organizations: Student Government, LPN Club, Phi Theta Kappa. Campus security: 24-hour emergency response devices and patrols, late night transport-escort service. College housing not available. 18,389 books, 110 serials, 3,397 audiovisual materials, an OPAC, and a Web page. 382 computers available on campus for general student use. Staffed computer lab on campus.

■ **IVY TECH COMMUNITY COLLEGE-NORTHWEST** *B-5*
1440 East 35th Ave.
Gary, IN 46409-1499
Tel: (219)981-1111
E-mail: tlewis@ivytech.edu
Web Site: http://www.ivytech.edu/

Description: State-supported, primarily 2-year, coed. Part of Ivy Tech State College System. Awards certificates, transfer associate, terminal associate, and bachelor's degrees. Founded 1963. Setting: 13-acre urban campus with easy access to Chicago. System endowment: $15.9 million. Total enrollment: 4,815. 738 applied, 100% were admitted. Full-time: 1,395 students, 67% women, 33% men. Part-time: 3,420 students, 66% women, 34% men. 0% from out-of-state, 0.2% Native American, 9% Hispanic, 30% black, 1% Asian American or Pacific Islander, 0.1% international, 64% 25 or older, 5% transferred in. Core. Calendar: semesters. Academic remediation for entering students, services for LD students, advanced placement, distance learning, summer session for credit, part-time degree program, adult/continuing education programs, internships.

Entrance Requirements: Open admission except for allied health programs in human services and health technology. Options: Peterson's Universal Application, deferred admission. Required: high school transcript. Required for some: interview. Entrance: noncompetitive. Application deadline: Rolling. Notification: continuous. Preference given to state residents.

Costs Per Year: Application fee: $0. State resident tuition: $2520 full-time, $83.95 per credit part-time. Nonresident tuition: $5108 full-time, $170.25 per credit part-time. Mandatory fees: $70 full-time, $35 per term part-time.

Collegiate Environment: Orientation program. Most popular organizations: Phi Theta Kappa, LPN Club, Computer Club, Student Government, Business Club. Campus security: 24-hour emergency response devices, late night transport-escort service. College housing not available. 13,805 books, 157 microform titles, 160 serials, 4,295 audiovisual materials, an OPAC, and a Web page. 267 computers available on campus for general student use. Staffed computer lab on campus.

■ **IVY TECH COMMUNITY COLLEGE-SOUTHEAST** *M-11*
590 Ivy Tech Dr., PO Box 209
Madison, IN 47250-1883
Tel: (812)265-4028
Admissions: (812)265-2580
E-mail: chutcher@ivytech.edu
Web Site: http://www.ivytech.edu/

Description: State-supported, 2-year, coed. Part of Ivy Tech State College System. Awards certificates, transfer associate, and terminal associate degrees. Founded 1963. Setting: 5-acre small town campus with easy access to Louisville. System endowment: $15.9 million. Total enrollment: 1,766. 280 applied, 100% were admitted. Full-time: 630 students, 72% women, 28% men. Part-time: 1,136 students, 72% women, 28% men. 2% from out-of-state, 0.1% Native American, 1% Hispanic, 1% black, 0.3% Asian American or Pacific Islander, 0.1% international, 56% 25 or older, 2% transferred in. Core. Calendar: semesters. Academic remediation for entering students, services for LD students, advanced placement, distance learning, summer session for credit, part-time degree program, internships.

Entrance Requirements: Open admission except for human services and health technology programs. Required: high school transcript. Required for some: interview. Entrance: noncompetitive. Application deadline: Rolling. Notification: continuous. Preference given to state residents.

Costs Per Year: Application fee: $0. State resident tuition: $2520 full-time, $83.95 per credit part-time. Nonresident tuition: $5108 full-time, $170.25 per credit part-time. Mandatory fees: $70 full-time, $35 per term part-time.

Collegiate Environment: Orientation program. Most popular organizations: Student Government, Phi Theta Kappa, LPN Club. Campus security: 24-hour emergency response devices. College housing not available. 9,027 books, 14,299 serials, 1,341 audiovisual materials, an OPAC, and a Web page. 123 computers available on campus for general student use. A campuswide network can be accessed. Staffed computer lab on campus.

■ **IVY TECH COMMUNITY COLLEGE-SOUTHERN INDIANA** *O-10*
8204 Hwy. 311
Sellersburg, IN 47172-1829
Tel: (812)246-3301
E-mail: msteinba@ivytech.edu
Web Site: http://www.ivytech.edu/

Description: State-supported, 2-year, coed. Part of Ivy Tech State College System. Awards certificates, transfer associate, and terminal associate degrees. Founded 1968. Setting: 63-acre small town campus with easy access to Louisville. System endowment: $15.9 million. Total enrollment: 3,112. 742 applied, 100% were admitted. Full-time: 904 students, 65% women, 35% men. Part-time: 2,208 students, 46% women, 54% men. 25% from out-of-state, 1% Native American, 1% Hispanic, 5% black, 0.5% Asian American or Pacific Islander, 0% international, 61% 25 or older, 5% transferred in. Core. Calendar: semesters. Academic remediation for entering students, services for LD students, advanced placement, distance learning, summer session for credit, part-time degree program, adult/continuing education programs, co-op programs and internships.

Entrance Requirements: Open admission except for human services and health programs. Options: early admission, deferred admission. Required: high school transcript. Required for some: interview. Entrance: noncompetitive. Application deadline: Rolling. Notification: continuous. Preference given to state residents.

Costs Per Year: Application fee: $0. State resident tuition: $2520 full-time, $83.95 per credit part-time. Nonresident tuition: $5108 full-time, $170.25 per credit part-time. Mandatory fees: $70 full-time, $35 per term part-time.

Collegiate Environment: Orientation program. Most popular organizations: Phi Theta Kappa, Practical Nursing Club, Medical Assistant Club, Accounting Club, Student Government. Campus security: late night transport-escort service. College housing not available. 7,634 books, 66 serials, 648 audiovisual materials, an OPAC, and a Web page. 187 computers available on campus for general student use. A campuswide network can be accessed. Staffed computer lab on campus.

■ **IVY TECH COMMUNITY COLLEGE-SOUTHWEST** *P-4*
3501 First Ave.
Evansville, IN 47710-3398
Tel: (812)426-2865
Admissions: (812)429-1430
E-mail: ajohnson@ivytech.edu
Web Site: http://www.ivytech.edu/

Description: State-supported, 2-year, coed. Part of Ivy Tech State College System. Awards certificates, transfer associate, and terminal associate degrees. Founded 1963. Setting: 15-acre suburban campus. System endowment: $15.9 million. Total enrollment: 4,858. 1,038 applied, 100% were admitted. Full-time: 1,526 students, 59% women, 41% men. Part-time: 3,332 students, 52% women, 48% men. 2% from out-of-state, 0.3% Native American, 1% Hispanic, 8% black, 0.5% Asian American or Pacific Islander, 0.05% international, 51% 25 or older, 4% transferred in. Core. Calendar: semesters. Academic remediation for entering students, services for LD students, advanced placement, independent study, distance learning, summer session for credit, part-time degree program, co-op programs and internships.

Entrance Requirements: Open admission except for human services and health technology programs. Options: early admission, deferred admission. Required: high school transcript. Required for some: interview. Entrance: noncompetitive. Application deadline: Rolling. Notification: continuous. Preference given to state residents.

Costs Per Year: Application fee: $0. State resident tuition: $2520 full-time, $83.95 per credit part-time. Nonresident tuition: $5108 full-time, $170.25 per credit part-time. Mandatory fees: $70 full-time, $35 per term part-time.

Collegiate Environment: Orientation program. Most popular organizations: Student Government, Phi Theta Kappa, LPN Club, National Association of Industrial Technology, Design Club. Campus security: late night transport-escort service. College housing not available. 7,082 books, 107 serials, 1,755 audiovisual materials, an OPAC, and a Web page. 362 computers available on campus for general student use. Staffed computer lab on campus.

■ **IVY TECH COMMUNITY COLLEGE-WABASH VALLEY** *J-5*
7999 US Hwy. 41, South
Terre Haute, IN 47802
Tel: (812)299-1121
Admissions: (812)298-2300

E-mail: mfisher@ivytech.edu

Web Site: http://www.ivytech.edu/

Description: State-supported, 2-year, coed. Part of Ivy Tech State College System. Awards certificates, transfer associate, and terminal associate degrees. Founded 1966. Setting: 55-acre suburban campus with easy access to Indianapolis. System endowment: $15.9 million. Total enrollment: 4,992. 1,300 applied, 100% were admitted. Full-time: 2,169 students, 64% women, 36% men. Part-time: 2,823 students, 52% women, 48% men. 2% from out-of-state, 1% Native American, 0.3% Hispanic, 3% black, 0.4% Asian American or Pacific Islander, 0.05% international, 55% 25 or older, 3% transferred in. Core. Calendar: semesters. Academic remediation for entering students, services for LD students, advanced placement, distance learning, summer session for credit, part-time degree program, adult/continuing education programs, internships.

Entrance Requirements: Open admission except for allied health programs in human services and health technology. Options: early admission, deferred admission. Required: high school transcript. Required for some: interview. Entrance: noncompetitive. Application deadline: Rolling. Notification: continuous. Preference given to state residents.

Costs Per Year: Application fee: $0. State resident tuition: $2520 full-time, $83.95 per credit part-time. Nonresident tuition: $5180 full-time, $170.25 per credit part-time. Mandatory fees: $70 full-time, $35 per term part-time.

Collegiate Environment: Orientation program. Most popular organizations: Student Government, Phi Theta Kappa, LPN Club, National Association of Industrial Technology. Student services: personal-psychological counseling, women's center. Campus security: 24-hour emergency response devices. College housing not available. 4,403 books, 77 serials, 406 audiovisual materials, an OPAC, and a Web page. 305 computers available on campus for general student use. A campuswide network can be accessed. Staffed computer lab on campus.

■ **IVY TECH COMMUNITY COLLEGE-WHITEWATER** *I-13*

2325 Chester Blvd.

Richmond, IN 47374-1220

Tel: (765)966-2656

E-mail: jplaster@ivytech.edu

Web Site: http://www.ivytech.edu/

Description: State-supported, 2-year, coed. Part of Ivy Tech State College System. Awards certificates, transfer associate, and terminal associate degrees. Founded 1963. Setting: 23-acre small town campus with easy access to Indianapolis. System endowment: $15.9 million. Total enrollment: 1,832. 347 applied, 100% were admitted. Full-time: 570 students, 72% women, 28% men. Part-time: 1,262 students, 75% women, 25% men. 4% from out-of-state, 0.3% Native American, 1% Hispanic, 5% black, 0.2% Asian American or Pacific Islander, 0% international, 62% 25 or older, 2% transferred in. Core. Calendar: semesters. Academic remediation for entering students, services for LD students, advanced placement, independent study, distance learning, summer session for credit, part-time degree program, adult/continuing education programs, internships. Off campus study at Indiana University East.

Entrance Requirements: Open admission except for human services and health technology programs. Option: early admission. Required: high school transcript. Required for some: interview. Entrance: noncompetitive. Application deadline: Rolling. Notification: continuous. Preference given to state residents.

Costs Per Year: Application fee: $0. State resident tuition: $2520 full-time, $83.95 per credit part-time. Nonresident tuition: $15,108 full-time, $170.25 per credit part-time. Mandatory fees: $70 full-time, $35 per term part-time.

Collegiate Environment: Orientation program. Student-run newspaper. Most popular organizations: Student Government, Phi Theta Kappa, LPN Club, CATS 2000, Business Professionals of America. Student services: personal-psychological counseling. Campus security: 24-hour emergency response devices, late night transport-escort service. College housing not available. 169 computers available on campus for general student use. A campuswide network can be accessed. Staffed computer lab on campus.

■ **LINCOLN TECHNICAL INSTITUTE** *I-9*

1201 Stadium Dr.

Indianapolis, IN 46202-2194

Tel: (317)632-5553

Free: 800-554-4465

Web Site: http://www.lincolntech.com/

Description: Proprietary, 2-year, coed. Part of Lincoln Technical Institute, Inc. Awards certificates and terminal associate degrees. Founded 1946. Set-

ting: urban campus. Total enrollment: 650. Students come from 2 states and territories, 1 other country, 25% 25 or older. Calendar: modular. Summer session for credit.

Entrance Requirements: Required: high school transcript, interview. Entrance: minimally difficult. Application deadline: Rolling.

Collegiate Environment: Orientation program. Student services: personal-psychological counseling. College housing not available. 800 books and 15 serials.

■ **MANCHESTER COLLEGE** *D-10*

604 East College Ave.

North Manchester, IN 46962-1225

Tel: (260)982-5000

Free: 800-852-3648

Admissions: (260)982-5055

Fax: (260)982-5043

E-mail: admitinfo@manchester.edu

Web Site: http://www.manchester.edu/

Description: Independent, comprehensive, coed, affiliated with Church of the Brethren. Awards associate, bachelor's, and master's degrees. Founded 1889. Setting: 125-acre small town campus. Endowment: $30 million. Research spending for 2004 fiscal year: $20,000. Educational spending for 2005 fiscal year: $4700 per student. Total enrollment: 1,104. Faculty: 89 (68 full-time, 21 part-time). Student-undergrad faculty ratio is 14:1. 1,487 applied, 73% were admitted. Full-time: 1,056 students, 53% women, 47% men. Part-time: 38 students, 42% women, 58% men. Students come from 23 states and territories, 29 other countries, 10% from out-of-state, 0.4% Native American, 2% Hispanic, 3% black, 1% Asian American or Pacific Islander, 6% international, 2% 25 or older, 74% live on campus, 3% transferred in. Retention: 71% of full-time freshmen returned the following year. Academic areas with the most degrees conferred: education; business/marketing; psychology. Core. Calendar: 4-1-4. Services for LD students, advanced placement, self-designed majors, honors program, independent study, double major, summer session for credit, part-time degree program, adult/continuing education programs, internships. Off campus study. Study abroad program.

Entrance Requirements: Options: Peterson's Universal Application, Common Application, electronic application, deferred admission, international baccalaureate accepted. Required: high school transcript, 1 recommendation, rank in upper 50% of high school class, SAT or ACT. Recommended: minimum 2.3 high school GPA, interview. Required for some: essay, minimum 3.0 high school GPA, interview. Entrance: moderately difficult. Application deadline: Rolling. Notification: continuous.

Costs Per Year: Application fee: $25. Tuition: $19,800 full-time, $670 per credit hour part-time. Mandatory fees: $700 full-time. College room only: $4500.

Collegiate Environment: Orientation program. Drama-theater group, choral group, student-run newspaper, radio station. Social organizations: 45 open to all. Most popular organizations: volunteer services, Campus Ministry Board, Accounting Club, Manchester Admissions Recruiting Corps, Student Alumni Council. Major annual events: Homecoming, Parents' Weekend, May Day Week. Student services: health clinic, personal-psychological counseling. Campus security: 24-hour emergency response devices and patrols, student patrols, late night transport-escort service, alarm system, locked residence hall entrances. 923 college housing spaces available; 815 were occupied in 2003-04. Freshmen guaranteed college housing. On-campus residence required through junior year. Options: coed, women-only housing available. Funderburg Library with an OPAC and a Web page. Operations spending for 2004 fiscal year: $531,000. 168 computers available on campus for general student use. Computer purchase/lease plans available. A campuswide network can be accessed from student residence rooms and from off campus. Staffed computer lab on campus.

Community Environment: North Manchester (population 6,000) is situated in north central Indiana, 35 miles west of Ft. Wayne, and 100 miles north of Indianapolis, and 3 hours from Chicago, enjoying a favorable climate. Bus facilities and airlines are within 30 miles. Community facilities include a library, indoor swimming pool, churches of many denominations, a medical clinic across the street from campus and a hospital within 20 minutes.

■ **MARIAN COLLEGE** *I-9*

3200 Cold Spring Rd.

Indianapolis, IN 46222-1997

Tel: (317)955-6000

Admissions: (317)955-6300

Web Site: http://www.marian.edu/

Description: Independent Roman Catholic, comprehensive, coed. Awards associate, bachelor's, and master's degrees. Founded 1851. Setting: 114-acre urban campus. Endowment: $6.2 million. Educational spending for 2005 fiscal year: $6200 per student. Total enrollment: 1,685. 911 applied, 73% were admitted. 11% from top 10% of their high school class, 29% from top quarter, 61% from top half. 2 valedictorians. Full-time: 1,091 students, 71% women, 29% men. Part-time: 575 students, 80% women, 20% men. Students come from 23 states and territories, 16 other countries, 10% from out-of-state, 0.4% Native American, 2% Hispanic, 19% black, 1% Asian American or Pacific Islander, 1% international, 42% 25 or older, 40% live on campus, 6% transferred in. Retention: 69% of full-time freshmen returned the following year. Core. Calendar: semesters. Academic remediation for entering students, services for LD students, advanced placement, accelerated degree program, honors program, independent study, double major, summer session for credit, part-time degree program, adult/continuing education programs, co-op programs and internships. Off campus study at Franklin College of Indiana, Indiana University-Purdue University at Indianapolis, University of Indianapolis, Christian Theological Seminary, Butler University. Study abroad program. ROTC: Army (c).

Entrance Requirements: Options: Common Application, electronic application, early admission, deferred admission. Required: high school transcript, minimum 2.00 high school GPA, SAT or ACT. Required for some: essay, recommendations, interview. Entrance: moderately difficult. Application deadline: 8/15. Notification: continuous until 8/24.

Costs Per Year: Application fee: $20. Comprehensive fee: $25,360 includes full-time tuition ($18,400), mandatory fees ($660), and college room and board ($6300). Full-time tuition and fees vary according to class time and course load. Room and board charges vary according to board plan and housing facility. Part-time tuition: $780 per credit hour. Part-time tuition varies according to class time and course load.

Collegiate Environment: Orientation program. Drama-theater group, choral group, student-run newspaper. Social organizations: 35 open to all. Most popular organizations: Fellowship of Christian Athletics, Marian College Student Association, Residence Hall Council, Business Club, Booster Club. Major annual events: October Fest, Homecoming (Mock Rock), Spring and Fall Formal. Student services: health clinic, personal-psychological counseling. Campus security: 24-hour patrols, late night transport-escort service. 500 college housing spaces available; 460 were occupied in 2003-04. Freshmen guaranteed college housing. On-campus residence required through senior year. Options: coed, men-only, women-only housing available. Mother Theresa Hackelmeier Memorial Library with 132,000 books, 1,200 microform titles, 300 serials, 100 audiovisual materials, an OPAC, and a Web page. Operations spending for 2004 fiscal year: $285,673. 130 computers available on campus for general student use. A campuswide network can be accessed from student residence rooms. Staffed computer lab on campus.

Community Environment: See Butler University.

■ **MARTIN UNIVERSITY** *I-9*

2171 Avondale Place, PO Box 18567
Indianapolis, IN 46218-3867
Tel: (317)543-3235
Admissions: (317)543-3237
Fax: (317)543-3257
Web Site: http://www.martin.edu/

Description: Independent, comprehensive, coed. Awards bachelor's and master's degrees. Founded 1977. Setting: 5-acre urban campus. Total enrollment: 571. Full-time: 219 students, 77% women, 23% men. Part-time: 246 students, 75% women, 25% men. Students come from 6 other countries, 0% from out-of-state, 0.2% Native American, 0.2% Hispanic, 92% black, 1% international, 80% 25 or older. Retention: 90% of full-time freshmen returned the following year. Core. Calendar: semesters. Academic remediation for entering students, advanced placement, accelerated degree program, self-designed majors, honors program, independent study, double major, summer session for credit, part-time degree program, adult/continuing education programs, internships, graduate courses open to undergrads. Off campus study at Consortium for Urban Education (CUE).

Entrance Requirements: Open admission. Options: early admission, deferred admission. Required: essay, high school transcript, interview, writing sample. Placement: Wonderlic aptitude test, Wide Range Achievement Test required for some. Entrance: noncompetitive. Application deadline: Rolling. Notification: continuous.

Costs Per Year: Application fee: $25. Tuition: $11,100 full-time, $370 per credit part-time. Mandatory fees: $320 full-time, $160 per term part-time.

Collegiate Environment: Drama-theater group, choral group. Student services: health clinic, personal-psychological counseling. Campus security: building security, security personnel from 7 a.m. to 9:30 p.m. College housing not available. 20 computers available on campus for general student use. Staffed computer lab on campus.

■ **MID-AMERICA COLLEGE OF FUNERAL SERVICE** *O-10*

3111 Hamburg Pike
Jeffersonville, IN 47130-9630
Tel: (812)288-8878
Free: 800-221-6158
Web Site: http://www.mid-america.edu/

Description: Independent, primarily 2-year, coed. Awards terminal associate and bachelor's degrees. Founded 1905. Setting: 3-acre small town campus with easy access to Louisville. Total enrollment: 120. Students come from 6 states and territories, 13% 25 or older. Core. Academic remediation for entering students.

Entrance Requirements: Open admission. Option: deferred admission. Required: high school transcript. Entrance: minimally difficult. Application deadline: Rolling.

Collegiate Environment: Orientation program. College housing not available. 1,500 books and 20 serials. 15 computers available on campus for general student use. Staffed computer lab on campus.

■ **OAKLAND CITY UNIVERSITY** *O-5*

138 North Lucretia St.
Oakland City, IN 47660-1099
Tel: (812)749-4781
Free: 800-737-5125
Admissions: (812)749-1222
Fax: (812)749-1233
Web Site: http://www.oak.edu/

Description: Independent General Baptist, comprehensive, coed. Awards associate, bachelor's, master's, doctoral, and first professional degrees. Founded 1885. Setting: 20-acre rural campus. Endowment: $2.8 million. Total enrollment: 1,900. Faculty: 183 (19 full-time, 164 part-time). Student-undergrad faculty ratio is 14:1. 7% from top 10% of their high school class, 26% from top quarter, 67% from top half. 3 valedictorians. Full-time: 1,275 students, 54% women, 46% men. Part-time: 291 students, 53% women, 47% men. Students come from 8 states and territories, 18 other countries, 16% from out-of-state, 0.3% Native American, 2% Hispanic, 10% black, 1% Asian American or Pacific Islander, 2% international, 65% 25 or older, 49% live on campus, 8% transferred in. Retention: 70% of full-time freshmen returned the following year. Core. Calendar: semesters. Academic remediation for entering students, services for LD students, advanced placement, accelerated degree program, summer session for credit, part-time degree program, external degree program, adult/continuing education programs.

Entrance Requirements: Options: Common Application, early admission, deferred admission. Required: essay, high school transcript, minimum 2.0 high school GPA, 1 recommendation, SAT or ACT. Recommended: interview. Entrance: minimally difficult. Application deadline: Rolling. Notification: continuous.

Costs Per Year: Application fee: $35. Comprehensive fee: $19,620 includes full-time tuition ($13,860), mandatory fees ($360), and college room and board ($5400). College room only: $1760. Part-time tuition: $462 per hour. Part-time mandatory fees: $15 per hour.

Collegiate Environment: Orientation program. Drama-theater group, choral group, student-run newspaper. Most popular organizations: Student Government Association, Good News Players, Art Guild. Major annual events: Founders' Day, Formal Tea. Student services: personal-psychological counseling. Campus security: 24-hour patrols, student patrols. 280 college housing spaces available; all were occupied in 2003-04. On-campus residence required in freshman year. Barger-Richardson Library with 87,724 books, 101,963 microform titles, 222 serials, 2,570 audiovisual materials, an OPAC, and a Web page. 92 computers available on campus for general student use. A campuswide network can be accessed from student residence rooms. Staffed computer lab on campus.

Community Environment: Oakland City is a friendly rural-suburban community with a Midwest climate, temperatures ranging from a high of 98 degrees to a low of ten degrees. Average rainfall is over 40 inches annually. Community facilities include six churches, both Protestant and Catholic, numerous civic and service groups, library, individual stores, and a shopping center 15 miles away. Some part time jobs are available for students.

■ PROFESSIONAL CAREERS INSTITUTE *I-9*

7302 Woodland Dr.
Indianapolis, IN 46278
Tel: (317)299-6001
Web Site: http://www.pcicareers.com/
Description: Independent, 2-year, coed. Awards certificates and terminal associate degrees. Total enrollment: 469. 107 applied, 66% were admitted. Part-time degree program, internships.
Entrance Requirements: Option: Common Application. Required: essay, high school transcript, minimum 1.7 high school GPA, 2 recommendations. Required for some: interview, CPAt, health exam, keyboard test. Entrance: minimally difficult.
Collegiate Environment: 25 computers available on campus for general student use.

■ PURDUE UNIVERSITY *G-7*

West Lafayette, IN 47907
Tel: (765)494-4600
Admissions: (765)494-1776
Fax: (765)494-0544
E-mail: admissions@adms.purdue.edu
Web Site: http://www.purdue.edu/
Description: State-supported, university, coed. Part of Purdue University System. Awards associate, bachelor's, master's, doctoral, and first professional degrees. Founded 1869. Setting: 1,579-acre suburban campus with easy access to Indianapolis. Endowment: $1.2 billion. Research spending for 2004 fiscal year: $394.5 million. Total enrollment: 38,712. Faculty: 2,293 (1,960 full-time, 333 part-time). Student-undergrad faculty ratio is 14:1. 24,052 applied, 85% were admitted. 27% from top 10% of their high school class, 58% from top quarter, 90% from top half. 69 National Merit Scholars, 187 valedictorians. Full-time: 29,196 students, 40% women, 60% men. Part-time: 1,679 students, 48% women, 52% men. 27% from out-of-state, 0.4% Native American, 3% Hispanic, 4% black, 5% Asian American or Pacific Islander, 6% international, 34% live on campus, 4% transferred in. Retention: 85% of full-time freshmen returned the following year. Academic areas with the most degrees conferred: engineering; business/marketing; engineering technologies. Core. Calendar: semesters. ESL program, services for LD students, advanced placement, accelerated degree program, freshman honors college, honors program, independent study, distance learning, double major, summer session for credit, part-time degree program, adult/continuing education programs, co-op programs and internships, graduate courses open to undergrads. Study abroad program. ROTC: Army, Naval, Air Force.
Entrance Requirements: Options: Common Application, electronic application, early admission, deferred admission. Required: high school transcript, SAT or ACT. Entrance: moderately difficult. Application deadline: 3/1. Notification: continuous.
Costs Per Year: Application fee: $30. State resident tuition: $7096 full-time, $254.15 per credit part-time. Nonresident tuition: $21,266 full-time, $706.25 per credit part-time.
Collegiate Environment: Orientation program. Drama-theater group, choral group, marching band, student-run newspaper, radio station. Social organizations: 601 open to all; national fraternities, national sororities; 17% of eligible men and 17% of eligible women are members. Most popular organizations: student government, Alpha Phi Omega, Society of Women Engineers, ballroom dancing, Golden Key National Honor Society. Major annual events: Grand Prix, Spring Funfest, homecoming. Student services: health clinic, personal-psychological counseling, women's center. Campus security: 24-hour emergency response devices and patrols, student patrols, late night transport-escort service, controlled dormitory access. 10,282 college housing spaces available; 10,220 were occupied in 2003-04. Freshmen given priority for college housing. Options: coed, men-only, women-only housing available. Hicks Undergraduate Library plus 13 others with 2.4 million books, 3.1 million microform titles, 19,957 serials, 11,905 audiovisual materials, an OPAC, and a Web page. Operations spending for 2004 fiscal year: $17.4 million. 2,925 computers available on campus for general student use. A campuswide network can be accessed from student residence rooms and from off campus. Staffed computer lab on campus.
Community Environment: Lafayette is located 65 miles northwest of Indianapolis and 120 miles southeast of Chicago. It is located on the Wabash River, in a rich grain-growing county where livestock and dairying are principal agricultural industries. All forms of commercial transportation are available. The community facilities include libraries, churches that represent 34 denominations, Lafayette Symphony Orchestra, Civic Theatre,

museums, hospitals, a TV station, and good shopping at downtown locations and 8 other shopping centers. Many hotel and motel accommodations are available for the conventions at Lafayette.

■ PURDUE UNIVERSITY CALUMET *B-5*

2200 169th St.
Hammond, IN 46323-2094
Tel: (219)989-2400
Admissions: (219)989-2213
Fax: (219)989-2775
E-mail: mcguinn@calumet.purdue.edu
Web Site: http://www.calumet.purdue.edu/
Description: State-supported, comprehensive, coed. Awards associate, bachelor's, and master's degrees. Founded 1951. Setting: 167-acre urban campus with easy access to Chicago. Endowment: $6 million. Research spending for 2004 fiscal year: $3.3 million. Educational spending for 2005 fiscal year: $6260 per student. Total enrollment: 9,302. Faculty: 471 (270 full-time, 201 part-time). Student-undergrad faculty ratio is 19:1. 2,405 applied, 80% were admitted. 7% from top 10% of their high school class, 22% from top quarter, 52% from top half. 2 National Merit Scholars, 6 valedictorians. Full-time: 5,029 students, 56% women, 44% men. Part-time: 3,330 students, 59% women, 41% men. Students come from 25 states and territories, 23 other countries, 8% from out-of-state, 0.5% Native American, 14% Hispanic, 16% black, 1% Asian American or Pacific Islander, 1% international, 35% 25 or older, 0% live on campus, 7% transferred in. Retention: 64% of full-time freshmen returned the following year. Academic areas with the most degrees conferred: social sciences; engineering technologies; computer and information sciences. Core. Calendar: semesters. Academic remediation for entering students, services for LD students, advanced placement, accelerated degree program, freshman honors college, honors program, independent study, distance learning, double major, summer session for credit, part-time degree program, adult/continuing education programs, co-op programs and internships, graduate courses open to undergrads. ROTC: Army (c).
Entrance Requirements: Options: Peterson's Universal Application, Common Application, electronic application, early admission. Required: high school transcript, minimum 2.0 high school GPA. Required for some: SAT or ACT. Entrance: moderately difficult. Application deadline: Rolling.
Costs Per Year: Application fee: $0. State resident tuition: $4368 full-time, $156 per credit hour part-time. Nonresident tuition: $10,260 full-time, $366 per credit hour part-time. Mandatory fees: $346 full-time, $14.80 per credit hour part-time. Full-time tuition and fees vary according to program. Part-time tuition and fees vary according to course load and program. College room only: $3990. Room charges vary according to housing facility.
Collegiate Environment: Orientation program. Drama-theater group, choral group, student-run newspaper. Social organizations: national fraternities, national sororities. Most popular organizations: Los Latinos, student government, Theater Club, Black Student Union, Song Company. Major annual events: Homecoming, Graduation, Gospel Fest. Student services: health clinic, personal-psychological counseling. Campus security: 24-hour emergency response devices and patrols, student patrols, late night transport-escort service. 376 college housing spaces available. No special consideration for freshman housing applicants. Purdue University Calumet Library with 269,648 books, 764,621 microform titles, 1,228 serials, 273 audiovisual materials, an OPAC, and a Web page. Operations spending for 2004 fiscal year: $1.7 million. 1,500 computers available on campus for general student use. A campuswide network can be accessed from off-campus. Staffed computer lab on campus.
Community Environment: Purdue University - Calumet primarily serves the communities located in the northwestern part of the state, adjacent to metropolitan Chicago. It is situated in the southeastern section of Hammond, just off the Borman Expressway and Indianapolis Boulevard.

■ PURDUE UNIVERSITY NORTH CENTRAL *B-7*

1401 South US Hwy. 421
Westville, IN 46391-9542
Tel: (219)785-5200
Admissions: (219)785-5283
Fax: (219)785-5538
Web Site: http://www.pnc.edu/
Description: State-supported, comprehensive, coed. Part of Purdue University System. Awards associate, bachelor's, and master's degrees. Founded 1967. Setting: 305-acre rural campus with easy access to Chicago. Endowment: $600,852. Research spending for 2004 fiscal year: $106,393.

Educational spending for 2005 fiscal year: $3848 per student. Total enrollment: 3,519. Faculty: 253 (103 full-time, 150 part-time). Student-undergrad faculty ratio is 17:1. 998 applied, 96% were admitted. 4% from top 10% of their high school class, 17% from top quarter, 49% from top half. 1 valedictorian. Full-time: 2,053 students, 55% women, 45% men. Part-time: 1,434 students, 63% women, 37% men. Students come from 5 states and territories, 1% from out-of-state, 1% Native American, 4% Hispanic, 4% black, 1% Asian American or Pacific Islander, 0.2% international, 39% 25 or older, 4% transferred in. Retention: 51% of full-time freshmen returned the following year. Academic areas with the most degrees conferred: business/marketing; liberal arts/general studies; engineering technologies. Calendar: semesters. Academic remediation for entering students, services for LD students, advanced placement, self-designed majors, honors program, distance learning, double major, summer session for credit, part-time degree program, adult/continuing education programs, co-op programs and internships, graduate courses open to undergrads. Study abroad program.

Entrance Requirements: Option: early admission. Required: high school transcript. Recommended: SAT, ACT. Required for some: essay, minimum 2.0 high school GPA, interview, SAT or ACT. Entrance: minimally difficult. Application deadline: 8/6. Notification: continuous.

Costs Per Year: State resident tuition: $5195 full-time, $173 per credit hour part-time. Nonresident tuition: $11,817 full-time, $407 per credit hour part-time. Mandatory fees: $388 full-time, $8.30 per credit hour part-time.

Collegiate Environment: Orientation program. Drama-theater group, student-run newspaper. Social organizations: 15 open to all. Most popular organizations: Student Cultural Society, Student Education Association, Construction Club. Major annual events: Chancellor's Series, Wednesday Lunch Series. Student services: personal-psychological counseling. Campus security: 24-hour emergency response devices, late night transport-escort service. College housing not available. Purdue University North Central Library with 87,675 books, 2,832 microform titles, 403 serials, 602 audiovisual materials, an OPAC, and a Web page. Operations spending for 2004 fiscal year: $446,328. 450 computers available on campus for general student use. Computer purchase/lease plans available. A campuswide network can be accessed from off-campus. Staffed computer lab on campus.

Community Environment: This small community (Westville population 1,170) located 12 miles south of Lake Michigan is progressing under a town and country zoning plan. Community facilities include six major civic organizations, two churches, a library, two parks, good transportation and shopping facilities.

■ ROSE-HULMAN INSTITUTE OF TECHNOLOGY *J-5*
5500 Wabash Ave.
Terre Haute, IN 47803-3999
Tel: (812)877-1511
Free: 800-248-7448
Admissions: (812)877-8213
Fax: (812)877-8941
E-mail: admis.ofc@rose-hulman.edu
Web Site: http://www.rose-hulman.edu/

Description: Independent, comprehensive, coed. Awards bachelor's and master's degrees. Founded 1874. Setting: 200-acre suburban campus with easy access to Indianapolis. Endowment: $163.5 million. Research spending for 2004 fiscal year: $8.4 million. Educational spending for 2005 fiscal year: $11,023 per student. Total enrollment: 1,887. Faculty: 157 (148 full-time, 9 part-time). Student-undergrad faculty ratio is 12:1. 3,294 applied, 69% were admitted. 64% from top 10% of their high school class, 93% from top quarter, 100% from top half. 17 National Merit Scholars, 50 valedictorians, 47 student government officers. Full-time: 1,766 students, 18% women, 82% men. Part-time: 9 students, 33% women, 67% men. Students come from 51 states and territories, 15 other countries, 55% from out-of-state, 0.1% Native American, 1% Hispanic, 2% black, 4% Asian American or Pacific Islander, 1% international, 1% 25 or older, 57% live on campus, 2% transferred in. Retention: 92% of full-time freshmen returned the following year. Academic areas with the most degrees conferred: engineering; computer and information sciences; mathematics. Core. Services for LD students, advanced placement, accelerated degree program, independent study, double major, summer session for credit, adult/continuing education programs, co-op programs, graduate courses open to undergrads. Off campus study at Indiana State University, St. Mary-of-the-Woods College. Study abroad program. ROTC: Army, Air Force.

Entrance Requirements: Options: Common Application, electronic application, deferred admission, international baccalaureate accepted. Required:

high school transcript, 1 recommendation, curricular, SAT or ACT. Recommended: essay, interview. Entrance: very difficult. Application deadline: 3/1. Notification: continuous.

Costs Per Year: Application fee: $40. Comprehensive fee: $34,557 includes full-time tuition ($26,688), mandatory fees ($450), and college room and board ($7419). College room only: $4236. Full-time tuition and fees vary according to course load. Room and board charges vary according to board plan. Part-time tuition: $768 per credit. Part-time tuition varies according to course load.

Collegiate Environment: Orientation program. Drama-theater group, choral group, student-run newspaper, radio station. Social organizations: 40 open to all; national fraternities, national sororities; 37% of eligible men and 43% of eligible women are members. Most popular organizations: intramurals, band, Drama Club, student government. Major annual events: Homecoming, Spring Fest, Campus Clean-up. Student services: health clinic, personal-psychological counseling. Campus security: 24-hour emergency response devices and patrols, late night transport-escort service, controlled dormitory access. 1,097 college housing spaces available; 1,034 were occupied in 2003-04. Freshmen guaranteed college housing. On-campus residence required in freshman year. Options: coed, men-only housing available. Logan Library with 77,839 books, 532 microform titles, 301 serials, 699 audiovisual materials, an OPAC, and a Web page. Operations spending for 2004 fiscal year: $605,759. 45 computers available on campus for general student use. Computer purchase/lease plans available. A campuswide network can be accessed from student residence rooms and from off campus. Staffed computer lab on campus.

Community Environment: See Indiana State University.

■ SAINT JOSEPH'S COLLEGE *D-6*
U.S. Hwy. 231, PO Box 890
Rensselaer, IN 47978
Tel: (219)866-6000
Free: 800-447-8781
Admissions: (219)866-6170
Fax: (219)866-6122
E-mail: admissions@saintjoe.edu
Web Site: http://www.saintjoe.edu/

Description: Independent Roman Catholic, comprehensive, coed. Awards associate, bachelor's, and master's degrees. Founded 1889. Setting: 180-acre small town campus with easy access to Chicago. Endowment: $12.6 million. Educational spending for 2005 fiscal year: $6744 per student. Total university enrollment: 9. Total unit enrollment: 1,003. Faculty: 77 (56 full-time, 21 part-time). Student-undergrad faculty ratio is 15:1. 1,363 applied, 78% were admitted. 13% from top 10% of their high school class, 40% from top quarter, 72% from top half. 24 valedictorians. Full-time: 886 students, 59% women, 41% men. Part-time: 117 students, 87% women, 13% men. Students come from 18 states and territories, 4 other countries, 28% from out-of-state, 0.1% Native American, 3% Hispanic, 6% black, 0.4% Asian American or Pacific Islander, 1% international, 14% 25 or older, 66% live on campus, 3% transferred in. Retention: 71% of full-time freshmen returned the following year. Academic areas with the most degrees conferred: business/marketing; education; security and protective services. Core. Calendar: semesters. Academic remediation for entering students, services for LD students, advanced placement, accelerated degree program, self-designed majors, honors program, independent study, double major, summer session for credit, part-time degree program, internships. Study abroad program.

Entrance Requirements: Options: electronic application, deferred admission, international baccalaureate accepted. Required: high school transcript, minimum 2.0 high school GPA, SAT or ACT. Required for some: essay, interview. Entrance: moderately difficult. Application deadline: Rolling. Notification: continuous.

Costs Per Year: Application fee: $25. Comprehensive fee: $26,240 includes full-time tuition ($19,600), mandatory fees ($160), and college room and board ($6480). Full-time tuition and fees vary according to reciprocity agreements. Room and board charges vary according to housing facility. Part-time tuition: $670 per credit. Part-time tuition varies according to course load and reciprocity agreements.

Collegiate Environment: Orientation program. Drama-theater group, choral group, marching band, student-run newspaper, radio station. Social organizations: 45 open to all. Most popular organizations: Student Association, Student Senate, Student Union, Campus Ministry, Business Club. Major annual events: Little 500, Homecoming Weekend, Little Siblings Weekend. Student services: health clinic, personal-psychological counseling. Campus security: 24-hour emergency response devices and patrols, student patrols, late night transport-escort service. 806 college housing spaces available; 670 were occupied in 2003-04. Freshmen guaranteed college housing. On-campus residence required through senior year. Options: coed, men-only, women-only housing available. Robinson Memorial Library with 157,021 books, 69,136 microform titles, 409 serials, 22,885 audiovisual materials, an OPAC, and a Web page. Operations spending for 2004 fiscal year: $319,805. 69 computers available on campus for general student use. A campuswide network can be accessed from student residence rooms. Staffed computer lab on campus.

■ SAINT MARY-OF-THE-WOODS COLLEGE

St. Mary-of-the-Woods, IN 47876
Tel: (812)535-5151
Free: 800-926-SMWC
Admissions: (812)535-5106
Fax: (812)535-5215
E-mail: adms@woods.smwc.edu
Web Site: http://www.smwc.edu/
Description: Independent Roman Catholic, comprehensive. Awards associate, bachelor's, and master's degrees and post-master's certificates (also offers external degree program with significant enrollment not reflected in profile). Founded 1840. Setting: 67-acre rural campus with easy access to Indianapolis. Endowment: $11.7 million. Educational spending for 2005 fiscal year: $6278 per student. Total enrollment: 1,757. Faculty: 67 (64 full-time, 3 part-time). Student-undergrad faculty ratio is 14:1. 266 applied. 24% from top 10% of their high school class, 46% from top quarter, 80% from top half. 3 valedictorians. Full-time: 510 students, 99% women, 0.2% men. Part-time: 1,116 students, 98% women, 2% men. Students come from 28 states and territories, 5 other countries, 30% from out-of-state, 1% Native American, 1% Hispanic, 3% black, 0.2% Asian American or Pacific Islander, 0.2% international, 60% 25 or older, 74% live on campus, 9% transferred in. Retention: 64% of full-time freshmen returned the following year. Academic areas with the most degrees conferred: education; business/marketing; visual and performing arts. Core. Calendar: semesters. Academic remediation for entering students, advanced placement, accelerated degree program, self-designed majors, independent study, distance learning, double major, summer session for credit, part-time degree program, external degree program, adult/continuing education programs, internships. Off campus study at Indiana State University, Rose-Hulman Institute of Technology, DePauw University, Wabash College. Study abroad program. ROTC: Army (c), Air Force (c).
Entrance Requirements: Options: Peterson's Universal Application, electronic application, early admission, deferred admission, international baccalaureate accepted. Required: minimum 2.5 high school GPA, 1 recommendation, SAT or ACT. Required for some: essay, high school transcript, interview. Entrance: moderately difficult. Application deadline: 8/15. Notification: continuous until 8/20.
Costs Per Year: Application fee: $30. Comprehensive fee: $25,480 includes full-time tuition ($18,060), mandatory fees ($600), and college room and board ($6820). College room only: $2660. Full-time tuition and fees vary according to program. Part-time tuition: $342 per hour. Part-time mandatory fees: $70 per year. Part-time tuition and fees vary according to course load and program.
Collegiate Environment: Orientation program. Drama-theater group, choral group, student-run newspaper. Social organizations: 25 open to all. Most popular organizations: Student Senate, In-Law, student newspaper, chorale, Diversity 'Worldwide Woodsies'. Major annual events: Ring Day, Parents' Weekend. Student services: health clinic, personal-psychological counseling. Campus security: 24-hour patrols. 360 college housing spaces available; 244 were occupied in 2003-04. Freshmen guaranteed college housing. On-campus residence required through senior year. Option: women-only housing available. Rooney Library with 155,771 books, 112 microform titles, 150 serials, 758 audiovisual materials, and an OPAC. Operations spending for 2004 fiscal year: $165,855. 65 computers available on campus for general student use. A campuswide network can be accessed from student residence rooms and from off campus. Staffed computer lab on campus.

■ SAINT MARY'S COLLEGE

Notre Dame, IN 46556
Tel: (574)284-4000
Free: 800-551-7621
Admissions: (574)284-4587
Fax: (574)284-4713

E-mail: admission@saintmarys.edu
Web Site: http://www.saintmarys.edu/
Description: Independent Roman Catholic, 4-year, women only. Awards bachelor's degrees. Founded 1844. Setting: 275-acre suburban campus. Endowment: $100.6 million. Educational spending for 2005 fiscal year: $13,286 per student. Total enrollment: 1,397. Student-undergrad faculty ratio is 10:1. 997 applied, 81% were admitted. 32% from top 10% of their high school class, 67% from top quarter, 96% from top half. 1 National Merit Scholar, 1 class president, 9 valedictorians, 66 student government officers. Full-time: 1,366 students. Part-time: 31 students. Students come from 45 states and territories, 9 other countries, 75% from out-of-state, 1% Native American, 4% Hispanic, 1% black, 2% Asian American or Pacific Islander, 1% international, 2% 25 or older, 81% live on campus, 3% transferred in. Retention: 87% of full-time freshmen returned the following year. Academic areas with the most degrees conferred: education; business/marketing; communications/journalism. Core. Calendar: semesters. Academic remediation for entering students, services for LD students, advanced placement, accelerated degree program, self-designed majors, independent study, double major, summer session for credit, part-time degree program, co-op programs and internships. Off campus study at University of Notre Dame, members of the Northern Indiana Consortium for Education. Study abroad program. ROTC: Army (c), Naval (c), Air Force (c).
Entrance Requirements: Options: Peterson's Universal Application, electronic application, early admission, early decision, deferred admission. Required: essay, high school transcript, 1 recommendation, SAT or ACT. Recommended: interview. Entrance: moderately difficult. Application deadlines: 3/1, 11/15 for early decision. Notification: continuous, 12/15 for early decision.
Costs Per Year: Application fee: $30. Comprehensive fee: $34,005 includes full-time tuition ($25,030), mandatory fees ($550), and college room and board ($8425). College room only: $5190. Part-time tuition: $989 per semester hour.
Collegiate Environment: Orientation program. Drama-theater group, choral group, marching band, student-run newspaper, radio station. Social organizations: 116 open to all. Most popular organizations: Circle K, Toastmasters, Volunteers in Support of Admissions (VISA), Student Government Association, academic clubs. Major annual events: Parents' Weekend, Hall and Class Dances, Student Activities Board events. Student services: health clinic, personal-psychological counseling, women's center. Campus security: 24-hour emergency response devices and patrols, late night transport-escort service, controlled dormitory access. 1,407 college housing spaces available; 1,155 were occupied in 2003-04. Freshmen guaranteed college housing. Option: women-only housing available. Cushwa-Leighton Library with 215,616 books, 14,627 microform titles, 759 serials, 2,528 audiovisual materials, an OPAC, and a Web page. Operations spending for 2004 fiscal year: $957,126. 187 computers available on campus for general student use. A campuswide network can be accessed from student residence rooms and from off campus. Staffed computer lab on campus.

■ SAWYER COLLEGE (HAMMOND) *B-5*

6040 Hohman Ave.
Hammond, IN 46320
Tel: (219)931-0436
Fax: (219)933-1239
Web Site: http://www.sawyercollege.edu/
Description: Proprietary, 2-year, coed. Awards transfer associate and terminal associate degrees. Founded 1962. Setting: 3-acre suburban campus. Total enrollment: 261.
Entrance Requirements: Required: Wonderlic aptitude test.

■ SAWYER COLLEGE (MERRILLVILLE) *B-5*

3803 East Lincoln Hwy.
Merrillville, IN 46410
Tel: (219)736-0436
Fax: (219)942-3762
Web Site: http://www.sawyercollege.edu/
Description: Proprietary, 2-year, coed. Awards transfer associate and terminal associate degrees. Founded 1968. Total enrollment: 395.
Entrance Requirements: Required: Wonderlic aptitude test.

■ TAYLOR UNIVERSITY *F-11*

236 West Reade Ave.
Upland, IN 46989-1001
Tel: (765)998-2751

Free: 800-882-3456
Admissions: (765)998-5206
Fax: (765)998-4925
E-mail: stmortland@tayloru.edu
Web Site: http://www.taylor.edu/

Description: Independent interdenominational, comprehensive, coed. Awards associate, bachelor's, and master's degrees. Founded 1846. Setting: 250-acre rural campus with easy access to Indianapolis. Endowment: $51 million. Research spending for 2004 fiscal year: $223,000. Educational spending for 2005 fiscal year: $7145 per student. Total enrollment: 1,865. Faculty: 187 (128 full-time, 59 part-time). Student-undergrad faculty ratio is 13:1. 1,517 applied, 82% were admitted. 37% from top 10% of their high school class, 68% from top quarter, 90% from top half. 9 National Merit Scholars, 29 valedictorians. Full-time: 1,794 students, 55% women, 45% men. Part-time: 57 students, 44% women, 56% men. Students come from 43 states and territories, 67% from out-of-state, 0.2% Native American, 1% Hispanic, 2% black, 1% Asian American or Pacific Islander, 1% international, 1% 25 or older, 91% live on campus, 2% transferred in. Retention: 88% of full-time freshmen returned the following year. Academic areas with the most degrees conferred: business/marketing; education; psychology. Core. Calendar: 4-1-4. Academic remediation for entering students, ESL program, services for LD students, advanced placement, self-designed majors, honors program, independent study, distance learning, double major, summer session for credit, part-time degree program, co-op programs and internships, graduate courses open to undergrads. Off campus study at members of the Christian College Coalition and the Christian College Consortium, Bowling Green University, Trinity Christian College. Study abroad program.

Entrance Requirements: Options: electronic application, early action, deferred admission. Required: essay, high school transcript, 2 recommendations, interview, SAT or ACT. Recommended: minimum 2.8 high school GPA. Entrance: very difficult. Application deadline: 12/1 for early action. Notification: 12/20 for early action. Preference given to Evangelical Christians.

Costs Per Year: Application fee: $25. Comprehensive fee: $26,376 includes full-time tuition ($20,520), mandatory fees ($226), and college room and board ($5630). College room only: $2732. Full-time tuition and fees vary according to course load. Room and board charges vary according to housing facility. Part-time tuition: $696 per credit. Part-time mandatory fees: $64 per year. Part-time tuition and fees vary according to course load.

Collegiate Environment: Orientation program. Drama-theater group, choral group, student-run newspaper, radio station. Social organizations: 200 open to all. Most popular organizations: Student Activities Council, World Outreach, Youth Conference, Inter-Class Council, Senate. Major annual events: Airband, Taylathon, Spiritual Renewal Week. Student services: health clinic, personal-psychological counseling. Campus security: 24-hour patrols, student patrols, late night transport-escort service. College housing designed to accommodate 1,452 students; 1,476 undergraduates lived in college housing during 2003-04. Freshmen guaranteed college housing. On-campus residence required through junior year. Options: men-only, women-only housing available. Zondervan Library with 189,007 books, 10,915 microform titles, 12,625 serials, 8,330 audiovisual materials, an OPAC, and a Web page. Operations spending for 2004 fiscal year: $813,651. 238 computers available on campus for general student use. A campuswide network can be accessed from student residence rooms and from off campus. Staffed computer lab on campus.

Community Environment: Upland (population 3,700) has all the advantages of quiet, country life with the nearby cities for activities. It is located 14 miles southeast of Marion and 23 miles north of Muncie. Buses and trains are accessible. The communities have churches of many denominations, health services and hospitals. Recreational activities are hunting, tennis, boating, fishing, golf and other sports.

■ TAYLOR UNIVERSITY FORT WAYNE *D-12*

1025 West Rudisill Blvd.
Fort Wayne, IN 46807-2197
Tel: (260)744-8600
Free: 800-233-3922
Admissions: (260)744-8689
Fax: (260)744-8660
E-mail: admissions@fw.taylor.edu
Web Site: http://www.tayloru.edu/

Description: Independent interdenominational, comprehensive, coed. Part of Taylor University. Awards associate, bachelor's, and master's degrees. Founded 1992. Setting: 32-acre suburban campus. Endowment: $9.4 million. Educational spending for 2005 fiscal year: $5500 per student. Total

enrollment: 595. Faculty: 55 (26 full-time, 29 part-time). Student-undergrad faculty ratio is 12:1. 266 applied, 83% were admitted. 13% from top 10% of their high school class, 27% from top quarter, 55% from top half. 3 valedictorians. Full-time: 337 students, 61% women, 39% men. Part-time: 207 students, 59% women, 41% men. Students come from 24 states and territories, 4 other countries, 19% from out-of-state, 0.2% Native American, 1% Hispanic, 10% black, 0.5% Asian American or Pacific Islander, 1% international, 23% 25 or older, 47% live on campus, 6% transferred in. Retention: 70% of full-time freshmen returned the following year. Academic areas with the most degrees conferred: theology and religious vocations; education; business/marketing. Core. Calendar: 4-1-4. Academic remediation for entering students, services for LD students, advanced placement, accelerated degree program, self-designed majors, independent study, distance learning, double major, summer session for credit, part-time degree program, external degree program, adult/continuing education programs, co-op programs and internships. Off campus study at Council for Christian Colleges and Universities, Christian College Consortium, Christian Center for Urban Studies. Study abroad program.

Entrance Requirements: Options: electronic application, deferred admission. Required: essay, high school transcript, 2 recommendations, SAT or ACT. Recommended: minimum 3.0 high school GPA, interview. Entrance: moderately difficult. Application deadline: Rolling.

Costs Per Year: Application fee: $20. Comprehensive fee: $22,674 includes full-time tuition ($17,600), mandatory fees ($114), and college room and board ($4960). College room only: $2160. Room and board charges vary according to board plan. Part-time tuition: $250 per credit hour. Part-time mandatory fees: $52 per year. Part-time tuition and fees vary according to course load.

Collegiate Environment: Orientation program. Drama-theater group, choral group, student-run newspaper. Social organizations: 11 open to all. Most popular organizations: Taylor Student Organization, Youth Conference Committee, Multicultrual Activities Council, World Outreach, Student Activities Council. Major annual events: Christmas Banquet, Annual Talent Show, Homecoming/Parents' Weekend. Student services: health clinic, personal-psychological counseling. Campus security: student patrols, late night transport-escort service, controlled dormitory access, 12-hour night patrols by trained personnel. 242 college housing spaces available; 225 were occupied in 2003-04. Freshmen given priority for college housing. On-campus residence required through junior year. Options: men-only, women-only housing available. Calvin H. English Library with 78,955 books, 29,815 microform titles, 670 serials, 5,063 audiovisual materials, an OPAC, and a Web page. Operations spending for 2004 fiscal year: $510,000. 72 computers available on campus for general student use. A campuswide network can be accessed from student residence rooms and from off campus. Staffed computer lab on campus.

■ TRI-STATE UNIVERSITY *B-12*

1 University Ave.
Angola, IN 46703-1764
Tel: (260)665-4100
Free: 800-347-4TSU
Admissions: (260)665-4365
Fax: (260)665-4292
E-mail: admit@alpha.tristate.edu
Web Site: http://www.tristate.edu/

Description: Independent, comprehensive, coed. Awards associate, bachelor's, and master's degrees. Founded 1884. Setting: 400-acre small town campus. Endowment: $16.8 million. Educational spending for 2005 fiscal year: $6218 per student. Total enrollment: 1,172. Faculty: 99 (69 full-time, 30 part-time). Student-undergrad faculty ratio is 13:1. 1,649 applied, 75% were admitted. 17% from top 10% of their high school class, 44% from top quarter, 74% from top half. 6 valedictorians. Full-time: 1,000 students, 30% women, 70% men. Part-time: 168 students, 61% women, 39% men. Students come from 23 states and territories, 17 other countries, 40% from out-of-state, 0.3% Native American, 1% Hispanic, 3% black, 1% Asian American or Pacific Islander, 1% international, 7% 25 or older, 48% live on campus, 6% transferred in. Retention: 65% of full-time freshmen returned the following year. Academic areas with the most degrees conferred: engineering technologies; education; business/marketing. Core. Calendar: semesters. Academic remediation for entering students, advanced placement, distance learning, double major, summer session for credit, part-time degree program, adult/continuing education programs, co-op programs and internships. Study abroad program.

Entrance Requirements: Options: Peterson's Universal Application, Common Application, electronic application, international baccalaureate accepted. Required: high school transcript, minimum 2.0 high school GPA, SAT or ACT. Recommended: recommendations, interview. Entrance: moderately difficult. Application deadline: 8/1. Notification: continuous until 8/15.

Costs Per Year: Application fee: $20. Comprehensive fee: $27,450 includes full-time tuition ($21,210) and college room and board ($6240). Part-time tuition: $663 per credit hour.

Collegiate Environment: Orientation program. Drama-theater group, choral group, student-run newspaper, radio station. Social organizations: 35 open to all; national fraternities, local sororities; 25% of eligible men and 15% of eligible women are members. Most popular organizations: Circle K, Drama Club, International Student Association, student newspaper, student radio station. Major annual event: Homecoming. Student services: personal-psychological counseling. Campus security: 24-hour emergency response devices and patrols, late night transport-escort service. 601 college housing spaces available; 570 were occupied in 2003-04. Freshmen guaranteed college housing. On-campus residence required through sophomore year. Option: coed housing available. Perry Ford Library with 73,859 books, 1,338 microform titles, 359 serials, 1,429 audiovisual materials, an OPAC, and a Web page. Operations spending for 2004 fiscal year: $276,432. 150 computers available on campus for general student use. A campuswide network can be accessed from student residence rooms and from off campus. Staffed computer lab on campus.

Community Environment: Angola, population 6,000, is situated at the intersection of U.S. Highways 20, 27, I-69 and the Indiana Toll Road. The city has a small airport. Recreational facilities include three golf courses, including one located on the Tri-State campus, Pokagon State Park five miles north, and many miles of shoreline surrounding more than 100 spring-fed lakes.

■ UNIVERSITY OF EVANSVILLE *P-4*

1800 Lincoln Ave.
Evansville, IN 47722
Tel: (812)488-2000
Free: 800-423-8633
Admissions: (812)488-2468
Fax: (812)474-4076
E-mail: dv9@evansville.edu
Web Site: http://www.evansville.edu/

Description: Independent, comprehensive, coed, affiliated with United Methodist Church. Awards associate, bachelor's, and master's degrees. Founded 1854. Setting: 75-acre suburban campus. Endowment: $69.2 million. Research spending for 2004 fiscal year: $119,330. Educational spending for 2005 fiscal year: $7819 per student. Total enrollment: 2,836. Faculty: 234 (175 full-time, 59 part-time). Student-undergrad faculty ratio is 13:1. 2,583 applied, 91% were admitted. 35% from top 10% of their high school class, 65% from top quarter, 92% from top half. 12 National Merit Scholars, 72 valedictorians. Full-time: 2,432 students, 62% women, 38% men. Part-time: 335 students, 61% women, 39% men. Students come from 42 states and territories, 38 other countries, 35% from out-of-state, 0.3% Native American, 1% Hispanic, 2% black, 1% Asian American or Pacific Islander, 5% international, 5% 25 or older, 67% live on campus, 3% transferred in. Retention: 81% of full-time freshmen returned the following year. Academic areas with the most degrees conferred: health professions and related sciences; visual and performing arts; business/marketing; education; engineering. Core. Calendar: semesters. ESL program, services for LD students, advanced placement, accelerated degree program, self-designed majors, freshman honors college, honors program, independent study, distance learning, double major, summer session for credit, part-time degree program, external degree program, adult/continuing education programs, co-op programs and internships, graduate courses open to undergrads. Study abroad program.

Entrance Requirements: Options: Peterson's Universal Application, Common Application, electronic application, early action, deferred admission, international baccalaureate accepted. Required: high school transcript, minimum 3.0 high school GPA, 1 recommendation, SAT or ACT. Recommended: interview. Required for some: essay, interview. Entrance: moderately difficult. Application deadlines: 2/1, 2/1 for nonresidents, 12/1 for early action. Notification: continuous until 3/1, continuous until 3/1 for nonresidents, 12/15 for early action.

Costs Per Year: Application fee: $35. Comprehensive fee: $28,320 includes full-time tuition ($21,120), mandatory fees ($540), and college room and board ($6660). College room only: $3280. Room and board charges vary according to board plan and housing facility. Part-time tuition: $580 per hour. Part-time mandatory fees: $35 per term. Part-time tuition and fees vary according to course load.

Collegiate Environment: Orientation program. Drama-theater group, choral group, student-run newspaper, radio station. Social organizations: 134 open to all; national fraternities, national sororities, local sororities; 22% of eligible men and 23% of eligible women are members. Most popular organizations: Kappa Chi, Admission Ambassadors, Student Activities Board, Phi Eta Sigma, Mortar Board. Major annual events: Fall Homecoming, Musical Madness, Bike Race Weekend. Student services: health clinic, personal-psychological counseling. Campus security: 24-hour emergency response devices and patrols, late night transport-escort service, controlled dormitory access. 1,774 college housing spaces available; 1,512 were occupied in 2003-04. Freshmen guaranteed college housing. On-campus residence required in freshman year. Option: coed housing available. Bower Suhrheinrich Library plus 1 other with 281,729 books, 465,300 microform titles, 1,200 serials, 11,230 audiovisual materials, an OPAC, and a Web page. Operations spending for 2004 fiscal year: $1.4 million. 312 computers available on campus for general student use. Computer purchase/lease plans available. A campuswide network can be accessed from student residence rooms and from off campus. Staffed computer lab on campus.

Community Environment: Evansville, population 136,000, is the fourth largest city in Indiana, and the largest in Southern Indiana. Cultural activities include a philharmonic orchestra, art museum, planetarium, zoo, civic and repertory theaters, and the remains of early Indian settlement.

■ UNIVERSITY OF INDIANAPOLIS *I-9*

1400 East Hanna Ave.
Indianapolis, IN 46227-3697
Tel: (317)788-3368
Free: 800-232-8634
Admissions: (317)788-3216
Fax: (317)788-3300
E-mail: admissions@uindy.edu
Web Site: http://www.uindy.edu/

Description: Independent, comprehensive, coed, affiliated with United Methodist Church. Awards associate, bachelor's, master's, and doctoral degrees. Founded 1902. Setting: 60-acre suburban campus. Endowment: $64.5 million. Research spending for 2004 fiscal year: $105,968. Educational spending for 2005 fiscal year: $8395 per student. Total enrollment: 4,462. Faculty: 416 (166 full-time, 250 part-time). Student-undergrad faculty ratio is 12:1. 3,519 applied, 76% were admitted. 20% from top 10% of their high school class, 54% from top quarter, 87% from top half. 19 valedictorians. Full-time: 2,389 students, 64% women, 36% men. Part-time: 972 students, 78% women, 22% men. Students come from 31 states and territories, 55 other countries, 7% from out-of-state, 0.3% Native American, 2% Hispanic, 11% black, 1% Asian American or Pacific Islander, 2% international, 27% 25 or older, 31% live on campus, 3% transferred in. Retention: 74% of full-time freshmen returned the following year. Academic areas with the most degrees conferred: business/marketing; education; psychology. Core. Calendar: 4-4-1. Academic remediation for entering students, ESL program, services for LD students, advanced placement, accelerated degree program, self-designed majors, honors program, independent study, distance learning, double major, summer session for credit, part-time degree program, adult/continuing education programs, co-op programs and internships, graduate courses open to undergrads. Off campus study at 7 members of the Consortium for Urban Education, 10 members of the May Term Consortium. Study abroad program. ROTC: Army (c).

Entrance Requirements: Options: Peterson's Universal Application, electronic application, deferred admission, international baccalaureate accepted. Required: high school transcript, minimum 2.0 high school GPA, SAT or ACT. Required for some: interview. Entrance: moderately difficult. Application deadline: Rolling. Notification: continuous.

Costs Per Year: Application fee: $20. Comprehensive fee: $24,990 includes full-time tuition ($17,980) and college room and board ($7010). Full-time tuition varies according to program. Room and board charges vary according to board plan and housing facility. Part-time tuition: $750 per hour. Part-time tuition varies according to class time.

Collegiate Environment: Orientation program. Drama-theater group, choral group, student-run newspaper, radio station. Social organizations: 37 open to all. Most popular organizations: Fellowship of Christian Athletes, Intercultural Association, Circle K, Indianapolis Student Government, Residence Hall Association. Major annual events: Late Nights, Winter Formal Dance, Cyclerama. Student services: health clinic, personal-psychological counseling. Campus security: 24-hour emergency response devices and patrols, student patrols, late night transport-escort service, emergency call boxes. 1,152 college housing spaces available; 1,029 were occupied in 2003-04. Options: coed, women-only housing available. Krannert Memorial Library with 173,363 books, 15,551 microform titles, 1,015 serials, 5,324 audiovisual materials, an OPAC, and a Web page. Operations spending for 2004 fiscal year: $1.1 million. 218 computers available on campus for general student use. A campuswide network can be accessed from student residence rooms and from off campus. Staffed computer lab on campus.

Community Environment: The university is located in the southern, residential suburb of Indianapolis known as University Heights. Indianapolis is the nation's third largest capital city and is known as the"Amateur Sports Capital of the World." The metropolitan area has a population of more than one million. Recreational, cultural, and social opportunities abound. Bus, train, and airline services are within minutes of the campus. There are also numerous shops, restaurants, hotels, and a major shopping mall nearby.

■ UNIVERSITY OF NOTRE DAME

Notre Dame, IN 46556
Tel: (574)631-5000
Admissions: (574)631-7505
Fax: (574)631-8865
E-mail: admissions@nd.edu
Web Site: http://www.nd.edu/

Description: Independent Roman Catholic, university, coed. Awards bachelor's, master's, doctoral, and first professional degrees. Founded 1842. Setting: 1,250-acre suburban campus. Endowment: $3.7 billion. Total enrollment: 11,417. Faculty: (877 full-time). Student-undergrad faculty ratio is 12:1. 11,317 applied, 32% were admitted. 86% from top 10% of their high school class, 97% from top quarter, 100% from top half. 151 National Merit Scholars, 179 class presidents, 261 valedictorians. Full-time: 8,260 students, 47% women, 53% men. Part-time: 15 students, 33% women, 67% men. Students come from 54 states and territories, 61 other countries, 88% from out-of-state, 1% Native American, 9% Hispanic, 4% black, 6% Asian American or Pacific Islander, 3% international, 0% 25 or older, 76% live on campus, 1% transferred in. Academic areas with the most degrees conferred: business/marketing; social sciences; engineering. Core. Calendar: semesters. Services for LD students, advanced placement, accelerated degree program, self-designed majors, honors program, independent study, distance learning, double major, summer session for credit, internships, graduate courses open to undergrads. Off campus study at Saint Mary's College (IN), Xavier University of Louisiana, Clark Atlanta University, St. Mary's University of San Antonio. Study abroad program. ROTC: Army, Naval, Air Force.

Entrance Requirements: Options: electronic application, early action, deferred admission, international baccalaureate accepted. Required: essay, high school transcript, 1 recommendation, SAT or ACT. Entrance: most difficult. Application deadlines: 12/31, 11/1 for early action. Notification: 4/1, 12/20 for early action.

Costs Per Year: Application fee: $50. Comprehensive fee: $42,172 includes full-time tuition ($32,900), mandatory fees ($542), and college room and board ($8730). Part-time tuition: $1371 per credit.

Collegiate Environment: Orientation program. Drama-theater group, choral group, marching band, student-run newspaper, radio station. Social organizations: 263 open to all. Most popular organizations: marching band, Circle K, Finance Club, Notre Dame/St. Mary's Right to Life. Major annual events: home football weekends, Bookstore Basketball Tournament, Junior Parents' Weekend. Student services: legal services, health clinic, personal-psychological counseling, women's center. Campus security: 24-hour emergency response devices and patrols, student patrols, late night transport-escort service, controlled dormitory access, crime prevention and personal safety workshops, full time trained police investigators, fire sprinklers in all residence halls. College housing designed to accommodate 6,284 students; 6,303 undergraduates lived in college housing during 2003-04. Freshmen guaranteed college housing. On-campus residence required in freshman year. Options: men-only, women-only housing available. University Libraries of Notre Dame plus 9 others with 2.8 million books, 2.1 million microform titles, 15,635 serials, 19,568 audiovisual materials, an OPAC, and a Web page. 400 computers available on campus for general student use. Computer purchase/lease plans available. A campuswide network can be accessed from student residence rooms and from off campus. Staffed computer lab on campus.

Community Environment: The South Bend area has a population of over 100,000. The downtown district, located 3 miles south of the campus, has enjoyed a complete urban renewal and offers attractive services to the students. A world-class water raceway provides excellent opportunities for challenging kayaking, tubing and canoeing. Home of the College Football Hall of Fame. Several major shopping malls with direct bus service to campus are less than 15 minutes away.

■ UNIVERSITY OF PHOENIX-INDIANAPOLIS CAMPUS *I-9*

7999 Knue Rd. Dr., Ste. 150
Indianapolis, IN 46250
Tel: (317)585-8610
Free: 800-228-7240
Admissions: (480)557-1712
Web Site: http://www.phoenix.edu/

Description: Proprietary, comprehensive, coed. Awards bachelor's and master's degrees. Founded 2003. Total enrollment: 616. Faculty: 82 (4 full-time, 78 part-time). Student-undergrad faculty ratio is 8:1. 48 applied. Full-time: 474 students, 65% women, 35% men. 0% Native American, 0.4% Hispanic, 5% black, 0.2% Asian American or Pacific Islander, 6% international, 84% 25 or older. Academic area with the most degrees conferred: business/marketing. Core. Calendar: continuous. Advanced placement, accelerated degree program, independent study, distance learning, external degree program, adult/continuing education programs, graduate courses open to undergrads.

Entrance Requirements: Open admission. Option: deferred admission. Required: 1 recommendation. Required for some: high school transcript. Entrance: noncompetitive. Application deadline: Rolling.

Costs Per Year: Application fee: $110. Tuition: $9780 full-time, $326 per credit part-time. Mandatory fees: $560 full-time, $70 per course part-time.

Collegiate Environment: College housing not available. University Library with 444 books, 666 serials, an OPAC, and a Web page. Operations spending for 2004 fiscal year: $3.2 million.

■ UNIVERSITY OF SAINT FRANCIS *D-12*

2701 Spring St.
Fort Wayne, IN 46808-3994
Tel: (260)434-3100
Free: 800-729-4732
Admissions: (260)434-3279
E-mail: admiss@sfc.edu
Web Site: http://www.sf.edu/

Description: Independent Roman Catholic, comprehensive, coed. Awards associate, bachelor's, and master's degrees. Founded 1890. Setting: 73-acre suburban campus. Endowment: $8.1 million. Educational spending for 2005 fiscal year: $6793 per student. Total enrollment: 2,003. Faculty: 229 (108 full-time, 121 part-time). Student-undergrad faculty ratio is 11:1. 1,129 applied, 59% were admitted. 10% from top 10% of their high school class, 34% from top quarter, 67% from top half. 8 valedictorians. Full-time: 1,343 students, 66% women, 34% men. Part-time: 425 students, 82% women, 18% men. Students come from 10 states and territories, 8 other countries, 9% from out-of-state, 1% Native American, 2% Hispanic, 4% black, 1% Asian American or Pacific Islander, 0% international, 32% 25 or older, 16% live on campus, 11% transferred in. Retention: 78% of full-time freshmen returned the following year. Academic areas with the most degrees conferred: business/marketing; health professions and related sciences; education. Core. Calendar: semesters. Academic remediation for entering students, services for LD students, advanced placement, freshman honors college, honors program, independent study, distance learning, double major, summer session for credit, part-time degree program, adult/continuing education programs, co-op programs and internships, graduate courses open to undergrads. Study abroad program.

Entrance Requirements: Options: Peterson's Universal Application, electronic application, deferred admission, international baccalaureate accepted. Required: high school transcript, minimum 2.3 high school GPA, SAT or ACT. Recommended: essay. Required for some: recommendations, interview. Entrance: moderately difficult. Application deadline: Rolling. Notification: continuous until 8/15.

Costs Per Year: Application fee: $20. Comprehensive fee: $24,312 includes full-time tuition ($17,760), mandatory fees ($718), and college room and board ($5834). Part-time tuition: $560 per hour. Part-time mandatory fees: $17 per hour.

Collegiate Environment: Orientation program. Drama-theater group, choral group, student-run newspaper. Social organizations: 25 open to all. Most popular organizations: Student Activities Council, Art Club, Student Government Organization, Student Nursing Association, Residence Hall Council. Major annual events: Homecoming, Spring Fling. Student services: personal-psychological counseling. Campus security: 24-hour emergency response devices and patrols, late night transport-escort service, controlled dormitory access. 350 college housing spaces available; 300 were occupied in 2003-04. Freshmen given priority for college housing. On-campus residence required through sophomore year. Option: coed housing available. University Library plus 1 other with 50,186 books, 631,345 microform titles, 449 serials, 2,105 audiovisual materials, an OPAC, and a Web page. Operations spending for 2004 fiscal year: $431,949. 217 computers available on campus for general student use. Computer purchase/lease plans available. A campuswide network can be accessed from student residence rooms. Staffed computer lab on campus.

■ **UNIVERSITY OF SOUTHERN INDIANA** *P-4*

8600 University Blvd.
Evansville, IN 47712-3590
Tel: (812)464-8600
Free: 800-467-1965
Admissions: (812)464-1765
Fax: (812)465-7154
Web Site: http://www.usi.edu/

Description: State-supported, comprehensive, coed. Part of Indiana Commission for Higher Education. Awards associate, bachelor's, and master's degrees. Founded 1965. Setting: 330-acre suburban campus. Research spending for 2004 fiscal year: $212,746. Total enrollment: 10,004. Faculty: 619 (303 full-time, 316 part-time). Student-undergrad faculty ratio is 18:1. 4,807 applied, 91% were admitted. 7% from top 10% of their high school class, 25% from top quarter, 56% from top half. 26 valedictorians. Full-time: 7,477 students, 59% women, 41% men. Part-time: 1,775 students, 64% women, 36% men. Students come from 34 states and territories, 34 other countries, 9% from out-of-state, 0.2% Native American, 1% Hispanic, 4% black, 1% Asian American or Pacific Islander, 1% international, 17% 25 or older, 31% live on campus, 7% transferred in. Retention: 59% of full-time freshmen returned the following year. Academic areas with the most degrees conferred: business/marketing; education; health professions and related sciences. Core. Calendar: semesters. Academic remediation for entering students, ESL program, services for LD students, advanced placement, honors program, independent study, distance learning, double major, summer session for credit, part-time degree program, adult/continuing education programs, co-op programs and internships, graduate courses open to undergrads. Study abroad program. ROTC: Army.
Entrance Requirements: Options: Common Application, electronic application. Required: high school transcript, SAT or ACT. Recommended: essay, minimum 2.0 high school GPA. Required for some: interview. Entrance: noncompetitive. Application deadline: 8/15. Notification: continuous until 8/27.
Costs Per Year: Application fee: $25. State resident tuition: $4244 full-time, $141.45 per credit hour part-time. Nonresident tuition: $10,118 full-time, $337.25 per credit hour part-time. Mandatory fees: $60 full-time, $22.75 per term part-time. College room and board: $6368. College room only: $3170.
Collegiate Environment: Orientation program. Drama-theater group, choral group, student-run newspaper, radio station. Social organizations: 82 open to all; national fraternities, national sororities. Most popular organization: student government. Major annual events: Student Involvement Fair, Midnight Breakfast, September Smash. Student services: health clinic, personal-psychological counseling. Campus security: 24-hour emergency response devices and patrols, student patrols, late night transport-escort service, controlled dormitory access. 3,200 college housing spaces available; 2,760 were occupied in 2003-04. No special consideration for freshman housing applicants. Option: coed housing available. David L. Rice Library plus 1 other with 247,329 books, 577,668 microform titles, 14,276 serials, 7,661 audiovisual materials, an OPAC, and a Web page. Operations spending for 2004 fiscal year: $1.9 million. 778 computers available on campus for general student use. A campuswide network can be accessed from student residence rooms and from off campus. Staffed computer lab on campus.
Community Environment: See University of Evansville.

■ **VALPARAISO UNIVERSITY** *B-6*

1700 Chapel Dr.
Valparaiso, IN 46383
Tel: (219)464-5000; 888-GO-VALPO
Admissions: (219)464-5011
Fax: (219)464-6898
E-mail: undergrad_admissions@valpo.edu
Web Site: http://www.valpo.edu/

Description: Independent, comprehensive, coed, affiliated with Lutheran Church. Awards associate, bachelor's, master's, and first professional degrees and post-master's certificates. Founded 1859. Setting: 310-acre small town campus with easy access to Chicago. Endowment: $143.1 million. Research spending for 2004 fiscal year: $565,916. Educational spending for 2005 fiscal year: $8289 per student. Total enrollment: 3,864. Faculty: 362 (243 full-time, 119 part-time). Student-undergrad faculty ratio is 13:1. 3,532 applied, 83% were admitted. 34% from top 10% of their high school class, 60% from top quarter, 85% from top half. 6 National Merit Scholars, 31 valedictorians. Full-time: 2,825 students, 51% women, 49% men. Part-time: 139 students, 71% women, 29% men. Students come from 49 states and territories, 32 other countries, 65% from out-of-state, 0.1% Native American, 3% Hispanic, 4% black, 2% Asian American or Pacific Islander, 2% international, 5% 25 or older, 65% live on campus, 4% transferred in. Retention: 84% of full-time freshmen returned the following year. Academic areas with the most degrees conferred: business/marketing; social sciences; education. Core. Calendar: semesters. ESL program, services for LD students, advanced placement, accelerated degree program, self-designed majors, freshman honors college, honors program, independent study, distance learning, double major, summer session for credit, part-time degree program, adult/continuing education programs, co-op programs and internships, graduate courses open to undergrads. Off campus study at Associated Colleges of the Midwest, American University, Lutheran College Washington Consortium, Drew University. Study abroad program. ROTC: Air Force.
Entrance Requirements: Options: Peterson's Universal Application, Common Application, electronic application, early admission, early action, deferred admission, international baccalaureate accepted. Required: essay, high school transcript, SAT or ACT. Recommended: 2 recommendations, interview. Required for some: interview. Entrance: moderately difficult. Application deadlines: 8/15, 11/1 for early action. Notification: 12/1 for early action.
Costs Per Year: Application fee: $30. Comprehensive fee: $28,970 includes full-time tuition ($22,000), mandatory fees ($750), and college room and board ($6220). College room only: $3910. Room and board charges vary according to housing facility and student level. Part-time tuition: $1000 per credit hour. Part-time mandatory fees: $20 per credit hour. Part-time tuition and fees vary according to course load.
Collegiate Environment: Orientation program. Drama-theater group, choral group, student-run newspaper, radio station. Social organizations: 100 open to all; national fraternities, local sororities; 30% of eligible men and 20% of eligible women are members. Most popular organizations: Union Board, student government, student volunteer organization, chapel programs. Major annual events: homecoming, Spring Weekend, Parents' Weekend. Student services: legal services, health clinic, personal-psychological counseling. Campus security: 24-hour emergency response devices and patrols, late night transport-escort service, controlled dormitory access. 1,989 college housing spaces available; 1,907 were occupied in 2003-04. Freshmen guaranteed college housing. On-campus residence required through junior year. Options: coed, women-only housing available. Christopher Center for Library and Information Resources plus 1 other with 1.1 million books, 2 million microform titles, 21,360 serials, 6,968 audiovisual materials, an OPAC, and a Web page. Operations spending for 2004 fiscal year: $3.1 million. 634 computers available on campus for general student use. A campuswide network can be accessed from student residence rooms and from off campus. Staffed computer lab on campus.
Community Environment: Valparaiso University is located 50 miles southeast of Chicago. For those interested in off-campus recreation and entertainment, it is a 20-minute drive to the Indiana Dunes National Lakeshore and less than an hour to the many theaters, museums, restaurants and athletic events of Chicago.

■ **VINCENNES UNIVERSITY** *M-5*

1002 North First St.
Vincennes, IN 47591-5202
Tel: (812)888-8888
Admissions: (812)888-4313
Fax: (812)888-5868
Web Site: http://www.vinu.edu/

Description: State-supported, 2-year, coed. Awards certificates, transfer associate, and terminal associate degrees. Founded 1801. Setting: 100-acre small town campus. Endowment: $25.6 million. Educational spending for 2005 fiscal year: $4558 per student. Total enrollment: 5,175. 4,553 applied, 94% were admitted. 5% from top 10% of their high school class, 10% from top quarter, 35% from top half. 1 National Merit Scholar, 5 class presidents, 20 valedictorians, 40 student government officers. Students come from 22 states and territories, 31 other countries, 7% from out-of-state, 0.3% Native American, 1% Hispanic, 8% black, 0.4% Asian American or Pacific Islander, 2% international, 22% 25 or older, 50% live on campus. Core. Calendar: semesters. Academic remediation for entering students, ESL program, services for LD students, advanced placement, self-designed majors, freshman honors college, honors program, independent study, distance learning, summer session for credit, part-time degree program, external degree program, adult/continuing education programs, co-op programs and internships. Off campus study at 30 universities in Indiana. ROTC: Army (c), Air Force (c).

Entrance Requirements: Open admission except for health-related programs. Options: Peterson's Universal Application, Common Application, electronic application, early admission, deferred admission. Required: high school transcript. Recommended: SAT or ACT. Required for some: interview, SAT or ACT. Entrance: noncompetitive. Application deadline: Rolling. Notification: continuous until 8/1.

Collegiate Environment: Orientation program. Drama-theater group, choral group, student-run newspaper, radio station. Social organizations: 53 open to all; national fraternities, national sororities, local fraternities, local sororities; 5% of eligible men and 1% of eligible women are members. Most popular organizations: Student Senate, Student Alumni Corporation, Intramurals, Law Enforcement Association, Campus Christian Fellowship. Major annual events: Tube Race, Homecoming, Parents' Weekends. Student services: health clinic, personal-psychological counseling. Campus security: 24-hour emergency response devices and patrols, student patrols, late night transport-escort service, controlled dormitory access, surveillance cameras. 3,000 college housing spaces available; 2,500 were occupied in 2003-04. Freshmen guaranteed college housing. On-campus residence required in freshman year. Options: coed, men-only, women-only housing available. Shake Learning Resource Center plus 1 other with 103,000 books, 5,012 microform titles, 557 serials, 5,260 audiovisual materials, an OPAC, and a Web page. Operations spending for 2004 fiscal year: $1.3 million. 600 computers available on campus for general student use. A campuswide network can be accessed from student residence rooms and from off campus. Staffed computer lab on campus.

Community Environment: Vincennes (population 20,000) is the oldest city in the state and was the capital of the Old Northwest. On the banks of the Wabash River, Vincennes is the distribution point for this area, which produces peaches, apples, cantaloupes, watermelons, sweet potatoes and wheat. Points of interest are the Cathedral Library, George Rogers Clark National Historic Park, Harrison Mansion, Indiana Territory State Memorial and the Old Cathedral.

■ **VINCENNES UNIVERSITY JASPER CAMPUS** *O-6*

850 College Ave.
Jasper, IN 47546-9393
Tel: (812)482-3030
Free: 800-809-VUJC
Fax: (812)481-5960
E-mail: lgilbert@indian.vinu.edu
Web Site: http://vujc.vinu.edu/

Description: State-supported, 2-year, coed. Part of Vincennes University. Awards certificates, transfer associate, and terminal associate degrees. Founded 1970. Setting: 120-acre small town campus. Total enrollment: 835. 247 applied, 99% were admitted. 3% from top 10% of their high school class, 20% from top quarter, 40% from top half. Students come from 1 other country, 0.2% Hispanic, 0.1% black, 0.1% Asian American or Pacific Islander, 0.1% international, 50% 25 or older. Core. Calendar: semesters. Academic remediation for entering students, advanced placement, distance learning, summer session for credit, part-time degree program, adult/continuing education programs.

Entrance Requirements: Open admission. Required: high school transcript. Placement: SAT or ACT recommended; SAT or ACT required for some. Entrance: noncompetitive. Application deadline: Rolling.

Collegiate Environment: Orientation program. Student-run newspaper. Student services: personal-psychological counseling. College housing not

available. Vincennes University Jasper Library with 14,000 books, 180 serials, and an OPAC. 140 computers available on campus for general student use. A campuswide network can be accessed from off-campus.

■ **WABASH COLLEGE** *H-7*

PO Box 352
Crawfordsville, IN 47933-0352
Tel: (765)361-6100
Free: 800-345-5385
Admissions: (765)361-6225
Fax: (765)361-6437
E-mail: admissions@wabash.edu
Web Site: http://www.wabash.edu/

Description: Independent, 4-year, men only. Awards bachelor's degrees. Founded 1832. Setting: 50-acre small town campus with easy access to Indianapolis. Endowment: $315.8 million. Research spending for 2004 fiscal year: $2.8 million. Educational spending for 2005 fiscal year: $48,281 per student. Total enrollment: 877. Student-undergrad faculty ratio is 10:1. 1,358 applied, 51% were admitted. 29% from top 10% of their high school class, 69% from top quarter, 93% from top half. 1 National Merit Scholar, 10 class presidents, 12 valedictorians, 97 student government officers. Full-time: 871 students. Part-time: 6 students. Students come from 35 states and territories, 22 other countries, 29% from out-of-state, 0.1% Native American, 4% Hispanic, 6% black, 3% Asian American or Pacific Islander, 4% international, 0% 25 or older, 87% live on campus, 0.1% transferred in. Retention: 89% of full-time freshmen returned the following year. Academic areas with the most degrees conferred: English; social sciences; history. Core. Calendar: semesters. Services for LD students, advanced placement, independent study, double major, internships. Off campus study at members of the Great Lakes Colleges Association. Study abroad program. ROTC: Army (c).

Entrance Requirements: Options: Peterson's Universal Application, Common Application, electronic application, early admission, early decision, early action, deferred admission. Required: high school transcript, 1 recommendation, SAT or ACT. Recommended: essay, interview. Entrance: moderately difficult. Application deadlines: 3/15, 11/15 for early decision, 12/15 for early action. Notification: continuous until 4/1, 12/15 for early decision, 1/31 for early action.

Costs Per Year: Application fee: $30. Comprehensive fee: $30,116 includes full-time tuition ($22,964), mandatory fees ($424), and college room and board ($6728). College room only: $2740. Room and board charges vary according to board plan and housing facility. Part-time tuition: $3827 per course. Part-time tuition varies according to course load.

Collegiate Environment: Orientation program. Drama-theater group, choral group, student-run newspaper, radio station. Social organizations: 45 open to all; national fraternities, language houses; 65% of eligible undergrads are members. Most popular organizations: Sphinx Club, Alpha Phi Omega, The Bachelor, Malcolm X Institute, Christian Fellowship. Major annual events: homecoming, Monon Bell football game. Student services: health clinic, personal-psychological counseling. Campus security: 24-hour emergency response devices and patrols, late night transport-escort service. 860 college housing spaces available; 742 were occupied in 2003-04. Freshmen guaranteed college housing. On-campus residence required through sophomore year. Option: men-only housing available. Lilly Library with 434,460 books, 11,359 microform titles, 5,530 serials, 11,151 audiovisual materials, an OPAC, and a Web page. Operations spending for 2004 fiscal year: $1.2 million. 310 computers available on campus for general student use. Computer purchase/lease plans available. A campuswide network can be accessed from student residence rooms and from off campus. Staffed computer lab on campus.

Community Environment: Crawfordsville (population 13,500), is located 45 miles northwest of Indianapolis. It is an historic small town community, and has many churches, a hospital, and motels. Recreational facilities include golf courses and swimming pools. Shades State Park is 14 miles away, and Turkey Run State Park is approximately 25 miles distant. Points of interest are the Lane Place Museum and Lew Wallace "Ben Hur" Museum.

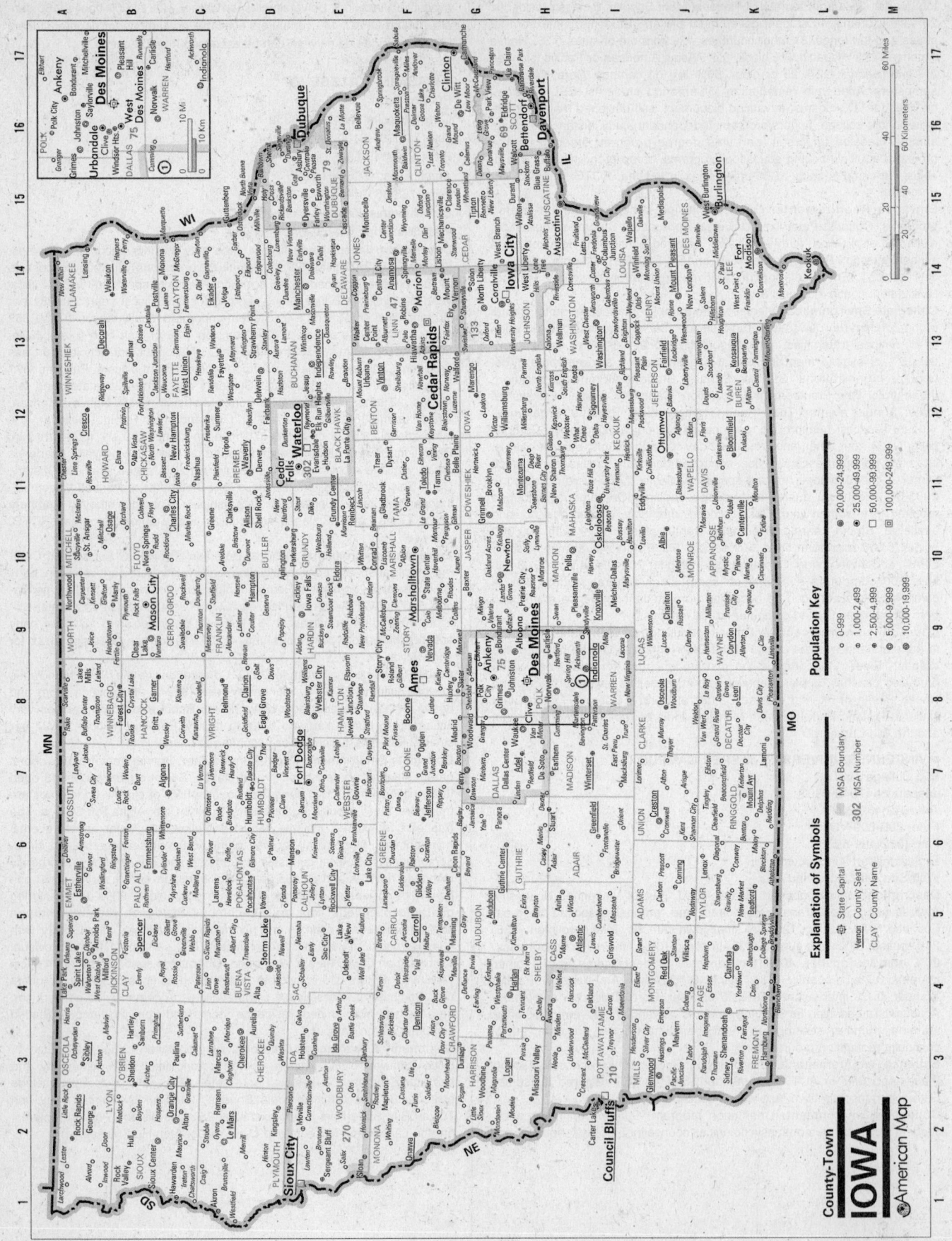

IOWA
County-Town

⊕American Map

Explanation of Symbols

⊕ State Capital
● County Seat

Vernon County Seat
CLAY County Name

302 MSA Boundary
302 MSA Number

Population Key

○ 0-999
○ 1,000-2,499
○ 2,500-4,999
◉ 5,000-9,999
⊙ 10,000-19,999

◉ 20,000-24,999
◉ 25,000-49,999
□ 50,000-99,999
⊡ 100,000-249,999

■ **AIB COLLEGE OF BUSINESS** *H-8*
2500 Fleur Dr.
Des Moines, IA 50321-1799
Tel: (515)244-4221
Free: 800-444-1921
Fax: (515)244-6773
E-mail: clineg@aib.edu
Web Site: http://www.aib.edu/
Description: Independent, 2-year, coed. Awards diplomas and terminal associate degrees. Founded 1921. Setting: 20-acre urban campus. Educational spending for 2005 fiscal year: $2322 per student. Total enrollment: 938. 546 applied, 74% were admitted. 5% from top 10% of their high school class, 21% from top quarter, 34% from top half. Full-time: 750 students, 70% women, 30% men. Part-time: 188 students, 66% women, 34% men. Students come from 5 states and territories, 5% from out-of-state, 0.2% Native American, 1% Hispanic, 2% black, 2% Asian American or Pacific Islander, 24% 25 or older, 48% live on campus, 21% transferred in. Core. Calendar: continuous. Academic remediation for entering students, accelerated degree program, double major, summer session for credit, part-time degree program, adult/continuing education programs, internships.
Entrance Requirements: Option: electronic application. Required: high school transcript. Recommended: interview, ACT. Entrance: minimally difficult. Application deadline: Rolling.
Costs Per Year: Application fee: $25. Comprehensive fee: $15,837 includes full-time tuition ($11,880) and college room and board ($3957). College room only: $2895. Part-time tuition: $330 per credit hour.
Collegiate Environment: Social organizations: 12 open to all; national fraternities, national sororities; 10% of eligible men and 10% of eligible women are members. Most popular organizations: Business Management Association, Institute of Management Accountants, International Association of Administrative Professionals, Association of Information Technology Professionals, Student Court Reporters Association. Major annual events: Fall Formal, All-Student Seminar, Graduation. Student services: personal-psychological counseling. Campus security: 24-hour emergency response devices, late night transport-escort service, controlled dormitory access, video security. 520 college housing spaces available. No special consideration for freshman housing applicants. On-campus residence required through sophomore year. Option: coed housing available. 5,400 books and 185 serials. Operations spending for 2004 fiscal year: $102,422. 188 computers available on campus for general student use. A campuswide network can be accessed from student residence rooms and from off campus. Staffed computer lab on campus.

■ **ALLEN COLLEGE** *E-12*
1825 Logan Ave.
Waterloo, IA 50703
Tel: (319)226-2000
Admissions: (319)226-2002
Fax: (319)226-2020
Web Site: http://www.allencollege.edu/
Description: Independent, comprehensive, coed. Administratively affiliated with Allen Health System/Iowa Health System. Awards associate, bachelor's, and master's degrees (liberal arts and general education courses offered at either University of North Iowa or Wartburg College). Founded 1989. Setting: 20-acre suburban campus. Endowment: $1 million. Educational spending for 2005 fiscal year: $10,712 per student. Total enrollment: 404. Faculty: 31 (19

full-time, 12 part-time). Student-undergrad faculty ratio is 13:1. 51 applied, 73% were admitted. 17% from top 10% of their high school class, 50% from top quarter, 89% from top half. Full-time: 318 students, 94% women, 6% men. Part-time: 56 students, 93% women, 7% men. 3% from out-of-state, 0.3% Native American, 1% Hispanic, 1% black, 1% Asian American or Pacific Islander, 0% international, 20% 25 or older, 15% live on campus, 22% transferred in. Retention: 76% of full-time freshmen returned the following year. Academic area with the most degrees conferred: health professions and related sciences. Core. Calendar: semesters. Advanced placement, independent study, distance learning, part-time degree program, internships, graduate courses open to undergrads. Off campus study. ROTC: Army (c).
Entrance Requirements: Option: electronic application. Required: essay, high school transcript, 1 recommendation, ACT. Recommended: minimum 2.3 high school GPA, rank in upper 50% of high school class, minimum ACT score of 18. Required for some: interview. Entrance: moderately difficult. Application deadlines: 7/1, 7/1 for nonresidents, 3/1 for early decision. Notification: continuous until 8/20, continuous until 8/20 for nonresidents, 3/15 for early decision.
Costs Per Year: Application fee: $50. Comprehensive fee: $19,184 includes full-time tuition ($11,958), mandatory fees ($1514), and college room and board ($5712). College room only: $2666. Part-time tuition: $415 per credit hour. Part-time mandatory fees: $37 per credit hour, $170 per term.
Collegiate Environment: Orientation program. Student-run newspaper. Social organizations: 4 open to all. Most popular organizations: Allen Student Nurses' Association, Nurses' Christian Fellowship, Allen Student Organization. Major annual events: Fall Fling, Holiday Party. Student services: health clinic, personal-psychological counseling, women's center. Campus security: 24-hour patrols. 50 undergraduates lived in college housing during 2003-04. Options: coed, men-only, women-only housing available. Barrett Library with 2,797 books, 199 serials, 433 audiovisual materials, an OPAC, and a Web page. Operations spending for 2004 fiscal year: $144,366. 26 computers available on campus for general student use. Staffed computer lab on campus.

■ **ASHFORD UNIVERSITY** *G-17*
400 North Bluff Blvd., PO Box 2967
Clinton, IA 52733-2967
Tel: (563)242-4023
Free: 800-242-4153
Fax: (563)242-2003
E-mail: admissns@tfu.edu
Web Site: http://www.ashford.edu/
Description: Proprietary, 4-year, coed. Awards bachelor's and master's degrees. Founded 1918. Setting: 24-acre small town campus with easy access to Chicago. Endowment: $1.4 million. Research spending for 2004 fiscal year: $26,474. Educational spending for 2005 fiscal year: $3227 per student. Total enrollment: 459. 298 applied, 71% were admitted. 8% from top 10% of their high school class, 21% from top quarter, 50% from top half. 1 class president, 3 student government officers. Full-time: 342 students, 56% women, 44% men. Part-time: 49 students, 65% women, 35% men. Students come from 9 states and territories, 38% from out-of-state, 1% Native American, 2% Hispanic, 7% black, 2% Asian American or Pacific Islander, 2% international, 27% 25 or older, 29% live on campus, 3% transferred in. Retention: 69% of full-time freshmen returned the following year. Core. Calendar: semesters. Academic remediation for entering students, ESL program, advanced placement, self-designed majors, freshman honors col-

lege, honors program, independent study, distance learning, double major, summer session for credit, part-time degree program, external degree program, internships. Study abroad program.

Entrance Requirements: Options: Common Application, electronic application, early admission, deferred admission. Required: high school transcript, SAT or ACT. Recommended: minimum 2.0 high school GPA, interview. Required for some: recommendations, interview. Entrance: minimally difficult. Application deadline: 8/15. Notification: continuous.

Collegiate Environment: Orientation program. Drama-theater group, choral group, student-run newspaper. Social organizations: 21 open to all. Most popular organizations: Student Senate, Student Ambassadors, Hall Council, Black Student Union, Student Iowa State Education Association. Major annual events: Brother/Sister Weekend, Matriculation Ceremony, Pep Rally and Homecoming. Student services: health clinic, personal-psychological counseling. Campus security: 24-hour emergency response devices and patrols, student patrols, late night transport-escort service, controlled dormitory access, self-defense education, lighted pathways. 234 college housing spaces available; 113 were occupied in 2003-04. Freshmen guaranteed college housing. On-campus residence required through junior year. Option: coed housing available. The Franciscan University of the Prairies Library with 98,974 books, 73,682 microform titles, 639 serials, 2,738 audiovisual materials, an OPAC, and a Web page. Operations spending for 2004 fiscal year: $159,661. 109 computers available on campus for general student use. Computer purchase/lease plans available. Staffed computer lab on campus.

Community Environment: Clinton, Iowa (population 28,000), situated midway between Chicago and Des Moines, is home to a minor league baseball team, a symphony orchestra, a pre-professional ballet company, summer stock theater, art shows, and other cultural events. Clinton is 45 minutes from the Quad Cities, three hours from Chicago, and five hours from Minneapolis. The quality of life in the city and on campus is typical of the wholesome lifestyle the Midwest is known for throughout the country.

■ BRIAR CLIFF UNIVERSITY *D-1*

3303 Rebecca St.
Sioux City, IA 51104-0100
Tel: (712)279-5321
Free: 800-662-3303
Admissions: (712)279-5200
Fax: (712)279-5410
E-mail: admissions@briar-cliff.edu
Web Site: http://www.briarcliff.edu/

Description: Independent Roman Catholic, comprehensive, coed. Awards associate, bachelor's, and master's degrees. Founded 1930. Setting: 70-acre suburban campus. Endowment: $8.5 million. Educational spending for 2005 fiscal year: $4225 per student. Total enrollment: 1,122. Faculty: 98 (56 full-time, 42 part-time). Student-undergrad faculty ratio is 13:1. 1,275 applied, 76% were admitted. 15% from top 10% of their high school class, 36% from top quarter, 61% from top half. Full-time: 970 students, 59% women, 41% men. Part-time: 126 students, 71% women, 29% men. Students come from 26 states and territories, 2 other countries, 32% from out-of-state, 1% Native American, 4% Hispanic, 2% black, 2% Asian American or Pacific Islander, 0.2% international, 27% 25 or older, 0% live on campus, 12% transferred in. Retention: 72% of full-time freshmen returned the following year. Academic areas with the most degrees conferred: business/marketing; education; health professions and related sciences. Core. Calendar: (3 10-week terms plus 2 5-week summer sessions). Academic remediation for entering students, services for LD students, advanced placement, accelerated degree program, self-designed majors, honors program, independent study, distance learning, double major, summer session for credit, part-time degree program, adult/continuing education programs, internships. Off campus study at Colleges of Mid-America. Study abroad program.

Entrance Requirements: Options: Peterson's Universal Application, Common Application, electronic application, early admission, deferred admission. Required: high school transcript, minimum 2.0 high school GPA, minimum ACT score of 18, SAT or ACT. Recommended: essay. Required for some: 3 recommendations, interview. Entrance: moderately difficult. Application deadlines: Rolling, Rolling for nonresidents.

Costs Per Year: Application fee: $20. Comprehensive fee: $23,550 includes full-time tuition ($17,490), mandatory fees ($495), and college room and board ($5565). College room only: $2760. Room and board charges vary according to board plan and housing facility. Part-time tuition: $583 per hour. Part-time mandatory fees: $16.50 per hour. Part-time tuition and fees vary according to class time and course load.

Collegiate Environment: Orientation program. Drama-theater group, choral group, student-run newspaper, radio station. Social organizations: 20 open to all; 65% of eligible men and 75% of eligible women are members. Most popular organizations: Student Government Association, Ethnic Relations Club, Residence Hall Association, Vision: Campus Programming Board, peer advising leaders. Major annual events: Homecoming, Welcome Week, Spring Fling. Student services: health clinic, personal-psychological counseling, career services. Campus security: 24-hour emergency response devices and patrols, student patrols, late night transport-escort service, controlled dormitory access. 581 college housing spaces available; 568 were occupied in 2003-04. Freshmen guaranteed college housing. On-campus residence required through junior year. Option: coed housing available. Mueller Library with 84,411 books, 21,592 microform titles, 7,786 serials, 10,761 audiovisual materials, an OPAC, and a Web page. Operations spending for 2004 fiscal year: $230,732. 350 computers available on campus for general student use. A campuswide network can be accessed from student residence rooms and from off campus. Staffed computer lab on campus.

■ BUENA VISTA UNIVERSITY *D-4*

610 West Fourth St.
Storm Lake, IA 50588
Tel: (712)749-2351
Free: 800-383-9600
Admissions: (712)749-2235
Fax: (712)749-2037
E-mail: admissions@bvu.edu
Web Site: http://www.bvu.edu/

Description: Independent, comprehensive, coed, affiliated with Presbyterian Church (U.S.A.). Awards bachelor's and master's degrees. Founded 1891. Setting: 60-acre small town campus. Endowment: $114.6 million. Educational spending for 2005 fiscal year: $6000 per student. Total enrollment: 1,283. Faculty: 116 (81 full-time, 35 part-time). Student-undergrad faculty ratio is 13:1. 1,183 applied, 83% were admitted. 16% from top 10% of their high school class, 38% from top quarter, 75% from top half. 20 valedictorians. Full-time: 1,198 students, 52% women, 48% men. Part-time: 16 students, 50% women, 50% men. Students come from 17 states and territories, 4 other countries, 22% from out-of-state, 0.3% Native American, 2% Hispanic, 3% black, 2% Asian American or Pacific Islander, 0% international, 3% 25 or older, 89% live on campus, 3% transferred in. Retention: 76% of full-time freshmen returned the following year. Academic areas with the most degrees conferred: business/marketing; education; interdisciplinary studies. Core. Calendar: 4-1-4. Academic remediation for entering students, ESL program, services for LD students, advanced placement, self-designed majors, freshman honors college, honors program, independent study, distance learning, double major, summer session for credit, part-time degree program, adult/continuing education programs, internships, graduate courses open to undergrads. Off campus study at Washington University in St. Louis. Study abroad program.

Entrance Requirements: Options: Peterson's Universal Application, Common Application, electronic application, deferred admission, international baccalaureate accepted. Required: high school transcript, recommendations, SAT or ACT. Recommended: minimum 3.0 high school GPA. Required for some: essay, interview. Entrance: moderately difficult. Notification: continuous.

Costs Per Year: Application fee: $25. Comprehensive fee: $27,742 includes full-time tuition ($21,688) and college room and board ($6054). Part-time tuition: $729 per semester hour.

Collegiate Environment: Orientation program. Drama-theater group, choral group, student-run newspaper, radio station. Social organizations: 50 open to all. Most popular organizations: Student Activities Board, student orientation staff, Esprit De Corps, Student Senate, Marketing Association. Major annual events: homecoming, Academic and Cultural Events Series (ACES), Buenafication Day. Student services: health clinic, personal-psychological counseling. Campus security: 24-hour emergency response devices, late night transport-escort service, controlled dormitory access, night security patrols. 1,137 college housing spaces available; 1,119 were occupied in 2003-04. Freshmen guaranteed college housing. On-campus residence required through senior year. Options: coed, men-only, women-only housing available. BVU Library with 145,085 books, 41,377 microform titles, 642 serials, 4,994 audiovisual materials, an OPAC, and a Web page. Operations spending for 2004 fiscal year: $820,733. 400 computers available on campus for general student use. Computer purchase/lease plans available. A campuswide network can be accessed from student residence rooms and from off campus. Staffed computer lab on campus.

Community Environment: Storm Lake (population 10,000) is the county seat of Buena Vista County, and is located 75 miles east of Sioux City and 160 miles northwest of Des Moines. Bus lines and nearby airport facilities provide adequate transportation. Several churches of various Christian denominations are represented in the community.

■ **CENTRAL COLLEGE** *H-10*
812 University St.
Pella, IA 50219-1999
Tel: (641)628-9000; 877-462-3689
Admissions: (641)628-7600
Fax: (641)628-5316
E-mail: admissions@central.edu
Web Site: http://www.central.edu/
Description: Independent, 4-year, coed, affiliated with Reformed Church in America. Awards bachelor's degrees. Founded 1853. Setting: 133-acre small town campus with easy access to Des Moines. Endowment: $65.9 million. Educational spending for 2005 fiscal year: $8487 per student. Total enrollment: 1,635. Student-undergrad faculty ratio is 13:1. 1,641 applied, 84% were admitted. 25% from top 10% of their high school class, 53% from top quarter, 78% from top half. Full-time: 1,601 students, 56% women, 44% men. Part-time: 34 students, 44% women, 56% men. Students come from 39 states and territories, 13 other countries, 14% from out-of-state, 0.2% Native American, 1% Hispanic, 1% black, 1% Asian American or Pacific Islander, 1% international, 3% 25 or older, 86% live on campus, 3% transferred in. Retention: 81% of full-time freshmen returned the following year. Academic areas with the most degrees conferred: business/marketing; education; parks and recreation. Core. Calendar: semesters. ESL program, services for LD students, self-designed majors, honors program, independent study, double major, summer session for credit, part-time degree program, internships. Off campus study. Study abroad program.
Entrance Requirements: Options: Peterson's Universal Application, Common Application, electronic application, deferred admission, international baccalaureate accepted. Required: high school transcript, SAT or ACT. Recommended: minimum 2.5 high school GPA, interview. Required for some: essay, 3 recommendations, interview. Entrance: moderately difficult. Application deadline: Rolling.
Costs Per Year: Application fee: $25. Comprehensive fee: $28,196 includes full-time tuition ($20,972) and college room and board ($7224). College room only: $3542. Part-time tuition: $728 per semester hour.
Collegiate Environment: Orientation program. Drama-theater group, choral group, student-run newspaper, radio station. Social organizations: 72 open to all; national fraternities, national sororities, local fraternities, local sororities; 15% of eligible men and 7% of eligible women are members. Most popular organizations: Students Concerned About the Environment, Inter-Varsity, FCA, Coalition for Multicultural Campus, Student Senate. Major annual events: Annual Lemming Race, Student Conference on Global Awareness, Interdisciplinary Research Symposium. Student services: health clinic, personal-psychological counseling. Campus security: 24-hour emergency response devices, student patrols, late night transport-escort service, controlled dormitory access. 1,384 college housing spaces available; 1,330 were occupied in 2003-04. Freshmen guaranteed college housing. On-campus residence required through senior year. Options: coed, men-only, women-only housing available. Geisler Library plus 3 others with 220,526 books, 55,313 microform titles, 1,161 serials, 13,160 audiovisual materials, an OPAC, and a Web page. Operations spending for 2004 fiscal year: $1.1 million. 300 computers available on campus for general student use. Computer purchase/lease plans available. A campuswide network can be accessed from student residence rooms and from off campus. Staffed computer lab on campus.
Community Environment: Pella (population 10,000), a rapidly growing agricultural and industrial community, is located 43 miles southeast of Des Moines. Active churches, libraries, and a community hospital serve the area. Pella is widely known for its attractive homes, gardens, and fine community spirit. Red Rock Dam and Lake is located four miles south. Tulip Time is an annual event here dedicated to preserving the Dutch heritage of the town.

■ **CLARKE COLLEGE** *D-16*
1550 Clarke Dr.
Dubuque, IA 52001-3198
Tel: (563)588-6300
Free: 800-383-2345
Admissions: (563)588-6316
Fax: (563)588-6789

E-mail: admissions@clarke.edu
Web Site: http://www.clarke.edu/
Description: Independent Roman Catholic, comprehensive, coed. Awards associate, bachelor's, and master's degrees. Founded 1843. Setting: 55-acre urban campus. Endowment: $15.2 million. Educational spending for 2005 fiscal year: $6780 per student. Total enrollment: 1,246. Faculty: 130 (83 full-time, 47 part-time). Student-undergrad faculty ratio is 11:1. 784 applied, 61% were admitted. 13% from top 10% of their high school class, 34% from top quarter, 75% from top half. Full-time: 857 students, 71% women, 29% men. Part-time: 164 students, 70% women, 30% men. Students come from 10 states and territories, 8 other countries, 35% from out-of-state, 0.4% Native American, 3% Hispanic, 3% black, 1% Asian American or Pacific Islander, 1% international, 32% 25 or older, 47% live on campus, 11% transferred in. Retention: 79% of full-time freshmen returned the following year. Academic areas with the most degrees conferred: education; business/marketing; health professions and related sciences. Core. Calendar: semesters. ESL program, advanced placement, self-designed majors, honors program, independent study, distance learning, double major, summer session for credit, part-time degree program, adult/continuing education programs, co-op programs and internships. Off campus study at Tri-College Cooperative Effort. Study abroad program.
Entrance Requirements: Options: Peterson's Universal Application, Common Application, electronic application, deferred admission, international baccalaureate accepted. Required: high school transcript, minimum 2.0 high school GPA, rank in upper 50% of high school class, minimum ACT score of 21 or SAT score of 1000, SAT or ACT. Required for some: interview. Entrance: moderately difficult. Application deadline: Rolling. Notification: continuous until 7/15.
Costs Per Year: Application fee: $25. Comprehensive fee: $25,390 includes full-time tuition ($18,360), mandatory fees ($585), and college room and board ($6445). College room only: $3135. Full-time tuition and fees vary according to class time. Room and board charges vary according to board plan and housing facility. Part-time tuition: $465 per credit hour. Part-time tuition varies according to class time.
Collegiate Environment: Orientation program. Drama-theater group, choral group, student-run newspaper, radio station. Social organizations: 63 open to all. Most popular organizations: Admissions Student Team, Student Multicultural Organization, concert choir, campus ministry, student government. Major annual events: homecoming, February beach party, Christmas dinner. Student services: health clinic, personal-psychological counseling. Campus security: 24-hour emergency response devices and patrols, late night transport-escort service, controlled dormitory access. 580 college housing spaces available; 486 were occupied in 2003-04. Freshmen guaranteed college housing. On-campus residence required through junior year. Options: coed, men-only, women-only housing available. Nicholas J. Schrupp Library with 157,576 books, 11,792 microform titles, 884 serials, 1,530 audiovisual materials, an OPAC, and a Web page. Operations spending for 2004 fiscal year: $631,132. 237 computers available on campus for general student use. A campuswide network can be accessed from student residence rooms and from off campus. Staffed computer lab on campus.
Community Environment: The small city of Dubuque is located on the Mississippi River where Iowa, Illinois and Wisconsin meet. The oldest city in Iowa, it features rugged bluffs and Victorian architecture. Excellent air connections with Chicago's O'Hare Airport and the Minneapolis-St. Paul Airport are available. The city is the cultural, recreational and commercial center of the tristate area, and offers theater, symphony, art galleries, museums, dog racing, riverboat gambling, and concerts as well as facilities for boating, skiing, golf and tennis.

■ **CLINTON COMMUNITY COLLEGE** *G-17*
1000 Lincoln Blvd.
Clinton, IA 52732-6299
Tel: (563)244-7001
Admissions: (563)244-7007
Fax: (563)244-7107
Web Site: http://www.eicc.edu/cco/
Description: State and locally supported, 2-year, coed. Part of Eastern Iowa Community College District. Awards certificates, diplomas, transfer associate, and terminal associate degrees. Founded 1946. Setting: 20-acre small town campus. Educational spending for 2005 fiscal year: $2249 per student. Total enrollment: 1,298. 215 applied, 100% were admitted. Full-time: 590 students, 63% women, 37% men. Part-time: 708 students, 70% women, 30% men. Students come from 9 states and territories, 8% from out-of-state, 1% Native American, 2% Hispanic, 3% black, 1% Asian American or Pacific

Islander, 0.4% international, 36% 25 or older. Core. Calendar: semesters. Academic remediation for entering students, ESL program, services for LD students, advanced placement, independent study, distance learning, double major, summer session for credit, part-time degree program, adult/continuing education programs, co-op programs and internships. Study abroad program.

Entrance Requirements: Open admission except for nursing program. Options: early admission, deferred admission. Required: high school transcript. Entrance: noncompetitive. Application deadline: Rolling. Notification: continuous.

Collegiate Environment: Drama-theater group. Student services: personal-psychological counseling. College housing not available. Clinton Community College Library with 18,701 books, 155 serials, and an OPAC. 37 computers available on campus for general student use. A campuswide network can be accessed from off-campus. Staffed computer lab on campus.

■ **COE COLLEGE** *F-13*
1220 1st Ave., NE
Cedar Rapids, IA 52402-5092
Tel: (319)399-8000; 877-225-5263
Admissions: (319)399-8500
Fax: (319)399-8816
E-mail: admission@coe.edu
Web Site: http://www.coe.edu/

Description: Independent, 4-year, coed, affiliated with Presbyterian Church. Awards bachelor's and master's degrees. Founded 1851. Setting: 53-acre urban campus. Endowment: $56.3 million. Research spending for 2004 fiscal year: $562,717. Educational spending for 2005 fiscal year: $10,467 per student. Total enrollment: 1,355. Faculty: 125 (76 full-time, 49 part-time). Student-undergrad faculty ratio is 12:1. 1,278 applied, 72% were admitted. 30% from top 10% of their high school class, 67% from top quarter, 95% from top half. 8 valedictorians. Full-time: 1,245 students, 57% women, 43% men. Part-time: 86 students, 63% women, 37% men. Students come from 36 states and territories, 15 other countries, 41% from out-of-state, 0.4% Native American, 2% Hispanic, 2% black, 1% Asian American or Pacific Islander, 4% international, 4% 25 or older, 84% live on campus, 4% transferred in. Retention: 81% of full-time freshmen returned the following year. Academic areas with the most degrees conferred: social sciences; business/marketing; psychology; visual and performing arts. Core. Calendar: 4-4-1. ESL program, services for LD students, advanced placement, accelerated degree program, self-designed majors, honors program, independent study, double major, summer session for credit, part-time degree program, internships. Off campus study at University of Iowa, Mount Mercy College, Associated Colleges of the Midwest, Washington University in St. Louis. Study abroad program. ROTC: Army (c), Air Force (c).

Entrance Requirements: Options: Peterson's Universal Application, Common Application, electronic application, early admission, early action, deferred admission, international baccalaureate accepted. Required: essay, high school transcript, 1 recommendation, SAT or ACT. Recommended: minimum 3.0 high school GPA, interview. Entrance: moderately difficult. Application deadlines: 3/1, 12/10 for early action. Notification: 3/15, 1/20 for early action.

Costs Per Year: Application fee: $30. Comprehensive fee: $31,670 includes full-time tuition ($24,830), mandatory fees ($290), and college room and board ($6550). College room only: $2990. Part-time tuition: $3200 per course.

Collegiate Environment: Orientation program. Drama-theater group, choral group, student-run newspaper, radio station. Social organizations: 60 open to all; national fraternities, national sororities; 26% of eligible men and 19% of eligible women are members. Most popular organizations: Student Activities Committee, International Club, Student Alumni Association, C-Club, Coe Alliance. Major annual events: Homecoming, Flunk Day, International Club Cultural Show and Dinner. Student services: health clinic, personal-psychological counseling. Campus security: 24-hour emergency response devices and patrols, late night transport-escort service, controlled dormitory access. 1,034 college housing spaces available; 1,020 were occupied in 2003-04. Freshmen guaranteed college housing. On-campus residence required through senior year. Options: coed, men-only, women-only housing available. Stewart Memorial Library plus 1 other with 218,881 books, 5,882 microform titles, 1,576 serials, 9,413 audiovisual materials, an OPAC, and a Web page. Operations spending for 2004 fiscal year: $944,383. 275 computers available on campus for general student use. A campuswide network can be accessed from student residence rooms and from off campus. Staffed computer lab on campus.

Community Environment: Cedar Rapids, a metropolitan community of 150,000 is located just 225 miles west of Chicago in east-central Iowa. All forms of commercial transportation are available. Community facilities include over 100 churches, a symphony orchestra, library, hospital, and shopping in the downtown area, plus three shopping centers. Part time employment is available. Cedar Rapids has over 59 city parks which offer a variety of recreational facilities. Points of interest are the Cedar Rapids Art Center, Iowa Masonic Library, Paramount Theater of Performing Arts, Five Seasons Civic Center, and Theatre Cedar Rapids.

■ **CORNELL COLLEGE** *G-14*
600 First St. West
Mount Vernon, IA 52314-1098
Tel: (319)895-4000
Free: 800-747-1112
Admissions: (319)895-4477
Fax: (319)895-4492
E-mail: admissions@cornellcollege.edu
Web Site: http://www.cornellcollege.edu/

Description: Independent Methodist, 4-year, coed. Awards bachelor's degrees. Founded 1853. Setting: 129-acre small town campus. Endowment: $65.2 million. Research spending for 2004 fiscal year: $200,664. Total enrollment: 1,179. Student-undergrad faculty ratio is 11:1. 1,653 applied, 66% were admitted. 24% from top 10% of their high school class, 56% from top quarter, 88% from top half. 15 valedictorians. Full-time: 1,166 students, 55% women, 45% men. Part-time: 13 students, 77% women, 23% men. Students come from 43 states and territories, 15 other countries, 68% from out-of-state, 0.4% Native American, 3% Hispanic, 4% black, 1% Asian American or Pacific Islander, 2% international, 1% 25 or older, 88% live on campus, 4% transferred in. Retention: 79% of full-time freshmen returned the following year. Academic areas with the most degrees conferred: social sciences; education; psychology. Core. Calendar: 9 3&S1/&I2-week terms. ESL program, advanced placement, self-designed majors, independent study, double major, adult/continuing education programs, internships. Off campus study at Associated Colleges of the Midwest, Fisk University, School for International Training. Study abroad program.

Entrance Requirements: Options: Common Application, electronic application, deferred admission, international baccalaureate accepted. Required: essay, high school transcript, 1 recommendation, SAT or ACT. Recommended: minimum 2.80 high school GPA, interview, SAT Subject Tests. Entrance: moderately difficult. Application deadlines: 3/1, 12/1 for early action. Notification: continuous, 2/1 for early action.

Costs Per Year: Application fee: $30. Comprehensive fee: $30,110 includes full-time tuition ($23,500), mandatory fees ($180), and college room and board ($6430). College room only: $3010. Full-time tuition and fees vary according to reciprocity agreements. Room and board charges vary according to board plan. Part-time tuition: $734 per credit. Part-time mandatory fees: $180 per year. Part-time tuition and fees vary according to course load.

Collegiate Environment: Orientation program. Drama-theater group, choral group, student-run newspaper, radio station. Social organizations: 76 open to all; local fraternities, local sororities; 30% of eligible men and 32% of eligible women are members. Most popular organizations: social groups, Student-initiated Living-learning Community, Lunch Buddies/Youth Mentoring, Chess and Games Club, PAAC (Performing Arts and Activities Council). Major annual events: Homecoming, music and cultural events, interactive entertainment. Student services: health clinic, personal-psychological counseling, women's center. Campus security: 24-hour emergency response devices and patrols. 1,038 college housing spaces available; 1,015 were occupied in 2003-04. Freshmen guaranteed college housing. On-campus residence required through senior year. Options: coed, men-only, women-only housing available. Cole Library plus 1 other with 186,318 books, 235,000 microform titles, 479 serials, 4,971 audiovisual materials, an OPAC, and a Web page. Operations spending for 2004 fiscal year: $1.3 million. 130 computers available on campus for general student use. A campuswide network can be accessed from student residence rooms and from off campus. Staffed computer lab on campus.

Community Environment: Mount Vernon is a small town located 15 miles east of Cedar Rapids and 22 miles north of Iowa City. Bus and airline service are available in Cedar Rapids. The community and college share many facilities. Community facilities include churches and various civic, fraternal and veteran's organizations. Opportunities for student employment off campus are limited. Excellent recreational facilities are available at the Palisades State Park, MacBride State Park and Coralville Reservoir, for fishing and boating, golf, bowling, swimming, and cross-country skiing. Downhill skiing facilities are available within 70 miles.

■ **DES MOINES AREA COMMUNITY COLLEGE** *G-8*

2006 South Ankeny Blvd.

Ankeny, IA 50021-8995

Tel: (515)964-6200

Admissions: (515)964-6216

Web Site: http://www.dmacc.edu/

Description: State and locally supported, 2-year, coed. Part of Iowa Area Community Colleges System. Awards certificates, diplomas, transfer associate, and terminal associate degrees (profile also includes information from the Boone, Carroll, Des Moines, and Newton campuses). Founded 1966. Setting: 362-acre small town campus. Endowment: $1.8 million. Educational spending for 2005 fiscal year: $2860 per student. Total enrollment: 13,719. Full-time: 6,002 students, 52% women, 48% men. Part-time: 7,717 students, 59% women, 41% men. Students come from 31 states and territories, 53 other countries, 1% from out-of-state, 0.3% Native American, 2% Hispanic, 4% black, 3% Asian American or Pacific Islander, 2% international, 30% 25 or older, 3% transferred in. Core. Calendar: semesters. Academic remediation for entering students, ESL program, services for LD students, advanced placement, self-designed majors, honors program, distance learning, summer session for credit, part-time degree program, adult/continuing education programs, co-op programs. Off campus study at Drake University, Grand View College, Iowa State University of Science and Technology, University of Northern Iowa.

Entrance Requirements: Open admission. Options: electronic application, early admission, deferred admission. Required for some: high school transcript, interview. Placement: ACT COMPASS required; ACT recommended. Entrance: noncompetitive. Application deadline: Rolling.

Costs Per Year: Application fee: $0. State resident tuition: $2850 full-time, $95 per credit hour part-time. Nonresident tuition: $5700 full-time, $190 per credit hour part-time. Full-time tuition varies according to course load. Part-time tuition varies according to course load.

Collegiate Environment: Drama-theater group, choral group, student-run newspaper. Social organizations: 30 open to all. Most popular organizations: Agri-Business Club, Horticulture Club, Hospitality Arts Club, Iowa Delta Epsilon Chi, Dental Hygienist Club. Major annual events: Orientation, Drive Into DMACC Days. Student services: health clinic, personal-psychological counseling. Campus security: 24-hour emergency response devices and patrols, late night transport-escort service. College housing not available. DMACC District Library plus 4 others with 62,986 books, 3,784 serials, 7,224 audiovisual materials, an OPAC, and a Web page. Operations spending for 2004 fiscal year: $935,000. 700 computers available on campus for general student use. Computer purchase/lease plans available. A campuswide network can be accessed from off-campus. Staffed computer lab on campus.

■ **DIVINE WORD COLLEGE** *E-15*

102 Jacoby Dr. SW

Epworth, IA 52045-0380

Tel: (563)876-3353

Free: 800-553-3321

Fax: (563)876-3407

Web Site: http://www.dwci.edu/

Description: Independent Roman Catholic, 4-year, coed. Awards associate and bachelor's degrees. Founded 1912. Setting: 28-acre rural campus. Total enrollment: 111. 8 applied, 50% were admitted. Full-time: 110 students, 1% women, 99% men. Part-time: 1 student, 100% women. Students come from 25 states and territories, 12 other countries, 92% from out-of-state, 53% 25 or older, 98% live on campus, 8% transferred in. Retention: 76% of full-time freshmen returned the following year. Core. Calendar: semesters. Academic remediation for entering students, ESL program, advanced placement, independent study, double major. Study abroad program.

Entrance Requirements: Options: Common Application, early admission. Required: essay, high school transcript, 3 recommendations, interview, medical history, SAT or ACT. Entrance: minimally difficult. Application deadline: 7/15. Notification: continuous until 8/1.

Collegiate Environment: Orientation program. Major annual events: Mission Sunday, Lunar New Year Celebration, International Nights. Student services: personal-psychological counseling. Campus security: controlled dormitory access. On-campus residence required through senior year. Option: men-only housing available. Matthew Jacoby Library with 94,583 books

and 372 serials. 26 computers available on campus for general student use. A campuswide network can be accessed from student residence rooms. Staffed computer lab on campus.

■ **DORDT COLLEGE** *B-2*

498 4th Ave., NE

Sioux Center, IA 51250-1697

Tel: (712)722-6000

Free: 800-343-6738

Admissions: (712)722-6080

Fax: (712)722-1967

E-mail: admissions@dordt.edu

Web Site: http://www.dordt.edu/

Description: Independent Christian Reformed, comprehensive, coed. Awards associate, bachelor's, and master's degrees. Founded 1955. Setting: 100-acre small town campus. Endowment: $28 million. Educational spending for 2005 fiscal year: $6515 per student. Total enrollment: 1,327. Faculty: 105 (73 full-time, 32 part-time). Student-undergrad faculty ratio is 15:1. 774 applied, 92% were admitted. 16% from top 10% of their high school class, 38% from top quarter, 68% from top half. 5 National Merit Scholars. Full-time: 1,192 students, 53% women, 47% men. Part-time: 62 students, 76% women, 24% men. Students come from 31 states and territories, 12 other countries, 65% from out-of-state, 0.1% Native American, 0.2% Hispanic, 0.5% black, 1% Asian American or Pacific Islander, 9% international, 10% 25 or older, 90% live on campus, 3% transferred in. Retention: 80% of full-time freshmen returned the following year. Academic areas with the most degrees conferred: business/marketing; education; English. Core. Calendar: semesters. Academic remediation for entering students, ESL program, services for LD students, advanced placement, self-designed majors, honors program, independent study, distance learning, double major, part-time degree program, internships. Off campus study at Christian College Coalition, Chicago Metro Program, American Studies Program, Los Angeles Film Studies Program. Study abroad program.

Entrance Requirements: Options: electronic application, deferred admission, international baccalaureate accepted. Required: high school transcript, minimum 2.25 high school GPA, minimum ACT composite score of 19 or SAT Reasoning score of 920, SAT or ACT. Required for some: essay, interview. Entrance: moderately difficult. Notification: continuous until 8/1.

Costs Per Year: Application fee: $25. Comprehensive fee: $22,540 includes full-time tuition ($17,400), mandatory fees ($240), and college room and board ($4900). College room only: $2580. Room and board charges vary according to board plan and housing facility. Part-time tuition: $690 per credit hour. Part-time mandatory fees: $120 per term.

Collegiate Environment: Orientation program. Drama-theater group, choral group, student-run newspaper, radio station. Social organizations: 40 open to all. Most popular organizations: PLIA, Future Teachers, Ag Club, Lacrosse Club, Defenders of Life. Major annual events: Talent Extravaganza, Homecoming, Parents' Weekend. Student services: health clinic, personal-psychological counseling. Campus security: 24-hour emergency response devices, student patrols, late night transport-escort service, controlled dormitory access. 1,275 college housing spaces available; 1,175 were occupied in 2003-04. Freshmen guaranteed college housing. On-campus residence required through senior year. Options: men-only, women-only housing available. Dordt College Library plus 1 other with 160,000 books, 121,622 microform titles, 6,597 serials, 1,989 audiovisual materials, an OPAC, and a Web page. Operations spending for 2004 fiscal year: $585,515. 250 computers available on campus for general student use. A campuswide network can be accessed from student residence rooms and from off campus. Staffed computer lab on campus.

Community Environment: Sioux Center, population 6,000 is a rural area with a temperate climate. College transportation serves the area. A public library, hospital, churches, clinics and shopping facilities are all available within the community. Recreational activities include swimming, golf, and fishing. Part-time employment may be found.

■ **DRAKE UNIVERSITY** *H-8*

2507 University Ave.

Des Moines, IA 50311-4516

Tel: (515)271-2011

Free: 800-44D-RAKE

Admissions: (515)271-3181

Fax: (515)271-2831

E-mail: laura.linn@drake.edu

Web Site: http://www.drake.edu/

Description: Independent, university, coed. Awards bachelor's, master's, doctoral, and first professional degrees and post-master's certificates. Founded 1881. Setting: 120-acre suburban campus. Endowment: $119 million. Research spending for 2004 fiscal year: $645,584. Educational spending for 2005 fiscal year: $5756 per student. Total enrollment: 5,277. Faculty: 388 (246 full-time, 142 part-time). Student-undergrad faculty ratio is 14:1. 3,668 applied, 82% were admitted. 37% from top 10% of their high school class, 73% from top quarter, 93% from top half. 6 National Merit Scholars. Full-time: 2,913 students, 57% women, 43% men. Part-time: 228 students, 55% women, 45% men. Students come from 47 states and territories, 53 other countries, 70% from out-of-state, 0.2% Native American, 2% Hispanic, 3% black, 4% Asian American or Pacific Islander, 5% international, 5% 25 or older, 57% live on campus, 5% transferred in. Retention: 85% of full-time freshmen returned the following year. Academic areas with the most degrees conferred: business/marketing; communications/journalism; social sciences. Calendar: semesters. ESL program, services for LD students, advanced placement, accelerated degree program, self-designed majors, honors program, independent study, distance learning, double major, summer session for credit, co-op programs and internships, graduate courses open to undergrads. Off campus study at Des Moines Consortium. Study abroad program. ROTC: Army, Air Force (c).

Entrance Requirements: Options: Peterson's Universal Application, Common Application, electronic application, early admission, deferred admission, international baccalaureate accepted. Required: high school transcript, SAT or ACT. Recommended: essay, interview. Required for some: PCAT for pharmacy transfers. Entrance: moderately difficult. Application deadline: 3/1. Notification: continuous.

Costs Per Year: Application fee: $25. Comprehensive fee: $27,632 includes full-time tuition ($21,100), mandatory fees ($362), and college room and board ($6170). College room only: $3000. Full-time tuition and fees vary according to class time, course load, and student level. Room and board charges vary according to board plan. Part-time tuition: $430 per hour. Part-time mandatory fees: $8 per hour. Part-time tuition and fees vary according to class time.

Collegiate Environment: Orientation program. Drama-theater group, choral group, marching band, student-run newspaper, radio station. Social organizations: 160 open to all; national fraternities, national sororities; 28% of eligible men and 23% of eligible women are members. Most popular organizations: Student Activities Board, international student organizations, Coalition of Black Students, Alpha Phi Omega Service Organization, Residence Hall Association. Major annual events: Drake Relays, Parent/Family Weekend, homecoming. Student services: legal services, health clinic, personal-psychological counseling. Campus security: 24-hour emergency response devices and patrols, late night transport-escort service, 24-hour desk attendants in residence halls. 1,761 college housing spaces available; 1,732 were occupied in 2003-04. Freshmen guaranteed college housing. On-campus residence required through sophomore year. Option: coed housing available. Cowles Library plus 1 other with 488,659 books, 920,666 microform titles, 15,363 serials, 1,960 audiovisual materials, an OPAC, and a Web page. Operations spending for 2004 fiscal year: $3.8 million. 1,000 computers available on campus for general student use. Computer purchase/lease plans available. A campuswide network can be accessed from student residence rooms and from off campus. Staffed computer lab on campus.

Community Environment: Des Moines is Iowa's capital city, and its metropolitan population of 400,000 is the largest in the state. The downtown area includes the Convention Center, a skywalk system linking office buildings and shops, and a major restoration and conversion of historic buildings in the former city market area. A Civic Center offers plays, concerts and other entertainment. The Art Center, in a park setting of trees and gardens, houses a permanent collection of paintings and sculpture, in addition to traveling exhibits. Major business interests include a concentration of home offices of insurance companies and the pivotal operation of a large publishing firm.

■ **ELLSWORTH COMMUNITY COLLEGE** *D-9*
1100 College Ave.
Iowa Falls, IA 50126-1199
Tel: (641)648-4611
Free: 800-ECC-9235
Fax: (641)648-3128
Web Site: http://www.iavalley.cc.ia.us/ecc/
Description: State and locally supported, 2-year, coed. Part of Iowa Valley Community College District System. Awards diplomas, transfer associate,

and terminal associate degrees. Founded 1890. Setting: 10-acre small town campus. Endowment: $2.3 million. Educational spending for 2005 fiscal year: $4600 per student. Total enrollment: 930. 610 applied, 93% were admitted. 5% from top 10% of their high school class, 40% from top half. Students come from 18 states and territories, 4 other countries, 9% from out-of-state, 0% Native American, 4% Hispanic, 8% black, 0.3% Asian American or Pacific Islander, 2% international, 18% 25 or older, 38% live on campus. Core. Calendar: semesters. Academic remediation for entering students, services for LD students, advanced placement, self-designed majors, honors program, distance learning, summer session for credit, part-time degree program, adult/continuing education programs, co-op programs and internships.

Entrance Requirements: Open admission for state residents. Options: Peterson's Universal Application, electronic application, early admission, deferred admission. Required: high school transcript. Placement: ACT recommended; ACT, COMPASS required for some. Entrance: noncompetitive. Application deadlines: Rolling, 8/1 for nonresidents. Notification: continuous.

Collegiate Environment: Orientation program. Drama-theater group, choral group, student-run newspaper. Most popular organizations: Agriculture-Science Club, Biotechnology Club, International Club, Criminal Justice Club, Rodeo Club. Major annual events: Winter Carnival, Family Day, Talent Show. Student services: personal-psychological counseling. Campus security: 24-hour emergency response devices and patrols. On-campus residence required in freshman year. Options: men-only, women-only housing available. Osgood Learning Resource Center with 25,500 books and 300 serials. Operations spending for 2004 fiscal year: $220,000. 80 computers available on campus for general student use. A campuswide network can be accessed from off-campus. Staffed computer lab on campus.

Community Environment: Iowa Falls (population 6,127) is a rural area situated on the Iowa River. Community facilities include 18 churches of all denominations, a hospital, library, motels, hotels, and various civic and service organizations. Part-time jobs are available. Recreational facilities include a theater, hunting, fishing, water skiing, swimming and two nine-hole golf courses.

■ **EMMAUS BIBLE COLLEGE** *D-16*
2570 Asbury Rd.
Dubuque, IA 52001-3097
Tel: (319)588-8000
Free: 800-397-2425
Admissions: (563)588-8000
Fax: (319)588-1216
Web Site: http://www.emmaus.edu/
Description: Independent nondenominational, 4-year, coed. Awards associate and bachelor's degrees. Founded 1941. Setting: 22-acre small town campus. Endowment: $1.2 million. Total enrollment: 296. 83 applied, 86% were admitted. 7% from top 10% of their high school class, 13% from top quarter, 26% from top half. Full-time: 270 students, 57% women, 43% men. Part-time: 26 students, 58% women, 42% men. Students come from 42 states and territories, 9 other countries, 72% from out-of-state, 1% Native American, 3% Hispanic, 1% black, 2% Asian American or Pacific Islander, 7% international, 14% 25 or older, 79% live on campus, 12% transferred in. Retention: 86% of full-time freshmen returned the following year. Core. Calendar: semesters. Advanced placement, independent study, double major, part-time degree program, internships. Off campus study.

Entrance Requirements: Open admission. Options: Common Application, electronic application, deferred admission. Required: essay, high school transcript, 3 recommendations. Placement: SAT or ACT required. Entrance: noncompetitive. Application deadline: 6/1. Notification: continuous.

Costs Per Year: Application fee: $25. Comprehensive fee: $12,372 includes full-time tuition ($7700), mandatory fees ($510), and college room and board ($4162). Full-time tuition and fees vary according to course load. Part-time tuition: $342 per credit hour. Part-time tuition varies according to course load.

Collegiate Environment: Orientation program. Drama-theater group, choral group, student-run radio station. Major annual events: Winterfest, Christmas Banquet, Spring Banquet. Student services: personal-psychological counseling. Campus security: 24-hour emergency response devices, student patrols, controlled dormitory access. 400 college housing spaces available. Freshmen guaranteed college housing. On-campus residence required through senior year. Options: men-only, women-only housing available. The Emmaus Bible College Library plus 1 other with 86,000 books, 259 microform titles, 330 serials, and an OPAC. Operations spending for 2004 fiscal year: $133,422. 60 computers available on campus for general student use. A campuswide network can be accessed from student residence rooms and from off campus. Staffed computer lab on campus.

Community Environment: Emmaus Bible College is located in Dubuque, Iowa, a Mississippi River City, of 60,000 people. It serves as the metropolitan center of 300,000 residents in the tri-state trading area. It is a city of traditional values and loyalties reflecting the past with a progressive spirit toward the future. Dubuque provides many wholesome activities for the Emmaus student. The Dubuque Symphony Orchestra performs regularly at the Five Flags Center. The Spirit of Dubuque, a paddlewheeler, plies the Mississippi and provides dining en route. Fall brings out the beauty of the variety of trees and foliage along the river and its tributaries. Dubuque is also a center for education, boasting three colleges in addition to Emmaus, as well as two seminaries. This healthy environment is a suitable setting for the Emmaus education and for the community outreach of Christian service and evangelism.

■ **FAITH BAPTIST BIBLE COLLEGE AND THEOLOGICAL SEMINARY** *G-8*
1900 Northwest 4th St.
Ankeny, IA 50021
Tel: (515)964-0601; 888-FAITH 4U
Fax: (515)964-1638
E-mail: fbblenroll@aol.com
Web Site: http://www.faith.edu/

Description: Independent, comprehensive, coed, affiliated with General Association of Regular Baptist Churches. Awards associate, bachelor's, master's, and first professional degrees. Founded 1921. Setting: 52-acre small town campus. Endowment: $2.9 million. Educational spending for 2005 fiscal year: $3445 per student. Total enrollment; 479. Faculty: 37 (21 full-time, 16 part-time). Student-undergrad faculty ratio is 12:1. 156 applied, 65% were admitted. 10% from top 10% of their high school class, 31% from top quarter, 60% from top half. 1 valedictorian. Full-time: 289 students, 53% women, 47% men. Part-time: 39 students, 59% women, 41% men. Students come from 31 states and territories, 7 other countries, 45% from out-of-state, 0.3% Native American, 1% Hispanic, 0% black, 2% Asian American or Pacific Islander, 1% international, 5% 25 or older, 81% live on campus, 5% transferred in. Retention: 76% of full-time freshmen returned the following year. Academic areas with the most degrees conferred: theology and religious vocations; education; visual and performing arts. Core. Calendar: semesters. Academic remediation for entering students, advanced placement, independent study, double major, summer session for credit, part-time degree program, adult/continuing education programs, internships, graduate courses open to undergrads.

Entrance Requirements: Option: deferred admission. Required: essay, high school transcript, 2 recommendations, SAT or ACT. Recommended: minimum 2.0 high school GPA. Required for some: interview. Entrance: minimally difficult. Application deadline: 8/1. Notification: continuous until 9/1.

Costs Per Year: Application fee: $25. Comprehensive fee: $15,520 includes full-time tuition ($10,804), mandatory fees ($400), and college room and board ($4316). College room only: $2010. Full-time tuition and fees vary according to course load. Room and board charges vary according to board plan. Part-time tuition: $395 per semester hour. Part-time mandatory fees: $95 per term.

Collegiate Environment: Orientation program. Drama-theater group, choral group. Social organizations: 6 open to all; 10% of eligible men and 10% of eligible women are members. Most popular organizations: Student Association, Student Missions Fellowship. Major annual events: Homecoming Week, Student Appreciation Night, Spring Banquet. Student services: personal-psychological counseling. Campus security: 24-hour emergency response devices and patrols, late night transport-escort service. 432 college housing spaces available; 313 were occupied in 2003-04. Freshmen guaranteed college housing. On-campus residence required through senior year. Options: men-only, women-only housing available. Patten Hall with 67,040 books, 3,284 microform titles, 435 serials, 9,086 audiovisual materials, an OPAC, and a Web page. Operations spending for 2004 fiscal year: $167,724. 50 computers available on campus for general student use. A campuswide network can be accessed from student residence rooms and from off campus. Staffed computer lab on campus.

■ **GRACELAND UNIVERSITY** *K-7*
1 University Place
Lamoni, IA 50140
Tel: (641)784-5000; (866)GRACELAND

Admissions: (641)784-5118
Fax: (641)784-5480
E-mail: admissions@graceland.edu
Web Site: http://www.graceland.edu/

Description: Independent Community of Christ, comprehensive, coed. Awards bachelor's and master's degrees and post-master's certificates. Founded 1895. Setting: 169-acre small town campus with easy access to Des Moines. Endowment: $55.4 million. Educational spending for 2005 fiscal year: $7003 per student. Total enrollment: 2,351. 1,170 applied, 55% were admitted. 13% from top 10% of their high school class, 18% from top quarter, 67% from top half. Full-time: 1,398 students, 55% women, 45% men. Part-time: 547 students, 80% women, 20% men. Students come from 49 states and territories, 34 other countries, 63% from out-of-state, 1% Native American, 3% Hispanic, 7% black, 2% Asian American or Pacific Islander, 8% international, 4% 25 or older, 66% live on campus, 5% transferred in. Retention: 70% of full-time freshmen returned the following year. Core. Calendar: 4-1-4. Academic remediation for entering students, ESL program, services for LD students, advanced placement, accelerated degree program, self-designed majors, honors program, independent study, distance learning, double major, summer session for credit, part-time degree program, external degree program, adult/continuing education programs, co-op programs and internships, graduate courses open to undergrads. Off campus study at Indian Hills Community College, North Central Missouri College. Study abroad program.

Entrance Requirements: Options: Peterson's Universal Application, Common Application, electronic application, early admission, deferred admission, international baccalaureate accepted. Required: high school transcript, minimum 2.5 high school GPA, minimum SAT score of 960 or ACT score of 21, SAT or ACT. Required for some: essay, 2 recommendations, interview. Entrance: moderately difficult. Application deadlines: Rolling, 1/31 for early decision. Notification: continuous.

Costs Per Year: Application fee: $50. Comprehensive fee: $21,550 includes full-time tuition ($16,000), mandatory fees ($150), and college room and board ($5400). Full-time tuition and fees vary according to course load and location. Room and board charges vary according to board plan, housing facility, and location. Part-time tuition: $500 per semester hour. Part-time tuition varies according to location.

Collegiate Environment: Orientation program. Drama-theater group, choral group, student-run newspaper. Social organizations: 72 open to all. Most popular organizations: student political organizations, Black Student Union (BSU), Habitat for Humanity, International Club, Students in Free Enterprise (SIFE). Major annual events: New Year's in November, Final Fling, Renaissance Week. Student services: health clinic, personal-psychological counseling. Campus security: 24-hour emergency response devices and patrols, late night transport-escort service, controlled dormitory access. 789 college housing spaces available; 660 were occupied in 2003-04. Freshmen guaranteed college housing. On-campus residence required through sophomore year. Options: men-only, women-only housing available. Frederick Madison Smith Library with 193,109 books, 125,773 microform titles, 503 serials, 3,556 audiovisual materials, an OPAC, and a Web page. Operations spending for 2004 fiscal year: $649,956. 106 computers available on campus for general student use. A campuswide network can be accessed from student residence rooms and from off campus. Staffed computer lab on campus.

Community Environment: Lamoni (population 2,700), a picturesque town in the rolling hills of south central Iowa, is within easy driving distance of Des Moines, Omaha, Council Bluffs, and Kansas City. Bus transportation is available to these urban centers. The city has an excellent library and shopping area including several antique malls. Churches play an important part in the life of the community and a county hospital is located in nearby Leon. Citizens enjoy world-renowned artists in concert and theater productions at the college fine arts center, movies, sports, clubs, and lodges. Nine Eagles State Park (12 miles southeast), Central Park, and Foreman Park provide facilities for recreation.

■ **GRAND VIEW COLLEGE** *H-8*
1200 Grandview Ave.
Des Moines, IA 50316-1599
Tel: (515)263-2800
Free: 800-444-6083
Admissions: (515)263-2810
Fax: (515)263-2974
E-mail: admissions@gvc.edu
Web Site: http://www.gvc.edu/

Description: Independent, 4-year, coed, affiliated with Evangelical Lutheran Church in America. Awards associate and bachelor's degrees. Founded 1896. Setting: 25-acre urban campus. Endowment: $9.3 million. Research spending for 2004 fiscal year: $2781. Educational spending for 2005 fiscal year: $4336 per student. Total enrollment: 1,761. Student-undergrad faculty ratio is 12:1. 442 applied, 95% were admitted. 11% from top 10% of their high school class, 32% from top quarter, 67% from top half. 5 valedictorians. Full-time: 1,372 students, 68% women, 32% men. Part-time: 389 students, 72% women, 28% men. Students come from 29 states and territories, 7 other countries, 10% from out-of-state, 0.5% Native American, 2% Hispanic, 4% black, 3% Asian American or Pacific Islander, 1% international, 41% 25 or older, 32% live on campus, 21% transferred in. Retention: 68% of full-time freshmen returned the following year. Academic areas with the most degrees conferred: health professions and related sciences; business/marketing; liberal arts/general studies. Core. Calendar: semesters. Academic remediation for entering students, services for LD students, advanced placement, accelerated degree program, self-designed majors, freshman honors college, honors program, independent study, distance learning, double major, summer session for credit, part-time degree program, adult/continuing education programs, co-op programs and internships. Off campus study at Drake University, Des Moines Area Community College. Study abroad program. ROTC: Army (c), Air Force (c).

Entrance Requirements: Options: Common Application, electronic application. Required: high school transcript, SAT or ACT. Recommended: minimum 2.0 high school GPA. Entrance: minimally difficult. Application deadline: 8/15. Notification: continuous until 9/15.

Costs Per Year: Application fee: $35. Comprehensive fee: $21,774 includes full-time tuition ($15,750), mandatory fees ($360), and college room and board ($5664). Full-time tuition and fees vary according to class time. Room and board charges vary according to board plan and housing facility. Part-time tuition: $425 per hour. Part-time tuition varies according to class time.

Collegiate Environment: Orientation program. Drama-theater group, choral group, student-run newspaper, radio station. Social organizations: 19 open to all. Most popular organizations: Nursing Student Association (NSA), Art Club, Science Club, Education Club, Business Club. Major annual events: Homecoming, Studenterfest. Student services: health clinic, personal-psychological counseling. Campus security: 24-hour emergency response devices, night security patrols. 438 college housing spaces available; 420 were occupied in 2003-04. Freshmen guaranteed college housing. On-campus residence required through sophomore year. Options: coed, men-only, women-only housing available. Grand View College Library with 104,225 books, 11,119 microform titles, 8,141 serials, 6,379 audiovisual materials, an OPAC, and a Web page. Operations spending for 2004 fiscal year: $335,963. 249 computers available on campus for general student use. A campuswide network can be accessed from student residence rooms and from off campus. Staffed computer lab on campus.

Community Environment: See Drake University.

■ **GRINNELL COLLEGE** *G-11*
1121 Park St.
Grinnell, IA 50112-1690
Tel: (641)269-4000
Free: 800-247-0113
Admissions: (641)269-3600
Fax: (641)269-3408
E-mail: askgrin@admin.grin.edu
Web Site: http://www.grinnell.edu/

Description: Independent, 4-year, coed. Awards bachelor's degrees. Founded 1846. Setting: 120-acre small town campus. Endowment: $1.4 billion. Research spending for 2004 fiscal year: $974,405. Educational spending for 2005 fiscal year: $17,736 per student. Total enrollment: 1,577. Student-undergrad faculty ratio is 9:1. 3,121 applied, 45% were admitted. 73% from top 10% of their high school class, 93% from top quarter, 99% from top half. 50 National Merit Scholars, 38 valedictorians, 97 student government officers. Full-time: 1,546 students, 55% women, 45% men. Part-time: 31 students, 58% women, 42% men. Students come from 53 states and territories, 59 other countries, 78% from out-of-state, 0.5% Native American, 4% Hispanic, 4% black, 6% Asian American or Pacific Islander, 11% international, 0% 25 or older, 75% live on campus, 1% transferred in. Retention: 92% of full-time freshmen returned the following year. Academic areas with the most degrees conferred: social sciences; foreign languages and literature; biological/life sciences. Calendar: semesters. Services for LD students, advanced placement, accelerated degree program, self-designed majors, independent study, double major, internships. Off campus study. Study abroad program.

Entrance Requirements: Options: Peterson's Universal Application, Common Application, electronic application, early admission, early decision, deferred admission, international baccalaureate accepted. Required: essay, high school transcript, 3 recommendations, SAT or ACT. Recommended: interview. Entrance: very difficult. Application deadlines: 1/20, 11/20 for early decision plan 1, 1/1 for early decision plan 2. Notification: 4/1, 12/20 for early decision plan 1, 2/1 for early decision plan 2.

Costs Per Year: Application fee: $30. Comprehensive fee: $34,814 includes full-time tuition ($27,060), mandatory fees ($444), and college room and board ($7310). College room only: $3424. Room and board charges vary according to board plan and housing facility. Part-time tuition: $846 per credit hour.

Collegiate Environment: Orientation program. Drama-theater group, choral group, student-run newspaper, radio station. Social organizations: 168 open to all. Most popular organizations: Dagorhir, International Student Organization, Alternative Happy Hour, Campus Democrats, Davi's Buddies. Major annual events: Winter Waltz, Spring Waltz, Disco Ball. Student services: health clinic, personal-psychological counseling. Campus security: 24-hour emergency response devices and patrols, student patrols, late night transport-escort service, controlled dormitory access. 1,252 college housing spaces available; 1,235 were occupied in 2003-04. Freshmen guaranteed college housing. On-campus residence required through sophomore year. Option: coed housing available. Burling Library plus 2 others with 1.1 million books, 392,573 microform titles, 5,147 serials, 29,452 audiovisual materials, an OPAC, and a Web page. Operations spending for 2004 fiscal year: $3 million. 188 computers available on campus for general student use. A campuswide network can be accessed from student residence rooms and from off campus. Staffed computer lab on campus.

Community Environment: Grinnell, population 9,500, is located 1 hour east of Des Moines and 1 hour west of Iowa City, on Interstate 80 and is within a five-hour drive from Chicago, St. Louis, Kansas City, and Minneapolis.

■ **HAMILTON COLLEGE (CEDAR FALLS)** *D-11*
7009 Nordic Dr.
Cedar Falls, IA 50613
Tel: (319)277-0220
Free: 800-728-1220
E-mail: jilines@hamiltoncf.com
Web Site: http://www.hamiltoncf.com/

Description: primarily 2-year. Awards transfer associate, terminal associate, and bachelor's degrees. Total enrollment: 695. Student-undergrad faculty ratio is 25:1. Full-time: 541 students, 76% women, 24% men. Part-time: 154 students, 75% women, 25% men. 0% from out-of-state, 0.3% Native American, 1% Hispanic, 10% black, 0% Asian American or Pacific Islander. Academic area with the most degrees conferred: business/marketing.

Entrance Requirements: Required: essay, high school transcript, recommendations, interview, Wonderlic. Entrance: noncompetitive. Application deadline: Rolling.

Costs Per Year: Application fee: $20.

Collegiate Environment: Student-run newspaper.

■ **HAMILTON COLLEGE (CEDAR RAPIDS)** *F-13*
3165 Edgewood Parkway, SW
Cedar Rapids, IA 52404
Tel: (319)363-0481
Free: 800-728-0481
Fax: (319)363-3812
Web Site: http://www.hamiltonia.edu/

Description: Proprietary, primarily 2-year, coed. Awards certificates, diplomas, transfer associate, terminal associate, and bachelor's degrees (branch locations in Des Moines, Mason City, and Cedar Falls with significant enrollment not reflected in profile). Founded 1900. Setting: 4-acre suburban campus. Educational spending for 2005 fiscal year: $8036 per student. Total enrollment: 511. Student-undergrad faculty ratio is 25:1. Full-time: 440 students, 58% women, 42% men. Part-time: 71 students, 76% women, 24% men. 1% Native American, 1% Hispanic, 3% black, 2% Asian American or Pacific Islander, 47% 25 or older. Retention: 52% of full-time freshmen returned the following year. Core. Academic remediation for entering students, distance learning, part-time degree program, adult/continuing education programs, co-op programs and internships.

Entrance Requirements: Options: Common Application, early admission, deferred admission. Required: high school transcript, interview, Wonderlic. Entrance: moderately difficult. Application deadline: Rolling.

Costs Per Year: Application fee: $50. Tuition: $17,040 full-time, $355 per credit hour part-time.

Collegiate Environment: Social organizations: 3 open to all. Most popular organizations: Phi Beta Lambda, Travel Club, Student Senate. Major annual events: End of Quarter Bash, Awards Program, Alumni Picnic. Campus security: 24-hour emergency response devices. College housing not available. Hamilton College Library with 5,500 books, 40 serials, an OPAC, and a Web page. 50 computers available on campus for general student use. A campuswide network can be accessed from off-campus. Staffed computer lab on campus.

■ **HAMILTON COLLEGE (COUNCIL BLUFFS)** *I-3*
1751 Madison Ave.
Council Bluffs, IA 51503
Free: 800-518-4212
Web Site: http://www.hamiltoncb.com/
Description: 2-year.

■ **HAMILTON TECHNICAL COLLEGE** *H-16*
1011 East 53rd St.
Davenport, IA 52807-2653
Tel: (319)386-3570
Admissions: (563)386-3570
Fax: (319)386-6756
Web Site: http://www.hamiltontechcollege.com/
Description: Proprietary, 4-year, coed. Awards associate and bachelor's degrees. Founded 1969. Setting: urban campus. Total enrollment: 420. Calendar: continuous.
Entrance Requirements: Open admission. Options: Peterson's Universal Application, Common Application, deferred admission. Required: high school transcript, interview. Entrance: noncompetitive. Application deadline: Rolling.
Costs Per Year: Application fee: $25. Tuition: $6900 full-time, $230 per credit part-time. Tuition guaranteed not to increase for student's term of enrollment.
Collegiate Environment: Campus security: 24-hour emergency response devices. College housing not available. Hamilton Technical College Library with 4,500 books and 30 serials. 110 computers available on campus for general student use. Staffed computer lab on campus.

■ **HAWKEYE COMMUNITY COLLEGE** *E-12*
PO Box 8015
Waterloo, IA 50704-8015
Tel: (319)296-2320
Free: 800-670-4769
Admissions: (319)296-4204
Fax: (319)296-2874
E-mail: dball@hawkeyecollege.edu
Web Site: http://www.hawkeyecollege.edu/
Description: State and locally supported, 2-year, coed. Awards certificates, diplomas, transfer associate, and terminal associate degrees. Founded 1966. Setting: 320-acre rural campus. Research spending for 2004 fiscal year: $103,898. Total enrollment: 5,272. Student-undergrad faculty ratio is 16:1. 4 valedictorians. Full-time: 2,751 students, 54% women, 46% men. Part-time: 2,521 students, 59% women, 41% men. Students come from 18 states and territories, 10 other countries, 1% from out-of-state, 0.3% Native American, 2% Hispanic, 7% black, 1% Asian American or Pacific Islander, 0% international, 27% 25 or older, 11% transferred in. Calendar: semesters. Academic remediation for entering students, ESL program, services for LD students, advanced placement, distance learning, summer session for credit, part-time degree program, external degree program, adult/continuing education programs, co-op programs. ROTC: Army (c).
Entrance Requirements: Open admission except for nursing, dental hygiene, medical laboratory technology programs. Options: Peterson's Universal Application, electronic application, deferred admission. Required: high school transcript. Required for some: ACT. Entrance: noncompetitive. Application deadline: Rolling. Notification: continuous.
Costs Per Year: Application fee: $0. State resident tuition: $2940 full-time, $98 per credit part-time. Nonresident tuition: $5880 full-time, $196 per credit part-time. Mandatory fees: $300 full-time, $10 per credit part-time.
Collegiate Environment: Orientation program. Social organizations: 10 open to all; academic fraternities; 2% of eligible men and 2% of eligible women are members. Most popular organizations: Student Senate, Phi Theta Kappa, Environmental Conservation Club/Ag Club, Law Enforcement/Criminal Justice, Fashion Merchandising. Major annual events: Fall Fest,

Spring Splurge, Color Me Human Food Festival. Student services: personal-psychological counseling, women's center. Campus security: 24-hour patrols. College housing not available. Hawkeye Community College Library with 37,155 books, 3,714 microform titles, 482 serials, 2,078 audiovisual materials, an OPAC, and a Web page. Operations spending for 2004 fiscal year: $466,647. 300 computers available on campus for general student use. A campuswide network can be accessed. Staffed computer lab on campus.

Community Environment: Waterloo, population 75,000, is an industrial city. The manufacture of tractors, and the horse racing cart known as the Sulky by the Jerald Sulky Company. Highlights of interest are the Museum of History and Science.

■ **INDIAN HILLS COMMUNITY COLLEGE** *J-11*
525 Grandview Ave., Bldg. No. 1
Ottumwa, IA 52501-1398
Tel: (641)683-5111
Free: 800-726-2585
Admissions: (641)683-5151
Web Site: http://www.ihcc.cc.ia.us/
Description: State and locally supported, 2-year, coed. Part of Iowa Area Community Colleges System. Awards certificates, diplomas, transfer associate, and terminal associate degrees. Founded 1966. Setting: 400-acre small town campus. Total enrollment: 2,867. 2,477 applied, 100% were admitted. Full-time: 2,046 students, 55% women, 45% men. Part-time: 821 students, 69% women, 31% men. Students come from 16 states and territories, 7% from out-of-state, 40% 25 or older, 15% live on campus, 0.4% transferred in. Academic remediation for entering students, ESL program, services for LD students, self-designed majors, honors program, summer session for credit, part-time degree program, adult/continuing education programs, co-op programs and internships.
Entrance Requirements: Open admission except for nursing, technology programs. Options: Peterson's Universal Application, Common Application, early admission. Required for some: high school transcript. Placement: ACT ASSET required; ACT required for some. Entrance: noncompetitive. Application deadline: Rolling.
Collegiate Environment: Orientation program. Drama-theater group. Most popular organizations: Student Senate, Warriors Club. Major annual events: Foundation Auction, Art on the Lawn Festival. Student services: personal-psychological counseling, women's center. Campus security: 24-hour emergency response devices and patrols. Option: coed housing available. Indian Hills Community College Library plus 2 others with 53,073 books, 350 serials, an OPAC, and a Web page. 150 computers available on campus for general student use. A campuswide network can be accessed. Staffed computer lab on campus.
Community Environment: The population of Ottumwa is 27,000. This community is located about 85 miles southwest of Des Moines. Recreational activities are available at Lake Rathbun, about six miles northwest of Centerville.

■ **IOWA CENTRAL COMMUNITY COLLEGE** *E-7*
330 Ave. M
Fort Dodge, IA 50501-5798
Tel: (515)576-7201
Admissions: (515)576-0099
Fax: (515)576-7724
Web Site: http://www.iccc.cc.ia.us/
Description: State and locally supported, 2-year, coed. Part of Iowa Department of Education Division of Community Colleges. Awards certificates, diplomas, transfer associate, and terminal associate degrees. Founded 1966. Setting: 110-acre small town campus. Total enrollment: 4,567. 10% from top 10% of their high school class, 20% from top quarter, 40% from top half. Students come from 25 states and territories, 18 other countries, 5% from out-of-state, 26% 25 or older, 22% live on campus. Core. Calendar: semesters. Academic remediation for entering students, services for LD students, advanced placement, independent study, distance learning, summer session for credit, part-time degree program, adult/continuing education programs, co-op programs and internships. Study abroad program.
Entrance Requirements: Open admission except for health occupations programs. Options: Peterson's Universal Application, early admission, deferred admission. Required: high school transcript. Placement: SAT or ACT, ACT ASSET or ACT COMPASS required. Entrance: noncompetitive. Application deadline: Rolling.

Costs Per Year: Application fee: $0. State resident tuition: $2790 full-time, $93 per credit part-time. Nonresident tuition: $4135 full-time, $139.50 per credit part-time. Mandatory fees: $300 full-time, $10 per credit part-time.

Collegiate Environment: Orientation program. Drama-theater group, choral group, student-run newspaper, radio station. Social organizations: 1 open to all. Most popular organizations: Student Senate, HOSA, BPA, Phi Beta Lambda. Major annual events: first week of fall semester activities, Hypnotist, theater productions. Student services: health clinic, personal-psychological counseling. Campus security: 24-hour emergency response devices and patrols, student patrols, late night transport-escort service, controlled dormitory access. Iowa Central Community College Library plus 1 other with 55,000 books, 350 serials, an OPAC, and a Web page. 510 computers available on campus for general student use. A campuswide network can be accessed from off-campus. Staffed computer lab on campus.

■ **IOWA LAKES COMMUNITY COLLEGE** *A-5*
19 South 7th St.
Estherville, IA 51334-2295
Tel: (712)362-2604
Free: 800-521-5054
E-mail: info@iowalakes.edu
Web Site: http://www.iowalakes.edu/

Description: State and locally supported, 2-year, coed. Part of Iowa Area Community Colleges System. Awards certificates, diplomas, transfer associate, and terminal associate degrees. Founded 1967. Setting: 20-acre small town campus. Endowment: $63,000. Educational spending for 2005 fiscal year: $1636 per student. Total enrollment: 2,993. 1,897 applied, 81% were admitted. Full-time: 1,371 students, 49% women, 51% men. Part-time: 1,622 students, 60% women, 40% men. Students come from 12 states and territories, 2 other countries, 13% from out-of-state, 0.3% Native American, 1% Hispanic, 1% black, 0.3% Asian American or Pacific Islander, 0.4% international, 35% 25 or older, 24% live on campus, 4% transferred in. Core. Calendar: semesters. Academic remediation for entering students, services for LD students, advanced placement, accelerated degree program, honors program, independent study, distance learning, summer session for credit, part-time degree program, adult/continuing education programs, co-op programs and internships. Study abroad program.

Entrance Requirements: Open admission except for allied health, aviation programs. Options: Peterson's Universal Application, deferred admission. Required: high school transcript. Required for some: recommendations, interview. Placement: ACT, ACT ASSET, ACT COMPASS required for some. Entrance: noncompetitive. Application deadline: Rolling.

Costs Per Year: Application fee: $0. State resident tuition: $3296 full-time. Nonresident tuition: $3360 full-time. Mandatory fees: $452 full-time. Full-time tuition and fees vary according to course load and program. College room and board: $4120. Room and board charges vary according to board plan.

Collegiate Environment: Orientation program. Drama-theater group, choral group, student-run newspaper, radio station. Social organizations: 37 open to all. Most popular organizations: Criminal Justice Club, Ecology Club, Nursing Club, Student Senate, BPA. Major annual events: homecoming, Convocations, Orientation. Student services: personal-psychological counseling, women's center. Campus security: 24-hour emergency response devices, student patrols. College housing designed to accommodate 306 students; 316 undergraduates lived in college housing during 2003-04. Freshmen guaranteed college housing. Option: coed housing available. Iowa Lakes Community College Library plus 2 others with 36,881 books, 353 serials, 1,133 audiovisual materials, and an OPAC. Operations spending for 2004 fiscal year: $624,435. 1,000 computers available on campus for general student use. A campuswide network can be accessed. Staffed computer lab on campus.

■ **IOWA STATE UNIVERSITY OF SCIENCE AND TECHNOLOGY** *F-8*
Ames, IA 50011
Tel: (515)294-4111
Free: 800-262-3810
Admissions: (515)294-0815
Fax: (515)294-2592
E-mail: admissions@iastate.edu
Web Site: http://www.iastate.edu/

Description: State-supported, university, coed. Awards bachelor's, master's, doctoral, and first professional degrees and post-master's certificates. Founded 1858. Setting: 1,788-acre suburban campus. Endowment: $456.6 million. Research spending for 2004 fiscal year: $157.9 million. Total enrollment: 25,741. Faculty: 1,636 (1,419 full-time, 217 part-time). Student-undergrad faculty ratio is 15:1. 9,101 applied, 90% were admitted. 24% from top 10% of their high school class, 52% from top quarter, 92% from top half. 69 National Merit Scholars. Full-time: 19,433 students, 44% women, 56% men. Part-time: 1,299 students, 42% women, 58% men. Students come from 54 states and territories, 114 other countries, 20% from out-of-state, 0.3% Native American, 2% Hispanic, 3% black, 3% Asian American or Pacific Islander, 3% international, 7% 25 or older, 31% live on campus, 7% transferred in. Retention: 86% of full-time freshmen returned the following year. Academic areas with the most degrees conferred: business/marketing; engineering; agriculture. Calendar: semesters. Academic remediation for entering students, ESL program, services for LD students, advanced placement, accelerated degree program, self-designed majors, freshman honors college, honors program, independent study, distance learning, double major, summer session for credit, part-time degree program, external degree program, adult/continuing education programs, co-op programs and internships, graduate courses open to undergrads. Off campus study at Iowa Regents' Universities Student Exchange, National Student Exchange. Study abroad program. ROTC: Army, Naval, Air Force.

Entrance Requirements: Options: Common Application, electronic application, early admission, deferred admission, international baccalaureate accepted. Required: high school transcript, rank in upper 50% of high school class, SAT or ACT. Entrance: moderately difficult. Application deadline: 7/1. Notification: 9/1.

Costs Per Year: Application fee: $30. State resident tuition: $4890 full-time, $204 per semester hour part-time. Nonresident tuition: $14,980 full-time, $625 per semester hour part-time. Mandatory fees: $744 full-time. Full-time tuition and fees vary according to class time, degree level, and program. Part-time tuition varies according to class time, course load, degree level, and program. College room and board: $6197. College room only: $3295. Room and board charges vary according to board plan and housing facility.

Collegiate Environment: Orientation program. Drama-theater group, choral group, marching band, student-run newspaper, radio station. Social organizations: 515 open to all; national fraternities, national sororities, local fraternities, local sororities; 13% of eligible men and 14% of eligible women are members. Most popular organizations: student government, Student Alumni Association, Residence Hall Associations. Major annual events: Veishea (student spring festival and university open house), Homecoming, Family Weekend. Student services: legal services, health clinic, personal-psychological counseling, women's center. Campus security: 24-hour emergency response devices and patrols, student patrols, late night transport-escort service, controlled dormitory access, crime prevention programs, threat assessment team, motor vehicle help van. 9,455 college housing spaces available; 8,174 were occupied in 2003-04. Freshmen given priority for college housing. Options: coed, men-only, women-only housing available. University Library plus 1 other with 2.4 million books, 3.4 million microform titles, 33,914 serials, 64,499 audiovisual materials, an OPAC, and a Web page. Operations spending for 2004 fiscal year: $16.7 million. 2,400 computers available on campus for general student use. Computer purchase/lease plans available. A campuswide network can be accessed from student residence rooms and from off campus. Staffed computer lab on campus.

■ **IOWA WESLEYAN COLLEGE** *J-14*
601 North Main St.
Mount Pleasant, IA 52641-1398
Tel: (319)385-8021
Free: 800-582-2383
Admissions: (319)385-6230
Fax: (319)385-6296
E-mail: admitrwl@iwc.edu
Web Site: http://www.iwc.edu/

Description: Independent United Methodist, 4-year, coed. Awards bachelor's degrees. Founded 1842. Setting: 60-acre small town campus. Endowment: $5.9 million. Research spending for 2004 fiscal year: $8970. Educational spending for 2005 fiscal year: $3291 per student. Total enrollment: 849. Student-undergrad faculty ratio is 14:1. 727 applied, 59% were admitted. 5% from top 10% of their high school class, 24% from top quarter, 51% from top half. Students come from 22 states and territories, 12 other countries, 46% from out-of-state, 0% Native American, 7% Hispanic, 11% black, 1% Asian American or Pacific Islander, 6% international, 40% 25 or older, 57% live on campus. Retention: 53% of full-time freshmen returned the following year. Core. Calendar: semesters. Academic remediation for entering students, ESL program, services for LD students, advanced placement, self-designed majors, independent study, distance learning, double major, summer session for credit, part-time degree program, adult/continuing education programs, internships. Off campus study at Southeastern Community College, Muscatine Community College. Study abroad program.

Entrance Requirements: Options: Peterson's Universal Application, Common Application, electronic application, early admission, deferred admission. Required: high school transcript, minimum 2.0 high school GPA, SAT or ACT. Recommended: interview. Required for some: essay, 2 recommendations. Placement: SAT or ACT required. Entrance: moderately difficult. Application deadline: 8/15.

Costs Per Year: Comprehensive fee: $23,330 includes full-time tuition ($17,800) and college room and board ($5530). College room only: $2280. Part-time tuition: $439 per credit hour.

Collegiate Environment: Orientation program. Drama-theater group, choral group, student-run newspaper, radio station. Social organizations: 38 open to all; national fraternities, national sororities; 10% of eligible men and 14% of eligible women are members. Most popular organizations: Commuter Club, Student Senate, International Club, Behavioral Science Club, Blue Key Society. Major annual events: Homecoming, Spring Thing, Christmas Thing. Student services: health clinic, personal-psychological counseling. Campus security: 24-hour patrols, late night transport-escort service, controlled dormitory access. 465 college housing spaces available; 314 were occupied in 2003-04. Freshmen guaranteed college housing. On-campus residence required through junior year. Options: men-only, women-only housing available. Chadwick Library plus 1 other with 107,227 books, 27,200 microform titles, 431 serials, 6,553 audiovisual materials, an OPAC, and a Web page. Operations spending for 2004 fiscal year: $216,160. 72 computers available on campus for general student use. Staffed computer lab on campus.

Community Environment: Mount Pleasant (population 8,000) is located at the intersection of U.S. Highways 218 and 34; Amtrak and a municipal airport serve the area. Community facilities include many churches, libraries, a hospital, motels, and civic and fraternal organizations. Part time employment is available. Two state parks are nearby which provide facilities for boating and fishing.

■ **IOWA WESTERN COMMUNITY COLLEGE** *I-3*
2700 College Rd., Box 4-C
Council Bluffs, IA 51502
Tel: (712)325-3200
Free: 800-432-5852
Admissions: (712)388-6878
Fax: (712)325-3720
Web Site: http://www.iwcc.edu/

Description: District-supported, 2-year, coed. Part of Iowa Department of Education Division of Community Colleges. Awards certificates, diplomas, transfer associate, and terminal associate degrees. Founded 1966. Setting: 282-acre suburban campus with easy access to Omaha. Total enrollment: 4,299. Students come from 27 states and territories, 10 other countries, 1% Native American, 1% Hispanic, 2% black, 1% Asian American or Pacific Islander, 2% international, 34% 25 or older, 19% live on campus. Core. Calendar: semesters. Academic remediation for entering students, ESL program, services for LD students, independent study, distance learning, summer session for credit, part-time degree program, adult/continuing education programs, co-op programs and internships. ROTC: Army (c), Air Force (c).

Entrance Requirements: Open admission except for nursing, technical programs. Options: early admission, deferred admission. Required: high school transcript. Placement: SAT Reasoning Test or ACT or ACT ASSET or ACT COMPASS required. Entrance: noncompetitive. Application deadline: Rolling.

Costs Per Year: State resident tuition: $3200 full-time, $100 per credit part-time. Nonresident tuition: $4800 full-time, $150 per credit part-time. Mandatory fees: $320 full-time, $10 per credit part-time. College room and board: $4350. Room and board charges vary according to board plan and housing facility.

Collegiate Environment: Orientation program. Drama-theater group, choral group, student-run newspaper, radio station. Social organizations: 21 open to all. Most popular organizations: Student Senate, Health Occupations Student Association, Volunteer Institute Program, Data Processing Student Association, Phi Theta Kappa. Major annual events: Career Awareness Fair, Renaissance Faire, Annual Job Expo. Student services: personal-psychological counseling. Campus security: 24-hour patrols, late night transport-escort service. Option: coed housing available. 59,200 books, 207 serials, and an OPAC. Operations spending for 2004 fiscal year: $256,000. 263 computers available on campus for general student use. A campuswide network can be accessed from off-campus. Staffed computer lab on campus.

■ **KAPLAN UNIVERSITY** *H-16*
1801 East Kimberly Rd., Ste. 1
Davenport, IA 52807-2095
Tel: (563)355-3500
Admissions: (563)441-2496
Web Site: http://www.kaplancollegeia.com/

Description: Proprietary, primarily 2-year, coed. Part of Kaplan Higher Education. Awards certificates, diplomas, transfer associate, terminal associate, and bachelor's degrees (profile includes both traditional and on-line students). Founded 1937. Setting: suburban campus. Educational spending for 2005 fiscal year: $2935 per student. Total enrollment: 9,194. 5,017 applied, 94% were admitted. Full-time: 1,648 students, 70% women, 30% men. Part-time: 7,546 students, 73% women, 27% men. Students come from 2 states and territories, 91% from out-of-state, 0.04% Native American, 0.4% Hispanic, 1% black, 0.1% Asian American or Pacific Islander, 0% international, 92% 25 or older, 16% transferred in. Core. Academic remediation for entering students, independent study, distance learning, double major, summer session for credit, part-time degree program, adult/continuing education programs, co-op programs and internships.

Entrance Requirements: Options: early admission, deferred admission. Required: high school transcript, interview. Entrance: minimally difficult. Application deadline: Rolling.

Collegiate Environment: Most popular organization: academic department clubs. Student services: personal-psychological counseling. College housing not available. Academic Resource Center with 7,000 books, 120 serials, 504 audiovisual materials, and an OPAC. Operations spending for 2004 fiscal year: $67,600. 120 computers available on campus for general student use. A campuswide network can be accessed. Staffed computer lab on campus.

■ **KIRKWOOD COMMUNITY COLLEGE** *F-13*
PO Box 2068
Cedar Rapids, IA 52406-2068
Tel: (319)398-5411
Free: 800-332-2055
Admissions: (319)398-5517
Fax: (319)398-1244
E-mail: dbannon@kirkwood.cc.ia.us
Web Site: http://www.kirkwood.cc.ia.us/

Description: State and locally supported, 2-year, coed. Part of Iowa Department of Education Division of Community Colleges. Awards certificates, diplomas, transfer associate, and terminal associate degrees. Founded 1966. Setting: 630-acre suburban campus. Endowment: $4.4 million. Educational spending for 2005 fiscal year: $3350 per student. Total enrollment: 15,032. Full-time: 8,319 students, 49% women, 51% men. Part-time: 6,713 students, 60% women, 40% men. Students come from 15 states and territories, 85 other countries, 2% from out-of-state, 1% Native American, 2% Hispanic, 4% black, 1% Asian American or Pacific Islander, 2% international, 29% 25 or older, 9% transferred in. Core. Calendar: semesters. Academic remediation for entering students, ESL program, services for LD students, advanced placement, accelerated degree program, self-designed majors, honors program, distance learning, summer session for credit, part-time degree program, external degree program, adult/continuing education programs, co-op programs and internships. Off campus study at Iowa State University of Science and Technology, University of Northern Iowa, St. Ambrose University.

Entrance Requirements: Open admission. Options: electronic application, early admission. Required: high school transcript. Placement: ACT, ACT COMPASS required. Entrance: noncompetitive. Application deadline: Rolling. Notification: continuous.

Collegiate Environment: Orientation program. Drama-theater group, choral group, student-run newspaper. Social organizations: 45 open to all. Major annual events: Homecoming, Fall Orientation, Graduation ceremonies. Student services: legal services, health clinic, personal-psychological counseling. Campus security: 24-hour patrols. College housing not available. Library with 60,622 books, 40,377 microform titles, 565 serials, 3,677 audiovisual materials, and an OPAC. Operations spending for 2004 fiscal year: $609,049. 1,000 computers available on campus for general student use. A campuswide network can be accessed. Staffed computer lab on campus.

Community Environment: Cedar Rapids/Marion is a dynamic community of 130,000, and Kirkwood students enjoy its many options for recreation, entertainment, and shopping. Located just five minutes north of the campus, downtown Cedar Rapids features Five Seasons Center, which holds an arena accommodating 8,000 persons for rock concerts, sports events, auto and ice shows, and more. Numerous restaurants, night spots, and movie theaters round out the entertainment scene, There are 62 parks for swimming, golfing, tennis, boating, and camping, and there is shopping in two large malls and the thriving downtown business districts of Cedar Rapids and Marion. Cultural activity centers around the Cedar Rapids Symphony, Art Museum, and Community Theater, as well as the area's four colleges. Religious activity is based in more than 125 congregations of all faiths. Apartment and condominium housing is available in all price ranges, and more new units are being built. Cedar Rapids/Marion is an attractive and stimulating place to live as well as learn. In addition to the Cedar Rapids campus, there are Kirkwood learning centers in each of the seven counties in the College's service area.

■ LORAS COLLEGE D-16

1450 Alta Vista
Dubuque, IA 52004-0178
Tel: (563)588-7100
Free: 800-245-6727
Admissions: (563)588-7829
Fax: (563)588-7964
E-mail: adms@loras.edu
Web Site: http://www.loras.edu/

Description: Independent Roman Catholic, comprehensive, coed. Awards associate, bachelor's, and master's degrees. Founded 1839. Setting: 60-acre suburban campus. Endowment: $24.3 million. Research spending for 2004 fiscal year: $221,051. Educational spending for 2005 fiscal year: $6447 per student. Total enrollment: 1,683. Faculty: 142 (112 full-time, 30 part-time). Student-undergrad faculty ratio is 13:1. 1,402 applied, 82% were admitted. 13% from top 10% of their high school class, 34% from top quarter, 69% from top half. Full-time: 1,512 students, 50% women, 50% men. Part-time: 82 students, 62% women, 38% men. Students come from 23 states and territories, 8 other countries, 45% from out-of-state, 0% Native American, 1% Hispanic, 1% black, 1% Asian American or Pacific Islander, 3% international, 6% 25 or older, 64% live on campus, 18% transferred in. Retention: 78% of full-time freshmen returned the following year. Academic areas with the most degrees conferred: business/marketing; education; security and protective services; social sciences. Core. Calendar: semesters. Academic remediation for entering students, ESL program, services for LD students, advanced placement, self-designed majors, honors program, independent study, double major, summer session for credit, part-time degree program, adult/continuing education programs, co-op programs and internships, graduate courses open to undergrads. Off campus study. Study abroad program.

Entrance Requirements: Options: Peterson's Universal Application, electronic application, deferred admission. Required: high school transcript, minimum 2.5 high school GPA, SAT or ACT. Recommended: essay, 1 recommendation. Required for some: interview. Entrance: moderately difficult. Application deadline: Rolling. Notification: continuous.

Costs Per Year: Application fee: $25. Comprehensive fee: $27,193 includes full-time tuition ($19,990), mandatory fees ($1108), and college room and board ($6095). College room only: $3100. Full-time tuition and fees vary according to course load and degree level. Room and board charges vary according to board plan and housing facility. Part-time tuition: $400 per credit.

Collegiate Environment: Orientation program. Drama-theater group, choral group, student-run newspaper, radio station. Social organizations: 59 open to all; national sororities; 10% of eligible men and 20% of eligible women are members. Most popular organizations: Student Senate, campus ministry, College Activities Board, residence hall councils. Major annual events: homecoming, End of Year Bash, Family Weekend. Student services: health clinic, personal-psychological counseling. Campus security: 24-hour emergency response devices and patrols, late night transport-escort service, controlled dormitory access. 1,098 college housing spaces available; 1,032 were occupied in 2003-04. Freshmen guaranteed college housing. On-campus residence required through junior year. Option: coed housing available. Academic Resource Center with 224,971 books, 77,389 microform titles, 750 serials, 1,854 audiovisual materials, an OPAC, and a Web page. Operations spending for 2004 fiscal year: $788,528. 20 computers available on campus for general student use. Computer purchase/lease plans available. A campuswide network can be accessed from student residence rooms and from off campus. Staffed computer lab on campus.

Community Environment: The small city of Dubuque is located on the Mississippi River where Iowa, Illinois, and Wisconsin meet. The oldest city in Iowa, it features rugged bluffs and Victorian architecture. Excellent air connections with Chicago's O'Hare Airport and with the Minneapolis-St. Paul Airport are available. The city is the commercial, cultural, and recreational center of the tri-state area. It offers concerts, theater, symphony, art galleries, museums, and riverboat gambling. Facilities are available for boating, skiing, golf, and tennis.

■ LUTHER COLLEGE B-13

700 College Dr.
Decorah, IA 52101-1045
Tel: (563)387-2000
Free: 800-458-8437
Admissions: (563)387-1430
Fax: (563)387-2159
E-mail: admissions@luther.edu
Web Site: http://www.luther.edu/

Description: Independent, 4-year, coed, affiliated with Evangelical Lutheran Church in America. Awards bachelor's degrees. Founded 1861. Setting: 800-acre small town campus. Endowment: $83.9 million. Research spending for 2004 fiscal year: $263,681. Educational spending for 2005 fiscal year: $9546 per student. Total enrollment: 2,545. Student-undergrad faculty ratio is 13:1. 2,121 applied, 75% were admitted. 32% from top 10% of their high school class, 61% from top quarter, 84% from top half. 9 National Merit Scholars, 20 class presidents, 48 valedictorians, 89 student government officers. Full-time: 2,476 students, 59% women, 41% men. Part-time: 69 students, 51% women, 49% men. Students come from 34 states and territories, 28 other countries, 65% from out-of-state, 0.4% Native American, 1% Hispanic, 1% black, 2% Asian American or Pacific Islander, 3% international, 2% 25 or older, 82% live on campus, 2% transferred in. Retention: 84% of full-time freshmen returned the following year. Academic areas with the most degrees conferred: business/marketing; visual and performing arts; biological/life sciences. Core. Calendar: 4-1-4. Academic remediation for entering students, services for LD students, advanced placement, self-designed majors, honors program, independent study, double major, summer session for credit, part-time degree program, internships. Off campus study. Study abroad program.

Entrance Requirements: Options: Peterson's Universal Application, Common Application, electronic application, deferred admission, international baccalaureate accepted. Required: essay, high school transcript, 1 recommendation, SAT or ACT. Recommended: interview. Entrance: moderately difficult. Notification: continuous.

Costs Per Year: Application fee: $25. Comprehensive fee: $30,670 includes full-time tuition ($26,380) and college room and board ($4290). College room only: $2100. Part-time tuition: $924 per semester hour.

Collegiate Environment: Orientation program. Drama-theater group, choral group, student-run newspaper, radio station. Social organizations: 139 open to all; national fraternities, local fraternities, local sororities; 7% of eligible men and 9% of eligible women are members. Most popular organizations: Alpha Phi Omega, Student Activities Council, intramural clubs and organizations, Campus Ministry. Major annual events: Homecoming, Parents' Weekend, Christmas at Luther Weekend. Student services: health clinic, personal-psychological counseling, women's center. Campus security: 24-hour emergency response devices and patrols, late night transport-escort service, controlled dormitory access. 2,133 college housing spaces available; 2,114 were occupied in 2003-04. Freshmen guaranteed college housing. On-campus residence required through senior year. Option: coed housing available. Preus Library with 339,173 books, 25,009 microform titles, 1,122 serials, 10,704 audiovisual materials, an OPAC, and a Web page. Operations spending for 2004 fiscal year: $1.5 million. 500 computers available on campus for general student use. A campuswide network can be accessed from student residence rooms and from off campus. Staffed computer lab on campus.

Community Environment: Decorah (population 8,000) is on the banks of the Upper Iowa River, in an area known as Little Switzerland, in northeast Iowa. Twin Springs and Siewer Springs state fish hatcheries are nearby. Decorah has set aside more than 328 acres for recreation. Outdoor activities include golf, skiing, hiking, hunting and fishing.

■ MAHARISHI UNIVERSITY OF MANAGEMENT J-13

1000 North 4th St.
Fairfield, IA 52557
Tel: (641)472-7000
Free: 800-369-6480
Admissions: (641)472-1110
Fax: (641)472-1189
E-mail: admissions@miu.edu
Web Site: http://www.mum.edu/

Description: Independent, university, coed. Awards bachelor's, master's, and doctoral degrees. Founded 1971. Setting: 272-acre small town campus. Endowment: $9.1 million. Research spending for 2004 fiscal year: $3.8 million. Educational spending for 2005 fiscal year: $11,665 per student. Total enrollment: 741. Faculty: 47 (39 full-time, 8 part-time). Student-undergrad faculty ratio is 16:1. 58 applied, 66% were admitted. Full-time: 206 students, 41% women, 59% men. Part-time: 12 students, 50% women, 50% men. Students come from 26 states and territories, 21 other countries, 40% from out-of-state, 1% Native American, 1% Hispanic, 3% black, 2% Asian American or Pacific Islander, 30% international, 15% 25 or older, 46% live on campus, 23% transferred in. Retention: 85% of full-time freshmen returned the following year. Academic areas with the most degrees conferred: visual and performing arts; biological/life sciences; business/marketing. Core. Calendar: semesters. Academic remediation for entering students, ESL program, services for LD students, advanced placement, self-designed majors, honors program, independent study, distance learning, double major, adult/continuing education programs, co-op programs and internships, graduate courses open to undergrads. Study abroad program.

Entrance Requirements: Options: Peterson's Universal Application, Common Application, electronic application, early admission, deferred admission, international baccalaureate accepted. Required: essay, high school transcript, minimum 2.5 high school GPA, 2 recommendations, minimum SAT score of 950 or ACT score of 19. Recommended: interview, SAT or ACT. Entrance: moderately difficult. Application deadline: 8/1. Notification: continuous until 8/15. Preference given to graduates of the Maharishi School of the Age of Enlightenment.

Costs Per Year: Application fee: $15. Comprehensive fee: $30,430 includes full-time tuition ($24,000), mandatory fees ($430), and college room and board ($6000).

Collegiate Environment: Orientation program. Drama-theater group, choral group, student-run newspaper, radio station. Social organizations: 10 open to all. Most popular organizations: Student Senate, Soccer Club, Global Student Council, Fencing Club, Knitting Club. Major annual events: International Cultural Festivals, Monthly World Peace Assemblies, Variety/Talent Show. Student services: legal services, health clinic, personal-psychological counseling. Campus security: 24-hour emergency response devices and patrols, late night transport-escort service, controlled dormitory access. 320 college housing spaces available; 105 were occupied in 2003-04. Freshmen guaranteed college housing. On-campus residence required through senior year. Options: men-only, women-only housing available. Maharishi University of Management Library with 137,775 books, 59,851 microform titles, 11,146 serials, 26,924 audiovisual materials, an OPAC, and a Web page. Operations spending for 2004 fiscal year: $138,946. 120 computers available on campus for general student use. A campuswide network can be accessed from student residence rooms and from off campus. Staffed computer lab on campus.

Community Environment: The University is located in the Fairfield, Iowa, 50 miles west of the Mississippi River in the heartland of the central United States. A thirty percent growth in the population and the appearance of numerous new businesses in Fairfield in recent years have spurred an unprecedented level of economic and cultural growth in the community. Fairfield is viewed as one of the great success stories in Iowa, and is recognized throughout the state for its creativity in business, the arts, and education. Located within easy access of Chicago, St. Louis, and Kansas City, it is only one hour south of Iowa City, home of the University of Iowa.

■ **MARSHALLTOWN COMMUNITY COLLEGE** *F-10*
3700 South Center St.
Marshalltown, IA 50158-4760
Tel: (641)752-7106; (866)622-4748
Fax: (641)752-8149
E-mail: dtrawny@iavalley.cc.ia.us
Web Site: http://www.marshalltowncommunitycollege.com/

Description: District-supported, 2-year, coed. Part of Iowa Valley Community College District System. Awards certificates, diplomas, transfer associate, and terminal associate degrees. Founded 1927. Setting: 200-acre small town campus. Endowment: $1.7 million. Educational spending for 2005 fiscal year: $2891 per student. Total enrollment: 1,421. Full-time: 903 students, 55% women, 45% men. Part-time: 518 students, 70% women, 30% men. Students come from 3 states and territories, 10 other countries, 1% from out-of-state, 3% Native American, 4% Hispanic, 3% black, 1% Asian American or Pacific Islander, 2% international, 35% 25 or older, 8% live on campus. Core. Calendar: semesters. Academic remediation for entering students, ESL program, services for LD students, advanced placement,

self-designed majors, freshman honors college, honors program, independent study, distance learning, summer session for credit, part-time degree program, adult/continuing education programs, co-op programs and internships. Study abroad program. ROTC: Air Force (c).

Entrance Requirements: Open admission. Options: Common Application, electronic application, early admission. Required: high school transcript, ACT COMPASS. Recommended: ACT. Required for some: recommendations, interview. Entrance: noncompetitive. Application deadline: Rolling. Notification: continuous.

Collegiate Environment: Drama-theater group, choral group, student-run newspaper, radio station. Social organizations: 10 open to all. Most popular organizations: Student Activities Council, Student Senate, College Community Connection, SAMS, International Student Association. Major annual events: Lip Sync Contest, popcorn days, hypnotist performance. Student services: personal-psychological counseling. 96 college housing spaces available; all were occupied in 2003-04. No special consideration for freshman housing applicants. Option: coed housing available. Learning Resource Center with 39,348 books, 216 serials, and a Web page. Operations spending for 2004 fiscal year: $195,489. 250 computers available on campus for general student use. A campuswide network can be accessed from student residence rooms. Staffed computer lab on campus.

Community Environment: Marshalltown, an industrial city in central Iowa, is an important bus and truck terminal. The community facilities include 32 churches, hospitals, a library and many civic service clubs, as well as a Chamber of Commerce. Opportunities for part time or seasonal employment are excellent. Recreational facilities include an expanding park system; three golf courses; YMCA; two swimming pools; large youth soccer, football, and Little League complexes; a five-mile in-city walk/jog/bike path with greenbelt environment; new playgrounds; two bowling alleys; and three theaters.

■ **MERCY COLLEGE OF HEALTH SCIENCES** *H-8*
928 Sixth Ave.
Des Moines, IA 50309-1239
Tel: (515)643-3180
Free: 800-637-2994
Fax: (515)643-6698
Web Site: http://www.mchs.edu/

Description: Independent, 4-year, coed, affiliated with Roman Catholic Church. Awards associate and bachelor's degrees. Founded 1995. Setting: 5-acre urban campus. Total enrollment: 660. 461 applied, 93% were admitted. 10% from top 10% of their high school class, 27% from top quarter, 46% from top half. Full-time: 411 students, 91% women, 9% men. Part-time: 249 students, 93% women, 7% men. 0% from out-of-state, 0.2% Native American, 2% Hispanic, 1% black, 2% Asian American or Pacific Islander, 0% international, 60% 25 or older. Retention: 78% of full-time freshmen returned the following year. Calendar: semesters.

Entrance Requirements: Open admission. Option: Common Application. Required: high school transcript, minimum 3.2 high school GPA, ACT. Required for some: interview. Application deadline: Rolling. Notification: continuous.

Costs Per Year: Application fee: $25. Tuition: $11,700 full-time, $395 per semester hour part-time. Mandatory fees: $25 full-time. Full-time tuition and fees vary according to program. Part-time tuition varies according to course load and program.

Collegiate Environment: Campus security: 24-hour emergency response devices, late night transport-escort service.

Community Environment: Des Moines is the setting for MCHS's four-acre campus, which is located just south of Interstate 235 and three blocks south of Mercy Medical Center.

■ **MORNINGSIDE COLLEGE** *D-1*
1501 Morningside Ave.
Sioux City, IA 51106
Tel: (712)274-5000
Free: 800-831-0806
Admissions: (712)274-5111
E-mail: mscadm@alpha.morningside.edu
Web Site: http://www.morningside.edu/

Description: Independent, comprehensive, coed, affiliated with United Methodist Church. Awards bachelor's and master's degrees. Founded 1894. Setting: 41-acre suburban campus. Endowment: $30.1 million. Educational spending for 2005 fiscal year: $4875 per student. Total enrollment: 1,440. Faculty: 132 (66 full-time, 66 part-time). Student-undergrad faculty ratio is 16:1. 1,296 applied, 74% were admitted. 17% from top 10% of their high school class, 39% from top quarter, 75% from top half. Full-time: 1,066 students, 54% women, 46% men. Part-time: 83 students, 63% women, 37% men. Students come from 24 states and territories, 11 other countries, 35% from out-of-state, 0.4% Native American, 3% Hispanic, 2% black, 1% Asian American or Pacific Islander, 2% international, 7% 25 or older, 70% live on campus, 8% transferred in. Retention: 65% of full-time freshmen returned the following year. Academic areas with the most degrees conferred: education; business/marketing; health professions and related sciences. Core. Calendar: semesters. Academic remediation for entering students, ESL program, services for LD students, advanced placement, self-designed majors, honors program, independent study, double major, summer session for credit, part-time degree program, adult/continuing education programs, internships, graduate courses open to undergrads. Off campus study at American University, Drew University. Study abroad program. ROTC: Army (c).

Entrance Requirements: Options: electronic application, deferred admission, international baccalaureate accepted. Required: high school transcript, minimum SAT score of 930 or ACT score of 20 and rank in top 50% of high school class or achieved GPA of 2.5 or better, SAT or ACT. Recommended: interview. Required for some: 2 recommendations. Entrance: moderately difficult. Application deadline: Rolling. Notification: continuous.

Costs Per Year: Application fee: $25. Comprehensive fee: $23,704 includes full-time tuition ($17,170), mandatory fees ($910), and college room and board ($5624). College room only: $2940. Full-time tuition and fees vary according to program. Room and board charges vary according to housing facility. Part-time tuition: $530 per semester hour. Part-time tuition varies according to course load.

Collegiate Environment: Orientation program. Drama-theater group, choral group, student-run newspaper, radio station. Social organizations: 45 open to all; national fraternities, national sororities; 12% of eligible men and 6% of eligible women are members. Most popular organizations: Student Government/Activities Council, Student Ambassadors, Homecoming Committee. Major annual events: Homecoming, Honors Assembly, Christmas at Morningside. Student services: health clinic, personal-psychological counseling, women's center. Campus security: 24-hour emergency response devices, student patrols, late night transport-escort service, controlled dormitory access, 18-hour patrols by trained security personnel. 720 college housing spaces available; 613 were occupied in 2003-04. Freshmen guaranteed college housing. On-campus residence required through junior year. Option: coed housing available. Hickman-Johnson-Furrow Library with 113,169 books, 295,215 microform titles, 528 serials, 5,601 audiovisual materials, an OPAC, and a Web page. Operations spending for 2004 fiscal year: $424,081. 800 computers available on campus for general student use. Computer purchase/lease plans available. A campuswide network can be accessed from student residence rooms and from off campus. Staffed computer lab on campus.

Community Environment: See Briar Cliff College.

■ **MOUNT MERCY COLLEGE** *F-13*
1330 Elmhurst Dr., NE
Cedar Rapids, IA 52402-4797
Tel: (319)363-8213
Free: 800-248-4504
Admissions: (319)368-6460
Fax: (319)368-6492
E-mail: admission@mtmercy.edu
Web Site: http://www.mtmercy.edu/
Description: Independent Roman Catholic, 4-year, coed. Awards bachelor's degrees. Founded 1928. Setting: 40-acre suburban campus. Endowment: $13.4 million. Educational spending for 2005 fiscal year: $5328 per student. Total university enrollment: 151. Total unit enrollment: 1,490. Student-undergrad faculty ratio is 12:1. 481 applied, 79% were admitted. 13% from top 10% of their high school class, 40% from top quarter, 78% from top half. Full-time: 1,019 students, 75% women, 25% men. Students come from 23 states and territories, 6% from out-of-state, 0.1% Native American, 1% Hispanic, 2% black, 1% Asian American or Pacific Islander, 0.5% international, 8% 25 or older, 28% live on campus, 20% transferred in. Retention: 76% of full-time freshmen returned the following year. Academic areas with the most degrees conferred: computer and information sciences; business/marketing; education. Core. Calendar: 4-1-4. Academic remediation for entering students, services for LD students, advanced placement, accelerated degree program, self-designed majors, freshman honors college, honors program, independent study, double major, summer session for credit, part-time degree program, adult/continuing education programs, internships. Off campus study at Coe College.

Entrance Requirements: Options: electronic application, early admission, deferred admission. Required: high school transcript, minimum 2.5 high school GPA, SAT and SAT Subject Tests or ACT. Recommended: minimum 3.0 high school GPA. Entrance: moderately difficult. Application deadline: 8/25. Notification: continuous.

Costs Per Year: Application fee: $20. Comprehensive fee: $23,710 includes full-time tuition ($18,030) and college room and board ($5680). Full-time tuition varies according to course load. Room and board charges vary according to board plan and housing facility. Part-time tuition: $500 per credit hour. Part-time tuition varies according to course load.

Collegiate Environment: Orientation program. Drama-theater group, choral group, student-run newspaper. Social organizations: 32 open to all. Most popular organizations: Student Government Association, Students in Free Enterprise, Tomorrow's Nurses Today, Student-Iowa State Education Association. Major annual events: Spring Fling, Hill Fest, homecoming. Student services: health clinic, personal-psychological counseling. Campus security: 24-hour emergency response devices and patrols, student patrols, late night transport-escort service, controlled dormitory access. 500 college housing spaces available; 391 were occupied in 2003-04. Freshmen guaranteed college housing. Option: coed housing available. Busse Center with 118,000 books, 34,000 microform titles, 1,000 serials, 5,000 audiovisual materials, an OPAC, and a Web page. Operations spending for 2004 fiscal year: $526,628. 115 computers available on campus for general student use. A campuswide network can be accessed from student residence rooms and from off campus. Staffed computer lab on campus.

Community Environment: See Kirkwood Community College.

■ **MUSCATINE COMMUNITY COLLEGE** *H-15*
152 Colorado St.
Muscatine, IA 52761-5396
Tel: (563)288-6001
Admissions: (563)288-6012
Fax: (563)288-6074
Web Site: http://www.eicc.edu/
Description: State-supported, 2-year, coed. Part of Eastern Iowa Community College District. Awards certificates, diplomas, transfer associate, and terminal associate degrees. Founded 1929. Setting: 25-acre small town campus. Educational spending for 2005 fiscal year: $2249 per student. Total enrollment: 1,280. 312 applied, 100% were admitted. Full-time: 552 students, 59% women, 41% men. Part-time: 728 students, 62% women, 38% men. Students come from 6 states and territories, 4% from out-of-state, 1% Native American, 10% Hispanic, 1% black, 1% Asian American or Pacific Islander, 1% international, 43% 25 or older. Core. Calendar: semesters. Academic remediation for entering students, ESL program, services for LD students, advanced placement, honors program, independent study, distance learning, double major, summer session for credit, part-time degree program, adult/continuing education programs, co-op programs and internships. Study abroad program.

Entrance Requirements: Open admission except for nursing program. Options: early admission, deferred admission. Required: high school transcript. Placement: ACT or DTLS, DTMS required. Entrance: noncompetitive. Application deadline: Rolling. Notification: continuous.

Collegiate Environment: Drama-theater group, choral group, student-run newspaper. Student services: personal-psychological counseling. 75 college housing spaces available; 70 were occupied in 2003-04. Muscatine Community College Library with 19,588 books, 176 serials, and an OPAC. 57 computers available on campus for general student use. A campuswide network can be accessed from off-campus. Staffed computer lab on campus.

Community Environment: Muscatine, an industrial center, is located on the Mississippi River, and has an annual mean temperature of 50 degrees, and an average rainfall of 34 inches. Vegetables and melons are raised in the vicinity; over three million bushels of grain are shipped from here each year. Community facilities include many churches and a library. Parks, a golf course, a bowling alley and skating rink offer recreation. The Mississippi River and nearby Cedar and Iowa rivers provide excellent picnicking, fishing and boat launching facilities. Points of interest are the Laura Musser Art Gallery and Museum, and Weed Park.

■ **NORTH IOWA AREA COMMUNITY COLLEGE** *B-9*
500 College Dr.
Mason City, IA 50401-7299
Tel: (641)423-1264; 888-GO NIACC
Admissions: (641)422-4104
Fax: (641)423-1711

Web Site: http://www.niacc.edu/

Description: State and locally supported, 2-year, coed. Part of Iowa Community Colleges System. Awards certificates, diplomas, transfer associate, and terminal associate degrees. Founded 1918. Setting: 320-acre rural campus. Total enrollment: 3,133. Student-undergrad faculty ratio is 13:1. 2% from top 10% of their high school class, 9% from top quarter, 36% from top half. Full-time: 1,698 students, 50% women, 50% men. Part-time: 1,435 students, 64% women, 36% men. Students come from 25 states and territories, 7 other countries, 4% from out-of-state, 0.3% Native American, 2% Hispanic, 3% black, 1% Asian American or Pacific Islander, 1% international, 22% 25 or older, 15% live on campus, 57% transferred in. Retention: 68% of full-time freshmen returned the following year. Core. Calendar: semesters. Academic remediation for entering students, ESL program, services for LD students, advanced placement, self-designed majors, honors program, independent study, distance learning, double major, summer session for credit, part-time degree program, external degree program, co-op programs and internships. Off campus study.

Entrance Requirements: Open admission except for nursing, information systems technology, e-commerce, web design and development, physical therapy assistant programs. Options: Common Application, electronic application. Required: high school transcript. Entrance: noncompetitive. Application deadline: Rolling. Notification: continuous.

Costs Per Year: Application fee: $0. State resident tuition: $2790 full-time, $93 per credit part-time. Nonresident tuition: $4184 full-time, $139.50 per credit part-time. Mandatory fees: $174 full-time, $11 per credit part-time. College room and board: $3920.

Collegiate Environment: Orientation program. Choral group, student-run newspaper. Social organizations: 18 open to all. Most popular organizations: Student Senate, school newspaper, intramurals, choral groups, band/orchestra. Major annual events: Quadilbet, Homecoming. Student services: personal-psychological counseling. Campus security: 24-hour emergency response devices, controlled dormitory access. 480 college housing spaces available; 325 were occupied in 2003-04. Freshmen given priority for college housing. On-campus residence required in freshman year. Option: coed housing available. North Iowa Area Community College Library with 29,540 books, 1,905 microform titles, 413 serials, 7,773 audiovisual materials, an OPAC, and a Web page. 365 computers available on campus for general student use. A campuswide network can be accessed from off-campus. Staffed computer lab on campus.

Community Environment: Mason City (population 30,379) is located in the north center of the state midway between Des Moines and Minneapolis - St. Paul, and has an average winter temperature of 28 degrees, summer average 63 degrees. One bus line and an airline offer transportation. The community facilities include hospitals, a library, Art Center, hotels and motels. Brick, tile and Portland cement are manufactured from the deposits of clay, limestone and sand in this area. Part-time work is available. Recreation activities include golf, water sports in summer, ice boating and fishing in winter, ice skating, pheasant deer and duck hunting.

■ **NORTHEAST IOWA COMMUNITY COLLEGE** *B-13*

Box 400

Calmar, IA 52132-0480

Tel: (563)562-3263

Free: 800-728-CALMAR

Fax: (563)562-3719

E-mail: keunem@nicc.edu

Web Site: http://www.nicc.edu/

Description: State and locally supported, 2-year, coed. Part of Iowa Area Community Colleges System. Awards certificates, diplomas, transfer associate, and terminal associate degrees. Founded 1966. Setting: 210-acre small town campus. Total enrollment: 4,833. Student-undergrad faculty ratio is 15:1. 1,161 applied, 66% were admitted. 4% from top quarter of their high school class, 14% from top half. Full-time: 2,140 students, 60% women, 40% men. Part-time: 2,693 students, 63% women, 37% men. Students come from 5 states and territories, 13% from out-of-state, 0.2% Native American, 1% Hispanic, 1% black, 0.5% Asian American or Pacific Islander, 0.3% international, 36% 25 or older. Core. Calendar: semesters. Academic remediation for entering students, ESL program, services for LD students, self-designed majors, independent study, distance learning, double major, summer session for credit, adult/continuing education programs, co-op programs and internships. Off campus study at Upper Iowa University, Clarke College, University of Dubuque, Loras College. Study abroad program.

Entrance Requirements: Open admission except for allied health programs. Recommended: high school transcript. Entrance: noncompetitive. Application deadline: Rolling. Notification: continuous.

Costs Per Year: Application fee: $0. State resident tuition: $3590 full-time, $105 per credit part-time. Nonresident tuition: $3590 full-time, $105 per credit part-time. Mandatory fees: $442 full-time, $13 per credit part-time.

Collegiate Environment: Orientation program. Student-run newspaper. Student services: personal-psychological counseling. Campus security: security personnel on week nights. College housing not available. Wilder Resource Center plus 1 other with 18,634 books, 302 serials, and an OPAC. 4,000 computers available on campus for general student use. A campuswide network can be accessed from off-campus. Staffed computer lab on campus.

Community Environment: Calmar is located 10 miles from Decorah, 25 miles from Cresco, 17 miles from Postville, and 24 miles from New Hampton. The town's primary business is agriculture and related fields. Two firms here manufacture furniture and truck racks. Recreational facilities are provided by Calmar Lake, Upper Iowa River, and Turkey River, which furnish great opportunity for fishing and hunting. Northeast Iowa operates a second campus at Peosta, Iowa, which is located approximately ten miles west of the city of Dubuque. The rural area of Peosta is similar to that of Calmar, except that it is close to the metropolitan area of Dubuque, which has a population of nearly 70,000. It offers a wide range of cultural and recreational activities and is situated on the Mississippi River. The popularity of Northeast Iowa is pointed out by the growing numbers of tourists who travel to the area from all over the Midwest.

■ **NORTHWEST IOWA COMMUNITY COLLEGE** *B-3*

603 West Park St.

Sheldon, IA 51201-1046

Tel: (712)324-5061

Free: 800-352-4907

Fax: (712)324-4136

Web Site: http://www.nwicc.edu/

Description: State-supported, 2-year, coed. Part of Iowa Department of Education Division of Community Colleges. Awards certificates, diplomas, transfer associate, and terminal associate degrees. Founded 1966. Setting: 263-acre small town campus with easy access to Sioux City, IA; Sioux Falls, SD. Educational spending for 2005 fiscal year: $3500 per student. Total enrollment: 1,079. 1,113 applied, 99% were admitted. Full-time: 533 students, 43% women, 57% men. Part-time: 546 students, 66% women, 34% men. Students come from 10 states and territories, 4% from out-of-state, 0.2% Native American, 1% Hispanic, 0.3% black, 1% Asian American or Pacific Islander, 20% 25 or older, 5% live on campus. Retention: 56% of full-time freshmen returned the following year. Calendar: semesters. Academic remediation for entering students, services for LD students, distance learning, summer session for credit, part-time degree program, adult/continuing education programs, co-op programs.

Entrance Requirements: Open admission. Options: Peterson's Universal Application, Common Application, electronic application. Required: high school transcript. Required for some: minimum 2.0 high school GPA, ACT COMPASS. Placement: ACT COMPASS required. Entrance: noncompetitive. Application deadline: Rolling. Notification: continuous.

Collegiate Environment: Student-run newspaper. Social organizations: 3 open to all. Major annual events: Fall Kick-off BBQ, Free Holiday Meals, SGA Special Entertainment. Student services: personal-psychological counseling. Campus security: 24-hour emergency response devices. 38 college housing spaces available; all were occupied in 2003-04. Option: coed housing available. Northwest Iowa Community College Library plus 1 other with 12,500 books, 340 serials, 2,500 audiovisual materials, an OPAC, and a Web page. Operations spending for 2004 fiscal year: $165,951. 142 computers available on campus for general student use. A campuswide network can be accessed. Staffed computer lab on campus.

Community Environment: Sheldon (population 5,100) is the trading center for a rich, five-county farmland area. Bus and train transportation are available, airline service is within 55 miles at Sioux City. Local parks and a golf club provide facilities for recreation. The Iowa Lakes Region is a 50 mile drive. Community facilities include public libraries, churches, a modern hospital, and an indoor swimming pool.

■ **NORTHWESTERN COLLEGE** *C-2*

101 Seventh St., SW

Orange City, IA 51041-1996

Tel: (712)707-7000

Free: 800-747-4757

Admissions: (712)737-7130
Fax: (712)707-7247
E-mail: markb@nwciowa.edu
Web Site: http://www.nwciowa.edu/

Description: Independent, 4-year, coed, affiliated with Reformed Church in America. Awards bachelor's degrees. Founded 1882. Setting: 45-acre rural campus. Endowment: $35.3 million. Research spending for 2004 fiscal year: $77,938. Educational spending for 2005 fiscal year: $6522 per student. Total enrollment: 1,273. Student-undergrad faculty ratio is 15:1. 1,185 applied, 93% were admitted. 28% from top 10% of their high school class, 55% from top quarter, 85% from top half. 19 valedictorians. Full-time: 1,226 students, 62% women, 38% men. Part-time: 47 students, 60% women, 40% men. Students come from 29 states and territories, 12 other countries, 43% from out-of-state, 0.1% Native American, 1% Hispanic, 1% black, 1% Asian American or Pacific Islander, 2% international, 3% 25 or older, 89% live on campus, 4% transferred in. Retention: 76% of full-time freshmen returned the following year. Academic areas with the most degrees conferred: business/marketing; education; biological/life sciences. Core. Calendar: semesters. Academic remediation for entering students, ESL program, advanced placement, self-designed majors, freshman honors college, honors program, independent study, double major, summer session for credit, part-time degree program, internships. Off campus study at 5 members of the Mid-America States Universities Association, Council for Christian Colleges and Universities. Study abroad program.

Entrance Requirements: Options: Peterson's Universal Application, Common Application, electronic application, early admission, deferred admission, international baccalaureate accepted. Required: essay, high school transcript, minimum 2.0 high school GPA, 1 recommendation, SAT and SAT Subject Tests or ACT. Recommended: minimum 2.5 high school GPA, interview. Entrance: moderately difficult. Application deadline: Rolling. Notification: continuous.

Costs Per Year: Application fee: $25. Comprehensive fee: $22,174 includes full-time tuition ($17,260) and college room and board ($4914). College room only: $2090. Room and board charges vary according to housing facility.

Collegiate Environment: Orientation program. Drama-theater group, choral group, student-run newspaper. Social organizations: 30 open to all. Most popular organizations: Phi Beta Lambda, Student Ministries Board, Student Iowa State Education Association, Fellowship of Christian Athletes, International Club. Major annual events: Homecoming, Springfest, Parents' Day. Student services: health clinic, personal-psychological counseling. Campus security: 24-hour emergency response devices, controlled dormitory access. 1,208 college housing spaces available; 1,075 were occupied in 2003-04. On-campus residence required through senior year. Options: men-only, women-only housing available. Ramaker Library plus 1 other with 125,000 books, 110,000 microform titles, 615 serials, 5,000 audiovisual materials, and an OPAC. Operations spending for 2004 fiscal year: $470,729. 250 computers available on campus for general student use. A campuswide network can be accessed from student residence rooms and from off campus. Staffed computer lab on campus.

■ **PALMER COLLEGE OF CHIROPRACTIC** *H-16*
1000 Brady St.
Davenport, IA 52803-5287
Tel: (563)884-5000
Free: 800-722-3648
Admissions: (563)884-5656
Fax: (563)884-5897
E-mail: pcadmit@palmer.edu
Web Site: http://www.palmer.edu/

Description: Independent, comprehensive, coed. Awards associate, incidental bachelor's, master's, and first professional degrees. Founded 1897. Setting: urban campus. Total enrollment: 2,171. Faculty: 136 (all full-time). Student-undergrad faculty ratio is 16:1. Full-time: 81 students, 65% women, 35% men. Part-time: 15 students, 47% women, 53% men. 0% Native American, 3% Hispanic, 4% black, 5% Asian American or Pacific Islander, 0% international. Core. Calendar: trimesters. Academic remediation for entering students, services for LD students, summer session for credit, internships.

Entrance Requirements: Options: Peterson's Universal Application, Common Application, electronic application, deferred admission. Required: high school transcript, minimum 2.0 high school GPA, minimum 2.0 in math, science, and English courses. Required for some: essay, interview. Entrance: moderately difficult. Application deadline: Rolling. Notification: continuous. Preference given to students from colleges with whom PCC has an articulation agreement.

Costs Per Year: Application fee: $50. Tuition: $5775 full-time, $145 per credit part-time. Mandatory fees: $255 full-time, $100 per term part-time.

Collegiate Environment: Orientation program. Student-run newspaper. Social organizations: 60 open to all; local fraternities, local sororities. Most popular organizations: Gonstead Club, intramural sports, campus guides, Student International Chiropractic Association, Palmer Student Alumni Foundation. Major annual events: homecoming, Chili Cook-off, Fall Harvest. Student services: health clinic, personal-psychological counseling. Campus security: 24-hour emergency response devices and patrols, late night transport-escort service. College housing not available. D. D. Palmer Health Sciences Library with 55,278 books, 2,297 microform titles, 525 serials, 22,225 audiovisual materials, an OPAC, and a Web page. Operations spending for 2004 fiscal year: $840,766. 75 computers available on campus for general student use. A campuswide network can be accessed from off-campus. Staffed computer lab on campus.

Community Environment: The Quad-Cities area, a community of about 400,000, offers a wide variety of entertainment options including more than 275 restaurants; professional basketball and ice hockey; Class A baseball; arena football; 60 miles of bike trails; theater, museums and the art galleries.

■ **ST. AMBROSE UNIVERSITY** *H-16*
518 West Locust St.
Davenport, IA 52803-2898
Tel: (563)333-6000
Free: 800-383-2627
Admissions: (563)333-6300
Fax: (563)383-8791
E-mail: higginsmegf@sau.edu
Web Site: http://www.sau.edu/

Description: Independent Roman Catholic, comprehensive, coed. Awards bachelor's, master's, and doctoral degrees and post-master's certificates. Founded 1882. Setting: 11-acre urban campus. Endowment: $39.3 million. Educational spending for 2005 fiscal year: $5960 per student. Total enrollment: 3,623. Faculty: 290 (160 full-time, 130 part-time). Student-undergrad faculty ratio is 15:1. 1,634 applied, 84% were admitted. 16% from top 10% of their high school class, 36% from top quarter, 65% from top half. 45 valedictorians. Full-time: 2,200 students, 58% women, 42% men. Part-time: 498 students, 67% women, 33% men. Students come from 23 states and territories, 12 other countries, 44% from out-of-state, 0.3% Native American, 3% Hispanic, 3% black, 1% Asian American or Pacific Islander, 1% international, 23% 25 or older, 52% live on campus, 12% transferred in. Retention: 80% of full-time freshmen returned the following year. Academic areas with the most degrees conferred: business/marketing; education; psychology. Core. Calendar: 4-1-4. Academic remediation for entering students, services for LD students, advanced placement, accelerated degree program, self-designed majors, independent study, distance learning, double major, summer session for credit, part-time degree program, external degree program, adult/continuing education programs, co-op programs and internships, graduate courses open to undergrads. Off campus study at Black Hawk College, Eastern Iowa Community Colleges. Study abroad program.

Entrance Requirements: Options: Peterson's Universal Application, Common Application, electronic application, deferred admission. Required: high school transcript, minimum 2.5 high school GPA, minimum ACT score of 20 or rank in top 50% of high school class, SAT or ACT. Recommended: interview, ACT. Required for some: recommendations, interview. Entrance: moderately difficult. Application deadline: Rolling. Notification: 10/1.

Costs Per Year: Application fee: $25. Comprehensive fee: $26,700 includes full-time tuition ($19,460) and college room and board ($7240). College room only: $3690. Part-time tuition: $605 per semester hour.

Collegiate Environment: Orientation program. Drama-theater group, choral group, student-run newspaper, radio station. Social organizations: 23 open to all. Most popular organizations: Student Government Association, Student Alumni Association, Social Action Group, College Activities Board, Ambrosians for Peace and Justice. Major annual events: Homecoming, Winter Carnival, Spring Fling. Student services: health clinic, personal-psychological counseling, women's center. Campus security: 24-hour emergency response devices and patrols, late night transport-escort service, controlled dormitory access, police officer on campus 10 p.m. to 6 a.m. 1,273 college housing spaces available; 1,212 were occupied in 2003-04. Freshmen guaranteed college housing. On-campus residence required through sophomore year. Options: coed, men-only, women-only housing available. O'Keefe Library plus 1 other with 143,634 books, 6,727 microform titles, 739 serials, 3,351 audiovisual materials, an OPAC, and a Web page. Operations spending for 2004 fiscal year: $838,329. 190 computers available on campus for general student use. Computer purchase/lease plans available. A campuswide network can be accessed from student residence rooms and from off campus. Staffed computer lab on campus.

■ **ST. LUKE'S COLLEGE** *D-1*

2720 Stone Park Blvd.
Sioux City, IA 51104
Tel: (712)279-3149
Free: 800-352-4660
Fax: (712)233-8017
E-mail: mccartsj@stlukes.org
Web Site: http://stlukescollege.edu/

Description: Independent, 2-year, coed. Part of St. Luke's Regional Medical Center. Awards certificates and terminal associate degrees. Setting: rural campus. Endowment: $883,130. Educational spending for 2005 fiscal year: $7568 per student. Total enrollment: 155. Student-undergrad faculty ratio is 11:1. 2% from top 10% of their high school class, 2% from top quarter, 39% from top half. Full-time: 128 students, 89% women, 11% men. Part-time: 27 students, 93% women, 7% men. Students come from 8 states and territories, 28% from out-of-state, 2% Native American, 1% Hispanic, 1% black, 0% Asian American or Pacific Islander, 0% international, 45% 25 or older, 15% live on campus, 7% transferred in. Retention: 83% of full-time freshmen returned the following year. Core. Calendar: semesters. Advanced placement, summer session for credit, part-time degree program, co-op programs.

Entrance Requirements: Options: electronic application, early admission, early action. Required: essay, high school transcript, minimum 2.50 high school GPA, interview, minimum ACT score of 19, ACT. Entrance: minimally difficult. Application deadlines: 8/1, 11/1 for early decision plan 1, 3/15 for early decision plan 2.

Costs Per Year: Application fee: $25. Tuition: $11,900 full-time, $340 per credit part-time. Mandatory fees: $600 full-time.

Collegiate Environment: Orientation program. Major annual events: Phone-a-thon, Spring Fling, Professionals Day. Student services: health clinic, personal-psychological counseling. Campus security: 24-hour emergency response devices and patrols, late night transport-escort service. 74 college housing spaces available; 20 were occupied in 2003-04. No special consideration for freshman housing applicants. Option: coed housing available. St. Luke's Library plus 1 other with 2,038 books, 119 serials, 324 audiovisual materials, an OPAC, and a Web page. Operations spending for 2004 fiscal year: $185,937. 10 computers available on campus for general student use. A campuswide network can be accessed. Staffed computer lab on campus.

■ **SCOTT COMMUNITY COLLEGE** *H-16*

500 Belmont Rd.
Bettendorf, IA 52722-6804
Tel: (563)441-4001
Admissions: (563)441-4007
Fax: (563)441-4066
Web Site: http://www.eicc.edu/scc/

Description: State and locally supported, 2-year, coed. Part of Eastern Iowa Community College District. Awards certificates, diplomas, transfer associate, and terminal associate degrees. Founded 1966. Setting: urban campus. Educational spending for 2005 fiscal year: $2249 per student. Total enrollment: 4,697. 1,422 applied, 100% were admitted. Full-time: 2,212 students, 58% women, 42% men. Part-time: 2,485 students, 64% women, 36% men. Students come from 36 states and territories, 8% from out-of-state, 1% Native American, 4% Hispanic, 8% black, 2% Asian American or Pacific Islander, 1% international, 44% 25 or older. Core. Calendar: semesters. Academic remediation for entering students, ESL program, services for LD students, advanced placement, honors program, independent study, distance learning, double major, summer session for credit, part-time degree program, adult/continuing education programs, co-op programs and internships. Off campus study at Black Hawk College. Study abroad program.

Entrance Requirements: Open admission except for nursing program. Options: early admission, deferred admission. Required: high school transcript. Placement: ACT, College Board Diagnostic Tests required. Entrance: noncompetitive. Application deadline: Rolling. Notification: continuous.

Collegiate Environment: Drama-theater group. Most popular organizations: student government, Campus Activities Board. Student services: personal-psychological counseling. Campus security: 24-hour emergency response devices. College housing not available. Scott Community College Library with 22,700 books, 183 serials, and an OPAC. 200 computers available on

campus for general student use. A campuswide network can be accessed from off-campus. Staffed computer lab on campus.

Community Environment: Davenport (population 100,400), part of the Iowa-Illinois Quad Cities (pop. 375,000), is situated on the north bank of the Mississippi River and has an average temperature of 57 degrees and average rainfall of 50 inches. Commercial transportation is available. Community facilities are excellent and include 91 churches, hotels, hospitals, four local radio stations, four TV stations, a public library, and numerous civic and service organizations. Some of its industries' products are brooms, clothing, food, machinery, foundry products, and aircraft instruments. The 27 city parks offer varied recreational facilities. Vandeer Veer Park has gardens with approximately 2,500 species of roses.

■ **SIMPSON COLLEGE** *I-8*

701 North C St.
Indianola, IA 50125-1297
Tel: (515)961-6251
Free: 800-362-2454
Admissions: (515)961-1624
Fax: (515)961-1498
E-mail: admiss@simpson.edu
Web Site: http://www.simpson.edu/

Description: Independent United Methodist, 4-year, coed. Awards bachelor's degrees. Founded 1860. Setting: 74-acre small town campus. Endowment: $64.4 million. Educational spending for 2005 fiscal year: $6986 per student. Total enrollment: 2,035. Student-undergrad faculty ratio is 14:1. 1,216 applied, 87% were admitted. 30% from top 10% of their high school class, 61% from top quarter, 90% from top half. 32 valedictorians. Full-time: 1,485 students, 58% women, 42% men. Part-time: 525 students, 62% women, 38% men. Students come from 21 states and territories, 16 other countries, 8% from out-of-state, 0.2% Native American, 1% Hispanic, 1% black, 1% Asian American or Pacific Islander, 1% international, 21% 25 or older, 82% live on campus, 4% transferred in. Retention: 82% of full-time freshmen returned the following year. Academic areas with the most degrees conferred: business/marketing; social sciences; education. Core. Calendar: 4-4-1. Services for LD students, advanced placement, honors program, independent study, distance learning, double major, summer session for credit, part-time degree program, external degree program, adult/continuing education programs, co-op programs and internships. Off campus study at Drew University, American University, Washington Center Internships and Symposia, George Washington Carver Teacher Initiative Consortium agreement with Iowa State University and Des Moines Area Community College. Study abroad program.

Entrance Requirements: Options: electronic application, early admission, deferred admission, international baccalaureate accepted. Required: high school transcript, 1 recommendation, SAT or ACT. Recommended: rank in upper 50% of high school class. Entrance: moderately difficult. Application deadline: 8/15. Notification: continuous.

Costs Per Year: Application fee: $0. Comprehensive fee: $26,833 includes full-time tuition ($20,693), mandatory fees ($218), and college room and board ($5922). College room only: $2842. Room and board charges vary according to board plan and housing facility.

Collegiate Environment: Orientation program. Drama-theater group, choral group, student-run newspaper, radio station. Social organizations: 81 open to all; national fraternities, national sororities, local fraternities; 18% of eligible men and 25% of eligible women are members. Most popular organizations: intramurals, Religious Life Council, Campus Activities Board, student government. Major annual events: Homecoming Week, All College Sing, Campus Day. Student services: health clinic, personal-psychological counseling, Carver Cultural Center. Campus security: 24-hour emergency response devices and patrols, student patrols, late night transport-escort service, controlled dormitory access. 1,139 college housing spaces available; 1,106 were occupied in 2003-04. Freshmen guaranteed college housing. On-campus residence required through junior year. Options: coed, men-only, women-only housing available. Dunn Library plus 1 other with 157,713 books, 12,492 microform titles, 558 serials, 6,242 audiovisual materials, an OPAC, and a Web page. Operations spending for 2004 fiscal year: $792,117. 284 computers available on campus for general student use. A campuswide network can be accessed from student residence rooms and from off campus. Staffed computer lab on campus.

Community Environment: Indianola (population 13,000) is located 20 minutes from Des Moines, the state capital, and enjoys the advantages of both a charming small town and a metropolitan center. Major transportation facilities are found in Des Moines, including the Des Moines International

Airport. While Des Moines is known as a commercial and industrial city in the heart of a great agricultural state, it is also known for its educational, cultural, philanthropic, and religious institutions.

■ **SOUTHEASTERN COMMUNITY COLLEGE, NORTH CAMPUS** *J-15*
1500 West Agency St.
PO Box 180
West Burlington, IA 52655-0180
Tel: (319)752-2731
Fax: (319)752-4957
Web Site: http://www.secc.cc.ia.us/
Description: State and locally supported, 2-year, coed. Part of Iowa Department of Education Division of Community Colleges. Awards diplomas, transfer associate, and terminal associate degrees. Founded 1968. Setting: 160-acre small town campus. Total enrollment: 2,045. Students come from 8 states and territories, 34% 25 or older, 3% live on campus. Core. Calendar: semesters. Academic remediation for entering students, ESL program, services for LD students, advanced placement, distance learning, summer session for credit, part-time degree program, adult/continuing education programs, co-op programs and internships.
Entrance Requirements: Open admission except for computer programming, nursing, electronics, medical assistant, medical laboratory technology, manufacturing technology, engineering design, occupational therapy assistant, physical therapy assistant programs. Options: early admission, deferred admission. Placement: ACT ASSET required; ACT recommended. Entrance: noncompetitive. Application deadline: Rolling.
Collegiate Environment: Choral group. Social organizations: 15 open to all. Most popular organizations: Student Senate, Criminal Justice Club, Art Club, Science Club. Major annual events: Welcome Picnic, Spring Fling. Campus security: controlled dormitory access, night patrols by trained security personnel. Options: men-only, women-only housing available. Yohe Memorial Library with 39,304 books and 282 serials. 100 computers available on campus for general student use. Staffed computer lab on campus.

■ **SOUTHEASTERN COMMUNITY COLLEGE, SOUTH CAMPUS** *L-14*
335 Messenger Rd., PO Box 6007
Keokuk, IA 52632-6007
Tel: (319)524-3221
Admissions: (319)752-2731
Fax: (319)524-8621
Web Site: http://www.secc.cc.ia.us/
Description: State and locally supported, 2-year, coed. Part of Iowa Department of Education Division of Community Colleges. Awards certificates, diplomas, transfer associate, and terminal associate degrees. Founded 1967. Setting: 3-acre small town campus. Total enrollment: 548. Core. Calendar: semesters. Academic remediation for entering students, services for LD students, advanced placement, independent study, distance learning, summer session for credit, part-time degree program. Off campus study at Carl Sandburg College, Iowa Wesleyan College.
Entrance Requirements: Open admission except for nursing program. Options: electronic application, early admission, deferred admission. Recommended: high school transcript. Entrance: noncompetitive. Application deadline: Rolling.
Collegiate Environment: Orientation program. Drama-theater group, choral group, student-run newspaper. Social organizations: 10 open to all. Most popular organizations: Business Professionals of America, Art Club, Student Nurses Association, Computer Club, Student Board. Major annual events: Chicago trip, Fall Pizza Party, Spring Picnic. Student services: personal-psychological counseling. College housing not available. Fred Karre Memorial Library with 10,000 books, 70 serials, and an OPAC. 80 computers available on campus for general student use. A campuswide network can be accessed from off-campus. Staffed computer lab on campus.

■ **SOUTHWESTERN COMMUNITY COLLEGE** *J-6*
1501 West Townline St.
Creston, IA 50801
Tel: (641)782-7081
Free: 800-247-4023
Fax: (641)782-3312
E-mail: carstens@swcc.cc.ia.us
Web Site: http://www.swcc.cc.ia.us/
Description: State-supported, 2-year, coed. Part of Iowa Department of Education Division of Community Colleges. Awards diplomas, transfer associate, and terminal associate degrees. Founded 1966. Setting: 420-acre

rural campus. Endowment: $691,031. Total enrollment: 1,254. 660 applied, 43% were admitted. 15% from top quarter of their high school class, 47% from top half. Full-time: 666 students, 59% women, 41% men. Part-time: 588 students, 54% women, 46% men. Students come from 11 states and territories, 4 other countries, 4% from out-of-state, 0% Native American, 1% Hispanic, 2% black, 0.2% Asian American or Pacific Islander, 0.5% international, 30% 25 or older, 5% live on campus, 5% transferred in. Core. Calendar: semesters. Academic remediation for entering students, services for LD students, advanced placement, self-designed majors, independent study, summer session for credit, part-time degree program, adult/continuing education programs, co-op programs and internships.
Entrance Requirements: Open admission except for allied health programs. Options: Peterson's Universal Application, Common Application, electronic application, early admission. Required: high school transcript. Required for some: SAT or ACT, ACT COMPASS. Entrance: noncompetitive. Application deadline: 9/5. Notification: continuous.
Costs Per Year: Application fee: $0. State resident tuition: $3104 full-time, $97 per credit hour part-time. Nonresident tuition: $4560 full-time, $142.50 per credit hour part-time. Mandatory fees: $384 full-time, $13 per credit hour part-time. College room and board: $3700.
Collegiate Environment: Choral group, student-run newspaper. Major annual events: Social Awareness Day, Cultural Diversity Day, Early Bird Scholarships. Student services: personal-psychological counseling. Campus security: 24-hour emergency response devices and patrols, controlled dormitory access. 60 undergraduates lived in college housing during 2003-04. No special consideration for freshman housing applicants. Options: men-only, women-only housing available. Learning Resources Center with 14,742 books, 1,044 microform titles, 170 serials, 1,174 audiovisual materials, an OPAC, and a Web page. Operations spending for 2004 fiscal year: $144,366. 115 computers available on campus for general student use. A campuswide network can be accessed from off-campus. Staffed computer lab on campus.

■ **UNIVERSITY OF DUBUQUE** *D-16*
2000 University Ave.
Dubuque, IA 52001-5099
Tel: (563)589-3000
Admissions: (563)589-3214
Fax: (563)589-3690
Web Site: http://www.dbq.edu/
Description: Independent Presbyterian, comprehensive, coed. Awards associate, bachelor's, master's, doctoral, and first professional degrees. Founded 1852. Setting: 56-acre suburban campus. Total enrollment: 1,441. Faculty: 158 (70 full-time, 88 part-time). Student-undergrad faculty ratio is 13:1. 885 applied, 77% were admitted. 10% from top 10% of their high school class, 25% from top quarter, 51% from top half. 1 National Merit Scholar, 15 class presidents, 2 valedictorians, 100 student government officers. Full-time: 1,127 students, 37% women, 63% men. Part-time: 52 students, 56% women, 44% men. Students come from 37 states and territories, 2 other countries, 60% from out-of-state, 2% Native American, 4% Hispanic, 12% black, 1% Asian American or Pacific Islander, 1% international, 1% 25 or older, 70% live on campus, 10% transferred in. Retention: 65% of full-time freshmen returned the following year. Academic areas with the most degrees conferred: health professions and related sciences; business/marketing; education. Core. Calendar: semesters. Academic remediation for entering students, ESL program, services for LD students, advanced placement, accelerated degree program, self-designed majors, independent study, distance learning, double major, summer session for credit, part-time degree program, adult/continuing education programs, internships, graduate courses open to undergrads. Off campus study at Loras College, Clarke College (IA). Study abroad program. ROTC: Army.
Entrance Requirements: Options: Peterson's Universal Application, Common Application, electronic application, international baccalaureate accepted. Required: essay, high school transcript, minimum 2.5 high school GPA, 2 recommendations, SAT or ACT. Recommended: interview. Entrance: moderately difficult. Application deadline: Rolling. Notification: continuous.
Costs Per Year: Application fee: $25. Comprehensive fee: $23,420 includes full-time tuition ($17,250), mandatory fees ($220), and college room and board ($5950). College room only: $3100. Part-time tuition: $390 per credit.
Collegiate Environment: Orientation program. Drama-theater group, choral group, student-run newspaper. Social organizations: 50 open to all; local fraternities, local sororities; 15% of eligible men and 13% of eligible women are members. Most popular organizations: Alpha Phi Omega, Students in Free Enterprise, Student Activities Board, Student Government Association,

Web of Life (environmental science). Major annual events: homecoming, Spring Founders' Day Ball, Christmas Candlelight Ceremony. Student services: health clinic, personal-psychological counseling. Campus security: 24-hour patrols, late night transport-escort service, controlled dormitory access. 700 college housing spaces available; all were occupied in 2003-04. Freshmen guaranteed college housing. On-campus residence required through junior year. Options: coed, men-only, women-only housing available. Charles C. Myer's Library with 168,579 books, 20,000 microform titles, 484 serials, 1,169 audiovisual materials, an OPAC, and a Web page. 220 computers available on campus for general student use. A campuswide network can be accessed from student residence rooms and from off campus. Staffed computer lab on campus.

■ **THE UNIVERSITY OF IOWA** *G-14*
Iowa City, IA 52242-1316
Tel: (319)335-3500
Free: 800-553-4692
Admissions: (319)335-3847
Fax: (319)335-1535
E-mail: admissions@uiowa.edu
Web Site: http://www.uiowa.edu/
Description: State-supported, university, coed. Awards bachelor's, master's, doctoral, and first professional degrees and post-master's and first professional certificates. Founded 1847. Setting: 1,900-acre small town campus. Endowment: $313.8 million. Research spending for 2004 fiscal year: $217.1 million. Educational spending for 2005 fiscal year: $9695 per student. Total enrollment: 28,426. Faculty: 1,693 (1,595 full-time, 98 part-time). Student-undergrad faculty ratio is 15:1. 13,241 applied, 84% were admitted. 22% from top 10% of their high school class, 53% from top quarter, 92% from top half. 25 National Merit Scholars, 168 valedictorians. Full-time: 18,194 students, 53% women, 47% men. Part-time: 2,106 students, 54% women, 46% men. Students come from 51 states and territories, 68 other countries, 39% from out-of-state, 0.5% Native American, 2% Hispanic, 2% black, 4% Asian American or Pacific Islander, 2% international, 9% 25 or older, 28% live on campus, 6% transferred in. Retention: 84% of full-time freshmen returned the following year. Academic areas with the most degrees conferred: business/marketing; social sciences; communications/journalism. Core. Calendar: semesters. Academic remediation for entering students, ESL program, services for LD students, advanced placement, accelerated degree program, self-designed majors, honors program, independent study, distance learning, double major, summer session for credit, part-time degree program, external degree program, adult/continuing education programs, co-op programs and internships, graduate courses open to undergrads. Off campus study at Iowa State University of Science and Technology, University of Northern Iowa, Committee on Institutional Cooperation. Study abroad program. ROTC: Army, Air Force.
Entrance Requirements: Options: electronic application, early admission, deferred admission, international baccalaureate accepted. Required: high school transcript, rank in upper 50% for residents, rank in top 30% for nonresidents, SAT or ACT. Entrance: moderately difficult. Application deadline: 4/1. Notification: continuous.
Costs Per Year: Application fee: $40. State resident tuition: $5110 full-time, $213 per semester hour part-time. Nonresident tuition: $17,334 full-time, $757 per semester hour part-time. Mandatory fees: $825 full-time, $413 per term part-time. College room and board: $6912.
Collegiate Environment: Orientation program. Drama-theater group, choral group, marching band, student-run newspaper, radio station. Social organizations: 408 open to all; national fraternities, national sororities; 7% of eligible men and 12% of eligible women are members. Most popular organizations: Association of Students of Engineering, Association of Residence Halls, Newman Center, Friendship Association of Chinese Scholars, May Co. Major annual events: River Fest Annual Spring Festival, Homecoming, Dance Marathon. Student services: legal services, health clinic, personal-psychological counseling, women's center. Campus security: 24-hour emergency response devices and patrols, late night transport-escort service, controlled dormitory access. 5,600 college housing spaces available; 5,515 were occupied in 2003-04. Freshmen given priority for college housing. Option: coed housing available. Main Library plus 12 others with 4 million books, 6.6 million microform titles, 44,644 serials, 267,192 audiovisual materials, an OPAC, and a Web page. Operations spending for 2004 fiscal year: $24.1 million. 1,200 computers available on campus for general student use. Computer purchase/lease plans available. A campuswide network can be accessed from student residence rooms and from off campus. Staffed computer lab on campus.

Community Environment: Greater Iowa City (population 70,085) is located in eastern Iowa. Major transportation facilities are accessible. The university hospital and medical and scientific research departments make Iowa City an important medical center for the area and state. Public and historical libraries and museums, churches of most denominations, hospitals, and civic, fraternal, and veterans' organizations are a part of the community.

■ **UNIVERSITY OF NORTHERN IOWA** *D-11*
1227 West 27th St.
Cedar Falls, IA 50614
Tel: (319)273-2311
Free: 800-772-2037
Admissions: (319)273-2701
Fax: (319)273-2885
E-mail: admissions@uni.edu
Web Site: http://www.uni.edu/
Description: State-supported, comprehensive, coed. Part of Board of Regents, State of Iowa. Awards bachelor's, master's, and doctoral degrees. Founded 1876. Setting: 916-acre small town campus. Endowment: $51.8 million. Research spending for 2004 fiscal year: $2.6 million. Educational spending for 2005 fiscal year: $10,242 per student. Total enrollment: 12,622. Faculty: 829 (641 full-time, 188 part-time). Student-undergrad faculty ratio is 16:1. 4,360 applied, 78% were admitted. 19% from top 10% of their high school class, 48% from top quarter, 90% from top half. Full-time: 9,753 students, 57% women, 43% men. Part-time: 1,241 students, 57% women, 43% men. Students come from 42 states and territories, 58 other countries, 5% from out-of-state, 0.2% Native American, 1% Hispanic, 3% black, 1% Asian American or Pacific Islander, 2% international, 9% 25 or older, 34% live on campus, 10% transferred in. Retention: 81% of full-time freshmen returned the following year. Academic areas with the most degrees conferred: business/marketing; education; social sciences. Core. Calendar: semesters. Academic remediation for entering students, ESL program, services for LD students, advanced placement, accelerated degree program, self-designed majors, honors program, independent study, distance learning, double major, summer session for credit, part-time degree program, external degree program, adult/continuing education programs, co-op programs and internships, graduate courses open to undergrads. Off campus study at Iowa Regents' Universities Student Exchange, National Student Exchange. Study abroad program. ROTC: Army.
Entrance Requirements: Options: electronic application, deferred admission, international baccalaureate accepted. Required: high school transcript, rank in upper 50% of high school class, SAT or ACT. Required for some: interview. Entrance: moderately difficult. Application deadline: 8/15. Notification: 9/1.
Costs Per Year: Application fee: $30. State resident tuition: $4890 full-time, $204 per hour part-time. Nonresident tuition: $12,502 full-time, $521 per hour part-time. Mandatory fees: $712 full-time, $313.75 per term part-time. Full-time tuition and fees vary according to course load. Part-time tuition and fees vary according to course load. College room and board: $5531. College room only: $2588. Room and board charges vary according to board plan and housing facility.
Collegiate Environment: Orientation program. Drama-theater group, choral group, marching band, student-run newspaper, radio station. Social organizations: 185 open to all; national fraternities, national sororities; 4% of eligible men and 3% of eligible women are members. Most popular organizations: American Marketing Association, Public Relations Student Society, Iowa State Education Association, United Students of Iowa, Golden Key. Major annual events: homecoming, Family Fest. Student services: health clinic, personal-psychological counseling. Campus security: 24-hour emergency response devices and patrols, student patrols, late night transport-escort service, controlled dormitory access. 4,921 college housing spaces available; 3,816 were occupied in 2003-04. No special consideration for freshman housing applicants. Options: coed, men-only, women-only housing available. Rod Library with 1.2 million books, 1.1 million microform titles, 6,814 serials, 28,342 audiovisual materials, an OPAC, and a Web page. Operations spending for 2004 fiscal year: $5.8 million. 1,900 computers available on campus for general student use. Computer purchase/lease plans available. A campuswide network can be accessed from student residence rooms and from off campus. Staffed computer lab on campus.
Community Environment: Cedar Falls is an active industrial community on the Cedar River, situated in northeast Iowa. Along with nearby Waterloo, the area population is well over 100,000. All forms of commercial transportation are available. Recreational facilities include many parks; Cedar River for fishing and boating, and two public golf courses. Part-time work is available.

■ UPPER IOWA UNIVERSITY *C-13*

605 Washington St., Box 1857
Fayette, IA 52142-1857
Tel: (563)425-5200
Free: 800-553-4150
Admissions: (563)425-5281
Fax: (563)425-5277
E-mail: admission@uiu.edu
Web Site: http://www.uiu.edu/

Description: Independent, comprehensive, coed. Awards associate, bachelor's, and master's degrees (also offers continuing education program with significant enrollment not reflected in profile). Founded 1857. Setting: 80-acre rural campus. Total enrollment: 887. 853 applied, 56% were admitted. 23% from top 10% of their high school class, 41% from top quarter, 80% from top half. 5 valedictorians. Full-time: 678 students, 40% women, 60% men. Part-time: 47 students, 74% women, 26% men. Students come from 25 states and territories, 7 other countries, 42% from out-of-state, 0.1% Native American, 5% Hispanic, 15% black, 5% Asian American or Pacific Islander, 2% international, 70% live on campus, 13% transferred in. Retention: 65% of full-time freshmen returned the following year. Core. Calendar: 4 8-week terms. Academic remediation for entering students, advanced placement, accelerated degree program, self-designed majors, independent study, distance learning, double major, summer session for credit, part-time degree program, external degree program, adult/continuing education programs, internships. Study abroad program.

Entrance Requirements: Options: Peterson's Universal Application, Common Application, early admission, deferred admission. Required: high school transcript, minimum 2.0 high school GPA, SAT or ACT. Required for some: essay, recommendations, interview. Entrance: moderately difficult. Application deadline: Rolling.

Costs Per Year: Application fee: $15. Comprehensive fee: $23,596 includes full-time tuition ($18,056) and college room and board ($5540). College room only: $2300. Full-time tuition varies according to course load. Room and board charges vary according to board plan and housing facility. Part-time tuition: $600 per credit hour.

Collegiate Environment: Orientation program. Drama-theater group, choral group, student-run newspaper. Social organizations: 35 open to all; local fraternities, local sororities; 30% of eligible men and 30% of eligible women are members. Most popular organizations: outdoor pursuits, Sigma Delta Phi, Alpha Nu Omega, Psychology Club, Campus Events Council. Major annual events: Greek Week, Homecoming, Spring Fest. Student services: health clinic, personal-psychological counseling. Campus security: late night transport-escort service, controlled dormitory access. 500 college housing spaces available; 288 were occupied in 2003-04. Freshmen guaranteed college housing. On-campus residence required through sophomore year. Options: coed, men-only, women-only housing available. Henderson Wilder Library with 64,043 books, 9,501 microform titles, 3,241 serials, 4,031 audiovisual materials, an OPAC, and a Web page. 75 computers available on campus for general student use. A campuswide network can be accessed. Staffed computer lab on campus.

Community Environment: Fayette (population 1,500) is a rural area in northeastern Iowa, 50 miles from the Mississippi River. Community facilities include five churches and hospital service in the county seat 8 miles away. The city has a Chamber of Commerce and other civic and fraternal organizations. Part-time work is available for students and families. Outdoor sports include hiking, cross-country skiing, hunting, fishing, and golf.

■ VATTEROTT COLLEGE *H-8*

6100 Thornton Ave., Ste. 290
Des Moines, IA 50321
Tel: (515)309-9000
Free: 800-353-7264
Fax: (515)309-0366
Web Site: http://www.vatterott-college.edu/

Description: Proprietary, primarily 2-year, coed. Awards certificates, diplomas, terminal associate, and bachelor's degrees. Setting: 25-acre urban campus. Total enrollment: 336. Student-undergrad faculty ratio is 15:1. 0% Native American, 3% Hispanic, 6% black, 3% Asian American or Pacific Islander, 0% international. Calendar: ten week periods.

Entrance Requirements: Required: high school transcript, interview.

■ VENNARD COLLEGE

PO Box 29
University Park, IA 52595

Tel: (515)673-8391
Free: 800-686-8391
Admissions: (641)673-8391
Fax: (515)673-8365
Web Site: http://www.vennard.edu/

Description: Independent interdenominational, 4-year, coed. Awards associate and bachelor's degrees. Founded 1996. Setting: 70-acre small town campus with easy access to Des Moines. Endowment: $479,742. Educational spending for 2005 fiscal year: $4377 per student. Total enrollment: 72. 49 applied, 33% were admitted. 0% from top 10% of their high school class, 12% from top quarter, 25% from top half. Full-time: 58 students, 43% women, 57% men. Part-time: 14 students, 64% women, 36% men. Students come from 17 states and territories, 82% from out-of-state, 0% Native American, 1% Hispanic, 0% black, 0% Asian American or Pacific Islander, 0% international, 29% 25 or older, 11% transferred in. Retention: 66% of full-time freshmen returned the following year. Core. Calendar: semesters. Academic remediation for entering students, advanced placement, self-designed majors, independent study, distance learning, double major, summer session for credit, part-time degree program, co-op programs and internships. Off campus study at William Penn University.

Entrance Requirements: Options: Common Application, electronic application, early admission. Required: essay, high school transcript, minimum 2.2 high school GPA, 3 recommendations. Required for some: interview, SAT or ACT, SAT and SAT Subject Tests or ACT. Entrance: moderately difficult. Application deadline: 8/11.

Collegiate Environment: Orientation program. Campus security: student patrols. 75 college housing spaces available; 30 were occupied in 2003-04. Freshmen guaranteed college housing. On-campus residence required through sophomore year. Options: men-only, women-only housing available. Jessop-Bruner Library with 19,619 books, 5,975 serials, 302 audiovisual materials, an OPAC, and a Web page. Operations spending for 2004 fiscal year: $69,514. 17 computers available on campus for general student use. Staffed computer lab on campus.

■ WALDORF COLLEGE *B-8*

106 South 6th St.
Forest City, IA 50436-1713
Tel: (641)585-2450
Free: 800-292-1903
Admissions: (641)585-8112
Fax: (641)585-8194
E-mail: admissions@waldorf.edu
Web Site: http://www.waldorf.edu/

Description: Independent Lutheran, 4-year, coed. Awards bachelor's degrees. Founded 1903. Setting: 29-acre small town campus. Total enrollment: 629. 761 applied, 63% were admitted. 5% from top 10% of their high school class, 28% from top quarter, 49% from top half. Full-time: 546 students, 52% women, 48% men. Part-time: 83 students, 65% women, 35% men. Students come from 20 states and territories, 11 other countries, 33% from out-of-state, 0% Native American, 0.5% Hispanic, 3% black, 0.5% Asian American or Pacific Islander, 5% international, 4% 25 or older, 93% live on campus, 11% transferred in. Retention: 75% of full-time freshmen returned the following year. Core. Calendar: semesters. Academic remediation for entering students, ESL program, services for LD students, advanced placement, accelerated degree program, freshman honors college, honors program, double major, summer session for credit, part-time degree program, adult/continuing education programs, co-op programs and internships. Study abroad program.

Entrance Requirements: Options: Peterson's Universal Application, Common Application, electronic application, early admission. Required: high school transcript, 1 recommendation, SAT or ACT. Recommended: minimum 2.0 high school GPA. Required for some: interview. Entrance: moderately difficult. Application deadline: Rolling. Notification: continuous.

Costs Per Year: Application fee: $0. Comprehensive fee: $20,140 includes full-time tuition ($14,785), mandatory fees ($735), and college room and board ($4620). College room only: $2150. Full-time tuition and fees vary according to class time, course load, and program. Room and board charges vary according to board plan and housing facility. Part-time tuition: $180 per credit. Part-time mandatory fees: $200 per credit.

Collegiate Environment: Orientation program. Drama-theater group, choral group, student-run newspaper, radio station. Social organizations: 13 open to all. Most popular organizations: student government, FCA, Drama Club, intramurals, Amnesty International. Major annual events: Homecoming, Bash on the Grass. Student services: health clinic, personal-psychological counseling. Campus security: late night transport-escort service, evening and night patrols by trained security personnel. 800 college housing spaces available; 425 were occupied in 2003-04. Freshmen guaranteed college housing. On-campus residence required through sophomore year. Options: coed, men-only, women-only housing available. Voss Memorial Library with 33,422 books, 43,718 microform titles, 55,989 serials, 274 audiovisual materials, and an OPAC. 700 computers available on campus for general student use. Computer purchase/lease plans available. A campuswide network can be accessed from student residence rooms and from off campus. Staffed computer lab on campus.

Community Environment: Forest City (population 5000), so named for the numerous trees covering the slopes of the rolling hills surrounding the city, is in north-central Iowa on the Winnebago River, near Mason City (population 35,000) and midway between Minneapolis and Des Moines. It is also the county seat and serves as both the manufacturing and administrative center for Winnebago Industries. A few miles to the east is Pilot Knob State Park, offering hiking and winter sports. Also available for recreation is the YMCA.

■ **WARTBURG COLLEGE** *D-11*
100 Wartburg Blvd., PO Box 1003
Waverly, IA 50677-0903
Tel: (319)352-8200
Free: 800-772-2085
Admissions: (319)352-8264
Fax: (319)352-8279
E-mail: admissions@wartburg.edu
Web Site: http://www.wartburg.edu/

Description: Independent Lutheran, 4-year, coed. Awards bachelor's degrees. Founded 1852. Setting: 118-acre small town campus. Endowment: $36.8 million. Educational spending for 2005 fiscal year: $9021 per student. Total enrollment: 1,811. Student-undergrad faculty ratio is 12:1. 1,681 applied, 88% were admitted. 31% from top 10% of their high school class, 61% from top quarter, 89% from top half. 43 valedictorians. Full-time: 1,732 students, 52% women, 48% men. Part-time: 79 students, 62% women, 38% men. Students come from 25 states and territories, 36 other countries, 23% from out-of-state, 0.3% Native American, 1% Hispanic, 3% black, 1% Asian American or Pacific Islander, 5% international, 2% 25 or older, 79% live on campus, 2% transferred in. Retention: 77% of full-time freshmen returned the following year. Academic areas with the most degrees conferred: business/marketing; education; communications/journalism. Core. Calendar: 4-4-1. Academic remediation for entering students, advanced placement, accelerated degree program, self-designed majors, honors program, independent study, double major, summer session for credit, part-time degree program, internships. Off campus study at members of the May Term Consortium. Study abroad program.

Entrance Requirements: Options: Peterson's Universal Application, Common Application, electronic application, early action, deferred admission. Required: high school transcript, minimum 2.0 high school GPA, SAT or ACT. Recommended: recommendations, secondary school report. Required for some: interview. Entrance: moderately difficult. Application deadline: 12/1 for early action. Notification: continuous.

Costs Per Year: Application fee: $20. Comprehensive fee: $26,895 includes full-time tuition ($20,500), mandatory fees ($630), and college room and board ($5765). College room only: $2815. Room and board charges vary according to board plan and housing facility. Part-time tuition: $760 per credit. Part-time mandatory fees: $50 per term. Part-time tuition and fees vary according to course load.

Collegiate Environment: Orientation program. Drama-theater group, choral group, student-run newspaper, radio station. Social organizations: 96 open to all. Most popular organizations: Entertainment To Knight, choir, Student Senate, campus ministry, band. Major annual events: Outfly, Homecoming, Family Weekend. Student services: health clinic, personal-psychological counseling. Campus security: 24-hour emergency response devices and patrols, late night transport-escort service, controlled dormitory access. 1,471 college housing spaces available; 1,415 were occupied in 2003-04. Freshmen guaranteed college housing. On-campus residence required through senior year. Options: coed, men-only, women-only housing available. Vogel Library with 186,089 books, 7,774 microform titles, 12,473 serials, 4,717 audiovisual materials, an OPAC, and a Web page. Operations spending for 2004 fiscal year: $687,216. 275 computers available on campus for general student use. A campuswide network can be accessed from student residence rooms and from off campus. Staffed computer lab on campus.

Community Environment: Waverly is a rural Iowa community (population 9,000), within 15 minutes of the Waterloo-Cedar Falls metro area (population

120,000). A variety of cultural events are available. The community provides libraries, a museum, a hospital, churches, clinics, shopping facilities and a community symphony. Part-time employment opportunities are limited.

■ **WESTERN IOWA TECH COMMUNITY COLLEGE** *D-1*
4647 Stone Ave., PO Box 5199
Sioux City, IA 51102-5199
Tel: (712)274-6400
Fax: (712)274-6412
Web Site: http://www.witcc.edu/

Description: State-supported, 2-year, coed. Part of Iowa Department of Education Division of Community Colleges. Awards certificates, diplomas, transfer associate, and terminal associate degrees. Founded 1966. Setting: 143-acre urban campus. Endowment: $337,763. Research spending for 2004 fiscal year: $40,502. Total enrollment: 5,334. Student-undergrad faculty ratio is 20:1. 581 applied, 100% were admitted. 12% from top 10% of their high school class, 33% from top quarter, 69% from top half. Full-time: 2,086 students, 59% women, 41% men. Part-time: 3,248 students, 54% women, 46% men. 10% from out-of-state, 2% Native American, 6% Hispanic, 2% black, 2% Asian American or Pacific Islander, 0.1% international, 30% 25 or older, 2% live on campus, 7% transferred in. Core. Calendar: semesters. Academic remediation for entering students, ESL program, services for LD students, accelerated degree program, honors program, independent study, distance learning, double major, summer session for credit, part-time degree program, adult/continuing education programs, internships.

Entrance Requirements: Open admission except health occupations programs. Options: early admission, deferred admission. Required: high school transcript. Entrance: noncompetitive. Application deadline: Rolling. Notification: continuous.

Costs Per Year: Application fee: $20. State resident tuition: $93 per credit hour part-time. Nonresident tuition: $133 per credit hour part-time. Mandatory fees: $15 per credit hour part-time.

Collegiate Environment: Orientation program. Most popular organization: Student Senate. Student services: health clinic, personal-psychological counseling. Campus security: 24-hour emergency response devices and patrols. Western Iowa Tech Community College Library Services with 25,696 books, 10,463 microform titles, 1,886 serials, 3,456 audiovisual materials, and an OPAC. Operations spending for 2004 fiscal year: $255,202. 640 computers available on campus for general student use. A campuswide network can be accessed from student residence rooms and from off campus. Staffed computer lab on campus.

Community Environment: See Briar Cliff University.

■ **WILLIAM PENN UNIVERSITY** *I-11*
201 Trueblood Ave.
Oskaloosa, IA 52577-1799
Tel: (641)673-1001
Free: 800-779-7366
Admissions: (641)673-1012
Fax: (641)673-1396
E-mail: admissions@wmpenn.edu
Web Site: http://www.wmpenn.edu/

Description: Independent, 4-year, coed, affiliated with Society of Friends. Awards associate and bachelor's degrees. Founded 1873. Setting: 60-acre rural campus with easy access to Des Moines. Endowment: $4.2 million. Educational spending for 2005 fiscal year: $2821 per student. Total enrollment: 1,892. Student-undergrad faculty ratio is 15:1. 9% from top 10% of their high school class, 20% from top quarter, 50% from top half. Full-time: 1,804 students, 57% women, 43% men. Part-time: 88 students, 44% women, 56% men. Students come from 42 states and territories, 12 other countries, 28% from out-of-state, 1% Native American, 5% Hispanic, 10% black, 2% Asian American or Pacific Islander, 0.1% international, 30% 25 or older, 40% live on campus, 6% transferred in. Retention: 55% of full-time freshmen returned the following year. Academic areas with the most degrees conferred: business/marketing; education; social sciences. Core. Calendar: semesters. Academic remediation for entering students, ESL program, services for LD students, advanced placement, self-designed majors, independent study, double major, summer session for credit, part-time degree program, adult/continuing education programs, co-op programs and internships. Study abroad program.

Entrance Requirements: Options: electronic application, deferred admission. Required: high school transcript, minimum 2.0 high school GPA, SAT or ACT. Required for some: essay, recommendations, interview. Entrance: moderately difficult. Notification: continuous.

Costs Per Year: Application fee: $20. Comprehensive fee: $20,927 includes full-time tuition ($15,575), mandatory fees ($370), and college room and board ($4982).

Collegiate Environment: Orientation program. Drama-theater group, choral group, student-run newspaper, radio station. Social organizations: 30 open to all; local fraternities, local sororities; 5% of eligible men and 5% of eligible women are members. Most popular organizations: Fellowship of Christian Athletes, Literacy Tutoring Project, student government. Major annual events: Homecoming, Campus Beautification Day, PennStock. Student services: health clinic, personal-psychological counseling. Campus security: 24-hour emergency response devices and patrols, controlled dormitory access. 540 college housing spaces available; 537 were occupied in 2003-04. Freshmen guaranteed college housing. On-campus residence required through junior year. Options: coed, men-only, women-only housing available. Wilcox Library with 72,907 books, 2,718 microform titles, 354 serials, 738 audiovisual materials, an OPAC, and a Web page. Operations spending for 2004 fiscal year: $238,525. 85 computers available on campus for general student use. Computer purchase/lease plans available. A campuswide network can be accessed from student residence rooms and from off campus. Staffed computer lab on campus.

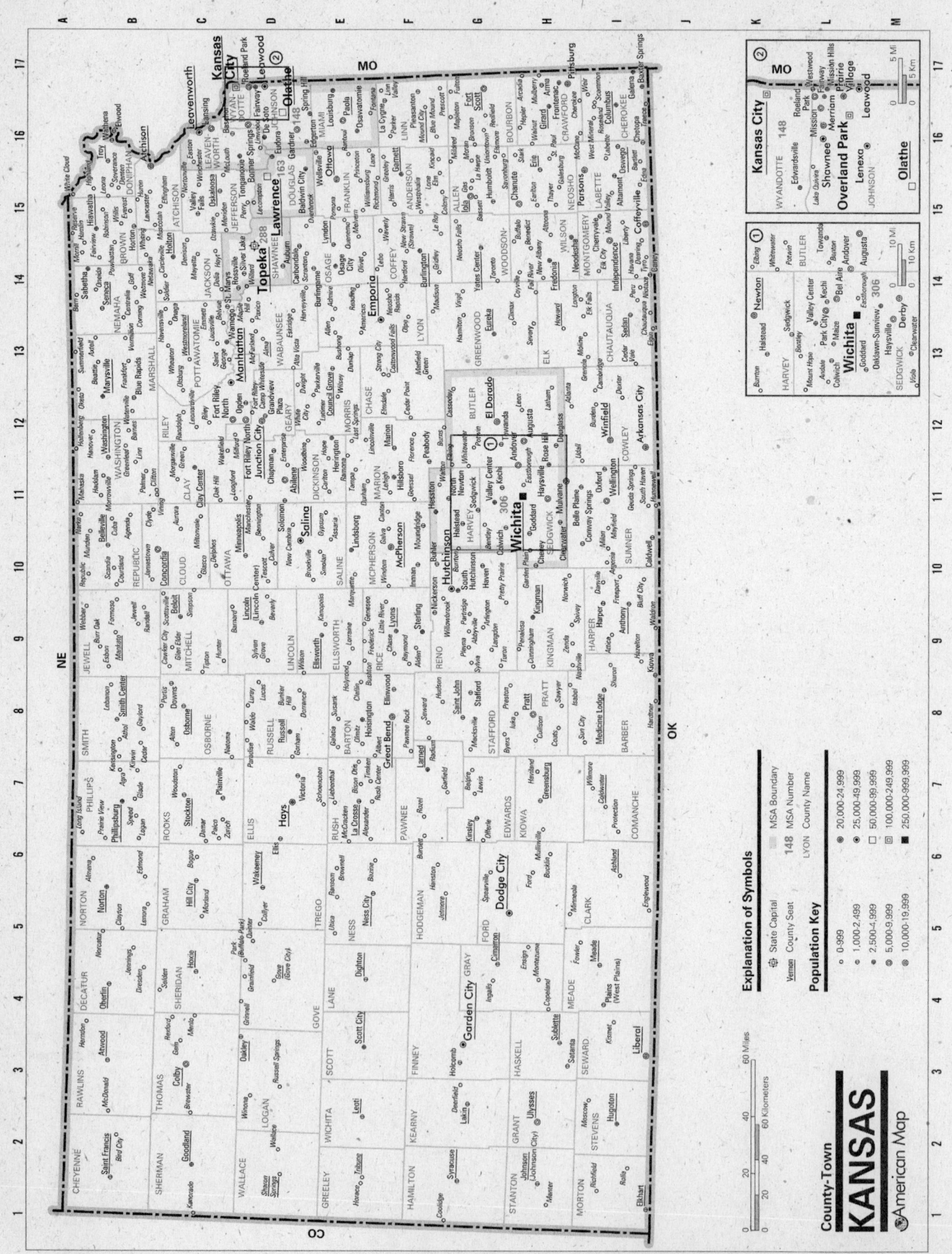

KANSAS

County-Town

● American Map

Explanation of Symbols

⊕ State Capital	▨ MSA Boundary
Vernon County Seat	**148** MSA Number
	LYON County Name

Population Key

○	0-999
●	1,000-2,499
●	2,500-4,999
◉	5,000-9,999
⊙	10,000-19,999
●	20,000-24,999
◉	25,000-49,999
☐	50,000-99,999
▨	100,000-249,999
■	250,000-999,999

■ **ALLEN COUNTY COMMUNITY COLLEGE** *G-15*
1801 North Cottonwood St.
Iola, KS 66749-1607
Tel: (620)365-5116
Fax: (620)365-7406
Web Site: http://www.allencc.net/
Description: State and locally supported, 2-year, coed. Part of Kansas State Board of Regents. Awards certificates, transfer associate, and terminal associate degrees. Founded 1923. Setting: 88-acre small town campus. Endowment: $2.7 million. Educational spending for 2005 fiscal year: $1833 per student. Total enrollment: 2,256. Student-undergrad faculty ratio is 17:1. 893 applied, 100% were admitted. 8% from top 10% of their high school class, 16% from top quarter, 29% from top half. Full-time: 824 students, 60% women, 40% men. Part-time: 1,432 students, 65% women, 35% men. Students come from 17 states and territories, 16 other countries, 4% from out-of-state, 1% Native American, 3% Hispanic, 4% black, 1% Asian American or Pacific Islander, 1% international, 35% 25 or older, 10% live on campus, 76% transferred in. Retention: 56% of full-time freshmen returned the following year. Core. Calendar: semesters. Academic remediation for entering students, services for LD students, self-designed majors, summer session for credit, part-time degree program, adult/continuing education programs, co-op programs.
Entrance Requirements: Open admission. Options: Common Application, early admission, deferred admission. Required: high school transcript. Entrance: noncompetitive. Application deadline: 8/24. Notification: continuous.
Costs Per Year: Application fee: $0. Area resident tuition: $1184 full-time, $37 per hour part-time. State resident tuition: $1280 full-time, $40 per hour part-time. Nonresident tuition: $1280 full-time, $40 per hour part-time. Mandatory fees: $512 full-time, $16 per hour part-time. College room and board: $3600. College room only: $2600.
Collegiate Environment: Drama-theater group, choral group, student-run newspaper. Most popular organizations: intramurals, Student Senate, Biology Club, student newspaper, Phi Theta Kappa. Major annual events: Homecoming, Outstanding Sophomore, Welcome Week. Student services: personal-psychological counseling. Campus security: controlled dormitory access. 190 college housing spaces available; all were occupied in 2003-04. On-campus residence required through sophomore year. Option: coed housing available. Learning Resource Center with 49,416 books, 159 serials, and an OPAC. Operations spending for 2004 fiscal year: $134,304. 65 computers available on campus for general student use. A campuswide network can be accessed. Staffed computer lab on campus.
Community Environment: Iola is a rural area with community facilities that provide a library, hospital, many churches and a fine arts center. Part-time employment is available. Fishing, boating, golf and bowling are some of the recreational activities. The County 4-H Fair is an annual event as is the Farm-City Day Celebration.

■ **BAKER UNIVERSITY** *E-16*
Box 65
Baldwin City, KS 66006-0065
Tel: (785)594-6451
Free: 800-873-4282
Admissions: (785)594-8307
Fax: (785)594-6721
E-mail: daniel.mckinney@bakeru.edu

Web Site: http://www.bakeru.edu/
Description: Independent United Methodist, comprehensive, coed. Awards bachelor's degrees. Founded 1858. Setting: 26-acre small town campus with easy access to Kansas City. Endowment: $32.8 million. Educational spending for 2005 fiscal year: $6047 per student. Total enrollment: 916. Student-undergrad faculty ratio is 10:1. 1,051 applied, 63% were admitted. 25% from top 10% of their high school class, 52% from top quarter, 81% from top half. 10 valedictorians. Full-time: 860 students, 53% women, 47% men. Part-time: 56 students, 52% women, 48% men. Students come from 18 states and territories, 5 other countries, 26% from out-of-state, 1% Native American, 3% Hispanic, 8% black, 1% Asian American or Pacific Islander, 0.5% international, 2% 25 or older, 82% live on campus, 6% transferred in. Retention: 81% of full-time freshmen returned the following year. Academic areas with the most degrees conferred: business/marketing; education; library science. Core. Calendar: 4-1-4, semesters for nursing program. Services for LD students, advanced placement, self-designed majors, honors program, independent study, double major, summer session for credit, internships. Study abroad program. ROTC: Army (c), Air Force (c).
Entrance Requirements: Options: electronic application, deferred admission, international baccalaureate accepted. Required: high school transcript, 1 recommendation, SAT or ACT. Recommended: minimum 3.0 high school GPA, minimum ACT score of 21. Required for some: essay, interview. Entrance: moderately difficult. Application deadline: Rolling.
Costs Per Year: Application fee: $0. Comprehensive fee: $22,190 includes full-time tuition ($16,100), mandatory fees ($460), and college room and board ($5630). College room only: $2580. Full-time tuition and fees vary according to location and program. Room and board charges vary according to board plan and housing facility. Part-time tuition: $485 per credit hour. Part-time mandatory fees: $45. Part-time tuition and fees vary according to course load.
Collegiate Environment: Orientation program. Drama-theater group, choral group, student-run newspaper, radio station. Social organizations: 75 open to all; national fraternities, national sororities, local fraternities; 39% of eligible men and 45% of eligible women are members. Most popular organizations: Delta Sigma Pi, Earth We Are, Mungano, Fellowship of Christian Athletes. Major annual events: Homecoming, Orientation, Baker Preview Weekend. Student services: health clinic, personal-psychological counseling. Campus security: 24-hour emergency response devices and patrols, student patrols, controlled dormitory access. 524 college housing spaces available; 422 were occupied in 2003-04. Freshmen guaranteed college housing. On-campus residence required through senior year. Options: coed, men-only, women-only housing available. Collins Library with 98,258 books, 207,943 microform titles, 482 serials, 3,344 audiovisual materials, an OPAC, and a Web page. Operations spending for 2004 fiscal year: $815,618. 222 computers available on campus for general student use. A campuswide network can be accessed from student residence rooms. Staffed computer lab on campus.
Community Environment: A rural town located 30 miles southwest of Kansas City and 15 miles south of Lawrence. The city is 10 miles from Lone Star Lake, which provides recreational facilities. Churches of many denominations are represented here. Shopping, a public library, and a clinic all serve the community. The larger shopping centers of Kansas City and

Topeka are excellent as are the cultural advantages of these two cities, which contribute to the enjoyment of the smaller surrounding areas.

■ BARCLAY COLLEGE
607 North Kingman
Haviland, KS 67059-0288
Tel: (620)862-5252
Free: 800-862-0226
Fax: (620)862-5403
E-mail: frahe@barclaycollege.edu
Web Site: http://www.barclaycollege.edu/
Description: Independent, 4-year, coed, affiliated with Society of Friends. Awards associate and bachelor's degrees. Founded 1917. Setting: 13-acre rural campus. Endowment: $812,000. Educational spending for 2005 fiscal year: $5929 per student. Total enrollment: 131. Student-undergrad faculty ratio is 7:1. 65 applied, 58% were admitted. Full-time: 90 students, 50% women, 50% men. Part-time: 41 students, 46% women, 54% men. Students come from 26 states and territories, 1 other country, 58% from out-of-state, 1% Native American, 3% Hispanic, 4% black, 2% Asian American or Pacific Islander, 1% international, 43% 25 or older, 14% transferred in. Retention: 69% of full-time freshmen returned the following year. Academic areas with the most degrees conferred: theology and religious vocations; psychology; business/marketing. Core. Calendar: semesters. Academic remediation for entering students, advanced placement, accelerated degree program, self-designed majors, independent study, distance learning, double major, part-time degree program, external degree program, adult/continuing education programs, internships.
Entrance Requirements: Options: early admission, deferred admission. Required: essay, high school transcript, minimum 2.3 high school GPA, 2 recommendations, interview, SAT or ACT. Entrance: minimally difficult. Application deadline: 9/1. Notification: continuous.
Costs Per Year: Application fee: $15. Comprehensive fee: $17,830 includes full-time tuition ($12,730) and college room and board ($5100). College room only: $2000. Part-time tuition: $390 per hour.
Collegiate Environment: Orientation program. Drama-theater group, choral group. Social organizations: 3 open to all. Most popular organizations: Pep Club, Drama Club, Missions Club. Major annual events: Homecoming, Christmas banquet. Student services: personal-psychological counseling. Campus security: student patrols. Freshmen guaranteed college housing. On-campus residence required through senior year. Options: men-only, women-only housing available. Worden Memorial Library with 63,759 books, 404 microform titles, 21,988 serials, 2,291 audiovisual materials, and an OPAC. Operations spending for 2004 fiscal year: $48,810. 20 computers available on campus for general student use. Computer purchase/lease plans available. A campuswide network can be accessed from off-campus. Staffed computer lab on campus.
Community Environment: Haviland is a small town in a rural area with a friendly and supportive atmosphere. Especially welcoming to young families.

■ BARTON COUNTY COMMUNITY COLLEGE *F-8*
245 Northeast 30th Rd.
Great Bend, KS 67530-9283
Tel: (620)792-2701
Free: 800-722-6842
Admissions: (620)792-9241
Fax: (620)792-3238
Web Site: http://www.bartonccc.edu/
Description: State and locally supported, 2-year, coed. Part of Kansas Board of Regents. Awards certificates, transfer associate, and terminal associate degrees. Founded 1969. Setting: 140-acre rural campus. Endowment: $4.3 million. Educational spending for 2005 fiscal year: $3728 per student. Total enrollment: 3,821. Student-undergrad faculty ratio is 18:1. Full-time: 943 students, 55% women, 45% men. Part-time: 2,878 students, 51% women, 49% men. Students come from 40 states and territories, 15 other countries, 17% from out-of-state, 1% Native American, 6% Hispanic, 13% black, 2% Asian American or Pacific Islander, 2% international, 47% 25 or older, 4% live on campus, 3% transferred in. Retention: 65% of full-time freshmen returned the following year. Calendar: semesters. Academic remediation for entering students, ESL program, services for LD students, advanced placement, accelerated degree program, self-designed majors, honors program, independent study, distance learning, summer session for credit, part-time degree program, external degree program, adult/continuing education programs, co-op programs and internships.

Entrance Requirements: Open admission. Options: Common Application, electronic application, early admission. Recommended: high school transcript. Entrance: noncompetitive. Application deadline: Rolling.
Costs Per Year: Application fee: $0. State resident tuition: $1568 full-time, $49 per credit hour part-time. Nonresident tuition: $2176 full-time, $68 per credit hour part-time. Mandatory fees: $576 full-time, $18 per credit hour part-time. College room and board: $3854.
Collegiate Environment: Orientation program. Drama-theater group, choral group, student-run newspaper. Social organizations: 20 open to all. Most popular organizations: Danceline, Business Professionals, Psychology Club, Agriculture Club, Cougarettes. Major annual events: homecoming, Parents' Day, Orientation/Welcome Back Days. Student services: health clinic, personal-psychological counseling. Campus security: 24-hour emergency response devices and patrols. 292 college housing spaces available; all were occupied in 2003-04. Freshmen guaranteed college housing. On-campus residence required in freshman year. Option: coed housing available. Barton County Community College Library with 26,322 books, 4,178 microform titles, 179 serials, 1,529 audiovisual materials, an OPAC, and a Web page. Operations spending for 2004 fiscal year: $146,481. 350 computers available on campus for general student use. A campuswide network can be accessed from student residence rooms and from off campus. Staffed computer lab on campus.
Community Environment: An urban area, Great Bend (population 18,000) is in the wheat belt and is a large oil producing area. Thirty churches, a library, a hospital and good shopping facilities are a part of the community. Brit Spaugh Park has recreational facilities for tennis, baseball, swimming, and picnicking. Cheyenne Bottoms, nearby, is a wildlife and waterfowl refuge of more than 18,000 acres of which 15,000 acres are covered by water. All forms of commercial transportation are available.

■ BENEDICTINE COLLEGE *B-16*
1020 North 2nd St.
Atchison, KS 66002-1499
Tel: (913)367-5340
Free: 800-467-5340
Fax: (913)367-3673
E-mail: mail@benedictine.edu
Web Site: http://www.benedictine.edu/
Description: Independent Roman Catholic, comprehensive, coed. Awards associate, bachelor's, and master's degrees. Founded 1859. Setting: 225-acre small town campus with easy access to Kansas City. Endowment: $9.6 million. Research spending for 2004 fiscal year: $15,000. Educational spending for 2005 fiscal year: $3458 per student. Total enrollment: 1,508. Faculty: 114 (68 full-time, 46 part-time). Student-undergrad faculty ratio is 16:1. 708 applied, 90% were admitted. Full-time: 1,176 students, 50% women, 50% men. Part-time: 280 students, 64% women, 36% men. Students come from 36 states and territories, 19 other countries, 55% from out-of-state, 0.2% Native American, 8% Hispanic, 4% black, 2% Asian American or Pacific Islander, 2% international, 3% 25 or older, 69% live on campus, 4% transferred in. Retention: 72% of full-time freshmen returned the following year. Academic areas with the most degrees conferred: business/marketing; social sciences; area and ethnic studies; education. Core. Calendar: semesters. Academic remediation for entering students, ESL program, advanced placement, self-designed majors, independent study, double major, summer session for credit, part-time degree program, co-op programs and internships, graduate courses open to undergrads. Off campus study at 16 members of the Kansas City Regional Council for Higher Education, Kansas State University. Study abroad program. ROTC: Army.
Entrance Requirements: Options: Peterson's Universal Application, Common Application, electronic application, deferred admission. Required: high school transcript, minimum 2.0 high school GPA, SAT or ACT. Required for some: interview. Entrance: moderately difficult. Notification: continuous.
Costs Per Year: Application fee: $25. Comprehensive fee: $22,968 includes full-time tuition ($15,110), mandatory fees ($650), and college room and board ($7208). College room only: $2730. Full-time tuition and fees vary according to course load and degree level. Room and board charges vary according to board plan and housing facility. Part-time tuition: $450 per credit hour. Part-time tuition varies according to course load and degree level.
Collegiate Environment: Orientation program. Drama-theater group, choral group, student-run newspaper. Social organizations: 42 open to all. Most popular organizations: student government, Students in Free Enterprise, Knights of Columbus, Concert Chorale/Chamber Singers, Campus Activities Board. Major annual events: Springfest, Homecoming, Parents' Weekend. Student services: health clinic, personal-psychological counseling. Campus

security: 24-hour emergency response devices and patrols, late night transport-escort service. College housing designed to accommodate 749 students; 750 undergraduates lived in college housing during 2003-04. Freshmen guaranteed college housing. On-campus residence required through senior year. Options: coed, men-only, women-only housing available. Benedictine College Library with 368,558 books, 37,482 microform titles, 504 serials, 857 audiovisual materials, an OPAC, and a Web page. Operations spending for 2004 fiscal year: $290,724. 80 computers available on campus for general student use. A campuswide network can be accessed from student residence rooms and from off campus. Staffed computer lab on campus.

Community Environment: Atchison is located on the Kansas-Missouri border, within 30-50 miles of St. Joseph and Kansas City, Missouri, and Topeka and Kansas City, Kansas.

■ **BETHANY COLLEGE** *E-10*
421 North First St.
Lindsborg, KS 67456-1897
Tel: (785)227-3311
Free: 800-826-2281
Fax: (785)227-2860
E-mail: admissions@bethanylb.edu
Web Site: http://www.bethanylb.edu/
Description: Independent Lutheran, 4-year, coed. Awards bachelor's degrees. Founded 1881. Setting: 80-acre small town campus. Endowment: $20.8 million. Educational spending for 2005 fiscal year: $6460 per student. Total enrollment: 588. Student-undergrad faculty ratio is 11:1. 868 applied, 63% were admitted. 17% from top 10% of their high school class, 41% from top quarter, 78% from top half. 12 valedictorians. Full-time: 552 students, 46% women, 54% men. Part-time: 36 students, 36% women, 64% men. Students come from 25 states and territories, 11 other countries, 41% from out-of-state, 1% Native American, 5% Hispanic, 8% black, 1% Asian American or Pacific Islander, 4% international, 4% 25 or older, 68% live on campus, 10% transferred in. Retention: 61% of full-time freshmen returned the following year. Academic areas with the most degrees conferred: education; business/marketing; biological/life sciences. Core. Calendar: 4-1-4. Academic remediation for entering students, services for LD students, advanced placement, accelerated degree program, self-designed majors, honors program, independent study, double major, summer session for credit, internships. Off campus study at 6 members of the Associated Colleges of Central Kansas. Study abroad program.
Entrance Requirements: Options: Common Application, electronic application, deferred admission, international baccalaureate accepted. Required: high school transcript, minimum 2.5 high school GPA, SAT or ACT. Required for some: essay, recommendations, interview. Entrance: moderately difficult. Application deadline: Rolling. Notification: continuous.
Costs Per Year: Application fee: $20. Comprehensive fee: $21,480 includes full-time tuition ($16,000), mandatory fees ($210), and college room and board ($5270). College room only: $2850. Part-time tuition: $300 per credit hour.
Collegiate Environment: Orientation program. Drama-theater group, choral group, student-run newspaper. Social organizations: 62 open to all; local fraternities, local sororities; 15% of eligible men and 18% of eligible women are members. Most popular organizations: Business Club, Bethany Student Education Association, Multicultural Student Association, Bethany Youth Ministry Team, Bio Chem Club. Major annual events: Handel's Messiah by the Bethany Oratorio Society, Homecoming events/talent show, Swedestock. Student services: health clinic, personal-psychological counseling. Campus security: 24-hour emergency response devices, student patrols, late night transport-escort service, controlled dormitory access, night patrols by security personnel. 547 college housing spaces available; 354 were occupied in 2003-04. Freshmen guaranteed college housing. On-campus residence required through junior year. Options: coed, men-only, women-only housing available. Wallerstedt Library plus 1 other with 84,730 books, 6,400 microform titles, 709 serials, 2,648 audiovisual materials, and an OPAC. Operations spending for 2004 fiscal year: $155,519. 50 computers available on campus for general student use. A campuswide network can be accessed from student residence rooms and from off campus. Staffed computer lab on campus.

■ **BETHEL COLLEGE** *G-11*
300 East 27th St.
North Newton, KS 67117
Tel: (316)283-2500

Free: 800-522-1887
Admissions: (316)284-5230
Fax: (316)284-5286
E-mail: admissions@bethelks.edu
Web Site: http://www.bethelks.edu/
Description: Independent, 4-year, coed, affiliated with Mennonite Church USA. Awards bachelor's degrees. Founded 1887. Setting: 60-acre small town campus with easy access to Wichita. Endowment: $17.4 million. Research spending for 2004 fiscal year: $10,775. Educational spending for 2005 fiscal year: $6783 per student. Total enrollment: 514. Student-undergrad faculty ratio is 9:1. 581 applied, 72% were admitted. 17% from top 10% of their high school class, 46% from top quarter, 79% from top half. 4 National Merit Scholars, 12 valedictorians. Full-time: 476 students, 49% women, 51% men. Part-time: 38 students, 71% women, 29% men. Students come from 19 states and territories, 14 other countries, 24% from out-of-state, 1% Native American, 4% Hispanic, 6% black, 2% Asian American or Pacific Islander, 5% international, 9% 25 or older, 68% live on campus, 12% transferred in. Retention: 66% of full-time freshmen returned the following year. Academic areas with the most degrees conferred: health professions and related sciences; business/marketing; public administration and social services; visual and performing arts. Core. Calendar: 4-1-4. Academic remediation for entering students, services for LD students, advanced placement, independent study, double major, summer session for credit, part-time degree program, internships. Off campus study at 6 members of the Associated Colleges of Central Kansas, Hesston College. Study abroad program.
Entrance Requirements: Options: Peterson's Universal Application, deferred admission, international baccalaureate accepted. Required: high school transcript, minimum 2.5 high school GPA, SAT or ACT. Recommended: interview. Required for some: essay, 2 recommendations. Entrance: moderately difficult. Application deadline: Rolling. Notification: continuous.
Costs Per Year: Application fee: $20. Comprehensive fee: $21,650 includes full-time tuition ($15,550) and college room and board ($6100). College room only: $3200. Full-time tuition varies according to course load. Room and board charges vary according to board plan and housing facility. Part-time tuition: $550 per credit hour. Part-time tuition varies according to course load.
Collegiate Environment: Orientation program. Drama-theater group, choral group, student-run newspaper, radio station. Social organizations: 25 open to all. Most popular organizations: Bethel College Service Corps, The Collegian (newspaper), Student Alumni Association, Student Senate, Student Activities Board. Major annual events: Fall Fest, Christmas Gala, Spring Fling. Student services: health clinic, personal-psychological counseling. Campus security: 24-hour emergency response devices, student patrols, community police patrols. 456 college housing spaces available; 345 were occupied in 2003-04. Freshmen guaranteed college housing. On-campus residence required through senior year. Option: coed housing available. Mantz Library plus 1 other with 137,130 books, 13,615 microform titles, 571 serials, 163,189 audiovisual materials, an OPAC, and a Web page. Operations spending for 2004 fiscal year: $290,496. 38 computers available on campus for general student use. A campuswide network can be accessed from student residence rooms and from off campus. Staffed computer lab on campus.

■ **BROWN MACKIE COLLEGE-KANSAS CITY** *L-16*
9705 Lenexa Dr.
Lenexa, KS 66215
Tel: (913)768-1900
Free: 800-635-9101
Fax: (913)823-7448
E-mail: dewhite@brownmackie.edu
Web Site: http://www.bmcaec.com/
Description: Proprietary, 2-year, coed. Part of The Brown Mackie College. Awards certificates, diplomas, and terminal associate degrees. Founded 1892. Setting: 3-acre suburban campus with easy access to Kansas City. Total enrollment: 370. Full-time: 370 students, 77% women, 23% men. Students come from 2 states and territories, 35% from out-of-state, 2% Native American, 8% Hispanic, 26% black, 1% Asian American or Pacific Islander, 0% international, 60% 25 or older. Core. Academic remediation for entering students, summer session for credit, adult/continuing education programs.
Entrance Requirements: Open admission. Option: deferred admission. Required: high school transcript, interview. Recommended: essay, minimum 2.0 high school GPA. Required for some: essay. Entrance: noncompetitive. Application deadline: Rolling. Notification: continuous.

Costs Per Year: Tuition: $7164 full-time. Mandatory fees: $432 full-time.

Collegiate Environment: Orientation program. Social organizations: 1 open to all. Most popular organization: Coffee Club (service and social organization). Major annual events: Summer Picnic, Halloween Costume Competition, Sweethearts Elections. Student services: personal-psychological counseling. Campus security: 24-hour emergency response devices. College housing not available. The Brown Mackie College Library plus 1 other with 48 serials, an OPAC, and a Web page. 185 computers available on campus for general student use. A campuswide network can be accessed from off-campus. Staffed computer lab on campus.

■ **BROWN MACKIE COLLEGE-SALINA** *D-10*

2106 South 9th St.

Salina, KS 67401-2810

Tel: (785)825-5422

Free: 800-365-0433

Fax: (785)827-7623

Web Site: http://www.brownmackie.edu/locations.asp?locid=13

Description: Proprietary, 2-year, coed. Awards certificates, diplomas, transfer associate, and terminal associate degrees. Founded 1892. Setting: 10-acre small town campus with easy access to Wichita. Educational spending for 2005 fiscal year: $1677 per student. Total enrollment: 367. Student-undergrad faculty ratio is 15:1. 136 applied, 96% were admitted. Full-time: 367 students, 68% women, 32% men. Students come from 10 states and territories, 2 other countries, 26% from out-of-state, 0% Native American, 8% Hispanic, 12% black, 1% Asian American or Pacific Islander, 0% international, 38% 25 or older, 3% transferred in. Core. Calendar: modular. Academic remediation for entering students, services for LD students, advanced placement, independent study, summer session for credit, adult/continuing education programs, co-op programs.

Entrance Requirements: Open admission. Options: Peterson's Universal Application, Common Application, deferred admission. Required: high school transcript, interview. Entrance: noncompetitive. Application deadline: Rolling. Notification: continuous.

Costs Per Year: Tuition: $9072 full-time. Mandatory fees: $576 full-time.

Collegiate Environment: Orientation program. Student-run newspaper. Social organizations: 2 open to all. Most popular organizations: Student Senate, Athletic Booster Club. Major annual events: Commencement, summer picnic, Thanksgiving/Christmas Dinner. College housing not available. Brown Mackie College Library plus 1 other with 14,788 books, 500 microform titles, 45 serials, 195 audiovisual materials, an OPAC, and a Web page. Operations spending for 2004 fiscal year: $44,886. 162 computers available on campus for general student use. Staffed computer lab on campus.

■ **BUTLER COMMUNITY COLLEGE** *G-12*

901 South Haverhill Rd.

El Dorado, KS 67042-3280

Tel: (316)321-2222

Fax: (316)322-3109

Web Site: http://www.butlercc.edu/

Description: State and locally supported, 2-year, coed. Part of Kansas Board of Regents. Awards certificates, transfer associate, and terminal associate degrees. Founded 1927. Setting: 80-acre small town campus. Educational spending for 2005 fiscal year: $2824 per student. Total enrollment: 8,863. Student-undergrad faculty ratio is 18:1. Full-time: 3,658 students, 56% women, 44% men. Part-time: 5,205 students, 63% women, 37% men. Students come from 28 states and territories, 21 other countries, 5% from out-of-state, 2% Native American, 6% Hispanic, 12% black, 2% Asian American or Pacific Islander, 3% international, 42% 25 or older, 4% live on campus, 5% transferred in. Retention: 57% of full-time freshmen returned the following year. Core. Calendar: semesters. Academic remediation for entering students, ESL program, services for LD students, advanced placement, accelerated degree program, self-designed majors, honors program, independent study, distance learning, double major, summer session for credit, part-time degree program, adult/continuing education programs, co-op programs.

Entrance Requirements: Open admission. Options: early admission, deferred admission. Required: high school transcript. Entrance: noncompetitive. Application deadline: 8/19. Notification: continuous.

Costs Per Year: Application fee: $0. State resident tuition: $1756 full-time, $55 per credit hour part-time. Nonresident tuition: $3164 full-time, $99 per credit hour part-time. Mandatory fees: $448 full-time, $14 per credit hour part-time. College room and board: $4335. Room and board charges vary according to housing facility.

Collegiate Environment: Orientation program. Drama-theater group, choral group, student-run newspaper, radio station. Most popular organizations: Agriculture Club, Art Club, Campus Crusade for Christ, Grizzly Ambassadors, intramurals. Student services: personal-psychological counseling. Campus security: 24-hour emergency response devices and patrols, controlled dormitory access, video cameras at dormitory entrances and parking lot. 377 college housing spaces available; all were occupied in 2003-04. No special consideration for freshman housing applicants. Options: coed, men-only, women-only housing available. L.W. Nixon Library with 38,000 books, 36,920 microform titles, 220 serials, 914 audiovisual materials, an OPAC, and a Web page. Operations spending for 2004 fiscal year: $108,482. 90 computers available on campus for general student use. Staffed computer lab on campus.

Community Environment: Butler County attracts visitors because of its location near the scenic Flint Hills in Kansas and the El Dorado Lake, a federal Corps of Engineers Project covering approximately 4,500 acres. Butler County has an approximate population of 50,000 persons in nine communities. Butler County communities offers good schools, numerous musical, writing and civic clubs with an emphasis toward educational and cultural opportunities. Located just 30 minutes east of Wichita, a city of approximately 300,000 residents, Butler County residents and BCCC students are also offered all the advantages of a major metropolitan city.

■ **CENTRAL CHRISTIAN COLLEGE OF KANSAS** *F-10*

1200 South Main

PO Box 1403

McPherson, KS 67460-5799

Tel: (620)241-0723

Free: 800-835-0078

Fax: (620)241-6032

E-mail: david.ferrell@centralchristian.edu

Web Site: http://www.centralchristian.edu/

Description: Independent Free Methodist, 4-year, coed. Awards associate and bachelor's degrees. Founded 1884. Setting: 16-acre small town campus. Endowment: $5.7 million. Educational spending for 2005 fiscal year: $4829 per student. Total enrollment: 336. Student-undergrad faculty ratio is 16:1. 289 applied, 98% were admitted. 15% from top 10% of their high school class, 42% from top quarter, 80% from top half. 4 valedictorians, 25 student government officers. Full-time: 314 students, 54% women, 46% men. Part-time: 22 students, 55% women, 45% men. Students come from 29 states and territories, 2 other countries, 61% from out-of-state, 2% Native American, 7% Hispanic, 8% black, 0% Asian American or Pacific Islander, 3% international, 12% 25 or older, 81% live on campus, 5% transferred in. Retention: 57% of full-time freshmen returned the following year. Academic areas with the most degrees conferred: business/marketing; liberal arts/general studies; theology and religious vocations. Core. Calendar: 4-1-4. Academic remediation for entering students, services for LD students, advanced placement, self-designed majors, independent study, double major, part-time degree program, adult/continuing education programs, co-op programs and internships. Off campus study at McPherson College, Christian Center for Urban Studies, Focus on the Family Institute, CCCU. Study abroad program.

Entrance Requirements: Options: Peterson's Universal Application, electronic application, deferred admission, international baccalaureate accepted. Required: high school transcript, minimum 2.5 high school GPA, 2 recommendations, SAT or ACT. Recommended: essay, interview. Entrance: moderately difficult. Application deadline: Rolling. Notification: continuous.

Costs Per Year: Application fee: $20. Comprehensive fee: $19,500 includes full-time tuition ($14,000), mandatory fees ($500), and college room and board ($5000). College room only: $2400. Part-time tuition: $405 per credit hour.

Collegiate Environment: Orientation program. Drama-theater group, choral group, student-run newspaper. Social organizations: 9 open to all. Most popular organizations: C.O.L.O.R.S. (Cross Over Lines of Racial Stereotype), Performing Arts Club, Student Activities Committee, Fellowship of Christian Athletes, Phi Beta Lambda Business Club. Major annual events: All College Picnic, Community Service Day, Christmas Banquet. Student services: health clinic, personal-psychological counseling. Campus security: controlled dormitory access. 258 college housing spaces available; 224 were occupied in 2003-04. Freshmen guaranteed college housing. On-campus residence required through junior year. Options: men-only, women-only housing available. Briner Library with 35,156 books, 524 microform titles, 95 serials, 779 audiovisual materials, an OPAC, and a Web page. Operations spending for 2004 fiscal year: $71,445. 37 computers available on campus for general student use. A campuswide network can be accessed. Staffed computer lab on campus.

Community Environment: The community of McPherson, Kansas is an attractive Midwestern agricultural and petroleum based city of 14,000. Located 50 miles north of Wichita, the community is rated the thirty-third best small town in the United States.

■ **CLOUD COUNTY COMMUNITY COLLEGE** *B-10*
2221 Campus Dr., PO Box 1002
Concordia, KS 66901-1002
Tel: (785)243-1435
Free: 800-729-5101
Fax: (785)243-1043
Web Site: http://www.cloud.edu/
Description: State and locally supported, 2-year, coed. Part of Kansas Community College System. Awards certificates, diplomas, transfer associate, and terminal associate degrees. Founded 1965. Setting: 35-acre rural campus. Total enrollment: 3,521. Students come from 12 states and territories, 5 other countries, 1% Native American, 2% Hispanic, 6% black, 1% Asian American or Pacific Islander, 0.4% international, 12% 25 or older. Core. Calendar: semesters. Academic remediation for entering students, services for LD students, advanced placement, summer session for credit, part-time degree program, adult/continuing education programs, co-op programs and internships.
Entrance Requirements: Open admission. Options: Common Application, early admission, deferred admission. Required: high school transcript. Placement: ACT ASSET required; ACT recommended. Entrance: noncompetitive. Application deadline: 9/11. Notification: continuous.
Costs Per Year: Application fee: $0. State resident tuition: $1560 full-time, $52 per credit hour part-time. Nonresident tuition: $2220 full-time, $74 per credit hour part-time. Mandatory fees: $540 full-time, $18 per credit hour part-time. College room and board: $3780.
Collegiate Environment: Orientation program. Drama-theater group, choral group, student-run newspaper, radio station. Most popular organizations: Fellowship of Christian Athletes, Block and Bridle Club, Student Senate. Major annual event: Homecoming. Student services: health clinic. Campus security: 24-hour emergency response devices. 18,010 books and 142 serials. 57 computers available on campus for general student use. Staffed computer lab on campus.
Community Environment: Located in the Republican River Valley, Concordia is a central shopping, industrial and medical district for the citizens of North Central Kansas. The city of approximately 7,000 is home to St. Joseph Hospital, which is operated by the Sisters of St. Joseph. The city features a large municipal swimming complex, a vigorous summer recreational program, tennis courts and spacious parks. Concordia hosts the annual North Central Kansas Rodeo and the annual Fall Fest Celebration, and is the home of the Cloud County Fair. The Brown Grand Theater, which is on the National Register of Historic Sites, features many cultural events throughout the year.

■ **COFFEYVILLE COMMUNITY COLLEGE** *I-15*
400 West 11th St.
Coffeyville, KS 67337-5063
Tel: (620)251-7700
Fax: (620)252-7098
Web Site: http://www.coffeyville.edu/
Description: State and locally supported, 2-year, coed. Part of Kansas Board of Regents. Awards certificates, transfer associate, and terminal associate degrees. Founded 1923. Setting: 39-acre small town campus with easy access to Tulsa. Endowment: $2.8 million. Educational spending for 2005 fiscal year: $4300 per student. Total enrollment: 1,766. 1,499 applied, 100% were admitted. 10% from top 10% of their high school class, 20% from top quarter, 20% from top half. Full-time: 665 students, 40% women, 60% men. Part-time: 1,101 students, 63% women, 37% men. Students come from 19 states and territories, 4 other countries, 8% from out-of-state, 2% Native American, 2% Hispanic, 12% black, 0.3% Asian American or Pacific Islander, 1% international, 43% 25 or older, 27% live on campus, 38% transferred in. Core. Calendar: semesters. Academic remediation for entering students, ESL program, services for LD students, advanced placement, self-designed majors, honors program, distance learning, double major, summer session for credit, part-time degree program, adult/continuing education programs, co-op programs and internships.

Entrance Requirements: Open admission. Options: Common Application, early admission, deferred admission. Required: high school transcript. Placement: ACT, ACT COMPASS required. Entrance: noncompetitive. Application deadline: Rolling. Notification: continuous.
Costs Per Year: Application fee: $0. State resident tuition: $896 full-time, $28 per credit hour part-time. Nonresident tuition: $2176 full-time, $68 per credit hour part-time. Mandatory fees: $704 full-time, $22 per credit hour part-time. College room and board: $3380.
Collegiate Environment: Drama-theater group, choral group, marching band. Social organizations: 30 open to all. Most popular organizations: Student Government Association, Phi Theta Kappa, Delta Psi Omega, Agriculture Club. Major annual events: Homecoming, musicals and plays. Student services: health clinic, personal-psychological counseling, women's center. Campus security: 24-hour patrols, late night transport-escort service. 304 college housing spaces available; 250 were occupied in 2003-04. No special consideration for freshman housing applicants. Option: coed housing available. Russell H. Graham Learning Resource Center plus 1 other with 27,482 books, 3,005 microform titles, 238 serials, 1,415 audiovisual materials, an OPAC, and a Web page. Operations spending for 2004 fiscal year: $116,000. 90 computers available on campus for general student use. A campuswide network can be accessed from off-campus. Staffed computer lab on campus.
Community Environment: A town of diversified industries, Coffeyville has churches of many denominations, a hospital and numerous civic, service and social organizations. A municipal airport, railroads and bus lines provide transportation. A significant point of interest is the Dalton Defenders Museum. Coffeyville was once the home of the famous baseball pitcher, Walter Johnson; a memorial to Johnson may be seen in Walter Johnson Park.

■ **COLBY COMMUNITY COLLEGE** *C-3*
1255 South Range
Colby, KS 67701-4099
Tel: (785)462-3984
Fax: (785)462-4600
Web Site: http://www.colbycc.edu/
Description: State and locally supported, 2-year, coed. Part of Kansas Board of Regents. Awards certificates, diplomas, transfer associate, and terminal associate degrees. Founded 1964. Setting: 80-acre small town campus. Endowment: $3.2 million. Educational spending for 2005 fiscal year: $2891 per student. Total enrollment: 1,784. Student-undergrad faculty ratio is 19:1. 647 applied, 100% were admitted. 12% from top 10% of their high school class, 25% from top quarter, 63% from top half. Students come from 14 states and territories, 5 other countries, 13% from out-of-state, 0.2% Native American, 2% Hispanic, 1% black, 1% Asian American or Pacific Islander, 2% international, 22% 25 or older, 30% live on campus. Core. Calendar: semesters. Academic remediation for entering students, services for LD students, advanced placement, self-designed majors, honors program, distance learning, double major, summer session for credit, part-time degree program, adult/continuing education programs, co-op programs and internships.
Entrance Requirements: Open admission except for animal science, health-related programs. Options: early admission, deferred admission, international baccalaureate accepted. Required: high school transcript. Entrance: noncompetitive. Application deadline: Rolling. Notification: continuous.
Costs Per Year: State resident tuition: $1536 full-time, $48 per credit hour part-time. Nonresident tuition: $2784 full-time, $87 per credit hour part-time. Mandatory fees: $768 full-time, $24 per credit hour part-time. College room and board: $3632.
Collegiate Environment: Orientation program. Drama-theater group, choral group, marching band, student-run newspaper, radio station. Social organizations: 16 open to all. Most popular organizations: KSNEA, Physical Therapist Assistants Club, Block and Bridle, SVTA, COPNS. Major annual events: Fall Formal, Spring Formal, End of Year Event. Student services: health clinic, personal-psychological counseling. Campus security: 24-hour emergency response devices and patrols. 264 college housing spaces available; 240 were occupied in 2003-04. No special consideration for freshman housing applicants. On-campus residence required in freshman year. Options: men-only, women-only housing available. Davis Library with 32,000 books, 350 serials, and an OPAC. 178 computers available on campus for general student use. A campuswide network can be accessed from student residence rooms and from off campus. Staffed computer lab on campus.
Community Environment: Colby is in the state's leading wheat-producing area, the northwest corner of the state. Population 6,000. Community facili-

ties include a fine hospital, library and churches of most faiths. Job opportunities are open with the city and community providing employment for students wherever possible.

■ **COWLEY COUNTY COMMUNITY COLLEGE AND AREA VOCATIONAL-TECHNICAL SCHOOL** *I-12*
125 South Second, PO Box 1147
Arkansas City, KS 67005-1147
Tel: (620)442-0430
Free: 800-593-CCCC
Admissions: (620)441-5245
Fax: (620)441-5350
E-mail: admissions@paws.cowley.cc.ks.us
Web Site: http://www.cowley.cc.ks.us/
Description: State and locally supported, 2-year, coed. Part of Kansas State Board of Education. Awards certificates, diplomas, transfer associate, and terminal associate degrees. Founded 1922. Setting: 19-acre small town campus. Endowment: $3 million. Educational spending for 2005 fiscal year: $2577 per student. Total enrollment: 4,679. Student-undergrad faculty ratio Is 31:1. 1,185 applied, 100% were admitted. 5% from top 10% of their high school class, 19% from top quarter, 45% from top half. Full-time: 2,386 students, 53% women, 47% men. Part-time: 2,293 students, 65% women, 35% men. Students come from 16 states and territories, 12 other countries, 6% from out-of-state, 1% Native American, 4% Hispanic, 8% black, 5% Asian American or Pacific Islander, 1% international, 19% 25 or older, 7% live on campus. Core. Calendar: semesters. Academic remediation for entering students, advanced placement, accelerated degree program, self-designed majors, independent study, distance learning, summer session for credit, part-time degree program, external degree program, adult/continuing education programs, co-op programs.
Entrance Requirements: Open admission. Options: early admission, deferred admission. Required: high school transcript. Recommended: ACT. Entrance: noncompetitive. Application deadline: Rolling.
Costs Per Year: Application fee: $0. Area resident tuition: $1290 full-time, $43 per credit hour part-time. State resident tuition: $1440 full-time, $48 per credit hour part-time. Nonresident tuition: $3000 full-time, $100 per credit hour part-time. Mandatory fees: $570 full-time, $19 per credit hour part-time. College room and board: $3530.
Collegiate Environment: Orientation program. Drama-theater group, choral group, student-run newspaper. Social organizations: 21 open to all. Most popular organizations: Volunteer Club, Peers Advocating for Wellness, Phi Theta Kappa, Student Government Association, Phi Beta Lambda. Major annual events: Mr. Cinderfella, Puttin' on the Hits, Homecoming. Student services: health clinic, personal-psychological counseling. Campus security: student patrols, late night transport-escort service, residence hall entrances are locked at night. Options: coed, men-only, women-only housing available. Renn Memorial Library with 26,000 books and 100 serials. Operations spending for 2004 fiscal year: $149,256. 53 computers available on campus for general student use. A campuswide network can be accessed. Staffed computer lab on campus.

■ **DODGE CITY COMMUNITY COLLEGE** *H-5*
2501 North 14th Ave.
Dodge City, KS 67801-2399
Tel: (620)225-1321
Admissions: (316)225-1321
Fax: (620)225-0918
E-mail: admin@dccc.dodge-city.cc.ks.us
Web Site: http://www.dccc.cc.ks.us/
Description: State and locally supported, 2-year, coed. Part of Kansas State Board of Education. Awards certificates, transfer associate, and terminal associate degrees. Founded 1935. Setting: 143-acre small town campus. Total enrollment: 1,956. 5% from top 10% of their high school class, 50% from top half. Students come from 20 states and territories, 5 other countries, 67% 25 or older, 20% live on campus. Core. Calendar: semesters. Academic remediation for entering students, ESL program, advanced placement, self-designed majors, summer session for credit, part-time degree program, external degree program, adult/continuing education programs, co-op programs and internships.
Entrance Requirements: Open admission. Options: Common Application, early admission, deferred admission. Required: high school transcript. Placement: ACT ASSET required. Entrance: noncompetitive. Application deadline: Rolling. Notification: continuous.

Costs Per Year: Application fee: $0. State resident tuition: $1120 full-time, $35 per credit hour part-time. Nonresident tuition: $1344 full-time, $42 per credit hour part-time. Mandatory fees: $806 full-time, $23 per credit hour part-time, $35 per term part-time. Full-time tuition and fees vary according to course load. Part-time tuition and fees vary according to course load. College room and board: $4060.
Collegiate Environment: Drama-theater group, choral group, student-run newspaper, radio station. Major annual events: Homecoming, Spring Fling, Multicultural Day. Student services: health clinic, personal-psychological counseling. Option: coed housing available. Learning Resource Center with 30,000 books and 225 serials. 125 computers available on campus for general student use. Staffed computer lab on campus.
Community Environment: Dodge City serves as a supply and trade center for a large agricultural area. It is located on the plains of western Kansas. All modes of transportation are accessible. Community facilities include a library, hospitals, churches of all major denominations, community concert association, and many fraternal, civic and veteran's organizations. Sports include golf, bowling, fishing, hunting and boating. Points of interest are Boot Hill, Fort Dodge and Point Rocks. Special events are Dodge City Days rodeo and the Square Dance Festival.

■ **DONNELLY COLLEGE** *D-17*
608 North 18th St.
Kansas City, KS 66102-4298
Tel: (913)621-6070
Admissions: (913)621-8769
Fax: (913)621-0354
Web Site: http://www.donnelly.edu/
Description: Independent Roman Catholic, 2-year, coed. Awards certificates, transfer associate, and terminal associate degrees. Founded 1949. Setting: 4-acre urban campus. Endowment: $4 million. Educational spending for 2005 fiscal year: $5141 per student. Total enrollment: 398. 327 applied, 100% were admitted. Full-time: 198 students, 75% women, 25% men. Part-time: 200 students, 66% women, 34% men. Students come from 15 states and territories, 12% from out-of-state, 1% Native American, 22% Hispanic, 54% black, 3% Asian American or Pacific Islander, 4% international, 85% 25 or older. Core. Calendar: semesters. Academic remediation for entering students, ESL program, services for LD students, advanced placement, independent study, double major, summer session for credit, part-time degree program, external degree program, internships.
Entrance Requirements: Open admission. Options: early admission, deferred admission. Recommended: high school transcript. Entrance: noncompetitive. Application deadline: Rolling.
Collegiate Environment: Student services: personal-psychological counseling. Campus security: 24-hour emergency response devices. 10 undergraduates lived in college housing during 2003-04. Trant Memorial Library with 33,752 books, 114 serials, 1,020 audiovisual materials, an OPAC, and a Web page. Operations spending for 2004 fiscal year: $86,469. 51 computers available on campus for general student use. A campuswide network can be accessed from off-campus. Staffed computer lab on campus.

■ **EMPORIA STATE UNIVERSITY** *F-14*
1200 Commercial St.
Emporia, KS 66801-5087
Tel: (620)341-1200; 877-468-6378
Admissions: (620)341-5465
E-mail: go2esu@emporia.edu
Web Site: http://www.emporia.edu/
Description: State-supported, comprehensive, coed. Part of Kansas Board of Regents. Awards bachelor's, master's, and doctoral degrees and post-master's certificates. Founded 1863. Setting: 207-acre small town campus with easy access to Wichita. Endowment: $52.1 million. Research spending for 2004 fiscal year: $550,554. Educational spending for 2005 fiscal year: $2632 per student. Total enrollment: 6,288. Faculty: 282 (252 full-time, 30 part-time). Student-undergrad faculty ratio is 18:1. 1,188 applied, 78% were admitted. Full-time: 3,797 students, 61% women, 39% men. Part-time: 554 students, 63% women, 37% men. Students come from 30 states and territories, 30 other countries, 5% from out-of-state, 1% Native American, 5% Hispanic, 4% black, 1% Asian American or Pacific Islander, 2% international, 16% 25 or older, 25% live on campus, 11% transferred in. Retention: 68% of full-time freshmen returned the following year. Academic areas with the most degrees conferred: education; business/marketing; social sciences. Core. Calendar: semesters. Academic remediation for entering students, ESL program, services for LD students, advanced placement, accelerated degree

program, honors program, independent study, distance learning, double major, summer session for credit, part-time degree program, adult/continuing education programs, internships, graduate courses open to undergrads. Off campus study. Study abroad program.

Entrance Requirements: Options: electronic application, early admission, deferred admission. Required: high school transcript, ACT, SAT or ACT. Recommended: minimum 2.0 high school GPA. Entrance: noncompetitive. Application deadline: Rolling.

Costs Per Year: Application fee: $30. State resident tuition: $2638 full-time, $88 per credit hour part-time. Nonresident tuition: $9990 full-time, $333 per credit hour part-time. Mandatory fees: $668 full-time, $41 per credit hour part-time. Full-time tuition and fees vary according to degree level. Part-time tuition and fees vary according to degree level. College room and board: $4787. College room only: $2363. Room and board charges vary according to board plan and housing facility.

Collegiate Environment: Orientation program. Drama-theater group, choral group, marching band, student-run newspaper. Social organizations: 112 open to all; national fraternities, national sororities; 13% of eligible men and 9% of eligible women are members. Most popular organizations: Union Activities Council, Associated Student Government, Black Student Union. Major annual events: Homecoming, Flintstock, Family Day. Student services: legal services, health clinic, personal-psychological counseling, women's center. Campus security: 24-hour emergency response devices and patrols, student patrols, late night transport-escort service, controlled dormitory access, 24-hour residence hall monitoring, safety and self-awareness programs. 1,148 college housing spaces available; 1,053 were occupied in 2003-04. Freshmen guaranteed college housing. On-campus residence required in freshman year. Options: coed, men-only, women-only housing available. William Allen White Library with 2.4 million books, 53,656 microform titles, 815 serials, 8,728 audiovisual materials, an OPAC, and a Web page. Operations spending for 2004 fiscal year: $1.9 million. 410 computers available on campus for general student use. A campuswide network can be accessed from student residence rooms and from off campus. Staffed computer lab on campus.

Community Environment: Emporia, close to the nation's geographical center, is an industrial city as well as a "university town." From this agricultural area more than 100,000 cattle are sent to market each year. The community facilities include a hospital, libraries, an auditorium and many civic, social and veteran's organizations. All forms of commercial transportation are available. Parks, golf courses, a skating rink, tennis courts, ball fields, bowling alley, and swimming pools are some of the facilities for recreation.

■ **FLINT HILLS TECHNICAL COLLEGE** *F-14*
3301 West 18th Ave.
Emporia, KS 66801
Tel: (620)341-2300
Free: 800-711-6947
Fax: (620)343-7252
Web Site: http://www.fhtc.net/
Description: State-supported, 2-year, coed. Founded 1963. Calendar: semesters.

■ **FORT HAYS STATE UNIVERSITY** *D-7*
600 Park St.
Hays, KS 67601-4099
Tel: (785)628-4000
Free: 800-628-FHSU
Admissions: (785)628-5666
Fax: (785)628-4014
E-mail: tigers@fhsuvm.fhsu.edu
Web Site: http://www.fhsu.edu/
Description: State-supported, comprehensive, coed. Part of Kansas Board of Regents. Awards associate, bachelor's, and master's degrees and post-master's certificates. Founded 1902. Setting: 200-acre small town campus. Endowment: $27.6 million. Research spending for 2004 fiscal year: $47,638. Educational spending for 2005 fiscal year: $5102 per student. Total enrollment: 7,373. 1,938 applied, 94% were admitted. 9% from top 10% of their high school class, 31% from top quarter, 65% from top half. Full-time: 4,126 students, 53% women, 47% men. Part-time: 1,794 students, 56% women, 44% men. Students come from 48 states and territories, 15 other countries, 10% from out-of-state, 0.5% Native American, 3% Hispanic, 1% black, 1% Asian American or Pacific Islander, 16% international, 18% 25 or older, 20% live on campus, 21% transferred in. Retention: 72% of full-time freshmen

returned the following year. Core. Calendar: semesters. Academic remediation for entering students, ESL program, services for LD students, advanced placement, self-designed majors, distance learning, double major, summer session for credit, part-time degree program, external degree program, adult/continuing education programs, internships, graduate courses open to undergrads. Off campus study at members of the National Student Exchange. Study abroad program.

Entrance Requirements: Options: Peterson's Universal Application, Common Application, electronic application, international baccalaureate accepted. Required: high school transcript, ACT, SAT or ACT. Entrance: noncompetitive. Application deadline: Rolling. Notification: continuous.

Costs Per Year: Application fee: $30. State resident tuition: $1886 full-time, $101.75 per credit hour part-time. Nonresident tuition: $7104 full-time, $319.17 per credit hour part-time. Mandatory fees: $556 full-time. Full-time tuition and fees vary according to course load, location, and reciprocity agreements. Part-time tuition varies according to course load and location. College room and board: $6190. College room only: $3577. Room and board charges vary according to board plan, housing facility, and student level.

Collegiate Environment: Orientation program. Drama-theater group, choral group, marching band, student-run newspaper, radio station. Social organizations: 105 open to all; national fraternities, national sororities; 2% of eligible men and 2% of eligible women are members. Most popular organizations: Student Government Association, University Activities Board, Residence Hall Association, International Student Union, Block and Bridle. Major annual events: homecoming, Back to School Picnic, Oktoberfest. Student services: health clinic, personal-psychological counseling, women's center. Campus security: 24-hour emergency response devices and patrols, late night transport-escort service, controlled dormitory access. 1,250 college housing spaces available; 1,000 were occupied in 2003-04. Freshmen guaranteed college housing. On-campus residence required in freshman year. Options: coed, men-only, women-only housing available. Forsyth Library with 624,637 books, 404,433 microform titles, 1,689 serials, an OPAC, and a Web page. Operations spending for 2004 fiscal year: $1.9 million. 813 computers available on campus for general student use. Computer purchase/lease plans available. A campuswide network can be accessed from student residence rooms and from off campus. Staffed computer lab on campus.

Community Environment: Fort Hays, a military post on the old frontier, gave this railroad town its name of Hays. Known as an agricultural, educational, and regional medical center Hays has vast interests in oil and livestock as well. Ellis county, the county in which Hays is located, is the largest oil producing county in the State of Kansas. Fort Hays Experiment Station, one of the largest dryland experiment stations in the world, is located here.

■ **FORT SCOTT COMMUNITY COLLEGE** *G-17*
2108 South Horton
Fort Scott, KS 66701
Tel: (316)223-2700
Free: 800-874-3722
Fax: (316)223-4927
Web Site: http://www.fortscott.edu/
Description: State and locally supported, 2-year, coed. Awards certificates, transfer associate, and terminal associate degrees. Founded 1919. Setting: 147-acre small town campus. Total enrollment: 1,923. 662 applied. Students come from 24 states and territories, 1% Native American, 1% Hispanic, 6% black, 0.5% Asian American or Pacific Islander, 0.3% international, 9% live on campus. Core. Calendar: semesters. Academic remediation for entering students, ESL program, services for LD students, advanced placement, self-designed majors, independent study, distance learning, summer session for credit, part-time degree program, external degree program, adult/continuing education programs, co-op programs and internships. Study abroad program. ROTC: Army (c).

Entrance Requirements: Open admission. Options: Peterson's Universal Application, early admission, deferred admission. Placement: ACT ASSET required; ACT required for some. Entrance: minimally difficult. Application deadline: 8/15.

Collegiate Environment: Orientation program. Drama-theater group, choral group, marching band. Most popular organizations: Aggie Club, Student Nurses Association, student government, Soccer Club, Phi Theta Kappa. Major annual events: homecoming, Spring Fling, Endowment Dinner. Student services: personal-psychological counseling. Campus security: controlled dormitory access, evening security from 9 pm to 6am. 200 college housing spaces available; 198 were occupied in 2003-04. Option: coed housing available. Learning Resource Center with 25,308 books, 124 serials, and an OPAC. Operations spending for 2004 fiscal year: $103,628. 95 computers available on campus for general student use. Staffed computer lab on campus.

Community Environment: FSCC is located in Fort Scott, Kansas, a thriving agricultural-industrial town at the intersection of U.S. highways 69 and 54 in southeast Kansas. About 9,000 persons live in Fort Scott and an additional 6,000 live in the surrounding Bourbon County area. Fort Scott citizens continue to value their historic background, dating from the time the town was established as a military outpost in 1842. The original army post on the Indian frontier, restored and operated by the National Park Service as the Fort Scott National Historic Site, draws thousands of tourists annually. The city is served by major highways and bus lines and has a municipal airport. Superb medical facilities, including a 164-bed hospital, provide medical services for much of southeast Kansas. Numerous cultural opportunities include an active arts council and civic symphony. Outstanding community recreational programs and facilities, 180 acres of parks and several area lakes enhance the college experience for FSCC students.

■ **FRIENDS UNIVERSITY** *H-11*
2100 West University St.
Wichita, KS 67213
Tel: (316)295-5000
Free: 800-577-2233
Admissions: (316)295-5100
Fax: (316)262-5027
E-mail: tmyers@friends.edu
Web Site: http://www.friends.edu/

Description: Independent, comprehensive, coed. Awards associate, bachelor's, and master's degrees. Founded 1898. Setting: 45-acre urban campus. Endowment: $22.2 million. Total enrollment: 3,190. 668 applied, 93% were admitted. Students come from 30 states and territories, 25 other countries, 10% from out-of-state, 0.3% 25 or older, 18% live on campus. Retention: 63% of full-time freshmen returned the following year. Core. Calendar: semesters. Academic remediation for entering students, advanced placement, accelerated degree program, self-designed majors, honors program, summer session for credit, part-time degree program, external degree program, adult/continuing education programs, co-op programs and internships, graduate courses open to undergrads. Off campus study at Newman University, Wichita Area Vocational/Technical Institute.

Entrance Requirements: Options: early admission, international baccalaureate accepted. Required: high school transcript, SAT or ACT. Recommended: interview. Required for some: essay, 1 recommendation. Entrance: moderately difficult. Application deadline: Rolling. Notification: continuous.

Collegiate Environment: Drama-theater group, choral group. Social organizations: local fraternities, local sororities. Most popular organizations: Singing Quakers, Phi Beta Lambda, Student Association. Major annual events: homecoming, Cherry Carnival, Falcon Frenzy. Student services: health clinic, personal-psychological counseling. Campus security: 24-hour patrols, late night transport-escort service. Options: men-only, women-only housing available. Edmund Stanley Library plus 3 others with 105,989 books, 857 serials, and an OPAC. 190 computers available on campus for general student use. A campuswide network can be accessed from student residence rooms and from off campus. Staffed computer lab on campus.

■ **GARDEN CITY COMMUNITY COLLEGE** *G-3*
801 Campus Dr.
Garden City, KS 67846-6399
Tel: (316)276-7611
Admissions: (620)276-7611
Web Site: http://www.gcccks.edu/

Description: County-supported, 2-year, coed. Part of Kansas Board of Regents. Awards certificates, transfer associate, and terminal associate degrees. Founded 1919. Setting: 63-acre rural campus. Endowment: $4.9 million. Educational spending for 2005 fiscal year: $4890 per student. Total enrollment: 2,174. 845 applied, 100% were admitted. 17% from top 10% of their high school class, 19% from top quarter, 34% from top half. Full-time: 925 students, 49% women, 51% men. Part-time: 1,249 students, 58% women, 42% men. Students come from 31 states and territories, 7% from out-of-state, 1% Native American, 20% Hispanic, 9% black, 2% Asian American or Pacific Islander, 1% international, 39% 25 or older, 12% live on campus. Retention: 78% of full-time freshmen returned the following year. Core. Calendar: semesters. Academic remediation for entering students,

ESL program, services for LD students, advanced placement, self-designed majors, distance learning, summer session for credit, part-time degree program, external degree program, adult/continuing education programs.

Entrance Requirements: Open admission except for transfer students. Required: high school transcript. Placement: ACT COMPASS required. Entrance: noncompetitive. Application deadline: Rolling.

Costs Per Year: Application fee: $0. State resident tuition: $1248 full-time, $39 per credit hour part-time. Nonresident tuition: $2080 full-time, $65 per credit hour part-time. Mandatory fees: $672 full-time, $21 per credit hour part-time. Full-time tuition and fees vary according to course load and location. Part-time tuition and fees vary according to course load and location. College room and board: $4500. Room and board charges vary according to housing facility.

Collegiate Environment: Orientation program. Drama-theater group, choral group, student-run newspaper. Social organizations: 23 open to all. Most popular organizations: student government, Hispanic American Leadership Organization, Business Professionals of America, Criminal Justice Organization, Phi Theta Kappa. Major annual events: Earth Day, Homecoming, Hispanic Day. Student services: health clinic, personal-psychological counseling. Campus security: 24-hour emergency response devices and patrols, student patrols, late night transport-escort service, controlled dormitory access. 306 college housing spaces available. No special consideration for freshman housing applicants. Option: coed housing available. Saffell Library with 42,080 books, 2,771 microform titles, 116 serials, 303 audiovisual materials, an OPAC, and a Web page. Operations spending for 2004 fiscal year: $166,111. 150 computers available on campus for general student use. A campuswide network can be accessed from student residence rooms. Staffed computer lab on campus.

Community Environment: Garden City is on the Arkansas River in a fertile agricultural area. Predominant crops are corn, alfalfa, wheat and grain sorgums, with beef cattle production very strong. Shopping facilities are good. Finnup Park, a large recreational development, contains a swimming pool, picnic sites, museum and zoo. Other facilities for recreation are golf courses and local parks. One of the largest buffalo herds is located at Garden City on the Buffalo Preserve. All forms of commercial transportation are available.

■ **HASKELL INDIAN NATIONS UNIVERSITY** *D-15*
155 Indian Ave., No. 5031
Lawrence, KS 66046-4800
Tel: (785)749-8404
Admissions: (785)749-8454
Fax: (785)749-8429
Web Site: http://www.haskell.edu/

Description: Federally supported, 4-year, coed. Awards associate and bachelor's degrees. Founded 1884. Setting: 320-acre suburban campus. Total enrollment: 1,028. 10% from top 10% of their high school class, 30% from top half. Full-time: 922 students, 47% women, 53% men. Part-time: 106 students, 47% women, 53% men. Students come from 37 states and territories, 100% Native American, 0% Hispanic, 0% black, 0% Asian American or Pacific Islander, 0% international, 1% 25 or older, 9% transferred in. Core. Calendar: semesters. Academic remediation for entering students, services for LD students, advanced placement, self-designed majors, independent study, distance learning, summer session for credit, part-time degree program, internships. Off campus study at members of the American Indian Higher Education Consortium, Kansas City Regional Council for Higher Education, University of Kansas. ROTC: Air Force (c).

Entrance Requirements: Options: Common Application, electronic application. Required: high school transcript, minimum 2.0 high school GPA, ACT. Required for some: 2 recommendations. Entrance: minimally difficult. Application deadline: 7/30. Notification: continuous. Preference given to applicants with at least one-fourth Native American ancestry or tribal membership.

Costs Per Year: Application fee: $10. State resident tuition: $0 full-time. Nonresident tuition: $0 full-time. Mandatory fees: $420 full-time, $70 per term part-time.

Collegiate Environment: Orientation program. Drama-theater group, student-run newspaper. Social organizations: 40 open to all. Most popular organizations: Phi Beta Lambda, Aises, H-Club, Navajo Club, Unity. Major annual events: Spring Graduation Pow-Wow, Haskell Indian Art Market, Welcome Back Pow Wow. Student services: health clinic, personal-psychological counseling. Campus security: night patrol only. 822 college housing spaces available; 762 were occupied in 2003-04. Freshmen given priority for college housing. Options: coed, men-only, women-only housing available. 50,000 books, 400 serials, and an OPAC. 35 computers available on campus for general student use. Staffed computer lab on campus.

Community Environment: See University of Kansas.

■ **HESSTON COLLEGE** *F-11*

Box 3000
Hesston, KS 67062-2093
Tel: (620)327-4221
Free: 800-995-2757
Admissions: (620)327-8222
Fax: (620)327-8300
E-mail: admissions@hesston.edu
Web Site: http://www.hesston.edu/

Description: Independent Mennonite, 2-year, coed. Awards transfer associate and terminal associate degrees. Founded 1909. Setting: 50-acre small town campus with easy access to Wichita. Total enrollment: 477. 710 applied, 83% were admitted. Full-time: 414 students, 48% women, 52% men. Part-time: 63 students, 65% women, 35% men. Students come from 30 states and territories, 13 other countries, 50% from out-of-state, 1% Native American, 3% Hispanic, 4% black, 1% Asian American or Pacific Islander, 9% international, 50% 25 or older, 74% live on campus, 9% transferred in. Retention: 76% of full-time freshmen returned the following year. Core. Calendar: semesters. Academic remediation for entering students, ESL program, services for LD students, advanced placement, independent study, double major, summer session for credit, part-time degree program, co-op programs and internships.

Entrance Requirements: Open admission except for nursing and pastoral ministries programs. Options: electronic application, early admission, deferred admission. Required: high school transcript, 2 recommendations, SAT or ACT. Required for some: interview. Entrance: noncompetitive. Application deadline: Rolling.

Costs Per Year: Application fee: $15. Comprehensive fee: $22,354 includes full-time tuition ($16,246), mandatory fees ($250), and college room and board ($5858). Part-time tuition: $676 per hour. Part-time mandatory fees: $60 per term.

Collegiate Environment: Orientation program. Drama-theater group, choral group, student-run newspaper. Major annual events: Thanksgiving Weekend, Feast of Carols, Spring Celebration. Student services: personal-psychological counseling. Campus security: 24-hour emergency response devices. 376 college housing spaces available; 75 were occupied in 2003-04. Freshmen guaranteed college housing. On-campus residence required through sophomore year. Options: men-only, women-only housing available. Mary Miller Library with 35,000 books, 234 serials, 2,409 audiovisual materials, an OPAC, and a Web page. 67 computers available on campus for general student use. A campuswide network can be accessed from student residence rooms and from off campus. Staffed computer lab on campus.

Community Environment: Hesston is a small, progressive, south central Kansas town with a population of 4,000. It is located 35 miles north of Wichita, and has ready access to air, rail, and bus transportation. Part-time employment for students is available in the area and is coordinated through the Cooperative Education office on campus. A temperate climate allows considerable outside activity. Recreational facilities located in or near Hesston include an 18-hole golf course, bike trails, tennis courts, year-round swimming pool, and numerous county and state parks and lakes.

■ **HIGHLAND COMMUNITY COLLEGE**

606 West Main St.
Highland, KS 66035
Tel: (785)442-6000
Admissions: (785)442-6020
Fax: (785)442-6100
Web Site: http://www.highlandcc.edu/

Description: State and locally supported, 2-year, coed. Part of Kansas Community College System. Awards certificates, transfer associate, and terminal associate degrees. Founded 1858. Setting: 20-acre rural campus. Total enrollment: 3,040. 11% from top 10% of their high school class, 38% from top quarter, 67% from top half. Students come from 9 states and territories, 31% 25 or older. Core. Calendar: semesters. Academic remediation for entering students, services for LD students, advanced placement, self-designed majors, summer session for credit, part-time degree program, adult/continuing education programs, co-op programs and internships. Off campus study. ROTC: Army (c).

Entrance Requirements: Open admission for state residents. Options: Peterson's Universal Application, early admission. Required: high school

transcript. Placement: ACT ASSET required; ACT recommended. Entrance: minimally difficult. Application deadline: 8/20. Notification: continuous. Preference given to state residents.

Costs Per Year: Application fee: $0. Area resident tuition: $888 full-time, $37 per credit hour part-time. State resident tuition: $1080 full-time, $45 per credit hour part-time. Nonresident tuition: $2280 full-time, $95 per credit hour part-time. Mandatory fees: $1056 full-time, $44 per credit hour part-time. College room and board: $3872. College room only: $2242.

Collegiate Environment: Drama-theater group, student-run newspaper. Option: coed housing available. 30,000 books and 268 serials. 94 computers available on campus for general student use. Staffed computer lab on campus.

■ **HUTCHINSON COMMUNITY COLLEGE AND AREA VOCATIONAL SCHOOL** *G-10*

1300 North Plum St.
Hutchinson, KS 67501-5894
Tel: (620)665-3500
Free: 800-289-3501
Admissions: (620)665-3536
Fax: (620)665-3310
E-mail: strobelc@hutchcc.edu
Web Site: http://www.hutchcc.edu/

Description: State and locally supported, 2-year, coed. Part of Kansas Board of Regents. Awards certificates, transfer associate, and terminal associate degrees. Founded 1928. Setting: 47-acre small town campus. Endowment: $3.6 million. Educational spending for 2005 fiscal year: $3345 per student. Total enrollment: 4,869. Student-undergrad faculty ratio is 16:1. 2,940 applied, 100% were admitted. 10% from top 10% of their high school class, 20% from top quarter, 50% from top half. Full-time: 1,956 students, 51% women, 49% men. Part-time: 2,913 students, 62% women, 38% men. Students come from 34 states and territories, 18 other countries, 7% from out-of-state, 1% Native American, 4% Hispanic, 4% black, 1% Asian American or Pacific Islander, 0.4% international, 32% 25 or older, 11% live on campus, 10% transferred in. Retention: 56% of full-time freshmen returned the following year. Core. Calendar: semesters. Academic remediation for entering students, ESL program, services for LD students, advanced placement, self-designed majors, honors program, independent study, distance learning, double major, summer session for credit, part-time degree program, adult/continuing education programs, co-op programs and internships. ROTC: Army (c).

Entrance Requirements: Open admission except for allied health programs. Options: electronic application, early admission, deferred admission. Recommended: high school transcript. Required for some: interview. Entrance: noncompetitive. Application deadline: Rolling.

Costs Per Year: Application fee: $0. Area resident tuition: $50 per hour part-time. State resident tuition: $1600 full-time, $50 per hour part-time. Nonresident tuition: $2816 full-time, $88 per hour part-time. Mandatory fees: $480 full-time, $15 per hour part-time. College room and board: $4060. Room and board charges vary according to board plan.

Collegiate Environment: Orientation program. Drama-theater group, choral group, student-run newspaper. Social organizations: 15 open to all. Most popular organizations: Student Government Association, Black Cultural Society, Hispanic-American Leadership Organization, Hutchinson Christian Fellowship, Campus Crusade for Christ. Student services: health clinic, personal-psychological counseling. Campus security: 24-hour emergency response devices and patrols, student patrols, late night transport-escort service, controlled dormitory access. 350 college housing spaces available; all were occupied in 2003-04. No special consideration for freshman housing applicants. Options: men-only, women-only housing available. John F. Kennedy Library plus 1 other with 41,812 books, 76,808 microform titles, 245 serials, 3,039 audiovisual materials, an OPAC, and a Web page. Operations spending for 2004 fiscal year: $86,614. 475 computers available on campus for general student use. A campuswide network can be accessed from off-campus. Staffed computer lab on campus.

■ **INDEPENDENCE COMMUNITY COLLEGE** *I-15*

Brookside Dr. and College Ave.
PO Box 708
Independence, KS 67301-0708
Tel: (620)331-4100
Free: 800-842-6063
Admissions: (620)332-5400
Fax: (620)331-5344

E-mail: sciufulescu@indycc.edu

Web Site: http://www.indycc.edu/

Description: State-supported, 2-year, coed. Part of Kansas State Board of Education. Awards certificates, transfer associate, and terminal associate degrees. Founded 1925. Setting: 68-acre small town campus. Total enrollment: 906. Student-undergrad faculty ratio is 17:1. Full-time: 478 students, 43% women, 57% men. Part-time: 428 students, 66% women, 34% men. Students come from 18 states and territories, 17 other countries, 9% from out-of-state, 2% Native American, 2% Hispanic, 2% black, 4% Asian American or Pacific Islander, 1% international, 44% 25 or older, 10% live on campus. Core. Calendar: semesters. Academic remediation for entering students, ESL program, advanced placement, honors program, summer session for credit, part-time degree program, adult/continuing education programs, co-op programs and internships.

Entrance Requirements: Open admission. Options: Common Application, electronic application, early admission. Required: high school transcript. Placement: SAT or ACT recommended. Entrance: noncompetitive. Application deadline: Rolling.

Costs Per Year: Application fee: $0. Area resident tuition: $800 full-time. State resident tuition: $800 full-time, $25 per credit hour part-time. Nonresident tuition: $2080 full-time, $65 per credit hour part-time. Mandatory fees: $800 full-time. College room and board: $4100.

Collegiate Environment: Drama-theater group, choral group, student-run newspaper. Most popular organizations: Student Senate, Phi Theta Kappa, Student Ambassadors, Campus Christians, multicultural student organization. Major annual events: homecoming, Winter Formal, fall/spring picnics. Student services: personal-psychological counseling. Campus security: night patrol. 300 college housing spaces available; 180 were occupied in 2003-04. Freshmen guaranteed college housing. On-campus residence required through sophomore year. Independence Community College Library plus 1 other with 32,408 books and 166 serials. 75 computers available on campus for general student use. A campuswide network can be accessed from student residence rooms and from off campus. Staffed computer lab on campus.

Community Environment: Independence, is in a predominately agricultural region that also produces oil. The community includes a number of churches, a hospital and numerous civic, fraternal and veteran's organizations. An airport is within a ten-minute drive. Montgomery County State Lake and the Elk City Reservoir provide facilities for all water sports. Other recreational activities are golf, tennis and bowling.

■ **JOHNSON COUNTY COMMUNITY COLLEGE** *L-16*

12345 College Blvd.

Overland Park, KS 66210-1299

Tel: (913)469-8500

Web Site: http://www.johnco.cc.ks.us/

Description: State and locally supported, 2-year, coed. Part of Kansas State Board of Education. Awards certificates, transfer associate, and terminal associate degrees. Founded 1967. Setting: 220-acre suburban campus with easy access to Kansas City. Endowment: $4.4 million. Educational spending for 2005 fiscal year: $3245 per student. Total enrollment: 18,612. Full-time: 6,378 students, 51% women, 49% men. Part-time: 12,234 students, 58% women, 42% men. Students come from 26 states and territories, 36 other countries, 5% from out-of-state, 1% Native American, 3% Hispanic, 4% black, 4% Asian American or Pacific Islander, 1% international, 43% 25 or older, 1% transferred in. Core. Calendar: semesters. Academic remediation for entering students, ESL program, services for LD students, advanced placement, self-designed majors, honors program, independent study, distance learning, double major, summer session for credit, part-time degree program, adult/continuing education programs, co-op programs and internships. Off campus study at Metropolitan Community College.

Entrance Requirements: Open admission except for nursing, dental hygiene, paralegal, respiratory care, interpreter training, emergency medical technology programs. Option: early admission. Required for some: high school transcript. Placement: ACT, ACT ASSET required for some. Entrance: noncompetitive. Application deadline: Rolling. Notification: continuous.

Costs Per Year: Application fee: $10. Area resident tuition: $1920 full-time, $64 per credit hour part-time. State resident tuition: $2370 full-time, $79 per credit hour part-time. Nonresident tuition: $4350 full-time, $145 per credit hour part-time. Full-time tuition varies according to course load. Part-time tuition varies according to course load.

Collegiate Environment: Drama-theater group, student-run newspaper. Campus security: 24-hour emergency response devices and patrols, late night transport-escort service. College housing not available. Johnson

County Community College Library with 89,400 books, 708 serials, 4,770 audiovisual materials, an OPAC, and a Web page. Operations spending for 2004 fiscal year: $1.2 million. 800 computers available on campus for general student use. A campuswide network can be accessed from off-campus. Staffed computer lab on campus.

■ **KANSAS CITY KANSAS COMMUNITY COLLEGE** *D-17*

7250 State Ave.

Kansas City, KS 66112-3003

Tel: (913)334-1100

Admissions: (913)288-7694

Fax: (913)696-9646

Web Site: http://www.kckcc.edu/

Description: State and locally supported, 2-year, coed. Awards certificates, diplomas, transfer associate, and terminal associate degrees. Founded 1923. Setting: 148-acre urban campus. Total enrollment: 5,419. Student-undergrad faculty ratio is 14:1. Full-time: 1,925 students, 61% women, 39% men. Part-time: 3,494 students, 67% women, 33% men. Students come from 29 states and territories, 23 other countries, 5% from out-of-state, 1% Native American, 7% Hispanic, 25% black, 2% Asian American or Pacific Islander, 2% international, 49% 25 or older, 7% transferred in. Core. Calendar: semesters. Academic remediation for entering students, ESL program, services for LD students, advanced placement, freshman honors college, honors program, independent study, distance learning, summer session for credit, part-time degree program, external degree program, adult/continuing education programs, co-op programs and internships.

Entrance Requirements: Open admission except for nursing program. Options: Common Application, electronic application, international baccalaureate accepted. Required: high school transcript. Entrance: noncompetitive. Application deadline: Rolling. Notification: continuous.

Costs Per Year: Application fee: $0. State resident tuition: $1470 full-time, $49 per credit hour part-time. Nonresident tuition: $4410 full-time, $147 per credit hour part-time. Mandatory fees: $300 full-time, $10 per credit hour part-time. Full-time tuition and fees vary according to course load. Part-time tuition and fees vary according to course load.

Collegiate Environment: Drama-theater group, choral group, student-run newspaper. Social organizations: 20 open to all. Most popular organizations: Student Senate, Phi Theta Kappa, Drama Club, The African American Student Union, Christian Student Union. Major annual events: Last Class Bash, Candle Lighting Program, First Class Bash. Student services: health clinic, personal-psychological counseling, women's center. Campus security: 24-hour emergency response devices and patrols, student patrols, late night transport-escort service. College housing not available. Kansas City Kansas Community College Library with 65,000 books, 250,000 microform titles, 200 serials, 12,000 audiovisual materials, an OPAC, and a Web page. 775 computers available on campus for general student use. A campuswide network can be accessed from off-campus. Staffed computer lab on campus.

■ **KANSAS STATE UNIVERSITY** *C-13*

Manhattan, KS 66506

Tel: (785)532-6011

Admissions: (785)532-6250

Fax: (785)532-6393

E-mail: kstate@ksu.edu

Web Site: http://www.ksu.edu/

Description: State-supported, university, coed. Part of Kansas Board of Regents. Awards associate, bachelor's, master's, doctoral, and first professional degrees. Founded 1863. Setting: 668-acre suburban campus with easy access to Kansas City. Endowment: $340.5 million. Research spending for 2004 fiscal year: $98.8 million. Educational spending for 2005 fiscal year: $5764 per student. Total enrollment: 23,182. Faculty: 792 (714 full-time, 78 part-time). Student-undergrad faculty ratio is 21:1. 8,207 applied, 59% were admitted. Full-time: 16,519 students, 49% women, 51% men. Part-time: 2,319 students, 54% women, 46% men. Students come from 50 states and territories, 100 other countries, 13% from out-of-state, 1% Native American, 3% Hispanic, 3% black, 1% Asian American or Pacific Islander, 1% international, 9% 25 or older, 37% live on campus, 9% transferred in. Retention: 81% of full-time freshmen returned the following year. Academic areas with the most degrees conferred: business/marketing; education; social sciences. Core. Calendar: semesters. Academic remediation for entering students, ESL program, services for LD students, advanced placement, accelerated degree program, freshman honors college, honors program, independent study, distance learning, double major, summer session for credit, part-time degree program, adult/continuing education programs, co-op programs and internships, graduate courses open to undergrads. Off campus study at Manhattan Christian College, University of Missouri-Kansas City, 19 Kansas community colleges. Study abroad program. ROTC: Army, Air Force.

Entrance Requirements: Options: Common Application, electronic application. Required: high school transcript, minimum 2.0 high school GPA, SAT or ACT. Entrance: noncompetitive. Application deadline: Rolling. Notification: continuous.

Costs Per Year: Application fee: $30. State resident tuition: $4560 full-time, $152 per credit hour part-time. Nonresident tuition: $13,890 full-time, $463 per credit hour part-time. Mandatory fees: $564 full-time. College room and board: $5772. Room and board charges vary according to board plan.

Collegiate Environment: Orientation program. Drama-theater group, choral group, marching band, student-run newspaper, radio station. Social organizations: 372 open to all; national fraternities, national sororities; 20% of eligible men and 20% of eligible women are members. Most popular organizations: athletic department groups, marching band, Union Governing Board, theater productions, debate team. Major annual events: Homecoming, Multicultural Week, open house. Student services: legal services, health clinic, personal-psychological counseling, women's center. Campus security: 24-hour emergency response devices and patrols, late night transport-escort service, controlled dormitory access. No special consideration for freshman housing applicants. Options: coed, men-only, women-only housing available. Hale Library plus 3 others with 1.6 million books, 2.5 million microform titles, 1,365 serials, 5,056 audiovisual materials, an OPAC, and a Web page. Operations spending for 2004 fiscal year: $11.9 million. 326 computers available on campus for general student use. A campuswide network can be accessed from student residence rooms and from off campus. Staffed computer lab on campus.

Community Environment: Manhattan, a beautiful city, situated on the Blue River and Kansas River, enjoys the excellent recreational facilities of Tuttle Creek Dam. The community offers libraries, churches, hospitals, hotels, motels, rooming houses and four attractive shopping centers including Manhattan Town Center. Numerous civic, service and social organizations exist. Part-time work is available. Historic Fort Riley is eight miles away.

■ **KANSAS WESLEYAN UNIVERSITY** *D-10*
100 East Claflin Ave.
Salina, KS 67401-6196
Tel: (785)827-5541
Free: 800-874-1154
Admissions: (785)829-5541
Fax: (785)827-0927
E-mail: jallen@kwu.edu
Web Site: http://www.kwu.edu/
Description: Independent United Methodist, comprehensive, coed. Awards associate, bachelor's, and master's degrees. Founded 1886. Setting: 28-acre urban campus. Endowment: $13.5 million. Educational spending for 2005 fiscal year: $3911 per student. Total enrollment: 805. 1,097 applied, 53% were admitted. 9% from top 10% of their high school class, 38% from top quarter, 71% from top half. Full-time: 597 students, 57% women, 43% men. Part-time: 171 students, 65% women, 35% men. Students come from 24 states and territories, 4 other countries, 39% from out-of-state, 1% Native American, 5% Hispanic, 6% black, 2% Asian American or Pacific Islander, 0.4% international, 26% 25 or older, 65% live on campus, 17% transferred in. Retention: 74% of full-time freshmen returned the following year. Core. Calendar: 2 semesters with a summer term. Academic remediation for entering students, ESL program, advanced placement, self-designed majors, independent study, distance learning, double major, summer session for credit, part-time degree program, external degree program, adult/continuing education programs, internships, graduate courses open to undergrads. Off campus study at Associated Colleges of Central Kansas. Study abroad program.

Entrance Requirements: Options: Peterson's Universal Application, Common Application, electronic application, deferred admission. Required: high school transcript, minimum 2.5 high school GPA, minimum ACT composite score of 18, SAT or ACT. Recommended: SAT, ACT. Entrance: moderately difficult. Application deadline: Rolling. Notification: continuous.

Costs Per Year: Application fee: $20. Comprehensive fee: $21,400 includes full-time tuition ($15,800) and college room and board ($5600). College room only: $2400. Part-time tuition: $200 per credit hour. Part-time tuition varies according to course load.

Collegiate Environment: Orientation program. Drama-theater group, choral group, student-run newspaper. Social organizations: 20 open to all; local

fraternities, local sororities, societies; 1% of eligible men and 1% of eligible women are members. Most popular organizations: Fellowship of Christian Athletes, student government, Wesleyan Chorale, Multicultural Student Association, Business Club. Major annual events: Homecoming, Sweetheart Dance, Spring Fling. Student services: personal-psychological counseling. Campus security: 24-hour emergency response devices, student patrols, late night transport-escort service, controlled dormitory access, evening patrols by security. 400 college housing spaces available; 360 were occupied in 2003-04. Freshmen guaranteed college housing. On-campus residence required through sophomore year. Options: men-only, women-only housing available. Memorial Library with 100,000 microform titles, 370 serials, 1,055 audiovisual materials, an OPAC, and a Web page. Operations spending for 2004 fiscal year: $177,612. 72 computers available on campus for general student use. A campuswide network can be accessed from student residence rooms and from off campus. Staffed computer lab on campus.

Community Environment: Salina (pop. 42,299), situated in the central part of the state, is the fifth largest city in Kansas. Major forms of transportation are available. Community facilities include a public library, municipal shopping center, museum, community theater, and numerous churches. Points of interest include Kanapolis Lake and Rock City.

■ **LABETTE COMMUNITY COLLEGE** *I-16*
200 South 14th St.
Parsons, KS 67357-4299
Tel: (620)421-6700
Web Site: http://www.labette.edu/
Description: State and locally supported, 2-year, coed. Part of Kansas State Board of Education. Awards certificates, transfer associate, and terminal associate degrees. Founded 1923. Setting: 4-acre small town campus. Total enrollment: 1,401. 212 applied, 100% were admitted. 20% from top 10% of their high school class, 59% from top half. Full-time: 466 students, 58% women, 42% men. Part-time: 935 students, 69% women, 31% men. Students come from 7 states and territories, 4 other countries, 1% Native American, 4% Hispanic, 4% black, 0.4% Asian American or Pacific Islander, 1% international, 40% 25 or older. Calendar: semesters. Academic remediation for entering students, services for LD students, advanced placement, accelerated degree program, independent study, distance learning, double major, summer session for credit, part-time degree program, adult/continuing education programs, co-op programs and internships. Off campus study. ROTC: Army (c).

Entrance Requirements: Open admission except for nursing program. Option: early admission. Recommended: high school transcript. Required for some: recommendations, interview. Placement: ACT COMPASS required; ACT recommended. Entrance: noncompetitive. Application deadline: Rolling. Notification: continuous.

Collegiate Environment: Choral group. Social organizations: 18 open to all. Most popular organizations: Adult Women Who Are Returning to Education (AWARE), Phi Beta Lambda. Student services: personal-psychological counseling. Option: coed housing available. Labette Community College Library with 26,000 books, 1,770 microform titles, 235 serials, 542 audiovisual materials, an OPAC, and a Web page. 66 computers available on campus for general student use. Staffed computer lab on campus.

Community Environment: This is an agricultural and industrial area, dairying being the principal source of income. Lake Parsons, which is municipally owned, provides facilities for picnicking, fishing and boating. Camping is available at Marvel Park and the Neosho Water Fowl Management Area, 12 miles north of the city, affords fishing and hunting as well.

■ **MANHATTAN AREA TECHNICAL COLLEGE** *C-13*
3136 Dickens Ave.
Manhattan, KS 66503-2499
Tel: (913)587-2800
Free: 800-352-7575
Admissions: (785)587-2800
Fax: (913)587-2804
Web Site: http://www.matc.net/
Description: State and locally supported, 2-year, coed. Awards certificates, diplomas, and terminal associate degrees. Founded 1965. Setting: 19-acre suburban campus. Educational spending for 2005 fiscal year: $3563 per student. Total enrollment: 401. Student-undergrad faculty ratio is 11:1. Full-time: 324 students, 34% women, 66% men. Part-time: 77 students, 36% women, 64% men. 2% Native American, 4% Hispanic, 4% black, 1% Asian American or Pacific Islander, 32% 25 or older, 37% transferred in. Core. Calendar: semesters.

Entrance Requirements: Recommended: high school transcript. Required for some: high school transcript.

Costs Per Year: Application fee: $40. State resident tuition: $2035 full-time, $55 per credit hour part-time. Mandatory fees: $400 full-time, $10 per credit hour part-time.

Collegiate Environment: College housing not available. Matc Library with an OPAC.

■ MANHATTAN CHRISTIAN COLLEGE *C-13*
1415 Anderson Ave.
Manhattan, KS 66502-4081
Tel: (785)539-3571; 877-246-4622
Fax: (785)539-0832
Web Site: http://www.mccks.edu/

Description: Independent, 4-year, coed, affiliated with Christian Churches and Churches of Christ. Awards associate and bachelor's degrees. Founded 1927. Setting: 10-acre small town campus. Endowment: $939,895. Educational spending for 2005 fiscal year: $3144 per student. Total enrollment: 331. 156 applied, 78% were admitted. 30% from top 10% of their high school class, 40% from top quarter, 70% from top half. Full-time: 262 students, 49% women, 51% men. Part-time: 69 students, 62% women, 38% men. Students come from 12 states and territories, 1 other country, 35% from out-of-state, 0% Native American, 2% Hispanic, 4% black, 0.3% Asian American or Pacific Islander, 0.3% international, 13% 25 or older, 65% live on campus, 7% transferred in. Retention: 60% of full-time freshmen returned the following year. Core. Calendar: semesters. Academic remediation for entering students, advanced placement, independent study, distance learning, double major, summer session for credit, adult/continuing education programs, internships. ROTC: Army (c), Air Force (c).

Entrance Requirements: Options: Peterson's Universal Application, electronic application, international baccalaureate accepted. Required: essay, high school transcript, minimum 2.0 high school GPA, 3 recommendations, SAT or ACT. Required for some: interview. Entrance: minimally difficult. Application deadline: 8/1. Notification: continuous.

Costs Per Year: Application fee: $25. Comprehensive fee: $15,228 includes full-time tuition ($9444), mandatory fees ($194), and college room and board ($5590). Room and board charges vary according to board plan. Part-time tuition: $389 per hour. Part-time tuition varies according to course load.

Collegiate Environment: Orientation program. Drama-theater group, choral group, student-run newspaper. Social organizations: 25 open to all. Most popular organizations: Student Council, Unspoken Message (drama and dance team), praise bands, Drama Team, Prison Ministry. Major annual events: Family Weekend, Oasis, Orientation. Student services: personal-psychological counseling. 182 college housing spaces available; 151 were occupied in 2003-04. Freshmen guaranteed college housing. On-campus residence required through sophomore year. Options: men-only, women-only housing available. Manhattan Christian College Library with 3,300 books, 1,800 microform titles, 3,000 serials, 2,200 audiovisual materials, an OPAC, and a Web page. Operations spending for 2004 fiscal year: $65,147. 16 computers available on campus for general student use. Computer purchase/lease plans available. A campuswide network can be accessed from student residence rooms. Staffed computer lab on campus.

Community Environment: See Kansas State University.

■ MCPHERSON COLLEGE *F-10*
1600 East Euclid, PO Box 1402
McPherson, KS 67460-1402
Tel: (620)241-0731
Free: 800-365-7402
Fax: (620)241-8443
Web Site: http://www.mcpherson.edu/

Description: Independent, 4-year, coed, affiliated with Church of the Brethren. Awards associate and bachelor's degrees. Founded 1887. Setting: 26-acre small town campus. Endowment: $31.4 million. Educational spending for 2005 fiscal year: $7338 per student. Total enrollment: 464. 555 applied, 75% were admitted. 10% from top 10% of their high school class, 27% from top quarter, 71% from top half. Full-time: 443 students, 36% women, 64% men. Part-time: 21 students, 52% women, 48% men. Students come from 30 states and territories, 0.4% Native American, 6% Hispanic, 9% black, 0.4% Asian American or Pacific Islander, 1% international, 24% 25 or older, 70% live on campus, 13% transferred in. Retention: 83% of full-time freshmen returned the following year. Core. Calendar: 4-1-4. Academic remediation for entering students, services for LD students, advanced placement, self-designed majors, independent study, double major, summer ses-

sion for credit, part-time degree program, adult/continuing education programs, internships. Off campus study at 6 members of the Associated Colleges of Central Kansas. Study abroad program.

Entrance Requirements: Options: electronic application, deferred admission. Required: high school transcript, minimum 2.0 high school GPA, SAT or ACT. Recommended: ACT. Entrance: moderately difficult. Application deadline: Rolling. Notification: continuous.

Costs Per Year: Application fee: $25. Comprehensive fee: $21,010 includes full-time tuition ($14,900), mandatory fees ($260), and college room and board ($5850). College room only: $2400. Part-time tuition: $450 per credit hour. Part-time mandatory fees: $280 per credit hour, $1580 per term. Part-time tuition and fees vary according to course load.

Collegiate Environment: Orientation program. Drama-theater group, choral group, student-run newspaper. Social organizations: 32 open to all. Most popular organizations: Today's Educators, Spectator (newspaper), drama productions, athletics, choir. Major annual events: homecoming, Alumni Weekend, graduation. Student services: health clinic, personal-psychological counseling. Campus security: student patrols, controlled dormitory access. On-campus residence required through senior year. Options: coed, men-only housing available. Miller Library with 89,946 books, 60,561 microform titles, 345 serials, 4,465 audiovisual materials, an OPAC, and a Web page. Operations spending for 2004 fiscal year: $105,692. 60 computers available on campus for general student use. A campuswide network can be accessed from student residence rooms and from off campus. Staffed computer lab on campus.

Community Environment: McPherson is a small city of 14,000 located near Highway I-135. The county seat, as well as the business center for the surrounding agricultural area, McPherson's principal industries include oil refining, insulation, plastic pipe, pharmaceuticals, mobile homes, and farm equipment. The community supports many cultural activities such as activities symphony, theatre guild, chorale, and art festival. Air transportation is available at nearby Wichita, Salina and Hutchinson, as well as churches, motels, and several parks.

■ MIDAMERICA NAZARENE UNIVERSITY *D-16*
2030 East College Way
Olathe, KS 66062-1899
Tel: (913)782-3750
Free: 800-800-8887
Admissions: (913)791-3380
Fax: (913)791-3481
E-mail: admissions@mnu.edu
Web Site: http://www.mnu.edu/

Description: Independent, comprehensive, coed, affiliated with Church of the Nazarene. Awards associate, bachelor's, and master's degrees. Founded 1966. Setting: 105-acre suburban campus with easy access to Kansas City. Endowment: $17.4 million. Educational spending for 2005 fiscal year: $4442 per student. Total enrollment: 1,779. Faculty: 173 (71 full-time, 102 part-time). Student-undergrad faculty ratio is 18:1. 750 applied, 69% were admitted. 1 National Merit Scholar, 4 valedictorians. Full-time: 1,198 students, 52% women, 48% men. Part-time: 159 students, 55% women, 45% men. Students come from 40 states and territories, 11 other countries, 34% from out-of-state, 1% Native American, 4% Hispanic, 7% black, 1% Asian American or Pacific Islander, 1% international, 22% 25 or older, 62% live on campus, 8% transferred in. Retention: 67% of full-time freshmen returned the following year. Academic areas with the most degrees conferred: business/marketing; education; health professions and related sciences. Core. Calendar: semesters. Academic remediation for entering students, services for LD students, advanced placement, accelerated degree program, independent study, double major, summer session for credit, part-time degree program, adult/continuing education programs, internships. Off campus study at Coalition for Christian Colleges and Universities. Study abroad program. ROTC: Army (c), Air Force (c).

Entrance Requirements: Options: electronic application, early admission, deferred admission, international baccalaureate accepted. Required: high school transcript, minimum 2.0 high school GPA, 1 recommendation, SAT or ACT. Entrance: minimally difficult. Application deadline: 8/1. Notification: continuous.

Costs Per Year: Application fee: $25. Comprehensive fee: $21,798 includes full-time tuition ($14,968), mandatory fees ($1000), and college room and board ($5830). Part-time tuition: $500 per semester hour. Part-time mandatory fees: $500 per term.

Collegiate Environment: Orientation program. Drama-theater group, choral group, student-run newspaper, radio station. Social organizations: 20 open

to all. Most popular organizations: Associated Student Government, Residence Hall Government, ministry groups, intramurals, Gospel Station. Major annual events: homecoming, Mock Rock, Welcome Week. Student services: health clinic, personal-psychological counseling. Campus security: 24-hour emergency response devices and patrols, student patrols, late night transport-escort service, controlled dormitory access. 715 college housing spaces available; 657 were occupied in 2003-04. Freshmen guaranteed college housing. On-campus residence required through senior year. Options: men-only, women-only housing available. Mabee Library with 132,991 books, 337,000 microform titles, 1,250 serials, 11,427 audiovisual materials, an OPAC, and a Web page. Operations spending for 2004 fiscal year: $427,946. 85 computers available on campus for general student use. A campuswide network can be accessed from student residence rooms and from off campus. Staffed computer lab on campus.

■ **NATIONAL AMERICAN UNIVERSITY** *L-16*
10310 Mastin
Overland Park, KS 66212
Tel: (913)217-2900
Web Site: http://www.national.edu/
Description: Independent, 2-year, coed.

■ **NEOSHO COUNTY COMMUNITY COLLEGE** *H-15*
800 West 14th St.
Chanute, KS 66720-2699
Tel: (620)431-2820
Free: 800-729-6222
Fax: (620)431-6222
E-mail: llast@neosho.edu
Web Site: http://www.neosho.edu/
Description: State and locally supported, 2-year, coed. Part of Kansas State Board of Education. Awards certificates, diplomas, transfer associate, and terminal associate degrees. Founded 1936. Setting: 50-acre small town campus. Endowment: $370,000. Total enrollment: 1,826. 573 applied, 100% were admitted. Full-time: 615 students, 61% women, 39% men. Part-time: 1,211 students, 69% women, 31% men. Students come from 15 states and territories, 1% Native American, 3% Hispanic, 5% black, 2% Asian American or Pacific Islander, 0% international, 58% 25 or older, 5% live on campus. Core. Calendar: semesters. Academic remediation for entering students, services for LD students, advanced placement, self-designed majors, summer session for credit, part-time degree program, adult/continuing education programs.
Entrance Requirements: Open admission. Options: Common Application, early admission. Required: high school transcript. Placement: ACT required. Entrance: noncompetitive. Application deadline: 9/15. Notification: continuous.
Collegiate Environment: Drama-theater group, choral group, student-run newspaper. Most popular organizations: Business Club, Science Club, Student Nurses Association, Fellowship of Christian Athletes, Nontraditional Student Organization. Major annual events: homecoming, Fun-in-the-Sun Week, Halloween Dance. Student services: personal-psychological counseling. Campus security: controlled dormitory access. On-campus residence required in freshman year. Option: coed housing available. Chapman Library with 33,000 books and 200 serials. 100 computers available on campus for general student use. Staffed computer lab on campus.
Community Environment: An industrial city with rural and urban sections, Chanute is the girlhood home of Osa Johnson, famous African and South Seas explorer. Oil production, manufacturing and agriculture are important to the city's economy. The varied industries include a cement plant, an oil field equipment manufacturing company, a garment factory and machine shops. Some part-time employment is available. Chanute has good shopping facilities, a hospital, many churches, a theater, a skating rink, commercial family recreation, a lake and a municipal golf course. A Mexican Fiesta, the Fall Festival, and a Horse Show are special annual events.

■ **NEWMAN UNIVERSITY** *H-11*
3100 McCormick Ave.
Wichita, KS 67213-2097
Tel: (316)942-4291; 877-NEWMANU
Fax: (316)942-4483
E-mail: admissions@newmanu.edu
Web Site: http://www.newmanu.edu/
Description: Independent Roman Catholic, comprehensive, coed. Awards associate, bachelor's, and master's degrees. Founded 1933. Setting: 61-

acre urban campus. Endowment: $17.2 million. Educational spending for 2005 fiscal year: $3809 per student. Total enrollment: 2,103. Faculty: 153 (85 full-time, 68 part-time). Student-undergrad faculty ratio is 17:1. 753 applied, 85% were admitted. 16% from top 10% of their high school class, 37% from top quarter, 74% from top half. Full-time: 1,123 students, 61% women, 39% men. Part-time: 609 students, 60% women, 40% men. Students come from 19 states and territories, 32 other countries, 9% from out-of-state, 1% Native American, 8% Hispanic, 6% black, 4% Asian American or Pacific Islander, 8% international, 37% 25 or older, 21% live on campus, 13% transferred in. Retention: 59% of full-time freshmen returned the following year. Academic areas with the most degrees conferred: business/marketing; education; health professions and related sciences. Core. Calendar: semesters. Academic remediation for entering students, services for LD students, advanced placement, accelerated degree program, independent study, distance learning, double major, summer session for credit, part-time degree program, external degree program, adult/continuing education programs, co-op programs and internships. Off campus study at Friends University. Study abroad program.
Entrance Requirements: Options: electronic application, early admission, deferred admission. Required: high school transcript, minimum 2.0 high school GPA, SAT or ACT. Recommended: interview. Entrance: minimally difficult. Application deadline: Rolling. Notification: continuous.
Costs Per Year: Application fee: $20. Comprehensive fee: $22,680 includes full-time tuition ($17,008), mandatory fees ($300), and college room and board ($5372). Part-time tuition: $567 per credit hour. Part-time mandatory fees: $10 per credit hour.
Collegiate Environment: Orientation program. Drama-theater group, choral group, student-run newspaper. Social organizations: 30 open to all. Most popular organizations: Student Activities Board, chorale, International Club, Chemistry/Pre-Med Club, Newman Occupational Therapy Student Association. Major annual events: Charity Week, Family Weekend, Homecoming. Student services: personal-psychological counseling. Campus security: 24-hour patrols, late night transport-escort service. 320 college housing spaces available; 255 were occupied in 2003-04. Freshmen guaranteed college housing. On-campus residence required through sophomore year. Options: coed, women-only housing available. Library Learning Resource Center with 107,057 books, 134,880 microform titles, 327 serials, 1,857 audiovisual materials, an OPAC, and a Web page. Operations spending for 2004 fiscal year: $208,437. 90 computers available on campus for general student use. Computer purchase/lease plans available. A campuswide network can be accessed from student residence rooms and from off campus. Staffed computer lab on campus.
Community Environment: See Wichita State University.

■ **NORTH CENTRAL KANSAS TECHNICAL COLLEGE** *C-9*
PO Box 507
Beloit, KS 67420
Tel: (913)738-2276
Free: 800-658-4655
E-mail: jheidrick@ncktc.tec.ks.us
Web Site: http://www.ncktc.tec.ks.us/
Description: State-supported, 2-year, coed. Founded 1963. Calendar: semesters.

■ **NORTHEAST KANSAS TECHNICAL COLLEGE** *B-16*
1501 West Riley St.
Atchison, KS 66002
Tel: (913)367-6204
Free: 800-567-4890
Fax: (913)367-3107
Web Site: http://www.nektc.net/
Description: State-supported, 2-year, coed. Founded 1965. Calendar: semesters.

■ **NORTHWEST KANSAS TECHNICAL COLLEGE** *C-2*
PO Box 668
1209 Harrison St.
Goodland, KS 67735
Tel: (785)899-3641
Free: 800-316-4127
Fax: (785)899-5711
Web Site: http://www.nwktc.org/

Description: State-supported, 2-year, coed. Founded 1964. Calendar: semesters.

■ **OTTAWA UNIVERSITY** *E-15*
1001 South Cedar
Ottawa, KS 66067-3399
Tel: (785)242-5200
Free: 800-755-5200
Fax: (785)242-7429
E-mail: admiss@ottawa.edu
Web Site: http://www.ottawa.edu/
Description: Independent American Baptist Churches in the USA, comprehensive, coed. Awards bachelor's degrees (also offers master's, adult, international and on-line education programs with significant enrollment not reflected in profile). Founded 1865. Setting: 60-acre small town campus with easy access to Kansas City. Endowment: $17.7 million. Educational spending for 2005 fiscal year: $2038 per student. Total enrollment: 440. Student-undergrad faculty ratio is 16:1. 789 applied, 71% were admitted. 17% from top 10% of their high school class, 39% from top quarter, 72% from top half. 1 valedictorian. Full-time: 401 students, 44% women, 56% men. Part-time: 39 students, 38% women, 62% men. Students come from 19 states and territories, 10 other countries, 37% from out-of-state, 3% Native American, 6% Hispanic, 9% black, 1% Asian American or Pacific Islander, 3% international, 10% 25 or older, 13% transferred in. Retention: 66% of full-time freshmen returned the following year. Academic areas with the most degrees conferred: business/marketing; education; biological/life sciences. Core. Calendar: semesters. Advanced placement, self-designed majors, independent study, double major, summer session for credit, part-time degree program, internships.
Entrance Requirements: Options: Peterson's Universal Application, electronic application, international baccalaureate accepted. Required: high school transcript, minimum 2.5 high school GPA, 18 or higher ACT; rank in upper 50% of class, SAT or ACT. Recommended: 2 recommendations, interview. Required for some: essay. Entrance: moderately difficult. Application deadline: Rolling. Notification: continuous.
Costs Per Year: Application fee: $15. Comprehensive fee: $20,042 includes full-time tuition ($14,500) and college room and board ($5542). College room only: $2400. Full-time tuition varies according to course load. Room and board charges vary according to board plan and housing facility.
Collegiate Environment: Orientation program. Drama-theater group, choral group, student-run newspaper, radio station. Social organizations: 35 open to all; 20% of eligible men and 25% of eligible women are members. Most popular organizations: Christian Faith In Action, Student Activities Force, Education Club, Whole Earth Club, Fellowship of Christian Athletes. Major annual events: Welcome Week, Casino Night, Late Night Finals Breakfast. Student services: health clinic, personal-psychological counseling. Campus security: 24-hour emergency response devices and patrols, locked residence hall entrances. 360 college housing spaces available. Freshmen guaranteed college housing. On-campus residence required through junior year. Options: men-only, women-only housing available. Myers Library with 80,500 books, 4,542 microform titles, and 310 serials. Operations spending for 2004 fiscal year: $146,329. 71 computers available on campus for general student use. A campuswide network can be accessed from student residence rooms and from off campus. Staffed computer lab on campus.
Community Environment: The city is named for the Indians who established a new reservation here in 1834. Pomona Dam and Reservoir, fifteen miles northwest, provides facilities for picnicking, camping, trailering, swimming, boating, fishing and hunting. Forest Park on the Marais des Cygnes River provides additional outdoor recreational facilities. Community facilities include libraries, municipal airport and trains and buses for transportation. Other cultural and recreational activities are enjoyed in Kansas City, which is an hour's drive away.

■ **PITTSBURG STATE UNIVERSITY** *H-17*
1701 South Broadway
Pittsburg, KS 66762
Tel: (620)231-7000
Free: 800-854-7488
Fax: (620)235-4080
Web Site: http://www.pittstate.edu/
Description: State-supported, comprehensive, coed. Part of Kansas Board of Regents. Awards bachelor's and master's degrees (associate, specialist in education). Founded 1903. Setting: 233-acre small town campus. Endowment: $44.7 million. Research spending for 2004 fiscal year: $2 million.

Educational spending for 2005 fiscal year: $4466 per student. Total enrollment: 6,628. Faculty: 373 (291 full-time, 82 part-time). Student-undergrad faculty ratio is 18:1. 1,935 applied, 90% were admitted. Full-time: 5,126 students, 48% women, 52% men. Part-time: 417 students, 51% women, 49% men. Students come from 25 states and territories, 48 other countries, 28% from out-of-state, 2% Native American, 2% Hispanic, 2% black, 1% Asian American or Pacific Islander, 4% international, 14% live on campus, 10% transferred in. Retention: 77% of full-time freshmen returned the following year. Academic areas with the most degrees conferred: education; business/marketing; science technologies. Core. Calendar: semesters. Academic remediation for entering students, ESL program, services for LD students, advanced placement, self-designed majors, freshman honors college, honors program, independent study, distance learning, double major, summer session for credit, part-time degree program, external degree program, adult/continuing education programs, co-op programs and internships, graduate courses open to undergrads. Off campus study at Southside Education Center, Wichita, KS, Kansas City Metro Center, Lenexa, KS. Study abroad program. ROTC: Army.
Entrance Requirements: Open admission for state residents. Options: Peterson's Universal Application, Common Application, electronic application, early admission, deferred admission, international baccalaureate accepted. Required: high school transcript, ACT. Required for some: minimum 2.0 high school GPA. Entrance: noncompetitive. Application deadline: Rolling.
Costs Per Year: Application fee: $30. State resident tuition: $2850 full-time, $95 per credit hour part-time. Nonresident tuition: $9732 full-time, $324 per credit hour part-time. Mandatory fees: $712 full-time, $32 per credit hour part-time. College room and board: $4550. Room and board charges vary according to board plan and housing facility.
Collegiate Environment: Orientation program. Drama-theater group, choral group, marching band, student-run newspaper, radio station. Social organizations: 140 open to all; national fraternities, national sororities; 3% of eligible men and 3% of eligible women are members. Most popular organizations: Student Government Association, student yearbook, student newspaper. Major annual events: homecoming, Family Day, Visit the Campus Day. Student services: legal services, health clinic, personal-psychological counseling, learning and writing center. Campus security: 24-hour emergency response devices and patrols, student patrols, controlled dormitory access. 1,066 college housing spaces available; 966 were occupied in 2003-04. Freshmen given priority for college housing. On-campus residence required in freshman year. Option: coed housing available. Leonard H. Axe Library plus 2 others with 639,136 books, 842,616 microform titles, 7,038 serials, 1,712 audiovisual materials, an OPAC, and a Web page. Operations spending for 2004 fiscal year: $1.9 million.
Community Environment: Pittsburg is the largest city in southeast Kansas. It is widely known for its fine homes, large churches, excellent schools, and many municipal facilities. Much of the coal mining in Kansas was done in this area. Some of the abandoned open pits have been flooded and stocked for fishing, swimming, boating, and water skiing. Other recreational activities within the city are bowling, tennis, and golf. Part-time employment opportunities are good.

■ **PRATT COMMUNITY COLLEGE** *H-8*
348 NE State Rd. 61
Pratt, KS 67124-8317
Tel: (620)672-9800
Admissions: (620)450-2222
Fax: (620)672-5288
E-mail: lynnp@prattcc.edu
Web Site: http://www.prattcc.edu/
Description: State and locally supported, 2-year, coed. Part of Kansas Board of Regents. Awards certificates, transfer associate, and terminal associate degrees. Founded 1938. Setting: 80-acre rural campus with easy access to Wichita. Educational spending for 2005 fiscal year: $2951 per student. Total enrollment: 1,546. Student-undergrad faculty ratio is 14:1. 904 applied, 100% were admitted. Full-time: 625 students, 46% women, 54% men. Part-time: 921 students, 56% women, 44% men. Students come from 21 states and territories, 16% from out-of-state, 1% Native American, 5% Hispanic, 5% black, 1% Asian American or Pacific Islander, 2% international, 22% live on campus. Retention: 51% of full-time freshmen returned the following year. Calendar: semesters. Academic remediation for entering students, advanced placement, distance learning, summer session for credit, part-time degree program, adult/continuing education programs, co-op programs and internships.

Entrance Requirements: Open admission. Options: Common Application, early admission. Required: high school transcript. Required for some: AS-SET. Entrance: noncompetitive. Application deadline: Rolling.

Costs Per Year: Application fee: $0. State resident tuition: $42 per credit hour part-time. Nonresident tuition: $1344 full-time, $42 per credit hour part-time. Mandatory fees: $928 full-time, $29 per credit hour part-time. College room and board: $3768.

Collegiate Environment: Drama-theater group, choral group, student-run newspaper. Social organizations: 20 open to all. Most popular organizations: Phi Theta Kappa, Student Senate, Baptist Student Union, Block and Bridle, Business Professionals Club. Major annual event: Spring Formal. Student services: health clinic, personal-psychological counseling. Campus security: 24-hour patrols, late night transport-escort service, controlled dormitory access. 282 college housing spaces available; 219 were occupied in 2003-04. No special consideration for freshman housing applicants. On-campus residence required through sophomore year. Options: coed, men-only, women-only housing available. 33,000 books, 100 microform titles, 250 serials, 1,200 audiovisual materials, an OPAC, and a Web page. Operations spending for 2004 fiscal year: $183,530. 100 computers available on campus for general student use. A campuswide network can be accessed from off-campus. Staffed computer lab on campus.

■ **SEWARD COUNTY COMMUNITY COLLEGE** *I-3*
PO Box 1137
Liberal, KS 67905-1137
Tel: (620)624-1951
Free: 800-373-9951
Fax: (620)629-2725
Web Site: http://www.sccc.edu/

Description: State and locally supported, 2-year, coed. Part of Kansas State Board of Regents. Awards certificates, diplomas, transfer associate, and terminal associate degrees. Founded 1969. Setting: 120-acre rural campus. Endowment: $8.5 million. Research spending for 2004 fiscal year: $94,000. Educational spending for 2005 fiscal year: $3800 per student. Total enrollment: 2,325. 14 National Merit Scholars, 31 class presidents, 24 valedictorians, 63 student government officers. Students come from 8 states and territories, 7 other countries, 11% from out-of-state, 67% 25 or older, 21% live on campus. Core. Calendar: semesters. Academic remediation for entering students, ESL program, self-designed majors, distance learning, summer session for credit, part-time degree program, external degree program, adult/continuing education programs, co-op programs and internships.

Entrance Requirements: Open admission. Options: early admission, deferred admission. Required: high school transcript. Required for some: minimum 2.0 high school GPA, 1 recommendation, interview. Placement: SAT or ACT recommended. Entrance: noncompetitive. Application deadline: 8/15. Notification: continuous.

Collegiate Environment: Orientation program. Drama-theater group, choral group, student-run newspaper. Social organizations: 28 open to all. Most popular organizations: HALO, ATLAS, Block and Bridle, DECA, Sigma Chi Chi. Major annual events: Homecoming/Family Day, Pancake Day, Oktoberfest. Campus security: 24-hour patrols, late night transport-escort service. Option: coed housing available. Learning Resource Center plus 1 other with 32,926 books and 318 serials. Operations spending for 2004 fiscal year: $157,000. 102 computers available on campus for general student use. Staffed computer lab on campus.

Community Environment: Liberal is the county seat of Seward County. Oil discoveries have added significantly to the economic importance of Liberal. Southwestern Kansas is rich in wheat, oil and gas, and growing agri-related industries such as cattle/swine feed operations and meat packing. Part time employment is available. All forms of commercial transportation are available. A golf course, parks and swimming pools are some of the recreational facilities. Shopping facilities are excellent.

■ **SOUTHWESTERN COLLEGE** *I-12*
100 College St.
Winfield, KS 67156-2499
Tel: (620)229-6000
Free: 800-846-1543
Admissions: (620)229-6236
Fax: (620)229-6224
E-mail: scadmit@jinx.sckans.edu
Web Site: http://www.sckans.edu/

Description: Independent United Methodist, comprehensive, coed. Awards bachelor's and master's degrees. Founded 1885. Setting: 70-acre small

town campus with easy access to Wichita. Endowment: $13.6 million. Educational spending for 2005 fiscal year: $9074 per student. Total enrollment: 1,416. Faculty: 144 (46 full-time, 98 part-time). Student-undergrad faculty ratio is 10:1. 494 applied, 28% were admitted. 21% from top 10% of their high school class, 45% from top quarter, 75% from top half. 9 valedictorians. Full-time: 569 students, 52% women, 48% men. Part-time: 694 students, 48% women, 52% men. Students come from 40 states and territories, 7 other countries, 2% Native American, 4% Hispanic, 8% black, 1% Asian American or Pacific Islander, 2% international, 53% 25 or older, 63% live on campus, 31% transferred in. Retention: 71% of full-time freshmen returned the following year. Academic areas with the most degrees conferred: business/marketing; education; health professions and related sciences. Core. Calendar: semesters. Academic remediation for entering students, advanced placement, self-designed majors, honors program, independent study, double major, summer session for credit, part-time degree program, external degree program, adult/continuing education programs, internships, graduate courses open to undergrads. Off campus study at Urban Life Center, Chicago. Study abroad program.

Entrance Requirements: Options: Common Application, electronic application, deferred admission. Required: essay, high school transcript, minimum 2.25 high school GPA, SAT or ACT. Required for some: interview. Entrance: moderately difficult. Application deadline: 8/1. Notification: continuous.

Costs Per Year: Application fee: $20. One-time mandatory fee: $100. Comprehensive fee: $22,238 includes full-time tuition ($16,800) and college room and board ($5438). College room only: $2428. Part-time tuition: $700 per semester hour.

Collegiate Environment: Orientation program. Drama-theater group, choral group, student-run newspaper, radio station. Social organizations: 19 open to all; national fraternities, local fraternities, local sororities; 10% of eligible men and 10% of eligible women are members. Most popular organizations: Student Activities Association, student government, Fellowship of Christian Athletes, Campus Council on Ministries, International Club. Major annual events: homecoming, Moundbuilding Ceremony, Kickback Day. Student services: health clinic, personal-psychological counseling. Campus security: 24-hour emergency response devices, late night transport-escort service. 450 college housing spaces available; 397 were occupied in 2003-04. Freshmen guaranteed college housing. On-campus residence required through sophomore year. Options: coed, men-only, women-only housing available. Memorial Library plus 1 other with 77,000 books, 3,740 microform titles, 320 serials, 320 audiovisual materials, an OPAC, and a Web page. Operations spending for 2004 fiscal year: $343,640. 55 computers available on campus for general student use. A campuswide network can be accessed from student residence rooms and from off campus. Staffed computer lab on campus.

■ **STERLING COLLEGE** *F-9*
PO Box 98
Sterling, KS 67579-0098
Tel: (620)278-2173
Free: 800-346-1017
Admissions: (620)278-4364
Fax: (620)278-3690
Web Site: http://www.sterling.edu/

Description: Independent Presbyterian, 4-year, coed. Awards bachelor's degrees. Founded 1887. Setting: 46-acre rural campus. Endowment: $5.6 million. Educational spending for 2005 fiscal year: $6203 per student. Total enrollment: 516. Student-undergrad faculty ratio is 10:1. 541 applied, 56% were admitted. 7% from top 10% of their high school class, 35% from top quarter, 70% from top half. 5 valedictorians. Full-time: 433 students, 47% women, 53% men. Part-time: 61 students, 54% women, 46% men. Students come from 29 states and territories, 9 other countries, 41% from out-of-state, 2% Native American, 5% Hispanic, 7% black, 0.5% Asian American or Pacific Islander, 2% international, 5% 25 or older, 83% live on campus, 9% transferred in. Retention: 46% of full-time freshmen returned the following year. Core. Calendar: 4-1-4. Services for LD students, advanced placement, self-designed majors, honors program, independent study, double major, internships. Off campus study at 6 members of the Associated Colleges of Central Kansas. Study abroad program.

Entrance Requirements: Options: Peterson's Universal Application, Common Application, electronic application, early action, deferred admission. Required: high school transcript, minimum 2.2 high school GPA, SAT or ACT. Recommended: essay, interview. Required for some: 2 recommendations, audition required for fine arts majors. Entrance: moderately difficult. Application deadlines: 7/15, 11/15 for early action. Notification: continuous, 12/1 for early action.

Costs Per Year: Application fee: $25. Comprehensive fee: $20,486 includes full-time tuition ($14,300), mandatory fees ($100), and college room and board ($6086).

Collegiate Environment: Orientation program. Drama-theater group, choral group, student-run newspaper, radio station. Social organizations: 23 open to all. Most popular organizations: Fellowship of Christian Athletes, Student Activities Council, My Brother's Keeper, Habitat for Humanity, youth ministries. Major annual events: homecoming, Last Blast, Convocations. Student services: personal-psychological counseling. Campus security: controlled dormitory access, late night security patrol. 520 college housing spaces available; 372 were occupied in 2003-04. Freshmen guaranteed college housing. On-campus residence required through senior year. Options: men-only, women-only housing available. Mabee Library with 76,637 books, 2,120 microform titles, 350 serials, 2,159 audiovisual materials, an OPAC, and a Web page. Operations spending for 2004 fiscal year: $212,000. 115 computers available on campus for general student use. A campuswide network can be accessed from student residence rooms. Staffed computer lab on campus.

Community Environment: Sterling is in a rich wheat-growing, oil producing area with community facilities that include churches, Medical Center and many businesses. Opportunities for part time work are good. Train and bus service are available as well as an airport in Hutchinson, 25 miles away. Recreational activities are baseball, fishing, picnicking, and swimming at the municipal lake and college swimming pool.

■ **TABOR COLLEGE** *F-11*

400 South Jefferson
Hillsboro, KS 67063
Tel: (620)947-3121
Free: 800-822-6799
Fax: (620)947-2607
Web Site: http://www.tabor.edu/

Description: Independent Mennonite Brethren, comprehensive, coed. Awards associate, bachelor's, and master's degrees. Founded 1908. Setting: 26-acre small town campus with easy access to Wichita. Endowment: $4 million. Educational spending for 2005 fiscal year: $5860 per student. Total enrollment: 606. 246 applied, 99% were admitted. 14% from top 10% of their high school class, 33% from top quarter, 69% from top half. Full-time: 463 students, 46% women, 54% men. Part-time: 123 students, 68% women, 32% men. Students come from 26 states and territories, 4 other countries, 33% from out-of-state, 1% Native American, 3% Hispanic, 5% black, 1% Asian American or Pacific Islander, 1% international, 8% 25 or older, 80% live on campus, 8% transferred in. Retention: 69% of full-time freshmen returned the following year. Core. Calendar: 4-1-4. Academic remediation for entering students, services for LD students, advanced placement, accelerated degree program, self-designed majors, honors program, independent study, double major, part-time degree program, adult/continuing education programs, internships, graduate courses open to undergrads. Off campus study at Associated Colleges of Central Kansas. Study abroad program.

Entrance Requirements: Options: Common Application, electronic application, early decision, international baccalaureate accepted. Required: essay, high school transcript, minimum 2.0 high school GPA, 2 recommendations, interview, minimum ACT score of 18, SAT or ACT. Recommended: minimum 3.0 high school GPA. Entrance: moderately difficult. Application deadlines: 8/1, 1/1 for early decision plan 1, 4/1 for early decision plan 2. Notification: continuous.

Costs Per Year: Application fee: $20. Comprehensive fee: $21,604 includes full-time tuition ($15,574), mandatory fees ($360), and college room and board ($5670). College room only: $2215. Full-time tuition and fees vary according to course load. Room and board charges vary according to board plan, housing facility, and location.

Collegiate Environment: Orientation program. Drama-theater group, choral group, student-run newspaper. Social organizations: 18 open to all. Most popular organizations: Student Activities Board, Student Senate, Campus Ministries Council, Fellowship of Christian Athletes, Share, Prayer, and Dare. Major annual events: homecoming, Missions/Services Emphasis Week, Opening Bible Conference. Student services: personal-psychological counseling. Campus security: student patrols. 424 college housing spaces available; 376 were occupied in 2003-04. Freshmen guaranteed college housing. On-campus residence required through senior year. Options: men-only, women-only housing available. Tabor College Library with 80,099 books, 435 microform titles, 265 serials, 1,640 audiovisual materials, an OPAC, and a Web page. Operations spending for 2004 fiscal year: $143,647. 57 computers available on campus for general student use. A

campuswide network can be accessed from student residence rooms and from off campus. Staffed computer lab on campus.

Community Environment: Situated in the wheat and dairy area of central Kansas, Hillsboro is the leading trade center of western Marion County. Community facilities include a hospital, park, swimming pool and golf course.

■ **UNIVERSITY OF KANSAS** *D-15*

Lawrence, KS 66045
Tel: (785)864-2700
Admissions: (785)864-3911
Fax: (785)864-5006
E-mail: be.a.jayhawk@st37.eds.ukans.edu
Web Site: http://www.ku.edu

Description: State-supported, university, coed. Awards bachelor's, master's, doctoral, and first professional degrees and post-master's certificates (University of Kansas is a single institution with academic programs and facilities at two primary locations: Lawrence and Kansas City.). Founded 1866. Setting: 1,100-acre suburban campus with easy access to Kansas City. Endowment: $1.2 billion. Research spending for 2004 fiscal year: $258 million. Total enrollment: 28,949. Faculty: 1,312 (1,185 full-time, 127 part-time). Student-undergrad faculty ratio is 20:1. 10,442 applied, 69% were admitted. 28% from top 10% of their high school class, 56% from top quarter, 87% from top half. 57 National Merit Scholars. Full-time: 18,888 students, 51% women, 49% men. Part-time: 2,503 students, 50% women, 50% men. Students come from 52 states and territories, 113 other countries, 24% from out-of-state, 1% Native American, 3% Hispanic, 4% black, 4% Asian American or Pacific Islander, 3% international, 8% 25 or older, 23% live on campus, 7% transferred in. Retention: 82% of full-time freshmen returned the following year. Academic areas with the most degrees conferred: business/marketing; health professions and related sciences; English. Core. Calendar: semesters. Academic remediation for entering students, ESL program, services for LD students, advanced placement, accelerated degree program, honors program, independent study, distance learning, double major, summer session for credit, part-time degree program, co-op programs and internships, graduate courses open to undergrads. Study abroad program. ROTC: Army, Naval, Air Force.

Entrance Requirements: Options: electronic application, deferred admission. Required: high school transcript, minimum 2.0 high school GPA, Kansas Board of Regents admissions criteria with GPA of 2.0/2.5; upper third of high school class; minimum 21/24 ACT score of 24 or minimum SAT score of 980/1090, SAT or ACT. Required for some: minimum 2.5 high school GPA. Entrance: moderately difficult. Application deadline: 4/1. Notification: continuous.

Costs Per Year: Application fee: $30. State resident tuition: $4824 full-time, $160.80 per credit hour part-time. Nonresident tuition: $13,277 full-time, $442.55 per credit hour part-time. Mandatory fees: $589 full-time, $49.08 per credit hour part-time. Full-time tuition and fees vary according to program and reciprocity agreements. Part-time tuition and fees vary according to program and reciprocity agreements. College room and board: $5502. College room only: $2752. Room and board charges vary according to board plan and housing facility.

Collegiate Environment: Orientation program. Drama-theater group, choral group, marching band, student-run newspaper, radio station. Social organizations: 400 open to all; national fraternities, national sororities; 14% of eligible men and 17% of eligible women are members. Most popular organizations: Center for Community Outreach, Graduate and Professional Association, St. Lawrence Catholic Campus Center, International Student Association. Major annual events: Homecoming, graduation, Parents' Day. Student services: legal services, health clinic, personal-psychological counseling, women's center, freshman-sophmore advising center, day care center, disability services, fi. Campus security: 24-hour emergency response devices and patrols, late night transport-escort service, controlled dormitory access, University police department; security guards are included. 5,299 college housing spaces available; 4,759 were occupied in 2003-04. No special consideration for freshman housing applicants. Options: coed, women-only housing available. Watson Library plus 11 others with 4.8 million books, 4.1 million microform titles, 41,830 serials, 55,284 audiovisual materials, an OPAC, and a Web page. Operations spending for 2004 fiscal year: $19.1 million. 1,500 computers available on campus for general student use. Computer purchase/lease plans available. A campuswide network can be accessed from student residence rooms and from off campus. Staffed computer lab on campus.

Community Environment: Lawrence, a town about 70,000, is set among the rolling hills of northeast Kansas. The cosmopolitan quality of the campus extends to the community, making a wide variety of cultural, ethnic, and recreational opportunities available to university students. Lawrence offers shopping areas, restaurants, entertainment, and recreational facilities that are either within easy walking distance of the campus or served by the university bus service. Near Lawrence there are several lakes for boating, fishing, and swimming. Metropolitan Kansas City, with its professional sports, ballet, opera, concerts, night spots, galleries, museums, festivals, and international airport, is about 40 miles east of Lawrence. Topeka, the state capital, is 30 miles west.

■ UNIVERSITY OF PHOENIX-WICHITA CAMPUS *H-11*

3020 North Cypress Dr., Ste. 150
Wichita, KS 67226
Tel: (316)630-8121
Free: 800-228-7240
Admissions: (480)557-1712
Web Site: http://www.phoenix.edu/

Description: Proprietary, comprehensive, coed. Awards bachelor's and master's degrees. Founded 2003. Total enrollment: 400. Faculty: 76 (2 full-time, 74 part-time). Student-undergrad faculty ratio is 5:1. 24 applied. Full-time: 331 students, 59% women, 41% men. 0% from out-of-state, 0% Native American, 1% Hispanic, 1% black, 0.3% Asian American or Pacific Islander, 16% international, 84% 25 or older. Core. Calendar: continuous. Advanced placement, accelerated degree program, independent study, distance learning, external degree program, adult/continuing education programs, graduate courses open to undergrads.

Entrance Requirements: Open admission. Option: deferred admission. Required: 1 recommendation. Required for some: high school transcript. Entrance: noncompetitive. Application deadline: Rolling.

Costs Per Year: Application fee: $110. Tuition: $10,440 full-time, $348 per credit part-time. Mandatory fees: $560 full-time, $70 per course part-time.

Collegiate Environment: University Library with 444 books, 666 serials, an OPAC, and a Web page. System-wide operations spending for 2004 fiscal year: $3.2 million.

■ UNIVERSITY OF SAINT MARY *C-16*

4100 South Fourth St. Trafficway
Leavenworth, KS 66048-5082
Tel: (913)682-5151
Free: 800-752-7043
Fax: (913)758-6140
E-mail: admiss@stmary.edu
Web Site: http://www.stmary.edu/

Description: Independent Roman Catholic, comprehensive, coed. Awards associate, bachelor's, and master's degrees. Founded 1923. Setting: 240-acre small town campus with easy access to Kansas City. Endowment: $8.3 million. Educational spending for 2005 fiscal year: $5258 per student. Total enrollment: 817. Faculty: 89 (39 full-time, 50 part-time). Student-undergrad faculty ratio is 10:1. 570 applied, 45% were admitted. 6% from top 10% of their high school class, 23% from top quarter, 70% from top half. Full-time: 376 students, 51% women, 49% men. Part-time: 152 students, 74% women, 26% men. Students come from 28 states and territories, 5 other countries, 35% from out-of-state, 0.5% Native American, 11% Hispanic, 13% black, 3% Asian American or Pacific Islander, 1% international, 20% 25 or older, 42% live on campus. Retention: 60% of full-time freshmen returned the following year. Academic areas with the most degrees conferred: psychology; business/marketing; education. Core. Calendar: semesters. Advanced placement, self-designed majors, honors program, independent study, distance learning, double major, summer session for credit, part-time degree program, adult/continuing education programs, co-op programs and internships, graduate courses open to undergrads. Off campus study at University of Kansas, members of the Council of Independent Colleges. Study abroad program. ROTC: Army (c), Air Force (c).

Entrance Requirements: Options: Peterson's Universal Application, Common Application, electronic application, international baccalaureate accepted. Required: high school transcript, minimum 2.5 high school GPA, SAT or ACT. Recommended: 1 recommendation, interview. Entrance: moderately difficult. Application deadline: Rolling. Notification: continuous.

Costs Per Year: Application fee: $25. Comprehensive fee: $22,510 includes full-time tuition ($16,100), mandatory fees ($310), and college room and board ($6100). College room only: $2600. Part-time tuition: $310 per credit. Part-time mandatory fees: $108 per term.

Collegiate Environment: Orientation program. Drama-theater group, choral group, student-run newspaper. Social organizations: 25 open to all. Most

popular organizations: Student Government Association, BACCHUS, Theatrical Union, Campus Ministry, Amnesty International. Major annual events: Family Weekend, Heritage Day, Spring Honors Convocation. Student services: health clinic, personal-psychological counseling. Campus security: late night transport-escort service, controlled dormitory access. 351 college housing spaces available; 187 were occupied in 2003-04. Freshmen guaranteed college housing. On-campus residence required through sophomore year. Option: coed housing available. De Paul Library with 118,195 books, 70,528 microform titles, 205 serials, 1,985 audiovisual materials, an OPAC, and a Web page. Operations spending for 2004 fiscal year: $177,594. 95 computers available on campus for general student use. A campuswide network can be accessed from student residence rooms. Staffed computer lab on campus.

Community Environment: Leavenworth is 26 miles northwest of Kansas City, which contributes to the economic and recreational interest of the community.

■ WASHBURN UNIVERSITY *D-15*

1700 SW College Ave.
Topeka, KS 66621
Tel: (785)670-1010
Admissions: (785)670-1812
Fax: (785)231-1089
E-mail: al.dickes@washburn.edu
Web Site: http://www.washburn.edu/

Description: City-supported, comprehensive, coed. Awards associate, bachelor's, master's, and first professional degrees. Founded 1865. Setting: 160-acre urban campus with easy access to Kansas City. Endowment: $100 million. Research spending for 2004 fiscal year: $126,561. Educational spending for 2005 fiscal year: $4300 per student. Total enrollment: 7,261. Faculty: 510 (258 full-time, 252 part-time). Student-undergrad faculty ratio is 16:1. 1,576 applied, 99% were admitted. 14% from top 10% of their high school class, 33% from top quarter, 66% from top half. 25 valedictorians. Full-time: 4,151 students, 60% women, 40% men. Part-time: 2,273 students, 65% women, 35% men. Students come from 49 states and territories, 45 other countries, 4% from out-of-state, 35% 25 or older, 13% live on campus, 8% transferred in. Retention: 69% of full-time freshmen returned the following year. Academic areas with the most degrees conferred: business/marketing; health professions and related sciences; security and protective services. Core. Calendar: semesters. Academic remediation for entering students, ESL program, services for LD students, advanced placement, self-designed majors, honors program, independent study, distance learning, double major, summer session for credit, part-time degree program, adult/continuing education programs, co-op programs and internships, graduate courses open to undergrads. Off campus study at Kansas City Kansas Community College, Johnson County Community College. Study abroad program. ROTC: Army, Naval (c), Air Force (c).

Entrance Requirements: Open admission except for nursing program. Options: electronic application, early admission. Required: high school transcript, ACT. Entrance: noncompetitive. Application deadline: 8/1. Notification: continuous.

Costs Per Year: Application fee: $20. State resident tuition: $4920 full-time, $164 per credit hour part-time. Nonresident tuition: $11,130 full-time, $371 per credit hour part-time. Mandatory fees: $62 full-time, $15 per term part-time. College room and board: $4752. College room only: $2772.

Collegiate Environment: Orientation program. Drama-theater group, choral group, marching band, student-run newspaper. Social organizations: 100 open to all; national fraternities, national sororities, local fraternities; 8% of eligible men and 6% of eligible women are members. Most popular organizations: Washburn Student Government Association, Campus Activities Board, Student Alumni Association, Learning in the Community, Washburn Education Association. Major annual events: homecoming, WU Stock, dance marathon. Student services: legal services, health clinic, personal-psychological counseling. Campus security: 24-hour emergency response devices and patrols, late night transport-escort service. 474 college housing spaces available; 464 were occupied in 2003-04. Option: coed housing available. Mabee Library plus 1 other with 1.5 million books, 14,000 serials, an OPAC, and a Web page. Operations spending for 2004 fiscal year: $3.3 million. 400 computers available on campus for general student use. A campuswide network can be accessed from off-campus. Staffed computer lab on campus.

Community Environment: Topeka, the state capital of Kansas, is situated on the edge of the wheat belt approximately 60 miles from Kansas City. The leading industries are meat packing, tire manufacturing, grain milling, printing and publishing, and the manufacture of steel products. Excellent community facilities include libraries, museums, many churches, and outstanding medical facilities. The Topeka Civic Theatre and Topeka Community Concert group provide the citizens with unusual cultural activities. Lake Shawnee is a popular recreation spot; Gage Park is a beautiful park within the city that has the finest facilities for picnicking and swimming, as well as lovely rose gardens. All major forms of commercial transportation are available. The Menninger Clinic located here is one of the world's largest psychiatric research and training centers.

■ WICHITA AREA TECHNICAL COLLEGE *H-11*
301 South Grove St.
Wichita, KS 67211
Tel: (316)677-9282
Admissions: (316)677-9400
E-mail: info@watc.edu
Web Site: http://www.wichitatech.com/

Description: District-supported, 2-year, coed. Awards certificates, diplomas, transfer associate, and terminal associate degrees. Founded 1963. Setting: urban campus. Educational spending for 2005 fiscal year: $9629 per student. Total enrollment: 1,044. Student-undergrad faculty ratio is 14:1. 719 applied, 49% were admitted. Full-time: 313 students, 54% women, 46% men. Part-time: 731 students, 43% women, 57% men. 0% from out-of-state, 2% Native American, 7% Hispanic, 16% black, 5% Asian American or Pacific Islander, 0.1% international. Calendar: semesters.

Entrance Requirements: Required for some: high school transcript, WorkKeys & COMPASS. Entrance: minimally difficult. Application deadline: Rolling.

Costs Per Year: Application fee: $16. State resident tuition: $2970 full-time, $99 per credit part-time. Nonresident tuition: $11,730 full-time, $345 per credit part-time. Mandatory fees: $236 full-time, $118 per term part-time.

■ WICHITA STATE UNIVERSITY *H-11*
1845 North Fairmount
Wichita, KS 67260
Tel: (316)978-3456
Free: 800-362-2594
Admissions: (316)978-3085
Fax: (316)978-3795
E-mail: crabtree@witchita.edu
Web Site: http://www.wichita.edu/

Description: State-supported, university, coed. Part of Kansas Board of Regents. Awards associate, bachelor's, master's, and doctoral degrees and post-master's certificates. Founded 1895. Setting: 335-acre urban campus. Endowment: $135.2 million. Research spending for 2004 fiscal year: $17.9 million. Educational spending for 2005 fiscal year: $2126 per student. Total enrollment: 14,076. Faculty: 515 (467 full-time, 48 part-time). Student-undergrad faculty ratio is 18:1. 2,066 applied, 84% were admitted. 19% from top 10% of their high school class, 47% from top quarter, 76% from top half. Full-time: 7,198 students, 56% women, 44% men. Part-time: 3,777 students, 56% women, 44% men. Students come from 45 states and territories, 77 other countries, 3% from out-of-state, 1% Native American, 5% Hispanic, 7% black, 7% Asian American or Pacific Islander, 5% international, 34% 25 or older, 7% live on campus, 11% transferred in. Retention: 67% of full-time freshmen returned the following year. Academic areas with the most degrees conferred: business/marketing; education; health professions and related

sciences. Core. Calendar: semesters. Academic remediation for entering students, ESL program, services for LD students, advanced placement, accelerated degree program, self-designed majors, freshman honors college, honors program, independent study, distance learning, double major, summer session for credit, part-time degree program, co-op programs and internships, graduate courses open to undergrads. Off campus study at National Student Exchange, Midwest Student Exchange. Study abroad program.

Entrance Requirements: Open admission for state residents who graduated from a Kansas high school before May 2001. Options: electronic application, deferred admission, international baccalaureate accepted. Required for some: minimum 2.0 high school GPA, minimum ACT score of 21; rank in top 1/3 of high school class, or minimum of 2.00 high school GPA, SAT and SAT Subject Tests or ACT. Entrance: noncompetitive. Application deadline: Rolling. Notification: continuous.

Costs Per Year: Application fee: $30. State resident tuition: $3434 full-time, $114.45 per credit hour part-time. Nonresident tuition: $10,887 full-time, $362.90 per credit hour part-time. Mandatory fees: $797 full-time, $25.45 per credit hour part-time, $17 per term part-time. Full-time tuition and fees vary according to course load. Part-time tuition and fees vary according to course load. College room and board: $5070. Room and board charges vary according to board plan and housing facility.

Collegiate Environment: Orientation program. Drama-theater group, choral group, student-run newspaper, radio station. Social organizations: 99 open to all; national fraternities, national sororities. Most popular organizations: Association of Malaysian Students, Organization of Pakistani Students, Psychology Club, nursing students organization, Institute of Aeronautics. Major annual events: Shocktoberfest, Hippodrome, Welcomefest. Student services: legal services, health clinic, personal-psychological counseling, women's center. Campus security: 24-hour emergency response devices and patrols, student patrols, late night transport-escort service, controlled dormitory access, bicycle patrols by campus security. 1,453 college housing spaces available; 757 were occupied in 2003-04. No special consideration for freshman housing applicants. On-campus residence required in freshman year. Option: coed housing available. Ablah Library plus 2 others with 1.6 million books, 1.1 million microform titles, 15,169 serials, 47,558 audiovisual materials, an OPAC, and a Web page. Operations spending for 2004 fiscal year: $5.3 million. 1,500 computers available on campus for general student use. A campuswide network can be accessed from student residence rooms and from off campus. Staffed computer lab on campus.

Community Environment: Wichita, population 300,000, is the largest city in Kansas. It is located 161 miles southeast of the center of the U.S. Primary economic factors contributing to the growth and development of the city have been aircraft manufacturing, oil and natural gas, air conditioners, heating and lighting units, as well as camping equipment and agriculture. It is the Aviation Center of the World. WSU is an important resource to the Wichita area business community. The university supports research and development through programs such as the Center for Productivity Enhancement, and the National Institute for Aviation Research. The corporate community utilizes programs offered by the University's Center for Management for continuing professional development. The Center for Entrepreneurship and Small Business Management encourages development of small businesses, while the Hugo Wall Center for Urban Studies supports local and state government facilities for canoeing, boating, and water skiing. Several theater groups stage productions throughout the year and the Wichita Symphony has provided more than 30 years of professional music. The city's civic an

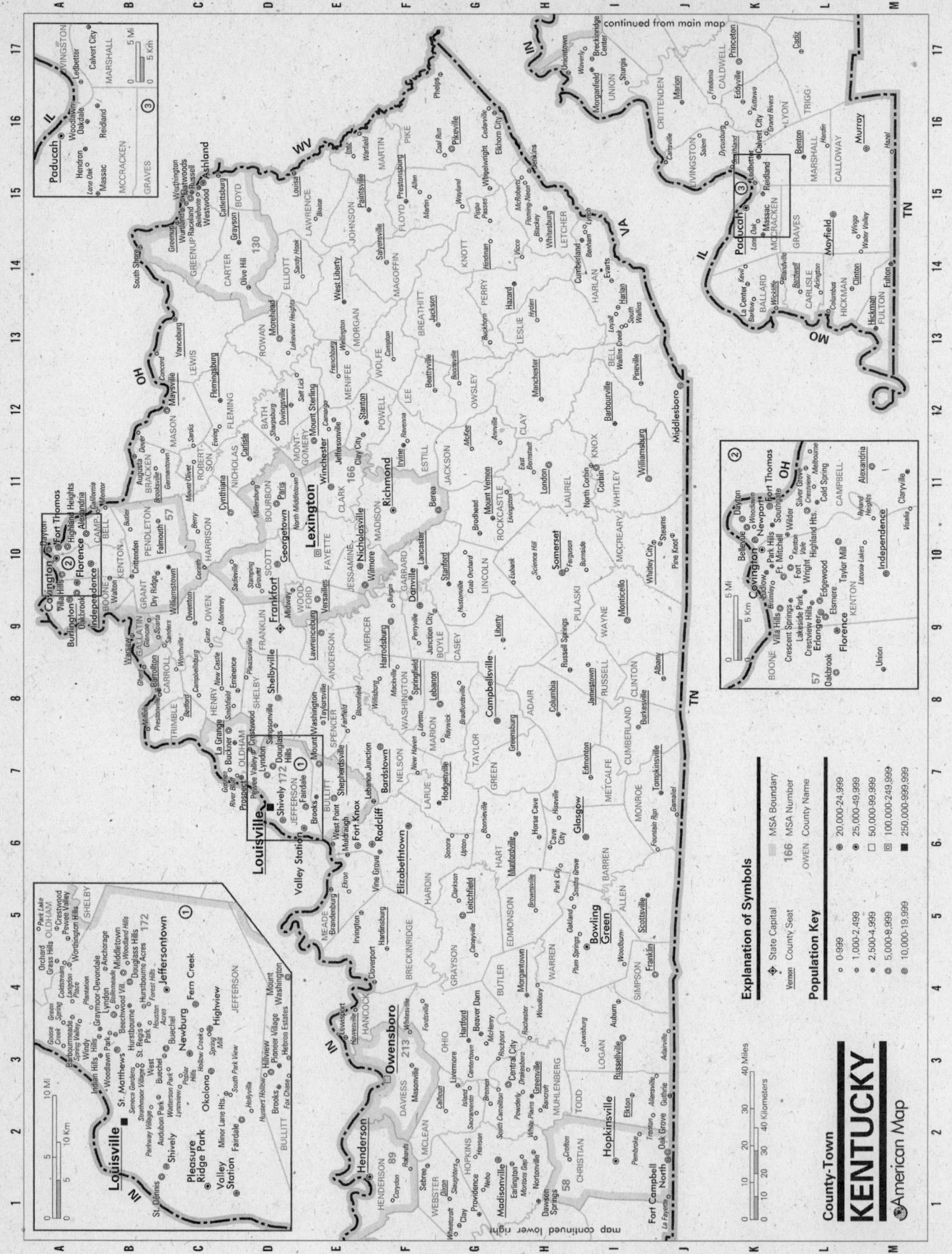

KENTUCKY

County-Town

American Map

Explanation of Symbols

✪	State Capital
⊛	County Seat
Vernon	County Seat
166	MSA Number
OWEN	County Name
	MSA Boundary

Population Key

○	0-999
⊙	1,000-2,499
●	2,500-4,999
⊡	5,000-9,999
⊚	10,000-19,999
⊕	20,000-24,999
⊕	25,000-49,999
□	50,000-99,999
⊡	100,000-249,999
■	250,000-999,999

continued from main map

map continued lower right

■ **ALICE LLOYD COLLEGE** *G-15*
100 Purpose Rd.
Pippa Passes, KY 41844
Tel: (606)368-2101
Admissions: (606)368-6134
Fax: (606)368-2125
Web Site: http://www.alc.edu/
Description: Independent, 4-year, coed. Awards bachelor's degrees. Founded 1923. Setting: 175-acre rural campus. Endowment: $21 million. Educational spending for 2005 fiscal year: $3000 per student. Total enrollment: 593. Student-undergrad faculty ratio is 18:1. 881 applied, 59% were admitted. 30% from top 10% of their high school class, 58% from top quarter, 86% from top half. 9 valedictorians. Full-time: 575 students, 53% women, 47% men. Part-time: 18 students, 56% women, 44% men. Students come from 6 states and territories, 1 other country, 16% from out-of-state, 0.2% Native American, 1% Hispanic, 1% black, 0.3% Asian American or Pacific Islander, 0.2% international, 5% 25 or older, 74% live on campus, 3% transferred in. Retention: 61% of full-time freshmen returned the following year. Academic areas with the most degrees conferred: education; business/marketing; biological/life sciences. Core. Calendar: semesters. Academic remediation for entering students, advanced placement, self-designed majors, independent study, double major, part-time degree program, internships. Study abroad program.
Entrance Requirements: Options: Peterson's Universal Application, deferred admission. Required: high school transcript, minimum 2.25 high school GPA, SAT or ACT. Required for some: essay, 2 recommendations, interview. Entrance: moderately difficult. Application deadline: Rolling. Notification: continuous.
Costs Per Year: Application fee: $0. Comprehensive fee: $4900 includes full-time tuition ($0), mandatory fees ($1150), and college room and board ($3750). College room only: $1730. Part-time tuition: $212 per credit hour. Full-time students in the 108-county service area are granted guaranteed tuition.
Collegiate Environment: Orientation program. Drama-theater group, choral group, student-run newspaper, radio station. Social organizations: 16 open to all; 16% of eligible men and 26% of eligible women are members. Most popular organizations: Phi Beta Lambda, All Scholastic Society, Math/Science Club, Allied Health Sciences Club. Major annual events: Religious Emphasis Week, Alcohol Awareness Week, Homecoming. Student services: health clinic, personal-psychological counseling. Campus security: 24-hour patrols, late night transport-escort service. 450 college housing spaces available; 440 were occupied in 2003-04. No special consideration for freshman housing applicants. On-campus residence required through senior year. McGaw Library and Learning Center with 74,216 books, 3,600 microform titles, 118 serials, 1,225 audiovisual materials, an OPAC, and a Web page. Operations spending for 2004 fiscal year: $189,193. 85 computers available on campus for general student use. A campuswide network can be accessed from student residence rooms. Staffed computer lab on campus.
Community Environment: Located in a small, rural town, the primary industries being coal mining and farming.

■ **ASBURY COLLEGE** *E-10*
1 Macklem Dr.
Wilmore, KY 40390-1198
Tel: (859)858-3511
Free: 800-888-1818

Fax: (859)858-3921
E-mail: admissions@asbury.edu
Web Site: http://www.asbury.edu/
Description: Independent nondenominational, comprehensive, coed. Awards bachelor's and master's degrees. Founded 1890. Setting: 400-acre small town campus with easy access to Lexington. Endowment: $28.1 million. Educational spending for 2005 fiscal year: $6843 per student. Total enrollment: 1,293. Faculty: 151 (86 full-time, 65 part-time). Student-undergrad faculty ratio is 11:1. 797 applied, 74% were admitted. 35% from top 10% of their high school class, 64% from top quarter, 85% from top half. Full-time: 1,124 students, 59% women, 41% men. Part-time: 105 students, 58% women, 42% men. Students come from 47 states and territories, 11 other countries, 67% from out-of-state, 0.4% Native American, 1% Hispanic, 1% black, 1% Asian American or Pacific Islander, 1% international, 4% 25 or older, 87% live on campus, 4% transferred in. Retention: 76% of full-time freshmen returned the following year. Academic areas with the most degrees conferred: communication technologies; English; theology and religious vocations. Core. Calendar: semesters. Academic remediation for entering students, ESL program, advanced placement, double major, summer session for credit, part-time degree program, internships. Study abroad program. ROTC: Army (c), Air Force (c).
Entrance Requirements: Options: Peterson's Universal Application, electronic application, early admission, deferred admission, international baccalaureate accepted. Required: essay, high school transcript, minimum 2.5 high school GPA, 3 recommendations, SAT or ACT. Required for some: interview. Entrance: moderately difficult. Application deadlines: Rolling, Rolling for nonresidents. Notification: continuous, continuous for nonresidents.
Costs Per Year: Application fee: $30. Comprehensive fee: $23,762 includes full-time tuition ($18,808), mandatory fees ($148), and college room and board ($4806). College room only: $2810. Full-time tuition and fees vary according to course load. Room and board charges vary according to board plan, housing facility, and location. Part-time tuition: $723 per semester hour. Part-time tuition varies according to course load.
Collegiate Environment: Orientation program. Drama-theater group, choral group, student-run newspaper, radio station. Social organizations: 35 open to all. Most popular organizations: Fellowship of Christian Athletes, Impact (community service), Christian Service Association, ministry teams, Student-Faculty Council. Major annual events: homecoming, Fall Revival, Missions Conference. Student services: health clinic, personal-psychological counseling. Campus security: 24-hour emergency response devices, late night transport-escort service, controlled dormitory access, late night security personnel. 1,253 college housing spaces available; 1,056 were occupied in 2003-04. Freshmen guaranteed college housing. On-campus residence required through senior year. Options: men-only, women-only housing available. Kinlaw Library with 145,424 books, 22,120 microform titles, 517 serials, 9,116 audiovisual materials, an OPAC, and a Web page. Operations spending for 2004 fiscal year: $406,070. 189 computers available on campus for general student use. Computer purchase/lease plans available. A campuswide network can be accessed from student residence rooms and from off campus. Staffed computer lab on campus.
Community Environment: This is rural town with air and bus service available in nearby Lexington, Kentucky. There are several natural and historic points of interest located nearby: High Bridge, Shakertown, Fort Harrod,

Boone's Tavern, National Cemetery at Camp Nelson, Kentucky Horse Park, world famous thoroughbred farms and Natural Bridge.

■ **ASHLAND COMMUNITY AND TECHNICAL COLLEGE** *C-15*
1400 College Dr.
Ashland, KY 41101-3683
Tel: (606)329-2999
Free: 800-370-7191
Admissions: (606)326-2114
Fax: (606)325-8124
E-mail: steve.flouhouse@kctcs.edu
Web Site: http://www.ashland.kctcs.edu/
Description: State-supported, 2-year, coed. Part of Kentucky Community and Technical College System. Awards certificates, diplomas, transfer associate, and terminal associate degrees. Founded 1937. Setting: 47-acre small town campus. Endowment: $870,926. Educational spending for 2005 fiscal year: $3241 per student. Total enrollment: 2,565. 404 applied, 100% were admitted. Students come from 6 states and territories, 10% from out-of-state, 41% 25 or older. Retention: 44% of full-time freshmen returned the following year. Core. Calendar: semesters. Academic remediation for entering students, services for LD students, advanced placement, honors program, distance learning, summer session for credit, part-time degree program, adult/continuing education programs, co-op programs and internships. Off campus study at University of Kentucky, other area colleges.
Entrance Requirements: Open admission except for nursing program. Options: Common Application, early admission, deferred admission. Required: high school transcript. Placement: ACT COMPASS required; ACT recommended. Entrance: noncompetitive. Application deadline: 8/20.
Costs Per Year: Application fee: $0. State resident tuition: $2940 full-time, $98 per credit hour part-time. Nonresident tuition: $8820 full-time, $294 per credit hour part-time. Full-time tuition varies according to reciprocity agreements. Part-time tuition varies according to reciprocity agreements.
Collegiate Environment: Orientation program. Drama-theater group, choral group, student-run newspaper. Social organizations: 11 open to all. Most popular organizations: Phi Theta Kappa, Phi Beta Lambda, Kentucky Association of Nursing Students, Baptist Student Union/Students for Christ, Circle K. Major annual events: Back to School Barbecue/United Way Fundraiser, Spring Fling, Red Cross Bloodmobiles. Student services: personal-psychological counseling. Campus security: 24-hour emergency response devices and patrols, late night transport-escort service, electronic surveillance of bookstore and business office. College housing not available. Joseph and Sylvia Mansbach Memorial Library with 41,379 books, 391 serials, and an OPAC. Operations spending for 2004 fiscal year: $378,995. 150 computers available on campus for general student use. A campuswide network can be accessed from off-campus. Staffed computer lab on campus.
Community Environment: On the Ohio River, Ashland has a temperate climate with an average annual temperature of 55 degrees. This city has 25 industries including steel, oil refining, a coal and coke-processing plant and a firebrick factory. More than 21 million tons of barge traffic on the river passes the city annually. The Greenup Locks and Dam complex consist of two adjacent chambers which elevate 1,100 foot modern tows in 20 minutes as opposed to the six hours previously required. Transportation is provided by bus and railroad. Part time work is available. City services include a public library, churches of 15 denominations, Y's (no overnight facilities), and hospitals. Recreational facilities easily accessible are indoor theatres, several drive-ins, golf courses, boating, fishing, two state parks, bowling alleys, municipal swimming pool and private swim club, baseball, tennis, and croquet.

■ **BECKFIELD COLLEGE** *A-10*
16 Spiral Dr.
Florence, KY 41042
Tel: (859)371-9393
Fax: (859)371-5096
E-mail: kleeds@beckfield.org
Web Site: http://www.beckfield.edu/
Description: Proprietary, primarily 2-year, coed. Awards certificates, diplomas, terminal associate, and bachelor's degrees. Founded 1984. Setting: suburban campus. Total enrollment: 480. Full-time: 320 students, 50% women, 50% men. Students come from 3 states and territories, 60% 25 or older.
Entrance Requirements: Open admission.

■ **BELLARMINE UNIVERSITY** *D-7*
2001 Newburg Rd.
Louisville, KY 40205-0671

Tel: (502)452-8000
Free: 800-274-4723
Admissions: (502)452-8131
Fax: (502)452-8002
Web Site: http://www.bellarmine.edu/
Description: Independent Roman Catholic, comprehensive, coed. Awards bachelor's, master's, and doctoral degrees and post-master's certificates. Founded 1950. Setting: 120-acre suburban campus. Endowment: $19.4 million. Educational spending for 2005 fiscal year: $6399 per student. Total enrollment: 2,800. Faculty: 251 (115 full-time, 136 part-time). Student-undergrad faculty ratio is 13:1. 2,024 applied, 71% were admitted. 18% from top 10% of their high school class, 51% from top quarter, 83% from top half. 1 National Merit Scholar, 3 class presidents, 72 student government officers. Full-time: 1,737 students, 66% women, 34% men. Part-time: 522 students, 65% women, 35% men. Students come from 39 states and territories, 22% from out-of-state, 0.2% Native American, 2% Hispanic, 4% black, 2% Asian American or Pacific Islander, 1% international, 15% 25 or older, 37% live on campus, 5% transferred in. Retention: 84% of full-time freshmen returned the following year. Core. Calendar: semesters. Services for LD students, advanced placement, accelerated degree program, self-designed majors, honors program, independent study, double major, summer session for credit, part-time degree program, adult/continuing education programs, internships, graduate courses open to undergrads. Off campus study at University of Louisville, Spalding University, Indiana University Southeast, Southern Baptist Theological Seminary, Presbyterian Seminary, Jefferson Community College. Study abroad program. ROTC: Army (c), Air Force (c).
Entrance Requirements: Options: Peterson's Universal Application, Common Application, electronic application, early admission, early action, deferred admission, international baccalaureate accepted. Required: essay, high school transcript, minimum 2.0 high school GPA, recommendations, SAT or ACT. Recommended: interview. Entrance: moderately difficult. Application deadlines: 2/1, 11/1 for early action. Notification: 12/1 for early action.
Costs Per Year: Application fee: $25. Comprehensive fee: $31,030 includes full-time tuition ($23,300), mandatory fees ($850), and college room and board ($6880). College room only: $3860. Part-time tuition: $550 per credit. Part-time mandatory fees: $35 per course.
Collegiate Environment: Orientation program. Drama-theater group, choral group, student-run newspaper. Social organizations: 61 open to all; national fraternities, national sororities; 2% of eligible men and 2% of eligible women are members. Most popular organizations: student government, Delta Sigma Pi, Fellowship of Christian Athletes, campus ministry, Bellarmine Activities Council. Major annual events: Ball on the Belle, Homecoming, Pioneer Dance. Student services: health clinic, personal-psychological counseling. Campus security: 24-hour emergency response devices and patrols, student patrols, late night transport-escort service, controlled dormitory access, 24-hour locked residence hall entrances, security cameras. 580 college housing spaces available; 520 were occupied in 2003-04. Freshmen guaranteed college housing. On-campus residence required through junior year. Options: coed, men-only, women-only housing available. W.L. Lyons Brown Library with 97,737 books, 609,287 microform titles, 401 serials, 3,853 audiovisual materials, an OPAC, and a Web page. Operations spending for 2004 fiscal year: $2 million. 160 computers available on campus for general student use. A campuswide network can be accessed from student residence rooms. Staffed computer lab on campus.

■ **BEREA COLLEGE** *G-11*
Berea, KY 40404
Tel: (859)985-3000
Free: 800-326-5948
Admissions: (859)985-3500
E-mail: admissions@berea.edu
Web Site: http://www.berea.edu/
Description: Independent, 4-year, coed. Awards bachelor's degrees. Founded 1855. Setting: 140-acre small town campus. Endowment: $861.7 million. Educational spending for 2005 fiscal year: $8572 per student. Total enrollment: 1,595. Student-undergrad faculty ratio is 11:1. 1,908 applied, 27% were admitted. 30% from top 10% of their high school class, 66% from top quarter, 91% from top half. Full-time: 1,529 students, 60% women, 40% men. Part-time: 66 students, 41% women, 59% men. Students come from 42 states and territories, 71 other countries, 57% from out-of-state, 1% Native American, 2% Hispanic, 19% black, 1% Asian American or Pacific Islander, 7% international, 6% 25 or older, 84% live on campus, 2% transferred in. Retention: 82% of full-time freshmen returned the following

year. Academic areas with the most degrees conferred: education; business/ marketing; engineering technologies. Core. Calendar: 4-1-4. Academic remediation for entering students, services for LD students, advanced placement, self-designed majors, honors program, independent study, double major, summer session for credit, internships. Off campus study at Hastings College, Salem College, Austin College, Birmingham-Southern College, Eckerd College, Whitworth College. Study abroad program.

Entrance Requirements: Option: electronic application. Required: essay, high school transcript, interview, financial aid application, SAT or ACT. Recommended: 2 recommendations. Entrance: very difficult. Application deadlines: 4/30, 4/30 for nonresidents. Notification: continuous until 12/20, continuous until 12/20 for nonresidents. Preference given to Appalachian residents with high ability and limited economic resources.

Costs Per Year: Application fee: $0. Comprehensive fee: $5496 includes full-time tuition ($0), mandatory fees ($516), and college room and board ($4980). Financial aid is provided to all students for tuition costs.

Collegiate Environment: Orientation program. Drama-theater group, choral group, student-run newspaper. Social organizations: 77 open to all. Most popular organizations: Campus Activities Board, Cosmopolitan Club, Students for Appalachia, flag football and basketball intramurals, Baptist Student Union. Major annual events: Mountain Day Eve, Graduation, Labor Day. Student services: health clinic, personal-psychological counseling, women's center. Campus security: 24-hour emergency response devices and patrols, late night transport-escort service, controlled dormitory access, crime prevention programs. 1,370 college housing spaces available; 1,265 were occupied in 2003-04. Freshmen guaranteed college housing. On-campus residence required through senior year. Options: men-only, women-only housing available. Hutchins Library plus 2 others with 358,556 books, 132,888 microform titles, 1,918 serials, 11,593 audiovisual materials, an OPAC, and a Web page. Operations spending for 2004 fiscal year: $869,669. 260 computers available on campus for general student use. A campuswide network can be accessed from student residence rooms and from off campus. Staffed computer lab on campus.

Community Environment: Nestled in the foothills of the Cumberland Mountains, Berea draws 80% of its students from the Appalachian regions of nine southern states. Excellent motels are found in the community as well as the college hotel. The Churchill Weavers, one of the largest hand-weaving companies in the country, is located here.

■ **BIG SANDY COMMUNITY AND TECHNICAL COLLEGE** *F-15*
One Bert T. Combs Dr.
Prestonsburg, KY 41653-1815
Tel: (606)886-3863; 888-641-4132
Fax: (606)886-6943
E-mail: ccsprerg@kctcs.edu
Web Site: http://www.bigsandy.kctcs.edu/
Description: State-supported, 2-year, coed. Part of Kentucky Community and Technical College System. Awards transfer associate and terminal associate degrees. Founded 1964. Setting: 50-acre rural campus. Endowment: $700,000. Total enrollment: 4,406. 0% from out-of-state, 0.1% Native American, 0.2% Hispanic, 1% black, 0.2% Asian American or Pacific Islander, 44% 25 or older. Core. Calendar: semesters. Academic remediation for entering students, services for LD students, advanced placement, independent study, distance learning, summer session for credit, part-time degree program, adult/continuing education programs, co-op programs. Off campus study at Morehead State University.

Entrance Requirements: Open admission except for nursing program. Options: Common Application, early admission, deferred admission. Required: high school transcript. Placement: ACT required; ACT ASSET recommended. Entrance: noncompetitive. Application deadline: Rolling.

Costs Per Year: Application fee: $0. Area resident tuition: $2940 full-time, $98 per credit hour part-time. State resident tuition: $3540 full-time, $118 per credit hour part-time. Nonresident tuition: $8820 full-time, $294 per credit hour part-time.

Collegiate Environment: Orientation program. Choral group. Social organizations: 8 open to all. Most popular organizations: Phi Theta Kappa, Baptist Student Union, Student Government Association, Phi Beta Lambda, Kentucky Association of Nursing Students. Major annual events: Spring Blowout, College Day Fair, Disabilities Awareness Day. Student services: health clinic, personal-psychological counseling. Campus security: 24-hour emergency response devices. College housing not available. Magoffin Learning Resource Center with 34,668 books, 259 serials, and an OPAC. Operations spending for 2004 fiscal year: $360,000. 200 computers available on campus for general student use. Staffed computer lab on campus.

Community Environment: Prestonsburg is the site of a revolutionary war battle and General Garfield's headquarters in 1862. Surrounding the city are eastern Kentucky's coal, oil and gas fields. The urban area has transportation provided by bus and car. The city has hospitals, churches of all denominations, average shopping facilities, and good opportunities for part-time employment. Recreational facilities are available at a state park with boating, fishing, swimming, water skiing, horseback riding, and high lift. Locally are a public park, bowling alley, golf course, swimming pool and tennis courts. The Kentucky Highland Folk Festival, The Jenny Wiley Festival and Horse Show are annual events.

■ **BOWLING GREEN TECHNICAL COLLEGE** *I-5*
1845 Loop Dr.
Bowling Green, KY 42101
Tel: (270)901-1000
Fax: (270)746-7466
Web Site: http://www.bowlinggreen.kctcs.edu/
Description: State-supported, 2-year, coed. Founded 1938. Calendar: semesters.

■ **BRESCIA UNIVERSITY** *F-3*
717 Frederica St.
Owensboro, KY 42301-3023
Tel: (270)685-3131; 877-273-7242
Admissions; (270)686-4241
Fax: (270)686-6422
Web Site: http://www.brescia.edu/
Description: Independent Roman Catholic, comprehensive, coed. Awards associate, bachelor's, and master's degrees. Founded 1950. Setting: 9-acre urban campus. Endowment: $9 million. Educational spending for 2005 fiscal year: $3695 per student. Total enrollment: 709. 216 applied, 93% were admitted. 16% from top 10% of their high school class, 37% from top quarter, 76% from top half. Full-time: 477 students, 57% women, 43% men. Part-time: 192 students, 56% women, 44% men. 0.4% Native American, 1% Hispanic, 4% black, 1% Asian American or Pacific Islander, 13% international, 44% 25 or older, 26% live on campus, 12% transferred in. Retention: 67% of full-time freshmen returned the following year. Core. Calendar: semesters. Academic remediation for entering students, ESL program, services for LD students, advanced placement, self-designed majors, honors program, independent study, double major, summer session for credit, part-time degree program, adult/continuing education programs, internships. Off campus study at Kentucky Wesleyan College. Study abroad program.

Entrance Requirements: Options: Peterson's Universal Application, Common Application, electronic application, deferred admission. Required: essay, high school transcript, minimum 2.5 high school GPA, SAT or ACT. Required for some: 1 recommendation, interview. Entrance: moderately difficult. Application deadline: Rolling. Notification: continuous.

Costs Per Year: Application fee: $25. Comprehensive fee: $15,330 includes full-time tuition ($12,400), mandatory fees ($220), and college room and board ($2710). College room only: $1560. Full-time tuition and fees vary according to class time. Room and board charges vary according to board plan and housing facility. Part-time tuition: $395 per credit hour. Part-time mandatory fees: $10 per credit hour, $100 per term.

Collegiate Environment: Orientation program. Drama-theater group, choral group, student-run newspaper. Social organizations: 23 open to all. Most popular organizations: Student Government Association, Ichabod Society, National Student Speech-Language-Hearing Association, Social Work Club, Spanish Club. Major annual events: Homecoming, Family Weekend, Inaugural Ball. Student services: personal-psychological counseling, women's center. Campus security: late night transport-escort service, controlled dormitory access. 269 college housing spaces available; 239 were occupied in 2003-04. On-campus residence required in freshman year. Options: coed, men-only, women-only housing available. Brescia University Library with 331,620 microform titles, 2,466 serials, 6,717 audiovisual materials, an OPAC, and a Web page. Operations spending for 2004 fiscal year: $203,469. 41 computers available on campus for general student use. A campuswide network can be accessed from student residence rooms and from off campus. Staffed computer lab on campus.

Community Environment: Brescia University is located in Owensboro, Kentucky, on the Ohio River. With a metropolitan population of 55,000, Owensboro is easily accessible from any direction. The college campus is within walking distance of the revitalized downtown area, the performing arts center, public library, art museum, natural science and history museum, as well as numerous restaurants, churches, and parks. Many Owensboro industries and professional organizations cooperate with Brescia in providing enriching off-campus learning opportunities for students, particularly in the areas of business, education, psychology, social work, speech and hearing, and special education.

■ **BROWN MACKIE COLLEGE-HOPKINSVILLE** *I-2*

4001 Ft. Cambell Blvd.
Hopkinsville, KY 42240
Tel: (270)886-1302
Free: 800-359-4753
Fax: (270)886-3544
E-mail: bcortez@borwnmackie.edu
Web Site: http://www.brownmackie.edu/locations.asp?locid=17

Description: Proprietary, 2-year, coed. Awards diplomas and transfer associate degrees. Setting: small town campus. Total enrollment: 146. Student-undergrad faculty ratio is 15:1. 89 applied, 100% were admitted. Full-time: 146 students, 88% women, 12% men. 0% from out-of-state, 1% Native American, 3% Hispanic, 25% black, 1% Asian American or Pacific Islander, 0% international.

Entrance Requirements: Required: high school transcript. Recommended: interview. Entrance: noncompetitive. Application deadline: Rolling. Notification: continuous.

Costs Per Year: Tuition: $8592 full-time, $179 per credit hour part-time. Mandatory fees: $480 full-time, $10 per credit hour part-time.

■ **BROWN MACKIE COLLEGE-LOUISVILLE** *D-7*

300 High Rise Dr.
Louisville, KY 40213
Tel: (502)968-7191
Free: 800-999-7387
Fax: (502)968-1727
E-mail: kbelanger@brownmackie.edu
Web Site: http://www.brownmackie.edu/locations.asp?locid=18

Description: Proprietary, 2-year, coed. Awards terminal associate degrees. Founded 1972. Setting: suburban campus. Total enrollment: 315. Student-undergrad faculty ratio is 18:1. 128 applied, 72% were admitted. Students come from 3 states and territories, 1 other country, 7% from out-of-state, 1% Native American, 2% Hispanic, 34% black, 1% Asian American or Pacific Islander, 0% international, 63% 25 or older. Core. Academic remediation for entering students.

Entrance Requirements: Options: early admission, deferred admission. Required: high school transcript, interview. Entrance: minimally difficult. Application deadline: Rolling. Notification: continuous.

Costs Per Year: Application fee: $0. Tuition: $8592 full-time. Mandatory fees: $480 full-time.

Collegiate Environment: Student services: personal-psychological counseling. Campus security: 24-hour emergency response devices, evening security guards, electronically operated building access. College housing not available. Main library plus 1 other with 1,210 books and 23 serials. 3 computers available on campus for general student use. A campuswide network can be accessed. Staffed computer lab on campus.

■ **BROWN MACKIE COLLEGE-NORTHERN KENTUCKY** *K-10*

309 Buttermilk Pike
Fort Mitchell, KY 41017-2191
Tel: (859)341-5627
Free: 800-888-1445
Fax: (859)341-6483
E-mail: jdellefield@brownmackie.edu
Web Site: http://www.brownmackie.edu

Description: Proprietary, 2-year, coed. Part of American Education Centers, Inc. Awards certificates, diplomas, transfer associate, and terminal associate degrees. Founded 1927. Setting: 5-acre suburban campus with easy access to Cincinnati. Total enrollment: 465. Student-undergrad faculty ratio is 14:1. 500 applied. 0% from top 10% of their high school class, 0% from top quarter, 0% from top half. Full-time: 465 students, 70% women, 30% men. Students come from 3 states and territories, 12% from out-of-state, 0% Native American, 1% Hispanic, 8% black, 1% Asian American or Pacific Islander, 0% international, 59% 25 or older. Retention: 81% of full-time freshmen returned the following year. Core. Academic remediation for entering students, summer session for credit, part-time degree program, adult/continuing education programs, internships.

Entrance Requirements: Open admission. Options: Common Application, international baccalaureate accepted. Required: interview. Application deadline: Rolling. Notification: continuous.

Collegiate Environment: Major annual events: Summer Cook-Out, Chili Cook-Off, Halloween. Student services: personal-psychological counseling. Campus security: 24-hour emergency response devices, late night transport-escort service. College housing not available. 1,500 books and 50 serials. 50 computers available on campus for general student use. Staffed computer lab on campus.

■ **CAMPBELLSVILLE UNIVERSITY** *G-8*

1 University Dr.
Campbellsville, KY 42718-2799
Tel: (270)789-5000
Free: 800-264-6014
Admissions: (270)789-5220
Fax: (270)789-5071
Web Site: http://www.campbellsville.edu/

Description: Independent, comprehensive, coed, affiliated with Kentucky Baptist Convention. Awards associate, bachelor's, and master's degrees. Founded 1906. Setting: 80-acre small town campus. Endowment: $5.4 million. Educational spending for 2005 fiscal year: $3748 per student. Total enrollment: 2,286. Faculty: 217 (86 full-time, 131 part-time). Student-undergrad faculty ratio is 12:1. 1,351 applied, 73% were admitted. 15% from top 10% of their high school class, 37% from top quarter, 65% from top half. 12 valedictorians. Full-time: 1,266 students, 52% women, 48% men. Part-time: 570 students, 65% women, 35% men. Students come from 27 states and territories, 18 other countries, 16% from out-of-state, 1% Hispanic, 6% black, 1% Asian American or Pacific Islander, 3% international, 18% 25 or older, 55% live on campus, 7% transferred in. Retention: 62% of full-time freshmen returned the following year. Academic areas with the most degrees conferred: business/marketing; education; theology and religious vocations. Core. Calendar: semesters. Academic remediation for entering students, ESL program, advanced placement, accelerated degree program, honors program, independent study, distance learning, double major, summer session for credit, part-time degree program, adult/continuing education programs, internships. Off campus study. Study abroad program.

Entrance Requirements: Options: Peterson's Universal Application, Common Application, electronic application, deferred admission. Required: high school transcript, minimum 2.0 high school GPA, SAT or ACT. Recommended: essay, minimum 3.0 high school GPA, recommendations, interview. Entrance: moderately difficult. Application deadline: Rolling. Notification: continuous.

Costs Per Year: Application fee: $20. Comprehensive fee: $22,272 includes full-time tuition ($15,960), mandatory fees ($380), and college room and board ($5932).

Collegiate Environment: Orientation program. Drama-theater group, choral group, marching band, student-run newspaper, radio station. Social organizations: 48 open to all. Most popular organizations: Student Government Association, Baptist Student Union, Phi Beta Lambda, African-American Leadership League, Fellowship of Christian Athletics. Major annual events: homecoming, Christmas celebration, Spring Formal. Student services: health clinic, personal-psychological counseling. Campus security: 24-hour emergency response devices and patrols, student patrols, late night transport-escort service, controlled dormitory access. 750 college housing spaces available; 748 were occupied in 2003-04. Freshmen guaranteed college housing. On-campus residence required through sophomore year. Options: men-only, women-only housing available. Montgomery Library plus 2 others with 172,000 books, 338,235 microform titles, 12,777 serials, 16,023 audiovisual materials, an OPAC, and a Web page. Operations spending for 2004 fiscal year: $388,464. 148 computers available on campus for general student use. Staffed computer lab on campus.

Community Environment: The 70-acre Campbellsville campus is situated precisely in the center of Kentucky, one-half mile from downtown Campbellsville (population 15,000), 40 minutes southeast of Elizabethtown, one and one-half hours from Louisville and Lexington, and just over two hours from Nashville. The college is located on KY55 and can be reached from the north by way of the Bluegrass Parkway and from the south by way of the Cumberland Parkway.

■ **CENTRE COLLEGE** *F-9*

600 West Walnut St.
Danville, KY 40422-1394
Tel: (859)238-5200

Free: 800-423-6236

Admissions: (859)238-5350

Fax: (859)238-5456

E-mail: admission@centre.edu

Web Site: http://www.centre.edu/

Description: Independent, 4-year, coed, affiliated with Presbyterian Church (U.S.A.). Awards bachelor's degrees. Founded 1819. Setting: 100-acre small town campus. Endowment: $149.9 million. Educational spending for 2005 fiscal year: $10,047 per student. Total enrollment: 1,130. Student-undergrad faculty ratio is 11:1. 1,989 applied, 63% were admitted. 55% from top 10% of their high school class, 85% from top quarter, 96% from top half. 30 valedictorians, 120 student government officers. Full-time: 1,127 students, 51% women, 49% men. Part-time: 3 students, 67% women, 33% men. Students come from 35 states and territories, 12 other countries, 33% from out-of-state, 0.2% Native American, 1% Hispanic, 2% black, 2% Asian American or Pacific Islander, 2% international, 0% 25 or older, 95% live on campus, 1% transferred in. Retention: 92% of full-time freshmen returned the following year. Academic areas with the most degrees conferred: social sciences; history; biological/life-sciences. Core. Calendar: 4-1-4. Services for LD students, advanced placement, self-designed majors, independent study, double major, part-time degree program, internships. Off campus study at Associated Colleges of the South. Study abroad program. ROTC: Army (c), Air Force (c).

Entrance Requirements: Options: Peterson's Universal Application, Common Application, electronic application, early admission, early action, deferred admission, international baccalaureate accepted. Required: essay, high school transcript, 1 recommendation, SAT or ACT. Recommended: interview. Entrance: very difficult. Application deadlines: 2/1, 12/1 for early action. Notification: 3/15, 1/15 for early action.

Costs Per Year: Application fee: $40. Comprehensive fee: $30,810 includes full-time tuition ($23,110) and college room and board ($7700). College room only: $3900. Room and board charges vary according to board plan. Part-time tuition: $830 per credit hour. Part-time tuition varies according to course load.

Collegiate Environment: Orientation program. Drama-theater group, choral group, student-run newspaper. Social organizations: 76 open to all; national fraternities, national sororities; 37% of eligible men and 38% of eligible women are members. Most popular organizations: CARE (Centre Action Reaches Everyone), Christian Fellowship, College Democrats and Republicans, Student Congress, Outdoors Club. Major annual events: Homecoming, Spring Carnival, Family Weekend. Student services: health clinic, personal-psychological counseling. Campus security: 24-hour emergency response devices and patrols, late night transport-escort service, controlled dormitory access. 1,000 college housing spaces available; all were occupied in 2003-04. Freshmen guaranteed college housing. On-campus residence required through sophomore year. Options: coed, men-only, women-only housing available. Doherty Library plus 1 other with 217,751 books, 52,512 microform titles, 750 serials, an OPAC, and a Web page. Operations spending for 2004 fiscal year: $811,184. 150 computers available on campus for general student use. A campuswide network can be accessed from student residence rooms and from off campus. Staffed computer lab on campus.

Community Environment: Danville is a prosperous community located on the southern edge of Kentucky's famous bluegrass region. The town has a rich historical heritage. It was the first seat of government west of the Alleghenies, and is also known for its early contributions in medicine, education, and government. Today, Danville is a model in Kentucky and the region as a center for light industry, with more than a dozen major employers. Midwinter days average 35 degrees; midsummer temperatures average 80 degrees. There is sunshine 60% of the time. Transportation is provided by a bus line and three main highways. Danville has fine horse farms, many churches, a library, a Regional Arts Center, bowling alley, fishing, boating, waterskiing, golf, and theaters. Part-time jobs are available.

■ **CLEAR CREEK BAPTIST BIBLE COLLEGE** *I-12*

300 Clear Creek Rd.

Pineville, KY 40977-9754

Tel: (606)337-3196

Web Site: http://www.ccbbc.edu/

Description: Independent Southern Baptist, 4-year, coed. Awards bachelor's degrees. Founded 1926. Setting: 700-acre rural campus. Total enrollment: 212. 85% 25 or older. Retention: 82% of full-time freshmen returned the following year. Core. Calendar: semesters. Summer session for credit, part-time degree program. Off campus study at University of Kentucky, Southeast Community College.

Entrance Requirements: Open admission. Options: Common Application, electronic application, deferred admission. Required: essay, 4 recommendations. Recommended: high school transcript, interview. Entrance: noncompetitive. Application deadline: 7/15. Notification: continuous.

Costs Per Year: Application fee: $40. Comprehensive fee: $7830 includes full-time tuition ($4520) and college room and board ($3310). College room only: $1870. Part-time tuition: $205 per semester hour.

Collegiate Environment: Orientation program. Choral group. Student services: health clinic, personal-psychological counseling. Campus security: 24-hour emergency response devices, student patrols. Option: coed housing available. Carolyn Boatman Brooks Memorial Library with 38,000 books, 300 serials, and an OPAC. 15 computers available on campus for general student use. A campuswide network can be accessed. Staffed computer lab on campus.

Community Environment: The campus bounds Pine Mountain State Park. Pineville, founded in 1799, is located in a rural area 16 miles north of Cumberland Gap, and is served by the Greyhound bus line. Churches, a small shopping area and some part-time employment are available.

■ **DAYMAR COLLEGE (LOUISVILLE)** *D-7*

4400 Breckenridge Ln., Ste. 415

Louisville, KY 40218

Tel: (502)495-1040

Web Site: http://www.daymarcollege.edu/

Description: Proprietary, 2-year, coed. Awards diplomas and terminal associate degrees. Founded 2001. Total enrollment: 227.

Entrance Requirements: Required: high school transcript, interview.

■ **DAYMAR COLLEGE (OWENSBORO)** *F-3*

3361 Buckland Square

Owensboro, KY 42301

Tel: (270)926-4040

Free: 800-960-4090

Fax: (270)685-4090

E-mail: mdowney@ojcb.com

Web Site: http://www.daymarcollege.edu/

Description: Proprietary, 2-year, coed. Awards certificates, diplomas, and transfer associate degrees. Founded 1963. Setting: 1-acre small town campus. Educational spending for 2005 fiscal year: $1200 per student. Total enrollment: 446. Full-time: 334 students, 85% women, 15% men. Part-time: 112 students, 84% women, 16% men. Students come from 2 states and territories, 14% from out-of-state, 0% Native American, 1% Hispanic, 3% black, 0% Asian American or Pacific Islander, 0% international, 0% transferred in. Retention: 72% of full-time freshmen returned the following year. Core. Academic remediation for entering students, advanced placement, accelerated degree program, independent study, double major, summer session for credit, part-time degree program, adult/continuing education programs, co-op programs and internships.

Entrance Requirements: Option: deferred admission. Required: high school transcript, interview, Wonderlic aptitude test. Required for some: SAT or ACT. Entrance: minimally difficult. Application deadline: Rolling.

Collegiate Environment: Orientation program. Student-run newspaper. Major annual events: quarterly awards ceremonies, Student Appreciation Week, Graduation. Student services: personal-psychological counseling. Campus security: 24-hour emergency response devices. College housing not available. Learning Resource Center with 3,215 books, 67 serials, 77 audiovisual materials, and a Web page. Operations spending for 2004 fiscal year: $10,000. 103 computers available on campus for general student use. A campuswide network can be accessed from off-campus. Staffed computer lab on campus.

■ **DRAUGHONS JUNIOR COLLEGE** *I-5*

2421 Fitzgerald Industrial Dr.

Bowling Green, KY 42101

Tel: (270)843-6750

Fax: (270)843-6976

Web Site: http://www.draughons.edu/

Description: Proprietary, 2-year, coed. Administratively affiliated with Draughons Junior College, Inc. Awards diplomas and transfer associate degrees. Founded 1989. Setting: suburban campus with easy access to Nashville. Educational spending for 2005 fiscal year: $10,800 per student. Total enrollment: 368. 120 applied, 100% were admitted. Full-time: 172 students, 85% women, 15% men. Part-time: 196 students, 86% women, 14% men. Students come from 2 states and territories, 1% from out-of-state,

0% Native American, 1% Hispanic, 10% black, 0% Asian American or Pacific Islander, 0% international, 27% 25 or older, 11% transferred in. Retention: 78% of full-time freshmen returned the following year. Core. Calendar: semesters. Part-time degree program, adult/continuing education programs, internships.

Entrance Requirements: Open admission. Options: Peterson's Universal Application, Common Application. Required: high school transcript. Placement: SAT or ACT recommended. Entrance: noncompetitive.

Costs Per Year: Application fee: $20. Tuition: $300 per credit part-time. Mandatory fees: $1000 full-time. Full-time fees vary according to course load and program. Part-time tuition varies according to course load and program. Tuition guaranteed not to increase for student's term of enrollment.

Collegiate Environment: Orientation program. Student-run newspaper. Social organizations: 1 open to all. Most popular organization: Student Council. Major annual events: food drives, blood drives, Cancer Walk-A-Thon. Student services: personal-psychological counseling. Campus security: 24-hour emergency response devices. College housing not available. Draughons Junior College Library with 5,000 books, 30 serials, 75 audiovisual materials, and a Web page. Operations spending for 2004 fiscal year: $2000. 52 computers available on campus for general student use. A campuswide network can be accessed. Staffed computer lab on campus.

■ **EASTERN KENTUCKY UNIVERSITY** *F-11*
521 Lancaster Ave.
Richmond, KY 40475-3102
Tel: (859)622-1000
Admissions: (859)622-2106
Fax: (859)622-1020
Web Site: http://www.eku.edu/
Description: State-supported, comprehensive, coed. Part of Kentucky Council on Post Secondary Education. Awards associate, bachelor's, and master's degrees and post-master's certificates. Founded 1906. Setting: 500-acre small town campus with easy access to Lexington. Endowment: $38.3 million. Research spending for 2004 fiscal year: $639,776. Educational spending for 2005 fiscal year: $5228 per student. Total enrollment: 16,219. Faculty: 1,010 (556 full-time, 454 part-time). Student-undergrad faculty ratio is 17:1. 6,205 applied, 75% were admitted. Full-time: 10,919 students, 60% women, 40% men. Part-time: 3,023 students, 64% women, 36% men. Students come from 41 states and territories, 42 other countries, 12% from out-of-state, 0.3% Native American, 1% Hispanic, 5% black, 1% Asian American or Pacific Islander, 1% international, 27% 25 or older, 33% live on campus, 7% transferred in. Retention: 66% of full-time freshmen returned the following year. Academic areas with the most degrees conferred: health professions and related sciences; education; security and protective services. Core. Calendar: semesters. Academic remediation for entering students, ESL program, services for LD students, advanced placement, accelerated degree program, self-designed majors, honors program, independent study, distance learning, double major, summer session for credit, part-time degree program, external degree program, adult/continuing education programs, co-op programs and internships, graduate courses open to undergrads. Study abroad program. ROTC: Army, Air Force (c).
Entrance Requirements: Open admission for state residents. Options: Peterson's Universal Application, electronic application, deferred admission. Required: high school transcript, minimum 2.0 high school GPA, ACT. Entrance: noncompetitive. Application deadline: 8/1. Notification: continuous.
Costs Per Year: Application fee: $30. State resident tuition: $4660 full-time, $194 per credit hour part-time. Nonresident tuition: $13,070 full-time, $545 per credit hour part-time. Mandatory fees: $460 full-time. Part-time tuition varies according to course load. College room and board: $4088. College room only: $2208. Room and board charges vary according to board plan and housing facility.
Collegiate Environment: Orientation program. Drama-theater group, choral group, marching band, student-run newspaper, radio station. Social organizations: 160 open to all; national fraternities, national sororities; 8% of eligible men and 6% of eligible women are members. Most popular organizations: Honor Society, Regular Society. Major annual events: Homecoming, Fall Festival, Spring Fling. Student services: health clinic, personal-psychological counseling. Campus security: 24-hour emergency response devices and patrols, student patrols, late night transport-escort service. 5,200 college housing spaces available. Freshmen guaranteed college housing. On-campus residence required through senior year. Options: coed, men-only, women-only housing available. John Grant Crabbe Library plus 2 others with 768,300 books, 1.3 million microform titles, 3,128 serials, 13,580 audiovisual materials, an OPAC, and a Web page. Operations spending for

2004 fiscal year: $4 million. 1,200 computers available on campus for general student use. Computer purchase/lease plans available. A campuswide network can be accessed from student residence rooms and from off campus. Staffed computer lab on campus.
Community Environment: Local industries are a miniature lamp plant and tool and die manufacturing. Richmond is located in the famous Bluegrass Region, 26 miles southeast of Lexington, and 55 miles to the State Capital of Frankfort on the Kentucky River. Recreational facilities are available at nearby parks and lakes. There are part-time work opportunities available.

■ **ELIZABETHTOWN COMMUNITY AND TECHNICAL COLLEGE** *F-6*
600 College St. Rd.
Elizabethtown, KY 42701-3081
Tel: (270)769-2371; 877-246-2322
Fax: (270)769-1632
Web Site: http://www.elizabethtown.kctcs.edu/
Description: State-supported, 2-year, coed. Part of Kentucky Community and Technical College System. Awards certificates, diplomas, transfer associate, and terminal associate degrees. Founded 1964. Setting: 40-acre small town campus with easy access to Louisville. Educational spending for 2005 fiscal year: $2715 per student. Total enrollment: 3,615. Full-time: 1,645 students, 69% women, 31% men. Part-time: 1,970 students, 68% women, 32% men. Students come from 10 states and territories, 1% Native American, 3% Hispanic, 11% black, 2% Asian American or Pacific Islander, 50% 25 or older. Core. Calendar: semesters. Academic remediation for entering students, services for LD students, advanced placement, summer session for credit, part-time degree program, external degree program, adult/continuing education programs, co-op programs and internships. Off campus study at Western Kentucky University.
Entrance Requirements: Open admission for state residents. Options: Common Application, early admission. Required: essay, high school transcript. Required for some: ACT. Entrance: noncompetitive. Application deadline: Rolling. Notification: continuous.
Costs Per Year: Application fee: $0. State resident tuition: $2352 full-time, $98 per credit hour part-time. Nonresident tuition: $7056 full-time, $294 per credit hour part-time. Full-time tuition varies according to course load. Part-time tuition varies according to course load.
Collegiate Environment: Orientation program. Drama-theater group, choral group, student-run newspaper. Social organizations: 18 open to all. Most popular organizations: Baptist Student Union, Kentucky Association of Nursing Students. Major annual events: Fall Festival, Hanging of the Greens, Social Science Seminar. Campus security: late night security. College housing not available. Elizabethtown Community College Media Center with 35,175 books, 240 serials, and an OPAC. Operations spending for 2004 fiscal year: $459,000. 70 computers available on campus for general student use. Staffed computer lab on campus.
Community Environment: Brown-Pusey Community House, formerly a stagecoach inn, has been restored and now serves as a community center and library. This is a rural area with rail and bus service, and a local airport. Elizabethtown provides recreation with two theaters, a recreational lake owned by the city, a park with olympic-size pool and a par-three golf course. Community services include the County Health Department, one hospital and 39 different organizations. A County Fair and City Festival are held annually.

■ **GATEWAY COMMUNITY AND TECHNICAL COLLEGE** *A-10*
1025 Amsterdam Rd.
Covington, KY 41011
Tel: (859)441-4500
Fax: (859)292-6415
Web Site: http://www.gateway.kctcs.edu/
Description: State-supported, 2-year, coed. Awards certificates, diplomas, and transfer associate degrees. Founded 1961. Total enrollment: 2,597. Calendar: semesters.
Entrance Requirements: Placement: ACT or ACT COMPASS required. Entrance: minimally difficult.
Costs Per Year: State resident tuition: $2940 full-time, $98 per credit hour part-time. Nonresident tuition: $8820 full-time, $294 per credit hour part-time.
Collegiate Environment: College housing not available.

■ **GEORGETOWN COLLEGE** *D-10*
400 East College St.
Georgetown, KY 40324-1696
Tel: (502)863-8000

Free: 800-788-9985
Admissions: (502)863-8009
Fax: (502)868-8891
Web Site: http://www.georgetowncollege.edu/
Description: Independent, comprehensive, coed, affiliated with Baptist Church. Awards bachelor's and master's degrees and post-master's certificates. Founded 1829. Setting: 110-acre suburban campus with easy access to Cincinnati. Endowment: $34.4 million. Educational spending for 2005 fiscal year: $4483 per student. Total enrollment: 1,904. Faculty: 167 (101 full-time, 66 part-time). Student-undergrad faculty ratio is 11:1. 1,063 applied, 95% were admitted. 31% from top 10% of their high school class, 58% from top quarter, 86% from top half. 15 valedictorians. Full-time: 1,310 students, 55% women, 45% men. Part-time: 55 students, 47% women, 53% men. Students come from 22 states and territories, 11 other countries, 17% from out-of-state, 0.1% Native American, 1% Hispanic, 4% black, 1% Asian American or Pacific Islander, 1% international, 2% 25 or older, 88% live on campus, 2% transferred in. Retention: 85% of full-time freshmen returned the following year. Academic areas with the most degrees conferred: business/marketing; biological/life sciences; communications/journalism. Core. Calendar: semesters. Advanced placement, self-designed majors, honors program, independent study, double major, summer session for credit, part-time degree program, co-op programs and internships. Off campus study at Central University of Iowa. Study abroad program. ROTC: Army (c), Air Force (c).
Entrance Requirements: Options: Peterson's Universal Application, electronic application, deferred admission. Required: essay, high school transcript, minimum 2.5 high school GPA, SAT or ACT. Recommended: ACT. Required for some: recommendations, interview. Entrance: moderately difficult. Application deadline: 7/1. Notification: continuous.
Costs Per Year: Application fee: $30. Comprehensive fee: $26,770 includes full-time tuition ($20,700) and college room and board ($6070). College room only: $2940. Part-time tuition: $860 per hour.
Collegiate Environment: Orientation program. Drama-theater group, choral group, student-run newspaper, radio station. Social organizations: 97 open to all; national fraternities, national sororities, local fraternities; 28% of eligible men and 40% of eligible women are members. Most popular organizations: Campus Ministries, Association of Georgetown Students, Harper-Gatton Leadership Center, President's Ambassadors, Phi Beta Lambda. Major annual events: Hanging of the Green, Homecoming/Festival of Song, Belle of the Blue. Student services: health clinic, personal-psychological counseling. Campus security: 24-hour patrols, late night transport-escort service. 1,238 college housing spaces available; 1,133 were occupied in 2003-04. Freshmen guaranteed college housing. On-campus residence required through senior year. Options: men-only, women-only housing available. Anna Ashcraft Ensor Learning Resource Center plus 1 other with 160,862 books, 189,419 microform titles, 541 serials, 5,547 audiovisual materials, an OPAC, and a Web page. Operations spending for 2004 fiscal year: $677,879. 175 computers available on campus for general student use. A campuswide network can be accessed from student residence rooms and from off campus. Staffed computer lab on campus.
Community Environment: This town was the site of McClelland's Fort, a log stockade that was completed about 1776. Today the city is a residential and educational community located 12 miles north of Lexington and 75 miles east of Louisville, and can be reached by several major highways. Recently identified as one of Kentucky's two "safest cities," Georgetown is also the site of the Toyota Corporation's manufacturing plant. The Kentucky State Horse Park is only 5 miles south of the campus.

■ **HAZARD COMMUNITY AND TECHNICAL COLLEGE** *H-14*
1 Community College Dr.
Hazard, KY 41701-2403
Tel: (606)436-5721
Free: 800-246-7521
Fax: (606)439-2988
Web Site: http://www.hazard.kctcs.edu/
Description: State-supported, 2-year, coed. Part of Kentucky Community and Technical College System. Awards certificates, diplomas, transfer associate, and terminal associate degrees. Founded 1968. Setting: 34-acre rural campus. Total enrollment: 3,500. 15% from top 10% of their high school class, 50% from top half. Students come from 3 states and territories, 5% from out-of-state, 35% 25 or older. Core. Calendar: semesters. Academic remediation for entering students, honors program, summer session for credit, part-time degree program, adult/continuing education programs.
Entrance Requirements: Open admission for state residents. Options:

Common Application, early admission. Required: high school transcript. Placement: ACT required. Entrance: noncompetitive. Application deadline: Rolling. Notification: continuous.
Collegiate Environment: Drama-theater group, choral group. Student services: personal-psychological counseling. Campus security: late night transport-escort service. Option: coed housing available. 36,550 books and 160 serials. 28 computers available on campus for general student use.
Community Environment: Hazard, the County Seat of Perry County, is the retail and cultural center of southeastern Kentucky. The college serves an 8-county (Breathitt, Knott, Leslie, Letcher, Wolfe, Lee, Owsley, and Perry) all rural area. The College's service area is also in the heart of the state's coal country, in the Cumberland Mountains of Kentucky.

■ **HENDERSON COMMUNITY COLLEGE** *F-1*
2660 South Green St.
Henderson, KY 42420-4623
Tel: (270)827-1867
E-mail: patty.mitchell@kctcs.edu
Web Site: http://www.henderson.kctcs.edu/
Description: State-supported, 2-year, coed. Part of Kentucky Community and Technical College System. Awards transfer associate and terminal associate degrees. Founded 1963. Setting: 120-acre small town campus. Total enrollment: 2,241. 1,923 applied, 100% were admitted. Students come from 12 states and territories, 1% from out-of-state, 1% Native American, 1% Hispanic, 5% black, 0.3% Asian American or Pacific Islander, 57% 25 or older. Core. Calendar: semesters. Academic remediation for entering students, ESL program, advanced placement, accelerated degree program, independent study, distance learning, double major, summer session for credit, part-time degree program, external degree program, adult/continuing education programs, co-op programs and internships. Off campus study.
Entrance Requirements: Open admission. Option: Common Application. Required: high school transcript, ACT, ACT COMPASS. Required for some: essay, recommendations, interview. Entrance: noncompetitive. Application deadline: 9/1.
Costs Per Year: State resident tuition: $2490 full-time, $98 per credit hour part-time. Nonresident tuition: $8820 full-time, $294 per credit hour part-time. Full-time tuition varies according to course load. Part-time tuition varies according to course load.
Collegiate Environment: Orientation program. Drama-theater group, student-run radio station. Student services: personal-psychological counseling. Campus security: 24-hour emergency response devices. College housing not available. Hartfield Learning Resource Center plus 1 other with 30,206 books, 21,126 microform titles, 231 serials, 1,053 audiovisual materials, an OPAC, and a Web page. Operations spending for 2004 fiscal year: $246,114. 200 computers available on campus for general student use.
Community Environment: An industrial city, Henderson is on the Ohio River in an important oil-producing and agricultural area. Principal crops are corn, soybeans and tobacco. Part-time employment is available. Transportation provided by rail and bus lines within the city and airlines located in Evansville, Indiana, nine miles away. Ellis Park Racetrack, three miles north, offers thoroughbred racing August through Labor Day and harness racing from in late May to late July. 95 organizations embrace all types of activities. There is a hospital and clinics, public library, YMCA, and 36 churches offering community service. This is the home of Audubon Museum which houses the world's finest collection of Audubon items. The city has one of the finest summer recreational programs in the state of Kentucky. the finest summer recreational programs in the state of Kentucky.

■ **HOPKINSVILLE COMMUNITY COLLEGE** *I-2*
PO Box 2100
Hopkinsville, KY 42241-2100
Tel: (270)886-3921
Fax: (270)886-0237
Web Site: http://www.hopcc.kctcs.edu/
Description: State-supported, 2-year, coed. Part of Kentucky Community and Technical College System. Awards certificates, diplomas, transfer associate, and terminal associate degrees. Founded 1965. Setting: 70-acre small town campus with easy access to Nashville. Endowment: $2.4 million. Educational spending for 2005 fiscal year: $6780 per student. Total enrollment: 3,104. Full-time: 1,413 students, 70% women, 30% men. Part-time: 1,691 students, 68% women, 32% men. Students come from 3 states and territories, 1 other country, 25% from out-of-state, 0.4% Native American, 4% Hispanic, 22% black, 1% Asian American or Pacific Islander, 0% international, 52% 25 or older, 61% transferred in. Retention: 55% of full-time fresh-

men returned the following year. Core. Calendar: semesters. Academic remediation for entering students, services for LD students, advanced placement, honors program, independent study, distance learning, summer session for credit, part-time degree program, adult/continuing education programs.

Entrance Requirements: Open admission except for nursing program. Options: Common Application, early admission, deferred admission. Required for some: high school transcript, interview. Placement: ACT, ACT COMPASS required. Entrance: noncompetitive. Application deadline: Rolling. Notification: continuous.

Costs Per Year: Application fee: $0. State resident tuition: $2940 full-time, $98 per credit hour part-time. Nonresident tuition: $8820 full-time, $294 per credit hour part-time. Full-time tuition varies according to location and reciprocity agreements. Part-time tuition varies according to location and reciprocity agreements.

Collegiate Environment: Orientation program. Student-run newspaper. Social organizations: 18 open to all; local fraternities. Most popular organizations: Baptist Student Union, Circle K, Minority Student Union, Donovan Scholars, Nursing Club. Major annual events: Fun Day, Appreciation Day, Circle of Love. Campus security: 24-hour emergency response devices, late night transport-escort service. College housing not available. HCC Library plus 1 other with 45,674 books, 25,613 microform titles, 147 serials, 4,377 audiovisual materials, an OPAC, and a Web page. Operations spending for 2004 fiscal year: $134,000. 400 computers available on campus for general student use. A campuswide network can be accessed from off-campus. Staffed computer lab on campus.

Community Environment: Hopkinsville is noted as an agricultural and industrial center with important livestock, grain, and dark tobacco markets, flour and feed production, and the manufacturing of shoes, clothing, hardwood flooring, lighting fixtures, industrial springs, and automotive products. The city is served by rail, bus, and air lines via nearby Clarksville and Nashville, Tennessee.

■ **ITT TECHNICAL INSTITUTE (LEXINGTON)** *E-10*
2473 Fortune Dr., Ste. 180
Lexington, KY 40509
Tel: (859)246-3300
Web Site: http://www.itt-tech.edu/

■ **ITT TECHNICAL INSTITUTE (LOUISVILLE)** *D-7*
10509 Timberwood Circle, Ste. 100
Louisville, KY 40223-5392
Tel: (502)327-7424
Web Site: http://www.itt-tech.edu/
Description: Proprietary, primarily 2-year, coed. Part of ITT Educational Services, Inc. Awards terminal associate and bachelor's degrees. Founded 1993. Setting: suburban campus. Core.

Entrance Requirements: Option: deferred admission. Required: high school transcript, interview, Wonderlic aptitude test. Recommended: recommendations. Entrance: minimally difficult. Application deadline: Rolling. Notification: continuous.

Costs Per Year: Application fee: $100.

Collegiate Environment: Orientation program. College housing not available.

■ **JEFFERSON COMMUNITY AND TECHNICAL COLLEGE** *D-7*
109 East Broadway
Louisville, KY 40202-2005
Tel: (502)213-5333
Admissions: (502)213-2183
Fax: (502)213-2115
Web Site: http://www.jctc.kctcs.edu/
Description: State-supported, 2-year, coed. Part of Kentucky Community and Technical College System. Awards certificates, diplomas, transfer associate, and terminal associate degrees. Founded 1968. Setting: 10-acre urban campus. Endowment: $1.1 million. Educational spending for 2005 fiscal year: $3580 per student. Total enrollment: 14,240. Student-undergrad faculty ratio is 19:1. Full-time: 4,941 students, 52% women, 48% men. Part-time: 9,299 students, 51% women, 49% men. Students come from 11 states and territories, 3% from out-of-state, 0.3% Native American, 2% Hispanic, 16% black, 1% Asian American or Pacific Islander, 0.3% international, 41% 25 or older, 11% transferred in. Core. Calendar: semesters. Academic remediation for entering students, ESL program, services for LD students, advanced placement, honors program, independent study, distance learning,

summer session for credit, part-time degree program, external degree program, adult/continuing education programs, co-op programs and internships. Off campus study at members of the Kentuckiana Metroversity. ROTC: Army (c).

Entrance Requirements: Open admission except for high school students in early admissions programs. Option: early admission. Entrance: noncompetitive. Application deadline: Rolling. Notification: continuous.

Costs Per Year: Application fee: $0. State resident tuition: $3270 full-time, $109 per credit hour part-time. Nonresident tuition: $9810 full-time, $327 per credit hour part-time. Mandatory fees: $50 full-time, $25 per term part-time.

Collegiate Environment: Drama-theater group, student-run newspaper. Student services: personal-psychological counseling. Campus security: 24-hour emergency response devices and patrols, late night transport-escort service. College housing not available. John T. Smith Learning Resource Center plus 2 others with 76,578 books, 156,316 microform titles, 391 serials, 15,103 audiovisual materials, an OPAC, and a Web page. Operations spending for 2004 fiscal year: $311,000. 895 computers available on campus for general student use. A campuswide network can be accessed from off-campus. Staffed computer lab on campus.

Community Environment: See University of Louisville.

■ **KENTUCKY CHRISTIAN UNIVERSITY** *D-14*
100 Academic Parkway
Grayson, KY 41143-2205
Tel: (606)474-3000
Free: 800-522-3181
Admissions: (606)474-3266
Fax: (606)474-3155
E-mail: sdeakins@email.kcc.edu
Web Site: http://www.kcu.edu/
Description: Independent, comprehensive, coed, affiliated with Christian Churches and Churches of Christ. Awards associate, bachelor's, and master's degrees. Founded 1919. Setting: 124-acre rural campus. Endowment: $3.4 million. Educational spending for 2005 fiscal year: $2609 per student. Total enrollment: 559. 285 applied, 76% were admitted. 18% from top 10% of their high school class, 43% from top quarter, 69% from top half. 4 valedictorians. Full-time: 530 students, 56% women, 44% men. Part-time: 14 students, 79% women, 21% men. Students come from 26 states and territories, 7 other countries, 67% from out-of-state, 1% Native American, 0.4% Hispanic, 1% black, 1% Asian American or Pacific Islander, 2% international, 12% 25 or older, 88% live on campus, 8% transferred in. Retention: 70% of full-time freshmen returned the following year. Core. Calendar: semesters. Academic remediation for entering students, services for LD students, advanced placement, accelerated degree program, independent study, double major, summer session for credit, part-time degree program, co-op programs and internships, graduate courses open to undergrads. Off campus study.

Entrance Requirements: Options: Common Application, electronic application, early action, deferred admission. Required: essay, high school transcript, 3 recommendations, SAT and SAT Subject Tests or ACT. Recommended: minimum 2.0 high school GPA. Required for some: interview. Entrance: moderately difficult. Application deadline: Rolling. Notification: continuous.

Collegiate Environment: Drama-theater group, choral group, student-run newspaper. Social organizations: 8 open to all. Most popular organizations: Rotaract, SIFE, Matheteuo, Pi Chi Delta, Laos Alpha. Major annual events: Feast of Christmas, Campus Drama, Basketball Homecoming. Student services: health clinic, personal-psychological counseling. Campus security: 24-hour emergency response devices, late night transport-escort service, controlled dormitory access, patrols by trained security personnel (6pm-6am). 589 college housing spaces available; 473 were occupied in 2003-04. On-campus residence required through senior year. Options: men-only, women-only housing available. Young Library with 103,323 books, 8,172 microform titles, 395 serials, 1,755 audiovisual materials, an OPAC, and a Web page. Operations spending for 2004 fiscal year: $293,339. 50 computers available on campus for general student use. A campuswide network can be accessed from student residence rooms and from off campus. Staffed computer lab on campus.

Community Environment: Grayson can be accessed via bus. It has many Protestant churches and several organizations, including the Creative Arts Club and Chamber of Commerce. Health services are provided by two clinic and two hospitals within 20 miles. Recreation available includes hunting, fishing, boating, bowling, swimming, horseback riding and miniature golf with three state parks in the area. Grayson is a friendly town with complete up-to-date modern stores comparable to a city twice its size.

■ **KENTUCKY MOUNTAIN BIBLE COLLEGE** *F-8*

PO Box 10
Vancleve, KY 41385-0010
Tel: (606)693-5000
Free: 800-879-KMBC
Fax: (606)693-7744
Web Site: http://www.kmbc.edu/

Description: Independent interdenominational, 4-year, coed. Awards associate and bachelor's degrees. Founded 1931. Setting: 35-acre rural campus. Endowment: $350,000. Total enrollment: 79. Student-undergrad faculty ratio is 6:1. 52 applied, 46% were admitted. Students come from 50 states and territories, 3 other countries, 71% from out-of-state, 0% Native American, 2% Hispanic, 4% black, 0% Asian American or Pacific Islander, 7% international, 24% 25 or older, 91% live on campus. Retention: 67% of full-time freshmen returned the following year. Core. Calendar: semesters. Academic remediation for entering students, part-time degree program, adult/continuing education programs, internships.

Entrance Requirements: Option: deferred admission. Required: essay, high school transcript, minimum 2.0 high school GPA, recommendations, ACT. Recommended: interview. Entrance: moderately difficult. Application deadline: Rolling. Notification: continuous. Preference given to Christians.

Costs Per Year: Application fee: $25. Comprehensive fee: $8460 includes full-time tuition ($4800), mandatory fees ($460), and college room and board ($3200). College room only: $1000. Full-time tuition and fees vary according to course load. Room and board charges vary according to housing facility. Part-time tuition: $160 per credit hour. Part-time mandatory fees: $30 per term. Part-time tuition and fees vary according to course load.

Collegiate Environment: Orientation program. Drama-theater group, choral group. Social organizations: 40 open to all. Most popular organizations: Drama Team, choral groups, Student Council, band, Student Involvement (missionary group). Major annual events: College Acquaintance Days, Missionary Convention, graduation. Student services: personal-psychological counseling. Campus security: student patrols. 100 college housing spaces available; 73 were occupied in 2003-04. Freshmen guaranteed college housing. On-campus residence required through senior year. Options: men-only, women-only housing available. Gibson Library with 23,520 books, 81 microform titles, 175 serials, 1,263 audiovisual materials, and an OPAC. Operations spending for 2004 fiscal year: $35,500. 12 computers available on campus for general student use. Staffed computer lab on campus.

Community Environment: Vancleve is a rural town located 7 miles northwest of Jackson just off State Highway 15. Radio Station WMTC is located here. Part-time employment found on campus.

■ **KENTUCKY STATE UNIVERSITY** *D-9*

400 East Main St.
Frankfort, KY 40601
Tel: (502)597-6000
Free: 800-325-1716
Admissions: (502)597-6322
Fax: (502)597-6239
Web Site: http://www.kysu.edu/

Description: State-related, comprehensive, coed. Awards associate, bachelor's, and master's degrees. Founded 1886. Setting: 485-acre small town campus with easy access to Louisville. Research spending for 2004 fiscal year: $8.8 million. Total enrollment: 2,386. Faculty: 160 (152 full-time, 8 part-time). Student-undergrad faculty ratio is 15:1. 5,013 applied, 28% were admitted. Full-time: 1,619 students, 57% women, 43% men. Part-time: 609 students, 58% women, 42% men. Students come from 29 states and territories, 24 other countries, 33% from out-of-state, 0.04% Native American, 0.4% Hispanic, 61% black, 1% Asian American or Pacific Islander, 0.04% international, 80% 25 or older, 26% live on campus, 5% transferred in. Retention: 59% of full-time freshmen returned the following year. Core. Calendar: semesters. Academic remediation for entering students, ESL program, services for LD students, advanced placement, accelerated degree program, self-designed majors, honors program, independent study, summer session for credit, part-time degree program, adult/continuing education programs, co-op programs and internships, graduate courses open to undergrads. Off campus study at Berea College. Study abroad program. ROTC: Air Force (c).

Entrance Requirements: Option: early admission. Required: high school transcript, SAT or ACT. Recommended: minimum 2.0 high school GPA, ACT. Required for some: essay, minimum 3.0 high school GPA, 2 recommendations, interview. Entrance: minimally difficult. Application deadline: Rolling.

Costs Per Year: Application fee: $22. State resident tuition: $3550 full-time, $148 per credit part-time. Nonresident tuition: $9992 full-time, $419 per credit part-time. Mandatory fees: $918 full-time, $20 per credit part-time, $49 per term part-time. Full-time tuition and fees vary according to class time, course level, course load, location, program, reciprocity agreements, and student level. Part-time tuition and fees vary according to class time, course level, course load, location, program, reciprocity agreements, and student level. College room and board: $5620. College room only: $2592. Room and board charges vary according to board plan, housing facility, location, and student level.

Collegiate Environment: Orientation program. Drama-theater group, choral group, marching band, student-run newspaper. Social organizations: 45 open to all; national fraternities, national sororities, local fraternities, local sororities; 6% of eligible men and 4% of eligible women are members. Most popular organizations: Baptist Student Union, student government. Major annual events: Coronation, Greek Step-Show, Homecoming Concert. Student services: health clinic, personal-psychological counseling. Campus security: 24-hour patrols, controlled dormitory access. 849 college housing spaces available. On-campus residence required through sophomore year. Options: men-only, women-only housing available. Blazer Library with 296,631 books, 320,739 microform titles, 1,097 serials, 3,025 audiovisual materials, and an OPAC. Operations spending for 2004 fiscal year: $887,261. 230 computers available on campus for general student use. A campuswide network can be accessed from off-campus. Staffed computer lab on campus.

Community Environment: Founded in 1786, Frankfort was selected as Kentucky's capital in 1792. Located at the western edge of the Bluegrass region, Frankfort, population 27,500, is home to several plants which manufacture electronic equipment, shoes, underwear, metal auto trim, precision parts and screws. There is access to rail and bus lines. The city has a public library, hospital, Y's, shopping facilities, theatres, and swimming. Organizations including major civic, fraternal, and veterans' are located in the area.

■ **KENTUCKY WESLEYAN COLLEGE** *F-3*

3000 Frederica St., PO Box 1039
Owensboro, KY 42302-1039
Tel: (270)926-3111
Free: 800-990-0592
Admissions: (270)852-3120
Fax: (270)926-3196
E-mail: admission@kwc.edu
Web Site: http://www.kwc.edu/

Description: Independent Methodist, 4-year, coed. Awards bachelor's degrees. Founded 1858. Setting: 52-acre suburban campus. Endowment: $24.5 million. Educational spending for 2005 fiscal year: $4043 per student. Total enrollment: 755. Student-undergrad faculty ratio is 16:1. 1,074 applied, 77% were admitted. 19% from top 10% of their high school class, 30% from top quarter, 75% from top half. 3 National Merit Scholars, 12 valedictorians. Full-time: 717 students, 49% women, 51% men. Part-time: 38 students, 53% women, 47% men. Students come from 22 states and territories, 8 other countries, 23% from out-of-state, 0.4% Native American, 2% Hispanic, 10% black, 1% Asian American or Pacific Islander, 1% international, 8% 25 or older, 46% live on campus, 8% transferred in. Retention: 71% of full-time freshmen returned the following year. Academic areas with the most degrees conferred: business/marketing; communications/journalism; education. Core. Calendar: semesters. Academic remediation for entering students, advanced placement, self-designed majors, independent study, distance learning, double major, summer session for credit, part-time degree program, internships. Off campus study at Brescia College, Owensboro Community College, University of Evansville. Study abroad program.

Entrance Requirements: Options: Peterson's Universal Application, Common Application, electronic application, early admission, deferred admission, international baccalaureate accepted. Required: high school transcript, SAT or ACT. Required for some: recommendations. Entrance: moderately difficult. Application deadline: 9/1. Notification: continuous.

Costs Per Year: Application fee: $0. Comprehensive fee: $19,350 includes full-time tuition ($13,200), mandatory fees ($400), and college room and board ($5750). College room only: $2600. Part-time tuition: $400 per credit hour.

Collegiate Environment: Orientation program. Drama-theater group, choral group, marching band, student-run newspaper, radio station. Social organizations: 40 open to all; national fraternities, national sororities; 15% of eligible men and 20% of eligible women are members. Most popular organizations: Student Government Association, Student Activities Programming Board, Leadership KWC, Pre-Professional Society, Wesley Club. Major annual events: homecoming, Annual Thanksgiving Dinner, Leadership Symposium. Student services: health clinic, personal-psychological counseling. Campus security: late night transport-escort service, 12-hour patrols by trained security personnel. 413 college housing spaces available; 299 were occupied in 2003-04. Freshmen guaranteed college housing. On-campus residence required through junior year. Options: coed, men-only, women-only housing available. Library Learning Center with a Web page. Operations spending for 2004 fiscal year: $332,825. 110 computers available on campus for general student use. A campuswide network can be accessed from student residence rooms. Staffed computer lab on campus.

Community Environment: Owensboro, population 54,000, with sunshine 52-60 percent of the year is the largest city in western Kentucky. There are good commercial bus and air transportation facilities. The city has public libraries, many churches, a hospital, three medical centers and a public health center. Recreation facilities include theaters, drive-ins, bowling alleys, golf courses as well as fishing, boating, swimming, indoor athletics and other activities.

■ **LEXINGTON COMMUNITY COLLEGE** *E-10*
Cooper Dr.
Lexington, KY 40506-0235
Tel: (859)257-4872
E-mail: shugl00@uky.edu
Web Site: http://www.uky.edu/lcc/
Description: State-supported, 2-year, coed. Part of Kentucky Community and Technical College System. Awards transfer associate and terminal associate degrees. Founded 1965. Setting: 10-acre urban campus. Endowment: $750,000. Total enrollment: 8,639. 5,828 applied, 100% were admitted. Full-time: 5,354 students, 54% women, 46% men. Part-time: 3,285 students, 61% women, 39% men. Students come from 35 states and territories, 5% from out-of-state, 1% Native American, 1% Hispanic, 11% black, 2% Asian American or Pacific Islander, 20% 25 or older, 5% live on campus, 9% transferred in. Core. Calendar: semesters. Academic remediation for entering students, services for LD students, advanced placement, accelerated degree program, distance learning, summer session for credit, part-time degree program, adult/continuing education programs, co-op programs. ROTC: Army (c), Air Force (c).
Entrance Requirements: Open admission except for health technology programs, computer information systems. Option: early admission. Required: high school transcript. Entrance: noncompetitive. Application deadline: 8/2. Preference given to state residents.
Collegiate Environment: Orientation program. Student-run newspaper. Social organizations: 8 open to all. Most popular organizations: Baptist Student Union, Unity, KANS, Veterans Union, Athena. Major annual events: Black History Month, Spring Fling, Career Fair. Student services: health clinic, personal-psychological counseling. Campus security: 24-hour emergency response devices and patrols, late night transport-escort service. 576 undergraduates lived in college housing during 2003-04. Freshmen given priority for college housing. Lexington Community College Library with 27,000 books, 250 serials, an OPAC, and a Web page. Operations spending for 2004 fiscal year: $498,588. 80 computers available on campus for general student use. A campuswide network can be accessed. Staffed computer lab on campus.

■ **LINDSEY WILSON COLLEGE** *H-8*
210 Lindsey Wilson St.
Columbia, KY 42728-1298
Tel: (270)384-2126
Free: 800-264-0138
Admissions: (270)384-8100
Fax: (270)384-8200
E-mail: poolert@lindsey.edu
Web Site: http://www.lindsey.edu/
Description: Independent United Methodist, comprehensive, coed. Awards associate, bachelor's, and master's degrees. Founded 1903. Setting: 45-acre rural campus. Endowment: $15 million. Educational spending for 2005 fiscal year: $4000 per student. Total enrollment: 1,902. Faculty: 111 (70 full-time, 41 part-time). Student-undergrad faculty ratio is 23:1. Full-time: 1,457 students, 64% women, 36% men. Part-time: 165 students, 79% women, 21% men. Students come from 22 states and territories, 31 other countries, 8% from out-of-state, 0.4% Native American, 2% Hispanic, 8% black, 1% Asian American or Pacific Islander, 3% international, 25% 25 or older, 47% live on campus, 12% transferred in. Retention: 53% of full-time freshmen

returned the following year. Core. Calendar: semesters. Academic remediation for entering students, ESL program, services for LD students, advanced placement, accelerated degree program, self-designed majors, independent study, double major, summer session for credit, part-time degree program, external degree program, adult/continuing education programs, co-op programs and internships, graduate courses open to undergrads. Off campus study. Study abroad program. ROTC: Army (c).
Entrance Requirements: Open admission. Options: Peterson's Universal Application, Common Application, electronic application. Required: high school transcript. Recommended: interview. Required for some: SAT or ACT. Entrance: minimally difficult. Application deadline: Rolling. Notification: continuous.
Costs Per Year: Application fee: $0. Comprehensive fee: $20,601 includes full-time tuition ($14,208), mandatory fees ($230), and college room and board ($6163). Part-time tuition: $592 per credit hour.
Collegiate Environment: Orientation program. Drama-theater group, choral group, student-run newspaper. Social organizations: 27 open to all. Major annual events: homecoming, Founders' Day, Malvina Farkie Day. Student services: health clinic, personal-psychological counseling. Campus security: 24-hour emergency response devices and patrols. 750 college housing spaces available; 720 were occupied in 2003-04. Freshmen guaranteed college housing. On-campus residence required through senior year. Options: men-only, women-only housing available. Katie Murrell Library with 80,000 books and 1,500 serials. Operations spending for 2004 fiscal year: $156,325. 80 computers available on campus for general student use. A campuswide network can be accessed from student residence rooms and from off campus. Staffed computer lab on campus.
Community Environment: Columbia is the seat of Adair County. The climate is moderate. The city is located 8 miles from Green River Lake State Park and 20 miles from Cumberland Lake State Park, both known for their boating, fishing, water skiing and other water activities. Community services include seven churches, a modern hospital, and adequate shopping. There are several service clubs, and an excellent relationship exists between the local population and the college.

■ **LOUISVILLE TECHNICAL INSTITUTE** *D-7*
3901 Atkinson Square Dr.
Louisville, KY 40218-4528
Tel: (502)456-6509
Free: 800-884-6528
Fax: (502)456-2341
Web Site: http://www.louisvilletech.com/
Description: Proprietary, 2-year, coed. Part of Sullivan University System. Awards certificates, diplomas, and terminal associate degrees. Founded 1961. Setting: 10-acre suburban campus. Educational spending for 2005 fiscal year: $3000 per student. Total enrollment: 667. 182 applied, 77% were admitted. 8% from top 10% of their high school class, 28% from top quarter, 64% from top half. Full-time: 626 students, 33% women, 67% men. Part-time: 41 students, 63% women, 37% men. Students come from 6 states and territories, 17% from out-of-state, 1% Native American, 2% Hispanic, 11% black, 1% Asian American or Pacific Islander, 0% international, 32% 25 or older, 6% live on campus, 11% transferred in. Retention: 68% of full-time freshmen returned the following year. Academic remediation for entering students, services for LD students, accelerated degree program, summer session for credit, part-time degree program, adult/continuing education programs, co-op programs and internships.
Entrance Requirements: Option: deferred admission. Required: high school transcript, minimum 2.0 high school GPA, interview, ACT, SAT or CPAt. Entrance: moderately difficult. Application deadline: Rolling.
Costs Per Year: Application fee: $90. One-time mandatory fee: $90. Tuition: $13,110 full-time, $270 per credit hour part-time. Mandatory fees: $435 full-time, $30 per course part-time. Full-time tuition and fees vary according to class time and program. Part-time tuition and fees vary according to program. College room only: $3960. Tuition guaranteed not to increase for student's term of enrollment.
Collegiate Environment: Orientation program. Student-run newspaper. Social organizations: 5 open to all. Most popular organizations: ASID, IIDA, ADDA, Robotics International. Major annual events: School Picnic, River Boat Cruise, picnics, dinners and luncheons. Campus security: late night transport-escort service. 42 college housing spaces available; 39 were occupied in 2003-04. Option: coed housing available. Louisville Tech Library plus 1 other with 3,463 books, 96 serials, 242 audiovisual materials, and an OPAC. Operations spending for 2004 fiscal year: $32,491. 193 computers available on campus for general student use. A campuswide network can be accessed from off-campus. Staffed computer lab on campus.

■ MADISONVILLE COMMUNITY COLLEGE *G-2*

2000 College Dr.
Madisonville, KY 42431-9185
Tel: (270)821-2250
Fax: (270)821-1555
Web Site: http://www.madcc.kctcs.edu/ .

Description: State-supported, 2-year, coed. Part of Kentucky Community and Technical College System. Awards certificates, diplomas, transfer associate, and terminal associate degrees. Founded 1968. Setting: 150-acre small town campus. Endowment: $2.4 million. Educational spending for 2005 fiscal year: $4341 per student. Total enrollment: 3,500. 0.2% from out-of-state, 42% 25 or older. Core. Calendar: semesters. Academic remediation for entering students, services for LD students, advanced placement, independent study, distance learning, summer session for credit, part-time degree program, external degree program, adult/continuing education programs, co-op programs and internships. Off campus study.
Entrance Requirements: Open admission. Options: electronic application, early admission, deferred admission. Required: high school transcript. Placement: ACT, ACT ASSET required. Entrance: noncompetitive. Application deadline: Rolling. Notification: continuous.
Collegiate Environment: Orientation program. Drama-theater group, choral group, student-run newspaper. Most popular organizations: student government, Baptist Student Union, Socratic Society, Student Ambassadors, Academic Team. Student services: personal-psychological counseling. Campus security: 24-hour emergency response devices, late night transport-escort service, evening patrols. College housing not available. Loman C. Trover Library plus 1 other with 26,793 books, 21,346 microform titles, 227 serials, 1,688 audiovisual materials, an OPAC, and a Web page. Operations spending for 2004 fiscal year: $211,216. 35 computers available on campus for general student use. A campuswide network can be accessed from off-campus. Staffed computer lab on campus.
Community Environment: Centered on a plateau between the Pond and Tradewater Rivers, Madisonville is one of the principal loose leaf tobacco markets in western Kentucky. Underground coal mining operations are in the vicinity. Good shopping facilities are available. The city has several churches, a public library, and one theatre. The climate is moderate and part-time employment is available.

■ MAYSVILLE COMMUNITY AND TECHNICAL COLLEGE *C-12*

1755 US 68
Maysville, KY 41056
Tel: (606)759-7141
E-mail: ccsmayrg@ukcc.uky.edu
Web Site: http://www.maycc.kctcs.net/

Description: State-supported, 2-year, coed. Part of Kentucky Community and Technical College System. Awards certificates, diplomas, transfer associate, and terminal associate degrees. Founded 1967. Setting: 12-acre rural campus. Educational spending for 2005 fiscal year: $1800 per student. Total enrollment: 1,917. 3 valedictorians. Full-time: 776 students, 74% women, 26% men. Part-time: 1,141 students, 63% women, 37% men. Students come from 2 states and territories, 7% from out-of-state, 0.1% Native American, 0.1% Hispanic, 2% black, 0.2% Asian American or Pacific Islander, 40% 25 or older, 1% transferred in. Core. Calendar: semesters. Academic remediation for entering students, ESL program, services for LD students, advanced placement, honors program, independent study, distance learning, summer session for credit, part-time degree program, external degree program, adult/continuing education programs, co-op programs and internships. Off campus study.
Entrance Requirements: Open admission except for nursing, early childhood education, respiratory care , surgical technologist programs. Option: early admission. Required: high school transcript. Placement: ACT required for some. Entrance: noncompetitive. Application deadline: Rolling. Notification: continuous.
Collegiate Environment: Orientation program. Social organizations: 1 open to all. Most popular organizations: Student Government Association, Math and Science Club, Retail Marketing Club, Student Education Association. Major annual events: Student Government Food and Coat Drive, Blood Drive, election of homecoming princess. Student services: personal-psychological counseling. Campus security: student patrols, evening parking lot security. College housing not available. Finch Library with 36,600 books, 7,700 microform titles, 288 serials, an OPAC, and a Web page. Operations spending for 2004 fiscal year: $60,717. 250 computers available on campus for general student use. A campuswide network can be accessed from off-campus. Staffed computer lab on campus.

Community Environment: From 1786 to 1789, Daniel Boone and his wife operated a tavern in Maysville, one of the first incorporated towns in Kentucky. Today this is a metropolitan city. The average temperature is 55.3 degrees with an average rainfall of 43.58 inches. Known as one of the largest burley tobacco markets in the world, the city has three large redrying plants and 18 loose-leaf sale warehouses. These warehouses are open daily from 10 to 2 during the tobacco sale and auction season. The manufacturer of power driven pulleys and bicycle parts are also among Maysville's chief industries. There is a hospital and clinic in town, and various civic, fraternal and veteran's organizations are represented. There are excellent shopping facilities. Cinema 4, boating, golf courses, and several private clubs are easily accessible for recreation. Part-time employment is available.

■ MID-CONTINENT UNIVERSITY *L-15*

99 Powell Rd. East
Mayfield, KY 42066-9007
Tel: (270)247-8521
Fax: (270)247-3115
E-mail: admissions@midcontinent.edu
Web Site: http://www.midcontinent.edu/

Description: Independent Southern Baptist, 4-year, coed. Awards associate and bachelor's degrees. Founded 1949. Setting: 60-acre small town campus. Endowment: $2.4 million. Educational spending for 2005 fiscal year: $2150 per student. Total enrollment: 649. Student-undergrad faculty ratio is 15:1. 285 applied. 10% from top 10% of their high school class, 22% from top quarter, 68% from top half. 1 valedictorian. Full-time: 587 students, 46% women, 54% men. Part-time: 62 students, 53% women, 47% men. Students come from 16 states and territories, 8 other countries, 19% from out-of-state, 81% 25 or older, 33% live on campus, 24% transferred in. Retention: 75% of full-time freshmen returned the following year. Academic areas with the most degrees conferred: business/marketing; psychology; English. Core. Calendar: semesters. Academic remediation for entering students, advanced placement, accelerated degree program, self-designed majors, independent study, double major, summer session for credit, part-time degree program. Off campus study. Study abroad program.
Entrance Requirements: Options: Common Application, electronic application, early admission. Required: essay, high school transcript, minimum 2.0 high school GPA, 1 recommendation, SAT or ACT. Required for some: interview. Entrance: minimally difficult. Application deadline: Rolling. Notification: continuous.
Costs Per Year: Application fee: $20. Comprehensive fee: $15,800 includes full-time tuition ($8850), mandatory fees ($1250), and college room and board ($5700). Full-time tuition and fees vary according to course load and program. Room and board charges vary according to board plan and housing facility. Part-time tuition: $295 per credit hour. Part-time tuition varies according to course load and program.
Collegiate Environment: Orientation program. Student-run newspaper. Social organizations: 5 open to all. Most popular organizations: SGA, Baptist Student Union, Psychology Club, International Club, Ministry Association. Major annual events: Homecoming Spirit Week, Blue and Gold Awards, Student Development Impact Week. Student services: personal-psychological counseling. Campus security: student patrols. 75 college housing spaces available; 65 were occupied in 2003-04. No special consideration for freshman housing applicants. On-campus residence required through sophomore year. Options: men-only, women-only housing available. Anne P. Markham Library with 32,697 books, 70 serials, 509 audiovisual materials, and an OPAC. Operations spending for 2004 fiscal year: $78,593. 30 computers available on campus for general student use. A campuswide network can be accessed from student residence rooms and from off campus. Staffed computer lab on campus.
Community Environment: Mayfield is centrally located in the Mississippi River Valley. Transportation, commerce, industry and agriculture contribute to the prosperity of the area. Religious, medical and social facilities are available in the area.

■ MIDWAY COLLEGE *D-10*

512 East Stephens St.
Midway, KY 40347-1120
Tel: (859)846-4421
Free: 800-755-0031
Admissions: (859)846-5799
Fax: (859)846-5823
Web Site: http://www.midway.edu/

Description: Independent, 4-year, women only, affiliated with Christian Church (Disciples of Christ). Awards associate and bachelor's degrees. Founded 1847. Setting: 105-acre small town campus with easy access to Louisville and Lexington. Endowment: $17 million. Educational spending for 2005 fiscal year: $4407 per student. Total enrollment: 1,279. Student-undergrad faculty ratio is 12:1. 423 applied, 75% were admitted. 13% from top 10% of their high school class, 35% from top quarter, 61% from top half. 1 class president, 38 student government officers. Full-time: 876 students. Part-time: 403 students. Students come from 33 states and territories, 6 other countries, 11% from out-of-state, 0.2% Native American, 0.4% Hispanic, 6% black, 0.2% Asian American or Pacific Islander, 1% international, 63% 25 or older, 23% live on campus, 20% transferred in. Retention: 53% of full-time freshmen returned the following year. Academic areas with the most degrees conferred: business/marketing; education; agriculture; health professions and related sciences. Core. Calendar: semesters. Academic remediation for entering students, services for LD students, advanced placement, honors program, independent study, distance learning, summer session for credit, part-time degree program, adult/continuing education programs, internships. Off campus study at Kentucky Institute of International Studies. Study abroad program. ROTC: Army (c).

Entrance Requirements: Options: Peterson's Universal Application, Common Application, electronic application, early admission, deferred admission. Required: high school transcript, SAT or ACT. Recommended: minimum 2.2 high school GPA. Required for some: essay, recommendations, interview. Entrance: minimally difficult. Application deadline: Rolling. Notification: continuous.

Costs Per Year: Application fee: $25. Comprehensive fee: $20,150 includes full-time tuition ($13,800), mandatory fees ($150), and college room and board ($6200). College room only: $3000. Full-time tuition and fees vary according to class time, location, and program. Room and board charges vary according to board plan and housing facility. Part-time tuition: $460 per semester hour. Part-time tuition varies according to class time, location, and program.

Collegiate Environment: Orientation program. Choral group, student-run newspaper. Social organizations: 21 open to all. Most popular organizations: student government, Midway Chorale, Midway Association of Nursing Students, Council on Religious Activities, Midway Horse Women's Association. Major annual events: Hanging of the Greens, Equine Gala, Night of Lights. Student services: health clinic, personal-psychological counseling, women's center. Campus security: 24-hour emergency response devices and patrols, late night transport-escort service. 220 college housing spaces available; 202 were occupied in 2003-04. Freshmen guaranteed college housing. On-campus residence required through sophomore year. Option: women-only housing available. Little Memorial Library with 96,236 books, 58,217 microform titles, 250 serials, 9,213 audiovisual materials, an OPAC, and a Web page. Operations spending for 2004 fiscal year: $179,000. 60 computers available on campus for general student use. A campuswide network can be accessed from student residence rooms and from off campus. Staffed computer lab on campus.

Community Environment: Appropriately named, Midway is located halfway between Lexington and Frankfort in Woodford County. The climate is moderate. Midway has seven churches of various denominations and several large horse farms.

■ **MOREHEAD STATE UNIVERSITY** *D-13*
University Blvd.
Morehead, KY 40351
Tel: (606)783-2221
Free: 800-585-6781
Admissions: (606)783-2000
Fax: (606)783-5038
Web Site: http://www.moreheadstate.edu/
Description: State-supported, comprehensive, coed. Awards associate, bachelor's, and master's degrees and post-master's certificates. Founded 1922. Setting: 1,016-acre small town campus. Endowment: $25.7 million. Research spending for 2004 fiscal year: $1.4 million. Educational spending for 2005 fiscal year: $5764 per student. Total enrollment: 9,062. Faculty: 534 (378 full-time, 156 part-time). Student-undergrad faculty ratio is 17:1. 5,092 applied, 69% were admitted. 17% from top 10% of their high school class, 39% from top quarter, 71% from top half. Full-time: 5,964 students, 58% women, 42% men. Part-time: 1,580 students, 77% women, 23% men. Students come from 39 states and territories, 22 other countries, 16% from out-of-state, 0.4% Native American, 1% Hispanic, 4% black, 0.3% Asian American or Pacific Islander, 0.4% international, 23% 25 or older, 33% live

on campus, 6% transferred in. Retention: 61% of full-time freshmen returned the following year. Academic areas with the most degrees conferred: business/marketing; education; liberal arts/general studies. Core. Calendar: semesters. Academic remediation for entering students, services for LD students, advanced placement, accelerated degree program, self-designed majors, honors program, independent study, distance learning, double major, summer session for credit, part-time degree program, adult/continuing education programs, co-op programs and internships, graduate courses open to undergrads. Off campus study at Pikeville College. Study abroad program. ROTC: Army.

Entrance Requirements: Options: electronic application, early admission, deferred admission. Required: high school transcript, SAT or ACT. Recommended: ACT. Required for some: recommendations. Entrance: minimally difficult. Application deadline: Rolling. Notification: continuous.

Costs Per Year: Application fee: $0. State resident tuition: $4320 full-time, $180 per credit hour part-time. Nonresident tuition: $11,480 full-time, $480 per credit hour part-time. Full-time tuition varies according to course load and reciprocity agreements. College room and board: $4830. Room and board charges vary according to board plan and housing facility.

Collegiate Environment: Orientation program. Drama-theater group, choral group, marching band, student-run newspaper, radio station. Social organizations: national fraternities, national sororities; 20% of eligible men and 20% of eligible women are members. Major annual events: homecoming, Appalachian Celebration. Student services: health clinic, personal-psychological counseling. Campus security: 24-hour emergency response devices and patrols, late night transport-escort service, controlled dormitory access. 3,651 college housing spaces available; 2,411 were occupied in 2003-04. Freshmen given priority for college housing. On-campus residence required through sophomore year. Options: coed, men-only, women-only housing available. Camden Carroll Library with 333,518 books, 781,060 microform titles, 2,627 serials, 1,808 audiovisual materials, an OPAC, and a Web page. Operations spending for 2004 fiscal year: $2.7 million. 1,000 computers available on campus for general student use. A campuswide network can be accessed from student residence rooms and from off campus. Staffed computer lab on campus.

Community Environment: The city of Morehead is located between Lexington, KY, and Huntington, WV. Community services include a hospital, several churches, five motels, several restaurants and 2 shopping centers. Area recreation includes the Daniel Boone National Forest. The campus is a 1-hour drive from several state parks, and 20 minutes from swimming, boating, fishing, and water skiing. The campus also has Eagle Lake for recreation with a golf course and horseback riding. Several annual local festivals and university-sponsored Appalachia celebrations provide further entertainment.

■ **MURRAY STATE UNIVERSITY** *M-16*
PO Box 9
Murray, KY 42071-0009
Tel: (270)762-3011
Free: 800-272-4678
Admissions: (270)762-3592
Fax: (270)762-3413
E-mail: jim.vaughan@murraystate.edu
Web Site: http://www.murraystate.edu/
Description: State-supported, comprehensive, coed. Part of Kentucky Council on Postsecondary Education. Awards bachelor's and master's degrees and post-master's certificates. Founded 1922. Setting: 238-acre small town campus. Endowment: $40.9 million. Research spending for 2004 fiscal year: $3.6 million. Educational spending for 2005 fiscal year: $5696 per student. Total enrollment: 10,266. Faculty: 537 (386 full-time, 151 part-time). Student-undergrad faculty ratio is 17:1. 3,057 applied, 64% were admitted. 28% from top 10% of their high school class, 65% from top quarter, 99% from top half. 62 valedictorians. Full-time: 7,155 students, 56% women, 44% men. Part-time: 1,422 students, 61% women, 39% men. Students come from 49 states and territories, 56 other countries, 32% from out-of-state, 0.5% Native American, 1% Hispanic, 6% black, 1% Asian American or Pacific Islander, 2% international, 17% 25 or older, 40% live on campus, 8% transferred in. Retention: 80% of full-time freshmen returned the following year. Academic areas with the most degrees conferred: education; business/marketing; communications/journalism. Core. Calendar: semesters. Academic remediation for entering students, ESL program, services for LD students, advanced placement, accelerated degree program, honors program, independent study, distance learning, double major, summer session for credit, part-time degree program, external degree program, adult/

continuing education programs, co-op programs and internships, graduate courses open to undergrads. Off campus study at National Student Exchange. Study abroad program. ROTC: Army (c).

Entrance Requirements: Option: electronic application. Required: high school transcript, minimum 3.0 high school GPA, ACT. Entrance: moderately difficult. Notification: continuous until 8/1, continuous until 8/1 for nonresidents.

Costs Per Year: Application fee: $30. State resident tuition: $3792 full-time, $185 per hour part-time. Nonresident tuition: $5464 full-time, $240 per hour part-time. Mandatory fees: $636 full-time, $23 per hour part-time. Full-time tuition and fees vary according to reciprocity agreements. Part-time tuition and fees vary according to reciprocity agreements. College room and board: $4472. College room only: $2366. Room and board charges vary according to board plan.

Collegiate Environment: Orientation program. Drama-theater group, choral group, marching band, student-run newspaper, radio station. Social organizations: 210 open to all; national fraternities, national sororities, local fraternities, local sororities; 16% of eligible men and 12% of eligible women are members. Most popular organizations: student government, Baptist Student Union, Phi Mu Alpha, Residential Colleges. Major annual events: Homecoming, All Campus Sing, Fall Family Weekend. Student services: legal services, health clinic, personal-psychological counseling, women's center. Campus security: 24-hour emergency response devices and patrols, student patrols, late night transport-escort service, controlled dormitory access. 3,200 college housing spaces available; 3,126 were occupied in 2003-04. No special consideration for freshman housing applicants. On-campus residence required through sophomore year. Options: coed, men-only, women-only housing available. Waterfield Library plus 1 other with 400,000 books, 200,814 microform titles, 2,500 serials, 10,500 audiovisual materials, an OPAC, and a Web page. Operations spending for 2004 fiscal year: $2.8 million. 1,800 computers available on campus for general student use. Computer purchase/lease plans available. A campuswide network can be accessed from student residence rooms and from off campus. Staffed computer lab on campus.

Community Environment: The area around Munas has a hospital and several churches. Recreation is available at nearby Kentucky Lake, the largest lake created by the Tennessee Valley Authority, Lake Barkley, and Land Between Lakes, a recreation area of 177,000 acres. Part-time employment is available.

■ **NATIONAL COLLEGE OF BUSINESS & TECHNOLOGY (DANVILLE)** *F-9*
115 East Lexington Ave.
Danville, KY 40422
Tel: (859)236-6991
Free: 800-664-1886
Web Site: http://www.ncbt.edu/
Description: Proprietary, 2-year, coed. Part of National College of Business and Technology. Awards diplomas and terminal associate degrees. Founded 1962. Total enrollment: 326. Core. Services for LD students, advanced placement, honors program, double major, summer session for credit, part-time degree program, internships.
Entrance Requirements: Open admission. Options: Common Application, electronic application. Required: high school transcript. Entrance: noncompetitive. Application deadline: Rolling. Notification: continuous.
Costs Per Year: Application fee: $30. Tuition: $6408 full-time, $178 per credit hour part-time. Mandatory fees: $75 full-time, $15 per term part-time.
Collegiate Environment: Orientation program. College housing not available. 30 computers available on campus for general student use. A campuswide network can be accessed. Staffed computer lab on campus.

■ **NATIONAL COLLEGE OF BUSINESS & TECHNOLOGY (FLORENCE)** *A-10*
7627 Ewing Blvd.
Florence, KY 41042
Tel: (859)525-6510
Free: 800-664-1886
Fax: (859)525-8961
Web Site: http://www.ncbt.edu/
Description: Proprietary, 2-year, coed. Part of National College of Business and Technology. Awards diplomas and terminal associate degrees. Founded 1941. Setting: suburban campus. Total enrollment: 189. Core. Services for LD students, advanced placement, honors program, double major, summer session for credit, part-time degree program, internships.

Entrance Requirements: Open admission. Option: electronic application. Recommended: interview. Required for some: high school transcript. Entrance: noncompetitive. Application deadline: Rolling. Notification: continuous.
Costs Per Year: Application fee: $30. Tuition: $6408 full-time, $178 per credit hour part-time. Mandatory fees: $75 full-time, $15 per term part-time.
Collegiate Environment: Orientation program. Campus security: 24-hour emergency response devices. College housing not available. 30 computers available on campus for general student use. Staffed computer lab on campus.

■ **NATIONAL COLLEGE OF BUSINESS & TECHNOLOGY (LEXINGTON)** *E-10*
628 East Main St.
Lexington, KY 40508-2312
Tel: (859)253-0621
Free: 800-664-1886
Admissions: (859)266-0401
Web Site: http://www.ncbt.edu/
Description: Proprietary, 2-year, coed. Part of National College of Business and Technology. Awards diplomas and terminal associate degrees. Founded 1947. Setting: urban campus. Total enrollment: 378. Core. Advanced placement, honors program, double major, summer session for credit, part-time degree program, internships.
Entrance Requirements: Open admission. Option: electronic application. Required: high school transcript. Entrance: noncompetitive. Application deadline: Rolling. Notification: continuous.
Costs Per Year: Application fee: $30. Tuition: $6408 full-time, $178 per credit hour part-time. Mandatory fees: $75 full-time, $15 per term part-time.
Collegiate Environment: Orientation program. Student services: personal-psychological counseling. College housing not available. 30 computers available on campus for general student use. Staffed computer lab on campus.

■ **NATIONAL COLLEGE OF BUSINESS & TECHNOLOGY (LOUISVILLE)** *D-7*
3950 Dixie Hwy.
Louisville, KY 40216
Tel: (502)447-7634
Free: 800-664-1886
Web Site: http://www.ncbt.edu/
Description: Proprietary, 2-year, coed. Part of National College of Business and Technology. Awards diplomas and terminal associate degrees. Founded 1990. Total enrollment: 678. Core. Services for LD students, advanced placement, honors program, double major, summer session for credit, part-time degree program, internships.
Entrance Requirements: Open admission. Option: electronic application. Recommended: interview. Required for some: high school transcript. Entrance: noncompetitive. Application deadline: Rolling. Notification: continuous.
Costs Per Year: Application fee: $30. Tuition: $6408 full-time, $178 per credit hour part-time. Mandatory fees: $75 full-time, $15 per term part-time. Full-time tuition and fees vary according to course load. Part-time tuition and fees vary according to course load.
Collegiate Environment: Orientation program. College housing not available. 55 computers available on campus for general student use. Staffed computer lab on campus.

■ **NATIONAL COLLEGE OF BUSINESS & TECHNOLOGY (PIKEVILLE)** *G-16*
288 South Mayo Trail, Ste. 2
Pikeville, KY 41501
Tel: (606)432-5477
Free: 800-664-1886
Fax: (606)437-4952
Web Site: http://www.ncbt.edu/
Description: Proprietary, 2-year, coed. Part of National College of Business and Technology. Awards diplomas and terminal associate degrees. Founded 1976. Setting: rural campus. Total enrollment: 219. Core. Services for LD students, advanced placement, honors program, double major, summer session for credit, part-time degree program, internships.
Entrance Requirements: Open admission. Recommended: interview. Required for some: high school transcript. Entrance: noncompetitive. Application deadline: Rolling. Notification: continuous.

Costs Per Year: Application fee: $30. Tuition: $6408 full-time, $178 per credit hour part-time. Mandatory fees: $75 full-time, $15 per term part-time.
Collegiate Environment: Orientation program. College housing not available. 24 computers available on campus for general student use. Staffed computer lab on campus.

■ NATIONAL COLLEGE OF BUSINESS & TECHNOLOGY (RICHMOND) F-11

139 South Killarney Ln.
Richmond, KY 40475
Tel: (859)623-8956
Free: 800-664-1886
Fax: (859)624-5544
Web Site: http://www.ncbt.edu/
Description: Proprietary, 2-year, coed. Part of National College of Business and Technology. Awards diplomas and terminal associate degrees. Founded 1951. Setting: suburban campus. Total enrollment: 363. Core. Advanced placement, honors program, double major, summer session for credit, part-time degree program, internships.
Entrance Requirements: Open admission. Option: electronic application. Recommended: interview. Required for some: high school transcript. Entrance: noncompetitive. Application deadline: Rolling. Notification: continuous.
Costs Per Year: Application fee: $30. Tuition: $6408 full-time, $178 per credit hour part-time. Mandatory fees: $75 full-time, $15 per term part-time.
Collegiate Environment: Orientation program. College housing not available. 20 computers available on campus for general student use. Staffed computer lab on campus.

■ NORTHERN KENTUCKY UNIVERSITY A-10

Louie B Nunn Dr.
Highland Heights, KY 41099
Tel: (859)572-5100
Free: 800-637-9948
Admissions: (859)572-5220
E-mail: admitnku@nku.edu
Web Site: http://www.nku.edu/
Description: State-supported, comprehensive, coed. Awards associate, bachelor's, master's, and first professional degrees. Founded 1968. Setting: 320-acre suburban campus with easy access to Cincinnati. Endowment: $1.5 million. Total enrollment: 13,908. Faculty: 788 (487 full-time, 301 part-time). Student-undergrad faculty ratio is 18:1. 4,369 applied, 81% were admitted. Full-time: 8,989 students, 59% women, 41% men. Part-time: 3,068 students, 59% women, 41% men. Students come from 32 states and territories, 11 other countries, 30% from out-of-state, 27% 25 or older, 9% live on campus, 6% transferred in. Retention: 63% of full-time freshmen returned the following year. Core. Calendar: semesters. Academic remediation for entering students, services for LD students, advanced placement, honors program, independent study, distance learning, double major, summer session for credit, part-time degree program, adult/continuing education programs, co-op programs and internships, graduate courses open to undergrads. Off campus study at all Kentucky state schools, members of the Greater Cincinnati Consortium of Colleges and Universities. Study abroad program. ROTC: Army, Air Force (c).
Entrance Requirements: Open admission. Options: electronic application, early admission, early action, deferred admission, international baccalaureate accepted. Required: high school transcript, minimum 2.0 high school GPA, SAT or ACT. Recommended: ACT. Entrance: noncompetitive. Application deadlines: 8/1, 2/1 for early action. Notification: continuous, 2/15 for early action.
Costs Per Year: Application fee: $30. State resident tuition: $4968 full-time, $207 per credit hour part-time. Nonresident tuition: $9696 full-time, $404 per credit hour part-time. Full-time tuition varies according to location. Part-time tuition varies according to location. College room and board: $4660. College room only: $2580. Room and board charges vary according to board plan, housing facility, and location.
Collegiate Environment: Orientation program. Drama-theater group, choral group, student-run newspaper, radio station. Social organizations: 100 open to all; national fraternities, national sororities; 4% of eligible men and 4% of eligible women are members. Most popular organizations: campus ministries, academic organizations, student government, Activities Program Board. Major annual events: Homecoming, Freshfusion, Rites of Spring. Student services: health clinic, personal-psychological counseling, women's center. Campus security: 24-hour emergency response devices and patrols,

late night transport-escort service, controlled dormitory access. 1,500 college housing spaces available; all were occupied in 2003-04. No special consideration for freshman housing applicants. Options: coed, men-only, women-only housing available. Steely Library plus 2 others with 325,721 books, 771,708 microform titles, 2,217 serials, an OPAC, and a Web page. 600 computers available on campus for general student use. A campuswide network can be accessed from student residence rooms and from off campus. Staffed computer lab on campus.
Community Environment: Located in the largest metropolitan area of any state university in Kentucky, NKU is seven miles southeast of Cincinnati, Ohio.

■ OWENSBORO COMMUNITY AND TECHNICAL COLLEGE F-3

4800 New Hartford Rd.
Owensboro, KY 42303-1899
Tel: (270)686-4400; (866)755-6282
Admissions: (270)686-4527
Fax: (270)686-4496
Web Site: http://www.octc.kctcs.edu/
Description: State-supported, 2-year, coed. Part of Kentucky Community and Technical College System. Awards certificates, transfer associate, and terminal associate degrees. Founded 1986. Setting: 102-acre suburban campus. Endowment: $109,305. Educational spending for 2005 fiscal year: $1348 per student. Total enrollment: 3,664. 789 applied, 100% were admitted. Full-time: 1,848 students, 60% women, 40% men. Part-time: 1,816 students, 60% women, 40% men. Students come from 6 states and territories, 2 other countries, 5% from out-of-state, 0.2% Native American, 0.3% Hispanic, 3% black, 0.5% Asian American or Pacific Islander, 0% international, 28% 25 or older, 2% transferred in. Core. Calendar: semesters. Academic remediation for entering students, advanced placement, honors program, distance learning, double major, summer session for credit, part-time degree program, external degree program, adult/continuing education programs, co-op programs and internships. Off campus study. Study abroad program.
Entrance Requirements: Open admission. Required: high school transcript. Placement: ACT required; ACT COMPASS required for some. Entrance: noncompetitive. Application deadline: Rolling. Notification: continuous.
Collegiate Environment: Orientation program. Drama-theater group, choral group, student-run newspaper, radio station. Social organizations: 20 open to all. Most popular organizations: student government, Psychology Club, Nursing Club. Major annual events: Fall Fling, Spring Fling, Hanging of Greens. Campus security: 24-hour emergency response devices, late night transport-escort service. College housing not available. Learning Resource Center with 18,200 books, 80 serials, an OPAC, and a Web page. Operations spending for 2004 fiscal year: $291,000. 90 computers available on campus for general student use. A campuswide network can be accessed. Staffed computer lab on campus.
Community Environment: A myriad of items including bread, soybean oil, paper, plastics, and electronic components are made in the Owensboro area. Thirty manufacturers have forty or more employees, including such national firms as Baskin-Robbins, General Electric, and Kimberly Clark. Eight percent of the land is used for farming. The fifth largest city in the state, population 53,549, it is home to the International Barbecue Festival, the International Bluegrass Museum Association, and the world's largest sassafras tree.

■ PADUCAH TECHNICAL COLLEGE K-15

509 South 30th St., PO Box 8252
Paducah, KY 42001
Tel: (270)444-9676
Admissions: (502)444-9676
Fax: (270)441-7202
Web Site: http://www.ptc-ky.com/
Description: Proprietary, 2-year, coed. Awards diplomas and terminal associate degrees. Founded 1964. Setting: small town campus. Total enrollment: 200. 82 applied, 100% were admitted. Students come from 4 states and territories, 48% from out-of-state. Calendar: trimesters. Summer session for credit, co-op programs.
Entrance Requirements: Open admission. Option: deferred admission. Required: high school transcript. Entrance: noncompetitive. Application deadline: Rolling.
Collegiate Environment: College housing not available. 17 computers available on campus for general student use.

■ **PIKEVILLE COLLEGE** *G-16*
147 Sycamore St.
Pikeville, KY 41501
Tel: (606)218-5250; (866)232-7700
Admissions: (606)218-5251
Fax: (606)218-5269
Web Site: http://www.pc.edu/
Description: Independent, comprehensive, coed, affiliated with Presbyterian Church (U.S.A.). Awards associate, bachelor's, and first professional degrees. Founded 1889. Setting: 25-acre small town campus. Endowment: $18.7 million. Educational spending for 2005 fiscal year: $6092 per student. Total enrollment: 1,129. Faculty: 61 (54 full-time, 7 part-time). Student-undergrad faculty ratio is 14:1. 520 applied, 100% were admitted. 40% from top quarter of their high school class, 81% from top half. Full-time: 778 students, 52% women, 48% men. Part-time: 66 students, 59% women, 41% men. Students come from 25 states and territories, 7 other countries, 19% from out-of-state, 0.4% Native American, 1% Hispanic, 8% black, 0.1% Asian American or Pacific Islander, 1% international, 18% 25 or older, 41% live on campus, 12% transferred in. Retention: 58% of full-time freshmen returned the following year. Academic areas with the most degrees conferred: psychology; business/marketing; education. Core. Calendar: semesters. Academic remediation for entering students, services for LD students, advanced placement, independent study, double major, summer session for credit, part-time degree program, internships. Off campus study. Study abroad program.
Entrance Requirements: Open admission except for nursing, education programs. Options: electronic application, deferred admission. Required: high school transcript. Required for some: SAT or ACT. Entrance: noncompetitive. Application deadline: 8/16. Notification: continuous.
Costs Per Year: Application fee: $0. Comprehensive fee: $16,500 includes full-time tuition ($11,500) and college room and board ($5000). Full-time tuition varies according to course load. Part-time tuition: $479 per credit hour.
Collegiate Environment: Orientation program. Drama-theater group, choral group, student-run newspaper. Social organizations: 22 open to all. Most popular organizations: Pre-Professional Club, Phi Beta Lambda, Rotaract, Psychology Round Table, Nursing Club. Major annual events: Homecoming, Founders' Day. Student services: personal-psychological counseling. Campus security: 24-hour patrols, controlled dormitory access. 529 college housing spaces available; 326 were occupied in 2003-04. Freshmen given priority for college housing. Options: coed, men-only, women-only housing available. Allara Library plus 2 others with 72,673 books, 39,128 microform titles, 219 serials, 1,811 audiovisual materials, and an OPAC. Operations spending for 2004 fiscal year: $282,004. 162 computers available on campus for general student use. A campuswide network can be accessed from student residence rooms and from off campus. Staffed computer lab on campus.
Community Environment: Located in the heart of Big Sandy Valley, Pikeville is an important mining and trade center in the midst of Elkhorn coalfield. Breaks Park, southeast of town and Jenny Wiley State Park north of town, provides recreational facilities. Part-time employment is available.

■ **ROWAN TECHNICAL COLLEGE** *D-13*
609 Viking Dr.
Morehead, KY 40351
Tel: (606)783-1538
Admissions: (606)759-7141
Fax: (606)784-9876
Web Site: http://www.rowtc.kctcs.edu/
Description: State-supported, 2-year, coed. Awards certificates, diplomas, and terminal associate degrees. Founded 1984. Total enrollment: 842. Full-time: 294 students, 35% women, 65% men. Part-time: 548 students, 26% women, 74% men. 0.1% Hispanic, 3% black, 0.2% Asian American or Pacific Islander. Calendar: semesters.

■ **ST. CATHARINE COLLEGE** *F-8*
2735 Bardstown Rd.
St. Catharine, KY 40061-9499
Tel: (859)336-5082
Fax: (859)336-5031
Web Site: http://www.sccky.edu/
Description: Independent Roman Catholic, 2-year, coed. Awards certificates, transfer associate, and terminal associate degrees. Founded 1931. Setting: 643-acre rural campus with easy access to Louisville. Endowment:

$300,000. Total enrollment: 751. 700 applied, 45% were admitted. Students come from 45 other countries, 0.1% Native American, 1% Hispanic, 9% black, 1% Asian American or Pacific Islander, 1% international, 32% 25 or older, 19% live on campus. Core. Calendar: semesters. Academic remediation for entering students, services for LD students, advanced placement, summer session for credit, part-time degree program, co-op programs and internships.
Entrance Requirements: Options: Common Application, electronic application, early admission. Required: minimum ACT score of 12, ACT. Required for some: high school transcript. Entrance: minimally difficult. Application deadline: Rolling.
Collegiate Environment: Drama-theater group, choral group, student-run newspaper. Most popular organizations: African-American Club, International Club, student government, Phi Theta Kappa. Major annual events: Homecoming Weekend, Christmas Dance, Awards Banquet. Student services: personal-psychological counseling. Campus security: 24-hour emergency response devices, night security guard. Option: coed housing available. St. Catharine College Library with 25,000 books, 110 serials, an OPAC, and a Web page. 60 computers available on campus for general student use. Staffed computer lab on campus.

■ **SOMERSET COMMUNITY COLLEGE** *H-10*
808 Monticello St.
Somerset, KY 42501-2973
Tel: (606)679-8501
Web Site: http://www.somerset.kctcs.edu/
Description: State-supported, 2-year, coed. Part of Kentucky Community and Technical College System. Awards certificates, diplomas, transfer associate, and terminal associate degrees. Founded 1965. Setting: 70-acre small town campus. Endowment: $419,000. Educational spending for 2005 fiscal year: $3018 per student. Total enrollment: 5,850. 825 applied, 100% were admitted. Students come from 3 states and territories, 0.2% Native American, 0.3% Hispanic, 1% black, 0.2% Asian American or Pacific Islander, 0% international, 50% 25 or older. Retention: 60% of full-time freshmen returned the following year. Core. Calendar: semesters. Academic remediation for entering students, ESL program, services for LD students, advanced placement, independent study, distance learning, double major, summer session for credit, part-time degree program, adult/continuing education programs, co-op programs and internships.
Entrance Requirements: Open admission except for nursing, clinical laboratory technology, physical therapy assistant, surgical technology, radiography programs. Options: Common Application, early admission. Required: high school transcript. Placement: ACT required. Entrance: noncompetitive. Application deadline: 8/22. Notification: continuous.
Collegiate Environment: Orientation program. Drama-theater group, choral group, student-run newspaper. Social organizations: 6 open to all. Most popular organizations: Student Government Association, Students in Free Enterprise, Phi Beta Lambda, Phi Theta Kappa. Major annual events: graduation, drama presentations, Multicultural Day Events. College housing not available. Somerset Community College Library with 58,918 books, 4,548 microform titles, 154 serials, 1,233 audiovisual materials, an OPAC, and a Web page. Operations spending for 2004 fiscal year: $102,000. 1,000 computers available on campus for general student use. A campuswide network can be accessed. Staffed computer lab on campus.
Community Environment: Located in an urban area in south central Kentucky, railroad and bus service are available to Somerset. It has a local YMCA, library, hospital and other health services and various organizations including Rotary, Kiwanis, Jaycees, and a Chamber of Commerce. Recreation is provided with 3 theatres, drive-ins, golf, tennis, and Lake Cumberland with 1,225 miles of shoreline.

■ **SOUTHEAST KENTUCKY COMMUNITY AND TECHNICAL COLLEGE** *I-14*
700 College Rd.
Cumberland, KY 40823-1099
Tel: (606)589-2145; 888-274-SECC
Fax: (606)589-5423
Web Site: http://www.soucc.kctcs.net/
Description: State-supported, 2-year, coed. Part of Kentucky Community and Technical College System. Awards certificates, diplomas, transfer associate, and terminal associate degrees. Founded 1960. Setting: 150-acre small town campus. Endowment: $1.8 million. Total enrollment: 4,519. 0.2% Native American, 0.3% Hispanic, 1% black, 0.2% Asian American or Pacific Islander, 0.02% international. Core. Calendar: semesters. Academic

remediation for entering students, advanced placement, accelerated degree program, distance learning, summer session for credit, part-time degree program, adult/continuing education programs, internships.

Entrance Requirements: Open admission except for allied health programs. Required: high school transcript. Entrance: noncompetitive. Application deadline: 8/20. Notification: continuous until 9/3.

Costs Per Year: Application fee: $0. State resident tuition: $2352 full-time, $98 per credit hour part-time. Nonresident tuition: $7056 full-time, $294 per credit hour part-time. Mandatory fees: $164 full-time.

Collegiate Environment: Orientation program. Drama-theater group, choral group, student-run newspaper. Social organizations: 10 open to all. Most popular organizations: Professional Business Leaders, Student Government Association, Phi Theta Kappa, Black Student Union, Nursing Club. Major annual events: Octoberfest, Swappin' Meetin', Spring on Cloverlick. College housing not available. Gertrude Dale Library with 25,921 books, 200 serials, an OPAC, and a Web page. Operations spending for 2004 fiscal year: $480,000. 46 computers available on campus for general student use. A campuswide network can be accessed from off-campus. Staffed computer lab on campus.

Community Environment: Cumberland is a rural town in Harlan County of southeastern Kentucky. The city has Protestant and Catholic churches, and a community hospital and other medical services. Recreation is provided by movie theaters, fishing at Kingdom Come State Park Lake, picnic areas, a lodge and trailer park and a city park. Local merchants employ college students since the town serves an area of approximately 20,000 persons. Various civic, service, fraternal and veteran's organizations, including a Chamber of Commerce, enhance the community spirit.

■ **SOUTHERN BAPTIST THEOLOGICAL SEMINARY** *D-7*
2825 Lexington Rd.
Louisville, KY 40280-0004
Tel: (502)897-4011
Web Site: http://www.sbts.edu/
Description: Independent Southern Baptist, comprehensive, coed. Awards associate and bachelor's degrees. Founded 1858. Total enrollment: 475.
Community Environment: See University of Louisville.

■ **SOUTHWESTERN COLLEGE OF BUSINESS** *A-10*
8095 Connector Dr.
Florence, KY 41042
Tel: (859)282-9999
Admissions: (859)341-6633
E-mail: bbudesheim@swcollege.net
Web Site: http://www.swcollege.net/
Description: Proprietary, 2-year, coed. Awards certificates, diplomas, and terminal associate degrees. Founded 1978. Setting: suburban campus with easy access to Cincinnati. Total enrollment: 240. 97% 25 or older. Academic remediation for entering students, double major.
Entrance Requirements: Open admission. Options: Common Application, early admission.
Collegiate Environment: College housing not available.

■ **SPALDING UNIVERSITY** *D-7*
851 South Fourth St.
Louisville, KY 40203-2188
Tel: (502)585-9911
Free: 800-896-8941
Fax: (502)585-7158
E-mail: admissions@spalding.edu
Web Site: http://www.spalding.edu/
Description: Independent, comprehensive, coed, affiliated with Roman Catholic Church. Awards associate, bachelor's, master's, and doctoral degrees and post-master's certificates. Founded 1814. Setting: 5-acre urban campus. Endowment: $6.8 million. Research spending for 2004 fiscal year: $50,935. Educational spending for 2005 fiscal year: $7725 per student. Total enrollment: 1,641. Faculty: 174 (76 full-time, 98 part-time). Student-undergrad faculty ratio is 12:1. 493 applied, 67% were admitted. 0% from top 10% of their high school class, 28% from top quarter, 61% from top half. Full-time: 645 students, 79% women, 21% men. Part-time: 255 students, 81% women, 19% men. Students come from 8 states and territories, 27 other countries, 16% from out-of-state, 0.4% Native American, 1% Hispanic, 20% black, 1% Asian American or Pacific Islander, 2% international, 54% 25 or older, 13% live on campus, 10% transferred in. Retention: 71% of full-time freshmen returned the following year. Academic areas with the most degrees

conferred: health professions and related sciences; business/marketing; psychology; public administration and social services. Core. Calendar: semesters. Academic remediation for entering students, services for LD students, advanced placement, accelerated degree program, independent study, double major, summer session for credit, part-time degree program, adult/continuing education programs, internships, graduate courses open to undergrads. Off campus study at 7 members of the Kentuckiana Metroversity. Study abroad program. ROTC: Army (c), Air Force (c).

Entrance Requirements: Options: electronic application, deferred admission. Required: high school transcript, minimum 2.5 high school GPA, SAT or ACT. Recommended: interview. Required for some: essay. Entrance: moderately difficult. Application deadline: Rolling. Notification: continuous.

Costs Per Year: Application fee: $20. Comprehensive fee: $19,572 includes full-time tuition ($15,300), mandatory fees ($600), and college room and board ($3672). College room only: $2100. Part-time tuition: $510 per hour. Part-time mandatory fees: $20 per hour.

Collegiate Environment: Orientation program. Drama-theater group, choral group, student-run newspaper. Social organizations: 27 open to all. Most popular organizations: student government, Model United Nations/International Club, Nursing Society, National Education Association, Student Occupational Therapy Association. Major annual events: Rat Race - Run for the Rodents, International Week, Homecoming Week. Student services: health clinic, personal-psychological counseling. Campus security: 24-hour emergency response devices and patrols, late night transport-escort service. 200 college housing spaces available; 83 were occupied in 2003-04. No special consideration for freshman housing applicants. Option: coed housing available. Spalding Library with 160,954 books, 16,273 microform titles, 655 serials, 30,140 audiovisual materials, an OPAC, and a Web page. Operations spending for 2004 fiscal year: $397,805. 80 computers available on campus for general student use. A campuswide network can be accessed. Staffed computer lab on campus.

Community Environment: See University of Louisville.

■ **SPENCERIAN COLLEGE** *D-7*
4627 Dixie Hwy.
Louisville, KY 40216
Tel: (502)447-1000
Free: 800-264-1799
Fax: (502)447-4574
Web Site: http://www.spencerian.edu/
Description: Proprietary, 2-year, coed. Part of The Sullivan University System. Awards certificates, diplomas, transfer associate, and terminal associate degrees. Founded 1892. Setting: 10-acre urban campus. Total enrollment: 1,326. 1 valedictorian. Students come from 11 states and territories, 16% from out-of-state, 1% Native American, 0.3% Hispanic, 25% black, 1% Asian American or Pacific Islander, 0% international, 50% 25 or older, 0% live on campus. Academic remediation for entering students, services for LD students, advanced placement, accelerated degree program, honors program, independent study, distance learning, double major, part-time degree program, external degree program, co-op programs and internships.

Entrance Requirements: Open admission. Options: Common Application, electronic application. Required: high school transcript, interview. Recommended: SAT or ACT. Required for some: essay, recommendations. Notification: continuous until 9/1. Preference given to nursing programs have preferential admission.

Costs Per Year: Application fee: $90. Tuition: $12,120 full-time, $202 per credit hour part-time. Mandatory fees: $575 full-time, $30. College room only: $3960.

Collegiate Environment: Orientation program. Student-run newspaper. Social organizations: local fraternities; 1% of eligible men and 50% of eligible women are members. Most popular organization: Spencerian Business Leaders. Major annual events: Belle of Louisville Cruise, annual picnic, Derby Activities. Student services: personal-psychological counseling. Campus security: 24-hour emergency response devices. Option: coed housing available. Laura Diener with an OPAC and a Web page. 81 computers available on campus for general student use. A campuswide network can be accessed from off-campus. Staffed computer lab on campus.

■ **SPENCERIAN COLLEGE-LEXINGTON** *E-10*
2355 Harrodsburg Rd.
Lexington, KY 40504
Tel: (859)223-9608
Admissions: 800-456-3253

Fax: (859)224-7744
Web Site: http://www.spencerian.edu/
Description: Proprietary, 2-year, coed. Part of Sullivan Colleges System. Awards certificates, diplomas, and terminal associate degrees. Setting: urban campus with easy access to Louisville. Educational spending for 2005 fiscal year: $2932 per student. Total enrollment: 376. 158 applied, 79% were admitted. Students come from 1 other country, 0% from out-of-state, 0.3% Native American, 2% Hispanic, 6% black, 0% Asian American or Pacific Islander, 0.3% international, 31% 25 or older, 13% live on campus. Retention: 0% of full-time freshmen returned the following year. Academic remediation for entering students, services for LD students, independent study, summer session for credit, part-time degree program, co-op programs.
Entrance Requirements: Option: Common Application. Required: high school transcript, interview. Required for some: CPAt. Entrance: moderately difficult. Application deadline: Rolling.
Collegiate Environment: Orientation program. Student-run newspaper. Major annual events: golf tournament, school picnic, Student Appreciation Week. Campus security: 24-hour emergency response devices. 90 college housing spaces available; 50 were occupied in 2003-04. No special consideration for freshman housing applicants. Options: men-only, women-only housing available. Spencerian College Library with 450 books, 30 serials, and 25 audiovisual materials. Operations spending for 2004 fiscal year: $4500. 14 computers available on campus for general student use. A campuswide network can be accessed from off-campus. Staffed computer lab on campus.

■ **SULLIVAN UNIVERSITY** *D-7*
3101 Bardstown Rd.
Louisville, KY 40205
Tel: (502)456-6504
Free: 800-844-1354
Admissions: (502)456-6505
Fax: (502)456-0040
E-mail: gcawthon@sullivan.edu
Web Site: http://www.sullivan.edu/
Description: Proprietary, comprehensive, coed. Administratively affiliated with Sullivan Colleges System. Awards associate, bachelor's, and master's degrees. Founded 1864. Setting: 10-acre suburban campus. Educational spending for 2005 fiscal year: $2100 per student. Total enrollment: 4,639. Faculty: 213 (93 full-time, 120 part-time). Student-undergrad faculty ratio is 20:1. 10% from top 10% of their high school class, 22% from top quarter, 76% from top half. Students come from 22 states and territories, 11 other countries, 13% from out-of-state, 52% 25 or older, 9% live on campus. Retention: 60% of full-time freshmen returned the following year. Academic remediation for entering students, advanced placement, accelerated degree program, independent study, distance learning, double major, summer session for credit, part-time degree program, adult/continuing education programs, co-op programs. ROTC: Army (c).
Entrance Requirements: Required: high school transcript, interview, ACT or CPAt. Entrance: minimally difficult. Application deadline: Rolling. Notification: continuous.
Costs Per Year: Application fee: $90. Tuition: $12,900 full-time, $215 per credit part-time. Mandatory fees: $435 full-time, $30 per course part-time. Full-time tuition and fees vary according to program. Part-time tuition and fees vary according to program. College room only: $3960. Tuition guaranteed not to increase for student's term of enrollment.
Collegiate Environment: Orientation program. Social organizations: 15 open to all. Most popular organizations: student government, Travel Club, Sullivan Student Paralegal Association, American Marketing Association, Society of Hosteurs. Major annual events: Belle of Louisville Cruise, Summer Picnic/Festival, ski trip. Student services: personal-psychological counseling. Campus security: 24-hour patrols. 300 college housing spaces available; 215 were occupied in 2003-04. Freshmen guaranteed college housing. Option: coed housing available. McWhorter Library with 22,500 books, 222 serials, an OPAC, and a Web page. Operations spending for 2004 fiscal year: $475,000. 125 computers available on campus for general student use. A campuswide network can be accessed from student residence rooms and from off campus. Staffed computer lab on campus.

■ **THOMAS MORE COLLEGE** *L-9*
333 Thomas More Parkway
Crestview Hills, KY 41017-3495
Tel: (859)341-5800

Free: 800-825-4557
Admissions: (859)344-3332
Fax: (859)344-3638
E-mail: admissions@thomasmore.edu
Web Site: http://www.thomasmore.edu/
Description: Independent Roman Catholic, comprehensive, coed. Awards associate, bachelor's, and master's degrees. Founded 1921. Setting: 100-acre suburban campus with easy access to Cincinnati. Endowment: $9.6 million. Educational spending for 2005 fiscal year: $6056 per student. Total enrollment: 1,434. Faculty: 134 (71 full-time, 63 part-time). Student-undergrad faculty ratio is 14:1. 1,007 applied, 63% were admitted. 14% from top 10% of their high school class, 37% from top quarter, 70% from top half. 12 valedictorians. Students come from 56 states and territories, 10 other countries, 32% from out-of-state, 0.4% Native American, 0.4% Hispanic, 6% black, 1% Asian American or Pacific Islander, 0.4% international, 31% 25 or older, 20% live on campus. Retention: 67% of full-time freshmen returned the following year. Academic areas with the most degrees conferred: business/marketing; education; history. Core. Calendar: semesters. Academic remediation for entering students, services for LD students, advanced placement, accelerated degree program, self-designed majors, honors program, independent study, double major, summer session for credit, part-time degree program, external degree program, adult/continuing education programs, co-op programs and internships. Off campus study at members of the Greater Cincinnati Consortium of Colleges and Universities. Study abroad program. ROTC: Army (c), Air Force (c).
Entrance Requirements: Options: Peterson's Universal Application, Common Application, electronic application, deferred admission, international baccalaureate accepted. Required: high school transcript, minimum 2.0 high school GPA, rank in upper 50% of high school class, admissions committee may consider those not meeting criteria, SAT or ACT. Recommended: interview. Required for some: essay, 2 recommendations. Entrance: moderately difficult. Application deadline: 8/15. Notification: continuous.
Costs Per Year: Application fee: $25. Comprehensive fee: $24,470 includes full-time tuition ($17,600), mandatory fees ($720), and college room and board ($6150). College room only: $2900. Full-time tuition and fees vary according to program. Room and board charges vary according to board plan and housing facility. Part-time tuition: $450 per credit hour. Part-time mandatory fees: $30 per credit hour, $15 per term. Part-time tuition and fees vary according to course load and program.
Collegiate Environment: Orientation program. Drama-theater group, choral group. Social organizations: 29 open to all. Most popular organizations: Student Government Association, orientation team, ACT More Program Board, Outdoors Club, Business Society. Major annual events: Homecoming, Senior Boat Cruise, Spring Fling Week/Spring Formal. Student services: health clinic, personal-psychological counseling. Campus security: 24-hour patrols, late night transport-escort service, controlled dormitory access. 400 college housing spaces available; 270 were occupied in 2003-04. No special consideration for freshman housing applicants. Options: coed, men-only, women-only housing available. Thomas More Library with 127,429 books, 51,551 microform titles, 609 serials, 2,178 audiovisual materials, and a Web page. Operations spending for 2004 fiscal year: $345,094. 100 computers available on campus for general student use. A campuswide network can be accessed from student residence rooms and from off campus. Staffed computer lab on campus.
Community Environment: The campus is located just 10 minutes south of downtown Cincinnati. The Greater Cincinnati International Airport is a five-minute drive from campus. Numerous activities and faculties include the Cincinnati Symphony Orchestra, jazz clubs, restaurants, shops, live theater and ballet, the Cincinnati Zoo, the annual Riverfest, Oktoberfest and Taste of Cincinnati. Teams include the Cincinnati Reds and the Bengals.

■ **TRANSYLVANIA UNIVERSITY** *E-10*
300 North Broadway
Lexington, KY 40508-1797
Tel: (859)233-8300
Free: 800-872-6798
Admissions: (859)233-8242
Fax: (859)233-8797
E-mail: dison@transi/.edu
Web Site: http://www.transy.edu/
Description: Independent, 4-year, coed, affiliated with Christian Church (Disciples of Christ). Awards bachelor's degrees. Founded 1780. Setting: 35-acre urban campus with easy access to Cincinnati and Louisville. Endowment: $127.1 million. Educational spending for 2005 fiscal year: $7523 per

student. Total enrollment: 1,151. Student-undergrad faculty ratio is 13:1. 1,222 applied, 84% were admitted. 50% from top 10% of their high school class, 75% from top quarter, 97% from top half. 7 National Merit Scholars, 31 valedictorians. Full-time: 1,135 students, 60% women, 40% men. Part-time: 16 students, 25% women, 75% men. Students come from 34 states and territories, 1 other country, 22% from out-of-state, 0.3% Native American, 1% Hispanic, 2% black, 2% Asian American or Pacific Islander, 0.1% international, 0.4% 25 or older, 80% live on campus, 1% transferred in. Retention: 89% of full-time freshmen returned the following year. Academic areas with the most degrees conferred: business/marketing; social sciences; biological/life sciences. Core. Calendar: 4-4-1. Advanced placement, self-designed majors, independent study, double major, summer session for credit, part-time degree program, internships. Off campus study at Washington Center for Internships and Academic Seminars, Kentucky Institute for International Studies. Study abroad program. ROTC: Army (c), Air Force (c).

Entrance Requirements: Options: Peterson's Universal Application, Common Application, electronic application, early admission, early action, deferred admission, international baccalaureate accepted. Required: essay, high school transcript, minimum 2.75 high school GPA, 2 recommendations, SAT or ACT. Recommended: interview. Required for some: interview. Entrance: very difficult. Application deadlines: 2/1, 12/1 for early action. Notification: 3/15, 1/15 for early action.

Costs Per Year: Application fee: $30. Comprehensive fee: $26,240 includes full-time tuition ($19,650) and college room and board ($6590). Room and board charges vary according to board plan and location. Part-time tuition: $2100 per course. Part-time mandatory fees: $84 per course.

Collegiate Environment: Orientation program. Drama-theater group, choral group, student-run newspaper, radio station. Social organizations: 51 open to all; national fraternities, national sororities; 50% of eligible men and 50% of eligible women are members. Most popular organizations: Student Alumni Association, Student Government Association, Student Activities Board, Crimson Crew, Alternative Spring Break. Major annual events: T-Day Week, Greek Week, Crimson Christmas. Student services: health clinic, personal-psychological counseling. Campus security: 24-hour emergency response devices and patrols, late night transport-escort service. 890 college housing spaces available; 850 were occupied in 2003-04. Freshmen guaranteed college housing. On-campus residence required through junior year. Options: coed, men-only, women-only housing available. Transylvania Library with 124,000 books, 13,348 microform titles, 500 serials, 2,214 audiovisual materials, an OPAC, and a Web page. Operations spending for 2004 fiscal year: $660,028. 250 computers available on campus for general student use. A campuswide network can be accessed from student residence rooms and from off campus. Staffed computer lab on campus.

Community Environment: See University of Kentucky.

■ UNION COLLEGE *I-12*

310 College St.
Barbourville, KY 40906-1499
Tel: (606)546-4151
Free: 800-489-8646
Admissions: (606)546-1222
Fax: (606)546-1667
E-mail: enroll@unionky.edu
Web Site: http://www.unionky.edu/

Description: Independent United Methodist, comprehensive, coed. Awards bachelor's and master's degrees. Founded 1879. Setting: 110-acre small town campus. Endowment: $14.4 million. Educational spending for 2005 fiscal year: $5065 per student. Total enrollment: 1,224. Faculty: 71 (46 full-time, 25 part-time). Student-undergrad faculty ratio is 14:1. 596 applied, 64% were admitted. 6% from top 10% of their high school class, 28% from top quarter, 60% from top half. Full-time: 555 students, 42% women, 58% men. Part-time: 56 students, 63% women, 38% men. Students come from 18 states and territories, 5 other countries, 19% from out-of-state, 1% Native American, 2% Hispanic, 9% black, 0.2% Asian American or Pacific Islander, 4% international, 24% 25 or older, 45% live on campus, 10% transferred in. Retention: 56% of full-time freshmen returned the following year. Academic areas with the most degrees conferred: education; business/marketing; psychology. Core. Calendar: semesters. Advanced placement, accelerated degree program, self-designed majors, independent study, distance learning, double major, summer session for credit, part-time degree program, co-op programs and internships, graduate courses open to undergrads. Off campus study at members of the Mid-Appalachian Colleges Council. Study abroad program. ROTC: Army (c).

Entrance Requirements: Options: Peterson's Universal Application, Common Application, electronic application, early admission, deferred admission.

Required: high school transcript, minimum 2.0 high school GPA, SAT and SAT Subject Tests or ACT. Required for some: essay, recommendations, interview. Entrance: moderately difficult. Application deadline: 8/1. Notification: continuous.

Costs Per Year: Application fee: $20. One-time mandatory fee: $800. Comprehensive fee: $19,890 includes full-time tuition ($14,950), mandatory fees ($340), and college room and board ($4600). College room only: $1700. Part-time tuition: $260 per hour. Part-time mandatory fees: $15 per semester hour.

Collegiate Environment: Orientation program. Drama-theater group, choral group, student-run newspaper. Social organizations: 18 open to all. Most popular organizations: Fellowship of Christian Athletes, Baptist Student Union, Thespian Society, Newman Club, Psychology Club. Major annual events: Special Olympics, Homecoming, Springfest. Student services: health clinic, personal-psychological counseling. Campus security: 24-hour emergency response devices and patrols, late night transport-escort service, controlled dormitory access. 325 college housing spaces available; 248 were occupied in 2003-04. Freshmen guaranteed college housing. On-campus residence required through sophomore year. Options: coed, men-only, women-only housing available. Weeks-Townsend Memorial Library with 142,667 books, 444,016 microform titles, 8,612 serials, 5,198 audiovisual materials, an OPAC, and a Web page. Operations spending for 2004 fiscal year: $327,564. 70 computers available on campus for general student use. A campuswide network can be accessed from student residence rooms and from off campus. Staffed computer lab on campus.

■ UNIVERSITY OF THE CUMBERLANDS *J-11*

6178 College Station Dr.
Williamsburg, KY 40769-1372
Tel: (606)549-2200
Free: 800-343-1609
Admissions: (606)539-4201
Fax: (606)539-4303
E-mail: swake@ucumberlands.edu
Web Site: http://www.cumberlandcollege.edu/

Description: Independent Kentucky Baptist, comprehensive, coed. Awards associate, bachelor's, and master's degrees. Founded 1889. Setting: 50-acre rural campus with easy access to Knoxville. Endowment: $55.1 million. Educational spending for 2005 fiscal year: $4962 per student. Total enrollment: 1,843. Faculty: 112 (86 full-time, 26 part-time). Student-undergrad faculty ratio is 15:1. 984 applied, 83% were admitted. 16% from top 10% of their high school class, 42% from top quarter, 70% from top half. 21 valedictorians. Full-time: 1,411 students, 52% women, 48% men. Part-time: 222 students, 56% women, 44% men. Students come from 34 states and territories, 23 other countries, 40% from out-of-state, 0.5% Native American, 2% Hispanic, 7% black, 1% Asian American or Pacific Islander, 2% international, 9% 25 or older, 53% live on campus, 4% transferred in. Retention: 63% of full-time freshmen returned the following year. Academic areas with the most degrees conferred: business/marketing; education; biological/life sciences. Core. Calendar: semesters. Academic remediation for entering students, advanced placement, accelerated degree program, self-designed majors, honors program, independent study, distance learning, double major, summer session for credit, part-time degree program, adult/continuing education programs, co-op programs and internships, graduate courses open to undergrads. Study abroad program. ROTC: Army.

Entrance Requirements: Options: Peterson's Universal Application, Common Application. Required: essay, high school transcript, minimum 2.0 high school GPA, 1 recommendation, SAT or ACT. Recommended: interview. Entrance: moderately difficult. Application deadline: Rolling. Notification: continuous.

Costs Per Year: Application fee: $30. Comprehensive fee: $19,984 includes full-time tuition ($13,298), mandatory fees ($360), and college room and board ($6326). Part-time tuition: $410 per hour. Part-time mandatory fees: $48.75 per term.

Collegiate Environment: Orientation program. Drama-theater group, choral group, marching band, student-run newspaper, radio station. Social organizations: 45 open to all. Most popular organizations: Baptist Student Union, Student Government Association, Campus Activity Board, Mountain Outreach, Fellowship of Christian Athletes. Major annual events: homecoming, Hanging of the Green, Spring Fever. Student services: health clinic, personal-psychological counseling. Campus security: 24-hour emergency response devices, student patrols, late night transport-escort service, patrols by trained security personnel 11pm-7am. 1,100 college housing spaces available; 929 were occupied in 2003-04. Freshmen guaranteed college housing. On-campus residence required through junior year. Options: men-only, women-only housing available. 300 computers available on campus for general student use. A campuswide network can be accessed from student residence rooms and from off campus. Staffed computer lab on campus.

Community Environment: Located in the southeastern part of Kentucky, Williamsburg is accessible via bus service and interstate highway. The city offers facilities that include 14 churches of various denominations, 4 medical clinics, civic organizations and city parks. Recreation is found at Cumberland Falls State Park, Cumberland Lake, Laurel Lake, cinemas and theaters. There is adequate modern housing available and motels nearby. Part-time employment opportunities are available for students.

■ **UNIVERSITY OF KENTUCKY** *E-10*
Lexington, KY 40506-0032
Tel: (859)257-9000
Admissions: (859)257-2000
Fax: (859)257-4000
Web Site: http://www.uky.edu/

Description: State-supported, university, coed. Awards bachelor's, master's, doctoral, and first professional degrees and post-master's certificates. Founded 1865. Setting: 685-acre urban campus with easy access to Cincinnati and Louisville. Endowment: $538.4 million. Research spending for 2004 fiscal year: $187.5 million. Educational spending for 2005 fiscal year: $10,365 per student. Total enrollment: 25,672. Faculty: 1,724 (1,211 full-time, 513 part-time). Student-undergrad faculty ratio is 17:1. 10,508 applied, 82% were admitted. 28% from top 10% of their high school class, 57% from top quarter, 86% from top half. 35 National Merit Scholars, 157 valedictorians. Full-time: 17,050 students, 52% women, 48% men. Part-time: 1,652 students, 49% women, 51% men. Students come from 52 states and territories, 91 other countries, 17% from out-of-state, 0.1% Native American, 1% Hispanic, 5% black, 2% Asian American or Pacific Islander, 1% international, 10% 25 or older, 31% live on campus, 6% transferred in. Retention: 79% of full-time freshmen returned the following year. Academic areas with the most degrees conferred: business/marketing; communications/journalism; social sciences. Core. Calendar: semesters. Academic remediation for entering students, ESL program, services for LD students, advanced placement, accelerated degree program, self-designed majors, honors program, independent study, distance learning, double major, summer session for credit, part-time degree program, adult/continuing education programs, co-op programs and internships, graduate courses open to undergrads. Off campus study at Academic Common Market, University of Florida. Study abroad program. ROTC: Army, Air Force.

Entrance Requirements: Options: electronic application, early admission, international baccalaureate accepted. Required: high school transcript, minimum 2.0 high school GPA, SAT or ACT. Entrance: moderately difficult. Application deadline: 2/15. Notification: continuous. Preference given to state residents for certain programs.

Costs Per Year: Application fee: $40. State resident tuition: $5162 full-time, $216 per credit hour part-time. Nonresident tuition: $12,148 full-time, $507 per credit hour part-time. Mandatory fees: $650 full-time, $16.25 per credit hour part-time. Full-time tuition and fees vary according to degree level, program, reciprocity agreements, and student level. Part-time tuition and fees vary according to degree level, program, reciprocity agreements, and student level. College room and board: $5129. College room only: $3363. Room and board charges vary according to board plan and housing facility.

Collegiate Environment: Orientation program. Drama-theater group, choral group, marching band, student-run newspaper, radio station. Social organizations: 305 open to all; national fraternities, national sororities; 15% of eligible men and 19% of eligible women are members. Most popular organizations: Student Activities Board, Student Government Association, Campus Progressive Coalition, Ski and Snowboard Club, Society of Women Engineers. Major annual events: Homecoming, Student Center Night, Cultural Diversity Festival. Student services: legal services, health clinic, personal-psychological counseling, women's center. Campus security: 24-hour emergency response devices and patrols, late night transport-escort service, controlled dormitory access. 5,600 college housing spaces available; all were occupied in 2003-04. No special consideration for freshman housing applicants. Options: coed, men-only, women-only housing available. William T. Young Library plus 15 others with 3.1 million books, 6.3 million microform titles, 29,633 serials, 86,690 audiovisual materials, an OPAC, and a Web page. Operations spending for 2004 fiscal year: $20.4 million. 1,400 computers available on campus for general student use. A campuswide network can be accessed from student residence rooms and from off campus. Staffed computer lab on campus.

Community Environment: Lexington is located in the famous Bluegrass area of Kentucky. It is centrally located with Louisville 80 miles to the west and Cincinnati 90 miles to the north. Travel is made easier with close access to Interstates 75 and 64. The Mountain Parkway connects the Bluegrass with eastern Kentucky, and the Bluegrass Parkway links the western part of the State and Interstate 65. Lexington, known throughout the world as the home of the thoroughbred, attracts thousands of horse fans and buyers each year. Keeneland, a thoroughbred race track, and the famous trotting track, the Red Mile draw racing fans. The thoroughbred is not Lexington's only equine citizen; the standardbred, the quarterhorse, the saddle horse, and the Arabian are some of the many other breeds that live on some of the world's most famous farms in the Bluegrass. Since 1974, Lexington has been governed by an urban county form of government. The Lexington-Fayette County population is approximately 250,000, and this second largest city in Kentucky has seen steady growth in population. Le

■ **UNIVERSITY OF LOUISVILLE** *D-7*
2301 South Third St.
Louisville, KY 40292-0001
Tel: (502)852-5555
Free: 800-334-8635
Admissions: (502)852-6531
Fax: (502)852-4776
E-mail: admitme@ulkyvm.louisville.edu
Web Site: http://www.louisville.edu/

Description: State-supported, university, coed. Awards associate, bachelor's, master's, doctoral, and first professional degrees and post-master's certificates. Founded 1798. Setting: 169-acre urban campus. Endowment: $607.6 million. Research spending for 2004 fiscal year: $100.4 million. Educational spending for 2005 fiscal year: $11,415 per student. Total enrollment: 20,734. Faculty: 1,313 (802 full-time, 511 part-time). Student-undergrad faculty ratio is 17:1. 5,712 applied, 79% were admitted. 22% from top 10% of their high school class, 51% from top quarter, 80% from top half. Full-time: 11,441 students, 53% women, 47% men. Part-time: 3,492 students, 51% women, 49% men. Students come from 51 states and territories, 65 other countries, 14% from out-of-state, 0.3% Native American, 1% Hispanic, 14% black, 3% Asian American or Pacific Islander, 1% international, 15% 25 or older, 15% live on campus, 6% transferred in. Retention: 76% of full-time freshmen returned the following year. Academic areas with the most degrees conferred: business/marketing; social sciences; engineering. Core. Calendar: semesters. Academic remediation for entering students, ESL program, services for LD students, advanced placement, accelerated degree program, self-designed majors, honors program, independent study, distance learning, double major, summer session for credit, part-time degree program, external degree program, adult/continuing education programs, co-op programs and internships, graduate courses open to undergrads. Off campus study at 6 members of the Kentuckiana Metroversity. Study abroad program. ROTC: Army, Air Force.

Entrance Requirements: Options: electronic application, early admission, deferred admission. Required: high school transcript, minimum 2.50 high school GPA, SAT or ACT. Entrance: moderately difficult. Application deadline: Rolling. Notification: continuous.

Costs Per Year: Application fee: $30. State resident tuition: $5532 full-time, $231 per hour part-time. Nonresident tuition: $15,092 full-time, $629 per hour part-time. Full-time tuition varies according to reciprocity agreements. Part-time tuition varies according to course load and reciprocity agreements. College room and board: $6036. College room only: $4490. Room and board charges vary according to board plan and housing facility.

Collegiate Environment: Orientation program. Drama-theater group, choral group, marching band, student-run newspaper, radio station. Social organizations: 202 open to all; national fraternities, national sororities; 7% of eligible men and 3% of eligible women are members. Most popular organizations: Spirit Club - 'L' Raisers, Baptist Student Union, Golden Key Society, Sigma Chi, Phi Eta Sigma. Major annual events: Homecoming events, NPHC Stepshow, Welcome. Student services: legal services, health clinic, personal-psychological counseling, women's center. Campus security: 24-hour emergency response devices and patrols, late night transport-escort service, controlled dormitory access. 1,674 college housing spaces available; 1,590 were occupied in 2003-04. Freshmen given priority for college housing. Option: coed housing available. William F. Ekstrom Library plus 5 others with 2 million books, 2.2 million microform titles, 24,910 serials, 35,429 audiovisual materials, an OPAC, and a Web page. Operations spending for 2004 fiscal year: $71.7 million. 265 computers available on campus for general student use. Computer purchase/lease plans available.

A campuswide network can be accessed from student residence rooms and from off campus. Staffed computer lab on campus.

Community Environment: Louisville is known as the Derby City for the annual running of the Kentucky Derby at Churchill Downs. The city was the base of supplies for Clark's expeditions, which culminated in the conquest of the northwest. U.S. river boats pass through the locks around 25-foot falls in the Ohio River. Louisville is an important distilling center and one of the largest tobacco product manufacturing centers in the world. There are many other local manufacturing firms in the area, and part-time employment is available. There is a community-wide fund for music, drama, and art, and the city has resident opera, ballet, orchestra, and theater companies.

■ **WEST KENTUCKY COMMUNITY AND TECHNICAL COLLEGE** *K-15*
4810 Alben Barkley Dr.
PO Box 7380
Paducah, KY 42002-7380
Tel: (270)554-9200
Fax: (270)554-6217
Web Site: http://www.westkentucky.kctcs.edu/
Description: State-supported, 2-year, coed. Part of University of Kentucky Community College System. Awards certificates, diplomas, transfer associate, and terminal associate degrees. Founded 1932. Setting: 117-acre small town campus. Educational spending for 2005 fiscal year: $2042 per student. Total enrollment: 3,545. 14% from top 10% of their high school class, 56% from top quarter, 71% from top half. Students come from 12 states and territories, 0.4% Native American, 1% Hispanic, 6% black, 0.4% Asian American or Pacific Islander, 41% 25 or older. Core. Calendar: semesters. Academic remediation for entering students, services for LD students, honors program, summer session for credit, part-time degree program, adult/continuing education programs, co-op programs and internships.
Entrance Requirements: Open admission. Option: early admission. Required for some: high school transcript. Placement: ACT required for some. Entrance: noncompetitive. Application deadline: Rolling.
Costs Per Year: Area resident tuition: $98 per credit hour part-time. State resident tuition: $118 per credit hour part-time. Nonresident tuition: $294 per credit hour part-time.
Collegiate Environment: Drama-theater group, choral group, student-run newspaper. Student services: women's center. Campus security: 14-hour patrols by trained security personnel. College housing not available. Paducah Community College Library with 31,339 books, 152 serials, an OPAC, and a Web page. Operations spending for 2004 fiscal year: $358,108. 160 computers available on campus for general student use. Staffed computer lab on campus.
Community Environment: A busy town with a leisurely atmosphere, Paducah was named for Indian Chief, Paduke, who is buried on the bank of the river. It is an important market for burley and dark tobacco. Diversified industries include boat and barge builders, electronics and chemicals plants. Part-time work is available. Located at the confluence of the Tennessee and Ohio Rivers, average winter temperature is 46.2 degrees, summer, 73.4 degrees. Highways, airlines, and bus lines serve the community. A public library, churches, two hospitals, hotels and motels and many civic organizations are available. Recreation areas include nearby Kentucky and Barkley Lakes and the "Land Between Lakes" area as well as three state parks, several public parks, a swimming pool, golf courses and theatres.

■ **WESTERN KENTUCKY UNIVERSITY** *I-5*
1 Big Red Way
Bowling Green, KY 42101-3576
Tel: (270)745-0111
Admissions: (270)745-2551
Fax: (270)745-6133

E-mail: admission@wku.edu
Web Site: http://www.wku.edu/
Description: State-supported, comprehensive, coed. Awards associate, bachelor's, and master's degrees and post-master's and first professional certificates. Founded 1906. Setting: 223-acre suburban campus with easy access to Nashville. Endowment: $75.3 million. Research spending for 2004 fiscal year: $8.5 million. Total enrollment: 18,634. Faculty: 1,107 (694 full-time, 413 part-time). Student-undergrad faculty ratio is 19:1. 6,781 applied, 92% were admitted. 15% from top 10% of their high school class, 36% from top quarter, 67% from top half. 4 National Merit Scholars, 105 valedictorians. Full-time: 13,053 students, 56% women, 44% men. Part-time: 2,914 students, 65% women, 35% men. Students come from 45 states and territories, 51 other countries, 17% from out-of-state, 0.3% Native American, 1% Hispanic, 9% black, 1% Asian American or Pacific Islander, 2% international, 20% 25 or older, 31% live on campus, 5% transferred in. Retention: 73% of full-time freshmen returned the following year. Academic areas with the most degrees conferred: education; business/marketing; communications/journalism. Core. Calendar: semesters. Academic remediation for entering students, ESL program, services for LD students, advanced placement, accelerated degree program, self-designed majors, honors program, independent study, distance learning, double major, summer session for credit, part-time degree program, adult/continuing education programs, co-op programs and internships, graduate courses open to undergrads. Study abroad program. ROTC: Army, Air Force (c).
Entrance Requirements: Open admission. Option: international baccalaureate accepted. Required: high school transcript, minimum 2.5 high school GPA, SAT or ACT. Entrance: moderately difficult. Application deadlines: 8/1, 6/1 for nonresidents. Notification: continuous, continuous for nonresidents.
Costs Per Year: Application fee: $35. State resident tuition: $5316 full-time, $228 per hour part-time. Nonresident tuition: $12,732 full-time, $537 per hour part-time. Full-time tuition varies according to course load, location, program, and reciprocity agreements. Part-time tuition varies according to course load, location, program, and reciprocity agreements. College room and board: $4876. College room only: $2800. Room and board charges vary according to board plan and housing facility.
Collegiate Environment: Orientation program. Drama-theater group, choral group, marching band, student-run newspaper, radio station. Social organizations: 215 open to all; national fraternities, national sororities, local sororities; 7% of eligible men and 9% of eligible women are members. Most popular organizations: Student Government Association, Campus Activities Board, Campus Crusade for Christ, campus ministries, Residence Hall Association. Major annual events: homecoming, football tailgating, step show. Student services: health clinic, personal-psychological counseling, women's center. Campus security: 24-hour emergency response devices and patrols, student patrols, late night transport-escort service, controlled dormitory access. College housing designed to accommodate 4,513 students; 4,887 undergraduates lived in college housing during 2003-04. Freshmen given priority for college housing. On-campus residence required in freshman year. Options: coed, men-only, women-only housing available. Helm-Cravens Library plus 3 others with an OPAC and a Web page. Operations spending for 2004 fiscal year: $5.8 million. 1,300 computers available on campus for general student use. A campuswide network can be accessed from student residence rooms and from off campus. Staffed computer lab on campus.
Community Environment: The city of Bowling Green is located on the Barrer River in Warren County in southern Kentucky. Situated 60 miles north of Nashville, and 103 miles south of Louisville, Bowling Green has about 80 churches of 26 denominations, a public library, and two hospitals. Recreation is provided by local theaters and parks, including nearby Mammoth Cave National Park.

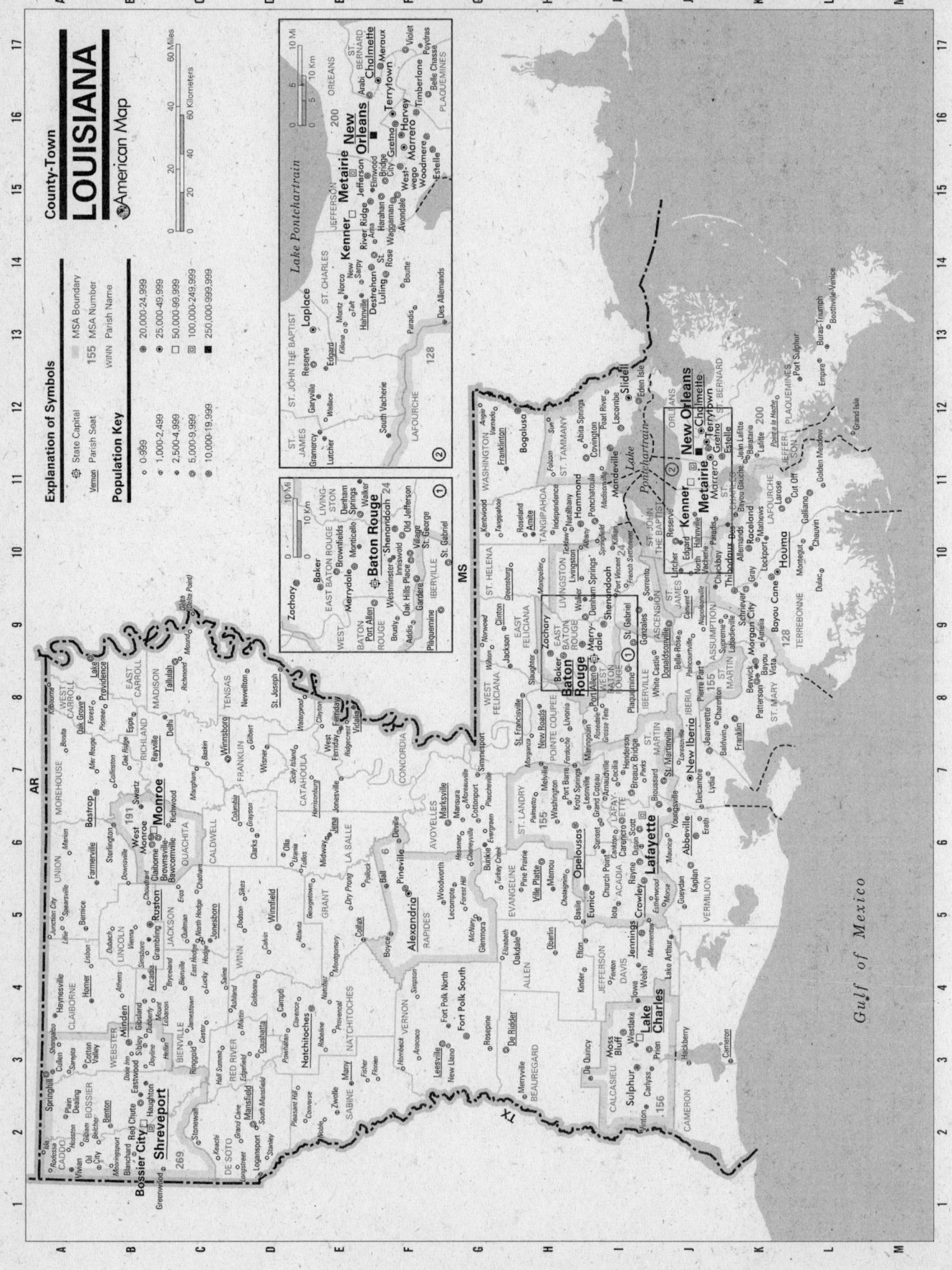

■ **BATON ROUGE COMMUNITY COLLEGE** *I-9*
5310 Florida Blvd.
Baton Rouge, LA 70806
Tel: (225)216-8000
Free: 800-601-4558
Admissions: (225)216-8700
Fax: (225)216-8100
Web Site: http://www.brcc.cc.la.us/
Description: State-supported, 2-year, coed. Awards transfer associate and terminal associate degrees. Founded 1995. Total enrollment: 5,761. Calendar: semesters.
Costs Per Year: State resident tuition: $1656 full-time. Nonresident tuition: $4464 full-time. Mandatory fees: $432 full-time. Full-time tuition and fees vary according to course load.

■ **BATON ROUGE SCHOOL OF COMPUTERS** *I-9*
10425 Plaza Americana
Baton Rouge, LA 70816
Tel: (504)923-2525
Fax: (504)923-2979
Web Site: http://www.brsc.net/
Description: Proprietary, 2-year, coed. Founded 1979.

■ **BLUE CLIFF COLLEGE-LAFAYETTE** *I-6*
100 Asma Blvd., Ste. 350
Lafayette, LA 70508-3862
Tel: (504)456-3141
Web Site: http://www.bluecliffcollege.com
Description: Proprietary, 2-year, coed.

■ **BLUE CLIFF COLLEGE-SHREVEPORT** *B-2*
200 N. Thomas Dr., Ste. A
Shreveport, LA 71107-6520
Tel: (504)456-3141
Web Site: http://www.bluecliffcollege.com
Description: Proprietary, 2-year, coed.

■ **BOSSIER PARISH COMMUNITY COLLEGE** *B-2*
2719 Airline Dr. North
Bossier City, LA 71111-5801
Tel: (318)746-9851
Admissions: (318)678-6166
Fax: (318)742-8664
Web Site: http://www.bpcc.edu/
Description: State-supported, 2-year, coed. Part of University of Louisiana System. Awards certificates, diplomas, transfer associate, and terminal associate degrees. Founded 1967. Setting: 64-acre urban campus. Total enrollment: 4,121. 0.1% Native American, 2% Hispanic, 24% black, 1% Asian American or Pacific Islander. Core. Calendar: semesters. Academic remediation for entering students, services for LD students, advanced placement, distance learning, double major, summer session for credit, part-time degree program, adult/continuing education programs.
Entrance Requirements: Open admission. Option: early admission. Required: high school transcript. Placement: ACT required. Entrance: noncompetitive. Application deadline: 8/10.

Costs Per Year: Application fee: $15. State resident tuition: $1720 full-time, $254 per credit part-time. Nonresident tuition: $3860 full-time, $414 per credit part-time. Mandatory fees: $448 full-time, $19 per credit part-time, $55 per term part-time.
Collegiate Environment: Orientation program. Drama-theater group, choral group, student-run newspaper. Most popular organizations: Student Government Association, Cavalier Players Drama Club, Data Processing Management Association. Major annual events: Basketball Homecoming, Halloween Dance, Doo Dah Parade. Student services: personal-psychological counseling. Campus security: student patrols. College housing not available. Bossier Parish Community College Library with 29,600 books, 384 serials, and an OPAC. Operations spending for 2004 fiscal year: $126,450. 83 computers available on campus for general student use. Staffed computer lab on campus.

■ **BRYMAN COLLEGE** *J-11*
1201 Elmwood Park Blvd., Ste. 600
New Orleans, LA 70123
Tel: (504)733-7117
Fax: (504)734-1217
Web Site: http://bryman-college.com/
Description: Proprietary, 2-year, coed. Founded 1989.

■ **CAMELOT COLLEGE** *I-9*
2618 Wooddale Blvd., Ste. A
Baton Rouge, LA 70805
Tel: (225)928-3005
Free: 800-470-3320
Fax: (225)927-3794
E-mail: home@camelotcollege.com
Web Site: http://www.camelotcollege.com/
Description: Proprietary, 2-year, coed. Founded 1986.

■ **CAMERON COLLEGE** *J-11*
2740 Canal St.
New Orleans, LA 70119
Tel: (504)821-5881
Web Site: http://www.cameroncollege.com/
Description: Proprietary, 2-year.

■ **CAREER TECHNICAL COLLEGE** *B-6*
2319 Louisville Ave.
Monroe, LA 71201
Tel: (318)323-2889
Free: 800-234-6766
Fax: (318)324-9883
Web Site: http://www.careertc.com/
Description: Proprietary, 2-year, coed. Founded 1985.

■ **CENTENARY COLLEGE OF LOUISIANA** *B-2*
2911 Centenary Blvd, PO Box 41188
Shreveport, LA 71104
Tel: (318)869-5011
Free: 800-234-4448
Admissions: (318)869-5104

Fax: (318)869-5005

E-mail: dcolson@centenary.edu

Web Site: http://www.centenary.edu/

Description: Independent United Methodist, comprehensive, coed. Awards bachelor's and master's degrees. Founded 1825. Setting: 65-acre suburban campus. Endowment: $112.3 million. Total enrollment: 1,044. Faculty: 122 (72 full-time, 50 part-time). Student-undergrad faculty ratio is 10:1. 1,348 applied, 64% were admitted. 40% from top 10% of their high school class, 70% from top quarter, 91% from top half. 57 class presidents, 25 valedictorians, 113 student government officers. Full-time: 882 students, 62% women, 38% men. Part-time: 22 students, 64% women, 36% men. Students come from 31 states and territories, 14 other countries, 38% from out-of-state, 1% Native American, 4% Hispanic, 7% black, 3% Asian American or Pacific Islander, 2% international, 2% 25 or older, 68% live on campus, 4% transferred in. Retention: 81% of full-time freshmen returned the following year. Academic areas with the most degrees conferred: business/marketing; biological/life sciences; visual and performing arts. Core. Calendar: 4-4-1. Advanced placement, self-designed majors, honors program, independent study, double major, summer session for credit, part-time degree program, adult/continuing education programs, internships, graduate courses open to undergrads. Off campus study at Associated Colleges of the South. Study abroad program.

Entrance Requirements: Options: Peterson's Universal Application, Common Application, electronic application, early admission, early decision, early action, deferred admission, international baccalaureate accepted. Required: high school transcript, minimum 2.0 high school GPA, 1 recommendation, SAT or ACT. Recommended: essay, interview, class rank. Entrance: moderately difficult. Application deadlines: 8/1, 12/15 for early decision, 1/15 for early action. Notification: 1/1 for early decision, 2/1 for early action.

Costs Per Year: Application fee: $30. Comprehensive fee: $25,680 includes full-time tuition ($18,900) and college room and board ($6780). College room only: $3310. Part-time tuition: $630 per semester hour. Part-time mandatory fees: $50 per term.

Collegiate Environment: Orientation program. Drama-theater group, choral group, student-run newspaper, radio station. Social organizations: 34 open to all; national fraternities, national sororities; 25% of eligible men and 20% of eligible women are members. Most popular organizations: intramural sports, Student Activities Board, crew, Church Career/Campus Ministries, student media. Major annual events: Fall Fest, Spring Fling, homecoming. Student services: health clinic, personal-psychological counseling. Campus security: 24-hour emergency response devices and patrols, late night transport-escort service, controlled dormitory access. 619 college housing spaces available; 68 were occupied in 2003-04. Freshmen guaranteed college housing. On-campus residence required through senior year. Options: coed, men-only, women-only housing available. Magale Library plus 1 other with 186,564 books, 1,454 microform titles, 59,899 serials, 5,945 audiovisual materials, an OPAC, and a Web page. Operations spending for 2004 fiscal year: $558,681. 250 computers available on campus for general student use. A campuswide network can be accessed from student residence rooms and from off campus. Staffed computer lab on campus.

Community Environment: See Louisiana State University Shreveport.

■ **DELGADO COMMUNITY COLLEGE** *J-11*

501 City Park Ave.

New Orleans, LA 70119-4399

Tel: (504)483-4400

Admissions: (504)483-4004

Fax: (504)483-1986

E-mail: jbolde@dcc.edu

Web Site: http://www.dcc.edu/

Description: State-supported, 2-year, coed. Part of Louisiana Community and Technical College System. Awards certificates, transfer associate, and terminal associate degrees. Founded 1921. Setting: 57-acre urban campus. Endowment: $1 million. Research spending for 2004 fiscal year: $58,000. Total enrollment: 16,501. Student-undergrad faculty ratio is 20:1. 2,657 applied. Full-time: 7,376 students, 68% women, 32% men. Part-time: 9,125 students, 72% women, 28% men. Students come from 33 states and territories, 3 other countries, 0.3% from out-of-state, 1% Native American, 4% Hispanic, 43% black, 2% Asian American or Pacific Islander, 0% international, 42% 25 or older. Retention: 53% of full-time freshmen returned the following year. Core. Calendar: semesters. Academic remediation for entering students, ESL program, services for LD students, advanced placement, self-designed majors, honors program, distance learning, summer session

for credit, part-time degree program, co-op programs. Off campus study at University of New Orleans, Southern University at New Orleans. ROTC: Army (c), Air Force (c).

Entrance Requirements: Open admission except for allied health, nursing, culinary arts programs. Recommended: high school transcript, proof of immunization. Required for some: high school transcript. Placement: ACT recommended; ACT required for some. Entrance: noncompetitive. Application deadline: Rolling.

Costs Per Year: Application fee: $15. State resident tuition: $1482 full-time, $420 per term part-time. Nonresident tuition: $4462 full-time, $1275 per term part-time. Mandatory fees: $362 full-time, $5 per credit part-time, $10 per term part-time. Part-time tuition and fees vary according to course load.

Collegiate Environment: Orientation program. Drama-theater group, choral group, student-run newspaper. Social organizations: 50 open to all. Most popular organizations: student government, Circle K, International Club, Phi Theta Kappa, Lambda Phi Nu. Major annual events: Homecoming Week, Spring Fest, International Week. Student services: health clinic, personal-psychological counseling. Campus security: 24-hour patrols, student patrols. College housing not available. Moss Memorial Library with 110,000 books, 1,299 serials, an OPAC, and a Web page. Operations spending for 2004 fiscal year: $1 million. 950 computers available on campus for general student use. A campuswide network can be accessed from off-campus. Staffed computer lab on campus.

Community Environment: See Tulane University.

■ **DELTA COLLEGE OF ARTS AND TECHNOLOGY** *I-9*

7380 Exchange Place

Baton Rouge, LA 70806-3851

Tel: (504)928-7770

Admissions: (225)928-7770

Fax: (504)927-9096

Web Site: http://www.deltacollege.com/

Description: Proprietary, 2-year, coed. Awards certificates, diplomas, and terminal associate degrees. Setting: 3-acre urban campus. Total enrollment: 434. Calendar: continuous (for most programs).

■ **DELTA SCHOOL OF BUSINESS & TECHNOLOGY** *I-3*

517 Broad St.

Lake Charles, LA 70601

Tel: (337)439-5765

Fax: (337)436-5151

E-mail: gholt@deltatech.edu

Web Site: http://www.deltatech.edu/

Description: Private, 2-year.

■ **DILLARD UNIVERSITY** *J-11*

2601 Gentilly Blvd.

New Orleans, LA 70122-3097

Tel: (504)283-8822

Free: 800-216-6637

Admissions: (504)816-4356

Fax: (504)286-4895

Web Site: http://www.dillard.edu/

Description: Independent interdenominational, 4-year, coed. Awards bachelor's degrees. Founded 1869. Setting: 55-acre urban campus. Endowment: $44.6 million. Educational spending for 2005 fiscal year: $5611 per student. Total enrollment: 2,155. 3,106 applied, 47% were admitted. 2% from top 10% of their high school class, 44% from top quarter, 74% from top half. Full-time: 1,920 students, 78% women, 22% men. Part-time: 235 students, 82% women, 18% men. Students come from 28 states and territories, 12 other countries, 50% from out-of-state, 0% Native American, 0.1% Hispanic, 99% black, 0.05% Asian American or Pacific Islander, 0.3% international, 10% 25 or older, 50% live on campus, 2% transferred in. Retention: 78% of full-time freshmen returned the following year. Core. Calendar: semesters. Academic remediation for entering students, services for LD students, advanced placement, honors program, double major, summer session for credit, part-time degree program, co-op programs and internships. Study abroad program. ROTC: Army (c), Air Force (c).

Entrance Requirements: Options: Common Application, electronic application, international baccalaureate accepted. Required: essay, high school transcript, 2 recommendations, SAT or ACT. Recommended: interview. Entrance: moderately difficult. Application deadline: 7/1. Notification: continuous until 8/1.

Collegiate Environment: Orientation program. Drama-theater group, choral group, student-run newspaper, radio station. Social organizations: 64 open to all; national fraternities, national sororities. Most popular organizations: SGA (Student Government Association), Pre-Alumni Council, SOUL-Students' Outreach of the Urban League, Students' Arts and Activities Committee. Major annual events: Coronation, Spring Fest, Black Heritage Ball. Student services: health clinic, personal-psychological counseling. Campus security: 24-hour patrols. 1,110 college housing spaces available; 1,000 were occupied in 2003-04. Freshmen guaranteed college housing. Options: coed, men-only, women-only housing available. Will W. Alexander Library with an OPAC and a Web page. Operations spending for 2004 fiscal year: $437,504.

Community Environment: See Tulane University.

■ **ELAINE P. NUNEZ COMMUNITY COLLEGE** *J-12*
3710 Paris Rd.
Chalmette, LA 70043-1249
Tel: (504)680-2240
Admissions: (504)680-2457
Fax: (504)680-2243
Web Site: http://www.nunez.edu/
Description: State-supported, 2-year, coed. Part of Louisiana Community and Technical Colleges System. Awards certificates, transfer associate, and terminal associate degrees. Founded 1992. Setting: 20-acre suburban campus with easy access to New Orleans. Endowment: $770,000. Educational spending for 2005 fiscal year: $3142 per student. Total enrollment: 2,363. 423 applied, 100% were admitted. Full-time: 1,213 students, 71% women, 29% men. Part-time: 1,150 students, 67% women, 33% men. Students come from 3 states and territories, 0% from out-of-state, 1% Native American, 3% Hispanic, 28% black, 2% Asian American or Pacific Islander, 1% international, 53% 25 or older, 19% transferred in. Core. Calendar: semesters. Academic remediation for entering students, ESL program, services for LD students, advanced placement, self-designed majors, independent study, distance learning, double major, summer session for credit, part-time degree program, adult/continuing education programs, co-op programs and internships. Off campus study at University of New Orleans, Southeastern Louisiana University, Delgado Community College.
Entrance Requirements: Open admission. Option: deferred admission. Recommended: minimum 2.0 high school GPA. Required for some: high school transcript. Placement: ACT recommended; ACT ASSET or ACT COMPASS required for some. Entrance: noncompetitive. Application deadline: 8/1.
Collegiate Environment: Orientation program. Drama-theater group, choral group, student-run newspaper. Social organizations: 1 open to all; national fraternities, coed fraternity; 5% of eligible men and 6% of eligible women are members. Most popular organization: Nunez Environmental Team. Major annual events: Spring Fling, Fall Fest. Student services: personal-psychological counseling. Campus security: 24-hour emergency response devices, late night transport-escort service. College housing not available. Nunez Community College Library with 37,626 books, 81,267 microform titles, 1,391 audiovisual materials, an OPAC, and a Web page. Operations spending for 2004 fiscal year: $368,692. 200 computers available on campus for general student use. A campuswide network can be accessed from student residence rooms. Staffed computer lab on campus.

■ **GRAMBLING STATE UNIVERSITY** *B-5*
PO Box 607
Grambling, LA 71245
Tel: (318)247-3811
Admissions: (318)274-6183
Fax: (318)274-6172
Web Site: http://www.gram.edu/
Description: State-supported, university, coed. Part of University of Louisiana System Board of Supervisors. Awards associate, bachelor's, master's, and doctoral degrees. Founded 1901. Setting: 380-acre small town campus. Endowment: $1.9 million. Total enrollment: 5,039. 2,793 applied, 65% were admitted. 18% from top quarter of their high school class, 53% from top half. Full-time: 4,088 students, 59% women, 41% men. Part-time: 352 students, 56% women, 44% men. Students come from 39 states and territories, 17 other countries, 40% from out-of-state, 0.2% Native American, 0.3% Hispanic, 95% black, 0.1% Asian American or Pacific Islander, 2% international, 14% 25 or older, 4% transferred in. Core. Calendar: semesters. Academic remediation for entering students, advanced placement, honors program, distance learning, summer session for credit, part-time degree

program, adult/continuing education programs, co-op programs and internships, graduate courses open to undergrads. Off campus study at Louisiana Tech University. Study abroad program. ROTC: Army, Air Force.
Entrance Requirements: Open admission for state residents. Options: Peterson's Universal Application, Common Application, early admission, early decision, deferred admission. Required: high school transcript, SAT or ACT. Entrance: noncompetitive. Application deadlines: 7/15, 4/15 for early decision. Notification: continuous until 8/1, 4/20 for early decision.
Costs Per Year: Application fee: $20. State resident tuition: $2232 full-time, $558 per term part-time. Nonresident tuition: $7582 full-time, $558 per term part-time. Mandatory fees: $1274 full-time. Part-time tuition varies according to course load. College room and board: $4034. College room only: $2138. Room and board charges vary according to housing facility.
Collegiate Environment: Orientation program. Drama-theater group, choral group, marching band, student-run newspaper, radio station. Social organizations: 81 open to all; national fraternities, national sororities, local fraternities, local sororities. Major annual events: Bayou Classic Football Game, Homecoming festivities, Springfest. Student services: health clinic, personal-psychological counseling. Campus security: 24-hour patrols, student patrols, controlled dormitory access. 3,304 college housing spaces available; 2,926 were occupied in 2003-04. On-campus residence required in freshman year. Options: men-only, women-only housing available. A. C. Lewis Memorial Library with 208,935 books, 642,843 microform titles, 1,253 serials, 5,661 audiovisual materials, an OPAC, and a Web page. 250 computers available on campus for general student use. Computer purchase/lease plans available. A campuswide network can be accessed from student residence rooms and from off campus. Staffed computer lab on campus.
Community Environment: Grambling is in a suburban location five miles from Ruston, 35 miles from Monroe, and 70 miles from Shreveport. There is easy access to several major air and bus lines. The town has many fraternal, athletic, social, and civic organizations, and there are theatres in nearby Ruston. Excellent hunting, fishing, and boating facilities in the area. This is the home of the annual North Louisiana Broiler Show and Fair, and an annual Housing Clinic.

■ **GRETNA CAREER COLLEGE** *J-11*
1415 Whitney Ave.
Gretna, LA 70053-5835
Tel: (504)366-5409
Fax: (504)365-1004
Web Site: http://www.gretnacareercollege.com/
Description: Proprietary, 2-year, coed.

■ **HERZING COLLEGE** *J-11*
2400 Veterans Blvd.
Kenner, LA 70062
Tel: (504)733-0074
Fax: (504)733-0020
Web Site: http://www.herzing.edu/
Description: Proprietary, primarily 2-year, coed. Awards diplomas, transfer associate, terminal associate, and bachelor's degrees. Founded 1996. Total enrollment: 220. 240 applied, 92% were admitted. Full-time: 153 students, 46% women, 54% men. Part-time: 67 students, 21% women, 79% men. Calendar: semesters.
Entrance Requirements: Entrance: moderately difficult.

■ **ITI TECHNICAL COLLEGE** *I-9*
13944 Airline Hwy.
Baton Rouge, LA 70817
Tel: (225)752-4233
Free: 800-467-4484
Admissions: (225)752-4230
Fax: (225)756-0903
E-mail: jmartin@iticollege.edu
Web Site: http://www.iticollege.edu/
Description: Proprietary, 2-year, coed. Awards certificates and terminal associate degrees. Founded 1973. Setting: 10-acre suburban campus. Total enrollment: 351. Student-undergrad faculty ratio is 10:1. 435 applied, 85% were admitted. Full-time: 226 students, 15% women, 85% men. Part-time: 125 students, 14% women, 86% men. 1% from out-of-state, 0.4% Native American, 2% Hispanic, 32% black, 0.4% Asian American or Pacific Islander. Calendar: continuous.
Entrance Requirements: Required: high school transcript, interview.

Costs Per Year: Application fee: $0.

■ **ITT TECHNICAL INSTITUTE**
140 James Dr. E
St. Rose, LA 70087
Tel: (504)463-0338
Web Site: http://www.itt-tech.edu/
Description: Proprietary, primarily 2-year, coed. Part of ITT Educational Services, Inc. Awards terminal associate and bachelor's degrees. Total enrollment: 541. Core.
Entrance Requirements: Option: deferred admission. Required: high school transcript, interview, Wonderlic aptitude test. Recommended: recommendations. Entrance: minimally difficult. Application deadline: Rolling. Notification: continuous.
Costs Per Year: Application fee: $100.
Collegiate Environment: Orientation program. College housing not available.

■ **LOUISIANA COLLEGE** *F-5*
1140 College Dr.
Pineville, LA 71359-0001
Tel: (318)487-7011
Free: 800-487-1906
Admissions: (318)487-7439
Fax: (318)487-7550
E-mail: admissions@lacollege.edu
Web Site: http://www.lacollege.edu/
Description: Independent Southern Baptist, 4-year, coed. Awards bachelor's degrees. Founded 1906. Setting: 81-acre small town campus. Endowment: $27.1 million. Educational spending for 2005 fiscal year: $6840 per student. Total enrollment: 1,085. 667 applied, 73% were admitted. 28% from top 10% of their high school class, 56% from top quarter, 83% from top half. 23 valedictorians. Full-time: 920 students, 56% women, 44% men. Part-time: 165 students, 66% women, 34% men. Students come from 17 states and territories, 8 other countries, 9% from out-of-state, 0.3% Native American, 2% Hispanic, 9% black, 1% Asian American or Pacific Islander, 1% international, 9% 25 or older, 55% live on campus, 6% transferred in. Retention: 59% of full-time freshmen returned the following year. Core. Calendar: semesters. Academic remediation for entering students, services for LD students, advanced placement, accelerated degree program, self-designed majors, honors program, independent study, double major, summer session for credit, part-time degree program, adult/continuing education programs, internships. Study abroad program. ROTC: Army.
Entrance Requirements: Options: electronic application, early admission. Required: high school transcript, minimum 2.0 high school GPA, recommendations, class rank, SAT or ACT. Recommended: interview. Required for some: 3 recommendations. Entrance: moderately difficult. Application deadline: 8/15. Notification: continuous.
Collegiate Environment: Orientation program. Drama-theater group, choral group, student-run newspaper. Social organizations: 40 open to all; local fraternities, local sororities; 20% of eligible men and 35% of eligible women are members. Most popular organizations: Baptist Student Union, Delta Xi Omega, Student Government Association, Union Board, Lambda Chi Beta. Major annual events: Gala Christmas, Homecoming, Cochon de Lait. Student services: health clinic, personal-psychological counseling. Campus security: 24-hour patrols, student patrols, late night transport-escort service, controlled dormitory access. 666 college housing spaces available; 547 were occupied in 2003-04. Freshmen guaranteed college housing. On-campus residence required through senior year. Options: men-only, women-only housing available. Richard W. Norton Memorial Library with 135,566 books, 116,433 microform titles, 380 serials, 3,000 audiovisual materials, an OPAC, and a Web page. Operations spending for 2004 fiscal year: $600,047. 226 computers available on campus for general student use. A campuswide network can be accessed from off-campus. Staffed computer lab on campus.
Community Environment: Alexandria-Pineville is in the geographic heart of the state. The urban population of 113,000 has access to several major shopping malls, movie theaters, cultural attractions, fine restaurants, historical landmarks and churches representing nearly every denomination. The area is particularly noted for outdoor recreation opportunities, including year-round water sports and public hunting land. Part-time job opportunities in the community are numerous for college students.

■ **LOUISIANA STATE UNIVERSITY AND AGRICULTURAL AND MECHANICAL COLLEGE** *I-9*
Baton Rouge, LA 70803
Tel: (225)578-3202

Admissions: (225)578-1175
Fax: (225)578-4433
E-mail: admissions@lsu.edu
Web Site: http://www.lsu.edu/
Description: State-supported, university, coed. Part of Louisiana State University System. Awards bachelor's, master's, doctoral, and first professional degrees and post-master's certificates. Founded 1860. Setting: 2,000-acre urban campus with easy access to New Orleans. Endowment: $268.7 million. Research spending for 2004 fiscal year: $106.1 million. Educational spending for 2005 fiscal year: $7552 per student. Total enrollment: 31,264. Faculty: 1,467 (1,277 full-time, 190 part-time). Student-undergrad faculty ratio is 22:1. 10,825 applied, 73% were admitted. 24% from top 10% of their high school class, 52% from top quarter, 83% from top half. 32 National Merit Scholars, 150 valedictorians. Full-time: 23,766 students, 52% women, 48% men. Part-time: 1,939 students, 54% women, 46% men. Students come from 51 states and territories, 89 other countries, 13% from out-of-state, 0.4% Native American, 3% Hispanic, 9% black, 3% Asian American or Pacific Islander, 2% international, 7% 25 or older, 23% live on campus, 3% transferred in. Retention: 83% of full-time freshmen returned the following year. Academic areas with the most degrees conferred: business/marketing; education; engineering. Core. Calendar: semesters. ESL program, services for LD students, advanced placement, accelerated degree program, self-designed majors, freshman honors college, honors program, independent study, distance learning, double major, summer session for credit, part-time degree program, adult/continuing education programs, co-op programs and internships, graduate courses open to undergrads. Off campus study at Southern University and Agricultural and Mechanical College, members of the National Student Exchange, Baton Rouge Community College. Study abroad program. ROTC: Army, Naval (c), Air Force.
Entrance Requirements: Options: early admission, deferred admission, international baccalaureate accepted. Required: high school transcript, minimum 3.0 high school GPA, minimum ACT score of 22 or SAT score of 1030, SAT or ACT. Required for some: essay, interview. Entrance: moderately difficult. Application deadline: 4/15. Notification: continuous.
Costs Per Year: Application fee: $40. State resident tuition: $2981 full-time. Nonresident tuition: $11,281 full-time. Mandatory fees: $1438 full-time. College room and board: $6330. College room only: $3930. Room and board charges vary according to board plan and housing facility.
Collegiate Environment: Orientation program. Drama-theater group, choral group, marching band, student-run newspaper, radio station. Social organizations: 335 open to all; national fraternities, national sororities; 10% of eligible men and 17% of eligible women are members. Most popular organizations: intramural athletics, student political organizations, student professional organizations, religious organizations. Major annual events: Fall Fest, Student Disability Week, Martin Luther King Day Celebration. Student services: legal services, health clinic, personal-psychological counseling, women's center. Campus security: 24-hour emergency response devices and patrols, late night transport-escort service, controlled dormitory access, self-defense education, crime prevention programs. 7,574 college housing spaces available; 6,200 were occupied in 2003-04. No special consideration for freshman housing applicants. Options: coed, men-only, women-only housing available. Troy H. Middleton Library plus 7 others with 1.4 million books, 5.4 million microform titles, 24,304 serials, 24,788 audiovisual materials, an OPAC, and a Web page. Operations spending for 2004 fiscal year: $11.8 million. 7,000 computers available on campus for general student use. A campuswide network can be accessed from student residence rooms and from off campus. Staffed computer lab on campus.
Community Environment: Baton Rouge, with a metropolitan-area population of more than 500,000, is the capital of Louisiana, the state's second largest port for ocean-going vessels, and the fifth largest inland port in the nation. A rich mixture of French, Spanish, and English cultures reflects Baton Rouge's history. Geographically, Baton Rouge is the center of South Louisiana's main cultural and recreational attractions. New Orleans is 80 miles to the southeast; the Feliciana parishes, noted for their antebellum homes, are less than an hour's drive to the north; and to the west lies the Acadian-French country of bayous, lakes, and marshes. Baton Rouge's industry is widely diversified. It is a major petrochemical center, as well as a center for banking and financial services and a major retail center. Cultural organizations include the Baton Rouge Symphony, the Baton Rouge Ballet,

and community theater groups. Baton Rouge has many recreation centers, golf courses, and parks. Mild temperatures make outdoor activities possible and enjoyable throughout the year.

■ LOUISIANA STATE UNIVERSITY AT ALEXANDRIA F-5

8100 Hwy. 71 South
Alexandria, LA 71302-9121
Tel: (318)445-3672; 888-473-6417
Admissions: (318)473-6542
Fax: (318)473-6418
Web Site: http://www.lsua.edu/
Description: State-supported, primarily 2-year, coed. Part of Louisiana State University System. Awards certificates, transfer associate, terminal associate, and bachelor's degrees. Founded 1960. Setting: 3,114-acre rural campus. Endowment: $588,481. Educational spending for 2005 fiscal year: $4397 per student. Total enrollment: 2,988. Student-undergrad faculty ratio is 16:1. 668 applied, 77% were admitted. Full-time: 1,572 students, 70% women, 30% men. Part-time: 1,416 students, 79% women, 21% men. Students come from 14 states and territories, 6 other countries, 1% from out-of-state, 2% Native American, 1% Hispanic, 19% black, 1% Asian American or Pacific Islander, 0.5% international, 41% 25 or older, 9% transferred in. Core. Calendar: semesters. Academic remediation for entering students, services for LD students, advanced placement, distance learning, summer session for credit, part-time degree program, adult/continuing education programs. ROTC: Army (c).
Entrance Requirements: Open admission for state residents. Option: early admission. Required: high school transcript, ACT. Entrance: noncompetitive. Application deadline: Rolling. Notification: continuous.
Costs Per Year: Application fee: $20. Area resident tuition: $3092 full-time. State resident tuition: $128 per credit hour part-time. Nonresident tuition: $5552 full-time, $231 per credit hour part-time.
Collegiate Environment: Orientation program. Drama-theater group, choral group, student-run newspaper. Social organizations: 15 open to all; national fraternities. Most popular organizations: Pentecostal Student Fellowship, Baptist Collegiate Ministries, Catholic Student Center, Student Government Association, Gamma Beta Phi. Student services: personal-psychological counseling. Campus security: 24-hour patrols. College housing not available. James C. Bolton Library with 154,935 books, 18,841 microform titles, 354 serials, 5,949 audiovisual materials, an OPAC, and a Web page. Operations spending for 2004 fiscal year: $405,157. 180 computers available on campus for general student use. A campuswide network can be accessed. Staffed computer lab on campus.

■ LOUISIANA STATE UNIVERSITY AT EUNICE I-5

PO Box 1129
Eunice, LA 70535-1129
Tel: (337)457-7311
Admissions: (337)550-1302
Fax: (337)457-7311
Web Site: http://www.lsue.edu/
Description: State-supported, 2-year, coed. Part of Louisiana State University System. Awards certificates, transfer associate, and terminal associate degrees. Founded 1967. Setting: 199-acre small town campus. Total enrollment: 2,833. 1,753 applied, 99% were admitted. Students come from 4 states and territories, 0.4% from out-of-state, 40% 25 or older. Core. Calendar: semesters. Academic remediation for entering students, services for LD students, advanced placement, honors program, distance learning, summer session for credit, part-time degree program, adult/continuing education programs, co-op programs.
Entrance Requirements: Open admission. Options: Common Application, early admission. Required: high school transcript. Placement: ACT recommended; ACT required for some. Entrance: noncompetitive. Application deadline: 8/7.
Collegiate Environment: Orientation program. Student-run newspaper. Social organizations: 14 open to all; local fraternities, local sororities; 3% of eligible men and 3% of eligible women are members. Most popular organizations: Student Government Association, Students in Free Enterprise, Criminal Justice Society, Student Nurses Association, Phi Theta Kappa. Major annual events: Festival of the Arts, Annual Blood Drive, End of Semester Bash. Student services: personal-psychological counseling. Campus security: 24-hour emergency response devices and patrols. Arnold LeDoux Library with 100,000 books, 253 serials, and an OPAC. 160 computers available on campus for general student use. A campuswide network can be accessed.

■ LOUISIANA STATE UNIVERSITY HEALTH SCIENCES CENTER J-11

433 Bolivar St.
New Orleans, LA 70112-2223
Tel: (504)568-4808
Admissions: (504)568-4829
Web Site: http://www.lsuhsc.edu/no/
Description: State-supported, university, coed. Part of Louisiana State University System. Awards associate, bachelor's, master's, doctoral, and first professional degrees. Founded 1931. Setting: 80-acre urban campus with easy access to New Orleans. Endowment: $56.2 million. Research spending for 2004 fiscal year: $83.8 million. Total enrollment: 2,240. Full-time: 585 students, 87% women, 13% men. Part-time: 57 students, 79% women, 21% men. Students come from 4 states and territories, 0.1% from out-of-state, 0.5% Native American, 4% Hispanic, 12% black, 8% Asian American or Pacific Islander, 0.5% international, 31% 25 or older, 11% live on campus. Calendar: semesters. Services for LD students, advanced placement, accelerated degree program, independent study, distance learning, double major, summer session for credit, co-op programs and internships, graduate courses open to undergrads.
Collegiate Environment: Orientation program. Choral group. Student services: health clinic, personal-psychological counseling. Campus security: 24-hour emergency response devices and patrols, late night transport-escort service, controlled dormitory access. 480 college housing spaces available; 73 were occupied in 2003-04. No special consideration for freshman housing applicants. Option: coed housing available. John P. Ische Library plus 2 others with 232,617 books, 2,359 serials, 3,200 audiovisual materials, an OPAC, and a Web page. Operations spending for 2004 fiscal year: $2.6 million. 100 computers available on campus for general student use. Computer purchase/lease plans available. A campuswide network can be accessed from student residence rooms and from off campus. Staffed computer lab on campus.

■ LOUISIANA STATE UNIVERSITY IN SHREVEPORT B-2

1 University Place
Shreveport, LA 71115-2399
Tel: (318)797-5000
Admissions: (318)797-5063
Fax: (318)797-5286
E-mail: admissions@pilot.lsus.edu
Web Site: http://www.lsus.edu/
Description: State-supported, comprehensive, coed. Part of Louisiana State University System. Awards bachelor's and master's degrees and post-master's certificates. Founded 1965. Setting: 200-acre urban campus. Endowment: $5.7 million. Research spending for 2004 fiscal year: $486,886. Educational spending for 2005 fiscal year: $1724 per student. Total enrollment: 4,401. 848 applied, 68% were admitted. Full-time: 2,648 students, 63% women, 37% men. Part-time: 1,105 students, 64% women, 36% men. Students come from 29 states and territories, 6 other countries, 4% from out-of-state, 1% Native American, 3% Hispanic, 23% black, 0% Asian American or Pacific Islander, 2% international, 33% 25 or older, 5% live on campus, 11% transferred in. Retention: 53% of full-time freshmen returned the following year. Core. Calendar: semesters plus 8-week and two 4-week summer terms. Academic remediation for entering students, services for LD students, advanced placement, accelerated degree program, self-designed majors, honors program, independent study, distance learning, double major, summer session for credit, part-time degree program, adult/continuing education programs, co-op programs and internships, graduate courses open to undergrads. Off campus study at Southern University at Shreveport-Bossier City Campus. ROTC: Army.
Entrance Requirements: Open admission for state residents. Options: early admission, deferred admission. Required: high school transcript, minimum 2.0 high school GPA. Recommended: ACT, SAT or ACT, SAT Subject Tests. Required for some: minimum ACT score of 17 for nonresidents. Entrance: noncompetitive. Application deadline: 8/1. Notification: continuous.
Collegiate Environment: Orientation program. Choral group, student-run newspaper. Social organizations: 45 open to all; national fraternities, national sororities; 5% of eligible men and 5% of eligible women are members. Most popular organizations: American Humanics, The Louisiana Association of Educators, Catholic Student Union, Biology/Health Club, Psychology Club. Major annual events: Spring Fling, Fall Fest, Pre-Cram Jam. Student services: personal-psychological counseling. Campus security: 24-hour patrols, student patrols, controlled dormitory access. 480 college housing spaces available; 292 were occupied in 2003-04. No special consideration

for freshman housing applicants. Options: coed, men-only, women-only housing available. Noel Memorial Library with 279,821 books, 364,744 microform titles, 1,190 serials, 1,914 audiovisual materials, an OPAC, and a Web page. Operations spending for 2004 fiscal year: $1.5 million.

■ LOUISIANA TECH UNIVERSITY B-5

PO Box 3168

Ruston, LA 71272

Tel: (318)257-0211

Free: 800-528-3241

Admissions: (318)257-3036

E-mail: usjba@latech.edu

Web Site: http://www.latech.edu/

Description: State-supported, university, coed. Part of University of Louisiana System. Awards associate, bachelor's, master's, and doctoral degrees and first professional certificates. Founded 1894. Setting: 247-acre small town campus. Endowment: $39.1 million. Research spending for 2004 fiscal year: $10.6 million. Educational spending for 2005 fiscal year: $3267 per student. Total enrollment: 11,691. 3,897 applied, 86% were admitted. 2 National Merit Scholars. Full-time: 7,553 students, 47% women, 53% men. Part-time: 1,765 students, 54% women, 46% men. Students come from 48 states and territories, 70 other countries, 12% from out-of-state, 19% 25 or older, 30% live on campus, 6% transferred in. Retention: 70% of full-time freshmen returned the following year. Core. Academic remediation for entering students, ESL program, advanced placement, honors program, independent study, distance learning, double major, summer session for credit, part-time degree program, adult/continuing education programs, co-op programs and internships, graduate courses open to undergrads. Off campus study at Grambling State University. Study abroad program. ROTC: Army (c), Naval.

Entrance Requirements: Option: early admission. Required: high school transcript, minimum 2.2 high school GPA, SAT or ACT. Recommended: ACT. Entrance: moderately difficult. Application deadline: 7/31. Notification: continuous.

Costs Per Year: Application fee: $20. State resident tuition: $3914 full-time. Nonresident tuition: $8819 full-time. Mandatory fees: $461 full-time. College room and board: $4035. College room only: $2130.

Collegiate Environment: Orientation program. Drama-theater group, choral group, marching band, student-run newspaper, radio station. Social organizations: 121 open to all; national fraternities, national sororities; 10% of eligible men and 12% of eligible women are members. Most popular organizations: Student Government Association, Association of Women's Studies, Union Board. Major annual events: homecoming, Spring Fling, Little Las Vegas Night. Student services: legal services, health clinic, personal-psychological counseling. Campus security: 24-hour emergency response devices and patrols, student patrols, late night transport-escort service, controlled dormitory access. On-campus residence required through sophomore year. Options: men-only, women-only housing available. Prescott Memorial Library with 3,319 books, 1.9 million microform titles, 2,469 serials, 14,532 audiovisual materials, an OPAC, and a Web page. Operations spending for 2004 fiscal year: $2.7 million. 1,800 computers available on campus for general student use. A campuswide network can be accessed from student residence rooms and from off campus. Staffed computer lab on campus.

Community Environment: This is an urban area with bus service available. City has a public library, several churches, its own hospital, medical clinics, and good shopping facilities. Theatres, drive-in, golf, fishing, boating, and a campus olympic swimming pool provide recreation opportunities. There is also a concert association.

■ LOUISIANA TECHNICAL COLLEGE I-9

150 3rd St.

Baton Rouge, LA 70801

Free: 800-351-7611

Web Site: http://www.ltc.edu/

Description: State-supported, 2-year, coed. Awards certificates, diplomas, and transfer associate degrees. Founded 1930. Endowment: $286,936. Educational spending for 2005 fiscal year: $3121 per student. Total enrollment: 13,414. Student-undergrad faculty ratio is 10:1. 2,094 applied, 100% were admitted. Full-time: 7,264 students, 55% women, 45% men. Part-time: 6,150 students, 39% women, 61% men. 1% from out-of-state, 1% Native American, 1% Hispanic, 37% black, 1% Asian American or Pacific Islander, 0% international.

Entrance Requirements: Required: high school transcript. Entrance: noncompetitive.

Costs Per Year: Application fee: $5. State resident tuition: $552 full-time, $23 per credit hour part-time. Nonresident tuition: $1104 full-time, $46 per credit hour part-time. Mandatory fees: $214 full-time, $9 per credit hour part-time, $5 per term part-time.

Collegiate Environment: College housing not available.

■ LOYOLA UNIVERSITY NEW ORLEANS J-11

6363 Saint Charles Ave.

New Orleans, LA 70118-6195

Tel: (504)865-2011

Free: 800-4-LOYOLA

Admissions: (504)865-3240

Fax: (504)865-3383

Web Site: http://www.loyno.edu/

Description: Independent Roman Catholic (Jesuit), comprehensive, coed. Awards bachelor's, master's, and first professional degrees and post-master's certificates. Founded 1912. Setting: 26-acre urban campus. Endowment: $304.2 million. Research spending for 2004 fiscal year: $775,074. Educational spending for 2005 fiscal year: $8770 per student. Total enrollment: 5,423. Faculty: 483 (306 full-time, 177 part-time). Student-undergrad faculty ratio is 11:1. 3,713 applied, 68% were admitted. 28% from top 10% of their high school class, 60% from top quarter, 90% from top half. 12 valedictorians. Full-time: 3,220 students, 60% women, 40% men. Part-time: 468 students, 67% women, 33% men. Students come from 52 states and territories, 56 other countries, 56% from out-of-state, 1% Native American, 11% Hispanic, 10% black, 4% Asian American or Pacific Islander, 3% international, 3% 25 or older, 40% live on campus, 6% transferred in. Retention: 82% of full-time freshmen returned the following year. Core. Calendar: semesters. Academic remediation for entering students, ESL program, services for LD students, advanced placement, accelerated degree program, self-designed majors, honors program, independent study, distance learning, double major, summer session for credit, part-time degree program, adult/continuing education programs, internships, graduate courses open to undergrads. Off campus study at Tulane University, Xavier University of Louisiana, Notre Dame Seminary, University of New Orleans, Southern University at New Orleans. Study abroad program. ROTC: Army (c), Naval (c), Air Force (c).

Entrance Requirements: Options: Common Application, electronic application, early admission, deferred admission, international baccalaureate accepted. Required: essay, high school transcript, 1 recommendation, SAT or ACT. Recommended: interview. Required for some: interview, PAA. Entrance: moderately difficult. Application deadline: 1/15. Notification: continuous.

Costs Per Year: Application fee: $20. Comprehensive fee: $33,558 includes full-time tuition ($24,410), mandatory fees ($836), and college room and board ($8312). College room only: $5166. Room and board charges vary according to board plan and housing facility. Part-time tuition: $696 per credit hour.

Collegiate Environment: Orientation program. Drama-theater group, choral group, student-run newspaper, radio station. Social organizations: 140 open to all; national fraternities, national sororities, local fraternities; 17% of eligible men and 18% of eligible women are members. Most popular organizations: University Programming Board, Community Action Program, Black Student Union, Student Government Association. Major annual events: Riverboat Party Charity Dance, Loyolapalooza Spring Festival, Loup Garou Fall Concert. Student services: health clinic, personal-psychological counseling, women's center. Campus security: 24-hour emergency response devices and patrols, late night transport-escort service, controlled dormitory access, self-defense education, bicycle patrols, closed circuit TV monitors, door alarms, crime prevention programs. 1,381 college housing spaces available; 1,295 were occupied in 2003-04. Freshmen guaranteed college housing. On-campus residence required in freshman year. Options: coed, women-only housing available. University Library plus 1 other with 401,548 books, 1.3 million microform titles, 4,948 serials, 15,484 audiovisual materials, an OPAC, and a Web page. Operations spending for 2004 fiscal year: $4.3 million. 458 computers available on campus for general student use. Computer purchase/lease plans available. A campuswide network can be accessed from student residence rooms and from off campus. Staffed computer lab on campus.

Community Environment: See Tulane University.

■ MCNEESE STATE UNIVERSITY *I-3*
4205 Ryan St.
Lake Charles, LA 70609
Tel: (337)475-5000
Free: 800-622-3352
Admissions: (337)475-5148
Web Site: http://www.mcneese.edu/
Description: State-supported, comprehensive, coed. Part of University of Louisiana System. Awards associate, bachelor's, and master's degrees and post-master's certificates. Founded 1939. Setting: 580-acre suburban campus. Endowment: $31.2 million. Research spending for 2004 fiscal year: $2.8 million. Educational spending for 2005 fiscal year: $2740 per student. Total enrollment: 8,785. 2,313 applied, 89% were admitted. 15% from top 10% of their high school class, 35% from top quarter, 66% from top half. Full-time: 6,399 students, 58% women, 42% men. Part-time: 1,327 students, 66% women, 34% men. Students come from 33 states and territories, 37 other countries, 6% from out-of-state, 1% Native American, 1% Hispanic, 20% black, 1% Asian American or Pacific Islander, 2% international, 23% 25 or older, 12% live on campus, 5% transferred in. Retention: 70% of full-time freshmen returned the following year. Core. Calendar: semesters. Academic remediation for entering students, ESL program, services for LD students, advanced placement, accelerated degree program, freshman honors college, honors program, independent study, distance learning, double major, summer session for credit, part-time degree program, adult/continuing education programs, co-op programs and internships, graduate courses open to undergrads. Off campus study at Council of Intercollegiate Nursing Consortium; Coushatta Project, Kinder, Louisiana. Study abroad program.
Entrance Requirements: Options: electronic application, early admission, international baccalaureate accepted. Required: high school transcript, SAT or ACT. Entrance: moderately difficult. Application deadline: Rolling. Notification: continuous.
Costs Per Year: Application fee: $20. State resident tuition: $2226 full-time, $571.50 per term part-time. Nonresident tuition: $8292 full-time, $571.50 per term part-time. Mandatory fees: $933 full-time, $292.50 per term part-time. College room and board: $4637.
Collegiate Environment: Orientation program. Drama-theater group, choral group, marching band, student-run newspaper. Social organizations: national fraternities, national sororities. Most popular organizations: Student Government Association, International Students Association, Resident Student Association. Major annual events: homecoming, Spring Fling. Student services: health clinic, personal-psychological counseling, women's center. Campus security: 24-hour emergency response devices and patrols, late night transport-escort service, controlled dormitory access. 1,270 college housing spaces available; 950 were occupied in 2003-04. No special consideration for freshman housing applicants. On-campus residence required in freshman year. Options: coed, men-only, women-only housing available. Frazer Memorial Library plus 2 others with 351,708 books, 1.4 million microform titles, 1,679 serials, 3,635 audiovisual materials, an OPAC, and a Web page. Operations spending for 2004 fiscal year: $1.5 million. 700 computers available on campus for general student use. A campuswide network can be accessed from student residence rooms and from off campus. Staffed computer lab on campus.
Community Environment: The city owes its development to the combination of Capt. J. B. Watkins, a variety of natural resources and a deepwater port. In 1887 Captain Watkins of New York moved his newspaper to Lake Charles and started an overwhelming advertising program, which, with the terminus of a railroad at New Orleans, resulted in the development of a 17-mill lumber industry. The discovery of oil in the early 1900s and a new process of mining sulfur further enriched the city. Forests are presently nearly depleted and the sulfur supply is no longer industrially profitable. This city with its vast oil companies in southwest Louisiana is a leader in the petrochemical industry. A deepwater port since 1926, it is currently the nation's leading rice port. Docks also handle general cargo, the output of chemical and petrochemical plants and products of the city's two large rice mills. Student employment is available. Transportation is provided by commercial passenger air lines, rail, and bus service. There are libraries, YMCA, a great number of churches, and three hospitals easily accessible. Recreation includes fishing, hunting, theatres, and an annual rodeo.

■ MEDVANCE INSTITUTE *I-9*
9255 Interline Ave.
Baton Rouge, LA 70809

Tel: (225)248-1015
Fax: (225)248-9571
Web Site: http://www.medvance.org/
Description: Proprietary, 2-year, coed. Awards diplomas and terminal associate degrees. Founded 1970. Setting: 4-acre urban campus. Total enrollment: 294. 105 applied, 57% were admitted. Full-time: 294 students, 90% women, 10% men. 0% from out-of-state, 50% 25 or older. Core. Internships.
Entrance Requirements: Options: Peterson's Universal Application, Common Application. Required: high school transcript, interview, Wonderlic aptitude test. Recommended: minimum 2.0 high school GPA, 2 recommendations. Entrance: noncompetitive. Application deadline: Rolling. Notification: continuous.
Collegiate Environment: College housing not available. 10 computers available on campus for general student use. Staffed computer lab on campus.

■ METROPOLITAN COMMUNITY COLLEGE *J-11*
2550 Belle Chasse Hwy.
Gretna, LA 70053
Tel: (504)366-4613
Fax: (504)366-4614
Web Site: http://www.metrocc.us/
Description: Proprietary, 2-year, coed. Awards certificates and terminal associate degrees.

■ NEW ORLEANS BAPTIST THEOLOGICAL SEMINARY *J-11*
3939 Gentilly Blvd.
New Orleans, LA 70126-4858
Tel: (504)282-4455
Free: 800-662-8701
Web Site: http://www.nobts.edu/
Description: Independent Southern Baptist, comprehensive, coed. Awards associate, bachelor's, master's, doctoral, and first professional degrees. Founded 1917. Setting: 81-acre suburban campus. Total enrollment: 2,712. 85 applied, 82% were admitted. Students come from 29 states and territories, 5 other countries, 0.2% Native American, 11% Hispanic, 18% black, 2% Asian American or Pacific Islander, 4% international, 100% 25 or older. Retention: 70% of full-time freshmen returned the following year. Core. Calendar: semesters. Academic remediation for entering students, ESL program, independent study, summer session for credit, part-time degree program, adult/continuing education programs, internships. Off campus study.
Entrance Requirements: Option: deferred admission. Recommended: minimum 2.0 high school GPA. Entrance: minimally difficult. Application deadline: 8/9. Notification: continuous.
Collegiate Environment: Orientation program. Choral group, student-run radio station. Major annual events: Campus Revival, Christmas Party. Student services: health clinic, personal-psychological counseling. Campus security: 24-hour emergency response devices and patrols. John Christian Library plus 1 other with 206,321 books. 10 computers available on campus for general student use.
Community Environment: See Tulane University.

■ NICHOLLS STATE UNIVERSITY *K-9*
906 East First St.
Thibodaux, LA 70310
Tel: (985)446-8111; 877-NICHOLLS
Admissions: (985)448-4507
Fax: (985)448-4929
E-mail: nicholls@nich-nsunet.nich.edu
Web Site: http://www.nicholls.edu
Description: State-supported, comprehensive, coed. Part of University of Louisiana System. Awards associate, bachelor's, and master's degrees and post-master's certificates. Founded 1948. Setting: 210-acre small town campus with easy access to New Orleans. Endowment: $11.8 million. Research spending for 2004 fiscal year: $770,000. Educational spending for 2005 fiscal year: $3807 per student. Total enrollment: 7,525. Faculty: 290 (289 full-time, 1 part-time). Student-undergrad faculty ratio is 21:1. 2,339 applied, 67% were admitted. 15% from top 10% of their high school class, 37% from top quarter, 65% from top half. 38 valedictorians. Full-time: 5,501 students, 61% women, 39% men. Part-time: 1,385 students, 68% women, 32% men. Students come from 32 states and territories, 25 other countries, 3% from out-of-state, 2% Native American, 1% Hispanic, 20% black, 1% Asian American or Pacific Islander, 1% international, 22% 25 or older, 18%

live on campus, 6% transferred in. Retention: 62% of full-time freshmen returned the following year. Academic areas with the most degrees conferred: health professions and related sciences; business/marketing; education. Core. Calendar: semesters. Academic remediation for entering students, ESL program, services for LD students, advanced placement, accelerated degree program, honors program, independent study, distance learning, double major, summer session for credit, part-time degree program, adult/continuing education programs, co-op programs and internships, graduate courses open to undergrads. Off campus study. Study abroad program.

Entrance Requirements: Options: Peterson's Universal Application, electronic application, early admission, deferred admission. Required: high school transcript. Recommended: SAT or ACT. Entrance: noncompetitive. Application deadline: Rolling. Notification: 9/1.

Costs Per Year: Application fee: $20. State resident tuition: $2230 full-time. Nonresident tuition: $7679 full-time. Mandatory fees: $1159 full-time. College room and board: $3720. College room only: $1900.

Collegiate Environment: Orientation program. Drama-theater group, choral group, marching band, student-run newspaper, radio station. Social organizations: 83 open to all; national fraternities, national sororities; 5% of eligible men and 4% of eligible women are members. Most popular organizations: Student Government Association, Student Programming Association, Residence Hall Association, Food Advisory Association. Major annual events: Homecoming, Spring Fest, Family Day. Student services: legal services, health clinic, personal-psychological counseling, women's center. Campus security: 24-hour emergency response devices and patrols, student patrols, late night transport-escort service. College housing designed to accommodate 1,174 students; 1,214 undergraduates lived in college housing during 2003-04. Freshmen guaranteed college housing. On-campus residence required in freshman year. Options: coed, men-only, women-only housing available. Allen J. Ellender Memorial Library with 303,962 books, 396,049 microform titles, 1,341 serials, 3,374 audiovisual materials, an OPAC, and a Web page. Operations spending for 2004 fiscal year: $1.6 million. 250 computers available on campus for general student use. A campuswide network can be accessed from student residence rooms and from off campus. Staffed computer lab on campus.

Community Environment: The campus is located in a sugar-belt town on the banks of picturesque Bayou Lafourche. Incorporated in 1838, this was the first trading post established between New Orleans and the country along Bayou Teche in southeastern Louisiana. There are many beautiful plantations in the vicinity. Thibodaux presents a small town atmosphere. It is a quick 45 miles from historic New Orleans by rail or bus. The year-round climate is mild to moderate. The city has a public library, churches representing all denominations, and a hospital. Recreation includes movies, theater, hunting, boating, fishing, golf, bowling, swimming, and tennis. Student employment is available in the area and on campus.

■ **NORTHWESTERN STATE UNIVERSITY OF LOUISIANA** *E-4*
350 Sam Sibley Dr.
Natchitoches, LA 71497
Tel: (318)357-6361
Free: 800-327-1903
Admissions: (318)357-4078
E-mail: admissions@nsula.edu
Web Site: http://www.nsula.edu/

Description: State-supported, comprehensive, coed. Part of University of Louisiana System. Awards associate, bachelor's, and master's degrees and post-master's certificates. Founded 1884. Setting: 916-acre small town campus. Endowment: $5.1 million. Research spending for 2004 fiscal year: $1.5 million. Educational spending for 2005 fiscal year: $3552 per student. Total enrollment: 9,847. Faculty: 546 (309 full-time, 237 part-time). Student-undergrad faculty ratio is 18:1. 2,852 applied, 77% were admitted. 14% from top 10% of their high school class, 35% from top quarter, 66% from top half. 39 valedictorians. Full-time: 6,460 students, 63% women, 37% men. Part-time: 2,328 students, 78% women, 22% men. Students come from 40 states and territories, 25 other countries, 7% from out-of-state, 2% Native American, 2% Hispanic, 31% black, 1% Asian American or Pacific Islander, 0.4% international, 27% 25 or older, 21% live on campus, 7% transferred in. Retention: 66% of full-time freshmen returned the following year. Academic areas with the most degrees conferred: health professions and related sciences; liberal arts/general studies; business/marketing. Core. Calendar: semesters. Academic remediation for entering students, advanced placement, freshman honors college, honors program, independent study, distance learning, double major, summer session for credit, part-time degree

program, adult/continuing education programs, co-op programs and internships, graduate courses open to undergrads. ROTC: Army.

Entrance Requirements: Options: Peterson's Universal Application, Common Application, electronic application, early action, deferred admission. Required: high school transcript, college preparatory curriculum; plus a 2.0 GPA, or a minimum ACT score of 20, or top 50% of class, SAT or ACT. Entrance: moderately difficult. Application deadline: 7/6. Notification: continuous.

Costs Per Year: Application fee: $20. State resident tuition: $2240 full-time, $240 per credit part-time. Nonresident tuition: $8318 full-time, $493 per credit part-time. Mandatory fees: $1153 full-time. Full-time tuition and fees vary according to course load. Part-time tuition varies according to course load. College room and board: $3626. College room only: $2050. Room and board charges vary according to board plan, housing facility, and location.

Collegiate Environment: Orientation program. Drama-theater group, choral group, marching band, student-run newspaper, radio station. Social organizations: 100 open to all; national fraternities, national sororities; 9% of eligible men and 5% of eligible women are members. Most popular organizations: Baptist Collegiate Ministry, Catholic Student Organization. Major annual events: Spring Fling Week, Homecoming Week, Welcome Week. Student services: health clinic, personal-psychological counseling. Campus security: 24-hour emergency response devices and patrols, late night transport-escort service, controlled dormitory access. 2,122 college housing spaces available; 1,923 were occupied in 2003-04. Freshmen given priority for college housing. On-campus residence required through junior year. Options: coed, men-only, women-only housing available. Eugene P. Watson Memorial Library with 325,829 books, 171,425 microform titles, 7,978 serials, 7,403 audiovisual materials, an OPAC, and a Web page. Operations spending for 2004 fiscal year: $1.7 million. 1,132 computers available on campus for general student use. Computer purchase/lease plans available. A campuswide network can be accessed from student residence rooms and from off campus. Staffed computer lab on campus.

■ **OUR LADY OF HOLY CROSS COLLEGE** *J-11*
4123 Woodland Dr.
New Orleans, LA 70131-7399
Tel: (504)394-7744
Free: 800-259-7744
Fax: (504)391-2421
Web Site: http://www.olhcc.edu/

Description: Independent Roman Catholic, comprehensive, coed. Awards associate, bachelor's, and master's degrees. Founded 1916. Setting: 40-acre suburban campus with easy access to New Orleans. Endowment: $7 million. Educational spending for 2005 fiscal year: $3200 per student. Total enrollment: 1,446. 320 applied, 97% were admitted. Full-time: 831 students, 78% women, 22% men. Part-time: 485 students, 79% women, 21% men. Students come from 4 states and territories, 3 other countries, 4% from out-of-state, 1% Native American, 4% Hispanic, 16% black, 3% Asian American or Pacific Islander, 0% international, 35% 25 or older, 11% transferred in. Retention: 64% of full-time freshmen returned the following year. Core. Calendar: semesters plus summer sessions. Academic remediation for entering students, services for LD students, advanced placement, independent study, distance learning, double major, summer session for credit, part-time degree program, adult/continuing education programs, co-op programs and internships, graduate courses open to undergrads. Off campus study at Delgado Community College, St. Joseph Seminary College, Notre Dame Seminary, Ochsner Clinical Foundation, Louisiana Universities Marine Consortium, Gulf Coast Research Laboratories. Study abroad program. ROTC: Army (c), Air Force (c).

Entrance Requirements: Options: Common Application, electronic application, deferred admission, international baccalaureate accepted. Required: high school transcript. Recommended: minimum 2.0 high school GPA. Placement: SAT or ACT required; ACT recommended. Entrance: minimally difficult. Application deadline: 7/20. Notification: continuous.

Collegiate Environment: Orientation program. Drama-theater group, student-run newspaper. Social organizations: 15 open to all. Most popular organizations: Innovators, student government, Association of Student Nurses, Delta Sigma Pi, Louisiana Association of Educators/Student Programs. Major annual events: Crawfish Boil, Christmas Dance, Fall Fest. Student services: personal-psychological counseling. Campus security: 24-hour patrols. College housing not available. Blaine Kern Library with 83,631 books, 222,522 microform titles, 1,002 serials, 11,949 audiovisual materials, an OPAC, and a Web page. Operations spending for 2004 fiscal year: $318,505. 68 computers available on campus for general student use. A campuswide network can be accessed. Staffed computer lab on campus.

Community Environment: See Tulane University.

■ OUR LADY OF THE LAKE COLLEGE *I-9*
7434 Perkins Rd.
Baton Rouge, LA 70808
Tel: (225)768-1700; 877-242-3509
Fax: (225)768-1726
Web Site: http://www.ololcollege.edu/
Description: Independent Roman Catholic, 4-year, coed. Awards associate, bachelor's, and master's degrees. Founded 1990. Setting: 5-acre suburban campus with easy access to New Orleans. Educational spending for 2005 fiscal year: $6782 per student. Total enrollment: 1,990. 241 applied, 91% were admitted. Students come from 3 states and territories, 1% from out-of-state, 1% Native American, 2% Hispanic, 20% black, 2% Asian American or Pacific Islander, 0% international. Retention: 55% of full-time freshmen returned the following year. Core. Calendar: semesters. Academic remediation for entering students, services for LD students, advanced placement, summer session for credit, part-time degree program, external degree program, adult/continuing education programs. Off campus study. ROTC: Army (c), Air Force (c).
Entrance Requirements: Open admission except for professional programs. Option: Common Application. Required: high school transcript, minimum 2.0 high school GPA, ACT, ACT ASSET. Entrance: minimally difficult. Application deadline: Rolling. Notification: 8/1.
Costs Per Year: Application fee: $35. Tuition: $6780 full-time, $226 per credit hour part-time. Mandatory fees: $500 full-time, $75 per term part-time.
Collegiate Environment: Student-run newspaper. Social organizations: 2 open to all. Most popular organizations: Student Government Association, Cultural Arts Association, Christian Fellowship Association, Mathematics/Science Association. Major annual events: Welcoming Ceremony, Spring Student Social, Fall Festival. Student services: health clinic, personal-psychological counseling. Campus security: 24-hour patrols. College housing not available. Learning Resource Center plus 1 other with 12,409 books, 328 serials, and an OPAC. Operations spending for 2004 fiscal year: $350,000. 100 computers available on campus for general student use. A campuswide network can be accessed. Staffed computer lab on campus.

■ REMINGTON COLLEGE-BATON ROUGE CAMPUS *I-9*
1900 North Lobdell
Baton Rouge, LA 70806
Tel: (225)922-3990
Fax: (225)922-9569
E-mail: gregg.falcon@remingtoncollege.edu
Web Site: http://www.remingtoncollege.edu/
Description: Proprietary, 2-year, coed. Calendar: continuous.

■ REMINGTON COLLEGE-LAFAYETTE CAMPUS *I-6*
303 Rue Louis XIV
Lafayette, LA 70508
Tel: (337)981-4010
Admissions: (337)981-9010
Fax: (337)983-7130
Web Site: http://www.remingtoncollege.edu/
Description: Proprietary, 2-year, coed. Part of Education America Inc. Awards diplomas and terminal associate degrees. Founded 1940. Setting: 4-acre urban campus. Total enrollment: 367. Student-undergrad faculty ratio is 18:1. 114 applied, 100% were admitted. 0% from out-of-state, 1% Native American, 2% Hispanic, 50% black, 2% Asian American or Pacific Islander, 0% international, 40% 25 or older. Core. Calendar: continuous. Honors program, independent study.
Entrance Requirements: Options: early admission, deferred admission, international baccalaureate accepted. Required: high school transcript, interview. Entrance: noncompetitive.
Costs Per Year: Application fee: $50. Tuition: $12,825 full-time.
Collegiate Environment: Major annual events: Career Fair, Blood Drive. Campus security: 24-hour emergency response devices. College housing not available. Remington College Library with 15,435 books, 85 serials, 182 audiovisual materials, and an OPAC. 120 computers available on campus for general student use. A campuswide network can be accessed from off-campus. Staffed computer lab on campus.

■ REMINGTON COLLEGE-NEW ORLEANS CAMPUS *J-11*
321 Veterans Memorial Blvd.
Metairie, LA 70005

Tel: (504)831-8889
Fax: (504)831-6803
Web Site: http://www.remingtoncollege.edu/
Description: Proprietary, 2-year, coed. Awards terminal associate degrees. Total enrollment: 650.
Entrance Requirements: Entrance: minimally difficult. Application deadline: Rolling. Notification: continuous.
Collegiate Environment: College housing not available.

■ RIVER PARISHES COMMUNITY COLLEGE *I-9*
PO Box 310
Sorrento, LA 70778
Tel: (225)675-8270
Fax: (225)675-5478
E-mail: adauzat@rpcc.cc.la.us
Web Site: http://rpcc.cc.la.us/
Description: State-supported, 2-year, coed. Awards certificates, diplomas, and transfer associate degrees. Founded 1997. Total enrollment: 724. Calendar: semesters.
Costs Per Year: Application fee: $10. State resident tuition: $1458 full-time, $66 per credit hour part-time. Nonresident tuition: $4174 full-time, $66 per credit hour part-time. Mandatory fees: $310 full-time, $40 per term part-time.

■ SAINT JOSEPH SEMINARY COLLEGE
St. Benedict, LA 70457
Tel: (504)892-1800
Admissions: (985)867-2225
Web Site: http://www.sjasc.edu/
Description: Independent Roman Catholic, 4-year, men only. Awards bachelor's degrees (Religious Studies Institute is coed). Founded 1891. Setting: 1,300-acre rural campus with easy access to New Orleans. Endowment: $127,793. Educational spending for 2005 fiscal year: $2383 per student. Total enrollment: 167. Full-time: 77 students. Part-time: 90 students. Students come from 8 states and territories, 42% from out-of-state, 21% Hispanic, 3% black, 6% Asian American or Pacific Islander, 31% 25 or older, 100% live on campus, 15% transferred in. Retention: 91% of full-time freshmen returned the following year. Core. Calendar: semesters. Academic remediation for entering students, ESL program, advanced placement, adult/continuing education programs.
Entrance Requirements: Options: early admission, deferred admission. Required: high school transcript, minimum 2.0 high school GPA, recommendations, interview, ACT. Entrance: minimally difficult. Application deadline: Rolling. Notification: continuous. Preference given to candidates for the priesthood.
Collegiate Environment: Orientation program. Drama-theater group, choral group, student-run newspaper. Social organizations: 5 open to all. Most popular organization: student government. Major annual events: Annual Bonfire, America Sings, homecoming. Student services: health clinic, personal-psychological counseling. Campus security: 24-hour emergency response devices, controlled dormitory access, entrance gate. 100 college housing spaces available; 77 were occupied in 2003-04. Freshmen guaranteed college housing. On-campus residence required through senior year. Option: men-only housing available. Pere Rouquette Library plus 1 other with 70,000 books, 137 serials, 1,500 audiovisual materials, an OPAC, and a Web page. Operations spending for 2004 fiscal year: $75,260. 15 computers available on campus for general student use. Staffed computer lab on campus.
Community Environment: Saint Benedict is located four miles north of Covington and 50 miles north of New Orleans. There is bus service available to Covington from New Orleans, Baton Rouge, and Hammond.

■ SCHOOL OF URBAN MISSIONS-NEW ORLEANS *J-11*
PO Box 53344
New Orleans, LA 70153
Tel: (504)362-6364
Free: 800-385-6364
Fax: (504)362-4895
Web Site: http://www.sumonline.org/
Description: Independent interdenominational, 2-year, coed. Founded 1991.

■ SOUTHEASTERN LOUISIANA UNIVERSITY *I-10*
Hammond, LA 70402
Tel: (985)549-2000

Free: 800-222-7358
Admissions: (985)549-2066
Fax: (985)549-5095
E-mail: Richard.Beaugh@selu.edu
Web Site: http://www.selu.edu/

Description: State-supported, comprehensive, coed. Part of University of Louisiana System. Awards associate, bachelor's, and master's degrees. Founded 1925. Setting: 375-acre small town campus with easy access to New Orleans. Endowment: $16.3 million. Research spending for 2004 fiscal year: $4.7 million. Educational spending for 2005 fiscal year: $2947 per student. Total enrollment: 15,472. Faculty: 730 (497 full-time, 233 part-time). Student-undergrad faculty ratio is 27:1. 3,297 applied, 94% were admitted. 9% from top 10% of their high school class, 28% from top quarter, 61% from top half. Full-time: 11,157 students, 60% women, 40% men. Part-time: 2,507 students, 69% women, 31% men. Students come from 42 states and territories, 39 other countries, 2% from out-of-state, 0.4% Native American, 1% Hispanic, 16% black, 1% Asian American or Pacific Islander, 1% international, 21% 25 or older, 11% live on campus, 5% transferred in. Retention: 67% of full-time freshmen returned the following year. Core. Calendar: semesters. Academic remediation for entering students, services for LD students, advanced placement, honors program, independent study, distance learning, double major, summer session for credit, part-time degree program, adult/continuing education programs, internships, graduate courses open to undergrads. Off campus study at Baton Rouge Center, St. Tammany Center. Study abroad program. ROTC: Army (c).

Entrance Requirements: Options: electronic application, early admission, deferred admission. Required: high school transcript, proof of immunization, SAT or ACT. Recommended: SAT Subject Tests. Required for some: minimum 2.0 high school GPA. Entrance: moderately difficult. Application deadline: 8/16. Notification: continuous.

Costs Per Year: Application fee: $20. State resident tuition: $3341 full-time, $139 per credit hour part-time. Nonresident tuition: $8669 full-time, $361 per credit hour part-time. Full-time tuition varies according to course load. Part-time tuition varies according to course load. College room and board: $5180. College room only: $3150. Room and board charges vary according to board plan and housing facility.

Collegiate Environment: Orientation program. Drama-theater group, choral group, student-run newspaper, radio station. Social organizations: 94 open to all; national fraternities, national sororities; 3% of eligible men and 5% of eligible women are members. Most popular organizations: Gamma Beta Phi, Alpha Omicron Pi, Management Honor Society, Baptist Collegiate Ministries, Black Student Union Caucus. Major annual events: Rush, Gumbo Ya Ya, Strawberry Jubilee. Student services: legal services, health clinic, personal-psychological counseling. Campus security: 24-hour emergency response devices and patrols, late night transport-escort service, controlled dormitory access, video cameras, motorist assistance. 2,000 college housing spaces available; 1,508 were occupied in 2003-04. Freshmen given priority for college housing. On-campus residence required through sophomore year. Options: coed, men-only, women-only housing available. Sims Memorial Library with 572,563 books, 769,303 microform titles, 2,387 serials, 48,752 audiovisual materials, an OPAC, and a Web page. Operations spending for 2004 fiscal year: $3.3 million. 837 computers available on campus for general student use. A campuswide network can be accessed from student residence rooms and from off campus. Staffed computer lab on campus.

Community Environment: City is located in the Southeastern section of the state. Climate is subtropical. Transportation to and from city available via Illinois Central Railroad and Greyhound Bus Co. There are five libraries, six local theatres, golf, hunting, fishing, boating at Lake Ponchartrain for recreation. Two hospitals, six motels and numerous apartments are available. Part-time employment for students is limited. There are 35 civic, fraternal, and veteran's organizations in Hammond.

■ SOUTHERN UNIVERSITY AND AGRICULTURAL AND MECHANICAL COLLEGE *I-9*

Baton Rouge, LA 70813
Tel: (225)771-4500
Free: 800-256-1531
Admissions: (225)771-2430
Web Site: http://www.subr.edu/

Description: State-supported, comprehensive, coed. Part of Southern University System. Awards associate, bachelor's, master's, and doctoral degrees and post-master's certificates. Founded 1880. Setting: 964-acre suburban campus. Endowment: $7.9 million. Research spending for 2004 fiscal year: $5.2 million. Educational spending for 2005 fiscal year: $3016

per student. Total enrollment: 9,941. Faculty: 573 (406 full-time, 167 part-time). Student-undergrad faculty ratio is 18:1. 4,703 applied, 53% were admitted. 11% from top 10% of their high school class, 30% from top quarter, 60% from top half. 5 class presidents, 11 valedictorians, 8 student government officers. Full-time: 7,729 students, 61% women, 39% men. Part-time: 847 students, 66% women, 34% men. Students come from 41 states and territories, 28 other countries, 17% from out-of-state, 0.1% Native American, 0.2% Hispanic, 96% black, 0.3% Asian American or Pacific Islander, 1% international, 17% 25 or older, 35% live on campus, 3% transferred in. Retention: 72% of full-time freshmen returned the following year. Academic areas with the most degrees conferred: business/marketing; health professions and related sciences; engineering. Core. Calendar: semesters. Academic remediation for entering students, services for LD students, advanced placement, honors program, distance learning, summer session for credit, part-time degree program, adult/continuing education programs, co-op programs and internships, graduate courses open to undergrads. Off campus study at Louisiana State University and Agricultural and Mechanical College, Southeastern Louisiana University, Southern University at New Orleans, Baton Rouge Community College. Study abroad program. ROTC: Army, Naval, Air Force (c).

Entrance Requirements: Options: Common Application, early admission. Required: high school transcript, minimum 2.2 high school GPA, SAT or ACT. Placement: SAT or ACT required. Entrance: moderately difficult. Application deadline: 7/1. Notification: continuous.

Costs Per Year: Application fee: $20. State resident tuition: $3592 full-time. Nonresident tuition: $9384 full-time. Full-time tuition varies according to course load and location. College room and board: $4646. College room only: $2816. Room and board charges vary according to board plan and housing facility.

Collegiate Environment: Orientation program. Drama-theater group, choral group, marching band, student-run newspaper. Social organizations: 63 open to all; national fraternities, national sororities, local fraternities, local sororities; 1% of eligible men and 2% of eligible women are members. Most popular organizations: Student Government Association, Association for Women Students (AWS), Men's Federation. Major annual events: homecoming, Founder's Day, Springfest. Student services: legal services, health clinic, personal-psychological counseling, women's center. Campus security: 24-hour emergency response devices and patrols, late night transport-escort service, controlled dormitory access. 3,015 college housing spaces available; 2,795 were occupied in 2003-04. Freshmen given priority for college housing. On-campus residence required in freshman year. Options: men-only, women-only housing available. John B. Cade Library plus 2 others with 808,365 books, 721,123 microform titles, 1,857 serials, 42,734 audiovisual materials, an OPAC, and a Web page. Operations spending for 2004 fiscal year: $2.1 million. 1,500 computers available on campus for general student use. A campuswide network can be accessed from student residence rooms and from off campus. Staffed computer lab on campus.

■ SOUTHERN UNIVERSITY AT NEW ORLEANS *J-11*

6400 Press Dr.
New Orleans, LA 70126-1009
Tel: (504)286-5000
Admissions: (504)286-5314
E-mail: tbailey@suno.edu
Web Site: http://www.suno.edu/

Description: State-supported, comprehensive, coed. Part of Southern University System. Awards associate, bachelor's, and master's degrees. Founded 1959. Setting: 17-acre campus. Total enrollment: 5,000. 1,000 applied, 100% were admitted. Students come from 13 states and territories, 8 other countries, 50% 25 or older. Core. Calendar: semesters. Academic remediation for entering students, part-time degree program, adult/continuing education programs. Off campus study at University of New Orleans, Delgado Community College. ROTC: Army (c), Air Force (c).

Entrance Requirements: Open admission. Options: Common Application, early admission, deferred admission. Required: high school transcript. Placement: SAT or ACT required. Entrance: noncompetitive. Application deadline: 7/1.

Costs Per Year: State resident tuition: $2990 full-time. Nonresident tuition: $6728 full-time.

Collegiate Environment: Drama-theater group, student-run newspaper. Social organizations: national fraternities, national sororities; 10% of eligible men and 10% of eligible women are members. Student services: health clinic. College housing not available. 100 computers available on campus for general student use. Staffed computer lab on campus.

■ **SOUTHERN UNIVERSITY AT SHREVEPORT** *B-2*

3050 Martin Luther King, Jr. Dr.

Shreveport, LA 71107

Tel: (318)674-3300

Admissions: (318)674-3426

Fax: (318)674-3489

E-mail: tscott@susla.edu

Web Site: http://www.susla.edu/

Description: State-supported, 2-year, coed. Part of Southern University System. Awards certificates, transfer associate, and terminal associate degrees. Founded 1964. Setting: 103-acre urban campus. Research spending for 2004 fiscal year: $42,522. Educational spending for 2005 fiscal year: $2521 per student. Total enrollment: 1,324. 10% from top 10% of their high school class, 30% from top quarter. Full-time: 921 students, 69% women, 31% men. Part-time: 403 students, 74% women, 26% men. Students come from 5 states and territories, 45% from out-of-state, 0.2% Native American, 0.2% Hispanic, 92% black, 0.2% Asian American or Pacific Islander, 0.1% international, 41% 25 or older, 10% transferred in. Core. Calendar: semesters. Academic remediation for entering students, advanced placement, self-designed majors, honors program, summer session for credit, part-time degree program, adult/continuing education programs, co-op programs and internships. Off campus study at Louisiana State University in Shreveport.

Entrance Requirements: Open admission. Option: early admission. Required: high school transcript. Recommended: ACT. Entrance: noncompetitive. Application deadline: Rolling. Notification: continuous until 8/15.

Collegiate Environment: Orientation program. Choral group, student-run newspaper. Social organizations: 38 open to all. Most popular organizations: Afro-American Society, SUSBO Gospel Choir, Student Center Board, Allied Health, Engineering Club. Major annual events: Career Day, Homecoming, Crawfish Boil. Student services: personal-psychological counseling. Campus security: 24-hour patrols. College housing not available. Library/Learning Resources Center with 25,733 microform titles, 380 serials, 24,016 audiovisual materials, and an OPAC. Operations spending for 2004 fiscal year: $308,227.

■ **TULANE UNIVERSITY** *J-11*

6823 St Charles Ave.

New Orleans, LA 70118-5669

Tel: (504)865-5000

Free: 800-873-9283

Admissions: (504)865-5731

Fax: (504)862-8715

E-mail: undergrad.admission@tulane.edu

Web Site: http://www.tulane.edu/

Description: Independent, university, coed. Awards associate, bachelor's, master's, doctoral, and first professional degrees. Founded 1834. Setting: 110-acre urban campus. Endowment: $782 million. Educational spending for 2005 fiscal year: $12,400 per student. Total enrollment: 12,691. Faculty: 1,371 (1,099 full-time, 272 part-time). Student-undergrad faculty ratio is 13:1. 17,572 applied, 45% were admitted. 59% from top 10% of their high school class, 75% from top quarter, 100% from top half. Full-time: 6,151 students, 51% women, 49% men. Part-time: 1,825 students, 60% women, 40% men. 70% from out-of-state, 1% Native American, 3% Hispanic, 9% black, 4% Asian American or Pacific Islander, 2% international, 16% 25 or older, 65% live on campus, 3% transferred in. Academic areas with the most degrees conferred: business/marketing; social sciences; biological/life sciences. Core. Calendar: semesters plus 3 summer sessions. ESL program, services for LD students, advanced placement, accelerated degree program, self-designed majors, freshman honors college, honors program, independent study, double major, summer session for credit, part-time degree program, adult/continuing education programs, co-op programs and internships, graduate courses open to undergrads. Off campus study at Xavier University of Louisiana, Loyola University New Orleans. Study abroad program. ROTC: Army, Naval, Air Force.

Entrance Requirements: Options: Common Application, electronic application, early admission, early decision, early action, deferred admission, international baccalaureate accepted. Required: essay, high school transcript, 1 recommendation, SAT or ACT. Entrance: very difficult. Application deadlines: 1/15, 11/1 for early decision, 11/1 for early action. Notification: continuous until 4/15, 12/15 for early decision, 12/15 for early action.

Costs Per Year: Application fee: $55. Comprehensive fee: $41,357 includes full-time tuition ($30,350), mandatory fees ($2596), and college room and board ($8411). College room only: $4841. Part-time tuition: $1340 per credit hour. Part-time mandatory fees: $20.

Collegiate Environment: Orientation program. Drama-theater group, choral group, marching band, student-run newspaper, radio station. Social organizations: 250 open to all; national fraternities, national sororities; 33% of eligible men and 35% of eligible women are members. Most popular organizations: Community Action Council, Campus Programming, African-American Congress, club sports, Tsunami. Major annual events: Outreach Tulane (Community Service Day for Freshmen), Student Activities Expo, Spring Arts Festival. Student services: legal services, health clinic, personal-psychological counseling, women's center. Campus security: 24-hour emergency response devices and patrols, student patrols, late night transport-escort service, controlled dormitory access, on and off-campus shuttle service, crime prevention programs, lighted pathways. College housing designed to accommodate 3,385 students; 5,184 undergraduates lived in college housing during 2003-04. Freshmen guaranteed college housing. On-campus residence required in freshman year. Options: coed, women-only housing available. Howard Tilton Memorial Library plus 8 others with 2.3 million books, 2.6 million microform titles, 15,499 serials, 94,404 audiovisual materials, an OPAC, and a Web page. 592 computers available on campus for general student use. Computer purchase/lease plans available. A campuswide network can be accessed from student residence rooms and from off campus. Staffed computer lab on campus.

Community Environment: Year-round New Orleans offers festivals and jazz bands, symphonies and operas, Broadway shows and concerts. But the City that Care Forgot also blends its unique French and Spanish heritage to offer quiet entertainment in museums, galleries, quaint restaurants or strolls through the European ambiance of the French Quarter. The 1.3 million people living in the metropolitan area succeed as well in running Louisiana's business, banking, judicial and cultural capital. Many students find the city to be as much a place of learning and intellectual challenge as the classroom. Moderate temperatures can be enjoyed year-round. New Orleans is one of the greatest distributing points in the South, and one of the largest ports in the United States; it is a marketing center for cotton, oil, salt, sulfur, natural gas, agricultural and forest products. Good transportation facilities are available. This is a paradise for those who fish or hunt. Since the city is a tourist attraction, there are many recreational facilities and community services available. Work opportunities are available for students.

■ **UNIVERSITY OF LOUISIANA AT LAFAYETTE** *I-6*

104 University Circle

PO Drawer 41008

Lafayette, LA 70504

Tel: (337)482-1000

Admissions: (337)482-6553

Fax: (337)482-6195

E-mail: dan@louisiana.edu

Web Site: http://www.louisiana.edu/

Description: State-supported, university, coed. Part of University of Louisiana System. Awards bachelor's, master's, and doctoral degrees and post-master's certificates. Founded 1898. Setting: 1,375-acre urban campus. Endowment: $80.1 million. Research spending for 2004 fiscal year: $61.1 million. Educational spending for 2005 fiscal year: $3324 per student. Total enrollment: 17,075. Faculty: 719 (548 full-time, 171 part-time). Student-undergrad faculty ratio is 22:1. 6,309 applied, 76% were admitted. 17% from top 10% of their high school class, 39% from top quarter, 72% from top half. 75 valedictorians. Full-time: 12,926 students, 58% women, 42% men. Part-time: 2,638 students, 65% women, 35% men. Students come from 50 states and territories, 80 other countries, 4% from out-of-state, 0.5% Native American, 2% Hispanic, 20% black, 2% Asian American or Pacific Islander, 2% international, 19% 25 or older, 12% live on campus, 5% transferred in. Retention: 71% of full-time freshmen returned the following year. Academic areas with the most degrees conferred: business/marketing; education; liberal arts/general studies. Core. Calendar: semesters. Academic remediation for entering students, services for LD students, advanced placement, accelerated degree program, self-designed majors, honors program, independent study, distance learning, double major, summer session for credit, part-time degree program, adult/continuing education programs, co-op programs and internships. Study abroad program. ROTC: Army.

Entrance Requirements: Options: early admission, deferred admission, international baccalaureate accepted. Required: high school transcript, minimum 2.0 high school GPA, core requirements, no remedials, SAT or ACT. Entrance: moderately difficult. Application deadline: Rolling.

Costs Per Year: Application fee: $25. State resident tuition: $3324 full-time, $92.75 per credit hour part-time. Nonresident tuition: $9504 full-time, $350.25 per credit hour part-time. Full-time tuition varies according to course load. Part-time tuition varies according to course load. College room and board: $3478. Room and board charges vary according to board plan and housing facility.

Collegiate Environment: Orientation program. Drama-theater group, choral group, marching band, student-run newspaper, radio station. Social organizations: 200 open to all; national fraternities, national sororities; 2% of eligible men and 5% of eligible women are members. Most popular organizations: Student Government Association, Resident Hall Association, Newman Club, Union Program Council, Chi Alpha. Major annual events: homecoming, Lagniappe Day, Mardi Gras. Student services: legal services, health clinic, personal-psychological counseling, women's center. Campus security: 24-hour emergency response devices and patrols, late night transport-escort service. 2,400 college housing spaces available; 1,984 were occupied in 2003-04. Freshmen guaranteed college housing. On-campus residence required in freshman year. Options: men-only, women-only housing available. Edith Garland Dupre Library with 986,000 books, 1.3 million microform titles, 5,174 serials, 9,245 audiovisual materials, an OPAC, and a Web page. Operations spending for 2004 fiscal year: $3.6 million. 1,000 computers available on campus for general student use. A campuswide network can be accessed from off-campus. Staffed computer lab on campus.

■ **UNIVERSITY OF LOUISIANA AT MONROE** *B-6*
700 University Ave.
Monroe, LA 71209-0001
Tel: (318)342-1000
Free: 800-372-5127
Admissions: (318)342-5272
Fax: (318)342-1049
E-mail: lmiller@ulm.edu
Web Site: http://www.ulm.edu/
Description: State-supported, university, coed. Awards associate, bachelor's, master's, doctoral, and first professional degrees and post-master's certificates. Founded 1931. Setting: 238-acre urban campus. Research spending for 2004 fiscal year: $7.9 million. Total enrollment: 9,056. Faculty: 455 (373 full-time, 82 part-time). 2,378 applied, 87% were admitted. Full-time: 6,251 students, 63% women, 37% men. Part-time: 1,496 students, 69% women, 31% men. Students come from 45 states and territories, 42 other countries, 7% from out-of-state, 0.4% Native American, 1% Hispanic, 29% black, 2% Asian American or Pacific Islander, 1% international, 27% 25 or older, 15% live on campus, 7% transferred in. Academic areas with the most degrees conferred: health professions and related sciences; liberal arts/general studies; education. Core. Calendar: semesters. Academic remediation for entering students, ESL program, advanced placement, honors program, independent study, distance learning, double major, summer session for credit, part-time degree program, co-op programs and internships, graduate courses open to undergrads. Off campus study at University of Southern Mississippi, Louisiana Tech University, Grambling State University. Study abroad program. ROTC: Army.
Entrance Requirements: Options: Common Application, electronic application, early admission, deferred admission. Required: high school transcript, ACT. Entrance: noncompetitive. Application deadline: Rolling. Notification: continuous.
Costs Per Year: Application fee: $20. State resident tuition: $2334 full-time, $93 per credit hour part-time. Nonresident tuition: $8284 full-time. Mandatory fees: $1068 full-time, $64 per credit hour part-time. Full-time tuition and fees vary according to course load and program. Part-time tuition and fees vary according to course load and program. College room and board: $4120. College room only: $2230. Room and board charges vary according to board plan and housing facility.
Collegiate Environment: Orientation program. Drama-theater group, choral group, marching band, student-run newspaper, radio station. Social organizations: 173 open to all; national fraternities, national sororities. Most popular organizations: Union Board, Student Government Association. Major annual events: Homecoming, Spring Fever Week, Miss ULM contest. Student services: health clinic, personal-psychological counseling. Campus security: 24-hour emergency response devices and patrols, student patrols, late night transport-escort service. 1,895 college housing spaces available; 1,474 were occupied in 2003-04. Freshmen guaranteed college housing. Options: coed, men-only, women-only housing available. University Library with 642,582 books, 614,669 microform titles, 2,761 serials, 1,138 audiovisual materials, and an OPAC. Operations spending for 2004 fiscal year: $2 million. 1,400 computers available on campus for general student use. A campuswide network can be accessed from student residence rooms and from off campus. Staffed computer lab on campus.

■ **UNIVERSITY OF NEW ORLEANS** *J-11*
Lake Front
New Orleans, LA 70148
Tel: (504)280-6000
Free: 800-256-5866
Admissions: (504)280-7013
Fax: (504)280-5522
Web Site: http://www.uno.edu/
Description: State-supported, university, coed. Part of Louisiana State University System. Awards bachelor's, master's, and doctoral degrees. Founded 1958. Setting: 345-acre urban campus. Endowment: $13.8 million. Research spending for 2004 fiscal year: $24.9 million. Educational spending for 2005 fiscal year: $4252 per student. Total enrollment: 17,350. Faculty: 785 (556 full-time, 229 part-time). Student-undergrad faculty ratio is 25:1. 6,197 applied, 63% were admitted. Full-time: 9,551 students, 55% women, 45% men. Part-time: 3,674 students, 59% women, 41% men. Students come from 50 states and territories, 81 other countries, 4% from out-of-state, 0.4% Native American, 7% Hispanic, 25% black, 6% Asian American or Pacific Islander, 2% international, 27% 25 or older, 9% live on campus, 9% transferred in. Retention: 67% of full-time freshmen returned the following year. Core. Calendar: semesters. Academic remediation for entering students, ESL program, services for LD students, advanced placement, self-designed majors, honors program, independent study, distance learning, double major, summer session for credit, part-time degree program, adult/continuing education programs, co-op programs and internships, graduate courses open to undergrads. Off campus study at Southern University at New Orleans, Delgado Community College, Nunez Community College. Study abroad program. ROTC: Army (c), Naval (c), Air Force (c).
Entrance Requirements: Options: Peterson's Universal Application, Common Application, electronic application, early admission, deferred admission, international baccalaureate accepted. Required: high school transcript, SAT or ACT. Required for some: essay, minimum 2.0 high school GPA, 3 recommendations, interview, 2.0 high school GPA on high school core program. Entrance: moderately difficult. Application deadline: Rolling. Notification: continuous.
Costs Per Year: Application fee: $20. State resident tuition: $3292 full-time, $133 per hour part-time. Nonresident tuition: $10,336 full-time, $426 per hour part-time. Mandatory fees: $518 full-time. Part-time tuition varies according to course load. College room only: $4590. Room charges vary according to housing facility.
Collegiate Environment: Orientation program. Drama-theater group, choral group, student-run newspaper. Social organizations: 100 open to all; national fraternities, national sororities, local fraternities. Most popular organizations: Student Government Association, Student Government Activities Council, Circle K International, International Student Organization, Progressive Black Student Union. Major annual events: Fall Fest, Spring Fest, Annual Crayfish Boil. Student services: legal services, health clinic, personal-psychological counseling, women's center. Campus security: 24-hour emergency response devices and patrols, late night transport-escort service, controlled dormitory access. 1,426 college housing spaces available; 1,282 were occupied in 2003-04. No special consideration for freshman housing applicants. Option: coed housing available. Earl K. Long Library with 896,000 books, 12.4 million microform titles, 4,950 serials, 125,600 audiovisual materials, an OPAC, and a Web page. Operations spending for 2004 fiscal year: $3.4 million. 1,084 computers available on campus for general student use. A campuswide network can be accessed from student residence rooms and from off campus. Staffed computer lab on campus.
Community Environment: See Tulane University.

■ **UNIVERSITY OF PHOENIX-LOUISIANA CAMPUS** *J-11*
1 Galleria Blvd., Ste. 725
Metairie, LA 70001-2082
Tel: (504)461-8852
Free: 800-228-7240
Admissions: (480)557-1712
Web Site: http://www.phoenix.edu/
Description: Proprietary, comprehensive, coed. Awards bachelor's and master's degrees. Founded 1976. Setting: urban campus. Total enrollment: 2,747. Faculty: 304 (2 full-time, 302 part-time). Student-undergrad faculty ratio is 6:1. 77 applied. Full-time: 2,085 students, 71% women, 29% men. 0% Native American, 1% Hispanic, 15% black, 0.2% Asian American or Pacific Islander, 20% international, 93% 25 or older. Academic areas with the most degrees conferred: business/marketing; computer and information sciences; security and protective services. Core. Calendar: continuous.

Advanced placement, accelerated degree program, independent study, distance learning, external degree program, adult/continuing education programs, graduate courses open to undergrads.

Entrance Requirements: Open admission. Option: deferred admission. Required: 1 recommendation. Required for some: high school transcript. Entrance: noncompetitive. Application deadline: Rolling.

Costs Per Year: Application fee: $110. Tuition: $9120 full-time, $304 per credit part-time. Mandatory fees: $560 full-time, $70 per course part-time. Full-time tuition and fees vary according to program.

Collegiate Environment: College housing not available. University Library with 444 books, 666 serials, an OPAC, and a Web page. System-wide operations spending for 2004 fiscal year: $3.2 million.

■ **XAVIER UNIVERSITY OF LOUISIANA** *J-11*
1 Drexel Dr.
New Orleans, LA 70125-1098
Tel: (504)486-7411; 877-XAVIERU
Admissions: (504)520-7388
E-mail: apply@xula.edu
Web Site: http://www.xula.edu/

Description: Independent Roman Catholic, comprehensive, coed. Awards bachelor's, master's, and first professional degrees. Founded 1925. Setting: 23-acre urban campus with easy access to New Orleans. Endowment: $48.5 million. Total enrollment: 4,121. Faculty: 289 (241 full-time, 48 part-time). Student-undergrad faculty ratio is 16:1. 4,248 applied, 83% were admitted. 30% from top 10% of their high school class, 55% from top quarter, 83% from top half. Full-time: 3,143 students, 75% women, 25% men. Part-time: 147 students, 74% women, 26% men. Students come from 41 states and territories, 15 other countries, 49% from out-of-state, 0.1% Native American, 0.4% Hispanic, 84% black, 5% Asian American or Pacific Islander, 2% international, 2% 25 or older, 30% live on campus, 5% transferred in. Retention: 73% of full-time freshmen returned the following year. Core. Calendar: semesters. Academic remediation for entering students, services for LD students, advanced placement, accelerated degree program, freshman honors college, honors program, independent study, double major, summer session for credit, part-time degree program, adult/continuing education programs, co-op programs and internships, graduate courses open to undergrads. Off campus study at 2 members of the New Orleans Consortium, St. Michael's College, University of Notre Dame. Study abroad program. ROTC: Army (c), Naval (c), Air Force (c).

Entrance Requirements: Options: Common Application, electronic application, early action. Required: high school transcript, minimum 2.0 high school GPA, 1 recommendation, SAT or ACT. Required for some: interview. Entrance: moderately difficult. Application deadlines: 3/1, 1/15 for early action. Notification: 4/15, 2/15 for early action.

Costs Per Year: Application fee: $25. Comprehensive fee: $20,200 includes full-time tuition ($12,100), mandatory fees ($1000), and college room and board ($7100). Room and board charges vary according to location. Part-time tuition: $500 per credit hour.

Collegiate Environment: Orientation program. Choral group, student-run newspaper. Social organizations: 64 open to all; national fraternities, national sororities; 2% of eligible men and 6% of eligible women are members. Most popular organizations: Mobilization at Xavier, AWARE, NAACP, California Club, Beta Beta Beta. Major annual events: Homecoming, Spring Fest, Martin Luther King Week for Peace. Student services: health clinic, personal-psychological counseling. Campus security: 24-hour emergency response devices and patrols, student patrols, bicycle patrols. 1,678 college housing spaces available; 1,306 were occupied in 2003-04. Freshmen given priority for college housing. Options: coed, men-only, women-only housing available. Xavier Library plus 1 other with 238,455 books, 785,994 microform titles, 1,868 serials, and 6,186 audiovisual materials. 250 computers available on campus for general student use. A campuswide network can be accessed from student residence rooms and from off campus. Staffed computer lab on campus.

Community Environment: See Tulane University.

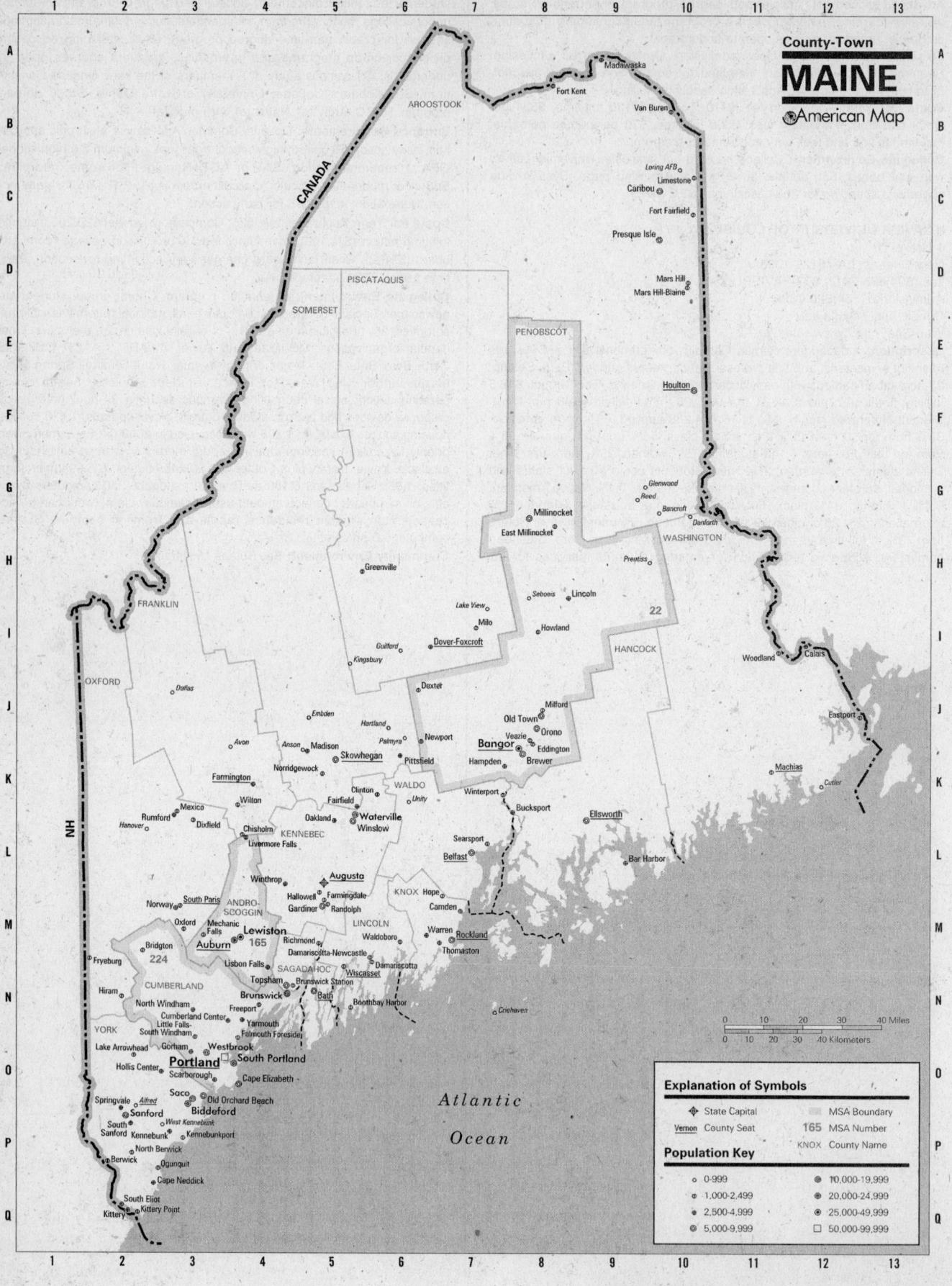

County-Town
MAINE
American Map

Explanation of Symbols

	State Capital		MSA Boundary
Vernon	County Seat	165	MSA Number
		KNOX	County Name

Population Key

○	0-999	◉	10,000-19,999
⊕	1,000-2,499	◉	20,000-24,999
⊛	2,500-4,999	◉	25,000-49,999
⊕	5,000-9,999	□	50,000-99,999

AROOSTOOK

PISCATAQUIS

SOMERSET

PENOBSCOT

WASHINGTON

FRANKLIN

OXFORD

HANCOCK

KENNEBEC

WALDO

ANDRO-SCOGGIN

KNOX

LINCOLN

SAGADAHOC

CUMBERLAND

YORK

CANADA

NH

Madawaska
Fort Kent
Van Buren
Loring AFB
Limestone
Caribou
Fort Fairfield
Presque Isle
Mars Hill
Mars Hill-Blaine
Houlton
Glenwood
Reed
Bancroft
Danforth
Millinocket
East Millinocket
Prentiss
Greenville
Seboeis
Lincoln
Lake View
Milo
Howland
Guilford
Dover-Foxcroft
Kingsbury
Woodland
Calais
Dexter
Milford
Eastport
Dallas
Old Town
Orono
Embden
Hartland
Veazie
Eddington
Avon
Anson
Madison
Palmyra
Newport
Bangor
Hampden
Brewer
Machias
Cutler
Skowhegan
Pittsfield
Norridgewock
Farmington
Clinton
Unity
Winterport
Wilton
Fairfield
Bucksport
Rumford
Mexico
Oakland
Waterville
Winslow
Ellsworth
Hanover
Dixfield
Chisholm
Livermore Falls
Searsport
Belfast
Bar Harbor
Winthrop
Augusta
Hope
Camden
Norway
South Paris
Hallowell
Farmingdale
Gardiner
Randolph
Oxford
Mechanic Falls
Lewiston
165
Warren
Rockland
Bridgton
224
Auburn
Richmond
Waldoboro
Thomaston
Fryeburg
Lisbon Falls
Damariscotta-Newcastle
Damariscotta
Hiram
Topsham
Wiscasset
Bath
North Windham
Brunswick Station
Brunswick
Boothbay Harbor
Cumberland Center
Freeport
Little Falls
Yarmouth
South Windham
Falmouth Foreside
Criehaven
Lake Arrowhead
Gorham
Westbrook
Hollis Center
Portland
South Portland
Scarborough
Cape Elizabeth
Springvale
Alfred
Saco
Old Orchard Beach
Sanford
Biddeford
South Sanford
West Kennebunk
Kennebunk
Kennebunkport
North Berwick
Berwick
Ogunquit
Cape Neddick
South Eliot
Kittery
Kittery Point

22

Atlantic
Ocean

0 10 20 30 40 Miles
0 10 20 30 40 Kilometers

■ **ANDOVER COLLEGE** *O-3*
901 Washington Ave.
Portland, ME 04103-2791
Tel: (207)774-6126
Free: 800-639-3110
Fax: (207)774-1715
Web Site: http://www.andovercollege.com/
Description: Proprietary, 2-year, coed. Awards certificates and terminal associate degrees. Founded 1966. Setting: 2-acre urban campus. Total enrollment: 502. 103 applied, 100% were admitted. Students come from 4 states and territories, 3 other countries, 70% 25 or older. Core. Calendar: modular. Academic remediation for entering students, independent study, summer session for credit, part-time degree program, adult/continuing education programs, co-op programs and internships.
Entrance Requirements: Open admission. Options: Common Application, early admission, deferred admission. Required: high school transcript. Recommended: interview. Entrance: noncompetitive. Application deadline: Rolling.
Collegiate Environment: Orientation program. Social organizations: 9 open to all. Most popular organizations: Student Advisors, Andover Computer, Student Advisors Group, Andover Student Medical Assistants, C.O.P.S. Major annual events: Campus Day, Career Day, Awards Banquet. Student services: personal-psychological counseling. Campus security: 24-hour emergency response devices. College housing not available. Andover Library with 6,500 books, 110 serials, and 59 audiovisual materials. 100 computers available on campus for general student use. Staffed computer lab on campus.
Community Environment: Portland, located just two hours north of Boston, lies in the southern part of Maine. Southern Maine is home to some of the country's best-known companies including L.L. Bean, UNUM Insurance, J.J. Nissen Bakery, and Hannaford Brothers. These companies combine with the shipping and fishing industries to give Portland a vibrant and thriving economy. Portland also boasts some of the finest restaurants on the east coast and has a unique and charming shopping district in the old city. The city is home to a championship minor league hockey team, The Portland Pirates, an affiliate of the Washington Capitals, and one of the minor league's most successful baseball teams, The Portland Sea Dogs, an affiliate of the Florida Marlins. Portland also has a highly regarded art museum, professional stage and dance companies, public recreation facilities, and breathtaking views of the Atlantic Ocean. Portland is easily accessible by car, plane, or bus.

■ **BATES COLLEGE** *M-4*
Andrews Rd.
Lewiston, ME 04240-6028
Tel: (207)786-6255
Admissions: (207)786-6000
Fax: (207)786-6025
E-mail: admissions@bates.edu
Web Site: http://www.bates.edu/
Description: Independent, 4-year, coed. Awards bachelor's degrees. Founded 1855. Setting: 109-acre small town campus. Endowment: $207.5 million. Research spending for 2004 fiscal year: $622,437. Educational spending for 2005 fiscal year: $16,100 per student. Total enrollment: 1,730. Student-undergrad faculty ratio is 10:1. 4,356 applied, 29% were admitted. 57% from top 10% of their high school class, 91% from top quarter, 99%

from top half. Full-time: 1,699 students, 51% women, 49% men. Part-time: 31 students, 58% women, 42% men. Students come from 48 states and territories, 72 other countries, 88% from out-of-state, 0.4% Native American, 2% Hispanic, 3% black, 4% Asian American or Pacific Islander, 5% international, 0.3% 25 or older, 90% live on campus. Retention: 94% of full-time freshmen returned the following year. Academic areas with the most degrees conferred: social sciences; psychology; biological/life sciences. Core. Calendar: 4-4-1. Services for LD students, advanced placement, accelerated degree program, self-designed majors, honors program, independent study, double major, co-op programs and internships. Off campus study at American University, Williams College (Mystic Seaport Program), McGill University, Washington and Lee University, Morehouse College, Spelman College. Study abroad program.
Entrance Requirements: Options: Peterson's Universal Application, Common Application, electronic application, early admission, early decision, deferred admission, international baccalaureate accepted. Required: essay, high school transcript, 3 recommendations. Recommended: interview. Entrance: most difficult. Application deadlines: 1/1, 1/1 for nonresidents, 11/15 for early decision plan 1, 1/1 for early decision plan 2. Notification: 3/31, 3/31 for nonresidents, 12/20 for early decision plan 1, 2/15 for early decision plan 2.
Costs Per Year: Application fee: $60. Comprehensive fee: $42,100.
Collegiate Environment: Orientation program. Drama-theater group, choral group, student-run newspaper, radio station. Social organizations: 91 open to all. Most popular organizations: Representative Assembly, International Club, Outing Club (outdoor recreation), student radio station, The Student (newspaper). Major annual events: Winter Carnival, Triad, St. Patrick's Day Puddle Jump. Student services: health clinic, personal-psychological counseling, women's center. Campus security: 24-hour emergency response devices and patrols, student patrols, late night transport-escort service, controlled dormitory access. 1,592 college housing spaces available; 1,524 were occupied in 2003-04. Freshmen guaranteed college housing. On-campus residence required in freshman year. Options: coed, men-only, women-only housing available. Ladd Library plus 1 other with 588,211 books, 298,706 microform titles, 25,674 serials, 31,656 audiovisual materials, an OPAC, and a Web page. Operations spending for 2004 fiscal year: $3.3 million. 1,150 computers available on campus for general student use. Computer purchase/lease plans available. A campuswide network can be accessed from student residence rooms and from off campus. Staffed computer lab on campus.
Community Environment: The second largest city in state, Lewiston is Maine's leading textile center. It is located on the Androscoggin River at Twin Falls, directly opposite the city of Auburn. Minimum-maximum temperatures are 0-50 degrees in the winter and 50-90 degrees in the summer. Commercial transportation is available via air and bus. The city has several churches, Ys, a public library, two hospitals, several movie theaters, and hotels and motels.

■ **BEAL COLLEGE** *K-8*
629 Main St.
Bangor, ME 04401-6896
Tel: (207)947-4591
Web Site: http://www.bealcollege.edu/
Description: Proprietary, 2-year, coed. Awards certificates, diplomas, and terminal associate degrees. Founded 1891. Setting: 4-acre small town campus. Total enrollment: 373. Student-undergrad faculty ratio is 16:1. Full-

time: 239 students, 85% women, 15% men. Part-time: 134 students, 85% women, 15% men. Students come from 2 states and territories, 0% from out-of-state, 1% Native American, 1% Hispanic, 1% black, 0% Asian American or Pacific Islander, 0% international, 54% 25 or older. Core. Calendar: modular. Academic remediation for entering students, advanced placement, accelerated degree program, double major, summer session for credit, part-time degree program, adult/continuing education programs, internships.

Entrance Requirements: Open admission. Option: deferred admission. Required: high school transcript. Recommended: interview. Entrance: noncompetitive. Application deadline: Rolling.

Collegiate Environment: Orientation program. Student-run newspaper. Most popular organizations: Sophomore Travel Club, Freshman Travel Club, yearbook staff. Major annual events: Holiday Hop, Spring Fling, Christmas Buffet. College housing not available. Beal College Library with 7,275 books, 100 serials, and a Web page. 85 computers available on campus for general student use.

■ **BOWDOIN COLLEGE** *N-4*
5000 College Station
Brunswick, ME 04011
Tel: (207)725-3000
Admissions: (207)725-3958
Fax: (207)725-3003
E-mail: admissions@bowdoin.edu
Web Site: http://www.bowdoin.edu/

Description: Independent, 4-year, coed. Awards bachelor's degrees. Founded 1794. Setting: 200-acre small town campus with easy access to Portland. Endowment: $578.2 million. Research spending for 2004 fiscal year: $2 million. Educational spending for 2005 fiscal year: $20,262 per student. Total enrollment: 1,666. Student-undergrad faculty ratio is 10:1. 5,026 applied, 25% were admitted. 23 National Merit Scholars, 44 valedictorians. Full-time: 1,661 students, 50% women, 50% men. Part-time: 5 students, 80% women, 20% men. Students come from 49 states and territories, 29 other countries, 87% from out-of-state, 1% Native American, 7% Hispanic, 6% black, 12% Asian American or Pacific Islander, 3% international, 1% 25 or older, 93% live on campus, 0.5% transferred in. Retention: 97% of full-time freshmen returned the following year. Academic areas with the most degrees conferred: social sciences; foreign languages and literature; biological/life sciences. Core. Calendar: semesters. Services for LD students, advanced placement, accelerated degree program, self-designed majors, independent study, double major. Off campus study at Twelve College Exchange Program. Study abroad program.

Entrance Requirements: Options: Peterson's Universal Application, Common Application, electronic application, early decision, deferred admission, international baccalaureate accepted. Required: essay, high school transcript, 3 recommendations. Recommended: interview. Entrance: most difficult. Application deadlines: 1/1, 11/15 for early decision plan 1, 1/1 for early decision plan 2. Notification: 4/5, 12/31 for early decision plan 1, 2/15 for early decision plan 2.

Costs Per Year: Application fee: $60. Comprehensive fee: $41,660 includes full-time tuition ($32,650), mandatory fees ($340), and college room and board ($8670). College room only: $3900. Room and board charges vary according to board plan.

Collegiate Environment: Orientation program. Drama-theater group, choral group, student-run newspaper, radio station. Social organizations: 109 open to all. Most popular organizations: Outing Club, men's and women's rugby, volunteer programs, Ballroom Dance Club, Campus Activities Board. Major annual events: Common Good Day, Spring Gala, Winter's Weekend. Student services: health clinic, personal-psychological counseling, women's center. Campus security: 24-hour emergency response devices and patrols, student patrols, late night transport-escort service, controlled dormitory access, self-defense education, whistle program. 1,597 college housing spaces available; 1,564 were occupied in 2003-04. Freshmen guaranteed college housing. On-campus residence required through sophomore year. Option: coed housing available. Hawthorne-Longfellow Library plus 6 others with 981,074 books, 110,537 microform titles, 5,665 serials, 21,992 audiovisual materials, an OPAC, and a Web page. Operations spending for 2004 fiscal year: $4.5 million. 400 computers available on campus for general student use. Computer purchase/lease plans available. A campuswide network can be accessed from student residence rooms and from off campus. Staffed computer lab on campus.

Community Environment: Brunswick, a community of 20,500, is located within brief driving distance of several fine beaches and summer resort

areas; skiing is available in winter. There are excellent highways and airline service to Portland, only 26 miles away. The area has several excellent motels. The town has a public library, Maine State Music Theatre, which features Broadway musicals each summer, and churches of many denominations, shopping centers and movie theaters; good restaurants. Recreational facilities include golf, hunting, boating, fishing, skiing, biking, backpacking, and other sports.

■ **CENTRAL MAINE COMMUNITY COLLEGE** *M-4*
1250 Turner St.
Auburn, ME 04210-6498
Tel: (207)755-5100
Free: 800-891-2002
Admissions: (207)755-5334
Fax: (207)755-5491
E-mail: admissions@cmtc.mtcs.tec.me.us
Web Site: http://www.cmcc.edu/

Description: State-supported, 2-year, coed. Part of Maine Technical College System. Awards certificates, diplomas, transfer associate, and terminal associate degrees. Founded 1964. Setting: 135-acre small town campus. Educational spending for 2005 fiscal year: $5515 per student. Total enrollment: 1,850. 858 applied, 54% were admitted. Students come from 5 states and territories, 1% Native American, 1% Hispanic, 1% black, 0.5% Asian American or Pacific Islander, 46% 25 or older, 11% live on campus. Retention: 77% of full-time freshmen returned the following year. Core. Calendar: semesters. Academic remediation for entering students, ESL program, services for LD students, advanced placement, independent study, distance learning, summer session for credit, part-time degree program, adult/continuing education programs, co-op programs and internships.

Entrance Requirements: Option: deferred admission. Required: essay, high school transcript. Recommended: minimum 2.0 high school GPA. Required for some: 2 recommendations, interview. Placement: SAT recommended; ACCUPLACER required for some. Entrance: minimally difficult. Application deadline: Rolling. Notification: continuous.

Collegiate Environment: Orientation program. Drama-theater group. Social organizations: 7 open to all. Most popular organizations: Student Senate, Drama Club, Outing Club, intramural sports, Phi Theta Kappa. Major annual events: Spring Fling, NCAA Basketball Championship. Student services: health clinic, personal-psychological counseling. Campus security: 24-hour emergency response devices, controlled dormitory access, night patrols by police. 130 college housing spaces available; all were occupied in 2003-04. Freshmen given priority for college housing. Options: coed, men-only, women-only housing available. Central Maine Technical College Library with 15,000 books, 240 serials, and a Web page. Operations spending for 2004 fiscal year: $190,480. 150 computers available on campus for general student use. Staffed computer lab on campus.

Community Environment: See Bates College.

■ **CENTRAL MAINE MEDICAL CENTER SCHOOL OF NURSING** *M-4*
70 Middle St.
Lewiston, ME 04240-0305
Tel: (207)795-2840
Admissions: (207)795-2868
Fax: (207)795-2849
Web Site: http://www.cmmcson.edu/

Description: Independent, 2-year, coed. Awards certificates and terminal associate degrees. Founded 1891. Setting: urban campus. Total enrollment: 114. 252 applied, 24% were admitted. 50% from top 10% of their high school class, 50% from top quarter, 100% from top half. Full-time: 22 students, 86% women, 14% men. Part-time: 92 students, 86% women, 14% men. Students come from 2 states and territories, 1% from out-of-state, 1% Native American, 0% Hispanic, 0% black, 0% Asian American or Pacific Islander, 0% international, 84% 25 or older, 2% live on campus. Core. Calendar: semesters. Advanced placement. Off campus study at University of Maine at Augusta, University of Southern Maine.

Entrance Requirements: Required: essay, high school transcript, 2 recommendations, SAT. Entrance: moderately difficult. Application deadline: 3/1. Notification: 3/15.

Costs Per Year: Application fee: $40. Tuition: $2898 full-time, $138 per credit part-time. Mandatory fees: $1205 full-time, $20 per term part-time. College room only: $1500.

Collegiate Environment: Orientation program. Social organizations: 3 open to all. Most popular organizations: Student Communication Council, student government, Student Nurses Association. Major annual events: Alumni

Banquet, President's Breakfast, Alumni Holiday Party. Student services: health clinic, personal-psychological counseling. Campus security: 24-hour emergency response devices and patrols, late night transport-escort service, controlled dormitory access. 10 college housing spaces available; 6 were occupied in 2003-04. No special consideration for freshman housing applicants. Option: coed housing available. Gerrish True Health Sciences Library plus 1 other with 1,975 books, 339 serials, an OPAC, and a Web page. 10 computers available on campus for general student use. Staffed computer lab on campus.

■ **COLBY COLLEGE** *L-5*
Mayflower Hill
Waterville, ME 04901-8840
Tel: (207)872-3000
Free: 800-723-3032
Admissions: (207)859-4802
Fax: (207)872-3474
E-mail: admissions@colby.edu
Web Site: http://www.colby.edu/

Description: Independent, 4-year, coed. Awards bachelor's degrees. Founded 1813. Setting: 714-acre small town campus. Endowment: $424.2 million. Research spending for 2004 fiscal year: $1.1 million. Educational spending for 2005 fiscal year: $16,048 per student. Total enrollment: 1,871. Student-undergrad faculty ratio is 10:1. 3,874 applied, 38% were admitted. 67% from top 10% of their high school class, 92% from top quarter, 99% from top half. 7 valedictorians. Full-time: 1,871 students, 54% women, 46% men. Students come from 45 states and territories, 66 other countries, 89% from out-of-state, 0.5% Native American, 3% Hispanic, 2% black, 6% Asian American or Pacific Islander, 6% international, 0% 25 or older, 93% live on campus, 1% transferred in. Retention: 94% of full-time freshmen returned the following year. Academic areas with the most degrees conferred: social sciences; area and ethnic studies; biological/life sciences. Core. Calendar: 4-1-4. Services for LD students, advanced placement, self-designed majors, honors program, independent study, double major, part-time degree program, internships. Off campus study at Pomona College, Pitzer College, Howard University, Claremont McKenna College, Scripps College, Boston University (Sea Semester), Williams College (Mystic Seaport Program), Clark Atlanta University. Study abroad program. ROTC: Army (c).

Entrance Requirements: Options: Common Application, electronic application, early admission, early decision, deferred admission, international baccalaureate accepted. Required: essay, high school transcript, 2 recommendations, SAT or ACT. Recommended: interview. Entrance: most difficult. Application deadlines: 1/1, 11/15 for early decision plan 1, 1/1 for early decision plan 2. Notification: 4/1, 12/15 for early decision plan 1, 2/1 for early decision plan 2.

Costs Per Year: Application fee: $0. Comprehensive fee: $41,770.

Collegiate Environment: Orientation program. Drama-theater group, choral group, student-run newspaper, radio station. Social organizations: 114 open to all. Most popular organizations: Outing Club, volunteer center, WMHB-FM (College Radio Station), student government, Powder and Wig (theater). Major annual events: Family Weekend, Junior/Senior Cotillion, Foss Arts Festival. Student services: health clinic, personal-psychological counseling, women's center. Campus security: 24-hour emergency response devices and patrols, late night transport-escort service, controlled dormitory access, campus lighting, student emergency response team, self-defense class, property id program, party monitors. 1,702 college housing spaces available; 1,696 were occupied in 2003-04. Freshmen guaranteed college housing. On-campus residence required through senior year. Option: coed housing available. Miller Library plus 2 others with 350,000 books, 301,700 microform titles, 1,850 serials, 20,645 audiovisual materials, an OPAC, and a Web page. Operations spending for 2004 fiscal year: $4.6 million. 300 computers available on campus for general student use. A campuswide network can be accessed from student residence rooms and from off campus. Staffed computer lab on campus.

Community Environment: Colby, located in the Kennebec River Valley, is one mile from downtown Waterville, a regional center for industry, professional, and retail trade. Major employers in the area include Maine General Medical Center, L.L. Bean, SAPPI Fine Paper, the Chinet Co., and The State of Maine. Transportation is available to Waterville by bus from Portland or Boston. Commercial airports serve Portland, Bangor, and Augusta.

■ **COLLEGE OF THE ATLANTIC** *L-9*
105 Eden St.
Bar Harbor, ME 04609-1198

Tel: (207)288-5015
Free: 800-528-0025
Fax: (207)288-4126
E-mail: inquiry@coa.edu
Web Site: http://www.coa.edu/

Description: Independent, comprehensive, coed. Awards bachelor's and master's degrees. Founded 1969. Setting: 35-acre small town campus. Endowment: $10 million. Research spending for 2004 fiscal year: $501,381. Educational spending for 2005 fiscal year: $10,000 per student. Total enrollment: 318. Faculty: 30 (19 full-time, 11 part-time). Student-undergrad faculty ratio is 9:1. 284 applied, 66% were admitted. 36% from top 10% of their high school class, 76% from top quarter, 95% from top half. 5 National Merit Scholars, 2 class presidents, 2 valedictorians, 23 student government officers. Full-time: 296 students, 64% women, 36% men. Part-time: 14 students, 64% women, 36% men. Students come from 33 states and territories, 31 other countries, 62% from out-of-state, 0% Native American, 1% Hispanic, 0% black, 0.3% Asian American or Pacific Islander, 17% international, 5% 25 or older, 40% live on campus, 4% transferred in. Retention: 86% of full-time freshmen returned the following year. Academic area with the most degrees conferred: biological/life sciences. Core. Calendar: 3 10-week terms. Academic remediation for entering students, services for LD students, advanced placement, accelerated degree program, self-designed majors, independent study, part-time degree program, co-op programs and internships, graduate courses open to undergrads. Off campus study at University of Maine, Landing School of Boatbuilding, SEA Education Association, Shoal's Marine Laboratory, Ecoleague consortium: Alaska Pacific University, Antioch College, Green Mountain College, Northland College and Prescott College. Study abroad program.

Entrance Requirements: Options: Peterson's Universal Application, Common Application, electronic application, early admission, early decision, deferred admission, international baccalaureate accepted. Required: essay, high school transcript, 3 recommendations. Recommended: minimum 3.0 high school GPA, interview, SAT or ACT. Required for some: interview. Entrance: very difficult. Application deadlines: 2/15, 12/1 for early decision plan 1, 1/10 for early decision plan 2. Notification: 4/1, 12/15 for early decision plan 1, 1/25 for early decision plan 2.

Costs Per Year: Application fee: $45. Comprehensive fee: $35,675 includes full-time tuition ($27,700), mandatory fees ($375), and college room and board ($7600). College room only: $4700. Part-time tuition: $9234 per term. Part-time mandatory fees: $125 per term.

Collegiate Environment: Orientation program. Drama-theater group, choral group, student-run newspaper. Social organizations: 12 open to all. Most popular organizations: Outing Club, Environmental Awareness Club, Students for a Free Tibet, All-Campus Meeting, choral group. Major annual events: Beech Hill Farm Harvest, Earth Day, Martin Luther King, Jr. Day. Student services: health clinic, personal-psychological counseling, women's center. Campus security: 24-hour emergency response devices and patrols, late night transport-escort service. 103 college housing spaces available; all were occupied in 2003-04. Freshmen guaranteed college housing. Option: coed housing available. Thorndike Library with 50,000 books, 37,000 microform titles, 3,000 serials, 302,500 audiovisual materials, an OPAC, and a Web page. Operations spending for 2004 fiscal year: $223,056. 53 computers available on campus for general student use. Computer purchase/lease plans available. A campuswide network can be accessed from student residence rooms and from off campus. Staffed computer lab on campus.

Community Environment: Bar Harbor and Mount Desert Island's natural environment provide excellent opportunities for environmental studies. Cooperative resource sharing is available with the Jackson Laboratory, Mount Desert Island Biological Laboratory, Acadia National Park and the local school system. In the summer, Bar Harbor is supported by the tourist trade. Other businesses which provide for the local economy are boatbuilding, fishing, and lobstering. Bar Harbor is easily accessible by Bar Harbor Airlines, Greyhound Bus or automobile via State Routes 1 and 3.

■ **EASTERN MAINE COMMUNITY COLLEGE** *K-8*
354 Hogan Rd.
Bangor, ME 04401-4206
Tel: (207)974-4600
Admissions: (207)974-4680
Fax: (207)974-4683
Web Site: http://www.emcc.edu/

Description: State-supported, 2-year, coed. Part of Maine Community College System. Awards certificates, diplomas, transfer associate, and terminal associate degrees. Founded 1966. Setting: 72-acre small town campus. Endowment: $1.5 million. Educational spending for 2005 fiscal year: $4918 per student. Total enrollment: 1,790. 1,407 applied, 50% were admitted. Full-time: 744 students, 40% women, 60% men. Part-time: 1,046 students, 61% women, 39% men. Students come from 2 states and territories, 1% from out-of-state, 1% Native American, 0.1% Hispanic, 0.1% black, 0.3% Asian American or Pacific Islander, 26% 25 or older, 20% live on campus. Calendar: semesters. Academic remediation for entering students, advanced placement, summer session for credit, part-time degree program, adult/continuing education programs.

Entrance Requirements: Option: deferred admission. Required: essay, high school transcript, recommendations, ACCUPLACER. Recommended: minimum 2.0 high school GPA. Required for some: interview, SAT. Entrance: minimally difficult. Application deadline: Rolling. Notification: continuous. Preference given to state residents.

Collegiate Environment: Orientation program. Student-run newspaper. Social organizations: 12 open to all. Most popular organizations: Student Senate, Phi Theta Kappa, Senior Council, Resident's Council, Associated General Contractors Student Chapter. Major annual events: Technology Day, Winter Carnival, Harvest Breakfast. Student services: health clinic, personal-psychological counseling. Campus security: late night transport-escort service, controlled dormitory access. 185 college housing spaces available; all were occupied in 2003-04. No special consideration for freshman housing applicants. Option: coed housing available. Eastern Maine Technical College Library plus 1 other with 17,554 books, 159 serials, an OPAC, and a Web page. Operations spending for 2004 fiscal year: $144,508. 85 computers available on campus for general student use. A campuswide network can be accessed from off-campus. Staffed computer lab on campus.

■ **HUSSON COLLEGE** *K-8*
One College Circle
Bangor, ME 04401-2999
Tel: (207)941-7000
Free: 800-4-HUSSON
Admissions: (207)941-7100
Fax: (207)941-7935
E-mail: admit@husson.husson.edu
Web Site: http://www.husson.edu/

Description: Independent, comprehensive, coed. Awards associate, bachelor's, and master's degrees and post-master's certificates. Founded 1898. Setting: 170-acre suburban campus. Endowment: $3.6 million. Educational spending for 2005 fiscal year: $2812 per student. Total enrollment: 2,245. Faculty: 54 (50 full-time, 4 part-time). Student-undergrad faculty ratio is 19:1. 677 applied, 95% were admitted. 11% from top 10% of their high school class, 28% from top quarter, 61% from top half. 9 class presidents, 2 valedictorians, 54 student government officers. Full-time: 1,605 students, 61% women, 39% men. Part-time: 372 students, 64% women, 36% men. Students come from 15 states and territories, 13 other countries, 12% from out-of-state, 0.1% Native American, 0.3% Hispanic, 2% black, 1% Asian American or Pacific Islander, 2% international, 13% 25 or older, 56% live on campus, 5% transferred in. Retention: 66% of full-time freshmen returned the following year. Academic areas with the most degrees conferred: business/marketing; health professions and related sciences; law/legal studies. Core. Calendar: semesters. Academic remediation for entering students, ESL program, services for LD students, advanced placement, self-designed majors, independent study, distance learning, double major, summer session for credit, part-time degree program, adult/continuing education programs, co-op programs and internships, graduate courses open to undergrads. ROTC: Army (c), Naval (c).

Entrance Requirements: Options: Peterson's Universal Application, Common Application, electronic application, early admission, early action, deferred admission. Required: essay, high school transcript, 1 recommendation, SAT or ACT. Recommended: interview. Required for some: 2 recommendations. Entrance: moderately difficult. Application deadlines: 9/1, 12/15 for early action. Notification: continuous, 1/2 for early action.

Costs Per Year: Application fee: $25. Comprehensive fee: $17,410 includes full-time tuition ($11,130), mandatory fees ($250), and college room and board ($6030). Full-time tuition and fees vary according to class time. Part-time tuition: $371 per credit hour. Part-time tuition varies according to class time and course load.

Collegiate Environment: Orientation program. Drama-theater group, student-run newspaper, radio station. Social organizations: 31 open to all; national fraternities, local fraternities, local sororities; 1% of eligible men and 3% of eligible women are members. Most popular organizations: student

government, Organization of Student Nurses, Organization of Physical Therapy Students, Accounting Society, Phi Beta Lambda. Major annual events: Chief Week, Spring Fling, homecoming. Student services: health clinic, personal-psychological counseling. Campus security: 24-hour emergency response devices and patrols. 790 college housing spaces available; 700 were occupied in 2003-04. Freshmen guaranteed college housing. On-campus residence required through senior year. Option: coed housing available. Sawyer Library with 37,871 books, 15,147 microform titles, 500 serials, 190 audiovisual materials, an OPAC, and a Web page. Operations spending for 2004 fiscal year: $143,239. 57 computers available on campus for general student use. A campuswide network can be accessed from student residence rooms. Staffed computer lab on campus.

■ **KENNEBEC VALLEY COMMUNITY COLLEGE** *K-5*
92 Western Ave.
Fairfield, ME 04937-1367
Tel: (207)453-5000
Admissions: (207)453-5033
Web Site: http://www.kvcc.me.edu/

Description: State-supported, 2-year, coed. Part of Maine Community College System. Awards certificates, diplomas, transfer associate, and terminal associate degrees. Founded 1970. Setting: 58-acre small town campus. Endowment: $229,488. Educational spending for 2005 fiscal year: $4652 per student. Total enrollment: 1,782. Student-undergrad faculty ratio is 22:1. 476 applied, 71% were admitted. Full-time: 523 students, 65% women, 35% men. Part-time: 1,259 students, 70% women, 30% men. Students come from 4 states and territories, 1% Native American, 2% Hispanic, 0.2% black, 0.5% Asian American or Pacific Islander, 0% international, 66% 25 or older. Core. Calendar: semesters. Academic remediation for entering students, services for LD students, advanced placement, accelerated degree program, independent study, distance learning, summer session for credit, part-time degree program, external degree program, adult/continuing education programs, internships.

Entrance Requirements: Open admission except for nursing, radiologic technology, physical therapy assisting, occupational therapy assisting. Options: electronic application, deferred admission. Required: essay, high school transcript. Recommended: SAT or ACT. Required for some: recommendations, interview, nursing exam, HOBET, ACCUPLACER. Entrance: minimally difficult. Application deadline: Rolling. Notification: continuous.

Costs Per Year: Application fee: $20. State resident tuition: $2220 full-time, $74 per credit part-time. Nonresident tuition: $4650 full-time, $155 per credit part-time. Mandatory fees: $600 full-time.

Collegiate Environment: Orientation program. Most popular organizations: Vocational Industrial Clubs of America (VICA) Skills USA, Student Senate, Phi Theta Kappa, Glee Club. Student services: personal-psychological counseling. Campus security: Evening security patrol. College housing not available. Lunder Library with 19,629 books, 25,734 serials, 1,373 audiovisual materials, an OPAC, and a Web page. Operations spending for 2004 fiscal year: $179,890. 250 computers available on campus for general student use. A campuswide network can be accessed from off-campus. Staffed computer lab on campus.

Community Environment: See Colby College.

■ **MAINE COLLEGE OF ART** *O-3*
97 Spring St.
Portland, ME 04101-3987
Tel: (207)775-3052
Free: 800-639-4808
Admissions: (207)775-5157
Fax: (207)772-5069
E-mail: admissions@meca.edu
Web Site: http://www.meca.edu/

Description: Independent, comprehensive, coed. Awards bachelor's and master's degrees. Founded 1882. Setting: urban campus with easy access to Boston. Endowment: $3.2 million. Educational spending for 2005 fiscal year: $9514 per student. Total enrollment: 490. Faculty: 69 (32 full-time, 37 part-time). Student-undergrad faculty ratio is 10:1. 472 applied, 69% were admitted. Full-time: 435 students, 65% women, 35% men. Part-time: 23 students, 78% women, 22% men. 0% from out-of-state, 1% Native American, 2% Hispanic, 2% black, 1% Asian American or Pacific Islander, 1% international, 25% live on campus, 11% transferred in. Academic area with the most degrees conferred: visual and performing arts. Core. Calendar: semesters. Services for LD students, self-designed majors, independent study, double major, part-time degree program, adult/continuing education programs, internships. Off campus study at Association of Independent Colleges of Art and Design Mobility Program. Study abroad program.

Entrance Requirements: Options: Peterson's Universal Application, Common Application, electronic application, early admission, deferred admission, international baccalaureate accepted. Required: essay, high school transcript, 2 recommendations, portfolio, SAT or ACT. Recommended: minimum 2.0 high school GPA, interview. Entrance: moderately difficult. Application deadline: Rolling. Notification: continuous until 8/31.

Costs Per Year: Application fee: $40. Comprehensive fee: $34,590 includes full-time tuition ($24,670), mandatory fees ($650), and college room and board ($9270).

Collegiate Environment: Orientation program. Student-run newspaper. Most popular organizations: Student Representative Association, outdoor group, The Canvas (student newspaper), Ski and Snowboard Club, Movie Club. Major annual events: Annual Meca Art Auction, Student-Alumni Sale, BFA Show. Student services: health clinic, personal-psychological counseling. Campus security: 24-hour emergency response devices and patrols, controlled dormitory access. 100 college housing spaces available; all were occupied in 2003-04. Freshmen given priority for college housing. Option: coed housing available. Joanne Waxman Library at the Maine College of Art with 24,609 books, 100 serials, 235 audiovisual materials, an OPAC, and a Web page. Operations spending for 2004 fiscal year: $200,128. 57 computers available on campus for general student use. Computer purchase/lease plans available. A campuswide network can be accessed. Staffed computer lab on campus.

■ **MAINE MARITIME ACADEMY** *L-8*
Castine, ME 04420
Tel: (207)326-4311
Free: 800-227-8465
Admissions: (207)326-2215
Fax: (207)326-2515
Web Site: http://www.mainemaritime.edu/

Description: State-supported, comprehensive, coed. Awards associate, bachelor's, and master's degrees. Founded 1941. Setting: 35-acre small town campus. Endowment: $20 million. Total enrollment: 861. Faculty: 66 (50 full-time, 16 part-time). Student-undergrad faculty ratio is 12:1. 720 applied, 67% were admitted. 25% from top 10% of their high school class, 42% from top quarter, 74% from top half. Full-time: 747 students, 17% women, 83% men. Part-time: 99 students, 8% women, 92% men. Students come from 37 states and territories, 8 other countries, 65% from out-of-state, 1% Native American, 1% Hispanic, 0.3% black, 0.3% Asian American or Pacific Islander, 4% international, 18% 25 or older, 80% live on campus, 0.4% transferred in. Retention: 80% of full-time freshmen returned the following year. Academic areas with the most degrees conferred: engineering technologies; transportation and materials moving; engineering. Core. Calendar: semesters. Academic remediation for entering students, advanced placement, independent study, distance learning, double major, adult/continuing education programs, internships. Off campus study at International Association of Maritime Universities. Study abroad program. ROTC: Army, Naval.

Entrance Requirements: Options: Peterson's Universal Application, electronic application, early admission, early decision, deferred admission, international baccalaureate accepted. Required: high school transcript, 1 recommendation, physical examination, SAT or ACT. Recommended: interview. Entrance: moderately difficult. Application deadlines: 7/1, 12/20 for early decision. Notification: 1/1 for early decision.

Costs Per Year: Application fee: $15. State resident tuition: $6380 full-time, $230 per credit hour part-time. Nonresident tuition: $9570 full-time, $410 per credit hour part-time. Mandatory fees: $1240 full-time. Full-time tuition and fees vary according to program. Part-time tuition varies according to program. College room and board: $6720. College room only: $2420. Room and board charges vary according to board plan.

Collegiate Environment: Orientation program. Drama-theater group, choral group, marching band. Social organizations: 30 open to all. Most popular organizations: Alpha Phi Omega, Yacht Club, Outing Club, Social Council, drill team. Major annual events: Parents' Weekend, Homecoming, Ring Dance. Student services: health clinic, personal-psychological counseling, women's center. Campus security: 24-hour patrols, student patrols. College housing designed to accommodate 625 students; 650 undergraduates lived in college housing during 2003-04. Freshmen guaranteed college housing. On-campus residence required through junior year. Option: coed housing available. Nutting Memorial Library with 177,800 books, 382 serials, an OPAC, and a Web page. 40 computers available on campus for general

student use. A campuswide network can be accessed from student residence rooms and from off campus. Staffed computer lab on campus.

Community Environment: The French erected the first fort here in 1613, but the first permanent settlement was made by the English in 1760. Fort George, partially restored, is maintained as a memorial today. Castine is on south central coast of Maine, 35 miles south of Bangor.

■ **NEW ENGLAND SCHOOL OF COMMUNICATIONS** *K-8*
1 College Circle
Bangor, ME 04401-2999
Tel: (207)941-7176; 888-877-1876
Fax: (207)947-3987
E-mail: grantl@nescom.edu
Web Site: http://www.nescom.edu/

Description: Independent, 4-year, coed. Awards associate and bachelor's degrees. Founded 1981. Setting: 200-acre small town campus. Total enrollment: 305. Student-undergrad faculty ratio is 18:1. 310 applied, 69% were admitted. Full-time: 295 students, 23% women, 77% men. Part-time: 10 students, 20% women, 80% men. Students come from 9 states and territories, 17% from out-of-state, 0% Native American, 0.3% Hispanic, 2% black, 1% Asian American or Pacific Islander, 0% international, 26% 25 or older, 54% live on campus, 4% transferred in. Academic area with the most degrees conferred: communication technologies. Core. Calendar: semesters. ESL program, services for LD students, advanced placement, self-designed majors, double major, summer session for credit, part-time degree program, adult/continuing education programs, internships.

Entrance Requirements: Open admission. Options: electronic application, early admission, deferred admission. Required: essay, high school transcript, 2 recommendations, interview, Wonderlic Scholastic Test, Wonderlic aptitude test. Recommended: SAT or ACT. Entrance: minimally difficult. Application deadline: Rolling. Notification: continuous.

Costs Per Year: Application fee: $15. Comprehensive fee: $15,620 includes full-time tuition ($8890), mandatory fees ($700), and college room and board ($6030). Part-time tuition: $275 per credit.

Collegiate Environment: Orientation program. Drama-theater group, choral group, marching band, student-run newspaper, radio station. Social organizations: 32 open to all; national fraternities, national sororities, local fraternities, local sororities; 10% of eligible men and 10% of eligible women are members. Most popular organizations: drama, newspaper, student government, radio station. Major annual events: Greek Week, Orientation, Winter Carnival. Student services: health clinic, personal-psychological counseling. Campus security: 24-hour emergency response devices and patrols, late night transport-escort service. 1,200 college housing spaces available; 120 were occupied in 2003-04. Freshmen given priority for college housing. Option: coed housing available. Husson College Library plus 1 other with an OPAC and a Web page. 150 computers available on campus for general student use. Computer purchase/lease plans available. A campuswide network can be accessed from student residence rooms and from off campus. Staffed computer lab on campus.

■ **NORTHERN MAINE COMMUNITY COLLEGE** *D-10*
33 Edgemont Dr.
Presque Isle, ME 04769-2016
Tel: (207)768-2700
Admissions: (207)768-2786
Fax: (207)768-2831
E-mail: ncasavant@nmcc.edu
Web Site: http://www.nmcc.edu/

Description: State-related, 2-year, coed. Part of Maine Technical College System. Awards certificates, diplomas, transfer associate, and terminal associate degrees. Founded 1963. Setting: 86-acre small town campus. Educational spending for 2005 fiscal year: $4697 per student. Total enrollment: 921. 759 applied, 52% were admitted. 75% from top half of their high school class. Full-time: 605 students, 44% women, 56% men. Part-time: 316 students, 69% women, 31% men. Students come from 5 states and territories, 1 other country, 4% from out-of-state, 4% Native American, 1% Hispanic, 1% black, 0.4% Asian American or Pacific Islander, 4% international, 45% 25 or older, 28% live on campus. Calendar: semesters. Academic remediation for entering students, services for LD students, advanced placement, independent study, double major, summer session for credit, part-time degree program, adult/continuing education programs, co-op programs and internships. Off campus study at University of Maine at Presque Isle.

Entrance Requirements: Open admission except for nursing, electrical engineering technology programs. Options: Peterson's Universal Application, Common Application, electronic application, early admission. Required: high school transcript, interview, ACCUPLACER. Recommended: essay, minimum 2.0 high school GPA. Required for some: recommendations, Net Test/RN. Entrance: minimally difficult. Application deadline: Rolling. Notification: continuous.

Costs Per Year: Application fee: $20. Area resident tuition: $2390 full-time, $78 per credit hour part-time. State resident tuition: $115 per credit hour part-time. Nonresident tuition: $4770 full-time, $159 per credit hour part-time. College room and board: $4930.

Collegiate Environment: Orientation program. Student services: health clinic, Career Planning, Counseling, Student Employment, student email web pages st. Campus security: 24-hour patrols. Option: coed housing available. Northern Maine Technical College Library with 11,200 books, 233 serials, 250 audiovisual materials, an OPAC, and a Web page. Operations spending for 2004 fiscal year: $124,000.

Community Environment: See University of Maine - Presque Isle.

■ SAINT JOSEPH'S COLLEGE OF MAINE *O-3*

278 Whites Bridge Rd.
Standish, ME 04084-5263
Tel: (207)892-6766
Free: 800-338-7057
Admissions: (207)893-7746
Fax: (207)893-7862
E-mail: vkloskow@sjcme.edu
Web Site: http://www.sjcme.edu/

Description: Independent, comprehensive, coed, affiliated with Roman Catholic Church. Awards bachelor's and master's degrees (profile does not include enrollment in distance learning master's program). Founded 1912. Setting: 330-acre small town campus. Endowment: $4.1 million. Research spending for 2004 fiscal year: $114,734. Educational spending for 2005 fiscal year: $3993 per student. Total enrollment: 955. Faculty: 108 (64 full-time, 44 part-time). Student-undergrad faculty ratio is 15:1. 1,178 applied, 77% were admitted. 15% from top 10% of their high school class, 40% from top quarter, 75% from top half. 2 valedictorians. Full-time: 925 students, 64% women, 36% men. Part-time: 30 students, 70% women, 30% men. Students come from 14 states and territories, 1 other country, 40% from out-of-state, 0.1% Native American, 1% Hispanic, 2% black, 0.4% Asian American or Pacific Islander, 0% international, 3% 25 or older, 83% live on campus, 3% transferred in. Retention: 81% of full-time freshmen returned the following year. Academic areas with the most degrees conferred: education; business/marketing; health professions and related sciences. Core. Calendar: semesters. Services for LD students, advanced placement, self-designed majors, honors program, independent study, distance learning, double major, summer session for credit, part-time degree program, adult/continuing education programs, co-op programs and internships. Off campus study at Greater Portland Alliance of Colleges and Universities, a consortium that includes University of Southern Maine, Maine College of Art, University of New England, Southern Maine Technical College, and Saint Joseph's College. Study abroad program. ROTC: Army (c).

Entrance Requirements: Options: Peterson's Universal Application, Common Application, electronic application, early action, deferred admission. Required: essay, high school transcript, minimum 2.0 high school GPA, 2 recommendations, SAT or ACT. Recommended: interview. Entrance: moderately difficult. Application deadlines: Rolling, 11/15 for early action. Notification: continuous, 12/15 for early action.

Costs Per Year: Application fee: $40. Comprehensive fee: $29,185 includes full-time tuition ($19,890), mandatory fees ($715), and college room and board ($8580). Full-time tuition and fees vary according to program. Part-time tuition: $350 per credit. Part-time mandatory fees: $125 per year. Part-time tuition and fees vary according to course load and program.

Collegiate Environment: Orientation program. Drama-theater group, choral group, student-run newspaper, radio station. Social organizations: 25 open to all. Most popular organizations: campus ministry, Superkids, Student Government Association and Senate, Business Club, Inter-Hall Council. Major annual events: Family Weekend, Spring Fling, Welcome Back Weekends. Student services: health clinic, personal-psychological counseling. Campus security: 24-hour emergency response devices and patrols, late night transport-escort service, controlled dormitory access. 829 college housing spaces available; 795 were occupied in 2003-04. Freshmen guaranteed college housing. Options: coed, men-only, women-only housing available. Wellehan Library with 98,626 books, 29,010 microform titles,

11,461 serials, 1,000 audiovisual materials, an OPAC, and a Web page. Operations spending for 2004 fiscal year: $403,893. 102 computers available on campus for general student use. Computer purchase/lease plans available. A campuswide network can be accessed from student residence rooms. Staffed computer lab on campus.

■ SOUTHERN MAINE COMMUNITY COLLEGE *O-4*

2 Fort Rd.
South Portland, ME 04106
Tel: (207)741-5500
Admissions: (207)741-5664
Fax: (207)741-5751
Web Site: http://www.smccme.edu/

Description: State-supported, 2-year, coed. Part of Maine Community College System. Awards certificates, diplomas, transfer associate, and terminal associate degrees. Founded 1946. Setting: 65-acre small town campus. Endowment: $513,726. Educational spending for 2005 fiscal year: $6095 per student. Total enrollment: 4,103. Full-time: 2,135 students, 44% women, 56% men. Part-time: 1,968 students, 58% women, 42% men. Students come from 9 states and territories, 6% from out-of-state, 1% Native American, 1% Hispanic, 3% black, 1% Asian American or Pacific Islander, 0.5% international, 48% 25 or older, 10% live on campus. Core. Calendar: semesters. Academic remediation for entering students, ESL program, services for LD students, advanced placement, distance learning, double major, summer session for credit, part-time degree program, co-op programs and internships. Off campus study at Great Portland Alliance of Colleges and Universities. Study abroad program.

Entrance Requirements: Option: electronic application. Required: high school transcript. Placement: SAT recommended; ACCUPLACER required for some. Entrance: minimally difficult. Application deadline: Rolling. Notification: continuous. Preference given to state residents.

Costs Per Year: Application fee: $20. State resident tuition: $2220 full-time. Nonresident tuition: $4650 full-time. College room and board: $5824. College room only: $2678.

Collegiate Environment: Orientation program. Drama-theater group, choral group, student-run newspaper. Most popular organizations: SEA Club, student government, Phi Theta Kappa, VICA. Major annual events: Earth Day, Awards Day. Student services: health clinic, personal-psychological counseling, women's center. Campus security: 24-hour emergency response devices, student patrols, late night transport-escort service. 200 college housing spaces available; all were occupied in 2003-04. Option: coed housing available. Southern Maine Community College Library with 15,000 books, 350 serials, an OPAC, and a Web page. Operations spending for 2004 fiscal year: $236,090. 200 computers available on campus for general student use. A campuswide network can be accessed from student residence rooms and from off campus. Staffed computer lab on campus.

■ THOMAS COLLEGE *L-5*

180 West River Rd.
Waterville, ME 04901-5097
Tel: (207)859-1111
Free: 800-339-7001
Admissions: (207)859-1101
Fax: (207)859-1114
E-mail: admiss@thomas.edu
Web Site: http://www.thomas.edu/

Description: Independent, comprehensive, coed. Awards associate, bachelor's, and master's degrees (associate). Founded 1894. Setting: 70-acre small town campus. Endowment: $5.8 million. Educational spending for 2005 fiscal year: $3199 per student. Total enrollment: 875. Faculty: 78 (23 full-time, 55 part-time). Student-undergrad faculty ratio is 17:1. 628 applied, 73% were admitted. 11% from top 10% of their high school class, 21% from top quarter, 55% from top half. Full-time: 598 students, 46% women, 54% men. Part-time: 133 students, 73% women, 27% men. Students come from 10 states and territories, 16% from out-of-state, 1% Native American, 1% Hispanic, 1% black, 1% Asian American or Pacific Islander, 0% international, 16% 25 or older, 65% live on campus, 5% transferred in. Retention: 58% of full-time freshmen returned the following year. Academic areas with the most degrees conferred: business/marketing; computer and information sciences; education. Core. Calendar: semesters. Academic remediation for entering students, advanced placement, double major, summer session for credit, part-time degree program, adult/continuing education programs, co-op programs and internships, graduate courses open to undergrads. Off campus study at Colby College, Kennebec Valley Community College, Unity College. Study abroad program.

Entrance Requirements: Options: Peterson's Universal Application, Common Application, electronic application, early action, deferred admission, international baccalaureate accepted. Required: essay, high school transcript, 1 recommendation. Recommended: minimum 2.0 high school GPA, interview, rank in upper 50% of high school class. Required for some: SAT or ACT. Entrance: minimally difficult. Application deadlines: Rolling, 12/15 for early action. Notification: continuous, 12/31 for early action.

Costs Per Year: Application fee: $50. Comprehensive fee: $25,160 includes full-time tuition ($17,280), mandatory fees ($450), and college room and board ($7430). Part-time tuition: $720 per credit hour.

Collegiate Environment: Orientation program. Drama-theater group, choral group, student-run newspaper. Social organizations: 17 open to all; national fraternities, national sororities, local fraternities, local sororities; 3% of eligible men and 5% of eligible women are members. Most popular organizations: Phi Beta Lambda, Students Club, GLOBE, Campus Activity Board, peer advisors. Major annual events: Homecoming, Parents' Day, Olympic Day. Student services: health clinic, personal-psychological counseling. Campus security: 24-hour emergency response devices and patrols, student patrols. 392 college housing spaces available; 390 were occupied in 2003-04. Freshmen guaranteed college housing. On-campus residence required through senior year. Option: coed housing available. Marriner Library with 20,000 books, 5,000 serials, 600 audiovisual materials, an OPAC, and a Web page. Operations spending for 2004 fiscal year: $145,469. 120 computers available on campus for general student use. A campuswide network can be accessed from student residence rooms and from off campus. Staffed computer lab on campus.

■ **UNITY COLLEGE** *K-6*

90 Quaker Hill Rd.
Unity, ME 04988
Tel: (207)948-3131
Fax: (207)948-6277
Web Site: http://www.unity.edu/

Description: Independent, 4-year, coed. Awards associate and bachelor's degrees. Founded 1965. Setting: 265-acre rural campus. Endowment: $2.4 million. Educational spending for 2005 fiscal year: $5026 per student. Total enrollment: 521. 436 applied, 88% were admitted. 8% from top 10% of their high school class, 29% from top quarter, 60% from top half. Full-time: 515 students, 36% women, 64% men. Part-time: 6 students, 17% women, 83% men. Students come from 21 states and territories, 2 other countries, 62% from out-of-state, 0% Native American, 0.4% Hispanic, 0.4% black, 0% Asian American or Pacific Islander, 1% international, 8% 25 or older, 66% live on campus, 9% transferred in. Retention: 98% of full-time freshmen returned the following year. Core. Calendar: semesters. Academic remediation for entering students, ESL program, services for LD students, advanced placement, accelerated degree program, self-designed majors, honors program, independent study, summer session for credit, part-time degree program, co-op programs and internships. Off campus study at The Washington Center. ROTC: Army (c).

Entrance Requirements: Options: Peterson's Universal Application, Common Application, electronic application, early admission, early action, deferred admission, international baccalaureate accepted. Required: essay, high school transcript, 2 recommendations. Recommended: minimum 2.0 high school GPA, interview. Required for some: interview. Placement: SAT or ACT recommended. Entrance: moderately difficult. Application deadlines: Rolling, 1/15 for early action. Notification: 2/1 for early action.

Costs Per Year: Application fee: $25. Comprehensive fee: $24,310 includes full-time tuition ($16,740), mandatory fees ($940), and college room and board ($6630). Room and board charges vary according to board plan. Part-time tuition: $630 per credit hour. Part-time tuition varies according to course load.

Collegiate Environment: Orientation program. Drama-theater group, student-run newspaper. Social organizations: 28 open to all. Student services: health clinic, personal-psychological counseling. Campus security: 24-hour patrols. College housing designed to accommodate 306 students; 312 undergraduates lived in college housing during 2003-04. On-campus residence required through sophomore year. Option: coed housing available. Dorothy Webb Quimby Library with 46,000 books, 650 serials, and a Web page. Operations spending for 2004 fiscal year: $266,787. 42 computers available on campus for general student use. A campuswide network can be accessed from student residence rooms and from off campus. Staffed computer lab on campus.

Community Environment: Located on Lake Winnecook, which is three miles long and has excellent fishing, canoeing, and sailing, Unity has several small businesses, two churches, a public library, and several fraternal organizations. Transportation is provided by air and bus lines. The climate is cool.

■ **UNIVERSITY OF MAINE** *J-8*

Orono, ME 04469
Tel: (207)581-1110; 877-486-2364
Admissions: (207)581-1561
Fax: (207)581-1213
E-mail: um-admit@maine.edu
Web Site: http://www.umaine.edu/

Description: State-supported, university, coed. Part of University of Maine System. Awards bachelor's, master's, and doctoral degrees and post-master's certificates. Founded 1865. Setting: 3,300-acre small town campus. Endowment: $159.6 million. Research spending for 2004 fiscal year: $51.9 million. Educational spending for 2005 fiscal year: $9972 per student. Total enrollment: 11,435. Faculty: 823 (496 full-time, 327 part-time). Student-undergrad faculty ratio is 16:1. 5,702 applied, 80% were admitted. 22% from top 10% of their high school class, 52% from top quarter, 86% from top half. 2 National Merit Scholars, 37 valedictorians, 304 student government officers. Full-time: 7,617 students, 49% women, 51% men. Part-time: 1,562 students, 63% women, 37% men. Students come from 41 states and territories, 47 other countries, 13% from out-of-state, 2% Native American, 1% Hispanic, 1% black, 1% Asian American or Pacific Islander, 2% international, 21% 25 or older, 30% live on campus, 5% transferred in. Retention: 79% of full-time freshmen returned the following year. Academic areas with the most degrees conferred: education; business/marketing; engineering; social sciences; health professions and related sciences. Core. Calendar: semesters. ESL program, services for LD students, advanced placement, accelerated degree program, self-designed majors, freshman honors college, honors program, independent study, distance learning, double major, summer session for credit, part-time degree program, external degree program, adult/continuing education programs, co-op programs and internships. Off campus study at Bangor Theological Seminary, other institutions of the University of Maine System. Study abroad program. ROTC: Army, Naval.

Entrance Requirements: Options: Peterson's Universal Application, Common Application, electronic application, early admission, deferred admission, international baccalaureate accepted. Required: essay, high school transcript, 1 recommendation, SAT or ACT. Required for some: interview. Entrance: moderately difficult. Application deadlines: Rolling, 12/15 for early action. Notification: continuous.

Costs Per Year: Application fee: $40. State resident tuition: $5520 full-time, $184 per credit hour part-time. Nonresident tuition: $15,660 full-time, $522 per credit hour part-time. Mandatory fees: $1390 full-time. Full-time tuition and fees vary according to reciprocity agreements. Part-time tuition varies according to reciprocity agreements. College room and board: $6732. College room only: $3390. Room and board charges vary according to board plan and housing facility.

Collegiate Environment: Orientation program. Drama-theater group, choral group, marching band, student-run newspaper, radio station. Social organizations: 234 open to all; national fraternities, national sororities, local fraternities. Most popular organizations: Volunteers in Community Efforts/VOICE, Circle K, Campus Crusade for Christ, Outing Club, Wilde Stein. Major annual events: Maine Day, Bumstock, Student Organizations Fair. Student services: legal services, health clinic, personal-psychological counseling, women's center. Campus security: 24-hour emergency response devices and patrols, late night transport-escort service, controlled dormitory access. 3,643 college housing spaces available; all were occupied in 2003-04. Freshmen guaranteed college housing. On-campus residence required in freshman year. Option: coed housing available. Fogler Library plus 2 others with 1 million books, 2.4 million microform titles, 13,041 serials, 26,647 audiovisual materials, an OPAC, and a Web page. Operations spending for 2004 fiscal year: $7.2 million. 500 computers available on campus for general student use. Computer purchase/lease plans available. A campuswide network can be accessed from student residence rooms and from off campus. Staffed computer lab on campus.

■ **THE UNIVERSITY OF MAINE AT AUGUSTA** *M-5*

46 University Dr.
Augusta, ME 04330-9410
Tel: (207)621-3000
Admissions: (207)621-3390
Fax: (207)621-3116
E-mail: umaar@maine.edu

Web Site: http://www.uma.maine.edu/
Description: State-supported, 4-year, coed. Part of University of Maine System. Awards associate and bachelor's degrees (also offers some graduate courses and continuing education programs with significant enrollment not reflected in profile). Founded 1965. Setting: 159-acre small town campus. Endowment: $1.4 million. Educational spending for 2005 fiscal year: $3668 per student. Total enrollment: 5,494. Student-undergrad faculty ratio is 19:1. 1,012 applied, 52% were admitted. Full-time: 1,544 students, 70% women, 30% men. Part-time: 3,950 students, 76% women, 24% men. Students come from 16 states and territories, 4 other countries, 1% from out-of-state, 3% Native American, 0.5% Hispanic, 1% black, 0.3% Asian American or Pacific Islander, 0.1% international, 65% 25 or older, 4% transferred in. Academic areas with the most degrees conferred: health professions and related sciences; business/marketing; library science. Core. Calendar: semesters. Academic remediation for entering students, services for LD students, advanced placement, self-designed majors, honors program, independent study, distance learning, double major, summer session for credit, part-time degree program, adult/continuing education programs, internships. Off campus study at other units of the University of Maine System. Study abroad program.
Entrance Requirements: Options: Peterson's Universal Application, Common Application, electronic application, early admission, deferred admission. Required: high school transcript. Recommended: essay. Required for some: recommendations, interview, music audition. Entrance: noncompetitive. Application deadline: 8/31. Notification: continuous until 9/15.
Costs Per Year: Application fee: $40. State resident tuition: $4290 full-time, $143 per credit hour part-time. Nonresident tuition: $10,380 full-time, $346 per credit hour part-time. Mandatory fees: $735 full-time, $24.50 per credit hour part-time. Full-time tuition and fees vary according to reciprocity agreements. Part-time tuition and fees vary according to reciprocity agreements.
Collegiate Environment: Orientation program. Student-run newspaper. Social organizations: 5 open to all. Most popular organizations: Honors Program Student Association, Arts and Architecture Students of UMA, Student Nurse Association, Student-American Dental Hygiene Association, International Student Club. Major annual events: UMA Day, Jazz Week, Poetry Festival. Student services: personal-psychological counseling. Campus security: late night transport-escort service. College housing not available. The Bennett D. Katz Library plus 1 other with 83,766 books, 6,600 microform titles, 546 serials, 3,296 audiovisual materials, and an OPAC. Operations spending for 2004 fiscal year: $822,318. 142 computers available on campus for general student use. Computer purchase/lease plans available. A campuswide network can be accessed from off-campus. Staffed computer lab on campus.

■ **UNIVERSITY OF MAINE AT FARMINGTON** *K-4*
224 Main St.
Farmington, ME 04938-1990
Tel: (207)778-7000
Admissions: (207)778-7087
Fax: (207)778-8182
E-mail: umfadmit@maine.edu
Web Site: http://www.umf.maine.edu/
Description: State-supported, 4-year, coed. Part of University of Maine System. Awards bachelor's degrees. Founded 1863. Setting: 50-acre small town campus. Research spending for 2004 fiscal year: $877,000. Educational spending for 2005 fiscal year: $5256 per student. Total enrollment: 2,452. Student-undergrad faculty ratio is 16:1. 1,602 applied, 74% were admitted. 12% from top 10% of their high school class, 38% from top quarter, 80% from top half. Full-time: 2,123 students, 66% women, 34% men. Part-time: 329 students, 70% women, 30% men. Students come from 21 states and territories, 7 other countries, 23% from out-of-state, 1% Native American, 1% Hispanic, 0.2% black, 1% Asian American or Pacific Islander, 0.4% international, 12% 25 or older, 44% live on campus, 5% transferred in. Retention: 70% of full-time freshmen returned the following year. Academic areas with the most degrees conferred: education; English; interdisciplinary studies. Core. Calendar: semesters plus May term and 2 5-week summer terms. Academic remediation for entering students, services for LD students, advanced placement, accelerated degree program, self-designed majors, honors program, independent study, distance learning, double major, summer session for credit, part-time degree program, internships. Off campus study at National Student Exchange, SALT Center for Documentary Field Studies, other institutions of the University of Maine System. Study abroad program.
Entrance Requirements: Options: Peterson's Universal Application, electronic application, early admission, early action, deferred admission,

international baccalaureate accepted. Required: essay, high school transcript, minimum 2.0 high school GPA, 1 recommendation. Recommended: interview. Required for some: minimum 2.5 GPA for elementary education majors, SAT or ACT. Entrance: moderately difficult. Application deadlines: Rolling, 12/1 for early action. Notification: continuous, 1/8 for early action.
Costs Per Year: Application fee: $40. State resident tuition: $5010 full-time, $167 per credit hour part-time. Nonresident tuition: $12,240 full-time, $408 per credit hour part-time. Mandatory fees: $621 full-time, $75 per term part-time. Full-time tuition and fees vary according to course load, reciprocity agreements, and student level. Part-time tuition and fees vary according to course load, reciprocity agreements, and student level. College room and board: $5984. College room only: $3200. Room and board charges vary according to board plan and housing facility.
Collegiate Environment: Orientation program. Drama-theater group, choral group, student-run newspaper, radio station. Social organizations: 52 open to all. Most popular organizations: Program Board, Intramural Board, Campus Residence Council, campus radio station, Commuter Council. Major annual events: Intramural All Niter, Spring Fling, Campus Residence Council Semi-Formal. Student services: health clinic, personal-psychological counseling. Campus security: 24-hour emergency response devices and patrols, late night transport-escort service, controlled dormitory access, safety whistles. 1,030 college housing spaces available; 1,000 were occupied in 2003-04. Freshmen guaranteed college housing. Options: coed, women-only housing available. Mantor Library with 98,248 books, 82,773 microform titles, 577 serials, 7,663 audiovisual materials, an OPAC, and a Web page. Operations spending for 2004 fiscal year: $566,305. 175 computers available on campus for general student use. A campuswide network can be accessed from student residence rooms and from off campus. Staffed computer lab on campus.

■ **UNIVERSITY OF MAINE AT FORT KENT** *B-8*
23 University Dr.
Fort Kent, ME 04743-1292
Tel: (207)834-7500; 888-TRY-UMFK
Admissions: (207)834-7600
Fax: (207)834-7609
E-mail: dbarley@maine.edu
Web Site: http://www.umfk.maine.edu/
Description: State-supported, 4-year, coed. Part of University of Maine System. Awards associate and bachelor's degrees. Founded 1878. Setting: 52-acre rural campus. Endowment: $1.5 million. Research spending for 2004 fiscal year: $2500. Educational spending for 2005 fiscal year: $2928 per student. Total enrollment: 1,076. 394 applied, 81% were admitted. 7% from top 10% of their high school class, 20% from top quarter, 60% from top half. 10 National Merit Scholars, 4 valedictorians, 20 student government officers. Students come from 30 states and territories, 12 other countries, 4% from out-of-state, 1% Native American, 0.5% Hispanic, 1% black, 0.1% Asian American or Pacific Islander, 27% international, 36% 25 or older, 30% live on campus. Retention: 59% of full-time freshmen returned the following year. Core. Calendar: semesters. ESL program, services for LD students, advanced placement, accelerated degree program, self-designed majors, honors program, independent study, distance learning, double major, summer session for credit, part-time degree program, external degree program, internships.
Entrance Requirements: Options: Peterson's Universal Application, Common Application, electronic application, early admission, early decision, deferred admission. Required: essay, high school transcript. Recommended: recommendations, SAT and SAT Subject Tests or ACT. Required for some: interview, SAT, SAT and SAT Subject Tests or ACT. Entrance: moderately difficult. Application deadline: Rolling. Notification: continuous.
Collegiate Environment: Orientation program. Drama-theater group, choral group. Social organizations: 12 open to all; national fraternities, national sororities; 5% of eligible men and 5% of eligible women are members. Most popular organizations: Performing Arts Club, Student Teachers Educational Professional Society, Student Nurses Organization, Diversity Club, Dorm Council. Major annual events: Quebec City Carnival Field Trip, Open Mic Nights, Spring Formal. Student services: health clinic, personal-psychological counseling. Campus security: controlled dormitory access, 8-hour night patrols by security personnel 11pm-7am. 300 college housing spaces available; 250 were occupied in 2003-04. No special consideration for freshman housing applicants. Option: coed housing available. Waneta Blake Library plus 1 other with 69,189 books, 335 serials, 4,254 audiovisual materials, an OPAC, and a Web page. Operations spending for 2004 fiscal

year: $246,483. 100 computers available on campus for general student use. A campuswide network can be accessed from student residence rooms and from off campus. Staffed computer lab on campus.

■ **UNIVERSITY OF MAINE AT MACHIAS** *K-11*
9 O'Brien Ave.
Machias, ME 04654-1321
Tel: (207)255-1200; 888-GOTOUMM
Admissions: (207)255-1318
Fax: (207)255-1363
E-mail: ummadmissions@maine.edu
Web Site: http://www.umm.maine.edu/
Description: State-supported, 4-year, coed. Part of University of Maine System. Awards bachelor's degrees. Founded 1909. Setting: 42-acre rural campus. Endowment: $1 million. Research spending for 2004 fiscal year: $268,937. Educational spending for 2005 fiscal year: $5302 per student. Total enrollment: 1,149. Student-undergrad faculty ratio is 14:1. 374 applied, 83% were admitted. 9% from top 10% of their high school class, 25% from top quarter, 64% from top half. Full-time: 462 students, 66% women, 34% men. Part-time: 687 students, 79% women, 21% men. Students come from 26 states and territories, 16 other countries, 23% from out-of-state, 4% Native American, 2% Hispanic, 1% black, 1% Asian American or Pacific Islander, 5% international, 27% 25 or older, 42% live on campus, 3% transferred in. Retention: 67% of full-time freshmen returned the following year. Academic areas with the most degrees conferred: business/marketing; interdisciplinary studies; biological/life sciences. Core. Calendar: semesters. Academic remediation for entering students, services for LD students, advanced placement, self-designed majors, honors program, independent study, distance learning, double major, summer session for credit, part-time degree program, external degree program, adult/continuing education programs, co-op programs and internships. Off campus study. Study abroad program.
Entrance Requirements: Options: Peterson's Universal Application, Common Application, electronic application, early admission, early action, deferred admission. Required: essay, high school transcript, 1 recommendation, SAT or ACT. Recommended: 2 recommendations, interview. Required for some: minimum 2.0 high school GPA, interview. Entrance: moderately difficult. Application deadlines: 8/15, 12/15 for early action. Notification: continuous, 1/15 for early action.
Costs Per Year: Application fee: $40. State resident tuition: $4290 full-time, $143 per credit hour part-time. Nonresident tuition: $11,640 full-time, $388 per credit hour part-time. Mandatory fees: $555 full-time, $17.50 per credit hour part-time, $45 per term part-time. College room and board: $5678. College room only: $2858. Room and board charges vary according to housing facility.
Collegiate Environment: Orientation program. Drama-theater group, choral group, student-run radio station. Social organizations: 25 open to all; national fraternities, national sororities, local fraternities, local sororities; 8% of eligible men and 4% of eligible women are members. Most popular organizations: Student Senate, 100% Society, International Club, MRPASS, Softball Club. Major annual events: homecoming, Winter Carnival, Spring Weekend. Student services: health clinic, personal-psychological counseling. Campus security: 24-hour emergency response devices, late night transport-escort service, controlled dormitory access, night security guard until 3:00 a.m., day security 8-5 p.m. 353 college housing spaces available; 309 were occupied in 2003-04. No special consideration for freshman housing applicants. Option: coed housing available. Merrill Library plus 1 other with 82,664 books, 4,750 microform titles, 316 serials, 3,647 audiovisual materials, an OPAC, and a Web page. Operations spending for 2004 fiscal year: $269,894. 185 computers available on campus for general student use. A campuswide network can be accessed from student residence rooms and from off campus. Staffed computer lab on campus.

■ **UNIVERSITY OF MAINE AT PRESQUE ISLE** *D-10*
181 Main St.
Presque Isle, ME 04769-2888
Tel: (207)768-9400
Admissions: (207)768-9453
Fax: (207)768-9608
E-mail: benson@umpi.maine.edu
Web Site: http://www.umpi.maine.edu/
Description: State-supported, 4-year, coed. Part of University of Maine System. Awards associate and bachelor's degrees. Founded 1903. Setting: 150-acre small town campus. Endowment: $1.1 million. Research spending

for 2004 fiscal year: $7820. Total enrollment: 1,548. Student-undergrad faculty ratio is 16:1. 480 applied, 87% were admitted. 8% from top 10% of their high school class, 23% from top quarter, 51% from top half. Full-time: 1,112 students, 63% women, 37% men. Part-time: 436 students, 73% women, 27% men. Students come from 17 states and territories, 4 other countries, 2% from out-of-state, 4% Native American, 1% Hispanic, 1% black, 1% Asian American or Pacific Islander, 9% international, 31% 25 or older, 28% live on campus, 15% transferred in. Retention: 55% of full-time freshmen returned the following year. Academic areas with the most degrees conferred: liberal arts/general studies; education; business/marketing. Core. Calendar: semesters. Academic remediation for entering students, services for LD students, advanced placement, accelerated degree program, self-designed majors, honors program, independent study, distance learning, double major, summer session for credit, part-time degree program, adult/continuing education programs, co-op programs and internships. Off campus study at Tri-Campus Exchange. Study abroad program.
Entrance Requirements: Options: Common Application, electronic application, early admission, early action, deferred admission, international baccalaureate accepted. Required: essay, high school transcript, minimum 2.0 high school GPA, recommendations. Required for some: 1 recommendation, interview. Entrance: minimally difficult. Application deadlines: Rolling, 10/31 for early action. Notification: continuous, 4/1 for early action.
Costs Per Year: Application fee: $40. State resident tuition: $4290 full-time, $143 per credit hour part-time. Nonresident tuition: $10,680 full-time, $356 per credit hour part-time. Mandatory fees: $530 full-time, $19 per credit hour part-time. Full-time tuition and fees vary according to course load and reciprocity agreements. Part-time tuition and fees vary according to course load and reciprocity agreements. College room and board: $5246. College room only: $3000. Room and board charges vary according to board plan.
Collegiate Environment: Orientation program. Drama-theater group, student-run newspaper, radio station. Social organizations: 25 open to all; national fraternities, national sororities; 1% of eligible men and 1% of eligible women are members. Most popular organizations: Student Senate, OAPI-Outdoor Adventure Program International, Student Activities Board, Student Organization of Social Work, Campus Crusade for Christ. Major annual events: Spring Fest, Winter Blast, Spring Ball. Student services: health clinic, personal-psychological counseling. Campus security: student patrols, late night transport-escort service, crime prevention programs, lighted pathways. College housing designed to accommodate 361 students; 368 undergraduates lived in college housing during 2003-04. Option: coed housing available. UMPI Library with 455,372 books, 440,453 microform titles, 2,500 serials, 1,281 audiovisual materials, an OPAC, and a Web page. Operations spending for 2004 fiscal year: $447,582. 82 computers available on campus for general student use. A campuswide network can be accessed from student residence rooms and from off campus. Staffed computer lab on campus.

■ **UNIVERSITY OF NEW ENGLAND** *P-3*
Hills Beach Rd.
Biddeford, ME 04005-9526
Tel: (207)283-0171
Free: 800-477-4UNE
Admissions: (207)283-0170
E-mail: admissions@une.edu
Web Site: http://www.une.edu/
Description: Independent, comprehensive, coed. Awards associate, bachelor's, master's, and first professional degrees and post-master's certificates. Founded 1831. Setting: 410-acre small town campus. Endowment: $22.5 million. Research spending for 2004 fiscal year: $1 million. Educational spending for 2005 fiscal year: $9375 per student. Total enrollment: 3,312. Faculty: 241 (137 full-time, 104 part-time). Student-undergrad faculty ratio is 11:1. 2,055 applied, 92% were admitted. 17% from top 10% of their high school class, 49% from top quarter, 86% from top half. Full-time: 1,519 students, 77% women, 23% men. Part-time: 217 students, 76% women, 24% men. Students come from 35 states and territories, 3 other countries, 59% from out-of-state, 0.2% Native American, 1% Hispanic, 1% black, 1% Asian American or Pacific Islander, 0.2% international, 13% 25 or older, 61% live on campus, 9% transferred in. Retention: 75% of full-time freshmen returned the following year. Academic areas with the most degrees conferred: health professions and related sciences; biological/life sciences; psychology. Core. Calendar: semesters. Academic remediation for entering students, services for LD students, advanced placement, accelerated degree program, self-designed majors, independent study, distance learning, double major, summer session for credit, part-time degree program, co-op programs

and internships, graduate courses open to undergrads. Off campus study at Greater Portland Alliance of Colleges and Universities. Study abroad program. ROTC: Army (c).

Entrance Requirements: Options: Peterson's Universal Application, Common Application, electronic application, deferred admission. Required: high school transcript, SAT or ACT. Recommended: essay, interview. Required for some: interview. Entrance: moderately difficult. Application deadline: Rolling. Notification: continuous.

Costs Per Year: Application fee: $40. Comprehensive fee: $31,005 includes full-time tuition ($21,540), mandatory fees ($735), and college room and board ($8730). Room and board charges vary according to housing facility. Part-time tuition: $775 per credit.

Collegiate Environment: Orientation program. Social organizations: 44 open to all. Most popular organizations: Student Government, Outing Club, Campus Programming Board, Earth's Eco, Dance Team. Major annual events: homecoming, Jam Fest, Winter Fest. Student services: health clinic, personal-psychological counseling. Campus security: 24-hour emergency response devices and patrols, late night transport-escort service, controlled dormitory access. College housing designed to accommodate 881 students; 909 undergraduates lived in college housing during 2003-04. Freshmen guaranteed college housing. On-campus residence required through junior year. Options: coed, women-only housing available. Ketchum Library plus 1 other with 142,181 books, 6,281 microform titles, 2,443 serials, 9,879 audiovisual materials, an OPAC, and a Web page. Operations spending for 2004 fiscal year: $1.6 million. 150 computers available on campus for general student use. A campuswide network can be accessed from student residence rooms and from off campus. Staffed computer lab on campus.

Community Environment: On the Saco River, the University of New England is located outside the small City of Biddeford (pop. 25,000) on the coast of Southern Maine, two hours from Boston and 25 minutes from Portland, Maine's largest city. Part-time work is available for students. Biddeford city services include hospital, churches, library, and Chamber of commerce. Recreational facilities good, with beaches of Biddeford Pool, Kennebunk, and Old Orchard; golf, fishing, swimming, skiing, are within easy reach.

■ **UNIVERSITY OF SOUTHERN MAINE** *O-3*
96 Falmouth St., PO Box 9300
Portland, ME 04104-9300
Tel: (207)780-4141
Free: 800-800-4USM
Admissions: (207)780-5670
Fax: (207)780-5640
E-mail: usmadm@usm.maine.edu
Web Site: http://www.usm.maine.edu/
Description: State-supported, comprehensive, coed. Part of University of Maine System. Awards associate, bachelor's, master's, doctoral, and first professional degrees and post-master's certificates. Founded 1878. Setting: 144-acre suburban campus. Endowment: $16.7 million. Research spending for 2004 fiscal year: $65.6 million. Educational spending for 2005 fiscal year: $7072 per student. Total enrollment: 10,944. Faculty: 704 (402 full-time, 302 part-time). Student-undergrad faculty ratio is 13:1. 3,599 applied, 79% were admitted. 10% from top 10% of their high school class, 31% from top quarter, 71% from top half. 4 valedictorians. Full-time: 4,788 students, 58% women, 42% men. Part-time: 3,834 students, 61% women, 39% men. Students come from 33 other countries, 8% from out-of-state, 2% Native American, 1% Hispanic, 1% black, 1% Asian American or Pacific Islander, 0.01% international, 32% 25 or older, 40% live on campus, 9% transferred in. Retention: 57% of full-time freshmen returned the following year. Academic areas with the most degrees conferred: health professions and related sciences; social sciences; business/marketing. Core. Calendar: semesters. Academic remediation for entering students, ESL program, services for LD students, advanced placement, accelerated degree program, self-designed majors, honors program, independent study, distance learning, double major, summer session for credit, part-time degree program, external degree program, adult/continuing education programs, co-op programs and internships, graduate courses open to undergrads. Off campus study at National Student Exchange. Study abroad program. ROTC: Army (c), Air Force (c).
Entrance Requirements: Options: Peterson's Universal Application, Common Application, electronic application, early admission, deferred admission, international baccalaureate accepted. Required: essay, high school transcript, SAT or ACT. Recommended: minimum 2.8 high school GPA, 1 recommendation, interview. Required for some: interview, auditions for music majors. Entrance: moderately difficult. Application deadline: 2/15. Notification: continuous.

Costs Per Year: Application fee: $40. State resident tuition: $4980 full-time, $166 per credit hour part-time. Nonresident tuition: $13,800 full-time, $460 per credit hour part-time. Mandatory fees: $926 full-time. Full-time tuition and fees vary according to course load, degree level, and reciprocity agreements. Part-time tuition varies according to course load, degree level, and reciprocity agreements. College room and board: $6755. College room only: $3586. Room and board charges vary according to board plan, housing facility, and location.

Collegiate Environment: Orientation program. Drama-theater group, choral group, student-run newspaper, radio station. Social organizations: 100 open to all; national fraternities, national sororities, local fraternities, local sororities; 2% of eligible men and 2% of eligible women are members. Most popular organizations: Outing and Ski Clubs, Gorham Events Board, Commuter Student Group, Circle K. Major annual events: Spring Fling, Winter Weekend, theatre and music performers. Student services: legal services, health clinic, personal-psychological counseling, women's center. Campus security: 24-hour emergency response devices and patrols, student patrols, late night transport-escort service, controlled dormitory access, security lighting, preventive programs within residence halls. College housing designed to accommodate 1,551 students; 1,599 undergraduates lived in college housing during 2003-04. Freshmen given priority for college housing. Option: coed housing available. University of Southern Maine Library plus 4 others with 545,246 books, 1 million microform titles, 2,585 serials, 2,705 audiovisual materials, an OPAC, and a Web page. Operations spending for 2004 fiscal year: $3.4 million. 485 computers available on campus for general student use. Computer purchase/lease plans available. A campuswide network can be accessed from student residence rooms and from off campus. Staffed computer lab on campus.

■ **WASHINGTON COUNTY COMMUNITY COLLEGE** *I-12*
RR No. 1, Box 22C River Rd.
Calais, ME 04619
Tel: (207)454-1000
Fax: (207)454-1026
Web Site: http://www.wccc.me.edu/
Description: State-supported, 2-year, coed. Part of Maine Technical College System. Awards certificates, diplomas, transfer associate, and terminal associate degrees. Founded 1969. Setting: 40-acre rural campus. Total enrollment: 350. 273 applied, 98% were admitted. 1% from top quarter of their high school class, 24% from top half. 2 student government officers. Students come from 12 states and territories, 1 other country, 4% from out-of-state, 59% 25 or older, 22% live on campus. Calendar: semesters. Academic remediation for entering students, services for LD students, advanced placement, independent study, distance learning, double major, part-time degree program, external degree program, adult/continuing education programs, co-op programs and internships. Off campus study. Study abroad program.
Entrance Requirements: Open admission. Options: Peterson's Universal Application, deferred admission. Required: essay, high school transcript, interview. Recommended: minimum 2.0 high school GPA, recommendations. Placement: ACT ASSET required. Entrance: noncompetitive. Application deadline: Rolling. Notification: continuous.
Collegiate Environment: Orientation program. Choral group. Social organizations: 2 open to all. Most popular organizations: Hiking Club, Native American Club. Major annual events: Technology Fair, Christmas Party, graduation. Student services: personal-psychological counseling. Campus security: 24-hour emergency response devices. Option: coed housing available. Washington County Technical College Library with 26,370 books, 232 serials, and 50 audiovisual materials. Operations spending for 2004 fiscal year: $104,175. 100 computers available on campus for general student use. A campuswide network can be accessed from off-campus. Staffed computer lab on campus.

■ **YORK COUNTY COMMUNITY COLLEGE** *P-3*
112 College Dr.
Wells, ME 04090
Tel: (207)646-9282
Free: 800-580-3820
Fax: (207)641-0837
E-mail: admissions@yctc.net
Web Site: http://www.yccc.edu/
Description: State-supported, 2-year, coed. Part of Maine Technical College System. Awards certificates, transfer associate, and terminal associate degrees. Founded 1994. Setting: 84-acre small town campus with easy ac-

cess to Boston. Educational spending for 2005 fiscal year: $3161 per student. Total enrollment: 990. 216 applied, 90% were admitted. Students come from 3 states and territories, 1% from out-of-state. Calendar: semesters. Accelerated degree program, independent study, distance learning, double major, summer session for credit, part-time degree program, co-op programs and internships.

Entrance Requirements: Open admission. Required: essay, high school transcript. Placement: SAT recommended. Entrance: noncompetitive. Application deadline: Rolling.

Collegiate Environment: Orientation program. Student-run newspaper.

Social organizations: 4 open to all. Most popular organizations: Student Senate, Veteran's Club, Early Childhood Education Club, Skills-USA Club. Major annual events: family Homecoming events, Holiday Party, Spring Fling. Campus security: 24-hour emergency response devices. College housing not available. Library and Learning Resource Center plus 1 other with 4,000 books, 75 serials, 200 audiovisual materials, an OPAC, and a Web page. Operations spending for 2004 fiscal year: $110,582. 35 computers available on campus for general student use. A campuswide network can be accessed. Staffed computer lab on campus.

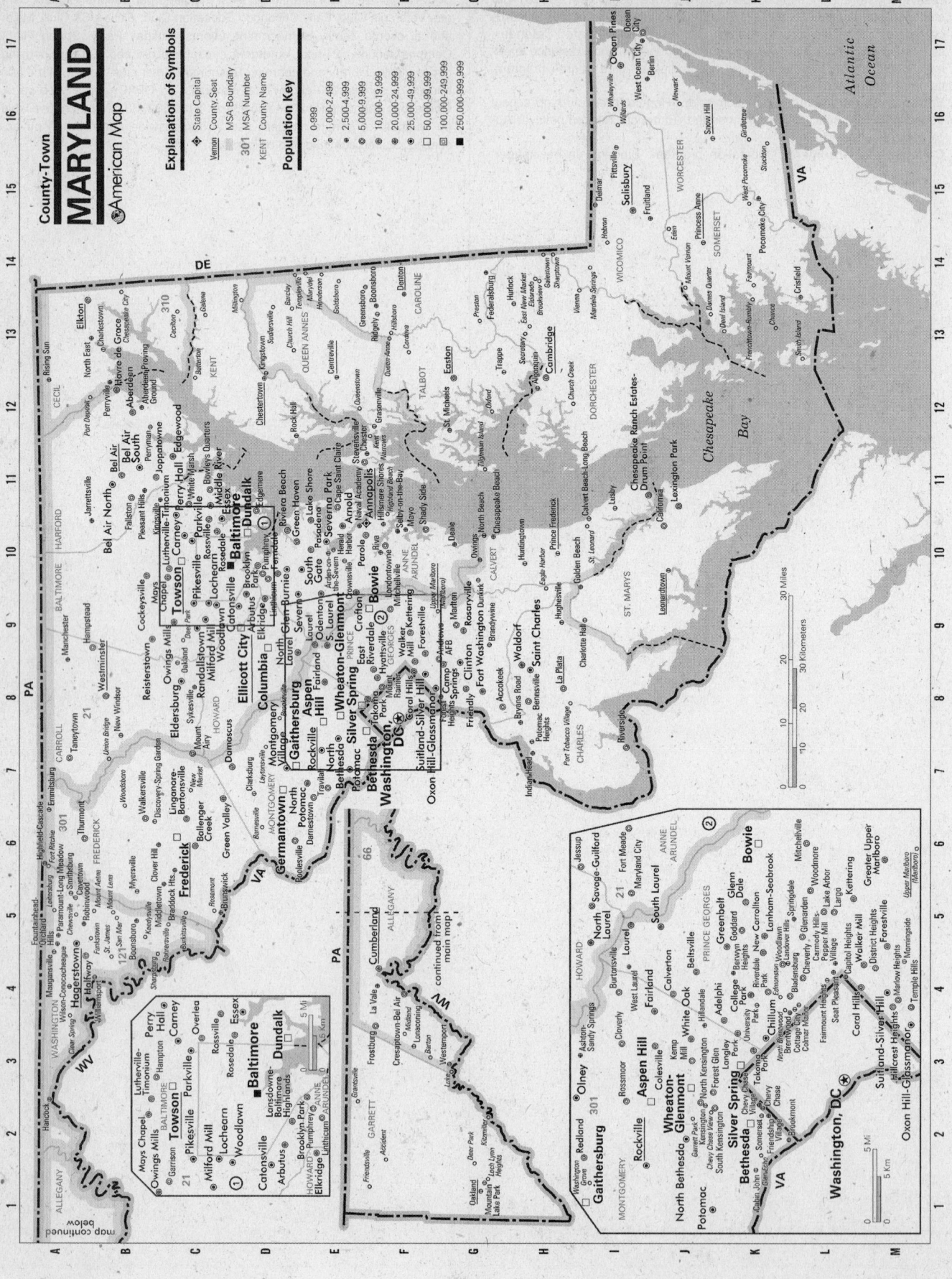

MARYLAND

County-Town

American Map

Explanation of Symbols

⊛ State Capital
Vernon County Seat
— MSA Boundary
301 MSA Number
KENT County Name

Population Key

○ 0-999
⊚ 1,000-2,499
⊙ 2,500-4,999
⊛ 5,000-9,999
⊛ 10,000-19,999
⊛ 20,000-24,999
⊛ 25,000-49,999
□ 50,000-99,999
▣ 100,000-249,999
■ 250,000-999,999

■ **ALLEGANY COLLEGE OF MARYLAND** *F-4*
12401 Willowbrook Rd., SE
Cumberland, MD 21502-2596
Tel: (301)784-5000
Fax: (301)784-5024
E-mail: cnolan@allegany.edu
Web Site: http://www.allegany.edu/
Description: State and locally supported, 2-year, coed. Part of Maryland State Community Colleges System. Awards certificates, transfer associate, and terminal associate degrees. Founded 1961. Setting: 311-acre small town campus. Endowment: $5.2 million. Research spending for 2004 fiscal year: $5042. Educational spending for 2005 fiscal year: $3445 per student. Total enrollment: 3,666. Student-undergrad faculty ratio is 17:1. 2,098 applied, 99% were admitted. Full-time: 2,073 students, 67% women, 33% men. Part-time: 1,593 students, 71% women, 29% men. Students come from 21 states and territories, 42% from out-of-state, 0.2% Native American, 1% Hispanic, 8% black, 1% Asian American or Pacific Islander, 0% international, 35% 25 or older. Calendar: semesters. Academic remediation for entering students, advanced placement, honors program, independent study, distance learning, double major, summer session for credit, part-time degree program, adult/continuing education programs, internships. ROTC: Army (c).
Entrance Requirements: Open admission except for allied health programs. Options: electronic application, early admission. Required: high school transcript. Required for some: ACT. Entrance: noncompetitive. Application deadline: Rolling.
Costs Per Year: Application fee: $0. Area resident tuition: $2700 full-time, $90 per credit part-time. State resident tuition: $5160 full-time, $172 per credit part-time. Nonresident tuition: $6060 full-time, $202 per credit part-time. Mandatory fees: $194 full-time, $8.30 per credit part-time, $41 per term part-time. Full-time tuition and fees vary according to course load and location. Part-time tuition and fees vary according to course load and location.
Collegiate Environment: Orientation program. Choral group. Social organizations: 24 open to all. Most popular organizations: SAHDA, Honors Club, EMT Club, Forestry Club. Major annual events: All College Awards Banquet, Welcome Back Picnic, Spring Fling Tension Breaker. Student services: personal-psychological counseling, women's center. Campus security: 24-hour emergency response devices and patrols, late night transport-escort service. College housing not available. Allegany College of Maryland Library with 86,636 books, 7,737 microform titles, 313 serials, 3,395 audiovisual materials, an OPAC, and a Web page. Operations spending for 2004 fiscal year: $563,784. 700 computers available on campus for general student use. A campuswide network can be accessed from off-campus. Staffed computer lab on campus.

■ **ANNE ARUNDEL COMMUNITY COLLEGE** *E-10*
101 College Parkway
Arnold, MD 21012-1895
Tel: (410)647-7100
Admissions: (410)777-2240
Fax: (410)541-2245
Web Site: http://www.aacc.edu/
Description: State and locally supported, 2-year, coed. Awards certificates, transfer associate, and terminal associate degrees. Founded 1961. Setting: 230-acre suburban campus with easy access to Baltimore and Washington, DC. Endowment: $2.4 million. Educational spending for 2005 fiscal year: $2836 per student. Total enrollment: 14,290. Full-time: 4,780 students, 55%

women, 45% men. Part-time: 9,510 students, 66% women, 34% men. Students come from 12 states and territories, 19 other countries, 1% from out-of-state, 1% Native American, 2% Hispanic, 12% black, 3% Asian American or Pacific Islander, 1% international, 43% 25 or older, 19% transferred in. Retention: 58% of full-time freshmen returned the following year. Core. Calendar: semesters. Academic remediation for entering students, ESL program, services for LD students, advanced placement, accelerated degree program, freshman honors college, honors program, independent study, distance learning, summer session for credit, part-time degree program, adult/continuing education programs, co-op programs and internships. ROTC: Army (c), Air Force (c).
Entrance Requirements: Open admission except for certain allied health programs. Options: early admission, deferred admission. Placement: SAT or ACT recommended. Entrance: noncompetitive. Application deadline: Rolling.
Costs Per Year: Application fee: $0. Area resident tuition: $1992 full-time, $83 per credit hour part-time. State resident tuition: $3816 full-time, $159 per credit hour part-time. Nonresident tuition: $6768 full-time, $282 per credit hour part-time. Mandatory fees: $232 full-time, $8 per credit hour part-time, $20 per term part-time. Full-time tuition and fees vary according to course load. Part-time tuition and fees vary according to course load.
Collegiate Environment: Orientation program. Drama-theater group, choral group, student-run newspaper. Social organizations: 45 open to all. Most popular organizations: Drama Club, student association, Black Student Union, International Student Association, Chemistry Club. Major annual events: Activities Fair, family performances, dramatic/theatrical performances. Student services: health clinic, personal-psychological counseling. Campus security: 24-hour emergency response devices and patrols, student patrols, late night transport-escort service. College housing not available. Andrew G. Truxal Library with 144,694 books, 7,875 microform titles, 403 serials, 8,060 audiovisual materials, an OPAC, and a Web page. Operations spending for 2004 fiscal year: $273,173. 250 computers available on campus for general student use. A campuswide network can be accessed from off-campus. Staffed computer lab on campus.

■ **BALTIMORE CITY COMMUNITY COLLEGE** *D-10*
2901 Liberty Heights Ave.
Baltimore, MD 21215-7893
Tel: (410)462-8300
Fax: (410)462-7677
Web Site: http://www.bccc.state.md.us/
Description: State-supported, 2-year, coed. Awards certificates, transfer associate, and terminal associate degrees. Founded 1947. Setting: 19-acre urban campus. Endowment: $139,215. Educational spending for 2005 fiscal year: $3218 per student. Total enrollment: 7,095. 1,380 applied. Students come from 4 states and territories, 1% from out-of-state, 57% 25 or older. Core. Calendar: semesters. Academic remediation for entering students, ESL program, services for LD students, advanced placement, honors program, distance learning, double major, summer session for credit, part-time degree program, adult/continuing education programs, co-op programs and internships. Study abroad program.
Entrance Requirements: Open admission except for allied health programs. Options: Common Application, early admission, deferred admission. Required: high school transcript. Recommended: interview. Placement: SAT Subject Tests recommended. Entrance: noncompetitive. Application deadline: 8/9. Notification: continuous.
Collegiate Environment: Orientation program. Choral group, student-run

newspaper, radio station. Student services: health clinic, personal-psychological counseling. College housing not available. Bard Library with 72,413 books, 150 serials, 1,074 audiovisual materials, an OPAC, and a Web page.

Community Environment: See University of Baltimore.

■ BALTIMORE HEBREW UNIVERSITY *D-10*

5800 Park Heights Ave.
Baltimore, MD 21215-3996
Tel: (410)578-6900; 888-248-7420
Admissions: (410)578-6967
Fax: (410)578-6940
E-mail: bhu@bhu.edu
Web Site: http://www.bhu.edu/

Description: Independent, comprehensive, coed. Awards associate, bachelor's, master's, and doctoral degrees. Founded 1919. Setting: 2-acre urban campus. Total enrollment: 161. Full-time: 43 students, 47% women, 53% men. Part-time: 53 students, 81% women, 19% men. Students come from 2 other countries, 0% Native American, 0% Hispanic, 3% black, 0% Asian American or Pacific Islander, 5% international, 90% 25 or older. Core. Calendar: semesters. ESL program, services for LD students, advanced placement, independent study, distance learning, double major, summer session for credit, part-time degree program, adult/continuing education programs, graduate courses open to undergrads. Off campus study at Baltimore Student Exchange Program.

Entrance Requirements: Options: Common Application, early admission, deferred admission. Required: essay, high school transcript, interview. Required for some: 3 recommendations. Entrance: moderately difficult. Application deadline: Rolling. Notification: continuous.

Collegiate Environment: Orientation program. Social organizations: 3 open to all. Most popular organizations: Israeli Dance, Chug Ivri Club for Advanced Hebrew Speakers, Yiddish Club. Major annual events: Convocation, Commencement, Maurice A. Stiller Award for Literature lecture. Campus security: 24-hour patrols, guards on duty during class hours, patrols by security, well-lit parking lots. College housing not available. Joseph Meyerhoff Library with 70,000 books, 15,000 microform titles, 250 serials, 600 audiovisual materials, an OPAC, and a Web page. 15 computers available on campus for general student use. Staffed computer lab on campus.

Community Environment: The university is located in residential northwest Baltimore, the center of Jewish life in the city and county. Tree-lined streets, numerous apartment complexes, convenient parking, public transportation and nearby shopping make the area amenable. There are orthodox, conservative, reform and reconstructionist synagogues in the area, along with kosher restaurants, delicatessens and two community centers, including one located on the campus. Affordable housing can be found near the university. Colleges and institutions that offer cooperative programs are less than 30 minutes away, and field work assignments are often within walking distance of the campus. Baltimore offers a colorful inner harbor, national aquarium, symphony orchestra, baseball and football teams, theaters, opera, and numerous museums.

■ BALTIMORE INTERNATIONAL COLLEGE *D-10*

Commerce Exchange
17 Commerce St.
Baltimore, MD 21202-3230
Tel: (410)752-4710
Free: 800-624-9926
Fax: (410)752-3730
Web Site: http://www.bic.edu/

Description: Independent, primarily 2-year, coed. Awards certificates, transfer associate, terminal associate, bachelor's, and master's degrees. Founded 1972. Setting: 6-acre urban campus with easy access to Washington, DC. Endowment: $83,144. Educational spending for 2005 fiscal year: $8640 per student. Total enrollment: 516. Faculty: 32 (14 full-time, 18 part-time). Full-time: 486 students, 53% women, 47% men. Part-time: 30 students, 53% women, 47% men. Students come from 19 states and territories, 5 other countries, 12% from out-of-state, 0.4% Native American, 2% Hispanic, 52% black, 3% Asian American or Pacific Islander, 1% international, 24% 25 or older, 24% live on campus, 21% transferred in. Retention: 39% of full-time freshmen returned the following year. Academic area with the most degrees conferred: personal and culinary services. Core. Calendar: semesters. Academic remediation for entering students, advanced placement, accelerated degree program, honors program, double major, adult/

continuing education programs, co-op programs and internships. Off campus study at Virginia Park Campus, County Cavan, Ireland. Study abroad program.

Entrance Requirements: Options: Peterson's Universal Application, Common Application, electronic application, early action, deferred admission. Required: high school transcript. Recommended: recommendations, interview. Required for some: essay, SAT or ACT, CPat or TOEFL. Entrance: minimally difficult. Application deadline: Rolling. Notification: continuous until 8/15.

Costs Per Year: Application fee: $35. Comprehensive fee: $20,313 includes full-time tuition ($14,751), mandatory fees ($107), and college room and board ($5455). College room only: $3255. Room and board charges vary according to housing facility.

Collegiate Environment: Orientation program. Student-run newspaper. Social organizations: local fraternities, local sororities; 10% of eligible men and 10% of eligible women are members. Most popular organizations: American Culinary Federation, Beta Iota Kappa. Major annual events: trip to New York Hotel/Restaurant Trade Show, student mixers. Student services: health clinic, personal-psychological counseling. Campus security: late night transport-escort service, controlled dormitory access. Freshmen guaranteed college housing. On-campus residence required in freshman year. Option: coed housing available. George A. Piendak Library plus 1 other with 13,000 books, 200 serials, and 1,000 audiovisual materials. Operations spending for 2004 fiscal year: $407,400. 35 computers available on campus for general student use. A campuswide network can be accessed from off-campus. Staffed computer lab on campus.

■ BOWIE STATE UNIVERSITY *F-9*

14000 Jericho Park Rd.
Bowie, MD 20715-9465
Tel: (301)860-4000; 877-772-6943
Admissions: (301)860-3427
Fax: (301)860-3510
E-mail: dkiah@bowiestate.edu
Web Site: http://www.bowiestate.edu/

Description: State-supported, comprehensive, coed. Part of University System of Maryland. Awards bachelor's, master's, and doctoral degrees. Founded 1865. Setting: 312-acre small town campus with easy access to Baltimore and Washington, DC. Endowment: $3 million. Research spending for 2004 fiscal year: $3.2 million. Educational spending for 2005 fiscal year: $5105 per student. Total enrollment: 5,415. 2,766 applied, 53% were admitted. Full-time: 3,216 students, 63% women, 37% men. Part-time: 811 students, 67% women, 33% men. Students come from 33 states and territories, 47 other countries, 8% from out-of-state, 0.3% Native American, 1% Hispanic, 89% black, 1% Asian American or Pacific Islander, 1% international, 28% 25 or older, 34% live on campus, 9% transferred in. Retention: 70% of full-time freshmen returned the following year. Core. Calendar: semesters. Academic remediation for entering students, services for LD students, advanced placement, honors program, independent study, distance learning, double major, summer session for credit, part-time degree program, external degree program, adult/continuing education programs, co-op programs and internships, graduate courses open to undergrads. Off campus study at other units of the University System of Maryland. Study abroad program. ROTC: Army.

Entrance Requirements: Options: electronic application, international baccalaureate accepted. Required: high school transcript, minimum 2.0 high school GPA, SAT or ACT. Recommended: recommendations. Required for some: recommendations. Entrance: minimally difficult. Application deadline: 4/1. Notification: continuous. Preference given to state residents.

Costs Per Year: Application fee: $40. State resident tuition: $5096 full-time. Nonresident tuition: $13,088 full-time. Mandatory fees: $1750 full-time. College room and board: $5219. College room only: $3859. Room and board charges vary according to board plan and housing facility.

Collegiate Environment: Orientation program. Drama-theater group, choral group, marching band, student-run newspaper, radio station. Social organizations: 52 open to all; national fraternities, national sororities; 2% of eligible men and 2% of eligible women are members. Most popular organizations: NSAP Student Leadership Institute, Honda Campus All-Star Challenge. Major annual events: Fall Convocation, Homecoming events, Honors Convocation. Student services: health clinic, personal-psychological counseling. Campus security: 24-hour emergency response devices and patrols, student patrols, late night transport-escort service, controlled dormitory access. 1,367 college housing spaces available; all were occupied in 2003-04. Freshmen given priority for college housing. Options: coed, men-only, women-only housing available. Thurgood Marshall Library with 331,640 books, 6,674 microform titles, 3,152 serials, 4,475 audiovisual materials, an OPAC, and a Web page. Operations spending for 2004 fiscal year: $1.9 million. 3,144 computers available on campus for general student use. A campuswide network can be accessed from student residence rooms and from off campus. Staffed computer lab on campus.

Community Environment: A suburban community with good transportation facilities. Baltimore-Washington Airport at Baltimore is 14 miles. Student employment is available in many commercial establishments and private homes. Bowie is near beaches and many recreation centers.

■ **CAPITOL COLLEGE** *E-9*
11301 Springfield Rd.
Laurel, MD 20708-9759
Tel: (301)369-2800
Free: 800-950-1992
Admissions: (301)953-3200
E-mail: admissions@capitol-college.edu
Web Site: http://www.capitol-college.edu/

Description: Independent, comprehensive, coed. Awards associate, bachelor's, and master's degrees. Founded 1964. Setting: 52-acre suburban campus with easy access to Baltimore and Washington, DC. Endowment: $3 million. Total enrollment: 801. 213 applied, 90% were admitted. Full-time: 319 students, 24% women, 76% men. Part-time: 311 students, 22% women, 78% men. Students come from 15 states and territories, 21 other countries, 14% from out-of-state, 0.4% Native American, 2% Hispanic, 37% black, 7% Asian American or Pacific Islander, 4% international, 17% live on campus, 5% transferred in. Core. Calendar: semesters. Academic remediation for entering students, ESL program, advanced placement, accelerated degree program, summer session for credit, part-time degree program, adult/continuing education programs, co-op programs. ROTC: Army (c).

Entrance Requirements: Options: Peterson's Universal Application, electronic application, deferred admission. Required: high school transcript, SAT or ACT. Recommended: minimum 2.2 high school GPA, interview. Required for some: essay, 2 recommendations, interview. Entrance: minimally difficult. Application deadline: Rolling.

Costs Per Year: Application fee: $25. Tuition: $17,688 full-time. College room only: $3869. Room charges vary according to housing facility.

Collegiate Environment: Orientation program. Student-run newspaper. Social organizations: 8 open to all. Most popular organizations: IEEE, NSDE, SWE. Student services: personal-psychological counseling. Campus security: night security patrols. 120 college housing spaces available; 90 were occupied in 2003-04. Freshmen guaranteed college housing. Option: coed housing available. Puente Library with 10,000 books, 100 serials, 117 audiovisual materials, and an OPAC. Operations spending for 2004 fiscal year: $119,953. 42 computers available on campus for general student use. A campuswide network can be accessed from off-campus. Staffed computer lab on campus.

Community Environment: The town is in Prince George's County, a suburban area within easy reach of Washington, DC, and Baltimore, MD. Much of Washington's electronic industry is located in this area. The Capital Beltway is only four minutes from the school, providing easy access to the metropolitan area.

■ **CARROLL COMMUNITY COLLEGE** *B-8*
1601 Washington Rd.
Westminster, MD 21157
Tel: (410)386-8000
Admissions: (410)386-8430
Fax: (410)876-8855
E-mail: cedwards@carrollcc.edu
Web Site: http://www.carrollcc.edu/

Description: State and locally supported, 2-year, coed. Part of Maryland Higher Education Commission. Awards certificates, transfer associate, and terminal associate degrees. Founded 1993. Setting: 80-acre small town campus with easy access to Baltimore. Endowment: $1.2 million. Total enrollment: 3,115. Student-undergrad faculty ratio is 17:1. 711 applied, 100% were admitted. Full-time: 1,327 students, 58% women, 42% men. Part-time: 1,788 students, 69% women, 31% men. Students come from 3 states and territories, 4 other countries, 1% from out-of-state, 0.4% Native American, 2% Hispanic, 3% black, 2% Asian American or Pacific Islander, 0.2% international, 31% 25 or older. Academic areas with the most degrees conferred: liberal arts/general studies; business/marketing; health professions and related sciences. Core. Calendar: semesters plus winter session.

Academic remediation for entering students, ESL program, services for LD students, advanced placement, honors program, independent study, distance learning, summer session for credit, part-time degree program, internships.

Entrance Requirements: Open admission. Option: early admission. Required: high school transcript. Entrance: noncompetitive. Application deadline: Rolling. Notification: continuous.

Costs Per Year: Application fee: $0. Area resident tuition: $3234 full-time, $92 per credit part-time. State resident tuition: $4476 full-time, $128 per credit part-time. Nonresident tuition: $6788 full-time, $195 per credit part-time.

Collegiate Environment: Orientation program. Drama-theater group, choral group, student-run newspaper. Most popular organizations: Student Government Organization, Carroll Community Chorus, Programming Board. Major annual events: Crab Feast, Health Fair. Student services: personal-psychological counseling. Campus security: late night transport-escort service. College housing not available. Random House Learning Resources Center with 39,187 books, 3,400 microform titles, 318 serials, 3,151 audiovisual materials, an OPAC, and a Web page. 674 computers available on campus for general student use. A campuswide network can be accessed. Staffed computer lab on campus.

■ **CECIL COMMUNITY COLLEGE** *B-13*
One Seahawk Dr.
North East, MD 21901-1999
Tel: (410)287-6060
Admissions: (410)287-1002
Fax: (410)287-1026
E-mail: dlane@cecilcc.edu
Web Site: http://www.cecilcc.edu/

Description: County-supported, 2-year, coed. Awards certificates and transfer associate degrees. Founded 1968. Setting: 100-acre small town campus with easy access to Baltimore. Total enrollment: 1,916. 481 applied, 100% were admitted. Full-time: 687 students, 57% women, 43% men. Part-time: 1,229 students, 70% women, 30% men. Students come from 5 states and territories, 4 other countries, 9% from out-of-state, 0.5% Native American, 2% Hispanic, 7% black, 1% Asian American or Pacific Islander, 0.3% international, 31% 25 or older, 1% transferred in. Academic areas with the most degrees conferred: health professions and related sciences; liberal arts/general studies; visual and performing arts. Core. Calendar: semesters. Academic remediation for entering students, ESL program, services for LD students, advanced placement, independent study, distance learning, double major, summer session for credit, part-time degree program, adult/continuing education programs, co-op programs and internships.

Entrance Requirements: Open admission. Options: Common Application, electronic application, early admission, deferred admission. Required: high school transcript. Entrance: noncompetitive. Application deadline: Rolling. Notification: continuous.

Costs Per Year: Area resident tuition: $2550 full-time, $85 per credit hour part-time. State resident tuition: $5250 full-time, $175 per credit hour part-time. Nonresident tuition: $6600 full-time, $220 per credit hour part-time.

Collegiate Environment: Drama-theater group, student-run newspaper. Social organizations: 14 open to all; national fraternities. Most popular organizations: student government, Non-traditional Student Organization, Student Nurses Association, student newspaper. Major annual events: Welcome Back Event, Spring Fling, Chautauqua Festival. Student services: personal-psychological counseling, women's center. Campus security: 24-hour emergency response devices, late night transport-escort service. College housing not available. Cecil County Veteran's Memorial Library with 35,575 books, 16 microform titles, 192 serials, 1,148 audiovisual materials, an OPAC, and a Web page. 69 computers available on campus for general student use. A campuswide network can be accessed from off-campus. Staffed computer lab on campus.

Community Environment: North East is approximately 5 miles west of Elkton, which is nestled in the valley where the Chesapeake Bay begins. It is within easy reach of the major cities on the East Coast with all forms of major commercial transportation available. Three interchanges on the John F. Kennedy Turnpike and super highways make New York or Washington, D.C., an easy two-hour drive. Elkton, rich in historical sites, has churches, health centers, and good shopping. The area offers hunting, fishing, camping, yachting, and racing and, with its beaches, parks, and marinas, is an ideal spot for vacationing.

■ **CHESAPEAKE COLLEGE**

PO Box 8
Wye Mills, MD 21679-0008
Tel: (410)822-5400
Fax: (410)827-9466
Web Site: http://www.chesapeake.edu/

Description: State and locally supported, 2-year, coed. Awards certificates, transfer associate, and terminal associate degrees. Founded 1965. Setting: 170-acre rural campus with easy access to Baltimore and Washington, DC. Total enrollment: 2,354. Full-time: 724 students, 62% women, 38% men. Part-time: 1,630 students, 74% women, 26% men. Students come from 2 states and territories, 1% from out-of-state, 0.2% Native American, 1% Hispanic, 21% black, 1% Asian American or Pacific Islander, 0.1% international, 45% 25 or older, 30% transferred in. Core. Calendar: semesters. Academic remediation for entering students, ESL program, services for LD students, advanced placement, self-designed majors, honors program, independent study, distance learning, summer session for credit, part-time degree program, adult/continuing education programs, co-op programs and internships.

Entrance Requirements: Open admission except for radiological technology, physical therapy assistant programs. Options: early admission, deferred admission. Required: high school transcript. Entrance: noncompetitive. Application deadline: Rolling. Notification: continuous.

Collegiate Environment: Orientation program. Drama-theater group, choral group. Social organizations: 6 open to all; 3% of eligible men and 5% of eligible women are members. Most popular organizations: student government action teams, Phi Theta Kappa, UHURU, Chesapeake Players. Major annual events: Spring Fling, Fall Fest, Concert Series. Student services: personal-psychological counseling, women's center. Campus security: 24-hour patrols. College housing not available. Learning Resource Center plus 1 other with 44,049 books, 8,545 microform titles, 132 serials, 1,600 audiovisual materials, an OPAC, and a Web page. Operations spending for 2004 fiscal year: $471,260.

■ **COLLEGE OF NOTRE DAME OF MARYLAND** *D-10*

4701 North Charles St.
Baltimore, MD 21210-2476
Tel: (410)435-0100
Free: 800-435-0300
Admissions: (410)532-5330
Fax: (410)532-6287
E-mail: admiss@ndm.edu
Web Site: http://www.ndm.edu/

Description: Independent Roman Catholic, comprehensive. Awards bachelor's, master's, and doctoral degrees. Founded 1873. Setting: 58-acre suburban campus. Total enrollment: 3,307. 450 applied, 72% were admitted. 15% from top 10% of their high school class, 43% from top quarter, 80% from top half. Full-time: 607 students, 100% women. Part-time: 1,079 students, 90% women, 10% men. Students come from 26 states and territories, 15 other countries, 8% from out-of-state, 0.5% Native American, 3% Hispanic, 26% black, 3% Asian American or Pacific Islander, 2% international, 61% 25 or older, 57% live on campus, 3% transferred in. Retention: 86% of full-time freshmen returned the following year. Core. Calendar: 4-1-4. ESL program, services for LD students, advanced placement, accelerated degree program, self-designed majors, honors program, independent study, double major, summer session for credit, part-time degree program, adult/continuing education programs, internships, graduate courses open to undergrads. Off campus study at Loyola College, Johns Hopkins University, Towson University, Goucher College, Morgan State University, Coppin State College, Maryland Institute College of Art. Study abroad program. ROTC: Army (c).

Entrance Requirements: Options: Common Application, electronic application, early admission, early action, deferred admission, international baccalaureate accepted. Required: essay, high school transcript, minimum 2.0 high school GPA, 2 recommendations, SAT or ACT. Recommended: minimum 3.0 high school GPA, interview, resume. Entrance: moderately difficult. Application deadlines: 2/15, 12/3 for early action. Notification: continuous until 6/30, 1/1 for early action.

Costs Per Year: Application fee: $25. Comprehensive fee: $29,600 includes

full-time tuition ($21,100), mandatory fees ($500), and college room and board ($8000). Part-time tuition: $345 per credit. Part-time mandatory fees: $60 per term.

Collegiate Environment: Orientation program. Drama-theater group, choral group, student-run newspaper, radio station. Social organizations: 24 open to all. Most popular organizations: Black Student Association, Kymry, Commuter Association, Community Service Organization, campus ministry. Major annual events: Honors Convocation, Notre Dame Day, Tree Trim. Student services: health clinic, personal-psychological counseling, women's center. Campus security: 24-hour emergency response devices and patrols, late night transport-escort service, controlled dormitory access, emergency call boxes. 406 college housing spaces available; 360 were occupied in 2003-04. Freshmen guaranteed college housing. On-campus residence required through sophomore year. Option: women-only housing available. Loyola/Notre Dame Library with 400,000 books, 1,800 serials, 27,000 audiovisual materials, an OPAC, and a Web page. 80 computers available on campus for general student use. Computer purchase/lease plans available. A campuswide network can be accessed from student residence rooms and from off campus. Staffed computer lab on campus.

Community Environment: Like Boston, Baltimore is a college town. There are nine nearby colleges and universities and over 60,000 students in the Baltimore metropolitan area which enhances academic and social opportunities. The Notre Dame campus is located 15 minutes from the nationally known Inner Harbor area where concerts, fairs and ethnic festivals are sponsored. Both mountains and ocean are only a few hours from Notre Dame, providing opportunities for skiing in the winter and relaxing on the beach in the summer. Annapolis, home of the U. S. Naval Academy, is about 45 minutes from Notre Dame, and Washington, D. C., with all of its resources, is less than an hour's drive from the college.

■ **COLLEGE OF SOUTHERN MARYLAND** *H-8*

8730 Mitchell Rd., PO Box 910
La Plata, MD 20646-0910
Tel: (301)934-2251
Free: 800-933-9177
Admissions: (301)934-7520
Fax: (301)934-5255
E-mail: juliap@csmd.edu
Web Site: http://www.csmd.edu/

Description: State and locally supported, 2-year, coed. Awards certificates, transfer associate, and terminal associate degrees. Founded 1958. Setting: 175-acre rural campus with easy access to Washington, DC. Educational spending for 2005 fiscal year: $3294 per student. Total enrollment: 7,546. Student-undergrad faculty ratio is 9:1. 2,731 applied, 55% were admitted. Full-time: 2,599 students, 58% women, 42% men. Part-time: 4,947 students, 69% women, 31% men. Students come from 10 states and territories, 1% from out-of-state, 1% Native American, 3% Hispanic, 19% black, 3% Asian American or Pacific Islander, 0% international, 37% 25 or older, 45% transferred in. Calendar: semesters. Academic remediation for entering students, services for LD students, advanced placement, accelerated degree program, honors program, distance learning, summer session for credit, part-time degree program, adult/continuing education programs, co-op programs and internships. Study abroad program.

Entrance Requirements: Open admission except for nursing program. Options: electronic application, early admission, deferred admission, international baccalaureate accepted. Recommended: high school transcript. Entrance: noncompetitive. Application deadline: Rolling. Notification: continuous.

Costs Per Year: Application fee: $0. Area resident tuition: $2650 full-time, $110 per credit part-time. State resident tuition: $4608 full-time, $192 per credit part-time. Nonresident tuition: $5789 full-time, $241 per credit part-time. Mandatory fees: $552 full-time. Full-time tuition and fees vary according to course load. Part-time tuition varies according to course load.

Collegiate Environment: Drama-theater group, choral group, student-run newspaper. Social organizations: 23 open to all. Most popular organizations: Spanish Club, Nursing Student Association, Science Club, Black Student Union, BACCHUS. Major annual events: Spring Fling Week, Fall Picnic. Student services: personal-psychological counseling, women's center. Campus security: 24-hour emergency response devices and patrols. College housing not available. College of Southern Maryland Library with 44,896 books, 2,214 microform titles, 166 serials, 14,013 audiovisual materials, an OPAC, and a Web page. Operations spending for 2004 fiscal year: $553,065. 130 computers available on campus for general student use. A campuswide network can be accessed from off-campus. Staffed computer lab on campus.

Community Environment: Southern Maryland is within a short distance of Washington, D.C. Community recreational activities include bowling, hunting, swimming, boating, camping, fishing, water sports, and fox hunting. Some of the special events are the annual county fair, and the Maryland Garden Tours.

■ **COLUMBIA UNION COLLEGE** *F-8*
7600 Flower Ave.
Takoma Park, MD 20912-7796
Tel: (301)891-4000
Free: 800-835-4212
Admissions: (301)891-4502
Fax: (301)891-4230
Web Site: http://www.cuc.edu/
Description: Independent Seventh-day Adventist, comprehensive, coed. Awards associate, bachelor's, and master's degrees. Founded 1904. Setting: 19-acre suburban campus with easy access to Washington, DC. Endowment: $4.3 million. Total enrollment: 1,047. Faculty: 56 (53 full-time, 3 part-time). Student-undergrad faculty ratio is 12:1. 1,351 applied, 35% were admitted. Full-time: 730 students, 63% women, 37% men. Part-time: 288 students, 65% women, 35% men. Students come from 40 states and territories, 38 other countries, 44% from out-of-state, 0% Native American, 8% Hispanic, 55% black, 6% Asian American or Pacific Islander, 3% international, 20% 25 or older, 50% live on campus, 8% transferred in. Retention: 59% of full-time freshmen returned the following year. Academic areas with the most degrees conferred: psychology; business/marketing; health professions and related sciences. Core. Calendar: semesters. Academic remediation for entering students, ESL program, advanced placement, accelerated degree program, self-designed majors, honors program, independent study, distance learning, double major, summer session for credit, part-time degree program, external degree program, adult/continuing education programs, co-op programs and internships. Off campus study at University of Maryland System. Study abroad program.
Entrance Requirements: Options: electronic application, early admission, deferred admission. Required: high school transcript, minimum 2.50 high school GPA, 2 recommendations, SAT or ACT. Required for some: essay, interview. Entrance: minimally difficult. Application deadline: 8/1. Notification: continuous.
Costs Per Year: Application fee: $25. Comprehensive fee: $23,536 includes full-time tuition ($16,514), mandatory fees ($1072), and college room and board ($5950). Part-time tuition: $688 per semester hour. Part-time mandatory fees: $670 per term. Part-time tuition and fees vary according to class time.
Collegiate Environment: Orientation program. Drama-theater group, choral group, student-run newspaper, radio station. Social organizations: 9 open to all. Most popular organization: Student Association. Major annual events: Barn Party, Christmas Party, Valentine Banquet. Student services: health clinic, personal-psychological counseling. Campus security: 24-hour emergency response devices, student patrols, late night transport-escort service. 362 undergraduates lived in college housing during 2003-04. Freshmen guaranteed college housing. Options: men-only, women-only housing available. Theofield G. Weis Library with 141,534 books, 9,000 serials, 7,500 audiovisual materials, an OPAC, and a Web page. 50 computers available on campus for general student use. A campuswide network can be accessed from student residence rooms and from off campus. Staffed computer lab on campus.
Community Environment: A suburb of Washington, D.C., the residents of Takoma Park enjoy the cultural and recreational facilities of that city. There are many opportunities for part-time employment. Shopping facilities are excellent.

■ **THE COMMUNITY COLLEGE OF BALTIMORE COUNTY** *D-10*
800 South Rolling Rd.
Baltimore, MD 21228-5381
Tel: (410)455-6050
Admissions: (410)455-4392
Fax: (410)719-6546
Web Site: http://www.ccbcmd.edu/
Description: County-supported, 2-year, coed. Awards certificates, transfer associate, and terminal associate degrees. Founded 1957. Setting: 350-acre suburban campus. Total enrollment: 19,622. Student-undergrad faculty ratio is 20:1. Full-time: 7,049 students, 55% women, 45% men. Part-time: 12,573 students, 67% women, 33% men. 0.4% Native American, 2% Hispanic, 30% black, 5% Asian American or Pacific Islander, 3% international. Calendar: semesters.

Costs Per Year: Area resident tuition: $2610 full-time, $87 per hour part-time. State resident tuition: $4500 full-time, $150 per hour part-time. Nonresident tuition: $6150 full-time, $205 per hour part-time. Mandatory fees: $316 full-time, $316 per term part-time.
Collegiate Environment: Student-run newspaper.

■ **COPPIN STATE UNIVERSITY** *D-10*
2500 West North Ave.
Baltimore, MD 21216-3698
Tel: (410)951-3000
Free: 800-635-3674
Admissions: (410)951-3600
Fax: (410)523-7238
Web Site: http://www.coppin.edu/
Description: State-supported, comprehensive, coed. Part of University System of Maryland. Awards bachelor's and master's degrees. Founded 1900. Setting: 33-acre urban campus. Total enrollment: 4,003. 2,270 applied, 47% were admitted. 10% from top 10% of their high school class, 20% from top quarter, 60% from top half. Students come from 20 states and territories, 19 other countries, 0.4% Native American, 1% Hispanic, 95% black, 0.2% Asian American or Pacific Islander, 2% international, 50% 25 or older, 10% live on campus. Core. Calendar: semesters. Academic remediation for entering students, ESL program, services for LD students, advanced placement, freshman honors college, honors program, double major, summer session for credit, part-time degree program, external degree program, adult/continuing education programs, co-op programs and internships, graduate courses open to undergrads. Off campus study at 6 members of the Cooperative Education Program. ROTC: Army.
Entrance Requirements: Options: Peterson's Universal Application, Common Application, electronic application, early admission, deferred admission. Required: high school transcript, SAT or ACT. Recommended: minimum 2.5 high school GPA, interview. Required for some: 2 recommendations. Entrance: moderately difficult. Application deadline: 7/15. Notification: continuous.
Costs Per Year: Application fee: $35. State resident tuition: $3527 full-time, $151 per credit hour part-time. Nonresident tuition: $10,048 full-time, $347 per credit hour part-time. Mandatory fees: $1352 full-time, $22 per credit hour part-time, $150 per term part-time. College room and board: $6239. College room only: $3881.
Collegiate Environment: Orientation program. Drama-theater group, choral group, student-run newspaper. Social organizations: 45 open to all; national fraternities, national sororities, local fraternities, local sororities; 5% of eligible men and 4% of eligible women are members. Most popular organizations: International Students Association, class government, Nursing Students' Association, Coppin Models Fashion Club, Student Honors Association. Major annual events: homecoming, athletic events. Student services: health clinic, personal-psychological counseling. Campus security: 24-hour emergency response devices and patrols, late night transport-escort service, controlled dormitory access. Option: coed housing available. Parlett L. Moore Library with 134,983 books, 665 serials, and an OPAC. 130 computers available on campus for general student use. A campuswide network can be accessed from off-campus. Staffed computer lab on campus.
Community Environment: See University of Baltimore.

■ **DEVRY UNIVERSITY** *F-8*
4550 Montgomery Ave.. Ste. 100 North
Bethesda, MD 20814-3304
Tel: (301)652-8477; (866)338-7934
Fax: (301)652-8577
Web Site: http://www.devry.edu/
Description: Proprietary, comprehensive, coed. Part of DeVry University. Awards bachelor's and master's degrees. Total enrollment: 96. Faculty: 15 (2 full-time, 13 part-time). Student-undergrad faculty ratio is 3:1. Full-time: 9 students, 56% women, 44% men. Part-time: 23 students, 52% women, 48% men. 0% Native American, 16% Hispanic, 56% black, 6% Asian American or Pacific Islander, 3% international. Academic area with the most degrees conferred: business/marketing. Calendar: semesters. Academic remediation for entering students, services for LD students, advanced placement, accelerated degree program, distance learning, summer session for credit, part-time degree program, adult/continuing education programs, co-op programs.
Entrance Requirements: Options: electronic application, deferred admission, international baccalaureate accepted. Required: high school transcript, interview. Entrance: minimally difficult. Application deadline: Rolling.

Costs Per Year: Application fee: $50. One-time mandatory fee: $40. Tuition: $13,060 full-time, $475 per credit part-time. Mandatory fees: $30 full-time, $30 per year part-time. Full-time tuition and fees vary according to course load. Part-time tuition and fees vary according to course load.

Collegiate Environment: Orientation program. College housing not available.

■ **FREDERICK COMMUNITY COLLEGE** *C-6*

7932 Opossumtown Pike
Frederick, MD 21702-2097
Tel: (301)846-2400
Admissions: (301)846-2432
Web Site: http://www.frederick.edu/

Description: State and locally supported, 2-year, coed. Awards certificates, transfer associate, and terminal associate degrees. Founded 1957. Setting: 125-acre small town campus with easy access to Baltimore and Washington, DC. Endowment: $4 million. Total enrollment: 4,822. Full-time: 1,855 students, 53% women, 47% men. Part-time: 2,967 students, 68% women, 32% men. Students come from 9 states and territories, 1% from out-of-state, 1% Native American, 4% Hispanic, 9% black, 3% Asian American or Pacific Islander, 0% international, 60% 25 or older, 56% transferred in. Core. Calendar: semesters. Academic remediation for entering students, services for LD students, advanced placement, honors program, independent study, distance learning, summer session for credit, part-time degree program, external degree program, adult/continuing education programs, co-op programs. Off campus study at Hood College, Mount Saint Mary's College. Study abroad program. ROTC: Army (c).

Entrance Requirements: Open admission except for nursing, some medical programs. Options: early admission, deferred admission. Entrance: noncompetitive. Application deadline: 9/1. Notification: continuous.

Costs Per Year: Application fee: $0. Area resident tuition: $2088 full-time, $87 per credit hour part-time. State resident tuition: $4560 full-time, $190 per credit hour part-time. Nonresident tuition: $6216 full-time, $259 per credit hour part-time. Mandatory fees: $300 full-time, $10.95 per credit hour part-time, $37 per year part-time.

Collegiate Environment: Orientation program. Drama-theater group, student-run newspaper. Social organizations: 15 open to all. Student services: personal-psychological counseling, women's center. Campus security: 24-hour emergency response devices and patrols. College housing not available. FCC Library with 40,000 books, 2,400 microform titles, 5,150 serials, 1,400 audiovisual materials, an OPAC, and a Web page.

Community Environment: See Hood College.

■ **FROSTBURG STATE UNIVERSITY** *F-4*

101 Braddock Rd.
Frostburg, MD 21532-1099
Tel: (301)687-4000
Admissions: (301)687-4201
Fax: (301)687-7074
Web Site: http://www.frostburg.edu/

Description: State-supported, comprehensive, coed. Part of University System of Maryland. Awards bachelor's and master's degrees and post-master's certificates. Founded 1898. Setting: 260-acre small town campus with easy access to Baltimore and Washington, DC. Endowment: $8.6 million. Educational spending for 2005 fiscal year: $5353 per student. Total enrollment: 5,041. Faculty: 351 (233 full-time, 118 part-time). Student-undergrad faculty ratio is 17:1. 3,430 applied, 76% were admitted. 10% from top 10% of their high school class, 32% from top quarter, 73% from top half. Full-time: 4,053 students, 49% women, 51% men. Part-time: 268 students, 49% women, 51% men. Students come from 23 states and territories, 27 other countries, 11% from out-of-state, 0.4% Native American, 2% Hispanic, 15% black, 2% Asian American or Pacific Islander, 1% international, 7% 25 or older, 35% live on campus, 8% transferred in. Retention: 71% of full-time freshmen returned the following year. Academic areas with the most degrees conferred: business/marketing; education; social sciences. Core. Calendar: semesters. Services for LD students, advanced placement, freshman honors college, honors program, independent study, distance learning, double major, summer session for credit, part-time degree program, adult/continuing education programs, internships, graduate courses open to undergrads. Off campus study at Cooperative Education Program. Study abroad program.

Entrance Requirements: Options: electronic application, early admission. Required: high school transcript, minimum 2.0 high school GPA, SAT or ACT. Recommended: recommendations, interview. Required for some: essay. Entrance: moderately difficult. Application deadline: Rolling.

Costs Per Year: Application fee: $30. State resident tuition: $5224 full-time, $216 per credit hour part-time. Nonresident tuition: $14,050 full-time, $396 per credit hour part-time. Mandatory fees: $1392 full-time, $67 per credit hour part-time, $9 per term part-time. College room and board: $6442. College room only: $3132.

Collegiate Environment: Orientation program. Drama-theater group, choral group, marching band, student-run newspaper, radio station. Social organizations: 80 open to all; national fraternities, national sororities; 10% of eligible men and 10% of eligible women are members. Most popular organizations: Student Government Association, Black Student Association, Campus Activities Board, Residence Hall Association. Major annual events: homecoming, Parents' Weekend, Greek Week. Student services: health clinic, personal-psychological counseling, women's center. Campus security: 24-hour emergency response devices and patrols, student patrols, late night transport-escort service, controlled dormitory access, bicycle patrols. 1,800 college housing spaces available; 1,590 were occupied in 2003-04. Options: coed, men-only, women-only housing available. Lewis J. Ort Library with 261,712 books, 293,802 microform titles, 2,430 serials, 32,224 audiovisual materials, an OPAC, and a Web page. Operations spending for 2004 fiscal year: $611,697. 577 computers available on campus for general student use. A campuswide network can be accessed from student residence rooms and from off campus. Staffed computer lab on campus.

Community Environment: The state university, in the City of Frostburg (population 7,623) is located in the mountains of western Maryland at an elevation of 2,200 feet. There are nearby state parks and winter sports activities including ice skating, skiing, and sleighing.

■ **GARRETT COLLEGE**

687 Mosser Rd.
McHenry, MD 21541
Tel: (301)387-3000
Admissions: (301)387-3046
Fax: (301)387-3055
E-mail: admission@garrett.ncin.com
Web Site: http://www.garrettcollege.edu/

Description: State and locally supported, 2-year, coed. Awards certificates, transfer associate, and terminal associate degrees. Founded 1966. Setting: 62-acre rural campus. Research spending for 2004 fiscal year: $19,371. Educational spending for 2005 fiscal year: $3638 per student. Total enrollment: 613. Full-time: 360 students, 52% women, 48% men. Part-time: 253 students, 58% women, 42% men. Students come from 12 states and territories, 1 other country, 20% from out-of-state, 1% Native American, 2% Hispanic, 9% black, 0% Asian American or Pacific Islander, 2% international, 22% 25 or older, 8% live on campus, 48% transferred in. Core. Calendar: semesters. Academic remediation for entering students, services for LD students, advanced placement, honors program, independent study, distance learning, double major, summer session for credit, part-time degree program, external degree program, adult/continuing education programs, internships.

Entrance Requirements: Open admission. Options: Common Application, early admission, deferred admission. Required: high school transcript, interview. Placement: SAT or ACT recommended. Entrance: noncompetitive. Application deadline: Rolling. Notification: continuous.

Costs Per Year: Application fee: $0. Area resident tuition: $2340 full-time, $78 per credit hour part-time. State resident tuition: $5460 full-time, $182 per credit hour part-time. Nonresident tuition: $6540 full-time, $218 per credit hour part-time. Mandatory fees: $570 full-time, $18 per credit hour part-time, $15. College room and board: $4970. College room only: $2550.

Collegiate Environment: Orientation program. Drama-theater group, student-run newspaper. Social organizations: 3 open to all; national fraternities; 20% of men are members. Most popular organizations: Wildlife Club, Raiders of the Lost Arts, student government. Major annual events: Back to College Event, GCC/ACC basketball game, Orientation. Student services: personal-psychological counseling. 60 college housing spaces available; all were occupied in 2003-04. No special consideration for freshman housing applicants. Option: coed housing available. Learning Resource Center with 24,230 books, 7,969 microform titles, 87 serials, 2,151 audiovisual materials, an OPAC, and a Web page. Operations spending for 2004 fiscal year: $254,723. 60 computers available on campus for general student use. Computer purchase/lease plans available. A campuswide network can be accessed. Staffed computer lab on campus.

Community Environment: Garrett County is a rural area of approximately 29,000 year-round inhabitants, most of whom are employed in small business, education, agriculture and tourism. It is also a four-season resort area with seasonal swells in population. The natural resources of the region are conducive to the college's three signature programs: Adventure sports, Agricultural Management, and Natural Resources and Wildlife Technology.

■ GEORGE MEANY CENTER FOR LABOR STUDIES-THE NATIONAL LABOR COLLEGE E-8

10000 New Hampshire Ave.
Silver Spring, MD 20903
Tel: (301)431-6400
Free: 800-GMC-4CDP
Admissions: (301)431-5404
Fax: (301)431-5411
E-mail: cspruill@georgemeany.org
Web Site: http://www.georgemeany.org/
Description: Independent, comprehensive, coed. Founded 1974.

■ GOUCHER COLLEGE D-10

1021 Dulaney Valley Rd.
Baltimore, MD 21204-2794
Tel: (410)337-6000
Free: 800-468-2437
Admissions: (410)337-6100
Fax: (410)337-6236
E-mail: admissions@goucher.edu
Web Site: http://www.goucher.edu/
Description: Independent, comprehensive, coed. Awards bachelor's and master's degrees. Founded 1885. Setting: 287-acre suburban campus. Endowment: $155.8 million. Educational spending for 2005 fiscal year: $12,100 per student. Total enrollment: 2,233. Faculty: 190 (112 full-time, 78 part-time). Student-undergrad faculty ratio is 10:1. 2,976 applied, 67% were admitted. 26% from top 10% of their high school class, 83% from top half. Full-time: 1,306 students, 66% women, 34% men. Part-time: 40 students, 73% women, 28% men. Students come from 40 states and territories, 8 other countries, 69% from out-of-state, 0.5% Native American, 3% Hispanic, 4% black, 3% Asian American or Pacific Islander, 1% international, 1% 25 or older, 80% live on campus, 4% transferred in. Retention: 83% of full-time freshmen returned the following year. Academic areas with the most degrees conferred: psychology; visual and performing arts; English. Core. Calendar: semesters. Services for LD students, advanced placement, self-designed majors, honors program, independent study, double major, adult/continuing education programs, internships, graduate courses open to undergrads. Off campus study at Johns Hopkins University, Morgan State University, Maryland Institute, College of Art, Loyola College, Towson University, Baltimore Hebrew University, College of Notre Dame of Maryland, Coppin State, Villa Julie College, University of Maryland Baltimore County, University of Baltimore. Study abroad program. ROTC: Army (c).
Entrance Requirements: Options: Common Application, electronic application, early admission, early action, deferred admission, international baccalaureate accepted. Required: essay, high school transcript, minimum 2.0 high school GPA, 3 recommendations, SAT or ACT. Recommended: minimum 2.8 high school GPA, interview. Entrance: moderately difficult. Application deadlines: 2/1, 12/15 for early action. Notification: 4/1, 2/15 for early action.
Costs Per Year: Application fee: $40. Comprehensive fee: $37,000 includes full-time tuition ($27,100), mandatory fees ($425), and college room and board ($9475). College room only: $5625. Room and board charges vary according to board plan and housing facility. Part-time tuition: $950 per credit hour.
Collegiate Environment: Orientation program. Drama-theater group, choral group, student-run newspaper, radio station. Social organizations: 38 open to all. Most popular organizations: CAUSE (Community Auxiliary for Service), Umoja: The African Alliance, Quindecim (newspaper), BGlad, Hillel. Major annual events: Pumpkin Bowl, Spring Gala, GIG. Student services: health clinic, personal-psychological counseling, women's center. Campus security: 24-hour emergency response devices and patrols, late night transport-escort service, controlled dormitory access. Freshmen guaranteed college housing. On-campus residence required through sophomore year. Options: coed, women-only housing available. Julia Rogers Library with 303,000 books, 24,800 microform titles, 22,000 serials, 4,278 audiovisual materials, an OPAC, and a Web page. Operations spending for 2004 fiscal year: $2 million. 150 computers available on campus for general student use. Computer purchase/lease plans available. A campuswide network can be accessed from student residence rooms and from off campus. Staffed computer lab on campus.

Community Environment: Goucher is located on 287 wooded acres in suburban Towson, seat of Baltimore County. The college is 20 minutes away from downtown Baltimore, an hour's drive from Washington, D.C., and 25 miles from the state capital of Annapolis, on the Chesapeake Bay. There are extensive walking, riding, and running trails that help create a small college atmosphere.

■ GRIGGS UNIVERSITY E-8

PO Box 4437, 12501 Old Columbia Pk
Silver Spring, MD 20914-4437
Tel: (301)680-6570
Admissions: (301)680-6579
Fax: (301)680-6577
E-mail: 74617.74@compuserve.com
Web Site: http://www.griggs.edu/
Description: Independent Seventh-day Adventist, 4-year, coed. Part of Seventh-day Adventist Parochial School System. Awards associate and bachelor's degrees (offers only external degree programs). Founded 1990. Setting: suburban campus with easy access to Washington D.C.. Total enrollment: 389. 28 applied, 100% were admitted. Core. Calendar: continuous. Advanced placement, accelerated degree program, independent study, distance learning, double major, summer session for credit, part-time degree program, external degree program, adult/continuing education programs.
Entrance Requirements: Options: Common Application, early admission, deferred admission. Required: essay, high school transcript, minimum 2.0 high school GPA. Entrance: minimally difficult. Application deadline: Rolling.
Costs Per Year: Application fee: $50. Tuition: $7350 full-time, $245 per semester hour part-time. Mandatory fees: $70 full-time, $70 per year part-time. Full-time tuition and fees vary according to course load. Part-time tuition and fees vary according to course load.
Collegiate Environment: College housing not available.

■ HAGERSTOWN BUSINESS COLLEGE A-5

18618 Crestwood Dr.
Hagerstown, MD 21742-2797
Tel: (301)739-2670
Free: 800-422-2670
Fax: (301)791-7661
E-mail: jklein@hagerstownbusinesscol.org
Web Site: http://www.hagerstownbusinesscol.org/
Description: Proprietary, 2-year, coed. Part of Kaplan Higher Education Corporation. Awards certificates and terminal associate degrees. Founded 1938. Setting: 8-acre small town campus with easy access to Baltimore and Washington, DC. Total enrollment: 932. Student-undergrad faculty ratio is 18:1. 64% from out-of-state, 0.1% Native American, 2% Hispanic, 10% black, 1% Asian American or Pacific Islander, 55% 25 or older, 3% live on campus. Academic remediation for entering students, advanced placement, accelerated degree program, summer session for credit, adult/continuing education programs, internships.
Entrance Requirements: Open admission. Options: early admission, deferred admission. Required: high school transcript, interview. Entrance: noncompetitive. Application deadline: Rolling.
Collegiate Environment: Orientation program. Social organizations: 5 open to all. Most popular organizations: Phi Beta Lambda, Association of Legal Students, Health Information Technology Students Organization, Student Government Association, Caduceus Club. Student services: personal-psychological counseling. Campus security: 24-hour emergency response devices. 36 college housing spaces available; 27 were occupied in 2003-04. No special consideration for freshman housing applicants. Option: coed housing available. HBC library plus 1 other with 8,000 books, 528 microform titles, 70 serials, and 400 audiovisual materials. 207 computers available on campus for general student use. A campuswide network can be accessed. Staffed computer lab on campus.

■ HAGERSTOWN COMMUNITY COLLEGE A-5

11400 Robinwood Dr.
Hagerstown, MD 21742-6590
Tel: (301)790-2800
Fax: (301)739-0737
E-mail: fisherj@hagerstowncc.edu
Web Site: http://www.hagerstowncc.edu/
Description: State and locally supported, 2-year, coed. Awards certificates, transfer associate, and terminal associate degrees. Founded 1946. Setting: 187-acre suburban campus with easy access to Baltimore and Washington,

DC. Endowment: $5.7 million. Educational spending for 2005 fiscal year: $3378 per student. Total enrollment: 3,521. Student-undergrad faculty ratio is 14:1. 1,373 applied, 100% were admitted. Full-time: 1,204 students, 55% women, 45% men. Part-time: 2,317 students, 67% women, 33% men. Students come from 6 states and territories, 1 other country, 23% from out-of-state, 1% Native American, 2% Hispanic, 7% black, 1% Asian American or Pacific Islander, 0% international, 37% 25 or older, 5% transferred in. Retention: 62% of full-time freshmen returned the following year. Core. Calendar: semesters. Academic remediation for entering students, ESL program, services for LD students, advanced placement, accelerated degree program, self-designed majors, honors program, independent study, distance learning, summer session for credit, part-time degree program, adult/continuing education programs, co-op programs and internships. Off campus study at HCC Valley Mall Center, Maryland Correctional Training Center.

Entrance Requirements: Open admission except for nursing (RN), radiological technology and practical nursing (LPN) programs. Options: Peterson's Universal Application, Common Application, electronic application, early admission, deferred admission. Required for some: high school transcript, ACT composite score of 21, 1 lab chemistry and algebra for admission into nursing and radiography programs. Entrance: noncompetitive. Application deadline: Rolling. Notification: continuous.

Costs Per Year: Application fee: $0. Area resident tuition: $2670 full-time, $89 per credit hour part-time. State resident tuition: $4260 full-time, $142 per credit hour part-time. Nonresident tuition: $5580 full-time, $186 per credit hour part-time. Mandatory fees: $280 full-time, $8 per credit hour part-time, $20. Full-time tuition and fees vary according to course load. Part-time tuition and fees vary according to course load.

Collegiate Environment: Orientation program. Drama-theater group, choral group, student-run newspaper. Social organizations: 10 open to all. Most popular organizations: Phi Theta Kappa, Robinwood Players, Association of Nursing Students, Theta Lambda Upsilon, Art Club. Student services: health clinic, personal-psychological counseling. Campus security: 24-hour patrols. College housing not available. William Brish Library with 45,705 books, 4,907 microform titles, 228 serials, 1,585 audiovisual materials, an OPAC, and a Web page. Operations spending for 2004 fiscal year: $378,321. 500 computers available on campus for general student use. Computer purchase/lease plans available. A campuswide network can be accessed from off-campus. Staffed computer lab on campus.

Community Environment: In the heart of Cumberland Valley, Hagerstown is manufacturing city nestled at an intersection of highway interstates and rail transportation. All forms of commercial transportation are available. Recreational facilities are numerous. Points of interest are Antietam Battlefield, Old Ft. Frederick State Park, Hager House, and Washington County Museum of Fine Arts. Special events include the annual Halloween Mummer's Parade.

■ HARFORD COMMUNITY COLLEGE B-11

401 Thomas Run Rd.
Bel Air, MD 21015-1698
Tel: (410)836-4000
Admissions: (410)836-4379
Fax: (410)836-4197
Web Site: http://www.harford.edu/

Description: State and locally supported, 2-year, coed. Awards certificates, diplomas, transfer associate, and terminal associate degrees. Founded 1957. Setting: 331-acre small town campus with easy access to Baltimore. Endowment: $4.1 million. Educational spending for 2005 fiscal year: $3681 per student. Total enrollment: 5,492. 1,197 applied, 100% were admitted. Full-time: 2,157 students, 56% women, 44% men. Part-time: 3,335 students, 66% women, 34% men. Students come from 10 states and territories, 17 other countries, 1% from out-of-state, 0.4% Native American, 3% Hispanic, 11% black, 2% Asian American or Pacific Islander, 0.5% international, 33% 25 or older, 60% transferred in. Retention: 66% of full-time freshmen returned the following year. Core. Calendar: semesters. Academic remediation for entering students, ESL program, services for LD students, advanced placement, self-designed majors, independent study, distance learning, double major, summer session for credit, part-time degree program, adult/continuing education programs, co-op programs and internships.

Entrance Requirements: Open admission. Options: electronic application, international baccalaureate accepted. Placement: ACCUPLACER required for some. Entrance: noncompetitive. Application deadline: Rolling.

Costs Per Year: Application fee: $0. Area resident tuition: $2250 full-time, $75 per credit part-time. State resident tuition: $4500 full-time, $150 per credit part-time. Nonresident tuition: $6750 full-time, $225 per credit part-time. Mandatory fees: $225 full-time, $7.50 per credit part-time. Full-time tuition and fees vary according to course load. Part-time tuition and fees vary according to course load.

Collegiate Environment: Orientation program. Drama-theater group, choral group, student-run newspaper, radio station. Social organizations: 18 open to all. Most popular organizations: Student Association, Paralegal Club, Multi-National Students Association, Student Nurses Association, Video Club. Major annual events: Welcome Picnic, Oktoberfest, Holiday Party. Student services: personal-psychological counseling. Campus security: 24-hour patrols, late night transport-escort service. College housing not available. Learning Resources Center with 74,731 books, 4,203 microform titles, 422 serials, 6,700 audiovisual materials, an OPAC, and a Web page. Operations spending for 2004 fiscal year: $1.3 million. 267 computers available on campus for general student use. A campuswide network can be accessed from off-campus. Staffed computer lab on campus.

■ HOOD COLLEGE C-6

401 Rosemont Ave.
Frederick, MD 21701-8575
Tel: (301)663-3131
Free: 800-922-1599
Admissions: (301)696-3400
E-mail: admissions@nimue.hood.edu
Web Site: http://www.hood.edu/

Description: Independent, comprehensive, coed. Awards bachelor's and master's degrees (also offers adult program with significant enrollment not reflected in profile). Founded 1893. Setting: 50-acre suburban campus with easy access to Baltimore and Washington, DC. Endowment: $50.5 million. Research spending for 2004 fiscal year: $356,475. Educational spending for 2005 fiscal year: $11,051 per student. Total enrollment: 2,117. Faculty: 202 (81 full-time, 121 part-time). Student-undergrad faculty ratio is 12:1. 1,852 applied, 51% were admitted. 33% from top 10% of their high school class, 64% from top quarter, 96% from top half. 4 valedictorians. Full-time: 1,007 students, 76% women, 24% men. Part-time: 176 students, 66% women, 34% men. Students come from 28 states and territories, 27 other countries, 19% from out-of-state, 0.3% Native American, 3% Hispanic, 12% black, 2% Asian American or Pacific Islander, 3% international, 19% 25 or older, 53% live on campus, 12% transferred in. Retention: 87% of full-time freshmen returned the following year. Academic areas with the most degrees conferred: education; psychology; social sciences. Core. Calendar: semesters. Academic remediation for entering students, ESL program, services for LD students, advanced placement, accelerated degree program, self-designed majors, honors program, independent study, distance learning, double major, summer session for credit, part-time degree program, adult/continuing education programs, internships, graduate courses open to undergrads. Off campus study at Washington Semester Program , Public Leadership Education Network (PLEN), Council of International Education Exchange (CIEE), Duke University Marine Science Consort Education (MSEC). Study abroad program. ROTC: Army (c).

Entrance Requirements: Options: Peterson's Universal Application, Common Application, electronic application, early action, deferred admission, international baccalaureate accepted. Required: high school transcript, minimum 2.0 high school GPA, SAT or ACT. Recommended: essay, interview. Required for some: recommendations. Entrance: moderately difficult. Application deadlines: 2/15, 10/1 for early action. Notification: continuous, 10/15 for early action.

Costs Per Year: Application fee: $35. Comprehensive fee: $30,085 includes full-time tuition ($22,000), mandatory fees ($335), and college room and board ($7750). College room only: $4050. Full-time tuition and fees vary according to course load. Room and board charges vary according to board plan. Part-time tuition: $635 per credit. Part-time mandatory fees: $105 per term. Part-time tuition and fees vary according to course load.

Collegiate Environment: Orientation program. Drama-theater group, choral group, student-run newspaper, radio station. Social organizations: 59 open to all. Most popular organizations: Education Club, Black Student Union, Campus Activities Board, International Club, Hood Today (newspaper). Major annual events: Policies for Dollars, spring parties, Messiah Holiday Weekend. Student services: health clinic, personal-psychological counseling, women's center. Campus security: 24-hour emergency response devices and patrols, late night transport-escort service, controlled dormitory access, residence hall security. 640 college housing spaces available; 525 were occupied in 2003-04. Freshmen guaranteed college housing. On-campus residence required through sophomore year. Options: coed, women-only housing available. Beneficial-Hodson Library and Information Technology Center with 182,786 books, 688,015 microform titles, 1,057 serials, 3,864 audiovisual materials, an OPAC, and a Web page. Operations spending for 2004 fiscal year: $713,454. 277 computers available on campus for general student use. A campuswide network can be accessed from student residence rooms and from off campus. Staffed computer lab on campus.

Community Environment: Hood College is located on almost 50 acres near downtown Frederick, Maryland, a community of approximately 49,000. The campus is 45 miles west of Baltimore and an equal distance northwest of Washington D.C. The proximity of the Hood campus to these major metropolitan areas increases the opportunities open to students to participate in social and cultural activities, to complete internships, and to explore prominent research facilities.

■ **HOWARD COMMUNITY COLLEGE** *D-9*

10901 Little Patuxent Parkway
Columbia, MD 21044-3197
Tel: (410)772-4800
Admissions: (410)772-4856
Fax: (410)772-4589
E-mail: hsinfo@howardcc.edu
Web Site: http://www.howardcc.edu/

Description: State and locally supported, 2-year, coed. Awards certificates, transfer associate, and terminal associate degrees. Founded 1966. Setting: 122-acre suburban campus with easy access to Baltimore and Washington, DC. Endowment: $2 million. Educational spending for 2005 fiscal year: $3657 per student. Total enrollment: 6,842. Student-undergrad faculty ratio is 18:1. Students come from 4 states and territories, 1% from out-of-state, 1% Native American, 4% Hispanic, 21% black, 11% Asian American or Pacific Islander, 43% 25 or older. Core. Calendar: semesters. Academic remediation for entering students, ESL program, services for LD students, advanced placement, honors program, distance learning, double major, summer session for credit, part-time degree program, adult/continuing education programs, co-op programs. Off campus study. Study abroad program.

Entrance Requirements: Open admission except for nursing, cardiovascular technology, Rouse scholars program, EMT-P. Options: electronic application, early admission, deferred admission, international baccalaureate accepted. Required for some: essay, high school transcript, 2 recommendations, SAT or ACT. Entrance: noncompetitive. Application deadline: Rolling. Notification: continuous.

Costs Per Year: Application fee: $25. Area resident tuition: $3300 full-time, $110 per credit part-time. State resident tuition: $5790 full-time, $193 per credit part-time. Nonresident tuition: $7140 full-time, $238 per credit part-time. Mandatory fees: $553 full-time, $18.43 per credit part-time.

Collegiate Environment: Orientation program. Drama-theater group, choral group, student-run newspaper. Social organizations: 16 open to all. Most popular organizations: Secretarial Club, Nursing Club, Black Leadership Organization, student newspaper, Student Government Association. Major annual events: Fall Cookout, Spring Fling, Weekly Block Time. Student services: personal-psychological counseling. Campus security: 24-hour emergency response devices and patrols, late night transport-escort service. College housing not available. Howard Community College Library with 40,380 books, 1,201 serials, 6,253 audiovisual materials, an OPAC, and a Web page. Operations spending for 2004 fiscal year: $550,260. 750 computers available on campus for general student use. Staffed computer lab on campus.

Community Environment: Columbia, a planned city of 100,000, was designed as a community of village centers. Small lakes, parks, and bicycle paths add charm and access to the outdoors. Situated between two major cities, Baltimore and Washington, there is quick access to transportation facilities at airports and rail stations. The Columbia Mall provides major shopping facilities, and each village center complements the mall with supermarkets and convenience stores. The college serves as a cultural center in the county and hosts a variety of concerts, stage productions and cultural activities in its theatre.

■ **ITT TECHNICAL INSTITUTE** *C-9*

11301 Red Run Blvd.
Owings Mills, MD 21117
Admissions: (443)394-7115
Web Site: http://www.itt-tech.edu/

Description: primarily 2-year, coed. Awards terminal associate and bachelor's degrees.

Entrance Requirements: Required: high school transcript, interview, Wonderlic aptitude test. Recommended: recommendations. Application deadline: Rolling. Notification: continuous.

Costs Per Year: Application fee: $100.

■ **THE JOHNS HOPKINS UNIVERSITY** *D-10*

3400 North Charles St.
Baltimore, MD 21218-2699
Tel: (410)516-8000
Admissions: (410)516-8341
Fax: (410)516-6025
E-mail: gotojhu@jhu.edu
Web Site: http://www.jhu.edu/

Description: Independent, university, coed. Awards bachelor's, master's, doctoral, and first professional degrees and post-master's certificates. Founded 1876. Setting: 140-acre urban campus with easy access to Washington, DC. Endowment: $2 billion. Total enrollment: 6,025. Faculty: 525 (451 full-time, 74 part-time). Student-undergrad faculty ratio is 9:1. 11,274 applied, 35% were admitted. 78% from top 10% of their high school class, 96% from top quarter, 100% from top half. 33 National Merit Scholars. Full-time: 4,351 students, 46% women, 54% men. Part-time: 66 students, 52% women, 48% men. Students come from 51 states and territories, 52 other countries, 85% from out-of-state, 1% Native American, 6% Hispanic, 5% black, 22% Asian American or Pacific Islander, 5% international, 0% 25 or older, 50% live on campus, 1% transferred in. Retention: 96% of full-time freshmen returned the following year. Academic areas with the most degrees conferred: health professions and related sciences; engineering; social sciences. Calendar: 4-1-4. Services for LD students, advanced placement, accelerated degree program, self-designed majors, honors program, independent study, double major, summer session for credit, part-time degree program, adult/continuing education programs, internships, graduate courses open to undergrads. Off campus study at University of Maryland, Baltimore County; Loyola College; Towson University; Morgan State University; College of Notre Dame of Maryland; Maryland Institute, College of Art; Goucher College; Baltimore Hebrew Academy. Study abroad program. ROTC: Army, Air Force (c).

Entrance Requirements: Options: Common Application, electronic application, early admission, early decision, deferred admission, international baccalaureate accepted. Required: essay, high school transcript, recommendations, SAT or ACT. Recommended: interview, SAT and SAT Subject Tests or ACT. Entrance: most difficult. Application deadlines: 1/1, 11/15 for early decision. Notification: 4/1, 12/15 for early decision.

Costs Per Year: Application fee: $60. Comprehensive fee: $45,022 includes full-time tuition ($33,900), mandatory fees ($500), and college room and board ($10,622). College room only: $6096. Part-time tuition: $1130 per credit.

Collegiate Environment: Orientation program. Drama-theater group, choral group, student-run newspaper, radio station. Social organizations: 180 open to all; national fraternities, national sororities; 21% of eligible men and 17% of eligible women are members. Most popular organizations: The Outdoors Club, The Hopkins Organization for Programs, The Barn Stormers (theater group), Inter-Asian Council, Ole (Latino Student organization). Major annual events: Spring Fair, Homecoming, Family Weekend. Student services: health clinic, personal-psychological counseling. Campus security: 24-hour emergency response devices and patrols, student patrols, late night transport-escort service, controlled dormitory access. 2,123 college housing spaces available; all were occupied in 2003-04. Freshmen guaranteed college housing. On-campus residence required through sophomore year. Options: coed, men-only, women-only housing available. Milton S. Eisenhower Library plus 6 others with 3.5 million books, 4.2 million microform titles, 30,023 serials, 299,605 audiovisual materials, an OPAC, and a Web page. 140 computers available on campus for general student use. A campuswide network can be accessed from student residence rooms and from off campus. Staffed computer lab on campus.

Community Environment: See University of Baltimore.

■ **LOYOLA COLLEGE IN MARYLAND** *D-10*

4501 North Charles St.
Baltimore, MD 21210-2699
Tel: (410)617-2000
Fax: (410)323-2768
Web Site: http://www.loyola.edu/

Description: Independent Roman Catholic (Jesuit), comprehensive, coed. Awards bachelor's, master's, and doctoral degrees and post-master's certificates. Founded 1852. Setting: 89-acre urban campus with easy access to Washington, DC. Endowment: $143.6 million. Research spending for 2004 fiscal year: $819,000. Total enrollment: 6,187. Faculty: 537 (305 full-time, 232 part-time). Student-undergrad faculty ratio is 12:1. 10,391 applied, 47% were admitted. 35% from top 10% of their high school class, 74% from top quarter, 97% from top half. Full-time: 3,501 students, 58% women, 42% men. Part-time: 55 students, 62% women, 38% men. Students come from 38 states and territories, 82% from out-of-state, 0.1% Native American, 3% Hispanic, 5% black, 2% Asian American or Pacific Islander, 1% international, 1% 25 or older, 79% live on campus, 1% transferred in. Retention: 90% of full-time freshmen returned the following year. Academic areas with the most degrees conferred: business/marketing; communications/journalism; psychology. Core. Calendar: semesters. Services for LD students, advanced placement, accelerated degree program, honors program, independent study, double major, summer session for credit, part-time degree program, internships, graduate courses open to undergrads. Off campus study at Johns Hopkins University; College of Notre Dame of Maryland; Goucher College; Towson State University; Morgan State University; Peabody Conservatory of Music of The Johns Hopkins University; Maryland Institute, College of Art. ROTC: Army, Air Force (c).

Entrance Requirements: Options: Common Application, early admission, deferred admission, international baccalaureate accepted. Required: essay, high school transcript, SAT or ACT. Recommended: interview. Entrance: moderately difficult. Application deadline: 1/15. Notification: 4/1.

Costs Per Year: Application fee: $50. Comprehensive fee: $38,898 includes full-time tuition ($28,683), mandatory fees ($1000), and college room and board ($9215). College room only: $7215. Full-time tuition and fees vary according to student level. Room and board charges vary according to board plan. Part-time tuition: $486 per credit. Part-time mandatory fees: $25 per term.

Collegiate Environment: Orientation program. Drama-theater group, choral group, student-run newspaper, radio station. Student services: health clinic, personal-psychological counseling. Campus security: 24-hour emergency response devices and patrols, late night transport-escort service, controlled dormitory access. 2,790 college housing spaces available; all were occupied in 2003-04. Freshmen given priority for college housing. On-campus residence required in freshman year. Option: coed housing available. Loyola/Notre Dame Library with 293,639 books, 312,725 microform titles, 2,126 serials, 28,878 audiovisual materials, an OPAC, and a Web page. Operations spending for 2004 fiscal year: $2.7 million. 292 computers available on campus for general student use. A campuswide network can be accessed from student residence rooms and from off campus. Staffed computer lab on campus.

■ **MAPLE SPRINGS BAPTIST BIBLE COLLEGE AND SEMINARY** *L-4*
4130 Belt Rd.
Capitol Heights, MD 20743
Tel: (301)736-3631
Fax: (301)735-6507
E-mail: percy.coker@msbbcs.edu
Web Site: http://www.msbbcs.edu/

Description: Independent Baptist, comprehensive, coed. Awards associate, bachelor's, master's, and doctoral degrees. Founded 1986. Setting: 1-acre suburban campus with easy access to Washington, DC. Educational spending for 2005 fiscal year: $867 per student. Total enrollment: 151. 24 applied, 100% were admitted. Full-time: 7 students, 57% women, 43% men. Part-time: 82 students, 55% women, 45% men. Students come from 4 states and territories, 50% from out-of-state, 90% 25 or older, 24% transferred in. Core. Calendar: semesters. Academic remediation for entering students, accelerated degree program, independent study, part-time degree program, external degree program, adult/continuing education programs, internships, graduate courses open to undergrads.

Entrance Requirements: Open admission. Option: deferred admission. Required: essay, high school transcript, 3 recommendations, interview. Placement: Bible examination required. Entrance: minimally difficult. Application deadline: Rolling. Notification: continuous.

Collegiate Environment: Orientation program. Student-run newspaper. Social organizations: 2 open to all. Most popular organizations: Student Government Association, newsletter. Campus security: 24-hour emergency response devices, part-time security personnel. College housing not available. 1,781 books, 37 serials, and 35 audiovisual materials. Operations spending for 2004 fiscal year: $4176.

■ **MARYLAND INSTITUTE COLLEGE OF ART** *D-10*
1300 Mount Royal Ave.
Baltimore, MD 21217
Tel: (410)669-9200
Admissions: (410)225-2222
Fax: (410)225-2337
E-mail: admissions@mica.edu
Web Site: http://www.mica.edu/

Description: Independent, comprehensive, coed. Awards bachelor's and master's degrees. Founded 1826. Setting: 12-acre urban campus with easy access to Washington, DC. Endowment: $38.9 million. Educational spending for 2005 fiscal year: $9493 per student. Total enrollment: 1,717. Faculty: 267 (118 full-time, 149 part-time). Student-undergrad faculty ratio is 10:1. 2,487 applied, 45% were admitted. 29% from top 10% of their high school class, 62% from top quarter, 91% from top half. 1 National Merit Scholar, 28 class presidents, 3 valedictorians, 64 student government officers. Full-time: 1,478 students, 62% women, 38% men. Part-time: 19 students, 58% women, 42% men. Students come from 47 states and territories, 48 other countries, 80% from out-of-state, 0.5% Native American, 5% Hispanic, 4% black, 8% Asian American or Pacific Islander, 5% international, 4% 25 or older, 88% live on campus, 4% transferred in. Retention: 86% of full-time freshmen returned the following year. Academic areas with the most degrees conferred: visual and performing arts; education. Core. Calendar: semesters. Academic remediation for entering students, services for LD students, advanced placement, accelerated degree program, self-designed majors, independent study, distance learning, double major, summer session for credit, adult/continuing education programs, internships. Off campus study at Association of Independent Colleges of Art and Design, Johns Hopkins University, Goucher College, University of Baltimore, Loyola College, Notre Dame College, Peabody Conservatory of Music of the Johns Hopkins University. Study abroad program. ROTC: Army (c).

Entrance Requirements: Options: early admission, early decision, early action, deferred admission, international baccalaureate accepted. Required: essay, high school transcript, art portfolio, SAT or ACT. Recommended: minimum 3.0 high school GPA, 3 recommendations, interview. Entrance: very difficult. Application deadlines: 2/15, 11/15 for early decision, 1/15 for early action. Notification: 3/15, 12/15 for early decision, 1/30 for early action.

Costs Per Year: Application fee: $50. Comprehensive fee: $34,450 includes full-time tuition ($26,140), mandatory fees ($780), and college room and board ($7530). College room only: $5500. Room and board charges vary according to board plan and housing facility. Part-time tuition: $1090 per credit. Part-time mandatory fees: $390 per term.

Collegiate Environment: Orientation program. Drama-theater group, choral group. Social organizations: 22 open to all. Most popular organizations: a Cappela, soccer teams, Black Student Union, Channel Organix, Knitting Club. Major annual events: bus trips to galleries and museums, dances, exhibition openings. Student services: health clinic, personal-psychological counseling. Campus security: 24-hour emergency response devices and patrols, student patrols, late night transport-escort service, controlled dormitory access, self-defense education, 24-hour building security, safety awareness programs, campus patrols by city police. 630 college housing spaces available; 615 were occupied in 2003-04. Freshmen guaranteed college housing. Option: coed housing available. Decker Library plus 1 other with 55,000 books, 366 serials, 4,200 audiovisual materials, an OPAC, and a Web page. Operations spending for 2004 fiscal year: $631,334. 305 computers available on campus for general student use. A campuswide network can be accessed from student residence rooms and from off campus. Staffed computer lab on campus.

Community Environment: See University of Baltimore.

■ **MCDANIEL COLLEGE** *B-8*
2 College Hill
Westminster, MD 21157-4390
Tel: (410)848-7000
Free: 800-638-5005
Admissions: (410)857-2230
Fax: (410)857-2729
E-mail: admissions@mcdaniel.edu
Web Site: http://www.mcdaniel.edu/

Description: Independent, comprehensive, coed. Awards bachelor's and master's degrees. Founded 1867. Setting: 160-acre suburban campus with easy access to Baltimore and Washington, DC. Endowment: $72.2 million. Research spending for 2004 fiscal year: $140,829. Educational spending for 2005 fiscal year: $8892 per student. Total enrollment: 3,524. Faculty: 190

(129 full-time, 61 part-time). Student-undergrad faculty ratio is 13:1. 2,256 applied, 79% were admitted. 26% from top 10% of their high school class, 55% from top quarter, 86% from top half. Full-time: 1,643 students, 57% women, 43% men. Part-time: 52 students, 56% women, 44% men. Students come from 30 states and territories, 9 other countries, 28% from out-of-state, 1% Native American, 2% Hispanic, 7% black, 2% Asian American or Pacific Islander, 1% international, 3% 25 or older, 80% live on campus, 4% transferred in. Retention: 80% of full-time freshmen returned the following year. Academic areas with the most degrees conferred: social sciences; business/marketing; psychology. Core. Calendar: 4-1-4. Academic remediation for entering students, services for LD students, advanced placement, self-designed majors, honors program, independent study, double major, summer session for credit, part-time degree program, adult/continuing education programs, internships, graduate courses open to undergrads. Off campus study at American University, Drew University, Gallaudet University. Study abroad program. ROTC: Army.

Entrance Requirements: Options: Peterson's Universal Application, Common Application, electronic application, early admission, early action, deferred admission, international baccalaureate accepted. Required: essay, high school transcript, minimum 2.5 high school GPA, SAT or ACT. Recommended: recommendations, interview, SAT Subject Tests. Required for some: interview. Entrance: moderately difficult. Application deadlines: 2/1, 12/1 for early action. Notification: 4/1, 1/15 for early action.

Costs Per Year: Application fee: $50. Comprehensive fee: $33,180 includes full-time tuition ($26,980), mandatory fees ($300), and college room and board ($5900). College room only: $3200. Part-time tuition: $843 per credit. Part-time mandatory fees: $150 per term.

Collegiate Environment: Orientation program. Drama-theater group, choral group, student-run newspaper, radio station. Social organizations: 128 open to all; national fraternities, national sororities, local fraternities, local sororities; 16% of eligible men and 12% of eligible women are members. Major annual events: homecoming, Jazz Nights, Spring Fling. Student services: health clinic, personal-psychological counseling. Campus security: 24-hour emergency response devices and patrols, late night transport-escort service, controlled dormitory access. 1,314 college housing spaces available; 1,250 were occupied in 2003-04. Freshmen guaranteed college housing. On-campus residence required through junior year. Options: coed, men-only, women-only housing available. Hoover Library with 629,965 books, 1.4 million microform titles, 3,500 serials, 11,125 audiovisual materials, an OPAC, and a Web page. Operations spending for 2004 fiscal year: $1.2 million. 171 computers available on campus for general student use. A campuswide network can be accessed from student residence rooms and from off campus. Staffed computer lab on campus.

■ **MONTGOMERY COLLEGE** *E-7*
900 Hungerford Dr.
Rockville, MD 20850
Tel: (301)279-5000
Admissions: (301)279-5034
Web Site: http://www.montgomerycollege.org/

Description: State and locally supported, 2-year, coed. Awards certificates, transfer associate, and terminal associate degrees. Setting: suburban campus with easy access to Washington D.C.. Total enrollment: 21,805. Full-time: 7,748 students, 51% women, 49% men. Part-time: 14,057 students, 60% women, 40% men. Students come from 169 other countries, 3% from out-of-state, 0.2% Native American, 14% Hispanic, 27% black, 13% Asian American or Pacific Islander, 8% international, 41% 25 or older, 40% transferred in. Calendar: semesters.

Entrance Requirements: Option: Common Application. Entrance: noncompetitive. Application deadline: Rolling. Notification: continuous.

Collegiate Environment: Drama-theater group, choral group, student-run newspaper, radio station. Student services: personal-psychological counseling, women's center. Campus security: 24-hour emergency response devices and patrols, late night transport-escort service. College housing not available.

■ **MORGAN STATE UNIVERSITY** *D-10*
1700 East Cold Spring Ln.
Baltimore, MD 21251
Tel: (443)885-3333
Free: 800-332-6674
Admissions: (443)885-3000
E-mail: ejohnson@moac.morgan.edu
Web Site: http://www.morgan.edu/

Description: State-supported, university, coed. Awards bachelor's, master's, and doctoral degrees. Founded 1867. Setting: 143-acre urban campus with easy access to Washington, DC. Educational spending for 2005 fiscal year: $14,500 per student. Total enrollment: 6,621. 11,387 applied, 34% were admitted. Full-time: 5,328 students, 58% women, 42% men. Part-time: 677 students, 58% women, 42% men. Students come from 47 states and territories, 30 other countries, 38% from out-of-state, 0.2% Native American, 0.5% Hispanic, 91% black, 1% Asian American or Pacific Islander, 4% international, 27% 25 or older, 30% live on campus, 5% transferred in. Retention: 71% of full-time freshmen returned the following year. Core. Calendar: semesters. Academic remediation for entering students, services for LD students, advanced placement, accelerated degree program, honors program, independent study, summer session for credit, part-time degree program, adult/continuing education programs, co-op programs and internships, graduate courses open to undergrads. Off campus study at Towson University, Coppin State College, University of Maryland. ROTC: Army.

Entrance Requirements: Options: Peterson's Universal Application, Common Application, electronic application, early admission, deferred admission, international baccalaureate accepted. Required: high school transcript, minimum 2.0 high school GPA, SAT or ACT. Recommended: essay. Required for some: 2 recommendations, interview. Entrance: moderately difficult. Application deadline: 5/1. Notification: continuous until 6/30. Preference given to state residents.

Costs Per Year: Application fee: $25. State resident tuition: $4280 full-time, $194 per credit part-time. Nonresident tuition: $11,690 full-time, $445 per credit part-time. Mandatory fees: $1830 full-time, $55 per credit part-time. College room and board: $6990. College room only: $4430. Room and board charges vary according to board plan and housing facility.

Collegiate Environment: Orientation program. Drama-theater group, choral group, marching band, student-run newspaper, radio station. Social organizations: 20 open to all; national fraternities, national sororities; 10% of eligible men and 10% of eligible women are members. Most popular organizations: Student Government Association, choir, band. Major annual event: homecoming. Student services: health clinic, personal-psychological counseling. Campus security: 24-hour emergency response devices and patrols, late night transport-escort service, controlled dormitory access. 2,351 college housing spaces available; all were occupied in 2003-04. Option: coed housing available. Morris Soper Library with 333,101 books, 2,526 serials, and an OPAC. 285 computers available on campus for general student use. A campuswide network can be accessed from student residence rooms and from off campus. Staffed computer lab on campus.

Community Environment: See University of Baltimore.

■ **MOUNT ST. MARY'S UNIVERSITY** *A-6*
16300 Old Emmitsburg Rd.
Emmitsburg, MD 21727-7799
Tel: (301)447-6122
Free: 800-448-4347
Admissions: (301)447-5214
E-mail: admissions@msmary.edu
Web Site: http://www.msmary.edu/

Description: Independent Roman Catholic, comprehensive, coed. Awards bachelor's, master's, and first professional degrees and post-master's certificates. Founded 1808. Setting: 1,400-acre rural campus with easy access to Baltimore and Washington, DC. Endowment: $33.3 million. Educational spending for 2005 fiscal year: $6772 per student. Total enrollment: 2,176. Faculty: 205 (105 full-time, 100 part-time). Student-undergrad faculty ratio is 13:1. 2,190 applied, 84% were admitted. 20% from top 10% of their high school class, 48% from top quarter, 81% from top half. 4 valedictorians. Full-time: 1,485 students, 59% women, 41% men. Part-time: 171 students, 75% women, 25% men. Students come from 26 states and territories, 11 other countries, 42% from out-of-state, 0.2% Native American, 3% Hispanic, 7% black, 2% Asian American or Pacific Islander, 1% international, 2% 25 or older, 80% live on campus, 3% transferred in. Retention: 84% of full-time freshmen returned the following year. Academic areas with the most degrees conferred: business/marketing; social sciences; education. Core. Calendar: semesters. Academic remediation for entering students, services for LD students, advanced placement, accelerated degree program, self-designed majors, honors program, independent study, double major, summer session for credit, part-time degree program, adult/continuing education programs, internships, graduate courses open to undergrads. Off campus study at Frederick Community College. Study abroad program. ROTC: Army (c).

Entrance Requirements: Options: Peterson's Universal Application, electronic application, early action, deferred admission. Required: high school transcript, minimum 2.0 high school GPA, 1 recommendation, SAT or ACT. Recommended: essay, minimum 3.0 high school GPA, interview. Entrance: moderately difficult. Application deadlines: Rolling, 12/1 for early action. Notification: continuous, 12/15 for early action.

Costs Per Year: Application fee: $35. Comprehensive fee: $32,720 includes full-time tuition ($23,630), mandatory fees ($400), and college room and board ($8690). College room only: $4380. Part-time tuition: $790 per credit hour. Part-time mandatory fees: $12 per credit hour.

Collegiate Environment: Orientation program. Drama-theater group, choral group, student-run newspaper, radio station. Social organizations: 50 open to all. Most popular organizations: campus ministry, Rugby Team Club, Ice Hockey Club, Circle K, International Affairs Organization. Major annual events: Opening Picnic, Spring Fling, Mountapalooza. Student services: health clinic, personal-psychological counseling. Campus security: 24-hour emergency response devices and patrols, late night transport-escort service, controlled dormitory access. 1,185 college housing spaces available; 1,112 were occupied in 2003-04. Freshmen guaranteed college housing. On-campus residence required in freshman year. Option: coed housing available. Phillips Library with 210,359 books, 18,675 microform titles, 926 serials, 4,825 audiovisual materials, an OPAC, and a Web page. Operations spending for 2004 fiscal year: $878,218. 150 computers available on campus for general student use. Computer purchase/lease plans available. A campuswide network can be accessed from student residence rooms and from off campus. Staffed computer lab on campus.

■ **NER ISRAEL RABBINICAL COLLEGE** *D-10*
400 Mount Wilson Ln.
Baltimore, MD 21208
Tel: (410)484-7200
Fax: (410)484-3060

Description: Independent Jewish, comprehensive, men only. Awards bachelor's, master's, doctoral, and first professional degrees. Founded 1933. Setting: 54-acre suburban campus. Total enrollment: 577. 134 applied, 50% were admitted. Full-time: 353 students. Students come from 36 states and territories, 74% from out-of-state, 8% 25 or older, 12% transferred in. Core. Calendar: semesters. Academic remediation for entering students, ESL program, honors program, summer session for credit, graduate courses open to undergrads. Study abroad program.

Entrance Requirements: Options: early admission, deferred admission. Required: recommendations. Recommended: interview. Entrance: moderately difficult. Application deadline: Rolling.

Collegiate Environment: Student services: health clinic. On-campus residence required through senior year.

Community Environment: See University of Baltimore.

■ **PEABODY CONSERVATORY OF MUSIC OF THE JOHNS HOPKINS UNIVERSITY** *D-10*
1 East Mount Vernon Place
Baltimore, MD 21202-2397
Tel: (410)659-8150
Free: 800-368-2521
Admissions: (410)659-8110
Web Site: http://www.peabody.jhu.edu/

Description: Independent, comprehensive, coed. Administratively affiliated with Johns Hopkins University. Awards bachelor's, master's, and doctoral degrees. Founded 1857. Setting: 1-acre urban campus with easy access to Washington, DC. Endowment: $75.5 million. Total enrollment: 647. Faculty: 165. Student-undergrad faculty ratio is 4:1. 713 applied, 43% were admitted. Full-time: 311 students, 45% women, 55% men. Part-time: 12 students, 58% women, 42% men. Students come from 37 states and territories, 12 other countries, 67% from out-of-state, 0.3% Native American, 2% Hispanic, 6% black, 9% Asian American or Pacific Islander, 16% international, 2% 25 or older, 3% transferred in. Retention: 88% of full-time freshmen returned the following year. Academic areas with the most degrees conferred: visual and performing arts; education. Core. Calendar: semesters. Academic remediation for entering students, ESL program, services for LD students, advanced placement, accelerated degree program, honors program, independent study, double major, internships, graduate courses open to undergrads. Off campus study at Johns Hopkins University; Loyola College; Maryland Institute, College of Art.

Entrance Requirements: Required: essay, high school transcript, 3 recommendations, interview, audition. Recommended: minimum 3.0 high school GPA. Required for some: SAT or ACT. Entrance: very difficult. Application deadline: 12/1. Notification: 4/1.

Costs Per Year: Application fee: $60. Comprehensive fee: $39,490 includes full-time tuition ($29,630), mandatory fees ($360), and college room and board ($9500). Part-time tuition: $840 per semester hour.

Collegiate Environment: Orientation program. Choral group. Social organizations: 84 open to all. Major annual events: beginning of the year events, Relaxation Day, End of Year Party. Student services: health clinic, personal-psychological counseling. Campus security: 24-hour emergency response devices and patrols, late night transport-escort service, controlled dormitory access. 180 college housing spaces available; 165 were occupied in 2003-04. Freshmen guaranteed college housing. On-campus residence required through sophomore year. Options: coed, women-only housing available. Arthur Friedheim Library with 90,706 books, 199 microform titles, 223 serials, 24,585 audiovisual materials, an OPAC, and a Web page. Operations spending for 2004 fiscal year: $469,818. 40 computers available on campus for general student use. A campuswide network can be accessed from student residence rooms and from off campus. Staffed computer lab on campus.

■ **PRINCE GEORGE'S COMMUNITY COLLEGE** *L-5*
301 Largo Rd.
Largo, MD 20774-2199
Tel: (301)336-6000
Admissions: (301)322-0801
Web Site: http://www.pgcc.edu/

Description: County-supported, 2-year, coed. Awards certificates, transfer associate, and terminal associate degrees. Founded 1958. Setting: 150-acre suburban campus with easy access to Washington, DC. Educational spending for 2005 fiscal year: $5638 per student. Total enrollment: 12,564. 4,570 applied, 100% were admitted. Full-time: 3,352 students, 58% women, 42% men. Part-time: 9,212 students, 69% women, 31% men. Students come from 20 states and territories, 98 other countries, 4% from out-of-state, 1% Native American, 3% Hispanic, 76% black, 4% Asian American or Pacific Islander, 3% international, 51% 25 or older, 13% transferred in. Retention: 58% of full-time freshmen returned the following year. Core. Calendar: semesters plus 2 summer sessions. Academic remediation for entering students, ESL program, services for LD students, advanced placement, honors program, distance learning, summer session for credit, part-time degree program, external degree program, adult/continuing education programs, co-op programs. ROTC: Army (c).

Entrance Requirements: Open admission. Option: early admission. Recommended: minimum 2.0 high school GPA. Required for some: high school transcript. Placement: ACCUPLACER required for some. Entrance: noncompetitive. Application deadline: Rolling. Notification: continuous.

Collegiate Environment: Orientation program. Drama-theater group, choral group, student-run newspaper. Social organizations: 40 open to all. Most popular organizations: Crusaders for Christ, Student Program Board, Union of Black Scholars, International Student Groups. Major annual events: International Festival, Bluebird Blues Jazz Festival, Jook Joint Saturday Night. Student services: health clinic, personal-psychological counseling. Campus security: 24-hour emergency response devices and patrols, late night transport-escort service. College housing not available. Accokeek Hall with 242,519 books, 226,390 microform titles, 750 serials, 16,645 audiovisual materials, and an OPAC. 450 computers available on campus for general student use. A campuswide network can be accessed from off-campus. Staffed computer lab on campus.

■ **ST. JOHN'S COLLEGE** *F-10*
PO Box 2800
Annapolis, MD 21404
Tel: (410)263-2371
Free: 800-727-9238
Admissions: (410)626-2522
E-mail: admissions@sjca.edu
Web Site: http://www.stjohnscollege.edu/

Description: Independent, comprehensive, coed. Awards bachelor's and master's degrees. Founded 1784. Setting: 36-acre small town campus with easy access to Baltimore and Washington, DC. Endowment: $56.9 million. Educational spending for 2005 fiscal year: $13,479 per student. Total enrollment: 566. Faculty: 78 (71 full-time, 7 part-time). Student-undergrad faculty ratio is 8:1. 494 applied, 76% were admitted. 40% from top 10% of their high school class, 69% from top quarter, 91% from top half. 8 National Merit Scholars. Full-time: 472 students, 46% women, 54% men. Part-time: 2 students, 100% women. Students come from 48 states and territories, 10 other countries, 85% from out-of-state, 1% Native American, 3% Hispanic,

1% black, 3% Asian American or Pacific Islander, 1% international, 2% 25 or older, 87% live on campus, 0% transferred in. Retention: 82% of full-time freshmen returned the following year. Academic area with the most degrees conferred: liberal arts/general studies. Core. Calendar: semesters. Internships. Off campus study at St. John's College (NM).

Entrance Requirements: Options: Peterson's Universal Application, Common Application, electronic application, early admission, deferred admission, international baccalaureate accepted. Required: essay, high school transcript, 2 recommendations. Recommended: interview, SAT or ACT. Required for some: SAT or ACT. Entrance: moderately difficult. Application deadline: Rolling. Notification: continuous.

Costs Per Year: Application fee: $0. Comprehensive fee: $40,451 includes full-time tuition ($32,375), mandatory fees ($200), and college room and board ($7876). Room and board charges vary according to board plan.

Collegiate Environment: Orientation program. Drama-theater group, choral group, marching band, student-run newspaper. Social organizations: 35 open to all; 85% of eligible men and 85% of eligible women are members. Most popular organizations: King William Players, Project Politae, Political Forum, Student Committee on Instruction, Rowing Club. Major annual events: Collegium Musicum, King William Players' Production, Annapolis Cup Croquet Match. Student services: health clinic, personal-psychological counseling. Campus security: 24-hour emergency response devices and patrols, late night transport-escort service, controlled dormitory access. 350 college housing spaces available; all were occupied in 2003-04. Freshmen guaranteed college housing. On-campus residence required through senior year. Option: coed housing available. Greenfield Library plus 1 other with 102,400 books, 412 microform titles, 123 serials, 2,100 audiovisual materials, and an OPAC. Operations spending for 2004 fiscal year: $383,388. 16 computers available on campus for general student use. A campuswide network can be accessed from student residence rooms and from off campus. Staffed computer lab on campus.

■ **ST. MARY'S COLLEGE OF MARYLAND**

18952 East Fisher Rd.
St. Mary's City, MD 20686-3001
Tel: (240)895-2000
Free: 800-492-7181
Admissions: (240)895-5000
Fax: (240)895-5001
E-mail: admissions@smcm.edu
Web Site: http://www.smcm.edu/

Description: State-supported, 4-year, coed. Part of Maryland State Colleges and Universities System. Awards bachelor's degrees. Founded 1840. Setting: 319-acre rural campus. Endowment: $29.6 million. Research spending for 2004 fiscal year: $498,828. Educational spending for 2005 fiscal year: $8019 per student. Total enrollment: 1,964. Student-undergrad faculty ratio is 12:1. 2,200 applied, 68% were admitted. 34% from top 10% of their high school class, 70% from top quarter, 94% from top half. 22 National Merit Scholars, 23 valedictorians. Full-time: 1,849 students, 57% women, 43% men. Part-time: 115 students, 57% women, 43% men. Students come from 36 states and territories, 18% from out-of-state, 0.2% Native American, 3% Hispanic, 8% black, 4% Asian American or Pacific Islander, 1% international, 3% 25 or older, 84% live on campus, 4% transferred in. Retention: 89% of full-time freshmen returned the following year. Academic areas with the most degrees conferred: social sciences; psychology; biological/life sciences. Core. Calendar: semesters. Services for LD students, advanced placement, self-designed majors, freshman honors college, honors program, independent study, double major, summer session for credit, part-time degree program, co-op programs and internships. Off campus study at National Student Exchange. Study abroad program.

Entrance Requirements: Options: Peterson's Universal Application, electronic application, early admission, early decision. Required: essay, high school transcript, minimum 2.0 high school GPA, SAT or ACT. Recommended: 2 recommendations, interview. Entrance: very difficult. Application deadlines: 1/15, 12/1 for early decision plan 1, 1/15 for early decision plan 2. Notification: 4/1, 1/1 for early decision plan 1, 2/15 for early decision plan 2.

Costs Per Year: Application fee: $40. State resident tuition: $9770 full-time, $160 per credit part-time. Nonresident tuition: $19,340 full-time, $160 per credit part-time. Mandatory fees: $1940 full-time. College room and board: $8505. College room only: $4820.

Collegiate Environment: Orientation program. Drama-theater group, choral group, student-run newspaper, radio station. Social organizations: 75 open to all. Most popular organizations: For Goodness Sake (community service), The Point News (student newspaper), FMLA (feminist group), Black Student

Union, Dance Club. Major annual events: World Carnival, Christmas in April (community service), Cardboard Boat Races. Student services: health clinic, personal-psychological counseling. Campus security: 24-hour emergency response devices and patrols, student patrols, late night transport-escort service, controlled dormitory access. College housing designed to accommodate 1,482 students; 1,522 undergraduates lived in college housing during 2003-04. Freshmen guaranteed college housing. Options: coed, men-only, women-only housing available. Baltimore Hall with 157,077 books, 44,816 microform titles, 1,343 serials, 16,463 audiovisual materials, an OPAC, and a Web page. Operations spending for 2004 fiscal year: $1.8 million. 180 computers available on campus for general student use. A campuswide network can be accessed from student residence rooms and from off campus. Staffed computer lab on campus.

■ **SALISBURY UNIVERSITY** *I-15*

1101 Camden Ave.
Salisbury, MD 21801-6837
Tel: (410)543-6000; 888-543-0148
Admissions: (410)543-6161
Fax: (410)548-2587
E-mail: admissions@salisbury.edu
Web Site: http://www.ssu.edu/

Description: State-supported, comprehensive, coed. Part of University System of Maryland. Awards bachelor's and master's degrees. Founded 1925. Setting: 144-acre small town campus. Endowment: $32.5 million. Research spending for 2004 fiscal year: $3.6 million. Educational spending for 2005 fiscal year: $4523 per student. Total enrollment: 7,009. Faculty: 494 (323 full-time, 171 part-time). Student-undergrad faculty ratio is 16:1. 5,296 applied, 57% were admitted. 18% from top 10% of their high school class, 50% from top quarter, 87% from top half. 3 National Merit Scholars, 7 valedictorians. Full-time: 5,798 students, 56% women, 44% men. Part-time: 639 students, 55% women, 45% men. Students come from 30 states and territories, 23 other countries, 14% from out-of-state, 0.3% Native American, 3% Hispanic, 9% black, 2% Asian American or Pacific Islander, 1% international, 8% 25 or older, 46% live on campus, 11% transferred in. Retention: 83% of full-time freshmen returned the following year. Academic areas with the most degrees conferred: business/marketing; education; social sciences. Core. Calendar: 4-1-4. Academic remediation for entering students, ESL program, services for LD students, advanced placement, self-designed majors, honors program, independent study, double major, summer session for credit, part-time degree program, adult/continuing education programs, internships, graduate courses open to undergrads. Off campus study at other units of the University System of Maryland. Study abroad program. ROTC: Army (c).

Entrance Requirements: Options: Common Application, electronic application, early admission, early action, international baccalaureate accepted. Required: high school transcript, minimum 2.0 high school GPA, SAT or ACT. Entrance: moderately difficult. Application deadlines: 1/15, 12/1 for early action. Notification: 3/15, 1/15 for early action.

Costs Per Year: Application fee: $45. State resident tuition: $4814 full-time, $200 per credit hour part-time. Nonresident tuition: $12,492 full-time, $520 per credit hour part-time. Mandatory fees: $1562 full-time, $50 per credit hour part-time. College room and board: $6932. College room only: $3554. Room and board charges vary according to board plan and housing facility.

Collegiate Environment: Orientation program. Drama-theater group, choral group, student-run newspaper, radio station. Social organizations: 104 open to all; national fraternities, national sororities; 5% of eligible men and 5% of eligible women are members. Most popular organizations: Student Government Association, campus radio station, Programming Board, Union of African-American Students. Major annual events: Welcome Week, Spring Fling, Family Weekend. Student services: health clinic, personal-psychological counseling. Campus security: 24-hour emergency response devices and patrols, student patrols, late night transport-escort service, controlled dormitory access. 1,704 college housing spaces available; all were occupied in 2003-04. Freshmen given priority for college housing. Options: coed, men-only, women-only housing available. Blackwell Library plus 1 other with 254,151 books, 747,871 microform titles, 1,271 serials, 4,467 audiovisual materials, an OPAC, and a Web page. Operations spending for 2004 fiscal year: $2.1 million. 275 computers available on campus for general student use. Computer purchase/lease plans available. A

campuswide network can be accessed from student residence rooms and from off campus. Staffed computer lab on campus.

■ **SOJOURNER-DOUGLASS COLLEGE** *D-10*
500 North Caroline St.
Baltimore, MD 21205-1814
Tel: (410)276-0306
Fax: (410)675-1810
Web Site: http://sdc.edu/
Description: Independent, comprehensive, coed. Awards bachelor's and master's degrees (offers only evening and weekend programs). Founded 1980. Setting: 15-acre urban campus. Total enrollment: 1,124. Full-time: 714 students, 85% women, 15% men. Part-time: 346 students, 82% women, 18% men. 0.1% Native American, 1% Hispanic, 98% black, 95% 25 or older. Retention: 78% of full-time freshmen returned the following year. Core. Calendar: trimesters. Academic remediation for entering students, services for LD students, accelerated degree program, self-designed majors, honors program, summer session for credit, part-time degree program, external degree program, adult/continuing education programs, internships.
Entrance Requirements: Options: Common Application, deferred admission. Required: essay, high school transcript, 2 recommendations, interview, resume. Entrance: noncompetitive. Application deadline: Rolling.
Costs Per Year: Tuition: $6540 full-time, $363 per credit part-time. Mandatory fees: $208 full-time, $104 per term part-time. Part-time tuition and fees vary according to course load.
Collegiate Environment: Student services: personal-psychological counseling. College housing not available. 10,000 books and 25 serials. 16 computers available on campus for general student use. A campuswide network can be accessed from off-campus. Staffed computer lab on campus.
Community Environment: The school is located in the heart of Baltimore, which is in the center of Maryland and accessible from every major state highway. The metropolitan area extends into five adjacent counties: Baltimore, Anne Arundel, Carroll, Harford, and Howard. The area has more than 1,000 different employers, primarily in the high technology and service industries. Recreational facilities are ample and can be found both on campus and in several public parks and indoor facilities.

■ **TESST COLLEGE OF TECHNOLOGY (BALTIMORE)** *D-10*
1520 South Caton Ave.
Baltimore, MD 21227-1063
Tel: (410)644-6400
Fax: (410)644-6481
E-mail: ssherwood@tesst.com
Web Site: http://www.tesst.com/
Description: Proprietary, 2-year, coed. Founded 1956.

■ **TESST COLLEGE OF TECHNOLOGY (BELTSVILLE)** *J-4*
4600 Powder Mill Rd.
Beltsville, MD 20705
Tel: (301)937-8448
Fax: (301)937-5327
E-mail: mcolling@tesst.com
Web Site: http://www.tesst.com/
Description: Proprietary, 2-year, coed. Founded 1967.

■ **TESST COLLEGE OF TECHNOLOGY (TOWSON)** *C-10*
803 Glen Eagles Ct.
Towson, MD 21286-2201
Tel: (410)296-5350
Free: 800-48-TESST
Fax: (410)296-5356
E-mail: dmcrae@tesst.com
Web Site: http://www.tesst.com/
Description: Proprietary, 2-year, coed. Awards terminal associate degrees. Founded 1992.
Entrance Requirements: Required: high school transcript, interview. Entrance: noncompetitive.
Collegiate Environment: Student-run newspaper.

■ **TOWSON UNIVERSITY** *C-10*
8000 York Rd.
Towson, MD 21252-0001
Tel: (410)704-2000; 888-4TOWSON
Admissions: (410)704-2113

Fax: (410)704-3030
E-mail: lshulack@towson.edu
Web Site: http://www.towson.edu/
Description: State-supported, university, coed. Part of University System of Maryland. Awards bachelor's, master's, and doctoral degrees and post-master's certificates. Founded 1866. Setting: 321-acre suburban campus with easy access to Baltimore and Washington, DC. Endowment: $4.5 million. Research spending for 2004 fiscal year: $3.5 million. Educational spending for 2005 fiscal year: $4204 per student. Total enrollment: 18,011. Faculty: 1,245 (663 full-time, 582 part-time). Student-undergrad faculty ratio is 17:1. 11,746 applied, 64% were admitted. 24% from top 10% of their high school class, 54% from top quarter, 91% from top half. Full-time: 12,812 students, 62% women, 38% men. Part-time: 1,683 students, 54% women, 46% men. Students come from 45 states and territories, 106 other countries, 18% from out-of-state, 0.3% Native American, 2% Hispanic, 11% black, 4% Asian American or Pacific Islander, 2% international, 12% 25 or older, 24% live on campus, 10% transferred in. Retention: 83% of full-time freshmen returned the following year. Academic areas with the most degrees conferred: business/marketing; education; public administration and social services. Core. Calendar: semesters. Academic remediation for entering students, ESL program, services for LD students, advanced placement, accelerated degree program, self-designed majors, freshman honors college, honors program, independent study, distance learning, double major, summer session for credit, part-time degree program, adult/continuing education programs, co-op programs and internships, graduate courses open to undergrads. Off campus study at all state colleges in Maryland, other institutions of higher education in the Baltimore metropolitan area, members of the National Student Exchange. Study abroad program. ROTC: Army (c), Air Force (c).
Entrance Requirements: Options: Peterson's Universal Application, electronic application, deferred admission, international baccalaureate accepted. Required: high school transcript, SAT or ACT. Recommended: essay, minimum 2.75 high school GPA, recommendations, interview. Required for some: interview. Entrance: moderately difficult. Application deadline: 2/15. Notification: continuous.
Costs Per Year: Application fee: $45. State resident tuition: $5180 full-time, $225 per credit part-time. Nonresident tuition: $14,114 full-time, $528 per credit part-time. Mandatory fees: $1916 full-time, $74 per credit part-time. Full-time tuition and fees vary according to course load. College room and board: $6828. College room only: $3968. Room and board charges vary according to board plan and housing facility.
Collegiate Environment: Orientation program. Drama-theater group, choral group, marching band, student-run newspaper, radio station. Social organizations: 175 open to all; national fraternities, national sororities; 10% of eligible men and 7% of eligible women are members. Most popular organizations: Black Student Union, Student Government Association, Habitat for Humanity, Circle K, University Residence Government. Major annual events: Homecoming Weekend, Welcome Week, Tiger Fest (spring festival). Student services: health clinic, personal-psychological counseling, women's center. Campus security: 24-hour emergency response devices and patrols, late night transport-escort service, controlled dormitory access. College housing designed to accommodate 3,266 students; 3,347 undergraduates lived in college housing during 2003-04. Freshmen guaranteed college housing. Option: coed housing available. Cook Library with 574,096 books, 880,434 microform titles, 4,154 serials, 16,413 audiovisual materials, an OPAC, and a Web page. Operations spending for 2004 fiscal year: $5 million.

■ **UNITED STATES NAVAL ACADEMY** *F-10*
121 Blake Rd.
Annapolis, MD 21402-5000
Tel: (410)293-1000
Admissions: (410)293-4361
Fax: (410)293-4348
Web Site: http://www.usna.edu/
Description: Federally supported, 4-year, coed. Awards bachelor's degrees. Founded 1845. Setting: 329-acre small town campus with easy access to Baltimore and Washington, DC. Endowment: $115.6 million. Total enrollment: 4,422. Student-undergrad faculty ratio is 7:1. 11,259 applied, 13% were admitted. 54% from top 10% of their high school class, 81% from top quarter, 96% from top half. 135 class presidents, 135 student government officers. Full-time: 4,422 students, 18% women, 82% men. Students come from 54 states and territories, 21 other countries, 96% from out-of-state, 2% Native American, 9% Hispanic, 6% black, 5% Asian American or Pacific

Islander, 1% international, 2% 25 or older, 100% live on campus, 0% transferred in. Retention: 96% of full-time freshmen returned the following year. Academic areas with the most degrees conferred: engineering; social sciences; history. Core. Calendar: semesters. Academic remediation for entering students, ESL program, advanced placement, honors program, independent study, double major, summer session for credit.

Entrance Requirements: Required: essay, high school transcript, minimum 2.0 high school GPA, 2 recommendations, interview, authorized nomination, SAT or ACT. Entrance: very difficult. Application deadline: 1/31. Notification: 4/15.

Costs Per Year: Application fee: $0.

Collegiate Environment: Orientation program. Drama-theater group, choral group, marching band, student-run radio station. Social organizations: 75 open to all. Most popular organizations: Mountaineering Club, Semper Fi, Black Studies Club, Midshipmen Action Club, Martial Arts Club. Major annual events: Parents' Weekend, Army-Navy football game, Commissioning Week. Student services: legal services, health clinic, personal-psychological counseling. Campus security: 24-hour emergency response devices and patrols, student patrols, front gate security. 4,500 college housing spaces available; 4,349 were occupied in 2003-04. Freshmen guaranteed college housing. On-campus residence required through senior year. Option: coed housing available. Nimitz Library plus 1 other with 800,000 books, 1,892 serials, and an OPAC. 6,100 computers available on campus for general student use. Computer purchase/lease plans available. A campuswide network can be accessed from student residence rooms and from off campus. Staffed computer lab on campus.

■ **UNIVERSITY OF BALTIMORE** *D-10*
1420 North Charles St.
Baltimore, MD 21201-5779
Tel: (410)837-4200; 877-APPLYUB
Admissions: (410)837-4777
Fax: (410)837-4793
E-mail: admissions@ubmail.ubalt.edu
Web Site: http://www.ubalt.edu/

Description: State-supported, upper-level, coed. Part of University System of Maryland. Awards bachelor's, master's, doctoral, and first professional degrees and post-master's certificates. Founded 1925. Setting: 49-acre urban campus. Endowment: $18.9 million. Research spending for 2004 fiscal year: $3.8 million. Educational spending for 2005 fiscal year: $6369 per student. Total enrollment: 4,987. 1,001 applied, 82% were admitted. Full-time: 1,051 students, 57% women, 43% men. Part-time: 1,066 students, 64% women, 36% men. Students come from 26 states and territories, 62 other countries, 7% from out-of-state, 1% Native American, 2% Hispanic, 33% black, 3% Asian American or Pacific Islander, 1% international, 61% 25 or older, 98% transferred in. Core. Calendar: semesters. Academic remediation for entering students, services for LD students, advanced placement, accelerated degree program, self-designed majors, honors program, independent study, distance learning, summer session for credit, part-time degree program, adult/continuing education programs, co-op programs and internships, graduate courses open to undergrads. Off campus study at University of Maryland Baltimore County, Coppin State College, Morgan State University, Towson University, Bowie State College, Maryland Institute, College of Art. ROTC: Army (c), Air Force (c).

Costs Per Year: Application fee: $35. State resident tuition: $5324 full-time, $243 per credit part-time. Nonresident tuition: $16,904 full-time, $704 per credit part-time. Mandatory fees: $1469 full-time, $27 per credit part-time. Full-time tuition and fees vary according to class time, course load, and degree level. Part-time tuition and fees vary according to class time, course load, and degree level.

Collegiate Environment: Orientation program. Student-run newspaper. Social organizations: 65 open to all; 9% of eligible men and 9% of eligible women are members. Most popular organizations: Psi Chi, APALSA, International Student Association, African Student Association, Forensics Student Association. Major annual events: Semi-Annual Block Party, Speaker Series. Student services: health clinic, personal-psychological counseling. Campus security: 24-hour emergency response devices and patrols, late night transport-escort service. College housing not available. Langsdale Library plus 1 other with 258,747 books, 368,607 microform titles, 10,738 serials, 883 audiovisual materials, an OPAC, and a Web page. Operations spending for 2004 fiscal year: $4 million. 135 computers available on campus for general student use. A campuswide network can be accessed from off-campus. Staffed computer lab on campus.

Community Environment: Baltimore is an important industrial and educational center for the state of Maryland and the regional northeastern

United States. The port has an active international market and foreign trade. Downtown Baltimore has become a popular tourist site; the Inner Harbor complex, including Harborplace and the National Aquarium, is recognized internationally. New stadiums to house the Baltimore Orioles and Baltimore Ravens have been completed at Camden Yards in downtown Baltimore. Pimlico Race Course is the home of the annual Preakness race. University of Baltimore is located in the cultural center of the city, adjacent to the Lyric Opera House, Meyerhoff Symphony Hall and the Maryland Institute of Art.

■ **UNIVERSITY OF MARYLAND, BALTIMORE COUNTY** *D-10*
1000 Hilltop Circle
Baltimore, MD 21250
Tel: (410)455-1000
Free: 800-862-2402
Admissions: (410)455-2291
Fax: (410)455-1210
E-mail: admissions@umbc.edu
Web Site: http://www.umbc.edu/

Description: State-supported, university, coed. Part of University System of Maryland. Awards bachelor's, master's, and doctoral degrees. Founded 1963. Setting: 530-acre suburban campus with easy access to Washington, D.C.. Endowment: $32.7 million. Research spending for 2004 fiscal year: $42.9 million. Educational spending for 2005 fiscal year: $8114 per student. Total enrollment: 11,650. Faculty: 753 (458 full-time, 295 part-time). Student-undergrad faculty ratio is 17:1. 5,229 applied, 71% were admitted. 30% from top 10% of their high school class, 59% from top quarter, 88% from top half. 5 National Merit Scholars. Full-time: 7,980 students, 46% women, 54% men. Part-time: 1,426 students, 49% women, 51% men. Students come from 43 states and territories, 91 other countries, 8% from out-of-state, 0.4% Native American, 4% Hispanic, 14% black, 20% Asian American or Pacific Islander, 4% international, 16% 25 or older, 33% live on campus, 12% transferred in. Retention: 81% of full-time freshmen returned the following year. Academic areas with the most degrees conferred: communication technologies; social sciences; biological/life sciences. Core. Calendar: 4-1-4. Academic remediation for entering students, ESL program, services for LD students, advanced placement, self-designed majors, freshman honors college, honors program, independent study, distance learning, double major, summer session for credit, part-time degree program, external degree program, adult/continuing education programs, co-op programs and internships, graduate courses open to undergrads. Off campus study at Johns Hopkins University, University System of Maryland. Study abroad program. ROTC: Army (c).

Entrance Requirements: Options: Common Application, electronic application, early admission, early action, deferred admission, international baccalaureate accepted. Required: essay, high school transcript, SAT or ACT. Recommended: minimum 3 high school GPA, 2 recommendations. Entrance: moderately difficult. Application deadlines: 2/1, 11/1 for early action. Notification: continuous, 12/15 for early action.

Costs Per Year: Application fee: $50. State resident tuition: $6484 full-time, $270 per credit hour part-time. Nonresident tuition: $14,560 full-time, $606 per credit hour part-time. Mandatory fees: $2036 full-time, $5 per credit hour part-time. College room and board: $8090. College room only: $4930.

Collegiate Environment: Orientation program. Drama-theater group, choral group, student-run newspaper, radio station. Social organizations: 180 open to all; national fraternities, national sororities; 3% of eligible men and 3% of eligible women are members. Most popular organizations: Student Government Association, Student Events Board, Retriever Weekly, Resident Student Association, Black Student Union. Major annual events: Quadmania, Fall Frenzy, Homecoming. Student services: legal services, health clinic, personal-psychological counseling, women's center. Campus security: 24-hour emergency response devices and patrols, late night transport-escort service. 3,780 college housing spaces available; 3,183 were occupied in 2003-04. Freshmen guaranteed college housing. Option: coed housing available. Albin O. Kuhn Library and Gallery plus 1 other with 766,261 books, 1.1 million microform titles, 4,170 serials, 35,659 audiovisual materials, an OPAC, and a Web page. Operations spending for 2004 fiscal year: $6.5 million. 762 computers available on campus for general student use. Computer purchase/lease plans available. A campuswide network can be accessed from student residence rooms and from off campus. Staffed computer lab on campus.

Community Environment: The ultramodern 500-acre campus is in an open-country setting in Catonsville, only minutes from the heart of Baltimore and less than an hour from the nation's capital. Baltimore, just six miles from the campus, is a rich resource for university students. Opportunities for musical, athletic, theatrical, and cultural events abound. The dynamic and dramatic Inner Harbor area features a convention center, the Maryland Science Center, Pier 7 Performing Arts Pavilion, the National Aquarium, and the lively collection of shops and restaurants called Harborplace. The Morris Mechanic Theatre brings Broadway to Baltimore, while the Baltimore Symphony Orchestra and internationally acclaimed artists perform in the striking Meyerhoff Concert Hall. The Walters Art Gallery, the Enoch Pratt Library, and Oriole Park at Camden Yards are also part of the city's rich tradition. Washington, only 32 miles from the campus, offers the student a wealth of academic, cultural, political, and leisure activities.

■ UNIVERSITY OF MARYLAND, COLLEGE PARK K-4

College Park, MD 20742
Tel: (301)405-1000
Free: 800-422-5867
Admissions: (301)314-8385
Fax: (301)314-9693
E-mail: um-admit@uga.umd.edu
Web Site: http://www.maryland.edu/

Description: State-supported, university, coed. Part of University System of Maryland. Awards bachelor's, master's, doctoral, and first professional degrees and post-master's certificates. Founded 1856. Setting: 3,688-acre suburban campus with easy access to Baltimore and Washington, DC. Endowment: $329.4 million. Research spending for 2004 fiscal year: $372 million. Educational spending for 2005 fiscal year: $10,834 per student. Total enrollment: 35,300. Faculty: 2,070 (1,508 full-time, 562 part-time). Student-undergrad faculty ratio is 19:1. 22,428 applied, 49% were admitted. 50% from top 10% of their high school class, 83% from top quarter, 99% from top half. 112 National Merit Scholars. Full-time: 23,226 students, 49% women, 51% men. Part-time: 2,147 students, 46% women, 54% men. Students come from 54 states and territories, 159 other countries, 24% from out-of-state, 0.4% Native American, 6% Hispanic, 13% black, 14% Asian American or Pacific Islander, 2% international, 7% 25 or older, 39% live on campus, 8% transferred in. Retention: 93% of full-time freshmen returned the following year. Academic areas with the most degrees conferred: social sciences; business/marketing; engineering. Core. Calendar: semesters. Academic remediation for entering students, ESL program, services for LD students, advanced placement, accelerated degree program, self-designed majors, honors program, independent study, distance learning, double major, summer session for credit, part-time degree program, external degree program, adult/continuing education programs, co-op programs and internships, graduate courses open to undergrads. Off campus study at 140 members of the National Student Exchange. Study abroad program. ROTC: Army, Naval (c), Air Force.

Entrance Requirements: Options: early admission, early action, international baccalaureate accepted. Required: essay, high school transcript, 1 recommendation, SAT or ACT. Recommended: 2 recommendations. Required for some: resume of activities, auditions. Entrance: moderately difficult. Application deadlines: 1/20, 12/1 for early action. Notification: continuous until 4/1, 2/15 for early action. Preference given to state residents.

Costs Per Year: Application fee: $55. State resident tuition: $6566 full-time, $273 per credit hour part-time. Nonresident tuition: $18,890 full-time, $787 per credit hour part-time. Mandatory fees: $1255 full-time, $288 per term part-time. Part-time tuition and fees vary according to course load. College room and board: $8075. College room only: $4784. Room and board charges vary according to board plan.

Collegiate Environment: Orientation program. Drama-theater group, choral group, marching band, student-run newspaper, radio station. Social organizations: 515 open to all; national fraternities, national sororities; 9% of eligible men and 11% of eligible women are members. Most popular organizations: Student Government Association, Residence Hall Association, Black Student Union, Asian-American Student Union/Jewish Student Union, Commuter Students Association. Major annual events: First Look Fair, All-Niter, Art Attack. Student services: legal services, health clinic, personal-psychological counseling, women's center. Campus security: 24-hour emergency response devices and patrols, student patrols, late night transport-escort service, controlled dormitory access, campus police, video camera surveillance. 10,771 college housing spaces available; all were occupied in 2003-04. Freshmen guaranteed college housing. Options: coed, women-only housing available. McKeldin Library plus 6 others with 3 million books, 541,175 microform titles, 34,091 serials, 244,911 audiovisual materials, an OPAC, and a Web page. Operations spending for 2004 fiscal year: $21.3 million. 773 computers available on campus for general student use.

Computer purchase/lease plans available. A campuswide network can be accessed from student residence rooms and from off campus. Staffed computer lab on campus.

■ UNIVERSITY OF MARYLAND EASTERN SHORE J-14

Princess Anne, MD 21853-1299
Tel: (410)651-2200
Admissions: (410)651-8410
Fax: (410)651-7922
Web Site: http://www.umes.edu/

Description: State-supported, university, coed. Part of University System of Maryland. Awards bachelor's, master's, and doctoral degrees. Founded 1886. Setting: 700-acre rural campus. Total enrollment: 3,762. 3,714 applied, 58% were admitted. Full-time: 2,902 students, 60% women, 40% men. Part-time: 424 students, 54% women, 46% men. Students come from 30 states and territories, 50 other countries, 28% from out-of-state, 0.4% Native American, 1% Hispanic, 76% black, 2% Asian American or Pacific Islander, 11% international, 13% 25 or older, 60% live on campus, 4% transferred in. Retention: 69% of full-time freshmen returned the following year. Core. Calendar: semesters. Academic remediation for entering students, services for LD students, advanced placement, accelerated degree program, self-designed majors, honors program, summer session for credit, part-time degree program, adult/continuing education programs, co-op programs and internships, graduate courses open to undergrads. Off campus study at Salisbury State University.

Entrance Requirements: Options: Peterson's Universal Application, Common Application, electronic application, early admission, early action, deferred admission. Required: essay, high school transcript, minimum 2.5 high school GPA, 2 recommendations, SAT or ACT, ACCUPLACER. Recommended: interview. Entrance: moderately difficult. Application deadlines: 7/15, 11/15 for early action. Preference given to state residents.

Costs Per Year: Application fee: $25. State resident tuition: $4112 full-time, $171 per credit hour part-time. Nonresident tuition: $10,268 full-time, $371 per credit hour part-time. Mandatory fees: $1696 full-time, $40 per term part-time. Full-time tuition and fees vary according to course load. Part-time tuition and fees vary according to course load. College room and board: $6130. College room only: $3430. Room and board charges vary according to board plan and housing facility.

Collegiate Environment: Orientation program. Drama-theater group, choral group, student-run newspaper. Social organizations: national fraternities, national sororities, local fraternities, local sororities; 25% of eligible men and 30% of eligible women are members. Major annual events: homecoming, Spring Fest, Spring Convocation. Student services: health clinic, personal-psychological counseling. Campus security: 24-hour emergency response devices and patrols, student patrols, late night transport-escort service, controlled dormitory access. 2,200 college housing spaces available; 1,900 were occupied in 2003-04. Options: coed, men-only, women-only housing available. Frederick Douglass Library with 150,000 books, 1,260 serials, an OPAC, and a Web page. 120 computers available on campus for general student use. Computer purchase/lease plans available. A campuswide network can be accessed. Staffed computer lab on campus.

■ UNIVERSITY OF MARYLAND UNIVERSITY COLLEGE K-4

3501 University Blvd. East
Adelphi, MD 20783
Tel: (301)985-7000
Fax: (301)985-7678
Web Site: http://www.umuc.edu/

Description: State-supported, comprehensive, coed. Part of University System of Maryland. Awards associate, bachelor's, master's, and doctoral degrees (offers primarily part-time evening and weekend degree programs at more than 30 off-campus locations in Maryland and the Washington, DC area, and more than 180 military communities in Europe and Asia with military enrollment not reflected in this profile; associate of arts program available to military students only). Founded 1947. Setting: suburban campus with easy access to Washington, DC. Total enrollment: 28,374. 950 applied, 100% were admitted. Full-time: 2,779 students, 62% women, 38% men. Part-time: 17,078 students, 57% women, 43% men. Students come from 54 states and territories, 41 other countries, 33% from out-of-state, 1% Native American, 5% Hispanic, 34% black, 5% Asian American or Pacific Islander, 2% international, 83% 25 or older, 24% transferred in. Core. Calendar: semesters. Services for LD students, advanced placement, accelerated degree program, distance learning, double major, summer session for credit, part-time degree program, external degree program, adult/continuing education programs, co-op programs. Off campus study.

Entrance Requirements: Open admission. Options: electronic application, deferred admission. Required: high school transcript. Entrance: noncompetitive. Application deadline: Rolling. Notification: continuous.

Costs Per Year: Application fee: $30. State resident tuition: $5520 full-time, $230 per semester hour part-time. Nonresident tuition: $10,152 full-time, $423 per semester hour part-time. Mandatory fees: $120 full-time, $5 per semester hour part-time.

Collegiate Environment: Campus security: 24-hour emergency response devices and patrols, late night transport-escort service. College housing not available. Information and Library Services plus 1 other with 5,807 books, 31 serials, an OPAC, and a Web page. 375 computers available on campus for general student use. A campuswide network can be accessed from off-campus. Staffed computer lab on campus.

Community Environment: The administrative site is located at College Park, a small town of 25,000. Programs are offered at more than 30 locations throughout Maryland, Northern Virginia, and the Washington, D.C. area.

■ UNIVERSITY OF PHOENIX-MARYLAND CAMPUS *D-9*

8830 Stanford Blvd., Ste. 100
Columbia, MD 21045-5424
Tel: (410)872-9001
Free: 800-228-7240
Admissions: (480)557-1712
Web Site: http://www.phoenix.edu/

Description: Proprietary, comprehensive, coed. Awards bachelor's and master's degrees. Setting: urban campus. Total enrollment: 2,028. Faculty: 218 (9 full-time, 209 part-time). Student-undergrad faculty ratio is 11:1. 98 applied. Full-time: 1,586 students, 60% women, 40% men. 0.3% Native American, 1% Hispanic, 14% black, 1% Asian American or Pacific Islander, 19% international, 94% 25 or older. Academic areas with the most degrees conferred: business/marketing; computer and information sciences. Core. Calendar: continuous. Advanced placement, accelerated degree program, independent study, distance learning, external degree program, adult/continuing education programs, graduate courses open to undergrads.

Entrance Requirements: Open admission. Option: deferred admission. Required: 1 recommendation. Required for some: high school transcript. Entrance: noncompetitive. Application deadline: Rolling.

Costs Per Year: Application fee: $110. Tuition: $11,950 full-time, $398 per credit part-time. Mandatory fees: $560 full-time, $70 per course part-time. Full-time tuition and fees vary according to program.

Collegiate Environment: College housing not available. University Library with 444 books, 666 serials, an OPAC, and a Web page. System-wide operations spending for 2004 fiscal year: $3.2 million.

■ VILLA JULIE COLLEGE

Green Spring Valley Rd.
Stevenson, MD 21153
Tel: (410)486-7000; 877-468-3852
Admissions: (410)486-7001
E-mail: admissions@mail.vjc.edu
Web Site: http://www.vjc.edu/

Description: Independent, comprehensive, coed. Awards associate, bachelor's, and master's degrees. Founded 1952. Setting: 60-acre suburban campus with easy access to Baltimore. Total enrollment: 2,956. Faculty: 349 (93 full-time, 256 part-time). Student-undergrad faculty ratio is 14:1. 2,166 applied, 70% were admitted. 17% from top 10% of their high school class, 42% from top quarter, 78% from top half. 3 valedictorians. Full-time: 2,304 students, 70% women, 30% men. Part-time: 503 students, 78% women, 22% men. Students come from 13 states and territories, 9 other countries, 4% from out-of-state, 0.3% Native American, 1% Hispanic, 15% black, 3% Asian American or Pacific Islander, 0.3% international, 19% 25 or older, 26% live on campus, 7% transferred in. Retention: 79% of full-time freshmen returned the following year. Academic areas with the most degrees conferred: health professions and related sciences; business/marketing; computer and information sciences. Core. Calendar: semesters. Academic remediation for entering students, ESL program, services for LD students, advanced placement, accelerated degree program, self-designed majors, freshman honors college, honors program, independent study, distance learning, double major, summer session for credit, part-time degree program, adult/continuing education programs, co-op programs and internships, graduate courses open to undergrads. Off campus study at Chesapeake Community College, Anne Arundel Community College, Howard Community College. Study abroad program. ROTC: Army (c).

Entrance Requirements: Options: Peterson's Universal Application, electronic application, early admission, deferred admission, international baccalaureate accepted. Required: essay, high school transcript, 2 recommendations, SAT or ACT. Recommended: interview. Entrance: moderately difficult. Application deadline: 3/1. Notification: continuous.

Costs Per Year: Application fee: $25. Comprehensive fee: $25,222 includes full-time tuition ($14,674), mandatory fees ($1000), and college room and board ($9548). College room only: $6550. Room and board charges vary according to board plan and housing facility. Part-time tuition: $415 per credit. Part-time mandatory fees: $75 per term.

Collegiate Environment: Orientation program. Drama-theater group, choral group, student-run newspaper. Social organizations: 30 open to all; national sororities; 2% of women are members. Most popular organizations: Student Government Association, Wilderness Club, Black Student Union, National Student Nurses Association, Phi Sigma. Major annual events: Welcome Picnic, SGA Haunted Trail and Bonfire, BSU Latin Dance. Student services: personal-psychological counseling. Campus security: 24-hour emergency response devices, late night transport-escort service, controlled dormitory access, patrols by trained security personnel during campus hours. College housing designed to accommodate 548 students; 550 undergraduates lived in college housing during 2003-04. Freshmen given priority for college housing. Options: men-only, women-only housing available. Villa Julie College Library with 64,930 books, 147,735 microform titles, 15,503 serials, 2,603 audiovisual materials, an OPAC, and a Web page. 300 computers available on campus for general student use. A campuswide network can be accessed from student residence rooms and from off campus. Staffed computer lab on campus.

Community Environment: Located in the open countryside of Baltimore County, 20 minutes from the center of urban Baltimore, the college offers a country setting with city conveniences.

■ WASHINGTON BIBLE COLLEGE

6511 Princess Garden Parkway
Lanham, MD 20706-3599
Tel: (301)552-1400; 877-793-7227
Fax: (301)552-2775
E-mail: admissions@bible.edu
Web Site: http://www.bible.edu/

Description: Independent nondenominational, 4-year, coed. Administratively affiliated with Capital Bible Seminary. Awards associate and bachelor's degrees. Founded 1938. Setting: 63-acre suburban campus with easy access to Washington, DC. Total enrollment: 331. 167 applied, 65% were admitted. Students come from 14 states and territories, 9 other countries, 24% from out-of-state, 0% Native American, 2% Hispanic, 39% black, 8% Asian American or Pacific Islander, 2% international, 63% 25 or older, 28% live on campus. Retention: 70% of full-time freshmen returned the following year. Core. Calendar: semesters. Academic remediation for entering students, ESL program, advanced placement, accelerated degree program, double major, summer session for credit, part-time degree program, adult/continuing education programs, co-op programs and internships. Off campus study at New Antioch Baptist Church, Randallstown, MD.

Entrance Requirements: Options: early admission, deferred admission. Required: essay, high school transcript, 2 recommendations, Christian testimony, SAT or ACT. Required for some: interview. Entrance: moderately difficult. Application deadline: 1/9. Notification: continuous until 8/15.

Costs Per Year: Application fee: $25. Comprehensive fee: $22,690 includes full-time tuition ($16,000), mandatory fees ($450), and college room and board ($6240). College room only: $3000. Full-time tuition and fees vary according to course load and location. Room and board charges vary according to board plan. Part-time tuition: $350 per credit. Part-time tuition varies according to course load and location.

Collegiate Environment: Orientation program. Drama-theater group, choral group. Most popular organizations: Student Missions Fellowship, school choir and ensemble, Korean Student Fellowship. Major annual events: homecoming, Christmas banquet. Student services: health clinic, personal-psychological counseling. Campus security: 24-hour patrols, student patrols, late night transport-escort service, secured campus entrances, trained guards on duty. 250 college housing spaces available; 120 were occupied in 2003-04. Freshmen given priority for college housing. On-campus residence required through senior year. Options: men-only, women-only housing available. Oyer Memorial Library plus 1 other with 78,000 books, 4,640 microform titles, 525 serials, 3,824 audiovisual materials, an OPAC, and a Web page. 25 computers available on campus for general student use. Staffed computer lab on campus.

Community Environment: Washington Bible College is 25 minutes outside of Washington, D.C., and within 30 minutes of historic Annapolis and Baltimore's Inner Harbor, making metropolitan recreational and cultural facilities easily accessible.

■ **WASHINGTON COLLEGE** *D-12*
300 Washington Ave.
Chestertown, MD 21620-1197
Tel: (410)778-2800
Free: 800-422-1782
Admissions: (410)778-7700
Fax: (410)778-7287
E-mail: admissions_office@washcoll.edu
Web Site: http://www.washcoll.edu/
Description: Independent, comprehensive, coed. Awards bachelor's and master's degrees. Founded 1782. Setting: 120-acre small town campus with easy access to Baltimore and Washington, DC. Endowment: $125.5 million. Research spending for 2004 fiscal year: $1.3 million. Educational spending for 2005 fiscal year: $8519 per student. Total enrollment: 1,412. Faculty: 144 (93 full-time, 51 part-time). Student-undergrad faculty ratio is 12:1. 2,223 applied, 59% were admitted. 28% from top 10% of their high school class, 66% from top quarter, 93% from top half. Full-time: 1,312 students, 61% women, 39% men. Part-time: 29 students, 83% women, 17% men. Students come from 36 states and territories, 40 other countries, 56% from out-of-state, 0.2% Native American, 1% Hispanic, 4% black, 1% Asian American or Pacific Islander, 3% international, 2% 25 or older, 80% live on campus, 3% transferred in. Retention: 84% of full-time freshmen returned the following year. Academic areas with the most degrees conferred: social sciences; business/marketing; English. Core. Calendar: semesters. ESL program, services for LD students, advanced placement, self-designed majors, independent study, double major, part-time degree program, internships, graduate courses open to undergrads. Off campus study. Study abroad program.
Entrance Requirements: Options: Peterson's Universal Application, Common Application, electronic application, early decision, early action, deferred admission, international baccalaureate accepted. Required: essay, high school transcript, 1 recommendation, SAT or ACT. Recommended: interview. Required for some: interview. Entrance: moderately difficult. Application deadlines: 3/1, 11/15 for early decision, 12/1 for early action. Notification: continuous, 12/15 for early decision, 12/20 for early action.
Costs Per Year: Application fee: $45. Comprehensive fee: $34,990 includes full-time tuition ($28,230), mandatory fees ($560), and college room and board ($6200). College room only: $3000. Full-time tuition and fees vary according to program and reciprocity agreements. Room and board charges vary according to board plan and housing facility. Part-time tuition: $4705 per course. Part-time tuition varies according to course load and program.
Collegiate Environment: Orientation program. Drama-theater group, choral group, student-run newspaper. Social organizations: 50 open to all; national fraternities, national sororities; 25% of eligible men and 25% of eligible women are members. Most popular organizations: Writers Union, Student Government Association, Hands Out, Omicron Delta Kappa, Dale Adams Society. Major annual events: Fall Weekend, Birthday Ball, May Day. Student services: health clinic, personal-psychological counseling. Campus security: 24-hour emergency response devices and patrols, student patrols, late night transport-escort service, controlled dormitory access. 1,004 college housing spaces available; all were occupied in 2003-04. Freshmen guaranteed college housing. On-campus residence required through sophomore year. Options: coed, men-only housing available. Clifton M. Miller Library with 243,030 books, 247,626 microform titles, 4,667 serials, 6,114 audiovisual materials, an OPAC, and a Web page. Operations spend-

ing for 2004 fiscal year: $1.3 million. 150 computers available on campus for general student use. Computer purchase/lease plans available. A campuswide network can be accessed from student residence rooms and from off campus. Staffed computer lab on campus.
Community Environment: Chestertown is on the eastern shore of Maryland, 40 miles from Chesapeake Bay Bridge. The community facilities include churches and numerous civic and service organizations. Boating, fishing and hunting are some of the outdoor sports of the area.

■ **WOR-WIC COMMUNITY COLLEGE** *I-15*
32000 Campus Dr.
Salisbury, MD 21804
Tel: (410)334-2800
Admissions: (410)334-2895
Web Site: http://www.worwic.edu/
Description: State and locally supported, 2-year, coed. Part of Maryland State Community Colleges System. Awards certificates, transfer associate, and terminal associate degrees. Founded 1976. Setting: 202-acre small town campus. Endowment: $4 million. Educational spending for 2005 fiscal year: $2987 per student. Total enrollment: 3,043. Student-undergrad faculty ratio is 20:1. 1,075 applied, 100% were admitted. Full-time: 970 students, 61% women, 39% men. Part-time: 2,073 students, 70% women, 30% men. Students come from 15 states and territories, 2% from out-of-state, 0.3% Native American, 2% Hispanic, 25% black, 2% Asian American or Pacific Islander, 0% international, 47% 25 or older, 8% transferred in. Core. Calendar: semesters. Academic remediation for entering students, ESL program, services for LD students, advanced placement, accelerated degree program, honors program, independent study, distance learning, double major, summer session for credit, part-time degree program, adult/continuing education programs, internships.
Entrance Requirements: Open admission except for emergency medical services, nursing and radiologic technology programs. Option: early admission. Recommended: high school transcript. Required for some: ACT. Entrance: noncompetitive. Application deadline: Rolling.
Costs Per Year: Application fee: $0. Area resident tuition: $2250 full-time, $75 per credit hour part-time. State resident tuition: $5700 full-time, $190 per credit hour part-time. Nonresident tuition: $6630 full-time, $221 per credit hour part-time. Mandatory fees: $86 full-time, $2 per credit hour part-time, $13 per term part-time.
Collegiate Environment: Orientation program. Drama-theater group, choral group, student-run newspaper. Social organizations: 9 open to all. Most popular organizations: Student Government Association, Arts Club, Bioneer Club, Future Educators of America Club, student newspaper. Major annual events: Fall Fest, Dolphin Days, Wellness Day. Student services: personal-psychological counseling. Campus security: 24-hour emergency response devices, late night transport-escort service, patrols by trained security personnel 9 a.m. to midnight. College housing not available. Patricia M. Hazel Media Center plus 2 others with 25 books, 37 serials, 272 audiovisual materials, and a Web page. Operations spending for 2004 fiscal year: $258,015. 478 computers available on campus for general student use. A campuswide network can be accessed from off-campus. Staffed computer lab on campus.

■ **YESHIVA COLLEGE OF THE NATION'S CAPITAL** *E-8*
1216 Arcola Ave.
Silver Spring, MD 20902
Tel: (301)593-2534
Fax: (301)949-7040
Description: Independent Jewish, 4-year.

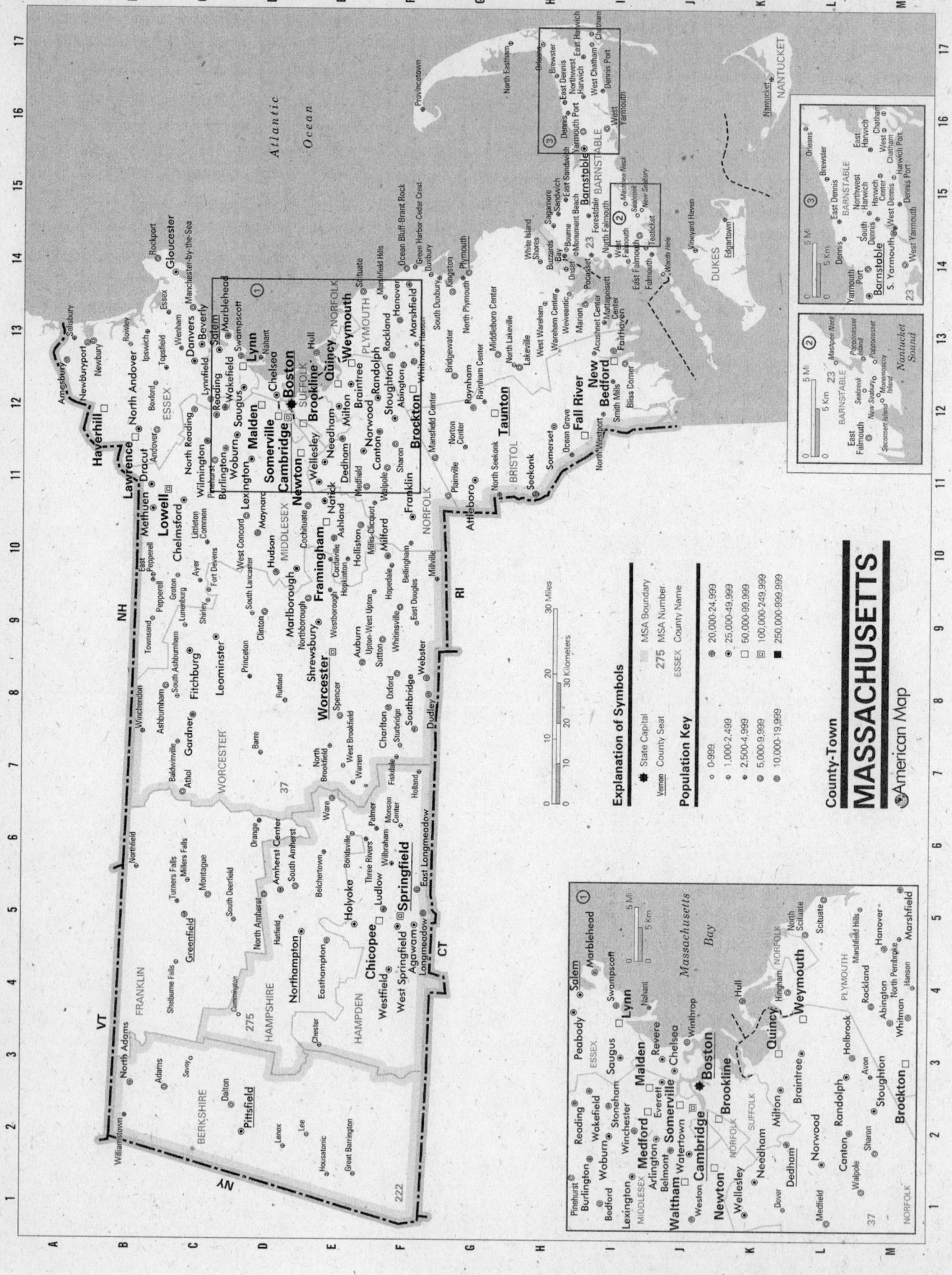

MASSACHUSETTS

County-Town

American Map

Explanation of Symbols

* State Capital
☐ County Seat

Vernon County Seat
ESSEX County Name

MSA Boundary
275 MSA Number

Population Key

* 0-999
⊙ 1,000-2,499
⊙ 2,500-4,999
⊙ 5,000-9,999
⊙ 10,000-19,999

⊙ 20,000-24,999
⊙ 25,000-49,999
⊙ 50,000-99,999
■ 100,000-249,999
■ 250,000-999,999

■ **AMERICAN INTERNATIONAL COLLEGE** *F-5*

1000 State St.
Springfield, MA 01109-3189
Tel: (413)737-7000
Admissions: (413)205-3201
Fax: (413)737-2803
E-mail: inquiry@acad.aic.edu
Web Site: http://www.aic.edu/

Description: Independent, comprehensive, coed. Awards associate, bachelor's, master's, and doctoral degrees and post-master's certificates. Founded 1885. Setting: 58-acre urban campus. Endowment: $7.4 million. Educational spending for 2005 fiscal year: $5132 per student. Total enrollment: 1,815. Faculty: 159 (72 full-time, 87 part-time). Student-undergrad faculty ratio is 12:1. 1,333 applied, 84% were admitted. 15% from top 10% of their high school class, 25% from top quarter, 90% from top half. 7 class presidents, 2 valedictorians, 107 student government officers. Full-time: 1,214 students, 58% women, 42% men. Part-time: 184 students, 65% women, 35% men. Students come from 30 states and territories, 52 other countries, 42% from out-of-state, 0.4% Native American, 9% Hispanic, 25% black, 2% Asian American or Pacific Islander, 1% international, 12% 25 or older, 55% live on campus, 13% transferred in. Retention: 60% of full-time freshmen returned the following year. Academic areas with the most degrees conferred: business/marketing; education; health professions and related sciences; security and protective services; psychology; liberal arts/general studies. Core. Calendar: semesters. Academic remediation for entering students, ESL program, services for LD students, advanced placement, accelerated degree program, freshman honors college, honors program, independent study, double major, summer session for credit, part-time degree program, adult/continuing education programs, internships, graduate courses open to undergrads. Off campus study at Cooperating Colleges of Greater Springfield. Study abroad program. ROTC: Army (c), Air Force (c).

Entrance Requirements: Options: Common Application, electronic application, early admission, deferred admission, international baccalaureate accepted. Required: high school transcript, 1 recommendation, SAT or ACT. Recommended: essay, interview. Required for some: interview. Entrance: moderately difficult. Application deadline: Rolling. Notification: continuous.

Costs Per Year: Application fee: $20. Comprehensive fee: $30,260 includes full-time tuition ($20,990) and college room and board ($9270). Part-time tuition: $470 per credit.

Collegiate Environment: Orientation program. Drama-theater group, choral group, student-run newspaper, radio station. Social organizations: 40 open to all; local fraternities, local sororities; 2% of eligible men and 3% of eligible women are members. Most popular organizations: Student Activities Committee, Golden Key Society, PRIDE (Persons Ready in Defense of Ebony), student government. Major annual events: homecoming, Model Congress, Press Forum. Student services: health clinic, personal-psychological counseling. Campus security: 24-hour emergency response devices and patrols, student patrols, late night transport-escort service, controlled dormitory access. 600 college housing spaces available; 562 were occupied in 2003-04. Freshmen guaranteed college housing. Options: coed, women-only housing available. James J. Shea Jr. Library with 118,000 books, 390 serials, an OPAC, and a Web page. Operations spending for 2004 fiscal year: $566,354. 125 computers available on campus for general student use. A campuswide network can be accessed. Staffed computer lab on campus.

Community Environment: Springfield is a city of 165,000 that offers a multitude of activities for college students, including a quadrangle of museums, the Stage West Theater Company, and the Springfield Civic Center.

■ **AMHERST COLLEGE** *D-5*

PO Box 5000
Amherst, MA 01002-5000
Tel: (413)542-2000
Admissions: (413)542-2328
Fax: (413)542-2040
E-mail: admissions@amherst.edu
Web Site: http://www.amherst.edu/

Description: Independent, 4-year, coed. Awards bachelor's degrees. Founded 1821. Setting: 1,000-acre small town campus. Endowment: $1.2 billion. Research spending for 2004 fiscal year: $3.1 million. Educational spending for 2005 fiscal year: $15,732 per student. Total enrollment: 1,623. Student-undergrad faculty ratio is 8:1. 6,284 applied, 19% were admitted. 87% from top 10% of their high school class, 95% from top quarter, 100% from top half. 98 National Merit Scholars, 44 valedictorians. Full-time: 1,623 students, 48% women, 52% men. Students come from 52 states and territories, 31 other countries, 87% from out-of-state, 0.2% Native American, 6% Hispanic, 10% black, 13% Asian American or Pacific Islander, 7% international, 0% 25 or older, 98% live on campus, 1% transferred in. Retention: 97% of full-time freshmen returned the following year. Academic areas with the most degrees conferred: public administration and social services; English; foreign languages and literature; psychology; visual and performing arts; history. Calendar: semesters. Self-designed majors, honors program, independent study, double major. Off campus study at Five Colleges, Inc., Twelve College Exchange Program. Study abroad program.

Entrance Requirements: Options: Common Application, electronic application, early admission, early decision, deferred admission. Required: essay, high school transcript, 3 recommendations, SAT and SAT Subject Tests or ACT. Entrance: most difficult. Application deadlines: 1/1, 11/15 for early decision. Notification: 4/5, 12/15 for early decision.

Costs Per Year: Application fee: $55. Comprehensive fee: $41,590 includes full-time tuition ($32,395), mandatory fees ($610), and college room and board ($8585). College room only: $4600.

Collegiate Environment: Orientation program. Drama-theater group, choral group, student-run newspaper, radio station. Social organizations: 100 open to all. Most popular organizations: choral groups, WAMH (campus radio station), OUTREACH (community service), literary magazines, The Amherst Student (school newspaper). Major annual events: homecoming, Casino Night, Newport Jazz. Student services: health clinic, personal-psychological counseling, women's center. Campus security: 24-hour emergency response devices and patrols, student patrols, late night transport-escort service, controlled dormitory access. 1,600 college housing spaces available; 1,550 were occupied in 2003-04. Freshmen guaranteed college housing. On-campus residence required in freshman year. Option: coed housing available. Robert Frost Library plus 5 others with 1 million books, 530,038 microform titles, 10,632 serials, 45,139 audiovisual materials, an OPAC, and a Web page. Operations spending for 2004 fiscal year: $4.9 million. 182 computers available on campus for general student use. Computer purchase/lease plans available. A campuswide network can be accessed from student residence rooms and from off campus. Staffed computer lab on campus.

Community Environment: Well-known American poets Emily Dickinson, Robert Frost and Eugene Field, and author Ray Stannard Baker (David Grayson) all lived in Amherst. Located on eastern edge of Connecticut Valley, the town has mean winter temperature of 25.2 degrees, and summer, 72 degrees. Annual rainfall is 43.8 inches. Rail and bus service is available. Free 5-college bus system connects all five institutions. Recreation provided at Mt. Sugarloaf and Mt. Tom Reservation nearby. Town has theatres, golf, tennis, fishing, and ice skating. Community opera performs annually. Nearby are the Pelham Hills, where Daniel Shays organized his rebellion; Deerfield, with its Bloody Brook, so named after a 17th-century clash between Indians and settlers; the Holyoke Range; and byways reminiscent of colonial days. Tobacco farms and apple orchards dot the Connecticut River valley, and throughout the neighboring hills are many opportunities for hiking, canoeing, and skiing amid the small villages, farms, and abandoned factories of another age. An exciting community lies in the midst of this bucolic setting. Amherst students and townspeople alike thrive on the contemporary vitality of a major academic center, since both Hampshire College and the University of Massachusetts are also located in Amherst, with Smith and Mount Holyoke Colleges nearby. The resulting concentration of students, teachers, practicing artists, and visiting speakers makes the area a hub of scholarship and creativity. It has even been said that, after Boston, the Pioneer Valley offers the richest array of cultural events in New England.

■ ANNA MARIA COLLEGE *E-8*
Sunset Ln.
Paxton, MA 01612
Tel: (508)849-3300
Free: 800-344-4586
Admissions: (508)849-3360
Web Site: http://www.annamaria.edu/

Description: Independent Roman Catholic, comprehensive, coed. Awards associate, bachelor's, and master's degrees and post-master's certificates. Founded 1946. Setting: 180-acre rural campus with easy access to Boston. Endowment: $1.3 million. Educational spending for 2005 fiscal year: $3335 per student. Total enrollment: 1,042. Faculty: 170 (38 full-time, 132 part-time). Student-undergrad faculty ratio is 9:1. 557 applied, 90% were admitted. 4% from top 10% of their high school class, 15% from top quarter, 47% from top half. Full-time: 540 students, 62% women, 38% men. Part-time: 205 students, 53% women, 47% men. Students come from 11 states and territories, 21% from out-of-state, 0.4% Native American, 3% Hispanic, 2% black, 1% Asian American or Pacific Islander, 1% international, 3% 25 or older, 60% live on campus, 2% transferred in. Retention: 59% of full-time freshmen returned the following year. Academic areas with the most degrees conferred: security and protective services; public administration and social services; business/marketing. Core. Calendar: semesters. Academic remediation for entering students, services for LD students, advanced placement, accelerated degree program, self-designed majors, independent study, double major, summer session for credit, part-time degree program, adult/continuing education programs, co-op programs and internships, graduate courses open to undergrads. Off campus study at Colleges of Worcester Consortium. Study abroad program. ROTC: Air Force (c).

Entrance Requirements: Options: Peterson's Universal Application, Common Application, deferred admission, international baccalaureate accepted. Required: essay, high school transcript, 2 recommendations, SAT and SAT Subject Tests or ACT. Recommended: minimum 2.0 high school GPA, interview. Required for some: audition for music programs, portfolio for art programs. Entrance: moderately difficult. Application deadline: Rolling. Notification: continuous.

Costs Per Year: Application fee: $40. Comprehensive fee: $29,815 includes full-time tuition ($19,900), mandatory fees ($1980), and college room and board ($7935). Part-time tuition: $663.33 per credit hour.

Collegiate Environment: Orientation program. Drama-theater group, choral group. Social organizations: 25 open to all. Most popular organizations: Student Government Association, Drama Club, Ski Club, chorus, Criminal Justice Club. Major annual events: Spring Weekend, Winter Semi-Formal, Harvest Weekend. Student services: health clinic, personal-psychological counseling. Campus security: 24-hour emergency response devices and patrols, late night transport-escort service, controlled dormitory access. 397 college housing spaces available; 329 were occupied in 2003-04. Freshmen guaranteed college housing. Option: coed housing available. Mondor-Eagen Library with 79,039 books, 1,738 microform titles, 318 serials, 895 audiovisual materials, and an OPAC. Operations spending for 2004 fiscal year: $302,994. 59 computers available on campus for general student use. A campuswide network can be accessed from student residence rooms and from off campus.

Community Environment: Paxton is located in the geographical center of Massachusetts, eight miles northwest of Worcester and a one-hour drive from Boston or Providence. Summer and winter sports are available in the area. Excellent job opportunities are available in the immediate area.

■ THE ART INSTITUTE OF BOSTON AT LESLEY UNIVERSITY *D-12*
700 Beacon St.
Boston, MA 02215-2598
Tel: (617)585-6600
Admissions: (617)585-6701
Fax: (617)437-1226
E-mail: broth@lesley.edu
Web Site: http://www.aiboston.edu/

Description: Independent, comprehensive, coed. Part of Education Management Corporation. Administratively affiliated with Lesley University. Awards bachelor's and master's degrees. Founded 1912. Setting: 1-acre urban campus. Endowment: $43.9 million. Research spending for 2004 fiscal year: $887,653. System-wide educational spending for 2005 fiscal year: $10,882 per student. Total enrollment: 6,521. 885 applied, 78% were admitted. 20% from top 10% of their high school class, 43% from top quarter, 83% from top half. 4 class presidents, 1 valedictorian, 37 student government officers. Full-time: 964 students, 80% women, 20% men. Part-time: 78 students, 77% women, 23% men. Students come from 34 states and territories, 24 other countries, 41% from out-of-state, 0.5% Native American, 4% Hispanic, 7% black, 5% Asian American or Pacific Islander, 5% international, 8% 25 or older, 66% live on campus, 11% transferred in. Retention: 67% of full-time freshmen returned the following year. Core. Calendar: semesters. Academic remediation for entering students, ESL program, services for LD students, advanced placement, accelerated degree program, self-designed majors, freshman honors college, honors program, independent study, distance learning, double major, summer session for credit, part-time degree program, external degree program, adult/continuing education programs, internships, graduate courses open to undergrads. Off campus study at Association of Independent Colleges of Art and Design, NY studio program, Parsons School of Design. Study abroad program.

Entrance Requirements: Options: Common Application, electronic application, deferred admission, international baccalaureate accepted. Required: essay, high school transcript, 3 recommendations, interview, portfolio, SAT or ACT. Entrance: moderately difficult. Application deadline: Rolling. Notification: continuous.

Costs Per Year: Application fee: $40. Comprehensive fee: $29,550 includes full-time tuition ($19,600) and college room and board ($9950). College room only: $6100. Full-time tuition varies according to program. Room and board charges vary according to housing facility. Part-time tuition: $824 per credit.

Collegiate Environment: Orientation program. Drama-theater group, choral group. Social organizations: 6 open to all. Most popular organizations: Peer Advisors, Ski Club, International Student Association, Student Gallery Committee, Literary Journal. Major annual events: Edible Art, student and faculty Coffee Hours, Student Lunches. Student services: health clinic, personal-psychological counseling. Campus security: 24-hour emergency response devices and patrols, late night transport-escort service, controlled dormitory access, lighted walkways. 500 college housing spaces available; all were occupied in 2003-04. Freshmen given priority for college housing. Options: coed, women-only housing available. The Art Institute of Boston Library plus 2 others with 100,000 books, 826,172 microform titles, 1,160 serials, 49,943 audiovisual materials, and an OPAC. Operations spending for 2004 fiscal year: $1.9 million. 175 computers available on campus for general student use. Computer purchase/lease plans available. A campuswide network can be accessed from student residence rooms and from off campus. Staffed computer lab on campus.

■ ASSUMPTION COLLEGE *E-9*
500 Salisbury St.
Worcester, MA 01609-1296
Tel: (508)767-7000; 888-882-7786
Admissions: (508)767-7110
Fax: (508)799-4412
Web Site: http://www.assumption.edu/

Description: Independent Roman Catholic, comprehensive, coed. Awards bachelor's and master's degrees and post-master's certificates. Founded 1904. Setting: 145-acre suburban campus with easy access to Boston. Endowment: $47.7 million. Educational spending for 2005 fiscal year: $6552 per student. Total enrollment: 2,451. Faculty: 216 (129 full-time, 87 part-time). Student-undergrad faculty ratio is 13:1. 3,357 applied, 76% were admitted. 12% from top 10% of their high school class, 41% from top quarter, 79% from top half. Full-time: 2,099 students, 60% women, 40% men. Part-time: 25 students, 72% women, 28% men. Students come from 20 states and territories, 8 other countries, 31% from out-of-state, 0.05% Native American, 2% Hispanic, 1% black, 2% Asian American or Pacific Islander, 0.3% international, 21% 25 or older, 90% live on campus, 2% transferred in. Retention: 84% of full-time freshmen returned the following year. Academic areas with the most degrees conferred: psychology; business/marketing; communications/journalism. Core. Calendar: semesters. Services for LD students, advanced placement, self-designed majors, honors program, independent study, double major, summer session for credit, part-time degree program, adult/continuing education programs, internships, graduate courses open to undergrads. Off campus study at Colleges of Worcester Consortium. Study abroad program. ROTC: Army (c), Air Force (c).

Entrance Requirements: Options: Peterson's Universal Application, Common Application, electronic application, early decision, deferred admission, international baccalaureate accepted. Required: essay, high school transcript, 1 recommendation, SAT or ACT. Recommended: interview. Entrance: moderately difficult. Application deadlines: 3/1, 11/15 for early decision. Notification: continuous until 5/1, 12/15 for early decision.

Costs Per Year: Application fee: $50. Comprehensive fee: $32,085 includes full-time tuition ($25,895), mandatory fees ($415), and college room and board ($5775). College room only: $3395.

Collegiate Environment: Orientation program. Drama-theater group, choral group, student-run newspaper. Social organizations: 40 open to all. Most popular organizations: Volunteer Center, Campus Activities Board, student government, Campus Ministry, resident assistants. Major annual events: Siblings' Weekend, Family Weekend, Welcome Back Week. Student services: health clinic, personal-psychological counseling. Campus security: 24-hour emergency response devices and patrols, student patrols, late night transport-escort service, front gate security, well-lit pathways. 1,942 college housing spaces available; 1,938 were occupied in 2003-04. Freshmen guaranteed college housing. Options: coed, women-only housing available. Emmanuel d'Alzon Library with 103,467 books, 17,690 microform titles, 1,119 serials, 1,450 audiovisual materials, an OPAC, and a Web page. Operations spending for 2004 fiscal year: $1.2 million. 190 computers available on campus for general student use. Computer purchase/lease plans available. A campuswide network can be accessed from student residence rooms and from off campus. Staffed computer lab on campus.

Community Environment: 175-acre park-like campus situated in residential section of city. See Clark University for area details.

■ **ATLANTIC UNION COLLEGE** *D-9*
PO Box 1000
South Lancaster, MA 01561-1000
Tel: (978)368-2000
Free: 800-282-2030
Admissions: (978)368-2239
Fax: (978)368-2015
E-mail: info@atlanticuc.edu
Web Site: http://www.atlanticuc.edu/

Description: Independent Seventh-day Adventist, comprehensive, coed. Awards associate, bachelor's, and master's degrees. Founded 1882. Setting: 314-acre small town campus with easy access to Boston. Endowment: $2 million. Total enrollment: 473. 713 applied, 39% were admitted. Students come from 15 states and territories, 18 other countries, 45% from out-of-state, 68% live on campus. Retention: 75% of full-time freshmen returned the following year. Core. Calendar: semesters. Academic remediation for entering students, ESL program, advanced placement, freshman honors college, honors program, summer session for credit, part-time degree program, external degree program, adult/continuing education programs, co-op programs and internships. Study abroad program.

Entrance Requirements: Options: Common Application, international baccalaureate accepted. Required: high school transcript, minimum 2.0 high school GPA, 2 recommendations. Required for some: essay, interview. Placement: SAT or ACT required; SAT recommended. Entrance: moderately difficult. Application deadline: 8/1.

Costs Per Year: Application fee: $25. Comprehensive fee: $17,600. Part-time tuition: $525 per credit hour. Part-time tuition varies according to class time and program. Tuition: $525 per credit hour part-time. Part-time tuition varies according to class time and program. Tuition guaranteed not to increase for student's term of enrollment.

Collegiate Environment: Orientation program. Drama-theater group, choral group, student-run newspaper, radio station. Social organizations: 10 open

to all. Most popular organizations: Student Association, Black Christian Union, choir, CHISPA (Hispanic group). Major annual events: Student Week of Prayer, Campus Clean-Up, Encore. Student services: health clinic, personal-psychological counseling. Campus security: 24-hour patrols, late night transport-escort service. Freshmen guaranteed college housing. On-campus residence required through senior year. Options: coed, men-only, women-only housing available. G. Eric Jones Library with 135,694 books, 15,742 microform titles, 533 serials, 4,544 audiovisual materials, an OPAC, and a Web page. 74 computers available on campus for general student use. A campuswide network can be accessed. Staffed computer lab on campus.

Community Environment: Rural community (population 6,500), located in the approximate center of the state. Moderate climate in spring and fall; winters are cold. fall; winters are cold.

■ **BABSON COLLEGE** *E-11*
Babson Park, MA 02457-0310
Tel: (781)235-1200
Free: 800-488-3696
Fax: (781)239-5614
E-mail: ugradadmission@babson.edu
Web Site: http://www.babson.edu/

Description: Independent, comprehensive, coed. Awards bachelor's and master's degrees and post-master's certificates. Founded 1919. Setting: 370-acre suburban campus with easy access to Boston. Endowment: $179.2 million. Research spending for 2004 fiscal year: $3.7 million. Total enrollment: 3,210. Faculty: 229 (151 full-time, 78 part-time). Student-undergrad faculty ratio is 14:1. 3,159 applied, 37% were admitted. 52% from top 10% of their high school class, 87% from top quarter, 99% from top half. Full-time: 1,725 students, 39% women, 61% men. Students come from 47 states and territories, 59 other countries, 70% from out-of-state, 0.4% Native American, 6% Hispanic, 3% black, 8% Asian American or Pacific Islander, 18% international, 83% live on campus, 3% transferred in. Retention: 95% of full-time freshmen returned the following year. Academic area with the most degrees conferred: business/marketing. Core. Calendar: semesters. Services for LD students, advanced placement, accelerated degree program, self-designed majors, freshman honors college, honors program, independent study, summer session for credit, internships. Off campus study at Pine Manor College, Regis College (MA), Brandeis University, Wellesley College, Olin College of Engineering. Study abroad program. ROTC: Army (c), Naval (c), Air Force (c).

Entrance Requirements: Options: Peterson's Universal Application, Common Application, electronic application, early decision, early action, deferred admission, international baccalaureate accepted. Required: essay, high school transcript, 2 recommendations, SAT or ACT. Recommended: interview, SAT Subject Test in math. Entrance: very difficult. Application deadlines: 1/15, 11/15 for early decision, 11/15 for early action. Notification: 4/1, 12/15 for early decision, 1/1 for early action.

Costs Per Year: Application fee: $60. Comprehensive fee: $43,478 includes full-time tuition ($32,256) and college room and board ($11,222). College room only: $7242.

Collegiate Environment: Orientation program. Drama-theater group, choral group, student-run newspaper, radio station. Social organizations: 60 open to all; national fraternities, national sororities; 9% of eligible men and 9% of eligible women are members. Most popular organizations: student government, Free Press, Dance Ensemble, Asian Pacific Student Association, college radio. Major annual events: Oktoberfest, Spring Weekend, Family Weekend. Student services: health clinic, personal-psychological counseling, women's center. Campus security: 24-hour emergency response devices and patrols, late night transport-escort service, controlled dormitory access. 1,435 college housing spaces available; 1,420 were occupied in 2003-04. Freshmen guaranteed college housing. On-campus residence required in freshman year. Options: coed, men-only housing available. Horn Library plus 1 other with 131,436 books, 346,933 microform titles, 626 serials, 5,411 audiovisual materials, an OPAC, and a Web page. Operations spending for 2004 fiscal year: $2.4 million. 290 computers available on campus for general student use. A campuswide network can be accessed from student residence rooms and from off campus. Staffed computer lab on campus.

Community Environment: Breadth distinguishes Babson from other undergraduate management programs. The focus of the Babson education blends professional (50%) and liberal arts (50%) courses with campus and field experiences in a small college setting where both halves of the faculty work together to help students perform well and to grow in response to change. Babson is located 30 minutes by car from Boston.

■ BAY PATH COLLEGE F-5
588 Longmeadow St.
Longmeadow, MA 01106-2292
Tel: (413)565-1000
Free: 800-782-7284
Fax: (413)567-0501
E-mail: admiss@baypath.edu
Web Site: http://www.baypath.edu/

Description: Independent, comprehensive. Awards associate, bachelor's, and master's degrees. Founded 1897. Setting: 48-acre suburban campus with easy access to Boston. Endowment: $19.3 million. Total enrollment: 1,456. Faculty: 162 (38 full-time, 124 part-time). Student-undergrad faculty ratio is 17:1. 599 applied, 69% were admitted. 2 class presidents, 6 student government officers. Full-time: 1,109 students, 100% women. Part-time: 234 students, 100% women. Students come from 17 states and territories, 6 other countries, 41% from out-of-state, 0.4% Native American, 7% Hispanic, 12% black, 1% Asian American or Pacific Islander, 1% international, 54% 25 or older, 40% live on campus, 3% transferred in. Retention: 70% of full-time freshmen returned the following year. Academic areas with the most degrees conferred: business/marketing; liberal arts/general studies; psychology. Core. Calendar: semesters. Academic remediation for entering students, ESL program, services for LD students, advanced placement, self-designed majors, freshman honors college, honors program, independent study, summer session for credit, part-time degree program, adult/continuing education programs, internships. Off campus study at Cooperating Colleges of Greater Springfield. Study abroad program. ROTC: Army (c), Air Force (c).

Entrance Requirements: Options: Peterson's Universal Application, Common Application, electronic application, early admission, early action, deferred admission, international baccalaureate accepted. Required: essay, high school transcript, 2 recommendations, SAT or ACT. Recommended: minimum 2.0 high school GPA, interview. Required for some: minimum 3.0 high school GPA, interview. Entrance: moderately difficult. Application deadlines: Rolling, 12/15 for early action. Notification: continuous, 1/2 for early action.

Costs Per Year: Application fee: $25. Comprehensive fee: $30,220 includes full-time tuition ($20,606) and college room and board ($9614). Room and board charges vary according to board plan. Part-time tuition: $440 per credit.

Collegiate Environment: Orientation program. Drama-theater group, choral group, student-run radio station. Social organizations: 36 open to all. Most popular organizations: student government, All Women Excel, Golden Z Service Club, Alliance, Women of Culture. Major annual events: Campus Day, Women in Culture. Student services: health clinic, personal-psychological counseling. Campus security: 24-hour emergency response devices and patrols, late night transport-escort service, controlled dormitory access. 410 college housing spaces available; 362 were occupied in 2003-04. Freshmen guaranteed college housing. Option: women-only housing available. Hatch Library with 55,060 books, 4,312 microform titles, 132 serials, 3,764 audiovisual materials, an OPAC, and a Web page. Operations spending for 2004 fiscal year: $382,825. 155 computers available on campus for general student use. A campuswide network can be accessed from student residence rooms and from off campus. Staffed computer lab on campus.

Community Environment: Longmeadow is a small, residential, historic town located on the Connecticut/Massachusetts border. Its location near two major cities provides cultural and social advantages.

■ BAY STATE COLLEGE D-12
122 Commonwealth Ave.
Boston, MA 02116-2975
Tel: (617)236-8000
Free: 800-81-LEARN
Fax: (617)536-1735
E-mail: admissions@baystate.edu
Web Site: http://www.baystate.edu/

Description: Independent, primarily 2-year, coed. Awards transfer associate, terminal associate, and bachelor's degrees. Founded 1946. Setting: urban campus. Total enrollment: 757. Student-undergrad faculty ratio is 13:1. 1,405 applied, 80% were admitted. Students come from 11 states and territories, 11 other countries, 11% from out-of-state, 0% Native American, 10% Hispanic, 18% black, 8% Asian American or Pacific Islander, 1% international, 12% 25 or older, 21% live on campus. Retention: 50% of full-time freshmen returned the following year. Core. Calendar: semesters. Academic remediation for entering students, ESL program, advanced placement,

independent study, part-time degree program, adult/continuing education programs, co-op programs and internships.

Entrance Requirements: Options: Peterson's Universal Application, Common Application, early admission. Required: essay, high school transcript. Recommended: minimum 2.0 high school GPA, interview. Entrance: minimally difficult. Application deadline: Rolling.

Costs Per Year: Application fee: $40. Comprehensive fee: $26,325 includes full-time tuition ($15,900), mandatory fees ($350), and college room and board ($10,075). Part-time tuition: $1530 per course.

Collegiate Environment: Orientation program. Social organizations: 9 open to all. Most popular organizations: Activities Club, Hospitality Travel Association, Fashion Club, Early Childhood Education Club, Student Medical Assisting Society. Major annual events: Senior Cruise, Celtics Game. Student services: personal-psychological counseling. Campus security: late night transport-escort service, controlled dormitory access, 14-hour patrols by trained security personnel. 174 college housing spaces available; all were occupied in 2003-04. Options: coed, women-only housing available. Bay State College Library with 4,490 books, 262 serials, 471 audiovisual materials, and an OPAC. Operations spending for 2004 fiscal year: $36,177. 55 computers available on campus for general student use. A campuswide network can be accessed. Staffed computer lab on campus.

Community Environment: See Boston University.

■ BECKER COLLEGE E-9
61 Sever St.
Worcester, MA 01609
Tel: (508)791-9241; 877-5BECKER
Fax: (508)831-7505
E-mail: admissions@go.becker.edu
Web Site: http://www.beckercollege.edu/

Description: Independent, 4-year, coed. Awards associate and bachelor's degrees (also includes Leicester, MA small town campus). Founded 1784. Setting: 100-acre urban campus with easy access to Boston. Total enrollment: 1,660. 1,790 applied, 65% were admitted. Full-time: 910 students, 75% women, 25% men. Part-time: 750 students, 85% women, 15% men. Students come from 18 states and territories, 2 other countries, 29% from out-of-state, 0.3% Native American, 3% Hispanic, 5% black, 1% Asian American or Pacific Islander, 0.3% international, 23% 25 or older, 40% live on campus, 11% transferred in. Retention: 61% of full-time freshmen returned the following year. Core. Calendar: semesters. Academic remediation for entering students, services for LD students, advanced placement, accelerated degree program, distance learning, summer session for credit, part-time degree program, adult/continuing education programs, co-op programs and internships. Off campus study at Colleges of Worcester Consortium. Study abroad program. ROTC: Army (c), Naval (c), Air Force (c).

Entrance Requirements: Options: Peterson's Universal Application, Common Application, electronic application, deferred admission. Required: high school transcript, minimum 2.0 high school GPA, recommendations, SAT or ACT. Recommended: essay, recommendations. Required for some: minimum 2.5 high school GPA, interview. Entrance: minimally difficult. Application deadline: Rolling. Notification: continuous.

Costs Per Year: Application fee: $30. Comprehensive fee: $26,425 includes full-time tuition ($18,000), mandatory fees ($425), and college room and board ($8000). Part-time tuition: $750 per credit hour. Part-time tuition varies according to program.

Collegiate Environment: Orientation program. Drama-theater group, student-run newspaper. Social organizations: 25 open to all. Most popular organizations: student government, Student Activities Committee, Black Student Union, Animal Health Club, Drama Club. Major annual events: Family Weekend, Halloween Week, Spring Week. Student services: health clinic, personal-psychological counseling. Campus security: 24-hour emergency response devices and patrols, late night transport-escort service, controlled dormitory access. 492 college housing spaces available; 40 were occupied in 2003-04. Freshmen guaranteed college housing. Options: coed, men-only, women-only housing available. Ruska Library plus 1 other with 75,000 books, 2,230 microform titles, 400 serials, 2,900 audiovisual materials, and an OPAC. 155 computers available on campus for general student use. A campuswide network can be accessed from student residence rooms and from off campus. Staffed computer lab on campus.

■ BENJAMIN FRANKLIN INSTITUTE OF TECHNOLOGY D-12
41 Berkeley St.
Boston, MA 02116-6296

Tel: (617)423-4630
Fax: (617)482-3706
E-mail: nkraft@bfit.edu
Web Site: http://www.bfit.edu/

Description: Independent, primarily 2-year, coed. Awards certificates, transfer associate, terminal associate, and bachelor's degrees. Founded 1908. Setting: 3-acre urban campus. Endowment: $8 million. Total enrollment: 386. Student-undergrad faculty ratio is 11:1. 668 applied, 91% were admitted. Students come from 12 states and territories, 0.3% Native American, 13% Hispanic, 38% black, 12% Asian American or Pacific Islander, 0.3% international, 10% 25 or older. Core. Calendar: semesters. Academic remediation for entering students, ESL program, advanced placement, summer session for credit, part-time degree program, adult/continuing education programs, internships. Off campus study at University of Massachusetts.

Entrance Requirements: Open admission. Options: Peterson's Universal Application, Common Application, electronic application, deferred admission, international baccalaureate accepted. Required: high school transcript. Recommended: essay, minimum 2.0 high school GPA, recommendations, interview, SAT or ACT. Entrance: minimally difficult. Application deadline: 8/15.

Costs Per Year: Application fee: $20. Tuition: $12,750 full-time, $531 per credit part-time.

Collegiate Environment: Orientation program. Social organizations: 4 open to all; local fraternities. Most popular organizations: Society of Manufacturing Engineers, student government, Yearbook Committee, athletics, Institute of Electrical and electronic Engineers (IEEE). Major annual events: Engineering Week Competition, Ben Franklin's Birthday, Spring Week. Student services: personal-psychological counseling. Campus security: 24-hour emergency response devices, student patrols. College housing not available. Lufkin Memorial Library with 10,000 books, 90 serials, and an OPAC. 100 computers available on campus for general student use. A campuswide network can be accessed. Staffed computer lab on campus.

■ **BENTLEY COLLEGE** *J-1*
175 Forest St.
Waltham, MA 02452-4705
Tel: (781)891-2000
Free: 800-523-2354
Admissions: (781)891-2244
Fax: (781)891-3414
E-mail: krinehart@bentley.edu
Web Site: http://www.bentley.edu

Description: Independent, comprehensive, coed. Awards associate, bachelor's, and master's degrees and post-master's certificates. Founded 1917. Setting: 143-acre suburban campus with easy access to Boston. Endowment: $199.2 million. Educational spending for 2005 fiscal year: $10,510 per student. Total enrollment: 5,565. Faculty: 475 (270 full-time, 205 part-time). Student-undergrad faculty ratio is 12:1. 5,802 applied, 43% were admitted. 39% from top 10% of their high school class, 81% from top quarter, 99% from top half. Full-time: 3,958 students, 41% women, 59% men. Part-time: 336 students, 44% women, 56% men. Students come from 40 states and territories, 69 other countries, 47% from out-of-state, 0.1% Native American, 4% Hispanic, 3% black, 8% Asian American or Pacific Islander, 8% international, 7% 25 or older, 79% live on campus, 4% transferred in. Retention: 94% of full-time freshmen returned the following year. Academic areas with the most degrees conferred: business/marketing; computer and information sciences; interdisciplinary studies. Core. Calendar: semesters. ESL program, services for LD students, advanced placement, accelerated degree program, self-designed majors, honors program, independent study, distance learning, double major, summer session for credit, part-time degree program, internships, graduate courses open to undergrads. Off campus study at The Bentley-Brandeis-Regis Exchange. Study abroad program. ROTC: Army (c).

Entrance Requirements: Options: Common Application, electronic application, early admission, early decision, early action, deferred admission, international baccalaureate accepted. Required: essay, high school transcript, 2 recommendations, SAT or ACT. Recommended: interview. Entrance: very difficult. Application deadlines: 2/1, 11/15 for early decision, 12/1 for early action. Notification: 4/1, 12/22 for early decision, 1/30 for early action.

Costs Per Year: Application fee: $50. Comprehensive fee: $38,784 includes full-time tuition ($28,390), mandatory fees ($224), and college room and board ($10,170). College room only: $6060. Full-time tuition and fees vary

according to student level. Room and board charges vary according to board plan and housing facility. Part-time tuition: $1368 per course. Part-time mandatory fees: $10 per term. Part-time tuition and fees vary according to class time and student level.

Collegiate Environment: Orientation program. Drama-theater group, choral group, student-run newspaper, radio station. Social organizations: 90 open to all; national fraternities, national sororities, local fraternities. Most popular organizations: Student Government Association, Campus Activities Board, Hall Council Advisory Board, WBTY. Major annual events: Homecoming Weekend, Spring Weekend, Midnight Madness. Student services: health clinic, personal-psychological counseling, women's center. Campus security: 24-hour emergency response devices and patrols, late night transport-escort service, controlled dormitory access, security cameras. College housing designed to accommodate 3,127 students; 3,128 undergraduates lived in college housing during 2003-04. Freshmen guaranteed college housing. Option: coed housing available. Baker Library plus 1 other with 136,094 books, 1,744 microform titles, 16,848 serials, 5,850 audiovisual materials, an OPAC, and a Web page. Operations spending for 2004 fiscal year: $1.7 million. 4,441 computers available on campus for general student use. Computer purchase/lease plans available. A campuswide network can be accessed from student residence rooms and from off campus. Staffed computer lab on campus.

Community Environment: The college represents the best of New England college campuses and provides an inviting atmosphere for study and socializing. Located in Waltham, Massachusetts, just 10 miles from Boston, Bentley's 163-acre suburban campus puts the city's many resources within easy reach. Boston is the country's ultimate college town. From theater to art exhibits, dance clubs to alternative rock concerts, championship sports to championship shopping, Boston has the proverbial "something for everyone." The college offers a shuttle service into Cambridge at Harvard Square, and from there, the entire city of Boston is accessible via public transportation.

■ **BERKLEE COLLEGE OF MUSIC** *D-12*
1140 Boylston St.
Boston, MA 02215-3693
Tel: (617)266-1400
Free: 800-BER-KLEE
Admissions: (617)747-2222
Fax: (617)747-2047
E-mail: admissions@berklee.edu
Web Site: http://www.berklee.edu/

Description: Independent, 4-year, coed. Awards bachelor's degrees. Founded 1945. Setting: urban campus. Endowment: $127.9 million. Educational spending for 2005 fiscal year: $11,151 per student. Total enrollment: 4,037. Student-undergrad faculty ratio is 13:1. 2,474 applied, 57% were admitted. Students come from 54 states and territories, 66 other countries, 78% from out-of-state, 0.4% Native American, 6% Hispanic, 6% black, 3% Asian American or Pacific Islander, 22% international, 20% live on campus. Core. Calendar: semesters. ESL program, services for LD students, advanced placement, accelerated degree program, self-designed majors, double major, summer session for credit, internships. Off campus study at Pro Arts Consortium.

Entrance Requirements: Options: electronic application, early action, deferred admission, international baccalaureate accepted. Required: essay, high school transcript, 2 recommendations, interview, 2 years of formal music study and audition. Required for some: SAT or ACT. Entrance: moderately difficult. Application deadlines: 2/1, 11/1 for early action. Notification: 3/31, 1/31 for early action.

Costs Per Year: Application fee: $100. Comprehensive fee: $37,997 includes full-time tuition ($21,790), mandatory fees ($4517), and college room and board ($11,690).

Collegiate Environment: Orientation program. Drama-theater group, choral group, student-run newspaper, radio station. Social organizations: 39 open to all. Most popular organizations: Musical Theater at Berklee Club, Yoga Society, Black Student Union, Christian Fellowship. Major annual events: Convocation, Welcoming Barbecue, International Night. Student services: personal-psychological counseling. Campus security: 24-hour patrols. 771 college housing spaces available; 760 were occupied in 2003-04. Freshmen given priority for college housing. Option: coed housing available. The Stan Getz Media Center and Library with 30,208 books, 77 serials, 19,480 audiovisual materials, an OPAC, and a Web page. Operations spending for 2004 fiscal year: $775,000. 45 computers available on campus for general student use. A campuswide network can be accessed from student residence rooms. Staffed computer lab on campus.

Community Environment: See Boston University.

■ BERKSHIRE COMMUNITY COLLEGE D-2

1350 West St.
Pittsfield, MA 01201-5786
Tel: (413)499-4660
Fax: (413)496-9511
E-mail: mbullock@berkshirecc.edu
Web Site: http://www.berkshirecc.edu/
Description: State-supported, 2-year, coed. Part of Massachusetts Public Higher Education System. Awards certificates, transfer associate, and terminal associate degrees. Founded 1960. Setting: 100-acre suburban campus. Endowment: $3 million. Educational spending for 2005 fiscal year: $3341 per student. Total enrollment: 2,328. Student-undergrad faculty ratio is 14:1. 399 applied, 100% were admitted. Full-time: 923 students, 55% women, 45% men. Part-time: 1,405 students, 68% women, 32% men. Students come from 4 states and territories, 14 other countries, 4% from out-of-state, 1% Native American, 3% Hispanic, 4% black, 2% Asian American or Pacific Islander, 2% international, 40% 25 or older, 13% transferred in. Core. Calendar: semesters. Academic remediation for entering students, ESL program, services for LD students, advanced placement, self-designed majors, honors program, independent study, distance learning, double major, summer session for credit, part-time degree program, adult/continuing education programs, internships. Off campus study at Massachusetts College of Liberal Arts, Williams College, Springfield Technical Community College.
Entrance Requirements: Open admission except for nursing and allied health. Options: Peterson's Universal Application, Common Application, deferred admission. Required: high school transcript. Recommended: interview. Entrance: noncompetitive. Application deadline: Rolling. Notification: continuous.
Costs Per Year: Application fee: $10. State resident tuition: $780 full-time, $26 per credit part-time. Nonresident tuition: $7800 full-time, $260 per credit part-time. Mandatory fees: $2820 full-time, $94 per credit part-time.
Collegiate Environment: Orientation program. Drama-theater group, choral group. Social organizations: 19 open to all. Most popular organizations: Mass PIRG, Student Nurse Organization, Student Senate, Diversity Club, LPN Organization. Major annual events: concerts, speakers, film presentations. Student services: personal-psychological counseling. Campus security: 24-hour emergency response devices and patrols. College housing not available. Jonathan Edwards Library plus 1 other with 74,271 books, 319 serials, 3,247 audiovisual materials, an OPAC, and a Web page. Operations spending for 2004 fiscal year: $126,014. 354 computers available on campus for general student use. Computer purchase/lease plans available. A campuswide network can be accessed from off-campus. Staffed computer lab on campus.
Community Environment: Set in the cultural mecca of the rolling Berkshire hills, this attractive area is also the home to long established plastics and paper industries. The city has three libraries, numerous churches, two hospitals, a museum, YMCA, and good shopping facilities. Regular transportation is available by rail bus and air. Theatres, bowling, three golf courses, two large lakes, many parks, and closeness to area festivals and summer attractions make this city a favorite recreation spot. Part-time employment is available.

■ BOSTON ARCHITECTURAL COLLEGE D-12

320 Newbury St.
Boston, MA 02115-2795
Tel: (617)262-5000; 877-585-0100
Admissions: (617)585-0256
Fax: (617)585-0111
Web Site: http://www.the-bac.edu/
Description: Independent, comprehensive, coed. Awards bachelor's and master's degrees. Founded 1889. Setting: 1-acre urban campus. Endowment: $6.1 million. Total enrollment: 910. Faculty: 327 (10 full-time, 317 part-time). Student-undergrad faculty ratio is 12:1. 338 applied, 70% were admitted. Full-time: 466 students, 37% women, 63% men. Part-time: 41 students, 22% women, 78% men. Students come from 43 states and territories, 47% from out-of-state, 1% Native American, 5% Hispanic, 2% black, 2% Asian American or Pacific Islander, 7% international, 67% 25 or older, 14% transferred in. Retention: 62% of full-time freshmen returned the following year. Core. Calendar: semesters. Advanced placement, independent study, distance learning, summer session for credit, adult/continuing education programs, internships. Off campus study at Art Institute of Boston at Lesley College, ProArts Consortium.

Entrance Requirements: Open admission. Options: Common Application, electronic application. Required: high school transcript. Recommended: resume. Entrance: noncompetitive. Application deadline: Rolling.
Costs Per Year: Application fee: $50. Tuition: $8610 full-time, $717 per credit part-time. Mandatory fees: $20 full-time, $150. Full-time tuition and fees vary according to course load, degree level, program, and reciprocity agreements. Part-time tuition and fees vary according to course load, degree level, program, and reciprocity agreements.
Collegiate Environment: Orientation program. Student-run newspaper. Most popular organization: student government. Major annual event: Sketch Problem Weekend. Campus security: 24-hour emergency response devices and patrols, electronically operated building access. College housing not available. Shaw and Stone Library with 27,000 books, 140 serials, an OPAC, and a Web page. Operations spending for 2004 fiscal year: $398,012. 63 computers available on campus for general student use. Computer purchase/lease plans available. A campuswide network can be accessed from off-campus. Staffed computer lab on campus.

■ BOSTON BAPTIST COLLEGE D-12

950 Metropolitan Ave.
Boston, MA 02136
Tel: (617)364-3510; 888-235-2014
Fax: (617)364-0723
E-mail: kfox@boston.edu
Web Site: http://www.boston.edu/
Description: Independent Baptist, 4-year, coed. Awards associate and bachelor's degrees. Founded 1976. Setting: 8-acre suburban campus with easy access to Providence. Total enrollment: 130. 3% from top 10% of their high school class, 21% from top quarter, 42% from top half. Full-time: 120 students, 37% women, 63% men. Part-time: 10 students, 20% women, 80% men. Students come from 22 states and territories, 3 other countries, 70% from out-of-state, 0% Native American, 2% Hispanic, 2% black, 2% Asian American or Pacific Islander, 4% international, 10% 25 or older, 65% live on campus, 12% transferred in. Academic area with the most degrees conferred: theology and religious vocations. Calendar: semesters. Academic remediation for entering students, honors program, summer session for credit, part-time degree program, internships.
Entrance Requirements: Option: Common Application. Required: essay, high school transcript, recommendations, SAT or ACT. Recommended: interview. Entrance: moderately difficult. Application deadline: Rolling.
Costs Per Year: Application fee: $40. Comprehensive fee: $14,784 includes full-time tuition ($6930), mandatory fees ($1600), and college room and board ($6254). College room only: $3594. Part-time tuition: $290 per hour. Part-time mandatory fees: $900 per term.
Collegiate Environment: Drama-theater group, choral group, student-run newspaper. Social organizations: local fraternities, local sororities. Major annual events: Christmas Concert, Missions Conference, Open House East. Student services: personal-psychological counseling. Campus security: 24-hour emergency response devices, student patrols. 100 college housing spaces available; 90 were occupied in 2003-04. 9 computers available on campus for general student use. Staffed computer lab on campus.

■ BOSTON COLLEGE E-12

140 Commonwealth Ave.
Chestnut Hill, MA 02467-3800
Tel: (617)552-8000
Free: 800-360-2522
Admissions: (617)552-3100
Fax: (617)552-0798
E-mail: admissions@bcvms.bc.edu
Web Site: http://www.bc.edu/
Description: Independent Roman Catholic (Jesuit), university, coed. Awards bachelor's, master's, doctoral, and first professional degrees and post-master's certificates (also offers continuing education program with significant enrollment not reflected in profile). Founded 1863. Setting: 240-acre suburban campus with easy access to Boston. Endowment: $1.2 billion. Research spending for 2004 fiscal year: $24.2 million. Educational spending for 2005 fiscal year: $19,808 per student. Total enrollment: 13,755. Faculty: 1,285 (662 full-time, 623 part-time). Student-undergrad faculty ratio is 13:1. 23,823 applied, 31% were admitted. 75% from top 10% of their high school class, 95% from top quarter, 99% from top half. 7 National Merit Scholars, 138 student government officers. Full-time: 9,019 students, 52% women, 48% men. Students come from 51 states and territories, 100 other countries, 71% from out-of-state, 0.3% Native American, 8% Hispanic, 6% black, 9%

Asian American or Pacific Islander, 2% international, 21% 25 or older, 78% live on campus, 1% transferred in. Retention: 96% of full-time freshmen returned the following year. Academic areas with the most degrees conferred: business/marketing; social sciences; communications/journalism. Core. Calendar: semesters. Services for LD students, advanced placement, accelerated degree program, self-designed majors, freshman honors college, honors program, independent study, double major, summer session for credit, part-time degree program, adult/continuing education programs, internships, graduate courses open to undergrads. Off campus study at Boston University, Brandeis University, Hebrew College, Pine Manor College, Regis College (MA), Tufts University. Study abroad program. ROTC: Army (c), Air Force (c).

Entrance Requirements: Options: Common Application, electronic application, early admission, early action, deferred admission, international baccalaureate accepted. Required: essay, high school transcript, 2 recommendations, SAT and SAT Subject Tests or ACT. Entrance: very difficult. Application deadlines: 1/1, 11/1 for early action. Notification: 4/15, 12/25 for early action.

Costs Per Year: Application fee: $70. One-time mandatory fee: $355. Comprehensive fee: $42,283 includes full-time tuition ($30,950), mandatory fees ($488), and college room and board ($10,845). College room only: $6945. Room and board charges vary according to housing facility.

Collegiate Environment: Orientation program. Drama-theater group, choral group, marching band, student-run newspaper, radio station. Social organizations: 171 open to all. Most popular organizations: Ski Club, The Bostonians, Boston College Bop. Major annual events: Homecoming, Middlemarch Ball, Student Leadership Awards Banquet. Student services: health clinic, personal-psychological counseling, women's center. Campus security: 24-hour emergency response devices and patrols, late night transport-escort service, controlled dormitory access. College housing designed to accommodate 7,068 students; 7,341 undergraduates lived in college housing during 2003-04. Freshmen guaranteed college housing. Options: coed, women-only housing available. Thomas P. O'Neill Library plus 6 others with 2.2 million books, 3.9 million microform titles, 22,266 serials, 162,202 audiovisual materials, an OPAC, and a Web page. Operations spending for 2004 fiscal year: $20.9 million. 1,000 computers available on campus for general student use. Computer purchase/lease plans available. A campuswide network can be accessed from student residence rooms and from off campus. Staffed computer lab on campus.

Community Environment: Boston College considers, and the students concur, that the suburban location of the campus six miles from Boston is the ideal setting for a University. The campus boasts superior academic, residential, and recreational facilities, and the dynamic Greater Boston area offers unlimited cultural, educational, and personal opportunities for individual development within a cosmopolitan atmosphere.

■ **THE BOSTON CONSERVATORY** *D-12*
8 The Fenway
Boston, MA 02215
Tel: (617)536-6340
Admissions: (617)912-9153
Fax: (617)536-3176
Web Site: http://www.bostonconservatory.edu/
Description: Independent, comprehensive, coed. Awards bachelor's and master's degrees and post-master's certificates. Founded 1867. Setting: urban campus. Total enrollment: 537. 989 applied, 43% were admitted. Full-time: 404 students, 64% women, 36% men. Part-time: 3 students, 67% women, 33% men. Students come from 42 states and territories, 60% from out-of-state, 0% 25 or older, 29% live on campus, 2% transferred in. Retention: 68% of full-time freshmen returned the following year. Core. Calendar: semesters. ESL program, advanced placement, double major, summer session for credit, adult/continuing education programs, graduate courses open to undergrads. Off campus study at members of the Pro Arts Consortium.
Entrance Requirements: Options: deferred admission, international baccalaureate accepted. Required: essay, high school transcript, minimum 2.7 high school GPA, 4 recommendations, audition, SAT or ACT. Required for some: interview. Entrance: moderately difficult. Application deadline: 12/1. Notification: 4/1.
Costs Per Year: Application fee: $105. Comprehensive fee: $42,155 includes full-time tuition ($26,400), mandatory fees ($1435), and college room and board ($14,320).
Collegiate Environment: Orientation program. Drama-theater group, choral group, student-run newspaper. Social organizations: 16 open to all; national fraternities, national sororities; 25% of eligible men and 15% of eligible

women are members. Most popular organizations: Student Government Association, Korean Student Association, Chinese Student Association, Sigma Alpha Iota. Major annual events: Spring Weekend, International Student Festival. Student services: health clinic, personal-psychological counseling. Campus security: 24-hour emergency response devices and patrols, controlled dormitory access. On-campus residence required in freshman year. Options: coed, women-only housing available. The Albert Alphin Music Library with 40,000 books and 92 serials. Operations spending for 2004 fiscal year: $130,000. 16 computers available on campus for general student use. A campuswide network can be accessed. Staffed computer lab on campus.

Community Environment: Located in an urban environment in central Boston near Symphony Hall and the Museum of Fine Arts. Public transportation, metropolitan shopping, artistic areas and fine dining are within walking distance.

■ **BOSTON UNIVERSITY** *D-12*
Boston, MA 02215
Tel: (617)353-2000
Admissions: (617)353-2300
Fax: (617)353-9695
E-mail: admissions@bu.edu
Web Site: http://www.bu.edu/
Description: Independent, university, coed. Awards bachelor's, master's, doctoral, and first professional degrees and post-master's and first professional certificates. Founded 1839. Setting: 132-acre urban campus. Endowment: $712.3 million. Research spending for 2004 fiscal year: $218.8 million. Educational spending for 2005 fiscal year: $19,796 per student. Total enrollment: 30,957. Faculty: 2,438 (1,454 full-time, 984 part-time). Student-undergrad faculty ratio is 12:1. 31,431 applied, 57% were admitted. 58% from top 10% of their high school class, 87% from top quarter, 99% from top half. 108 valedictorians. Full-time: 17,384 students, 59% women, 41% men. Part-time: 1,310 students, 49% women, 51% men. Students come from 54 states and territories, 103 other countries, 77% from out-of-state, 0.4% Native American, 6% Hispanic, 3% black, 13% Asian American or Pacific Islander, 6% international, 3% 25 or older, 74% live on campus, 1% transferred in. Retention: 91% of full-time freshmen returned the following year. Academic areas with the most degrees conferred: communications/journalism; social sciences; business/marketing. Core. Calendar: semesters. ESL program, services for LD students, advanced placement, accelerated degree program, self-designed majors, honors program, independent study, distance learning, double major, summer session for credit, part-time degree program, adult/continuing education programs, co-op programs and internships, graduate courses open to undergrads. Off campus study at Boston College, Brandeis University, Hebrew College, Tufts University. Study abroad program. ROTC: Army, Naval, Air Force.

Entrance Requirements: Options: Peterson's Universal Application, Common Application, electronic application, early admission, early decision, deferred admission, international baccalaureate accepted. Required: essay, high school transcript, 2 recommendations, SAT or ACT. Recommended: minimum 3.0 high school GPA. Required for some: interview, audition, portfolio, SAT Subject Tests. Entrance: very difficult. Application deadlines: 1/1, 11/1 for early decision plan 1, 1/1 for early decision plan 2. Notification: continuous until 4/15, 12/15 for early decision plan 1, 2/15 for early decision plan 2.

Costs Per Year: Application fee: $70. Comprehensive fee: $42,046 includes full-time tuition ($31,530), mandatory fees ($436), and college room and board ($10,080). College room only: $6450. Full-time tuition and fees vary according to class time and degree level. Room and board charges vary according to board plan and housing facility. Part-time tuition: $985 per credit. Part-time mandatory fees: $40. Part-time tuition and fees vary according to class time, course load, and degree level.

Collegiate Environment: Orientation program. Drama-theater group, choral group, marching band, student-run newspaper, radio station. Social organizations: 380 open to all; national fraternities, national sororities; 3% of eligible men and 5% of eligible women are members. Most popular organizations: performing and acappella groups, cultural organizations, service organizations, student government, residence hall associations. Major annual events: Head of the Charles River Regatta, Homecoming Weekend, World Fair. Student services: health clinic, personal-psychological counseling, women's center. Campus security: 24-hour emergency response devices and patrols, late night transport-escort service, controlled dormitory access, security personnel at residence hall entrances, self-defense education, well-lit sidewalks. College housing designed to accommodate 10,818 students; 10,914 undergraduates lived in college housing during 2003-04. Freshmen guaranteed college housing. On-campus residence required in freshman year. Options: coed, women-only housing available. Mugar Memorial Library plus 18 others with 2.3 million books, 4.5 million microform titles, 30,067 serials, 72,153 audiovisual materials, an OPAC, and a Web page. Operations spending for 2004 fiscal year: $17.4 million. 750 computers available on campus for general student use. Computer purchase/lease plans available. A campuswide network can be accessed from student residence rooms and from off campus. Staffed computer lab on campus.

Community Environment: Historic capital of Massachusetts, Boston is a contrast of past and present with broad avenues disappearing into crooked, narrow streets of colonial Boston. Modern stores and buildings stand next to Revolutionary shrines. With one in every five residents a college student, Boston is America's ultimate college town.

■ **BRANDEIS UNIVERSITY** *J-1*
415 South St.
Waltham, MA 02454-9110
Tel: (781)736-2000
Free: 800-622-0622
Admissions: (781)736-3500
Fax: (781)736-3536
E-mail: admissions@brandeis.edu
Web Site: http://www.brandeis.edu/

Description: Independent, university, coed. Awards bachelor's, master's, and doctoral degrees. Founded 1948. Setting: 235-acre suburban campus with easy access to Boston. Endowment: $519 million. Research spending for 2004 fiscal year: $36.7 million. Total enrollment: 5,189. Faculty: 472 (343 full-time, 129 part-time). Student-undergrad faculty ratio is 8:1. 7,343 applied, 38% were admitted. 74% from top 10% of their high school class, 96% from top quarter, 99% from top half. 21 National Merit Scholars. Full-time: 3,242 students, 55% women, 45% men. Part-time: 25 students, 72% women, 28% men. Students come from 46 states and territories, 57 other countries, 63% from out-of-state, 0.1% Native American, 4% Hispanic, 3% black, 7% Asian American or Pacific Islander, 8% international, 0% 25 or older, 82% live on campus, 1% transferred in. Retention: 94% of full-time freshmen returned the following year. Academic areas with the most degrees conferred: social sciences; area and ethnic studies; biological/life sciences. Core. Calendar: semesters. ESL program, services for LD students, advanced placement, self-designed majors, honors program, independent study, double major, summer session for credit, part-time degree program, adult/continuing education programs, internships, graduate courses open to undergrads. Off campus study at Tufts University, Babson College, Bentley College, Boston University, Wellesley College, Boston College. Study abroad program. ROTC: Army (c), Air Force (c).

Entrance Requirements: Options: Common Application, electronic application, early decision, deferred admission, international baccalaureate accepted. Required: essay, high school transcript, 2 recommendations, SAT and SAT Subject Tests or ACT. Recommended: minimum 3.0 high school GPA, interview. Entrance: most difficult. Application deadlines: 1/15, 1/1 for early decision. Notification: 4/1, 12/1 for early decision.

Costs Per Year: Application fee: $55. Comprehensive fee: $41,551 includes full-time tuition ($31,532), mandatory fees ($969), and college room and board ($9050). College room only: $5083. Room and board charges vary according to board plan and housing facility. Part-time tuition: $986 per credit. Part-time tuition varies according to course load.

Collegiate Environment: Orientation program. Drama-theater group, choral group, student-run newspaper, radio station. Social organizations: 184 open to all. Most popular organizations: Waltham Group, Student Programming Board, performing groups, student government. Major annual events: Louis, Louis Weekend, Bronstein Weekend, Community Service Day. Student services: health clinic, personal-psychological counseling, women's center. Campus security: 24-hour emergency response devices and patrols, late night transport-escort service, controlled dormitory access. College housing designed to accommodate 2,456 students; 2,536 undergraduates lived in college housing during 2003-04. Freshmen guaranteed college housing. Option: coed housing available. Goldfarb Library plus 2 others with 938,835 books, 914,322 microform titles, 15,835 serials, 35,287 audiovisual materials, an OPAC, and a Web page. Operations spending for 2004 fiscal year: $11.5 million. 104 computers available on campus for general student use. Computer purchase/lease plans available. A campuswide network can be accessed from student residence rooms and from off campus. Staffed computer lab on campus.

Community Environment: Waltham is a city of 58,000, ten miles west of Boston on the Charles River. It is a traditional manufacturing community that now hosts extensive high-tech industries. The City is served by commuter railroad and excellent bus lines for easy access to Boston and Cambridge. The locale has two colleges, four hospitals, a wide range of religious institutions, public library, Federal Archives and Records Center, parks, and a variety of ethnic restaurants. Good job and community service opportunities for students are available.

■ **BRIDGEWATER STATE COLLEGE** *G-12*
Bridgewater, MA 02325-0001
Tel: (508)531-1000
Admissions: (508)531-1237
Fax: (508)531-1707
E-mail: admission@bridgew.edu
Web Site: http://www.bridgew.edu/

Description: State-supported, comprehensive, coed. Part of Massachusetts Public Higher Education System. Awards bachelor's and master's degrees and post-master's certificates. Founded 1840. Setting: 235-acre suburban campus with easy access to Boston. Endowment: $11.4 million. Educational spending for 2005 fiscal year: $3836 per student. Total enrollment: 9,649. Faculty: 494 (261 full-time, 233 part-time). Student-undergrad faculty ratio is 20:1. 5,446 applied, 80% were admitted. 6% from top 10% of their high school class, 30% from top quarter, 69% from top half. Students come from 32 states and territories, 28 other countries, 3% from out-of-state, 0.3% Native American, 2% Hispanic, 4% black, 1% Asian American or Pacific Islander, 1% international, 16% 25 or older, 31% live on campus. Retention: 75% of full-time freshmen returned the following year. Academic areas with the most degrees conferred: psychology; business/marketing; education. Core. Calendar: semesters. Academic remediation for entering students, ESL program, services for LD students, advanced placement, accelerated degree program, honors program, independent study, distance learning, double major, summer session for credit, part-time degree program, adult/continuing education programs, internships. Off campus study at 8 members of the Southeastern Association for Cooperation in Higher Education in Massachusetts, 9 members of the College Academic Program Sharing. Study abroad program. ROTC: Army (c), Air Force (c).

Entrance Requirements: Options: Common Application, electronic application, early admission, early action, deferred admission, international baccalaureate accepted. Required: essay, high school transcript, minimum 3.0 high school GPA, SAT or ACT. Recommended: recommendations. Entrance: moderately difficult. Application deadlines: 2/15, 11/15 for early action. Notification: continuous, 12/15 for early action.

Costs Per Year: Application fee: $25. State resident tuition: $910 full-time, $38 per credit hour part-time. Nonresident tuition: $7050 full-time, $294 per credit hour part-time. Mandatory fees: $4596 full-time, $188 per credit hour part-time. College room and board: $6614. College room only: $4114. Room and board charges vary according to board plan and housing facility.

Collegiate Environment: Orientation program. Drama-theater group, choral group, marching band, student-run newspaper, radio station. Social organizations: 76 open to all; national fraternities, national sororities, coed fraternities. Most popular organizations: Children's Developmental Clinic, Student Government Association, Afro-American/Latino Club, Program Committee. Major annual events: Homecoming, Springfest, Parents' Weekend. Student services: health clinic, personal-psychological counseling, women's center. Campus security: 24-hour emergency response devices and patrols, late night transport-escort service, controlled dormitory access. College housing designed to accommodate 2,045 students; 2,220 undergraduates lived in college housing during 2003-04. Freshmen given priority for college housing. Options: coed, women-only housing available. Clement Maxwell Library with 326,662 books, 756,874 microform titles, 1,100 serials, 10,590 audiovisual materials, an OPAC, and a Web page. Operations spending for 2004 fiscal year: $788,068. 780 computers available on campus for general student use. Computer purchase/lease plans available. A campuswide network can be accessed from student residence rooms and from off campus. Staffed computer lab on campus.

Community Environment: This largely residential, colonial town, 30 miles southeast of Boston, has among its manufactures, shoes, leatherboard, nails, and bricks. Extensive excavations by archaeologists have revealed the remains of two Indian civilizations in the area. Boston provides the area with all the cultural, and recreational advantages of a large city.

■ **BRISTOL COMMUNITY COLLEGE** *I-12*
777 Elsbree St.
Fall River, MA 02720-7395
Tel: (508)678-2811

Fax: (508)674-8838
E-mail: rclark@bristol.mass.edu
Web Site: http://www.bristol.mass.edu/

Description: State-supported, 2-year, coed. Awards certificates, transfer associate, and terminal associate degrees. Founded 1965. Setting: 105-acre urban campus with easy access to Boston. Endowment: $2.9 million. Total enrollment: 6,873. Student-undergrad faculty ratio is 19:1. 3,684 applied, 80% were admitted. Full-time: 3,097 students, 59% women, 41% men. Part-time: 3,776 students, 67% women, 33% men. Students come from 7 states and territories, 25 other countries, 7% from out-of-state, 1% Native American, 3% Hispanic, 5% black, 2% Asian American or Pacific Islander, 0.2% international, 35% 25 or older, 5% transferred in. Core. Calendar: semesters. Academic remediation for entering students, ESL program, services for LD students, self-designed majors, honors program, independent study, distance learning, summer session for credit, part-time degree program, adult/continuing education programs, co-op programs and internships. Off campus study at Southeastern Association for Cooperation in Higher Education in Massachusetts.

Entrance Requirements: Open admission except for nursing, dental hygiene, medical laboratory technology, occupational therapy assistant programs. Option: Common Application. Required: high school transcript. Entrance: noncompetitive. Notification: continuous. Preference given to state residents.

Costs Per Year: Application fee: $10. State resident tuition: $576 full-time, $24 per credit part-time. Nonresident tuition: $5520 full-time, $230 per credit part-time. Mandatory fees: $2544 full-time, $99 per credit part-time, $30 per term part-time.

Collegiate Environment: Orientation program. Drama-theater group, student-run newspaper. Social organizations: 32 open to all. Most popular organizations: International Club, MASS/PIRG WaterWatch, Criminal Justice Society, Society for Students in Free Enterprise, Portuguese Club. Major annual events: Orientation, Student Awards Night, International Festival. Student services: health clinic, personal-psychological counseling, women's center. Campus security: 24-hour emergency response devices and patrols, student patrols, late night transport-escort service. College housing not available. Learning Resources Center with 65,000 books, 380 serials, an OPAC, and a Web page. Operations spending for 2004 fiscal year: $990,128. 150 computers available on campus for general student use. A campuswide network can be accessed from off-campus. Staffed computer lab on campus.

Community Environment: Located approximately 50 miles south of Boston, Massachusetts and 18 miles southeast of Providence, Rhode Island on the New England Coast, the City is easily accessible by train, bus and air. Fall River's major industries include textiles, needlecrafts, and rubber and chemicals. The city, the factory outlet capital of New England, is experiencing a revitalization in its business and residential districts. Many opportunities exist for part-time and full-time work for students.

■ **BUNKER HILL COMMUNITY COLLEGE** *D-12*
250 New Rutherford Ave.
Boston, MA 02129-2925
Tel: (617)228-2000
Admissions: (617)228-2420
Fax: (617)228-2120
Web Site: http://www.bhcc.mass.edu/

Description: State-supported, 2-year, coed. Awards certificates, transfer associate, and terminal associate degrees. Founded 1973. Setting: 21-acre urban campus. Endowment: $2.1 million. Educational spending for 2005 fiscal year: $10,496 per student. Total enrollment: 7,837. Student-undergrad faculty ratio is 19:1. 3,697 applied, 69% were admitted. Full-time: 2,388 students, 56% women, 44% men. Part-time: 5,449 students, 61% women, 39% men. Students come from 18 states and territories, 93 other countries, 1% from out-of-state, 1% Native American, 14% Hispanic, 29% black, 14% Asian American or Pacific Islander, 6% international, 52% 25 or older, 3% transferred in. Core. Calendar: semesters. Academic remediation for entering students, ESL program, services for LD students, advanced placement, honors program, independent study, distance learning, summer session for credit, part-time degree program, external degree program, co-op programs and internships. Study abroad program.

Entrance Requirements: Open admission except for health career programs. Option: deferred admission. Required: high school transcript. Entrance: noncompetitive. Application deadline: Rolling. Notification: continuous.

Costs Per Year: Application fee: $10. State resident tuition: $576 full-time, $24 per credit part-time. Nonresident tuition: $5520 full-time, $230 per credit part-time. Mandatory fees: $1824 full-time, $76 per credit part-time.

Collegiate Environment: Orientation program. Drama-theater group, choral group, student-run radio station. Social organizations: 28 open to all. Most popular organizations: African-American Cultural Society, Asian-Pacific Students Association, Arab Students Association, Hospitality Club, Radio station. Major annual events: Holiday Stroll, Family Day, Spring Day. Student services: health clinic, personal-psychological counseling. Campus security: 24-hour emergency response devices and patrols, late night transport-escort service. College housing not available. Bunker Hill Community College Library with 65,953 books, 5,554 microform titles, 330 serials, 934 audiovisual materials, an OPAC, and a Web page. Operations spending for 2004 fiscal year: $388,584. 585 computers available on campus for general student use. A campuswide network can be accessed from off-campus. Staffed computer lab on campus.

Community Environment: The college is located on a 21-acre site in the Charlestown District of Boston. The campus is very near the Bunker Hill Monument and the U.S.S. Constitution. The school is within immediate access to Boston's bus-streetcar-subway system.

■ **CAMBRIDGE COLLEGE** *D-12*
1000 Massachusetts Ave.
Cambridge, MA 02138-5304
Tel: (617)868-1000
Free: 800-877-4723
Fax: (617)349-3545
Web Site: http://www.cambridgecollege.edu/

Description: Independent, comprehensive, coed. Awards bachelor's, master's, and doctoral degrees and post-master's certificates. Founded 1971. Setting: urban campus with easy access to Boston. Endowment: $6.4 million. Educational spending for 2005 fiscal year: $13,101 per student. Total enrollment: 4,031. Faculty: 806 (33 full-time, 773 part-time). Student-undergrad faculty ratio is 10:1. 503 applied, 99% were admitted. Full-time: 226 students, 66% women, 34% men. Part-time: 685 students, 74% women, 26% men. Students come from 15 states and territories, 6 other countries, 12% from out-of-state, 1% Native American, 24% Hispanic, 34% black, 3% Asian American or Pacific Islander, 2% international, 16% 25 or older, 49% transferred in. Retention: 28% of full-time freshmen returned the following year. Academic areas with the most degrees conferred: psychology; interdisciplinary studies; business/marketing. Core. Calendar: trimesters. ESL program, accelerated degree program, summer session for credit, part-time degree program, adult/continuing education programs, internships.

Entrance Requirements: Open admission. Option: deferred admission. Required: essay, high school transcript, recommendations, interview. Recommended: 3 years of work experience. Entrance: minimally difficult. Application deadline: Rolling. Notification: continuous.

Costs Per Year: Application fee: $30. One-time mandatory fee: $110. Tuition: $8040 full-time, $335 per credit part-time. Mandatory fees: $150 full-time.

Collegiate Environment: Orientation program. College housing not available. Cambridge College Online Library with an OPAC and a Web page. Operations spending for 2004 fiscal year: $168,758.

■ **CAPE COD COMMUNITY COLLEGE** *I-15*
2240 Iyanough Rd.
West Barnstable, MA 02668-1599
Tel: (508)362-2131
Web Site: http://www.capecod.mass.edu/

Description: State-supported, 2-year, coed. Part of Massachusetts Public Higher Education System. Awards certificates, transfer associate, and terminal associate degrees. Founded 1961. Setting: 120-acre rural campus with easy access to Boston. Endowment: $3.8 million. Educational spending for 2005 fiscal year: $8081 per student. Total enrollment: 4,243. 1,179 applied, 98% were admitted. 10% from top quarter of their high school class, 31% from top half. Full-time: 1,470 students, 58% women, 42% men. Part-time: 2,773 students, 68% women, 32% men. Students come from 24 states and territories, 5 other countries, 1% from out-of-state, 1% Native American, 2% Hispanic, 4% black, 1% Asian American or Pacific Islander, 1% international, 58% 25 or older, 10% transferred in. Core. Calendar: semesters. Academic remediation for entering students, ESL program, services for LD students, advanced placement, freshman honors college, honors program, independent study, distance learning, summer session for credit, part-time degree program, adult/continuing education programs, co-op programs and internships. Off campus study at Bridgewater State College, Bristol Community College, Dean College, Massasoit Community College, Stonehill College, University of Massachusetts Dartmouth. Study abroad program.

Entrance Requirements: Open admission except for nursing, dental hygiene, physical therapy programs. Options: deferred admission, international baccalaureate accepted. Required: high school transcript. Required for some: essay, recommendations. Entrance: noncompetitive. Application deadline: 8/10. Notification: continuous. Preference given to state residents.

Costs Per Year: Application fee: $10. State resident tuition: $720 full-time, $24 per credit hour part-time. Nonresident tuition: $6900 full-time, $230 per credit hour part-time. Mandatory fees: $2940 full-time, $98 per credit hour part-time.

Collegiate Environment: Orientation program. Drama-theater group, choral group, student-run newspaper, radio station. Social organizations: 31 open to all. Most popular organizations: Innkeepers Club, Phi Theta Kappa, Student Senate, Learning Disabilities Support Group, Ethnic Diversity. Major annual events: Spree Day, Commencement festivities, Annual Arts Festival. Student services: health clinic, personal-psychological counseling, women's center. Campus security: 24-hour patrols. College housing not available. Cape Cod Community College Learning Resource Center with 54,342 books, 30,740 microform titles, 705 serials, 6,107 audiovisual materials, and an OPAC. Operations spending for 2004 fiscal year: $588,557. 240 computers available on campus for general student use. A campuswide network can be accessed from off-campus. Staffed computer lab on campus.

Community Environment: A rural village in the town of Barnstable on Cape Cod with several museums dedicated to early Americana in the area. The community has excellent facilities for all sports, yacht races and tournaments, and many historic celebrations. Part-time employment is available with exceptional opportunities in the summer. Transportation provided by air and bus. Shopping facilities are excellent.

■ **CLARK UNIVERSITY** *E-9*

950 Main St.
Worcester, MA 01610-1477
Tel: (508)793-7711
Free: 800-GO-CLARK
Admissions: (508)793-7431
Fax: (508)793-8821
E-mail: admissions@clarku.edu
Web Site: http://www.clarku.edu/

Description: Independent, university, coed. Awards bachelor's, master's, and doctoral degrees and post-master's certificates. Founded 1887. Setting: 50-acre urban campus with easy access to Boston. Endowment: $206 million. Research spending for 2004 fiscal year: $3195. Educational spending for 2005 fiscal year: $10,154 per student. Total enrollment: 3,118. Faculty: 263 (167 full-time, 96 part-time). Student-undergrad faculty ratio is 10:1. 4,463 applied, 62% were admitted. 34% from top 10% of their high school class, 70% from top quarter, 97% from top half. Full-time: 2,097 students, 60% women, 40% men. Part-time: 158 students, 54% women, 46% men. Students come from 48 states and territories, 55 other countries, 61% from out-of-state, 0.3% Native American, 2% Hispanic, 2% black, 4% Asian American or Pacific Islander, 7% international, 1% 25 or older, 77% live on campus, 2% transferred in. Retention: 86% of full-time freshmen returned the following year. Academic areas with the most degrees conferred: social sciences; psychology; biological/life sciences. Core. Calendar: semesters. Academic remediation for entering students, ESL program, services for LD students, advanced placement, accelerated degree program, self-designed majors, honors program, independent study, double major, summer session for credit, part-time degree program, adult/continuing education programs, internships, graduate courses open to undergrads. Off campus study at Worcester Consortium for Higher Education, Howard University. Study abroad program. ROTC: Army (c), Naval (c), Air Force (c).

Entrance Requirements: Options: Peterson's Universal Application, Common Application, early admission, early decision, deferred admission. Required: essay, high school transcript, 2 recommendations, SAT or ACT. Recommended: interview. Entrance: moderately difficult. Application deadlines: 1/15, 11/15 for early decision. Notification: 4/1, 12/15 for early decision.

Costs Per Year: Application fee: $50. Comprehensive fee: $37,365 includes full-time tuition ($31,200), mandatory fees ($265), and college room and board ($5900). College room only: $3550. Room and board charges vary according to board plan and housing facility. Part-time tuition: $915.63 per credit hour.

Collegiate Environment: Orientation program. Drama-theater group, choral group, marching band, student-run newspaper, radio station. Social organizations: 74 open to all. Most popular organizations: Student Activities

Board, Hillel, Pub Entertainment Committee, Massachusetts PIRG, Film Society. Major annual events: Academic Spree Day, Student Spree Day, G and P Variety Show. Student services: health clinic, personal-psychological counseling, women's center. Campus security: 24-hour emergency response devices and patrols, student patrols, late night transport-escort service, controlled dormitory access. 1,570 college housing spaces available; 1,545 were occupied in 2003-04. Freshmen guaranteed college housing. On-campus residence required through sophomore year. Options: coed, women-only housing available. Robert Hutchings Goddard Library plus 4 others with 289,658 books, 60,084 microform titles, 1,383 serials, 1,007 audiovisual materials, an OPAC, and a Web page. Operations spending for 2004 fiscal year: $2.8 million. 200 computers available on campus for general student use. A campuswide network can be accessed from student residence rooms and from off campus. Staffed computer lab on campus.

Community Environment: An industrial center and state center for biotechnology and related research, Worcester is the second largest city in all of New England. Good transportation facilities make area easily accessible. Located 38 miles west of Boston, city has several religious groups of all denominations, as well as significant libraries, museums, parks, theatre, and music facilities and municipal recreation opportunities and the Centrum (seating 13,000) houses concerts, sport events, and exhibits. Many students take advantage of the city's offerings through paid and unpaid internships with area corporations and institutions.

■ **COLLEGE OF THE HOLY CROSS** *E-9*

1 College St.
Worcester, MA 01610-2395
Tel: (508)793-2011
Free: 800-442-2421
Admissions: (508)793-2443
Fax: (508)793-3888
E-mail: admissions@holycross.edu
Web Site: http://www.holycross.edu/

Description: Independent Roman Catholic (Jesuit), 4-year, coed. Awards bachelor's degrees. Founded 1843. Setting: 174-acre suburban campus with easy access to Boston. Endowment: $465.3 million. Research spending for 2004 fiscal year: $2.1 million. Educational spending for 2005 fiscal year: $13,777 per student. Total enrollment: 2,816. Student-undergrad faculty ratio is 11:1. 4,744 applied, 48% were admitted. 66% from top 10% of their high school class, 93% from top quarter, 100% from top half. 3 National Merit Scholars, 19 valedictorians. Full-time: 2,788 students, 55% women, 45% men. Part-time: 28 students, 86% women, 14% men. Students come from 51 states and territories, 18 other countries, 63% from out-of-state, 0.4% Native American, 6% Hispanic, 4% black, 5% Asian American or Pacific Islander, 1% international, 0% 25 or older, 88% live on campus, 1% transferred in. Retention: 97% of full-time freshmen returned the following year. Academic areas with the most degrees conferred: social sciences; English; history. Core. Calendar: semesters. Advanced placement, accelerated degree program, self-designed majors, honors program, independent study, double major, internships. Off campus study at Colleges of Worcester Consortium of Higher Education. Study abroad program. ROTC: Army (c), Naval, Air Force (c).

Entrance Requirements: Options: Peterson's Universal Application, Common Application, electronic application, early admission, early decision, deferred admission, international baccalaureate accepted. Required: essay, high school transcript, 2 recommendations. Recommended: interview. Entrance: very difficult. Application deadlines: 1/15, 12/15 for early decision. Notification: 4/1, 1/15 for early decision.

Costs Per Year: Application fee: $50. Comprehensive fee: $40,664 includes full-time tuition ($30,960), mandatory fees ($484), and college room and board ($9220). College room only: $4610. Room and board charges vary according to board plan and housing facility.

Collegiate Environment: Orientation program. Drama-theater group, choral group, marching band, student-run newspaper, radio station. Social organizations: 94 open to all. Most popular organizations: SPUD (community service organization), choral and music groups, Campus Activities Board, Student Government Association, Purple Key Society. Major annual events: homecoming, Family Weekend, Spring Weekend. Student services: health clinic, personal-psychological counseling, women's center. Campus security: 24-hour emergency response devices and patrols, late night transport-escort service, controlled dormitory access. 2,353 college housing spaces available; 2,272 were occupied in 2003-04. Freshmen guaranteed college housing. On-campus residence required through sophomore year. Option: coed housing available. Dinand Library plus 5 others with 606,647 books, 15,913 microform titles, 1,626 serials, 26,675 audiovisual materials, an OPAC, and a Web page. Operations spending for 2004 fiscal year: $2.9 million. 482 computers available on campus for general student use. Computer purchase/lease plans available. A campuswide network can be accessed from student residence rooms and from off campus. Staffed computer lab on campus.

Community Environment: See Clark University.

■ **CURRY COLLEGE** *E-12*
1071 Blue Hill Ave.
Milton, MA 02186-9984
Tel: (617)333-0500
Free: 800-669-0686
Admissions: (617)333-2210
Fax: (617)333-6860
E-mail: curryadm@curry.edu
Web Site: http://www.curry.edu/

Description: Independent, comprehensive, coed. Awards bachelor's and master's degrees. Founded 1879. Setting: 131-acre suburban campus with easy access to Boston. Endowment: $13.9 million. Educational spending for 2005 fiscal year: $9544 per student. Total enrollment: 3,202. Faculty: 372 (102 full-time, 270 part-time). Student-undergrad faculty ratio is 12:1. 3,006 applied, 69% were admitted. 4% from top 10% of their high school class, 27% from top quarter, 57% from top half. Full-time: 2,203 students, 48% women, 52% men. Part-time: 752 students, 68% women, 32% men. Students come from 26 states and territories, 15 other countries, 34% from out-of-state, 0.1% Native American, 3% Hispanic, 8% black, 1% Asian American or Pacific Islander, 1% international, 4% 25 or older, 65% live on campus, 4% transferred in. Retention: 69% of full-time freshmen returned the following year. Academic areas with the most degrees conferred: health professions and related sciences; security and protective services; business/marketing. Core. Calendar: semesters. Academic remediation for entering students, services for LD students, advanced placement, accelerated degree program, self-designed majors, honors program, independent study, double major, summer session for credit, part-time degree program, external degree program, adult/continuing education programs, internships. Off campus study. Study abroad program. ROTC: Army (c).

Entrance Requirements: Options: Common Application, electronic application, early admission, early decision, deferred admission. Required: essay, high school transcript, minimum 2.0 high school GPA, 1 recommendation. Recommended: interview. Required for some: interview, SAT or ACT, Wechsler Adult Intelligence Scale-Revised for PAL candidates. Entrance: moderately difficult. Application deadlines: 4/1, 12/1 for early decision. Notification: continuous, 12/15 for early decision.

Costs Per Year: Application fee: $40. Comprehensive fee: $33,940 includes full-time tuition ($23,400), mandatory fees ($900), and college room and board ($9640). College room only: $5640.

Collegiate Environment: Orientation program. Drama-theater group, choral group, student-run newspaper, radio station. Social organizations: 22 open to all. Most popular organizations: student radio station, student government, Community Campus Activities Board, student newspaper, Drama Club. Major annual events: Homecoming, Midnight Madness, Spring Fest. Student services: health clinic, personal-psychological counseling. Campus security: 24-hour emergency response devices and patrols, late night transport-escort service, controlled dormitory access. 1,285 college housing spaces available; 1,235 were occupied in 2003-04. No special consideration for freshman housing applicants. Options: coed, men-only, women-only housing available. Levin Library plus 1 other with 90,000 books, 24,000 microform titles, 675 serials, 1,050 audiovisual materials, an OPAC, and a Web page. Operations spending for 2004 fiscal year: $850,915. 120 computers available on campus for general student use. A campuswide network can be accessed from student residence rooms and from off campus. Staffed computer lab on campus.

Community Environment: Suburban location about seven miles south of Boston near the Neponset River in the town of Milton. All forms of transportation easily accessible. Shuttle bus to Boston, rapid transit. Blue Hills Reservation, a summer and winter sports center with golf course, ice rink, ski slopes, is located nearby. Job opportunities, community services, and cultural advantages will be found in neighboring Boston, as well as on campus.

■ **DEAN COLLEGE** *F-10*
99 Main St.
Franklin, MA 02038-1994

Tel: (508)541-1900; 877-TRY-DEAN
Admissions: (508)541-1508
Fax: (508)541-8726
E-mail: admissions@dean.edu
Web Site: http://www.dean.edu/

Description: Independent, primarily 2-year, coed. Awards certificates, transfer associate, terminal associate, and bachelor's degrees. Founded 1865. Setting: 100-acre small town campus with easy access to Boston and Providence. Endowment: $20.7 million. Total enrollment: 1,249. Student-undergrad faculty ratio is 19:1. 1,816 applied, 74% were admitted. Full-time: 925 students, 45% women, 55% men. Part-time: 324 students, 69% women, 31% men. Students come from 25 states and territories, 14 other countries, 48% from out-of-state, 0.4% Native American, 3% Hispanic, 5% black, 2% Asian American or Pacific Islander, 7% international, 3% 25 or older, 90% live on campus, 3% transferred in. Retention: 69% of full-time freshmen returned the following year. Academic area with the most degrees conferred: visual and performing arts. Core. Calendar: semesters. Academic remediation for entering students, ESL program, services for LD students, advanced placement, accelerated degree program, self-designed majors, freshman honors college, honors program, independent study, summer session for credit, part-time degree program, adult/continuing education programs, internships. Off campus study at Washington Center for Internships and Academic Seminars.

Entrance Requirements: Options: Peterson's Universal Application, Common Application, electronic application, deferred admission, international baccalaureate accepted. Required: essay, high school transcript, recommendations, SAT or ACT. Recommended: minimum 2.0 high school GPA, interview. Entrance: minimally difficult. Application deadline: Rolling. Notification: continuous.

Costs Per Year: Application fee: $35. One-time mandatory fee: $200. Comprehensive fee: $34,350 includes full-time tuition ($24,000) and college room and board ($10,350). College room only: $6550. Part-time tuition: $690 per course.

Collegiate Environment: Orientation program. Drama-theater group, choral group, student-run radio station. Social organizations: 30 open to all. Most popular organizations: Emerging Leaders, College Success Staff, Student Ambassadors, student government, Phi Theta Kappa. Major annual events: Homecoming, Harvest Weekend, Leadership Conference. Student services: health clinic, personal-psychological counseling. Campus security: 24-hour emergency response devices and patrols, late night transport-escort service, controlled dormitory access. 817 college housing spaces available Free: 800 were occupied in 2003-04. Freshmen guaranteed college housing. On-campus residence required through sophomore year. Option: coed housing available. E. Ross Anderson Library with 46,226 books and 185 serials. 150 computers available on campus for general student use. A campuswide network can be accessed from student residence rooms. Staffed computer lab on campus.

Community Environment: Franklin is located 30 miles southwest of Boston and is the birthplace of Horace Mann. This is a rapidly growing area easily accessible by bus and rail. The community has swimming pools, tennis courts, ski facilities, riding, golf, movies, bowling, and dancing. There are many shopping centers nearby. Some part-time employment is available for students.

■ **EASTERN NAZARENE COLLEGE** *E-12*
23 East Elm Ave.
Quincy, MA 02170-2999
Tel: (617)745-3000
Free: 800-88-ENC88
Admissions: (617)745-3732
Fax: (617)745-3907
E-mail: webbd@enc.edu
Web Site: http://www.enc.edu/

Description: Independent, comprehensive, coed, affiliated with Church of the Nazarene. Awards associate, bachelor's, and master's degrees. Founded 1918. Setting: 15-acre suburban campus with easy access to Boston. Endowment: $8 million. Educational spending for 2005 fiscal year: $4532 per student. Total enrollment: 1,212. 552 applied, 62% were admitted. 17 class presidents, 10 valedictorians, 25 student government officers. Full-time: 1,043 students, 61% women, 39% men. Part-time: 26 students, 54% women, 46% men. Students come from 32 states and territories, 18 other countries, 57% from out-of-state, 1% Native American, 4% Hispanic, 10% black, 2% Asian American or Pacific Islander, 1% international, 50% 25 or older, 82% live on campus, 3% transferred in. Retention: 77% of full-time freshmen returned the following year. Core. Calendar: 4-1-4. Academic remediation for entering students, ESL program, services for LD students, advanced placement, accelerated degree program, honors program, independent study, double major, summer session for credit, part-time degree program, adult/continuing education programs, internships, graduate courses open to undergrads. Off campus study at Coalition for Christian Colleges and Universities, Boston University, Massachusetts College of Pharmacy and Allied Health Sciences, Boston College. Study abroad program. ROTC: Army (c).

Entrance Requirements: Options: early admission, deferred admission. Required: essay, high school transcript, minimum 2.3 high school GPA, 2 recommendations, interview, SAT or ACT. Entrance: moderately difficult. Application deadline: Rolling. Notification: continuous.

Costs Per Year: Application fee: $25. Comprehensive fee: $24,900 includes full-time tuition ($17,700), mandatory fees ($610), and college room and board ($6590). Full-time tuition and fees vary according to course load. Room and board charges vary according to board plan, gender, and housing facility. Part-time tuition: $750 per credit hour. Part-time tuition varies according to course load.

Collegiate Environment: Orientation program. Drama-theater group, choral group, student-run newspaper, radio station. Social organizations: 26 open to all. Most popular organizations: AMS Associated Men Students, AWS Associated Women Students, gospel choir, ACTS Actors Christians Teachers Singers, Kid's Club. Major annual events: Festival of Life, Homecoming, Heritage Day/Alumni Day. Student services: health clinic, personal-psychological counseling. Campus security: 24-hour emergency response devices and patrols, student patrols, late night transport-escort service, controlled dormitory access. On-campus residence required through senior year. Options: men-only, women-only housing available. Nease Library with 117,540 books, 57,030 microform titles, 466 serials, 1,290 audiovisual materials, and an OPAC. Operations spending for 2004 fiscal year: $473,409. 98 computers available on campus for general student use. A campuswide network can be accessed from student residence rooms and from off campus. Staffed computer lab on campus.

Community Environment: See Quincy College.

■ **ELMS COLLEGE** *F-5*
291 Springfield St.
Chicopee, MA 01013-2839
Tel: (413)594-2761
Free: 800-255-ELMS
Admissions: (413)592-3189
Fax: (413)594-2781
Web Site: http://www.elms.edu/
Description: Independent Roman Catholic, comprehensive, coed. Awards associate, bachelor's, and master's degrees. Founded 1928. Setting: 32-acre suburban campus. Endowment: $6 million. Research spending for 2004 fiscal year: $53,003. Educational spending for 2005 fiscal year: $7359 per student. Total enrollment: 1,234. Faculty: 146 (59 full-time, 87 part-time). Student-undergrad faculty ratio is 12:1. 447 applied, 89% were admitted. 15% from top 10% of their high school class, 45% from top quarter, 70% from top half. Full-time: 681 students, 75% women, 25% men. Part-time: 385 students, 90% women, 10% men. Students come from 11 states and territories, 1 other country, 19% from out-of-state, 0.1% Native American, 3% Hispanic, 4% black, 1% Asian American or Pacific Islander, 0.2% international, 40% 25 or older, 39% live on campus, 4% transferred in. Retention: 80% of full-time freshmen returned the following year. Core. Calendar: semesters. Academic remediation for entering students, ESL program, advanced placement, accelerated degree program, self-designed majors, honors program, double major, summer session for credit, part-time degree program, adult/continuing education programs, internships, graduate courses open to undergrads. Off campus study at Cooperating Colleges of Greater Springfield, Sisters of Saint Joseph Colleges Consortium. Study abroad program. ROTC: Army (c), Air Force (c).

Entrance Requirements: Options: Peterson's Universal Application, Common Application, early admission, deferred admission, international baccalaureate accepted. Required: essay, high school transcript, 2 recommendations, SAT or ACT. Recommended: interview. Entrance: moderately difficult. Application deadline: Rolling. Notification: continuous.

Costs Per Year: Application fee: $30. Comprehensive fee: $29,920 includes full-time tuition ($21,520) and college room and board ($8400). Part-time tuition: $440 per credit. Part-time mandatory fees: $20 per term.

Collegiate Environment: Orientation program. Drama-theater group, choral group, student-run newspaper, radio station. Social organizations: 25 open

to all. Most popular organizations: Student Government Association, Zonta, Elmscript, Umoja, Social Work Club. Major annual events: Midnight Madness, Semi-Formal, Soph Show. Student services: health clinic, personal-psychological counseling. Campus security: 24-hour emergency response devices and patrols, late night transport-escort service, controlled dormitory access. 313 college housing spaces available; 229 were occupied in 2003-04. Freshmen guaranteed college housing. Options: coed, women-only housing available. Alumnae Library with 111,379 books, 3,334 microform titles, 529 serials, 2,948 audiovisual materials, and an OPAC. Operations spending for 2004 fiscal year: $466,344. 70 computers available on campus for general student use. A campuswide network can be accessed from student residence rooms and from off campus. Staffed computer lab on campus.

Community Environment: Elms is located in western Massachusetts, two and one half miles from Springfield, near the junction of I-91 and I-90 (Mass. Turnpike). The climate is temperate. The community has several churches, museums, a library, theatre, sports center, cultural and social events at many of the nearby colleges, shopping, and major civic, fraternal, and veteran's organizations. Part-time employment is available.

■ **EMERSON COLLEGE** *D-12*
120 Boylston St.
Boston, MA 02116-4624
Tel: (617)824-8500
Admissions: (617)824-8600
Fax: (617)824-8609
E-mail: admission@emerson.edu
Web Site: http://www.emerson.edu/
Description: Independent, comprehensive, coed. Awards bachelor's, master's, and doctoral degrees. Founded 1880. Setting: urban campus. Endowment: $86.5 million. Educational spending for 2005 fiscal year: $8292 per student. Total enrollment: 4,326. Faculty: 381 (143 full-time, 238 part-time). Student-undergrad faculty ratio is 14:1. 5,008 applied, 45% were admitted. 36% from top 10% of their high school class, 83% from top quarter, 99% from top half. 8 valedictorians. Full-time: 3,092 students, 56% women, 44% men. Part-time: 281 students, 60% women, 40% men. Students come from 47 states and territories, 43 other countries, 63% from out-of-state, 1% Native American, 5% Hispanic, 2% black, 4% Asian American or Pacific Islander, 3% international, 3% 25 or older, 45% live on campus, 7% transferred in. Retention: 89% of full-time freshmen returned the following year. Academic areas with the most degrees conferred: visual and performing arts; communications/journalism; business/marketing; English. Core. Calendar: semesters. Services for LD students, advanced placement, self-designed majors, honors program, independent study, double major, summer session for credit, part-time degree program, adult/continuing education programs, internships, graduate courses open to undergrads. Off campus study. Study abroad program.

Entrance Requirements: Options: Peterson's Universal Application, electronic application, early admission, early action, deferred admission, international baccalaureate accepted. Required: essay, high school transcript, 2 recommendations, SAT or ACT. Required for some: interview, audition, essay, portfolio, or resume for performing arts applicants. Entrance: very difficult. Application deadlines: 1/5, 11/1 for early action. Notification: 4/1, 12/15 for early action.

Costs Per Year: Application fee: $60. Comprehensive fee: $35,042 includes full-time tuition ($24,064), mandatory fees ($558), and college room and board ($10,420). College room only: $6200. Part-time tuition: $752 per credit hour.

Collegiate Environment: Orientation program. Drama-theater group, choral group, student-run newspaper, radio station. Social organizations: 60 open to all; national fraternities, national sororities, local fraternities, local sororities; 3% of eligible men and 3% of eligible women are members. Most popular organizations: EIV (Emerson Independent Video), WERS 88.9 FM, Musical Theatre Society, Berkeley Beacon, International Student Association. Major annual events: EVVY's, Spring Musical, Hand Me Down Night. Student services: health clinic, personal-psychological counseling. Campus security: 24-hour emergency response devices and patrols, late night transport-escort service, controlled dormitory access. 1,207 college housing spaces available; all were occupied in 2003-04. Freshmen given priority for college housing. Option: coed housing available. Emerson Library plus 1 other with 174,782 books, 9,129 microform titles, 16,426 serials, 9,760 audiovisual materials, an OPAC, and a Web page. Operations spending for 2004 fiscal year: $2.8 million. 385 computers available on campus for general student use. A campuswide network can be accessed from student residence rooms and from off campus. Staffed computer lab on campus.

Community Environment: See Boston University.

■ **EMMANUEL COLLEGE** *D-12*
400 The Fenway
Boston, MA 02115
Tel: (617)277-9340
Admissions: (617)735-9715
Fax: (617)735-9801
E-mail: enroll@emmanuel.edu
Web Site: http://www.emmanuel.edu/
Description: Independent Roman Catholic, comprehensive, coed. Awards bachelor's and master's degrees and post-master's certificates. Founded 1919. Setting: 16-acre urban campus. Endowment: $62 million. Educational spending for 2005 fiscal year: $3518 per student. Total enrollment: 2,296. Faculty: 222 (67 full-time, 155 part-time). Student-undergrad faculty ratio is 16:1. 3,107 applied, 61% were admitted. 15% from top 10% of their high school class, 41% from top quarter, 78% from top half. Full-time: 1,503 students, 74% women, 26% men. Part-time: 593 students, 80% women, 20% men. Students come from 34 states and territories, 39 other countries, 28% from out-of-state, 0.3% Native American, 4% Hispanic, 7% black, 4% Asian American or Pacific Islander, 3% international, 29% 25 or older, 65% live on campus, 3% transferred in. Retention: 83% of full-time freshmen returned the following year. Academic areas with the most degrees conferred: business/marketing; health professions and related sciences; education. Core. Calendar: semesters. Academic remediation for entering students, ESL program, services for LD students, advanced placement, accelerated degree program, self-designed majors, honors program, independent study, double major, summer session for credit, part-time degree program, adult/continuing education programs, internships, graduate courses open to undergrads. Off campus study at College of Notre Dame (CA), Colleges of the Fenway. Study abroad program. ROTC: Army (c).
Entrance Requirements: Options: Peterson's Universal Application, Common Application, electronic application, early admission, early decision, deferred admission, international baccalaureate accepted. Required: essay, high school transcript, 2 recommendations, SAT or ACT. Required for some: interview. Entrance: moderately difficult. Application deadlines: 3/1, 11/1 for early decision. Notification: 12/1, 12/1 for early decision.
Costs Per Year: Application fee: $40. Comprehensive fee: $32,000 includes full-time tuition ($21,900), mandatory fees ($400), and college room and board ($9700). Full-time tuition and fees vary according to course load, degree level, and program. Room and board charges vary according to housing facility. Part-time tuition: $684 per credit. Part-time tuition varies according to program.
Collegiate Environment: Orientation program. Drama-theater group, choral group, student-run newspaper, radio station. Social organizations: 25 open to all. Most popular organizations: Hellas, Student Government Association, Peace and Justice Club, Theatre Guild, L.E.A.D.E.R.S. Major annual events: Family Weekend, Clam Bake, Tap-Off Tournament. Student services: personal-psychological counseling. Campus security: 24-hour emergency response devices and patrols, late night transport-escort service, controlled dormitory access, 24-hour security personnel on duty at front desk in residence halls. College housing designed to accommodate 1,023 students; 1,029 undergraduates lived in college housing during 2003-04. Freshmen guaranteed college housing. Option: coed housing available. Cardinal Cushing Library with 97,627 books, 2,128 microform titles, 394 serials, 567 audiovisual materials, an OPAC, and a Web page. Operations spending for 2004 fiscal year: $590,561. 115 computers available on campus for general student use. A campuswide network can be accessed from student residence rooms and from off campus. Staffed computer lab on campus.

■ **ENDICOTT COLLEGE** *C-13*
376 Hale St.
Beverly, MA 01915-2096
Tel: (978)927-0585
Free: 800-325-1114
Admissions: (978)921-1000
Fax: (978)927-0084
E-mail: admissio@endicott.edu
Web Site: http://www.endicott.edu/
Description: Independent, comprehensive, coed. Awards associate, bachelor's, and master's degrees. Founded 1939. Setting: 240-acre suburban campus with easy access to Boston. Endowment: $14.9 million. Total enrollment: 3,326. Faculty: 146 (66 full-time, 80 part-time). Student-undergrad faculty ratio is 16:1. 3,081 applied, 47% were admitted. 9% from

top 10% of their high school class, 35% from top quarter, 79% from top half. Full-time: 1,860 students, 59% women, 41% men. Part-time: 178 students, 54% women, 46% men. Students come from 28 states and territories, 33 other countries, 53% from out-of-state, 0.4% Native American, 1% Hispanic, 1% black, 0.5% Asian American or Pacific Islander, 4% international, 10% 25 or older, 84% live on campus, 3% transferred in. Retention: 82% of full-time freshmen returned the following year. Academic areas with the most degrees conferred: business/marketing; visual and performing arts; psychology. Core. Calendar: semesters. Academic remediation for entering students, ESL program, advanced placement, accelerated degree program, self-designed majors, honors program, independent study, distance learning, summer session for credit, part-time degree program, adult/continuing education programs, internships. Off campus study at 10 members of the Northeast Consortium of Colleges and Universities in Massachusetts. Study abroad program. ROTC: Army (c).
Entrance Requirements: Options: Common Application, electronic application, deferred admission, international baccalaureate accepted. Required: essay, high school transcript, minimum 2.5 high school GPA, SAT or ACT. Recommended: interview. Required for some: interview. Entrance: moderately difficult. Application deadline: 2/15. Notification: continuous.
Costs Per Year: Application fee: $40. Comprehensive fee: $30,156 includes full-time tuition ($19,690), mandatory fees ($700), and college room and board ($9766). College room only: $6846. Full-time tuition and fees vary according to student level. Room and board charges vary according to board plan and housing facility. Part-time tuition: $615 per credit. Part-time mandatory fees: $200 per term. Part-time tuition and fees vary according to student level.
Collegiate Environment: Orientation program. Drama-theater group, choral group, student-run newspaper, radio station. Social organizations: 20 open to all. Most popular organizations: Student Activities Committee, student government, yearbook, Admissions Ambassadors, Adventure Base Council. Major annual events: Spring Week, Halloween activities, Winter Carnival. Student services: health clinic, personal-psychological counseling. Campus security: 24-hour emergency response devices and patrols, late night transport-escort service, controlled dormitory access. 1,369 college housing spaces available; all were occupied in 2003-04. Freshmen guaranteed college housing. On-campus residence required through senior year. Options: coed, women-only housing available. Endicott College Library with 121,000 books, 23,500 microform titles, 3,500 serials, 475 audiovisual materials, an OPAC, and a Web page. Operations spending for 2004 fiscal year: $446,243. 150 computers available on campus for general student use. A campuswide network can be accessed from student residence rooms and from off campus. Staffed computer lab on campus.
Community Environment: Suburban.

■ **FINE MORTUARY COLLEGE, LLC** *E-11*
150 Kerry Place
Norwood, MA 02062
Tel: (781)762-1211
Fax: (781)762-7177
Web Site: http://www.fine-ne.com/
Description: Proprietary, 2-year, coed. Founded 1996. Calendar: continuous.

■ **FISHER COLLEGE** *D-12*
118 Beacon St.
Boston, MA 02116-1500
Tel: (617)236-8800
Free: 800-446-1226
Admissions: (617)236-8822
Fax: (617)236-8858
Web Site: http://www.fisher.edu/
Description: Independent, primarily 2-year, coed. Awards transfer associate, terminal associate, and bachelor's degrees. Founded 1903. Setting: urban campus. Endowment: $12.9 million. Total enrollment: 507. Student-undergrad faculty ratio is 18:1. 1,700 applied, 62% were admitted. Full-time: 507 students, 66% women, 34% men. Students come from 14 states and territories, 21 other countries, 21% from out-of-state, 0.2% Native American, 16% Hispanic, 19% black, 4% Asian American or Pacific Islander, 11% international, 47% 25 or older, 50% live on campus, 18% transferred in. Core. Calendar: semesters. Academic remediation for entering students, ESL program, advanced placement, summer session for credit, part-time degree program, adult/continuing education programs, internships. Off campus study at Emerson College.

Entrance Requirements: Options: Peterson's Universal Application, deferred admission. Required: high school transcript. Recommended: minimum 2.0 high school GPA. Required for some: essay, recommendations, interview. Entrance: minimally difficult. Application deadline: Rolling. Notification: continuous.

Costs Per Year: Application fee: $25. Comprehensive fee: $30,280 includes full-time tuition ($18,330), mandatory fees ($950), and college room and board ($11,000).

Collegiate Environment: Orientation program. Drama-theater group, choral group. Most popular organizations: Drama Club, student government, Student Activity Club, Inter-Cultural Club. Major annual events: Parents' Weekend, Fashion Show, All-College Outing. Student services: health clinic, personal-psychological counseling, women's center. Campus security: 24-hour emergency response devices and patrols, controlled dormitory access. Options: coed, women-only housing available. Fisher College Library plus 1 other with 30,000 books, 160 serials, and an OPAC. 112 computers available on campus for general student use. A campuswide network can be accessed from off-campus. Staffed computer lab on campus.

Community Environment: See Boston University.

■ **FITCHBURG STATE COLLEGE** *C-9*
160 Pearl St.
Fitchburg, MA 01420-2697
Tel: (978)345-2151
Free: 800-705-9692
Fax: (978)665-4540
Web Site: http://www.fsc.edu/
Description: State-supported, comprehensive, coed. Part of Massachusetts Public Higher Education System. Awards bachelor's and master's degrees and post-master's certificates. Founded 1894. Setting: 45-acre small town campus with easy access to Boston. Endowment: $9.9 million. Total enrollment: 5,340. Faculty: 242 (166 full-time, 76 part-time). Student-undergrad faculty ratio is 16:1. 3,070 applied, 67% were admitted. Full-time: 2,950 students, 55% women, 45% men. Part-time: 703 students, 59% women, 41% men. Students come from 20 states and territories, 7% from out-of-state, 0.3% Native American, 3% Hispanic, 3% black, 2% Asian American or Pacific Islander, 1% international, 16% 25 or older, 48% live on campus, 8% transferred in. Retention: 78% of full-time freshmen returned the following year. Academic areas with the most degrees conferred: business/marketing; visual and performing arts; education. Core. Calendar: semesters. Academic remediation for entering students, services for LD students, advanced placement, accelerated degree program, self-designed majors, honors program, independent study, distance learning, double major, summer session for credit, part-time degree program, adult/continuing education programs, internships. Study abroad program. ROTC: Air Force (c).

Entrance Requirements: Options: Peterson's Universal Application, Common Application, electronic application, deferred admission. Required: essay, high school transcript, minimum 2.0 high school GPA, SAT or ACT. Recommended: recommendations. Entrance: moderately difficult. Notification: continuous, continuous for nonresidents.

Costs Per Year: Application fee: $10. State resident tuition: $970 full-time, $40.42 per credit part-time. Nonresident tuition: $7050 full-time, $293.75 per credit part-time. Mandatory fees: $4032 full-time, $168 per credit part-time. College room and board: $6274.

Collegiate Environment: Orientation program. Drama-theater group, choral group, student-run newspaper, radio station. Social organizations: 65 open to all; national fraternities, national sororities; 10% of eligible men and 15% of eligible women are members. Most popular organizations: Student Government Association, Residence Hall Council, student radio station, student newspaper, Dance Club. Major annual events: film festivals, student Convocations, Falcon Fest. Student services: health clinic, personal-psychological counseling. Campus security: 24-hour emergency response devices and patrols, student patrols, late night transport-escort service, controlled dormitory access. College housing designed to accommodate 1,400 students; 1,470 undergraduates lived in college housing during 2003-04. Freshmen given priority for college housing. Option: coed housing available. Hammond Library with 238,743 books, 455,651 microform titles, 2,039 serials, 1,489 audiovisual materials, an OPAC, and a Web page. 135 computers available on campus for general student use. A campuswide network can be accessed from student residence rooms and from off campus. Staffed computer lab on campus.

Community Environment: The college is located in an urban setting, 50 miles from Boston.

■ **FRAMINGHAM STATE COLLEGE** *E-10*
100 State St., PO Box 9101
Framingham, MA 01701-9101
Tel: (508)620-1220
Admissions: (508)626-4500
Fax: (508)626-4017
E-mail: admiss@frc.mass.edu
Web Site: http://www.framingham.edu/
Description: State-supported, comprehensive, coed. Part of Massachusetts Public Higher Education System. Awards bachelor's and master's degrees. Founded 1839. Setting: 73-acre suburban campus with easy access to Boston. Endowment: $5.4 million. Research spending for 2004 fiscal year: $13,294. Educational spending for 2005 fiscal year: $4077 per student. Total enrollment: 5,874. Faculty: 234 (167 full-time, 67 part-time). Student-undergrad faculty ratio is 15:1. 3,955 applied, 64% were admitted. 8% from top 10% of their high school class, 31% from top quarter, 74% from top half. Full-time: 3,045 students, 67% women, 33% men. Part-time: 727 students, 62% women, 38% men. Students come from 15 states and territories, 20 other countries, 4% from out-of-state, 0.4% Native American, 3% Hispanic, 3% black, 3% Asian American or Pacific Islander, 1% international, 10% 25 or older, 45% live on campus, 8% transferred in. Retention: 75% of full-time freshmen returned the following year. Academic areas with the most degrees conferred: business/marketing; social sciences; psychology. Core. Calendar: semesters. ESL program, advanced placement, honors program, independent study, distance learning, double major, summer session for credit, part-time degree program, adult/continuing education programs, internships, graduate courses open to undergrads. Off campus study at College Academic Program Sharing, 8 members of the other Massachusetts State colleges. Study abroad program. ROTC: Army.

Entrance Requirements: Options: Peterson's Universal Application, electronic application, early admission, early action, deferred admission. Required: high school transcript, SAT or ACT. Recommended: essay, minimum 3.0 high school GPA, recommendations. Required for some: essay, interview. Entrance: moderately difficult. Application deadlines: 2/15, 11/15 for early action. Notification: 3/31, 12/15 for early action. Preference given to state residents.

Costs Per Year: Application fee: $25. State resident tuition: $970 full-time, $41 per credit part-time. Nonresident tuition: $7050 full-time, $294 per credit part-time. Mandatory fees: $4029 full-time, $184 per credit part-time. Full-time tuition and fees vary according to class time. Part-time tuition and fees vary according to class time and course load. College room and board: $6157. Room and board charges vary according to board plan and housing facility.

Collegiate Environment: Orientation program. Drama-theater group, choral group, student-run newspaper, radio station. Social organizations: 35 open to all. Most popular organizations: Student Union Activities Board, Student Government Association, Gatepost (student newspaper), Hilltop Players, literary magazine. Major annual events: homecoming, All College Day, Sandbox Festival. Student services: health clinic, personal-psychological counseling. Campus security: 24-hour emergency response devices and patrols, student patrols, late night transport-escort service, controlled dormitory access. 1,500 college housing spaces available; all were occupied in 2003-04. Freshmen given priority for college housing. Options: coed, women-only housing available. Whittemore Library with 165,219 books, 658,878 microform titles, 409 serials, 3,313 audiovisual materials, an OPAC, and a Web page. Operations spending for 2004 fiscal year: $1.6 million. 575 computers available on campus for general student use. Computer purchase/lease plans available. A campuswide network can be accessed from student residence rooms and from off campus. Staffed computer lab on campus.

Community Environment: Area is located 20 miles west of Boston and has transportation facilities. Part-time job opportunities are available for students. This diversified community offers many opportunities in the areas of high technology, retailing, and manufacturing, as well as being a major residential center.

■ **FRANKLIN W. OLIN COLLEGE OF ENGINEERING** *E-11*
Olin Way
Needham, MA 02492-1200
Tel: (781)292-2300
Admissions: (781)292-2250

E-mail: duncan.murdoch@olin.edu

Web Site: http://www.olin.edu/

Description: Independent, 4-year, coed. Awards bachelor's degrees. Endowment: $419 million. Total enrollment: 285. Student-undergrad faculty ratio is 9:1. 546 applied, 23% were admitted. 94% from top 10% of their high school class, 100% from top quarter. Full-time: 285 students, 43% women, 57% men. 90% from out-of-state, 0% Native American, 6% Hispanic, 2% black, 9% Asian American or Pacific Islander, 1% international, 0% 25 or older, 100% live on campus. Retention: 99% of full-time freshmen returned the following year. Self-designed majors, independent study, internships. Study abroad program.

Entrance Requirements: Option: deferred admission. Required: essay, high school transcript, 3 recommendations, SAT or ACT. Recommended: interview, SAT Subject Tests. Application deadline: 1/6. Notification: 3/21.

Costs Per Year: Application fee: $60.

Collegiate Environment: Drama-theater group, choral group, student-run newspaper. Student services: legal services, health clinic, personal-psychological counseling. Option: coed housing available.

■ **GIBBS COLLEGE** *D-12*

126 Newbury St.

Boston, MA 02116-2904

Tel: (617)578-7100

Free: 800-6SK-ILLS

Admissions: (617)578-7150

Fax: (617)262-2610

Web Site: http://www.katharinegibbs.com/

Description: Proprietary, 2-year, coed. Part of Career Education Corporation. Awards certificates, transfer associate, and terminal associate degrees. Founded 1917. Setting: urban campus. 1% from top 10% of their high school class, 10% from top quarter, 30% from top half. Students come from 15 states and territories, 6 other countries, 35% 25 or older. Core. Academic remediation for entering students, summer session for credit, part-time degree program, adult/continuing education programs, internships.

Entrance Requirements: Required: high school transcript, CPAt, SAT, or ACT. Entrance: minimally difficult. Application deadline: Rolling.

Collegiate Environment: Most popular organizations: student council, yearbook, International Student Organization. Major annual events: Holiday Toys for Tots Drive, Spring Formal, Graduation Cruise. Student services: personal-psychological counseling. College housing not available. William F. Reilly Library plus 1 other with 3,270 books and 81 serials. 70 computers available on campus for general student use. Staffed computer lab on campus.

■ **GORDON COLLEGE** *C-13*

255 Grapevine Rd.

Wenham, MA 01984-1899

Tel: (978)927-2300; (866)464-6736

Admissions: (978)867-4218

Fax: (978)524-3704

E-mail: admissions@hope.gordonc.edu

Web Site: http://www.gordon.edu/

Description: Independent nondenominational, comprehensive, coed. Awards bachelor's and master's degrees. Founded 1889. Setting: 500-acre small town campus with easy access to Boston. Endowment: $30.5 million. Educational spending for 2005 fiscal year: $10,965 per student. Total enrollment: 1,650. Faculty: 145 (93 full-time, 52 part-time). Student-undergrad faculty ratio is 14:1. 1,098 applied, 84% were admitted. 33% from top 10% of their high school class, 69% from top quarter, 87% from top half. 9 National Merit Scholars. Full-time: 1,555 students, 63% women, 37% men. Part-time: 34 students, 59% women, 41% men. Students come from 46 states and territories, 28 other countries, 75% from out-of-state, 0.4% Native American, 3% Hispanic, 1% black, 2% Asian American or Pacific Islander, 2% international, 1% 25 or older, 88% live on campus, 5% transferred in. Retention: 85% of full-time freshmen returned the following year. Academic areas with the most degrees conferred: education; English; business/marketing; social sciences. Core. Calendar: semesters. Academic remediation for entering students, services for LD students, advanced placement, self-designed majors, honors program, independent study, double major, part-time degree program, co-op programs and internships. Off campus study at members of the Christian College Consortium, Northeast Consortium of Colleges and Universities in Massachusetts. Study abroad program. ROTC: Army (c), Air Force (c).

Entrance Requirements: Options: Common Application, electronic application, early admission, early decision, early action, deferred admission, international baccalaureate accepted. Required: essay, high school transcript, 2 recommendations, interview, pastoral recommendation, statement of Christian faith, SAT or ACT. Recommended: minimum 3.0 high school GPA. Entrance: moderately difficult. Application deadlines: Rolling, 11/15 for early decision, 12/1 for early action. Notification: continuous, 12/15 for early decision, 1/1 for early action.

Costs Per Year: Application fee: $50. Comprehensive fee: $29,194 includes full-time tuition ($21,930), mandatory fees ($994), and college room and board ($6270). College room only: $4200. Room and board charges vary according to board plan and housing facility. Part-time mandatory fees: $1550 per credit, $248.50 per term. Part-time fees vary according to course load.

Collegiate Environment: Orientation program. Drama-theater group, choral group, student-run newspaper. Social organizations: 35 open to all. Most popular organizations: Student Government Association, student ministries, diverse music ensembles. Major annual events: Center for Christian Studies Spring Symposium, Homecoming, Day of Prayer and Fasting. Student services: health clinic, personal-psychological counseling. Campus security: 24-hour emergency response devices and patrols, late night transport-escort service, controlled dormitory access. College housing designed to accommodate 1,420 students; 1,422 undergraduates lived in college housing during 2003-04. Freshmen guaranteed college housing. On-campus residence required through senior year. Options: coed, men-only, women-only housing available. Jenks Learning Resource Center with 142,688 books, 31,285 microform titles, 8,555 serials, 10,266 audiovisual materials, and an OPAC. Operations spending for 2004 fiscal year: $626,107. 141 computers available on campus for general student use. A campuswide network can be accessed from student residence rooms and from off campus. Staffed computer lab on campus.

■ **GREENFIELD COMMUNITY COLLEGE** *C-5*

1 College Dr.

Greenfield, MA 01301-9739

Tel: (413)775-1000

Admissions: (413)775-1806

Fax: (413)773-5129

Web Site: http://www.gcc.mass.edu/

Description: State-supported, 2-year, coed. Awards certificates, transfer associate, and terminal associate degrees. Founded 1962. Setting: 120-acre small town campus. Total enrollment: 2,217. Student-undergrad faculty ratio is 23:1. 727 applied, 100% were admitted. Full-time: 994 students, 57% women, 43% men. Part-time: 1,223 students, 69% women, 31% men. Students come from 5 states and territories, 7 other countries, 5% from out-of-state, 0.4% Native American, 3% Hispanic, 3% black, 3% Asian American or Pacific Islander, 0% international, 46% 25 or older, 12% transferred in. Core. Calendar: semesters. Academic remediation for entering students, ESL program, services for LD students, advanced placement, honors program, independent study, distance learning, double major, summer session for credit, part-time degree program, adult/continuing education programs, co-op programs and internships.

Entrance Requirements: Open admission except for allied health, outdoor leadership programs. Required for some: high school transcript, interview, Psychological Corporation Practical Nursing Entrance Examination. Entrance: noncompetitive. Application deadline: Rolling. Preference given to state residents.

Costs Per Year: Application fee: $10. State resident tuition: $780 full-time, $26 per credit part-time. Nonresident tuition: $8430 full-time, $281 per credit part-time. Mandatory fees: $3227 full-time, $103.50 per credit part-time, $61. Full-time tuition and fees vary according to class time. Part-time tuition and fees vary according to class time.

Collegiate Environment: Orientation program. Drama-theater group, choral group. Major annual event: Spring Weekend. Student services: health clinic, personal-psychological counseling, women's center. Campus security: 24-hour emergency response devices and patrols, late night transport-escort service. College housing not available. Greenfield Community College Library with 52,690 books and 356 serials. 115 computers available on campus for general student use. A campuswide network can be accessed from off-campus. Staffed computer lab on campus.

Community Environment: The world's largest producer of taps and dies, Greenfield is a center for winter sports, and hunting and fishing in season. This is a combined rural and suburban area with bus service and limited rail service available. Climate is temperate. Recreational facilities include excellent ski area, 13 movie theatres, and all water sports on Connecticut River. Limited part-time employment for students. County fair held annually in September; Winter Carnival in February; Spring Farmers' Market.

■ **HAMPSHIRE COLLEGE** *D-5*
893 West St.
Amherst, MA 01002
Tel: (413)549-4600; 877-937-4267
Admissions: (413)559-5471
Fax: (413)582-5631
E-mail: admissions@hampshire.edu
Web Site: http://www.hampshire.edu/
Description: Independent, 4-year, coed. Awards bachelor's degrees. Founded 1965. Setting: 800-acre rural campus. Endowment: $25.4 million. Research spending for 2004 fiscal year: $940,930. Educational spending for 2005 fiscal year: $10,463 per student. Total enrollment: 1,376. Student-undergrad faculty ratio is 12:1. 2,243 applied, 64% were admitted. 28% from top 10% of their high school class, 63% from top quarter, 90% from top half. 7 National Merit Scholars, 74 class presidents, 2 valedictorians, 67 student government officers. Full-time: 1,376 students, 59% women, 41% men. Students come from 46 states and territories, 26 other countries, 82% from out-of-state, 0.4% Native American, 4% Hispanic, 3% black, 4% Asian American or Pacific Islander, 3% international, 1% 25 or older, 93% live on campus, 4% transferred in. Retention: 82% of full-time freshmen returned the following year. Academic areas with the most degrees conferred: visual and performing arts; social sciences; English. Core. Calendar: 4-1-4. Services for LD students, advanced placement, accelerated degree program, self-designed majors, independent study, double major, internships. Off campus study at members of Five Colleges, Inc. Study abroad program. ROTC: Army (c).
Entrance Requirements: Options: Peterson's Universal Application, Common Application, electronic application, early admission, early decision, early action, deferred admission, international baccalaureate accepted. Required: essay, high school transcript, 2 recommendations. Recommended: interview. Entrance: moderately difficult. Application deadlines: 1/15, 11/15 for early decision, 12/1 for early action. Notification: 4/1, 12/15 for early decision, 1/15 for early action.
Costs Per Year: Application fee: $55. Comprehensive fee: $41,038 includes full-time tuition ($31,939), mandatory fees ($580), and college room and board ($8519). College room only: $5433. Room and board charges vary according to board plan.
Collegiate Environment: Orientation program. Drama-theater group, choral group, student-run newspaper. Social organizations: 80 open to all. Most popular organizations: Alternative Music Collective, Jewish Student Union, Student Action for Radical Change, Theatre Board, Red Scare Ultimate Frisbee. Major annual events: Spring Jam, Hampshire Halloween, The QCA Drag Ball. Student services: health clinic, personal-psychological counseling, women's center. Campus security: 24-hour emergency response devices and patrols, student patrols, late night transport-escort service. 1,179 college housing spaces available; all were occupied in 2003-04. Freshmen guaranteed college housing. On-campus residence required through senior year. Options: coed, men-only, women-only housing available. Harold F. Johnson Library with 136,326 books, 5,429 microform titles, 2,288 serials, 39,135 audiovisual materials, an OPAC, and a Web page. Operations spending for 2004 fiscal year: $1.3 million. 186 computers available on campus for general student use. A campuswide network can be accessed from student residence rooms and from off campus. Staffed computer lab on campus.
Community Environment: See Amherst College.

■ **HARVARD UNIVERSITY** *D-12*
Cambridge, MA 02138
Tel: (617)495-1000
Admissions: (617)495-1551
E-mail: college@harvard.edu
Web Site: http://www.harvard.edu/
Description: Independent, university, coed. Awards bachelor's, master's, doctoral, and first professional degrees. Founded 1636. Setting: 380-acre urban campus with easy access to Boston. Endowment: $25.9 billion. Total enrollment: 19,376. Faculty: 2,035 (1,592 full-time, 443 part-time). Student-undergrad faculty ratio is 7:1. 22,796 applied, 9% were admitted. 96% from top 10% of their high school class, 99% from top quarter, 100% from top half. Full-time: 6,649 students, 49% women, 51% men. Students come from 53 states and territories, 82 other countries, 1% Native American, 8% Hispanic,

8% black, 18% Asian American or Pacific Islander, 9% international, 1% 25 or older, 96% live on campus, 1% transferred in. Retention: 98% of full-time freshmen returned the following year. Core. Calendar: semesters. Academic remediation for entering students, ESL program, services for LD students, advanced placement, accelerated degree program, self-designed majors, honors program, independent study, double major, summer session for credit, adult/continuing education programs, internships, graduate courses open to undergrads. Off campus study at Massachusetts Institute of Technology. Study abroad program. ROTC: Army (c), Air Force (c).
Entrance Requirements: Options: Peterson's Universal Application, Common Application, early action, deferred admission. Required: essay, high school transcript, 2 recommendations, interview, SAT and SAT Subject Tests or ACT. Entrance: most difficult. Application deadlines: 1/1, 11/1 for early action. Notification: 4/1, 12/15 for early action.
Costs Per Year: Application fee: $65. Comprehensive fee: $43,655 includes full-time tuition ($30,275), mandatory fees ($3434), and college room and board ($9946). College room only: $5328.
Collegiate Environment: Orientation program. Drama-theater group, choral group, marching band, student-run newspaper, radio station. Social organizations: 250 open to all; 'House' system; 99% of eligible men and 99% of eligible women are members. Most popular organizations: Phillips Brooks House, Asian-American Association, International Relations Council, Harvard Crimson (newspaper), Harvard/Radcliffe Chorus. Major annual event: Commencement. Student services: legal services, health clinic, personal-psychological counseling, women's center. Campus security: 24-hour emergency response devices and patrols, late night transport-escort service, controlled dormitory access, required and optional safety courses. 6,660 college housing spaces available; 6,425 were occupied in 2003-04. On-campus residence required in freshman year. Option: coed housing available. Widener Library plus 90 others with 14 million books and 97,568 serials. Operations spending for 2004 fiscal year: $91 million.
Community Environment: Settled in 1630, Cambridge has been the home of such famous writers as Henry Wadsworth Longfellow, James Russell Lowell, and Oliver Wendell Holmes. It is also the birthplace in Massachusetts of high technology industry. With a population of about 95,000 concentrated in 6.25 square miles, Cambridge today is the sixth largest city in the state. A vital university town, Cambridge is also a city of long-established neighborhoods with strong ethnic roots and traditions. Just across the Charles River and connected by an efficient transit system, Boston offers historical landmarks, professional sports, cosmopolitan shopping, world-famous hospitals and outstanding cultural opportunities.

■ **HEBREW COLLEGE** *E-12*
160 Herrick Rd.
Newton Centre, MA 02459
Tel: (617)559-8600
Free: 800-866-4814
Admissions: (617)559-8610
Fax: (617)559-8601
Web Site: http://www.hebrewcollege.edu/
Description: Independent Jewish, comprehensive, coed. Awards bachelor's and master's degrees. Founded 1921. Setting: 3-acre suburban campus with easy access to Boston. Endowment: $8 million. Total enrollment: 6. Full-time: 5 students, 80% women, 20% men. Part-time: 1 student, 100% women. Students come from 6 states and territories, 1 other country, 1% from out-of-state, 99% 25 or older. Core. Calendar: semesters. Distance learning, summer session for credit, part-time degree program, adult/continuing education programs, internships, graduate courses open to undergrads. Off campus study at Boston College, Boston University, Northeastern University, Simmons College, University of Massachusetts Boston, Brandeis University, Andover Newton Theological School, Tufts University.
Entrance Requirements: Open admission. Options: Peterson's Universal Application, early admission, early decision, deferred admission, international baccalaureate accepted. Required: essay, high school transcript, 3 recommendations, interview. Required for some: GRE, audition. Placement: SAT required. Entrance: minimally difficult. Application deadlines: Rolling, 12/15 for early decision. Notification: continuous.
Costs Per Year: Application fee: $50. Tuition: $18,600 full-time, $775 per credit part-time. Mandatory fees: $200 full-time, $100 per semester hour part-time.
Collegiate Environment: Orientation program. College housing not available. Rae and Joseph Gann Library with 125,000 books, 3,600 microform

titles, 280 serials, and a Web page. Operations spending for 2004 fiscal year: $211,820. 10 computers available on campus for general student use. Staffed computer lab on campus.

■ **HELLENIC COLLEGE** E-12

50 Goddard Ave.

Brookline, MA 02445-7496

Tel: (617)731-3500; (866)424-2338

Fax: (617)232-7819

E-mail: sdaly@hchc.edu

Web Site: http://www.hchc.edu/

Description: Independent Greek Orthodox, 4-year, coed. Awards bachelor's degrees (also offers graduate degree programs through Holy Cross Greek Orthodox School of Theology). Founded 1937. Setting: 52-acre suburban campus with easy access to Boston. Endowment: $23 million. Educational spending for 2005 fiscal year: $10,409 per student. Total enrollment: 191. Student-undergrad faculty ratio is 9:1. 22 applied, 50% were admitted. Full-time: 84 students, 39% women, 61% men. Students come from 39 states and territories, 10 other countries, 85% from out-of-state, 1% Native American, 0% Hispanic, 1% black, 0% Asian American or Pacific Islander, 19% international, 10% 25 or older, 90% live on campus, 6% transferred in. Retention: 94% of full-time freshmen returned the following year. Academic area with the most degrees conferred: liberal arts/general studies. Core. Calendar: semesters. Academic remediation for entering students, advanced placement, independent study, double major, summer session for credit, part-time degree program, internships. Off campus study at Boston Theological Institute.

Entrance Requirements: Options: Common Application, electronic application, early action, deferred admission. Required: essay, high school transcript, minimum 2.0 high school GPA, recommendations, interview, health certificate, SAT or ACT. Required for some: SAT Subject Tests. Entrance: minimally difficult. Application deadlines: Rolling, 12/1 for early action. Notification: continuous.

Costs Per Year: Application fee: $50. Comprehensive fee: $25,075 includes full-time tuition ($15,435), mandatory fees ($380), and college room and board ($9260). Part-time tuition: $643 per credit. Part-time mandatory fees: $260 per term. Part-time tuition and fees vary according to course load.

Collegiate Environment: Orientation program. Choral group, student-run newspaper. Student services: health clinic, personal-psychological counseling. Campus security: controlled dormitory access. 190 college housing spaces available. Freshmen guaranteed college housing. On-campus residence required through senior year. Option: coed housing available. Archbishop Iakoros Library with 115,805 books, 863 microform titles, 721 serials, 2,911 audiovisual materials, an OPAC, and a Web page. Operations spending for 2004 fiscal year: $6437. 9 computers available on campus for general student use. Staffed computer lab on campus.

■ **HOLYOKE COMMUNITY COLLEGE** E-5

303 Homestead Ave.

Holyoke, MA 01040-1099

Tel: (413)538-7000; (413)552-2850

Admissions: (413)552-2321

Web Site: http://www.hcc.mass.edu/

Description: State-supported, 2-year, coed. Part of Massachusetts Public Higher Education System. Awards certificates, transfer associate, and terminal associate degrees. Founded 1946. Setting: 135-acre suburban campus. Endowment: $5.8 million. Total enrollment: 6,258. Student-undergrad faculty ratio is 15:1. Full-time: 3,075 students, 58% women, 42% men. Part-time: 3,183 students, 72% women, 28% men. Students come from 18 states and territories, 11 other countries, 1% from out-of-state, 1% Native American, 13% Hispanic, 6% black, 2% Asian American or Pacific Islander, 0.4% international, 31% 25 or older, 5% transferred in. Core. Calendar: semesters. Academic remediation for entering students, ESL program, services for LD students, advanced placement, self-designed majors, honors program, independent study, summer session for credit, part-time degree program, adult/continuing education programs, co-op programs and internships. Off campus study at the Cooperating Colleges of Greater Springfield. Study abroad program. ROTC: Army (c), Air Force (c).

Entrance Requirements: Open admission except for nursing, radiological science, ophthalmic technology programs. Options: Common Application, electronic application, early admission, deferred admission. Required: high school transcript. Recommended: interview. Entrance: noncompetitive. Application deadline: Rolling. Notification: continuous.

Costs Per Year: Application fee: $10. State resident tuition: $2570 full-time, $103 per credit part-time. Nonresident tuition: $7514 full-time, $309 per credit part-time.

Collegiate Environment: Orientation program. Drama-theater group, choral group, student-run newspaper, radio station. Most popular organizations: Drama Club, Music Club, Student Advisory Board. Major annual events: Spring Fling Week, Welcome Week, Black History Month. Student services: health clinic, personal-psychological counseling, women's center. Campus security: 24-hour emergency response devices and patrols, student patrols, late night transport-escort service. College housing not available. Elaine Marieb Library with 75,222 books, 135,807 microform titles, 365 serials, 7,489 audiovisual materials, an OPAC, and a Web page. Operations spending for 2004 fiscal year: $511,775. 450 computers available on campus for general student use. A campuswide network can be accessed from off-campus. Staffed computer lab on campus.

Community Environment: Holyoke is located 87 miles west of Boston on the shores of the Connecticut River and was the first planned industrial center in the country. Industries include the production of fine writing paper and various mills. The game of volleyball, first known as minonette, was invented here in 1895. The city has historical points of interest, museums, three movie theatres, public beaches and marinas, a community concert series featuring nationally known artists, and Mt. Tom Ski area. Westover Air Force Base is five miles from town. Part-time employment is available.

■ **ITT TECHNICAL INSTITUTE (NORWOOD)** E-11

333 Providence Hwy.

Norwood, MA 02062

Tel: (781)278-7200

Free: 800-879-8324

Web Site: http://www.itt-tech.edu/

Description: Proprietary, 2-year, coed. Part of ITT Educational Services, Inc. Awards terminal associate degrees. Founded 1990. Setting: suburban campus with easy access to Boston. Core.

Entrance Requirements: Option: deferred admission. Required: high school transcript, interview, Wonderlic aptitude test. Recommended: recommendations. Entrance: minimally difficult. Application deadline: Rolling. Notification: continuous.

Costs Per Year: Application fee: $100.

Collegiate Environment: Orientation program. College housing not available.

■ **ITT TECHNICAL INSTITUTE (WOBURN)** D-12

10 Forbes Rd.

Woburn, MA 01801

Tel: (781)937-8324

Web Site: http://www.itt-tech.edu/

Description: Proprietary, 2-year, coed. Part of ITT Educational Services, Inc. Awards terminal associate degrees. Core.

Entrance Requirements: Open admission. Option: deferred admission. Required: high school transcript, interview, Wonderlic aptitude test. Recommended: recommendations. Entrance: minimally difficult. Application deadline: Rolling. Notification: continuous.

Costs Per Year: Application fee: $100.

Collegiate Environment: Orientation program. College housing not available.

■ **LABOURÉ COLLEGE** D-12

2120 Dorchester Ave.

Boston, MA 02124-5698

Tel: (617)296-8300

Web Site: http://www.laboure.edu/

Description: Independent Roman Catholic, 2-year, coed. Awards certificates, transfer associate, and terminal associate degrees. Founded 1971. Setting: urban campus. Endowment: $951,296. Total enrollment: 432. 88 applied, 22% were admitted. 25% from top quarter of their high school class, 25% from top half. Students come from 3 states and territories, 4 other countries, 1% from out-of-state, 0% Native American, 6% Hispanic, 31% black, 4% Asian American or Pacific Islander, 0% international, 72% 25 or older. Retention: 65% of full-time freshmen returned the following year. Core. Calendar: semesters. Academic remediation for entering students, services for LD students, accelerated degree program, independent study, summer session for credit, part-time degree program, adult/continuing education programs.

Entrance Requirements: Option: deferred admission. Required: high school transcript, recommendations. Entrance: minimally difficult. Application deadline: Rolling.

Collegiate Environment: Orientation program. Student-run newspaper. Most popular organizations: Student Government Association, college yearbook, peer advisors. Student services: health clinic, personal-psychological counseling. Campus security: 24-hour emergency response devices. College housing not available. Helen Stubblefield Law Library with 10,975 books, 24 microform titles, 155 serials, 650 audiovisual materials, and an OPAC. 20 computers available on campus for general student use. Staffed computer lab on campus.

■ **LASELL COLLEGE** *E-11*
1844 Commonwealth Ave.
Newton, MA 02466-2709
Tel: (617)243-2000; 888-LASELL-4
Admissions: (617)243-2225
Fax: (617)796-4343
E-mail: info@lasell.edu
Web Site: http://www.lasell.edu/

Description: Independent, comprehensive, coed. Awards bachelor's and master's degrees. Founded 1851. Setting: 50-acre suburban campus with easy access to Boston. Endowment: $12.5 million. Educational spending for 2005 fiscal year: $5680 per student. Total enrollment: 1,253. Faculty: 162 (55 full-time, 107 part-time). Student-undergrad faculty ratio is 13:1. 2,652 applied, 67% were admitted. 6% from top 10% of their high school class, 32% from top quarter, 62% from top half. Full-time: 1,194 students, 69% women, 31% men. Part-time: 22 students, 59% women, 41% men. Students come from 16 states and territories, 15 other countries, 48% from out-of-state, 1% Native American, 6% Hispanic, 6% black, 3% Asian American or Pacific Islander, 3% international, 5% 25 or older, 80% live on campus, 6% transferred in. Retention: 80% of full-time freshmen returned the following year. Core. Calendar: semesters. ESL program, advanced placement, self-designed majors, honors program, independent study, double major, part-time degree program, co-op programs and internships. Study abroad program.

Entrance Requirements: Options: Common Application, electronic application, deferred admission, international baccalaureate accepted. Required: high school transcript, minimum 2.0 high school GPA, 1 recommendation, SAT or ACT. Recommended: essay, interview. Entrance: moderately difficult. Application deadline: Rolling. Notification: continuous.

Costs Per Year: Application fee: $40. Comprehensive fee: $30,100 includes full-time tuition ($19,900), mandatory fees ($1000), and college room and board ($9200). Part-time tuition: $660 per credit hour. Part-time mandatory fees: $250.

Collegiate Environment: Orientation program. Drama-theater group, choral group, student-run newspaper, radio station. Social organizations: 20 open to all. Most popular organizations: Center for Public Service, student government, Umoja-Nia, yearbook, Fashion Board. Major annual events: River Day/Family and Friends Weekend, Torchlight Parade, spring/winter balls. Student services: health clinic, personal-psychological counseling. Campus security: 24-hour emergency response devices and patrols, late night transport-escort service, controlled dormitory access. 910 undergraduates lived in college housing during 2003-04. Freshmen guaranteed college housing. Options: coed, women-only housing available. Brennan Library with 60,250 books, 50,083 microform titles, 474 serials, 9,844 audiovisual materials, and an OPAC. Operations spending for 2004 fiscal year: $251,333. 150 computers available on campus for general student use. Computer purchase/lease plans available. A campuswide network can be accessed from student residence rooms and from off campus. Staffed computer lab on campus.

Community Environment: See Boston University.

■ **LESLEY UNIVERSITY** *D-12*
29 Everett St.
Cambridge, MA 02138-2790
Tel: (617)868-9600
Free: 800-999-1959
Admissions: (617)349-8800
Fax: (617)349-8150
E-mail: lcadmissions@lesley.edu
Web Site: http://www.lesley.edu/

Description: Independent, comprehensive, coed. Awards associate, bachelor's, master's, and doctoral degrees and post-master's certificates.

Founded 1909. Setting: 5-acre urban campus with easy access to Boston. Endowment: $45.6 million. Research spending for 2004 fiscal year: $887,653. Educational spending for 2005 fiscal year: $24,200 per student. Total enrollment: 7,298. Faculty: 184 (53 full-time, 131 part-time). Student-undergrad faculty ratio is 11:1. 1,351 applied, 72% were admitted. 23% from top 10% of their high school class, 50% from top quarter, 78% from top half. 4 class presidents, 1 valedictorian, 37 student government officers. Full-time: 1,023 students, 77% women, 23% men. Part-time: 242 students, 75% women, 25% men. Students come from 34 states and territories, 24 other countries, 37% from out-of-state, 0.5% Native American, 5% Hispanic, 6% black, 4% Asian American or Pacific Islander, 3% international, 8% 25 or older, 66% live on campus, 9% transferred in. Retention: 79% of full-time freshmen returned the following year. Academic areas with the most degrees conferred: liberal arts/general studies; business/marketing; visual and performing arts. Core. Calendar: semesters. Academic remediation for entering students, ESL program, services for LD students, advanced placement, accelerated degree program, self-designed majors, freshman honors college, honors program, independent study, distance learning, double major, summer session for credit, part-time degree program, external degree program, adult/continuing education programs, internships, graduate courses open to undergrads. Off campus study at Harvard University Extension Program, National Audubon Society Expedition Institute. Study abroad program.

Entrance Requirements: Options: Peterson's Universal Application, Common Application, electronic application, deferred admission, international baccalaureate accepted. Required: high school transcript, 2 recommendations, SAT or ACT. Recommended: essay, minimum 2.5 high school GPA, interview. Required for some: portfolio. Entrance: moderately difficult. Application deadlines: 3/1, 12/1 for early action. Notification: continuous, 1/1 for early action.

Costs Per Year: Application fee: $40. One-time mandatory fee: $950. Comprehensive fee: $34,950 includes full-time tuition ($24,200), mandatory fees ($250), and college room and board ($10,500). College room only: $6400. Full-time tuition and fees vary according to program. Room and board charges vary according to housing facility. Part-time tuition: $1020 per credit.

Collegiate Environment: Orientation program. Drama-theater group, choral group, student-run newspaper. Social organizations: 20 open to all. Most popular organizations: Student Senate, Women for Social Justice, Hillel, Swim Club, Third Wave. Major annual events: Family and Friends Weekend, Quad Fest, World Fest. Student services: health clinic, personal-psychological counseling. Campus security: 24-hour emergency response devices and patrols, late night transport-escort service, controlled dormitory access, self-defense education, lighted pathways. 500 college housing spaces available; all were occupied in 2003-04. Freshmen guaranteed college housing. Options: coed, women-only housing available. Eleanor DeWolfe Ludcke Library plus 2 others with 118,729 books, 826,172 microform titles, 1,150 serials, 49,943 audiovisual materials, an OPAC, and a Web page. Operations spending for 2004 fiscal year: $1.9 million. 175 computers available on campus for general student use. Computer purchase/lease plans available. A campuswide network can be accessed from student residence rooms and from off campus. Staffed computer lab on campus.

■ **MARIAN COURT COLLEGE** *D-13*
35 Little's Point Rd.
Swampscott, MA 01907-2840
Tel: (781)595-6768
Fax: (781)595-3560
E-mail: lparker@mariancourt.edu
Web Site: http://www.mariancourt.edu/

Description: Independent Roman Catholic, 2-year, coed. Awards certificates and transfer associate degrees. Founded 1964. Setting: 6-acre suburban campus with easy access to Boston. Total enrollment: 281. 136 applied, 97% were admitted. Students come from 5 other countries, 45% 25 or older. Calendar: semesters. Academic remediation for entering students, advanced placement, honors program, independent study, summer session for credit, part-time degree program, adult/continuing education programs, internships. Off campus study at members of the Northeast Consortium of Colleges and Universities in Massachusetts.

Entrance Requirements: Options: Peterson's Universal Application, Common Application, electronic application, deferred admission. Required: essay, high school transcript, minimum 2.0 high school GPA, 2 recommendations, interview. Entrance: minimally difficult. Application deadline: Rolling.

Collegiate Environment: Orientation program. Choral group. Most popular organizations: Travel Club, student government, Yearbook Committee, Theater Club. Major annual events: International Supper, Winter Dance, Luau. Student services: personal-psychological counseling. Campus security: well-lit parking lots. College housing not available. Lindsay Library with 5,006 books, 122 serials, and an OPAC. 43 computers available on campus for general student use. Staffed computer lab on campus.

■ **MASSACHUSETTS BAY COMMUNITY COLLEGE** *E-11*
50 Oakland St.
Wellesley Hills, MA 02481
Tel: (781)239-3000
Admissions: (781)239-2501
Fax: (781)239-1047
Web Site: http://www.massbay.edu/
Description: State-supported, 2-year, coed. Awards certificates, transfer associate, and terminal associate degrees. Founded 1961. Setting: 84-acre suburban campus with easy access to Boston. Total enrollment: 5,015. Student-undergrad faculty ratio is 19:1. 2,557 applied, 99% were admitted. Full-time: 2,145 students, 46% women, 54% men. Part-time: 2,870 students, 67% women, 33% men. Students come from 7 states and territories, 50 other countries, 2% from out-of-state, 0.3% Native American, 7% Hispanic, 12% black, 4% Asian American or Pacific Islander, 2% international, 42% 25 or older, 38% transferred in. Core. Calendar: semesters. Academic remediation for entering students, services for LD students, advanced placement, honors program, distance learning, summer session for credit, part-time degree program, adult/continuing education programs, co-op programs and internships.
Entrance Requirements: Open admission except for nursing program. Options: electronic application, deferred admission. Entrance: noncompetitive. Application deadline: Rolling. Notification: continuous.
Costs Per Year: Application fee: $20. State resident tuition: $720 full-time. Nonresident tuition: $6900 full-time.
Collegiate Environment: Drama-theater group, student-run newspaper. Social organizations: 18 open to all. Most popular organizations: Student Government Association, Latino Student Organization, New World Society Club, Mass Bay Players, Student Occupational Therapy Association. Major annual events: Spring Barbeque, Health Fair, Career Fair. Student services: health clinic, personal-psychological counseling. Campus security: 24-hour emergency response devices and patrols. College housing not available. Perkins Library with 50,333 books, 12,820 microform titles, 291 serials, 4,650 audiovisual materials, an OPAC, and a Web page. Operations spending for 2004 fiscal year: $427,680. 400 computers available on campus for general student use. A campuswide network can be accessed from off-campus. Staffed computer lab on campus.
Community Environment: See Wellesley College.

■ **MASSACHUSETTS COLLEGE OF ART** *D-12*
621 Huntington Ave.
Boston, MA 02115-5882
Tel: (617)879-7000
Admissions: (617)879-7225
Fax: (617)879-7250
E-mail: admissions@massart.edu
Web Site: http://www.massart.edu/
Description: State-supported, comprehensive, coed. Part of Massachusetts Public Higher Education System. Awards bachelor's and master's degrees. Founded 1873. Setting: 5-acre urban campus. Endowment: $4 million. Total enrollment: 2,130. Faculty: 209 (86 full-time, 123 part-time). Student-undergrad faculty ratio is 13:1. 1,210 applied, 61% were admitted. 21% from top 10% of their high school class, 41% from top quarter, 86% from top half. Full-time: 1,379 students, 63% women, 37% men. Part-time: 615 students, 66% women, 34% men. Students come from 23 states and territories, 48 other countries, 29% from out-of-state, 1% Native American, 5% Hispanic, 4% black, 5% Asian American or Pacific Islander, 3% international, 15% 25 or older, 26% live on campus, 9% transferred in. Retention: 83% of full-time freshmen returned the following year. Academic areas with the most degrees conferred: visual and performing arts; education; architecture. Core. Calendar: semesters. Self-designed majors, independent study, double major, summer session for credit, part-time degree program, external degree program, internships, graduate courses open to undergrads. Off campus study at members of the Pro Arts Consortium, Association of Independent Colleges of Art and Design, CAPS, Colleges of the Fenway. Study abroad program.

Entrance Requirements: Options: electronic application, early admission, early action, deferred admission. Required: essay, high school transcript, minimum 3.0 high school GPA, recommendations, portfolio, SAT or ACT. Entrance: very difficult. Application deadlines: 2/15, 12/1 for early action. Notification: 4/15. Preference given to state residents.
Costs Per Year: Application fee: $30. State resident tuition: $6850 full-time. Nonresident tuition: $19,200 full-time. College room and board: $9800.
Collegiate Environment: Orientation program. Drama-theater group, student-run newspaper, radio station. Social organizations: 30 open to all. Most popular organizations: International Students' Club, Design Research Unit, Spectrum, film society, Event Works. Major annual events: All School Show, Annual Holiday Sale, Service Learning Day. Student services: health clinic, personal-psychological counseling, women's center. Campus security: 24-hour emergency response devices and patrols, late night transport-escort service, security lighting, self-defense workshops. 367 undergraduates lived in college housing during 2003-04. Freshmen guaranteed college housing. Option: coed housing available. Morton R. Godine Library with 231,586 books, 8,700 microform titles, 757 serials, and 125,000 audiovisual materials. 250 computers available on campus for general student use. A campuswide network can be accessed from off-campus. Staffed computer lab on campus.
Community Environment: See Boston University.

■ **MASSACHUSETTS COLLEGE OF LIBERAL ARTS** *B-3*
375 Church St.
North Adams, MA 01247-4100
Tel: (413)662-5000
Admissions: (413)662-5410
Fax: (413)662-5179
E-mail: admissions@nasc.mass.edu
Web Site: http://www.mcla.edu/
Description: State-supported, comprehensive, coed. Part of Massachusetts Public Higher Education System. Awards bachelor's and master's degrees. Founded 1894. Setting: 80-acre small town campus. Endowment: $3.9 million. Research spending for 2004 fiscal year: $10,635. Educational spending for 2005 fiscal year: $6200 per student. Total enrollment: 1,811. 1,106 applied, 71% were admitted. Full-time: 1,193 students, 59% women, 41% men. Part-time: 265 students, 72% women, 28% men. Students come from 13 states and territories, 21% from out-of-state, 0.3% Native American, 2% Hispanic, 4% black, 1% Asian American or Pacific Islander, 1% international, 14% 25 or older, 65% live on campus, 10% transferred in. Retention: 77% of full-time freshmen returned the following year. Core. Calendar: semesters. Academic remediation for entering students, services for LD students, advanced placement, self-designed majors, honors program, independent study, distance learning, double major, summer session for credit, part-time degree program, internships, graduate courses open to undergrads. Off campus study at College Academic Program Sharing, Williams College, Berkshire Community College. Study abroad program.
Entrance Requirements: Options: Peterson's Universal Application, Common Application, electronic application, early action, deferred admission. Required: essay, high school transcript, minimum 3.0 high school GPA, SAT or ACT. Recommended: recommendations, interview, SAT. Required for some: interview. Entrance: moderately difficult. Application deadlines: Rolling, 12/1 for early action. Notification: continuous, 12/15 for early action.
Collegiate Environment: Orientation program. Drama-theater group, choral group, student-run newspaper, radio station. Social organizations: 45 open to all; national fraternities, national sororities, local fraternities, local sororities; 1% of eligible men and 1% of eligible women are members. Most popular organizations: Student Activities Council, Weightlifting Club, Non-Traditional Student Organization, Outing Club, Lacrosse Club. Major annual events: Spring Fling, Academic Convocation, semi-formal dances. Student services: health clinic, personal-psychological counseling, women's center. Campus security: 24-hour emergency response devices and patrols, late night transport-escort service, controlled dormitory access. On-campus residence required through junior year. Option: coed housing available. Freel Library with 241,000 microform titles, 541 serials, 4,567 audiovisual materials, an OPAC, and a Web page. Operations spending for 2004 fiscal year: $547,718.
Community Environment: In the northwestern corner of state, this Berkshire town produces a diversity of small business establishments and cultural activities. Bus lines are accessible. A regional hospital, Sterling and Francine Clark Art Institute, Massachusetts Museum of Contemporary Art, and numerous civic and service organizations are found here. There are 6 major ski areas within 25 miles and Mohawk and Taconic Trails. Part-time employment is seasonal for students. The city has an annual Fall Festival.

■ **MASSACHUSETTS COLLEGE OF PHARMACY AND HEALTH SCIENCES** *D-12*
179 Longwood Ave.
Boston, MA 02115-5896
Tel: (617)732-2800
Free: 800-225-5506
Admissions: (617)732-2850
Fax: (617)732-2801
E-mail: admissions@mcphs.edu
Web Site: http://www.mcphs.edu/
Description: Independent, university, coed. Awards bachelor's, master's, doctoral, and first professional degrees. Founded 1823. Setting: 2-acre urban campus. Endowment: $45.4 million. Total enrollment: 2,896. Faculty: 162 (157 full-time, 5 part-time). Student-undergrad faculty ratio is 17:1. 1,200 applied, 76% were admitted. 28% from top 10% of their high school class, 64% from top quarter, 90% from top half. Full-time: 1,764 students, 68% women, 32% men. Part-time: 122 students, 72% women, 28% men. Students come from 40 states and territories, 34 other countries, 38% from out-of-state, 0.3% Native American, 2% Hispanic, 5% black, 32% Asian American or Pacific Islander, 3% international, 26% 25 or older, 30% live on campus, 12% transferred in. Retention: 88% of full-time freshmen returned the following year. Core. Calendar: semesters. ESL program, services for LD students, advanced placement, accelerated degree program, independent study, distance learning, double major, summer session for credit, part-time degree program, adult/continuing education programs, internships, graduate courses open to undergrads. Off campus study at Colleges of the Fenway. ROTC: Army (c), Air Force (c).
Entrance Requirements: Options: Peterson's Universal Application, Common Application, electronic application, early admission, early decision, deferred admission, international baccalaureate accepted. Required: essay, high school transcript, 2 recommendations, SAT or ACT. Required for some: 3 recommendations, interview. Entrance: moderately difficult. Application deadlines: 2/1, 2/1 for early action. Notification: continuous, 2/1 for early action.
Costs Per Year: Application fee: $70. Comprehensive fee: $32,270 includes full-time tuition ($20,400), mandatory fees ($650), and college room and board ($11,220). College room only: $7900. Part-time tuition: $750 per credit. Part-time mandatory fees: $160 per term.
Collegiate Environment: Orientation program. Drama-theater group, choral group, student-run newspaper. Social organizations: 30 open to all; national fraternities, national sororities, local fraternities, local sororities; 35% of eligible men and 30% of eligible women are members. Most popular organizations: Academy of Students of Pharmacy, Vietnamese Student Association, Student Government Association, Students of American Dental Hygienists. Major annual events: Fall Harvest Ball, Culture Fest, Activities Fair. Student services: health clinic, personal-psychological counseling, stress management, crisis management consultation to student groups. Campus security: 24-hour emergency response devices and patrols, controlled dormitory access, electronically operated academic area entrances, security guards at entrance. 495 college housing spaces available; 484 were occupied in 2003-04. Freshmen guaranteed college housing. Options: coed, women-only housing available. Sheppard Library with 32,000 books, 700 serials, 525 audiovisual materials, an OPAC, and a Web page. 250 computers available on campus for general student use. A campuswide network can be accessed from student residence rooms and from off campus. Staffed computer lab on campus.

■ **MASSACHUSETTS INSTITUTE OF TECHNOLOGY** *D-12*
77 Massachusetts Ave.
Cambridge, MA 02139-4307
Tel: (617)253-1000
Admissions: (617)253-4791
Fax: (617)258-8304
E-mail: admissions@mit.edu
Web Site: http://web.mit.edu/
Description: Independent, university, coed. Awards bachelor's, master's, and doctoral degrees. Founded 1861. Setting: 154-acre urban campus with easy access to Boston. Endowment: $6.7 billion. Research spending for 2004 fiscal year: $529.5 million. Educational spending for 2005 fiscal year: $49,800 per student. Total enrollment: 10,206. Faculty: 1,554 (1,177 full-time, 377 part-time). Student-undergrad faculty ratio is 7:1. 10,440 applied, 14% were admitted. 97% from top 10% of their high school class, 100% from top quarter. 233 valedictorians. Full-time: 4,014 students, 44% women, 56% men. Part-time: 52 students, 23% women, 77% men. Students come from 55 states and territories, 78 other countries, 91% from out-of-state, 2% Native American, 11% Hispanic, 6% black, 27% Asian American or Pacific Islander, 8% international, 1% 25 or older, 93% live on campus, 0.05% transferred in. Retention: 98% of full-time freshmen returned the following year. Academic areas with the most degrees conferred: engineering; computer and information sciences; biological/life sciences. Core. Calendar: 4-1-4. ESL program, services for LD students, advanced placement, summer session for credit, co-op programs and internships, graduate courses open to undergrads. Off campus study at Wellesley College, Harvard University, Massachusetts College of Art, School of the Museum of Fine Arts. ROTC: Army, Naval, Air Force.
Entrance Requirements: Options: electronic application, early action, deferred admission, international baccalaureate accepted. Required: essay, high school transcript, 2 recommendations, SAT or ACT, SAT Subject Tests. Recommended: interview. Entrance: most difficult. Application deadlines: 1/1, 11/1 for early action. Notification: 3/25, 12/15 for early action.
Costs Per Year: Application fee: $65. Comprehensive fee: $41,800 includes full-time tuition ($32,100), mandatory fees ($200), and college room and board ($9500). College room only: $5250. Room and board charges vary according to board plan and housing facility. Part-time tuition: $505 per unit. Part-time tuition varies according to course load.
Collegiate Environment: Orientation program. Drama-theater group, choral group, marching band, student-run newspaper, radio station. Social organizations: 330 open to all; national fraternities, national sororities, local fraternities. Most popular organizations: Tech Catholic Community, Outing Club, Society of Women Engineers, Hillel, South Asian-American Students. Major annual events: Orientation, Commencement, Spring Weekend. Student services: health clinic, personal-psychological counseling. Campus security: 24-hour emergency response devices and patrols, late night transport-escort service, controlled dormitory access. College housing designed to accommodate 3,025 students; 3,050 undergraduates lived in college housing during 2003-04. Freshmen guaranteed college housing. On-campus residence required in freshman year. Options: coed, women-only housing available. MIT Libraries plus 10 others with 2.7 million books, 2.4 million microform titles, 22,597 serials, 596,928 audiovisual materials, an OPAC, and a Web page. Operations spending for 2004 fiscal year: $18.1 million. 1,100 computers available on campus for general student use. Computer purchase/lease plans available. A campuswide network can be accessed from student residence rooms and from off campus. Staffed computer lab on campus.
Community Environment: See Harvard University.

■ **MASSACHUSETTS MARITIME ACADEMY** *H-14*
101 Academy Dr.
Buzzards Bay, MA 02532-1803
Tel: (508)830-5000
Free: 800-544-3411
Admissions: (508)830-6441
Fax: (508)830-5077
Web Site: http://www.maritime.edu/
Description: State-supported, comprehensive, coed. Part of Massachusetts Public Higher Education System. Awards bachelor's and master's degrees and first professional certificates. Founded 1891. Setting: 55-acre small town campus with easy access to Boston. Endowment: $7.9 million. Total enrollment: 1,008. Faculty: 70 (59 full-time, 11 part-time). Student-undergrad faculty ratio is 15:1. 901 applied, 61% were admitted. Full-time: 923 students, 11% women, 89% men. Part-time: 46 students, 20% women, 80% men. Students come from 24 states and territories, 4 other countries, 30% from out-of-state, 0.2% Native American, 1% Hispanic, 1% black, 1% Asian American or Pacific Islander, 1% international, 100% live on campus. Retention: 79% of full-time freshmen returned the following year. Core. Calendar: semesters plus sea term. Academic remediation for entering students, services for LD students, advanced placement, double major, summer session for credit, adult/continuing education programs, co-op programs and internships. ROTC: Army (c), Naval.
Entrance Requirements: Options: Peterson's Universal Application, electronic application, early decision, deferred admission. Required: essay, high school transcript, minimum 2.0 high school GPA, 2 recommendations, physical examination, SAT or ACT. Recommended: interview. Entrance: moderately difficult. Application deadlines: Rolling, Rolling for nonresidents, 11/1 for early action. Notification: continuous, continuous for nonresidents, 12/15 for early decision, 12/15 for early action.

Costs Per Year: Application fee: $50. Area resident tuition: $1062 full-time. State resident tuition: $1591 full-time. Nonresident tuition: $11,591 full-time. Mandatory fees: $4045 full-time. College room and board: $6464. College room only: $3286.

Collegiate Environment: Orientation program. Drama-theater group, marching band, student-run newspaper. Social organizations: 15 open to all; 70% of eligible men and 70% of eligible women are members. Most popular organizations: Club Hockey, water sports, sailing/cruising, Rugby Club, Scuba Club. Major annual events: Emery Rice Day, Homecoming, Winter Sea Cruise. Student services: health clinic, personal-psychological counseling. Campus security: 24-hour emergency response devices and patrols, late night transport-escort service. 1,000 college housing spaces available; all were occupied in 2003-04. Freshmen guaranteed college housing. On-campus residence required through senior year. Option: coed housing available. Hurley Library with 55,000 books, 253 serials, 200 audiovisual materials, and an OPAC. Operations spending for 2004 fiscal year: $202,218. 100 computers available on campus for general student use. Computer purchase/lease plans available. A campuswide network can be accessed from student residence rooms. Staffed computer lab on campus.

Community Environment: Bourne is the second largest town on Cape Cod and has a New England climate. It is located 60 miles from Boston, and bus service and air service from Hyannis are available. The Trading Post, located here, is a replica of the trading post built in 1627. Bourne Scenic Park is a good area for picnics and camping. Boating, fishing, swimming and golf are available for recreation in this resort community.

■ **MASSASOIT COMMUNITY COLLEGE** *F-12*
1 Massasoit Blvd.
Brockton, MA 02302-3996
Tel: (508)588-9100
Fax: (508)427-1220
Web Site: http://www.massasoit.mass.edu/
Description: State-supported, 2-year, coed. Awards certificates, transfer associate, and terminal associate degrees. Founded 1966. Setting: suburban campus with easy access to Boston. Total enrollment: 6,808. Full-time: 3,178 students, 53% women, 47% men. Part-time: 3,630 students, 64% women, 36% men. Students come from 4 states and territories, 3 other countries, 1% from out-of-state, 1% Native American, 2% Hispanic, 15% black, 1% Asian American or Pacific Islander, 0.4% international, 35% 25 or older, 5% transferred in. Core. Calendar: semesters. Academic remediation for entering students, ESL program, services for LD students, accelerated degree program, distance learning, summer session for credit, part-time degree program, adult/continuing education programs, co-op programs and internships. Off campus study at 9 members of the Southeastern Association for Cooperation in Higher Education in Massachusetts.
Entrance Requirements: Open admission except for allied health programs. Entrance: noncompetitive. Application deadline: Rolling. Notification: continuous. Preference given to state residents.
Costs Per Year: Application fee: $0. State resident tuition: $576 full-time. Nonresident tuition: $5520 full-time. Mandatory fees: $2088 full-time. Full-time tuition and fees vary according to course load.
Collegiate Environment: Drama-theater group, student-run newspaper, radio station. Social organizations: 32 open to all. Most popular organizations: Drama Club, student newspaper, Phi Theta Kappa, International Student Association, Student Senate. Student services: health clinic, personal-psychological counseling, women's center. Campus security: 24-hour patrols. College housing not available. 75,000 books and 396 serials. 350 computers available on campus for general student use. Staffed computer lab on campus.
Community Environment: Brockton is located 20 miles south of downtown Boston and the center of the second fastest growing area of the State. The college service area encompasses one million people in 51 cities and towns south of Boston and includes the city of Quincy.

■ **MERRIMACK COLLEGE** *B-12*
315 Turnpike St.
North Andover, MA 01845-5800
Tel: (978)837-5000
Fax: (978)837-5222
Web Site: http://www.merrimack.edu/
Description: Independent Roman Catholic, comprehensive, coed. Awards associate, bachelor's, and master's degrees. Founded 1947. Setting: 220-acre suburban campus with easy access to Boston. Endowment: $31.2 million. Research spending for 2004 fiscal year: $97,269. Educational spending

for 2005 fiscal year: $9447 per student. Total enrollment: 2,188. Faculty: 223 (143 full-time, 80 part-time). Student-undergrad faculty ratio is 12:1. 3,412 applied, 71% were admitted. 19% from top 10% of their high school class, 47% from top quarter, 85% from top half. 20 class presidents, 4 valedictorians, 197 student government officers. Full-time: 1,950 students, 54% women, 46% men. Part-time: 204 students, 42% women, 58% men. Students come from 29 states and territories, 16 other countries, 28% from out-of-state, 0.1% Native American, 2% Hispanic, 1% black, 1% Asian American or Pacific Islander, 1% international, 2% 25 or older, 74% live on campus, 4% transferred in. Retention: 79% of full-time freshmen returned the following year. Academic areas with the most degrees conferred: business/marketing; social sciences; psychology. Core. Calendar: semesters. Academic remediation for entering students, ESL program, services for LD students, advanced placement, self-designed majors, honors program, independent study, double major, summer session for credit, part-time degree program, adult/continuing education programs, co-op programs and internships. Off campus study at Northeast Consortium of Colleges and Universities in Massachusetts, American University, Massachusetts Bay Marine Studies Consortium. Study abroad program. ROTC: Air Force (c).
Entrance Requirements: Options: Peterson's Universal Application, Common Application, electronic application, early admission, early action, deferred admission, international baccalaureate accepted. Required: essay, high school transcript, first quarter senior grades, SAT or ACT. Recommended: minimum 2.8 high school GPA, 1 recommendation, interview. Required for some: interview. Entrance: moderately difficult. Application deadlines: 2/1, 11/30 for early action. Notification: continuous until 4/1, 12/20 for early action.
Costs Per Year: Application fee: $50. Comprehensive fee: $34,380 includes full-time tuition ($24,200), mandatory fees ($450), and college room and board ($9730). College room only: $5500. Full-time tuition and fees vary according to program and student level. Room and board charges vary according to board plan and housing facility. Part-time tuition: $900 per credit. Part-time mandatory fees: $55 per term. Part-time tuition and fees vary according to class time, course level, course load, and degree level.
Collegiate Environment: Orientation program. Drama-theater group, choral group. Social organizations: 48 open to all; national fraternities, national sororities, local fraternities, local sororities; 16% of eligible men and 19% of eligible women are members. Most popular organizations: Merrimaction Community Outreach, MORE Retreat Program, Merrimack Marketing Association, Orientation Committee Coordinators, Developing Leaders Program. Major annual events: Parents' Weekend, Homecoming, Winter Weekend. Student services: health clinic, personal-psychological counseling. Campus security: 24-hour emergency response devices and patrols, student patrols, late night transport-escort service, controlled dormitory access. 1,590 college housing spaces available; 1,497 were occupied in 2003-04. Freshmen given priority for college housing. Option: coed housing available. McQuade Library with 115,639 books, 11,624 microform titles, 1,044 serials, 1,972 audiovisual materials, an OPAC, and a Web page. Operations spending for 2004 fiscal year: $1.1 million. 175 computers available on campus for general student use. A campuswide network can be accessed from student residence rooms. Staffed computer lab on campus.
Community Environment: North Andover is approximately 25 miles north of Boston and has rail and bus service to the city. Andover is used extensively for relaxation, shopping and eating. The local area is rich in cultural and historic attractions.

■ **MIDDLESEX COMMUNITY COLLEGE** *I-1*
Springs Rd.
Bedford, MA 01730-1655
Tel: (781)280-3200
Admissions: (978)656-3207
Fax: (978)656-3322
E-mail: orellanad@middlesex.cc.ma.us
Web Site: http://www.middlesex.mass.edu/
Description: State-supported, 2-year, coed. Part of Massachusetts Public Higher Education System. Awards certificates, transfer associate, and terminal associate degrees. Founded 1970. Setting: 200-acre suburban campus with easy access to Boston. Endowment: $1.1 million. Total enrollment: 8,016. Students come from 5 states and territories, 5% from out-of-state, 39% 25 or older. Core. Calendar: semesters. Academic remediation for entering students, ESL program, services for LD students, advanced placement, accelerated degree program, honors program, independent study, distance learning, summer session for credit, part-time degree program, adult/continuing education programs, co-op programs and intern-

ships. Off campus study at members of the Northeast Consortium of Colleges and Universities in Massachusetts. Study abroad program. ROTC: Air Force (c).

Entrance Requirements: Open admission for most programs. Options: Peterson's Universal Application, Common Application, electronic application, early admission. Required for some: essay, high school transcript, 3 recommendations, interview, CPT. Entrance: noncompetitive. Application deadline: Rolling. Notification: continuous. Preference given to state residents.

Collegiate Environment: Orientation program. Drama-theater group, student-run newspaper. Social organizations: 31 open to all. Most popular organizations: Mental Health Club, International Club, Early Childhood Education Club, Student Union Government Association, Student Activities Board. Major annual events: Annual Speaker Series, Annual Recognition Banquet, Annual Semi-Formal. Student services: legal services, health clinic, personal-psychological counseling. Campus security: 24-hour emergency response devices and patrols. College housing not available. Main library plus 1 other with 52,960 books, 538 serials, an OPAC, and a Web page. Operations spending for 2004 fiscal year: $577,053. 325 computers available on campus for general student use. A campuswide network can be accessed from off-campus. Staffed computer lab on campus.

■ **MONTSERRAT COLLEGE OF ART** *C-13*
23 Essex St., Box 26
Beverly, MA 01915
Tel: (978)922-8222
Free: 800-836-0487
Admissions: (978)921-4242
Fax: (978)922-4268
E-mail: admiss@montserrat.edu
Web Site: http://www.montserrat.edu/
Description: Independent, 4-year, coed. Awards bachelor's degrees. Founded 1970. Setting: 10-acre suburban campus with easy access to Boston. Endowment: $645,166. Educational spending for 2005 fiscal year: $5739 per student. Total enrollment: 308. Student-undergrad faculty ratio is 7:1. 326 applied, 85% were admitted. Full-time: 279 students, 62% women, 38% men. Part-time: 29 students, 59% women, 41% men. Students come from 20 states and territories, 1 other country, 50% from out-of-state, 0% Native American, 2% Hispanic, 1% black, 2% Asian American or Pacific Islander, 0% international, 7% 25 or older, 53% live on campus, 6% transferred in. Retention: 51% of full-time freshmen returned the following year. Academic area with the most degrees conferred: visual and performing arts. Core. Calendar: semesters. ESL program, services for LD students, advanced placement, self-designed majors, independent study, double major, part-time degree program, adult/continuing education programs, internships. Off campus study at Northeast Consortium of Colleges and Universities in Massachusetts, Association of Independent Colleges of Art and Design. Study abroad program. ROTC: Air Force (c).
Entrance Requirements: Options: deferred admission, international baccalaureate accepted. Required: essay, high school transcript, minimum 2.25 high school GPA, 2 recommendations, portfolio. Recommended: minimum 2.5 high school GPA, interview. Required for some: SAT or ACT. Entrance: moderately difficult. Application deadline: 8/1. Notification: continuous until 8/20.
Costs Per Year: Application fee: $40. One-time mandatory fee: $725. Tuition: $19,934 full-time, $831 per credit part-time. Mandatory fees: $745 full-time, $22 per credit part-time. Full-time tuition and fees vary according to course load. Part-time tuition and fees vary according to course load. College room only: $5300. Room charges vary according to housing facility.
Collegiate Environment: Orientation program. Social organizations: 8 open to all. Most popular organizations: Student Council, Language Partners, peer leaders, Fashion Show Committee, coed intramural sports. Major annual events: Global Holiday, Halloween Party, Tropical Party. Student services: personal-psychological counseling. Campus security: late night transport-escort service. 198 college housing spaces available; 153 were occupied in 2003-04. Freshmen given priority for college housing. Option: coed housing available. Paul Scott Library plus 1 other with 12,025 books, 76 serials, 50,031 audiovisual materials, and an OPAC. Operations spending for 2004 fiscal year: $135,724. 98 computers available on campus for general student use. A campuswide network can be accessed. Staffed computer lab on campus.
Community Environment: Just 30 minutes north of Boston, Beverly is a residential city with a population of 52,000. The historic rocky coast of the north shore of Boston offers a contemplative setting with its harborside parks

and beaches, access to the nearby fishing and yachting harbors of Gloucester, Marblehead and Rockport, and to the historic city of Salem, immediately adjacent to Beverly. The environment of the north shore is offset by the accessibility to a large metropolitan city with galleries, museums, cultural events, and nightlife.

■ **MOUNT HOLYOKE COLLEGE** *E-5*
50 College St.
South Hadley, MA 01075
Tel: (413)538-2000
Admissions: (413)538-2023
Fax: (413)538-2409
E-mail: admission@mtholyoke.edu
Web Site: http://www.mtholyoke.edu/
Description: Independent, comprehensive, women only. Awards bachelor's and master's degrees. Founded 1837. Setting: 800-acre small town campus with easy access to Springfield. Endowment: $460.8 million. Research spending for 2004 fiscal year: $2.7 million. Educational spending for 2005 fiscal year: $19,304 per student. Total enrollment: 2,127. Faculty: 241 (207 full-time, 34 part-time). Student-undergrad faculty ratio is 10:1. 2,924 applied, 52% were admitted. 51% from top 10% of their high school class, 80% from top quarter, 95% from top half. 2 National Merit Scholars, 26 valedictorians, 142 student government officers. Full-time: 2,052 students. Part-time: 73 students. Students come from 48 states and territories, 72 other countries, 75% from out-of-state, 1% Native American, 5% Hispanic, 4% black, 12% Asian American or Pacific Islander, 14% international, 6% 25 or older, 93% live on campus, 2% transferred in. Retention: 94% of full-time freshmen returned the following year. Academic areas with the most degrees conferred: social sciences; biological/life sciences; psychology. Core. Calendar: 4-1-4. Services for LD students, advanced placement, self-designed majors, honors program, independent study, double major, part-time degree program, adult/continuing education programs, co-op programs and internships. Off campus study at members of the Twelve College Exchange Program, Five Colleges, Inc., Spelman College, Mills College. Study abroad program. ROTC: Army (c), Air Force (c).
Entrance Requirements: Options: Common Application, electronic application, early admission, early decision, deferred admission, international baccalaureate accepted. Required: essay, high school transcript, 2 recommendations. Recommended: interview. Required for some: SAT Subject Tests. Entrance: very difficult. Application deadlines: 1/15, 11/15 for early decision plan 1, 1/1 for early decision plan 2. Notification: 4/1, 1/1 for early decision plan 1, 2/1 for early decision plan 2.
Costs Per Year: Application fee: $60. Comprehensive fee: $42,148 includes full-time tuition ($32,430), mandatory fees ($168), and college room and board ($9550). College room only: $4670. Room and board charges vary according to board plan and housing facility. Part-time tuition: $1015 per credit hour.
Collegiate Environment: Orientation program. Drama-theater group, choral group, student-run newspaper, radio station. Social organizations: 145 open to all. Most popular organizations: Student Government Association, WMHC (radio station), Mount Holyoke News, cultural organizations, a cappella groups. Major annual events: A Cappella Jams, Junior Show, Las Vegas Night. Student services: health clinic, personal-psychological counseling, women's center. Campus security: 24-hour emergency response devices and patrols, student patrols, late night transport-escort service, controlled dormitory access, police officers on-campus. 2,022 college housing spaces available; 1,983 were occupied in 2003-04. Freshmen guaranteed college housing. On-campus residence required through senior year. Option: women-only housing available. Williston Memorial Library plus 2 others with 909,720 books, 23,088 microform titles, 2,325 serials, 6,453 audiovisual materials, an OPAC, and a Web page. Operations spending for 2004 fiscal year: $3.8 million. 561 computers available on campus for general student use. A campuswide network can be accessed from student residence rooms and from off campus. Staffed computer lab on campus.
Community Environment: Across from campus in South Hadley Center is the Village Commons, apartments, movie theaters, a restaurant, an ice cream shop, a pub, a video rental shop, clothing stores, and offices, all attract people from across the five college areas. South Hadley is approximately 3 hours from the city of New York and only an hour and 30 minutes away from Boston. The Bradley International Airport is 40 minutes away and serves the Hartford and Springfield areas. Springfield, only 12 miles away, is accessible by Amtrak. There are buses running from Boston, Hartford, and Springfield to the campus gates. A free bus runs every half hour, taking students to the four other schools (Smith, Amherst, Hampshire, and The University of Massachusetts at Amherst).

■ MOUNT IDA COLLEGE *E-11*

777 Dedham St.
Newton, MA 02459-3310
Tel: (617)928-4500
Fax: (617)928-4507
Web Site: http://www.mountida.edu/

Description: Independent, 4-year, coed. Awards associate and bachelor's degrees. Founded 1899. Setting: 72-acre suburban campus with easy access to Boston. Endowment: $9.4 million. Educational spending for 2005 fiscal year: $3908 per student. Total enrollment: 1,297. 1,994 applied, 79% were admitted. Full-time: 1,191 students, 69% women, 31% men. Part-time: 106 students, 76% women, 24% men. Students come from 23 states and territories, 33 other countries, 0.1% Native American, 6% Hispanic, 12% black, 3% Asian American or Pacific Islander, 8% international, 38% live on campus. Core. Calendar: semesters. Academic remediation for entering students, ESL program, services for LD students, accelerated degree program, self-designed majors, freshman honors college, honors program, part-time degree program, adult/continuing education programs, co-op programs and internships. Study abroad program.

Entrance Requirements: Options: Peterson's Universal Application, Common Application, electronic application, early action, deferred admission. Required: high school transcript, 1 recommendation, SAT or ACT. Recommended: essay, minimum 2.0 high school GPA, interview. Entrance: moderately difficult. Application deadline: Rolling. Notification: continuous.

Costs Per Year: Application fee: $35. Comprehensive fee: $28,926 includes full-time tuition ($18,500), mandatory fees ($596), and college room and board ($9830). Part-time tuition: $515 per credit hour. Part-time mandatory fees: $15 per credit.

Collegiate Environment: Orientation program. Drama-theater group, choral group, student-run newspaper, radio station. Social organizations: 25 open to all. Most popular organizations: Leadership Students, student government, Phi Theta Kappa, Residence Council, Alpha Chi. Major annual events: Homecomng/Parents' Weekend, Winter Fest, Spring Fling. Student services: health clinic, personal-psychological counseling. Campus security: 24-hour emergency response devices and patrols, student patrols, late night transport-escort service, controlled residence hall entrances, secured campus entrance. 800 college housing spaces available; 764 were occupied in 2003-04. Options: coed, men-only, women-only housing available. Wadsworth Learning Resource Center plus 1 other with 100,695 books, 533 serials, and a Web page. 101 computers available on campus for general student use. A campuswide network can be accessed. Staffed computer lab on campus.

■ MOUNT WACHUSETT COMMUNITY COLLEGE *C-8*

444 Green St.
Gardner, MA 01440-1000
Tel: (978)632-6600
Fax: (978)632-8925
Web Site: http://www.mwcc.mass.edu/

Description: State-supported, 2-year, coed. Part of Massachusetts Public Higher Education System. Awards certificates, transfer associate, and terminal associate degrees. Founded 1963. Setting: 270-acre small town campus with easy access to Boston. Endowment: $1.7 million. Educational spending for 2005 fiscal year: $4083 per student. Total enrollment: 4,170. Student-undergrad faculty ratio is 22:1. 1,542 applied, 98% were admitted. Full-time: 1,958 students, 61% women, 39% men. Part-time: 2,212 students, 73% women, 27% men. Students come from 6 states and territories, 8 other countries, 5% from out-of-state, 0.5% Native American, 9% Hispanic, 4% black, 3% Asian American or Pacific Islander, 2% international, 42% 25 or older, 8% transferred in. Retention: 49% of full-time freshmen returned the following year. Core. Calendar: semesters. Academic remediation for entering students, ESL program, services for LD students, advanced placement, honors program, independent study, distance learning, double major, summer session for credit, part-time degree program, adult/continuing education programs, co-op programs and internships. Study abroad program.

Entrance Requirements: Open admission except for nursing, physical therapy assistant programs. Options: Common Application, early admission. Required: high school transcript. Required for some: essay, 2 recommendations. Entrance: noncompetitive. Application deadline: Rolling. Notification: continuous. Preference given to state residents.

Costs Per Year: Application fee: $10. State resident tuition: $750 full-time, $25 per credit part-time. Nonresident tuition: $6900 full-time, $230 per credit part-time. Mandatory fees: $3480 full-time, $111 per credit part-time, $55 per term part-time.

Collegiate Environment: Orientation program. Drama-theater group, choral group, student-run newspaper. Social organizations: 18 open to all. Most popular organizations: Sophomore Nursing Club, Freshman Nursing Club, Alpha Beta Gamma, Physical Therapist Assistant Club, Multicultural Club. Major annual events: Orientation, Commencement Dinner/Awards Ceremony. Student services: health clinic, personal-psychological counseling, women's center. Campus security: 24-hour emergency response devices and patrols. College housing not available. Mount Wachusett Community College Library with 56,344 books, 6,051 microform titles, 532 serials, 2,185 audiovisual materials, an OPAC, and a Web page. Operations spending for 2004 fiscal year: $348,122. 415 computers available on campus for general student use. A campuswide network can be accessed. Staffed computer lab on campus.

Community Environment: City has airport and bus service. Community services include three libraries, many churches of most denominations, the Henry Heywood Memorial Hospital, and a downtown shopping center. Recreational facilities are swimming pool, golf course, lakes, bowling and theatre. Excellent opportunities for part-time employment.

■ NEW ENGLAND COLLEGE OF FINANCE *D-12*

10 High St.
Ste. 204
Boston, MA 02111-2645
Tel: (617)951-2350; 888-696-NECF
Fax: (617)951-2533
Web Site: http://www.finance.edu/

Description: Independent, 2-year, coed. Awards certificates and terminal associate degrees (offers primarily part-time evening degree programs; bachelor's degree offered jointly with Bentley College, Assumption College, Providence College, University of Hartford, and University System College for Lifelong Learning). Founded 1909. Setting: urban campus. Total enrollment: 412. Student-undergrad faculty ratio is 11:1. Students come from 4 states and territories, 5% from out-of-state, 0.5% Native American, 9% Hispanic, 9% black, 8% Asian American or Pacific Islander, 22% 25 or older. Core. Calendar: 8 week terms (6 per academic year). Academic remediation for entering students, independent study, distance learning, summer session for credit, part-time degree program, adult/continuing education programs, internships.

Entrance Requirements: Open admission. Option: Common Application. Required: essay, high school transcript, 1 recommendation, interview. Entrance: noncompetitive. Application deadline: Rolling. Notification: continuous.

Costs Per Year: Application fee: $0. Tuition: $242 per semester hour part-time.

Collegiate Environment: Campus security: reception desk in lobby of building. College housing not available. 10 computers available on campus for general student use.

■ NEW ENGLAND CONSERVATORY OF MUSIC *D-12*

290 Huntington Ave.
Boston, MA 02115-5000
Tel: (617)585-1100
Admissions: (617)585-1101
Fax: (617)585-1115
E-mail: tnovak@newenglandconservatory.edu
Web Site: http://www.newenglandconservatory.edu/

Description: Independent, comprehensive, coed. Awards bachelor's, master's, and doctoral degrees. Founded 1867. Setting: 2-acre urban campus. Endowment: $65.6 million. Educational spending for 2005 fiscal year: $12,743 per student. Total enrollment: 801. Faculty: 210 (83 full-time, 127 part-time). Student-undergrad faculty ratio is 4:1. 968 applied, 30% were admitted. Full-time: 388 students, 44% women, 56% men. Part-time: 24 students, 54% women, 46% men. Students come from 46 states and territories, 39 other countries, 86% from out-of-state, 1% Native American, 5% Hispanic, 2% black, 9% Asian American or Pacific Islander, 17% international, 4% 25 or older, 40% live on campus, 5% transferred in. Retention: 84% of full-time freshmen returned the following year. Academic area with the most degrees conferred: visual and performing arts. Core. Calendar: semesters. ESL program, services for LD students, advanced placement, independent study, summer session for credit, part-time degree program, adult/continuing education programs, internships, graduate courses open to undergrads. Off campus study at Simmons College, Tufts University, Northeastern University. Study abroad program.

Entrance Requirements: Option: deferred admission. Required: essay, high school transcript, minimum 2.75 high school GPA, 2 recommendations, audition, SAT or ACT. Entrance: very difficult. Application deadline: 12/1. Notification: 4/1.

Costs Per Year: Application fee: $100. Comprehensive fee: $40,389 includes full-time tuition ($29,000), mandatory fees ($300), and college room and board ($11,089). Part-time tuition: $950 per credit.

Collegiate Environment: Orientation program. Choral group. Social organizations: 8 open to all; local fraternities; 15% of eligible men and 15% of eligible women are members. Most popular organizations: NEC Student Association, Chinese Student Association, Christian Fellowship, Vegetarian Club, Soccer Club. Major annual events: spring and fall barbecues, International Day, Chinese New Year. Student services: health clinic, personal-psychological counseling. Campus security: 24-hour patrols, late night transport-escort service. 169 college housing spaces available; 163 were occupied in 2003-04. Freshmen guaranteed college housing. On-campus residence required in freshman year. Option: coed housing available. Spaulding Library plus 1 other with 78,853 books, 298 microform titles, 275 serials, 46,384 audiovisual materials, an OPAC, and a Web page. Operations spending for 2004 fiscal year: $645,921. 48 computers available on campus for general student use. A campuswide network can be accessed. Staffed computer lab on campus.

Community Environment: See Boston University.

■ **THE NEW ENGLAND INSTITUTE OF ART** *E-12*
10 Brookline Place West
Brookline, MA 02445
Tel: (617)267-7910
Admissions: (617)739-1700
Fax: (617)236-7883
E-mail: aine_admissions@aii.edu
Web Site: http://www.neia.aii.edu/

Description: Proprietary, 4-year, coed. Part of Education Management Corporation. Awards associate and bachelor's degrees. Setting: urban campus with easy access to Boston. Educational spending for 2005 fiscal year: $3145 per student. Total enrollment: 1,293. Student-undergrad faculty ratio is 18:1. 919 applied, 97% were admitted. Full-time: 1,004 students, 30% women, 70% men. Part-time: 289 students, 31% women, 69% men. Students come from 36 states and territories, 63% from out-of-state, 0.2% Native American, 2% Hispanic, 2% black, 1% Asian American or Pacific Islander, 1% international. Retention: 100% of full-time freshmen returned the following year. Academic areas with the most degrees conferred: visual and performing arts; computer and information sciences; engineering technologies. Core. Calendar: semesters. Academic remediation for entering students, services for LD students, advanced placement, independent study, distance learning, adult/continuing education programs, internships.

Entrance Requirements: Options: Common Application, electronic application. Required: essay, high school transcript, minimum X high school GPA, interview. Required for some: recommendations, portfolios. Entrance: minimally difficult. Application deadline: Rolling. Notification: continuous.

Costs Per Year: Application fee: $50. Comprehensive fee: $28,053 includes full-time tuition ($17,850), mandatory fees ($225), and college room and board ($9978). College room only: $7718. Part-time tuition: $595 per credit.

Collegiate Environment: Orientation program. Student-run radio station. Social organizations: 8 open to all. Most popular organizations: Graphic Design Club, Naked Truth, Naked Eye Video, Naked Ear Records, Web Raisers. Major annual events: Fall Festival, Spring Festival, Summer Festival. Student services: personal-psychological counseling. Campus security: late night transport-escort service, controlled dormitory access. 190 college housing spaces available; 185 were occupied in 2003-04. No special consideration for freshman housing applicants. Option: coed housing available. The New England Institute of Art Library with 8,800 books, 175 serials, 660 audiovisual materials, and an OPAC. 200 computers available on campus for general student use. A campuswide network can be accessed. Staffed computer lab on campus.

■ **NEWBURY COLLEGE** *E-12*
129 Fisher Ave.
Brookline, MA 02445
Tel: (617)730-7000
Free: 800-NEW-BURY
Admissions: (617)730-7007
Fax: (617)731-9618
E-mail: info@newbury.edu

Web Site: http://www.newbury.edu/

Description: Independent, 4-year, coed. Awards associate and bachelor's degrees. Founded 1962. Setting: 10-acre suburban campus with easy access to Boston. Endowment: $1.5 million. Educational spending for 2005 fiscal year: $5560 per student. Total enrollment: 1,311. Student-undergrad faculty ratio is 15:1. 1,950 applied, 74% were admitted. 11% from top 10% of their high school class, 21% from top quarter, 54% from top half. 1 National Merit Scholar, 1 class president, 40 student government officers. Full-time: 928 students, 61% women, 39% men. Part-time: 383 students, 68% women, 32% men. Students come from 20 states and territories, 30 other countries, 30% from out-of-state, 0% Native American, 9% Hispanic, 19% black, 6% Asian American or Pacific Islander, 5% international, 10% 25 or older, 47% live on campus, 4% transferred in. Retention: 80% of full-time freshmen returned the following year. Core. Calendar: semesters. Academic remediation for entering students, ESL program, services for LD students, advanced placement, accelerated degree program, freshman honors college, honors program, independent study, double major, summer session for credit, part-time degree program, adult/continuing education programs, co-op programs and internships. Off campus study. Study abroad program.

Entrance Requirements: Options: Peterson's Universal Application, electronic application, early admission, early action, deferred admission. Required: essay, high school transcript, recommendations. Recommended: minimum 2.0 high school GPA, interview, SAT or ACT. Required for some: SAT or ACT. Entrance: minimally difficult. Application deadlines: Rolling, 12/1 for early action. Notification: continuous until 8/1, 1/1 for early action.

Costs Per Year: Application fee: $50. Comprehensive fee: $24,350 includes full-time tuition ($15,500), mandatory fees ($600), and college room and board ($8250). Full-time tuition and fees vary according to class time, course load, and program. Room and board charges vary according to board plan and housing facility. Part-time tuition: $220 per credit. Part-time tuition varies according to class time, course load, and program.

Collegiate Environment: Orientation program. Student-run newspaper, radio station. Social organizations: 23 open to all. Most popular organizations: student government, Newbury College Programming Board, Inn Keepers Club, Speech and Debate Team, International Student Organization. Major annual events: Family Day, Multicultural Week, Spring Formal. Student services: personal-psychological counseling. Campus security: 24-hour emergency response devices and patrols, late night transport-escort service, controlled dormitory access. 450 college housing spaces available; all were occupied in 2003-04. Options: coed, women-only housing available. Newbury College Library plus 1 other with 32,500 books, 1,115 serials, and an OPAC. Operations spending for 2004 fiscal year: $620,000. 85 computers available on campus for general student use. A campuswide network can be accessed from off-campus. Staffed computer lab on campus.

Community Environment: The main campus of Newbury College is nestled in a beautiful residential section of Brookline, Massachusetts, just 4 miles from downtown Boston, and easily accessible by public transportation.

■ **NICHOLS COLLEGE** *F-8*
PO Box 5000
Dudley, MA 01571-5000
Tel: (508)213-1560
Free: 800-470-3379
Admissions: (508)213-2203
Fax: (508)213-9885
E-mail: joe.bellavance@nichols.edu
Web Site: http://www.nichols.edu/

Description: Independent, comprehensive, coed. Awards associate, bachelor's, and master's degrees. Founded 1815. Setting: 210-acre rural campus with easy access to Boston. Total enrollment: 1,792. 1,195 applied, 84% were admitted. 2% from top 10% of their high school class, 25% from top quarter, 49% from top half. Full-time: 938 students, 35% women, 65% men. Part-time: 494 students, 55% women, 45% men. Students come from 26 states and territories, 50 other countries, 35% from out-of-state, 0.3% Native American, 4% Hispanic, 7% black, 2% Asian American or Pacific Islander, 0% international, 30% 25 or older, 80% live on campus, 4% transferred in. Retention: 76% of full-time freshmen returned the following year. Core. Calendar: semesters. Academic remediation for entering students, advanced placement, accelerated degree program, independent study, distance learning, double major, summer session for credit, part-time degree program, adult/continuing education programs, co-op programs and internships. Study abroad program. ROTC: Army (c).

Entrance Requirements: Options: Peterson's Universal Application, Common Application, electronic application, early admission, deferred admission.

Required: essay, high school transcript, 1 recommendation, SAT or ACT. Required for some: interview. Entrance: moderately difficult. Application deadline: Rolling. Notification: continuous.

Collegiate Environment: Orientation program. Drama-theater group, student-run newspaper, radio station. Social organizations: 30 open to all. Most popular organizations: Rugby Club, Accounting Club, Racquetball Club, student publications, Theater Club. Major annual events: Homecoming, Spring Weekend, Commencement. Student services: health clinic, personal-psychological counseling. Campus security: 24-hour patrols, late night transport-escort service. 737 college housing spaces available; all were occupied in 2003-04. Freshmen guaranteed college housing. On-campus residence required through senior year. Option: coed housing available. Conant Library plus 1 other with 43,989 books, 3,808 microform titles, 211 serials, 1,711 audiovisual materials, an OPAC, and a Web page. 850 computers available on campus for general student use. Computer purchase/lease plans available. A campuswide network can be accessed from student residence rooms and from off campus. Staffed computer lab on campus.

■ **NORTH SHORE COMMUNITY COLLEGE** C-13

1 Ferncroft Rd.
Danvers, MA 01923-4093
Tel: (978)762-4000
Fax: (978)762-4021
Web Site: http://www.northshore.edu/

Description: State-supported, 2-year, coed. Awards certificates, transfer associate, and terminal associate degrees. Founded 1965. Setting: suburban campus with easy access to Boston. Endowment: $4.1 million. Educational spending for 2005 fiscal year: $4310 per student. Total enrollment: 6,604. Student-undergrad faculty ratio is 18:1. 3,061 applied, 90% were admitted. Full-time: 2,764 students, 56% women, 44% men. Part-time: 3,840 students, 67% women, 33% men. Students come from 5 states and territories, 8 other countries, 1% from out-of-state, 0.3% Native American, 12% Hispanic, 8% black, 3% Asian American or Pacific Islander, 0.1% international, 45% 25 or older, 9% transferred in. Core. Calendar: semesters. Academic remediation for entering students, ESL program, services for LD students, advanced placement, honors program, independent study, distance learning, summer session for credit, part-time degree program, adult/continuing education programs, co-op programs and internships.

Entrance Requirements: Open admission except for nursing, engineering, health-related programs. Options: electronic application, early admission. Required for some: high school transcript, interview. Entrance: noncompetitive. Application deadline: Rolling. Notification: continuous. Preference given to state residents.

Costs Per Year: Application fee: $0. State resident tuition: $600 full-time, $25 per credit part-time. Nonresident tuition: $6168 full-time, $257 per credit part-time. Mandatory fees: $2184 full-time, $91 per credit part-time.

Collegiate Environment: Orientation program. Drama-theater group, student-run newspaper. Social organizations: 23 open to all. Most popular organizations: Program Council, student government, performing arts, student newspaper, Phi Theta Kappa. Major annual events: multicultural fair, Spring Fling, Alcohol Awareness Week. Student services: health clinic, personal-psychological counseling, women's center. Campus security: 24-hour emergency response devices and patrols, late night transport-escort service. College housing not available. Learning Resource Center plus 2 others with 97,818 books, 78,311 microform titles, 408 serials, 7,795 audiovisual materials, and an OPAC. Operations spending for 2004 fiscal year: $1.1 million. 380 computers available on campus for general student use. A campuswide network can be accessed. Staffed computer lab on campus.

Community Environment: Suburban.

■ **NORTHEASTERN UNIVERSITY** D-12

360 Huntington Ave.
Boston, MA 02115-5096
Tel: (617)373-2000
Admissions: (617)373-2200
Fax: (617)373-8780
E-mail: admissions@neu.edu
Web Site: http://www.northeastern.edu

Description: Independent, university, coed. Awards bachelor's, master's, doctoral, and first professional degrees and post-master's certificates. Founded 1898. Setting: 67-acre urban campus. Endowment: $557.5 million. Total enrollment: 19,541. Faculty: 1,257 (853 full-time, 404 part-time).

Student-undergrad faculty ratio is 16:1. 25,467 applied, 47% were admitted. 36% from top 10% of their high school class, 73% from top quarter, 94% from top half. Full-time: 14,730 students, 51% women, 49% men. Students come from 50 states and territories, 123 other countries, 66% from out-of-state, 0.4% Native American, 5% Hispanic, 6% black, 7% Asian American or Pacific Islander, 5% international, 4% 25 or older, 4% transferred in. Retention: 90% of full-time freshmen returned the following year. Academic areas with the most degrees conferred: business/marketing; engineering; social sciences. Core. Calendar: semesters. Academic remediation for entering students, ESL program, services for LD students, advanced placement, accelerated degree program, self-designed majors, honors program, independent study, distance learning, double major, summer session for credit, part-time degree program, adult/continuing education programs, co-op programs and internships, graduate courses open to undergrads. Off campus study at New England Conservatory of Music, Hebrew College. Study abroad program. ROTC: Army, Naval (c), Air Force (c).

Entrance Requirements: Options: Common Application, electronic application, early admission, deferred admission, international baccalaureate accepted. Required: essay, high school transcript, SAT or ACT. Recommended: minimum 2.0 high school GPA, 2 recommendations. Required for some: interview. Entrance: very difficult. Application deadline: 1/15. Notification: continuous until 4/1.

Costs Per Year: Application fee: $75. Comprehensive fee: $39,342 includes full-time tuition ($28,400), mandatory fees ($392), and college room and board ($10,550). College room only: $5620. Room and board charges vary according to board plan and housing facility.

Collegiate Environment: Orientation program. Drama-theater group, choral group, student-run newspaper, radio station. Social organizations: 200 open to all; national fraternities, national sororities, local fraternities; 4% of eligible men and 4% of eligible women are members. Most popular organizations: Student Government Association, NU Hus-kiers and Outing Club, International Student Association, Council for University Programs, Resident Student Association. Major annual events: Homecoming Week, Springfest, International Week. Student services: health clinic, personal-psychological counseling, women's center. Campus security: 24-hour emergency response devices and patrols, late night transport-escort service, controlled dormitory access. 7,244 college housing spaces available; all were occupied in 2003-04. Freshmen guaranteed college housing. Options: coed, women-only housing available. Snell Library plus 4 others with 965,833 books, 2.3 million microform titles, 7,636 serials, 17,215 audiovisual materials, an OPAC, and a Web page. 1,993 computers available on campus for general student use. A campuswide network can be accessed from student residence rooms and from off campus. Staffed computer lab on campus.

Community Environment: Students at Northeastern University have access to the full range of cultural, educational, historical, and recreational offerings of Boston, the higher education capital of the world. The cultural opportunities include the Museum of Fine Arts, Symphony Hall, and the Boston Public Library. The University is adjacent to the Fenway, a spacious park that includes a beautiful rose garden and paths.

■ **NORTHERN ESSEX COMMUNITY COLLEGE** B-12

100 Elliott St.
Haverhill, MA 01830
Tel: (978)556-3000
Free: 800-NECC-123
Admissions: (978)556-3616
E-mail: nsheridan@necc.mass.edu
Web Site: http://www.necc.mass.edu/

Description: State-supported, 2-year, coed. Awards certificates, transfer associate, and terminal associate degrees. Founded 1960. Setting: 106-acre suburban campus with easy access to Boston. Endowment: $2.1 million. Educational spending for 2005 fiscal year: $12,363 per student. Total enrollment: 6,362. Student-undergrad faculty ratio is 20:1. 3,347 applied, 95% were admitted. Students come from 4 states and territories, 16% from out-of-state, 0.3% Native American, 20% Hispanic, 2% black, 2% Asian American or Pacific Islander, 1% international, 51% 25 or older. Retention: 54% of full-time freshmen returned the following year. Core. Calendar: semesters. Academic remediation for entering students, ESL program, services for LD students, advanced placement, freshman honors college, honors program, independent study, distance learning, double major, summer session for credit, part-time degree program, adult/continuing education programs, co-op programs and internships. Off campus study at Bradford College, members of the Northeast Consortium of Colleges and Universities in Massachusetts. Study abroad program. ROTC: Air Force (c).

Entrance Requirements: Open admission except for health, human services, technology programs. Option: early admission. Required: high school transcript, Psychological Corporation Aptitude Test for Practical Nursing. Entrance: noncompetitive. Application deadline: Rolling. Notification: continuous. Preference given to state residents.

Costs Per Year: Application fee: $0. State resident tuition: $3150 full-time, $105 per credit part-time. Nonresident tuition: $3660 full-time, $346 per credit part-time. Full-time tuition varies according to course load, degree level, program, and reciprocity agreements. Part-time tuition varies according to course load, degree level, program, and reciprocity agreements.

Collegiate Environment: Drama-theater group, student-run newspaper. Student services: health clinic, personal-psychological counseling, women's center. Campus security: 24-hour emergency response devices and patrols. College housing not available. Bentley Library with 61,120 books, 598 serials, and an OPAC. Operations spending for 2004 fiscal year: $529,028. 250 computers available on campus for general student use. A campuswide network can be accessed from off-campus. Staffed computer lab on campus.

■ **PINE MANOR COLLEGE** *E-12*
400 Heath St.
Chestnut Hill, MA 02467
Tel: (617)731-7000
Free: 800-762-1357
Admissions: (617)731-7104
Fax: (617)731-7199
E-mail: admisson@pmc.edu
Web Site: http://www.pmc.edu/

Description: Independent, 4-year, women only. Awards associate and bachelor's degrees. Founded 1911. Setting: 65-acre suburban campus with easy access to Boston. Endowment: $11.2 million. Educational spending for 2005 fiscal year: $6252 per student. Total enrollment: 461. Student-undergrad faculty ratio is 10:1. 387 applied, 94% were admitted. 8% from top 10% of their high school class, 23% from top quarter, 58% from top half. Full-time: 448 students. Part-time: 13 students. Students come from 26 states and territories, 24 other countries, 24% from out-of-state, 1% Native American, 12% Hispanic, 42% black, 5% Asian American or Pacific Islander, 9% international, 13% 25 or older, 74% live on campus, 4% transferred in. Retention: 64% of full-time freshmen returned the following year. Academic areas with the most degrees conferred: psychology; business/marketing; biological/life sciences. Core. Calendar: semesters. Academic remediation for entering students, ESL program, services for LD students, advanced placement, self-designed majors, honors program, independent study, double major, summer session for credit, part-time degree program, external degree program, adult/continuing education programs, internships. Off campus study at Marine Studies Consortium, Boston College, Babson College. Study abroad program.

Entrance Requirements: Options: Common Application, electronic application, deferred admission, international baccalaureate accepted. Required: essay, high school transcript, 1 recommendation, SAT or ACT. Recommended: minimum 2.0 high school GPA, interview. Entrance: moderately difficult. Application deadline: Rolling. Notification: continuous. Preference given to students from colleges with whom PMC has an articulation agreement.

Costs Per Year: Application fee: $25. Comprehensive fee: $25,288 includes full-time tuition ($15,538), mandatory fees ($250), and college room and board ($9500). Full-time tuition and fees vary according to course load. Part-time tuition: $460 per credit. Part-time tuition varies according to course load.

Collegiate Environment: Orientation program. Drama-theater group, choral group, student-run newspaper, radio station. Social organizations: 25 open to all. Most popular organizations: Student Government Association, ALANA, LOVES (Ladies of Various Ebony Shades), CVSA (Cape Veraean Student Alliance), Campus Activities Board. Major annual events: Family and Friends Weekend, Fall Fest Weekend, Spring Formal. Student services: health clinic, personal-psychological counseling, women's center. Campus security: 24-hour emergency response devices and patrols, student patrols, late night transport-escort service, controlled dormitory access. 481 college housing spaces available; 371 were occupied in 2003-04. Freshmen given priority for college housing. Option: women-only housing available. Annenberg Library with 65,359 books, 62,027 microform titles, 313 serials, 1,907 audiovisual materials, an OPAC, and a Web page. Operations spending for 2004 fiscal year: $307,946. 126 computers available on campus for general student use. A campuswide network can be accessed from student residence rooms and from off campus. Staffed computer lab on campus.

■ **QUINCY COLLEGE** *E-12*
34 Coddington St.
Quincy, MA 02169-4522
Tel: (617)984-1600
Admissions: (617)984-1775
Fax: (617)984-1669
Web Site: http://www.quincycollege.edu/

Description: City-supported, 2-year, coed. Awards certificates, transfer associate, and terminal associate degrees. Founded 1958. Setting: 2-acre suburban campus with easy access to Boston. Endowment: $112,021. Total enrollment: 4,000. Students come from 11 states and territories, 92 other countries, 0.1% Native American, 3% Hispanic, 20% black, 13% Asian American or Pacific Islander, 45% 25 or older. Core. Calendar: semesters. Academic remediation for entering students, ESL program, advanced placement, summer session for credit, part-time degree program, adult/continuing education programs, internships.

Entrance Requirements: Open admission except for nursing, surgical technology programs. Options: Peterson's Universal Application, Common Application, early admission, deferred admission. Required: high school transcript. Placement: CPT required. Entrance: noncompetitive. Application deadline: Rolling. Notification: continuous.

Costs Per Year: Application fee: $20. State resident tuition: $4500 full-time.

Collegiate Environment: Orientation program. Most popular organizations: Student Government Association, Phi Theta Kappa, campus newspaper. Campus security: 24-hour emergency response devices and patrols. College housing not available. Anselmo Library plus 1 other with 32,000 books and 125 serials. 130 computers available on campus for general student use. A campuswide network can be accessed. Staffed computer lab on campus.

Community Environment: An important business and industrial city today, Quincy has given the nation some of its most important patriots. Quincy was the birthplace of two presidents, John Adams and his son, John Quincy Adams. This South Shore suburb is located about seven miles from downtown Boston, a 15-minute ride by public transportation. There is easy access to all Boston facilities.

■ **QUINSIGAMOND COMMUNITY COLLEGE** *E-9*
670 West Boylston St.
Worcester, MA 01606-2092
Tel: (508)853-2300
Admissions: (508)854-4262
Fax: (508)852-6943
E-mail: qccadm@qcc.mass.edu
Web Site: http://www.qcc.mass.edu/

Description: State-supported, 2-year, coed. Awards certificates, transfer associate, and terminal associate degrees. Founded 1963. Setting: 57-acre urban campus with easy access to Boston. Total enrollment: 5,970. 1,433 applied, 100% were admitted. Full-time: 2,761 students, 55% women, 45% men. Part-time: 3,209 students, 65% women, 35% men. Students come from 3 states and territories, 13 other countries, 0.5% Native American, 9% Hispanic, 8% black, 3% Asian American or Pacific Islander, 0.5% international, 45% 25 or older, 4% transferred in. Core. Calendar: semesters. Academic remediation for entering students, ESL program, services for LD students, advanced placement, accelerated degree program, double major, summer session for credit, part-time degree program, adult/continuing education programs, co-op programs and internships. Off campus study at members of the Colleges of Worcester Consortium. ROTC: Army (c).

Entrance Requirements: Open admission for business administration, general studies programs. Option: Common Application. Required: high school transcript. Required for some: interview. Entrance: moderately difficult. Application deadline: Rolling. Notification: continuous.

Costs Per Year: Application fee: $20. State resident tuition: $576 full-time, $24 per credit part-time. Nonresident tuition: $5520 full-time, $230 per credit part-time. Mandatory fees: $2479 full-time, $96 per credit part-time, $85 per term part-time.

Collegiate Environment: Orientation program. Drama-theater group, student-run newspaper. Social organizations: 24 open to all. Most popular organizations: Phi Theta Kappa, Nursing Club, Rad Tech Club, Gay Straight Alliance, Criminal Justice Club. Major annual events: Welcome Week, Spring Fling, Honors and Awards Banquet. Student services: health clinic, personal-psychological counseling, women's center, disability services, academic advising, career planning, tutoring. Campus security: 24-hour emergency response devices and patrols, late night transport-escort service. College housing not available. Quinsigamond Library plus 1 other with 54,000 books, 11 microform titles, 310 serials, 230 audiovisual materials, and an OPAC.

Operations spending for 2004 fiscal year: $459,484. 200 computers available on campus for general student use. A campuswide network can be accessed from off-campus. Staffed computer lab on campus.

Community Environment: See Clark University.

■ **REGIS COLLEGE** *J-1*
235 Wellesley St.
Weston, MA 02493
Tel: (781)768-7000; (866)438-7344
Admissions: (781)768-7100
Fax: (781)768-8339
Web Site: http://www.regiscollege.edu/

Description: Independent Roman Catholic, comprehensive. Awards associate, bachelor's, and master's degrees and post-master's certificates. Founded 1927. Setting: 168-acre small town campus with easy access to Boston. Endowment: $15.8 million. Educational spending for 2005 fiscal year: $7889 per student. Total enrollment: 1,303. Faculty: 113 (55 full-time, 58 part-time). Student-undergrad faculty ratio is 13:1. 908 applied, 76% were admitted. 20% from top 10% of their high school class, 58% from top quarter, 83% from top half. Full-time: 621 students, 99% women, 1% men. Part-time: 222 students, 91% women, 9% men. Students come from 15 states and territories, 8 other countries, 11% from out-of-state, 0.2% Native American, 10% Hispanic, 14% black, 7% Asian American or Pacific Islander, 1% international, 13% 25 or older, 46% live on campus, 6% transferred in. Retention: 78% of full-time freshmen returned the following year. Academic areas with the most degrees conferred: health professions and related sciences; biological/life sciences; business/marketing. Core. Calendar: semesters. Academic remediation for entering students, services for LD students, advanced placement, accelerated degree program, self-designed majors, honors program, independent study, double major, summer session for credit, part-time degree program, adult/continuing education programs, internships. Off campus study at Babson College, Bentley College, Boston College, American University, National Federation of Carondolet Colleges. Study abroad program. ROTC: Army (c).

Entrance Requirements: Options: Peterson's Universal Application, Common Application, electronic application, deferred admission, international baccalaureate accepted. Required: essay, high school transcript, minimum 2.0 high school GPA, 2 recommendations, SAT or ACT. Recommended: minimum 3.0 high school GPA, interview, rank in upper 50% of high school class. Required for some: interview. Entrance: moderately difficult. Application deadline: Rolling.

Costs Per Year: Application fee: $40. Comprehensive fee: $31,350 includes full-time tuition ($21,525) and college room and board ($9825). College room only: $4995.

Collegiate Environment: Orientation program. Drama-theater group, choral group, student-run radio station. Social organizations: 30 open to all. Most popular organizations: Board of Programmers, student government, Glee Club, Amigos, AHANA Club. Major annual events: Family Weekend, Cultural Enlightenment, Spring Weekend. Student services: health clinic, personal-psychological counseling. Campus security: 24-hour emergency response devices and patrols, late night transport-escort service, controlled dormitory access. 600 college housing spaces available; 416 were occupied in 2003-04. Freshmen guaranteed college housing. Option: women-only housing available. Regis College Library with 137,070 books, 19,704 microform titles, 805 serials, 6,204 audiovisual materials, an OPAC, and a Web page. Operations spending for 2004 fiscal year: $702,107. 159 computers available on campus for general student use. A campuswide network can be accessed from student residence rooms and from off campus. Staffed computer lab on campus.

Community Environment: Regis College is in a suburban community located approximately 12 miles west of Boston. Community services, cultural, and recreational facilities are located in Boston.

■ **ROXBURY COMMUNITY COLLEGE** *E-12*
1234 Columbus Ave.
Roxbury Crossing, MA 02120-3400
Tel: (617)427-0060
Admissions: (617)541-5310
Web Site: http://www.rcc.mass.edu/

Description: State-supported, 2-year, coed. Part of Massachusetts Public Higher Education System. Awards certificates, transfer associate, and terminal associate degrees. Founded 1973. Setting: 12-acre urban campus with easy access to Boston. Total enrollment: 2,382. 1,290 applied, 83% were admitted. Full-time: 1,124 students, 62% women, 38% men. Part-time:

1,258 students, 65% women, 35% men. Students come from 14 states and territories, 0.1% Native American, 16% Hispanic, 48% black, 4% Asian American or Pacific Islander, 0.4% international, 61% 25 or older, 1% transferred in. Core. Calendar: semesters. Academic remediation for entering students, ESL program, services for LD students, self-designed majors, honors program, summer session for credit, part-time degree program, adult/continuing education programs, internships. Off campus study.

Entrance Requirements: Open admission except for nursing program. Option: deferred admission. Required: high school transcript. Entrance: noncompetitive. Application deadline: Rolling. Notification: continuous. Preference given to local residents.

Collegiate Environment: Drama-theater group, choral group, student-run newspaper. Student services: personal-psychological counseling. Campus security: 24-hour emergency response devices and patrols, late night transport-escort service. College housing not available. Roxbury Community College Library with 12,800 books. 100 computers available on campus for general student use. A campuswide network can be accessed from off-campus. Staffed computer lab on campus.

■ **SALEM STATE COLLEGE** *C-13*
352 Lafayette St.
Salem, MA 01970-5353
Tel: (978)542-6000
Admissions: (978)542-6200
Fax: (978)542-6126
Web Site: http://www.salemstate.edu/

Description: State-supported, comprehensive, coed. Part of Massachusetts Public Higher Education System. Awards bachelor's and master's degrees and post-master's certificates. Founded 1854. Setting: 62-acre small town campus with easy access to Boston. Endowment: $6.6 million. Research spending for 2004 fiscal year: $93,258. Educational spending for 2005 fiscal year: $4252 per student. Total enrollment: 9,863. Faculty: 668 (296 full-time, 372 part-time). Student-undergrad faculty ratio is 17:1. 4,827 applied, 90% were admitted. Full-time: 5,468 students, 63% women, 37% men. Part-time: 1,828 students, 65% women, 35% men. Students come from 18 states and territories, 10% from out-of-state, 0.4% Native American, 5% Hispanic, 6% black, 3% Asian American or Pacific Islander, 4% international, 18% 25 or older, 22% live on campus, 12% transferred in. Retention: 75% of full-time freshmen returned the following year. Academic areas with the most degrees conferred: business/marketing; education; psychology. Core. Calendar: semesters. Academic remediation for entering students, ESL program, services for LD students, advanced placement, self-designed majors, honors program, independent study, double major, summer session for credit, part-time degree program, adult/continuing education programs, internships, graduate courses open to undergrads. Off campus study at other Massachusetts state colleges, Northeast Consortium of Colleges and Universities in Massachusetts. Study abroad program.

Entrance Requirements: Options: early admission, international baccalaureate accepted. Required: high school transcript, minimum 2.0 high school GPA, SAT and SAT Subject Tests or ACT. Required for some: interview. Entrance: minimally difficult. Application deadline: Rolling. Notification: continuous. Preference given to state residents.

Costs Per Year: Application fee: $25. State resident tuition: $910 full-time, $37.92 per credit part-time. Nonresident tuition: $7050 full-time, $293.75 per credit part-time. Mandatory fees: $4,374 full-time, $182.24 per credit part-time, $13.50 per term part-time. Full-time tuition and fees vary according to class time. Part-time tuition and fees vary according to class time. College room and board: $7350. College room only: $5047. Room and board charges vary according to board plan and housing facility.

Collegiate Environment: Orientation program. Drama-theater group, choral group, student-run newspaper, radio station. Social organizations: 44 open to all. Most popular organizations: Student Government Association, Program Council, Hispanic American Student Association, GLBT Alliance, WMWM Radio. Major annual events: 'Big Name' Spring Concert, Spring Fling Dance, NCAA Athletic Events. Student services: legal services, health clinic, personal-psychological counseling, women's center. Campus security: 24-hour emergency response devices and patrols, late night transport-escort service. 1,404 college housing spaces available; all were occupied in 2003-04. Freshmen given priority for college housing. Option: coed housing available. Salem State College Library with 217,842 books, 230,788 microform titles, 1,914 serials, 79,000 audiovisual materials, an OPAC, and a Web page. Operations spending for 2004 fiscal year: $1.9 million. 426 computers available on campus for general student use. Computer purchase/lease plans available. A campuswide network can be accessed from student residence rooms and from off campus. Staffed computer lab on campus.

Community Environment: Salem State College is located in Salem, Massachusetts. Salem was founded in 1626, and is one of the oldest cities in the country. It was one of the most active seaports in the New World, and was the capital of the Massachusetts Bay Colony until 1630. Salem was the site of the witchcraft trials in which the accusations of group of children and women caused 19 people to be hanged and one pressed to death. Many handsome old houses reminiscent of the days when sea captains and China merchants grew rich from importing are still to be seen. Marblehead harbor, one of the yachting capitals of the world, is only three miles away. The city is located approximately 14 miles north of Boston, is suburban in nature and has good bus and train service.

■ **SCHOOL OF THE MUSEUM OF FINE ARTS, BOSTON** *D-12*
230 The Fenway
Boston, MA 02115
Tel: (617)267-6100
Admissions: (617)369-3626
Fax: (617)369-3679
E-mail: info@smfa.edu
Web Site: http://www.smfa.edu/
Description: Independent, comprehensive, coed. Administratively affiliated with Tufts University; Museum of Fine Arts, Boston. Awards bachelor's and master's degrees. Founded 1876. Setting: 14-acre urban campus. Endowment: $19.5 million. Educational spending for 2005 fiscal year: $7300 per student. Total enrollment: 773. Faculty: 180 (51 full-time, 129 part-time). Student-undergrad faculty ratio is 9:1. 858 applied, 84% were admitted. Full-time: 611 students, 65% women, 35% men. Part-time: 66 students, 73% women, 27% men. Students come from 40 states and territories, 26 other countries, 58% from out-of-state, 1% Native American, 5% Hispanic, 2% black, 3% Asian American or Pacific Islander, 6% international, 18% 25 or older, 9% live on campus, 14% transferred in. Retention: 81% of full-time freshmen returned the following year. Academic areas with the most degrees conferred: visual and performing arts; education. Calendar: semesters. ESL program, services for LD students, self-designed majors, independent study, double major, summer session for credit, part-time degree program, adult/continuing education programs, internships. Off campus study at Pro Arts Consortium, Association of Independent Colleges of Art and Design. Study abroad program.
Entrance Requirements: Option: deferred admission. Required: essay, high school transcript, portfolio. Required for some: recommendations, interview, SAT or ACT. Entrance: moderately difficult. Application deadline: 2/1. Notification: continuous.
Costs Per Year: Application fee: $65. Tuition: $23,850 full-time, $1000 per credit hour part-time. Mandatory fees: $910 full-time, $455 per term part-time. Full-time tuition and fees vary according to course load, degree level, and program. Part-time tuition and fees vary according to class time, course load, and program. College room only: $10,795. Room charges vary according to housing facility.
Collegiate Environment: Orientation program. Most popular organizations: Gay/Lesbian/Bisexual Alliance, Student Body, Inc., film, video and animation screening nights, Chess Club, Animation Club. Major annual events: juried and unjuried art exhibitions, Halloween Costume Contest, Open Studios. Student services: personal-psychological counseling. Campus security: 24-hour emergency response devices and patrols. 60 college housing spaces available; all were occupied in 2003-04. Freshmen given priority for college housing. Options: coed, women-only housing available. William Morris Hunt Memorial Library plus 2 others with 280,000 books, 47 microform titles, 497 serials, 274 audiovisual materials, an OPAC, and a Web page. Operations spending for 2004 fiscal year: $202,527. 46 computers available on campus for general student use. Computer purchase/lease plans available. A campuswide network can be accessed. Staffed computer lab on campus.
Community Environment: See Boston University.

■ **SIMMONS COLLEGE** *D-12*
300 The Fenway
Boston, MA 02115
Tel: (617)521-2000
Free: 800-345-8468
Admissions: (617)521-2057
Fax: (617)521-3199
E-mail: ugadm@simmons.edu
Web Site: http://www.simmons.edu/
Description: Independent, university. Awards bachelor's, master's, and doctoral degrees and post-master's certificates. Founded 1899. Setting: 12-acre urban campus. Endowment: $152.9 million. Research spending for 2004 fiscal year: $1.3 million. Educational spending for 2005 fiscal year: $12,864 per student. Total enrollment: 4,805. Faculty: 374 (193 full-time, 181 part-time). Student-undergrad faculty ratio is 12:1. 2,303 applied, 64% were admitted. 25% from top 10% of their high school class, 59% from top quarter, 93% from top half. 7 National Merit Scholars. Full-time: 1,688 students, 100% women. Part-time: 277 students, 90% women, 10% men. Students come from 38 states and territories, 26 other countries, 39% from out-of-state, 0.5% Native American, 3% Hispanic, 7% black, 7% Asian American or Pacific Islander, 2% international, 16% 25 or older, 70% live on campus, 2% transferred in. Retention: 84% of full-time freshmen returned the following year. Academic areas with the most degrees conferred: health professions and related sciences; social sciences; psychology. Core. Calendar: semesters. Academic remediation for entering students, ESL program, services for LD students, advanced placement, accelerated degree program, self-designed majors, freshman honors college, honors program, independent study, double major, summer session for credit, part-time degree program, adult/continuing education programs, internships, graduate courses open to undergrads. Off campus study at members of Colleges of the Fenway, Fisk University, Mills College, Spelman College. Study abroad program. ROTC: Army (c), Naval (c), Air Force (c).
Entrance Requirements: Options: Common Application, electronic application, early admission, early action, deferred admission, international baccalaureate accepted. Required: essay, high school transcript, 2 recommendations, SAT or ACT. Recommended: minimum 3.0 high school GPA, interview. Entrance: moderately difficult. Application deadlines: 2/2, 12/1 for early action. Notification: 4/15, 1/20 for early action.
Costs Per Year: Application fee: $35. Comprehensive fee: $35,640 includes full-time tuition ($24,680), mandatory fees ($760), and college room and board ($10,200). Full-time tuition and fees vary according to course load. Part-time tuition: $770 per semester hour. Part-time tuition varies according to course load.
Collegiate Environment: Orientation program. Drama-theater group, choral group, student-run newspaper. Social organizations: 70 open to all; 30% of women are members. Most popular organizations: Student Government Association, Simmons Community Outreach, Campus Activities Board, class councils, Simmons Voice. Major annual events: Winter Wonderland Dinner, Spring Spree Weekend, Simmons Cup. Student services: health clinic, personal-psychological counseling, women's center. Campus security: 24-hour emergency response devices and patrols, late night transport-escort service, controlled dormitory access. 1,103 undergraduates lived in college housing during 2003-04. Freshmen given priority for college housing. Option: women-only housing available. Beatley Library plus 4 others with 253,145 books, 35,549 microform titles, 1,749 serials, 4,843 audiovisual materials, an OPAC, and a Web page. Operations spending for 2004 fiscal year: $2.5 million. 420 computers available on campus for general student use. A campuswide network can be accessed from student residence rooms and from off campus. Staffed computer lab on campus.
Community Environment: Simmons College is next door to the Isabella Stewart Gardner Museum and two blocks away from the Museum of Fine Arts. Other nearby attractions are Fenway Park, the Charles River, Beacon Hill, Back Bay, Cambridge and the North End. Complete intercity transportation is available.

■ **SIMON'S ROCK COLLEGE OF BARD** *E-1*
84 Alford Rd.
Great Barrington, MA 01230-9702
Tel: (413)528-0771
Free: 800-235-7186
Admissions: (413)528-7245
Fax: (413)528-7334
E-mail: admit@simons-rock.edu
Web Site: http://www.simons-rock.edu/
Description: Independent, 4-year, coed. Administratively affiliated with Bard College. Awards associate and bachelor's degrees. Founded 1964. Setting: 275-acre rural campus with easy access to Albany and Springfield. Endowment: $9.2 million. Educational spending for 2005 fiscal year: $10,554 per student. Total enrollment: 386. Student-undergrad faculty ratio is 8:1. 247 applied, 79% were admitted. Full-time: 369 students, 58% women, 42% men. Part-time: 17 students, 53% women, 47% men. Students come from 39 states and territories, 1 other country, 79% from out-of-state, 2% Native American, 4% Hispanic, 4% black, 6% Asian American or Pacific Islander, 1% international, 1% 25 or older, 81% live on campus, 0% transferred in. Retention: 78% of full-time freshmen returned the following year. Academic

areas with the most degrees conferred: area and ethnic studies; visual and performing arts; English; social sciences. Core. Calendar: semesters. Services for LD students, self-designed majors, independent study, double major, part-time degree program, external degree program, adult/continuing education programs, internships. Off campus study at Bard College. Study abroad program.

Entrance Requirements: Options: electronic application, early admission, deferred admission. Required: essay, high school transcript, minimum 2.0 high school GPA, 2 recommendations, interview, parent application, SAT, PSAT. Recommended: minimum 3.0 high school GPA, ACT. Entrance: very difficult. Application deadline: 6/15. Notification: continuous.

Costs Per Year: Application fee: $40. Comprehensive fee: $41,988 includes full-time tuition ($32,834), mandatory fees ($500), and college room and board ($8654). Full-time tuition and fees vary according to course load and program. Part-time tuition: $285 per credit hour. Part-time mandatory fees: $650. Part-time tuition and fees vary according to course load and program.

Collegiate Environment: Orientation program. Drama-theater group, choral group, student-run newspaper, radio station. Social organizations: 21 open to all. Most popular organizations: Women's Center, Math and Sciences Club, multicultural student organization, Community Health Institute, Community Service Program. Major annual events: The Anti-Prom, Winter Solstice, Mayfest. Student services: health clinic, personal-psychological counseling, women's center. Campus security: 24-hour emergency response devices, late night transport-escort service, controlled dormitory access, 24-hour weekend patrols by trained security personnel. 356 college housing spaces available; 313 were occupied in 2003-04. Freshmen guaranteed college housing. On-campus residence required through sophomore year. Option: coed housing available. Alumni Library with 73,514 books, 7,619 microform titles, 417 serials, 4,623 audiovisual materials, an OPAC, and a Web page. Operations spending for 2004 fiscal year: $456,474. 50 computers available on campus for general student use. A campuswide network can be accessed from student residence rooms and from off campus. Staffed computer lab on campus.

■ **SMITH COLLEGE** *E-5*
Northampton, MA 01063
Tel: (413)584-2700
Free: 800-383-3232
Admissions: (413)585-2500
Fax: (413)585-2123
E-mail: admission@smith.edu
Web Site: http://www.smith.edu/

Description: Independent, comprehensive. Awards bachelor's, master's, and doctoral degrees and post-master's certificates. Founded 1871. Setting: 125-acre small town campus with easy access to Hartford. Endowment: $1 billion. Research spending for 2004 fiscal year: $3.8 million. Educational spending for 2005 fiscal year: $18,744 per student. Total enrollment: 3,093. Faculty: 316 (288 full-time, 28 part-time). Student-undergrad faculty ratio is 9:1. 3,304 applied, 52% were admitted. 61% from top 10% of their high school class, 90% from top quarter, 98% from top half. Full-time: 2,612 students, 99.9% women, 0.1% men. Part-time: 30 students, 100% women. Students come from 53 states and territories, 65 other countries, 78% from out-of-state, 1% Native American, 6% Hispanic, 6% black, 11% Asian American or Pacific Islander, 7% international, 8% 25 or older, 91% live on campus, 3% transferred in. Retention: 89% of full-time freshmen returned the following year. Academic areas with the most degrees conferred: social sciences; history; psychology. Calendar: semesters. Services for LD students, advanced placement, accelerated degree program, self-designed majors, independent study, double major, part-time degree program, adult/continuing education programs, internships, graduate courses open to undergrads. Off campus study at Pomona College, Amherst College, Bowdoin College, Connecticut College, Dartmouth College, Mount Holyoke College, Trinity College, Vassar College, Wellesley College, Wesleyan University, Wheaton College, Williams College, several historically black colleges. Study abroad program. ROTC: Army (c).

Entrance Requirements: Options: Peterson's Universal Application, Common Application, electronic application, early admission, early decision, deferred admission, international baccalaureate accepted. Required: essay, high school transcript, 3 recommendations, SAT or ACT. Recommended: interview. Entrance: very difficult. Application deadlines: 1/15, 11/15 for early decision plan 1, 1/2 for early decision plan 2. Notification: 4/1, 12/15 for early decision plan 1, 2/2 for early decision plan 2.

Costs Per Year: Application fee: $60. Comprehensive fee: $41,474 includes full-time tuition ($30,520), mandatory fees ($234), and college room and

board ($10,720). College room only: $5160. Room and board charges vary according to housing facility. Part-time tuition: $955 per credit hour.

Collegiate Environment: Orientation program. Drama-theater group, choral group, student-run newspaper, radio station. Social organizations: 112 open to all. Most popular organizations: Recreation Council, Service Organizations of Smith, Glee Club and choirs, Athletic Association, Black Student Alliance. Major annual events: International Students' Bazaar, Otelia Cromwell Day (Diversity Day), Rally Day. Student services: health clinic, personal-psychological counseling, women's center. Campus security: 24-hour emergency response devices and patrols, late night transport-escort service, self-defense workshops, emergency telephones, programs in crime and sexual assault prevention. 2,449 college housing spaces available. Freshmen guaranteed college housing. On-campus residence required through senior year. Option: women-only housing available. Neilson Library plus 3 others with 1.3 million books, 141,932 microform titles, 6,530 serials, 65,135 audiovisual materials, an OPAC, and a Web page. Operations spending for 2004 fiscal year: $7 million. 585 computers available on campus for general student use. Computer purchase/lease plans available. A campuswide network can be accessed from student residence rooms and from off campus. Staffed computer lab on campus.

Community Environment: The early frontier town of Northampton, settled in 1654, has been transformed over the intervening three-and-one-half centuries into a lively and sophisticated center of culture, commerce, and entertainment. Northampton has been named the Number 1 small town for the arts in the country by writer John Villani. Today there is a population of over 30,000. Located in the western-central part of state, about 18 miles north of Springfield, the area is easily accessible to good recreational sites. The city has a community hospital, theatres, art galleries, parks, and several hotels and motels. Part-time work is available for students.

■ **SPRINGFIELD COLLEGE** *F-5*
263 Alden St.
Springfield, MA 01109-3797
Tel: (413)748-3000
Free: 800-343-1257
Admissions: (413)748-3136
Fax: (413)748-3764
E-mail: admissions@spfldcol.edu
Web Site: http://www.spfldcol.edu/

Description: Independent, comprehensive, coed. Awards bachelor's, master's, and doctoral degrees. Founded 1885. Setting: 167-acre suburban campus. Total enrollment: 3,155. Faculty: 342 (174 full-time, 168 part-time). Student-undergrad faculty ratio is 12:1. 2,326 applied, 69% were admitted. 13% from top 10% of their high school class, 35% from top quarter, 72% from top half. Full-time: 2,172 students, 48% women, 52% men. Part-time: 45 students, 62% women, 38% men. Students come from 37 states and territories, 65% from out-of-state, 0.2% Native American, 2% Hispanic, 3% black, 1% Asian American or Pacific Islander, 0.2% international, 85% live on campus, 0.2% transferred in. Retention: 82% of full-time freshmen returned the following year. Academic areas with the most degrees conferred: parks and recreation; health professions and related sciences; business/marketing. Core. Calendar: semesters. ESL program, services for LD students, advanced placement, accelerated degree program, independent study, double major, summer session for credit, part-time degree program, adult/continuing education programs, co-op programs and internships, graduate courses open to undergrads. Off campus study at 4 members of the Private Colleges of Greater Springfield, 7 members of the Cooperating Colleges of Greater Springfield. Study abroad program. ROTC: Army (c), Air Force (c).

Entrance Requirements: Options: Common Application, electronic application, early admission, early decision, deferred admission. Required: essay, high school transcript, 1 recommendation, SAT or ACT. Recommended: interview. Required for some: portfolio. Entrance: moderately difficult. Application deadlines: 4/1, 12/1 for early decision. Notification: continuous until 4/15, 2/1 for early decision. Preference given to children of alumni.

Costs Per Year: Application fee: $50. Comprehensive fee: $30,845 includes full-time tuition ($22,390), mandatory fees ($325), and college room and board ($8130). College room only: $4400. Part-time tuition: $679 per credit.

Collegiate Environment: Orientation program. Drama-theater group, choral group, student-run newspaper, radio station. Social organizations: 50 open to all. Student services: health clinic, personal-psychological counseling. Freshmen guaranteed college housing. On-campus residence required through junior year. Options: coed, men-only, women-only housing available. Babson Library with 125,000 books and 850 serials. 95 computers available on campus for general student use. Computer purchase/lease plans available. A campuswide network can be accessed from student residence rooms and from off campus.

Community Environment: Established as a trading post in 1636, Springfield is located on the Connecticut River in Southwestern part of the state. City is noted today for its diversified industries including the manufacture of firearms, plastics, chemicals, radio equipment, tires, paper, and electrical equipment. Ample part-time job opportunities available. Several movie theatres, municipal auditorium, drive-ins, summer theatre, two municipal golf courses, 150 parks, civic center, and playgrounds, swimming, skating, quadrangle of museums, public libraries, provide excellent recreational and cultural opportunities. Easy access to commercial, bus and rail service.

■ **SPRINGFIELD TECHNICAL COMMUNITY COLLEGE** *F-5*
1 Armory Square, PO Box 9000
Springfield, MA 01102-9000
Tel: (413)781-7822
Fax: (413)781-5805
E-mail: admissions@stccadm.stcc.mass.edu
Web Site: http://www.stcc.edu/
Description: State-supported, 2-year, coed. Awards certificates, transfer associate, and terminal associate degrees. Founded 1967. Setting: 34-acre urban campus. Total enrollment: 5,823. Student-undergrad faculty ratio is 15:1. 2,211 applied, 93% were admitted. Full-time: 2,658 students, 54% women, 46% men. Part-time: 3,165 students, 61% women, 39% men. Students come from 10 states and territories, 4% from out-of-state, 0.4% Native American, 16% Hispanic, 15% black, 2% Asian American or Pacific Islander, 1% international, 42% 25 or older. Calendar: semesters. Academic remediation for entering students, ESL program, services for LD students, advanced placement, honors program, independent study, distance learning, summer session for credit, part-time degree program, adult/continuing education programs, co-op programs and internships. Off campus study at the Cooperating Colleges of Greater Springfield.
Entrance Requirements: Open admission except for certain vocational programs. Required: high school transcript. Required for some: interview, SAT. Entrance: noncompetitive. Application deadline: Rolling.
Costs Per Year: Application fee: $10. State resident tuition: $750 full-time, $25 per credit hour part-time. Nonresident tuition: $7260 full-time, $242 per credit hour part-time. Mandatory fees: $2604 full-time, $80 per credit hour part-time, $109 per term part-time. Full-time tuition and fees vary according to course load. Part-time tuition and fees vary according to course load. Tuition guaranteed not to increase for student's term of enrollment.
Collegiate Environment: Orientation program. Drama-theater group. Social organizations: 25 open to all. Most popular organizations: Phi Theta Kappa Honor Society, Landscape Club, Dental Hygiene Club, Clinical Lab Club, Physical Therapist Assistant Club. Major annual events: Multicultural Luncheon, Spring Fling, Opening Picnic. Student services: health clinic, personal-psychological counseling. Campus security: 24-hour emergency response devices and patrols, late night transport-escort service. College housing not available. Springfield Technical Community College Library with 63,945 books, 96,688 microform titles, 259 serials, 17,586 audiovisual materials, an OPAC, and a Web page. 1,175 computers available on campus for general student use. A campuswide network can be accessed from off-campus. Staffed computer lab on campus.
Community Environment: See Springfield College.

■ **STONEHILL COLLEGE** *G-12*
320 Washington St.
Easton, MA 02357-5510
Tel: (508)565-1000
Admissions: (508)565-1373
Fax: (508)565-1500
E-mail: admissions@stonehill.edu
Web Site: http://www.stonehill.edu/
Description: Independent Roman Catholic, comprehensive, coed. Awards bachelor's and master's degrees. Founded 1948. Setting: 375-acre suburban campus with easy access to Boston. Endowment: $118.2 million. Research spending for 2004 fiscal year: $102,167. Educational spending for 2005 fiscal year: $7423 per student. Total enrollment: 2,443. Faculty: 253 (132 full-time, 121 part-time). Student-undergrad faculty ratio is 13:1. 4,848 applied, 57% were admitted. 48% from top 10% of their high school class, 87% from top quarter, 99% from top half. 4 class presidents, 5 valedictorians, 37 student government officers. Full-time: 2,260 students, 59% women, 41%

men. Part-time: 171 students, 71% women, 29% men. Students come from 27 states and territories, 8 other countries, 42% from out-of-state, 0.3% Native American, 3% Hispanic, 3% black, 3% Asian American or Pacific Islander, 1% international, 7% 25 or older, 82% live on campus, 1% transferred in. Retention: 90% of full-time freshmen returned the following year. Academic areas with the most degrees conferred: business/marketing; social sciences; psychology. Core. Calendar: semesters. Services for LD students, advanced placement, self-designed majors, honors program, independent study, double major, summer session for credit, part-time degree program, adult/continuing education programs, internships, graduate courses open to undergrads. Off campus study at 8 members of the Southeastern Association for Cooperation of Higher Education in Massachusetts. Study abroad program. ROTC: Army.
Entrance Requirements: Options: Common Application, electronic application, early admission, early decision, deferred admission, international baccalaureate accepted. Required: essay, high school transcript, 2 recommendations, SAT or ACT. Recommended: campus visit. Required for some: interview. Entrance: very difficult. Application deadlines: 1/15, 11/1 for early decision. Notification: 4/1, 12/15 for early decision.
Costs Per Year: Application fee: $50. Comprehensive fee: $36,104 includes full-time tuition ($25,540) and college room and board ($10,564). Part-time tuition: $840 per course. Part-time mandatory fees: $25 per term. Part-time tuition and fees vary according to course load.
Collegiate Environment: Orientation program. Drama-theater group, choral group, student-run newspaper, radio station. Social organizations: 66 open to all. Most popular organizations: Into the Streets, student radio station, student government, Summit (student newspaper), sports clubs. Major annual events: Winter Week, Spring Weekend, Halloween Masquerade Mixer. Student services: health clinic, personal-psychological counseling, women's center. Campus security: 24-hour emergency response devices and patrols, late night transport-escort service. College housing designed to accommodate 1,825 students; 1,907 undergraduates lived in college housing during 2003-04. Freshmen given priority for college housing. Options: coed, women-only housing available. Bartley MacPhaidin, C.S.C. Library with 215,581 books, 360,232 microform titles, 2,196 serials, 6,089 audiovisual materials, an OPAC, and a Web page. Operations spending for 2004 fiscal year: $1.5 million. 300 computers available on campus for general student use. A campuswide network can be accessed from student residence rooms and from off campus. Staffed computer lab on campus.
Community Environment: The College is in Easton, adjoining Brockton and 20 miles south of Boston. Transportation is available to Brockton, and the Boston subway system. Cultural, recreational and community services are all quite accessible.

■ **SUFFOLK UNIVERSITY** *D-12*
8 Ashburton Place
Boston, MA 02108-2770
Tel: (617)573-8000
Free: 800-6-SUFFOLK
Admissions: (617)573-8749
Fax: (617)742-4291
E-mail: admission@admin.suffolk.edu
Web Site: http://www.suffolk.edu/
Description: Independent, comprehensive, coed. Awards associate, bachelor's, master's, doctoral, and first professional degrees and post-master's and first professional certificates (doctoral degree in law). Founded 1906. Setting: 2-acre urban campus. Endowment: $74.9 million. Research spending for 2004 fiscal year: $4.8 million. Educational spending for 2005 fiscal year: $9470 per student. Total enrollment: 8,474. Faculty: 779 (255 full-time, 524 part-time). Student-undergrad faculty ratio is 12:1. 6,244 applied, 82% were admitted. 10% from top 10% of their high school class, 25% from top quarter, 69% from top half. Full-time: 4,075 students, 59% women, 41% men. Part-time: 709 students, 63% women, 37% men. Students come from 35 states and territories, 100 other countries, 24% from out-of-state, 0.4% Native American, 4% Hispanic, 3% black, 7% Asian American or Pacific Islander, 9% international, 9% 25 or older, 19% live on campus, 7% transferred in. Retention: 73% of full-time freshmen returned the following year. Academic areas with the most degrees conferred: business/marketing; social sciences; communications/journalism. Core. Calendar: semesters. Academic remediation for entering students, ESL program, services for LD students, advanced placement, accelerated degree program, freshman honors college, honors program, independent study, distance learning, double major, summer session for credit, part-time degree program, adult/

continuing education programs, co-op programs and internships, graduate courses open to undergrads. Off campus study. Study abroad program. ROTC: Army (c).

Entrance Requirements: Options: Peterson's Universal Application, Common Application, electronic application, early action, deferred admission, international baccalaureate accepted. Required: essay, high school transcript, 2 recommendations, SAT or ACT. Recommended: minimum 2.5 high school GPA. Required for some: interview. Entrance: moderately difficult. Application deadlines: 3/15, 11/15 for early action. Notification: continuous, 12/1 for early action.

Costs Per Year: Application fee: $50. Comprehensive fee: $33,160 includes full-time tuition ($21,140), mandatory fees ($80), and college room and board ($11,940). College room only: $10,020. Room and board charges vary according to board plan and housing facility. Part-time tuition: $526 per credit. Part-time mandatory fees: $10 per term.

Collegiate Environment: Orientation program. Drama-theater group, choral group, student-run newspaper, radio station. Social organizations: 75 open to all; national fraternities, local sororities; 25% of eligible men and 29% of eligible women are members. Most popular organizations: Student Government Association, Program Council, Black Student Union, Evening Student Association, International Student Association. Major annual events: Cultural Unity Week, Commencement Ball, Temple Street Fair. Student services: health clinic, personal-psychological counseling, women's center. Campus security: 24-hour emergency response devices, late night transport-escort service, controlled dormitory access. 827 college housing spaces available; all were occupied in 2003-04. Freshmen given priority for college housing. Option: coed housing available. Mildred Sawyer Library plus 3 others with 129,562 books, 135,749 microform titles, 8,644 serials, 380 audiovisual materials, an OPAC, and a Web page. Operations spending for 2004 fiscal year: $5.1 million. 400 computers available on campus for general student use. A campuswide network can be accessed from student residence rooms and from off campus. Staffed computer lab on campus.

Community Environment: Suffolk University is located in the heart of Boston, a city rich in history and culture. In addition to being an international center for high-technology, finance, architecture, and medicine, Boston boasts over 50 of the finest colleges and universities in the nation. Founded in 1630, ten years after the Pilgrims landed at Plymouth, Boston is the capital of the Commonwealth of Massachusetts and is the largest city in New England. The city of Boston has a population of over 600,000 people whose heritage is drawn worldwide. The Freedom Trail includes 16 landmarks significant to our nation's history, including Faneuil Hall, the Old North Church, Paul Revere's house, Old Ironsides and the Bunker Hill Monument. Hidden throughout Boston are treasures such as the Isabella Stewart Gardner Museum and the African Meeting House, which is the oldest black church building still standing in this country. There is various entertainment such as the Boston Ballet, the Boston Symphony Orchestra, and the theatre, as well as comedy clubs and clubs featuring many different types of music. In addition, Boston offers some of the finest shopping and dining facilities in the country. Boston is also the home of four professional sports teams -- the Boston Bruins, the Boston Celtics, the Boston Red Sox, and the New England Patriots. The city is accessible by public transportation, commuter rail, bus service,

■ **TUFTS UNIVERSITY** *D-12*
Medford, MA 02155
Tel: (617)628-5000
Admissions: (617)627-3170
Fax: (617)627-3860
E-mail: admissions.inquiry@ase.tufts.edu
Web Site: http://www.tufts.edu/

Description: Independent, university, coed. Awards bachelor's, master's, doctoral, and first professional degrees and post-master's certificates. Founded 1852. Setting: 150-acre suburban campus with easy access to Boston. Endowment: $880.5 million. Total enrollment: 9,780. Faculty: 1,194 (765 full-time, 429 part-time). Student-undergrad faculty ratio is 9:1. 15,536 applied, 28% were admitted. 80% from top 10% of their high school class, 96% from top quarter, 100% from top half. Full-time: 4,971 students, 52% women, 48% men. Part-time: 107 students, 54% women, 46% men. Students come from 51 states and territories, 67 other countries, 74% from out-of-state, 0.4% Native American, 7% Hispanic, 7% black, 13% Asian American or Pacific Islander, 6% international, 75% live on campus, 2% transferred in. Retention: 95% of full-time freshmen returned the following year. Academic areas with the most degrees conferred: social sciences; engineering; visual and performing arts. Core. Calendar: semesters.

Services for LD students, advanced placement, self-designed majors, honors program, independent study, double major, summer session for credit, adult/continuing education programs, internships, graduate courses open to undergrads. Off campus study at Boston College, Boston University, Brandeis University, Swarthmore College, American University, Lincoln University. Study abroad program. ROTC: Army (c), Naval (c), Air Force (c).

Entrance Requirements: Options: Common Application, electronic application, early admission, early decision, deferred admission, international baccalaureate accepted. Required: essay, high school transcript, 1 recommendation, SAT and SAT Subject Tests or ACT. Recommended: interview. Entrance: most difficult. Application deadlines: 1/1, 11/15 for early decision plan 1, 1/1 for early decision plan 2. Notification: 4/1, 12/15 for early decision plan 1, 2/1 for early decision plan 2.

Costs Per Year: Application fee: $70. Comprehensive fee: $42,018 includes full-time tuition ($31,828), mandatory fees ($793), and college room and board ($9397). College room only: $4827. Room and board charges vary according to board plan.

Collegiate Environment: Orientation program. Drama-theater group, choral group, marching band, student-run newspaper, radio station. Social organizations: 160 open to all; national fraternities, national sororities; 15% of eligible men and 4% of eligible women are members. Most popular organizations: Leonard Carmichael Society, Mountain Club, Environmental Consciousness Outreach. Major annual events: Homecoming, Spring Fling, Supershow. Student services: legal services, health clinic, personal-psychological counseling, women's center. Campus security: 24-hour emergency response devices and patrols, late night transport-escort service, controlled dormitory access, security lighting, call boxes to campus police. Freshmen guaranteed college housing. On-campus residence required through sophomore year. Options: coed, women-only housing available. Tisch Library plus 1 other with 1.6 million books, 1.2 million microform titles, 5,204 serials, 33,731 audiovisual materials, an OPAC, and a Web page. 254 computers available on campus for general student use. A campuswide network can be accessed from student residence rooms and from off campus. Staffed computer lab on campus.

Community Environment: Medford is a residential suburb of Boston, located approximately five miles northwest of the city. One of the oldest settlements in the Commonwealth and in the United States, Medford was founded in 1630 and has many historical points of interest. Beautiful Mystic Lakes are located on the northwest border of the city, and further recreational opportunities are provided by the Middlesex Fells, a mountainous reservation of approximately 4,000 acres. Part-time employment is available in Boston.

■ **UNIVERSITY OF MASSACHUSETTS AMHERST** *D-5*
Amherst, MA 01003
Tel: (413)545-0111
Admissions: (413)545-0222
Fax: (413)545-4312
E-mail: kk@admissions.umass.edu
Web Site: http://www.umass.edu/

Description: State-supported, university, coed. Part of University of Massachusetts. Awards associate, bachelor's, master's, and doctoral degrees and post-master's certificates. Founded 1863. Setting: 1,463-acre small town campus with easy access to Hartford. Endowment: $91.2 million. Research spending for 2004 fiscal year: $113.5 million. Total enrollment: 25,093. Faculty: 1,338 (1,148 full-time, 190 part-time). Student-undergrad faculty ratio is 17:1. 20,205 applied, 80% were admitted. 19% from top 10% of their high school class, 51% from top quarter, 88% from top half. Full-time: 18,054 students, 49% women, 51% men. Part-time: 1,340 students, 57% women, 43% men. Students come from 56 states and territories, 97 other countries, 15% from out-of-state, 0.3% Native American, 3% Hispanic, 5% black, 7% Asian American or Pacific Islander, 1% international, 7% 25 or older, 61% live on campus, 6% transferred in. Retention: 84% of full-time freshmen returned the following year. Academic areas with the most degrees conferred: business/marketing; social sciences; education. Core. Calendar: semesters. Academic remediation for entering students, ESL program, services for LD students, advanced placement, self-designed majors, freshman honors college, honors program, independent study, distance learning, double major, summer session for credit, part-time degree program, adult/continuing education programs, co-op programs and internships, graduate courses open to undergrads. Off campus study at members of the National Student Exchange, Five Colleges, Inc., other units of the University of Massachusetts System. Study abroad program. ROTC: Army, Air Force.

Entrance Requirements: Options: Peterson's Universal Application, electronic application, early action, international baccalaureate accepted.

Required: essay, high school transcript, SAT or ACT. Recommended: minimum 3.0 high school GPA, recommendations. Entrance: moderately difficult. Application deadlines: 1/15, 11/1 for early action. Notification: continuous, 12/15 for early action.

Costs Per Year: Application fee: $40. State resident tuition: $2031 full-time. Nonresident tuition: $10,857 full-time. Mandatory fees: $7564 full-time.

Collegiate Environment: Orientation program. Drama-theater group, choral group, marching band, student-run newspaper, radio station. Social organizations: 200 open to all; national fraternities, national sororities, local fraternities, local sororities; 1% of eligible men and 1% of eligible women are members. Most popular organizations: Minutemen Marching Band, Theater Guild, Ski Club, Outing Club, student newspaper. Major annual events: First Week, Family Weekend. Student services: legal services, health clinic, personal-psychological counseling, women's center. Campus security: 24-hour emergency response devices and patrols, student patrols, controlled dormitory access, residence halls locked nights and weekends. College housing designed to accommodate 10,864 students; 11,020 undergraduates lived in college housing during 2003-04. Freshmen guaranteed college housing. On-campus residence required through sophomore year. Options: coed, men-only, women-only housing available. W. E. B. Du Bois Library plus 1 other with 3.2 million books, 2.5 million microform titles, 37,716 serials, 22,781 audiovisual materials, an OPAC, and a Web page. Operations spending for 2004 fiscal year: $12.1 million. 450 computers available on campus for general student use. A campuswide network can be accessed from student residence rooms and from off campus. Staffed computer lab on campus.

Community Environment: See Amherst College.

■ **UNIVERSITY OF MASSACHUSETTS BOSTON** *D-12*

100 Morrissey Blvd.
Boston, MA 02125-3393
Tel: (617)287-5000
Admissions: (617)287-6100
E-mail: undergrad@umassp.edu
Web Site: http://www.umb.edu/

Description: State-supported, university, coed. Part of University of Massachusetts. Awards bachelor's, master's, and doctoral degrees and post-master's certificates. Founded 1964. Setting: 177-acre urban campus. Endowment: $8.1 million. Research spending for 2004 fiscal year: $14.2 million. Total enrollment: 11,862. Faculty: 813 (445 full-time, 368 part-time). Student-undergrad faculty ratio is 14:1. 3,174 applied, 60% were admitted. Full-time: 5,768 students, 58% women, 42% men. Part-time: 3,190 students, 56% women, 44% men. Students come from 35 states and territories, 64 other countries, 4% from out-of-state, 1% Native American, 7% Hispanic, 15% black, 12% Asian American or Pacific Islander, 4% international, 51% 25 or older, 13% transferred in. Retention: 71% of full-time freshmen returned the following year. Academic areas with the most degrees conferred: business/marketing; social sciences; psychology. Core. Calendar: semesters. Academic remediation for entering students, ESL program, services for LD students, advanced placement, accelerated degree program, self-designed majors, freshman honors college, honors program, independent study, distance learning, double major, summer session for credit, part-time degree program, adult/continuing education programs, co-op programs and internships, graduate courses open to undergrads. Off campus study at members of the National Student Exchange, New England Regional Student Exchange, Boston Five Course Exchange Program. Study abroad program.

Entrance Requirements: Options: Common Application, electronic application, deferred admission, international baccalaureate accepted. Required: high school transcript, minimum 2.75 high school GPA, SAT or ACT. Recommended: essay. Required for some: essay, recommendations, interview. Entrance: moderately difficult. Application deadline: 6/1. Notification: continuous.

Costs Per Year: Application fee: $40. State resident tuition: $1714 full-time, $71.50 per credit hour part-time. Nonresident tuition: $9758 full-time, $406.50 per credit hour part-time. Mandatory fees: $6551 full-time, $273 per credit hour part-time. Full-time tuition and fees vary according to class time, course load, program, reciprocity agreements, and student level. Part-time tuition and fees vary according to class time, course load, program, reciprocity agreements, and student level.

Collegiate Environment: Orientation program. Drama-theater group, choral group, student-run newspaper, radio station. Social organizations: 72 open to all. Most popular organizations: Women's Center, Black Student Center, Asian Student Center, Veterans Student Center, Disabilities Student Center. Major annual events: Convocation, Commencement, fall and spring festivals.

Student services: legal services, health clinic, personal-psychological counseling, women's center. Campus security: 24-hour emergency response devices and patrols, late night transport-escort service, crime prevention program, bicycle patrols. College housing not available. Joseph P. Healey Library with 584,015 books, 827,112 microform titles, 25,575 serials, 2,011 audiovisual materials, an OPAC, and a Web page. Operations spending for 2004 fiscal year: $2.8 million. 260 computers available on campus for general student use. Computer purchase/lease plans available. A campuswide network can be accessed from off-campus. Staffed computer lab on campus.

Community Environment: See Boston University.

■ **UNIVERSITY OF MASSACHUSETTS DARTMOUTH** *I-13*

285 Old Westport Rd.
North Dartmouth, MA 02747-2300
Tel: (508)999-8000
Admissions: (508)999-8605
Fax: (508)999-8755
E-mail: sbriggs@umassd.edu
Web Site: http://www.umassd.edu/

Description: State-supported, university, coed. Part of University of Massachusetts. Awards bachelor's, master's, and doctoral degrees and post-master's certificates. Founded 1895. Setting: 710-acre suburban campus with easy access to Boston and Providence. Endowment: $18.3 million. Research spending for 2004 fiscal year: $16.9 million. Educational spending for 2005 fiscal year: $5500 per student. Total enrollment: 8,549. Faculty: 571 (355 full-time, 216 part-time). Student-undergrad faculty ratio is 17:1. 6,432 applied, 74% were admitted. 9% from top 10% of their high school class, 39% from top quarter, 65% from top half. Full-time: 6,449 students, 49% women, 51% men. Part-time: 1,070 students, 60% women, 40% men. Students come from 29 states and territories, 29 other countries, 5% from out-of-state, 1% Native American, 2% Hispanic, 1% black, 3% Asian American or Pacific Islander, 0.5% international, 10% 25 or older, 48% live on campus, 7% transferred in. Retention: 76% of full-time freshmen returned the following year. Academic areas with the most degrees conferred: business/marketing; social sciences; visual and performing arts. Core. Calendar: semesters. Academic remediation for entering students, services for LD students, advanced placement, self-designed majors, honors program, independent study, distance learning, double major, summer session for credit, part-time degree program, adult/continuing education programs, co-op programs and internships, graduate courses open to undergrads. Off campus study at members of the Southeastern Association for Cooperation in Higher Education in Massachusetts. Study abroad program. ROTC: Army (c).

Entrance Requirements: Options: Common Application, early admission, early decision, deferred admission. Required: essay, high school transcript, minimum 3.0 high school GPA, SAT or ACT. Recommended: recommendations. Entrance: moderately difficult. Application deadlines: Rolling, 11/15 for early decision. Notification: continuous, 12/15 for early decision.

Costs Per Year: Application fee: $35, $55 for nonresidents. State resident tuition: $1417 full-time, $59.04 per credit part-time. Nonresident tuition: $8099 full-time, $454.88 per credit part-time. Mandatory fees: $6619 full-time, $275.79 per credit part-time. Full-time tuition and fees vary according to reciprocity agreements. Part-time tuition and fees vary according to course load and reciprocity agreements. College room and board: $7634. College room only: $4460. Room and board charges vary according to board plan and housing facility.

Collegiate Environment: Orientation program. Drama-theater group, choral group, student-run newspaper, radio station. Social organizations: 90 open to all; national fraternities, national sororities; 1% of eligible men and 1% of eligible women are members. Most popular organizations: Student Activities Board, Outing Club, Phi Sigma Sigma, Portuguese Language Club, United Brothers and Sisters. Major annual events: Senior Week, Welcome Back Week, Spring Semi-Formal. Student services: legal services, health clinic, personal-psychological counseling, women's center. Campus security: 24-hour emergency response devices and patrols, student patrols, late night transport-escort service, controlled dormitory access. 3,250 college housing spaces available; 3,113 were occupied in 2003-04. No special consideration for freshman housing applicants. Option: coed housing available. University of Massachusetts Dartmouth Library with 947,000 books, 810,127 microform titles, 2,925 serials, 12,980 audiovisual materials, an OPAC, and a Web page. 368 computers available on campus for general student use. Computer purchase/lease plans available. A campuswide network can be accessed from student residence rooms and from off campus. Staffed computer lab on campus.

Community Environment: North Dartmouth is located near the larger city of New Bedford, MA. This city, on Buzzard's Bay, was once the greatest whaling port in the world. Fishing fleets and allied industries contribute one-fifth of New Bedford's income. The city is also known for the manufacture of fine textile goods, plastics, tire fabrics, boats, golf balls, cut glass, and other products. The area is easily accessible by rail, bus, and air. The city has a library and whaling museum. Major community services are located in the immediate area. Part-time jobs opportunities are available.

■ **UNIVERSITY OF MASSACHUSETTS LOWELL** *C-11*
1 University Ave.
Lowell, MA 01854-2881
Tel: (978)934-4000
Free: 800-410-4607
Admissions: (978)934-3944
Fax: (978)934-3000
Web Site: http://www.uml.edu/
Description: State-supported, university, coed. Part of University of Massachusetts. Awards associate, bachelor's, master's, and doctoral degrees and post-master's certificates. Founded 1894. Setting: 100-acre urban campus with easy access to Boston. Endowment: $18.8 million. Research spending for 2004 fiscal year: $24.5 million. Educational spending for 2005 fiscal year: $9536 per student. Total enrollment: 10,666. Faculty: 623 (383 full-time, 240 part-time). Student-undergrad faculty ratio is 17:1. 4,766 applied, 63% were admitted. Students come from 30 states and territories, 12 other countries, 10% from out-of-state, 0.2% Native American, 5% Hispanic, 4% black, 7% Asian American or Pacific Islander, 1% international, 13% 25 or older, 40% live on campus. Retention: 75% of full-time freshmen returned the following year. Academic areas with the most degrees conferred: business/marketing; computer and information sciences; engineering. Core. Calendar: semesters. Services for LD students, advanced placement, accelerated degree program, honors program, distance learning, double major, summer session for credit, part-time degree program, adult/continuing education programs, co-op programs and internships, graduate courses open to undergrads. Off campus study at Northeast Consortium of Colleges and Universities in Massachusetts. Study abroad program. ROTC: Air Force.
Entrance Requirements: Options: electronic application, deferred admission, international baccalaureate accepted. Required: essay, high school transcript, minimum 3.0 high school GPA, SAT or ACT. Required for some: interview. Entrance: moderately difficult. Application deadline: Rolling. Notification: continuous.
Costs Per Year: Application fee: $20. State resident tuition: $1454 full-time, $60.58 per credit part-time. Nonresident tuition: $8567 full-time, $356.96 per credit part-time. Mandatory fees: $6712 full-time, $291.33 per credit part-time. College room and board: $6311. College room only: $3810. Room and board charges vary according to board plan and housing facility.
Collegiate Environment: Orientation program. Drama-theater group, choral group, marching band, student-run newspaper, radio station. Social organizations: 100 open to all. Major annual events: Spring Carnival, Family Day, Culture Fest. Student services: health clinic, personal-psychological counseling, women's center. Campus security: 24-hour emergency response devices and patrols, late night transport-escort service, controlled dormitory access. 2,175 college housing spaces available; 2,080 were occupied in 2003-04. No special consideration for freshman housing applicants. Options: coed, men-only, women-only housing available. O'Leary Library plus 2 others with 549,243 books, 534,974 microform titles, an OPAC, and a Web page. Operations spending for 2004 fiscal year: $4.1 million. 4,000 computers available on campus for general student use. A campuswide network can be accessed from student residence rooms and from off campus. Staffed computer lab on campus.
Community Environment: in the metropolitan area, the cotton and woolen plants once caused city to be known as"the spindle city." Today, textile manufacture has been de-emphasized and industry is diversified with electronics paramount. Lowell is the home of the only federal Urban National Park. Part-time employment available for students. Commercial air, rail, and bus service is easily accessible. Community has public library, churches of all denominations, YMCA, YWCA, art gallery, and hospitals. All sports facilities are available as well as beaches, theatres, and famous ski area within a short distance.

■ **UNIVERSITY OF PHOENIX-BOSTON CAMPUS** *E-12*
100 Grossman Dr.
Braintree, MA 02184-4949
Tel: (781)843-0844

Free: 800-228-7240
Admissions: (480)557-1712
Web Site: http://www.phoenix.edu/
Description: Proprietary, comprehensive, coed. Awards bachelor's and master's degrees. Founded 2001. Total enrollment: 628. Faculty: 119 (4 full-time, 115 part-time). Student-undergrad faculty ratio is 5:1. 20 applied. Full-time: 421 students, 54% women, 46% men. 0.2% Native American, 0.5% Hispanic, 5% black, 1% Asian American or Pacific Islander, 9% international, 93% 25 or older. Academic areas with the most degrees conferred: business/marketing; computer and information sciences. Core. Calendar: continuous. Advanced placement, accelerated degree program, independent study, distance learning, external degree program, adult/continuing education programs, graduate courses open to undergrads.
Entrance Requirements: Open admission. Option: deferred admission. Required: 1 recommendation. Required for some: high school transcript. Entrance: noncompetitive. Application deadline: Rolling.
Costs Per Year: Application fee: $110. Tuition: $13,020 full-time, $434 per credit part-time. Mandatory fees: $560 full-time, $70 per course part-time.
Collegiate Environment: College housing not available. University Library with 444 books, 666 serials, an OPAC, and a Web page. System-wide operations spending for 2004 fiscal year: $3.2 million.

■ **UNIVERSITY OF PHOENIX-CENTRAL MASSACHUSETTS CAMPUS** *E-9*
One Research Dr.
Westborough, MA 01581
Tel: (508)614-4100
Free: 800-228-7240
Admissions: (480)557-1712
Web Site: http://www.phoenix.edu/
Description: Proprietary, comprehensive, coed. Awards bachelor's and master's degrees. Founded 2003. Total enrollment: 339. Faculty: 51 (2 full-time, 49 part-time). Student-undergrad faculty ratio is 4:1. 22 applied. Full-time: 233 students, 46% women, 54% men. 5% Hispanic, 3% black, 2% Asian American or Pacific Islander, 13% international, 98% 25 or older. Academic area with the most degrees conferred: business/marketing. Core. Calendar: continuous. Advanced placement, accelerated degree program, independent study, distance learning, external degree program, adult/continuing education programs, graduate courses open to undergrads.
Entrance Requirements: Open admission. Option: deferred admission. Required: 1 recommendation. Required for some: high school transcript. Entrance: noncompetitive. Application deadline: Rolling.
Costs Per Year: Application fee: $110. Tuition: $13,020 full-time, $434 per credit part-time. Mandatory fees: $560 full-time, $70 per course part-time.
Collegiate Environment: College housing not available. University Library with 444 books, 666 serials, an OPAC, and a Web page. System-wide operations spending for 2004 fiscal year: $3.2 million.

■ **URBAN COLLEGE OF BOSTON** *D-12*
178 Tremont St.
Boston, MA 02111
Tel: (617)292-4723
Fax: (617)423-4758
Web Site: http://www.urbancollegeofboston.org/
Description: Independent, 2-year, coed. Awards certificates and terminal associate degrees. Founded 1993. Setting: urban campus. Total enrollment: 609. 10 applied, 100% were admitted. Full-time: 12 students, 92% women, 8% men. Part-time: 597 students, 95% women, 5% men. 38% Hispanic, 31% black, 17% Asian American or Pacific Islander, 0% international, 100% 25 or older. Core. Calendar: semesters. Part-time degree program.
Collegiate Environment: College housing not available.

■ **WELLESLEY COLLEGE** *E-11*
106 Central St.
Wellesley, MA 02481
Tel: (781)283-1000
Admissions: (781)283-2257
Fax: (781)283-3678
E-mail: admission@wellesley.edu
Web Site: http://www.wellesley.edu/
Description: Independent, 4-year, women only. Awards bachelor's degrees (double bachelor's degree with Massachusetts Institute of Technology). Founded 1870. Setting: 500-acre suburban campus with easy access to Boston. Endowment: $1.3 billion. Research spending for 2004 fiscal year:

$12.9 million. Educational spending for 2005 fiscal year: $22,427 per student. Total enrollment: 2,331. Student-undergrad faculty ratio is 9:1. 4,347 applied, 34% were admitted. 77% from top 10% of their high school class, 95% from top quarter, 100% from top half. Full-time: 2,216 students. Part-time: 115 students. Students come from 52 states and territories, 79 other countries, 84% from out-of-state, 0.5% Native American, 7% Hispanic, 6% black, 27% Asian American or Pacific Islander, 8% international, 3% 25 or older, 97% live on campus, 1% transferred in. Retention: 94% of full-time freshmen returned the following year. Academic areas with the most degrees conferred: social sciences; psychology; foreign languages and literature. Core. Calendar: semesters. Services for LD students, advanced placement, self-designed majors, independent study, double major, summer session for credit, part-time degree program, adult/continuing education programs, internships. Off campus study at Brandeis University, Babson College, Massachusetts Institute of Technology, members of the Twelve College Exchange Program, Spelman College, Mills College. Study abroad program. ROTC: Army (c), Air Force (c).

Entrance Requirements: Options: Common Application, electronic application, early admission, early decision, deferred admission. Required: essay, high school transcript, 3 recommendations, SAT and SAT Subject Tests or ACT. Recommended: interview. Required for some: interview. Entrance: most difficult. Application deadlines: 1/15, 11/1 for early decision. Notification: 4/1, 12/15 for early decision.

Costs Per Year: Application fee: $50. Comprehensive fee: $41,030 includes full-time tuition ($30,696), mandatory fees ($652), and college room and board ($9682). College room only: $4906. Room and board charges vary according to board plan.

Collegiate Environment: Orientation program. Drama-theater group, choral group, student-run newspaper, radio station. Social organizations: 160 open to all. Most popular organizations: student government, radio station, cultural clubs, Rugby Club, theater groups. Major annual events: Spring Weekend, Fall Gala, Junior Show. Student services: health clinic, personal-psychological counseling, women's center. Campus security: 24-hour emergency response devices and patrols, late night transport-escort service, controlled dormitory access. Freshmen guaranteed college housing. Option: women-only housing available. Margaret Clapp Library plus 3 others with 765,530 books, 488,721 microform titles, 4,945 serials, 22,777 audiovisual materials, an OPAC, and a Web page. Operations spending for 2004 fiscal year: $5.6 million. 200 computers available on campus for general student use. Computer purchase/lease plans available. A campuswide network can be accessed from student residence rooms and from off campus. Staffed computer lab on campus.

Community Environment: The campus is located in a suburb of Boston 15 miles from the heart of the city. Railroad and bus transportation is available. Community services, and cultural and recreational facilities are found in adjacent Boston.

■ **WENTWORTH INSTITUTE OF TECHNOLOGY** D-12
550 Huntington Ave.
Boston, MA 02115-5998
Tel: (617)989-4590
Free: 800-556-0610
Fax: (617)989-4010
Web Site: http://www.wit.edu/

Description: Independent, 4-year, coed. Awards associate and bachelor's degrees. Founded 1904. Setting: 35-acre urban campus. Endowment: $73.5 million. Research spending for 2004 fiscal year: $66,000. Educational spending for 2005 fiscal year: $3476 per student. Total enrollment: 3,636. Student-undergrad faculty ratio is 24:1. 3,040 applied, 60% were admitted. Full-time: 3,141 students, 21% women, 79% men. Part-time: 495 students, 15% women, 85% men. Students come from 36 states and territories, 41 other countries, 40% from out-of-state, 0.1% Native American, 3% Hispanic, 4% black, 5% Asian American or Pacific Islander, 3% international, 12% 25 or older, 41% live on campus, 4% transferred in. Retention: 80% of full-time freshmen returned the following year. Academic areas with the most degrees conferred: engineering; computer and information sciences; architecture. Calendar: semesters for freshmen and sophomores, trimesters for juniors and seniors. Academic remediation for entering students, ESL program, services for LD students, advanced placement, accelerated degree program, freshman honors college, summer session for credit, part-time degree program, co-op programs and internships. Off campus study at Emmanuel College (MA), Massachusetts College of Pharmacy and Allied Sciences, Simmons College, Wheelock College. Study abroad program. ROTC: Army (c), Air Force (c).

Entrance Requirements: Options: Peterson's Universal Application, Common Application, electronic application, deferred admission. Required: essay, high school transcript, recommendations, SAT or ACT. Recommended: minimum 2.0 high school GPA, interview. Entrance: moderately difficult. Application deadline: Rolling. Notification: continuous.

Costs Per Year: Application fee: $30. Comprehensive fee: $27,500 includes full-time tuition ($18,500) and college room and board ($9000).

Collegiate Environment: Orientation program. Drama-theater group, student-run newspaper, radio station. Social organizations: 43 open to all. Most popular organizations: intramural sports, Wentworth Events Board, Asian Students Association, Ski and Adventure Club. Major annual events: Beaux Arts Ball, Family Weekend, Design Lecture Series. Student services: health clinic, personal-psychological counseling, women's center. Campus security: 24-hour emergency response devices and patrols, student patrols, late night transport-escort service, controlled dormitory access. 41 undergraduates lived in college housing during 2003-04. Freshmen guaranteed college housing. Option: coed housing available. Wentworth Alumni Library with 77,000 books, 500 serials, an OPAC, and a Web page. Operations spending for 2004 fiscal year: $778,000. 400 computers available on campus for general student use. A campuswide network can be accessed from student residence rooms and from off campus. Staffed computer lab on campus.

Community Environment: See Boston University.

■ **WESTERN NEW ENGLAND COLLEGE** F-5
1215 Wilbraham Rd.
Springfield, MA 01119
Tel: (413)782-3111
Free: 800-325-1122
Admissions: (413)782-1321
Fax: (413)782-1777
E-mail: ugradmis@wnec.edu
Web Site: http://www.wnec.edu/

Description: Independent, comprehensive, coed. Awards associate, bachelor's, master's, and first professional degrees. Founded 1919. Setting: 215-acre suburban campus. Endowment: $36.7 million. Research spending for 2004 fiscal year: $38,597. Total enrollment: 3,729. Faculty: 320 (164 full-time, 156 part-time). Student-undergrad faculty ratio is 15:1. 4,243 applied, 75% were admitted. 10% from top 10% of their high school class, 32% from top quarter, 73% from top half. Full-time: 2,363 students, 40% women, 60% men. Part-time: 477 students, 29% women, 71% men. Students come from 28 states and territories, 5 other countries, 51% from out-of-state, 0.3% Native American, 3% Hispanic, 4% black, 2% Asian American or Pacific Islander, 0.2% international, 20% 25 or older, 57% live on campus, 3% transferred in. Retention: 75% of full-time freshmen returned the following year. Academic areas with the most degrees conferred: security and protective services; business/marketing; psychology. Core. Calendar: semesters. Services for LD students, advanced placement, accelerated degree program, self-designed majors, honors program, independent study, distance learning, double major, summer session for credit, part-time degree program, adult/continuing education programs, internships, graduate courses open to undergrads. Off campus study at Cooperating Colleges of Greater Springfield. Study abroad program. ROTC: Army, Air Force (c).

Entrance Requirements: Options: Peterson's Universal Application, Common Application, electronic application, international baccalaureate accepted. Required: high school transcript, 1 recommendation, SAT or ACT. Recommended: essay, interview. Entrance: moderately difficult. Application deadline: Rolling. Notification: continuous.

Costs Per Year: Application fee: $50. Comprehensive fee: $32,054 includes full-time tuition ($21,600), mandatory fees ($1564), and college room and board ($8890). Full-time tuition and fees vary according to program and student level. Room and board charges vary according to board plan and housing facility. Part-time tuition: $452 per credit hour. Part-time mandatory fees: $21 per term. Part-time tuition and fees vary according to program.

Collegiate Environment: Orientation program. Drama-theater group, choral group, student-run newspaper, radio station. Social organizations: 60 open to all. Most popular organizations: Student Senate, Residence Hall Association, Campus Activities Board, student radio station, Management Association. Major annual events: homecoming, Family Weekend, Spring Concert. Student services: health clinic, personal-psychological counseling. Campus security: 24-hour emergency response devices and patrols, student patrols, controlled dormitory access, security cameras. 1,950 college housing spaces available; 1,880 were occupied in 2003-04. Freshmen guaranteed college housing. Options: coed, men-only, women-only housing available.

D'Amour Library plus 1 other with 100,010 books, 361,460 microform titles, 787 serials, 2,989 audiovisual materials, an OPAC, and a Web page. Operations spending for 2004 fiscal year: $1.1 million. 460 computers available on campus for general student use. A campuswide network can be accessed from student residence rooms and from off campus. Staffed computer lab on campus.

Community Environment: The College is located in a residential section of Springfield, Massachusetts, about four miles from the city's downtown area. Because Springfield is a city of 157,000 people, there are a variety of social, cultural, and athletic activities from which to choose. Some of the city's special features are live theater ant City Stage; the Springfield Symphony; the Quadrangle, a complex of museums; the Basketball Hall of Fame; the Springfield Falcons hockey team; Six Flags New England Amusement Park; the Eastern States Exposition fairgrounds; and many activities, shows, and concerts held in the Springfield Civic Center. Public transportation is available to locations throughout the greater Springfield area. The College is also a member of the Cooperating Colleges of Greater Springfield, a group of 8 private and public colleges in the immediate area.

■ **WESTFIELD STATE COLLEGE** *F-4*
Western Ave.
Westfield, MA 01086
Tel: (413)572-5300
Admissions: (413)572-5218
E-mail: admission@wsc.mass.edu
Web Site: http://www.wsc.ma.edu/

Description: State-supported, comprehensive, coed. Part of Massachusetts Public Higher Education System. Awards bachelor's and master's degrees and post-master's certificates. Founded 1838. Setting: 227-acre small town campus. Endowment: $2.7 million. Educational spending for 2005 fiscal year: $4446 per student. Total enrollment: 5,345. Faculty: 344 (179 full-time, 165 part-time). Student-undergrad faculty ratio is 18:1. 4,248 applied, 74% were admitted. Full-time: 4,112 students, 55% women, 45% men. Part-time: 555 students, 58% women, 42% men. Students come from 13 states and territories, 7% from out-of-state, 9% 25 or older, 54% live on campus, 8% transferred in. Retention: 77% of full-time freshmen returned the following year. Academic areas with the most degrees conferred: security and protective services; business/marketing; liberal arts/general studies. Core. Calendar: semesters. Services for LD students, advanced placement, self-designed majors, honors program, independent study, distance learning, double major, summer session for credit, part-time degree program, adult/continuing education programs, co-op programs and internships. Off campus study at National Student Exchange, New England Student Exchange Program. Study abroad program. ROTC: Army (c), Air Force (c).

Entrance Requirements: Option: deferred admission. Required: high school transcript, SAT or ACT. Recommended: recommendations, SAT. Entrance: moderately difficult. Application deadline: 3/1.

Costs Per Year: Application fee: $25. State resident tuition: $970 full-time. Nonresident tuition: $7050 full-time. Mandatory fees: $4687 full-time. College room and board: $6470.

Collegiate Environment: Orientation program. Drama-theater group, choral group, student-run newspaper, radio station. Social organizations: 67 open to all. Major annual events: Spring Weekend, Student Senate Banquet. Student services: legal services, health clinic, personal-psychological counseling. Campus security: 24-hour emergency response devices and patrols, student patrols, late night transport-escort service. College housing designed to accommodate 2,114 students; 2,156 undergraduates lived in college housing during 2003-04. Option: coed housing available. Ely Library with 124,363 books, 547,002 microform titles, 819 serials, 2,379 audiovisual materials, an OPAC, and a Web page. Operations spending for 2004 fiscal year: $1 million. 238 computers available on campus for general student use. A campuswide network can be accessed from student residence rooms and from off campus. Staffed computer lab on campus.

Community Environment: Founded in 1669, city is located in southwestern part of state approximately nine miles northwest of Springfield. This is an industrial city manufacturing paper, machinery, and toys. Part-time employment is available for students. Several historical sites are found in the immediate area, including Grandmother's Garden, a municipally owned garden of old-fashioned flowers and herbs. Nearby Stanley Park offers 85 acres of

floral gardens, arboretum, concerts, 96-foot high Carillon, covered bridge, old mill, blacksmith shop, and multicolored fountain. Adjacent cities offer many community services.

■ **WHEATON COLLEGE** *G-11*
East Main St.
Norton, MA 02766
Tel: (508)285-7722
Free: 800-394-6003
Admissions: (508)286-8251
Fax: (508)285-8271
E-mail: admission@wheatonma.edu
Web Site: http://www.wheatoncollege.edu/

Description: Independent, 4-year, coed. Awards bachelor's degrees. Founded 1834. Setting: 385-acre small town campus with easy access to Boston. Endowment: $150.9 million. Educational spending for 2005 fiscal year: $11,500 per student. Total enrollment: 1,568. Student-undergrad faculty ratio is 11:1. 3,697 applied, 44% were admitted. 56% from top 10% of their high school class, 82% from top quarter, 97% from top half. 103 student government officers. Full-time: 1,558 students, 62% women, 38% men. Part-time: 10 students, 90% women, 10% men. Students come from 47 states and territories, 31 other countries, 65% from out-of-state, 0.3% Native American, 4% Hispanic, 3% black, 3% Asian American or Pacific Islander, 3% international, 97% live on campus, 1% transferred in. Retention: 86% of full-time freshmen returned the following year. Academic areas with the most degrees conferred: social sciences; English; psychology. Core. Calendar: semesters. Advanced placement, accelerated degree program, self-designed majors, independent study, double major, part-time degree program, internships. Off campus study at members of the Twelve College Exchange Program, American University, Williams College, Brown University, members of the Southeastern Association for Cooperation in Higher Education in Massachusetts, Connecticut College (National Theatre Institute), SALT Center for Documentary Field Studies, Marine Biological Laboratory (Woods Hole, MA). Study abroad program. ROTC: Army (c).

Entrance Requirements: Options: Peterson's Universal Application, Common Application, electronic application, early admission, early decision, deferred admission, international baccalaureate accepted. Required: essay, high school transcript, 2 recommendations. Recommended: interview. Entrance: very difficult. Application deadlines: 1/15, 11/15 for early decision plan 1, 1/15 for early decision plan 2. Notification: 4/1, 12/15 for early decision plan 1, 2/15 for early decision plan 2.

Costs Per Year: Application fee: $55. Comprehensive fee: $40,180 includes full-time tuition ($32,115), mandatory fees ($235), and college room and board ($7830). College room only: $4130.

Collegiate Environment: Orientation program. Drama-theater group, choral group, student-run newspaper, radio station. Social organizations: 65 open to all; 50% of eligible men and 50% of eligible women are members. Most popular organizations: Student Government Association, Community Service Network, Amnesty International, a cappella singing groups, Programming Council. Major annual events: Academic Festival, Spring Weekend, Wheaton Family Homecoming. Student services: health clinic, personal-psychological counseling, women's center. Campus security: 24-hour emergency response devices and patrols, student patrols, late night transport-escort service, controlled dormitory access. 1,471 undergraduates lived in college housing during 2003-04. Freshmen guaranteed college housing. On-campus residence required through senior year. Options: coed, men-only, women-only housing available. Madeleine Clark Wallace Library plus 1 other with 372,322 books, 85,105 microform titles, 3,726 serials, 14,078 audiovisual materials, an OPAC, and a Web page. Operations spending for 2004 fiscal year: $2.4 million. 285 computers available on campus for general student use. Computer purchase/lease plans available. A campuswide network can be accessed from student residence rooms and from off campus. Staffed computer lab on campus.

■ **WHEELOCK COLLEGE** *D-12*
200 The Riverway
Boston, MA 02215-4176
Tel: (617)879-2000
Free: 800-734-5212
Admissions: (617)879-2209
Fax: (617)566-7531
E-mail: undergrad@wheelock.edu
Web Site: http://www.wheelock.edu/

Description: Independent, comprehensive, coed. Awards associate, bachelor's, and master's degrees and post-master's certificates. Founded 1888. Setting: 7-acre urban campus. Endowment: $34.6 million. Research spending for 2004 fiscal year: $120,000. Educational spending for 2005 fiscal year: $15,317 per student. Total enrollment: 1,016. Faculty: 95 (65 full-time, 30 part-time). Student-undergrad faculty ratio is 11:1. 703 applied, 77% were admitted. 12% from top 10% of their high school class, 35% from top quarter, 66% from top half. Full-time: 623 students, 95% women, 5% men. Part-time: 40 students, 93% women, 8% men. Students come from 17 states and territories, 63% from out-of-state, 1% Native American, 5% Hispanic, 7% black, 2% Asian American or Pacific Islander, 0.3% international, 2% 25 or older, 69% live on campus, 6% transferred in. Retention: 71% of full-time freshmen returned the following year. Academic areas with the most degrees conferred: education; family and consumer sciences; public administration and social services. Core. Calendar: semesters. Academic remediation for entering students, services for LD students, advanced placement, independent study, double major, part-time degree program, internships, graduate courses open to undergrads. Off campus study at 5 other members of Colleges of the Fenway. Study abroad program.

Entrance Requirements: Options: Peterson's Universal Application, Common Application, electronic application, early decision, deferred admission. Required: essay, high school transcript, 1 recommendation, SAT or ACT. Recommended: minimum 2.0 high school GPA, interview. Entrance: moderately difficult. Application deadlines: 3/1, 12/1 for early decision, 12/1 for early action. Notification: continuous until 4/15.

Costs Per Year: Application fee: $35. Comprehensive fee: $33,075 includes full-time tuition ($23,100), mandatory fees ($525), and college room and board ($9450). Part-time tuition: $722 per credit.

Collegiate Environment: Orientation program. Drama-theater group, choral group. Social organizations: 25 open to all; 6% of eligible men and 94% of eligible women are members. Most popular organizations: Student Government Association, Campus Activities Board, AHANA Club, residence hall councils, class councils. Major annual events: Fall Fest Weekend, Semi-Formal Banquet, Spring Weekend. Student services: health clinic, personal-psychological counseling, women's center. Campus security: 24-hour patrols, late night transport-escort service, controlled dormitory access, self-defense education. 475 college housing spaces available; 371 were occupied in 2003-04. Freshmen guaranteed college housing. Options: coed, women-only housing available. Wheelock College Library with 93,534 books, 587,044 microform titles, 536 serials, 5,058 audiovisual materials, an OPAC, and a Web page. Operations spending for 2004 fiscal year: $623,000. 120 computers available on campus for general student use. A campuswide network can be accessed from student residence rooms and from off campus. Staffed computer lab on campus.

Community Environment: See Boston University.

■ **WILLIAMS COLLEGE** *B-2*
PO Box 687
Williamstown, MA 01267
Tel: (413)597-3131
Admissions: (413)597-2211
Fax: (413)597-4018
E-mail: admission@williams.edu
Web Site: http://www.williams.edu/

Description: Independent, comprehensive, coed. Awards bachelor's and master's degrees. Founded 1793. Setting: 450-acre small town campus with easy access to Albany. Endowment: $1.3 billion. Educational spending for 2005 fiscal year: $22,702 per student. Total enrollment: 2,070. Faculty: 312 (257 full-time, 55 part-time). Student-undergrad faculty ratio is 7:1. 5,822 applied, 19% were admitted. 85% from top 10% of their high school class, 97% from top quarter, 100% from top half. Full-time: 1,984 students, 51% women, 49% men. Part-time: 33 students, 61% women, 39% men. Students come from 45 states and territories, 63 other countries, 87% from out-of-state, 0.3% Native American, 9% Hispanic, 9% black, 9% Asian American or Pacific Islander, 6% international, 0% 25 or older, 93% live on campus, 0.2% transferred in. Retention: 97% of full-time freshmen returned the following year. Academic areas with the most degrees conferred: social sciences; visual and performing arts; English; psychology. Core. Calendar: 4-1-4. Services for LD students, advanced placement, accelerated degree program, self-designed majors, honors program, independent study, double major, internships, graduate courses open to undergrads. Off campus study at members of the Twelve College Exchange Program, Bennington College, Rensselaer Polytechnic Institute, California Institute of Technology, Dartmouth College, Massachusetts College of Liberal Arts, Columbia University. Study abroad program.

Entrance Requirements: Options: Peterson's Universal Application, Common Application, electronic application, early admission, early decision, deferred admission, international baccalaureate accepted. Required: essay, high school transcript, 2 recommendations, SAT and SAT Subject Tests or ACT. Entrance: most difficult. Application deadlines: 1/1, 11/10 for early decision. Notification: 4/1, 12/15 for early decision.

Costs Per Year: Application fee: $60. Comprehensive fee: $40,310 includes full-time tuition ($31,548), mandatory fees ($212), and college room and board ($8550). College room only: $4330. Room and board charges vary according to board plan.

Collegiate Environment: Orientation program. Drama-theater group, choral group, marching band, student-run newspaper, radio station. Social organizations: 110 open to all. Major annual events: homecoming, Winter Carnival, Spring Weekend. Student services: health clinic, personal-psychological counseling, women's center. Campus security: 24-hour emergency response devices and patrols, student patrols, late night transport-escort service, controlled dormitory access. 2,020 college housing spaces available; 1,880 were occupied in 2003-04. Freshmen guaranteed college housing. On-campus residence required through senior year. Option: coed housing available. Sawyer Library plus 10 others with 932,000 books, 491,623 microform titles, 12,063 serials, 38,076 audiovisual materials, an OPAC, and a Web page. Operations spending for 2004 fiscal year: $5.2 million. 252 computers available on campus for general student use. A campuswide network can be accessed from student residence rooms and from off campus. Staffed computer lab on campus.

Community Environment: This pleasant colonial town was named for its founder, Col. Ephraim Williams. It is located in the Berkshire Mountains within easy commuting distance of Albany, Boston, and New York. Heavy tourist trade is found here, and the area is known as "Village Beautiful." Excellent facilities are available for skiing, horseback riding, hunting in season, fishing, hiking, and golf. The town has several art museum and its own symphony orchestra. The Tanglewood Music Festival is held nearby annually.

■ **WORCESTER POLYTECHNIC INSTITUTE** *E-9*
100 Institute Rd.
Worcester, MA 01609-2280
Tel: (508)831-5000
Admissions: (508)831-5286
Fax: (508)831-5875
E-mail: admissiosn@wpi.edu
Web Site: http://www.wpi.edu/

Description: Independent, university, coed. Awards bachelor's, master's, and doctoral degrees and post-master's certificates. Founded 1865. Setting: 80-acre suburban campus with easy access to Boston. Endowment: $327.4 million. Research spending for 2004 fiscal year: $11.7 million. Educational spending for 2005 fiscal year: $16,633 per student. Total enrollment: 3,910. Faculty: 317 (232 full-time, 85 part-time). Student-undergrad faculty ratio is 13:1. 3,575 applied, 71% were admitted. 46% from top 10% of their high school class, 77% from top quarter, 96% from top half. 23 National Merit Scholars, 117 valedictorians. Full-time: 2,811 students, 25% women, 75% men. Part-time: 81 students, 21% women, 79% men. Students come from 42 states and territories, 49% from out-of-state, 0.4% Native American, 4% Hispanic, 2% black, 6% Asian American or Pacific Islander, 5% international, 0% 25 or older, 60% live on campus, 1% transferred in. Retention: 92% of full-time freshmen returned the following year. Academic areas with the most degrees conferred: engineering; computer and information sciences; biological/life sciences. Core. Calendar: 4 7-week terms. ESL program, services for LD students, advanced placement, accelerated degree program, self-designed majors, independent study, double major, summer session for credit, part-time degree program, adult/continuing education programs, co-op programs, graduate courses open to undergrads. Off campus study at Colleges of Worcester Consortium. Study abroad program. ROTC: Army, Naval (c), Air Force.

Entrance Requirements: Options: Peterson's Universal Application, Common Application, electronic application, early admission, early decision, early action, deferred admission, international baccalaureate accepted. Required: essay, high school transcript, 2 recommendations, SAT or ACT. Recommended: SAT Subject Tests. Required for some: interview. Entrance: very difficult. Application deadlines: 2/1, 2/1 for nonresidents, 11/15 for early action. Notification: 4/1, 4/1 for nonresidents, 12/15 for early action.

Costs Per Year: Application fee: $60. Comprehensive fee: $43,110 includes full-time tuition ($32,850), mandatory fees ($420), and college room and board ($9840). College room only: $5720. Part-time tuition: $2738 per unit.

Collegiate Environment: Orientation program. Drama-theater group, choral group, marching band, student-run newspaper, radio station. Social organizations: 100 open to all; national fraternities, national sororities; 33% of eligible men and 33% of eligible women are members. Most popular organizations: student government, Masque (drama group), music groups, intramural sports, ethnic clubs. Major annual events: Homecoming/Parents' Weekend, Traditions Day, Winter Weekend. Student services: health clinic, personal-psychological counseling, women's center. Campus security: 24-hour emergency response devices and patrols, student patrols, late night transport-escort service. College housing designed to accommodate 1,242 students; 1,260 undergraduates lived in college housing during 2003-04. Freshmen guaranteed college housing. Options: coed, men-only, women-only housing available. George C. Gordon Library with 275,299 books, 109,800 microform titles, 7,822 serials, 2,614 audiovisual materials, an OPAC, and a Web page. Operations spending for 2004 fiscal year: $2.9 million. 700 computers available on campus for general student use. A campuswide network can be accessed from student residence rooms and from off campus. Staffed computer lab on campus.

Community Environment: See Clark University.

■ **WORCESTER STATE COLLEGE** *E-9*
486 Chandler St.
Worcester, MA 01602-2597
Tel: (508)929-8000; (866)WSC-CALL
Admissions: (508)929-8825
Fax: (508)929-8131
Web Site: http://www.worcester.edu/

Description: State-supported, comprehensive, coed. Part of Massachusetts Public Higher Education System. Awards bachelor's and master's degrees. Founded 1874. Setting: 53-acre urban campus with easy access to Boston. Endowment: $8.7 million. Educational spending for 2005 fiscal year: $5673 per student. Total enrollment: 5,471. Faculty: 400 (167 full-time, 233 part-time). Student-undergrad faculty ratio is 17:1. 3,113 applied, 59% were admitted. Full-time: 3,242 students, 59% women, 41% men. Part-time: 1,356 students, 64% women, 36% men. Students come from 18 states and territories, 46 other countries, 3% from out-of-state, 0.4% Native American, 4% Hispanic, 4% black, 3% Asian American or Pacific Islander, 3% international, 17% 25 or older, 35% live on campus, 10% transferred in. Retention: 75% of full-time freshmen returned the following year. Academic areas with the most degrees conferred: business/marketing; health professions and related sciences; psychology. Core. Calendar: semesters. Advanced placement, accelerated degree program, honors program, independent study, double major, summer session for credit, part-time degree program, adult/continuing education programs, internships, graduate courses open to undergrads. Off

campus study at Worcester Consortium for Higher Education, other Massachusetts state colleges. Study abroad program. ROTC: Army (c), Naval (c), Air Force (c).

Entrance Requirements: Options: electronic application, early admission, deferred admission. Required: high school transcript, minimum 2.0 high school GPA. Required for some: SAT or ACT. Entrance: moderately difficult. Application deadline: 6/1. Notification: continuous.

Costs Per Year: Application fee: $20. State resident tuition: $970 full-time, $40.42 per credit part-time. Nonresident tuition: $7050 full-time, $293.75 per credit part-time. Mandatory fees: $4109 full-time, $167.04 per credit part-time. Full-time tuition and fees vary according to class time, course load, and reciprocity agreements. Part-time tuition and fees vary according to class time, course load, and reciprocity agreements. College room and board: $7420. College room only: $4730. Room and board charges vary according to board plan and housing facility.

Collegiate Environment: Drama-theater group, choral group, student-run newspaper, radio station. Social organizations: 14 open to all. Most popular organizations: Senate, SEC (Student Events Committee), TWA (Third World Alliance), WSCW (Radio Station), Dance Company/Club. Major annual events: Multicultural Festival, Homecoming, SGA Auction to Benefit the Homeless. Student services: personal-psychological counseling, women's center. Campus security: 24-hour emergency response devices and patrols, late night transport-escort service, controlled dormitory access, well-lit campus, limited access to campus at night. College housing designed to accommodate 693 students; 961 undergraduates lived in college housing during 2003-04. Options: men-only, women-only housing available. Learning Resources Center with 150,419 books, 15,602 microform titles, 1,021 serials, 12,127 audiovisual materials, an OPAC, and a Web page. Operations spending for 2004 fiscal year: $762,356. 102 computers available on campus for general student use. Computer purchase/lease plans available. A campuswide network can be accessed from student residence rooms. Staffed computer lab on campus.

Community Environment: The Worcester State College location has the advantages of a suburban setting in the west side of Worcester, while less than two miles from downtown Worcester. A shuttle service provides free student transportation to the other nine college in the Colleges of Worcester Consortium and to City Hall, the Worcester Public Library, and several cultural centers. Worcester, the"Heart of New England," is about 40 miles from Boston, 45 miles from Providence, Rhode Island and 60 miles from Hartford, Connecticut. More than 700,000 people live within an hour's drive. The Worcester Centrum and Convention Center, with a seating capacity of 15,500, hosts a variety of sports and entertainment events. Lakes, rivers, city parks and beaches make fishing and boating, and a variety of activities, available. Hiking and skiing are available in nearby Mt. Wachusett.

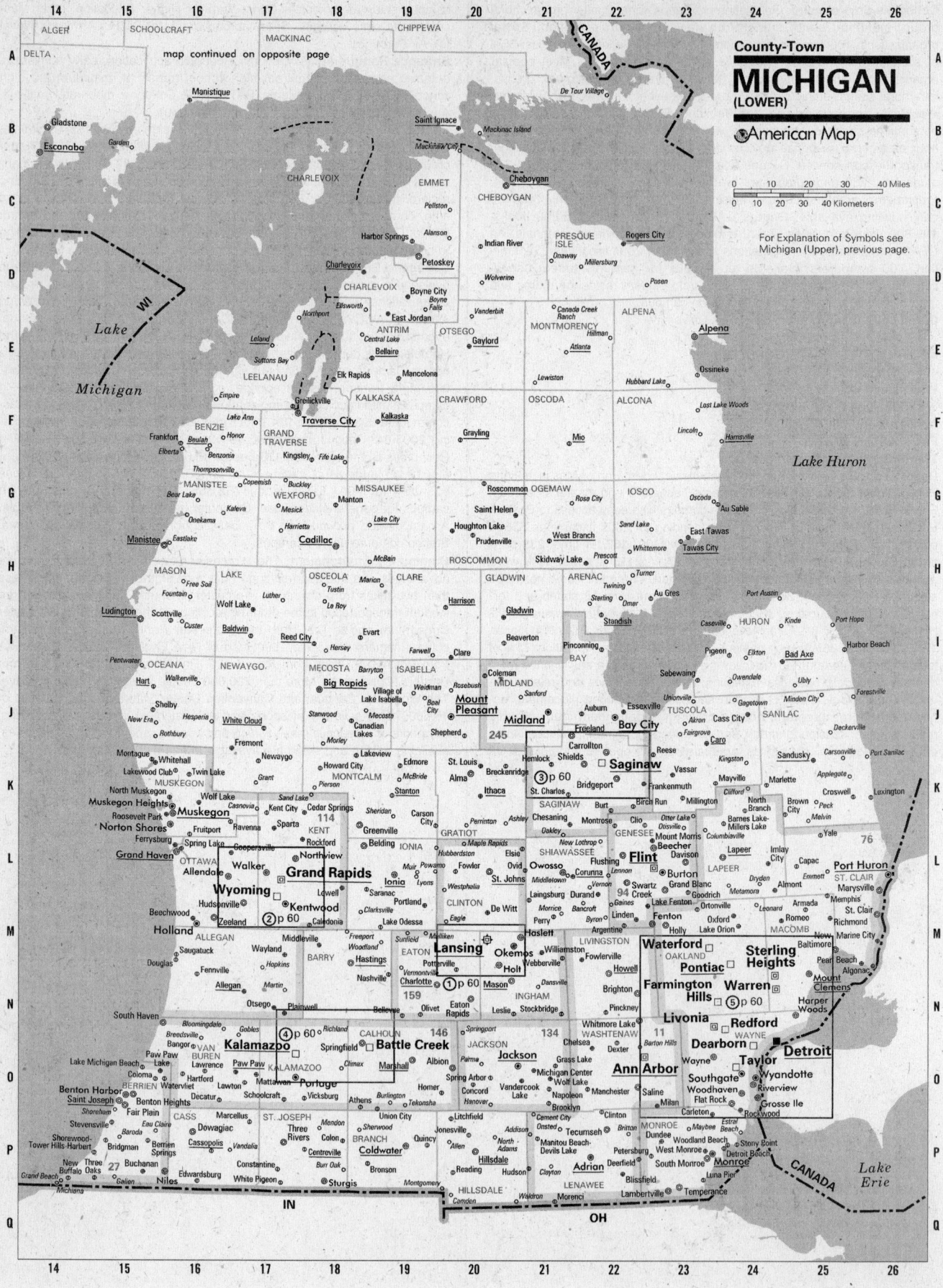

County-Town
MICHIGAN
(LOWER)

American Map

0 10 20 30 40 Miles
0 10 20 30 40 Kilometers

For Explanation of Symbols see
Michigan (Upper), previous page.

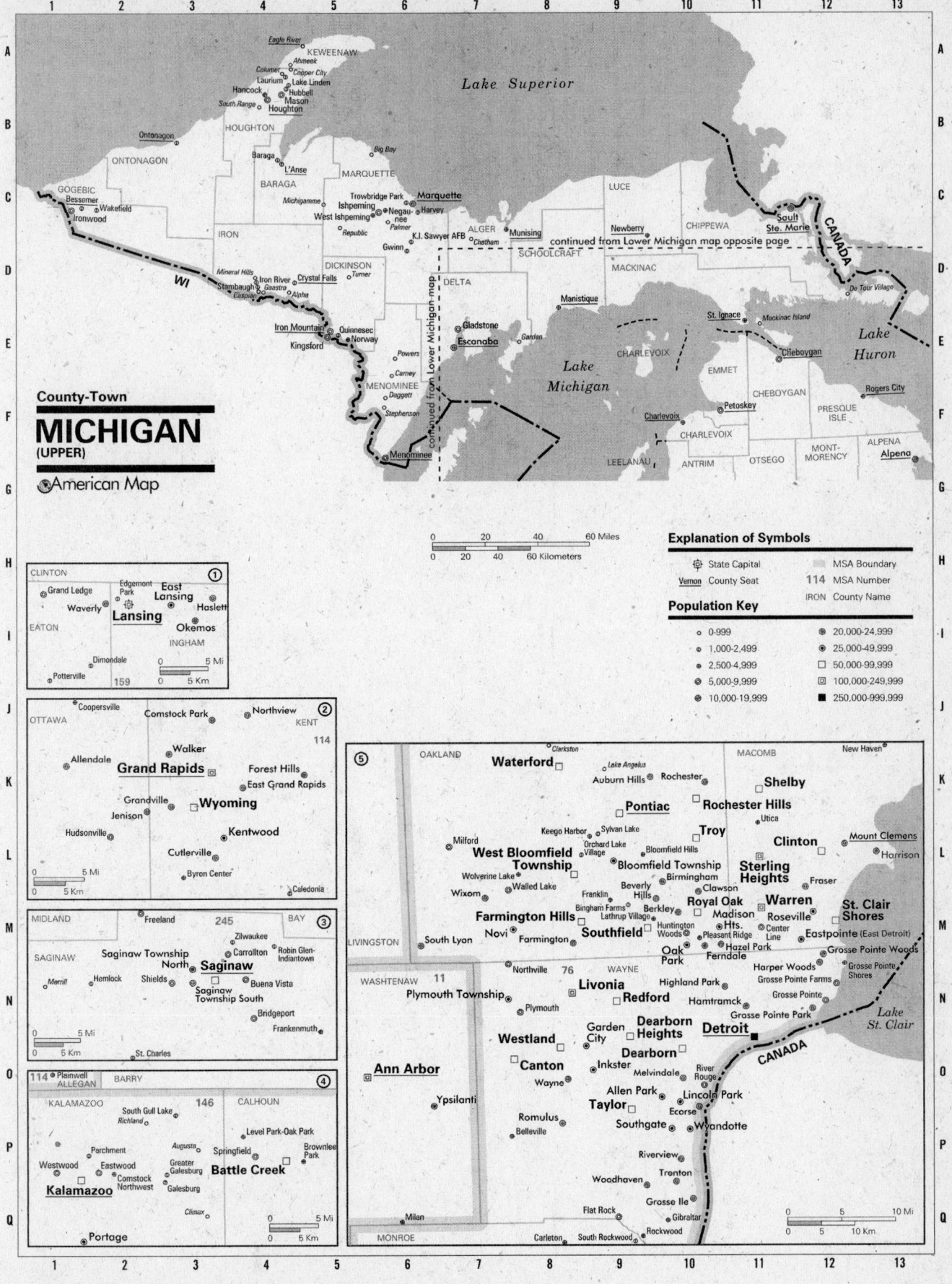

■ **ADRIAN COLLEGE** *P-22*

110 South Madison St.
Adrian, MI 49221-2575
Tel: (517)265-5161
Free: 800-877-2246
Fax: (517)265-3331
E-mail: admission@adrian.adrian.edu
Web Site: http://www.adrian.edu/

Description: Independent, 4-year, coed, affiliated with United Methodist Church. Awards associate and bachelor's degrees. Founded 1859. Setting: 100-acre small town campus with easy access to Detroit and Toledo. Endowment: $37.8 million. Educational spending for 2005 fiscal year: $5672 per student. Total enrollment: 1,013. 1,209 applied, 84% were admitted. 13% from top 10% of their high school class, 33% from top quarter, 61% from top half. Full-time: 959 students, 53% women, 47% men. Part-time: 54 students, 76% women, 24% men. Students come from 16 states and territories, 8 other countries, 15% from out-of-state, 0.4% Native American, 1% Hispanic, 6% black, 1% Asian American or Pacific Islander, 1% international, 1% 25 or older, 77% live on campus, 3% transferred in. Retention: 66% of full-time freshmen returned the following year. Core. Calendar: semesters. Academic remediation for entering students, ESL program, services for LD students, advanced placement, self-designed majors, honors program, independent study, double major, summer session for credit, part-time degree program, adult/continuing education programs, co-op programs and internships. Off campus study at Urban Life Center (Chicago), The Washington Center. Study abroad program.

Entrance Requirements: Options: Peterson's Universal Application, Common Application, electronic application, deferred admission, international baccalaureate accepted. Required: high school transcript, SAT or ACT. Recommended: interview, ACT. Required for some: essay. Entrance: moderately difficult. Application deadline: 8/15. Notification: continuous.

Costs Per Year: Application fee: $20. Comprehensive fee: $24,900 includes full-time tuition ($18,530), mandatory fees ($100), and college room and board ($6270). College room only: $2880. Room and board charges vary according to board plan.

Collegiate Environment: Orientation program. Drama-theater group, choral group, student-run newspaper, radio station. Social organizations: 70 open to all; national fraternities, national sororities; 29% of eligible men and 29% of eligible women are members. Most popular organizations: student government, volunteerism, Adrian College Theatre, musical ensembles. Major annual events: Homecoming, International Week, Greek Week. Student services: health clinic, personal-psychological counseling. Campus security: 24-hour patrols, student patrols, late night transport-escort service. 1,115 college housing spaces available; 761 were occupied in 2003-04. Freshmen guaranteed college housing. On-campus residence required through junior year. Option: coed housing available. Shipman Library with 148,407 books, 48,257 microform titles, 600 serials, 1,961 audiovisual materials, an OPAC, and a Web page. Operations spending for 2004 fiscal year: $569,904. 140 computers available on campus for general student use. A campuswide network can be accessed from student residence rooms and from off campus. Staffed computer lab on campus.

Community Environment: Adrian is 35 miles southwest of Ann Arbor and 35 miles northwest of Toledo, Ohio, located in the center of a large industrial, agricultural and recreational area. Leading manufactured products include aircraft, automobile, and refrigerator parts, paper, wood cabinetry, plastics, tools, and chemicals. Water sports and fishing are easily accessible with many lakes within a 25-mile radius. Part-time job opportunities are available.

■ **ALBION COLLEGE** *O-20*

611 East Porter St.
Albion, MI 49224-1831
Tel: (517)629-1000
Free: 800-858-6770
Admissions: (517)629-0600
Fax: (517)629-0569
E-mail: admissions@albion.edu
Web Site: http://www.albion.edu/

Description: Independent Methodist, 4-year, coed. Awards bachelor's degrees. Founded 1835. Setting: 565-acre small town campus with easy access to Detroit. Endowment: $136.6 million. Research spending for 2004 fiscal year: $859,670. Educational spending for 2005 fiscal year: $10,261 per student. Total enrollment: 1,979. Student-undergrad faculty ratio is 13:1. 1,946 applied, 82% were admitted. 30% from top 10% of their high school class, 64% from top quarter, 90% from top half. 1 National Merit Scholar, 19 class presidents, 23 valedictorians, 124 student government officers. Full-time: 1,941 students, 56% women, 44% men. Part-time: 38 students, 42% women, 58% men. Students come from 32 states and territories, 19 other countries, 10% from out-of-state, 1% Native American, 1% Hispanic, 4% black, 2% Asian American or Pacific Islander, 1% international, 0% 25 or older, 93% live on campus, 2% transferred in. Retention: 86% of full-time freshmen returned the following year. Academic areas with the most degrees conferred: social sciences; psychology; biological/life sciences. Core. Calendar: semesters. Services for LD students, advanced placement, self-designed majors, honors program, independent study, double major, summer session for credit, part-time degree program, internships. Off campus study at Great Lakes Colleges Association. Study abroad program.

Entrance Requirements: Options: Peterson's Universal Application, Common Application, electronic application, early admission, early action, deferred admission, international baccalaureate accepted. Required: essay, high school transcript, 1 recommendation. Recommended: minimum 3.0 high school GPA. Required for some: interview, SAT or ACT. Entrance: moderately difficult. Application deadlines: 3/1, 12/1 for early action. Notification: continuous, 1/1 for early action.

Costs Per Year: Application fee: $20. Comprehensive fee: $31,224 includes full-time tuition ($24,012), mandatory fees ($284), and college room and board ($6928). College room only: $3388. Room and board charges vary according to housing facility. Part-time tuition: $1020 per semester hour.

Collegiate Environment: Orientation program. Drama-theater group, choral group, marching band, student-run newspaper, radio station. Social organizations: 122 open to all; national fraternities, national sororities; 32% of eligible men and 32% of eligible women are members. Most popular organizations: Alpha Phi Omega, Union Board, Inter-Varsity Christian Fellowship, Student Senate. Major annual events: homecoming, Briton Bash (activities fair and organization expo), Annual Leadership Recognition Night. Student services: health clinic, personal-psychological counseling, women's center. Campus security: 24-hour emergency response devices and patrols, student patrols, late night transport-escort service, controlled dormitory access. 1,722 college housing spaces available; 1,495 were occupied in 2003-04. Freshmen guaranteed college housing. On-campus residence required through senior year. Options: coed, men-only, women-only housing available. Stockwell Mudd Libraries with 363,000 books, 69,572 microform titles,

2,016 serials, 6,540 audiovisual materials, an OPAC, and a Web page. Operations spending for 2004 fiscal year: $1.4 million. 411 computers available on campus for general student use. A campuswide network can be accessed from student residence rooms and from off campus. Staffed computer lab on campus.

Community Environment: Located one and one-half hours west of Detroit and three hours east of Chicago, the city of Albion combines small town life, a strong industrial base, and the amenities of a college town to form a unique community for its citizens. Albion boasts a rich history of educational and industrial accomplishment and prides itself on its ethnic and cultural diversity. Part-time employment is available. The area is served by Greyhound Bus and Amtrak and has a library, hospital, parks, and several civic and service organizations. Facilities are provided for tennis, golf, skating, and water sports.

■ **ALMA COLLEGE** *K-20*
614 West Superior St.
Alma, MI 48801-1599
Tel: (989)463-7111
Free: 800-321-ALMA
Fax: (989)463-7057
E-mail: admissions@alma.edu
Web Site: http://www.alma.edu/

Description: Independent Presbyterian, 4-year, coed. Awards bachelor's degrees. Founded 1886. Setting: 125-acre small town campus. Endowment: $95 million. Research spending for 2004 fiscal year: $69,785. Educational spending for 2005 fiscal year: $6926 per student. Total enrollment: 1,284. Student-undergrad faculty ratio is 13:1. 1,471 applied, 81% were admitted. 32% from top 10% of their high school class, 62% from top quarter, 89% from top half. 1 National Merit Scholar, 16 valedictorians. Full-time: 1,242 students, 58% women, 42% men. Part-time: 42 students, 74% women, 26% men. Students come from 21 states and territories, 12 other countries, 5% from out-of-state, 1% Native American, 2% Hispanic, 2% black, 1% Asian American or Pacific Islander, 1% international, 5% 25 or older, 84% live on campus, 3% transferred in. Retention: 80% of full-time freshmen returned the following year. Academic areas with the most degrees conferred: business/marketing; biological/life sciences; health professions and related sciences. Core. Calendar: 4-4-1. Academic remediation for entering students, services for LD students, advanced placement, self-designed majors, independent study, double major, summer session for credit, internships. Off campus study at New York Arts program, Philadelphia Center Internship, Urban Life Center, Washington Semester. Study abroad program. ROTC: Army (c).

Entrance Requirements: Options: Peterson's Universal Application, Common Application, electronic application, early admission, early action, deferred admission, international baccalaureate accepted. Required: high school transcript, minimum 3.0 high school GPA, minimum SAT score of 1030 or ACT score of 22, SAT or ACT. Recommended: interview. Required for some: essay, recommendations. Entrance: moderately difficult. Application deadline: Rolling. Notification: continuous.

Costs Per Year: Application fee: $25. Comprehensive fee: $28,544 includes full-time tuition ($20,934), mandatory fees ($200), and college room and board ($7410). College room only: $3650. Room and board charges vary according to board plan and housing facility. Part-time tuition: $810 per credit. Part-time tuition varies according to course load.

Collegiate Environment: Orientation program. Drama-theater group, choral group, marching band, student-run newspaper, radio station. Social organizations: 96 open to all; national fraternities, national sororities, local fraternities, local sororities; 17% of eligible men and 26% of eligible women are members. Most popular organizations: Ambassadors, Alma College Union Board, Trinity Baptist Fellowship, student government, SOS (Students Offering Service). Major annual events: homecoming, All Nighter, Songfest. Student services: health clinic, personal-psychological counseling, women's center. Campus security: 24-hour emergency response devices and patrols. 1,211 college housing spaces available; 1,018 were occupied in 2003-04. Freshmen guaranteed college housing. On-campus residence required through senior year. Options: coed, women-only housing available. Kerhl Building-Monteith Library with 261,393 books, 244,135 microform titles, 1,175 serials, 8,037 audiovisual materials, an OPAC, and a Web page. Operations spending for 2004 fiscal year: $901,145. 717 computers available on campus for general student use. A campuswide network can be accessed from student residence rooms and from off campus. Staffed computer lab on campus.

Community Environment: Alma is located in a rural area in the center of Michigan's lower peninsula. Major industries include manufacturing of automotive parts, plastic extrusions, drainage and metal products. Some part-time work available for students. Area has access to rail service and airport. Alma has its own public library, hospital and motels. Recreation facilities include golf, Community Center, swimming pool, parks and the Pine River for boating and fishing. Alma College is within two hours of Michigan's beaches and ski resorts.

■ **ALPENA COMMUNITY COLLEGE** *E-23*
666 Johnson St.
Alpena, MI 49707-1495
Tel: (989)356-9021
Admissions: (989)358-7339
Fax: (989)358-7553
Web Site: http://www.alpenacc.edu/

Description: State and locally supported, 2-year, coed. Awards certificates, transfer associate, and terminal associate degrees. Founded 1952. Setting: 700-acre small town campus. Endowment: $3.3 million. Educational spending for 2005 fiscal year: $7628 per student. Total enrollment: 1,937. 1,163 applied, 100% were admitted. 10% from top 10% of their high school class, 25% from top quarter, 50% from top half. Full-time: 984 students, 55% women, 45% men. Part-time: 953 students, 62% women, 38% men. Students come from 4 states and territories, 0.01% from out-of-state, 0.4% Native American, 0.2% Hispanic, 1% black, 1% Asian American or Pacific Islander, 0% international, 40% 25 or older, 2% live on campus, 2% transferred in. Retention: 55% of full-time freshmen returned the following year. Core. Calendar: semesters. Academic remediation for entering students, services for LD students, advanced placement, distance learning, double major, summer session for credit, part-time degree program, internships.

Entrance Requirements: Open admission except for nursing, utility technician programs. Options: electronic application, early admission, deferred admission. Required: high school transcript. Placement: ACT COMPASS required; ACT recommended. Entrance: noncompetitive. Application deadline: Rolling. Notification: continuous.

Costs Per Year: Application fee: $0. Area resident tuition: $2532 full-time, $67.75 per contact hour part-time. State resident tuition: $3545 full-time, $101.50 per contact hour part-time. Nonresident tuition: $4550 full-time, $135 per contact hour part-time. Mandatory fees: $500 full-time, $16 per contact hour part-time, $10 per term part-time. College room only: $3000.

Collegiate Environment: Orientation program. Drama-theater group, choral group, student-run newspaper. Social organizations: 8 open to all. Most popular organizations: Nursing Association, Student Senate, Phi Theta Kappa, Lumberjack Newspaper, Law Enforcement Club. Major annual events: homecoming, Awards Night, Spring Fling. Student services: personal-psychological counseling, women's center. Campus security: 24-hour emergency response devices. 64 college housing spaces available; 48 were occupied in 2003-04. No special consideration for freshman housing applicants. Options: coed, men-only, women-only housing available. Stephen Fletcher Library with 29,000 books, 183 serials, an OPAC, and a Web page. Operations spending for 2004 fiscal year: $324,807. 75 computers available on campus for general student use. A campuswide network can be accessed from off-campus. Staffed computer lab on campus.

Community Environment: Located on Thunder Bay, 94 miles south of the Straits of Mackinac and 235 miles north of Detroit, Alpena is the largest port on northern Lake Huron. Industries include a cement plant, paper mill, and shale quarry. The mean annual temperature is 42.2 degrees. Air and bus service are available. The community has several churches, theatres, a hospital, museum, and planetarium. Alpena is well known for fine fishing, hunting, and winter sports. There are five city parks and over 240,000 acres of public land within a one-hour drive. Recreation facilities include golf, sailboat racing, tennis, and skating. Part-time employment is available for students.

■ **ANDREWS UNIVERSITY** *P-15*
Berrien Springs, MI 49104
Tel: (269)471-7771
Free: 800-253-2874
Fax: (269)471-3228
Web Site: http://www.andrews.edu/

Description: Independent Seventh-day Adventist, university, coed. Awards associate, bachelor's, master's, doctoral, and first professional degrees and post-master's certificates. Founded 1874. Setting: 1,650-acre small town campus. Endowment: $20.6 million. Research spending for 2004 fiscal year: $950,358. Total enrollment: 3,087. Faculty: 268 (207 full-time, 61 part-time).

Student-undergrad faculty ratio is 10:1. 1,324 applied, 40% were admitted. 16% from top 10% of their high school class, 38% from top quarter, 72% from top half. Full-time: 1,489 students, 55% women, 45% men. Part-time: 237 students, 55% women, 45% men. Students come from 45 states and territories, 46 other countries, 54% from out-of-state, 0.3% Native American, 11% Hispanic, 20% black, 8% Asian American or Pacific Islander, 12% international, 15% 25 or older, 54% live on campus, 9% transferred in. Retention: 78% of full-time freshmen returned the following year. Academic areas with the most degrees conferred: health professions and related sciences; business/marketing; visual and performing arts. Core. Calendar: semesters. Academic remediation for entering students, ESL program, advanced placement, accelerated degree program, self-designed majors, freshman honors college, honors program, distance learning, double major, summer session for credit, part-time degree program, adult/continuing education programs, co-op programs and internships, graduate courses open to undergrads. Off campus study. Study abroad program.

Entrance Requirements: Options: electronic application, deferred admission, international baccalaureate accepted. Required: essay, high school transcript, minimum 2.25 high school GPA, 2 recommendations, SAT or ACT. Entrance: moderately difficult. Application deadline: Rolling. Notification: continuous.

Costs Per Year: Application fee: $30. Comprehensive fee: $21,786 includes full-time tuition ($16,030), mandatory fees ($476), and college room and board ($5280). College room only: $2850. Full-time tuition and fees vary according to course load. Room and board charges vary according to board plan. Part-time tuition: $670 per credit hour. Part-time tuition varies according to course load.

Collegiate Environment: Orientation program. Drama-theater group, choral group, student-run newspaper, radio station. Social organizations: 30 open to all. Major annual events: College Days, Feast of Lights, homecoming. Student services: health clinic, personal-psychological counseling. Campus security: 24-hour emergency response devices and patrols, controlled dormitory access. 1,148 college housing spaces available; 925 were occupied in 2003-04. Freshmen guaranteed college housing. On-campus residence required through senior year. Options: men-only, women-only housing available. James White Library plus 2 others with 512,100 books, 795,060 microform titles, 3,032 serials, 41,503 audiovisual materials, an OPAC, and a Web page. Operations spending for 2004 fiscal year: $2.1 million. 130 computers available on campus for general student use. Computer purchase/lease plans available. A campuswide network can be accessed from student residence rooms and from off campus. Staffed computer lab on campus.

Community Environment: Andrews is located in a small town in the southwest part of Michigan. The area is accessible by bus, airplane, or Amtrak. Shopping and cultural activities are located in South Bend, Indiana, which is 25 miles away, and St. Joseph/Benton Harbor, Michigan, which is 10 miles away, and are approximately 30 minutes away. Lake Michigan, with its 200-foot high sand dunes and water activities, is less than 30 minutes distant. Chicago is less than two hours distant.

■ **AQUINAS COLLEGE** *L-17*
1607 Robinson Rd., SE
Grand Rapids, MI 49506-1799
Tel: (616)459-8281
Free: 800-678-9593
Admissions: (616)632-2852
Fax: (616)459-2563
E-mail: admissions@aquinas.edu
Web Site: http://www.aquinas.edu/

Description: Independent Roman Catholic, comprehensive, coed. Awards associate, bachelor's, and master's degrees. Founded 1886. Setting: 107-acre suburban campus with easy access to Detroit. Endowment: $14.6 million. Educational spending for 2005 fiscal year: $4923 per student. Total enrollment: 2,193. Faculty: 199 (94 full-time, 105 part-time). Student-undergrad faculty ratio is 14:1. 1,646 applied, 86% were admitted. 17% from top 10% of their high school class, 41% from top quarter, 77% from top half. 12 valedictorians. Full-time: 1,469 students, 65% women, 35% men. Part-time: 313 students, 64% women, 36% men. Students come from 22 states and territories, 9 other countries, 4% from out-of-state, 0.3% Native American, 4% Hispanic, 4% black, 2% Asian American or Pacific Islander, 1% international, 24% 25 or older, 75% live on campus, 4% transferred in. Retention: 79% of full-time freshmen returned the following year. Academic areas with the most degrees conferred: education; business/marketing; social sciences. Core. Calendar: semesters. Academic remediation for enter-

ing students, services for LD students, advanced placement, accelerated degree program, self-designed majors, honors program, independent study, distance learning, double major, summer session for credit, part-time degree program, external degree program, adult/continuing education programs, co-op programs and internships, graduate courses open to undergrads. Off campus study at members of the Dominican College Interchange. Study abroad program.

Entrance Requirements: Options: Common Application, electronic application, early admission, deferred admission. Required: high school transcript, minimum 2.5 high school GPA, SAT or ACT. Required for some: essay, interview. Entrance: moderately difficult. Application deadline: Rolling.

Costs Per Year: Application fee: $0. Comprehensive fee: $23,750 includes full-time tuition ($17,926) and college room and board ($5824). College room only: $2690. Full-time tuition varies according to course load. Room and board charges vary according to board plan and housing facility. Part-time tuition: $361 per credit. Part-time tuition varies according to course load.

Collegiate Environment: Orientation program. Drama-theater group, choral group, student-run newspaper, radio station. Social organizations: 48 open to all. Most popular organizations: Community Senate Programming Board, Aquinas Times, JAMMIN (multicultural group). Major annual events: Homecoming, St. Thomas Aquinas Celebration Week, Spring Fling. Student services: health clinic, personal-psychological counseling, women's center. Campus security: 24-hour emergency response devices and patrols, student patrols, late night transport-escort service, controlled dormitory access. 705 college housing spaces available; 641 were occupied in 2003-04. Freshmen guaranteed college housing. On-campus residence required through sophomore year. Option: coed housing available. Woodhouse Library with 112,458 books, 223,804 microform titles, 14,725 serials, 4,907 audiovisual materials, an OPAC, and a Web page. Operations spending for 2004 fiscal year: $835,621. 176 computers available on campus for general student use. A campuswide network can be accessed from student residence rooms and from off campus. Staffed computer lab on campus.

Community Environment: Grand Rapids is an urban setting. The greater Grand Rapids area has a population of 640,000, and is one of the fastest growing areas in the nation. It is the commercial, medical and cultural center of west Michigan.

■ **AVE MARIA COLLEGE** *P-6*
300 West Forest Ave.
Ypsilanti, MI 48197
Tel: (734)337-4100; (866)866-3030
Admissions: (734)337-4528
Fax: (734)337-4140
Web Site: http://www.avemaria.edu/

Description: Independent Roman Catholic, 4-year, coed. Awards bachelor's degrees. Founded 1998. Setting: urban campus with easy access to Detroit. Total enrollment: 308. 214 applied, 78% were admitted. Students come from 39 states and territories, 13 other countries, 72% from out-of-state, 0% Native American, 3% Hispanic, 1% black, 1% Asian American or Pacific Islander, 12% international, 10% 25 or older, 95% live on campus. Retention: 72% of full-time freshmen returned the following year. Calendar: semesters. Study abroad program.

Entrance Requirements: Required: essay, high school transcript, minimum 2.4 high school GPA, 2 recommendations, SAT or ACT. Recommended: interview. Required for some: minimum SAT score of 1000 or ACT score of 21. Entrance: very difficult.

Collegiate Environment: Drama-theater group, choral group, student-run newspaper. Social organizations: 12 open to all; local fraternities, local sororities. Most popular organizations: Pro-Life Organization, Student Government, yearbook, newspaper, Liturgical Ministries. Major annual events: Opening of the Year Mass, Fall Bash, Spring Formal. Student services: personal-psychological counseling. Campus security: 24-hour emergency response devices, late night transport-escort service, controlled dormitory access, 12-hour evening patrols by trained security personnel. On-campus residence required through senior year. Options: men-only, women-only housing available.

■ **BAKER COLLEGE OF ALLEN PARK** *O-10*
4500 Enterprise Dr.
Allen Park, MI 48101
Tel: (313)425-3700
Web Site: http://www.baker.edu/

Description: Independent, 4-year, coed. Part of Baker College System. Awards associate and bachelor's degrees. Founded 2003. Setting: 13-acre suburban campus with easy access to Detroit. Total enrollment: 1,522. Student-undergrad faculty ratio is 34:1. 819 applied, 100% were admitted. 0% from out-of-state, 1% Native American, 5% Hispanic, 29% black, 1% Asian American or Pacific Islander, 0% international.

Entrance Requirements: Required: high school transcript, interview. Application deadline: 9/24.

Costs Per Year: Application fee: $0. Tuition: $6480 full-time, $180 per quarter hour part-time.

Collegiate Environment: Student services: personal-psychological counseling. Campus security: 24-hour patrols. College housing not available.

■ **BAKER COLLEGE OF AUBURN HILLS** *K-10*
1500 University Dr.
Auburn Hills, MI 48326-1586
Tel: (248)340-0600
E-mail: love_j@auburnhills.baker.edu
Web Site: http://www.baker.edu/

Description: Independent, 4-year, coed. Part of Baker College System. Awards associate and bachelor's degrees. Founded 1911. Setting: 7-acre urban campus with easy access to Detroit. Total enrollment: 3,517. Student-undergrad faculty ratio is 59:1. 1,306 applied, 100% were admitted. 0% from out-of-state, 1% Native American, 4% Hispanic, 19% black, 3% Asian American or Pacific Islander, 0% international, 41% 25 or older. Core. Academic remediation for entering students, services for LD students, advanced placement, accelerated degree program, independent study, distance learning, double major, summer session for credit, part-time degree program, external degree program, co-op programs and internships.

Entrance Requirements: Open admission. Options: Peterson's Universal Application, early admission, deferred admission. Required: high school transcript. Entrance: noncompetitive. Application deadline: Rolling.

Costs Per Year: Application fee: $20. Tuition: $6480 full-time, $180 per quarter hour part-time.

Collegiate Environment: Social organizations: 3 open to all. Most popular organizations: Baker Business Club, Interior Design Society, Students Action in Engineering, Marketing Club. Major annual events: Fall Kick Day, Spring Spirit Day. Campus security: 24-hour emergency response devices. College housing not available. Baker College of Auburn Hills Library with 5,400 books, 95 serials, an OPAC, and a Web page. 110 computers available on campus for general student use. A campuswide network can be accessed from off-campus. Staffed computer lab on campus.

■ **BAKER COLLEGE OF CADILLAC** *H-18*
9600 East 13th St.
Cadillac, MI 49601
Tel: (231)876-3100
Fax: (231)775-8505
E-mail: mike.tisdale@baker.edu
Web Site: http://www.baker.edu/

Description: Independent, 4-year, coed. Part of Baker College System. Awards associate and bachelor's degrees. Founded 1986. Setting: 40-acre small town campus. Total enrollment: 1,559. Student-undergrad faculty ratio is 42:1. 621 applied, 100% were admitted. Students come from 4 states and territories, 0% from out-of-state, 0.1% Native American, 0.2% Hispanic, 0.3% black, 0.1% Asian American or Pacific Islander, 0% international, 56% 25 or older. Retention: 69% of full-time freshmen returned the following year. Core. Academic remediation for entering students, services for LD students, advanced placement, independent study, distance learning, double major, summer session for credit, part-time degree program, external degree program, co-op programs and internships.

Entrance Requirements: Open admission. Options: early admission, deferred admission. Required: high school transcript. Recommended: interview. Required for some: SAT or ACT. Entrance: noncompetitive. Application deadline: Rolling.

Costs Per Year: Application fee: $20. Tuition: $6480 full-time, $180 per quarter hour part-time.

Collegiate Environment: Campus security: 24-hour emergency response devices. College housing not available. Baker College of Cadillac Library with 4,000 books, 78 serials, an OPAC, and a Web page. 77 computers available on campus for general student use. A campuswide network can be accessed from off-campus. Staffed computer lab on campus.

■ **BAKER COLLEGE OF CLINTON TOWNSHIP** *L-12*
34950 Little Mack Ave.
Clinton Township, MI 48035-4701

Tel: (586)791-6610; 888-272-2842
Admissions: (586)790-9580
Fax: (586)791-6611
E-mail: annette.looser@baker.edu
Web Site: http://www.baker.edu/

Description: Independent, 4-year, coed. Part of Baker College System. Awards associate and bachelor's degrees. Founded 1990. Setting: 25-acre urban campus with easy access to Detroit. Total enrollment: 5,103. Student-undergrad faculty ratio is 60:1. 2,606 applied, 100% were admitted. Students come from 2 states and territories, 0% from out-of-state, 1% Native American, 2% Hispanic, 17% black, 2% Asian American or Pacific Islander, 0% international, 42% 25 or older. Core. Academic remediation for entering students, services for LD students, advanced placement, summer session for credit, part-time degree program, external degree program, co-op programs and internships.

Entrance Requirements: Open admission. Options: electronic application, early admission, deferred admission, international baccalaureate accepted. Required: high school transcript. Required for some: SAT or ACT. Entrance: noncompetitive. Application deadline: Rolling.

Costs Per Year: Application fee: $20. Tuition: $6480 full-time, $180 per quarter hour part-time.

Collegiate Environment: Student services: personal-psychological counseling. Campus security: 24-hour emergency response devices and patrols, evening security guard. College housing not available. Baker College of Mt. Clemens Library with 8,000 books, 97 serials, an OPAC, and a Web page. 127 computers available on campus for general student use. A campuswide network can be accessed from off-campus. Staffed computer lab on campus.

■ **BAKER COLLEGE OF FLINT** *L-23*
1050 West Bristol Rd.
Flint, MI 48507-5508
Tel: (810)767-7600
Free: 800-964-4299
Admissions: (810)766-4015
Fax: (810)766-4049
Web Site: http://www.baker.edu/

Description: Independent, 4-year, coed. Part of Baker College System. Awards associate and bachelor's degrees. Founded 1911. Setting: 30-acre urban campus with easy access to Detroit. Total enrollment: 6,065. Student-undergrad faculty ratio is 42:1. 2,848 applied, 100% were admitted. Students come from 5 states and territories, 1% from out-of-state, 0.5% Native American, 2% Hispanic, 28% black, 1% Asian American or Pacific Islander, 0% international, 2% live on campus. Core. Academic remediation for entering students, services for LD students, advanced placement, accelerated degree program, independent study, distance learning, double major, summer session for credit, part-time degree program, external degree program, co-op programs and internships.

Entrance Requirements: Open admission. Options: early admission, deferred admission, international baccalaureate accepted. Required: high school transcript. Entrance: noncompetitive. Application deadline: 9/20.

Costs Per Year: Application fee: $20. Tuition: $6480 full-time, $180 per quarter hour part-time. College room only: $2600.

Collegiate Environment: Most popular organizations: Occupational Therapy Club, Interior Design Society, Medical Assistants Student Organization, Physical Therapist Assistant Club. Major annual events: Campus Spirit Day, Student Club Day. Student services: personal-psychological counseling. Campus security: 24-hour patrols, late night transport-escort service, controlled dormitory access, video monitoring of high traffic areas. 500 college housing spaces available. On-campus residence required in freshman year. Option: coed housing available. Marianne Jewell Library with 168,700 books, an OPAC, and a Web page. 412 computers available on campus for general student use. A campuswide network can be accessed from off-campus. Staffed computer lab on campus.

■ **BAKER COLLEGE OF JACKSON** *O-21*
2800 Springport Rd.
Jackson, MI 49202
Tel: (517)789-6123; 888-343-3683
Admissions: (517)788-7800
E-mail: heldt_v@jackson.baker.edu
Web Site: http://www.baker.edu/

Description: Independent, 4-year, coed. Part of Baker College System. Awards associate and bachelor's degrees. Founded 1994. Setting: 42-acre urban campus with easy access to Lansing. Total enrollment: 1,625. Student-undergrad faculty ratio is 50:1. 659 applied, 100% were admitted. Students come from 2 states and territories, 1% from out-of-state, 0.2% Native American, 2% Hispanic, 5% black, 0.1% Asian American or Pacific Islander, 0% international, 56% 25 or older. Core. Academic remediation for entering students, services for LD students, advanced placement, accelerated degree program, independent study, distance learning, double major, summer session for credit, part-time degree program, external degree program, co-op programs and internships.

Entrance Requirements: Open admission. Options: electronic application, early admission, deferred admission, international baccalaureate accepted. Required: high school transcript. Entrance: noncompetitive. Application deadline: 9/19. Notification: continuous.

Costs Per Year: Application fee: $20. Tuition: $6480 full-time, $180 per quarter hour part-time.

Collegiate Environment: Student services: personal-psychological counseling. Campus security: 24-hour emergency response devices. College housing not available. Baker College of Jackson Library with 7,000 books, 150 serials, an OPAC, and a Web page. 110 computers available on campus for general student use. A campuswide network can be accessed from off-campus. Staffed computer lab on campus.

■ **BAKER COLLEGE OF MUSKEGON** *K-16*
1903 Marquette Ave.
Muskegon, MI 49442-3497
Tel: (231)777-5200
Admissions: (231)777-5207
Fax: (231)777-5201
E-mail: jacobs_k@muskegon.baker.edu
Web Site: http://www.baker.edu/
Description: Independent, 4-year, coed. Part of Baker College System. Awards associate and bachelor's degrees. Founded 1888. Setting: 40-acre suburban campus with easy access to Grand Rapids. Educational spending for 2005 fiscal year: $1417 per student. Total enrollment: 4,744. Student-undergrad faculty ratio is 63:1. 1,937 applied, 100% were admitted. Students come from 13 states and territories, 1% from out-of-state, 1% Native American, 4% Hispanic, 13% black, 1% Asian American or Pacific Islander, 0% international, 45% 25 or older, 11% live on campus. Core. Academic remediation for entering students, services for LD students, advanced placement, accelerated degree program, independent study, distance learning, double major, summer session for credit, part-time degree program, external degree program, adult/continuing education programs, co-op programs and internships.

Entrance Requirements: Open admission. Options: electronic application, early admission, deferred admission, international baccalaureate accepted. Required: high school transcript. Entrance: noncompetitive. Application deadline: 9/24. Notification: continuous.

Costs Per Year: Application fee: $20. Tuition: $6480 full-time, $180 per quarter hour part-time. College room only: $2400.

Collegiate Environment: Orientation program. Social organizations: 4 open to all. Most popular organizations: Accounting Club, Rehab Club, Travel Club, Culinary Club. Major annual event: Career/Job Fair. Student services: personal-psychological counseling. Campus security: 24-hour emergency response devices and patrols, late night transport-escort service, controlled dormitory access, 24-hour security camera surveillance. 800 college housing spaces available; 500 were occupied in 2003-04. Freshmen given priority for college housing. On-campus residence required in freshman year. Option: coed housing available. Marianne Jewell Library with 32,000 books, 90 microform titles, 140 serials, an OPAC, and a Web page. Operations spending for 2004 fiscal year: $241,725. 165 computers available on campus for general student use. A campuswide network can be accessed from student residence rooms and from off campus. Staffed computer lab on campus.

■ **BAKER COLLEGE OF OWOSSO** *L-21*
1020 South Washington St.
Owosso, MI 48867-4400
Tel: (989)729-3300
Free: 800-879-3797
Admissions: (989)729-3350
Fax: (989)729-3411
E-mail: mike.konopacke@baker.edu
Web Site: http://www.baker.edu/
Description: Independent, 4-year, coed. Part of Baker College System. Awards associate and bachelor's degrees. Founded 1984. Setting: 32-acre

small town campus. Total enrollment: 2,823. Student-undergrad faculty ratio is 50:1. 1,218 applied, 100% were admitted. Students come from 4 states and territories, 0% from out-of-state, 0.3% Native American, 2% Hispanic, 2% black, 0.3% Asian American or Pacific Islander, 0% international, 41% 25 or older, 15% live on campus. Core. Academic remediation for entering students, services for LD students, advanced placement, accelerated degree program, summer session for credit, part-time degree program, external degree program, adult/continuing education programs, co-op programs and internships.

Entrance Requirements: Open admission. Options: Common Application, early admission, deferred admission, international baccalaureate accepted. Required: high school transcript. Entrance: noncompetitive. Application deadline: Rolling.

Costs Per Year: Application fee: $20. Tuition: $6480 full-time, $180 per quarter hour part-time. College room only: $2400.

Collegiate Environment: Orientation program. Student-run newspaper. Most popular organizations: Accounting Club, Travel Club, Management Club, Baker Health Information Management Club, RAD Club. Major annual event: Spirit Day. Student services: personal-psychological counseling. Campus security: 24-hour emergency response devices and patrols, late night transport-escort service, controlled dormitory access. Option: coed housing available. Baker College of Owosso Library with 35,424 books, 71 microform titles, 215 serials, and 344 audiovisual materials. Operations spending for 2004 fiscal year: $244,284. 190 computers available on campus for general student use. A campuswide network can be accessed from off-campus. Staffed computer lab on campus.

■ **BAKER COLLEGE OF PORT HURON** *L-26*
3403 Lapeer Rd.
Port Huron, MI 48060-2597
Tel: (810)985-7000; 888-262-2442
Fax: (810)985-7066
Web Site: http://www.baker.edu/
Description: Independent, 4-year, coed. Part of Baker College System. Awards associate and bachelor's degrees. Founded 1990. Setting: 10-acre urban campus with easy access to Detroit. Total enrollment: 1,578. Student-undergrad faculty ratio is 28:1. 596 applied, 100% were admitted. 0% from out-of-state, 1% Native American, 2% Hispanic, 3% black, 0.4% Asian American or Pacific Islander, 0% international, 51% 25 or older. Core. Academic remediation for entering students, services for LD students, advanced placement, accelerated degree program, independent study, distance learning, double major, summer session for credit, part-time degree program, external degree program, co-op programs and internships.

Entrance Requirements: Open admission. Options: early admission, deferred admission, international baccalaureate accepted. Required: high school transcript, interview. Entrance: noncompetitive. Application deadline: 9/24. Notification: continuous.

Costs Per Year: Application fee: $20. Tuition: $6480 full-time, $180 per quarter hour part-time.

Collegiate Environment: Most popular organizations: Travel Club, Student Association Dental Hygienists of America. Major annual events: Spirit Days, collections for the underprivileged. Student services: personal-psychological counseling. Campus security: 24-hour emergency response devices, late night transport-escort service. College housing not available. Baker College of Port Huron Library with 16,823 books, 181 serials, 135 audiovisual materials, an OPAC, and a Web page. Operations spending for 2004 fiscal year: $99,399. 145 computers available on campus for general student use. A campuswide network can be accessed from off-campus. Staffed computer lab on campus.

■ **BAY MILLS COMMUNITY COLLEGE** *C-11*
12214 West Lakeshore Dr.
Brimley, MI 49715
Tel: (906)248-3354
Free: 800-844-BMCC
Fax: (906)248-3351
Web Site: http://www.bmcc.edu/
Description: District-supported, 2-year, coed. Awards certificates, diplomas, and transfer associate degrees. Founded 1984. Setting: rural campus. Total enrollment: 489. 75% 25 or older. Calendar: semesters. Academic remediation for entering students, part-time degree program, internships.

Entrance Requirements: Open admission. Options: Common Application, early admission. Required: high school transcript. Placement: ACT ASSET required. Entrance: noncompetitive. Application deadline: Rolling.

Costs Per Year: Application fee: $0. State resident tuition: $2040 full-time, $85 per credit hour part-time. Mandatory fees: $300 full-time, $10 per credit hour part-time, $30 per term part-time.

Collegiate Environment: Major annual events: Veteran's Day, Pow Wow. Student services: personal-psychological counseling. Campus security: 24-hour emergency response devices. 60 computers available on campus for general student use. A campuswide network can be accessed. Staffed computer lab on campus.

■ **BAY DE NOC COMMUNITY COLLEGE** *B-14*

2001 North Lincoln Rd.
Escanaba, MI 49829-2511
Tel: (906)786-5802
Free: 800-221-2001
Fax: (906)786-6555
Web Site: http://www.baydenoc.cc.mi.us/

Description: County-supported, 2-year, coed. Part of Michigan Department of Education. Awards certificates, transfer associate, and terminal associate degrees. Founded 1963. Setting: 150-acre rural campus. Endowment: $2.1 million. Total enrollment: 2,549. 10% from top 10% of their high school class, 25% from top quarter, 50% from top half. Students come from 2 states and territories, 2 other countries, 1% from out-of-state, 4% Native American, 0.2% Hispanic, 0.4% black, 0.1% Asian American or Pacific Islander, 0.1% international, 36% 25 or older. Core. Calendar: semesters. Academic remediation for entering students, advanced placement, distance learning, summer session for credit, part-time degree program, adult/continuing education programs, co-op programs and internships.

Entrance Requirements: Open admission. Option: early admission. Required: high school transcript. Placement: ACT COMPASS required. Entrance: noncompetitive. Application deadline: 8/15. Notification: continuous.

Collegiate Environment: Orientation program. Student-run newspaper. Campus security: evening housing security personnel. 100 college housing spaces available; 70 were occupied in 2003-04. No special consideration for freshman housing applicants. Learning Resources Center plus 1 other with 30,000 books and 200 serials. Operations spending for 2004 fiscal year: $373,920. 200 computers available on campus for general student use. A campuswide network can be accessed from off-campus. Staffed computer lab on campus.

Community Environment: An industrial city, Escanaba has an excellent deepwater harbor and mammoth ore docks from which about six million tons of iron ore are shipped annually. Local manufactures include paper, welding machines and lumber products. Part-time employment is available for students. City services include a library, hospital, and major transportation facilities. Recreation includes swimming, boating, golf, tennis, fishing and winter sports.

■ **CALVIN COLLEGE** *L-17*

3201 Burton St., SE
Grand Rapids, MI 49546-4388
Tel: (616)526-6000
Free: 800-688-0122
Admissions: (616)526-6106
Fax: (616)526-8551
E-mail: admissions@calvin.edu
Web Site: http://www.calvin.edu/

Description: Independent, comprehensive, coed, affiliated with Christian Reformed Church. Awards bachelor's and master's degrees. Founded 1876. Setting: 370-acre suburban campus. Endowment: $82.1 million. Research spending for 2004 fiscal year: $1.4 million. Educational spending for 2005 fiscal year: $9543 per student. Total enrollment: 4,177. Faculty: 398 (309 full-time, 89 part-time). Student-undergrad faculty ratio is 12:1. 2,156 applied, 98% were admitted. 26% from top 10% of their high school class, 54% from top quarter, 80% from top half. 19 National Merit Scholars, 41 valedictorians. Full-time: 3,968 students, 54% women, 46% men. Part-time: 157 students, 48% women, 52% men. Students come from 50 states and territories, 45 other countries, 41% from out-of-state, 0.3% Native American, 1% Hispanic, 1% black, 3% Asian American or Pacific Islander, 7% international, 1% 25 or older, 56% live on campus, 2% transferred in. Retention: 88% of full-time freshmen returned the following year. Academic areas with the most degrees conferred: business/marketing; education; health professions and related sciences. Core. Calendar: 4-1-4. Academic remediation for entering students, services for LD students, advanced placement, accelerated degree program, self-designed majors, honors program,

independent study, double major, summer session for credit, part-time degree program, adult/continuing education programs, internships, graduate courses open to undergrads. Off campus study at Council for Christian Colleges and Universities, Central College, Trinity Christian College, Au Sable Institute. Study abroad program. ROTC: Army (c).

Entrance Requirements: Options: Peterson's Universal Application, Common Application, deferred admission, international baccalaureate accepted. Required: essay, high school transcript, minimum 2.5 high school GPA, 1 recommendation, SAT and SAT Subject Tests or ACT. Recommended: interview. Entrance: moderately difficult. Application deadline: 8/15. Notification: continuous.

Costs Per Year: Application fee: $35. Comprehensive fee: $25,735 includes full-time tuition ($18,925), mandatory fees ($225), and college room and board ($6585). College room only: $3580. Full-time tuition and fees vary according to program. Room and board charges vary according to board plan. Part-time tuition: $460 per credit hour. Part-time tuition varies according to course load.

Collegiate Environment: Orientation program. Drama-theater group, choral group, student-run newspaper, radio station. Social organizations: 52 open to all. Most popular organizations: Association for Supervision and Curriculum Development, Environmental Stewardship Coalition, China Club, Young Life, Dance Guild. Major annual events: Rangeela (international student talent showcase), Fall and Spring Music and Arts Festivals, Chaos Day. Student services: health clinic, personal-psychological counseling. Campus security: 24-hour emergency response devices and patrols, student patrols, late night transport-escort service, controlled dormitory access, crime prevention programs, crime alert bulletins. 2,331 college housing spaces available; 2,211 were occupied in 2003-04. Freshmen guaranteed college housing. On-campus residence required through sophomore year. Options: men-only, women-only housing available. Hekman Library plus 1 other with 824,806 books, 790,885 microform titles, 14,464 serials, 26,191 audiovisual materials, an OPAC, and a Web page. Operations spending for 2004 fiscal year: $2 million. 700 computers available on campus for general student use. Computer purchase/lease plans available. A campuswide network can be accessed from student residence rooms and from off campus. Staffed computer lab on campus.

Community Environment: The city of Grand Rapids provides additional service, internship, recreational, and employment opportunities for students in the area's six colleges. It has a lively interest in the arts, as evidenced by an active symphony orchestra, civic theatre, ballet association, and art museum. Recreational opportunities abound with professional hockey, basketball, baseball, and arena football or concerts at DeVos Hall or Van Andel Arena.

■ **CENTRAL MICHIGAN UNIVERSITY** *J-20*

Mount Pleasant, MI 48859
Tel: (989)774-4000; 888-292-5366
Admissions: (989)774-3076
Fax: (989)774-3537
Web Site: http://www.cmich.edu/

Description: State-supported, university, coed. Awards bachelor's, master's, and doctoral degrees and post-master's certificates. Founded 1892. Setting: 854-acre small town campus. Endowment: $59.3 million. Research spending for 2004 fiscal year: $6 million. Educational spending for 2005 fiscal year: $4769 per student. Total enrollment: 27,221. Faculty: 1,095 (704 full-time, 391 part-time). Student-undergrad faculty ratio is 22:1. 13,550 applied, 75% were admitted. 15% from top 10% of their high school class, 38% from top quarter, 75% from top half. Full-time: 17,620 students, 57% women, 43% men. Part-time: 2,377 students, 57% women, 43% men. Students come from 42 states and territories, 39 other countries, 2% from out-of-state, 1% Native American, 2% Hispanic, 6% black, 1% Asian American or Pacific Islander, 1% international, 7% 25 or older, 35% live on campus, 6% transferred in. Retention: 77% of full-time freshmen returned the following year. Academic areas with the most degrees conferred: business/marketing; education; social sciences. Core. Calendar: semesters. Academic remediation for entering students, ESL program, advanced placement, accelerated degree program, self-designed majors, freshman honors college, honors program, independent study, distance learning, double major, summer session for credit, part-time degree program, external degree program, adult/continuing education programs, internships, graduate courses open to undergrads. Study abroad program. ROTC: Army.

Entrance Requirements: Options: Peterson's Universal Application, electronic application, early admission, deferred admission. Required: high school transcript, ACT. Recommended: minimum 3.0 high school GPA.

Required for some: essay, recommendations, interview. Entrance: moderately difficult. Application deadline: Rolling.

Costs Per Year: Application fee: $35. State resident tuition: $5868 full-time, $195.60 per credit part-time. Nonresident tuition: $13,632 full-time, $454.40 per credit part-time. Full-time tuition varies according to student level. Part-time tuition varies according to student level. College room and board: $6376. College room only: $3188. Room and board charges vary according to board plan, housing facility, and location. Tuition guaranteed not to increase for student's term of enrollment.

Collegiate Environment: Orientation program. Drama-theater group, choral group, marching band, student-run newspaper, radio station. Social organizations: 250 open to all; national fraternities, national sororities; 6% of eligible men and 7% of eligible women are members. Most popular organizations: Residence Hall Assembly, Student Government Association, Program Board. Major annual events: Homecoming, Siblings' Weekend, Mainstage. Student services: health clinic, personal-psychological counseling, women's center. Campus security: 24-hour emergency response devices and patrols, student patrols, late night transport-escort service, controlled dormitory access. 5,985 college housing spaces available; 5,975 were occupied in 2003-04. Freshmen guaranteed college housing. Options: coed, men-only, women-only housing available. Charles V. Park Library plus 1 other with 1 million books, 1.3 million microform titles, 3,330 serials, 26,694 audiovisual materials, an OPAC, and a Web page. Operations spending for 2004 fiscal year: $8.3 million. 1,585 computers available on campus for general student use. Computer purchase/lease plans available. A campuswide network can be accessed from student residence rooms and from off campus. Staffed computer lab on campus.

Community Environment: Located in the approximate center of the state, Mount Pleasant is the largest city in the county. Average temperature is 45.6 degrees; rainfall, 26.14; snowfall, 45.7 inches. The area has a hospital, auditoriums, theatres, motels, a public stadium, and its own airport. Ten lakes and a ski range nearby offer excellent recreational facilities. An Indian reservation is located four miles east of the city.

■ **CLEARY UNIVERSITY** *O-5*
3601 Plymouth Rd.
Ann Arbor, MI 48105-2659
Tel: (734)332-4477; 888-5-CLEARY
Admissions: (517)548-3670
Fax: (734)332-4646
Web Site: http://www.cleary.edu/

Description: Independent, comprehensive, coed. Awards associate, bachelor's, and master's degrees. Founded 1883. Setting: 32-acre suburban campus with easy access to Detroit and Lansing. Endowment: $1.7 million. Educational spending for 2005 fiscal year: $750 per student. Total enrollment: 597. Faculty: 106 (12 full-time, 94 part-time). Student-undergrad faculty ratio is 10:1. Students come from 4 states and territories, 6 other countries, 1% from out-of-state, 1% Native American, 1% Hispanic, 7% black, 1% Asian American or Pacific Islander, 0% international, 81% 25 or older. Retention: 67% of full-time freshmen returned the following year. Core. Advanced placement, accelerated degree program, independent study, distance learning, summer session for credit, part-time degree program, adult/continuing education programs, co-op programs and internships.

Entrance Requirements: Options: Common Application, electronic application, early admission, deferred admission, international baccalaureate accepted. Required: high school transcript, minimum 2.0 high school GPA. Recommended: interview. Required for some: essay, 2 recommendations, SAT or ACT, SAT Subject Tests, TOEFL. Entrance: moderately difficult. Application deadline: 8/15.

Costs Per Year: Application fee: $25. Tuition: $13,680 full-time, $285 per quarter hour part-time.

Collegiate Environment: Orientation program. Social organizations: ; 1% of women are members. Campus security: 24-hour emergency response devices. College housing not available. Cleary University Library plus 1 other with 4,500 books, 22 serials, 100 audiovisual materials, an OPAC, and a Web page. Operations spending for 2004 fiscal year: $95,000. 60 computers available on campus for general student use. A campuswide network can be accessed from off-campus. Staffed computer lab on campus.

■ **COLLEGE FOR CREATIVE STUDIES** *O-24*
201 East Kirby
Detroit, MI 48202-4034
Tel: (313)664-7400
Free: 800-952-ARTS

Fax: (313)872-2739
Web Site: http://www.ccscad.edu/

Description: Independent, 4-year, coed. Awards bachelor's degrees. Founded 1926. Setting: 11-acre urban campus. Endowment: $11.8 million. Total enrollment: 1,291. Student-undergrad faculty ratio is 10:1. 598 applied, 60% were admitted. Full-time: 1,067 students, 39% women, 61% men. Part-time: 224 students, 50% women, 50% men. Students come from 35 states and territories, 18 other countries, 17% from out-of-state, 0.5% Native American, 4% Hispanic, 7% black, 5% Asian American or Pacific Islander, 5% international, 22% 25 or older, 23% live on campus, 12% transferred in. Retention: 77% of full-time freshmen returned the following year. Academic area with the most degrees conferred: visual and performing arts. Core. Calendar: semesters. Academic remediation for entering students, ESL program, services for LD students, advanced placement, independent study, double major, summer session for credit, part-time degree program, co-op programs and internships. Off campus study at Association of Independent Colleges of Art and Design.

Entrance Requirements: Options: electronic application, deferred admission. Required: essay, high school transcript, portfolio, SAT or ACT. Recommended: minimum 2.5 high school GPA. Required for some: essay, recommendations, interview. Entrance: moderately difficult. Application deadline: Rolling.

Costs Per Year: Application fee: $35. Tuition: $23,490 full-time, $788 per credit hour part-time. Mandatory fees: $1145 full-time, $563 per term part-time. College room only: $3900.

Collegiate Environment: Orientation program. Major annual events: Annual Student Exhibition, Noel Night. Student services: personal-psychological counseling. Campus security: 24-hour patrols, late night transport-escort service, controlled dormitory access. 300 college housing spaces available; all were occupied in 2003-04. Option: coed housing available. Center for Creative Studies Library with 24,000 books and 75 serials.

■ **CONCORDIA UNIVERSITY** *O-5*
4090 Geddes Rd.
Ann Arbor, MI 48105-2797
Tel: (734)995-7300
Free: 800-253-0680
Admissions: (734)995-7311
Fax: (734)995-4610
E-mail: admissions@ccaa.edu or neumag@cuaa.edu
Web Site: http://www.cuaa.edu/

Description: Independent, comprehensive, coed, affiliated with Lutheran Church-Missouri Synod. Part of Concordia University System. Awards associate, bachelor's, and master's degrees. Founded 1963. Setting: 234-acre suburban campus with easy access to Detroit. Endowment: $5.4 million. Educational spending for 2005 fiscal year: $5608 per student. Total enrollment: 600. Faculty: 85 (35 full-time, 50 part-time). Student-undergrad faculty ratio is 11:1. 550 applied, 82% were admitted. Full-time: 506 students, 56% women, 44% men. Part-time: 53 students, 57% women, 43% men. Students come from 20 states and territories, 2 other countries, 18% from out-of-state, 1% Native American, 2% Hispanic, 10% black, 1% Asian American or Pacific Islander, 1% international, 24% 25 or older, 56% live on campus, 9% transferred in. Retention: 72% of full-time freshmen returned the following year. Academic areas with the most degrees conferred: education; business/marketing; security and protective services. Core. Calendar: semesters. Academic remediation for entering students, services for LD students, advanced placement, accelerated degree program, self-designed majors, independent study, distance learning, double major, summer session for credit, part-time degree program, adult/continuing education programs, internships, graduate courses open to undergrads. Off campus study at Concordia University System. Study abroad program. ROTC: Army (c), Air Force (c).

Entrance Requirements: Options: electronic application, deferred admission. Required: high school transcript, SAT or ACT. Recommended: minimum 2.5 high school GPA, 1 recommendation, ACT. Required for some: essay, interview. Entrance: moderately difficult. Application deadlines: Rolling, Rolling for nonresidents.

Costs Per Year: Application fee: $25. One-time mandatory fee: $100. Comprehensive fee: $25,153 includes full-time tuition ($18,035), mandatory fees ($170), and college room and board ($6948). College room only: $5042. Full-time tuition and fees vary according to course load, degree level, and program. Part-time tuition: $590 per credit hour. Part-time tuition varies according to course load, degree level, and program.

Collegiate Environment: Orientation program. Drama-theater group, choral group, student-run newspaper. Social organizations: 16 open to all. Most

popular organizations: Student Activities Committee, Drama Club, Student Senate, Spiritual Life Committee, off-campus ministries. Major annual events: Lyceum Day, Homecoming, Spring Formal. Student services: health clinic, personal-psychological counseling. Campus security: student patrols, late night transport-escort service. 436 college housing spaces available; 283 were occupied in 2003-04. Freshmen guaranteed college housing. On-campus residence required through sophomore year. Options: men-only, women-only housing available. Zimmerman Library with 120,000 books, 300,000 microform titles, 3,950 serials, 10,500 audiovisual materials, an OPAC, and a Web page. Operations spending for 2004 fiscal year: $334,000. 60 computers available on campus for general student use. A campuswide network can be accessed from student residence rooms and from off campus. Staffed computer lab on campus.

■ **CORNERSTONE UNIVERSITY** *L-17*
1001 East Beltline Ave., NE
Grand Rapids, MI 49525-5897
Tel: (616)949-5300
Free: 800-787-9778
Admissions: (616)222-1426
Fax: (616)222-1540
E-mail: admissions@cornerstone.edu
Web Site: http://www.cornerstone.edu/
Description: Independent nondenominational, comprehensive, coed. Awards associate, bachelor's, master's, and first professional degrees. Founded 1941. Setting: 132-acre suburban campus. Endowment: $5.4 million. Educational spending for 2005 fiscal year: $3597 per student. Total enrollment: 2,515. Faculty: 140 (76 full-time, 64 part-time). Student-undergrad faculty ratio is 15:1. 1,122 applied, 76% were admitted. 16% from top 10% of their high school class, 41% from top quarter, 74% from top half. 1 National Merit Scholar, 17 valedictorians. Full-time: 1,653 students, 63% women, 37% men. Part-time: 519 students, 58% women, 42% men. Students come from 31 states and territories, 1 other country, 5% from out-of-state, 0.5% Native American, 3% Hispanic, 18% black, 1% Asian American or Pacific Islander, 1% international, 6% 25 or older, 56% live on campus, 5% transferred in. Retention: 78% of full-time freshmen returned the following year. Academic areas with the most degrees conferred: education; theology and religious vocations; psychology. Core. Calendar: semesters. Academic remediation for entering students, advanced placement, accelerated degree program, independent study, double major, summer session for credit, part-time degree program, adult/continuing education programs, internships, graduate courses open to undergrads. Off campus study at Calvin College, Reformed Bible College, Grace Bible College. ROTC: Army (c).
Entrance Requirements: Option: deferred admission. Required: essay, high school transcript, minimum 2.5 high school GPA, 1 recommendation, pastoral letter, SAT or ACT. Recommended: interview. Entrance: moderately difficult. Application deadline: Rolling.
Costs Per Year: Application fee: $25. Comprehensive fee: $20,500 includes full-time tuition ($14,700) and college room and board ($5800). College room only: $2650. Room and board charges vary according to board plan. Part-time tuition: $595 per hour. Part-time tuition varies according to course load.
Collegiate Environment: Orientation program. Drama-theater group, choral group, student-run newspaper. Social organizations: 13 open to all. Most popular organizations: student government, Student Education Association, Breakpoint, Student Activities Council. Major annual events: homecoming, Winter Banquet, Spring Splash. Student services: health clinic, personal-psychological counseling. Campus security: 24-hour emergency response devices and patrols, student patrols, late night transport-escort service, controlled dormitory access. College housing designed to accommodate 718 students; 737 undergraduates lived in college housing during 2003-04. Freshmen guaranteed college housing. On-campus residence required through junior year. Options: men-only, women-only housing available. Miller Library with 109,376 books, 287,358 microform titles, 1,073 serials, 19,702 audiovisual materials, an OPAC, and a Web page. Operations spending for 2004 fiscal year: $680,609. 531 computers available on campus for general student use. A campuswide network can be accessed from student residence rooms and from off campus. Staffed computer lab on campus.

■ **DAVENPORT UNIVERSITY (ALMA)** *K-20*
1500 North Pine St.
Alma, MI 48801
Tel: (989)463-8922
Free: 800-632-9569

Fax: (989)463-4540
Web Site: http://www.davenport.edu/
Description: Independent, primarily 2-year, coed. Part of Davenport Educational System. Awards diplomas, transfer associate, terminal associate, and bachelor's degrees. Founded 1977. Total university enrollment: 13,124. Calendar: semesters. ESL program, accelerated degree program, self-designed majors, independent study, distance learning, internships.
Entrance Requirements: Open admission. Option: deferred admission. Entrance: noncompetitive. Application deadline: Rolling. Notification: continuous.
Costs Per Year: Application fee: $25. Tuition: $6216 full-time, $259 per credit hour part-time. Mandatory fees: $120 full-time.

■ **DAVENPORT UNIVERSITY (BAD AXE)** *I-24*
150 Nugent Rd.
Bad Axe, MI 48413
Tel: (989)269-9288
Free: 800-632-9569
Fax: (989)269-2772
Web Site: http://www.davenport.edu/
Description: Independent, primarily 2-year, coed. Part of Davenport Educational System. Awards diplomas, transfer associate, terminal associate, and bachelor's degrees. Founded 1996. Total university enrollment: 13,124. Calendar: semesters. ESL program, accelerated degree program, self-designed majors, independent study, distance learning, internships.
Entrance Requirements: Open admission. Option: deferred admission. Entrance: noncompetitive. Application deadline: Rolling. Notification: continuous.
Costs Per Year: Application fee: $25. Tuition: $6600 full-time, $275 per credit hour part-time. Mandatory fees: $120 full-time.

■ **DAVENPORT UNIVERSITY (BAY CITY)** *J-22*
3930 Traxler Ct.
Bay City, MI 48706
Tel: (989)686-1572
Free: 800-632-9569
Fax: (989)686-2380
Web Site: http://www.davenport.edu/
Description: Independent, primarily 2-year, coed. Part of Davenport Educational System. Awards diplomas, transfer associate, terminal associate, and bachelor's degrees. Founded 1996. Total university enrollment: 13,124. Calendar: semesters. ESL program, accelerated degree program, self-designed majors, independent study, distance learning, internships.
Entrance Requirements: Open admission. Option: deferred admission. Entrance: noncompetitive. Application deadline: Rolling. Notification: continuous.
Costs Per Year: Application fee: $25. Tuition: $6600 full-time, $275 per credit hour part-time. Mandatory fees: $120 full-time.

■ **DAVENPORT UNIVERSITY (CARO)** *J-23*
1231 Cleaver Rd.
Caro, MI 48723
Tel: (989)673-5857
Free: 800-632-9569
Fax: (989)673-7543
Web Site: http://www.davenport.edu/
Description: Independent, primarily 2-year, coed. Part of Davenport Educational System. Awards diplomas, transfer associate, terminal associate, and bachelor's degrees. Founded 1996. Total university enrollment: 13,124. Calendar: semesters. ESL program, accelerated degree program, self-designed majors, independent study, distance learning, internships.
Entrance Requirements: Open admission. Option: deferred admission. Entrance: noncompetitive. Application deadline: Rolling. Notification: continuous.
Costs Per Year: Application fee: $25. Tuition: $6600 full-time, $275 per credit hour part-time. Mandatory fees: $120 full-time.

■ **DAVENPORT UNIVERSITY (DEARBORN)** *O-24*
4801 Oakman Blvd.
Dearborn, MI 48126-3799
Tel: (313)581-4400
Free: 800-632-9569
Admissions: (616)451-3511
Fax: (313)581-1853

E-mail: lynnae.selberg@davenport.edu
Web Site: http://www.davenport.edu/
Description: Independent, comprehensive, coed. Part of Davenport Educational System. Awards associate, bachelor's, and master's degrees. Founded 1985. Setting: 17-acre suburban campus with easy access to Detroit. Endowment: $10.5 million. Educational spending for 2005 fiscal year: $2888 per student. Total enrollment: 12,822. Faculty: 1,096 (130 full-time, 966 part-time). Student-undergrad faculty ratio is 13:1. 1,231 applied, 100% were admitted. Full-time: 3,104 students, 67% women, 33% men. Part-time: 8,962 students, 79% women, 21% men. 2% from out-of-state, 0.5% Native American, 4% Hispanic, 24% black, 1% Asian American or Pacific Islander, 0.1% international. Retention: 61% of full-time freshmen returned the following year. Academic areas with the most degrees conferred: business/marketing; computer and information sciences; health professions and related sciences. Core. Calendar: semesters. Academic remediation for entering students, ESL program, advanced placement, accelerated degree program, self-designed majors, independent study, distance learning, double major, summer session for credit, part-time degree program, co-op programs and internships.
Entrance Requirements: Open admission. Option: deferred admission. Required: high school transcript. Recommended: interview. Entrance: noncompetitive. Application deadline: Rolling. Notification: continuous.
Costs Per Year: Application fee: $25. Tuition: $8760 full-time, $365 per credit hour part-time. Mandatory fees: $120 full-time.
Collegiate Environment: Social organizations: 18 open to all. Most popular organizations: Health Occupations Students of America (HOSA), student newspaper, Student Council, Allman Rafiki Society (ARS), President's Council. Major annual events: Spring Carnival, MLK Volunteer Day, Recognition Dinner. Campus security: late night transport-escort service. 295 computers available on campus for general student use. A campuswide network can be accessed. Staffed computer lab on campus.
Community Environment: See Henry Ford Community College.

■ **DAVENPORT UNIVERSITY (MIDLAND)** *J-21*
3555 East Patrick Rd.
Midland, MI 48642
Tel: (989)835-5588
Free: 800-632-9569
Fax: (989)835-8363
Web Site: http://www.davenport.edu/
Description: Independent, primarily 2-year, coed. Part of Davenport Educational System. Awards certificates, transfer associate, terminal associate, and bachelor's degrees. Founded 1996. Setting: urban campus. Total university enrollment: 13,124. Core. Calendar: semesters. Academic remediation for entering students, ESL program, accelerated degree program, self-designed majors, independent study, distance learning, double major, summer session for credit, part-time degree program, co-op programs and internships.
Entrance Requirements: Open admission. Option: deferred admission. Required: high school transcript. Entrance: noncompetitive. Application deadline: Rolling. Notification: continuous.
Costs Per Year: Application fee: $25. Tuition: $6600 full-time, $275 per credit hour part-time. Mandatory fees: $120 full-time.
Collegiate Environment: Social organizations: 1 open to all. Major annual events: Honors Convocations, Commencement. Campus security: 24-hour emergency response devices. College housing not available. 197 computers available on campus for general student use. A campuswide network can be accessed. Staffed computer lab on campus.

■ **DAVENPORT UNIVERSITY (ROMEO)** *M-24*
71180 Van Dyke Rd.
Romeo, MI 48065
Tel: (586)752-5229
Free: 800-632-9569
Fax: (586)752-5756
Web Site: http://www.davenport.edu/
Description: Independent, primarily 2-year, coed. Part of Davenport Educational System. Awards diplomas, transfer associate, terminal associate, and bachelor's degrees. Founded 1985. Total university enrollment: 13,124. Calendar: semesters. ESL program, accelerated degree program, self-designed majors, independent study, distance learning, internships.
Entrance Requirements: Open admission. Option: deferred admission. Entrance: noncompetitive. Application deadline: Rolling. Notification: continuous.

Costs Per Year: Application fee: $25. Tuition: $6216 full-time, $259 per credit hour part-time. Mandatory fees: $120 full-time.

■ **DAVENPORT UNIVERSITY (SAGINAW)** *K-22*
5300 Bay Rd.
Saginaw, MI 48604
Tel: (989)799-7800
Free: 800-632-9569
Fax: (989)799-9696
Web Site: http://www.davenport.edu/
Description: Independent, primarily 2-year, coed. Part of Davenport Educational System. Awards diplomas, transfer associate, terminal associate, and bachelor's degrees. Founded 1996. Total university enrollment: 13,124. Calendar: semesters. ESL program, accelerated degree program, self-designed majors, independent study, distance learning, internships.
Entrance Requirements: Open admission. Option: deferred admission. Entrance: noncompetitive. Application deadline: Rolling. Notification: continuous.
Costs Per Year: Application fee: $25. Tuition: $6600 full-time, $275 per credit hour part-time. Mandatory fees: $120 full-time.

■ **DELTA COLLEGE** *J-22*
1961 Delta Rd.
University Center, MI 48710
Tel: (989)686-9000
Free: 800-285-1705
Admissions: (989)686-9449
Fax: (989)686-8736
Web Site: http://www.delta.edu/
Description: District-supported, 2-year, coed. Awards certificates, transfer associate, and terminal associate degrees. Founded 1961. Setting: 640-acre rural campus. Endowment: $8.6 million. Educational spending for 2005 fiscal year: $4470 per student. Total enrollment: 10,210. Student-undergrad faculty ratio is 20:1. 4,054 applied, 100% were admitted. Full-time: 3,938 students, 52% women, 48% men. Part-time: 6,272 students, 59% women, 41% men. Students come from 22 other countries, 0% from out-of-state, 1% Native American, 4% Hispanic, 7% black, 1% Asian American or Pacific Islander, 1% international, 34% 25 or older, 4% transferred in. Core. Calendar: semesters. Academic remediation for entering students, services for LD students, advanced placement, self-designed majors, freshman honors college, honors program, independent study, distance learning, double major, summer session for credit, part-time degree program, external degree program, adult/continuing education programs, co-op programs and internships. Off campus study.
Entrance Requirements: Open admission except for international applicants. Options: Common Application, electronic application, early admission, deferred admission. Recommended: high school transcript. Required for some: essay. Entrance: noncompetitive. Application deadline: Rolling.
Costs Per Year: Application fee: $20. Area resident tuition: $1740 full-time, $72.50 per credit hour part-time. State resident tuition: $2496 full-time, $104 per credit hour part-time. Nonresident tuition: $3564 full-time, $148.50 per credit hour part-time. Mandatory fees: $192 full-time, $5.50 per credit part-time, $30 per term part-time.
Collegiate Environment: Student-run newspaper, radio station. Social organizations: 10 open to all. Most popular organizations: intramural activities, Student Senate, Phi Theta Kappa, Inter-Varsity Christian Fellowship, DECA. Major annual events: Earth Day, Bienvenidos, Global Awareness Week. Student services: personal-psychological counseling. Campus security: 24-hour emergency response devices and patrols, student patrols, late night transport-escort service. College housing not available. Library Learning Information Center with 93,167 books, 29,618 microform titles, 400 serials, 4,200 audiovisual materials, an OPAC, and a Web page. Operations spending for 2004 fiscal year: $735,588. 550 computers available on campus for general student use. A campuswide network can be accessed from off-campus. Staffed computer lab on campus.
Community Environment: University Center encompasses the tri-county area of Bay, Midland and Saginaw counties. The area has good shopping, commuter bus service and very active churches. Saginaw Arts Council promotes and encourages the area's cultural and educational organizations. There are excellent part-time employment opportunities for students. Summer and winter sports resort areas are located nearby. Some areas are highly industrialized.

■ **EASTERN MICHIGAN UNIVERSITY** *P-6*
Ypsilanti, MI 48197
Tel: (734)487-1849

Free: 800-GO TO EMU
Admissions: (734)487-3060
Fax: (734)487-1484
Web Site: http://www.emich.edu/
Description: State-supported, comprehensive, coed. Awards bachelor's, master's, and doctoral degrees and post-master's certificates. Founded 1849. Setting: 460-acre suburban campus with easy access to Detroit. Endowment: $39.8 million. Research spending for 2004 fiscal year: $4.9 million. Educational spending for 2005 fiscal year: $4671 per student. Total enrollment: 23,240. Faculty: 1,196 (769 full-time, 427 part-time). Student-undergrad faculty ratio is 19:1. 10,151 applied, 79% were admitted. 12% from top 10% of their high school class, 35% from top quarter, 68% from top half. 18 valedictorians. Full-time: 12,998 students, 60% women, 40% men. Part-time: 5,580 students, 59% women, 41% men. Students come from 43 states and territories, 68 other countries, 7% from out-of-state, 1% Native American, 2% Hispanic, 17% black, 2% Asian American or Pacific Islander, 1% international, 23% 25 or older, 20% live on campus, 9% transferred in. Retention: 73% of full-time freshmen returned the following year. Core. Calendar: semesters. Academic remediation for entering students, ESL program, services for LD students, advanced placement, accelerated degree program, self-designed majors, honors program, independent study, distance learning, double major, summer session for credit, part-time degree program, adult/continuing education programs, co-op programs and internships, graduate courses open to undergrads. Study abroad program. ROTC: Army, Naval (c), Air Force (c).
Entrance Requirements: Options: deferred admission, international baccalaureate accepted. Required: high school transcript, minimum 2.0 high school GPA. Required for some: 1 recommendation, interview, ACT. Entrance: moderately difficult. Notification: continuous.
Costs Per Year: Application fee: $30. State resident tuition: $5463 full-time, $182.10 per credit hour part-time. Nonresident tuition: $16,818 full-time, $560.60 per credit hour part-time. Mandatory fees: $1078 full-time, $33.25 per credit hour part-time, $40 per term part-time. College room and board: $6356.
Collegiate Environment: Orientation program. Drama-theater group, choral group, marching band, student-run newspaper, radio station. Social organizations: 215 open to all; national fraternities, national sororities, local fraternities, local sororities; 8% of eligible men and 12% of eligible women are members. Major annual events: homecoming, Family Weekend, Founders' Day. Student services: health clinic, personal-psychological counseling, women's center. Campus security: 24-hour emergency response devices and patrols, student patrols, late night transport-escort service, controlled dormitory access, bicycle patrols, local police in dormitories, self-defense education, lighted pathways, bike lock lease program. 3,750 college housing spaces available; 3,200 were occupied in 2003-04. No special consideration for freshman housing applicants. On-campus residence required through sophomore year. Options: coed, women-only housing available. Bruce T. Halle Library with 658,648 books, 973,380 microform titles, 4,457 serials, 11,524 audiovisual materials, an OPAC, and a Web page. Operations spending for 2004 fiscal year: $7.2 million. 1,500 computers available on campus for general student use. Computer purchase/lease plans available. A campuswide network can be accessed from student residence rooms and from off campus. Staffed computer lab on campus.
Community Environment: Named for the Greek general of the 1820s Demetrius Ypsilanti, the community became a city in 1858. Ypsilanti is located in southeastern Michigan, approximately 40 miles west of Detroit and 7 miles from Ann Arbor. In addition to the extensive cultural opportunities at Eastern, the resources of the University of Michigan are 15 minutes away and downtown Detroit is a 45 minute drive. Regular bus service is available. Ypsilanti has an impressive historic district (Depot Town) and hosts a Heritage Festival annually in late August.

■ **FERRIS STATE UNIVERSITY** *J-18*
1201 South State St.
Big Rapids, MI 49307
Tel: (231)591-2000
Free: 800-433-7747
Admissions: (231)591-2797
Fax: (231)591-2978
E-mail: admissions@act01.ferris.edu
Web Site: http://www.ferris.edu/
Description: State-supported, comprehensive, coed. Awards associate, bachelor's, master's, and first professional degrees (Associate). Founded 1884. Setting: 850-acre small town campus with easy access to Grand

Rapids. Endowment: $25.2 million. Research spending for 2004 fiscal year: $386,674. Educational spending for 2005 fiscal year: $5939 per student. Total enrollment: 12,547. Faculty: 823 (545 full-time, 278 part-time). Student-undergrad faculty ratio is 17:1. 12,877 applied, 47% were admitted. Full-time: 8,868 students, 45% women, 55% men. Part-time: 2,569 students, 54% women, 46% men. Students come from 43 states and territories, 46 other countries, 4% from out-of-state, 1% Native American, 1% Hispanic, 6% black, 2% Asian American or Pacific Islander, 1% international, 18% 25 or older, 38% live on campus, 12% transferred in. Retention: 70% of full-time freshmen returned the following year. Academic areas with the most degrees conferred: business/marketing; engineering technologies; visual and performing arts. Core. Calendar: semesters. Academic remediation for entering students, ESL program, services for LD students, advanced placement, accelerated degree program, freshman honors college, honors program, independent study, distance learning, double major, summer session for credit, part-time degree program, adult/continuing education programs, co-op programs and internships, graduate courses open to undergrads. Off campus study at Delta College, Henry Ford Community College (CC), Lansing CC, Mott CC, Macomb CC, Macomb CC, St. Clair County CC, North Central Michigan College, Northwestern Michigan College, University Center, Gaylord, Westshore Community College, Muskegon CC, Southwestern Michigan College. Study abroad program. ROTC: Army (c).
Entrance Requirements: Open admission. Options: Peterson's Universal Application, electronic application. Required: high school transcript, minimum 2.35 high school GPA, SAT or ACT. Entrance: minimally difficult. Application deadline: 8/4. Notification: continuous.
Costs Per Year: Application fee: $30. State resident tuition: $6740 full-time, $265 per credit hour part-time. Nonresident tuition: $13,480 full-time, $530 per credit hour part-time. Mandatory fees: $142 full-time. Full-time tuition and fees vary according to reciprocity agreements. College room and board: $6816. College room only: $3462. Room and board charges vary according to board plan and housing facility.
Collegiate Environment: Orientation program. Drama-theater group, choral group, student-run newspaper, radio station. Social organizations: 220 open to all; national fraternities, national sororities, local fraternities, local sororities; 6% of eligible men and 2% of eligible women are members. Most popular organizations: Student Government of Ferris State University, Intramural Sports Club, University theatre, Music Club, Forensics Club. Major annual events: Homecoming, Ferris Fest, January Jams. Student services: health clinic, personal-psychological counseling. Campus security: 24-hour emergency response devices, student patrols, late night transport-escort service. 4,427 college housing spaces available; 4,043 were occupied in 2003-04. Freshmen guaranteed college housing. On-campus residence required through sophomore year. Option: coed housing available. FLITE: Ferris Library for Information, Technology and Education with 344,496 books, 443 microform titles, 21,445 serials, 10,195 audiovisual materials, an OPAC, and a Web page. Operations spending for 2004 fiscal year: $3.7 million. 2,373 computers available on campus for general student use. Computer purchase/lease plans available. A campuswide network can be accessed from student residence rooms and from off campus. Staffed computer lab on campus.
Community Environment: Home for Ferris is Big Rapids, a city of approximately 15,000 residents. The county seat of Mecosta County, Big Rapids is at the junction of U.S. 131 and M-20, 54 miles north of Michigan's second-largest city, Grand Rapids, and within approximately 200 miles of Detroit and Chicago. As one might guess from its name, Big Rapids' primary natural feature is a river, the Muskegon, whose wooded banks wind through town and form the eastern border of the Ferris campus. The former logging community is located in the heart of an extensive recreation area of which Mecosta County, with its 101 lakes and four county parks is a significant part. The city is served by a daily newspaper, one AM and two FM radio stations, a cable television system, a movie theater, roller skating and ice skating rinks, 18-hole college golf course, community pool, diverse commercial districts, four banks, three motels, Holiday Inn Hotel and Conference center, bus lines, 24 churches, a 74-bed hospital, and a community library holding nearly 50,000 volumes.

■ **FINLANDIA UNIVERSITY** *B-4*
601 Quincy St.
Hancock, MI 49930-1882
Tel: (906)482-5300; 877-202-5491
Admissions: (906)487-7311
Fax: (906)487-7300
E-mail: ben.larson@finlandia.edu

Web Site: http://www.finlandia.edu/

Description: Independent, 4-year, coed, affiliated with Evangelical Lutheran Church in America. Awards associate and bachelor's degrees. Founded 1896. Setting: 25-acre small town campus. Endowment: $2.1 million. Educational spending for 2005 fiscal year: $8908 per student. Total enrollment: 548. Student-undergrad faculty ratio is 11:1. 502 applied, 95% were admitted. 5 valedictorians. Full-time: 469 students, 66% women, 34% men. Part-time: 79 students, 70% women, 30% men. Students come from 15 states and territories, 9% from out-of-state, 1% Native American, 0% Hispanic, 1% black, 0% Asian American or Pacific Islander, 5% international, 24% 25 or older, 27% live on campus, 2% transferred in. Retention: 72% of full-time freshmen returned the following year. Academic areas with the most degrees conferred: education; business/marketing; liberal arts/general studies. Core. Calendar: semesters. Academic remediation for entering students, ESL program, services for LD students, advanced placement, accelerated degree program, independent study, distance learning, summer session for credit, part-time degree program, adult/continuing education programs, internships. Off campus study. Study abroad program. ROTC: Army (c), Air Force (c).

Entrance Requirements: Options: Peterson's Universal Application, Common Application, electronic application, early admission, international baccalaureate accepted. Required: essay, high school transcript, minimum 2.0 high school GPA. Recommended: SAT or ACT. Required for some: recommendations, interview. Entrance: minimally difficult. Application deadline: 8/15. Notification: continuous.

Costs Per Year: Application fee: $30. Comprehensive fee: $20,847 includes full-time tuition ($15,434), mandatory fees ($99), and college room and board ($5314). Full-time tuition and fees vary according to program. Room and board charges vary according to housing facility. Part-time tuition: $520 per credit. Part-time mandatory fees: $99 per year. Part-time tuition and fees vary according to course load, degree level, and program.

Collegiate Environment: Orientation program. Drama-theater group, choral group, student-run newspaper. Most popular organizations: Student Senate, Community Action, Campus Enrichment, Hall Government, International Group. Major annual events: Winter Carnival, Campus Play. Student services: personal-psychological counseling. Campus security: 24-hour patrols, late night transport-escort service. 192 college housing spaces available; 143 were occupied in 2003-04. No special consideration for freshman housing applicants. On-campus residence required through junior year. Option: coed housing available. Sulo and Aileen Maki Library with 46,092 books, 1,867 microform titles, 280 serials, 3,570 audiovisual materials, an OPAC, and a Web page. Operations spending for 2004 fiscal year: $162,178. 65 computers available on campus for general student use. Staffed computer lab on campus.

Community Environment: The campus is located near downtown Hancock, within a day's drive of Detroit, Chicago, Milwaukee, Duluth, and Minneapolis. The city, in "Copper County" sprang up amid the region's copper mining industry at the turn of the century. The area still has historical remnants of the mining but it is also know for its autumn when the expansive forests are ablaze with color. Community services include two hospitals, four theaters, and all major civic, fraternal, and service organizations. Recreational activities include fishing, camping, skiing, hunting, golf, hockey, and basketball, as well as the cold water and clean beaches of Lake Superior. Limited off-campus employment is available.

■ **GLEN OAKS COMMUNITY COLLEGE** *P-18*
62249 Shimmel Rd.
Centreville, MI 49032-9719
Tel: (616)467-9945; 888-994-7818
Admissions: (269)467-9945
Fax: (616)467-9068
Web Site: http://www.glenoaks.edu/

Description: State and locally supported, 2-year, coed. Part of Michigan Department of Career Development. Awards certificates, transfer associate, and terminal associate degrees. Founded 1965. Setting: 300-acre rural campus. Endowment: $1.4 million. Total enrollment: 1,710. Full-time: 659 students, 63% women, 37% men. Part-time: 1,051 students, 59% women, 41% men. Students come from 3 states and territories, 6% from out-of-state, 1% Native American, 2% Hispanic, 2% black, 1% Asian American or Pacific Islander, 0.1% international, 53% 25 or older. Core. Calendar: semesters. Academic remediation for entering students, services for LD students, advanced placement, distance learning, summer session for credit, part-time degree program, adult/continuing education programs, internships.

Entrance Requirements: Open admission. Option: Peterson's Universal

Application. Required: high school transcript. Placement: ACT ASSET required. Entrance: noncompetitive. Application deadline: Rolling.

Costs Per Year: Application fee: $0. Area resident tuition: $1800 full-time, $60 per credit hour part-time. State resident tuition: $2670 full-time, $89 per credit hour part-time. Nonresident tuition: $3450 full-time, $114 per credit hour part-time. Mandatory fees: $255 full-time, $7.50 per credit hour part-time, $31 per term part-time.

Collegiate Environment: Social organizations: 5 open to all. Most popular organizations: student government, choir, band, Phi Theta Kappa. Major annual events: College Picnic, Olympics. Student services: personal-psychological counseling. Campus security: 24-hour emergency response devices. College housing not available. E. J. Shaheen Library with 37,087 books, 347 serials, and an OPAC. 50 computers available on campus for general student use. A campuswide network can be accessed. Staffed computer lab on campus.

Community Environment: Glen Oaks is located in the center of St. Joseph County, almost equidistant between Three Rivers and Sturgis, the county's two largest cities. Nestled in the hills of Sherman Township, it overlooks a county population of approximately 60,000 people. The area is primarily agricultural, with heavy-to-light industry focused in Strugis and Three Rivers. Located midway between Chicago and Detroit on the "Chicago Trail," it has the potential for vast economic and population growth. The area also abounds in lakes and rolling hills, affording many opportunities for a variety of recreational activities throughout the year. The citizens are fortunate to be served by modern medical facilities and by well-supported public educational facilities. An energetic civic outreach program provides support for the educational, cultural, civil and economic community and assures its growth and progress.

■ **GOGEBIC COMMUNITY COLLEGE** *C-1*
E-4946 Jackson Rd.
Ironwood, MI 49938
Tel: (906)932-4231
Fax: (906)932-5541
Web Site: http://www.gogebic.edu/

Description: State and locally supported, 2-year, coed. Part of Michigan Department of Education. Awards certificates, transfer associate, and terminal associate degrees. Founded 1932. Setting: 195-acre small town campus. Endowment: $675,000. Total enrollment: 981. Full-time: 517 students, 53% women, 47% men. Part-time: 464 students, 72% women, 28% men. Students come from 7 states and territories, 4 other countries, 22% from out-of-state, 3% Native American, 1% Hispanic, 1% black, 0.4% Asian American or Pacific Islander, 1% international, 3% transferred in. Core. Calendar: semesters. Academic remediation for entering students, services for LD students, advanced placement, honors program, distance learning, summer session for credit, part-time degree program, adult/continuing education programs, co-op programs and internships.

Entrance Requirements: Open admission except nursing program. Options: electronic application, early admission, deferred admission. Required: high school transcript. Entrance: noncompetitive. Application deadlines: Rolling, 8/15 for nonresidents. Notification: continuous.

Costs Per Year: Application fee: $10. Area resident tuition: $2294 full-time, $74 per credit part-time. State resident tuition: $2914 full-time, $94 per credit part-time. Nonresident tuition: $3720 full-time, $120 per credit part-time. Mandatory fees: $442 full-time, $5 per credit part-time. Full-time tuition and fees vary according to course load and reciprocity agreements. Part-time tuition and fees vary according to course load and reciprocity agreements.

Collegiate Environment: Orientation program. Drama-theater group, choral group. Most popular organizations: Drama Club, Student Senate, Phi Theta Kappa, intramural sports. Major annual events: Snow Week, Rock the Z. Student services: personal-psychological counseling. College housing not available. Alex D. Chisholm Learning Resources Center with 22,000 books, 220 serials, an OPAC, and a Web page. 210 computers available on campus for general student use. A campuswide network can be accessed from off-campus. Staffed computer lab on campus.

Community Environment: On the Michigan-Wisconsin border, in the heart of the Midwest ski area, Ironwood is the trading center and lumbering headquarters of the Gogebic Range. The area has refreshing summers and snowy invigorating winters. The city has a library, churches, a hospital, and passenger transportation via air and bus lines. The community has two theatres, hunting, boating, fishing, and excellent skiing for recreation.

■ **GRACE BIBLE COLLEGE** *L-17*
1011 Aldon St. SW
PO Box 910

Grand Rapids, MI 49509-0910
Tel: (616)538-2330
Free: 800-968-1887
Fax: (616)538-0599
Web Site: http://www.gbcol.edu/
Description: Independent, 4-year, coed, affiliated with Grace Gospel Fellowship. Awards associate and bachelor's degrees. Founded 1945. Setting: 16-acre suburban campus. Endowment: $40,134. Educational spending for 2005 fiscal year: $6090 per student. Total enrollment: 161. Student-undergrad faculty ratio is 9:1. 133 applied, 64% were admitted. 15% from top 10% of their high school class, 35% from top quarter, 62% from top half. Full-time: 150 students, 48% women, 52% men. Part-time: 11 students, 45% women, 55% men. Students come from 16 states and territories, 1 other country, 28% from out-of-state, 2% Native American, 1% Hispanic, 2% black, 1% Asian American or Pacific Islander, 1% international, 9% 25 or older, 53% live on campus, 11% transferred in. Retention: 61% of full-time freshmen returned the following year. Academic areas with the most degrees conferred: education; visual and performing arts; communication technologies. Calendar: semesters. Academic remediation for entering students, ESL program, advanced placement, independent study, internships. Off campus study at Grand Rapids Community College, Davenport University, Cornerstone University. ROTC: Army (c).
Entrance Requirements: Options: early admission, deferred admission. Required: high school transcript, 2 recommendations, SAT and SAT Subject Tests or ACT. Recommended: minimum 2.5 high school GPA. Required for some: interview. Entrance: minimally difficult. Application deadline: 7/15. Notification: continuous until 8/1.
Costs Per Year: Application fee: $0. Comprehensive fee: $17,810 includes full-time tuition ($10,450), mandatory fees ($500), and college room and board ($6860). Room and board charges vary according to housing facility. Part-time tuition: $450 per semester hour. Part-time tuition varies according to course load.
Collegiate Environment: Orientation program. Drama-theater group, choral group. Social organizations: 5 open to all. Most popular organizations: Ambassador Fellowship, Student Activities Committee, Student Council, Ambassador Staff, Campus Ministry Team. Major annual events: Campus 'Clean-Up' Days, Fridays at Grace. Student services: personal-psychological counseling. Campus security: student patrols, controlled dormitory access. 104 college housing spaces available; 91 were occupied in 2003-04. Freshmen guaranteed college housing. On-campus residence required through sophomore year. Options: men-only, women-only housing available. Bultema Memorial Library with 39,079 books, 53 microform titles, 183 serials, 2,293 audiovisual materials, and an OPAC. Operations spending for 2004 fiscal year: $65,315. 25 computers available on campus for general student use. A campuswide network can be accessed from student residence rooms. Staffed computer lab on campus.

■ **GRAND RAPIDS COMMUNITY COLLEGE** *L-17*
143 Bostwick Ave., NE
Grand Rapids, MI 49503-3201
Tel: (616)234-4000
Admissions: (616)234-4100
Fax: (616)234-4005
Web Site: http://www.grcc.edu/
Description: District-supported, 2-year, coed. Part of Michigan Department of Education. Awards certificates, transfer associate, and terminal associate degrees. Founded 1914. Setting: 35-acre urban campus. Endowment: $10.3 million. Educational spending for 2005 fiscal year: $3788 per student. Total enrollment: 14,798. Student-undergrad faculty ratio is 25:1. 6,454 applied, 93% were admitted. Full-time: 6,483 students, 49% women, 51% men. Part-time: 8,315 students, 54% women, 46% men. Students come from 13 states and territories, 35 other countries, 1% from out-of-state, 1% Native American, 6% Hispanic, 10% black, 2% Asian American or Pacific Islander, 1% international, 28% 25 or older, 41% transferred in. Retention: 65% of full-time freshmen returned the following year. Academic areas with the most degrees conferred: liberal arts/general studies; health professions and related sciences; personal and culinary services. Core. Calendar: semesters. Academic remediation for entering students, ESL program, services for LD students, advanced placement, distance learning, summer session for credit, part-time degree program, adult/continuing education programs, co-op programs. Off campus study. Study abroad program.
Entrance Requirements: Open admission except for international applicants or allied health programs. Options: early admission, deferred admission. Required: high school transcript. Recommended: SAT or ACT.

Required for some: ACT ASSET. Entrance: noncompetitive. Application deadline: 8/30. Notification: continuous.
Costs Per Year: Application fee: $20. Area resident tuition: $2205 full-time, $73.50 per contact hour part-time. State resident tuition: $4260 full-time, $142 per contact hour part-time. Nonresident tuition: $6060 full-time, $202 per contact hour part-time. Mandatory fees: $100 full-time, $70 per term part-time.
Collegiate Environment: Orientation program. Drama-theater group, choral group, student-run newspaper. Social organizations: 32 open to all; national fraternities, national sororities. Most popular organizations: Student Congress, Phi Theta Kappa, Hispanic Student Organization, Asian Student Organization, Service Learning Advisory Board. Major annual events: Finals Relaxer, Orientation Week, Entertainment Series. Student services: personal-psychological counseling. Campus security: 24-hour emergency response devices, late night transport-escort service. College housing not available. Arthur Andrews Memorial Library plus 1 other with 101,077 books, 10,552 serials, an OPAC, and a Web page. Operations spending for 2004 fiscal year: $1.5 million. 1,048 computers available on campus for general student use. A campuswide network can be accessed from off-campus. Staffed computer lab on campus.
Community Environment: See Calvin College.

■ **GRAND VALLEY STATE UNIVERSITY** *L-16*
1 Campus Dr.
Allendale, MI 49401-9403
Tel: (616)331-5000
Free: 800-748-0246
Admissions: (616)331-2025
Fax: (616)331-2000
E-mail: go2gvsu@gvsu.edu
Web Site: http://www.gvsu.edu/
Description: State-supported, comprehensive, coed. Awards bachelor's and master's degrees and post-master's certificates. Founded 1960. Setting: 900-acre small town campus with easy access to Grand Rapids. Endowment: $42.6 million. Research spending for 2004 fiscal year: $4.1 million. Educational spending for 2005 fiscal year: $4957 per student. Total enrollment: 22,565. Faculty: 1,370 (910 full-time, 460 part-time). Student-undergrad faculty ratio is 18:1. 13,255 applied, 68% were admitted. 22% from top 10% of their high school class, 55% from top quarter, 91% from top half. Full-time: 16,457 students, 61% women, 39% men. Part-time: 2,446 students, 61% women, 39% men. Students come from 55 states and territories, 51 other countries, 4% from out-of-state, 1% Native American, 3% Hispanic, 5% black, 3% Asian American or Pacific Islander, 1% international, 11% 25 or older, 29% live on campus, 8% transferred in. Retention: 82% of full-time freshmen returned the following year. Academic areas with the most degrees conferred: business/marketing; health professions and related sciences; psychology. Core. Calendar: semesters. Academic remediation for entering students, ESL program, services for LD students, advanced placement, accelerated degree program, freshman honors college, honors program, independent study, distance learning, double major, summer session for credit, part-time degree program, adult/continuing education programs, co-op programs and internships, graduate courses open to undergrads. Study abroad program.
Entrance Requirements: Options: Peterson's Universal Application, electronic application. Required: high school transcript, SAT or ACT. Required for some: essay, interview. Entrance: moderately difficult. Application deadline: 5/1. Notification: continuous until 5/1.
Costs Per Year: Application fee: $30. State resident tuition: $6220 full-time, $271 per credit hour part-time. Nonresident tuition: $12,510 full-time, $532 per credit hour part-time. Full-time tuition varies according to course level, program, and student level. Part-time tuition varies according to course level, course load, program, and student level. College room and board: $6360. Room and board charges vary according to board plan, housing facility, and location.
Collegiate Environment: Orientation program. Drama-theater group, choral group, marching band, student-run newspaper, radio station. Social organizations: 136 open to all; national fraternities, national sororities, local fraternities, local sororities; 3% of eligible men and 2% of eligible women are members. Most popular organizations: Black Student Union, Residence Hall Association, Crew Club, Student Senate, Student Organization Network. Major annual events: Family Day, Homecoming. Student services: health clinic, personal-psychological counseling, women's center. Campus security: 24-hour emergency response devices and patrols, student patrols, late night transport-escort service, controlled dormitory access. 5,292 college housing

spaces available; 5,289 were occupied in 2003-04. Freshmen guaranteed college housing. Option: coed housing available. James H. Zumberge Library plus 2 others with 634,000 books, 23,200 microform titles, 5,000 serials, an OPAC, and a Web page. Operations spending for 2004 fiscal year: $6.4 million. 2,600 computers available on campus for general student use. A campuswide network can be accessed from student residence rooms and from off campus. Staffed computer lab on campus.

Community Environment: This is a rural community that has Protestant and Catholic churches and a small library. Many part-time job opportunities are available for students. Allendale has facilities for bowling, water sports, and winter sports. The area features an annual winter carnival and spring arts festival.

■ **GREAT LAKES CHRISTIAN COLLEGE** *M-20*
6211 West Willow Hwy.
Lansing, MI 48917-1299
Tel: (517)321-0242
Free: 800-YES-GLCC
Fax: (517)321-5902
Web Site: http://www.glcc.edu/
Description: Independent, 4-year, coed, affiliated with Christian Churches and Churches of Christ. Awards associate and bachelor's degrees. Founded 1949. Setting: 50-acre suburban campus. Total enrollment: 207. Students come from 8 states and territories, 3 other countries, 1% Hispanic, 6% black, 2% international, 36% 25 or older, 68% live on campus. Retention: 99% of full-time freshmen returned the following year. Core. Calendar: semesters. Advanced placement, independent study, double major, part-time degree program, external degree program, adult/continuing education programs, internships. Off campus study at Cornerstone College, Davenport College of Business.
Entrance Requirements: Options: early admission, deferred admission. Required: essay, high school transcript, minimum 2.25 high school GPA, 3 recommendations, SAT and SAT Subject Tests or ACT. Entrance: moderately difficult. Application deadline: 8/1. Notification: continuous until 8/15.
Costs Per Year: Application fee: $30. Comprehensive fee: $14,898 includes full-time tuition ($8448), mandatory fees ($1250), and college room and board ($5200). Full-time tuition and fees vary according to program, reciprocity agreements, and student level. Room and board charges vary according to board plan and housing facility. Part-time tuition: $264 per hour.
Collegiate Environment: Orientation program. Choral group. Student services: personal-psychological counseling. Campus security: evening security patrols. 139 college housing spaces available; 123 were occupied in 2003-04. On-campus residence required through senior year. Options: men-only, women-only housing available. Louis M. Detro Memorial Library with 34,000 books and 213 serials. 10 computers available on campus for general student use. Staffed computer lab on campus.
Community Environment: See Lansing Community College.

■ **HENRY FORD COMMUNITY COLLEGE** *O-24*
5101 Evergreen Rd.
Dearborn, MI 48128-1495
Tel: (313)845-9615
Fax: (313)845-9658
Web Site: http://www.hfcc.edu/
Description: District-supported, 2-year, coed. Awards certificates, transfer associate, and terminal associate degrees. Founded 1938. Setting: 75-acre suburban campus with easy access to Detroit. Total enrollment: 12,123. Students come from 3 states and territories, 1% Native American, 3% Hispanic, 17% black, 2% Asian American or Pacific Islander, 0.2% international, 44% 25 or older. Core. Calendar: semesters. Academic remediation for entering students, services for LD students, advanced placement, freshman honors college, honors program, summer session for credit, part-time degree program, adult/continuing education programs, co-op programs and internships.
Entrance Requirements: Open admission except for nursing, allied health, honors programs. Options: early admission, deferred admission. Recommended: high school transcript. Placement: ACT recommended. Entrance: noncompetitive. Application deadline: Rolling. Notification: continuous.
Collegiate Environment: Drama-theater group, choral group, student-run newspaper, radio station. Social organizations: 10 open to all. Most popular organizations: Phi Theta Kappa, Student Nurses, Future Teachers, ASAD (American Students of African Descent), Inter-Varsity Christian Fellowship. Major annual events: theater/concerts, Welcome Back Week. Student services: personal-psychological counseling, women's center. Campus

security: 24-hour emergency response devices and patrols, late night transport-escort service. College housing not available. Eshleman Library with 80,000 books, 650 serials, an OPAC, and a Web page. 250 computers available on campus for general student use. A campuswide network can be accessed from off-campus. Staffed computer lab on campus.
Community Environment: Dearborn's boundaries have been extended to join those of Detroit, and it is difficult to discern where one city ends and the other begins. Dearborn is a distinct entity with history, government and industries of its own. The area is called the city with no slums. There are limited job opportunities within the immediate area, though Detroit offers good part-time employment. Camp Dearborn 35 miles northwest offers 6 lakes, a trout stream, picnic groves, a 1/2 mile beach, and camping facilities. Community services include two general hospitals, five public libraries, and limited access to all major forms of public transportation. The city has outstanding public recreation facilities.

■ **HILLSDALE COLLEGE** *P-20*
33 East College St.
Hillsdale, MI 49242-1298
Tel: (517)437-7341
Admissions: (517)607-2327
Fax: (517)437-0190
E-mail: jefflantis@hillsdale.edu
Web Site: http://www.hillsdale.edu/
Description: Independent, 4-year, coed. Awards bachelor's degrees. Founded 1844. Setting: 200-acre small town campus. Endowment: $215 million. Educational spending for 2005 fiscal year: $12,500 per student. Total enrollment: 1,304. Student-undergrad faculty ratio is 10:1. 1,093 applied, 82% were admitted. 39% from top 10% of their high school class, 78% from top quarter, 98% from top half. 11 National Merit Scholars, 42 class presidents, 29 valedictorians, 175 student government officers. Full-time: 1,262 students, 51% women, 49% men. Part-time: 42 students, 81% women, 19% men. Students come from 48 states and territories, 14 other countries, 56% from out-of-state, 99% 25 or older, 83% live on campus, 2% transferred in. Retention: 88% of full-time freshmen returned the following year. Academic areas with the most degrees conferred: business/marketing; education; history. Core. Calendar: semesters. Advanced placement, accelerated degree program, honors program, independent study, double major, summer session for credit, part-time degree program, external degree program, internships. Study abroad program.
Entrance Requirements: Options: Peterson's Universal Application, Common Application, electronic application, early admission, deferred admission, international baccalaureate accepted. Required: essay, high school transcript, minimum 3.15 high school GPA, 1 recommendation, SAT or ACT. Recommended: 2 recommendations, interview, SAT Subject Tests. Required for some: 2 recommendations, interview. Entrance: very difficult. Application deadlines: 2/15, 2/19 for nonresidents, 11/15 for early decision, 1/15 for early action. Notification: continuous until 4/1, 4/1 for nonresidents, 12/1 for early decision, 12/15 for early action.
Costs Per Year: Application fee: $35. Comprehensive fee: $24,160 includes full-time tuition ($17,000), mandatory fees ($410), and college room and board ($6750). College room only: $3350. Room and board charges vary according to board plan. Part-time tuition: $670 per semester hour.
Collegiate Environment: Orientation program. Drama-theater group, choral group, student-run newspaper. Social organizations: 45 open to all; national fraternities, national sororities; 35% of eligible men and 45% of eligible women are members. Most popular organizations: Inter-Varsity Christian Fellowship, Varsity H-Club, Student Federation, Young Life, College Republicans. Major annual events: homecoming, Parents' Weekend, Greek Week. Student services: health clinic, personal-psychological counseling. Campus security: 24-hour emergency response devices and patrols, late night transport-escort service, controlled dormitory access. 900 college housing spaces available; all were occupied in 2003-04. Freshmen guaranteed college housing. On-campus residence required through sophomore year. Options: men-only, women-only housing available. Mossey Learning Center plus 3 others with 240,000 books, 61,400 microform titles, 1,650 serials, 8,000 audiovisual materials, an OPAC, and a Web page. Operations spending for 2004 fiscal year: $1.1 million. 188 computers available on campus for general student use. A campuswide network can be accessed from student residence rooms and from off campus. Staffed computer lab on campus.
Community Environment: Hillsdale is a county seat located in the south central part of the lower peninsula. In an agricultural region, it is a resort and industrial community, manufacturing automobile parts and accessories, and tool and die products. The area has bus service and a municipal airport.

■ **HOPE COLLEGE** *M-16*
141 East 12th St., PO Box 9000
Holland, MI 49422-9000
Tel: (616)395-7000
Free: 800-968-7850
Admissions: (616)395-7850
Fax: (616)395-7130
E-mail: admissions@hope.edu
Web Site: http://www.hope.edu/
Description: Independent, 4-year, coed, affiliated with Reformed Church in America. Awards bachelor's degrees. Founded 1866. Setting: 45-acre small town campus with easy access to Grand Rapids. Endowment: $118.1 million. Research spending for 2004 fiscal year: $5.3 million. Educational spending for 2005 fiscal year: $8300 per student. Total enrollment: 3,141. Student-undergrad faculty ratio is 13:1. 2,674 applied, 77% were admitted. 34% from top 10% of their high school class, 61% from top quarter, 95% from top half. 14 National Merit Scholars. Full-time: 3,029 students, 61% women, 39% men. Part-time: 112 students, 56% women, 44% men. Students come from 47 states and territories, 33 other countries, 25% from out-of-state, 0.4% Native American, 2% Hispanic, 2% black, 2% Asian American or Pacific Islander, 1% international, 67% 25 or older, 79% live on campus, 2% transferred in. Academic areas with the most degrees conferred: education; business/marketing; psychology. Core. Calendar: semesters. ESL program, services for LD students, advanced placement, self-designed majors, independent study, double major, summer session for credit, part-time degree program, internships. Off campus study at members of the Great Lakes Colleges Association, Associated Colleges of the Midwest, Institute of European Studies, Council for International Educational Exchange. Study abroad program. ROTC: Army (c).
Entrance Requirements: Options: Peterson's Universal Application, Common Application, electronic application, early admission, deferred admission, international baccalaureate accepted. Required: essay, high school transcript, SAT or ACT. Recommended: interview. Required for some: 1 recommendation. Entrance: moderately difficult. Application deadline: Rolling. Notification: continuous.
Costs Per Year: Application fee: $35. Comprehensive fee: $28,208 includes full-time tuition ($21,420), mandatory fees ($120), and college room and board ($6668). College room only: $3040. Full-time tuition and fees vary according to course load. Room and board charges vary according to board plan.
Collegiate Environment: Orientation program. Drama-theater group, choral group, student-run newspaper, radio station. Social organizations: 67 open to all; local fraternities, local sororities; 6% of eligible men and 15% of eligible women are members. Most popular organizations: Fellowship of Christian Athletes, Social Activities Committee. Major annual events: Winter Fantasia, Casino Night, All-College Sing. Student services: health clinic, personal-psychological counseling. Campus security: 24-hour emergency response devices and patrols, late night transport-escort service, controlled dormitory access. College housing designed to accommodate 2,265 students; 2,275 undergraduates lived in college housing during 2003-04. Freshmen guaranteed college housing. On-campus residence required through junior year. Options: coed, men-only, women-only housing available. Van Wylen Library plus 1 other with 358,329 books, 385,597 microform titles, 2,878 serials, 13,263 audiovisual materials, an OPAC, and a Web page. Operations spending for 2004 fiscal year: $2.5 million. 300 computers available on campus for general student use. Computer purchase/lease plans available. A campuswide network can be accessed from student residence rooms and from off campus. Staffed computer lab on campus.
Community Environment: Settled by the Dutch in 1847, the city still has many of the characteristics of a Dutch town. This is the tulip center of America, and millions of these flowers bloom in the parks and residential sections during May. Located on Lake Macatawa and Lake Michigan, the area offers many opportunities for water and other outdoor sports activities. Holland is surrounded by a large fruit-growing and farming area, and is also an industrial and resort town. The city has bus and train service, two airports, a public library, several churches, a hospital and several parks. The Greater Holland area has a population of approximately 90,000; it is a very friendly, safe and clean community.

■ **ITT TECHNICAL INSTITUTE (CANTON)** *O-8*
1905 South Haggerty Rd.
Canton, MI 48188-2025
Tel: (734)397-7800
Free: 800-247-4477

Fax: (734)397-1945
Web Site: http://www.itt-tech.edu/
Description: Proprietary, 2-year, coed. Part of ITT Educational Services, Inc. Awards terminal associate degrees. Founded 2002. Core.
Entrance Requirements: Option: deferred admission. Required: high school transcript, interview. Recommended: recommendations. Entrance: minimally difficult. Application deadline: Rolling. Notification: continuous.
Costs Per Year: Application fee: $100.
Collegiate Environment: Orientation program. College housing not available.

■ **ITT TECHNICAL INSTITUTE (GRAND RAPIDS)** *L-17*
4020 Sparks Dr., SE
Grand Rapids, MI 49546
Tel: (616)956-1060
Web Site: http://www.itt-tech.edu/
Description: Proprietary, 2-year, coed. Part of ITT Educational Services, Inc. Awards terminal associate degrees. Core.
Entrance Requirements: Option: deferred admission. Required: high school transcript, interview, Wonderlic aptitude test. Recommended: recommendations. Entrance: minimally difficult. Application deadline: Rolling. Notification: continuous.
Costs Per Year: Application fee: $100.
Collegiate Environment: Orientation program. College housing not available.

■ **ITT TECHNICAL INSTITUTE (TROY)** *L-10*
1522 East Big Beaver Rd.
Troy, MI 48083-1905
Tel: (248)524-1800
Web Site: http://www.itt-tech.edu/
Description: Proprietary, 2-year, coed. Part of ITT Educational Services, Inc. Awards terminal associate degrees. Founded 1987. Core.
Entrance Requirements: Option: deferred admission. Required: high school transcript, interview, Wonderlic aptitude test. Recommended: recommendations. Entrance: minimally difficult. Application deadline: Rolling. Notification: continuous.
Costs Per Year: Application fee: $100.
Collegiate Environment: Orientation program. College housing not available.

■ **JACKSON COMMUNITY COLLEGE** *O-21*
2111 Emmons Rd.
Jackson, MI 49201-8399
Tel: (517)787-0800; 888-522-7344
Admissions: (517)796-8425
Web Site: http://www.jccmi.edu
Description: County-supported, 2-year, coed. Awards certificates, transfer associate, and terminal associate degrees. Founded 1928. Setting: 580-acre suburban campus with easy access to Detroit. Endowment: $10.7 million. Total enrollment: 5,870. Student-undergrad faculty ratio is 19:1. Full-time: 2,108 students, 59% women, 41% men. Part-time: 3,762 students, 67% women, 33% men. 1% from out-of-state, 1% Native American, 4% Hispanic, 5% black, 1% Asian American or Pacific Islander, 0.1% international, 44% 25 or older. Retention: 65% of full-time freshmen returned the following year. Core. Calendar: semesters. Academic remediation for entering students, ESL program, services for LD students, advanced placement, independent study, distance learning, summer session for credit, part-time degree program, adult/continuing education programs, co-op programs and internships.
Entrance Requirements: Open admission except for allied health programs. Options: Peterson's Universal Application, electronic application, early admission. Entrance: noncompetitive. Application deadline: Rolling. Notification: continuous.
Costs Per Year: Application fee: $0. Area resident tuition: $1776 full-time, $74 per credit hour part-time. State resident tuition: $2496 full-time, $104 per credit hour part-time. Nonresident tuition: $3192 full-time, $133 per credit hour part-time. Mandatory fees: $384 full-time, $4.50 per credit hour part-time, $18 per term part-time. Full-time tuition and fees vary according to location. Part-time tuition and fees vary according to location.
Collegiate Environment: Orientation program. Drama-theater group, choral group, student-run newspaper. Social organizations: 16 open to all. Major annual event: Fall Semester Welcome Picnic. Campus security: 24-hour patrols. College housing not available. Atkinson Learning Resources Center

plus 1 other with 67,000 books, 24,000 microform titles, 300 serials, 2,000 audiovisual materials, an OPAC, and a Web page. 356 computers available on campus for general student use. A campuswide network can be accessed from off-campus. Staffed computer lab on campus.

Community Environment: The college is located seven miles south of Jackson, an important industrial city that manufactures mainly automobile and airplane parts and supplies. Major highways provide access to Chicago and Detroit. The county has numerous lakes, golf courses and parks. Cultural activities include a symphony orchestra, music, and dance and theater groups. Also located in the area are the Illuminated Cascades, the Ella Sharp Museum and the Michigan Space and Science Center.

■ **KALAMAZOO COLLEGE** *O-17*
1200 Academy St.
Kalamazoo, MI 49006-3295
Tel: (269)337-7000
Free: 800-253-3602
Admissions: (269)337-7166
Fax: (269)337-7251
E-mail: admissions@kzoo.edu
Web Site: http://www.kzoo.edu/
Description: Independent, 4-year, coed, affiliated with American Baptist Churches in the U.S.A.. Awards bachelor's degrees. Founded 1833. Setting: 60-acre suburban campus. Endowment: $135.5 million. Educational spending for 2005 fiscal year: $10,537 per student. Total enrollment: 1,263. Student-undergrad faculty ratio is 12:1. 1,669 applied, 68% were admitted. 43% from top 10% of their high school class, 72% from top quarter, 97% from top half. 8 National Merit Scholars, 16 valedictorians. Full-time: 1,263 students, 57% women, 43% men. Students come from 38 states and territories, 13 other countries, 27% from out-of-state, 0.1% Native American, 2% Hispanic, 2% black, 5% Asian American or Pacific Islander, 2% international, 0% 25 or older, 75% live on campus, 1% transferred in. Retention: 86% of full-time freshmen returned the following year. Academic areas with the most degrees conferred: social sciences; biological/life sciences; English. Core. Services for LD students, advanced placement, independent study, double major, internships. Off campus study at Western Michigan University. Study abroad program. ROTC: Army (c).
Entrance Requirements: Options: Peterson's Universal Application, Common Application, electronic application, early decision, early action, deferred admission, international baccalaureate accepted. Required: essay, high school transcript, 2 recommendations, SAT or ACT. Recommended: minimum 3.0 high school GPA, interview. Entrance: very difficult. Application deadlines: 2/15, 11/15 for early decision, 12/1 for early action. Notification: 4/1, 12/1 for early decision, 12/20 for early action.
Costs Per Year: Application fee: $35. Comprehensive fee: $32,353 includes full-time tuition ($25,644) and college room and board ($6709). College room only: $3273. Room and board charges vary according to board plan.
Collegiate Environment: Orientation program. Drama-theater group, choral group, student-run newspaper, radio station. Social organizations: 50 open to all. Most popular organizations: Student Activities Committee, Student Commission, Index (college newspaper), Inter-Varsity Christian Fellowship, Project Brave Volunteer Organization. Major annual events: homecoming, Monte Carlo Night, Spring Fling. Student services: health clinic, personal-psychological counseling, women's center. Campus security: 24-hour emergency response devices and patrols, late night transport-escort service, controlled dormitory access. 855 college housing spaces available; 746 were occupied in 2003-04. On-campus residence required in freshman year. Option: coed housing available. Upjohn Library plus 1 other with 342,939 books, 23,862 microform titles, 1,495 serials, 6,967 audiovisual materials, an OPAC, and a Web page. Operations spending for 2004 fiscal year: $1.4 million. 130 computers available on campus for general student use. A campuswide network can be accessed from student residence rooms and from off campus. Staffed computer lab on campus.
Community Environment: Kalamazoo is a college-centered community, 130 miles from Detroit and Chicago. The airport serves nine major airlines. Locally, many companies, hospitals and local governments make internships available to students.

■ **KALAMAZOO VALLEY COMMUNITY COLLEGE** *O-17*
PO Box 4070
Kalamazoo, MI 49003-4070
Tel: (269)488-4400
Admissions: (269)488-4207
Fax: (269)448-4555

Web Site: http://www.kvcc.edu/
Description: State and locally supported, 2-year, coed. Awards certificates, transfer associate, and terminal associate degrees. Founded 1966. Setting: 187-acre suburban campus. Total enrollment: 10,634. Full-time: 3,959 students, 50% women, 50% men. Part-time: 6,675 students, 55% women, 45% men. Students come from 3 states and territories, 46 other countries, 1% from out-of-state, 1% Native American, 3% Hispanic, 9% black, 1% Asian American or Pacific Islander, 1% international, 50% 25 or older. Core. Calendar: semesters. Academic remediation for entering students, ESL program, services for LD students, advanced placement, self-designed majors, honors program, independent study, distance learning, summer session for credit, part-time degree program, co-op programs and internships. Off campus study at 5 members of the Kalamazoo Consortium. ROTC: Army (c).
Entrance Requirements: Open admission. Options: early admission, deferred admission. Placement: ACT recommended. Entrance: noncompetitive. Application deadline: Rolling. Notification: continuous.
Costs Per Year: Application fee: $0. Area resident tuition: $1320 full-time, $55 per credit part-time. State resident tuition: $2256 full-time, $94 per credit part-time. Nonresident tuition: $3072 full-time, $128 per credit part-time.
Collegiate Environment: Orientation program. Choral group, student-run newspaper. Social organizations: 20 open to all. Student services: personal-psychological counseling, women's center. Campus security: 24-hour emergency response devices and patrols, late night transport-escort service. College housing not available. Kalamazoo Valley Community College Library with 88,791 books, 420 serials, an OPAC, and a Web page. 1,000 computers available on campus for general student use. A campuswide network can be accessed from off-campus. Staffed computer lab on campus.
Community Environment: See Western Michigan University.

■ **KELLOGG COMMUNITY COLLEGE** *O-19*
450 North Ave.
Battle Creek, MI 49017-3397
Tel: (616)965-3931
Admissions: (269)965-3931
Fax: (616)965-4133
Web Site: http://www.kellogg.edu/
Description: State and locally supported, 2-year, coed. Part of Michigan Department of Education. Awards certificates, transfer associate, and terminal associate degrees. Founded 1956. Setting: 120-acre urban campus. Endowment: $91,005. Research spending for 2004 fiscal year: $103,704. Educational spending for 2005 fiscal year: $4395 per student. Total enrollment: 6,200. Student-undergrad faculty ratio is 22:1. 2,085 applied, 87% were admitted. Full-time: 1,954 students, 60% women, 40% men. Part-time: 4,246 students, 65% women, 35% men. Students come from 3 states and territories, 11 other countries, 1% from out-of-state, 1% Native American, 2% Hispanic, 7% black, 1% Asian American or Pacific Islander, 1% international, 47% 25 or older, 3% transferred in. Core. Calendar: semesters. Academic remediation for entering students, services for LD students, advanced placement, accelerated degree program, freshman honors college, honors program, independent study, distance learning, double major, summer session for credit, part-time degree program, adult/continuing education programs, internships. Off campus study at Kalamazoo Valley Community College, Southwestern Michigan College, Lake Michigan College, Jackson Community College.
Entrance Requirements: Open admission except for allied health programs. Options: Common Application, early admission, deferred admission. Required for some: high school transcript, minimum 2.0 high school GPA, ACT, SAT or ACT. Entrance: noncompetitive. Application deadline: 8/30. Notification: continuous.
Costs Per Year: Application fee: $0. Area resident tuition: $1950 full-time, $65 per credit hour part-time. State resident tuition: $3165 full-time, $105.50 per credit hour part-time. Nonresident tuition: $4770 full-time, $159 per credit hour part-time. Mandatory fees: $210 full-time, $7 per credit hour part-time.
Collegiate Environment: Orientation program. Drama-theater group, choral group, student-run newspaper. Social organizations: 23 open to all. Most popular organizations: Tech Club, Phi Theta Kappa, Student Nurses Association, Crude Arts Club, Art League. Major annual events: KCC Family Fest, Leadership Conference, Blood Drive. Campus security: 24-hour emergency response devices and patrols, late night transport-escort service. College housing not available. Emory W. Morris Learning Resource Center with 42,131 books, 78,179 microform titles, 172 serials, 4,145 audiovisual materials, an OPAC, and a Web page. Operations spending for 2004 fiscal

year: $747,172. 550 computers available on campus for general student use. A campuswide network can be accessed from off-campus. Staffed computer lab on campus.

Community Environment: This is the home of cereal manufacturers. Other manufacturers produce packaging machines and auto parts. Commercial passenger facilities include bus, rail, and air. Some part-time employment is available for students. The city has good recreational areas for picnicking, golf, camping, tobogganing and skiing. All are easily accessible. The American Amateur Baseball Series is held here annually.

■ KETTERING UNIVERSITY *L-23*
1700 West Third Ave.
Flint, MI 48504-4898
Tel: (810)762-9500
Free: 800-955-4464
Admissions: (810)762-7865
Fax: (810)762-9837
E-mail: admissions@kettering.edu
Web Site: http://www.kettering.edu/

Description: Independent, comprehensive, coed. Awards bachelor's and master's degrees. Founded 1919. Setting: 85-acre suburban campus with easy access to Detroit. Endowment: $51.7 million. Research spending for 2004 fiscal year: $1.5 million. Educational spending for 2005 fiscal year: $7221 per student. Total enrollment: 2,935. Faculty: 157 (140 full-time, 17 part-time). Student-undergrad faculty ratio is 11:1. 2,127 applied, 73% were admitted. 31% from top 10% of their high school class, 62% from top quarter, 91% from top half. 18 valedictorians. Full-time: 2,411 students, 15% women, 85% men. Students come from 52 states and territories, 17 other countries, 37% from out-of-state, 0.2% Native American, 2% Hispanic, 5% black, 5% Asian American or Pacific Islander, 2% international, 3% 25 or older, 48% live on campus, 2% transferred in. Retention: 87% of full-time freshmen returned the following year. Academic areas with the most degrees conferred: engineering; business/marketing; computer and information sciences. Core. Calendar: semesters (11 weeks of full-time study plus 12 weeks of paid co-op experience per semester). Services for LD students, advanced placement, accelerated degree program, independent study, distance learning, double major, co-op programs and internships, graduate courses open to undergrads. Study abroad program.

Entrance Requirements: Options: Peterson's Universal Application, electronic application, deferred admission, international baccalaureate accepted. Required: high school transcript, SAT or ACT. Recommended: minimum 3.0 high school GPA, interview, SAT Subject Tests. Required for some: essay. Entrance: very difficult. Application deadline: Rolling. Notification: continuous.

Costs Per Year: Application fee: $35. Comprehensive fee: $29,188 includes full-time tuition ($23,360), mandatory fees ($388), and college room and board ($5440). College room only: $3432. Room and board charges vary according to student level. Part-time tuition: $730 per credit.

Collegiate Environment: Orientation program. Drama-theater group, choral group, student-run newspaper, radio station. Social organizations: 40 open to all; national fraternities, national sororities; 40% of eligible men and 33% of eligible women are members. Most popular organizations: student government, Society of Automotive Engineers, National Society of Black Engineers, Outdoors Club, Christians in Action. Major annual events: Greek Week, Spring Homecoming, Midnight Breakfast. Student services: health clinic, personal-psychological counseling, women's center. Campus security: 24-hour emergency response devices and patrols, late night transport-escort service, controlled dormitory access. 623 college housing spaces available; all were occupied in 2003-04. Freshmen guaranteed college housing. On-campus residence required in freshman year. Option: coed housing available. Kettering University Library plus 1 other with 122,000 books, 35,000 microform titles, 1,200 serials, 800 audiovisual materials, an OPAC, and a Web page. Operations spending for 2004 fiscal year: $981,830. 300 computers available on campus for general student use. A campuswide network can be accessed from student residence rooms and from off campus. Staffed computer lab on campus.

Community Environment: A pioneer in the early days of the automobile industry, Flint is located about one hour north of Detroit and within an hour of Ann Arbor and East Lansing. Commercial transportation is provided by air, bus, and rail lines. The Flint area has several hospitals, churches of most faiths, the Flint Cultural Center with museums and institutes of arts and music, and shopping. Recreational facilities are abundant, from the university Recreation Center and playing fields, to nearby golf courses, ski slopes, lakes, theatres, and more.

■ KIRTLAND COMMUNITY COLLEGE *G-20*
10775 North St Helen Rd.
Roscommon, MI 48653-9699
Tel: (989)275-5000
Fax: (989)275-8210
Web Site: http://www.kirtland.edu/

Description: District-supported, 2-year, coed. Part of Michigan Department of Education. Awards certificates, transfer associate, and terminal associate degrees. Founded 1966. Setting: 180-acre rural campus. Total enrollment: 1,918. 355 applied, 100% were admitted. Full-time: 609 students, 59% women, 41% men. Part-time: 1,309 students, 58% women, 42% men. 1% Native American, 1% Hispanic, 1% black, 0.1% Asian American or Pacific Islander, 0.1% international, 52% 25 or older. Core. Calendar: semesters. Academic remediation for entering students, services for LD students, advanced placement, summer session for credit, part-time degree program, adult/continuing education programs, co-op programs and internships.

Entrance Requirements: Open admission. Options: early admission, deferred admission. Placement: ACT ASSET required; SAT or ACT recommended. Entrance: noncompetitive. Application deadline: Rolling. Notification: continuous until 8/22.

Collegiate Environment: Drama-theater group, choral group, student-run newspaper. Student services: personal-psychological counseling. Campus security: student patrols, late night transport-escort service. Kirtland Community College Library with 35,000 books and 317 serials. 125 computers available on campus for general student use.

Community Environment: The college is located in the heart of Michigan's four-season vacationland amidst excellent hunting, fishing, swimming, boating, skiing and snowmobiling lands and lakes. Interstate Route I-75 provides the most direct means of approach to within twelve miles of the campus, which is located at the juncture of Roscommon, Ogemaw, Oscoda and Crawford counties on County Road F-97.

■ KUYPER COLLEGE *L-17*
3333 East Beltline, NE
Grand Rapids, MI 49525-9749
Tel: (616)222-3000
Free: 800-511-3749
Admissions: (616)988-3695
Fax: (616)222-3045
E-mail: llighthiser@kuyper.edu
Web Site: http://www.kuyper.edu/

Description: Independent religious, 4-year, coed. Awards associate and bachelor's degrees. Founded 1939. Setting: 34-acre suburban campus. Endowment: $7.5 million. Educational spending for 2005 fiscal year: $7002 per student. Total enrollment: 274. Student-undergrad faculty ratio is 15:1. 233 applied, 61% were admitted. 3% from top 10% of their high school class, 17% from top quarter, 42% from top half. Full-time: 220 students, 59% women, 41% men. Part-time: 50 students, 48% women, 52% men. Students come from 21 states and territories, 11 other countries, 10% from out-of-state, 0% Native American, 3% Hispanic, 3% black, 3% Asian American or Pacific Islander, 8% international, 18% 25 or older, 44% live on campus, 11% transferred in. Retention: 64% of full-time freshmen returned the following year. Academic areas with the most degrees conferred: theology and religious vocations; public administration and social services; education. Core. Calendar: semesters. Academic remediation for entering students, ESL program, services for LD students, advanced placement, independent study, double major, summer session for credit, part-time degree program, adult/continuing education programs, co-op programs and internships. Off campus study at Grand Rapids Community College, Cornerstone University, Calvin College. Study abroad program.

Entrance Requirements: Options: Peterson's Universal Application, Common Application, electronic application, deferred admission. Required: essay, high school transcript, minimum 2.5 high school GPA, SAT or ACT. Required for some: interview. Entrance: moderately difficult. Application deadline: Rolling.

Costs Per Year: Application fee: $25. Comprehensive fee: $17,908 includes full-time tuition ($11,700), mandatory fees ($508), and college room and board ($5700). College room only: $2300. Full-time tuition and fees vary according to course load and student level. Room and board charges vary according to board plan, housing facility, and student level. Part-time tuition: $525 per credit hour. Part-time tuition varies according to course load.

Collegiate Environment: Orientation program. Drama-theater group, choral group. Social organizations: 9 open to all. Most popular organizations: Bible study and prayer groups, Student Council, yearbook, Wellspring Drama

Club. Major annual events: Christmas Banquet, Fall Retreat, Mall Madness. Student services: health clinic, personal-psychological counseling. Campus security: student patrols, late night transport-escort service, controlled dormitory access. 160 college housing spaces available; 127 were occupied in 2003-04. Freshmen guaranteed college housing. On-campus residence required through sophomore year. Zondervan Library with 56,177 books, 4,866 microform titles, 254 serials, 6,833 audiovisual materials, an OPAC, and a Web page. Operations spending for 2004 fiscal year: $168,195. 56 computers available on campus for general student use. A campuswide network can be accessed from student residence rooms and from off campus. Staffed computer lab on campus.

Community Environment: See Calvin College.

■ **LAKE MICHIGAN COLLEGE** *O-15*

2755 East Napier

Benton Harbor, MI 49022-1899

Tel: (616)927-8100

Admissions: (269)927-8120

Web Site: http://www.lmc.cc.mi.us/

Description: District-supported, 2-year, coed. Part of Michigan Department of Education. Awards certificates, transfer associate, and terminal associate degrees. Founded 1946. Setting: 260-acre small town campus. Endowment: $5 million. Educational spending for 2005 fiscal year: $3309 per student. Total enrollment: 4,043. Student-undergrad faculty ratio is 18:1. 826 applied, 76% were admitted. 3% from top 10% of their high school class, 12% from top quarter, 40% from top half. Full-time: 1,235 students, 56% women, 44% men. Part-time: 2,808 students, 63% women, 38% men. Students come from 5 states and territories, 2% from out-of-state, 1% Native American, 4% Hispanic, 15% black, 2% Asian American or Pacific Islander, 1% international, 56% 25 or older. Core. Calendar: semesters. Academic remediation for entering students, self-designed majors, honors program, summer session for credit, part-time degree program, adult/continuing education programs.

Entrance Requirements: Open admission. Options: Common Application, early admission, deferred admission. Required: high school transcript. Required for some: interview. Entrance: noncompetitive. Application deadline: Rolling. Notification: continuous.

Costs Per Year: Application fee: $0. Area resident tuition: $2175 full-time, $72.50 per credit hour part-time. State resident tuition: $3060 full-time, $102 per credit hour part-time. Nonresident tuition: $4080 full-time, $136 per credit hour part-time. Mandatory fees: $930 full-time, $31 per credit hour part-time.

Collegiate Environment: Drama-theater group, choral group. Most popular organizations: Hospitality Club, International Club, Pride Club II, DECA. Major annual event: Winner Within Scholarship Auction. Student services: personal-psychological counseling, women's center. College housing not available. Lake Michigan College Library with 79,000 books and 280 serials. Operations spending for 2004 fiscal year: $276,507. 124 computers available on campus for general student use.

■ **LAKE SUPERIOR STATE UNIVERSITY** *C-11*

650 W Easterday Ave.

Sault Sainte Marie, MI 49783

Tel: (906)632-6841; 888-800-LSSU

Admissions: (906)635-2231

Fax: (906)635-6669

E-mail: admissions@lssu.edu

Web Site: http://www.lssu.edu/

Description: State-supported, 4-year, coed. Awards associate, bachelor's, and master's degrees. Founded 1946. Setting: 121-acre small town campus. Endowment: $9.7 million. Research spending for 2004 fiscal year: $312,131. Educational spending for 2005 fiscal year: $4660 per student. Total enrollment: 2,888. Faculty: 211 (112 full-time, 99 part-time). Student-undergrad faculty ratio is 17:1. 1,566 applied, 85% were admitted. 9% from top 10% of their high school class, 28% from top quarter, 60% from top half. Full-time: 2,315 students, 49% women, 51% men. Part-time: 573 students, 59% women, 41% men. Students come from 20 states and territories, 12 other countries, 17% from out-of-state, 9% Native American, 1% Hispanic, 1% black, 1% Asian American or Pacific Islander, 11% international, 26% 25 or older, 29% live on campus, 9% transferred in. Retention: 61% of full-time freshmen returned the following year. Academic areas with the most degrees conferred: security and protective services; business/marketing; engineering. Core. Calendar: semesters. Services for LD students, advanced placement, self-designed majors, freshman honors college, honors program,

independent study, distance learning, double major, summer session for credit, part-time degree program, adult/continuing education programs, co-op programs and internships.

Entrance Requirements: Options: Peterson's Universal Application, deferred admission. Required: high school transcript, ACT. Required for some: minimum 2.0 high school GPA. Entrance: moderately difficult. Application deadline: 8/15. Notification: continuous.

Costs Per Year: Application fee: $20. State resident tuition: $5988 full-time, $249.50 per credit hour part-time. Nonresident tuition: $11,976 full-time, $499 per credit hour part-time. Mandatory fees: $318 full-time, $7 per credit hour part-time, $75 per term part-time. Full-time tuition and fees vary according to reciprocity agreements. Part-time tuition and fees vary according to course load and reciprocity agreements. College room and board: $6536. Room and board charges vary according to board plan and housing facility.

Collegiate Environment: Orientation program. Drama-theater group, choral group, student-run newspaper, radio station. Social organizations: 14 open to all; national fraternities, national sororities, local fraternities, local sororities. Major annual events: Winter Carnival, Beach Party. Student services: health clinic, personal-psychological counseling. Campus security: 24-hour patrols, student patrols, late night transport-escort service. On-campus residence required through sophomore year. Options: coed, men-only, women-only housing available. Kenneth Shouldice Library with 200,449 books, 139,742 microform titles, 850 serials, 594 audiovisual materials, and an OPAC. Operations spending for 2004 fiscal year: $887,578. 350 computers available on campus for general student use. A campuswide network can be accessed from off-campus. Staffed computer lab on campus.

■ **LANSING COMMUNITY COLLEGE** *M-20*

PO Box 40010

Lansing, MI 48901-7210

Tel: (517)483-1957

Free: 800-644-4LCC

Admissions: (517)483-9886

Fax: (517)483-9668

E-mail: grossbt@lcc.edu

Web Site: http://www.lcc.edu/

Description: State and locally supported, 2-year, coed. Part of Michigan Department of Education. Awards certificates, transfer associate, and terminal associate degrees. Founded 1957. Setting: 28-acre urban campus. Endowment: $3.5 million. Educational spending for 2005 fiscal year: $3331 per student. Total enrollment: 20,057. Student-undergrad faculty ratio is 14:1. 3,322 applied, 100% were admitted. Full-time: 6,154 students, 52% women, 48% men. Part-time: 13,903 students, 57% women, 43% men. Students come from 29 states and territories, 69 other countries, 1% from out-of-state, 1% Native American, 4% Hispanic, 9% black, 2% Asian American or Pacific Islander, 2% international, 18% 25 or older. Core. Calendar: semesters. Academic remediation for entering students, ESL program, services for LD students, advanced placement, honors program, independent study, distance learning, double major, summer session for credit, part-time degree program, external degree program, adult/continuing education programs, co-op programs and internships. Study abroad program. ROTC: Army (c), Air Force (c).

Entrance Requirements: Open admission except for international students or allied health, fire science, automotive technologies, law enforcement programs. Options: Common Application, electronic application, early admission, deferred admission. Required for some: essay, high school transcript, 2 recommendations, interview. Entrance: noncompetitive. Application deadline: Rolling. Preference given to district residents.

Costs Per Year: Application fee: $0. Area resident tuition: $1975 full-time, $65 per contact hour part-time. State resident tuition: $3175 full-time, $105 per contact hour part-time. Nonresident tuition: $4375 full-time, $145 per contact hour part-time. Mandatory fees: $50 full-time, $25 per term part-time.

Collegiate Environment: Orientation program. Drama-theater group, choral group, student-run newspaper, radio station. Social organizations: 145 open to all; national fraternities, national sororities; 25% of eligible men and 75% of eligible women are members. Most popular organizations: Student Marketing, Legal Assistants Club, Student Nursing Club, Phi Theta Kappa, Student Advising Club. Major annual events: Graduation, Student Recognition Banquet, Welcome Week. Student services: personal-psychological counseling, women's center. Campus security: 24-hour emergency response devices and patrols, student patrols, late night transport-escort service. College housing not available. Abel Sykes Technology and Learning Center plus 1 other with 98,125 books, 4,900 microform titles, 600 serials, 11,653 audiovisual materials, an OPAC, and a Web page. Operations spending for

2004 fiscal year: $1.8 million. 1,146 computers available on campus for general student use. A campuswide network can be accessed from off-campus. Staffed computer lab on campus.

Community Environment: Named capital of the state in 1847, Lansing is well-known for its automotive industries. Over two-thirds of its products are gas engines, automobile parts, drop forgings and castings. The State Historical Museum is located here. The area has golf courses, theatres, a baseball team, museums, parks, and a riverfront walk. Excellent part-time employment is available for students.

■ LAWRENCE TECHNOLOGICAL UNIVERSITY M-9

21000 West Ten Mile Rd.
Southfield, MI 48075-1058
Tel: (248)204-4000
Free: 800-225-5588
Admissions: (248)204-3160
Fax: (248)204-3727
E-mail: admissions@ltu.edu
Web Site: http://www.ltu.edu/

Description: Independent, university, coed. Awards associate, bachelor's, master's, and doctoral degrees. Founded 1932. Setting: 115-acre suburban campus with easy access to Detroit. Endowment: $21.7 million. Research spending for 2004 fiscal year: $969,057. Educational spending for 2005 fiscal year: $7220 per student. Total enrollment: 4,122. Faculty: 389 (113 full-time, 276 part-time). Student-undergrad faculty ratio is 12:1. 1,298 applied, 76% were admitted. 20% from top 10% of their high school class, 41% from top quarter, 77% from top half. Full-time: 1,604 students, 25% women, 75% men. Part-time: 1,264 students, 18% women, 82% men. Students come from 16 states and territories, 14 other countries, 1% from out-of-state, 0.4% Native American, 2% Hispanic, 12% black, 3% Asian American or Pacific Islander, 2% international, 29% 25 or older, 15% live on campus, 9% transferred in. Retention: 69% of full-time freshmen returned the following year. Academic areas with the most degrees conferred: engineering; architecture; engineering technologies. Core. Calendar: semesters. Academic remediation for entering students, ESL program, services for LD students, advanced placement, independent study, distance learning, double major, summer session for credit, part-time degree program, adult/continuing education programs, co-op programs and internships, graduate courses open to undergrads. Off campus study at Macomb University Center, Oakland Technical Center. Study abroad program. ROTC: Army (c), Air Force (c).

Entrance Requirements: Options: electronic application, international baccalaureate accepted. Required: high school transcript, minimum 2.5 high school GPA, SAT or ACT. Recommended: SAT. Required for some: essay, recommendations, interview. Entrance: moderately difficult. Application deadline: 8/15. Notification: continuous until 8/26.

Costs Per Year: Application fee: $30. Comprehensive fee: $26,709 includes full-time tuition ($19,073), mandatory fees ($370), and college room and board ($7266). College room only: $5286. Part-time tuition: $635 per credit hour. Part-time mandatory fees: $185 per term.

Collegiate Environment: Orientation program. Student-run newspaper. Social organizations: 40 open to all; national fraternities, national sororities, local fraternities, local sororities; 5% of eligible men and 9% of eligible women are members. Most popular organizations: Society of Automotive Engineers, Institute of Electric and Electronic Engineers, American Institute of Architecture Students, American Society of Civil Engineers, Campus Crusade for Christ. Major annual events: Open House, Discovery Orientation Weekend, Greek Week. Student services: personal-psychological counseling. Campus security: 24-hour emergency response devices and patrols, late night transport-escort service, controlled dormitory access. 547 college housing spaces available; 414 were occupied in 2003-04. Freshmen given priority for college housing. Option: coed housing available. Lawrence Technological University Library plus 1 other with 110,250 books, 28,000 microform titles, 700 serials, 420 audiovisual materials, an OPAC, and a Web page. Operations spending for 2004 fiscal year: $1 million. 60 computers available on campus for general student use. Computer purchase/lease plans available. A campuswide network can be accessed from student residence rooms and from off campus. Staffed computer lab on campus.

Community Environment: The city is a northern suburb of Detroit, with excellent full-time and part-time employment opportunities for students. Good recreational facilities are nearby. Southfield has excellent shopping

areas and a Civic Center that includes a 166-acre park. Transportation and other facilities of Detroit are easily accessible.

■ LEWIS COLLEGE OF BUSINESS O-24

17370 Meyers Rd.
Detroit, MI 48235-1423
Tel: (313)862-6300
Fax: (313)862-1027
Web Site: http://www.lewiscollege.edu/

Description: Independent, 2-year, coed. Awards transfer associate and terminal associate degrees. Founded 1929. Setting: 11-acre urban campus. Total enrollment: 324. 1% Hispanic, 99% black. Calendar: semesters. Academic remediation for entering students, summer session for credit, part-time degree program, co-op programs.

Entrance Requirements: Open admission. Options: Common Application, early admission, deferred admission. Required: high school transcript. Entrance: noncompetitive. Application deadline: Rolling. Notification: continuous until 8/30.

Collegiate Environment: Orientation program. Student-run newspaper. Social organizations: 5 open to all; national sororities, local sororities; 10% of women are members. Most popular organizations: Sister to Sister, Brother to Brother, The Voice, Student Government Association, Business Club. Student services: personal-psychological counseling. Campus security: parking lot security. College housing not available. Main library plus 1 other with 3,355 books and 90 serials. 54 computers available on campus for general student use. Staffed computer lab on campus.

■ MACOMB COMMUNITY COLLEGE N-24

14500 East Twelve Mile Rd.
Warren, MI 48088-3896
Tel: (586)445-7000; (866)622-6624
Admissions: (586)445-7183
Fax: (586)445-7140
E-mail: hughesr@macomb.edu
Web Site: http://www.macomb.edu/

Description: District-supported, 2-year, coed. Awards certificates, transfer associate, and terminal associate degrees. Founded 1954. Setting: 384-acre suburban campus with easy access to Detroit. Endowment: $8 million. Educational spending for 2005 fiscal year: $6841 per student. Total enrollment: 20,596. Student-undergrad faculty ratio is 28:1. Full-time: 7,520 students, 50% women, 50% men. Part-time: 13,076 students, 53% women, 47% men. Students come from 5 states and territories, 0% from out-of-state, 0.5% Native American, 1% Hispanic, 6% black, 4% Asian American or Pacific Islander, 1% international, 45% 25 or older. Calendar: semesters. Academic remediation for entering students, ESL program, services for LD students, advanced placement, self-designed majors, honors program, summer session for credit, part-time degree program, adult/continuing education programs, co-op programs and internships. Off campus study at Wayne State University, Wayne County Community College, Benjamin Davis Vocational Technical Center, Oakland Community College.

Entrance Requirements: Open admission except for nursing, occupational therapy, respiratory therapy, veterinary technician, physical therapy programs. Options: Common Application, early admission, deferred admission. Entrance: noncompetitive. Application deadline: Rolling.

Costs Per Year: Application fee: $0. Area resident tuition: $2108 full-time, $68 per credit hour part-time. State resident tuition: $3224 full-time, $104 per credit hour part-time. Nonresident tuition: $4185 full-time, $135 per credit hour part-time. Mandatory fees: $40 full-time, $20 per term part-time.

Collegiate Environment: Orientation program. Drama-theater group. Social organizations: 20 open to all. Most popular organizations: Phi Beta Kappa, Adventure Unlimited, Alpha Rho Rho, SADD. Major annual events: Welcome Back Picnic, Spring Fling, Bandemonium. Student services: health clinic, personal-psychological counseling. Campus security: 24-hour emergency response devices and patrols, late night transport-escort service, security phones in parking lots, surveillance cameras. College housing not available. 159,226 books, 4,240 serials, and an OPAC. Operations spending for 2004 fiscal year: $1.4 million. 2,000 computers available on campus for general student use. A campuswide network can be accessed from off-campus. Staffed computer lab on campus.

Community Environment: Community has many libraries, churches of various denominations, hospitals, and excellent shopping facilities. Some part-time work is available for students. City has major recreational facilities, and borders Lake St. Clair.

■ MADONNA UNIVERSITY *N-23*

36600 Schoolcraft Rd.
Livonia, MI 48150-1173
Tel: (734)432-5300
Free: 800-852-4951
Admissions: (734)432-5317
Fax: (734)432-5393
E-mail: muinfo@smtp.munet.edu
Web Site: http://www.madonna.edu

Description: Independent Roman Catholic, comprehensive, coed. Awards associate, bachelor's, and master's degrees and post-master's certificates. Founded 1947. Setting: 49-acre suburban campus with easy access to Detroit. Endowment: $28.8 million. Educational spending for 2005 fiscal year: $4850 per student. Total enrollment: 4,308. Faculty: 400 (127 full-time, 273 part-time). Student-undergrad faculty ratio is 17:1. 573 applied, 86% were admitted. Full-time: 1,679 students, 76% women, 24% men. Part-time: 1,697 students, 75% women, 25% men. Students come from 32 states and territories, 42 other countries, 2% from out-of-state, 0.4% Native American, 3% Hispanic, 14% black, 2% Asian American or Pacific Islander, 3% international, 53% 25 or older, 3% live on campus, 57% transferred in. Retention: 70% of full-time freshmen returned the following year. Academic areas with the most degrees conferred: business/marketing; health professions and related sciences; security and protective services. Core. Calendar: semesters. Academic remediation for entering students, ESL program, services for LD students, advanced placement, accelerated degree program, self-designed majors, independent study, distance learning, double major, summer session for credit, part-time degree program, adult/continuing education programs, co-op programs and internships, graduate courses open to undergrads. Off campus study at 5 members of the Detroit Area Consortium of Catholic Colleges. Study abroad program.

Entrance Requirements: Options: Peterson's Universal Application, Common Application, electronic application, early admission, deferred admission. Required: essay, high school transcript, minimum 2.75 high school GPA, SAT or ACT. Recommended: interview. Required for some: 2 recommendations. Entrance: moderately difficult. Application deadline: Rolling. Notification: continuous.

Costs Per Year: Application fee: $25. Comprehensive fee: $16,168 includes full-time tuition ($10,300), mandatory fees ($100), and college room and board ($5768). College room only: $2318. Room and board charges vary according to board plan. Part-time tuition: $340 per credit hour. Part-time mandatory fees: $50 per term.

Collegiate Environment: Orientation program. Choral group, student-run newspaper, radio station. Social organizations: 16 open to all; national sororities; 2% of eligible men and 2% of eligible women are members. Most popular organizations: Campus Ministry, Gerontology Association, Madonna University Nursing Student Association, Society of Future Teachers. Major annual events: Welcome Week activities, Commencement, Peace and Justice Week activities. Student services: personal-psychological counseling. Campus security: 24-hour emergency response devices and patrols, late night transport-escort service. 250 college housing spaces available; 126 were occupied in 2003-04. Freshmen guaranteed college housing. Option: coed housing available. Madonna University Library with 199,144 books, 1,679 serials, an OPAC, and a Web page. Operations spending for 2004 fiscal year: $1.2 million. 175 computers available on campus for general student use. Computer purchase/lease plans available. A campuswide network can be accessed from student residence rooms and from off campus. Staffed computer lab on campus.

Community Environment: See Schoolcraft College.

■ MARYGROVE COLLEGE *O-24*

8425 West McNichols Rd.
Detroit, MI 48221-2599
Tel: (313)927-1200; (866)313-1297
Admissions: (313)927-1236
Fax: (313)927-1345
E-mail: info@marygrove.edu
Web Site: http://www.marygrove.edu/

Description: Independent Roman Catholic, comprehensive, coed. Awards associate, bachelor's, and master's degrees. Founded 1905. Setting: 50-acre urban campus. Endowment: $14.9 million. Total enrollment: 3,591. Faculty: 71 (65 full-time, 6 part-time). Student-undergrad faculty ratio is 51:1. 412 applied, 42% were admitted. Full-time: 398 students, 72% women, 28% men. Part-time: 334 students, 84% women, 16% men. Students come from 2 states and territories, 15 other countries, 0.1% from out-of-state, 0% Native American, 1% Hispanic, 65% black, 0% Asian American or Pacific Islander, 3% international, 67% 25 or older, 7% live on campus, 14% transferred in. Retention: 71% of full-time freshmen returned the following year. Academic areas with the most degrees conferred: social sciences; visual and performing arts; business/marketing. Core. Calendar: semesters. Academic remediation for entering students, advanced placement, self-designed majors, distance learning, double major, summer session for credit, part-time degree program, co-op programs and internships, graduate courses open to undergrads. Off campus study at Detroit Area Consortium of Catholic Colleges.

Entrance Requirements: Options: Peterson's Universal Application, early admission, deferred admission. Required: high school transcript, minimum 2.7 high school GPA, ACT. Required for some: recommendations, interview. Entrance: moderately difficult. Application deadline: 8/15. Notification: continuous until 9/1.

Costs Per Year: Application fee: $25. Comprehensive fee: $19,335 includes full-time tuition ($12,800), mandatory fees ($335), and college room and board ($6200). Part-time tuition: $478 per credit.

Collegiate Environment: Orientation program. Choral group. Social organizations: 16 open to all. Most popular organizations: Association of Black Social Workers, Council of Student Organization, Political Science Club, United Brotherhood, Marygrove Business Association. Major annual events: Fall Fest, Welcome Picnic and New Student Welcome, Martin Luther King, Jr. Celebration. Student services: personal-psychological counseling. Campus security: 24-hour emergency response devices and patrols, late night transport-escort service. 110 college housing spaces available; 44 were occupied in 2003-04. Freshmen given priority for college housing. Option: coed housing available. Main library plus 1 other with 83,483 books, 65,650 microform titles, 459 serials, 2,132 audiovisual materials, and an OPAC. Operations spending for 2004 fiscal year: $772,455. 115 computers available on campus for general student use. Computer purchase/lease plans available. A campuswide network can be accessed from student residence rooms. Staffed computer lab on campus.

Community Environment: Located 15 minutes from downtown Detroit, Marygrove offers considerable cultural and social opportunities. Theater, symphony, ballet, opera, and the nationally famous Detroit Institute of Arts are within easy commuting distance. Shopping centers, art galleries, sports arenas, and recreation centers are nearby.

■ MICHIGAN JEWISH INSTITUTE *M-10*

25401 Coolidge Hwy.
Oak Park, MI 48237-1304
Tel: (248)414-6900
Fax: (248)414-6907
E-mail: thgardin@mji.edu
Web Site: http://www.mji.edu/

Description: Independent, 4-year, coed. Awards associate and bachelor's degrees. Founded 1994. Core. Calendar: semesters. Academic remediation for entering students, ESL program, services for LD students, advanced placement, accelerated degree program, independent study, double major, summer session for credit, adult/continuing education programs, co-op programs and internships. Study abroad program.

Entrance Requirements: Open admission. Options: early admission, early decision, early action, deferred admission, international baccalaureate accepted. Required: high school transcript.

Costs Per Year: Application fee: $50. Tuition: $320 full-time, $320 per credit part-time. Mandatory fees: $50 full-time.

Collegiate Environment: Orientation program. College housing not available. Michigan Jewish Institute Library plus 1 other with an OPAC.

■ MICHIGAN STATE UNIVERSITY *I-3*

East Lansing, MI 48824
Tel: (517)355-1855
Admissions: (517)355-8332
E-mail: admis@msu.edu
Web Site: http://www.msu.edu/

Description: State-supported, university, coed. Awards bachelor's, master's, doctoral, and first professional degrees and post-master's certificates. Founded 1855. Setting: 5,192-acre suburban campus with easy access to Detroit. Endowment: $909.5 million. Research spending for 2004 fiscal year: $214.5 million. Total enrollment: 45,166. Faculty: 2,762 (2,411 full-time, 351 part-time). Student-undergrad faculty ratio is 18:1. 21,844 applied, 76% were admitted. 26% from top 10% of their high school class, 64% from top quarter, 94% from top half. Full-time: 32,200 students, 54% women, 46% men. Part-time: 3,478 students, 51% women, 49% men. Students come from 54 states and territories, 125 other countries, 7% from out-of-state, 1% Native American, 3% Hispanic, 9% black, 5% Asian American or Pacific Islander, 3% international, 6% 25 or older, 42% live on campus, 5% transferred in. Retention: 91% of full-time freshmen returned the following year. Academic areas with the most degrees conferred: business/marketing; communications/journalism; social sciences. Core. Calendar: semesters. Academic remediation for entering students, ESL program, services for LD students, advanced placement, accelerated degree program, self-designed majors, freshman honors college, honors program, independent study, distance learning, double major, summer session for credit, part-time degree program, adult/continuing education programs, co-op programs and internships, graduate courses open to undergrads. Off campus study at Committee on Institutional Cooperation. Study abroad program. ROTC: Army, Air Force.

Entrance Requirements: Options: Peterson's Universal Application, electronic application, deferred admission. Required: essay, high school transcript, SAT or ACT. Entrance: moderately difficult. Application deadline: Rolling. Notification: continuous until 9/1.

Costs Per Year: Application fee: $35. State resident tuition: $6705 full-time, $223.50 per credit part-time. Nonresident tuition: $18,458 full-time, $615.25 per credit part-time. Mandatory fees: $882 full-time, $882 per year part-time. Full-time tuition and fees vary according to course load, degree level, program, and student level. Part-time tuition and fees vary according to course load, degree level, program, and student level. College room and board: $5744. College room only: $2488. Room and board charges vary according to board plan and housing facility.

Collegiate Environment: Orientation program. Drama-theater group, choral group, marching band, student-run newspaper, radio station. Social organizations: 500 open to all; national fraternities, national sororities. Major annual events: football game against University of Michigan, Homecoming game, basketball game with University of Michigan. Student services: legal services, health clinic, personal-psychological counseling, women's center. Campus security: 24-hour emergency response devices and patrols, late night transport-escort service, self-defense workshops. 17,151 college housing spaces available; 14,500 were occupied in 2003-04. Freshmen guaranteed college housing. On-campus residence required in freshman year. Options: coed, women-only housing available. Main Library plus 14 others with 4.4 million books, 5.6 million microform titles, 29,470 serials, 290,206 audiovisual materials, an OPAC, and a Web page. Operations spending for 2004 fiscal year: $24.3 million. 2,000 computers available on campus for general student use. Computer purchase/lease plans available. A campuswide network can be accessed from student residence rooms and from off campus. Staffed computer lab on campus.

Community Environment: Located in a metropolitan area adjacent to Lansing, the state capital of Michigan. There are four hospitals, access to houses of worship, various entertainment venues, and good shopping facilities within the immediate area.

■ MICHIGAN TECHNOLOGICAL UNIVERSITY *B-4*

1400 Townsend Dr.
Houghton, MI 49931-1295
Tel: (906)487-1885; 888-MTU-1885
Admissions: (906)487-2335
Fax: (906)487-3343
E-mail: mtu4u@mtu.edu
Web Site: http://www.mtu.edu/

Description: State-supported, university, coed. Awards associate, bachelor's, master's, and doctoral degrees. Founded 1885. Setting: 240-acre small town campus. Endowment: $59 million. Research spending for 2004 fiscal year: $20.2 million. Educational spending for 2005 fiscal year: $7836 per student. Total enrollment: 6,510. Faculty: 389 (343 full-time, 46 part-time). Student-undergrad faculty ratio is 11:1. 3,928 applied, 85% were admitted. 25% from top 10% of their high school class, 56% from top quarter, 87% from top half. 6 National Merit Scholars, 70 valedictorians. Full-time: 5,159 students, 21% women, 79% men. Part-time: 455 students, 29% women, 71% men. Students come from 45 states and territories, 80 other countries, 25% from out-of-state, 1% Native American, 1% Hispanic, 2% black, 1% Asian American or Pacific Islander, 4% international, 11% 25 or older, 40% live on campus, 3% transferred in. Retention: 81% of full-time freshmen returned the following year. Academic areas with the most degrees conferred: engineering; business/marketing; engineering technologies. Core. Calendar: semesters. ESL program, services for LD students, advanced placement, self-designed majors, distance learning, double major, summer

session for credit, part-time degree program, co-op programs and internships, graduate courses open to undergrads. Off campus study at National Student Exchange. Study abroad program. ROTC: Army, Air Force.

Entrance Requirements: Options: Peterson's Universal Application, Common Application, electronic application, deferred admission. Required: high school transcript, SAT or ACT. Recommended: interview. Entrance: moderately difficult. Application deadline: Rolling.

Costs Per Year: Application fee: $40. State resident tuition: $7560 full-time, $252 per credit hour part-time. Nonresident tuition: $18,750 full-time, $625 per credit hour part-time. Mandatory fees: $634 full-time, $316.86 per term part-time. Full-time tuition and fees vary according to course load, location, and program. Part-time tuition and fees vary according to course load, location, and program. College room and board: $6375. College room only: $3120. Room and board charges vary according to board plan and housing facility.

Collegiate Environment: Orientation program. Drama-theater group, choral group, student-run newspaper, radio station. Social organizations: 145 open to all; national fraternities, national sororities, local fraternities, local sororities; 9% of eligible men and 15% of eligible women are members. Most popular organizations: Film Board, Undergraduate Student Government, Inter-Residence Hall Council, Blue Key National Honor Fraternity. Major annual events: homecoming, Winter Carnival, K-Day. Student services: health clinic, personal-psychological counseling. Campus security: 24-hour emergency response devices and patrols, late night transport-escort service. 2,639 college housing spaces available; 2,502 were occupied in 2003-04. Freshmen guaranteed college housing. On-campus residence required in freshman year. Options: coed, men-only, women-only housing available. J. R. Van Pelt Library with 820,414 books, 535,707 microform titles, 10,369 serials, 4,529 audiovisual materials, an OPAC, and a Web page. Operations spending for 2004 fiscal year: $3.6 million. 1,555 computers available on campus for general student use. A campuswide network can be accessed from student residence rooms and from off campus. Staffed computer lab on campus.

Community Environment: The main campus is located in Houghton, at the heart of the colorful Keweenaw Peninsula in Upper Michigan. Houghton is part of the Houghton-Hancock twin-city center of approximately 12,000. Numerous water and winter sports are available. The community has public libraries, churches for all major religions, a hospital, and opportunities for a variety of recreational and cultural activities. Part-time employment is available.

■ MID MICHIGAN COMMUNITY COLLEGE *I-20*

1375 South Clare Ave.
Harrison, MI 48625-9447
Tel: (989)386-6622
Admissions: (989)386-6660
Fax: (989)386-9088
Web Site: http://www.midmich.cc.mi.us/

Description: State and locally supported, 2-year, coed. Part of Michigan Department of Education. Awards certificates, transfer associate, and terminal associate degrees. Founded 1965. Setting: 560-acre rural campus. Educational spending for 2005 fiscal year: $903 per student. Total enrollment: 3,232. 1,383 applied, 100% were admitted. Full-time: 1,465 students, 58% women, 42% men. Part-time: 1,767 students, 67% women, 33% men. Students come from 6 states and territories, 1% from out-of-state, 2% Native American, 2% Hispanic, 2% black, 1% Asian American or Pacific Islander, 0.3% international, 32% 25 or older, 6% transferred in. Retention: 8% of full-time freshmen returned the following year. Core. Calendar: semesters. Academic remediation for entering students, services for LD students, advanced placement, honors program, independent study, distance learning, summer session for credit, part-time degree program, adult/continuing education programs, co-op programs and internships.

Entrance Requirements: Open admission except for allied health programs. Option: early admission. Recommended: high school transcript. Required for some: interview. Placement: ACT recommended. Entrance: noncompetitive. Application deadline: Rolling. Notification: continuous.

Costs Per Year: Application fee: $0. Area resident tuition: $2000 full-time. State resident tuition: $3500 full-time. Nonresident tuition: $6400 full-time. Mandatory fees: $150 full-time.

Collegiate Environment: Drama-theater group, choral group, student-run newspaper. Social organizations: 6 open to all. Most popular organizations: Commission of Student Activities Services, Phi Theta Kappa. Major annual events: Spring Picnic, Fall Festival, Christmas canned food drive and coats for kids programs. Campus security: 24-hour emergency response devices.

College housing not available. Charles A. Amble Library with 29,450 books and 200 serials. 175 computers available on campus for general student use. A campuswide network can be accessed. Staffed computer lab on campus.

■ **MONROE COUNTY COMMUNITY COLLEGE** *P-23*

1555 South Raisinville Rd.
Monroe, MI 48161-9047
Tel: (734)242-7300
Admissions: (734)384-4261
Fax: (734)242-9711
Web Site: http://www.monroeccc.edu/

Description: County-supported, 2-year, coed. Part of Michigan Department of Education. Awards certificates, transfer associate, and terminal associate degrees. Founded 1964. Setting: 150-acre small town campus with easy access to Detroit and Toledo. Total enrollment: 3,943. 1,700 applied, 99% were admitted. Full-time: 1,501 students, 48% women, 52% men. Part-time: 2,442 students, 61% women, 39% men. Students come from 3 states and territories, 1 other country, 4% from out-of-state, 45% 25 or older, 5% transferred in. Core. Calendar: semesters. Academic remediation for entering students, services for LD students, advanced placement, independent study, summer session for credit, part-time degree program.

Entrance Requirements: Open admission except for allied health, culinary arts programs. Options: early admission, deferred admission. Required: high school transcript, ACT ASSET, ACT COMPASS. Recommended: ACT. Required for some: ACT. Entrance: noncompetitive. Notification: continuous.

Collegiate Environment: Orientation program. Drama-theater group, choral group, student-run newspaper. Most popular organizations: student government, Society of Auto Engineers, Oasis, Nursing Students Organization. Major annual events: Family Fun Night, Santa's Winter Wonderland, Honors Reception. Campus security: police patrols during open hours. College housing not available. Campbell Learning Resource Center with 47,352 books, 321 serials, and an OPAC. 140 computers available on campus for general student use. Staffed computer lab on campus.

Community Environment: The third oldest community in the state, Monroe was founded in 1780 by the French. This early settlement, called Frenchtown, was the scene of the River Raisin Massacre in 1813. The only Michigan port on Lake Erie, Monroe includes among its industries large nurseries, paper mills, a limestone quarry, recreation, and a branch automotive factory. It is a suburban city with a community airport and bus lines easily accessible. There are many civic, fraternal and veteran's organizations in this area. Community has a library, YMCA, museum, hospital, theater, 9 golf courses, many public parks and 6 shopping centers.

■ **MONTCALM COMMUNITY COLLEGE** *K-19*

2800 College Dr.
Sidney, MI 48885-9723
Tel: (989)328-2111
Admissions: (989)328-1206
Fax: (989)328-2950
E-mail: admissions@montcalm.cc.mi.us
Web Site: http://www.montcalm.edu/

Description: State and locally supported, 2-year, coed. Part of Michigan Department of Education. Awards certificates, transfer associate, and terminal associate degrees. Founded 1965. Setting: 240-acre rural campus with easy access to Grand Rapids. Endowment: $3.4 million. Educational spending for 2005 fiscal year: $3685 per student. Total enrollment: 2,080. 589 applied, 100% were admitted. Full-time: 674 students, 68% women, 32% men. Part-time: 1,406 students, 69% women, 31% men. 0% from out-of-state, 1% Native American, 2% Hispanic, 0.2% black, 0.3% Asian American or Pacific Islander, 0% international, 45% 25 or older, 6% transferred in. Core. Calendar: semesters. Academic remediation for entering students, services for LD students, advanced placement, independent study, distance learning, double major, summer session for credit, part-time degree program, adult/continuing education programs, co-op programs and internships. Off campus study.

Entrance Requirements: Open admission except for nursing program. Options: early admission, deferred admission. Recommended: high school transcript. Placement: ACT ASSET, ACT COMPASS required; ACT recommended. Entrance: noncompetitive. Application deadline: Rolling. Notification: continuous.

Costs Per Year: Application fee: $0. Area resident tuition: $1920 full-time, $64 per credit hour part-time. State resident tuition: $2940 full-time, $98 per credit hour part-time. Nonresident tuition: $3810 full-time, $127 per credit

hour part-time. Mandatory fees: $165 full-time, $5.50 per credit hour part-time. Full-time tuition and fees vary according to course load. Part-time tuition and fees vary according to course load.

Collegiate Environment: Orientation program. Drama-theater group, choral group. Social organizations: 12 open to all. Most popular organizations: Nursing Club, Native American Club, Phi Theta Kappa, Business Club, Judo Club. Major annual events: Welcome Week, Heritage Village Festival. Student services: personal-psychological counseling. College housing not available. Montcalm Community College Library with 29,848 books, 3,670 serials, 580 audiovisual materials, an OPAC, and a Web page. Operations spending for 2004 fiscal year: $200,895. 450 computers available on campus for general student use. A campuswide network can be accessed from off-campus. Staffed computer lab on campus.

Community Environment: Located in a rural area, air transportation is accessible within a one-hour drive. A neighboring city has theatres, libraries and hospitals. There are 104 lakes in the county providing excellent recreational opportunities. Some part-time employment is available for students.

■ **MOTT COMMUNITY COLLEGE** *L-23*

1401 East Ct. St.
Flint, MI 48503-2089
Tel: (810)762-0200
Admissions: (810)762-0315
Fax: (810)762-0292
E-mail: marc.payne@mcc.edu
Web Site: http://www.mcc.edu/

Description: District-supported, 2-year, coed. Part of Michigan Labor and Economic Growth Department. Awards certificates, transfer associate, and terminal associate degrees. Founded 1923. Setting: 20-acre urban campus with easy access to Detroit. Endowment: $35.1 million. Educational spending for 2005 fiscal year: $4341 per student. Total enrollment: 10,299. Student-undergrad faculty ratio is 22:1. 2,838 applied, 39% were admitted. Full-time: 3,663 students, 55% women, 45% men. Part-time: 6,636 students, 64% women, 36% men. Students come from 10 states and territories, 33 other countries, 0.01% from out-of-state, 1% Native American, 2% Hispanic, 18% black, 1% Asian American or Pacific Islander, 0.3% international, 46% 25 or older, 3% transferred in. Core. Calendar: semesters. Academic remediation for entering students, ESL program, services for LD students, advanced placement, accelerated degree program, honors program, independent study, distance learning, double major, summer session for credit, part-time degree program, adult/continuing education programs, co-op programs and internships.

Entrance Requirements: Open admission. Options: electronic application, early admission, deferred admission. Required: high school transcript. Entrance: noncompetitive. Application deadline: 8/31.

Costs Per Year: Application fee: $0. Area resident tuition: $2385 full-time, $79.50 per contact hour part-time. State resident tuition: $3572 full-time, $119.05 per contact hour part-time. Nonresident tuition: $4766 full-time, $158.85 per contact hour part-time. Mandatory fees: $107 full-time, $53.50 per term part-time.

Collegiate Environment: Orientation program. Choral group. Social organizations: 24 open to all. Most popular organizations: Criminal Justice Association, Phi Theta Kappa, Dental Assisting Club, Connoisseur's Club, Social Work Club. Major annual events: College Night, Spring Fest, Fall Fest. Student services: health clinic, personal-psychological counseling. Campus security: 24-hour emergency response devices and patrols, student patrols, late night transport-escort service. College housing not available. Charles Stewart Mott Library with 112,251 books, 211,586 microform titles, 325 serials, an OPAC, and a Web page. Operations spending for 2004 fiscal year: $707,949. 1,290 computers available on campus for general student use. A campuswide network can be accessed from off-campus. Staffed computer lab on campus.

■ **MUSKEGON COMMUNITY COLLEGE** *K-16*

221 South Quarterline Rd.
Muskegon, MI 49442-1493
Tel: (231)773-9131
Admissions: (231)777-0261
Fax: (231)777-0255
E-mail: bamfiej@muskegoncc.edu
Web Site: http://www.muskegon.cc.mi.us/

Description: State and locally supported, 2-year, coed. Part of Michigan Department of Education. Awards transfer associate and terminal associate degrees. Founded 1926. Setting: 112-acre urban campus with easy access to Grand Rapids. Total enrollment: 5,000. Students come from 3 states and territories, 5 other countries, 52% 25 or older. Core. Calendar: semesters. Academic remediation for entering students, self-designed majors, honors program, summer session for credit, part-time degree program, adult/continuing education programs, co-op programs.

Entrance Requirements: Open admission. Options: early admission, deferred admission. Placement: SAT or ACT recommended. Entrance: noncompetitive. Application deadline: Rolling. Notification: continuous.

Collegiate Environment: Drama-theater group, choral group. Student services: personal-psychological counseling. College housing not available. 48,597 books and 450 serials. 30 computers available on campus for general student use.

Community Environment: Formerly known as the Lumber Queen of the World, cutting 800 million board feet of lumber in 1888, Muskegon is the largest city on the east bank of Lake Michigan. Today it is an important lake port and a manufacturing and resort center. Numerous industries produce automotive parts, foundry products, paper, oil, chemicals and recreational equipment. Area has an international airport and a seaway-depth port. There are art galleries, museums, and historical sites located within the immediate vicinity. The nearby Muskegon River offers excellent fishing, boating, and canoeing.

■ NORTH CENTRAL MICHIGAN COLLEGE D-19
1515 Howard St.
Petoskey, MI 49770-8717
Tel: (231)348-6600; 888-298-6605
Admissions: (231)439-6511
Web Site: http://www.ncmc.cc.mi.us/

Description: County-supported, 2-year, coed. Part of Michigan Department of Education. Awards certificates, transfer associate, and terminal associate degrees. Founded 1958. Setting: 270-acre small town campus. Total enrollment: 2,738. 424 applied, 100% were admitted. Students come from 4 states and territories, 4% Native American, 1% Hispanic, 0.1% black, 1% Asian American or Pacific Islander, 0% international, 55% 25 or older, 3% live on campus. Core. Calendar: semesters. Academic remediation for entering students, services for LD students, advanced placement, independent study, distance learning, double major, summer session for credit, part-time degree program, co-op programs and internships.

Entrance Requirements: Open admission except for nursing program. Required: high school transcript. Placement: ACT required. Entrance: noncompetitive. Application deadline: Rolling. Notification: continuous.

Collegiate Environment: Orientation program. Choral group. Major annual events: NCMC Cookout, lecture series, Polynesian Week. Student services: personal-psychological counseling. Campus security: 24-hour emergency response devices. 124 college housing spaces available; 55 were occupied in 2003-04. Option: coed housing available. North Central Michigan College Library with 29,249 books, 325 serials, an OPAC, and a Web page. 133 computers available on campus for general student use. A campuswide network can be accessed. Staffed computer lab on campus.

Community Environment: A resort and health center, the city is located on Little Traverse Bay. Within a 30-minute drive are 6 major ski resorts. Other recreational facilities include water sports on Lake Michigan, summer concerts, golf and tennis. The area has good transportation provided by air and bus service. There is some part-time employment available for students. Community services include a library, an arts center, many churches, 2 hospitals, and a clinic.

■ NORTHERN MICHIGAN UNIVERSITY C-6
1401 Presque Isle Ave.
Marquette, MI 49855-5301
Tel: (906)227-1000
Free: 800-682-9797
Admissions: (906)227-2650
Fax: (906)227-1747
E-mail: admiss@nmu.edu
Web Site: http://www.nmu.edu/

Description: State-supported, comprehensive, coed. Awards associate, bachelor's, and master's degrees and post-master's certificates. Founded 1899. Setting: 300-acre small town campus with easy access to Sawyer International. Endowment: $33.1 million. Educational spending for 2005 fiscal year: $4276 per student. Total enrollment: 9,379. Faculty: 422 (305 full-time, 117 part-time). Student-undergrad faculty ratio is 23:1. 4,772 applied, 84% were admitted. Full-time: 7,841 students, 53% women, 47% men. Part-

time: 873 students, 57% women, 43% men. 19% from out-of-state, 2% Native American, 1% Hispanic, 2% black, 1% Asian American or Pacific Islander, 0.4% international, 32% live on campus, 6% transferred in. Retention: 73% of full-time freshmen returned the following year. Academic areas with the most degrees conferred: education; business/marketing; social sciences. Core. Calendar: semesters. Academic remediation for entering students, services for LD students, advanced placement, accelerated degree program, self-designed majors, honors program, independent study, distance learning, double major, summer session for credit, part-time degree program, adult/continuing education programs, internships, graduate courses open to undergrads. Off campus study at other public institutions in Michigan. Study abroad program. ROTC: Army.

Entrance Requirements: Options: Peterson's Universal Application, Common Application, electronic application, deferred admission, international baccalaureate accepted. Required: high school transcript, SAT or ACT. Required for some: minimum 2.25 high school GPA. Entrance: minimally difficult. Application deadline: Rolling. Notification: continuous.

Costs Per Year: Application fee: $30. One-time mandatory fee: $150. State resident tuition: $5328 full-time, $222 per credit hour part-time. Nonresident tuition: $9072 full-time, $378 per credit hour part-time. Mandatory fees: $630 full-time, $30 per term part-time. Part-time tuition and fees vary according to location. College room and board: $6013. Room and board charges vary according to board plan and housing facility.

Collegiate Environment: Orientation program. Drama-theater group, choral group, marching band, student-run newspaper, radio station. Social organizations: 200 open to all; national fraternities, national sororities; 2% of eligible men and 2% of eligible women are members. Most popular organizations: Associated Students of Northern Michigan University, Platform Personalities, campus cinema, Northern Arts and Entertainment, Student Leader Fellowship Program. Major annual events: homecoming, Winterfest, Fallfest. Student services: health clinic, personal-psychological counseling. Campus security: 24-hour emergency response devices and patrols, student patrols, late night transport-escort service. College housing designed to accommodate 2,360 students; 2,712 undergraduates lived in college housing during 2003-04. Freshmen guaranteed college housing. On-campus residence required through sophomore year. Option: coed housing available. Lydia Olson Library plus 1 other with 592,689 books, 830,197 microform titles, 2,588 serials, 7,369 audiovisual materials, an OPAC, and a Web page. Operations spending for 2004 fiscal year: $1.1 million. 9,000 computers available on campus for general student use. Computer purchase/lease plans available. A campuswide network can be accessed from student residence rooms and from off campus. Staffed computer lab on campus.

Community Environment: Located on Lake Superior, Marquette is a day's driving distance from Chicago, Minneapolis, Duluth and Milwaukee. It is an important service and distribution center.

■ NORTHWESTERN MICHIGAN COLLEGE F-17
1701 East Front St.
Traverse City, MI 49686-3061
Tel: (231)995-1000
Free: 800-748-0566
Admissions: (231)995-1034
Fax: (231)995-1680
Web Site: http://www.nmc.edu/

Description: State and locally supported, 2-year, coed. Awards certificates, transfer associate, and terminal associate degrees. Founded 1951. Setting: 180-acre small town campus. Educational spending for 2005 fiscal year: $5840 per student. Total enrollment: 4,609. 2,521 applied, 95% were admitted. Full-time: 2,011 students, 53% women, 47% men. Part-time: 2,598 students, 64% women, 36% men. Students come from 19 states and territories, 2% from out-of-state, 2% Native American, 1% Hispanic, 0.5% black, 1% Asian American or Pacific Islander, 0% international, 37% 25 or older, 5% live on campus, 11% transferred in. Retention: 49% of full-time freshmen returned the following year. Core. Calendar: semesters. Academic remediation for entering students, services for LD students, advanced placement, honors program, independent study, distance learning, summer session for credit, part-time degree program, adult/continuing education programs, co-op programs and internships.

Entrance Requirements: Open admission residents of sponsoring counties. Options: Peterson's Universal Application, Common Application, early admission, deferred admission. Recommended: minimum 2.0 high school GPA. Required for some: high school transcript. Placement: ACT COMPASS required. Entrance: noncompetitive. Application deadline: Rolling. Notification: continuous until 8/28.

Costs Per Year: Application fee: $15. Area resident tuition: $2339 full-time, $68.80 per contact hour part-time. State resident tuition: $4077 full-time, $119.92 per contact hour part-time. Nonresident tuition: $5087 full-time, $149 per contact hour part-time. Mandatory fees: $383 full-time, $10.33 per contact hour part-time, $16 per term part-time. Part-time tuition and fees vary according to course load. College room and board: $6285. Room and board charges vary according to board plan and housing facility.
Collegiate Environment: Orientation program. Drama-theater group, choral group, student-run newspaper, radio station. Social organizations: 15 open to all. Most popular organizations: Residence Hall Council, honors fraternity, student newspaper, student magazine, student radio station. Major annual events: Campus Clean-Up Day, Annual Barbecue, graduation. Student services: health clinic, personal-psychological counseling. Campus security: 24-hour emergency response devices and patrols, student patrols, late night transport-escort service, controlled dormitory access, well-lit campus. 350 college housing spaces available; 238 were occupied in 2003-04. Options: coed, men-only, women-only housing available. Mark and Helen Osterlin Library plus 1 other with 97,458 books, 155,643 microform titles, 9,820 serials, 3,000 audiovisual materials, an OPAC, and a Web page. Operations spending for 2004 fiscal year: $491,000. 625 computers available on campus for general student use. A campuswide network can be accessed from student residence rooms and from off campus. Staffed computer lab on campus.
Community Environment: The Grand Traverse region is the center of Michigan's cherry-growing belt, with Traverse City marketing more cherries than any other city in the country. This is also an important year-round resort area. The temperature averages about 70 degrees in summer. Bus and air transportation are easily accessible. There are many churches, 2 hospitals, 2 libraries, 2 museums, and other major community services. Recreational activities include sailing, golf, hunting, tennis, swimming, water skiing, fishing, bowling, skating, and all winter sports. Concerts and travel lectures are given here, and the National Cherry Festival is an annual event.

■ **NORTHWOOD UNIVERSITY** *J-21*
4000 Whiting Dr.
Midland, MI 48640-2398
Tel: (989)837-4200
Free: 800-457-7878
Admissions: (989)837-4367
Fax: (989)837-4490
E-mail: admissions@northwood.edu
Web Site: http://www.northwood.edu/
Description: Independent, comprehensive, coed. Awards associate, bachelor's, and master's degrees. Founded 1959. Setting: 434-acre small town campus. System endowment: $58.2 million. Educational spending for 2005 fiscal year: $4029 per student. Total enrollment: 3,888. Faculty: 77 (46 full-time, 31 part-time). Student-undergrad faculty ratio is 34:1. 1,638 applied, 85% were admitted. 7% from top 10% of their high school class, 24% from top quarter, 51% from top half. Full-time: 2,587 students, 43% women, 57% men. Part-time: 990 students, 51% women, 49% men. Students come from 38 states and territories, 29 other countries, 15% from out-of-state, 0% Native American, 2% Hispanic, 13% black, 2% Asian American or Pacific Islander, 9% international, 1% 25 or older, 39% live on campus, 6% transferred in. Retention: 72% of full-time freshmen returned the following year. Academic areas with the most degrees conferred: business/marketing; parks and recreation; communications/journalism. Core. Academic remediation for entering students, ESL program, advanced placement, accelerated degree program, honors program, independent study, distance learning, double major, summer session for credit, part-time degree program, external degree program, adult/continuing education programs, co-op programs and internships. Off campus study. Study abroad program.
Entrance Requirements: Options: Peterson's Universal Application, Common Application, electronic application, early admission, deferred admission, international baccalaureate accepted. Required: essay, high school transcript, SAT or ACT. Recommended: minimum 2.0 high school GPA, 1 recommendation, interview. Entrance: moderately difficult. Application deadline: Rolling. Notification: continuous.
Costs Per Year: Application fee: $25. Comprehensive fee: $22,475 includes full-time tuition ($15,216), mandatory fees ($317), and college room and board ($6942). College room only: $3567. Part-time tuition: $317 per credit hour.
Collegiate Environment: Orientation program. Drama-theater group, choral group, student-run newspaper. Social organizations: 12 open to all; national fraternities, national sororities, local fraternities, local sororities. Most popular organizations: Student Senate, intramural sports/club sports, campus art, Northwood University International Auto Show (NUTAS). Major annual events: Auto Show/Homecoming, Values Emphasis Week, Basketball Homecoming. Student services: health clinic, personal-psychological counseling. Campus security: 24-hour emergency response devices and patrols, late night transport-escort service. 812 college housing spaces available; 699 were occupied in 2003-04. Freshmen guaranteed college housing. On-campus residence required in freshman year. Options: coed, men-only, women-only housing available. Strosacker Library with 41,275 books, 47,090 microform titles, 335 serials, 59 audiovisual materials, an OPAC, and a Web page. Operations spending for 2004 fiscal year: $717,383. 215 computers available on campus for general student use. A campuswide network can be accessed from student residence rooms and from off campus. Staffed computer lab on campus.

■ **OAKLAND COMMUNITY COLLEGE** *L-9*
2480 Opdyke Rd.
Bloomfield Hills, MI 48304-2266
Tel: (248)341-2000
Admissions: (248)341-2186
Fax: (248)341-2099
Web Site: http://www.oaklandcc.edu/
Description: State and locally supported, 2-year, coed. Part of Michigan Department of Career Development. Awards certificates, transfer associate, and terminal associate degrees. Founded 1964. Setting: 540-acre suburban campus with easy access to Detroit. Endowment: $1.4 million. Educational spending for 2005 fiscal year: $3894 per student. Total enrollment: 24,287. Student-undergrad faculty ratio is 27:1. 2,615 applied, 100% were admitted. Full-time: 7,705 students, 51% women, 49% men. Part-time: 16,582 students, 61% women, 39% men. Students come from 12 states and territories, 73 other countries, 0.01% from out-of-state, 1% Native American, 2% Hispanic, 16% black, 2% Asian American or Pacific Islander, 8% international, 47% 25 or older, 2% transferred in. Retention: 66% of full-time freshmen returned the following year. Core. Calendar: semesters. Academic remediation for entering students, ESL program, services for LD students, advanced placement, distance learning, summer session for credit, part-time degree program, adult/continuing education programs, co-op programs and internships. Off campus study at Macomb Community College and Eastern Michigan University. Study abroad program.
Entrance Requirements: Open admission. Option: deferred admission. Recommended: high school transcript, interview. Entrance: noncompetitive. Application deadline: Rolling. Notification: continuous.
Costs Per Year: Application fee: $0. Area resident tuition: $1704 full-time, $56.80 per credit hour part-time. State resident tuition: $2885 full-time, $96.15 per credit hour part-time. Nonresident tuition: $4045 full-time, $134.83 per credit hour part-time. Mandatory fees: $70 full-time, $35 per term part-time.
Collegiate Environment: Orientation program. Drama-theater group, choral group. Social organizations: 20 open to all. Most popular organizations: Phi Theta Kappa, International Student Organization, organizations related to student majors. Major annual events: Welcome Days, Distinguished Speaker Series. Student services: personal-psychological counseling, women's center. Campus security: 24-hour emergency response devices, late night transport-escort service. College housing not available. Main library plus 5 others with 243,137 books, 1.3 million microform titles, 2,139 serials, 8,315 audiovisual materials, an OPAC, and a Web page. Operations spending for 2004 fiscal year: $3.3 million. 2,065 computers available on campus for general student use. A campuswide network can be accessed from off-campus. Staffed computer lab on campus.
Community Environment: Oakland County is composed of both rural and urban towns and has all types of public transportation. Average temperature in winter is 20 degrees, with 70 degrees in summer. The average precipitation is 30 inches. There are good summer and winter sports facilities within the immediate area, with more than 400 lakes nearby. Extensive health services are available.

■ **OAKLAND UNIVERSITY** *K-10*
Rochester, MI 48309-4401
Tel: (248)370-2100
Free: 800-OAK-UNIV
Admissions: (248)370-4467
Fax: (248)370-4462
E-mail: ouinfo@oakland.edu
Web Site: http://www.oakland.edu/

Description: State-supported, university, coed. Awards bachelor's, master's, and doctoral degrees and post-master's certificates. Founded 1957. Setting: 1,444-acre suburban campus with easy access to Detroit. Endowment: $30.6 million. Educational spending for 2005 fiscal year: $4838 per student. Total enrollment: 17,339. Faculty: 890 (449 full-time, 441 part-time). Student-undergrad faculty ratio is 23:1. 5,948 applied, 82% were admitted. 38% from top quarter of their high school class, 85% from top half. Full-time: 9,760 students, 62% women, 38% men. Part-time: 3,688 students, 61% women, 39% men. Students come from 32 states and territories, 36 other countries, 1% from out-of-state, 0.5% Native American, 2% Hispanic, 9% black, 4% Asian American or Pacific Islander, 1% international, 21% 25 or older, 13% live on campus, 10% transferred in. Retention: 71% of full-time freshmen returned the following year. Academic areas with the most degrees conferred: psychology; business/marketing; education. Core. Calendar: semesters. Academic remediation for entering students, ESL program, services for LD students, advanced placement, accelerated degree program, self-designed majors, honors program, independent study, distance learning, double major, summer session for credit, part-time degree program, co-op programs and internships, graduate courses open to undergrads. Off campus study at Macomb Community College, Beaumont Hospital-Troy. Study abroad program. ROTC: Air Force (c).

Entrance Requirements: Options: electronic application, early action, deferred admission, international baccalaureate accepted. Required: high school transcript, minimum 2.5 high school GPA. Recommended: SAT and SAT Subject Tests or ACT. Required for some: minimum 3.0 high school GPA, recommendations, interview, audition. Entrance: moderately difficult. Application deadline: Rolling. Notification: continuous.

Costs Per Year: Application fee: $40. State resident tuition: $6443 full-time, $204.75 per credit part-time. Nonresident tuition: $14,869 full-time, $478.50 per credit part-time. Full-time tuition varies according to program and student level. Part-time tuition varies according to program and student level. College room and board: $6080. Room and board charges vary according to housing facility.

Collegiate Environment: Orientation program. Drama-theater group, choral group, student-run newspaper, radio station. Social organizations: national fraternities, national sororities, local sororities; 1% of eligible men and 1% of eligible women are members. Most popular organizations: Golden Key National Honor Society, Association of Black Students, SATE (Student Association for Teacher Education), Psi Chi Psychology Club, Student Nurses Association. Major annual events: Weekend of Champions at OU, Meadow Brook Ball, Midnight Madness. Student services: health clinic, personal-psychological counseling. Campus security: 24-hour emergency response devices and patrols, student patrols, late night transport-escort service, controlled dormitory access, security lighting, self-defense classes. 1,870 college housing spaces available; 1,715 were occupied in 2003-04. Freshmen given priority for college housing. On-campus residence required in freshman year. Option: coed housing available. Kresge Library plus 1 other with an OPAC and a Web page.

Community Environment: This is a suburban community with access to nearby Detroit via Interstate 75, and Michigan Highway 59. The immediate area has a hospital, shopping facilities, Oakland Technology Park, and several churches. Recreation is extensive both on and off campus. On campus cultural opportunities include Meadow Brook Theater, Meadow Brook Music Festival, Meadow Brook Art Gallery, and the Oakland University Center for Performing Arts. In addition, roller rinks, bowling centers, golf courses, Silverdome, the Palace (Home of the Detroit Pistons), theatres, and the local Avon Players offer recreational and cultural activities off campus. There is seasonal part-time employment for students. Special events held annually include Meadowbrook Music Festival in summer and the Christmas Parade; the annual Arts and Apples Festival is in September.

■ **OLIVET COLLEGE** *N-19*
320 South Main St.
Olivet, MI 49076-9701
Tel: (269)749-7000
Free: 800-456-7189
Fax: (616)749-3821
E-mail: kleonard@olivetcollege.edu
Web Site: http://www.olivetcollege.edu/

Description: Independent, comprehensive, coed, affiliated with Congregational Christian Church. Awards bachelor's and master's degrees. Founded 1844. Setting: 92-acre small town campus. Endowment: $11.5 million. Educational spending for 2005 fiscal year: $2100 per student. Total enrollment: 1,069. 750 applied, 54% were admitted. 45% from top 10% of their high school class, 59% from top quarter, 87% from top half. 3 National Merit Scholars, 18 class presidents, 18 valedictorians, 51 student government officers. Full-time: 954 students, 42% women, 58% men. Part-time: 69 students, 62% women, 38% men. Students come from 15 states and territories, 16 other countries, 16% from out-of-state, 1% Native American, 2% Hispanic, 14% black, 0.3% Asian American or Pacific Islander, 4% international, 12% 25 or older, 59% live on campus, 12% transferred in. Retention: 78% of full-time freshmen returned the following year. Core. Calendar: 4-4-1. Services for LD students, advanced placement, accelerated degree program, self-designed majors, honors program, independent study, double major, summer session for credit, part-time degree program, co-op programs and internships. Study abroad program.

Entrance Requirements: Options: Peterson's Universal Application, Common Application, electronic application, deferred admission. Required: high school transcript, SAT or ACT. Recommended: minimum 2.6 high school GPA. Required for some: essay, recommendations, interview. Entrance: minimally difficult. Application deadline: Rolling. Notification: continuous.

Costs Per Year: Application fee: $25. Comprehensive fee: $21,944 includes full-time tuition ($15,970), mandatory fees ($494), and college room and board ($5480). College room only: $2980. Full-time tuition and fees vary according to reciprocity agreements. Room and board charges vary according to board plan and housing facility. Part-time tuition: $515 per credit. Part-time tuition varies according to course load and reciprocity agreements.

Collegiate Environment: Orientation program. Drama-theater group, choral group, marching band, student-run newspaper, radio station. Social organizations: 32 open to all; local fraternities, local sororities; 15% of eligible men and 15% of eligible women are members. Most popular organizations: Campus Activities Board, Black Student Union, International Club, non-traditional student organization, Omicron Delta Kappa. Major annual events: Homecoming, Honors Convocation, Welcome Week. Student services: health clinic, personal-psychological counseling, women's center. Campus security: 24-hour emergency response devices and patrols, late night transport-escort service. 620 college housing spaces available; 615 were occupied in 2003-04. No special consideration for freshman housing applicants. On-campus residence required through junior year. Options: coed, men-only, women-only housing available. Burrage Library with 90,000 books, 200 microform titles, 415 serials, and an OPAC. Operations spending for 2004 fiscal year: $232,500. 60 computers available on campus for general student use. A campuswide network can be accessed from student residence rooms and from off campus.

Community Environment: Olivet, population 1,700, is located 30 miles south of Lansing and 125 miles west of Detroit.

■ **ROCHESTER COLLEGE** *K-10*
800 West Avon Rd.
Rochester Hills, MI 48307-2764
Tel: (248)218-2000
Free: 800-521-6010
Admissions: (248)218-2032
Fax: (248)218-2005
E-mail: admissions@rc.edu
Web Site: http://www.rc.edu/

Description: Independent, 4-year, coed, affiliated with Church of Christ. Awards associate, bachelor's, and master's degrees. Founded 1959. Setting: 83-acre suburban campus with easy access to Detroit. Endowment: $1.6 million. Educational spending for 2005 fiscal year: $2500 per student. Total university enrollment: 101. Total unit enrollment: 1,055. Faculty: 135 (45 full-time, 90 part-time). Student-undergrad faculty ratio is 14:1. 351 applied, 87% were admitted. 12% from top 10% of their high school class, 30% from top quarter, 59% from top half. 1 valedictorian, 11 student government officers. Full-time: 690 students, 61% women, 39% men. Part-time: 357 students, 63% women, 37% men. Students come from 24 states and territories, 8 other countries, 6% from out-of-state, 1% Native American, 1% Hispanic, 18% black, 1% Asian American or Pacific Islander, 1% international, 51% 25 or older, 26% live on campus, 19% transferred in. Retention: 55% of full-time freshmen returned the following year. Academic areas with the most degrees conferred: business/marketing; education; psychology. Core. Calendar: semesters. Academic remediation for entering students, advanced placement, accelerated degree program, independent study, distance learning, double major, summer session for credit, part-time degree program, external degree program, adult/continuing education programs, internships. Off campus study at Madonna University, Macomb Community College, Oakland Community College, Mott Community College, Specs Howard School of Broadcasters. Study abroad program.

Entrance Requirements: Options: Peterson's Universal Application, electronic application, early admission, deferred admission. Required: high school transcript, minimum 2.25 high school GPA, ACT or SAT. Recommended: essay, 2 recommendations. Required for some: interview. Entrance: minimally difficult. Application deadline: Rolling. Notification: continuous.

Costs Per Year: Application fee: $25. Comprehensive fee: $18,916 includes full-time tuition ($11,120), mandatory fees ($1236), and college room and board ($6560). Room and board charges vary according to board plan and housing facility. Part-time tuition: $360 per credit hour. Part-time mandatory fees: $180 per term. Part-time tuition and fees vary according to course load.

Collegiate Environment: Orientation program. Drama-theater group, choral group, student-run newspaper. Social organizations: 4 open to all; local fraternities, local sororities; 10% of eligible men and 10% of eligible women are members. Most popular organizations: Image, Student Government, American Marketing Association, Rotoract. Major annual event: Celebration. Student services: personal-psychological counseling. Campus security: 24-hour emergency response devices, late night transport-escort service, controlled dormitory access, evening security guards. 358 college housing spaces available; 240 were occupied in 2003-04. Freshmen guaranteed college housing. On-campus residence required through sophomore year. Options: men-only, women-only housing available. Ennis and Nancy Ham Library with 55,000 books, 17,500 microform titles, 200 serials, 2,009 audiovisual materials, an OPAC, and a Web page. Operations spending for 2004 fiscal year: $239,899. 59 computers available on campus for general student use. A campuswide network can be accessed from student residence rooms and from off campus. Staffed computer lab on campus.

Community Environment: See Oakland University.

■ **SACRED HEART MAJOR SEMINARY** *O-24*
2701 Chicago Blvd.
Detroit, MI 48206-1799
Tel: (313)883-8500
Admissions: (313)883-8710
Web Site: http://www.archdioceseofdetroit.org/shms/shms.htm

Description: Independent Roman Catholic, comprehensive, coed. Awards associate, bachelor's, master's, and first professional degrees. Founded 1919. Setting: 24-acre urban campus. Endowment: $3 million. Educational spending for 2005 fiscal year: $9950 per student. Total enrollment: 445. Faculty: 40 (27 full-time, 13 part-time). Student-undergrad faculty ratio is 10:1. 1 applied, 100% were admitted. 0% from top 10% of their high school class, 0% from top quarter, 0% from top half. Full-time: 45 students, 4% women, 96% men. Part-time: 254 students, 50% women, 50% men. Students come from 2 states and territories, 1% from out-of-state, 9% Hispanic, 2% Asian American or Pacific Islander, 4% international, 55% 25 or older, 2% transferred in. Retention: 100% of full-time freshmen returned the following year. Academic area with the most degrees conferred: liberal arts/general studies. Core. Calendar: semesters. Academic remediation for entering students, services for LD students, advanced placement, independent study, part-time degree program. Off campus study at Detroit Area Catholic Higher Education Consortium.

Entrance Requirements: Option: deferred admission. Required: essay, high school transcript, minimum 2.0 high school GPA, 1 recommendation, interview, SAT or ACT. Entrance: moderately difficult. Application deadline: 7/31. Notification: continuous until 8/15. Preference given to candidates for the priesthood.

Costs Per Year: Application fee: $30. Comprehensive fee: $16,671 includes full-time tuition ($10,341), mandatory fees ($80), and college room and board ($6250). Full-time tuition and fees vary according to course load. Part-time tuition: $245 per credit hour. Part-time mandatory fees: $40 per term. Part-time tuition and fees vary according to course load.

Collegiate Environment: Orientation program. Choral group. Student services: personal-psychological counseling. Campus security: 24-hour emergency response devices, late night transport-escort service. 40 college housing spaces available; 29 were occupied in 2003-04. Freshmen guaranteed college housing. On-campus residence required through senior year. Option: men-only housing available. Szoka Library with 136,975 books, 6,460 microform titles, 513 serials, an OPAC, and a Web page. Operations spending for 2004 fiscal year: $373,843. 23 computers available on campus for general student use. Staffed computer lab on campus.

Community Environment: At the turn of the 20th century, Detroit was a quiet, tree-shaded community brewing beer and producing comfortable carriages and comforting stoves. The serenity was broken by Henry Ford's creation, a vehicle "propelled by power generated from within itself." Today it is the greatest automobile-manufacturing city in the world. It is also rapidly becoming a steel center and a leader in the manufacturing of pharmaceuticals, office equipment, rubber products, salt, television components, synthetic resins and paints, meat products, marine engines, and more than half the garden seed used throughout the country. Annual mean temperature is 49.3 degrees, and annual rainfall is 31.03 inches. Definitely an industrial city, Detroit has a civic center complex on the riverfront, an excellent park system, and numerous museums and art galleries.

■ **SAGINAW CHIPPEWA TRIBAL COLLEGE** *J-20*
2274 Enterprise Dr.
Mount Pleasant, MI 48858
Tel: (989)775-4123
Fax: (989)775-4528
E-mail: treed@sagchip.org
Web Site: http://www.sagchip.org/tribalcollege/

Description: Independent, 2-year, coed. Awards transfer associate and terminal associate degrees. Founded 1998. Educational spending for 2005 fiscal year: $3380 per student. Total enrollment: 123. Student-undergrad faculty ratio is 9:1. 36 applied, 100% were admitted. Full-time: 43 students, 70% women, 30% men. Part-time: 80 students, 78% women, 23% men. 0% from out-of-state, 85% Native American, 3% Hispanic, 2% black, 0% Asian American or Pacific Islander, 0% international. Calendar: semesters.

Entrance Requirements: Required: high school transcript. Entrance: noncompetitive.

Costs Per Year: Application fee: $0. Tuition: $1320 full-time, $55 per credit hour part-time. Mandatory fees: $136 full-time, $68 per term part-time.

Collegiate Environment: Student-run newspaper.

■ **SAGINAW VALLEY STATE UNIVERSITY** *J-22*
7400 Bay Rd.
University Center, MI 48710
Tel: (989)964-4000
Free: 800-968-9500
Admissions: (989)964-4200
Fax: (989)964-0180
E-mail: admissions@svsu.edu
Web Site: http://www.svsu.edu/

Description: State-supported, comprehensive, coed. Awards bachelor's and master's degrees and post-master's certificates. Founded 1963. Setting: 782-acre rural campus. Endowment: $28.9 million. Research spending for 2004 fiscal year: $502,034. Educational spending for 2005 fiscal year: $3991 per student. Total enrollment: 9,569. Faculty: 560 (260 full-time, 300 part-time). Student-undergrad faculty ratio is 20:1. 3,796 applied, 89% were admitted. 110 valedictorians. Full-time: 6,044 students, 60% women, 40% men. Part-time: 1,885 students, 60% women, 40% men. Students come from 18 states and territories, 46 other countries, 1% from out-of-state, 0.4% Native American, 2% Hispanic, 7% black, 1% Asian American or Pacific Islander, 3% international, 24% 25 or older, 13% live on campus, 8% transferred in. Retention: 71% of full-time freshmen returned the following year. Academic areas with the most degrees conferred: education; business/marketing; health professions and related sciences. Core. Calendar: semesters plus summer session. Academic remediation for entering students, ESL program, services for LD students, advanced placement, accelerated degree program, self-designed majors, honors program, independent study, distance learning, double major, summer session for credit, part-time degree program, adult/continuing education programs, co-op programs and internships, graduate courses open to undergrads. Study abroad program.

Entrance Requirements: Options: Peterson's Universal Application, electronic application, deferred admission, international baccalaureate accepted. Required: high school transcript, ACT. Recommended: minimum 2.5 high school GPA. Entrance: moderately difficult. Application deadline: Rolling.

Costs Per Year: Application fee: $25. State resident tuition: $4,876 full-time, $162.55 per credit hour part-time. Nonresident tuition: $11,486 full-time, $382.85 per credit hour part-time. Mandatory fees: $405 full-time, $13.50 per credit hour part-time. Full-time tuition and fees vary according to course level, course load, location, and program. Part-time tuition and fees vary according to course level, course load, location, and program. College room and board: $6150. College room only: $3600. Room and board charges vary according to board plan, housing facility, and student level.

Collegiate Environment: Orientation program. Drama-theater group; choral group, marching band, student-run newspaper. Social organizations: 75

open to all; national fraternities, national sororities; 3% of eligible men and 2% of eligible women are members. Most popular organizations: Alpha Sigma Alpha, Sigma Pi, Organization of Black Unity, International Students Association, University Residence Association. Major annual events: Card's Party, Homecoming Week, Concert Series. Student services: health clinic, personal-psychological counseling. Campus security: 24-hour emergency response devices, late night transport-escort service, controlled dormitory access, rape prevention program. 1,700 college housing spaces available; 969 were occupied in 2003-04. Freshmen guaranteed college housing. Option: coed housing available. Zahnow Library with 226,952 books, 367,918 microform titles, 11,512 serials, 22,445 audiovisual materials, an OPAC, and a Web page. Operations spending for 2004 fiscal year: $1.9 million. 1,033 computers available on campus for general student use. Computer purchase/lease plans available. A campuswide network can be accessed from student residence rooms and from off campus. Staffed computer lab on campus.

Community Environment: The college has a 782-acre campus located 3 miles south of I-75 on M-84. Combined with this rural atmosphere are urban advantages available in neighboring Saginaw, Bay City and Midland, where tri-county populations total 410,000.

■ **ST. CLAIR COUNTY COMMUNITY COLLEGE** *L-26*
323 Erie St., PO Box 5015
Port Huron, MI 48061-5015
Tel: (810)984-3881
Admissions: (810)989-5500
Fax: (810)984-4730
Web Site: http://www.sc4.edu/

Description: State and locally supported, 2-year, coed. Part of Michigan Department of Education. Awards certificates, transfer associate, and terminal associate degrees. Founded 1923. Setting: 25-acre small town campus with easy access to Detroit. Endowment: $2.5 million. Research spending for 2004 fiscal year: $78,511. Educational spending for 2005 fiscal year: $3024 per student. Total enrollment: 4,523. 2,696 applied, 100% were admitted. Students come from 6 other countries, 0.1% from out-of-state, 38% 25 or older. Core. Calendar: semesters. Academic remediation for entering students, services for LD students, advanced placement, accelerated degree program, self-designed majors, honors program, independent study, distance learning, double major, summer session for credit, part-time degree program, adult/continuing education programs, co-op programs and internships.

Entrance Requirements: Open admission except for nursing program specifically. Option: early admission. Required: high school transcript. Placement: ACT recommended. Entrance: noncompetitive. Application deadline: Rolling.

Collegiate Environment: Orientation program. Drama-theater group, choral group, student-run newspaper, radio station. Social organizations: 16 open to all. Most popular organizations: ADN Nursing Club, LPN Nursing Club, Phi Theta Kappa, DECA, student government. Major annual events: Stress Breaker, athletic events, plays/music performances. Student services: personal-psychological counseling. Campus security: patrols by security until 10 p.m. Learning Resources Center with 59,134 books, 47,441 microform titles, 610 serials, 4,311 audiovisual materials, and an OPAC. Operations spending for 2004 fiscal year: $669,248. 450 computers available on campus for general student use. A campuswide network can be accessed. Staffed computer lab on campus.

■ **SCHOOLCRAFT COLLEGE** *N-23*
18600 Haggerty Rd.
Livonia, MI 48152-2696
Tel: (734)462-4400
Admissions: (734)462-4426
Fax: (734)462-4553
Web Site: http://www.schoolcraft.edu/

Description: District-supported, 2-year, coed. Part of Michigan Department of Education. Awards certificates, transfer associate, and terminal associate degrees. Founded 1961. Setting: 183-acre suburban campus with easy access to Detroit. Endowment: $8.9 million. Research spending for 2004 fiscal year: $295,249. Educational spending for 2005 fiscal year: $2516 per student. Total enrollment: 10,213. 3,570 applied, 100% were admitted. 93% from top 10% of their high school class, 94% from top quarter, 96% from top half. Full-time: 3,377 students, 52% women, 48% men. Part-time: 6,836 students, 60% women, 40% men. Students come from 4 states and territories, 1% from out-of-state, 1% Native American, 2% Hispanic, 8% black,

2% Asian American or Pacific Islander, 0.2% international, 38% 25 or older, 13% transferred in. Core. Calendar: semesters. Academic remediation for entering students, services for LD students, advanced placement, accelerated degree program, distance learning, summer session for credit, part-time degree program, adult/continuing education programs, co-op programs.

Entrance Requirements: Open admission. Options: early admission, deferred admission. Recommended: high school transcript. Required for some: high school transcript. Placement: ACT or CPT required; ACT recommended. Entrance: noncompetitive. Application deadline: Rolling.

Costs Per Year: Application fee: $0. Area resident tuition: $1950 full-time, $65 per credit hour part-time. State resident tuition: $2910 full-time, $97 per credit hour part-time. Nonresident tuition: $4290 full-time, $143 per credit hour part-time. Mandatory fees: $130 full-time.

Collegiate Environment: Orientation program. Drama-theater group, choral group, student-run newspaper. Social organizations: 11 open to all; national fraternities; 3% of men are members. Most popular organizations: Student Activities Board, Ski Club, student newspaper, Music Club, Phi Theta Kappa. Major annual events: School Daze, Wildlife Education Program, Children's Safe Halloween Party. Student services: legal services, health clinic, women's center. Campus security: 24-hour emergency response devices and patrols, late night transport-escort service. College housing not available. Bradner Library plus 1 other with 96,216 books, 176,413 microform titles, 634 serials, and an OPAC. Operations spending for 2004 fiscal year: $1.1 million. 775 computers available on campus for general student use. A campuswide network can be accessed from off-campus. Staffed computer lab on campus.

Community Environment: Livonia is in a suburban area, population 260,000, located 20 miles west of Detroit and is convenient to airports. Good part-time employment opportunities are available for students.

■ **SIENA HEIGHTS UNIVERSITY** *P-22*
1247 East Siena Heights Dr.
Adrian, MI 49221-1796
Tel: (517)263-0731
Free: 800-521-0009
Admissions: (517)264-7180
Fax: (517)264-7745
E-mail: admissions@sienahts.edu
Web Site: http://www.sienahts.edu

Description: Independent Roman Catholic, comprehensive, coed. Awards associate, bachelor's, and master's degrees. Founded 1919. Setting: 140-acre small town campus with easy access to Detroit. Total enrollment: 2,153. 979 applied, 64% were admitted. 19% from top 10% of their high school class, 30% from top quarter, 77% from top half. 6 valedictorians. Students come from 8 states and territories, 0.2% Native American, 2% Hispanic, 10% black, 0.4% Asian American or Pacific Islander, 1% international, 51% 25 or older, 33% live on campus. Retention: 69% of full-time freshmen returned the following year. Core. Calendar: semesters. Academic remediation for entering students, services for LD students, advanced placement, accelerated degree program, self-designed majors, independent study, double major, summer session for credit, part-time degree program, external degree program, adult/continuing education programs, co-op programs and internships, graduate courses open to undergrads. Off campus study at Adrian College. Study abroad program.

Entrance Requirements: Options: Peterson's Universal Application, Common Application, electronic application, deferred admission. Required: high school transcript, SAT or ACT. Recommended: minimum 2.3 high school GPA, interview. Required for some: essay, recommendations, interview. Entrance: moderately difficult. Application deadline: Rolling.

Collegiate Environment: Orientation program. Drama-theater group, choral group, student-run newspaper. Social organizations: 30 open to all; national fraternities, national sororities, local fraternities, local sororities; 5% of eligible men and 5% of eligible women are members. Most popular organizations: Student Programming Association, Residence Hall Counsel, Student Senate, Siena Heights African American Knowledge Association. Major annual events: Leadership Luncheon, Alumni Weekend, Sister Carmie Day. Student services: health clinic, personal-psychological counseling. Campus security: 24-hour patrols, student patrols, late night transport-escort service. On-campus residence required through sophomore year. Option: coed housing available. 120,407 books and 451 serials. 75 computers available on campus for general student use. A campuswide network can be accessed from student residence rooms and from off campus. Staffed computer lab on campus.

Community Environment: See Adrian College.

■ SOUTHWESTERN MICHIGAN COLLEGE *P-16*

58900 Cherry Grove Rd.
Dowagiac, MI 49047-9793
Tel: (269)782-1000
Free: 800-456-8675
Fax: (269)782-8414
E-mail: mhay@swmich.edu
Web Site: http://www.swmich.edu/

Description: State and locally supported, 2-year, coed. Part of Michigan Department of Education. Awards certificates, transfer associate, and terminal associate degrees. Founded 1964. Setting: 240-acre rural campus. Total enrollment: 2,676. Student-undergrad faculty ratio is 19:1. 459 applied, 100% were admitted. Full-time: 1,015 students, 63% women, 37% men. Part-time: 1,661 students, 67% women, 33% men. Students come from 4 states and territories, 29 other countries, 9% from out-of-state, 1% Native American, 4% Hispanic, 9% black, 1% Asian American or Pacific Islander, 4% international, 40% 25 or older. Core. Calendar: semesters. Academic remediation for entering students, ESL program, services for LD students, advanced placement, accelerated degree program, self-designed majors, honors program, independent study, distance learning, double major, summer session for credit, part-time degree program, adult/continuing education programs, co-op programs and internships.

Entrance Requirements: Open admission except for nursing program. Options: Peterson's Universal Application, electronic application, deferred admission. Required: high school transcript. Required for some: recommendations, interview. Entrance: noncompetitive. Application deadline: Rolling. Notification: continuous until 9/10.

Costs Per Year: Application fee: $0. Area resident tuition: $2101 full-time. State resident tuition: $2659 full-time. Nonresident tuition: $2868 full-time. Mandatory fees: $465 full-time. Full-time tuition and fees vary according to course load.

Collegiate Environment: Orientation program. Drama-theater group, choral group, student-run newspaper. Most popular organization: Phi Theta Kappa. Major annual event: Fall Student/Staff Picnic. Campus security: 24-hour emergency response devices, evening police patrols. College housing not available. Fred L. Mathews Library with 38,000 books, 30,375 microform titles, 1,100 serials, 1,750 audiovisual materials, an OPAC, and a Web page. 200 computers available on campus for general student use. A campuswide network can be accessed. Staffed computer lab on campus.

■ SPRING ARBOR UNIVERSITY *O-20*

106 East Main St.
Spring Arbor, MI 49283-9799
Tel: (517)750-1200
Free: 800-968-0011
Fax: (517)750-1604
E-mail: admissions@arbor.edu
Web Site: http://www.arbor.edu/

Description: Independent Free Methodist, comprehensive, coed. Awards associate, bachelor's, and master's degrees. Founded 1873. Setting: 123-acre small town campus. Endowment: $8.4 million. Educational spending for 2005 fiscal year: $5372 per student. Total enrollment: 3,701. Faculty: 138 (80 full-time, 58 part-time). Student-undergrad faculty ratio is 15:1. 1,313 applied, 75% were admitted. 20% from top 10% of their high school class, 46% from top quarter, 75% from top half. Full-time: 1,913 students, 66% women, 34% men. Part-time: 697 students, 73% women, 27% men. Students come from 22 states and territories, 4 other countries, 12% from out-of-state, 0.3% Native American, 2% Hispanic, 7% black, 1% Asian American or Pacific Islander, 1% international, 63% live on campus, 4% transferred in. Retention: 78% of full-time freshmen returned the following year. Academic areas with the most degrees conferred: business/marketing; family and consumer sciences; education. Core. Calendar: 4-1-4. Academic remediation for entering students, ESL program, services for LD students, advanced placement, accelerated degree program, self-designed majors, honors program, independent study, double major, summer session for credit, part-time degree program, external degree program, adult/continuing education programs, internships, graduate courses open to undergrads. Off campus study at Christian College Consortium. ROTC: Army (c).

Entrance Requirements: Options: early admission, deferred admission. Required: high school transcript, SAT or ACT. Recommended: minimum 2.6 high school GPA, ACT. Required for some: essay, recommendations, interview. Entrance: moderately difficult. Application deadline: 8/1. Notification: continuous.

Costs Per Year: Application fee: $30. Comprehensive fee: $22,476 includes full-time tuition ($16,270), mandatory fees ($396), and college room and board ($5810). College room only: $2730. Room and board charges vary according to board plan, housing facility, and location. Part-time tuition: $350 per credit. Part-time mandatory fees: $306 per year. Part-time tuition and fees vary according to course load and reciprocity agreements.

Collegiate Environment: Orientation program. Drama-theater group, choral group, student-run newspaper, radio station. Most popular organizations: Action Jackson, Cougarettes, Multicultural Organization. Major annual events: Arbor Games, Homecoming, Ormston Porchfest. Student services: health clinic, personal-psychological counseling. Campus security: late night transport-escort service. College housing designed to accommodate 919 students; 932 undergraduates lived in college housing during 2003-04. On-campus residence required in freshman year. Options: men-only, women-only housing available. Hugh A. White Library with 100,094 books, 351,759 microform titles, 667 serials, 6,181 audiovisual materials, and a Web page. Operations spending for 2004 fiscal year: $278,000. 168 computers available on campus for general student use. A campuswide network can be accessed from student residence rooms and from off campus. Staffed computer lab on campus.

■ UNIVERSITY OF DETROIT MERCY *O-24*

4001 W McNichols Rd, PO Box 19900
Detroit, MI 48219-0900
Tel: (313)993-1000
Free: 800-635-5020
Admissions: (313)993-1245
Fax: (313)993-3326
Web Site: http://www.udmercy.edu/

Description: Independent Roman Catholic (Jesuit), university, coed. Awards associate, bachelor's, master's, doctoral, and first professional degrees and post-master's and first professional certificates. Founded 1877. Setting: 70-acre urban campus. Total enrollment: 5,521. 2,214 applied, 68% were admitted. 31% from top 10% of their high school class, 63% from top quarter, 85% from top half. Full-time: 1,901 students, 62% women, 38% men. Part-time: 1,410 students, 73% women, 27% men. Students come from 27 states and territories, 19 other countries, 4% from out-of-state, 1% Native American, 2% Hispanic, 31% black, 2% Asian American or Pacific Islander, 3% international, 44% 25 or older, 21% live on campus, 13% transferred in. Retention: 76% of full-time freshmen returned the following year. Core. Calendar: semesters. Academic remediation for entering students, ESL program, advanced placement, honors program, independent study, double major, summer session for credit, part-time degree program, adult/continuing education programs, co-op programs and internships, graduate courses open to undergrads. Off campus study at 4 members of the Detroit Area Consortium of Catholic Colleges. Study abroad program.

Entrance Requirements: Options: Peterson's Universal Application, Common Application, deferred admission. Required: high school transcript, minimum 2.50 high school GPA, SAT or ACT. Recommended: essay, recommendations, interview. Required for some: 1 recommendation, interview. Entrance: moderately difficult. Application deadline: Rolling. Notification: continuous.

Costs Per Year: Application fee: $25. Comprehensive fee: $29,798 includes full-time tuition ($21,900), mandatory fees ($570), and college room and board ($7328). College room only: $4288. Part-time tuition: $535 per credit hour.

Collegiate Environment: Orientation program. Drama-theater group, choral group, student-run newspaper, radio station. Social organizations: 5 open to all; national sororities, local fraternities, local sororities. Major annual events: Homecoming, Black History Month, Greek Week. Student services: legal services, health clinic, personal-psychological counseling. Campus security: 24-hour emergency response devices and patrols, student patrols, late night transport-escort service. 955 college housing spaces available; 709 were occupied in 2003-04. Freshmen guaranteed college housing. Option: coed housing available. McNichols Campus Library plus 3 others with 998,417 microform titles, 9,340 serials, 32,053 audiovisual materials, an OPAC, and a Web page. 250 computers available on campus for general student use. A campuswide network can be accessed from student residence rooms and from off campus. Staffed computer lab on campus.

Community Environment: See Wayne State University.

■ UNIVERSITY OF MICHIGAN *O-5*

Ann Arbor, MI 48109
Tel: (734)764-1817

Admissions: (734)764-7433

Fax: (734)936-0740

E-mail: ugadmiss@umich.edu

Web Site: http://www.umich.edu/

Description: State-supported, university, coed. Awards bachelor's, master's, doctoral, and first professional degrees and post-master's certificates. Founded 1817. Setting: 8,070-acre suburban campus with easy access to Detroit. Endowment: $4.9 billion. Research spending for 2004 fiscal year: $753.3 million. Total enrollment: 39,993. Faculty: 2,936 (2,347 full-time, 589 part-time). Student-undergrad faculty ratio is 15:1. 23,882 applied, 57% were admitted. Full-time: 24,446 students, 51% women, 49% men. Part-time: 1,021 students, 50% women, 50% men. Students come from 55 states and territories, 84 other countries, 31% from out-of-state, 1% Native American, 5% Hispanic, 7% black, 12% Asian American or Pacific Islander, 5% international, 4% 25 or older, 37% live on campus, 3% transferred in. Retention: 96% of full-time freshmen returned the following year. Academic areas with the most degrees conferred: engineering; social sciences; psychology. Calendar: trimesters. ESL program, services for LD students, advanced placement, accelerated degree program, self-designed majors, honors program, independent study, distance learning, double major, summer session for credit, part-time degree program, adult/continuing education programs, co-op programs and internships, graduate courses open to undergrads. Off campus study at Committee on Institutional Cooperation. Study abroad program. ROTC: Army, Air Force.

Entrance Requirements: Options: electronic application, deferred admission. Required: essay, high school transcript, SAT or ACT. Required for some: recommendations, interview, SAT Subject Tests. Entrance: very difficult. Application deadline: 2/1. Notification: continuous until 4/1. Preference given to state residents.

Costs Per Year: Application fee: $40. State resident tuition: $9213 full-time, $349 per hour part-time. Nonresident tuition: $27,602 full-time, $1115 per hour part-time. Mandatory fees: $187 full-time, $94.69 per term part-time. Full-time tuition and fees vary according to course load, degree level, location, program, and student level. Part-time tuition and fees vary according to course load, degree level, location, program, and student level. College room and board: $7374. Room and board charges vary according to board plan and housing facility.

Collegiate Environment: Orientation program. Drama-theater group, choral group, marching band, student-run newspaper, radio station. Social organizations: 900 open to all; national fraternities, national sororities, local fraternities, local sororities; 16% of eligible men and 15% of eligible women are members. Most popular organizations: University Activities Center, Hillel, Project Serve, Residence Hall Association, Black Student Union. Major annual events: Martin Luther King Day Symposium, Annual Fall/Winter Leadership Conference, Festifall. Student services: legal services, health clinic, personal-psychological counseling, women's center. Campus security: 24-hour emergency response devices and patrols, student patrols, late night transport-escort service, controlled dormitory access, bicycle patrols. 14,000 college housing spaces available. Freshmen guaranteed college housing. Options: coed, women-only housing available. University Library plus 20 others with 8 million books, 8.2 million microform titles, 67,554 serials, 87,705 audiovisual materials, an OPAC, and a Web page. Operations spending for 2004 fiscal year: $43.2 million. 2,600 computers available on campus for general student use. Computer purchase/lease plans available. A campuswide network can be accessed from student residence rooms and from off campus. Staffed computer lab on campus.

Community Environment: Predominantly a college community, Ann Arbor also serves as a center for scientific and industrial research and development. Products manufactured in the area include precision instruments, automotive parts, ball bearings, computer components and machine tools. Part-time employment is available for students. Average summer temperature is 79 degrees; winter, 27.8 degrees; average rainfall is 30.7 inches. Average snowfall is 35.3 inches. City has excellent transportation facilities including rail, bus, air service, and expressways out of Detroit. Area offers many cultural and recreational advantages usually found only in a large metropolis. For instance, the Ann Arbor Musical Society provides classical concerts of major world orchestras, chamber music groups and soloists. The Ann Arbor May Festival is an additional musical attraction each year.

■ **UNIVERSITY OF MICHIGAN-DEARBORN** *O-24*

4901 Evergreen Rd.

Dearborn, MI 48128-1491

Tel: (313)593-5000

Admissions: (313)593-5100

E-mail: cwtrem@umd.umich.edu

Web Site: http://www.umd.umich.edu/

Description: State-supported, comprehensive, coed. Part of University of Michigan System. Awards bachelor's and master's degrees. Founded 1959. Setting: 210-acre suburban campus with easy access to Detroit. Endowment: $19.1 million. Research spending for 2004 fiscal year: $1.4 million. Total enrollment: 8,613. Faculty: 512 (287 full-time, 225 part-time). Student-undergrad faculty ratio is 16:1. 2,605 applied, 71% were admitted. 27% from top 10% of their high school class, 58% from top quarter, 89% from top half. Full-time: 4,031 students, 51% women, 49% men. Part-time: 2,540 students, 56% women, 44% men. Students come from 25 states and territories, 22 other countries, 0.2% from out-of-state, 1% Native American, 3% Hispanic, 9% black, 6% Asian American or Pacific Islander, 2% international, 27% 25 or older, 10% transferred in. Retention: 82% of full-time freshmen returned the following year. Academic areas with the most degrees conferred: business/marketing; engineering; education. Core. Calendar: semesters. Academic remediation for entering students, services for LD students, accelerated degree program, self-designed majors, honors program, independent study, distance learning, double major, summer session for credit, part-time degree program, adult/continuing education programs, co-op programs and internships, graduate courses open to undergrads. Off campus study at University of Michigan. Study abroad program. ROTC: Army (c), Naval (c), Air Force (c).

Entrance Requirements: Options: deferred admission, international baccalaureate accepted. Required: high school transcript, minimum 3.0 high school GPA, SAT or ACT. Recommended: ACT. Required for some: interview. Entrance: moderately difficult. Application deadline: Rolling. Notification: continuous.

Costs Per Year: Application fee: $30. State resident tuition: $6718 full-time, $256.10 per credit hour part-time. Nonresident tuition: $14,858 full-time, $581.50 per credit hour part-time. Mandatory fees: $123 full-time, $123.50 per term part-time. Full-time tuition and fees vary according to course level, course load, program, and student level. Part-time tuition and fees vary according to course level, course load, program, and student level.

Collegiate Environment: Orientation program. Drama-theater group, student-run newspaper, radio station. Social organizations: national fraternities, national sororities; 25% of eligible men and 25% of eligible women are members. Most popular organizations: Dearborn Campus Engineers, student radio station, Association for African-American Students. Major annual events: Native American Pow-Wow, Fall Fest, Human Dignity Week. Student services: health clinic, personal-psychological counseling, women's center. Campus security: 24-hour emergency response devices and patrols, late night transport-escort service. College housing not available. Mardigian Library with 340,897 books, 547,481 microform titles, 1,099 serials, 4,734 audiovisual materials, an OPAC, and a Web page. Operations spending for 2004 fiscal year: $92,001. 350 computers available on campus for general student use. A campuswide network can be accessed from off-campus. Staffed computer lab on campus.

Community Environment: The university is situated in the middle of a rapidly expanding industrial, residential and social area. Nearby is the Ford Motor Company World Headquarters Complex, the Fairlane Town Center, the Hyatt Regency Hotel and several new apartment and townhouse complexes. Within one hour's driving distance are the cultural opportunities available in Ann Arbor, Meadow Brook Theatre in Rochester, the Michigan Opera Theatre and the Fisher Theatre of Detroit and the various social and cultural events in the city of Dearborn.

■ **UNIVERSITY OF MICHIGAN-FLINT** *L-23*

303 East Kearsley St.

Flint, MI 48502-1950

Tel: (810)762-3000

Admissions: (810)762-3434

E-mail: maryjoss@umflint.edu

Web Site: http://www.umflint.edu/

Description: State-supported, comprehensive, coed. Part of University of Michigan System. Awards bachelor's, master's, and first professional degrees. Founded 1956. Setting: 72-acre urban campus with easy access to Detroit. Endowment: $55.4 million. Research spending for 2004 fiscal year: $680,000. Educational spending for 2005 fiscal year: $5271 per student. Total enrollment: 6,423. Faculty: 420 (213 full-time, 207 part-time). Student-undergrad faculty ratio is 15:1. 1,651 applied, 85% were admitted. 16% from top 10% of their high school class, 42% from top quarter, 75% from top half. Full-time: 3,458 students, 63% women, 37% men. Part-time: 2,213 students, 65% women, 35% men. Students come from 21 states and territories, 19 other countries, 1% from out-of-state, 1% Native American, 3% Hispanic, 11% black, 2% Asian American or Pacific Islander, 1% international, 34% 25 or older, 12% transferred in. Retention: 80% of full-time freshmen returned the following year. Academic areas with the most degrees conferred: education; business/marketing; health professions and related sciences. Core. Calendar: semesters. Academic remediation for entering students, services for LD students, advanced placement, self-designed majors, honors program, independent study, distance learning, double major, summer session for credit, part-time degree program, co-op programs and internships, graduate courses open to undergrads. Study abroad program.

Entrance Requirements: Options: Peterson's Universal Application, Common Application, deferred admission. Required: high school transcript, minimum 2.0 high school GPA, SAT or ACT. Recommended: essay, recommendations. Required for some: essay, recommendations. Entrance: moderately difficult. Notification: continuous.

Costs Per Year: Application fee: $30. State resident tuition: $6082 full-time, $240 per credit part-time. Nonresident tuition: $11,834 full-time, $480 per credit part-time. Mandatory fees: $316 full-time, $124 per term part-time. Full-time tuition and fees vary according to program. Part-time tuition and fees vary according to program.

Collegiate Environment: Orientation program. Drama-theater group, choral group, student-run newspaper. Social organizations: 54 open to all; national fraternities, national sororities, local fraternities, local sororities; 1% of eligible men and 1% of eligible women are members. Most popular organizations: Business Club, International Student Organization, Muslim Student Association, Students Organizing Fun Activities Sober (SOFAS), Inter-Varsity Christian Fellowship. Major annual events: Welcome Back Picnic, Spring Finale, CPB Movie Nights. Student services: health clinic, personal-psychological counseling, women's center. Campus security: 24-hour emergency response devices and patrols, student patrols, late night transport-escort service. College housing not available. Frances Willson Thompson Library with 253,182 books, 592,924 microform titles, 900 serials, 18,789 audiovisual materials, an OPAC, and a Web page. Operations spending for 2004 fiscal year: $1.7 million. 213 computers available on campus for general student use. A campuswide network can be accessed from off-campus. Staffed computer lab on campus.

Community Environment: See Kettering University.

■ **UNIVERSITY OF PHOENIX-METRO DETROIT CAMPUS** *L-10*
5480 Corporate Dr., Ste. 240
Troy, MI 48098-2623
Tel: (248)925-4100
Free: 800-228-7240
Admissions: (480)557-1712
Fax: (248)267-0147
Web Site: http://www.phoenix.edu/

Description: Proprietary, comprehensive, coed. Awards bachelor's and master's degrees. Setting: urban campus. Total enrollment: 3,993. Faculty: 341 (11 full-time, 330 part-time). Student-undergrad faculty ratio is 11:1. 175 applied. Full-time: 2,970 students, 69% women, 31% men. 0.1% Native American, 0.4% Hispanic, 16% black, 0.4% Asian American or Pacific Islander, 3% international, 93% 25 or older. Academic areas with the most degrees conferred: business/marketing; computer and information sciences; health professions and related sciences. Core. Calendar: continuous. Advanced placement, accelerated degree program, independent study, distance learning, external degree program, adult/continuing education programs, graduate courses open to undergrads.

Entrance Requirements: Open admission. Option: deferred admission. Required: 1 recommendation. Required for some: high school transcript. Entrance: noncompetitive. Application deadline: Rolling.

Costs Per Year: Application fee: $110. Tuition: $11,340 full-time, $378 per credit part-time. Mandatory fees: $560 full-time, $70 per course part-time.

Collegiate Environment: College housing not available. University Library with 444 books, 666 serials, an OPAC, and a Web page. System-wide operations spending for 2004 fiscal year: $3.2 million.

■ **UNIVERSITY OF PHOENIX-WEST MICHIGAN CAMPUS** *L-17*
318 River Ridge Dr. NW
Grand Rapids, MI 49544-1683
Tel: (616)647-5100
Free: 800-228-7240
Admissions: (480)557-1712
Web Site: http://www.phoenix.edu/

Description: Proprietary, comprehensive, coed. Awards bachelor's and master's degrees. Founded 2000. Setting: urban campus. Total enrollment: 1,156. Faculty: 203 (8 full-time, 195 part-time). Student-undergrad faculty ratio is 6:1. 33 applied. Full-time: 959 students, 60% women, 40% men. 0% from out-of-state, 0.1% Native American, 1% Hispanic, 3% black, 1% Asian American or Pacific Islander, 6% international, 92% 25 or older. Academic areas with the most degrees conferred: business/marketing; computer and information sciences; health professions and related sciences. Core. Calendar: continuous. Advanced placement, accelerated degree program, independent study, distance learning, external degree program, adult/continuing education programs, graduate courses open to undergrads.

Entrance Requirements: Open admission. Option: deferred admission. Required: 1 recommendation. Required for some: high school transcript. Entrance: noncompetitive. Application deadline: Rolling.

Costs Per Year: Application fee: $110. Tuition: $11,100 full-time, $370 per credit part-time. Mandatory fees: $560 full-time, $70 per course part-time.

Collegiate Environment: College housing not available. University Library with 444 books, 666 serials, an OPAC, and a Web page. System-wide operations spending for 2004 fiscal year: $3.2 million.

■ **WALSH COLLEGE OF ACCOUNTANCY AND BUSINESS ADMINISTRATION** *L-10*
3838 Livernois Rd., PO Box 7006
Troy, MI 48007-7006
Tel: (248)689-8282
Admissions: (248)823-1209
Fax: (248)524-2520
Web Site: http://www.walshcollege.edu/

Description: Independent, upper-level, coed. Awards bachelor's and master's degrees. Founded 1922. Setting: 29-acre suburban campus with easy access to Detroit. Endowment: $2.7 million. Educational spending for 2005 fiscal year: $3555 per student. Total enrollment: 3,105. Full-time: 145 students, 45% women, 55% men. Part-time: 764 students, 60% women, 40% men. Students come from 4 states and territories, 36 other countries, 1% from out-of-state, 0.1% Native American, 1% Hispanic, 6% black, 3% Asian American or Pacific Islander, 9% international, 61% 25 or older, 95% transferred in. Calendar: 4-11week terms. Services for LD students, advanced placement, independent study, distance learning, double major, summer session for credit, part-time degree program, adult/continuing education programs, internships. Off campus study.

Costs Per Year: Application fee: $25. Tuition: $9000 full-time, $250 per credit part-time. Mandatory fees: $230 full-time, $115 per term part-time.

Collegiate Environment: Orientation program. Social organizations: 7 open to all. Most popular organizations: student government, American Marketing Association, Economics/Finance Club, Accounting Club, National Association of Black Accountants. Campus security: 24-hour emergency response devices. College housing not available. Vollbrecht Library plus 1 other with 26,300 books, 123,000 microform titles, 8,210 serials, 121 audiovisual materials, an OPAC, and a Web page. Operations spending for 2004 fiscal year: $763,800. 300 computers available on campus for general student use. A campuswide network can be accessed from off-campus. Staffed computer lab on campus.

Community Environment: The college is located north of Detroit in the city of Troy, population 75,025. The city serves as headquarters for many large corporations.

■ **WASHTENAW COMMUNITY COLLEGE** *O-5*
4800 East Huron River Dr., PO Box D-1
Ann Arbor, MI 48106
Tel: (734)973-3300
Admissions: (734)973-3315
Fax: (734)677-5408
Web Site: http://www.wccnet.edu/

Description: State and locally supported, 2-year, coed. Awards certificates, transfer associate, and terminal associate degrees. Founded 1965. Setting: 235-acre suburban campus with easy access to Detroit. Endowment: $3.5 million. Research spending for 2004 fiscal year: $110,000. Total enrollment: 12,070. Full-time: 3,432 students, 53% women, 47% men. Part-time: 8,638 students, 57% women, 43% men. Students come from 12 states and territories, 37 other countries, 1% from out-of-state, 1% Native American, 2% Hispanic, 15% black, 3% Asian American or Pacific Islander, 5% international, 48% 25 or older. Core. Calendar: semesters. Academic remediation for entering students, ESL program, services for LD students, advanced placement, self-designed majors, honors program, independent study, distance learning, summer session for credit, part-time degree program, external degree program, adult/continuing education programs, co-op programs and internships. ROTC: Army (c), Naval (c), Air Force (c).

Entrance Requirements: Open admission except for health occupations programs. Options: Peterson's Universal Application, Common Application, electronic application, early admission, deferred admission, international baccalaureate accepted. Recommended: SAT or ACT. Required for some: high school transcript. Placement: SAT or ACT recommended. Entrance: noncompetitive. Application deadline: Rolling. Notification: continuous. Preference given to county residents for over-subscribed programs.

Collegiate Environment: Orientation program. Drama-theater group, choral group, student-run newspaper, radio station. Social organizations: 30 open to all. Most popular organizations: African-American Student Association, Delta Epsilon Chi, Muslim Student Association, Phi Theta Kappa, Anime Club. Major annual events: Job Fair, Student Activities Showcase Day, student/staff softball game. Student services: personal-psychological counseling, women's center. Campus security: 24-hour emergency response devices and patrols, late night transport-escort service. College housing not available. Media Resource Center with 76,500 books, 565 serials, an OPAC, and a Web page. Operations spending for 2004 fiscal year: $1.8 million. 300 computers available on campus for general student use. A campuswide network can be accessed from off-campus. Staffed computer lab on campus.

Community Environment: See University of Michigan.

■ **WAYNE COUNTY COMMUNITY COLLEGE DISTRICT** *O-24*
801 West Fort St.
Detroit, MI 48226-3010
Tel: (313)496-2600
Admissions: (313)496-2884
Fax: (313)961-2791
E-mail: caafjh@wccc.edu
Web Site: http://www.wcccd.edu/

Description: State and locally supported, 2-year, coed. Awards certificates, transfer associate, and terminal associate degrees. Founded 1967. Setting: urban campus. Research spending for 2004 fiscal year: $244,498. Educational spending for 2005 fiscal year: $5026 per student. Total enrollment: 11,673. 62% 25 or older. Core. Calendar: semesters. Academic remediation for entering students, ESL program, honors program, summer session for credit, part-time degree program, adult/continuing education programs, co-op programs.

Entrance Requirements: Open admission. Options: Peterson's Universal Application, Common Application, early admission, deferred admission. Placement: ACT ASSET required. Entrance: noncompetitive. Application deadline: Rolling.

Collegiate Environment: Orientation program. Student-run newspaper. Social organizations: national sororities, local sororities. Major annual events: Career Day, College Night, Jobs Fair. Campus security: 24-hour emergency response devices. College housing not available. Learning Resource Center with 70,000 books and an OPAC. Operations spending for 2004 fiscal year: $963,597. 118 computers available on campus for general student use.

■ **WAYNE STATE UNIVERSITY** *O-24*
656 West Kirby St.
Detroit, MI 48202
Tel: (313)577-2424
Free: 800-WSU-INFO
Admissions: (313)577-3577
Fax: (313)577-7536
E-mail: admissions@wayne.edu
Web Site: http://www.wayne.edu/

Description: State-supported, university, coed. Awards bachelor's, master's, doctoral, and first professional degrees and post-master's certificates. Founded 1868. Setting: 203-acre urban campus. Endowment: $192.2 million. Research spending for 2004 fiscal year: $143.6 million. Educational spending for 2005 fiscal year: $10,159 per student. Total enrollment: 33,137. Faculty: 1,917 (1,004 full-time, 913 part-time). Student-undergrad faculty ratio is 16:1. 11,410 applied, 60% were admitted. 25% from top 10% of their high school class, 50% from top quarter, 76% from top half. Full-time: 11,924 students, 58% women, 42% men. Part-time: 8,813 students, 61% women, 39% men. Students come from 34 states and territories, 57 other countries, 1% from out-of-state, 0.5% Native American, 3% Hispanic, 33% black, 5% Asian American or Pacific Islander, 4% international, 34% 25 or older, 7% live on campus, 11% transferred in. Academic areas with the most degrees

conferred: business/marketing; education; health professions and related sciences. Core. Calendar: semesters. Academic remediation for entering students, ESL program, services for LD students, advanced placement, accelerated degree program, self-designed majors, honors program, independent study, distance learning, double major, summer session for credit, part-time degree program, adult/continuing education programs, co-op programs and internships, graduate courses open to undergrads. Off campus study at University of Michigan, University of Windsor. Study abroad program. ROTC: Air Force (c).

Entrance Requirements: Options: deferred admission, international baccalaureate accepted. Required: high school transcript, minimum 2.0 high school GPA, SAT or ACT. Required for some: recommendations, interview, portfolio. Entrance: moderately difficult. Application deadline: 8/1. Notification: continuous until 9/1.

Costs Per Year: Application fee: $30. State resident tuition: $5682 full-time, $189.40 per semester hour part-time. Nonresident tuition: $13,014 full-time, $433.80 per semester hour part-time. Mandatory fees: $757 full-time, $15.80 per semester hour part-time, $141.70 per term part-time. Full-time tuition and fees vary according to student level. Part-time tuition and fees vary according to student level. College room and board: $5350. Room and board charges vary according to housing facility.

Collegiate Environment: Orientation program. Drama-theater group, choral group, marching band, student-run newspaper. Social organizations: 104 open to all; national fraternities, national sororities, local fraternities, local sororities; 2% of eligible men and 2% of eligible women are members. Most popular organizations: Indian Student Association, Golden Key Honor Society, Campus Crusade for Christ, Friendship Association of Chinese Students, Project Volunteer/Students of Service. Major annual events: Student Organization Days, Homecoming Week, International Fair. Student services: legal services, health clinic, personal-psychological counseling, women's center. Campus security: 24-hour emergency response devices and patrols, late night transport-escort service, controlled dormitory access. 1,700 college housing spaces available; 1,347 were occupied in 2003-04. Freshmen given priority for college housing. Option: coed housing available. David Adamany Undergraduate Library plus 6 others with 1.9 million books, 3.8 million microform titles, 18,645 serials, 70,131 audiovisual materials, an OPAC, and a Web page. 1,800 computers available on campus for general student use. A campuswide network can be accessed from student residence rooms and from off campus. Staffed computer lab on campus.

Community Environment: At the turn of the 20th Century, Detroit was a quiet, tree-shaded community brewing beer and producing comfortable carriages and comforting stoves. The serenity was broken by Henry Ford's creation, a vehicle "propelled by power generated from within itself." Today, it is the greatest automobile-manufacturing city in the world. It is also rapidly becoming a steel center and a leader in the manufacturing of pharmaceuticals, office equipment, rubber products, salt, television components, synthetic resins and paints, meat products, marine engines and more than half the garden seed used throughout the country. Annual mean temperature is 49.3 degrees, and annual rainfall is 31.03 inches. Definitely an industrial city, Detroit has a civic center complex on the riverfront, an excellent park system and numerous museums and art galleries.

■ **WEST SHORE COMMUNITY COLLEGE** *I-16*
PO Box 277, 3000 North Stiles Rd.
Scottville, MI 49454-0277
Tel: (231)845-6211
Fax: (231)845-0207
E-mail: admissions@westshore.cc.mi.us
Web Site: http://www.westshore.edu/

Description: District-supported, 2-year, coed. Part of Michigan Department of Education. Awards certificates, transfer associate, and terminal associate degrees. Founded 1967. Setting: 375-acre rural campus. Endowment: $291,972. Educational spending for 2005 fiscal year: $3249 per student. Total enrollment: 1,372. 323 applied, 100% were admitted. Students come from 3 states and territories, 1% from out-of-state, 43% 25 or older. Core. Calendar: semesters. Academic remediation for entering students, services for LD students, advanced placement, self-designed majors, independent study, distance learning, summer session for credit, part-time degree program, adult/continuing education programs, co-op programs and internships. Off campus study.

Entrance Requirements: Open admission except for applicants under 18 or nursing program. Options: Peterson's Universal Application, Common Application, early admission, deferred admission. Required: high school transcript. Placement: ACT recommended; ACT ASSET required for some. Entrance: noncompetitive. Application deadline: Rolling. Notification: continuous.

Collegiate Environment: Orientation program. Drama-theater group, choral group, student-run newspaper. Social organizations: 13 open to all. Most popular organizations: Art Club, Student Senate, Phi Theta Kappa, Science Club, Law Enforcement Club. Student services: personal-psychological counseling. Campus security: 24-hour emergency response devices and patrols. College housing not available. West Shore Library plus 1 other with 2,500 books, 910 microform titles, 150 serials, 1,100 audiovisual materials, an OPAC, and a Web page. Operations spending for 2004 fiscal year: $196,537. 185 computers available on campus for general student use. A campuswide network can be accessed from off-campus. Staffed computer lab on campus.

Community Environment: Scottville is a rural city located 80 miles northwest of Grand Rapids. Agriculture is the main economic feature of the city with a Stokley canning factory second. Recreation is provided by local Riverside Park, with camping, boating and fishing. In addition, duck and small game hunting is available in the surrounding area. Community services include a library, and five churches. Bus, rail and air transportation are easily accessible.

■ **WESTERN MICHIGAN UNIVERSITY** *O-17*

1903 West Michigan Ave.
Kalamazoo, MI 49008-5202
Tel: (269)387-1000
Admissions: (269)387-2000
Fax: (269)387-2096
E-mail: ask-wmu@wmich.edu
Web Site: http://www.wmich.edu/

Description: State-supported, university, coed. Awards bachelor's, master's, and doctoral degrees (specialist). Founded 1903. Setting: 1,200-acre urban campus. Endowment: $150.2 million. Research spending for 2004 fiscal year: $21 million. Educational spending for 2005 fiscal year: $5432 per student. Total enrollment: 26,239. Faculty: 1,460 (922 full-time, 538 part-time). Student-undergrad faculty ratio is 20:1. 12,928 applied, 85% were admitted. 13% from top 10% of their high school class, 33% from top quarter, 70% from top half. Full-time: 18,760 students, 51% women, 49% men. Part-time: 2,674 students, 51% women, 49% men. Students come from 53 states and territories, 109 other countries, 5% from out-of-state, 0.5% Native American, 2% Hispanic, 6% black, 2% Asian American or Pacific Islander, 2% international, 9% 25 or older, 24% live on campus, 8% transferred in. Retention: 73% of full-time freshmen returned the following year. Academic areas with the most degrees conferred: business/marketing; education; communications/journalism. Core. Calendar: semesters. Academic remediation for entering students, ESL program, services for LD students, advanced placement, accelerated degree program, self-designed majors, freshman honors college, honors program, independent study, distance learning, double major, summer session for credit, part-time degree program, adult/continuing education programs, co-op programs and internships, graduate courses open to undergrads. Off campus study at Kalamazoo College, Kalamazoo Valley Community College, Davenport College of Business. Study abroad program. ROTC: Army.

Entrance Requirements: Options: Peterson's Universal Application, electronic application, deferred admission. Required: high school transcript, minimum X high school GPA, SAT or ACT. Required for some: interview. Entrance: moderately difficult. Application deadline: Rolling. Notification: continuous.

Costs Per Year: Application fee: $35. State resident tuition: $5826 full-time, $194.18 per credit hour part-time. Nonresident tuition: $15,204 full-time, $506.81 per credit hour part-time. Mandatory fees: $652 full-time, $165.75 per term part-time. Full-time tuition and fees vary according to course load, location, and student level. Part-time tuition and fees vary according to course load, location, and student level. College room and board: $6651. College room only: $3518. Room and board charges vary according to board plan.

Collegiate Environment: Orientation program. Drama-theater group, choral group, marching band, student-run newspaper, radio station. Social organizations: 275 open to all; national fraternities, national sororities, local fraternities, local sororities; 8% of eligible men and 8% of eligible women are members. Most popular organizations: Golden Key Society, Inter-Varsity Christian Fellowship, Malaysian Student Organization. Major annual events: Homecoming, Bronco Bash, Gold Rush. Student services: legal services, health clinic, personal-psychological counseling, women's center. Campus security: 24-hour emergency response devices and patrols, student patrols, late night transport-escort service, controlled dormitory access. 6,300 college housing spaces available; 5,701 were occupied in 2003-04. No special consideration for freshman housing applicants. Options: coed, men-only, women-only housing available. Waldo Library plus 4 others with 2 million books, 1.9 million microform titles, 9,715 serials, 25,711 audiovisual materials, an OPAC, and a Web page. Operations spending for 2004 fiscal year: $12.6 million. 2,000 computers available on campus for general student use. A campuswide network can be accessed from student residence rooms and from off campus. Staffed computer lab on campus.

Community Environment: At one time a gathering place of the Potawatomies, the city received its name from the Indian word meaning"place where the water boils." Today the city is an important paper-manufacturing center with an annual production of over three million tons. The city is also prominent in the manufacture of pharmaceutical drugs. Part-time work is available for students. The largest city in southwest Michigan, Kalamazoo has many parks and picnic areas, 9 golf courses, ski areas, sandy beaches, and good hunting in season. Community service is provided by several churches, 2 hospitals, and shopping malls. The municipal library, art center, civic players, and symphony orchestra provide cultural outlets.

■ **YESHIVA GEDDOLAH OF GREATER DETROIT RABBINICAL COLLEGE** *M-10*

24600 Greenfield
Oak Park, MI 48237-1544
Tel: (810)968-3360
Description: Independent Jewish, 4-year, men only. Awards bachelor's degrees. Founded 1985. Setting: 1-acre campus with easy access to Detroit.

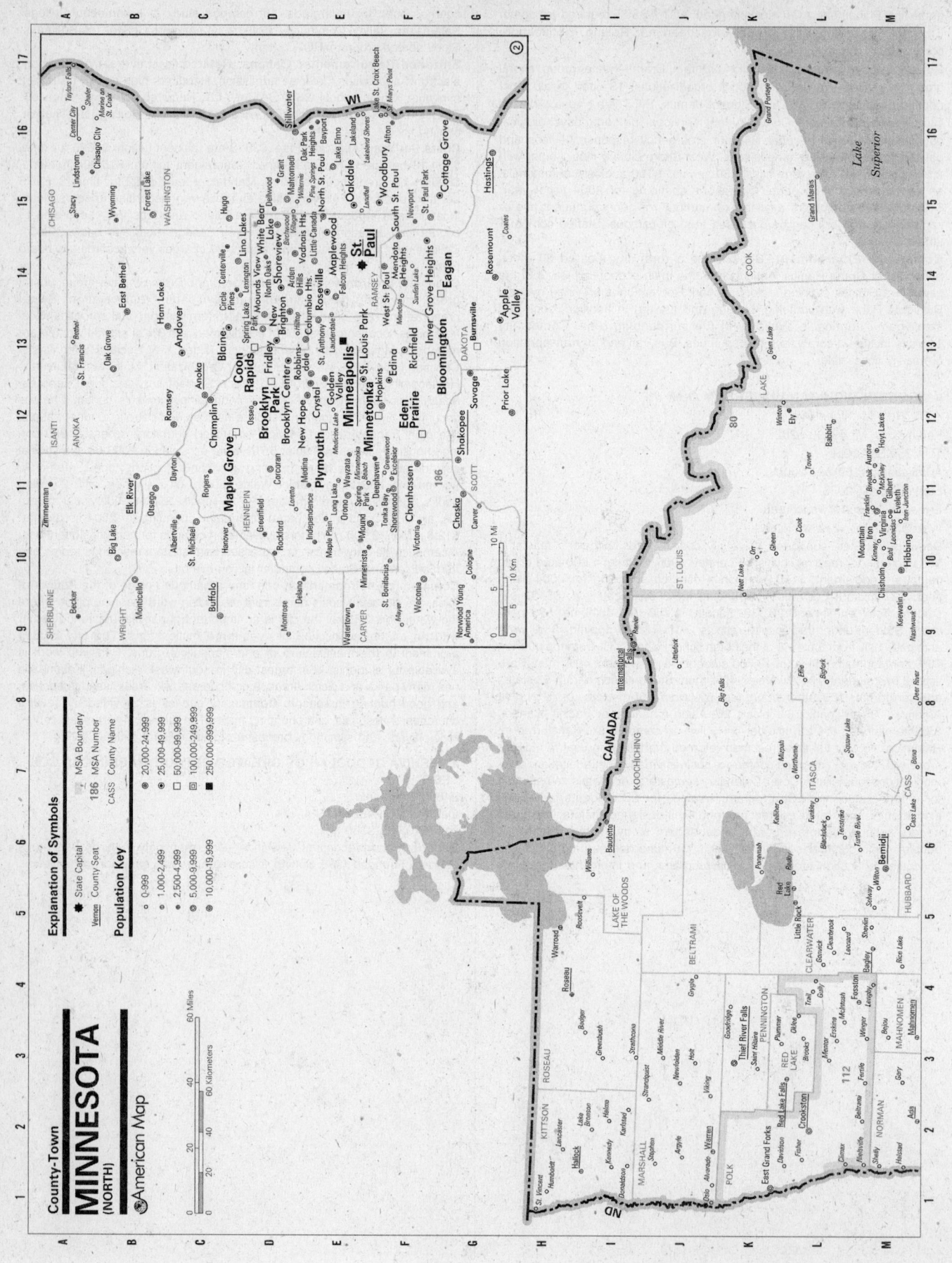

County-Town
MINNESOTA
(NORTH)

🌎 American Map

0   20   40   60 Miles
0   20   40   60 Kilometers

Explanation of Symbols

★	State Capital
Vernon	County Seat
186	MSA Number
	MSA Boundary
CASS	County Name

Population Key

○	0-999
⊙	1,000-2,499
◉	2,500-4,999
◎	5,000-9,999
⊚	10,000-19,999
⊛	20,000-24,999
⊗	25,000-49,999
▢	50,000-99,999
▣	100,000-249,999
■	250,000-999,999

②

Lake Superior

CANADA

ND

WI

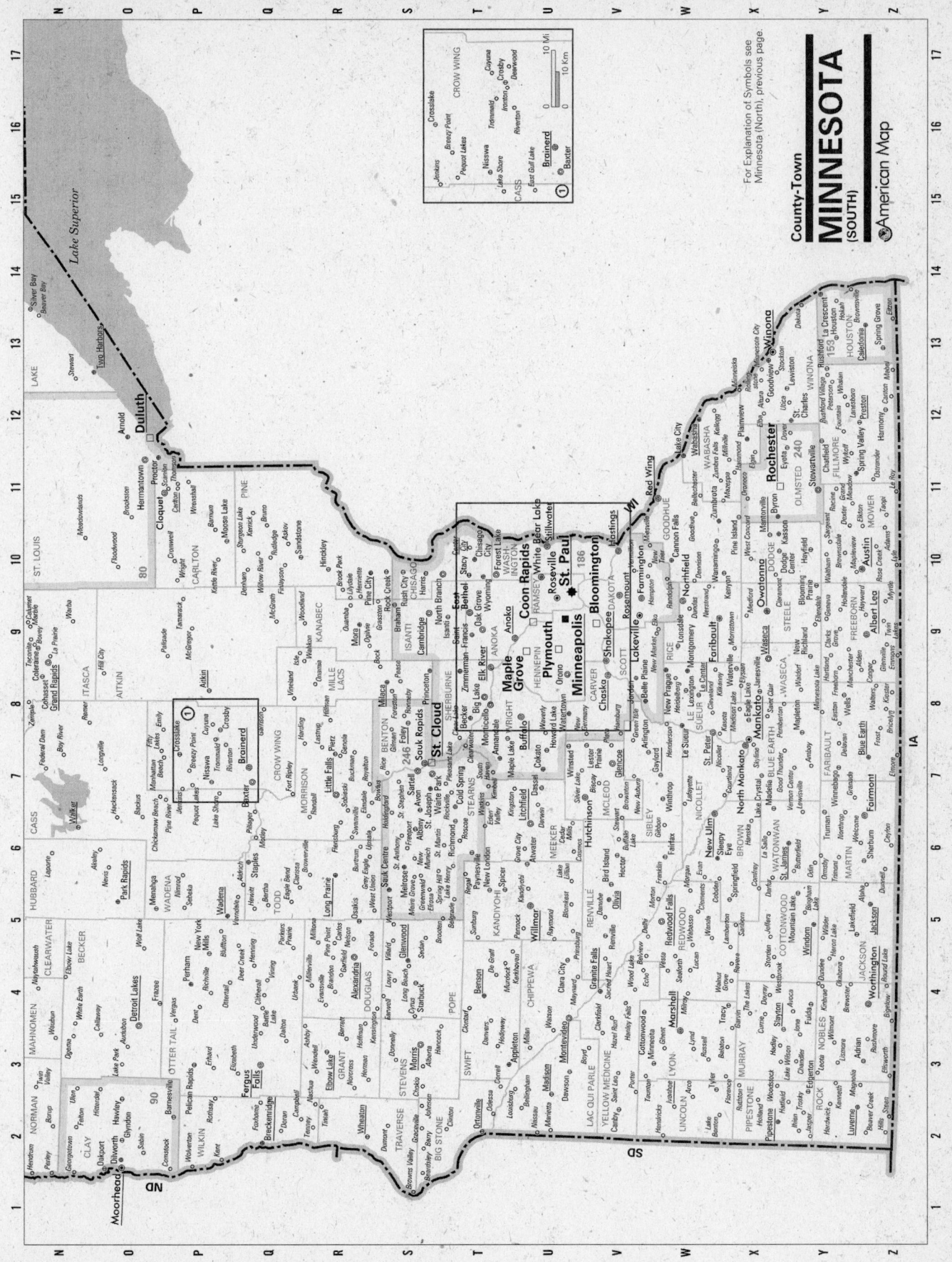

MINNESOTA
(SOUTH)

County-Town

American Map

For Explanation of Symbols see
Minnesota (North), previous page.

■ **ACADEMY COLLEGE** *U-9*

1101 East 78th St., Ste. 100
Minneapolis, MN 55420
Tel: (952)851-0066
Free: 800-292-9149
Fax: (952)851-0094
Web Site: http://www.academycollege.edu/

Description: Proprietary, primarily 2-year, coed. Awards certificates, transfer associate, terminal associate, and bachelor's degrees. Setting: urban campus. Total enrollment: 320. Students come from 5 states and territories. Core. Academic remediation for entering students, ESL program, services for LD students, advanced placement, accelerated degree program, honors program, distance learning, double major, summer session for credit, part-time degree program, adult/continuing education programs, co-op programs and internships.

Entrance Requirements: Open admission. Options: Common Application, electronic application, early admission, deferred admission, international baccalaureate accepted. Required: high school transcript, interview. Entrance: minimally difficult. Notification: continuous.

Collegiate Environment: Orientation program. College housing not available. Learning Resource Center plus 1 other with 1,309 books, 22 serials, 88 audiovisual materials, an OPAC, and a Web page. 75 computers available on campus for general student use. A campuswide network can be accessed. Staffed computer lab on campus.

■ **ALEXANDRIA TECHNICAL COLLEGE** *R-5*

1601 Jefferson St.
Alexandria, MN 56308-3707
Tel: (320)762-0221; 888-234-1222
Fax: (320)762-4430
E-mail: admissionsrep@alextech.edu
Web Site: http://www.alextech.edu/

Description: State-supported, 2-year, coed. Part of Minnesota State Colleges and Universities System. Awards certificates, diplomas, transfer associate, and terminal associate degrees. Founded 1961. Setting: 40-acre small town campus. Total enrollment: 1,971. Student-undergrad faculty ratio is 20:1. 1,838 applied, 67% were admitted. Students come from 14 states and territories, 4% from out-of-state, 1% Native American, 1% Hispanic, 0.4% black, 1% Asian American or Pacific Islander, 23% 25 or older. Calendar: semesters. Academic remediation for entering students, services for LD students, advanced placement, distance learning, double major, part-time degree program, internships.

Entrance Requirements: Open admission. Options: Common Application, electronic application, early admission. Required: high school transcript, interview. Entrance: minimally difficult. Application deadline: Rolling.

Costs Per Year: Application fee: $20. State resident tuition: $4318 full-time, $127 per credit part-time. Nonresident tuition: $8636 full-time, $254 per credit part-time. Mandatory fees: $401 full-time, $11.80 per credit part-time.

Collegiate Environment: Orientation program. Social organizations: 3 open to all. Most popular organizations: VICA (Vocational Industrial Clubs of America) Skills USA, BPA (Business Professionals of America), DECA (Delta Epsilon Club), Student Senate, Phi Theta Kappa. Major annual events: Open House, College for a Day, Sno-Daze. Student services: personal-psychological counseling. Campus security: late night transport-escort service, security cameras inside and outside. College housing not available. Learning Resource Center with 16,636 books, 346 serials, 1,219 audiovisual materials, an OPAC, and a Web page. 467 computers available on campus for general student use. Computer purchase/lease plans available. A campuswide network can be accessed from off-campus. Staffed computer lab on campus.

■ **ANOKA-RAMSEY COMMUNITY COLLEGE** *U-9*

11200 Mississippi Blvd., NW
Coon Rapids, MN 55433-3470
Tel: (763)427-2600
Admissions: (763)422-3420
Fax: (763)576-5944
Web Site: http://www.anokaramsey.edu/

Description: State-supported, 2-year, coed. Part of Minnesota State Colleges and Universities System. Awards certificates, transfer associate, and terminal associate degrees. Founded 1965. Setting: 100-acre suburban campus with easy access to Minneapolis-St. Paul. Total enrollment: 5,793. Student-undergrad faculty ratio is 25:1. 3,138 applied, 99% were admitted. 1% from out-of-state, 1% Native American, 1% Hispanic, 4% black, 3% Asian American or Pacific Islander, 0.5% international, 34% 25 or older. Core. Calendar: semesters. Academic remediation for entering students, services for LD students, advanced placement, accelerated degree program, honors program, independent study, distance learning, summer session for credit, part-time degree program, co-op programs and internships. Off campus study at other colleges in the Minnesota State Colleges and Universities System; evening courses at area community centers and high schools.. Study abroad program. ROTC: Air Force (c).

Entrance Requirements: Open admission for state residents only; the nursing program and some technical programs have additional admission requirements. Options: Peterson's Universal Application, early admission, deferred admission. Required for some: high school transcript. Entrance: noncompetitive. Application deadline: Rolling. Notification: continuous.

Costs Per Year: Application fee: $20. State resident tuition: $3390 full-time, $113 per credit part-time. Nonresident tuition: $6780 full-time, $226 per credit part-time. Mandatory fees: $414 full-time, $13.80 per credit part-time.

Collegiate Environment: Orientation program. Drama-theater group, choral group, student-run newspaper. Social organizations: 15 open to all. Most popular organizations: Phi Theta Kappa, Student Senate, student newspaper, International Student Club, Inter-Varsity Christian Fellowship. Major annual events: Fall Picnic, Spring Picnic. Student services: personal-psychological counseling. Campus security: 24-hour emergency response devices and patrols, late night transport-escort service. College housing not available. Coon Rapids Campus Library with 40,651 books, 25,588 microform titles, 232 serials, 1,517 audiovisual materials, an OPAC, and a Web page. Operations spending for 2004 fiscal year: $431,917. 600 computers available on campus for general student use. A campuswide network can be accessed from off-campus. Staffed computer lab on campus.

Community Environment: A suburban area with a temperate climate, Coon Rapids (population 53,000) enjoys all the recreational, social and cultural advantages of the Twin Cities. All forms of commercial transportation are available. Community facilities include churches, a public library and a community hospital nearby.

■ **ANOKA-RAMSEY COMMUNITY COLLEGE, CAMBRIDGE CAMPUS** *S-9*

300 Polk St. South
Cambridge, MN 55008-5706

Tel: (763)689-7000
Fax: (763)689-7050
Web Site: http://www.anokaramsey.edu/
Description: State-supported, 2-year, coed. Part of Minnesota State Colleges and Universities System. Awards certificates, transfer associate, and terminal associate degrees. Setting: small town campus. Total enrollment: 1,737. Student-undergrad faculty ratio is 25:1. 910 applied, 99% were admitted. 1% from out-of-state, 1% Native American, 1% Hispanic, 1% black, 1% Asian American or Pacific Islander, 0% international, 45% 25 or older. Core. Calendar: semesters. Academic remediation for entering students, services for LD students, advanced placement, accelerated degree program, honors program, independent study, distance learning, summer session for credit, part-time degree program, co-op programs and internships. Off campus study at other colleges in the Minnesota State College and Universities System. Study abroad program. ROTC: Air Force (c).
Entrance Requirements: Open admission for state residents only; the nursing program and some technical programs have additional admission requirements.. Options: early admission, deferred admission. Required for some: high school transcript. Entrance: noncompetitive. Application deadline: Rolling. Notification: continuous.
Costs Per Year: Application fee: $20. State resident tuition: $3390 full-time, $113 per credit part-time. Nonresident tuition: $6780 full-time, $226 per credit part-time. Mandatory fees: $414 full-time, $13.80 per credit part-time.
Collegiate Environment: Orientation program. Drama-theater group, choral group, student-run newspaper. Student services: personal-psychological counseling. College housing not available. Cambridge Campus Library with 18,927 books, 7,825 microform titles, 122 serials, 1,536 audiovisual materials, an OPAC, and a Web page. 200 computers available on campus for general student use. A campuswide network can be accessed from off-campus. Staffed computer lab on campus.

■ ANOKA TECHNICAL COLLEGE *U-9*
1355 West Hwy. 10
Anoka, MN 55303
Tel: (612)576-4700
Admissions: (763)576-4746
Web Site: http://www.ank.tec.mn.us/
Description: State-supported, 2-year, coed. Part of Minnesota State Colleges and Universities System. Awards certificates, diplomas, transfer associate, and terminal associate degrees. Founded 1967. Setting: small town campus with easy access to Minneapolis-St. Paul. Total enrollment: 2,371. 1,165 applied, 82% were admitted. Full-time: 1,058 students, 51% women, 49% men. Part-time: 1,313 students, 48% women, 52% men. 0.3% Native American, 1% Hispanic, 8% black, 2% Asian American or Pacific Islander, 1% international, 53% 25 or older. Retention: 59% of full-time freshmen returned the following year. Calendar: semesters. Academic remediation for entering students, ESL program, services for LD students, advanced placement, distance learning, double major, part-time degree program, co-op programs and internships.
Entrance Requirements: Open admission. Options: Common Application, electronic application, deferred admission. Required: high school transcript. Required for some: interview. Entrance: noncompetitive. Application deadline: 8/1.
Costs Per Year: Application fee: $20. State resident tuition: $3886 full-time, $129.55 per credit part-time. Nonresident tuition: $7772 full-time, $259.10 per credit part-time. Mandatory fees: $421 full-time, $14.05 per credit part-time. Full-time tuition and fees vary according to program and reciprocity agreements. Part-time tuition and fees vary according to program and reciprocity agreements.
Collegiate Environment: Orientation program. Student services: personal-psychological counseling. Campus security: late night transport-escort service. College housing not available. 100 computers available on campus for general student use. A campuswide network can be accessed. Staffed computer lab on campus.

■ THE ART INSTITUTES INTERNATIONAL MINNESOTA *U-9*
15 South 9th St.
Minneapolis, MN 55402-3137
Tel: (612)332-3361
Free: 800-777-3643
Fax: (612)332-3934
Web Site: http://www.aim.artinstitutes.edu/
Description: Proprietary, 4-year, coed. Part of Education Management Corporation. Awards associate and bachelor's degrees. Founded 1964. Set-

ting: urban campus. Total enrollment: 1,594. Student-undergrad faculty ratio is 20:1. 914 applied, 100% were admitted. Students come from 10 states and territories, 6 other countries, 6% from out-of-state, 1% Native American, 1% Hispanic, 2% black, 2% Asian American or Pacific Islander, 0% international, 31% 25 or older, 13% live on campus. Core. Academic remediation for entering students, services for LD students, advanced placement, independent study, summer session for credit, part-time degree program, co-op programs and internships.
Entrance Requirements: Options: Common Application, electronic application, deferred admission, international baccalaureate accepted. Required: essay, high school transcript, interview, ACT COMPASS. Recommended: ACT. Placement: ACT recommended. Entrance: minimally difficult. Application deadline: Rolling.
Costs Per Year: Application fee: $50. Tuition: $17,904 full-time, $373 per credit part-time.
Collegiate Environment: Orientation program. Student-run newspaper. Social organizations: 8 open to all. Most popular organizations: Siggraph, AIGA, ASID, ACF Jr., GSA. Major annual events: Summerfest Carnival, Adobe Design Competition, Thanksgiving Dinner. Student services: personal-psychological counseling. Campus security: security personnel during hours of operation. 200 college housing spaces available; 10 were occupied in 2003-04. Option: coed housing available. Learning Resource Center with 42,752 books, 160 serials, 2,259 audiovisual materials, an OPAC, and a Web page. 212 computers available on campus for general student use. A campuswide network can be accessed from off-campus. Staffed computer lab on campus.

■ AUGSBURG COLLEGE *U-9*
2211 Riverside Ave.
Minneapolis, MN 55454-1351
Tel: (612)330-1000
Free: 800-788-5678
Admissions: (612)330-1001
Fax: (612)330-1649
E-mail: admissions@augsburg.edu
Web Site: http://www.augsburg.edu/
Description: Independent Lutheran, comprehensive, coed. Awards bachelor's and master's degrees and post-master's certificates. Founded 1869. Setting: 23-acre urban campus. Endowment: $26.7 million. Research spending for 2004 fiscal year: $775,095. Educational spending for 2005 fiscal year: $14,612 per student. Total enrollment: 3,508. Faculty: 370 (163 full-time, 207 part-time). Student-undergrad faculty ratio is 15:1. 996 applied, 76% were admitted. 18% from top 10% of their high school class, 45% from top quarter, 70% from top half. Full-time: 2,269 students, 55% women, 45% men. Part-time: 566 students, 69% women, 31% men. Students come from 40 states and territories, 33 other countries, 13% from out-of-state, 1% Native American, 1% Hispanic, 5% black, 3% Asian American or Pacific Islander, 2% international, 38% 25 or older, 54% live on campus, 11% transferred in. Retention: 78% of full-time freshmen returned the following year. Academic areas with the most degrees conferred: business/marketing; education; social sciences. Core. Calendar: semesters for undergraduate programs; trimesters for graduate programs and weekend college. Academic remediation for entering students, ESL program, services for LD students, advanced placement, self-designed majors, freshman honors college, honors program, independent study, double major, summer session for credit, part-time degree program, adult/continuing education programs, co-op programs and internships. Off campus study at Associated Colleges of the Twin Cities. Study abroad program. ROTC: Army (c), Naval (c), Air Force (c).
Entrance Requirements: Options: Peterson's Universal Application, electronic application, deferred admission, international baccalaureate accepted. Required: essay, high school transcript, minimum 2.5 high school GPA, interview, SAT or ACT. Required for some: 2 recommendations. Entrance: moderately difficult. Application deadline: 8/15. Notification: continuous.
Costs Per Year: Application fee: $25. Comprehensive fee: $30,026 includes full-time tuition ($22,900), mandatory fees ($522), and college room and board ($6604). College room only: $3396. Part-time tuition: $2866 per course. Part-time mandatory fees: $86 per course.
Collegiate Environment: Orientation program. Drama-theater group, choral group, student-run newspaper, radio station. Social organizations: 60 open to all. Most popular organizations: Student Activities Council, student government, newspaper/yearbook, campus ministry, intramurals. Major annual events: Days in May, Advent Vespers/Velkommen Yul, Spring Affair. Student

services: health clinic, personal-psychological counseling, women's center. Campus security: 24-hour emergency response devices and patrols, late night transport-escort service, controlled dormitory access. College housing designed to accommodate 950 students; 955 undergraduates lived in college housing during 2003-04. Freshmen given priority for college housing. Options: coed, men-only, women-only housing available. James G. Lindell Library with 146,166 books, 19,719 microform titles, 754 serials, 2,908 audiovisual materials, an OPAC, and a Web page. Operations spending for 2004 fiscal year: $1 million. 260 computers available on campus for general student use. A campuswide network can be accessed from student residence rooms and from off campus. Staffed computer lab on campus.

Community Environment: Augsburg's campus is located in the heart of the Twin Cities, surrounding Murphy Square, the first of 155 parks in the "City of Lakes." The University of Minnesota West Bank campus and two of the city's largest hospitals, Fairview and St. Mary's, are adjacent to the campus. Downtown Minneapolis and St. Paul are minutes west and east via Interstate 94 which forms the southern border of the campus, or on bus routes that also connect with the suburbs.

■ **BEMIDJI STATE UNIVERSITY** *M-6*

1500 Birchmont Dr., NE
Bemidji, MN 56601-2699
Tel: (218)755-2000
Free: 800-652-9747
Admissions: (218)755-2040
Fax: (218)755-2074
E-mail: admissions@bemidjistate.edu
Web Site: http://www.bemidjistate.edu/

Description: State-supported, comprehensive, coed. Part of Minnesota State Colleges and Universities System. Awards associate, bachelor's, and master's degrees. Founded 1919. Setting: 89-acre small town campus. Endowment: $8.2 million. Total enrollment: 4,893. Faculty: 362 (246 full-time, 116 part-time). Student-undergrad faculty ratio is 19:1. 1,489 applied, 73% were admitted. 10% from top 10% of their high school class, 50% from top quarter, 90% from top half. Full-time: 3,248 students, 50% women, 50% men. Part-time: 1,208 students, 66% women, 34% men. Students come from 40 states and territories, 39 other countries, 8% from out-of-state, 3% Native American, 0.2% Hispanic, 1% black, 1% Asian American or Pacific Islander, 5% international, 20% 25 or older, 26% live on campus, 10% transferred in. Retention: 68% of full-time freshmen returned the following year. Academic areas with the most degrees conferred: education; engineering technologies; business/marketing. Core. Calendar: semesters. Academic remediation for entering students, ESL program, services for LD students, advanced placement, honors program, independent study, distance learning, double major, summer session for credit, part-time degree program, external degree program, adult/continuing education programs, co-op programs and internships, graduate courses open to undergrads. Off campus study at other colleges in MNSCU system. Study abroad program.

Entrance Requirements: Options: Common Application, electronic application, deferred admission, international baccalaureate accepted. Required: high school transcript, ACT. Required for some: essay, recommendations, interview. Entrance: moderately difficult. Application deadline: Rolling. Notification: continuous.

Costs Per Year: Application fee: $20. State resident tuition: $5246 full-time, $190.50 per credit part-time. Mandatory fees: $768 full-time, $83.89 per credit part-time. Part-time tuition and fees vary according to course load. College room and board: $5014. College room only: $3214. Room and board charges vary according to board plan and housing facility.

Collegiate Environment: Orientation program. Drama-theater group, choral group, student-run newspaper, radio station. Social organizations: 85 open to all; national fraternities, national sororities, local fraternities; 2% of eligible men and 1% of eligible women are members. Most popular organizations: International Students Organization, Jazz Band Club, Madrigal Dinner Club, Student Senate, Council of Indian Students. Major annual events: homecoming, Funtastic Dance Follies, Feast of Nations. Student services: health clinic, personal-psychological counseling, women's center. Campus security: 24-hour emergency response devices and patrols, late night transport-escort service, controlled dormitory access. 1,600 college housing spaces available; 1,482 were occupied in 2003-04. Freshmen given priority for college housing. Options: coed, men-only, women-only housing available. A. C. Clark Library with 554,087 books, 980,000 microform titles, 991 serials, 5,521 audiovisual materials, an OPAC, and a Web page. Operations spending for 2004 fiscal year: $574,701. 1,200 computers available on campus for general student use. A campuswide network can be accessed from student residence rooms and from off campus. Staffed computer lab on campus.

Community Environment: A regional home for outdoor sports and cultural arts activities, Bemidji (population 12,000) lies in Minnesota North Country on the shores of Lake Bemidji. This area is noted for its scenic forests and lakes that are enjoyed by recreational enthusiasts during all seasons. From excellent fishing in the summer to cross-country and downhill skiing in the winter, residents and visitors alike have found Bemidji to be a community that satisfies a great diversity of interests.

■ **BETHANY LUTHERAN COLLEGE** *X-8*

700 Luther Dr.
Mankato, MN 56001-6163
Tel: (507)344-7000
Free: 800-944-3066
Admissions: (507)344-7320
Fax: (507)344-7376
E-mail: admiss@blc.edu
Web Site: http://www.blc.edu/

Description: Independent Lutheran, 4-year, coed. Awards associate and bachelor's degrees. Founded 1927. Setting: 50-acre small town campus with easy access to Minneapolis-St. Paul. Endowment: $33.3 million. Educational spending for 2005 fiscal year: $6776 per student. Total enrollment: 566. Student-undergrad faculty ratio is 11:1. 346 applied, 84% were admitted. 12% from top 10% of their high school class, 35% from top quarter, 64% from top half. Full-time: 530 students, 56% women, 44% men. Part-time: 36 students, 72% women, 28% men. Students come from 28 states and territories, 13 other countries, 37% from out-of-state, 0.2% Native American, 1% Hispanic, 3% black, 1% Asian American or Pacific Islander, 2% international, 4% 25 or older, 77% live on campus, 8% transferred in. Retention: 75% of full-time freshmen returned the following year. Academic areas with the most degrees conferred: communications/journalism; business/marketing; liberal arts/general studies. Core. Calendar: semesters. Academic remediation for entering students, ESL program, services for LD students, advanced placement, honors program, independent study, double major, internships. Study abroad program. ROTC: Army (c).

Entrance Requirements: Options: Common Application, electronic application, international baccalaureate accepted. Required: essay, high school transcript, minimum 2.4 high school GPA, SAT or ACT. Recommended: minimum 3.2 high school GPA, interview. Required for some: interview. Entrance: moderately difficult. Application deadline: 7/15.

Costs Per Year: Application fee: $0. One-time mandatory fee: $130. Comprehensive fee: $21,786 includes full-time tuition ($16,248), mandatory fees ($260), and college room and board ($5278). College room only: $1988. Part-time tuition: $690 per credit. Part-time mandatory fees: $130 per term.

Collegiate Environment: Orientation program. Drama-theater group, choral group, student-run newspaper. Social organizations: 8 open to all. Most popular organizations: Student Senate, Paul Ylvisaker Center, BLC Scholastic Leadership Society, SIFE Students In Free Enterprise, Lutherans for Life. Major annual events: Parents and Family Weekend, Christmas/Holiday Services and Activities, Snow Week. Student services: personal-psychological counseling. Campus security: 24-hour emergency response devices, late night transport-escort service, controlled dormitory access. 500 college housing spaces available; 417 were occupied in 2003-04. Freshmen guaranteed college housing. On-campus residence required through junior year. Options: men-only, women-only housing available. Memorial Library plus 1 other with 72,392 books, 23,266 serials, 4,628 audiovisual materials, an OPAC, and a Web page. Operations spending for 2004 fiscal year: $324,038. 100 computers available on campus for general student use. A campuswide network can be accessed from student residence rooms and from off campus. Staffed computer lab on campus.

Community Environment: See Minnesota State University-Mankato.

■ **BETHEL UNIVERSITY** *U-10*

3900 Bethel Dr.
St. Paul, MN 55112-6999
Tel: (651)638-6400
Free: 800-255-8706
Admissions: (651)638-6371
Web Site: http://www.bethel.edu/

Description: Independent, comprehensive, coed, affiliated with Baptist General Conference. Awards associate, bachelor's, and master's degrees and post-master's certificates. Founded 1871. Setting: 231-acre suburban campus with easy access to Twin Cities. Endowment: $22 million. Educational spending for 2005 fiscal year: $7117 per student. Total enrollment: 3,857. Faculty: 306 (175 full-time, 131 part-time). Student-undergrad faculty ratio is 14:1. 1,636 applied, 87% were admitted. 32% from top 10% of their high school class, 63% from top quarter, 87% from top half. 4 National Merit Scholars, 30 valedictorians. Full-time: 2,875 students, 60% women, 40% men. Part-time: 322 students, 74% women, 26% men. Students come from 38 states and territories, 23 other countries, 26% from out-of-state, 0.3% Native American, 2% Hispanic, 3% black, 3% Asian American or Pacific Islander, 0.4% international, 11% 25 or older, 72% live on campus, 6% transferred in. Retention: 84% of full-time freshmen returned the following year. Academic areas with the most degrees conferred: business/marketing; education; health professions and related sciences. Core. Calendar: 4-1-4. Services for LD students, advanced placement, accelerated degree program, self-designed majors, honors program, independent study, double major, summer session for credit, part-time degree program, adult/continuing education programs, internships. Off campus study at members of the Christian College Consortium, Au Sable Institute, Coalition for Christian Colleges and Universities. Study abroad program. ROTC: Army (c), Air Force (c).

Entrance Requirements: Options: electronic application, early admission, early action. Required: essay, high school transcript, 2 recommendations, rank in upper 50% of high school class, minimum ACT score of 21 or SAT score of 920, SAT or ACT. Recommended: interview. Required for some: interview. Entrance: moderately difficult. Application deadlines: 3/1, 12/1 for early action. Notification: 4/1, 1/15 for early action.

Costs Per Year: Application fee: $25. Comprehensive fee: $29,840 includes full-time tuition ($22,590), mandatory fees ($110), and college room and board ($7140). College room only: $4260. Part-time tuition: $865 per credit.

Collegiate Environment: Orientation program. Drama-theater group, choral group, student-run newspaper, radio station. Social organizations: 37 open to all. Most popular organizations: United Cultures, Student Senate, Student Association, Habitat for Humanity, Tri Beta. Major annual events: Homecoming Week, Snow Week, Spring Banquet. Student services: health clinic, personal-psychological counseling. Campus security: 24-hour emergency response devices and patrols, student patrols, late night transport-escort service, controlled dormitory access. 1,880 college housing spaces available; all were occupied in 2003-04. Freshmen given priority for college housing. On-campus residence required through sophomore year. Option: coed housing available. Bethel College Library plus 1 other with 194,000 books, 195,650 microform titles, 18,000 serials, 15,789 audiovisual materials, an OPAC, and a Web page. Operations spending for 2004 fiscal year: $1.1 million. 124 computers available on campus for general student use. Computer purchase/lease plans available. A campuswide network can be accessed from student residence rooms and from off campus. Staffed computer lab on campus.

■ **BROWN COLLEGE** *F-14*
1440 Northland Dr.
Mendota Heights, MN 55120
Tel: (651)905-3400
Free: 800-6BR-OWN6
Fax: (651)905-3550
Web Site: http://www.browncollege.edu/
Description: Proprietary, primarily 2-year, coed. Part of Career Education Corporation. Awards certificates, transfer associate, terminal associate, and bachelor's degrees. Founded 1946. Setting: 20-acre suburban campus with easy access to Minneapolis-St. Paul. Endowment: $352,500. Educational spending for 2005 fiscal year: $4127 per student. Total enrollment: 2,054. Student-undergrad faculty ratio is 21:1. 1,116 applied, 48% were admitted. Full-time: 1,891 students, 35% women, 65% men. Part-time: 163 students, 36% women, 64% men. Students come from 15 states and territories, 21% from out-of-state, 1% Native American, 2% Hispanic, 6% black, 4% Asian American or Pacific Islander. Academic remediation for entering students, summer session for credit, part-time degree program, internships.
Entrance Requirements: Option: deferred admission. Required: high school transcript, interview. Recommended: recommendations. Required for some: minimum 2.0 high school GPA. Entrance: moderately difficult. Application deadline: Rolling.
Collegiate Environment: Student-run radio station. Most popular organization: Student Senate. Major annual events: Summer Fling, Portfolio Preview, Cultural Diversity Week. Campus security: 24-hour emergency response devices, student patrols, late night transport-escort service. College housing

not available. Career Resource Center with 768 books and 33 serials. 60 computers available on campus for general student use.

■ **CAPELLA UNIVERSITY** *U-9*
225 South 6th St., 9th Floor
Minneapolis, MN 55402
Tel: (612)252-4200; 888-CAPELLA
Admissions: 800-227-3552
Fax: (612)337-5396
Web Site: http://www.capella.edu/
Description: Proprietary, upper-level, coed. Awards bachelor's, master's, doctoral, and first professional degrees and first professional certificates (offers only distance learning degree programs). Founded 1993. Total enrollment: 12,000. Core. Services for LD students, self-designed majors, independent study, distance learning, double major, summer session for credit, part-time degree program, external degree program, adult/continuing education programs, internships, graduate courses open to undergrads. Off campus study.
Costs Per Year: Application fee: $75.
Collegiate Environment: Orientation program. College housing not available. Sheridan Library System at Johns Hopkins University with an OPAC and a Web page.

■ **CARLETON COLLEGE** *W-9*
One North College St.
Northfield, MN 55057-4001
Tel: (507)646-4000
Free: 800-995-2275
Admissions: (507)646-4190
Fax: (507)646-4526
E-mail: admissions@acs.carleton.edu
Web Site: http://www.carleton.edu/
Description: Independent, 4-year, coed. Awards bachelor's degrees. Founded 1866. Setting: 955-acre small town campus with easy access to Minneapolis-St. Paul. Endowment: $540 million. Research spending for 2004 fiscal year: $2 million. Educational spending for 2005 fiscal year: $24,462 per student. Total enrollment: 1,959. Student-undergrad faculty ratio is 9:1. 5,036 applied, 29% were admitted. 71% from top 10% of their high school class, 91% from top quarter, 100% from top half. 78 National Merit Scholars, 65 valedictorians. Full-time: 1,936 students, 52% women, 48% men. Part-time: 23 students, 61% women, 39% men. Students come from 51 states and territories, 30 other countries, 73% from out-of-state, 1% Native American, 5% Hispanic, 6% black, 10% Asian American or Pacific Islander, 6% international, 0.01% 25 or older, 89% live on campus, 0.1% transferred in. Retention: 97% of full-time freshmen returned the following year. Academic areas with the most degrees conferred: social sciences; biological/life sciences; visual and performing arts. Core. Calendar: three courses for each of three terms. Services for LD students, advanced placement, accelerated degree program, self-designed majors, independent study, double major, internships. Off campus study at Cooperative programs/St. Olaf College, memberships in Associated Colleges of the Midwest, Higher Education Consortium for Urban Affairs. Study abroad program.
Entrance Requirements: Options: Common Application, electronic application, early admission, early decision, deferred admission, international baccalaureate accepted. Required: essay, high school transcript, 2 recommendations, common application supplement, SAT or ACT. Recommended: interview, SAT Subject Tests. Entrance: very difficult. Application deadlines: 1/15, 11/15 for early decision plan 1, 1/15 for early decision plan 2. Notification: 4/15, 12/15 for early decision plan 1, 2/15 for early decision plan 2.
Costs Per Year: Application fee: $30. Comprehensive fee: $42,864 includes full-time tuition ($34,083), mandatory fees ($189), and college room and board ($8592). College room only: $4299.
Collegiate Environment: Orientation program. Drama-theater group, choral group, student-run newspaper, radio station. Social organizations: 132 open to all. Most popular organizations: CANOE (Carleton Association of Nature and Outdoor Enthusiasts), Farm Club, Amnesty International, WHIMS (Women in Math and Science), Ebony II. Major annual events: Halloween Concert and Masquerade Ball, Spring Concert, Mid-Winter Ball. Student services: health clinic, personal-psychological counseling, women's center. Campus security: 24-hour emergency response devices and patrols, student patrols, late night transport-escort service, controlled dormitory access. 1,627 college housing spaces available; 1,620 were occupied in 2003-04. Freshmen guaranteed college housing. On-campus residence required through senior year. Option: coed housing available. Laurence McKinley

Gould Library plus 1 other with 662,871 books, 127,753 microform titles, 10,964 serials, 778 audiovisual materials, an OPAC, and a Web page. Operations spending for 2004 fiscal year: $3.5 million. 221 computers available on campus for general student use. A campuswide network can be accessed from student residence rooms and from off campus. Staffed computer lab on campus.

Community Environment: Northfield (population 15,250), a two-college town, located 40 miles south of Minneapolis and St. Paul, is the home of several major industries that contribute to the prosperity of the community. Part-time employment is limited. Good shopping facilities, library, churches, a hospital and an arts guild are a part of the community. A Carleton - St. Olaf bus also makes round trips daily to the Twin Cities. The Defeat of Jesse James Days in September is a special annual event.

■ **CENTRAL LAKES COLLEGE** *Q-7*
501 West College Dr.
Brainerd, MN 56401-3904
Tel: (218)855-8000
Admissions: (218)828-2525
Fax: (218)855-8220
E-mail: cdaniels@clcmn.edu
Web Site: http://www.clcmn.edu/
Description: State-supported, 2-year, coed. Part of Minnesota State Colleges and Universities System. Awards certificates, diplomas, transfer associate, and terminal associate degrees. Founded 1938. Setting: 1-acre small town campus. Educational spending for 2005 fiscal year: $6268 per student. Total enrollment: 2,768. Student-undergrad faculty ratio is 17:1. Students come from 10 states and territories, 1 other country, 0.3% from out-of-state, 1% Native American, 1% Hispanic, 1% black, 1% Asian American or Pacific Islander, 0% international, 33% 25 or older. Core. Calendar: semesters. Academic remediation for entering students, advanced placement, summer session for credit, part-time degree program, external degree program. Off campus study at other colleges in the Minnesota State Colleges and Universities System.
Entrance Requirements: Open admission except for nonresidents. Option: deferred admission. Required: high school transcript. Entrance: noncompetitive. Application deadline: Rolling.
Costs Per Year: Application fee: $20. Area resident tuition: $3940 full-time.
Collegiate Environment: Drama-theater group, choral group, student-run newspaper. Major annual events: Homecoming, Snow Daze Festival. Campus security: late night transport-escort service. College housing not available. Learning Resource Center with 16,052 books, 286 serials, and an OPAC. 100 computers available on campus for general student use. A campuswide network can be accessed. Staffed computer lab on campus.
Community Environment: One of the state's best developed vacation areas, Brainerd (population 12,000) is on the Mississippi River near the center of the state. The town is the supply point for resorts along 464 lakes within a 25-mile radius of the town. There are opportunities for varied types of sports activities such as fishing, golfing, skiing, snowmobiling and water sports. Other activities include summer theatre, yacht club regatta, antique shows and concerts. Shopping areas, churches, a public library, a hospital and a YMCA are available. Transportation is provided by bus, railway and airlines.

■ **CENTURY COLLEGE** *U-10*
3300 Century Ave. North
White Bear Lake, MN 55110
Tel: (651)779-3200
Free: 800-228-1978
Admissions: (651)779-2619
Fax: (651)779-5810
Web Site: http://www.century.edu/
Description: State-supported, 2-year, coed. Part of Minnesota State Colleges and Universities System. Awards certificates, diplomas, transfer associate, and terminal associate degrees. Founded 1970. Setting: 150-acre suburban campus with easy access to Minneapolis-St. Paul. Endowment: $1 million. Educational spending for 2005 fiscal year: $3528 per student. Total enrollment: 8,553. Student-undergrad faculty ratio is 23:1. 2,713 applied, 100% were admitted. Full-time: 4,042 students, 54% women, 46% men. Part-time: 4,511 students, 63% women, 37% men. Students come from 28 states and territories, 60 other countries, 1% Native American, 2% Hispanic, 8% black, 10% Asian American or Pacific Islander, 1% international, 33% 25 or older, 22% transferred in. Retention: 48% of full-time freshmen returned the following year. Calendar: semesters. Academic remediation for entering

students, ESL program, services for LD students, advanced placement, honors program, distance learning, double major, summer session for credit, part-time degree program, external degree program, adult/continuing education programs, internships. ROTC: Air Force (c).
Entrance Requirements: Open admission. Option: international baccalaureate accepted. Required: high school transcript. Entrance: noncompetitive. Application deadline: Rolling.
Costs Per Year: Application fee: $20. State resident tuition: $4233 full-time, $141 per credit part-time. Nonresident tuition: $8043 full-time, $254 per credit part-time. Mandatory fees: $423 full-time, $14.11 per credit part-time.
Collegiate Environment: Orientation program. Drama-theater group, choral group, student-run newspaper. Social organizations: 15 open to all. Most popular organizations: Student Senate, Phi Theta Kappa, Dental Assistants Club, Creative Arts Alliance, Christian Club. Major annual events: Wood Duck Day, Winter Carnival, October Fest. Student services: personal-psychological counseling, women's center. Campus security: late night transport-escort service, day patrols. College housing not available. Century College Main Library plus 1 other with 56,867 books, 6,656 microform titles, 486 serials, 3,569 audiovisual materials, an OPAC, and a Web page. Operations spending for 2004 fiscal year: $630,696. 985 computers available on campus for general student use. A campuswide network can be accessed from off-campus. Staffed computer lab on campus.

■ **COLLEGE OF SAINT BENEDICT** *S-7*
37 South College Ave.
St. Joseph, MN 56374
Tel: (320)363-5011
Free: 800-544-1489
Fax: (320)363-5010
E-mail: admissions@csbsju.edu
Web Site: http://www.csbsju.edu/
Description: Independent Roman Catholic, 4-year, coed, coordinate with Saint John's University (MN). Awards bachelor's degrees (coordinate with Saint John's University for men). Founded 1887. Setting: 315-acre small town campus with easy access to Minneapolis-St. Paul. Endowment: $29.9 million. Research spending for 2004 fiscal year: $21,151. Educational spending for 2005 fiscal year: $8022 per student. Total enrollment: 2,045. Student-undergrad faculty ratio is 13:1. 1,472 applied, 86% were admitted. 44% from top 10% of their high school class, 79% from top quarter, 97% from top half. Full-time: 1,993 students, 100% women. Part-time: 52 students, 100% women. Students come from 27 states and territories, 29 other countries, 14% from out-of-state, 0.2% Native American, 1% Hispanic, 1% black, 3% Asian American or Pacific Islander, 4% international, 1% 25 or older, 84% live on campus, 2% transferred in. Retention: 88% of full-time freshmen returned the following year. Academic areas with the most degrees conferred: English; business/marketing; psychology. Core. Calendar: semesters. ESL program, services for LD students, advanced placement, accelerated degree program, self-designed majors, honors program, independent study, double major, internships. Off campus study at Tri-College Exchange Program (MN), Saint John's University (MN). Study abroad program. ROTC: Army (c).
Entrance Requirements: Options: Peterson's Universal Application, Common Application, electronic application, deferred admission, international baccalaureate accepted. Required: essay, high school transcript, 1 recommendation, SAT or ACT. Recommended: minimum 3.0 high school GPA, interview. Entrance: moderately difficult. Application deadline: 12/1. Notification: continuous until 10/1.
Costs Per Year: Application fee: $0. Comprehensive fee: $30,091 includes full-time tuition ($23,064), mandatory fees ($390), and college room and board ($6637). College room only: $3419. Room and board charges vary according to board plan and housing facility. Part-time tuition: $961 per credit. Part-time mandatory fees: $195 per term. Part-time tuition and fees vary according to course load.
Collegiate Environment: Orientation program. Drama-theater group, choral group, student-run newspaper, radio station. Social organizations: 90 open to all. Most popular organizations: Volunteers in Service to Others, ultimate Frisbee, Joint Events Council, Students in Free Enterprise, Cultural Affairs Board. Major annual events: Festival of Cultures, Little Sibs Weekend, Asian New Year. Student services: health clinic, personal-psychological counseling, women's center. Campus security: 24-hour emergency response devices and patrols, student patrols, late night transport-escort service, controlled dormitory access, well-lit pathways. 1,532 college housing spaces available; 1,480 were occupied in 2003-04. Freshmen guaranteed college housing. On-campus residence required through sophomore year. Option:

women-only housing available. Clemens Library plus 2 others with 805,376 books, 196,563 microform titles, 5,735 serials, 22,452 audiovisual materials, an OPAC, and a Web page. Operations spending for 2004 fiscal year: $2.7 million. 549 computers available on campus for general student use. A campuswide network can be accessed from student residence rooms and from off campus. Staffed computer lab on campus.

■ **COLLEGE OF ST. CATHERINE** *U-10*
2004 Randolph Ave.
St. Paul, MN 55105-1789
Tel: (651)690-6000
Admissions: (651)690-6505
Fax: (651)690-6042
E-mail: stkate@stkate.edu
Web Site: http://www.stkate.edu/
Description: Independent Roman Catholic, comprehensive. Awards associate, bachelor's, master's, and doctoral degrees. Founded 1905. Setting: 110-acre urban campus with easy access to Minneapolis. Endowment: $33.2 million. Research spending for 2004 fiscal year: $36,608. Educational spending for 2005 fiscal year: $6292 per student. Total enrollment: 4,907. Faculty: 483 (246 full-time, 237 part-time). Student-undergrad faculty ratio is 11:1. 1,475 applied, 78% were admitted. 34% from top 10% of their high school class, 75% from top quarter, 95% from top half. 4 National Merit Scholars, 8 valedictorians. Full-time: 2,362 students, 99% women, 0.5% men. Part-time: 1,243 students, 92% women, 8% men. Students come from 31 states and territories, 30 other countries, 10% from out-of-state, 0.5% Native American, 3% Hispanic, 8% black, 7% Asian American or Pacific Islander, 2% international, 16% 25 or older, 38% live on campus, 22% transferred in. Retention: 81% of full-time freshmen returned the following year. Academic areas with the most degrees conferred: health professions and related sciences; business/marketing; education. Core. Calendar: 4-1-4. Academic remediation for entering students, ESL program, services for LD students, advanced placement, self-designed majors, honors program, independent study, distance learning, double major, summer session for credit, part-time degree program, external degree program, adult/continuing education programs, internships. Off campus study at Associated Colleges of the Twin Cities, Sisters of St. Joseph College Consortium, Higher Education Consortium for Urban Affairs. Study abroad program. ROTC: Air Force (c).
Entrance Requirements: Options: Peterson's Universal Application, Common Application, deferred admission, international baccalaureate accepted. Required: high school transcript, 1 recommendation, SAT or ACT. Recommended: interview. Required for some: essay, interview. Entrance: moderately difficult. Application deadline: Rolling. Notification: continuous.
Costs Per Year: Application fee: $0. Comprehensive fee: $27,505 includes full-time tuition ($21,060), mandatory fees ($325), and college room and board ($6120). College room only: $3420. Full-time tuition and fees vary according to class time. Room and board charges vary according to board plan and housing facility. Part-time tuition: $702 per credit. Part-time tuition varies according to class time.
Collegiate Environment: Orientation program. Drama-theater group, choral group, student-run newspaper. Social organizations: 42 open to all; local sororities; 8% of women are members. Most popular organizations: student government, Residence Hall Association, Women Helping Women, Student Nursing Association, Social Work Club. Major annual events: Johnny Holm Traveling Fun Show, Dew Drop Bop, Family Weekend. Student services: health clinic, personal-psychological counseling, women's center. Campus security: 24-hour emergency response devices and patrols, student patrols, late night transport-escort service, controlled dormitory access. 850 college housing spaces available; 815 were occupied in 2003-04. Freshmen guaranteed college housing. Option: women-only housing available. St. Catherine Library plus 2 others with 263,495 books, 169,236 microform titles, 1,141 serials, 13,627 audiovisual materials, an OPAC, and a Web page. Operations spending for 2004 fiscal year: $3.1 million. 350 computers available on campus for general student use. Computer purchase/lease plans available. A campuswide network can be accessed from student residence rooms and from off campus. Staffed computer lab on campus.

■ **COLLEGE OF ST. CATHERINE-MINNEAPOLIS** *U-9*
601 25th Ave. South
Minneapolis, MN 55454-1494
Tel: (651)690-7700
Free: 800-945-4599
Admissions: (651)690-8600
Fax: (651)690-8107

E-mail: careerinfo@stkate.edu
Web Site: http://www.stkate.edu/
Description: Independent Roman Catholic, comprehensive, coed. Administratively affiliated with College of St. Catherine. Awards associate degrees. Founded 1964. Setting: 1-acre urban campus. Endowment: $33.2 million. Research spending for 2004 fiscal year: $35,622. Educational spending for 2005 fiscal year: $5611 per student. Total enrollment: 4,807. 1,170 applied, 77% were admitted. 31% from top 10% of their high school class, 64% from top quarter, 93% from top half. Full-time: 2,393 students, 99% women, 1% men. Part-time: 1,288 students, 94% women, 6% men. Students come from 18 states and territories, 4% from out-of-state, 1% Native American, 2% Hispanic, 7% black, 5% Asian American or Pacific Islander, 2% international, 57% 25 or older, 9% live on campus, 8% transferred in. Retention: 78% of full-time freshmen returned the following year. Core. Calendar: semesters. Academic remediation for entering students, ESL program, services for LD students, independent study, summer session for credit, part-time degree program, adult/continuing education programs, internships.
Entrance Requirements: Option: deferred admission. Required: essay, high school transcript, 2 recommendations. Recommended: minimum 2.0 high school GPA, interview. Required for some: minimum 3.0 high school GPA. Placement: ACT recommended. Entrance: minimally difficult. Application deadline: Rolling. Notification: continuous.
Costs Per Year: Application fee: $20. Comprehensive fee: $20,870 includes full-time tuition ($14,720), mandatory fees ($30), and college room and board ($6120). College room only: $3420. Room and board charges vary according to board plan and housing facility. Part-time tuition: $460 per credit. Part-time mandatory fees: $20 per term.
Collegiate Environment: Orientation program. Most popular organizations: Christian Healthcare Fellowship, Occupational Therapy Club, Student Nurses Association. Major annual event: Cinco de Mayo. Student services: health clinic, personal-psychological counseling. Campus security: 24-hour emergency response devices and patrols, late night transport-escort service, controlled dormitory access. 73 undergraduates lived in college housing during 2003-04. Freshmen guaranteed college housing. Option: coed housing available. Minneapolis Campus Library with 267,558 books, 185,443 microform titles, 1,141 serials, 13,627 audiovisual materials, an OPAC, and a Web page. Operations spending for 2004 fiscal year: $2.3 million. 40 computers available on campus for general student use. Computer purchase/lease plans available. A campuswide network can be accessed from student residence rooms and from off campus. Staffed computer lab on campus.

■ **THE COLLEGE OF ST. SCHOLASTICA** *O-12*
1200 Kenwood Ave.
Duluth, MN 55811-4199
Tel: (218)723-6000
Free: 800-249-6412
Admissions: (218)723-6053
Fax: (218)723-6290
E-mail: admissions@css1.css.edu
Web Site: http://www.css.edu/
Description: Independent, comprehensive, coed, affiliated with Roman Catholic Church. Awards bachelor's, master's, and first professional degrees and post-master's certificates. Founded 1912. Setting: 186-acre suburban campus. Endowment: $21.1 million. Educational spending for 2005 fiscal year: $7902 per student. Total enrollment: 3,238. Faculty: 252 (142 full-time, 110 part-time). Student-undergrad faculty ratio is 13:1. 1,459 applied, 87% were admitted. 25% from top 10% of their high school class, 54% from top quarter, 82% from top half. 8 valedictorians. Full-time: 2,296 students, 70% women, 30% men. Part-time: 317 students, 71% women, 29% men. Students come from 38 states and territories, 19 other countries, 11% from out-of-state, 2% Native American, 1% Hispanic, 2% black, 2% Asian American or Pacific Islander, 3% international, 28% 25 or older, 44% live on campus, 6% transferred in. Retention: 77% of full-time freshmen returned the following year. Academic areas with the most degrees conferred: business/marketing; health professions and related sciences; computer and information sciences. Core. Calendar: semesters. Academic remediation for entering students, services for LD students, advanced placement, accelerated degree program, self-designed majors, honors program, independent study, distance learning, double major, summer session for credit, part-time degree program, external degree program, adult/continuing education programs, internships, graduate courses open to undergrads. Off campus study at University of Wisconsin-Superior, University of Minnesota, Duluth. Study abroad program. ROTC: Air Force (c).

Entrance Requirements: Options: Peterson's Universal Application, Common Application, electronic application, early admission, deferred admission. Required: high school transcript, SAT or ACT. Recommended: interview. Required for some: minimum 2.0 high school GPA, interview. Entrance: moderately difficult. Application deadline: Rolling. Notification: continuous.

Costs Per Year: Application fee: $25. Comprehensive fee: $28,456 includes full-time tuition ($22,110), mandatory fees ($130), and college room and board ($6216). College room only: $3556. Full-time tuition and fees vary according to class time. Room and board charges vary according to board plan and housing facility. Part-time tuition: $688 per credit hour. Part-time tuition varies according to class time and course load.

Collegiate Environment: Orientation program. Drama-theater group, choral group, student-run newspaper. Social organizations: 45 open to all. Most popular organizations: Campus Activity Board (CAB), Inter-Varsity, SOTA, SHIMA, Social Work Club. Major annual events: Mayfest, Fallfest, Welcome Back Week. Student services: health clinic, personal-psychological counseling. Campus security: 24-hour emergency response devices and patrols, late night transport-escort service, controlled dormitory access, student door monitor at night. College housing designed to accommodate 742 students; 804 undergraduates lived in college housing during 2003-04. Freshmen guaranteed college housing. On-campus residence required through sophomore year. Option: coed housing available. College of St. Scholastica Library with 127,328 books, 1,818 microform titles, 4,488 serials, 13,435 audiovisual materials, an OPAC, and a Web page. Operations spending for 2004 fiscal year: $699,488. 129 computers available on campus for general student use. A campuswide network can be accessed from student residence rooms and from off campus. Staffed computer lab on campus.

■ **COLLEGE OF VISUAL ARTS** *U-10*
344 Summit Ave.
St. Paul, MN 55102-2124
Tel: (651)224-3416
Free: 800-224-1536
Fax: (651)224-8854
E-mail: jnorhorn@cva.edu
Web Site: http://www.cva.edu/

Description: Independent, 4-year, coed. Awards bachelor's degrees. Founded 1924. Setting: 2-acre urban campus with easy access to Minneapolis. Endowment: $304,762. Educational spending for 2005 fiscal year: $4673 per student. Total enrollment: 202. Student-undergrad faculty ratio is 8:1. 131 applied, 64% were admitted. 3% from top quarter of their high school class, 16% from top half. Full-time: 171 students, 59% women, 41% men. Part-time: 31 students, 81% women, 19% men. Students come from 13 states and territories, 3 other countries, 12% from out-of-state, 1% Native American, 0.5% Hispanic, 1% black, 3% Asian American or Pacific Islander, 21% 25 or older, 9% transferred in. Retention: 60% of full-time freshmen returned the following year. Academic area with the most degrees conferred: visual and performing arts. Core. Calendar: semesters. Academic remediation for entering students, advanced placement, honors program, independent study, double major, summer session for credit, part-time degree program, internships. Study abroad program.

Entrance Requirements: Options: Peterson's Universal Application, Common Application, electronic application, deferred admission. Required: essay, high school transcript, minimum 2.7 high school GPA, portfolio, SAT or ACT. Recommended: minimum 3.0 high school GPA, recommendations, interview. Entrance: moderately difficult. Application deadline: Rolling. Notification: continuous.

Costs Per Year: Application fee: $40. Tuition: $17,510 full-time, $875 per credit part-time. Mandatory fees: $530 full-time, $53 per course part-time. Full-time tuition and fees vary according to course load. Part-time tuition and fees vary according to course load.

Collegiate Environment: Orientation program. Most popular organization: AIGA Student Chapter. Major annual events: Senior Show, Annual Student Exhibition, Symposium Series. Student services: personal-psychological counseling. Campus security: 24-hour emergency response devices, late night transport-escort service. College housing not available. College of Visual Arts Library with 7,100 books, 55 serials, 30,370 audiovisual materials, an OPAC, and a Web page. Operations spending for 2004 fiscal year: $9037. 60 computers available on campus for general student use. A campuswide network can be accessed. Staffed computer lab on campus.

Community Environment: See University of Minnesota - Twin Cities.

■ **CONCORDIA COLLEGE** *O-2*
901 South 8th St.
Moorhead, MN 56562

Tel: (218)299-4000
Free: 800-699-9897
Admissions: (218)299-3004
Fax: (218)299-3947
E-mail: admissions@gloria.cord.edu
Web Site: http://www.concordiacollege.edu/

Description: Independent, 4-year, coed, affiliated with Evangelical Lutheran Church in America. Awards bachelor's and master's degrees. Founded 1891. Setting: 120-acre suburban campus. Endowment: $69.1 million. Total enrollment: 2,764. Faculty: 252 (190 full-time, 62 part-time). Student-undergrad faculty ratio is 15:1. 2,645 applied, 83% were admitted. 30% from top 10% of their high school class, 59% from top quarter, 86% from top half. Full-time: 2,693 students, 63% women, 37% men. Part-time: 66 students, 59% women, 41% men. Students come from 37 states and territories, 36 other countries, 29% from out-of-state, 0.4% Native American, 1% Hispanic, 1% black, 2% Asian American or Pacific Islander, 4% international, 2% 25 or older, 66% live on campus, 3% transferred in. Retention: 79% of full-time freshmen returned the following year. Core. Calendar: semesters. ESL program, services for LD students, advanced placement, honors program, independent study, double major, summer session for credit, part-time degree program, adult/continuing education programs, co-op programs and internships. Off campus study at Tri-College University. Study abroad program. ROTC: Army (c), Air Force (c).

Entrance Requirements: Options: Peterson's Universal Application, Common Application, electronic application, early admission, deferred admission, international baccalaureate accepted. Required: high school transcript, 2 recommendations, SAT or ACT. Entrance: moderately difficult. Application deadline: Rolling.

Costs Per Year: Application fee: $20. Comprehensive fee: $24,664 includes full-time tuition ($19,520), mandatory fees ($154), and college room and board ($4990). College room only: $2300. Room and board charges vary according to board plan and housing facility. Part-time tuition: $3045 per course. Part-time tuition varies according to course load.

Collegiate Environment: Orientation program. Drama-theater group, choral group, student-run newspaper, radio station. Social organizations: 80 open to all; local fraternities, local sororities, local coed fraternity; 4% of eligible men and 4% of eligible women are members. Most popular organizations: Sources of Service, Habitat for Humanity, Student Minnesota Education Association, language clubs, Health Professions Interest Club. Major annual events: Family Weekend, Homecoming, symposium. Student services: health clinic, personal-psychological counseling, women's center. Campus security: 24-hour emergency response devices and patrols, student patrols, late night transport-escort service, well-lit campus, 24-hour locked wing doors. 1,873 college housing spaces available; 1,786 were occupied in 2003-04. Freshmen given priority for college housing. On-campus residence required through sophomore year. Options: coed, men-only, women-only housing available. Carl B. Ylvisaker Library with 306,644 books, 43,671 microform titles, 3,460 serials, 21,302 audiovisual materials, an OPAC, and a Web page. Operations spending for 2004 fiscal year: $1.4 million. 460 computers available on campus for general student use. A campuswide network can be accessed from student residence rooms and from off campus. Staffed computer lab on campus.

■ **CONCORDIA UNIVERSITY, ST. PAUL** *U-10*
275 Syndicate St. North
St. Paul, MN 55104-5494
Tel: (651)641-8278
Free: 800-333-4705
Admissions: (651)641-8230
Fax: (651)659-0207
E-mail: admiss@csp.edu
Web Site: http://www.csp.edu/

Description: Independent, comprehensive, coed, affiliated with Lutheran Church-Missouri Synod. Part of Concordia University System. Awards associate, bachelor's, and master's degrees. Founded 1893. Setting: 37-acre urban campus. Endowment: $17.5 million. Educational spending for 2005 fiscal year: $5185 per student. Total enrollment: 2,069. Faculty: 438 (82 full-time, 356 part-time). Student-undergrad faculty ratio is 11:1. 651 applied, 64% were admitted. 16% from top 10% of their high school class, 33% from top quarter, 61% from top half. Full-time: 1,472 students, 61% women, 39% men. Part-time: 264 students, 63% women, 37% men. Students come from 43 states and territories, 6 other countries, 23% from out-of-state, 0.3% Native American, 2% Hispanic, 7% black, 5% Asian American or Pacific Islander, 0.4% international, 53% 25 or older, 23% live on campus, 17%

transferred in. Retention: 74% of full-time freshmen returned the following year. Academic areas with the most degrees conferred: business/marketing; education; family and consumer sciences; security and protective services. Core. Calendar: semesters. Academic remediation for entering students, ESL program, services for LD students, advanced placement, accelerated degree program, self-designed majors, independent study, distance learning, double major, summer session for credit, part-time degree program, adult/continuing education programs, internships, graduate courses open to undergrads. Off campus study at University of Minnesota-Twin Cities Campus, University of St. Thomas, Oak Hill College. Study abroad program. ROTC: Army (c), Naval (c), Air Force (c).

Entrance Requirements: Options: Peterson's Universal Application, Common Application, electronic application, early admission, deferred admission, international baccalaureate accepted. Required: high school transcript, 2 recommendations, ACT. Recommended: minimum 2.0 high school GPA, interview. Required for some: essay. Entrance: minimally difficult. Application deadline: 8/1. Notification: continuous.

Costs Per Year: Application fee: $30. Comprehensive fee: $28,974 includes full-time tuition ($22,378) and college room and board ($6596). Part-time tuition: $466 per credit.

Collegiate Environment: Orientation program. Drama-theater group, choral group, student-run newspaper. Social organizations: 40 open to all. Most popular organizations: church vocations, Minority Students' Club, ministry, Community Based Outreach. Major annual events: Homecoming, Festival of Beginnings, winter formal. Student services: health clinic, personal-psychological counseling. Campus security: 24-hour emergency response devices and patrols, student patrols, late night transport-escort service. 486 college housing spaces available; 402 were occupied in 2003-04. Freshmen guaranteed college housing. On-campus residence required in freshman year. Options: coed, men-only, women-only housing available. Library Technology Center with 134,200 books, 13,549 microform titles, 6,920 audiovisual materials, an OPAC, and a Web page. Operations spending for 2004 fiscal year: $550,547. 1,000 computers available on campus for general student use. Computer purchase/lease plans available. A campuswide network can be accessed from student residence rooms and from off campus. Staffed computer lab on campus.

■ **CROSSROADS COLLEGE** *X-11*
920 Mayowood Rd., SW
Rochester, MN 55902-2382
Tel: (507)288-4563
Free: 800-456-7651
Fax: (507)288-9046
Web Site: http://www.crossroadscollege.edu/
Description: Independent, 4-year, coed, affiliated with Christian Churches and Churches of Christ. Awards associate and bachelor's degrees. Founded 1913. Setting: 40-acre urban campus with easy access to Minneapolis-St. Paul. Endowment: $744,600. Educational spending for 2005 fiscal year: $4479 per student. Total enrollment: 149. Student-undergrad faculty ratio is 9:1. 53 applied, 79% were admitted. 58% from top quarter of their high school class, 63% from top half. Full-time: 130 students, 43% women, 57% men. Part-time: 19 students, 47% women, 53% men. Students come from 10 states and territories, 4 other countries, 25% from out-of-state, 0% Native American, 0% Hispanic, 5% black, 3% Asian American or Pacific Islander, 3% international, 21% 25 or older, 78% live on campus, 13% transferred in. Retention: 68% of full-time freshmen returned the following year. Core. Calendar: semesters. Academic remediation for entering students, advanced placement, self-designed majors, independent study, double major, adult/continuing education programs, internships.

Entrance Requirements: Option: deferred admission. Required: essay, high school transcript, 3 recommendations, SAT or ACT. Required for some: interview. Entrance: noncompetitive. Application deadline: 8/15. Notification: continuous until 9/1.

Costs Per Year: Application fee: $30. Tuition: $10,950 full-time, $330 per semester hour part-time. Mandatory fees: $320 full-time, $220 per year part-time. College room only: $3400.

Collegiate Environment: Orientation program. Drama-theater group, choral group, student-run newspaper. Social organizations: 5 open to all. Most popular organizations: Christian Outdoors, Musical Outreach, Ambassadors Mission Group. Major annual events: Spiritual Emphasis Week, Missions Emphasis Week, Fall Conference. Student services: personal-psychological counseling. Campus security: student patrols, late night transport-escort service. College housing designed to accommodate 100 students; 101 undergraduates lived in college housing during 2003-04. Freshmen

guaranteed college housing. On-campus residence required through sophomore year. Options: men-only, women-only housing available. G. H. Cachiaras Memorial Library with 33,697 books, 2,088 microform titles, 300 serials, and 1,755 audiovisual materials. Operations spending for 2004 fiscal year: $73,910. 15 computers available on campus for general student use. A campuswide network can be accessed from student residence rooms and from off campus. Staffed computer lab on campus.

Community Environment: See Rochester Community and Technical College.

■ **CROWN COLLEGE** *F-10*
8700 College View Dr.
St. Bonifacius, MN 55375-9001
Tel: (952)446-4100
Free: 800-68-CROWN
Admissions: (952)446-4144
Fax: (952)446-4149
E-mail: fiskm@crown.edu
Web Site: http://www.crown.edu
Description: Independent, comprehensive, coed, affiliated with The Christian and Missionary Alliance. Awards associate, bachelor's, and master's degrees. Founded 1916. Setting: 215-acre suburban campus with easy access to Minneapolis-St. Paul. Endowment: $5.9 million. Educational spending for 2005 fiscal year: $3236 per student. Total enrollment: 1,304. Faculty: 64 (39 full-time, 25 part-time). Student-undergrad faculty ratio is 14:1. 435 applied, 71% were admitted. 8% from top 10% of their high school class, 32% from top quarter, 64% from top half. Full-time: 843 students, 56% women, 44% men. Part-time: 345 students, 66% women, 34% men. Students come from 37 states and territories, 23% from out-of-state, 1% Native American, 2% Hispanic, 3% black, 6% Asian American or Pacific Islander, 0.2% international, 34% 25 or older, 70% live on campus, 5% transferred in. Retention: 70% of full-time freshmen returned the following year. Academic areas with the most degrees conferred: business/marketing; education; psychology. Core. Calendar: semesters. Academic remediation for entering students, ESL program, services for LD students, advanced placement, honors program, independent study, distance learning, double major, summer session for credit, part-time degree program, adult/continuing education programs, internships, graduate courses open to undergrads. Study abroad program.

Entrance Requirements: Options: electronic application, early admission, deferred admission, international baccalaureate accepted. Required: essay, high school transcript, minimum 2.0 high school GPA, 2 recommendations, ACT 18/SAT 870, SAT or ACT. Required for some: interview. Entrance: minimally difficult. Application deadline: Rolling.

Costs Per Year: Application fee: $35. Comprehensive fee: $24,070 includes full-time tuition ($17,054) and college room and board ($7016). College room only: $3652. Part-time tuition: $713 per credit.

Collegiate Environment: Orientation program. Drama-theater group, choral group, student-run newspaper. Social organizations: 14 open to all. Most popular organizations: Global Impact Team, Hmong Student Fellowship, Married Student Fellowship, Senate/Student Services Board, newspaper/yearbook staff. Major annual events: homecoming, Christmas Student Event, Spring Banquet. Student services: health clinic, personal-psychological counseling. Campus security: 24-hour emergency response devices, late night transport-escort service, controlled dormitory access. 544 college housing spaces available; 417 were occupied in 2003-04. Freshmen guaranteed college housing. On-campus residence required through senior year. Options: men-only, women-only housing available. Peter Watne Memorial Library with 79,386 books, 73,700 microform titles, 15,000 serials, 2,400 audiovisual materials, an OPAC, and a Web page. Operations spending for 2004 fiscal year: $299,658. 52 computers available on campus for general student use. Computer purchase/lease plans available. A campuswide network can be accessed from student residence rooms and from off campus. Staffed computer lab on campus.

Community Environment: The College is located in a small community about 20 miles west of Minneapolis.

■ **DAKOTA COUNTY TECHNICAL COLLEGE** *V-10*
1300 East 145th St.
Rosemount, MN 55068
Tel: (651)423-8000; 877-YES-DCTC
Admissions: (651)423-8399
Web Site: http://www.dctc.edu/

Description: State-supported, 2-year, coed. Part of Minnesota State Colleges and Universities System. Awards certificates, diplomas, transfer associate, and terminal associate degrees. Founded 1970. Setting: 100-acre suburban campus with easy access to Minneapolis and St. Paul. Endowment: $1.3 million. Research spending for 2004 fiscal year: $108,667. Educational spending for 2005 fiscal year: $5560 per student. Total enrollment: 6,069. 2,578 applied. Full-time: 2,956 students, 50% women, 50% men. Part-time: 3,113 students, 34% women, 66% men. Students come from 8 states and territories, 21 other countries, 3% from out-of-state, 0.5% Native American, 1% Hispanic, 2% black, 1% Asian American or Pacific Islander, 1% international, 55% 25 or older, 8% transferred in. Core. Calendar: semesters. Academic remediation for entering students, ESL program, services for LD students, independent study, distance learning, double major, summer session for credit, part-time degree program, co-op programs and internships.

Entrance Requirements: Open admission. Options: Common Application, electronic application. Recommended: interview. Required for some: high school transcript, recommendations. Placement: ACCUPLACER/CPT required for some. Entrance: noncompetitive.

Costs Per Year: Application fee: $20. State resident tuition: $3999 full-time, $124.96 per semester hour part-time. Nonresident tuition: $7997 full-time, $249.92 per semester hour part-time. Mandatory fees: $538 full-time, $16.80 per semester hour part-time. Full-time tuition and fees vary according to reciprocity agreements. Part-time tuition and fees vary according to reciprocity agreements.

Collegiate Environment: Orientation program. Student-run newspaper. Social organizations: 10 open to all. Most popular organizations: Student Senate, Visual Communications Club, SKILLS/VICA, Landscape Horticulture Club, Multicultural Club. Major annual events: Fall Follies, Spring Fling, Fall Welcome Week. Student services: health clinic, personal-psychological counseling. Campus security: 24-hour emergency response devices, late night transport-escort service. College housing not available. DCTC Library with 15,693 books, 258 serials, 1,164 audiovisual materials, an OPAC, and a Web page. Operations spending for 2004 fiscal year: $260,000. 200 computers available on campus for general student use. A campuswide network can be accessed from off-campus. Staffed computer lab on campus.

■ **DEVRY UNIVERSITY** *F-13*
7700 France Ave. South
Ste. 575
Edina, MN 55435
Tel: (952)838-1860
Fax: (952)838-3737
Web Site: http://www.devry.edu/locations/campuses/loc_edina.jsp
Description: Proprietary, comprehensive, coed. Awards associate, bachelor's, and master's degrees. Total enrollment: 94. Faculty: 22 (all part-time). Student-undergrad faculty ratio is 4:1. Full-time: 16 students, 31% women, 69% men. Part-time: 29 students, 34% women, 66% men. 2% Native American, 0% Hispanic, 9% black, 2% Asian American or Pacific Islander, 0% international.
Entrance Requirements: Required: high school transcript, interview. Application deadline: Rolling. Notification: continuous.
Costs Per Year: Application fee: $50. One-time mandatory fee: $40. Tuition: $11,790 full-time. Mandatory fees: $30 full-time.

■ **DULUTH BUSINESS UNIVERSITY** *O-12*
4724 Mike Colalillo Dr.
Duluth, MN 55807
Tel: (218)722-4000
Free: 800-777-8406
Web Site: http://www.dbumn.edu/
Description: Proprietary, 2-year, coed. Awards diplomas and terminal associate degrees. Founded 1891. Setting: urban campus. Total enrollment: 325.

■ **DUNWOODY COLLEGE OF TECHNOLOGY** *U-9*
818 Dunwoody Blvd.
Minneapolis, MN 55403
Tel: (612)374-5800
Free: 800-292-4625
Fax: (612)374-4128
Web Site: http://www.dunwoody.edu/
Description: Independent, 2-year, coed. Awards diplomas and terminal associate degrees. Founded 1914. Setting: 12-acre urban campus. Endow-

ment: $31.2 million. Educational spending for 2005 fiscal year: $6521 per student. Total enrollment: 1,611. 798 applied, 62% were admitted. 1% from top 10% of their high school class, 7% from top quarter, 32% from top half. Full-time: 1,236 students, 9% women, 91% men. Part-time: 375 students, 13% women, 87% men. Students come from 12 states and territories, 3 other countries, 5% from out-of-state, 2% Native American, 1% Hispanic, 7% black, 5% Asian American or Pacific Islander, 0.3% international, 28% 25 or older, 8% transferred in. Retention: 67% of full-time freshmen returned the following year. Academic remediation for entering students, ESL program, independent study, summer session for credit, internships.
Entrance Requirements: Options: electronic application, early admission, deferred admission. Required: high school transcript, interview, institutional entrance test. Entrance: noncompetitive. Application deadline: Rolling. Notification: continuous.
Collegiate Environment: Orientation program. Major annual event: Fall Fling. Student services: personal-psychological counseling. Campus security: 24-hour emergency response devices, late night transport-escort service. College housing not available. Learning Resource Center with 8,000 books, 115 serials, 250 audiovisual materials, and an OPAC. Operations spending for 2004 fiscal year: $139,800. 300 computers available on campus for general student use. A campuswide network can be accessed from off-campus. Staffed computer lab on campus.

■ **FOND DU LAC TRIBAL AND COMMUNITY COLLEGE** *P-11*
2101 14th St.
Cloquet, MN 55720
Tel: (218)879-0800
Free: 800-657-3712
Admissions: (218)879-0820
Fax: (218)879-0814
E-mail: darla@asab.fdl.cc.mn.us
Web Site: http://www.fdltcc.edu/
Description: State-supported, 2-year, coed. Part of Minnesota State Colleges and Universities System. Awards certificates, transfer associate, and terminal associate degrees. Founded 1987. Setting: 31-acre rural campus. Endowment: $270,000. Research spending for 2004 fiscal year: $2590. Educational spending for 2005 fiscal year: $1945 per student. Total enrollment: 1,735. 751 applied, 100% were admitted. 2% from out-of-state, 20% Native American, 0.5% Hispanic, 1% black, 1% Asian American or Pacific Islander, 32% 25 or older, 10% live on campus. Core. Calendar: semesters. Academic remediation for entering students, services for LD students, advanced placement, independent study, distance learning, double major, summer session for credit, part-time degree program, external degree program, adult/continuing education programs, co-op programs and internships. Off campus study.
Entrance Requirements: Open admission. Options: Common Application, electronic application, early admission, deferred admission. Required for some: high school transcript. Placement: ASAP required. Entrance: noncompetitive. Notification: continuous until 8/20.
Collegiate Environment: Orientation program. Drama-theater group, choral group, student-run newspaper. Most popular organizations: Human Services Club, Anishinaabe Club, Phi Theta Kappa, Law Enforcement Club, Student Senate. Major annual events: Giving Thanks Feast, Winter Fest, All-School Picnic. Student services: personal-psychological counseling. Campus security: 24-hour emergency response devices, late night transport-escort service, controlled dormitory access, video surveillance system. 100 college housing spaces available. No special consideration for freshman housing applicants. Option: coed housing available. Ruth Meyers Library with 3,482 books, 216 serials, 307 audiovisual materials, and an OPAC. Operations spending for 2004 fiscal year: $97,103. 117 computers available on campus for general student use. A campuswide network can be accessed from student residence rooms and from off campus. Staffed computer lab on campus.

■ **GLOBE COLLEGE** *E-15*
7166 North 10th St.
Oakdale, MN 55128
Tel: (651)730-5100
Admissions: (651)714-7331
Fax: (651)730-5151
Web Site: http://www.globecollege.com/
Description: Private, primarily 2-year, coed. Awards certificates, diplomas, terminal associate, and bachelor's degrees. Founded 1885. Setting: suburban campus. Total enrollment: 845. Student-undergrad faculty ratio is

15:1. Students come from 1 other country, 8% from out-of-state, 48% 25 or older. Academic remediation for entering students, accelerated degree program, distance learning, summer session for credit, part-time degree program, adult/continuing education programs, co-op programs and internships.

Entrance Requirements: Open admission. Options: Common Application, electronic application. Required: high school transcript, interview, CPAt. Required for some: essay. Entrance: minimally difficult. Application deadline: 10/5.

Costs Per Year: Application fee: $50. Tuition: $12,600 full-time, $350 per credit part-time. Mandatory fees: $500 full-time.

Collegiate Environment: Orientation program. Globe College Library with 1,432 books, 106 serials, 13 audiovisual materials, an OPAC, and a Web page. Operations spending for 2004 fiscal year: $16,737. 180 computers available on campus for general student use. Staffed computer lab on campus.

■ **GUSTAVUS ADOLPHUS COLLEGE** *W-8*
800 West College Ave.
St. Peter, MN 56082-1498
Tel: (507)933-8000
Free: 800-GUSTAVU(S)
Admissions: (507)933-7676
E-mail: admission@gac.edu
Web Site: http://www.gustavus.edu/
Description: Independent, 4-year, coed, affiliated with Evangelical Lutheran Church in America. Awards bachelor's degrees. Founded 1862. Setting: 330-acre small town campus with easy access to Minneapolis-St. Paul. Endowment: $86.9 million. Research spending for 2004 fiscal year: $91,726. Educational spending for 2005 fiscal year: $11,917 per student. Total enrollment: 2,603. Student-undergrad faculty ratio is 12:1. 2,691 applied, 80% were admitted. 41% from top 10% of their high school class, 71% from top quarter, 95% from top half. 6 National Merit Scholars, 37 valedictorians. Full-time: 2,571 students, 57% women, 43% men. Part-time: 32 students, 53% women, 47% men. Students come from 41 states and territories, 19 other countries, 19% from out-of-state, 0.2% Native American, 2% Hispanic, 1% black, 4% Asian American or Pacific Islander, 1% international, 0% 25 or older, 85% live on campus, 1% transferred in. Retention: 88% of full-time freshmen returned the following year. Academic areas with the most degrees conferred: social sciences; business/marketing; biological/life sciences. Core. Calendar: 4-1-4. Services for LD students, advanced placement, accelerated degree program, self-designed majors, honors program, independent study, double major, summer session for credit, co-op programs and internships. Off campus study at Minnesota State University, Mankato. Study abroad program. ROTC: Army (c).

Entrance Requirements: Options: Peterson's Universal Application, Common Application, electronic application, early admission, early action, deferred admission, international baccalaureate accepted. Required: essay, high school transcript, 2 recommendations, SAT or ACT. Recommended: interview. Placement: SAT or ACT required. Entrance: very difficult. Application deadlines: 4/1, 11/1 for early action. Notification: continuous until 5/1, 11/20 for early action.

Costs Per Year: Application fee: $0. Comprehensive fee: $30,930 includes full-time tuition ($24,500), mandatory fees ($365), and college room and board ($6065). College room only: $3665. Full-time tuition and fees vary according to student level. Room and board charges vary according to board plan, housing facility, and student level. Part-time tuition: $3000 per course. Tuition guaranteed not to increase for student's term of enrollment.

Collegiate Environment: Orientation program. Drama-theater group, choral group, student-run newspaper, radio station. Social organizations: 110 open to all; local fraternities, local sororities; 20% of eligible men and 17% of eligible women are members. Most popular organizations: Campus Activity Board, Gustavus Choir, Greens, Fellowship of Christian Athletes, Big Partner/Little Partner. Major annual events: Nobel Conference, Christmas in Christ Chapel, Mayday. Student services: health clinic, personal-psychological counseling, women's center. Campus security: 24-hour emergency response devices and patrols, late night transport-escort service, controlled dormitory access. 2,081 college housing spaces available; 2,013 were occupied in 2003-04. Freshmen guaranteed college housing. On-campus residence required through senior year. Option: coed housing available. Folke Bernadotte Memorial Library plus 2 others with 288,685 books, 35,440 microform titles, 996 serials, 16,623 audiovisual materials, an OPAC, and a Web page. Operations spending for 2004 fiscal year: $1.6 million. 441 computers available on campus for general student use. A campuswide

network can be accessed from student residence rooms and from off campus. Staffed computer lab on campus.

Community Environment: St. Peter is located 68 miles south of Minneapolis with the usual community facilities. Bus transportation is convenient.

■ **HAMLINE UNIVERSITY** *U-10*
1536 Hewitt Ave.
St. Paul, MN 55104-1284
Tel: (651)523-2800
Free: 800-753-9753
Admissions: (651)523-2207
Fax: (651)523-2458
E-mail: cla-admis@hamline.edu
Web Site: http://www.hamline.edu/
Description: Independent, comprehensive, coed, affiliated with United Methodist Church. Awards bachelor's, master's, doctoral, and first professional degrees. Founded 1854. Setting: 50-acre urban campus. Endowment: $59.2 million. Research spending for 2004 fiscal year: $215,085. Educational spending for 2005 fiscal year: $8957 per student. Total enrollment: 4,550. Faculty: 500 (174 full-time, 326 part-time). Student-undergrad faculty ratio is 13:1. 1,806 applied, 78% were admitted. 26% from top 10% of their high school class, 54% from top quarter, 86% from top half. 3 National Merit Scholars, 8 valedictorians. Full-time: 1,945 students, 60% women, 40% men. Part-time: 101 students, 65% women, 35% men. Students come from 24 states and territories, 28 other countries, 15% from out-of-state, 1% Native American, 2% Hispanic, 3% black, 6% Asian American or Pacific Islander, 3% international, 6% 25 or older, 41% live on campus, 6% transferred in. Retention: 84% of full-time freshmen returned the following year. Academic areas with the most degrees conferred: social sciences; psychology; business/marketing. Core. Calendar: 4-1-4. Academic remediation for entering students, ESL program, services for LD students, advanced placement, self-designed majors, honors program, independent study, double major, summer session for credit, part-time degree program, adult/continuing education programs, internships, graduate courses open to undergrads. Off campus study at members of the Associated Colleges of the Twin Cities, American University, Southern College Student Exchange Program, Higher Education Consortium for Urban Affairs, Drew University. Study abroad program. ROTC: Air Force (c).

Entrance Requirements: Options: Peterson's Universal Application, electronic application, early admission, early action, deferred admission. Required: essay, high school transcript, 2 recommendations, SAT or ACT. Recommended: interview, activity resume. Entrance: moderately difficult. Application deadlines: Rolling, 12/1 for early action. Notification: continuous until 1/1, 12/15 for early action.

Costs Per Year: Application fee: $0. Comprehensive fee: $30,067 includes full-time tuition ($22,758), mandatory fees ($399), and college room and board ($6910). College room only: $3484. Full-time tuition and fees vary according to student level. Room and board charges vary according to board plan and housing facility. Part-time tuition: $700 per credit. Part-time tuition varies according to course load and student level.

Collegiate Environment: Orientation program. Drama-theater group, choral group, student-run newspaper, radio station. Social organizations: 85 open to all; international dining club. Most popular organizations: Student Congress (HUSC), Acting in the Community Together, Minnesota Public Interest Research Group, residential hall councils, Affordable Arts. Major annual events: homecoming, End of the Year Celebration, Ethnic and Multicultural Festival. Student services: health clinic, personal-psychological counseling, women's center. Campus security: 24-hour emergency response devices and patrols, student patrols, late night transport-escort service, controlled dormitory access. 910 college housing spaces available; 789 were occupied in 2003-04. Freshmen guaranteed college housing. Option: coed housing available. Bush Library plus 1 other with 556,450 books, 588,139 microform titles, 3,858 serials, 2,642 audiovisual materials, an OPAC, and a Web page. Operations spending for 2004 fiscal year: $1.6 million. 130 computers available on campus for general student use. A campuswide network can be accessed from student residence rooms and from off campus. Staffed computer lab on campus.

■ **HENNEPIN TECHNICAL COLLEGE** *D-13*
9000 Brooklyn Blvd.
Brooklyn Park, MN 55445
Tel: (763)425-3800
Admissions: (763)488-2415

Fax: (763)550-2119

Web Site: http://www.hennepintech.edu/

Description: State-supported, 2-year, coed. Part of Minnesota State Colleges and Universities System. Awards certificates, diplomas, transfer associate, and terminal associate degrees. Founded 1972. Setting: 100-acre urban campus with easy access to Minneapolis-St. Paul. Total enrollment: 8,623. 11,773 applied, 96% were admitted. 1% Native American, 1% Hispanic, 10% black, 5% Asian American or Pacific Islander, 0.2% international. Core. Calendar: semesters. Academic remediation for entering students, ESL program, services for LD students, advanced placement, independent study, distance learning, double major, co-op programs and internships.

Entrance Requirements: Open admission. Recommended: high school transcript, interview. Entrance: minimally difficult. Application deadline: Rolling. Notification: continuous.

Collegiate Environment: Orientation program. Student services: personal-psychological counseling, women's center. Campus security: late night transport-escort service, security service. College housing not available.

■ **HERZING COLLEGE** *U-9*

5700 West Broadway

Minneapolis, MN 55428

Tel: (763)535-3000

Free: 800-878-DRAW

Admissions: (763)231-3152

Web Site: http://www.herzing.edu/

Description: Proprietary, primarily 2-year, coed. Part of Herzing College. Awards certificates, diplomas, terminal associate, and bachelor's degrees. Setting: 1-acre suburban campus. Educational spending for 2005 fiscal year: $4261 per student. Total enrollment: 346. 128 applied, 75% were admitted. Full-time: 205 students, 74% women, 26% men. Part-time: 141 students, 87% women, 13% men. Students come from 3 states and territories, 1% from out-of-state, 1% Native American, 1% Hispanic, 14% black, 5% Asian American or Pacific Islander, 0% international, 43% 25 or older. Core. Calendar: semesters. Distance learning, part-time degree program, adult/continuing education programs, internships.

Entrance Requirements: Open admission. Required: high school transcript, interview, ACCUPLACER. Recommended: SAT and SAT Subject Tests or ACT. Entrance: moderately difficult.

Costs Per Year: Application fee: $0. Tuition: $11,029 full-time, $367 per credit part-time. Mandatory fees: $25 full-time. Full-time tuition and fees vary according to course load and program. Part-time tuition varies according to course load and program.

Collegiate Environment: Orientation program. Major annual event: Dental Assistants State Convention. Student services: personal-psychological counseling. Campus security: 24-hour emergency response devices, late night transport-escort service. College housing not available. Operations spending for 2004 fiscal year: $53,173. 50 computers available on campus for general student use. Staffed computer lab on campus.

■ **HIBBING COMMUNITY COLLEGE** *M-10*

1515 East 25th St.

Hibbing, MN 55746-3300

Tel: (218)262-7200

Free: 800-224-4HCC

Admissions: (218)262-6713

E-mail: admissions@hibbing.edu

Web Site: http://www.hcc.mnscu.edu/

Description: State-supported, 2-year, coed. Part of Minnesota State Colleges and Universities System. Awards certificates, diplomas, transfer associate, and terminal associate degrees. Founded 1916. Setting: 100-acre small town campus. Educational spending for 2005 fiscal year: $3950 per student. Total enrollment: 1,176. Student-undergrad faculty ratio is 14:1. 1,312 applied, 100% were admitted. 7% from top 10% of their high school class, 54% from top half. Students come from 20 states and territories, 2% Native American, 1% Hispanic, 5% black, 1% Asian American or Pacific Islander, 55% 25 or older, 10% live on campus. Core. Calendar: semesters. Academic remediation for entering students, services for LD students, advanced placement, distance learning, summer session for credit, part-time degree program, adult/continuing education programs, co-op programs and internships. Off campus study at other colleges in the Minnesota State Colleges and Universities System. Study abroad program.

Entrance Requirements: Open admission except for nursing, law enforcement programs. Options: Common Application, early admission, deferred

admission. Required: high school transcript. Entrance: noncompetitive. Application deadline: Rolling. Notification: continuous.

Costs Per Year: Application fee: $20. State resident tuition: $3950 full-time, $116.60 per credit part-time. Nonresident tuition: $145.75 per credit part-time. Mandatory fees: $459 full-time, $15.30 per credit part-time. Full-time tuition and fees vary according to course load and reciprocity agreements. Part-time tuition and fees vary according to course load and reciprocity agreements. College room and board: $4500. College room only: $2900.

Collegiate Environment: Orientation program. Drama-theater group, choral group, marching band. Most popular organizations: Phi Theta Kappa, Performing Music Ensembles Club, Student Senate, Engineering Club, VICA. Student services: personal-psychological counseling. Campus security: late night transport-escort service. Hibbing Community College Library with 19,536 books, 190 serials, and a Web page. 150 computers available on campus for general student use. A campuswide network can be accessed from off-campus. Staffed computer lab on campus.

Community Environment: Hibbing (population 21,000) is the largest of the Mesabi Range towns where there are many open pits for mining ore. Located 70 miles from Duluth, plants in the area mine taconite, an ore-bearing rock that yields a rich iron ore concentrate when processed. The community facilities include a library, churches of major denominations, a hospital, 3 clinics, and shopping areas. Some part-time employment is available. Recreational activities include bowling, hunting, skiing, snowmobiling, fishing, tennis, water sports and curling. Points of interest are the Hibbing-Chisholm Pit Crossing Route and the Hull-Rust-Mahoning Mine. The Last Chance International Curling Bonspeil and the Winter Carnival are annual events.

■ **HIGH-TECH INSTITUTE** *F-13*

5100 Gamble Dr.

St. Louis Park, MN 55416

Tel: (763)560-9700

Free: 800-987-0110

Fax: (763)560-9777

Web Site: http://www.high-techinstitute.com/

Description: Proprietary, 2-year, coed. Founded 1996. Calendar: semesters.

■ **INVER HILLS COMMUNITY COLLEGE** *F-15*

2500 East 80th St.

Inver Grove Heights, MN 55076-3224

Tel: (651)450-8500

Admissions: (651)450-8680

Fax: (651)450-8679

E-mail: lpirius@inverhills.edu

Web Site: http://www.inverhills.edu/

Description: State-supported, 2-year, coed. Part of Minnesota State Colleges and Universities System. Awards certificates, transfer associate, and terminal associate degrees. Founded 1969. Setting: 100-acre suburban campus with easy access to Minneapolis-St. Paul. Research spending for 2004 fiscal year: $36,356. Educational spending for 2005 fiscal year: $2889 per student. Total enrollment: 4,325. Students come from 13 states and territories, 56% 25 or older. Core. Calendar: semesters. Academic remediation for entering students, ESL program, services for LD students, advanced placement, honors program, independent study, summer session for credit, part-time degree program, external degree program, co-op programs and internships. Off campus study at other colleges in the Minnesota State Colleges and Universities System.

Entrance Requirements: Open admission except for nursing, emergency medical technology programs. Recommended: high school transcript. Required for some: high school transcript. Entrance: noncompetitive. Application deadline: 8/15. Notification: continuous.

Costs Per Year: Application fee: $20. State resident tuition: $3343 full-time, $125.78 per credit part-time. Nonresident tuition: $6362 full-time, $251.56 per credit part-time. Mandatory fees: $400 full-time, $13.52 per credit part-time. Full-time tuition and fees vary according to program and reciprocity agreements. Part-time tuition and fees vary according to program and reciprocity agreements.

Collegiate Environment: Orientation program. Drama-theater group, choral group, student-run newspaper. Social organizations: 15 open to all. Most popular organizations: PTK, Black Student Union, Student Senate, Biology Club. Student services: health clinic, personal-psychological counseling. Campus security: late night transport-escort service, evening police patrol. College housing not available. 42,073 books, 300 serials, an OPAC, and a Web page. Operations spending for 2004 fiscal year: $340,783. 250 comput-

ers available on campus for general student use. A campuswide network can be accessed. Staffed computer lab on campus.
Community Environment: See Bethel College.

■ **ITASCA COMMUNITY COLLEGE** *N-9*
1851 Hwy. 169 East
Grand Rapids, MN 55744
Tel: (218)327-4460
Free: 800-996-6422
Admissions: (218)327-4464
Fax: (218)327-4350
E-mail: iccinfo@itascacc.edu
Web Site: http://www.itascacc.edu/
Description: State-supported, 2-year, coed. Part of Minnesota State Colleges and Universities System. Awards certificates, diplomas, transfer associate, and terminal associate degrees. Founded 1922. Setting: 24-acre rural campus. Endowment: $3.8 million. Research spending for 2004 fiscal year: $23,482. Educational spending for 2005 fiscal year: $3556 per student. Total enrollment: 1,137. Student-undergrad faculty ratio is 16:1. 661 applied, 100% were admitted. Students come from 10 states and territories, 2 other countries, 4% from out-of-state, 4% Native American, 0.4% Hispanic, 2% black, 1% Asian American or Pacific Islander, 2% international, 20% 25 or older. Retention: 54% of full-time freshmen returned the following year. Core. Calendar: semesters. Academic remediation for entering students, services for LD students, advanced placement, independent study, double major, summer session for credit, part-time degree program, adult/continuing education programs, co-op programs and internships. Off campus study. Study abroad program.
Entrance Requirements: Open admission. Options: Peterson's Universal Application, Common Application, electronic application, international baccalaureate accepted. Required: high school transcript. Required for some: 3 recommendations. Entrance: noncompetitive. Application deadline: 9/6. Notification: continuous.
Costs Per Year: Application fee: $20. State resident tuition: $4100 full-time, $128.12 per credit part-time. Nonresident tuition: $5125 full-time, $160.15 per credit part-time. Mandatory fees: $490 full-time, $15.30 per credit part-time. College room and board: $4190. College room only: $3290.
Collegiate Environment: Orientation program. Social organizations: 10 open to all. Most popular organizations: student association, Circle K, Student Ambassadors, Minority Student Club, Psychology Club. Major annual events: Christmas Dinner, Winter Ice Fishing, Bowling for Prizes. Student services: legal services. Campus security: late night transport-escort service, evening patrols by trained security personnel. 36 college housing spaces available; all were occupied in 2003-04. No special consideration for freshman housing applicants. Itasca Community College Library with 28,790 books, 16,900 microform titles, 280 serials, 2,443 audiovisual materials, an OPAC, and a Web page. Operations spending for 2004 fiscal year: $100,183. 250 computers available on campus for general student use. A campuswide network can be accessed from student residence rooms and from off campus. Staffed computer lab on campus.
Community Environment: A rural community beautifully situated on the Mississippi River and 5 lakes, Grand Rapids (population 8,000) is the county seat of Itasca County, a bustling community with a strong tourist trade. Over 1,000 lakes in the county provide the facilities for all water sports; fishing, hunting, bowling and golf are some of the other recreational activities available. Quadna Mt. ski resort is nearby. Part-time employment opportunities are good.

■ **ITT TECHNICAL INSTITUTE** *F-12*
8911 Columbine Rd.
Eden Prairie, MN 55347
Tel: (952)914-5300
Web Site: http://www.itt-tech.edu/
Description: Proprietary, primarily 2-year, coed. Awards terminal associate and bachelor's degrees. Founded 2003.
Entrance Requirements: Required: high school transcript, interview, Wonderlic aptitude test. Recommended: recommendations. Application deadline: Rolling. Notification: continuous.
Costs Per Year: Application fee: $100.

■ **LAKE SUPERIOR COLLEGE** *O-12*
2101 Trinity Rd.
Duluth, MN 55811
Tel: (218)733-7600

Free: 800-432-2884
Admissions: (218)733-5928
Web Site: http://www.lsc.edu/
Description: State-supported, 2-year, coed. Part of Minnesota State Colleges and Universities System. Awards certificates, diplomas, transfer associate, and terminal associate degrees. Founded 1995. Setting: 105-acre urban campus. Endowment: $148,576. Educational spending for 2005 fiscal year: $33,783 per student. Total enrollment: 4,200. Student-undergrad faculty ratio is 20:1. 13% from out-of-state, 2% Native American, 1% Hispanic, 2% black, 1% Asian American or Pacific Islander, 0% international, 33% 25 or older. Calendar: semesters. Academic remediation for entering students, ESL program, services for LD students, advanced placement, independent study, distance learning, double major, summer session for credit, part-time degree program, internships.
Entrance Requirements: Open admission. Options: early admission, deferred admission. Required for some: high school transcript. Entrance: noncompetitive. Application deadline: Rolling. Notification: continuous.
Costs Per Year: Application fee: $20. State resident tuition: $3450 full-time, $115 per credit part-time. Nonresident tuition: $6900 full-time, $230 per credit part-time. Mandatory fees: $477 full-time, $16 per credit part-time.
Collegiate Environment: Orientation program. Social organizations: 11 open to all. Most popular organizations: Business Professionals of America, Gus Gus Players, Art Club, All Nations, PTK Phi Theta Kappa. Major annual events: Christmas Party, Halloween Party, Game Show. Student services: health clinic, personal-psychological counseling, women's center. Campus security: late night transport-escort service, 15-hour patrols by trained security personnel. College housing not available. Harold P. Erickson Library with 2,869 books, 100 microform titles, 100 serials, 280 audiovisual materials, an OPAC, and a Web page. Operations spending for 2004 fiscal year: $308,033. 230 computers available on campus for general student use. A campuswide network can be accessed from off-campus. Staffed computer lab on campus.

■ **LEECH LAKE TRIBAL COLLEGE** *M-6*
PO Box 180
Cass Lake, MN 56633-0180
Tel: (218)335-4200; 888-829-4240
Fax: (218)335-4209
Web Site: http://www.lltc.org/
Description: Independent, 2-year, coed. Founded 1992. Calendar: semesters.

■ **MACALESTER COLLEGE** *U-10*
1600 Grand Ave.
St. Paul, MN 55105-1899
Tel: (651)696-6000
Free: 800-231-7974
Admissions: (651)696-6357
Fax: (651)696-6500
E-mail: admissions@macalester.edu
Web Site: http://www.macalester.edu/
Description: Independent Presbyterian, 4-year, coed. Awards bachelor's degrees. Founded 1874. Setting: 53-acre urban campus. Endowment: $525 million. Research spending for 2004 fiscal year: $1.1 million. Educational spending for 2005 fiscal year: $14,169 per student. Total enrollment: 1,869. Student-undergrad faculty ratio is 11:1. 4,317 applied, 44% were admitted. 65% from top 10% of their high school class, 94% from top quarter, 100% from top half. 52 National Merit Scholars, 41 valedictorians. Full-time: 1,827 students, 58% women, 42% men. Part-time: 42 students, 60% women, 40% men. Students come from 50 states and territories, 89 other countries, 75% from out-of-state, 1% Native American, 4% Hispanic, 4% black, 7% Asian American or Pacific Islander, 12% international, 0.3% 25 or older, 69% live on campus, 1% transferred in. Retention: 93% of full-time freshmen returned the following year. Academic areas with the most degrees conferred: social sciences; interdisciplinary studies; foreign languages and literature. Core. Calendar: semesters. Self-designed majors, honors program, independent study, double major, part-time degree program, internships. Off campus study at College of St. Catherine, University of St. Thomas, Augsburg College, Hamline University, Minneapolis College of Art and Design. Study abroad program. ROTC: Naval (c), Air Force (c).
Entrance Requirements: Options: Common Application, electronic application, early admission, early decision, deferred admission, international baccalaureate accepted. Required: essay, high school transcript, 3 recommendations, SAT or ACT. Recommended: interview. Entrance: very difficult.

Application deadlines: 1/15, 11/15 for early decision plan 1, 1/3 for early decision plan 2. Notification: 4/1, 12/15 for early decision plan 1, 2/7 for early decision plan 2.

Costs Per Year: Application fee: $40. Comprehensive fee: $39,020 includes full-time tuition ($30,870), mandatory fees ($168), and college room and board ($7982). College room only: $4208. Part-time tuition: $965 per semester hour.

Collegiate Environment: Orientation program. Drama-theater group, choral group, student-run newspaper, radio station. Social organizations: 70 open to all. Most popular organizations: Community Service Organization, student publications, multicultural organization, International Organization, Outing Club. Major annual events: Fall Festival, Springfest, Organization Fair/ Welcome Back. Student services: health clinic, personal-psychological counseling. Campus security: 24-hour emergency response devices and patrols, late night transport-escort service, controlled dormitory access. 1,280 college housing spaces available. Freshmen guaranteed college housing. On-campus residence required through sophomore year. Option: coed housing available. DeWitt Wallace Library with 448,968 books, 78,180 microform titles, 2,119 serials, 10,107 audiovisual materials, an OPAC, and a Web page. Operations spending for 2004 fiscal year: $2.2 million. 400 computers available on campus for general student use. Computer purchase/lease plans available. A campuswide network can be accessed from student residence rooms and from off campus. Staffed computer lab on campus.

Community Environment: The Twin Cities, Minneapolis and St. Paul, with their suburbs, comprise a metropolitan area with a population of 3 million people. The area is the cultural and economic gateway to the northwest and it abounds in cultural advantages of every sort for students. Great art galleries, theaters for the performing arts, notable choral and instrumental music organizations as well as parks, lakes, and professional sports enrich community life.

■ **MARTIN LUTHER COLLEGE** *W-6*
1995 Luther Ct.
New Ulm, MN 56073
Tel: (507)354-8221
Fax: (507)354-8225
E-mail: sebaldja-fac@mlc-wels.edu
Web Site: http://www.mlc-wels.edu/

Description: Independent, 4-year, coed, affiliated with Wisconsin Evangelical Lutheran Synod. Awards bachelor's degrees. Founded 1995. Setting: 50-acre small town campus. Educational spending for 2005 fiscal year: $2933 per student. Total enrollment: 945. 270 applied, 97% were admitted. 21% from top 10% of their high school class, 41% from top quarter, 68% from top half. 7 valedictorians. Full-time: 936 students, 50% women, 50% men. Part-time: 9 students, 33% women, 67% men. Students come from 35 states and territories, 9 other countries, 85% from out-of-state, 0.2% Native American, 1% Hispanic, 0.4% black, 1% Asian American or Pacific Islander, 1% international, 3% 25 or older, 85% live on campus, 3% transferred in. Retention: 83% of full-time freshmen returned the following year. Core. Calendar: semesters. Academic remediation for entering students, ESL program, advanced placement, independent study, double major, summer session for credit, internships.

Entrance Requirements: Option: deferred admission. Required: high school transcript, minimum 2.0 high school GPA, recommendations, ACT. Entrance: moderately difficult. Application deadline: 4/15. Notification: continuous.

Costs Per Year: Application fee: $25. Comprehensive fee: $12,390 includes full-time tuition ($8925) and college room and board ($3465). Part-time tuition: $175 per credit hour.

Collegiate Environment: Orientation program. Drama-theater group, choral group. Social organizations: 23 open to all. Most popular organizations: Drama Club, Color Guard, Pom Poms. Major annual events: Homecoming, Winter Carnival, Children's Theater. Student services: health clinic, personal-psychological counseling. Campus security: 24-hour emergency response devices, student patrols, controlled dormitory access. On-campus residence required through junior year. Options: men-only, women-only housing available. Martin Luther College Library with 115,309 books, 31,583 microform titles, 519 serials, 5,786 audiovisual materials, and an OPAC. Operations spending for 2004 fiscal year: $188,649. 125 computers available on campus for general student use. A campuswide network can be accessed from student residence rooms. Staffed computer lab on campus.

Community Environment: New Ulm (population 14,000), a rural area 100 miles from Minneapolis and St. Paul, is a city where German immigrants

carefully planned wide streets and numerous park areas in such a way that it has not been necessary to change the original plan. Part-time employment opportunities are good. Historical points of interest include the Brown County Historical Museum, Hermann's Monument, and Glockenspiel.

■ **MCNALLY SMITH COLLEGE OF MUSIC** *U-10*
19 Exchange St. East
St. Paul, MN 55101
Tel: (651)291-0177
Free: 800-594-9500
Fax: (651)291-0366
E-mail: dsandridge@mcnallysmith.edu
Web Site: http://www.mcnallysmith.edu/

Description: Proprietary, primarily 2-year, coed. Awards certificates, diplomas, transfer associate, terminal associate, and bachelor's degrees. Founded 1985. Setting: urban campus. Educational spending for 2005 fiscal year: $13,920 per student. Total enrollment: 471. Student-undergrad faculty ratio is 10:1. 160 applied, 84% were admitted. Full-time: 378 students, 16% women, 84% men. Part-time: 93 students, 20% women, 80% men. Students come from 23 states and territories, 45% from out-of-state, 1% Native American, 3% Hispanic, 6% black, 1% Asian American or Pacific Islander, 1% international, 10% 25 or older, 7% transferred in. Core. Calendar: semesters. Advanced placement, independent study, summer session for credit, adult/continuing education programs, internships.

Entrance Requirements: Open admission. Required: essay, high school transcript, 2 recommendations, interview. Recommended: ACT. Required for some: audition. Entrance: noncompetitive. Application deadline: 8/1. Notification: 8/1.

Costs Per Year: Application fee: $75. Tuition: $15,240 full-time, $635 per credit part-time. Mandatory fees: $575 full-time, $75 per term part-time.

Collegiate Environment: Orientation program. Student-run newspaper. Social organizations: 3 open to all. Most popular organizations: Student Advisory Board, Audio Engineering Society, Minnesota Songwriters Association. Student services: personal-psychological counseling. Campus security: 24-hour emergency response devices. College housing not available. Operations spending for 2004 fiscal year: $150,000. 20 computers available on campus for general student use. Staffed computer lab on campus.

■ **MESABI RANGE COMMUNITY AND TECHNICAL COLLEGE** *M-11*
1001 Chestnut St. West
Virginia, MN 55792-3448
Tel: (218)741-3095
Admissions: (218)749-0314
E-mail: b.kochevar@mr.mnscu.edu
Web Site: http://www.mr.mnscu.edu/

Description: State-supported, 2-year, coed. Part of Minnesota State Colleges and Universities System. Awards certificates, diplomas, transfer associate, and terminal associate degrees. Founded 1918. Setting: 30-acre small town campus. Total enrollment: 1,371. Student-undergrad faculty ratio is 25:1. Students come from 6 states and territories, 1% Native American, 0.3% Hispanic, 5% black, 1% Asian American or Pacific Islander, 32% 25 or older, 10% live on campus. Core. Calendar: semesters. Academic remediation for entering students, services for LD students, advanced placement, self-designed majors, summer session for credit, part-time degree program, adult/continuing education programs, co-op programs and internships. Off campus study at other colleges in the Minnesota State Colleges and Universities System.

Entrance Requirements: Open admission. Options: Common Application, early admission, deferred admission. Entrance: noncompetitive. Application deadline: Rolling. Notification: continuous.

Costs Per Year: Application fee: $20. State resident tuition: $4252 full-time. Nonresident tuition: $5197 full-time. College room only: $3352.

Collegiate Environment: Drama-theater group, choral group, student-run newspaper. Social organizations: 20 open to all. Most popular organizations: Student Senate, Human Services Club, Native American Club, Student Life Club, Black Awareness Club. Student services: personal-psychological counseling. Campus security: late night transport-escort service. 108 college housing spaces available; 100 were occupied in 2003-04. Option: coed housing available. Mesabi Library with 23,000 books and 167 serials. 120 computers available on campus for general student use. Staffed computer lab on campus.

Community Environment: The hub of Minnesota Arrowhead country and Taconite capital of the world, Virginia offers ready access to countless waterways and forestland, including Voyageurs National Park and the

Boundary Waters Canoe Area. The Giants Ridge Ski Area features excellent alpine and cross country skiing. The city also has 2 municipal parks, 2 lakes and an 18-hole golf course. Part-time employment is available.

■ METROPOLITAN STATE UNIVERSITY *U-10*
700 East 7th St.
St. Paul, MN 55106-5000
Tel: (651)793-1212
Admissions: (651)793-1303
Fax: (651)772-7632
Web Site: http://www.metrostate.edu
Description: State-supported, comprehensive, coed. Part of Minnesota State Colleges and Universities System. Awards bachelor's and master's degrees (offers primarily part-time evening degree programs). Founded 1971. Setting: urban campus. Endowment: $635,257. Research spending for 2004 fiscal year: $170,129. Educational spending for 2005 fiscal year: $3035 per student. Total enrollment: 6,516. 257 applied, 74% were admitted. Full-time: 1,948 students, 59% women, 41% men. Part-time: 3,953 students, 61% women, 39% men. Students come from 16 states and territories, 53 other countries, 2% from out-of-state, 1% Native American, 2% Hispanic, 9% black, 7% Asian American or Pacific Islander, 2% international, 71% 25 or older, 16% transferred in. Retention: 51% of full-time freshmen returned the following year. Core. Calendar: semesters. ESL program, self-designed majors, independent study, double major, summer session for credit, part-time degree program, external degree program, adult/continuing education programs, internships. Off campus study at other colleges in the Minnesota State College and University System.
Entrance Requirements: Options: Peterson's Universal Application, deferred admission. Required: high school transcript, minimum 2.0 high school GPA. Required for some: SAT or ACT. Entrance: minimally difficult. Application deadline: 6/15.
Costs Per Year: Application fee: $20. State resident tuition: $4,430 full-time, $147.65 per credit part-time. Nonresident tuition: $8859 full-time, $295.30 per credit part-time. Mandatory fees: $252 full-time, $8.39 per credit part-time. Full-time tuition and fees vary according to program and reciprocity agreements. Part-time tuition and fees vary according to course load, program, and reciprocity agreements.
Collegiate Environment: Orientation program. Drama-theater group, student-run newspaper. Social organizations: 21 open to all. Most popular organizations: Psychology Club, Lavender Bridge, International Student Organization, Student Senate, African-American Student Association. Major annual events: Fall Fest (Homecoming), Cultural Heritage Night. Student services: personal-psychological counseling. Campus security: late night transport-escort service. College housing not available. Library and Learning Center with 29,385 books, 385 serials, 1,726 audiovisual materials, an OPAC, and a Web page. Operations spending for 2004 fiscal year: $1.5 million. 525 computers available on campus for general student use. A campuswide network can be accessed from off-campus. Staffed computer lab on campus.
Community Environment: See Bethel College.

■ MINNEAPOLIS BUSINESS COLLEGE *U-10*
1711 West County Rd. B
Roseville, MN 55113
Tel: (612)636-7406
Free: 800-279-5200
Admissions: (651)604-4118
Fax: (612)636-8185
Web Site: http://www.minneapolisbusinesscollege.edu/
Description: Proprietary, 2-year, coed. Part of The Bradford School. Awards diplomas and terminal associate degrees. Founded 1874. Total enrollment: 350. Student-undergrad faculty ratio is 30:1. Students come from 2 states and territories, 11% from out-of-state, 1% 25 or older.
Entrance Requirements: Required: high school transcript. Entrance: minimally difficult.
Costs Per Year: Application fee: $50. Tuition: $12,240 full-time. College room only: $6360.
Collegiate Environment: Campus security: 24-hour emergency response devices.

■ MINNEAPOLIS COLLEGE OF ART AND DESIGN *U-9*
2501 Stevens Ave. South
Minneapolis, MN 55404-4347
Tel: (612)874-3700
Free: 800-874-6223
Admissions: (612)874-3762
Fax: (612)874-3704
E-mail: admissions@mn.mcad.edu
Web Site: http://www.mcad.edu/
Description: Independent, comprehensive, coed. Awards bachelor's and master's degrees. Founded 1886. Setting: 7-acre urban campus. Endowment: $37.4 million. Educational spending for 2005 fiscal year: $12,158 per student. Total enrollment: 722. Faculty: 105 (38 full-time, 67 part-time). Student-undergrad faculty ratio is 13:1. 332 applied, 77% were admitted. 2 valedictorians. Full-time: 626 students, 49% women, 51% men. Part-time: 49 students, 57% women, 43% men. Students come from 39 states and territories, 36% from out-of-state, 1% Native American, 3% Hispanic, 1% black, 3% Asian American or Pacific Islander, 1% international, 5% 25 or older, 45% live on campus, 9% transferred in. Retention: 91% of full-time freshmen returned the following year. Academic area with the most degrees conferred: visual and performing arts. Core. Calendar: semesters. Services for LD students, advanced placement, independent study, distance learning, summer session for credit, part-time degree program, adult/continuing education programs, co-op programs and internships. Off campus study at members of the Association of Independent Colleges of Art and Design, Macalester College. Study abroad program.
Entrance Requirements: Options: deferred admission, international baccalaureate accepted. Required: essay, high school transcript, 1 recommendation, SAT or ACT. Recommended: minimum 2.75 high school GPA, interview. Required for some: portfolio. Entrance: moderately difficult. Application deadline: 6/1. Notification: continuous.
Costs Per Year: Application fee: $35. Comprehensive fee: $31,010 includes full-time tuition ($24,800), mandatory fees ($240), and college room and board ($5970). College room only: $3770. Room and board charges vary according to housing facility. Part-time tuition: $827 per credit. Part-time mandatory fees: $120 per term. Part-time tuition and fees vary according to course load.
Collegiate Environment: Orientation program. Student-run radio station. Social organizations: 2 open to all. Major annual events: art sale, Thanksgiving Dinner. Student services: personal-psychological counseling. Campus security: 24-hour emergency response devices and patrols, late night transport-escort service. 265 college housing spaces available; all were occupied in 2003-04. Freshmen given priority for college housing. Option: coed housing available. Minneapolis College of Art and Design Library with 47,166 books, 1,193 microform titles, 196 serials, 139,245 audiovisual materials, and a Web page. Operations spending for 2004 fiscal year: $305,596. 110 computers available on campus for general student use. A campuswide network can be accessed from off-campus. Staffed computer lab on campus.
Community Environment: See University of Minnesota - Twin Cities.

■ MINNEAPOLIS COMMUNITY AND TECHNICAL COLLEGE *U-9*
1501 Hennepin Ave.
Minneapolis, MN 55403-1779
Tel: (612)659-6000
Admissions: (612)659-6206
Fax: (612)659-6210
Web Site: http://www.mctc.mnscu.edu/
Description: State-supported, 2-year, coed. Part of Minnesota State Colleges and Universities System. Awards certificates, diplomas, transfer associate, and terminal associate degrees. Founded 1965. Setting: 4-acre urban campus. Total enrollment: 7,091. 4,022 applied, 98% were admitted. Students come from 45 states and territories, 81 other countries, 3% from out-of-state, 2% Native American, 3% Hispanic, 25% black, 5% Asian American or Pacific Islander, 3% international, 44% 25 or older. Retention: 51% of full-time freshmen returned the following year. Core. Calendar: semesters. Academic remediation for entering students, ESL program, services for LD students, advanced placement, self-designed majors, honors program, independent study, distance learning, summer session for credit, part-time degree program, adult/continuing education programs, internships. Off campus study at other colleges in the Minnesota State Colleges and Universities System.
Entrance Requirements: Open admission except for nursing, law enforcement, aviation mechanics, air traffic control, some technical programs. Options: early admission, deferred admission. Required: high school transcript. Entrance: noncompetitive. Application deadline: 8/31. Notification: continuous.
Costs Per Year: Application fee: $20. State resident tuition: $4028 full-time, $134.25 per credit part-time. Nonresident tuition: $7694 full-time, $256.45

per credit part-time. Full-time tuition varies according to program and reciprocity agreements. Part-time tuition varies according to program and reciprocity agreements.

Collegiate Environment: Orientation program. Drama-theater group, choral group, student-run newspaper. Most popular organizations: Student Senate, National Vocational-Technical Honor Society, Phi Theta Kappa, Association of Black Collegiates, Soccer Club. Major annual events: 'Chase Your Dreams' open house, Martin Luther King Birthday tribute, MCTC Career Fair. Student services: personal-psychological counseling, women's center. Campus security: 24-hour emergency response devices, late night transport-escort service. College housing not available. Minneapolis Community and Technical College Library with 60,352 books, 1,968 microform titles, 600 serials, 1,374 audiovisual materials, and an OPAC. 150 computers available on campus for general student use. A campuswide network can be accessed. Staffed computer lab on campus.

Community Environment: Minneapolis Community College's beautiful campus borders a city park and is within walking distance of cultural centers (Guthrie Theatre, Walker Art Center) and downtown Minneapolis.

■ MINNESOTA SCHOOL OF BUSINESS *X-11*

2521 Pennington Dr., NW
Rochester, MN 55901
Tel: (507)536-9500; 888-662-8772
Admissions: (507)586-9500
Fax: (507)535-8011
Web Site: http://www.msbcollege.edu/oncampus/rochester/

■ MINNESOTA SCHOOL OF BUSINESS-BROOKLYN CENTER *D-13*

5910 Shingle Creek Parkway
Brooklyn Center, MN 55430
Tel: (763)566-7777
Admissions: (763)585-7777
Fax: (763)566-7030
Web Site: http://www.msbcollege.edu/

Description: Proprietary, primarily 2-year, coed. Awards certificates, diplomas, terminal associate, bachelor's, and master's degrees. Founded 1989. Setting: suburban campus. Total enrollment: 809. Student-undergrad faculty ratio is 13:1. Academic remediation for entering students, accelerated degree program, distance learning, part-time degree program, adult/continuing education programs, co-op programs and internships.

Entrance Requirements: Open admission. Options: Common Application, electronic application. Required: high school transcript, interview, CPAt. Required for some: essay. Application deadline: 10/6.

Costs Per Year: Application fee: $50. Tuition: $15,750 full-time, $350 per credit hour part-time.

Collegiate Environment: College housing not available. Minnesota School of Business Brooklyn Center with 1,534 books, 99 serials, 53 audiovisual materials, an OPAC, and a Web page. 179 computers available on campus for general student use. A campuswide network can be accessed. Staffed computer lab on campus.

■ MINNESOTA SCHOOL OF BUSINESS-PLYMOUTH *U-9*

1455 Country Rd. 101 North
Minneapolis, MN 55447
Tel: (763)476-2000
Web Site: http://www.msbcollege.edu/

Description: Proprietary, primarily 2-year, coed. Awards certificates, diplomas, terminal associate, bachelor's, and master's degrees. Founded 2002. Setting: 3-acre suburban campus. Total enrollment: 500. Student-undergrad faculty ratio is 10:1. Academic remediation for entering students, accelerated degree program, distance learning, summer session for credit, part-time degree program, adult/continuing education programs, co-op programs and internships.

Entrance Requirements: Open admission. Options: Common Application, electronic application. Required: high school transcript, interview, CPAt. Required for some: essay. Entrance: minimally difficult. Application deadline: 10/6.

Costs Per Year: Application fee: $50. Tuition: $15,750 full-time, $350 per credit part-time.

Collegiate Environment: Orientation program. College housing not available. Minnesota School of Business-Plymouth with 1,189 books, 106 serials, 12 audiovisual materials, an OPAC, and a Web page. 62 computers avail-

able on campus for general student use. A campuswide network can be accessed. Staffed computer lab on campus.

■ MINNESOTA SCHOOL OF BUSINESS-RICHFIELD *F-13*

1401 West 76th St.
Richfield, MN 55423
Tel: (612)861-2000
Fax: (612)861-5548
E-mail: pmurray@msbcollege.edu
Web Site: http://www.msbcollege.edu/

Description: Proprietary, primarily 2-year, coed. Awards certificates, diplomas, terminal associate, bachelor's, and master's degrees. Founded 1877. Setting: 3-acre urban campus with easy access to Minneapolis-St. Paul. Total enrollment: 944. Student-undergrad faculty ratio is 14:1. Students come from 5 states and territories, 40% 25 or older. Academic remediation for entering students, accelerated degree program, distance learning, summer session for credit, part-time degree program, adult/continuing education programs, co-op programs and internships.

Entrance Requirements: Open admission. Options: Common Application, electronic application. Required: high school transcript, interview, CPAt. Required for some: essay. Entrance: minimally difficult. Application deadline: 10/6.

Costs Per Year: Application fee: $50. Tuition: $15,750 full-time, $350 per credit hour part-time.

Collegiate Environment: Orientation program. College housing not available. Minnesota School of Business-Richfield with 2,420 books, 93 serials, 93 audiovisual materials, an OPAC, and a Web page. 168 computers available on campus for general student use. A campuswide network can be accessed from off-campus. Staffed computer lab on campus.

■ MINNESOTA SCHOOL OF BUSINESS-ST. CLOUD *S-7*

1201 2nd St. South
Waite Park, MN 56387
Tel: (320)257-2000; (866)403-3333
Web Site: http://www.msbcollege.edu/

Description: Proprietary, primarily 2-year, coed. Awards certificates, diplomas, terminal associate, bachelor's, and master's degrees. Total enrollment: 609. Student-undergrad faculty ratio is 13:1. Academic remediation for entering students, accelerated degree program, distance learning, summer session for credit, part-time degree program, adult/continuing education programs, co-op programs and internships.

Entrance Requirements: Open admission. Options: Common Application, electronic application. Required: high school transcript, interview, CPAt. Required for some: essay. Entrance: minimally difficult. Application deadline: 10/6.

Costs Per Year: Application fee: $50. Tuition: $15,750 full-time, $350 per credit hour part-time.

Collegiate Environment: Orientation program. College housing not available. Minnesota School of Business-St. Cloud with 724 books, 88 serials, an OPAC, and a Web page. 52 computers available on campus for general student use. A campuswide network can be accessed.

■ MINNESOTA SCHOOL OF BUSINESS-SHAKOPEE *V-9*

1200 Shakopee Town Square
Shakopee, MN 55379
Tel: (952)345-1200; (866)766-1200
Admissions: (952)516-7015
Fax: (952)345-1201
Web Site: http://www.msbcollege.edu/

Description: Proprietary, primarily 2-year, coed. Awards certificates, diplomas, terminal associate, bachelor's, and master's degrees. Total enrollment: 360. Student-undergrad faculty ratio is 12:1. Academic remediation for entering students, accelerated degree program, distance learning, summer session for credit, part-time degree program, adult/continuing education programs, co-op programs and internships.

Entrance Requirements: Open admission. Options: Common Application, electronic application. Required: high school transcript, interview, CPAt. Required for some: essay. Entrance: minimally difficult. Application deadline: 10/6.

Costs Per Year: Application fee: $50. Tuition: $15,750 full-time, $350 per credit part-time.

Collegiate Environment: Orientation program. College housing not available. Minnesota School of Business-Shakopee with 919 books, 95 serials, an OPAC, and a Web page. 48 computers available on campus for general student use. A campuswide network can be accessed. Staffed computer lab on campus.

■ MINNESOTA STATE COLLEGE-SOUTHEAST TECHNICAL *X-13*

1250 Homer Rd., PO Box 409
Winona, MN 55987
Tel: (507)453-2700
Free: 800-372-8164
Fax: (507)453-2715
Web Site: http://www.southeastmn.edu/

Description: State-supported, 2-year, coed. Part of Minnesota State Colleges and Universities System. Awards certificates, diplomas, transfer associate, and terminal associate degrees. Founded 1992. Setting: small town campus with easy access to Minneapolis-St. Paul. Endowment: $110,000. Total enrollment: 1,817. 1,263 applied, 87% were admitted. Full-time: 1,060 students, 48% women, 52% men. Part-time: 757 students, 68% women, 32% men. Students come from 20 states and territories, 1% Native American, 1% Hispanic, 2% black, 1% Asian American or Pacific Islander, 0.1% international, 46% 25 or older. Calendar: semesters. Academic remediation for entering students, ESL program, services for LD students, part-time degree program, internships.

Entrance Requirements: Open admission. Options: Common Application, electronic application. Required: high school transcript. Entrance: noncompetitive. Application deadline: Rolling.

Costs Per Year: Application fee: $20. State resident tuition: $124.43 per credit part-time. Nonresident tuition: $248.86 per credit part-time. Mandatory fees: $11.90 per credit part-time. Part-time tuition and fees vary according to reciprocity agreements.

Collegiate Environment: Orientation program. Social organizations: 4 open to all. Most popular organization: Student Senate. Major annual events: holiday dinners, Spring Picnic/Golf Outing, National Vocational Education Week activities. Campus security: 24-hour emergency response devices, late night transport-escort service. College housing not available. Learning Resource Center plus 1 other with 8,000 books, 150 serials, an OPAC, and a Web page. 50 computers available on campus for general student use. A campuswide network can be accessed from off-campus. Staffed computer lab on campus.

■ MINNESOTA STATE COMMUNITY AND TECHNICAL COLLEGE-FERGUS FALLS *Q-3*

1414 College Way
Fergus Falls, MN 56537-1009
Tel: (218)739-7500; 888-MY-MSCTC
Admissions: (218)736-1528
Fax: (218)739-7475
E-mail: carrie.brimhall@minnesota.edu
Web Site: http://www.minnesota.edu/

Description: State-supported, 2-year, coed. Part of Minnesota State Colleges and Universities System. Awards certificates, diplomas, transfer associate, and terminal associate degrees. Founded 1960. Setting: 146-acre rural campus. Endowment: $1.8 million. Educational spending for 2005 fiscal year: $4144 per student. Total enrollment: 5,631. Student-undergrad faculty ratio is 18:1. 3,320 applied, 81% were admitted. Full-time: 3,587 students, 51% women, 49% men. Part-time: 2,044 students, 71% women, 29% men. Students come from 12 states and territories, 2 other countries, 3% from out-of-state, 3% Native American, 1% Hispanic, 2% black, 1% Asian American or Pacific Islander, 0.1% international, 20% 25 or older, 22% live on campus, 1% transferred in. Core. Calendar: semesters. Academic remediation for entering students, ESL program, services for LD students, advanced placement, independent study, summer session for credit, part-time degree program. Off campus study at other colleges in the Minnesota State Colleges and Universities System. Study abroad program.

Entrance Requirements: Open admission for state residents, except for nursing program. Options: Common Application, electronic application, early admission, deferred admission. Required: high school transcript. Recommended: ACT. Entrance: noncompetitive. Application deadline: Rolling. Notification: continuous.

Costs Per Year: Application fee: $20. State resident tuition: $3900 full-time, $133 per credit part-time. Nonresident tuition: $3900 full-time, $133 per credit part-time. Mandatory fees: $569 full-time, $18 per credit part-time. College room only: $3000.

Collegiate Environment: Orientation program. Drama-theater group, choral group, student-run newspaper. Most popular organizations: Student Senate,

Students In Free Enterprise, Phi Theta Kappa. Major annual events: Homecoming, Minnesota Meltdown, Health Awareness Week. Student services: personal-psychological counseling, women's center. Campus security: late night transport-escort service, security for special events. 152 college housing spaces available; all were occupied in 2003-04. No special consideration for freshman housing applicants. Option: coed housing available. Fergus Falls Community College Library with 30,000 books, 68 microform titles, 173 serials, and an OPAC. Operations spending for 2004 fiscal year: $228,463. 144 computers available on campus for general student use. A campuswide network can be accessed from off-campus. Staffed computer lab on campus.

Community Environment: One of the largest dairy products and poultry shipping points in the northwest, Fergus Falls (population 12,443) also has the largest cooperative creamery in this region. Trains and buses are convenient for transportation. There are 1,000 lakes in the area which are within a 10 minute drive to an hour's drive. A fine park system, public golf course, municipal swimming beach, trap-shooting facilities, tennis courts, archery range, ice skating rinks, skiing facilities and rope tows provide the recreational activities. The hunting and fishing opportunities are unsurpassed.

■ MINNESOTA STATE UNIVERSITY MANKATO *X-8*

228 Wiecking Center
Mankato, MN 56001
Tel: (507)389-2463
Free: 800-722-0544
Admissions: (507)389-6670
E-mail: walter.wolff@mnsu.edu
Web Site: http://www.mnsu.edu/

Description: State-supported, comprehensive, coed. Part of Minnesota State Colleges and Universities System. Awards associate, bachelor's, and master's degrees and post-master's certificates. Founded 1868. Setting: 303-acre small town campus with easy access to Minneapolis-St. Paul. Research spending for 2004 fiscal year: $928,730. Educational spending for 2005 fiscal year: $3712 per student. Total enrollment: 14,335. Faculty: 717 (491 full-time, 226 part-time). Student-undergrad faculty ratio is 22:1. 5,605 applied, 90% were admitted. 8% from top 10% of their high school class, 27% from top quarter, 70% from top half. Full-time: 11,337 students, 52% women, 48% men. Part-time: 1,347 students, 56% women, 44% men. Students come from 44 states and territories, 68 other countries, 10% from out-of-state, 0.3% Native American, 1% Hispanic, 2% black, 2% Asian American or Pacific Islander, 3% international, 11% 25 or older, 22% live on campus, 8% transferred in. Retention: 76% of full-time freshmen returned the following year. Academic areas with the most degrees conferred: business/marketing; education; health professions and related sciences. Core. Calendar: semesters. Academic remediation for entering students, ESL program, services for LD students, advanced placement, self-designed majors, honors program, independent study, distance learning, double major, summer session for credit, part-time degree program, adult/continuing education programs, internships, graduate courses open to undergrads. Off campus study at other colleges in the Minnesota State College and University System. Study abroad program. ROTC: Army.

Entrance Requirements: Options: electronic application, early admission, deferred admission, international baccalaureate accepted. Required: high school transcript, ACT. Required for some: essay, 3 recommendations, personal statement. Entrance: moderately difficult. Application deadline: Rolling. Notification: continuous.

Costs Per Year: Application fee: $20. State resident tuition: $5104 full-time, $204.10 per credit part-time. Nonresident tuition: $10,932 full-time, $436 per credit part-time. Mandatory fees: $742 full-time, $29.89 per credit part-time. Full-time tuition and fees vary according to course load and reciprocity agreements. Part-time tuition and fees vary according to course load and reciprocity agreements. College room and board: $5083. Room and board charges vary according to board plan.

Collegiate Environment: Orientation program. Drama-theater group, choral group, marching band, student-run newspaper, radio station. Social organizations: 170 open to all; national fraternities, national sororities. Major annual events: homecoming events, Welcome Week activities, Frost Days. Student services: legal services, health clinic, personal-psychological counseling, women's center. Campus security: 24-hour emergency response devices and patrols, student patrols, late night transport-escort service, Night Owl security program in residence halls, closed circuit cameras in parking lots. 2,900 college housing spaces available. Option: coed housing available. Memorial Library with 474,252 books, 281,817 microform titles, 3,400 serials, 34,186 audiovisual materials, an OPAC, and a Web page. Operations spending for 2004 fiscal year: $4.6 million. 900 computers available on campus for general student use. A campuswide network can be accessed from student residence rooms and from off campus. Staffed computer lab on campus.

Community Environment: Mankato (population 41,000), on a great bend in the Minnesota River, is the trade and distributing center for agricultural southwestern Minnesota. Bus and air service is available. Community facilities include a number of churches, hospitals, and the usual civic and service organizations. About 30 lakes within a 25-mile area provide facilities for all water sports and fishing; other activities include golf, hunting and skiing. Points of interest are the Blue Earth County Historical Society Museum, Minneopa State Park and Sibley Park.

■ **MINNESOTA STATE UNIVERSITY MOORHEAD** *O-2*

1104 7th Ave. South
Moorhead, MN 56563-0002
Tel: (218)236-2011
Free: 800-593-7246
Admissions: (218)477-2161
Fax: (218)236-2168
E-mail: dragon@mastate.edu
Web Site: http://www.mnstate.edu/

Description: State-supported, comprehensive, coed. Part of Minnesota State Colleges and Universities System. Awards associate, bachelor's, and master's degrees and post-master's certificates. Founded 1885. Setting: 118-acre urban campus. Research spending for 2004 fiscal year: $45,586. Educational spending for 2005 fiscal year: $4133 per student. Total enrollment: 7,652. Faculty: 303 (270 full-time, 33 part-time). Student-undergrad faculty ratio is 20:1. 2,783 applied, 83% were admitted. 10% from top 10% of their high school class, 28% from top quarter, 63% from top half. Full-time: 6,198 students, 59% women, 41% men. Part-time: 1,044 students, 59% women, 41% men. Students come from 34 states and territories, 32 other countries, 43% from out-of-state, 1% Native American, 1% Hispanic, 1% black, 1% Asian American or Pacific Islander, 3% international, 19% 25 or older, 27% live on campus, 9% transferred in. Retention: 68% of full-time freshmen returned the following year. Academic areas with the most degrees conferred: education; business/marketing; communications/journalism. Core. Calendar: semesters. Academic remediation for entering students, services for LD students, advanced placement, self-designed majors, freshman honors college, honors program, independent study, distance learning, double major, summer session for credit, part-time degree program, external degree program, adult/continuing education programs, internships, graduate courses open to undergrads. Off campus study at North Dakota State University, Concordia College (Moorhead, MN), other colleges of the Minnesota State Colleges and Universities System. Study abroad program. ROTC: Army (c), Air Force (c).

Entrance Requirements: Options: early admission, deferred admission, international baccalaureate accepted. Required: high school transcript, ACT, SAT or ACT. Entrance: moderately difficult. Application deadline: 8/7. Notification: continuous.

Costs Per Year: Application fee: $20. State resident tuition: $4464 full-time, $148.80 per credit hour part-time. Nonresident tuition: $4464 full-time, $148.80 per credit hour part-time. Mandatory fees: $761 full-time, $88.85 per credit hour part-time. Full-time tuition and fees vary according to reciprocity agreements. Part-time tuition and fees vary according to reciprocity agreements. College room and board: $4974. College room only: $3044. Room and board charges vary according to board plan and housing facility.

Collegiate Environment: Orientation program. Drama-theater group, choral group, student-run newspaper, radio station. Social organizations: 110 open to all; national sororities, local fraternities; 3% of eligible men and 2% of eligible women are members. Most popular organizations: residence hall associations, Campus Activities Board, Pi Sigma Epsilon, Campus Crusade for Christ, ATransfer Club. Major annual events: Mall Music Madness, Homecoming, Graduation Ceremony. Student services: health clinic, personal-psychological counseling, women's center. Campus security: 24-hour emergency response devices and patrols, student patrols, late night transport-escort service, controlled dormitory access. Options: coed, men-only, women-only housing available. Livingston Lord Library with 367,334 books, 1,539 serials, an OPAC, and a Web page. Operations spending for 2004 fiscal year: $1.4 million. 450 computers available on campus for general student use. A campuswide network can be accessed from student residence rooms and from off campus. Staffed computer lab on campus.

Community Environment: Consistently ranked as one of the best places to live in the country by leading publications, the cities of Moorhead, Minn., and

Fargo, N.D. boast a high quality of life based on excellent schools and hospitals, booming business and job growth, superior educational, professional and recreational opportunities, and a safe, clean environment. In 2000 Fargo/Moorhead was awarded The prestigious All-American City Award. More than 20,000 students attend six educational institutions in Fargo-Moorhead. With a metro population of 165,000, the community is a regional center for education, business, communication, finance, health care and entertainment. MSU is just 4 hours from Minneapolis-St. Paul, 3 1/2 hours from Winnipeg, 3 hours from Bismarck, N.D., and 45 minutes from some of the best lake country in Minnesota.

■ **MINNESOTA WEST COMMUNITY AND TECHNICAL COLLEGE** *X-2*

1314 North Hiawatha Ave.
Pipestone, MN 56164
Tel: (507)825-6800
Free: 800-658-2330
Admissions: (507)825-6804
Fax: (507)825-4656
E-mail: garygillin@mnwest.edu
Web Site: http://www.mnwest.edu/

Description: State-supported, 2-year, coed. Part of Minnesota State Colleges and Universities System. Awards certificates, diplomas, transfer associate, and terminal associate degrees (profile contains information from Canby, Granite Falls, Jackson, and Worthington campuses). Founded 1967. Setting: 103-acre rural campus. Total enrollment: 2,783. Student-undergrad faculty ratio is 13:1. 2,160 applied, 81% were admitted. 1% from top 10% of their high school class, 5% from top quarter, 20% from top half. Full-time: 1,439 students, 50% women, 50% men. Part-time: 1,344 students, 54% women, 46% men. Students come from 25 states and territories, 3 other countries, 11% from out-of-state, 1% Native American, 3% Hispanic, 3% black, 1% Asian American or Pacific Islander, 0% international, 43% 25 or older, 5% transferred in. Retention: 63% of full-time freshmen returned the following year. Core. Calendar: semesters. Academic remediation for entering students, services for LD students, advanced placement, honors program, independent study, distance learning, double major, summer session for credit, part-time degree program, external degree program, co-op programs and internships.

Entrance Requirements: Open admission. Options: Peterson's Universal Application, Common Application, electronic application. Required: high school transcript. Entrance: noncompetitive. Application deadline: Rolling.

Costs Per Year: Application fee: $20. State resident tuition: $4085 full-time, $136.18 per credit part-time. Nonresident tuition: $8171 full-time, $272.36 per credit part-time. Mandatory fees: $377 full-time, $12.58 per credit part-time.

Collegiate Environment: Orientation program. Major annual events: Snow Week, Campus Olympics. Student services: personal-psychological counseling. College housing not available. Minnesota West Library plus 4 others with 46,057 books, 313 serials, 4,632 audiovisual materials, and an OPAC.

■ **NATIONAL AMERICAN UNIVERSITY (BLOOMINGTON)** *V-9*

112 West Market
Bloomington, MN 55425
Tel: (605)394-4800
Web Site: http://www.national.edu/
Description: Proprietary, 2-year, coed.

■ **NATIONAL AMERICAN UNIVERSITY (BROOKLYN CENTER)** *D-13*

6120 Earle Brown Dr.
Ste. 100
Brooklyn Center, MN 55430
Tel: (763)560-8377
Fax: (763)549-9955
Web Site: http://www.national.edu/
Description: Proprietary, 2-year, coed.

■ **NATIONAL AMERICAN UNIVERSITY (ROSEVILLE)** *U-10*

1500 West Hwy. 36
Roseville, MN 55113-4035
Tel: (651)644-1265
Fax: (651)644-0690
Web Site: http://www.national.edu/
Description: Proprietary, 4-year, coed. Part of National American University. Awards associate and bachelor's degrees. Setting: 1-acre urban campus. Total enrollment: 446. 259 applied, 100% were admitted. Full-time: 220

students, 49% women, 51% men. Part-time: 226 students, 47% women, 53% men. Students come from 5 states and territories, 0.4% Native American, 3% Hispanic, 18% black, 16% Asian American or Pacific Islander, 5% international, 50% 25 or older. Retention: 52% of full-time freshmen returned the following year.

Entrance Requirements: Required: high school transcript. Recommended: minimum 2 high school GPA, interview. Required for some: essay. Application deadline: Rolling. Notification: continuous.

Collegiate Environment: Student-run newspaper. Social organizations: 3 open to all. Most popular organizations: Southeast Asian Student Organization, Phi Beta Lambda/Lambda Beta Omicron, Student Government Association, International Student Organization. Major annual event: Grad Fest. Campus security: late night transport-escort service. College housing not available.

■ **NORMANDALE COMMUNITY COLLEGE** *V-9*
9700 France Ave. South
Bloomington, MN 55431-4399
Tel: (952)487-8200; (866)880-8740
Admissions: (952)487-8494
Fax: (612)487-8101
Web Site: http://www.normandale.edu/

Description: State-supported, 2-year, coed. Part of Minnesota State Colleges and Universities System. Awards certificates, transfer associate, and terminal associate degrees. Founded 1968. Setting: 90-acre suburban campus with easy access to Minneapolis-St. Paul. Endowment: $1.4 million. Research spending for 2004 fiscal year: $140,000. Educational spending for 2005 fiscal year: $4200 per student. Total enrollment: 8,261. Student-undergrad faculty ratio is 28:1. 4,186 applied, 71% were admitted. 8% from top 10% of their high school class, 18% from top quarter, 39% from top half. Students come from 22 states and territories, 2% from out-of-state, 1% Native American, 2% Hispanic, 10% black, 7% Asian American or Pacific Islander, 1% international, 34% 25 or older. Core. Calendar: semesters. Academic remediation for entering students, ESL program, services for LD students, advanced placement, accelerated degree program, self-designed majors, independent study, distance learning, summer session for credit, part-time degree program, adult/continuing education programs, co-op programs and internships. Off campus study at other colleges in the Minnesota State Colleges and Universities System. Study abroad program. ROTC: Army (c), Air Force (c).

Entrance Requirements: Open admission except for health programs. Options: Common Application, early admission, deferred admission. Required for some: high school transcript. Entrance: noncompetitive. Application deadline: Rolling. Notification: continuous.

Costs Per Year: Application fee: $20. State resident tuition: $3614 full-time, $133 per credit part-time. Nonresident tuition: $7227 full-time, $253 per credit part-time. Mandatory fees: $362 full-time.

Collegiate Environment: Orientation program. Drama-theater group, choral group, student-run newspaper. Social organizations: 30 open to all. Most popular organizations: Program Board (NPB), Student Senate, Phi Theta Kappa, Inter-Varsity Christian Fellowship Club, Spanish Club. Major annual events: Spring Fling, Winter Festival Breakfast, 3 on 3 Basketball Tourney. Student services: personal-psychological counseling. Campus security: 24-hour emergency response devices, student patrols, late night transport-escort service. College housing not available. Library plus 1 other with 98,141 books, 5,071 microform titles, 623 serials, 43,561 audiovisual materials, and an OPAC. Operations spending for 2004 fiscal year: $821,951. 450 computers available on campus for general student use. A campuswide network can be accessed from off-campus. Staffed computer lab on campus.

Community Environment: The college is located in Bloomington, a suburb of 85,000 people located 10 miles south of Minneapolis and 7 miles west of the Minneapolis/St. Paul Airport.

■ **NORTH CENTRAL UNIVERSITY** *U-9*
910 Elliot Ave.
Minneapolis, MN 55404-1322
Tel: (612)332-3491
Free: 800-289-6222
Admissions: (612)343-4460
Fax: (612)343-4778
E-mail: jghubert@northcentral.edu
Web Site: http://www.northcentral.edu/

Description: Independent, 4-year, coed, affiliated with Assemblies of God. Awards associate and bachelor's degrees. Founded 1930. Setting: 9-acre

urban campus. Endowment: $969,948. Educational spending for 2005 fiscal year: $2312 per student. Total enrollment: 1,241. 433 applied, 86% were admitted. 9% from top 10% of their high school class, 26% from top quarter, 56% from top half. Full-time: 1,143 students, 57% women, 43% men. Part-time: 98 students, 54% women, 46% men. Students come from 40 states and territories, 11 other countries, 56% from out-of-state, 1% Native American, 2% Hispanic, 4% black, 1% Asian American or Pacific Islander, 1% international, 10% 25 or older, 65% live on campus, 10% transferred in. Retention: 77% of full-time freshmen returned the following year. Core. Calendar: semesters plus January and May terms. Academic remediation for entering students, services for LD students, advanced placement, self-designed majors, summer session for credit, part-time degree program, external degree program, adult/continuing education programs, co-op programs and internships. Off campus study. Study abroad program. ROTC: Army (c), Air Force (c).

Entrance Requirements: Options: Common Application, deferred admission. Required: essay, high school transcript, minimum 2.2 high school GPA, recommendations, Christian testimony, SAT or ACT. Required for some: interview. Entrance: noncompetitive. Application deadline: 6/1. Notification: 6/15.

Costs Per Year: Application fee: $25. One-time mandatory fee: $115. Comprehensive fee: $16,646 includes full-time tuition ($11,280), mandatory fees ($886), and college room and board ($4480). College room only: $2050. Room and board charges vary according to board plan and housing facility. Part-time tuition: $376 per credit. Part-time mandatory fees: $35 per credit.

Collegiate Environment: Orientation program. Drama-theater group, choral group, student-run newspaper, radio station. Social organizations: 31 open to all. Most popular organizations: athletics, Mu Kappa, musical organizations, student government, student ministries. Major annual events: All College Pic-Nic, Fall Friend-See, Battle of the Floors. Student services: personal-psychological counseling. Campus security: 24-hour emergency response devices and patrols, late night transport-escort service, controlled dormitory access. 950 college housing spaces available; all were occupied in 2003-04. Freshmen guaranteed college housing. On-campus residence required through senior year. Options: men-only, women-only housing available. T. J. Jones Information Resource Center with 70,041 books and 384 serials. Operations spending for 2004 fiscal year: $282,286. 30 computers available on campus for general student use. A campuswide network can be accessed. Staffed computer lab on campus.

Community Environment: See University of Minnesota - Twin Cities.

■ **NORTH HENNEPIN COMMUNITY COLLEGE** *D-13*
7411 85th Ave. North
Brooklyn Park, MN 55445-2231
Tel: (763)424-0702
Admissions: (763)424-0713
Fax: (763)424-0929
E-mail: lkirkeby@nhcc.edu
Web Site: http://www.nhcc.edu/

Description: State-supported, 2-year, coed. Part of Minnesota State Colleges and Universities System. Awards certificates, transfer associate, and terminal associate degrees. Founded 1966. Setting: 80-acre suburban campus. Endowment: $838,054. Research spending for 2004 fiscal year: $63,175. Educational spending for 2005 fiscal year: $5300 per student. Total enrollment: 6,382. Student-undergrad faculty ratio is 29:1. 1,852 applied, 100% were admitted. Students come from 4 states and territories, 96 other countries, 2% from out-of-state, 1% Native American, 1% Hispanic, 15% black, 8% Asian American or Pacific Islander, 1% international, 35% 25 or older. Retention: 99% of full-time freshmen returned the following year. Core. Calendar: semesters. Academic remediation for entering students, ESL program, services for LD students, advanced placement, accelerated degree program, honors program, independent study, distance learning, summer session for credit, part-time degree program, adult/continuing education programs, internships. Off campus study. Study abroad program.

Entrance Requirements: Open admission except for nursing program, nonresident Aliens, Graphic Design, NICT, MLT Bus ASAP. Options: early admission, deferred admission. Recommended: high school transcript. Entrance: noncompetitive. Application deadline: Rolling. Notification: continuous.

Costs Per Year: Application fee: $20. State resident tuition: $3,158 full-time, $131.60 per credit part-time. Mandatory fees: $309 full-time, $10.30 per credit part-time.

Collegiate Environment: Orientation program. Drama-theater group, choral group, student-run newspaper. Student services: personal-psychological counseling. Campus security: 24-hour patrols, late night transport-escort service. College housing not available. Learning Resource Center with 69,375 books, 7,595 microform titles, 2,500 serials, 3,406 audiovisual materials, an OPAC, and a Web page. Operations spending for 2004 fiscal year: $460,701. 250 computers available on campus for general student use. A campuswide network can be accessed. Staffed computer lab on campus.

■ NORTHLAND COMMUNITY AND TECHNICAL COLLEGE-EAST GRAND FORKS *K-1*

2022 Central Ave., NW
East Grand Forks, MN 56721-2702
Tel: (218)773-3441
Free: 800-451-3441
Admissions: (218)773-4546
Fax: (218)773-4502
Web Site: http://www.northlandcollege.edu/
Description: State-supported, 2-year, coed. Awards certificates, diplomas, transfer associate, and terminal associate degrees. Founded 1973. Total enrollment: 1,442. Calendar: semesters.

■ NORTHLAND COMMUNITY AND TECHNICAL COLLEGE-THIEF RIVER FALLS *K-3*

1101 Hwy. One East
Thief River Falls, MN 56701
Tel: (218)681-0701
Free: 800-959-6282
Admissions: (218)681-0862
Fax: (218)681-6405
Web Site: http://www.northlandcollege.edu/
Description: State-supported, 2-year, coed. Part of Minnesota State Colleges and Universities System. Awards certificates, diplomas, transfer associate, and terminal associate degrees. Founded 1965. Setting: rural campus. Total enrollment: 3,652. Student-undergrad faculty ratio is 23:1. 2,137 applied, 100% were admitted. Students come from 27 states and territories, 3 other countries, 26% from out-of-state, 4% Native American, 2% Hispanic; 3% black, 1% Asian American or Pacific Islander, 0.1% international, 26% 25 or older. Core. Calendar: semesters. Academic remediation for entering students, services for LD students, advanced placement, distance learning, summer session for credit, part-time degree program, adult/continuing education programs, internships. Off campus study at other colleges in the Minnesota State Colleges and Universities System.
Entrance Requirements: Open admission for state residents, except for nursing program. Options: Peterson's Universal Application, Common Application, electronic application, early admission, deferred admission. Required: high school transcript. Entrance: noncompetitive. Application deadline: 9/1. Notification: continuous.
Costs Per Year: Application fee: $20. State resident tuition: $4170 full-time, $139 per credit part-time. Mandatory fees: $490 full-time, $16.12 per credit part-time.
Collegiate Environment: Orientation program. Drama-theater group, choral group, student-run newspaper, radio station. Most popular organizations: Law Enforcement Club, All-Nations Club, Environmental Club, PAMA, VICA. Major annual events: homecoming, Snow-Fest, Spring Fling. Student services: personal-psychological counseling, women's center. Campus security: student patrols, late night transport-escort service. College housing not available. 567 computers available on campus for general student use. Computer purchase/lease plans available. A campuswide network can be accessed from off-campus. Staffed computer lab on campus.
Community Environment: Thief River Falls (population 9,000) is in northwest Minnesota. The facilities for outdoor recreation are numerous. Commercial transportation is available. The community provides a complete downtown shopping center, a public library, hospitals and an employment office.

■ NORTHWEST TECHNICAL COLLEGE *M-6*

905 Grant Ave., SE
Bemidji, MN 56601-4907
Tel: (218)755-4270
Free: 800-942-8324
Admissions: (218)846-7444
Web Site: http://bemidji.ntcmn.edu/
Description: State-supported, 2-year, coed. Part of Minnesota State Colleges and Universities System. Awards certificates, diplomas, and terminal associate degrees. Founded 1993. Setting: small town campus. Total enrollment: 4,500. Calendar: semesters. Services for LD students, independent study, distance learning, summer session for credit, part-time degree program, external degree program, co-op programs and internships.
Entrance Requirements: Open admission. Placement: ACCUPLACER required. Entrance: noncompetitive.
Collegiate Environment: Orientation program. Student-run newspaper. Student services: personal-psychological counseling. Campus security: late night transport-escort service. College housing not available.

■ NORTHWEST TECHNICAL INSTITUTE *F-12*

11995 Singletree Ln.
Eden Prairie, MN 55344-5351
Tel: (952)944-0080
Free: 800-443-4223
Fax: (952)944-9274
Web Site: http://www.nti.edu/
Description: Proprietary, 2-year, coed. Awards transfer associate and terminal associate degrees. Founded 1957. Setting: 2-acre suburban campus with easy access to Minneapolis-St. Paul. Total enrollment: 108. 25 applied, 100% were admitted. 10% from top 10% of their high school class, 25% from top quarter, 50% from top half. Full-time: 108 students, 11% women, 89% men. Students come from 2 states and territories, 25% from out-of-state, 1% Hispanic, 2% black, 0% Asian American or Pacific Islander, 10% 25 or older, 6% transferred in. Core. Calendar: semesters. Honors program, independent study.
Entrance Requirements: Open admission. Required: high school transcript, interview. Entrance: noncompetitive. Application deadline: Rolling. Notification: continuous.
Collegiate Environment: Orientation program. Major annual events: Annual Softball Picnic, Student/Staff Holiday Luncheon. Campus security: 24-hour emergency response devices and patrols, late night transport-escort service. College housing not available. 565 books and 4 serials. 120 computers available on campus for general student use. A campuswide network can be accessed. Staffed computer lab on campus.

■ NORTHWESTERN COLLEGE *U-10*

3003 Snelling Ave. North
St. Paul, MN 55113-1598
Tel: (651)631-5100
Free: 800-827-6827
Admissions: (651)631-5111
Fax: (651)631-5680
E-mail: admissions@nwc.edu
Web Site: http://www.nwc.edu/
Description: Independent nondenominational, 4-year, coed. Awards associate, bachelor's, and master's degrees. Founded 1902. Setting: 100-acre suburban campus. Endowment: $9.8 million. Educational spending for 2005 fiscal year: $4521 per student. Total enrollment: 1,785. Faculty: 165 (85 full-time, 80 part-time). Student-undergrad faculty ratio is 16:1. 918 applied, 98% were admitted. 26% from top 10% of their high school class, 51% from top quarter, 79% from top half. 15 valedictorians. Full-time: 1,726 students, 60% women, 40% men. Part-time: 41 students, 56% women, 44% men. Students come from 36 states and territories, 13 other countries, 32% from out-of-state, 0.4% Native American, 2% Hispanic, 2% black, 4% Asian American or Pacific Islander, 1% international, 24% 25 or older, 42% live on campus, 24% transferred in. Retention: 79% of full-time freshmen returned the following year. Academic areas with the most degrees conferred: business/marketing; theology and religious vocations; education; psychology. Core. Calendar: semesters. Academic remediation for entering students, services for LD students, advanced placement, self-designed majors, honors program, independent study, distance learning, double major, summer session for credit, part-time degree program, adult/continuing education programs, internships. Off campus study at Council for Christian Colleges and Universities, Focus on the Family Institute, William Mitchell College of Law,. Study abroad program. ROTC: Army (c), Air Force (c).
Entrance Requirements: Options: electronic application, early admission, deferred admission, international baccalaureate accepted. Required: essay, high school transcript, minimum 2.0 high school GPA, 2 recommendations, lifestyle agreement, statement of Christian faith, SAT or ACT. Recommended: minimum 3.0 high school GPA. Required for some: interview. Entrance: moderately difficult. Application deadline: 7/1. Notification: continuous.

Costs Per Year: Application fee: $30. Comprehensive fee: $25,220 includes full-time tuition ($19,100) and college room and board ($6120). College room only: $3400. Full-time tuition varies according to course load. Room and board charges vary according to board plan. Part-time tuition: $810 per credit. Part-time tuition varies according to course load.

Collegiate Environment: Orientation program. Drama-theater group, choral group, student-run newspaper, radio station. Social organizations: 25 open to all. Most popular organizations: NWSA (student government association), Edge (religious group), Transfer Connection, Guardian Angels, Mu Kappa. Major annual events: Variety Show, Christmas at Northwestern, graduation. Student services: health clinic, personal-psychological counseling. Campus security: 24-hour patrols, late night transport-escort service, controlled dormitory access. 1,056 college housing spaces available; 950 were occupied in 2003-04. Freshmen guaranteed college housing. On-campus residence required through sophomore year. Options: men-only, women-only housing available. Berntsen Library with 87,877 books, 79,044 microform titles, 560 serials, 5,674 audiovisual materials, an OPAC, and a Web page. Operations spending for 2004 fiscal year: $706,357. 100 computers available on campus for general student use. Computer purchase/lease plans available. A campuswide network can be accessed from student residence rooms and from off campus. Staffed computer lab on campus.

■ OAK HILLS CHRISTIAN COLLEGE *M-6*
1600 Oak Hills Rd., SW
Bemidji, MN 56601-8832
Tel: (218)751-8670; 888-751-8670
Fax: (218)751-8825
E-mail: admissions@oakhills.edu
Web Site: http://www.oakhills.edu/

Description: Independent interdenominational, 4-year, coed. Awards associate and bachelor's degrees. Founded 1946. Setting: 180-acre rural campus. Endowment: $291,015. Educational spending for 2005 fiscal year: $3610 per student. Total enrollment: 167. Student-undergrad faculty ratio is 14:1. 79 applied, 53% were admitted. 11% from top 10% of their high school class, 26% from top quarter, 55% from top half. Full-time: 152 students, 42% women, 58% men. Part-time: 15 students, 40% women, 60% men. Students come from 22 states and territories, 1 other country, 30% from out-of-state, 2% Native American, 2% Hispanic, 1% black, 1% Asian American or Pacific Islander, 2% international, 14% 25 or older, 80% live on campus, 15% transferred in. Retention: 59% of full-time freshmen returned the following year. Academic area with the most degrees conferred: theology and religious vocations. Core. Calendar: semesters. Academic remediation for entering students, services for LD students, advanced placement, honors program, independent study, double major, part-time degree program, internships. Off campus study.

Entrance Requirements: Options: Peterson's Universal Application, deferred admission. Required: essay, high school transcript, minimum 2.0 high school GPA, 2 recommendations, ACT. Required for some: interview. Entrance: minimally difficult. Application deadline: Rolling. Notification: continuous.

Costs Per Year: Application fee: $25. Comprehensive fee: $16,390 includes full-time tuition ($11,940) and college room and board ($4450). Part-time tuition: $145 per semester hour.

Collegiate Environment: Choral group. Social organizations: 2 open to all. Most popular organizations: Student Council, Students Older Than Average. Major annual events: Spring Banquet, Christmas Festival, Soul Clean-Up Day. Student services: health clinic, personal-psychological counseling. Campus security: 24-hour emergency response devices, student patrols, controlled dormitory access, evening patrols by trained security personnel. 173 college housing spaces available; 130 were occupied in 2003-04. Freshmen guaranteed college housing. On-campus residence required through sophomore year. Options: men-only, women-only housing available. Cummings Library with 24,410 books, 86 serials, 1,428 audiovisual materials, an OPAC, and a Web page. Operations spending for 2004 fiscal year: $73,063. 10 computers available on campus for general student use. A campuswide network can be accessed from student residence rooms. Staffed computer lab on campus.

■ PILLSBURY BAPTIST BIBLE COLLEGE *X-9*
315 South Grove Ave.
Owatonna, MN 55060-3097
Tel: (507)451-2710
Free: 800-747-4557
Fax: (507)451-6459

Web Site: http://www.pillsbury.edu/

Description: Independent Baptist, 4-year, coed. Awards associate and bachelor's degrees. Founded 1957. Setting: 14-acre small town campus with easy access to Minneapolis-St. Paul. Endowment: $1.1 million. Educational spending for 2005 fiscal year: $3955 per student. Total enrollment: 172. 76 applied, 57% were admitted. Full-time: 150 students, 59% women, 41% men. Part-time: 22 students, 68% women, 32% men. Students come from 22 states and territories, 1 other country, 33% from out-of-state, 0% Native American, 3% Hispanic, 0% black, 1% Asian American or Pacific Islander, 2% international, 4% 25 or older, 83% live on campus, 3% transferred in. Retention: 72% of full-time freshmen returned the following year. Core. Calendar: semesters. Academic remediation for entering students, services for LD students, advanced placement, accelerated degree program, independent study, double major, summer session for credit, part-time degree program, internships. Study abroad program.

Entrance Requirements: Open admission. Option: deferred admission. Required: essay, high school transcript, 2 recommendations, 2 photographs, ACT. Recommended: interview. Entrance: noncompetitive. Application deadline: 8/20. Notification: continuous.

Costs Per Year: Application fee: $25. Comprehensive fee: $11,522 includes full-time tuition ($6750), mandatory fees ($888), and college room and board ($3884). Full-time tuition and fees vary according to course load. Part-time tuition: $225 per semester hour. Part-time mandatory fees: $21 per semester hour. Part-time tuition and fees vary according to course load.

Collegiate Environment: Drama-theater group, choral group, student-run newspaper. Social organizations: 5 open to all. Major annual events: Valentine Banquet, Junior/Senior Banquet, Harvest Home. Student services: personal-psychological counseling. Campus security: student patrols. 500 college housing spaces available; 159 were occupied in 2003-04. Freshmen guaranteed college housing. On-campus residence required through senior year. Options: men-only, women-only housing available. Pillsbury College Library with 53,732 books, 312 microform titles, 15,371 serials, 1,632 audiovisual materials, and an OPAC. Operations spending for 2004 fiscal year: $47,407. 33 computers available on campus for general student use. A campuswide network can be accessed. Staffed computer lab on campus.

■ PINE TECHNICAL COLLEGE *S-10*
900 4th St. SE
Pine City, MN 55063
Tel: (320)629-5100
Free: 800-521-7463
Fax: (320)629-5101
Web Site: http://www.pinetech.edu/

Description: State-supported, 2-year, coed. Part of Minnesota State Colleges and Universities System. Awards certificates, diplomas, transfer associate, and terminal associate degrees. Founded 1965. Setting: 6-acre small town campus with easy access to Minneapolis-St. Paul. Total enrollment: 770. Full-time: 258 students, 64% women, 36% men. Part-time: 512 students, 75% women, 25% men. Students come from 5 states and territories, 10% from out-of-state, 2% Native American, 0.4% Hispanic, 1% black, 1% Asian American or Pacific Islander, 0% international, 45% 25 or older, 3% transferred in. Core. Calendar: semesters. Academic remediation for entering students, services for LD students, advanced placement, independent study, distance learning, double major, summer session for credit, part-time degree program, internships.

Entrance Requirements: Open admission except for gunsmithing. Option: early admission. Required: high school transcript. Required for some: recommendations. Placement: ASAP required. Entrance: noncompetitive. Application deadline: Rolling.

Collegiate Environment: Orientation program. Student services: personal-psychological counseling, women's center. Campus security: late night transport-escort service. College housing not available. Media Center plus 1 other with 6,000 books, 30 serials, an OPAC, and a Web page. 150 computers available on campus for general student use. A campuswide network can be accessed from off-campus. Staffed computer lab on campus.

■ RAINY RIVER COMMUNITY COLLEGE *I-9*
1501 Hwy. 71
International Falls, MN 56649
Tel: (218)285-7722
Free: 800-456-3996
Admissions: (218)285-2207
Fax: (218)285-2239
E-mail: admissions@rr.mn.us

Web Site: http://www.rrcc.mnscu.edu/

Description: State-supported, 2-year, coed. Part of Minnesota State Colleges and Universities System. Awards certificates, diplomas, transfer associate, and terminal associate degrees. Founded 1967. Setting: 80-acre small town campus. Total enrollment: 384. 230 applied, 100% were admitted. Students come from 8 states and territories, 3% Native American, 1% Hispanic, 18% black, 1% Asian American or Pacific Islander, 54% 25 or older, 10% live on campus. Core. Calendar: semesters. Academic remediation for entering students, ESL program, services for LD students, advanced placement, honors program, independent study, summer session for credit, part-time degree program, adult/continuing education programs, co-op programs and internships.

Entrance Requirements: Open admission. Options: Common Application, early admission, deferred admission. Required: high school transcript. Placement: CPT required; ACT recommended. Entrance: noncompetitive. Application deadline: Rolling. Notification: continuous.

Collegiate Environment: Drama-theater group. Social organizations: 3 open to all. Most popular organizations: Anishinaabe Student Coalition, Student Senate, Black Student Association. Major annual events: Awareness Week, Diversity Week. Student services: personal-psychological counseling. Campus security: 24-hour emergency response devices, late night transport-escort service, controlled dormitory access. Option: coed housing available. Rainy River Community College Library with 20,000 books and an OPAC. 70 computers available on campus for general student use. A campuswide network can be accessed from off-campus. Staffed computer lab on campus.

Community Environment: Located on the Rainy River, which is the Minnesota-Ontario border. International Falls (population 8,000) is the supply point for an immense wilderness region famous for hunting, fishing and canoe trips. It is also an important port of entry from Ontario vacation country. Community facilities include complete church representation, good medical services, downtown and mall shopping areas, and numerous service organizations. Because of the great influx of summer tourists, many part-time jobs are available. Millions of acres are in the wilderness including Voyageurs National Park, which is close to International Falls. Rainy Lake, the biggest tourist attraction in the area, is 3 miles from town and features year-round good fishing. Other sports are swimming, water skiing, camping, hunting, boating and winter sports.

■ **RASMUSSEN COLLEGE EAGAN** *G-14*

3500 Federal Dr.
Eagan, MN 55122-1346
Tel: (651)687-9000
Free: 800-852-6367
Web Site: http://www.rasmussen.edu/

Description: Proprietary, 2-year, coed. Part of Rasmussen College System. Awards certificates, diplomas, and terminal associate degrees. Founded 1904. Setting: 10-acre suburban campus with easy access to Minneapolis-St. Paul. Total enrollment: 340. Full-time: 273 students, 77% women, 23% men. Part-time: 67 students, 69% women, 31% men. Students come from 3 states and territories, 5 other countries, 0.3% Native American, 3% Hispanic, 6% black, 4% Asian American or Pacific Islander, 3% international, 35% 25 or older. Retention: 64% of full-time freshmen returned the following year. Academic remediation for entering students, part-time degree program, adult/continuing education programs, internships.

Entrance Requirements: Option: Common Application. Required: high school transcript, minimum 2.0 high school GPA, interview, ACT COMPASS. Entrance: moderately difficult. Application deadline: Rolling.

Collegiate Environment: Student-run newspaper. Social organizations: 1 open to all. Most popular organizations: Student Senate, community league softball. Major annual events: Diversity Activities Quarterly, Student Awards Quarterly, Commencement Celebration Quarterly. Campus security: safety and security programs. College housing not available.

■ **RASMUSSEN COLLEGE EDEN PRAIRIE** *F-12*

7905 Golden Triangle Dr., Ste. 100
Eden Prairie, MN 55344
Tel: (952)545-2000
Web Site: http://www.rasmussen.edu/

Description: Proprietary, 2-year, coed. Part of Rasmussen College System. Awards certificates, diplomas, and terminal associate degrees. Founded 1904. Setting: 2-acre suburban campus with easy access to Minneapolis-St. Paul. Total enrollment: 363. Student-undergrad faculty ratio is 11:1. Full-time: 209 students, 81% women, 19% men. Part-time: 154 students, 74% women, 26% men. 1% Native American, 2% Hispanic, 13% black, 3% Asian

American or Pacific Islander, 0% international, 80% 25 or older. Core. Academic remediation for entering students, summer session for credit, part-time degree program, internships.

Entrance Requirements: Options: early admission, deferred admission. Required: high school transcript, interview, COMPASS. Entrance: moderately difficult. Application deadline: Rolling.

Collegiate Environment: Campus security: late night transport-escort service. College housing not available. 3,400 books and 10 serials. 300 computers available on campus for general student use. Staffed computer lab on campus.

■ **RASMUSSEN COLLEGE MANKATO** *X-8*

501 Holly Ln.
Mankato, MN 56001-6803
Tel: (507)625-6556
Fax: (507)625-6557
E-mail: kathyc@rasmussen.edu
Web Site: http://www.rasmussen.edu/

Description: Proprietary, 2-year, coed. Part of Rasmussen College System. Awards certificates, diplomas, and terminal associate degrees. Founded 1904. Setting: suburban campus with easy access to Minneapolis-St. Paul. Total enrollment: 463. Student-undergrad faculty ratio is 18:1. 4% Hispanic, 1% black, 1% Asian American or Pacific Islander, 40% 25 or older. Core. Academic remediation for entering students, services for LD students, advanced placement, summer session for credit, part-time degree program, co-op programs and internships.

Entrance Requirements: Options: Common Application, deferred admission. Required: high school transcript, minimum 2.0 high school GPA, interview, ACT COMPASS. Entrance: minimally difficult.

Costs Per Year: Application fee: $60. Tuition: $295 per credit part-time.

Collegiate Environment: Student-run newspaper. Social organizations: 3 open to all. Most popular organizations: Student Senate, Student Ambassadors, Student Life Organization. Major annual events: Perfect Attendance Banquet, Awards Banquet, Graduation ceremony. Campus security: limited access to buildings after hours. College housing not available. Media Center with 1,000 books and 3 serials. 70 computers available on campus for general student use. Staffed computer lab on campus.

■ **RASMUSSEN COLLEGE ST. CLOUD** *S-7*

226 Park Ave. South
St. Cloud, MN 56301-3713
Tel: (320)251-5600
Fax: (320)251-3702
Web Site: http://www.rasmussen.edu/

Description: Proprietary, 2-year, coed. Part of Rasmussen College System. Awards certificates, diplomas, transfer associate, and terminal associate degrees. Founded 1904. Setting: urban campus with easy access to Minneapolis-St. Paul. Total enrollment: 533. Full-time: 252 students, 85% women, 15% men. Part-time: 281 students, 80% women, 20% men. Students come from 3 states and territories, 1% from out-of-state, 2% Native American, 2% Hispanic, 2% black, 1% Asian American or Pacific Islander, 0% international, 43% 25 or older. Core. Academic remediation for entering students, distance learning, double major, summer session for credit, part-time degree program, adult/continuing education programs, internships.

Entrance Requirements: Options: Common Application, electronic application, early admission, deferred admission. Required: high school transcript, minimum 2.0 high school GPA, interview, ACT COMPASS. Entrance: minimally difficult. Application deadline: Rolling.

Collegiate Environment: Orientation program. Student-run newspaper. Social organizations: 1 open to all. Most popular organization: Student Senate. Major annual events: Awards Ceremony, Student Social, advisory meetings. College housing not available. St. Cloud Rasmussen College Library with 689 books, 31 serials, 173 audiovisual materials, an OPAC, and a Web page. 123 computers available on campus for general student use. A campuswide network can be accessed from off-campus. Staffed computer lab on campus.

■ **RIDGEWATER COLLEGE** *U-5*

PO Box 1097
Willmar, MN 56201-1097
Tel: (320)235-5114
Free: 800-722-1151
Admissions: (320)231-2907
Fax: (320)231-6602

E-mail: skerfield@ridgewater.mnscu.edu

Web Site: http://www.ridgewater.mnscu.edu/

Description: State-supported, 2-year, coed. Part of Minnesota State Colleges and Universities System. Awards certificates, diplomas, transfer associate, and terminal associate degrees. Founded 1961. Setting: 83-acre small town campus. Total enrollment: 3,915. Student-undergrad faculty ratio is 19:1. 26 student government officers. Full-time: 2,419 students, 52% women, 48% men. Part-time: 1,496 students, 63% women, 37% men. Students come from 12 states and territories, 5 other countries, 2% from out-of-state, 1% Native American, 3% Hispanic, 1% black, 1% Asian American or Pacific Islander, 0.1% international, 28% 25 or older, 6% transferred in. Calendar: semesters. Academic remediation for entering students, ESL program, services for LD students, advanced placement, accelerated degree program, self-designed majors, distance learning, summer session for credit, part-time degree program, adult/continuing education programs, co-op programs and internships. Off campus study at other colleges in the Minnesota State Colleges and Universities System.

Entrance Requirements: Open admission except for nursing, chemical dependency practitioner, radiological technology, veterinary technology programs. Options: early admission, deferred admission. Required: high school transcript. Required for some: recommendations, interview. Entrance: noncompetitive. Preference given to state residents.

Costs Per Year: Application fee: $20. State resident tuition: $3896 full-time, $129.85 per credit part-time. Nonresident tuition: $3895 full-time. Mandatory fees: $459 full-time, $15.31 per credit part-time. Full-time tuition and fees vary according to program and reciprocity agreements. Part-time tuition and fees vary according to program and reciprocity agreements.

Collegiate Environment: Orientation program. Drama-theater group, choral group, student-run newspaper. Social organizations: 9 open to all. Most popular organizations: Student Senate, Ski Club, Nontraditional Students Club, BACCHUS, Creative Writers, Unlimited. Major annual events: Homecoming, Snow Days, graduation. Student services: personal-psychological counseling, women's center. Campus security: late night transport-escort service. College housing not available. 30,000 books, 401 serials, an OPAC, and a Web page. Operations spending for 2004 fiscal year: $150,000. 215 computers available on campus for general student use. A campuswide network can be accessed from off-campus. Staffed computer lab on campus.

Community Environment: Greater Willmar, with a population of approximately 23,000, is the largest city within a 60-mile radius. It is an important shipping point for grain and livestock. The division headquarters of the Burlington Northern Railway and a large Hormel turkey-processing plant are located here. Other products manufactured here are plastics, furniture, sheet metal, concrete, clothing, machinery, cookies, and dairy products. The many lakes in the area provide good fishing and recreation. The campus is located in prime hunting country. The community offers a semirural setting with many cultural opportunities and, at the same time, is two hours from the Twin Cities of Minneapolis and St. Paul. The city of Hutchinson is a population center of approximately 13,000 and is located 60 miles west of the Twin Cities on Highway 7. Hutchinson has the second oldest park system in the United States and takes pride in its adaptation to the local environment, such as the Crow River, which flows through the community. In addition, there are a dozen lakes within 15 minutes which are ideal for boating and fishing. Major employers in Hutchinson include 3M Company, Hutchinson Technology, Inc., Hutchinson Manufacturing, and Mid-America Dairymen, Inc. A small town atmosphere with a high-tech future.

■ **RIVERLAND COMMUNITY COLLEGE** *Z-10*

1900 8th Ave., NW

Austin, MN 55912

Tel: (507)433-0600

Free: 800-247-5039

Admissions: (507)433-0517

Fax: (507)433-0515

E-mail: admissions@riverland.edu

Web Site: http://www.riverland.edu/

Description: State-supported, 2-year, coed. Part of Minnesota State Colleges and Universities System. Awards certificates, diplomas, transfer associate, and terminal associate degrees. Founded 1940. Setting: 187-acre small town campus with easy access to Minneapolis-St. Paul. Educational spending for 2005 fiscal year: $4500 per student. Total enrollment: 3,600. Student-undergrad faculty ratio is 18:1. Students come from 5 states and territories, 3% from out-of-state, 0.3% Native American, 4% Hispanic, 3% black, 1% Asian American or Pacific Islander, 42% 25 or older, 2% live on campus. Core. Calendar: semesters. Academic remediation for entering students, ESL program, services for LD students, advanced placement, independent study, distance learning, double major, summer session for credit, part-time degree program, adult/continuing education programs, internships. Off campus study at other colleges in the Minnesota State Colleges and Universities System. Study abroad program.

Entrance Requirements: Open admission except for nursing, human services, occupational therapy assistant, physical therapy assistant, law enforcement programs. Option: early admission. Required: high school transcript. Entrance: noncompetitive. Application deadline: Rolling.

Costs Per Year: Application fee: $20. State resident tuition: $3915 full-time, $130.50 per credit part-time. Nonresident tuition: $3915 full-time, $130.50 per credit part-time. Mandatory fees: $17 per credit part-time. College room only: $2600.

Collegiate Environment: Orientation program. Drama-theater group, choral group, student-run newspaper. Social organizations: 8 open to all. Most popular organizations: College Choir, student newspaper, Student Activities Board, Phi Theta Kappa, Theater Club. Major annual events: Multicultural Week, College Fair, Technology Day. Student services: personal-psychological counseling, women's center. Campus security: late night transport-escort service. 84 college housing spaces available; 72 were occupied in 2003-04. No special consideration for freshman housing applicants. Riverland Community College Library plus 2 others with 33,500 books, 278 serials, and an OPAC. Operations spending for 2004 fiscal year: $114,000. 175 computers available on campus for general student use. A campuswide network can be accessed from student residence rooms. Staffed computer lab on campus.

■ **ROCHESTER COMMUNITY AND TECHNICAL COLLEGE** *X-11*

851 30th Ave., SE

Rochester, MN 55904-4999

Tel: (507)285-7210

Admissions: (507)280-3509

Fax: (507)285-7496

Web Site: http://www.roch.edu/

Description: State-supported, primarily 2-year, coed. Part of Minnesota State Colleges and Universities System. Awards certificates, diplomas, transfer associate, terminal associate, and bachelor's degrees (also offers 13 programs that lead to a bachelor's degree with Winona State University or University of Minnesota). Founded 1915. Setting: 460-acre small town campus. Endowment: $437,000. Total enrollment: 5,862. 2,428 applied, 99% were admitted. Students come from 39 states and territories, 36 other countries, 10% from out-of-state, 34% 25 or older. Core. Calendar: semesters. Academic remediation for entering students, ESL program, services for LD students, advanced placement, honors program, independent study, distance learning, summer session for credit, part-time degree program, internships. Off campus study at other colleges in the Minnesota State Colleges and Universities System, Winona State University-Rochester Center.

Entrance Requirements: Open admission except for allied health, technology programs. Option: early admission. Required: high school transcript. Entrance: noncompetitive. Application deadline: 8/24. Notification: continuous.

Collegiate Environment: Orientation program. Drama-theater group, choral group, student-run newspaper. Social organizations: 34 open to all. Most popular organizations: choir, band, football, theater, Program Council. Major annual events: Spring Fling, Christmas Concert, theatre productions. Student services: health clinic, personal-psychological counseling. Campus security: student patrols, late night transport-escort service. College housing not available. Goddard Library plus 1 other with 62,000 books and 600 serials. 170 computers available on campus for general student use. A campuswide network can be accessed. Staffed computer lab on campus.

Community Environment: The Mayo Clinic, founded by Drs. William and Charles Mayo, has made Rochester (population 73,000) world famous. The transient population is estimated at 8,000 to 10,000 at any given time. Visitors are estimated at 550,000 annually. All forms of commercial transportation are available. Community cultural facilities include the Rochester Symphony Orchestra, Rochester Municipal Band, Oratorio Society, summer open-air concerts, Carillon concerts 3 times a week, and a civic theater with a full-time director.

■ **ST. CLOUD STATE UNIVERSITY** *S-7*

720 4th Ave. South

St. Cloud, MN 56301-4498

Tel: (320)308-0121; 877-654-7278
Admissions: (320)308-2244
E-mail: scsu4u@stcloudstate.edu
Web Site: http://www.stcloudstate.edu/
Description: State-supported, comprehensive, coed. Part of Minnesota State Colleges and Universities System. Awards associate, bachelor's, and master's degrees. Founded 1869. Setting: 922-acre suburban campus with easy access to Minneapolis-St. Paul. Research spending for 2004 fiscal year: $2 million. Total enrollment: 15,964. Faculty: 861 (650 full-time, 211 part-time). Student-undergrad faculty ratio is 17:1. 5,912 applied, 78% were admitted. 7% from top 10% of their high school class, 29% from top quarter, 76% from top half. Full-time: 11,611 students, 54% women, 46% men. Part-time: 2,875 students, 59% women, 41% men. Students come from 50 states and territories, 85 other countries, 8% from out-of-state, 1% Native American, 1% Hispanic, 2% black, 2% Asian American or Pacific Islander, 4% international, 12% 25 or older, 21% live on campus, 9% transferred in. Retention: 71% of full-time freshmen returned the following year. Academic areas with the most degrees conferred: business/marketing; education; social sciences. Core. Calendar: semesters. Academic remediation for entering students, ESL program, services for LD students, advanced placement, accelerated degree program, self-designed majors, honors program, independent study, distance learning, double major, summer session for credit, part-time degree program, adult/continuing education programs, internships, graduate courses open to undergrads. Off campus study at members of the Tri-College Exchange Program, other colleges in the Minnesota State Colleges and University System. Study abroad program. ROTC: Army.
Entrance Requirements: Options: electronic application, early admission, deferred admission, international baccalaureate accepted. Required: high school transcript, SAT or ACT. Required for some: recommendations. Entrance: moderately difficult. Application deadline: 6/1. Notification: continuous.
Costs Per Year: Application fee: $20. State resident tuition: $4760 full-time, $159 per credit part-time. Nonresident tuition: $10,332 full-time, $344 per credit part-time. Mandatory fees: $562 full-time, $23 per credit part-time. Full-time tuition and fees vary according to course load and reciprocity agreements. Part-time tuition and fees vary according to course load and reciprocity agreements. College room and board: $4688. College room only: $3340. Room and board charges vary according to board plan and housing facility.
Collegiate Environment: Orientation program. Drama-theater group, choral group, student-run newspaper, radio station. Social organizations: 240 open to all; national fraternities, national sororities, local sororities. Student services: health clinic, personal-psychological counseling, women's center. Campus security: 24-hour emergency response devices and patrols, late night transport-escort service. 3,100 college housing spaces available; all were occupied in 2003-04. Freshmen given priority for college housing. Option: coed housing available. James W. Miller Learning Resources Center with 897,973 books, 1.8 million microform titles, 1,737 serials, 24,929 audiovisual materials, an OPAC, and a Web page. Operations spending for 2004 fiscal year: $10.3 million. 1,335 computers available on campus for general student use. Computer purchase/lease plans available. A campuswide network can be accessed from student residence rooms and from off campus. Staffed computer lab on campus.

■ **ST. CLOUD TECHNICAL COLLEGE** *S-7*
1540 Northway Dr.
St. Cloud, MN 56303-1240
Tel: (320)654-5000
Admissions: (320)308-5089
Fax: (320)654-5981
E-mail: enroll@sctc.edu
Web Site: http://www.sctc.edu/
Description: State-supported, 2-year, coed. Part of Minnesota State Colleges and Universities System. Awards certificates, diplomas, and terminal associate degrees. Founded 1948. Setting: 35-acre urban campus with easy access to Minneapolis-St. Paul. Total enrollment: 3,348. Student-undergrad faculty ratio is 17:1. 2,653 applied, 62% were admitted. Full-time: 2,188 students, 46% women, 54% men. Part-time: 1,160 students, 61% women, 39% men. Students come from 19 states and territories, 5 other countries, 2% from out-of-state, 1% Native American, 0.3% Hispanic, 2% black, 1% Asian American or Pacific Islander, 0.2% international, 25% 25 or older, 8% transferred in. Calendar: semesters. Academic remediation for entering students, ESL program, services for LD students, advanced placement,

distance learning, summer session for credit, part-time degree program, adult/continuing education programs, co-op programs and internships.
Entrance Requirements: Open admission except for dental hygiene, echocardiography, sonography, nursing, invasive cardiovascular technology. Options: Peterson's Universal Application, electronic application, early admission, deferred admission. Required: high school transcript. Required for some: interview. Entrance: noncompetitive. Application deadline: Rolling. Notification: continuous until 8/1.
Costs Per Year: Application fee: $20. State resident tuition: $3678 full-time, $122.60 per credit part-time. Nonresident tuition: $7356 full-time, $145.20 per credit part-time. Mandatory fees: $302 full-time, $10.06 per credit part-time.
Collegiate Environment: Orientation program. Student-run newspaper. Social organizations: 10 open to all. Most popular organizations: Student Senate, Distributive Education Club of America, Business Professionals of America, Child and Adult Care Education, Central Minnesota Builders Association. Major annual events: graduation, Annual Job Fair, Fall Welcome Back Activities. Student services: personal-psychological counseling, women's center. Campus security: late night transport-escort service. College housing not available. Learning Resource Center plus 1 other with 10,000 books, 600 serials, an OPAC, and a Web page. 500 computers available on campus for general student use. Computer purchase/lease plans available. A campuswide network can be accessed. Staffed computer lab on campus.

■ **SAINT JOHN'S UNIVERSITY** *S-7*
PO Box 2000
Collegeville, MN 56321
Tel: (320)363-2011
Free: 800-544-1489
Fax: (320)363-3206
E-mail: admissions@csbsju.edu
Web Site: http://www.csbsju.edu/
Description: Independent Roman Catholic, comprehensive, coed, coordinate with College of Saint Benedict. Awards bachelor's, master's, and first professional degrees (coordinate with College of Saint Benedict for women). Founded 1857. Setting: 2,400-acre rural campus with easy access to Minneapolis-St. Paul. Endowment: $114 million. Research spending for 2004 fiscal year: $665,264. Educational spending for 2005 fiscal year: $10,116 per student. Total enrollment: 1,996. Faculty: 176 (147 full-time, 29 part-time). Student-undergrad faculty ratio is 12:1. 1,167 applied, 87% were admitted. 22% from top 10% of their high school class, 51% from top quarter, 91% from top half. 4 National Merit Scholars. Full-time: 1,845 students, 100% men. Part-time: 30 students, 100% men. Students come from 32 states and territories, 27 other countries, 14% from out-of-state, 0.3% Native American, 1% Hispanic, 1% black, 2% Asian American or Pacific Islander, 4% international, 1% 25 or older, 83% live on campus, 2% transferred in. Retention: 87% of full-time freshmen returned the following year. Academic areas with the most degrees conferred: social sciences; business/marketing; English. Core. Calendar: semesters. ESL program, services for LD students, advanced placement, accelerated degree program, self-designed majors, honors program, independent study, double major, internships, graduate courses open to undergrads. Off campus study at College of Saint Benedict, Tri-College Exchange Program. Study abroad program. ROTC: Army.
Entrance Requirements: Options: Peterson's Universal Application, Common Application, electronic application, deferred admission, international baccalaureate accepted. Required: essay, high school transcript, 1 recommendation, SAT or ACT. Recommended: minimum 3.0 high school GPA, interview. Entrance: moderately difficult. Application deadline: 12/1. Notification: continuous until 10/1.
Costs Per Year: Application fee: $0. Comprehensive fee: $29,749 includes full-time tuition ($23,064), mandatory fees ($410), and college room and board ($6275). College room only: $3151. Room and board charges vary according to board plan and housing facility. Part-time tuition: $961 per credit. Part-time mandatory fees: $205 per term. Part-time tuition and fees vary according to course load.
Collegiate Environment: Orientation program. Drama-theater group, choral group, student-run newspaper, radio station. Social organizations: 90 open to all. Most popular organizations: Volunteers in Service to Others, Joint Events Council, Cultural Affairs Board, Students in Free Enterprise, ultimate Frisbee. Major annual events: Festival of Cultures, Pinestock, Asian New Year. Student services: health clinic, personal-psychological counseling. Campus security: 24-hour emergency response devices and patrols, late night transport-escort service, well-lit pathways, 911 center on campus,

closed circuit TV monitors. 1,488 college housing spaces available; 1,456 were occupied in 2003-04. Freshmen guaranteed college housing. On-campus residence required through sophomore year. Option: men-only housing available. Alcuin Library plus 2 others with 805,376 books, 196,563 microform titles, 5,735 serials, 22,452 audiovisual materials, an OPAC, and a Web page. Operations spending for 2004 fiscal year: $2.7 million. 549 computers available on campus for general student use. A campuswide network can be accessed from student residence rooms and from off campus. Staffed computer lab on campus.

■ SAINT MARY'S UNIVERSITY OF MINNESOTA *X-13*

700 Terrace Heights
Winona, MN 55987-1399
Tel: (507)452-4430
Free: 800-635-5987
Admissions: (507)457-1700
Fax: (507)457-1722
E-mail: admissions@smumn.edu
Web Site: http://www.smumn.edu/

Description: Independent Roman Catholic, comprehensive, coed. Awards bachelor's, master's, and doctoral degrees and post-master's certificates. Founded 1912. Setting: 350-acre small town campus. Endowment: $31.4 million. Research spending for 2004 fiscal year: $313,855. Total enrollment: 5,222. Faculty: 561 (101 full-time, 460 part-time). Student-undergrad faculty ratio is 12:1. 1,048 applied, 83% were admitted. 19% from top 10% of their high school class, 47% from top quarter, 70% from top half. 7 valedictorians. Full-time: 1,286 students, 54% women, 46% men. Part-time: 394 students, 49% women, 51% men. Students come from 29 states and territories, 9 other countries, 29% from out-of-state, 0.2% Native American, 2% Hispanic, 4% black, 2% Asian American or Pacific Islander, 1% international, 1% 25 or older, 77% live on campus, 8% transferred in. Retention: 75% of full-time freshmen returned the following year. Academic areas with the most degrees conferred: business/marketing; computer and information sciences; visual and performing arts. Core. Calendar: semesters. Academic remediation for entering students, ESL program, services for LD students, advanced placement, accelerated degree program, self-designed majors, honors program, independent study, double major, summer session for credit, part-time degree program, external degree program, adult/continuing education programs, co-op programs and internships, graduate courses open to undergrads. Off campus study at Winona State University. Study abroad program. ROTC: Army (c).

Entrance Requirements: Options: Peterson's Universal Application, Common Application, electronic application, early admission, deferred admission, international baccalaureate accepted. Required: essay, high school transcript, minimum 2.5 high school GPA, SAT or ACT. Recommended: 2 recommendations. Required for some: interview. Entrance: moderately difficult. Application deadline: 5/1. Notification: continuous.

Costs Per Year: Application fee: $25. Comprehensive fee: $26,639 includes full-time tuition ($20,294), mandatory fees ($445), and college room and board ($5900). College room only: $3300.

Collegiate Environment: Orientation program. Drama-theater group, choral group, student-run newspaper, radio station. Social organizations: 84 open to all; national fraternities, national sororities; 6% of eligible men and 3% of eligible women are members. Most popular organizations: Student Activity Committee, Habitat for Humanity, Volunteers in Service to Others, Serving Others United in Love (Soul), concert choir/chamber singers. Major annual events: BLUE Angel, Gaslight, Taylor Richmond Benefit Dance. Student services: health clinic, personal-psychological counseling, women's center. Campus security: 24-hour emergency response devices and patrols, late night transport-escort service, controlled dormitory access. 1,103 college housing spaces available; 971 were occupied in 2003-04. Freshmen guaranteed college housing. On-campus residence required through sophomore year. Options: coed, men-only, women-only housing available. Fitzgerald Library with 168,923 books, 161,060 microform titles, 4,389 serials, 7,963 audiovisual materials, an OPAC, and a Web page. Operations spending for 2004 fiscal year: $729,411. 374 computers available on campus for general student use. A campuswide network can be accessed from student residence rooms and from off campus. Staffed computer lab on campus.

■ ST. OLAF COLLEGE *W-9*

1520 St. Olaf Ave.
Northfield, MN 55057-1098
Tel: (507)646-2222

Free: 800-800-3025
Admissions: (507)646-3025
Fax: (507)646-3832
E-mail: admiss@stolaf.edu
Web Site: http://www.stolaf.edu/

Description: Independent Lutheran, 4-year, coed. Awards bachelor's degrees. Founded 1874. Setting: 300-acre small town campus with easy access to Minneapolis-St. Paul. Endowment: $231.8 million. Research spending for 2004 fiscal year: $642,789. Educational spending for 2005 fiscal year: $13,164 per student. Total enrollment: 3,058. Student-undergrad faculty ratio is 12:1. 2,991 applied, 73% were admitted. 49% from top 10% of their high school class, 76% from top quarter, 96% from top half. 50 National Merit Scholars, 72 valedictorians. Full-time: 3,005 students, 58% women, 42% men. Part-time: 53 students, 43% women, 57% men. Students come from 48 states and territories, 18 other countries, 43% from out-of-state, 0.3% Native American, 1% Hispanic, 1% black, 5% Asian American or Pacific Islander, 1% international, 1% 25 or older, 96% live on campus, 1% transferred in. Retention: 92% of full-time freshmen returned the following year. Academic areas with the most degrees conferred: public administration and social services; visual and performing arts; English. Core. Calendar: 4-1-4. Services for LD students, advanced placement, self-designed majors, independent study, double major, summer session for credit, part-time degree program, internships. Off campus study at Augsburg College, Minnesota Intercollegiate Nursing Consortium, Oak Ridge Science semester-,Biosphere 2 Earth semester, HECUA programs, Environmental Science at Superior Studies site. Study abroad program.

Entrance Requirements: Options: Common Application, electronic application, early decision, early action, deferred admission, international baccalaureate accepted. Required: essay, high school transcript, 2 recommendations, SAT or ACT. Recommended: interview. Entrance: very difficult. Application deadlines: Rolling, 11/15 for early decision, 12/15 for early action. Notification: continuous, 12/6 for early decision, 2/1 for early action.

Costs Per Year: Application fee: $35. Comprehensive fee: $35,600 includes full-time tuition ($28,200) and college room and board ($7400). College room only: $3450. Part-time tuition: $880 per credit hour.

Collegiate Environment: Orientation program. Drama-theater group, choral group, student-run newspaper, radio station. Social organizations: 114 open to all. Most popular organizations: Student Government Association, Alpha Phi Omega, Habitat for Humanity, College Democrats, College Republicans. Major annual events: Homecoming/Family Weekend, Christmas Festival, Co-curricular Extravaganza. Student services: health clinic, personal-psychological counseling. Campus security: 24-hour emergency response devices and patrols, late night transport-escort service, controlled dormitory access, lighted pathways and sidewalks. 2,725 college housing spaces available; all were occupied in 2003-04. Freshmen guaranteed college housing. On-campus residence required through senior year. Option: coed housing available. Rolvaag Memorial Library plus 2 others with 697,516 books, 6,567 microform titles, 2,149 serials, 12,672 audiovisual materials, an OPAC, and a Web page. Operations spending for 2004 fiscal year: $1.7 million. 755 computers available on campus for general student use. A campuswide network can be accessed from student residence rooms. Staffed computer lab on campus.

■ SAINT PAUL COLLEGE-A COMMUNITY & TECHNICAL COLLEGE *U-10*

235 Marshall Ave.
St. Paul, MN 55102-1800
Tel: (651)846-1600
Free: 800-227-6029
Admissions: (651)846-1362
Fax: (651)221-1416
Web Site: http://www.saintpaul.edu/

Description: State-related, 2-year, coed. Part of Minnesota State Colleges and Universities System. Awards certificates, diplomas, transfer associate, and terminal associate degrees. Founded 1919. Setting: urban campus. Research spending for 2004 fiscal year: $200,000. Total enrollment: 5,169. Student-undergrad faculty ratio is 16:1. 3,379 applied, 89% were admitted. Full-time: 1,529 students, 50% women, 50% men. Part-time: 3,640 students, 42% women, 58% men. 2% Native American, 3% Hispanic, 24% black, 8% Asian American or Pacific Islander, 0.2% international, 6% transferred in. Calendar: semesters. Academic remediation for entering students, ESL program, honors program, distance learning, adult/continuing education programs, internships. Off campus study.

Entrance Requirements: Open admission. Options: Peterson's Universal

Application, electronic application, early admission. Required for some: high school transcript, interview. Entrance: noncompetitive. Application deadline: Rolling.

Costs Per Year: Application fee: $20. State resident tuition: $3,068 full-time, $127.85 per credit part-time. Nonresident tuition: $6,137 full-time, $255.70 per credit part-time. Mandatory fees: $232 full-time, $8.90 per credit part-time.

Collegiate Environment: Most popular organization: Student Senate. Student services: personal-psychological counseling, women's center. Campus security: late night transport-escort service. College housing not available. Saint Paul College Library with 12,000 books, 47 microform titles, 110 serials, 260 audiovisual materials, and an OPAC. Operations spending for 2004 fiscal year: $200,000.

■ **SOUTH CENTRAL TECHNICAL COLLEGE** *X-7*

1920 Lee Blvd.
North Mankato, MN 56003
Tel: (507)389-7200
Admissions: (507)389-7334
Web Site: http://www.sctc.mnscu.edu/

Description: State-supported, 2-year, coed. Part of Minnesota State Colleges and Universities System. Awards certificates, diplomas, transfer associate, and terminal associate degrees. Founded 1946. Setting: urban campus. Total enrollment: 2,350. 1,100 applied, 100% were admitted. Full-time: 2,350 students, 57% women, 43% men. Students come from 7 states and territories, 3 other countries, 0.2% Native American, 1% Hispanic, 1% black, 1% Asian American or Pacific Islander, 30% 25 or older, 11% transferred in. Calendar: semesters. Academic remediation for entering students, services for LD students, advanced placement, independent study, distance learning, part-time degree program, co-op programs.

Entrance Requirements: Open admission. Required: high school transcript. Application deadline: 8/1. Notification: continuous.

Costs Per Year: Application fee: $20. Area resident tuition: $115 per credit part-time. State resident tuition: $3800 full-time. Mandatory fees: $16 per credit part-time.

Collegiate Environment: Orientation program. College housing not available. 700 computers available on campus for general student use. A campuswide network can be accessed from student residence rooms and from off campus. Staffed computer lab on campus.

■ **SOUTHWEST MINNESOTA STATE UNIVERSITY** *W-3*

1501 State St.
Marshall, MN 56258
Tel: (507)537-7021
Free: 800-642-0684
Admissions: (507)537-6286
Fax: (507)537-7154
E-mail: shearerr@southwest.msus.edu
Web Site: http://www.southwest.msus.edu/

Description: State-supported, comprehensive, coed. Part of Minnesota State Colleges and Universities System. Awards associate, bachelor's, and master's degrees. Founded 1963. Setting: 216-acre small town campus. Endowment: $2.9 million. Research spending for 2004 fiscal year: $233,321. Educational spending for 2005 fiscal year: $3464 per student. Total enrollment: 5,636. 10% from top 10% of their high school class, 28% from top quarter, 72% from top half. Full-time: 2,310 students, 56% women, 44% men. Part-time: 2,857 students, 63% women, 37% men. Students come from 27 states and territories, 29 other countries, 12% from out-of-state, 0.2% Native American, 0.4% Hispanic, 1% black, 1% Asian American or Pacific Islander, 3% international, 10% 25 or older, 53% live on campus, 4% transferred in. Retention: 86% of full-time freshmen returned the following year. Core. Calendar: semesters. Academic remediation for entering students, services for LD students, advanced placement, accelerated degree program, self-designed majors, freshman honors college, honors program, independent study, distance learning, double major, summer session for credit, part-time degree program, external degree program, adult/continuing education programs, internships, graduate courses open to undergrads. Off campus study at other colleges in the Minnesota State College and University System. Study abroad program.

Entrance Requirements: Options: Common Application, electronic application, early admission, deferred admission. Required: essay, high school transcript, interview, SAT or ACT. Recommended: SAT and SAT Subject Tests or ACT. Entrance: minimally difficult. Application deadline: Rolling.

Collegiate Environment: Orientation program. Drama-theater group, choral group, marching band, student-run newspaper, radio station. Social organizations: 65 open to all. Major annual events: Red Cross Blood Drive, Fall Fest (Homecoming). Student services: health clinic, personal-psychological counseling, women's center. Campus security: 24-hour emergency response devices and patrols, student patrols, late night transport-escort service. 984 college housing spaces available; 731 were occupied in 2003-04. Options: coed, men-only, women-only housing available. Southwest State University with 167,888 books, 32,654 microform titles, 695 serials, 4,324 audiovisual materials, an OPAC, and a Web page. Operations spending for 2004 fiscal year: $966,523. 350 computers available on campus for general student use. A campuswide network can be accessed from student residence rooms and from off campus. Staffed computer lab on campus.

Community Environment: Marshall (population 11,900) is in the heart of rural, southwestern Minnesota. Air service, bus service and major highways make it accessible to parks, Minneapolis-St. Paul, Duluth and Sioux Falls, S.D. Marshall is a"college town" with restaurants, a shopping mall, churches, 3 movie theaters and a modern downtown area. It is also an expanding commercial center with a large industrial park and is the headquarters for several national agribusinesses and related firms. Marshall has a new, multimillion dollar hospital and health care facility. 5 city parks, a county park and 2 state parks are within a short drive. The community and university combine to offer concerts, theater and art/craft exhibits. Part-time job opportunities are available for students.

■ **UNIVERSITY OF MINNESOTA, CROOKSTON** *L-2*

2900 University Ave.
Crookston, MN 56716-5001
Tel: (218)281-6510
Free: 800-862-6466
Admissions: (218)281-8569
Fax: (218)281-8050
E-mail: info@crk.umn.edu
Web Site: http://www.crk.umn.edu/

Description: State-supported, 4-year, coed. Part of University of Minnesota System. Awards associate and bachelor's degrees. Founded 1966. Setting: 95-acre rural campus. Endowment: $8.8 million. Research spending for 2004 fiscal year: $578,406. Educational spending for 2005 fiscal year: $9072 per student. Total enrollment: 2,134. Student-undergrad faculty ratio is 19:1. 408 applied, 92% were admitted. 13% from top 10% of their high school class, 32% from top quarter, 66% from top half. Full-time: 966 students, 46% women, 54% men. Part-time: 1,168 students, 55% women, 45% men. Students come from 33 states and territories, 6 other countries, 1% Native American, 2% Hispanic, 4% black, 1% Asian American or Pacific Islander, 3% international, 23% 25 or older, 38% live on campus, 6% transferred in. Retention: 64% of full-time freshmen returned the following year. Academic areas with the most degrees conferred: business/marketing; agriculture; natural resources/environmental science. Core. Calendar: semesters. Academic remediation for entering students, services for LD students, advanced placement, independent study, distance learning, double major, summer session for credit, part-time degree program, adult/continuing education programs, internships. Study abroad program. ROTC: Air Force (c).

Entrance Requirements: Options: Peterson's Universal Application, Common Application, electronic application, deferred admission, international baccalaureate accepted. Required: high school transcript, ACT. Entrance: moderately difficult. Application deadline: Rolling. Notification: continuous.

Costs Per Year: Application fee: $30. State resident tuition: $5865 full-time, $195.50 per credit part-time. Nonresident tuition: $6865 full-time, $195.50 per credit part-time. Mandatory fees: $2254 full-time, $145 per credit part-time. Full-time tuition and fees vary according to reciprocity agreements. Part-time tuition and fees vary according to course load and reciprocity agreements. College room and board: $5038. College room only: $2458. Room and board charges vary according to board plan and housing facility. Tuition guaranteed not to increase for student's term of enrollment.

Collegiate Environment: Orientation program. Drama-theater group, choral group. Social organizations: 33 open to all; national fraternities, national sororities, local fraternities, local sororities; 3% of eligible men and 2% of eligible women are members. Most popular organizations: Students in Free Enterprise, Natural Resources Club, Horseman's Association, Multicultural and International Club, Ag-Arama Planning Club. Major annual events: homecoming, Sno-Daze, Ag Arama. Student services: health clinic, personal-psychological counseling. Campus security: student patrols, controlled dormitory access. 480 college housing spaces available; 350 were occupied in 2003-04. Freshmen guaranteed college housing. Option: coed housing available. UMC Library with 30,000 books, 1,200 serials, an OPAC, and a Web page. Operations spending for 2004 fiscal year: $645,357. 900 computers available on campus for general student use. Computer purchase/lease plans available. A campuswide network can be accessed from student residence rooms and from off campus. Staffed computer lab on campus.

Community Environment: Crookston (population 8,300) is the county seat of Polk County, one of the largest rural counties in the state. It is an agricultural processing center for the Red River Valley that produces wheat, barley, and sugar beets. Trains and buses are convenient for transportation. Recreational activities include swimming, camping, roller skating, ice skating, golf and bowling. The Old Crossing Treaty State Historic Park and the Polk County Pioneer Museum are some of the points of interest.

■ **UNIVERSITY OF MINNESOTA, DULUTH** *O-12*
10 University Dr.
Duluth, MN 55812-2496
Tel: (218)726-8000
Free: 800-232-1339
Admissions: (218)726-7171
Fax: (218)726-6394
E-mail: umdadmis@d.umn.edu
Web Site: http://www.d.umn.edu/

Description: State-supported, comprehensive, coed. Part of University of Minnesota System. Awards bachelor's, master's, and first professional degrees. Founded 1947. Setting: 250-acre suburban campus. Endowment: $38.4 million. Research spending for 2004 fiscal year: $11 million. Educational spending for 2005 fiscal year: $5011 per student. Total enrollment: 10,496. Faculty: 506 (407 full-time, 99 part-time). Student-undergrad faculty ratio is 22:1. 6,900 applied, 79% were admitted. 15% from top 10% of their high school class, 41% from top quarter, 73% from top half. 1 National Merit Scholar, 78 valedictorians. Full-time: 8,393 students, 49% women, 51% men. Part-time: 1,145 students, 49% women, 51% men. Students come from 36 states and territories, 32 other countries, 13% from out-of-state, 1% Native American, 1% Hispanic, 1% black, 3% Asian American or Pacific Islander, 2% international, 10% 25 or older, 30% live on campus, 4% transferred in. Retention: 74% of full-time freshmen returned the following year. Core. Calendar: semesters. Academic remediation for entering students, ESL program, services for LD students, advanced placement, self-designed majors, honors program, independent study, distance learning, double major, summer session for credit, part-time degree program, adult/continuing education programs, internships, graduate courses open to undergrads. Off campus study at University of Wisconsin-Superior, College of St. Scholastica. Study abroad program. ROTC: Air Force.

Entrance Requirements: Options: electronic application, international baccalaureate accepted. Required: high school transcript, SAT or ACT. Entrance: moderately difficult. Application deadline: 2/1. Notification: continuous.

Costs Per Year: Application fee: $35. State resident tuition: $7170 full-time, $239 per credit part-time. Nonresident tuition: $18,270 full-time, $609 per credit part-time. Mandatory fees: $1758 full-time. Full-time tuition and fees vary according to course load, degree level, program, and reciprocity agreements. Part-time tuition varies according to course load, degree level, program, and reciprocity agreements. College room and board: $5546.

Collegiate Environment: Orientation program. Drama-theater group, choral group, student-run newspaper. Social organizations: 120 open to all; national fraternities, national sororities, local fraternities, local sororities; 1% of eligible men and 1% of eligible women are members. Most popular organizations: recreational sports, departmental clubs, outdoor recreation clubs. Major annual events: Winter Carnival, Homecoming. Student services: legal services, health clinic, personal-psychological counseling, women's center. Campus security: 24-hour emergency response devices and patrols, late night transport-escort service. 3,050 college housing spaces available; 3,005 were occupied in 2003-04. Freshmen given priority for college housing. Options: coed, men-only, women-only housing available. University of Minnesota Duluth Library with 709,150 books, 750,000 microform titles, 4,500 serials, 15,250 audiovisual materials, an OPAC, and a Web page. Operations spending for 2004 fiscal year: $2.2 million. 680 computers available on campus for general student use. A campuswide network can be accessed from student residence rooms and from off campus. Staffed computer lab on campus.

Community Environment: On picturesque slopes, Duluth (population 80,000) commands splendid views of the St. Louis River, the harbor and Lake Superior. The city is headquarters for the Superior National Forest, which is the largest in the nation.

■ **UNIVERSITY OF MINNESOTA, MORRIS** *S-3*
600 East 4th St.
Morris, MN 56267-2134
Tel: (320)589-2211
Free: 800-992-8863
Admissions: (320)539-6035
Fax: (320)589-6399
Web Site: http://www.mrs.umn.edu/

Description: State-supported, 4-year, coed. Part of University of Minnesota System. Awards bachelor's degrees. Founded 1959. Setting: 130-acre small town campus. Endowment: $6.6 million. Research spending for 2004 fiscal year: $64,915. Educational spending for 2005 fiscal year: $5525 per student. Total enrollment: 1,678. Student-undergrad faculty ratio is 13:1. 1,097 applied, 82% were admitted. 31% from top 10% of their high school class, 60% from top quarter, 87% from top half. 27 class presidents, 36 valedictorians, 99 student government officers. Full-time: 1,527 students, 59% women, 41% men. Part-time: 151 students, 68% women, 32% men. Students come from 26 states and territories, 18 other countries, 14% from out-of-state, 9% Native American, 1% Hispanic, 2% black, 3% Asian American or Pacific Islander, 1% international, 4% 25 or older, 51% live on campus, 4% transferred in. Retention: 86% of full-time freshmen returned the following year. Academic areas with the most degrees conferred: social sciences; English; biological/life sciences; education. Core. Calendar: semesters. Services for LD students, advanced placement, accelerated degree program, self-designed majors, freshman honors college, honors program, independent study, distance learning, double major, summer session for credit, part-time degree program, external degree program, adult/continuing education programs, internships. Off campus study at other units of the University of Minnesota System, National Student Exchange. Study abroad program.

Entrance Requirements: Options: Peterson's Universal Application, electronic application, early admission, early action, deferred admission, international baccalaureate accepted. Required: essay, high school transcript, SAT or ACT. Recommended: minimum 3.0 high school GPA. Required for some: 1 recommendation, interview. Entrance: moderately difficult. Application deadlines: 3/15, 12/1 for early action. Notification: 4/1, 12/15 for early action.

Costs Per Year: Application fee: $35. State resident tuition: $8204 full-time, $273.47 per credit part-time. Nonresident tuition: $8204 full-time, $273.47 per credit part-time. Mandatory fees: $1517 full-time. Full-time tuition and fees vary according to reciprocity agreements. Part-time tuition varies according to course load and reciprocity agreements. College room and board: $5750. College room only: $2730. Room and board charges vary according to board plan and housing facility.

Collegiate Environment: Orientation program. Drama-theater group, choral group, student-run newspaper, radio station. Social organizations: 91 open to all. Most popular organizations: student radio station, Inter-Varsity Christian Fellowship, jazz ensemble/concert choir, Big Friend, Little Friend, student newspaper. Major annual events: homecoming, Jazz Fest, The Great Finals Pancake Break. Student services: legal services, health clinic, personal-psychological counseling, women's center. Campus security: 24-hour emergency response devices and patrols, late night transport-escort service, controlled dormitory access. 1,022 college housing spaces available; 850 were occupied in 2003-04. Freshmen guaranteed college housing. Option: coed housing available. Rodney A. Briggs Library plus 1 other with 191,469 books, 221,216 microform titles, 9,042 serials, 2,140 audiovisual materials, an OPAC, and a Web page. Operations spending for 2004 fiscal year: $1.2 million. 124 computers available on campus for general student use. A campuswide network can be accessed from student residence rooms and from off campus. Staffed computer lab on campus.

Community Environment: The rural setting of Morris (population 5,600) is ideal for outdoor activities year round. Students participate in the community through the many churches, the library, hospital and ambulance service, nursing home, community education, and parks. Employment is available for students that seek work.

■ **UNIVERSITY OF MINNESOTA, TWIN CITIES CAMPUS** *U-9*
100 Church St., SE
Minneapolis, MN 55455-0213
Tel: (612)625-5000

Free: 800-752-1000
Admissions: (612)625-2008
Fax: (612)626-1693
E-mail: admissions@tc.umn.edu
Web Site: http://www.umn.edu/tc/
Description: State-supported, university, coed. Part of University of Minnesota System. Awards bachelor's, master's, doctoral, and first professional degrees and post-master's and first professional certificates. Founded 1851. Setting: 2,000-acre urban campus. Total enrollment: 51,175. Faculty: 1,933 (1,680 full-time, 253 part-time). Student-undergrad faculty ratio is 15:1. 20,641 applied, 71% were admitted. 34% from top 10% of their high school class, 74% from top quarter, 97% from top half. 347 valedictorians. Full-time: 26,957 students, 53% women, 47% men. Part-time: 5,860 students, 54% women, 46% men. Students come from 55 states and territories, 85 other countries, 26% from out-of-state, 1% Native American, 2% Hispanic, 5% black, 9% Asian American or Pacific Islander, 2% international, 11% 25 or older, 22% live on campus, 5% transferred in. Retention: 87% of full-time freshmen returned the following year. Academic areas with the most degrees conferred: social sciences; engineering; business/marketing. Core. Calendar: semesters. Academic remediation for entering students, ESL program, services for LD students, advanced placement, accelerated degree program, self-designed majors, freshman honors college, honors program, independent study, distance learning, double major, summer session for credit, part-time degree program, external degree program, adult/continuing education programs, co-op programs and internships, graduate courses open to undergrads. Off campus study at National Student Exchange, Minnesota Community College System. Study abroad program. ROTC: Army, Air Force.
Entrance Requirements: Options: electronic application, early admission, deferred admission. Required: high school transcript, SAT or ACT. Recommended: minimum 2.0 high school GPA. Entrance: moderately difficult. Application deadline: Rolling. Notification: continuous.
Costs Per Year: Application fee: $45. State resident tuition: $7140 full-time, $275 per credit part-time. Nonresident tuition: $19,670 full-time, $722 per credit part-time. Mandatory fees: $1482 full-time. Full-time tuition and fees vary according to program and reciprocity agreements. Part-time tuition varies according to course load, program, and reciprocity agreements. College room and board: $6722. College room only: $3886. Room and board charges vary according to board plan, housing facility, and location. Tuition guaranteed not to increase for student's term of enrollment.
Collegiate Environment: Orientation program. Drama-theater group, choral group, marching band, student-run newspaper, radio station. Social organizations: 350 open to all; national fraternities, national sororities, local sororities; 3% of eligible men and 3% of eligible women are members. Most popular organizations: sports clubs, student government, religious organizations, departmental/professional organizations. Major annual event: homecoming. Student services: legal services, health clinic, personal-psychological counseling, women's center. Campus security: 24-hour emergency response devices and patrols, student patrols, late night transport-escort service, controlled dormitory access, safety/security orientation, security lighting. 6,500 college housing spaces available; 6,000 were occupied in 2003-04. Freshmen guaranteed college housing. Option: coed housing available. Wilson Library plus 17 others with 5.7 million books, 5.7 million microform titles, 45,000 serials, 1.2 million audiovisual materials, an OPAC, and a Web page.

■ **UNIVERSITY OF ST. THOMAS** *U-10*
2115 Summit Ave.
St. Paul, MN 55105-1096
Tel: (651)962-5000
Free: 800-328-6819
Admissions: (651)962-6150
Fax: (651)962-6160
E-mail: admissions@stthomas.edu
Web Site: http://www.stthomas.edu/
Description: Independent Roman Catholic, university, coed. Awards bachelor's, master's, doctoral, and first professional degrees and post-master's certificates. Founded 1885. Setting: 78-acre urban campus with easy access to Minneapolis. Endowment: $314.1 million. Research spending for 2004 fiscal year: $338,371. Educational spending for 2005 fiscal year: $10,569 per student. Total enrollment: 10,474. 4,249 applied, 81% were admitted. 22% from top 10% of their high school class, 53% from top quarter, 86% from top half. 11 National Merit Scholars, 34 valedictorians. Full-time: 4,788 students, 50% women, 50% men. Part-time: 514 students, 51%

women, 49% men. Students come from 45 states and territories, 54 other countries, 16% from out-of-state, 0.5% Native American, 2% Hispanic, 3% black, 5% Asian American or Pacific Islander, 1% international, 10% 25 or older, 39% live on campus, 5% transferred in. Retention: 85% of full-time freshmen returned the following year. Core. Calendar: 4-1-4. ESL program, services for LD students, advanced placement, self-designed majors, honors program, independent study, double major, summer session for credit, part-time degree program, adult/continuing education programs, internships, graduate courses open to undergrads. Off campus study at 5 members of the Associated Colleges of the Twin Cities. Study abroad program. ROTC: Army (c), Air Force.
Entrance Requirements: Options: Peterson's Universal Application, electronic application, deferred admission, international baccalaureate accepted. Required: essay, high school transcript, SAT or ACT. Recommended: recommendations, interview, ACT. Entrance: moderately difficult. Application deadline: Rolling. Notification: continuous.
Costs Per Year: Application fee: $0. Comprehensive fee: $30,380. Part-time tuition: $715 per credit hour. Part-time tuition varies according to class time, course load, and program. Tuition: $715 per credit hour part-time. Part-time tuition varies according to class time, course load, and program.
Collegiate Environment: Orientation program. Drama-theater group, choral group, student-run newspaper. Social organizations: 94 open to all. Major annual events: Taste of St. Thomas, Homecoming, Spring Fling. Student services: legal services, health clinic, personal-psychological counseling, women's center. Campus security: 24-hour emergency response devices and patrols, late night transport-escort service, controlled dormitory access. College housing designed to accommodate 1,888 students; 1,953 undergraduates lived in college housing during 2003-04. Freshmen given priority for college housing. Options: men-only, women-only housing available. O'Shaughnessy-Frey Library plus 2 others with 440,023 books, 964,335 microform titles, 4,168 serials, 3,516 audiovisual materials, an OPAC, and a Web page. Operations spending for 2004 fiscal year: $7.6 million. 1,549 computers available on campus for general student use. A campuswide network can be accessed from student residence rooms and from off campus. Staffed computer lab on campus.

■ **VERMILION COMMUNITY COLLEGE** *L-12*
1900 East Camp St.
Ely, MN 55731-1996
Tel: (218)365-7200
Free: 800-657-3608
Admissions: (218)365-7224
Web Site: http://www.vcc.edu/
Description: State-supported, 2-year, coed. Part of Minnesota State Colleges and Universities System. Awards certificates, diplomas, transfer associate, and terminal associate degrees. Founded 1922. Setting: 5-acre rural campus. Total enrollment: 745. Student-undergrad faculty ratio is 13:1. 595 applied, 57% were admitted. Students come from 42 states and territories, 3 other countries, 1% Native American, 3% Hispanic, 9% black, 1% Asian American or Pacific Islander, 10% 25 or older, 50% live on campus. Core. Calendar: semesters. Academic remediation for entering students, services for LD students, advanced placement, honors program, summer session for credit, part-time degree program, adult/continuing education programs, co-op programs and internships. Off campus study at other colleges in the Minnesota State Colleges and Universities System.
Entrance Requirements: Open admission. Options: Common Application, electronic application, early admission, deferred admission. Required: high school transcript. Entrance: noncompetitive. Application deadline: Rolling. Notification: continuous.
Costs Per Year: Application fee: $20. State resident tuition: $4190 full-time, $140 per credit part-time. Nonresident tuition: $5120 full-time, $171 per credit part-time. College room and board: $4560. College room only: $2900.
Collegiate Environment: Orientation program. Most popular organizations: Student Life Committee, student government, Drama Club. Major annual events: New Student Week, New Year's Dance, Karaoke Night. Student services: personal-psychological counseling, women's center. Campus security: student patrols, late night transport-escort service, controlled dormitory access. 260 college housing spaces available; all were occupied in 2003-04. No special consideration for freshman housing applicants. On-campus residence required in freshman year. Option: coed housing available. Vermilion Community College Library with 19,500 books, 100 serials, and an OPAC. 60 computers available on campus for general student use. A campuswide network can be accessed from student residence rooms and from off campus. Staffed computer lab on campus.

Community Environment: Located on the edge of the Boundary Waters Canoe Area, Vermilion offers its students one of the most beautiful wilderness areas in America for a college setting. The town of Ely, with a population of about 4,000, provides nearby shopping facilities, churches, a golf course, tennis courts, restaurants and an excellent hospital. Limited part-time work is available in the community. The area provides exceptional opportunities for camping, canoeing, fishing, hunting, snowmobiling, cross-country skiing, downhill skiing, and even dog sledding.

■ **WALDEN UNIVERSITY** *U-9*
155 Fifth Ave. South
Minneapolis, MN 55401
Tel: (612)338-7224; (866)492-5336
E-mail: request@walden.edu
Web Site: http://www.waldenu.edu/
Description: Proprietary, upper-level, coed. Awards bachelor's, master's, and doctoral degrees. Founded 1970. Total enrollment: 22,168. Faculty: 1,084 (68 full-time, 1,016 part-time). Student-undergrad faculty ratio is 20:1. Full-time: 55 students, 65% women, 35% men. Part-time: 1,174 students, 61% women, 39% men. 99% from out-of-state, 0.1% Native American, 30% Hispanic, 2% black, 0.4% Asian American or Pacific Islander, 0% international. Academic areas with the most degrees conferred: business/marketing; computer and information sciences. Calendar: quarter/semester depending on program.
Costs Per Year: Tuition: $8280 full-time, $230 per credit part-time.

■ **WINONA STATE UNIVERSITY** *X-13*
PO Box 5838
Winona, MN 55987-5838
Tel: (507)457-5000
Free: 800-DIAL WSU
Admissions: (507)457-5100
Fax: (507)457-5620
E-mail: admissions@winona.edu
Description: State-supported, comprehensive, coed. Part of Minnesota State Colleges and Universities System. Awards associate, bachelor's, and master's degrees and post-master's certificates. Founded 1858. Setting: 40-acre small town campus. Endowment: $3.1 million. Research spending for 2004 fiscal year: $850,000. Educational spending for 2005 fiscal year: $3700 per student. Total enrollment: 8,236. Faculty: 357 (315 full-time, 42 part-time). Student-undergrad faculty ratio is 21:1. 4,802 applied, 79% were admitted. 20% from top 10% of their high school class, 50% from top quarter, 96% from top half. 2 National Merit Scholars, 51 class presidents, 28 valedictorians. Full-time: 6,776 students, 63% women, 37% men. Part-time: 793 students, 60% women, 40% men. Students come from 21 states and territories, 48 other countries, 34% from out-of-state, 0.3% Native American, 1% Hispanic, 1% black, 1% Asian American or Pacific Islander, 4%

international, 11% 25 or older, 28% live on campus, 7% transferred in. Retention: 75% of full-time freshmen returned the following year. Core. Calendar: semesters. Academic remediation for entering students, ESL program, services for LD students, advanced placement, accelerated degree program, self-designed majors, honors program, independent study, distance learning, double major, summer session for credit, part-time degree program, external degree program, adult/continuing education programs, internships, graduate courses open to undergrads. Off campus study at Saint Mary's University of Minnesota, other colleges in the Minnesota State Colleges and Universities System. Study abroad program. ROTC: Army (c).
Entrance Requirements: Options: Peterson's Universal Application, Common Application, electronic application, early admission, early action, deferred admission, international baccalaureate accepted. Required: high school transcript, class rank, SAT or ACT. Required for some: essay, recommendations, interview. Entrance: moderately difficult. Application deadline: Rolling. Notification: continuous.
Costs Per Year: Application fee: $20. State resident tuition: $5877 full-time. Nonresident tuition: $10,297 full-time. Mandatory fees: $1850 full-time. College room and board: $5000. Room and board charges vary according to board plan and housing facility.
Collegiate Environment: Orientation program. Drama-theater group, choral group, marching band, student-run newspaper, radio station. Social organizations: 130 open to all; national fraternities, national sororities, local fraternities, local sororities; 3% of eligible men and 3% of eligible women are members. Most popular organizations: University Program Activities Committee, Student Senate, Inter-Residence Hall Council. Major annual events: homecoming, Family Weekend, Spring Fest. Student services: legal services, health clinic, personal-psychological counseling, women's center. Campus security: 24-hour emergency response devices and patrols, student patrols, late night transport-escort service, controlled dormitory access, security cameras. 2,500 college housing spaces available; all were occupied in 2003-04. Freshmen guaranteed college housing. Options: coed, men-only, women-only housing available. The Library with 243,500 books, 1,950 serials, an OPAC, and a Web page. Operations spending for 2004 fiscal year: $2.3 million. 1,400 computers available on campus for general student use. Computer purchase/lease plans available. A campuswide network can be accessed from student residence rooms and from off campus. Staffed computer lab on campus.
Community Environment: Winona (population 30,000) is a large town in southeastern Minnesota, in a sector known as Hiawatha Valley. Limestone from the quarries here is comparable to much of Italy's finest travertine. Winona is headquarters for the Upper Mississippi River Wildlife and Fish Refuge. Trains and buses provide commercial transportation. Community facilities include many churches, a public library, a hospital, hotels and motels. Part-time employment is available. Recreational activities include fishing, golf, swimming, hunting, boating and skiing.

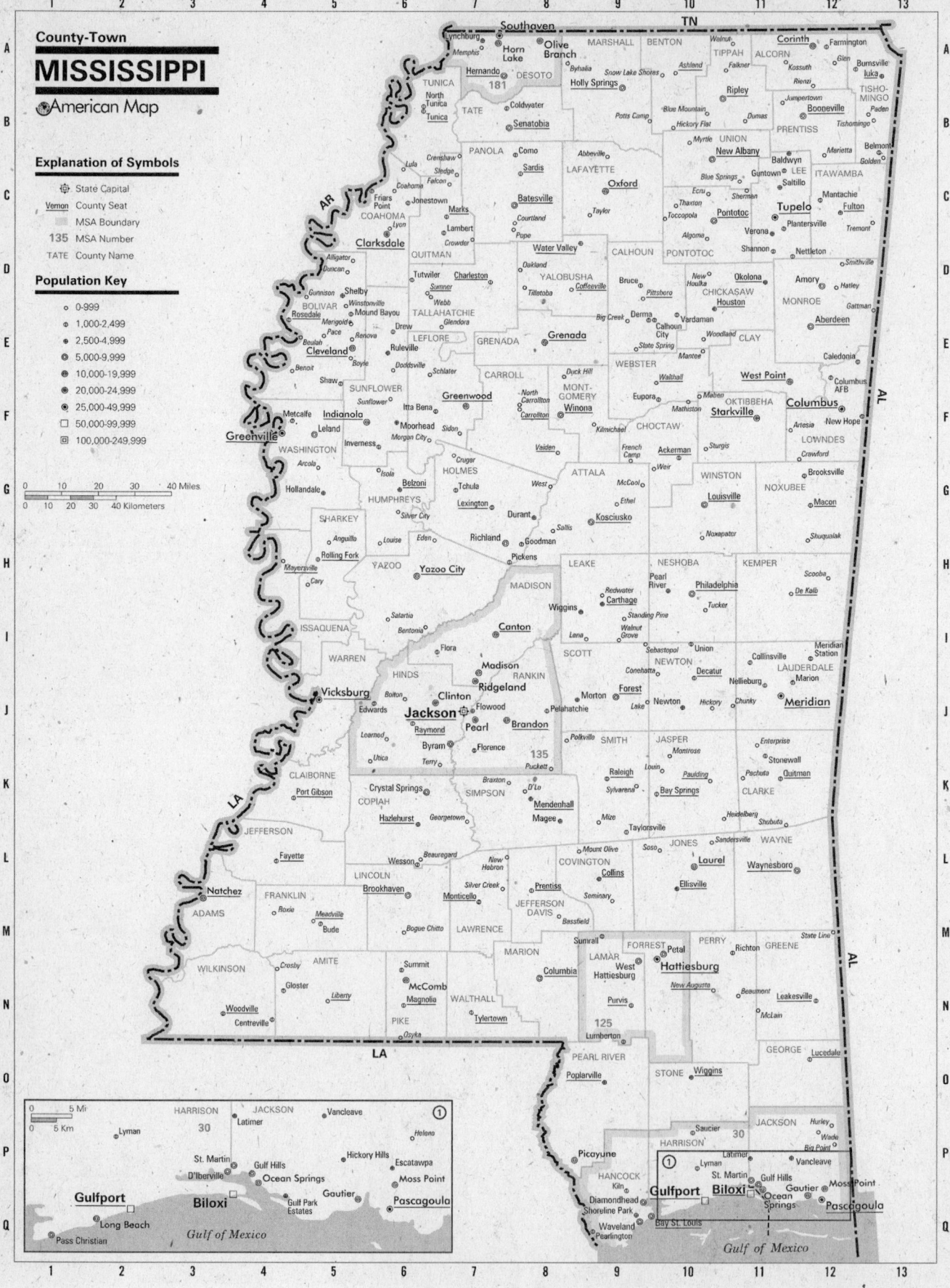

County-Town

MISSISSIPPI

American Map

Explanation of Symbols

- State Capital
- *Vernon* County Seat
- MSA Boundary
- 135 MSA Number
- TATE County Name

Population Key

- ○ 0-999
- ⊕ 1,000-2,499
- ⊙ 2,500-4,999
- ⊛ 5,000-9,999
- ⊜ 10,000-19,999
- ⊚ 20,000-24,999
- ⦿ 25,000-49,999
- ▢ 50,000-99,999
- ▣ 100,000-249,999

■ **ALCORN STATE UNIVERSITY**
1000 ASU Dr.
Alcorn State, MS 39096-7500
Tel: (601)877-6100
Free: 800-222-6790
Admissions: (601)877-6147
Fax: (601)877-6347
E-mail: ebarnes@alcorn.edu
Web Site: http://www.alcorn.edu/
Description: State-supported, comprehensive, coed. Part of Mississippi Institutions of Higher Learning. Awards associate, bachelor's, and master's degrees and post-master's certificates. Founded 1871. Setting: 1,756-acre rural campus. Endowment: $209,871. Research spending for 2004 fiscal year: $7 million. Educational spending for 2005 fiscal year: $6049 per student. Total enrollment: 3,544. Faculty: 209 (175 full-time, 34 part-time). Student-undergrad faculty ratio is 16:1. 2,335 applied, 68% were admitted. 75% from top half of their high school class. Full-time: 2,676 students, 61% women, 39% men. Part-time: 286 students, 79% women, 21% men. Students come from 31 states and territories, 13 other countries, 16% from out-of-state, 0.03% Native American, 0.2% Hispanic, 92% black, 0.4% Asian American or Pacific Islander, 2% international, 23% 25 or older, 52% live on campus, 9% transferred in. Retention: 74% of full-time freshmen returned the following year. Academic areas with the most degrees conferred: liberal arts/general studies; health professions and related sciences; business/marketing; education. Core. Calendar: semesters. Academic remediation for entering students, advanced placement, honors program, independent study, distance learning, double major, part-time degree program, co-op programs and internships, graduate courses open to undergrads. ROTC: Army.
Entrance Requirements: Options: electronic application, early admission, deferred admission. Required: high school transcript, minimum 2.0 high school GPA, SAT or ACT. Entrance: minimally difficult. Application deadline: Rolling. Notification: continuous. Preference given to state residents.
Costs Per Year: Application fee: $0. State resident tuition: $3919 full-time, $163 per hour part-time. Nonresident tuition: $8887 full-time, $370 per hour part-time. Mandatory fees: $807 full-time. College room and board: $4272. College room only: $2428.
Collegiate Environment: Orientation program. Drama-theater group, choral group, marching band, student-run newspaper, radio station. Social organizations: 74 open to all; national fraternities, national sororities; 7% of eligible men and 12% of eligible women are members. Most popular organizations: intramural sports, marching band, gospel choir, inter-faith choir. Major annual events: Greek Step Show, concerts, Homecoming. Student services: health clinic, personal-psychological counseling. Campus security: 24-hour patrols. 2,519 college housing spaces available; 1,460 were occupied in 2003-04. Freshmen guaranteed college housing. Options: men-only, women-only housing available. John Dewey Boyd Library with 210,036 books, 562,030 microform titles, 1,046 serials, 11,504 audiovisual materials, and an OPAC. Operations spending for 2004 fiscal year: $1.2 million. 500 computers available on campus for general student use. A campuswide network can be accessed from student residence rooms and from off campus. Staffed computer lab on campus.
Community Environment: This rural community has a population of less than 2,500. Multidenominational churches serve the area. It is an ideal place for hiking, camping and other outdoor recreational activities. The university is

located in Claiborne County, seven miles west of Lorman, seventeen miles southwest of Poet Gibson, and forty-five miles south of Vicksburg.

■ **ANTONELLI COLLEGE (HATTIESBURG)** *M-10*
1500 North 31st Ave.
Hattiesburg, MS 39401
Tel: (601)583-4100
Fax: (601)583-0839
Web Site: http://www.antonellic.com/
Description: Proprietary, 2-year, coed.

■ **ANTONELLI COLLEGE (JACKSON)** *J-7*
480 East Woodrow Wilson Dr.
Jackson, MS 39216
Tel: (601)362-9991
Fax: (601)362-2333
Web Site: http://www.antonellic.com/
Description: Proprietary, 2-year, coed. Awards diplomas, transfer associate, and terminal associate degrees. Total enrollment: 214.

■ **BELHAVEN COLLEGE** *J-7*
1500 Peachtree St.
Jackson, MS 39202-1789
Tel: (601)968-5928
Free: 800-960-5940
Admissions: (601)968-5940
Fax: (601)968-9998
Web Site: http://www.belhaven.edu/
Description: Independent Presbyterian, comprehensive, coed. Awards associate, bachelor's, and master's degrees. Founded 1883. Setting: 42-acre urban campus. Endowment: $3.6 million. Research spending for 2004 fiscal year: $31,003. Educational spending for 2005 fiscal year: $2971 per student. Total enrollment: 2,580. Faculty: 225 (70 full-time, 155 part-time). Student-undergrad faculty ratio is 21:1. 734 applied, 57% were admitted. 20% from top 10% of their high school class, 30% from top quarter, 56% from top half. 5 National Merit Scholars, 4 valedictorians. Full-time: 2,166 students, 68% women, 32% men. Part-time: 72 students, 71% women, 29% men. Students come from 30 states and territories, 17 other countries, 27% from out-of-state, 1% Native American, 3% Hispanic, 38% black, 0.5% Asian American or Pacific Islander, 1% international, 54% 25 or older, 32% live on campus, 2% transferred in. Retention: 69% of full-time freshmen returned the following year. Academic areas with the most degrees conferred: business/marketing; education; psychology. Core. Calendar: semesters. Academic remediation for entering students, ESL program, advanced placement, accelerated degree program, self-designed majors, honors program, independent study, double major, summer session for credit, part-time degree program, adult/continuing education programs, internships. Off campus study at Coalition for Christian Colleges and Universities. Study abroad program.
Entrance Requirements: Options: early admission, deferred admission, international baccalaureate accepted. Required: essay, high school transcript, minimum 2.0 high school GPA, 1 recommendation, 1 academic reference, SAT or ACT. Required for some: interview. Entrance: moderately difficult. Application deadline: Rolling. Notification: continuous.

Costs Per Year: Application fee: $25. Comprehensive fee: $20,478 includes full-time tuition ($14,124), mandatory fees ($650), and college room and board ($5704). Part-time tuition: $350 per semester hour.

Collegiate Environment: Orientation program. Drama-theater group, choral group, student-run newspaper. Social organizations: 20 open to all. Most popular organizations: Student Government Association, Reformed University Fellowship, Kappa Delta Epsilon, Black Student Association, Math/Computer Science Club. Major annual events: Homecoming, Lake Day, Christmas Formal. Student services: health clinic, personal-psychological counseling. Campus security: 24-hour emergency response devices and patrols, late night transport-escort service, controlled dormitory access. 475 undergraduates lived in college housing during 2003-04. Freshmen guaranteed college housing. On-campus residence required through sophomore year. Options: men-only, women-only housing available. Hood Library with 99,765 books, 11,271 microform titles, 467 serials, 3,546 audiovisual materials, an OPAC, and a Web page. Operations spending for 2004 fiscal year: $254,208. 40 computers available on campus for general student use. A campuswide network can be accessed from student residence rooms and from off campus. Staffed computer lab on campus.

Community Environment: See Jackson State University.

■ **BLUE MOUNTAIN COLLEGE**

PO Box 160
Blue Mountain, MS 38610-9509
Tel: (662)685-4771
Free: 800-235-0136
Admissions: (662)685-4161
Fax: (662)685-4776
E-mail: eteel@bmc.edu
Web Site: http://www.bmc.edu/

Description: Independent Southern Baptist, 4-year, coed. Awards bachelor's degrees. Founded 1873. Setting: 44-acre rural campus with easy access to Memphis. Endowment: $6.6 million. Educational spending for 2005 fiscal year: $6152 per student. Total enrollment: 365. Student-undergrad faculty ratio is 11:1. 170 applied, 55% were admitted. 30% from top 10% of their high school class, 58% from top quarter, 82% from top half. Full-time: 283 students, 73% women, 27% men. Part-time: 82 students, 91% women, 9% men. Students come from 8 states and territories, 2 other countries, 10% from out-of-state, 0% Native American, 0% Hispanic, 14% black, 0.3% Asian American or Pacific Islander, 0.3% international, 35% 25 or older, 34% live on campus, 15% transferred in. Retention: 58% of full-time freshmen returned the following year. Academic areas with the most degrees conferred: education; social sciences; psychology; visual and performing arts. Core. Calendar: semesters. Advanced placement, accelerated degree program, honors program, double major, summer session for credit, part-time degree program, internships.

Entrance Requirements: Options: Peterson's Universal Application, electronic application, early admission. Required: high school transcript, SAT or ACT. Recommended: minimum 2.0 high school GPA. Required for some: essay, 2 recommendations, interview. Entrance: minimally difficult. Application deadline: 9/3. Notification: continuous.

Costs Per Year: Application fee: $10. Comprehensive fee: $11,086 includes full-time tuition ($6780), mandatory fees ($540), and college room and board ($3766). College room only: $1400. Full-time tuition and fees vary according to course load. Room and board charges vary according to board plan and gender. Part-time tuition: $230 per hour. Part-time mandatory fees: $80 per term. Part-time tuition and fees vary according to course load.

Collegiate Environment: Orientation program. Drama-theater group, choral group. Social organizations: ; 50% of women are members. Most popular organizations: Baptist Student Union, Student Government Association, Athletic Association, Commuter Club, Mississippi Association of Educators/Student Program. Major annual events: BSU/SGA Welcome Back Parties, Society Rush, Field Day. Campus security: 24-hour patrols. 234 college housing spaces available; 127 were occupied in 2003-04. No special consideration for freshman housing applicants. On-campus residence required through senior year. Option: women-only housing available. Guyton Library with 59,431 books, 380 microform titles, 186 serials, 3,645 audiovisual materials, and an OPAC. Operations spending for 2004 fiscal year: $145,603. 55 computers available on campus for general student use. A campuswide network can be accessed from student residence rooms. Staffed computer lab on campus.

Community Environment: A rural community, Blue Mountain has a warm and pleasant climate with an average temperature of 68 degrees. Blue Mountain is about 70 miles from Memphis. Recreational facilities include a swimming pool, golf course, athletic field, physical education center, tennis courts, student center and 2 auditoriums for productions.

■ **COAHOMA COMMUNITY COLLEGE** *D-6*

3240 Friars Point Rd.
Clarksdale, MS 38614-9799
Tel: (662)627-2571
Admissions: (662)621-4205
Web Site: http://www.ccc.cc.ms.us/

Description: State and locally supported, 2-year, coed. Part of Mississippi State Board for Community and Junior Colleges. Awards certificates, transfer associate, and terminal associate degrees. Founded 1949. Setting: 29-acre small town campus with easy access to Memphis. Educational spending for 2005 fiscal year: $5172 per student. Total enrollment: 1,946. Student-undergrad faculty ratio is 26:1. Full-time: 1,801 students, 70% women, 30% men. Part-time: 145 students, 80% women, 20% men. Students come from 8 states and territories, 3% from out-of-state, 0% Native American, 0.1% Hispanic, 95% black, 0% Asian American or Pacific Islander, 0% international, 10% 25 or older. Core. Calendar: semesters. Part-time degree program, adult/continuing education programs.

Entrance Requirements: Open admission. Option: Common Application. Required: high school transcript. Required for some: minimum X high school GPA, recommendations, interview. Entrance: noncompetitive. Application deadline: Rolling. Notification: continuous.

Costs Per Year: Application fee: $0. Area resident tuition: $1600 full-time, $90 per semester hour part-time. Nonresident tuition: $2900 full-time. Mandatory fees: $140 full-time, $60 per term part-time. College room and board: $2914.

Collegiate Environment: Drama-theater group, choral group, marching band, student-run newspaper. Most popular organizations: Student Government Association, VICA, Phi Theta Kappa Honor Society. Major annual events: High School Day, Coronation of Miss Coahoma Community College, Graduation. Student services: health clinic, personal-psychological counseling. Campus security: 24-hour patrols. 400 college housing spaces available; 285 were occupied in 2003-04. 25 computers available on campus for general student use. A campuswide network can be accessed.

Community Environment: Clarksdale, an important distributing outlet in an agricultural region, is a prime example of the state's "Balance Agriculture with Industry" program. The city gins large amounts of cotton and manufactures conveyor equipment, corrugated boxes, farm machinery, tire tubes, agricultural chemicals and fertilizers, builder's hardware, electronic equipment and furniture. The Greyhound Bus line serves the city. The area has a public library, hospital, churches of all major denominations and movie theatres.

■ **COPIAH-LINCOLN COMMUNITY COLLEGE** *L-6*

PO Box 649
Wesson, MS 39191-0649
Tel: (601)643-5101
Admissions: (601)643-8307
Fax: (601)643-8212
E-mail: phil.broome@colin.edu
Web Site: http://www.colin.edu/

Description: State and locally supported, 2-year, coed. Part of Mississippi State Board for Community and Junior Colleges. Awards certificates, transfer associate, and terminal associate degrees. Founded 1928. Setting: 525-acre rural campus with easy access to Jackson. Total enrollment: 2,161. Students come from 7 states and territories, 2 other countries, 2% from out-of-state, 22% 25 or older, 30% live on campus. Calendar: semesters. Academic remediation for entering students, advanced placement, self-designed majors, honors program, summer session for credit, part-time degree program, adult/continuing education programs.

Entrance Requirements: Open admission. Option: early admission. Required: high school transcript. Entrance: noncompetitive. Application deadline: Rolling. Preference given to state residents.

Costs Per Year: Application fee: $0. State resident tuition: $1700 full-time. Nonresident tuition: $1800 full-time. Mandatory fees: $100 full-time.

Collegiate Environment: Orientation program. Drama-theater group, choral group, marching band, student-run newspaper, radio station. Student services: health clinic, personal-psychological counseling. Campus security: 24-hour patrols. 1,200 college housing spaces available; all were occupied in 2003-04. Oswalt Memorial Library with 38,900 books and 255 serials. 300 computers available on campus for general student use. Staffed computer lab on campus.

Community Environment: Wesson is located on U.S. Highway 51, approximately 150 miles north of New Orleans. The climate is pleasant. Transportation is provided by the Illinois Central railroad. Some part-time employment is available for students.

■ **COPIAH-LINCOLN COMMUNITY COLLEGE-NATCHEZ CAMPUS**
M-3
11 Co-Lin Circle
Natchez, MS 39120-8446
Tel: (601)442-9111
Fax: (601)446-9967
Web Site: http://www.colin.edu/
Description: State and locally supported, 2-year, coed. Part of Mississippi State Board for Community and Junior Colleges. Awards certificates, transfer associate, and terminal associate degrees. Founded 1972. Setting: 24-acre small town campus. Educational spending for 2005 fiscal year: $1800 per student. Total enrollment: 900. Full-time: 554 students, 71% women, 29% men. Part-time: 346 students, 76% women, 24% men. Students come from 4 states and territories, 0.3% Hispanic, 53% black, 0.3% Asian American or Pacific Islander, 50% 25 or older. Core. Calendar: semesters. Academic remediation for entering students, advanced placement, self-designed majors, distance learning, summer session for credit, part-time degree program, adult/continuing education programs, internships.
Entrance Requirements: Open admission. Option: early admission. Required: high school transcript. Required for some: ACT, TABE. Entrance: noncompetitive. Application deadline: Rolling. Notification: continuous.
Costs Per Year: Application fee: $0. State resident tuition: $1600 full-time, $100 per semester hour part-time. Nonresident tuition: $3400 full-time, $175 per semester hour part-time. Mandatory fees: $100 full-time, $5 per semester hour part-time, $10 per year part-time. College room and board: $2600.
Collegiate Environment: Orientation program. Student-run newspaper. Most popular organization: student newspaper. Campus security: 24-hour patrols. Willie Mae Dunn Library with 19,000 books, 112 serials, 700 audiovisual materials, an OPAC, and a Web page. 175 computers available on campus for general student use. A campuswide network can be accessed from off-campus. Staffed computer lab on campus.

■ **DELTA STATE UNIVERSITY** *E-5*
Hwy. 8 West
Cleveland, MS 38733-0001
Tel: (662)846-3000
Free: 800-468-6378
Admissions: (662)846-4658
Fax: (662)846-4016
E-mail: dheslep@deltastate.edu
Web Site: http://www.deltastate.edu/
Description: State-supported, comprehensive, coed. Part of Mississippi Institutions of Higher Learning. Awards bachelor's, master's, and doctoral degrees and post-master's certificates. Founded 1924. Setting: 332-acre small town campus. Endowment: $10.3 million. Research spending for 2004 fiscal year: $13,000. Educational spending for 2005 fiscal year: $4801 per student. Total enrollment: 3,998. Faculty: 275 (165 full-time, 110 part-time). Student-undergrad faculty ratio is 18:1. 40% from top quarter of their high school class, 65% from top half. Full-time: 2,754 students, 58% women, 42% men. Part-time: 504 students, 71% women, 29% men. Students come from 26 states and territories, 21 other countries, 8% from out-of-state, 0.3% Native American, 1% Hispanic, 39% black, 1% Asian American or Pacific Islander, 0% international, 24% 25 or older, 35% live on campus, 18% transferred in. Retention: 71% of full-time freshmen returned the following year. Academic areas with the most degrees conferred: business/marketing; education; health professions and related sciences. Core. Calendar: semesters. Academic remediation for entering students, services for LD students, advanced placement, honors program, independent study, distance learning, double major, summer session for credit, part-time degree program, co-op programs and internships. ROTC: Air Force.
Entrance Requirements: Options: electronic application, deferred admission. Required: high school transcript, minimum X high school GPA, SAT and SAT Subject Tests or ACT. Required for some: interview for art, music majors. Entrance: minimally difficult. Application deadline: 8/1. Notification: continuous.
Costs Per Year: Application fee: $15. State resident tuition: $3762 full-time, $155 per semester hour part-time. Nonresident tuition: $8950 full-time, $370

per semester hour part-time. Mandatory fees: $490 full-time. College room and board: $4272. Room and board charges vary according to board plan and housing facility.
Collegiate Environment: Orientation program. Drama-theater group, choral group, marching band, student-run newspaper. Social organizations: 86 open to all; national fraternities, national sororities; 16% of eligible men and 16% of eligible women are members. Most popular organizations: Student Government Association, Student Alumni Association, Baptist Student Union, Fellowship of Christian Athletes, Delta Volunteers. Major annual events: Homecoming, Renaissance Faire, Springfest. Student services: health clinic, personal-psychological counseling. Campus security: 24-hour emergency response devices and patrols, late night transport-escort service, controlled dormitory access. 1,113 undergraduates lived in college housing during 2003-04. No special consideration for freshman housing applicants. Options: men-only, women-only housing available. Roberts-LaForge Library plus 1 other with 345,565 books, 828,979 microform titles, 1,268 serials, 18,493 audiovisual materials, an OPAC, and a Web page. Operations spending for 2004 fiscal year: $1.4 million. 293 computers available on campus for general student use. A campuswide network can be accessed from student residence rooms and from off campus. Staffed computer lab on campus.
Community Environment: Located midway between Memphis, Tennessee and Vicksburg, Mississippi, the city has a public library, several churches representing the major denominations, and a hospital. Bus lines are accessible to the area and a regional airport is located 30 miles from campus in Greenville. Recreation is provided in the community through a local Little Theatre, movies, swimming pools, 4 municipal parks, a nine-hole golf course, bowling, and fishing and hunting in the nearby lake region. Average living facilities are provided by a hotel, motel, several apartments, rooming houses and dormitories. The city has over 35 civic, fraternal and business organizations. Some part-time employment is available for students.

■ **EAST CENTRAL COMMUNITY COLLEGE** *J-10*
PO Box 129
Decatur, MS 39327-0129
Tel: (601)635-2111; 877-462-3222
Fax: (601)635-2150
Web Site: http://www.eccc.cc.ms.us/
Description: State and locally supported, 2-year, coed. Part of Mississippi State Board for Community and Junior Colleges. Awards certificates, transfer associate, and terminal associate degrees. Founded 1928. Setting: 200-acre rural campus. Total enrollment: 2,382. Students come from 9 states and territories, 2% from out-of-state, 32% 25 or older, 27% live on campus. Core. Calendar: semesters. Academic remediation for entering students, services for LD students, advanced placement, honors program, summer session for credit, part-time degree program, adult/continuing education programs.
Entrance Requirements: Open admission. Options: Common Application, early admission. Required: high school transcript. Placement: ACT required. Entrance: noncompetitive. Application deadline: Rolling. Notification: continuous.
Collegiate Environment: Orientation program. Drama-theater group, choral group, marching band, student-run newspaper. Student services: health clinic, personal-psychological counseling. Campus security: 24-hour patrols. Options: men-only, women-only housing available. 80 computers available on campus for general student use. A campuswide network can be accessed from off-campus. Staffed computer lab on campus.
Community Environment: Located in a rural area with a healthful atmosphere, Decatur has 2 churches and very active civic, fraternal and veteran's organizations. Hunting in the local area, fishing and swimming provide recreation for the city.

■ **EAST MISSISSIPPI COMMUNITY COLLEGE**
PO Box 158
Scooba, MS 39358-0158
Tel: (662)476-8442
Admissions: (662)476-5041
Web Site: http://www.eastms.edu/
Description: State and locally supported, 2-year, coed. Part of Mississippi State Board for Community and Junior Colleges. Awards certificates, transfer associate, and terminal associate degrees. Founded 1927. Setting: 25-acre rural campus. Endowment: $134,022. Educational spending for 2005 fiscal year: $3980 per student. Total enrollment: 3,417. 2,245 applied, 62% were admitted. Students come from 4 states and territories, 1% from

out-of-state, 0.1% Native American, 0.5% Hispanic, 51% black, 0.4% Asian American or Pacific Islander, 0.03% international, 30% 25 or older, 25% live on campus. Core. Calendar: semesters. Academic remediation for entering students, services for LD students, advanced placement, honors program, distance learning, double major, summer session for credit, part-time degree program, adult/continuing education programs, co-op programs.

Entrance Requirements: Open admission. Options: Common Application, electronic application, deferred admission. Required: high school transcript. Placement: ACT required for some. Entrance: noncompetitive. Application deadline: Rolling.

Collegiate Environment: Orientation program. Drama-theater group, choral group, marching band, student-run newspaper. Social organizations: local fraternities. Student services: personal-psychological counseling. Campus security: 24-hour emergency response devices and patrols. 700 college housing spaces available; 435 were occupied in 2003-04. No special consideration for freshman housing applicants. Options: men-only, women-only housing available. Tubb-May Library with 27,840 books, 116 serials, 3,478 audiovisual materials, an OPAC, and a Web page. Operations spending for 2004 fiscal year: $274,922. 100 computers available on campus for general student use. A campuswide network can be accessed from student residence rooms and from off campus.

Community Environment: Scooba is located in the east central part of Mississippi, 35 miles north of Meridian. The area is accessible by railroad and U.S. Highway 45. There are excellent bus, train and air facilities in nearby Meridian.

■ **HINDS COMMUNITY COLLEGE** *J-6*
PO Box 1100
Raymond, MS 39154-1100
Tel: (601)857-5261
Admissions: (601)857-3280
Web Site: http://www.hindscc.edu/

Description: State and locally supported, 2-year, coed. Part of Mississippi State Board for Community and Junior Colleges. Awards certificates, diplomas, transfer associate, and terminal associate degrees. Founded 1917. Setting: 671-acre small town campus. Endowment: $948,556. Educational spending for 2005 fiscal year: $3009 per student. Total enrollment: 9,961. 21% from top quarter of their high school class, 59% from top half. Full-time: 7,145 students, 63% women, 37% men. Part-time: 2,816 students, 69% women, 31% men. Students come from 16 states and territories, 1 other country, 3% from out-of-state, 0.2% Native American, 1% Hispanic, 52% black, 0.5% Asian American or Pacific Islander, 0.03% international, 40% 25 or older, 15% live on campus. Core. Calendar: semesters. Academic remediation for entering students, services for LD students, advanced placement, accelerated degree program, freshman honors college, honors program, independent study, distance learning, double major, summer session for credit, part-time degree program, adult/continuing education programs, co-op programs. ROTC: Army (c).

Entrance Requirements: Open admission. Options: Common Application, early admission. Required: high school transcript. Required for some: SAT and SAT Subject Tests or ACT. Entrance: noncompetitive. Application deadline: Rolling. Notification: continuous.

Collegiate Environment: Drama-theater group, choral group, marching band, student-run newspaper. Social organizations: 51 open to all. Most popular organizations: Phi Theta Kappa, Baptist Student Union, Residence Hall Association, Hi-Steppers Dance Team, band. Major annual events: Homecoming Week, Substance Abuse Week, Spring Fling. Student services: personal-psychological counseling, women's center. Campus security: 24-hour emergency response devices and patrols, controlled dormitory access. Options: men-only, women-only housing available. McLendon Library with 165,260 books, 8 microform titles, 1,178 serials, and an OPAC. Operations spending for 2004 fiscal year: $1.8 million. 55 computers available on campus for general student use. A campuswide network can be accessed. Staffed computer lab on campus.

Community Environment: Raymond is a suburban area 15 miles east of Jackson. The community has a regional library and a general hospital 8 miles east. There are several churches of various denominations in the immediate area. Local clubs include Lions, Business & Professional Women, and the Jaycees. Hinds Community College has a part-time employment agreement with a local industry.

■ **HOLMES COMMUNITY COLLEGE** *H-8*
PO Box 369
Goodman, MS 39079-0369

Tel: (662)472-2312
Admissions: (601)472-2312
Fax: (662)472-9156
Web Site: http://www.holmescc.edu/

Description: State and locally supported, 2-year, coed. Part of Mississippi State Board for Community and Junior Colleges. Awards certificates, transfer associate, and terminal associate degrees. Founded 1928. Setting: 196-acre small town campus. Endowment: $2.4 million. Educational spending for 2005 fiscal year: $3428 per student. Total enrollment: 4,494. Full-time: 3,251 students, 64% women, 36% men. Part-time: 1,243 students, 72% women, 28% men. Students come from 11 states and territories, 1% from out-of-state, 0.1% Native American, 0.3% Hispanic, 45% black, 26% 25 or older, 12% live on campus. Retention: 55% of full-time freshmen returned the following year. Core. Calendar: semesters. Academic remediation for entering students, services for LD students, advanced placement, distance learning, summer session for credit, adult/continuing education programs, co-op programs.

Entrance Requirements: Open admission. Option: early admission. Required: high school transcript. Placement: ACT required. Entrance: noncompetitive. Application deadline: Rolling. Notification: continuous.

Costs Per Year: Application fee: $0. State resident tuition: $1100 full-time, $65 per semester hour part-time. Nonresident tuition: $1750 full-time. Mandatory fees: $330 full-time, $10 per term part-time. Part-time tuition and fees vary according to course load. College room and board: $3330. Room and board charges vary according to housing facility.

Collegiate Environment: Drama-theater group, choral group, marching band, student-run newspaper. Social organizations: 23 open to all. Most popular organizations: Student Government Association, Drama/Theater Club, Baptist Student Union, FCA, Vocational Industrial Clubs of America. Major annual events: Homecoming, Beauty Pageant, Spring Fling. Student services: personal-psychological counseling. Campus security: 24-hour emergency response devices and patrols. 660 college housing spaces available. No special consideration for freshman housing applicants. Options: men-only, women-only housing available. McMorrough Library plus 2 others with 53,000 books, 550 serials, and an OPAC. Operations spending for 2004 fiscal year: $124,696. 150 computers available on campus for general student use. A campuswide network can be accessed from off-campus. Staffed computer lab on campus.

Community Environment: Located in a rural area, there is bus service to Goodman. The climate is mild and humid. Railroad service is available in nearby Durant, Mississippi. Several churches of various denominations are located here. Many cultural, recreational and community services available in Jackson, the State Capital, 48 miles away. There is some work available for students requiring financial assistance.

■ **ITAWAMBA COMMUNITY COLLEGE** *C-12*
602 West Hill St.
Fulton, MS 38843
Tel: (662)862-8000
Admissions: (662)862-8032
Fax: (662)862-8036
E-mail: hgjefcoat@iccms.edu
Web Site: http://www.icc.cc.ms.us/

Description: State and locally supported, 2-year, coed. Part of Mississippi State Board for Community and Junior Colleges. Awards transfer associate and terminal associate degrees. Founded 1947. Setting: 300-acre small town campus. Total enrollment: 4,000. 15% from top 10% of their high school class, 25% from top quarter, 70% from top half. Students come from 9 states and territories, 3 other countries, 8% 25 or older. Core. Calendar: semesters. Academic remediation for entering students, services for LD students, honors program, summer session for credit, part-time degree program, adult/continuing education programs. ROTC: Army.

Entrance Requirements: Open admission except for allied health programs. Option: early admission. Required: high school transcript. Placement: ACT required. Entrance: noncompetitive. Application deadline: Rolling. Notification: continuous.

Collegiate Environment: 36,816 books and 231 serials. 40 computers available on campus for general student use. Staffed computer lab on campus.

Community Environment: Fulton is a rural community in northeast Mississippi. The climate is moderate to warm. The area is accessible to bus and rail lines and has several churches of various denominations. Recreation is provided by local theatres, boating water skiing, fishing, and golf. Community services include the County Health Department, a hospital, and fine shopping facilities. There are many active civic and fraternal organizations within the immediate area.

■ JACKSON STATE UNIVERSITY J-7

1400 John R Lynch St.
Jackson, MS 39217
Tel: (601)979-2121
Free: 800-848-6817
Admissions: (601)979-2100
Fax: (601)979-2358
E-mail: schatman@jsums.edu
Web Site: http://www.jsums.edu/

Description: State-supported, university, coed. Part of Mississippi Institutions of Higher Learning. Awards bachelor's, master's, and doctoral degrees and post-master's certificates. Founded 1877. Setting: 150-acre urban campus. Endowment: $6 million. Research spending for 2004 fiscal year: $20.8 million. Total enrollment: 8,351. 8,725 applied, 40% were admitted. 38% from top quarter of their high school class, 75% from top half. Full-time: 5,714 students, 61% women, 39% men. Part-time: 891 students, 70% women, 30% men. Students come from 40 states and territories, 38 other countries, 21% from out-of-state, 0.1% Native American, 0.2% Hispanic, 97% black, 0.3% Asian American or Pacific Islander, 1% international, 27% 25 or older, 34% live on campus, 5% transferred in. Retention: 75% of full-time freshmen returned the following year. Core. Calendar: semesters. Academic remediation for entering students, services for LD students, advanced placement, honors program, distance learning, summer session for credit, part-time degree program, adult/continuing education programs, co-op programs and internships, graduate courses open to undergrads. Off campus study at Mississippi State University, Auburn University, Southern Illinois University, National Student Exchange. Study abroad program. ROTC: Army.
Entrance Requirements: Options: electronic application, early admission, deferred admission. Required: high school transcript, minimum 2.0 high school GPA, SAT or ACT. Required for some: 3 recommendations. Entrance: minimally difficult. Application deadline: 8/1. Notification: continuous.
Costs Per Year: Application fee: $0. State resident tuition: $3964 full-time, $166 per credit hour part-time. Nonresident tuition: $8872 full-time, $371 per credit hour part-time. College room and board: $5044. College room only: $2998. Room and board charges vary according to board plan.
Collegiate Environment: Orientation program. Drama-theater group, choral group, marching band, student-run newspaper, radio station. Social organizations: 160 open to all; national fraternities, national sororities; 11% of eligible men and 19% of eligible women are members. Most popular organizations: Tiger Pride Connection, Sonic Boom of the South, Students In Free Enterprise, Interfaith, NAACP. Major annual events: homecoming, Founders' Day, Capital City Classic. Student services: health clinic, personal-psychological counseling. Campus security: 24-hour emergency response devices and patrols, late night transport-escort service, controlled dormitory access. 2,222 college housing spaces available; 1,969 were occupied in 2003-04. No special consideration for freshman housing applicants. Options: men-only, women-only housing available. H. T. Sampson Library plus 1 other with 236,933 books, 670,035 microform titles, 3,409 serials, 4,285 audiovisual materials, and an OPAC. Operations spending for 2004 fiscal year: $545,276.
Community Environment: On the Pearl River, Jackson is the capital and largest city of Mississippi. It was first established as a trading post by the French. In the early days, many Virginians and Carolinians passed through here as they followed the Old Natchez Trace to the Southwest. The area enjoys year-round pleasant weather. Being a major city, there are good facilities for rail and air transportation. Community associations sponsoring cultural pursuits include Jackson Music Association, Little Theatre, Municipal Art Gallery and Symphony Orchestra. Local services are supplied by 5 hospitals, libraries and many churches. Recreation facilities include 12 parks, 4 municipal swimming pools, a zoo, golf courses, tennis courts, and fishing and hunting nearby.

■ JONES COUNTY JUNIOR COLLEGE L-10

900 South Ct. St.
Ellisville, MS 39437-3901
Tel: (601)477-4000
Admissions: (601)477-4025
Fax: (601)477-4212
Web Site: http://www.jcjc.edu/

Description: State and locally supported, 2-year, coed. Part of Mississippi State Board for Community and Junior Colleges. Awards certificates, transfer associate, and terminal associate degrees. Founded 1928. Setting: 360-acre small town campus. Total enrollment: 5,640. Students come from 9 states and territories, 22% 25 or older, 20% live on campus. Core. Calendar: semesters. Academic remediation for entering students, advanced placement, honors program, distance learning, summer session for credit, part-time degree program, co-op programs. ROTC: Army (c), Air Force (c).
Entrance Requirements: Open admission. Options: Common Application, early admission. Required: high school transcript, SAT or ACT. Entrance: noncompetitive. Application deadline: 8/26. Notification: continuous. Preference given to district residents.
Collegiate Environment: Drama-theater group, choral group, marching band, student-run newspaper. Most popular organization: student government. Major annual events: homecoming, Spring Fever Week. Student services: health clinic, personal-psychological counseling. Campus security: 24-hour patrols. 1,000 college housing spaces available; all were occupied in 2003-04. Options: men-only, women-only housing available. Memorial Library with 62,349 books and 654 serials. 600 computers available on campus for general student use. Staffed computer lab on campus.
Community Environment: The city is located 7 miles from Laurel. The climate is mild. Churches, libraries and museums all contribute to the pleasant living of the area. Transportation is provided by rail and air lines, and the town is easily accessible by highway. Fishing, hunting, and golf are the major recreational pastimes. There are some part-time job opportunities for students.

■ MAGNOLIA BIBLE COLLEGE G-9

PO Box 1109
Kosciusko, MS 39090-1109
Tel: (601)289-2896
Admissions: (662)289-2896
Web Site: http://www.magnolia.edu/

Description: Independent, 4-year, coed, affiliated with Church of Christ. Awards bachelor's degrees. Founded 1976. Setting: 5-acre small town campus. Endowment: $224,876. Educational spending for 2005 fiscal year: $10,675 per student. Total enrollment: 41. Student-undergrad faculty ratio is 11:1. 1 applied, 100% were admitted. 100% from top half of their high school class. Full-time: 20 students, 10% women, 90% men. Part-time: 21 students, 29% women, 71% men. Students come from 11 states and territories, 1 other country, 10% from out-of-state, 0% Native American, 0% Hispanic, 25% black, 0% Asian American or Pacific Islander, 4% international, 76% 25 or older, 48% live on campus, 10% transferred in. Retention: 100% of full-time freshmen returned the following year. Academic area with the most degrees conferred: theology and religious vocations. Core. Calendar: semesters. Academic remediation for entering students, independent study, summer session for credit, part-time degree program, internships.
Entrance Requirements: Open admission. Required: essay, high school transcript, 3 recommendations. Entrance: noncompetitive. Application deadline: 8/31. Notification: continuous. Preference given to Christians.
Costs Per Year: Application fee: $0. Tuition: $4800 full-time, $200 per semester hour part-time. Mandatory fees: $90 full-time, $45 per term part-time. College room only: $1500.
Collegiate Environment: Orientation program. Student services: personal-psychological counseling. Campus security: 24-hour emergency response devices. 34 college housing spaces available; 15 were occupied in 2003-04. No special consideration for freshman housing applicants. On-campus residence required through senior year. Option: coed housing available. Paul and Philip Gaunt Library with 32,589 books, 896 microform titles, 268 serials, and 1,123 audiovisual materials. Operations spending for 2004 fiscal year: $53,092. 8 computers available on campus for general student use. Staffed computer lab on campus.

■ MERIDIAN COMMUNITY COLLEGE J-11

910 Hwy. 19 North
Meridian, MS 39307
Tel: (601)483-8241
Admissions: (601)484-8895
Web Site: http://www.meridiancc.edu

Description: State and locally supported, 2-year, coed. Part of Mississippi State Board for Community and Junior Colleges. Awards certificates, transfer associate, and terminal associate degrees. Founded 1937. Setting: 62-acre small town campus. Endowment: $4.8 million. Total enrollment: 3,572. Students come from 16 states and territories, 3% from out-of-state,

2% Native American, 1% Hispanic, 39% black, 0.4% Asian American or Pacific Islander, 0.1% international, 30% 25 or older, 12% live on campus. Core. Calendar: semesters. Academic remediation for entering students, ESL program, services for LD students, advanced placement, independent study, distance learning, summer session for credit, part-time degree program, adult/continuing education programs, co-op programs.

Entrance Requirements: Open admission. Option: early admission. Required: high school transcript, minimum 2.0 high school GPA, AC-CUPLACER. Recommended: ACT. Required for some: essay. Entrance: noncompetitive. Application deadline: Rolling.

Costs Per Year: Application fee: $0. State resident tuition: $1450 full-time, $80 per credit hour part-time. Nonresident tuition: $2740 full-time, $137 per credit hour part-time. Mandatory fees: $4 per credit hour part-time, $5 per term part-time. College room and board: $2600. Room and board charges vary according to board plan.

Collegiate Environment: Orientation program. Drama-theater group, choral group, student-run newspaper, radio station. Social organizations: 22 open to all. Most popular organizations: Phi Theta Kappa, Vocational Industrial Clubs of America, Health Occupations Students of America, Organization of Student Nurses, Distributive Education Clubs of America. Major annual events: Spring Fest, Octoberfest, Fall Picnic. Student services: health clinic, personal-psychological counseling. Campus security: 24-hour patrols, student patrols. 360 college housing spaces available; all were occupied in 2003-04. No special consideration for freshman housing applicants. Options: coed, men-only, women-only housing available. L.O. Todd Library with 50,000 books and 600 serials. Operations spending for 2004 fiscal year: $647,419. 123 computers available on campus for general student use. A campuswide network can be accessed from student residence rooms and from off campus. Staffed computer lab on campus.

Community Environment: Neither destruction by fire during the Civil War, a riot in 1871, a yellow fever epidemic in 1878, nor a cyclone in 1906 could keep Meridian down. It survived these disasters to become the state's leading industrial city. In an area providing abundant raw agricultural and industrial materials, local industries produce wood products, clothing, clay pipes, metal windows, asphalt roofing, fabricated steel and dairy and meat products. The region also produces timber, corn, cotton and cattle. Passenger air, rail and bus service is available. The city has private hospitals. Cultural activities include Little Theatre, Symphony Orchestra, Meridian Chorale and Art Association. The economic base is evenly divided between agriculture, industry and military payrolls.

■ MILLSAPS COLLEGE J-7

1701 North State St.
Jackson, MS 39210-0001
Tel: (601)974-1000
Free: 800-352-1050
Admissions: (601)974-1050
Fax: (601)974-1059
E-mail: admissions@millsaps.edu
Web Site: http://www.millsaps.edu/

Description: Independent United Methodist, comprehensive, coed. Awards bachelor's and master's degrees. Founded 1890. Setting: 100-acre urban campus. Endowment: $90.3 million. Educational spending for 2005 fiscal year: $9919 per student. Total enrollment: 1,154. Faculty: 97 (92 full-time, 5 part-time). Student-undergrad faculty ratio is 12:1. 1,008 applied, 82% were admitted. 38% from top 10% of their high school class, 63% from top quarter, 87% from top half. Full-time: 1,039 students, 49% women, 51% men. Part-time: 46 students, 46% women, 54% men. Students come from 30 states and territories, 50% from out-of-state, 0.4% Native American, 1% Hispanic, 12% black, 3% Asian American or Pacific Islander, 1% international, 4% 25 or older, 82% live on campus, 6% transferred in. Retention: 83% of full-time freshmen returned the following year. Academic areas with the most degrees conferred: business/marketing; social sciences; psychology. Core. Calendar: semesters. Services for LD students, advanced placement, accelerated degree program, self-designed majors, honors program, independent study, double major, summer session for credit, part-time degree program, adult/continuing education programs, co-op programs and internships, graduate courses open to undergrads. Off campus study at American University. Study abroad program. ROTC: Army (c).

Entrance Requirements: Options: Peterson's Universal Application, Common Application, electronic application, early admission, early action, deferred admission, international baccalaureate accepted. Required: essay, high school transcript, minimum 2.5 high school GPA, recommendations,

SAT or ACT. Recommended: interview. Entrance: moderately difficult. Application deadlines: 6/1, 12/1 for early action. Notification: continuous until 11/1, 12/15 for early action.

Costs Per Year: Application fee: $25. Comprehensive fee: $28,256 includes full-time tuition ($19,490), mandatory fees ($1200), and college room and board ($7566). College room only: $4248. Room and board charges vary according to housing facility. Part-time tuition: $604 per credit hour. Part-time mandatory fees: $30 per credit hour. Part-time tuition and fees vary according to course load.

Collegiate Environment: Orientation program. Drama-theater group, choral group, student-run newspaper. Social organizations: 80 open to all; national fraternities, national sororities; 54% of eligible men and 52% of eligible women are members. Most popular organizations: Campus Ministry Team, Major Productions, Outdoors Club, Student Body Association, Black Student Association. Major annual events: homecoming, Major Madness, Multicultural Festival. Student services: health clinic, personal-psychological counseling. Campus security: 24-hour emergency response devices and patrols, student patrols, late night transport-escort service, controlled dormitory access, self-defense education, lighted pathways. 922 college housing spaces available

Free: 800 were occupied in 2003-04. Freshmen guaranteed college housing. On-campus residence required through sophomore year. Options: coed, men-only, women-only housing available. Millsaps Wilson Library with 190,982 books, 79,248 microform titles, 874 serials, 8,409 audiovisual materials, an OPAC, and a Web page. Operations spending for 2004 fiscal year: $830,277. 120 computers available on campus for general student use. Computer purchase/lease plans available. A campuswide network can be accessed from student residence rooms and from off campus. Staffed computer lab on campus.

Community Environment: See Jackson State University.

■ MISSISSIPPI COLLEGE J-6

200 South Capitol St.
Clinton, MS 39058
Tel: (601)925-3000
Free: 800-738-1236
Admissions: (601)925-3315
Fax: (601)925-3804
E-mail: admissions@mc.edu
Web Site: http://www.mc.edu/

Description: Independent Southern Baptist, comprehensive, coed. Awards bachelor's, master's, and first professional degrees. Founded 1826. Setting: 320-acre suburban campus. Endowment: $42.6 million. Educational spending for 2005 fiscal year: $6419 per student. Total enrollment: 3,905. Faculty: 308 (161 full-time, 147 part-time). Student-undergrad faculty ratio is 11:1. 2,038 applied, 57% were admitted. 27% from top 10% of their high school class, 56% from top quarter, 80% from top half. Full-time: 2,211 students, 57% women, 43% men. Part-time: 342 students, 73% women, 27% men. Students come from 26 states and territories, 15% from out-of-state, 0.2% Native American, 1% Hispanic, 21% black, 1% Asian American or Pacific Islander, 2% international, 18% 25 or older, 61% live on campus, 15% transferred in. Retention: 73% of full-time freshmen returned the following year. Academic areas with the most degrees conferred: business/marketing; education; health professions and related sciences. Core. Calendar: semesters. Academic remediation for entering students, services for LD students, advanced placement, freshman honors college, honors program, independent study, double major, summer session for credit, part-time degree program, adult/continuing education programs, co-op programs and internships, graduate courses open to undergrads. Study abroad program. ROTC: Army (c).

Entrance Requirements: Options: Peterson's Universal Application, Common Application, electronic application, early admission, early decision, deferred admission, international baccalaureate accepted. Required: essay, high school transcript, 1 recommendation, SAT or ACT. Recommended: minimum 2.0 high school GPA, interview. Entrance: moderately difficult. Application deadlines: Rolling, Rolling for nonresidents, 12/15 for early decision. Notification: continuous, continuous for nonresidents, 12/31 for early decision.

Costs Per Year: Comprehensive fee: $18,182 includes full-time tuition ($11,600), mandatory fees ($688), and college room and board ($5894). Part-time tuition: $365 per credit hour. Part-time mandatory fees: $133 per term.

Collegiate Environment: Orientation program. Drama-theater group, choral group, marching band, student-run newspaper, radio station. Social organizations: 26 open to all. Most popular organizations: Baptist Student Union, Nenamoosha Social Tribe, Laguna Social Tribe, Civitan Service Club, Shawreth Service Club. Major annual events: Welcome Week, Homecoming, Spring Fever Week. Student services: health clinic, personal-psychological counseling. Campus security: 24-hour emergency response devices and patrols, late night transport-escort service, controlled dormitory access. 1,667 college housing spaces available; 1,475 were occupied in 2003-04. Freshmen given priority for college housing. On-campus residence required through senior year. Options: men-only, women-only housing available. Leland Speed Library plus 1 other with 362,296 books, 500,409 microform titles, 4,254 serials, 14,909 audiovisual materials, an OPAC, and a Web page. Operations spending for 2004 fiscal year: $2.2 million. 250 computers available on campus for general student use. A campuswide network can be accessed from student residence rooms and from off campus. Staffed computer lab on campus.

Community Environment: This is a suburban community located adjacent to Jackson's city limits. The climate is warm. The area has a shopping center, and rapid expansion of businesses and residential areas is anticipated. Clinton has excellent highway, air, and rail connections.

■ **MISSISSIPPI DELTA COMMUNITY COLLEGE** *F-6*

PO Box 668
Moorhead, MS 38761-0668
Tel: (662)246-6322
Admissions: (662)246-6308
Web Site: http://www.msdelta.edu/

Description: District-supported, 2-year, coed. Part of Mississippi State Board for Community and Junior Colleges. Awards certificates, diplomas, transfer associate, and terminal associate degrees. Founded 1926. Setting: 425-acre small town campus. Educational spending for 2005 fiscal year: $2372 per student. Total enrollment: 4,000. 909 applied, 100% were admitted. Students come from 6 states and territories, 19% 25 or older, 25% live on campus. Calendar: semesters. Academic remediation for entering students, advanced placement, summer session for credit, part-time degree program, adult/continuing education programs.

Entrance Requirements: Option: deferred admission. Required: high school transcript. Required for some: ACT. Entrance: noncompetitive. Application deadline: 7/27. Preference given to district residents.

Costs Per Year: Application fee: $0. State resident tuition: $1850 full-time, $83 per semester hour part-time. Nonresident tuition: $3528 full-time. Mandatory fees: $70 full-time, $10 per semester hour part-time. College room and board: $1330. College room only: $800.

Collegiate Environment: Drama-theater group, choral group, marching band, student-run newspaper. Social organizations: 16 open to all. Student services: personal-psychological counseling. Campus security: 24-hour emergency response devices and patrols, late night transport-escort service. Stanny Sanders Library with 33,020 books, 250 serials, and an OPAC. Operations spending for 2004 fiscal year: $443,719. 80 computers available on campus for general student use. Staffed computer lab on campus.

Community Environment: This is a rural area with bus and air transportation 8 miles distant. The immediate area supports a clinic and small stores. There is some part-time employment for men over 18. Better employment opportunities for students are available in the neighboring community. The city has a theater, swimming pool and tennis courts. 5 local lakes provide hunting and fishing within the area.

■ **MISSISSIPPI GULF COAST COMMUNITY COLLEGE**

PO Box 609
Perkinston, MS 39573-0609
Tel: (601)928-5211
Admissions: (601)928-6264
Fax: (601)928-6299
Web Site: http://www.mgccc.edu/

Description: District-supported, 2-year, coed. Part of Mississippi State Board for Community and Junior Colleges. Awards certificates, diplomas, transfer associate, and terminal associate degrees. Founded 1911. Setting: 600-acre small town campus with easy access to New Orleans. Endowment: $3 million. Educational spending for 2005 fiscal year: $2606 per student. Total enrollment: 7,806. Student-undergrad faculty ratio is 26:1. 2,363 applied, 100% were admitted. Full-time: 5,209 students, 61% women, 39% men. Part-time: 2,597 students, 64% women, 36% men. Students come from 15 states and territories, 4% from out-of-state, 0.4% Native American, 2% Hispanic, 19% black, 2% Asian American or Pacific Islander, 0% international, 0% 25 or older, 7% live on campus. Retention: 62% of full-time

freshmen returned the following year. Core. Calendar: semesters. Academic remediation for entering students, ESL program, services for LD students, advanced placement, honors program, distance learning, summer session for credit, part-time degree program, adult/continuing education programs, co-op programs and internships.

Entrance Requirements: Open admission except for allied health programs. Options: Common Application, electronic application, early admission. Required: high school transcript. Entrance: noncompetitive. Application deadline: Rolling. Notification: continuous. Preference given to district residents.

Costs Per Year: Application fee: $0. Area resident tuition: $1522 full-time, $75 per hour part-time. Nonresident tuition: $3368 full-time, $152 per hour part-time. College room and board: $3800.

Collegiate Environment: Orientation program. Drama-theater group, choral group, marching band, student-run newspaper. Social organizations: 33 open to all. Most popular organizations: VICA, SIFE, Student Government Association. Major annual events: homecoming, Vocational Awareness Week, Drug/Alcohol Awareness Week. Student services: personal-psychological counseling, women's center. Campus security: 24-hour emergency response devices and patrols. Options: men-only, women-only housing available. Main library plus 3 others with 100,472 books, 933 serials, and an OPAC. Operations spending for 2004 fiscal year: $949,826. 435 computers available on campus for general student use. A campuswide network can be accessed from student residence rooms. Staffed computer lab on campus.

Community Environment: The city lies 25 miles north of Gulfport. Area is reached by Interstate 10 and Highway 49. Air service is available.

■ **MISSISSIPPI STATE UNIVERSITY**

Mississippi State, MS 39762
Tel: (662)325-2323
Admissions: (662)325-2224
Fax: (662)325-3299
E-mail: admit@admissions.msstate.edu
Web Site: http://www.msstate.edu/

Description: State-supported, university, coed. Part of Mississippi Board of Trustees of State Institutions of Higher Learning. Awards bachelor's, master's, doctoral, and first professional degrees and post-master's certificates. Founded 1878. Setting: 4,200-acre small town campus. Endowment: $178.5 million. Research spending for 2004 fiscal year: $143.5 million. Educational spending for 2005 fiscal year: $6158 per student. Total enrollment: 16,101. Faculty: 1,139 (974 full-time, 165 part-time). Student-undergrad faculty ratio is 14:1. 5,778 applied, 69% were admitted. 26% from top 10% of their high school class, 55% from top quarter, 82% from top half. 33 National Merit Scholars. Full-time: 11,098 students, 47% women, 53% men. Part-time: 1,457 students, 51% women, 49% men. Students come from 51 states and territories, 39 other countries, 19% from out-of-state, 0.4% Native American, 1% Hispanic, 21% black, 1% Asian American or Pacific Islander, 1% international, 16% 25 or older, 21% live on campus, 12% transferred in. Retention: 80% of full-time freshmen returned the following year. Core. Calendar: semesters. Academic remediation for entering students, ESL program, services for LD students, advanced placement, accelerated degree program, self-designed majors, freshman honors college, honors program, independent study, distance learning, double major, summer session for credit, part-time degree program, adult/continuing education programs, co-op programs and internships, graduate courses open to undergrads. Off campus study at Meridian Campus, Vicksburg Graduate Center, Stennis Center (Hancock County). Study abroad program. ROTC: Army, Air Force.

Entrance Requirements: Options: electronic application, early admission, deferred admission, international baccalaureate accepted. Required: high school transcript, minimum 2.0 high school GPA, SAT or ACT. Required for some: recommendations. Entrance: moderately difficult. Application deadline: 8/1. Notification: continuous.

Costs Per Year: Application fee: $0. State resident tuition: $4312 full-time, $179.75 per hour part-time. Nonresident tuition: $9772 full-time, $407.25 per hour part-time. Part-time tuition varies according to course load. College room and board: $5859. College room only: $2824. Room and board charges vary according to board plan, housing facility, and student level.

Collegiate Environment: Orientation program. Drama-theater group, choral group, marching band, student-run newspaper, radio station. Social organizations: 283 open to all; national fraternities, national sororities; 17% of eligible men and 18% of eligible women are members. Most popular organizations: Student Association, Black Student Alliance, Residence Hall

Association, Fashion Board, Campus Activities Board. Major annual events: Bulldog Bash, Homecoming, athletic events. Student services: health clinic, personal-psychological counseling. Campus security: 24-hour emergency response devices and patrols, late night transport-escort service, controlled dormitory access, bicycle patrols, crime prevention program, RAD program, general law enforcement services. 3,266 college housing spaces available; 2,754 were occupied in 2003-04. Freshmen given priority for college housing. Options: coed, men-only, women-only housing available. Mitchell Memorial Library plus 2 others with 2.5 million books, 2.9 million microform titles, 18,104 serials, 137,200 audiovisual materials, an OPAC, and a Web page. Operations spending for 2004 fiscal year: $7.8 million. 2,000 computers available on campus for general student use. A campuswide network can be accessed from student residence rooms and from off campus. Staffed computer lab on campus.

■ **MISSISSIPPI UNIVERSITY FOR WOMEN** *F-12*
1100 College St., MUW-1600
Columbus, MS 39701-9998
Tel: (662)329-4750; 877-GO 2 THE W
Admissions: (601)329-7106
Fax: (662)329-7297
E-mail: admissions@muw.edu
Web Site: http://www.muw.edu/
Description: State-supported, comprehensive, coed. Part of Mississippi Institutions of Higher Learning. Awards associate, bachelor's, and master's degrees. Founded 1884. Setting: 110-acre small town campus. Endowment: $16.2 million. Educational spending for 2005 fiscal year: $1835 per student. Total enrollment: 2,328. 609 applied, 65% were admitted. 60% from top quarter of their high school class, 88% from top half. 10 class presidents, 23 valedictorians, 26 student government officers. Students come from 26 states and territories, 11% from out-of-state, 0.4% Native American, 1% Hispanic, 28% black, 1% Asian American or Pacific Islander, 2% international, 42% 25 or older, 21% live on campus. Retention: 70% of full-time freshmen returned the following year. Core. Calendar: semesters. Academic remediation for entering students, ESL program, services for LD students, advanced placement, accelerated degree program, freshman honors college, honors program, distance learning, double major, summer session for credit, part-time degree program, adult/continuing education programs, co-op programs and internships, graduate courses open to undergrads. Off campus study at Mississippi State University. Study abroad program. ROTC: Army (c), Air Force (c).
Entrance Requirements: Options: Peterson's Universal Application, Common Application, electronic application, early admission. Required: high school transcript. Recommended: SAT or ACT. Required for some: minimum 2.0 high school GPA, recommendations, rank in upper 50% of high school class, SAT or ACT. Entrance: moderately difficult. Application deadline: Rolling. Notification: continuous.
Collegiate Environment: Orientation program. Drama-theater group, choral group, student-run newspaper, radio station. Social organizations: 84 open to all; national fraternities, national sororities, local fraternities, local sororities; 10% of eligible men and 20% of eligible women are members. Most popular organizations: Student Government Association, Union Advisory Cabinet, Black Student Council, W Angels, Student Alumni Ambassadors. Major annual events: homecoming, Oktoberfest, Gala Fall Weekend. Student services: health clinic, personal-psychological counseling. Campus security: 24-hour patrols, student patrols, late night transport-escort service. Options: men-only, women-only housing available. John Clayton Fant Memorial Library with 426,543 books, 602,113 microform titles, 1,629 serials, 164 audiovisual materials, and an OPAC. Operations spending for 2004 fiscal year: $708,933. 250 computers available on campus for general student use. A campuswide network can be accessed from student residence rooms and from off campus. Staffed computer lab on campus.

■ **MISSISSIPPI VALLEY STATE UNIVERSITY** *F-6*
14000 Hwy. 82 West
Itta Bena, MS 38941-1400
Tel: (662)254-9041
Admissions: (662)254-3344
Fax: (662)254-7900
E-mail: nbtaylor@mvsu.edu
Web Site: http://www.mvsu.edu/
Description: State-supported, comprehensive, coed. Part of Mississippi Institutions of Higher Learning. Awards bachelor's and master's degrees. Founded 1946. Setting: 450-acre small town campus. Research spending

for 2004 fiscal year: $257,978. Total enrollment: 3,165. Faculty: 183 (117 full-time, 66 part-time). Student-undergrad faculty ratio is 19:1. 4,832 applied, 25% were admitted. Full-time: 2,434 students, 67% women, 33% men. Part-time: 314 students, 79% women, 21% men. Students come from 24 states and territories, 1 other country, 7% from out-of-state, 0% Native American, 0.3% Hispanic, 94% black, 0.04% Asian American or Pacific Islander, 0% international, 45% 25 or older, 30% live on campus, 8% transferred in. Retention: 59% of full-time freshmen returned the following year. Academic areas with the most degrees conferred: education; public administration and social services; business/marketing. Core. Calendar: semesters. Academic remediation for entering students, freshman honors college, honors program, summer session for credit, part-time degree program, adult/continuing education programs, co-op programs and internships, graduate courses open to undergrads. ROTC: Army, Air Force.
Entrance Requirements: Option: deferred admission. Required: high school transcript, SAT or ACT. Recommended: interview. Required for some: 2.5 GPA for non-residents. Entrance: minimally difficult. Application deadline: Rolling. Notification: continuous.
Costs Per Year: Application fee: $0. State resident tuition: $4024 full-time, $168 per semester hour part-time. Nonresident tuition: $9282 full-time, $219 per semester hour part-time. Mandatory fees: $50 full-time, $25 per term part-time. Full-time tuition and fees vary according to course load and degree level. Part-time tuition and fees vary according to course load and degree level. College room and board: $3946. College room only: $2142. Room and board charges vary according to board plan and housing facility.
Collegiate Environment: Orientation program. Drama-theater group, choral group, marching band, student-run newspaper, radio station. Social organizations: 53 open to all; national fraternities, national sororities, local fraternities, local sororities; 20% of eligible men and 25% of eligible women are members. Most popular organizations: Student Government Association, Baptist Student Union, Black Student Fellowship, National Education Association. Major annual events: Homecoming, Black History Month, Founders' Day. Student services: health clinic, personal-psychological counseling. Campus security: 24-hour emergency response devices and patrols, controlled dormitory access. 1,800 college housing spaces available; 1,048 were occupied in 2003-04. No special consideration for freshman housing applicants. On-campus residence required through senior year. Options: men-only, women-only housing available. James H. White Library with 101,109 books, 355,603 microform titles, 347 serials, 500 audiovisual materials, an OPAC, and a Web page. Operations spending for 2004 fiscal year: $904,678. 250 computers available on campus for general student use. A campuswide network can be accessed from student residence rooms and from off campus. Staffed computer lab on campus.
Community Environment: This is a rural community with a mild, temperate climate. Bus service provides transportation for the city and adjacent areas. Community services within the immediate area include churches of major denominations and a clinic. Shopping facilities are available within the surrounding communities. There is no part-time employment available for students.

■ **NORTHEAST MISSISSIPPI COMMUNITY COLLEGE** *B-12*
101 Cunningham Blvd.
Booneville, MS 38829
Tel: (662)728-7751
Free: 800-555-2154
Fax: (662)728-1165
E-mail: lgibson@necc.cc.ms.us
Web Site: http://www.nemcc.edu/
Description: State-supported, 2-year, coed. Part of Mississippi State Board for Community and Junior Colleges. Awards certificates, transfer associate, and terminal associate degrees. Founded 1948. Setting: 100-acre small town campus. Total enrollment: 3,224. Full-time: 2,777 students, 58% women, 42% men. Part-time: 447 students, 63% women, 37% men. Students come from 18 states and territories, 0.4% Native American, 0.4% Hispanic, 18% black, 0.4% Asian American or Pacific Islander, 0% international, 20% 25 or older, 25% live on campus. Core. Calendar: semesters. Academic remediation for entering students, services for LD students, advanced placement, self-designed majors, summer session for credit, part-time degree program, adult/continuing education programs, co-op programs.
Entrance Requirements: Open admission. Option: early admission. Required for some: SAT or ACT. Entrance: noncompetitive. Application deadline: Rolling. Notification: continuous.
Collegiate Environment: Orientation program. Drama-theater group, choral group, marching band, student-run newspaper. Student services: personal-

psychological counseling. Campus security: 24-hour patrols, student patrols, controlled dormitory access. 724 college housing spaces available; all were occupied in 2003-04. Eula Dees Library with 29,879 books and 378 serials. 350 computers available on campus for general student use. Staffed computer lab on campus.

Community Environment: The city is located in the northeast corner of Mississippi, 100 miles southeast of Memphis, Tennessee. It has a warm and pleasant climate.

■ NORTHWEST MISSISSIPPI COMMUNITY COLLEGE *B-8*

4975 Hwy. 51 North
Senatobia, MS 38668-1701
Tel: (662)562-3200
Admissions: (662)562-3222
Fax: (662)562-3911
Web Site: http://www.northwestms.edu/

Description: State and locally supported, 2-year, coed. Part of Mississippi State Board for Community and Junior Colleges. Awards transfer associate and terminal associate degrees. Founded 1927. Setting: 75-acre rural campus with easy access to Memphis. Total enrollment: 6,300. 2,000 applied, 100% were admitted. Core. Calendar: semesters. Academic remediation for entering students, services for LD students, honors program, summer session for credit, part-time degree program, adult/continuing education programs. ROTC: Air Force.

Entrance Requirements: Open admission. Options: Common Application, early admission, deferred admission. Required: high school transcript. Placement: ACT required. Entrance: noncompetitive. Application deadline: 9/7. Notification: continuous.

Collegiate Environment: Drama-theater group, choral group, marching band, student-run newspaper, radio station. Major annual events: Homecoming, Career Week, Senior Round-Ups. Student services: health clinic. Campus security: 24-hour emergency response devices, late night transport-escort service, controlled dormitory access. R. C. Pugh Library with 38,000 books and 325 serials. 50 computers available on campus for general student use.

Community Environment: Senatobia is the seat of Tate County, lying 40 miles south of Memphis, Tennessee. The area is served by Illinois Central Railroad. The city itself is located off Interstate Highway 55. Nearby is Arkabutla Reservoir and Dam, a well-known recreation facility.

■ PEARL RIVER COMMUNITY COLLEGE *O-9*

101 Hwy. 11 North
Poplarville, MS 39470
Tel: (601)403-1000
Admissions: (601)795-6801
Fax: (601)403-1135
E-mail: dford@prcc.cc.ms.us
Web Site: http://www.prcc.edu/

Description: State and locally supported, 2-year, coed. Part of Mississippi State Board for Community and Junior Colleges. Awards certificates, transfer associate, and terminal associate degrees. Founded 1909. Setting: 240-acre rural campus with easy access to New Orleans. Total enrollment: 3,700. Students come from 11 states and territories, 27% 25 or older, 20% live on campus. Core. Calendar: semesters. Academic remediation for entering students, advanced placement, self-designed majors, summer session for credit, part-time degree program, adult/continuing education programs, co-op programs.

Entrance Requirements: Open admission except for nursing, data processing programs. Options: Peterson's Universal Application, early admission, deferred admission. Required: high school transcript. Placement: ACT required. Entrance: minimally difficult. Application deadline: Rolling. Notification: continuous until 8/15. Preference given to state residents.

Collegiate Environment: Drama-theater group, choral group, marching band, student-run newspaper. Social organizations: 4 open to all. Major annual events: Homecoming, Fall Fest, Spring Fest. Student services: health clinic, personal-psychological counseling, women's center. Campus security: 24-hour patrols. Pearl River Community College Library with 40,000 books and 340 serials. 90 computers available on campus for general student use. Staffed computer lab on campus.

Community Environment: Poplarville is located in the southern portion of the state and has a temperate climate. New Orleans may be reached 70 miles southwest via Interstate Highway 59. Poplarville has its own hospital.

■ RUST COLLEGE *B-9*

150 Rust Ave.
Holly Springs, MS 38635-2328

Tel: (662)252-8000; 888-886-8492
Admissions: (601)252-8000
Fax: (662)252-6107
E-mail: jmcdonald@rustcollege.edu
Web Site: http://www.rustcollege.edu/

Description: Independent United Methodist, 4-year, coed. Awards associate and bachelor's degrees. Founded 1866. Setting: 126-acre rural campus with easy access to Memphis. Endowment: $19 million. Research spending for 2004 fiscal year: $400. Total enrollment: 1,001. Student-undergrad faculty ratio is 15:1. 3,641 applied, 39% were admitted. 15% from top 10% of their high school class, 30% from top quarter, 50% from top half. Full-time: 839 students, 65% women, 35% men. Part-time: 162 students, 64% women, 36% men. Students come from 22 states and territories, 7 other countries, 31% from out-of-state, 93% black, 6% international, 27% 25 or older, 65% live on campus, 3% transferred in. Retention: 58% of full-time freshmen returned the following year. Academic areas with the most degrees conferred: computer and information sciences; biological/life sciences; communications/journalism. Core. Calendar: semesters. Academic remediation for entering students, accelerated degree program, honors program, independent study, summer session for credit, part-time degree program, adult/continuing education programs, co-op programs and internships. Study abroad program. ROTC: Army.

Entrance Requirements: Options: Peterson's Universal Application, Common Application, deferred admission. Required: high school transcript, minimum 2.0 high school GPA, 2 recommendations, ACT. Required for some: essay. Entrance: moderately difficult. Application deadline: 7/15. Notification: 7/15.

Costs Per Year: Application fee: $10. Comprehensive fee: $8950 includes full-time tuition ($6200) and college room and board ($2750). College room only: $1212. Part-time tuition: $267 per credit hour. Part-time tuition varies according to class time and course load.

Collegiate Environment: Orientation program. Drama-theater group, choral group, student-run newspaper, radio station. Social organizations: 32 open to all; national fraternities, national sororities; 10% of eligible men and 14% of eligible women are members. Major annual events: Founders' Day, Commencement, Career Day. Campus security: 24-hour emergency response devices and patrols, late night transport-escort service, controlled dormitory access. 856 college housing spaces available; 651 were occupied in 2003-04. Freshmen guaranteed college housing. Options: men-only, women-only housing available. Leontyne Price Library with 123,055 books, 340 serials, 1,448 audiovisual materials, and an OPAC. Operations spending for 2004 fiscal year: $408,633. 150 computers available on campus for general student use. A campuswide network can be accessed from student residence rooms and from off campus. Staffed computer lab on campus.

Community Environment: A typical antebellum town, Holly Springs grew up during the great cotton boom before the Civil War. The fine old mansions and churches of the town reflect the prosperity of the cotton era. There are shopping areas in nearby Memphis. No part-time employment is available for students.

■ SOUTHEASTERN BAPTIST COLLEGE *L-10*

4229 Hwy. 15 North
Laurel, MS 39440-1096
Tel: (601)426-6346

Description: Independent Baptist, 4-year, coed. Awards associate and bachelor's degrees. Founded 1949. Setting: 23-acre small town campus. Endowment: $177,930. Total enrollment: 104. 19 applied, 100% were admitted. 31% live on campus. Retention: 50% of full-time freshmen returned the following year. Core. Calendar: semesters. Academic remediation for entering students, advanced placement, summer session for credit, part-time degree program, adult/continuing education programs.

Entrance Requirements: Open admission. Options: early admission, deferred admission. Required: high school transcript, 2 recommendations. Required for some: interview. Entrance: noncompetitive. Application deadline: Rolling.

Costs Per Year: Application fee: $25. Tuition: $140 per semester hour part-time.

Collegiate Environment: Choral group. A. R. Reddin Memorial Library with 24,119 books and 314 serials. Operations spending for 2004 fiscal year: $26,109.

Community Environment: Laurel's growth from a small village in 1900 to its present metropolitan size has been due to its pine forests and oil development. Lumber represents an important industry, but other firms manufacture clothing, machines, doors, furniture, agricultural implements, distribution transformers, oil well drilling equipment, walk-in refrigerators, condiments and janitorial supplies. There is a complete recreation program in the city, and it is close to resorts and state parks. Railroad, bus and air transportation is available in the immediate area. Laurel is considered the medical center of the surrounding area.

■ SOUTHWEST MISSISSIPPI COMMUNITY COLLEGE *N-6*
College Dr.
Summit, MS 39666
Tel: (601)276-2000
Admissions: (601)276-2001
Fax: (601)276-3888
E-mail: mattc@smcc.edu
Web Site: http://www.smcc.cc.ms.us/
Description: State and locally supported, 2-year, coed. Part of Mississippi State Board for Community and Junior Colleges. Awards certificates, transfer associate, and terminal associate degrees. Founded 1918. Setting: 701-acre rural campus. Total enrollment: 1,895. Student-undergrad faculty ratio is 25:1. Students come from 6 states and territories, 10% from out-of-state, 1% Native American, 0% Hispanic, 40% black, 0.3% Asian American or Pacific Islander, 31% 25 or older, 35% live on campus. Core. Calendar: semesters. Academic remediation for entering students, distance learning, summer session for credit, part-time degree program, adult/continuing education programs.
Entrance Requirements: Open admission. Required: high school transcript. Entrance: noncompetitive. Application deadline: 8/1.
Costs Per Year: Application fee: $0. State resident tuition: $1700 full-time, $75 per hour part-time. Nonresident tuition: $3900 full-time, $170 per hour part-time. Mandatory fees: $100 full-time, $50 per term part-time. College room and board: $2180.
Collegiate Environment: Choral group, marching band, student-run newspaper. Campus security: 24-hour patrols. Library Learning Resources Center (LLRC) with 34,000 books, 150 serials, and an OPAC. 300 computers available on campus for general student use. A campuswide network can be accessed from off-campus. Staffed computer lab on campus.
Community Environment: Summit is a suburban area near McComb, Mississippi. The city is served by bus and rail. Health services, a library, and churches, are to be found in the neighboring city. There are shopping facilities in the immediate area. Some part-time employment is available. Recreation in the area includes boating, fishing and camping.

■ TOUGALOO COLLEGE
500 West County Line Rd.
Tougaloo, MS 39174
Tel: (601)977-7700; 888-42GALOO
Admissions: (601)977-7765
Fax: (601)977-7739
Web Site: http://www.tougaloo.edu/
Description: Independent, 4-year, coed, affiliated with United Church of Christ. Awards associate and bachelor's degrees. Founded 1869. Setting: 500-acre suburban campus. Endowment: $4.7 million. Research spending for 2004 fiscal year: $236,232. Total enrollment: 940. 627 applied, 99% were admitted. 14% from top 10% of their high school class, 34% from top quarter, 55% from top half. Full-time: 883 students, 69% women, 31% men. Part-time: 57 students, 77% women, 23% men. Students come from 24 states and territories, 1 other country, 14% from out-of-state, 0% Native American, 0% Hispanic, 99% black, 0% Asian American or Pacific Islander, 1% international, 10% 25 or older, 5% transferred in. Retention: 78% of full-time freshmen returned the following year. Core. Calendar: semesters. Academic remediation for entering students, accelerated degree program, self-designed majors, honors program, part-time degree program, adult/continuing education programs, co-op programs and internships. Off campus study at Brown University, New York University, Boston University. Study abroad program. ROTC: Army.
Entrance Requirements: Options: Peterson's Universal Application, Common Application, early admission. Required: high school transcript, minimum 2.0 high school GPA, SAT or ACT. Entrance: minimally difficult. Application deadline: Rolling. Notification: continuous.
Costs Per Year: Application fee: $5. Comprehensive fee: $15,497 includes full-time tuition ($8800), mandatory fees ($477), and college room and board ($6220). College room only: $4400. Part-time tuition: $367 per credit hour.
Collegiate Environment: Orientation program. Drama-theater group, choral group, student-run newspaper. Social organizations: 8 open to all; national fraternities, national sororities; 30% of eligible men and 35% of eligible

women are members. Most popular organizations: concert choir, Student Government Association, gospel choir, NAACP, Pre-Alumni Club. Major annual events: Founders' Weekend, Humanities Festival, Faculty Recognition Day. Student services: health clinic, personal-psychological counseling. Campus security: 24-hour emergency response devices and patrols. Options: men-only, women-only housing available. L. Zenobiz Coleman Library with 137,000 books and 432 serials. 43 computers available on campus for general student use. Staffed computer lab on campus.
Community Environment: See Jackson State University.

■ UNIVERSITY OF MISSISSIPPI
University, MS 38677
Tel: (662)915-7211
Admissions: (662)915-7226
Fax: (662)915-5869
E-mail: admissions@olemiss.edu
Web Site: http://www.olemiss.edu/
Description: State-supported, university, coed. Part of Mississippi Institutions of Higher Learning. Awards bachelor's, master's, doctoral, and first professional degrees. Founded 1844. Setting: 2,500-acre small town campus with easy access to Memphis. Research spending for 2004 fiscal year: $47.2 million. Educational spending for 2005 fiscal year: $7241 per student. Total enrollment: 14,901. Faculty: (622 full-time). Student-undergrad faculty ratio is 19:1. 6,763 applied, 73% were admitted. 28 National Merit Scholars. Full-time: 11,143 students, 53% women, 47% men. Part-time: 1,054 students, 55% women, 45% men. Students come from 47 states and territories, 67 other countries, 32% from out-of-state, 0.3% Native American, 1% Hispanic, 13% black, 1% Asian American or Pacific Islander, 1% international, 33% live on campus, 10% transferred in. Retention: 79% of full-time freshmen returned the following year. Academic areas with the most degrees conferred: business/marketing; education; social sciences. Core. Calendar: semesters. Academic remediation for entering students, ESL program, services for LD students, advanced placement, accelerated degree program, freshman honors college, honors program, independent study, double major, summer session for credit, part-time degree program, adult/continuing education programs, internships, graduate courses open to undergrads. Study abroad program. ROTC: Army, Air Force.
Entrance Requirements: Options: electronic application, early admission. Required: high school transcript, minimum 2.0 high school GPA. Recommended: SAT or ACT. Entrance: moderately difficult. Application deadline: 7/20. Notification: continuous until 8/16.
Costs Per Year: Application fee: $25, $40 for nonresidents. State resident tuition: $4320 full-time, $180 per credit part-time. Nonresident tuition: $9744 full-time, $406 per credit part-time. College room and board: $5762. College room only: $2972. Room and board charges vary according to board plan and housing facility.
Collegiate Environment: Orientation program. Drama-theater group, choral group, marching band, student-run newspaper, radio station. Social organizations: 200 open to all; national fraternities, national sororities. Most popular organizations: Associated Student Body, School Spirit Club, sport clubs, Black Student Union, Student Programming Board. Major annual events: Homecoming, Red/Blue Week followed by the Red/Blue Game, Awards of Distinction. Student services: legal services, health clinic, personal-psychological counseling, women's center. Campus security: 24-hour emergency response devices and patrols, late night transport-escort service, controlled dormitory access, crime prevention programs. 3,700 college housing spaces available; 3,400 were occupied in 2003-04. Freshmen guaranteed college housing. On-campus residence required in freshman year. Options: men-only, women-only housing available. J. D. Williams Library plus 3 others with 1.3 million books, 3.5 million microform titles, 11,600 serials, 156,603 audiovisual materials, an OPAC, and a Web page. Operations spending for 2004 fiscal year: $8.3 million. 3,500 computers available on campus for general student use. Computer purchase/lease plans available. A campuswide network can be accessed from student residence rooms and from off campus. Staffed computer lab on campus.
Community Environment: University is a part of Oxford. Located in a cotton, corn and cattle region, Oxford is the seat of Lafayette County. Annual average temperature is 80 degrees in July and 40 degrees in January, with average rainfall 54.55 inches. Total snowfall yearly averages 1.2 inches. Bus service and shuttle service from Memphis Airport are available to the city. Area has 3 recreational parks, swimming pools, movie theaters, bowling and golf facilities. Oxford is near Holly Springs National Forest which encompasses over 90,000 acres and numerous lakes. The lakes provide excellent hunting, swimming, boating and vacation facilities.

■ **UNIVERSITY OF MISSISSIPPI MEDICAL CENTER** *J-7*
2500 North State St.
Jackson, MS 39216-4505
Tel: (601)984-1000
Admissions: (601)984-1080
Fax: (601)984-1080
Web Site: http://umc.edu/
Description: State-supported, upper-level, coed. Administratively affiliated with University of Mississippi. Awards bachelor's, master's, doctoral, and first professional degrees. Founded 1955. Setting: 164-acre urban campus. Endowment: $33.5 million. Research spending for 2004 fiscal year: $35.3 million. Educational spending for 2005 fiscal year: $5134 per student. Total enrollment: 1,993. Faculty: 844 (683 full-time, 161 part-time). Student-undergrad faculty ratio is 2:1. Full-time: 452 students, 79% women, 21% men. Part-time: 71 students, 85% women, 15% men. 0% from out-of-state, 1% Hispanic, 19% black, 1% Asian American or Pacific Islander, 0% international, 62% transferred in. Academic area with the most degrees conferred: health professions and related sciences. Calendar: semesters. Services for LD students, distance learning, internships. Study abroad program.
Costs Per Year: Application fee: $10. State resident tuition: $3519 full-time, $141 per credit part-time. Nonresident tuition: $7195 full-time, $294 per credit part-time. Full-time tuition varies according to program. Part-time tuition varies according to course load and program. College room only: $3354. Room charges vary according to housing facility.
Collegiate Environment: Orientation program. Student-run newspaper. Student services: health clinic, personal-psychological counseling. Campus security: 24-hour emergency response devices and patrols, late night transport-escort service, controlled dormitory access. 132 college housing spaces available; 80 were occupied in 2003-04. Option: women-only housing available. Rowland Medical Library with 310,016 books, 62,134 microform titles, 2,732 serials, 18,076 audiovisual materials, an OPAC, and a Web page. Operations spending for 2004 fiscal year: $3.3 million. 90 computers available on campus for general student use. Computer purchase/lease plans available. A campuswide network can be accessed from off-campus. Staffed computer lab on campus.
Community Environment: See Jackson State University.

■ **UNIVERSITY OF SOUTHERN MISSISSIPPI** *M-10*
118 College Dr.
Hattiesburg, MS 39406-0001
Tel: (601)266-7011
Admissions: (601)266-5000
E-mail: kristi.motter@usm.edu
Web Site: http://www.usm.edu/
Description: State-supported, university, coed. Awards bachelor's, master's, and doctoral degrees. Founded 1910. Setting: 1,090-acre suburban campus with easy access to New Orleans. Research spending for 2004 fiscal year: $38.9 million. Educational spending for 2005 fiscal year: $7146 per student. Total enrollment: 15,030. Faculty: 846 (713 full-time, 133 part-time). Student-undergrad faculty ratio is 18:1. 5,153 applied, 61% were admitted. 19% from top 10% of their high school class, 47% from top quarter, 79% from top half. Full-time: 10,727 students, 60% women, 40% men. Part-time: 1,741 students, 63% women, 37% men. Students come from 42 states and territories, 40 other countries, 25% from out-of-state, 0.4% Native American, 1% Hispanic, 28% black, 1% Asian American or Pacific Islander, 1% international, 24% 25 or older, 31% live on campus, 14% transferred in. Retention: 75% of full-time freshmen returned the following year. Academic areas with the most degrees conferred: business/marketing; education; health professions and related sciences. Core. Calendar: semesters. Academic remediation for entering students, ESL program, services for LD students, advanced placement, accelerated degree program, honors program, distance learning, double major, summer session for credit, part-time degree program, adult/continuing education programs, co-op programs, graduate courses open to undergrads. Off campus study at Gulf Coast Research Laboratory, Marine Science Laboratory, Stennis Space Center. Study abroad program. ROTC: Army, Air Force.
Entrance Requirements: Options: Common Application, electronic application, early admission, deferred admission. Required: high school transcript, minimum 2.0 high school GPA, SAT or ACT. Required for some: interview. Entrance: moderately difficult. Application deadline: Rolling. Notification: continuous.
Costs Per Year: Application fee: $0. State resident tuition: $4312 full-time,

$180 per credit hour part-time. Nonresident tuition: $9742 full-time, $407 per credit hour part-time. Mandatory fees: $30 full-time. College room and board: $5800. College room only: $2620.
Collegiate Environment: Orientation program. Drama-theater group, choral group, marching band, student-run newspaper, radio station. Social organizations: 200 open to all; national fraternities, national sororities; 16% of eligible men and 15% of eligible women are members. Most popular organizations: University Activities Council, residence halls associations. Major annual events: Fall Festival, UAC sponsored events, homecoming. Student services: legal services, health clinic, personal-psychological counseling, women's center. Campus security: 24-hour emergency response devices and patrols, late night transport-escort service, controlled dormitory access. 3,932 college housing spaces available; 3,469 were occupied in 2003-04. No special consideration for freshman housing applicants. Options: men-only, women-only housing available. Cook Memorial Library plus 4 others with 1.4 million books, 4.9 million microform titles, 21,259 serials, 19,452 audiovisual materials, an OPAC, and a Web page. Operations spending for 2004 fiscal year: $4.5 million. 600 computers available on campus for general student use. Staffed computer lab on campus.
Community Environment: Primarily a thriving industrial city, Hattiesburg produces chemicals, clothing, concrete and corrugated containers, and has food processing plants, lumber mills and an oil refinery. Passenger bus, rail and air service is accessible. The city is a well-rounded community with a splendid balance among agriculture, commerce and industry. There are a public library and two hospitals located within the city limits. Each year, the Hattiesburg Concert Association brings concerts, symphonies and choral groups to the city. A full-time recreation department is operated, with both indoor and outdoor programs year-round. There is good hunting and fishing in the general area.

■ **VIRGINIA COLLEGE AT JACKSON** *J-7*
5360 I-55 North
Jackson, MS 39211
Tel: (601)977-0960
Fax: (601)956-4325
Web Site: http://www.vc.edu/
Description: Proprietary, 2-year, coed. Awards diplomas and terminal associate degrees. Founded 2000. Setting: 3-acre urban campus. Total enrollment: 1,108.
Entrance Requirements: Required: high school transcript, interview, GED, CPAt.
Collegiate Environment: Campus security: 24-hour emergency response devices and patrols. College housing not available.

■ **WESLEY COLLEGE** *K-7*
PO Box 1070
Florence, MS 39073-1070
Tel: (601)845-2265
Free: 800-748-9972
Fax: (601)845-2266
E-mail: admissions@wesleycollege.edu
Web Site: http://www.wesleycollege.com/
Description: Independent Congregational Methodist, 4-year, coed. Awards bachelor's degrees. Founded 1944. Setting: 40-acre small town campus with easy access to Jackson. Endowment: $353,038. Educational spending for 2005 fiscal year: $10,250 per student. Total enrollment: 80. Student-undergrad faculty ratio is 6:1. 22 applied, 100% were admitted. Full-time: 60 students, 43% women, 57% men. Part-time: 20 students, 40% women, 60% men. Students come from 10 states and territories, 3 other countries, 35% from out-of-state, 0% Native American, 4% Hispanic, 31% black, 1% Asian American or Pacific Islander, 3% international, 40% 25 or older, 69% live on campus, 13% transferred in. Core. Calendar: semesters. Academic remediation for entering students, advanced placement, independent study, double major, part-time degree program, adult/continuing education programs, internships.
Entrance Requirements: Open admission. Required: essay, high school transcript, 3 recommendations, SAT or ACT. Recommended: interview. Entrance: noncompetitive. Application deadline: 8/1. Notification: continuous.
Costs Per Year: Application fee: $20. Comprehensive fee: $10,980 includes full-time tuition ($6900), mandatory fees ($700), and college room and board ($3380). Part-time tuition: $230 per credit hour.
Collegiate Environment: Orientation program. Drama-theater group, choral group. Social organizations: 2 open to all. Most popular organizations: Missionary Prayer Band, Ministerial Union. Major annual events: Youth Retreat,

Missions Convention. Campus security: 24-hour emergency response devices. 60 college housing spaces available; 30 were occupied in 2003-04. Options: men-only, women-only housing available. 25,000 books, 250 microform titles, 96 serials, and 51 audiovisual materials. Operations spending for 2004 fiscal year: $28,515. 2 computers available on campus for general student use. Staffed computer lab on campus.

■ **WILLIAM CAREY COLLEGE** *M-10*
498 Tuscan Ave.
Hattiesburg, MS 39401-5499
Tel: (601)318-6051
Fax: (601)318-6454
E-mail: admiss@mail.wmcarey.edu
Web Site: http://www.wmcarey.edu/
Description: Independent Southern Baptist, comprehensive, coed. Awards bachelor's and master's degrees. Founded 1906. Setting: 64-acre small town campus with easy access to New Orleans. Endowment: $7 million. Educational spending for 2005 fiscal year: $3138 per student. Total enrollment: 2,758. 276 applied, 71% were admitted. Full-time: 1,576 students, 72% women, 28% men. Part-time: 277 students, 78% women, 22% men. Students come from 18 states and territories, 17 other countries, 25% from out-of-state, 0.5% Native American, 2% Hispanic, 34% black, 1% Asian American or Pacific Islander, 2% international, 42% 25 or older, 23% live on campus, 21% transferred in. Retention: 67% of full-time freshmen returned the following year. Core. Calendar: trimesters. Academic remediation for entering students, services for LD students, advanced placement, accelerated degree program, honors program, independent study, distance learning, double major, summer session for credit, part-time degree program, adult/continuing education programs, internships, graduate courses open to undergrads. Off campus study. ROTC: Army (c), Air Force (c).

Entrance Requirements: Options: Common Application, early admission, deferred admission, international baccalaureate accepted. Required: high school transcript, SAT or ACT. Recommended: minimum 2.0 high school GPA. Required for some: recommendations. Entrance: moderately difficult. Application deadline: Rolling. Notification: continuous until 8/15.
Costs Per Year: Application fee: $20. Comprehensive fee: $11,880 includes full-time tuition ($8100), mandatory fees ($315), and college room and board ($3465). College room only: $1305. Full-time tuition and fees vary according to degree level and location. Room and board charges vary according to board plan, housing facility, and location. Part-time tuition: $270 per hour. Part-time mandatory fees: $105 per term. Part-time tuition and fees vary according to degree level and location.
Collegiate Environment: Orientation program. Drama-theater group, choral group, student-run newspaper. Social organizations: 32 open to all; local fraternities, local sororities; 4% of eligible men and 59% of eligible women are members. Most popular organizations: Student Government Association, Baptist Student Union, Phi Beta Lambda, intramurals, Hope Project. Major annual events: Homecoming, Honors Convocation, Carey Fest. Student services: personal-psychological counseling. Campus security: 24-hour patrols, controlled dormitory access. 612 college housing spaces available; 419 were occupied in 2003-04. Freshmen guaranteed college housing. On-campus residence required through senior year. Options: men-only, women-only housing available. Smith-Rouse Library with 98,139 books, 15,568 microform titles, 472 serials, 789 audiovisual materials, an OPAC, and a Web page. Operations spending for 2004 fiscal year: $500,171. 50 computers available on campus for general student use. A campuswide network can be accessed from student residence rooms and from off campus. Staffed computer lab on campus.
Community Environment: See University of Southern Mississippi.

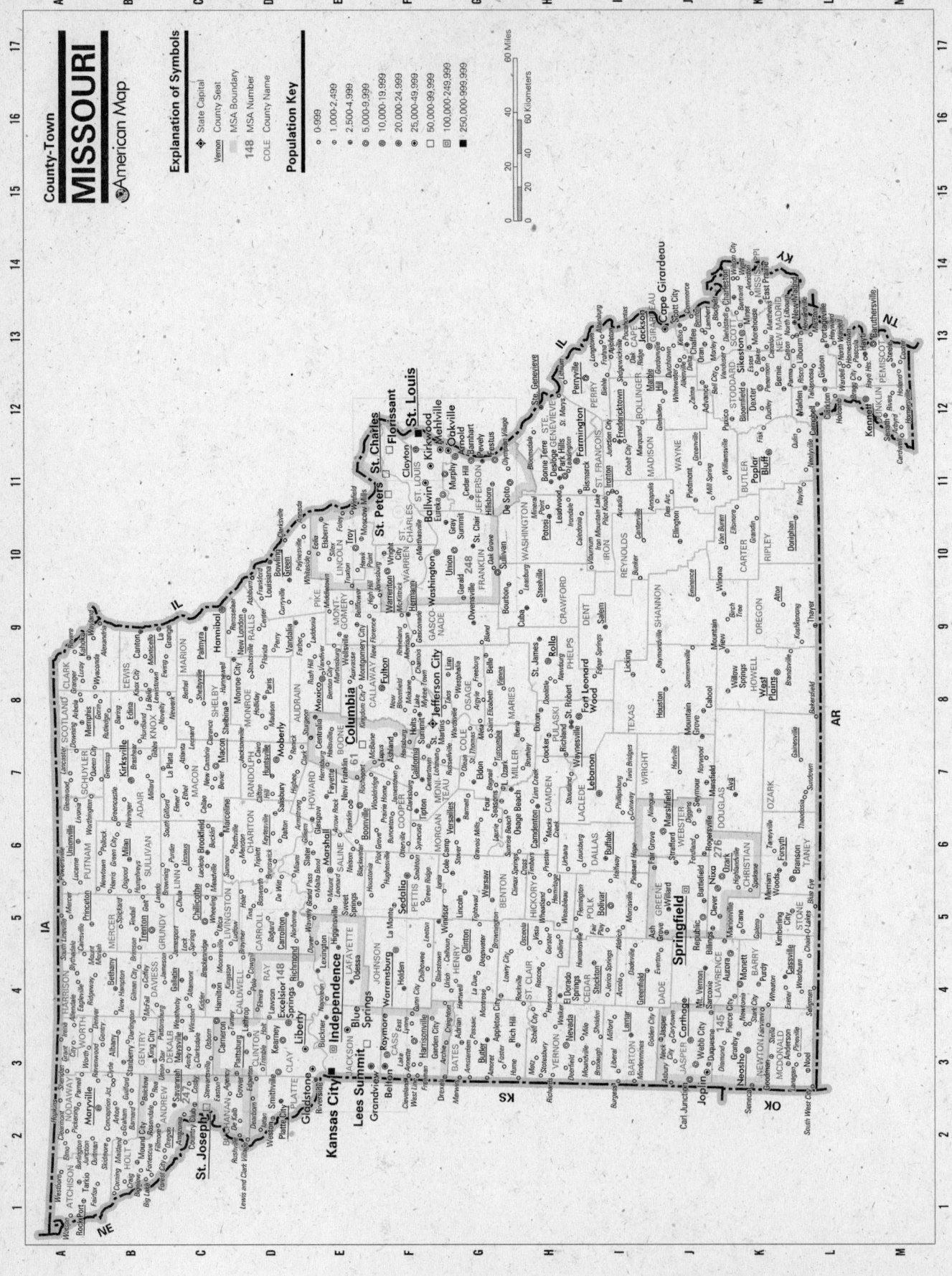

MISSOURI
County-Town
● American Map

Explanation of Symbols

◆ State Capital
Vernon County Seat
148 MSA Number
COLE County Name

Population Key

○ 0-999
⊙ 1,000-2,499
⊙ 2,500-4,999
⊛ 5,000-9,999
⊛ 10,000-19,999
⊛ 20,000-24,999
⊛ 25,000-49,999
□ 50,000-99,999
⊡ 100,000-249,999
■ 250,000-999,999

60 Miles
60 Kilometers

■ **ALLIED COLLEGE** *R-15*
13723 Riverport Dr., Ste. 103
Maryland Heights, MO 63043
Tel: (314)739-4450
Fax: (314)739-5133
Web Site: http://www.hightechinstitute.edu/
Description: Proprietary, 2-year, coed.

■ **AVIATION INSTITUTE OF MAINTENANCE-KANSAS CITY** *E-3*
3130 Terrace St.
Kansas City, MO 64111
Tel: (816)753-9920; 877-538-5627
Fax: (816)753-9941
E-mail: directoramk@aviationmaintenance.edu
Web Site: http://www.aviationmaintenance.edu/aviation-kansascity.asp
Description: Proprietary, 2-year. Awards certificates and terminal associate degrees.
Entrance Requirements: Required: High School Diploma or GED.

■ **AVILA UNIVERSITY** *E-3*
11901 Wornall Rd.
Kansas City, MO 64145-1698
Tel: (816)942-8400
Free: 800-GO-AVILA
Admissions: (816)501-3773
Fax: (816)942-3362
E-mail: paige.illum@avila.edu
Web Site: http://www.avila.edu/
Description: Independent Roman Catholic, comprehensive, coed. Administratively affiliated with Affiliation with the Sisters of Saint Joseph of Carondelet, St. Louise Province. Awards bachelor's and master's degrees. Founded 1916. Setting: 50-acre suburban campus. Endowment: $6.5 million. Educational spending for 2005 fiscal year: $5373 per student. Total enrollment: 1,697. Faculty: 199 (64 full-time, 135 part-time). Student-undergrad faculty ratio is 12:1. 898 applied, 56% were admitted. Full-time: 910 students, 65% women, 35% men. Part-time: 304 students, 69% women, 31% men. Students come from 25 states and territories, 30 other countries, 36% from out-of-state, 1% Native American, 5% Hispanic, 17% black, 2% Asian American or Pacific Islander, 5% international, 37% 25 or older, 17% live on campus, 24% transferred in. Retention: 80% of full-time freshmen returned the following year. Academic areas with the most degrees conferred: business/marketing; health professions and related sciences; psychology. Core. Calendar: semesters. Academic remediation for entering students, ESL program, services for LD students, advanced placement, accelerated degree program, independent study, distance learning, double major, summer session for credit, part-time degree program, adult/continuing education programs, co-op programs and internships. Off campus study at Sisters of St. Joseph Consortium, Council of Independent Colleges Exchange Program. Study abroad program. ROTC: Army (c).
Entrance Requirements: Options: Peterson's Universal Application, Common Application, early admission, international baccalaureate accepted. Required: high school transcript, minimum 2.5 high school GPA, SAT or ACT. Recommended: interview. Required for some: essay, recommendations. Entrance: minimally difficult. Application deadline: Rolling. Notification: continuous.

Costs Per Year: Application fee: $0. Comprehensive fee: $22,100 includes full-time tuition ($16,300), mandatory fees ($400), and college room and board ($5400). Full-time tuition and fees vary according to course load. Room and board charges vary according to board plan and housing facility. Part-time tuition: $365 per credit hour. Part-time mandatory fees: $13 per credit hour. Part-time tuition and fees vary according to course load. Tuition guaranteed not to increase for student's term of enrollment.
Collegiate Environment: Orientation program. Drama-theater group, choral group, student-run newspaper. Social organizations: 30 open to all. Most popular organizations: Group Activities Programming, Avila Student Nurses Association, Residence Hall Association, Student Senate, Black Student Union. Major annual events: Homecoming Week, Spring Fling Week, Harmony Month. Student services: health clinic, personal-psychological counseling. Campus security: 24-hour emergency response devices, student patrols, late night transport-escort service, controlled dormitory access. 220 college housing spaces available; 186 were occupied in 2003-04. Freshmen guaranteed college housing. On-campus residence required through sophomore year. Options: coed, men-only, women-only housing available. Hooley Bundshu Library with 80,865 books, 460,080 microform titles, 7,179 serials, 3,265 audiovisual materials, an OPAC, and a Web page. Operations spending for 2004 fiscal year: $283,483. 68 computers available on campus for general student use. A campuswide network can be accessed from student residence rooms. Staffed computer lab on campus.
Community Environment: See University of Missouri - Kansas City.

■ **BAPTIST BIBLE COLLEGE** *J-5*
628 East Kearney
Springfield, MO 65803-3498
Tel: (417)268-6000
Fax: (417)831-8029
Web Site: http://www.baptist.edu/index.htm
Description: Independent Baptist, comprehensive, coed. Awards associate, bachelor's, master's, and first professional degrees. Founded 1950. Setting: 38-acre suburban campus. Total enrollment: 653. 264 applied, 76% were admitted. Students come from 46 states and territories, 5 other countries, 80% from out-of-state, 1% Native American, 3% Hispanic, 1% black, 0.3% Asian American or Pacific Islander, 2% international, 61% live on campus. Core. Calendar: semesters. Academic remediation for entering students, summer session for credit, part-time degree program, internships, graduate courses open to undergrads. ROTC: Army (c).
Entrance Requirements: Open admission. Options: early admission, deferred admission. Required: high school transcript, 1 recommendation. Entrance: noncompetitive. Application deadline: Rolling. Notification: continuous. Preference given to members of supporting churches.
Costs Per Year: Application fee: $40. Comprehensive fee: $18,300 includes full-time tuition ($13,000) and college room and board ($5300).
Collegiate Environment: Drama-theater group, choral group, student-run radio station. Student services: health clinic, personal-psychological counseling. On-campus residence required through senior year. Options: men-only, women-only housing available. 36,844 books and 226 serials. 50 computers available on campus for general student use. Staffed computer lab on campus.

Community Environment: See Southwest Missouri State University.

■ **BARNES-JEWISH COLLEGE OF NURSING AND ALLIED HEALTH**
F-12
306 South Kingshighway Blvd.
St. Louis, MO 63110-1091
Tel: (314)454-7055
Admissions: (314)454-7538
Fax: (314)454-5239
E-mail: cal7374@bjcmail.carenet.org
Web Site: http://www.barnesjewishcollege.edu/
Description: Independent, comprehensive, coed. Awards associate, bachelor's, and master's degrees and post-master's certificates. Founded 1902. Setting: urban campus. Endowment: $4.2 million. Total enrollment: 781. 310 applied, 91% were admitted. 39% from top 10% of their high school class, 90% from top quarter, 100% from top half. Full-time: 200 students, 88% women, 12% men. Part-time: 486 students, 90% women, 10% men. Students come from 7 states and territories, 14% from out-of-state, 1% Native American, 1% Hispanic, 9% black, 1% Asian American or Pacific Islander, 0% international, 68% 25 or older, 1% live on campus, 16% transferred in. Retention: 72% of full-time freshmen returned the following year. Core. Calendar: semesters. Services for LD students, advanced placement, independent study, double major, summer session for credit, part-time degree program, graduate courses open to undergrads. Off campus study at Washington University in St. Louis.
Entrance Requirements: Option: Common Application. Required: high school transcript, minimum 2.0 high school GPA, 2 recommendations, SAT or ACT. Entrance: moderately difficult. Application deadline: Rolling.
Collegiate Environment: Orientation program. Most popular organization: Student Nurses Association. Student services: personal-psychological counseling. Campus security: 24-hour patrols, late night transport-escort service, controlled dormitory access. No special consideration for freshman housing applicants. Option: coed housing available. George and Juanita Way Library plus 4 others with 3,765 books, 232 serials, 400 audiovisual materials, an OPAC, and a Web page. Operations spending for 2004 fiscal year: $147,000. 21 computers available on campus for general student use. A campuswide network can be accessed from off-campus. Staffed computer lab on campus.

■ **BLUE RIVER COMMUNITY COLLEGE** *E-3*
20301 East 78 Hwy.
Independence, MO 64057
Tel: (816)655-6000
Admissions: (816)655-6118
Fax: (816)655-6014
Web Site: http://www.mcckc.edu
Description: State and locally supported, 2-year, coed. Part of Metropolitan Community Colleges System. Awards certificates, transfer associate, and terminal associate degrees. Setting: suburban campus with easy access to Kansas City. Endowment: $2.4 million. Educational spending for 2005 fiscal year: $3488 per student. Total enrollment: 2,662. Student-undergrad faculty ratio is 13:1. 487 applied, 100% were admitted. Full-time: 1,053 students, 58% women, 42% men. Part-time: 1,609 students, 61% women, 39% men. Students come from 2 states and territories, 0.2% from out-of-state, 1% Native American, 2% Hispanic, 2% black, 1% Asian American or Pacific Islander, 0% international, 32% 25 or older, 5% transferred in. Retention: 57% of full-time freshmen returned the following year. Core. Calendar: semesters. Academic remediation for entering students, ESL program, services for LD students, advanced placement, accelerated degree program, honors program, distance learning, summer session for credit, part-time degree program, adult/continuing education programs, co-op programs and internships. Off campus study at Johnson County Community College.
Entrance Requirements: Open admission. Options: early admission, deferred admission. Entrance: noncompetitive. Application deadline: Rolling.
Costs Per Year: Application fee: $0. Area resident tuition: $2190 full-time, $73 per hour part-time. State resident tuition: $3990 full-time, $133 per hour part-time. Nonresident tuition: $5400 full-time, $180 per hour part-time. Mandatory fees: $150 full-time, $5 per hour part-time.
Collegiate Environment: Choral group. Campus security: 24-hour emergency response devices and patrols. College housing not available. Blue River Community College Library with 10,312 books, 28,297 microform titles, 66 serials, 567 audiovisual materials, an OPAC, and a Web page. Operations spending for 2004 fiscal year: $231,156. 375 computers avail-able on campus for general student use. A campuswide network can be accessed from off-campus. Staffed computer lab on campus.

■ **CALVARY BIBLE COLLEGE AND THEOLOGICAL SEMINARY** *E-3*
15800 Calvary Rd.
Kansas City, MO 64147-1341
Tel: (816)322-0110
Free: 800-326-3960
Web Site: http://www.calvary.edu/
Description: Independent nondenominational, comprehensive, coed. Awards associate, bachelor's, master's, and first professional degrees. Founded 1932. Setting: 55-acre suburban campus. Endowment: $183,313. Educational spending for 2005 fiscal year: $14,642 per student. Total enrollment: 348. Faculty: 35 (12 full-time, 23 part-time). Student-undergrad faculty ratio is 12:1. 50 applied, 98% were admitted. Full-time: 230 students, 45% women, 55% men. Part-time: 58 students, 34% women, 66% men. Students come from 22 states and territories, 4 other countries, 53% from out-of-state, 0% Native American, 1% Hispanic, 2% black, 1% Asian American or Pacific Islander, 1% international, 50% 25 or older. Retention: 73% of full-time fresh-men returned the following year. Academic areas with the most degrees conferred: theology and religious vocations; business/marketing; education. Core. Calendar: semesters. Academic remediation for entering students, advanced placement, independent study, double major, summer session for credit, part-time degree program, adult/continuing education programs, graduate courses open to undergrads.
Entrance Requirements: Options: early admission, deferred admission, international baccalaureate accepted. Required: essay, high school transcript, 2 recommendations, statement of faith, SAT or ACT. Required for some: interview. Entrance: minimally difficult. Application deadline: 7/15.
Costs Per Year: Application fee: $25. Comprehensive fee: $10,996 includes full-time tuition ($6720), mandatory fees ($576), and college room and board ($3700). College room only: $1750. Part-time tuition: $240 per credit hour. Part-time mandatory fees: $19 per credit.
Collegiate Environment: Orientation program. Drama-theater group, choral group, student-run radio station. Social organizations: 2 open to all. Most popular organizations: Missions Encounter, Masterworks (Fine Arts). Major annual events: Day of Prayer, Missions Emphasis Week, All-Calvary Workday. Student services: health clinic, personal-psychological counseling. Campus security: late night transport-escort service, night patrols by trained security personnel. 200 college housing spaces available; 180 were oc-cupied in 2003-04. Freshmen guaranteed college housing. On-campus residence required through senior year. Options: men-only, women-only housing available. Hilda Kroeker Library with 56,087 books, 2,725 microform titles, 249 serials, 1,583 audiovisual materials, an OPAC, and a Web page. Operations spending for 2004 fiscal year: $105,328. 23 computers available on campus for general student use. A campuswide network can be accessed from student residence rooms. Staffed computer lab on campus.
Community Environment: See University of Missouri Kansas City.

■ **CENTRAL BIBLE COLLEGE** *J-5*
3000 North Grant Ave.
Springfield, MO 65803-1096
Tel: (417)833-2551
Free: 800-831-4222
Fax: (417)833-5141
Web Site: http://www.cbcag.edu/
Description: Independent Assemblies of God, 4-year, coed. Awards associ-ate and bachelor's degrees. Founded 1922. Setting: 108-acre suburban campus. Total enrollment: 817. 265 applied, 71% were admitted. 7% from top 10% of their high school class, 14% from top quarter, 43% from top half. Full-time: 742 students, 41% women, 59% men. Part-time: 75 students, 32% women, 68% men. Students come from 48 states and territories, 74% from out-of-state, 1% Native American, 3% Hispanic, 2% black, 2% Asian American or Pacific Islander, 1% international, 18% 25 or older, 65% live on campus, 9% transferred in. Retention: 75% of full-time freshmen returned the following year. Core. Calendar: semesters. Academic remediation for entering students, services for LD students, advanced placement, independent study, distance learning, double major, summer session for credit, part-time degree program, internships.
Entrance Requirements: Options: early admission, deferred admission. Required: essay, high school transcript, 3 recommendations. Recom-mended: minimum 2.0 high school GPA. Required for some: interview. Placement: SAT or ACT required. Entrance: moderately difficult. Application deadline: Rolling. Preference given to Christians.

Collegiate Environment: Orientation program. Drama-theater group, choral group, student-run newspaper, radio station. Major annual events: Annual School Picnic, Missions Convention, Spiritual Emphasis Week. Student services: health clinic, personal-psychological counseling. Campus security: 24-hour emergency response devices and patrols, student patrols, controlled dormitory access. 665 college housing spaces available; 493 were occupied in 2003-04. No special consideration for freshman housing applicants. On-campus residence required through senior year. Options: men-only, women-only housing available. Meyer Pearlman Library with 107,023 books, 38,341 microform titles, 1,074 serials, 6,894 audiovisual materials, an OPAC, and a Web page. Operations spending for 2004 fiscal year: $186,610. 20 computers available on campus for general student use. A campuswide network can be accessed. Staffed computer lab on campus.

Community Environment: See Southwest Missouri State University.

■ **CENTRAL CHRISTIAN COLLEGE OF THE BIBLE** *D-7*
911 Urbandale Dr. East
Moberly, MO 65270-1997
Tel: (660)263-3900
Fax: (660)263-3936
Web Site: http://www.cccb.edu/
Description: Independent, 4-year, coed, affiliated with Christian Churches and Churches of Christ. Awards associate and bachelor's degrees. Founded 1957. Setting: 40-acre small town campus. Total enrollment: 531. Student-undergrad faculty ratio is 31:1. Full-time: 523 students, 47% women, 53% men. Part-time: 8 students, 50% women, 50% men. Students come from 10 states and territories, 1 other country, 40% from out-of-state, 20% 25 or older, 75% live on campus, 1% transferred in. Core. Calendar: semesters. Academic remediation for entering students, self-designed majors, part-time degree program, internships. Off campus study at Fort Hays State University, Tabor College, Johnson Bible College, Moberly Area Community College.
Entrance Requirements: Options: Peterson's Universal Application, early admission, deferred admission. Required: high school transcript, 3 recommendations, SAT or ACT. Entrance: noncompetitive. Application deadline: Rolling. Preference given to Christians.
Costs Per Year: Application fee: $25.
Collegiate Environment: Orientation program. Choral group. Most popular organization: Harvesters. Major annual events: Missions Emphasis, Agape Banquet, Revival. Student services: personal-psychological counseling. On-campus residence required through senior year. Options: men-only, women-only housing available. 35,000 books, 6 microform titles, and 196 serials. 25 computers available on campus for general student use. Staffed computer lab on campus.

■ **CENTRAL METHODIST UNIVERSITY** *E-7*
411 Central Methodist Square
Fayette, MO 65248-1198
Tel: (660)248-3391
Admissions: (660)248-6247
Fax: (660)248-2287
E-mail: admissions@cmc.edu
Web Site: http://www.centralmethodist.edu/
Description: Independent Methodist, comprehensive, coed. Awards associate, bachelor's, and master's degrees. Founded 1854. Setting: 80-acre small town campus. Endowment: $20.9 million. Educational spending for 2005 fiscal year: $4124 per student. Total enrollment: 781. 1,183 applied, 62% were admitted. 8% from top 10% of their high school class, 33% from top quarter, 70% from top half. 3 valedictorians. Full-time: 751 students, 50% women, 50% men. Part-time: 30 students, 67% women, 33% men. Students come from 17 states and territories, 9% from out-of-state, 1% Native American, 2% Hispanic, 9% black, 1% Asian American or Pacific Islander, 2% international, 9% 25 or older, 71% live on campus, 10% transferred in. Retention: 57% of full-time freshmen returned the following year. Core. Calendar: semesters. Academic remediation for entering students, services for LD students, advanced placement, accelerated degree program, self-designed majors, honors program, independent study, distance learning, double major, summer session for credit, part-time degree program, internships. Off campus study at Mineral Area College, East Central College. Study abroad program. ROTC: Army (c), Air Force (c).
Entrance Requirements: Options: Peterson's Universal Application, Common Application, electronic application, deferred admission. Required: high school transcript, minimum 2.5 high school GPA, SAT or ACT. Recom-

mended: ACT. Required for some: 2 recommendations. Entrance: moderately difficult. Application deadline: Rolling. Notification: continuous.
Costs Per Year: Application fee: $20. Comprehensive fee: $20,560 includes full-time tuition ($14,490), mandatory fees ($710), and college room and board ($5360). College room only: $2640. Room and board charges vary according to board plan and housing facility. Part-time tuition: $140 per credit hour. Part-time tuition varies according to course load.
Collegiate Environment: Orientation program. Drama-theater group, choral group, marching band, student-run newspaper, radio station. Social organizations: 37 open to all; local fraternities, local sororities; 12% of eligible men and 14% of eligible women are members. Most popular organizations: Student Government Association, Wesley Foundation, Alpha Phi Omega, Christian Students United in Christ, Big Brothers/Big Sisters program. Major annual events: Family Day, Homecoming, Hall of Sponsors Competition. Student services: health clinic, personal-psychological counseling. Campus security: 24-hour emergency response devices, late night transport-escort service, controlled dormitory access. No special consideration for freshman housing applicants. On-campus residence required through senior year. Options: coed, men-only, women-only housing available. Smiley Library plus 1 other with 97,793 books, 140,742 microform titles, 316 serials, 379 audiovisual materials, an OPAC, and a Web page. 72 computers available on campus for general student use. A campuswide network can be accessed from student residence rooms and from off campus. Staffed computer lab on campus.
Community Environment: Fayette (population 3,520) is the county seat of Howard County and is in an area that is noted for the production of purebred cattle. Both Kansas City and St. Louis are about a two-hour drive away. The cultural facilities of both large cities are available and add charm to the community.

■ **CENTRAL MISSOURI STATE UNIVERSITY** *F-5*
PO Box 800
Warrensburg, MO 64093
Tel: (660)543-4111
Admissions: (660)543-4290
Fax: (660)543-8517
E-mail: admit@cmsuvmb.cmsu.edu
Web Site: http://www.cmsu.edu/
Description: State-supported, comprehensive, coed. Awards associate, bachelor's, and master's degrees and post-master's certificates. Founded 1871. Setting: 1,561-acre small town campus with easy access to Kansas City. Endowment: $23.2 million. Research spending for 2004 fiscal year: $1.9 million. Educational spending for 2005 fiscal year: $6061 per student. Total enrollment: 10,604. Faculty: 705 (439 full-time, 266 part-time). Student-undergrad faculty ratio is 16:1. 3,619 applied, 85% were admitted. 14% from top 10% of their high school class, 40% from top quarter, 75% from top half. Full-time: 7,168 students, 55% women, 45% men. Part-time: 1,649 students, 59% women, 41% men. Students come from 43 states and territories, 51 other countries, 6% from out-of-state, 0.5% Native American, 2% Hispanic, 6% black, 1% Asian American or Pacific Islander, 2% international, 28% 25 or older, 34% live on campus, 9% transferred in. Retention: 71% of full-time freshmen returned the following year. Academic areas with the most degrees conferred: education; business/marketing; engineering technologies. Core. Calendar: semesters. Academic remediation for entering students, ESL program, services for LD students, advanced placement, self-designed majors, honors program, distance learning, double major, summer session for credit, part-time degree program, adult/continuing education programs, co-op programs and internships, graduate courses open to undergrads. Off campus study. Study abroad program. ROTC: Army, Air Force (c).
Entrance Requirements: Options: Common Application, electronic application, deferred admission, international baccalaureate accepted. Required: high school transcript, rank in upper two-thirds of high school class, minimum ACT score of 20, ACT. Required for some: recommendations. Entrance: moderately difficult. Application deadline: Rolling. Notification: continuous.
Costs Per Year: Application fee: $30. State resident tuition: $5835 full-time. Nonresident tuition: $11,250 full-time. College room and board: $5109. College room only: $3406.
Collegiate Environment: Orientation program. Drama-theater group, choral group, marching band, student-run newspaper, radio station. Social organizations: 150 open to all; national fraternities, national sororities; 15% of eligible men and 11% of eligible women are members. Most popular organizations: Student Government Association, Campus Activities Board, Association of Black Collegiates, International Student Organization. Major

annual events: Homecoming, Greek Week activities, Welcome Week. Student services: health clinic, personal-psychological counseling, women's center. Campus security: 24-hour emergency response devices and patrols, student patrols, late night transport-escort service, controlled dormitory access, canine patrol. 3,495 college housing spaces available; 2,640 were occupied in 2003-04. Freshmen guaranteed college housing. On-campus residence required in freshman year. Options: coed, men-only, women-only housing available. James C. Kirkpatrick Library with 1.3 million books, 829,084 microform titles, 2,552 serials, 25,240 audiovisual materials, an OPAC, and a Web page. Operations spending for 2004 fiscal year: $4.3 million. 1,220 computers available on campus for general student use. A campuswide network can be accessed from student residence rooms and from off campus. Staffed computer lab on campus.

Community Environment: Surrounded by rolling prairie and scenic woodlands, Warrensburg is located just south of Interstate 70 at the junction of highways 50 and 13. An hour's drive southeast of Kansas City, it is directly en route to a number of popular Missouri attractions, including the Lake of the Ozarks and Branson. Warrensburg's 18,500 residents are in the enviable position of being close to a metropolitan area while able to enjoy the safety and advantages of small-town life. Bus and train lines serve the town. Employment and housing are available both on and off campus.

■ **CHAMBERLAIN COLLEGE OF NURSING** *F-12*
6150 Oakland Ave.
St. Louis, MO 63139-3215
Tel: (314)768-3044
Free: 800-942-4310
Admissions: (314)768-3179
Fax: (314)768-5673
Web Site: http://www.deaconess.edu/

Description: Proprietary, 4-year, coed. Administratively affiliated with Tenet Healthcare Corporation. Awards associate and bachelor's degrees. Founded 1889. Setting: 15-acre urban campus. Educational spending for 2005 fiscal year: $3156 per student. Total enrollment: 324. 13% from top 10% of their high school class, 52% from top quarter, 81% from top half. 1 student government officer. Full-time: 137 students, 99% women, 1% men. Part-time: 187 students, 97% women, 3% men. Students come from 15 states and territories, 0% Native American, 2% Hispanic, 30% black, 1% Asian American or Pacific Islander, 0% international, 32% 25 or older, 21% live on campus, 3% transferred in. Retention: 62% of full-time freshmen returned the following year. Core. Calendar: semesters. Academic remediation for entering students, ESL program, advanced placement, summer session for credit, part-time degree program. Off campus study at Fontbonne College. ROTC: Army (c).

Entrance Requirements: Options: Peterson's Universal Application, deferred admission. Required: essay, high school transcript, ACT. Recommended: minimum 2.5 high school GPA. Required for some: recommendations, interview. Entrance: moderately difficult. Application deadline: Rolling. Notification: continuous.

Collegiate Environment: Orientation program. Student-run newspaper. Social organizations: 4 open to all. Most popular organizations: Deaconess Ambassadors, National Student Nurses Association, Student Government Association, Campus Crusade for Christ. Major annual events: Convocation, Christmas Tea, Annual Student Picnic. Student services: personal-psychological counseling. Campus security: 24-hour patrols, late night transport-escort service, controlled dormitory access. 88 college housing spaces available; 50 were occupied in 2003-04. Options: coed, women-only housing available. Drusch Professional Library with 8,700 books, 233 serials, and an OPAC. 20 computers available on campus for general student use. Staffed computer lab on campus.

■ **CLEVELAND CHIROPRACTIC COLLEGE-KANSAS CITY CAMPUS** *E-3*
6401 Rockhill Rd.
Kansas City, MO 64131-1181
Tel: (816)501-0100
Free: 800-467-2252
Fax: (816)361-0272
E-mail: mdenton@cleveland.edu
Web Site: http://www.cleveland.edu/

Description: Independent, upper-level, coed. Awards bachelor's and first professional degrees. Founded 1922. Setting: urban campus. Total enrollment: 459. Full-time: 61 students, 34% women, 66% men. Part-time: 10 students, 50% women, 50% men. Students come from 18 states and ter-

ritories, 1 other country, 43% from out-of-state, 0% Native American, 0% Hispanic, 4% black, 1% Asian American or Pacific Islander, 1% international, 30% 25 or older. Core. Calendar: trimesters. Academic remediation for entering students, services for LD students, accelerated degree program, summer session for credit, co-op programs and internships.

Collegiate Environment: Orientation program. College housing not available. Ruth R. Cleveland Memorial Library with 14,000 books, 36,500 microform titles, 268 serials, 12,320 audiovisual materials, an OPAC, and a Web page. 14 computers available on campus for general student use. A campuswide network can be accessed.

■ **COLLEGE OF THE OZARKS** *L-5*
PO Box 17
Point Lookout, MO 65726
Tel: (417)334-6411
Free: 800-222-0525
Fax: (417)335-2618
E-mail: admiss4@cofo.edu
Web Site: http://www.cofo.edu/

Description: Independent Presbyterian, 4-year, coed. Awards bachelor's degrees. Founded 1906. Setting: 1,000-acre small town campus. Endowment: $295.7 million. Educational spending for 2005 fiscal year: $9091 per student. Total enrollment: 1,333. Student-undergrad faculty ratio is 16:1. 2,424 applied, 10% were admitted. 25% from top 10% of their high school class, 52% from top quarter, 85% from top half. Full-time: 1,311 students, 54% women, 46% men. Part-time: 22 students, 73% women, 27% men. Students come from 38 states and territories, 16 other countries, 32% from out-of-state, 1% Native American, 1% Hispanic, 1% black, 1% Asian American or Pacific Islander, 2% international, 4% 25 or older, 84% live on campus, 2% transferred in. Retention: 76% of full-time freshmen returned the following year. Academic areas with the most degrees conferred: business/marketing; education; agriculture. Core. Calendar: semesters. Academic remediation for entering students, advanced placement, accelerated degree program, self-designed majors, honors program, independent study, double major, part-time degree program, co-op programs and internships. ROTC: Army.

Entrance Requirements: Option: electronic application. Required: high school transcript, 2 recommendations, interview, medical history, financial statement, ACT. Recommended: minimum 2.5 high school GPA. Entrance: moderately difficult. Application deadline: 2/15. Notification: continuous. Preference given to needy students.

Costs Per Year: Application fee: $0. Comprehensive fee: $4380 includes full-time tuition ($0), mandatory fees ($280), and college room and board ($4100). College room only: $2000. Part-time tuition: $295 per credit hour. Part-time mandatory fees: $140 per term.

Collegiate Environment: Orientation program. Drama-theater group, choral group, student-run newspaper, radio station. Social organizations: 49 open to all. Most popular organizations: Aviation Club, Student Senate, Baptist Student Union, Aggie Club, Business Undergraduate Society. Major annual events: Homecoming, Mud Fest, Spring Formal. Student services: health clinic, personal-psychological counseling. Campus security: 24-hour emergency response devices and patrols, controlled dormitory access, front gate closed 1 a.m. to 6 a.m., gate security 5:30 p.m. to 1 a.m. 1,031 college housing spaces available; all were occupied in 2003-04. No special consideration for freshman housing applicants. On-campus residence required through junior year. Options: men-only, women-only housing available. Lyons Memorial Library plus 1 other with 119,765 books, 30,730 microform titles, 452 serials, 5,370 audiovisual materials, and an OPAC. Operations spending for 2004 fiscal year: $556,734. 160 computers available on campus for general student use. A campuswide network can be accessed from student residence rooms and from off campus. Staffed computer lab on campus.

Community Environment: Point Lookout is a rural area near Branson, 38 miles south of Springfield. Bus service is available and air travel is a little more than 60 minutes away. Shopping areas, a library, and churches of major denominations are part of the community. A great deal of part-time employment is available especially during the April-December tourist season. All recreational facilities are available in the summer resort area.

■ **COLUMBIA COLLEGE** *E-7*
1001 Rogers St.
Columbia, MO 65216-0002
Tel: (573)875-8700
Free: 800-231-2391

Admissions: (573)875-7352

Fax: (573)875-7506

E-mail: admissions@ccis.edu

Web Site: http://www.ccis.edu/

Description: Independent, comprehensive, coed, affiliated with Christian Church (Disciples of Christ). Awards associate, bachelor's, and master's degrees (offers continuing education program with significant enrollment not reflected in profile). Founded 1851. Setting: 29-acre small town campus. Endowment: $14.9 million. Educational spending for 2005 fiscal year: $6980 per student. Total enrollment: 1,149. Faculty: 82 (56 full-time, 26 part-time). Student-undergrad faculty ratio is 13:1. 819 applied, 62% were admitted. 6% from top 10% of their high school class, 28% from top quarter, 58% from top half. 4 valedictorians. Full-time: 757 students, 58% women, 42% men. Part-time: 252 students, 62% women, 38% men. Students come from 25 states and territories, 27 other countries, 7% from out-of-state, 1% Native American, 3% Hispanic, 6% black, 1% Asian American or Pacific Islander, 4% international, 23% 25 or older, 36% live on campus, 12% transferred in. Retention: 55% of full-time freshmen returned the following year. Academic areas with the most degrees conferred: business/marketing; liberal arts/general studies; security and protective services. Core. Calendar: semesters. ESL program, advanced placement, accelerated degree program, self-designed majors, honors program, independent study, distance learning, double major, summer session for credit, part-time degree program, adult/continuing education programs, co-op programs and internships, graduate courses open to undergrads. Off campus study at local institutions. Study abroad program. ROTC: Army (c), Air Force (c).

Entrance Requirements: Options: Common Application, early admission, deferred admission, international baccalaureate accepted. Required: high school transcript, minimum 2.5 high school GPA, SAT or ACT. Recommended: rank in upper 50% of high school class. Required for some: essay, recommendations, interview. Entrance: moderately difficult. Application deadline: Rolling. Notification: continuous.

Costs Per Year: Application fee: $25. Comprehensive fee: $17,006 includes full-time tuition ($11,995) and college room and board ($5011). College room only: $3152. Full-time tuition varies according to class time and course load. Room and board charges vary according to board plan. Part-time tuition: $257 per credit hour. Part-time tuition varies according to class time, course load, and location.

Collegiate Environment: Orientation program. Drama-theater group, choral group, student-run newspaper. Social organizations: 26 open to all. Most popular organizations: Students in Free Enterprise, Campus Community Government, Student Leaders Advocating Teaching Excellence, Spanish Club, Criminal Justice Association. Major annual events: Family Day, Paper in Particular (national juried art show), Career Day. Student services: health clinic, personal-psychological counseling. Campus security: 24-hour emergency response devices and patrols, late night transport-escort service, controlled dormitory access. College housing designed to accommodate 305 students; 320 undergraduates lived in college housing during 2003-04. Freshmen guaranteed college housing. On-campus residence required through sophomore year. Options: coed, women-only housing available. Stafford Library with 62,265 books, 13,729 microform titles, 382 serials, 3,613 audiovisual materials, an OPAC, and a Web page. Operations spending for 2004 fiscal year: $508,593. 137 computers available on campus for general student use. Computer purchase/lease plans available. A campuswide network can be accessed from student residence rooms and from off campus. Staffed computer lab on campus.

■ **CONCEPTION SEMINARY COLLEGE** *B-3*

PO Box 502

Conception, MO 64433-0502

Tel: (660)944-3105

Admissions: (660)944-2886

Fax: (660)944-2829

Web Site: http://www.conceptionabbey.org/

Description: Independent Roman Catholic, 4-year, men only. Awards bachelor's degrees. Founded 1886. Setting: 30-acre rural campus. Total enrollment: 100. 10 applied, 100% were admitted. 20% from top 10% of their high school class, 30% from top quarter, 80% from top half. Full-time: 90 students. Part-time: 10 students. Students come from 18 states and territories, 5 other countries, 67% from out-of-state, 0% Native American, 6% Hispanic, 1% black, 10% Asian American or Pacific Islander, 8% international, 55% 25 or older, 100% live on campus, 24% transferred in. Retention: 82% of full-time freshmen returned the following year. Core. Calendar:

semesters. Academic remediation for entering students, ESL program, advanced placement, independent study, double major. Off campus study at Northwest Missouri State University.

Entrance Requirements: Option: electronic application. Required: essay, high school transcript, minimum 2.0 high school GPA, 2 recommendations, church certificate, medical history, ACT. Entrance: noncompetitive. Application deadline: 7/31. Notification: continuous until 8/15. Preference given to Catholic seminarians.

Costs Per Year: Application fee: $0. Comprehensive fee: $19,498 includes full-time tuition ($12,118), mandatory fees ($180), and college room and board ($7200). College room only: $3046. Part-time tuition: $150 per credit.

Collegiate Environment: Orientation program. Drama-theater group, choral group, student-run newspaper. Social organizations: 12 open to all. Most popular organizations: Vocation Committee, Drama Club, Apostolics, Fine Arts Committee, Social Concerns Committee. Major annual events: May Day, Encounter with God's Call, Parents' Weekend. Student services: health clinic, personal-psychological counseling. 125 college housing spaces available; all were occupied in 2003-04. On-campus residence required through senior year. Option: men-only housing available. Conception Seminary College Library with 115,000 books, 180 microform titles, 300 serials, 5,000 audiovisual materials, and a Web page. 12 computers available on campus for general student use. A campuswide network can be accessed from off-campus. Staffed computer lab on campus.

Community Environment: Conception is located in northwest Missouri, 85 miles north of Kansas City. The Abbey contains a collection of rare manuscripts dating back to the 10th century. See also Missouri Western State College for information about St. Joseph, the nearest large city.

■ **CONCORDE CAREER INSTITUTE** *E-3*

3239 Broadway

Kansas City, MO 64111-2407

Tel: (816)531-5223

Fax: (816)756-3231

Web Site: http://www.concordecareercolleges.com/

Description: Proprietary, 2-year, coed. Founded 1983.

■ **COTTEY COLLEGE** *H-3*

1000 West Austin

Nevada, MO 64772

Tel: (417)667-8181; 888-526-8839

Fax: (417)667-8103

E-mail: enrollmgt@cottey.edu

Web Site: http://www.cottey.edu/

Description: Independent, 2-year, women only. Awards transfer associate degrees. Founded 1884. Setting: 51-acre small town campus. Endowment: $78.4 million. Total enrollment: 308. Student-undergrad faculty ratio is 10:1. 507 applied, 36% were admitted. 13% from top 10% of their high school class, 46% from top quarter, 83% from top half. 2 class presidents, 3 valedictorians, 20 student government officers. Students come from 42 states and territories, 15 other countries, 78% from out-of-state, 0.3% Native American, 6% Hispanic, 3% black, 2% Asian American or Pacific Islander, 11% international, 1% 25 or older, 98% live on campus. Retention: 75% of full-time freshmen returned the following year. Core. Calendar: semesters. Advanced placement, part-time degree program.

Entrance Requirements: Options: electronic application, early admission, deferred admission. Required: essay, high school transcript, 1 recommendation, SAT or ACT. Recommended: minimum 2.6 high school GPA, interview. Entrance: moderately difficult. Application deadline: Rolling.

Costs Per Year: Application fee: $20. Comprehensive fee: $17,510 includes full-time tuition ($11,600), mandatory fees ($710), and college room and board ($5200).

Collegiate Environment: Orientation program. Drama-theater group, choral group, student-run newspaper. Social organizations: 13 open to all. Most popular organizations: International Friendship Circle, Cottey Intramural Association, Ozarks Explorers Club, Inter-Varsity Club, Golden Keys. Major annual events: Hanging of the Greens, Quad C Week, Humanities Film Festival. Student services: health clinic, personal-psychological counseling. Campus security: 24-hour emergency response devices and patrols, late night transport-escort service, controlled dormitory access. 350 college housing spaces available; 311 were occupied in 2003-04. On-campus residence required through sophomore year. Option: women-only housing available. Blanche Skiff Ross Memorial Library with 54,200 books, 246 serials, and an OPAC. Operations spending for 2004 fiscal year: $194,423. 50

computers available on campus for general student use. A campuswide network can be accessed. Staffed computer lab on campus.

Community Environment: Located 100 miles south of Kansas City, 60 miles north of Joplin, and 90 miles north of Springfield, Nevada has a population of 10,000 and is the county seat of Vernon County. Although historically an agricultural community, Nevada has a diverse economic base. The Jefferson Bus Lines connect Nevada to the International Airport in Kansas City and the municipal airport in Joplin. The community facilities include 27 churches, a number of civic, fraternal, and veterans' organizations, a municipal hospital, and a community center. Part-time employment for students is available. Recreational activities are hunting, fishing, golf, and bowling. The Chamber of Commerce holds a number of special events during the year.

■ **COX COLLEGE OF NURSING AND HEALTH SCIENCES** *J-5*
1423 North Jefferson
Springfield, MO 65802
Tel: (417)269-3401
Admissions: (417)269-3038
Web Site: http://www.coxcollege.edu/

Description: Independent, 4-year, coed. Administratively affiliated with Cox Health Systems. Awards associate and bachelor's degrees. Founded 1994. Setting: urban campus. Total enrollment: 592. Student-undergrad faculty ratio is 13:1. Full-time: 279 students, 92% women, 8% men. Part-time: 313 students, 91% women, 9% men. Students come from 4 states and territories, 1% from out-of-state, 1% Native American, 1% Hispanic, 2% black, 1% Asian American or Pacific Islander, 0% international, 55% 25 or older, 15% live on campus, 19% transferred in. Core. Calendar: semesters. Academic remediation for entering students, accelerated degree program, summer session for credit, part-time degree program.

Entrance Requirements: Options: Common Application, early decision. Required: high school transcript, minimum 2.5 high school GPA. Recommended: SAT or ACT. Application deadlines: 2/1, 11/1 for early decision. Notification: 3/1, 12/1 for early decision.

Costs Per Year: Application fee: $30. Tuition: $9240 full-time, $308 per credit hour part-time. Mandatory fees: $1050 full-time, $35 per credit hour part-time. Full-time tuition and fees vary according to course load and program. Part-time tuition and fees vary according to course load and program. College room only: $2000.

Collegiate Environment: Orientation program. Social organizations: 7 open to all. Most popular organizations: Student Nurses Association, National Student Nurses Association, Student Council, Residence Hall Council, Christian Fellowship. Major annual events: Diversity Day, Day of Caring. Student services: personal-psychological counseling. Campus security: 24-hour patrols, late night transport-escort service. 60 college housing spaces available; 30 were occupied in 2003-04. No special consideration for freshman housing applicants. Option: coed housing available. 48 computers available on campus for general student use. A campuswide network can be accessed from student residence rooms and from off campus. Staffed computer lab on campus.

■ **CROWDER COLLEGE** *K-3*
601 Laclede Ave.
Neosho, MO 64850-9160
Tel: (417)451-3223; (866)238-7788
Fax: (417)451-4280
Web Site: http://www.crowder.edu/

Description: State and locally supported, 2-year, coed. Part of Missouri Coordinating Board for Higher Education. Awards certificates, transfer associate, and terminal associate degrees. Founded 1963. Setting: 608-acre rural campus. Total enrollment: 2,615. Student-undergrad faculty ratio is 19:1. 1,253 applied, 100% were admitted. Full-time: 1,319 students, 61% women, 39% men. Part-time: 1,296 students, 69% women, 31% men. Students come from 15 states and territories, 15 other countries, 4% from out-of-state, 2% Native American, 5% Hispanic, 1% black, 1% Asian American or Pacific Islander, 1% international, 23% 25 or older, 10% live on campus, 5% transferred in. Core. Calendar: semesters. Academic remediation for entering students, ESL program, advanced placement, freshman honors college, honors program, summer session for credit, part-time degree program, adult/continuing education programs, co-op programs and internships. Study abroad program.

Entrance Requirements: Open admission except for nursing program. Required: high school transcript. Entrance: noncompetitive. Application deadline: Rolling. Notification: continuous.

Costs Per Year: Application fee: $25. Area resident tuition: $1860 full-time. State resident tuition: $2640 full-time. Nonresident tuition: $3450 full-time. Mandatory fees: $360 full-time. College room and board: $3870.

Collegiate Environment: Orientation program. Drama-theater group, choral group, student-run newspaper. Social organizations: 15 open to all. Most popular organizations: Phi Beta Lambda, Students in Free Enterprise, Baptist Student Union, Student Senate, Student Ambassadors. Major annual events: Homecoming, Spring Fling, Spirit Week. Student services: personal-psychological counseling. Campus security: 24-hour patrols. 200 college housing spaces available; 150 were occupied in 2003-04. No special consideration for freshman housing applicants. Options: men-only, women-only housing available. Crowder College Learning Resources Center with 37,452 books, 167,829 microform titles, 163 serials, 3,632 audiovisual materials, an OPAC, and a Web page. Operations spending for 2004 fiscal year: $175,280. 515 computers available on campus for general student use. A campuswide network can be accessed. Staffed computer lab on campus.

Community Environment: Neosho (population 10,000) is the birthplace of Thomas Hart Benton, 18 miles from Joplin. All forms of commercial transportation are available. Churches of most of the major denominations, two libraries, a museum, two hospitals and numerous civic and fraternal organizations are represented. Part time jobs are available in Neosho and the two county districts. Neosho provides the area with a full time recreation director and planned activities for the community. The Government Fish Hatchery is nearby.

■ **CULVER-STOCKTON COLLEGE** *B-9*
1 College Hill
Canton, MO 63435-1299
Tel: (573)288-6000
Free: 800-537-1883
Fax: (573)288-6617
E-mail: bsmith@culver.edu
Web Site: http://www.culver.edu/

Description: Independent, 4-year, coed, affiliated with Christian Church (Disciples of Christ). Awards bachelor's degrees. Founded 1853. Setting: 143-acre rural campus. Endowment: $20.7 million. Educational spending for 2005 fiscal year: $3827 per student. Total enrollment: 840. Student-undergrad faculty ratio is 13:1. 959 applied, 76% were admitted. 16% from top 10% of their high school class, 37% from top quarter, 68% from top half. 7 valedictorians. Full-time: 766 students, 57% women, 43% men. Part-time: 74 students, 66% women, 34% men. Students come from 21 states and territories, 6 other countries, 34% from out-of-state, 0.5% Native American, 3% Hispanic, 7% black, 0.5% Asian American or Pacific Islander, 1% international, 9% 25 or older, 71% live on campus, 10% transferred in. Retention: 68% of full-time freshmen returned the following year. Academic areas with the most degrees conferred: business/marketing; health professions and related sciences; education. Core. Calendar: semesters. Advanced placement, self-designed majors, honors program, independent study, double major, summer session for credit, part-time degree program, internships. Off campus study at Central College. Study abroad program.

Entrance Requirements: Options: Peterson's Universal Application, electronic application, deferred admission, international baccalaureate accepted. Required: high school transcript, minimum 2.0 high school GPA, rank in upper 50% of high school class, SAT or ACT. Recommended: essay, recommendations, interview. Required for some: interview. Entrance: moderately difficult.

Costs Per Year: Application fee: $25. Comprehensive fee: $21,796 includes full-time tuition ($15,250) and college room and board ($6546). College room only: $3030. Part-time tuition: $400 per credit hour. Part-time mandatory fees: $10 per credit hour.

Collegiate Environment: Orientation program. Drama-theater group, choral group, student-run newspaper, radio station. Social organizations: 37 open to all; national fraternities, national sororities; 12% of eligible men and 24% of eligible women are members. Most popular organizations: C-S Teachers Organization, Student Ambassadors, Christian Fellowship Group, Student Government Association, Student Nurses Organization. Major annual events: Homecoming, Family Weekend, Rush. Student services: personal-psychological counseling. Campus security: 24-hour emergency response devices, late night transport-escort service. 706 college housing spaces available; 593 were occupied in 2003-04. Freshmen guaranteed college housing. On-campus residence required through senior year. Options: coed, men-only, women-only housing available. Johann Memorial Library with 155,487 books, 5,117 microform titles, 777 serials, 4,327 audiovisual materials, an QPAC, and a Web page. Operations spending for 2004 fiscal year: $258,779. 70 computers available on campus for general student use. A campuswide network can be accessed from student residence rooms and from off campus. Staffed computer lab on campus.

Community Environment: Canton, population 2,623, is 20 miles north of Quincy, IL, 30 miles south of Keokuk, IA, and approximately two hours north of St. Louis, MO. On the Mississippi River, it is the site of the U.S. Lock and Dam No. 20, which is one of the series of navigation dams built between Minneapolis and St. Louis. Libraries, museums, many churches, and good shopping facilities all provide service to the community. A state park is nearby for recreational and outdoor play. The college homecoming is a community affair. Part-time employment is available.

■ DEVRY UNIVERSITY (KANSAS CITY) *E-3*

City Center Square
1100 Main St., Ste. 118
Kansas City, MO 64105-2112
Tel: (816)221-1300
Fax: (816)474-0318
Web Site: http://www.devry.edu/
Description: Proprietary, comprehensive, coed. Calendar: semesters.
Costs Per Year: One-time mandatory fee: $40. Tuition: $11,790 full-time, $440 per credit part-time. Mandatory fees: $60 full-time, $30 per year part-time.

■ DEVRY UNIVERSITY (KANSAS CITY) *E-3*

11224 Holmes Rd.
Kansas City, MO 64131-3698
Tel: (816)941-0430
Free: 800-821-3766
Fax: (816)941-0896
Web Site: http://www.devry.edu/
Description: Proprietary, 4-year, coed. Part of DeVry University. Awards associate, bachelor's, and master's degrees. Founded 1931. Setting: 12-acre urban campus. Total enrollment: 1,233. Faculty: 88 (49 full-time, 39 part-time). Student-undergrad faculty ratio is 16:1. Full-time: 809 students, 46% women, 54% men. Part-time: 292 students, 54% women, 46% men. 1% Native American, 4% Hispanic, 19% black, 3% Asian American or Pacific Islander, 0.5% international. Academic areas with the most degrees conferred: computer and information sciences; business/marketing; engineering technologies. Calendar: semesters. Academic remediation for entering students, services for LD students, advanced placement, accelerated degree program, distance learning, summer session for credit, part-time degree program, adult/continuing education programs, co-op programs.
Entrance Requirements: Options: electronic application, deferred admission, international baccalaureate accepted. Required: high school transcript, interview. Entrance: minimally difficult. Application deadline: Rolling.
Costs Per Year: Application fee: $50. One-time mandatory fee: $40. Tuition: $11,790 full-time, $440 per credit part-time. Mandatory fees: $270 full-time, $160 per year part-time. Full-time tuition and fees vary according to course load. Part-time tuition and fees vary according to course load.
Collegiate Environment: Orientation program. Social organizations: 8 open to all. Most popular organizations: Phi Beta Lambda, Institution of Electrical and Electronic Engineers, Tau Alpha Pi, Association of Information Technology Professionals, Cutting Edge Bible Club. Major annual events: Tryathlon, Student Picnic, Casino Night. Campus security: 24-hour emergency response devices and patrols, lighted pathways/sidewalks. College housing not available. James E. Lovan Library with 15,000 books, 49 microform titles, 68 serials, 457 audiovisual materials, an OPAC, and a Web page. 334 computers available on campus for general student use. Computer purchase/lease plans available. A campuswide network can be accessed from off-campus. Staffed computer lab on campus.

■ DEVRY UNIVERSITY (ST. LOUIS) *F-12*

1801 Park 270 Dr., Ste. 260
St. Louis, MO 63146-4020
Tel: (314)542-4222
Fax: (314)542-4004
Web Site: http://www.devry.edu/
Description: Proprietary, comprehensive, coed. Calendar: semesters.
Costs Per Year: One-time mandatory fee: $40. Tuition: $11,790 full-time, $440 per credit part-time. Mandatory fees: $60 full-time, $30 per year part-

time. Full-time tuition and fees vary according to course load. Part-time tuition and fees vary according to course load.

■ DRURY UNIVERSITY *J-5*

900 North Benton Ave.
Springfield, MO 65802-3791
Tel: (417)873-7879
Free: 800-922-2274
Admissions: (417)873-7205
Fax: (417)873-7529
E-mail: druryad@drury.edu
Web Site: http://www.drury.edu/
Description: Independent, comprehensive, coed. Awards bachelor's and master's degrees (also offers evening program with significant enrollment not reflected in profile). Founded 1873. Setting: 80-acre urban campus. Endowment: $74.4 million. Research spending for 2004 fiscal year: $412,641. Educational spending for 2005 fiscal year: $10,716 per student. Total enrollment: 1,961. Faculty: 185 (123 full-time, 62 part-time). Student-undergrad faculty ratio is 13:1. 1,106 applied, 78% were admitted. 38% from top 10% of their high school class, 67% from top quarter, 91% from top half. 5 National Merit Scholars, 73 valedictorians. Full-time: 1,541 students, 57% women, 43% men. Part-time: 39 students, 31% women, 69% men. Students come from 34 states and territories, 21 other countries, 19% from out-of-state, 1% Native American, 2% Hispanic, 1% black, 2% Asian American or Pacific Islander, 4% international, 5% 25 or older, 50% live on campus, 7% transferred in. Retention: 78% of full-time freshmen returned the following year. Academic areas with the most degrees conferred: business/marketing; biological/life sciences; communications/journalism. Core. Calendar: semesters. ESL program, services for LD students, advanced placement, accelerated degree program, self-designed majors, honors program, independent study, distance learning, double major, summer session for credit, part-time degree program, adult/continuing education programs, co-op programs and internships, graduate courses open to undergrads. Off campus study. Study abroad program. ROTC: Army (c).
Entrance Requirements: Options: Peterson's Universal Application, electronic application, deferred admission, international baccalaureate accepted. Required: essay, high school transcript, minimum 2.7 high school GPA, 1 recommendation, minimum ACT score of 21, SAT or ACT. Recommended: interview. Entrance: moderately difficult. Application deadline: 3/15. Notification: continuous.
Costs Per Year: Application fee: $25. Comprehensive fee: $21,302 includes full-time tuition ($15,173), mandatory fees ($339), and college room and board ($5790). Part-time tuition: $500 per semester hour.
Collegiate Environment: Orientation program. Drama-theater group, choral group, student-run newspaper, radio station. Social organizations: 60 open to all; national fraternities, national sororities; 42% of eligible men and 38% of eligible women are members. Most popular organizations: Student Union Board, Community Outreach/Taking a Stand for Kids, choral groups and bands, International Student Organization, academic department clubs. Major annual events: Fall Festival, Homecoming, Spring Wellness Week. Student services: health clinic, personal-psychological counseling. Campus security: 24-hour emergency response devices and patrols, student patrols, late night transport-escort service, controlled dormitory access, security cameras in parking areas. 952 college housing spaces available; 811 were occupied in 2003-04. Freshmen guaranteed college housing. On-campus residence required in freshman year. Options: coed, men-only, women-only housing available. F. W. Olin Library plus 1 other with 177,794 books, 119,683 microform titles, 868 serials, 60,098 audiovisual materials, an OPAC, and a Web page. Operations spending for 2004 fiscal year: $1 million. 323 computers available on campus for general student use. A campuswide network can be accessed from student residence rooms and from off campus. Staffed computer lab on campus.
Community Environment: See Southwest Missouri State University.

■ EAST CENTRAL COLLEGE *G-10*

1964 Prairie Dell Rd.
Union, MO 63084
Tel: (636)583-5193
Admissions: (636)583-5195
Fax: (636)583-1897
Web Site: http://www.eastcentral.edu/
Description: District-supported, 2-year, coed. Part of Missouri Coordinating Board for Higher Education. Awards certificates, transfer associate, and terminal associate degrees. Founded 1959. Setting: 207-acre rural campus

with easy access to St. Louis. Endowment: $2.8 million. Educational spending for 2005 fiscal year: $2681 per student. Total enrollment: 3,486. Student-undergrad faculty ratio is 21:1. 9% from top 10% of their high school class, 56% from top half. Full-time: 1,447 students, 61% women, 39% men. Part-time: 2,039 students, 63% women, 37% men. Students come from 4 states and territories, 0.4% Native American, 1% Hispanic, 1% black, 1% Asian American or Pacific Islander, 0.04% international, 25% 25 or older, 6% transferred in. Core. Calendar: semesters. Academic remediation for entering students, ESL program, services for LD students, advanced placement, honors program, independent study, distance learning, summer session for credit, part-time degree program, adult/continuing education programs, internships. Study abroad program.

Entrance Requirements: Open admission. Options: Peterson's Universal Application, Common Application, early admission, deferred admission. Required: high school transcript. Entrance: noncompetitive. Application deadline: Rolling. Preference given to district residents.

Costs Per Year: Application fee: $0. Area resident tuition: $1464 full-time, $61 per credit hour part-time. State resident tuition: $2088 full-time, $87 per credit hour part-time. Nonresident tuition: $3144 full-time, $131 per credit hour part-time. Mandatory fees: $240 full-time, $10 per credit hour part-time.

Collegiate Environment: Orientation program. Drama-theater group, choral group, student-run newspaper. Social organizations: 3 open to all. Most popular organizations: student government, Phi Theta Kappa, Amnesty International, Multicultural Club. Major annual events: Homecoming, All Campus Day, Blood Drive. Campus security: 24-hour emergency response devices, late night transport-escort service. College housing not available. East Central College Library with 38,863 books, 5,148 microform titles, 278 serials, 1,420 audiovisual materials, an OPAC, and a Web page. Operations spending for 2004 fiscal year: $222,715. 372 computers available on campus for general student use. A campuswide network can be accessed from off-campus. Staffed computer lab on campus.

Community Environment: Union (population 6,000) is the county seat of Franklin County, and is located 40 miles west of St. Louis; see Washington University for information about St. Louis.

■ **EVANGEL UNIVERSITY** *J-5*
1111 North Glenstone
Springfield, MO 65802-2191
Tel: (417)865-2811
Fax: (417)865-9599
E-mail: admissions@evangel.edu
Web Site: http://www.evangel.edu/

Description: Independent, comprehensive, coed, affiliated with Assemblies of God. Awards associate, bachelor's, and master's degrees. Founded 1955. Setting: 80-acre urban campus. Endowment: $3.8 million. Educational spending for 2005 fiscal year: $4728 per student. Total enrollment: 1,801. Faculty: 158 (96 full-time, 62 part-time). Student-undergrad faculty ratio is 18:1. 883 applied, 96% were admitted. 16% from top 10% of their high school class, 42% from top quarter, 67% from top half. 21 valedictorians. Full-time: 1,646 students, 60% women, 40% men. Part-time: 75 students, 57% women, 43% men. Students come from 49 states and territories, 59% from out-of-state, 1% Native American, 4% Hispanic, 3% black, 2% Asian American or Pacific Islander, 0.2% international, 3% 25 or older, 82% live on campus, 8% transferred in. Retention: 75% of full-time freshmen returned the following year. Core. Calendar: semesters. Academic remediation for entering students, services for LD students, advanced placement, accelerated degree program; double major, summer session for credit, part-time degree program, adult/continuing education programs, internships. ROTC: Army.

Entrance Requirements: Options: electronic application, deferred admission, international baccalaureate accepted. Required: high school transcript, SAT or ACT. Recommended: minimum 2.0 high school GPA. Entrance: moderately difficult. Application deadline: 8/1. Notification: continuous.

Costs Per Year: Application fee: $25. Comprehensive fee: $17,370 includes full-time tuition ($12,040), mandatory fees ($710), and college room and board ($4620). College room only: $2270. Full-time tuition and fees vary according to course load. Room and board charges vary according to board plan. Part-time tuition: $469 per credit hour. Part-time mandatory fees: $235 per term.

Collegiate Environment: Orientation program. Drama-theater group, choral group, student-run newspaper, radio station. Social organizations: 36 open to all. Most popular organizations: Evangel Student Government Association, Student Missouri State Teachers Association, Crosswalk, Students in Free Enterprise. Major annual events: homecoming, Harvest Fest, Spring Fling.

Student services: health clinic, personal-psychological counseling. Campus security: 24-hour emergency response devices and patrols, student patrols, late night transport-escort service, controlled dormitory access. 1,292 college housing spaces available; 1,254 were occupied in 2003-04. Freshmen guaranteed college housing. On-campus residence required through senior year. Option: coed housing available. Claude Kendrick Library with 100,691 books, 10,773 microform titles, 1,060 serials, 6,962 audiovisual materials, and an OPAC. Operations spending for 2004 fiscal year: $741,723. 136 computers available on campus for general student use. Staffed computer lab on campus.

Community Environment: See Southwest Missouri State University.

■ **FONTBONNE UNIVERSITY** *F-12*
6800 Wydown Blvd.
St. Louis, MO 63105-3098
Tel: (314)862-3456
Admissions: (314)889-1400
Fax: (314)719-8021
E-mail: pmusen@fontbonne.edu
Web Site: http://www.fontbonne.edu/

Description: Independent Roman Catholic, comprehensive, coed. Awards bachelor's and master's degrees. Founded 1917. Setting: 13-acre suburban campus. Total enrollment: 2,836. Faculty: 372 (72 full-time, 300 part-time). Student-undergrad faculty ratio is 13:1. 618 applied, 66% were admitted. 12% from top 10% of their high school class, 31% from top quarter, 70% from top half. 17 class presidents, 3 valedictorians, 51 student government officers. Full-time: 1,547 students, 76% women, 24% men. Part-time: 531 students, 74% women, 26% men. Students come from 18 states and territories, 1 other country, 10% from out-of-state, 0.4% Native American, 1% Hispanic, 32% black, 1% Asian American or Pacific Islander, 0.4% international, 35% 25 or older, 19% live on campus, 14% transferred in. Retention: 65% of full-time freshmen returned the following year. Academic areas with the most degrees conferred: business/marketing; education; visual and performing arts. Core. Calendar: semesters. Academic remediation for entering students, ESL program, services for LD students, advanced placement, accelerated degree program, self-designed majors, honors program, independent study, distance learning, double major, summer session for credit, adult/continuing education programs, co-op programs and internships, graduate courses open to undergrads. Off campus study at Webster University, Maryville College, Lindenwood College, Missouri Baptist College. ROTC: Army (c).

Entrance Requirements: Options: Common Application, electronic application, early admission, deferred admission. Required: essay, high school transcript, minimum 2.5 high school GPA, SAT or ACT. Recommended: 2 recommendations, interview. Entrance: moderately difficult. Application deadline: 8/1. Notification: continuous.

Costs Per Year: Application fee: $25. Comprehensive fee: $24,428 includes full-time tuition ($17,120), mandatory fees ($320), and college room and board ($6988). Part-time tuition: $465 per credit hour. Part-time mandatory fees: $16 per credit hour.

Collegiate Environment: Orientation program. Drama-theater group, choral group, student-run newspaper. Social organizations: 24 open to all. Most popular organizations: Future Teachers Association, Students for the Enhancement of Black Awareness, Fontbonne Athletic Association, Fontbonne in Service and Humility, Student Government Association. Major annual events: homecoming, Christmas Ball, Springfest. Student services: health clinic, personal-psychological counseling. Campus security: 24-hour patrols, late night transport-escort service, controlled dormitory access. 288 college housing spaces available; 244 were occupied in 2003-04. Freshmen guaranteed college housing. Options: coed, women-only housing available. Fontbonne Library with 52,980 books, 500 serials, 18,319 audiovisual materials, an OPAC, and a Web page. Operations spending for 2004 fiscal year: $454,881. 120 computers available on campus for general student use. A campuswide network can be accessed from student residence rooms and from off campus. Staffed computer lab on campus.

■ **GLOBAL UNIVERSITY OF THE ASSEMBLIES OF GOD** *J-5*
1211 South Glenstone Ave.
Springfield, MO 65804
Tel: (417)862-9533
Free: 800-443-1083
Fax: (417)862-5318
E-mail: jdorn@globaluniversity.edu
Web Site: http://www.globaluniversity.edu/

Description: Independent, comprehensive, coed, affiliated with Assemblies of God. Awards associate, bachelor's, master's, and first professional degrees (offers only external degree programs). Founded 1948. Educational spending for 2005 fiscal year: $1280 per student. Total enrollment: 6,665. Faculty: 618 (57 full-time, 561 part-time). Student-undergrad faculty ratio is 11:1. Students come from 50 states and territories, 127 other countries, 98% from out-of-state, 91% 25 or older. Academic area with the most degrees conferred: theology and religious vocations. Core. Calendar: continuous. Academic remediation for entering students, advanced placement, accelerated degree program, honors program, independent study, distance learning, part-time degree program, external degree program, adult/continuing education programs, co-op programs and internships, graduate courses open to undergrads.

Entrance Requirements: Open admission. Option: international baccalaureate accepted. Required: high school transcript. Recommended: essay. Required for some: 1 recommendation. Entrance: noncompetitive. Application deadline: Rolling.

Costs Per Year: Application fee: $35. Tuition: $2160 full-time, $90 per credit hour part-time. Part-time tuition varies according to class time.

Collegiate Environment: Campus security: 24-hour emergency response devices. College housing not available. Global University Library with 180 serials and a Web page.

■ **GRANTHAM UNIVERSITY** *E-3*
7200 NW 86th St., Ste. M
Kansas City, MO 64153
Free: 800-955-2527
Fax: (816)595-5757
E-mail: admissions@grantham.edu
Web Site: http://www.grantham.edu/

Description: Proprietary, comprehensive, coed. Awards associate, bachelor's, and master's degrees (offers only external degree programs). Founded 1951. Setting: small town campus. Total enrollment: 8,500. Students come from 52 states and territories, 25 other countries, 0% from out-of-state, 96% 25 or older. Core. Calendar: continuous. Advanced placement, accelerated degree program, honors program, independent study, distance learning, part-time degree program, external degree program, adult/continuing education programs.

Entrance Requirements: Open admission. Options: Peterson's Universal Application, electronic application. Required: high school transcript. Entrance: noncompetitive. Application deadline: Rolling. Notification: continuous.

Costs Per Year: Application fee: $0. Tuition: $6978 full-time, $335 per credit hour part-time.

Collegiate Environment: College housing not available.

■ **HANNIBAL-LAGRANGE COLLEGE** *C-9*
2800 Palmyra Rd.
Hannibal, MO 63401-1999
Tel: (573)221-3675
Free: 800-HLG-1119
Admissions: (573)221-3113
Fax: (573)221-6594
E-mail: admissio@hlg.edu
Web Site: http://www.hlg.edu/

Description: Independent Southern Baptist, 4-year, coed. Awards associate and bachelor's degrees. Founded 1858. Setting: 110-acre small town campus. Endowment: $3.3 million. Educational spending for 2005 fiscal year: $5263 per student. Total enrollment: 1,057. Student-undergrad faculty ratio is 12:1. 363 applied, 96% were admitted. 14% from top 10% of their high school class, 33% from top quarter, 59% from top half. Full-time: 873 students, 67% women, 33% men. Part-time: 184 students, 38% women, 62% men. Students come from 22 states and territories, 8 other countries, 20% from out-of-state, 0.1% Native American, 1% Hispanic, 2% black, 0.4% Asian American or Pacific Islander, 3% international, 15% 25 or older, 50% live on campus, 10% transferred in. Retention: 66% of full-time freshmen returned the following year. Academic areas with the most degrees conferred: business/marketing; education; law/legal studies. Core. Calendar: semesters. Academic remediation for entering students, services for LD students, advanced placement, accelerated degree program, honors program, independent study, distance learning, double major, summer session for credit, part-time degree program, adult/continuing education programs, co-op programs and internships. Study abroad program.

Entrance Requirements: Options: Peterson's Universal Application, Common Application, early admission, deferred admission. Required: high school transcript, minimum 2.0 high school GPA, 2 recommendations, SAT or ACT. Entrance: moderately difficult. Application deadline: Rolling. Notification: continuous.

Costs Per Year: Application fee: $25. Comprehensive fee: $16,390 includes full-time tuition ($11,420), mandatory fees ($360), and college room and board ($4610). Full-time tuition and fees vary according to course load. Room and board charges vary according to board plan and housing facility. Part-time tuition: $380 per hour. Part-time mandatory fees: $90 per term. Part-time tuition and fees vary according to course load.

Collegiate Environment: Orientation program. Drama-theater group, choral group, student-run newspaper. Social organizations: 27 open to all. Most popular organizations: Phi Beta Lambda, Student Government, Student Teachers Organization, Phi Beta Delta, Association of Women Students. Major annual events: homecoming, Booster Banquet, Parents' Day. Student services: health clinic, personal-psychological counseling. Campus security: 24-hour emergency response devices and patrols, late night transport-escort service, controlled dormitory access. 481 college housing spaces available; 447 were occupied in 2003-04. Freshmen guaranteed college housing. Options: men-only, women-only housing available. L. A. Foster Library with 71,680 books, 20,692 microform titles, 516 serials, 6,605 audiovisual materials, and an OPAC. Operations spending for 2004 fiscal year: $354,247. 76 computers available on campus for general student use. A campuswide network can be accessed from student residence rooms and from off campus. Staffed computer lab on campus.

Community Environment: The boyhood home of Mark Twain, Hannibal (population 18,698), is located on the west bank of the Mississippi River, 120 miles north of St. Louis. Buses and trains are the principal forms of transportation as well as a municipal airport that serves the area. A public library, YMCA, churches, a music association, and numerous civic and service organizations are a part of the community. Some recreational activities include swimming, bowling, and fishing.

■ **HARRIS-STOWE STATE UNIVERSITY** *F-12*
3026 Laclede Ave.
St. Louis, MO 63103-2136
Tel: (314)340-3366
Admissions: (314)340-3301
Fax: (314)340-3322
Web Site: http://www.hssu.edu/

Description: State-supported, 4-year, coed. Part of Missouri Coordinating Board for Higher Education. Awards bachelor's degrees. Founded 1857. Setting: 22-acre urban campus. Educational spending for 2005 fiscal year: $4100 per student. Total enrollment: 1,662. Student-undergrad faculty ratio is 16:1. 21 valedictorians. Full-time: 970 students, 69% women, 31% men. Part-time: 692 students, 73% women, 27% men. Students come from 9 states and territories, 19 other countries, 7% from out-of-state, 0.3% Native American, 0.4% Hispanic, 87% black, 0.1% Asian American or Pacific Islander, 1% international, 42% 25 or older, 14% transferred in. Academic areas with the most degrees conferred: business/marketing; education; interdisciplinary studies. Core. Calendar: semesters. Academic remediation for entering students, services for LD students, advanced placement, self-designed majors, summer session for credit, part-time degree program, co-op programs and internships. Off campus study at Saint Louis University, University of Missouri-St. Louis. ROTC: Air Force (c).

Entrance Requirements: Open admission. Options: early admission, deferred admission. Required: high school transcript, SAT or ACT. Entrance: noncompetitive. Application deadline: Rolling.

Costs Per Year: Application fee: $15. State resident tuition: $4650 full-time, $145 per hour part-time. Nonresident tuition: $8570 full-time, $285.65 per hour part-time. Mandatory fees: $150 full-time, $150 per term part-time. College room only: $5400.

Collegiate Environment: Drama-theater group, choral group. Social organizations: 43 open to all; national fraternities, national sororities; 1% of eligible men and 1% of eligible women are members. Most popular organizations: Drama Club, concert chorale, Student Government Association, Multicultural Council, Student Ambassadors. Major annual events: Homecoming, Commencement, Organization Day. Student services: health clinic, personal-psychological counseling. Campus security: 24-hour emergency response devices, student patrols, late night transport-escort service, 16-hour patrols by trained security personnel Monday through Friday, 24-hour weekend and holiday patrols. College housing not available. Southwestern Bell Library and Technology Center with 60,000 books, 8,700 microform titles, 340 serials, 15 audiovisual materials, and an OPAC. Operations spending for 2004 fiscal year: $354,589. 251 computers available on campus for general student use. A campuswide network can be accessed from off-campus. Staffed computer lab on campus.

■ **HERITAGE COLLEGE** *E-3*
534 East 99th St.
Kansas City, MO 64131-4203
Tel: (816)942-5474
Fax: (816)942-5405
Web Site: http://www.heritage-education.com/
Description: Proprietary, 2-year, coed.

■ **HICKEY COLLEGE** *F-12*
940 West Port Plaza, Ste. 101
St. Louis, MO 63146
Tel: (314)434-2212
Free: 800-777-1544
Fax: (314)434-1974
Web Site: http://www.hickeycollege.edu/
Description: Proprietary, primarily 2-year, coed. Awards diplomas, terminal associate, and bachelor's degrees. Founded 1933. Setting: suburban campus. Total enrollment: 610. Student-undergrad faculty ratio is 38:1. 33% from out-of-state. Calendar: semesters. Accelerated degree program.
Entrance Requirements: Required: high school transcript, interview. Entrance: minimally difficult. Application deadline: Rolling.
Collegiate Environment: 109 computers available on campus for general student use.

■ **HIGH-TECH INSTITUTE** *E-3*
9001 State Line Rd.
Kansas City, MO 64114
Tel: (602)279-9700
Web Site: http://www.high-techinstitute.com/
Description: Proprietary, 2-year, coed. Founded 2003. Calendar: semesters.

■ **IHM HEALTH STUDIES CENTER** *F-12*
2500 Abbott Place
St. Louis, MO 63143-2636
Tel: (314)768-1234
Fax: (314)768-1595
E-mail: meyer@abbottems.org
Web Site: http://www.ihmhealthstudies.com/
Description: Independent, 2-year, coed. Awards certificates and terminal associate degrees. Founded 1977. Setting: suburban campus. Total enrollment: 136. 1% Native American, 1% Hispanic, 18% black, 1% Asian American or Pacific Islander, 0% international. Calendar: trimesters.

■ **ITT TECHNICAL INSTITUTE (ARNOLD)** *R-15*
1930 Meyer Drury Dr.
Arnold, MO 63010
Tel: (636)464-6600; 888-488-1082
Web Site: http://www.itt-tech.edu/
Description: Proprietary, primarily 2-year, coed. Part of ITT Educational Services, Inc. Awards terminal associate and bachelor's degrees. Core.
Entrance Requirements: Option: deferred admission. Required: high school transcript, interview, Wonderlic aptitude test. Recommended: recommendations. Entrance: minimally difficult. Application deadline: Rolling. Notification: continuous.
Costs Per Year: Application fee: $100.
Collegiate Environment: Orientation program. College housing not available.

■ **ITT TECHNICAL INSTITUTE (EARTH CITY)** *F-11*
13505 Lakefront Dr.
Earth City, MO 63045-1412
Tel: (314)298-7800
Free: 800-235-5488
Fax: (314)298-0559
Web Site: http://www.itt-tech.edu/
Description: Proprietary, primarily 2-year, coed. Part of ITT Educational Services, Inc. Awards terminal associate and bachelor's degrees. Founded 1936. Setting: 2-acre suburban campus with easy access to St. Louis. Core.

Entrance Requirements: Option: deferred admission. Required: high school transcript, interview, Wonderlic aptitude test. Recommended: recommendations. Entrance: minimally difficult. Application deadline: Rolling. Notification: continuous.
Costs Per Year: Application fee: $100.
Collegiate Environment: Orientation program. College housing not available.

■ **ITT TECHNICAL INSTITUTE (KANSAS CITY)** *E-3*
1740 West 92nd St., Ste. 10
Kansas City, MO 64114
877-488-1442
Admissions: (816)276-1400
Web Site: http://www.itt-tech.edu/
Description: primarily 2-year, coed. Awards terminal associate and bachelor's degrees.
Entrance Requirements: Required: high school transcript, interview, Wonderlic aptitude test. Recommended: recommendations. Application deadline: Rolling. Notification: continuous.
Costs Per Year: Application fee: $100.

■ **JEFFERSON COLLEGE** *G-11*
1000 Viking Dr.
Hillsboro, MO 63050-2441
Tel: (636)797-3000
Fax: (636)789-4012
Web Site: http://www.jeffco.edu/
Description: State-supported, 2-year, coed. Part of Missouri Coordinating Board for Higher Education. Awards certificates, transfer associate, and terminal associate degrees. Founded 1963. Setting: 480-acre rural campus with easy access to St. Louis. Endowment: $769,631. Educational spending for 2005 fiscal year: $2651 per student. Total enrollment: 4,065. 2,927 applied, 100% were admitted. 8% from top 10% of their high school class, 24% from top quarter, 57% from top half. Full-time: 2,176 students, 59% women, 41% men. Part-time: 1,889 students, 63% women, 37% men. Students come from 6 states and territories, 1% from out-of-state, 1% Native American, 1% Hispanic, 1% black, 0.3% Asian American or Pacific Islander, 1% international, 17% 25 or older, 15% live on campus, 5% transferred in. Core. Calendar: semesters. Academic remediation for entering students, ESL program, services for LD students, advanced placement, freshman honors college, honors program, independent study, distance learning, double major, summer session for credit, part-time degree program, adult/continuing education programs, internships. Off campus study at St. Louis Community College, Heremac and Forest Park campuses. Study abroad program.
Entrance Requirements: Open admission except for veterinary technology, nursing, emergency medical technician programs and police training academy. Options: Peterson's Universal Application, electronic application, early admission. Required: high school transcript. Placement: ACT COMPASS required; ACT recommended. Entrance: noncompetitive. Application deadline: Rolling.
Collegiate Environment: Orientation program. Drama-theater group, choral group, student-run newspaper. Social organizations: 15 open to all. Most popular organizations: Student Senate, nursing associations, Baptist Student Unit, Phi Beta Lambda, Phi Theta Kappa. Major annual events: Special Olympics, Shocktober Night, Spring Fling. Student services: personal-psychological counseling. Campus security: 24-hour patrols. 216 college housing spaces available; 150 were occupied in 2003-04. No special consideration for freshman housing applicants. Jefferson College Library plus 1 other with 70,402 books, 45,014 microform titles, 242 serials, 5,085 audiovisual materials, an OPAC, and a Web page. Operations spending for 2004 fiscal year: $357,546. 350 computers available on campus for general student use. A campuswide network can be accessed. Staffed computer lab on campus.
Community Environment: Hillsboro (population 1,508) is a rural community with a temperate climate. It is located within a 30-minute drive of metropolitan St. Louis. The town is situated near several small lakes, which are excellent for fishing and boating. Hillsboro is the headquarters for the county health unit. The community facilities include civic clubs, a shopping center, churches of major denominations, and a college library. The recreational, social and cultural facilities of St. Louis are accessible. Opportunities for part-time employment are good. See also Washington University for information on St. Louis.

■ KANSAS CITY ART INSTITUTE *E-3*

4415 Warwick Blvd.
Kansas City, MO 64111-1874
Tel: (816)472-4852
Free: 800-522-5224
Admissions: (816)474-5224
Fax: (816)531-6296
E-mail: admiss@kcai.edu
Web Site: http://www.kcai.edu/

Description: Independent, 4-year, coed. Awards bachelor's degrees. Founded 1885. Setting: 18-acre urban campus. Endowment: $19.3 million. Educational spending for 2005 fiscal year: $4523 per student. Total enrollment: 588. Student-undergrad faculty ratio is 12:1. 436 applied, 74% were admitted. 12% from top 10% of their high school class, 33% from top quarter, 69% from top half. Full-time: 576 students, 56% women, 44% men. Part-time: 12 students, 92% women, 8% men. Students come from 38 states and territories, 14 other countries, 62% from out-of-state, 1% Native American, 6% Hispanic, 4% black, 4% Asian American or Pacific Islander, 3% international, 9% 25 or older, 25% live on campus, 10% transferred in. Retention: 70% of full-time freshmen returned the following year. Academic area with the most degrees conferred: visual and performing arts. Core. Calendar: semesters. Academic remediation for entering students, ESL program, services for LD students, advanced placement, independent study, double major, summer session for credit, adult/continuing education programs, co-op programs and internships. Off campus study at New York Studio Program, AICAD School Exchange. Study abroad program.
Entrance Requirements: Option: deferred admission. Required: essay, high school transcript, minimum 2.5 high school GPA, 2 recommendations, portfolio, statement of purpose, SAT or ACT. Recommended: interview. Entrance: moderately difficult. Application deadline: Rolling. Notification: continuous until 8/1.
Costs Per Year: Application fee: $35. Comprehensive fee: $29,542 includes full-time tuition ($21,446), mandatory fees ($946), and college room and board ($7150). Full-time tuition and fees vary according to program. Room and board charges vary according to board plan and housing facility. Part-time tuition: $850 per credit hour. Part-time mandatory fees: $46 per credit hour. Part-time tuition and fees vary according to program.
Collegiate Environment: Orientation program. Most popular organizations: Student Union, Student Gallery Committee, Ethnic Student Association. Major annual events: Department Openings, Visiting Artist Series, Student Film Series. Student services: personal-psychological counseling. Campus security: 24-hour emergency response devices and patrols, late night transport-escort service, controlled dormitory access. 160 college housing spaces available; 155 were occupied in 2003-04. Freshmen given priority for college housing. On-campus residence required in freshman year. Option: coed housing available. Jannes Library and Learning Center plus 1 other with 32,235 books, 133 serials, 101,688 audiovisual materials, an OPAC, and a Web page. Operations spending for 2004 fiscal year: $245,000. 100 computers available on campus for general student use. Computer purchase/lease plans available. A campuswide network can be accessed from student residence rooms and from off campus. Staffed computer lab on campus.
Community Environment: See University of Missouri - Kansas City.

■ KANSAS CITY COLLEGE *E-3*

402 East Bannister Rd., Ste. A
Kansas City, MO 64131
Tel: (816)444-2232; 877-582-3963
Fax: (816)444-3142
Web Site: http://www.metropolitancollege.edu/

Description: Proprietary, 4-year, coed. Awards associate and bachelor's degrees. Total enrollment: 123. 42 applied, 90% were admitted. Calendar: trimesters.
Entrance Requirements: Required: high school transcript, interview. Required for some: ACT. Application deadline: 9/24.
Collegiate Environment: College housing not available.

■ LINCOLN UNIVERSITY *F-8*

820 Chestnut St.
Jefferson City, MO 65102
Tel: (573)681-5000
Free: 800-521-5052
Admissions: (573)681-5599
Fax: (573)681-6074

E-mail: enroll@lincolnu.edu
Web Site: http://www.lincolnu.edu/

Description: State-supported, comprehensive, coed. Part of Missouri Coordinating Board for Higher Education. Awards associate, bachelor's, and master's degrees and post-master's certificates. Founded 1866. Setting: 152-acre small town campus. Endowment: $1.3 million. Research spending for 2004 fiscal year: $1.8 million. Educational spending for 2005 fiscal year: $4536 per student. Total enrollment: 3,180. Faculty: 174 (127 full-time, 47 part-time). Student-undergrad faculty ratio is 17:1. 1,487 applied, 94% were admitted. 5% from top 10% of their high school class, 17% from top quarter, 43% from top half. Full-time: 2,017 students, 56% women, 44% men. Part-time: 936 students, 69% women, 31% men. Students come from 33 states and territories, 27 other countries, 15% from out-of-state, 0.5% Native American, 2% Hispanic, 46% black, 1% Asian American or Pacific Islander, 5% international, 25% 25 or older, 28% live on campus, 7% transferred in. Retention: 55% of full-time freshmen returned the following year. Academic areas with the most degrees conferred: business/marketing; education; computer and information sciences. Core. Calendar: semesters. Academic remediation for entering students, services for LD students, advanced placement, accelerated degree program, self-designed majors, freshman honors college, honors program, independent study, double major, summer session for credit, part-time degree program, adult/continuing education programs, co-op programs and internships, graduate courses open to undergrads. ROTC: Army.
Entrance Requirements: Open admission for state residents. Options: early admission, deferred admission. Required: high school transcript. Required for some: minimum 2.0 high school GPA. Entrance: noncompetitive. Application deadline: 7/15. Notification: continuous.
Costs Per Year: Application fee: $17. State resident tuition: $4412 full-time, $147.08 per credit hour part-time. Nonresident tuition: $8059 full-time, $268.62 per credit hour part-time. Mandatory fees: $190 full-time, $5 per credit hour part-time, $20 per term part-time. College room and board: $3790. College room only: $1850.
Collegiate Environment: Orientation program. Drama-theater group, choral group, marching band, student-run newspaper, radio station. Social organizations: 40 open to all; national fraternities, national sororities, local fraternities, local sororities. Major annual events: homecoming, Campus Visitation Day, Founders' Day. Student services: health clinic, personal-psychological counseling. Campus security: 24-hour emergency response devices and patrols, student patrols, late night transport-escort service, controlled dormitory access. 814 college housing spaces available; 744 were occupied in 2003-04. No special consideration for freshman housing applicants. On-campus residence required through sophomore year. Options: coed, men-only, women-only housing available. Inman Page Library with 187,956 books, 91,582 microform titles, 397 serials, 14,521 audiovisual materials, an OPAC, and a Web page. Operations spending for 2004 fiscal year: $828,132. 141 computers available on campus for general student use. Computer purchase/lease plans available. A campuswide network can be accessed. Staffed computer lab on campus.

■ LINDENWOOD UNIVERSITY *F-11*

209 South Kingshighway
St. Charles, MO 63301-1695
Tel: (636)949-2000
Admissions: (636)949-4993
Fax: (636)949-4910
E-mail: sguffey@lindenwood.edu
Web Site: http://www.lindenwood.edu/

Description: Independent Presbyterian, comprehensive, coed. Awards bachelor's and master's degrees and post-master's certificates (education specialist). Founded 1827. Setting: 420-acre suburban campus with easy access to St. Louis. Endowment: $32.8 million. Educational spending for 2005 fiscal year: $4316 per student. Total enrollment: 9,076. Faculty: 608 (208 full-time, 400 part-time). Student-undergrad faculty ratio is 15:1. 2,906 applied, 43% were admitted. 14% from top 10% of their high school class, 39% from top quarter, 75% from top half. 4 National Merit Scholars, 18 class presidents, 15 valedictorians, 211 student government officers. Full-time: 5,092 students, 56% women, 44% men. Part-time: 646 students, 65% women, 35% men. Students come from 44 states and territories, 61 other countries, 17% from out-of-state, 0.4% Native American, 1% Hispanic, 12% black, 1% Asian American or Pacific Islander, 7% international, 33% 25 or older, 76% live on campus, 14% transferred in. Retention: 69% of full-time freshmen returned the following year. Academic areas with the most degrees conferred: business/marketing; education; communications/journalism;

social sciences; visual and performing arts. Core. Calendar: 4-1-4 for daytime programs; quarters and trimesters for evening programs. Academic remediation for entering students, services for LD students, advanced placement, accelerated degree program, self-designed majors, freshman honors college, honors program, independent study, double major, summer session for credit, part-time degree program, adult/continuing education programs, co-op programs and internships, graduate courses open to undergrads. Off campus study at St. Louis Private College Consortium, Washington University in St. Louis, University of Missouri-Columbia. Study abroad program. ROTC: Army, Air Force (c).

Entrance Requirements: Options: Peterson's Universal Application, early admission, deferred admission, international baccalaureate accepted. Required: high school transcript, minimum ACT score of 20 or minimum SAT score of 900, SAT or ACT. Recommended: minimum 2.25 high school GPA, interview. Required for some: essay, recommendations, interview. Entrance: moderately difficult. Application deadline: Rolling.

Costs Per Year: Application fee: $30. Comprehensive fee: $18,240 includes full-time tuition ($12,000), mandatory fees ($240), and college room and board ($6000). College room only: $3000. Part-time tuition: $330 per credit hour.

Collegiate Environment: Orientation program. Drama-theater group, choral group, marching band, student-run newspaper, radio station. Social organizations: 65 open to all; national fraternities, national sororities, local fraternities, local sororities; 6% of eligible men and 10% of eligible women are members. Most popular organizations: Lindenwood Student Government, American Humanics, Delta Zeta, Honors College, Inter-cultural Club. Major annual events: Spring Fling, Homecoming, Welcome Week. Student services: career placement services. Campus security: 24-hour emergency response devices and patrols, late night transport-escort service, controlled dormitory access. 2,856 college housing spaces available; 2,775 were occupied in 2003-04. Freshmen guaranteed college housing. Options: men-only, women-only housing available. Butler Library with 122,461 books, 19,250 microform titles, 28,830 serials, 1,531 audiovisual materials, an OPAC, and a Web page. Operations spending for 2004 fiscal year: $762,885. 160 computers available on campus for general student use. Computer purchase/lease plans available. A campuswide network can be accessed from student residence rooms and from off campus. Staffed computer lab on campus.

Community Environment: St. Charles was one of the first settlements on the Missouri River. It is located 20 miles from St. Louis. An airport is located ten miles away. Community facilities include restaurants, shopping, churches, hospital, hotels, motels, and recreation centers. Swimming, boating, and skating are some of the recreational activities found in St. Charles County.

■ **LINN STATE TECHNICAL COLLEGE** *G-8*
One Technology Dr.
Linn, MO 65051-9606
Tel: (573)897-5000
Free: 800-743-TECH
Admissions: (573)897-5196
Web Site: http://www.linnstate.edu/

Description: State-supported, 2-year, coed. Awards certificates and terminal associate degrees. Founded 1961. Setting: 249-acre rural campus. Endowment: $48,357. Educational spending for 2005 fiscal year: $6540 per student. Total enrollment: 878. Student-undergrad faculty ratio is 10:1. 976 applied, 61% were admitted. 6% from top 10% of their high school class, 14% from top quarter, 28% from top half. Full-time: 785 students, 9% women, 91% men. Part-time: 93 students, 19% women, 81% men. Students come from 11 states and territories, 2 other countries, 1% from out-of-state, 0.4% Native American, 1% Hispanic, 1% black, 0.4% Asian American or Pacific Islander, 1% international, 13% 25 or older, 15% live on campus, 9% transferred in. Retention: 58% of full-time freshmen returned the following year. Core. Calendar: semesters. Academic remediation for entering students, ESL program, services for LD students, advanced placement, accelerated degree program, independent study, distance learning, double major, summer session for credit, part-time degree program, adult/continuing education programs, co-op programs and internships. Off campus study at PTA-Jefferson City, MO, LPH, MIM, MNT-Mexico, MO. ROTC: Army.

Entrance Requirements: Options: Common Application, electronic application. Required: high school transcript, ACT ASSET, ACT COMPASS. Required for some: essay, recommendations, interview, driving record, physical examination, ACT. Placement: ACT, ACT ASSET, ACT COMPASS required for some. Entrance: moderately difficult. Notification: continuous.

Costs Per Year: Application fee: $0. State resident tuition: $4080 full-time, $136 per credit part-time. Nonresident tuition: $8160 full-time, $272 per credit part-time. Mandatory fees: $630 full-time, $21 per credit part-time. College room and board: $1870. College room only: $1445.

Collegiate Environment: Orientation program. Social organizations: 12 open to all. Most popular organizations: Skills USA-VICA, Phi Theta Kappa, Student Government Association, Aviation Club, Electricity Club. Major annual events: Welcome Back Bash, Casino Night, Valentine Dance. Student services: personal-psychological counseling. Campus security: 24-hour emergency response devices, student patrols, controlled dormitory access, indoor and outdoor surveillance cameras. 144 college housing spaces available; 131 were occupied in 2003-04. No special consideration for freshman housing applicants. Options: coed, men-only, women-only housing available. Linn State Technical College Library plus 2 others with 13,774 books, 132 serials, 729 audiovisual materials, an OPAC, and a Web page. Operations spending for 2004 fiscal year: $236,863. 51 computers available on campus for general student use. A campuswide network can be accessed from student residence rooms. Staffed computer lab on campus.

■ **LOGAN UNIVERSITY-COLLEGE OF CHIROPRACTIC** *P-14*
1851 Schoettler Rd., Box 1065
Chesterfield, MO 63006-1065
Tel: (636)227-2100
Free: 800-533-9210
Fax: (636)227-9338
E-mail: loganadm@logan.edu
Web Site: http://www.logan.edu/

Description: Independent, upper-level, coed. Awards bachelor's and first professional degrees. Founded 1935. Setting: 111-acre suburban campus with easy access to St. Louis. Endowment: $11 million. Research spending for 2004 fiscal year: $475,268. Educational spending for 2005 fiscal year: $6590 per student. Total enrollment: 1,076. Faculty: 87 (41 full-time, 46 part-time). Student-undergrad faculty ratio is 12:1. 207 applied, 96% were admitted. Full-time: 76 students, 22% women, 78% men. Part-time: 35 students, 34% women, 66% men. Students come from 24 states and territories, 1 other country, 61% from out-of-state, 1% Native American, 5% Hispanic, 4% black, 1% Asian American or Pacific Islander, 2% international, 42% 25 or older, 86% transferred in. Academic area with the most degrees conferred: biological/life sciences. Core. Calendar: trimesters. Services for LD students, advanced placement, independent study, distance learning, adult/continuing education programs, internships, graduate courses open to undergrads.

Costs Per Year: Application fee: $50. Tuition: $3420 full-time, $95 per credit hour part-time. Mandatory fees: $330 full-time, $110 per term part-time.

Collegiate Environment: Orientation program. Student-run newspaper. Social organizations: 24 open to all; national fraternities, national sororities. Most popular organizations: Pi Kappa Chi, Lambda Kappa Chi, Omega Sigma Pi, Student American Chiropractic Association, Student International Chiropractic Association. Major annual events: Field Day, Homecoming, Graduation celebrations. Student services: health clinic, personal-psychological counseling. Campus security: 24-hour patrols. College housing not available. Learning Resources Center with 10,777 books, 225 serials, 1,972 audiovisual materials, an OPAC, and a Web page. Operations spending for 2004 fiscal year: $525,743. 75 computers available on campus for general student use. A campuswide network can be accessed. Staffed computer lab on campus.

■ **LONGVIEW COMMUNITY COLLEGE** *E-4*
500 Southwest Longview Rd.
Lee's Summit, MO 64081-2105
Tel: (816)672-2000
Admissions: (816)672-2249
Web Site: http://www.mcckc.edu

Description: State and locally supported, 2-year, coed. Part of Metropolitan Community Colleges System. Awards certificates, transfer associate, and terminal associate degrees. Founded 1969. Setting: 147-acre suburban campus with easy access to Kansas City. System endowment: $2.4 million. Educational spending for 2005 fiscal year: $2970 per student. Total enrollment: 5,667. Student-undergrad faculty ratio is 19:1. 963 applied, 100% were admitted. Full-time: 2,419 students, 52% women, 48% men. Part-time: 3,248 students, 62% women, 38% men. Students come from 6 states and territories, 1% from out-of-state, 0.2% Native American, 2% Hispanic, 11% black, 1% Asian American or Pacific Islander, 0.03% international, 29% 25 or older, 5% transferred in. Retention: 55% of full-time freshmen returned the following year. Core. Calendar: semesters. Academic remediation for entering students, ESL program, services for LD students, advanced placement, accelerated degree program, honors program, distance learning, summer session for credit, part-time degree program, adult/continuing education programs, co-op programs and internships. Off campus study at Johnson County Community College.

Entrance Requirements: Open admission. Options: early admission, deferred admission. Entrance: noncompetitive. Application deadline: Rolling.

Costs Per Year: Application fee: $0. Area resident tuition: $2190 full-time, $73 per hour part-time. State resident tuition: $3990 full-time, $133 per hour part-time. Nonresident tuition: $5400 full-time, $180 per hour part-time. Mandatory fees: $150 full-time.

Collegiate Environment: Drama-theater group, choral group, student-run newspaper. Social organizations: national fraternities. Most popular organizations: student newspaper, student government, Phi Theta Kappa, Longview Mighty Voices Choir, Longview Broadcasting Network. Major annual events: family Easter celebration, Fall Dance, College Transfer Day. Student services: personal-psychological counseling. Campus security: 24-hour patrols. College housing not available. Longview Community College Library with 56,266 books, 1,583 microform titles, 288 serials, 806 audiovisual materials, an OPAC, and a Web page. Operations spending for 2004 fiscal year: $452,150. 650 computers available on campus for general student use. A campuswide network can be accessed from off-campus. Staffed computer lab on campus.

Community Environment: See University of Missouri Kansas City.

■ **MAPLE WOODS COMMUNITY COLLEGE** *E-3*

2601 Northeast Barry Rd.
Kansas City, MO 64156-1299
Tel: (816)437-3000
Admissions: (816)437-3108
Web Site: http://www.mcckc.edu

Description: State and locally supported, 2-year, coed. Part of Metropolitan Community Colleges System. Awards certificates, transfer associate, and terminal associate degrees. Founded 1969. Setting: 205-acre suburban campus. System endowment: $2.4 million. Educational spending for 2005 fiscal year: $2705 per student. Total enrollment: 4,442. Student-undergrad faculty ratio is 18:1. 856 applied, 100% were admitted. Full-time: 1,817 students, 57% women, 43% men. Part-time: 2,625 students, 62% women, 38% men. Students come from 4 states and territories, 1% from out-of-state, 0.3% Native American, 2% Hispanic, 3% black, 1% Asian American or Pacific Islander, 0% international, 26% 25 or older, 5% transferred in. Retention: 59% of full-time freshmen returned the following year. Core. Calendar: semesters. Academic remediation for entering students, ESL program, services for LD students, advanced placement, accelerated degree program, honors program, distance learning, summer session for credit, part-time degree program, adult/continuing education programs, co-op programs and internships. Off campus study at Johnson County Community College.

Entrance Requirements: Open admission except for veterinary technology. Options: early admission, deferred admission. Entrance: noncompetitive. Application deadline: Rolling. Notification: continuous.

Costs Per Year: Application fee: $0. Area resident tuition: $2190 full-time, $73 per hour part-time. State resident tuition: $3990 full-time, $133 per hour part-time. Nonresident tuition: $5400 full-time, $180 per hour part-time. Mandatory fees: $150 full-time, $5 per hour part-time.

Collegiate Environment: Drama-theater group, choral group, student-run newspaper. Social organizations: national fraternities. Most popular organizations: Student Activities Council, Art Club, Friends of All Cultures, Phi Theta Kappa, Engineering Club. Major annual events: Spring Fest, Family Christmas, Blood Drive. Student services: personal-psychological counseling. Campus security: 24-hour patrols, late night transport-escort service. College housing not available. Maple Woods Community College Library with 32,906 books, 21,488 microform titles, 250 serials, 783 audiovisual materials, and an OPAC. Operations spending for 2004 fiscal year: $405,755. 400 computers available on campus for general student use. A campuswide network can be accessed from off-campus. Staffed computer lab on campus.

Community Environment: See University of Missouri - Kansas City.

■ **MARYVILLE UNIVERSITY OF SAINT LOUIS** *F-12*

13550 Conway Rd.
St. Louis, MO 63141-7299
Tel: (314)529-9300
Free: 800-627-9855
Admissions: (314)529-9350

Fax: (314)529-9927
E-mail: admissions@maryville.edu
Web Site: http://www.maryville.edu/

Description: Independent, comprehensive, coed. Awards bachelor's, master's, and doctoral degrees. Founded 1872. Setting: 130-acre suburban campus. Endowment: $29.9 million. Research spending for 2004 fiscal year: $63,580. Educational spending for 2005 fiscal year: $6848 per student. Total enrollment: 3,223. Faculty: 343 (99 full-time, 244 part-time). Student-undergrad faculty ratio is 13:1. 1,357 applied, 73% were admitted. 24% from top 10% of their high school class, 54% from top quarter, 84% from top half. 12 valedictorians, 3 student government officers. Full-time: 1,610 students, 74% women, 26% men. Part-time: 1,049 students, 74% women, 26% men. Students come from 18 states and territories, 21 other countries, 12% from out-of-state, 0.5% Native American, 1% Hispanic, 6% black, 2% Asian American or Pacific Islander, 1% international, 39% 25 or older, 32% live on campus, 14% transferred in. Retention: 77% of full-time freshmen returned the following year. Academic areas with the most degrees conferred: business/marketing; health professions and related sciences; psychology. Core. Calendar: semesters. ESL program, services for LD students, advanced placement, accelerated degree program, self-designed majors, freshman honors college, honors program, independent study, distance learning, double major, summer session for credit, part-time degree program, adult/continuing education programs, co-op programs and internships, graduate courses open to undergrads. Off campus study at Fontbonne University, Lindenwood University, Webster University, Missouri Baptist University. Study abroad program. ROTC: Army (c).

Entrance Requirements: Options: Peterson's Universal Application, electronic application, early admission, deferred admission, international baccalaureate accepted. Required: high school transcript, minimum 2.5 high school GPA, SAT or ACT. Required for some: essay, recommendations, interview, audition, portfolio. Entrance: moderately difficult. Application deadline: 8/15. Notification: continuous.

Costs Per Year: Application fee: $25. Comprehensive fee: $24,670 includes full-time tuition ($17,000), mandatory fees ($320), and college room and board ($7350). College room only: $6425. Full-time tuition and fees vary according to course load. Room and board charges vary according to housing facility. Part-time tuition: $510 per credit hour. Part-time mandatory fees: $80 per term. Part-time tuition and fees vary according to class time.

Collegiate Environment: Orientation program. Drama-theater group, choral group, student-run newspaper. Social organizations: 33 open to all. Most popular organizations: Campus Activity Board, Physical Therapy Club, Maryville University Student Government, Community Service Club, Campus Crusade for Christ. Major annual events: NEXFALAWANACYA ('Next Fall I Want to See You' spring semester send-off programs), Cram Jam, Activities Fair. Student services: health clinic, personal-psychological counseling. Campus security: 24-hour emergency response devices and patrols, late night transport-escort service, controlled dormitory access, video security system in residence halls, self-defense and education programs. 576 college housing spaces available; 538 were occupied in 2003-04. No special consideration for freshman housing applicants. Option: coed housing available. Maryville University Library with 209,418 books, 521,965 microform titles, 4,920 serials, 11,257 audiovisual materials, an OPAC, and a Web page. Operations spending for 2004 fiscal year: $1.1 million. 401 computers available on campus for general student use. A campuswide network can be accessed from student residence rooms and from off campus. Staffed computer lab on campus.

Community Environment: The campus is located at Highway 40/I-64 and Woods Mill Road, 2 miles west of I-270 in West St. Louis County. The campus is nestled on 130 acres of rolling hills, with wooded areas, creeks, and two lakes. It is within 20 minutes of downtown St. Louis which provides many social, cultural, athletic, and entertainment facilities including, the St. Louis Art Museum, St. Louis Symphony Orchestra, St. Louis Science Center, Missouri Botanical Garden, Municipal Opera, ballet, rock performances, theaters, restaurants, a world renown zoo, a large park system, as well as professional baseball, hockey, soccer, and football, and an International airport.

■ **MESSENGER COLLEGE** *J-3*

PO Box 4050
Joplin, MO 64803
Tel: (417)624-7070
Fax: (417)624-5070
E-mail: tstump@messengercollege.edu
Web Site: http://www.messengercollege.edu/

Description: Independent Pentecostal, 4-year, coed. Awards associate and bachelor's degrees. Founded 1987. Setting: 16-acre suburban campus with easy access to Springfield. Endowment: $289,532. Educational spending for 2005 fiscal year: $1286 per student. Total enrollment: 100. 45 applied, 87% were admitted. 5 valedictorians, 5 student government officers. Full-time: 84 students, 45% women, 55% men. Part-time: 16 students, 56% women, 44% men. Students come from 17 states and territories, 49% from out-of-state, 6% Native American, 8% Hispanic, 4% black, 0% Asian American or Pacific Islander, 0% international, 23% 25 or older, 7% transferred in. Retention: 71% of full-time freshmen returned the following year. Core. Calendar: semesters. Academic remediation for entering students, honors program, independent study, distance learning, double major, part-time degree program, external degree program, co-op programs and internships.

Entrance Requirements: Options: Common Application, electronic application. Required: essay, high school transcript, minimum 2.0 high school GPA, 3 recommendations, health form, SAT or ACT. Required for some: interview. Entrance: moderately difficult. Application deadline: 8/1. Notification: continuous until 8/15.

Costs Per Year: Application fee: $35. Comprehensive fee: $8910 includes full-time tuition ($4950), mandatory fees ($460), and college room and board ($3500). Room and board charges vary according to housing facility. Part-time tuition: $165 per credit hour.

Collegiate Environment: Orientation program. Drama-theater group, choral group. Social organizations: 2 open to all. Most popular organizations: Special Projects Team-Community Service, H.I.M Club-Heart in Missions Club. Major annual events: Spring Banquet, sports events, College Days. Student services: personal-psychological counseling. Campus security: 24-hour emergency response devices, student patrols. 98 college housing spaces available; 64 were occupied in 2003-04. No special consideration for freshman housing applicants. On-campus residence required through sophomore year. Options: men-only, women-only housing available. McDole-McDonald Library with 28,874 books, 114 serials, 326 audiovisual materials, and an OPAC. Operations spending for 2004 fiscal year: $20,000. 5 computers available on campus for general student use. Staffed computer lab on campus.

■ **METRO BUSINESS COLLEGE (CAPE GIRARDEAU)** *J-13*
1732 North Kingshighway
Cape Girardeau, MO 63701
Tel: (573)334-9181
Fax: (573)334-0617
Web Site: http://www.metrobusinesscollege.edu/
Description: Proprietary, primarily 2-year, coed. Awards certificates, diplomas, terminal associate, and bachelor's degrees. Total enrollment: 118. 50% 25 or older.
Entrance Requirements: Entrance: minimally difficult.
Collegiate Environment: College housing not available.

■ **METRO BUSINESS COLLEGE (JEFFERSON CITY)** *F-8*
1407 Southwest Blvd.
Jefferson City, MO 65109
Tel: (573)635-6600
Free: 800-467-0786
Fax: (573)635-6999
E-mail: cheri@metrobusinesscollege.edu
Web Site: http://www.metrobusinesscollege.edu/
Description: Proprietary, 2-year, coed. Awards certificates, diplomas, and terminal associate degrees. Founded 1979. Educational spending for 2005 fiscal year: $10,905 per student. Total enrollment: 155. Student-undergrad faculty ratio is 14:1. 61 applied, 75% were admitted. Full-time: 140 students, 89% women, 11% men. Part-time: 15 students, 100% women. 1% from out-of-state, 0% Native American, 1% Hispanic, 19% black, 0% Asian American or Pacific Islander, 0% international.
Entrance Requirements: Required: essay, high school transcript, interview, Wonderlic. Application deadline: Rolling. Notification: continuous.
Costs Per Year: Application fee: $25. Tuition: $8385 full-time. Mandatory fees: $125 full-time.
Collegiate Environment: Student-run newspaper. Student services: personal-psychological counseling.

■ **METRO BUSINESS COLLEGE (ROLLA)** *H-8*
1202 East State Route 72
Rolla, MO 65401
Tel: (573)364-8464

Free: 800-467-0785
Admissions: (314)364-8464
Fax: (573)364-8077
E-mail: cbarker@metrobusinesscollege.edu
Web Site: http://www.metrobusinesscollege.edu/
Description: Proprietary, 2-year, coed. Founded 1979.

■ **METROPOLITAN COMMUNITY COLLEGE-BUSINESS & TECHNOLOGY COLLEGE** *E-3*
1775 Universal Ave.
Kansas City, MO 64120
Tel: (816)482-5210
Free: 800-841-7158
Web Site: http://www.mcckc.edu
Description: State and locally supported, 2-year, coed. Part of Metropolitan Community Colleges. Awards certificates, transfer associate, and terminal associate degrees. Founded 1995. Setting: 23-acre urban campus. Endowment: $2.4 million. Educational spending for 2005 fiscal year: $7742 per student. Total enrollment: 602. Student-undergrad faculty ratio is 13:1. 68 applied, 100% were admitted. Full-time: 118 students, 9% women, 91% men. Part-time: 484 students, 10% women, 90% men. Students come from 2 states and territories, 2 other countries, 2% from out-of-state, 0.4% Native American, 1% Hispanic, 5% black, 0.4% Asian American or Pacific Islander, 0% international, 64% 25 or older, 2% transferred in. Retention: 26% of full-time freshmen returned the following year. Calendar: semesters.
Costs Per Year: Area resident tuition: $2190 full-time, $730 per hour part-time. State resident tuition: $3990 full-time, $133 per hour part-time. Nonresident tuition: $5400 full-time, $180 per hour part-time. Mandatory fees: $150 full-time, $5 per hour part-time.
Collegiate Environment: Campus security: 24-hour patrols, late night transport-escort service. College housing not available. Learning Resource Center/Library with an OPAC. Operations spending for 2004 fiscal year: $887. 355 computers available on campus for general student use.

■ **MIDWEST INSTITUTE (EARTH CITY)** *F-11*
4260 Shoreline Dr.
Earth City, MO 63045
Tel: (314)344-3334
Fax: (314)344-0495
Web Site: http://www.midwestinstitute.com/
Description: Proprietary, 2-year, coed.

■ **MIDWEST INSTITUTE (KIRKWOOD)** *F-11*
10910 Manchester Rd.
Kirkwood, MO 63122
Tel: (314)965-8363
Fax: (314)965-1558
Web Site: http://www.midwestinstitute.com/
Description: Proprietary, 2-year, coed. Founded 1963.

■ **MINERAL AREA COLLEGE** *H-11*
PO Box 1000
Park Hills, MO 63601-1000
Tel: (573)431-4593
Admissions: (573)518-2206
E-mail: jsheets@mineralarea.edu
Web Site: http://www.mineralarea.edu/
Description: District-supported, 2-year, coed. Part of Missouri Coordinating Board for Higher Education. Awards certificates, transfer associate, and terminal associate degrees. Founded 1922. Setting: 240-acre rural campus with easy access to St. Louis. Endowment: $2.1 million. Educational spending for 2005 fiscal year: $3969 per student. Total enrollment: 2,820. 697 applied, 100% were admitted. 9% from top 10% of their high school class, 31% from top quarter, 67% from top half. Full-time: 1,605 students, 65% women, 35% men. Part-time: 1,215 students, 71% women, 29% men. Students come from 6 states and territories, 1% from out-of-state, 1% Native American, 1% Hispanic, 2% black, 0.3% Asian American or Pacific Islander, 0.4% international, 36% 25 or older, 3% transferred in. Core. Calendar: semesters. Academic remediation for entering students, services for LD students, advanced placement, honors program, distance learning, summer session for credit, part-time degree program, internships. Off campus study at East Central College, Jefferson College.
Entrance Requirements: Open admission except for allied health programs, law enforcement programs. Options: electronic application, early

admission. Required: high school transcript. Placement: ACT, ACT COMPASS required for some. Entrance: noncompetitive. Application deadline: Rolling. Notification: continuous.

Costs Per Year: Application fee: $15. Area resident tuition: $2160 full-time, $72 per credit hour part-time. State resident tuition: $2880 full-time, $96 per credit hour part-time. Nonresident tuition: $3540 full-time, $118 per credit hour part-time. College room only: $2475.

Collegiate Environment: Orientation program. Drama-theater group, choral group. Most popular organizations: Student Senate, Phi Theta Kappa, Psi Beta, MAC Ambassadors, Phi Beta Lambda. Major annual events: Spring Picnic, Club Awareness Day. Student services: personal-psychological counseling. Campus security: 24-hour patrols. 208 college housing spaces available; 119 were occupied in 2003-04. Option: coed housing available. C. H. Cozen Learning Resource Center with 32,228 books, 3,068 microform titles, 214 serials, 4,859 audiovisual materials, an OPAC, and a Web page. Operations spending for 2004 fiscal year: $227,861. 226 computers available on campus for general student use. A campuswide network can be accessed from student residence rooms and from off campus. Staffed computer lab on campus.

Community Environment: Park Hills (population 10,000) is located in east-central Missouri, 60 miles south of St. Louis. Kentucky, Illinois and Arkansas are not too distant. District facilities include most denominations of churches, four newspapers, four radio station and parks. Outdoor activities are hunting and fishing, tennis, golf.

■ MISSOURI BAPTIST UNIVERSITY *F-12*
One College Park Dr.
St. Louis, MO 63141-8660
Tel: (314)434-1115; 877-434-1115
Admissions: (314)392-2291
Fax: (314)434-7596
E-mail: admissions@mobap.edu
Web Site: http://www.mobap.edu/

Description: Independent Southern Baptist, comprehensive, coed. Awards associate, bachelor's, and master's degrees. Founded 1964. Setting: 65-acre suburban campus. Endowment: $3 million. Educational spending for 2005 fiscal year: $2919 per student. Total enrollment: 4,460. Faculty: 191 (58 full-time, 133 part-time). Student-undergrad faculty ratio is 15:1. 551 applied, 52% were admitted. 14% from top 10% of their high school class, 31% from top quarter, 61% from top half. Full-time: 1,202 students, 55% women, 45% men. Part-time: 2,283 students, 60% women, 40% men. Students come from 26 states and territories, 29 other countries, 13% from out-of-state, 0.3% Native American, 1% Hispanic, 11% black, 0.3% Asian American or Pacific Islander, 6% international, 27% 25 or older, 17% live on campus, 7% transferred in. Retention: 67% of full-time freshmen returned the following year. Academic areas with the most degrees conferred: education; business/marketing; psychology. Core. Calendar: semesters. Services for LD students, advanced placement, accelerated degree program, self-designed majors, independent study, distance learning, double major, summer session for credit, part-time degree program, adult/continuing education programs, internships, graduate courses open to undergrads. Off campus study at Maryville University of Saint Louis, Lindenwood University, Fontbonne College, Webster University. Study abroad program. ROTC: Army (c).

Entrance Requirements: Option: electronic application. Required: high school transcript, minimum 2.0 high school GPA, recommendations, interview. Required for some: SAT or ACT. Entrance: moderately difficult. Application deadline: Rolling. Notification: continuous.

Costs Per Year: Application fee: $25. Comprehensive fee: $19,640 includes full-time tuition ($13,230), mandatory fees ($610), and college room and board ($5800). Full-time tuition and fees vary according to course load, degree level, and location. Room and board charges vary according to housing facility. Part-time tuition: $460 per credit. Part-time mandatory fees: $30 per credit. Part-time tuition and fees vary according to course load, degree level, and location.

Collegiate Environment: Orientation program. Drama-theater group, choral group, student-run newspaper, radio station. Social organizations: 11 open to all. Most popular organizations: Baptist Collegiate Ministry, Students in Free Enterprise (SIFE), Missouri State Teacher's Association, Fellowship of Christian Athletes, Ministerial Alliance. Major annual events: homecoming, Hanging of the Green, The MoBap Perk. Student services: personal-psychological counseling. Campus security: 24-hour patrols, late night transport-escort service, controlled dormitory access, self-defense classes. 239 college housing spaces available; 231 were occupied in 2003-04. Options: men-only, women-only housing available. Jung-Kellogg Library with

91,115 books, 45,595 microform titles, 450 serials, 4,596 audiovisual materials, and an OPAC. Operations spending for 2004 fiscal year: $288,125. 122 computers available on campus for general student use. A campuswide network can be accessed from student residence rooms and from off campus.

Community Environment: See Washington University.

■ MISSOURI COLLEGE *F-12*
10121 Manchester Rd.
St. Louis, MO 63122-1583
Tel: (314)821-7700
Web Site: http://www.mocollege.com/

Description: Proprietary, 2-year, coed. Awards diplomas and terminal associate degrees. Founded 1963. Total enrollment: 560. Students come from 4 states and territories, 42% 25 or older.

Entrance Requirements: Open admission. Required: essay, interview. Application deadline: Rolling.

Collegiate Environment: College housing not available. 60 computers available on campus for general student use. Computer purchase/lease plans available. A campuswide network can be accessed. Staffed computer lab on campus.

■ MISSOURI SOUTHERN STATE UNIVERSITY *J-3*
3950 East Newman Rd.
Joplin, MO 64801-1595
Tel: (417)625-9300; (866)818-MSSU
Admissions: (417)625-9537
Fax: (417)659-4429
E-mail: admissions@mssu.edu
Web Site: http://www.mssu.edu/

Description: State-supported, 4-year, coed. Awards associate, bachelor's, and master's degrees. Founded 1937. Setting: 350-acre small town campus. Educational spending for 2005 fiscal year: $2115 per student. Total enrollment: 5,473. Faculty: 308 (206 full-time, 102 part-time). Student-undergrad faculty ratio is 18:1. 1,576 applied, 99% were admitted. 18% from top 10% of their high school class, 43% from top quarter, 72% from top half. Full-time: 3,849 students, 58% women, 42% men. Part-time: 1,624 students, 63% women, 37% men. Students come from 27 states and territories, 34 other countries, 14% from out-of-state, 2% Native American, 2% Hispanic, 3% black, 1% Asian American or Pacific Islander, 2% international, 38% 25 or older, 10% live on campus. Retention: 64% of full-time freshmen returned the following year. Academic areas with the most degrees conferred: business/marketing; education; health professions and related sciences; security and protective services. Core. Calendar: semesters. Academic remediation for entering students, ESL program, services for LD students, advanced placement, accelerated degree program, honors program, independent study, distance learning, double major, summer session for credit, part-time degree program, external degree program, adult/continuing education programs, co-op programs and internships. Off campus study at Nevada Consortium. Study abroad program.

Entrance Requirements: Options: Common Application, electronic application, deferred admission, international baccalaureate accepted. Required: high school transcript, standardized test scores; class rank, SAT or ACT. Recommended: ACT. Required for some: 2 recommendations, Michigan Test of English Language Proficiency. Entrance: moderately difficult. Application deadline: 8/1. Notification: continuous.

Costs Per Year: Application fee: $15. State resident tuition: $3750 full-time, $125 per credit part-time. Nonresident tuition: $7500 full-time, $250 per credit part-time. Mandatory fees: $166 full-time, $83 per term part-time. Full-time tuition and fees vary according to course load. College room and board: $4480. Room and board charges vary according to board plan and housing facility.

Collegiate Environment: Orientation program. Drama-theater group, choral group, marching band, student-run newspaper, radio station. Social organizations: 81 open to all; national fraternities, national sororities, local fraternities; 1% of eligible men and 1% of eligible women are members. Most popular organizations: Koinonia, Campus Activities Board, Residence Hall Association, Baptist Student Union, Student Senate. Major annual events: Spring Fling, Homecoming, Career Fair. Student services: health clinic, personal-psychological counseling. Campus security: 24-hour emergency response devices and patrols, late night transport-escort service, controlled dormitory access, security at campus events, emergency vehicle assistance, safety awareness information to students. 750 college housing spaces available; 530 were occupied in 2003-04. Freshmen guaranteed college housing.

On-campus residence required in freshman year. Options: coed, men-only, women-only housing available. Spiva Library with an OPAC and a Web page. Operations spending for 2004 fiscal year: $1.1 million. 448 computers available on campus for general student use. A campuswide network can be accessed from student residence rooms and from off campus. Staffed computer lab on campus.

Community Environment: Located in southwest Missouri at the northern gateway of the Ozark Resort area, Joplin (population 46,000) is surrounded by numerous spring fed fishing streams in scenic hill country. The city has many manufacturing and wholesale firms as well as industry involving the mining and processing of zinc ore. All forms of commercial transportation are available. Part-time employment is available. There are over 100 churches, 14 elementary schools, 1 junior high school, 1 high school, 2 four-year colleges, and 2 hospitals.

■ **MISSOURI STATE UNIVERSITY** *J-5*
901 South National
Springfield, MO 65804-0094
Tel: (417)836-5000
Free: 800-492-7900
Admissions: (417)836-5521
Fax: (417)836-6334
E-mail: smsuinfo@vma.smsu.edu
Web Site: http://www.missouristate.edu/

Description: State-supported, comprehensive, coed. Awards bachelor's, master's, and doctoral degrees and post-master's certificates. Founded 1905. Setting: 225-acre suburban campus. Endowment: $38.2 million. Research spending for 2004 fiscal year: $6.2 million. Educational spending for 2005 fiscal year: $2076 per student. Total enrollment: 18,928. Faculty: 1,027 (728 full-time, 299 part-time). Student-undergrad faculty ratio is 18:1. 6,866 applied, 77% were admitted. 22% from top 10% of their high school class, 49% from top quarter, 81% from top half. 86 valedictorians. Full-time: 12,630 students, 56% women, 44% men. Part-time: 3,527 students, 58% women, 42% men. Students come from 49 states and territories, 82 other countries, 7% from out-of-state, 1% Native American, 1% Hispanic, 2% black, 1% Asian American or Pacific Islander, 2% international, 16% 25 or older, 24% live on campus, 7% transferred in. Retention: 73% of full-time freshmen returned the following year. Core. Calendar: semesters. ESL program, services for LD students, advanced placement, accelerated degree program, self-designed majors, freshman honors college, honors program, independent study, distance learning, double major, summer session for credit, part-time degree program, adult/continuing education programs, co-op programs and internships, graduate courses open to undergrads. Off campus study at National Student Exchange. Study abroad program. ROTC: Army.

Entrance Requirements: Options: Peterson's Universal Application, electronic application, international baccalaureate accepted. Required: high school transcript, SAT or ACT. Required for some: essay, recommendations, interview. Entrance: moderately difficult. Application deadline: 7/20. Notification: continuous.

Costs Per Year: Application fee: $30. State resident tuition: $4920 full-time, $164 per credit hour part-time. Nonresident tuition: $9840 full-time, $328 per credit hour part-time. Mandatory fees: $534 full-time. College room and board: $5294. College room only: $3462.

Collegiate Environment: Orientation program. Drama-theater group, choral group, marching band, student-run newspaper, radio station. Social organizations: 260 open to all; national fraternities, national sororities. Most popular organizations: Residence Hall Association, Campus Crusade, Gamma Sigma Sigma, Student Government Association. Major annual events: New Student Festival, Homecoming, May Day. Student services: legal services, health clinic, personal-psychological counseling. Campus security: 24-hour emergency response devices and patrols, late night transport-escort service, controlled dormitory access, on-campus police substation. 4,034 college housing spaces available; 3,970 were occupied in 2003-04. Freshmen guaranteed college housing. On-campus residence required in freshman year. Option: coed housing available. Meyer Library plus 3 others with 1.7 million books, 1 million microform titles, 4,238 serials, 33,547 audiovisual materials, an OPAC, and a Web page. Operations spending for 2004 fiscal year: $3.6 million. 1,800 computers available on campus for general student use. Computer purchase/lease plans available. A campuswide network can be accessed from student residence rooms and from off campus. Staffed computer lab on campus.

Community Environment: Springfield (population 140,000) is Missouri's third largest city and is within one hour's drive from many of the popular resort and vacation areas of the southwest Missouri Ozark region. Springfield has become a major health care center for the region and is home to several major businesses and industries including Bass Pro Shops, General Electric, Kraft, and Associated Wholesale Grocers.

■ **MISSOURI STATE UNIVERSITY-WEST PLAINS** *K-8*
128 Garfield
West Plains, MO 65775
Tel: (417)255-7255
Admissions: (417)255-7955
E-mail: melissajett@missouristate.edu
Web Site: http://www.wp.missouristate.edu/

Description: State-supported, 2-year, coed. Part of Missouri State University. Awards certificates, transfer associate, and terminal associate degrees. Founded 1963. Setting: 11-acre small town campus. Total enrollment: 1,675. Student-undergrad faculty ratio is 17:1. 469 applied, 100% were admitted. Full-time: 886 students, 67% women, 33% men. Part-time: 789 students, 64% women, 36% men. Students come from 15 states and territories, 6 other countries, 4% from out-of-state, 1% Native American, 1% Hispanic, 1% black, 0.5% Asian American or Pacific Islander, 1% international, 10% 25 or older, 6% live on campus, 3% transferred in. Core. Calendar: semesters. Academic remediation for entering students, services for LD students, advanced placement, honors program, distance learning, summer session for credit, part-time degree program, co-op programs and internships. Study abroad program.

Entrance Requirements: Open admission except for the nursing program which requires a separate application with a March 1 deadline. Admission eligibility requirements include a ranking score computation based on GPA and ACT. Required for some: high school transcript. Entrance: noncompetitive. Application deadline: Rolling.

Costs Per Year: Application fee: $15. State resident tuition: $102 per credit hour part-time. Nonresident tuition: $204 per credit hour part-time. Mandatory fees: $77 per term part-time. College room and board: $4586.

Collegiate Environment: Orientation program. Drama-theater group, choral group. Social organizations: 12 open to all. Most popular organizations: Student Government Association, Chi Alpha, Adult Students in Higher Education, Lambda Lambda Lambda, Programming Board. Major annual events: Homecoming, University Life Talent Show, Welcome Week Dance. Student services: personal-psychological counseling. Campus security: late night transport-escort service, controlled dormitory access. 60 college housing spaces available; all were occupied in 2003-04. Option: coed housing available. Garnett Library with 21,210 books, 10,836 microform titles, 189 serials, 714 audiovisual materials, an OPAC, and a Web page. Operations spending for 2004 fiscal year: $214,473. 58 computers available on campus for general student use. A campuswide network can be accessed from student residence rooms and from off campus. Staffed computer lab on campus.

■ **MISSOURI TECH** *F-12*
1167 Corporate Lake Dr.
St. Louis, MO 63132-1716
Tel: (314)569-3600
Fax: (314)569-1167
Web Site: http://www.motech.edu/

Description: Proprietary, 4-year, coed. Awards associate and bachelor's degrees. Founded 1932. Setting: suburban campus. Total enrollment: 201. 27 applied, 56% were admitted. Full-time: 44 students, 5% women, 95% men. Part-time: 157 students, 13% women, 87% men. Students come from 4 states and territories, 20% from out-of-state, 0% Native American, 1% Hispanic, 17% black, 0% Asian American or Pacific Islander, 3% international, 56% 25 or older, 6% live on campus, 7% transferred in. Calendar: semesters. Advanced placement, accelerated degree program, summer session for credit, part-time degree program, adult/continuing education programs, internships.

Entrance Requirements: Options: Peterson's Universal Application, Common Application, electronic application. Required: high school transcript. Recommended: ACT. Required for some: interview, minimum ACT score of 20. Entrance: moderately difficult. Application deadline: Rolling.

Collegiate Environment: Most popular organizations: student council, President's Club. Major annual events: Graduation Ceremony, Picnic. Campus security: 24-hour emergency response devices. 15 undergraduates lived in college housing during 2003-04. Options: men-only, women-only housing available. 100 computers available on campus for general student use. A campuswide network can be accessed from off-campus. Staffed computer lab on campus.

■ MISSOURI VALLEY COLLEGE *E-6*

500 East College
Marshall, MO 65340-3197
Tel: (660)831-4000
Admissions: (660)831-4157
Fax: (660)831-4039
Web Site: http://www.moval.edu/

Description: Independent, 4-year, coed, affiliated with Presbyterian Church. Awards associate and bachelor's degrees. Founded 1889. Setting: 140-acre small town campus with easy access to Kansas City. Endowment: $3.4 million. Educational spending for 2005 fiscal year: $2415 per student. Total enrollment: 1,623. 1,345 applied, 67% were admitted. 6% from top 10% of their high school class, 19% from top quarter, 41% from top half. 12 class presidents, 14 valedictorians, 47 student government officers. Full-time: 1,377 students, 43% women, 57% men. Part-time: 246 students, 68% women, 32% men. Students come from 40 states and territories, 29 other countries, 34% from out-of-state, 1% Native American, 4% Hispanic, 13% black, 4% Asian American or Pacific Islander, 8% international, 12% 25 or older, 73% live on campus, 9% transferred in. Retention: 45% of full-time freshmen returned the following year. Core. Calendar: semesters plus 2 summer sessions. ESL program, services for LD students, advanced placement, independent study, double major, summer session for credit, part-time degree program, adult/continuing education programs, co-op programs and internships. ROTC: Army (c).

Entrance Requirements: Options: Peterson's Universal Application, Common Application, electronic application, early admission, deferred admission. Required: high school transcript, SAT or ACT. Recommended: minimum 2.0 high school GPA, interview. Required for some: essay, 3 recommendations, interview. Entrance: minimally difficult. Application deadline: Rolling. Notification: continuous.

Costs Per Year: Application fee: $15. Comprehensive fee: $20,250 includes full-time tuition ($14,500) and college room and board ($5750).

Collegiate Environment: Orientation program. Drama-theater group, choral group, student-run newspaper, radio station. Social organizations: 33 open to all; national fraternities, national sororities; 30% of eligible men and 25% of eligible women are members. Most popular organizations: student government, Valley players, American Humanics. Major annual events: Homecoming, Family Weekend, Spring Fest. Student services: health clinic. Campus security: 24-hour emergency response devices, student patrols, controlled dormitory access. 1,117 college housing spaces available; 1,043 were occupied in 2003-04. Freshmen guaranteed college housing. Options: coed, men-only, women-only housing available. Murrell Memorial Library plus 1 other with 61,907 books, 25,463 microform titles, 391 serials, 1,399 audiovisual materials, an OPAC, and a Web page. Operations spending for 2004 fiscal year: $240,653. 250 computers available on campus for general student use. A campuswide network can be accessed from student residence rooms and from off campus. Staffed computer lab on campus.

Community Environment: Marshall, population 15,000, is located 80 miles east of Kansas City and bus transportation is available. Community recreational facilities include a bowling alley, skating rink, and a philharmonic orchestra. The Indian Foothills Park, at the eastern city limits, provides tennis courts, ball fields, a golf course, swimming, fishing, and picnic grounds.

■ MISSOURI WESTERN STATE UNIVERSITY *C-2*

4525 Downs Dr.
St. Joseph, MO 64507-2294
Tel: (816)271-4200
Free: 800-662-7041
Admissions: (816)271-4267
Fax: (816)271-5833
E-mail: admission@missouriwestern.edu
Web Site: http://www.missouriwestern.edu/

Description: State-supported, 4-year, coed. Awards associate and bachelor's degrees. Founded 1915. Setting: 744-acre suburban campus with easy access to Kansas City. Endowment: $6.1 million. Research spending for 2004 fiscal year: $69,501. Educational spending for 2005 fiscal year: $5600 per student. Total enrollment: 5,248. Student-undergrad faculty ratio is 19:1. 2,606 applied, 100% were admitted. 8% from top 10% of their high school class, 27% from top quarter, 55% from top half. Full-time: 3,800 students, 59% women, 41% men. Part-time: 1,448 students, 63% women, 38% men. Students come from 31 states and territories, 7 other countries, 7% from out-of-state, 1% Native American, 2% Hispanic, 12% black, 1% Asian American or Pacific Islander, 0.2% international, 22% 25 or older, 28% live on campus, 5% transferred in. Retention: 59% of full-time freshmen

returned the following year. Academic areas with the most degrees conferred: business/marketing; education; security and protective services. Core. Calendar: semesters. Academic remediation for entering students, advanced placement, accelerated degree program, freshman honors college, honors program, distance learning, double major, summer session for credit, part-time degree program, internships. ROTC: Army.

Entrance Requirements: Open admission. Option: early admission. Required: high school transcript. Entrance: noncompetitive. Application deadline: 6/1. Notification: continuous until 8/10.

Costs Per Year: Application fee: $15. State resident tuition: $4380 full-time, $146 per credit part-time. Nonresident tuition: $8010 full-time, $267 per credit part-time. Mandatory fees: $398 full-time, $12 per credit part-time, $35. College room and board: $4756. Room and board charges vary according to board plan and housing facility.

Collegiate Environment: Orientation program. Drama-theater group, choral group, marching band, student-run newspaper. Social organizations: 50 open to all; national fraternities, national sororities; 6% of eligible men and 3% of eligible women are members. Major annual events: homecoming, Family Day, Springfest. Student services: health clinic, personal-psychological counseling, women's center. Campus security: 24-hour emergency response devices and patrols, student patrols, late night transport-escort service, controlled dormitory access. 1,045 college housing spaces available; all were occupied in 2003-04. Option: coed housing available. Warren E. Hearnes Library with 147,509 books, 110,808 microform titles, 1,068 serials, 13,705 audiovisual materials, an OPAC, and a Web page. Operations spending for 2004 fiscal year: $1.1 million. 300 computers available on campus for general student use. A campuswide network can be accessed from student residence rooms and from off campus. Staffed computer lab on campus.

Community Environment: Located in America's heartland, St. Joseph was one of only 10 cities nationwide to receive the prestigious 1997 All-America City Award. A thriving business community has seen St. Joseph grow from a booming frontier town to the market place for the four-state area of Missouri, Iowa, Kansas, and Nebraska. With a population of 72,000, St. Joseph boasts metropolitan advantages blended with small town flavor. The city offers 26-miles of parkway system, Olympic-size ice rink, YMCA and YWCA, St. Joseph Symphony, Performing Arts Association Arts Association, Robidoux Resident Theatre, and 13 museums, including the Albrecht-Kemper Museum of Art; Jesse James House; Pony Express Stables and the St. Joseph Museum.

■ MOBERLY AREA COMMUNITY COLLEGE *D-7*

101 College Ave.
Moberly, MO 65270-1304
Tel: (660)263-4110
Free: 800-622-2070
Fax: (660)263-6252
Web Site: http://www.macc.edu/

Description: State and locally supported, 2-year, coed. Awards certificates, transfer associate, and terminal associate degrees. Founded 1927. Setting: 32-acre small town campus. Total enrollment: 3,835. Student-undergrad faculty ratio is 20:1. 25% from top quarter of their high school class, 58% from top half. Full-time: 1,818 students, 61% women, 39% men. Part-time: 2,017 students, 63% women, 37% men. Students come from 17 states and territories, 12 other countries, 1% from out-of-state, 0.4% Native American, 1% Hispanic, 6% black, 1% Asian American or Pacific Islander, 0.2% international, 24% 25 or older, 1% live on campus, 4% transferred in. Retention: 57% of full-time freshmen returned the following year. Core. Calendar: semesters. Academic remediation for entering students, services for LD students, advanced placement, distance learning, summer session for credit, part-time degree program, adult/continuing education programs, co-op programs and internships. Study abroad program.

Entrance Requirements: Open admission except for nursing, law enforcement programs. Options: electronic application, international baccalaureate accepted. Required: high school transcript. Recommended: ACT, ACT ASSET. Required for some: ACT, ACT ASSET. Entrance: noncompetitive. Application deadline: Rolling. Notification: continuous until 9/1.

Costs Per Year: Application fee: $0. Area resident tuition: $1740 full-time, $58 per credit hour part-time. State resident tuition: $2550 full-time, $85 per credit hour part-time. Nonresident tuition: $3960 full-time, $132 per credit hour part-time. Mandatory fees: $300 full-time, $10 per credit hour part-time. College room only: $1800.

Collegiate Environment: Drama-theater group, choral group, student-run newspaper. Social organizations: 9 open to all; local fraternities, local sororities; 10% of eligible men and 10% of eligible women are members. Most popular organizations: Phi Theta Kappa, Student Nurses Association, Child Care Club, Delta Epsilon Chi, Brother Ox. Major annual events: theatrical production, Fall Picnic, Spring Picnic. Campus security: student patrols, extensive surveillance. 42 college housing spaces available; 25 were occupied in 2003-04. No special consideration for freshman housing applicants. Options: men-only, women-only housing available. Kate Stamper Wilhite Library with 23,027 books, 80 microform titles, 88 serials, 1,393 audiovisual materials, an OPAC, and a Web page. Operations spending for 2004 fiscal year: $189,446. 750 computers available on campus for general student use. A campuswide network can be accessed from off-campus. Staffed computer lab on campus.

Community Environment: Moberly (population 13,000) is the county seat of Randolph County, in central Missouri. The town is served by one major railroad and the Omar Bradley Airport. Community facilities include churches of all denominations, a regional hospital, and Little Dixie Regional Library. A moderately large shopping district is available. Student employment is available in retail, restaurants, filling stations, and warehouses. Housing may be found in hotels, motels, and apartments. Outdoor activities are golf, boating, fishing, hunting, baseball, and tennis.

■ **NATIONAL AMERICAN UNIVERSITY** *E-3*
4200 Blue Ridge Blvd.
Kansas City, MO 64133-1612
Tel: (816)353-4554
Fax: (816)353-1176
E-mail: jjoy@national.edu
Web Site: http://www.national.edu/
Description: Proprietary, 4-year, coed. Part of National College. Awards associate and bachelor's degrees. Founded 1941. Setting: 1-acre urban campus. Total enrollment: 380. Students come from 2 states and territories, 5 other countries, 97% 25 or older. Retention: 81% of full-time freshmen returned the following year. Core. Independent study, distance learning, summer session for credit, part-time degree program, external degree program, co-op programs. Study abroad program.
Entrance Requirements: Open admission. Options: early admission, deferred admission, international baccalaureate accepted. Required: high school transcript, interview. Entrance: noncompetitive. Application deadline: Rolling. Notification: continuous until 9/12.
Collegiate Environment: Student-run newspaper. Social organizations: 2 open to all. Most popular organizations: Phi Beta Lambda, Student Senate. Major annual events: Martin Luther King Day, Annual Student Picnic, Christmas Festival. Student services: personal-psychological counseling. Campus security: 24-hour patrols. College housing not available. Learning Resource Center plus 1 other with 1,500 books and 60 serials. 60 computers available on campus for general student use. A campuswide network can be accessed. Staffed computer lab on campus.

■ **NORTH CENTRAL MISSOURI COLLEGE** *B-5*
1301 Main St.
Trenton, MO 64683-1824
Tel: (660)359-3948
Free: 800-880-6180
E-mail: bbirdsong@mail.ncmissouri.edu
Web Site: http://www.ncmissouri.edu/
Description: District-supported, 2-year, coed. Awards certificates, transfer associate, and terminal associate degrees. Founded 1925. Setting: 2-acre small town campus. Endowment: $423,653. Educational spending for 2005 fiscal year: $2881 per student. Total enrollment: 1,342. Student-undergrad faculty ratio is 17:1. 519 applied, 58% were admitted. Full-time: 702 students, 71% women, 29% men. Part-time: 640 students, 70% women, 30% men. Students come from 7 states and territories, 1 other country, 1% from out-of-state, 1% Native American, 1% Hispanic, 3% black, 0.1% Asian American or Pacific Islander, 0.4% international, 25% 25 or older, 9% live on campus, 4% transferred in. Calendar: semesters. Academic remediation for entering students, services for LD students, advanced placement, accelerated degree program, distance learning, summer session for credit, part-time degree program, adult/continuing education programs, co-op programs and internships.
Entrance Requirements: Open admission except for health occupations programs. Option: Peterson's Universal Application. Required: high school transcript. Entrance: noncompetitive. Application deadline: Rolling.
Costs Per Year: Application fee: $0. Area resident tuition: $1680 full-time, $56 per credit part-time. State resident tuition: $2550 full-time, $85 per credit

part-time. Nonresident tuition: $3570 full-time, $119 per credit part-time. Mandatory fees: $450 full-time, $15 per credit part-time. Full-time tuition and fees vary according to course load and location. Part-time tuition and fees vary according to location. College room and board: $4149. Room and board charges vary according to board plan.
Collegiate Environment: Drama-theater group. Social organizations: local fraternities, local sororities. Student services: personal-psychological counseling. Campus security: controlled dormitory access. 140 college housing spaces available; 123 were occupied in 2003-04. No special consideration for freshman housing applicants. Options: men-only, women-only housing available. North Central Missouri College Library with 20,627 books and 104 serials. Operations spending for 2004 fiscal year: $86,603. 159 computers available on campus for general student use. A campuswide network can be accessed. Staffed computer lab on campus.
Community Environment: A rural location in central north Missouri, Trenton (population 6,700) has 11 churches, libraries, a hospital, and numerous civic, fraternal, and veteran's organizations. Several lakes are nearby offering excellent fishing, swimming, and boating. City parks also provide facilities for recreation. Part-time employment is available.

■ **NORTHWEST MISSOURI STATE UNIVERSITY** *B-2*
800 University Dr.
Maryville, MO 64468-6001
Tel: (660)562-1212
Free: 800-633-1175
Admissions: (660)562-1587
Fax: (660)562-1121
E-mail: admissions@acad.nwmissouri.edu
Web Site: http://www.nwmissouri.edu/
Description: State-supported, comprehensive, coed. Part of Missouri Coordinating Board for Higher Education. Awards bachelor's and master's degrees. Founded 1905. Setting: 240-acre small town campus with easy access to Kansas City. Research spending for 2004 fiscal year: $332,801. Educational spending for 2005 fiscal year: $6092 per student. Total enrollment: 6,249. Faculty: 259 (243 full-time, 16 part-time). Student-undergrad faculty ratio is 24:1. 3,655 applied, 45% were admitted. 19% from top 10% of their high school class, 45% from top quarter, 80% from top half. Full-time: 4,719 students, 56% women, 44% men. Part-time: 642 students, 57% women, 43% men. Students come from 36 states and territories, 12 other countries, 34% from out-of-state, 1% Native American, 2% Hispanic, 5% black, 1% Asian American or Pacific Islander, 2% international, 7% 25 or older, 49% live on campus, 6% transferred in. Retention: 72% of full-time freshmen returned the following year. Core. Calendar: trimesters. Academic remediation for entering students, ESL program, services for LD students, advanced placement, accelerated degree program, independent study, distance learning, double major, summer session for credit, part-time degree program, internships, graduate courses open to undergrads. Off campus study at Missouri Western State College, Truman State University, North Central Missouri College. Study abroad program. ROTC: Army.
Entrance Requirements: Options: Peterson's Universal Application, electronic application, deferred admission, international baccalaureate accepted. Required: high school transcript, minimum 2.0 high school GPA, SAT or ACT. Required for some: recommendations, interview. Entrance: moderately difficult. Application deadline: Rolling. Notification: continuous. Preference given to state residents.
Costs Per Year: Application fee: $25. State resident tuition: $5535 full-time, $172.50 per credit hour part-time. Nonresident tuition: $9540 full-time, $306 per credit hour part-time. Mandatory fees: $465 full-time, $12 per credit hour part-time, $105 per term part-time. Full-time tuition and fees vary according to course load. Part-time tuition and fees vary according to course load. College room and board: $5492. Room and board charges vary according to board plan.
Collegiate Environment: Orientation program. Drama-theater group, choral group, marching band, student-run newspaper, radio station. Social organizations: 125 open to all; national fraternities, national sororities; 16% of eligible men and 16% of eligible women are members. Most popular organization: student government. Major annual events: Homecoming, Family Day, Greek Week. Student services: health clinic, women's center. Campus security: 24-hour patrols, student patrols, late night transport-escort service. 2,500 college housing spaces available; 2,150 were occupied in 2003-04. Freshmen guaranteed college housing. On-campus residence required in freshman year. Option: coed housing available. B. D. Owens Library plus 1 other with 326,919 books, 962,095 microform titles, 8,873 serials, 5,624 audiovisual materials, an OPAC, and a Web page. Operations

spending for 2004 fiscal year: $1.8 million. 2,450 computers available on campus for general student use. A campuswide network can be accessed from student residence rooms and from off campus. Staffed computer lab on campus.

Community Environment: Maryville (population 10,000) is a rural area in northwest Missouri. Dormitories, fraternity houses, and private homes provide housing. Community facilities include a library, 13 churches, a hospital, and several civic, national, and international branches of clubs and organizations are represented. Train and bus transportation is available. 90 miles from Kansas City, 45 from St. Joseph, 110 from Omaha and 125 from Des Moines.

■ OZARK CHRISTIAN COLLEGE *J-3*

1111 North Main St.
Joplin, MO 64801-4804
Tel: (417)624-2518
Free: 800-299-4622
Fax: (417)624-0090
Web Site: http://www.occ.edu/

Description: Independent Christian, 4-year, coed. Awards associate and bachelor's degrees. Founded 1942. Setting: 110-acre suburban campus. Total enrollment: 799. 332 applied, 100% were admitted. Students come from 33 states and territories, 13 other countries, 57% from out-of-state, 2% Native American, 2% Hispanic, 2% black, 1% Asian American or Pacific Islander, 2% international, 25% 25 or older, 63% live on campus. Retention: 70% of full-time freshmen returned the following year. Calendar: semesters. Academic remediation for entering students, ESL program, services for LD students, double major, summer session for credit, part-time degree program, adult/continuing education programs, internships.

Entrance Requirements: Open admission. Options: Common Application, electronic application. Required: essay, high school transcript, 4 recommendations, SAT or ACT. Required for some: interview. Entrance: noncompetitive. Application deadline: 8/5.

Collegiate Environment: Orientation program. Drama-theater group, choral group, student-run radio station. Social organizations: 3 open to all. Most popular organizations: Family Outreach Group, God's Spokesman, Imagine. Major annual events: Parents' Day, Living Christmas Tree, preaching/teaching convention. Student services: health clinic, personal-psychological counseling. Campus security: 24-hour emergency response devices, 12-hour patrols by trained security personnel. 577 college housing spaces available; 511 were occupied in 2003-04. Freshmen guaranteed college housing. On-campus residence required through senior year. Options: men-only, women-only housing available. Seth Wilson Library with 59,808 books, 182 microform titles, 362 serials, 21,289 audiovisual materials, an OPAC, and a Web page. 28 computers available on campus for general student use. Staffed computer lab on campus.

■ OZARKS TECHNICAL COMMUNITY COLLEGE *J-5*

PO Box 5958
Springfield, MO 65801
Tel: (417)895-7000
Admissions: (417)895-7136
Fax: (417)895-7161
Web Site: http://www.otc.edu/

Description: District-supported, 2-year, coed. Part of Missouri Coordinating Board for Higher Education. Awards certificates, diplomas, transfer associate, and terminal associate degrees. Founded 1990. Setting: 20-acre urban campus. Endowment: $3867. Total enrollment: 8,488. 1% from top 10% of their high school class, 21% from top quarter, 32% from top half. Full-time: 4,232 students, 54% women, 46% men. Part-time: 4,256 students, 53% women, 47% men. Students come from 37 states and territories, 2% from out-of-state, 1% Native American, 1% Hispanic, 2% black, 1% Asian American or Pacific Islander, 0.1% international, 25% 25 or older, 38% transferred in. Core. Calendar: semesters. Academic remediation for entering students, ESL program, services for LD students, summer session for credit, part-time degree program, adult/continuing education programs, co-op programs and internships. Off campus study at Southwest Missouri State University.

Entrance Requirements: Open admission. Options: Common Application, early admission. Required: high school transcript. Placement: ACT ASSET, ACT COMPASS required. Entrance: noncompetitive. Notification: continuous.

Collegiate Environment: Orientation program. Student-run newspaper. Most popular organizations: Phi Theta Kappa, Phi Beta Lambda. Major an-

nual event: Annual Student Picnic. Student services: personal-psychological counseling. Campus security: 24-hour emergency response devices. College housing not available. Learning Resource Center plus 1 other with 6,000 books, 190 serials, and an OPAC. 150 computers available on campus for general student use. Staffed computer lab on campus.

■ PARK UNIVERSITY *Q-2*

8700 NW River Park Dr.
Parkville, MO 64152-3795
Tel: (816)741-2000
Free: 800-745-7275
Admissions: (816)584-6728
Fax: (816)741-4462
Web Site: http://www.park.edu/

Description: Independent, comprehensive, coed. Awards associate, bachelor's, and master's degrees. Founded 1875. Setting: 800-acre suburban campus with easy access to Kansas City. Endowment: $39 million. Educational spending for 2005 fiscal year: $4226 per student. Total university enrollment: 5,448. Total unit enrollment: 13,253. Faculty: 889 (97 full-time, 792 part-time). Student-undergrad faculty ratio is 13:1. 352 applied, 74% were admitted. 11% from top 10% of their high school class, 36% from top quarter, 73% from top half. 2 class presidents, 1 valedictorian, 20 student government officers. Full-time: 1,002 students, 62% women, 38% men. Part-time: 11,686 students, 47% women, 53% men. Students come from 50 states and territories, 91 other countries, 80% from out-of-state, 1% Native American, 16% Hispanic, 21% black, 3% Asian American or Pacific Islander, 2% international, 73% 25 or older, 1% live on campus, 16% transferred in. Retention: 66% of full-time freshmen returned the following year. Academic areas with the most degrees conferred: business/marketing; psychology; security and protective services. Core. Calendar: semesters. Academic remediation for entering students, ESL program, services for LD students, advanced placement, self-designed majors, honors program, independent study, distance learning, double major, summer session for credit, part-time degree program, external degree program, adult/continuing education programs, internships, graduate courses open to undergrads. Off campus study at members of the Kansas City Professional Development Council. ROTC: Army.

Entrance Requirements: Options: Peterson's Universal Application, electronic application, early admission, deferred admission, international baccalaureate accepted. Required: high school transcript, minimum 2.0 high school GPA, SAT or ACT. Recommended: essay. Required for some: 2 recommendations, interview. Entrance: moderately difficult. Application deadline: 8/1. Notification: continuous.

Costs Per Year: Application fee: $25. Comprehensive fee: $11,956 includes full-time tuition ($6776) and college room and board ($5180). Part-time tuition: $242 per credit hour.

Collegiate Environment: Orientation program. Drama-theater group, choral group, student-run newspaper, radio station. Social organizations: 15 open to all. Most popular organizations: World Student Union, Student Senate, Radio Club, Latin American Student Organization, Marketing Club. Major annual events: Harvest Fest, Spring Fling, Christmas on the River. Student services: health clinic, personal-psychological counseling. Campus security: 24-hour patrols, student patrols, late night transport-escort service. 227 college housing spaces available; 162 were occupied in 2003-04. Freshmen guaranteed college housing. On-campus residence required through junior year. Option: coed housing available. McAfee Memorial Library with 150,503 books, 90,000 microform titles, 591 serials, 1,233 audiovisual materials, and an OPAC. Operations spending for 2004 fiscal year: $874,128. 143 computers available on campus for general student use. A campuswide network can be accessed from student residence rooms. Staffed computer lab on campus.

Community Environment: See University of Missouri - Kansas City.

■ PATRICIA STEVENS COLLEGE *F-12*

330 North Fourth St., Ste. 306
St. Louis, MO 63102
Tel: (314)421-0949
Free: 800-871-0949
Fax: (314)421-0304
Web Site: http://www.patriciastevenscollege.edu/

Description: Proprietary, 2-year, coed. Awards diplomas, transfer associate, and terminal associate degrees. Founded 1947. Setting: urban campus. Educational spending for 2005 fiscal year: $3700 per student. Total enrollment: 212. Students come from 4 states and territories, 42% from out-of-state, 0% Native American, 0.5% Hispanic, 47% black, 0.5% Asian American or Pacific Islander, 0% international, 37% 25 or older. Core. Academic remediation for entering students, advanced placement, honors program, independent study, summer session for credit, part-time degree program, adult/continuing education programs, co-op programs and internships.

Entrance Requirements: Option: deferred admission. Required: high school transcript, interview. Recommended: essay, recommendations. Application deadline: Rolling.

Collegiate Environment: Orientation program. Student services: personal-psychological counseling. Campus security: 24-hour emergency response devices and patrols. 35 computers available on campus for general student use. Staffed computer lab on campus.

■ **PENN VALLEY COMMUNITY COLLEGE** *E-3*
3201 Southwest Trafficway
Kansas City, MO 64111
Tel: (816)759-4000
Admissions: (816)759-4101
Web Site: http://www.mcckc.edu

Description: State and locally supported, 2-year, coed. Part of Metropolitan Community Colleges System. Awards certificates, transfer associate, and terminal associate degrees. Founded 1969. Setting: 25-acre urban campus. System endowment: $2.4 million. Educational spending for 2005 fiscal year: $4599 per student. Total enrollment: 4,627. Student-undergrad faculty ratio is 12:1. 785 applied, 100% were admitted. Full-time: 1,457 students, 70% women, 30% men. Part-time: 3,170 students, 73% women, 27% men. Students come from 6 states and territories, 5% from out-of-state, 1% Native American, 5% Hispanic, 29% black, 3% Asian American or Pacific Islander, 0.03% international, 54% 25 or older, 5% transferred in. Retention: 52% of full-time freshmen returned the following year. Core. Calendar: semesters. Academic remediation for entering students, ESL program, services for LD students, advanced placement, accelerated degree program, honors program, distance learning, summer session for credit, part-time degree program, adult/continuing education programs, co-op programs and internships. Off campus study at Johnson County Community College.

Entrance Requirements: Open admission except for allied health programs. Options: Common Application, early admission. Required: high school transcript. Entrance: noncompetitive. Application deadline: Rolling.

Costs Per Year: Application fee: $0. Area resident tuition: $2190 full-time, $73 per hour part-time. State resident tuition: $3990 full-time, $133 per hour part-time. Nonresident tuition: $5400 full-time, $180 per hour part-time. Mandatory fees: $150 full-time, $5 per hour part-time.

Collegiate Environment: Drama-theater group, choral group, student-run newspaper. Social organizations: national fraternities. Most popular organizations: Black Student Association, Los Americanos, Phi Theta Kappa, Fashion Club. Major annual events: Black History Month, Spring Fling, homecoming. Student services: personal-psychological counseling. Campus security: 24-hour patrols. College housing not available. Penn Valley Community College Library with 91,428 books, 89 microform titles, 89,242 serials, 355 audiovisual materials, and an OPAC. Operations spending for 2004 fiscal year: $449,705. 1,058 computers available on campus for general student use. A campuswide network can be accessed from off-campus. Staffed computer lab on campus.

Community Environment: See University of Missouri Kansas City.

■ **PINNACLE CAREER INSTITUTE** *E-3*
15329 Kensington Ave.
Kansas City, MO 64147-1212
Tel: (816)331-5700
Web Site: http://www.pcitraining.edu/

Description: Proprietary, 2-year, coed. Awards certificates and transfer associate degrees. Total enrollment: 170. 354 applied, 57% were admitted.

Entrance Requirements: Application deadline: 6/1.

■ **RANKEN TECHNICAL COLLEGE** *F-12*
4431 Finney Ave.
St. Louis, MO 63113
Tel: (314)371-0233; (866)4RA-NKEN
Fax: (314)371-0241
Web Site: http://www.ranken.edu/

Description: Independent, primarily 2-year, coed. Awards certificates, transfer associate, terminal associate, and bachelor's degrees. Founded 1907. Setting: 10-acre urban campus. Endowment: $39 million. Educational spending for 2005 fiscal year: $2598 per student. Total enrollment: 1,423.

920 applied, 92% were admitted. Full-time: 743 students, 4% women, 96% men. Part-time: 680 students, 4% women, 96% men. Students come from 3 states and territories, 40% from out-of-state, 40% 25 or older, 1% live on campus. Calendar: semesters. Academic remediation for entering students, services for LD students, advanced placement, independent study, distance learning, summer session for credit, part-time degree program, adult/continuing education programs, co-op programs and internships.

Entrance Requirements: Options: Common Application, electronic application. Required: essay, high school transcript, interview. Placement: SAT or ACT required. Entrance: moderately difficult. Application deadline: Rolling.

Costs Per Year: Application fee: $95. Tuition: $10,000 full-time, $725 per term part-time. Mandatory fees: $140 full-time, $95 per term part-time.

Collegiate Environment: Orientation program. Student-run newspaper. Social organizations: 6 open to all. Most popular organizations: Phi Theta Kappa, student government, Women's Support Group, Instrumentation Society of America, Vocational Industrial Clubs of America. Major annual events: Spirit Days, Wacky Olympics, Canned Food and Toy Drive. Student services: personal-psychological counseling, women's center. Campus security: 24-hour emergency response devices and patrols. 12 undergraduates lived in college housing during 2003-04. Options: men-only, women-only housing available. Ashley Gray Jr. Learning Center with 11,000 books, 182 serials, an OPAC, and a Web page. 85 computers available on campus for general student use. A campuswide network can be accessed. Staffed computer lab on campus.

■ **RESEARCH COLLEGE OF NURSING** *E-3*
2252 East Meyer Blvd.
Kansas City, MO 64132
Tel: (816)995-2800
Free: 800-842-6776
Admissions: (816)276-4733
Fax: (816)276-3526
E-mail: leslie.mendenhall@researchcollege.edu
Web Site: http://www.researchcollege.edu/

Description: Independent, comprehensive, coed. Part of Rockhurst University. Awards bachelor's and master's degrees (bachelor's degree offered jointly with Rockhurst College). Founded 1980. Setting: 66-acre urban campus. Total enrollment: 213. 94 applied, 77% were admitted. 24% from top 10% of their high school class, 67% from top quarter, 95% from top half. Full-time: 184 students, 93% women, 7% men. Part-time: 3 students, 100% women. Students come from 7 states and territories, 0% Native American, 3% Hispanic, 5% black, 2% Asian American or Pacific Islander, 0% international, 30% 25 or older, 5% transferred in. Core. Calendar: semesters. Services for LD students, advanced placement, accelerated degree program, honors program, independent study, double major, summer session for credit, graduate courses open to undergrads. Study abroad program. ROTC: Army (c).

Entrance Requirements: Options: Common Application, electronic application, deferred admission. Required: high school transcript, 1 recommendation, SAT or ACT. Recommended: minimum 2.8 high school GPA, interview, minimum ACT score of 20. Entrance: moderately difficult. Application deadline: 6/30. Notification: continuous until 8/15.

Costs Per Year: Application fee: $25. Comprehensive fee: $25,640 includes full-time tuition ($18,900), mandatory fees ($640), and college room and board ($6100). College room only: $3100. Full-time tuition and fees vary according to program. Room and board charges vary according to board plan, housing facility, and location. Part-time tuition: $630 per credit hour. Part-time tuition varies according to class time and program.

Collegiate Environment: Orientation program. Drama-theater group, choral group, student-run newspaper, radio station. Social organizations: 40 open to all; national fraternities, national sororities, local sororities; 75% of eligible men and 75% of eligible women are members. Major annual events: Mass of the Holy Spirit, Polar Walk, homecoming. Student services: health clinic, personal-psychological counseling. Campus security: 24-hour emergency response devices and patrols, late night transport-escort service, controlled dormitory access. 1,800 college housing spaces available; 1,000 were occupied in 2003-04. Freshmen guaranteed college housing. On-campus residence required in freshman year. Options: coed, men-only, women-only housing available. Greenlease Library with 150,000 books, 675 serials, an OPAC, and a Web page. 125 computers available on campus for general student use. A campuswide network can be accessed from student residence rooms and from off campus. Staffed computer lab on campus.

■ **ROCKHURST UNIVERSITY** *E-3*
1100 Rockhurst Rd.
Kansas City, MO 64110-2561
Tel: (816)501-4000
Free: 800-842-6776
Admissions: (816)501-4100
Fax: (816)501-4241
E-mail: admission@rockhurst.edu
Web Site: http://www.rockhurst.edu/
Description: Independent Roman Catholic (Jesuit), comprehensive, coed. Awards bachelor's, master's, and doctoral degrees. Founded 1910. Setting: 35-acre urban campus. Endowment: $39.4 million. Educational spending for 2005 fiscal year: $7667 per student. Total enrollment: 2,944. Faculty: 217 (127 full-time, 90 part-time). Student-undergrad faculty ratio is 10:1. 1,775 applied, 74% were admitted. 31% from top 10% of their high school class, 65% from top quarter, 87% from top half. 6 valedictorians. Full-time: 1,261 students, 55% women, 45% men. Part-time: 830 students, 63% women, 37% men. Students come from 26 states and territories, 16 other countries, 33% from out-of-state, 1% Native American, 5% Hispanic, 7% black, 2% Asian American or Pacific Islander, 1% international, 14% 25 or older, 49% live on campus, 5% transferred in. Retention: 89% of full-time freshmen returned the following year. Academic areas with the most degrees conferred: business/marketing; health professions and related sciences; psychology. Core. Calendar: semesters. Academic remediation for entering students, services for LD students, advanced placement, accelerated degree program, freshman honors college, honors program, independent study, distance learning, double major, summer session for credit, part-time degree program, adult/continuing education programs, co-op programs and internships, graduate courses open to undergrads. Off campus study at Kansas City Area Student Exchange. Study abroad program. ROTC: Army (c).
Entrance Requirements: Options: Peterson's Universal Application, Common Application, electronic application, deferred admission, international baccalaureate accepted. Required: high school transcript, minimum 2.0 high school GPA, 1 recommendation, SAT or ACT. Required for some: essay, interview. Entrance: moderately difficult. Application deadline: 6/30. Notification: continuous.
Costs Per Year: Application fee: $25. One-time mandatory fee: $60. Comprehensive fee: $25,110 includes full-time tuition ($18,500), mandatory fees ($710), and college room and board ($5900). Full-time tuition and fees vary according to class time and course load. Room and board charges vary according to board plan and housing facility. Part-time tuition: $630 per semester hour. Part-time mandatory fees: $25 per term. Part-time tuition and fees vary according to class time and course load.
Collegiate Environment: Orientation program. Drama-theater group, choral group, student-run newspaper. Social organizations: 54 open to all; national fraternities, national sororities, local sororities; 7% of eligible men and 8% of eligible women are members. Most popular organizations: Student Activities Board, Organization of Collegiate Women, Black Student Union, Student Organization of Latinos, College Players. Major annual events: homecoming, Greek Week, Family Weekend. Student services: health clinic, personal-psychological counseling. Campus security: 24-hour emergency response devices and patrols, student patrols, late night transport-escort service, controlled dormitory access, closed-circuit TV monitors. 700 college housing spaces available; 627 were occupied in 2003-04. No special consideration for freshman housing applicants. On-campus residence required through sophomore year. Options: coed, men-only, women-only housing available. Greenlease Library with 597,800 books, 223,100 microform titles, 750 serials, 3,494 audiovisual materials, an OPAC, and a Web page. Operations spending for 2004 fiscal year: $699,000. 500 computers available on campus for general student use. A campuswide network can be accessed from student residence rooms and from off campus. Staffed computer lab on campus.
Community Environment: See University of Missouri - Kansas City.

■ **SAINT CHARLES COMMUNITY COLLEGE** *F-11*
4601 Mid Rivers Mall Dr.
St. Peters, MO 63376-0975
Tel: (636)922-8000
Admissions: (636)922-8229
Fax: (636)922-8236
E-mail: regist@stchas.edu

Web Site: http://www.stchas.edu/
Description: State-supported, 2-year, coed. Part of Missouri Coordinating Board for Higher Education. Awards certificates, transfer associate, and terminal associate degrees. Founded 1986. Setting: 234-acre small town campus with easy access to St. Louis. Endowment: $5.7 million. Educational spending for 2005 fiscal year: $3715 per student. Total enrollment: 6,870. Student-undergrad faculty ratio is 21:1. 1,677 applied, 100% were admitted. Full-time: 3,378 students, 55% women, 45% men. Part-time: 3,492 students, 66% women, 34% men. Students come from 4 states and territories, 6 other countries, 0% from out-of-state, 0.3% Native American, 2% Hispanic, 4% black, 2% Asian American or Pacific Islander, 0.3% international, 52% 25 or older, 5% transferred in. Core. Calendar: semesters. Academic remediation for entering students, ESL program, services for LD students, advanced placement, independent study, distance learning, double major, summer session for credit, part-time degree program, adult/continuing education programs, internships.
Entrance Requirements: Open admission except for nursing, allied health programs. Options: Common Application, early admission, deferred admission. Recommended: high school transcript. Required for some: high school transcript. Entrance: noncompetitive. Application deadline: Rolling. Notification: continuous.
Costs Per Year: Application fee: $0. Area resident tuition: $2280 full-time. State resident tuition: $3360 full-time. Nonresident tuition: $4980 full-time.
Collegiate Environment: Orientation program. Drama-theater group, choral group. Social organizations: 12 open to all. Most popular organizations: Phi Theta Kappa, SCCCC Roller Hockey Club, Student Senate, Criminal Justice Student Organization, Human Services Student Organization. Major annual events: Spring Fling, Fall Fun Blitz, lunchtime seminars. Student services: personal-psychological counseling. Campus security: 24-hour emergency response devices and patrols, late night transport-escort service. College housing not available. Learning Resource Center with 54,110 books, 37,219 microform titles, 8,282 serials, 7,624 audiovisual materials, an OPAC, and a Web page. Operations spending for 2004 fiscal year: $684,379. 117 computers available on campus for general student use. A campuswide network can be accessed from off-campus. Staffed computer lab on campus.

■ **ST. LOUIS CHRISTIAN COLLEGE** *F-11*
1360 Grandview Dr.
Florissant, MO 63033-6499
Tel: (314)837-6777
Free: 800-887-SLCC
Fax: (314)837-8291
Web Site: http://www.slcconline.edu/
Description: Independent Christian, 4-year, coed. Awards associate and bachelor's degrees. Founded 1956. Setting: 20-acre suburban campus with easy access to St. Louis. Endowment: $577,910. Educational spending for 2005 fiscal year: $4758 per student. Total enrollment: 213. 55 applied, 76% were admitted. 19% from top 10% of their high school class, 38% from top quarter, 69% from top half. Full-time: 143 students, 44% women, 56% men. Part-time: 70 students, 51% women, 49% men. Students come from 11 states and territories, 3 other countries, 37% from out-of-state, 1% Native American, 2% Hispanic, 27% black, 1% Asian American or Pacific Islander, 1% international, 42% 25 or older, 38% live on campus, 6% transferred in. Retention: 65% of full-time freshmen returned the following year. Core. Calendar: semesters. Academic remediation for entering students, services for LD students, advanced placement, accelerated degree program, part-time degree program, adult/continuing education programs, internships.
Entrance Requirements: Option: early admission. Required: essay, high school transcript, 2 recommendations, ACT. Recommended: minimum 2.0 high school GPA. Required for some: interview. Entrance: minimally difficult. Application deadline: 8/15. Notification: continuous.
Costs Per Year: Application fee: $0. Comprehensive fee: $13,450 includes full-time tuition ($8000), mandatory fees ($450), and college room and board ($5000). Room and board charges vary according to housing facility. Part-time tuition: $250 per credit. Part-time mandatory fees: $450 per semester hour.
Collegiate Environment: Orientation program. Drama-theater group, choral group. Social organizations: 3 open to all. Most popular organizations: World Christians Unlimited, Drama Club, pep band. Major annual events: Jam Fest, Jesus Encounter, Junior High Winterfest. Student services: personal-psychological counseling. Campus security: 24-hour emergency response devices and patrols, controlled dormitory access, night security. 150 college housing spaces available; 92 were occupied in 2003-04. On-campus residence required through senior year. Options: men-only, women-only

housing available. St. Louis Christian College Library with 39,728 books, 144 serials, and a Web page. Operations spending for 2004 fiscal year: $70,631. 11 computers available on campus for general student use. Staffed computer lab on campus.

■ **ST. LOUIS COLLEGE OF HEALTH CAREERS** *F-12*
909 South Taylor Ave.
St. Louis, MO 63110-1511
Web Site: http://www.slchc.com/
Description: Proprietary, 2-year, coed.

■ **ST. LOUIS COLLEGE OF PHARMACY** *F-12*
4588 Parkview Place
St. Louis, MO 63110-1088
Tel: (314)367-8700
Admissions: (314)446-8313
Fax: (314)367-2784
E-mail: pbryant@stlcop.edu
Web Site: http://www.stlcop.edu/
Description: Independent, comprehensive, coed. Awards master's and first professional degrees. Founded 1864. Setting: 5-acre urban campus. Endowment: $62.7 million. Educational spending for 2005 fiscal year: $9826 per student. Total enrollment: 1,093. Faculty: 105 (60 full-time, 45 part-time). Student-undergrad faculty ratio is 15:1. 686 applied, 35% were admitted. 34% from top 10% of their high school class, 75% from top quarter, 97% from top half. 23 valedictorians. 53% from out-of-state, 0.2% Native American, 1% Hispanic, 3% black, 12% Asian American or Pacific Islander, 1% international, 40% live on campus. Retention: 85% of full-time freshmen returned the following year. Academic area with the most degrees conferred: health professions and related sciences. Core. Calendar: semesters. Academic remediation for entering students, advanced placement, summer session for credit, internships, graduate courses open to undergrads. ROTC: Army (c), Air Force (c).
Entrance Requirements: Options: Peterson's Universal Application, electronic application. Required: essay, high school transcript, minimum 3.0 high school GPA, 2 recommendations, SAT or ACT. Required for some: interview. Entrance: moderately difficult. Application deadlines: 2/1, 11/1 for early decision plan 1, 1/1 for early decision plan 2. Notification: 4/1; 11/30 for early decision plan 1, 1/30 for early decision plan 2.
Costs Per Year: Application fee: $50. Comprehensive fee: $26,690 includes full-time tuition ($18,900), mandatory fees ($280), and college room and board ($7510). Part-time tuition: $810 per credit.
Collegiate Environment: Orientation program. Drama-theater group, choral group, student-run newspaper. Social organizations: 15 open to all; national fraternities, national sororities; 70% of eligible men and 65% of eligible women are members. Most popular organizations: Gateway Academy of Student Pharmacists, Student Council, International Student Council, student ambassadors, Student Alumni Association. Major annual events: homecoming, Organization Fair (Welcome Week). Student services: personal-psychological counseling. Campus security: 24-hour emergency response devices and patrols, late night transport-escort service, controlled dormitory access. 380 college housing spaces available; all were occupied in 2003-04. Freshmen given priority for college housing. On-campus residence required in freshman year. Option: coed housing available. O. J. Cloughly Alumni Library with 68,187 books, 5,259 microform titles, 234 serials, 802 audiovisual materials, an OPAC, and a Web page. Operations spending for 2004 fiscal year: $480,817. 75 computers available on campus for general student use. Computer purchase/lease plans available. A campuswide network can be accessed from student residence rooms and from off campus. Staffed computer lab on campus.

■ **ST. LOUIS COMMUNITY COLLEGE AT FLORISSANT VALLEY** *F-12*
3400 Pershall Rd.
St. Louis, MO 63135-1499
Tel: (314)513-4200
Admissions: (314)595-4258
Fax: (314)513-2224
Web Site: http://www.stlcc.edu/
Description: District-supported, 2-year, coed. Part of St. Louis Community College System. Awards certificates, transfer associate, and terminal associate degrees. Founded 1963. Setting: 108-acre suburban campus. Students come from 31 other countries, 53% 25 or older. Core. Calendar: semesters. Academic remediation for entering students, ESL program, services for LD students, advanced placement, honors program, summer session for credit,

part-time degree program, adult/continuing education programs, co-op programs. Study abroad program. ROTC: Army (c).
Entrance Requirements: Open admission. Options: electronic application, early admission. Required: high school transcript. Entrance: noncompetitive. Application deadline: 8/19. Notification: continuous.
Costs Per Year: Application fee: $0. Area resident tuition: $78 per credit hour part-time. State resident tuition: $103 per credit hour part-time. Nonresident tuition: $138 per credit hour part-time.
Collegiate Environment: Orientation program. Drama-theater group, student-run newspaper, radio station. Social organizations: 20 open to all; national fraternities, national sororities; 20% of eligible men and 15% of eligible women are members. Most popular organizations: Phi Theta Kappa, Student Nurses Association, Women in New Goals, Florissant Valley Association of the Deaf, Student Government Association. Major annual events: awareness days, school spirit days, Children's Christmas Party. Student services: health clinic, personal-psychological counseling. Campus security: 24-hour emergency response devices and patrols, late night transport-escort service. College housing not available. 90,021 books and 655 serials. 470 computers available on campus for general student use. A campuswide network can be accessed. Staffed computer lab on campus.

■ **ST. LOUIS COMMUNITY COLLEGE AT FOREST PARK** *F-12*
5600 Oakland Ave.
St. Louis, MO 63110-1316
Tel: (314)644-9100
Admissions: (314)644-9131
E-mail: bdevoti@stlcc.edu
Web Site: http://www.stlcc.edu/
Description: District-supported, 2-year, coed. Part of St. Louis Community College System. Awards transfer associate and terminal associate degrees. Founded 1962. Setting: 34-acre suburban campus. Total enrollment: 7,610. 1,282 applied, 100% were admitted. Students come from 11 states and territories, 4% from out-of-state, 0.4% Native American, 1% Hispanic, 43% black, 4% Asian American or Pacific Islander, 0.2% international, 60% 25 or older. Core. Calendar: semesters. Academic remediation for entering students, ESL program, services for LD students, honors program, distance learning, summer session for credit, part-time degree program, adult/continuing education programs. Study abroad program.
Entrance Requirements: Open admission except for allied medical programs. Options: electronic application, early admission. Required: high school transcript. Entrance: noncompetitive. Application deadline: 8/22. Notification: continuous. Preference given to district residents.
Collegiate Environment: Orientation program. Drama-theater group, student-run newspaper. Student services: personal-psychological counseling. Campus security: 24-hour patrols. College housing not available. St. Louis Community College Library with 72,713 books, 511 serials, an OPAC, and a Web page. 369 computers available on campus for general student use. A campuswide network can be accessed from off-campus. Staffed computer lab on campus.

■ **ST. LOUIS COMMUNITY COLLEGE AT MERAMEC** *F-11*
11333 Big Bend Blvd.
Kirkwood, MO 63122-5720
Tel: (314)984-7500
Admissions: (314)984-7609
Fax: (314)984-7117
Web Site: http://www.stlcc.edu/
Description: District-supported, 2-year, coed. Part of St. Louis Community College System. Awards certificates, transfer associate, and terminal associate degrees. Founded 1963. Setting: 80-acre suburban campus with easy access to St. Louis. Educational spending for 2005 fiscal year: $1304 per student. Total enrollment: 12,607. Students come from 10 states and territories, 1% Native American, 2% Hispanic, 4% black, 3% Asian American or Pacific Islander, 42% 25 or older. Core. Calendar: semesters. Academic remediation for entering students, ESL program, services for LD students, advanced placement, freshman honors college, honors program, summer session for credit, part-time degree program, adult/continuing education programs, internships. Off campus study at The New England Banking Institute. Study abroad program. ROTC: Army (c), Air Force (c).
Entrance Requirements: Open admission except for nursing, paramedic, occupational therapy, physical therapy programs. Options: early admission, deferred admission. Required for some: high school transcript, interview. Placement: Michigan Test of English Language Proficiency required for some. Entrance: noncompetitive. Application deadline: Rolling. Notification: continuous.

Collegiate Environment: Drama-theater group, choral group, student-run newspaper. Social organizations: 50 open to all. Most popular organizations: Phi Theta Kappa, Scuba Club, International Club, Inter-Varsity Christian Fellowship, Horticulture Club. Major annual events: Las Vegas Night, Friday Night Movies, barbecues. Student services: health clinic, personal-psychological counseling. Campus security: 24-hour emergency response devices and patrols. College housing not available. Meramec Library with 58,911 books and 500 serials. 420 computers available on campus for general student use. Staffed computer lab on campus.

■ **SAINT LOUIS UNIVERSITY** *F-12*
221 North Grand Blvd.
St. Louis, MO 63103-2097
Tel: (314)977-2222
Free: 800-758-3678
Admissions: (314)977-3415
Fax: (314)977-7136
E-mail: admitme@sluvca.slu.edu
Web Site: http://www.slu.edu
Description: Independent Roman Catholic (Jesuit), university, coed. Awards bachelor's, master's, doctoral, and first professional degrees and post-master's certificates. Founded 1818. Setting: 373-acre urban campus. Endowment: $750.7 million. Educational spending for 2005 fiscal year: $13,653 per student. Total enrollment: 11,823. Faculty: 1,094 (616 full-time, 478 part-time). Student-undergrad faculty ratio is 12:1. 8,105 applied, 78% were admitted. 36% from top 10% of their high school class, 66% from top quarter, 90% from top half. 9 National Merit Scholars. Full-time: 6,817 students, 57% women, 43% men. Part-time: 604 students, 61% women, 39% men. Students come from 51 states and territories, 51 other countries, 54% from out-of-state, 0.5% Native American, 3% Hispanic, 8% black, 5% Asian American or Pacific Islander, 2% international, 4% 25 or older, 52% live on campus, 5% transferred in. Retention: 86% of full-time freshmen returned the following year. Academic areas with the most degrees conferred: business/marketing; health professions and related sciences; psychology. Core. Calendar: semesters. Academic remediation for entering students, ESL program, services for LD students, advanced placement, accelerated degree program, self-designed majors, honors program, independent study, distance learning, double major, summer session for credit, part-time degree program, adult/continuing education programs, co-op programs and internships, graduate courses open to undergrads. Off campus study at Washington University in St. Louis. Study abroad program. ROTC: Army (c), Air Force.
Entrance Requirements: Options: Peterson's Universal Application, Common Application, electronic application, deferred admission, international baccalaureate accepted. Required: essay, high school transcript, secondary school report form, SAT or ACT. Recommended: minimum 2.5 high school GPA, 2 recommendations, interview. Entrance: moderately difficult. Application deadline: Rolling. Notification: continuous until 10/1.
Costs Per Year: Application fee: $25. Comprehensive fee: $34,678 includes full-time tuition ($26,250), mandatory fees ($198), and college room and board ($8230). College room only: $4700.
Collegiate Environment: Orientation program. Drama-theater group, choral group, student-run newspaper, radio station. Social organizations: 100 open to all; national fraternities, national sororities; 19% of eligible men and 15% of eligible women are members. Most popular organizations: Student Government Association, Student Activities Board, Black Student Alliance, International Student Federation. Major annual events: Student Activities Fair, Spring Fever, Billiken World Festival. Student services: legal services, health clinic, personal-psychological counseling. Campus security: 24-hour emergency response devices and patrols, student patrols, late night transport-escort service, controlled dormitory access, crime prevention program, bicycle patrols, pamphlets, posters, films. 3,442 college housing spaces available; 3,137 were occupied in 2003-04. No special consideration for freshman housing applicants. Option: coed housing available. Pius XII Memorial Library plus 2 others with 1.9 million books, 2.6 million microform titles, 13,999 serials, 195,126 audiovisual materials, an OPAC, and a Web page. Operations spending for 2004 fiscal year: $9 million. 1,350 computers available on campus for general student use. Computer purchase/lease plans available. A campuswide network can be accessed from student residence rooms and from off campus. Staffed computer lab on campus.
Community Environment: See Washington University.

■ **SAINT LUKE'S COLLEGE** *E-3*
4426 Wornall Rd.
Kansas City, MO 64111

Tel: (816)932-2233
Admissions: (816)932-2073
E-mail: mjthomas@saint-lukes.org
Web Site: http://www.saintlukescollege.edu/
Description: Independent Episcopal, upper-level, coed. Administratively affiliated with Saint Luke's Hospital. Awards bachelor's degrees. Founded 1903. Setting: 3-acre urban campus. Endowment: $1.8 million. Total enrollment: 109. Full-time: 96 students, 91% women, 9% men. Part-time: 13 students, 100% women. Students come from 5 states and territories, 6 other countries, 0% Native American, 1% Hispanic, 9% black, 5% Asian American or Pacific Islander, 0% international, 51% 25 or older, 48% transferred in. Retention: 90% of full-time entering class returned the following year. Core. Calendar: semesters. Summer session for credit, co-op programs.
Costs Per Year: Application fee: $20. Tuition: $8850 full-time, $295 per credit part-time. Mandatory fees: $620 full-time, $180 per term part-time.
Collegiate Environment: Orientation program. Social organizations: 1 open to all. Most popular organization: Saint Luke's Student Nurse Association. Major annual events: College Picnic, College Spring Banquet. Student services: health clinic, personal-psychological counseling. Campus security: 24-hour emergency response devices and patrols. College housing not available. 20 computers available on campus for general student use. Staffed computer lab on campus.

■ **SANFORD-BROWN COLLEGE (FENTON)** *Q-15*
1203 Smizer Mill Rd.
Fenton, MO 63026
Tel: (636)349-4900
Free: 800-456-7222
Fax: (636)349-9170
Web Site: http://www.sanford-brown.edu/
Description: Proprietary, primarily 2-year, coed. Part of Education Management Corporation. Awards certificates, diplomas, terminal associate, and bachelor's degrees. Founded 1868. Setting: 6-acre suburban campus with easy access to St. Louis. Total enrollment: 440. 92 applied, 86% were admitted. Full-time: 394 students, 68% women, 32% men. Part-time: 46 students, 48% women, 52% men. Students come from 2 states and territories, 8% from out-of-state, 75% 25 or older. Core. Services for LD students, independent study, adult/continuing education programs, internships.
Entrance Requirements: Open admission. Options: Common Application, deferred admission. Required: high school transcript, interview, CPAt. Entrance: minimally difficult.
Collegiate Environment: Orientation program. Most popular organizations: Paralegal Club, peer advisors, student council, Accounting Club, student ambassadors. Major annual events: Christmas Party, Summer Party. Student services: personal-psychological counseling. Campus security: late night transport-escort service, trained security personnel from 7:30 p.m. to 10:30 p.m. College housing not available. 150 computers available on campus for general student use. Computer purchase/lease plans available. A campuswide network can be accessed from off-campus. Staffed computer lab on campus.

■ **SANFORD-BROWN COLLEGE (HAZELWOOD)** *O-15*
75 Village Square
Hazelwood, MO 63042
Tel: (314)731-1101
Admissions: (314)731-5200
Web Site: http://www.sanford-brown.edu/
Description: Proprietary, 2-year, coed. Awards diplomas, transfer associate, and terminal associate degrees. Founded 1868. Setting: 1-acre campus with easy access to St. Louis. Total enrollment: 600. Students come from 3 other countries. Core. Academic remediation for entering students, services for LD students, part-time degree program, adult/continuing education programs, internships.
Entrance Requirements: Options: Peterson's Universal Application, Common Application, deferred admission. Required: high school transcript, interview. Entrance: minimally difficult. Application deadline: Rolling.
Collegiate Environment: Social organizations: 4 open to all. Most popular organizations: Paralegal Club, peer advisors, student council, Accounting Club. Major annual events: Christmas Party, Nursing Graduation Party, Summer Party. Student services: personal-psychological counseling. Campus security: 24-hour emergency response devices and patrols. 32 computers available on campus for general student use. Staffed computer lab on campus.

■ **SANFORD-BROWN COLLEGE (NORTH KANSAS CITY)** *Q-2*
520 East 19th Ave.
North Kansas City, MO 64116
Tel: (816)472-7400
Free: 800-456-7222
Admissions: (816)472-0275
Fax: (816)472-0688
E-mail: edward.beauchamp@wix.net
Web Site: http://www.sanford-brown.edu/
Description: Proprietary, 2-year, coed. Awards certificates, diplomas, and terminal associate degrees. Founded 1992. Setting: suburban campus. Total enrollment: 300. Students come from 2 states and territories. Services for LD students, internships.
Entrance Requirements: Options: Common Application, deferred admission. Entrance: minimally difficult. Application deadline: Rolling. Notification: continuous.
Collegiate Environment: Student services: personal-psychological counseling. Campus security: 24-hour patrols. 18 computers available on campus for general student use. Staffed computer lab on campus.

■ **SANFORD-BROWN COLLEGE (ST. CHARLES)** *F-11*
3555 Franks Dr.
St. Charles, MO 63301
Tel: (314)949-2620
Admissions: (636)949-2620
E-mail: karl.peterson@wix.net
Web Site: http://www.sanford-brown.edu/
Description: Proprietary, 2-year, coed. Awards diplomas, transfer associate, and terminal associate degrees. Founded 1868. Setting: 2-acre suburban campus with easy access to St. Louis. Educational spending for 2005 fiscal year: $2500 per student. 500 applied, 80% were admitted. Students come from 2 states and territories, 60% 25 or older, 5% live on campus. Academic remediation for entering students, services for LD students, summer session for credit, part-time degree program, adult/continuing education programs, co-op programs and internships.
Entrance Requirements: Options: Common Application, deferred admission. Required: high school transcript, interview. Required for some: Thurston Mental Alertness Test. Entrance: minimally difficult. Application deadline: Rolling.
Collegiate Environment: Social organizations: 3 open to all. Most popular organizations: student council, PBL, Paralegal Club. Major annual events: Campus Bar-B-Que, Summer Picnic, Christmas Luncheon. Student services: personal-psychological counseling. Campus security: 24-hour emergency response devices. Option: coed housing available. Learning Resource Center with 1,350 books and 60 serials. 40 computers available on campus for general student use. Staffed computer lab on campus.

■ **SOUTHEAST MISSOURI HOSPITAL COLLEGE OF NURSING AND HEALTH SCIENCES** *J-13*
1819 Broadway
Cape Girardeau, MO 63701
Tel: (573)334-6825
Fax: (573)339-7805
E-mail: tbuttry@sehosp.org
Web Site: http://www.southeastmissourihospital.com/college/
Description: Independent, 2-year, coed. Founded 1928. Calendar: six 7-week terms per year.

■ **SOUTHEAST MISSOURI STATE UNIVERSITY** *J-13*
One University Plaza
Cape Girardeau, MO 63701-4799
Tel: (573)651-2000
Admissions: (573)651-2590
Web Site: http://www.semo.edu/
Description: State-supported, comprehensive, coed. Part of Missouri Coordinating Board for Higher Education. Awards associate, bachelor's, and master's degrees and post-master's certificates. Founded 1873. Setting: 693-acre small town campus with easy access to St. Louis. Endowment: $35.8 million. Research spending for 2004 fiscal year: $411,394. Educational spending for 2005 fiscal year: $5684 per student. Total enrollment: 10,292. Faculty: 608 (400 full-time, 208 part-time). Student-undergrad faculty ratio is 17:1. 4,060 applied, 89% were admitted. 15% from top 10% of their high school class, 35% from top quarter, 65% from top half. 2 National Merit

Scholars, 37 valedictorians. Full-time: 6,796 students, 58% women, 42% men. Part-time: 2,172 students, 62% women, 38% men. Students come from 39 states and territories, 35 other countries, 12% from out-of-state, 1% Native American, 1% Hispanic, 9% black, 0.5% Asian American or Pacific Islander, 2% international, 18% 25 or older, 28% live on campus, 6% transferred in. Retention: 70% of full-time freshmen returned the following year. Academic areas with the most degrees conferred: education; business/marketing; liberal arts/general studies. Core. Calendar: semesters. Academic remediation for entering students, ESL program, services for LD students, advanced placement, accelerated degree program, self-designed majors, honors program, independent study, distance learning, double major, summer session for credit, part-time degree program, adult/continuing education programs, co-op programs and internships, graduate courses open to undergrads. Study abroad program. ROTC: Air Force.
Entrance Requirements: Options: Peterson's Universal Application, Common Application, electronic application, deferred admission, international baccalaureate accepted. Required: high school transcript, minimum 2.0 high school GPA, ACT. Entrance: moderately difficult. Notification: 10/1.
Costs Per Year: Application fee: $20. State resident tuition: $4764 full-time, $158.80 per credit hour part-time. Nonresident tuition: $8619 full-time, $287.30 per credit hour part-time. Mandatory fees: $381 full-time, $12.70 per credit hour part-time. Full-time tuition and fees vary according to course load and location. Part-time tuition and fees vary according to course load and location. College room and board: $5351. College room only: $3270. Room and board charges vary according to board plan and housing facility.
Collegiate Environment: Orientation program. Drama-theater group, choral group, marching band, student-run newspaper, radio station. Social organizations: 14 open to all; national fraternities, national sororities; 14% of eligible men and 10% of eligible women are members. Most popular organizations: student government, Residence Hall Association, Marketing Club, Student Activities Council. Major annual events: Family Weekend, Homecoming Week, Greek Week. Student services: health clinic, personal-psychological counseling. Campus security: 24-hour emergency response devices and patrols, late night transport-escort service, controlled dormitory access. 2,748 college housing spaces available; 2,400 were occupied in 2003-04. Freshmen given priority for college housing. On-campus residence required through sophomore year. Option: coed housing available. Kent Library with 411,992 books, 1.3 million microform titles, 2,781 serials, 9,400 audiovisual materials, an OPAC, and a Web page. Operations spending for 2004 fiscal year: $1.7 million. 1,022 computers available on campus for general student use. A campuswide network can be accessed from student residence rooms and from off campus. Staffed computer lab on campus.
Community Environment: Cape Girardeau (population 35,800) was founded in 1793 as an Indian trading post. It is now a progressive industrial city. Commercial transportation is convenient; other community facilities include many churches, hospitals, shopping areas and a library. Part time employment is available.

■ **SOUTHWEST BAPTIST UNIVERSITY** *I-5*
1600 University Ave.
Bolivar, MO 65613-2597
Tel: (417)326-5281
Free: 800-526-5859
Admissions: (417)328-1817
Fax: (417)328-1514
E-mail: dcrowder@sbuniv.edu
Web Site: http://www.sbuniv.edu/
Description: Independent Southern Baptist, comprehensive, coed. Awards associate, bachelor's, master's, and doctoral degrees and post-master's certificates. Founded 1878. Setting: 152-acre small town campus. Endowment: $15.2 million. Educational spending for 2005 fiscal year: $5400 per student. Total enrollment: 3,440. Faculty: 246 (105 full-time, 141 part-time). Student-undergrad faculty ratio is 15:1. 720 applied, 85% were admitted. 20% from top 10% of their high school class, 43% from top quarter, 74% from top half. Full-time: 1,778 students, 61% women, 39% men. Part-time: 923 students, 75% women, 25% men. Students come from 43 states and territories, 13 other countries, 30% from out-of-state, 1% Native American, 1% Hispanic, 2% black, 1% Asian American or Pacific Islander, 1% international, 27% 25 or older, 64% live on campus, 4% transferred in. Retention: 68% of full-time freshmen returned the following year. Academic areas with the most degrees conferred: education; psychology; business/marketing. Core. Calendar: 4-1-4. Academic remediation for entering students, ESL program, services for LD students, advanced placement, honors program, independent study, double major, summer session for

credit, part-time degree program, co-op programs and internships, graduate courses open to undergrads. Off campus study at Mountain View Center, Salem Center, Springfield Center. Study abroad program. ROTC: Army (c).

Entrance Requirements: Options: electronic application, international baccalaureate accepted. Required: high school transcript, SAT or ACT. Recommended: interview. Required for some: 3 recommendations. Entrance: moderately difficult. Application deadline: Rolling. Notification: continuous.

Costs Per Year: Application fee: $30. Comprehensive fee: $18,300 includes full-time tuition ($13,300), mandatory fees ($800), and college room and board ($4200). College room only: $2200. Part-time tuition: $530 per hour.

Collegiate Environment: Orientation program. Drama-theater group, choral group, student-run newspaper. Social organizations: 27 open to all. Most popular organizations: small group ministries, Christian Service Organization, Student Government Association, Student Missouri State Teachers Association, revival teams. Major annual events: homecoming, Mass Advisement Day, Commencement. Student services: health clinic, personal-psychological counseling. Campus security: 24-hour emergency response devices and patrols. 1,126 college housing spaces available; 940 were occupied in 2003-04. Freshmen guaranteed college housing. On-campus residence required through junior year. Options: men-only, women-only housing available. Harriett K. Hutchens Library plus 3 others with 193,821 books, 481,593 microform titles, 10,939 serials, 11,202 audiovisual materials, an OPAC, and a Web page. Operations spending for 2004 fiscal year: $1 million. 261 computers available on campus for general student use. A campuswide network can be accessed from student residence rooms and from off campus. Staffed computer lab on campus.

Community Environment: The county seat of Polk County, Bolivar (population 8,000) is in the midst of a recreational area and is the center of a developing lake region. There is bus transportation to Springfield and Kansas City from Bolivar. A community concert association, allied with Columbia Artists Management of New York, brings quality musical attractions to Bolivar each season. The Southwest Regional Library which serves three counties is located here.

■ **SPRINGFIELD COLLEGE** *J-5*
1010 West Sunshine
Springfield, MO 65807-2488
Tel: (417)864-7220
Free: 800-475-2669
Fax: (417)865-5697
E-mail: gterrebr@cci.edu
Web Site: http://www.Springfield-college.com/

Description: Proprietary, 2-year, coed. Part of Corinthian Colleges, Inc. Awards terminal associate degrees. Founded 1976. Setting: 2-acre urban campus. Total enrollment: 520. 60% 25 or older. Core. Academic remediation for entering students, advanced placement, summer session for credit, part-time degree program, internships.

Entrance Requirements: Open admission. Option: deferred admission. Required: high school transcript, interview, CPAt. Entrance: noncompetitive. Application deadline: Rolling.

Collegiate Environment: Orientation program. Social organizations: 6 open to all; local fraternities. Most popular organizations: student government, Medical Assistant Club, Legal Club, Phi Beta Lambda, Collegiate Secretaries International. College housing not available. Springfield College Library with 3,000 books and 32 serials. 75 computers available on campus for general student use. Staffed computer lab on campus.

Community Environment: Established as a trading post in 1636, Springfield is located on the Connecticut River in Southwestern part of the state. City is noted today for its diversified industries including the manufacture of firearms, plastics, chemicals, radio equipment, tires, paper, and electrical equipment. Ample part-time job opportunities available. Several movie theatres, municipal auditorium, drive-ins, summer theatre, two municipal golf courses, 150 parks, civic center, and playgrounds, swimming, skating, quadrangle of museums, public libraries, provide excellent recreational and cultural opportunities. Easy access to commercial, bus and rail service.

■ **STATE FAIR COMMUNITY COLLEGE** *F-6*
3201 West 16th St.
Sedalia, MO 65301-2199
Tel: (660)530-5800; 877-311-SFCC
Fax: (660)530-5820
Web Site: http://www.sfcc.cc.mo.us/

Description: District-supported, 2-year, coed. Part of Missouri Coordinating Board for Higher Education. Awards certificates, transfer associate, and terminal associate degrees. Founded 1966. Setting: 128-acre small town campus. Educational spending for 2005 fiscal year: $1176 per student. Total enrollment: 3,391. 8% from top 10% of their high school class, 25% from top quarter, 40% from top half. Full-time: 1,690 students, 63% women, 37% men. Part-time: 1,701 students, 54% women, 46% men. Students come from 16 states and territories, 1% Native American, 3% Hispanic, 6% black, 1% Asian American or Pacific Islander, 0% international, 54% 25 or older. Retention: 55% of full-time freshmen returned the following year. Core. Calendar: semesters. Academic remediation for entering students, services for LD students, advanced placement, accelerated degree program, distance learning, summer session for credit, part-time degree program, adult/continuing education programs, internships. Off campus study at Midwest Student Exchange Program.

Entrance Requirements: Open admission except for allied health programs. Option: early admission. Required: high school transcript. Placement: ACT, ACT ASSET, ACT COMPASS required for some. Entrance: noncompetitive. Application deadline: Rolling.

Collegiate Environment: Orientation program. Drama-theater group, choral group. Campus security: security during evening class hours. Options: coed, men-only, women-only housing available. Learning Resources Center with 36,000 books and 100 serials. 218 computers available on campus for general student use. A campuswide network can be accessed from off-campus. Staffed computer lab on campus.

Community Environment: Sedalia (population 20,000) is a rural community, and is the home of the Missouri State Fair. It is also an industrial area that produces truck bodies, brooms, mops, wheels, toolboxes, restaurant equipment, and fans. All forms of commercial transportation are available. Good shopping facilities, many churches, and various service clubs are a part of the community's facilities. Many part-time employment opportunities are available. Parks provide opportunities for recreation.

■ **STEPHENS COLLEGE** *E-7*
1200 East Broadway
Columbia, MO 65215-0002
Tel: (573)442-2211
Free: 800-876-7207
Admissions: (573)876-7207
Fax: (573)876-7237
E-mail: apply@stephens.edu
Web Site: http://www.stephens.edu/

Description: Independent, comprehensive. Awards bachelor's and master's degrees. Founded 1833. Setting: 86-acre urban campus. Endowment: $19.7 million. Research spending for 2004 fiscal year: $98,000. Educational spending for 2005 fiscal year: $6464 per student. Total enrollment: 824. Faculty: 91 (41 full-time, 50 part-time). Student-undergrad faculty ratio is 12:1. 546 applied, 77% were admitted. 19% from top 10% of their high school class, 59% from top quarter, 88% from top half. Full-time: 574 students, 98% women, 2% men. Part-time: 180 students, 94% women, 6% men. Students come from 41 states and territories, 3 other countries, 55% from out-of-state, 1% Native American, 3% Hispanic, 7% black, 2% Asian American or Pacific Islander, 1% international, 26% 25 or older, 70% live on campus, 4% transferred in. Retention: 73% of full-time freshmen returned the following year. Academic areas with the most degrees conferred: visual and performing arts; communications/journalism; business/marketing; health professions and related sciences. Core. Calendar: semesters. Academic remediation for entering students, ESL program, services for LD students, advanced placement, accelerated degree program, self-designed majors, freshman honors college, honors program, independent study, distance learning, double major, part-time degree program, external degree program, adult/continuing education programs, co-op programs and internships, graduate courses open to undergrads. Off campus study at University of Missouri, Columbia College (MO). Study abroad program. ROTC: Army (c), Air Force (c).

Entrance Requirements: Options: Peterson's Universal Application, Common Application, electronic application, early admission, deferred admission, international baccalaureate accepted. Required: essay, high school transcript, minimum 2.5 high school GPA, 1 recommendation, SAT or ACT. Recommended: interview. Entrance: moderately difficult. Application deadline: 8/1. Notification: continuous until 8/15.

Costs Per Year: Application fee: $25. Comprehensive fee: $28,475 includes full-time tuition ($20,500) and college room and board ($7975). College room only: $4760. Part-time tuition: $220 per hour.

Collegiate Environment: Orientation program. Drama-theater group, choral group, student-run newspaper, radio station. Social organizations: 45 open to all; national sororities; 10% of women are members. Most popular organizations: Student Government Association, Martin Luther King Jr. Student Union, Stephens Ambassadors Association, Stephens Christian Fellowship, Young Women's Political Caucus. Major annual events: Opening Convocation, Winter Formal, Honors Convocation. Student services: health clinic, personal-psychological counseling, women's center. Campus security: 24-hour emergency response devices and patrols, student patrols, late night transport-escort service, controlled dormitory access. 817 college housing spaces available; 320 were occupied in 2003-04. Freshmen guaranteed college housing. On-campus residence required through junior year. Option: women-only housing available. Hugh Stephens Library with 121,084 books, 11,067 microform titles, 534 serials, 4,764 audiovisual materials, an OPAC, and a Web page. Operations spending for 2004 fiscal year: $306,765. 64 computers available on campus for general student use. A campuswide network can be accessed from student residence rooms and from off campus. Staffed computer lab on campus.

Community Environment: Stephens College is located in Columbia, Missouri. Situated between Kansas City and St. Louis, Columbia is the cultural, medical, and business center of mid-Missouri. Often called "College Town, USA", Columbia is also the home of Columbia College and the University of Missouri. Stephens students have easy access to Columbia's shopping, dining, and entertainment offerings.

■ **THREE RIVERS COMMUNITY COLLEGE** *K-11*

2080 Three Rivers Blvd.

Poplar Bluff, MO 63901-2393

Tel: (573)840-9600; 877-TRY-TRCC

Admissions: (573)840-9675

Web Site: http://www.trcc.edu/

Description: State and locally supported, 2-year, coed. Part of Missouri Coordinating Board for Higher Education. Awards certificates, transfer associate, and terminal associate degrees. Founded 1966. Setting: 70-acre rural campus. Endowment: $655,356. Educational spending for 2005 fiscal year: $2260 per student. Total enrollment: 2,935. Student-undergrad faculty ratio is 22:1. 619 applied, 100% were admitted. 7% from top 10% of their high school class, 25% from top quarter, 58% from top half. 8 valedictorians. Full-time: 1,622 students, 63% women, 37% men. Part-time: 1,313 students, 71% women, 29% men. Students come from 11 states and territories, 2% from out-of-state, 1% Native American, 1% Hispanic, 9% black, 1% Asian American or Pacific Islander, 0% international, 38% 25 or older, 10% live on campus, 1% transferred in. Core. Calendar: semesters. Academic remediation for entering students, ESL program, services for LD students, advanced placement, accelerated degree program, honors program, independent study, distance learning, double major, summer session for credit, part-time degree program, external degree program, adult/continuing education programs, internships.

Entrance Requirements: Open admission. Option: early admission. Required: high school transcript. Entrance: noncompetitive.

Costs Per Year: Application fee: $20. Area resident tuition: $1830 full-time, $61 per credit hour part-time. State resident tuition: $2940 full-time, $98 per credit hour part-time. Nonresident tuition: $3660 full-time, $122 per credit hour part-time. Mandatory fees: $375 full-time, $8.50 per credit hour part-time. College room only: $3114.

Collegiate Environment: Orientation program. Social organizations: 10 open to all. Most popular organizations: student government, PTK, PBL, Alpha Beta Gamma, Lambda Alpha Epsilon. Major annual events: Fall Celebration, Spring Celebration, Annual Monter Mass. Campus security: 24-hour patrols. 188 college housing spaces available; 167 were occupied in 2003-04. No special consideration for freshman housing applicants. Option: coed housing available. Rutland Library with 36,960 books, 7,527 microform titles, 238 serials, 1,027 audiovisual materials, an OPAC, and a Web page. Operations spending for 2004 fiscal year: $177,500. 200 computers available on campus for general student use. A campuswide network can be accessed from student residence rooms. Staffed computer lab on campus.

Community Environment: Poplar Bluff, population 25,000, is a metropolitan area in southeast Missouri where the climate is temperate and living is pleasant. The community has two private general hospitals, one veteran's hospital, many churches, a library, and numerous civic organizations. Many natural streams and lakes within driving distance of the city provide excellent facilities for all outdoor sports. Part-time jobs are available.

■ **TRUMAN STATE UNIVERSITY** *B-7*

100 East Normal St.

Kirksville, MO 63501-4221

Tel: (660)785-4000

Admissions: (660)785-4114

Fax: (660)785-7456

E-mail: admissions@truman.edu

Web Site: http://www.truman.edu/

Description: State-supported, comprehensive, coed. Awards bachelor's and master's degrees. Founded 1867. Setting: 140-acre small town campus. Endowment: $21.1 million. Research spending for 2004 fiscal year: $573,413. Educational spending for 2005 fiscal year: $6707 per student. Total enrollment: 5,803. Faculty: 378 (353 full-time, 25 part-time). Student-undergrad faculty ratio is 15:1. 4,883 applied, 83% were admitted. 48% from top 10% of their high school class, 80% from top quarter, 99% from top half. 16 National Merit Scholars, 137 valedictorians. Full-time: 5,460 students, 58% women, 42% men. Part-time: 111 students, 45% women, 55% men. Students come from 44 states and territories, 51 other countries, 23% from out-of-state, 0.4% Native American, 2% Hispanic, 4% black, 2% Asian American or Pacific Islander, 4% international, 1% 25 or older, 48% live on campus, 2% transferred in. Retention: 86% of full-time freshmen returned the following year. Academic areas with the most degrees conferred: business/marketing; social sciences; biological/life sciences. Core. Calendar: semesters. ESL program, services for LD students, advanced placement, accelerated degree program, self-designed majors, honors program, double major, summer session for credit, part-time degree program, internships, graduate courses open to undergrads. Off campus study at Gulf Coast Research Laboratory, Reis Biological Station. Study abroad program. ROTC: Army.

Entrance Requirements: Options: Peterson's Universal Application, Common Application, electronic application, early admission, early action, deferred admission, international baccalaureate accepted. Required: essay, high school transcript, SAT or ACT. Recommended: minimum 3.0 high school GPA, interview, ACT. Entrance: moderately difficult. Application deadlines: 3/1, 11/15 for early action. Notification: continuous, 12/15 for early action. Preference given to state residents.

Costs Per Year: Application fee: $0. One-time mandatory fee: $150. State resident tuition: $5740 full-time, $239 per credit hour part-time. Nonresident tuition: $9920 full-time, $413 per credit hour part-time. Mandatory fees: $72 full-time. Part-time tuition varies according to course load. College room and board: $5380. Room and board charges vary according to housing facility.

Collegiate Environment: Orientation program. Drama-theater group, choral group, marching band, student-run newspaper, radio station. Social organizations: 210 open to all; national fraternities, national sororities, local sororities; 30% of eligible men and 20% of eligible women are members. Most popular organizations: Campus Christian Fellowship, Alpha Phi Omega, Student Ambassadors, Alpha Sigma Gamma, Baptist Student Union. Major annual events: Homecoming, Dog Days (spring carnival), Lyceum Series. Student services: health clinic, personal-psychological counseling, women's center. Campus security: 24-hour emergency response devices and patrols, student patrols, late night transport-escort service, patrols by commissioned officers. 2,926 college housing spaces available; 2,794 were occupied in 2003-04. Freshmen guaranteed college housing. On-campus residence required in freshman year. Options: coed, women-only housing available. Pickler Memorial Library with 492,916 books, 1.5 million microform titles, 3,468 serials, 39,284 audiovisual materials, an OPAC, and a Web page. Operations spending for 2004 fiscal year: $2.5 million. 900 computers available on campus for general student use. Computer purchase/lease plans available. A campuswide network can be accessed from student residence rooms and from off campus. Staffed computer lab on campus.

Community Environment: Kirksville, Missouri, is located in the northeastern part of the state, a 3 to 4-hour drive from Kansas City, St. Louis, and Des Moines, Iowa, and 80 miles west of historic Hannibal, Missouri, and Quincy, Illinois. The town is served by a direct Amtrak connection from Chicago and Quincy, IL. A municipal airport provides daily flights to and from Kansas City. Kirksville offers an environment for serious study in a community where higher education is the focal point. Besides University students, the community is home to 17,000 townspeople and nearly 250 medical students at the Kirksville College of Osteopathic Medicine.

■ **UNIVERSITY OF MISSOURI-COLUMBIA** *E-7*

Columbia, MO 65211

Tel: (573)882-2121

Admissions: (573)882-7786

Fax: (573)882-7887

E-mail: mu4u@missouri.edu

Web Site: http://www.missouri.edu/

Description: State-supported, university, coed. Part of University of Missouri System. Awards bachelor's, master's, doctoral, and first professional degrees and post-master's and first professional certificates. Founded 1839. Setting: 1,358-acre small town campus. Endowment: $442.8 million. Research spending for 2004 fiscal year: $162.9 million. Total enrollment: 27,985. Faculty: 1,149 (1,066 full-time, 83 part-time). Student-undergrad faculty ratio is 18:1. 12,404 applied, 83% were admitted. 27% from top 10% of their high school class, 57% from top quarter, 88% from top half. 31 National Merit Scholars. Full-time: 19,979 students, 52% women, 48% men. Part-time: 1,396 students, 50% women, 50% men. Students come from 52 states and territories, 85 other countries, 19% from out-of-state, 1% Native American, 2% Hispanic, 6% black, 3% Asian American or Pacific Islander, 1% international, 5% 25 or older, 39% live on campus, 6% transferred in. Retention: 84% of full-time freshmen returned the following year. Academic areas with the most degrees conferred: business/marketing; communications/journalism; engineering. Core. Calendar: semesters. ESL program, services for LD students, advanced placement, accelerated degree program, self-designed majors, freshman honors college, honors program, independent study, distance learning, double major, summer session for credit, part-time degree program, external degree program, adult/continuing education programs, co-op programs and internships, graduate courses open to undergrads. Off campus study at Mid-Missouri Associated Colleges and Universities, National Student Exchange. Study abroad program. ROTC: Army, Naval, Air Force.

Entrance Requirements: Options: electronic application, deferred admission. Required: high school transcript, specific high school curriculum, SAT or ACT, specific high school curriculum. Recommended: ACT. Entrance: moderately difficult. Application deadline: Rolling. Notification: continuous.

Costs Per Year: Application fee: $35. State resident tuition: $6495 full-time, $216.50 per credit hour part-time. Nonresident tuition: $16,272 full-time, $542.40 per credit hour part-time. Mandatory fees: $1250 full-time, $32.07 per credit hour part-time. Full-time tuition and fees vary according to course load, program, and reciprocity agreements. Part-time tuition and fees vary according to course load, program, and reciprocity agreements. College room and board: $6245. Room and board charges vary according to board plan and housing facility.

Collegiate Environment: Orientation program. Drama-theater group, choral group, marching band, student-run newspaper, radio station. Social organizations: 442 open to all; national fraternities, national sororities; 21% of eligible men and 24% of eligible women are members. Most popular organizations: Students Association, Residence Hall Association, Honors International Organization. Major annual events: Homecoming, Student Activities Mart, Journalism Week. Student services: legal services, health clinic, personal-psychological counseling, women's center. Campus security: 24-hour emergency response devices and patrols, late night transport-escort service, controlled dormitory access. 9,207 college housing spaces available; 8,210 were occupied in 2003-04. Freshmen guaranteed college housing. On-campus residence required in freshman year. Options: coed, men-only, women-only housing available. Ellis Library plus 11 others with 3.2 million books, 6.9 million microform titles, 15,808 serials, 22,705 audiovisual materials, an OPAC, and a Web page. Operations spending for 2004 fiscal year: $14.2 million. 1,615 computers available on campus for general student use. Computer purchase/lease plans available. A campuswide network can be accessed from student residence rooms and from off campus. Staffed computer lab on campus.

Community Environment: The University rests in the heart of Columbia, a growing city of more than 76,000. Cited for its excellent educational opportunities and quality of life, Columbia has ranked among the top most livable cities in the United States for more than a decade, according to Money Magazine. Columbia combines the benefits of a large city - a wide selection of lodging, dining, shopping, cultural and sporting opportunities - with the friendly atmosphere and convenience of a small town. All forms of public transportation are available. Situated midway between St. Louis and Kansas City (each about two hours away), Columbia also is within a two-hour drive for the Lake of the Ozarks recreation area, which provides opportunities for many outdoor sports.

■ **UNIVERSITY OF MISSOURI-KANSAS CITY** *E-3*

5100 Rockhill Rd.

Kansas City, MO 64110-2499

Tel: (816)235-1000

Free: 800-775-8652

Admissions: (816)235-1111

Fax: (816)235-1717

E-mail: admit@umkc.edu

Web Site: http://www.umkc.edu/

Description: State-supported, university, coed. Part of University of Missouri System. Awards bachelor's, master's, doctoral, and first professional degrees and post-master's and first professional certificates. Founded 1929. Setting: 191-acre urban campus. Endowment: $189.9 million. Research spending for 2004 fiscal year: $35.6 million. Total enrollment: 14,310. Faculty: 1,055 (641 full-time, 414 part-time). Student-undergrad faculty ratio is 11:1. 3,018 applied, 75% were admitted. 30% from top 10% of their high school class, 55% from top quarter, 84% from top half. Full-time: 5,676 students, 59% women, 41% men. Part-time: 3,815 students, 60% women, 40% men. Students come from 45 states and territories, 46 other countries, 24% from out-of-state, 1% Native American, 4% Hispanic, 15% black, 6% Asian American or Pacific Islander, 3% international, 30% 25 or older, 13% live on campus, 12% transferred in. Retention: 71% of full-time freshmen returned the following year. Academic areas with the most degrees conferred: liberal arts/general studies; business/marketing; education. Core. Calendar: semesters. ESL program, services for LD students, advanced placement, accelerated degree program, honors program, independent study, distance learning, double major, summer session for credit, part-time degree program, adult/continuing education programs, co-op programs and internships, graduate courses open to undergrads. Off campus study at other campuses of the University of Missouri System. Study abroad program. ROTC: Army, Air Force (c).

Entrance Requirements: Options: electronic application, deferred admission, international baccalaureate accepted. Required: high school transcript, SAT or ACT. Entrance: moderately difficult. Application deadline: Rolling. Notification: continuous.

Costs Per Year: Application fee: $35. State resident tuition: $6819 full-time, $227.30 per credit hour part-time. Nonresident tuition: $17,085 full-time, $569.50 per credit hour part-time.

Collegiate Environment: Orientation program. Drama-theater group, choral group, student-run newspaper. Social organizations: 75 open to all; national fraternities, national sororities, local sororities; 13% of eligible men and 20% of eligible women are members. Most popular organizations: African-American Student Association, International Student Council, Alpha Phi Omega, Activities and Programs Council. Major annual events: International Food and Culture Night, Welcome Fest/Roo Fair, Greek Week. Student services: legal services, health clinic, personal-psychological counseling, women's center. Campus security: 24-hour emergency response devices and patrols, late night transport-escort service, controlled dormitory access. 1,700 college housing spaces available; 867 were occupied in 2003-04. Option: coed housing available. Miller-Nichols Library plus 3 others with 1.3 million books, 2.4 million microform titles, 7,222 serials, 451,563 audiovisual materials, an OPAC, and a Web page. Operations spending for 2004 fiscal year: $6.3 million. 671 computers available on campus for general student use. Computer purchase/lease plans available. A campuswide network can be accessed from student residence rooms and from off campus. Staffed computer lab on campus.

Community Environment: One of the country's largest railroad centers, Kansas City is also a great manufacturing city and an important distributing point located at the confluence of the Kansas and Missouri Rivers. All forms of commercial transportation are convenient. Extensive cultural activities are available. Recreational facilities are numerous. Swope Park is one the largest municipal playgrounds in the country that contains 1,705 acres, two golf courses, tennis courts, picnic grounds, a zoo, swimming pool and a lagoon for boating. Kansas City is the home of the Chiefs of the National Football League and Royals baseball team of the American League. The Country Club district in the southern part of the city has gained international attention as a model for city planning. Each home in this district is planned to harmonize with its surroundings, and careful selection of European art objects beautify street corners.

■ UNIVERSITY OF MISSOURI-ROLLA *H-8*

1870 Miner Circle
Rolla, MO 65409-0910
Tel: (573)341-4111
Free: 800-522-0938
Admissions: (573)341-4164
E-mail: umrolla@umr.edu
Web Site: http://www.umr.edu/

Description: State-supported, university, coed. Part of University of Missouri System. Awards bachelor's, master's, and doctoral degrees. Founded 1870. Setting: 284-acre small town campus. Endowment: $63.8 million. Research spending for 2004 fiscal year: $28.9 million. Educational spending for 2005 fiscal year: $10,061 per student. Total enrollment: 5,407. 1,942 applied, 90% were admitted. 40% from top 10% of their high school class, 71% from top quarter, 94% from top half. 44 National Merit Scholars, 37 valedictorians. Full-time: 3,747 students, 22% women, 78% men. Part-time: 374 students, 31% women, 69% men. Students come from 45 states and territories, 33 other countries, 20% from out-of-state, 0.5% Native American, 2% Hispanic, 4% black, 3% Asian American or Pacific Islander, 2% international, 8% 25 or older, 56% live on campus, 7% transferred in. Retention: 83% of full-time freshmen returned the following year. Core. Calendar: semesters. Academic remediation for entering students, ESL program, services for LD students, advanced placement, accelerated degree program, freshman honors college, honors program, independent study, distance learning, double major, summer session for credit, part-time degree program, adult/continuing education programs, co-op programs and internships, graduate courses open to undergrads. Off campus study at University of Missouri-Columbia. Study abroad program. ROTC: Army, Naval (c), Air Force.

Entrance Requirements: Options: Common Application, electronic application, early admission, deferred admission, international baccalaureate accepted. Required: high school transcript, SAT or ACT. Entrance: very difficult. Application deadline: 7/1. Notification: continuous.

Costs Per Year: Application fee: $35. State resident tuition: $6451 full-time, $216.50 per credit hour part-time. Nonresident tuition: $15,576 full-time, $542.40 per credit hour part-time. Mandatory fees: $1041 full-time. Full-time tuition and fees vary according to course load, degree level, and program. Part-time tuition varies according to course load, degree level, and program. College room and board: $5840. College room only: $3570. Room and board charges vary according to board plan, housing facility, and location.

Collegiate Environment: Orientation program. Drama-theater group, choral group, marching band, student-run newspaper, radio station. Social organizations: 197 open to all; national fraternities, national sororities, local sororities; 27% of eligible men and 24% of eligible women are members. Most popular organizations: student government, service organizations, academic organizations. Major annual events: homecoming, St. Patrick's celebration, Parents' Day. Student services: legal services, health clinic, personal-psychological counseling. Campus security: 24-hour emergency response devices and patrols, student patrols, late night transport-escort service, controlled dormitory access, crime prevention programs. 1,400 college housing spaces available. On-campus residence required through sophomore year. Options: coed, men-only, women-only housing available. Curtis Laws Wilson Library with 255,768 books, 45,827 microform titles, 1,495 serials, 6,353 audiovisual materials, an OPAC, and a Web page. Operations spending for 2004 fiscal year: $2.6 million. 800 computers available on campus for general student use. A campuswide network can be accessed from student residence rooms and from off campus. Staffed computer lab on campus.

Community Environment: Rolla, population 15,000, is one of the most scenic sections of the Ozarks, where excellent fishing and hunting are available. Situated in the center of Missouri, on Interstate 44. A number of churches of most denominations, a hospital, clinics, a library and civic organizations are all a part of the community services. Lake and river recreation available, caves to explore, tennis courts, baseball diamonds, golf courses, and bowling alleys provide recreation. Part time employment for students is available. Rolla originally was an Ozarks farm trade center. After the establishment of the university campus, several large and important federal and state government agencies located here. Today the community is unusual in its concentration of about 1,000 professional engineers, geologists, cartographers, mathematicians, and technicians who are employed by these offices.

■ UNIVERSITY OF MISSOURI-ST. LOUIS *F-12*

One University Blvd.
St. Louis, MO 63121
Tel: (314)516-5000
Admissions: (314)516-5451
Fax: (314)516-5310
E-mail: kundelj@umsl.edu
Web Site: http://www.umsl.edu/

Description: State-supported, university, coed. Part of University of Missouri System. Awards bachelor's, master's, doctoral, and first professional degrees. Founded 1963. Setting: 350-acre suburban campus. Endowment: $43.3 million. Research spending for 2004 fiscal year: $6.2 million. Educational spending for 2005 fiscal year: $3358 per student. Total enrollment: 15,561. Faculty: 693 (371 full-time, 322 part-time). Student-undergrad faculty ratio is 19:1. 2,207 applied, 52% were admitted. 21% from top 10% of their high school class, 50% from top quarter, 83% from top half. Full-time: 5,887 students, 59% women, 41% men. Part-time: 6,732 students, 63% women, 37% men. Students come from 34 states and territories, 88 other countries, 5% from out-of-state, 0.3% Native American, 2% Hispanic, 17% black, 3% Asian American or Pacific Islander, 2% international, 38% 25 or older, 8% live on campus, 21% transferred in. Retention: 73% of full-time freshmen returned the following year. Academic areas with the most degrees conferred: business/marketing; education; social sciences. Core. Calendar: semesters. ESL program, services for LD students, advanced placement, accelerated degree program, self-designed majors, freshman honors college, honors program, independent study, distance learning, double major, summer session for credit, part-time degree program, adult/continuing education programs, co-op programs and internships, graduate courses open to undergrads. Off campus study at Southern Illinois University, Saint Louis University, Washington University in St. Louis, St. Charles Community College, Mineral Area Community College, East Central Community College, Jefferson Community College. Study abroad program. ROTC: Army (c), Air Force (c).

Entrance Requirements: Options: electronic application, deferred admission, international baccalaureate accepted. Required: high school transcript, CBHE Core Requirements, SAT or ACT. Entrance: moderately difficult. Application deadline: Rolling. Notification: continuous.

Costs Per Year: Application fee: $35. State resident tuition: $6495 full-time, $216.50 per credit hour part-time. Nonresident tuition: $16,272 full-time, $542.40 per credit hour part-time. Mandatory fees: $1123 full-time, $43.20 per credit hour part-time. Full-time tuition and fees vary according to course load, program, and reciprocity agreements. Part-time tuition and fees vary according to course load, program, and reciprocity agreements. College room and board: $6428. College room only: $4561. Room and board charges vary according to board plan and housing facility.

Collegiate Environment: Orientation program. Drama-theater group, choral group, student-run newspaper. Social organizations: 120 open to all; national fraternities, national sororities; 1% of eligible men and 1% of eligible women are members. Most popular organizations: Student Government Association, Associated Black Collegians, Pierre laclede Honors College Student Association, Residence Hall Council, International Student Association. Major annual events: Fall Expo/Campus Picnic, Mirthday, Welcome Week. Student services: health clinic, personal-psychological counseling, women's center. Campus security: 24-hour emergency response devices and patrols, late night transport-escort service, controlled dormitory access. 1,000 college housing spaces available; 960 were occupied in 2003-04. No special consideration for freshman housing applicants. Options: coed, women-only housing available. Thomas Jefferson Library plus 2 others with 1.1 million books, 1.3 million microform titles, 3,305 serials, 3,878 audiovisual materials, an OPAC, and a Web page. Operations spending for 2004 fiscal year: $4.4 million. 1,000 computers available on campus for general student use. Computer purchase/lease plans available. A campuswide network can be accessed from student residence rooms and from off campus. Staffed computer lab on campus.

■ UNIVERSITY OF PHOENIX-KANSAS CITY CAMPUS *E-3*

901 East 104th St., Ste. 301
Kansas City, MO 64131-4517
Tel: (816)943-9600
Free: 800-228-7240
Admissions: (480)557-1712
Fax: (816)943-6675
Web Site: http://www.phoenix.edu/

Description: Proprietary, comprehensive, coed. Awards bachelor's and master's degrees. Founded 2002. Total enrollment: 1,297. Faculty: 127 (8 full-time, 119 part-time). Student-undergrad faculty ratio is 8:1. 52 applied. Full-time: 1,020 students, 61% women, 39% men. 0.3% Native American, 1% Hispanic, 7% black, 1% Asian American or Pacific Islander, 13% international, 88% 25 or older. Academic areas with the most degrees conferred: business/marketing; computer and information sciences. Core. Calendar: continuous. Advanced placement, accelerated degree program, independent study, distance learning, external degree program, adult/continuing education programs, graduate courses open to undergrads.
Entrance Requirements: Open admission. Option: deferred admission. Required: 1 recommendation. Required for some: high school transcript. Entrance: noncompetitive. Application deadline: Rolling.
Costs Per Year: Application fee: $110. Tuition: $11,145 full-time, $371.50 per credit part-time. Mandatory fees: $560 full-time.
Collegiate Environment: College housing not available. University Library with 444 books, 666 serials, an OPAC, and a Web page. System-wide operations spending for 2004 fiscal year: $3.2 million.

■ **UNIVERSITY OF PHOENIX-ST. LOUIS CAMPUS** *F-12*
Riverport Lakes West
13801 Riverport Dr., Ste. 102
St. Louis, MO 63043-4828
Tel: (314)298-9755
Free: 800-228-7240
Admissions: (480)557-1712
Fax: (314)291-2901
Web Site: http://www.phoenix.edu/
Description: Proprietary, comprehensive, coed. Awards bachelor's and master's degrees. Founded 2000. Setting: urban campus. Total enrollment: 1,026. Faculty: 167 (12 full-time, 155 part-time). Student-undergrad faculty ratio is 6:1. 50 applied. Full-time: 869 students, 57% women, 43% men. 0% from out-of-state, 0.1% Native American, 0.3% Hispanic, 8% black, 0.5% Asian American or Pacific Islander, 7% international, 88% 25 or older. Academic areas with the most degrees conferred: business/marketing; computer and information sciences. Core. Calendar: continuous. Advanced placement, accelerated degree program, independent study, distance learning, external degree program, adult/continuing education programs, graduate courses open to undergrads.
Entrance Requirements: Open admission. Option: deferred admission. Required: 1 recommendation. Required for some: high school transcript. Entrance: noncompetitive. Application deadline: Rolling.
Costs Per Year: Application fee: $110. Tuition: $11,550 full-time, $385 per credit part-time. Mandatory fees: $560 full-time, $70 per course part-time.
Collegiate Environment: College housing not available. University Library with 444 books, 666 serials, an OPAC, and a Web page. System-wide operations spending for 2004 fiscal year: $3.2 million.

■ **UNIVERSITY OF PHOENIX-SPRINGFIELD CAMPUS** *J-5*
1260 E. Kingsley St.
Springfield, MO 65804-7211
Free: 800-228-7240
Admissions: (480)557-1712
Web Site: http://www.phoenix.edu/
Description: Proprietary, comprehensive, coed. Awards bachelor's and master's degrees. Total enrollment: 259. Faculty: 35 (3 full-time, 32 part-time). Student-undergrad faculty ratio is 4:1. 33 applied. Full-time: 220 students, 54% women, 46% men. 0% from out-of-state, 3% international. Core. Advanced placement, accelerated degree program, independent study, distance learning, external degree program, adult/continuing education programs, graduate courses open to undergrads.
Entrance Requirements: Open admission. Option: deferred admission. Required: 1 recommendation. Required for some: high school transcript. Entrance: noncompetitive. Application deadline: Rolling.
Costs Per Year: Application fee: $110. Tuition: $9450 full-time, $315 per credit part-time. Mandatory fees: $560 full-time, $70 per course part-time.
Collegiate Environment: College housing not available. University Library with 444 books, 666 serials, and a Web page. System-wide operations spending for 2004 fiscal year: $3.2 million.

■ **VATTEROTT COLLEGE (KANSAS CITY)** *E-3*
8955 East 38th Terrace
Kansas City, MO 64129
Tel: (816)861-1000

Free: 800-466-3997
Fax: (816)861-1400
Web Site: http://www.vatterott-college.com/
Description: Proprietary, 2-year, coed. Calendar: semesters.

■ **VATTEROTT COLLEGE (O'FALLON)**
927 East Terra Ln.
O'Fallon, MO 63366
Tel: (636)978-7488
Fax: (636)978-5121
Web Site: http://www.vatterott-college.com/
Description: Proprietary, 2-year, coed.

■ **VATTEROTT COLLEGE (ST. ANN)** *F-11*
3925 Industrial Dr.
St. Ann, MO 63074-1807
Tel: (314)428-5900
Free: 800-345-6018
Web Site: http://www.vatterott-college.edu/
Description: Proprietary, primarily 2-year, coed. Awards diplomas, terminal associate, and bachelor's degrees. Founded 1969. Setting: 5-acre suburban campus with easy access to St. Louis. Total enrollment: 580. Full-time: 580 students, 19% women, 81% men. 0.3% Hispanic, 56% black, 0.2% Asian American or Pacific Islander. Calendar: continuous.
Entrance Requirements: Option: Common Application.
Collegiate Environment: Orientation program. College housing not available. Main library plus 7 others with a Web page. 240 computers available on campus for general student use. A campuswide network can be accessed. Staffed computer lab on campus.

■ **VATTEROTT COLLEGE (ST. JOSEPH)** *C-2*
3131 Frederick Ave.
St. Joseph, MO 64506
Tel: (816)364-5399
Free: 800-282-5327
Fax: (816)364-1593
Web Site: http://www.vatterott-college.com/
Description: Proprietary, 2-year, coed. Awards diplomas and terminal associate degrees. Setting: urban campus. Total enrollment: 260. Calendar: semesters.
Costs Per Year: Tuition guaranteed not to increase for student's term of enrollment.

■ **VATTEROTT COLLEGE (ST. LOUIS)** *F-12*
12970 Maurer Industrial Dr.
St. Louis, MO 63127
Tel: (314)843-4200
Fax: (314)843-1709
Web Site: http://www.vatterott-college.edu/
Description: Proprietary, primarily 2-year, coed. Awards diplomas, terminal associate, and bachelor's degrees. Total enrollment: 600. Calendar: semesters.

■ **VATTEROTT COLLEGE (SPRINGFIELD)** *J-5*
1258 East Trafficway St.
Springfield, MO 65802
Tel: (417)831-8116
Free: 800-766-5829
Fax: (417)831-5099
Web Site: http://www.vatterott-college.edu/
Description: Proprietary, 2-year, coed. Part of Vatterott College. Awards diplomas and terminal associate degrees. Setting: 2-acre urban campus. Core. Internships.
Entrance Requirements: Required: high school transcript, interview.
Costs Per Year: Tuition: $8800 full-time. Mandatory fees: $900 full-time. Full-time tuition and fees vary according to degree level and program. Tuition guaranteed not to increase for student's term of enrollment.
Collegiate Environment: Orientation program. Social organizations: 1 open to all. Most popular organization: Computer Club. Major annual events: Fall Student Appreciation, Summer Appreciation. Campus security: alarm devices and personnel during open hours; security alarms during closed

hours. College housing not available. 200 computers available on campus for general student use. A campuswide network can be accessed. Staffed computer lab on campus.

■ WASHINGTON UNIVERSITY IN ST. LOUIS *F-12*

1 Brookings Dr.
St. Louis, MO 63130-4899
Tel: (314)935-5000
Free: 800-638-0700
Admissions: (314)935-6000
Fax: (314)935-4290
E-mail: admission@wustl.edu
Web Site: http://www.wustl.edu

Description: Independent, university, coed. Awards bachelor's, master's, doctoral, and first professional degrees. Founded 1853. Setting: 169-acre suburban campus. Endowment: $4.4 billion. Research spending for 2004 fiscal year: $369.6 million. Total enrollment: 13,383. Faculty: 1,081 (850 full-time, 231 part-time). Student-undergrad faculty ratio is 7:1. 21,515 applied, 19% were admitted. Full-time: 6,169 students, 51% women, 49% men. Part-time: 1,297 students, 59% women, 41% men. Students come from 53 states and territories, 66 other countries, 88% from out-of-state, 0.2% Native American, 3% Hispanic, 9% black, 10% Asian American or Pacific Islander, 4% international, 1% 25 or older, 75% live on campus, 2% transferred in. Retention: 96% of full-time freshmen returned the following year. Academic areas with the most degrees conferred: engineering; social sciences; psychology. Core. Calendar: semesters. ESL program, services for LD students, advanced placement, accelerated degree program, self-designed majors, independent study, double major, summer session for credit, part-time degree program, adult/continuing education programs, co-op programs and internships, graduate courses open to undergrads. Off campus study at Consortium on Financing Higher Education. Study abroad program. ROTC: Army, Air Force (c).

Entrance Requirements: Options: Common Application, electronic application, early admission, early decision, deferred admission, international baccalaureate accepted. Required: essay, high school transcript, 2 recommendations, SAT or ACT. Recommended: minimum 3.0 high school GPA, portfolio for art and architecture programs. Entrance: most difficult. Application deadlines: 1/15, 11/15 for early decision plan 1. Notification: 4/1, 12/15 for early decision plan 1.

Costs Per Year: Application fee: $55. Comprehensive fee: $44,240 includes full-time tuition ($32,800), mandatory fees ($988), and college room and board ($10,452). College room only: $6402.

Collegiate Environment: Orientation program. Drama-theater group, choral group, student-run newspaper, radio station. Social organizations: 200 open to all; national fraternities, national sororities; 25% of eligible men and 25% of eligible women are members. Most popular organizations: community service organizations, student government/programming groups, performing arts groups, multicultural interest groups. Major annual events: Thurtene Carnival, W.I.L.D. (concert festival), Homecoming. Student services: health clinic, personal-psychological counseling, women's center. Campus security: 24-hour emergency response devices and patrols, student patrols, late night transport-escort service, controlled dormitory access. 4,590 college housing spaces available; 4,519 were occupied in 2003-04. Freshmen guaranteed college housing. On-campus residence required in freshman year. Options: coed, men-only, women-only housing available. John M. Olin Library plus 13 others with 1.6 million books, 3.3 million microform titles, 47,266 serials, 72,672 audiovisual materials, an OPAC, and a Web page. Operations spending for 2004 fiscal year: $29.4 million. 2,500 computers available on campus for general student use. Computer purchase/lease plans available. A campuswide network can be accessed from student residence rooms and from off campus. Staffed computer lab on campus.

■ WEBSTER UNIVERSITY *F-12*

470 East Lockwood Ave.
St. Louis, MO 63119-3194
Tel: (314)968-6900
Free: 800-75-ENROL
Admissions: (314)968-6991
Fax: (314)968-7115
E-mail: admit@webster.edu
Web Site: http://www.webster.edu/

Description: Independent, comprehensive, coed. Awards bachelor's, master's, and doctoral degrees and post-master's certificates. Founded 1915. Setting: 47-acre suburban campus. Endowment: $40.9 million.

Educational spending for 2005 fiscal year: $4178 per student. Total enrollment: 7,327. Faculty: 807 (172 full-time, 635 part-time). Student-undergrad faculty ratio is 12:1. 1,468 applied, 55% were admitted. 23% from top 10% of their high school class, 48% from top quarter, 83% from top half. 20 class presidents, 11 valedictorians, 69 student government officers. Full-time: 2,558 students, 59% women, 41% men. Part-time: 965 students, 65% women, 35% men. Students come from 39 states and territories, 40 other countries, 20% from out-of-state, 0.1% Native American, 2% Hispanic, 12% black, 1% Asian American or Pacific Islander, 3% international, 32% 25 or older, 27% live on campus, 14% transferred in. Retention: 80% of full-time freshmen returned the following year. Academic areas with the most degrees conferred: business/marketing; communications/journalism; visual and performing arts. Core. Calendar: semesters. Academic remediation for entering students, ESL program, services for LD students, advanced placement, accelerated degree program, self-designed majors, independent study, distance learning, double major, summer session for credit, part-time degree program, adult/continuing education programs, co-op programs and internships, graduate courses open to undergrads. Off campus study at Fontbonne College, Lindenwood College, Maryville University of Saint Louis, Eden Theological Seminary, Missouri Baptist College. Study abroad program. ROTC: Army (c), Air Force (c).

Entrance Requirements: Options: Common Application, electronic application, early admission, deferred admission, international baccalaureate accepted. Required: essay, high school transcript, minimum 2.5 high school GPA, 1 recommendation, SAT or ACT. Recommended: minimum 3.0 high school GPA, interview. Required for some: minimum 3.0 high school GPA, audition. Entrance: moderately difficult. Application deadline: 6/1. Notification: continuous.

Costs Per Year: Application fee: $25. Comprehensive fee: $23,947 includes full-time tuition ($17,210) and college room and board ($6737). College room only: $3586. Full-time tuition varies according to program. Room and board charges vary according to board plan and housing facility. Part-time tuition: $445 per credit hour. Part-time tuition varies according to location.

Collegiate Environment: Orientation program. Drama-theater group, choral group, student-run newspaper, radio station. Social organizations: 47 open to all. Most popular organizations: Student Government Association, Habitat for Humanity, Big Brothers/Big Sisters, Marketing Communications Club, Residential Housing Association. Major annual events: Webster Works Worldwide Community Service Day, Springfest, Homecoming. Student services: health clinic, personal-psychological counseling, women's center. Campus security: 24-hour emergency response devices and patrols, student patrols, late night transport-escort service. 500 college housing spaces available; all were occupied in 2003-04. Freshmen given priority for college housing. Option: coed housing available. Emerson Library with 271,047 books, 137,000 microform titles, 1,598 serials, 16,303 audiovisual materials, an OPAC, and a Web page. Operations spending for 2004 fiscal year: $2.6 million. 330 computers available on campus for general student use. A campuswide network can be accessed. Staffed computer lab on campus.

Community Environment: A suburban area 10 miles from St. Louis, Webster Groves (population 27,455) has the convenience of all major forms of transportation. The shopping facilities here are excellent, numerous civic and service organizations are active. Webster Groves also enjoys the recreational and cultural advantages of St. Louis. Other facilities include a library, and churches of major denominations. Some part-time employment is available.

■ WENTWORTH MILITARY ACADEMY AND JUNIOR COLLEGE *E-4*

1880 Washington Ave.
Lexington, MO 64067
Tel: (660)259-2221
Fax: (660)259-2677
E-mail: rhamilton@wma1880.org
Web Site: http://www.wma1880.org/

Description: Independent, 2-year, coed. Awards transfer associate degrees. Founded 1880. Setting: 130-acre small town campus with easy access to Kansas City. Educational spending for 2005 fiscal year: $7960 per student. Total enrollment: 561. Student-undergrad faculty ratio is 10:1. 456 applied, 100% were admitted. Full-time: 234 students, 46% women, 54% men. Part-time: 327 students, 60% women, 40% men. Students come from 22 states and territories, 4 other countries, 18% from out-of-state, 0.2% Native American, 2% Hispanic, 4% black, 3% Asian American or Pacific Islander, 0.4% international, 10% 25 or older, 0.2% transferred in. Core. Calendar: semesters. Academic remediation for entering students, ESL program, advanced placement, self-designed majors, summer session for credit, part-time degree program, adult/continuing education programs. ROTC: Army.

Entrance Requirements: Option: Common Application. Required: high school transcript. Recommended: SAT or ACT. Required for some: SAT or ACT. Entrance: moderately difficult. Application deadline: 9/11. Notification: 9/11.

Costs Per Year: Application fee: $100. One-time mandatory fee: $25. Tuition: $3480 full-time, $145 per hour part-time.

Collegiate Environment: Orientation program. Choral group, marching band, student-run newspaper. Major annual events: Kansas City Symphony concert, Artist Series, Field Days. Student services: health clinic, personal-psychological counseling. Campus security: 24-hour emergency response devices and patrols. 100 college housing spaces available; 80 were occupied in 2003-04. On-campus residence required through sophomore year. Options: men-only, women-only housing available. Sellers-Coombs Library with 18,890 books, 6,655 microform titles, 49 serials, 919 audiovisual materials, and a Web page. Operations spending for 2004 fiscal year: $15,704. 35 computers available on campus for general student use. Staffed computer lab on campus.

■ **WESTMINSTER COLLEGE** *F-8*
501 Westminster Ave.
Fulton, MO 65251-1299
Tel: (573)642-3361
Free: 800-475-3361
Admissions: (573)592-5251
Fax: (573)592-5227
E-mail: admissions@westminster-mo.edu
Web Site: http://www.westminster-mo.edu/
Description: Independent, 4-year, coed, affiliated with Presbyterian Church. Awards bachelor's degrees. Founded 1851. Setting: 65-acre small town campus. Endowment: $39.8 million. Research spending for 2004 fiscal year: $140,000. Educational spending for 2005 fiscal year: $6167 per student. Total enrollment: 918. Student-undergrad faculty ratio is 14:1. 1,155 applied, 79% were admitted. 14% from top 10% of their high school class, 35% from top quarter, 64% from top half. 7 valedictorians. Full-time: 896 students, 42% women, 58% men. Part-time: 22 students, 77% women, 23% men. Students come from 24 states and territories, 16 other countries, 29% from out-of-state, 2% Native American, 2% Hispanic, 4% black, 1% Asian American or Pacific Islander, 10% international, 1% 25 or older, 80% live on campus, 4% transferred in. Retention: 75% of full-time freshmen returned the following year. Academic areas with the most degrees conferred: business/marketing; social sciences; education. Core. Calendar: semesters. Academic remediation for entering students, services for LD students, advanced placement, self-designed majors, honors program, independent study, double major, summer session for credit, part-time degree program, co-op programs and internships. Off campus study at Chicago Urban Studies Semester, American University. Study abroad program. ROTC: Army (c), Air Force (c).
Entrance Requirements: Options: Peterson's Universal Application, Common Application, electronic application, early admission, deferred admission, international baccalaureate accepted. Required: high school transcript, 1 recommendation, minimum ACT score of 21 or minimum SAT score of 970, SAT or ACT. Recommended: essay, minimum 2.5 high school GPA. Required for some: interview. Entrance: moderately difficult. Notification: continuous until 8/1.
Costs Per Year: Application fee: $0. Comprehensive fee: $21,170 includes full-time tuition ($14,600), mandatory fees ($430), and college room and board ($6140). College room only: $3170. Part-time tuition: $750 per credit hour.
Collegiate Environment: Orientation program. Drama-theater group, choral group, student-run newspaper. Social organizations: 40 open to all; national fraternities, national sororities; 68% of eligible men and 64% of eligible women are members. Most popular organizations: Student Government Association, Environmentally Concerned Students, International Student Club, Habitat for Humanity, Little Brother/Little Sister. Major annual events: Leadership Challenge, Take Back the Night, Wellness Week. Student services: health clinic, personal-psychological counseling, women's center. Campus security: 24-hour emergency response devices and patrols, late night transport-escort service, controlled dormitory access, well-lit campus. 460 college housing spaces available; 427 were occupied in 2003-04. Freshmen guaranteed college housing. On-campus residence required through junior year. Options: coed, women-only housing available. Reeves Memorial Library plus 1 other with 114,402 books, 19,012 microform titles, 3,074 serials, 9,095 audiovisual materials, an OPAC, and a Web page. Operations spending for 2004 fiscal year: $339,913. 140 computers available on campus for general student use. Computer purchase/lease plans available.

A campuswide network can be accessed from student residence rooms and from off campus. Staffed computer lab on campus.

■ **WILLIAM JEWELL COLLEGE** *E-3*
500 College Hill
Liberty, MO 64068-1843
Tel: (816)781-7700; 888-2JEWELL
Fax: (816)415-5027
E-mail: admission@william.jewell.edu
Web Site: http://www.jewell.edu/
Description: Independent Baptist, 4-year, coed. Awards bachelor's degrees (also offers evening program with significant enrollment not reflected in profile). Founded 1849. Setting: 200-acre small town campus with easy access to Kansas City. Endowment: $66.7 million. Educational spending for 2005 fiscal year: $8196 per student. Total enrollment: 1,331. Student-undergrad faculty ratio is 13:1. 1,681 applied, 64% were admitted. 33% from top 10% of their high school class, 65% from top quarter, 91% from top half. 18 valedictorians. Full-time: 1,285 students, 59% women, 41% men. Part-time: 46 students, 61% women, 39% men. Students come from 32 states and territories, 12 other countries, 1% Native American, 3% Hispanic, 5% black, 1% Asian American or Pacific Islander, 0.4% international, 6% 25 or older, 62% live on campus, 8% transferred in. Retention: 81% of full-time freshmen returned the following year. Academic areas with the most degrees conferred: business/marketing; health professions and related sciences; psychology. Core. Calendar: semesters. Academic remediation for entering students, ESL program, advanced placement, self-designed majors, honors program, independent study, double major, summer session for credit, part-time degree program, adult/continuing education programs, co-op programs and internships. Study abroad program.
Entrance Requirements: Options: Peterson's Universal Application, Common Application, electronic application, early action, deferred admission, international baccalaureate accepted. Required: high school transcript, minimum 2.0 high school GPA, SAT or ACT. Recommended: essay, minimum 2.5 high school GPA, 2 recommendations, interview. Required for some: SAT Subject Tests. Entrance: moderately difficult. Application deadline: 8/15. Notification: continuous until 9/1.
Costs Per Year: Application fee: $25. Comprehensive fee: $25,660 includes full-time tuition ($20,150) and college room and board ($5510). College room only: $2320.
Collegiate Environment: Orientation program. Drama-theater group, choral group, student-run newspaper, radio station. Social organizations: 47 open to all; national fraternities, national sororities; 33% of eligible men and 31% of eligible women are members. Most popular organizations: Christian student ministries, College Union activities, Fellowship of Christian Athletes, UNITY, Amnesty International. Major annual events: homecoming, Hanging of the Green/Lighting of the Quad, Undergraduate Research Colloquium. Student services: health clinic, personal-psychological counseling. Campus security: 24-hour emergency response devices and patrols, late night transport-escort service, controlled dormitory access. 906 college housing spaces available; 725 were occupied in 2003-04. Freshmen guaranteed college housing. On-campus residence required through junior year. Options: coed, men-only, women-only housing available. Charles F. Curry Library with 260,119 books, 207,784 microform titles, 868 serials, 27,617 audiovisual materials, an OPAC, and a Web page. Operations spending for 2004 fiscal year: $1.3 million. 160 computers available on campus for general student use. A campuswide network can be accessed from student residence rooms and from off campus. Staffed computer lab on campus.
Community Environment: A suburban community, Liberty is 13 miles northeast of Kansas City and enjoys all of the cultural and recreational advantages afforded by its proximity to a major metropolitan area of 1.5 million people. Several points of interest are the State Ballet of Missouri, the Kansas city Symphony, and the Nelson-Atkins Museum of Art. Kansas City also offers professional football and baseball. The Harriman Fine Arts Program provides great performances from such artists as Itzhak Perlman, Paul Taylor Dance Company, and Yo Yo Ma.

■ **WILLIAM WOODS UNIVERSITY** *F-8*
One University Ave.
Fulton, MO 65251-1098
Tel: (573)642-2251
Free: 800-995-3159
Admissions: (573)592-4221
Fax: (573)592-1146
E-mail: jclay@williamwoods.edu

Web Site: http://www.williamwoods.edu/

Description: Independent, comprehensive, coed, affiliated with Christian Church (Disciples of Christ). Awards associate, bachelor's, and master's degrees and post-master's certificates. Founded 1870. Setting: 170-acre small town campus with easy access to St. Louis. Endowment: $10.1 million. Educational spending for 2005 fiscal year: $1108 per student. Total enrollment: 3,047. Faculty: 114 (50 full-time, 64 part-time). Student-undergrad faculty ratio is 13:1. 792 applied, 68% were admitted. 15% from top 10% of their high school class, 40% from top quarter, 77% from top half. Full-time: 808 students, 76% women, 24% men. Part-time: 365 students, 72% women, 28% men. Students come from 37 states and territories, 13 other countries, 19% from out-of-state, 1% Native American, 2% Hispanic, 3% black, 0.4% Asian American or Pacific Islander, 4% international, 31% 25 or older, 80% live on campus, 6% transferred in. Retention: 76% of full-time freshmen returned the following year. Academic areas with the most degrees conferred: business/marketing; computer and information sciences; agriculture. Core. Calendar: semesters. Academic remediation for entering students, advanced placement, accelerated degree program, self-designed majors, honors program, independent study, double major, summer session for credit, part-time degree program, adult/continuing education programs, internships. Off campus study at University of Missouri-Columbia, Westminster College (MO), Stephens College, Lincoln University (MO). Study abroad program. ROTC: Army (c), Naval (c), Air Force (c).

Entrance Requirements: Options: electronic application, early admission, deferred admission, international baccalaureate accepted. Required: high school transcript, minimum 2.5 high school GPA, 16 hours college prep; SAT or ACT, SAT or ACT. Recommended: interview. Required for some: essay, 2 recommendations. Entrance: moderately difficult. Application deadlines: Rolling, Rolling for nonresidents. Notification: continuous, continuous for nonresidents.

Costs Per Year: Application fee: $25. Comprehensive fee: $21,020 includes full-time tuition ($14,700), mandatory fees ($420), and college room and board ($5900). Full-time tuition and fees vary according to program. Room and board charges vary according to board plan and housing facility. Part-time tuition: $490 per credit. Part-time mandatory fees: $15 per term. Part-time tuition and fees vary according to course load and program.

Collegiate Environment: Orientation program. Drama-theater group, choral group, student-run newspaper, radio station. Social organizations: national fraternities, national sororities; 22% of eligible men and 29% of eligible women are members. Most popular organizations: Campus Crusade for Christ, Leader Scholars, Hunter Jumper Show Team. Major annual events: student organization activities fair, Snowball (campus-wide formal), Casino Night. Student services: health clinic, personal-psychological counseling. Campus security: 24-hour patrols, controlled dormitory access. 670 college housing spaces available; 565 were occupied in 2003-04. Freshmen guaranteed college housing. On-campus residence required through senior year. Options: coed, men-only, women-only housing available. Dulany Library with 139,986 books, 11,129 microform titles, 11,713 serials, 19,556 audiovisual materials, an OPAC, and a Web page. Operations spending for 2004 fiscal year: $165,469. 105 computers available on campus for general student use. Computer purchase/lease plans available. A campuswide network can be accessed from student residence rooms. Staffed computer lab on campus.

Community Environment: The wooded Missouri landscape provides a scenic setting for residents of the area. Colleges, state educational and health facilities and professional industries are primary employers. Part-time employment is available. The regional area provides major medical centers, churches, libraries, restaurants, and recreational and entertainment facilities.

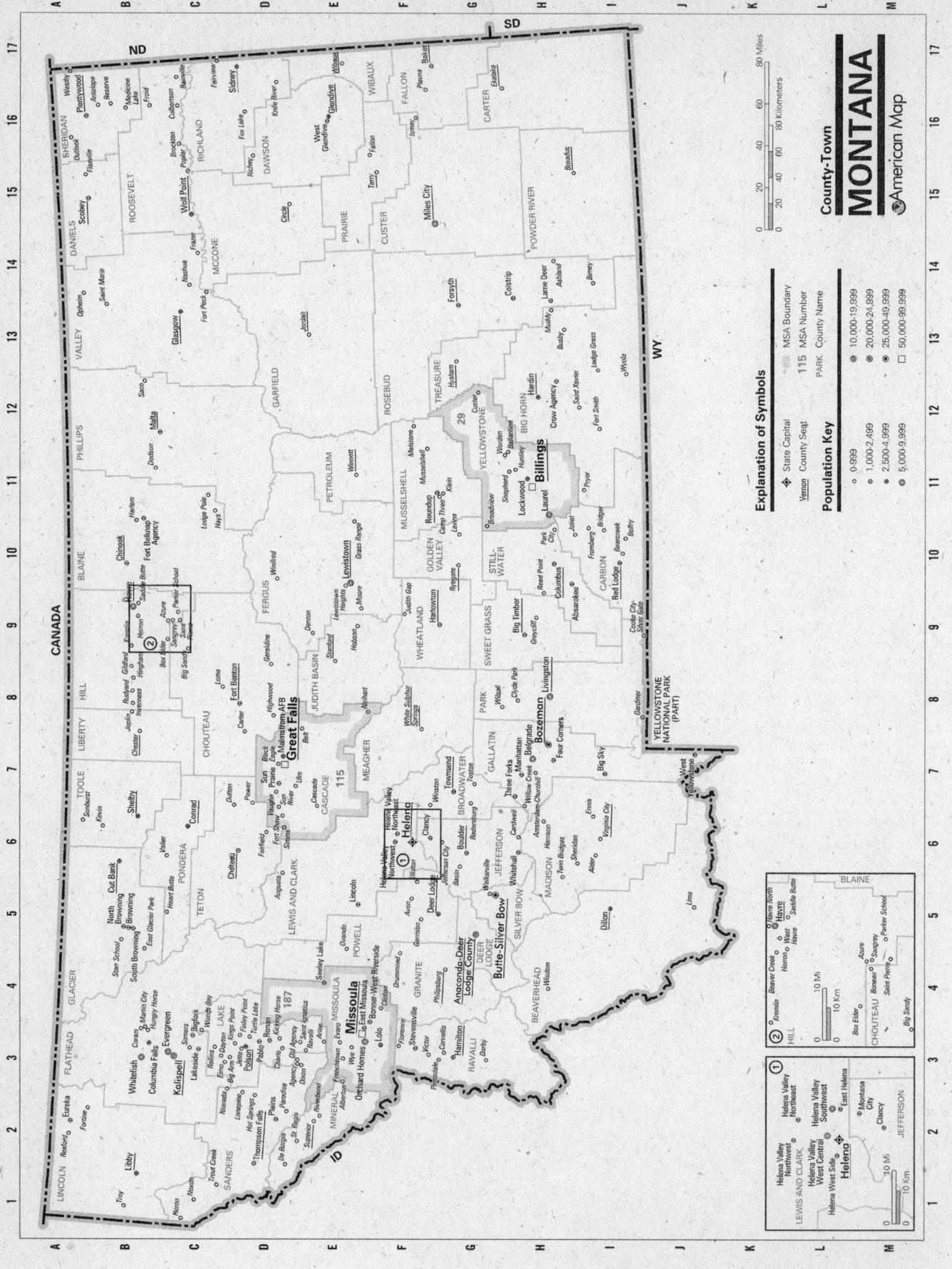

MONTANA
County-Town
American Map

Explanation of Symbols

◆ State Capital
Vernon County Seat
Population Key

▦ MSA Boundary
115 MSA Number
PARK County Name

○ 0-999
⊙ 1,000-2,499
◉ 2,500-4,999
◎ 5,000-9,999
● 10,000-19,999
⊛ 20,000-24,999
⦿ 25,000-49,999
□ 50,000-99,999

■ **BLACKFEET COMMUNITY COLLEGE** *B-5*
PO Box 819
Browning, MT 59417-0819
Tel: (406)338-5441
Free: 800-549-7457
Admissions: (406)338-5421
Fax: (406)338-3272
Web Site: http://www.bfcc.org/
Description: Independent, 2-year, coed. Awards certificates, diplomas, transfer associate, and terminal associate degrees. Founded 1974. Setting: 5-acre small town campus. Endowment: $300,688. Research spending for 2004 fiscal year: $125,543. Educational spending for 2005 fiscal year: $2837 per student. Total enrollment: 503. Full-time: 424 students, 63% women, 37% men. Part-time: 79 students, 72% women, 28% men. Students come from 2 states and territories, 92% Native American, 0.4% Hispanic, 61% 25 or older, 6% transferred in. Core. Calendar: semesters. Academic remediation for entering students, part-time degree program, adult/continuing education programs. Off campus study at members of the American Indian Higher Education Consortium.
Entrance Requirements: Open admission. Option: early admission. Required: high school transcript, immunization with 2nd MMR, certificate of Indian blood. Entrance: noncompetitive. Application deadline: 8/29. Notification: continuous.
Costs Per Year: Application fee: $20. One-time mandatory fee: $20. State resident tuition: $1650 full-time, $69 per credit part-time. Nonresident tuition: $1650 full-time, $69 per credit part-time. Mandatory fees: $350 full-time, $80 per term part-time. Full-time tuition and fees vary according to course load. Part-time tuition and fees vary according to course load.
Collegiate Environment: Orientation program. Campus security: 16 hour patrols by security personnel. College housing not available. 10,000 books and 175 serials. Operations spending for 2004 fiscal year: $89,452. 55 computers available on campus for general student use. A campuswide network can be accessed. Staffed computer lab on campus.

■ **CARROLL COLLEGE** *F-6*
1601 North Benton Ave.
Helena, MT 59625-0002
Tel: (406)447-4300
Free: 800-992-3648
Admissions: (406)447-4384
Fax: (406)447-4533
E-mail: enroll@carroll.edu
Web Site: http://www.carroll.edu/
Description: Independent Roman Catholic, 4-year, coed. Awards associate and bachelor's degrees. Founded 1909. Setting: 64-acre small town campus. Endowment: $23.1 million. Educational spending for 2005 fiscal year: $4260 per student. Total enrollment: 1,452. Student-undergrad faculty ratio is 13:1. 1,048 applied, 79% were admitted. 22% from top 10% of their high school class, 44% from top quarter, 80% from top half. 27 valedictorians. Full-time: 1,245 students, 57% women, 43% men. Part-time: 207 students, 60% women, 40% men. Students come from 33 states and territories, 14 other countries, 35% from out-of-state, 1% Native American, 1% Hispanic, 0.3% black, 1% Asian American or Pacific Islander, 1% international, 7% 25 or older, 58% live on campus, 5% transferred in. Retention: 79% of full-time freshmen returned the following year. Academic areas with the most degrees conferred: business/marketing; education; biological/life

sciences; social sciences. Core. Calendar: semesters. ESL program, advanced placement, accelerated degree program, self-designed majors, freshman honors college, honors program, independent study, double major, summer session for credit, part-time degree program, adult/continuing education programs, co-op programs and internships. Study abroad program. ROTC: Army.
Entrance Requirements: Options: Peterson's Universal Application, Common Application, electronic application, deferred admission, international baccalaureate accepted. Required: essay, high school transcript, minimum 2.0 high school GPA, 1 recommendation, SAT or ACT. Recommended: minimum 3.0 high school GPA, interview. Required for some: interview, SAT Subject Tests. Entrance: moderately difficult. Application deadline: 6/1. Notification: continuous.
Costs Per Year: Application fee: $35. Comprehensive fee: $23,484 includes full-time tuition ($16,778), mandatory fees ($300), and college room and board ($6406). College room only: $3046. Full-time tuition and fees vary according to course load. Room and board charges vary according to board plan and housing facility. Part-time tuition: $558 per credit hour. Part-time tuition varies according to course load.
Collegiate Environment: Orientation program. Drama-theater group, choral group, student-run newspaper, radio station. Social organizations: 35 open to all. Most popular organizations: student government, Drama Club, Into the Streets, Radio Club, Soccer Club. Major annual events: Homecoming, Casino Night, Spring Softball Tournament. Student services: health clinic, personal-psychological counseling. Campus security: late night transport-escort service, controlled dormitory access. 830 college housing spaces available; 780 were occupied in 2003-04. Freshmen guaranteed college housing. On-campus residence required through sophomore year. Options: coed, men-only, women-only housing available. Corette Library plus 1 other with 89,003 books, 64,500 microform titles, 2,721 serials, 3,890 audiovisual materials, an OPAC, and a Web page. Operations spending for 2004 fiscal year: $374,825. 91 computers available on campus for general student use. A campuswide network can be accessed from student residence rooms and from off campus. Staffed computer lab on campus.

■ **CHIEF DULL KNIFE COLLEGE** *H-13*
PO Box 98
Lame Deer, MT 59043-0098
Tel: (406)477-6215
Fax: (406)477-6219
Web Site: http://www.cdkc.edu/
Description: Independent, 2-year, coed. Awards certificates, transfer associate, and terminal associate degrees. Founded 1975. Setting: 3-acre rural campus. Total enrollment: 460. 60% 25 or older. Core. Calendar: semesters. Academic remediation for entering students, services for LD students, summer session for credit, part-time degree program, adult/continuing education programs, co-op programs and internships. Off campus study at members of the American Indian Higher Education Consortium.
Entrance Requirements: Open admission. Option: early admission. Required: high school transcript. Placement: ACT ASSET required; ACT recommended. Entrance: noncompetitive. Application deadline: Rolling. Notification: continuous.
Collegiate Environment: Student-run newspaper. Student services: personal-psychological counseling. College housing not available. 10,000 books and 128 serials. 25 computers available on campus for general student use. Staffed computer lab on campus.

■ **DAWSON COMMUNITY COLLEGE** *E-16*

Box 421
Glendive, MT 59330-0421
Tel: (406)377-3396
Free: 800-821-8320
Fax: (406)377-8132
Web Site: http://www.dawson.edu/

Description: State and locally supported, 2-year, coed. Part of Montana University System. Awards certificates, transfer associate, and terminal associate degrees. Founded 1940. Setting: 300-acre rural campus. Endowment: $344,944. Research spending for 2004 fiscal year: $3000. Educational spending for 2005 fiscal year: $3897 per student. Total enrollment: 539. 208 applied, 100% were admitted. Full-time: 395 students, 50% women, 50% men. Part-time: 144 students, 70% women, 30% men. Students come from 10 states and territories, 2 other countries, 0.02% from out-of-state, 3% Native American, 1% Hispanic, 2% black, 0% Asian American or Pacific Islander, 0% international, 31% 25 or older, 19% live on campus, 6% transferred in. Core. Calendar: semesters. Academic remediation for entering students, services for LD students, independent study, summer session for credit, part-time degree program, adult/continuing education programs, internships.

Entrance Requirements: Open admission. Option: deferred admission. Required: high school transcript. Placement: ACT recommended; ACT required for some. Entrance: noncompetitive. Application deadline: Rolling. Notification: continuous.

Costs Per Year: Application fee: $30. Area resident tuition: $1232 full-time, $44 per credit part-time. State resident tuition: $2,103 full-time, $75.10 per credit part-time. Nonresident tuition: $5,762 full-time, $205.80 per credit part-time. Mandatory fees: $1092 full-time, $39 per credit part-time. Full-time tuition and fees vary according to reciprocity agreements. Part-time tuition and fees vary according to reciprocity agreements. College room only: $1950.

Collegiate Environment: Orientation program. Drama-theater group, choral group. Social organizations: 6 open to all. Most popular organizations: Human Services Club, Law Enforcement Club, Associated Student Body, VICA, United Badlands Indian Club. Major annual events: Halloween Party, Home Rodeo, Homecoming. Campus security: 24-hour emergency response devices. 140 college housing spaces available; all were occupied in 2003-04. No special consideration for freshman housing applicants. Option: coed housing available. Jane Carey Memorial Library with 18,870 books, 1,112 audiovisual materials, an OPAC, and a Web page. Operations spending for 2004 fiscal year: $169,351. 70 computers available on campus for general student use. A campuswide network can be accessed from student residence rooms and from off campus. Staffed computer lab on campus.

Community Environment: Dawson is located in Glendive, the county seat of Dawson County. It is a transportation, agricultural and energy resource center located on the Yellowstone River on I-94. The city has a library, Frontier Gateway Museum, several churches, a hospital, and most major civic, fraternal and veteran's organizations within the immediate area. Recreation facilities include indoor and outdoor theaters, good hunting, limited boating and fishing, golf, and other outdoor sports. Some part-time work is available for students.

■ **FLATHEAD VALLEY COMMUNITY COLLEGE** *C-3*

777 Grandview Dr.
Kalispell, MT 59901-2622
Tel: (406)756-3822
Free: 800-313-3822
Admissions: (406)756-3846
Fax: (406)756-3815
E-mail: mstoltz@fvcc.cc.mt.us
Web Site: http://www.fvcc.edu/

Description: State and locally supported, 2-year, coed. Awards certificates, transfer associate, and terminal associate degrees. Founded 1967. Setting: 40-acre small town campus. Endowment: $865,025. Educational spending for 2005 fiscal year: $2690 per student. Total enrollment: 2,100. 381 applied, 89% were admitted. Full-time: 972 students, 60% women, 40% men. Part-time: 1,128 students, 69% women, 31% men. Students come from 25 states and territories, 2 other countries, 2% from out-of-state, 2% Native American, 1% Hispanic, 0.5% black, 1% Asian American or Pacific Islander, 1% international, 50% 25 or older, 2% transferred in. Retention: 55% of full-time freshmen returned the following year. Core. Calendar: semesters. Academic remediation for entering students, services for LD students, advanced place-

ment, independent study, distance learning, double major, summer session for credit, part-time degree program, adult/continuing education programs, internships.

Entrance Requirements: Open admission. Options: early admission, deferred admission. Required: high school transcript. Entrance: noncompetitive. Application deadline: Rolling.

Costs Per Year: Application fee: $15. Area resident tuition: $1739 full-time, $62.10 per credit part-time. State resident tuition: $2856 full-time, $102 per credit part-time. Nonresident tuition: $7146 full-time, $255.20 per credit part-time. Mandatory fees: $25.75 per credit part-time, $609.50 per year part-time. Part-time tuition and fees vary according to course load.

Collegiate Environment: Orientation program. Drama-theater group, student-run newspaper. Social organizations: 10 open to all. Most popular organizations: Forestry Club, Pi-Ta Club. Student services: personal-psychological counseling. College housing not available. Flathead Valley Community College Library with 19,038 books, 495 microform titles, 125 serials, 514 audiovisual materials, an OPAC, and a Web page. Operations spending for 2004 fiscal year: $188,636. 132 computers available on campus for general student use. A campuswide network can be accessed. Staffed computer lab on campus.

Community Environment: The campus is located 3 miles north of Kalispell city center in the beautiful Flathead Valley, a region noted for the production of seed potatoes, wheat, cattle, Christmas trees, plywood, lumber and sweet cherries. The city is circled by dense forests, lakes, and mountains, with more than 2,000 miles of good fishing streams. Transportation for the area is provided by air, rail, and bus lines. There are 28 churches, one library, a hospital and a medical center. Convenient shopping is easily accessible. Although Kalispell is a resort area, the local industries include plywood production, camper and camp trailer manufacturing, log-skidding machinery, and chemical and concrete products. Part-time employment is available for students.

■ **FORT BELKNAP COLLEGE**

PO Box 159
Harlem, MT 59526-0159
Tel: (406)353-2607
Fax: (406)353-2898
Web Site: http://www.fbcc.edu/

Description: Federally supported, 2-year, coed. Awards certificates and transfer associate degrees. Founded 1984. Setting: 3-acre rural campus. Endowment: $291,263. Total enrollment: 158. Full-time: 117 students, 71% women, 29% men. Part-time: 41 students, 68% women, 32% men. 95% Native American, 67% 25 or older. Core. Academic remediation for entering students, part-time degree program, co-op programs.

Entrance Requirements: Open admission. Options: early admission, deferred admission. Required: high school transcript. Placement: TABE required. Entrance: noncompetitive. Application deadline: Rolling. Notification: continuous.

Collegiate Environment: Orientation program. Student-run radio station. Most popular organizations: student government, Red Nations Society Indian Club, American Indian Business Leaders, American Indians Society in Engineering and Science. Major annual events: Orientation, Native American Day, Spring Fling. Campus security: 24-hour patrols. College housing not available. Fort Belknap College Library with 16,000 books, 95 serials, an OPAC, and a Web page. Operations spending for 2004 fiscal year: $42,495. 48 computers available on campus for general student use. Staffed computer lab on campus.

■ **FORT PECK COMMUNITY COLLEGE**

PO Box 398
Poplar, MT 59255-0398
Tel: (406)768-5551
Admissions: (406)768-6329
Web Site: http://www.fpcc.edu/

Description: District-supported, 2-year, coed. Awards certificates, transfer associate, and terminal associate degrees. Founded 1978. Setting: small town campus. Total enrollment: 428. 80% 25 or older. Core. Calendar: semesters. Summer session for credit, part-time degree program. Off campus study at members of the American Indian Higher Education Consortium.

Entrance Requirements: Open admission. Options: electronic application, early admission. Placement: ACT ASSET required. Entrance: noncompetitive. Application deadline: Rolling.

Collegiate Environment: College housing not available. 50 computers available on campus for general student use. Staffed computer lab on campus.

■ **LITTLE BIG HORN COLLEGE** *H-12*
Box 370
Crow Agency, MT 59022-0370
Tel: (406)638-2228
Admissions: (406)638-3116
Web Site: http://www.lbhc.cc.mt.us/
Description: Independent, 2-year, coed. Awards certificates, transfer associate, and terminal associate degrees. Founded 1980. Setting: 5-acre rural campus. Total enrollment: 317. 50% 25 or older. Core. Part-time degree program. Off campus study at members of the American Indian Higher Education Consortium.
Entrance Requirements: Open admission. Required: high school transcript. Placement: ACT ASSET required. Entrance: noncompetitive. Application deadline: Rolling. Notification: continuous.
Collegiate Environment: Student-run newspaper. College housing not available. 30 computers available on campus for general student use. Staffed computer lab on campus.

■ **MILES COMMUNITY COLLEGE** *G-15*
2715 Dickinson
Miles City, MT 59301-4799
Tel: (406)874-6100
Free: 800-541-9281
Admissions: (406)874-6159
Fax: (406)874-6282
Web Site: http://www.milescc.edu/
Description: State and locally supported, 2-year, coed. Part of Montana University System. Awards certificates, transfer associate, and terminal associate degrees. Founded 1939. Setting: 8-acre small town campus. Endowment: $2.7 million. Total enrollment: 474. 205 applied, 100% were admitted. 15% from top 10% of their high school class, 40% from top half. Full-time: 360 students, 54% women, 46% men. Part-time: 114 students, 79% women, 21% men. Students come from 6 states and territories, 5% from out-of-state, 1% Native American, 1% Hispanic, 1% black, 0.5% Asian American or Pacific Islander, 2% international, 19% 25 or older, 20% live on campus, 11% transferred in. Core. Calendar: semesters. Academic remediation for entering students, ESL program, services for LD students, advanced placement, accelerated degree program, independent study, distance learning, double major, summer session for credit, part-time degree program, adult/continuing education programs, co-op programs and internships. Off campus study.
Entrance Requirements: Open admission except for nursing program. Options: Common Application, early admission, deferred admission. Required: high school transcript. Placement: SAT or ACT recommended; SAT or ACT required for some. Entrance: noncompetitive. Application deadline: Rolling.
Collegiate Environment: Orientation program. Drama-theater group, choral group, student-run newspaper. Social organizations: 6 open to all. Most popular organizations: Campus Ministry, Multicultural Club, Student Nurses Association, Vocational Industrial Club, Western Club. Major annual events: Homecoming, awards banquets, All-Campus Picnics. Student services: personal-psychological counseling. Campus security: 24-hour emergency response devices. 150 college housing spaces available. Option: coed housing available. Library Resource Center with 17,563 books, 36 microform titles, 310 serials, 174 audiovisual materials, an OPAC, and a Web page. Operations spending for 2004 fiscal year: $172,000. 165 computers available on campus for general student use. A campuswide network can be accessed from off-campus. Staffed computer lab on campus.
Community Environment: Vast livestock ranches around Miles City raise more than one-fourth of the cattle and sheep produced in Montana. Wheat is the primary crop grown in the dryland area. The city itself is a pleasant residential town with a mean annual temperature of 44.4 degrees, and an average rainfall of 13.79 inches. Local area is served by airlines and bus lines. The community has 17 churches, tennis courts, two theaters, bowling alley, golf course, radio and TV station and various civic and fraternal organizations. Local homes, apartments and rooms provide student housing in addition to dormitories. There are limited part-time work opportunities for students.

■ **MONTANA STATE UNIVERSITY** *H-7*
Bozeman, MT 59717
Tel: (406)994-0211; 888-MSU-CATS

Admissions: (406)994-2601
E-mail: zam1202@msu.oscs.montana.edu
Web Site: http://www.montana.edu/
Description: State-supported, university, coed. Part of Montana University System. Awards bachelor's, master's, and doctoral degrees and post-master's certificates. Founded 1893. Setting: 1,170-acre small town campus. Endowment: $73.7 million. Research spending for 2004 fiscal year: $88 million. Educational spending for 2005 fiscal year: $9109 per student. Total enrollment: 12,166. Faculty: 828 (553 full-time, 275 part-time). Student-undergrad faculty ratio is 16:1. 5,124 applied, 74% were admitted. 17% from top 10% of their high school class, 41% from top quarter, 71% from top half. 17 National Merit Scholars, 94 valedictorians. Full-time: 9,285 students, 46% women, 54% men. Part-time: 1,557 students, 51% women, 49% men. Students come from 50 states and territories, 59 other countries, 30% from out-of-state, 2% Native American, 1% Hispanic, 0.5% black, 1% Asian American or Pacific Islander, 1% international, 16% 25 or older, 25% live on campus, 7% transferred in. Retention: 71% of full-time freshmen returned the following year. Academic areas with the most degrees conferred: business/marketing; engineering; visual and performing arts. Core. Calendar: semesters. Academic remediation for entering students, ESL program, services for LD students, advanced placement, self-designed majors, honors program, independent study, distance learning, double major, summer session for credit, part-time degree program, adult/continuing education programs, internships, graduate courses open to undergrads. Off campus study at members of the National Student Exchange. Study abroad program. ROTC: Army, Air Force.
Entrance Requirements: Options: electronic application, early admission, deferred admission, international baccalaureate accepted. Required: high school transcript, minimum 2.5 high school GPA, SAT or ACT. Entrance: moderately difficult. Application deadline: Rolling. Notification: continuous.
Costs Per Year: Application fee: $30. State resident tuition: $5221 full-time, $171.10 per credit part-time. Nonresident tuition: $14,945 full-time, $572.70 per credit part-time. Full-time tuition varies according to course load. Part-time tuition varies according to course load. College room and board: $6150. Room and board charges vary according to board plan and housing facility.
Collegiate Environment: Orientation program. Drama-theater group, choral group, marching band, student-run newspaper, radio station. Social organizations: 150 open to all; national fraternities, national sororities; 3% of eligible men and 2% of eligible women are members. Most popular organizations: Spurs, Inter-Varsity Christian Fellowship, Campus Crusade for Christ, Fangs, Mortar Board. Major annual events: International Food Bazaar, Native American Pow-wow, Day of Student Recognition. Student services: legal services, health clinic, personal-psychological counseling, women's center. Campus security: 24-hour emergency response devices and patrols, student patrols, late night transport-escort service, 24-hour residence hall monitoring. 3,260 college housing spaces available; 2,704 were occupied in 2003-04. Freshmen guaranteed college housing. On-campus residence required in freshman year. Options: coed, men-only, women-only housing available. Renne Library plus 1 other with 574,634 books, 2.1 million microform titles, 6,643 serials, 4,822 audiovisual materials, an OPAC, and a Web page. Operations spending for 2004 fiscal year: $4.6 million. 850 computers available on campus for general student use. A campuswide network can be accessed from student residence rooms and from off campus. Staffed computer lab on campus.
Community Environment: At the heart of the Gallatin Valley, known for its scenic beauty, the city is headquarters for Gallatin National Forest. The Bridger Bowl Ski Area, 18 miles northwest, and Big Sky, Inc. 33 miles south offer skiing from mid-November to mid-March. Immediately south of Bozeman, Highway 191 follows Gallatin River through the forest to Yellowstone National Park 90 miles away. The Gallatin Field airport is 8 miles from Bozeman and is served by Delta and Northwest. Community services include many churches, public library, one hospital, and many hotels and motels. Various service clubs, veteran's clubs, and many fraternal organizations are represented within the immediate area. Recreation other than skiing is provided by local picnic areas, swimming pools, five parks, tennis courts, dude ranches, golf courses, hunting, boating, and fishing. Bozeman is known for its year-round outdoor recreational opportunities.

■ **MONTANA STATE UNIVERSITY-BILLINGS** *H-11*
1500 University Dr.
Billings, MT 59101-0298
Tel: (406)657-2011
Free: 800-565-6782
Admissions: (406)657-2158

Fax: (406)657-2302
E-mail: cjohannes@msubillings.edu
Web Site: http://www.msubillings.edu/
Description: State-supported, comprehensive, coed. Part of Montana University System. Awards associate, bachelor's, and master's degrees and post-master's certificates. Founded 1927. Setting: 92-acre urban campus. Endowment: $10 million. Research spending for 2004 fiscal year: $528,143. Educational spending for 2005 fiscal year: $3532 per student. Total enrollment: 4,872. Faculty: 257 (156 full-time, 101 part-time). Student-undergrad faculty ratio is 20:1. 1,546 applied, 96% were admitted. 10% from top 10% of their high school class, 30% from top quarter, 66% from top half. 8 valedictorians. Full-time: 3,170 students, 62% women, 38% men. Part-time: 1,237 students, 70% women, 30% men. Students come from 39 states and territories, 16 other countries, 10% from out-of-state, 5% Native American, 3% Hispanic, 1% black, 1% Asian American or Pacific Islander, 1% international, 37% 25 or older, 10% live on campus, 9% transferred in. Retention: 56% of full-time freshmen returned the following year. Academic areas with the most degrees conferred: education; business/marketing; liberal arts/general studies. Core. Calendar: semesters. Academic remediation for entering students, ESL program, services for LD students, advanced placement, accelerated degree program, honors program, independent study, distance learning, double major, summer session for credit, part-time degree program, external degree program, adult/continuing education programs, co-op programs and internships, graduate courses open to undergrads. Off campus study. Study abroad program.
Entrance Requirements: Options: Common Application, early admission, deferred admission. Required: high school transcript, minimum 2.5 high school GPA, SAT or ACT. Entrance: moderately difficult. Application deadline: 7/1. Notification: continuous.
Costs Per Year: Application fee: $30. State resident tuition: $3762 full-time, $135 per credit hour part-time. Nonresident tuition: $13,096 full-time, $364 per credit hour part-time. Mandatory fees: $1094 full-time. Full-time tuition and fees vary according to course load, degree level, and location. Part-time tuition varies according to course load, degree level, and location. College room and board: $4050. Room and board charges vary according to board plan and housing facility.
Collegiate Environment: Orientation program. Drama-theater group, choral group, student-run newspaper, radio station. Social organizations: 53 open to all; local fraternities, local sororities; 5% of eligible men and 10% of eligible women are members. Most popular organizations: Art Student League, Band Club, Inter-Varsity Christian Fellowship, Residence Hall Association, Student Council for Exceptional Children. Major annual events: Homecoming, Welcome Week events; Summerfest. Student services: legal services, health clinic, personal-psychological counseling, women's center. Campus security: 24-hour emergency response devices and patrols, late night transport-escort service, controlled dormitory access. 550 college housing spaces available; 460 were occupied in 2003-04. Freshmen given priority for college housing. On-campus residence required in freshman year. Options: coed, men-only, women-only housing available. Montana State University-Billings Library plus 2 others with 488,004 books, 850,000 microform titles, 3,276 serials, 2,125 audiovisual materials, an OPAC, and a Web page. Operations spending for 2004 fiscal year: $464,475. 863 computers available on campus for general student use. A campuswide network can be accessed from student residence rooms and from off campus. Staffed computer lab on campus.
Community Environment: Billings is an expanding city located in the Yellowstone River Valley between rugged mountains and sweeping plains. The city is the largest in Montana, and has a population of approximately 125,000 people living in the metropolitan area. The "Magic City" is a transportation, medical, agricultural, wholesale, and retail trade center. It is served by major air, bus, and rail lines, and excellent interstate highways. Community services include many churches representing most denominations, a city library, theatres, museums, art galleries, two hospitals, YMCA, YWCA, and various civic and fraternal organizations. Recreational sites are numerous and include opportunities for fishing, hunting, boating, bowling, golf, skiing, and hiking.

■ **MONTANA STATE UNIVERSITY-GREAT FALLS COLLEGE OF TECHNOLOGY** *D-7*
2100 16th Ave., South
Great Falls, MT 59405
Tel: (406)771-4300
Fax: (406)771-4317
E-mail: zgf2001@maia.oscs.montana.edu

Web Site: http://www.msugf.edu/
Description: State-supported, 2-year, coed. Part of Montana University System. Awards certificates, transfer associate, and terminal associate degrees. Founded 1969. Setting: 35-acre urban campus. Total enrollment: 1,463. 422 applied, 99% were admitted. Full-time: 716 students, 70% women, 30% men. Part-time: 747 students, 69% women, 31% men. Students come from 10 states and territories, 1% from out-of-state, 3% Native American, 2% Hispanic, 2% black, 1% Asian American or Pacific Islander, 0% international, 54% 25 or older, 8% transferred in. Retention: 47% of full-time freshmen returned the following year. Calendar: semesters. Academic remediation for entering students, services for LD students, advanced placement, independent study, distance learning, double major, summer session for credit, part-time degree program, adult/continuing education programs, internships. Off campus study.
Entrance Requirements: Open admission except for physical therapist assistant program. Option: deferred admission. Required: high school transcript, proof of immunization. Required for some: essay, 3 recommendations. Placement: SAT, ACT, or ACT ASSET required. Entrance: noncompetitive. Application deadline: Rolling.
Collegiate Environment: Orientation program. Student-run newspaper. Campus security: 24-hour emergency response devices. College housing not available. Montana State University College of Technology - Great Falls Library with 4,000 books, 200 serials, an OPAC, and a Web page. 150 computers available on campus for general student use. A campuswide network can be accessed from off-campus. Staffed computer lab on campus.

■ **MONTANA STATE UNIVERSITY-NORTHERN** *B-9*
PO Box 7751
Havre, MT 59501-7751
Tel: (406)265-3700
Admissions: (406)265-3704
Fax: (406)265-3777
Web Site: http://www.msun.edu/
Description: State-supported, comprehensive, coed. Part of Montana University System. Awards associate, bachelor's, and master's degrees. Founded 1929. Setting: 105-acre small town campus. Endowment: $162,838. Educational spending for 2005 fiscal year: $3500 per student. Total enrollment: 1,589. 868 applied, 82% were admitted. Full-time: 1,060 students, 48% women, 52% men. Part-time: 368 students, 67% women, 33% men. Students come from 7 states and territories, 3 other countries, 1% from out-of-state, 14% Native American, 1% Hispanic, 1% black, 1% Asian American or Pacific Islander, 1% international, 65% 25 or older. Retention: 65% of full-time freshmen returned the following year. Core. Calendar: semesters. Academic remediation for entering students, ESL program, services for LD students, advanced placement, honors program, distance learning, double major, summer session for credit, part-time degree program, adult/continuing education programs, co-op programs and internships, graduate courses open to undergrads.
Entrance Requirements: Options: early admission, deferred admission. Required: high school transcript. Required for some: minimum 2.0 high school GPA. Placement: ACT required. Entrance: moderately difficult. Application deadline: Rolling. Notification: continuous.
Collegiate Environment: Orientation program. Drama-theater group, student-run newspaper, radio station. Social organizations: 26 open to all. Most popular organizations: Vocational and Industrial Clubs of America, Student Nurses Association of America, Student Education Association. Major annual events: Founders' Week, Convocation, Native American Pow-Wow. Student services: health clinic, personal-psychological counseling. On-campus residence required in freshman year. Option: coed housing available. Vande Bogart Libraries with 128,000 books, 1,729 serials, an OPAC, and a Web page. Operations spending for 2004 fiscal year: $317,148. 140 computers available on campus for general student use. A campuswide network can be accessed from student residence rooms and from off campus. Staffed computer lab on campus.
Community Environment: Havre is the transportation hub of the Northern Great Plains, America's agricultural heartland. Montana's panoramic Big Sky meets a horizon of rolling foothills and abundant lakes and reservoirs. The community is easily accessible from all directions by highway, Amtrak, and a commuter airline with links to major international airports. Rugged environments such as Glacier National Park, the Cypress Hills of Canada, the Bears Paw Mountains and the Little Rockies, are only a few hours away. Picnicking, camping, abundant wildlife, lakes with great fishing, boating, and water skiing, and numerous winter and summer sports offer recreation for outdoor enthusiasts.

■ MONTANA TECH OF THE UNIVERSITY OF MONTANA *G-5*

1300 West Park St.
Butte, MT 59701-8997
Tel: (406)496-4101
Free: 800-445-TECH
Admissions: (406)496-4178
Fax: (406)496-4710
E-mail: tcampeau@mtech.edu
Web Site: http://www.mtech.edu/

Description: State-supported, comprehensive, coed. Part of Montana University System. Awards associate, bachelor's, and master's degrees. Founded 1895. Setting: 56-acre small town campus. Endowment: $17.7 million. Research spending for 2004 fiscal year: $8.6 million. Educational spending for 2005 fiscal year: $9344 per student. Total enrollment: 2,230. Faculty: 149 (110 full-time, 39 part-time). Student-undergrad faculty ratio is 16:1. 414 applied, 98% were admitted. 10% from top 10% of their high school class, 40% from top quarter, 70% from top half. 44 valedictorians. Full-time: 1,729 students, 40% women, 60% men. Part-time: 413 students, 64% women, 36% men. Students come from 39 states and territories, 16 other countries, 12% from out-of-state, 1% Native American, 2% Hispanic, 1% black, 1% Asian American or Pacific Islander, 4% international, 34% 25 or older, 15% live on campus, 6% transferred in. Retention: 63% of full-time freshmen returned the following year. Academic areas with the most degrees conferred: engineering; health professions and related sciences; business/marketing. Core. Calendar: semesters. Academic remediation for entering students, services for LD students, advanced placement, self-designed majors, independent study, distance learning, double major, summer session for credit, part-time degree program, adult/continuing education programs, co-op programs and internships, graduate courses open to undergrads.

Entrance Requirements: Open admission for students attending the College of Technology.. Options: Common Application, electronic application, early admission. Required: high school transcript, minimum 2.5 high school GPA, proof of immunization, standardized test scores, SAT or ACT. Entrance: moderately difficult. Application deadline: Rolling. Notification: continuous.

Costs Per Year: Application fee: $30. State resident tuition: $4816 full-time, $233 per credit part-time. Nonresident tuition: $13,807 full-time, $607 per credit part-time. Mandatory fees: $43 per credit part-time, $49. College room and board: $5106. College room only: $2294.

Collegiate Environment: Orientation program. Choral group, student-run newspaper, radio station. Social organizations: 35 open to all. Most popular organizations: Environmental Engineering Club, SH/IH Club, Petroleum Club SPE, Marcus Daly Mining, Chemistry Club. Major annual events: Homecoming, M-Days, Comedy Night. Student services: health clinic, personal-psychological counseling. Campus security: 24-hour patrols, controlled dormitory access. 339 college housing spaces available; 303 were occupied in 2003-04. Freshmen guaranteed college housing. On-campus residence required in freshman year. Option: coed housing available. Montana Tech Library plus 1 other with 165,734 books, 369,372 microform titles, 20,233 serials, 3,284 audiovisual materials, an OPAC, and a Web page. Operations spending for 2004 fiscal year: $569,920. 500 computers available on campus for general student use. A campuswide network can be accessed from student residence rooms and from off campus. Staffed computer lab on campus.

Community Environment: Known as the "richest hill on earth," Butte has the reputation of being the world's greatest mining city. Mine workings consist of more than 10,000 miles of underground excavation. They produce a substantial percentage of the total amount of copper mined in the United States and a quantity of zinc ore. The Butte mining district is on the edge of one of the broad, faulted valleys characteristic of western Montana. During the more than 100 years of its active existence, this district has yielded manganese, copper, zinc, silver, lead, gold, and minor amounts of other metals. Three mountain ranges surround the city from the Continental Divide. The area is served by two transcontinental railroads, airlines, and bus lines. Butte community service facilities include many churches, two hospitals, five radio stations, and two TV stations. The city has a wholesale and retail shopping center. Many civic, fraternal, and professional organizations meet regularly in the immediate area. Recreation in the forms of skiing, hiking, fishing, hunting, boating, and golf are within minutes of the city.

■ ROCKY MOUNTAIN COLLEGE *H-11*

1511 Poly Dr.
Billings, MT 59102-1796
Tel: (406)657-1000
Free: 800-877-6259
Admissions: (406)657-1026
Fax: (406)259-9751
E-mail: admissions@rocky.edu
Web Site: http://www.rocky.edu/

Description: Independent interdenominational, 4-year, coed. Awards associate, bachelor's, and master's degrees. Founded 1878. Setting: 60-acre urban campus. Endowment: $19.2 million. Educational spending for 2005 fiscal year: $6028 per student. Total enrollment: 1,009. Faculty: 113 (53 full-time, 60 part-time). Student-undergrad faculty ratio is 13:1. 728 applied, 78% were admitted. 15% from top 10% of their high school class, 40% from top quarter, 73% from top half. 8 valedictorians, 72 student government officers. Full-time: 895 students, 54% women, 46% men. Part-time: 69 students, 62% women, 38% men. Students come from 37 states and territories, 19 other countries, 32% from out-of-state, 7% Native American, 2% Hispanic, 1% black, 1% Asian American or Pacific Islander, 6% international, 17% 25 or older, 43% live on campus, 8% transferred in. Retention: 72% of full-time freshmen returned the following year. Academic areas with the most degrees conferred: business/marketing; education; health professions and related sciences. Core. Calendar: semesters. Academic remediation for entering students, services for LD students, advanced placement, accelerated degree program, self-designed majors, honors program, independent study, distance learning, double major, summer session for credit, part-time degree program, adult/continuing education programs, internships. Study abroad program.

Entrance Requirements: Options: Peterson's Universal Application, Common Application, electronic application, early admission, deferred admission, international baccalaureate accepted. Required: high school transcript, minimum 2.5 high school GPA, SAT or ACT. Recommended: ACT. Required for some: essay, 2 recommendations, interview. Entrance: moderately difficult. Application deadline: Rolling. Notification: continuous.

Costs Per Year: Application fee: $25. Comprehensive fee: $23,013 includes full-time tuition ($16,136), mandatory fees ($253), and college room and board ($6624). College room only: $3628. Part-time tuition: $674 per credit. Part-time mandatory fees: $67 per term.

Collegiate Environment: Orientation program. Drama-theater group, choral group, student-run newspaper. Social organizations: 23 open to all. Most popular organizations: Sojourners, Equestrian Club, Oysters, STARs, Martial Arts Club. Major annual events: homecoming, Candlelight Dinner, campus-wide holiday dinners. Student services: health clinic, personal-psychological counseling. Campus security: 24-hour emergency response devices, student patrols, controlled dormitory access, security cameras. 477 college housing spaces available; 407 were occupied in 2003-04. Freshmen guaranteed college housing. On-campus residence required through sophomore year. Option: coed housing available. Paul M. Adams Memorial Library with 42,674 books, 12,666 microform titles, 324 serials, 1,613 audiovisual materials, an OPAC, and a Web page. Operations spending for 2004 fiscal year: $214,025. 104 computers available on campus for general student use. A campuswide network can be accessed from student residence rooms and from off campus. Staffed computer lab on campus.

■ SALISH KOOTENAI COLLEGE *D-3*

PO Box 117
Pablo, MT 59855-0117
Tel: (406)275-4800
Admissions: (406)275-4866
Fax: (406)275-4801
Web Site: http://www.skc.edu/

Description: Independent, primarily 2-year, coed. Awards certificates, transfer associate, terminal associate, and bachelor's degrees. Founded 1977. Setting: 4-acre rural campus. Total enrollment: 1,088. 344 applied, 64% were admitted. 50% from top half of their high school class. Full-time: 585 students, 63% women, 37% men. Part-time: 503 students, 58% women, 42% men. Students come from 3 states and territories, 79% Native American, 0.3% Hispanic, 0.2% black, 48% 25 or older. Core. Academic remediation for entering students, services for LD students, summer session for credit, part-time degree program, adult/continuing education programs, co-op programs. Off campus study at members of the American Indian Higher Education Consortium.

Entrance Requirements: Open admission. Option: deferred admission. Required: high school transcript, proof of immunization, tribal enrollment. Placement: TABE required. Entrance: noncompetitive. Application deadline: Rolling. Notification: continuous. Preference given to Native Americans.

Collegiate Environment: Drama-theater group. Student services: personal-psychological counseling. College housing not available. 24,000 books and 200 serials. 30 computers available on campus for general student use.

■ STONE CHILD COLLEGE
RR1, Box 1082
Box Elder, MT 59521
Tel: (406)395-4313
Fax: (406)395-4836
E-mail: uanet337@quest.ocsc.montana.edu
Web Site: http://www.montana.edu/wwwscc/

Description: Independent, 2-year, coed. Awards certificates and transfer associate degrees. Founded 1984. Setting: rural campus. Total enrollment: 240. 11 applied, 100% were admitted. Calendar: semesters.

Entrance Requirements: Open admission. Required: high school transcript. Entrance: noncompetitive.

Collegiate Environment: 42 computers available on campus for general student use. Staffed computer lab on campus.

■ UNIVERSITY OF GREAT FALLS *D-7*
1301 Twentieth St. South
Great Falls, MT 59405
Tel: (406)761-8210
Free: 800-856-9544
Admissions: (406)791-5200
Fax: (406)791-5209
E-mail: enroll@ugf.edu
Web Site: http://www.ugf.edu/

Description: Independent Roman Catholic, comprehensive, coed. Administratively affiliated with Providence Services. Awards associate, bachelor's, and master's degrees. Founded 1932. Setting: 40-acre urban campus. Endowment: $6.2 million. Educational spending for 2005 fiscal year: $5123 per student. Total enrollment: 778. Faculty: 94 (33 full-time, 61 part-time). Student-undergrad faculty ratio is 11:1. 242 applied, 79% were admitted. Full-time: 485 students, 61% women, 39% men. Part-time: 188 students, 71% women, 29% men. Students come from 32 states and territories, 5 other countries, 24% from out-of-state, 4% Native American, 4% Hispanic, 3% black, 2% Asian American or Pacific Islander, 1% international, 48% 25 or older, 21% live on campus, 15% transferred in. Retention: 42% of full-time freshmen returned the following year. Academic areas with the most degrees conferred: education; psychology; public administration and social services. Core. Calendar: semesters. Academic remediation for entering students, services for LD students, advanced placement, independent study, distance learning, double major, summer session for credit, part-time degree program, external degree program, adult/continuing education programs, co-op programs and internships, graduate courses open to undergrads. Off campus study at Flathead Valley Community College; Bellevue University, NE.

Entrance Requirements: Open admission. Options: Common Application, electronic application, early admission, deferred admission, international baccalaureate accepted. Required: essay. Recommended: high school transcript, interview, SAT and SAT Subject Tests or ACT. Entrance: noncompetitive. Application deadlines: 8/1, 8/1 for nonresidents. Notification: 9/1, 9/1 for nonresidents.

Costs Per Year: Application fee: $35. Comprehensive fee: $20,720 includes full-time tuition ($14,600), mandatory fees ($620), and college room and board ($5500). College room only: $2400. Part-time tuition: $460 per credit. Part-time mandatory fees: $15 per credit.

Collegiate Environment: Orientation program. Drama-theater group, choral group, student-run newspaper, radio station. Social organizations: 19 open to all. Most popular organizations: Student Montana Education Association, Student Senate, International Law and Justice Club, Students In Free Enterprise, Science Club (medical, forensic and computer science students). Major annual events: Spookaroo, Homecoming, student coffee houses. Student services: health clinic, personal-psychological counseling, women's center. Campus security: 24-hour emergency response devices and patrols, late night transport-escort service, controlled dormitory access. 300 college housing spaces available; 141 were occupied in 2003-04. Freshmen guaranteed college housing. On-campus residence required through sophomore year. Option: coed housing available. University of Great Falls Library with 107,541 books, 21,423 microform titles, 581 serials, 4,164 audiovisual materials, an OPAC, and a Web page. Operations spending for 2004 fiscal year: $482,545. 110 computers available on campus for general student use. A campuswide network can be accessed from student residence rooms. Staffed computer lab on campus.

Community Environment: Montana's second largest city, Great Falls is an industrial, financial, wholesale and distributing center. Major agricultural pursuits in the area are livestock farming and wood production. Known as the city "between the parks," Great Falls is almost equidistant to Yellowstone and Glacier National Parks. The winters are moderate. Summer evenings are cool. The area is served by air, rail, and bus lines. Local attractions include dude and guest ranches, fishing, hunting, and skiing. Some employment opportunities are available in the area.

■ THE UNIVERSITY OF MONTANA-HELENA COLLEGE OF TECHNOLOGY *F-6*
1115 North Roberts St.
Helena, MT 59601
Tel: (406)444-6800
Fax: (406)444-6892
Web Site: http://www.umhelena.edu/

Description: State-supported, 2-year, coed. Part of Montana University System. Awards certificates, transfer associate, and terminal associate degrees. Founded 1939. Setting: small town campus. Total enrollment: 850. Calendar: semesters. Academic remediation for entering students, services for LD students, summer session for credit, part-time degree program, adult/continuing education programs.

Entrance Requirements: Open admission. Options: early admission, deferred admission. Placement: ACT ASSET required. Entrance: noncompetitive. Application deadline: Rolling.

Collegiate Environment: Orientation program. Most popular organization: Student Senate. Major annual events: Fall and Spring Barbecues, Christmas Party, Open House. College housing not available. 2,500 books and 30 serials. 45 computers available on campus for general student use. A campuswide network can be accessed. Staffed computer lab on campus.

■ THE UNIVERSITY OF MONTANA-MISSOULA *F-3*
Missoula, MT 59812-0002
Tel: (406)243-0211
Free: 800-462-8636
Admissions: (406)243-2361
Fax: (406)243-5711
E-mail: admiss@umontana.edu
Web Site: http://www.umt.edu/

Description: State-supported, university, coed. Part of Montana University System. Awards associate, bachelor's, master's, doctoral, and first professional degrees and post-master's certificates. Founded 1893. Setting: 220-acre urban campus. Endowment: $78.3 million. Research spending for 2004 fiscal year: $20 million. Educational spending for 2005 fiscal year: $4633 per student. Total enrollment: 13,602. Faculty: 734 (547 full-time, 187 part-time). Student-undergrad faculty ratio is 19:1. 5,802 applied, 83% were admitted. 17% from top 10% of their high school class, 41% from top quarter, 71% from top half. 18 National Merit Scholars, 52 valedictorians. Full-time: 9,620 students, 54% women, 46% men. Part-time: 1,884 students, 55% women, 45% men. Students come from 52 states and territories, 61 other countries, 27% from out-of-state, 4% Native American, 2% Hispanic, 1% black, 1% Asian American or Pacific Islander, 1% international, 21% 25 or older, 23% live on campus, 26% transferred in. Retention: 70% of full-time freshmen returned the following year. Academic areas with the most degrees conferred: business/marketing; social sciences; communications/journalism; natural resources/environmental science; education. Core. Calendar: semesters. Academic remediation for entering students, ESL program, services for LD students, advanced placement, freshman honors college, honors program, independent study, distance learning, double major, summer session for credit, part-time degree program, adult/continuing education programs, co-op programs and internships, graduate courses open to undergrads. Off campus study at members of the National Student Exchange. Study abroad program. ROTC: Army.

Entrance Requirements: Options: Peterson's Universal Application, Common Application, electronic application, early admission, deferred admission, international baccalaureate accepted. Required: high school transcript, minimum 2.5 high school GPA, SAT 1540 (M-V-Wr) or ACT 22; and SAT Math 420 or ACT Math 17, SAT or ACT. Required for some: ACT ASSET or ACT COMPASS. Entrance: moderately difficult. Application deadline: 3/1. Notification: continuous.

Costs Per Year: Application fee: $30. State resident tuition: $3739 full-time, $164 per credit part-time. Nonresident tuition: $13,246 full-time, $573 per credit part-time. Mandatory fees: $1291 full-time, $40 per credit part-time. College room and board: $5860. College room only: $2660.

Collegiate Environment: Orientation program. Drama-theater group, choral group, marching band, student-run newspaper, radio station. Social organizations: 125 open to all; national fraternities, national sororities; 10% of eligible men and 7% of eligible women are members. Most popular organizations: Forestry Club, Honors Student Association, Campus Outdoor Program, International Organization, Kyio Indian Club. Major annual events: Aber Day (clean earth day), Foresters' Ball, Homecoming. Student services: legal services, health clinic, personal-psychological counseling, women's center. Campus security: 24-hour emergency response devices and patrols, student patrols, late night transport-escort service, controlled dormitory access. 3,413 college housing spaces available; 3,037 were occupied in 2003-04. On-campus residence required in freshman year. Options: coed, men-only, women-only housing available. Maureen and Mike Mansfield Library plus 2 others with 570,287 books, 238,184 microform titles, 6,248 serials, 118,190 audiovisual materials, an OPAC, and a Web page. Operations spending for 2004 fiscal year: $5.3 million. 545 computers available on campus for general student use. A campuswide network can be accessed from student residence rooms and from off campus. Staffed computer lab on campus.

■ **THE UNIVERSITY OF MONTANA-WESTERN** *I-5*

710 South Atlantic
Dillon, MT 59725-3598
Tel: (406)683-7011; (866)869-6668
Admissions: (406)683-7665
Fax: (406)683-7493
E-mail: e_murray@wmc.edu
Web Site: http://www.umwestern.edu/

Description: State-supported, 4-year, coed. Part of Montana University System. Awards associate and bachelor's degrees. Founded 1893. Setting: 36-acre small town campus. Endowment: $6 million. Research spending for 2004 fiscal year: $171,202. Educational spending for 2005 fiscal year: $4769 per student. Total enrollment: 1,159. Student-undergrad faculty ratio is 17:1. 428 applied, 99% were admitted. 5% from top 10% of their high school class, 17% from top quarter, 47% from top half. 3 valedictorians. Full-time: 941 students, 53% women, 47% men. Part-time: 218 students, 85% women, 15% men. Students come from 12 states and territories, 2 other countries, 15% from out-of-state, 4% Native American, 2% Hispanic, 1% black, 2% Asian American or Pacific Islander, 1% international, 33% 25 or older, 35% live on campus, 11% transferred in. Retention: 62% of full-time freshmen returned the following year. Academic areas with the most degrees conferred: education; business/marketing; social sciences. Core. Calendar: semesters. Academic remediation for entering students, services for LD students, advanced placement, accelerated degree program, self-designed majors, honors program, independent study, distance learning, double major, summer session for credit, part-time degree program, adult/continuing education programs, co-op programs and internships.

Entrance Requirements: Options: Peterson's Universal Application, Common Application, electronic application, early admission, deferred admission. Required: high school transcript, minimum 2.5 high school GPA, SAT or ACT. Entrance: minimally difficult. Application deadline: 7/1. Notification: continuous.

Costs Per Year: Application fee: $30. State resident tuition: $3538 full-time, $295 per credit part-time. Nonresident tuition: $12,080 full-time, $503 per credit part-time. Mandatory fees: $815 full-time. College room and board: $4920. College room only: $1970.

Collegiate Environment: Orientation program. Drama-theater group, choral group, student-run newspaper, radio station. Social organizations: 18 open to all. Most popular organizations: soccer, IGNU (poetry club), admissions volunteers, Rodeo Club, Chi Alpha-Christian Fellowship. Major annual events: Homecoming, Alumni Weekend, Campus Olympics. Student services: legal services, personal-psychological counseling. Campus security: 24-hour emergency response devices and patrols, late night transport-escort service. 481 college housing spaces available; 181 were occupied in 2003-04. Freshmen guaranteed college housing. On-campus residence required in freshman year. Options: coed, men-only, women-only housing available. Lucy Carson Memorial Library with 90,431 books, 5,792 microform titles, 7,127 serials, 3,718 audiovisual materials, an OPAC, and a Web page. Operations spending for 2004 fiscal year: $549,987. 140 computers available on campus for general student use. A campuswide network can be accessed from student residence rooms and from off campus. Staffed computer lab on campus.

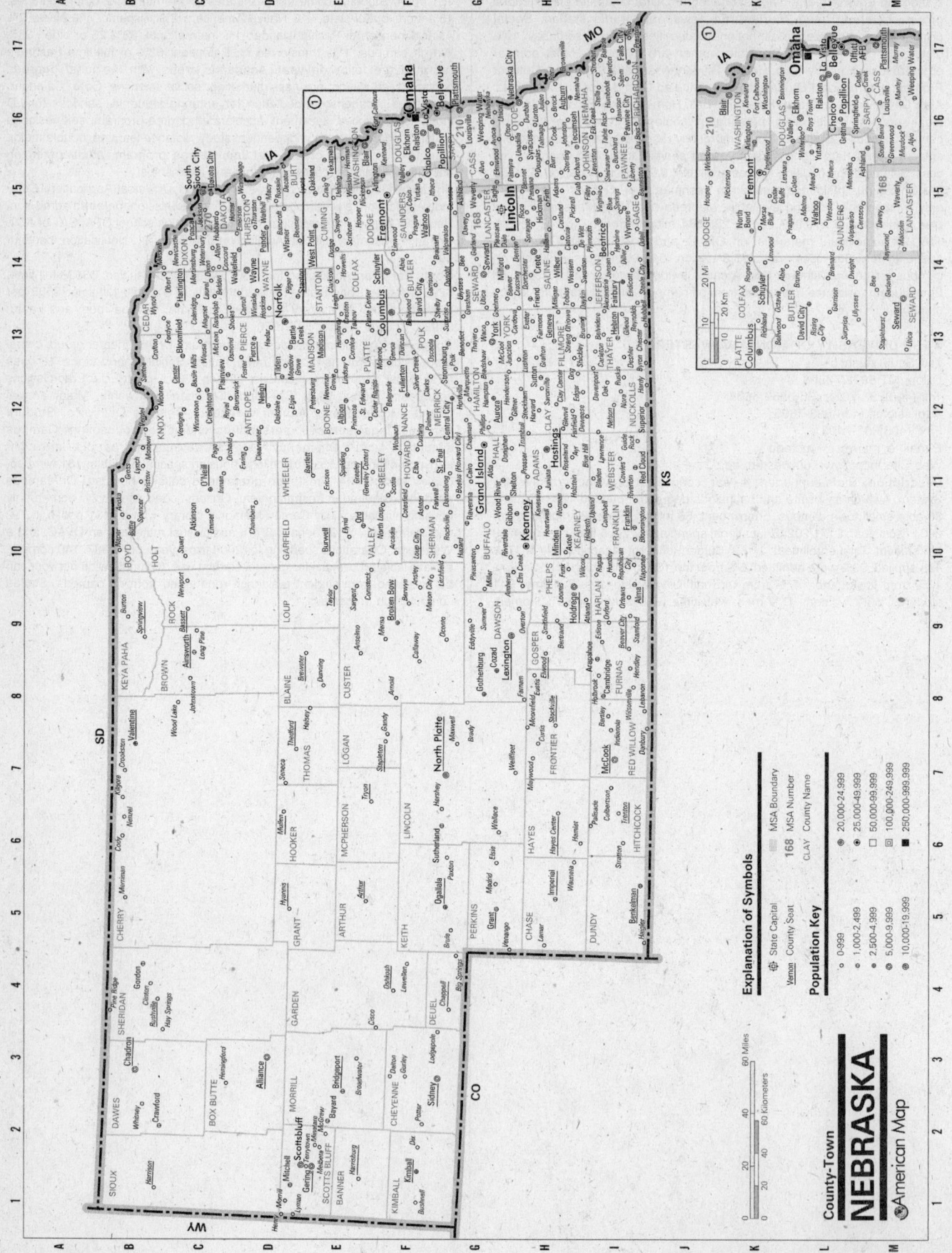

County-Town
NEBRASKA
American Map

■ BELLEVUE UNIVERSITY *F-16*

1000 Galvin Rd. South
Bellevue, NE 68005-3098
Tel: (402)291-8100
Free: 800-756-7920
Admissions: (402)505-5512
Fax: (402)293-2020
E-mail: sandusky@bellevue.edu
Web Site: http://www.bellevue.edu/

Description: Independent, comprehensive, coed. Awards bachelor's and master's degrees. Founded 1965. Setting: 35-acre suburban campus with easy access to Omaha. Endowment: $22.5 million. Educational spending for 2005 fiscal year: $2350 per student. Total enrollment: 5,929. Faculty: 398 (72 full-time, 326 part-time). Student-undergrad faculty ratio is 15:1. Full-time: 2,849 students, 47% women, 53% men. Part-time: 1,598 students, 53% women, 47% men. Students come from 42 states and territories, 66 other countries, 28% from out-of-state, 1% Native American, 6% Hispanic, 10% black, 2% Asian American or Pacific Islander, 6% international, 82% 25 or older. Academic areas with the most degrees conferred: business/marketing; health professions and related sciences; security and protective services. Core. Calendar: semesters for day division, trimesters for evening division. Academic remediation for entering students, ESL program, advanced placement, accelerated degree program, independent study, distance learning, double major, summer session for credit, part-time degree program, external degree program, adult/continuing education programs, co-op programs and internships. ROTC: Army (c), Air Force (c).

Entrance Requirements: Open admission. Option: deferred admission. Required: high school transcript. Entrance: noncompetitive. Application deadline: Rolling.

Costs Per Year: Application fee: $50. Tuition: $5250 full-time, $175 per credit hour part-time. Mandatory fees: $95 full-time, $45 per term part-time.

Collegiate Environment: Major annual events: Student Appreciation Days, Halloween, Christmas. Student services: personal-psychological counseling. Campus security: 24-hour emergency response devices. College housing not available. Freeman/Lozier Library plus 1 other with 100,904 books, 6,500 microform titles, 12,468 serials, 4,200 audiovisual materials, an OPAC, and a Web page. Operations spending for 2004 fiscal year: $718,428. 1,000 computers available on campus for general student use. A campuswide network can be accessed from off-campus. Staffed computer lab on campus.

Community Environment: The oldest continuous settlement in Nebraska, Bellevue is located on the bluffs of the Missouri River, just south of Omaha and adjoining Offutt Air Force Base, the headquarters of the Strategic Air Command. The Fontenelle Forest Nature Center between Bellevue and the Missouri River contains displays of regional habitats.

■ CENTRAL COMMUNITY COLLEGE-COLUMBUS CAMPUS *F-13*

4500 63rd St., PO Box 1027
Columbus, NE 68602-1027
Tel: (402)564-7132
Admissions: (402)562-1296
Fax: (402)562-1201
E-mail: myoung@cccneb.edu
Web Site: http://www.cccneb.edu/

Description: State and locally supported, 2-year, coed. Part of Central Community College. Awards certificates, diplomas, transfer associate, and terminal associate degrees. Founded 1968. Setting: 90-acre small town

campus. Educational spending for 2005 fiscal year: $3156 per student. Total enrollment: 1,999. Student-undergrad faculty ratio is 15:1. Full-time: 445 students, 54% women, 46% men. Part-time: 1,554 students, 64% women, 36% men. Students come from 21 states and territories, 4% from out-of-state, 0.2% Native American, 7% Hispanic, 1% black, 0.4% Asian American or Pacific Islander, 0% international, 50% 25 or older, 17% live on campus, 2% transferred in. Core. Calendar: semesters plus six-week summer session. Academic remediation for entering students, ESL program, services for LD students, advanced placement, accelerated degree program, self-designed majors, independent study, distance learning, summer session for credit, part-time degree program, external degree program, adult/continuing education programs, co-op programs and internships. Off campus study.

Entrance Requirements: Open admission. Options: Common Application, electronic application, early admission. Required: high school transcript. Required for some: 3 recommendations, interview. Entrance: noncompetitive. Application deadline: Rolling. Notification: continuous.

Costs Per Year: Application fee: $0. State resident tuition: $1860 full-time, $62 per credit part-time. Nonresident tuition: $2790 full-time, $93 per credit part-time. Mandatory fees: $120 full-time, $4 per credit part-time.

Collegiate Environment: Orientation program. Choral group. Social organizations: 12 open to all. Most popular organizations: Phi Theta Kappa, Drama Club, Art Club, Cantari, Chorale. Major annual events: East Central Nebraska College Fair, Ethnic Festival, plays. Student services: personal-psychological counseling, women's center. Campus security: late night transport-escort service, controlled dormitory access, night security. 106 college housing spaces available; 93 were occupied in 2003-04. No special consideration for freshman housing applicants. Option: coed housing available. Learning Resources Center with 22,000 books, 118 serials, 1,390 audiovisual materials, and an OPAC. Operations spending for 2004 fiscal year: $87,621. 100 computers available on campus for general student use. A campuswide network can be accessed from student residence rooms and from off campus. Staffed computer lab on campus.

Community Environment: Columbus was originally an agricultural area, but in the late 1940s, as the town was dying from the loss of young people to the larger cities, a concerted effort was begun to introduce industry to the community. This effort has been very successful, and to date the area has more industrial workers per capita than any other city in the Midwest. Products range from agricultural equipment to medical equipment. Commercial transportation is available. Pawnee Park offers swimming, tennis, picnic grounds, and athletic fields. Lake North offers swimming, water skiing, and boating. Lake Babcok offers fishing and boating, plus free camp grounds equipped with electrical outlets and tables. Columbus is 85 miles from Omaha and 80 miles from Lincoln. The community facilities include 22 churches and one library.

■ CENTRAL COMMUNITY COLLEGE-GRAND ISLAND CAMPUS *G-12*

PO Box 4903
Grand Island, NE 68802-4903
Tel: (308)398-4222
Admissions: (308)398-7406
Fax: (308)398-7398
E-mail: lkohout@cccneb.edu
Web Site: http://www.cccneb.edu/

Description: State and locally supported, 2-year, coed. Part of Central Community College. Awards certificates, diplomas, transfer associate, and terminal associate degrees. Founded 1976. Setting: 64-acre small town campus. Educational spending for 2005 fiscal year: $2566 per student. Total enrollment: 2,916. Student-undergrad faculty ratio is 15:1. Full-time: 399 students, 67% women, 33% men. Part-time: 2,517 students, 66% women, 34% men. Students come from 22 states and territories, 1 other country, 4% from out-of-state, 0.3% Native American, 9% Hispanic, 1% black, 1% Asian American or Pacific Islander, 0.1% international, 57% 25 or older, 10% live on campus, 2% transferred in. Core. Calendar: semesters plus six-week summer session. Academic remediation for entering students, ESL program, services for LD students, advanced placement, accelerated degree program, self-designed majors, independent study, distance learning, summer session for credit, part-time degree program, external degree program, adult/continuing education programs, co-op programs and internships. Off campus study.

Entrance Requirements: Open admission. Options: Peterson's Universal Application, Common Application, electronic application, early admission. Required: high school transcript. Required for some: 3 recommendations, interview. Entrance: noncompetitive. Application deadline: Rolling. Notification: continuous.

Costs Per Year: Application fee: $0. State resident tuition: $1860 full-time, $62 per credit part-time. Nonresident tuition: $2790 full-time, $93 per credit part-time. Mandatory fees: $120 full-time, $4 per credit part-time.

Collegiate Environment: Orientation program. Social organizations: 3 open to all. Most popular organizations: Mid-Nebraska Users of Computers, Student Activities Organization, intramurals. Major annual events: Christmas Party, Spring Picnic, Halloween Party. Student services: personal-psychological counseling. 40 college housing spaces available; 12 were occupied in 2003-04. Freshmen given priority for college housing. Option: coed housing available. Central Community College-Grand Island Campus Library with 5,700 books, 94 serials, 150 audiovisual materials, an OPAC, and a Web page. Operations spending for 2004 fiscal year: $80,609. 156 computers available on campus for general student use. A campuswide network can be accessed from off-campus. Staffed computer lab on campus.

Community Environment: Grand Island is located in Central Nebraska and is a leading agricultural center for retailing and industry. Due to agricultural production, industry has quickly expanded, with a resulting rapid population growth. There are many recreational opportunities available to residents and visitors, including swimming, golfing, horse racing, bowling, hunting, and a variety of health-related activities. A large museum complex is located at Grand Island and reflects the Old West tradition. More than 40 churches, two hospitals, a children's zoo and a major library are available.

■ **CENTRAL COMMUNITY COLLEGE-HASTINGS CAMPUS** *H-11*
PO Box 1024
Hastings, NE 68902-1024
Tel: (402)463-9811
Admissions: (402)461-2428
E-mail: rglenn@cccneb.edu
Web Site: http://www.cccneb.edu/
Description: State and locally supported, 2-year, coed. Part of Central Community College. Awards certificates, diplomas, transfer associate, and terminal associate degrees. Founded 1966. Setting: 600-acre small town campus. Educational spending for 2005 fiscal year: $3265 per student. Total enrollment: 2,534. Student-undergrad faculty ratio is 15:1. Full-time: 933 students, 47% women, 53% men. Part-time: 1,601 students, 62% women, 38% men. Students come from 36 states and territories, 4% from out-of-state, 0.4% Native American, 5% Hispanic, 0.4% black, 1% Asian American or Pacific Islander, 0.04% international, 44% 25 or older, 26% live on campus, 3% transferred in. Core. Calendar: semesters plus six-week summer session. Academic remediation for entering students, ESL program, services for LD students, advanced placement, accelerated degree program, self-designed majors, independent study, distance learning, summer session for credit, part-time degree program, external degree program, adult/continuing education programs, co-op programs and internships. Off campus study.

Entrance Requirements: Open admission. Options: Common Application, electronic application, early admission. Required: high school transcript. Required for some: 3 recommendations, interview. Entrance: noncompetitive. Application deadline: Rolling. Notification: continuous.

Costs Per Year: Application fee: $0. State resident tuition: $1860 full-time, $62 per credit part-time. Nonresident tuition: $2790 full-time, $93 per credit part-time. Mandatory fees: $120 full-time, $4 per credit part-time.

Collegiate Environment: Orientation program. Student-run radio station. Social organizations: 13 open to all. Most popular organizations: Student Senate, Central Dormitory Council, Judicial Board, Seeds and Soils, Young

Farmers and Ranchers. Major annual events: back-to-school week events, Christmas Party. Student services: personal-psychological counseling, women's center. Campus security: 24-hour patrols, controlled dormitory access. 320 college housing spaces available; 311 were occupied in 2003-04. No special consideration for freshman housing applicants. Option: coed housing available. Nuckolls Library with 4,025 books, 52 serials, 150 audiovisual materials, and an OPAC. Operations spending for 2004 fiscal year: $35,176. 190 computers available on campus for general student use. A campuswide network can be accessed from student residence rooms and from off campus. Staffed computer lab on campus.

Community Environment: See Hastings College.

■ **CHADRON STATE COLLEGE** *B-3*
1000 Main St.
Chadron, NE 69337
Tel: (308)432-6000
Admissions: (308)432-6263
Fax: (308)432-6229
E-mail: admissions@csc1.csc.edu
Web Site: http://www.csc.edu/
Description: State-supported, comprehensive, coed. Part of Nebraska State College System. Awards bachelor's and master's degrees. Founded 1911. Setting: 281-acre small town campus. Endowment: $6.3 million. Research spending for 2004 fiscal year: $147,715. Educational spending for 2005 fiscal year: $3565 per student. Total enrollment: 2,636. Faculty: 110 (101 full-time, 9 part-time). Student-undergrad faculty ratio is 19:1. 2% from top 10% of their high school class, 19% from top quarter, 47% from top half. Full-time: 1,634 students, 54% women, 46% men. Part-time: 682 students, 68% women, 32% men. Students come from 36 states and territories, 5 other countries, 34% from out-of-state, 2% Native American, 2% Hispanic, 1% black, 1% Asian American or Pacific Islander, 1% international, 15% 25 or older, 65% live on campus, 7% transferred in. Retention: 70% of full-time freshmen returned the following year. Academic areas with the most degrees conferred: education; business/marketing; biological/life sciences. Core. Calendar: semesters. Services for LD students, advanced placement, self-designed majors, honors program, independent study, distance learning, double major, summer session for credit, part-time degree program, external degree program, adult/continuing education programs, co-op programs and internships, graduate courses open to undergrads. Off campus study. Study abroad program.

Entrance Requirements: Open admission. Options: electronic application, early admission. Required: high school transcript, health forms. Entrance: noncompetitive. Application deadline: Rolling. Notification: continuous.

Costs Per Year: Application fee: $15. State resident tuition: $2933 full-time, $97.25 per credit part-time. Nonresident tuition: $5865 full-time, $195.50 per credit part-time. Mandatory fees: $729 full-time. Full-time tuition and fees vary according to course load, location, and program. Part-time tuition varies according to course load, location, and program. College room and board: $4074. College room only: $1924. Room and board charges vary according to board plan and housing facility.

Collegiate Environment: Orientation program. Drama-theater group, choral group, student-run newspaper, radio station. Major annual events: Spring Days, Homecoming. Student services: health clinic, personal-psychological counseling. Campus security: 24-hour emergency response devices and patrols, student patrols, late night transport-escort service. 1,200 college housing spaces available; 774 were occupied in 2003-04. Freshmen guaranteed college housing. On-campus residence required in freshman year. Options: coed, men-only, women-only housing available. Reta King Library with 593,140 books, 381,890 microform titles, 619 serials, 5,596 audiovisual materials, an OPAC, and a Web page. Operations spending for 2004 fiscal year: $662,266. 75 computers available on campus for general student use. A campuswide network can be accessed from student residence rooms and from off campus. Staffed computer lab on campus.

Community Environment: Chadron, located in northwestern Nebraska, is near the Nebraska National Forest where hunting is popular as well as trout fishing. Chadron is also a short drive from snow skiing, water skiing, and the Black Hills of South Dakota. The community facilities include a public library, hospital, churches, and numerous civic organizations.

■ **CLARKSON COLLEGE** *F-16*
101 South 42nd St.
Omaha, NE 68131-2739
Tel: (402)552-3100
Free: 800-647-5500

Fax: (402)552-6057

E-mail: admiss@clrkcol.crhsnet.edu

Web Site: http://www.clarksoncollege.edu/

Description: Independent, comprehensive, coed. Part of Nebraska Health System. Awards associate, bachelor's, and master's degrees. Founded 1888. Setting: 3-acre urban campus. Endowment: $2.2 million. Educational spending for 2005 fiscal year: $5525 per student. Total enrollment: 507. 15% from top 10% of their high school class, 30% from top quarter, 70% from top half. Full-time: 260 students, 92% women, 8% men. Part-time: 161 students, 89% women, 11% men. Students come from 35 states and territories, 33% from out-of-state, 0.2% Native American, 1% Hispanic, 6% black, 1% Asian American or Pacific Islander, 0% international, 41% 25 or older, 20% live on campus, 20% transferred in. Retention: 85% of full-time freshmen returned the following year. Core. Calendar: semesters. Advanced placement, accelerated degree program, independent study, distance learning, double major, summer session for credit, part-time degree program, external degree program, adult/continuing education programs, co-op programs and internships, graduate courses open to undergrads. Study abroad program. ROTC: Army (c), Air Force (c).

Entrance Requirements: Options: Peterson's Universal Application, electronic application, deferred admission. Required: essay, high school transcript, minimum 2.5 high school GPA. Recommended: minimum 3.0 high school GPA. Required for some: 2 recommendations, SAT or ACT. Entrance: moderately difficult. Application deadline: Rolling. Notification: continuous.

Costs Per Year: Application fee: $15. Comprehensive fee: $15,030 includes full-time tuition ($10,350), mandatory fees ($690), and college room and board ($3990). Part-time tuition: $345 per credit hour. Part-time mandatory fees: $22 per credit hour, $15 per term.

Collegiate Environment: Orientation program. Social organizations: 10 open to all. Most popular organizations: Clarkson Student Nurses Association, Clarkson Radiology Student Association, Student Government Association, Student Ambassadors, Clarkson Fellows Program. Major annual events: Alcohol Awareness Week, Student Leadership Convention, staff vs. student softball game. Student services: health clinic, personal-psychological counseling. Campus security: 24-hour emergency response devices and patrols, late night transport-escort service, controlled dormitory access. 78 college housing spaces available; 70 were occupied in 2003-04. Option: coed housing available. Clarkson College Library with 8,807 books, 25,000 microform titles, 262 serials, 530 audiovisual materials, an OPAC, and a Web page. Operations spending for 2004 fiscal year: $258,319. 40 computers available on campus for general student use. A campuswide network can be accessed from off-campus. Staffed computer lab on campus.

■ **COLLEGE OF SAINT MARY** *F-16*

1901 South 72nd St.

Omaha, NE 68124-2377

Tel: (402)399-2400

Free: 800-926-5534

Admissions: (402)399-2407

Fax: (402)399-2412

E-mail: enroll@csm.edu

Web Site: http://www.csm.edu/

Description: Independent Roman Catholic, 4-year, women only. Awards associate, bachelor's, and master's degrees. Founded 1923. Setting: 25-acre suburban campus. Endowment: $6.3 million. Total enrollment: 1,015. Faculty: 54 (all full-time). Student-undergrad faculty ratio is 10:1. 417 applied, 56% were admitted. 11% from top 10% of their high school class, 46% from top quarter, 75% from top half. Full-time: 641 students. Part-time: 358 students. Students come from 14 states and territories, 8 other countries, 10% from out-of-state, 1% Native American, 3% Hispanic, 7% black, 1% Asian American or Pacific Islander, 1% international, 53% 25 or older, 17% live on campus, 23% transferred in. Retention: 71% of full-time freshmen returned the following year. Academic areas with the most degrees conferred: business/marketing; health professions and related sciences; education. Core. Calendar: semesters. Academic remediation for entering students, services for LD students, advanced placement, accelerated degree program, independent study, double major, summer session for credit, part-time degree program, adult/continuing education programs, internships. Study abroad program. ROTC: Army (c), Air Force (c).

Entrance Requirements: Options: Peterson's Universal Application, Common Application, electronic application. Required: high school transcript, minimum 2.0 high school GPA, SAT or ACT. Required for some: essay, minimum 3.0 high school GPA, 2 recommendations, interview. Entrance: minimally difficult. Application deadline: Rolling. Notification: continuous until 8/24.

Costs Per Year: Application fee: $30. Comprehensive fee: $24,010 includes full-time tuition ($17,750), mandatory fees ($360), and college room and board ($5900). Room and board charges vary according to housing facility. Part-time tuition: $550 per credit hour. Part-time mandatory fees: $12 per credit hour. Part-time tuition and fees vary according to class time.

Collegiate Environment: Orientation program. Choral group. Social organizations: 16 open to all; 2% of eligible undergrads are members. Most popular organizations: Student Senate, Campus Activities Board, Student Education Association of Nebraska, Student Occupational Therapy Club, Sigma Rho Lambda. Major annual events: Senate Casino Night, service-learning projects, Queen of Hearts Formal. Student services: personal-psychological counseling. Campus security: 24-hour emergency response devices and patrols, late night transport-escort service, controlled dormitory access, external cameras at residence hall entrances. 250 college housing spaces available; 150 were occupied in 2003-04. Freshmen guaranteed college housing. On-campus residence required through sophomore year. Option: women-only housing available. College of Saint Mary Library with 81,268 books, 12,800 serials, 2,398 audiovisual materials, an OPAC, and a Web page. Operations spending for 2004 fiscal year: $270,119. 153 computers available on campus for general student use. A campuswide network can be accessed from student residence rooms. Staffed computer lab on campus.

■ **CONCORDIA UNIVERSITY** *G-14*

800 North Columbia Ave.

Seward, NE 68434-1599

Tel: (402)643-3651

Free: 800-535-5494

Admissions: (402)643-7233

Fax: (402)643-4073

E-mail: admiss@cune.edu

Web Site: http://www.cune.edu/

Description: Independent, comprehensive, coed, affiliated with Lutheran Church-Missouri Synod. Part of Concordia University System. Awards bachelor's and master's degrees. Founded 1894. Setting: 120-acre small town campus with easy access to Omaha. Endowment: $15 million. Educational spending for 2005 fiscal year: $3565 per student. Total enrollment: 1,317. 728 applied, 89% were admitted. 25% from top 10% of their high school class, 52% from top quarter, 85% from top half. Full-time: 1,122 students, 56% women, 44% men. Part-time: 80 students, 64% women, 36% men. Students come from 38 states and territories, 59% from out-of-state, 0% Native American, 1% Hispanic, 1% black, 1% Asian American or Pacific Islander, 0% international, 3% 25 or older, 3% transferred in. Retention: 80% of full-time freshmen returned the following year. Core. Calendar: 4-4-1. Academic remediation for entering students, ESL program, services for LD students, advanced placement, accelerated degree program, honors program, independent study, distance learning, double major, summer session for credit, part-time degree program, adult/continuing education programs, co-op programs and internships, graduate courses open to undergrads. Off campus study at University of Nebraska-Lincoln. Study abroad program. ROTC: Army (c), Air Force (c).

Entrance Requirements: Options: electronic application, deferred admission. Required: high school transcript, SAT or ACT. Recommended: minimum 2.0 high school GPA, interview. Required for some: recommendations. Entrance: moderately difficult. Application deadline: 7/31.

Costs Per Year: Application fee: $25. Comprehensive fee: $22,434 includes full-time tuition ($17,724) and college room and board ($4710). Room and board charges vary according to board plan.

Collegiate Environment: Orientation program. Drama-theater group, choral group, student-run newspaper. Social organizations: 25 open to all. Most popular organizations: Student Activities Council, musical groups, men's and women's C-Club, Student Senate, Concordia Youth Ministry. Major annual events: homecoming, Spring Weekend, LEAD Conference. Student services: health clinic, personal-psychological counseling. Campus security: 24-hour emergency response devices and patrols, controlled dormitory access. 903 college housing spaces available; 793 were occupied in 2003-04. Freshmen guaranteed college housing. On-campus residence required through senior year. Options: men-only, women-only housing available. Link Library with 171,688 books, 11,093 microform titles, 575 serials, 12,068 audiovisual materials, an OPAC, and a Web page. Operations spending for 2004 fiscal year: $346,633. 75 computers available on campus for general student use. A campuswide network can be accessed from student residence rooms and from off campus. Staffed computer lab on campus.

■ THE CREATIVE CENTER *F-16*

10850 Emmet St.
Omaha, NE 68164
Tel: (402)898-1000; 888-898-1789
Fax: (402)898-1301
Web Site: http://www.thecreativecenter.com/
Description: Proprietary, 2-year, coed. Awards terminal associate degrees. Setting: urban campus. Calendar: semesters.
Entrance Requirements: Required: essay, high school transcript, 1 recommendation, interview.

■ CREIGHTON UNIVERSITY *F-16*

2500 California Plaza
Omaha, NE 68178-0001
Tel: (402)280-2700
Free: 800-282-5835
Admissions: (402)280-2162
Fax: (402)280-2685
E-mail: admissions@creighton.edu
Web Site: http://www.creighton.edu/
Description: Independent Roman Catholic (Jesuit), university, coed. Awards associate, bachelor's, master's, doctoral, and first professional degrees. Founded 1878. Setting: 110-acre urban campus. Endowment: $239.5 million. Educational spending for 2005 fiscal year: $15,545 per student. Total enrollment: 6,791. Faculty: 649 (475 full-time, 174 part-time). Student-undergrad faculty ratio is 12:1. 3,435 applied, 87% were admitted. 40% from top 10% of their high school class, 73% from top quarter, 95% from top half. 155 class presidents, 69 valedictorians, 350 student government officers. Full-time: 3,731 students, 60% women, 40% men. Part-time: 257 students, 58% women, 42% men. Students come from 45 states and territories, 52 other countries, 55% from out-of-state, 1% Native American, 4% Hispanic, 3% black, 7% Asian American or Pacific Islander, 1% international, 4% 25 or older, 56% live on campus, 3% transferred in. Retention: 87% of full-time freshmen returned the following year. Academic areas with the most degrees conferred: health professions and related sciences; business/marketing; biological/life sciences. Core. Calendar: semesters. ESL program, services for LD students, advanced placement, accelerated degree program, honors program, independent study, distance learning, double major, summer session for credit, part-time degree program, adult/continuing education programs, internships, graduate courses open to undergrads. Off campus study at Creighton University; West Omaha Campus. Study abroad program. ROTC: Army, Air Force (c).
Entrance Requirements: Options: Common Application, electronic application, deferred admission, international baccalaureate accepted. Required: essay, high school transcript, minimum 2.75 high school GPA, 1 recommendation, SAT or ACT. Entrance: moderately difficult. Application deadline: 8/1. Notification: continuous.
Costs Per Year: Application fee: $40. Comprehensive fee: $29,918 includes full-time tuition ($21,576), mandatory fees ($802), and college room and board ($7540). College room only: $4250. Room and board charges vary according to board plan and housing facility. Part-time tuition: $675 per semester hour. Part-time mandatory fees: $134 per semester hour.
Collegiate Environment: Orientation program. Drama-theater group, choral group, student-run newspaper, radio station. Social organizations: 190 open to all; national fraternities, national sororities, local fraternities, local sororities; 23% of eligible men and 28% of eligible women are members. Most popular organizations: Bird Cage, Freshman Leadership Program, Alpha Pi Omega, Alpha Kappa Psi, Omecron Delta Kappa. Major annual events: Spring Fling, J Jam, Fallapalooza. Student services: legal services, health clinic, personal-psychological counseling, women's center. Campus security: 24-hour emergency response devices and patrols, student patrols, late night transport-escort service, controlled dormitory access. 2,000 college housing spaces available; 1,969 were occupied in 2003-04. Freshmen guaranteed college housing. On-campus residence required through sophomore year. Options: coed, women-only housing available. Reinert Alumni Memorial Library plus 2 others with 481,848 books, 823,736 microform titles, 1,666 serials, 2,500 audiovisual materials, an OPAC, and a Web page. 505 computers available on campus for general student use. Computer purchase/lease plans available. A campuswide network can be accessed from student residence rooms and from off campus. Staffed computer lab on campus.

Community Environment: Metropolitan Omaha has a population of over 650,000 and serves as a communication and cultural center for the Plains States. Urban Omaha is in a period of rapid renewal through publicly and privately supported programs. It is a major insurance center of the nation, other industries such as railroads, telecommunications, creative enterprises, and health care institutions are well represented. It is best known, however, as a food processing center because of its location in the area known as the "bread basket of America". Cultural attractions include the Omaha Symphony Orchestra, Ballet and Opera Company, Community Playhouse, the Joslyn Art Museum, and the Henry Dvorly Zoo, rated the no. 1 family attraction in America by Family Life Magazine.

■ DANA COLLEGE *E-16*

2848 College Dr.
Blair, NE 68008-1099
Tel: (402)426-9000
Free: 800-444-3262
Admissions: (402)426-7220
Fax: (402)426-7386
E-mail: admissions@dana.edu
Web Site: http://www.dana.edu/
Description: Independent, 4-year, coed, affiliated with Evangelical Lutheran Church in America. Awards bachelor's degrees. Founded 1884. Setting: 150-acre small town campus with easy access to Omaha. Endowment: $11.6 million. Educational spending for 2005 fiscal year: $7286 per student. Total enrollment: 676. Student-undergrad faculty ratio is 12:1. 901 applied, 76% were admitted. 10% from top 10% of their high school class, 35% from top quarter, 66% from top half. Full-time: 653 students, 45% women, 55% men. Part-time: 23 students, 65% women, 35% men. Students come from 35 states and territories, 1 other country, 45% from out-of-state, 1% Native American, 3% Hispanic, 5% black, 1% Asian American or Pacific Islander, 1% international, 4% 25 or older, 67% live on campus, 7% transferred in. Retention: 58% of full-time freshmen returned the following year. Academic areas with the most degrees conferred: education; business/marketing; parks and recreation. Core. Calendar: 4-1-4. ESL program, services for LD students, advanced placement, accelerated degree program, self-designed majors, honors program, independent study, double major, summer session for credit, part-time degree program, adult/continuing education programs, internships. Off campus study at Consortium of Eastern Nebraska Colleges. Study abroad program. ROTC: Army (c), Air Force (c).
Entrance Requirements: Options: Peterson's Universal Application, electronic application, deferred admission. Required: high school transcript, minimum 2.0 high school GPA, SAT or ACT. Recommended: ACT. Required for some: essay, 1 recommendation, interview. Entrance: moderately difficult. Application deadline: Rolling. Notification: continuous.
Costs Per Year: Application fee: $0. Comprehensive fee: $22,770 includes full-time tuition ($16,850), mandatory fees ($600), and college room and board ($5320). College room only: $2060. Room and board charges vary according to board plan and housing facility. Part-time tuition: $510 per semester hour. Part-time mandatory fees: $35 per term. Part-time tuition and fees vary according to course load.
Collegiate Environment: Orientation program. Drama-theater group, choral group, student-run newspaper, radio station. Social organizations: 25 open to all. Most popular organizations: Residence Hall Association, Social Awareness Organization, Fellowship of Christian Athletes, campus ministry, HOPE (Helping Our People Expand). Major annual events: homecoming, Sights and Sounds of Christmas, Winterfest. Student services: health clinic, personal-psychological counseling. Campus security: 24-hour emergency response devices and patrols, late night transport-escort service, controlled dormitory access. 600 college housing spaces available; 422 were occupied in 2003-04. Freshmen guaranteed college housing. On-campus residence required through junior year. Options: coed, women-only housing available. C. A. Dana-Life Library plus 1 other with 145,909 books, 16,274 microform titles, 12,577 serials, 6,979 audiovisual materials, an OPAC, and a Web page. Operations spending for 2004 fiscal year: $222,305. 110 computers available on campus for general student use. A campuswide network can be accessed from student residence rooms and from off campus. Staffed computer lab on campus.
Community Environment: Blair is a suburban community located in a large farming area. Small industries contribute to the economic stability of the community. The college provides transportation to Omaha for the train and bus, and to Eppley Airfield, 25 minutes away. Community facilities include 11 churches, a public library, community theatre, hospital, and clinics as well as many civic, fraternal, and veterans' organizations. Recreational facilities

provide for golf, swimming, tennis, and hiking; the DeSoto National Wildlife Refuge is 3 miles from Blair; the Missouri River near Blair provides boating and fishing opportunities. Student employment opportunities are good.

■ **DOANE COLLEGE** *H-14*
1014 Boswell Ave.
Crete, NE 68333-2430
Tel: (402)826-2161
Free: 800-333-6263
Admissions: (402)826-8222
Fax: (402)826-8600
E-mail: admissions@doane.edu
Web Site: http://www.doane.edu/
Description: Independent, comprehensive, coed, affiliated with United Church of Christ. Awards bachelor's and master's degrees (non-traditional undergraduate programs and graduate programs offered at Lincoln campus). Founded 1872. Setting: 300-acre small town campus with easy access to Omaha. Endowment: $79.1 million. Total enrollment: 2,394. Faculty: 140 (77 full-time, 63 part-time). Student-undergrad faculty ratio is 10:1. 1,144 applied, 80% were admitted. 23% from top 10% of their high school class, 52% from top quarter, 80% from top half. Full-time: 1,349 students, 46% women, 54% men. Part-time: 247 students, 62% women, 38% men. Students come from 23 states and territories, 2 other countries, 17% from out-of-state, 0.4% Native American, 1% Hispanic, 3% black, 2% Asian American or Pacific Islander, 0.3% international, 1% transferred in. Retention: 71% of full-time freshmen returned the following year. Academic areas with the most degrees conferred: business/marketing; education; biological/life sciences. Core. Calendar: 4-1-4. Academic remediation for entering students, ESL program, advanced placement, accelerated degree program, self-designed majors, honors program, independent study, double major, summer session for credit, part-time degree program, adult/continuing education programs, co-op programs and internships, graduate courses open to undergrads. Off campus study at Association of Nebraska Interterm Colleges. Study abroad program. ROTC: Army (c), Air Force (c).
Entrance Requirements: Options: electronic application, early admission, deferred admission, international baccalaureate accepted. Required: high school transcript, 2 recommendations, SAT or ACT. Recommended: minimum 2.0 high school GPA, SAT or ACT. Required for some: interview. Entrance: moderately difficult. Application deadline: Rolling. Notification: continuous.
Costs Per Year: Application fee: $15. Comprehensive fee: $22,458 includes full-time tuition ($17,186), mandatory fees ($350), and college room and board ($4922). College room only: $1850. Full-time tuition and fees vary according to location. Room and board charges vary according to board plan, housing facility, and location. Part-time tuition: $573 per credit hour. Part-time mandatory fees: $120 per year. Part-time tuition and fees vary according to degree level and location.
Collegiate Environment: Orientation program. Drama-theater group, choral group, marching band, student-run newspaper, radio station. Social organizations: 60 open to all; local fraternities, local sororities; 31% of eligible men and 28% of eligible women are members. Most popular organizations: Student Activities Council, Hansen Leadership Program, band/choir, Doane Ambassadors. Major annual events: Homecoming, Big Event, Stop Day. Student services: health clinic, personal-psychological counseling. Campus security: student patrols, evening patrols by trained security personnel. 900 college housing spaces available; 96 were occupied in 2003-04. Freshmen guaranteed college housing. On-campus residence required through senior year. Option: coed housing available. Perkins Library plus 1 other with 299,471 books, an OPAC, and a Web page. Operations spending for 2004 fiscal year: $533,750. 240 computers available on campus for general student use. A campuswide network can be accessed from student residence rooms and from off campus. Staffed computer lab on campus.
Community Environment: Crete, a community of 5,000 persons, is located 25 miles southwest of Lincoln. The community includes nine churches of different denominations, a hospital, library, and numerous civic, fraternal and veterans' organizations. Recreation includes bowling, fishing, hunting, golf, and numerous other activities.

■ **GRACE UNIVERSITY** *F-16*
1311 South Ninth St.
Omaha, NE 68108
Tel: (402)449-2800
Free: 800-383-1422

Admissions: (402)449-2831
Fax: (402)341-9587
E-mail: admissions@graceuniversity.edu
Web Site: http://www.graceuniversity.edu/
Description: Independent interdenominational, comprehensive, coed. Awards associate, bachelor's, and master's degrees. Founded 1943. Setting: 15-acre urban campus. Endowment: $890,668. Educational spending for 2005 fiscal year: $3885 per student. Total enrollment: 513. 325 applied, 46% were admitted. Full-time: 375 students, 58% women, 42% men. Part-time: 52 students, 52% women, 48% men. Students come from 30 states and territories, 4 other countries, 36% from out-of-state, 0.5% Native American, 2% Hispanic, 5% black, 0% Asian American or Pacific Islander, 61% live on campus, 11% transferred in. Retention: 68% of full-time freshmen returned the following year. Core. Calendar: semesters. Services for LD students, advanced placement, accelerated degree program, self-designed majors, independent study, distance learning, double major, summer session for credit, part-time degree program, external degree program, adult/continuing education programs, co-op programs and internships, graduate courses open to undergrads. Off campus study at Iowa Western Community College, Metropolitan Community College (NE), University of Nebraska at Omaha, Bellevue University, Clarkson College. Study abroad program. ROTC: Army (c), Air Force (c).
Entrance Requirements: Options: electronic application, early admission, deferred admission, international baccalaureate accepted. Required: essay, high school transcript, minimum 2.0 high school GPA, 3 recommendations, ACT. Required for some: interview. Entrance: moderately difficult. Application deadline: Rolling.
Costs Per Year: Application fee: $35. Comprehensive fee: $17,380 includes full-time tuition ($11,700), mandatory fees ($280), and college room and board ($5400). College room only: $2400. Part-time tuition: $390 per credit hour. Part-time mandatory fees: $15 per term.
Collegiate Environment: Orientation program. Choral group, student-run radio station. Social organizations: ; 12% of eligible men and 20% of eligible women are members. Most popular organizations: choral group, band, radio station, yearbook. Major annual events: Spiritual Orientation (Welcome Week), Bible Conference, World Christian Conference. Student services: health clinic, personal-psychological counseling. Campus security: student patrols, late night transport-escort service, controlled dormitory access. 322 college housing spaces available; 244 were occupied in 2003-04. Freshmen given priority for college housing. On-campus residence required through sophomore year. Options: men-only, women-only housing available. Grace University Library with 46,736 books, 623 microform titles, 3,721 serials, 3,882 audiovisual materials, an OPAC, and a Web page. Operations spending for 2004 fiscal year: $116,023. 45 computers available on campus for general student use. A campuswide network can be accessed. Staffed computer lab on campus.
Community Environment: Grace University adheres to four values that revolve around community living: honesty, integrity, responsibility, and accountability.

■ **HAMILTON COLLEGE-LINCOLN** *G-15*
1821 K St., PO Box 82826
Lincoln, NE 68501-2826
Tel: (402)474-5315
Fax: (402)474-5302
E-mail: losc@ix.netcom.com
Web Site: http://www.hamiltonlincoln.com/
Description: Proprietary, 2-year, coed. Part of Quest Education Corporation. Awards certificates, diplomas, transfer associate, and terminal associate degrees. Founded 1884. Setting: 5-acre urban campus with easy access to Omaha. Total enrollment: 1,000. 10% from top 10% of their high school class, 40% from top quarter, 50% from top half. Students come from 3 states and territories, 1% from out-of-state, 0% Native American, 2% Hispanic, 4% black, 1% Asian American or Pacific Islander, 0% international, 38% 25 or older. Core. Services for LD students, accelerated degree program, independent study, double major, summer session for credit, adult/continuing education programs, co-op programs and internships.
Entrance Requirements: Open admission. Option: early admission. Required: essay, high school transcript, recommendations, interview, CPAt. Entrance: minimally difficult. Application deadline: Rolling. Notification: continuous.
Collegiate Environment: Orientation program. Social organizations: 7 open to all. Most popular organizations: Travel Club, Secretarial Club, Business Club, Court Reporting Club, Legal Assistant Club. Major annual events:

Spring Picnic, Fall Picnic, Spring Dance. Campus security: late night transport-escort service. 140 college housing spaces available; 120 were occupied in 2003-04. Option: coed housing available. Lincoln School of Commerce Library with 7,500 books, 1,872 serials, 300 audiovisual materials, and an OPAC. 99 computers available on campus for general student use. A campuswide network can be accessed. Staffed computer lab on campus.

■ **HAMILTON COLLEGE-OMAHA** *F-16*
3350 North 90th St.
Omaha, NE 68134
Tel: (402)572-8500
Free: 800-642-1456
Fax: (402)573-1341
Web Site: http://www.hamiltonomaha.edu/
Description: Proprietary, primarily 2-year, coed. Part of Educational Medical, Inc. Awards diplomas, terminal associate, and bachelor's degrees. Founded 1891. Setting: 3-acre urban campus. Total enrollment: 700. 850 applied. Full-time: 700 students, 64% women, 36% men. Students come from 5 states and territories, 60% 25 or older, 0% transferred in. Core. Academic remediation for entering students, advanced placement, summer session for credit, part-time degree program, adult/continuing education programs, co-op programs and internships.
Entrance Requirements: Options: early admission, deferred admission. Required: high school transcript, interview, CPAt. Entrance: minimally difficult. Application deadline: Rolling.
Collegiate Environment: Orientation program. Student-run newspaper. Student services: personal-psychological counseling. Campus security: 24-hour emergency response devices. College housing not available. Nebraska College of Business Library with 4,800 books, 50 serials, and a Web page. 110 computers available on campus for general student use. Staffed computer lab on campus.

■ **HASTINGS COLLEGE** *H-11*
800 North Turner Ave.
Hastings, NE 68901-7696
Tel: (402)463-2402
Free: 800-532-7642
Admissions: (402)461-7320
Fax: (402)463-3002
E-mail: mmolliconi@hastings.edu
Web Site: http://www.hastings.edu/
Description: Independent Presbyterian, comprehensive, coed. Awards bachelor's and master's degrees. Founded 1882. Setting: 109-acre small town campus. Endowment: $56.3 million. Educational spending for 2005 fiscal year: $6414 per student. Total enrollment: 1,189. Faculty: 121 (79 full-time, 42 part-time). Student-undergrad faculty ratio is 12:1. 1,413 applied, 79% were admitted. 14% from top 10% of their high school class, 37% from top quarter, 72% from top half. 21 valedictorians. Full-time: 1,121 students, 49% women, 51% men. Part-time: 23 students, 52% women, 48% men. Students come from 22 states and territories, 8 other countries, 20% from out-of-state, 0.4% Native American, 2% Hispanic, 2% black, 1% Asian American or Pacific Islander, 1% international, 3% 25 or older, 67% live on campus, 5% transferred in. Retention: 78% of full-time freshmen returned the following year. Academic areas with the most degrees conferred: education; business/marketing; psychology. Core. Calendar: 4-1-4. Services for LD students, advanced placement, self-designed majors, independent study, double major, summer session for credit, part-time degree program, adult/continuing education programs, internships, graduate courses open to undergrads. Off campus study. Study abroad program.
Entrance Requirements: Options: Peterson's Universal Application, Common Application, international baccalaureate accepted. Required: high school transcript, minimum 2.0 high school GPA, counselor's recommendation, SAT or ACT. Required for some: essay, 2 recommendations, interview. Entrance: moderately difficult. Application deadline: 8/1. Notification: continuous.
Costs Per Year: Application fee: $20. Comprehensive fee: $22,218 includes full-time tuition ($16,578), mandatory fees ($690), and college room and board ($4950). College room only: $2116. Full-time tuition and fees vary according to course level and program. Room and board charges vary according to board plan and housing facility. Part-time tuition: $686 per semester hour. Part-time mandatory fees: $182 per term. Part-time tuition and fees vary according to course level, course load, and program.
Collegiate Environment: Orientation program. Drama-theater group, choral group, marching band, student-run newspaper, radio station. Social

organizations: 60 open to all; local fraternities, local sororities; 20% of eligible men and 30% of eligible women are members. Most popular organizations: Student Association, Student Alumni Ambassadors, Fellowship of Christian Athletes, Phi Mu Alpha Sinfonia, Hastings College Singers. Major annual events: homecoming, Boar's Head Dinner, Greek Dinner Dance. Student services: health clinic, personal-psychological counseling. Campus security: 24-hour emergency response devices, student patrols, late night transport-escort service, controlled dormitory access, security cameras at entrances and parking lots. 760 college housing spaces available; 721 were occupied in 2003-04. Freshmen guaranteed college housing. On-campus residence required through junior year. Options: coed, men-only, women-only housing available. Perkins Library with 113,318 books, 120,500 microform titles, 636 serials, 1,875 audiovisual materials, an OPAC, and a Web page. Operations spending for 2004 fiscal year: $550,309. 181 computers available on campus for general student use. Computer purchase/lease plans available. A campuswide network can be accessed from student residence rooms and from off campus. Staffed computer lab on campus.
Community Environment: Located in the south central section of the state, Hastings is in the heart of an important irrigated agricultural and stock-raising area. All commercial transportation is available. Part-time jobs are available for students. Community facilities include a library, churches of all denominations and numerous fraternal organizations. Prospect Park contains the Aquacourt, an ultramodern swimming pool, fishing and skiing. A municipal pool is in Libs Park. Lake Hastings, one mile north, offers water sports and fishing. Points of interest are the Fisher Rainbow Fountain, the Hastings Museum, which includes the J.M. McDonald Planetarium, and the Imax theater.

■ **ITT TECHNICAL INSTITUTE** *F-16*
9814 M St.
Omaha, NE 68127-2056
Tel: (402)331-2900
Free: 800-677-9260
Fax: (402)331-9495
Web Site: http://www.itt-tech.edu/
Description: Proprietary, primarily 2-year, coed. Part of ITT Educational Services, Inc. Awards terminal associate and bachelor's degrees. Founded 1991. Setting: 1-acre urban campus. Core.
Entrance Requirements: Option: deferred admission. Required: high school transcript, interview, Wonderlic aptitude test. Recommended: recommendations. Entrance: minimally difficult. Application deadline: Rolling. Notification: continuous.
Costs Per Year: Application fee: $100.
Collegiate Environment: Orientation program. College housing not available.

■ **LITTLE PRIEST TRIBAL COLLEGE**
PO Box 270
Winnebago, NE 68071
Tel: (402)878-2380
Fax: (402)878-2355
Web Site: http://www.lptc.bia.edu/
Description: Independent, 2-year. Awards certificates, diplomas, transfer associate, and terminal associate degrees. Setting: rural campus. Total enrollment: 130. 24 applied, 100% were admitted. 10% from top 10% of their high school class, 10% from top quarter, 70% from top half. Full-time: 67 students, 73% women, 27% men. Part-time: 63 students, 83% women, 17% men. 83% Native American, 2% Hispanic, 1% black, 1% Asian American or Pacific Islander.

■ **METROPOLITAN COMMUNITY COLLEGE** *F-16*
PO Box 3777
Omaha, NE 68103-0777
Tel: (402)457-2400
Free: 800-228-9553
Admissions: (402)457-2717
Fax: (402)457-2564
E-mail: bnicks@mccneb.edu
Web Site: http://www.mccneb.edu/
Description: State and locally supported, 2-year, coed. Part of Nebraska Coordinating Commission for Postsecondary Education. Awards certificates, diplomas, transfer associate, and terminal associate degrees. Founded 1974. Setting: 172-acre urban campus. Endowment: $1.4 million. Educational spending for 2005 fiscal year: $2551 per student. Total enrollment:

12,461. Student-undergrad faculty ratio is 13:1. 3,674 applied, 100% were admitted. Full-time: 4,798 students, 56% women, 44% men. Part-time: 7,663 students, 56% women, 44% men. 3% from out-of-state, 47% 25 or older, 9% transferred in. Retention: 46% of full-time freshmen returned the following year. Core. Academic remediation for entering students, ESL program, services for LD students, advanced placement, independent study, distance learning, summer session for credit, part-time degree program, adult/continuing education programs, co-op programs and internships. ROTC: Army (c).

Entrance Requirements: Open admission. Options: Peterson's Universal Application, early admission. Recommended: high school transcript. Entrance: noncompetitive. Application deadline: Rolling. Notification: continuous.

Costs Per Year: Application fee: $0. State resident tuition: $1733 full-time, $38.50 per credit hour part-time. Nonresident tuition: $2610 full-time, $71 per credit hour part-time. Mandatory fees: $135 full-time, $3 per credit hour part-time.

Collegiate Environment: Orientation program. Student services: personal-psychological counseling. Campus security: 24-hour emergency response devices and patrols, late night transport-escort service, security on duty 9 pm to 6 am. College housing not available. Metropolitan Community College plus 2 others with 41,161 books, 1,325 microform titles, 544 serials, 10,702 audiovisual materials, an OPAC, and a Web page. Operations spending for 2004 fiscal year: $891,473. 1,700 computers available on campus for general student use. A campuswide network can be accessed from off-campus. Staffed computer lab on campus.

Community Environment: See Creighton University.

■ **MID-PLAINS COMMUNITY COLLEGE** *G-7*
601 West State Farm Rd.
North Platte, NE 69101
Tel: (308)535-3600
Free: 800-658-4348
Admissions: (308)535-3610
Fax: (308)532-8590
Web Site: http://www.mpcca.cc.ne.us/
Description: District-supported, 2-year, coed. Awards certificates, diplomas, transfer associate, and terminal associate degrees. Setting: small town campus. Educational spending for 2005 fiscal year: $7134 per student. Total enrollment: 3,084. 816 applied, 77% were admitted. 4% from top 10% of their high school class, 20% from top quarter, 51% from top half. Full-time: 1,083 students, 59% women, 41% men. Part-time: 2,001 students, 57% women, 43% men. Students come from 11 states and territories, 0.1% from out-of-state, 1% Native American, 2% Hispanic, 1% black, 0.4% Asian American or Pacific Islander, 0.4% international, 67% 25 or older, 8% live on campus. Core. Calendar: semesters. Academic remediation for entering students, advanced placement, independent study, distance learning, summer session for credit, part-time degree program, adult/continuing education programs, co-op programs and internships.

Entrance Requirements: Open admission. Required: high school transcript. Placement: ACT COMPASS required; ACT recommended. Entrance: minimally difficult. Application deadline: Rolling. Notification: continuous.

Collegiate Environment: Drama-theater group, choral group, student-run newspaper. Social organizations: 10 open to all; local fraternities. Most popular organizations: Student Senate, Phi Theta Kappa, Phi Beta Lamda, SEAN. Campus security: controlled dormitory access, patrols by trained security personnel. 300 college housing spaces available; 180 were occupied in 2003-04. No special consideration for freshman housing applicants. Option: coed housing available. McDonald-Belton L R C plus 1 other with 64,284 books, 65,119 microform titles, 277 serials, and 6,318 audiovisual materials. Operations spending for 2004 fiscal year: $189,260. 300 computers available on campus for general student use. A campuswide network can be accessed from off-campus. Staffed computer lab on campus.

Community Environment: A rural and agricultural community, North Platte is a railroad division point with extensive railroad shops. Important crops raised are corn, wheat, and alfalfa. Maloney Reservoir, six miles south of North Platte, offers boating, fishing and hunting. Community facilities include many churches, a regional medical center, shopping areas, a community playhouse, civic music association and numerous social and service organizations. Part-time employment opportunities are good.

■ **MIDLAND LUTHERAN COLLEGE** *F-15*
900 North Clarkson St.
Fremont, NE 68025-4200

Tel: (402)721-5480
Free: 800-642-8382
Admissions: (402)941-6521
Fax: (402)721-0250
E-mail: watson@mlc.edu
Web Site: http://www.mlc.edu/
Description: Independent Lutheran, 4-year, coed. Awards associate and bachelor's degrees. Founded 1883. Setting: 27-acre small town campus with easy access to Omaha. Endowment: $25.6 million. Educational spending for 2005 fiscal year: $4325 per student. Total enrollment: 909. Student-undergrad faculty ratio is 14:1. 898 applied, 86% were admitted. 9% from top 10% of their high school class, 26% from top quarter, 57% from top half. 17 valedictorians. Full-time: 888 students, 54% women, 46% men. Part-time: 21 students, 76% women, 24% men. Students come from 25 states and territories, 4 other countries, 19% from out-of-state, 0.3% Native American, 2% Hispanic, 3% black, 1% Asian American or Pacific Islander, 0% international, 8% 25 or older, 62% live on campus, 6% transferred in. Retention: 80% of full-time freshmen returned the following year. Core. Calendar: 4-1-4. Academic remediation for entering students, ESL program, services for LD students, advanced placement, accelerated degree program, self-designed majors, honors program, independent study, double major, summer session for credit, part-time degree program, co-op programs and internships. Off campus study at Concordia University, Doane College, Dana College, Hastings College, Central College. Study abroad program.

Entrance Requirements: Options: Peterson's Universal Application, electronic application, early admission, international baccalaureate accepted. Required: high school transcript, SAT or ACT. Recommended: essay, minimum 3.0 high school GPA, recommendations. Required for some: interview. Entrance: moderately difficult. Application deadline: Rolling. Notification: continuous until 9/1.

Costs Per Year: Application fee: $30. Comprehensive fee: $24,460 includes full-time tuition ($19,510) and college room and board ($4950). College room only: $2190.

Collegiate Environment: Orientation program. Drama-theater group, student-run newspaper. Social organizations: 48 open to all; local fraternities, local sororities; 40% of eligible men and 40% of eligible women are members. Most popular organizations: Student Nurses Association, Student Education Association, Phi Beta Lambda, Fellowship of Christian Athletics (FCA), Circle K. Major annual events: homecoming, Snow Days, Spring Fling. Student services: health clinic, personal-psychological counseling. Campus security: 24-hour emergency response devices, student patrols, late night transport-escort service, controlled dormitory access. 650 college housing spaces available; 592 were occupied in 2003-04. On-campus residence required through sophomore year. Options: coed, men-only, women-only housing available. Luther Library with 110,000 books, 900 serials, an OPAC, and a Web page. Operations spending for 2004 fiscal year: $277,877. 180 computers available on campus for general student use. A campuswide network can be accessed from student residence rooms and from off campus. Staffed computer lab on campus.

Community Environment: Situated near the Platte River, Fremont, the trading center of a dairying and livestock area, is located 35 miles northwest of Omaha and 51 miles north of Lincoln, Nebraska. Fremont is also recognized as the hybrid seed corn center of the state. Some of the products of industry are poultry, butter, flour, soybeans, and animal food. Some nationally known manufacturers such as Campbell Soup, Fel-Tex Ammonia, Magnus Metal, and Hormel Meats have plants in the area. Part-time employment is available. Boating, fishing and hunting are some of the outdoor sports available.

■ **MYOTHERAPY INSTITUTE** *H-5*
6020 South 58th St.
Lincoln, NE 68516
Tel: (402)421-7410
Free: 800-896-3363
Fax: (402)421-6736
E-mail: admissions@myomassage.net
Web Site: http://www.myotherapy.edu/
Description: Proprietary, 2-year, coed.

■ **NEBRASKA CHRISTIAN COLLEGE** *D-13*
1800 Syracuse Ave.
Norfolk, NE 68701-2458
Tel: (402)379-5000
Web Site: http://www.nechristian.edu/

Description: Independent, 4-year, coed, affiliated with Christian Churches and Churches of Christ. Awards associate and bachelor's degrees. Founded 1944. Setting: 85-acre small town campus. Endowment: $324,000. Total enrollment: 167. 175 applied, 45% were admitted. 14% from top 10% of their high school class, 28% from top quarter, 67% from top half. Full-time: 152 students, 49% women, 51% men. Part-time: 15 students, 40% women, 60% men. Students come from 15 states and territories, 3 other countries, 49% from out-of-state, 0% Native American, 4% Hispanic, 0% black, 1% Asian American or Pacific Islander, 2% international, 10% 25 or older, 85% live on campus, 8% transferred in. Retention: 63% of full-time freshmen returned the following year. Core. Calendar: semesters. Part-time degree program, internships. Off campus study at Northeast Community College, Wayne State College, York College (NE), Fort Hays State University.

Entrance Requirements: Option: Peterson's Universal Application. Required: high school transcript, 2 recommendations, ACT. Required for some: interview. Entrance: minimally difficult. Application deadline: Rolling. Notification: continuous until 9/1.

Collegiate Environment: Orientation program. Drama-theater group, choral group, student-run newspaper. Social organizations: 4 open to all. Major annual events: Fall Formal, Challenge Week, Spring Formal. Student services: health clinic, personal-psychological counseling. 165 college housing spaces available. Freshmen guaranteed college housing. On-campus residence required through junior year. Swedberg Library with 250,000 books and 149 serials. 10 computers available on campus for general student use. A campuswide network can be accessed. Staffed computer lab on campus.

Community Environment: Primarily a rural community, Norfolk depends very heavily on agriculture and the raising of beef as its primary industries. The livestock business is valued at almost a $40 million industry. Community facilities include a public library, 20 churches representing 16 denominations, a YMCA and civic organizations such as Rotary, Kiwanis and the Lions Club. Part-time employment is available. Lewis and Clark Lake and other facilities provide swimming, boating, fishing and golf. The Norfolk Historical Museum exhibits a collection of local historical relics.

■ NEBRASKA COLLEGE OF TECHNICAL AGRICULTURE

RR3, Box 23A
Curtis, NE 69025-9205
Tel: (308)367-4124
Free: 800-3CU-RTIS
Fax: (308)367-5203
E-mail: gsundquist1@unl.edu
Web Site: http://www.ncta.unl.edu/

Description: State-supported, 2-year, coed. Part of University of Nebraska System. Awards transfer associate and terminal associate degrees. Founded 1965. Setting: small town campus. Endowment: $80,000. Total enrollment: 189. 161 applied, 100% were admitted. 10% from top 10% of their high school class, 20% from top quarter, 30% from top half. Students come from 8 states and territories, 24% 25 or older, 44% live on campus. Core. Calendar: 8-week modular system. Academic remediation for entering students, part-time degree program, adult/continuing education programs, internships.

Entrance Requirements: Open admission. Option: early admission. Required: high school transcript. Recommended: interview. Placement: ACT required. Entrance: noncompetitive. Application deadline: Rolling.

Costs Per Year: Application fee: $10. State resident tuition: $3006 full-time. Nonresident tuition: $6012 full-time. Mandatory fees: $433 full-time. College room and board: $4149. College room only: $1824.

Collegiate Environment: Social organizations: local fraternities; 10% of men are members. Most popular organizations: Aggie Livestock Association, Student Technicians Veterinary Medicine Association, Activities Without Alcohol and Drugs, Business Club, Phi Theta Kappa. Major annual event: Annual Open House. Student services: health clinic, personal-psychological counseling. Campus security: 24-hour emergency response devices, controlled dormitory access. Nebraska College of Technical Agriculture Library with 5,500 books, 230 serials, and a Web page. 60 computers available on campus for general student use. A campuswide network can be accessed from off-campus. Staffed computer lab on campus.

■ NEBRASKA INDIAN COMMUNITY COLLEGE

PO Box 428
Macy, NE 68039-0428
Tel: (402)837-5078; 888-843-6432
Admissions: (402)344-8428
Fax: (402)878-2522

Web Site: http://www.thenicc.edu/

Description: Federally supported, 2-year, coed. Awards certificates, transfer associate, and terminal associate degrees. Founded 1979. Setting: 2-acre rural campus with easy access to Omaha, NE. Endowment: $68,020. Educational spending for 2005 fiscal year: $4066 per student. Total enrollment: 190. Full-time: 97 students, 62% women, 38% men. Part-time: 93 students, 75% women, 25% men. Students come from 2 states and territories, 13% from out-of-state, 82% Native American, 1% Hispanic, 4% black, 0% Asian American or Pacific Islander, 66% 25 or older. Core. Calendar: semesters. Academic remediation for entering students, double major, summer session for credit, part-time degree program, adult/continuing education programs.

Entrance Requirements: Open admission. Options: early admission, deferred admission. Required: high school transcript, certificate of tribal enrollment if applicable. Entrance: noncompetitive. Application deadline: Rolling. Notification: continuous.

Collegiate Environment: Orientation program. College housing not available. 10 computers available on campus for general student use. Staffed computer lab on campus.

■ NEBRASKA METHODIST COLLEGE *F-16*

720 N. 87th St.
Omaha, NE 68114
Tel: (402)354-4879
Free: 800-335-5510
Admissions: (402)354-7205
Fax: (402)354-4819
E-mail: deann.sterner@methodistcollege.edu
Web Site: http://www.methodistcollege.edu/

Description: Independent, comprehensive, coed, affiliated with United Methodist Church. Awards associate, bachelor's, and master's degrees and post-master's certificates. Founded 1891. Setting: 5-acre urban campus. Endowment: $30.2 million. Educational spending for 2005 fiscal year: $10,400 per student. Total enrollment: 524. Faculty: 57 (33 full-time, 24 part-time). Student-undergrad faculty ratio is 10:1. 119 applied, 50% were admitted. 15% from top 10% of their high school class, 25% from top quarter, 100% from top half. Full-time: 333 students, 92% women, 8% men. Part-time: 126 students, 89% women, 11% men. Students come from 5 states and territories, 3 other countries, 25% from out-of-state, 0% Native American, 0.4% Hispanic, 2% black, 1% Asian American or Pacific Islander, 0.4% international, 25% 25 or older, 20% live on campus, 13% transferred in. Retention: 74% of full-time freshmen returned the following year. Academic area with the most degrees conferred: health professions and related sciences. Core. Calendar: semesters. Academic remediation for entering students, services for LD students, advanced placement, accelerated degree program, independent study, distance learning, summer session for credit, internships. ROTC: Army (c).

Entrance Requirements: Options: electronic application, deferred admission. Required: essay, high school transcript, minimum 2.0 high school GPA, 3 recommendations, interview, SAT or ACT. Entrance: moderately difficult. Application deadline: 4/1. Notification: 4/15.

Costs Per Year: Application fee: $25. Tuition: $11,340 full-time, $378 per credit hour part-time. Mandatory fees: $600 full-time, $20 per credit hour part-time. College room only: $2270.

Collegiate Environment: Orientation program. Social organizations: 5 open to all. Most popular organizations: Student Senate, Student Nurses Association, Methodist Allied Health Student Association, Student Ambassadors, Residence Hall Council. Major annual events: holiday events, Welcome Week. Student services: health clinic, personal-psychological counseling. Campus security: 24-hour emergency response devices, late night transport-escort service, controlled dormitory access. 70 college housing spaces available; 65 were occupied in 2003-04. Freshmen given priority for college housing. Option: coed housing available. John Moritz Library plus 1 other with 8,656 books, 181 microform titles, 475 serials, 985 audiovisual materials, and a Web page. Operations spending for 2004 fiscal year: $300,000. 45 computers available on campus for general student use. A campuswide network can be accessed. Staffed computer lab on campus.

■ NEBRASKA WESLEYAN UNIVERSITY *G-15*

5000 Saint Paul Ave.
Lincoln, NE 68504-2796
Tel: (402)466-2371
Free: 800-541-3818
Admissions: (402)465-2218

Fax: (402)465-2179
E-mail: admissions@nebrwesleyan.edu
Web Site: http://www.nebrwesleyan.edu/
Description: Independent United Methodist, comprehensive, coed. Awards bachelor's and master's degrees and post-master's certificates. Founded 1887. Setting: 50-acre suburban campus with easy access to Omaha. Endowment: $35.4 million. Educational spending for 2005 fiscal year: $6505 per student. Total enrollment: 2,016. Faculty: 225 (102 full-time, 123 part-time). Student-undergrad faculty ratio is 13:1. 1,508 applied, 84% were admitted. 22% from top 10% of their high school class, 57% from top quarter, 88% from top half. 28 valedictorians. Full-time: 1,606 students, 56% women, 44% men. Part-time: 236 students, 67% women, 33% men. Students come from 24 states and territories, 9 other countries, 8% from out-of-state, 1% Native American, 2% Hispanic, 1% black, 1% Asian American or Pacific Islander, 0.1% international, 2% 25 or older, 54% live on campus, 3% transferred in. Retention: 82% of full-time freshmen returned the following year. Academic areas with the most degrees conferred: business/marketing; education; health professions and related sciences. Core. Calendar: semesters. Services for LD students, advanced placement, independent study, double major, summer session for credit, part-time degree program, adult/continuing education programs, internships, graduate courses open to undergrads. Off campus study at Chicago Urban Life Center, Capitol Hill Internship Program. Study abroad program. ROTC: Army (c), Air Force (c).
Entrance Requirements: Options: Peterson's Universal Application, Common Application, electronic application, early admission, early decision, deferred admission, international baccalaureate accepted. Required: high school transcript, minimum 2.0 high school GPA, SAT or ACT. Recommended: interview. Required for some: essay, resume of activities. Entrance: moderately difficult. Application deadlines: 8/15, 11/15 for early decision. Notification: continuous, 12/15 for early decision.
Costs Per Year: Application fee: $20. Comprehensive fee: $23,425 includes full-time tuition ($18,100), mandatory fees ($310), and college room and board ($5015). Room and board charges vary according to board plan and housing facility. Part-time tuition: $683 per credit hour. Part-time tuition varies according to class time, course load, degree level, location, and program.
Collegiate Environment: Orientation program. Drama-theater group, choral group, student-run newspaper. Social organizations: 65 open to all; national fraternities, national sororities, local fraternities, local sororities; 24% of eligible men and 22% of eligible women are members. Most popular organizations: Student Affairs Senate, Union programs, Ambassadors, FCA. Major annual events: Wesleyan Weekend (Homecoming), Jim Wand Hypnotist (annual orientation event), Big Event (comedian). Student services: health clinic, personal-psychological counseling, women's center. Campus security: 24-hour emergency response devices, late night transport-escort service, controlled dormitory access. 1,108 college housing spaces available; 988 were occupied in 2003-04. Freshmen guaranteed college housing. On-campus residence required through junior year. Options: coed, men-only, women-only housing available. Cochrane Woods Library with 178,531 books, 4,309 microform titles, 743 serials, 7,951 audiovisual materials, an OPAC, and a Web page. Operations spending for 2004 fiscal year: $703,739. 336 computers available on campus for general student use. Computer purchase/lease plans available. A campuswide network can be accessed from student residence rooms and from off campus. Staffed computer lab on campus.
Community Environment: The capital, Lincoln, in southeastern Nebraska, is in a vast agricultural area where irrigation is an important factor. Many insurance firms have their home offices here. Major forms of transportation are available. Pershing Municipal Auditorium and the Bob Devaney Sports Center is used for conventions, concerts and athletic activities. Recreational facilities and sporting events are numerous. Some of the points of interest are Antelope Park, the Sunken Garden, Fairview, a home occupied by the William Jennings Bryan family for 15 years, Pioneer Park, Holmes Lake with bike trails, Sheldon Memorial Art Gallery, the University of Nebraska State Museum, and the Haymarket District. Part-time jobs are available on and off campus.

■ NORTHEAST COMMUNITY COLLEGE *D-13*
801 East Benjamin Ave, PO Box 469
Norfolk, NE 68702-0469
Tel: (402)371-2020
Admissions: (402)844-7258
Fax: (402)644-0650
Web Site: http://www.northeastcollege.com/
Description: State and locally supported, 2-year, coed. Part of Nebraska Coordinating Commission for Postsecondary Education. Awards certificates, diplomas, transfer associate, and terminal associate degrees. Founded 1973. Setting: 205-acre small town campus. Endowment: $1.5 million. Educational spending for 2005 fiscal year: $2975 per student. Total enrollment: 5,101. Student-undergrad faculty ratio is 17:1. Full-time: 2,127 students, 48% women, 52% men. Part-time: 2,974 students, 45% women, 55% men. Students come from 15 states and territories, 15 other countries, 4% from out-of-state, 39% 25 or older, 11% live on campus. Core. Calendar: semesters. Academic remediation for entering students, ESL program, services for LD students, advanced placement, accelerated degree program, independent study, distance learning, summer session for credit, part-time degree program, adult/continuing education programs, co-op programs and internships. Off campus study.
Entrance Requirements: Open admission. Options: electronic application, early admission. Recommended: high school transcript. Entrance: noncompetitive. Application deadline: Rolling. Notification: continuous.
Costs Per Year: Application fee: $0. State resident tuition: $1770 full-time, $59 per credit hour part-time. Nonresident tuition: $2,212 full-time, $73.75 per credit hour part-time. Mandatory fees: $315 full-time, $10.50 per credit hour part-time. College room and board: $4586.
Collegiate Environment: Orientation program. Drama-theater group, choral group, student-run newspaper, radio station. Social organizations: 42 open to all. Most popular organizations: Phi Theta Kappa, Campus Crusade for Christ, Diversified Ag Club, Electricians Club, Utility Line Club. Major annual events: Welcome Back Breakfast, Extreme Bowling Hypnotist, Fall Student/Staff Picnic. Student services: personal-psychological counseling. Campus security: 24-hour patrols, controlled dormitory access. 204 college housing spaces available; all were occupied in 2003-04. No special consideration for freshman housing applicants. Option: coed housing available. Resource Center plus 1 other with 28,000 books, 3,025 serials, 1,298 audiovisual materials, an OPAC, and a Web page. Operations spending for 2004 fiscal year: $200,000. 300 computers available on campus for general student use. A campuswide network can be accessed. Staffed computer lab on campus.
Community Environment: See Nebraska Christian College.

■ PERU STATE COLLEGE
PO Box 10
Peru, NE 68421
Tel: (402)872-3815
Admissions: (402)872-2221
E-mail: mwillis@oakmail.peru.edu
Web Site: http://www.peru.edu/
Description: State-supported, comprehensive, coed. Part of Nebraska State College System. Awards bachelor's and master's degrees. Founded 1867. Setting: 104-acre rural campus. Total enrollment: 1,959. Faculty: 130 (40 full-time, 90 part-time). Student-undergrad faculty ratio is 20:1. 740 applied, 29% were admitted. 10% from top 10% of their high school class, 20% from top quarter, 45% from top half. Full-time: 1,017 students, 56% women, 44% men. Part-time: 693 students, 52% women, 48% men. Students come from 27 states and territories, 7 other countries, 12% from out-of-state, 1% Native American, 2% Hispanic, 4% black, 1% Asian American or Pacific Islander, 0.2% international, 32% 25 or older, 12% transferred in. Retention: 65% of full-time freshmen returned the following year. Academic areas with the most degrees conferred: education; business/marketing; engineering technologies. Core. Calendar: semesters. Academic remediation for entering students, services for LD students, advanced placement, accelerated degree program, freshman honors college, honors program, distance learning, double major, summer session for credit, part-time degree program, external degree program, adult/continuing education programs, co-op programs and internships, graduate courses open to undergrads. Off campus study. ROTC: Army (c), Air Force (c).
Entrance Requirements: Open admission. Options: Peterson's Universal Application, Common Application, early admission, deferred admission. Required: high school transcript. Required for some: minimum 2.0 high school GPA, SAT or ACT. Entrance: noncompetitive. Application deadline: Rolling. Notification: continuous.
Costs Per Year: Application fee: $0. Area resident tuition: $97.75 per credit hour part-time. State resident tuition: $2933 full-time, $195.50 per credit hour part-time. Nonresident tuition: $5865 full-time. Mandatory fees: $706 full-time. Part-time tuition varies according to course load, location, and reciprocity agreements. College room and board: $4486. Room and board charges vary according to board plan and housing facility.
Collegiate Environment: Orientation program. Choral group, student-run newspaper. Social organizations: 13 open to all. Most popular organizations:

Peru Chorus, Campus Activities Board, marching band, student government, Peru Players. Major annual events: homecoming, Spring Fling. Student services: health clinic, personal-psychological counseling. Campus security: 24-hour patrols. 365 undergraduates lived in college housing during 2003-04. On-campus residence required through sophomore year. Options: coed, men-only, women-only housing available. Peru State College Library with 177,373 books, 450,631 microform titles, 232 serials, and a Web page. 120 computers available on campus for general student use. A campuswide network can be accessed from student residence rooms. Staffed computer lab on campus.

Community Environment: Peru is situated in an agricultural region of southeast Nebraska on bluffs overlooking the Missouri River. Corn, wheat, apples, and many other crops are raised in the area. The town is 65 miles from Omaha and 75 miles from Lincoln.

■ **SOUTHEAST COMMUNITY COLLEGE, BEATRICE CAMPUS** *I-15*
4771 W. Scott Rd.
Beatrice, NE 68310-7042
Tel: (402)228-3468
Free: 800-233-5027
Fax: (402)228-2218
Web Site: http://www.southeast.edu/

Description: District-supported, 2-year, coed. Part of Southeast Community College System. Awards certificates, diplomas, transfer associate, and terminal associate degrees. Founded 1976. Setting: 640-acre small town campus. Total enrollment: 1,220. Students come from 9 states and territories, 7 other countries, 3% from out-of-state, 40% 25 or older, 22% live on campus. Core. Calendar: semesters. Academic remediation for entering students, services for LD students, advanced placement, distance learning, summer session for credit, part-time degree program, adult/continuing education programs, co-op programs and internships. Off campus study at Peru State College.

Entrance Requirements: Open admission. Options: Common Application, electronic application, early admission, deferred admission. Required: high school transcript. Recommended: minimum 2.0 high school GPA, SAT or ACT, ACT ASSET, ACT COMPASS. Required for some: ACT ASSET, ACT COMPASS. Entrance: noncompetitive. Application deadline: Rolling.

Collegiate Environment: Orientation program. Drama-theater group, choral group, student-run newspaper, radio station. Social organizations: 12 open to all. Most popular organizations: Student Senate, Agricultural Club, Residence Hall Association, Licensed Practical Association of Nebraska, International Student Association. Major annual events: homecoming, All Campus Spaghetti Feed, Bowling Night. Student services: personal-psychological counseling. Campus security: controlled dormitory access, evening security. 250 college housing spaces available; 230 were occupied in 2003-04. Option: coed housing available. Learning Resource Center with 13,287 books, 40,762 microform titles, 225 serials, 1,681 audiovisual materials, and an OPAC. Operations spending for 2004 fiscal year: $53,639. 75 computers available on campus for general student use. Staffed computer lab on campus.

■ **SOUTHEAST COMMUNITY COLLEGE, LINCOLN CAMPUS** *G-15*
8800 O St.
Lincoln, NE 68520-1299
Tel: (402)471-3333
Free: 800-642-4075
Admissions: (402)437-2619
Web Site: http://www.southeast.edu/

Description: District-supported, 2-year, coed. Part of Southeast Community College System. Awards certificates, diplomas, transfer associate, and terminal associate degrees. Founded 1973. Setting: 115-acre suburban campus with easy access to Omaha. Educational spending for 2005 fiscal year: $3115 per student. Total enrollment: 7,917. Full-time: 4,095 students, 55% women, 45% men. Part-time: 3,822 students, 60% women, 40% men. Students come from 23 states and territories, 4% from out-of-state, 0.5% Native American, 3% Hispanic, 3% black, 2% Asian American or Pacific Islander, 0.1% international, 35% 25 or older. Core. Academic remediation for entering students, ESL program, services for LD students, advanced placement, independent study, distance learning, summer session for credit, part-time degree program, adult/continuing education programs, co-op programs and internships. Off campus study at University of Nebraska-Lincoln.

Entrance Requirements: Open admission. Options: electronic application, early admission, deferred admission. Required: high school transcript. Placement: SAT or ACT recommended. Entrance: noncompetitive. Application deadline: Rolling.

Costs Per Year: Application fee: $0. State resident tuition: $1755 full-time, $39 per quarter hour part-time. Nonresident tuition: $2138 full-time, $47.50 per quarter hour part-time. Mandatory fees: $45 full-time, $1 per quarter hour part-time. Full-time tuition and fees vary according to course load. Part-time tuition and fees vary according to course load.

Collegiate Environment: Orientation program. Social organizations: 5 open to all. Most popular organizations: Student Senate, Phi Theta Kappa, Multicultural Student Organization, Single Parents Club, Vocational Industrial Clubs of America. Major annual event: open house. Student services: personal-psychological counseling. Campus security: late night transport-escort service. College housing not available. Lincoln Campus Learning Resource Center with 14,081 books, 375 serials, and an OPAC. Operations spending for 2004 fiscal year: $392,525. 380 computers available on campus for general student use. A campuswide network can be accessed. Staffed computer lab on campus.

■ **SOUTHEAST COMMUNITY COLLEGE, MILFORD CAMPUS** *G-14*
600 State St.
Milford, NE 68405-8498
Tel: (402)761-2131
Free: 800-933-7223
Web Site: http://www.southeast.edu/

Description: District-supported, 2-year, coed. Part of Southeast Community College System. Awards diplomas and terminal associate degrees. Founded 1941. Setting: 50-acre small town campus with easy access to Omaha. Total enrollment: 922. Full-time: 890 students, 6% women, 94% men. Part-time: 32 students, 3% women, 97% men. 1% Native American, 1% Hispanic, 0.4% Asian American or Pacific Islander, 20% 25 or older, 33% live on campus. Academic remediation for entering students, services for LD students, distance learning, co-op programs and internships.

Entrance Requirements: Open admission. Option: Common Application. Required: high school transcript. Recommended: SAT, ACT. Entrance: noncompetitive. Application deadline: Rolling. Notification: continuous.

Collegiate Environment: Major annual events: Convocation, dances, Orientation. Campus security: 24-hour patrols, late night transport-escort service. 330 college housing spaces available; 310 were occupied in 2003-04. No special consideration for freshman housing applicants. Options: men-only, women-only housing available. Milford Campus Learning Resource Center with 10,000 books and 300 serials. 72 computers available on campus for general student use. Staffed computer lab on campus.

■ **UNION COLLEGE** *G-15*
3800 South 48th St.
Lincoln, NE 68506-4300
Tel: (402)486-2600
Free: 800-228-4600
Admissions: (402)486-2504
Fax: (402)486-2895
E-mail: ucenroll@ucollege.edu
Web Site: http://www.ucollege.edu/

Description: Independent Seventh-day Adventist, comprehensive, coed. Awards associate, bachelor's, and master's degrees. Founded 1891. Setting: 26-acre suburban campus with easy access to Omaha. Endowment: $8.2 million. Educational spending for 2005 fiscal year: $5881 per student. Total enrollment: 930. Faculty: 98 (57 full-time, 41 part-time). Student-undergrad faculty ratio is 13:1. 635 applied, 43% were admitted. 14% from top 10% of their high school class, 17% from top quarter, 57% from top half. Full-time: 757 students, 55% women, 45% men. Part-time: 128 students, 54% women, 46% men. Students come from 42 states and territories, 29 other countries, 89% from out-of-state, 1% Native American, 6% Hispanic, 2% black, 2% Asian American or Pacific Islander, 10% international, 14% 25 or older, 13% live on campus, 9% transferred in. Retention: 72% of full-time freshmen returned the following year. Academic areas with the most degrees conferred: health professions and related sciences; business/marketing; education. Core. Calendar: semesters. ESL program, services for LD students, advanced placement, accelerated degree program, self-designed majors, honors program, independent study, double major, summer session for credit, part-time degree program, adult/continuing education programs, co-op programs and internships. Off campus study at University of Nebraska, Southeast Community College. Study abroad program.

Entrance Requirements: Options: Peterson's Universal Application, Common Application, electronic application. Required: high school transcript, minimum 2.5 high school GPA, 3 recommendations, ACT. Required for some: essay, interview. Entrance: moderately difficult. Application deadline: Rolling. Notification: continuous.

Costs Per Year: Application fee: $0. Comprehensive fee: $19,448 includes full-time tuition ($14,790), mandatory fees ($440), and college room and board ($4218). College room only: $2898. Part-time tuition: $625 per semester hour.

Collegiate Environment: Orientation program. Drama-theater group, choral group, student-run newspaper. Student services: health clinic, personal-psychological counseling. Campus security: 24-hour emergency response devices, student patrols, late night transport-escort service. 547 undergraduates lived in college housing during 2003-04. Freshmen guaranteed college housing. On-campus residence required through sophomore year. Options: men-only, women-only housing available. Ella Johnson Crandall Library with 147,813 books, 1,026 microform titles, 1,357 serials, 3,278 audiovisual materials, an OPAC, and a Web page. Operations spending for 2004 fiscal year: $471,957. 520 computers available on campus for general student use. Computer purchase/lease plans available. A campuswide network can be accessed from student residence rooms and from off campus. Staffed computer lab on campus.

■ **UNIVERSITY OF NEBRASKA AT KEARNEY** *H-10*
905 West 25th St.
Kearney, NE 68849-0001
Tel: (308)865-8441
Free: 800-532-7639
Admissions: (308)865-8702
Fax: (308)865-8987
E-mail: admissionsug@plattc.unk.edu
Web Site: http://www.unk.edu/

Description: State-supported, comprehensive, coed. Part of University of Nebraska System. Awards bachelor's and master's degrees and post-master's certificates. Founded 1903. Setting: 235-acre small town campus. Research spending for 2004 fiscal year: $494,232. Educational spending for 2005 fiscal year: $4179 per student. Total enrollment: 6,445. Faculty: 380 (306 full-time, 74 part-time). Student-undergrad faculty ratio is 17:1. 2,443 applied, 84% were admitted. 13% from top 10% of their high school class, 37% from top quarter, 72% from top half. Full-time: 4,895 students, 54% women, 46% men. Part-time: 486 students, 58% women, 42% men. Students come from 38 states and territories, 46 other countries, 6% from out-of-state, 0.3% Native American, 3% Hispanic, 1% black, 1% Asian American or Pacific Islander, 7% international, 11% 25 or older, 33% live on campus, 6% transferred in. Retention: 84% of full-time freshmen returned the following year. Academic areas with the most degrees conferred: business/marketing; education; communications/journalism; English; security and protective services. Core. Calendar: semesters. Academic remediation for entering students, ESL program, services for LD students, advanced placement, honors program, independent study, distance learning, double major, summer session for credit, part-time degree program, co-op programs and internships, graduate courses open to undergrads. Off campus study at National Student Exchange. Study abroad program.

Entrance Requirements: Option: electronic application. Required: high school transcript, SAT and SAT Subject Tests or ACT. Required for some: 3 recommendations. Entrance: moderately difficult. Application deadline: Rolling. Notification: continuous.

Costs Per Year: Application fee: $45. State resident tuition: $3668 full-time, $122.25 per hour part-time. Nonresident tuition: $7508 full-time, $250.25 per hour part-time. Mandatory fees: $825 full-time, $16.25 per hour part-time. Full-time tuition and fees vary according to course load and degree level. Part-time tuition and fees vary according to course load and degree level. College room and board: $5326. Room and board charges vary according to board plan and housing facility.

Collegiate Environment: Orientation program. Drama-theater group, choral group, marching band, student-run newspaper, radio station. Social organizations: 153 open to all; national fraternities, national sororities; 9% of eligible men and 9% of eligible women are members. Most popular organizations: Student Activities Council, Intramurals Council, Residence Hall Association, International Student Association. Major annual events: Midwest Conference on World Affairs, Homecoming, Blue and Gold Welcome Week. Student services: health clinic, personal-psychological counseling. Campus security: 24-hour emergency response devices and patrols, late night transport-escort service. 2,313 college housing spaces available; 1,965 were

occupied in 2003-04. On-campus residence required in freshman year. Options: coed, men-only, women-only housing available. Calvin T. Ryan Library with 320,915 books, 1 million microform titles, 1,657 serials, 75,881 audiovisual materials, an OPAC, and a Web page. 277 computers available on campus for general student use. A campuswide network can be accessed from student residence rooms and from off campus. Staffed computer lab on campus.

■ **UNIVERSITY OF NEBRASKA-LINCOLN** *G-15*
14th and R Sts.
Lincoln, NE 68588
Tel: (402)472-7211
Free: 800-742-8800
Admissions: (402)472-2030
Fax: (402)472-0670
E-mail: admissions@unc.edu
Web Site: http://www.unl.edu/

Description: State-supported, university, coed. Part of University of Nebraska System. Awards associate, bachelor's, master's, doctoral, and first professional degrees and post-master's certificates. Founded 1869. Setting: 623-acre urban campus with easy access to Omaha. Endowment: $179.8 million. Research spending for 2004 fiscal year: $116.5 million. Educational spending for 2005 fiscal year: $7691 per student. Total enrollment: 21,675. Faculty: 1,058 (1,048 full-time, 10 part-time). Student-undergrad faculty ratio is 19:1. 7,474 applied, 75% were admitted. 27% from top 10% of their high school class, 54% from top quarter, 84% from top half. 65 National Merit Scholars. Full-time: 15,768 students, 47% women, 53% men. Part-time: 1,269 students, 42% women, 58% men. Students come from 52 states and territories, 110 other countries, 20% from out-of-state, 1% Native American, 3% Hispanic, 2% black, 3% Asian American or Pacific Islander, 3% international, 8% 25 or older, 24% live on campus, 5% transferred in. Retention: 84% of full-time freshmen returned the following year. Academic areas with the most degrees conferred: business/marketing; education; engineering. Core. Calendar: semesters. ESL program, services for LD students, advanced placement, accelerated degree program, self-designed majors, honors program, independent study, distance learning, double major, summer session for credit, part-time degree program, adult/continuing education programs, co-op programs and internships, graduate courses open to undergrads. Off campus study at University of Missouri, Kansas State University, University of South Dakota. Study abroad program. ROTC: Army, Naval, Air Force.

Entrance Requirements: Options: electronic application, international baccalaureate accepted. Required: high school transcript, SAT and SAT Subject Tests or ACT. Recommended: ACT. Required for some: rank in upper 50% of high school class. Entrance: moderately difficult. Application deadline: 5/1. Notification: continuous.

Costs Per Year: Application fee: $45. State resident tuition: $4530 full-time, $151 per credit hour part-time. Nonresident tuition: $13,440 full-time, $448 per credit hour part-time. Mandatory fees: $1010 full-time, $8.50 per credit hour part-time, $202.10 per term part-time. Full-time tuition and fees vary according to course load. Part-time tuition and fees vary according to course load. College room and board: $6008. College room only: $3239. Room and board charges vary according to board plan and housing facility.

Collegiate Environment: Orientation program. Drama-theater group, choral group, marching band, student-run newspaper, radio station. Social organizations: 335 open to all; national fraternities, national sororities, local fraternities, local sororities; 14% of eligible men and 18% of eligible women are members. Most popular organizations: Student Alumni Association, University Ambassadors, University Program Council, Golden Key. Major annual events: homecoming, Big Red Welcome, UPC Lecture Series. Student services: legal services, health clinic, personal-psychological counseling, women's center. Campus security: 24-hour emergency response devices and patrols, student patrols, late night transport-escort service, controlled dormitory access. 5,558 college housing spaces available; 4,115 were occupied in 2003-04. Freshmen guaranteed college housing. On-campus residence required in freshman year. Options: coed, men-only, women-only housing available. Love Memorial Library plus 10 others with 3.3 million books, 4.6 million microform titles, 22,774 serials, 303,120 audiovisual materials, an OPAC, and a Web page. Operations spending for 2004 fiscal year: $13.4 million. 600 computers available on campus for general student use. Computer purchase/lease plans available. A campuswide network can be accessed from student residence rooms and from off campus. Staffed computer lab on campus.

Community Environment: UNL is located in the capital city of Lincoln, a community of more than 209,000 that combines a college-town atmosphere with the entertainment and nightlife of a larger city. Lincoln boasts a thriving arts community with dozens of art galleries and the Lied Center for Performing Arts, which hosts major productions such as Les Miserables, Cats, and performances by the Russian Ballet, Celine Dion, and cellist Yo-yo Ma. Lincoln has more parks per capita than any other U.S. city and a growing network of bike paths that extend far beyond the city limits. There are 16 golf courses, hundreds of restaurants, more than 30 movie screens, major shopping malls, and a restored downtown historic district complete with specialty shops, coffeehouses, and a dinner theater. Major metropolitan cities like Omaha, Kansas City, Chicago, and Denver are within a day's driving distance, and Lincoln is easily accessible by plane, train, and bus.

■ UNIVERSITY OF NEBRASKA MEDICAL CENTER *F-16*

Nebraska Medical Center
Omaha, NE 68198
Tel: (402)559-4000
Free: 800-626-8431
Admissions: (402)559-6409
Fax: (402)559-6796
Web Site: http://www.unmc.edu/

Description: State-supported, upper-level, coed. Part of University of Nebraska System. Awards bachelor's, master's, doctoral, and first professional degrees and post-master's and first professional certificates. Founded 1869. Setting: 51-acre urban campus. Endowment: $7.7 million. Research spending for 2004 fiscal year: $73.8 million. Educational spending for 2005 fiscal year: $37,932 per student. Total enrollment: 2,995. Faculty: 1,007 (783 full-time, 224 part-time). Full-time: 779 students, 90% women, 10% men. Part-time: 72 students, 93% women, 7% men. Students come from 15 states and territories, 6 other countries, 9% from out-of-state, 0.5% Native American, 2% Hispanic, 1% black, 1% Asian American or Pacific Islander, 1% international, 30% 25 or older, 25% transferred in. Academic area with the most degrees conferred: health professions and related sciences. Calendar: semesters. Services for LD students, accelerated degree program, honors program, distance learning, summer session for credit, part-time degree program, internships, graduate courses open to undergrads. Off campus study at University of Nebraska-Lincoln, University of Nebraska at Omaha, University of Nebraska at Kearney. ROTC: Army (c), Air Force (c).

Costs Per Year: Application fee: $45. State resident tuition: $6685 full-time, $191 per credit hour part-time. Nonresident tuition: $16,591 full-time, $559.75 per credit hour part-time. Mandatory fees: $733 full-time. Full-time tuition and fees vary according to course level, course load, and program. Part-time tuition varies according to program.

Collegiate Environment: Orientation program. Social organizations: 5 open to all; national fraternities, national sororities. Most popular organizations: student government, Toastmasters, Student Alliance for Global Health, Christian Medical Society, Student Research Group. Major annual event: Spring Dance. Student services: health clinic, personal-psychological counseling. Campus security: 24-hour emergency response devices and patrols, late night transport-escort service. College housing not available. McGoogan Medical Library with 241,551 books, 9 microform titles, 4,280 serials, 2,908 audiovisual materials, an OPAC, and a Web page. Operations spending for 2004 fiscal year: $3.2 million. 65 computers available on campus for general student use. A campuswide network can be accessed from student residence rooms and from off campus. Staffed computer lab on campus.

Community Environment: See Creighton University.

■ UNIVERSITY OF NEBRASKA AT OMAHA *F-16*

6001 Dodge St.
Omaha, NE 68182
Tel: (402)554-2200
Admissions: (402)554-2416
Fax: (402)554-3472
E-mail: jadams@mail.unomaha.edu
Web Site: http://www.unomaha.edu/

Description: State-supported, university, coed. Part of University of Nebraska System. Awards bachelor's, master's, and doctoral degrees and post-master's certificates. Founded 1908. Setting: 158-acre urban campus. Endowment: $180 million. Research spending for 2004 fiscal year: $14 million. Educational spending for 2005 fiscal year: $5613 per student. Total enrollment: 14,093. Faculty: 842 (482 full-time, 360 part-time). Student-undergrad faculty ratio is 18:1. 3,732 applied, 89% were admitted. 13% from top 10% of their high school class, 35% from top quarter, 68% from top half.

Full-time: 8,532 students, 53% women, 47% men. Part-time: 2,797 students, 54% women, 46% men. Students come from 32 states and territories, 68 other countries, 7% from out-of-state, 0.5% Native American, 3% Hispanic, 6% black, 3% Asian American or Pacific Islander, 2% international, 21% 25 or older, 9% live on campus, 9% transferred in. Retention: 75% of full-time freshmen returned the following year. Academic areas with the most degrees conferred: business/marketing; education; security and protective services. Core. Calendar: semesters. ESL program, services for LD students, advanced placement, self-designed majors, honors program, distance learning, double major, summer session for credit, part-time degree program, adult/continuing education programs, co-op programs and internships, graduate courses open to undergrads. Off campus study at other units of the University of Nebraska System. Study abroad program. ROTC: Army (c), Air Force.

Entrance Requirements: Option: deferred admission. Required: high school transcript, minimum ACT score of 20 or rank in upper 50% of high school class, SAT or ACT. Placement: SAT or ACT required for some. Entrance: minimally difficult. Application deadlines: 8/1, 8/1 for nonresidents. Notification: continuous, continuous for nonresidents.

Costs Per Year: Application fee: $45. State resident tuition: $4133 full-time, $137.75 per semester hour part-time. Nonresident tuition: $12,180 full-time, $406 per semester hour part-time. Mandatory fees: $692 full-time, $19.55 per semester hour part-time, $81.50 per term part-time. Full-time tuition and fees vary according to course load and student level. Part-time tuition and fees vary according to course load and student level. College room and board: $6140. College room only: $3690. Room and board charges vary according to board plan.

Collegiate Environment: Orientation program. Drama-theater group, choral group, marching band, student-run newspaper, radio station. Social organizations: 126 open to all; national fraternities, national sororities; 2% of eligible men and 2% of eligible women are members. Most popular organization: Student Programming Organization. Major annual events: Homecoming, Magical Dinner, Welcome Back Week. Student services: legal services, health clinic, personal-psychological counseling, women's center. Campus security: 24-hour emergency response devices and patrols, late night transport-escort service, controlled dormitory access. 1,212 college housing spaces available; 927 were occupied in 2003-04. No special consideration for freshman housing applicants. Option: coed housing available. University Library with 700,000 books, 2 million microform titles, 3,000 serials, 7,000 audiovisual materials, an OPAC, and a Web page. Operations spending for 2004 fiscal year: $4.8 million. 2,000 computers available on campus for general student use. A campuswide network can be accessed from student residence rooms and from off campus. Staffed computer lab on campus.

■ VATTEROTT COLLEGE (OMAHA) *F-16*

225 North 80th St.
Omaha, NE 68114
Tel: (402)392-1300
Fax: (402)392-2828
Web Site: http://www.vatterott-college.edu/

Description: Proprietary, 2-year, coed. Awards diplomas and transfer associate degrees. Founded 1967. Setting: 1-acre urban campus. Total enrollment: 414. 230 applied, 81% were admitted. 10% from top 10% of their high school class, 40% from top quarter, 50% from top half. Students come from 5 states and territories, 12% from out-of-state, 1% Native American, 4% Hispanic, 29% black, 0.2% Asian American or Pacific Islander, 58% 25 or older. Calendar: semesters. Summer session for credit, internships.

Entrance Requirements: Options: early admission, deferred admission. Required: high school transcript, Wonderlic aptitude test. Recommended: SAT or ACT. Entrance: moderately difficult. Application deadline: Rolling. Notification: continuous.

Collegiate Environment: Orientation program. Campus security: 24-hour emergency response devices. Main library plus 1 other with 1,900 books, 22 serials, and an OPAC. 50 computers available on campus for general student use. Staffed computer lab on campus.

■ VATTEROTT COLLEGE (OMAHA-SPRING VALLEY)

11818 I St.
Omaha, NE 68137
Tel: (402)891-9411
Fax: (402)891-9413
Web Site: http://www.vatterott-college.edu/

Description: Proprietary, 2-year, coed. Calendar: semesters.

■ WAYNE STATE COLLEGE *D-14*

1111 Main St.
Wayne, NE 68787
Tel: (402)375-7000
Admissions: (402)375-7234
Fax: (402)375-7204
E-mail: admit1@wsc.edu
Web Site: http://www.wsc.edu/

Description: State-supported, comprehensive, coed. Part of Nebraska State College System. Awards bachelor's and master's degrees and post-master's certificates. Founded 1910. Setting: 128-acre small town campus. Endowment: $8.7 million. Total enrollment: 3,322. Faculty: 205 (126 full-time, 79 part-time). Student-undergrad faculty ratio is 18:1. 1,202 applied, 100% were admitted. 13% from top 10% of their high school class, 33% from top quarter, 64% from top half. Full-time: 2,483 students, 55% women, 45% men. Part-time: 223 students, 68% women, 32% men. Students come from 28 states and territories, 13 other countries, 14% from out-of-state, 1% Native American, 2% Hispanic, 3% black, 1% Asian American or Pacific Islander, 1% international, 12% 25 or older, 42% live on campus, 9% transferred in. Retention: 67% of full-time freshmen returned the following year. Academic areas with the most degrees conferred: business/marketing; education; psychology. Core. Calendar: semesters. Services for LD students, self-designed majors, honors program, independent study, distance learning, double major, summer session for credit, part-time degree program, adult/continuing education programs, co-op programs and internships, graduate courses open to undergrads. Off campus study at Northeast Community College, Central Community College. ROTC: Army (c).

Entrance Requirements: Open admission. Options: Peterson's Universal Application, electronic application, deferred admission. Required: high school transcript. Entrance: noncompetitive. Application deadline: Rolling. Notification: continuous.

Costs Per Year: Application fee: $30. State resident tuition: $2933 full-time, $97.75 per credit hour part-time. Nonresident tuition: $5865 full-time, $195.50 per credit hour part-time. Mandatory fees: $870 full-time, $34.75 per credit hour part-time. Full-time tuition and fees vary according to course level and course load. Part-time tuition and fees vary according to course level and course load. College room and board: $4300. College room only: $2080. Room and board charges vary according to board plan and housing facility.

Collegiate Environment: Orientation program. Drama-theater group, choral group, marching band, student-run newspaper, radio station. Social organizations: 92 open to all; national fraternities, national sororities. Student services: health clinic, personal-psychological counseling. Campus security: 24-hour patrols, student patrols, late night transport-escort service, controlled dormitory access. 1,587 college housing spaces available; 1,170 were occupied in 2003-04. Freshmen guaranteed college housing. On-campus residence required in freshman year. Options: coed, women-only housing available. U. S. Conn Library plus 1 other with 147,205 books, 650,000 microform titles, 656 serials, 5,300 audiovisual materials, an OPAC, and a Web page. 365 computers available on campus for general student use. A campuswide network can be accessed from student residence rooms and from off campus. Staffed computer lab on campus.

Community Environment: Located 45 miles southwest of Sioux City, Iowa, Wayne is the county seat. Bus transportation and chartered air service are available. Dormitories, motels, and rooming houses provide housing for students. Community facilities include churches of most denominations and a hospital. Hunting, swimming and golf are some of the outdoor activities available.

■ WESTERN NEBRASKA COMMUNITY COLLEGE *F-3*

371 College Dr.
Sidney, NE 69162
Tel: (308)254-5450
Free: 800-348-4435
Admissions: (308)635-6015
Fax: (308)254-7444
E-mail: rhovey@wncc.net
Web Site: http://www.wncc.net/

Description: State and locally supported, 2-year, coed. Part of Western Community College Area System. Awards certificates, diplomas, transfer associate, and terminal associate degrees. Founded 1926. Setting: 20-acre rural campus. Research spending for 2004 fiscal year: $35,512. Educational spending for 2005 fiscal year: $3881 per student. Total enrollment: 3,151. 613 applied, 100% were admitted. 10% from top 10% of their high school class, 18% from top quarter, 50% from top half. Students come from 18 states and territories, 10% from out-of-state, 43% 25 or older, 5% live on campus. Core. Calendar: semesters. Academic remediation for entering students, services for LD students, advanced placement, accelerated degree program, independent study, distance learning, summer session for credit, part-time degree program, adult/continuing education programs, co-op programs and internships.

Entrance Requirements: Open admission. Options: Common Application, electronic application. Recommended: high school transcript. Placement: ACT ASSET required. Entrance: noncompetitive. Application deadline: Rolling. Notification: continuous until 8/21.

Collegiate Environment: Orientation program. Drama-theater group, choral group, student-run newspaper. Social organizations: 6 open to all; national sororities; 2% of women are members. Most popular organizations: Choices, Phi Theta Kappa, student government, SEAN. Student services: personal-psychological counseling. Campus security: 24-hour emergency response devices and patrols, late night transport-escort service, controlled dormitory access, patrols by trained security personnel from 12:30 a.m. to 6 a.m. 100 college housing spaces available; all were occupied in 2003-04. Option: coed housing available. Western Nebraska Community College Library with 34,539 books, 19 microform titles, 2,631 serials, 2,631 audiovisual materials, and an OPAC. Operations spending for 2004 fiscal year: $373,391. 355 computers available on campus for general student use. A campuswide network can be accessed from off-campus. Staffed computer lab on campus.

Community Environment: In the valley of the North Platte River, Scottsbluff is an agriculture center. It is also called the Capital of America's Valley of the Nile. This is the location of the largest continuous area of irrigated land in the country. Recreational activities include hunting, fishing, golf, swimming and winter sports nearby.

■ YORK COLLEGE *G-13*

1125 East 8th St.
York, NE 68467
Tel: (402)363-5600
Free: 800-950-9675
Admissions: (402)363-5608
Fax: (402)363-5666
E-mail: tjmartin@york.edu
Web Site: http://www.york.edu/

Description: Independent, 4-year, coed, affiliated with Church of Christ. Awards associate and bachelor's degrees. Founded 1890. Setting: 44-acre small town campus. Endowment: $6.3 million. Educational spending for 2005 fiscal year: $3921 per student. Total enrollment: 450. Student-undergrad faculty ratio is 10:1. 206 applied, 99% were admitted. 10% from top 10% of their high school class, 21% from top quarter, 46% from top half. Full-time: 412 students, 50% women, 50% men. Part-time: 38 students, 55% women, 45% men. Students come from 30 states and territories, 14 other countries, 66% from out-of-state, 0.2% Native American, 4% Hispanic, 5% black, 2% Asian American or Pacific Islander, 2% international, 3% 25 or older, 60% live on campus, 10% transferred in. Retention: 68% of full-time freshmen returned the following year. Academic areas with the most degrees conferred: engineering; business/marketing; biological/life sciences. Core. Calendar: semesters. Academic remediation for entering students, services for LD students, advanced placement, honors program, independent study, double major, summer session for credit, part-time degree program, external degree program, adult/continuing education programs, co-op programs and internships. Study abroad program. ROTC: Army (c), Naval (c), Air Force (c).

Entrance Requirements: Options: Peterson's Universal Application, Common Application, electronic application, early admission, deferred admission, international baccalaureate accepted. Required: high school transcript, minimum 2.0 high school GPA, 2 recommendations, SAT or ACT. Entrance: moderately difficult. Application deadline: Rolling.

Costs Per Year: Application fee: $20. Comprehensive fee: $16,330 includes full-time tuition ($11,400), mandatory fees ($1030), and college room and board ($3900). Full-time tuition and fees vary according to course load. Room and board charges vary according to board plan and housing facility. Part-time tuition: $355 per credit hour. Part-time mandatory fees: $177 per credit hour. Part-time tuition and fees vary according to course load.

Collegiate Environment: Orientation program. Drama-theater group, choral group, student-run newspaper. Social organizations: 8 open to all; local fraternities, local sororities; 46% of eligible men and 64% of eligible women are members. Most popular organizations: concert choir, Student Association, Promethians, Marksmen. Major annual events: Homecoming, Songfest, All-School Banquet. Student services: personal-psychological counseling. Campus security: 24-hour patrols, student patrols, controlled dormitory access. 472 college housing spaces available; 282 were occupied in 2003-04. Freshmen guaranteed college housing. On-campus residence required through sophomore year. Options: men-only, women-only housing available. Levitt Library with 106,994 books, 21,075 microform titles, 338 serials, 5,867 audiovisual materials, an OPAC, and a Web page. Operations spending for 2004 fiscal year: $234,848. 57 computers available on campus for general student use. A campuswide network can be accessed from student residence rooms and from off campus. Staffed computer lab on campus.

Community Environment: York is located about 50 miles from Lincoln, where all forms of commercial transportation are available. Various civic and service organizations are active here as well as churches of many denominations. Recreational facilities include parks, playgrounds, a swimming pool, baseball park, basketball courts, and a community center.

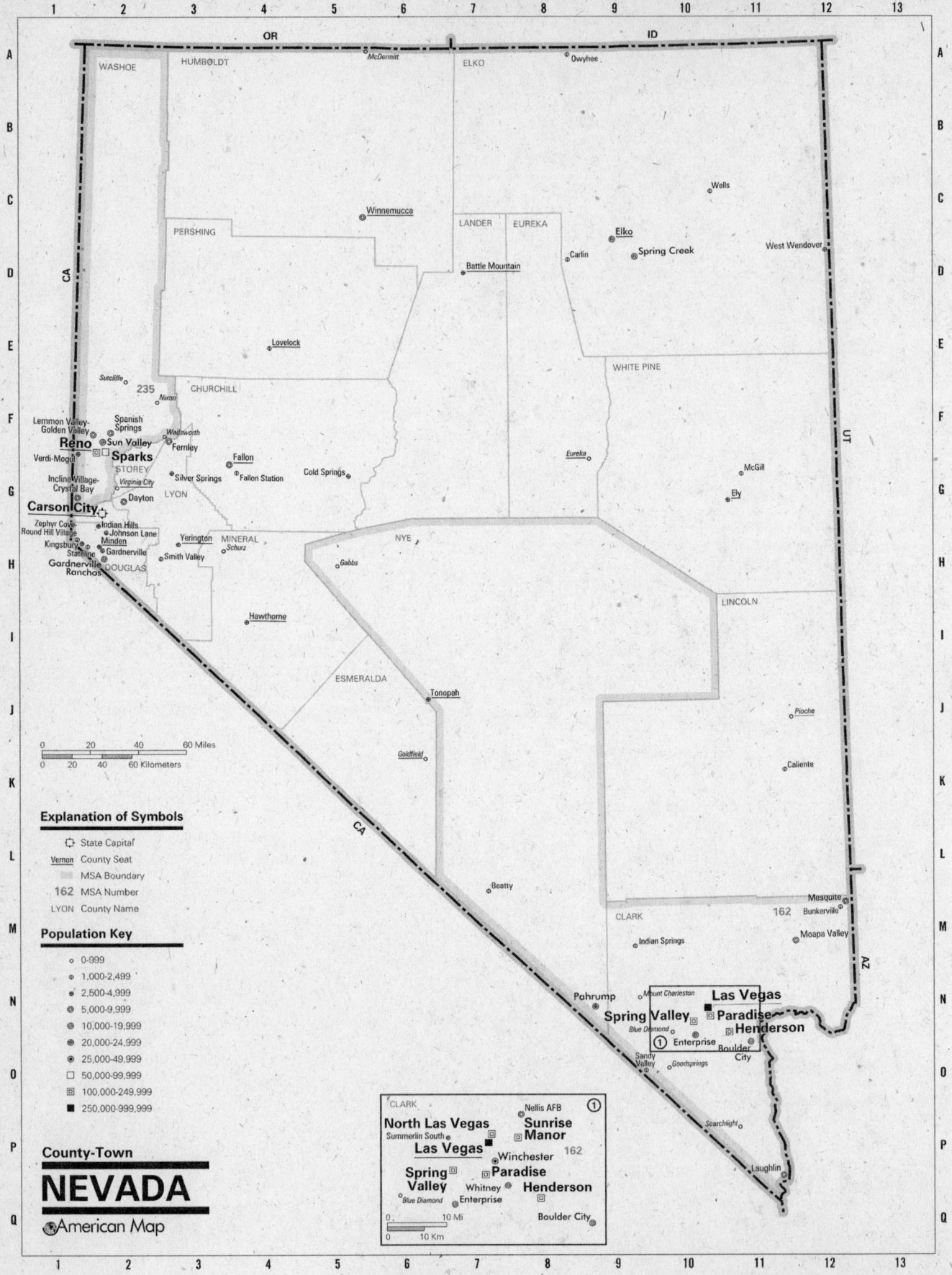

NEVADA

County-Town

Explanation of Symbols

⌖ State Capital
Vernon County Seat
MSA Boundary
162 MSA Number
LYON County Name

Population Key

- ○ 0-999
- ◔ 1,000-2,499
- ◑ 2,500-4,999
- ◕ 5,000-9,999
- ◉ 10,000-19,999
- ◉ 20,000-24,999
- ◉ 25,000-49,999
- ☐ 50,000-99,999
- ▣ 100,000-249,999
- ■ 250,000-999,999

Ⓐ American Map

■ **THE ART INSTITUTE OF LAS VEGAS** *N-11*
2350 Corporate Circle Dr.
Henderson, NV 89074
Tel: (702)369-9944
Fax: (702)992-8558
E-mail: snoel@aii.edu
Web Site: http://www.ailv.artinstitutes.edu/
Description: Proprietary, 4-year, coed. Part of Education Management Corporation. Awards associate and bachelor's degrees. Founded 2002. Educational spending for 2005 fiscal year: $1000 per student. Total enrollment: 1,046. Student-undergrad faculty ratio is 19:1. Full-time: 951 students, 46% women, 54% men. Part-time: 95 students, 49% women, 51% men. 23% from out-of-state, 2% Native American, 16% Hispanic, 8% black, 9% Asian American or Pacific Islander, 0% international, 7% live on campus. Retention: 56% of full-time freshmen returned the following year. Academic area with the most degrees conferred: visual and performing arts. Core.
Entrance Requirements: Open admission. Options: Common Application, electronic application. Required: essay, high school transcript, interview. Recommended: minimum X high school GPA, SAT and SAT Subject Tests or ACT. Entrance: moderately difficult. Application deadline: Rolling. Notification: continuous.
Costs Per Year: Application fee: $50. Tuition: $16,740 full-time, $372 per credit part-time. Mandatory fees: $1000 full-time. College room only: $4725.
Collegiate Environment: Orientation program. Student services: health clinic, personal-psychological counseling. 200 college housing spaces available; 70 were occupied in 2003-04. Options: men-only, women-only housing available.

■ **CAREER COLLEGE OF NORTHERN NEVADA** *G-2*
1195-A Corporate Blvd.
Reno, NV 89502
Tel: (775)856-2266
E-mail: lgoldhammer@ccnn4u.com
Web Site: http://www.ccnn.edu/
Description: Proprietary, 2-year, coed. Awards diplomas and terminal associate degrees. Founded 1984. Setting: 1-acre urban campus. Total enrollment: 283. Student-undergrad faculty ratio is 20:1. 419 applied, 100% were admitted. Students come from 2 states and territories, 5% from out-of-state, 6% Native American, 17% Hispanic, 8% black, 6% Asian American or Pacific Islander. Core. Calendar: six-week terms. Academic remediation for entering students, accelerated degree program, double major, summer session for credit, co-op programs and internships.
Entrance Requirements: Open admission. Required: essay, high school transcript, interview. Entrance: noncompetitive. Application deadline: Rolling. Notification: continuous.
Costs Per Year: Application fee: $25. Tuition: $175 per credit hour part-time.
Collegiate Environment: Orientation program. Student-run newspaper. Major annual events: Annual School Picnic, Christmas Party. Campus security: 24-hour emergency response devices. College housing not available. 380 books and 7 serials. Operations spending for 2004 fiscal year: $7000. 120 computers available on campus for general student use. A campuswide network can be accessed. Staffed computer lab on campus.

■ **COMMUNITY COLLEGE OF SOUTHERN NEVADA** *P-7*
3200 East Cheyenne Ave.
North Las Vegas, NV 89030-4296
Tel: (702)651-4000
Free: 800-492-5728
Admissions: (702)651-4060
Fax: (702)643-6243
E-mail: stops@ccmail.ccsn.nevada.edu
Web Site: http://www.ccsn.nevada.edu/
Description: State-supported, 2-year, coed. Part of University and Community College System of Nevada. Awards certificates and transfer associate degrees. Founded 1971. Setting: 89-acre suburban campus with easy access to Las Vegas. Endowment: $2.6 million. Research spending for 2004 fiscal year: $3287. Total enrollment: 34,204. Full-time: 7,850 students, 56% women, 44% men. Part-time: 26,354 students, 57% women, 43% men. Students come from 55 states and territories, 13 other countries, 2% from out-of-state, 60% 25 or older, 1% transferred in. Core. Calendar: semesters. Academic remediation for entering students, ESL program, services for LD students, advanced placement, accelerated degree program, honors program, independent study, distance learning, double major, summer session for credit, part-time degree program, adult/continuing education programs, co-op programs and internships. ROTC: Army.
Entrance Requirements: Open admission except for allied health programs. Option: early admission. Required: student data form. Entrance: noncompetitive. Application deadline: Rolling.
Costs Per Year: Application fee: $5. State resident tuition: $1523 full-time, $50.75 per credit part-time. Nonresident tuition: $6557 full-time, $106.75 per credit part-time. Mandatory fees: $120 full-time, $4 per credit part-time.
Collegiate Environment: Orientation program. Drama-theater group, choral group, student-run newspaper. Social organizations: 10 open to all. Most popular organizations: Culinary Club, Art Club, Black Student Association, Student Organization of Latinos, Student Nurses Club. Major annual events: Black History Week, Career Day, Cinco de Mayo. Student services: legal services, health clinic, personal-psychological counseling, women's center. Campus security: 24-hour emergency response devices and patrols. College housing not available. Learning Assistance Center with 100,000 books, 200 microform titles, 500 serials, 5,400 audiovisual materials, an OPAC, and a Web page. Operations spending for 2004 fiscal year: $1.1 million. 500 computers available on campus for general student use. A campuswide network can be accessed from off-campus. Staffed computer lab on campus.
Community Environment: See University of Nevada - Las Vegas.

■ **DEEP SPRINGS COLLEGE**
HC 72, Box 45001
Dyer, NV 89010-9803
Tel: (760)872-2000
E-mail: apcom@deepsprings.edu
Web Site: http://www.deepsprings.edu/
Description: Independent, 2-year, men only. Awards transfer associate degrees. Founded 1917. Setting: 3,000-acre rural campus in Deep Springs, CA; mailing address is in Dyer, NV. Endowment: $9 million. Educational spending for 2005 fiscal year: $43,350 per student. Total enrollment: 27. Student-undergrad faculty ratio is 3:1. 160 applied, 8% were admitted. 82% from top 10% of their high school class, 100% from top quarter. 1 class president, 1 valedictorian, 1 student government officer. Students come from 14 states and territories, 3 other countries, 85% from out-of-state, 4% international, 0% 25 or older, 100% live on campus. Retention: 87% of full-time freshmen returned the following year. Calendar: 6 seven-week terms.

Accelerated degree program, self-designed majors, freshman honors college, honors program, independent study, summer session for credit, co-op programs and internships.

Entrance Requirements: Options: Common Application, international baccalaureate accepted. Required: essay, high school transcript, recommendations, interview, SAT and SAT Subject Tests or ACT. Entrance: most difficult. Application deadline: 11/15. Notification: 4/15.

Collegiate Environment: Orientation program. Drama-theater group, choral group. Most popular organizations: Student Self-Government, Labor Program, Applications Committee, Review Committee, Curriculum Committee. Major annual events: Potato Harvest, Cattle Round-up, Thanksgiving Football Game. Student services: legal services, personal-psychological counseling. On-campus residence required through sophomore year. Option: men-only housing available. Mossner Library of Deep Springs with 20,000 books, 60 serials, an OPAC, and a Web page. Operations spending for 2004 fiscal year: $16,500. 6 computers available on campus for general student use.

■ **DEVRY UNIVERSITY** *N-11*
2490 Paseo Verde Parkway, Ste. 150
Henderson, NV 89074-7120
Tel: (702)933-9700; (866)783-3879
Fax: (702)933-9717
Web Site: http://www.devry.edu/

Description: Proprietary, comprehensive, coed. Part of DeVry University. Awards associate, bachelor's, and master's degrees. Total enrollment: 122. Faculty: 31 (all part-time). Student-undergrad faculty ratio is 7:1. Full-time: 55 students, 44% women, 56% men. Part-time: 34 students, 35% women, 65% men. 0% Native American, 17% Hispanic, 13% black, 13% Asian American or Pacific Islander, 0% international. Academic area with the most degrees conferred: business/marketing. Calendar: semesters. Academic remediation for entering students, services for LD students, advanced placement, accelerated degree program, distance learning, summer session for credit, part-time degree program, adult/continuing education programs, co-op programs.

Entrance Requirements: Options: electronic application, deferred admission, international baccalaureate accepted. Required: high school transcript, interview. Entrance: minimally difficult. Application deadline: Rolling.

Costs Per Year: Application fee: $50. One-time mandatory fee: $40. Tuition: $11,790 full-time, $440 per credit part-time. Mandatory fees: $270 full-time, $30 per year part-time.

Collegiate Environment: Orientation program. College housing not available.

■ **GREAT BASIN COLLEGE** *D-9*
1500 College Parkway
Elko, NV 89801-3348
Tel: (775)738-8493
Admissions: (775)753-2271
E-mail: bjulie@gbcnv.edu
Web Site: http://www.gbcnv.edu/

Description: State-supported, primarily 2-year, coed. Part of University and Community College System of Nevada. Awards certificates, transfer associate, terminal associate, and bachelor's degrees. Founded 1967. Setting: 45-acre small town campus. Endowment: $150,000. Total enrollment: 3,095. Student-undergrad faculty ratio is 13:1. Full-time: 853 students, 70% women, 30% men. Part-time: 2,242 students, 58% women, 42% men. 1% from out-of-state, 4% Native American, 9% Hispanic, 1% black, 1% Asian American or Pacific Islander, 0% international, 60% 25 or older. Core. Calendar: semesters. Academic remediation for entering students, ESL program, services for LD students, independent study, distance learning, summer session for credit, part-time degree program, external degree program, adult/continuing education programs, co-op programs.

Entrance Requirements: Open admission except for nursing program. Options: Common Application, electronic application, early admission, deferred admission. Required: high school transcript. Entrance: noncompetitive. Application deadline: Rolling. Notification: continuous.

Costs Per Year: Application fee: $5. State resident tuition: $1575 full-time, $52.50 per credit part-time. Nonresident tuition: $4962 full-time, $110.25 per credit part-time. College room and board: $4520. College room only: $1900.

Collegiate Environment: Orientation program. Drama-theater group, choral group. Social organizations: local sororities; 1% of women are members. Student services: personal-psychological counseling. Campus security: evening patrols by trained security personnel. 90 college housing spaces

available; all were occupied in 2003-04. Learning Resources Center with 27,521 books, 250 serials, and an OPAC. Operations spending for 2004 fiscal year: $349,787. 95 computers available on campus for general student use. A campuswide network can be accessed from off-campus. Staffed computer lab on campus.

Community Environment: Primarily involved in mining, ranching, and government business, Elko is the largest city in Elko County and is at the heart of the nation's finest hunting and fishing areas, along with such historic landmarks as old ghost towns and deserted mining camps. Located at the base of the Ruby Mountains, Elko is also near Jarbidge Wilderness area and Great Basin National Park.

■ **HERITAGE COLLEGE** *N-10*
3305 Spring Mountain Rd., Ste. 7
Las Vegas, NV 89102
Tel: (702)368-2338
Fax: (702)638-3853
Web Site: http://www.heritagecollege.com/
Description: Proprietary, 2-year.

■ **HIGH-TECH INSTITUTE** *N-10*
2320 South Rancho Dr.
Las Vegas, NV 89102
Tel: (702)385-6700
Free: 800-987-0110
Fax: (702)388-4463
E-mail: ajhollander@hightechinstitute.com
Web Site: http://www.high-techinstitute.com/
Description: Proprietary, 2-year, coed. Founded 2002. Calendar: semesters.

■ **ITT TECHNICAL INSTITUTE** *N-11*
168 Gibson Rd.
Henderson, NV 89014
Tel: (702)558-5404
Web Site: http://www.itt-tech.edu/
Description: Proprietary, primarily 2-year, coed. Part of ITT Educational Services, Inc. Awards terminal associate and bachelor's degrees. Core.

Entrance Requirements: Option: deferred admission. Required: high school transcript, interview, Wonderlic aptitude test. Recommended: recommendations. Entrance: minimally difficult. Application deadline: Rolling. Notification: continuous.

Costs Per Year: Application fee: $100.

Collegiate Environment: Orientation program. College housing not available.

■ **LAS VEGAS COLLEGE** *N-10*
4100 West Flamingo Rd., Ste. 2100
Las Vegas, NV 89103-3926
Tel: (702)368-6200
Free: 800-903-3101
Fax: (702)368-6464
Web Site: http://www.lasvegas-college.com/
Description: Proprietary, 2-year, coed. Part of Corinthian Colleges, Inc. Awards diplomas and terminal associate degrees. Founded 1979. Setting: urban campus. Total enrollment: 651. Full-time: 412 students, 86% women, 14% men. Part-time: 239 students, 84% women, 16% men. 1% Native American, 9% Hispanic, 10% black, 5% Asian American or Pacific Islander, 0% international, 64% 25 or older. Core. Independent study, double major, part-time degree program, adult/continuing education programs, co-op programs and internships.

Entrance Requirements: Open admission. Option: Common Application. Required: high school transcript, interview. Placement: CPAt required. Entrance: noncompetitive.

Collegiate Environment: Orientation program. Student-run newspaper. Social organizations: 1 open to all. Most popular organization: student association. Major annual events: Christmas baskets, student appreciation days. College housing not available. 35 computers available on campus for general student use. A campuswide network can be accessed from off-campus.

■ **LE CORDON BLEU COLLEGE OF CULINARY ARTS, LAS VEGAS** *N-10*
1451 Center Crossing Rd.
Las Vegas, NV 89144

Tel: (702)365-7690
Fax: (702)365-7911
Web Site: http://www.vegasculinary.com/
Description: Proprietary, 2-year, coed. Awards terminal associate degrees. Founded 2003.

■ **MORRISON UNIVERSITY** *G-2*
10315 Professional Circle
Reno, NV 89521
Tel: (775)850-0700
Free: 800-369-6144
Fax: (775)850-0711
E-mail: richard.farmer@morrison.edu
Web Site: http://www.morrison.neumont.edu/
Description: Proprietary, comprehensive, coed. Awards associate, bachelor's, and master's degrees. Founded 1902. Setting: 2-acre urban campus. Total enrollment: 130. 10% from top 10% of their high school class, 60% from top quarter, 90% from top half. Students come from 8 states and territories, 5 other countries, 8% Native American, 7% Hispanic, 4% black, 5% Asian American or Pacific Islander, 74% 25 or older. Retention: 73% of full-time freshmen returned the following year. Core. Calendar: 5 sessions per year. Academic remediation for entering students, ESL program, accelerated degree program, summer session for credit, part-time degree program, adult/continuing education programs, internships.
Entrance Requirements: Open admission. Options: early admission, deferred admission. Required: high school transcript, interview. Recommended: CPAt of 160 for paralegal program. Required for some: essay. Entrance: noncompetitive. Notification: continuous.
Costs Per Year: Application fee: $25. Tuition: $12,000 full-time.
Collegiate Environment: Student-run newspaper. Social organizations: 1 open to all; national fraternities, national sororities; 25% of eligible men and 35% of eligible women are members. Most popular organization: Phi Beta Lambda. Major annual events: Summer Picnic, Christmas Party, Holiday Potlucks. Student services: personal-psychological counseling. Campus security: 24-hour emergency response devices, late night transport-escort service, evening patrols by security. College housing not available. Morrison College Library with 6,000 books and 20 serials. 50 computers available on campus for general student use. A campuswide network can be accessed. Staffed computer lab on campus.

■ **NEVADA STATE COLLEGE AT HENDERSON** *N-11*
1125 Nevada State Dr.
Henderson, NV 89015
Tel: (702)992-2000
Fax: (702)992-2226
Web Site: http://www.nsc.nevada.edu/
Description: State-supported, 4-year, coed. Part of Nevada System of Higher Education. Awards bachelor's degrees. Founded 2002. Setting: 520-acre suburban campus with easy access to Las Vegas. Educational spending for 2005 fiscal year: $7197 per student. Total enrollment: 535. 603 applied, 58% were admitted. Full-time: 248 students, 75% women, 25% men. Part-time: 287 students, 70% women, 30% men. Students come from 8 states and territories, 9% from out-of-state, 55% transferred in. Retention: 52% of full-time freshmen returned the following year. Calendar: semesters.
Entrance Requirements: Required: high school transcript, minimum 2.0 high school GPA. Recommended: SAT or ACT. Application deadline: 8/20. Notification: continuous.
Collegiate Environment: Student-run newspaper. Social organizations: 6 open to all. Most popular organizations: Teachers of Principle, Nursing Club, Psychology Club, Running Team, Student Government. Student services: personal-psychological counseling. College housing not available.

■ **PIMA MEDICAL INSTITUTE** *N-10*
3333 East Flamingo Rd.
Las Vegas, NV 89121
Tel: (702)458-9650
Free: 800-477-PIMA
Web Site: http://www.pmi.edu
Description: Proprietary, 2-year, coed. Part of Vocational Training Institutes, Inc. Awards certificates and terminal associate degrees. Founded 2003. Setting: urban campus. Total enrollment: 329. 34 applied, 82% were admitted. Full-time: 329 students, 87% women, 13% men. 10% from out-of-state. Core. Calendar: modular. Advanced placement, internships.

Entrance Requirements: Required: interview, Wonderlic Scholastic Level Exam. Required for some: essay, high school transcript. Entrance: moderately difficult.
Collegiate Environment: Orientation program. College housing not available. 25 computers available on campus for general student use.

■ **SIERRA NEVADA COLLEGE**
999 Tahoe Blvd.
Incline Village, NV 89451
Tel: (775)831-1314
Admissions: (775)831-7799
Fax: (775)831-1347
E-mail: admissions@sierranevada.edu
Web Site: http://www.sierranevada.edu/
Description: Independent, comprehensive, coed. Awards bachelor's and master's degrees. Founded 1969. Setting: 20-acre small town campus with easy access to Reno. Endowment: $3.5 million. Educational spending for 2005 fiscal year: $19,500 per student. Total enrollment: 492. 383 applied, 68% were admitted. 10% from top 10% of their high school class, 35% from top quarter, 70% from top half. 1 class president, 1 valedictorian, 18 student government officers. Full-time: 302 students, 51% women, 49% men. Students come from 32 states and territories, 5 other countries, 71% from out-of-state, 1% Native American, 3% Hispanic, 1% black, 3% Asian American or Pacific Islander, 3% international, 8% 25 or older, 45% live on campus, 12% transferred in. Retention: 70% of full-time freshmen returned the following year. Core. Calendar: semesters. Academic remediation for entering students, services for LD students, advanced placement, accelerated degree program, honors program, independent study, double major, summer session for credit, part-time degree program, adult/continuing education programs, co-op programs and internships, graduate courses open to undergrads. Study abroad program. ROTC: Army (c).
Entrance Requirements: Options: Peterson's Universal Application, Common Application, electronic application, early admission, deferred admission, international baccalaureate accepted. Required: essay, high school transcript, minimum 2.0 high school GPA, SAT and SAT Subject Tests or ACT. Recommended: interview. Required for some: recommendations, school report form for high school seniors. Entrance: moderately difficult. Application deadline: Rolling. Notification: continuous.
Collegiate Environment: Orientation program. Drama-theater group, choral group, student-run newspaper. Most popular organizations: Recycling Club, Ski Club (NASIS), Enviroaction Club, Snowboard Club, Rotaract. Major annual events: Jamaica Jam, Halloween Bash, Snowfest. Student services: health clinic, personal-psychological counseling. Campus security: 24-hour emergency response devices and patrols. 176 college housing spaces available; 156 were occupied in 2003-04. Freshmen guaranteed college housing. On-campus residence required through sophomore year. Option: coed housing available. MacLean Library with 18,500 books, 175 serials, an OPAC, and a Web page. Operations spending for 2004 fiscal year: $150,000. 50 computers available on campus for general student use. A campuswide network can be accessed from student residence rooms and from off campus.

■ **TRUCKEE MEADOWS COMMUNITY COLLEGE** *G-2*
7000 Dandini Blvd.
Reno, NV 89512-3901
Tel: (775)673-7000
Admissions: (775)674-7623
Fax: (775)673-7028
E-mail: dharbeck@tmcc.edu
Web Site: http://www.tmcc.edu/
Description: State-supported, 2-year, coed. Part of University and Community College System of Nevada. Awards certificates, transfer associate, and terminal associate degrees. Founded 1971. Setting: 63-acre suburban campus. Endowment: $5.6 million. Educational spending for 2005 fiscal year: $2572 per student. Total enrollment: 9,697. Full-time: 1,963 students, 54% women, 46% men. Part-time: 7,734 students, 55% women, 45% men. Students come from 12 states and territories, 3 other countries, 2% Native American, 9% Hispanic, 2% black, 6% Asian American or Pacific Islander, 2% international, 54% 25 or older. Core. Calendar: semesters. Academic remediation for entering students, ESL program, services for LD students, advanced placement, distance learning, summer session for credit, part-time degree program, adult/continuing education programs, co-op programs and internships. ROTC: Army (c).

Entrance Requirements: Open admission except for allied health programs. Options: early admission, deferred admission. Placement: SAT or ACT recommended. Entrance: noncompetitive. Application deadline: Rolling.

Costs Per Year: Application fee: $10. State resident tuition: $0 full-time. Nonresident tuition: $4915 full-time, $55.75 per credit part-time. Mandatory fees: $1314 full-time, $54.75 per credit part-time.

Collegiate Environment: Drama-theater group, choral group, student-run newspaper. Most popular organizations: Associated Students of Truckee Meadows, Phi Theta Kappa, International Students Organization, Latino Student Organization, Asian and Pacific Islander Student Association. Major annual events: Student Welcome Back, Annual Student Blood Drive. Student services: health clinic, personal-psychological counseling. Campus security: 24-hour emergency response devices and patrols, late night transport-escort service. College housing not available. Elizabeth Storm Library plus 1 other with 42,110 books, 816 serials, an OPAC, and a Web page. Operations spending for 2004 fiscal year: $507,540.

Community Environment: Reno/Sparks, cities of approximately 240,000, are bounded on the west by the majestic Sierra Nevada, and on the east by the rolling basin and range province. The climate is cool and dry, and is marked by the full pageant of the seasons. A mixture of metropolitan and quietly provincial, the area is noted on the one hand for its fashionable hotels and tourist attractions, and on the other for its beautiful parks, which line the Truckee River, and its modern residential areas. Recreational activities abound, both in Reno and its environs. Within a one-hour drive of the campus are the Lake Tahoe resort area in the high Sierra, and the unique prehistoric desert sea, Pyramid Lake. The adjoining Sierra is also the site of a number of nationally famed ski areas, including Squaw Valley, site of the 1960 Winter Olympics. Other scenic attractions include Virginia City, setting for one of the West's richest mining bonanzas, and Genoa, the state's first pioneer settlement.

■ UNIVERSITY OF NEVADA, LAS VEGAS *N-10*

4505 Maryland Parkway
Las Vegas, NV 89154-9900
Tel: (702)895-3011
Admissions: (702)895-5292
Fax: (702)895-1118
E-mail: stephanie.brown@unlv.edu
Web Site: http://www.unlv.edu/

Description: State-supported, university, coed. Part of University and Community College System of Nevada. Awards bachelor's, master's, doctoral, and first professional degrees and post-master's certificates. Founded 1957. Setting: 335-acre urban campus. Endowment: $108.5 million. Research spending for 2004 fiscal year: $73.4 million. Educational spending for 2005 fiscal year: $5556 per student. Total enrollment: 27,344. Faculty: 1,542 (810 full-time, 732 part-time). Student-undergrad faculty ratio is 20:1. 6,952 applied, 81% were admitted. 18% from top 10% of their high school class, 45% from top quarter, 79% from top half. 7 National Merit Scholars, 37 valedictorians. Full-time: 15,570 students, 56% women, 44% men. Part-time: 6,213 students, 55% women, 45% men. Students come from 51 states and territories, 65 other countries, 21% from out-of-state, 1% Native American, 11% Hispanic, 8% black, 14% Asian American or Pacific Islander, 4% international, 26% 25 or older, 4% live on campus, 13% transferred in. Retention: 72% of full-time freshmen returned the following year. Academic areas with the most degrees conferred: business/marketing; education; communications/journalism. Core. Calendar: semesters. Academic remediation for entering students, ESL program, services for LD students, advanced placement, accelerated degree program, self-designed majors, honors program, independent study, distance learning, double major, summer session for credit, part-time degree program, adult/continuing education programs, co-op programs and internships, graduate courses open to undergrads. Off campus study at National Student Exchange, Western Interstate Commission for Higher Education, Western Undergraduate Exchange. Study abroad program.

Entrance Requirements: Options: deferred admission, international baccalaureate accepted. Required: high school transcript, minimum 2.5 high school GPA. Recommended: SAT or ACT. Required for some: 2 recommendations, SAT or ACT. Entrance: moderately difficult. Application deadline: 2/1. Notification: continuous.

Costs Per Year: Application fee: $60. State resident tuition: $3278 full-time, $105.25 per credit hour part-time. Nonresident tuition: $13,189 full-time, $225 per credit hour part-time. Mandatory fees: $540 full-time. College room and board: $8326. College room only: $5278.

Collegiate Environment: Orientation program. Drama-theater group, choral group, marching band, student-run newspaper, radio station. Social organizations: 140 open to all; national fraternities, national sororities; 6% of eligible men and 4% of eligible women are members. Most popular organizations: Inter-Varsity Christian Fellowship, Rebel Ski Club, Student Organization of Latinos, Latter Day Saints, Hawaii Club. Major annual events: Premier UNLV, Spring Fling, Unityfest. Student services: health clinic, personal-psychological counseling, women's center, free legal education courses through law school. Campus security: 24-hour emergency response devices and patrols, late night transport-escort service, controlled dormitory access. 2,000 college housing spaces available; 1,490 were occupied in 2003-04. Freshmen given priority for college housing. On-campus residence required in freshman year. Option: coed housing available. Lied Library with 1 million books, 2.5 million microform titles, 9,536 serials, 120,128 audiovisual materials, an OPAC, and a Web page. Operations spending for 2004 fiscal year: $13.5 million. 1,900 computers available on campus for general student use. A campuswide network can be accessed from student residence rooms and from off campus. Staffed computer lab on campus.

Community Environment: Situated in southeast Nevada, Las Vegas is a great vacation and convention center located near Lake Mead and the mountains. Las Vegas is one of the fastest growing cities in the United States; some 1.3 million people live in southern Nevada. Community facilities include churches of most denominations, hospitals and clinics, and good shopping centers. The hotels feature some of the best entertainers in America. Nearby Charleston Peak provides expert ski runs and other snow sports facilities.

■ UNIVERSITY OF NEVADA, RENO *G-2*

Reno, NV 89557
Tel: (775)784-1110; (866)263-8232
Admissions: (775)784-4700
E-mail: unrug@unr.edu
Web Site: http://www.unr.edu/

Description: State-supported, university, coed. Part of University and Community College System of Nevada. Awards bachelor's, master's, doctoral, and first professional degrees and post-master's and first professional certificates. Founded 1874. Setting: 200-acre urban campus. Endowment: $161.1 million. Research spending for 2004 fiscal year: $59.2 million. Educational spending for 2005 fiscal year: $12,419 per student. Total enrollment: 16,336. Faculty: 960 (489 full-time, 471 part-time). Student-undergrad faculty ratio is 20:1. 4,793 applied, 86% were admitted. Full-time: 10,257 students, 55% women, 45% men. Part-time: 2,680 students, 52% women, 48% men. Students come from 52 states and territories, 70 other countries, 16% from out-of-state, 1% Native American, 7% Hispanic, 2% black, 7% Asian American or Pacific Islander, 3% international, 17% 25 or older, 14% live on campus, 8% transferred in. Retention: 75% of full-time freshmen returned the following year. Academic areas with the most degrees conferred: business/marketing; education; health professions and related sciences. Core. Calendar: semesters. Academic remediation for entering students, ESL program, services for LD students, advanced placement, honors program, independent study, distance learning, double major, summer session for credit, part-time degree program, adult/continuing education programs, internships, graduate courses open to undergrads. Off campus study at National Student Exchange. Study abroad program. ROTC: Army.

Entrance Requirements: Options: Peterson's Universal Application, electronic application, early action, deferred admission. Required: high school transcript, minimum 2.5 high school GPA. Entrance: moderately difficult. Application deadlines: Rolling, 11/15 for early action. Notification: continuous.

Costs Per Year: Application fee: $60. State resident tuition: $3060 full-time, $102 per credit part-time. Nonresident tuition: $11,735 full-time, $209.75 per credit part-time. Mandatory fees: $210 full-time. Full-time tuition and fees vary according to course load. Part-time tuition varies according to course load. College room and board: $7785. College room only: $4190. Room and board charges vary according to board plan and housing facility.

Collegiate Environment: Orientation program. Drama-theater group, choral group, marching band, student-run newspaper, radio station. Social organizations: 130 open to all; national fraternities, national sororities; 7% of eligible men and 5% of eligible women are members. Most popular organizations: Asian-American Student Association, Ambassadors, Non-Traditional Student Union, The Alliance, Orvis Nursing Student Association. Major annual events: Homecoming, MacKay Days, Night of All Nations. Student services: legal services, health clinic, personal-psychological counseling, women's center. Campus security: 24-hour emergency response devices and patrols, late night transport-escort service, controlled dormitory access. 1,763 college housing spaces available; 1,646 were occupied in 2003-04.

Freshmen given priority for college housing. Options: coed, men-only, women-only housing available. Getchell Library plus 6 others with 1.1 million books, 3.3 million microform titles, 15,000 serials, 65,453 audiovisual materials, an OPAC, and a Web page. 298 computers available on campus for general student use. Computer purchase/lease plans available. A campuswide network can be accessed from student residence rooms and from off campus. Staffed computer lab on campus.

Community Environment: When Reno was laid out as a townsite in 1868, it was named in honor of Major General Jesse L. Reno, who died in the Battle of the South Mountain during the Civil War. Reno is situated on the Truckee River near the base of the Sierra Nevada and has a cool, dry climate. Mining, livestock raising, lumber products, agriculture and tourism are the important industries of the area. Part-time employment is available. The city has a number of parks with facilities for swimming, tennis and picnicking; within a 25 to 90 minute drive from Reno, winter sports are available at a number of major resorts. Annual events are the Reno Rodeo, Reno Balloon Race, Air Races, and Holiday Festival of Trees.

■ **UNIVERSITY OF PHOENIX-NEVADA CAMPUS** *N-10*

7455 Washington Ave., Ste. 317
Las Vegas, NV 89128
Tel: (702)638-7279
Free: 800-228-7240
Admissions: (480)557-1712
Fax: (702)638-8035
Web Site: http://www.phoenix.edu/

Description: Proprietary, comprehensive, coed. Awards bachelor's and master's degrees and post-master's certificates. Founded 1994. Setting: urban campus. Total enrollment: 4,238. Faculty: 317 (7 full-time, 310 part-time). Student-undergrad faculty ratio is 8:1. 87 applied. Full-time: 2,976 students, 61% women, 39% men. 1% Native American, 4% Hispanic, 5% black, 2% Asian American or Pacific Islander, 12% international, 90% 25 or older. Academic areas with the most degrees conferred: business/marketing; computer and information sciences; security and protective services. Core. Calendar: continuous. Advanced placement, accelerated degree program, independent study, distance learning, external degree program, adult/continuing education programs, graduate courses open to undergrads.

Entrance Requirements: Open admission. Option: deferred admission. Required: 1 recommendation. Required for some: high school transcript. Entrance: noncompetitive. Application deadline: Rolling.

Costs Per Year: Application fee: $110. Tuition: $9750 full-time, $325 per credit part-time. Mandatory fees: $560 full-time, $70 per course part-time.

Collegiate Environment: College housing not available. University Library with 444 books, 666 serials, an OPAC, and a Web page. System-wide operations spending for 2004 fiscal year: $3.2 million.

■ **WESTERN NEVADA COMMUNITY COLLEGE** *G-2*

2201 West College Parkway
Carson City, NV 89703-7316
Tel: (775)445-3000
Admissions: (775)445-3271
Fax: (775)887-3141
E-mail: hull@wncc.edu
Web Site: http://www.wncc.edu/

Description: State-supported, 2-year, coed. Part of University and Community College System of Nevada. Awards certificates, diplomas, transfer associate, and terminal associate degrees. Founded 1971. Setting: 200-acre small town campus. Endowment: $126,000. Educational spending for 2005 fiscal year: $3986 per student. Total enrollment: 4,907. Student-undergrad faculty ratio is 15:1. 750 applied, 100% were admitted. 1 student government officer. 4% Native American, 9% Hispanic, 2% black, 5% Asian American or Pacific Islander, 0% international, 68% 25 or older. Core. Calendar: semesters. Academic remediation for entering students, ESL program, services for LD students, advanced placement, honors program, independent study, distance learning, summer session for credit, part-time degree program, adult/continuing education programs, co-op programs and internships.

Entrance Requirements: Open admission. Option: early admission. Required for some: high school transcript. Entrance: noncompetitive. Application deadline: Rolling.

Costs Per Year: Application fee: $15. Area resident tuition: $52.50 per credit part-time. State resident tuition: $1575 full-time, $88 per credit part-time. Nonresident tuition: $6695 full-time, $114.25 per credit part-time. Mandatory fees: $120 full-time, $4 per credit part-time.

Collegiate Environment: Orientation program. Drama-theater group, choral group. Social organizations: 7 open to all. Most popular organizations: Phi Theta Kappa, writers group, Infinity Society, Golf Club, Physics and Engineering Club. Major annual events: picnics, Career Fair, graduation. Student services: personal-psychological counseling. Campus security: late night transport-escort service. College housing not available. Western Nevada Community College Library and Media Services plus 2 others with 42,500 books, 36,933 microform titles, 228 serials, 26,695 audiovisual materials, an OPAC, and a Web page. Operations spending for 2004 fiscal year: $1.1 million. 678 computers available on campus for general student use. A campuswide network can be accessed from off-campus. Staffed computer lab on campus.

Community Environment: Carson City (pop. 40,443), the Capital of Nevada, is located near scenic Lake Tahoe and the Carson River. It is an agricultural region formerly important for silver production.

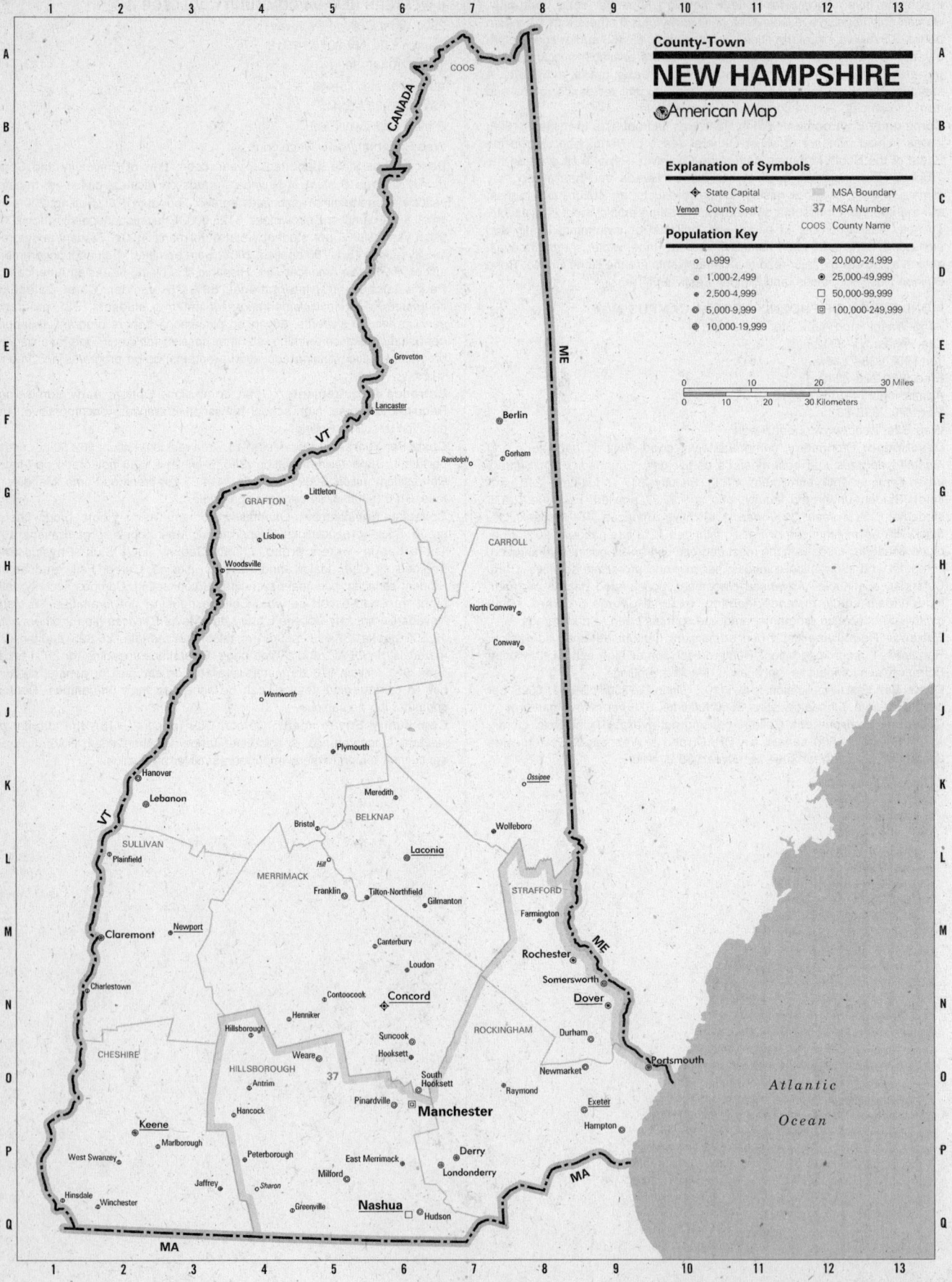

County-Town
NEW HAMPSHIRE
American Map

Explanation of Symbols

✦ State Capital   MSA Boundary
Vernon County Seat   37 MSA Number
                       COOS County Name

Population Key

○ 0-999   ◉ 20,000-24,999
◦ 1,000-2,499   ◉ 25,000-49,999
• 2,500-4,999   ☐ 50,000-99,999
◉ 5,000-9,999   ☒ 100,000-249,999
◉ 10,000-19,999

CANADA

COOS

VT

ME

Groveton

Lancaster   Berlin

Randolph   Gorham

GRAFTON   Littleton

Lisbon

Woodsville

CARROLL

North Conway

Conway

Wentworth

Plymouth

Ossipee

Hanover   Meredith

Lebanon   Wolfeboro

VT   Bristol   BELKNAP

SULLIVAN   Laconia

Plainfield   Hill   STRAFFORD

MERRIMACK   Tilton-Northfield

Franklin   Gilmanton   Farmington

Claremont   Newport   Rochester   ME

Canterbury   Somersworth

Loudon

Charlestown   Dover

Contoocook   Concord

Henniker   ROCKINGHAM   Durham

Hillsborough   Newmarket

CHESHIRE   Weare   Suncook

HILLSBOROUGH   Hooksett   Portsmouth

37   Antrim   Raymond

South   Atlantic
Hooksett

Pinardville   Manchester   Ocean

Keene   Hancock   Exeter

Marlborough   Hampton

West Swanzey   Peterborough   East Merrimack   Derry

Milford   Londonderry

Jaffrey   Sharon   MA

Hinsdale   Greenville   Nashua

Winchester   Hudson

MA

■ **CHESTER COLLEGE OF NEW ENGLAND** *P-7*
40 Chester St.
Chester, NH 03036-4331
Tel: (603)887-4401
Free: 800-974-6372
Admissions: (603)887-7400
E-mail: svogell@chestercollege.edu
Web Site: http://www.chestercollege.edu/
Description: Independent, 4-year, coed. Awards bachelor's degrees. Founded 1965. Setting: 75-acre rural campus with easy access to Boston. Endowment: $3.1 million. Educational spending for 2005 fiscal year: $3868 per student. Total enrollment: 217. Student-undergrad faculty ratio is 10:1. 219 applied, 57% were admitted. 7% from top 10% of their high school class, 24% from top quarter, 29% from top half. Students come from 11 states and territories, 1 other country, 44% from out-of-state, 0% Native American, 1% Hispanic, 1% black, 1% Asian American or Pacific Islander, 0.5% international, 6% 25 or older, 52% live on campus. Retention: 69% of full-time freshmen returned the following year. Academic areas with the most degrees conferred: visual and performing arts; English. Core. Calendar: semesters. Academic remediation for entering students, ESL program, advanced placement, self-designed majors, independent study, double major, summer session for credit, part-time degree program, adult/continuing education programs, co-op programs and internships. Study abroad program.
Entrance Requirements: Options: Peterson's Universal Application, Common Application, electronic application, deferred admission. Required: essay, high school transcript, minimum 2.2 high school GPA, 2 recommendations, interview. Recommended: minimum 2.7 high school GPA, portfolio. Entrance: moderately difficult. Application deadline: Rolling. Notification: continuous.
Costs Per Year: Application fee: $35. Comprehensive fee: $22,565 includes full-time tuition ($14,700), mandatory fees ($265), and college room and board ($7600). Part-time tuition: $465 per credit. Part-time mandatory fees: $500 per year.
Collegiate Environment: Orientation program. Drama-theater group, choral group, student-run newspaper. Social organizations: 7 open to all; 15% of eligible men and 24% of eligible women are members. Most popular organizations: student government, Running Club, Green Life (Recycling), Filmmakers Club, Drama Club. Major annual events: Commencement, Fall/Spring Convocation, Open House. Student services: personal-psychological counseling. Campus security: late night transport-escort service, controlled dormitory access, regular patrols by trained security personnel. 102 college housing spaces available; 90 were occupied in 2003-04. Freshmen guaranteed college housing. Option: coed housing available. Wadleigh Library with 27,000 books, 355 microform titles, 60 serials, 400 audiovisual materials, an OPAC, and a Web page. Operations spending for 2004 fiscal year: $52,635. 29 computers available on campus for general student use. A campuswide network can be accessed from student residence rooms. Staffed computer lab on campus.
Community Environment: Chester is a small town in close proximity to larger towns and cities such as Derry, Manchester and Boston.

■ **COLBY-SAWYER COLLEGE** *M-4*
541 Main St.
New London, NH 03257-7835
Tel: (603)526-3000
Free: 800-272-1015
Admissions: (603)526-3700
Fax: (603)526-3452
E-mail: csadmiss@colby-sawyer.edu
Web Site: http://www.colby-sawyer.edu/
Description: Independent, 4-year, coed. Awards associate and bachelor's degrees. Founded 1837. Setting: 200-acre small town campus. Endowment: $21.3 million. Educational spending for 2005 fiscal year: $6486 per student. Total enrollment: 971. Student-undergrad faculty ratio is 11:1. 1,474 applied, 90% were admitted. Full-time: 954 students, 64% women, 36% men. Part-time: 17 students, 65% women, 35% men. Students come from 23 states and territories, 5 other countries, 70% from out-of-state, 0% Native American, 0.3% Hispanic, 1% black, 1% Asian American or Pacific Islander, 1% international, 3% 25 or older, 87% live on campus, 4% transferred in. Retention: 79% of full-time freshmen returned the following year. Academic areas with the most degrees conferred: business/marketing; psychology; parks and recreation. Core. Calendar: semesters. ESL program, services for LD students, advanced placement, accelerated degree program, self-designed majors, honors program, independent study, double major, part-time degree program, internships. Off campus study at The New Hampshire College and University Council, American University. Study abroad program. ROTC: Army (c), Air Force (c).
Entrance Requirements: Options: Peterson's Universal Application, Common Application, electronic application, early admission, early action, deferred admission, international baccalaureate accepted. Required: essay, high school transcript, minimum 2.0 high school GPA, 2 recommendations, minimum of 15 units of college preparatory work, SAT or ACT. Recommended: interview. Entrance: moderately difficult. Application deadlines: 4/1, 12/1 for early decision. Notification: 1/1, 12/15 for early decision.
Costs Per Year: Application fee: $45. Comprehensive fee: $36,250 includes full-time tuition ($26,350) and college room and board ($9900). College room only: $5600. Part-time tuition: $880 per credit hour.
Collegiate Environment: Orientation program. Drama-theater group, choral group, student-run newspaper, radio station. Social organizations: 40 open to all. Most popular organizations: Student Government Association, campus radio station, Alpha Chi Honor Society, Outing Club. Major annual events: Mountain Day, Spring Weekend, Hogan Games. Student services: health clinic, personal-psychological counseling. Campus security: 24-hour emergency response devices and patrols, late night transport-escort service, controlled dormitory access, awareness seminars. 867 college housing spaces available; 826 were occupied in 2003-04. Freshmen guaranteed college housing. On-campus residence required in freshman year. Options: coed, women-only housing available. Susan Colgate Cleveland Library Learning Center with 90,055 books, 203,532 microform titles, 514 serials, 2,099 audiovisual materials, an OPAC, and a Web page. Operations spending for 2004 fiscal year: $465,625. 189 computers available on campus for general student use. A campuswide network can be accessed from student residence rooms. Staffed computer lab on campus.
Community Environment: Located in west central New Hampshire, New London enjoys a very agreeable climate and is a summer and winter tourist haven. Lake Sunapee is ten minutes west of New London and Mount Sunapee Ski Area is approximately twenty minutes away. There are excellent stores and specialty shops along with hotels, inns and lodges that are

found in a resort area. Recreation includes winter skiing, hiking, biking, and seasonal fishing in lakes and streams.

■ DANIEL WEBSTER COLLEGE *Q-6*

20 University Dr.
Nashua, NH 03063-1300
Tel: (603)577-6000
Free: 800-325-6876
Admissions: (603)577-6604
Fax: (603)577-6001
E-mail: thatcher@dwc.edu
Web Site: http://www.dwc.edu/

Description: Independent, 4-year, coed. Awards associate and bachelor's degrees. Founded 1965. Setting: 50-acre suburban campus with easy access to Boston. Endowment: $1.3 million. Educational spending for 2005 fiscal year: $7065 per student. Total enrollment: 1,109. 642 applied, 79% were admitted. 9% from top 10% of their high school class, 23% from top quarter, 51% from top half. Full-time: 823 students, 25% women, 75% men. Part-time: 227 students, 33% women, 67% men. Students come from 24 states and territories, 17 other countries, 46% from out-of-state, 0% Native American, 1% Hispanic, 2% black, 1% Asian American or Pacific Islander, 1% international, 10% 25 or older, 80% live on campus, 3% transferred in. Retention: 56% of full-time freshmen returned the following year. Core. Calendar: semesters. Advanced placement, accelerated degree program, independent study, distance learning, double major, summer session for credit, part-time degree program, adult/continuing education programs, internships. Off campus study at members of the New Hampshire College and University Council. Study abroad program. ROTC: Army (c), Air Force (c).

Entrance Requirements: Options: Peterson's Universal Application, Common Application, electronic application, early admission, deferred admission. Required: high school transcript, SAT or ACT. Recommended: 1 recommendation, interview. Entrance: moderately difficult. Application deadline: Rolling. Notification: continuous.

Costs Per Year: Application fee: $35. Comprehensive fee: $31,405 includes full-time tuition ($22,130), mandatory fees ($825), and college room and board ($8450).

Collegiate Environment: Orientation program. Drama-theater group, choral group, student-run newspaper. Social organizations: 17 open to all. Most popular organizations: Student Activities Board, Theatre Guild, Ice Hockey Club, student government, jazz band. Major annual events: Parents' Weekend-Casino Night, Commencement, Ski Day. Student services: health clinic, personal-psychological counseling. Campus security: 24-hour emergency response devices and patrols, student patrols, late night transport-escort service, controlled dormitory access. 500 college housing spaces available. Freshmen guaranteed college housing. On-campus residence required through sophomore year. Options: coed, men-only, women-only housing available. Ann Bridge Baddour Library and Learning Center with 34,195 books, 60,064 microform titles, 440 serials, 1,439 audiovisual materials, an OPAC, and a Web page. Operations spending for 2004 fiscal year: $460,000. 137 computers available on campus for general student use. A campuswide network can be accessed from student residence rooms and from off campus. Staffed computer lab on campus.

Community Environment: See Rivier College.

■ DARTMOUTH COLLEGE

Hanover, NH 03755
Tel: (603)646-1110
Admissions: (603)646-2875
Fax: (603)646-1216
E-mail: admissions.office@dartmouth.edu
Web Site: http://www.dartmouth.edu/

Description: Independent, university, coed. Awards bachelor's, master's, doctoral, and first professional degrees. Founded 1769. Setting: 265-acre small town campus. Endowment: $2.1 billion. Research spending for 2004 fiscal year: $156.7 million. Total enrollment: 5,780. Faculty: 633 (493 full-time, 140 part-time). Student-undergrad faculty ratio is 8:1. 12,756 applied, 17% were admitted. 88% from top 10% of their high school class, 100% from top half. Full-time: 4,050 students, 50% women, 50% men. Part-time: 60 students, 50% women, 50% men. Students come from 54 states and territories, 47 other countries, 96% from out-of-state, 3% Native American, 6% Hispanic, 7% black, 13% Asian American or Pacific Islander, 5% international, 0% 25 or older, 83% live on campus, 0.3% transferred in. Retention: 98% of full-time freshmen returned the following year. Academic areas with

the most degrees conferred: social sciences; history; psychology. Core. Services for LD students, advanced placement, self-designed majors, honors program, independent study, double major, summer session for credit, internships, graduate courses open to undergrads. Off campus study at members of the Twelve College Exchange Program, University of California, San Diego, McGill University, Morehouse College, Spelman College, Stanford University. Study abroad program. ROTC: Army (c).

Entrance Requirements: Options: Peterson's Universal Application, Common Application, electronic application, early admission, early decision, deferred admission, international baccalaureate accepted. Required: essay, high school transcript, 2 recommendations, peer evaluation, SAT and SAT Subject Tests or ACT. Recommended: interview. Entrance: most difficult. Application deadlines: 1/1, 11/1 for early decision. Notification: 4/10, 12/15 for early decision.

Costs Per Year: Application fee: $70. Comprehensive fee: $41,436 includes full-time tuition ($31,770), mandatory fees ($276), and college room and board ($9390). College room only: $5640. Room and board charges vary according to board plan.

Collegiate Environment: Orientation program. Drama-theater group, choral group, marching band, student-run newspaper, radio station. Social organizations: 250 open to all; national fraternities, national sororities, local fraternities, local sororities; 50% of eligible men and 48% of eligible women are members. Most popular organizations: student government, Outing Club, intramural sports, community service, performing arts organizations. Major annual events: Dartmouth Night/Homecoming, Winter Carnival, Green Key Weekend. Student services: health clinic, personal-psychological counseling, women's center. Campus security: 24-hour emergency response devices and patrols, student patrols, late night transport-escort service, controlled dormitory access. Freshmen guaranteed college housing. On-campus residence required in freshman year. Option: coed housing available. Baker-Berry Library plus 10 others with an OPAC and a Web page. 200 computers available on campus for general student use. A campuswide network can be accessed from student residence rooms and from off campus. Staffed computer lab on campus.

Community Environment: The northern New England surroundings and the small town pleasantness of Hanover are very much a part of undergraduate life. Located in the central western part of New Hampshire, Hanover is bordered by the Connecticut River dividing New Hampshire and Vermont. The rural location provides unsurpassed facilities and opportunities for all forms of outdoor recreation. Hanover provides convenient student shopping facilities, and is easily accessible to all major transportation centers in New England and New York by interstate highway, bus and commuter airline service. Boston, two hours away by car, is the nearest large metropolitan area.

■ FRANKLIN PIERCE COLLEGE *Q-3*

20 College Rd., PO Box 60
Rindge, NH 03461-0060
Tel: (603)899-4000
Free: 800-437-0048
Admissions: (603)899-4050
Fax: (603)899-4372
E-mail: admissions@rindge.fpc.edu
Web Site: http://www.fpc.edu/

Description: Independent, comprehensive, coed. Awards bachelor's degrees (profile does not reflect significant enrollment at 6 continuing education sites; master's degree is only offered at these sites). Founded 1962. Setting: 1,000-acre rural campus. Endowment: $6.2 million. Total enrollment: 1,635. Student-undergrad faculty ratio is 16:1. 4,068 applied, 74% were admitted. 1% from top 10% of their high school class, 21% from top quarter, 51% from top half. Full-time: 1,596 students, 49% women, 51% men. Part-time: 39 students, 67% women, 33% men. Students come from 32 states and territories, 18 other countries, 83% from out-of-state, 0.2% Native American, 2% Hispanic, 4% black, 1% Asian American or Pacific Islander, 2% international, 2% 25 or older, 87% live on campus, 2% transferred in. Retention: 66% of full-time freshmen returned the following year. Academic areas with the most degrees conferred: visual and performing arts; business/marketing; communications/journalism. Core. Calendar: semesters. Academic remediation for entering students, ESL program, services for LD students, advanced placement, self-designed majors, honors program, independent study, distance learning, double major, summer session for credit, part-time degree program, adult/continuing education programs, internships. Off campus study at 12 members of the New Hampshire College and University Council. Study abroad program. ROTC: Army (c), Air Force (c).

Entrance Requirements: Options: Peterson's Universal Application, Common Application, electronic application, early admission, deferred admission, international baccalaureate accepted. Required: essay, high school transcript, 1 recommendation, SAT or ACT. Recommended: minimum 2.0 high school GPA, interview. Entrance: moderately difficult. Application deadline: Rolling. Notification: continuous.

Costs Per Year: Application fee: $0. Comprehensive fee: $33,500 includes full-time tuition ($24,300), mandatory fees ($1000), and college room and board ($8200). College room only: $4600. Part-time tuition: $810 per credit.

Collegiate Environment: Orientation program. Drama-theater group, choral group, student-run newspaper, radio station. Social organizations: 32 open to all. Most popular organizations: Outing Club, WFPR-Radio, Student Senate, Law Club, Business Club. Major annual events: Fall Weekend, Crimson and Grey Cultural Series, Alternative Spring Break. Student services: health clinic, personal-psychological counseling. Campus security: 24-hour emergency response devices and patrols, student patrols, late night transport-escort service, controlled dormitory access. 1,389 college housing spaces available; 1,370 were occupied in 2003-04. Freshmen guaranteed college housing. On-campus residence required through senior year. Option: coed housing available. Franklin Pierce College Library plus 1 other with 110,210 books, 26,111 microform titles, 10,985 serials, 10,589 audiovisual materials, an OPAC, and a Web page. 109 computers available on campus for general student use. Computer purchase/lease plans available. A campuswide network can be accessed from student residence rooms. Staffed computer lab on campus.

Community Environment: Rindge is a rural community with a temperate climate. Cathedral of the Pines, an outdoor international shrine for people of all faiths, is located here. Numerous lakes in the area provide facilities for boating and fishing. There is limited part-time work for students off campus.

■ **GRANITE STATE COLLEGE** *N-6*
125 North State St.
Concord, NH 03301
Tel: (603)228-3000
Fax: (603)229-0964
Web Site: http://www.granite.edu/

Description: State and locally supported, 4-year, coed. Part of University System of New Hampshire. Awards associate and bachelor's degrees (offers primarily part-time degree programs; courses offered at 50 locations in New Hampshire). Founded 1972. Setting: rural campus. Research spending for 2004 fiscal year: $1.1 million. Educational spending for 2005 fiscal year: $4337 per student. Total enrollment: 1,827. Students come from 7 states and territories, 7% from out-of-state, 1% Native American, 1% Hispanic, 1% black, 1% Asian American or Pacific Islander, 0.1% international, 79% 25 or older. Core. Calendar: semesters. Academic remediation for entering students, services for LD students, advanced placement, accelerated degree program, self-designed majors, independent study, distance learning, double major, summer session for credit, part-time degree program, adult/continuing education programs, co-op programs and internships. Off campus study at other units of the University System of New Hampshire and the New Hampshire College and University Council.

Entrance Requirements: Required for some: ACCUPLACER. Entrance: noncompetitive. Application deadline: Rolling. Notification: continuous.

Collegiate Environment: Social organizations: 1 open to all. Most popular organization: Alumni Learner Association. College housing not available. 128 computers available on campus for general student use. A campuswide network can be accessed from off-campus. Staffed computer lab on campus.

■ **HESSER COLLEGE** *O-6*
3 Sundial Ave.
Manchester, NH 03103-7245
Tel: (603)668-6660
Free: 800-526-9231
Web Site: http://www.hesser.edu/

Description: Proprietary, primarily 2-year, coed. Part of Quest Education Corporation. Awards certificates, diplomas, transfer associate, terminal associate, and bachelor's degrees (also offers a graduate law program with Massachusetts School of Law at Andover). Founded 1900. Setting: 1-acre urban campus with easy access to Boston. Total enrollment: 3,398. 1,725 applied, 91% were admitted. 12% from top 10% of their high school class, 20% from top quarter, 68% from top half. Full-time: 2,104 students, 67% women, 33% men. Part-time: 1,294 students, 78% women, 22% men. Students come from 12 states and territories, 25% 25 or older, 50% live on campus. Core. Calendar: semesters. Advanced placement, accelerated

degree program, self-designed majors, double major, summer session for credit, part-time degree program, adult/continuing education programs, co-op programs and internships.

Entrance Requirements: Options: Peterson's Universal Application, Common Application, electronic application, deferred admission. Required: high school transcript, interview. Recommended: minimum 2.0 high school GPA, SAT. Required for some: essay, recommendations. Entrance: moderately difficult. Application deadline: Rolling. Notification: continuous.

Costs Per Year: Application fee: $10. Comprehensive fee: $18,940 includes full-time tuition ($11,340), mandatory fees ($1000), and college room and board ($6600). College room only: $3600. Part-time tuition: $410 per credit.

Collegiate Environment: Orientation program. Student-run radio station. Social organizations: 7 open to all; local fraternities. Most popular organizations: student government, Ski Club, Amnesty International, yearbook, student ambassadors. Major annual events: Job Fair, Orientation. Student services: health clinic, personal-psychological counseling. Campus security: 24-hour emergency response devices and patrols, student patrols, late night transport-escort service, controlled dormitory access. 400 college housing spaces available; 350 were occupied in 2003-04. Freshmen guaranteed college housing. Option: coed housing available. Kenneth W. Galeucia Memorial Library with 38,000 books, 200 serials, 60 audiovisual materials, an OPAC, and a Web page. 60 computers available on campus for general student use. A campuswide network can be accessed from student residence rooms. Staffed computer lab on campus.

Community Environment: See Saint Anselm College.

■ **KEENE STATE COLLEGE** *P-2*
229 Main St.
Keene, NH 03435
Tel: (603)352-1909
Free: 800-572-1909
Admissions: (603)358-2273
Fax: (603)358-2767
E-mail: admissions@keene.edu
Web Site: http://www.keene.edu/

Description: State-supported, comprehensive, coed. Part of University System of New Hampshire. Awards bachelor's and master's degrees and post-master's certificates. Founded 1909. Setting: 160-acre small town campus. Endowment: $10 million. Educational spending for 2005 fiscal year: $4485 per student. Total enrollment: 4,846. Faculty: 409 (187 full-time, 222 part-time). Student-undergrad faculty ratio is 17:1. 3,527 applied, 76% were admitted. 4% from top 10% of their high school class, 21% from top quarter, 60% from top half. Full-time: 4,170 students, 57% women, 43% men. Part-time: 559 students, 54% women, 46% men. Students come from 30 states and territories, 11 other countries, 47% from out-of-state, 0.1% Native American, 1% Hispanic, 0.4% black, 1% Asian American or Pacific Islander, 1% international, 11% 25 or older, 56% live on campus, 4% transferred in. Retention: 77% of full-time freshmen returned the following year. Academic areas with the most degrees conferred: education; psychology; social sciences. Core. Calendar: semesters. ESL program, services for LD students, advanced placement, self-designed majors, honors program, independent study, double major, summer session for credit, part-time degree program, co-op programs and internships, graduate courses open to undergrads. Off campus study at members of the New Hampshire College and University Council. Study abroad program. ROTC: Air Force (c).

Entrance Requirements: Option: deferred admission. Required: essay, high school transcript, 1 recommendation, SAT or ACT. Recommended: interview. Required for some: interview. Entrance: moderately difficult. Application deadline: 4/1. Notification: continuous.

Costs Per Year: Application fee: $35. State resident tuition: $5780 full-time, $241 per credit part-time. Nonresident tuition: $13,050 full-time, $544 per credit part-time. Mandatory fees: $2038 full-time, $77 per credit part-time. Part-time tuition and fees vary according to course load and degree level. College room and board: $7027. College room only: $4700. Room and board charges vary according to board plan and housing facility.

Collegiate Environment: Orientation program. Drama-theater group, choral group, student-run newspaper, radio station. Social organizations: 80 open to all; national fraternities, national sororities, local fraternities, local sororities; 3% of eligible men and 3% of eligible women are members. Most popular organizations: Social Activities Council, Concerned Students Coalition, Pride, Habitat for Humanity, Sports Club. Major annual events: Pumpkin Festival, Parent and Family Weekend, Spring Weekend. Student services: health clinic, personal-psychological counseling, women's center. Campus security: 24-hour emergency response devices and patrols, late night transport-escort service, controlled dormitory access. 2,391 college housing spaces available; 2,340 were occupied in 2003-04. Freshmen guaranteed college housing. Options: coed, women-only housing available. Mason Library with 1 million microform titles, 958 serials, an OPAC, and a Web page. Operations spending for 2004 fiscal year: $1.8 million. 500 computers available on campus for general student use. Computer purchase/lease plans available. A campuswide network can be accessed from student residence rooms and from off campus. Staffed computer lab on campus.

Community Environment: Keene, population 22,000, is located in the southwest corner of New Hampshire, 90 miles from Boston. All forms of commercial transportation are available. Keene is a city of diversified industry with metal and machine industries the most important. There are a number of churches, a community hospital and library serving the area. One of the most popular resorts in the state, Keene has many lakes and ponds within a 20-mile radius as well as golf courses and facilities for winter sports. A number of covered bridges may be seen on side roads off State Highway 10 between Keene and Winchester.

■ **MAGDALEN COLLEGE** *N-4*
511 Kearsarge Mountain Rd.
Warner, NH 03278
Tel: (603)456-2656; 877-498-1723
Fax: (603)456-2660
E-mail: jfout@magdalen.edu
Web Site: http://www.magdalen.edu/

Description: Independent Roman Catholic, 4-year, coed. Awards associate and bachelor's degrees. Founded 1973. Setting: 135-acre small town campus. Endowment: $1 million. Educational spending for 2005 fiscal year: $3800 per student. Total enrollment: 73. Student-undergrad faculty ratio is 8:1. 49 applied, 78% were admitted. Full-time: 72 students, 53% women, 47% men. Part-time: 1 student, 100% women. Students come from 17 states and territories, 1 other country, 93% from out-of-state, 0% Native American, 13% Hispanic, 1% black, 4% Asian American or Pacific Islander, 4% international, 3% 25 or older, 100% live on campus, 0% transferred in. Retention: 85% of full-time freshmen returned the following year. Academic area with the most degrees conferred: liberal arts/general studies. Core. Calendar: semesters. Academic remediation for entering students, part-time degree program, co-op programs.

Entrance Requirements: Options: early admission, early decision. Required: essay, high school transcript, 2 recommendations, interview, medical examination form, SAT or ACT. Entrance: moderately difficult. Application deadlines: 5/1, 1/1 for early decision.

Costs Per Year: Application fee: $35. Comprehensive fee: $17,250 includes full-time tuition ($10,750) and college room and board ($6500).

Collegiate Environment: Orientation program. Choral group. Most popular organizations: performance choir, polophony choir, Drama Club, intramural sports, leisure activities programs. Major annual events: Parents' Weekend, Christmas Party, Winter Rest. Student services: personal-psychological counseling. Campus security: 24-hour emergency response devices, student patrols. 120 college housing spaces available; 65 were occupied in 2003-04. Freshmen guaranteed college housing. On-campus residence required through senior year. Options: men-only, women-only housing available. St. Augustine Learning Center plus 1 other with 26,000 books and 10 serials. Operations spending for 2004 fiscal year: $2500. 6 computers available on campus for general student use. Staffed computer lab on campus.

■ **MCINTOSH COLLEGE** *N-9*
23 Cataract Ave.
Dover, NH 03820-3990
Tel: (603)742-1234
Free: 800-McINTOSH
Fax: (603)742-7292
Web Site: http://www.mcintoshcollege.edu/

Description: Proprietary, 2-year, coed. Awards certificates, transfer associate, and terminal associate degrees. Founded 1896. Setting: 11-acre small town campus with easy access to Boston. Total enrollment: 750. 2,250 applied, 33% were admitted. 8% from top 10% of their high school class, 23% from top quarter, 69% from top half. Students come from 20 states and territories, 10% from out-of-state, 2% Native American, 6% Hispanic, 9% black, 2% Asian American or Pacific Islander, 1% international, 65% 25 or older, 25% live on campus. Retention: 96% of full-time freshmen returned the following year. Core. Calendar: trimesters. Services for LD students, advanced placement, accelerated degree program, double major, summer session for credit, part-time degree program, adult/continuing education programs, co-op programs and internships.

Entrance Requirements: Open admission. Options: Peterson's Universal Application, Common Application, electronic application, early admission, deferred admission. Required: high school transcript. Recommended: interview. Entrance: noncompetitive. Application deadline: Rolling. Notification: continuous.

Costs Per Year: Application fee: $15. Comprehensive fee: $25,085 includes full-time tuition ($15,600), mandatory fees ($125), and college room and board ($9360). Part-time tuition: $443 per credit. Tuition guaranteed not to increase for student's term of enrollment.

Collegiate Environment: Orientation program. Drama-theater group. Social organizations: 10 open to all. Most popular organizations: Student Activities Committee, Drama Club, Business Club, Culture Club, Collegiate Secretaries International. Major annual events: Octoberfest, Spring Fling, Graduation Dinner/Dance. Student services: personal-psychological counseling. Campus security: 24-hour emergency response devices and patrols, student patrols, controlled dormitory access. 240 college housing spaces available; 185 were occupied in 2003-04. Option: coed housing available. McIntosh College Library with 11,000 books and 130 serials. Operations spending for 2004 fiscal year: $45,000. 150 computers available on campus for general student use. Staffed computer lab on campus.

Community Environment: The oldest permanent settlement in New Hampshire, Dover was founded in 1623 by fishermen and traders. Primarily a manufacturing center, industries produce electrical and electronic equipment, shoes, machinery and sporting goods. Part-time jobs are available. Trains and buses are convenient; airlines service nearby Portsmouth, and Dover does enjoy all the cultural and recreational advantages of that city.

■ **NEW ENGLAND COLLEGE** *N-4*
7 Main St.
Henniker, NH 03242-3293
Tel: (603)428-2211
Free: 800-521-7642
Admissions: (603)428-2223
E-mail: admission@nec.edu
Web Site: http://www.nec.edu/

Description: Independent, comprehensive, coed. Awards associate, bachelor's, and master's degrees. Founded 1946. Setting: 225-acre small town campus with easy access to Boston. Endowment: $4.9 million. Educational spending for 2005 fiscal year: $5436 per student. Total enrollment: 1,380. Faculty: 152 (57 full-time, 95 part-time). Student-undergrad faculty ratio is 11:1. 1,817 applied, 83% were admitted. 9% from top 10% of their high school class, 29% from top quarter, 68% from top half. 5 class presidents, 22 student government officers. Full-time: 972 students, 51% women, 49% men. Part-time: 69 students, 68% women, 32% men. Students come from 33 states and territories, 16 other countries, 67% from out-of-state, 0.4% Native American, 2% Hispanic, 2% black, 2% Asian American or Pacific Islander, 3% international, 6% 25 or older, 68% live on campus, 5% transferred in. Retention: 63% of full-time freshmen returned the following year. Academic areas with the most degrees conferred: business/marketing; psychology; parks and recreation. Core. Calendar: semesters. Academic remediation for entering students, ESL program, services for LD students, advanced placement, self-designed majors, honors program, independent study, distance learning, double major, summer session for credit, part-time degree program, external degree program, adult/continuing education programs, internships, graduate courses open to undergrads. Off campus study at members of the New Hampshire College and University Council. Study abroad program. ROTC: Army (c), Air Force (c).

Entrance Requirements: Options: Common Application, electronic application, deferred admission, international baccalaureate accepted. Required: essay, high school transcript, 3 recommendations. Recommended: interview. Entrance: moderately difficult. Application deadline: Rolling. Notification: continuous.

Costs Per Year: Application fee: $30. Comprehensive fee: $31,466 includes full-time tuition ($22,366), mandatory fees ($644), and college room and board ($8456). College room only: $4398. Full-time tuition and fees vary according to class time, course load, degree level, location, and program. Room and board charges vary according to board plan and housing facility. Part-time tuition: $1065 per credit. Part-time mandatory fees: $198 per term. Part-time tuition and fees vary according to class time, course load, degree level, location, and program.

Collegiate Environment: Orientation program. Drama-theater group, choral group, student-run newspaper, radio station. Social organizations: 27 open to all; national sororities, local fraternities, local sororities; 10% of eligible men and 10% of eligible women are members. Most popular organizations:

Student Senate, Campus Activities Board, T.E.A.C.H. (Taking Education Across Children's Horizons), International Student Association. Major annual events: Midnight Madness, Winter Carnival, Spring Fling Weekend. Student services: health clinic, personal-psychological counseling, women's center. Campus security: 24-hour emergency response devices and patrols, student patrols, late night transport-escort service. 671 college housing spaces available; 636 were occupied in 2003-04. Freshmen guaranteed college housing. On-campus residence required through sophomore year. Option: coed housing available. Danforth Library with 100,000 books, 35,000 microform titles, 15,300 serials, 950 audiovisual materials, and an OPAC. Operations spending for 2004 fiscal year: $376,195. 148 computers available on campus for general student use. Computer purchase/lease plans available. A campuswide network can be accessed from student residence rooms and from off campus. Staffed computer lab on campus.

Community Environment: The campus is situated in an area abounding in natural beauty. Henniker, a village of 3,200, is located on the Contoocook River in a mountainous area of New Hampshire 85 miles from Boston and 15 miles from Concord, the capital. The campus facilities are located throughout Henniker allowing students easy walking access to stores and restaurants. Alpine skiing and snowboarding are available at Pat's Peak two miles from Henniker. Other outdoor recreational facilities abound in the surrounding area.

■ **NEW HAMPSHIRE COMMUNITY TECHNICAL COLLEGE, BERLIN/ LACONIA** *F-7*

2020 Riverside Dr.
Berlin, NH 03570-3717
Tel: (603)752-1113
Free: 800-445-4525
Web Site: http://www.berlin.nhctc.edu/

Description: State-supported, 2-year, coed. Part of New Hampshire Community Technical College System. Awards certificates, diplomas, transfer associate, and terminal associate degrees. Founded 1966. Setting: 325-acre rural campus. Total enrollment: 2,080. 5% from top 10% of their high school class, 12% from top quarter, 65% from top half. Full-time: 708 students, 46% women, 54% men. Part-time: 1,372 students, 67% women, 33% men. Students come from 6 states and territories, 9% from out-of-state, 0.1% Native American, 0.1% Hispanic, 0.1% black, 0.2% Asian American or Pacific Islander, 0% international, 3% transferred in. Core. Calendar: semesters. Academic remediation for entering students, services for LD students, advanced placement, independent study, distance learning, double major, summer session for credit, part-time degree program, external degree program, adult/continuing education programs, internships.

Entrance Requirements: Required: high school transcript, placement test, ACT ASSET. Required for some: essay. Entrance: minimally difficult. Application deadline: Rolling. Notification: continuous.

Costs Per Year: Application fee: $10. State resident tuition: $164 per credit part-time. Nonresident tuition: $376 per credit part-time. Mandatory fees: $4 per credit part-time.

Collegiate Environment: Orientation program. Student-run newspaper. Most popular organization: Student Senate. Student services: personal-psychological counseling, women's center. College housing not available. Fortier Library with 10,000 books, 15 microform titles, 160 serials, 50 audiovisual materials, and an OPAC. 65 computers available on campus for general student use. A campuswide network can be accessed from off-campus. Staffed computer lab on campus.

■ **NEW HAMPSHIRE COMMUNITY TECHNICAL COLLEGE, MANCHESTER/STRATHAM** *O-6*

1066 Front St.
Manchester, NH 03102-8518
Tel: (603)668-6706
E-mail: ntravers@nhctc.edu
Web Site: http://www.manchester.nhctc.edu/

Description: State-supported, 2-year, coed. Part of New Hampshire Community Technical College System. Awards certificates, diplomas, transfer associate, and terminal associate degrees. Founded 1945. Setting: 60-acre urban campus with easy access to Boston. Research spending for 2004 fiscal year: $35,000. Total enrollment: 2,944. Student-undergrad faculty ratio is 14:1. 2,800 applied, 90% were admitted. Students come from 5 states and territories. Core. Calendar: semesters. Academic remediation for entering students, ESL program, services for LD students, advanced placement, independent study, distance learning, summer session for credit, part-time

degree program, external degree program, adult/continuing education programs, co-op programs and internships.

Entrance Requirements: Options: early admission, deferred admission. Required: high school transcript, interview. Recommended: recommendations. Entrance: minimally difficult. Application deadline: Rolling. Notification: continuous.

Costs Per Year: Application fee: $10. Area resident tuition: $3936 full-time, $164 per credit part-time. State resident tuition: $5904 full-time, $246 per credit part-time. Nonresident tuition: $9024 full-time, $376 per credit part-time. Mandatory fees: $5 per credit part-time.

Collegiate Environment: Orientation program. Social organizations: 4 open to all. Most popular organizations: Student Senate, Phi Theta Kappa, American Society of Welders, Student Nurses Association. Major annual events: Spring Formal, graduation. Student services: personal-psychological counseling. Campus security: trained security personnel. College housing not available. New Hampshire Community Technical College Library plus 1 other with 18,000 books, 160 serials, and an OPAC. Operations spending for 2004 fiscal year: $66,600. 210 computers available on campus for general student use. A campuswide network can be accessed. Staffed computer lab on campus.

■ **NEW HAMPSHIRE COMMUNITY TECHNICAL COLLEGE, NASHUA/ CLAREMONT** *Q-6*

505 Amherst St.
Nashua, NH 03063-1026
Tel: (603)882-6923
Fax: (603)882-8690
E-mail: nashua@nhctc.edu
Web Site: http://www.ncctc.edu/

Description: State-supported, 2-year, coed. Part of New Hampshire Community Technical College System. Awards certificates, diplomas, transfer associate, and terminal associate degrees. Founded 1967. Setting: 66-acre urban campus with easy access to Boston. Total enrollment: 1,639. Student-undergrad faculty ratio is 9:1. 1 valedictorian. Core. Calendar: semesters. Academic remediation for entering students, ESL program, services for LD students, self-designed majors, distance learning, summer session for credit, part-time degree program, external degree program, adult/continuing education programs, co-op programs and internships.

Entrance Requirements: Option: deferred admission. Required: high school transcript, interview. Recommended: recommendations. Required for some: recommendations, nursing exam. Entrance: minimally difficult. Application deadline: Rolling. Notification: continuous.

Costs Per Year: Application fee: $10. State resident tuition: $5248 full-time, $164 per credit part-time. Nonresident tuition: $12,032 full-time, $376 per credit part-time. Mandatory fees: $512 full-time, $16 per credit part-time.

Collegiate Environment: Orientation program. Drama-theater group, student-run newspaper. Social organizations: 11 open to all. Most popular organizations: Student Senate, Phi Theta Kappa, AmeriCorp, Paralegal Club, Ski Club. Student services: personal-psychological counseling. Campus security: 24-hour emergency response devices. College housing not available. Walter B. Peterson Library and Media Center with 22,000 books, 250 serials, and an OPAC. 150 computers available on campus for general student use. A campuswide network can be accessed. Staffed computer lab on campus.

■ **NEW HAMPSHIRE INSTITUTE OF ART** *O-6*

148 Concord St.
Manchester, NH 03104-4158
Tel: (603)623-0313
Admissions: (866)241-4918
Fax: (603)641-1832
E-mail: lsullivan@nhia.edu
Web Site: http://www.nhia.edu/

Description: Proprietary, 4-year, coed. Awards bachelor's degrees. Founded 1898. Setting: urban campus with easy access to Boston, MA. Total enrollment: 180. 75 applied, 83% were admitted. Full-time: 135 students, 66% women, 34% men. Part-time: 45 students, 84% women, 16% men. Students come from 6 states and territories, 9% from out-of-state, 1% Hispanic, 3% Asian American or Pacific Islander, 2% international, 33% 25 or older, 15% transferred in. Core. Calendar: semesters. Summer session for credit, part-time degree program.

Entrance Requirements: Open admission. Required: essay, high school transcript, recommendations, portfolio, SAT or ACT. Recommended: interview. Entrance: minimally difficult.

Costs Per Year: Application fee: $25. Tuition: $10,950 full-time, $365 per credit part-time. Mandatory fees: $1130 full-time, $466 per year part-time. College room only: $5700. Room charges vary according to housing facility.

Collegiate Environment: Orientation program. Major annual event: Student Art Exhibitions. 72 college housing spaces available; 30 were occupied in 2003-04. No special consideration for freshman housing applicants. Options: coed, women-only housing available. New Hampshire Institute of Art Library with 5,000 books, 5 microform titles, 55 serials, 1,000 audiovisual materials, an OPAC, and a Web page. 5 computers available on campus for general student use.

■ **NEW HAMPSHIRE TECHNICAL INSTITUTE** *N-6*
11 Institute Dr.
Concord, NH 03301-7412
Tel: (603)271-6484
Free: 800-247-0179
Admissions: (603)271-7131
Fax: (603)271-7734
Web Site: http://www.nhti.edu/

Description: State-supported, 2-year, coed. Part of New Hampshire Community Technical College System. Awards certificates, diplomas, and transfer associate degrees. Founded 1964. Setting: 225-acre small town campus with easy access to Boston. Total enrollment: 3,650. Student-undergrad faculty ratio is 12:1. 1,919 applied, 73% were admitted. 22% from top quarter of their high school class, 41% from top half. 1 valedictorian. Students come from 12 states and territories, 24 other countries, 2% from out-of-state, 0.3% Native American, 2% Hispanic, 1% black, 1% Asian American or Pacific Islander, 50% 25 or older, 23% live on campus. Calendar: semesters. Academic remediation for entering students, ESL program, services for LD students, advanced placement, distance learning, double major, summer session for credit, part-time degree program, external degree program, adult/continuing education programs.

Entrance Requirements: Options: Peterson's Universal Application, electronic application. Required: high school transcript. Recommended: minimum 2.0 high school GPA, SAT or ACT. Required for some: essay, recommendations, interview, National League of Nursing Exam. Entrance: moderately difficult. Application deadline: Rolling. Notification: continuous. Preference given to state residents.

Costs Per Year: Application fee: $10. State resident tuition: $4920 full-time, $164 per credit part-time. Nonresident tuition: $11,280 full-time, $376 per credit part-time. Mandatory fees: $480 full-time, $16 per credit part-time. College room and board: $6110. College room only: $4150.

Collegiate Environment: Orientation program. Drama-theater group. Most popular organizations: Phi Theta Kappa, Student Senate, Student Nurses Association, Criminal Justice Club, Outing Club. Student services: health clinic, personal-psychological counseling. Campus security: 24-hour patrols, late night transport-escort service, controlled dormitory access. Option: coed housing available. Farnum Library plus 1 other with 32,000 books, 12,000 microform titles, 500 serials, 1,000 audiovisual materials, an OPAC, and a Web page. 160 computers available on campus for general student use. Staffed computer lab on campus.

Community Environment: Bisected by the Merrimack River, Concord is the capital of New Hampshire, and is the economic and political center of the state. It is a key city on the interstate highway system. Community facilities include three libraries, numerous churches, a YMCA, hospitals, and good shopping. Job opportunities are good.

■ **PLYMOUTH STATE UNIVERSITY** *K-5*
17 High St.
Plymouth, NH 03264-1595
Tel: (603)535-5000
Free: 800-842-6900
Fax: (603)535-2714
E-mail: plymouthadmit@plymouth.edu
Web Site: http://www.plymouth.edu/

Description: State-supported, comprehensive, coed. Part of University System of New Hampshire. Awards bachelor's and master's degrees and post-master's certificates. Founded 1871. Setting: 170-acre small town campus. Endowment: $4.1 million. Research spending for 2004 fiscal year: $1.9 million. Total enrollment: 5,264. Faculty: 452 (175 full-time, 277 part-time). Student-undergrad faculty ratio is 17:1. 3,655 applied, 77% were admitted. 4% from top 10% of their high school class, 16% from top quarter, 52% from top half. Full-time: 3,956 students, 49% women, 51% men. Part-time: 236 students, 53% women, 47% men. Students come from 31 states

and territories, 10 other countries, 40% from out-of-state, 0.3% Native American, 1% Hispanic, 1% black, 1% Asian American or Pacific Islander, 1% international, 4% 25 or older, 53% live on campus, 5% transferred in. Retention: 76% of full-time freshmen returned the following year. Academic areas with the most degrees conferred: education; business/marketing; visual and performing arts. Core. Calendar: semesters. Services for LD students, advanced placement, accelerated degree program, self-designed majors, honors program, independent study, double major, summer session for credit, part-time degree program, internships, graduate courses open to undergrads. Off campus study at members of the New Hampshire College and University Council. Study abroad program. ROTC: Army (c), Air Force (c).

Entrance Requirements: Options: electronic application, deferred admission. Required: essay, high school transcript, 1 recommendation, SAT or ACT. Required for some: interview. Entrance: moderately difficult. Application deadline: 4/1. Notification: continuous until 7/1.

Costs Per Year: Application fee: $35. State resident tuition: $5410 full-time, $226 per credit hour part-time. Nonresident tuition: $12,250 full-time, $510 per credit hour part-time. Mandatory fees: $1618 full-time, $74 per credit hour part-time. Full-time tuition and fees vary according to reciprocity agreements. Part-time tuition and fees vary according to course load and reciprocity agreements. College room and board: $6780. College room only: $4650. Room and board charges vary according to board plan and housing facility.

Collegiate Environment: Orientation program. Drama-theater group, choral group, student-run newspaper, radio station. Social organizations: 100 open to all; national fraternities, national sororities, local fraternities, local sororities; 1% of eligible men and 1% of eligible women are members. Most popular organizations: Programming Activities in College Environment, Student Senate, alternative spring break, Childhood Studies Club, Health, Physical Ed, & Recreation Club. Major annual events: Spring Fling, Family Weekend, Homecoming Weekend. Student services: health clinic, personal-psychological counseling, women's center, career services, campus ministries, academic support services, veterans ser. Campus security: 24-hour emergency response devices and patrols, student patrols, late night transport-escort service, controlled dormitory access, shuttle bus service, crime prevention programs, self-defense education. 2,164 college housing spaces available; 2,119 were occupied in 2003-04. Freshmen given priority for college housing. On-campus residence required in freshman year. Option: coed housing available. Lamson Library with 306,314 books, 796,924 microform titles, 1,043 serials, 23,095 audiovisual materials, an OPAC, and a Web page. Operations spending for 2004 fiscal year: $1.9 million. 500 computers available on campus for general student use. Computer purchase/lease plans available. A campuswide network can be accessed from student residence rooms and from off campus. Staffed computer lab on campus.

Community Environment: With the White Mountains to the north, the Lakes Region to the south, and the Pemigewasset Rivers bordering the town to the east, Plymouth, NH is home to some of the country's most spectacular wilderness. PSC students step outside every morning into a natural landscape that provides four seasons of recreational and educational adventure. Here, the outdoors offer a natural laboratory, a classroom, and a playground. The campus is nestled in the town of Plymouth, which has been ranked seventh in The 100 Best Small Towns in America. Plymouth is less than 2 hours' drive from Boston. Portland , Maine is 2 hours east; Burlington, Vermont, is 2 hours to the northwest; and Montreal, Canada is only 3 1/2 hours to the north. Recreational activities include skiing and other winter sports, hiking, fishing, boating, and hunting.

■ **RIVIER COLLEGE** *Q-6*
420 Main St.
Nashua, NH 03060-5086
Tel: (603)888-1311
Free: 800-44RIVIER
Admissions: (603)897-8502
Fax: (603)891-1799
E-mail: rivadmit@rivier.edu
Web Site: http://www.rivier.edu/

Description: Independent Roman Catholic, comprehensive, coed. Awards associate, bachelor's, and master's degrees and post-master's certificates. Founded 1933. Setting: 64-acre suburban campus with easy access to Boston. Endowment: $19 million. Educational spending for 2005 fiscal year: $4638 per student. Total enrollment: 2,123. Faculty: 180 (71 full-time, 109 part-time). Student-undergrad faculty ratio is 9:1. 1,132 applied, 72% were admitted. 11% from top 10% of their high school class, 39% from top quarter,

75% from top half. Full-time: 845 students, 79% women, 21% men. Part-time: 543 students, 78% women, 22% men. Students come from 10 states and territories, 7 other countries, 45% from out-of-state, 0.2% Native American, 3% Hispanic, 2% black, 1% Asian American or Pacific Islander, 0% international, 38% 25 or older, 46% live on campus, 9% transferred in. Academic areas with the most degrees conferred: education; health professions and related sciences; social sciences. Core. Calendar: semesters. ESL program, services for LD students, advanced placement, accelerated degree program, honors program, independent study, double major, part-time degree program, adult/continuing education programs, internships. Off campus study at members of the New Hampshire College and University Council. ROTC: Air Force (c).

Entrance Requirements: Options: Common Application, early action, deferred admission. Required: essay, high school transcript, 1 recommendation, SAT or ACT. Recommended: minimum 2.3 high school GPA, interview. Required for some: interview, nursing exam. Entrance: moderately difficult. Application deadlines: Rolling, 11/15 for early action. Notification: continuous, 12/1 for early action.

Costs Per Year: Application fee: $25. Comprehensive fee: $28,144 includes full-time tuition ($19,980), mandatory fees ($600), and college room and board ($7564). Room and board charges vary according to board plan and housing facility. Part-time tuition: $666 per credit. Part-time tuition varies according to class time.

Collegiate Environment: Orientation program. Drama-theater group, choral group, student-run newspaper. Social organizations: 32 open to all. Most popular organizations: Student Government Association, Residence Hall Council, Student Business Organization, Student Admissions Committee, Behavioral Sciences Association. Major annual events: Rivier Theater Company Productions, International Week, R-Aid Day. Student services: health clinic, personal-psychological counseling. Campus security: 24-hour emergency response devices and patrols, late night transport-escort service, controlled dormitory access. 450 college housing spaces available; 420 were occupied in 2003-04. Freshmen guaranteed college housing. Option: coed housing available. Regina Library plus 1 other with 92,000 books, 130,000 microform titles, 500 serials, 4,000 audiovisual materials, an OPAC, and a Web page. Operations spending for 2004 fiscal year: $764,283. 93 computers available on campus for general student use. A campuswide network can be accessed from student residence rooms and from off campus. Staffed computer lab on campus.

Community Environment: Nashua is the second largest city in New Hampshire. It is conveniently located within an hour's drive of Boston, the White Mountains, and the seacoast, and is home to a large technology industry. Buses provide ample transportation to shopping malls, libraries, banking facilities, and many other services within just a few miles of the campus.

■ **SAINT ANSELM COLLEGE** *O-6*
100 Saint Anselm Dr.
Manchester, NH 03102-1310
Tel: (603)641-7000; 888-4ANSELM
Admissions: (603)641-7500
Fax: (603)641-7550
E-mail: admission@anselm.edu
Web Site: http://www.anselm.edu/

Description: Independent Roman Catholic, 4-year, coed. Awards bachelor's degrees. Founded 1889. Setting: 450-acre suburban campus with easy access to Boston. Endowment: $48.6 million. Research spending for 2004 fiscal year: $304,793. Educational spending for 2005 fiscal year: $5888 per student. Total enrollment: 1,986. Student-undergrad faculty ratio is 13:1. 3,258 applied, 73% were admitted. 15% from top 10% of their high school class, 45% from top quarter, 83% from top half. Full-time: 1,937 students, 58% women, 42% men. Part-time: 49 students, 65% women, 35% men. Students come from 28 states and territories, 15 other countries, 0.1% Native American, 1% Hispanic, 1% black, 1% Asian American or Pacific Islander, 1% international, 1% 25 or older, 95% live on campus, 1% transferred in. Retention: 82% of full-time freshmen returned the following year. Academic areas with the most degrees conferred: business/marketing; social sciences; security and protective services. Core. Calendar: semesters. Services for LD students, advanced placement, honors program, independent study, summer session for credit, part-time degree program, internships. Off campus study at members of the New Hampshire College and University Council. Study abroad program. ROTC: Army (c), Air Force (c).

Entrance Requirements: Options: Peterson's Universal Application, Common Application, electronic application, early admission, early decision,

deferred admission, international baccalaureate accepted. Required: essay, high school transcript, minimum 2.0 high school GPA, 2 recommendations, SAT or ACT. Recommended: interview. Entrance: moderately difficult. Application deadlines: Rolling, 11/15 for early decision. Notification: continuous, 12/1 for early decision.

Costs Per Year: Application fee: $55. Comprehensive fee: $33,730 includes full-time tuition ($23,990), mandatory fees ($670), and college room and board ($9070). Part-time tuition: $2400 per course.

Collegiate Environment: Orientation program. Social organizations: 64 open to all. Most popular organizations: Center for Volunteers, Anselmian Abbey Players, Knights of Columbus, spring break alternative, International Relations Club. Major annual events: Homecoming, Spring Weekend, Family Weekend. Student services: health clinic, personal-psychological counseling. Campus security: 24-hour emergency response devices and patrols, late night transport-escort service, controlled dormitory access. College housing designed to accommodate 1,643 students; 1,692 undergraduates lived in college housing during 2003-04. Freshmen guaranteed college housing. On-campus residence required in freshman year. Options: men-only, women-only housing available. Geisel Library with 222,000 books, 66,000 microform titles, 1,900 serials, 8,000 audiovisual materials, an OPAC, and a Web page. Operations spending for 2004 fiscal year: $1.3 million. 400 computers available on campus for general student use. A campuswide network can be accessed from student residence rooms and from off campus. Staffed computer lab on campus.

Community Environment: On the banks of Merrimack River, Manchester is the largest city in the state. The city is a retail, industrial, distribution and financial center. All means of commercial transportation are available. Community facilities include 54 churches, 8 hospitals, a public library, hotels and motels. The recreational activities are numerous. They include golf, swimming, bowling, tennis, roller skating, fishing, sailing, skiing, ice skating, and tobogganing. Points of interest are the Currier Gallery of Art, Manchester Historic Association and the Old Blodgett Canal.

■ **SOUTHERN NEW HAMPSHIRE UNIVERSITY** *O-6*
2500 North River Rd.
Manchester, NH 03106-1045
Tel: (603)668-2211
Free: 800-642-4968
Admissions: (603)645-9611
Fax: (603)645-9693
E-mail: admission@nhc.edu
Web Site: http://www.snhu.edu/

Description: Independent, comprehensive, coed. Awards associate, bachelor's, master's, and doctoral degrees. Founded 1932. Setting: 280-acre suburban campus with easy access to Boston. Endowment: $11.8 million. Educational spending for 2005 fiscal year: $6493 per student. Total enrollment: 3,887. Faculty: 389 (114 full-time, 275 part-time). Student-undergrad faculty ratio is 14:1. 2,654 applied, 74% were admitted. 6% from top 10% of their high school class, 26% from top quarter, 66% from top half. Full-time: 1,784 students, 55% women, 45% men. Part-time: 60 students, 50% women, 50% men. Students come from 23 states and territories, 63 other countries, 52% from out-of-state, 0.2% Native American, 1% Hispanic, 1% black, 2% Asian American or Pacific Islander, 2% international, 78% live on campus, 5% transferred in. Retention: 75% of full-time freshmen returned the following year. Academic areas with the most degrees conferred: business/marketing; personal and culinary services; psychology. Core. Calendar: semesters. Academic remediation for entering students, ESL program, services for LD students, advanced placement, accelerated degree program, honors program, independent study, distance learning, double major, summer session for credit, part-time degree program, adult/continuing education programs, co-op programs and internships, graduate courses open to undergrads. Off campus study at members of the New Hampshire College and University Council. Study abroad program. ROTC: Army (c), Air Force (c).

Entrance Requirements: Options: Peterson's Universal Application, Common Application, electronic application, early action, deferred admission, international baccalaureate accepted. Required: essay, high school transcript, minimum 2.0 high school GPA, recommendations, 1 letter of recommendation from guidance counselor or 2 letters from teachers, SAT or ACT. Recommended: interview. Entrance: moderately difficult. Application deadlines: Rolling, 11/15 for early action. Notification: continuous, 12/15 for early action.

Costs Per Year: Application fee: $35. Comprehensive fee: $30,194 includes full-time tuition ($21,384), mandatory fees ($330), and college room and board ($8480). College room only: $6080. Part-time tuition: $891 per credit.

Collegiate Environment: Orientation program. Drama-theater group, student-run newspaper, radio station. Social organizations: 40 open to all; national fraternities, national sororities, local fraternities, local sororities; 3% of eligible men and 3% of eligible women are members. Most popular organizations: Student Government Association, Student Programming Board, Association Cultural Exchange, Commuter Club. Major annual events: Family Weekend, New Student Fall Orientation, Fall/Spring Weekend. Student services: health clinic, personal-psychological counseling. Campus security: 24-hour emergency response devices and patrols, student patrols, late night transport-escort service, controlled dormitory access. 1,426 college housing spaces available; all were occupied in 2003-04. Freshmen guaranteed college housing. On-campus residence required in freshman year. Option: coed housing available. Harry A. B. and Gertrude C. Shapiro Library with 89,338 books, 350,000 microform titles, 14,400 serials, an OPAC, and a Web page. Operations spending for 2004 fiscal year: $1.4 million. 557 computers available on campus for general student use. Computer purchase/lease plans available. A campuswide network can be accessed from student residence rooms and from off campus. Staffed computer lab on campus.

Community Environment: Combining the tradition of the past with the sophistication of the future, Manchester has everything to be expected in a city with a population of more than 100,000, offering a thriving business environment as well as numerous cultural facilities. It is also within an hour of Boston, many ski resorts, and beaches that provide opportunities for jobs and recreation.

■ **THOMAS MORE COLLEGE OF LIBERAL ARTS** *P-6*
6 Manchester St.
Merrimack, NH 03054-4818
Tel: (603)880-8308
Free: 800-880-8308
Fax: (603)880-9280
Web Site: http://www.thomasmorecollege.edu/
Description: Independent, 4-year, coed, affiliated with Roman Catholic Church. Awards bachelor's degrees. Founded 1978. Setting: 14-acre small town campus with easy access to Boston. Educational spending for 2005 fiscal year: $4044 per student. Total enrollment: 86. 43 applied, 84% were admitted. Full-time: 86 students, 49% women, 51% men. Students come from 24 states and territories, 4 other countries, 78% from out-of-state, 1% Native American, 6% Hispanic, 1% Asian American or Pacific Islander, 3% international, 3% 25 or older, 97% live on campus, 13% transferred in. Retention: 85% of full-time freshmen returned the following year. Core. Calendar: semesters. Independent study. Study abroad program.
Entrance Requirements: Options: electronic application, early admission, deferred admission. Required: essay, high school transcript, 2 recommendations, SAT or ACT. Required for some: interview. Entrance: moderately difficult. Application deadline: Rolling. Notification: continuous.
Costs Per Year: Application fee: $0. Comprehensive fee: $18,650 includes full-time tuition ($10,600), mandatory fees ($50), and college room and board ($8000). Part-time tuition: $175 per credit hour.
Collegiate Environment: Orientation program. Choral group. Major annual events: Graduation, Convocation, visiting lectures. Student services: personal-psychological counseling. Campus security: student patrols, late night transport-escort service. 80 college housing spaces available; all were occupied in 2003-04. Freshmen guaranteed college housing. On-campus residence required through senior year. Options: men-only, women-only housing available. Warren Memorial Library plus 1 other with 45,000 books, 20 serials, and 1,000 audiovisual materials. Operations spending for 2004 fiscal year: $16,806. 6 computers available on campus for general student use. Staffed computer lab on campus.

■ **UNIVERSITY OF NEW HAMPSHIRE** *O-9*
Durham, NH 03824
Tel: (603)862-1234
Admissions: (603)862-1360
E-mail: admissions@unh.edu
Web Site: http://www.unh.edu/
Description: State-supported, university, coed. Part of University System of New Hampshire. Awards associate, bachelor's, master's, and doctoral degrees and post-master's certificates. Founded 1866. Setting: 2,600-acre small town campus with easy access to Boston. Endowment: $186.8 million. Research spending for 2004 fiscal year: $93.8 million. Educational spending for 2005 fiscal year: $8602 per student. Total enrollment: 14,564. Faculty: 962 (694 full-time, 268 part-time). Student-undergrad faculty ratio is 16:1.

12,310 applied, 72% were admitted. 20% from top 10% of their high school class, 61% from top quarter, 97% from top half. 33 valedictorians. Full-time: 10,911 students, 57% women, 43% men. Part-time: 618 students, 51% women, 49% men. Students come from 44 states and territories, 28 other countries, 42% from out-of-state, 0.3% Native American, 2% Hispanic, 1% black, 2% Asian American or Pacific Islander, 1% international, 4% 25 or older, 56% live on campus, 4% transferred in. Retention: 86% of full-time freshmen returned the following year. Academic areas with the most degrees conferred: business/marketing; social sciences; English. Core. Calendar: semesters. ESL program, services for LD students, advanced placement, self-designed majors, honors program, independent study, double major, summer session for credit, part-time degree program, external degree program, adult/continuing education programs, internships, graduate courses open to undergrads. Off campus study at National Student Exchange, New Hampshire College and University Council Exchange, New England Land Grant Universities Exchange, University of California, Santa Cruz Exchange, The Washington (D.C.) Center Internship. Study abroad program. ROTC: Army, Air Force.
Entrance Requirements: Options: Common Application, electronic application, early action, deferred admission, international baccalaureate accepted. Required: essay, high school transcript, 1 recommendation, SAT or ACT. Recommended: minimum 3.0 high school GPA. Entrance: moderately difficult. Application deadlines: 2/1, 12/1 for early action. Notification: 4/15, 1/15 for early action. Preference given to state residents.
Costs Per Year: Application fee: $45. State resident tuition: $8240 full-time. Nonresident tuition: $20,690 full-time. Mandatory fees: $2161 full-time. College room and board: $7584. College room only: $4606.
Collegiate Environment: Orientation program. Drama-theater group, choral group, marching band, student-run newspaper, radio station. Social organizations: 160 open to all; national fraternities, national sororities, local fraternities; 4% of eligible men and 5% of eligible women are members. Most popular organizations: Outing Club, Student Committee on Popular Entertainment, Diversity Support Coalition, Campus Activities Board, Student Environmental Action Coalition. Major annual events: Homecoming, Jukebox, Winter Carnival. Student services: legal services, health clinic, personal-psychological counseling, women's center. Campus security: 24-hour emergency response devices and patrols, student patrols, late night transport-escort service, controlled dormitory access, lighted pathways and sidewalks. College housing designed to accommodate 5,900 students; 6,180 undergraduates lived in college housing during 2003-04. Freshmen guaranteed college housing. Options: coed, women-only housing available. Dimond Library plus 4 others with 1.8 million books, 3 million microform titles, 25,962 serials, 37,114 audiovisual materials, an OPAC, and a Web page. Operations spending for 2004 fiscal year: $14 million. 389 computers available on campus for general student use. A campuswide network can be accessed from student residence rooms and from off campus. Staffed computer lab on campus.
Community Environment: Situated in southeastern New Hampshire, Durham is a quiet college town with many small restaurants, shops, and pubs located near the university. The cultural and recreational advantages of Portland to the northeast and nearby Boston to the south are both within one hour's drive. The University is 10 miles from the Atlantic coastline and historic Portsmouth. The White Mountains and ski areas are 60 miles to the northwest.

■ **UNIVERSITY OF NEW HAMPSHIRE AT MANCHESTER** *O-6*
400 Commercial St.
Manchester, NH 03101-1113
Tel: (603)641-4321
Admissions: (603)641-4150
Fax: (603)641-4125
Web Site: http://www.unhm.unh.edu/
Description: State-supported, comprehensive, coed. Part of University System of New Hampshire. Awards associate, bachelor's, and master's degrees. Founded 1967. Setting: 800-acre urban campus with easy access to Boston. Total enrollment: 1,165. Faculty: 91 (33 full-time, 58 part-time). Student-undergrad faculty ratio is 12:1. 286 applied, 63% were admitted. 3% from top 10% of their high school class, 15% from top quarter, 52% from top half. Full-time: 561 students, 58% women, 42% men. Part-time: 437 students, 57% women, 43% men. Students come from 4 states and territories, 5 other countries, 2% from out-of-state, 0.4% Native American, 2% Hispanic, 2% black, 2% Asian American or Pacific Islander, 1% international, 13% transferred in. Core. Calendar: semesters. Academic remediation for entering students, services for LD students, advanced placement, self-

designed majors, independent study, double major, summer session for credit, part-time degree program, external degree program, adult/continuing education programs, internships. Off campus study at 12 members of the New Hampshire College and University Council. Study abroad program. ROTC: Army (c), Air Force (c).

Entrance Requirements: Options: Common Application, electronic application, deferred admission. Required: essay, high school transcript, 1 recommendation, SAT. Recommended: interview. Entrance: moderately difficult. Application deadline: 6/15. Notification: continuous.

Costs Per Year: Application fee: $35. State resident tuition: $6960 full-time, $290 per credit part-time. Nonresident tuition: $17,610 full-time, $734 per credit part-time. Mandatory fees: $203 full-time. Full-time tuition and fees vary according to course load and program. Part-time tuition varies according to course load and program.

Collegiate Environment: Orientation program. Most popular organization: Student Council. Major annual events: Jazz in the Mills Series, Cultural Connections, New England Voices poetry series. Campus security: late night transport-escort service. College housing not available. UNH Manchester Library plus 1 other with 32,261 books, 11,397 microform titles, 259 serials, 1,979 audiovisual materials, an OPAC, and a Web page. 47 computers available on campus for general student use. Computer purchase/lease plans available. A campuswide network can be accessed from off-campus. Staffed computer lab on campus.

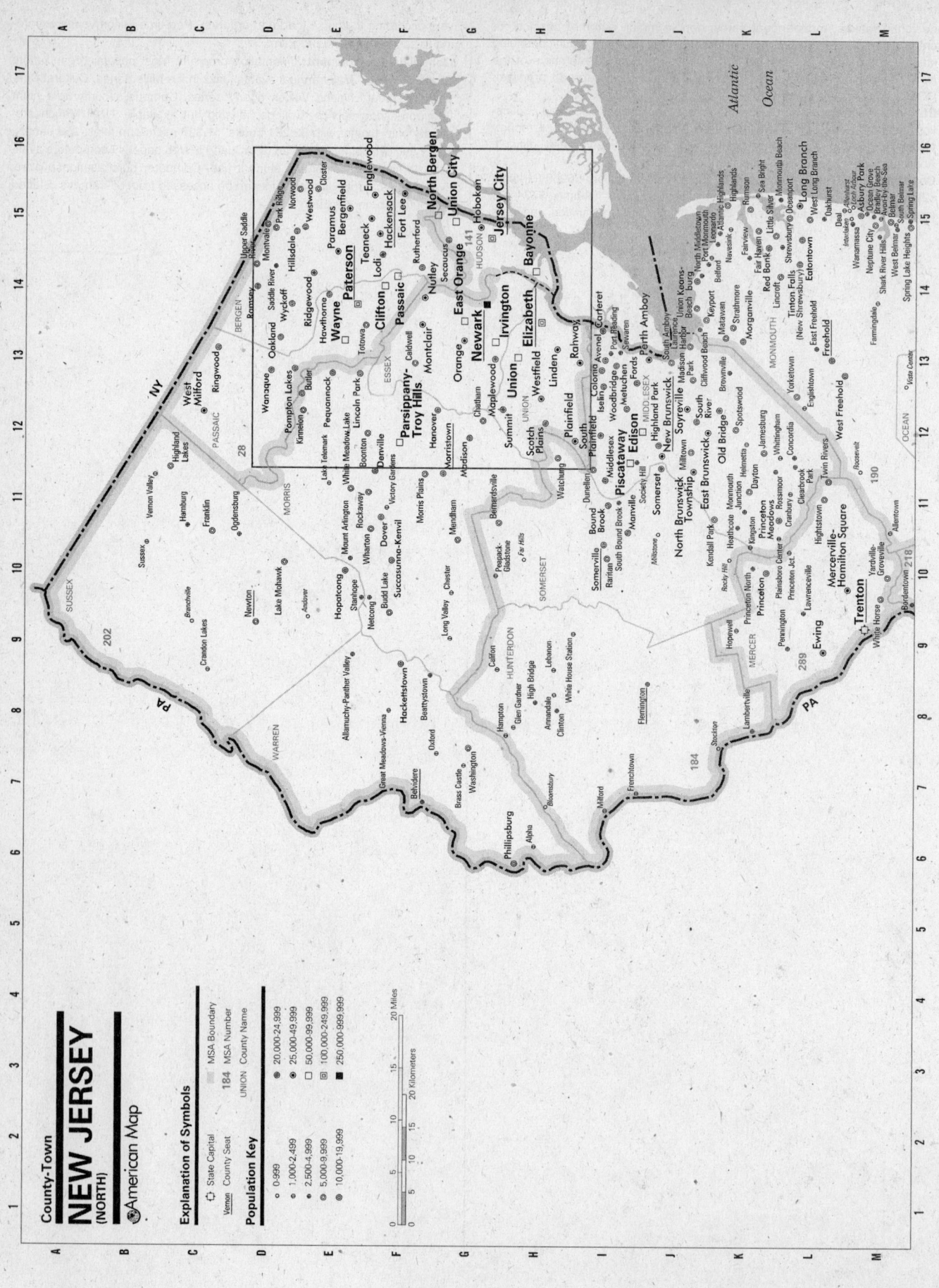

County-Town

NEW JERSEY
(NORTH)

◆American Map

Explanation of Symbols

✪ State Capital   MSA Boundary

Vernon County Seat   184 MSA Number

UNION County Name

Population Key

○ 0-999   ◉ 20,000-24,999

◦ 1,000-2,499   ◉ 25,000-49,999

● 2,500-4,999   ☐ 50,000-99,999

◉ 5,000-9,999   ⊡ 100,000-249,999

◎ 10,000-19,999   ■ 250,000-999,999

20 Miles

Atlantic Ocean

NEW JERSEY
County-Town
(SOUTH)

American Map

For Explanation of Symbols see
New Jersey (North), previous page.

Atlantic

Ocean

OCEAN
MONMOUTH
BURLINGTON
ATLANTIC
CAMDEN
GLOUCESTER
SALEM
CUMBERLAND
CAPE MAY
PA
DE

Camden
Cherry Hill
Toms River
Brick
Lakewood
Vineland
Bridgeton
Millville
Atlantic City
Hammonton

Allenwood · Sea Girt · Manasquan · Point Pleasant Beach · Point Pleasant
Brielle · Bay Head · Mantoloking
Ramtown
Leisure Village East · Holiday City-Berkeley
Dover Beaches North · Lavallette · Dover Beaches South
Silver Ridge · Holiday City · Seaside Heights · Seaside Park
South Toms River · Pine Beach · Ocean Gate
Beachwood · Island Heights
Forked River
Waretown
Barnegat Light
Barnegat
Harvey Cedars
Surf City
Ship Bottom
North Beach Haven
Beach Haven
Tuckerton
Mystic Island
Beach Haven West
Manahawkin
Ocean Acres
New Egypt
McGuire AFB
Fort Dix
Wrightstown
Pemberton
Browns Mills
Cedar Glen West · Leisure Village
Lakehurst · Leisure Knoll
Leisure Village West-Pine Lake Park
Pine Ridge at Crestwood
Cedar Glen Lakes
Crestwood Village
Country Lake Estates
Presidential Lakes Estates
Leisuretowne
Medford Lakes
Pemberton Heights
Mount Holly
Willingboro
Moorestown-Lenola
Florence-Roebling
Burlington
Edgewater Park
Beverly
Delran
Cinnaminson
Riverton
Riverside
Palmyra
National Park
Gloucester City
Bellmawr
Runnemede
Woodbury
Wenonah
Oak Valley
Mantua
Paulsboro
Gibbstown
Beckett
Swedesboro
Woodstown
Penns Grove
Carneys Point
Pennsville
Salem
Alloway
Elmer
Olivet
Shiloh
Seabrook Farms
Rosenhayn
Fairton
Cedarville
Port Norris
Laurel Lake
Port Republic
Pomona
Absecon
Pleasantville
Northfield
Linwood
Somers Point
Ventnor City
Margate City
Longport
Ocean City
Brigantine
May's Landing
Elwood-Magnolia
Egg Harbor City
Buena
Newfield
Victory Lakes
Clayton
Glassboro
Pitman
Turnersville
Mullica Hill
Williamstown
Chesilhurst
Folsom
Collings Lakes
Greentree · Marlton
Springdale · Berlin
Ashland · Lindenwold
Audubon · Echelon
Erlton-Ellisburg · Pine Hill
Blackwood
Maple Shade
Estell Manor (Risley)
Woodbine
Corbin City
Strathmere
Sea Isle City
Avalon
Stone Harbor
North Wildwood
Wildwood
West Wildwood
Wildwood Crest
Diamond Beach
Cape May
Rio Grande
Whitesboro-Burleigh
Cape May Court House
North Cape May
Cape May Point
West Cape May
Villas
Erma

17
190
218
298

■ **ASSUMPTION COLLEGE FOR SISTERS** *G-10*
350 Bernardsville Rd.
Mendham, NJ 07945-0800
Tel: (973)543-6528
Fax: (973)543-9459
Web Site: http://www.acscollegeforsisters.org/
Description: Independent Roman Catholic, 2-year, women only. Awards certificates, diplomas, and transfer associate degrees. Founded 1953. Setting: 112-acre rural campus with easy access to New York City. Endowment: $86,392. Educational spending for 2005 fiscal year: $2327 per student. Total enrollment: 37. Student-undergrad faculty ratio is 5:1. 16 applied, 100% were admitted. Full-time: 30 students. Part-time: 7 students. Students come from 3 states and territories, 5 other countries, 60% from out-of-state, 0% Hispanic, 84% international, 86% 25 or older, 0% transferred in. Core. Calendar: semesters. Academic remediation for entering students, ESL program, services for LD students, advanced placement, summer session for credit, part-time degree program.
Entrance Requirements: Required: high school transcript, 1 recommendation, women religious or women in religious formation. Required for some: essay, interview. Entrance: noncompetitive.
Costs Per Year: Application fee: $0. Tuition: $3300 full-time, $100 per credit part-time. Mandatory fees: $50 full-time.
Collegiate Environment: Orientation program. Choral group. Major annual events: Orientation, Christmas Program, Graduation. Campus security: 24-hour emergency response devices. College housing not available. Assumption College for Sisters Library with 25,000 books, 50 serials, 3,000 audiovisual materials, and an OPAC. Operations spending for 2004 fiscal year: $39,675. 16 computers available on campus for general student use. A campuswide network can be accessed. Staffed computer lab on campus.

■ **ATLANTIC CAPE COMMUNITY COLLEGE** *U-9*
5100 Black Horse Pike
Mays Landing, NJ 08330-2699
Tel: (609)625-1111
Free: 800-645-CHIEF
Admissions: (609)343-5500
Fax: (609)343-4921
E-mail: accadmit@atlantic.edu
Web Site: http://www.atlantic.edu/
Description: County-supported, 2-year, coed. Awards certificates, diplomas, transfer associate, and terminal associate degrees. Founded 1964. Setting: 537-acre small town campus with easy access to Philadelphia. Endowment: $673,167. Educational spending for 2005 fiscal year: $2882 per student. Total enrollment: 6,845. Student-undergrad faculty ratio is 24:1. 3,170 applied. Full-time: 3,074 students, 59% women, 41% men. Part-time: 3,771 students, 66% women, 34% men. Students come from 3 states and territories, 17 other countries, 1% from out-of-state, 0.3% Native American, 10% Hispanic, 14% black, 8% Asian American or Pacific Islander, 1% international, 68% 25 or older, 3% transferred in. Core. Calendar: semesters. Academic remediation for entering students, ESL program, services for LD students, advanced placement, independent study, distance learning, double major, summer session for credit, part-time degree program, adult/continuing education programs, co-op programs and internships.
Entrance Requirements: Open admission except for culinary arts, nursing, allied health, occupation therapy, physical therapy, respiratory therapy assistant programs. Options: Common Application, electronic application, early

admission, deferred admission. Recommended: high school transcript. Entrance: noncompetitive. Application deadline: 7/1.
Costs Per Year: Application fee: $35. Area resident tuition: $2370 full-time, $79 per credit part-time. State resident tuition: $4740 full-time, $158 per credit part-time. Nonresident tuition: $9480 full-time, $316 per credit part-time. Mandatory fees: $550 full-time, $18 per credit part-time, $2.50 per term part-time.
Collegiate Environment: Orientation program. Drama-theater group, student-run newspaper, radio station. Social organizations: 20 open to all. Most popular organizations: Culinary Student Association, Phi Theta Kappa, History/Government Club, Student Nurses Club, Occupational Therapy Club. Major annual events: Buccaneer Day, Earth Day, New Student Day. Student services: personal-psychological counseling. Campus security: 24-hour emergency response devices and patrols. College housing not available. William Spangler Library with 78,000 books, 300 microform titles, 300 serials, 1,000 audiovisual materials, an OPAC, and a Web page. Operations spending for 2004 fiscal year: $356,200. 350 computers available on campus for general student use. A campuswide network can be accessed from off-campus. Staffed computer lab on campus.
Community Environment: Population 8,000. Mays Landing is the county seat of Atlantic County, 18 miles from Atlantic City.

■ **BERGEN COMMUNITY COLLEGE** *E-14*
400 Paramus Rd.
Paramus, NJ 07652-1595
Tel: (201)447-7100
Fax: (201)444-7036
Web Site: http://www.bergen.edu/
Description: County-supported, 2-year, coed. Awards certificates, transfer associate, and terminal associate degrees. Founded 1965. Setting: 167-acre suburban campus with easy access to New York City. Total enrollment: 14,812. Student-undergrad faculty ratio is 22:1. Full-time: 7,486 students, 52% women, 48% men. Part-time: 7,326 students, 62% women, 38% men. Students come from 120 other countries, 0.2% Native American, 23% Hispanic, 7% black, 11% Asian American or Pacific Islander, 8% international, 31% 25 or older. Core. Calendar: semesters. Academic remediation for entering students, ESL program, services for LD students, honors program, distance learning, summer session for credit, part-time degree program, adult/continuing education programs, co-op programs and internships. Study abroad program.
Entrance Requirements: Open admission except for allied health programs. Option: Peterson's Universal Application. Entrance: noncompetitive. Notification: continuous. Preference given to county residents for nursing and dental hygiene programs.
Costs Per Year: Area resident tuition: $2249 full-time, $93.70 per credit part-time. State resident tuition: $4632 full-time, $193 per credit part-time. Nonresident tuition: $4872 full-time, $203 per credit part-time. Mandatory fees: $568 full-time, $23 per credit part-time, $8 per term part-time.
Collegiate Environment: Orientation program. Drama-theater group, choral group, student-run newspaper. Social organizations: 50 open to all. Student services: health clinic, personal-psychological counseling. Campus security: 24-hour patrols. College housing not available. Sidney Silverman Library and Learning Resources Center plus 1 other with an OPAC.
Community Environment: Bergen Community College is located in Paramus, which is the geographic center of Bergen County in northern New Jersey. With more than 300,000 households and nearly 1 million residents,

Bergen County is one of the largest counties in the state. The college is located on a 167-acre campus that is bordered by two golf courses and a county park. There is convenient transportation to New York City by bus, train, and ferry. The college is approximately 20 minutes from the George Washington Bridge.

■ **BERKELEY COLLEGE** *F-6*
44 Rifle Camp Rd.
West Paterson, NJ 07424-3353
Tel: (973)278-5400
Free: 800-446-5400
Fax: (973)278-2242
Web Site: http://www.berkeleycollege.edu/
Description: Proprietary, primarily 2-year, coed. Awards certificates, transfer associate, terminal associate, and bachelor's degrees. Founded 1931. Setting: 25-acre suburban campus with easy access to New York City. Total enrollment: 2,422. Student-undergrad faculty ratio is 22:1. 1,955 applied, 84% were admitted. Full-time: 2,040 students, 71% women, 29% men. Part-time: 382 students, 84% women, 16% men. Students come from 8 states and territories, 25 other countries, 4% from out-of-state, 0.2% Native American, 34% Hispanic, 17% black, 5% Asian American or Pacific Islander, 2% international, 26% 25 or older, 1% live on campus, 5% transferred in. Retention: 55% of full-time freshmen returned the following year. Academic area with the most degrees conferred: business/marketing. Core. Academic remediation for entering students, ESL program, advanced placement, distance learning, summer session for credit, part-time degree program, adult/continuing education programs, co-op programs and internships. Off campus study at Berkeley College, New York; Berkeley College, White Plains. Study abroad program.
Entrance Requirements: Options: Peterson's Universal Application, electronic application, deferred admission. Required: high school transcript, SAT or ACT. Recommended: interview. Entrance: minimally difficult. Application deadline: Rolling.
Costs Per Year: Application fee: $50. Comprehensive fee: $26,700 includes full-time tuition ($16,950), mandatory fees ($750), and college room and board ($9000).
Collegiate Environment: Student-run newspaper. Social organizations: 9 open to all; local fraternities, local sororities; 5% of eligible men and 15% of eligible women are members. Most popular organizations: Student Government Association, Athletics Club, Paralegal Student Association, International Club, Fashion and Marketing Club. Major annual events: Berkeley Day, Mardi Gras, Spring Fling. Student services: personal-psychological counseling. Campus security: 24-hour emergency response devices, controlled dormitory access, security patrols. 110 college housing spaces available; all were occupied in 2003-04. Option: coed housing available. Walter A. Brower Library with 49,584 books, 6,419 microform titles, 224 serials, 2,659 audiovisual materials, an OPAC, and a Web page. 300 computers available on campus for general student use. A campuswide network can be accessed from student residence rooms and from off campus. Staffed computer lab on campus.

■ **BETH MEDRASH GOVOHA** *N-13*
617 Sixth St.
Lakewood, NJ 08701-2797
Tel: (732)367-1060
Admissions: (908)367-1060
Description: Independent Jewish, upper-level, men only. Awards bachelor's and master's degrees. Founded 1943. Setting: small town campus with easy access to New York City and Philadelphia. 29 applied, 59% were admitted. Students come from 15 states and territories, 6 other countries, 2% 25 or older. Calendar: semesters. Part-time degree program.
Community Environment: See Georgian Court College.

■ **BLOOMFIELD COLLEGE** *H-6*
467 Franklin St.
Bloomfield, NJ 07003-9981
Tel: (973)748-9000
Free: 800-848-4555
Fax: (973)748-0916
Web Site: http://www.bloomfield.edu/
Description: Independent, 4-year, coed, affiliated with Presbyterian Church (U.S.A.). Awards bachelor's degrees. Founded 1868. Setting: 12-acre suburban campus with easy access to New York City. Endowment: $8.1 million. Educational spending for 2005 fiscal year: $5273 per student. Total enrollment: 2,212. Student-undergrad faculty ratio is 14:1. 2,531 applied, 47% were admitted. 1% from top 10% of their high school class, 11% from top quarter, 42% from top half. Full-time: 1,721 students, 66% women, 34% men. Part-time: 491 students, 78% women, 22% men. Students come from 13 states and territories, 29 other countries, 3% from out-of-state, 0.2% Native American, 18% Hispanic, 53% black, 4% Asian American or Pacific Islander, 2% international, 38% 25 or older, 16% live on campus, 10% transferred in. Retention: 65% of full-time freshmen returned the following year. Academic areas with the most degrees conferred: business/marketing; social sciences; psychology. Core. Calendar: semesters. Academic remediation for entering students, ESL program, services for LD students, advanced placement, accelerated degree program, self-designed majors, honors program, independent study, distance learning, double major, summer session for credit, part-time degree program, co-op programs and internships. Study abroad program. ROTC: Army (c).
Entrance Requirements: Options: Peterson's Universal Application, Common Application, electronic application, early admission, early action, deferred admission, international baccalaureate accepted. Required: essay, high school transcript, minimum 2.70 high school GPA, 2 recommendations, graded essay/term paper, SAT or ACT. Recommended: interview. Entrance: minimally difficult. Application deadlines: 7/1, 1/7 for early action. Notification: continuous, 1/21 for early action.
Costs Per Year: Application fee: $35. Comprehensive fee: $22,500 includes full-time tuition ($14,850), mandatory fees ($250), and college room and board ($7400). College room only: $3700. Part-time tuition: $1495 per course. Part-time mandatory fees: $30 per term. Part-time tuition and fees vary according to course load.
Collegiate Environment: Orientation program. Drama-theater group, choral group, student-run radio station. Social organizations: 25 open to all; national fraternities, national sororities; 1% of eligible men and 1% of eligible women are members. Most popular organizations: Versatile Entertainment, Team Infinite, Residence Life Development, Haitian Student Organization, Sisters in Support. Major annual events: Spring Festival, End of Year Formal, Welcome Back Barbeque. Student services: health clinic, personal-psychological counseling. Campus security: 24-hour emergency response devices and patrols, late night transport-escort service, controlled dormitory access, security cameras in high-traffic areas. College housing designed to accommodate 262 students; 339 undergraduates lived in college housing during 2003-04. No special consideration for freshman housing applicants. Option: coed housing available. Bloomfield College Library plus 1 other with 64,700 books, 59 microform titles, 456 serials, 1,437 audiovisual materials, an OPAC, and a Web page. Operations spending for 2004 fiscal year: $595,000. 300 computers available on campus for general student use. Computer purchase/lease plans available. A campuswide network can be accessed from student residence rooms and from off campus. Staffed computer lab on campus.
Community Environment: Located between Newark and Montclair, Bloomfield, population 55,000, is a suburban, residential city. Excellent shopping facilities, libraries, churches, numerous civic and service organizations and hospitals are a part of the community. Part-time employment is available. Commercial transportation is convenient.

■ **BROOKDALE COMMUNITY COLLEGE** *L-14*
765 Newman Springs Rd.
Lincroft, NJ 07738-1597
Tel: (732)842-1900
Admissions: (732)224-2268
Fax: (732)576-1643
Web Site: http://www.brookdalecc.edu/
Description: County-supported, 2-year, coed. Part of New Jersey Commission on Higher Education. Awards certificates, transfer associate, and terminal associate degrees. Founded 1967. Setting: 221-acre small town campus with easy access to New York City. Total enrollment: 12,724. 4,081 applied, 100% were admitted. Full-time: 6,588 students, 51% women, 49% men. Part-time: 6,136 students, 64% women, 36% men. Students come from 6 states and territories, 50 other countries, 0.1% from out-of-state, 0.2% Native American, 7% Hispanic, 12% black, 4% Asian American or Pacific Islander, 1% international, 28% 25 or older, 5% transferred in. Retention: 66% of full-time freshmen returned the following year. Core. Calendar: semesters plus 1 ten-week and 2 six-week summer terms. Academic remediation for entering students, ESL program, services for LD students, advanced placement, honors program, independent study, distance learning, summer session for credit, part-time degree program, adult/continuing education programs, co-op programs and internships. Study abroad program. ROTC: Army (c), Air Force (c).

Entrance Requirements: Open admission. Options: early admission, deferred admission. Required: high school transcript. Placement: AC-CUPLACER required for some. Entrance: noncompetitive. Application deadline: Rolling. Notification: continuous. Preference given to county residents.

Costs Per Year: Application fee: $25. Area resident tuition: $2202 full-time, $91.75 per credit part-time. State resident tuition: $4404 full-time, $183.50 per credit part-time. Nonresident tuition: $5400 full-time, $225 per credit part-time. Mandatory fees: $462 full-time, $19.25 per credit part-time.

Collegiate Environment: Orientation program. Drama-theater group, student-run newspaper, radio station. Social organizations: 30 open to all. Most popular organizations: Circle K, SAGE, Outdoor Club. Major annual events: May Fest, International Fair. Student services: personal-psychological counseling, women's center. Campus security: 24-hour emergency response devices and patrols. College housing not available. Brookdale Community College Library with 150,000 books, 17,987 microform titles, 709 serials, 33,000 audiovisual materials, and an OPAC. 1,100 computers available on campus for general student use. A campus-wide network can be accessed from off-campus. Staffed computer lab on campus.

Community Environment: Bounded by Sandy Hook Bay and the Navesink River, the Lincroft countryside area is located along the eastern shore of central New Jersey. The area abounds in orchards and horse farms. Community facilities include a library, churches of various faiths, above-average shopping facilities and many civic and service organizations. Railroads and buses furnish public transportation. Recreational facilities are very good including 7 miles of seashore for bay fishing, swimming and water sports.

■ **BURLINGTON COUNTY COLLEGE** *O-9*

Route 530
Pemberton, NJ 08068-1599
Tel: (609)894-9311
Fax: (609)894-0183
Web Site: http://www.bcc.edu/

Description: County-supported, 2-year, coed. Part of New Jersey Commission on Higher Education. Awards certificates, transfer associate, and terminal associate degrees. Founded 1966. Setting: 225-acre suburban campus with easy access to Philadelphia. Educational spending for 2005 fiscal year: $1967 per student. Total enrollment: 7,519. 2,442 applied, 100% were admitted. Full-time: 3,411 students, 53% women, 47% men. Part-time: 4,108 students, 62% women, 38% men. Students come from 7 states and territories, 1% from out-of-state, 0.4% Native American, 5% Hispanic, 22% black, 4% Asian American or Pacific Islander, 39% 25 or older. Core. Calendar: semesters plus 2 summer terms. Academic remediation for entering students, ESL program, services for LD students, advanced placement, honors program, independent study, distance learning, double major, summer session for credit, part-time degree program, adult/continuing education programs, co-op programs and internships.

Entrance Requirements: Open admission except for nursing program. Options: Peterson's Universal Application, Common Application, electronic application, early admission, deferred admission. Required: high school transcript. Placement: New Jersey Basic Skills Exam required. Entrance: noncompetitive. Application deadline: Rolling. Notification: continuous.

Collegiate Environment: Orientation program. Drama-theater group, student-run radio station. Social organizations: 25 open to all. Most popular organizations: Student Government Association, Phi Theta Kappa, Creative Writing Guild. Major annual events: AIDS Awareness Week, Drugs/Alcohol Awareness Week, Black History Month. Student services: health clinic, personal-psychological counseling. Campus security: 24-hour emergency response devices and patrols, late night transport-escort service, electronic entrances to buildings and rooms, surveillance cameras. College housing not available. Burlington County College Library plus 1 other with 92,400 books, 15,400 microform titles, 1,750 serials, 11,600 audiovisual materials, an OPAC, and a Web page. Operations spending for 2004 fiscal year: $806,400. 500 computers available on campus for general student use. A campuswide network can be accessed from off-campus. Staffed computer lab on campus.

Community Environment: The main campus is located in a rural setting where the principal agricultural pursuit is the raising of berries. Bus transportation is available. The campus is located 35 minutes from Center City Philadelphia and 90 minutes from New York City. Fort Dix and McGuire Air Force Base are nearby. Burlington County, the largest of New Jersey's 21 counties, has numerous churches and synagogues and excellent health care and recreational facilities.

■ **CALDWELL COLLEGE** *F-13*

9 Ryerson Ave.
Caldwell, NJ 07006-6195
Tel: (973)618-3000; 888-864-9516
Admissions: (973)618-3226
Web Site: http://www.caldwell.edu/

Description: Independent Roman Catholic, comprehensive, coed. Awards bachelor's and master's degrees and post-master's certificates. Founded 1939. Setting: 100-acre suburban campus with easy access to New York City. Endowment: $4.5 million. Research spending for 2004 fiscal year: $30,000. Educational spending for 2005 fiscal year: $5084 per student. Total enrollment: 2,229. Faculty: 184 (83 full-time, 101 part-time). Student-undergrad faculty ratio is 12:1. 1,234 applied, 78% were admitted. 6% from top 10% of their high school class, 23% from top quarter, 56% from top half. Full-time: 1,059 students, 64% women, 36% men. Part-time: 612 students, 74% women, 26% men. Students come from 18 states and territories, 28 other countries, 14% from out-of-state, 0.2% Native American, 11% Hispanic, 16% black, 2% Asian American or Pacific Islander, 5% international, 38% 25 or older, 26% live on campus, 8% transferred in. Retention: 73% of full-time freshmen returned the following year. Academic areas with the most degrees conferred: psychology; business/marketing; education. Core. Calendar: semesters. Academic remediation for entering students, ESL program, services for LD students, advanced placement, accelerated degree program, self-designed majors, honors program, independent study, distance learning, double major, summer session for credit, part-time degree program, external degree program, adult/continuing education programs, co-op programs and internships, graduate courses open to undergrads. Off campus study. Study abroad program. ROTC: Army. (c).

Entrance Requirements: Options: Peterson's Universal Application, Common Application, electronic application, early admission, early action, deferred admission, international baccalaureate accepted. Required: essay, high school transcript, minimum 2.0 high school GPA, 1 recommendation, SAT or ACT. Required for some: interview. Entrance: moderately difficult. Application deadlines: 3/15, 1/1 for early action. Notification: continuous, 1/15 for early action.

Costs Per Year: Application fee: $40. Comprehensive fee: $26,650 includes full-time tuition ($18,700), mandatory fees ($300), and college room and board ($7650). Room and board charges vary according to board plan and housing facility. Part-time tuition: $458 per credit. Part-time tuition varies according to course load.

Collegiate Environment: Orientation program. Drama-theater group, choral group, student-run newspaper. Social organizations: 20 open to all. Most popular organizations: Student Government Association, International Students Organization, Caldwell College Education Association, Circle K, Black Student Cooperative Unit. Major annual events: Founders' Day, Semi-Formal Banquet, Fall Festival. Student services: health clinic, personal-psychological counseling. Campus security: 24-hour patrols, late night transport-escort service, controlled dormitory access, dusk-to-dawn patrols by trained security personnel. 371 college housing spaces available; 355 were occupied in 2003-04. Freshmen given priority for college housing. Option: coed housing available. Jennings Library with 144,698 books, 6,121 microform titles, 426 serials, 2,007 audiovisual materials, an OPAC, and a Web page. Operations spending for 2004 fiscal year: $912,238. 197 computers available on campus for general student use. A campuswide network can be accessed from student residence rooms and from off campus. Staffed computer lab on campus.

Community Environment: The birthplace of President Grover Cleveland, Caldwell is situated in Western Essex County with bus lines serving the area, and New York City only 20 miles away. Community services include a number of churches, a public library, hospitals and various civic organizations. The Grover Cleveland County Park, golf courses and tennis courts provide facilities for recreation. Skiing and ice skating are available during the winter season.

■ **CAMDEN COUNTY COLLEGE** *Q-6*

PO Box 200
Blackwood, NJ 08012-0200
Tel: (856)227-7200; 888-228-2466
Web Site: http://www.camdencc.edu/

Description: State and locally supported, 2-year, coed. Part of New Jersey Commission on Higher Education. Awards certificates, transfer associate, and terminal associate degrees. Founded 1967. Setting: 320-acre suburban campus with easy access to Philadelphia. Educational spending for 2005 fiscal year: $5211 per student. Total enrollment: 14,829. 9,472 applied, 100%

were admitted. Students come from 2 states and territories, 21 other countries, 4% from out-of-state, 0.3% Native American, 7% Hispanic, 21% black, 5% Asian American or Pacific Islander, 39% 25 or older. Core. Calendar: semesters. Academic remediation for entering students, ESL program, services for LD students, freshman honors college, honors program, independent study, distance learning, double major, summer session for credit, part-time degree program, external degree program, adult/continuing education programs, co-op programs and internships. Off campus study. Study abroad program.

Entrance Requirements: Open admission. Options: Common Application, early admission. Required for some: high school transcript. Entrance: noncompetitive. Application deadline: Rolling.

Costs Per Year: Application fee: $0. Area resident tuition: $73 per credit part-time. State resident tuition: $77 per credit part-time. Mandatory fees: $13 per credit part-time.

Collegiate Environment: Drama-theater group, choral group, student-run radio station. Social organizations: 45 open to all. Most popular organizations: Phi Theta Kappa, Circle K, Laser Club, Math Club, Chess Club. Major annual events: Welcome Back Barbecue, College Community Day, Military Career Day. Campus security: 24-hour emergency response devices. College housing not available. Learning Resource Center with 91,366 books, 19,970 microform titles, 449 serials, 2,038 audiovisual materials, and an OPAC. 700 computers available on campus for general student use. A campuswide network can be accessed. Staffed computer lab on campus.

Community Environment: Blackwood is located in Gloucester Township (population 30,461), near Philadelphia, PA.

■ **CENTENARY COLLEGE** *F-9*

400 Jefferson St.
Hackettstown, NJ 07840-2100
Tel: (908)852-1400
Free: 800-236-8679
Fax: (908)852-3454
Web Site: http://www.centenarycollege.edu/

Description: Independent, comprehensive, coed, affiliated with United Methodist Church. Awards associate, bachelor's, and master's degrees. Founded 1867. Setting: 42-acre suburban campus with easy access to New York City. Endowment: $2 million. Educational spending for 2005 fiscal year: $5741 per student. Total enrollment: 2,472. Faculty: 304 (63 full-time, 241 part-time). Student-undergrad faculty ratio is 18:1. 693 applied, 75% were admitted. 3% from top 10% of their high school class, 18% from top quarter, 55% from top half. Full-time: 1,617 students, 63% women, 37% men. Part-time: 270 students, 66% women, 34% men. Students come from 23 states and territories, 17 other countries, 12% from out-of-state, 0.1% Native American, 4% Hispanic, 5% black, 2% Asian American or Pacific Islander, 2% international, 35% 25 or older, 58% live on campus, 11% transferred in. Retention: 73% of full-time freshmen returned the following year. Academic areas with the most degrees conferred: business/marketing; social sciences; agriculture; psychology. Core. Calendar: semesters. Academic remediation for entering students, ESL program, services for LD students, advanced placement, accelerated degree program, self-designed majors, honors program, independent study, double major, summer session for credit, part-time degree program, internships, graduate courses open to undergrads. Off campus study at Center for Adult and Professional Studies. Study abroad program.

Entrance Requirements: Options: Peterson's Universal Application, Common Application, electronic application, deferred admission, international baccalaureate accepted. Required: essay, high school transcript, SAT or ACT. Recommended: minimum 2.0 high school GPA, recommendations, interview. Required for some: interview, portfolio. Entrance: moderately difficult. Application deadline: Rolling. Notification: continuous.

Costs Per Year: Application fee: $30. Comprehensive fee: $28,770 includes full-time tuition ($19,840), mandatory fees ($1030), and college room and board ($7900). Full-time tuition and fees vary according to location and program. Part-time tuition: $395 per credit. Part-time mandatory fees: $10 per term. Part-time tuition and fees vary according to location and program.

Collegiate Environment: Orientation program. Drama-theater group, student-run newspaper, radio station. Social organizations: 25 open to all; local fraternities, local sororities; 10% of eligible men and 30% of eligible women are members. Most popular organizations: Student Activities Council, equestrian teams, Quill, student government, Kappa Delta Epsilon. Major annual events: Homecoming/Alumni Weekend, Christmas Semi-Formal, President's Ball. Student services: health clinic, personal-psychological counseling, women's center. Campus security: late night

transport-escort service, controlled dormitory access, patrols by trained security personnel 4 p.m. to 8 a.m. 625 college housing spaces available; 620 were occupied in 2003-04. Freshmen given priority for college housing. Options: coed, women-only housing available. Taylor Memorial Learning Resource Center with 67,272 books, 20,591 microform titles, 211 serials, 4,965 audiovisual materials, and an OPAC. Operations spending for 2004 fiscal year: $263,936. 30 computers available on campus for general student use. A campuswide network can be accessed from student residence rooms and from off campus. Staffed computer lab on campus.

Community Environment: Population 16,000, Hackettstown is a suburban and residential community. The area industry has not destroyed the natural surroundings. There is easy access to New York City by bus and train. The ski resorts of the Pocono Mountains are only 30 minutes via Route 80 West. State parks maintained by New Jersey are minutes away.

■ **THE COLLEGE OF NEW JERSEY** *L-9*

PO Box 7718
Ewing, NJ 08628
Tel: (609)771-1855
Free: 800-624-0967
Admissions: (609)771-2131
E-mail: admiss@tcnj.edu
Web Site: http://www.tcnj.edu/

Description: State-supported, comprehensive, coed. Awards bachelor's and master's degrees and post-master's certificates. Founded 1855. Setting: 255-acre suburban campus with easy access to Philadelphia. Endowment: $6.9 million. Research spending for 2004 fiscal year: $4.6 million. Educational spending for 2005 fiscal year: $6962 per student. Total enrollment: 6,768. Faculty: 705 (341 full-time, 364 part-time). Student-undergrad faculty ratio is 12:1. 7,300 applied, 45% were admitted. 68% from top 10% of their high school class, 94% from top quarter, 99% from top half. 10 National Merit Scholars. Full-time: 5,726 students, 58% women, 42% men. Part-time: 169 students, 63% women, 37% men. Students come from 16 states and territories, 20 other countries, 5% from out-of-state, 0.1% Native American, 7% Hispanic, 6% black, 5% Asian American or Pacific Islander, 0.1% international, 6% 25 or older, 65% live on campus, 4% transferred in. Retention: 95% of full-time freshmen returned the following year. Academic areas with the most degrees conferred: education; business/marketing; English. Core. Calendar: semesters. Academic remediation for entering students, services for LD students, advanced placement, self-designed majors, honors program, independent study, double major, summer session for credit, part-time degree program, internships, graduate courses open to undergrads. Off campus study at members of the National Student Exchange, Philadelphia College of Pharmacy and Science, New Jersey Marine Sciences Consortium (Sandy Hook and Sea Isle City). Study abroad program. ROTC: Army (c), Air Force (c).

Entrance Requirements: Options: electronic application, early admission, early decision, deferred admission. Required: essay, high school transcript, SAT or ACT. Recommended: minimum 3.5 high school GPA, 3 recommendations. Required for some: interview, art portfolio or music audition. Entrance: very difficult. Application deadlines: 2/15, 11/15 for early decision. Notification: continuous until 4/1, 12/15 for early decision.

Costs Per Year: Application fee: $50. State resident tuition: $7051 full-time, $249.75 per credit part-time. Nonresident tuition: $12,314 full-time, $436 per credit part-time. Mandatory fees: $2656 full-time, $93.10 per credit part-time. Part-time tuition and fees vary according to course load. College room and board: $8458. College room only: $6090. Room and board charges vary according to board plan.

Collegiate Environment: Orientation program. Drama-theater group, choral group, student-run newspaper, radio station. Social organizations: 185 open to all; national fraternities, national sororities, local fraternities, local sororities; 20% of eligible men and 20% of eligible women are members. Most popular organizations: Student Government Association, College Union Board, The Signal, intramurals. Major annual events: Family Fest Performing Arts Series, Homecoming, Student Center Late Nighter. Student services: legal services, health clinic, personal-psychological counseling, women's center. Campus security: 24-hour emergency response devices and patrols, student patrols, late night transport-escort service, controlled dormitory access. 3,594 college housing spaces available; all were occupied in 2003-04. Option: coed housing available. Roscoe L. West Library with 550,000 books, 319,000 microform titles, 7,900 serials, 4,000 audiovisual materials, an OPAC, and a Web page. Operations spending for 2004 fiscal year: $3.8 million. 800 computers available on campus for general student use. A campuswide network can be accessed from student residence rooms and from off campus. Staffed computer lab on campus.

Community Environment: See Rider University.

■ COLLEGE OF SAINT ELIZABETH *G-11*

2 Convent Rd.
Morristown, NJ 07960-6989
Tel: (973)290-4000
Free: 800-210-7900
Admissions: (973)290-4700
Fax: (973)290-4710
E-mail: apply@liza.st-elizabeth.edu
Web Site: http://www.cse.edu/

Description: Independent Roman Catholic, comprehensive. Awards bachelor's and master's degrees (also offers coed adult undergraduate degree program and coed graduate programs). Founded 1899. Setting: 188-acre suburban campus with easy access to New York City. Endowment: $19.9 million. Educational spending for 2005 fiscal year: $7755 per student. Total enrollment: 1,858. Faculty: 178 (65 full-time, 113 part-time). Student-undergrad faculty ratio is 10:1. 422 applied, 79% were admitted. 16% from top 10% of their high school class, 44% from top quarter, 71% from top half. Full-time: 671 students, 98% women, 2% men. Part-time: 534 students, 85% women, 15% men. Students come from 13 states and territories, 40 other countries, 6% from out-of-state, 0.2% Native American, 15% Hispanic, 16% black, 6% Asian American or Pacific Islander, 4% international, 43% 25 or older, 68% live on campus, 7% transferred in. Retention: 78% of full-time freshmen returned the following year. Academic areas with the most degrees conferred: business/marketing; communications/journalism; psychology. Core. Calendar: semesters. Academic remediation for entering students, ESL program, services for LD students, advanced placement, accelerated degree program, self-designed majors, honors program, independent study, distance learning, double major, summer session for credit, part-time degree program, internships, graduate courses open to undergrads. Off campus study at 4 members of the Seton Colleges, Drew University, Fairleigh Dickinson University. Study abroad program.

Entrance Requirements: Options: Peterson's Universal Application, electronic application, early admission, deferred admission, international baccalaureate accepted. Required: high school transcript, minimum 2.0 high school GPA, 2 recommendations, SAT or ACT. Recommended: essay, interview. Entrance: moderately difficult. Application deadline: 8/15. Notification: 11/15.

Costs Per Year: Application fee: $35. Comprehensive fee: $28,715 includes full-time tuition ($18,640), mandatory fees ($1100), and college room and board ($8975). Full-time tuition and fees vary according to program. Part-time tuition: $587 per credit. Part-time mandatory fees: $170. Part-time tuition and fees vary according to course load, location, and program.

Collegiate Environment: Orientation program. Drama-theater group, choral group, student-run newspaper. Social organizations: 28 open to all. Most popular organizations: Student Government Association, Students Take Action Committee, International/Intercultural Club, College Activities Board, campus ministry. Major annual events: Oktoberfest/Parents' Day, International Night, Christmas Celebration. Student services: health clinic, personal-psychological counseling. Campus security: 24-hour emergency response devices and patrols, late night transport-escort service, controlled dormitory access. 423 college housing spaces available; all were occupied in 2003-04. Freshmen guaranteed college housing. Option: women-only housing available. Mahoney Library with 110,230 books, 88,581 microform titles, 852 serials, 853 audiovisual materials, an OPAC, and a Web page. Operations spending for 2004 fiscal year: $1.9 million. 152 computers available on campus for general student use. A campuswide network can be accessed from student residence rooms and from off campus. Staffed computer lab on campus.

Community Environment: Situated in northern New Jersey, two miles east of Morristown (population 16,839), the college is near enough to New York to enjoy the educational, cultural and social advantages of that city. All forms of commercial transportation are convenient.

■ COUNTY COLLEGE OF MORRIS *F-11*

214 Center Grove Rd.
Randolph, NJ 07869-2086
Tel: (973)328-5000; 888-226-8001
Admissions: (973)328-5100
Fax: (973)328-1282
E-mail: admiss@ccm.edu
Web Site: http://www.ccm.edu/

Description: County-supported, 2-year, coed. Part of New Jersey Commission on Higher Education. Awards certificates, transfer associate, and terminal associate degrees. Founded 1966. Setting: 218-acre suburban campus with easy access to New York City. Endowment: $1.3 million. Educational spending for 2005 fiscal year: $3791 per student. Total enrollment: 8,496. 1% from top 10% of their high school class, 4% from top quarter, 22% from top half. Students come from 4 states and territories, 0.3% from out-of-state, 0.4% Native American, 11% Hispanic, 4% black, 7% Asian American or Pacific Islander, 0% international, 27% 25 or older. Core. Calendar: semesters. Academic remediation for entering students, ESL program, services for LD students, advanced placement, honors program, distance learning, summer session for credit, part-time degree program, adult/continuing education programs, co-op programs and internships.

Entrance Requirements: Open admission. Options: Common Application, early admission. Required: high school transcript. Required for some: recommendations. Placement: New Jersey Basic Skills Exam required; SAT or ACT required for some. Entrance: noncompetitive. Notification: continuous.

Collegiate Environment: Orientation program. Drama-theater group, choral group, student-run newspaper, radio station. Social organizations: 25 open to all. Most popular organizations: Student Government Association, Student Activities Programming Board, Black Student Union, United Latino Organization, student newspaper. Major annual event: Spring Festival. Student services: health clinic, personal-psychological counseling, women's center. Campus security: 24-hour emergency response devices and patrols, late night transport-escort service. College housing not available. Matsen Learning Resource Center with 102,550 books, 819 serials, an OPAC, and a Web page. Operations spending for 2004 fiscal year: $1.5 million. 51 computers available on campus for general student use. A campuswide network can be accessed from off-campus. Staffed computer lab on campus.

Community Environment: Morristown, population 16,839 is a suburban area 27 miles west of New York City, and was the winter encampment of General Washington's army during the winter of 1777 and 1779-80. Many historical events took place in Morristown. The sites have been restored and are incorporated in the Morristown National Historical Park. Commercial transportation is available. Excellent shopping and recreational facilities are available, including all water sports. Part-time employment opportunities are good.

■ CUMBERLAND COUNTY COLLEGE *U-6*

PO Box 1500, College Dr.
Vineland, NJ 08362-1500
Tel: (856)691-8600
Fax: (856)691-6157
Web Site: http://www.cccnj.edu/

Description: State and locally supported, 2-year, coed. Part of New Jersey Commission on Higher Education. Awards certificates, transfer associate, and terminal associate degrees. Founded 1963. Setting: 100-acre small town campus with easy access to Philadelphia. Total enrollment: 3,176. 2% Native American, 16% Hispanic, 19% black, 2% Asian American or Pacific Islander, 0% international, 50% 25 or older. Retention: 64% of full-time freshmen returned the following year. Core. Calendar: semesters. Academic remediation for entering students, ESL program, services for LD students, advanced placement, honors program, distance learning, double major, summer session for credit, part-time degree program, adult/continuing education programs, co-op programs.

Entrance Requirements: Open admission except for nursing, radiography programs. Options: electronic application, early admission, deferred admission. Required: high school transcript. Entrance: noncompetitive. Application deadline: Rolling. Notification: continuous.

Costs Per Year: Application fee: $25. Area resident tuition: $1848 full-time, $77 per credit part-time. State resident tuition: $3696 full-time, $154 per credit part-time. Nonresident tuition: $7392 full-time, $308 per credit part-time. Mandatory fees: $600 full-time, $25 per credit part-time.

Collegiate Environment: Drama-theater group, choral group, student-run newspaper. Social organizations: 20 open to all. Most popular organizations: Student Activities Board, Student Senate. Student services: personal-psychological counseling. Campus security: 24-hour emergency response devices, late night transport-escort service. College housing not available. Cumberland County College Library with 51,000 books, 3,900 microform titles, 213 serials, 480 audiovisual materials, an OPAC, and a Web page. Operations spending for 2004 fiscal year: $261,000. 275 computers available on campus for general student use. A campuswide network can be accessed from off-campus. Staffed computer lab on campus.

Community Environment: Cumberland County's population lies mainly in the tri-city area of Vineland, Bridgeton, and Millville. Industries include glass production, clothing manufacturing, and food processing and canning. Most church denominations are represented, and a hospital, shopping facilities, and numerous service and civic groups all contribute to the general well-being of the Cumberland area. Golf, tennis, and water sports are the main recreational activities in the county.

■ **DEVRY UNIVERSITY** *J-11*
630 US Hwy. 1
North Brunswick, NJ 08902-3362
Tel: (732)435-4880; (866)338-7934
Web Site: http://www.devry.edu/

Description: Proprietary, 4-year, coed. Part of DeVry University. Awards associate and bachelor's degrees. Founded 1969. Setting: 10-acre urban campus with easy access to New York City. Total enrollment: 1,503. Student-undergrad faculty ratio is 15:1. Full-time: 1,154 students, 38% women, 62% men. Part-time: 349 students, 42% women, 58% men. 0.3% Native American, 21% Hispanic, 22% black, 9% Asian American or Pacific Islander, 1% international, 45% 25 or older. Retention: 45% of full-time freshmen returned the following year. Academic areas with the most degrees conferred: computer and information sciences; engineering technologies. Calendar: semesters. Academic remediation for entering students, services for LD students, advanced placement, accelerated degree program, distance learning, summer session for credit, part-time degree program, adult/continuing education programs, co-op programs.

Entrance Requirements: Options: Peterson's Universal Application, electronic application, deferred admission, international baccalaureate accepted. Required: high school transcript, interview. Entrance: minimally difficult. Application deadline: Rolling.

Costs Per Year: Application fee: $50. One-time mandatory fee: $40. Tuition: $11,890 full-time, $505 per credit part-time. Mandatory fees: $270 full-time, $160 per year part-time. Full-time tuition and fees vary according to course load. Part-time tuition and fees vary according to course load.

Collegiate Environment: Orientation program. Social organizations: 10 open to all. Most popular organizations: Phi Theta Kappa, Data Processing Management Association, Telecommunications Management Association, Institute of Electrical and Electronics Engineering. Major annual event: Student Appreciation Day. Campus security: 24-hour emergency response devices and patrols, late night transport-escort service. College housing not available. Learning Resource Center with 32,109 books, 210 serials, 1,870 audiovisual materials, an OPAC, and a Web page. 575 computers available on campus for general student use. Computer purchase/lease plans available. A campuswide network can be accessed from off-campus. Staffed computer lab on campus.

Community Environment: North Brunswick is a suburban community within easy access to New York City, and Philadelphia and all their cultural and recreational resources. In addition, the 125-mile New Jersey Seacoast provides all forms of water sports.

■ **DREW UNIVERSITY** *G-12*
36 Madison Ave.
Madison, NJ 07940-1493
Tel: (973)408-3000
Admissions: (973)408-3739
Fax: (973)408-3939
E-mail: cadm@drew.edu
Web Site: http://www.drew.edu/

Description: Independent, university, coed, affiliated with United Methodist Church. Awards bachelor's, master's, doctoral, and first professional degrees. Founded 1867. Setting: 186-acre suburban campus with easy access to New York City. Endowment: $225,393. Educational spending for 2005 fiscal year: $12,221 per student. Total enrollment: 2,627. Faculty: 233 (148 full-time, 85 part-time). Student-undergrad faculty ratio is 11:1. 3,802 applied, 77% were admitted. 36% from top 10% of their high school class, 66% from top quarter, 90% from top half. Full-time: 1,561 students, 57% women, 43% men. Part-time: 52 students, 67% women, 33% men. Students come from 43 states and territories, 12 other countries, 44% from out-of-state, 0.3% Native American, 6% Hispanic, 3% black, 6% Asian American or Pacific Islander, 1% international, 3% 25 or older, 88% live on campus, 2% transferred in. Retention: 84% of full-time freshmen returned the following year. Academic areas with the most degrees conferred: social sciences; psychology; visual and performing arts. Core. Calendar: semesters. Academic remediation for entering students, services for LD students,

advanced placement, accelerated degree program, self-designed majors, independent study, double major, summer session for credit, part-time degree program, adult/continuing education programs, internships, graduate courses open to undergrads. Off campus study at College of Saint Elizabeth, Fairleigh Dickinson University. Study abroad program. ROTC: Army (c), Air Force (c).

Entrance Requirements: Options: Peterson's Universal Application, Common Application, early admission, early decision, deferred admission. Required: essay, high school transcript, 1 recommendation. Recommended: interview. Entrance: moderately difficult. Application deadlines: 2/15, 12/1 for early decision plan 1, 1/15 for early decision plan 2. Notification: 3/15, 12/24 for early decision plan 1, 2/15 for early decision plan 2.

Costs Per Year: Application fee: $50. Comprehensive fee: $39,698 includes full-time tuition ($30,740), mandatory fees ($546), and college room and board ($8412). College room only: $5438. Full-time tuition and fees vary according to course load. Room and board charges vary according to board plan and housing facility. Part-time tuition: $1280 per credit. Part-time mandatory fees: $22.75 per credit, $273. Part-time tuition and fees vary according to course load.

Collegiate Environment: Orientation program. Drama-theater group, choral group, student-run newspaper, radio station. Social organizations: 80 open to all. Most popular organizations: The Acorn (student newspaper), Student Government Association, Volunteer Resource Center, University Program Board, WMNJ (student radio station). Major annual events: First Annual Picnic, Holiday Ball, Midnight Breakfast. Student services: health clinic, personal-psychological counseling. Campus security: 24-hour emergency response devices and patrols, late night transport-escort service, controlled dormitory access. 1,337 college housing spaces available; 1,325 were occupied in 2003-04. Freshmen guaranteed college housing. Option: coed housing available. Drew University Library with 499,758 books, 373,236 microform titles, 2,609 serials, 2,445 audiovisual materials, an OPAC, and a Web page. Operations spending for 2004 fiscal year: $2.7 million. 200 computers available on campus for general student use. Computer purchase/lease plans available. A campuswide network can be accessed from student residence rooms and from off campus. Staffed computer lab on campus.

Community Environment: Madison, population approximately 16,000, is a suburban community in historical surroundings. Bordering a rural area that features numerous horse farms and a 6,000-acre national wildlife preserve, Madison is on a commuter rail line, just 30 miles from Manhattan. Some part-time employment is available.

■ **ESSEX COUNTY COLLEGE** *G-14*
303 University Ave.
Newark, NJ 07102-1798
Tel: (973)877-3000
Admissions: (973)877-3119
Fax: (973)623-6449
Web Site: http://www.essex.edu/

Description: County-supported, 2-year, coed. Part of New Jersey Commission on Higher Education. Awards certificates, transfer associate, and terminal associate degrees. Founded 1966. Setting: 22-acre urban campus with easy access to New York City. Total enrollment: 10,435. Student-undergrad faculty ratio is 28:1. 4,957 applied, 100% were admitted. Full-time: 5,683 students, 61% women, 39% men. Part-time: 4,752 students, 64% women, 36% men. Students come from 10 states and territories, 69 other countries, 2% from out-of-state, 0.1% Native American, 18% Hispanic, 50% black, 3% Asian American or Pacific Islander, 8% international, 50% 25 or older, 2% transferred in. Retention: 57% of full-time freshmen returned the following year. Core. Calendar: semesters. Academic remediation for entering students, ESL program, services for LD students, advanced placement, accelerated degree program, independent study, distance learning, double major, summer session for credit, part-time degree program, adult/continuing education programs, co-op programs and internships. Off campus study at New Jersey Institute of Technology; Rutgers, The State University of New Jersey; University of Medicine and Dentistry of New Jersey. ROTC: Army (c).

Entrance Requirements: Open admission except for allied health programs. Option: deferred admission. Required: high school transcript. Entrance: noncompetitive. Application deadline: 8/15. Notification: continuous.

Costs Per Year: Application fee: $25. Area resident tuition: $2318 full-time, $77.25 per credit hour part-time. State resident tuition: $4635 full-time, $154.50 per credit hour part-time. Mandatory fees: $650 full-time, $26 per credit hour part-time.

Collegiate Environment: Orientation program. Drama-theater group, choral group, student-run newspaper. Social organizations: 20 open to all. Most popular organizations: Fashion Entertainment Board, Phi Theta Kappa, Latin Student Union, DECA, Black Student Association. Student services: health clinic, personal-psychological counseling, women's center. Campus security: 24-hour emergency response devices and patrols. College housing not available. Martin Luther King, Jr. Library with 91,000 books, 29,607 microform titles, 639 serials, 3,618 audiovisual materials, an OPAC, and a Web page. 700 computers available on campus for general student use. A campuswide network can be accessed from off-campus. Staffed computer lab on campus.

Community Environment: See New Jersey Institute of Technology.

■ **FAIRLEIGH DICKINSON UNIVERSITY, COLLEGE AT FLORHAM**
G-12

285 Madison Ave.
Madison, NJ 07940-1099
Tel: (973)443-8500
Free: 800-338-8803
Admissions: (201)692-7304
Web Site: http://www.fdu.edu/

Description: Independent, comprehensive, coed. Awards associate, bachelor's, and master's degrees and post-master's certificates. Founded 1942. Setting: 178-acre suburban campus with easy access to New York City. System-wide research spending for 2004 fiscal year: $126,669. Total enrollment: 3,481. Faculty: 309 (113 full-time, 196 part-time). Student-undergrad faculty ratio is 16:1. 2,829 applied, 72% were admitted. 10% from top 10% of their high school class, 28% from top quarter, 64% from top half. Full-time: 2,300 students, 52% women, 48% men. Part-time: 295 students, 57% women, 43% men. Students come from 28 states and territories, 21 other countries, 18% from out-of-state, 0.3% Native American, 7% Hispanic, 8% black, 3% Asian American or Pacific Islander, 2% international, 11% 25 or older, 56% live on campus, 6% transferred in. Retention: 20% of full-time freshmen returned the following year. Academic areas with the most degrees conferred: business/marketing; psychology; liberal arts/general studies. Core. Calendar: semesters. Academic remediation for entering students, services for LD students, advanced placement, accelerated degree program, honors program, independent study, distance learning, double major, summer session for credit, part-time degree program, adult/continuing education programs, co-op programs and internships, graduate courses open to undergrads. Off campus study at College of Saint Elizabeth, Drew University, Cornell University, University of Hawaii at Hilo. Study abroad program. ROTC: Army (c).

Entrance Requirements: Options: Common Application, deferred admission. Required: high school transcript, 2 recommendations, SAT and SAT Subject Tests or ACT. Required for some: essay, interview. Entrance: moderately difficult. Notification: continuous.

Costs Per Year: Application fee: $40. Comprehensive fee: $33,932 includes full-time tuition ($24,364), mandatory fees ($540), and college room and board ($9028). College room only: $5404. Room and board charges vary according to board plan and housing facility. Part-time tuition: $725 per credit. Part-time mandatory fees: $130 per term. Part-time tuition and fees vary according to course load.

Collegiate Environment: Orientation program. Drama-theater group, choral group, student-run newspaper, radio station. Social organizations: 40 open to all; national fraternities, national sororities; 20% of eligible men and 30% of eligible women are members. Most popular organizations: student government, Florham Programming Committee, Association of Black Collegians, 'Metro' newspaper. Major annual events: Homecoming, Spring Fling, Greek Week. Student services: health clinic, personal-psychological counseling, women's center. Campus security: 24-hour emergency response devices and patrols, late night transport-escort service, trained law enforcement personnel on staff. 1,580 college housing spaces available; all were occupied in 2003-04. Freshmen given priority for college housing. Option: coed housing available. Friendship Library plus 1 other with an OPAC. 300 computers available on campus for general student use. A campuswide network can be accessed from student residence rooms and from off campus. Staffed computer lab on campus.

■ **FAIRLEIGH DICKINSON UNIVERSITY, METROPOLITAN CAMPUS**
F-15

1000 River Rd.
Teaneck, NJ 07666-1914
Tel: (201)692-2000

Free: 800-338-8803
Admissions: (201)692-7304
Web Site: http://www.fdu.edu/

Description: Independent, comprehensive, coed. Awards associate, bachelor's, master's, and doctoral degrees and post-master's certificates. Founded 1942. Setting: 88-acre suburban campus with easy access to New York City. System-wide research spending for 2004 fiscal year: $159,331. Total enrollment: 7,937. Faculty: 561 (182 full-time, 379 part-time). Student-undergrad faculty ratio is 15:1. 2,775 applied, 65% were admitted. 11% from top 10% of their high school class, 31% from top quarter, 69% from top half. Full-time: 1,833 students, 54% women, 46% men. Part-time: 3,611 students, 53% women, 47% men. Students come from 25 states and territories, 52 other countries, 13% from out-of-state, 0.3% Native American, 18% Hispanic, 20% black, 6% Asian American or Pacific Islander, 8% international, 38% 25 or older, 26% live on campus, 9% transferred in. Retention: 76% of full-time freshmen returned the following year. Academic areas with the most degrees conferred: liberal arts/general studies; business/marketing; communications/journalism. Core. Calendar: semesters. Academic remediation for entering students, ESL program, services for LD students, advanced placement, accelerated degree program, self-designed majors, honors program, independent study, distance learning, double major, summer session for credit, part-time degree program, adult/continuing education programs, co-op programs and internships, graduate courses open to undergrads. Off campus study at Cornell University, University of Hawaii at Hilo, Duke University. Study abroad program. ROTC: Army (c).

Entrance Requirements: Options: Common Application, early admission, deferred admission. Required: SAT and SAT Subject Tests or ACT. Required for some: essay, interview. Entrance: moderately difficult. Notification: continuous.

Costs Per Year: Application fee: $40. Comprehensive fee: $32,646 includes full-time tuition ($22,604), mandatory fees ($540), and college room and board ($9502). College room only: $5878. Room and board charges vary according to board plan and housing facility. Part-time tuition: $725 per credit. Part-time mandatory fees: $130 per term. Part-time tuition and fees vary according to course load.

Collegiate Environment: Orientation program. Drama-theater group, choral group, student-run newspaper, radio station. Social organizations: 63 open to all; national fraternities, national sororities; 1% of eligible men and 1% of eligible women are members. Most popular organizations: Indian Cultural Experience, Student Program Board, Student Government Association, International Student Association, Multicultural Council. Major annual events: Springfest, Welcome Week, International Fashion Show. Student services: health clinic, personal-psychological counseling. Campus security: 24-hour emergency response devices and patrols, late night transport-escort service, controlled dormitory access, trained law enforcement personnel on staff. 1,012 college housing spaces available; 850 were occupied in 2003-04. Option: coed housing available. Weiner Library plus 2 others with an OPAC. System-wide operations spending for 2004 fiscal year: $1.9 million. 210 computers available on campus for general student use. A campuswide network can be accessed from student residence rooms and from off campus. Staffed computer lab on campus.

■ **FELICIAN COLLEGE** *F-14*
262 South Main St.
Lodi, NJ 07644-2117
Tel: (201)559-6000
Admissions: (201)559-6187
Fax: (973)778-4111
E-mail: admissions@inet.felician.edu
Web Site: http://www.felician.edu/

Description: Independent Roman Catholic, comprehensive, coed. Awards associate, bachelor's, and master's degrees. Founded 1942. Setting: 37-acre suburban campus with easy access to New York City. Endowment: $716,953. Educational spending for 2005 fiscal year: $6023 per student. Total enrollment: 1,806. Faculty: 148 (83 full-time, 65 part-time). Student-undergrad faculty ratio is 13:1. 1,250 applied, 87% were admitted. Full-time: 1,157 students, 76% women, 24% men. Part-time: 393 students, 75% women, 25% men. Students come from 10 states and territories, 0.3% Native American, 17% Hispanic, 12% black, 7% Asian American or Pacific Islander, 60% 25 or older, 14% transferred in. Retention: 64% of full-time freshmen returned the following year. Core. Calendar: semesters. Academic remediation for entering students, ESL program, services for LD students, advanced placement, accelerated degree program, self-designed majors, honors program, independent study, distance learning, double major, summer session for credit, part-time degree program, external degree program, adult/continuing education programs, co-op programs and internships, graduate courses open to undergrads. Off campus study at University of Medicine and Dentistry of New Jersey. Study abroad program.

Entrance Requirements: Option: Common Application. Required: high school transcript, minimum 2.0 high school GPA, SAT or ACT. Required for some: essay, interview, ACT, SAT Subject Tests. Entrance: moderately difficult. Application deadline: Rolling. Notification: continuous.

Costs Per Year: Application fee: $30. Comprehensive fee: $26,150 includes full-time tuition ($17,300), mandatory fees ($900), and college room and board ($7950). Part-time tuition: $575 per credit.

Collegiate Environment: Orientation program. Drama-theater group, choral group. Social organizations: 20 open to all; local fraternities, local sororities. Most popular organizations: Student Nurses Association, Zeta Alpha Zeta teaching sorority, Campus Activity Board, Students In Free Enterprise, Student Government Association. Major annual events: Homecoming/ College Festival, Midnight Madness, Springfest. Student services: health clinic, personal-psychological counseling. Campus security: 24-hour patrols, student patrols, late night transport-escort service. 500 college housing spaces available. Freshmen given priority for college housing. Options: coed, men-only, women-only housing available. Felician College Library with 101,040 books, 77,143 microform titles, 563 serials, 3,991 audiovisual materials, an OPAC, and a Web page. Operations spending for 2004 fiscal year: $393,821. 100 computers available on campus for general student use. A campuswide network can be accessed from student residence rooms and from off campus. Staffed computer lab on campus.

Community Environment: Felician is located on two campuses, in Lodi and in Rutherford, in Bergen County, New Jersey, 12 miles from New York City and 10 minutes from the Meadowlands Sports Complex.

■ **GEORGIAN COURT UNIVERSITY** *N-13*
900 Lakewood Ave.
Lakewood, NJ 08701-2697
Tel: (732)987-2760
Free: 800-458-8422
Admissions: (732)364-2202
Fax: (732)987-2000
E-mail: admissions@georgian.edu
Web Site: http://www.georgian.edu/

Description: Independent Roman Catholic, comprehensive. Awards bachelor's and master's degrees and post-master's certificates. Founded 1908. Setting: 150-acre suburban campus with easy access to New York City and Philadelphia. Endowment: $40 million. Research spending for 2004 fiscal year: $173,946. Total enrollment: 3,153. Faculty: 298 (110 full-time, 188 part-time). Student-undergrad faculty ratio is 13:1. 532 applied, 75% were admitted. 8% from top 10% of their high school class, 31% from top quarter, 63% from top half. Full-time: 1,345 students, 95% women, 5% men. Part-time: 654 students, 82% women, 18% men. Students come from 9 states and territories, 11 other countries, 1% from out-of-state, 0.2% Native American, 6% Hispanic, 6% black, 2% Asian American or Pacific Islander, 1% international, 39% 25 or older, 15% live on campus, 13% transferred in. Retention: 84% of full-time freshmen returned the following year. Academic areas with the most degrees conferred: education; psychology; business/ marketing. Core. Calendar: semesters. Academic remediation for entering students, ESL program, services for LD students, advanced placement, accelerated degree program, honors program, independent study, distance learning, double major, summer session for credit, part-time degree program, adult/continuing education programs, internships, graduate courses open to undergrads. Off campus study. Study abroad program.

Entrance Requirements: Options: Peterson's Universal Application, electronic application, early action. Required: high school transcript, minimum 2.5 high school GPA, recommendations, SAT or ACT. Recommended: essay, interview. Entrance: moderately difficult. Application deadlines: 8/1, 11/15 for early action. Notification: 12/30 for early action.

Costs Per Year: Application fee: $40. Comprehensive fee: $26,700 includes full-time tuition ($18,380), mandatory fees ($720), and college room and board ($7600). Full-time tuition and fees vary according to program. Room and board charges vary according to board plan. Part-time tuition: $495 per credit. Part-time mandatory fees: $180 per term. Part-time tuition and fees vary according to course load and program.

Collegiate Environment: Orientation program. Choral group, student-run newspaper. Social organizations: 44 open to all. Most popular organizations: Social Work Club, Athletic Training Club, Re-Entry Women, Commuter Life, Phi Alpha Theta. Major annual events: Family Day, Irish Afternoon, Fall

Convocation. Student services: health clinic, personal-psychological counseling. Campus security: 24-hour emergency response devices and patrols, late night transport-escort service, controlled dormitory access. 356 college housing spaces available; 271 were occupied in 2003-04. Freshmen guaranteed college housing. Option: women-only housing available. The Sister Mary Joseph Cunningham Library with 145,413 books, 693,370 microform titles, 1,123 serials, 2,313 audiovisual materials, an OPAC, and a Web page. Operations spending for 2004 fiscal year: $2 million. 180 computers available on campus for general student use. A campuswide network can be accessed from student residence rooms. Staffed computer lab on campus.

Community Environment: Lakewood, population 46,000, is located in the central part of New Jersey and is convenient to the Route 9 corridor, Garden State Parkway, and Interstate 95. New York City, Philadelphia, and Atlantic City are each less than one and one-half hours from the college. Lakewood offers the services of a public library, hospital, various houses of worship, and numerous major civic and service organizations. The famous New Jersey shore is less than one-half hour away. Nearby are also the Naval Air Engineering Center, a sport parachuting center, and shopping centers.

■ **GIBBS COLLEGE (LIVINGSTON)**
630 West Mount Pleasant Ave.
Livingston, NJ 07039
Tel: (973)369-1360
Web Site: http://www.gibbsmontclair.com
Description: Proprietary, 2-year, coed.

■ **GIBBS COLLEGE (MONTCLAIR)** *F-13*
33 Plymouth St.
Montclair, NJ 07042-2699
Tel: (973)744-2010
Admissions: (201)744-2010
E-mail: mgreco@njgibbscollege.net
Web Site: http://www.njgibbscollege.net/
Description: Proprietary, 2-year, coed. Awards certificates, transfer associate, and terminal associate degrees. Founded 1950. Setting: 2-acre urban campus with easy access to New York City. Total enrollment: 600. 450 applied, 78% were admitted.

Entrance Requirements: Required: high school transcript, CPAt. Application deadline: Rolling.

Collegiate Environment: College housing not available.

■ **GLOUCESTER COUNTY COLLEGE** *R-6*
1400 Tanyard Rd.
Sewell, NJ 08080
Tel: (856)468-5000
Admissions: (856)415-2209
Fax: (856)468-8498
Web Site: http://www.gccnj.edu/

Description: County-supported, 2-year, coed. Part of New Jersey Commission on Higher Education. Awards certificates, transfer associate, and terminal associate degrees. Founded 1967. Setting: 270-acre rural campus with easy access to Philadelphia. Total enrollment: 5,610. 2,219 applied, 100% were admitted. Full-time: 2,950 students, 56% women, 44% men. Part-time: 2,660 students, 65% women, 35% men. 0.4% Native American, 2% Hispanic, 9% black, 2% Asian American or Pacific Islander, 1% international. Core. Calendar: semesters. Academic remediation for entering students, services for LD students, advanced placement, distance learning, summer session for credit, part-time degree program, co-op programs.

Entrance Requirements: Open admission except for nursing, respiratory therapy, nuclear medicine, ultrasound, auto technology programs. Options: electronic application, deferred admission. Required: high school transcript. Required for some: SAT or ACT. Entrance: noncompetitive. Application deadline: Rolling.

Collegiate Environment: Drama-theater group, choral group, student-run newspaper, radio station. Most popular organizations: Student Activities Board, student government, Accounting Club, Student Nurses Club, student newspaper. Major annual events: St. Nicholas Day, Earth Day, Spring Fling. Student services: health clinic, personal-psychological counseling, women's center. Campus security: 24-hour emergency response devices and patrols, late night transport-escort service. College housing not available. Gloucester County College Library with 55,710 books, 127,705 microform titles, 875 serials, 13,407 audiovisual materials, and an OPAC. 120 computers available on campus for general student use. A campuswide network can be accessed. Staffed computer lab on campus.

Community Environment: See Rutgers, The State University of New Jersey - Camden College of Arts and Sciences.

■ **HUDSON COUNTY COMMUNITY COLLEGE** *G-15*

25 Journal Square
Jersey City, NJ 07306
Tel: (201)656-2020
Admissions: (201)714-2115
Fax: (201)714-2136
Web Site: http://www.hccc.edu/

Description: State and locally supported, 2-year, coed. Part of New Jersey Commission on Higher Education. Awards certificates, diplomas, transfer associate, and terminal associate degrees. Founded 1974. Setting: urban campus with easy access to New York City. Endowment: $56,000. Educational spending for 2005 fiscal year: $2369 per student. Total enrollment: 6,489. 6,350 applied, 100% were admitted. Full-time: 4,277 students, 66% women, 34% men. Part-time: 2,212 students, 72% women, 28% men. 0.2% Native American, 42% Hispanic, 19% black, 18% Asian American or Pacific Islander, 3% international, 42% 25 or older. Core. Calendar: semesters. Academic remediation for entering students, ESL program, services for LD students, advanced placement, honors program, independent study, distance learning, double major, summer session for credit, part-time degree program, adult/continuing education programs, internships.

Entrance Requirements: Open admission. Required: high school transcript. Placement: ACCUPLACER required. Entrance: noncompetitive. Application deadline: 9/1. Notification: continuous until 9/1. Preference given to county residents.

Collegiate Environment: Drama-theater group, choral group, student-run newspaper. Social organizations: ; 25% of eligible men and 30% of eligible women are members. Most popular organizations: Psychology Club, Hispanos Unidos Pura El Progreso, International Student Organization, Drama Society. Major annual events: International Festival, Senior Dinner Dance. Student services: personal-psychological counseling. Campus security: 24-hour emergency response devices. College housing not available. Hudson County Community College Library/Learning Resources Center with 32,000 books, 11,000 microform titles, 251 serials, and 940 audiovisual materials. Operations spending for 2004 fiscal year: $710,000. 351 computers available on campus for general student use. A campuswide network can be accessed from off-campus. Staffed computer lab on campus.

■ **KEAN UNIVERSITY** *H-13*

1000 Morris Ave.
Union, NJ 07083
Tel: (908)737-KEAN
Admissions: (908)737-7100
Fax: (908)737-3415
E-mail: admitme@kean.edu
Web Site: http://www.kean.edu/

Description: State-supported, comprehensive, coed. Part of New Jersey State College System. Awards bachelor's and master's degrees and post-master's certificates. Founded 1855. Setting: 151-acre urban campus with easy access to New York City. Endowment: $3.7 million. Research spending for 2004 fiscal year: $290,000. Educational spending for 2005 fiscal year: $7818 per student. Total enrollment: 12,958. Faculty: 1,160 (382 full-time, 778 part-time). Student-undergrad faculty ratio is 15:1. 4,289 applied, 71% were admitted. 7% from top 10% of their high school class, 22% from top quarter, 57% from top half. Full-time: 7,591 students, 61% women, 39% men. Part-time: 2,444 students, 71% women, 29% men. Students come from 22 states and territories, 74 other countries, 2% from out-of-state, 0.3% Native American, 20% Hispanic, 21% black, 6% Asian American or Pacific Islander, 2% international, 32% 25 or older, 12% live on campus, 11% transferred in. Retention: 77% of full-time freshmen returned the following year. Academic areas with the most degrees conferred: business/marketing; education; psychology. Core. Calendar: semesters. Academic remediation for entering students, ESL program, services for LD students, advanced placement, accelerated degree program, honors program, independent study, distance learning, double major, summer session for credit, part-time degree program, adult/continuing education programs, co-op programs and internships, graduate courses open to undergrads. Off campus study at members of the Consortium of East New Jersey. Study abroad program. ROTC: Army (c), Air Force (c).

Entrance Requirements: Option: electronic application. Required: essay, high school transcript, minimum 2.0 high school GPA, SAT or ACT. Recommended: 2 recommendations. Required for some: interview. Entrance: moderately difficult. Application deadline: 5/31. Notification: continuous.

Costs Per Year: Application fee: $50. State resident tuition: $4898 full-time, $163.25 per credit part-time. Nonresident tuition: $7530 full-time, $251 per credit part-time. Mandatory fees: $2609 full-time, $87.70 per credit part-time. Part-time tuition and fees vary according to course load. College room and board: $8374. College room only: $5892. Room and board charges vary according to board plan and housing facility.

Collegiate Environment: Orientation program. Drama-theater group, choral group, student-run newspaper, radio station. Social organizations: 130 open to all; national fraternities, national sororities, local fraternities, local sororities. Most popular organization: Student Organization. Major annual events: homecoming, Campus Awareness Festival, Celebration of Diversity. Student services: health clinic, personal-psychological counseling, women's center. Campus security: 24-hour emergency response devices and patrols, student patrols, late night transport-escort service, controlled dormitory access, 24-hour patrols by campus police. 1,300 college housing spaces available; all were occupied in 2003-04. No special consideration for freshman housing applicants. On-campus residence required in freshman year. Options: coed, men-only, women-only housing available. Nancy Thompson Library plus 2 others with 280,000 books, 16,053 serials, an OPAC, and a Web page. Operations spending for 2004 fiscal year: $3.7 million. 2,000 computers available on campus for general student use. Computer purchase/lease plans available. A campuswide network can be accessed from student residence rooms and from off campus. Staffed computer lab on campus.

Community Environment: The township of Union, population 53,400, and its proximity to major automobile, bus, rail, and air transportation networks makes access to the university excellent. This provides continuous cultural, intellectual and social interchange between the cities and the university. Community facilities include library, numerous churches, hospitals and clinics, major civic and service organizations. A recreation center provides facilities for special activities.

■ **MERCER COUNTY COMMUNITY COLLEGE** *M-9*

1200 Old Trenton Rd., PO Box B
Trenton, NJ 08690-1004
Tel: (609)586-4800
Free: 800-392-MCCC
Fax: (609)586-6944
Web Site: http://www.mccc.edu/

Description: State and locally supported, 2-year, coed. Awards certificates, transfer associate, and terminal associate degrees. Founded 1966. Setting: 292-acre suburban campus with easy access to New York City and Philadelphia. Total enrollment: 8,928. Student-undergrad faculty ratio is 20:1. 2,049 applied, 100% were admitted. Full-time: 3,404 students, 51% women, 49% men. Part-time: 5,524 students, 61% women, 39% men. Students come from 5 states and territories, 7% from out-of-state, 0.2% Native American, 8% Hispanic, 24% black, 5% Asian American or Pacific Islander, 5% international, 41% 25 or older, 4% transferred in. Core. Calendar: semesters. Academic remediation for entering students, ESL program, services for LD students, advanced placement, accelerated degree program, self-designed majors, independent study, distance learning, double major, summer session for credit, part-time degree program, external degree program, adult/continuing education programs, co-op programs and internships. ROTC: Army (c), Air Force (c).

Entrance Requirements: Open admission. Options: Peterson's Universal Application, Common Application, electronic application, deferred admission. Required: high school transcript. Recommended: interview. Entrance: noncompetitive. Application deadline: Rolling. Notification: continuous. Preference given to county residents.

Costs Per Year: Application fee: $0. Area resident tuition: $2940 full-time, $98 per credit part-time. State resident tuition: $3945 full-time, $131.50 per credit part-time. Nonresident tuition: $6045 full-time, $201.50 per credit part-time. Mandatory fees: $495 full-time, $16.50 per credit part-time.

Collegiate Environment: Orientation program. Drama-theater group, choral group, student-run newspaper, radio station. Social organizations: 38 open to all. Most popular organizations: Student Government Association, student radio station, African-American Student Organization, Student Activities Board, Phi Theta Kappa. Major annual events: NJCAA National Soccer Tournament, Club Day, Spring Day. Student services: personal-psychological counseling. Campus security: 24-hour emergency response devices and patrols. College housing not available. Mercer County Community College

Library plus 1 other with 57,317 books, 251,470 microform titles, 8,934 audiovisual materials, an OPAC, and a Web page. Operations spending for 2004 fiscal year: $555,239.

Community Environment: See Rider University.

■ **MIDDLESEX COUNTY COLLEGE** *J-12*
2600 Woodbridge Ave., PO Box 3050
Edison, NJ 08818-3050
Tel: (732)548-6000
Admissions: (732)906-4243
Web Site: http://www.middlesexcc.edu/

Description: County-supported, 2-year, coed. Awards certificates, transfer associate, and terminal associate degrees. Founded 1964. Setting: 200-acre suburban campus with easy access to New York City. Total enrollment: 11,276. Student-undergrad faculty ratio is 21:1. 9,394 applied, 69% were admitted. Students come from 4 states and territories, 44% 25 or older. Core. Calendar: semesters. Academic remediation for entering students, ESL program, services for LD students, advanced placement, independent study, distance learning, summer session for credit, part-time degree program, adult/continuing education programs, co-op programs and internships. Off campus study. Study abroad program. ROTC: Army (c).

Entrance Requirements: Open admission exceptions: dental hygiene, nursing, radiography, medical laboratory technology, psychosocial rehabilitation, respiratory care and automotive technology programs. Options: Peterson's Universal Application, early admission, deferred admission. Required: high school transcript. Required for some: National League of Nursing Exam for most health-related programs. Entrance: noncompetitive. Application deadline: Rolling. Notification: continuous. Preference given to county residents.

Costs Per Year: Application fee: $25. Area resident tuition: $1,957 full-time, $81.55 per credit part-time. State resident tuition: $4,526 full-time, $188.60 per credit part-time. Mandatory fees: $612 full-time, $25.50 per credit part-time.

Collegiate Environment: Orientation program. Drama-theater group, choral group, student-run newspaper, radio station. Student services: health clinic, personal-psychological counseling. Campus security: 24-hour emergency response devices and patrols. College housing not available. Middlesex County College Library plus 1 other with 85,160 books, 8,583 microform titles, 599 serials, 5,642 audiovisual materials, an OPAC, and a Web page. 1,290 computers available on campus for general student use. A campus-wide network can be accessed from off-campus. Staffed computer lab on campus.

Community Environment: Edison (population, 67,120) is located in a major metropolitan area, and is both a residential and industrial city with train and bus service available. It is located 45 minutes from New York City. Community facilities include a library, churches of all denominations, several hospitals, museums and various civic and service organizations. Edison offers fine shopping facilities. Part-time jobs are available. Parks and the Raritan River provide for boating and swimming, etc.

■ **MONMOUTH UNIVERSITY** *L-15*
400 Cedar Ave.
West Long Branch, NJ 07764-1898
Tel: (732)571-3400
Free: 800-543-9671
Admissions: (732)571-3456
Fax: (732)263-5166
E-mail: admission@monmouth.edu
Web Site: http://www.monmouth.edu/

Description: Independent, comprehensive, coed. Awards associate, bachelor's, and master's degrees and post-master's certificates. Founded 1933. Setting: 153-acre suburban campus with easy access to New York City and Philadelphia. Endowment: $38.1 million. Research spending for 2004 fiscal year: $630,249. Educational spending for 2005 fiscal year: $6402 per student. Total enrollment: 6,350. Faculty: 513 (246 full-time, 267 part-time). Student-undergrad faculty ratio is 15:1. 5,089 applied, 69% were admitted. 11% from top 10% of their high school class, 33% from top quarter, 72% from top half. Full-time: 4,116 students, 57% women, 43% men. Part-time: 439 students, 68% women, 32% men. Students come from 28 states and territories, 12 other countries, 8% from out-of-state, 0.3% Native American, 4% Hispanic, 4% black, 2% Asian American or Pacific Islander, 0.3% international, 11% 25 or older, 43% live on campus, 8% transferred in. Retention: 75% of full-time freshmen returned the following year. Academic areas with the most degrees conferred: business/marketing; education; com-

munications/journalism. Core. Calendar: semesters. Academic remediation for entering students, services for LD students, advanced placement, accelerated degree program, self-designed majors, honors program, independent study, distance learning, double major, summer session for credit, part-time degree program, co-op programs and internships, graduate courses open to undergrads. Study abroad program. ROTC: Air Force (c).

Entrance Requirements: Options: Peterson's Universal Application, early admission, early decision, early action, deferred admission, international baccalaureate accepted. Required: high school transcript, resume of activities including community involvement and leadership positions, SAT or ACT. Recommended: essay, recommendations, interview. Entrance: moderately difficult. Application deadlines: 3/1, 12/1 for early decision, 12/15 for early action. Notification: 4/1, 1/1 for early decision, 1/15 for early action.

Costs Per Year: Application fee: $35. Comprehensive fee: $28,956 includes full-time tuition ($20,066), mandatory fees ($620), and college room and board ($8270). College room only: $4440. Room and board charges vary according to board plan and housing facility. Part-time tuition: $581 per credit hour. Part-time mandatory fees: $155 per term.

Collegiate Environment: Orientation program. Drama-theater group, choral group, student-run newspaper, radio station. Social organizations: 67 open to all; national fraternities, national sororities; 8% of eligible men and 9% of eligible women are members. Most popular organizations: student-run radio station, Student Government Association, student newspaper (Outlook), Student Activities Board, Shadows (yearbook). Major annual events: Homecoming, Winter Ball, Spring Fest. Student services: legal services, health clinic, personal-psychological counseling, women's center. Campus security: 24-hour emergency response devices and patrols, late night transport-escort service, controlled dormitory access. 1,742 college housing spaces available; all were occupied in 2003-04. Freshmen given priority for college housing. Option: coed housing available. Murry and Leonie Guggenheim Memorial Library with 260,400 books, 16,000 serials, an OPAC, and a Web page. Operations spending for 2004 fiscal year: $1.9 million. 673 computers available on campus for general student use. A campuswide network can be accessed from student residence rooms and from off campus. Staffed computer lab on campus.

Community Environment: The university is located in West Long Branch, a suburban community of 7,700 people. The campus is located just one mile from the Atlantic Ocean. Both New York and Philadelphia are about a one and a half hour trip away. Newark airport is 45 miles distant. Train and bus service are available 2 miles from campus.

■ **MONTCLAIR STATE UNIVERSITY** *F-13*
1 Normal Ave.
Montclair, NJ 07043-1624
Tel: (973)655-4000
Free: 800-331-9205
Admissions: (973)655-5116
Fax: (973)893-5455
E-mail: msuadm@saturn.montclair.edu
Web Site: http://www.montclair.edu/

Description: State-supported, comprehensive, coed. Awards bachelor's, master's, and doctoral degrees and post-master's certificates. Founded 1908. Setting: 275-acre suburban campus with easy access to New York City. Research spending for 2004 fiscal year: $1.2 million. Educational spending for 2005 fiscal year: $5300 per student. Total enrollment: 16,063. Faculty: 1,172 (477 full-time, 695 part-time). Student-undergrad faculty ratio is 17:1. 8,877 applied, 54% were admitted. 19% from top 10% of their high school class, 45% from top quarter, 83% from top half. 50 valedictorians. Full-time: 9,909 students, 60% women, 40% men. Part-time: 2,265 students, 64% women, 36% men. Students come from 13 states and territories, 87 other countries, 5% from out-of-state, 0.4% Native American, 17% Hispanic, 10% black, 6% Asian American or Pacific Islander, 3% international, 23% 25 or older, 27% live on campus, 10% transferred in. Retention: 82% of full-time freshmen returned the following year. Academic areas with the most degrees conferred: business/marketing; family and consumer sciences; psychology. Core. Calendar: semesters. Academic remediation for entering students, ESL program, services for LD students, advanced placement, accelerated degree program, freshman honors college, honors program, independent study, double major, summer session for credit, part-time degree program, adult/continuing education programs, co-op programs and internships, graduate courses open to undergrads. Off campus study at New Jersey School of Conservation, New Jersey Marine Science Consortium. Study abroad program. ROTC: Air Force (c).

Entrance Requirements: Options: electronic application, deferred admission, international baccalaureate accepted. Required: essay, high school transcript, SAT or ACT. Required for some: interview. Entrance: moderately difficult. Application deadline: 3/1. Notification: continuous.

Costs Per Year: Application fee: $55. State resident tuition: $5581 full-time, $186.04 per credit part-time. Nonresident tuition: $10,029 full-time, $334.22 per credit part-time. Mandatory fees: $2128 full-time, $69.61 per credit part-time, $20 per term part-time. College room and board: $8618. College room only: $5768. Room and board charges vary according to board plan and housing facility.

Collegiate Environment: Orientation program. Drama-theater group, choral group, marching band, student-run newspaper, radio station. Social organizations: 87 open to all; national fraternities, national sororities, local fraternities, local sororities. Most popular organizations: Latin American Student Organization, Campus Recreation, Players (A Theatrical Organization), WMSC-FM (The Student-Run Radio Station), Human Relations and Leadership Association. Major annual events: homecoming, Welcome Week, World's Fair. Student services: legal services, health clinic, personal-psychological counseling, women's center. Campus security: 24-hour emergency response devices and patrols, late night transport-escort service, controlled dormitory access, video surveillance, student escorts. 3,149 college housing spaces available; all were occupied in 2003-04. Freshmen given priority for college housing. Options: coed, women-only housing available. Sprague Library with 426,583 books, 1.2 million microform titles, 2,955 serials, 47,408 audiovisual materials, an OPAC, and a Web page. Operations spending for 2004 fiscal year: $4.1 million. 218 computers available on campus for general student use. Computer purchase/lease plans available. A campuswide network can be accessed from student residence rooms and from off campus. Staffed computer lab on campus.

Community Environment: Population about 40,000, the township of Montclair is a residential suburb about 14 miles west of New York City and about six miles northwest of Newark. Residents can commute to Manhattan by bus or railroad. An art museum, theater groups, music societies, and a library are provided by the community as well as two hospitals, several shopping areas and numerous active civic and social organizations.

■ **NEW JERSEY CITY UNIVERSITY** G-15

2039 Kennedy Blvd.
Jersey City, NJ 07305-1597
Tel: (201)200-2000; 888-441-NJCU
Admissions: (201)200-3234
Fax: (201)200-2044
E-mail: admissions@jcs1.jcstate.edu
Web Site: http://www.njcu.edu/

Description: State-supported, comprehensive, coed. Awards bachelor's and master's degrees and post-master's certificates. Founded 1927. Setting: 46-acre urban campus with easy access to New York City. Total enrollment: 8,464. Faculty: 524 (251 full-time, 273 part-time). Student-undergrad faculty ratio is 16:1. 2,719 applied, 54% were admitted. 10% from top 10% of their high school class, 23% from top quarter, 66% from top half. Full-time: 4,192 students, 62% women, 38% men. Part-time: 1,812 students, 64% women, 36% men. Students come from 10 states and territories, 1% from out-of-state, 0.1% Native American, 33% Hispanic, 20% black, 8% Asian American or Pacific Islander, 1% international, 26% 25 or older, 4% live on campus, 13% transferred in. Retention: 74% of full-time freshmen returned the following year. Academic areas with the most degrees conferred: business/marketing; psychology; social sciences. Core. Calendar: semesters. Academic remediation for entering students, ESL program, services for LD students, advanced placement, accelerated degree program, honors program, independent study, distance learning, double major, summer session for credit, part-time degree program, adult/continuing education programs, co-op programs and internships, graduate courses open to undergrads. Off campus study at Hudson County Consortium. Study abroad program.

Entrance Requirements: Options: electronic application, deferred admission. Required: essay, high school transcript, minimum 2.0 high school GPA, SAT or ACT. Recommended: 1 recommendation. Required for some: interview. Entrance: moderately difficult. Application deadline: 4/1. Notification: continuous.

Costs Per Year: Application fee: $35. State resident tuition: $5190 full-time, $173 per credit hour part-time. Nonresident tuition: $10,230 full-time, $341 per credit hour part-time. Mandatory fees: $1850 full-time, $59.95 per credit part-time. College room and board: $7306. College room only: $4630.

Collegiate Environment: Orientation program. Drama-theater group, choral group, student-run newspaper, radio station. Social organizations: 40 open to all; national fraternities, local fraternities, local sororities, frorority; 1% of

eligible men and 1% of eligible women are members. Most popular organizations: International Student Association, Black Freedom Society, Latin Power Association. Major annual events: Unity Banquet, Spring and Fall Formals, Club and Greek Day. Student services: legal services, health clinic, personal-psychological counseling, women's center. Campus security: 24-hour emergency response devices and patrols, late night transport-escort service. Option: coed housing available. Congressman Frank J. Guarini Library with 212,786 books, 465,875 microform titles, 1,260 serials, 2,234 audiovisual materials, an OPAC, and a Web page. 1,400 computers available on campus for general student use. A campuswide network can be accessed from student residence rooms and from off campus. Staffed computer lab on campus.

Community Environment: Jersey City, the second largest in the state with a population of 260,545, is just across the Hudson River (via the Holland Tunnel or PATH trains) from New York City. A manufacturing center, Jersey City is home to roughly 600 industrial plants. It is a major shipping port and the terminus for some of the nation's largest railroads and transcontinental motor freight lines. Transportation is convenient for all the entertainment, recreational, cultural, and historical offerings to be had in either New Jersey or throughout the tri-state area.

■ **NEW JERSEY INSTITUTE OF TECHNOLOGY** G-14

University Heights
Newark, NJ 07102
Tel: (973)596-3000
Free: 800-925-NJIT
Admissions: (973)596-3300
Fax: (973)802-1854
E-mail: admissions@njit.edu
Web Site: http://www.njit.edu/

Description: State-supported, university, coed. Awards bachelor's, master's, and doctoral degrees. Founded 1881. Setting: 45-acre urban campus with easy access to New York City. Endowment: $73 million. Research spending for 2004 fiscal year: $70 million. Educational spending for 2005 fiscal year: $9600 per student. Total enrollment: 8,058. Faculty: 654 (416 full-time, 238 part-time). Student-undergrad faculty ratio is 13:1. 2,562 applied, 71% were admitted. 24% from top 10% of their high school class, 50% from top quarter, 79% from top half. Full-time: 4,082 students, 20% women, 80% men. Part-time: 1,181 students, 19% women, 81% men. Students come from 24 states and territories, 65 other countries, 4% from out-of-state, 0.3% Native American, 13% Hispanic, 11% black, 21% Asian American or Pacific Islander, 6% international, 24% 25 or older, 28% live on campus, 8% transferred in. Retention: 82% of full-time freshmen returned the following year. Academic areas with the most degrees conferred: engineering; computer and information sciences; engineering technologies. Core. Calendar: semesters. Academic remediation for entering students, ESL program, services for LD students, advanced placement, accelerated degree program, freshman honors college, honors program, independent study, distance learning, double major, summer session for credit, part-time degree program, adult/continuing education programs, co-op programs and internships, graduate courses open to undergrads. Off campus study at Essex County College, Rutgers, The State University of New Jersey, University of Medicine and Dentistry of New Jersey; Camden County College. Study abroad program. ROTC: Air Force.

Entrance Requirements: Options: Common Application, electronic application, early admission, early decision, deferred admission. Required: high school transcript, SAT or ACT. Recommended: 1 recommendation. Required for some: essay, interview, SAT Subject Tests. Entrance: moderately difficult. Application deadline: 4/1. Notification: continuous. Preference given to state residents.

Costs Per Year: Application fee: $50. State resident tuition: $8472 full-time, $321 per credit part-time. Nonresident tuition: $14,676 full-time, $628 per credit part-time. Mandatory fees: $1350 full-time, $64 per credit part-time, $102 per term part-time. Full-time tuition and fees vary according to course load and degree level. Part-time tuition and fees vary according to course load and degree level. College room and board: $8572. College room only: $5974. Room and board charges vary according to board plan and housing facility.

Collegiate Environment: Orientation program. Drama-theater group, student-run newspaper, radio station. Social organizations: 70 open to all; national fraternities, national sororities, local fraternities, local sororities; 9% of eligible men and 4% of eligible women are members. Most popular organizations: Student Senate, Student Activities Council, Microcomputer Users Group, Chess Club. Major annual events: World Week, Spring Week,

Miniversity. Student services: health clinic, personal-psychological counseling, women's center. Campus security: 24-hour emergency response devices and patrols, late night transport-escort service, controlled dormitory access, bicycle patrols, sexual assault response team. 1,434 college housing spaces available; 1,393 were occupied in 2003-04. No special consideration for freshman housing applicants. Option: coed housing available. Van Houten Library plus 1 other with 160,000 books, 1,100 serials, an OPAC, and a Web page. Operations spending for 2004 fiscal year: $2.6 million. 1,938 computers available on campus for general student use. Computer purchase/lease plans available. A campuswide network can be accessed from student residence rooms and from off campus. Staffed computer lab on campus.

Community Environment: Newark is the largest metropolis of New Jersey and contains some of the state's greatest cultural institutions: the Newark Museum, the Newark Public Library, and Symphony Hall. Construction has begun on the 12.5 acre New Jersey Center for the Performing Arts. Part-time employment opportunities are good.

■ **OCEAN COUNTY COLLEGE** *P-13*
College Dr., PO Box 2001
Toms River, NJ 08754-2001
Tel: (732)255-0400
Admissions: (732)255-0304
Web Site: http://www.ocean.edu/
Description: County-supported, 2-year, coed. Part of New Jersey Commission on Higher Education. Awards certificates, diplomas, transfer associate, and terminal associate degrees. Founded 1964. Setting: 275-acre small town campus with easy access to Philadelphia. Total enrollment: 8,449. Full-time: 4,023 students, 53% women, 47% men. Part-time: 4,426 students, 64% women, 36% men. Students come from 6 other countries. 0.3% Native American, 6% Hispanic, 4% black, 2% Asian American or Pacific Islander, 0.4% international. Core. Calendar: semesters. Academic remediation for entering students, ESL program, services for LD students, advanced placement, accelerated degree program, freshman honors college, honors program, distance learning, summer session for credit, part-time degree program, adult/continuing education programs, co-op programs. Study abroad program.
Entrance Requirements: Open admission except for nursing program. Options: early admission, deferred admission. Required for some: high school transcript. Entrance: noncompetitive. Application deadline: Rolling. Notification: continuous. Preference given to county residents for nursing program.
Costs Per Year: Application fee: $15. Area resident tuition: $2460 full-time, $82 per credit part-time. State resident tuition: $3360 full-time, $112 per credit part-time. Nonresident tuition: $5520 full-time, $184 per credit part-time. Mandatory fees: $720 full-time, $24.
Collegiate Environment: Orientation program. Drama-theater group, choral group, student-run newspaper, radio station. Student services: health clinic, personal-psychological counseling. Campus security: 24-hour emergency response devices and patrols, late night transport-escort service. College housing not available. Ocean County College Library with 74,215 books and 428 serials. 100 computers available on campus for general student use. Staffed computer lab on campus.
Community Environment: A principality in Dover Township, Toms River is the business, vacation, financial, and industrial hub of Ocean County. The city is located four miles inland from the New Jersey shoreline where buses and trains are convenient. An airport is within 20 miles. Community facilities include churches of the major denominations, hospitals, libraries, and civic and service organizations. Recreational activities offered are swimming, picnicking, hiking, camping and canoeing. Some part-time work is available.

■ **PASSAIC COUNTY COMMUNITY COLLEGE** *E-14*
One College Blvd.
Paterson, NJ 07505-1179
Tel: (973)684-6800
Admissions: (973)684-6304
Web Site: http://www.pccc.cc.nj.us/
Description: County-supported, 2-year, coed. Awards certificates, transfer associate, and terminal associate degrees. Founded 1968. Setting: 6-acre urban campus with easy access to New York City. Endowment: $78,695. Research spending for 2004 fiscal year: $97,474. Educational spending for 2005 fiscal year: $3777 per student. Total enrollment: 6,308. 2,076 applied, 100% were admitted. 1% from out-of-state, 41% 25 or older. Core. Calendar: semesters. Academic remediation for entering students, ESL program, advanced placement, honors program, independent study, distance learning,

double major, summer session for credit, part-time degree program, co-op programs and internships. Study abroad program. ROTC: Army (c).
Entrance Requirements: Open admission except for nursing, respiratory therapy, radiological technology programs. Options: early admission, deferred admission. Placement: New Jersey Basic Skills Exam required. Entrance: noncompetitive. Application deadline: Rolling. Preference given to county residents.
Collegiate Environment: Choral group, student-run newspaper. Most popular organizations: Latin American Club, Christian Club, International Club, Soccer Club, Volleyball Club. Student services: personal-psychological counseling. Campus security: late night transport-escort service. College housing not available. Passaic County Community College Learning Resource Center plus 1 other with 90,000 books, 250 microform titles, 263 serials, and 2,000 audiovisual materials. Operations spending for 2004 fiscal year: $482,542. 150 computers available on campus for general student use. Staffed computer lab on campus.
Community Environment: See Bergen Community College.

■ **PRINCETON UNIVERSITY** *K-10*
Princeton, NJ 08544-1019
Tel: (609)258-3000
Admissions: (609)258-3062
Web Site: http://www.princeton.edu/
Description: Independent, university, coed. Awards bachelor's, master's, and doctoral degrees. Founded 1746. Setting: 600-acre suburban campus with easy access to New York City and Philadelphia. Endowment: $11.2 billion. Research spending for 2004 fiscal year: $187.3 million. Educational spending for 2005 fiscal year: $31,450 per student. Total enrollment: 6,916. Faculty: 1,060 (809 full-time, 251 part-time). Student-undergrad faculty ratio is 5:1. 16,510 applied, 11% were admitted. 94% from top 10% of their high school class, 99% from top quarter, 100% from top half. Full-time: 4,719 students, 46% women, 54% men. Part-time: 187 students, 45% women, 55% men. Students come from 53 states and territories, 75 other countries, 85% from out-of-state, 1% Native American, 7% Hispanic, 9% black, 13% Asian American or Pacific Islander, 9% international, 0% 25 or older, 98% live on campus. Retention: 98% of full-time freshmen returned the following year. Academic areas with the most degrees conferred: social sciences; engineering; history. Core. Calendar: semesters. Services for LD students, advanced placement, self-designed majors, independent study, adult/continuing education programs, graduate courses open to undergrads. Off campus study at Rutgers, The State University of New Jersey, Westminster Choir College of Rider University, Princeton Theological Seminary. Study abroad program. ROTC: Army, Air Force (c).
Entrance Requirements: Options: Common Application, electronic application, early decision, deferred admission, international baccalaureate accepted. Required: essay, high school transcript, 3 recommendations, SAT and SAT Subject Tests or ACT. Recommended: interview. Entrance: most difficult. Application deadlines: 1/1; 11/1 for early decision. Notification: 4/3, 12/15 for early decision.
Costs Per Year: Application fee: $65. Comprehensive fee: $42,200 includes full-time tuition ($33,000) and college room and board ($9200). College room only: $4885.
Collegiate Environment: Orientation program. Drama-theater group, choral group, marching band, student-run newspaper, radio station. Social organizations: 250 open to all. Student services: legal services, health clinic, personal-psychological counseling, women's center. Campus security: 24-hour emergency response devices and patrols, student patrols, late night transport-escort service, controlled dormitory access. 4,535 college housing spaces available. Freshmen guaranteed college housing. On-campus residence required through sophomore year. Options: coed, men-only, women-only housing available. Harvey S. Firestone Memorial Library plus 14 others with 7 million books, 6.4 million microform titles, 44,634 serials, 522,790 audiovisual materials, an OPAC, and a Web page. Operations spending for 2004 fiscal year: $40.8 million. 500 computers available on campus for general student use. Computer purchase/lease plans available. A campuswide network can be accessed from student residence rooms and from off campus. Staffed computer lab on campus.
Community Environment: Numerous historical events have taken place at Princeton since the time of its founding in 1746. The first state legislature met here in 1776, as well as in 1873; the Continental Congress Sessions were held here. Princeton is 50 miles southwest of New York City and 45 miles northeast of Philadelphia. All forms of commercial transportation are available. Community facilities are excellent, housing is available for students. The James Forrestal Campus which adjoins Princeton University's

campus is an integral part of the University's advanced training and research in the basic and engineering sciences. The largest single project at Forrestal is the Plasma Physics Laboratory, a long range effort to develop a controlled thermonuclear reactor which would provide an infinite energy source. Many of the facilities of the Department of Aerospace and Mechanical Sciences for the Aerospace Propulsion Sciences and the Gas Dynamics Laboratories are here. Rockingham, five miles north is also known as the Berrien Mansion which was used as General Washington's headquarters during 1783. His"Farewell Address to the Armies" was delivered here.

■ **RABBI JACOB JOSEPH SCHOOL** *J-12*
One Plainfield Ave
Edison, NJ 08817
Tel: (908)985-6533
Description: Independent Jewish, 4-year.

■ **RABBINICAL COLLEGE OF AMERICA** *G-11*
226 Sussex Ave., PO Box 1996
Morristown, NJ 07962-1996
Tel: (973)267-9404
Fax: (973)267-5208
Description: Independent Jewish, 4-year, men only. Awards bachelor's degrees. Founded 1956. Setting: 81-acre small town campus with easy access to New York City. Total enrollment: 259. 60 applied, 100% were admitted. Students come from 24 states and territories, 10 other countries. Calendar: semesters. Academic remediation for entering students, accelerated degree program, summer session for credit, internships. Off campus study at Yeshivah Gedolah of New England, Yeshivah Gedolah of Miami. Study abroad program.
Entrance Requirements: Required: interview. Required for some: recommendations. Entrance: minimally difficult. Application deadline: Rolling.
Collegiate Environment: Student services: health clinic, personal-psychological counseling. On-campus residence required through senior year. 10,000 books.

■ **RAMAPO COLLEGE OF NEW JERSEY** *E-14*
505 Ramapo Valley Rd.
Mahwah, NJ 07430-1680
Tel: (201)684-7500
Admissions: (201)684-7300
Fax: (201)684-7508
E-mail: admissions@ramapo.edu
Web Site: http://www.ramapo.edu/
Description: State-supported, comprehensive, coed. Part of New Jersey State College System. Awards bachelor's and master's degrees. Founded 1969. Setting: 300-acre suburban campus with easy access to New York City. Endowment: $1.3 million. Research spending for 2004 fiscal year: $60,000. Educational spending for 2005 fiscal year: $6116 per student. Total enrollment: 5,538. Faculty: 433 (187 full-time, 246 part-time). Student-undergrad faculty ratio is 16:1. 4,507 applied, 41% were admitted. 31% from top 10% of their high school class, 80% from top quarter, 99% from top half. Full-time: 4,254 students, 60% women, 40% men. Part-time: 979 students, 61% women, 39% men. Students come from 24 states and territories, 60 other countries, 7% from out-of-state, 0.3% Native American, 8% Hispanic, 7% black, 4% Asian American or Pacific Islander, 3% international, 18% 25 or older, 51% live on campus, 10% transferred in. Retention: 89% of full-time freshmen returned the following year. Academic areas with the most degrees conferred: biological/life sciences; business/marketing; social sciences. Core. Calendar: semesters. Academic remediation for entering students, ESL program, services for LD students, advanced placement, accelerated degree program, self-designed majors, freshman honors college, honors program, independent study, double major, summer session for credit, part-time degree program, external degree program, adult/continuing education programs, co-op programs and internships, graduate courses open to undergrads. Off campus study at New Jersey Institute of Technology; SUNY State College of Optometry; University of Medical and Dental of N.J.; NY Chiropractic College. Study abroad program. ROTC: Air Force (c).
Entrance Requirements: Options: Peterson's Universal Application, electronic application, early admission, early action, deferred admission. Required: essay, high school transcript, recommendations, SAT. Recommended: minimum 3.0 high school GPA. Required for some: ACT. Entrance: moderately difficult. Application deadline: 3/1. Notification: continuous until 3/1.

Costs Per Year: Application fee: $55. State resident tuition: $6091 full-time, $190.35 per credit part-time. Nonresident tuition: $11,008 full-time, $344 per credit part-time. Mandatory fees: $2701 full-time, $84.40 per credit part-time. College room and board: $9464. College room only: $6840.
Collegiate Environment: Orientation program. Drama-theater group, choral group, student-run newspaper, radio station. Social organizations: 60 open to all; national fraternities, national sororities; 5% of eligible men and 6% of eligible women are members. Most popular organizations: History Club, Organization for Latin Unity, Sci-Fi Club, Ramapo Pride, Future Educators of America. Major annual events: Unity Barbeque, Family Day, Haunted Mansion. Student services: health clinic, personal-psychological counseling, women's center. Campus security: 24-hour emergency response devices and patrols, late night transport-escort service, controlled dormitory access, surveillance cameras, patrols by trained security personnel. 2,531 college housing spaces available; 2,497 were occupied in 2003-04. Freshmen guaranteed college housing. Option: coed housing available. George T. Potter Library plus 1 other with 172,639 books, 20,251 microform titles, 662 serials, 2,994 audiovisual materials, an OPAC, and a Web page. Operations spending for 2004 fiscal year: $1.8 million. 580 computers available on campus for general student use. A campuswide network can be accessed from student residence rooms and from off campus. Staffed computer lab on campus.
Community Environment: Mahwah, population 12,000, is a suburban community near the foothills of the Ramapo Mountains on the New York-New Jersey border. Darlington County Park offers two lakes for swimming and a third for boating. Sports facilities, skiing, nature trails and picnic areas exist at nearby Campgaw Mountain.

■ **RARITAN VALLEY COMMUNITY COLLEGE** *I-10*
PO Box 3300
Somerville, NJ 08876-1265
Tel: (908)526-1200
Fax: (908)704-3442
E-mail: momalley@raritanval.edu
Web Site: http://www.raritanval.edu/
Description: County-supported, 2-year, coed. Awards certificates, transfer associate, and terminal associate degrees. Founded 1965. Setting: 225-acre small town campus with easy access to New York City and Philadelphia. Research spending for 2004 fiscal year: $78,196. Educational spending for 2005 fiscal year: $3295 per student. Total enrollment: 6,251. Student-undergrad faculty ratio is 19:1. 2,433 applied, 68% were admitted. Full-time: 2,575 students, 50% women, 50% men. Part-time: 3,676 students, 64% women, 36% men. 7% from out-of-state, 0.2% Native American, 11% Hispanic, 8% black, 8% Asian American or Pacific Islander, 3% international, 40% 25 or older, 8% transferred in. Retention: 66% of full-time freshmen returned the following year. Core. Calendar: semesters. Academic remediation for entering students, ESL program, services for LD students, advanced placement, honors program, independent study, distance learning, summer session for credit, part-time degree program, adult/continuing education programs, co-op programs and internships. Off campus study at Somerset County Technical Institute. ROTC: Army (c), Air Force (c).
Entrance Requirements: Open admission except for foreign students or respiratory care, nursing programs. Options: electronic application, early admission. Required: high school transcript. Entrance: noncompetitive. Application deadline: Rolling.
Costs Per Year: Application fee: $25. State resident tuition: $2430 full-time, $81 per credit part-time. Nonresident tuition: $2430 full-time, $81 per credit part-time. Mandatory fees: $850 full-time, $23 per credit part-time, $80 per term part-time.
Collegiate Environment: Orientation program. Drama-theater group, choral group, student-run newspaper. Social organizations: 20 open to all. Most popular organizations: International Club, The Latin Pride Club, Student Nurses Association, The Record (student newspaper), Christian Fellowship Club. Major annual events: Fall Picnic, Spring Picnic, Student Awards Banquet. Student services: personal-psychological counseling. Campus security: 24-hour emergency response devices and patrols, 24-hour outdoor surveillance cameras. College housing not available. Evelyn S. Field Learning Resources Center with 82,942 books, 7,863 microform titles, 354 serials, 1,140 audiovisual materials, an OPAC, and a Web page. Operations spending for 2004 fiscal year: $857,730. 844 computers available on campus for general student use. A campuswide network can be accessed from off-campus. Staffed computer lab on campus.
Community Environment: Somerville is the county seat for Somerset County. It is a suburban community located ten miles west of Plainfield and ten miles northwest of New Brunswick.

■ THE RICHARD STOCKTON COLLEGE OF NEW JERSEY *U-10*

PO Box 195, Jimmie Leeds Rd.
Pomona, NJ 08240-0195
Tel: (609)652-1776
Admissions: (609)652-4261
Fax: (609)748-5541
E-mail: admissions@pollux.stockton.edu
Web Site: http://www.stockton.edu/

Description: State-supported, comprehensive, coed. Part of New Jersey State College System. Awards bachelor's and master's degrees. Founded 1969. Setting: 1,600-acre suburban campus with easy access to Philadelphia. Endowment: $1.5 million. Research spending for 2004 fiscal year: $331,743. Educational spending for 2005 fiscal year: $5519 per student. Total enrollment: 7,034. Faculty: 426 (242 full-time, 184 part-time). Student-undergrad faculty ratio is 19:1. 3,448 applied, 52% were admitted. 1% from top 10% of their high school class, 75% from top quarter, 93% from top half. 22 class presidents, 3 valedictorians, 245 student government officers. Full-time: 5,650 students, 57% women, 43% men. Part-time: 920 students, 61% women, 39% men. Students come from 10 states and territories, 30 other countries, 3% from out-of-state, 0.5% Native American, 6% Hispanic, 8% black, 4% Asian American or Pacific Islander, 0.5% international, 22% 25 or older, 38% live on campus, 13% transferred in. Retention: 83% of full-time freshmen returned the following year. Academic areas with the most degrees conferred: business/marketing; social sciences; psychology. Core. Calendar: semesters. Academic remediation for entering students, services for LD students, advanced placement, self-designed majors, freshman honors college, honors program, independent study, distance learning, double major, summer session for credit, part-time degree program, adult/continuing education programs, internships, graduate courses open to undergrads. Off campus study at Washington Center for Internships and Academic Seminars. Study abroad program.

Entrance Requirements: Options: Peterson's Universal Application, Common Application, electronic application, early admission, early action, international baccalaureate accepted. Required: essay, high school transcript, minimum 2.0 high school GPA, SAT or ACT. Recommended: minimum 3.0 high school GPA, recommendations. Entrance: very difficult. Application deadline: 5/1. Notification: continuous until 5/15.

Costs Per Year: Application fee: $50. State resident tuition: $5498 full-time, $171.82 per credit part-time. Nonresident tuition: $8896 full-time, $278 per credit part-time. Mandatory fees: $2896 full-time, $90.50 per credit part-time. College room and board: $7902. College room only: $5370. Room and board charges vary according to board plan and housing facility.

Collegiate Environment: Orientation program. Drama-theater group, choral group, student-run newspaper, radio station. Social organizations: 81 open to all; national fraternities, national sororities; 3% of eligible men and 3% of eligible women are members. Most popular organizations: Stockton Action Volunteers for the Environment, Board of Activities, Los Latinos Unidos, Unified Black Student Society, Stockton Residents Association. Major annual events: Osprey Ball, Spring Fling, Student, Faculty and Staff Dinner. Student services: health clinic, personal-psychological counseling, women's center. Campus security: 24-hour emergency response devices and patrols, late night transport-escort service, controlled dormitory access, on-campus sworn/commissioned police force. College housing designed to accommodate 2,080 students; 2,090 undergraduates lived in college housing during 2003-04. Freshmen guaranteed college housing. Option: coed housing available. The Richard Stockton College of New Jersey Library with 258,822 books, 1.1 million microform titles, 16,826 serials, 13,523 audiovisual materials, and a Web page. Operations spending for 2004 fiscal year: $3.5 million. 1,375 computers available on campus for general student use. A campuswide network can be accessed from student residence rooms and from off campus. Staffed computer lab on campus.

Community Environment: Pomona is located about 12 miles northwest of Atlantic City in an undeveloped forest area.

■ RIDER UNIVERSITY *L-9*

2083 Lawrenceville Rd.
Lawrenceville, NJ 08648-3001
Tel: (609)896-5000
Free: 800-257-9026
Admissions: (609)895-5768
Fax: (609)895-6645
E-mail: admissions@rider.edu
Web Site: http://www.rider.edu/

Description: Independent, comprehensive, coed. Awards associate, bachelor's, and master's degrees and post-master's certificates. Founded 1865. Setting: 340-acre suburban campus with easy access to New York City and Philadelphia. Endowment: $51.8 million. Research spending for 2004 fiscal year: $1.3 million. Educational spending for 2005 fiscal year: $9358 per student. Total enrollment: 5,552. Faculty: 501 (234 full-time, 267 part-time). Student-undergrad faculty ratio is 13:1. 4,463 applied, 81% were admitted. 10% from top 10% of their high school class, 34% from top quarter, 69% from top half. Full-time: 3,611 students, 58% women, 42% men. Part-time: 764 students, 63% women, 37% men. Students come from 32 states and territories, 16 other countries, 24% from out-of-state, 0.1% Native American, 5% Hispanic, 9% black, 3% Asian American or Pacific Islander, 2% international, 13% 25 or older, 56% live on campus, 4% transferred in. Retention: 79% of full-time freshmen returned the following year. Academic areas with the most degrees conferred: business/marketing; education; psychology. Core. Calendar: semesters. Academic remediation for entering students, ESL program, services for LD students, advanced placement, honors program, independent study, double major, summer session for credit, part-time degree program, adult/continuing education programs, co-op programs and internships, graduate courses open to undergrads. Study abroad program. ROTC: Army (c).

Entrance Requirements: Options: Peterson's Universal Application, Common Application, electronic application, early admission, early action, deferred admission. Required: essay, high school transcript, 2 recommendations, audition, music examination, SAT or ACT. Recommended: minimum 2.5 high school GPA. Required for some: interview. Entrance: moderately difficult. Application deadline: Rolling. Notification: continuous.

Costs Per Year: Application fee: $45. Comprehensive fee: $32,310 includes full-time tuition ($22,910), mandatory fees ($560), and college room and board ($8840). College room only: $4940. Part-time tuition: $432 per credit. Part-time mandatory fees: $35 per course.

Collegiate Environment: Orientation program. Drama-theater group, choral group, student-run newspaper, radio station. Social organizations: 106 open to all; national fraternities, national sororities; 17% of eligible men and 16% of eligible women are members. Most popular organizations: Student Government Association, Student Entertainment Council, Association of Commuter Students, Latin American Student Organization. Major annual events: Cranberry Fest, Homecoming, Family Day. Student services: health clinic, personal-psychological counseling. Campus security: 24-hour emergency response devices and patrols, student patrols, late night transport-escort service, controlled dormitory access. 2,741 college housing spaces available; 2,265 were occupied in 2003-04. Freshmen guaranteed college housing. Options: coed, women-only housing available. Franklin F. Moore Library plus 1 other with 404,353 books, 810,051 microform titles, 13,600 serials, 9,650 audiovisual materials, an OPAC, and a Web page. Operations spending for 2004 fiscal year: $2.8 million. 403 computers available on campus for general student use. Computer purchase/lease plans available. A campuswide network can be accessed from student residence rooms and from off campus. Staffed computer lab on campus.

Community Environment: The capital of the state, Trenton's slogan is "Trenton Makes-the World Takes" and more than 400 industries support this claim. Products include pottery, wire, rope, rubber and cigars. Situated midway between New York City and Philadelphia, all forms of commercial transportation are available. Along with the usual community facilities, Trenton supports a symphony orchestra and provides community concerts. There are many part-time job opportunities in the New York to Philadelphia corridor. The mountains and seashore are a short distance, providing excellent recreational facilities. Some of the numerous points of interest are the Friends Meetinghouse, New Jersey State Museum, Old Barracks, Trent House and Washington Crossing State Park.

■ ROWAN UNIVERSITY *R-6*

201 Mullica Hill Rd.
Glassboro, NJ 08028-1701
Tel: (856)256-4500
Admissions: (856)256-4200
E-mail: admissions@rowan.edu
Web Site: http://www.rowan.edu/

Description: State-supported, comprehensive, coed. Part of New Jersey State College System. Awards bachelor's, master's, and doctoral degrees. Founded 1923. Setting: 200-acre small town campus with easy access to Philadelphia. Endowment: $92.3 million. Research spending for 2004 fiscal year: $2 million. Total enrollment: 9,762. Faculty: 886 (436 full-time, 450 part-time). Student-undergrad faculty ratio is 14:1. 7,303 applied, 47% were admitted. 10% from top 10% of their high school class, 55% from top quarter, 90% from top half. Full-time: 7,283 students, 53% women, 47% men. Part-time: 1,201 students, 62% women, 38% men. Students come from 20 states and territories, 29 other countries, 2% from out-of-state, 0.4% Native American, 6% Hispanic, 9% black, 3% Asian American or Pacific Islander, 15% 25 or older, 36% live on campus, 9% transferred in. Retention: 87% of full-time freshmen returned the following year. Academic areas with the most degrees conferred: education; communications/journalism; business/marketing. Core. Calendar: semesters. Academic remediation for entering students, ESL program, services for LD students, advanced placement, freshman honors college, honors program, independent study, double major, summer session for credit, part-time degree program, adult/continuing education programs, internships, graduate courses open to undergrads. Study abroad program. ROTC: Army (c).

Entrance Requirements: Option: deferred admission. Required: high school transcript, SAT or ACT. Recommended: minimum 3.0 high school GPA, recommendations, interview. Required for some: interview. Entrance: moderately difficult. Application deadline: 3/15. Notification: 4/15.

Costs Per Year: Application fee: $50. State resident tuition: $6294 full-time, $262 per credit hour part-time. Nonresident tuition: $12,588 full-time, $524 per credit hour part-time. Mandatory fees: $2313 full-time, $107.20 per credit hour part-time. Full-time tuition and fees vary according to degree level. Part-time tuition and fees vary according to degree level. College room and board: $8242. Room and board charges vary according to board plan and housing facility.

Collegiate Environment: Orientation program. Drama-theater group, choral group, marching band, student-run newspaper, radio station. Social organizations: 150 open to all; national fraternities, national sororities, local fraternities, local sororities; 12% of eligible men and 8% of eligible women are members. Most popular organizations: Student Government Association, Student Activities Board. Major annual events: Project Santa, Homecoming Week, Spring Festival Weekend. Student services: legal services, health clinic, personal-psychological counseling, women's center. Campus security: 24-hour emergency response devices and patrols, late night transport-escort service, controlled dormitory access. College housing designed to accommodate 1,545 students; 2,868 undergraduates lived in college housing during 2003-04. Freshmen guaranteed college housing. On-campus residence required in freshman year. Option: coed housing available. Keith and Shirley Campbell Library plus 2 others with 316,500 books, 478,692 microform titles, 1,858 serials, 52,834 audiovisual materials, an OPAC, and a Web page. 350 computers available on campus for general student use. A campuswide network can be accessed from student residence rooms and from off campus. Staffed computer lab on campus.

Community Environment: Glassboro was established in 1775 when a German widow and her seven sons organized Stanger & Co., the first successful glass factory in North America. Hollybush, a mansion of a glass manufacturer, which formed part of the original campus, was the site of a summit conference between President Lyndon Johnson and Russian Premier Alexei Kosygin in 1967. Glassboro is near enough to large cities that all forms of commercial transportation are available. Philadelphia Airport is 35 minutes away. Part-time employment is available. Nearby lakes and beaches provide recreational facilities.

■ **RUTGERS, THE STATE UNIVERSITY OF NEW JERSEY, CAMDEN** *P-6*

311 North Fifth St.
Camden, NJ 08102-1401
Tel: (856)225-1766
Admissions: (732)932-4636
Web Site: http://camden-www.rutgers.edu/

Description: State-supported, university, coed. Part of Rutgers, The State University of New Jersey. Awards bachelor's, master's, and first professional degrees. Founded 1927. System endowment: $496.3 million. System-wide research spending for 2004 fiscal year: $150.7 million. System-wide educational spending for 2005 fiscal year: $9536 per student. Total enrollment: 5,321. Faculty: 401 (229 full-time, 172 part-time). Student-undergrad faculty ratio is 11:1. 6,153 applied, 53% were admitted. 27% from top 10% of their high school class, 64% from top quarter, 96% from top half. Full-time: 2,949 students, 57% women, 43% men. Part-time: 897 students, 61% women, 39% men. 3% out-of-state, 0.3% Native American, 6% Hispanic, 15% black, 8% Asian American or Pacific Islander, 1% international, 31% 25 or older, 13% live on campus, 11% transferred in. Retention: 84% of full-time freshmen returned the following year. Academic areas with the most degrees conferred: business/marketing; science technologies;

social sciences. Core. Calendar: semesters. Academic remediation for entering students, ESL program, services for LD students, advanced placement, accelerated degree program, self-designed majors, freshman honors college, honors program, independent study, distance learning, double major, summer session for credit, part-time degree program, co-op programs and internships. Study abroad program. ROTC: Army (c), Air Force (c).

Entrance Requirements: Options: electronic application, early admission. Required: high school transcript, SAT or ACT. Entrance: moderately difficult. Application deadline: Rolling. Notification: 2/28. Preference given to state residents.

Costs Per Year: Application fee: $50. State resident tuition: $7336 full-time, $236.50 per credit hour part-time. Nonresident tuition: $14,934 full-time, $484.05 per credit hour part-time. Mandatory fees: $1692 full-time. College room and board: $8088. College room only: $5778.

Collegiate Environment: Orientation program. Drama-theater group, student-run radio station. Option: coed housing available. Paul Robeson Library plus 2 others with 714,447 books, 259,982 microform titles, 5,189 serials, and 326 audiovisual materials. System-wide operations spending for 2004 fiscal year: $29.4 million. 184 computers available on campus for general student use. A campuswide network can be accessed from student residence rooms and from off campus. Staffed computer lab on campus.

■ **RUTGERS, THE STATE UNIVERSITY OF NEW JERSEY, NEW BRUNSWICK/PISCATAWAY** *J-12*

New Brunswick, NJ 08901-1281
Tel: (732)932-4636
Web Site: http://www.rutgers.edu/

Description: State-supported, university, coed. Part of Rutgers, The State University of New Jersey. Awards bachelor's, master's, doctoral, and first professional degrees and post-master's certificates. Founded 1766. System endowment: $496.3 million. System-wide research spending for 2004 fiscal year: $150.7 million. System-wide educational spending for 2005 fiscal year: $9536 per student. Total enrollment: 34,449. Faculty: 2,224 (1,535 full-time, 689 part-time). Student-undergrad faculty ratio is 14:1. 25,462 applied, 61% were admitted. 36% from top 10% of their high school class, 78% from top quarter, 99% from top half. Full-time: 24,361 students, 51% women, 49% men. Part-time: 2,352 students, 53% women, 47% men. Students come from 9 other countries, 9% from out-of-state, 0.2% Native American, 8% Hispanic, 9% black, 22% Asian American or Pacific Islander, 2% international, 8% 25 or older, 46% live on campus, 5% transferred in. Retention: 89% of full-time freshmen returned the following year. Academic areas with the most degrees conferred: social sciences; psychology; biological/life sciences. Core. Calendar: semesters. Academic remediation for entering students, ESL program, advanced placement, accelerated degree program, self-designed majors, honors program, independent study, distance learning, double major, co-op programs, graduate courses open to undergrads. Study abroad program. ROTC: Army, Air Force.

Entrance Requirements: Options: electronic application, early admission. Required: high school transcript, SAT or ACT. Entrance: moderately difficult. Application deadline: Rolling. Notification: 2/28. Preference given to state residents.

Costs Per Year: Application fee: $50. State resident tuition: $7336 full-time, $236.50 per credit hour part-time. Nonresident tuition: $14,934 full-time, $484 per credit hour part-time. Mandatory fees: $1885 full-time. Part-time tuition varies according to course level. College room and board: $8838. College room only: $5378. Room and board charges vary according to board plan and housing facility.

Collegiate Environment: Orientation program. Drama-theater group, choral group, marching band, student-run newspaper, radio station. Social organizations: national fraternities, national sororities. Student services: health clinic. Options: coed, men-only, women-only housing available. Archibald S. Alexander Library plus 14 others with 4.7 million books, 3.3 million microform titles, 17,182 serials, 91,657 audiovisual materials, an OPAC, and a Web page. System-wide operations spending for 2004 fiscal year: $29.4 million. 1,450 computers available on campus for general student use. A campuswide network can be accessed from student residence rooms and from off campus. Staffed computer lab on campus.

■ **RUTGERS, THE STATE UNIVERSITY OF NEW JERSEY, NEWARK** *G-14*

Newark, NJ 07102
Tel: (973)353-1766
Admissions: (732)932-4636
Fax: (973)353-1048

Web Site: http://www.newark.rutgers.edu/

Description: State-supported, university, coed. Part of Rutgers, The State University of New Jersey. Awards bachelor's, master's, doctoral, and first professional degrees. Founded 1892. System endowment: $496.3 million. System-wide research spending for 2004 fiscal year: $150.7 million. System-wide educational spending for 2005 fiscal year: $9536 per student. Total enrollment: 10,246. Faculty: 653 (422 full-time, 231 part-time). Student-undergrad faculty ratio is 11:1. 9,927 applied, 47% were admitted. 35% from top 10% of their high school class, 70% from top quarter, 100% from top half. Full-time: 4,911 students, 58% women, 42% men. Part-time: 1,602 students, 56% women, 44% men. 6% from out-of-state, 0.3% Native American, 18% Hispanic, 21% black, 23% Asian American or Pacific Islander, 2% international, 24% 25 or older, 15% live on campus, 7% transferred in. Retention: 86% of full-time freshmen returned the following year. Academic areas with the most degrees conferred: business/marketing; health professions and related sciences; computer and information sciences. Core. Calendar: semesters. Academic remediation for entering students, ESL program, services for LD students, advanced placement, accelerated degree program, self-designed majors, freshman honors college, honors program, independent study, distance learning, double major, summer session for credit, part-time degree program, adult/continuing education programs, co-op programs. Off campus study at New Jersey Institute of Technology. Study abroad program. ROTC: Army, Air Force.

Entrance Requirements: Options: electronic application, early admission. Required: high school transcript, SAT or ACT. Entrance: moderately difficult. Application deadline: Rolling. Notification: 2/28. Preference given to state residents.

Costs Per Year: Application fee: $50. State resident tuition: $7336 full-time, $236.50 per credit hour part-time. Nonresident tuition: $14,934 full-time, $484.05 per credit hour part-time. Mandatory fees: $1476 full-time. College room and board: $8984. College room only: $5654. Room and board charges vary according to board plan and housing facility.

Collegiate Environment: Orientation program. Drama-theater group, choral group, student-run newspaper, radio station. Option: coed housing available. John Cotton Dana Library plus 4 others with 941,103 books, 1.5 million microform titles, 6,408 serials, and 34,994 audiovisual materials. System-wide operations spending for 2004 fiscal year: $29.4 million. 708 computers available on campus for general student use. A campuswide network can be accessed from student residence rooms and from off campus. Staffed computer lab on campus.

■ **SAINT PETER'S COLLEGE** *G-15*
2641 Kennedy Blvd.
Jersey City, NJ 07306-5997
Tel: (201)915-9000; 888-SPC-9933
Admissions: (201)915-9495
Fax: (201)432-5860
E-mail: admissions@spcvxa.spc.edu
Web Site: http://www.spc.edu/

Description: Independent Roman Catholic (Jesuit), comprehensive, coed. Awards associate, bachelor's, and master's degrees. Founded 1872. Setting: 15-acre urban campus with easy access to New York City. Endowment: $20 million. Research spending for 2004 fiscal year: $1.9 million. Total enrollment: 3,282. 2,041 applied, 67% were admitted. 13% from top 10% of their high school class, 30% from top quarter, 64% from top half. 5 valedictorians. Students come from 28 states and territories, 9 other countries, 13% from out-of-state, 19% 25 or older, 27% live on campus. Retention: 69% of full-time freshmen returned the following year. Core. Calendar: semesters. Academic remediation for entering students, services for LD students, advanced placement, accelerated degree program, self-designed majors, honors program, independent study, distance learning, double major, summer session for credit, part-time degree program, adult/continuing education programs, co-op programs and internships, graduate courses open to undergrads. Off campus study at members of the Jesuit Student Exchange. Study abroad program. ROTC: Army, Air Force (c).

Entrance Requirements: Options: Peterson's Universal Application, Common Application, early admission, deferred admission, international baccalaureate accepted. Required: essay, high school transcript, minimum 2.0 high school GPA, 2 recommendations, SAT or ACT. Recommended: interview. Required for some: interview. Entrance: moderately difficult. Application deadline: Rolling. Notification: continuous.

Collegiate Environment: Orientation program. Drama-theater group, choral group, student-run newspaper, radio station. Social organizations: 42 open to all. Most popular organizations: Caribbean Culture Club, Black Action

Committee, Asian American Student Union, Argus Eyes Dramatic Society, Voices of Praise Gospel Choir. Major annual events: Spring Fest, Winter Fest, All-Nighter. Student services: health clinic, personal-psychological counseling. Campus security: 24-hour emergency response devices and patrols, late night transport-escort service, controlled dormitory access, ID checks at residence halls and library. 763 college housing spaces available; 692 were occupied in 2003-04. Options: coed, women-only housing available. Theresa and Edward O'Toole Library plus 1 other with 178,587 books, 66,439 microform titles, 1,741 serials, 330 audiovisual materials, an OPAC, and a Web page. Operations spending for 2004 fiscal year: $1.2 million. 150 computers available on campus for general student use. A campuswide network can be accessed from student residence rooms and from off campus. Staffed computer lab on campus.

■ **SALEM COMMUNITY COLLEGE** *R-3*
460 Hollywood Ave.
Carneys Point, NJ 08069-2799
Tel: (856)299-2100
Admissions: (856)351-2707
Fax: (856)299-9193
Web Site: http://www.salemcc.org/

Description: County-supported, 2-year, coed. Part of New Jersey Commission on Higher Education. Awards certificates, transfer associate, and terminal associate degrees. Founded 1972. Setting: small town campus with easy access to Philadelphia. Educational spending for 2005 fiscal year: $3305 per student. Total enrollment: 1,251. Student-undergrad faculty ratio is 19:1. Full-time: 598 students, 59% women, 41% men. Part-time: 653 students, 68% women, 32% men. Students come from 6 states and territories, 15% from out-of-state, 1% Native American, 4% Hispanic, 22% black, 1% Asian American or Pacific Islander, 5% international, 52% 25 or older, 3% transferred in. Core. Calendar: semesters. Academic remediation for entering students, ESL program, services for LD students, advanced placement, independent study, distance learning, double major, summer session for credit, part-time degree program, adult/continuing education programs, co-op programs. Off campus study.

Entrance Requirements: Open admission. Options: early admission, deferred admission. Required: essay, high school transcript. Entrance: noncompetitive. Application deadline: Rolling. Notification: continuous.

Costs Per Year: Application fee: $25. Area resident tuition: $2385 full-time, $79.50 per credit part-time. State resident tuition: $2685 full-time, $89.50 per credit part-time. Nonresident tuition: $2685 full-time, $89.50 per credit part-time. Mandatory fees: $920 full-time, $29 per credit part-time, $25 per term part-time. Full-time tuition and fees vary according to course load. Part-time tuition and fees vary according to course load.

Collegiate Environment: Orientation program. Choral group. Most popular organizations: Drama Club, Science Club, Multicultural Exchange Club. Major annual events: Talent Show, Graduation, Children's Christmas Party. Student services: personal-psychological counseling, women's center. Campus security: 24-hour emergency response devices and patrols, late night transport-escort service. College housing not available. Michael S. Cettei Memorial Library with 28,951 books, 240 serials, and an OPAC. Operations spending for 2004 fiscal year: $153,676. 200 computers available on campus for general student use. A campuswide network can be accessed from off-campus. Staffed computer lab on campus.

■ **SETON HALL UNIVERSITY** *J-5*
400 South Orange Ave.
South Orange, NJ 07079-2697
Tel: (973)761-9000
Free: 800-THE HALL
Admissions: (973)761-9688
Fax: (973)761-9452
E-mail: terrybry@shu.edu
Web Site: http://www.shu.edu/

Description: Independent Roman Catholic, university, coed. Awards bachelor's, master's, doctoral, and first professional degrees and post-master's certificates. Founded 1856. Setting: 58-acre suburban campus with easy access to New York City. Endowment: $197.7 million. Research spending for 2004 fiscal year: $2.2 million. Educational spending for 2005 fiscal year: $8705 per student. Total enrollment: 9,637. Faculty: 926 (441 full-time, 485 part-time). Student-undergrad faculty ratio is 14:1. 4,982 applied, 84% were admitted. 25% from top 10% of their high school class, 51% from top quarter, 84% from top half. Full-time: 4,801 students, 53% women, 47% men. Part-time: 534 students, 57% women, 43% men. Students come from

45 states and territories, 49 other countries, 26% from out-of-state, 0.1% Native American, 9% Hispanic, 11% black, 7% Asian American or Pacific Islander, 1% international, 7% 25 or older, 45% live on campus, 6% transferred in. Retention: 83% of full-time freshmen returned the following year. Academic areas with the most degrees conferred: business/marketing; health professions and related sciences; communications/journalism. Core. Calendar: semesters. Academic remediation for entering students, ESL program, services for LD students, advanced placement, accelerated degree program, honors program, independent study, distance learning, double major, summer session for credit, part-time degree program, co-op programs and internships, graduate courses open to undergrads. Study abroad program. ROTC: Army, Air Force (c).

Entrance Requirements: Options: Peterson's Universal Application, Common Application, electronic application, deferred admission, international baccalaureate accepted. Required: essay, high school transcript, counselor report, SAT or ACT. Recommended: minimum 3.0 high school GPA, recommendations, interview. Required for some: minimum 3.0 high school GPA, interview. Entrance: moderately difficult. Application deadline: 3/1. Notification: continuous until 12/1.

Costs Per Year: Application fee: $55. Comprehensive fee: $35,186 includes full-time tuition ($22,770), mandatory fees ($1950), and college room and board ($10,466). College room only: $6664. Part-time tuition: $759 per credit. Part-time mandatory fees: $185 per term.

Collegiate Environment: Orientation program. Drama-theater group, choral group, student-run newspaper, radio station. Social organizations: 116 open to all; national fraternities, national sororities, local fraternities, local sororities; 5% of eligible men and 3% of eligible women are members. Most popular organizations: Martin Luther King Jr. Scholars Association, Adelante/Caribe, Black Student Union, National Council of Negro Women. Major annual events: University Day, Deck The Hall, Career Day. Student services: health clinic, personal-psychological counseling, women's center. Campus security: 24-hour emergency response devices and patrols, late night transport-escort service, controlled dormitory access. 2,209 college housing spaces available; 2,198 were occupied in 2003-04. No special consideration for freshman housing applicants. Option: coed housing available. Walsh Library plus 1 other with 506,042 books, 530,000 microform titles, 1,475 serials, 2,225 audiovisual materials, an OPAC, and a Web page. Operations spending for 2004 fiscal year: $9 million. 300 computers available on campus for general student use. Computer purchase/lease plans available. A campuswide network can be accessed from student residence rooms and from off campus. Staffed computer lab on campus.

Community Environment: A upper middle class suburb, South Orange enjoys the cultural and recreational advantages of New York City and Newark. Mass transportation is available. Community facilities include a public library, two hospitals in nearby Livingston and Summit, and Catholic, Methodist, Episcopal and Presbyterian churches.

■ **SOMERSET CHRISTIAN COLLEGE** *I-11*
10 Liberty Square
PO Box 9035
Zarephath, NJ 08890-9035
Tel: (732)356-1595
Free: 800-234-9305
Fax: (732)356-4846
Web Site: http://www.somerset.edu/
Description: Independent religious, 2-year, coed. Awards transfer associate degrees. Founded 1908. Total enrollment: 142. 93 applied, 96% were admitted. Students come from 3 states and territories, 0% from out-of-state, 1% Native American, 5% Hispanic, 26% black, 4% Asian American or Pacific Islander, 0% international, 95% 25 or older. Retention: 13% of full-time freshmen returned the following year. Core. Calendar: semesters plus 'FastTrack' semesters. Part-time degree program, adult/continuing education programs.
Entrance Requirements: Options: electronic application, deferred admission, international baccalaureate accepted. Required: essay, recommendations. Required for some: high school transcript, minimum 2.5 high school GPA, interview, SAT or ACT. Entrance: minimally difficult. Application deadline: 9/1. Notification: continuous.
Collegiate Environment: Student-run newspaper, radio station. Most popular organization: Nursing Home Visitation. Major annual events: chapels, Convocation, picnics. Student services: personal-psychological

counseling. College housing not available. Arthur K. White Library with 60,000 books, 95 serials, 150 audiovisual materials, an OPAC, and a Web page.

■ **STEVENS INSTITUTE OF TECHNOLOGY** *G-15*
Castle Point on Hudson
Hoboken, NJ 07030
Tel: (201)216-5000
Free: 800-458-5323
Admissions: (201)216-5194
Fax: (201)216-8348
E-mail: admissions@stevens.edu
Web Site: http://www.stevens.edu/
Description: Independent, university, coed. Awards bachelor's, master's, and doctoral degrees. Founded 1870. Setting: 55-acre urban campus with easy access to New York City. Endowment: $130.2 million. Research spending for 2004 fiscal year: $25.2 million. Educational spending for 2005 fiscal year: $20,594 per student. Total enrollment: 4,689. Faculty: 331 (210 full-time, 121 part-time). Student-undergrad faculty ratio is 7:1. 2,418 applied, 47% were admitted. 49% from top 10% of their high school class, 81% from top quarter, 96% from top half. 11 valedictorians. Full-time: 1,788 students, 25% women, 75% men. Part-time: 1 student, 100% men. Students come from 41 states and territories, 52 other countries, 34% from out-of-state, 0.3% Native American, 9% Hispanic, 5% black, 13% Asian American or Pacific Islander, 5% international, 2% 25 or older, 80% live on campus, 2% transferred in. Retention: 88% of full-time freshmen returned the following year. Academic areas with the most degrees conferred: engineering; computer and information sciences; business/marketing. Core. Calendar: semesters. Advanced placement, accelerated degree program, honors program, independent study, double major, summer session for credit, co-op programs and internships, graduate courses open to undergrads. Off campus study at New York University Dual-degree program. Study abroad program. ROTC: Army (c), Air Force (c).
Entrance Requirements: Options: Peterson's Universal Application, Common Application, electronic application, early admission, early decision, deferred admission, international baccalaureate accepted. Required: essay, high school transcript, recommendations, interview, SAT or ACT. Required for some: SAT Subject Tests. Entrance: very difficult. Application deadlines: 2/15, 11/15 for early decision plan 1, 1/15 for early decision plan 2. Notification: 3/15, 12/15 for early decision plan 1, 2/15 for early decision plan 2.
Costs Per Year: Application fee: $55. Comprehensive fee: $41,335 includes full-time tuition ($30,240), mandatory fees ($1595), and college room and board ($9500). College room only: $4800. Full-time tuition and fees vary according to student level. Room and board charges vary according to board plan and housing facility. Part-time tuition: $1008 per credit. Part-time mandatory fees: $528 per term.
Collegiate Environment: Orientation program. Drama-theater group, choral group, student-run newspaper, radio station. Social organizations: 70 open to all; national fraternities, national sororities, local sororities; 34% of eligible men and 31% of eligible women are members. Most popular organizations: Drama Society, Student Council (including Ethnic Student Council), foreign student clubs, Inter-Dormitory Council, student newspaper. Major annual events: Boken, Techfest, Midnight Breakfast. Student services: health clinic, personal-psychological counseling, women's center. Campus security: 24-hour emergency response devices and patrols, late night transport-escort service, controlled dormitory access. 75 undergraduates lived in college housing during 2003-04. Freshmen guaranteed college housing. Option: coed housing available. S. C. Williams Library with 115,234 books, 11,062 microform titles, 134 serials, an OPAC, and a Web page. Operations spending for 2004 fiscal year: $1.8 million. 175 computers available on campus for general student use. Computer purchase/lease plans available. A campuswide network can be accessed from student residence rooms and from off campus. Staffed computer lab on campus.
Community Environment: Hoboken, a quaint, park-like community, is just one mile square and easily accessible to Manhattan. Recently it has become a residential center for young professionals. Many new shops, restaurants, and clubs have opened in the past ten years. The recreational and cultural advantages of New York are convenient for Hoboken, as well as many job opportunities. Stevens takes advantage of its location and has a popular cooperative education program, in addition to providing internships and research opportunities with leading companies.

■ **SUSSEX COUNTY COMMUNITY COLLEGE** *D-9*
1 College Hill
Newton, NJ 07860

Tel: (973)300-2100
Admissions: (973)300-2219
Web Site: http://www.sussex.edu/
Description: State and locally supported, 2-year, coed. Part of New Jersey Commission on Higher Education. Awards certificates, transfer associate, and terminal associate degrees. Founded 1981. Setting: 160-acre small town campus with easy access to New York City. Endowment: $883,431. Educational spending for 2005 fiscal year: $3628 per student. Total enrollment: 3,461. Student-undergrad faculty ratio is 22:1. 629 applied, 100% were admitted. Full-time: 1,706 students, 52% women, 48% men. Part-time: 1,755 students, 68% women, 32% men. Students come from 3 states and territories, 12% from out-of-state, 0.3% Native American, 6% Hispanic, 2% black, 1% Asian American or Pacific Islander, 1% international, 41% 25 or older, 5% transferred in. Retention: 46% of full-time freshmen returned the following year. Core. Calendar: semesters. Academic remediation for entering students, ESL program, services for LD students, advanced placement, distance learning, double major, summer session for credit, part-time degree program, internships.
Entrance Requirements: Open admission. Required: high school transcript. Entrance: noncompetitive. Application deadline: Rolling. Notification: continuous.
Costs Per Year: Application fee: $15. Area resident tuition: $2310 full-time, $77 per credit part-time. State resident tuition: $4620 full-time, $154 per credit part-time. Nonresident tuition: $4620 full-time, $154 per credit part-time. Mandatory fees: $510 full-time, $13 per credit part-time, $15 per term part-time.
Collegiate Environment: Drama-theater group, choral group, student-run newspaper. Social organizations: 23 open to all. Most popular organizations: Student Government Association, 'The College Hill' (newspaper), Human Services Club, Arts Club, Returning Adult Support Group. Major annual events: Fall Festival, Talent Show, International Festival. Student services: personal-psychological counseling, women's center. Campus security: late night transport-escort service, trained security personnel. College housing not available. Sussex County Community College Library with 34,346 books, 173 microform titles, 266 serials, 602 audiovisual materials, an OPAC, and a Web page. 302 computers available on campus for general student use. A campuswide network can be accessed. Staffed computer lab on campus.

■ **TALMUDICAL ACADEMY OF NEW JERSEY** *M-13*
Route 524
Adelphia, NJ 07710
Tel: (732)431-1600
Admissions: (201)431-1600
Description: Independent Jewish, comprehensive, men only. Awards bachelor's and master's degrees. Founded 1967. Setting: small town campus. Calendar: semesters.

■ **THOMAS EDISON STATE COLLEGE** *M-9*
101 West State St.
Trenton, NJ 08608-1176
Tel: (609)984-1100; 888-442-8372
Fax: (609)292-9000
E-mail: admissions@tesc.edu
Web Site: http://www.tesc.edu/
Description: State-supported, comprehensive, coed. Awards associate, bachelor's, and master's degrees (offers only distance learning degree programs). Founded 1972. Setting: 2-acre urban campus with easy access to Philadelphia. Total enrollment: 11,224. Part-time: 10,904 students, 44% women, 56% men. Students come from 55 states and territories, 74 other countries, 45% from out-of-state, 1% Native American, 6% Hispanic, 12% black, 2% Asian American or Pacific Islander, 2% international, 86% 25 or older. Academic areas with the most degrees conferred: liberal arts/general studies; engineering technologies; business/marketing. Core. Calendar: continuous. Services for LD students, advanced placement, independent study, distance learning, double major, summer session for credit, part-time degree program, external degree program, adult/continuing education programs, graduate courses open to undergrads.
Entrance Requirements: Open admission. Option: electronic application. Required: age 21 or over and a high school graduate. Entrance: noncompetitive.
Costs Per Year: Application fee: $75. State resident tuition: $3780 per year part-time. Nonresident tuition: $5400 per year part-time.
Collegiate Environment: Campus security: guard from 7 a.m. to 11 p.m., local police patrol. College housing not available.

■ **UNION COUNTY COLLEGE** *L-4*
1033 Springfield Ave.
Cranford, NJ 07016-1599
Tel: (908)709-7000
Admissions: (908)709-7127
Fax: (908)709-0527
Web Site: http://www.ucc.edu/
Description: State and locally supported, 2-year, coed. Part of New Jersey Commission on Higher Education. Awards certificates, diplomas, transfer associate, and terminal associate degrees. Founded 1933. Setting: 48-acre suburban campus with easy access to New York City. Endowment: $7.2 million. Educational spending for 2005 fiscal year: $3743 per student. Total enrollment: 10,976. Student-undergrad faculty ratio is 25:1. 6,593 applied, 98% were admitted. Full-time: 5,327 students, 61% women, 39% men. Part-time: 5,649 students, 70% women, 30% men. Students come from 8 states and territories, 82 other countries, 2% from out-of-state, 0.4% Native American, 25% Hispanic, 24% black, 6% Asian American or Pacific Islander, 3% international, 50% 25 or older, 9% transferred in. Retention: 77% of full-time freshmen returned the following year. Core. Calendar: semesters. Academic remediation for entering students, ESL program, services for LD students, advanced placement, accelerated degree program, self-designed majors, honors program, independent study, distance learning, summer session for credit, part-time degree program, adult/continuing education programs, internships. Off campus study. ROTC: Air Force (c).
Entrance Requirements: Open admission except for allied health programs. Options: electronic application, early admission, deferred admission. Required: high school transcript. Required for some: interview. Entrance: noncompetitive. Application deadline: Rolling. Notification: continuous.
Costs Per Year: Application fee: $30. Area resident tuition: $2460 full-time, $82 per credit part-time. State resident tuition: $4920 full-time, $164 per credit part-time. Mandatory fees: $780 full-time.
Collegiate Environment: Orientation program. Drama-theater group, student-run newspaper, radio station. Social organizations: 17 open to all. Most popular organizations: SIGN, Spanish Club, Black Students Heritage Organization, Student Government Organization, International Cultural Exchange Students. Major annual events: new student mixers, international cultural festivals, Hip-Hop Appreciation Week and Spring Fling. Student services: personal-psychological counseling. Campus security: 24-hour emergency response devices and patrols, late night transport-escort service. College housing not available. MacKay Library plus 2 others with 135,783 books, 8,565 microform titles, 2,609 serials, 3,455 audiovisual materials, an OPAC, and a Web page. Operations spending for 2004 fiscal year: $1.2 million. 881 computers available on campus for general student use. A campuswide network can be accessed from off-campus. Staffed computer lab on campus.
Community Environment: A suburban area, 10 miles southwest of Newark, Cranford enjoys all the cultural and recreational advantages of nearby New York. Major forms of commercial transportation are available.

■ **WARREN COUNTY COMMUNITY COLLEGE** *G-8*
475 Route 57 West
Washington, NJ 07882-4343
Tel: (908)689-1090
Admissions: (908)835-2300
Web Site: http://www.warren.edu/
Description: State and locally supported, 2-year, coed. Part of New Jersey Commission on Higher Education. Awards certificates, transfer associate, and terminal associate degrees. Founded 1981. Setting: 77-acre rural campus. Total enrollment: 1,129. 480 applied, 100% were admitted. Full-time: 347 students, 53% women, 47% men. Part-time: 358 students, 73% women, 27% men. Students come from 4 states and territories, 57% 25 or older. Core. Calendar: semesters. Academic remediation for entering students, ESL program, services for LD students, advanced placement, independent study, distance learning, double major, summer session for credit, part-time degree program, co-op programs and internships. Off campus study at Raritan Valley Community College, Union County College, Northampton County Area Community College.
Entrance Requirements: Open admission. Options: early admission, deferred admission. Placement: New Jersey Basic Skills Exam required. Entrance: noncompetitive. Application deadline: Rolling.
Collegiate Environment: Drama-theater group, student-run newspaper. Social organizations: national fraternities. Campus security: evening and weekend security. College housing not available. 23,143 books, 70

microform titles, 375 serials, and 1,300 audiovisual materials. 85 computers available on campus for general student use. A campuswide network can be accessed from off-campus. Staffed computer lab on campus.

■ WESTMINSTER CHOIR COLLEGE OF RIDER UNIVERSITY *K-10*
101 Walnut Ln.
Princeton, NJ 08540-3899
Tel: (609)921-7100
Free: 800-96-CHOIR
Admissions: (609)921-9100
Fax: (609)921-2538
E-mail: wccadmission@rider.edu
Web Site: http://westminster.rider.edu/
Description: Independent, comprehensive, coed. Administratively affiliated with Rider University. Awards bachelor's and master's degrees. Founded 1926. Setting: 23-acre small town campus with easy access to New York City and Philadelphia. Endowment: $15.7 million. Educational spending for 2005 fiscal year: $9358 per student. Total enrollment: 452. Faculty: 101 (35 full-time, 66 part-time). Student-undergrad faculty ratio is 7:1. 206 applied, 76% were admitted. 15% from top 10% of their high school class, 39% from top quarter, 71% from top half. 1 class president, 10 student government officers. Full-time: 323 students, 64% women, 36% men. Part-time: 10 students, 40% women, 60% men. Students come from 40 states and territories, 56% from out-of-state, 1% Native American, 4% Hispanic, 7% black, 1% Asian American or Pacific Islander, 4% international, 3% 25 or older, 58% live on campus, 4% transferred in. Retention: 79% of full-time freshmen returned the following year. Academic area with the most degrees conferred: visual and performing arts. Calendar: semesters. Academic remediation for entering students, ESL program, services for LD students, advanced placement, honors program, independent study, double major, summer session for credit, part-time degree program, adult/continuing education programs, internships. Off campus study at Princeton University, Rider University, Princeton Theological Seminary. ROTC: Army (c).
Entrance Requirements: Option: deferred admission. Required: essay, high school transcript, 2 recommendations, audition, music examination, SAT or ACT. Recommended: minimum 2.5 high school GPA, interview. Entrance: moderately difficult. Application deadline: Rolling. Notification: continuous.
Costs Per Year: Application fee: $45. One-time mandatory fee: $560. Comprehensive fee: $32,670 includes full-time tuition ($22,910), mandatory fees ($560), and college room and board ($9200). College room only: $4380. Room and board charges vary according to board plan. Part-time tuition: $870 per credit. Part-time mandatory fees: $35 per course. Part-time tuition and fees vary according to course load and program.
Collegiate Environment: Orientation program. Drama-theater group, choral group, student-run newspaper, radio station. Most popular organizations: Westminster Choir, Westminster Singers, Westminster Handbell Choir, Black and Hispanic Alliance, Student Activities Committee. Major annual events: Homecoming/Alumni Weekend, Christmas at Westminster, opera performance. Student services: health clinic, personal-psychological counseling. Campus security: 24-hour emergency response devices and patrols, late night transport-escort service. 208 college housing spaces available; 190 were occupied in 2003-04. Freshmen guaranteed college housing. On-campus residence required through sophomore year. Option: coed housing available. Talbott Library-Learning Center with 55,000 books and 160 serials. 60 computers available on campus for general student use. Staffed computer lab on campus.
Community Environment: See Princeton University.

■ WILLIAM PATERSON UNIVERSITY OF NEW JERSEY *E-13*
300 Pompton Rd.
Wayne, NJ 07470-8420

Tel: (973)720-2000
Admissions: (973)720-2906
Fax: (973)720-2910
E-mail: mccoyj@wpunj.edu
Web Site: http://ww2.wpunj.edu/
Description: State-supported, comprehensive, coed. Part of New Jersey State College System. Awards bachelor's and master's degrees and post-master's certificates. Founded 1855. Setting: 300-acre suburban campus with easy access to New York City. Total enrollment: 10,970. Faculty: 1,071 (372 full-time, 699 part-time). Student-undergrad faculty ratio is 15:1. 5,380 applied, 67% were admitted. 12% from top 10% of their high school class, 30% from top quarter, 68% from top half. Full-time: 7,472 students, 57% women, 43% men. Part-time: 1,638 students, 63% women, 37% men. Students come from 39 states and territories, 55 other countries, 0.2% Native American, 17% Hispanic, 13% black, 6% Asian American or Pacific Islander, 1% international, 22% 25 or older, 24% live on campus, 10% transferred in. Retention: 77% of full-time freshmen returned the following year. Academic areas with the most degrees conferred: business/marketing; social sciences; communications/journalism. Core. Calendar: semesters. Academic remediation for entering students, ESL program, services for LD students, advanced placement, accelerated degree program, honors program, independent study, distance learning, double major, summer session for credit, part-time degree program, adult/continuing education programs, internships, graduate courses open to undergrads. Off campus study at members of the National Student Exchange. Study abroad program. ROTC: Air Force (c).
Entrance Requirements: Options: Common Application, electronic application, early action, deferred admission. Required: essay, high school transcript, SAT or ACT. Recommended: minimum 2.5 high school GPA. Required for some: recommendations, interview. Entrance: moderately difficult. Application deadline: 5/1. Notification: continuous.
Costs Per Year: Application fee: $50. State resident tuition: $5358 full-time, $172.16 per credit part-time. Nonresident tuition: $10,474 full-time, $339.16 per credit part-time. Mandatory fees: $3382 full-time, $108.84 per credit part-time. College room and board: $9070. College room only: $6040. Room and board charges vary according to board plan and housing facility.
Collegiate Environment: Orientation program. Drama-theater group, choral group, student-run newspaper, radio station. Social organizations: 50 open to all; national fraternities, national sororities, local fraternities, local sororities; 1% of eligible men and 2% of eligible women are members. Most popular organizations: Caribbean Student Association, Organization of Latin American Students (OLAS), Sisters of Awareness, Student Activities Committee. Major annual event: Homecoming. Student services: legal services, health clinic, personal-psychological counseling, women's center. Campus security: 24-hour emergency response devices and patrols, controlled dormitory access. 2,299 college housing spaces available; 2,284 were occupied in 2003-04. No special consideration for freshman housing applicants. Options: coed, women-only housing available. David and Lorraine Cheng Library with 305,155 books, 1.1 million microform titles, 4,112 serials, 19,661 audiovisual materials, an OPAC, and a Web page. 700 computers available on campus for general student use. A campuswide network can be accessed from student residence rooms and from off campus. Staffed computer lab on campus.
Community Environment: Population 50,000, Wayne is a suburban community located in the center of Passaic County's Wayne Township. The University lies twenty miles west of New York City and is easily accessed by all major New Jersey arteries and nearby Newark Airport. Community facilities include excellent shopping, hospitals, churches of all denominations and numerous clubs and organizations. The University is located within an hour of New York City, the Jersey shore, the Delaware Water Gap and the Meadowlands all of which offer facilities for recreation.

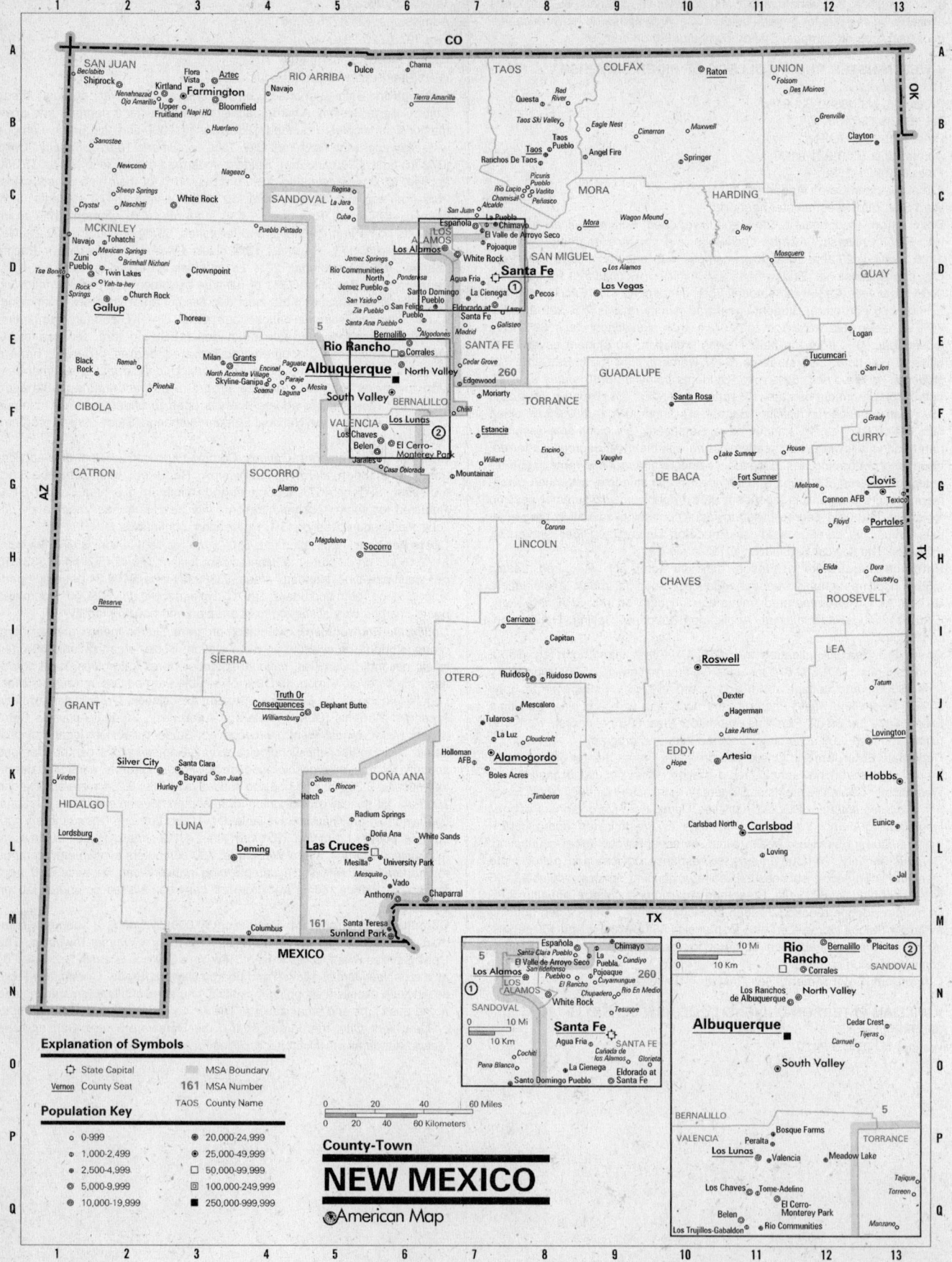

County-Town
NEW MEXICO
American Map

Explanation of Symbols

✪ State Capital	▨ MSA Boundary
Vernon County Seat	**161** MSA Number
	TAOS County Name

Population Key

○	0-999	◉	20,000-24,999
◦	1,000-2,499	◉	25,000-49,999
◉	2,500-4,999	□	50,000-99,999
◉	5,000-9,999	▣	100,000-249,999
◉	10,000-19,999	■	250,000-999,999

■ **THE ART CENTER DESIGN COLLEGE** *E-6*

5000 Marble NE
Albuquerque, NM 87110
Tel: (505)254-7575
Free: 800-825-8753
Admissions: (520)325-0123
Fax: (505)254-4754
Web Site: http://www.theartcenter.edu/
Description: Proprietary, 2-year, coed. Awards certificates, diplomas, and terminal associate degrees. Founded 1989. Total enrollment: 275. Part-time degree program.
Entrance Requirements: Required for some: ACT ASSET. Entrance: moderately difficult. Application deadline: Rolling.
Collegiate Environment: College housing not available.

■ **CENTRAL NEW MEXICO COMMUNITY COLLEGE** *E-6*

525 Buena Vista, SE
Albuquerque, NM 87106-4096
Tel: (505)224-3000
Fax: (505)224-4740
Web Site: http://www.tvi.cc.nm.us/
Description: State-supported, 2-year, coed. Awards transfer associate and terminal associate degrees. Founded 1965. Setting: 60-acre urban campus. Endowment: $1.2 million. Educational spending for 2005 fiscal year: $3080 per student. Total enrollment: 23,107. Student-undergrad faculty ratio is 21:1. 4,388 applied, 100% were admitted. Full-time: 6,925 students, 57% women, 43% men. Part-time: 16,182 students, 61% women, 39% men. 1% from out-of-state, 8% Native American, 42% Hispanic, 3% black, 2% Asian American or Pacific Islander, 0.3% international, 54% 25 or older, 8% transferred in. Calendar: trimesters. Academic remediation for entering students, ESL program, services for LD students, advanced placement, distance learning, double major, summer session for credit, part-time degree program, adult/continuing education programs, co-op programs and internships. ROTC: Air Force (c).
Entrance Requirements: Open admission except for nursing, respiratory therapy, medical laboratory technology programs. Options: electronic application, early admission. Recommended: high school transcript. Entrance: noncompetitive. Application deadline: Rolling. Notification: continuous.
Costs Per Year: Application fee: $0. Area resident tuition: $1,490 full-time, $41.40 per credit hour part-time. State resident tuition: $1,796 full-time, $49.90 per credit hour part-time. Nonresident tuition: $7,945 full-time, $220.70 per credit hour part-time. Mandatory fees: $90 full-time, $30 per term part-time.
Collegiate Environment: Orientation program. Student-run newspaper. Most popular organizations: Phi Theta Kappa, student government, Hispanic Club, TVI Times (student newspaper). Student services: health clinic, personal-psychological counseling. Campus security: 24-hour emergency response devices and patrols, late night transport-escort service. College housing not available. Main Campus Library with an OPAC and a Web page.

■ **CLOVIS COMMUNITY COLLEGE** *G-13*

417 Schepps Blvd.
Clovis, NM 88101-8381
Tel: (505)769-2811
Admissions: (505)769-4021

E-mail: yosic.corrie@clovis.edu
Web Site: http://www.clovis.edu/
Description: State-supported, 2-year, coed. Awards certificates, transfer associate, and terminal associate degrees. Founded 1990. Setting: 25-acre small town campus. Endowment: $558,291. Educational spending for 2005 fiscal year: $5693 per student. Total enrollment: 3,937. Student-undergrad faculty ratio is 15:1. 648 applied, 100% were admitted. Full-time: 688 students, 71% women, 29% men. Part-time: 3,249 students, 64% women, 36% men. Students come from 47 states and territories, 29% from out-of-state, 1% Native American, 37% Hispanic, 5% black, 2% Asian American or Pacific Islander, 0.05% international, 52% 25 or older, 5% transferred in. Retention: 55% of full-time freshmen returned the following year. Core. Calendar: semesters. Academic remediation for entering students, ESL program, services for LD students, advanced placement, independent study, distance learning, double major, summer session for credit, part-time degree program, co-op programs and internships.
Entrance Requirements: Open admission except for nursing, radiological technician, cosmetology, construction programs. Option: Common Application. Required: high school transcript. Required for some: interview. Entrance: noncompetitive.
Costs Per Year: Application fee: $0. Area resident tuition: $736 full-time, $29 per credit hour part-time. State resident tuition: $784 full-time, $31 per credit hour part-time. Nonresident tuition: $1480 full-time, $60 per credit hour part-time. Mandatory fees: $36 full-time, $3 per credit part-time, $20 per term part-time.
Collegiate Environment: Orientation program. Drama-theater group, choral group. Social organizations: 11 open to all. Most popular organizations: Student Senate, Student Nursing Association, Black Advisory Council, Hispanic Advisory Council, student ambassadors. Major annual events: campus-wide socials, Health and Fitness Fair, concert series. Student services: personal-psychological counseling. Campus security: student patrols, late night transport-escort service. College housing not available. Clovis Community College Library and Learning Resources Center with 52,000 books, 138,000 microform titles, 370 serials, 2,900 audiovisual materials, and an OPAC. Operations spending for 2004 fiscal year: $319,757. 280 computers available on campus for general student use. A campuswide network can be accessed. Staffed computer lab on campus.

■ **COLLEGE OF SANTA FE** *D-7*

1600 Saint Michael's Dr.
Santa Fe, NM 87505-7634
Tel: (505)473-6011
Free: 800-456-2673
Admissions: (505)473-6133
Fax: (505)473-6127
E-mail: admissions@csf.edu
Web Site: http://www.csf.edu
Description: Independent, comprehensive, coed. Awards associate, bachelor's, and master's degrees. Founded 1947. Setting: 100-acre suburban campus with easy access to Albuquerque. Total enrollment: 1,661. Faculty: 275 (76 full-time, 199 part-time). Student-undergrad faculty ratio is 7:1. 598 applied, 73% were admitted. 9% from top 10% of their high school class, 30% from top quarter, 65% from top half. Full-time: 640 students, 56% women, 44% men. Part-time: 702 students, 60% women, 40% men. 67% from out-of-state, 3% Native American, 26% Hispanic, 3% black, 1% Asian American or Pacific Islander, 1% international, 14% 25 or older, 62% live on

campus, 4% transferred in. Retention: 75% of full-time freshmen returned the following year. Academic areas with the most degrees conferred: visual and performing arts; business/marketing; education. Core. Calendar: semesters. Academic remediation for entering students, services for LD students, advanced placement, accelerated degree program, self-designed majors, independent study, double major, summer session for credit, part-time degree program, adult/continuing education programs, co-op programs and internships, graduate courses open to undergrads. Off campus study at Great Lakes Colleges Association, New York City Arts Program. Study abroad program. ROTC: Air Force (c).

Entrance Requirements: Options: Peterson's Universal Application, Common Application, electronic application, early admission, early decision, deferred admission, international baccalaureate accepted. Required: essay, high school transcript, 2 recommendations, interview, SAT or ACT. Recommended: minimum 3.0 high school GPA, portfolio or audition for visual and performing arts programs. Entrance: moderately difficult. Application deadline: Rolling. Notification: continuous.

Costs Per Year: Application fee: $35. Comprehensive fee: $28,978 includes full-time tuition ($21,530), mandatory fees ($746), and college room and board ($6702). College room only: $3204. Room and board charges vary according to board plan and housing facility. Part-time tuition: $720 per credit hour. Part-time mandatory fees: $16 per credit hour.

Collegiate Environment: Orientation program. Drama-theater group, choral group, student-run newspaper. Social organizations: 14 open to all. Major annual events: Annual Day of Service, Christmas Semi-Formal, Fiesta De Santa Fe. Student services: health clinic, personal-psychological counseling. Campus security: 24-hour patrols, late night transport-escort service. 499 college housing spaces available; 457 were occupied in 2003-04. Freshmen guaranteed college housing. On-campus residence required through sophomore year. Options: coed, men-only, women-only housing available. Fogelson Library Center plus 2 others with an OPAC and a Web page. 180 computers available on campus for general student use. A campuswide network can be accessed from student residence rooms and from off campus. Staffed computer lab on campus.

Community Environment: Santa Fe, the oldest state capital in the United States, is one of the country's top art markets and cultural centers. According to Conde Nast Traveler magazine, Santa Fe is one of the top tourist destinations in the world. The charm of narrow, winding streets and fascinating architecture, combined with such exciting annual events as the Indian Market and Fiestas, make Santa Fe a fun place to visit and a great place in which to live and study. Outdoors, Santa Fe has an ideal four-season climate. Recreation includes world-class skiing, white water rafting on the Rio Grande, biking, and hiking. Any time of the year, Sante Fe's sunsets are notoriously beautiful.

■ **COLLEGE OF THE SOUTHWEST** *K-13*
6610 Lovington Hwy.
Hobbs, NM 88240-9129
Tel: (505)392-6561
Free: 800-530-4400
Admissions: (505)392-6563
Web Site: http://www.csw.edu/
Description: Independent, comprehensive, coed. Awards bachelor's and master's degrees. Founded 1962. Setting: 162-acre small town campus. Endowment: $486,583. Educational spending for 2005 fiscal year: $4812 per student. Total enrollment: 741. 1,994 applied, 46% were admitted. 9% from top 10% of their high school class, 35% from top quarter, 68% from top half. Full-time: 427 students, 61% women, 39% men. Part-time: 181 students, 66% women, 34% men. Students come from 11 states and territories, 11 other countries, 26% from out-of-state, 3% Native American, 30% Hispanic, 3% black, 0.5% Asian American or Pacific Islander, 4% international, 42% 25 or older, 23% live on campus, 15% transferred in. Retention: 63% of full-time freshmen returned the following year. Core. Calendar: semesters. Services for LD students, advanced placement, distance learning, double major, summer session for credit, part-time degree program, external degree program, adult/continuing education programs, internships, graduate courses open to undergrads.

Entrance Requirements: Options: electronic application, early admission, deferred admission. Required: high school transcript, minimum 2.0 high school GPA, SAT or ACT. Entrance: moderately difficult. Application deadline: Rolling. Notification: continuous.

Costs Per Year: Application fee: $25. Comprehensive fee: $14,300 includes full-time tuition ($9300) and college room and board ($5000). Full-time tuition varies according to course load. Room and board charges vary according to housing facility. Part-time tuition: $310 per semester hour. Part-time tuition varies according to course load.

Collegiate Environment: Orientation program. Drama-theater group, choral group, student-run newspaper. Social organizations: 6 open to all. Most popular organizations: student government, Students in Free Enterprise, Southwest Association of Future Educators, Fellowship of Christian Athletes. Major annual events: homecoming, Family Week. Student services: personal-psychological counseling. Campus security: student patrols, night security. 156 college housing spaces available; 134 were occupied in 2003-04. Freshmen given priority for college housing. On-campus residence required through sophomore year. Option: coed housing available. Scarborough Memorial Library plus 1 other with 76,217 books, 24,195 microform titles, 287 serials, 1,333 audiovisual materials, and an OPAC. Operations spending for 2004 fiscal year: $183,225. 35 computers available on campus for general student use. A campuswide network can be accessed from student residence rooms. Staffed computer lab on campus.

Community Environment: See New Mexico Junior College.

■ **CROWNPOINT INSTITUTE OF TECHNOLOGY** *D-3*
PO Box 849
Crownpoint, NM 87313
Tel: (505)786-4100
Fax: (505)786-5644
Web Site: http://crownpointtech.org/
Description: Independent, 2-year, coed. Founded 1979. Calendar: semesters.

■ **DOÑA ANA BRANCH COMMUNITY COLLEGE** *L-6*
MSC-3DA, Box 30001
3400 South Espina St.
Las Cruces, NM 88003-8001
Tel: (505)527-7500
Fax: (505)527-7515
Web Site: http://dabcc-www.nmsu.edu/
Description: State and locally supported, 2-year, coed. Part of New Mexico State University System. Awards certificates, transfer associate, and terminal associate degrees. Founded 1973. Setting: 15-acre urban campus with easy access to Ciudad Juarez and El Paso. Total enrollment: 6,347. 1,629 applied, 99% were admitted. Full-time: 3,596 students, 56% women, 44% men. Part-time: 2,751 students, 56% women, 44% men. 2% Native American, 63% Hispanic, 2% black, 1% Asian American or Pacific Islander, 1% international, 3% transferred in. Retention: 80% of full-time freshmen returned the following year. Core. Calendar: semesters. Academic remediation for entering students, ESL program, services for LD students, advanced placement, freshman honors college, honors program, summer session for credit, part-time degree program, adult/continuing education programs, co-op programs and internships. ROTC: Army (c), Air Force (c).

Entrance Requirements: Open admission except for radiological technology, nursing, respiratory care, paramedic, electrical apprenticeship, area vocational school programs. Option: deferred admission. Required: high school transcript. Required for some: recommendations. Placement: ACT, ACT ASSET, or ACT COMPASS recommended. Entrance: noncompetitive. Application deadline: Rolling.

Costs Per Year: Application fee: $15. Area resident tuition: $1080 full-time, $45 per credit part-time. State resident tuition: $1320 full-time, $55 per credit part-time. Nonresident tuition: $3240 full-time, $135 per credit part-time.

Collegiate Environment: Orientation program. Drama-theater group, choral group, marching band, student-run newspaper, radio station. Social organizations: 10 open to all. Major annual events: Homecoming, Spring Fling, Return to Campus. Student services: legal services, health clinic, personal-psychological counseling, women's center. Campus security: 24-hour emergency response devices and patrols, late night transport-escort service. Option: coed housing available. Library/Media Center with 17,140 books, 213 serials, and an OPAC. Operations spending for 2004 fiscal year: $184,000. 433 computers available on campus for general student use. A campuswide network can be accessed from off-campus. Staffed computer lab on campus.

■ **EASTERN NEW MEXICO UNIVERSITY** *H-13*
1200 West University
Portales, NM 88130
Tel: (505)562-1011
Free: 800-367-3668

Admissions: (505)562-2178
Fax: (505)562-2118
E-mail: donna.kittrell@enmu.edu
Web Site: http://www.enmu.edu/
Description: State-supported, comprehensive, coed. Part of Eastern New Mexico University System. Awards associate, bachelor's, and master's degrees. Founded 1934. Setting: 240-acre rural campus. Endowment: $7.2 million. Research spending for 2004 fiscal year: $569,683. Educational spending for 2005 fiscal year: $5279 per student. Total enrollment: 4,033. Faculty: 263 (149 full-time, 114 part-time). Student-undergrad faculty ratio is 17:1. 1,804 applied, 65% were admitted. 12% from top 10% of their high school class, 34% from top quarter, 67% from top half. Full-time: 2,510 students, 53% women, 47% men. Part-time: 781 students, 68% women, 32% men. Students come from 37 states and territories, 16 other countries, 19% from out-of-state, 3% Native American, 30% Hispanic, 7% black, 1% Asian American or Pacific Islander, 1% international, 25% 25 or older, 28% live on campus, 10% transferred in. Retention: 58% of full-time freshmen returned the following year. Academic areas with the most degrees conferred: education; business/marketing; liberal arts/general studies. Core. Calendar: semesters. Academic remediation for entering students, ESL program, services for LD students, advanced placement, accelerated degree program, self-designed majors, honors program, distance learning, double major, summer session for credit, part-time degree program, external degree program, adult/continuing education programs, co-op programs and internships, graduate courses open to undergrads. Study abroad program.
Entrance Requirements: Options: Peterson's Universal Application, electronic application, early admission, deferred admission, international baccalaureate accepted. Required: high school transcript, minimum 2.0 high school GPA, SAT or ACT. Entrance: minimally difficult. Application deadline: Rolling.
Costs Per Year: Application fee: $0. State resident tuition: $1992 full-time, $83 per credit hour part-time. Nonresident tuition: $7548 full-time, $314.50 per credit hour part-time. Mandatory fees: $792 full-time, $33 per credit hour part-time. College room and board: $4480. College room only: $2090. Room and board charges vary according to housing facility.
Collegiate Environment: Orientation program. Drama-theater group, choral group, marching band, student-run newspaper, radio station. Social organizations: 51 open to all; national fraternities, national sororities. Most popular organizations: Student Government Association, Student Activities Board, Residence Hall Association, IFC. Major annual events: Peanut Valley Festival, Homecoming, Spring Fling. Student services: health clinic, personal-psychological counseling. Campus security: 24-hour emergency response devices and patrols, late night transport-escort service, controlled dormitory access. 1,176 college housing spaces available; 837 were occupied in 2003-04. Freshmen guaranteed college housing. On-campus residence required in freshman year. Options: coed, women-only housing available. Golden Library with 305,108 books, 738,873 microform titles, 7,621 serials, 26,408 audiovisual materials, an OPAC, and a Web page. Operations spending for 2004 fiscal year: $1.4 million. 493 computers available on campus for general student use. A campuswide network can be accessed from student residence rooms and from off campus. Staffed computer lab on campus.

■ **EASTERN NEW MEXICO UNIVERSITY-ROSWELL** *J-10*
PO Box 6000
Roswell, NM 88202-6000
Tel: (505)624-7000
Admissions: (505)624-7145
Fax: (505)624-7119
Web Site: http://www.enmu.edu/
Description: State-supported, 2-year, coed. Part of Eastern New Mexico University System. Awards certificates, transfer associate, and terminal associate degrees. Founded 1958. Setting: 241-acre small town campus. Endowment: $494,460. Educational spending for 2005 fiscal year: $2427 per student. Total enrollment: 3,522. 860 applied, 55% were admitted. Students come from 6 states and territories, 3 other countries, 1% from out-of-state, 2% Native American, 47% Hispanic, 2% black, 0.3% Asian American or Pacific Islander, 0.1% international, 55% 25 or older, 5% live on campus. Core. Calendar: semesters. Academic remediation for entering students, ESL program, services for LD students, advanced placement, independent study, distance learning, summer session for credit, part-time degree program, adult/continuing education programs, co-op programs and internships. Off campus study at other units of the Eastern New Mexico University System. ROTC: Army (c), Naval (c), Air Force (c).

Entrance Requirements: Open admission except for nursing, occupational therapy programs. Options: Common Application, early admission. Required: high school transcript. Recommended: ACT. Entrance: noncompetitive. Application deadline: Rolling.
Collegiate Environment: Orientation program. Drama-theater group, choral group, student-run newspaper. Social organizations: 20 open to all. Most popular organizations: student government, Spanish Club, Drama Club, Phi Theta Kappa. Campus security: 24-hour emergency response devices, student patrols, late night transport-escort service. Option: coed housing available. Learning Resource Center with 251,449 microform titles, 327 serials, 5,727 audiovisual materials, and an OPAC. Operations spending for 2004 fiscal year: $304,720. 60 computers available on campus for general student use. A campuswide network can be accessed from off-campus. Staffed computer lab on campus.

■ **INSTITUTE OF AMERICAN INDIAN ARTS** *D-7*
83 Avan Nu Po Rd.
Santa Fe, NM 87508
Tel: (505)424-2300
Admissions: (505)424-2328
Fax: (505)424-0505
Web Site: http://www.iaia.edu/
Description: Federally supported, primarily 2-year, coed. Awards transfer associate and bachelor's degrees. Founded 1962. Setting: 120-acre urban campus. Endowment: $4 million. Total enrollment: 183. 109 applied, 69% were admitted. Full-time: 156 students, 47% women, 53% men. Part-time: 27 students, 41% women, 59% men. Students come from 29 states and territories, 88% Native American, 1% Asian American or Pacific Islander, 51% 25 or older. Retention: 46% of full-time freshmen returned the following year. Core. Calendar: semesters. Academic remediation for entering students, internships. Off campus study at College of Santa Fe, Santa Fe Community College, University of Arizona, Haystack School of Crafts, University of New Mexico.
Entrance Requirements: Option: deferred admission. Required: high school transcript, minimum 2.0 high school GPA, 3 recommendations. Recommended: interview. Placement: ACT recommended. Entrance: minimally difficult. Application deadline: 4/15. Notification: continuous until 7/1.
Costs Per Year: Application fee: $0. State resident tuition: $2400 full-time, $100 per credit hour part-time. Nonresident tuition: $2400 full-time, $100 per credit hour part-time. Mandatory fees: $200 full-time, $20 per term part-time. College room and board: $4648. College room only: $2212. Room and board charges vary according to housing facility.
Collegiate Environment: Orientation program. Drama-theater group, student-run newspaper. Social organizations: 10 open to all. Most popular organizations: Powwow Club, Museum Club, Ski Club, Spring Break Club. Major annual events: Powwow, gallery openings, visit to Indian reservations. Student services: personal-psychological counseling. Campus security: 24-hour patrols, late night transport-escort service. 100 college housing spaces available; 97 were occupied in 2003-04. Option: coed housing available. Fogelson Library with 15,200 books and 60 serials. 20 computers available on campus for general student use. Staffed computer lab on campus.

■ **INTERNATIONAL INSTITUTE OF THE AMERICAS** *E-6*
4201 Central Ave. NW, Ste. J
Albuquerque, NM 87105-1649
Tel: (505)880-2877; 888-660-2428
Fax: (505)352-0199
E-mail: esigman@iia.edu
Web Site: http://www.aibtonline.com/
Description: Independent, primarily 2-year, coed. Awards diplomas, terminal associate, and bachelor's degrees. Setting: 1-acre urban campus. Total enrollment: 232. Student-undergrad faculty ratio is 15:1. 13% Native American, 67% Hispanic, 3% black, 1% Asian American or Pacific Islander, 0% international. Retention: 100% of full-time freshmen returned the following year. Calendar: continuous.
Entrance Requirements: Required: interview. Entrance: noncompetitive. Application deadline: Rolling. Notification: continuous.
Costs Per Year: One-time mandatory fee: $200. Tuition: $9850 full-time. Mandatory fees: $350 full-time.

■ **ITT TECHNICAL INSTITUTE** *E-6*
5100 Masthead, NE
Albuquerque, NM 87109-4366

Tel: (505)828-1114
Fax: (505)828-1849
Web Site: http://www.itt-tech.edu/
Description: Proprietary, primarily 2-year, coed. Part of ITT Educational Services, Inc. Awards terminal associate and bachelor's degrees. Founded 1989. Core.
Entrance Requirements: Option: deferred admission. Required: high school transcript, interview, Wonderlic aptitude test. Recommended: recommendations. Entrance: minimally difficult. Application deadline: Rolling. Notification: continuous.
Costs Per Year: Application fee: $100.
Collegiate Environment: Orientation program. College housing not available.

■ **LUNA COMMUNITY COLLEGE** *D-9*
PO Box 1510
Las Vegas, NM 87701
Tel: (505)454-2500
Free: 800-588-7232
Admissions: (505)454-2020
E-mail: hgriego@luna.cc.nm.us
Web Site: http://www.luna.cc.nm.us/
Description: State-supported, 2-year, coed. Awards certificates, diplomas, transfer associate, and terminal associate degrees. Setting: 25-acre rural campus. Endowment: $12,911. Educational spending for 2005 fiscal year: $1779 per student. Total enrollment: 2,041. 154 applied, 100% were admitted. Full-time: 502 students, 65% women, 35% men. Part-time: 1,539 students, 59% women, 41% men. 0.5% Native American, 88% Hispanic, 0.5% black, 0.5% Asian American or Pacific Islander, 25% 25 or older. Core. Calendar: semesters. Academic remediation for entering students, honors program, independent study, distance learning, part-time degree program, co-op programs.
Entrance Requirements: Open admission. Options: Common Application, electronic application. Required: high school transcript. Entrance: noncompetitive.
Costs Per Year: Area resident tuition: $600 full-time, $25 per credit hour part-time. State resident tuition: $888 full-time, $37 per credit hour part-time. Nonresident tuition: $1824 full-time, $76 per credit hour part-time. Mandatory fees: $44 full-time, $22 per term part-time. Full-time tuition and fees vary according to course load, program, and reciprocity agreements. Part-time tuition and fees vary according to course load, program, and reciprocity agreements.
Collegiate Environment: Orientation program. College housing not available. Samuel F. Vigil Learning Resource Center plus 1 other with 37,343 books, 178 serials, 5,000 audiovisual materials, and an OPAC. Operations spending for 2004 fiscal year: $421,509.

■ **MESALANDS COMMUNITY COLLEGE** *E-12*
911 South Tenth St.
Tucumcari, NM 88401
Tel: (505)461-4413
Fax: (505)461-1901
Web Site: http://www.mesalands.edu/
Description: State-supported, 2-year, coed. Awards certificates, transfer associate, and terminal associate degrees. Founded 1979. Setting: small town campus. Endowment: $16,000. Total enrollment: 563. Students come from 10 states and territories, 5% from out-of-state, 3% Native American, 35% Hispanic, 2% black, 1% Asian American or Pacific Islander, 2% international, 52% 25 or older. Calendar: semesters.
Entrance Requirements: Required: high school transcript. Placement: ACT COMPASS required. Entrance: minimally difficult. Application deadline: Rolling.
Costs Per Year: State resident tuition: $1050 full-time, $37 per credit hour part-time. Nonresident tuition: $1890 full-time, $66 per credit hour part-time. Mandatory fees: $284 full-time, $7 per credit hour part-time, $27 per term part-time.
Collegiate Environment: Social organizations: 11 open to all. Most popular organizations: Student Senate, Chi Alpha, Phi Theta Kappa, SHOE, Natural Sciences Club. Major annual events: Student Appreciation Days, Cinco de Mayo Celebration. Campus security: 24-hour emergency response devices. College housing not available.

■ **METROPOLITAN COLLEGE OF COURT REPORTING** *E-6*
8100 Mountain Rd. NE, Ste. 200
Albuquerque, NM 87110-4129

Tel: (505)888-3400
Fax: (505)254-3738
Web Site: http://www.metropolitancollege.edu/
Description: Proprietary, 4-year, coed. Founded 1980. Setting: urban campus. Total enrollment: 147. 60 applied, 80% were admitted. Calendar: trimesters.

■ **NATIONAL AMERICAN UNIVERSITY (ALBUQUERQUE)** *E-6*
4775 Indian School, NE, Ste. 200
Albuquerque, NM 87110
Tel: (505)265-7517
Free: 800-843-8892
Fax: (505)265-7542
Web Site: http://www.national.edu/
Description: Proprietary, 4-year, coed. Awards associate, bachelor's, and master's degrees. Founded 1941. Setting: 5-acre suburban campus. Total enrollment: 519. Students come from 2 other countries, 0% from out-of-state, 6% Native American, 38% Hispanic, 6% black, 2% Asian American or Pacific Islander, 1% international, 92% 25 or older. Retention: 60% of full-time freshmen returned the following year. Core. Accelerated degree program, independent study, distance learning, double major, summer session for credit, part-time degree program, external degree program, adult/continuing education programs, co-op programs and internships. Off campus study.
Entrance Requirements: Open admission. Required: high school transcript. Entrance: noncompetitive. Application deadline: Rolling.
Costs Per Year: Application fee: $25. Tuition: $11,280 full-time, $235 per quarter hour part-time. Mandatory fees: $420 full-time. Full-time tuition and fees vary according to course load and program. Part-time tuition varies according to course load and program.
Collegiate Environment: Orientation program. Major annual events: Spring Graduation, Galas. Campus security: 24-hour patrols, late night transport-escort service. College housing not available. 70 computers available on campus for general student use. A campuswide network can be accessed from off-campus. Staffed computer lab on campus.

■ **NATIONAL AMERICAN UNIVERSITY (RIO RANCHO)** *E-6*
1601 Rio Rancho
Ste. 200
Rio Rancho, NM 87124
Tel: (505)891-1111
Web Site: http://www.national.edu/
Description: Proprietary, 2-year, coed.

■ **NATIONAL COLLEGE OF MIDWIFERY** *B-8*
209 State Rd. 240
Taos, NM 87571
Tel: (505)758-8914
Fax: (505)758-0302
Web Site: http://www.midwiferycollege.org/
Description: Independent, comprehensive, women only. Awards associate, bachelor's, master's, and doctoral degrees. Founded 1989. Total enrollment: 59. 30 applied, 100% were admitted. Full-time: 30 students. Part-time: 27 students. 2% Native American, 5% Hispanic, 0% international. Calendar: trimesters.
Collegiate Environment: College housing not available.

■ **NEW MEXICO HIGHLANDS UNIVERSITY** *D-9*
PO Box 9000
Las Vegas, NM 87701
Tel: (505)454-3000
Free: 800-338-6648
Admissions: (505)454-3405
Fax: (505)454-3311
E-mail: johncoca@nmhu.edu
Web Site: http://www.nmhu.edu/
Description: State-supported, comprehensive, coed. Awards associate, bachelor's, and master's degrees. Founded 1893. Setting: 120-acre small town campus. Endowment: $2 million. Research spending for 2004 fiscal year: $3.6 million. Educational spending for 2005 fiscal year: $3578 per student. Total enrollment: 3,750. Faculty: 109 (73 full-time, 36 part-time). Student-undergrad faculty ratio is 25:1. 1,193 applied, 69% were admitted. 5% from top 10% of their high school class, 14% from top quarter, 41% from top half. Full-time: 1,245 students, 56% women, 44% men. Part-time: 741

students, 71% women, 29% men. Students come from 19 states and territories, 3 other countries, 8% from out-of-state, 9% Native American, 59% Hispanic, 4% black, 1% Asian American or Pacific Islander, 0.4% international, 44% 25 or older, 10% live on campus, 14% transferred in. Retention: 54% of full-time freshmen returned the following year. Academic areas with the most degrees conferred: health professions and related sciences; education; business/marketing. Core. Calendar: semesters. Academic remediation for entering students, services for LD students, advanced placement, accelerated degree program, honors program, independent study, distance learning, double major, summer session for credit, part-time degree program, co-op programs and internships, graduate courses open to undergrads. Off campus study at San Juan Community College, Santa Fe Community College, NMHU Center at Roswell; NMHU Center at Rio Rancho.

Entrance Requirements: Options: Peterson's Universal Application, Common Application, electronic application, early admission, deferred admission, international baccalaureate accepted. Required: high school transcript, minimum 2.0 high school GPA. Required for some: 2 recommendations, interview. Entrance: minimally difficult. Application deadline: Rolling. Notification: continuous.

Costs Per Year: Application fee: $15. State resident tuition: $2280 full-time, $95 per credit hour part-time. Nonresident tuition: $3420 full-time, $95 per credit hour part-time. Mandatory fees: $20 full-time. Full-time tuition and fees vary according to course load and location. Part-time tuition varies according to course load and location. College room and board: $3992. College room only: $2056. Room and board charges vary according to board plan and housing facility.

Collegiate Environment: Orientation program. Drama-theater group, choral group, marching band, student-run newspaper, radio station. Social organizations: 30 open to all. Most popular organizations: BESO Club, Activities Board, Campus Crusade, AISES, Cowboy Cheerleaders. Major annual events: Homecoming activities, Performing Arts Series, Welcome Back Weeks. Student services: health clinic, personal-psychological counseling. Campus security: 24-hour emergency response devices and patrols, late night transport-escort service, controlled dormitory access. 474 college housing spaces available; 284 were occupied in 2003-04. No special consideration for freshman housing applicants. Options: coed, men-only, women-only housing available. Donnelly Library with 386,489 books, 183,913 microform titles, 740 serials, 826 audiovisual materials, an OPAC, and a Web page. Operations spending for 2004 fiscal year: $1.3 million. 500 computers available on campus for general student use. A campuswide network can be accessed from student residence rooms and from off campus. Staffed computer lab on campus.

Community Environment: Las Vegas has grown considerably since its days as a Mormon outpost on the Santa Fe Trail. The city is in the foothills of the Sangre de Cristo Mountains and produces lumber, dairy and wool products. The area has a stimulating, dry climate with winters that are bracing but sunny. Recreational facilities nearby include hunting, fishing and skiing. Some part-time employment is available for students.

■ **NEW MEXICO INSTITUTE OF MINING AND TECHNOLOGY** *H-5*
801 Leroy Place
Socorro, NM 87801
Tel: (505)835-5011
Free: 800-428-TECH
Admissions: (505)835-5424
Fax: (505)835-5989
E-mail: admission@admin.nmt.edu
Web Site: http://www.nmt.edu/

Description: State-supported, university, coed. Awards associate, bachelor's, master's, and doctoral degrees. Founded 1889. Setting: 320-acre small town campus with easy access to Albuquerque. Endowment: $16.2 million. Total enrollment: 1,891. Faculty: 147 (125 full-time, 22 part-time). Student-undergrad faculty ratio is 11:1. 428 applied, 81% were admitted. 41% from top 10% of their high school class, 71% from top quarter, 88% from top half. Full-time: 1,125 students, 26% women, 74% men. Part-time: 263 students, 56% women, 44% men. Students come from 24 states and territories, 29 other countries, 12% from out-of-state, 3% Native American, 20% Hispanic, 1% black, 3% Asian American or Pacific Islander, 3% international, 11% 25 or older, 49% live on campus, 6% transferred in. Retention: 68% of full-time freshmen returned the following year. Academic areas with the most degrees conferred: engineering; physical sciences; computer and information sciences. Core. Calendar: semesters. Services for LD students, advanced placement, accelerated degree program, self-

designed majors, independent study, distance learning, double major, summer session for credit, part-time degree program, co-op programs and internships, graduate courses open to undergrads.

Entrance Requirements: Options: Peterson's Universal Application, electronic application, deferred admission. Required: high school transcript, minimum 2.5 high school GPA, SAT or ACT. Recommended: interview, ACT. Required for some: 2 recommendations. Entrance: moderately difficult. Application deadline: 8/1. Notification: continuous.

Costs Per Year: Application fee: $15. State resident tuition: $3156 full-time, $131.48 per hour part-time. Nonresident tuition: $9975 full-time, $415.63 per hour part-time. Mandatory fees: $448 full-time. Part-time tuition varies according to course load. College room and board: $4866. College room only: $2116. Room and board charges vary according to board plan and housing facility.

Collegiate Environment: Orientation program. Drama-theater group, choral group, student-run newspaper, radio station. Social organizations: 55 open to all. Most popular organizations: Search and Rescue, Society for Creative Anachronism, Amateur Astronomers, Ski Club. Major annual events: 49'ers, Spring Fling, International Fair. Student services: health clinic, personal-psychological counseling. Campus security: 24-hour emergency response devices and patrols, late night transport-escort service. 644 college housing spaces available. Options: coed, men-only, women-only housing available. New Mexico Tech Library plus 1 other with 321,829 books, 217,540 microform titles, 884 serials, 2,526 audiovisual materials, and a Web page. 225 computers available on campus for general student use. A campuswide network can be accessed from student residence rooms and from off campus. Staffed computer lab on campus.

Community Environment: Located 75 miles south of Albuquerque, Socorro (Spanish meaning"help") is in the valley of the Rio Grande. Socorro is the county seat of Socorro County and relies primarily on a service economy and serves a trade territory encompassing both Socorro and Catron Counties. The town draws trade and population from those who work at Stallion Site on the northern end of the White Sands Missile Range, and at the Very Large Array (VLA), the largest radio telescope complex in the world, located on the San Augustin Plains, about 50 miles west of Socorro. The Tech campus provides facilities for golf, tennis, and swimming. The surrounding area provides mountain biking, hiking, and fishing. The town also supports an improving public school system, a general hospital, and 14 churches. Opportunities for part-time employment on the Tech campus are excellent.

■ **NEW MEXICO JUNIOR COLLEGE** *K-13*
5317 Lovington Hwy.
Hobbs, NM 88240-9123
Tel: (505)392-4510
Admissions: (505)392-5092
Fax: (505)392-2527
Web Site: http://www.nmjc.edu/

Description: State and locally supported, 2-year, coed. Part of New Mexico Commission on Higher Education. Awards certificates, transfer associate, and terminal associate degrees. Founded 1965. Setting: 185-acre small town campus. Research spending for 2004 fiscal year: $21,370. Total enrollment: 3,222. 9% from top 10% of their high school class, 24% from top quarter, 72% from top half. 5 valedictorians. Students come from 17 states and territories, 7 other countries, 10% from out-of-state, 1% Native American, 32% Hispanic, 4% black, 1% Asian American or Pacific Islander, 0.2% international, 52% 25 or older, 15% live on campus. Core. Calendar: semesters. Academic remediation for entering students, services for LD students, advanced placement, distance learning, summer session for credit, part-time degree program, adult/continuing education programs, co-op programs and internships.

Entrance Requirements: Open admission. Options: early admission, deferred admission. Placement: ACT recommended. Entrance: noncompetitive. Application deadline: Rolling.

Collegiate Environment: Drama-theater group, choral group. Most popular organizations: Student Nurses Association, Phi Theta Kappa, Fellowship of Christian Athletes. Major annual events: Cowboy Roundup Days, Southwest Poets' Conference, New Mexico Junior College Rodeo. Student services: health clinic, personal-psychological counseling. Campus security: 24-hour emergency response devices and patrols, late night transport-escort service, controlled dormitory access. 200 college housing spaces available; all were occupied in 2003-04. On-campus residence required in freshman year. Option: coed housing available. Pannell Library with 118,500 books, 45 serials, an OPAC, and a Web page. 275 computers available on campus for general student use. A campuswide network can be accessed from off-campus. Staffed computer lab on campus.

Community Environment: A tent city sprang up in this once little-known ranchland corner of New Mexico when oil was discovered in 1927. The settlement soon became the terminal point for oil companies, producing 90% of the state's petroleum. Farmlands in the surrounding area are irrigated by artesian wells and produce alfalfa, cotton and grain sorghums. The city has an airport and bus service for transportation. Community facilities include churches representing major denominations, a library, a hospital, and various civic and fraternal organizations. Recreational areas within reasonable distance provide hunting, fishing, golf, boating and other water sports. Part-time employment is available for students.

■ **NEW MEXICO MILITARY INSTITUTE** *J-10*
101 West College Blvd.
Roswell, NM 88201-5173
Tel: (505)622-6250
Free: 800-421-5376
Admissions: (505)624-8050
Fax: (505)624-8067
E-mail: admissions@nmmi.edu
Web Site: http://www.nmmi.edu/
Description: State-supported, 2-year, coed. Part of New Mexico Commission on Higher Education. Awards transfer associate degrees. Founded 1891. Setting: 42-acre small town campus. Endowment: $298.5 million. Total enrollment: 455. Student-undergrad faculty ratio is 7:1. 601 applied, 62% were admitted. Students come from 42 states and territories, 13 other countries, 55% from out-of-state, 2% Native American, 16% Hispanic, 11% black, 5% Asian American or Pacific Islander, 3% international, 0% 25 or older, 100% live on campus. Core. Calendar: semesters. Academic remediation for entering students, ESL program, advanced placement, summer session for credit. ROTC: Army.
Entrance Requirements: Options: early admission, deferred admission. Required: high school transcript, minimum 2.0 high school GPA, SAT or ACT. Entrance: moderately difficult. Application deadline: 8/1. Notification: continuous. Preference given to state residents.
Costs Per Year: Application fee: $60. State resident tuition: $1304 full-time. Nonresident tuition: $4258 full-time. Mandatory fees: $1558 full-time. College room and board: $3645.
Collegiate Environment: Orientation program. Drama-theater group, choral group, marching band, student-run newspaper. Social organizations: 30 open to all. Most popular organizations: band, chorus, drill teams, Officer's Club. Major annual events: Parents' Weekend, Homecoming, Open House. Student services: health clinic, personal-psychological counseling. Campus security: 24-hour emergency response devices and patrols, controlled dormitory access. On-campus residence required through sophomore year. Option: coed housing available. Paul Horgan Library plus 2 others with 65,000 books, 200 serials, and an OPAC. Operations spending for 2004 fiscal year: $165,220. 700 computers available on campus for general student use. Computer purchase/lease plans available. A campuswide network can be accessed from student residence rooms and from off campus. Staffed computer lab on campus.
Community Environment: With a population of approximately 45,000, Roswell, a Pecos Valley City, noted for its fine climate, is the distributing and supply point for a great agricultural, stockraising and oil producing territory. The summer mean temperature is 77.5 degrees, and the winter mean temperature is 41.2 degrees. The area is reached by bus, rail and air lines. Community services include several churches, a public library, a community museum and art center, a community concert association and 2 hospitals. A local park offers a swimming pool, tennis courts and golf courses.

■ **NEW MEXICO STATE UNIVERSITY** *L-6*
PO Box 30001
Las Cruces, NM 88003-8001
Tel: (505)646-0111
Free: 800-662-6678
Admissions: (505)646-3121
Fax: (505)646-6330
E-mail: admssions@nmsu.edu
Web Site: http://www.nmsu.edu/
Description: State-supported, university, coed. Part of New Mexico State University System. Awards associate, bachelor's, master's, and doctoral degrees and post-master's certificates. Founded 1888. Setting: 900-acre suburban campus with easy access to El Paso. Endowment: $52.7 million. Research spending for 2004 fiscal year: $97.7 million. Educational spending for 2005 fiscal year: $5682 per student. Total enrollment: 16,072. Faculty:

833 (667 full-time, 166 part-time). Student-undergrad faculty ratio is 19:1. 5,522 applied, 81% were admitted. 20% from top 10% of their high school class, 49% from top quarter, 82% from top half. Full-time: 10,238 students, 55% women, 45% men. Part-time: 2,418 students, 59% women, 41% men. Students come from 52 states and territories, 44 other countries, 16% from out-of-state, 3% Native American, 45% Hispanic, 3% black, 1% Asian American or Pacific Islander, 1% international, 20% 25 or older, 16% live on campus, 4% transferred in. Retention: 70% of full-time freshmen returned the following year. Academic areas with the most degrees conferred: business/marketing; education; engineering. Core. Calendar: semesters. Academic remediation for entering students, services for LD students, advanced placement, accelerated degree program, self-designed majors, honors program, independent study, distance learning, double major, summer session for credit, part-time degree program, adult/continuing education programs, co-op programs and internships, graduate courses open to undergrads. Off campus study at members of the National Student Exchange, other units of the New Mexico State University System. Study abroad program. ROTC: Army, Air Force.
Entrance Requirements: Options: Peterson's Universal Application, electronic application, early admission, deferred admission. Required: high school transcript, minimum 2.0 high school GPA, SAT or ACT. Entrance: moderately difficult. Application deadline: 8/19. Notification: continuous.
Costs Per Year: Application fee: $15. State resident tuition: $2868 full-time, $163.25 per credit part-time. Nonresident tuition: $12,156 full-time, $550.25 per credit part-time. Mandatory fees: $1050 full-time. College room and board: $5332. College room only: $3072. Room and board charges vary according to board plan and gender.
Collegiate Environment: Orientation program. Drama-theater group, choral group, marching band, student-run newspaper, radio station. Social organizations: 253 open to all; national fraternities, national sororities; 4% of eligible men and 3% of eligible women are members. Major annual events: homecoming, Earth Day, Noche de Luminarias. Student services: legal services, health clinic, personal-psychological counseling, women's center. Campus security: 24-hour emergency response devices and patrols, late night transport-escort service, controlled dormitory access. 2,255 college housing spaces available; 2,061 were occupied in 2003-04. No special consideration for freshman housing applicants. Options: coed, men-only, women-only housing available. New Mexico State University Library plus 2 others with 1.6 million books, 1.4 million microform titles, 5,975 serials, 34,845 audiovisual materials, an OPAC, and a Web page. Operations spending for 2004 fiscal year: $6.4 million. 500 computers available on campus for general student use. A campuswide network can be accessed from student residence rooms and from off campus. Staffed computer lab on campus.

■ **NEW MEXICO STATE UNIVERSITY-ALAMOGORDO** *K-7*
2400 North Scenic Dr.
Alamogordo, NM 88311-0477
Tel: (505)439-3600
Admissions: (505)439-3700
E-mail: advisor@nmsua.nmsu.edu
Web Site: http://alamo.nmsu.edu/
Description: State-supported, 2-year, coed. Part of New Mexico State University System. Awards certificates, transfer associate, and terminal associate degrees. Founded 1958. Setting: 540-acre small town campus. Educational spending for 2005 fiscal year: $3024 per student. Total enrollment: 1,915. Student-undergrad faculty ratio is 14:1. 268 applied, 100% were admitted. Full-time: 714 students, 68% women, 32% men. Part-time: 1,201 students, 64% women, 36% men. Students come from 5 other countries, 4% Native American, 28% Hispanic, 5% black, 3% Asian American or Pacific Islander, 1% international, 70% 25 or older, 14% transferred in. Core. Calendar: semesters. Academic remediation for entering students, ESL program, services for LD students, advanced placement, self-designed majors, honors program, distance learning, summer session for credit, part-time degree program, adult/continuing education programs, internships. Off campus study at other branches of New Mexico State University.
Entrance Requirements: Open admission except for medical laboratory technology, nursing programs. Options: Common Application, electronic application, early admission, deferred admission. Required: high school transcript, minimum 2.0 high school GPA. Entrance: noncompetitive. Application deadline: Rolling. Notification: continuous.
Costs Per Year: Application fee: $15. Area resident tuition: $1248 full-time, $52 per credit hour part-time. State resident tuition: $1416 full-time, $59 per

credit hour part-time. Nonresident tuition: $3960 full-time, $165 per credit hour part-time. Mandatory fees: $48 full-time, $2 per credit hour part-time.
Collegiate Environment: Orientation program. Drama-theater group, choral group. Social organizations: 12 open to all. Most popular organizations: Social Science Club, Phi Theta Kappa, Student/NEA, Christian Fellowship, Epsilon Tau Sigma. Student services: personal-psychological counseling. Campus security: 24-hour emergency response devices. College housing not available. David H. Townsend Library with 39,000 books, 350 serials, an OPAC, and a Web page. Operations spending for 2004 fiscal year: $274,000. 200 computers available on campus for general student use. A campuswide network can be accessed from off-campus. Staffed computer lab on campus.

■ **NEW MEXICO STATE UNIVERSITY-CARLSBAD** *L-11*
1500 University Dr.
Carlsbad, NM 88220-3509
Tel: (505)234-9200
Admissions: (505)234-9220
Fax: (505)885-4951
Web Site: http://www.cavern.nmsu.edu/
Description: State-supported, 2-year, coed. Part of New Mexico State University System. Awards certificates, transfer associate, and terminal associate degrees. Founded 1950. Setting: 40-acre small town campus. Total enrollment: 1,236. Students come from 6 states and territories, 2 other countries, 1% Native American, 39% Hispanic, 1% black, 1% Asian American or Pacific Islander, 0.2% international, 70% 25 or older. Core. Calendar: semesters. Academic remediation for entering students, ESL program, services for LD students, advanced placement, self-designed majors, honors program, independent study, distance learning, double major, summer session for credit, part-time degree program, adult/continuing education programs, co-op programs and internships.
Entrance Requirements: Open admission except for nursing, radiological technology programs. Options: electronic application, early admission, deferred admission. Required: high school transcript. Placement: ACT recommended; ACT required for some. Entrance: noncompetitive. Application deadline: Rolling. Notification: continuous.
Collegiate Environment: Orientation program. Drama-theater group. Social organizations: 10 open to all. Most popular organizations: Student Nurses Association, Alpha Sigma Phi (criminal justice), Phi Theta Kappa, Associated Students. Major annual events: Haunted House, Kramer Entertainment. Campus security: 24-hour emergency response devices. College housing not available. 300 computers available on campus for general student use. A campuswide network can be accessed. Staffed computer lab on campus.

■ **NEW MEXICO STATE UNIVERSITY-GRANTS** *E-3*
1500 3rd St.
Grants, NM 87020-2025
Tel: (505)287-7981
Web Site: http://grants.nmsu.edu/
Description: State-supported, 2-year, coed. Part of New Mexico State University System. Awards certificates, transfer associate, and terminal associate degrees. Founded 1968. Setting: small town campus. Total enrollment: 636. Full-time: 233 students, 73% women, 27% men. Part-time: 403 students, 70% women, 30% men. 41% Native American, 29% Hispanic, 1% black, 0.3% Asian American or Pacific Islander, 0% international. Core. Calendar: semesters. Summer session for credit, part-time degree program.
Entrance Requirements: Open admission. Options: Common Application, early admission. Required: high school transcript, CPT. Entrance: noncompetitive. Application deadline: 7/30.
Collegiate Environment: College housing not available. 30,000 books and 20 serials. 150 computers available on campus for general student use. A campuswide network can be accessed. Staffed computer lab on campus.

■ **NORTHERN NEW MEXICO COMMUNITY COLLEGE** *D-7*
921 Paseo de Oñate
Espanola, NM 87532
Tel: (505)747-2100
Admissions: (505)747-2193
Web Site: http://www.nnmcc.edu/
Description: State-supported, 2-year, coed. Part of New Mexico Commission on Higher Education. Awards certificates, transfer associate, and terminal associate degrees. Founded 1909. Setting: 35-acre rural campus. Endowment: $829,791. Total enrollment: 2,272. 320 applied, 100% were admitted. 5% from top 10% of their high school class, 23% from top quarter,

52% from top half. Students come from 5 states and territories, 1% from out-of-state, 60% 25 or older, 1% live on campus. Core. Calendar: semesters. Academic remediation for entering students, services for LD students, advanced placement, distance learning, summer session for credit, part-time degree program.
Entrance Requirements: Open admission. Options: early admission, deferred admission. Required: high school transcript. Entrance: noncompetitive. Application deadline: Rolling.
Collegiate Environment: Social organizations: 9 open to all. Most popular organizations: nursing organization, radiography organization, AISES, Aikido, Phi Theta Kappa. Campus security: 24-hour emergency response devices and patrols. Option: coed housing available. Northern New Mexico Community College Library with 18,065 books and 222 serials. Operations spending for 2004 fiscal year: $112,638. 12 computers available on campus for general student use. A campuswide network can be accessed from off-campus. Staffed computer lab on campus.

■ **PIMA MEDICAL INSTITUTE** *E-6*
2201 San Pedro NE, Bldg. 3, Ste. 100
Albuquerque, NM 87110
Tel: (505)881-1234; 888-898-9048
Fax: (505)884-8371
Web Site: http://www.pmi.edu
Description: Proprietary, 2-year, coed. Part of Vocational Training Institutes, Inc. Awards certificates and terminal associate degrees. Founded 1985. Setting: urban campus. Total enrollment: 420. Student-undergrad faculty ratio is 20:1. 85 applied, 66% were admitted. Full-time: 420 students, 88% women, 12% men. Calendar: modular. Academic remediation for entering students, services for LD students, co-op programs and internships.
Entrance Requirements: Option: early admission. Required: interview, Wonderlic Scholastic Level Exam. Required for some: high school transcript. Entrance: minimally difficult.
Costs Per Year: Application fee: $0.
Collegiate Environment: Orientation program. College housing not available. 56 computers available on campus for general student use. A campuswide network can be accessed from off-campus. Staffed computer lab on campus.

■ **ST. JOHN'S COLLEGE** *D-7*
1160 Camino Cruz Blanca
Santa Fe, NM 87505-4599
Tel: (505)984-6000
Free: 800-331-5232
Admissions: (505)984-6060
E-mail: admissions@sjcsf.edu
Web Site: http://www.stjohnscollege.edu/
Description: Independent, comprehensive, coed. Administratively affiliated with St. John's College (MD). Awards bachelor's and master's degrees. Founded 1964. Setting: 250-acre small town campus. Endowment: $81.9 million. Educational spending for 2005 fiscal year: $15,159 per student. Total enrollment: 533. Faculty: 71 (68 full-time, 3 part-time). Student-undergrad faculty ratio is 6:1. 318 applied, 83% were admitted. 38% from top 10% of their high school class, 54% from top quarter, 86% from top half. 2 National Merit Scholars, 3 class presidents, 2 valedictorians. Full-time: 431 students, 46% women, 54% men. Part-time: 4 students, 75% women, 25% men. Students come from 56 states and territories, 8 other countries, 90% from out-of-state, 0.5% Native American, 6% Hispanic, 1% black, 2% Asian American or Pacific Islander, 2% international, 5% 25 or older, 75% live on campus, 7% transferred in. Retention: 76% of full-time freshmen returned the following year. Core. Calendar: semesters. Summer session for credit, internships. Off campus study at St. John's College (MD).
Entrance Requirements: Options: Peterson's Universal Application, Common Application, early admission, deferred admission, international baccalaureate accepted. Required: essay, high school transcript, 2 recommendations. Recommended: 3 recommendations, interview. Required for some: interview, SAT or ACT. Entrance: very difficult. Application deadline: Rolling. Notification: continuous.
Costs Per Year: Application fee: $0. Comprehensive fee: $42,776 includes full-time tuition ($34,306), mandatory fees ($200), and college room and board ($8270). College room only: $3938. Part-time tuition: $1009 per unit.
Collegiate Environment: Orientation program. Drama-theater group, choral group, student-run newspaper. Social organizations: 32 open to all. Most popular organizations: student government, film society, Search and Rescue Team, student newspaper, theatre group. Major annual events: Reality

(graduation party), Fashing Ball, Halloween Dance and Costume Party. Student services: health clinic, personal-psychological counseling. Campus security: 24-hour emergency response devices and patrols, student patrols, late night transport-escort service. College housing designed to accommodate 329 students; 335 undergraduates lived in college housing during 2003-04. Freshmen guaranteed college housing. On-campus residence required in freshman year. Options: coed, men-only, women-only housing available. Meem Library with 65,000 books, 140 serials, an OPAC, and a Web page. Operations spending for 2004 fiscal year: $390,000. 30 computers available on campus for general student use. A campuswide network can be accessed from student residence rooms and from off campus. Staffed computer lab on campus.

■ **SAN JUAN COLLEGE** *B-3*
4601 College Blvd.
Farmington, NM 87402-4699
Tel: (505)326-3311
Admissions: (505)566-3300
Fax: (505)599-3385
E-mail: florezr@sanjuancollege.edu
Web Site: http://www.sanjuancollege.edu/
Description: State-supported, 2-year, coed. Part of New Mexico Commission on Higher Education. Awards certificates, transfer associate, and terminal associate degrees. Founded 1958. Setting: 698-acre small town campus. Endowment: $10.5 million. Educational spending for 2005 fiscal year: $4602 per student. Total enrollment: 5,064. Student-undergrad faculty ratio is 19:1. 1,184 applied, 100% were admitted. Full-time: 2,606 students, 58% women, 42% men. Part-time: 2,458 students, 61% women, 39% men. Students come from 18 states and territories, 7% from out-of-state, 33% Native American, 12% Hispanic, 1% black, 1% Asian American or Pacific Islander, 0.3% international, 37% 25 or older. Core. Calendar: semesters. Academic remediation for entering students, ESL program, services for LD students, advanced placement, honors program, independent study, distance learning, summer session for credit, part-time degree program, adult/continuing education programs, co-op programs and internships.
Entrance Requirements: Open admission. Options: electronic application, early admission, deferred admission. Required: high school transcript. Entrance: noncompetitive. Application deadline: Rolling. Notification: continuous.
Costs Per Year: Application fee: $0. State resident tuition: $720 full-time, $30 per credit hour part-time. Nonresident tuition: $960 full-time, $40 per credit hour part-time.
Collegiate Environment: Orientation program. Drama-theater group, choral group, student-run newspaper, radio station. Social organizations: national fraternities, national sororities; 1% of men are members. Student services: personal-psychological counseling. Campus security: 24-hour patrols, late night transport-escort service. College housing not available. San Juan College Library with 81,116 books, 134,776 microform titles, 6,677 serials, 1,779 audiovisual materials, an OPAC, and a Web page. Operations spending for 2004 fiscal year: $607,642. 900 computers available on campus for general student use. A campuswide network can be accessed from off-campus. Staffed computer lab on campus.
Community Environment: At the junction of the San Juan, Las Animas and La Plata Rivers, Farmington is a producer of gas and oil. This is the starting point for two large natural gas pipelines, one leading to Los Angeles, San Diego and San Francisco, the other to the Pacific Northwest. Irrigated lands surrounding the general locale produce farm crops and grazing for livestock. The region is also noted for apple and peach raising. Some part-time employment is available for students.

■ **SANTA FE COMMUNITY COLLEGE** *D-7*
6401 Richards Ave.
Santa Fe, NM 87508-4887
Tel: (505)428-1000
Admissions: (505)428-1261
Fax: (505)428-1237
E-mail: atupler@sfccnm.edu
Web Site: http://www.sfccnm.edu/
Description: State and locally supported, 2-year, coed. Awards certificates, transfer associate, and terminal associate degrees. Founded 1983. Setting: 366-acre suburban campus. Educational spending for 2005 fiscal year: $2062 per student. Total enrollment: 5,452. Full-time: 915 students, 65% women, 35% men. Part-time: 4,537 students, 63% women, 37% men. Students come from 50 states and territories, 6 other countries, 10% from

out-of-state, 5% Native American, 51% Hispanic, 1% black, 1% Asian American or Pacific Islander, 0.5% international, 64% 25 or older, 1% transferred in. Retention: 47% of full-time freshmen returned the following year. Core. Calendar: semesters. Academic remediation for entering students, ESL program, services for LD students, advanced placement, honors program, independent study, distance learning, double major, summer session for credit, part-time degree program, external degree program, adult/continuing education programs, co-op programs and internships.
Entrance Requirements: Open admission except for nursing, early childhood education programs. Options: early admission, deferred admission, international baccalaureate accepted. Required: high school transcript. Entrance: noncompetitive. Application deadline: Rolling. Notification: continuous.
Collegiate Environment: Orientation program. Choral group, student-run radio station. Social organizations: 9 open to all. Most popular organizations: Student Nurses Association, Native American Student Association, Service-Learning Club, MECHA (Movimiento Estudiantil Chicano de Aztlan), Phi Theta Kappa. Major annual events: Graduation, Welcome Back Week, Margaret Mead Film Festival. Student services: personal-psychological counseling, women's center. Campus security: 24-hour emergency response devices and patrols, late night transport-escort service. College housing not available. Learning Resource Center with 38,226 books, 9,808 microform titles, 206 serials, 2,010 audiovisual materials, an OPAC, and a Web page. Operations spending for 2004 fiscal year: $288,100. 340 computers available on campus for general student use. Computer purchase/lease plans available. A campuswide network can be accessed from off-campus. Staffed computer lab on campus.

■ **SOUTHWESTERN INDIAN POLYTECHNIC INSTITUTE** *E-6*
9169 Coors, NW, Box 10146
Albuquerque, NM 87184-0146
Tel: (505)346-2347
Admissions: (505)346-2362
Fax: (505)346-2343
E-mail: mgarro@sipi.bia.edu
Web Site: http://www.sipi.bia.edu/
Description: Federally supported, 2-year, coed. Awards certificates, transfer associate, and terminal associate degrees. Founded 1971. Setting: 174-acre suburban campus. Research spending for 2004 fiscal year: $72,958. Total enrollment: 818. 337 applied, 95% were admitted. 3% from top 10% of their high school class, 11% from top quarter, 32% from top half. Students come from 33 states and territories, 35% 25 or older. Core. Calendar: trimesters. Academic remediation for entering students, services for LD students, advanced placement, double major, summer session for credit, part-time degree program, co-op programs and internships.
Entrance Requirements: Open admission. Option: Common Application. Required: high school transcript, certificate of Indian Blood form. Placement: TABE or ACT COMPASS required. Entrance: noncompetitive. Application deadline: Rolling. Notification: continuous. Preference given to Native Americans.
Collegiate Environment: Student services: health clinic, personal-psychological counseling. Campus security: 24-hour emergency response devices, late night transport-escort service. College housing not available. 26,000 books and 120 serials. 124 computers available on campus for general student use. Staffed computer lab on campus.

■ **UNIVERSITY OF NEW MEXICO** *E-6*
Albuquerque, NM 87131-2039
Tel: (505)277-0111
Admissions: (505)277-2446
Fax: (505)277-6686
E-mail: apply@unm.edu
Web Site: http://www.unm.edu/
Description: State-supported, university, coed. Awards associate, bachelor's, master's, doctoral, and first professional degrees and post-master's certificates. Founded 1889. Setting: 875-acre urban campus with easy access to Albuquerque. Endowment: $245.2 million. Research spending for 2004 fiscal year: $149.7 million. Educational spending for 2005 fiscal year: $8522 per student. Total enrollment: 26,172. Faculty: 1,411 (885 full-time, 526 part-time). Student-undergrad faculty ratio is 19:1. 7,134 applied, 74% were admitted. 20% from top 10% of their high school class, 48% from top quarter, 78% from top half. Full-time: 14,839 students, 58% women, 42% men. Part-time: 3,886 students, 61% women, 39% men. Students come from 51 states and territories, 56 other countries, 11% from out-of-state, 6%

Native American, 35% Hispanic, 3% black, 3% Asian American or Pacific Islander, 1% international, 24% 25 or older, 11% live on campus, 6% transferred in. Retention: 76% of full-time freshmen returned the following year. Academic areas with the most degrees conferred: business/marketing; education; health professions and related sciences. Core. Calendar: semesters. Academic remediation for entering students, ESL program, services for LD students, advanced placement, accelerated degree program, self-designed majors, honors program, independent study, distance learning, double major, summer session for credit, part-time degree program, adult/continuing education programs, co-op programs and internships, graduate courses open to undergrads. Off campus study at National Student Exchange, Western Undergraduate Exchange, Western Interstate Commission for Higher Education, International Student Exchange. Study abroad program. ROTC: Army, Naval, Air Force.

Entrance Requirements: Options: electronic application, early admission, deferred admission, international baccalaureate accepted. Required: high school transcript, minimum 2.25 high school GPA, SAT or ACT. Required for some: essay, recommendations. Entrance: moderately difficult. Application deadline: 6/15. Notification: continuous.

Costs Per Year: Application fee: $20. Area resident tuition: $171.20 per credit hour part-time. State resident tuition: $4108 full-time. Nonresident tuition: $13,438 full-time. Part-time tuition varies according to course load. College room and board: $6518. College room only: $3818. Room and board charges vary according to board plan and housing facility.

Collegiate Environment: Orientation program. Drama-theater group, choral group, marching band, student-run newspaper, radio station. Social organizations: 300 open to all; national fraternities, national sororities; 3% of eligible men and 3% of eligible women are members. Most popular organizations: Associated Students of UNM, Graduate and Professional Students Association, Golden Key National Honor Society. Major annual events: Spring Fiestas, Welcome Back Days, Homecoming. Student services: health clinic, personal-psychological counseling, women's center. Campus security: 24-hour emergency response devices and patrols, student patrols, late night transport-escort service, controlled dormitory access. 2,245 college housing spaces available; 2,104 were occupied in 2003-04. Option: coed housing available. The University of New Mexico General Library plus 7 others with 2.7 million books, 3.8 million microform titles, 592,243 serials, 58,405 audiovisual materials, an OPAC, and a Web page. Operations spending for 2004 fiscal year: $15.7 million. 446 computers available on campus for general student use. Computer purchase/lease plans available. A campuswide network can be accessed from student residence rooms and from off campus. Staffed computer lab on campus.

■ **UNIVERSITY OF NEW MEXICO-GALLUP** *D-2*
200 College Rd.
Gallup, NM 87301-5603
Tel: (505)863-7500
Admissions: (505)863-7576
Fax: (505)863-7532
Web Site: http://www.gallup.unm.edu/
Description: State-supported, primarily 2-year, coed. Part of New Mexico Commission on Higher Education. Awards certificates, diplomas, transfer associate, terminal associate, and bachelor's degrees. Founded 1968. Setting: 80-acre small town campus. Total enrollment: 2,858. 2% from top 10% of their high school class, 5% from top quarter, 30% from top half. Students come from 10 states and territories, 4 other countries, 76% Native American, 10% Hispanic, 0.3% black, 1% Asian American or Pacific Islander, 0.2% international, 50% 25 or older. Core. Calendar: semesters. Academic remediation for entering students, services for LD students, advanced placement, self-designed majors, honors program, summer session for credit, part-time degree program, adult/continuing education programs, co-op programs and internships.

Entrance Requirements: Open admission. Option: early admission. Required for some: high school transcript, SAT, ACT. Entrance: noncompetitive. Application deadline: Rolling. Notification: continuous.

Collegiate Environment: Orientation program. Student-run newspaper. Campus security: late night transport-escort service. College housing not available. Zollinger Library plus 1 other with 36,172 books and 354 serials. 300 computers available on campus for general student use. Staffed computer lab on campus.

■ **UNIVERSITY OF NEW MEXICO-LOS ALAMOS BRANCH** *D-6*
4000 University Dr.
Los Alamos, NM 87544-2233

Tel: (505)662-5919
Admissions: (505)661-4692
E-mail: aapodaca@la.unm.edu
Web Site: http://www.la.unm.edu/
Description: State-supported, 2-year, coed. Part of New Mexico Commission on Higher Education. Awards certificates, transfer associate, and terminal associate degrees. Founded 1980. Setting: 5-acre small town campus. Total enrollment: 890. 213 applied, 100% were admitted. Students come from 12 states and territories, 3 other countries, 3% Native American, 39% Hispanic, 1% black, 3% Asian American or Pacific Islander, 1% international, 40% 25 or older. Core. Calendar: semesters. Academic remediation for entering students, ESL program, services for LD students, advanced placement, summer session for credit, part-time degree program, adult/continuing education programs, co-op programs and internships. Off campus study at University of New Mexico, Northern New Mexico Community College, Santa Fe Community College.

Entrance Requirements: Open admission. Options: early admission, deferred admission. Placement: SAT or ACT required for some. Entrance: noncompetitive. Application deadline: 8/12. Notification: continuous.

Collegiate Environment: Orientation program. Choral group, student-run newspaper. Social organizations: 4 open to all. 10,000 books and 160 serials. 60 computers available on campus for general student use. Staffed computer lab on campus.

■ **UNIVERSITY OF NEW MEXICO-TAOS** *B-8*
115 Civic Plaza Dr.
Taos, NM 87571
Tel: (505)758-7667
Web Site: http://taos.unm.edu/
Description: State-supported, 2-year, coed. Calendar: semesters.

■ **UNIVERSITY OF NEW MEXICO-VALENCIA CAMPUS** *F-6*
280 La Entrada
Los Lunas, NM 87031-7633
Tel: (505)925-8500
Admissions: (505)925-8580
Fax: (505)925-8563
Web Site: http://www.unm.edu/~unmvc/
Description: State-supported, 2-year, coed. Part of New Mexico Commission on Higher Education. Awards certificates, transfer associate, and terminal associate degrees. Founded 1981. Setting: small town campus with easy access to Albuquerque. Total enrollment: 1,544. Students come from 4 states and territories, 2 other countries, 76% 25 or older. Core. Calendar: semesters. Academic remediation for entering students, ESL program, services for LD students, honors program, summer session for credit, part-time degree program, adult/continuing education programs.

Entrance Requirements: Open admission. Options: early admission, deferred admission. Recommended: high school transcript. Required for some: minimum 2.0 high school GPA. Placement: ACT COMPASS recommended; SAT or ACT, ACT COMPASS required for some. Entrance: noncompetitive. Application deadline: Rolling. Notification: continuous until 8/25.

Collegiate Environment: Major annual events: Halloween Carnival, Cultural Festival. Student services: personal-psychological counseling. Campus security: 24-hour emergency response devices and patrols, late night transport-escort service. College housing not available. 9,500 books and 150 serials. Operations spending for 2004 fiscal year: $140,091. 65 computers available on campus for general student use. A campuswide network can be accessed from off-campus. Staffed computer lab on campus.

■ **UNIVERSITY OF PHOENIX-NEW MEXICO CAMPUS** *E-6*
7471 Pan American Freeway NE
Albuquerque, NM 87109-4645
Tel: (505)821-4800
Free: 800-228-7240
Admissions: (480)557-1712
Web Site: http://www.phoenix.edu/
Description: Proprietary, comprehensive, coed. Awards bachelor's and master's degrees. Setting: urban campus. Total enrollment: 4,724. Faculty: 448 (17 full-time, 431 part-time). Student-undergrad faculty ratio is 11:1. 119 applied. Full-time: 3,669 students, 61% women, 39% men. 1% Native American, 24% Hispanic, 1% black, 0.5% Asian American or Pacific Islander, 16% international, 91% 25 or older. Academic areas with the most degrees conferred: business/marketing; computer and information sciences; public

administration and social services. Core. Calendar: continuous. Advanced placement, accelerated degree program, independent study, distance learning, external degree program, adult/continuing education programs, graduate courses open to undergrads.

Entrance Requirements: Open admission. Option: deferred admission. Required: 1 recommendation. Required for some: high school transcript. Entrance: noncompetitive. Application deadline: Rolling.

Costs Per Year: Application fee: $110. Tuition: $9390 full-time, $313 per credit part-time. Mandatory fees: $560 full-time, $70 per course part-time.

Collegiate Environment: College housing not available. University Library with 444 books, 666 serials, an OPAC, and a Web page. System-wide operations spending for 2004 fiscal year: $3.2 million.

■ **WESTERN NEW MEXICO UNIVERSITY** *K-2*
PO Box 680
Silver City, NM 88062-0680
Tel: (505)538-6336
Admissions: (505)538-6106
Fax: (505)538-6155
Web Site: http://www.wnmu.edu/

Description: State-supported, comprehensive, coed. Awards associate, bachelor's, and master's degrees. Founded 1893. Setting: 83-acre rural campus. Endowment: $2.2 million. Research spending for 2004 fiscal year: $38,500. Total enrollment: 3,074. 8% from top 10% of their high school class, 21% from top quarter, 40% from top half. Students come from 33 states and territories, 6 other countries, 46% 25 or older. Retention: 52% of full-time freshmen returned the following year. Core. Calendar: semesters. Academic remediation for entering students, services for LD students, advanced place-

ment, accelerated degree program, self-designed majors, summer session for credit, part-time degree program, adult/continuing education programs, co-op programs and internships, graduate courses open to undergrads.

Entrance Requirements: Open admission. Options: Common Application, early admission, deferred admission, international baccalaureate accepted. Required: high school transcript. Recommended: ACT. Placement: ACT COMPASS required. Entrance: noncompetitive. Application deadline: 8/1. Notification: continuous.

Costs Per Year: Application fee: $10. State resident tuition: $2733 full-time, $95 per credit part-time. Nonresident tuition: $10,293 full-time. Mandatory fees: $85 full-time, $42.50 per term part-time.

Collegiate Environment: Orientation program. Drama-theater group, choral group, marching band, student-run newspaper. Student services: personal-psychological counseling, women's center. Campus security: 24-hour emergency response devices and patrols, student patrols, late night transport-escort service. 425 college housing spaces available; 294 were occupied in 2003-04. Freshmen guaranteed college housing. On-campus residence required in freshman year. Option: coed housing available. Miller Library plus 2 others with 245,146 books, 236 serials, an OPAC, and a Web page. Operations spending for 2004 fiscal year: $707,000. 85 computers available on campus for general student use. Staffed computer lab on campus.

Community Environment: Once an Apache Indian campsite and later a booming gold, silver, and zinc mining town, Silver City is a trading center for the cattle ranching and copper-mining area today. The city, located in the foothills of the mountains, has various active civic, fraternal, and veteran's organizations, and is served by commuter airline. Recreational activities include football, hunting, fishing, camping, and picnicking.

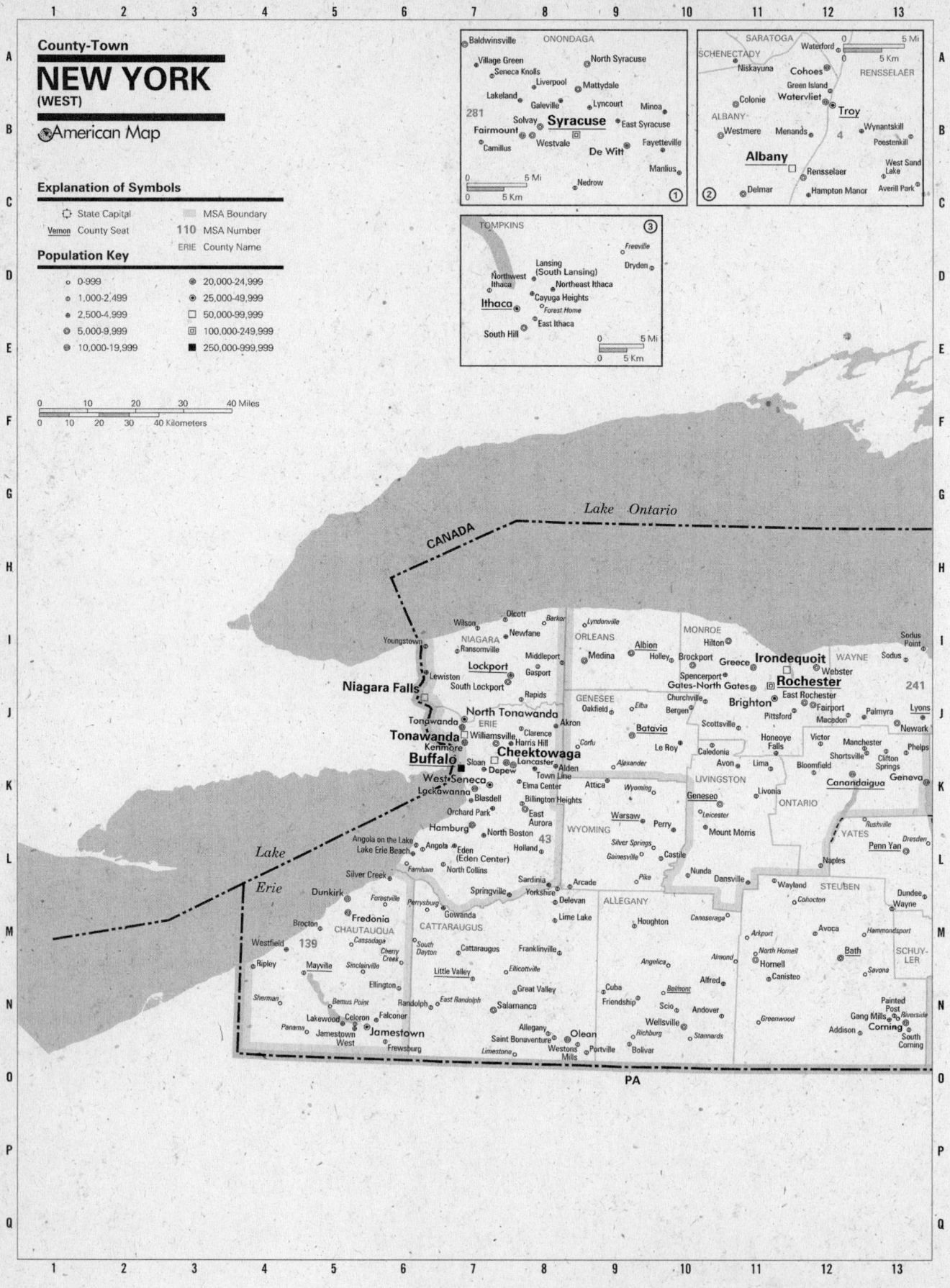

County-Town

NEW YORK

(WEST)

American Map

Explanation of Symbols

◇ State Capital
Vernon County Seat
ERIE County Name

▨ MSA Boundary
110 MSA Number

Population Key

○ 0-999
⊙ 1,000-2,499
⊙ 2,500-4,999
⊙ 5,000-9,999
⊙ 10,000-19,999

⊙ 20,000-24,999
⊙ 25,000-49,999
□ 50,000-99,999
▣ 100,000-249,999
■ 250,000-999,999

0   10   20   30   40 Miles
0   10   20   30   40 Kilometers

Inset ①

ONONDAGA
Baldwinsville
Village Green
North Syracuse
Seneca Knolls
Liverpool
Lakeland
Mattydale
Galeville
Lyncourt
Minoa
281
Solvay
Syracuse
East Syracuse
Fairmount
Westvale
De Witt
Fayetteville
Camillus
Manlius
Nedrow
0   5 Mi
0   5 Km

Inset ②

SARATOGA
SCHENECTADY
Waterford
Niskayuna
Cohoes
RENSSELAER
Green Island
Colonie
Watervliet
ALBANY
Westmere
Menands
Troy
Wynantskill
Poestenkill
4
Albany
West Sand Lake
Rensselaer
Averill Park
Delmar
Hampton Manor
0   5 Mi
0   5 Km

Inset ③

TOMKINS
Freeville
Lansing (South Lansing)
Dryden
Northwest Ithaca
Northeast Ithaca
Cayuga Heights
Ithaca
Forest Home
East Ithaca
South Hill
0   5 Mi
0   5 Km

Lake Ontario

CANADA

Lake Erie

Wilson
Olcott
Barker
Lyndonville
MONROE
Sodus Point
Youngstown
Newfane
NIAGARA
Ransomville
ORLEANS
Albion
Hilton
WAYNE
Sodus
Middleport
Medina
Holley
Brockport
Greece
Irondequoit
Lewiston
Lockport
Gasport
Spencerport
Gates-North Gates
Rochester
Webster
South Lockport
Rapids
GENESEE
Churchville
Elba
East Rochester
241
Niagara Falls
Akron
Oakfield
Bergen
Brighton
Fairport
Palmyra
Newark
North Tonawanda
Clarence
Batavia
Le Roy
Scottsville
Pittsford
Macedon
Lyons
Tonawanda
Williamsville
Harris Hill
Corfu
Caledonia
Honeoye Falls
Victor
Manchester
Phelps
Tonawanda
Kenmore
Cheektowaga
Alexander
Avon
Lima
Shortsville
Clifton Springs
Geneva
Buffalo
Sloan
Lancaster
Alden
LIVINGSTON
Bloomfield
Canandaigua
Depew
Town Line
Attica
Wyoming
Geneseo
Livonia
ONTARIO
West Seneca
Elma Center
Leicester
Rushville
Lackawanna
Blasdell
Billington Heights
Warsaw
Perry
YATES
Dresden
Orchard Park
East Aurora
Mount Morris
Naples
Penn Yan
Hamburg
North Boston
WYOMING
Silver Springs
Nunda
Dansville
Wayland
STEUBEN
Angola on the Lake
Angola
Eden (Eden Center)
Holland
43
Gainesville
Castile
Cohocton
Dundee
Lake Erie Beach
Farnham
North Collins
Pike
Wayne
Silver Creek
Sardinia
Arcade
Naples
Dunkirk
Forestville
Perrysburg
Yorkshire
Delevan
ALLEGANY
Arkport
Avoca
Hammondsport
Springville
Gowanda
Lime Lake
Houghton
Canaseraga
North Hornell
Brocton
CATTARAUGUS
Cassadaga
Cattaraugus
Franklinville
Angelica
Almond
Hornell
SCHUY-LER
Fredonia
South Dayton
Ellicottville
Canisteo
Bath
Westfield
139
Cherry Creek
Little Valley
Great Valley
Cuba
Alfred
Savona
Ripley
Mayville
Sinclairville
Belmont
Ellington
East Randolph
Salamanca
Friendship
Scio
Andover
Greenwood
Painted Post
Riverside
Sherman
Randolph
Allegany
Wellsville
Richburg
Stannards
Gang Mills
Corning
Bemus Point
Lakewood
Celoron
Falconer
Saint Bonaventure
Olean
Addison
South Corning
Panama
Jamestown West
Jamestown
Limestone
Westons Mills
Portville
Bolivar
Frewsburg

PA

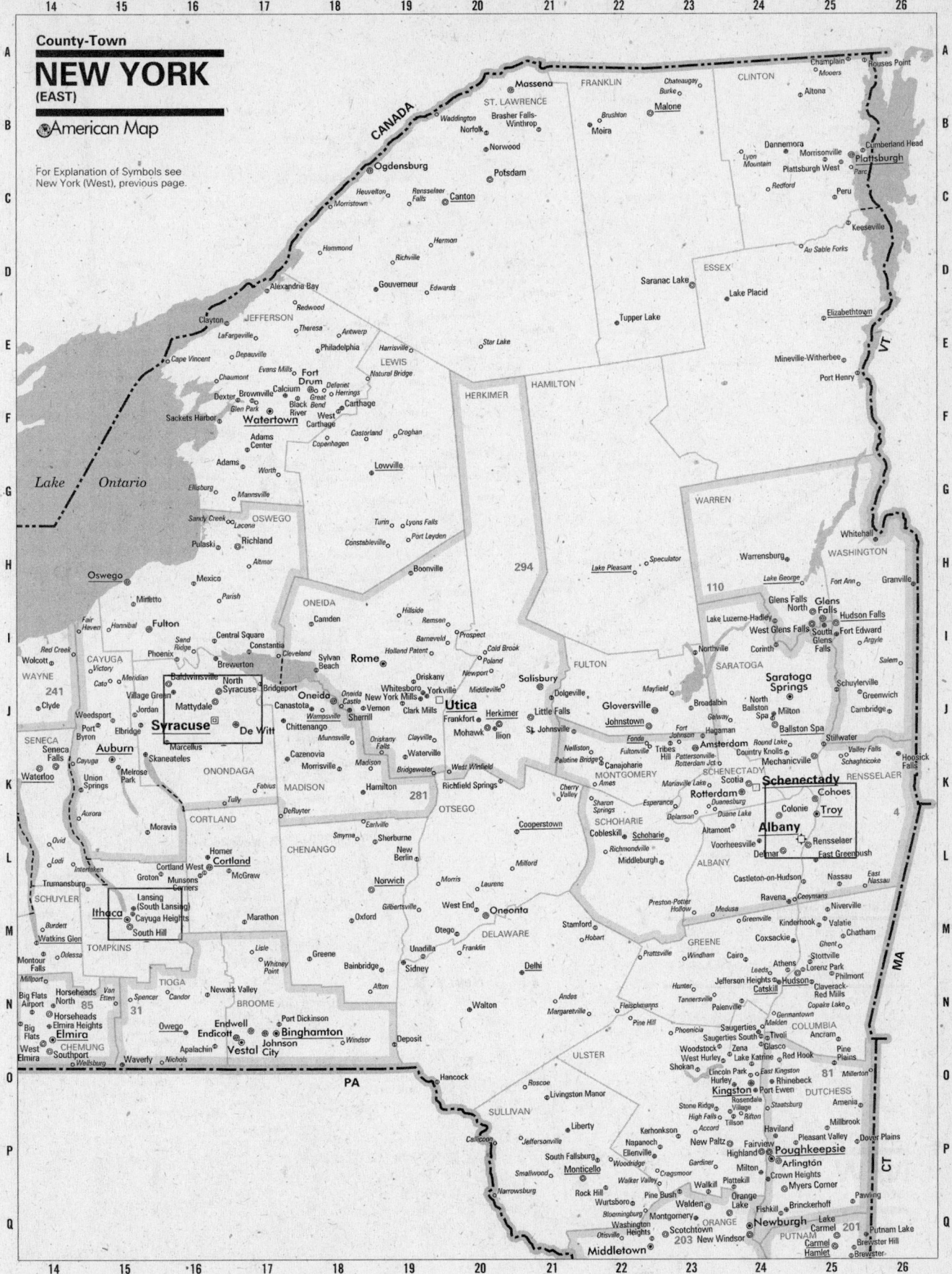

County-Town
NEW YORK
(EAST)

American Map

For Explanation of Symbols see
New York (West), previous page.

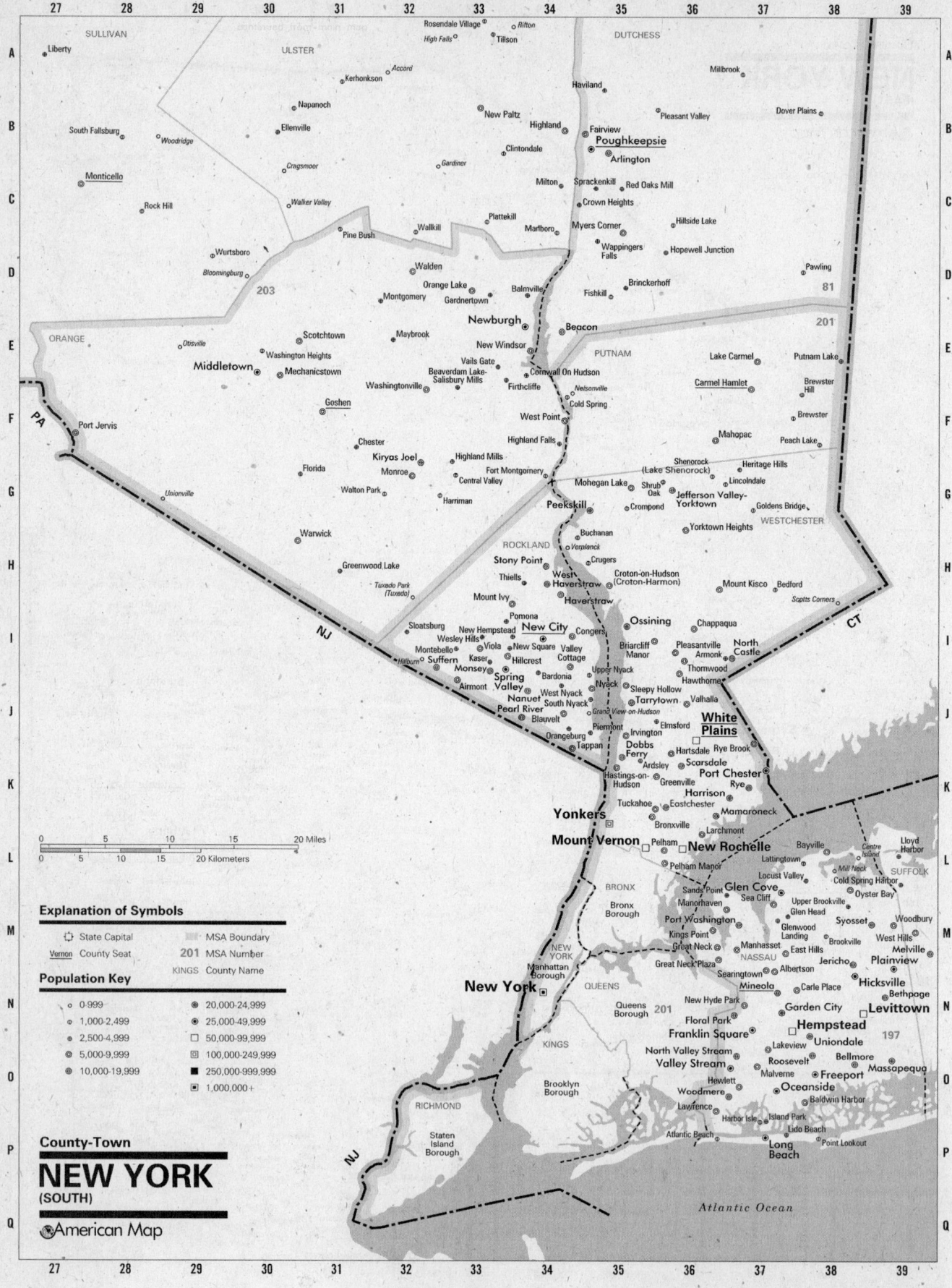

County-Town

NEW YORK

(SOUTH)

American Map

Explanation of Symbols

State Capital | MSA Boundary
Vernon County Seat | 201 MSA Number
| KINGS County Name

Population Key

o 0-999 | ⊚ 20,000-24,999
● 1,000-2,499 | ◉ 25,000-49,999
● 2,500-4,999 | □ 50,000-99,999
● 5,000-9,999 | ▣ 100,000-249,999
● 10,000-19,999 | ■ 250,000-999,999
| ▣ 1,000,000+

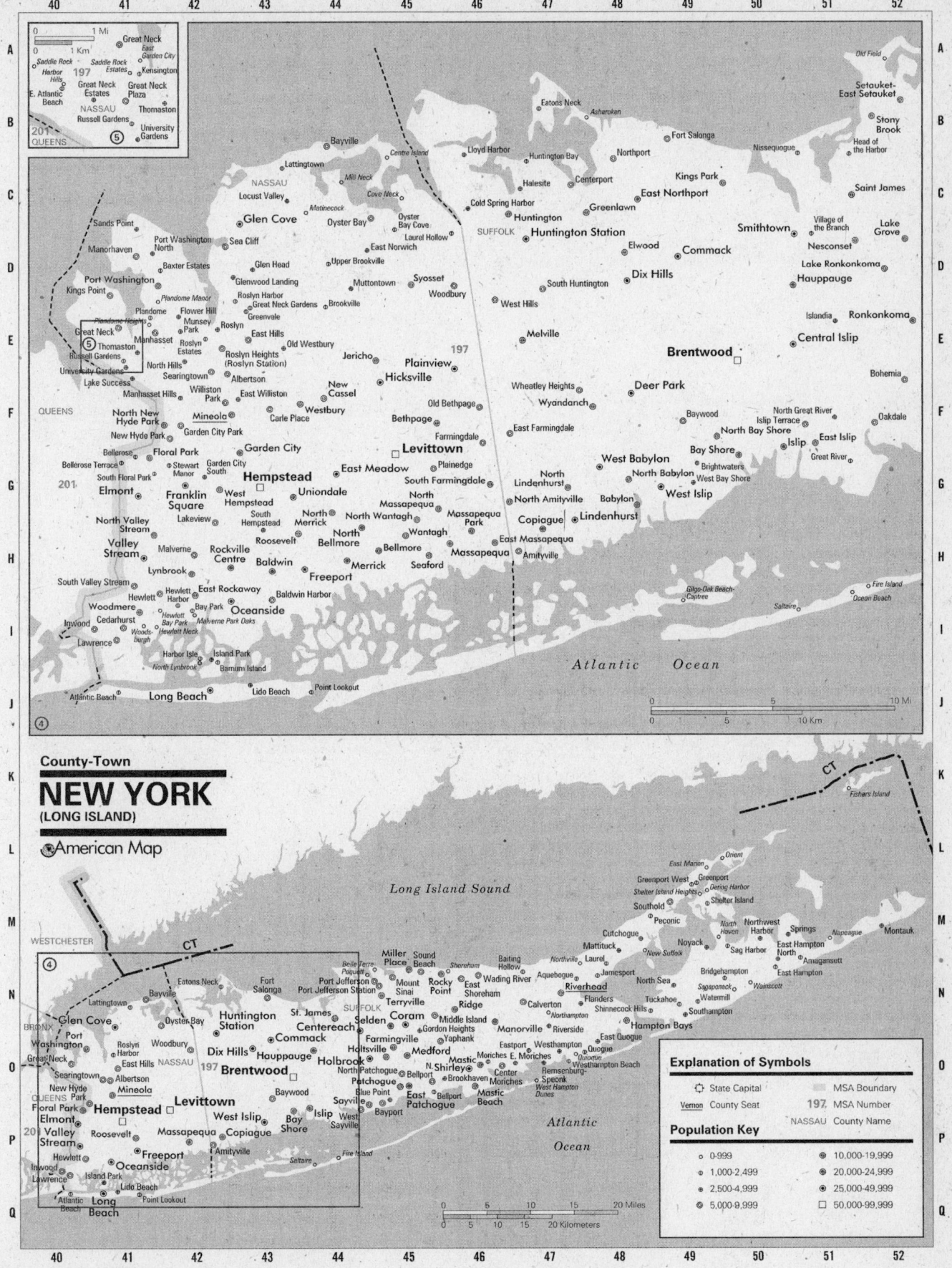

■ **ADELPHI UNIVERSITY** *G-43*
One South Ave.
PO Box 701
Garden City, NY 11530-0701
Tel: (516)877-3000
Free: 800-ADE-LPHI
Admissions: (516)877-3050
Fax: (516)877-3039
E-mail: admissions@adelphi.edu
Web Site: http://www.adelphi.edu/
Description: Independent, university, coed. Awards associate, bachelor's, master's, and doctoral degrees and post-master's certificates. Founded 1896. Setting: 75-acre suburban campus with easy access to New York City. Endowment: $75 million. Research spending for 2004 fiscal year: $166,000. Educational spending for 2005 fiscal year: $8838 per student. Total enrollment: 7,898. Faculty: 857 (257 full-time, 600 part-time). Student-undergrad faculty ratio is 11:1. 5,197 applied, 68% were admitted. 23% from top 10% of their high school class, 58% from top quarter, 88% from top half. Full-time: 3,961 students, 71% women, 29% men. Part-time: 797 students, 76% women, 24% men. Students come from 38 states and territories, 47 other countries, 8% from out-of-state, 0.04% Native American, 8% Hispanic, 13% black, 5% Asian American or Pacific Islander, 3% international, 22% 25 or older, 24% live on campus, 12% transferred in. Retention: 82% of full-time freshmen returned the following year. Academic areas with the most degrees conferred: business/marketing; social sciences; health professions and related sciences. Core. Calendar: semesters. Services for LD students, advanced placement, accelerated degree program, self-designed majors, freshman honors college, honors program, independent study, distance learning, double major, summer session for credit, part-time degree program, internships, graduate courses open to undergrads. Study abroad program. ROTC: Army (c), Air Force (c).
Entrance Requirements: Options: Peterson's Universal Application, Common Application, electronic application, early admission, early action, deferred admission, international baccalaureate accepted. Required: essay, high school transcript, 1 recommendation, SAT or ACT. Recommended: minimum 3.0 high school GPA, interview. Required for some: 2 recommendations, interview, auditions/portfolios for performing and fine arts. Entrance: moderately difficult. Application deadlines: Rolling, 12/1 for early action. Notification: continuous, 12/31 for early action.
Costs Per Year: Application fee: $35. Comprehensive fee: $28,910 includes full-time tuition ($18,620), mandatory fees ($1100), and college room and board ($9190). College room only: $5990. Full-time tuition and fees vary according to course level, location, and program. Room and board charges vary according to board plan and housing facility. Part-time tuition: $600 per credit. Part-time mandatory fees: $550 per year. Part-time tuition and fees vary according to course level, location, and program.
Collegiate Environment: Orientation program. Drama-theater group, choral group, student-run newspaper, radio station. Social organizations: 76 open to all; national fraternities, national sororities, local fraternities, local sororities; 6% of eligible men and 4% of eligible women are members. Most popular organizations: Student Activities Board, Student Government Association, Caliber, Caribbean Cultural Awareness Club, Umoja. Major annual events: Senior Week, Halloween Party, Fall Fest. Student services: health clinic, personal-psychological counseling. Campus security: 24-hour emergency response devices and patrols, late night transport-escort service, controlled dormitory access. 1,050 college housing spaces available; 1,049 were occupied in 2003-04. Freshmen guaranteed college housing. Option: coed housing available. Swirbul Library plus 1 other with 631,023 books, 836,186 microform titles, 1,642 serials, 44,191 audiovisual materials, an OPAC, and a Web page. Operations spending for 2004 fiscal year: $4.1 million. 540 computers available on campus for general student use. Computer purchase/lease plans available. A campuswide network can be accessed from student residence rooms and from off campus. Staffed computer lab on campus.
Community Environment: Garden City, Long Island, was one of the first planned residential communities in the country. The settlement was established around the Cathedral of the Incarnation. The climate is temperate. Located near New York City, the area has good transportation connections with the adjoining metropolis. A library, churches of major denominations, and hospitals nearby all serve the city. There is some part-time employment in the immediate area. The locale has good shopping facilities and active civic, fraternal, and veteran's organizations.

■ **ADIRONDACK COMMUNITY COLLEGE** *I-25*
640 Bay Rd.
Queensbury, NY 12804
Tel: (518)743-2200
Admissions: (518)743-2264
Fax: (518)745-1433
Web Site: http://www.sunyacc.edu/
Description: State and locally supported, 2-year, coed. Part of State University of New York System. Awards certificates, transfer associate, and terminal associate degrees. Founded 1960. Setting: 141-acre small town campus. Endowment: $1 million. Educational spending for 2005 fiscal year: $3280 per student. Total enrollment: 3,200. 1,328 applied, 91% were admitted. 4% from top 10% of their high school class, 22% from top quarter, 48% from top half. Students come from 5 states and territories, 5 other countries, 2% from out-of-state, 46% 25 or older. Core. Calendar: semesters. Academic remediation for entering students, services for LD students, advanced placement, accelerated degree program, independent study, double major, summer session for credit, part-time degree program, external degree program, adult/continuing education programs, co-op programs and internships. Study abroad program.
Entrance Requirements: Open admission. Options: early admission, deferred admission. Required: high school transcript. Required for some: minimum 2.0 high school GPA. Entrance: minimally difficult. Application deadline: 8/15. Notification: continuous until 9/1.
Collegiate Environment: Orientation program. Drama-theater group, choral group, student-run radio station. Social organizations: 25 open to all. Most popular organizations: New Horizons, Broadcasting Club, Humanities Club, College Activity Board, Ski and Adventure Club. Major annual events: Hot Air Balloon Festival, Children's Holiday Party, Annual Beach Party. Student services: personal-psychological counseling. Campus security: late night transport-escort service, patrols by trained security personnel 8 a.m. to 10 p.m. College housing not available. Adirondack Community College Library with 65,000 books, 391 serials, an OPAC, and a Web page. Operations spending for 2004 fiscal year: $406,890. 250 computers available on campus for general student use. A campuswide network can be accessed. Staffed computer lab on campus.

■ **ALBANY COLLEGE OF PHARMACY OF UNION UNIVERSITY** *L-25*
106 New Scotland Ave.
Albany, NY 12208-3425

Tel: (518)445-7200; 888-203-8010

Admissions: (518)445-7221

Fax: (518)445-7202

E-mail: connorsc@acp.edu

Web Site: http://www.acp.edu/

Description: Independent, comprehensive, coed. Part of Union University (Albany Law School, Albany Medical College, Union College, NY). Awards bachelor's and first professional degrees. Founded 1881. Setting: 1-acre urban campus. Endowment: $6.6 million. Research spending for 2004 fiscal year: $1.3 million. Educational spending for 2005 fiscal year: $7879 per student. Total enrollment: 1,138. Faculty: 69 (63 full-time, 6 part-time). Student-undergrad faculty ratio is 14:1. 1,014 applied, 58% were admitted. 48% from top 10% of their high school class, 77% from top quarter, 99% from top half. 5 valedictorians. Full-time: 856 students, 56% women, 44% men. Students come from 10 states and territories, 7 other countries, 20% from out-of-state, 0.1% Native American, 1% Hispanic, 1% black, 10% Asian American or Pacific Islander, 8% international, 4% 25 or older, 30% live on campus, 8% transferred in. Retention: 76% of full-time freshmen returned the following year. Academic area with the most degrees conferred: health professions and related sciences. Core. Calendar: semesters. Academic remediation for entering students, services for LD students, advanced placement, accelerated degree program, summer session for credit, internships. Off campus study at Hudson-Mohawk Association of Colleges and Universities. ROTC: Army (c), Air Force (c).

Entrance Requirements: Options: electronic application, early decision. Required: essay, high school transcript, 2 recommendations, SAT or ACT. Recommended: minimum 3.0 high school GPA. Required for some: interview. Entrance: moderately difficult. Application deadlines: 2/1, 11/1 for early decision. Notification: continuous until 8/1, 12/15 for early decision.

Costs Per Year: Application fee: $75. Comprehensive fee: $24,870 includes full-time tuition ($18,300), mandatory fees ($470), and college room and board ($6100). Room and board charges vary according to board plan and housing facility. Part-time tuition: $610 per credit.

Collegiate Environment: Orientation program. Choral group, marching band, student-run newspaper. Social organizations: 14 open to all; national fraternities, national sororities; 12% of eligible men and 12% of eligible women are members. Major annual events: Parents' Weekend, Orientation, Springfest. Student services: health clinic, personal-psychological counseling. Campus security: 24-hour emergency response devices and patrols, controlled dormitory access. 529 college housing spaces available; 389 were occupied in 2003-04. Freshmen guaranteed college housing. On-campus residence required through sophomore year. Option: coed housing available. George and Leona Lewis Library with 16,124 books, 28,388 microform titles, 3,576 serials, 319 audiovisual materials, an OPAC, and a Web page. Operations spending for 2004 fiscal year: $256,096. 47 computers available on campus for general student use. Computer purchase/lease plans available. A campuswide network can be accessed from student residence rooms and from off campus. Staffed computer lab on campus.

■ **ALFRED UNIVERSITY** *N-11*

One Saxon Dr.

Alfred, NY 14802-1205

Tel: (607)871-2111

Free: 800-541-9229

Admissions: (607)871-2115

Fax: (607)871-2198

E-mail: spencer@alfred.edu

Web Site: http://www.alfred.edu/

Description: Independent, university, coed. Awards bachelor's, master's, and doctoral degrees and post-master's certificates. Founded 1836. Setting: 232-acre rural campus with easy access to Rochester. Endowment: $84.5 million. Research spending for 2004 fiscal year: $5.6 million. Educational spending for 2005 fiscal year: $13,709 per student. Total enrollment: 2,235. Faculty: 205 (165 full-time, 40 part-time). Student-undergrad faculty ratio is 12:1. 2,134 applied, 77% were admitted. 19% from top 10% of their high school class, 48% from top quarter, 83% from top half. 4 National Merit Scholars, 8 valedictorians, 42 student government officers. Full-time: 1,863 students, 49% women, 51% men. Part-time: 98 students, 59% women, 41% men. Students come from 38 states and territories, 32 other countries, 33% from out-of-state, 5% 25 or older, 67% live on campus, 5% transferred in. Retention: 78% of full-time freshmen returned the following year. Academic areas with the most degrees conferred: visual and performing arts; business/marketing; engineering. Core. Calendar: semesters. Academic remediation for entering students, services for LD students, advanced placement, ac-

celerated degree program, self-designed majors, honors program, independent study, double major, summer session for credit, part-time degree program, co-op programs and internships, graduate courses open to undergrads. Off campus study. Study abroad program. ROTC: Army (c).

Entrance Requirements: Options: Common Application, electronic application, early admission, early decision, deferred admission, international baccalaureate accepted. Required: essay, high school transcript, 1 recommendation, SAT or ACT. Recommended: interview. Required for some: interview, portfolio. Entrance: moderately difficult. Application deadlines: 2/1, 12/1 for early decision. Notification: continuous, 12/15 for early decision.

Costs Per Year: Application fee: $40. Comprehensive fee: $30,706 includes full-time tuition ($20,150), mandatory fees ($810), and college room and board ($9746). College room only: $5076. Full-time tuition and fees vary according to student level. Room and board charges vary according to board plan and housing facility. Part-time tuition: $658 per credit hour. Part-time tuition varies according to course load.

Collegiate Environment: Orientation program. Drama-theater group, choral group, student-run newspaper, radio station. Social organizations: 90 open to all. Most popular organizations: Student Activities Board, Spectrum, WALF, Student Senate, Fiat Lux. Major annual events: homecoming, Hot Dog Day Weekend, Parents' Weekend. Student services: health clinic, personal-psychological counseling, women's center. Campus security: 24-hour emergency response devices, student patrols, late night transport-escort service. 1,395 college housing spaces available; 1,377 were occupied in 2003-04. Freshmen guaranteed college housing. On-campus residence required through sophomore year. Option: coed housing available. Herrick Memorial Library plus 1 other with 288,137 books, 94,325 microform titles, 1,478 serials, 166,301 audiovisual materials, an OPAC, and a Web page. Operations spending for 2004 fiscal year: $1.7 million. 450 computers available on campus for general student use. Computer purchase/lease plans available. A campuswide network can be accessed from student residence rooms and from off campus. Staffed computer lab on campus.

Community Environment: Alfred is a small residential community situated among the foothills of the Allegheny Mountains near the Finger Lakes Region of New York. It is served by air service in nearby cities (Rochester/Elmira), and also bus service. It is the home of the Davis Memorial Carillon, which contains the oldest carillon bells in the western hemisphere. Outdoor activities including hiking, white water rafting, downhill and cross-country skiing, and horseback riding are located a short distance from campus. Numerous groups sponsor appearances by visiting professors, speakers, and artists. Student groups sponsor a number of popular entertainers and rock and folk concerts. Both a current movie series and a classics series provide weekly films. The Fosdick Nelson Gallery shows exhibits of sculpture, glass, ceramics, paintings, lithographs and photographs. Additionally, student theatre and dance productions, as well as performances by musical ensembles, are scheduled throughout the year.

■ **AMERICAN ACADEMY OF DRAMATIC ARTS** *N-34*

120 Madison Ave.

New York, NY 10016-7004

Tel: (212)686-9244

Free: 800-463-8990

Web Site: http://www.aada.org/

Description: Independent, 2-year, coed. Awards certificates and terminal associate degrees. Founded 1884. Setting: urban campus. Endowment: $4.9 million. Educational spending for 2005 fiscal year: $5759 per student. Total enrollment: 220. Student-undergrad faculty ratio is 16:1, 349 applied, 38% were admitted. 11% from top 10% of their high school class, 27% from top quarter, 81% from top half. Full-time: 220 students, 63% women, 37% men. Students come from 2 states and territories, 14 other countries, 84% from out-of-state, 0% Native American, 6% Hispanic, 4% black, 3% Asian American or Pacific Islander, 18% international, 14% 25 or older, 0% transferred in. Retention: 61% of full-time freshmen returned the following year. Core. Calendar: continuous.

Entrance Requirements: Option: deferred admission. Required: essay, high school transcript, minimum 2.00 high school GPA, 2 recommendations, interview, audition. Recommended: high school transcript. Required for some: high school transcript. Entrance: moderately difficult. Application deadline: Rolling. Notification: continuous.

Costs Per Year: Application fee: $50. Tuition: $16,900 full-time. Mandatory fees: $500 full-time.

Collegiate Environment: Orientation program. Major annual events: Christmas party, graduation, seminars by guest lecturers. Campus security: 24-hour emergency response devices, trained security guard during hours of operation. College housing not available. Academy/CBS Library with 7,467 books, 24 serials, and 570 audiovisual materials. Operations spending for 2004 fiscal year: $51,710. 2 computers available on campus for general student use. A campuswide network can be accessed.

■ **AMERICAN ACADEMY MCALLISTER INSTITUTE OF FUNERAL SERVICE** *N-34*
450 West 56th St.
New York, NY 10019-3602
Tel: (212)757-1190
Admissions: (212)220-4275
Fax: (212)765-5923
Web Site: http://www.a-a-m-i.org/
Description: Independent, 2-year, coed. Awards diplomas and terminal associate degrees. Founded 1926. Setting: urban campus. Total enrollment: 130. Full-time: 130 students, 58% women, 42% men. Students come from 9 states and territories, 4 other countries, 26% from out-of-state, 5% Hispanic, 44% black, 7% international, 29% 25 or older, 36% transferred in. Core. Calendar: semesters.
Entrance Requirements: Open admission. Options: early admission, deferred admission. Required: high school transcript, 2 recommendations. Recommended: interview. Entrance: noncompetitive. Application deadline: Rolling. Notification: continuous until 8/15.
Collegiate Environment: College housing not available. American Academy MacAllister Institute Library with 1,672 books, 78 serials, and 165 audiovisual materials. 12 computers available on campus for general student use.

■ **THE ART INSTITUTE OF NEW YORK CITY** *N-34*
75 Varick St., 16th Floor
New York, NY 10013
Tel: (212)226-5500
Free: 800-654-2433
Fax: (212)226-5644
Web Site: http://www.ainyc.aii.edu/
Description: Proprietary, 2-year, coed. Part of Education Management Corporation. Awards certificates, diplomas, transfer associate, and terminal associate degrees. Founded 1980. Setting: urban campus. Total enrollment: 1,477. Student-undergrad faculty ratio is 16:1. Students come from 3 states and territories, 25% from out-of-state, 2% Native American, 30% Hispanic, 30% black, 7% Asian American or Pacific Islander, 0% international, 40% 25 or older. Core. Academic remediation for entering students, advanced placement, summer session for credit, co-op programs and internships.
Entrance Requirements: Open admission. Option: Common Application. Required: essay, high school transcript, interview. Entrance: minimally difficult. Application deadline: Rolling. Notification: continuous.
Costs Per Year: Application fee: $50. Tuition: $431 per credit part-time. Part-time tuition varies according to course load and degree level. Contact school directly as tuition and fees vary according to program. Tuition guaranteed not to increase for student's term of enrollment.
Collegiate Environment: Orientation program. College housing not available. 20 computers available on campus for general student use. Staffed computer lab on campus.

■ **ASA INSTITUTE, THE COLLEGE OF ADVANCED TECHNOLOGY** *O-34*
151 Lawrence St., 2nd Floor
Brooklyn, NY 11201
Tel: (718)522-9073
Admissions: (718)534-0773
Fax: (718)834-0835
E-mail: alice_perez@asa-institute.com
Web Site: http://www.asa-institute.com/
Description: Proprietary, 2-year, coed. Founded 1985. Calendar: semesters.

■ **BARD COLLEGE** *O-24*
PO Box 5000
Annandale-on-Hudson, NY 12504
Tel: (845)758-6822
Admissions: (845)758-7472
E-mail: admission@bard.edu
Web Site: http://www.bard.edu/
Description: Independent, comprehensive, coed. Awards associate, bachelor's, master's, and doctoral degrees. Founded 1860. Setting: 600-

acre rural campus. Research spending for 2004 fiscal year: $1.7 million. Total enrollment: 1,858. Faculty: 230 (130 full-time, 100 part-time). Student-undergrad faculty ratio is 9:1. 4,142 applied, 32% were admitted. 63% from top 10% of their high school class, 85% from top quarter, 99% from top half. Full-time: 1,521 students, 57% women, 43% men. Part-time: 64 students, 52% women, 48% men. Students come from 50 states and territories, 51 other countries, 69% from out-of-state, 0.5% Native American, 4% Hispanic, 2% black, 4% Asian American or Pacific Islander, 8% international, 1% 25 or older, 80% live on campus, 2% transferred in. Retention: 88% of full-time freshmen returned the following year. Academic areas with the most degrees conferred: visual and performing arts; social sciences; English. Core. Calendar: semesters. ESL program, services for LD students, advanced placement, accelerated degree program, self-designed majors, independent study, double major, part-time degree program, adult/continuing education programs, internships, graduate courses open to undergrads. Off campus study at Vassar College, State University of New York at New Paltz. Study abroad program.
Entrance Requirements: Options: Peterson's Universal Application, Common Application, electronic application, early admission, early action, deferred admission, international baccalaureate accepted. Required: essay, high school transcript, 3 recommendations. Recommended: minimum 3.0 high school GPA, interview. Required for some: interview. Entrance: very difficult. Application deadlines: 1/15, 11/1 for early action. Notification: 4/1, 1/1 for early action.
Costs Per Year: Application fee: $50. Comprehensive fee: $43,930 includes full-time tuition ($34,080) and college room and board ($9850). College room only: $4950. Part-time tuition: $1066 per credit. Part-time mandatory fees: $351 per term.
Collegiate Environment: Orientation program. Drama-theater group, choral group, student-run newspaper, radio station. Social organizations: 70 open to all. Most popular organizations: student government, Social Action Workshop, Model United Nations, student newspaper, International Student Organization. Major annual events: Carnivale, Spring Fling, Senior Project Shows. Student services: legal services, health clinic, personal-psychological counseling, women's center. Campus security: 24-hour emergency response devices and patrols, student patrols, late night transport-escort service, controlled dormitory access. 1,170 college housing spaces available; all were occupied in 2003-04. Freshmen guaranteed college housing. On-campus residence required in freshman year. Options: coed, women-only housing available. Stevenson Library plus 3 others with 350,000 books, 1,200 microform titles, 15,000 serials, 3,200 audiovisual materials, an OPAC, and a Web page. Operations spending for 2004 fiscal year: $1.3 million. 425 computers available on campus for general student use. Computer purchase/lease plans available. A campuswide network can be accessed from student residence rooms and from off campus. Staffed computer lab on campus.
Community Environment: The town is situated on the Hudson River in eastern New York. The area is accessible via Metro North and Amtrak Railroad nearby, the Taconic State Parkway, or the New York Thruway, using Exit 19 and the Kingston-Rhinecliff Bridge.

■ **BARNARD COLLEGE** *N-34*
3009 Broadway
New York, NY 10027-6598
Tel: (212)854-5262
Admissions: (212)854-2014
Fax: (212)854-6220
E-mail: admissions@barnard.edu
Web Site: http://www.barnard.edu/
Description: Independent, 4-year, women only. Part of Columbia University. Awards bachelor's degrees. Founded 1889. Setting: 4-acre urban campus. Endowment: $152.6 million. Research spending for 2004 fiscal year: $2.9 million. Educational spending for 2005 fiscal year: $15,175 per student. Total enrollment: 2,356. Student-undergrad faculty ratio is 10:1. 4,431 applied, 27% were admitted. 83% from top 10% of their high school class, 99% from top quarter, 100% from top half. 6 National Merit Scholars. Full-time: 2,296 students. Part-time: 60 students. Students come from 50 states and territories, 40 other countries, 66% from out-of-state, 0.4% Native American, 7% Hispanic, 5% black, 17% Asian American or Pacific Islander, 3% international, 1% 25 or older, 90% live on campus, 4% transferred in. Retention: 95% of full-time freshmen returned the following year. Academic areas with the most degrees conferred: social sciences; English; psychology. Core. Calendar: semesters. Services for LD students, advanced placement, accelerated degree program, self-designed majors, honors program,

independent study, double major, internships. Off campus study at Manhattan School of Music, Jewish Theological Seminary of America, Juilliard School, Columbia University School of International and Public Affairs, Spelman College. Study abroad program.

Entrance Requirements: Options: Peterson's Universal Application, Common Application, early admission, early decision, deferred admission, international baccalaureate accepted. Required: essay, high school transcript, 3 recommendations, SAT and SAT Subject Tests or ACT. Recommended: interview. Entrance: most difficult. Application deadlines: 1/1, 11/15 for early decision. Notification: 4/1, 12/15 for early decision.

Costs Per Year: Application fee: $45. Comprehensive fee: $41,802 includes full-time tuition ($29,364), mandatory fees ($1312), and college room and board ($11,126). College room only: $6764. Room and board charges vary according to board plan and housing facility. Part-time tuition: $980 per credit.

Collegiate Environment: Orientation program. Drama-theater group, choral group, marching band, student-run newspaper, radio station. Social organizations: 100 open to all. Most popular organizations: Community Impact, Student Government Association, Student Activities Council, WBAR Radio, Asian-American Alliance. Major annual events: Winterfest and Springfest Celebration, Founder's Day, Take Back the Night. Student services: health clinic, personal-psychological counseling, women's center. Campus security: 24-hour emergency response devices and patrols, late night transport-escort service, 4 permanent security posts. 2,112 college housing spaces available; 2,065 were occupied in 2003-04. Freshmen guaranteed college housing. Options: coed, women-only housing available. Wollman Library with 204,906 books, 17,705 microform titles, 543 serials, 17,448 audiovisual materials, an OPAC, and a Web page. Operations spending for 2004 fiscal year: $2.3 million. 208 computers available on campus for general student use. A campuswide network can be accessed from student residence rooms and from off campus. Staffed computer lab on campus.

Community Environment: See Columbia University.

■ **BEIS MEDRASH HEICHAL DOVID**
257 Beach 17th St.
Far Rockaway, NY 11691
Tel: (718)868-2300
Fax: (718)868-0517
Description: Proprietary, 4-year.

■ **BERKELEY COLLEGE-NEW YORK CITY CAMPUS** *N-34*
3 East 43rd St.
New York, NY 10017-4604
Tel: (212)986-4343
Free: 800-446-5400
Fax: (212)697-3371
Web Site: http://www.berkeleycollege.edu/
Description: Proprietary, primarily 2-year, coed. Awards certificates, transfer associate, terminal associate, and bachelor's degrees. Founded 1936. Setting: urban campus. Total enrollment: 2,321. Student-undergrad faculty ratio is 26:1. 2,279 applied, 73% were admitted. Full-time: 2,138 students, 69% women, 31% men. Part-time: 183 students, 74% women, 26% men. Students come from 14 states and territories, 66 other countries, 9% from out-of-state, 0.4% Native American, 23% Hispanic, 22% black, 5% Asian American or Pacific Islander, 15% international, 31% 25 or older, 6% transferred in. Retention: 48% of full-time freshmen returned the following year. Academic area with the most degrees conferred: business/marketing. Core. Academic remediation for entering students, ESL program, advanced placement, distance learning, summer session for credit, part-time degree program, adult/continuing education programs, co-op programs and internships. Off campus study at Berkeley College, White Plains; Berkeley College, West Paterson. Study abroad program.

Entrance Requirements: Options: electronic application, deferred admission. Required: high school transcript, SAT or ACT. Recommended: interview. Entrance: minimally difficult. Application deadline: Rolling.

Costs Per Year: Application fee: $50. Tuition: $16,950 full-time. Mandatory fees: $750 full-time.

Collegiate Environment: Student-run newspaper. Social organizations: local fraternities, local sororities; 33% of eligible men and 75% of eligible women are members. Most popular organizations: student government, International Club, Paralegal Club, Accounting Club. Major annual events: International Day, Graduation Ball. Student services: personal-psychological counseling. Campus security: 24-hour emergency response devices. Col-

lege housing not available. 13,164 books, 138 serials, 949 audiovisual materials, an OPAC, and a Web page. 200 computers available on campus for general student use. A campuswide network can be accessed from off-campus. Staffed computer lab on campus.

■ **BERKELEY COLLEGE-WESTCHESTER CAMPUS** *J-36*
99 Church St.
White Plains, NY 10601
Tel: (914)694-1122
Free: 800-446-5400
Fax: (914)694-5832
Web Site: http://www.berkeleycollege.edu/
Description: Proprietary, primarily 2-year, coed. Awards certificates, transfer associate, terminal associate, and bachelor's degrees. Founded 1945. Setting: 10-acre suburban campus with easy access to New York City. Total enrollment: 610. Student-undergrad faculty ratio is 22:1. Full-time: 564 students, 71% women, 29% men. Part-time: 46 students, 83% women, 17% men. Students come from 9 states and territories, 28 other countries, 15% from out-of-state, 0% Native American, 21% Hispanic, 26% black, 3% Asian American or Pacific Islander, 6% international, 20% 25 or older, 10% live on campus, 14% transferred in. Retention: 55% of full-time freshmen returned the following year. Academic areas with the most degrees conferred: business/marketing; law/legal studies. Core. Academic remediation for entering students, ESL program, services for LD students, advanced placement, distance learning, summer session for credit, part-time degree program, adult/continuing education programs, co-op programs and internships. Off campus study at Berkeley College, West Paterson; Berkeley College, New York. Study abroad program.

Entrance Requirements: Options: electronic application, deferred admission. Required: high school transcript, SAT or ACT. Recommended: interview. Entrance: minimally difficult. Application deadline: Rolling.

Costs Per Year: Application fee: $50. Comprehensive fee: $26,700 includes full-time tuition ($16,950), mandatory fees ($750), and college room and board ($9000).

Collegiate Environment: Student-run newspaper. Social organizations: 8 open to all; local sororities. Most popular organizations: student government, Paralegal Club, Fashion Club, Phi Theta Kappa. Major annual events: Multicultural Month, Commuter Appreciation Day, Unity Week. Student services: personal-psychological counseling. Campus security: monitored entrance with front desk security guard. 140 college housing spaces available; all were occupied in 2003-04. Option: coed housing available. 9,526 books, 66 serials, 777 audiovisual materials, an OPAC, and a Web page. 175 computers available on campus for general student use. A campuswide network can be accessed from off-campus. Staffed computer lab on campus.

■ **BERNARD M. BARUCH COLLEGE OF THE CITY UNIVERSITY OF NEW YORK** *N-34*
1 Bernard Baruch Way
New York, NY 10010-5585
Tel: (646)312-1000
Admissions: (212)312-1400
E-mail: udgbb@cunyvm.edu
Web Site: http://www.baruch.cuny.edu/
Description: State and locally supported, comprehensive, coed. Part of City University of New York System. Awards bachelor's, master's, and doctoral degrees and post-master's certificates. Founded 1919. Setting: urban campus. Endowment: $86.4 million. Research spending for 2004 fiscal year: $1.9 million. Total enrollment: 15,756. Faculty: 925 (473 full-time, 452 part-time). Student-undergrad faculty ratio is 20:1. 14,917 applied, 33% were admitted. 23% from top 10% of their high school class, 56% from top quarter, 81% from top half. Full-time: 9,753 students, 53% women, 47% men. Part-time: 3,091 students, 61% women, 39% men. Students come from 14 states and territories, 120 other countries, 2% from out-of-state, 0.1% Native American, 17% Hispanic, 13% black, 28% Asian American or Pacific Islander, 11% international, 26% 25 or older, 10% transferred in. Retention: 88% of full-time freshmen returned the following year. Academic areas with the most degrees conferred: business/marketing; computer and information sciences; communications/journalism. Core. Calendar: semesters. ESL program, services for LD students, advanced placement, accelerated degree program, self-designed majors, honors program, independent study, distance learning, double major, summer session for credit, part-time degree program, adult/continuing education programs, internships, graduate courses open to undergrads. Study abroad program.

Entrance Requirements: Options: early admission, early decision, early action. Required: high school transcript, minimum 2.5 high school GPA, 16 academic units, SAT or ACT. Required for some: recommendations, interview. Entrance: very difficult. Application deadlines: 2/1, 12/13 for early decision, 12/15 for early action. Notification: continuous until 5/15, 1/7 for early decision, 1/7 for early action.

Costs Per Year: Application fee: $65. State resident tuition: $4000 full-time, $170 per credit part-time. Nonresident tuition: $8640 full-time, $360 per credit part-time. Mandatory fees: $320 full-time, $80 per term part-time.

Collegiate Environment: Orientation program. Drama-theater group, choral group, student-run newspaper, radio station. Social organizations: 126 open to all; national fraternities, national sororities, local fraternities, local sororities; 20% of eligible men and 25% of eligible women are members. Most popular organizations: Accounting Society, Computer Information Systems Society, Association of Latino Professionals in Finance and Accounting, Golden Key International Society, Helpline. Major annual events: Street Fair, Club Fair, Caribbean Cultural Festival. Student services: legal services, health clinic, personal-psychological counseling. Campus security: 24-hour emergency response devices and patrols, late night transport-escort service, controlled access by ID card. College housing not available. The William and Anita Newman Library plus 1 other with 297,959 books, 2.1 million microform titles, 4,038 serials, 1,044 audiovisual materials, an OPAC, and a Web page. Operations spending for 2004 fiscal year: $3.4 million. 1,294 computers available on campus for general student use. A campuswide network can be accessed. Staffed computer lab on campus.

■ **BETH HAMEDRASH SHAAREI YOSHER INSTITUTE** *O-34*

4102-10 Sixteenth Ave.
Brooklyn, NY 11204
Tel: (718)854-2290

Description: Independent Jewish, comprehensive, men only. Awards bachelor's and master's degrees. Founded 1962. Total enrollment: 150. Calendar: semesters.

■ **BETH HATALMUD RABBINICAL COLLEGE** *O-34*

2127 Eighty-second St.
Brooklyn, NY 11214
Tel: (718)259-2525

Description: Independent Jewish, comprehensive, men only. Awards bachelor's and master's degrees. Founded 1950. Total enrollment: 230. Calendar: semesters.

■ **BORICUA COLLEGE** *N-34*

3755 Broadway
New York, NY 10032-1560
Tel: (212)694-1000
Web Site: http://www.boricuacollege.edu/

Description: Independent, comprehensive, coed. Awards associate, bachelor's, and master's degrees. Founded 1974. Setting: urban campus. Endowment: $50,000. Educational spending for 2005 fiscal year: $1862 per student. Total enrollment: 1,520. 986 applied, 47% were admitted. 89% 25 or older. Retention: 85% of full-time freshmen returned the following year. Core. Calendar: 15-15-8. Accelerated degree program, honors program, summer session for credit, adult/continuing education programs, internships. Study abroad program.

Entrance Requirements: Options: Common Application, deferred admission. Required: high school transcript, 2 recommendations, interview, proficiency in English and Spanish, CAT. Entrance: moderately difficult. Application deadline: Rolling.

Costs Per Year: Application fee: $25. Tuition: $9000 full-time. Mandatory fees: $50 full-time.

Collegiate Environment: Choral group. Campus security: 24-hour emergency response devices. College housing not available. Boricua College Library plus 1 other with 112,600 books and 780 serials. Operations spending for 2004 fiscal year: $58,539. 63 computers available on campus for general student use. Staffed computer lab on campus.

■ **BOROUGH OF MANHATTAN COMMUNITY COLLEGE OF THE CITY UNIVERSITY OF NEW YORK** *N-34*

199 Chambers St.
New York, NY 10007-1097
Tel: (212)346-8000
Admissions: (212)220-1265
Fax: (212)346-8816

Web Site: http://www.bmcc.cuny.edu/

Description: State and locally supported, 2-year, coed. Part of City University of New York System. Awards certificates, transfer associate, and terminal associate degrees. Founded 1963. Setting: 5-acre urban campus. Endowment: $3.3 million. Total enrollment: 18,776. Student-undergrad faculty ratio is 22:1. 6,446 applied, 89% were admitted. 4% from top 10% of their high school class, 11% from top quarter, 37% from top half. Full-time: 10,809 students, 59% women, 41% men. Part-time: 7,967 students, 67% women, 33% men. Students come from 3 states and territories, 100 other countries, 12% from out-of-state, 0.1% Native American, 29% Hispanic, 36% black, 10% Asian American or Pacific Islander, 11% international, 42% 25 or older, 10% transferred in. Core. Calendar: semesters. Academic remediation for entering students, ESL program, services for LD students, advanced placement, honors program, independent study, distance learning, summer session for credit, part-time degree program, adult/continuing education programs, co-op programs and internships. Off campus study at other units of the City University of New York System. Study abroad program.

Entrance Requirements: Open admission. Options: electronic application, deferred admission. Required: high school transcript. Entrance: noncompetitive. Application deadline: Rolling. Notification: continuous. Preference given to city residents.

Costs Per Year: Application fee: $65. State resident tuition: $2800 full-time, $120 per credit hour part-time. Nonresident tuition: $4560 full-time, $190 per credit hour part-time. Mandatory fees: $268 full-time.

Collegiate Environment: Orientation program. Drama-theater group, choral group, student-run newspaper. Social organizations: 50 open to all. Most popular organizations: Caribbean Students Association, Dominican Students Association, When One Voice is Not Enough (WOVINE), Students of Indian Descent Association, Asian Society. Major annual events: Club Fair, Women's Herstory Month, African Heritage Month. Student services: health clinic, personal-psychological counseling, women's center. Campus security: 24-hour patrols. College housing not available. A. Philip Randolph Library with 101,869 books, 17,960 microform titles, 8,594 serials, 1,343 audiovisual materials, an OPAC, and a Web page.

■ **BRAMSON ORT COLLEGE**

69-30 Austin St.
Forest Hills, NY 11375-4239
Tel: (718)261-5800
Web Site: http://www.bramsonort.edu/

Description: Independent, 2-year, coed. Awards certificates and terminal associate degrees. Founded 1977. Total enrollment: 600. Students come from 3 states and territories, 5 other countries, 80% 25 or older. Calendar: semesters. Academic remediation for entering students, ESL program, advanced placement, summer session for credit, part-time degree program, internships.

Entrance Requirements: Open admission. Options: early admission, deferred admission. Required: high school transcript. Entrance: noncompetitive. Application deadline: Rolling.

Collegiate Environment: Student-run newspaper. Student services: personal-psychological counseling, women's center. College housing not available. 8,000 books and 110 serials. 50 computers available on campus for general student use.

■ **BRIARCLIFFE COLLEGE** *N-39*

1055 Stewart Ave.
Bethpage, NY 11714
Tel: (516)918-3600
Admissions: (516)918-3705
Fax: (516)470-6020
E-mail: donohuet@bcl.org
Web Site: http://www.briarcliffe.edu/

Description: Proprietary, 4-year, coed. Part of Career Education Corporation. Awards associate and bachelor's degrees. Founded 1966. Setting: 18-acre suburban campus with easy access to New York City. Total enrollment: 3,009. Student-undergrad faculty ratio is 16:1. 10% from top 10% of their high school class, 40% from top quarter, 70% from top half. Full-time: 2,373 students, 49% women, 51% men. Part-time: 636 students, 57% women, 43% men. Students come from 10 states and territories, 7 other countries, 0% from out-of-state, 0.3% Native American, 9% Hispanic, 14% black, 1% Asian American or Pacific Islander, 0% international, 42% 25 or older, 4% live on campus, 20% transferred in. Retention: 65% of full-time freshmen returned the following year. Core. Calendar: semesters. Academic remediation for entering students, services for LD students, advanced placement, accelerated degree program, independent study, distance learning, summer session for credit, part-time degree program, external degree program, adult/continuing education programs, co-op programs and internships.

Entrance Requirements: Options: Peterson's Universal Application, electronic application, deferred admission. Required: high school transcript. Recommended: interview. Entrance: moderately difficult. Application deadline: Rolling. Notification: continuous.

Costs Per Year: Application fee: $35. Comprehensive fee: $23,730 includes full-time tuition ($14,592), mandatory fees ($1200), and college room and board ($7938). Part-time tuition: $608 per credit.

Collegiate Environment: Orientation program. Student-run newspaper, radio station. Social organizations: 4 open to all; national fraternities; 10% of eligible men and 10% of eligible women are members. Most popular organizations: Student Government Association, Telecommunication Club, Graphic Design Club, Law Club. Campus security: late night transport-escort service. 104 college housing spaces available; all were occupied in 2003-04. No special consideration for freshman housing applicants. Option: coed housing available. Briarcliffe Library with 11,834 books and 191 serials. 350 computers available on campus for general student use. A campuswide network can be accessed. Staffed computer lab on campus.

■ BRONX COMMUNITY COLLEGE OF THE CITY UNIVERSITY OF NEW YORK *M-35*

University Ave. & West 181st St.
Bronx, NY 10453
Tel: (718)289-5100
Admissions: (718)289-5888
Web Site: http://www.bcc.cuny.edu/

Description: State and locally supported, 2-year, coed. Part of City University of New York System. Awards certificates, transfer associate, and terminal associate degrees. Founded 1959. Setting: 50-acre urban campus. Total enrollment: 8,470. Student-undergrad faculty ratio is 15:1. 5,061 applied, 98% were admitted. Full-time: 5,088 students, 62% women, 38% men. Part-time: 3,382 students, 67% women, 33% men. Students come from 16 states and territories, 100 other countries, 0.2% Native American, 48% Hispanic, 35% black, 3% Asian American or Pacific Islander, 11% international, 48% 25 or older, 5% transferred in. Retention: 65% of full-time freshmen returned the following year. Core. Calendar: semesters. Academic remediation for entering students, ESL program, services for LD students, advanced placement, honors program, independent study, distance learning, summer session for credit, part-time degree program, adult/continuing education programs, co-op programs and internships. Study abroad program.

Entrance Requirements: Open admission. Required: high school transcript. Entrance: noncompetitive. Application deadline: 7/1. Notification: 8/15.

Costs Per Year: Application fee: $65. State resident tuition: $2800 full-time, $120 per credit part-time. Nonresident tuition: $4560 full-time, $190 per credit part-time. Mandatory fees: $284 full-time, $90 per term part-time.

Collegiate Environment: Orientation program. Drama-theater group, choral group, student-run newspaper. Social organizations: national fraternities, national sororities. Student services: health clinic, personal-psychological counseling. Campus security: 24-hour patrols. College housing not available. 75,000 books and 800 serials. 300 computers available on campus for general student use.

■ BROOKLYN COLLEGE OF THE CITY UNIVERSITY OF NEW YORK *O-34*

2900 Bedford Ave.
Brooklyn, NY 11210-2889
Tel: (718)951-5000
Admissions: (718)951-5001
E-mail: admissions@brooklyn.cuny.edu
Web Site: http://www.brooklyn.cuny.edu/

Description: State and locally supported, comprehensive, coed. Part of City University of New York System. Awards bachelor's and master's degrees and post-master's certificates. Founded 1930. Setting: 26-acre urban campus. Total enrollment: 15,281. Faculty: 1,103 (517 full-time, 586 part-time). Student-undergrad faculty ratio is 15:1. 7,083 applied, 33% were admitted. 14% from top 10% of their high school class, 42% from top quarter, 77% from top half. Full-time: 8,109 students, 59% women, 41% men. Part-time: 3,255 students, 62% women, 38% men. Students come from 25 states and territories, 75 other countries, 1% from out-of-state, 0.2% Native American, 12% Hispanic, 28% black, 11% Asian American or Pacific

Islander, 7% international, 33% 25 or older, 13% transferred in. Retention: 76% of full-time freshmen returned the following year. Core. Calendar: semesters. ESL program, services for LD students, advanced placement, freshman honors college, honors program, independent study, distance learning, double major, summer session for credit, part-time degree program, adult/continuing education programs, internships, graduate courses open to undergrads. Off campus study at other units of the City University of New York System. Study abroad program.

Entrance Requirements: Options: early admission, deferred admission, international baccalaureate accepted. Required: high school transcript, minimum 3.0 high school GPA, SAT or ACT. Recommended: SAT Subject Tests. Required for some: essay, recommendations, interview. Entrance: moderately difficult. Application deadline: Rolling. Notification: continuous.

Costs Per Year: Application fee: $65. State resident tuition: $4000 full-time, $170 per credit part-time. Nonresident tuition: $8640 full-time, $360 per credit part-time. Mandatory fees: $375 full-time, $139.05 per term part-time.

Collegiate Environment: Orientation program. Drama-theater group, choral group, student-run newspaper, radio station. Social organizations: 150 open to all; national fraternities, national sororities, local fraternities, local sororities; 3% of eligible men and 3% of eligible women are members. Most popular organizations: Academic Club Association, Kingsman and Excelsior Newspaper, NY Public Interest Group (NYPIRG), Student Government CIAS, SGS, and GSO, Student Forensics. Major annual events: Presidential Convocation, Graduation Ceremony, student government elections. Student services: health clinic, personal-psychological counseling, women's center. Campus security: 24-hour emergency response devices and patrols, late night transport-escort service. College housing not available. Brooklyn College Library plus 1 other with 1.3 million books, 1.6 million microform titles, 13,500 serials, 21,731 audiovisual materials, an OPAC, and a Web page. 800 computers available on campus for general student use. A campuswide network can be accessed from off-campus. Staffed computer lab on campus.

■ BROOME COMMUNITY COLLEGE *N-17*

PO Box 1017
Binghamton, NY 13902-1017
Tel: (607)778-5000
Admissions: (607)778-5001
Web Site: http://www.sunybroome.edu/

Description: State and locally supported, 2-year, coed. Part of State University of New York System. Awards certificates, transfer associate, and terminal associate degrees. Founded 1946. Setting: 223-acre suburban campus. Total enrollment: 6,231. Student-undergrad faculty ratio is 21:1. 2,703 applied, 52% were admitted. Full-time: 3,946 students, 54% women, 46% men. Part-time: 2,285 students, 62% women, 38% men. Students come from 36 states and territories, 30 other countries, 4% from out-of-state, 0.3% Native American, 2% Hispanic, 3% black, 1% Asian American or Pacific Islander, 2% international, 10% 25 or older. Retention: 62% of full-time freshmen returned the following year. Core. Calendar: semesters. Academic remediation for entering students, ESL program, services for LD students, advanced placement, self-designed majors, honors program, independent study, distance learning, summer session for credit, part-time degree program, external degree program, adult/continuing education programs, internships. Off campus study at State University of New York at Binghamton. Study abroad program.

Entrance Requirements: Open admission except for allied health, engineering technology, computer science programs. Options: electronic application, early admission. Required: high school transcript. Required for some: interview. Entrance: noncompetitive. Application deadline: Rolling. Notification: continuous. Preference given to county residents.

Costs Per Year: Application fee: $0. One-time mandatory fee: $45. State resident tuition: $2814 full-time, $118 per credit hour part-time. Nonresident tuition: $5628 full-time, $236 per credit hour part-time. Mandatory fees: $267 full-time, $5 per credit hour part-time, $29 per term part-time. Full-time tuition and fees vary according to course load and location. Part-time tuition and fees vary according to course load and location.

Collegiate Environment: Orientation program. Choral group, student-run newspaper. Social organizations: 44 open to all. Most popular organizations: Broome Early Childhood Organization, Differentially Disabled Student Association, Ecology Club, Phi Theta Kappa, Criminal Justice Club. Major annual events: Student Activities Day, Convocation, Festival of the Arts. Student services: health clinic, personal-psychological counseling. Campus security: 24-hour emergency response devices and patrols. College housing not available. Cecil C. Tyrrell Learning Resources Center plus 1 other with 60,518 books, 27 microform titles, 301 serials, 2,145 audiovisual materials, an OPAC, and a Web page. Operations spending for 2004 fiscal year: $833,029. 550 computers available on campus for general student use. A campuswide network can be accessed from off-campus. Staffed computer lab on campus.

■ BRYANT AND STRATTON COLLEGE (ALBANY) L-25

1259 Central Ave.
Albany, NY 12205-5230
Tel: (518)437-1802
Fax: (518)437-1048
Web Site: http://www.bryantstratton.edu/
Description: Proprietary, 2-year, coed. Part of Bryant and Stratton College, Inc. Awards terminal associate degrees. Founded 1857. Setting: suburban campus. Total enrollment: 470. Full-time: 354 students, 79% women, 21% men. Part-time: 116 students, 74% women, 26% men. 0% from out-of-state, 1% Native American, 7% Hispanic, 48% black, 2% Asian American or Pacific Islander, 0% international, 51% 25 or older. Retention: 45% of full-time freshmen returned the following year. Core. Calendar: semesters. Academic remediation for entering students, services for LD students, independent study, distance learning, double major, summer session for credit, part-time degree program, internships.
Entrance Requirements: Option: deferred admission. Required: high school transcript, interview, entrance and placement evaluations, CPAt, ACCUPLACER. Recommended: SAT or ACT. Required for some: recommendations. Entrance: minimally difficult. Application deadline: Rolling.
Costs Per Year: Tuition: $18,675 full-time, $415 per credit hour part-time. Mandatory fees: $25 full-time. Full-time tuition and fees vary according to course load. Part-time tuition varies according to course load.
Collegiate Environment: Orientation program. Student-run newspaper. Campus security: 24-hour emergency response devices. College housing not available. Library with 3,500 books, 5 serials, 136 audiovisual materials, an OPAC, and a Web page. 110 computers available on campus for general student use. A campuswide network can be accessed. Staffed computer lab on campus.

■ BRYANT AND STRATTON COLLEGE, AMHERST CAMPUS J-7

Audubon Business Center, 40 Hazelwood Dr.
Amherst, NY 14228
Tel: (716)691-0012
Fax: (716)691-6716
E-mail: mzachary@bryantstratton.edu
Web Site: http://www.bryantstratton.edu/
Description: Proprietary, primarily 2-year, coed. Part of Bryant and Stratton College. Awards terminal associate and bachelor's degrees. Founded 1977. Setting: 12-acre suburban campus with easy access to Buffalo. Total enrollment: 403. 73 applied, 79% were admitted. Full-time: 240 students, 73% women, 27% men. Part-time: 163 students, 74% women, 26% men. 0% from out-of-state, 1% Native American, 2% Hispanic, 15% black, 0.5% Asian American or Pacific Islander, 0% international, 56% 25 or older, 17% transferred in. Core. Calendar: trimesters. Academic remediation for entering students, advanced placement, independent study, distance learning, double major, summer session for credit, part-time degree program, co-op programs and internships.
Entrance Requirements: Options: Common Application, deferred admission. Required: high school transcript, interview, entrance evaluation and placement evaluation, TABE, CPAt or ACCUPLACER. Recommended: SAT or ACT. Required for some: recommendations. Entrance: minimally difficult. Application deadline: Rolling.
Costs Per Year: Tuition: $18,675 full-time, $415 per credit hour part-time. Mandatory fees: $25 full-time. Full-time tuition and fees vary according to class time and course load. Part-time tuition varies according to class time and course load.
Collegiate Environment: Orientation program. Most popular organizations: Phi Beta Lambda, Student Government Association, Information Technology Club, Ambassadors. Major annual events: Picnic, Bring a Friend Day, Field Trip Day. College housing not available. Library Resource Center with 4,500 books, 25 serials, 150 audiovisual materials, an OPAC, and a Web page. 70 computers available on campus for general student use. Staffed computer lab on campus.

■ BRYANT AND STRATTON COLLEGE, BUFFALO CAMPUS K-7

465 Main St.
Ste. 400
Buffalo, NY 14203

Tel: (716)884-9120
Web Site: http://www.bryantstratton.edu/
Description: Proprietary, 2-year, coed. Part of Bryant and Stratton College. Awards terminal associate degrees. Founded 1854. Setting: 2-acre urban campus. Total enrollment: 603. 305 applied, 75% were admitted. Full-time: 495 students, 72% women, 28% men. Part-time: 108 students, 86% women, 14% men. 0% from out-of-state, 1% Native American, 5% Hispanic, 65% black, 0.2% Asian American or Pacific Islander, 0% international, 46% 25 or older, 4% transferred in. Core. Calendar: trimesters. Academic remediation for entering students, advanced placement, independent study, distance learning, double major, summer session for credit, part-time degree program, co-op programs and internships.
Entrance Requirements: Options: Peterson's Universal Application, Common Application, deferred admission. Required: high school transcript, interview, entrance and placement evaluation, TABE, CPAt or ACCUPLACER. Recommended: SAT or ACT. Required for some: recommendations. Entrance: minimally difficult. Application deadline: Rolling.
Costs Per Year: Tuition: $18,675 full-time, $415 per credit hour part-time. Mandatory fees: $25 full-time. Full-time tuition and fees vary according to class time and course load. Part-time tuition varies according to course load.
Collegiate Environment: Orientation program. Most popular organizations: Med-Assisting Club, Secretarial Club, Accounting/Business Club. Major annual events: Dean's List Ceremony, Commencement, NVTHS. College housing not available. Learning Center/Library with 30,000 books, 28,217 serials, 252 audiovisual materials, and an OPAC. 125 computers available on campus for general student use. Staffed computer lab on campus.
Community Environment: See Canisius College.

■ BRYANT AND STRATTON COLLEGE, LACKAWANNA CAMPUS K-7

1214 Abbott Rd.
Lackawanna, NY 14218-1989
Tel: (716)821-9331
Admissions: (716)677-9500
E-mail: prkehr@bryantstratton.edu
Web Site: http://www.bryantstratton.edu/
Description: Proprietary, 2-year, coed. Part of Bryant and Stratton College. Awards terminal associate degrees. Founded 1989. Setting: suburban campus with easy access to Buffalo. Total enrollment: 269. 98 applied, 73% were admitted. Full-time: 189 students, 72% women, 28% men. Part-time: 80 students, 88% women, 13% men. 0% from out-of-state, 1% Native American, 2% Hispanic, 4% black, 0% Asian American or Pacific Islander, 0% international, 49% 25 or older. Core. Calendar: trimesters. Academic remediation for entering students, advanced placement, independent study, distance learning, double major, summer session for credit, part-time degree program, co-op programs and internships.
Entrance Requirements: Options: Common Application, deferred admission. Required: high school transcript, interview, entrance and placement evaluations, TABE, CPAt or ACCUPLACER. Recommended: SAT or ACT. Required for some: recommendations. Entrance: minimally difficult. Application deadline: Rolling.
Costs Per Year: Tuition: $18,675 full-time, $415 per credit hour part-time. Mandatory fees: $25 full-time. Full-time tuition and fees vary according to course load. Part-time tuition varies according to course load.
Collegiate Environment: Orientation program. Most popular organizations: Accounting/Business Club, Administrative Professionals Club, Micro Club, Honor Society, student newsletter. Major annual events: Career Fair, Health Fair, Fall Festival. Student services: women's center, life long placement service. Campus security: 24-hour emergency response devices, late night transport-escort service. College housing not available. Southtowns Library with 1,402 books, 42 serials, 128 audiovisual materials, an OPAC, and a Web page. 112 computers available on campus for general student use. Staffed computer lab on campus.

■ BRYANT AND STRATTON COLLEGE, NORTH CAMPUS A-8

8687 Carling Rd.
Liverpool, NY 13090-1315
Tel: (315)652-6500
Web Site: http://www.bryantstratton.edu/
Description: Proprietary, 2-year, coed. Part of Bryant and Stratton Business Institute, Inc. Awards diplomas and terminal associate degrees. Founded 1983. Setting: 1-acre rural campus with easy access to Syracuse. Educational spending for 2005 fiscal year: $4115 per student. Total enrollment: 357. Full-time: 324 students, 69% women, 31% men. Part-time: 33 students, 88% women, 12% men. 0.3% Native American, 2% Hispanic, 3%

black, 0% Asian American or Pacific Islander, 0% international. Core. Calendar: semesters. Academic remediation for entering students, services for LD students, advanced placement, independent study, distance learning, double major, summer session for credit, part-time degree program, adult/continuing education programs, co-op programs and internships.

Entrance Requirements: Option: deferred admission. Required: high school transcript, interview, entrance evaluation and placement evaluation, TABE, CPAt. Recommended: minimum 2.0 high school GPA. Required for some: recommendations. Entrance: minimally difficult. Application deadline: Rolling. Notification: continuous.

Collegiate Environment: Orientation program. Social organizations: 4 open to all; national fraternities. Most popular organizations: Institute of Managerial Accountants, Students Helping Santa, Computer Club, Bryant & Stratton Business Club (BSBC), Alpha Beta Gamma. Major annual event: Graduation Breakfast. Student services: personal-psychological counseling. Campus security: 24-hour emergency response devices. College housing not available. Resource Center plus 1 other with 1,936 books, 13 serials, 85 audiovisual materials, and an OPAC. Operations spending for 2004 fiscal year: $12,500. 73 computers available on campus for general student use. Staffed computer lab on campus.

■ **BRYANT AND STRATTON COLLEGE (ROCHESTER-GREECE CAMPUS)** *J-11*
150 Bellwood Dr.
Rochester, NY 14606
Tel: (585)720-0660
Fax: (585)720-9226
Web Site: http://www.bryantstratton.edu/
Description: Proprietary, 2-year, coed. Part of Bryant and Stratton College. Awards terminal associate degrees. Founded 1973. Setting: urban campus. Total enrollment: 194. Full-time: 152 students, 85% women, 15% men. Part-time: 42 students, 88% women, 12% men. Students come from 4 states and territories, 0% from out-of-state, 1% Native American, 12% Hispanic, 26% black, 0% Asian American or Pacific Islander, 0% international, 97% 25 or older, 14% transferred in. Retention: 0% of full-time freshmen returned the following year. Core. Calendar: semesters. Academic remediation for entering students, services for LD students, independent study, distance learning, double major, summer session for credit, part-time degree program, adult/continuing education programs, internships.
Entrance Requirements: Options: electronic application, deferred admission. Required: high school transcript, interview, entrance evaluation and placement evaluation, CPAt. Recommended: SAT or ACT. Required for some: recommendations. Entrance: minimally difficult. Application deadline: Rolling.
Costs Per Year: Tuition: $18,675 full-time, $415 per credit hour part-time. Mandatory fees: $25 full-time.
Collegiate Environment: Orientation program. Social organizations: 5 open to all. Most popular organizations: BASSA, SAMS Club. Major annual events: Holiday Party, Backyard Bar-B-Cue, Spring Fling. Campus security: 24-hour emergency response devices, late night transport-escort service. College housing not available. Campus Library with 250 books and 27 serials. 195 computers available on campus for general student use. Staffed computer lab on campus.

■ **BRYANT AND STRATTON COLLEGE (ROCHESTER-HENRIETTA CAMPUS)** *J-11*
1225 Jefferson Rd.
Rochester, NY 14623-3136
Tel: (585)292-5627
Fax: (585)292-6015
Web Site: http://www.bryantstratton.edu/
Description: Proprietary, 2-year, coed. Part of Bryant and Stratton College. Awards terminal associate degrees. Founded 1985. Setting: 1-acre suburban campus. Total enrollment: 297. Student-undergrad faculty ratio is 10:1. Full-time: 238 students, 81% women, 19% men. Part-time: 59 students, 63% women, 37% men. Students come from 4 states and territories, 0% from out-of-state, 0.3% Native American, 5% Hispanic, 36% black, 1% Asian American or Pacific Islander, 0% international, 60% 25 or older, 6% transferred in. Retention: 0% of full-time freshmen returned the following year. Core. Calendar: semesters. Academic remediation for entering students, services for LD students, independent study, distance learning, double major, summer session for credit, part-time degree program, adult/continuing education programs, internships.

Entrance Requirements: Options: electronic application, deferred admission. Required: high school transcript, interview, entrance evaluation and placement evaluation, CPAt. Recommended: minimum 2.0 high school GPA, SAT or ACT. Required for some: recommendations. Entrance: minimally difficult. Application deadline: Rolling.
Costs Per Year: Tuition: $18,675 full-time, $415 per credit hour part-time. Mandatory fees: $25 full-time.
Collegiate Environment: Orientation program. Student-run newspaper. Social organizations: 3 open to all. Major annual events: student Christmas parties, Spring Fling. Campus security: late night transport-escort service. College housing not available. Campus Library with 250 books and 27 serials. 195 computers available on campus for general student use. Staffed computer lab on campus.

■ **BRYANT AND STRATTON COLLEGE (SYRACUSE)** *J-16*
953 James St.
Syracuse, NY 13203-2502
Tel: (315)472-6603
Fax: (315)474-4383
Web Site: http://www.bryantstratton.edu/
Description: Proprietary, 2-year, coed. Part of Bryant and Stratton Business Institute, Inc. Awards terminal associate degrees. Founded 1854. Setting: urban campus. Total enrollment: 636. 2% from top 10% of their high school class, 10% from top quarter, 88% from top half. Full-time: 494 students, 77% women, 23% men. Part-time: 142 students, 77% women, 23% men. Students come from 2 other countries, 1% from out-of-state, 2% Native American, 5% Hispanic, 47% black, 1% Asian American or Pacific Islander, 1% international, 26% 25 or older, 26% live on campus, 3% transferred in. Core. Calendar: semesters. Academic remediation for entering students, services for LD students, distance learning, double major, summer session for credit, part-time degree program, internships.
Entrance Requirements: Required: high school transcript, interview, entrance, placement evaluations, CPAt. Recommended: SAT or ACT. Required for some: recommendations. Entrance: minimally difficult. Application deadline: Rolling.
Costs Per Year: Tuition: $18,675 full-time, $415 per credit hour part-time. Mandatory fees: $25 full-time.
Collegiate Environment: Orientation program. Student-run newspaper. Most popular organizations: Management Club, Travel Club, Medical Club, Computer Club. Major annual events: Summer Picnic, Fall Pep Rally, Career Day. Campus security: 24-hour emergency response devices, controlled dormitory access. Option: coed housing available. Bryant and Stratton, Syracuse Campus with 1,325 books, 40 serials, and 40 audiovisual materials. 114 computers available on campus for general student use. Staffed computer lab on campus.

■ **BUFFALO STATE COLLEGE, STATE UNIVERSITY OF NEW YORK** *K-7*
1300 Elmwood Ave.
Buffalo, NY 14222-1095
Tel: (716)878-4000
Admissions: (716)878-5519
Fax: (716)878-6100
E-mail: admissions@buffalostate.edu
Web Site: http://www.buffalostate.edu/
Description: State-supported, comprehensive, coed. Awards bachelor's and master's degrees and post-master's certificates. Founded 1867. Setting: 115-acre urban campus. Endowment: $12.4 million. Research spending for 2004 fiscal year: $33 million. Educational spending for 2005 fiscal year: $3681 per student. Total enrollment: 11,056. Faculty: 715 (393 full-time, 322 part-time). Student-undergrad faculty ratio is 17:1. 8,563 applied, 44% were admitted. 6% from top 10% of their high school class, 25% from top quarter, 73% from top half. Full-time: 7,818 students, 61% women, 39% men. Part-time: 1,192 students, 49% women, 51% men. Students come from 30 states and territories, 21 other countries, 1% from out-of-state, 0.5% Native American, 4% Hispanic, 13% black, 2% Asian American or Pacific Islander, 0.4% international, 17% 25 or older, 21% live on campus, 10% transferred in. Retention: 75% of full-time freshmen returned the following year. Academic areas with the most degrees conferred: education; visual and performing arts; communications/journalism. Core. Calendar: semesters. Academic remediation for entering students, ESL program, services for LD students, advanced placement, freshman honors college, honors program, independent study, distance learning, double major, summer session for credit, part-time degree program, adult/continuing education programs,

co-op programs and internships, graduate courses open to undergrads. Off campus study at Western New York Consortium, National Student Exchange. Study abroad program. ROTC: Army (c).

Entrance Requirements: Options: early admission, early decision, deferred admission, international baccalaureate accepted. Required: high school transcript, minimum 3.0 high school GPA, SAT and SAT Subject Tests or ACT. Required for some: essay, recommendations, interview. Entrance: moderately difficult. Application deadlines: Rolling, 11/15 for early decision. Notification: continuous, 12/15 for early decision.

Costs Per Year: Application fee: $30. State resident tuition: $4350 full-time, $181 per semester hour part-time. Nonresident tuition: $10,610 full-time, $442 per semester hour part-time. Mandatory fees: $881 full-time, $36.60 per credit hour part-time. College room and board: $6672. College room only: $4136. Room and board charges vary according to board plan, housing facility, and student level.

Collegiate Environment: Orientation program. Drama-theater group, choral group, student-run newspaper, radio station. Social organizations: 75 open to all; national fraternities, national sororities, local fraternities, local sororities; 1% of eligible men and 1% of eligible women are members. Most popular organizations: United Student Government, African-American Student Organization, Caribbean Student Organization, The Record, WBNY radio. Major annual events: homecoming, Commuter Daze. Student services: legal services, health clinic, personal-psychological counseling, women's center. Campus security: 24-hour emergency response devices and patrols, student patrols, late night transport-escort service, controlled dormitory access. 1,862 college housing spaces available; 1,853 were occupied in 2003-04. Freshmen guaranteed college housing. On-campus residence required through sophomore year. Option: coed housing available. E. H. Butler Library with 489,069 books, 943,930 microform titles, 2,847 serials, 22,189 audiovisual materials, an OPAC, and a Web page. Operations spending for 2004 fiscal year: $3.3 million. 836 computers available on campus for general student use. A campuswide network can be accessed from student residence rooms and from off campus. Staffed computer lab on campus.

■ BUSINESS INFORMATICS CENTER, INC. *O-37*

134 South Central Ave.
Valley Stream, NY 11580-5431
Tel: (516)561-0050
Fax: (516)561-0074
Description: Proprietary, 2-year, coed. Founded 1982.

■ CANISIUS COLLEGE *K-7*

2001 Main St.
Buffalo, NY 14208-1098
Tel: (716)883-7000
Free: 800-843-1517
Admissions: (716)888-2200
Fax: (716)888-2377
E-mail: inquiry@gort.canisius.edu
Web Site: http://www.canisius.edu/
Description: Independent Roman Catholic (Jesuit), comprehensive, coed. Awards bachelor's and master's degrees and post-master's certificates. Founded 1870. Setting: 36-acre urban campus. Endowment: $48.6 million. Educational spending for 2005 fiscal year: $6781 per student. Total enrollment: 4,979. Faculty: 531 (215 full-time, 316 part-time). Student-undergrad faculty ratio is 13:1. 4,123 applied, 72% were admitted. 22% from top 10% of their high school class, 51% from top quarter, 82% from top half. 12 valedictorians. Full-time: 3,310 students, 57% women, 43% men. Part-time: 281 students, 59% women, 41% men. Students come from 28 states and territories, 31 other countries, 5% from out-of-state, 0.4% Native American, 2% Hispanic, 6% black, 2% Asian American or Pacific Islander, 3% international, 4% 25 or older, 42% live on campus, 5% transferred in. Retention: 84% of full-time freshmen returned the following year. Academic areas with the most degrees conferred: education; business/marketing; communications/journalism. Core. Calendar: semesters. Academic remediation for entering students, ESL program, services for LD students, advanced placement, honors program, independent study, distance learning, double major, summer session for credit, part-time degree program, external degree program, internships, graduate courses open to undergrads. Off campus study at members of the Western New York Consortium. Study abroad program. ROTC: Army.

Entrance Requirements: Options: Peterson's Universal Application, Common Application, electronic application, early admission, deferred admission,

international baccalaureate accepted. Required: high school transcript, minimum 2.5 high school GPA, SAT or ACT. Recommended: essay, recommendations, interview. Required for some: interview. Entrance: moderately difficult. Application deadline: 5/1. Notification: continuous until 12/15.

Costs Per Year: Application fee: $40. Comprehensive fee: $32,257 includes full-time tuition ($22,370), mandatory fees ($927), and college room and board ($8960). College room only: $5250. Room and board charges vary according to board plan, housing facility, and student level. Part-time tuition: $638 per credit hour. Part-time mandatory fees: $20.50 per credit, $18 per term.

Collegiate Environment: Orientation program. Drama-theater group, choral group, student-run newspaper, radio station. Social organizations: 100 open to all; national fraternities, national sororities; 1% of eligible men and 1% of eligible women are members. Most popular organizations: Campus Programming Board, Undergraduate Student Association, Afro-American Society, Residence Hall Association, Student Association. Major annual events: Parents' Weekend, Spring Fest, International Fest Week. Student services: health clinic, personal-psychological counseling. Campus security: 24-hour emergency response devices and patrols, late night transport-escort service, controlled dormitory access, crime prevention programs, closed-circuit television monitors. 1,596 college housing spaces available; 1,450 were occupied in 2003-04. Freshmen given priority for college housing. Option: coed housing available. Andrew L. Bouwhuis Library plus 1 other with 328,278 books, 570,475 microform titles, 1,637 serials, 7,710 audiovisual materials, an OPAC, and a Web page. Operations spending for 2004 fiscal year: $1.7 million. 348 computers available on campus for general student use. Computer purchase/lease plans available. A campuswide network can be accessed from student residence rooms and from off campus. Staffed computer lab on campus.

Community Environment: The Buffalo metropolitan area of over 1.2 million people offers varied cultural, athletic, and entertainment facilities. Among them are the world-famous Albright-Knox Art Gallery, renowned for its modern and contemporary collection; the Buffalo Philharmonic Orchestra, among the top ranked orchestras in North America, which makes its home in the acoustically excellent Kleinhans Music Hall; the Studio Arena, which offers legitimate theater; and the Buffalo Zoo, one of the leading zoos in the United States. For sports fans, there are the Buffalo Bills football team, the Buffalo Sabres hockey team, and the Buffalo Bisons baseball team. Niagara Falls, the ski areas of western New York, and many attractions in Canada are within easy driving distance of the College. The central location of the College also provides many opportunities for students interested in community service, internships, and employment.

■ CAYUGA COUNTY COMMUNITY COLLEGE *K-15*

197 Franklin St.
Auburn, NY 13021-3099
Tel: (315)255-1743
Web Site: http://www.cayuga-cc.edu/
Description: State and locally supported, 2-year, coed. Part of State University of New York System. Awards certificates, transfer associate, and terminal associate degrees. Founded 1953. Setting: 50-acre small town campus with easy access to Rochester and Syracuse. Endowment: $6.5 million. Total enrollment: 3,896. 1,429 applied, 84% were admitted. Full-time: 2,220 students, 55% women, 45% men. Part-time: 1,676 students, 65% women, 35% men. Students come from 9 states and territories, 3 other countries, 1% from out-of-state, 1% Native American, 1% Hispanic, 3% black, 1% Asian American or Pacific Islander, 0.5% international, 35% 25 or older, 4% transferred in. Core. Calendar: semesters. Academic remediation for entering students, services for LD students, advanced placement, accelerated degree program, honors program, independent study, distance learning, double major, summer session for credit, part-time degree program, adult/continuing education programs, internships. Study abroad program.

Entrance Requirements: Open admission. Options: electronic application, deferred admission. Required: high school transcript. Required for some: interview. Placement: SAT or ACT recommended; ACT ASSET, ACCUPLACER required for some. Entrance: noncompetitive. Application deadline: Rolling. Notification: continuous.

Costs Per Year: Application fee: $0. State resident tuition: $2900 full-time, $105 per credit part-time. Nonresident tuition: $5800 full-time, $210 per credit part-time. Mandatory fees: $311 full-time, $12 per credit part-time, $2 per term part-time. Full-time tuition and fees vary according to class time, course load, and program. Part-time tuition and fees vary according to class time, course load, and program.

Collegiate Environment: Orientation program. Drama-theater group, choral group, student-run newspaper, radio station. Social organizations: 5 open to all. Most popular organizations: Student Government Association, Student Activities Board, Radio and Television Guild, honors and business fraternities, Phi Beta Lambda. Major annual events: Folk Art Festival, Transfer Day. Student services: health clinic, personal-psychological counseling. Campus security: security from 8 a.m. to 9 p.m. 100 college housing spaces available; 65 were occupied in 2003-04. Norman F. Bourke Memorial Library with 82,205 books, 10,318 microform titles, 527 serials, 8,930 audiovisual materials, an OPAC, and a Web page. Operations spending for 2004 fiscal year: $591,260. 240 computers available on campus for general student use. A campuswide network can be accessed from off-campus. Staffed computer lab on campus.

■ **CAZENOVIA COLLEGE** *K-17*
22 Sullivan St.
Cazenovia, NY 13035-1084
Tel: (315)655-7000
Free: 800-654-3210
Admissions: (315)655-7208
Fax: (315)655-2190
E-mail: rcroot@cazenovia.edu
Web Site: http://www.cazenovia.edu/
Description: Independent, 4-year, coed. Awards associate and bachelor's degrees. Founded 1824. Setting: 40-acre small town campus with easy access to Syracuse. Endowment: $27 million. Educational spending for 2005 fiscal year: $7309 per student. Total enrollment: 1,124. Student-undergrad faculty ratio is 14:1. 1,286 applied, 82% were admitted. 9% from top 10% of their high school class, 29% from top quarter, 67% from top half. Full-time: 812 students, 78% women, 22% men. Part-time: 312 students, 88% women, 13% men. Students come from 20 states and territories, 2 other countries, 21% from out-of-state, 1% Native American, 2% Hispanic, 3% black, 1% Asian American or Pacific Islander, 0.2% international, 5% 25 or older, 81% live on campus, 4% transferred in. Retention: 74% of full-time freshmen returned the following year. Academic areas with the most degrees conferred: visual and performing arts; business/marketing; public administration and social services. Core. Calendar: semesters. Academic remediation for entering students, services for LD students, advanced placement, self-designed majors, honors program, independent study, distance learning, summer session for credit, part-time degree program, adult/continuing education programs, co-op programs and internships. Off campus study. Study abroad program. ROTC: Army (c), Air Force (c).
Entrance Requirements: Options: Common Application, early admission, deferred admission, international baccalaureate accepted. Required: high school transcript. Recommended: essay, minimum 2.0 high school GPA, recommendations, interview, portfolio for art and design students, SAT and SAT Subject Tests or ACT. Entrance: minimally difficult. Application deadline: Rolling. Notification: continuous.
Costs Per Year: Application fee: $30. Comprehensive fee: $26,450 includes full-time tuition ($18,940) and college room and board ($7510). College room only: $4200. Full-time tuition varies according to course load. Room and board charges vary according to board plan. Part-time tuition: $400 per credit. Part-time mandatory fees: $100. Part-time tuition and fees vary according to class time and course load.
Collegiate Environment: Orientation program. Drama-theater group, choral group, student-run newspaper, radio station. Social organizations: 22 open to all. Most popular organizations: Activities Board, Multicultural Student Group, performing arts, student radio station, yearbook. Major annual events: Spring Day, Parents' Weekend, Quad Day. Student services: health clinic, personal-psychological counseling. Campus security: 24-hour emergency response devices and patrols, late night transport-escort service, controlled dormitory access. 683 college housing spaces available; 653 were occupied in 2003-04. Freshmen given priority for college housing. On-campus residence required through sophomore year. Option: coed housing available. Witheral Library with 79,920 books, 14,144 microform titles, 430 serials, 3,736 audiovisual materials, an OPAC, and a Web page. Operations spending for 2004 fiscal year: $387,987. 75 computers available on campus for general student use. A campuswide network can be accessed from student residence rooms and from off campus. Staffed computer lab on campus.
Community Environment: The village of Cazenovia is a rural community near Syracuse with a population of 3,000. The climate is temperate with 4 definite seasons. Cazenovia has a local library, churches of many denominations, motels, inns, and restaurants, and various civic, fraternal, and

veteran's organizations. Recreational activities include water sports, summer and winter mountain sports including hiking and skiing, as well as local and regional sports teams and cultural events.

■ **CENTRAL YESHIVA TOMCHEI TMIMIM-LUBAVITCH** *O-34*
841-853 Ocean Parkway
Brooklyn, NY 11230
Tel: (718)434-0784
Admissions: (718)859-7600
Description: Independent Jewish, comprehensive, men only. Awards bachelor's and master's degrees. Founded 1941. Total enrollment: 1,000. Calendar: semesters.

■ **CITY COLLEGE OF THE CITY UNIVERSITY OF NEW YORK** *N-34*
138th St. and Convent Ave.
New York, NY 10031-9198
Tel: (212)650-7000
Admissions: (212)650-6977
Fax: (212)650-6417
E-mail: admissions@ccny.cuny.edu
Web Site: http://www.ccny.cuny.edu/
Description: State and locally supported, university, coed. Part of City University of New York. System. Awards bachelor's, master's, and first professional degrees and post-master's certificates. Founded 1847. Setting: 35-acre urban campus. Total enrollment: 12,440. Faculty: 1,122 (534 full-time, 588 part-time). Student-undergrad faculty ratio is 11:1. 12,327 applied, 37% were admitted. 28% from top 10% of their high school class, 86% from top half. Full-time: 6,740 students, 48% women, 52% men. Part-time: 2,754 students, 51% women, 49% men. Students come from 130 other countries, 4% from out-of-state, 0.1% Native American, 34% Hispanic, 25% black, 18% Asian American or Pacific Islander, 13% international, 40% 25 or older, 13% transferred in. Retention: 79% of full-time freshmen returned the following year. Academic areas with the most degrees conferred: social sciences; engineering; architecture. Core. Calendar: semesters. Academic remediation for entering students, ESL program, services for LD students, advanced placement, accelerated degree program, self-designed majors, freshman honors college, honors program, independent study, summer session for credit, part-time degree program, adult/continuing education programs, co-op programs and internships, graduate courses open to undergrads. Off campus study at other units of the City University of New York System. Study abroad program. ROTC: Army (c), Air Force (c).
Entrance Requirements: Options: early admission, deferred admission, international baccalaureate accepted. Required: high school transcript, SAT or ACT. Entrance: moderately difficult. Application deadline: 3/1. Notification: continuous until 8/1.
Costs Per Year: Application fee: $65. State resident tuition: $4080 full-time, $170 per credit part-time. Nonresident tuition: $8640 full-time, $360 per credit part-time. Full-time tuition varies according to class time and program. Part-time tuition varies according to class time, course load, and program.
Collegiate Environment: Orientation program. Drama-theater group, student-run newspaper, radio station. Social organizations: 140 open to all; national fraternities, local fraternities. Most popular organizations: LAESA-SHPE, NSBE, BSA, Salsa-Mambo, IVCF. Major annual events: Fashion Show-FIC, Harlemween-USG, End of Semester Party-USG. Student services: health clinic, personal-psychological counseling. Campus security: 24-hour patrols. College housing not available. Morris Raphael Cohen Library plus 3 others with 1.4 million books, 887,471 microform titles, 22,027 serials, 38,300 audiovisual materials, an OPAC, and a Web page. 3,000 computers available on campus for general student use. A campuswide network can be accessed from off-campus. Staffed computer lab on campus.

■ **CLARKSON UNIVERSITY** *C-20*
Potsdam, NY 13699
Tel: (315)268-6400
Free: 800-527-6577
Admissions: (315)268-6463
Fax: (315)268-7647
E-mail: admission@clarkson.edu
Web Site: http://www.clarkson.edu/
Description: Independent, university, coed. Awards bachelor's, master's, and doctoral degrees. Founded 1896. Setting: 640-acre small town campus. Endowment: $128.5 million. Research spending for 2004 fiscal year: $16.3 million. Educational spending for 2005 fiscal year: $10,843 per student. Total enrollment: 3,045. Faculty: 192 (170 full-time, 22 part-time). Student-

undergrad faculty ratio is 17:1. 2,405 applied, 86% were admitted. 35% from top 10% of their high school class, 69% from top quarter, 94% from top half. 13 valedictorians. Full-time: 2,633 students, 24% women, 76% men. Part-time: 15 students, 53% women, 47% men. Students come from 35 states and territories, 23 other countries, 27% from out-of-state, 0.4% Native American, 2% Hispanic, 2% black, 2% Asian American or Pacific Islander, 3% international, 2% 25 or older, 83% live on campus, 4% transferred in. Retention: 86% of full-time freshmen returned the following year. Academic areas with the most degrees conferred: engineering; business/marketing; interdisciplinary studies. Core. Calendar: semesters. ESL program, services for LD students, advanced placement, accelerated degree program, self-designed majors, honors program, independent study, double major, summer session for credit, part-time degree program, co-op programs and internships, graduate courses open to undergrads. Off campus study at Associated Colleges of the St. Lawrence Valley. Study abroad program. ROTC: Army, Air Force.

Entrance Requirements: Options: Peterson's Universal Application, Common Application, early admission, early decision, deferred admission. Required: high school transcript, 2 recommendations, SAT or ACT. Recommended: interview, SAT Subject Tests. Entrance: very difficult. Application deadlines: 3/15, 12/1 for early decision plan 1, 1/15 for early decision plan 2. Notification: continuous, 12/15 for early decision plan 1, 2/1 for early decision plan 2.

Costs Per Year: Application fee: $50. Comprehensive fee: $34,930 includes full-time tuition ($25,185), mandatory fees ($400), and college room and board ($9345). College room only: $4896. Full-time tuition and fees vary according to course load. Room and board charges vary according to housing facility. Part-time tuition: $840 per credit. Part-time tuition varies according to course load.

Collegiate Environment: Orientation program. Drama-theater group, choral group, student-run newspaper, radio station. Social organizations: 62 open to all; national fraternities, national sororities, local fraternities; 15% of eligible men and 13% of eligible women are members. Most popular organizations: Ski Club, Outing Club, Pep Band, Crew Club, Racquetball Club. Major annual events: Alumni Reunion, Homecoming, Winter Carnival. Student services: legal services, health clinic, personal-psychological counseling. Campus security: 24-hour emergency response devices and patrols, late night transport-escort service, controlled dormitory access. 2,179 college housing spaces available; 2,114 were occupied in 2003-04. Freshmen guaranteed college housing. On-campus residence required through senior year. Options: coed, men-only, women-only housing available. Andrew S. Schuler Educational Resources Center plus 1 other with 257,958 books, 259,253 microform titles, 1,806 serials, 2,058 audiovisual materials, an OPAC, and a Web page. Operations spending for 2004 fiscal year: $1.4 million. 400 computers available on campus for general student use. Computer purchase/lease plans available. A campuswide network can be accessed from student residence rooms and from off campus.

Community Environment: This is a college community with a population of 9,500. Bus and air lines serve the area. Local community services include a library, a museum, a hospital, churches of major denominations, and several civic, fraternal, and veterans' organizations. There are part-time jobs available at the campus and with businesses in the area. Recreational activities include bowling, canoeing, fishing, hiking, golfing, mountain biking, swimming, skiing, and theater.

■ **CLINTON COMMUNITY COLLEGE** *C-25*
136 Clinton Point Dr.
Plattsburgh, NY 12901-9573
Tel: (518)562-4200
Free: 800-552-1160
Admissions: (518)562-4170
Fax: (518)562-8621
Web Site: http://clintoncc.suny.edu/

Description: State and locally supported, 2-year, coed. Part of State University of New York System. Awards certificates, transfer associate, and terminal associate degrees. Founded 1969. Setting: 100-acre small town campus. Endowment: $1 million. Educational spending for 2005 fiscal year: $3082 per student. Total enrollment: 2,192. 1,714 applied, 82% were admitted. Full-time: 1,259 students, 56% women, 44% men. Part-time: 933 students, 59% women, 41% men. Students come from 5 states and territories, 9 other countries, 1% from out-of-state, 1% Native American, 2% Hispanic, 3% black, 1% Asian American or Pacific Islander, 2% international, 31% 25 or older, 6% live on campus, 6% transferred in. Core. Calendar: semesters. Academic remediation for entering students, ESL program,

services for LD students, advanced placement, self-designed majors, independent study, distance learning, summer session for credit, part-time degree program, external degree program, adult/continuing education programs, co-op programs and internships. Off campus study at Plattsburgh State University of New York.

Entrance Requirements: Open admission except for nursing, medical laboratory technology, electronics technology. Options: Common Application, electronic application, deferred admission. Required: high school transcript. Required for some: essay, minimum 2.5 high school GPA, 3 recommendations, interview. Placement: SAT or ACT recommended. Entrance: noncompetitive. Application deadline: 8/26. Notification: continuous. Preference given to county residents.

Costs Per Year: Application fee: $0. State resident tuition: $3020 full-time, $125 per credit hour part-time. Nonresident tuition: $7550 full-time, $312 per credit hour part-time. Mandatory fees: $166 full-time, $5 per credit hour part-time. College room and board: $6340. College room only: $3800.

Collegiate Environment: Orientation program. Drama-theater group, choral group, student-run newspaper. Social organizations: 12 open to all. Most popular organizations: Criminal Justice Club, Business Club, Tomorrow's New Teachers, Ski Club, Nursing Club. Major annual events: Carnival, Spring Picnic, College Club Day. Student services: health clinic, personal-psychological counseling. Campus security: 24-hour emergency response devices, late night transport-escort service, controlled dormitory access, security during class hours. 160 college housing spaces available; 116 were occupied in 2003-04. Freshmen guaranteed college housing. Option: coed housing available. Clinton Community College Learning Resource Center plus 1 other with 33,862 books, 38,600 microform titles, 288 serials, 257 audiovisual materials, an OPAC, and a Web page. Operations spending for 2004 fiscal year: $375,633. 250 computers available on campus for general student use. A campuswide network can be accessed from off-campus. Staffed computer lab on campus.

■ **COCHRAN SCHOOL OF NURSING** *L-35*
967 North Broadway
Yonkers, NY 10701
Tel: (914)964-4283
Admissions: (914)964-4296
Web Site: http://www.riversidehealth.org/

Description: Independent, 2-year, coed. Awards terminal associate degrees. Founded 1894. Setting: urban campus with easy access to New York City. Educational spending for 2005 fiscal year: $7000 per student. Total enrollment: 157. 16 applied, 13% were admitted. Full-time: 101 students, 84% women, 16% men. Part-time: 56 students, 91% women, 9% men. Students come from 2 states and territories, 0% from out-of-state, 0% Native American, 14% Hispanic, 25% black, 12% Asian American or Pacific Islander, 76% 25 or older, 50% transferred in. Retention: 75% of full-time freshmen returned the following year. Core. Calendar: semesters. Advanced placement, part-time degree program.

Entrance Requirements: Option: deferred admission. Required: essay, high school transcript, interview, nursing exam. Required for some: SAT. Entrance: moderately difficult. Application deadline: Rolling. Notification: continuous.

Collegiate Environment: Major annual events: Spring Fling Dance, Boat Trip, Holiday Luncheon. Student services: health clinic, personal-psychological counseling. Campus security: 24-hour emergency response devices and patrols, late night transport-escort service. College housing not available. Cochran School of Nursing Library with 4,314 books, 115 serials, 500 audiovisual materials, and an OPAC. Operations spending for 2004 fiscal year: $45,000. 6 computers available on campus for general student use. Staffed computer lab on campus.

■ **COLGATE UNIVERSITY** *K-18*
13 Oak Dr.
Hamilton, NY 13346-1386
Tel: (315)228-1000
Admissions: (315)228-7401
Fax: (315)228-7798
E-mail: admission@mail.colgate.edu
Web Site: http://www.colgate.edu/

Description: Independent, comprehensive, coed. Awards bachelor's and master's degrees. Founded 1819. Setting: 515-acre rural campus. Endowment: $508.7 million. Research spending for 2004 fiscal year: $974,126. Educational spending for 2005 fiscal year: $13,190 per student. Total enrollment: 2,779. Faculty: 315 (245 full-time, 70 part-time). Student-undergrad faculty ratio is 10:1. 8,008 applied, 27% were admitted. 68% from top 10% of their high school class, 90% from top quarter, 100% from top half. 38 valedictorians. Full-time: 2,747 students, 51% women, 49% men. Part-time: 24 students, 42% women, 58% men. Students come from 49 states and territories, 34 other countries, 69% from out-of-state, 1% Native American, 4% Hispanic, 4% black, 6% Asian American or Pacific Islander, 5% international, 0% 25 or older, 90% live on campus, 1% transferred in. Retention: 92% of full-time freshmen returned the following year. Academic areas with the most degrees conferred: social sciences; English; foreign languages and literature. Core. Calendar: semesters. Services for LD students, advanced placement, self-designed majors, honors program, independent study, double major, internships, graduate courses open to undergrads. Off campus study at New York State Visiting Student Program. Study abroad program. ROTC: Army (c).

Entrance Requirements: Options: Peterson's Universal Application, Common Application, electronic application, early decision, deferred admission, international baccalaureate accepted. Required: essay, high school transcript, 3 recommendations, SAT or ACT. Entrance: most difficult. Application deadlines: 1/15, 11/15 for early decision plan 1, 1/15 for early decision plan 2. Notification: 4/1, 12/15 for early decision plan 1, 2/15 for early decision plan 2.

Costs Per Year: Application fee: $55. Comprehensive fee: $41,170 includes full-time tuition ($32,885), mandatory fees ($220), and college room and board ($8065). College room only: $3895. Full-time tuition and fees vary according to course load. Room and board charges vary according to board plan and housing facility. Part-time tuition: $4111 per course. Part-time tuition varies according to course load.

Collegiate Environment: Orientation program. Drama-theater group, choral group, student-run newspaper, radio station. Social organizations: 125 open to all; national fraternities, national sororities, local fraternities; 42% of eligible men and 39% of eligible women are members. Most popular organizations: Volunteer Colgate, student government, cultural/ethnic interest groups, student publications, Outdoor Education. Major annual events: Winterfest, Spring Party Weekend, World Expo. Student services: legal services, health clinic, personal-psychological counseling, women's center. Campus security: 24-hour emergency response devices and patrols, student patrols, late night transport-escort service, controlled dormitory access. 2,220 college housing spaces available; 2,107 were occupied in 2003-04. Freshmen guaranteed college housing. On-campus residence required through senior year. Options: coed, men-only, women-only housing available. Everett Needham Case Library plus 1 other with 1.2 million books, 684,817 microform titles, 2,227 serials, 9,161 audiovisual materials, an OPAC, and a Web page. Operations spending for 2004 fiscal year: $4.6 million. 192 computers available on campus for general student use. Computer purchase/lease plans available. A campuswide network can be accessed from student residence rooms and from off campus. Staffed computer lab on campus.

Community Environment: Hamilton (population 2,500) lies 25 miles south of Utica and 38 miles southeast of Syracuse, New York. Bus and airline connections are to be found in the neighboring cities. The climate is moderate. Part-time employment is available for students. The village has a library, a small museum with library, a movie theater, coffee house, restaurants, hospital, and numerous civic, fraternal and veterans' organizations. Local recreational facilities include hunting, fishing, boating, skiing, and golf.

■ **COLLEGE OF MOUNT SAINT VINCENT**
6301 Riverdale Ave.
Riverdale, NY 10471-1093
Tel: (718)405-3200
Free: 800-665-CMSV
Admissions: (718)405-3268
Fax: (718)549-7945
E-mail: tim.nash@mountsaintvincent.edu
Web Site: http://www.mountsaintvincent.edu/
Description: Independent, comprehensive, coed. Administratively affiliated with Manhattan College. Awards associate, bachelor's, and master's degrees and post-master's certificates. Founded 1911. Setting: 70-acre suburban campus with easy access to New York City. Endowment: $5.5 million. Research spending for 2004 fiscal year: $117,959. Educational spending for 2005 fiscal year: $6059 per student. Total enrollment: 1,855. Faculty: 161 (77 full-time, 84 part-time). Student-undergrad faculty ratio is 14:1. 1,907 applied, 69% were admitted. 17% from top 10% of their high school class, 47% from top quarter, 77% from top half. Full-time: 1,249 students, 72% women, 28% men. Part-time: 278 students, 83% women, 17% men.

Students come from 23 states and territories, 5 other countries, 14% from out-of-state, 0.2% Native American, 29% Hispanic, 12% black, 11% Asian American or Pacific Islander, 0.1% international, 14% 25 or older, 47% live on campus, 7% transferred in. Retention: 81% of full-time freshmen returned the following year. Academic areas with the most degrees conferred: health professions and related sciences; business/marketing; communications/journalism. Core. Calendar: semesters. Academic remediation for entering students, ESL program, services for LD students, advanced placement, accelerated degree program, self-designed majors, freshman honors college, honors program, independent study, double major, summer session for credit, part-time degree program, adult/continuing education programs, internships, graduate courses open to undergrads. Off campus study at Manhattan College. Study abroad program. ROTC: Army (c), Air Force (c).

Entrance Requirements: Options: Common Application, electronic application, early admission, early decision, deferred admission, international baccalaureate accepted. Required: essay, high school transcript, minimum 2.0 high school GPA, 1 recommendation, SAT or ACT. Recommended: 2 recommendations, interview. Required for some: interview. Entrance: moderately difficult. Application deadlines: Rolling, 11/15 for early action. Notification: continuous, 12/1 for early action.

Costs Per Year: Application fee: $35. Comprehensive fee: $30,050 includes full-time tuition ($21,000), mandatory fees ($550), and college room and board ($8500). Part-time tuition: $685 per credit. Part-time mandatory fees: $75 per term.

Collegiate Environment: Orientation program. Drama-theater group, choral group, student-run newspaper, radio station. Social organizations: 36 open to all. Most popular organizations: Latino Club, Players, Dance Club, Student Nurse Association, Black Student Union. Major annual events: La Gala Latina, Block Party, Battle of the Dorms. Student services: health clinic, personal-psychological counseling. Campus security: 24-hour emergency response devices and patrols, late night transport-escort service, controlled dormitory access, emergency call boxes. College housing designed to accommodate 580 students; 581 undergraduates lived in college housing during 2003-04. Freshmen guaranteed college housing. Options: coed, women-only housing available. Elizabeth Seton Library with 160,696 books, 10,054 microform titles, 362 serials, 5,775 audiovisual materials, an OPAC, and a Web page. Operations spending for 2004 fiscal year: $449,265. 184 computers available on campus for general student use. A campuswide network can be accessed from student residence rooms and from off campus. Staffed computer lab on campus.

Community Environment: See Fordham University.

■ **THE COLLEGE OF NEW ROCHELLE** L-36
29 Castle Place
New Rochelle, NY 10805-2308
Tel: (914)654-5000
Free: 800-933-5923
Admissions: (914)654-5452
Fax: (914)654-5554
Web Site: http://cnr.edu/
Description: Independent, comprehensive, coed. Awards bachelor's and master's degrees and post-master's certificates (also offers a non-traditional adult program with significant enrollment not reflected in profile). Founded 1904. Setting: 20-acre suburban campus with easy access to New York City. Endowment: $19.9 million. Total enrollment: 2,306. Faculty: 219 (85 full-time, 134 part-time). Student-undergrad faculty ratio is 8:1. 1,430 applied, 50% were admitted. 15% from top 10% of their high school class, 46% from top quarter, 82% from top half. Full-time: 710 students, 98% women, 2% men. Part-time: 396 students, 87% women, 13% men. Students come from 16 states and territories, 10 other countries, 12% from out-of-state, 0.1% Native American, 13% Hispanic, 36% black, 6% Asian American or Pacific Islander, 1% international, 43% 25 or older, 37% live on campus, 16% transferred in. Retention: 71% of full-time freshmen returned the following year. Core. Calendar: semesters. Academic remediation for entering students, services for LD students, advanced placement, accelerated degree program, self-designed majors, honors program, independent study, double major, summer session for credit, part-time degree program, adult/continuing education programs, co-op programs and internships, graduate courses open to undergrads. Off campus study at Iona College, Concordia College (NY), Marymount College, Dominican College of San Rafael. Study abroad program.

Entrance Requirements: Options: Peterson's Universal Application, Common Application, early admission, early decision, deferred admission. Required: high school transcript, SAT or ACT. Recommended: essay, 1 recommendation, interview. Entrance: moderately difficult. Application deadlines: Rolling, 11/1 for early decision. Notification: continuous, 12/15 for early decision.

Costs Per Year: Application fee: $20. Comprehensive fee: $28,476 includes full-time tuition ($20,246), mandatory fees ($350), and college room and board ($7880). Full-time tuition and fees vary according to course load and program. Room and board charges vary according to housing facility. Part-time tuition: $682 per credit. Part-time mandatory fees: $60 per term. Part-time tuition and fees vary according to course load.

Collegiate Environment: Orientation program. Drama-theater group, choral group, student-run newspaper. Social organizations: 23 open to all. Most popular organizations: Drama Club, Science and Math Society, Latin-American Women's Society. Major annual events: Strawberry Festival, Family Weekend, Health Fair. Student services: health clinic, personal-psychological counseling, women's center. Campus security: 24-hour emergency response devices and patrols, late night transport-escort service, controlled dormitory access, 24-hour monitored security cameras at residence hall entrances. 493 college housing spaces available; 339 were occupied in 2003-04. Freshmen guaranteed college housing. Option: women-only housing available. Gill Library with 220,000 books, 284 microform titles, 1,450 serials, 4,350 audiovisual materials, and an OPAC. Operations spending for 2004 fiscal year: $1.5 million. 120 computers available on campus for general student use. Computer purchase/lease plans available. A campuswide network can be accessed from off-campus. Staffed computer lab on campus.

Community Environment: See Iona College.

■ **THE COLLEGE OF SAINT ROSE** *L-25*
432 Western Ave.
Albany, NY 12203-1419
Tel: (518)454-5111
Free: 800-637-8556
Admissions: (518)454-5150
Fax: (518)451-2013
E-mail: admit@strose.edu
Web Site: http://www.strose.edu/

Description: Independent, comprehensive, coed. Awards bachelor's and master's degrees and post-master's certificates. Founded 1920. Setting: 28-acre urban campus. Endowment: $18.8 million. Educational spending for 2005 fiscal year: $4849 per student. Total enrollment: 5,149. Faculty: 481 (175 full-time, 306 part-time). Student-undergrad faculty ratio is 15:1. 3,134 applied, 71% were admitted. 12% from top 10% of their high school class, 39% from top quarter, 77% from top half. Full-time: 2,795 students, 73% women, 27% men. Part-time: 283 students, 68% women, 32% men. Students come from 20 states and territories, 8% from out-of-state, 0.3% Native American, 3% Hispanic, 2% black, 1% Asian American or Pacific Islander, 0.1% international, 15% 25 or older, 30% live on campus, 10% transferred in. Retention: 85% of full-time freshmen returned the following year. Academic areas with the most degrees conferred: education; business/marketing; communication technologies. Core. Calendar: semesters. Academic remediation for entering students, services for LD students, advanced placement, accelerated degree program, self-designed majors, independent study, double major, summer session for credit, part-time degree program, external degree program, adult/continuing education programs, internships, graduate courses open to undergrads. Off campus study at Hudson-Mohawk Association of Colleges and Universities. Study abroad program.

Entrance Requirements: Options: Peterson's Universal Application, Common Application, electronic application, early admission, deferred admission. Required: essay, high school transcript, 1 recommendation, SAT or ACT. Recommended: minimum 3.0 high school GPA, interview. Required for some: interview. Entrance: moderately difficult. Application deadlines: 2/1, 12/1 for early action. Notification: continuous, 10/1 for early action.

Costs Per Year: Application fee: $35. Comprehensive fee: $25,770 includes full-time tuition ($17,368), mandatory fees ($586), and college room and board ($7816). College room only: $3684. Full-time tuition and fees vary according to course load and program. Room and board charges vary according to board plan. Part-time tuition: $578 per credit hour. Part-time tuition varies according to class time.

Collegiate Environment: Orientation program. Drama-theater group, choral group, student-run newspaper. Social organizations: 35 open to all. Most popular organizations: Student Association, Student Events Board, Circle K, Student Education Association, Student Speech, Hearing and Language Association. Major annual events: Family Weekend, Spring Fling, Fall Fest.

Student services: health clinic, personal-psychological counseling. Campus security: 24-hour emergency response devices and patrols, student patrols, late night transport-escort service, controlled dormitory access. 1,075 college housing spaces available; all were occupied in 2003-04. Freshmen given priority for college housing. Options: coed, women-only housing available. Neil Hellman Library plus 1 other with 205,938 books, 300,216 microform titles, 925 serials, 1,513 audiovisual materials, an OPAC, and a Web page. Operations spending for 2004 fiscal year: $1 million. 322 computers available on campus for general student use. A campuswide network can be accessed from student residence rooms and from off campus. Staffed computer lab on campus.

Community Environment: See State University of New York at Albany.

■ **COLLEGE OF STATEN ISLAND OF THE CITY UNIVERSITY OF NEW YORK** *P-32*
2800 Victory Blvd.
Staten Island, NY 10314-6600
Tel: (718)982-2000
Admissions: (718)982-2011
Fax: (718)982-2500
E-mail: admissions@mail.cuny.csi.edu
Web Site: http://www.csi.cuny.edu/

Description: State and locally supported, comprehensive, coed. Part of City University of New York System. Awards associate, bachelor's, and master's degrees and post-master's certificates. Founded 1955. Setting: 204-acre urban campus with easy access to New York City. Endowment: $4.8 million. Research spending for 2004 fiscal year: $2.7 million. Educational spending for 2005 fiscal year: $4091 per student. Total enrollment: 12,083. Faculty: 842 (330 full-time, 512 part-time). Student-undergrad faculty ratio is 17:1. 7,393 applied, 99% were admitted. Full-time: 7,293 students, 57% women, 43% men. Part-time: 3,627 students, 66% women, 34% men. Students come from 5 states and territories, 111 other countries, 1% from out-of-state, 0.2% Native American, 10% Hispanic, 9% black, 7% Asian American or Pacific Islander, 4% international, 29% 25 or older, 3% transferred in. Retention: 81% of full-time freshmen returned the following year. Academic areas with the most degrees conferred: business/marketing; social sciences; psychology. Core. Calendar: semesters. Academic remediation for entering students, ESL program, services for LD students, advanced placement, accelerated degree program, freshman honors college, honors program, independent study, distance learning, double major, summer session for credit, part-time degree program, adult/continuing education programs, co-op programs and internships, graduate courses open to undergrads. Off campus study at other units of the City University of New York System. Study abroad program.

Entrance Requirements: Open admission for Associate degree programs. Options: electronic application, early admission, deferred admission, international baccalaureate accepted. Required: high school transcript, minimum 2.0 high school GPA. Required for some: essay, recommendations, interview, SAT Subject Tests. Entrance: moderately difficult. Application deadline: Rolling. Notification: 3/15.

Costs Per Year: Application fee: $65. State resident tuition: $4000 full-time, $250 per credit part-time. Nonresident tuition: $8640 full-time, $530 per credit part-time. Mandatory fees: $328 full-time, $90.35 per term part-time. Full-time tuition and fees vary according to course load. Part-time tuition and fees vary according to course load.

Collegiate Environment: Orientation program. Drama-theater group, choral group, student-run newspaper, radio station. Social organizations: 50 open to all. Most popular organizations: Latin Club, Spanish Club, Southasian Cultural Club, Apostolic Christian Life Center. Major annual events: Kwanza, Spring Festival, Fall Carnival. Student services: health clinic, personal-psychological counseling, women's center. Campus security: 24-hour emergency response devices and patrols, late night transport-escort service, emergency call boxes, blue light system, bicycle patrols, radar-controlled traffic monitoring, lighted pathways. College housing not available. College of Staten Island Library with 220,025 books, 877,822 microform titles, 18,796 serials, 8,076 audiovisual materials, an OPAC, and a Web page. Operations spending for 2004 fiscal year: $1.9 million. 1,100 computers available on campus for general student use. A campuswide network can be accessed from off-campus. Staffed computer lab on campus.

■ **THE COLLEGE OF WESTCHESTER** *J-36*
325 Central Ave., PO Box 710
White Plains, NY 10602
Tel: (914)948-4442

Free: 800-333-4924
Fax: (914)948-5441
Web Site: http://www.cw.edu/

Description: Proprietary, 2-year, coed. Awards certificates, transfer associate, and terminal associate degrees. Founded 1915. Setting: suburban campus with easy access to New York City. Total enrollment: 1,039. Student-undergrad faculty ratio is 15:1. 4% from top 10% of their high school class, 19% from top quarter, 55% from top half. 1 National Merit Scholar. Full-time: 829 students, 49% women, 51% men. Part-time: 210 students, 50% women, 50% men. Students come from 3 states and territories, 4 other countries, 8% from out-of-state, 0.4% Native American, 30% Hispanic, 28% black, 2% Asian American or Pacific Islander, 0% international, 48% 25 or older, 7% transferred in. Core. Calendar: for day division, semesters for evening and weekend divisions. Academic remediation for entering students, accelerated degree program, honors program, double major, summer session for credit, part-time degree program, adult/continuing education programs, co-op programs and internships.

Entrance Requirements: Options: Peterson's Universal Application, Common Application, electronic application, deferred admission. Required: high school transcript, interview. Recommended: SAT. Required for some: essay. Entrance: minimally difficult. Application deadline: Rolling.

Costs Per Year: Application fee: $40. Tuition: $18,315 full-time, $385 per credit part-time. Mandatory fees: $795 full-time, $200 per term part-time.

Collegiate Environment: Orientation program. Student-run newspaper. Student services: personal-psychological counseling. College housing not available. 214 computers available on campus for general student use. A campuswide network can be accessed. Staffed computer lab on campus.

■ **COLUMBIA COLLEGE** *N-34*
116th St. and Broadway
New York, NY 10027
Tel: (212)854-1754
Admissions: (212)854-2522
Fax: (212)854-1209
E-mail: ugrad-admiss@columbia.edu
Web Site: http://www.college.columbia.edu/

Description: Independent, 4-year, coed. Part of Columbia University. Awards bachelor's degrees. Founded 1754. Setting: 35-acre urban campus. System endowment: $5.2 billion. Educational spending for 2005 fiscal year: $42,686 per student. Total enrollment: 4,225. Student-undergrad faculty ratio is 6:1. 15,793 applied, 11% were admitted. 86% from top 10% of their high school class, 97% from top quarter, 100% from top half. 303 National Merit Scholars. Full-time: 4,225 students, 52% women, 48% men. Students come from 54 states and territories, 72 other countries, 74% from out-of-state, 0.4% Native American, 9% Hispanic, 9% black, 13% Asian American or Pacific Islander, 6% international, 0% 25 or older, 96% live on campus, 1% transferred in. Retention: 97% of full-time freshmen returned the following year. Academic areas with the most degrees conferred: social sciences; English; history. Core. Calendar: semesters. ESL program, services for LD students, advanced placement, self-designed majors, honors program, independent study, double major, summer session for credit, internships. Off campus study at Howard University, The Juilliard School. Study abroad program. ROTC: Army (c), Naval (c), Air Force (c).

Entrance Requirements: Options: electronic application, early admission, early decision, deferred admission, international baccalaureate accepted. Required: essay, high school transcript, 3 recommendations, SAT and SAT Subject Tests or ACT. Entrance: most difficult. Application deadlines: 1/2, 11/1 for early decision. Notification: 4/4, 12/15 for early decision.

Costs Per Year: Application fee: $65. Comprehensive fee: $42,584 includes full-time tuition ($31,924), mandatory fees ($1322), and college room and board ($9338). College room only: $5448.

Collegiate Environment: Orientation program. Drama-theater group, choral group, marching band, student-run newspaper, radio station. Social organizations: 300 open to all; national fraternities, national sororities, coed fraternities; 19% of eligible men and 25% of eligible women are members. Most popular organizations: community service, cultural organizations, performing arts. Major annual events: Bacchanal (Spring Fest), Activities Day, Columbia Community Outreach. Student services: health clinic, personal-psychological counseling, women's center. Campus security: 24-hour emergency response devices and patrols, student patrols, late night transport-escort service, 24-hour ID check at door. 5,000 college housing spaces available; 970 were occupied in 2003-04. Freshmen guaranteed college housing. On-campus residence required in freshman year. Options: coed, men-only, women-only housing available. Butler Library plus 20 others

with 7.2 million books, 5.1 million microform titles, 66,000 serials, an OPAC, and a Web page. 400 computers available on campus for general student use. Computer purchase/lease plans available. A campuswide network can be accessed from student residence rooms and from off campus. Staffed computer lab on campus.

■ **COLUMBIA-GREENE COMMUNITY COLLEGE** *N-24*
4400 Route 23
Hudson, NY 12534-0327
Tel: (518)828-4181
Fax: (518)828-8543
E-mail: hallenbeck@sunycgcc.edu
Web Site: http://www.sunycgcc.edu/

Description: State and locally supported, 2-year, coed. Part of State University of New York System. Awards certificates, transfer associate, and terminal associate degrees. Founded 1969. Setting: 143-acre rural campus. Endowment: $450,000. Educational spending for 2005 fiscal year: $3371 per student. Total enrollment: 1,715. 631 applied, 79% were admitted. 2% from top 10% of their high school class, 15% from top quarter, 52% from top half. Full-time: 938 students, 59% women, 41% men. Part-time: 777 students, 71% women, 29% men. Students come from 5 states and territories, 5 other countries, 1% from out-of-state, 41% 25 or older, 5% transferred in. Core. Calendar: semesters. Academic remediation for entering students, services for LD students, advanced placement, self-designed majors, honors program, distance learning, summer session for credit, part-time degree program, adult/continuing education programs, internships.

Entrance Requirements: Open admission except for nursing, automotive technology, massage therapy programs. Options: early admission, deferred admission. Required: high school transcript. Required for some: interview. Placement: College Qualifying Test required; SAT or ACT recommended. Entrance: noncompetitive. Application deadline: Rolling. Notification: continuous. Preference given to residents of sponsoring counties.

Collegiate Environment: Orientation program. Drama-theater group, choral group, student-run radio station. Most popular organizations: student council/government, Student Ambassadors, Nursing Club. Major annual event: student play productions. Campus security: 24-hour patrols, late night transport-escort service. College housing not available. 52,484 books, 627 serials, an OPAC, and a Web page. Operations spending for 2004 fiscal year: $407,430. 150 computers available on campus for general student use. A campuswide network can be accessed from off-campus. Staffed computer lab on campus.

■ **COLUMBIA UNIVERSITY, SCHOOL OF GENERAL STUDIES** *N-34*
2970 Broadway
New York, NY 10027-6939
Tel: (212)854-2772
Free: 800-895-1169
E-mail: gs-admit@columbia.edu
Web Site: http://www.gs.columbia.edu/

Description: Independent, 4-year, coed. Part of Columbia University. Awards bachelor's degrees. Founded 1754. Setting: 36-acre urban campus. Endowment: $5.2 billion. Educational spending for 2005 fiscal year: $42,686 per student. Total enrollment: 1,579. Student-undergrad faculty ratio is 7:1. 254 applied, 48% were admitted. Full-time: 647 students, 46% women, 54% men. Part-time: 499 students, 55% women, 45% men. Students come from 36 states and territories, 42% from out-of-state, 1% Native American, 8% Hispanic, 6% black, 11% Asian American or Pacific Islander, 9% international, 75% 25 or older. Academic areas with the most degrees conferred: social sciences; English; liberal arts/general studies. Core. Calendar: semesters. Academic remediation for entering students, ESL program, services for LD students, advanced placement, accelerated degree program, self-designed majors, honors program, double major, summer session for credit, part-time degree program, adult/continuing education programs, internships. Off campus study. Study abroad program.

Entrance Requirements: Options: electronic application, deferred admission. Required: essay, high school transcript, recommendations, General Studies Admissions Exam. Recommended: SAT or ACT, SAT Subject Tests. Required for some: interview. Entrance: most difficult. Application deadlines: 7/1, 3/1 for early action. Notification: continuous, 5/1 for early action.

Costs Per Year: Application fee: $65. Comprehensive fee: $40,716 includes full-time tuition ($30,900), mandatory fees ($1276), and college room and board ($8540). College room only: $5450. Full-time tuition and fees vary according to course load. Room and board charges vary according to housing facility. Part-time tuition: $1030 per credit. Part-time tuition varies according to course load.

Collegiate Environment: Orientation program. Drama-theater group, choral group, student-run newspaper, radio station. Social organizations: national fraternities, national sororities. Most popular organizations: Columbia Dramatists, Writers Club, General Studies Student Council, The Observer. Student services: health clinic, personal-psychological counseling, women's center. Campus security: 24-hour emergency response devices and patrols, late night transport-escort service. 300 college housing spaces available; all were occupied in 2003-04. Option: coed housing available. Butler Library plus 21 others with 5.6 million books, 59,400 serials, and a Web page. 250 computers available on campus for general student use. A campuswide network can be accessed from student residence rooms.

■ **COLUMBIA UNIVERSITY, THE FU FOUNDATION SCHOOL OF ENGINEERING AND APPLIED SCIENCE** *N-34*
500 West 120th St.
New York, NY 10027
Tel: (212)854-1754
Admissions: (212)854-2522
Fax: (212)854-1209
E-mail: ugrad-admiss@columbia.edu
Web Site: http://www.engineering.columbia.edu/

Description: Independent, university, coed. Part of Columbia University. Awards bachelor's, master's, and doctoral degrees. Founded 1864. Setting: urban campus. Educational spending for 2005 fiscal year: $42,686 per student. Total enrollment: 1,436. Faculty: 137 (all full-time). Student-undergrad faculty ratio is 10:1. 2,332 applied, 45% were admitted. 91% from top 10% of their high school class, 99% from top quarter, 100% from top half. 136 National Merit Scholars. Full-time: 1,436 students, 27% women, 73% men. Students come from 44 states and territories, 59 other countries, 69% from out-of-state, 0.1% Native American, 6% Hispanic, 3% black, 32% Asian American or Pacific Islander, 12% international, 0% 25 or older, 99% live on campus, 1% transferred in. Retention: 98% of full-time freshmen returned the following year. Academic areas with the most degrees conferred: engineering; social sciences; computer and information sciences. Core. Calendar: semesters. ESL program, services for LD students, advanced placement, honors program, independent study, double major, summer session for credit, adult/continuing education programs, internships, graduate courses open to undergrads. Study abroad program. ROTC: Army (c), Naval (c), Air Force (c).

Entrance Requirements: Options: electronic application, early admission, early decision, deferred admission, international baccalaureate accepted. Required: essay, high school transcript, 3 recommendations, SAT and SAT Subject Tests or ACT. Recommended: interview. Entrance: most difficult. Application deadlines: 1/2, 11/1 for early decision. Notification: 4/4, 12/15 for early decision.

Costs Per Year: Application fee: $65. Comprehensive fee: $42,584 includes full-time tuition ($31,924), mandatory fees ($1322), and college room and board ($9338). College room only: $5448. Room and board charges vary according to board plan.

Collegiate Environment: Orientation program. Drama-theater group, choral group, marching band, student-run newspaper, radio station. Social organizations: 300 open to all; national fraternities, national sororities; 19% of eligible men and 25% of eligible women are members. Most popular organizations: community service, cultural organizations, performing arts. Major annual events: Bacchanal (Spring Fest), Activities Day, Columbia Community Outreach. Student services: health clinic, personal-psychological counseling, women's center. Campus security: 24-hour emergency response devices and patrols, late night transport-escort service, 24-hour ID check at door. 5,000 college housing spaces available; 98 were occupied in 2003-04. Freshmen guaranteed college housing. On-campus residence required in freshman year. Options: coed, men-only, women-only housing available. Butler Library plus 20 others with 7.2 million books, 5.1 million microform titles, 66,000 serials, an OPAC, and a Web page. 400 computers available on campus for general student use. Computer purchase/lease plans available. A campuswide network can be accessed from student residence rooms and from off campus. Staffed computer lab on campus.

■ **CONCORDIA COLLEGE** *L-35*
171 White Plains Rd.
Bronxville, NY 10708-1998
Tel: (914)337-9300
Free: 800-YES-COLLEGE
Fax: (914)395-4500
E-mail: djh@concordia-ny.edu

Web Site: http://www.concordia-ny.edu/

Description: Independent Lutheran, 4-year, coed. Part of Concordia University System. Awards associate and bachelor's degrees. Founded 1881. Setting: 33-acre suburban campus with easy access to New York City. Endowment: $6.4 million. Educational spending for 2005 fiscal year: $6410 per student. Total enrollment: 649. Student-undergrad faculty ratio is 16:1. 688 applied, 66% were admitted. 11% from top 10% of their high school class, 25% from top quarter, 57% from top half. 8 class presidents, 3 valedictorians, 30 student government officers. Full-time: 592 students, 56% women, 44% men. Part-time: 57 students, 68% women, 32% men. Students come from 34 states and territories, 29 other countries, 16% from out-of-state, 0.3% Native American, 7% Hispanic, 10% black, 2% Asian American or Pacific Islander, 8% international, 13% 25 or older, 68% live on campus, 7% transferred in. Retention: 78% of full-time freshmen returned the following year. Academic areas with the most degrees conferred: business/marketing; social sciences; liberal arts/general studies. Core. Calendar: semesters. Academic remediation for entering students, ESL program, services for LD students, advanced placement, accelerated degree program, self-designed majors, honors program, independent study, distance learning, double major, part-time degree program, adult/continuing education programs, internships. Off campus study at Concordia University System. Study abroad program.

Entrance Requirements: Options: Peterson's Universal Application, Common Application, electronic application, early admission, early action, deferred admission. Required: essay, high school transcript, 1 recommendation, common application supplement, SAT or ACT. Recommended: minimum 2.7 high school GPA. Required for some: interview. Entrance: moderately difficult. Application deadlines: 3/15, 11/15 for early action. Notification: continuous until 6/15, 12/1 for early action.

Costs Per Year: Application fee: $40. Comprehensive fee: $28,640 includes full-time tuition ($19,800), mandatory fees ($900), and college room and board ($7940). College room only: $4400. Room and board charges vary according to board plan. Part-time tuition: $528 per credit hour. Part-time tuition varies according to course load.

Collegiate Environment: Orientation program. Drama-theater group, choral group, student-run newspaper. Social organizations: 22 open to all; national fraternities, national sororities; 12% of eligible men and 15% of eligible women are members. Most popular organizations: Campus Christian Ministries, Drama Club, Student Government Association, International and Afro/Latin American Club, yearbook and newspaper. Major annual events: Homecoming events, Spring Formal, Band Bash. Student services: health clinic, personal-psychological counseling. Campus security: 24-hour emergency response devices and patrols, late night transport-escort service, controlled dormitory access. 450 college housing spaces available; 315 were occupied in 2003-04. Freshmen guaranteed college housing. Options: men-only, women-only housing available. Scheele Memorial Library with 71,500 books, 20,850 microform titles, 467 serials, 7,660 audiovisual materials, an OPAC, and a Web page. Operations spending for 2004 fiscal year: $276,825. 50 computers available on campus for general student use. A campuswide network can be accessed from student residence rooms and from off campus. Staffed computer lab on campus.

■ **COOPER UNION FOR THE ADVANCEMENT OF SCIENCE AND ART** *N-34*
30 Cooper Square
New York, NY 10003-7120
Tel: (212)353-4100
Admissions: (212)353-4120
Fax: (212)353-4343
E-mail: admissions@cooper.edu
Web Site: http://www.cooper.edu/

Description: Independent, 4-year, coed. Awards bachelor's degrees (also offers master's program primarily made up of currently-enrolled students). Founded 1859. Setting: urban campus. Endowment: $261.3 million. Research spending for 2004 fiscal year: $401,540. Educational spending for 2005 fiscal year: $15,082 per student. Total enrollment: 1,003. Student-undergrad faculty ratio is 7:1. 2,301 applied, 13% were admitted. 85% from top 10% of their high school class, 98% from top quarter, 99% from top half. Full-time: 943 students, 36% women, 64% men. Part-time: 6 students, 50% women, 50% men. Students come from 41 states and territories, 40% from out-of-state, 0.4% Native American, 9% Hispanic, 5% black, 20% Asian American or Pacific Islander, 12% international, 7% 25 or older, 19% live on campus, 4% transferred in. Retention: 97% of full-time freshmen returned the following year. Academic areas with the most degrees conferred: education; visual and performing arts; architecture. Core. Calendar: semesters. Advanced placement, self-designed majors, honors program, independent study, summer session for credit, internships. Off campus study at East Coast members of the National Association of Schools of Art and Design, New York University, Eugene Lang College, New School University. Study abroad program.

Entrance Requirements: Options: electronic application, early admission, early decision, deferred admission. Required: high school transcript, minimum 2.0 high school GPA, 2 recommendations, SAT or ACT. Recommended: minimum 3.0 high school GPA. Required for some: essay, minimum 3 high school GPA, 3 recommendations, portfolio, home examination, SAT Subject Tests. Entrance: most difficult. Application deadlines: 1/1, 12/1 for early decision plan 1, 12/1 for early decision plan 2. Notification: 4/1, 12/24 for early decision plan 1, 2/1 for early decision plan 2.

Costs Per Year: Application fee: $50. One-time mandatory fee: $150. Comprehensive fee: $14,860 includes full-time tuition ($0), mandatory fees ($1500), and college room and board ($13,360). College room only: $9360.

Collegiate Environment: Orientation program. Drama-theater group, choral group, student-run newspaper. Social organizations: 65 open to all; national fraternities, national sororities; 20% of eligible men and 10% of eligible women are members. Most popular organizations: Campus Crusade for Christ, Chinese Students Association, Kesher, Athletic Association, Muslim Students Organization. Major annual events: Fall Club Day, Pro Musica Jam. Student services: personal-psychological counseling, health referrals provided and career services offered. Campus security: 24-hour emergency response devices and patrols, controlled dormitory access, security guards. 182 college housing spaces available; all were occupied in 2003-04. Freshmen given priority for college housing. Option: coed housing available. Cooper Union Library with 97,000 books, 100,000 microform titles, 370 serials, 200,000 audiovisual materials, an OPAC, and a Web page. Operations spending for 2004 fiscal year: $821,628. 400 computers available on campus for general student use. A campuswide network can be accessed from student residence rooms and from off campus. Staffed computer lab on campus.

■ **CORNELL UNIVERSITY** *M-15*
Ithaca, NY 14853-0001
Tel: (607)255-2000
Admissions: (607)255-3316
Fax: (607)255-0659
E-mail: admissions_mailbox@cornell.edu
Description: Independent, university, coed. Awards bachelor's, master's, doctoral, and first professional degrees. Founded 1865. Setting: 745-acre small town campus with easy access to Syracuse. Endowment: $3.9 billion. Research spending for 2004 fiscal year: $327.5 million. Educational spending for 2005 fiscal year: $20,720 per student. Total enrollment: 19,447. Faculty: 1,844 (1,675 full-time, 169 part-time). Student-undergrad faculty ratio is 9:1. 24,452 applied, 27% were admitted. 80% from top 10% of their high school class, 96% from top quarter, 99% from top half. 235 National Merit Scholars. Full-time: 13,515 students, 50% women, 50% men. Students come from 55 states and territories, 109 other countries, 61% from out-of-state, 0.5% Native American, 5% Hispanic, 5% black, 16% Asian American or Pacific Islander, 8% international, 1% 25 or older, 44% live on campus, 4% transferred in. Retention: 96% of full-time freshmen returned the following year. Academic areas with the most degrees conferred: engineering; agriculture; biological/life sciences; social sciences; business/marketing. Calendar: semesters. Academic remediation for entering students, ESL program, services for LD students, advanced placement, accelerated degree program, self-designed majors, honors program, independent study, distance learning, double major, summer session for credit, co-op programs and internships, graduate courses open to undergrads. Off campus study at Ithaca College, Wells College. Study abroad program. ROTC: Army, Air Force.

Entrance Requirements: Options: electronic application, early admission, early decision, deferred admission, international baccalaureate accepted. Required: essay, high school transcript, 2 recommendations, SAT and SAT Subject Tests or ACT, SAT Subject Tests. Required for some: interview. Entrance: most difficult. Application deadlines: 1/1, 11/1 for early decision. Notification: 4/3, 12/15 for early decision. Preference given to state residents for state-supported programs.

Costs Per Year: Application fee: $65. Comprehensive fee: $41,717 includes full-time tuition ($31,300), mandatory fees ($167), and college room and board ($10,250). College room only: $6080. Room and board charges vary according to board plan and housing facility.

Collegiate Environment: Orientation program. Drama-theater group, choral group, marching band, student-run newspaper, radio station. Social organizations: 754 open to all; national fraternities, national sororities, local fraternities; 28% of eligible men and 22% of eligible women are members. Most popular organizations: Student Assembly, Residence Hall Association, Catholic Community, Hillel, Concert Commission. Major annual events: Undergraduate Research Forum, Dragon Day, Cornell Ice Hockey games. Student services: health clinic, personal-psychological counseling, women's center. Campus security: 24-hour emergency response devices and patrols; late night transport-escort service, controlled dormitory access, escort service. 5,947 college housing spaces available; 5,727 were occupied in 2003-04. Freshmen guaranteed college housing. Options: coed, men-only, women-only housing available. Olin Library plus 17 others with 7.2 million books, 7.8 million microform titles, 64,760 serials, 427,798 audiovisual materials, an OPAC, and a Web page. Operations spending for 2004 fiscal year: $28.5 million. 3,000 computers available on campus for general student use. Computer purchase/lease plans available. A campuswide network can be accessed from student residence rooms and from off campus. Staffed computer lab on campus.

Community Environment: Population 30,000. Located at the southern tip of Cayuga Lake, the city encompasses scenic, deep gorges through which flow Six Mile, Fall and Cascadilla Creeks. Ithaca is in the heart of central New York's Finger Lakes region. Good transportation is provided by bus and airlines, as well as state highways. Ithaca has various fraternal, civic and veteran's organizations, and over 30 churches representative of most major denominations. Part-time employment is available for students. Recreational facilities within the vicinity include YMCA, theatres, 3 state parks, indoor ice rink, fishing, boating, swimming, hunting, horseback riding, bowling, a pistol range, archery, museums, golf courses, and 14 public parks.

■ **CORNING COMMUNITY COLLEGE** *N-13*
One Academic Dr.
Corning, NY 14830-3297
Tel: (607)962-9011
Admissions: (607)962-9427
Fax: (607)962-9456
E-mail: admissions@corning-cc.edu
Web Site: http://www.corning-cc.edu/
Description: State and locally supported, 2-year, coed. Part of State University of New York System. Awards certificates, transfer associate, and terminal associate degrees. Founded 1956. Setting: 275-acre rural campus. Endowment: $2.3 million. Educational spending for 2005 fiscal year: $7556 per student. Total enrollment: 5,310. Student-undergrad faculty ratio is 18:1. 1,252 applied, 98% were admitted. 3% from top 10% of their high school class, 16% from top quarter, 46% from top half. Full-time: 2,638 students, 54% women, 46% men. Part-time: 2,672 students, 60% women, 40% men. Students come from 13 states and territories, 5% from out-of-state, 1% Native American, 1% Hispanic, 2% black, 1% Asian American or Pacific Islander, 0.1% international, 41% 25 or older, 3% transferred in. Core. Calendar: semesters. Academic remediation for entering students, services for LD students, advanced placement, accelerated degree program, self-designed majors, honors program, independent study, distance learning, double major, summer session for credit, part-time degree program, internships. ROTC: Army (c), Naval (c), Air Force (c).

Entrance Requirements: Open admission. Options: electronic application, early admission. Required: high school transcript. Required for some: interview. Entrance: noncompetitive. Application deadline: Rolling. Notification: continuous. Preference given to residents of sponsoring counties.

Costs Per Year: Application fee: $25. State resident tuition: $3100 full-time, $128 per credit part-time. Nonresident tuition: $6200 full-time, $258 per credit part-time.

Collegiate Environment: Orientation program. Drama-theater group, choral group, student-run newspaper, radio station. Social organizations: 23 open to all. Most popular organizations: student association, WCEB, Two-Bit Players, Activities Programming Committee, Nursing Society. Major annual events: Springfest/Fallfest, Job Fair, Campus Life Fair. Student services: health clinic, personal-psychological counseling. Campus security: 24-hour emergency response devices and patrols, late night transport-escort service. College housing not available. Arthur A. Houghton, Jr. Library with 71,233 books, 26,123 microform titles, 2,500 serials, 4,290 audiovisual materials, an OPAC, and a Web page. Operations spending for 2004 fiscal year: $700,222. 350 computers available on campus for general student use. A campuswide network can be accessed from off-campus. Staffed computer lab on campus.

■ **CROUSE HOSPITAL SCHOOL OF NURSING** *J-16*

736 Irving Ave.
Syracuse, NY 13210
Tel: (315)470-7481
Web Site: http://www.crouse.org/nursing/

Description: Independent, 2-year, coed. Awards transfer associate and terminal associate degrees. Founded 1913. Setting: urban campus. Total enrollment: 252. Full-time: 140 students, 92% women, 8% men. Part-time: 112 students, 82% women, 18% men. Students come from 4 states and territories, 2% from out-of-state, 0% Native American, 1% Hispanic, 7% black, 2% Asian American or Pacific Islander, 0% international, 64% 25 or older, 14% live on campus. Calendar: semesters. Part-time degree program.

Entrance Requirements: Option: deferred admission. Required: essay, high school transcript, minimum 2.5 high school GPA, 3 recommendations, interview. Recommended: SAT or ACT. Required for some: SAT or ACT. Application deadline: 2/1.

Costs Per Year: Application fee: $30. Tuition: $7352 full-time, $225 per credit hour part-time. Mandatory fees: $360 full-time, $130 per term part-time. College room only: $1750.

Collegiate Environment: Student services: health clinic, personal-psychological counseling. Campus security: 24-hour emergency response devices and patrols, late night transport-escort service, controlled dormitory access.

■ **THE CULINARY INSTITUTE OF AMERICA** *P-24*

1946 Campus Dr.
Hyde Park, NY 12538-1499
Tel: (845)452-9600
Free: 800-CULINARY
Fax: (845)452-8629
Web Site: http://www.ciachef.edu/

Description: Independent, 4-year, coed. Awards bachelor's degrees. Founded 1946. Setting: 150-acre small town campus. Endowment: $43.4 million. Educational spending for 2005 fiscal year: $38,061 per student. Total enrollment: 2,713. Student-undergrad faculty ratio is 18:1. 903 applied, 69% were admitted. 9% from top 10% of their high school class, 25% from top quarter, 50% from top half. Students come from 53 states and territories, 25 other countries, 76% from out-of-state, 1% Native American, 5% Hispanic, 3% black, 5% Asian American or Pacific Islander, 5% international, 21% 25 or older, 70% live on campus. Core. Calendar: semesters plus 18 or 21 week externship program. Academic remediation for entering students, services for LD students, distance learning, adult/continuing education programs, co-op programs and internships. Off campus study at The Associated Colleges of the Mid-Hudson Valley.

Entrance Requirements: Open admission. Options: Common Application, electronic application, deferred admission, international baccalaureate accepted. Required: essay, high school transcript, 2 recommendations. Recommended: SAT or ACT. Required for some: an Affidavit of Support. Entrance: moderately difficult. Application deadline: Rolling. Preference given to candidates with 6 months of prior food service experience.

Costs Per Year: Application fee: $30. Comprehensive fee: $26,980 includes full-time tuition ($19,180), mandatory fees ($980), and college room and board ($6820). Full-time tuition and fees vary according to degree level. Room and board charges vary according to housing facility.

Collegiate Environment: Orientation program. Student-run newspaper. Social organizations: 20 open to all; 10% of eligible men and 12% of eligible women are members. Most popular organizations: Epicures of Wine, Baker's Club, Food Art Club, Oye Me, Gourmet Society. Major annual events: Halloween Party, Chili Cook-off, Summer Cook-Out. Student services: health clinic, personal-psychological counseling. Campus security: 24-hour emergency response devices and patrols, late night transport-escort service, controlled dormitory access. 1,534 college housing spaces available; 1,416 were occupied in 2003-04. Freshmen guaranteed college housing. Option: coed housing available. Conrad N. Hilton Library with 69,000 books, 282 microform titles, 300 serials, 4,195 audiovisual materials, and an OPAC. Operations spending for 2004 fiscal year: $557,310. 154 computers available on campus for general student use. A campuswide network can be accessed from student residence rooms and from off campus. Staffed computer lab on campus.

■ **DAEMEN COLLEGE** *J-7*

4380 Main St.
Amherst, NY 14226-3592
Tel: (716)839-3600
Free: 800-462-7652
Admissions: (716)839-8225
Fax: (716)839-8516
E-mail: dshaffne@daemen.edu
Web Site: http://www.daemen.edu/

Description: Independent, comprehensive, coed. Awards bachelor's, master's, and first professional degrees and post-master's certificates. Founded 1947. Setting: 35-acre suburban campus with easy access to Buffalo. Endowment: $682,941. Educational spending for 2005 fiscal year: $5685 per student. Total enrollment: 2,315. Faculty: 259 (80 full-time, 179 part-time). Student-undergrad faculty ratio is 13:1. 1,609 applied, 79% were admitted. 15% from top 10% of their high school class, 45% from top quarter, 75% from top half. Full-time: 1,271 students, 76% women, 24% men. Part-time: 332 students, 79% women, 21% men. Students come from 19 states and territories, 14 other countries, 4% from out-of-state, 1% Native American, 2% Hispanic, 15% black, 1% Asian American or Pacific Islander, 1% international, 18% 25 or older, 42% live on campus, 10% transferred in. Retention: 67% of full-time freshmen returned the following year. Academic areas with the most degrees conferred: health professions and related sciences; biological/life sciences; education. Core. Calendar: semesters. Academic remediation for entering students, services for LD students, advanced placement, accelerated degree program, self-designed majors, honors program, independent study, double major, summer session for credit, part-time degree program, adult/continuing education programs, co-op programs and internships, graduate courses open to undergrads. Off campus study at Western New York Consortium. Study abroad program. ROTC: Army (c).

Entrance Requirements: Options: Peterson's Universal Application, Common Application, electronic application, early admission, early action, deferred admission, international baccalaureate accepted. Required: high school transcript, minimum 2.0 high school GPA, SAT or ACT. Required for some: essay, 3 recommendations, interview. Entrance: moderately difficult. Application deadlines: Rolling, 8/30 for early action. Notification: continuous, 9/1 for early action.

Costs Per Year: Application fee: $25. Comprehensive fee: $24,580 includes full-time tuition ($16,350), mandatory fees ($450), and college room and board ($7780). Room and board charges vary according to board plan and housing facility. Part-time tuition: $545 per credit. Part-time mandatory fees: $4 per credit, $68 per term. Part-time tuition and fees vary according to course load.

Collegiate Environment: Orientation program. Drama-theater group, choral group, student-run newspaper. Social organizations: 42 open to all; local fraternities, local sororities; 24% of eligible men and 16% of eligible women are members. Most popular organizations: Students Without Borders, Student Physical Therapy Association, Physician Assistant Student Society, Step Team, cheerleaders. Major annual events: Campus Bonfire, Boobar (Halloween party), Springfest. Student services: personal-psychological counseling. Campus security: 24-hour emergency response devices and patrols, late night transport-escort service, 24-hour security cameras. 592 college housing spaces available; 588 were occupied in 2003-04. Freshmen guaranteed college housing. On-campus residence required through sophomore year. Option: coed housing available. Marian Library plus 1 other with 127,232 books, 26,782 microform titles, 889 serials, 10,584 audiovisual materials, an OPAC, and a Web page. Operations spending for 2004 fiscal year: $767,490. 99 computers available on campus for general student use. A campuswide network can be accessed from student residence rooms and from off campus. Staffed computer lab on campus.

Community Environment: The college is located in a quiet suburban environment accessible to the City of Buffalo and the international boundary with Canada. Transportation hubs-plane, train, and bus-are located a short distance from the campus.

■ **DARKEI NOAM RABBINICAL COLLEGE** *O-34*

2822 Ave. J
Brooklyn, NY 11210
Tel: (718)338-6464

Description: Independent Jewish, comprehensive, men only. Awards bachelor's and master's degrees. Founded 1977. Setting: urban campus. Total enrollment: 50. 13 applied, 77% were admitted. Students come from 6 states and territories, 2% 25 or older. Core. Calendar: semesters.

Entrance Requirements: Required: interview. Entrance: minimally difficult.

Collegiate Environment: Kat Lowitz Library with 53,000 books and 2 serials.

■ **DAVIS COLLEGE** *N-17*
400 Riverside Dr.
Johnson City, NY 13790
Tel: (607)729-1581
Free: 800-331-4137
Fax: (607)729-2962
E-mail: admissions@davisny.edu
Web Site: http://www.davisny.edu/

Description: Independent nondenominational, 4-year, coed. Awards associate and bachelor's degrees. Founded 1900. Setting: 22-acre suburban campus with easy access to Syracuse. Educational spending for 2005 fiscal year: $16,000 per student. Total enrollment: 255. Student-undergrad faculty ratio is 17:1. 60 applied, 68% were admitted. 1% from top 10% of their high school class, 27% from top quarter, 61% from top half. Students come from 13 states and territories, 4 other countries, 23% from out-of-state, 0.4% Native American, 0.4% Hispanic, 5% black, 0.4% Asian American or Pacific Islander, 5% international, 22% 25 or older, 61% live on campus. Retention: 84% of full-time freshmen returned the following year. Academic area with the most degrees conferred: theology and religious vocations. Core. Calendar: semesters. Academic remediation for entering students, ESL program, services for LD students, advanced placement, independent study, summer session for credit, part-time degree program, adult/continuing education programs, co-op programs and internships.
Entrance Requirements: Options: Common Application, electronic application, deferred admission. Required: high school transcript, 2 recommendations, references, SAT or ACT. Recommended: minimum 2.0 high school GPA, interview, ACT. Required for some: essay. Entrance: minimally difficult. Application deadline: Rolling. Notification: continuous.
Costs Per Year: Application fee: $25. Comprehensive fee: $15,240 includes full-time tuition ($9440), mandatory fees ($700), and college room and board ($5100). Part-time tuition: $325 per credit. Part-time mandatory fees: $175 per term.
Collegiate Environment: Orientation program. Drama-theater group, choral group. Social organizations: 4 open to all. Most popular organizations: Student Missionary Fellowship, Student Wives Fellowship, Student Life Committee, Married Couples Fellowship. Major annual events: Annual Missions Conference, Fall Bible Conference, Prayer Days. Student services: health clinic, personal-psychological counseling. Campus security: 24-hour emergency response devices and patrols, student patrols, late night transport-escort service. 300 college housing spaces available. On-campus residence required through senior year. Options: men-only, women-only housing available. Alice E. Chatlos Library with 77,000 books, 8,494 microform titles, 644 serials, 8,500 audiovisual materials, an OPAC, and a Web page. Operations spending for 2004 fiscal year: $125,317. 12 computers available on campus for general student use. A campuswide network can be accessed. Staffed computer lab on campus.

■ **DEVRY INSTITUTE OF TECHNOLOGY**
30-20 Thomson Ave.
Long Island City, NY 11101
Tel: (718)472-2728; (866)338-7934
Web Site: http://www.devry.edu/

Description: Proprietary, 4-year, coed. Part of DeVry University. Awards associate, bachelor's, and master's degrees. Founded 1998. Setting: 4-acre urban campus. Total enrollment: 1,376. Faculty: 89 (47 full-time, 42 part-time). Student-undergrad faculty ratio is 18:1. Full-time: 937 students, 31% women, 69% men. Part-time: 333 students, 37% women, 63% men. 1% Native American, 30% Hispanic, 45% black, 10% Asian American or Pacific Islander, 2% international, 45% 25 or older. Academic areas with the most degrees conferred: computer and information sciences; business/marketing; engineering technologies. Calendar: semesters. Academic remediation for entering students, advanced placement, accelerated degree program, distance learning, summer session for credit, part-time degree program, adult/continuing education programs, co-op programs.
Entrance Requirements: Options: electronic application, deferred admission, international baccalaureate accepted. Required: high school transcript, interview. Entrance: minimally difficult. Application deadline: Rolling.
Costs Per Year: Application fee: $50. One-time mandatory fee: $40. Tuition: $13,060 full-time, $475 per credit part-time. Mandatory fees: $270 full-time, $160 per year part-time.

Collegiate Environment: Orientation program. Social organizations: 7 open to all. Most popular organizations: International Students Club, Video Games Club, DeVry Student Association, Chess Club, Muslim Student Association. Major annual events: DSA Time Out, Post-Ramadan Celebration. Campus security: 24-hour emergency response devices and patrols, student patrols, late night transport-escort service, lighted pathways/sidewalks. College housing not available. Learning Resource Center with 14,078 books, 62 serials, 2,057 audiovisual materials, an OPAC, and a Web page. 478 computers available on campus for general student use. Computer purchase/lease plans available. A campuswide network can be accessed from off-campus. Staffed computer lab on campus.

■ **DOMINICAN COLLEGE** *J-34*
470 Western Hwy.
Orangeburg, NY 10962-1210
Tel: (845)359-7800; (866)432-4636
Admissions: (845)359-3533
Fax: (845)359-2313
E-mail: joyce.elbe@dc.edu
Web Site: http://www.dc.edu/

Description: Independent, comprehensive, coed. Awards associate, bachelor's, master's, and doctoral degrees. Founded 1952. Setting: 26-acre suburban campus with easy access to New York City. Endowment: $320,000. Educational spending for 2005 fiscal year: $5280 per student. Total enrollment: 1,530. Faculty: 163 (51 full-time, 112 part-time). Student-undergrad faculty ratio is 14:1. 1,228 applied, 83% were admitted. Full-time: 1,071 students, 64% women, 36% men. Part-time: 338 students, 77% women, 23% men. Students come from 14 states and territories, 19% from out-of-state, 0.3% Native American, 14% Hispanic, 17% black, 6% Asian American or Pacific Islander, 0% international, 37% 25 or older, 20% live on campus, 6% transferred in. Retention: 68% of full-time freshmen returned the following year. Academic areas with the most degrees conferred: business/marketing; health professions and related sciences; social sciences. Core. Calendar: semesters. Academic remediation for entering students, services for LD students, advanced placement, accelerated degree program, honors program, independent study, distance learning, double major, summer session for credit, part-time degree program, adult/continuing education programs, co-op programs and internships.
Entrance Requirements: Options: Peterson's Universal Application, Common Application, electronic application, deferred admission, international baccalaureate accepted. Required: high school transcript, SAT or ACT. Entrance: noncompetitive. Application deadline: Rolling. Notification: continuous.
Costs Per Year: Application fee: $35. Comprehensive fee: $26,630 includes full-time tuition ($17,240), mandatory fees ($670), and college room and board ($8720). Part-time tuition: $515 per credit. Part-time mandatory fees: $160 per term.
Collegiate Environment: Orientation program. Drama-theater group, choral group, student-run newspaper. Most popular organizations: Student Government Association, Business Club, Aquin Players, school newspaper, Nursing Association. Major annual events: Spring Formal, Spring Festival, Family Day. Student services: health clinic, personal-psychological counseling. Campus security: 24-hour emergency response devices and patrols, student patrols, late night transport-escort service, controlled dormitory access. Option: coed housing available. Pius X Hall plus 1 other with 103,350 books, 650 serials, and an OPAC. Operations spending for 2004 fiscal year: $400,302. 38 computers available on campus for general student use. A campuswide network can be accessed from student residence rooms.
Community Environment: Orangeburg, population 50,000, is located in southeast New York, located 3 miles southwest of Nyack on the northern border of New Jersey. The area may be reached by the New York State Thruway, Exit 12, or Palisades Parkway, Exit 6E.

■ **DOROTHEA HOPFER SCHOOL OF NURSING AT THE MOUNT VERNON HOSPITAL** *L-35*
53 Valentine St.
Mount Vernon, NY 10550
Tel: (914)664-8000
Fax: (914)665-7047
Web Site: http://www.ssmc.org/
Description: Independent, 2-year. Total enrollment: 120.

■ **DOWLING COLLEGE** *F-52*
Idle Hour Blvd.
Oakdale, NY 11769-1999

Tel: (631)244-3000
Free: 800-DOW-LING
Admissions: (631)244-3030
Fax: (631)563-3827
E-mail: admissions@dowling.edu
Web Site: http://www.dowling.edu/
Description: Independent, comprehensive, coed. Awards bachelor's, master's, and doctoral degrees and post-master's certificates. Founded 1955. Setting: 157-acre suburban campus with easy access to New York City. Endowment: $11.1 million. Research spending for 2004 fiscal year: $134,095. Educational spending for 2005 fiscal year: $3264 per student. Total enrollment: 6,379. Faculty: 500 (124 full-time, 376 part-time). Student-undergrad faculty ratio is 17:1. 2,399 applied, 87% were admitted. 6% from top 10% of their high school class, 19% from top quarter, 50% from top half. Full-time: 2,298 students, 61% women, 39% men. Part-time: 1,329 students, 60% women, 40% men. Students come from 28 states and territories, 56 other countries, 10% from out-of-state, 0.2% Native American, 9% Hispanic, 9% black, 2% Asian American or Pacific Islander, 4% international, 41% 25 or older, 17% live on campus, 9% transferred in. Retention: 66% of full-time freshmen returned the following year. Academic areas with the most degrees conferred: business/marketing; education; liberal arts/general studies. Core. Calendar: semesters. Academic remediation for entering students, ESL program, services for LD students, advanced placement, accelerated degree program, self-designed majors, honors program, independent study, double major, summer session for credit, part-time degree program, co-op programs and internships, graduate courses open to undergrads. Off campus study at Long Island Regional Advisory Council for Higher Education. ROTC: Air Force (c).
Entrance Requirements: Options: Common Application, electronic application, deferred admission. Required: high school transcript. Entrance: moderately difficult. Application deadline: Rolling. Notification: continuous.
Costs Per Year: Application fee: $25. Tuition: $12,960 full-time, $540 per credit hour part-time. Mandatory fees: $840 full-time, $137.50 per term part-time. Part-time tuition and fees vary according to course load and degree level. College room only: $5748. Room charges vary according to housing facility and location.
Collegiate Environment: Orientation program. Drama-theater group, choral group, student-run newspaper, radio station. Social organizations: 30 open to all. Most popular organizations: Student Government Association, Residence Hall Council, Pan African-American-Caribbean Club, Aeronautics Club, Lion's Voice (student newspaper). Major annual events: Holiday Ball, Spring Cotillion, Adopt-a-Child Holiday Event. Student services: health clinic, personal-psychological counseling. Campus security: 24-hour emergency response devices and patrols, late night transport-escort service. 625 college housing spaces available; all were occupied in 2003-04. No special consideration for freshman housing applicants. Option: coed housing available. Dowling College Library with 118,830 books, 3,131 serials, and an OPAC. Operations spending for 2004 fiscal year: $2 million. 118 computers available on campus for general student use. A campuswide network can be accessed. Staffed computer lab on campus.
Community Environment: Population 3,000. Oakdale is a suburban community west of Sayville with temperate climate. The area is served by the Long Island Railroad, and a main bus route to Patchogue and Freeport. There are 3 hospitals within 20 miles and a college health service. Adjoining cities furnish community services as well as recreational and cultural opportunities. Some part-time employment is available for students.

■ **DUTCHESS COMMUNITY COLLEGE** *P-24*
53 Pendell Rd.
Poughkeepsie, NY 12601-1595
Tel: (845)431-8000
Admissions: (845)431-8010
E-mail: banner@sunydutchess.edu
Web Site: http://www.sunydutchess.edu/
Description: State and locally supported, 2-year, coed. Part of State University of New York System. Awards certificates, transfer associate, and terminal associate degrees. Founded 1957. Setting: 130-acre suburban campus with easy access to New York City. Total enrollment: 7,810. 1,030 applied, 98% were admitted. 48% 25 or older. Calendar: semesters. Academic remediation for entering students, ESL program, advanced placement, freshman honors college, honors program, summer session for credit, part-time degree program, adult/continuing education programs, internships. Off campus study at Marist College, Vassar College, State University of New York College at New Paltz, Culinary Institute of America, Bard College.

Entrance Requirements: Open admission for most programs. Options: early admission, deferred admission. Required: high school transcript. Entrance: noncompetitive. Application deadline: Rolling. Notification: continuous. Preference given to county residents.
Costs Per Year: State resident tuition: $2600 full-time, $105 per credit part-time. Nonresident tuition: $5200 full-time, $210 per credit part-time. Mandatory fees: $387 full-time, $8 per credit part-time, $24.75 per term part-time.
Collegiate Environment: Orientation program. Drama-theater group, choral group, student-run newspaper, radio station. Major annual events: Fall Freshmen Day, Family Festival, Lyceum Series of Speakers. Student services: health clinic, personal-psychological counseling. Campus security: 24-hour emergency response devices and patrols, late night transport-escort service. College housing not available. Dutchess Library with 103,272 books, 540 serials, an OPAC, and a Web page. 50 computers available on campus for general student use. A campuswide network can be accessed from off-campus. Staffed computer lab on campus.

■ **D'YOUVILLE COLLEGE** *K-7*
320 Porter Ave.
Buffalo, NY 14201-1084
Tel: (716)829-8000
Free: 800-777-3921
Admissions: (716)829-7600
Fax: (716)829-7790
Web Site: http://www.dyc.edu/
Description: Independent, comprehensive, coed. Awards bachelor's, master's, doctoral, and first professional degrees and post-master's certificates. Founded 1908. Setting: 7-acre urban campus. Endowment: $16.5 million. Total enrollment: 2,906. Faculty: 216 (110 full-time, 106 part-time). Student-undergrad faculty ratio is 14:1. 1,408 applied, 73% were admitted. 9 class presidents, 4 valedictorians, 45 student government officers. Full-time: 1,220 students, 74% women, 26% men. Part-time: 262 students, 78% women, 22% men. Students come from 18 states and territories, 28 other countries, 11% from out-of-state, 1% Native American, 5% Hispanic, 17% black, 1% Asian American or Pacific Islander, 11% international, 43% 25 or older, 20% live on campus, 40% transferred in. Retention: 81% of full-time freshmen returned the following year. Academic areas with the most degrees conferred: health professions and related sciences; business/marketing; interdisciplinary studies. Core. Calendar: semesters plus summer session. Academic remediation for entering students, services for LD students, accelerated degree program, independent study, distance learning, double major, summer session for credit, part-time degree program, adult/continuing education programs, internships, graduate courses open to undergrads. Off campus study at Western New York Consortium. Study abroad program. ROTC: Army (c).
Entrance Requirements: Options: Common Application, electronic application, deferred admission, international baccalaureate accepted. Required: high school transcript, minimum 2.0 high school GPA, SAT or ACT. Required for some: essay, minimum 3.0 high school GPA, recommendations, interview. Entrance: moderately difficult. Application deadline: Rolling. Notification: continuous.
Costs Per Year: Application fee: $25. Comprehensive fee: $23,600 includes full-time tuition ($15,600), mandatory fees ($200), and college room and board ($7800). College room only: $6400. Full-time tuition and fees vary according to course level, degree level, and program. Room and board charges vary according to board plan and housing facility. Part-time tuition: $455 per credit. Part-time mandatory fees: $100 per term. Part-time tuition and fees vary according to course load. Tuition guaranteed not to increase for student's term of enrollment.
Collegiate Environment: Orientation program. Drama-theater group, choral group, student-run newspaper. Social organizations: 35 open to all. Most popular organizations: Student Association, Occupational Therapy Student Association, Physical Therapy Student Association, Student Nurses Association, Black Student Union. Major annual events: Family and Friends, Honors Convocation, Moving Up Days. Student services: health clinic, personal-psychological counseling. Campus security: 24-hour emergency response devices and patrols, late night transport-escort service, controlled dormitory access. 473 college housing spaces available; 232 were occupied in 2003-04. Freshmen guaranteed college housing. On-campus residence required in freshman year. Options: coed, men-only, women-only housing available. D'Youville College Library with 122,057 books, 195,079 microform titles, 665 serials, 3,160 audiovisual materials, an OPAC, and a Web page. Operations spending for 2004 fiscal year: $951,681. 72 computers available on campus for general student use. Computer purchase/lease plans available. A

campuswide network can be accessed from student residence rooms and from off campus. Staffed computer lab on campus.

■ ELLIS HOSPITAL SCHOOL OF NURSING K-24

1101 Nott St.
Schenectady, NY 12308
Tel: (518)243-4471
Web Site: http://www.ehson.org/
Description: Independent, 2-year, coed. Awards transfer associate and terminal associate degrees. Total enrollment: 69. 101 applied; 50% were admitted. 0% Native American, 1% Hispanic, 3% black, 1% Asian American or Pacific Islander, 0% international, 80% 25 or older.
Entrance Requirements: Required: essay, high school transcript, 3 recommendations. Recommended: SAT. Application deadline: Rolling.

■ ELMIRA BUSINESS INSTITUTE O-14

303 North Main St.
Elmira, NY 14901
Tel: (607)733-7177
Free: 800-843-1812
Fax: (607)733-7178
Web Site: http://www.ebi-college.com/
Description: Private, 2-year, coed. Awards certificates, transfer associate, and terminal associate degrees. Founded 1858. Total enrollment: 361. 108 applied. 0% from top 10% of their high school class, 10% from top quarter, 30% from top half. Full-time: 283 students, 90% women, 10% men. Part-time: 78 students, 86% women, 14% men. Students come from 2 states and territories, 13% from out-of-state, 1% Hispanic, 7% black, 0.3% Asian American or Pacific Islander, 70% 25 or older, 1% transferred in. Calendar: semesters. Academic remediation for entering students, advanced placement, part-time degree program, internships.
Entrance Requirements: Open admission. Options: Common Application, electronic application. Required: high school transcript, interview. Application deadline: Rolling.
Collegiate Environment: Orientation program. College housing not available. Elmira Business Institute Library with 800 books, 14 serials, and 15 audiovisual materials. 50 computers available on campus for general student use.

■ ELMIRA COLLEGE O-14

One Park Place
Elmira, NY 14901
Tel: (607)735-1800
Free: 800-935-6472
Admissions: (607)735-1724
Fax: (607)735-1718
E-mail: gfallis@elmira.edu
Web Site: http://www.elmira.edu/
Description: Independent, 4-year, coed. Awards bachelor's and master's degrees. Founded 1855. Setting: 42-acre small town campus. Endowment: $40.3 million. Educational spending for 2005 fiscal year: $11,620 per student. Total enrollment: 1,853. Faculty: 99 (82 full-time, 17 part-time). Student-undergrad faculty ratio is 12:1. 1,966 applied, 64% were admitted. 28% from top 10% of their high school class, 72% from top quarter, 100% from top half. 33 class presidents, 26 valedictorians, 206 student government officers. Full-time: 1,175 students, 70% women, 30% men. Part-time: 309 students, 76% women, 24% men. Students come from 35 states and territories, 23 other countries, 51% from out-of-state, 0.1% Native American, 1% Hispanic, 2% black, 1% Asian American or Pacific Islander, 4% international, 19% 25 or older, 95% live on campus, 5% transferred in. Retention: 84% of full-time freshmen returned the following year. Academic areas with the most degrees conferred: education; business/marketing; health professions and related sciences; psychology. Core. Calendar: 4-4-1. ESL program, advanced placement, accelerated degree program, self-designed majors, independent study, double major, summer session for credit, part-time degree program, adult/continuing education programs, internships. Off campus study at members of the May Term Consortium. Study abroad program. ROTC: Army, Air Force (c).
Entrance Requirements: Options: Peterson's Universal Application, Common Application, electronic application, early admission, early decision, deferred admission, international baccalaureate accepted. Required: essay, high school transcript, minimum 2.0 high school GPA, 2 recommendations, SAT or ACT. Recommended: interview. Required for some: interview. Entrance: moderately difficult. Application deadlines: 4/15, 11/15 for early

decision plan 1, 1/15 for early decision plan 2. Notification: continuous until 4/30, 12/15 for early decision plan 1, 2/1 for early decision plan 2.
Costs Per Year: Application fee: $50. Comprehensive fee: $39,150 includes full-time tuition ($29,000), mandatory fees ($1050), and college room and board ($9100). Part-time tuition: $270 per credit.
Collegiate Environment: Orientation program. Drama-theater group, choral group, student-run newspaper, radio station. Social organizations: 80 open to all. Most popular organizations: student radio station, Student Activities Board, Psychology Club, Ski Club, Pal Program. Major annual events: Octagon Fair, Holiday Banquet and Ball, Spring Weekend. Student services: health clinic, personal-psychological counseling. Campus security: 24-hour patrols, late night transport-escort service, 24-hour locked residence hall entrances. 1,098 college housing spaces available; 1,076 were occupied in 2003-04. Freshmen guaranteed college housing. On-campus residence required through senior year. Options: coed, women-only housing available. Gannett-Tripp Library with 391,038 books, 1.7 million microform titles, 859 serials, 4,428 audiovisual materials, an OPAC, and a Web page. Operations spending for 2004 fiscal year: $553,431. 105 computers available on campus for general student use. Computer purchase/lease plans available. A campuswide network can be accessed from student residence rooms. Staffed computer lab on campus.
Community Environment: Founded as a commercial and transportation center, Elmira, population 35,000, dominates south-central New York State and nearby Pennsylvania as the trade, industrial, financial, and transportation hub of the southern Finger Lakes region. Light industrial activity remains as the economic base for the county, though a large portion of Chemung County is still rural in activity and atmosphere. Transportation is available with the Elmira-Corning Airport, buses, and car via Routes 13, 14, and 17. There are two hospitals, approximately 60 churches, a public library, theatres, good shopping centers, and more than 200 fraternal, service, and social organizations. Recreational facilities include parks, playgrounds, golf, swimming, bowling, tennis, horseback riding, picnic areas, fishing, ice skating, and skiing nearby. Located within walking distance of the campus is the Samuel Clemens Performing Arts Center.

■ ERIE COMMUNITY COLLEGE K-7

121 Ellicott St.
Buffalo, NY 14203-2698
Tel: (716)851-1001
Admissions: (716)851-1588
Fax: (716)842-1972
Web Site: http://www.ecc.edu/
Description: State and locally supported, 2-year, coed. Part of State University of New York System. Awards certificates, diplomas, transfer associate, and terminal associate degrees. Founded 1971. Setting: 1-acre urban campus. Educational spending for 2005 fiscal year: $3743 per student. Total enrollment: 2,949. Student-undergrad faculty ratio is 17:1. 1,458 applied, 76% were admitted. 7% from top 10% of their high school class, 63% from top half. Full-time: 2,188 students, 63% women, 37% men. Part-time: 761 students, 65% women, 35% men. Students come from 12 states and territories, 3 other countries, 1% from out-of-state, 1% Native American, 8% Hispanic, 42% black, 2% Asian American or Pacific Islander, 0.2% international, 44% 25 or older, 5% transferred in. Core. Calendar: semesters. Academic remediation for entering students, ESL program, services for LD students, advanced placement, self-designed majors, honors program, independent study, distance learning, double major, summer session for credit, part-time degree program, adult/continuing education programs, co-op programs and internships. Study abroad program. ROTC: Army (c).
Entrance Requirements: Open admission except for nursing and radiologic technology programs. Options: Common Application, electronic application. Required: high school transcript. Required for some: interview. Entrance: noncompetitive. Application deadline: Rolling. Notification: continuous.
Costs Per Year: Application fee: $0. Area resident tuition: $2900 full-time, $121 per credit hour part-time. State resident tuition: $5800 full-time, $242 per credit hour part-time. Nonresident tuition: $5800 full-time, $242 per credit hour part-time. Mandatory fees: $320 full-time, $5 per credit hour part-time, $30 per term part-time.
Collegiate Environment: Orientation program. Drama-theater group, choral group, student-run newspaper, radio station. Social organizations: 12 open to all. Most popular organizations: Alpha Beta Gamma, Anthropology Club, Black Student Union, Business Club, Campus Ministry Club. Major annual events: Back to School Bash, Club Day. Student services: health clinic, personal-psychological counseling, women's center, child care. Campus

security: 24-hour emergency response devices and patrols, late night transport-escort service. College housing not available. Leon E. Butler Library with 24,927 books, 26,834 microform titles, 208 serials, 2,492 audiovisual materials, an OPAC, and a Web page. Operations spending for 2004 fiscal year: $1.9 million. 341 computers available on campus for general student use. A campuswide network can be accessed from off-campus. Staffed computer lab on campus.

■ **ERIE COMMUNITY COLLEGE, NORTH CAMPUS** *J-7*
6205 Main St.
Williamsville, NY 14221-7095
Tel: (716)851-1002
Admissions: (716)851-1588
Fax: (716)634-3802
Web Site: http://www.ecc.edu

Description: State and locally supported, 2-year, coed. Part of State University of New York System. Awards certificates, diplomas, transfer associate, and terminal associate degrees. Founded 1946. Setting: 20-acre suburban campus with easy access to Buffalo. Educational spending for 2005 fiscal year: $3743 per student. Total enrollment: 5,641. Student-undergrad faculty ratio is 17:1. 1,856 applied, 91% were admitted. 12% from top 10% of their high school class, 76% from top half. Full-time: 3,779 students, 50% women, 50% men. Part-time: 1,862 students, 52% women, 48% men. Students come from 17 states and territories, 24 other countries, 1% from out-of-state, 1% Native American, 2% Hispanic, 12% black, 2% Asian American or Pacific Islander, 1% international, 29% 25 or older, 5% transferred in. Core. Calendar: semesters plus summer sessions. Academic remediation for entering students, ESL program, services for LD students, advanced placement, self-designed majors, honors program, independent study, distance learning, double major, summer session for credit, part-time degree program, adult/continuing education programs, co-op programs and internships. Study abroad program. ROTC: Army (c).

Entrance Requirements: Open admission except for nursing, engineering science, occupational therapy programs. Options: Common Application, electronic application. Required: high school transcript. Required for some: interview. Entrance: noncompetitive. Application deadline: Rolling. Notification: continuous.

Costs Per Year: Area resident tuition: $2900 full-time, $121 per credit hour part-time. State resident tuition: $5800 full-time, $242 per credit hour part-time. Nonresident tuition: $5800 full-time, $242 per credit hour part-time. Mandatory fees: $320 full-time, $5 per credit hour part-time, $30 per term part-time.

Collegiate Environment: Orientation program. Drama-theater group, choral group, student-run newspaper, radio station. Social organizations: 9 open to all. Most popular organizations: APWA (American Public Works Association), Dental Hygiene Club, Environmental Awareness Club, Flame and Ice, Future Teachers. Major annual events: Holiday Charity Luncheon, Halloween Party, Christmas Party. Student services: health clinic, personal-psychological counseling, women's center, child care. Campus security: 24-hour emergency response devices and patrols, late night transport-escort service. College housing not available. Richard R. Dry Memorial Library with 71,220 books, 50,216 microform titles, 359 serials, 8,084 audiovisual materials, an OPAC, and a Web page. Operations spending for 2004 fiscal year: $1.9 million. 457 computers available on campus for general student use. A campuswide network can be accessed from off-campus. Staffed computer lab on campus.

■ **ERIE COMMUNITY COLLEGE, SOUTH CAMPUS** *K-7*
4041 Southwestern Blvd.
Orchard Park, NY 14127-2199
Tel: (716)851-1003
Admissions: (716)851-1588
Fax: (716)648-9953
Web Site: http://www.ecc.edu/

Description: State and locally supported, 2-year, coed. Part of State University of New York System. Awards certificates, diplomas, transfer associate, and terminal associate degrees. Founded 1974. Setting: 20-acre suburban campus with easy access to Buffalo. Educational spending for 2005 fiscal year: $3743 per student. Total enrollment: 4,067. Student-undergrad faculty ratio is 17:1. 1,377 applied, 89% were admitted. 10% from top 10% of their high school class, 77% from top half. Full-time: 2,521 students, 42% women, 58% men. Part-time: 1,546 students, 47% women, 53% men. Students come from 19 states and territories, 4 other countries, 1% from out-of-state, 1% Native American, 3% Hispanic, 5% black, 1%

Asian American or Pacific Islander, 0.1% international, 20% 25 or older, 5% transferred in. Core. Calendar: semesters plus summer sessions. Academic remediation for entering students, ESL program, services for LD students, advanced placement, self-designed majors, honors program, independent study, distance learning, double major, summer session for credit, part-time degree program, adult/continuing education programs, co-op programs and internships. Study abroad program. ROTC: Army (c).

Entrance Requirements: Open admission except for computer technology program or dental laboratory technology. Options: Common Application, electronic application. Required: high school transcript. Required for some: interview. Entrance: noncompetitive. Application deadline: Rolling. Notification: continuous.

Costs Per Year: Area resident tuition: $2900 full-time, $121 per credit hour part-time. State resident tuition: $5800 full-time, $242 per credit hour part-time. Nonresident tuition: $5800 full-time, $242 per credit hour part-time. Mandatory fees: $320 full-time, $5 per credit hour part-time, $30 per term part-time.

Collegiate Environment: Orientation program. Drama-theater group, student-run newspaper, radio station. Social organizations: 7 open to all. Most popular organizations: Habitat for Humanity, Honors Society, Phi Theta Kappa, Photo Club, Recreation Leadership Club. Major annual events: Christmas Party, Paczki Day, Halloween Party. Student services: health clinic, personal-psychological counseling, women's center, child care. Campus security: 24-hour emergency response devices and patrols, late night transport-escort service. College housing not available. 57,029 books, 16,366 microform titles, 286 serials, 5,401 audiovisual materials, an OPAC, and a Web page. Operations spending for 2004 fiscal year: $1.9 million. 434 computers available on campus for general student use. A campuswide network can be accessed from off-campus. Staffed computer lab on campus.

■ **EUGENE LANG COLLEGE THE NEW SCHOOL FOR LIBERAL ARTS** *N-34*
65 West 11th St.
New York, NY 10011-8601
Tel: (212)229-5600; 877-528-3321
Admissions: (212)229-5665
Fax: (212)229-5355
E-mail: lang@newschool.edu
Web Site: http://www.lang.edu/

Description: Independent, 4-year, coed. Part of New School University. Awards bachelor's degrees. Founded 1978. Setting: 5-acre urban campus. System endowment: $18 million. System-wide research spending for 2004 fiscal year: $6.4 million. Educational spending for 2005 fiscal year: $8218 per student. Total enrollment: 985. Student-undergrad faculty ratio is 14:1. 1,244 applied, 61% were admitted. 17% from top 10% of their high school class, 51% from top quarter, 87% from top half. Full-time: 939 students, 68% women, 32% men. Part-time: 46 students, 28% women, 72% men. Students come from 36 states and territories, 15 other countries, 68% from out-of-state, 0.3% Native American, 5% Hispanic, 4% black, 4% Asian American or Pacific Islander, 2% international, 4% 25 or older, 34% live on campus, 10% transferred in. Retention: 73% of full-time freshmen returned the following year. Academic area with the most degrees conferred: liberal arts/general studies. Calendar: semesters. Advanced placement, accelerated degree program, self-designed majors, independent study, distance learning, summer session for credit, part-time degree program, adult/continuing education programs, internships. Off campus study at Cooper Union for the Advancement of Science and Art, Bank Street College of Education, Sarah Lawrence College. Study abroad program.

Entrance Requirements: Options: Peterson's Universal Application, Common Application, early admission, early decision, deferred admission, international baccalaureate accepted. Required: essay, high school transcript, minimum 2.0 high school GPA, 2 recommendations, interview, SAT or ACT. Recommended: minimum 3.0 high school GPA. Entrance: moderately difficult. Application deadlines: 2/1, 11/15 for early decision. Notification: 4/1, 12/15 for early decision.

Costs Per Year: Application fee: $40. Comprehensive fee: $38,860 includes full-time tuition ($26,540), mandatory fees ($570), and college room and board ($11,750). College room only: $8750. Full-time tuition and fees vary according to program. Room and board charges vary according to board plan and housing facility. Part-time tuition: $976 per credit. Part-time tuition varies according to course load, program, and reciprocity agreements.

Collegiate Environment: Orientation program. Drama-theater group, choral group, student-run newspaper, radio station. Social organizations: 10 open to all. Most popular organizations: Student Union, Theater Club, student newspaper, literary journal, ethnic organizations. Major annual events: Open-Mike Readings, Talking Book Festival, New School Block Party. Student services: health clinic, personal-psychological counseling. Campus security: 24-hour emergency response devices, controlled dormitory access, 24-hour desk attendants in residence halls. 948 college housing spaces available; 266 were occupied in 2003-04. Freshmen guaranteed college housing. Option: coed housing available. Raymond Fogelman Library plus 2 others with 4.1 million books, 4.7 million microform titles, 22,150 serials, 48,379 audiovisual materials, an OPAC, and a Web page. System-wide operations spending for 2004 fiscal year: $2.8 million. 934 computers available on campus for general student use. A campuswide network can be accessed from student residence rooms and from off campus. Staffed computer lab on campus.

■ **EUGENIO MARÍA DE HOSTOS COMMUNITY COLLEGE OF THE CITY UNIVERSITY OF NEW YORK** *M-35*

500 Grand Concourse
Bronx, NY 10451
Tel: (718)518-4444
Admissions: (718)518-4406
Fax: (718)518-4256
Web Site: http://www.hostos.cuny.edu/

Description: State and locally supported, 2-year, coed. Part of City University of New York System. Awards certificates, transfer associate, and terminal associate degrees. Founded 1968. Setting: 8-acre urban campus. Endowment: $211,655. Research spending for 2004 fiscal year: $2.6 million. Educational spending for 2005 fiscal year: $4780 per student. Total enrollment: 4,340. 1,316 applied, 100% were admitted. 2% from top 10% of their high school class, 9% from top quarter, 25% from top half. Full-time: 2,917 students, 73% women, 27% men. Part-time: 1,423 students, 75% women, 25% men. Students come from 4 states and territories, 91 other countries, 1% from out-of-state, 0.1% Native American, 58% Hispanic, 29% black, 2% Asian American or Pacific Islander, 8% international, 54% 25 or older, 12% transferred in. Core. Calendar: semesters. Academic remediation for entering students, ESL program, services for LD students, distance learning, double major, summer session for credit, part-time degree program, adult/continuing education programs, internships. Study abroad program.

Entrance Requirements: Open admission. Option: Common Application. Required: high school transcript. Placement: CUNY Skills Assessment Tests required; SAT, ACT, SAT Subject Tests required for some. Entrance: noncompetitive. Application deadline: Rolling. Notification: continuous until 8/15.

Costs Per Year: Application fee: $65. State resident tuition: $2500 full-time, $105 per credit part-time. Nonresident tuition: $3076 full-time, $130 per credit part-time.

Collegiate Environment: Orientation program. Student-run newspaper. Social organizations: 30 open to all. Most popular organizations: Dominican Association, Puerto Rican Student Organization, Student Government Association, Black Student Union, Veterans Club. Major annual events: Graduation, ethnic weeks, Prom Social. Student services: legal services, health clinic, personal-psychological counseling, women's center. Campus security: 24-hour emergency response devices and patrols, late night transport-escort service. College housing not available. Hostos Community College Library with 56,100 books, 6,715 microform titles, 846 serials, 710 audiovisual materials, an OPAC, and a Web page. Operations spending for 2004 fiscal year: $963,590. 800 computers available on campus for general student use. A campuswide network can be accessed from off-campus. Staffed computer lab on campus.

■ **EXCELSIOR COLLEGE** *L-25*

7 Columbia Circle
Albany, NY 12203-5159
Tel: (518)464-8500; 888-647-2388
Fax: (518)464-8777
E-mail: info@excelsior.edu
Web Site: http://www.excelsior.edu/

Description: Independent, comprehensive, coed. Awards associate, bachelor's, and master's degrees (offers only external degree programs). Founded 1970. Setting: urban campus. Total enrollment: 28,464. Part-time: 27,844 students, 56% women, 44% men. Students come from 50 states and territories, 51 other countries, 90% from out-of-state, 1% Native American, 6% Hispanic, 16% black, 7% Asian American or Pacific Islander, 1% international, 97% 25 or older, 50% transferred in. Academic areas with the most degrees conferred: liberal arts/general studies; business/marketing;

health professions and related sciences. Core. Calendar: continuous. Advanced placement, accelerated degree program, self-designed majors, independent study, distance learning, part-time degree program, external degree program, adult/continuing education programs, graduate courses open to undergrads.

Entrance Requirements: Open admission except for applicants to nursing program without certain health care experience. Option: electronic application. Entrance: noncompetitive. Application deadline: Rolling. Notification: continuous.

Costs Per Year: Application fee: $65. Tuition: $250 per credit hour part-time. Mandatory fees: $515 per year part-time.

Collegiate Environment: Orientation program. Major annual event: Commencement. College housing not available. Excelsior College Virtual Library with a Web page.

■ **FARMINGDALE STATE UNIVERSITY OF NEW YORK** *G-46*

Route 110, 2350 Broadhollow Rd.
Farmingdale, NY 11735
Tel: (631)420-2000; 877-4-FARMINGDALE
Admissions: (631)420-2457
Fax: (631)420-2633
Web Site: http://www.farmingdale.edu/

Description: State-supported, 4-year, coed. Part of State University of New York System. Awards associate and bachelor's degrees. Founded 1912. Setting: 380-acre small town campus with easy access to New York City. Endowment: $2.8 million. Research spending for 2004 fiscal year: $306,344. Educational spending for 2005 fiscal year: $5740 per student. Total enrollment: 6,461. Student-undergrad faculty ratio is 19:1. 4,115 applied, 61% were admitted. 2% from top 10% of their high school class, 11% from top quarter, 53% from top half. Full-time: 4,020 students, 36% women, 64% men. Part-time: 2,441 students, 51% women, 49% men. Students come from 9 states and territories, 13 other countries, 0.01% from out-of-state, 0.2% Native American, 9% Hispanic, 13% black, 5% Asian American or Pacific Islander, 1% international, 28% 25 or older, 10% live on campus, 9% transferred in. Retention: 74% of full-time freshmen returned the following year. Academic areas with the most degrees conferred: business/marketing; computer and information sciences; engineering technologies. Core. Calendar: semesters. Academic remediation for entering students, services for LD students, advanced placement, distance learning, double major, summer session for credit, part-time degree program, internships. Study abroad program. ROTC: Army (c), Air Force (c).

Entrance Requirements: Options: electronic application, early admission, international baccalaureate accepted. Required: high school transcript, minimum 2.0 high school GPA, SAT or ACT. Required for some: portfolio. Entrance: moderately difficult. Application deadline: Rolling. Notification: continuous.

Costs Per Year: Application fee: $40. State resident tuition: $4350 full-time, $181 per credit part-time. Nonresident tuition: $10,610 full-time, $442 per credit part-time. Mandatory fees: $907 full-time, $30.85 per credit part-time. College room and board: $9660. College room only: $5670. Room and board charges vary according to board plan.

Collegiate Environment: Orientation program. Drama-theater group, student-run newspaper, radio station. Social organizations: 35 open to all. Most popular organizations: Liberal Arts Club, Campus Activities Board, Farmingdale Student Government, student radio station, Rambler Newspaper. Major annual events: Farewell to Farmingdale, Spring Fling. Student services: health clinic, personal-psychological counseling. Campus security: 24-hour emergency response devices and patrols, controlled dormitory access. 500 college housing spaces available; all were occupied in 2003-04. No special consideration for freshman housing applicants. Option: coed housing available. Greenley Hall with 125,000 books, 89,135 microform titles, 800 serials, 1,500 audiovisual materials, an OPAC, and a Web page. Operations spending for 2004 fiscal year: $880,032. 950 computers available on campus for general student use. Computer purchase/lease plans available. A campuswide network can be accessed from student residence rooms and from off campus. Staffed computer lab on campus.

■ **FASHION INSTITUTE OF TECHNOLOGY** *N-34*

Seventh Ave. at 27th St.
New York, NY 10001-5992
Tel: (212)217-7999
Free: 800-GOT-OFIT
Admissions: (212)217-7675
Fax: (212)217-7481

Web Site: http://www.fitnyc.edu/

Description: State and locally supported, comprehensive, coed. Part of State University of New York System. Awards associate, bachelor's, and master's degrees. Founded 1944. Setting: 5-acre urban campus. Endowment: $18.5 million. Educational spending for 2005 fiscal year: $5722 per student. Total enrollment: 10,381. Faculty: 918 (210 full-time, 708 part-time). Student-undergrad faculty ratio is 17:1. 3,498 applied, 41% were admitted. 13% from top 10% of their high school class, 45% from top quarter, 82% from top half. Full-time: 6,661 students, 85% women, 15% men. Part-time: 3,538 students, 82% women, 18% men. Students come from 51 states and territories, 60 other countries, 30% from out-of-state, 0.3% Native American, 10% Hispanic, 7% black, 10% Asian American or Pacific Islander, 10% international, 28% 25 or older, 16% live on campus, 8% transferred in. Retention: 84% of full-time freshmen returned the following year. Academic areas with the most degrees conferred: business/marketing; visual and performing arts; communications/journalism. Core. Calendar: 4-1-4. Academic remediation for entering students, ESL program, services for LD students, advanced placement, honors program, distance learning, summer session for credit, part-time degree program, adult/continuing education programs, co-op programs and internships. Study abroad program.

Entrance Requirements: Options: electronic application, early action, deferred admission, international baccalaureate accepted. Required: essay, high school transcript, portfolio for art and design programs. Entrance: moderately difficult. Application deadlines: 2/15, 11/15 for early action. Notification: continuous, 1/31 for early action.

Costs Per Year: Application fee: $40. State resident tuition: $4350 full-time, $181 per credit part-time. Nonresident tuition: $10,610 full-time, $442 per credit part-time. Mandatory fees: $420 full-time, $30 per term part-time. College room and board: $8409. College room only: $7519.

Collegiate Environment: Orientation program. Drama-theater group, choral group, student-run newspaper, radio station. Social organizations: 60 open to all. Most popular organizations: Public Relations Student Society of America, Delta Epsilon Chi, Merchandising Society, Student Government. Major annual events: Freshman Fair, Semi-Formal Dinner Cruise, Clubs Carnival. Student services: health clinic, personal-psychological counseling. Campus security: 24-hour emergency response devices and patrols. 1,234 college housing spaces available; 1,209 were occupied in 2003-04. Freshmen given priority for college housing. Options: coed, women-only housing available. Gladys Marcus Library with 176,987 books, 4,796 microform titles, 467 serials, 177,801 audiovisual materials, an OPAC, and a Web page. Operations spending for 2004 fiscal year: $3.5 million. 300 computers available on campus for general student use. A campuswide network can be accessed from student residence rooms and from off campus. Staffed computer lab on campus.

■ **FINGER LAKES COMMUNITY COLLEGE** *K-12*

4355 Lakeshore Dr.
Canandaigua, NY 14424-8395
Tel: (585)394-3500
Fax: (585)394-5005
E-mail: admissions@flcc.edu
Web Site: http://www.flcc.edu/

Description: State and locally supported, 2-year, coed. Part of State University of New York System. Awards certificates, transfer associate, and terminal associate degrees. Founded 1965. Setting: 300-acre small town campus with easy access to Rochester. Total enrollment: 4,910. Student-undergrad faculty ratio is 20:1. 4,023 applied. Full-time: 2,599 students, 52% women, 48% men. Part-time: 2,311 students, 63% women, 37% men. Students come from 6 states and territories, 3 other countries, 1% from out-of-state, 1% Native American, 2% Hispanic, 4% black, 1% Asian American or Pacific Islander, 32% 25 or older. Core. Calendar: semesters. Academic remediation for entering students, ESL program, services for LD students, advanced placement, honors program, distance learning, summer session for credit, part-time degree program, internships. Off campus study at the Rochester Area Colleges. ROTC: Army (c).

Entrance Requirements: Open admission except for nursing, therapeutic massage and integrative health care programs. Options: electronic application, early admission, deferred admission. Required: high school transcript. Recommended: interview. Entrance: noncompetitive. Application deadline: Rolling. Notification: continuous until 8/31. Preference given to state residents.

Costs Per Year: Application fee: $0. State resident tuition: $2900 full-time, $117 per credit hour part-time. Nonresident tuition: $5800 full-time, $234 per credit hour part-time. Mandatory fees: $260 full-time, $7 per credit hour part-time.

Collegiate Environment: Orientation program. Drama-theater group, choral group, student-run newspaper, radio station. Social organizations: 45 open to all; national fraternities, national sororities. Student services: legal services, health clinic, personal-psychological counseling. Campus security: 24-hour emergency response devices and patrols, late night transport-escort service. College housing not available. Charles Meder Library with 73,305 books, 464 serials, and an OPAC. 425 computers available on campus for general student use. A campuswide network can be accessed from off-campus. Staffed computer lab on campus.

■ **FIORELLO H. LAGUARDIA COMMUNITY COLLEGE OF THE CITY UNIVERSITY OF NEW YORK**

31-10 Thomson Ave.
Long Island City, NY 11101-3071
Tel: (718)482-7200
Admissions: (718)482-5114
Fax: (718)482-5599
E-mail: lavorad@lagcc.cuny.edu
Web Site: http://www.lagcc.cuny.edu/

Description: State and locally supported, 2-year, coed. Part of City University of New York System. Awards certificates, transfer associate, and terminal associate degrees. Founded 1970. Setting: 6-acre urban campus. Endowment: $351,000. Research spending for 2004 fiscal year: $6 million. Educational spending for 2005 fiscal year: $7464 per student. Total enrollment: 13,489. Student-undergrad faculty ratio is 21:1. 3,606 applied, 100% were admitted. 4% from top 10% of their high school class, 21% from top quarter, 46% from top half. Full-time: 7,453 students, 63% women, 37% men. Part-time: 6,036 students, 65% women, 35% men. Students come from 9 states and territories, 135 other countries, 1% from out-of-state, 0.2% Native American, 31% Hispanic, 17% black, 14% Asian American or Pacific Islander, 16% international, 40% 25 or older, 7% transferred in. Core. Calendar: modified semester. Academic remediation for entering students, ESL program, services for LD students, advanced placement, self-designed majors, honors program, independent study, double major, part-time degree program, adult/continuing education programs, co-op programs and internships. Off campus study at Vassar College, other units of the City University of New York System. Study abroad program.

Entrance Requirements: Open admission. Options: electronic application, early admission, deferred admission. Required: high school transcript. Entrance: noncompetitive. Application deadline: Rolling. Notification: continuous.

Costs Per Year: Application fee: $65. Area resident tuition: $3072 full-time, $120 per credit part-time. State resident tuition: $5700 full-time, $190 per credit hour part-time. Nonresident tuition: $5700 full-time, $190 per credit hour part-time. Mandatory fees: $272 full-time.

Collegiate Environment: Orientation program. Drama-theater group, student-run newspaper, radio station. Social organizations: 31 open to all. Most popular organizations: Latinos Unidos Club, Bangladesh Club, Dominican Club, Law Club. Major annual event: multicultural appreciation week. Student services: health clinic, personal-psychological counseling, women's center. Campus security: 24-hour patrols. College housing not available. Fiorello H. LaGuardia Community College Library Media Resources Center plus 1 other with 121,631 books, 583,009 microform titles, 760 serials, 5,529 audiovisual materials, and an OPAC. Operations spending for 2004 fiscal year: $2.2 million. 997 computers available on campus for general student use. A campuswide network can be accessed from off-campus. Staffed computer lab on campus.

■ **FIVE TOWNS COLLEGE** *O-43*

305 North Service Rd.
Dix Hills, NY 11746-6055
Tel: (631)424-7000
Fax: (631)656-2172
Web Site: http://www.fivetowns.edu/

Description: Independent, comprehensive, coed. Awards associate, bachelor's, master's, and doctoral degrees. Founded 1972. Setting: 40-acre suburban campus with easy access to New York City. Total enrollment: 1,162. Faculty: 109 (45 full-time, 64 part-time). Student-undergrad faculty ratio is 13:1. 713 applied, 77% were admitted. 5% from top 10% of their high school class, 25% from top quarter, 45% from top half. Full-time: 1,042 students, 38% women, 62% men. Part-time: 46 students, 63% women, 37% men. Students come from 10 states and territories, 0% from out-of-state, 0.5% Native American, 13% Hispanic, 19% black, 3% Asian American or Pacific Islander, 0% international, 10% live on campus. Retention: 74% of full-time freshmen returned the following year. Core. Calendar: semesters. Academic remediation for entering students, services for LD students, advanced placement, independent study, distance learning, summer session for credit, part-time degree program, co-op programs and internships, graduate courses open to undergrads. Off campus study at Long Island Regional Advisory Council for Higher Education.

Entrance Requirements: Options: Peterson's Universal Application, Common Application, electronic application, early admission, deferred admission, international baccalaureate accepted. Required: essay, high school transcript, minimum 2.3 high school GPA, recommendations. Required for some: interview. Entrance: moderately difficult. Application deadline: Rolling. Notification: continuous.

Costs Per Year: Application fee: $35. Comprehensive fee: $24,350 includes full-time tuition ($14,100) and college room and board ($10,250). Room and board charges vary according to board plan and location. Part-time tuition: $585 per credit.

Collegiate Environment: Orientation program. Drama-theater group, choral group, student-run newspaper. Social organizations: 7 open to all. Most popular organizations: concert choir, Live Audio Club, Dance Club, musical theatre, yearbook. Major annual events: Long Island Music Industry Conference, College Senior Picnic, L.I. Media Art Show. Student services: health clinic, personal-psychological counseling. Campus security: 24-hour emergency response devices and patrols, late night transport-escort service, controlled dormitory access. 200 college housing spaces available; all were occupied in 2003-04. Freshmen given priority for college housing. Option: coed housing available. Five Towns College Library with 35,000 books, 565 serials, 6,500 audiovisual materials, and an OPAC. 110 computers available on campus for general student use. Computer purchase/lease plans available. A campuswide network can be accessed. Staffed computer lab on campus.

Community Environment: See Adelphi University.

■ **FORDHAM UNIVERSITY** *M-35*
441 East Fordham Rd.
Bronx, NY 10458
Tel: (718)817-1000
Free: 800-FOR-DHAM
Admissions: (718)817-4000
Fax: (718)367-9404
E-mail: ad_buckley@lars.fordham.edu
Web Site: http://www.fordham.edu/

Description: Independent Roman Catholic (Jesuit), university, coed. Awards bachelor's, master's, doctoral, and first professional degrees and post-master's certificates (branch locations at Rose Hill and Lincoln Center). Founded 1841. Setting: 85-acre urban campus. Endowment: $307.2 million. Total enrollment: 14,664. Faculty: 1,326 (645 full-time, 681 part-time). Student-undergrad faculty ratio is 11:1. 15,225 applied, 50% were admitted. 39% from top 10% of their high school class, 75% from top quarter, 96% from top half. Full-time: 6,887 students, 59% women, 41% men. Part-time: 641 students, 67% women, 33% men. Students come from 53 states and territories, 44 other countries, 44% from out-of-state, 0.2% Native American, 11% Hispanic, 5% black, 6% Asian American or Pacific Islander, 1% international, 7% 25 or older, 60% live on campus, 3% transferred in. Retention: 90% of full-time freshmen returned the following year. Core. Calendar: semesters. ESL program, services for LD students, advanced placement, accelerated degree program, self-designed majors, honors program, independent study, double major, summer session for credit, part-time degree program, adult/continuing education programs, internships, graduate courses open to undergrads. Off campus study at University of San Francisco. Study abroad program. ROTC: Army, Naval (c), Air Force (c).

Entrance Requirements: Options: Peterson's Universal Application, Common Application, electronic application, early admission, early action, deferred admission. Required: essay, high school transcript, 1 recommendation, SAT or ACT. Recommended: minimum 3.0 high school GPA, interview, SAT Subject Tests. Required for some: interview. Entrance: very difficult. Application deadlines: 1/15, 11/1 for early action. Notification: 4/1, 12/25 for early action.

Costs Per Year: Application fee: $50. Comprehensive fee: $38,620 includes full-time tuition ($27,725) and college room and board ($10,895). College room only: $7260.

Collegiate Environment: Orientation program. Drama-theater group, choral group, marching band, student-run newspaper, radio station. Social organizations: 133 open to all. Most popular organizations: United Student Government, Commuting Student Association, Residence Hall Association,

Ambassador Program. Major annual events: Under the Tent Dance, Give a Child a Christmas, Spring Weekend. Student services: health clinic, personal-psychological counseling. Campus security: 24-hour emergency response devices and patrols, student patrols, late night transport-escort service, controlled dormitory access, security at each campus entrance and at residence halls. Option: coed housing available. Walsh Library plus 3 others with 2.5 million books, 3.1 million microform titles, 15,943 serials, 20,550 audiovisual materials, an OPAC, and a Web page. 1,400 computers available on campus for general student use. Computer purchase/lease plans available. A campuswide network can be accessed from student residence rooms and from off campus. Staffed computer lab on campus.

■ **FULTON-MONTGOMERY COMMUNITY COLLEGE** *J-22*
2805 State Hwy. 67
Johnstown, NY 12095-3790
Tel: (518)762-4651
Fax: (518)762-6518
E-mail: jkelley@fmcc.suny.edu
Web Site: http://www.fmcc.suny.edu/

Description: State and locally supported, 2-year, coed. Part of State University of New York System. Awards certificates, transfer associate, and terminal associate degrees. Founded 1964. Setting: 195-acre rural campus. Endowment: $1.5 million. Educational spending for 2005 fiscal year: $3800 per student. Total enrollment: 2,071. 1,375 applied, 100% were admitted. Full-time: 1,404 students, 55% women, 45% men. Part-time: 667 students, 66% women, 34% men. Students come from 2 states and territories, 20 other countries, 0.01% from out-of-state, 0.3% Native American, 5% Hispanic, 4% black, 1% Asian American or Pacific Islander, 7% international, 27% 25 or older, 2% transferred in. Core. Calendar: semesters plus winter session. Academic remediation for entering students, ESL program, services for LD students, advanced placement, accelerated degree program, self-designed majors, honors program, independent study, distance learning, double major, summer session for credit, part-time degree program, external degree program, adult/continuing education programs, co-op programs and internships. Off campus study at State University of New York College of Technology at Canton, State University of New York College of Agriculture and Technology at Cobleskill. Study abroad program.

Entrance Requirements: Open admission except for nursing program, radiologic technology. Options: Common Application, electronic application, early admission, deferred admission. Required: high school transcript. Entrance: noncompetitive. Application deadline: 9/10. Notification: continuous.

Costs Per Year: Application fee: $0. State resident tuition: $2925 full-time, $122 per credit hour part-time. Nonresident tuition: $5850 full-time, $244 per credit hour part-time. Mandatory fees: $205 full-time, $2 per credit hour part-time, $38 per term part-time. Part-time tuition and fees vary according to course load.

Collegiate Environment: Orientation program. Drama-theater group, choral group, student-run newspaper. Social organizations: 30 open to all. Most popular organizations: Business Students' Association, Criminal Justice Club, WAU (We Are United), Ski Club. Major annual events: Spring Fling, Orientation. Student services: personal-psychological counseling. Campus security: weekend and night security. College housing not available. Evans Library with 51,517 books, 4,844 microform titles, 143 serials, 1,041 audiovisual materials, an OPAC, and a Web page. Operations spending for 2004 fiscal year: $337,848. 400 computers available on campus for general student use. A campuswide network can be accessed from off-campus. Staffed computer lab on campus.

■ **GAMLA COLLEGE** *O-34*
1213 Elm Ave.
Brooklyn, NY 11230
Tel: (718)339-4747
Fax: (718)998-5766
Description: Independent, 2-year, coed. Calendar: semesters.

■ **GENESEE COMMUNITY COLLEGE** *J-9*
1 College Rd.
Batavia, NY 14020-9704
Tel: (585)343-0055
Free: 800-CALL GCC
Fax: (585)345-4541
Web Site: http://www.genesee.edu/

Description: State and locally supported, 2-year, coed. Part of State University of New York System. Awards certificates, transfer associate, and terminal associate degrees. Founded 1966. Setting: 256-acre small town campus with easy access to Buffalo. Endowment: $1.7 million. Educational spending for 2005 fiscal year: $2784 per student. Total enrollment: 6,490. Student-undergrad faculty ratio is 20:1. 2,547 applied, 100% were admitted. Full-time: 3,113 students, 65% women, 35% men. Part-time: 3,377 students, 65% women, 35% men. Students come from 13 states and territories, 26 other countries, 1% from out-of-state, 1% Native American, 1% Hispanic, 4% black, 1% Asian American or Pacific Islander, 3% international, 19% 25 or older, 5% transferred in. Core. Calendar: semesters. Academic remediation for entering students, services for LD students, advanced placement, honors program, independent study, distance learning, summer session for credit, part-time degree program, adult/continuing education programs, co-op programs and internships. ROTC: Army (c).

Entrance Requirements: Open admission except for nursing, physical therapy assistant, occupational therapy assistant, paralegal, respiratory care, dietetic technician programs. Options: Common Application, electronic application. Required: high school transcript. Required for some: 1 recommendation. Entrance: noncompetitive. Application deadline: Rolling. Notification: continuous. Preference given to county residents.

Costs Per Year: Application fee: $0. State resident tuition: $3200 full-time. Nonresident tuition: $3600 full-time. Mandatory fees: $290 full-time. College room only: $4250.

Collegiate Environment: Orientation program. Drama-theater group, choral group, student-run newspaper, radio station. Most popular organizations: Student Government Association, Phi Theta Kappa, DECA, Student Activities Council, Forum Players. Major annual events: Outdoor Festivals, Up All Night, Fashion Show. Student services: health clinic, personal-psychological counseling. Campus security: 24-hour emergency response devices and patrols, late night transport-escort service. 247 college housing spaces available; all were occupied in 2003-04. No special consideration for freshman housing applicants. Alfred C. O'Connell Library with 78,273 books, 11,667 microform titles, 332 serials, 4,729 audiovisual materials, an OPAC, and a Web page. Operations spending for 2004 fiscal year: $452,417. 408 computers available on campus for general student use. A campuswide network can be accessed from off-campus. Staffed computer lab on campus.

■ GLOBE INSTITUTE OF TECHNOLOGY *N-34*

291 Broadway, Second Floor
New York, NY 10007
Tel: (212)349-4330; 877-394-5623
Fax: (212)227-5920
E-mail: admissions@globe.edu
Web Site: http://www.globe.edu/

Description: Proprietary, 4-year, coed. Awards associate and bachelor's degrees. Setting: urban campus. Educational spending for 2005 fiscal year: $4543 per student. Total enrollment: 1,671. Student-undergrad faculty ratio is 15:1. 550 applied, 82% were admitted. Full-time: 1,655 students, 64% women, 36% men. Part-time: 16 students, 56% women, 44% men. Students come from 7 states and territories, 3% from out-of-state, 0.1% Native American, 8% Hispanic, 10% black, 35% Asian American or Pacific Islander, 0.4% international, 63% 25 or older. Retention: 45% of full-time freshmen returned the following year. Academic areas with the most degrees conferred: business/marketing; computer and information sciences. Core. Calendar: semesters. Academic remediation for entering students, ESL program, services for LD students, advanced placement, accelerated degree program, part-time degree program, internships.

Entrance Requirements: Open admission. Options: Common Application, electronic application. Required: high school transcript, interview. Required for some: SAT or ACT. Entrance: minimally difficult.

Costs Per Year: Application fee: $50. Tuition: $8950 full-time, $370 per credit part-time. Mandatory fees: $136 full-time, $136 per year part-time. College room only: $3600.

Collegiate Environment: Orientation program. Drama-theater group. Student services: personal-psychological counseling. 100 college housing spaces available; 80 were occupied in 2003-04. Globe Institute of Technology's Library with 6,678 books, 1,237 serials, 60 audiovisual materials, and a Web page. Operations spending for 2004 fiscal year: $231,500. 140 computers available on campus for general student use. A campuswide network can be accessed from off-campus. Staffed computer lab on campus.

■ HAMILTON COLLEGE *O-24*

198 College Hill Rd.
Clinton, NY 13323-1296

Tel: (315)859-4011
Free: 800-843-2655
Admissions: (315)859-4421
Fax: (315)859-4124
E-mail: admission@hamilton.edu
Web Site: http://www.hamilton.edu/

Description: Independent, 4-year, coed. Awards bachelor's degrees. Founded 1812. Setting: 1,200-acre small town campus. Endowment: $596 million. Research spending for 2004 fiscal year: $1.2 million. Educational spending for 2005 fiscal year: $19,590 per student. Total enrollment: 1,812. Student-undergrad faculty ratio is 10:1. 4,189 applied, 36% were admitted. 70% from top 10% of their high school class, 91% from top quarter, 99% from top half. 5 National Merit Scholars, 12 valedictorians. Full-time: 1,800 students, 50% women, 50% men. Part-time: 12 students, 58% women, 42% men. Students come from 41 states and territories, 40 other countries, 64% from out-of-state, 1% Native American, 4% Hispanic, 4% black, 6% Asian American or Pacific Islander, 5% international, 1% 25 or older, 98% live on campus, 1% transferred in. Retention: 93% of full-time freshmen returned the following year. Academic areas with the most degrees conferred: social sciences; foreign languages and literature; English. Calendar: semesters. ESL program, services for LD students, advanced placement, accelerated degree program, self-designed majors, independent study, double major, part-time degree program, adult/continuing education programs, internships. Off campus study at Colgate University, Syracuse University, Utica College of Syracuse University. Study abroad program. ROTC: Army (c), Air Force (c).

Entrance Requirements: Options: Peterson's Universal Application, Common Application, electronic application, early admission, early decision, deferred admission, international baccalaureate accepted. Required: essay, high school transcript, 1 recommendation, sample of expository prose. Recommended: interview. Entrance: very difficult. Application deadlines: 1/1, 11/15 for early decision. Notification: 4/1, 1/1 for early decision.

Costs Per Year: Application fee: $50. Comprehensive fee: $41,660 includes full-time tuition ($33,150), mandatory fees ($200), and college room and board ($8310). College room only: $4460. Room and board charges vary according to board plan.

Collegiate Environment: Orientation program. Drama-theater group, choral group, student-run newspaper, radio station. Social organizations: 80 open to all; national fraternities, local sororities; 29% of eligible men and 19% of eligible women are members. Most popular organizations: community service groups, Outing Club, student newspaper, club/intramural sports, performing arts groups. Major annual events: Fallcoming, Winter Carnival, Class and Charter Day. Student services: health clinic, personal-psychological counseling, women's center. Campus security: 24-hour emergency response devices and patrols, late night transport-escort service, controlled dormitory access, student safety program. 1,750 college housing spaces available; 1,700 were occupied in 2003-04. Freshmen guaranteed college housing. On-campus residence required through senior year. Option: coed housing available. Burke Library plus 3 others with 538,377 books, 419,461 microform titles, 3,585 serials, 52,051 audiovisual materials, an OPAC, and a Web page. Operations spending for 2004 fiscal year: $3.3 million. 522 computers available on campus for general student use. A campuswide network can be accessed from student residence rooms and from off campus. Staffed computer lab on campus.

Community Environment: Clinton, population 2,200, is a suburban community 10 miles southwest of Utica, population 75,600. The climate is temperate. Access via bus, rail, and air lines are through Utica. Nearby Kirkland has a library, five churches, an art center, a Chamber of Commerce, and civic, fraternal, and veteran's organizations. Hockey, skiing, camping, and ice skating are popular recreational activities in the area.

■ HARTWICK COLLEGE *M-20*

One Hartwick Dr.
Oneonta, NY 13820-4020
Tel: (607)431-4200; 888-HARTWICK
Admissions: (607)431-4150
Fax: (607)431-4138
E-mail: admissions@hartwick.edu
Web Site: http://www.hartwick.edu/

Description: Independent, 4-year, coed. Awards bachelor's degrees. Founded 1797. Setting: 425-acre small town campus with easy access to Albany. Endowment: $59.9 million. Total enrollment: 1,463. Student-undergrad faculty ratio is 11:1. 2,211 applied, 87% were admitted. 24% from top 10% of their high school class, 80% from top half. Full-time: 1,405 students, 56% women, 44% men. Part-time: 58 students, 57% women, 43% men. Students come from 30 states and territories, 34 other countries, 35% from out-of-state, 1% Native American, 4% Hispanic, 5% black, 1% Asian American or Pacific Islander, 4% international, 4% 25 or older, 86% live on campus, 3% transferred in. Retention: 76% of full-time freshmen returned the following year. Academic areas with the most degrees conferred: social sciences; business/marketing; visual and performing arts. Core. Calendar: 4-1-4. Services for LD students, advanced placement, accelerated degree program, self-designed majors, honors program, independent study, double major, part-time degree program, internships. Off campus study at State University of New York College at Oneonta, American University, Central University of Iowa, Syracuse University, The School for International Training. Study abroad program. ROTC: Army (c), Air Force (c).

Entrance Requirements: Options: Common Application, electronic application, early admission, early decision, early action, deferred admission, international baccalaureate accepted. Required: essay, high school transcript, 2 recommendations, audition for music program. Recommended: minimum 3.0 high school GPA, interview, SAT or ACT. Entrance: moderately difficult. Application deadlines: 2/15, 1/15 for early decision. Notification: 3/5.

Costs Per Year: Application fee: $35. Comprehensive fee: $34,490 includes full-time tuition ($26,480), mandatory fees ($530), and college room and board ($7480). College room only: $3940. Room and board charges vary according to board plan and housing facility. Part-time tuition: $883 per hour.

Collegiate Environment: Orientation program. Drama-theater group, choral group, student-run newspaper, radio station. Social organizations: 60 open to all; national fraternities, national sororities, local fraternities, local sororities. Most popular organizations: Student Union, student radio station, Student Senate, Hilltops, Cardboard Alley Players. Major annual events: Alumni Weekend, Parents' Weekend, Holiday Ball. Student services: health clinic, personal-psychological counseling, women's center. Campus security: 24-hour emergency response devices and patrols, late night transport-escort service. 1,100 college housing spaces available; 90 were occupied in 2003-04. On-campus residence required through junior year. Options: coed, men-only, women-only housing available. Stevens-German Library plus 1 other with 353,776 books, 8,291 microform titles, 571 serials, 6,171 audiovisual materials, an OPAC, and a Web page. Operations spending for 2004 fiscal year: $538,710. 80 computers available on campus for general student use. Computer purchase/lease plans available. A campuswide network can be accessed from student residence rooms and from off campus. Staffed computer lab on campus.

Community Environment: Oneonta, population 14,000, is large enough to support industries and two colleges, and serves as a regional commerce center. Cooperstown is 20 miles away and attracts many people annually who discover Oneonta (home of the National Soccer Hall of Fame) and its restaurants, motels, bed and breakfasts, and who use its local parks and facilities for swimming, golf, fishing, skiing, and boating. Public transportation is available in town. Oneonta is on Interstate 88, a freeway that connects Albany, New York, and central-eastern Pennsylvania.

■ **HELENE FULD COLLEGE OF NURSING OF NORTH GENERAL HOSPITAL** *N-34*
1879 Madison Ave.
New York, NY 10035-2709
Tel: (212)423-1000
Web Site: http://www.helenefuld.edu/
Description: Independent, 2-year, coed. Awards transfer associate and terminal associate degrees (program only open to licensed practical nurses). Founded 1945. Setting: urban campus. Total enrollment: 363. 16 applied, 100% were admitted. Students come from 3 states and territories, 3% from out-of-state, 96% 25 or older. Core. Accelerated degree program, summer session for credit, part-time degree program.

Entrance Requirements: Option: deferred admission. Required: essay, high school transcript, 1 recommendation, interview, must be Licensed Practical Nurse, nursing exam, Nelson Denny Reading Test, math exam. Entrance: moderately difficult. Application deadline: Rolling. Preference given to all students admitted must be licensed practical nurses.

Collegiate Environment: Orientation program. Student services: personal-psychological counseling. Campus security: security guard during open hours. College housing not available. 6,200 books, 82 serials, and 131 audiovisual materials. 24 computers available on campus for general student use. Staffed computer lab on campus.

■ **HERKIMER COUNTY COMMUNITY COLLEGE** *J-20*
Reservoir Rd.
Herkimer, NY 13350

Tel: (315)866-0300
Fax: (315)866-7253
Web Site: http://www.herkimer.edu
Description: State and locally supported, 2-year, coed. Part of State University of New York System. Awards certificates, transfer associate, and terminal associate degrees. Founded 1966. Setting: 500-acre small town campus with easy access to Syracuse. Endowment: $1.7 million. Educational spending for 2005 fiscal year: $2523 per student. Total enrollment: 3,477. Students come from 23 states and territories, 17 other countries, 2% from out-of-state, 23% 25 or older, 25% live on campus. Calendar: semesters. Academic remediation for entering students, ESL program, services for LD students, advanced placement, honors program, summer session for credit, part-time degree program, adult/continuing education programs, internships.

Entrance Requirements: Open admission except for occupational therapy assistant, physical therapy assistant programs. Option: early admission. Required: high school transcript. Placement: SAT or ACT recommended. Entrance: noncompetitive. Application deadline: 8/20. Notification: continuous. Preference given to county residents.

Collegiate Environment: Orientation program. Drama-theater group, student-run newspaper, radio station. Social organizations: 41 open to all. Most popular organizations: Criminal Justice Club, Travel Club, Student Senate, Physical Therapy Club. Major annual event: Arts and Crafts Show. Student services: personal-psychological counseling. Campus security: 24-hour emergency response devices and patrols. Option: coed housing available. Herkimer County Community College Library with 70,000 books, 220 serials, and an OPAC. Operations spending for 2004 fiscal year: $378,636. 222 computers available on campus for general student use. A campuswide network can be accessed from off-campus. Staffed computer lab on campus.

■ **HILBERT COLLEGE** *L-7*
5200 South Park Ave.
Hamburg, NY 14075-1597
Tel: (716)649-7900
Fax: (716)649-0702
Web Site: http://www.hilbert.edu/
Description: Independent, 4-year, coed. Awards associate and bachelor's degrees. Founded 1957. Setting: 40-acre small town campus with easy access to Buffalo. Endowment: $2.9 million. Educational spending for 2005 fiscal year: $5640 per student. Total enrollment: 1,109. Student-undergrad faculty ratio is 16:1. 423 applied, 94% were admitted. 4% from top 10% of their high school class, 17% from top quarter, 48% from top half. Full-time: 723 students, 59% women, 41% men. Part-time: 386 students, 69% women, 31% men. Students come from 6 states and territories, 2 other countries, 76% from out-of-state, 2% Native American, 2% Hispanic, 4% black, 1% Asian American or Pacific Islander, 0.2% international, 31% 25 or older, 10% live on campus, 14% transferred in. Retention: 83% of full-time freshmen returned the following year. Core. Calendar: semesters. Academic remediation for entering students, services for LD students, advanced placement, honors program, independent study, summer session for credit, part-time degree program, co-op programs and internships.

Entrance Requirements: Options: electronic application, early admission, deferred admission, international baccalaureate accepted. Required: high school transcript. Recommended: recommendations, interview, SAT or ACT. Required for some: interview. Entrance: minimally difficult. Application deadline: 9/1. Notification: continuous.

Costs Per Year: Application fee: $20. Comprehensive fee: $20,480 includes full-time tuition ($14,300), mandatory fees ($600), and college room and board ($5580). College room only: $2400. Full-time tuition and fees vary according to course load. Room and board charges vary according to board plan and housing facility. Part-time tuition: $332 per credit hour. Part-time mandatory fees: $13 per credit hour, $55 per term. Part-time tuition and fees vary according to course load.

Collegiate Environment: Orientation program. Drama-theater group, student-run newspaper. Social organizations: 20 open to all. Most popular organizations: Student Government Association, Student Business and Accounting Association, SADD, Students in Free Enterprise (SIFE), Criminal Justice Association. Major annual events: Quad Party, Fall Fest, Student Life Awards. Student services: personal-psychological counseling. Campus security: 24-hour emergency response devices and patrols, student patrols, late night transport-escort service, controlled dormitory access. 134 college housing spaces available; 130 were occupied in 2003-04. Freshmen guaranteed college housing. Option: coed housing available. McGrath Library with 41,322 books, 22,089 microform titles, 12,300 serials, 1,066 audiovisual materials, an OPAC, and a Web page. Operations spending for

2004 fiscal year: $381,684. 146 computers available on campus for general student use. A campuswide network can be accessed from student residence rooms. Staffed computer lab on campus.

Community Environment: Hamburg, population 10,000, is a suburban area adjacent to Buffalo. Within the immediate vicinity there are 18 churches, a theater, shopping center, and major civic, fraternal, and veteran's organizations. Some part-time employment is available for students in the immediate area. The Buffalo Raceway and annual Erie County Fair are here. Rich Stadium, home of the Buffalo Bills, is 5 minutes away and area ski resorts are nearby. All the cultural, community service, and recreational facilities of Buffalo are easily accessible.

■ **HOBART AND WILLIAM SMITH COLLEGES** *K-13*

Geneva, NY 14456-3397
Tel: (315)781-3000
Free: 800-245-0100
Admissions: (315)781-3472
Fax: (315)781-5471
Web Site: http://www.hws.edu/

Description: Independent, 4-year, coed. Awards bachelor's degrees. Founded 1822. Setting: 200-acre small town campus with easy access to Rochester and Syracuse. Endowment: $142 million. Research spending for 2004 fiscal year: $616,940. Educational spending for 2005 fiscal year: $11,244 per student. Total enrollment: 1,883. Student-undergrad faculty ratio is 11:1. 3,410 applied, 65% were admitted. 33% from top 10% of their high school class, 67% from top quarter, 95% from top half. 5 National Merit Scholars, 18 class presidents, 3 valedictorians, 48 student government officers. Full-time: 1,865 students, 54% women, 46% men. Part-time: 3 students, 67% women, 33% men. Students come from 44 states and territories, 10 other countries, 55% from out-of-state, 0.1% Native American, 4% Hispanic, 3% black, 2% Asian American or Pacific Islander, 2% international, 0% 25 or older, 92% live on campus, 0.5% transferred in. Retention: 85% of full-time freshmen returned the following year. Academic areas with the most degrees conferred: social sciences; English; history. Core. Calendar: semesters. ESL program, services for LD students, advanced placement, accelerated degree program, self-designed majors, honors program, independent study, double major, adult/continuing education programs, internships. Off campus study at New York State Visiting Student Program. Study abroad program.

Entrance Requirements: Options: Peterson's Universal Application, Common Application, electronic application, early admission, early decision, deferred admission, international baccalaureate accepted. Required: essay, high school transcript, 1 recommendation, SAT or ACT. Recommended: interview, SAT Subject Tests. Entrance: very difficult. Application deadlines: 2/1, 11/15 for early decision plan 1, 1/1 for early decision plan 2. Notification: 4/1, 12/15 for early decision plan 1, 2/1 for early decision plan 2.

Costs Per Year: Application fee: $45. Comprehensive fee: $41,123 includes full-time tuition ($31,850), mandatory fees ($887), and college room and board ($8386). Room and board charges vary according to board plan.

Collegiate Environment: Orientation program. Drama-theater group, choral group, student-run newspaper, radio station. Social organizations: 60 open to all; national fraternities; 15% of men are members. Most popular organizations: Student Life and Leadership, student government, African-American Student Coalition, Service Network, sports clubs. Major annual events: Folk Festival, Celebrate Service/Celebrate Geneva, Charter Day/Moving Up Day. Student services: legal services, health clinic, personal-psychological counseling, women's center. Campus security: 24-hour emergency response devices and patrols, late night transport-escort service, controlled dormitory access. 1,420 college housing spaces available; all were occupied in 2003-04. Freshmen guaranteed college housing. On-campus residence required through senior year. Options: coed, men-only, women-only housing available. Warren Hunting Smith Library plus 1 other with 380,419 books, 77,510 microform titles, 2,469 serials, 10,733 audiovisual materials, an OPAC, and a Web page. Operations spending for 2004 fiscal year: $2.3 million. 250 computers available on campus for general student use. Computer purchase/lease plans available. A campuswide network can be accessed from student residence rooms and from off campus. Staffed computer lab on campus.

Community Environment: Geneva, population 15,000, is on Seneca Lake, the largest of the Finger Lakes. It is the center of a rich agricultural and nursery region with a number of diversified industries adding to the city's economy. There are several churches of major denominations, a public library, historical museum, YMCA, and many service and fraternal organizations within the town. Seneca lake offers excellent facilities for fishing, boating, and other water sports. Some part-time employment is available.

■ **HOFSTRA UNIVERSITY** *N-37*

100 Hofstra University
Hempstead, NY 11549
Tel: (516)463-6600
Free: 800-HOF-STRA
Admissions: (516)463-6700
Fax: (516)560-7660
E-mail: admitme@hofstra.edu
Web Site: http://www.hofstra.edu/

Description: Independent, university, coed. Awards bachelor's, master's, doctoral, and first professional degrees and post-master's certificates. Founded 1935. Setting: 240-acre suburban campus with easy access to New York City. Endowment: $169.5 million. Research spending for 2004 fiscal year: $3.1 million. Educational spending for 2005 fiscal year: $10,076 per student. Total enrollment: 12,890. Faculty: 1,246 (527 full-time, 719 part-time). Student-undergrad faculty ratio is 14:1. 15,981 applied, 62% were admitted. 24% from top 10% of their high school class, 47% from top quarter, 77% from top half. 36 valedictorians. Full-time: 8,031 students, 54% women, 46% men. Part-time: 853 students, 49% women, 51% men. Students come from 48 states and territories, 51 other countries, 30% from out-of-state, 0.2% Native American, 8% Hispanic, 9% black, 5% Asian American or Pacific Islander, 2% international, 9% 25 or older, 44% live on campus, 8% transferred in. Retention: 78% of full-time freshmen returned the following year. Academic areas with the most degrees conferred: business/marketing; communications/journalism; psychology. Core. Calendar: 4-1-4. ESL program, services for LD students, advanced placement, accelerated degree program, self-designed majors, freshman honors college, honors program, independent study, double major, summer session for credit, part-time degree program, external degree program, adult/continuing education programs, internships, graduate courses open to undergrads. Study abroad program. ROTC: Army.

Entrance Requirements: Options: Peterson's Universal Application, Common Application, electronic application, early admission, early action, deferred admission, international baccalaureate accepted. Required: essay, high school transcript, 1 recommendation, proof of degree required for all; TOEFL required for international students. Recommended: essay, SAT Subject Tests. Required for some: interview, proof of degree required for all; TOEFL required for international students, SAT or ACT. Entrance: moderately difficult. Application deadlines: Rolling, 11/15 for early action. Notification: 2/1, 12/15 for early action.

Costs Per Year: Application fee: $50. Comprehensive fee: $30,830 includes full-time tuition ($20,500), mandatory fees ($1030), and college room and board ($9300). College room only: $6200. Full-time tuition and fees vary according to course load and program. Room and board charges vary according to board plan and housing facility. Part-time tuition: $670 per semester hour. Part-time mandatory fees: $155 per term. Part-time tuition and fees vary according to course load and program.

Collegiate Environment: Orientation program. Drama-theater group, choral group, student-run newspaper, radio station. Social organizations: 144 open to all; national fraternities, national sororities, local fraternities, local sororities; 6% of eligible men and 7% of eligible women are members. Most popular organizations: Student Government Association, Hillel, Entertainment Unlimited, Danceworks. Major annual events: homecoming, Sinterklaas, Freak Formal. Student services: health clinic, personal-psychological counseling. Campus security: 24-hour emergency response devices and patrols, student patrols, late night transport-escort service, controlled dormitory access, security booths and cameras at each residence hall entrance. 4,200 college housing spaces available; 3,880 were occupied in 2003-04. Freshmen given priority for college housing. Options: coed, women-only housing available. Axinn Library plus 1 other with 1.2 million books, 3.5 million microform titles, 8,576 serials, 11,118 audiovisual materials, an OPAC, and a Web page. Operations spending for 2004 fiscal year: $6.9 million. 1,175 computers available on campus for general student use. Computer purchase/lease plans available. A campuswide network can be accessed from student residence rooms and from off campus. Staffed computer lab on campus.

Community Environment: Population 39,500. A residential community and retail shopping center, Hempstead is particularly interesting for its 3 historic churches. A suburban area, it is situated 25 miles east of New York City. The immediate vicinity has a public library, the Nassau Coliseum, shopping mall, YMCA, YWCA, a hospital, churches and synagogues. There are theaters, water sports, and several civic, fraternal and veterans organizations in the city. Kennedy and La Guardia airports are within 30 minutes of the campus.

■ HOLY TRINITY ORTHODOX SEMINARY *K-20*

PO Box 36
Jordanville, NY 13361
Tel: (315)858-0945
Fax: (315)858-0945
Web Site: http://www.hts.edu/

Description: Independent Russian Orthodox, 5-year, men only. Awards bachelor's degrees. Founded 1948. Setting: 900-acre rural campus. Total enrollment: 26. Student-undergrad faculty ratio is 2:1. 10 applied, 80% were admitted. Full-time: 20 students. Part-time: 6 students. Students come from 9 states and territories, 11 other countries, 80% from out-of-state, 0% Native American, 4% Hispanic, 0% black, 0% Asian American or Pacific Islander, 42% international, 8% 25 or older, 100% live on campus, 0% transferred in. Retention: 100% of full-time freshmen returned the following year. Academic area with the most degrees conferred: theology and religious vocations. Core. Calendar: semesters. ESL program, accelerated degree program, distance learning.

Entrance Requirements: Required: essay, high school transcript, recommendations, special examination, proficiency in Russian, Eastern Orthodox baptism. Recommended: minimum 3.0 high school GPA. Entrance: noncompetitive. Application deadline: 5/1.

Costs Per Year: Application fee: $0. Comprehensive fee: $5525 includes full-time tuition ($3000), mandatory fees ($25), and college room and board ($2500). Part-time tuition: $300 per course.

Collegiate Environment: Choral group, student-run newspaper. Social organizations: 1 open to all. Most popular organization: Student Union. Major annual event: Holy Trinity Seminary Colloquium. Student services: health clinic, personal-psychological counseling. Campus security: 24-hour emergency response devices. 50 college housing spaces available; 32 were occupied in 2003-04. Freshmen guaranteed college housing. On-campus residence required through senior year. Option: men-only housing available. Holy Trinity Orthodox Seminary Library plus 1 other with 25,000 books, 200 serials, and 250 audiovisual materials. 8 computers available on campus for general student use. Staffed computer lab on campus.

■ HOUGHTON COLLEGE *M-9*

One Willard Ave.
Houghton, NY 14744
Tel: (585)567-9200
Free: 800-777-2556
Admissions: (585)567-9353
Fax: (585)567-9522
E-mail: admissions@houghton.edu
Web Site: http://www.houghton.edu/

Description: Independent Wesleyan, comprehensive, coed. Awards associate, bachelor's, and master's degrees. Founded 1883. Setting: 1,300-acre rural campus with easy access to Buffalo and Rochester. Endowment: $32.3 million. Research spending for 2004 fiscal year: $19,290. Educational spending for 2005 fiscal year: $8921 per student. Total enrollment: 1,411. Faculty: 103 (88 full-time, 15 part-time). Student-undergrad faculty ratio is 13:1. 1,176 applied, 77% were admitted. 32% from top 10% of their high school class, 68% from top quarter, 91% from top half. 5 National Merit Scholars, 21 valedictorians. Full-time: 1,337 students, 67% women, 33% men. Part-time: 61 students, 57% women, 43% men. Students come from 41 states and territories, 21 other countries, 37% from out-of-state, 0.1% Native American, 1% Hispanic, 3% black, 1% Asian American or Pacific Islander, 3% international, 10% 25 or older, 82% live on campus, 7% transferred in. Retention: 84% of full-time freshmen returned the following year. Academic areas with the most degrees conferred: business/marketing; education; English. Core. Calendar: semesters. Services for LD students, advanced placement, honors program, independent study, double major, summer session for credit, part-time degree program, adult/continuing education programs, internships, graduate courses open to undergrads. Off campus study at members of the Western New York Consortium and the Christian College Consortium. Study abroad program. ROTC: Army (c).

Entrance Requirements: Options: electronic application, deferred admission, international baccalaureate accepted. Required: essay, high school transcript, 1 recommendation, pastoral recommendation, SAT or ACT. Recommended: minimum 2.5 high school GPA, interview. Entrance: moderately difficult. Application deadline: Rolling. Notification: continuous. Preference given to Evangelical Christians and members of the Wesleyan Church.

Costs Per Year: Application fee: $40. Comprehensive fee: $25,980 includes full-time tuition ($19,420) and college room and board ($6560). Full-time tuition varies according to class time, program, and reciprocity agreements. Room and board charges vary according to board plan and housing facility. Part-time tuition: $812 per hour.

Collegiate Environment: Orientation program. Drama-theater group, choral group, student-run newspaper. Social organizations: 50 open to all. Most popular organizations: One Thing, Allegany County Outreach, World Mission Fellowship, Campus Activities Board, International Student Organization. Major annual events: SPOT, Midnight Breakfast, International Student banquet. Student services: health clinic, personal-psychological counseling. Campus security: 24-hour patrols, late night transport-escort service, controlled dormitory access, phone connection to security patrols. 1,059 college housing spaces available; 999 were occupied in 2003-04. Freshmen guaranteed college housing. On-campus residence required through senior year. Options: men-only, women-only housing available. Willard J. Houghton Library plus 1 other with 242,866 books, 39,550 microform titles, 4,110 serials, 2,918 audiovisual materials, an OPAC, and a Web page. Operations spending for 2004 fiscal year: $868,879. 50 computers available on campus for general student use. A campuswide network can be accessed from student residence rooms and from off campus. Staffed computer lab on campus.

Community Environment: Houghton is a small rural community in southwestern New York, just south of Letchworth State Park. Nearby state park makes available good fishing, hunting, and skiing in season. The college also has its own ski slopes with rope-tow, an initiatives rope course, an equestrian riding program and miles of cross-country ski trails.

■ HUDSON VALLEY COMMUNITY COLLEGE *K-25*

80 Vandenburgh Ave.
Troy, NY 12180-6096
Tel: (518)629-4822
Admissions: (518)629-4603
Web Site: http://www.hvcc.edu/

Description: State and locally supported, 2-year, coed. Part of State University of New York System. Awards certificates, transfer associate, and terminal associate degrees. Founded 1953. Setting: 135-acre suburban campus. Endowment: $3.7 million. Educational spending for 2005 fiscal year: $6736 per student. Total enrollment: 12,205. Student-undergrad faculty ratio is 19:1. 8,000 applied, 90% were admitted. 10% from top 10% of their high school class, 20% from top quarter, 50% from top half. Students come from 21 states and territories, 18 other countries, 5% from out-of-state, 0.3% Native American, 3% Hispanic, 8% black, 2% Asian American or Pacific Islander, 1% international, 35% 25 or older. Retention: 60% of full-time freshmen returned the following year. Calendar: semesters. Academic remediation for entering students, services for LD students, advanced placement, self-designed majors, summer session for credit, part-time degree program, external degree program, adult/continuing education programs, co-op programs and internships. Off campus study at 14 members of the Hudson-Mohawk Association of Colleges and Universities. ROTC: Army, Air Force (c).

Entrance Requirements: Open admission for individual studies program. Options: early admission, deferred admission. Required: high school transcript. Entrance: minimally difficult. Application deadline: Rolling. Notification: continuous.

Costs Per Year: Application fee: $30. State resident tuition: $2700 full-time, $112 per credit hour part-time. Nonresident tuition: $8100 full-time, $336 per credit hour part-time. Mandatory fees: $480 full-time, $14 per credit hour part-time.

Collegiate Environment: Drama-theater group, student-run newspaper, radio station. Student services: legal services, health clinic, personal-psychological counseling, women's center. Campus security: 24-hour emergency response devices and patrols, late night transport-escort service. College housing not available. Marvin Library with 148,189 books and 691 serials. 500 computers available on campus for general student use. A campuswide network can be accessed from off-campus. Staffed computer lab on campus.

■ HUNTER COLLEGE OF THE CITY UNIVERSITY OF NEW YORK *N-34*

695 Park Ave.
New York, NY 10021-5085
Tel: (212)772-4000
Admissions: (212)772-4490

Web Site: http://www.hunter.cuny.edu/

Description: State and locally supported, comprehensive, coed. Part of City University of New York System. Awards bachelor's and master's degrees and post-master's certificates. Founded 1870. Setting: urban campus. Total enrollment: 20,843. Faculty: 1,435 (633 full-time, 802 part-time). Student-undergrad faculty ratio is 14:1. 20,985 applied, 35% were admitted. 19% from top 10% of their high school class, 50% from top quarter, 78% from top half. Full-time: 10,406 students, 69% women, 31% men. Part-time: 5,225 students, 68% women, 32% men. Students come from 35 states and territories, 153 other countries, 4% from out-of-state, 0.2% Native American, 20% Hispanic, 14% black, 17% Asian American or Pacific Islander, 7% international, 31% 25 or older, 1% live on campus, 9% transferred in. Retention: 82% of full-time freshmen returned the following year. Academic areas with the most degrees conferred: social sciences; English; psychology. Core. Calendar: semesters. ESL program, services for LD students, advanced placement, self-designed majors, freshman honors college, honors program, independent study, distance learning, double major, summer session for credit, part-time degree program, internships, graduate courses open to undergrads. Off campus study at Marymount Manhattan College, New School for Social Research, YIVD Institute, other units of the City University of New York System. Study abroad program.

Entrance Requirements: Options: early admission, international baccalaureate accepted. Required: high school transcript, SAT or ACT. Entrance: moderately difficult. Application deadline: 3/15. Notification: continuous until 1/3.

Costs Per Year: Application fee: $65. State resident tuition: $4000 full-time, $170 per credit part-time. Nonresident tuition: $10,800 full-time, $360 per credit part-time. Mandatory fees: $349 full-time, $107 per term part-time. College room only: $3478.

Collegiate Environment: Orientation program. Drama-theater group, choral group, student-run newspaper, radio station. Social organizations: local fraternities, local sororities. Student services: personal-psychological counseling, women's center. Campus security: 24-hour emergency response devices and patrols. 612 college housing spaces available. Option: coed housing available. Hunter College Library with 789,718 books, 1.2 million microform titles, 4,282 serials, 13,489 audiovisual materials, an OPAC, and a Web page. 750 computers available on campus for general student use. A campuswide network can be accessed. Staffed computer lab on campus.

■ **INSTITUTE OF DESIGN AND CONSTRUCTION** *O-34*
141 Willoughby St.
Brooklyn, NY 11201-5317
Tel: (718)855-3661
Fax: (718)852-5889
Web Site: http://www.idcbrooklyn.org/

Description: Independent, 2-year, coed. Awards transfer associate degrees. Founded 1947. Setting: urban campus. Total enrollment: 246. 84 applied, 86% were admitted. Students come from 3 states and territories, 3% from out-of-state, 0% Native American, 21% Hispanic, 36% black, 8% Asian American or Pacific Islander, 2% international, 59% 25 or older. Core. Calendar: semesters. Academic remediation for entering students, advanced placement, summer session for credit, part-time degree program, adult/continuing education programs, co-op programs.

Entrance Requirements: Option: Common Application. Required: high school transcript. Recommended: interview. Entrance: noncompetitive. Application deadline: Rolling. Notification: continuous until 9/30.

Collegiate Environment: Student services: personal-psychological counseling. College housing not available. 17 computers available on campus for general student use.

■ **INTERBORO INSTITUTE** *N-34*
450 West 56th St.
New York, NY 10019-3602
Tel: (212)399-0093
Admissions: (212)399-0091
Fax: (212)765-5772
E-mail: ryan@interboro.com
Web Site: http://www.interboro.com/

Description: Proprietary, 2-year, coed. Awards terminal associate degrees. Founded 1888. Setting: urban campus. Educational spending for 2005 fiscal year: $518 per student. Total enrollment: 1,891. 1,765 applied, 58% were admitted. Full-time: 1,891 students, 66% women, 34% men. Students come from 10 other countries, 0% from out-of-state, 0% Native American, 38% Hispanic, 46% black, 4% Asian American or Pacific Islander, 1% interna-

tional, 27% 25 or older. Core. Calendar: semesters. Academic remediation for entering students, advanced placement, accelerated degree program, independent study, summer session for credit, adult/continuing education programs, co-op programs and internships.

Entrance Requirements: Open admission. Option: deferred admission. Required: essay, interview. Recommended: high school transcript. Placement: CPAt required for some. Entrance: noncompetitive. Application deadline: Rolling. Notification: continuous.

Collegiate Environment: Orientation program. Student-run newspaper. Social organizations: local fraternities, local sororities. Most popular organization: OPT Society. Major annual events: Interboro Day, Senior Dinner. Student services: personal-psychological counseling. Campus security: student patrols. College housing not available. Interboro Library with 5,986 books, 70 serials, 50 audiovisual materials, an OPAC, and a Web page. Operations spending for 2004 fiscal year: $200,000. 200 computers available on campus for general student use. A campuswide network can be accessed from off-campus. Staffed computer lab on campus.

■ **IONA COLLEGE** *L-36*
715 North Ave.
New Rochelle, NY 10801-1890
Tel: (914)633-2000
Admissions: (914)633-2502
Fax: (914)633-2096
E-mail: TWeede@iona.edu
Web Site: http://www.iona.edu/

Description: Independent, comprehensive, coed, affiliated with Roman Catholic Church. Awards bachelor's and master's degrees and post-master's certificates. Founded 1940. Setting: 35-acre suburban campus with easy access to New York City. Endowment: $21.3 million. Research spending for 2004 fiscal year: $220,968. Educational spending for 2005 fiscal year: $7230 per student. Total enrollment: 4,184. Faculty: 373 (176 full-time, 197 part-time). Student-undergrad faculty ratio is 15:1. 4,802 applied, 67% were admitted. 29% from top 10% of their high school class, 51% from top quarter, 94% from top half. 28 class presidents, 16 valedictorians, 151 student government officers. Full-time: 3,122 students, 54% women, 46% men. Part-time: 243 students, 49% women, 51% men. Students come from 37 states and territories, 51 other countries, 19% from out-of-state, 0.2% Native American, 11% Hispanic, 7% black, 2% Asian American or Pacific Islander, 2% international, 9% 25 or older, 30% live on campus, 5% transferred in. Retention: 80% of full-time freshmen returned the following year. Academic areas with the most degrees conferred: business/marketing; communications/journalism; education. Core. Calendar: semesters. Services for LD students, advanced placement, accelerated degree program, honors program, distance learning, double major, summer session for credit, part-time degree program, adult/continuing education programs, internships, graduate courses open to undergrads. Off campus study at College of New Rochelle, Concordia College (NY), Marymount College. Study abroad program. ROTC: Army (c).

Entrance Requirements: Options: Peterson's Universal Application, Common Application, early admission, early action, deferred admission, international baccalaureate accepted. Required: high school transcript, SAT or ACT. Recommended: essay, minimum 2.5 high school GPA, recommendations, interview, SAT Subject Tests. Entrance: moderately difficult. Application deadlines: 2/15, 12/1 for early action. Notification: 12/21 for early action.

Costs Per Year: Application fee: $50. Comprehensive fee: $30,878 includes full-time tuition ($20,110), mandatory fees ($870), and college room and board ($9898). Full-time tuition and fees vary according to class time. Room and board charges vary according to housing facility. Part-time tuition: $667 per credit. Part-time mandatory fees: $370 per term. Part-time tuition and fees vary according to class time and course load.

Collegiate Environment: Orientation program. Drama-theater group, choral group, marching band, student-run newspaper, radio station. Social organizations: 65 open to all; national fraternities, national sororities, local fraternities, local sororities; 4% of eligible men and 6% of eligible women are members. Most popular organizations: Council of Multicultural Leaders, student government, The Ionian, LASO, WICR. Major annual events: Founders' Day, Homecoming, Club Day. Student services: health clinic, personal-psychological counseling. Campus security: 24-hour emergency response devices and patrols, controlled dormitory access. 1,028 college housing spaces available; 1,017 were occupied in 2003-04. Freshmen given priority for college housing. Option: coed housing available. Ryan Library plus 2 others with 269,933 books, 509,742 microform titles, 763 serials,

3,018 audiovisual materials, an OPAC, and a Web page. Operations spending for 2004 fiscal year: $1.5 million. 500 computers available on campus for general student use. Computer purchase/lease plans available. A campuswide network can be accessed from student residence rooms and from off campus. Staffed computer lab on campus.

Community Environment: Population 75,400. An attractive residential suburb is 35 minutes from the center of Manhattan. Located on Long Island Sound, New Rochelle was settled by the Huguenots in 1688. Many houses date from the days of Dutch and English occupancy. Easy access to New York City is provided by rail and bus lines. There are many churches, a YMCA, hospital, public library, and various fraternal, civic, and veteran's organizations. Recreation in the area is provided by 8 miles of Long Island Sound frontage, inland lakes, and public parks as well as facilities for golf, tennis, canoeing, fishing, skating, and hockey. Part-time employment is available.

■ **ISLAND DRAFTING AND TECHNICAL INSTITUTE** *P-42*
128 Broadway
Amityville, NY 11701
Tel: (631)691-8733
Fax: (631)691-8738
E-mail: info@idti.edu
Web Site: http://www.idti.edu/
Description: Proprietary, 2-year, coed. Awards certificates, diplomas, transfer associate, and terminal associate degrees. Founded 1957. Setting: suburban campus. Total enrollment: 185. Student-undergrad faculty ratio is 15:1. 77 applied, 100% were admitted. 5% from top 10% of their high school class, 25% from top quarter, 80% from top half. Full-time: 185 students, 15% women, 85% men. 2% Native American, 18% Hispanic, 14% black, 1% Asian American or Pacific Islander, 0% international, 56% 25 or older. Core. Calendar: semesters. Accelerated degree program, summer session for credit, adult/continuing education programs.
Entrance Requirements: Open admission. Options: early admission, international baccalaureate accepted. Required: interview. Recommended: high school transcript. Entrance: noncompetitive. Notification: continuous.
Costs Per Year: Tuition: $11,850 full-time, $395 per credit part-time. Mandatory fees: $350 full-time.
Collegiate Environment: College housing not available.

■ **ITHACA COLLEGE** *M-15*
100 Job Hall
Ithaca, NY 14850-7020
Tel: (607)274-3011
Free: 800-429-4274
Admissions: (607)274-3124
Fax: (607)274-1900
E-mail: admission@ithaca.edu
Web Site: http://www.ithaca.edu/
Description: Independent, comprehensive, coed. Awards bachelor's, master's, and doctoral degrees. Founded 1892. Setting: 757-acre small town campus with easy access to Syracuse. Endowment: $128.1 million. Research spending for 2004 fiscal year: $2.4 million. Educational spending for 2005 fiscal year: $10,116 per student. Total enrollment: 6,412. Faculty: 656 (442 full-time, 214 part-time). Student-undergrad faculty ratio is 12:1. 10,421 applied, 76% were admitted. 29% from top 10% of their high school class, 64% from top quarter, 94% from top half. 8 National Merit Scholars, 26 valedictorians. Full-time: 5,961 students, 55% women, 45% men. Part-time: 137 students, 66% women, 34% men. Students come from 51 states and territories, 67 other countries, 53% from out-of-state, 0.4% Native American, 3% Hispanic, 3% black, 3% Asian American or Pacific Islander, 3% international, 1% 25 or older, 70% live on campus, 2% transferred in. Retention: 86% of full-time freshmen returned the following year. Academic areas with the most degrees conferred: communications/journalism; visual and performing arts; business/marketing. Calendar: semesters. Services for LD students, advanced placement, accelerated degree program, self-designed majors, freshman honors college, honors program, independent study, double major, summer session for credit, part-time degree program, adult/continuing education programs, internships, graduate courses open to undergrads. Off campus study at Cornell University, Wells College. Study abroad program. ROTC: Army (c), Air Force (c).
Entrance Requirements: Options: Common Application, electronic application, early admission, early decision, deferred admission, international baccalaureate accepted. Required: essay, high school transcript, 1 recommendation, SAT or ACT. Recommended: minimum 3.0 high school GPA,

interview. Required for some: audition. Entrance: moderately difficult. Application deadlines: 2/1, 11/1 for early decision. Notification: continuous until 4/15, 12/15 for early decision.
Costs Per Year: Application fee: $55. Comprehensive fee: $35,144 includes full-time tuition ($25,194) and college room and board ($9950). College room only: $5120. Part-time tuition: $840 per credit hour.
Collegiate Environment: Orientation program. Drama-theater group, choral group, student-run newspaper, radio station. Social organizations: 165 open to all; national fraternities, national sororities, local fraternities; 1% of eligible men and 1% of eligible women are members. Most popular organizations: student government, Student Activities Board, African-Latino Society, Residence Hall Association, Community Service Network. Major annual events: major concerts, Winterfest, Leadership Weekend. Student services: health clinic, personal-psychological counseling. Campus security: 24-hour emergency response devices, student patrols, late night transport-escort service, controlled dormitory access, patrols by trained security personnel 11 p.m. to 7 a.m. 4,296 college housing spaces available; 4,218 were occupied in 2003-04. Freshmen guaranteed college housing. On-campus residence required through junior year. Options: coed, women-only housing available. Ithaca College Library with 376,000 books, 250,100 microform titles, 37,000 serials, 33,000 audiovisual materials, an OPAC, and a Web page. Operations spending for 2004 fiscal year: $3.2 million. 640 computers available on campus for general student use. Computer purchase/lease plans available. A campuswide network can be accessed from student residence rooms and from off campus. Staffed computer lab on campus.
Community Environment: See Cornell University.

■ **ITT TECHNICAL INSTITUTE (ALBANY)** *L-25*
13 Airline Dr.
Albany, NY 12205
Tel: (518)452-9300
Web Site: http://www.itt-tech.edu/
Description: Proprietary, 2-year, coed. Part of ITT Educational Services, Inc. Awards terminal associate degrees. Core.
Entrance Requirements: Option: deferred admission. Required: high school transcript, interview, Wonderlic aptitude test. Recommended: recommendations. Entrance: minimally difficult. Application deadline: Rolling. Notification: continuous.
Costs Per Year: Application fee: $100.
Collegiate Environment: Orientation program. College housing not available.

■ **ITT TECHNICAL INSTITUTE (GETZVILLE)** *J-7*
2295 Millersport Hwy.
PO Box 327
Getzville, NY 14068
Tel: (716)689-2200
Web Site: http://www.itt-tech.edu/
Description: Proprietary, 2-year, coed. Part of ITT Educational Services, Inc. Awards terminal associate degrees. Core.
Entrance Requirements: Option: deferred admission. Required: high school transcript, interview, Wonderlic aptitude test. Recommended: recommendations. Entrance: minimally difficult. Application deadline: Rolling. Notification: continuous.
Costs Per Year: Application fee: $100.
Collegiate Environment: Orientation program. College housing not available.

■ **ITT TECHNICAL INSTITUTE (LIVERPOOL)** *A-8*
235 Greenfield Parkway
Liverpool, NY 13088
Tel: (315)461-8000
Web Site: http://www.itt-tech.edu/
Description: Proprietary, 2-year, coed. Part of ITT Educational Services, Inc. Awards terminal associate degrees. Core. Calendar: semesters.
Entrance Requirements: Option: deferred admission. Required: high school transcript, interview, Wonderlic aptitude test. Recommended: recommendations. Entrance: minimally difficult. Application deadline: Rolling. Notification: continuous.
Costs Per Year: Application fee: $100.
Collegiate Environment: Orientation program. College housing not available.

■ **JAMESTOWN BUSINESS COLLEGE** *N-5*
7 Fairmount Ave., Box 429
Jamestown, NY 14702-0429

Tel: (716)664-5100
Fax: (716)664-3144
E-mail: jbc@epix.net
Web Site: http://www.jbcny.org/
Description: Proprietary, 2-year, coed. Awards certificates and terminal associate degrees. Founded 1886. Setting: 1-acre small town campus. Total enrollment: 327. 112 applied, 72% were admitted. 2% from top 10% of their high school class, 8% from top quarter, 34% from top half. Full-time: 327 students, 81% women, 19% men. Students come from 2 states and territories, 17% from out-of-state, 1% Native American, 4% Hispanic, 2% black, 0.3% Asian American or Pacific Islander, 0% international, 55% 25 or older, 14% transferred in. Core. Academic remediation for entering students, advanced placement, double major, summer session for credit, part-time degree program, internships.
Entrance Requirements: Required: essay, high school transcript, interview. Entrance: minimally difficult. Application deadline: Rolling.
Costs Per Year: Application fee: $25. Tuition: $8400 full-time, $233 per credit hour part-time. Mandatory fees: $450 full-time, $75 per term part-time.
Collegiate Environment: Orientation program. Major annual events: food drives, Halloween Party, Christmas Party. Campus security: 24-hour emergency response devices. College housing not available. James Prendergast Library with 279,270 books, 372 serials, an OPAC, and a Web page. 106 computers available on campus for general student use. A campuswide network can be accessed from off-campus. Staffed computer lab on campus.

■ **JAMESTOWN COMMUNITY COLLEGE** *N-5*
525 Falconer St.
Jamestown, NY 14701-1999
Tel: (716)665-5220
Web Site: http://www.sunyjcc.edu/
Description: State and locally supported, 2-year, coed. Part of State University of New York System. Awards certificates, transfer associate, and terminal associate degrees. Founded 1950. Setting: 107-acre small town campus. Endowment: $274,625. Total enrollment: 3,672. Student-undergrad faculty ratio is 18:1. 1,668 applied, 82% were admitted. 54% from top half of their high school class. Full-time: 2,460 students, 57% women, 43% men. Part-time: 1,212 students, 63% women, 37% men. Students come from 11 states and territories, 9% from out-of-state, 1% Native American, 2% Hispanic, 3% black, 1% Asian American or Pacific Islander, 32% 25 or older. Core. Calendar: semesters. Academic remediation for entering students, services for LD students, advanced placement, honors program, independent study, distance learning, double major, summer session for credit, part-time degree program, adult/continuing education programs, co-op programs and internships. Off campus study at State University of New York College at Fredonia, Jamestown Business College. Study abroad program.
Entrance Requirements: Open admission except for nursing, human services, occupational therapy assistant programs. Option: deferred admission. Required: high school transcript. Required for some: standardized test scores. Entrance: noncompetitive. Application deadline: Rolling. Notification: continuous. Preference given to Chautauqua and Cattaraugus county residents.
Costs Per Year: Application fee: $40. State resident tuition: $3150 full-time, $132 per credit hour part-time. Nonresident tuition: $6300 full-time, $238 per credit hour part-time. Mandatory fees: $530 full-time, $16.75 per credit hour part-time. Full-time tuition and fees vary according to program.
Collegiate Environment: Drama-theater group, choral group, student-run radio station. Social organizations: 12 open to all. Most popular organizations: Nursing Club, Inter-Varsity Christian Fellowship, Earth Awareness, Adult Student Network, Student Senate. Major annual events: Fall Picnic, Spring Picnic/Spring Fling, Orientation. Student services: health clinic, personal-psychological counseling. College housing not available. Hultquist Library with 66,808 books, 49,364 microform titles, 370 serials, 4,605 audiovisual materials, an OPAC, and a Web page. 400 computers available on campus for general student use. A campuswide network can be accessed from off-campus. Staffed computer lab on campus.

■ **JEFFERSON COMMUNITY COLLEGE** *F-17*
1220 Coffeen St.
Watertown, NY 13601
Tel: (315)786-2200
Admissions: (315)786-2277
Fax: (315)786-0158
E-mail: admissions@sunyjefferson.edu

Web Site: http://www.sunyjefferson.edu/
Description: State and locally supported, 2-year, coed. Part of State University of New York System. Awards certificates, transfer associate, and terminal associate degrees. Founded 1961. Setting: 90-acre small town campus with easy access to Syracuse. Endowment: $2.1 million. Educational spending for 2005 fiscal year: $2623 per student. Total enrollment: 3,545. Student-undergrad faculty ratio is 20:1. Full-time: 1,822 students, 61% women, 39% men. Part-time: 1,723 students, 56% women, 44% men. Students come from 26 states and territories, 3 other countries, 1% from out-of-state, 1% Native American, 4% Hispanic, 5% black, 2% Asian American or Pacific Islander, 0.2% international, 37% 25 or older, 3% transferred in. Calendar: semesters. Academic remediation for entering students, services for LD students, advanced placement, self-designed majors, honors program, independent study, distance learning, double major, summer session for credit, part-time degree program, co-op programs and internships.
Entrance Requirements: Options: early admission, deferred admission. Required: high school transcript. Recommended: SAT or ACT. Required for some: recommendations, interview. Entrance: minimally difficult. Application deadline: 9/6. Notification: continuous. Preference given to county residents.
Costs Per Year: Application fee: $0. State resident tuition: $3294 full-time, $122 per credit hour part-time. Nonresident tuition: $4724 full-time, $182 per credit hour part-time. Mandatory fees: $366 full-time, $13 per credit hour part-time, $21.
Collegiate Environment: Orientation program. Drama-theater group, choral group, student-run newspaper. Social organizations: 25 open to all. Most popular organizations: Student Nursing Association, newspaper, The Melting Pot, Paralegal Club, Criminal Justice Club. Major annual events: Fall Fest/Spring Fest, Stage/Theater Production, Black History Month. Student services: health clinic, personal-psychological counseling. Campus security: 24-hour emergency response devices and patrols. College housing not available. Melvil Dewey Library with 62,503 books, 27,854 microform titles, 247 serials, 4,097 audiovisual materials, an OPAC, and a Web page. Operations spending for 2004 fiscal year: $321,415. 354 computers available on campus for general student use. A campuswide network can be accessed. Staffed computer lab on campus.

■ **THE JEWISH THEOLOGICAL SEMINARY** *N-34*
3080 Broadway
New York, NY 10027-4649
Tel: (212)678-8000
Fax: (212)678-8947
Web Site: http://www.jtsa.edu/
Description: Independent Jewish, university, coed. Awards bachelor's, master's, doctoral, and first professional degrees (double bachelor's degree with Barnard College, Columbia University, joint bachelor's degree with Columbia University). Founded 1886. Setting: 1-acre urban campus. Endowment: $80 million. Total enrollment: 669. 120 applied, 68% were admitted. Students come from 23 states and territories, 2 other countries, 65% from out-of-state, 4% Hispanic, 1% 25 or older, 77% live on campus. Retention: 92% of full-time freshmen returned the following year. Core. Calendar: semesters. Academic remediation for entering students, services for LD students, advanced placement, self-designed majors, freshman honors college, honors program, distance learning, double major, summer session for credit, part-time degree program, adult/continuing education programs, internships, graduate courses open to undergrads. Off campus study at Barnard College, Columbia University. Study abroad program.
Entrance Requirements: Options: early admission, early decision, deferred admission, international baccalaureate accepted. Required: essay, high school transcript, 2 recommendations, SAT and SAT Subject Tests or ACT. Recommended: minimum 3.0 high school GPA, interview. Entrance: very difficult. Application deadlines: 2/15, 11/15 for early decision plan 1, 1/15 for early decision plan 2. Notification: continuous until 4/15, 12/15 for early decision plan 1, 2/15 for early decision plan 2.
Collegiate Environment: Orientation program. Drama-theater group, choral group, student-run newspaper, radio station. Student services: health clinic, personal-psychological counseling, women's center. Campus security: 24-hour emergency response devices and patrols, late night transport-escort service, controlled dormitory access. Freshmen guaranteed college housing. Option: coed housing available. Library of the Jewish Theological Seminary with 380,000 books, 720 serials, an OPAC, and a Web page. 50 computers available on campus for general student use. A campuswide network can be accessed from student residence rooms and from off campus. Staffed computer lab on campus.

Community Environment: See Columbia University.

■ **JOHN JAY COLLEGE OF CRIMINAL JUSTICE OF THE CITY UNIVERSITY OF NEW YORK** *N-34*
899 Tenth Ave.
New York, NY 10019-1093
Tel: (212)237-8000; 877-JOHNJAY
Admissions: (212)237-8878
Web Site: http://www.jjay.cuny.edu/
Description: State and locally supported, comprehensive, coed. Part of City University of New York System. Awards associate, bachelor's, master's, and doctoral degrees. Founded 1964. Setting: urban campus. Endowment: $221,000. Educational spending for 2005 fiscal year: $3790 per student. Total enrollment: 12,984. 6,123 applied, 44% were admitted. 20% from top quarter of their high school class, 66% from top half. Students come from 52 states and territories, 0.2% Native American, 36% Hispanic, 25% black, 6% Asian American or Pacific Islander, 35% 25 or older. Retention: 72% of full-time freshmen returned the following year. Core. Calendar: semesters. Academic remediation for entering students, ESL program, services for LD students, advanced placement, honors program, summer session for credit, part-time degree program, co-op programs and internships, graduate courses open to undergrads. Off campus study at other units of the City University of New York System. ROTC: Air Force (c).
Entrance Requirements: Open admission for Associate degree programs. Options: early admission, deferred admission. Required: high school transcript, minimum 2.0 high school GPA, SAT or ACT. Entrance: moderately difficult. Application deadline: 3/15. Notification: continuous.
Costs Per Year: Application fee: $50. State resident tuition: $4000 full-time, $170 per credit part-time. Nonresident tuition: $8640 full-time, $360 per credit part-time. Mandatory fees: $259 full-time, $82.35 per term part-time. Full-time tuition and fees vary according to course level and course load. Part-time tuition and fees vary according to course level and course load.
Collegiate Environment: Drama-theater group, choral group, student-run newspaper, radio station. Social organizations: 38 open to all. Most popular organizations: Organization of Black Students, Latino Diversity Club, Lex Review, Women's Awareness Club, Forensic Psychology Society. Student services: legal services, health clinic, personal-psychological counseling, women's center. Campus security: 24-hour emergency response devices and patrols. College housing not available. Lloyd George Sealy Library with 310,000 books, 1,325 serials, and an OPAC. Operations spending for 2004 fiscal year: $1.5 million. 250 computers available on campus for general student use. A campuswide network can be accessed from off-campus. Staffed computer lab on campus.

■ **THE JUILLIARD SCHOOL** *N-34*
60 Lincoln Center Plaza
New York, NY 10023-6588
Tel: (212)799-5000
Fax: (212)724-0263
Web Site: http://www.juilliard.edu/
Description: Independent, comprehensive, coed. Awards bachelor's, master's, and doctoral degrees and post-master's certificates. Founded 1905. Setting: urban campus. Endowment: $478.1 million. Educational spending for 2005 fiscal year: $24,330 per student. Total enrollment: 808. Faculty: 266 (114 full-time, 152 part-time). 2,523 applied, 5% were admitted. Full-time: 478 students, 48% women, 52% men. Part-time: 3 students, 100% women. Students come from 41 states and territories, 29 other countries, 85% from out-of-state, 0.4% Native American, 4% Hispanic, 12% black, 13% Asian American or Pacific Islander, 20% international, 60% live on campus, 6% transferred in. Retention: 94% of full-time freshmen returned the following year. Academic area with the most degrees conferred: visual and performing arts. Core. Calendar: semesters. ESL program, accelerated degree program, double major, adult/continuing education programs, graduate courses open to undergrads. Off campus study at Barnard College, Columbia University. Study abroad program.
Entrance Requirements: Option: electronic application. Required: essay, high school transcript, audition. Entrance: most difficult. Application deadline: 12/1. Notification: 4/1.
Costs Per Year: Application fee: $100. Comprehensive fee: $34,500 includes full-time tuition ($24,330), mandatory fees ($600), and college room and board ($9570). Room and board charges vary according to housing facility.
Collegiate Environment: Orientation program. Drama-theater group, choral group, student-run newspaper. Social organizations: 15 open to all. Most

popular organizations: ArtREACH, Korean Campus Crusade for Christ, Julliard Christian Fellowship, The Forum, Artists Inspired. Major annual events: Opening Day Picnic on the Plaza, Halloween Dance, Spring Picnic on the Plaza. Student services: legal services, health clinic, personal-psychological counseling. Campus security: 24-hour emergency response devices and patrols, controlled dormitory access, electronically operated main building entrances. 348 college housing spaces available; 300 were occupied in 2003-04. Freshmen guaranteed college housing. On-campus residence required in freshman year. Option: coed housing available. Lila Acheson Wallace Library with 80,793 books, 153 microform titles, 220 serials, 21,867 audiovisual materials, an OPAC, and a Web page. 34 computers available on campus for general student use. A campuswide network can be accessed from off-campus. Staffed computer lab on campus.
Community Environment: See New York University.

■ **KATHARINE GIBBS SCHOOL (MELVILLE)** *M-39*
320 South Service Rd.
Melville, NY 11747-3785
Tel: (631)370-3300
Admissions: (631)370-3307
Fax: (631)293-1276
Web Site: http://www.gibbsmelville.com/
Description: Proprietary, 2-year, coed. Part of Career Education Corporation. Awards certificates, transfer associate, and terminal associate degrees. Founded 1971. Setting: suburban campus with easy access to New York City. Total enrollment: 897. 0% Native American, 6% Hispanic, 12% black, 1% Asian American or Pacific Islander, 0% international. Internships. ROTC: Army (c).
Entrance Requirements: Option: deferred admission. Required: high school transcript, interview. Recommended: recommendations, SAT. Required for some: CPAt. Entrance: minimally difficult. Application deadline: Rolling. Notification: continuous.
Collegiate Environment: Student-run newspaper. Student services: personal-psychological counseling. Campus security: security guard. Katherine Gibbs School Library with 26 serials. 120 computers available on campus for general student use.

■ **KATHARINE GIBBS SCHOOL (NEW YORK)** *N-34*
200 Park Ave.
New York, NY 10166-0005
Tel: (212)867-9300
Web Site: http://www.katharinegibbs.com/
Description: Proprietary, 2-year, coed. Part of Career Education Corporation. Awards certificates, transfer associate, and terminal associate degrees. Founded 1918. Setting: urban campus. Total enrollment: 2,717. Full-time: 2,717 students, 59% women, 41% men. Students come from 6 states and territories, 1% from out-of-state, 56% 25 or older. Core. Accelerated degree program, part-time degree program, adult/continuing education programs, co-op programs and internships.
Entrance Requirements: Options: deferred admission, international baccalaureate accepted. Required: essay, high school transcript, interview. Recommended: SAT. Required for some: CPAt. Entrance: minimally difficult. Application deadline: Rolling. Notification: continuous.
Collegiate Environment: Drama-theater group, student-run newspaper. Student services: personal-psychological counseling. College housing not available. 50 computers available on campus for general student use.

■ **KEHILATH YAKOV RABBINICAL SEMINARY** *O-34*
206 Wilson St.
Brooklyn, NY 11211-7207
Tel: (718)963-1212
Fax: (718)387-8586
Description: Independent Jewish, comprehensive, men only. Awards bachelor's and master's degrees. Founded 1950. Total enrollment: 135. 40 applied, 75% were admitted. 15% 25 or older. Calendar: semesters.
Collegiate Environment: College housing not available.

■ **KEUKA COLLEGE** *L-13*
Keuka Park, NY 14478-0098
Tel: (315)279-5000
Free: 800-33-KEUKA
Admissions: (315)279-5262
Fax: (315)279-5216
E-mail: admissions@mail.keuka.edu

Web Site: http://www.keuka.edu/

Description: Independent, comprehensive, coed, affiliated with American Baptist Churches in the U.S.A.. Awards bachelor's and master's degrees. Founded 1890. Setting: 173-acre rural campus with easy access to Rochester. Endowment: $4.3 million. Educational spending for 2005 fiscal year: $4896 per student. Total enrollment: 1,368. Faculty: 99 (57 full-time, 42 part-time). Student-undergrad faculty ratio is 14:1. 818 applied, 81% were admitted. 9% from top 10% of their high school class, 27% from top quarter, 62% from top half. Full-time: 1,115 students, 69% women, 31% men. Part-time: 153 students, 86% women, 14% men. Students come from 18 states and territories, 2 other countries, 9% from out-of-state, 1% Native American, 2% Hispanic, 6% black, 1% Asian American or Pacific Islander, 0.1% international, 14% 25 or older, 68% live on campus, 5% transferred in. Retention: 73% of full-time freshmen returned the following year. Academic areas with the most degrees conferred: health professions and related sciences; business/marketing; education. Core. Calendar: 4-1-4. Academic remediation for entering students, services for LD students, advanced placement, accelerated degree program, self-designed majors, independent study, double major, summer session for credit, part-time degree program, adult/continuing education programs, co-op programs and internships. Off campus study at Rochester Area Colleges. Study abroad program.

Entrance Requirements: Options: Peterson's Universal Application, Common Application, electronic application, early admission, deferred admission. Required: essay, high school transcript, recommendations, SAT or ACT. Recommended: minimum 2.75 high school GPA, interview. Required for some: interview. Entrance: moderately difficult. Application deadline: Rolling.

Costs Per Year: Application fee: $30. Comprehensive fee: $25,850 includes full-time tuition ($17,800), mandatory fees ($270), and college room and board ($7780). College room only: $3790. Full-time tuition and fees vary according to program. Room and board charges vary according to board plan and housing facility. Part-time tuition: $595 per credit hour. Part-time tuition varies according to program.

Collegiate Environment: Orientation program. Drama-theater group, choral group, student-run newspaper, radio station. Social organizations: 42 open to all. Most popular organizations: Student Senate, Campus Activities Board, OTTERS (occupational therapy club), Education Club, BAKU. Major annual events: May Day Weekend, Homecoming, Spring Weekend. Student services: health clinic, personal-psychological counseling. Campus security: 24-hour emergency response devices and patrols, late night transport-escort service. On-campus residence required through senior year. Options: coed, women-only housing available. Lightner Library with 117,192 books, 4,830 microform titles, 3,145 audiovisual materials, and an OPAC. Operations spending for 2004 fiscal year: $414,521. 105 computers available on campus for general student use. A campuswide network can be accessed from student residence rooms and from off campus. Staffed computer lab on campus.

Community Environment: The college is located on the western shore of Keuka Lake near Penn Yan, population 6,500. This pleasant rural setting is accessible by major roadways. The area provides boating, fishing, water sports, hunting, and winter sports.

■ **THE KING'S COLLEGE** *N-34*
350 Fifth Ave.
15th Floor Empire State Bldg.
New York, NY 10118
Tel: (212)659-7200; 888-969-7200
E-mail: bbell@tkc.edu
Web Site: http://www.tkc.edu/

Description: Independent religious, 4-year, coed. Awards bachelor's degrees. Setting: urban campus. Educational spending for 2005 fiscal year: $12,346 per student. Total enrollment: 240. Student-undergrad faculty ratio is 14:1. 348 applied, 57% were admitted. 48% from top 10% of their high school class, 80% from top quarter, 93% from top half. 2 class presidents, 4 valedictorians, 10 student government officers. Full-time: 217 students, 62% women, 38% men. Part-time: 23 students, 57% women, 43% men. Students come from 29 states and territories, 7 other countries, 76% from out-of-state, 0% Native American, 8% Hispanic, 7% black, 3% Asian American or Pacific Islander, 12% international, 11% 25 or older, 55% live on campus, 7% transferred in. Retention: 77% of full-time freshmen returned the following year. Academic areas with the most degrees conferred: business/marketing; education. Core. Calendar: semesters. Academic remediation for entering students, ESL program, advanced placement, independent study, summer session for credit, internships. Off campus study. Study abroad program.

Entrance Requirements: Options: electronic application, early action, deferred admission, international baccalaureate accepted. Required: high

school transcript, interview, SAT or ACT. Recommended: minimum 3.0 high school GPA, recommendations. Required for some: essay. Entrance: very difficult. Application deadlines: 2/1, 11/15 for early action. Notification: 3/8, 12/15 for early action.

Costs Per Year: Application fee: $30. Tuition: $18,590 full-time, $775 per credit part-time. Mandatory fees: $350 full-time, $175 per term part-time. College room only: $7980.

Collegiate Environment: Orientation program. Drama-theater group, choral group, student-run newspaper, radio station. Most popular organizations: student newspaper, E-teams, student radio, Business Club, Freshman Small Groups. Major annual events: Spring Formal, Homecoming, Fall Retreat. Campus security: 24-hour emergency response devices, late night transport-escort service, controlled dormitory access. 115 undergraduates lived in college housing during 2003-04. No special consideration for freshman housing applicants. Options: men-only, women-only housing available. Battles Library with 12,000 books, 75 serials, 300 audiovisual materials, an OPAC, and a Web page. Operations spending for 2004 fiscal year: $91,147. 20 computers available on campus for general student use. A campuswide network can be accessed from student residence rooms and from off campus. Staffed computer lab on campus.

■ **KINGSBOROUGH COMMUNITY COLLEGE OF THE CITY UNIVERSITY OF NEW YORK** *O-34*
2001 Oriental Blvd, Manhattan Beach
Brooklyn, NY 11235
Tel: (718)368-5000
Admissions: (718)368-6800
Web Site: http://www.kbcc.cuny.edu/

Description: State and locally supported, 2-year, coed. Part of City University of New York System. Awards transfer associate and terminal associate degrees. Founded 1963. Setting: 72-acre urban campus with easy access to New York City. Research spending for 2004 fiscal year: $383,053. Educational spending for 2005 fiscal year: $3912 per student. Total enrollment: 15,265. Student-undergrad faculty ratio is 25:1. 3% from top 10% of their high school class, 9% from top quarter, 31% from top half. Full-time: 7,968 students, 56% women, 44% men. Part-time: 7,297 students, 59% women, 41% men. 2% from out-of-state, 0.1% Native American, 14% Hispanic, 32% black, 9% Asian American or Pacific Islander, 10% international, 31% 25 or older, 9% transferred in. Core. Calendar: semesters. Academic remediation for entering students, ESL program, services for LD students, advanced placement, self-designed majors, honors program, summer session for credit, part-time degree program, adult/continuing education programs, internships. Off campus study at other units of the City University of New York System.

Entrance Requirements: Open admission. Option: Common Application. Required: high school transcript. Entrance: noncompetitive. Application deadline: 8/23.

Costs Per Year: Application fee: $60. State resident tuition: $2800 full-time, $120 per credit part-time. Nonresident tuition: $4560 full-time, $190 per credit part-time. Mandatory fees: $300 full-time, $79.50 per term part-time.

Collegiate Environment: Orientation program. Drama-theater group, choral group, student-run newspaper, radio station. Social organizations: 80 open to all. Most popular organizations: Peer Advisors, Caribbean Club, DECA. Major annual events: Club Fair, Family Day. Student services: health clinic, personal-psychological counseling, women's center. Campus security: 24-hour emergency response devices and patrols. College housing not available. Robert J. Kibbee Library with 185,912 books, 10,318 microform titles, 458 serials, 2,388 audiovisual materials, and an OPAC. Operations spending for 2004 fiscal year: $1.1 million. 900 computers available on campus for general student use. A campuswide network can be accessed. Staffed computer lab on campus.

■ **KOL YAAKOV TORAH CENTER** *J-33*
29 West Maple Ave.
Monsey, NY 10952-2954
Tel: (914)425-3863
Web Site: http://horizons.edu/

Description: Independent Jewish, comprehensive, men only. Awards bachelor's and master's degrees. Founded 1980. Setting: 3-acre small town campus with easy access to New York City. Total enrollment: 25. 10 applied, 50% were admitted. 100% from top 10% of their high school class. Students come from 15 states and territories, 7% 25 or older. Core. Calendar: semesters. Academic remediation for entering students, ESL program, self-designed majors, honors program, summer session for credit, part-time degree program, adult/continuing education programs, co-op programs. Off campus study. Study abroad program.

Entrance Requirements: Options: Peterson's Universal Application, early admission. Required: high school transcript, interview. Recommended: recommendations. Entrance: minimally difficult. Application deadline: Rolling.

Collegiate Environment: Orientation program. Student services: personal-psychological counseling. Campus security: 24-hour emergency response devices. 2,000 books. 3 computers available on campus for general student use.

■ **LABORATORY INSTITUTE OF MERCHANDISING** *N-34*

12 East 53rd St.
New York, NY 10022-5268
Tel: (212)752-1530
Free: 800-677-1323
Fax: (212)832-6708
E-mail: khamill@limcollege.edu
Web Site: http://www.limcollege.edu/

Description: Proprietary, 4-year, coed. Awards associate and bachelor's degrees. Founded 1939. Setting: urban campus. Total enrollment: 792. Student-undergrad faculty ratio is 19:1. 514 applied, 66% were admitted. 11% from top 10% of their high school class, 19% from top quarter, 55% from top half. Full-time: 776 students, 95% women, 5% men. Part-time: 16 students, 100% women. Students come from 33 states and territories, 5 other countries, 54% from out-of-state, 0.3% Native American, 15% Hispanic, 8% black, 6% Asian American or Pacific Islander, 1% international, 23% 25 or older, 14% live on campus, 13% transferred in. Retention: 80% of full-time freshmen returned the following year. Academic area with the most degrees conferred: business/marketing. Core. Calendar: semesters. Academic remediation for entering students, advanced placement, accelerated degree program, summer session for credit, part-time degree program, co-op programs and internships. Study abroad program.

Entrance Requirements: Options: Peterson's Universal Application, electronic application, deferred admission. Required: essay, high school transcript, 2 recommendations, interview, SAT or ACT. Recommended: minimum 2.5 high school GPA. Entrance: moderately difficult. Application deadline: Rolling. Notification: continuous.

Costs Per Year: Application fee: $40. Comprehensive fee: $30,700 includes full-time tuition ($17,250), mandatory fees ($450), and college room and board ($13,000). Part-time tuition: $545 per credit. Part-time mandatory fees: $112.50 per term.

Collegiate Environment: Orientation program. Social organizations: 6 open to all. Most popular organizations: student government, LIMlight Club (yearbook), Fashion Club, Latin Cultures Club, Marketing Club/SIFE. Major annual events: student-run fashion show, ski trip, holiday parties. Student services: personal-psychological counseling. 87 college housing spaces available; all were occupied in 2003-04. No special consideration for freshman housing applicants. Option: coed housing available. Adrian G. Marcuse Library with 10,300 books, 100 serials, 500 audiovisual materials, and an OPAC. 166 computers available on campus for general student use. A campuswide network can be accessed from student residence rooms and from off campus. Staffed computer lab on campus.

Community Environment: LIM's location right in the center of the greatest fashion city, New York, gives its students the best of all possible worlds. Within a block of the school are internationally known department stores, French and Italian designers' boutiques, retailing establishments of every kind, with goods imported from every continent of the world. Only a few blocks away is the heart of the garment district, Seventh Avenue. Merchandising creativity originates here and finds its way into the shopping centers of America, Europe, and the Far East.

■ **LE MOYNE COLLEGE** *J-16*

1419 Salt Springs Rd.
Syracuse, NY 13214
Tel: (315)445-4100
Free: 800-333-4733
Admissions: (315)445-4707
Fax: (315)445-4711
E-mail: admission@lemoyne.edu
Web Site: http://www.lemoyne.edu/

Description: Independent Roman Catholic (Jesuit), comprehensive, coed. Awards bachelor's and master's degrees and post-master's certificates. Founded 1946. Setting: 151-acre suburban campus. Endowment: $36.9 million. Research spending for 2004 fiscal year: $49,878. Educational spending

for 2005 fiscal year: $7466 per student. Total enrollment: 3,580. Faculty: 324 (154 full-time, 170 part-time). Student-undergrad faculty ratio is 13:1. 2,946 applied, 72% were admitted. 23% from top 10% of their high school class, 52% from top quarter, 82% from top half. 5 valedictorians. Full-time: 2,318 students, 61% women, 39% men. Part-time: 471 students, 76% women, 24% men. Students come from 27 states and territories, 6 other countries, 6% from out-of-state, 1% Native American, 4% Hispanic, 5% black, 2% Asian American or Pacific Islander, 1% international, 11% 25 or older, 60% live on campus, 6% transferred in. Retention: 87% of full-time freshmen returned the following year. Academic areas with the most degrees conferred: business/marketing; psychology; social sciences. Core. Calendar: semesters. Academic remediation for entering students, services for LD students, advanced placement, accelerated degree program, honors program, independent study, double major, summer session for credit, part-time degree program, adult/continuing education programs, internships, graduate courses open to undergrads. Off campus study at Syracuse Consortium for the Cultural Foundations of Medicine. Study abroad program. ROTC: Army (c), Air Force (c).

Entrance Requirements: Options: Peterson's Universal Application, Common Application, electronic application, early admission, early decision, deferred admission, international baccalaureate accepted. Required: essay, high school transcript, 2 recommendations, SAT or ACT. Recommended: interview. Entrance: moderately difficult. Application deadlines: 2/1, 12/1 for early decision. Notification: continuous, 12/15 for early decision.

Costs Per Year: Application fee: $35. Comprehensive fee: $29,570 includes full-time tuition ($20,770), mandatory fees ($510), and college room and board ($8290). College room only: $5240. Room and board charges vary according to board plan and housing facility. Part-time tuition: $441 per credit hour. Part-time tuition varies according to class time.

Collegiate Environment: Orientation program. Drama-theater group, choral group, student-run newspaper, radio station. Social organizations: 70 open to all. Most popular organizations: Student Programming Board, Outing Club, performing arts groups, Student Dancers, New Student Orientation Committee. Major annual events: winter/spring formals, Spring Olympics, Halloween Dance. Student services: health clinic, personal-psychological counseling. Campus security: 24-hour emergency response devices and patrols, late night transport-escort service, controlled dormitory access, self-defense education, lighted pathways, closed-circuit security cameras. 1,575 college housing spaces available; 1,460 were occupied in 2003-04. Freshmen guaranteed college housing. On-campus residence required through senior year. Options: coed, men-only, women-only housing available. Noreen Reale Falcone Library with 256,565 books, 577,468 microform titles, 13,589 serials, 10,935 audiovisual materials, an OPAC, and a Web page. Operations spending for 2004 fiscal year: $1.5 million. 325 computers available on campus for general student use. A campuswide network can be accessed from student residence rooms and from off campus. Staffed computer lab on campus.

Community Environment: See Syracuse University.

■ **LEHMAN COLLEGE OF THE CITY UNIVERSITY OF NEW YORK** *M-35*

250 Bedford Park Blvd. West
Bronx, NY 10468-1589
Tel: (718)960-8000; 877-Lehman1
Admissions: (718)960-8706
Fax: (718)960-8712
Web Site: http://www.lehman.cuny.edu/

Description: State and locally supported, comprehensive, coed. Part of City University of New York System. Awards bachelor's and master's degrees and post-master's certificates. Founded 1931. Setting: 37-acre urban campus. Research spending for 2004 fiscal year: $229,000. Educational spending for 2005 fiscal year: $6158 per student. Total enrollment: 10,615. 10,193 applied, 35% were admitted. Full-time: 5,119 students, 70% women, 30% men. Part-time: 3,323 students, 75% women, 25% men. Students come from 5 states and territories, 110 other countries, 1% from out-of-state, 0.1% Native American, 47% Hispanic, 34% black, 4% Asian American or Pacific Islander, 5% international, 52% 25 or older, 12% transferred in. Retention: 74% of full-time freshmen returned the following year. Academic areas with the most degrees conferred: social sciences; health professions and related sciences; business/marketing. Core. Calendar: semesters. ESL program, services for LD students, advanced placement, self-designed majors, freshman honors college, honors program, independent study, distance learning, double major, summer session for credit, part-time degree program, adult/continuing education programs, co-op programs and internships, graduate courses open to undergrads. Off campus study at other units of the City University of New York System. Study abroad program. ROTC: Army (c).

Entrance Requirements: Options: deferred admission, international baccalaureate accepted. Required: high school transcript, minimum 3.0 high school GPA, SAT or ACT. Required for some: essay, interview. Entrance: moderately difficult. Application deadline: Rolling. Notification: continuous.

Costs Per Year: Application fee: $50. State resident tuition: $4000 full-time, $170 per credit part-time. Nonresident tuition: $10,800 full-time, $360 per credit part-time. Mandatory fees: $288 full-time.

Collegiate Environment: Orientation program. Drama-theater group, choral group, student-run newspaper, radio station. Social organizations: 33 open to all. Most popular organizations: Club Mac, African Students Association, Dominican Student Association, The Sociology Club, Club Live. Major annual events: Multicultural Festival, Student Life Fair, Student Organization Open House. Student services: health clinic, personal-psychological counseling, women's center. Campus security: 24-hour emergency response devices and patrols, student patrols, late night transport-escort service. College housing not available. Lehman College Library plus 1 other with 541,944 books, 1,350 serials, an OPAC, and a Web page. Operations spending for 2004 fiscal year: $960,000. 600 computers available on campus for general student use. Staffed computer lab on campus.

■ **LONG ISLAND BUSINESS INSTITUTE** *O-43*

6500 Jericho Turnpike
Commack, NY 11725
Tel: (631)499-7100
Fax: (631)499-7114
E-mail: rnazar@libi.edu
Web Site: http://www.libi.edu/commack/index.html

Description: Proprietary, 2-year, coed. Awards certificates, diplomas, and transfer associate degrees. Founded 1968. Setting: suburban campus with easy access to New York City. Total enrollment: 890. Student-undergrad faculty ratio is 15:1. 325 applied, 100% were admitted. Full-time: 676 students, 72% women, 28% men. Part-time: 214 students, 93% women, 7% men. 0% from out-of-state, 0% Native American, 20% Hispanic, 3% black, 44% Asian American or Pacific Islander, 5% international, 95% 25 or older, 0% transferred in. Retention: 0% of full-time freshmen returned the following year. Calendar: trimesters. Academic remediation for entering students, advanced placement, independent study, summer session for credit, part-time degree program, adult/continuing education programs, internships.

Entrance Requirements: Open admission. Required: essay, high school transcript, interview. Entrance: noncompetitive. Application deadline: Rolling.

Costs Per Year: Application fee: $50. Tuition: $8500 full-time, $325 per credit part-time. Mandatory fees: $400 full-time, $50 per year part-time. Full-time tuition and fees vary according to course load and program. Part-time tuition and fees vary according to course load and program.

Collegiate Environment: Orientation program. Campus security: 24-hour emergency response devices. College housing not available. Mendon W. Smith Memorial Library with 1,484 books, 15 serials, 184 audiovisual materials, and an OPAC. Operations spending for 2004 fiscal year: $5000. 77 computers available on campus for general student use. Staffed computer lab on campus.

■ **LONG ISLAND COLLEGE HOSPITAL SCHOOL OF NURSING** *O-34*

340 Ct. St.
Brooklyn, NY 11231
Tel: (718)780-1953
Admissions: (718)780-1898
Fax: (718)780-1936
Web Site: http://www.futurenurselich.org/

Description: Independent, 2-year, coed. Awards transfer associate and terminal associate degrees. Founded 1883. Setting: urban campus. Total enrollment: 147. Student-undergrad faculty ratio is 12:1. 65 applied, 3% were admitted. 80% from top quarter of their high school class, 100% from top half. Full-time: 73 students, 85% women, 15% men. Part-time: 74 students, 72% women, 28% men. Students come from 2 states and territories, 1% from out-of-state, 0% Native American, 7% Hispanic, 45% black, 14% Asian American or Pacific Islander, 0% international, 81% 25 or older, 32% transferred in. Core. Calendar: semesters. Advanced placement, independent study, summer session for credit, part-time degree program, co-op programs and internships.

Entrance Requirements: Required: essay, high school transcript, minimum 2.0 high school GPA, 2 recommendations, interview. Recommended:

minimum 2.0 high school GPA. Entrance: moderately difficult. Application deadline: 4/28. Notification: continuous.

Costs Per Year: Application fee: $50. Tuition: $23,025 full-time. Mandatory fees: $370 full-time.

Collegiate Environment: Orientation program. Social organizations: 1 open to all. Most popular organization: Student Government Association. Major annual events: Open House, Atlantic Antic Street Fair, Awards and Recognition Ceremony. Student services: health clinic, personal-psychological counseling. Campus security: 24-hour emergency response devices, late night transport-escort service. College housing not available. E. King Morgan M.D. Health Sciences Library plus 1 other with 16,000 books and 400 serials. 14 computers available on campus for general student use. Staffed computer lab on campus.

■ **LONG ISLAND UNIVERSITY, BRENTWOOD CAMPUS** *O-43*

100 Second Ave.
Brentwood, NY 11717
Tel: (631)273-5112
Fax: (631)952-0809
Web Site: http://www.liu.edu/

Description: Independent, upper-level, coed. Part of Long Island University. Awards bachelor's and master's degrees and post-master's certificates. Founded 1959. Setting: 172-acre suburban campus. Total enrollment: 1,115. Full-time: 17 students, 71% women, 29% men. Part-time: 45 students, 67% women, 33% men. 1% from out-of-state, 0% Native American, 13% Hispanic, 16% black, 0% Asian American or Pacific Islander, 0% international, 95% 25 or older, 29% transferred in. Core. Calendar: semesters. Services for LD students, advanced placement, honors program, independent study, summer session for credit, part-time degree program, internships.

Costs Per Year: Tuition: $651 per credit part-time.

Collegiate Environment: Orientation program. Student services: health clinic, personal-psychological counseling. Campus security: evening security guard. College housing not available. Brentwood Campus Library with 55,000 books, 285 serials, 12 audiovisual materials, and a Web page. 42 computers available on campus for general student use. Computer purchase/lease plans available. A campuswide network can be accessed. Staffed computer lab on campus.

■ **LONG ISLAND UNIVERSITY, BROOKLYN CAMPUS** *O-34*

One University Plaza
Brooklyn, NY 11201-8423
Tel: (718)488-1000
Free: 800-LIU-PLAN
Admissions: (718)488-1011
E-mail: adm_sunday@eagle.liunet.edu
Web Site: http://www.liu.edu/

Description: Independent, university, coed. Part of Long Island University. Awards associate, bachelor's, master's, doctoral, and first professional degrees and post-master's and first professional certificates. Founded 1926. Setting: 10-acre urban campus. Total enrollment: 8,144. Faculty: 954 (259 full-time, 695 part-time). Student-undergrad faculty ratio is 13:1. 5,068 applied, 61% were admitted. Full-time: 4,412 students, 71% women, 29% men. Part-time: 919 students, 80% women, 20% men. Students come from 36 states and territories, 11% from out-of-state, 0.2% Native American, 12% Hispanic, 40% black, 15% Asian American or Pacific Islander, 2% international, 33% 25 or older, 10% transferred in. Retention: 67% of full-time freshmen returned the following year. Academic areas with the most degrees conferred: health professions and related sciences; business/marketing; communications/journalism; psychology; social sciences. Core. Calendar: semesters. Academic remediation for entering students, ESL program, services for LD students, advanced placement, self-designed majors, honors program, independent study, double major, summer session for credit, part-time degree program, adult/continuing education programs, co-op programs and internships, graduate courses open to undergrads.

Entrance Requirements: Options: Peterson's Universal Application, Common Application, electronic application, deferred admission. Required: high school transcript, minimum 2.0 high school GPA. Recommended: minimum 2.5 high school GPA. Required for some: essay, minimum 3.0 high school GPA, recommendations, interview, SAT or ACT. Entrance: minimally difficult. Application deadline: Rolling.

Costs Per Year: Application fee: $30. Comprehensive fee: $32,138 includes full-time tuition ($23,188), mandatory fees ($1140), and college room and board ($7810). College room only: $4640. Full-time tuition and fees vary according to program. Room and board charges vary according to board plan and housing facility. Part-time tuition: $689 per credit. Part-time mandatory fees: $590 per year. Part-time tuition and fees vary according to course load and program.

Collegiate Environment: Orientation program. Drama-theater group, choral group, student-run newspaper, radio station. Social organizations: 54 open to all; national fraternities, national sororities, local fraternities, local sororities. Most popular organizations: Caribbean Students Movement, Hillel, Muslim Student Organization, Student Government Association, WLIU-BK Radio (campus radio station). Major annual events: homecoming, Spring Day, Orientation Day. Student services: health clinic, personal-psychological counseling. Campus security: 24-hour emergency response devices and patrols. 638 college housing spaces available. Freshmen given priority for college housing. Option: coed housing available. Salena Library with an OPAC and a Web page. 345 computers available on campus for general student use. A campuswide network can be accessed from student residence rooms and from off campus. Staffed computer lab on campus.

Community Environment: The campus in downtown Brooklyn, at Flatbush and DeKalb Avenues, within easy distance of the Brooklyn Academy of Music, Prospect Park, the Brooklyn Museum, and midtown Manhattan.

■ **LONG ISLAND UNIVERSITY, C.W. POST CAMPUS** *M-38*
720 Northern Blvd.
Brookville, NY 11548-1300
Tel: (516)299-2000
Free: 800-LIU-PLAN
Admissions: (516)299-2900
Web Site: http://www.liu.edu/

Description: Independent, comprehensive, coed. Part of Long Island University. Awards bachelor's, master's, and doctoral degrees and post-master's certificates. Founded 1954. Setting: 308-acre suburban campus with easy access to New York City. Total enrollment: 8,472. Faculty: 1,165 (355 full-time, 810 part-time). Student-undergrad faculty ratio is 10:1. 5,162 applied, 78% were admitted. 14% from top 10% of their high school class, 32% from top quarter, 63% from top half. Full-time: 4,476 students, 60% women, 40% men. Part-time: 693 students, 68% women, 32% men. Students come from 30 states and territories, 9% from out-of-state, 0.3% Native American, 8% Hispanic, 10% black, 3% Asian American or Pacific Islander, 3% international, 16% 25 or older, 30% live on campus, 10% transferred in. Retention: 74% of full-time freshmen returned the following year. Academic areas with the most degrees conferred: education; business/marketing; visual and performing arts. Core. Calendar: semesters. Academic remediation for entering students, ESL program, services for LD students, advanced placement, accelerated degree program, self-designed majors, honors program, independent study, double major, summer session for credit, part-time degree program, adult/continuing education programs, co-op programs and internships, graduate courses open to undergrads. Off campus study. Study abroad program. ROTC: Army (c), Air Force (c).

Entrance Requirements: Options: Peterson's Universal Application, Common Application, electronic application, deferred admission. Required: essay, high school transcript, minimum 2.5 high school GPA, SAT or ACT. Recommended: recommendations. Required for some: interview. Entrance: moderately difficult. Application deadline: Rolling. Notification: continuous.

Costs Per Year: Application fee: $30. Comprehensive fee: $31,930 includes full-time tuition ($22,100), mandatory fees ($1130), and college room and board ($8700). College room only: $5730. Full-time tuition and fees vary according to program. Room and board charges vary according to board plan and housing facility. Part-time tuition: $689 per credit. Part-time mandatory fees: $7 per credit, $420 per year. Part-time tuition and fees vary according to course load and program.

Collegiate Environment: Orientation program. Drama-theater group, choral group, student-run newspaper, radio station. Social organizations: 50 open to all; national fraternities, national sororities; 40% of eligible men and 40% of eligible women are members. Most popular organizations: Student Government Association, Association for Campus Programming, African People's Organization, Resident Student Association, Post TV and Newman. Major annual events: homecoming, Spring Fling, Orientation Day. Student services: health clinic, personal-psychological counseling. Campus security: 24-hour emergency response devices and patrols, late night transport-escort service, controlled dormitory access. 1,673 college housing spaces available. Freshmen guaranteed college housing. Option: coed housing available. B. Davis Schwartz Memorial Library with an OPAC and a Web page. 357 computers available on campus for general student use. A campuswide network can be accessed from student residence rooms and from off campus. Staffed computer lab on campus.

■ **LONG ISLAND UNIVERSITY, FRIENDS WORLD PROGRAM** *N-49*
239 Montauk Hwy.
Southampton, NY 11968
Tel: (631)287-8474
Free: 800-287-8093
Admissions: (631)287-8465
Fax: (631)287-8463
E-mail: fw@southampton.liunet.edu
Web Site: http://www.southampton.liu.edu/fw/

Description: Independent, 4-year, coed. Part of Long Island University. Awards bachelor's degrees. Founded 1965. Setting: 110-acre rural campus. Total enrollment: 195. Full-time: 189 students, 69% women, 31% men. Part-time: 6 students, 67% women, 33% men. Students come from 29 states and territories, 5 other countries, 80% from out-of-state, 2% Native American, 2% Hispanic, 1% black, 7% Asian American or Pacific Islander, 0% international, 20% live on campus, 13% transferred in. Retention: 66% of full-time freshmen returned the following year. Core. Calendar: semesters. Advanced placement, self-designed majors, independent study, external degree program, internships. Off campus study at Long Island University (C.W. Post campus, Brooklyn campus). Study abroad program.

Entrance Requirements: Open admission except for the Comparative Religion and Culture program. Options: electronic application, early admission, deferred admission, international baccalaureate accepted. Required: essay, high school transcript, interview. Recommended: minimum 3.0 high school GPA. Entrance: noncompetitive. Application deadline: Rolling. Notification: continuous.

Costs Per Year: Application fee: $30. Comprehensive fee: $34,100 includes full-time tuition ($22,100), mandatory fees ($6000), and college room and board ($6000). Full-time tuition and fees vary according to location. Room and board charges vary according to location. Part-time tuition: $659 per credit.

Collegiate Environment: Orientation program. Drama-theater group, student-run newspaper, radio station. Social organizations: 32 open to all. Most popular organizations: Activist Club, P.E.A.C.E., LaFuenza Latina, Caribbean Student Association, Women's Issues Collective. Major annual events: Ingathering, World Conference, Graduation/Senior Recognition ceremony. Student services: health clinic, personal-psychological counseling. Freshmen guaranteed college housing. On-campus residence required through sophomore year. Option: coed housing available. Southampton College with 115,380 books, 140,000 microform titles, 665 serials, and 886 audiovisual materials. 175 computers available on campus for general student use. Computer purchase/lease plans available. A campuswide network can be accessed from student residence rooms and from off campus. Staffed computer lab on campus.

■ **MACHZIKEI HADATH RABBINICAL COLLEGE** *O-34*
5407 Sixteenth Ave.
Brooklyn, NY 11204-1805
Tel: (718)854-8777

Description: Independent Jewish, comprehensive, men only. Awards bachelor's and master's degrees. Founded 1956. Total enrollment: 137. Students come from 4 states and territories. Core. Calendar: semesters. Academic remediation for entering students. Study abroad program.

Entrance Requirements: Required: interview. Entrance: moderately difficult. Application deadline: Rolling. Notification: continuous.

Collegiate Environment: Abraham Koppel Library plus 1 other with 20,000 books.

■ **MANHATTAN COLLEGE**
Manhattan College Parkway
Riverdale, NY 10471
Tel: (718)862-8000
Admissions: (718)862-7200
Fax: (718)862-8019
E-mail: admit@manhattan.edu
Web Site: http://www.manhattan.edu/

Description: Independent, comprehensive, coed, affiliated with Roman Catholic Church. Awards bachelor's and master's degrees and post-master's certificates. Founded 1853. Setting: 31-acre urban campus with easy access to New York City. Endowment: $39.1 million. Research spending for 2004 fiscal year: $1.3 million. Educational spending for 2005 fiscal year: $7340 per student. Total enrollment: 3,425. Faculty: 332 (172 full-time, 160 part-time). Student-undergrad faculty ratio is 14:1. 4,712 applied, 57% were admitted. Full-time: 2,879 students, 47% women, 53% men. Part-time: 147

students, 34% women, 66% men. Students come from 42 states and territories, 27 other countries, 28% from out-of-state, 0.1% Native American, 10% Hispanic, 2% black, 3% Asian American or Pacific Islander, 1% international, 6% 25 or older, 54% live on campus, 5% transferred in. Retention: 84% of full-time freshmen returned the following year. Academic areas with the most degrees conferred: engineering; education; business/marketing. Core. Calendar: semesters. Academic remediation for entering students, ESL program, services for LD students, advanced placement, accelerated degree program, honors program, independent study, double major, summer session for credit, part-time degree program, adult/continuing education programs, co-op programs and internships, graduate courses open to undergrads. Off campus study at College of Mount Saint Vincent. Study abroad program. ROTC: Army (c), Air Force.

Entrance Requirements: Options: Peterson's Universal Application, Common Application, early admission, early decision, deferred admission, international baccalaureate accepted. Required: essay, high school transcript, minimum 2.5 high school GPA, 1 recommendation, SAT or ACT. Recommended: minimum 3.0 high school GPA, interview. Required for some: interview. Entrance: moderately difficult. Application deadlines: 4/15, 11/15 for early decision. Notification: continuous until 4/15, 12/1 for early decision.

Costs Per Year: Application fee: $50. Comprehensive fee: $29,675 includes full-time tuition ($20,350) and college room and board ($9325).

Collegiate Environment: Orientation program. Drama-theater group, choral group, marching band, student-run newspaper, radio station. Social organizations: 70 open to all; national fraternities, national sororities, local fraternities; 7% of eligible men and 5% of eligible women are members. Most popular organizations: Minority Student Union, student government, student radio station, Manhattan College Singers, Resident/Commuter Student Association. Major annual events: Springfest, Jasper Jingle Christmas Ball, Fall Festival. Student services: health clinic, personal-psychological counseling. Campus security: 24-hour patrols, late night transport-escort service, controlled dormitory access. 1,653 college housing spaces available; 1,629 were occupied in 2003-04. Option: coed housing available. O'Malley Library plus 1 other with 211,376 books, 649,695 microform titles, 1,190 serials, 1,122 audiovisual materials, an OPAC, and a Web page. Operations spending for 2004 fiscal year: $1.5 million. 375 computers available on campus for general student use. A campuswide network can be accessed from student residence rooms and from off campus. Staffed computer lab on campus.

Community Environment: See Fordham University.

■ **MANHATTAN SCHOOL OF MUSIC** *N-34*
120 Claremont Ave.
New York, NY 10027-4698
Tel: (212)749-2802
Fax: (212)749-5471
E-mail: admission@msnnyc.edu
Web Site: http://www.msmnyc.edu/

Description: Independent, comprehensive, coed. Awards bachelor's, master's, and doctoral degrees and post-master's certificates. Founded 1917. Setting: 1-acre urban campus. Endowment: $13 million. Educational spending for 2005 fiscal year: $24,500 per student. Total enrollment: 891. Faculty: 365 (73 full-time, 292 part-time). Student-undergrad faculty ratio is 5:1. 863 applied, 33% were admitted. Full-time: 408 students, 48% women, 52% men. Part-time: 8 students, 88% women, 13% men. Students come from 35 states and territories, 37 other countries, 65% from out-of-state, 0.2% Native American, 4% Hispanic, 3% black, 7% Asian American or Pacific Islander, 21% international, 3% 25 or older, 57% live on campus, 3% transferred in. Retention: 82% of full-time freshmen returned the following year. Academic area with the most degrees conferred: visual and performing arts. Core. Calendar: semesters. Academic remediation for entering students, ESL program, services for LD students, advanced placement, graduate courses open to undergrads. Off campus study at Barnard College.

Entrance Requirements: Options: electronic application, deferred admission. Required: essay, high school transcript, minimum 2.8 high school GPA, 1 recommendation, audition. Recommended: minimum 3.0 high school GPA, interview, SAT or ACT. Entrance: very difficult. Application deadline: 12/1. Notification: 4/1.

Costs Per Year: Application fee: $100. Comprehensive fee: $42,760 includes full-time tuition ($27,400), mandatory fees ($2560), and college room and board ($12,800). College room only: $8400. Part-time tuition: $1200 per credit.

Collegiate Environment: Orientation program. Choral group. Social organizations: 7 open to all. Most popular organizations: Pan-African

Student Union, International Student Association, Student Council, Resident Community Council, Gay/Lesbian/Bisexual Students Association. Major annual events: Winter Formal, Cafe Jazz, Rite of Spring. Student services: Specialized Career Center. Campus security: 24-hour patrols, controlled dormitory access. 336 college housing spaces available; 233 were occupied in 2003-04. No special consideration for freshman housing applicants. On-campus residence required through sophomore year. Option: coed housing available. Peter J. Sharp Library plus 1 other with 107,000 books, 110 serials, 24,000 audiovisual materials, an OPAC, and a Web page. Operations spending for 2004 fiscal year: $479,114. 9 computers available on campus for general student use. A campuswide network can be accessed from student residence rooms. Staffed computer lab on campus.

Community Environment: See Columbia University.

■ **MANHATTANVILLE COLLEGE**
2900 Purchase St.
Purchase, NY 10577-2132
Tel: (914)694-2200
Free: 800-328-4553
Admissions: (914)323-5124
Fax: (914)694-1732
E-mail: admission@mville.edu
Web Site: http://www.manhattanville.edu/

Description: Independent, comprehensive, coed. Awards bachelor's and master's degrees. Founded 1841. Setting: 100-acre suburban campus with easy access to New York City. Endowment: $13.5 million. Educational spending for 2005 fiscal year: $8811 per student. Total enrollment: 2,806. Faculty: 298 (90 full-time, 208 part-time). Student-undergrad faculty ratio is 11:1. 3,184 applied, 60% were admitted. Full-time: 1,651 students, 69% women, 31% men. Part-time: 130 students, 65% women, 35% men. Students come from 35 states and territories, 49 other countries, 37% from out-of-state, 1% Native American, 16% Hispanic, 7% black, 4% Asian American or Pacific Islander, 3% international, 1% 25 or older, 68% live on campus, 1% transferred in. Retention: 74% of full-time freshmen returned the following year. Academic areas with the most degrees conferred: business/marketing; psychology; visual and performing arts. Core. Calendar: semesters. Academic remediation for entering students, ESL program, services for LD students, advanced placement, accelerated degree program, self-designed majors, freshman honors college, honors program, independent study, distance learning, double major, summer session for credit, part-time degree program, adult/continuing education programs, internships, graduate courses open to undergrads. Off campus study at Purchase College, State University of New York, Mills College, American University (Washington Semester), New York State Visiting Student Program. Study abroad program.

Entrance Requirements: Options: Peterson's Universal Application, Common Application, electronic application, early admission, early decision, deferred admission, international baccalaureate accepted. Required: essay, high school transcript, minimum 2.0 high school GPA, 2 recommendations, SAT or ACT. Recommended: minimum 3.0 high school GPA, interview. Required for some: ACT. Entrance: moderately difficult. Application deadlines: 3/1, 12/1 for early decision. Notification: continuous, 12/31 for early decision.

Costs Per Year: Application fee: $55. Comprehensive fee: $39,550 includes full-time tuition ($26,920), mandatory fees ($1080), and college room and board ($11,550). College room only: $6860. Part-time tuition: $620 per credit. Part-time mandatory fees: $40.

Collegiate Environment: Orientation program. Drama-theater group, choral group, student-run newspaper, radio station. Social organizations: 45 open to all; 8% of eligible men and 12% of eligible women are members. Most popular organizations: Latin American Student Organization, International Student Organization, Black Student Union, WMVL (radio station), Connie Hogarth Center. Major annual events: Quad Jam, 200 Nights, Midnight Brunch. Student services: health clinic, personal-psychological counseling, women's center. Campus security: 24-hour emergency response devices and patrols, late night transport-escort service, controlled dormitory access. 1,114 college housing spaces available; all were occupied in 2003-04. Freshmen guaranteed college housing. Option: coed housing available. Manhattanville College Library with 292,846 books, 532,732 microform titles, 18,930 serials, 3,957 audiovisual materials, an OPAC, and a Web page. Operations spending for 2004 fiscal year: $1.1 million. 200 computers available on campus for general student use. Computer purchase/lease plans available. A campuswide network can be accessed from student residence rooms and from off campus. Staffed computer lab on campus.

Community Environment: Located approximately 25 miles from New York City, Purchase enjoys the cultural, civic, educational, and recreational facilities of its neighbor. There are railroad connections at nearby White Plains and Rye. Job opportunities are available within the immediate area.

■ MANNES COLLEGE THE NEW SCHOOL FOR MUSIC N-34

150 West 85th St.

New York, NY 10024-4402

Tel: (212)580-0210

Free: 800-292-3040

Fax: (212)580-1738

Web Site: http://www.newschool.mannes.edu/

Description: Independent, comprehensive, coed. Part of New School University. Awards bachelor's and master's degrees. Founded 1916. Setting: urban campus. System endowment: $129.2 million. System-wide research spending for 2004 fiscal year: $6.4 million. Educational spending for 2005 fiscal year: $8218 per student. Total enrollment: 366. Faculty: 256 (5 full-time, 251 part-time). Student-undergrad faculty ratio is 4:1. 371 applied, 29% were admitted. Full-time: 188 students, 58% women, 42% men. Part-time: 20 students, 40% women, 60% men. Students come from 16 states and territories, 14 other countries, 43% from out-of-state, 0.5% Native American, 5% Hispanic, 2% black, 5% Asian American or Pacific Islander, 32% international, 20% 25 or older, 13% live on campus, 9% transferred in. Retention: 89% of full-time freshmen returned the following year. Academic area with the most degrees conferred: visual and performing arts. Core. Calendar: semesters. Academic remediation for entering students, ESL program, advanced placement, double major, summer session for credit, adult/continuing education programs, graduate courses open to undergrads.

Entrance Requirements: Option: deferred admission. Required: high school transcript, minimum 2.5 high school GPA, 1 recommendation, audition. Entrance: very difficult. Application deadline: 12/1. Notification: 4/15.

Costs Per Year: Application fee: $100. Comprehensive fee: $37,880 includes full-time tuition ($25,560), mandatory fees ($570), and college room and board ($11,750). College room only: $8750. Full-time tuition and fees vary according to degree level and program. Room and board charges vary according to board plan. Part-time tuition: $842 per credit.

Collegiate Environment: Orientation program. Choral group. Major annual events: Block Party, University Convocation. Student services: health clinic, personal-psychological counseling. Campus security: 24-hour emergency response devices, controlled dormitory access. 948 college housing spaces available; 13 were occupied in 2003-04. Freshmen given priority for college housing. Option: coed housing available. Harry Scherman Library plus 2 others with 4.1 million books, 4.7 million microform titles, 22,150 serials, 48,379 audiovisual materials, an OPAC, and a Web page. System-wide operations spending for 2004 fiscal year: $2.8 million. 934 computers available on campus for general student use. A campuswide network can be accessed from student residence rooms and from off campus. Staffed computer lab on campus.

■ MARIA COLLEGE L-25

700 New Scotland Ave.

Albany, NY 12208-1798

Tel: (518)438-3111

Web Site: http://www.mariacollege.edu/

Description: Independent, 2-year, coed. Awards certificates, transfer associate, and terminal associate degrees. Founded 1958. Setting: 9-acre urban campus. Total enrollment: 788. Student-undergrad faculty ratio is 10:1. 232 applied, 72% were admitted. Full-time: 277 students, 91% women, 9% men. Part-time: 511 students, 86% women, 14% men. Students come from 5 states and territories, 4 other countries, 2% from out-of-state, 1% Native American, 3% Hispanic, 20% black, 2% Asian American or Pacific Islander, 1% international, 75% 25 or older, 30% transferred in. Core. Calendar: semesters. Academic remediation for entering students, services for LD students, advanced placement, independent study, summer session for credit, part-time degree program, adult/continuing education programs. Off campus study at members of the Hudson-Mohawk Association of Colleges and Universities. ROTC: Air Force (c).

Entrance Requirements: Option: early admission. Required: essay, high school transcript, minimum 2.0 high school GPA, 1 recommendation, interview, SAT or ACT. Entrance: minimally difficult. Application deadline: 8/25.

Costs Per Year: Application fee: $35. Tuition: $7800 full-time, $285 per credit part-time. Mandatory fees: $200 full-time.

Collegiate Environment: Orientation program. Student services: personal-psychological counseling. Campus security: late night transport-escort service. College housing not available. Maria College Library with 56,746 books, 17 microform titles, 160 serials, 375 audiovisual materials, an OPAC, and a Web page. 78 computers available on campus for general student use. A campuswide network can be accessed. Staffed computer lab on campus.

Community Environment: See State University of New York at Albany.

■ MARIST COLLEGE P-24

3399 North Rd.

Poughkeepsie, NY 12601-1387

Tel: (845)575-3000

Free: 800-436-5483

Admissions: (845)575-3226

Fax: (845)471-6213

E-mail: admissions@marist.edu

Web Site: http://www.marist.edu/

Description: Independent, comprehensive, coed. Awards bachelor's and master's degrees. Founded 1929. Setting: 150-acre small town campus with easy access to Albany and New York City. Endowment: $19.3 million. Research spending for 2004 fiscal year: $638,561. Educational spending for 2005 fiscal year: $7095 per student. Total enrollment: 5,744. Faculty: 596 (201 full-time, 395 part-time). Student-undergrad faculty ratio is 15:1. 7,077 applied, 50% were admitted. 29% from top 10% of their high school class, 67% from top quarter, 97% from top half. 4 National Merit Scholars, 13 class presidents, 2 valedictorians, 32 student government officers. Full-time: 4,413 students, 58% women, 42% men. Part-time: 483 students, 50% women, 50% men. Students come from 37 states and territories, 19 other countries, 40% from out-of-state, 0.3% Native American, 6% Hispanic, 3% black, 2% Asian American or Pacific Islander, 0.3% international, 13% 25 or older, 75% live on campus. Retention: 89% of full-time freshmen returned the following year. Academic areas with the most degrees conferred: business/marketing; communications/journalism; education; liberal arts/general studies. Core. Calendar: semesters. Academic remediation for entering students, ESL program, services for LD students, advanced placement, accelerated degree program, honors program, independent study, distance learning, double major, summer session for credit, part-time degree program, adult/continuing education programs, co-op programs and internships, graduate courses open to undergrads. Off campus study at Associated Colleges of the Mid-Hudson Area. Study abroad program. ROTC: Army.

Entrance Requirements: Options: Peterson's Universal Application, electronic application, early admission, early action, deferred admission, international baccalaureate accepted. Required: essay, high school transcript, 2 recommendations, SAT or ACT. Entrance: moderately difficult. Application deadlines: 2/15, 11/15 for early decision, 12/1 for early action. Notification: 3/15, 12/15 for early decision, 1/15 for early action.

Costs Per Year: Application fee: $40. Comprehensive fee: $30,566 includes full-time tuition ($20,712), mandatory fees ($490), and college room and board ($9364). College room only: $5964. Part-time tuition: $475 per credit. Part-time mandatory fees: $65 per term.

Collegiate Environment: Orientation program. Drama-theater group, choral group, marching band, student-run newspaper, radio station. Social organizations: 75 open to all; national fraternities, local sororities; 1% of eligible men and 3% of eligible women are members. Most popular organizations: Outback Club, student newspaper, student government, Theater Club, community service and campus ministry. Major annual events: Giving Tree, Homecoming, River Festival. Student services: health clinic, personal-psychological counseling. Campus security: 24-hour emergency response devices and patrols, student patrols, late night transport-escort service, controlled dormitory access, night residence hall monitors. 2,700 college housing spaces available; all were occupied in 2003-04. Freshmen guaranteed college housing. Option: coed housing available. James A. Cannavino Library with 176,347 books, 251,683 microform titles, 13,826 serials, 4,940 audiovisual materials, an OPAC, and a Web page. Operations spending for 2004 fiscal year: $1.7 million. 585 computers available on campus for general student use. Computer purchase/lease plans available. A campuswide network can be accessed from student residence rooms and from off campus. Staffed computer lab on campus.

Community Environment: See Vassar College.

■ MARYMOUNT MANHATTAN COLLEGE N-34

221 East 71st St.

New York, NY 10021-4597

Tel: (212)517-0400
Free: 800-MARYMOUNT
Admissions: (212)517-0430
E-mail: admissions@mmm.edu
Web Site: http://www.mmm.edu/

Description: Independent, 4-year, coed. Awards bachelor's degrees. Founded 1936. Setting: 3-acre urban campus. Endowment: $11.7 million. Educational spending for 2005 fiscal year: $6868 per student. Total enrollment: 2,007. Student-undergrad faculty ratio is 11:1. 2,033 applied, 77% were admitted. 11 class presidents, 11 valedictorians, 31 student government officers. Full-time: 1,603 students, 75% women, 25% men. Part-time: 404 students, 86% women, 14% men. Students come from 47 states and territories, 36 other countries, 66% from out-of-state, 0.5% Native American, 11% Hispanic, 12% black, 5% Asian American or Pacific Islander, 2% international, 19% 25 or older, 21% live on campus, 6% transferred in. Retention: 72% of full-time freshmen returned the following year. Academic areas with the most degrees conferred: visual and performing arts; communications/journalism; business/marketing. Core. Calendar: semesters plus summer and January mini-semesters. Academic remediation for entering students, ESL program, services for LD students, advanced placement, accelerated degree program, honors program, independent study, double major, summer session for credit, part-time degree program, adult/continuing education programs, internships. Off campus study at Hunter College of the City University of New York. Study abroad program.

Entrance Requirements: Options: Peterson's Universal Application, electronic application, early decision, deferred admission, international baccalaureate accepted. Required: essay, high school transcript, minimum 2 high school GPA, 2 recommendations, SAT or ACT. Recommended: interview. Required for some: audition for dance and theater programs. Entrance: moderately difficult. Application deadlines: Rolling, 11/1 for early decision. Notification: continuous, 12/15 for early decision.

Costs Per Year: Application fee: $60. Comprehensive fee: $31,728 includes full-time tuition ($18,748), mandatory fees ($890), and college room and board ($12,090). College room only: $10,090. Part-time tuition: $590 per credit. Part-time mandatory fees: $393 per term.

Collegiate Environment: Orientation program. Drama-theater group, student-run newspaper, radio station. Social organizations: 20 open to all; local sororities; 35% of women are members. Most popular organizations: Education Club, African-American Heritage Club, Asian-American Heritage Club, Latino Heritage Club, Business Club. Major annual event: Strawberry Festival. Student services: personal-psychological counseling. Campus security: 24-hour emergency response devices and patrols, student patrols, 24-hour security in residence halls. 675 college housing spaces available; 674 were occupied in 2003-04. Freshmen given priority for college housing. Option: coed housing available. Shanahan Library with 102,000 books, 26,565 microform titles, 600 serials, 13,285 audiovisual materials, an OPAC, and a Web page. Operations spending for 2004 fiscal year: $966,120. 175 computers available on campus for general student use. A campuswide network can be accessed from student residence rooms and from off campus. Staffed computer lab on campus.

Community Environment: See New York University.

■ **MEDAILLE COLLEGE** *K-7*
18 Agassiz Circle
Buffalo, NY 14214-2695
Tel: (716)884-3281
Fax: (716)884-0291
E-mail: gflorczak@medaille.edu
Web Site: http://www.medaille.edu/

Description: Independent, comprehensive, coed. Awards associate, bachelor's, and master's degrees. Founded 1875. Setting: 13-acre urban campus. Endowment: $700,000. Educational spending for 2005 fiscal year: $4700 per student. Total enrollment: 3,018. Faculty: 312 (91 full-time, 221 part-time). Student-undergrad faculty ratio is 17:1. 978 applied, 73% were admitted. 12% from top 10% of their high school class, 33% from top quarter, 55% from top half. 1 valedictorian. Full-time: 1,580 students, 65% women, 35% men. Part-time: 197 students, 63% women, 37% men. Students come from 2 other countries, 4% from out-of-state, 0.3% Native American, 3% Hispanic, 14% black, 1% Asian American or Pacific Islander, 0.2% international, 51% 25 or older, 21% live on campus, 10% transferred in. Retention: 70% of full-time freshmen returned the following year. Academic areas with the most degrees conferred: business/marketing; education; liberal arts/general studies. Core. Calendar: semesters (modular courses available for evening studies and weekend college program). Academic

remediation for entering students, services for LD students, advanced placement, accelerated degree program, self-designed majors, honors program, independent study, double major, summer session for credit, part-time degree program, adult/continuing education programs, internships, graduate courses open to undergrads. Off campus study at 16 members of the Western New York Consortium. ROTC: Army (c).

Entrance Requirements: Options: Common Application, electronic application, early admission, deferred admission. Required: high school transcript, interview, SAT or ACT. Recommended: essay, minimum 2.0 high school GPA, 1 recommendation, SAT. Required for some: essay, 2.5 high school GPA for veterinary technology and elementary teacher education majors. Entrance: moderately difficult. Application deadline: 8/1. Notification: continuous.

Costs Per Year: Application fee: $25. Comprehensive fee: $22,460 includes full-time tuition ($15,030) and college room and board ($7430). Full-time tuition varies according to location. Room and board charges vary according to housing facility. Part-time tuition: $532 per credit hour. Part-time tuition varies according to course load.

Collegiate Environment: Orientation program. Drama-theater group, student-run newspaper, radio station. Social organizations: 20 open to all. Most popular organizations: student government, radio station, ASRA (admissions club), Student Activities Board, Teach. Major annual events: Holiday Party, fall and spring picnics, Awards Banquet. Student services: health clinic, personal-psychological counseling. Campus security: 24-hour emergency response devices, late night transport-escort service, controlled dormitory access. 450 college housing spaces available; 340 were occupied in 2003-04. No special consideration for freshman housing applicants. Options: coed, men-only, women-only housing available. Medaille College Library with 56,854 books, 208 microform titles, 238 serials, 2,423 audiovisual materials, an OPAC, and a Web page. Operations spending for 2004 fiscal year: $550,000. 105 computers available on campus for general student use. A campuswide network can be accessed from student residence rooms and from off campus. Staffed computer lab on campus.

Community Environment: See Canisius College.

■ **MEDGAR EVERS COLLEGE OF THE CITY UNIVERSITY OF NEW YORK** *O-34*
1650 Bedford St.
Brooklyn, NY 11225-2298
Tel: (718)270-4900
Admissions: (718)270-6025
Web Site: http://www.mec.cuny.edu/

Description: State and locally supported, 4-year, coed. Part of City University of New York System. Awards associate and bachelor's degrees. Founded 1969. Setting: 1-acre urban campus. Research spending for 2004 fiscal year: $590,866. Total enrollment: 5,212. Student-undergrad faculty ratio is 15:1. 4,069 applied, 96% were admitted. 7% from top 10% of their high school class, 13% from top quarter, 42% from top half. Full-time: 3,134 students, 75% women, 25% men. Part-time: 2,078 students, 79% women, 21% men. Students come from 3 states and territories, 50 other countries, 1% from out-of-state, 0.2% Native American, 4% Hispanic, 89% black, 1% Asian American or Pacific Islander, 3% international, 61% 25 or older, 13% transferred in. Retention: 61% of full-time freshmen returned the following year. Academic areas with the most degrees conferred: business/marketing; psychology; biological/life sciences. Core. Calendar: semesters. Academic remediation for entering students, ESL program, services for LD students, advanced placement, honors program, independent study, summer session for credit, part-time degree program, external degree program, adult/continuing education programs, co-op programs and internships. Off campus study at other units of the City University of New York System. Study abroad program.

Entrance Requirements: Open admission except for nursing program. Options: Common Application, deferred admission. Required: high school transcript, GED. Required for some: SAT and SAT Subject Tests or ACT. Entrance: noncompetitive. Application deadline: Rolling. Notification: continuous. Preference given to city residents.

Costs Per Year: Application fee: $60. State resident tuition: $4000 full-time, $170 per credit part-time. Nonresident tuition: $8640 full-time, $360 per credit part-time. Mandatory fees: $230 full-time, $78.35 per term part-time.

Collegiate Environment: Drama-theater group, choral group, student-run newspaper, radio station. Social organizations: 30 open to all. Most popular organizations: Caribbean American Student Association, African Heritage, Phi Beta Sigma, Black Social Workers, Latino Club. Major annual events: Presidential Lecture Series, Black Solidarity Day, Club Fair. Student services: legal services, women's center. Campus security: 24-hour patrols. College housing not available. Charles Innis Memorial Library with 111,000 books, 23,379 microform titles, 24,410 serials, 20,000 audiovisual materials, an OPAC, and a Web page. Operations spending for 2004 fiscal year: $16,000. 1,570 computers available on campus for general student use. A campuswide network can be accessed from off-campus. Staffed computer lab on campus.

■ **MEMORIAL HOSPITAL SCHOOL OF NURSING** *L-25*
600 Northern Blvd.
Albany, NY 12204
Tel: (518)471-3260
Fax: (518)447-3559
Web Site: http://www.nehealth.com/html/NEH_Schools.asp?L1=6&L2=31
Description: Independent, 2-year, coed. Calendar: semesters.

■ **MERCY COLLEGE** *K-35*
555 Broadway
Dobbs Ferry, NY 10522-1189
Tel: (914)693-4500
Free: 800-MERCY-NY
Admissions: 800-MERCY-GO
Fax: (914)674-7382
E-mail: admissions@mercy.edu
Web Site: http://www.mercy.edu/
Description: Independent, comprehensive, coed. Awards associate, bachelor's, and master's degrees. Founded 1951. Setting: 60-acre suburban campus with easy access to New York City. Endowment: $24 million. Total enrollment: 9,539. Faculty: 830 (175 full-time, 655 part-time). Student-undergrad faculty ratio is 17:1. 2,110 applied, 42% were admitted. Full-time: 3,694 students, 70% women, 30% men. Part-time: 1,942 students, 73% women, 27% men. Students come from 6 states and territories, 49 other countries, 4% from out-of-state, 0.3% Native American, 34% Hispanic, 31% black, 3% Asian American or Pacific Islander, 2% international, 58% 25 or older, 21% transferred in. Retention: 61% of full-time freshmen returned the following year. Academic areas with the most degrees conferred: social sciences; business/marketing; health professions and related sciences. Core. Calendar: semesters. Academic remediation for entering students, ESL program, services for LD students, advanced placement, accelerated degree program, self-designed majors, honors program, independent study, distance learning, double major, summer session for credit, part-time degree program, adult/continuing education programs, co-op programs and internships, graduate courses open to undergrads. Off campus study at Westchester Conservatory of Music, New York Medical College. Study abroad program. ROTC: Air Force (c).
Entrance Requirements: Open admission. Options: Peterson's Universal Application, electronic application, early admission, deferred admission. Required: high school transcript, 1 recommendation. Recommended: interview, SAT. Application deadline: Rolling. Notification: continuous.
Costs Per Year: Application fee: $37. Comprehensive fee: $21,248 includes full-time tuition ($12,370), mandatory fees ($200), and college room and board ($8678). Part-time tuition: $520 per credit. Part-time mandatory fees: $100 per term.
Collegiate Environment: Orientation program. Student-run newspaper, radio station. Most popular organizations: Latin American Student Association, African Descendants of One Mind, Veterinarian Technology Club, The Reporters Impact, Resident Student Association. Major annual events: Campus Conversations with the President, Korean Food Festival, Hispanic Food Festival. Student services: personal-psychological counseling. Campus security: 24-hour patrols. Option: coed housing available. Mercy College Library with 322,610 books, 1,765 serials, an OPAC, and a Web page. 138 computers available on campus for general student use. A campuswide network can be accessed from off-campus. Staffed computer lab on campus.
Community Environment: Population 10,353. Primarily a residential community, Dobbs Ferry is located on the banks of the Hudson River and is 15 miles from New York City.

■ **MESIVTA OF EASTERN PARKWAY RABBINICAL SEMINARY** *O-34*
510 Dahill Rd.
Brooklyn, NY 11218-5559
Tel: (718)438-1002
Description: Independent Jewish, comprehensive, men only. Awards bachelor's and master's degrees. Founded 1947. Setting: 1-acre campus.

Total enrollment: 81. 25% from top 10% of their high school class, 100% from top half. Core. Calendar: semesters. Academic remediation for entering students, honors program, graduate courses open to undergrads.
Entrance Requirements: Required: high school transcript, 1 recommendation, interview, Orthodox Jewish commitment. Entrance: moderately difficult. Application deadline: Rolling.
Collegiate Environment: 7,500 books and 15 serials.

■ **MESIVTA TIFERETH JERUSALEM OF AMERICA** *N-34*
145 East Broadway
New York, NY 10002-6301
Tel: (212)964-2830
Description: Independent Jewish, comprehensive, men only. Awards bachelor's and master's degrees. Founded 1907. Calendar: semesters.

■ **MESIVTA TORAH VODAATH RABBINICAL SEMINARY** *O-34*
425 East Ninth St.
Brooklyn, NY 11218-5299
Tel: (718)941-8000
Fax: (718)941-8032
Description: Independent Jewish, comprehensive, men only. Awards bachelor's and master's degrees. Founded 1918. Core. Calendar: semesters. Summer session for credit, part-time degree program. Study abroad program.
Entrance Requirements: Options: early admission, deferred admission. Required: high school transcript, 2 recommendations. Entrance: moderately difficult. Application deadline: Rolling. Notification: continuous. Preference given to Orthodox Jews.
Collegiate Environment: Student services: personal-psychological counseling. 40,000 books and 12 serials.

■ **METROPOLITAN COLLEGE OF NEW YORK** *N-34*
75 Varick St.
New York, NY 10013-1919
Tel: (212)343-1234
Fax: (212)343-8470
Web Site: http://www.metropolitan.edu/
Description: Independent, comprehensive, coed. Awards associate, bachelor's, and master's degrees. Founded 1964. Setting: urban campus. Endowment: $4.5 million. Total enrollment: 1,555. Faculty: 297 (38 full-time, 259 part-time). Student-undergrad faculty ratio is 16:1. 208 applied, 98% were admitted. Students come from 5 states and territories, 2% from out-of-state, 0.3% Native American, 22% Hispanic, 66% black, 1% Asian American or Pacific Islander, 0.3% international, 65% 25 or older. Academic areas with the most degrees conferred: business/marketing; liberal arts/general studies. Core. Calendar: 3 15-week semesters. Academic remediation for entering students, ESL program, services for LD students, accelerated degree program, summer session for credit, adult/continuing education programs, co-op programs and internships. Study abroad program.
Entrance Requirements: Options: electronic application, deferred admission, international baccalaureate accepted. Required: essay, high school transcript, 2 recommendations, interview. Recommended: minimum 3.0 high school GPA, SAT, SAT or ACT. Required for some: college entrance exam, TABE. Entrance: moderately difficult. Application deadline: 8/15. Notification: continuous until 8/31.
Costs Per Year: Application fee: $30. Tuition: $14,240 full-time, $505 per credit part-time. Mandatory fees: $300 full-time. Full-time tuition and fees vary according to degree level and program. Part-time tuition varies according to degree level and program. Tuition guaranteed not to increase for student's term of enrollment.
Collegiate Environment: Orientation program. Student-run newspaper. Social organizations: 10 open to all. Most popular organizations: student government, student newsletter, honor societies, Networking Club, yearbook committee. Major annual events: Graduation Ceremony, New Student Orientation. Student services: personal-psychological counseling. Campus security: 24-hour patrols. College housing not available. Main Library with 26,800 books, 60 microform titles, 3,414 serials, 45 audiovisual materials, an OPAC, and a Web page. Operations spending for 2004 fiscal year: $789,823. 130 computers available on campus for general student use. A campuswide network can be accessed from off-campus. Staffed computer lab on campus.

■ **MILDRED ELLEY** *B-11*
800 New Louden Rd.
Latham, NY 12110

Tel: (518)786-0855
Free: 800-622-6327
Admissions: (518)786-3171
Web Site: http://www.mildred-elley.edu/
Description: Private, 2-year. Awards certificates, diplomas, transfer associ-ate, and terminal associate degrees. Setting: suburban campus with easy access to Albany. Total enrollment: 394. 121 applied, 98% were admitted. Full-time: 394 students, 82% women, 18% men. Students come from 3 states and territories, 3% from out-of-state, 6% Hispanic, 21% black, 64% 25 or older, 2% transferred in.
Entrance Requirements: Required: CPAt.
Collegiate Environment: Student services: legal services. College housing not available.

■ **MIRRER YESHIVA** *O-34*
1795 Ocean Parkway
Brooklyn, NY 11223-2010
Tel: (718)645-0536
Description: Independent Jewish, comprehensive, men only. Awards bachelor's and master's degrees. Founded 1926. Total enrollment: 236. Calendar: semesters.

■ **MOHAWK VALLEY COMMUNITY COLLEGE** *J-19*
1101 Sherman Dr.
Utica, NY 13501-5394
Tel: (315)792-5400
Admissions: (315)792-5354
Fax: (315)792-5527
E-mail: dkennelty@mvcc.edu
Web Site: http://www.mvcc.edu/
Description: State and locally supported, 2-year, coed. Part of State University of New York System. Awards certificates, transfer associate, and terminal associate degrees. Founded 1946. Setting: 80-acre suburban campus. Endowment: $3.1 million. Total enrollment: 5,984. Student-undergrad faculty ratio is 24:1. 3,440 applied, 90% were admitted. 3% from top 10% of their high school class, 8% from top quarter, 35% from top half. Full-time: 3,779 students, 51% women, 49% men. Part-time: 2,205 students, 58% women, 42% men. Students come from 18 states and territories, 11 other countries, 2% from out-of-state, 0.5% Native American, 3% Hispanic, 6% black, 2% Asian American or Pacific Islander, 0.4% international, 26% 25 or older, 6% live on campus, 5% transferred in. Retention: 58% of full-time freshmen returned the following year. Core. Calendar: semesters. Academic remediation for entering students, ESL program, services for LD students, advanced placement, self-designed majors, honors program, independent study, distance learning, double major, summer session for credit, part-time degree program, adult/continuing education programs, internships. Off campus study at Mohawk Valley College Consortium. Study abroad program. ROTC: Army (c).
Entrance Requirements: Open admission. Options: electronic application, early admission, early decision, deferred admission. Required: high school transcript. Entrance: noncompetitive. Application deadline: Rolling.
Costs Per Year: Application fee: $0. State resident tuition: $2950 full-time, $115 per credit hour part-time. Nonresident tuition: $5900 full-time, $230 per credit hour part-time. Mandatory fees: $344 full-time, $1 per credit hour part-time, $35 per term part-time. College room and board: $6260. College room only: $3530.
Collegiate Environment: Drama-theater group, choral group, student-run newspaper, radio station. Social organizations: 48 open to all. Most popular organizations: Drama Club, Student Congress, Returning Adult Student As-sociation, Black Student Union, Program Board. Major annual events: Open House, Student Orientation. Student services: health clinic, personal-psychological counseling. Campus security: 24-hour emergency response devices and patrols, late night transport-escort service, controlled dormitory access. 349 college housing spaces available; all were occupied in 2003-04. Freshmen guaranteed college housing. Option: coed housing available. Mohawk Valley Community College Library plus 2 others with 91,000 books, 925 serials, an OPAC, and a Web page. Operations spending for 2004 fiscal year: $921,708. 380 computers available on campus for general student use. A campuswide network can be accessed from off-campus. Staffed computer lab on campus.

■ **MOLLOY COLLEGE** *H-42*
1000 Hempstead Ave.
Rockville Centre, NY 11571-5002

Tel: (516)678-5000; 888-4MOLLOY
Web Site: http://www.molloy.edu/
Description: Independent, comprehensive, coed. Awards associate, bachelor's, and master's degrees and post-master's certificates. Founded 1955. Setting: 30-acre suburban campus with easy access to New York City. Total enrollment: 3,585. Faculty: 475 (147 full-time, 328 part-time). Student-undergrad faculty ratio is 10:1. 1,093 applied, 65% were admitted. 12% from top 10% of their high school class, 44% from top quarter, 86% from top half. Full-time: 1,875 students, 75% women, 25% men. Part-time: 857 students, 84% women, 16% men. Students come from 4 states and territories, 9 other countries, 0% from out-of-state, 0.1% Native American, 8% Hispanic, 20% black, 6% Asian American or Pacific Islander, 0.1% international, 34% 25 or older, 16% transferred in. Retention: 76% of full-time freshmen returned the following year. Core. Calendar: 4-1-4. Academic remediation for entering students, ESL program, services for LD students, advanced placement, self-designed majors, honors program, double major, summer session for credit, part-time degree program, adult/continuing education programs, co-op programs and internships. Study abroad program. ROTC: Army (c), Naval (c), Air Force (c).
Entrance Requirements: Options: Common Application, electronic applica-tion, early admission, early decision, deferred admission, international bac-calaureate accepted. Required: essay, high school transcript, SAT or ACT. Recommended: interview. Required for some: 1 recommendation. Entrance: moderately difficult. Application deadlines: Rolling, 11/1 for early decision. Notification: continuous, 12/1 for early decision.
Costs Per Year: Application fee: $30. Tuition: $15,760 full-time, $525 per credit part-time. Mandatory fees: $700 full-time.
Collegiate Environment: Orientation program. Drama-theater group, choral group, student-run newspaper. Social organizations: 23 open to all. Most popular organizations: Nursing Student Association, African-American Carib-bean Organization, Gaelic Society, Education Club, International Society. Major annual events: International Day, End of the Year Picnic, Career Day. Student services: health clinic, personal-psychological counseling, women's center. Campus security: 24-hour emergency response devices and patrols, late night transport-escort service. College housing not available. James Edward Tobin Library with 135,000 books, 13,850 microform titles, 9,675 audiovisual materials, and an OPAC. 246 computers available on campus for general student use. A campuswide network can be accessed. Staffed computer lab on campus.
Community Environment: Rockville Centre, population 35,000, is a suburb of New York City on Long Island. Good transportation facilities make all the cultural, recreational, civic services, and employment opportunities of New York easily accessible. Within the immediate area there are a public library, churches of major denominations, and a hospital. Some part-time work is available in the local area.

■ **MONROE COLLEGE (BRONX)** *M-35*
Monroe College Way
Bronx, NY 10468-5407
Tel: (718)933-6700
Free: 800-55MONROE
Web Site: http://www.monroecollege.edu/
Description: Proprietary, comprehensive, coed. Awards associate, bachelor's, and master's degrees. Founded 1933. Setting: urban campus. Total enrollment: 4,285. Faculty: 237 (57 full-time, 180 part-time). Student-undergrad faculty ratio is 21:1. 1,508 applied, 61% were admitted. Full-time: 3,637 students, 73% women, 27% men. Part-time: 648 students, 72% women, 28% men. Students come from 7 states and territories, 8 other countries, 1% from out-of-state, 0.2% Native American, 53% Hispanic, 41% black, 1% Asian American or Pacific Islander, 1% international, 46% 25 or older, 1% live on campus, 7% transferred in. Retention: 71% of full-time freshmen returned the following year. Academic areas with the most degrees conferred: business/marketing; computer and information sciences; security and protective services. Core. Calendar: trimesters. Academic remediation for entering students, ESL program, distance learning, summer session for credit, part-time degree program, adult/continuing education programs, co-op programs and internships.
Entrance Requirements: Options: early admission, deferred admission. Required: high school transcript, interview. Entrance: moderately difficult. Application deadline: 8/26. Notification: continuous until 9/3.
Costs Per Year: Application fee: $35. Comprehensive fee: $16,660 includes full-time tuition ($9160), mandatory fees ($600), and college room and board ($6900). Part-time tuition: $382 per credit hour. Part-time mandatory fees: $150 per term.

Collegiate Environment: Drama-theater group, student-run newspaper. Social organizations: 5 open to all. Student services: personal-psychological counseling. Campus security: late night transport-escort service. 525 college housing spaces available; all were occupied in 2003-04. Freshmen given priority for college housing. Option: coed housing available. Main library plus 1 other with 28,000 books, 301 serials, an OPAC, and a Web page. 541 computers available on campus for general student use. A campuswide network can be accessed. Staffed computer lab on campus.

■ **MONROE COLLEGE (NEW ROCHELLE)** *L-36*
434 Main St.
New Rochelle, NY 10801-6410
Tel: (914)632-5400
Free: 800-55MONROE
Admissions: (914)654-3200
Fax: (914)632-5462
Web Site: http://www.monroecollege.edu/

Description: Proprietary, 4-year, coed. Awards associate, bachelor's, and master's degrees. Founded 1983. Setting: suburban campus with easy access to New York City. Total enrollment: 1,781. Faculty: 72 (17 full-time, 55 part-time). Student-undergrad faculty ratio is 20:1. 896 applied, 60% were admitted. Full-time: 1,574 students, 67% women, 33% men. Part-time: 207 students, 67% women, 33% men. Students come from 9 states and territories, 10 other countries, 2% from out-of-state, 0.2% Native American, 17% Hispanic, 59% black, 1% Asian American or Pacific Islander, 15% international, 31% 25 or older, 20% live on campus, 8% transferred in. Retention: 74% of full-time freshmen returned the following year. Academic areas with the most degrees conferred: business/marketing; computer and information sciences; health professions and related sciences; security and protective services. Core. Calendar: trimesters. Academic remediation for entering students, ESL program, distance learning, summer session for credit, part-time degree program, external degree program, adult/continuing education programs, co-op programs and internships.
Entrance Requirements: Options: Peterson's Universal Application, Common Application, electronic application, early admission, deferred admission. Required: high school transcript, interview. Entrance: moderately difficult. Application deadline: 8/26. Notification: 9/3.
Costs Per Year: Application fee: $35. Comprehensive fee: $16,660 includes full-time tuition ($9160), mandatory fees ($600), and college room and board ($6900). Room and board charges vary according to board plan. Part-time tuition: $382 per credit. Part-time mandatory fees: $150 per term.
Collegiate Environment: Drama-theater group, student-run newspaper. Social organizations: 5 open to all. Student services: personal-psychological counseling. Campus security: late night transport-escort service. 525 college housing spaces available; all were occupied in 2003-04. Freshmen given priority for college housing. Option: coed housing available. Main library plus 1 other with 8,400 books and 211 serials. 214 computers available on campus for general student use. A campuswide network can be accessed from student residence rooms. Staffed computer lab on campus.

■ **MONROE COMMUNITY COLLEGE** *J-11*
1000 East Henrietta Rd.
Rochester, NY 14623-5780
Tel: (585)292-2000
Fax: (585)427-2749
Web Site: http://www.monroecc.edu/

Description: State and locally supported, 2-year, coed. Part of State University of New York System. Awards certificates, transfer associate, and terminal associate degrees. Founded 1961. Setting: 314-acre suburban campus with easy access to Buffalo. Endowment: $3.6 million. Educational spending for 2005 fiscal year: $3071 per student. Total enrollment: 16,596. Full-time: 9,398 students, 52% women, 48% men. Part-time: 7,198 students, 58% women, 42% men. Students come from 45 other countries, 1% Native American, 5% Hispanic, 17% black, 3% Asian American or Pacific Islander, 1% international, 35% 25 or older, 6% transferred in. Calendar: semesters. Academic remediation for entering students, ESL program, services for LD students, advanced placement, accelerated degree program, honors program, summer session for credit, part-time degree program, adult/continuing education programs, co-op programs and internships. Off campus study at the Rochester Area Colleges. ROTC: Army (c), Air Force (c).
Entrance Requirements: Open admission except for allied health, business, computer science, engineering science programs. Options: Peterson's Universal Application, electronic application, early admission. Required: high

school transcript. Entrance: noncompetitive. Application deadline: Rolling. Notification: continuous. Preference given to county residents.
Collegiate Environment: Orientation program. Drama-theater group, choral group, student-run newspaper, radio station. Social organizations: 52 open to all. Most popular organizations: student newspaper, Phi Theta Kappa, student government. Student services: health clinic, personal-psychological counseling. Campus security: 24-hour emergency response devices, late night transport-escort service. LeRoy V. Good Library plus 1 other with 110,748 books, 12,975 microform titles, 745 serials, 4,100 audiovisual materials, and an OPAC. Operations spending for 2004 fiscal year: $1.4 million. 150 computers available on campus for general student use. A campuswide network can be accessed from off-campus. Staffed computer lab on campus.

■ **MOUNT SAINT MARY COLLEGE** *Q-24*
330 Powell Ave.
Newburgh, NY 12550-3494
Tel: (845)561-0800; 888-937-6762
Admissions: (845)569-3248
Fax: (845)562-6762
E-mail: ogrady@msmc.edu
Web Site: http://www.msmc.edu/

Description: Independent, comprehensive, coed. Awards bachelor's and master's degrees. Founded 1960. Setting: 72-acre suburban campus with easy access to New York City. Endowment: $4.1 million. Educational spending for 2005 fiscal year: $4452 per student. Total enrollment: 2,574. Faculty: 221 (71 full-time, 150 part-time). Student-undergrad faculty ratio is 17:1. 1,625 applied, 79% were admitted. 8% from top 10% of their high school class, 27% from top quarter, 66% from top half. Full-time: 1,615 students, 74% women, 26% men. Part-time: 424 students, 70% women, 30% men. Students come from 15 states and territories, 1 other country, 12% from out-of-state, 0.3% Native American, 9% Hispanic, 11% black, 3% Asian American or Pacific Islander, 0% international, 26% 25 or older, 41% live on campus, 10% transferred in. Retention: 70% of full-time freshmen returned the following year. Academic areas with the most degrees conferred: business/marketing; English; history. Core. Calendar: semesters. Academic remediation for entering students, advanced placement, accelerated degree program, self-designed majors, freshman honors college, honors program, independent study, distance learning, double major, summer session for credit, part-time degree program, adult/continuing education programs, co-op programs and internships, graduate courses open to undergrads. Off campus study at Associated Colleges of the Mid-Hudson Area. Study abroad program. ROTC: Army (c).
Entrance Requirements: Options: Peterson's Universal Application, Common Application, electronic application, deferred admission. Required: high school transcript, SAT or ACT. Recommended: essay, minimum 3.0 high school GPA, 3 recommendations, interview. Required for some: essay, 3 recommendations, interview. Entrance: moderately difficult. Application deadline: Rolling. Notification: continuous.
Costs Per Year: Application fee: $35. Comprehensive fee: $25,250 includes full-time tuition ($16,410), mandatory fees ($520), and college room and board ($8320). College room only: $4680. Full-time tuition and fees vary according to degree level. Room and board charges vary according to board plan, housing facility, and student level. Part-time tuition: $547 per credit hour. Part-time mandatory fees: $35 per term. Part-time tuition and fees vary according to degree level.
Collegiate Environment: Orientation program. Drama-theater group, choral group, student-run newspaper, radio station. Social organizations: 31 open to all. Most popular organizations: Student Government Association, Different Stages, Big Brothers/Big Sisters, Black and Latin Student Unions, Habitat for Humanity. Major annual events: Siblings' Week, Parents' Weekend, Spring Weekend. Student services: health clinic, personal-psychological counseling. Campus security: 24-hour emergency response devices and patrols, student patrols, late night transport-escort service, controlled dormitory access, monitored surveillance cameras in all residence halls. 901 college housing spaces available; 841 were occupied in 2003-04. Freshmen given priority for college housing. Options: men-only, women-only housing available. Curtin Memorial Library plus 1 other with 113,676 books, 714,375 microform titles, 870 serials, 21,297 audiovisual materials, an OPAC, and a Web page. Operations spending for 2004 fiscal year: $732,994. 336 computers available on campus for general student use. A campuswide network can be accessed from student residence rooms and from off campus. Staffed computer lab on campus.
Community Environment: Mount Saint Mary College is located in the

historic Hudson Valley Region, at the foothills of the Catskill Mountains, 60 miles north of New York City. Cultural, historical, and outdoor activities abound.

■ NASSAU COMMUNITY COLLEGE *G-43*

1 Education Dr.
Garden City, NY 11530-6793
Tel: (516)572-7500
Admissions: (516)572-7345
Web Site: http://www.ncc.edu/

Description: State and locally supported, 2-year, coed. Part of State University of New York System. Awards certificates, transfer associate, and terminal associate degrees. Founded 1959. Setting: 225-acre suburban campus with easy access to New York City. Educational spending for 2005 fiscal year: $4990 per student. Total enrollment: 20,979. Student-undergrad faculty ratio is 18:1. 7,821 applied, 92% were admitted. Full-time: 13,528 students, 49% women, 51% men. Part-time: 7,451 students, 62% women, 38% men. 0.3% Native American, 13% Hispanic, 19% black, 7% Asian American or Pacific Islander, 5% international, 20% 25 or older, 9% transferred in. Calendar: semesters. Academic remediation for entering students, ESL program, services for LD students, advanced placement, honors program, distance learning, summer session for credit, part-time degree program, adult/continuing education programs, co-op programs and internships. Off campus study at members of the Long Island Regional Advisory Council for Higher Education. ROTC: Army (c).

Entrance Requirements: Option: deferred admission. Required: high school transcript. Recommended: minimum 2.0 high school GPA, SAT or ACT. Required for some: minimum 3.0 high school GPA, interview. Entrance: noncompetitive. Application deadline: 8/1. Notification: continuous.

Costs Per Year: Application fee: $30. State resident tuition: $3310 full-time, $138 per credit part-time. Nonresident tuition: $6620 full-time, $276 per credit part-time. Mandatory fees: $242 full-time.

Collegiate Environment: Drama-theater group, choral group, student-run newspaper, radio station. Social organizations: 60 open to all. Most popular organizations: Student Organization of Latinos, Student Government Association, Programming Board, Caribbean Student Organization, NYPIRG. Major annual events: Spring Festival, Multicultural Fair, Folk Festival. Student services: health clinic, personal-psychological counseling, women's center. Campus security: 24-hour emergency response devices and patrols, late night transport-escort service. College housing not available. A. Holly Patterson Library with 171,938 books, 14,935 microform titles, 753 serials, 55,514 audiovisual materials, an OPAC, and a Web page. 700 computers available on campus for general student use. A campuswide network can be accessed from off-campus. Staffed computer lab on campus.

■ NAZARETH COLLEGE OF ROCHESTER *J-11*

4245 East Ave.
Rochester, NY 14618-3790
Tel: (585)389-2525
Admissions: (585)389-2860
Fax: (585)389-2826
E-mail: tkdarin@naz.edu
Web Site: http://www.naz.edu/

Description: Independent, comprehensive, coed. Awards bachelor's, master's, and doctoral degrees and post-master's certificates. Founded 1924. Setting: 150-acre suburban campus. Endowment: $51 million. Educational spending for 2005 fiscal year: $8536 per student. Total enrollment: 3,120. Faculty: 301 (135 full-time, 166 part-time). Student-undergrad faculty ratio is 13:1. 1,972 applied, 79% were admitted. 29% from top 10% of their high school class, 66% from top quarter, 92% from top half. 5 valedictorians. Full-time: 1,864 students, 76% women, 24% men. Part-time: 193 students, 76% women, 24% men. Students come from 23 states and territories, 58% from out-of-state, 0.5% Native American, 2% Hispanic, 5% black, 2% Asian American or Pacific Islander, 0.5% international, 13% 25 or older, 57% live on campus, 8% transferred in. Retention: 84% of full-time freshmen returned the following year. Academic areas with the most degrees conferred: health professions and related sciences; psychology; business/marketing; English. Core. Calendar: semesters. Academic remediation for entering students, services for LD students, advanced placement, honors program, independent study, double major, summer session for credit, part-time degree program, adult/continuing education programs, co-op programs and internships. Off campus study at 14 members of the Rochester Area Colleges. Study abroad program. ROTC: Army (c), Air Force (c).

Entrance Requirements: Options: Peterson's Universal Application, Common Application, electronic application, early admission, early decision, early action, deferred admission, international baccalaureate accepted. Required: essay, high school transcript, 1 recommendation, SAT or ACT. Recommended: 2 recommendations, interview. Required for some: audition/portfolio review. Entrance: moderately difficult. Application deadlines: 2/15, 11/15 for early decision, 12/15 for early action. Notification: continuous, 12/15 for early decision, 1/15 for early action.

Costs Per Year: Application fee: $40. Comprehensive fee: $28,234 includes full-time tuition ($19,214), mandatory fees ($660), and college room and board ($8360). College room only: $4680. Room and board charges vary according to board plan and housing facility. Part-time tuition: $460 per credit hour.

Collegiate Environment: Orientation program. Drama-theater group, choral group, student-run newspaper, radio station. Social organizations: 33 open to all. Most popular organizations: Student Activities Council, French Club, Theater Club, Campus Ministry Council, Coffeehouse, Arts, Lecture, Entertainment Board (CALEB). Major annual events: Spring Fest, Siblings' Weekend, Parents' Weekend. Student services: health clinic, personal-psychological counseling. Campus security: 24-hour emergency response devices and patrols, student patrols, late night transport-escort service, controlled dormitory access, alarm system, security beeper, lighted pathways. 1,173 college housing spaces available; 1,106 were occupied in 2003-04. Freshmen guaranteed college housing. Options: coed, women-only housing available. Lorette Wilmot Library with 162,593 books, 438,204 microform titles, 1,888 serials, 12,236 audiovisual materials, an OPAC, and a Web page. Operations spending for 2004 fiscal year: $2.1 million. 150 computers available on campus for general student use. A campuswide network can be accessed from student residence rooms and from off campus. Staffed computer lab on campus.

Community Environment: See University of Rochester.

■ THE NEW SCHOOL FOR GENERAL STUDIES *N-34*

66 West 12th St.
New York, NY 10011-8603
Tel: (212)229-5600
Free: 800-862-5039
Admissions: (212)229-5630
Fax: (212)645-0661
E-mail: admissions@dialnsa.edu
Web Site: http://www.nsu.newschool.edu/

Description: Independent, upper-level, coed. Part of New School University. Awards bachelor's, master's, and doctoral degrees. Founded 1919. Setting: urban campus. Endowment: $150.9 million. Research spending for 2004 fiscal year: $6.4 million. Total enrollment: 1,650. Faculty: 506 (36 full-time, 470 part-time). 297 applied, 85% were admitted. Students come from 28 states and territories, 25 other countries, 33% from out-of-state, 1% Native American, 6% Hispanic, 12% black, 3% Asian American or Pacific Islander, 4% international, 72% 25 or older. Academic area with the most degrees conferred: liberal arts/general studies. Calendar: semesters. ESL program, advanced placement, accelerated degree program, self-designed majors, independent study, distance learning, summer session for credit, part-time degree program, adult/continuing education programs, internships, graduate courses open to undergrads.

Costs Per Year: Application fee: $40. Comprehensive fee: $30,128 includes full-time tuition ($17,808), mandatory fees ($570), and college room and board ($11,750). College room only: $8750. Room and board charges vary according to board plan. Part-time tuition: $742 per credit.

Collegiate Environment: Orientation program. Most popular organizations: university committees, B.A. program committees, student advisory committees, publications. Major annual events: Block Party, University Convocation, New Student Orientation. Student services: health clinic, personal-psychological counseling. Campus security: 24-hour emergency response devices, controlled dormitory access, trained security personnel in central buildings. 948 college housing spaces available. Option: coed housing available. Raymond Fogelman Library plus 2 others with 368,890 books, 20,972 microform titles, 1,155 serials, and 433,123 audiovisual materials. Operations spending for 2004 fiscal year: $2.8 million. 705 computers available on campus for general student use. A campuswide network can be accessed from off-campus. Staffed computer lab on campus.

■ THE NEW SCHOOL FOR JAZZ AND CONTEMPORARY MUSIC *N-34*

55 West 13th St., 5th Floor
New York, NY 10011

Tel: (212)229-5896
Web Site: http://www.jazz.newschool.edu
Description: Independent, 4-year, coed. Total enrollment: 287. Calendar: semesters.
Costs Per Year: Comprehensive fee: $38,600 includes full-time tuition ($27,600) and college room and board ($11,000). Part-time tuition: $900 per credit.

■ **NEW YORK CAREER INSTITUTE** *N-34*
11 Park Place- 4th Floor
New York, NY 10007
Tel: (212)962-0002
Fax: (212)385-7574
E-mail: cmcmahon@nyci.com
Web Site: http://www.nyci.com/
Description: Proprietary, 2-year, coed. Awards terminal associate degrees. Founded 1942. Setting: urban campus. Total enrollment: 716. 716 applied, 100% were admitted. 0.3% Native American, 19% Hispanic, 33% black, 1% Asian American or Pacific Islander, 0% international. Core. Calendar: trimesters (semesters for evening division). Summer session for credit, part-time degree program, co-op programs and internships.
Entrance Requirements: Required: high school transcript, interview. Required for some: recommendations. Entrance: noncompetitive. Application deadlines: 9/6, 9/6 for nonresidents. Notification: continuous.
Costs Per Year: Application fee: $25. Tuition: $9600 full-time, $300 per credit part-time. Mandatory fees: $35 full-time, $35 per term part-time. Full-time tuition and fees vary according to class time, course load, and degree level. Part-time tuition and fees vary according to class time, course load, and degree level.
Collegiate Environment: Orientation program. Student-run newspaper. College housing not available. 5,010 books and 23 serials. 50 computers available on campus for general student use.

■ **NEW YORK CITY COLLEGE OF TECHNOLOGY OF THE CITY UNIVERSITY OF NEW YORK** *O-34*
300 Jay St.
Brooklyn, NY 11201-2983
Tel: (718)260-5000
Admissions: (718)260-5500
Fax: (718)260-5198
Web Site: http://www.citytech.cuny.edu/
Description: State and locally supported, primarily 2-year, coed. Part of City University of New York System. Awards certificates, transfer associate, terminal associate, and bachelor's degrees. Founded 1946. Setting: urban campus. Endowment: $11.6 million. Research spending for 2004 fiscal year: $11,000. Educational spending for 2005 fiscal year: $3995 per student. Total enrollment: 11,380. 5,833 applied, 84% were admitted. 3% from top 10% of their high school class, 12% from top quarter, 49% from top half. Full-time: 7,053 students, 47% women, 53% men. Part-time: 4,327 students, 53% women, 47% men. Students come from 6 states and territories, 108 other countries, 0.2% Native American, 26% Hispanic, 44% black, 13% Asian American or Pacific Islander, 3% international, 38% 25 or older, 4% transferred in. Retention: 78% of full-time freshmen returned the following year. Core. Calendar: semesters. Academic remediation for entering students, ESL program, services for LD students, advanced placement, self-designed majors, freshman honors college, honors program, independent study, distance learning, summer session for credit, part-time degree program, internships. Off campus study. Study abroad program. ROTC: Air Force (c).
Entrance Requirements: Open admission except for upper-level bachelor's degree programs. Required: high school transcript. Entrance: noncompetitive. Application deadline: Rolling.
Collegiate Environment: Orientation program. Drama-theater group, choral group, student-run newspaper. Social organizations: 46 open to all. Most popular organizations: IBO, NUTREX, Human Services, Seekers Christian Fellowship Gospel Choir. Student services: health clinic, personal-psychological counseling, women's center. Campus security: 24-hour emergency response devices and patrols. College housing not available. Ursula C. Schwerin Library with 177,569 books, 630 serials, an OPAC, and a Web page. Operations spending for 2004 fiscal year: $1.5 million. 500 computers available on campus for general student use. A campuswide network can be accessed from off-campus. Staffed computer lab on campus.

■ **NEW YORK COLLEGE OF HEALTH PROFESSIONS** *M-39*
6801 Jericho Turnpike
Syosset, NY 11791-4413

Tel: (516)364-0808
Free: 800-922-7337
Fax: (516)364-0989
E-mail: rdodas@nycollege.edu
Web Site: http://www.nycollege.edu/
Description: Independent, primarily 2-year, coed. Awards terminal associate, incidental bachelor's, and master's degrees. Founded 1981. Setting: suburban campus with easy access to New York City. Total enrollment: 879. Full-time: 332 students, 77% women, 23% men. Part-time: 469 students, 75% women, 25% men. 0.3% Native American, 12% Hispanic, 11% black, 8% Asian American or Pacific Islander. Academic area with the most degrees conferred: health professions and related sciences. Core. Calendar: trimesters. Academic remediation for entering students, advanced placement, accelerated degree program, distance learning, double major, summer session for credit, part-time degree program, adult/continuing education programs, internships, graduate courses open to undergrads. Study abroad program.
Entrance Requirements: Options: Common Application, electronic application, deferred admission. Required: essay, high school transcript, minimum 2.0 high school GPA, interview. Entrance: moderately difficult. Application deadline: Rolling. Notification: continuous.
Costs Per Year: Application fee: $85. Tuition: $9900 full-time, $275 per credit part-time.
Collegiate Environment: Orientation program. Student services: health clinic. Campus security: 24-hour patrols, security guard evening and weekend hours. College housing not available. James and Lenore Jacobson Library at the New Center with 4,600 books, 100 serials, and an OPAC. 3 computers available on campus for general student use. Staffed computer lab on campus.

■ **NEW YORK INSTITUTE OF TECHNOLOGY** *E-43*
PO Box 8000
Old Westbury, NY 11568-8000
Tel: (516)686-7516
Free: 800-345-NYIT
Admissions: (516)686-7871
Fax: (516)686-7613
E-mail: admissions@aol.nuit.edu
Web Site: http://www.nyit.edu/
Description: Independent, university, coed. Awards associate, bachelor's, master's, doctoral, and first professional degrees and post-master's certificates. Founded 1955. Setting: 1,050-acre suburban campus with easy access to New York City. Endowment: $37.3 million. Research spending for 2004 fiscal year: $5.9 million. Educational spending for 2005 fiscal year: $6102 per student. Total enrollment: 11,141. Faculty: 675 (217 full-time, 458 part-time). Student-undergrad faculty ratio is 16:1. 3,941 applied, 67% were admitted. Full-time: 4,163 students, 39% women, 61% men. Part-time: 2,323 students, 53% women, 47% men. Students come from 48 states and territories, 82 other countries, 19% from out-of-state, 0.3% Native American, 10% Hispanic, 12% black, 9% Asian American or Pacific Islander, 5% international, 26% 25 or older, 9% live on campus, 9% transferred in. Retention: 71% of full-time freshmen returned the following year. Academic areas with the most degrees conferred: business/marketing; architecture; computer and information sciences. Core. Calendar: semesters. Academic remediation for entering students, ESL program, services for LD students, advanced placement, accelerated degree program, self-designed majors, honors program, independent study, distance learning, double major, summer session for credit, part-time degree program, external degree program, adult/continuing education programs, co-op programs and internships, graduate courses open to undergrads. Off campus study at New York State Teachers' Centers. Study abroad program. ROTC: Army, Air Force.
Entrance Requirements: Options: electronic application, deferred admission, international baccalaureate accepted. Required: essay, high school transcript, SAT or ACT. Required for some: minimum X high school GPA, recommendations, interview, proof of volunteer or work experience required for physical therapy, physician assistant and occupational therapy programs; portfolio for fine arts programs. Entrance: moderately difficult. Application deadline: Rolling. Notification: continuous.
Costs Per Year: Application fee: $50. Comprehensive fee: $30,040 includes full-time tuition ($18,696), mandatory fees ($540), and college room and board ($10,804). College room only: $5600. Full-time tuition and fees vary according to course load and program. Room and board charges vary according to board plan, housing facility, and location. Part-time tuition: $630 per credit. Part-time mandatory fees: $230 per term. Part-time tuition and fees vary according to course load.

Collegiate Environment: Orientation program. Drama-theater group, choral group, student-run newspaper, radio station. Social organizations: 100 open to all; national fraternities, national sororities, local fraternities, local sororities; 2% of eligible men and 1% of eligible women are members. Most popular organizations: Physical Therapy Society, Occupational Therapy Association, ASHRAM, Bio-Medical Society, National Society of Black Engineers. Major annual events: Career Expo, Oktoberfest, Mayfest. Student services: health clinic, personal-psychological counseling, women's center. Campus security: 24-hour emergency response devices and patrols, late night transport-escort service, controlled dormitory access. 1,000 college housing spaces available; 590 were occupied in 2003-04. Freshmen guaranteed college housing. Option: coed housing available. George and Gertrude Wisser Memorial Library plus 4 others with 208,620 books, 893,244 microform titles, 14,857 serials, 49,239 audiovisual materials, an OPAC, and a Web page. Operations spending for 2004 fiscal year: $2.6 million. 815 computers available on campus for general student use. A campuswide network can be accessed from student residence rooms and from off campus. Staffed computer lab on campus.

■ **NEW YORK SCHOOL OF INTERIOR DESIGN** *N-34*

170 East 70th St.
New York, NY 10021-5110
Tel: (212)472-1500
Free: 800-336-9743
Fax: (212)472-1867
E-mail: david@nysid.edu
Web Site: http://www.nysid.edu/

Description: Independent, comprehensive, coed. Awards associate, bachelor's, and master's degrees. Founded 1916. Setting: 1-acre urban campus. Endowment: $2.1 million. Total enrollment: 739. Faculty: 79 (2 full-time, 77 part-time). Student-undergrad faculty ratio is 10:1. 119 applied, 37% were admitted. Full-time: 168 students, 92% women, 8% men. Part-time: 556 students, 92% women, 8% men. Students come from 17 states and territories, 25 other countries, 33% from out-of-state, 0% Native American, 6% Hispanic, 3% black, 7% Asian American or Pacific Islander, 7% international, 73% 25 or older, 11% transferred in. Retention: 50% of full-time freshmen returned the following year. Core. Calendar: semesters. ESL program, services for LD students, advanced placement, independent study, summer session for credit, part-time degree program, internships. Study abroad program.

Entrance Requirements: Options: Peterson's Universal Application, Common Application, deferred admission, international baccalaureate accepted. Required: essay, high school transcript, minimum 2.8 high school GPA, 2 recommendations, portfolio, SAT or ACT. Entrance: moderately difficult. Application deadline: 3/1. Notification: 4/1.

Costs Per Year: Application fee: $50. Tuition: $18,600 full-time, $620 per credit part-time. Mandatory fees: $220 full-time, $110 per term part-time.

Collegiate Environment: Orientation program. Social organizations: 1 open to all. Most popular organization: American Society of Interior Designers. Major annual events: lecture series, ASID student auction, gallery exhibition openings. Campus security: security during school hours. College housing not available. NYSID Library with 12,000 books, 110 serials, 100 audiovisual materials, an OPAC, and a Web page. Operations spending for 2004 fiscal year: $217,916. 135 computers available on campus for general student use. A campuswide network can be accessed from off-campus. Staffed computer lab on campus.

■ **NEW YORK UNIVERSITY** *N-34*

70 Washington Square South
New York, NY 10012-1019
Tel: (212)998-1212
Admissions: (212)998-4500
Fax: (212)995-4902
E-mail: nyuadmit@uccvm.nyu.edu
Web Site: http://www.nyu.edu/

Description: Independent, university, coed. Awards associate, bachelor's, master's, doctoral, and first professional degrees and post-master's and first professional certificates. Founded 1831. Setting: urban campus. Endowment: $1.5 billion. Research spending for 2004 fiscal year: $219.8 million. Total enrollment: 40,004. Faculty: 4,073 (1,952 full-time, 2,121 part-time). Student-undergrad faculty ratio is 11:1. 34,509 applied, 37% were admitted. 68% from top 10% of their high school class, 95% from top quarter, 100% from top half. Full-time: 18,981 students, 61% women, 39% men. Part-time: 1,585 students, 62% women, 38% men. Students come from 52 states and

territories, 91 other countries, 57% from out-of-state, 0.2% Native American, 8% Hispanic, 5% black, 17% Asian American or Pacific Islander, 4% international, 10% 25 or older, 54% live on campus, 3% transferred in. Retention: 93% of full-time freshmen returned the following year. Academic areas with the most degrees conferred: business/marketing; visual and performing arts; social sciences. Core. Calendar: semesters. ESL program, services for LD students, advanced placement, accelerated degree program, self-designed majors, freshman honors college, honors program, independent study, distance learning, double major, summer session for credit, part-time degree program, adult/continuing education programs, co-op programs and internships, graduate courses open to undergrads. Off campus study at Spelman College, Morehouse College, Bennett College, Tougaloo College; American University. Study abroad program.

Entrance Requirements: Options: Peterson's Universal Application, Common Application, electronic application, early decision, deferred admission, international baccalaureate accepted. Required: essay, high school transcript, minimum 3.0 high school GPA, 2 recommendations, SAT or ACT. Recommended: SAT Subject Tests. Required for some: interview, audition, portfolio, SAT Subject Tests. Entrance: most difficult. Application deadlines: 1/15, 11/1 for early decision. Notification: 4/1, 12/15 for early decision.

Costs Per Year: Application fee: $65. Comprehensive fee: $43,170 includes full-time tuition ($29,890), mandatory fees ($1800), and college room and board ($11,480). Full-time tuition and fees vary according to program. Room and board charges vary according to board plan and housing facility. Part-time tuition: $881 per credit. Part-time mandatory fees: $53 per credit, $267 per term. Part-time tuition and fees vary according to program.

Collegiate Environment: Orientation program. Drama-theater group, choral group, student-run newspaper, radio station. Social organizations: 300 open to all; national fraternities, national sororities, local sororities; 4% of eligible men and 2% of eligible women are members. Most popular organizations: Inter-Varsity Christian Fellowship, Asian Cultural Union, Hillel, Latinos Unidos Con Honor y Amistad (LUCHA), South Asian Student Association (SHRUTI). Major annual events: Career Services Fair, Strawberry Festival, Community Service Week. Student services: health clinic, personal-psychological counseling, women's center. Campus security: 24-hour emergency response devices and patrols, student patrols, late night transport-escort service, controlled dormitory access, 24-hour security in residence halls. 10,766 college housing spaces available; 10,695 were occupied in 2003-04. Freshmen guaranteed college housing. Option: coed housing available. Elmer H. Bobst Library plus 11 others with 5.2 million books, 6.3 million microform titles, 48,958 serials, 1.4 million audiovisual materials, an OPAC, and a Web page. Operations spending for 2004 fiscal year: $47.7 million. 4,500 computers available on campus for general student use. Computer purchase/lease plans available. A campuswide network can be accessed from student residence rooms and from off campus. Staffed computer lab on campus.

Community Environment: New York City, the largest city in the nation, is also its business, entertainment, and artistic capital. This teeming city is considered the greatest center of higher education in the country, and claims the largest library outside the Library of Congress. Its intellectual and cultural opportunities are limitless and virtually impossible to duplicate elsewhere. Broadway, one of the great theatre districts of the world, Lincoln Center for the Performing Arts, more than 60 museums, and many historic sites dating from the pre-Revolutionary period are among New York's cultural attractions. More than one-sixth of the city is park land, offering facilities for many sports and activities in beautifully planned areas such as Central Park and Riverside Park. The financial district, with famous Wall Street, houses the complex mechanism of banking and security markets. A vast system of subways, roadways and buses span the areas of New York's 5 boroughs, connecting richly diverse communities and people from virtually all walks of life. Points of interest on Manhattan island include: the United Nations co

■ **NIAGARA COUNTY COMMUNITY COLLEGE** *J-7*

3111 Saunders Settlement Rd.
Sanborn, NY 14132-9460
Tel: (716)614-6222
Admissions: (716)614-6201
Fax: (716)731-4053
E-mail: saunders@niagaracc.suny.edu
Web Site: http://www.niagaracc.suny.edu/

Description: State and locally supported, 2-year, coed. Part of State University of New York System. Awards certificates, transfer associate, and terminal associate degrees. Founded 1962. Setting: 287-acre rural campus with easy access to Buffalo. Endowment: $2.1 million. Total enrollment:

5,572. Student-undergrad faculty ratio is 17:1. 2,282 applied, 100% were admitted. 6% from top 10% of their high school class, 26% from top quarter, 63% from top half. Full-time: 3,605 students, 59% women, 41% men. Part-time: 1,967 students, 62% women, 38% men. Students come from 15 states and territories, 1% from out-of-state, 2% Native American, 1% Hispanic, 6% black, 2% Asian American or Pacific Islander, 1% international, 31% 25 or older, 5% transferred in. Calendar: semesters. Academic remediation for entering students, services for LD students, advanced placement, self-designed majors, honors program, independent study, double major, summer session for credit, part-time degree program, adult/continuing education programs, co-op programs and internships. Off campus study at 17 members of the Western New York Consortium. Study abroad program. ROTC: Army (c).

Entrance Requirements: Open admission. Options: electronic application, early admission. Required: high school transcript. Required for some: minimum 2.0 high school GPA. Entrance: noncompetitive. Notification: continuous until 8/31.

Costs Per Year: Application fee: $0. State resident tuition: $3096 full-time, $129 per credit hour part-time. Nonresident tuition: $4644 full-time, $194 per credit hour part-time. Mandatory fees: $300 full-time, $62 per term part-time. Full-time tuition and fees vary according to program. Part-time tuition and fees vary according to program.

Collegiate Environment: Orientation program. Drama-theater group, choral group, student-run newspaper, radio station. Social organizations: 40 open to all. Most popular organizations: student radio station, Student Nurses Association, Phi Theta Kappa, Alpha Beta Gamma, Physical Education Club. Major annual events: All College Picnics, Orientation, theatrical/musical events. Student services: health clinic, personal-psychological counseling. Campus security: student patrols, late night transport-escort service, emergency telephones. College housing not available. Library Learning Center with 93,055 books, 122,936 microform titles, 524 serials, 20,207 audiovisual materials, an OPAC, and a Web page. Operations spending for 2004 fiscal year: $938,856. 414 computers available on campus for general student use. A campuswide network can be accessed. Staffed computer lab on campus.

■ NIAGARA UNIVERSITY *J-6*

Niagara University, NY 14109
Tel: (716)285-1212
Free: 800-462-2111
Admissions: (716)286-8700
Fax: (716)286-8355
E-mail: admissions@niagara.edu
Web Site: http://www.niagara.edu/

Description: Independent, comprehensive, coed, affiliated with Roman Catholic Church. Awards associate, bachelor's, and master's degrees and post-master's certificates. Founded 1856. Setting: 160-acre suburban campus with easy access to Buffalo and Toronto. Endowment: $54 million. Research spending for 2004 fiscal year: $335,387. Educational spending for 2005 fiscal year: $4859 per student. Total enrollment: 3,853. Faculty: 334 (137 full-time, 197 part-time). Student-undergrad faculty ratio is 17:1. 3,246 applied, 79% were admitted. 14% from top 10% of their high school class, 40% from top quarter, 73% from top half. Full-time: 2,816 students, 61% women, 39% men. Part-time: 126 students, 67% women, 33% men. Students come from 31 states and territories, 16 other countries, 7% from out-of-state, 1% Native American, 1% Hispanic, 4% black, 1% Asian American or Pacific Islander, 5% international, 7% 25 or older, 55% live on campus, 6% transferred in. Retention: 80% of full-time freshmen returned the following year. Academic areas with the most degrees conferred: business/marketing; education; security and protective services. Core. Calendar: semesters. Academic remediation for entering students, ESL program, services for LD students, advanced placement, accelerated degree program, freshman honors college, honors program, double major, summer session for credit, part-time degree program, adult/continuing education programs, co-op programs and internships, graduate courses open to undergrads. Off campus study at members of the New York State Visiting Student Program, the Western New York Consortium. Study abroad program. ROTC: Army.

Entrance Requirements: Options: Peterson's Universal Application, electronic application, early admission, deferred admission. Required: high school transcript, SAT or ACT. Recommended: minimum 3.0 high school GPA, 3 recommendations, interview. Entrance: moderately difficult. Application deadline: 8/1.

Costs Per Year: Application fee: $30. Comprehensive fee: $28,250 includes

full-time tuition ($19,000), mandatory fees ($800), and college room and board ($8450). Part-time tuition: $635 per credit hour. Part-time mandatory fees: $20 per term.

Collegiate Environment: Orientation program. Drama-theater group, choral group, student-run newspaper, radio station. Social organizations: 70 open to all; national fraternities. Most popular organizations: Niagara University Community Action Program, student government, Programming Board. Major annual events: Family Weekend, The University Ball, Spring Weekend. Student services: health clinic, personal-psychological counseling. Campus security: 24-hour emergency response devices and patrols, late night transport-escort service, controlled dormitory access, 24-hour escort service. 1,497 college housing spaces available; 1,450 were occupied in 2003-04. Freshmen guaranteed college housing. On-campus residence required through sophomore year. Options: coed, women-only housing available. Our Lady of Angels Library with 279,793 books, 76,987 microform titles, 8,600 serials, and an OPAC. Operations spending for 2004 fiscal year: $977,624. 150 computers available on campus for general student use. A campuswide network can be accessed from student residence rooms. Staffed computer lab on campus.

■ NORTH COUNTRY COMMUNITY COLLEGE *D-23*

23 Santanoni Ave., PO Box 89
Saranac Lake, NY 12983-0089
Tel: (518)891-2915; 888-TRY-NCCC
Fax: (518)891-2915
Web Site: http://www.nccc.edu/

Description: State and locally supported, 2-year, coed. Part of State University of New York System. Awards certificates, transfer associate, and terminal associate degrees. Founded 1967. Setting: 100-acre rural campus. Total enrollment: 1,605. Student-undergrad faculty ratio is 17:1. 1,802 applied, 94% were admitted. 6% from top 10% of their high school class, 28% from top quarter, 65% from top half. Full-time: 999 students, 61% women, 39% men. Part-time: 606 students, 69% women, 31% men. Students come from 13 states and territories, 4 other countries, 3% from out-of-state, 2% Native American, 1% Hispanic, 2% black, 1% Asian American or Pacific Islander, 1% international, 33% 25 or older, 7% live on campus, 8% transferred in. Core. Calendar: semesters. Academic remediation for entering students, services for LD students, advanced placement, self-designed majors, distance learning, double major, summer session for credit, part-time degree program, internships.

Entrance Requirements: Open admission except for radiologic technology, nursing, massage therapy programs. Options: electronic application, early admission, early decision, deferred admission. Required: high school transcript. Recommended: essay, interview, SAT or ACT. Entrance: minimally difficult. Application deadline: Rolling. Notification: continuous. Preference given to residents of sponsoring counties.

Costs Per Year: Application fee: $0. State resident tuition: $3250 full-time, $160 per credit hour part-time. Nonresident tuition: $8000 full-time, $375 per credit hour part-time. Mandatory fees: $730 full-time, $37.50 per credit hour part-time, $225 per term part-time. College room and board: $8150. College room only: $4750.

Collegiate Environment: Drama-theater group, student-run newspaper. Most popular organizations: Student Government Association, Wilderness Recreation Club, Nursing Club, Radiology Club, Criminal Justice Club. Major annual events: Winter Carnival, Winter Fest, May Fest. Student services: personal-psychological counseling. 96 college housing spaces available; 91 were occupied in 2003-04. No special consideration for freshman housing applicants. Option: coed housing available. North Country Community College Library with 58,556 books, 12,475 microform titles, 177 serials, and 1,217 audiovisual materials. Operations spending for 2004 fiscal year: $310,237. 140 computers available on campus for general student use. Staffed computer lab on campus.

■ NYACK COLLEGE *J-35*

One South Blvd.
Nyack, NY 10960-3698
Tel: (845)358-1710
Free: 800-33-NYACK
Fax: (845)358-3047
Web Site: http://www.nyack.edu

Description: Independent, comprehensive, coed, affiliated with The Christian and Missionary Alliance. Awards associate, bachelor's, master's, and first professional degrees. Founded 1882. Setting: 102-acre suburban campus with easy access to New York City. Endowment: $4.7 million. Total enrollment: 3,000. Faculty: 288 (107 full-time, 181 part-time). 9% from top 10% of their high school class, 24% from top quarter, 55% from top half. Full-time: 1,703 students, 59% women, 41% men. Part-time: 327 students, 71% women, 29% men. Students come from 41 states and territories, 30 other countries, 32% from out-of-state, 0.2% Native American, 20% Hispanic, 35% black, 6% Asian American or Pacific Islander, 5% international, 44% 25 or older, 33% live on campus, 18% transferred in. Retention: 64% of full-time freshmen returned the following year. Core. Calendar: semesters. Academic remediation for entering students, ESL program, advanced placement, accelerated degree program, honors program, independent study, distance learning, double major, summer session for credit, part-time degree program, adult/continuing education programs, internships. Off campus study at Council for Christian Colleges and Universities. Study abroad program.

Entrance Requirements: Options: electronic application, early admission, deferred admission. Required: essay, high school transcript, 1 recommendation. Required for some: interview, evidence of faith commitment, SAT or ACT. Entrance: moderately difficult. Application deadline: Rolling. Notification: continuous.

Costs Per Year: Application fee: $25. Comprehensive fee: $23,000 includes full-time tuition ($15,400) and college room and board ($7600). Part-time tuition: $600 per credit.

Collegiate Environment: Orientation program. Drama-theater group, choral group, student-run newspaper, radio station. Social organizations: 20 open to all. Most popular organizations: gospel teams, Drama Club, Student Government Association. Major annual events: Homecoming, Sadie Hawkins Day, Spiritual Emphasis Week. Student services: health clinic, personal-psychological counseling. Campus security: 24-hour emergency response devices and patrols, student patrols, late night transport-escort service. 748 college housing spaces available; 680 were occupied in 2003-04. Freshmen guaranteed college housing. Options: men-only, women-only housing available. The Bailey Library plus 2 others with 127,271 books, 11,997 microform titles, 958 serials, 4,739 audiovisual materials, an OPAC, and a Web page. Operations spending for 2004 fiscal year: $711,949. 180 computers available on campus for general student use. A campuswide network can be accessed from student residence rooms and from off campus. Staffed computer lab on campus.

Community Environment: Suburban village setting about 20 miles from New York City, Nyack is on the west bank of the Hudson River where it widens out to lake proportions. Early Dutch settlers called it the Tappan Zee. It has a local hospital, library, YMCA, and churches of all major denominations. The area has motels, hotels and shopping centers. Recreational facilities include bowling alleys, swimming pools, tennis, field sports, boating, lakes, ice skating, hunting, and fishing. There is ample part-time employment available for students.

■ **OHR HAMEIR THEOLOGICAL SEMINARY** *G-35*
Furnace Woods Rd.
Peekskill, NY 10566
Tel: (914)736-1500
Description: Independent Jewish, comprehensive, men only. Awards bachelor's and master's degrees. Founded 1962. 15 applied, 67% were admitted. Calendar: semesters.

■ **OHR SOMAYACH/JOSEPH TANENBAUM EDUCATIONAL CENTER** *J-33*
PO Box 334, 244 Route 306
Monsey, NY 10952-0334
Tel: (914)425-1370
Web Site: http://www.ohrsomayach.edu/
Description: Independent Jewish, 5-year, men only. Awards bachelor's and first professional degrees. Founded 1979. Setting: 7-acre small town campus with easy access to New York City. Research spending for 2004 fiscal year: $23,000. Total enrollment: 110. 100 applied, 65% were admitted. Full-time: 98 students. Students come from 10 states and territories, 8 other countries, 39% from out-of-state, 41% international, 75% 25 or older, 5% transferred in. Core. Calendar: semesters. Academic remediation for entering students, services for LD students, honors program, summer session for credit, part-time degree program, adult/continuing education programs, internships.
Entrance Requirements: Option: early admission. Required: recommendations, interview. Recommended: high school transcript. Required for some: essay. Entrance: moderately difficult. Application deadline: Rolling.
Collegiate Environment: Student services: personal-psychological counseling. Campus security: 24-hour emergency response devices and

patrols, controlled dormitory access. College housing designed to accommodate 70 students; 100 undergraduates lived in college housing during 2003-04. No special consideration for freshman housing applicants. On-campus residence required through senior year. Option: men-only housing available. Finer Library with 2,300 books.

■ **OLEAN BUSINESS INSTITUTE** *O-8*
301 North Union St.
Olean, NY 14760-2691
Tel: (716)372-7978
Fax: (716)372-2120
Web Site: http://www.obi.edu/
Description: Proprietary, 2-year, coed. Awards diplomas and terminal associate degrees. Founded 1961. Setting: small town campus. Total enrollment: 138. Students come from 2 states and territories, 34% from out-of-state, 52% 25 or older. Calendar: semesters. Double major, summer session for credit, part-time degree program, internships.
Entrance Requirements: Required: high school transcript. Required for some: essay, interview. Entrance: noncompetitive. Application deadline: 8/31. Notification: continuous until 9/1.
Collegiate Environment: Orientation program. Major annual events: Christmas Dinner/Dance, Graduation Dinner. Student services: personal-psychological counseling. Campus security: 24-hour emergency response devices, late night transport-escort service. College housing not available. 1,800 books, 25 serials, and an OPAC. 80 computers available on campus for general student use. Staffed computer lab on campus.

■ **ONONDAGA COMMUNITY COLLEGE** *J-16*
4941 Onondaga Rd.
Syracuse, NY 13215-2099
Tel: (315)498-2622
Admissions: (315)498-2201
Fax: (315)469-2107
Web Site: http://www.sunyocc.edu/
Description: State and locally supported, 2-year, coed. Part of State University of New York System. Awards certificates, diplomas, transfer associate, and terminal associate degrees. Founded 1962. Setting: 180-acre suburban campus. Total enrollment: 8,400. 3,581 applied, 76% were admitted. 10% from top 10% of their high school class, 20% from top quarter, 50% from top half. Students come from 9 states and territories, 34 other countries, 1% from out-of-state, 48% 25 or older. Core. Calendar: semesters. Academic remediation for entering students, ESL program, services for LD students, advanced placement, accelerated degree program, honors program, summer session for credit, part-time degree program, external degree program, adult/continuing education programs, co-op programs and internships. Study abroad program. ROTC: Army (c), Air Force (c).
Entrance Requirements: Open admission except for allied health, engineering, computer science, technology, art, music programs. Options: Peterson's Universal Application, Common Application, electronic application, early admission, deferred admission. Required: high school transcript. Recommended: 1 recommendation. Required for some: minimum 2.0 high school GPA, interview. Entrance: noncompetitive. Application deadline: 9/1. Notification: continuous. Preference given to county residents, members of the Armed Forces.
Collegiate Environment: Orientation program. Choral group, student-run newspaper, radio station. Social organizations: 22 open to all. Most popular organizations: Jamal, Music Club, Photo Club, Outing Club, Veterans Club. Major annual events: Party on the Quad, Orientation, Holiday Celebration. Student services: health clinic, personal-psychological counseling. Campus security: 24-hour patrols. College housing not available. Sidney B. Coulter Library with 96,611 books, 802 serials, an OPAC, and a Web page. Operations spending for 2004 fiscal year: $815,590. 525 computers available on campus for general student use. A campuswide network can be accessed from off-campus. Staffed computer lab on campus.

■ **ORANGE COUNTY COMMUNITY COLLEGE** *Q-22*
115 South St.
Middletown, NY 10940-6437
Tel: (845)344-6222
Admissions: (845)341-4030
Fax: (845)343-1228
Web Site: http://www.orange.cc.ny.us/

Description: State and locally supported, 2-year, coed. Part of State University of New York System. Awards certificates, transfer associate, and terminal associate degrees. Founded 1950. Setting: 37-acre suburban campus with easy access to New York City. Educational spending for 2005 fiscal year: $7900 per student. Total enrollment: 6,441. Student-undergrad faculty ratio is 16:1. 2,024 applied, 100% were admitted. Full-time: 3,344 students, 55% women, 45% men. Part-time: 3,097 students, 68% women, 32% men. Students come from 22 states and territories, 20 other countries, 1% from out-of-state, 0.4% Native American, 13% Hispanic, 10% black, 2% Asian American or Pacific Islander, 0.05% international, 29% 25 or older, 2% transferred in. Core. Calendar: semesters. Academic remediation for entering students, ESL program, services for LD students, accelerated degree program, honors program, summer session for credit, part-time degree program, external degree program, adult/continuing education programs, internships.

Entrance Requirements: Open admission except for dental hygiene, engineering, occupational therapy, physical therapy, computer science programs. Options: Common Application, early admission, deferred admission. Required: high school transcript. Entrance: noncompetitive. Application deadline: 8/1. Notification: continuous. Preference given to county residents.

Costs Per Year: Application fee: $30. State resident tuition: $3000 full-time, $125 per credit part-time. Nonresident tuition: $6000 full-time, $250 per credit part-time. Mandatory fees: $350 full-time.

Collegiate Environment: Orientation program. Drama-theater group, choral group, student-run newspaper, radio station. Social organizations: 21 open to all; local sororities. Most popular organizations: Phi Theta Kappa, Masters of the Elements, Computer Club, Agassiz Society, Apprentice Players. Student services: health clinic, personal-psychological counseling. Campus security: 24-hour emergency response devices, late night transport-escort service. College housing not available. Learning Resource Center with 101,342 books, 63,450 microform titles, 345 serials, 1,408 audiovisual materials, an OPAC, and a Web page. Operations spending for 2004 fiscal year: $653,163. 200 computers available on campus for general student use. A campuswide network can be accessed. Staffed computer lab on campus.

■ **PACE UNIVERSITY** *N-34*
One Pace Plaza
New York, NY 10038
Tel: (212)346-1200
Free: 800-874-7223
Admissions: (212)346-1781
Fax: (212)346-1040
E-mail: infoctr@pace.edu
Web Site: http://www.pace.edu/

Description: Independent, university, coed. Awards associate, bachelor's, master's, doctoral, and first professional degrees and post-master's and first professional certificates. Founded 1906. Endowment: $95.6 million. Research spending for 2004 fiscal year: $3 million. Educational spending for 2005 fiscal year: $11,357 per student. Total enrollment: 14,177. Faculty: 1,238 (478 full-time, 760 part-time). Student-undergrad faculty ratio is 15:1. 9,015 applied, 73% were admitted. 19% from top 10% of their high school class, 47% from top quarter, 86% from top half. Full-time: 6,879 students, 62% women, 38% men. Part-time: 2,049 students, 55% women, 45% men. Students come from 41 states and territories, 28 other countries, 28% from out-of-state, 0.3% Native American, 12% Hispanic, 10% black, 11% Asian American or Pacific Islander, 4% international, 20% 25 or older, 34% live on campus, 7% transferred in. Retention: 76% of full-time freshmen returned the following year. Academic areas with the most degrees conferred: business/marketing; computer and information sciences; communications/journalism. Core. Calendar: semesters. Academic remediation for entering students, ESL program, advanced placement, accelerated degree program, freshman honors college, honors program, independent study, distance learning, double major, summer session for credit, part-time degree program, adult/continuing education programs, co-op programs and internships, graduate courses open to undergrads. Study abroad program. ROTC: Army (c).

Entrance Requirements: Options: Peterson's Universal Application, Common Application, electronic application, early action, deferred admission, international baccalaureate accepted. Required: essay, high school transcript, 2 recommendations, SAT or ACT. Recommended: minimum 3.0 high school GPA, interview. Entrance: moderately difficult. Application deadlines: 3/1, 11/1 for early action. Notification: continuous, 12/15 for early action.

Costs Per Year: Application fee: $45. Comprehensive fee: $34,328 includes full-time tuition ($24,756), mandatory fees ($632), and college room and board ($8940). Full-time tuition and fees vary according to student level. Room and board charges vary according to board plan and housing facility. Part-time tuition: $710 per credit. Part-time mandatory fees: $240 per term. Part-time tuition and fees vary according to course load. Tuition guaranteed not to increase for student's term of enrollment.

Collegiate Environment: Orientation program. Drama-theater group, choral group, student-run newspaper, radio station. Social organizations: 105 open to all; national fraternities, national sororities, local fraternities, local sororities; 5% of eligible men and 3% of eligible women are members. Most popular organizations: student government, Pace Press Newspaper, United Chinese Students Association, Alianza Latina, National Association of Black Accountants. Major annual events: Spirit Night, Chill Out Day, Spring Festival. Student services: health clinic, personal-psychological counseling. Campus security: 24-hour emergency response devices and patrols, late night transport-escort service, controlled dormitory access. 2,672 college housing spaces available; 2,298 were occupied in 2003-04. No special consideration for freshman housing applicants. Option: coed housing available. Henry Birnbaum Library plus 3 others with 813,997 books, 56,536 microform titles, 1,729 serials, an OPAC, and a Web page. Operations spending for 2004 fiscal year: $4.3 million. 246 computers available on campus for general student use. A campuswide network can be accessed from student residence rooms and from off campus. Staffed computer lab on campus.

Community Environment: The New York City campus is just a short walk from Wall Street and the South Street Seaport. Lincoln Center, the theater district, the Metropolitan Museum, and other world-famous centers of the arts are just a few minutes away by subway or cab. The Pleasantville/Briarcliff campus is in a suburban setting in Westchester County, with access to twenty-three international corporate headquarters and excellent shopping nearby. The campus offers an environmental center, riding stables, and a variety of recreational facilities. The White Plains campus is adjacent to the train station.

■ **PARSONS THE NEW SCHOOL FOR DESIGN** *N-34*
66 Fifth Ave.
New York, NY 10011-8878
Tel: (212)229-8900; 877-528-3321
Fax: (212)229-8975
Web Site: http://www.parsons.newschool.edu/

Description: Independent, comprehensive, coed. Part of New School University. Awards associate, bachelor's, and master's degrees. Founded 1896. Setting: 2-acre urban campus. System endowment: $114.9 million. System-wide research spending for 2004 fiscal year: $6.4 million. System-wide educational spending for 2005 fiscal year: $8218 per student. Total enrollment: 3,502. Faculty: 951 (72 full-time, 879 part-time). Student-undergrad faculty ratio is 8:1. 2,106 applied, 47% were admitted. 13% from top 10% of their high school class, 49% from top quarter, 79% from top half. Full-time: 2,861 students, 79% women, 21% men. Part-time: 211 students, 85% women, 15% men. Students come from 48 states and territories, 66 other countries, 47% from out-of-state, 0.2% Native American, 6% Hispanic, 3% black, 17% Asian American or Pacific Islander, 33% international, 21% 25 or older, 21% live on campus, 15% transferred in. Retention: 85% of full-time freshmen returned the following year. Academic areas with the most degrees conferred: visual and performing arts; business/marketing; physical sciences. Core. Calendar: semesters. ESL program, services for LD students, advanced placement, accelerated degree program, self-designed majors, honors program, independent study, distance learning, summer session for credit, adult/continuing education programs, co-op programs and internships, graduate courses open to undergrads. Off campus study at Association of Independent Colleges of Art and Design. Study abroad program.

Entrance Requirements: Option: early admission. Required: high school transcript, minimum 2.0 high school GPA, portfolio, home examination, SAT or ACT. Recommended: minimum 3.0 high school GPA. Required for some: essay, interview. Entrance: very difficult. Application deadline: 3/1. Notification: continuous.

Costs Per Year: Application fee: $50. Comprehensive fee: $40,930 includes full-time tuition ($28,560), mandatory fees ($620), and college room and board ($11,750). College room only: $8750. Room and board charges vary according to board plan and housing facility. Part-time tuition: $974 per credit.

Collegiate Environment: Orientation program. Social organizations: 11 open to all. Most popular organizations: gallery committees, Latino/Latina

Student Group, Chinese Student Association, American Institute of Architectural Students. Major annual events: senior shows, Fashion Critics Award Show. Student services: health clinic, personal-psychological counseling. Campus security: 24-hour emergency response devices, controlled dormitory access. 948 college housing spaces available; 518 were occupied in 2003-04. Freshmen given priority for college housing. Option: coed housing available. Adam and Sophie Gimbel Design Library plus 2 others with 4.1 million books, 4.7 million microform titles, 22,150 serials, 48,379 audiovisual materials, an OPAC, and a Web page. System-wide operations spending for 2004 fiscal year: $2.8 million. 934 computers available on campus for general student use. A campuswide network can be accessed from student residence rooms and from off campus. Staffed computer lab on campus.

■ **PAUL SMITH'S COLLEGE OF ARTS AND SCIENCES** *D-22*
PO Box 265
Paul Smiths, NY 12970-0265
Tel: (518)327-6000
Free: 800-421-2605
Admissions: (518)327-6227
Fax: (518)327-6060
Web Site: http://www.paulsmiths.edu/

Description: Independent, 4-year, coed. Awards associate and bachelor's degrees. Founded 1937. Setting: 14,200-acre rural campus. Endowment: $12.6 million. Educational spending for 2005 fiscal year: $7500 per student. Total enrollment: 846. Student-undergrad faculty ratio is 14:1. 879 applied, 83% were admitted. 6% from top 10% of their high school class, 18% from top quarter, 48% from top half. Full-time: 821 students, 32% women, 68% men. Part-time: 25 students, 52% women, 48% men. Students come from 29 states and territories, 11 other countries, 32% from out-of-state, 0.5% Native American, 2% Hispanic, 2% black, 1% Asian American or Pacific Islander, 0.4% international, 7% 25 or older, 95% live on campus, 9% transferred in. Retention: 62% of full-time freshmen returned the following year. Academic areas with the most degrees conferred: natural resources/environmental science; personal and culinary services; business/marketing. Core. Calendar: semesters. Academic remediation for entering students, ESL program, services for LD students, advanced placement, self-designed majors, honors program, double major, summer session for credit, adult/continuing education programs, co-op programs and internships. Study abroad program.

Entrance Requirements: Options: Peterson's Universal Application, Common Application, electronic application, early admission, deferred admission. Required: high school transcript, SAT or ACT. Recommended: essay, 2 recommendations. Required for some: interview. Entrance: minimally difficult. Application deadline: Rolling.

Costs Per Year: Application fee: $30. Comprehensive fee: $25,590 includes full-time tuition ($16,910), mandatory fees ($1260), and college room and board ($7420). College room only: $3710. Part-time tuition: $450 per credit hour.

Collegiate Environment: Orientation program. Choral group, student-run radio station. Social organizations: 30 open to all. Most popular organizations: Forestry Club, Adirondack Experience Club, student radio station, Emergency Wilderness Response Team, Junior American Culinary. Major annual events: Fall Weekend, Winter Carnival, Winter Weekend. Student services: health clinic, personal-psychological counseling. Campus security: 24-hour emergency response devices and patrols, late night transport-escort service. 90 undergraduates lived in college housing during 2003-04. On-campus residence required through sophomore year. Option: coed housing available. Frank C. Cubley Library with 56,000 books, 504 serials, an OPAC, and a Web page. 65 computers available on campus for general student use. A campuswide network can be accessed from student residence rooms and from off campus. Staffed computer lab on campus.

■ **PHILLIPS BETH ISRAEL SCHOOL OF NURSING** *N-34*
310 East 22nd St., 9th Floor
New York, NY 10010-5702
Tel: (212)614-6110
Admissions: (212)614-6176
Fax: (212)614-6109
E-mail: bstern@bethisraelny.org
Web Site: http://www.futurenursebi.org

Description: Independent, 2-year, coed. Awards transfer associate and terminal associate degrees. Founded 1904. Setting: urban campus. Endowment: $1.2 million. Educational spending for 2005 fiscal year: $5400 per

student. Total enrollment: 200. Student-undergrad faculty ratio is 9:1. 57 applied, 12% were admitted. 18% from top 10% of their high school class, 50% from top quarter, 100% from top half. 1 student government officer. Students come from 8 states and territories, 5 other countries, 10% from out-of-state, 0% Native American, 14% Hispanic, 15% black, 22% Asian American or Pacific Islander, 4% international, 65% 25 or older. Core. Calendar: semesters. Advanced placement, part-time degree program. Off campus study at Pace University.

Entrance Requirements: Option: deferred admission. Required: essay, high school transcript, minimum 2.5 high school GPA, 2 recommendations, interview, nursing exam. Recommended: SAT. Entrance: moderately difficult. Application deadline: 4/1. Notification: continuous.

Costs Per Year: Application fee: $50. Tuition: $12,300 full-time, $300 per credit part-time. Mandatory fees: $2180 full-time.

Collegiate Environment: Orientation program. Choral group, student-run newspaper. Social organizations: 2 open to all. Most popular organizations: Student Government Organization, National Student Nurses Association. Major annual events: Holiday Party, Senior Luncheon, Senior Gala. Student services: health clinic, personal-psychological counseling. Campus security: 24-hour emergency response devices. College housing not available. Phillips Health Science Library with 600 serials and an OPAC. Operations spending for 2004 fiscal year: $150,000. 15 computers available on campus for general student use. Staffed computer lab on campus.

■ **PLAZA COLLEGE**
7409 37th Ave.
Jackson Heights, NY 11372-6300
Tel: (718)779-1430
Fax: (718)779-1456
Web Site: http://www.plazacollege.edu/

Description: Proprietary, 2-year, coed. Awards transfer associate and terminal associate degrees. Founded 1916. Setting: urban campus with easy access to New York City. 43% 25 or older. Core. Academic remediation for entering students, ESL program, services for LD students, summer session for credit, internships.

Entrance Requirements: Recommended: SAT and SAT Subject Tests or ACT. Entrance: moderately difficult. Application deadline: Rolling.

Collegiate Environment: Orientation program. Drama-theater group, student-run newspaper. Student services: personal-psychological counseling, women's center. Campus security: 24-hour emergency response devices. College housing not available. 90 computers available on campus for general student use.

■ **POLYTECHNIC UNIVERSITY, BROOKLYN CAMPUS** *O-34*
Six Metrotech Center
Brooklyn, NY 11201-2990
Tel: (718)260-3600
Free: 800-POLYTECH
Admissions: (718)260-5938
Fax: (718)260-3136
E-mail: uadmit@poly.edu
Web Site: http://www.poly.edu/

Description: Independent, university, coed. Awards bachelor's, master's, and doctoral degrees. Founded 1854. Setting: 3-acre urban campus. System endowment: $127.7 million. System-wide research spending for 2004 fiscal year: $17.6 million. System-wide educational spending for 2005 fiscal year: $16,593 per student. Total enrollment: 2,801. Faculty: 266 (126 full-time, 140 part-time). Student-undergrad faculty ratio is 13:1. 1,240 applied, 69% were admitted. 43% from top 10% of their high school class, 68% from top quarter, 92% from top half. 25 National Merit Scholars, 2 valedictorians, 15 student government officers. Full-time: 1,451 students, 18% women, 82% men. Part-time: 68 students, 19% women, 81% men. Students come from 18 states and territories, 44 other countries, 5% from out-of-state, 0.3% Native American, 11% Hispanic, 12% black, 32% Asian American or Pacific Islander, 8% international, 5% 25 or older, 13% live on campus, 4% transferred in. Retention: 80% of full-time freshmen returned the following year. Academic areas with the most degrees conferred: engineering; computer and information sciences; business/marketing. Core. Calendar: semesters. Academic remediation for entering students, ESL program, advanced placement, accelerated degree program, honors program, double major, summer session for credit, part-time degree program, co-op programs and internships, graduate courses open to undergrads. ROTC: Air Force (c).

Entrance Requirements: Options: Common Application, electronic application, deferred admission. Required: essay, high school transcript, 2 recommendations, SAT or ACT. Recommended: interview, SAT Subject Tests. Entrance: very difficult. Application deadline: 2/1.

Costs Per Year: Application fee: $60. Comprehensive fee: $37,150 includes full-time tuition ($27,640), mandatory fees ($1010), and college room and board ($8500). College room only: $6500. Full-time tuition and fees vary according to course load. Room and board charges vary according to housing facility. Part-time tuition: $880 per credit. Part-time mandatory fees: $320 per term. Part-time tuition and fees vary according to course load.

Collegiate Environment: Orientation program. Student-run newspaper. Social organizations: 58 open to all; national fraternities, national sororities, local fraternities, local sororities, a coed fraternity; 6% of eligible men and 3% of eligible women are members. Most popular organizations: National Society of Black Engineers, Society of Hispanic Professional Engineers, Association for Computing Machinery, Alpha Phi Omega, Chinese Student Society. Major annual events: Club Day/Club Rush, Career Fair, Poly Pride Day Mini-Fair. Student services: health clinic, personal-psychological counseling, women's center. Campus security: 24-hour patrols, controlled dormitory access. 400 college housing spaces available; 192 were occupied in 2003-04. Freshmen given priority for college housing. Option: coed housing available. Bern Dibner Library plus 1 other with 150,000 books, 60,106 microform titles, 1,621 serials, 337 audiovisual materials, an OPAC, and a Web page. Operations spending for 2004 fiscal year: $903,639. 1,334 computers available on campus for general student use. Computer purchase/lease plans available. A campuswide network can be accessed from student residence rooms and from off campus. Staffed computer lab on campus.

■ **PRATT INSTITUTE** *O-34*
200 Willoughby Ave.
Brooklyn, NY 11205-3899
Tel: (718)636-3600
Free: 800-331-0834
Admissions: (718)636-3669
Fax: (718)636-3670
E-mail: jaaron@pratt.edu
Web Site: http://www.pratt.edu/

Description: Independent, comprehensive, coed. Awards associate, bachelor's, master's, and first professional degrees (Associate). Founded 1887. Setting: 25-acre urban campus. Endowment: $65,000. Educational spending for 2005 fiscal year: $7528 per student. Total enrollment: 4,588. Faculty: 897 (121 full-time, 776 part-time). Student-undergrad faculty ratio is 11:1. 3,870 applied, 50% were admitted. Full-time: 2,898 students, 60% women, 40% men. Part-time: 149 students, 49% women, 51% men. Students come from 46 states and territories, 38 other countries, 60% from out-of-state, 0% Native American, 9% Hispanic, 8% black, 12% Asian American or Pacific Islander, 10% international, 12% 25 or older, 55% live on campus, 7% transferred in. Retention: 89% of full-time freshmen returned the following year. Academic areas with the most degrees conferred: visual and performing arts; architecture; communication technologies. Core. Calendar: semesters plus optional May term and summer session. ESL program, services for LD students, advanced placement, independent study, summer session for credit, part-time degree program, internships, graduate courses open to undergrads. Off campus study at members of the New York State Visiting Student Program, the Consortium of East Coast Art Schools. Study abroad program. ROTC: Army (c).

Entrance Requirements: Options: Peterson's Universal Application, Common Application, electronic application, early decision, international baccalaureate accepted. Required: essay, high school transcript, 1 recommendation, SAT or ACT. Recommended: minimum 3.0 high school GPA. Required for some: interview, portfolio. Entrance: very difficult. Application deadlines: 2/1, 11/15 for early action. Notification: continuous until 4/11, 1/10 for early action.

Costs Per Year: Application fee: $40. Comprehensive fee: $38,082 includes full-time tuition ($28,100), mandatory fees ($1130), and college room and board ($8852). College room only: $5552. Part-time tuition: $910 per credit. Part-time mandatory fees: $303 per term.

Collegiate Environment: Orientation program. Drama-theater group, student-run newspaper. Social organizations: 50 open to all; national fraternities, local fraternities, local sororities; 5% of eligible men and 5% of eligible women are members. Most popular organizations: travel and recreation, student newspaper, athletic clubs, Performing Arts Committee. Major annual events: Holiday Ball, Graduate Symposium, President's Lecture Series. Student services: health clinic, personal-psychological counseling. Campus security: 24-hour emergency response devices and

patrols, late night transport-escort service. 1,500 college housing spaces available; 1,465 were occupied in 2003-04. Freshmen guaranteed college housing. Option: coed housing available. Pratt Institute Library with 172,000 books, 40,000 microform titles, 540 serials, 2,851 audiovisual materials, an OPAC, and a Web page. Operations spending for 2004 fiscal year: $1.5 million. 250 computers available on campus for general student use. A campuswide network can be accessed from student residence rooms and from off campus. Staffed computer lab on campus.

■ **PURCHASE COLLEGE, STATE UNIVERSITY OF NEW YORK**
735 Anderson Hill Rd.
Purchase, NY 10577-1400
Tel: (914)251-6000
Admissions: (914)251-6300
E-mail: admissn@brick.purchase.edu
Web Site: http://www.purchase.edu/

Description: State-supported, comprehensive, coed. Part of State University of New York System. Awards bachelor's and master's degrees and post-master's certificates. Founded 1967. Setting: 500-acre small town campus with easy access to New York City. Endowment: $36.6 million. Educational spending for 2005 fiscal year: $4250 per student. Total enrollment: 3,826. Faculty: 340 (143 full-time, 197 part-time). Student-undergrad faculty ratio is 11:1. 6,946 applied, 31% were admitted. 9% from top 10% of their high school class, 29% from top quarter, 71% from top half. Full-time: 3,231 students, 54% women, 46% men. Part-time: 457 students, 58% women, 42% men. Students come from 44 states and territories, 24 other countries, 18% from out-of-state, 0.4% Native American, 10% Hispanic, 8% black, 4% Asian American or Pacific Islander, 1% international, 12% 25 or older, 64% live on campus, 9% transferred in. Retention: 78% of full-time freshmen returned the following year. Academic areas with the most degrees conferred: visual and performing arts; liberal arts/general studies; social sciences. Core. Calendar: semesters. Academic remediation for entering students, ESL program, advanced placement, self-designed majors, independent study, distance learning, double major, summer session for credit, part-time degree program, adult/continuing education programs, internships. Off campus study at Manhattanville College. Study abroad program.

Entrance Requirements: Options: early admission, early decision, deferred admission. Required: high school transcript, minimum 3.0 high school GPA, SAT or ACT. Required for some: essay, 1 recommendation, interview, audition, portfolio. Entrance: moderately difficult. Application deadlines: 6/1, 11/1 for early decision. Notification: 5/1, 12/5 for early decision.

Costs Per Year: Application fee: $40. State resident tuition: $4350 full-time, $181 per credit part-time. Nonresident tuition: $10,610 full-time, $442 per credit part-time. Mandatory fees: $1258 full-time, $.85 per credit part-time, $48.08 per term part-time. College room and board: $8466. College room only: $5378.

Collegiate Environment: Orientation program. Drama-theater group, choral group, student-run newspaper, radio station. Social organizations: 40 open to all. Most popular organizations: Student Union, WPUR radio station, Latinos Unidos, Gay/Lesbian/Bi-Sexual/Transgender Union, Organization of African People in America. Major annual events: Culture Shock, Fall Ball, Pancake Madness. Student services: legal services, health clinic, personal-psychological counseling, women's center. Campus security: 24-hour emergency response devices and patrols, late night transport-escort service, controlled dormitory access, 24-hour patrols by police officers. Option: coed housing available. Purchase College Library with 281,686 books, 247,057 microform titles, 1,990 serials, 15,578 audiovisual materials, an OPAC, and a Web page. Operations spending for 2004 fiscal year: $1.5 million. 350 computers available on campus for general student use. A campuswide network can be accessed from student residence rooms and from off campus. Staffed computer lab on campus.

■ **QUEENS COLLEGE OF THE CITY UNIVERSITY OF NEW YORK**
65-30 Kissena Blvd.
Flushing, NY 11367-1597
Tel: (718)997-5000
Admissions: (718)997-5600
Fax: (718)997-5617
E-mail: admissions@qc.edu
Web Site: http://www.qc.edu/

Description: State and locally supported, comprehensive, coed. Part of City University of New York System. Awards bachelor's and master's degrees and post-master's certificates. Founded 1937. Setting: 77-acre urban campus. Endowment: $10.6 million. Research spending for 2004 fiscal year: $7.1 million. Educational spending for 2005 fiscal year: $5138 per student. Total enrollment: 17,638. Faculty: 1,271 (575 full-time, 696 part-time). Student-undergrad faculty ratio is 16:1. 12,023 applied, 43% were admitted. 19% from top 10% of their high school class, 36% from top quarter, 92% from top half. Full-time: 8,816 students, 60% women, 40% men. Part-time: 4,202 students, 65% women, 35% men. Students come from 15 states and territories, 130 other countries, 1% from out-of-state, 0.1% Native American, 16% Hispanic, 10% black, 19% Asian American or Pacific Islander, 6% international, 33% 25 or older, 13% transferred in. Retention: 86% of full-time freshmen returned the following year. Academic areas with the most degrees conferred: social sciences; business/marketing; psychology. Core. Calendar: semesters. ESL program, services for LD students, advanced placement, accelerated degree program, self-designed majors, freshman honors college, honors program, independent study, double major, summer session for credit, part-time degree program, adult/continuing education programs, co-op programs and internships, graduate courses open to undergrads. Off campus study at other units of the City University of New York System. Study abroad program. ROTC: Army (c), Naval (c).

Entrance Requirements: Options: electronic application, deferred admission. Required: high school transcript, minimum 3.0 high school GPA, SAT or ACT. Recommended: SAT Subject Tests. Required for some: SAT Subject Tests. Entrance: very difficult. Application deadline: 1/1. Notification: continuous.

Costs Per Year: Application fee: $65. State resident tuition: $4000 full-time, $170 per credit part-time. Nonresident tuition: $10,800 full-time, $360 per credit part-time. Mandatory fees: $377 full-time, $120.10 per term part-time.

Collegiate Environment: Orientation program. Drama-theater group, choral group, student-run newspaper, radio station. Social organizations: 100 open to all; national fraternities, national sororities; 10% of eligible men and 10% of eligible women are members. Most popular organizations: Alliance of Latin American Students, Black Student Union, Caribbean Student Association, Hillel-Jewish Student Organization, India Cultural Exchange. Major annual events: Fall Campus Fest (Carnival theme), Spring Campus Fest (multicultural theme), Career Week. Student services: health clinic, personal-psychological counseling. Campus security: 24-hour emergency response devices and patrols. College housing not available. Benjamin S. Rosenthal Library plus 1 other with 985,550 books, 900,573 microform titles, 2,756 serials, 30,505 audiovisual materials, an OPAC, and a Web page. Operations spending for 2004 fiscal year: $3.1 million. 1,000 computers available on campus for general student use. A campuswide network can be accessed from off-campus. Staffed computer lab on campus.

■ **QUEENSBOROUGH COMMUNITY COLLEGE OF THE CITY UNIVERSITY OF NEW YORK**
222-05 56th Ave.
Bayside, NY 11364
Tel: (718)631-6262
Admissions: (718)631-6044
Fax: (718)281-5189
Web Site: http://www.qcc.cuny.edu/

Description: State and locally supported, 2-year, coed. Part of City University of New York System. Awards certificates, transfer associate, and terminal associate degrees. Founded 1958. Setting: 34-acre urban campus with easy access to New York City. Endowment: $1 million. Educational spending for 2005 fiscal year: $3000 per student. Total enrollment: 12,798. 3,485 applied, 100% were admitted. Full-time: 6,195 students, 53% women, 47% men. Part-time: 6,603 students, 64% women, 36% men. Students come from 2 states and territories, 132 other countries, 1% from out-of-state, 0.2% Native American, 22% Hispanic, 27% black, 20% Asian American or Pacific Islander, 6% international, 32% 25 or older, 5% transferred in. Core. Calendar: semesters. Academic remediation for entering students, ESL program, services for LD students, advanced placement, self-designed majors, honors program, summer session for credit, part-time degree program, adult/continuing education programs, co-op programs and internships. ROTC: Army (c).

Entrance Requirements: Open admission. Options: electronic application, deferred admission. Required: high school transcript. Entrance: noncompetitive. Application deadline: Rolling. Notification: continuous.

Costs Per Year: Application fee: $40. Area resident tuition: $2800 full-time. State resident tuition: $4560 full-time, $120 per credit part-time. Nonresident tuition: $4560 full-time, $190 per credit part-time. Mandatory fees: $266 full-time, $70 per term part-time. Full-time tuition and fees vary according to course load. Part-time tuition and fees vary according to course load.

Collegiate Environment: Drama-theater group, choral group, student-run newspaper, radio station. Social organizations: 42 open to all. Most popular organizations: Student Orientation Leaders, Student Nurses Association, Newman Club, Accounting Club, Flip Culture Society. Major annual events: Multicultural Festival, Transfer Day, Job Fair. Student services: health clinic, personal-psychological counseling. Campus security: 24-hour patrols, late night transport-escort service. College housing not available. The Kurt R. Schmeller with 140,000 books and 600 serials. Operations spending for 2004 fiscal year: $1.3 million. 1,001 computers available on campus for general student use. Staffed computer lab on campus.

■ **RABBINICAL ACADEMY MESIVTA RABBI CHAIM BERLIN** *O-34*
1605 Coney Island Ave.
Brooklyn, NY 11230-4715
Tel: (718)377-0777
Description: Independent Jewish, comprehensive, men only. Awards bachelor's and master's degrees. Founded 1939. Total enrollment: 400. 40 applied, 100% were admitted. Core. Calendar: semesters. Academic remediation for entering students, services for LD students.
Entrance Requirements: Entrance: moderately difficult.
Collegiate Environment: Student services: personal-psychological counseling.

■ **RABBINICAL COLLEGE BETH SHRAGA** *J-33*
28 Saddle River Rd.
Monsey, NY 10952-3035
Tel: (914)356-1980
Description: Independent Jewish, comprehensive, men only. Awards bachelor's and master's degrees. Founded 1965. Setting: small town campus. Total enrollment: 30. Calendar: semesters.

■ **RABBINICAL COLLEGE BOBOVER YESHIVA B'NEI ZION** *O-34*
1577 Forty-eighth St.
Brooklyn, NY 11219
Tel: (718)438-2018
Description: Independent Jewish, comprehensive, men only. Awards bachelor's and master's degrees. Founded 1947. Total enrollment: 270. 36 applied, 81% were admitted. 1% 25 or older. Core. Calendar: semesters.
Entrance Requirements: Entrance: moderately difficult.

■ **RABBINICAL COLLEGE CH'SAN SOFER** *O-34*
1876 Fiftieth St.
Brooklyn, NY 11204
Tel: (718)236-1171
Description: Independent Jewish, comprehensive, men only. Awards bachelor's and master's degrees. Founded 1940. Total enrollment: 124. Calendar: semesters.

■ **RABBINICAL COLLEGE OF LONG ISLAND** *P-37*
201 Magnolia Blvd.
Long Beach, NY 11561-3305
Tel: (516)431-7414
Description: Independent Jewish, comprehensive, men only. Awards bachelor's and master's degrees. Founded 1965. Setting: small town campus. Total enrollment: 114. Calendar: semesters.

■ **RABBINICAL COLLEGE OF OHR SHIMON YISROEL** *O-34*
215-217 Hewes St.
Brooklyn, NY 11211
Tel: (718)855-4092
Description: Independent Jewish, 4-year.

■ **RABBINICAL SEMINARY ADAS YEREIM** *O-34*
185 Wilson St.
Brooklyn, NY 11211-7206
Tel: (718)388-1751
Description: Independent religious, 4-year, men only. Awards bachelor's degrees. Founded 1961. Total enrollment: 105. Calendar: semesters.
Collegiate Environment: College housing not available.

■ **RABBINICAL SEMINARY OF AMERICA**
76-01 147th St.
Flushing, NY 11367
Tel: (718)268-4700

Description: Independent Jewish, comprehensive, men only. Awards bachelor's, master's, and first professional degrees. Founded 1933. Setting: urban campus with easy access to New York City. Total enrollment: 317. Students come from 18 states and territories, 2 other countries, 2% 25 or older, 90% live on campus. Core. Calendar: semesters. Academic remediation for entering students, honors program, adult/continuing education programs. Study abroad program.

Entrance Requirements: Option: early admission. Required: high school transcript, interview. Entrance: very difficult. Application deadline: 12/1. Notification: continuous.

Collegiate Environment: Major annual events: Purim, Simchat Torah, Chanukah Chagigah. Student services: personal-psychological counseling. Rabbinical Seminary of America Otzar HaSeforim Library plus 3 others with 30,000 books and 50 serials.

Community Environment: See Queens College of the City University of New York.

■ **RABBINICAL SEMINARY M'KOR CHAIM** *O-34*
1571 Fifty-fifth St.
Brooklyn, NY 11219
Tel: (718)851-0183
Description: Independent Jewish, comprehensive, men only. Awards bachelor's and master's degrees. Founded 1965. Total enrollment: 45. Calendar: semesters.

■ **RENSSELAER POLYTECHNIC INSTITUTE** *K-25*
110 8th St.
Troy, NY 12180-3590
Tel: (518)276-6000
Free: 800-448-6562
Admissions: (518)276-6216
Fax: (518)276-4072
E-mail: admissions@rpi.edu
Web Site: http://www.rpi.edu/
Description: Independent, university, coed. Awards bachelor's, master's, and doctoral degrees. Founded 1824. Setting: 260-acre suburban campus with easy access to Albany. Endowment: $624.3 million. Research spending for 2004 fiscal year: $67.5 million. Educational spending for 2005 fiscal year: $20,550 per student. Total enrollment: 7,241. Faculty: 481 (400 full-time, 81 part-time). Student-undergrad faculty ratio is 14:1. 5,574 applied, 78% were admitted. 61% from top 10% of their high school class, 95% from top quarter, 99% from top half. 25 National Merit Scholars, 56 valedictorians. Full-time: 4,926 students, 24% women, 76% men. Part-time: 25 students, 52% women, 48% men. Students come from 51 states and territories, 37 other countries, 52% from out-of-state, 0.4% Native American, 5% Hispanic, 4% black, 11% Asian American or Pacific Islander, 3% international, 3% 25 or older, 55% live on campus, 3% transferred in. Retention: 92% of full-time freshmen returned the following year. Academic areas with the most degrees conferred: engineering; computer and information sciences; business/marketing. Core. Calendar: semesters. ESL program, services for LD students, advanced placement, accelerated degree program, self-designed majors, honors program, independent study, distance learning, double major, summer session for credit, part-time degree program, adult/continuing education programs, co-op programs and internships, graduate courses open to undergrads. Off campus study at Williams College, Harvey Mudd College. Study abroad program. ROTC: Army, Naval, Air Force.

Entrance Requirements: Options: Common Application, electronic application, early admission, early decision, deferred admission. Required: essay, high school transcript, 1 recommendation, SAT or ACT. Required for some: portfolio for Electronic Arts is required; portfolio for Architecture highly recommended., SAT and SAT Subject Tests or ACT, . Entrance: very difficult. Application deadlines: 1/1, 11/15 for early decision. Notification: 3/20, 12/31 for early decision.

Costs Per Year: Application fee: $70. Comprehensive fee: $41,288 includes full-time tuition ($31,000), mandatory fees ($857), and college room and board ($9431). College room only: $5290. Room and board charges vary according to board plan and location. Part-time tuition: $969 per credit hour.

Collegiate Environment: Orientation program. Drama-theater group, choral group, student-run newspaper, radio station. Social organizations: 130 open to all; national fraternities, national sororities, local fraternities, local sororities; 39% of eligible men and 18% of eligible women are members. Most popular organizations: Ski Club, musical organizations, weightlifting, ballroom dance, campus radio station. Major annual events: Grand Marshal Week, Communiversity, Big Red Freakout. Student services: legal services,

health clinic, personal-psychological counseling, women's center. Campus security: 24-hour emergency response devices and patrols, late night transport-escort service, controlled dormitory access, campus foot patrols at night. 2,878 college housing spaces available; 2,700 were occupied in 2003-04. Freshmen guaranteed college housing. On-campus residence required in freshman year. Option: coed housing available. Folsom Library plus 1 other with 309,171 books, 10,210 serials, 91,435 audiovisual materials, an OPAC, and a Web page. Operations spending for 2004 fiscal year: $4.4 million. 5,588 computers available on campus for general student use. Computer purchase/lease plans available. A campuswide network can be accessed from student residence rooms and from off campus. Staffed computer lab on campus.

Community Environment: Troy, a city of 55,000, located at the head of navigation on the Hudson River, is an important industrial city and the eastern terminus of the New York State Barge Canal. The city, within 15 miles of Albany and Schenectady, is served by air, bus, and rail lines, houses of worship, 3 hospitals, and various civic, fraternal, and veteran's organizations. There are numerous opportunities for part-time student employment.

■ **ROBERTS WESLEYAN COLLEGE** *J-11*
2301 Westside Dr.
Rochester, NY 14624-1997
Tel: (585)594-6000
Free: 800-777-4RWC
Admissions: (585)594-6400
Fax: (585)594-6371
E-mail: admissions@roberts.edu
Web Site: http://www.roberts.edu/
Description: Independent, comprehensive, coed, affiliated with Free Methodist Church of North America. Awards associate, bachelor's, and master's degrees. Founded 1866. Setting: 75-acre suburban campus. Endowment: $11.2 million. Educational spending for 2005 fiscal year: $8676 per student. Total enrollment: 1,948. Faculty: 117 (98 full-time, 19 part-time). Student-undergrad faculty ratio is 13:1. 703 applied, 82% were admitted. 23% from top 10% of their high school class, 50% from top quarter, 81% from top half. 15 valedictorians. Full-time: 1,265 students, 69% women, 31% men. Part-time: 143 students, 68% women, 32% men. Students come from 24 states and territories, 19 other countries, 13% from out-of-state, 0.5% Native American, 3% Hispanic, 6% black, 1% Asian American or Pacific Islander, 3% international, 23% 25 or older, 69% live on campus, 7% transferred in. Retention: 81% of full-time freshmen returned the following year. Academic areas with the most degrees conferred: business/marketing; education; health professions and related sciences. Core. Calendar: semesters. Academic remediation for entering students, ESL program, services for LD students, advanced placement, freshman honors college, honors program, independent study, double major, summer session for credit, adult/continuing education programs, co-op programs and internships, graduate courses open to undergrads. Off campus study at Rochester Area Colleges, Council of Christian Colleges and Universities. Study abroad program. ROTC: Army (c), Air Force (c).

Entrance Requirements: Options: electronic application, early admission, deferred admission, international baccalaureate accepted. Required: essay, high school transcript, 2 recommendations, SAT or ACT. Recommended: minimum 2.5 high school GPA, interview. Entrance: moderately difficult. Application deadline: 2/1.

Costs Per Year: Application fee: $35. Comprehensive fee: $27,734 includes full-time tuition ($19,264), mandatory fees ($1022), and college room and board ($7448). College room only: $5280. Part-time tuition: $422 per credit.

Collegiate Environment: Orientation program. Drama-theater group, choral group, student-run newspaper, radio station. Social organizations: 25 open to all. Most popular organizations: Habitat for Humanity, Foot of the Cross, Radiant Light, Nursing Club, Drama Club. Major annual events: Spring Formal, Winter Weekend, Homecoming. Student services: health clinic, personal-psychological counseling. Campus security: 24-hour emergency response devices and patrols, late night transport-escort service, controlled dormitory access, 24-hour Resident Life staff on-call. 792 college housing spaces available; 756 were occupied in 2003-04. Freshmen guaranteed college housing. On-campus residence required through senior year. Options: men-only, women-only housing available. Ora A. Sprague Library with 123,434 books, 171,162 microform titles, 1,057 serials, 3,895 audiovisual materials, an OPAC, and a Web page. Operations spending for 2004 fiscal year: $774,430. 170 computers available on campus for general student use. A campuswide network can be accessed from student residence rooms and from off campus. Staffed computer lab on campus.

Community Environment: North Chili is a suburb of Rochester, New York. A municipal airport and bus service and railroad provide transportation to Rochester which has all major transportation facilities, as well as community services, public library, museums, art gallery, and hospitals. Part-time employment is available for students. Local recreational facilities include skiing, skating, tennis, swimming and golf.

■ **ROCHESTER BUSINESS INSTITUTE** *J-11*

1630 Portland Ave.
Rochester, NY 14621
Tel: (716)266-0430
Admissions: (585)266-0430
Fax: (716)266-8243
Web Site: http://www.rochester-institute.com/
Description: Proprietary, 2-year, coed. Part of Corinthian Colleges, Inc. Awards certificates, diplomas, and terminal associate degrees. Founded 1863. Setting: 2-acre suburban campus. Total enrollment: 1,223. Full-time: 1,032 students, 71% women, 29% men. Part-time: 191 students, 65% women, 35% men. Students come from 2 states and territories, 0.3% Native American, 10% Hispanic, 38% black, 1% Asian American or Pacific Islander, 0% international, 57% 25 or older. Academic remediation for entering students, advanced placement, independent study, distance learning, double major, summer session for credit, part-time degree program, adult/continuing education programs, co-op programs and internships.
Entrance Requirements: Options: early admission, deferred admission. Required: high school transcript, interview, CPAt. Entrance: minimally difficult. Application deadline: Rolling. Notification: continuous.
Collegiate Environment: Orientation program. College housing not available. Rochester Business Institute Library plus 2 others with 7,500 books, 26 serials, and an OPAC. Operations spending for 2004 fiscal year: $25,000. 125 computers available on campus for general student use. A campuswide network can be accessed. Staffed computer lab on campus.

■ **ROCHESTER INSTITUTE OF TECHNOLOGY** *J-11*

One Lomb Memorial Dr.
Rochester, NY 14623-5603
Tel: (585)475-2411
Admissions: (585)475-6631
Fax: (585)475-7424
E-mail: admissions@rit.edu
Web Site: http://www.rit.edu/
Description: Independent, comprehensive, coed. Awards associate, bachelor's, master's, and doctoral degrees and post-master's certificates. Founded 1829. Setting: 1,300-acre suburban campus with easy access to Buffalo. Endowment: $504.1 million. Research spending for 2004 fiscal year: $25.7 million. Total enrollment: 15,200. Faculty: 1,204 (798 full-time, 406 part-time). Student-undergrad faculty ratio is 14:1. 9,384 applied, 69% were admitted. 28% from top 10% of their high school class, 59% from top quarter, 90% from top half. 19 National Merit Scholars, 28 valedictorians. Full-time: 11,440 students, 30% women, 70% men. Part-time: 1,493 students, 34% women, 66% men. Students come from 50 states and territories, 90 other countries, 45% from out-of-state, 0.3% Native American, 3% Hispanic, 4% black, 6% Asian American or Pacific Islander, 11% international, 15% 25 or older, 60% live on campus, 6% transferred in. Retention: 90% of full-time freshmen returned the following year. Academic areas with the most degrees conferred: computer and information sciences; visual and performing arts; business/marketing. Core. ESL program, services for LD students, advanced placement, accelerated degree program, self-designed majors, honors program, independent study, distance learning, summer session for credit, part-time degree program, adult/continuing education programs, co-op programs and internships, graduate courses open to undergrads. Off campus study at members of the Rochester Area Colleges. Study abroad program. ROTC: Army, Naval (c), Air Force.
Entrance Requirements: Options: Peterson's Universal Application, Common Application, electronic application, early admission, early decision, deferred admission, international baccalaureate accepted. Required: essay, high school transcript, SAT or ACT. Recommended: minimum 3.0 high school GPA, 1 recommendation, interview. Required for some: portfolio. Entrance: moderately difficult. Application deadlines: 3/15, 12/1 for early decision. Notification: continuous, 1/15 for early decision.
Costs Per Year: Application fee: $50. Comprehensive fee: $32,070 includes full-time tuition ($23,247), mandatory fees ($372), and college room and board ($8451). College room only: $4863. Full-time tuition and fees vary according to course load, program, and student level. Room and board

charges vary according to board plan and housing facility. Part-time tuition: $518 per credit hour. Part-time mandatory fees: $31 per term. Part-time tuition and fees vary according to class time, course load, program, and student level.
Collegiate Environment: Orientation program. Drama-theater group, choral group, student-run newspaper, radio station. Social organizations: 170 open to all; national fraternities, national sororities, local fraternities, local sororities; 5% of eligible men and 5% of eligible women are members. Most popular organizations: campus radio station, campus weekly magazine, student government, Off-Campus Student Association, Music Association. Major annual events: Fall Weekend/Parents' Weekend, New Student Convocation, Spring Weekend. Student services: legal services, health clinic, personal-psychological counseling, women's center. Campus security: 24-hour emergency response devices and patrols, student patrols, late night transport-escort service. 6,600 college housing spaces available; all were occupied in 2003-04. Freshmen guaranteed college housing. On-campus residence required in freshman year. Options: coed, men-only, women-only housing available. Wallace Memorial Library with 408,000 books, 509,000 microform titles, 2,800 serials, 47,600 audiovisual materials, an OPAC, and a Web page. Operations spending for 2004 fiscal year: $4.8 million. 2,500 computers available on campus for general student use. A campuswide network can be accessed from student residence rooms and from off campus. Staffed computer lab on campus.
Community Environment: The Greater Rochester area - the city and its immediate suburbs - has a population of about 713,000. Per capital income is among the highest for metropolitan areas in the nation. The area's many internationally known industries employ a high proportion of scientists, technologists and skilled workers. Rochester is the world center of photography, the largest producer of optical goods in the United States, and among the leaders in graphic arts and reproduction and in production of electronic equipment and precision instruments. Rochester's industries have always been closely associated with RIT's programs and progress to the mutual benefit of all.

■ **ROCKLAND COMMUNITY COLLEGE** *I-32*

145 College Rd.
Suffern, NY 10901-3699
Tel: (914)574-4000
Free: 800-722-7666
Fax: (914)574-4433
Web Site: http://www.sunyrockland.edu/
Description: State and locally supported, 2-year, coed. Part of State University of New York System. Awards certificates, transfer associate, and terminal associate degrees. Founded 1959. Setting: 150-acre suburban campus with easy access to New York City. Research spending for 2004 fiscal year: $1.3 million. Total enrollment: 6,549. 1,904 applied, 100% were admitted. Full-time: 3,697 students, 49% women, 51% men. Part-time: 2,852 students, 64% women, 36% men. Students come from 4 states and territories, 25 other countries, 4% from out-of-state, 0.3% Native American, 10% Hispanic, 18% black, 6% Asian American or Pacific Islander, 5% international, 39% 25 or older, 8% transferred in. Core. Calendar: semesters. Academic remediation for entering students, ESL program, services for LD students, advanced placement, self-designed majors, honors program, summer session for credit, part-time degree program, external degree program, adult/continuing education programs, co-op programs and internships. Study abroad program. ROTC: Naval, Air Force.
Entrance Requirements: Open admission. Options: early admission, deferred admission. Required: high school transcript. Placement: SAT or ACT recommended. Entrance: noncompetitive. Application deadline: Rolling.
Collegiate Environment: Orientation program. Drama-theater group, student-run newspaper, radio station. Social organizations: 35 open to all. Most popular organizations: Hospitality Club, Student Senate, Student Ambassadors, Student Nurses Association, Latino Club. Major annual events: Club Fest, intercultural programs, Spring Fest. Student services: legal services, personal-psychological counseling. Campus security: 24-hour emergency response devices and patrols, student patrols, late night transport-escort service. College housing not available. Rockland Community College Library with 122,194 books, 541 serials, and an OPAC. Operations spending for 2004 fiscal year: $1 million. 177 computers available on campus for general student use. A campuswide network can be accessed. Staffed computer lab on campus.

■ **RUSSELL SAGE COLLEGE** *K-25*

45 Ferry St.
Troy, NY 12180-4115

Tel: (518)244-2000; 888-VERY SAGE
Admissions: (518)244-2018
Fax: (518)244-6880
E-mail: rscadmin@sage.edu
Web Site: http://www.sage.edu/rsc/index.php

Description: Independent, 4-year, women only. Part of The Sage Colleges. Awards bachelor's degrees. Founded 1916. Setting: 8-acre urban campus. System endowment: $26.4 million. System-wide research spending for 2004 fiscal year: $1.6 million. Educational spending for 2005 fiscal year: $6452 per student. Total enrollment: 838. Student-undergrad faculty ratio is 12:1. 394 applied, 81% were admitted. 30% from top 10% of their high school class, 67% from top quarter, 95% from top half. Full-time: 759 students. Part-time: 79 students. Students come from 15 states and territories, 3 other countries, 9% from out-of-state, 0.1% Native American, 3% Hispanic, 4% black, 2% Asian American or Pacific Islander, 0.3% international, 18% 25 or older, 47% live on campus, 13% transferred in. Retention: 79% of full-time freshmen returned the following year. Academic areas with the most degrees conferred: health professions and related sciences; psychology; biological/life sciences; English. Core. Calendar: semesters. Academic remediation for entering students, ESL program, services for LD students, advanced placement, accelerated degree program, self-designed majors, freshman honors college, honors program, independent study, double major, summer session for credit, part-time degree program, adult/continuing education programs, co-op programs and internships. Off campus study at Hudson-Mohawk Association of Colleges and Universities. Study abroad program. ROTC: Army (c), Air Force (c).

Entrance Requirements: Options: Peterson's Universal Application, Common Application, electronic application, early admission, early decision, deferred admission, international baccalaureate accepted. Required: essay, high school transcript, minimum 2.0 high school GPA, 2 recommendations, SAT or ACT. Recommended: interview. Entrance: moderately difficult. Application deadlines: Rolling, 12/1 for early decision. Notification: continuous, 12/15 for early decision.

Costs Per Year: Application fee: $30. Comprehensive fee: $31,060 includes full-time tuition ($22,650), mandatory fees ($870), and college room and board ($7540). College room only: $3650. Part-time tuition: $755 per credit hour.

Collegiate Environment: Orientation program. Drama-theater group, choral group, student-run newspaper. Social organizations: 26 open to all. Most popular organizations: student government, Sage Recreation Association, Physical Therapy Club, Crew Club, Black-Latin Student Alliance. Major annual events: Gospel Extravaganza, Sage Fest, Rally Day. Student services: health clinic, personal-psychological counseling, women's center. Campus security: 24-hour emergency response devices and patrols, late night transport-escort service, controlled dormitory access. 520 college housing spaces available; 375 were occupied in 2003-04. Freshmen guaranteed college housing. On-campus residence required through senior year. Option: women-only housing available. James Wheelock Clark Library plus 1 other with 337,694 books, 3,341 microform titles, 19,416 serials, 31,928 audiovisual materials, and an OPAC. Operations spending for 2004 fiscal year: $1.4 million. 145 computers available on campus for general student use. A campuswide network can be accessed from student residence rooms and from off campus. Staffed computer lab on campus.

Community Environment: The campus is located in the heart of New York State's Capital Region overlooking the Hudson River in historic Troy, New York, a regional center for music, art, and theatre with a rapidly developing artists' district. Troy is within easy driving distance of recreation opportunities in the nearby Adirondack, Berkshire, Catskill, and Green Mountains. There is also easy access to major Northeastern cities, including Boston, New York, Providence, and Montreal. Fourteen colleges and universities are within a 30-mile radius of Albany, the state capital and center of government, including two research universities that are lending strong development to the technology industry.

■ **SAGE COLLEGE OF ALBANY** *L-25*
140 New Scotland Ave.
Albany, NY 12208-3425
Tel: (518)292-1730; 888-VERY-SAGE
Fax: (518)292-1912
E-mail: scaadm@sage.edu
Web Site: http://www.sage.edu/sca/index.php

Description: Independent, 4-year, coed. Part of The Sage Colleges. Awards associate and bachelor's degrees. Founded 1957. Setting: 15-acre urban campus. System endowment: $26.4 million. System-wide research spending

for 2004 fiscal year: $1.6 million. Educational spending for 2005 fiscal year: $6452 per student. Total enrollment: 1,031. Student-undergrad faculty ratio is 12:1. 348 applied, 28% were admitted. 1% from top 10% of their high school class, 22% from top quarter, 66% from top half. Full-time: 620 students, 69% women, 31% men. Part-time: 411 students, 75% women, 25% men. Students come from 9 states and territories, 2 other countries, 3% from out-of-state, 0% Native American, 3% Hispanic, 9% black, 2% Asian American or Pacific Islander, 0.2% international, 46% 25 or older, 29% live on campus, 17% transferred in. Retention: 73% of full-time freshmen returned the following year. Academic areas with the most degrees conferred: business/marketing; interdisciplinary studies; visual and performing arts. Core. Calendar: semesters. Academic remediation for entering students, ESL program, services for LD students, advanced placement, self-designed majors, freshman honors college, honors program, independent study, summer session for credit, part-time degree program, external degree program, adult/continuing education programs, co-op programs and internships. Off campus study at members of the Hudson-Mohawk Association of Colleges and Universities.

Entrance Requirements: Options: Peterson's Universal Application, Common Application, electronic application, deferred admission. Required: high school transcript, 1 recommendation, portfolio for fine arts program, SAT or ACT. Recommended: essay, interview. Entrance: minimally difficult. Application deadline: Rolling. Notification: continuous until 8/15.

Costs Per Year: Application fee: $30. Comprehensive fee: $24,410 includes full-time tuition ($16,000), mandatory fees ($870), and college room and board ($7540). College room only: $3890. Part-time tuition: $535 per credit hour.

Collegiate Environment: Orientation program. Student-run newspaper. Social organizations: 13 open to all. Most popular organizations: student government, Phi Theta Kappa, Psychology Club, Ski Club, 'Vernacular' (art and literary publication). Major annual events: Activities Fair, Town Meeting, Earth Day. Student services: health clinic, personal-psychological counseling. Campus security: 24-hour emergency response devices and patrols, late night transport-escort service, controlled dormitory access, 24-hour security cameras. 200 college housing spaces available; 152 were occupied in 2003-04. Freshmen given priority for college housing. Options: coed, women-only housing available. Troy and Albany Campus Libraries with 337,694 books, 3,341 microform titles, 19,416 serials, 31,928 audiovisual materials, and an OPAC. System-wide operations spending for 2004 fiscal year: $1.4 million. 199 computers available on campus for general student use. A campuswide network can be accessed from student residence rooms and from off campus. Staffed computer lab on campus.

■ **ST. BONAVENTURE UNIVERSITY** *N-8*
Route 417
St. Bonaventure, NY 14778-2284
Tel: (716)375-2000
Free: 800-462-5050
Admissions: (716)375-2400
Fax: (716)375-2005
E-mail: jdirisio@sbu.edu
Web Site: http://www.sbu.edu/

Description: Independent, comprehensive, coed, affiliated with Roman Catholic Church. Awards bachelor's and master's degrees and post-master's certificates. Founded 1858. Setting: 600-acre small town campus. Endowment: $32.5 million. Research spending for 2004 fiscal year: $642,674. Total enrollment: 2,614. Faculty: 207 (153 full-time, 54 part-time). Student-undergrad faculty ratio is 16:1. 1,730 applied, 86% were admitted. 11% from top 10% of their high school class, 31% from top quarter, 68% from top half. 4 valedictorians. Full-time: 2,026 students, 49% women, 51% men. Part-time: 115 students, 43% women, 57% men. Students come from 36 states and territories, 24% from out-of-state, 0.4% Native American, 2% Hispanic, 3% black, 1% Asian American or Pacific Islander, 2% international, 2% 25 or older, 77% live on campus, 3% transferred in. Retention: 76% of full-time freshmen returned the following year. Academic areas with the most degrees conferred: business/marketing; communications/journalism; social sciences. Core. Calendar: semesters. Services for LD students, advanced placement, self-designed majors, freshman honors college, honors program, independent study, double major, summer session for credit, part-time degree program, internships, graduate courses open to undergrads. Off campus study at American University. Study abroad program. ROTC: Army.

Entrance Requirements: Options: Peterson's Universal Application, Common Application, early admission, deferred admission, international baccalaureate accepted. Required: high school transcript, 1 recommendation,

SAT or ACT. Recommended: essay, minimum 3.0 high school GPA, 3 recommendations, interview. Required for some: essay, SAT Subject Tests. Placement: SAT or ACT required for some. Entrance: moderately difficult. Application deadline: 4/15. Notification: continuous.

Costs Per Year: Application fee: $30. One-time mandatory fee: $325. Comprehensive fee: $30,275 includes full-time tuition ($21,650), mandatory fees ($865), and college room and board ($7760). College room only: $3960. Part-time tuition: $650 per credit hour.

Collegiate Environment: Orientation program. Drama-theater group, choral group, student-run newspaper, radio station. Social organizations: 50 open to all; 50% of eligible men and 50% of eligible women are members. Most popular organizations: student government, Student Programming Board, campus media, Bonaventure Business Association, Student Ambassadors. Major annual events: Family Weekend, Spring Weekend, Junior Prom. Student services: health clinic, personal-psychological counseling. Campus security: 24-hour emergency response devices and patrols, student patrols, late night transport-escort service. 1,634 undergraduates lived in college housing during 2003-04. Freshmen guaranteed college housing. On-campus residence required through junior year. Options: coed, men-only, women-only housing available. Friedsam Library with 287,622 books, 630 microform titles, 1,584 serials, 8,891 audiovisual materials, an OPAC, and a Web page. Operations spending for 2004 fiscal year: $1 million. 200 computers available on campus for general student use. A campuswide network can be accessed from student residence rooms and from off campus. Staffed computer lab on campus.

Community Environment: Allegany (population 2,050) is a rural community located in southwest New York a short distance from Allegany State Park. The area is accessible by bus and the Southern Tier Expressway. Climate is temperate with 4 definite seasons. Allegany has 1 library, several churches of different denominations. Various civic and fraternal organizations are active here. Part-time work for students is available. Olean (population 19,169) is a manufacturing and regional commercial center where part-time employment is available for students. Transportation is provided by bus or airlines. Nearby "Enchanted Mountains" resort area provides hunting, fishing, skiing, and other sports. The city has a hospital, numerous restaurants, movie theaters, shopping areas, and most of the major service clubs found in larger cities.

■ **ST. ELIZABETH COLLEGE OF NURSING** *J-19*
2215 Genesee St.
Utica, NY 13501
Tel: (315)798-8253
E-mail: mmonahan@stemc.org
Web Site: http://www.stemc.org/
Description: Independent, 2-year, coed. Founded 1904. Calendar: semesters.

■ **ST. FRANCIS COLLEGE** *O-34 H*
180 Remsen St.
Brooklyn Heights, NY 11201-4398
Tel: (718)522-2300
Admissions: (718)489-5200
Fax: (718)522-1274
Web Site: http://www.stfranciscollege.edu/
Description: Independent Roman Catholic, 4-year, coed. Awards associate, bachelor's, and master's degrees. Founded 1884. Setting: 1-acre urban campus with easy access to New York City. Endowment: $70.8 million. Research spending for 2004 fiscal year: $10,000. Educational spending for 2005 fiscal year: $3381 per student. Total enrollment: 2,336. Faculty: 214 (71 full-time, 143 part-time). Student-undergrad faculty ratio is 18:1. 1,566 applied, 92% were admitted. 3 valedictorians. Full-time: 2,019 students, 52% women, 48% men. Part-time: 317 students, 69% women, 31% men. Students come from 4 states and territories, 54 other countries, 2% from out-of-state, 0.1% Native American, 16% Hispanic, 20% black, 2% Asian American or Pacific Islander, 9% international, 18% 25 or older, 10% transferred in. Retention: 76% of full-time freshmen returned the following year. Academic areas with the most degrees conferred: business/marketing; liberal arts/general studies; communications/journalism; computer and information sciences; psychology. Core. Calendar: semesters. Academic remediation for entering students, ESL program, advanced placement, accelerated degree program, self-designed majors, honors program, independent study, double major, summer session for credit, part-time degree program, external degree program, adult/continuing education programs, co-op programs and internships. Study abroad program.

Entrance Requirements: Options: Peterson's Universal Application, electronic application, deferred admission, international baccalaureate accepted. Required: essay, high school transcript, minimum 2.0 high school GPA, 1 recommendation, SAT. Recommended: interview. Entrance: moderately difficult. Application deadline: Rolling. Notification: continuous.

Costs Per Year: Application fee: $35. Comprehensive fee: $20,710 includes full-time tuition ($12,450), mandatory fees ($260), and college room and board ($8000). College room only: $6500. Full-time tuition and fees vary according to course level, course load, degree level, program, and student level. Part-time tuition: $440 per credit. Part-time mandatory fees: $70 per term. Part-time tuition and fees vary according to course level, course load, degree level, program, and student level.

Collegiate Environment: Orientation program. Drama-theater group, choral group, student-run newspaper, radio station. Social organizations: 25 open to all; national fraternities, national sororities, local fraternities, local sororities. Most popular organizations: Latin American Society, Fine Arts Society, Power Lifting Club, Games Club, Haitian American Students Alliance. Major annual events: International Night, Franciscan Spirit Week, Community Day. Student services: personal-psychological counseling. Campus security: ID checks, crime awareness workshops, pamphlets, posters, films. McGarry Library with 120,000 books, 13,350 microform titles, 571 serials, 2,150 audiovisual materials, an OPAC, and a Web page. Operations spending for 2004 fiscal year: $758,319. 138 computers available on campus for general student use. Computer purchase/lease plans available. A campuswide network can be accessed from off-campus. Staffed computer lab on campus.

■ **ST. JOHN FISHER COLLEGE** *J-11*
3690 East Ave.
Rochester, NY 14618-3597
Tel: (585)385-8000
Free: 800-444-4640
Admissions: (585)385-8064
Fax: (585)385-8129
E-mail: admissions@fisher.sjfc.edu
Web Site: http://www.sjfc.edu/
Description: Independent, comprehensive, coed, affiliated with Roman Catholic Church. Awards bachelor's and master's degrees and post-master's certificates. Founded 1948. Setting: 136-acre suburban campus. Endowment: $35.4 million. Educational spending for 2005 fiscal year: $5639 per student. Total enrollment: 3,528. Faculty: 305 (152 full-time, 153 part-time). Student-undergrad faculty ratio is 14:1. 2,753 applied, 65% were admitted. 15% from top 10% of their high school class, 53% from top quarter, 91% from top half. 2 valedictorians. Full-time: 2,448 students, 58% women, 42% men. Part-time: 248 students, 61% women, 39% men. Students come from 17 states and territories, 6 other countries, 2% from out-of-state, 0.4% Native American, 3% Hispanic, 3% black, 2% Asian American or Pacific Islander, 0% international, 12% 25 or older, 58% live on campus, 10% transferred in. Retention: 84% of full-time freshmen returned the following year. Academic areas with the most degrees conferred: education; business/marketing; communications/journalism. Core. Calendar: semesters. Academic remediation for entering students, services for LD students, advanced placement, accelerated degree program, self-designed majors, honors program, independent study, double major, summer session for credit, part-time degree program, adult/continuing education programs, internships, graduate courses open to undergrads. Off campus study at members of the Rochester Area Colleges. Study abroad program. ROTC: Army (c), Naval (c), Air Force (c).

Entrance Requirements: Options: Common Application, electronic application, early admission, early decision, deferred admission, international baccalaureate accepted. Required: high school transcript, minimum 2.0 high school GPA, 1 recommendation, SAT or ACT. Recommended: essay, interview. Entrance: moderately difficult. Application deadlines: Rolling, 12/1 for early decision. Notification: continuous until 9/1, 12/15 for early decision.

Costs Per Year: Application fee: $30. Comprehensive fee: $27,860 includes full-time tuition ($19,300), mandatory fees ($260), and college room and board ($8300). College room only: $5400. Room and board charges vary according to board plan. Part-time tuition: $525 per credit hour. Part-time mandatory fees: $25 per term. Part-time tuition and fees vary according to course load.

Collegiate Environment: Orientation program. Drama-theater group, choral group, student-run newspaper, radio station. Social organizations: 40 open to all. Most popular organizations: student government, Student Activities Board, Commuter Council, Resident Student Association. Major annual events: Teddi Project Dance Marathon, Family Weekend, Fisherpalooza.

Student services: health clinic, personal-psychological counseling. Campus security: 24-hour emergency response devices and patrols, late night transport-escort service, controlled dormitory access. 1,372 college housing spaces available; all were occupied in 2003-04. Freshmen guaranteed college housing. Options: coed, women-only housing available. Charles J. Lavery Library with 190,903 books, 206,358 microform titles, 8,964 serials, 29,700 audiovisual materials, an OPAC, and a Web page. Operations spending for 2004 fiscal year: $1.1 million. 260 computers available on campus for general student use. A campuswide network can be accessed from student residence rooms and from off campus. Staffed computer lab on campus.

■ **ST. JOHN'S UNIVERSITY** *N-35*

8000 Utopia Parkway
Queens, NY 11439
Tel: (718)990-6161; 888-9ST JOHNS
Admissions: (718)990-2000
E-mail: admissions@stjohns.edu
Web Site: http://www.stjohns.edu/

Description: Independent, university, coed, affiliated with Roman Catholic Church. Awards associate, bachelor's, master's, doctoral, and first professional degrees and post-master's certificates. Founded 1870. Setting: 98-acre urban campus with easy access to New York City. Endowment: $265 million. Research spending for 2004 fiscal year: $7.7 million. Educational spending for 2005 fiscal year: $6719 per student. Total enrollment: 20,346. Faculty: 1,428 (599 full-time, 829 part-time). Student-undergrad faculty ratio is 18:1. 20,669 applied, 63% were admitted. 18% from top 10% of their high school class, 43% from top quarter, 75% from top half. Full-time: 11,855 students, 58% women, 42% men. Part-time: 3,237 students, 61% women, 39% men. Students come from 45 states and territories, 98 other countries, 12% from out-of-state, 0.2% Native American, 15% Hispanic, 17% black, 16% Asian American or Pacific Islander, 3% international, 5% 25 or older, 17% live on campus, 4% transferred in. Retention: 79% of full-time freshmen returned the following year. Academic areas with the most degrees conferred: business/marketing; communications/journalism; education. Core. Calendar: semesters. ESL program, services for LD students, advanced placement, accelerated degree program, honors program, independent study, distance learning, double major, summer session for credit, part-time degree program, adult/continuing education programs, internships, graduate courses open to undergrads. Off campus study at American Academy McAllister Institute of Funeral Service. Study abroad program. ROTC: Army.

Entrance Requirements: Options: Common Application, electronic application, deferred admission, international baccalaureate accepted. Required: high school transcript, SAT or ACT. Recommended: interview. Required for some: minimum X high school GPA, SAT. Entrance: moderately difficult. Application deadline: Rolling. Notification: continuous.

Costs Per Year: Application fee: $30. Comprehensive fee: $36,440 includes full-time tuition ($24,400), mandatory fees ($570), and college room and board ($11,470). College room only: $7200. Part-time tuition: $813 per credit. Part-time mandatory fees: $205 per term.

Collegiate Environment: Orientation program. Drama-theater group, choral group, student-run newspaper, radio station. Social organizations: 175 open to all; national fraternities, national sororities, local fraternities, local sororities; 8% of eligible men and 7% of eligible women are members. Most popular organizations: Student Government, Incorporated, Student Programming Board, Community and University Services in Education, Haraya, American Pharmaceutical Association. Major annual events: Black Music Fest, Winter Carnival, Spring Fling. Student services: health clinic, personal-psychological counseling. Campus security: 24-hour emergency response devices and patrols, student patrols, late night transport-escort service, controlled dormitory access. 2,557 college housing spaces available; 2,485 were occupied in 2003-04. Freshmen given priority for college housing. Option: coed housing available. St. John's University Library plus 1 other with 14.5 million books, 2.8 million microform titles, 19,249 serials, 22,918 audiovisual materials, an OPAC, and a Web page. Operations spending for 2004 fiscal year: $11 million. 1,025 computers available on campus for general student use. Computer purchase/lease plans available. A campuswide network can be accessed from student residence rooms and from off campus. Staffed computer lab on campus.

■ **ST. JOSEPH'S COLLEGE, NEW YORK** *O-34*

245 Clinton Ave.
Brooklyn, NY 11205-3688
Tel: (718)636-6800

Admissions: (718)636-6868
Fax: (718)636-7242
Web Site: http://www.sjcny.edu/

Description: Independent, comprehensive, coed. Awards bachelor's and master's degrees. Founded 1916. Setting: urban campus. Endowment: $23.4 million. Educational spending for 2005 fiscal year: $7839 per student. Total enrollment: 1,318. Faculty: 137 (52 full-time, 85 part-time). Student-undergrad faculty ratio is 17:1. 635 applied, 80% were admitted. Full-time: 708 students, 79% women, 21% men. Part-time: 414 students, 74% women, 26% men. Students come from 4 states and territories, 8 other countries, 1% from out-of-state, 0.1% Native American, 12% Hispanic, 37% black, 5% Asian American or Pacific Islander, 1% international, 61% 25 or older, 13% transferred in. Retention: 73% of full-time freshmen returned the following year. Academic areas with the most degrees conferred: health professions and related sciences; business/marketing; education. Core. Calendar: semesters. Advanced placement, honors program, independent study, distance learning, summer session for credit, part-time degree program, adult/continuing education programs, internships.

Entrance Requirements: Options: early admission, deferred admission. Required: high school transcript, minimum 3.0 high school GPA, SAT or ACT. Recommended: essay, 2 recommendations. Required for some: interview. Entrance: moderately difficult. Application deadline: 8/15. Notification: continuous until 8/30.

Costs Per Year: Application fee: $25. Tuition: $11,854 full-time, $382 per credit part-time. Mandatory fees: $382 full-time, $13 per credit part-time, $30 per term part-time.

Collegiate Environment: Orientation program. Drama-theater group, choral group, student-run newspaper. Social organizations: 24 open to all; local fraternities, local sororities; 10% of eligible men and 6% of eligible women are members. Most popular organizations: Admissions Club, Science Club, dramatics, Shild Study Club, Dance Team. Major annual events: Annual Dinner and Awards Night, Murder Mystery Dinner, Holiday Festival. Student services: personal-psychological counseling. Campus security: late night transport-escort service. College housing not available. McEntegart Hall Library with 100,000 books, 4,198 microform titles, 432 serials, and 4,482 audiovisual materials. Operations spending for 2004 fiscal year: $1.1 million. 90 computers available on campus for general student use. Staffed computer lab on campus.

■ **ST. JOSEPH'S COLLEGE, SUFFOLK CAMPUS** *O-45*

155 West Roe Blvd.
Patchogue, NY 11772-2399
Tel: (631)447-3200
Admissions: (631)447-3219
Fax: (631)447-1734
Web Site: http://www.sjcny.edu/

Description: Independent, comprehensive, coed. Administratively affiliated with St. Joseph's College, Brooklyn Campus. Awards bachelor's and master's degrees. Founded 1916. Setting: 28-acre small town campus with easy access to New York City. Total enrollment: 4,146. Faculty: 384 (120 full-time, 264 part-time). Student-undergrad faculty ratio is 17:1. 1,267 applied, 86% were admitted. 17% from top 10% of their high school class, 55% from top quarter, 85% from top half. 1 valedictorian, 22 student government officers. Full-time: 2,929 students, 74% women, 26% men. Part-time: 932 students, 79% women, 21% men. Students come from 4 states and territories, 6 other countries, 0.2% Native American, 6% Hispanic, 4% black, 1% Asian American or Pacific Islander, 0.1% international, 35% 25 or older, 13% transferred in. Retention: 83% of full-time freshmen returned the following year. Academic areas with the most degrees conferred: education; business/marketing; health professions and related sciences; psychology. Core. Calendar: 4-1-4. Services for LD students, advanced placement, honors program, independent study, distance learning, double major, summer session for credit, part-time degree program, adult/continuing education programs, co-op programs and internships. Off campus study at Long Island Regional Advisory Council for Higher Education. Study abroad program. ROTC: Army (c), Air Force (c).

Entrance Requirements: Options: early admission, deferred admission. Required: high school transcript, minimum 3.0 high school GPA, SAT or ACT. Recommended: essay, interview. Required for some: 2 recommendations. Entrance: moderately difficult. Application deadline: Rolling. Notification: continuous.

Costs Per Year: Application fee: $25. Tuition: $12,424 full-time, $402 per credit part-time. Mandatory fees: $342 full-time, $13 per credit part-time, $207 per term part-time. Part-time tuition and fees vary according to course load.

Collegiate Environment: Orientation program. Drama-theater group, choral group, student-run newspaper. Social organizations: 28 open to all; local fraternities, local sororities; 2% of eligible men and 2% of eligible women are members. Most popular organizations: Council for Exceptional Children, Child Study Club, Campus Activities Board, Society of Human Resources Management, National Student Speech Language Hearing Association. Major annual events: Homecoming/Fall Fest, Fine Arts Festival, Senior Week activities. Student services: personal-psychological counseling. Campus security: 24-hour patrols, late night transport-escort service. College housing not available. Callahan Library with 82,600 books, 3,755 microform titles, 323 serials, 1,331 audiovisual materials, an OPAC, and a Web page. 223 computers available on campus for general student use. A campuswide network can be accessed from off-campus. Staffed computer lab on campus.

■ **SAINT JOSEPH'S HOSPITAL HEALTH CENTER SCHOOL OF NURSING** *J-16*
206 Prospect Ave.
Syracuse, NY 13203
Tel: (315)448-5040
Fax: (315)448-5745
Web Site: http://www.sjhsyr.org/nursing/
Description: Independent, 2-year, coed. Awards terminal associate degrees. Setting: urban campus. Educational spending for 2005 fiscal year: $10,000 per student. Total enrollment: 293. Student-undergrad faculty ratio is 9:1. 42 applied, 55% were admitted. 0% from top 10% of their high school class, 50% from top quarter, 100% from top half. Students come from 2 states and territories, 0% from out-of-state, 2% Native American, 2% Hispanic, 3% black, 1% Asian American or Pacific Islander, 0% international, 51% 25 or older, 25% live on campus. Core. Calendar: semesters. Academic remediation for entering students, services for LD students, advanced placement, part-time degree program, adult/continuing education programs, co-op programs and internships.
Entrance Requirements: Option: deferred admission. Required: essay, high school transcript, minimum 3.0 high school GPA, 4 recommendations, interview, SAT or ACT. Entrance: moderately difficult.
Costs Per Year: Application fee: $30. Tuition: $8735 full-time. Mandatory fees: $1900 full-time. College room only: $3400.
Collegiate Environment: Orientation program. Social organizations: 10 open to all. Most popular organizations: New York State Student Nurse's Association, Syracuse Area Black Nurses Association, Student Body Organization. Major annual events: holiday parties, WalkRun Charity Events, Commitment to Nursing Ceremony. Student services: legal services, health clinic, personal-psychological counseling. Campus security: 24-hour patrols. Option: coed housing available. St. Joseph's Hospital Health Center School of Nursing Library with 4,500 books, 900 microform titles, 230 serials, 500 audiovisual materials, and an OPAC. Operations spending for 2004 fiscal year: $27,000. 30 computers available on campus for general student use. Staffed computer lab on campus.

■ **ST. LAWRENCE UNIVERSITY** *C-19*
Canton, NY 13617-1455
Tel: (315)229-5011
Free: 800-285-1856
Admissions: (315)229-5261
Fax: (315)229-5502
E-mail: admiss@music.stlawu.edu
Web Site: http://www.stlawu.edu/
Description: Independent, comprehensive, coed. Awards bachelor's and master's degrees and post-master's certificates. Founded 1856. Setting: 1,000-acre small town campus with easy access to Ottawa. Endowment: $211.5 million. Research spending for 2004 fiscal year: $338,560. Educational spending for 2005 fiscal year: $13,411 per student. Total enrollment: 2,264. Faculty: 190 (167 full-time, 23 part-time). Student-undergrad faculty ratio is 11:1. 2,989 applied, 59% were admitted. 38% from top 10% of their high school class, 71% from top quarter, 96% from top half. 18 valedictorians. Full-time: 2,111 students, 52% women, 48% men. Part-time: 20 students, 45% women, 55% men. Students come from 41 states and territories, 21 other countries, 50% from out-of-state, 1% Native American, 2% Hispanic, 2% black, 2% Asian American or Pacific Islander, 5% international, 4% 25 or older, 96% live on campus, 1% transferred in. Retention: 90% of full-time freshmen returned the following year. Academic areas with the most degrees conferred: social sciences; English; psychology. Core. Calendar: semesters. Services for LD students, advanced placement, self-designed

majors, independent study, double major, summer session for credit, part-time degree program, internships, graduate courses open to undergrads. Off campus study at Clarkson University, State University of New York College of Technology at Canton, State University of New York College at Potsdam, Fisk University, American University. Study abroad program. ROTC: Army (c), Air Force (c).
Entrance Requirements: Options: Common Application, electronic application, early decision, deferred admission, international baccalaureate accepted. Required: essay, high school transcript, 2 recommendations. Recommended: minimum 2.0 high school GPA, interview. Entrance: very difficult. Application deadlines: 2/15, 11/15 for early decision plan 1, 1/15 for early decision plan 2. Notification: 3/31, 12/15 for early decision plan 1, 2/15 for early decision plan 2.
Costs Per Year: Application fee: $50. Comprehensive fee: $40,330 includes full-time tuition ($31,935), mandatory fees ($215), and college room and board ($8180). College room only: $4400. Room and board charges vary according to board plan. Part-time tuition: $3990 per course.
Collegiate Environment: Orientation program. Drama-theater group, choral group, student-run newspaper, radio station. Social organizations: 100 open to all; national fraternities, national sororities, local sororities; 11% of eligible men and 27% of eligible women are members. Most popular organizations: Outing Club, student newspaper, student government, Circle K, Habitat for Humanity. Major annual events: Springfest, Peak Weekend, Festival of the Arts. Student services: health clinic, personal-psychological counseling, women's center. Campus security: 24-hour emergency response devices and patrols, student patrols, late night transport-escort service, controlled dormitory access. College housing designed to accommodate 1,928 students; 1,950 undergraduates lived in college housing during 2003-04. Freshmen guaranteed college housing. On-campus residence required through senior year. Option: coed housing available. Owen D. Young Library plus 1 other with 555,364 books, 594,961 microform titles, 1,961 serials, 5,281 audiovisual materials, an OPAC, and a Web page. Operations spending for 2004 fiscal year: $3.1 million. 550 computers available on campus for general student use. A campuswide network can be accessed from student residence rooms and from off campus. Staffed computer lab on campus.

■ **ST. THOMAS AQUINAS COLLEGE**
125 Route 340
Sparkill, NY 10976
Tel: (845)398-4000
Free: 800-999-STAC
Admissions: (845)398-4100
E-mail: vcrapanz@stac.edu
Web Site: http://www.stac.edu/
Description: Independent, comprehensive, coed. Awards associate, bachelor's, and master's degrees. Founded 1952. Setting: 46-acre suburban campus with easy access to New York City. Endowment: $13.5 million. Educational spending for 2005 fiscal year: $16,200 per student. Total enrollment: 2,194. Faculty: 139 (61 full-time, 78 part-time). Student-undergrad faculty ratio is 16:1. 1,243 applied, 76% were admitted. 50% from top half of their high school class. 2 National Merit Scholars, 8 class presidents, 1 valedictorian, 68 student government officers. Full-time: 1,328 students, 56% women, 44% men. Part-time: 658 students, 54% women, 46% men. Students come from 17 states and territories, 10 other countries, 27% from out-of-state, 0.1% Native American, 16% Hispanic, 5% black, 2% Asian American or Pacific Islander, 1% international, 25% 25 or older, 7% transferred in. Retention: 68% of full-time freshmen returned the following year. Academic areas with the most degrees conferred: business/marketing; social sciences; security and protective services. Core. Calendar: semesters. Academic remediation for entering students, services for LD students, advanced placement, accelerated degree program, freshman honors college, honors program, independent study, double major, summer session for credit, part-time degree program, adult/continuing education programs, internships, graduate courses open to undergrads. Off campus study at Barry University, Aquinas College, Dominican College of San Rafael. Study abroad program.
Entrance Requirements: Options: Peterson's Universal Application, Common Application, electronic application, early action, deferred admission. Required: high school transcript, minimum 2.0 high school GPA, SAT or ACT. Recommended: essay, 2 recommendations, interview. Required for some: 3 recommendations. Entrance: moderately difficult. Application deadlines: Rolling, 12/1 for early decision, 12/15 for early action. Notification: continuous until 10/1, 1/15 for early decision, 1/15 for early action.
Costs Per Year: Application fee: $30. Comprehensive fee: $25,450 includes full-time tuition ($16,200), mandatory fees ($400), and college room and

board ($8850). College room only: $4780. Part-time tuition: $540 per credit. Part-time mandatory fees: $100 per term.

Collegiate Environment: Orientation program. Drama-theater group, choral group, student-run newspaper, radio station. Major annual events: Spring Fest, Oktoberfest, Holiday Semi-Formal. Student services: personal-psychological counseling. Campus security: 24-hour emergency response devices and patrols, late night transport-escort service, controlled dormitory access. 465 undergraduates lived in college housing during 2003-04. Freshmen guaranteed college housing. Options: men-only, women-only housing available. Lougheed Library plus 1 other with 96,444 books, 277,820 microform titles, 1,090 serials, 3,084 audiovisual materials, an OPAC, and a Web page. 200 computers available on campus for general student use. A campuswide network can be accessed from student residence rooms and from off campus. Staffed computer lab on campus.

■ **SAINT VINCENT CATHOLIC MEDICAL CENTERS SCHOOL OF NURSING**
175-05 Horace Harding Expressway
Fresh Meadows, NY 11365
Tel: (718)357-0500
Fax: (718)357-4683
Web Site: http://www.svcmcny.org/

Description: Independent, 2-year, coed. Awards terminal associate degrees. Founded 1969. Setting: 2-acre suburban campus. Total enrollment: 93. 37 applied, 16% were admitted. 0% from out-of-state, 0% Native American, 18% Hispanic, 22% black, 23% Asian American or Pacific Islander, 0% international, 70% 25 or older. Core. Calendar: semesters. Part-time degree program.

Entrance Requirements: Option: deferred admission. Required: essay, high school transcript, nursing exam. Entrance: moderately difficult. Application deadline: 4/30. Notification: continuous.

Collegiate Environment: Orientation program. Campus security: 24-hour patrols. College housing not available. Crouse Library with 2,326 books and 42 serials. 6 computers available on campus for general student use.

■ **SAMARITAN HOSPITAL SCHOOL OF NURSING** *K-25*
2215 Burdett Ave.
Troy, NY 12180
Tel: (518)271-3285
Admissions: (518)271-3734
Fax: (518)271-3303
E-mail: deBlois@nehealth.com
Web Site: http://www.nehealth.com/

Description: Independent, 2-year. Awards diplomas, transfer associate, and terminal associate degrees. Total enrollment: 70. 65 applied, 38% were admitted. 60% 25 or older.

■ **SARAH LAWRENCE COLLEGE** *L-35*
1 Mead Way
Bronxville, NY 10708-5999
Tel: (914)337-0700
Free: 800-888-2858
Admissions: (914)395-2510
Fax: (914)395-2668
E-mail: slcadmit@mail.slc.edu
Web Site: http://www.sarahlawrence.edu/

Description: Independent, comprehensive, coed. Awards bachelor's and master's degrees. Founded 1926. Setting: 40-acre suburban campus with easy access to New York City. Endowment: $53.1 million. Research spending for 2004 fiscal year: $267,405. Educational spending for 2005 fiscal year: $20,119 per student. Total enrollment: 1,662. Faculty: 222 (188 full-time, 34 part-time). Student-undergrad faculty ratio is 6:1. 2,634 applied, 45% were admitted. 33% from top 10% of their high school class, 72% from top quarter, 95% from top half. 3 National Merit Scholars, 3 valedictorians. Full-time: 1,266 students, 73% women, 27% men. Part-time: 73 students, 84% women, 16% men. 77% from out-of-state, 1% Native American, 4% Hispanic, 5% black, 4% Asian American or Pacific Islander, 2% international, 5% 25 or older, 86% live on campus, 1% transferred in. Retention: 91% of full-time freshmen returned the following year. Academic area with the most degrees conferred: liberal arts/general studies. Core. Calendar: semesters. Services for LD students, advanced placement, self-designed majors, independent study, double major, part-time degree program, adult/continuing

education programs, internships, graduate courses open to undergrads. Off campus study at Reed College, Eugene Lang College, New School University. Study abroad program.

Entrance Requirements: Options: Peterson's Universal Application, Common Application, electronic application, early admission, early decision, deferred admission, international baccalaureate accepted. Required: essay, high school transcript, 3 recommendations. Recommended: minimum 3.0 high school GPA, interview. Entrance: very difficult. Application deadlines: 1/1, 11/15 for early decision plan 1, 1/1 for early decision plan 2. Notification: 4/1, 12/15 for early decision plan 1, 2/15 for early decision plan 2.

Costs Per Year: Application fee: $60. Comprehensive fee: $45,506 includes full-time tuition ($33,270), mandatory fees ($772), and college room and board ($11,464). College room only: $7600. Full-time tuition and fees vary according to course load. Room and board charges vary according to board plan. Part-time tuition: $1109 per credit. Part-time mandatory fees: $386 per term. Part-time tuition and fees vary according to course load.

Collegiate Environment: Orientation program. Drama-theater group, choral group, student-run newspaper, radio station. Social organizations: 30 open to all. Most popular organizations: Student Senate, APICAD, UNIDAD, Harambe, Amnesty International. Major annual events: Students for Students Scholarship Auction, Mayfair. Student services: health clinic, personal-psychological counseling. Campus security: 24-hour emergency response devices and patrols, student patrols, late night transport-escort service, controlled dormitory access. 965 college housing spaces available. Freshmen guaranteed college housing. On-campus residence required in freshman year. Options: coed, men-only, women-only housing available. Esther Rauschenbush Library plus 2 others with 193,581 books, 21,172 microform titles, 1,260 serials, 8,674 audiovisual materials, an OPAC, and a Web page. Operations spending for 2004 fiscal year: $2.6 million. 110 computers available on campus for general student use. A campuswide network can be accessed from student residence rooms and from off campus. Staffed computer lab on campus.

Community Environment: Population 7,000, Bronxville is a residential suburb in Westchester County. Public transportation in the area and to New York City is very accessible. Grand Central Station is only a 30 minute trip on the Metro North train.

■ **SCHENECTADY COUNTY COMMUNITY COLLEGE** *K-24*
78 Washington Ave.
Schenectady, NY 12305-2294
Tel: (518)381-1200
Admissions: (518)381-1370
Web Site: http://www.sunysccc.edu/

Description: State and locally supported, 2-year, coed. Part of State University of New York System. Awards certificates, transfer associate, and terminal associate degrees. Founded 1969. Setting: 50-acre urban campus. Total enrollment: 4,140. 2,190 applied, 98% were admitted. Full-time: 2,052 students, 54% women, 46% men. Part-time: 2,088 students, 61% women, 39% men. 1% Native American, 3% Hispanic, 8% black, 2% Asian American or Pacific Islander, 0% international, 47% 25 or older, 9% transferred in. Retention: 43% of full-time freshmen returned the following year. Core. Calendar: semesters. Academic remediation for entering students, ESL program, services for LD students, advanced placement, honors program, distance learning, double major, summer session for credit, part-time degree program, adult/continuing education programs, internships. Off campus study at 14 members of the Hudson-Mohawk Association of Colleges and Universities.

Entrance Requirements: Open admission. Options: Peterson's Universal Application, electronic application, early admission, deferred admission. Required: high school transcript. Placement: SAT or ACT recommended. Entrance: noncompetitive. Application deadline: Rolling. Notification: continuous. Preference given to county residents.

Collegiate Environment: Orientation program. Drama-theater group, choral group. Social organizations: 22 open to all; local fraternities, local sororities; 1% of eligible men and 2% of eligible women are members. Most popular organizations: Black and Latino Student Alliance, Culinary Arts Club, Student Government Association, Spanish Club, Rhythms Literary Magazine. Major annual events: SCCC Foundation Dinner, Honors Convocation, Annual Dinner Theater. Student services: personal-psychological counseling. Campus security: 24-hour emergency response devices and patrols, late night transport-escort service. College housing not available. Begley Library with 85,000 books, 75,000 microform titles, 640 serials, 2,600 audiovisual materials, an OPAC, and a Web page. 400 computers available on campus for general student use. A campuswide network can be accessed from off-campus. Staffed computer lab on campus.

■ SCHOOL OF VISUAL ARTS *N-34*

209 East 23rd St.
New York, NY 10010-3994
Tel: (212)592-2000
Free: 800-436-4204
Admissions: (212)592-2100
Fax: (212)592-2116
E-mail: jvega@sva.edu
Web Site: http://www.schoolofvisualarts.edu/

Description: Proprietary, comprehensive, coed. Awards bachelor's and master's degrees. Founded 1947. Setting: 1-acre urban campus. Educational spending for 2005 fiscal year: $5695 per student. Total enrollment: 3,575. Faculty: 760 (120 full-time, 640 part-time). 2,130 applied, 70% were admitted. Full-time: 2,923 students, 51% women, 49% men. Part-time: 240 students, 61% women, 39% men. Students come from 45 states and territories, 42 other countries, 40% from out-of-state, 0.3% Native American, 11% Hispanic, 4% black, 13% Asian American or Pacific Islander, 11% international, 16% 25 or older, 27% live on campus, 10% transferred in. Retention: 87% of full-time freshmen returned the following year. Academic area with the most degrees conferred: visual and performing arts. Core. Calendar: semesters. Academic remediation for entering students, ESL program, services for LD students, advanced placement, freshman honors college, honors program, independent study, summer session for credit, part-time degree program, internships. Study abroad program.

Entrance Requirements: Options: Common Application, electronic application, early decision, deferred admission. Required: essay, high school transcript, minimum 2.5 high school GPA, portfolio, SAT or ACT. Recommended: recommendations, interview. Entrance: moderately difficult. Application deadlines: Rolling, 12/1 for early decision. Notification: continuous, 1/1 for early decision.

Costs Per Year: Application fee: $50. Comprehensive fee: $32,580 includes full-time tuition ($20,080), mandatory fees ($1000), and college room and board ($11,500). College room only: $9000. Full-time tuition and fees vary according to program. Room and board charges vary according to board plan, gender, housing facility, and location. Part-time tuition: $670 per credit.

Collegiate Environment: Orientation program. Student-run newspaper, radio station. Social organizations: 15 open to all; 50% of eligible men and 50% of eligible women are members. Most popular organizations: Visual Arts Student Association, Film Club, Korean Christian Organization, Asian Association, Bible study. Major annual events: End of the Year Picnic, Great Adventure, ski trip. Student services: health clinic, personal-psychological counseling. Campus security: 24-hour patrols. 1,000 college housing spaces available; all were occupied in 2003-04. Freshmen given priority for college housing. Options: coed, women-only housing available. School of Visual Arts Library with 71,490 books, 1,170 microform titles, 340 serials, 158,000 audiovisual materials, and an OPAC. Operations spending for 2004 fiscal year: $572,680. 600 computers available on campus for general student use. Computer purchase/lease plans available. A campuswide network can be accessed from student residence rooms and from off campus. Staffed computer lab on campus.

■ SH'OR YOSHUV RABBINICAL COLLEGE

1 Cedarlawn Ave.
Lawrence, NY 11559-1714
Tel: (718)327-2048
Admissions: (718)327-7244
Web Site: http://www.shoryoshuv.org/

Description: Independent Jewish, comprehensive, men only. Awards bachelor's and master's degrees. Founded 1963. Total enrollment: 155. 12 applied, 100% were admitted. 5% from top 10% of their high school class, 90% from top half. Students come from 20 states and territories, 4 other countries, 60% 25 or older. Core. Calendar: semesters. Academic remediation for entering students, self-designed majors, honors program, summer session for credit, part-time degree program, adult/continuing education programs, co-op programs and internships, graduate courses open to undergrads.

Entrance Requirements: Open admission. Recommended: recommendations. Required for some: essay, high school transcript, interview. Placement: SAT required for some. Entrance: noncompetitive. Application deadline: 9/20.

Collegiate Environment: Student services: legal services, personal-psychological counseling. 20,000 books.

■ SIENA COLLEGE *B-12*

515 Loudon Rd.
Loudonville, NY 12211-1462
Tel: (518)783-2300; 888-AT-SIENA
Admissions: (518)783-2423
Fax: (518)783-4293
E-mail: admit@siena.edu
Web Site: http://www.siena.edu/

Description: Independent Roman Catholic, 4-year, coed. Awards bachelor's degrees. Founded 1937. Setting: 163-acre suburban campus. Endowment: $112.5 million. Educational spending for 2005 fiscal year: $7886 per student. Total enrollment: 3,336. Student-undergrad faculty ratio is 14:1. 4,326 applied, 61% were admitted. 21% from top 10% of their high school class, 58% from top quarter, 92% from top half. Full-time: 3,056 students, 57% women, 43% men. Part-time: 280 students, 61% women, 39% men. Students come from 30 states and territories, 7 other countries, 13% from out-of-state, 0.2% Native American, 4% Hispanic, 2% black, 3% Asian American or Pacific Islander, 1% international, 10% 25 or older, 70% live on campus, 5% transferred in. Retention: 89% of full-time freshmen returned the following year. Academic areas with the most degrees conferred: business/marketing; psychology; biological/life sciences. Core. Calendar: semesters. Academic remediation for entering students, services for LD students, advanced placement, accelerated degree program, honors program, independent study, distance learning, double major, summer session for credit, part-time degree program, adult/continuing education programs, internships. Off campus study at members of the Hudson-Mohawk Association of Colleges and Universities. Study abroad program. ROTC: Army, Air Force (c).

Entrance Requirements: Options: electronic application, early admission, early decision, early action, deferred admission, international baccalaureate accepted. Required: essay, high school transcript, 1 recommendation, SAT or ACT. Recommended: interview. Required for some: interview. Entrance: moderately difficult. Application deadlines: 3/1, 12/1 for early decision, 12/1 for early action. Notification: 3/15, 12/15 for early decision, 1/1 for early action.

Costs Per Year: Application fee: $50. Comprehensive fee: $30,000 includes full-time tuition ($21,285), mandatory fees ($240), and college room and board ($8475). College room only: $5280. Part-time tuition: $410 per credit hour. Part-time mandatory fees: $50 per term.

Collegiate Environment: Orientation program. Drama-theater group, student-run newspaper, radio station. Social organizations: 78 open to all. Most popular organizations: Student Senate, Student Events Board, Big Brothers/Big Sisters, Gaelic Society, Outing Club. Major annual events: Family Weekend, Women in Science Fair, Spring Weekend. Student services: health clinic, personal-psychological counseling, women's center. Campus security: 24-hour emergency response devices and patrols, late night transport-escort service, controlled dormitory access, call boxes in parking lots and on roadways. 2,329 college housing spaces available; 2,268 were occupied in 2003-04. Freshmen given priority for college housing. On-campus residence required through senior year. Option: coed housing available. J. Spencer and Patricia Standish Library with 326,332 books, 27,586 microform titles, 5,275 serials, 5,410 audiovisual materials, an OPAC, and a Web page. Operations spending for 2004 fiscal year: $1.6 million. 1,233 computers available on campus for general student use. A campuswide network can be accessed from student residence rooms and from off campus. Staffed computer lab on campus.

Community Environment: Population 11,000, Loudonville is a suburban community of Albany easily reached by bus, railroad, all major airlines, and interstate highways. The community provides a local church, hospital, and shopping facilities. Part-time employment is available for students. The Saratoga Performing Arts Center and Lake George are nearby.

■ SIMMONS INSTITUTE OF FUNERAL SERVICE *J-16*

1828 South Ave.
Syracuse, NY 13207
Tel: (315)475-5142
Free: 800-727-3536
Fax: (315)477-3817
Web Site: http://www.simmonsinstitute.com/

Description: Proprietary, 2-year, coed. Awards transfer associate and terminal associate degrees. Founded 1900. Setting: 1-acre urban campus. Total enrollment: 60. Full-time: 37 students, 43% women, 57% men. Part-time: 23 students, 39% women, 61% men. Students come from 3 states and territories, 1 other country, 5% from out-of-state, 0% Native American, 2% Hispanic, 7% black, 0% Asian American or Pacific Islander, 2% international, 45% 25 or older, 23% transferred in. Calendar: semesters. Advanced placement, part-time degree program.

Entrance Requirements: Open admission. Required: essay, high school transcript, interview. Entrance: minimally difficult. Application deadline: 6/30. Notification: 7/30.

Collegiate Environment: Orientation program. Most popular organization: Sigma Phi Sigma. Campus security: 24-hour emergency response devices. College housing not available. Simmons Library with 1,326 books and 52 serials. 18 computers available on campus for general student use. Staffed computer lab on campus.

■ SKIDMORE COLLEGE *J-24*

815 North Broadway
Saratoga Springs, NY 12866-1632
Tel: (518)580-5000
Free: 800-867-6007
Admissions: (518)580-5570
Fax: (518)581-7462
E-mail: admissions@scott.skidmore.edu
Web Site: http://www.skidmore.edu/

Description: Independent, comprehensive, coed. Awards bachelor's and master's degrees. Founded 1903. Setting: 800-acre small town campus with easy access to Albany. Endowment: $199.7 million. Research spending for 2004 fiscal year: $959,000. Educational spending for 2005 fiscal year: $15,170 per student. Total enrollment: 2,828. Faculty: 321 (228 full-time, 93 part-time). Student-undergrad faculty ratio is 9:1. 6,055 applied, 44% were admitted. 46% from top 10% of their high school class, 78% from top quarter, 96% from top half. Full-time: 2,524 students, 60% women, 40% men. Part-time: 249 students, 65% women, 35% men. Students come from 41 states and territories, 28 other countries, 70% from out-of-state, 1% Native American, 4% Hispanic, 3% black, 6% Asian American or Pacific Islander, 1% international, 0% 25 or older, 76% live on campus, 2% transferred in. Retention: 92% of full-time freshmen returned the following year. Academic areas with the most degrees conferred: visual and performing arts; social sciences; business/marketing. Core. Calendar: semesters plus optional 6-week internship period. Advanced placement, accelerated degree program, self-designed majors, honors program, independent study, distance learning, double major, summer session for credit, external degree program, adult/continuing education programs, internships. Off campus study at members of the Hudson-Mohawk Association of Colleges and Universities. Study abroad program. ROTC: Army (c), Air Force (c).

Entrance Requirements: Options: Common Application, electronic application, early admission, early decision, deferred admission, international baccalaureate accepted. Required: essay, high school transcript, 2 recommendations, SAT or ACT. Recommended: interview, SAT Subject Tests. Entrance: very difficult. Application deadlines: 1/15, 11/15 for early decision plan 1, 1/15 for early decision plan 2. Notification: 4/1, 12/15 for early decision plan 1, 2/15 for early decision plan 2.

Costs Per Year: Application fee: $60. Comprehensive fee: $41,779 includes full-time tuition ($32,340), mandatory fees ($319), and college room and board ($9120). College room only: $5100. Full-time tuition and fees vary according to course load. Room and board charges vary according to board plan and housing facility. Part-time tuition: $1080 per credit hour. Part-time mandatory fees: $25 per term. Part-time tuition and fees vary according to course load.

Collegiate Environment: Orientation program. Drama-theater group, choral group, student-run newspaper, radio station. Social organizations: 80 open to all. Most popular organizations: Student Government Association, student radio station, Student Volunteer Bureau, Outing Club, Skidmore News. Major annual events: Fall Convocation, Spring Convocation, Homecoming/Oktoberfest. Student services: health clinic, personal-psychological counseling. Campus security: 24-hour emergency response devices and patrols, late night transport-escort service, controlled dormitory access, well-lit campus. 1,700 college housing spaces available; all were occupied in 2003-04. Freshmen guaranteed college housing. On-campus residence required through sophomore year. Options: coed, men-only, women-only housing available. Scribner Library plus 1 other with 352,802 books, 65,608 microform titles, 984 serials, 140,927 audiovisual materials, an OPAC, and a Web page. Operations spending for 2004 fiscal year: $2.6 million. 173 computers available on campus for general student use. A campuswide network can be accessed from student residence rooms and from off campus. Staffed computer lab on campus.

Community Environment: This resort is famous for the beauty of its setting, the reputed health-giving properties of its water and the gaiety of its summer life. It is also gaining popularity as a winter sport center with downhill and cross-country skiing available nearby. The area has rail, bus, and airline service. Activities to be found within the area include Saratoga Performing Arts Center (summer home of the New York Ballet, Philadelphia Orchestra, and the Acting Company), thoroughbred racing, night harness racing, Yaddo Artist's Colony, Congress Park, Newport Jazz Festival, Petrified Sea Gardens, State Tree Nursery, Grant's Cottage on Mount McGregor, and the Saratoga Historical Museum in the Canfield Casino. Saratoga has churches representing the major denominations. Part-time employment is available.

■ STATE UNIVERSITY OF NEW YORK AT BINGHAMTON *N-17*

PO Box 6000
Binghamton, NY 13902-6000
Tel: (607)777-2000
Admissions: (607)777-2171
E-mail: admit@binghamton.edu
Web Site: http://www.binghamton.edu/

Description: State-supported, university, coed. Part of State University of New York System. Awards bachelor's, master's, and doctoral degrees and post-master's certificates. Founded 1946. Setting: 887-acre suburban campus. Endowment: $52.3 million. Research spending for 2004 fiscal year: $28.2 million. Total enrollment: 14,018. Faculty: 769 (537 full-time, 232 part-time). Student-undergrad faculty ratio is 21:1. 21,658 applied, 43% were admitted. 87% from top quarter of their high school class, 99% from top half. Full-time: 10,734 students, 48% women, 52% men. Part-time: 440 students, 48% women, 52% men. Students come from 39 states and territories, 67 other countries, 6% from out-of-state, 0.2% Native American, 6% Hispanic, 5% black, 15% Asian American or Pacific Islander, 7% international, 5% 25 or older, 58% live on campus, 7% transferred in. Retention: 90% of full-time freshmen returned the following year. Academic areas with the most degrees conferred: social sciences; business/marketing; psychology. Core. Calendar: semesters. Academic remediation for entering students, ESL program, services for LD students, advanced placement, accelerated degree program, self-designed majors, honors program, independent study, distance learning, double major, summer session for credit, part-time degree program, adult/continuing education programs, internships, graduate courses open to undergrads. Off campus study at National Student Exchange, New York State Visiting Student Program. Study abroad program. ROTC: Air Force (c).

Entrance Requirements: Options: Common Application, early admission, early action, deferred admission. Required: essay, high school transcript, SAT or ACT. Required for some: 1 recommendation, portfolio, audition. Entrance: very difficult. Application deadlines: Rolling, 11/15 for early action. Notification: continuous, 12/22 for early action.

Costs Per Year: Application fee: $40. State resident tuition: $4350 full-time, $181 per credit hour part-time. Nonresident tuition: $10,610 full-time, $442 per credit hour part-time. Mandatory fees: $1488 full-time, $133.15 per credit hour part-time. College room and board: $8150. College room only: $4970. Room and board charges vary according to board plan and housing facility.

Collegiate Environment: Orientation program. Drama-theater group, choral group, student-run newspaper, radio station. Social organizations: 176 open to all; national fraternities, national sororities, local fraternities, local sororities; 8% of eligible men and 9% of eligible women are members. Most popular organizations: student radio station, Student Association, student newspaper, cultural organizations, Peer Counseling/Mentoring/Volunteering Program. Major annual events: Caribbean Carnival, Spring Fling, University Fest. Student services: legal services, health clinic, personal-psychological counseling, women's center. Campus security: 24-hour emergency response devices and patrols, student patrols, late night transport-escort service, controlled dormitory access, safety awareness programs, well-lit campus, self-defense education, secured campus entrance 12 a.m. to 5 a.m., emergency telephones. 6,556 college housing spaces available; 6,344 were occupied in 2003-04. Freshmen guaranteed college housing. On-campus residence required in freshman year. Option: coed housing available. Glenn G. Bartle Library plus 1 other with 1.9 million books, 1.9 million microform titles, 8,915 serials, 122,518 audiovisual materials, an OPAC, and a Web page. Operations spending for 2004 fiscal year: $10.8 million. 7,200 computers available on campus for general student use. Computer purchase/lease plans available. A campuswide network can be accessed from student residence rooms and from off campus. Staffed computer lab on campus.

■ STATE UNIVERSITY OF NEW YORK AT BUFFALO K-7

Capen Hall
Buffalo, NY 14260
Tel: (716)645-2000; 888-UB-ADMIT
Admissions: (716)645-6900
Fax: (716)645-6411
E-mail: ub-admissions@buffalo.edu
Web Site: http://www.buffalo.edu/

Description: State-supported, university, coed. Part of State University of New York System. Awards bachelor's, master's, doctoral, and first professional degrees and post-master's and first professional certificates. Founded 1846. Setting: 1,350-acre suburban campus. Endowment: $463.2 million. Research spending for 2004 fiscal year: $111.5 million. Educational spending for 2005 fiscal year: $9754 per student. Total enrollment: 27,220. Faculty: 1,748 (1,159 full-time, 589 part-time). Student-undergrad faculty ratio is 15:1. 18,391 applied, 57% were admitted. 24% from top 10% of their high school class, 59% from top quarter, 93% from top half. 15 valedictorians. Full-time: 16,911 students, 46% women, 54% men. Part-time: 1,254 students, 45% women, 55% men. Students come from 40 states and territories, 78 other countries, 3% from out-of-state, 0.4% Native American, 4% Hispanic, 7% black, 9% Asian American or Pacific Islander, 7% international, 10% 25 or older, 38% live on campus, 9% transferred in. Retention: 88% of full-time freshmen returned the following year. Academic areas with the most degrees conferred: business/marketing; engineering; communications/journalism; psychology. Core. Calendar: semesters. Academic remediation for entering students, ESL program, services for LD students, advanced placement, accelerated degree program, self-designed majors, freshman honors college, honors program, independent study, distance learning, double major, summer session for credit, part-time degree program, adult/continuing education programs, co-op programs and internships, graduate courses open to undergrads. Off campus study at all institutions in the western New York area, Association of Colleges and Universities of the State of New York. Study abroad program. ROTC: Army (c).

Entrance Requirements: Options: electronic application, early admission, early decision, international baccalaureate accepted. Required: high school transcript, SAT or ACT. Recommended: essay, interview. Required for some: portfolio, audition. Entrance: moderately difficult. Application deadline: 11/1 for early decision. Notification: continuous, 12/15 for early decision.

Costs Per Year: Application fee: $40. State resident tuition: $4350 full-time, $181 per credit hour part-time. Nonresident tuition: $10,610 full-time, $442 per credit hour part-time. Mandatory fees: $1718 full-time, $76 per credit hour part-time. Part-time tuition and fees vary according to course load. College room and board: $7626. College room only: $4636. Room and board charges vary according to board plan and housing facility.

Collegiate Environment: Orientation program. Drama-theater group, choral group, marching band, student-run newspaper, radio station. Social organizations: national fraternities, national sororities, local fraternities, local sororities; 3% of eligible men and 4% of eligible women are members. Most popular organizations: PODER-Latinos Unidos, Black Student Union, Caribbean Student Association, Crew, LaCross. Major annual events: September Welcome, Fallfest/Springfest, Homecoming/Parents' Weekend. Student services: legal services, health clinic, personal-psychological counseling, women's center. Campus security: 24-hour emergency response devices and patrols, student patrols, late night transport-escort service, controlled dormitory access, self-defense and awareness programs. College housing designed to accommodate 6,673 students; 6,843 undergraduates lived in college housing during 2003-04. Freshmen guaranteed college housing. Option: coed housing available. Lockwood Library plus 7 others with 3.4 million books, 5.4 million microform titles, 34,126 serials, 188,300 audiovisual materials, an OPAC, and a Web page. Operations spending for 2004 fiscal year: $20.2 million. 2,391 computers available on campus for general student use. A campuswide network can be accessed from student residence rooms and from off campus. Staffed computer lab on campus.

■ STATE UNIVERSITY OF NEW YORK COLLEGE OF AGRICULTURE AND TECHNOLOGY AT COBLESKILL L-22

Cobleskill, NY 12043
Tel: (518)255-5011
Free: 800-295-8988
Fax: (518)255-5333
Web Site: http://www.cobleskill.edu/

Description: State-supported, 4-year, coed. Part of State University of New York System. Awards associate and bachelor's degrees. Founded 1916. Setting: 750-acre rural campus. Endowment: $1.7 million. Research spending for 2004 fiscal year: $20,175. Educational spending for 2005 fiscal year: $4130 per student. Total enrollment: 2,482. Student-undergrad faculty ratio is 21:1. 3,394 applied, 74% were admitted. 3% from top 10% of their high school class, 11% from top quarter, 35% from top half. Full-time: 2,372 students, 46% women, 54% men. Part-time: 110 students, 65% women, 35% men. Students come from 16 states and territories, 8 other countries, 10% from out-of-state, 0.1% Native American, 4% Hispanic, 6% black, 1% Asian American or Pacific Islander, 2% international, 11% 25 or older, 62% live on campus, 14% transferred in. Retention: 81% of full-time freshmen returned the following year. Academic areas with the most degrees conferred: agriculture; computer and information sciences. Core. Calendar: semesters. Academic remediation for entering students, ESL program, services for LD students, advanced placement, freshman honors college, honors program, distance learning, summer session for credit, part-time degree program, adult/continuing education programs, internships. Off campus study at other units of the State University of New York System. Study abroad program.

Entrance Requirements: Options: electronic application, early admission, deferred admission. Required: high school transcript. Recommended: SAT or ACT. Required for some: essay, minimum 2.0 high school GPA, 3 recommendations, interview, SAT or ACT. Entrance: moderately difficult. Application deadline: Rolling. Notification: continuous.

Costs Per Year: Application fee: $40. State resident tuition: $4350 full-time, $181 per credit hour part-time. Nonresident tuition: $7210 full-time, $300 per credit hour part-time. Mandatory fees: $995 full-time, $59.12 per credit hour part-time. Full-time tuition and fees vary according to course level and degree level. Part-time tuition and fees vary according to course level and degree level. College room and board: $7270. College room only: $4300. Room and board charges vary according to board plan and housing facility.

Collegiate Environment: Orientation program. Drama-theater group, choral group, student-run newspaper. Social organizations: 35 open to all. Most popular organizations: Orange Key, American Animal Producers Club, Outing Club, Phi Theta Kappa, Little Theater. Major annual events: Parents' Weekend, Tiger Fest, Spring Festival. Student services: health clinic, personal-psychological counseling. Campus security: 24-hour emergency response devices and patrols, late night transport-escort service, controlled dormitory access, bicycle patrols. 1,893 college housing spaces available; all were occupied in 2003-04. On-campus residence required in freshman year. Options: coed, men-only, women-only housing available. Jared van Wagenen Library with 76,919 books, 32,405 microform titles, 327 serials, 12,601 audiovisual materials, an OPAC, and a Web page. Operations spending for 2004 fiscal year: $645,017. 200 computers available on campus for general student use. A campuswide network can be accessed from student residence rooms and from off campus. Staffed computer lab on campus.

■ STATE UNIVERSITY OF NEW YORK COLLEGE OF AGRICULTURE AND TECHNOLOGY AT MORRISVILLE K-18

PO Box 901
Morrisville, NY 13408-0901
Tel: (315)684-6000
Admissions: (315)684-6046
Fax: (315)684-6116
Web Site: http://www.morrisville.edu/

Description: State-supported, primarily 2-year, coed. Part of State University of New York System. Awards certificates, transfer associate, terminal associate, and bachelor's degrees. Founded 1908. Setting: 185-acre rural campus with easy access to Syracuse. Endowment: $681,026. Research spending for 2004 fiscal year: $1.3 million. Educational spending for 2005 fiscal year: $4555 per student. Total enrollment: 3,269. 3,028 applied, 42% were admitted. Full-time: 2,820 students, 42% women, 58% men. Part-time: 449 students, 69% women, 31% men. Students come from 14 states and territories, 11 other countries, 1% from out-of-state, 1% Native American, 4% Hispanic, 12% black, 1% Asian American or Pacific Islander, 1% international, 22% 25 or older, 60% live on campus, 9% transferred in. Core. Calendar: semesters. Academic remediation for entering students, services for LD students, advanced placement, self-designed majors, honors program, distance learning, double major, summer session for credit, part-time degree program, co-op programs and internships. Off campus study at other units of the State University of New York System. ROTC: Army (c).

Entrance Requirements: Options: electronic application, early admission, deferred admission. Required: high school transcript. Recommended:

minimum 2.0 high school GPA, recommendations, interview, SAT and SAT Subject Tests or ACT. Required for some: essay, recommendations, SAT. Entrance: moderately difficult. Application deadline: Rolling. Notification: continuous.

Collegiate Environment: Orientation program. Drama-theater group, choral group, student-run newspaper, radio station. Social organizations: 60 open to all; local fraternities, local sororities; 15% of eligible men and 15% of eligible women are members. Most popular organizations: African Student Union Black Alliance, Student Government Organization, Agriculture Club, Latino-American Student Association, WCVM (student radio station). Major annual events: College/Community Picnic, Parents' Weekend, Alumni Weekend. Student services: health clinic, personal-psychological counseling. Campus security: 24-hour emergency response devices and patrols, late night transport-escort service, controlled dormitory access. 2,000 college housing spaces available; 1,700 were occupied in 2003-04. Freshmen guaranteed college housing. On-campus residence required in freshman year. Option: coed housing available. SUNY Morrisville Library plus 1 other with 99,258 books, 12,000 microform titles, 568 serials, 2,100 audiovisual materials, an OPAC, and a Web page. Operations spending for 2004 fiscal year: $143,626. 90 computers available on campus for general student use. Computer purchase/lease plans available. A campuswide network can be accessed from student residence rooms and from off campus. Staffed computer lab on campus.

■ **STATE UNIVERSITY OF NEW YORK COLLEGE AT BROCKPORT**
I-10

350 New Campus Dr.
Brockport, NY 14420-2997
Tel: (585)395-2211
Admissions: (585)395-2751
Fax: (585)395-5452
E-mail: admit@brockport.edu
Web Site: http://www.brockport.edu/

Description: State-supported, comprehensive, coed. Part of State University of New York System. Awards bachelor's and master's degrees and post-master's certificates. Founded 1867. Setting: 435-acre small town campus with easy access to Rochester. Endowment: $3.1 million. Research spending for 2004 fiscal year: $1.1 million. Educational spending for 2005 fiscal year: $6658 per student. Total enrollment: 8,484. Faculty: 615 (320 full-time, 295 part-time). Student-undergrad faculty ratio is 19:1. 7,816 applied, 46% were admitted. 16% from top 10% of their high school class, 56% from top quarter, 89% from top half. 6 valedictorians. Full-time: 6,178 students, 56% women, 44% men. Part-time: 787 students, 61% women, 39% men. Students come from 35 states and territories, 26 other countries, 2% from out-of-state, 0.3% Native American, 3% Hispanic, 5% black, 1% Asian American or Pacific Islander, 1% international, 18% 25 or older, 35% live on campus, 13% transferred in. Retention: 83% of full-time freshmen returned the following year. Academic areas with the most degrees conferred: business/marketing; education; health professions and related sciences. Core. Calendar: semesters. Academic remediation for entering students, services for LD students, advanced placement, accelerated degree program, self-designed majors, freshman honors college, honors program, independent study, distance learning, double major, summer session for credit, part-time degree program, co-op programs and internships, graduate courses open to undergrads. Off campus study at Rochester Area Colleges, New York State Visiting Student Program. Study abroad program. ROTC: Army, Naval (c), Air Force (c).

Entrance Requirements: Options: electronic application, deferred admission, international baccalaureate accepted. Required: high school transcript, SAT or ACT. Recommended: minimum 2.6 high school GPA, recommendations. Required for some: essay, recommendations, interview. Entrance: moderately difficult. Application deadline: Rolling. Notification: continuous. Preference given to exceptional talent in arts, dance, and athletics.

Costs Per Year: Application fee: $40. State resident tuition: $181 per credit part-time. Nonresident tuition: $429 per credit part-time.

Collegiate Environment: Orientation program. Drama-theater group, choral group, student-run newspaper, radio station. Social organizations: 60 open to all; national fraternities, national sororities; 1% of eligible men and 2% of eligible women are members. Most popular organizations: fine arts clubs, Organization for Students of African Descent, Communication Club, student radio station, sports clubs. Major annual events: Homecoming/Family Weekend, Scholars' Day, Green and Gold Week. Student services: legal services, health clinic, personal-psychological counseling, women's center. Campus security: 24-hour emergency response devices and patrols, student

patrols, late night transport-escort service, controlled dormitory access. 2,450 college housing spaces available; 2,190 were occupied in 2003-04. Freshmen guaranteed college housing. On-campus residence required in freshman year. Option: coed housing available. Drake Memorial Library with 584,687 books, 2 million microform titles, 1,800 serials, 8,228 audiovisual materials, an OPAC, and a Web page. Operations spending for 2004 fiscal year: $2.7 million. 750 computers available on campus for general student use. A campuswide network can be accessed from student residence rooms and from off campus. Staffed computer lab on campus.

■ **STATE UNIVERSITY OF NEW YORK COLLEGE AT CORTLAND**
L-16

PO Box 2000
Cortland, NY 13045
Tel: (607)753-2011
Admissions: (607)753-4711
Fax: (607)753-5999
E-mail: admissions@cortland.edu
Web Site: http://www.cortland.edu/

Description: State-supported, comprehensive, coed. Part of State University of New York System. Awards bachelor's and master's degrees and post-master's certificates. Founded 1868. Setting: 191-acre small town campus with easy access to Syracuse. Total enrollment: 7,260. Faculty: 555 (334 full-time, 221 part-time). Student-undergrad faculty ratio is 16:1. 9,751 applied, 48% were admitted. 8% from top 10% of their high school class, 38% from top quarter, 85% from top half. Full-time: 5,731 students, 57% women, 43% men. Part-time: 256 students, 53% women, 47% men. Students come from 26 states and territories, 2% from out-of-state, 1% Native American, 4% Hispanic, 3% black, 1% Asian American or Pacific Islander, 1% international, 8% 25 or older, 50% live on campus, 11% transferred in. Retention: 78% of full-time freshmen returned the following year. Academic areas with the most degrees conferred: education; social sciences; parks and recreation. Core. Calendar: semesters. Academic remediation for entering students, services for LD students, advanced placement, self-designed majors, honors program, independent study, distance learning, double major, summer session for credit, part-time degree program, adult/continuing education programs, co-op programs and internships, graduate courses open to undergrads. Off campus study at other units of the State University of New York System. Study abroad program. ROTC: Army (c), Air Force (c).

Entrance Requirements: Options: electronic application, early admission, early decision, deferred admission, international baccalaureate accepted. Required: essay, high school transcript, minimum 2.3 high school GPA, 1 recommendation, SAT or ACT. Recommended: minimum 3.0 high school GPA, 3 recommendations, interview. Entrance: moderately difficult. Application deadlines: Rolling, 11/15 for early decision. Notification: continuous, 12/15 for early decision.

Costs Per Year: Application fee: $40. State resident tuition: $4350 full-time, $181 per credit hour part-time. Nonresident tuition: $10,610 full-time, $442 per credit hour part-time. College room and board: $7850. College room only: $4460.

Collegiate Environment: Orientation program. Drama-theater group, choral group, student-run newspaper, radio station. Social organizations: 100 open to all; national fraternities, national sororities, local sororities; 4% of eligible men and 9% of eligible women are members. Major annual events: sporting events, Scholars' Day. Student services: legal services, health clinic, personal-psychological counseling, women's center. Campus security: 24-hour emergency response devices and patrols, late night transport-escort service. 2,953 college housing spaces available; all were occupied in 2003-04. On-campus residence required through sophomore year. Option: coed housing available. Memorial Library with 82,257 books, an OPAC, and a Web page. 832 computers available on campus for general student use. A campuswide network can be accessed from student residence rooms and from off campus. Staffed computer lab on campus.

■ **STATE UNIVERSITY OF NEW YORK COLLEGE OF ENVIRONMENTAL SCIENCE AND FORESTRY** *J-16*

1 Forestry Dr.
Syracuse, NY 13210-2779
Tel: (315)470-6500
Free: 800-777-7373
Admissions: (315)470-6600
Fax: (315)470-6933
E-mail: esfinfo@lmailbox.syr.edu

Web Site: http://www.esf.edu/

Description: State-supported, university, coed. Part of State University of New York System. Awards associate, bachelor's, master's, and doctoral degrees. Founded 1911. Setting: 12-acre urban campus. Endowment: $8.5 million. Research spending for 2004 fiscal year: $11.5 million. Total enrollment: 1,934. Faculty: 145 (128 full-time, 17 part-time). Student-undergrad faculty ratio is 12:1. 921 applied, 66% were admitted. 14% from top 10% of their high school class, 49% from top quarter, 90% from top half. 1 class president, 2 valedictorians. Full-time: 1,348 students, 37% women, 63% men. Part-time: 44 students, 36% women, 64% men. Students come from 25 states and territories, 8 other countries, 11% from out-of-state, 1% Native American, 3% Hispanic, 1% black, 2% Asian American or Pacific Islander, 1% international, 12% 25 or older, 40% live on campus, 15% transferred in. Retention: 89% of full-time freshmen returned the following year. Academic areas with the most degrees conferred: natural resources/environmental science; biological/life sciences; engineering. Core. Calendar: semesters. Academic remediation for entering students, ESL program, services for LD students, advanced placement, accelerated degree program, freshman honors college, honors program, independent study, distance learning, double major, part-time degree program, adult/continuing education programs, co-op programs and internships, graduate courses open to undergrads. Off campus study at Syracuse University. Study abroad program. ROTC: Army (c), Air Force (c).

Entrance Requirements: Options: electronic application, early admission, early action, deferred admission, international baccalaureate accepted. Required: essay, high school transcript, minimum 3.3 high school GPA, supplemental application, SAT or ACT. Recommended: 3 recommendations, interview. Entrance: moderately difficult. Application deadlines: Rolling, 12/1 for early action. Notification: continuous, 1/2 for early action.

Costs Per Year: Application fee: $40. State resident tuition: $4350 full-time, $181 per credit hour part-time. Nonresident tuition: $10,610 full-time, $442 per credit hour part-time. Mandatory fees: $682 full-time, $32.85 per credit hour part-time, $19.10 per year part-time. College room and board: $10,180. College room only: $5090.

Collegiate Environment: Orientation program. Drama-theater group, choral group, marching band, student-run newspaper, radio station. Social organizations: 300 open to all; national fraternities, national sororities; 33% of eligible men and 33% of eligible women are members. Most popular organizations: Bob Marshall/Outing Club, Forestry Club, Student Environmental Action Coalition. Major annual events: Earth Day, Family and Friends Fall Barbecue, Awards Banquet. Student services: legal services, health clinic, personal-psychological counseling, women's center. Campus security: 24-hour emergency response devices and patrols, late night transport-escort service, controlled dormitory access. Freshmen guaranteed college housing. On-campus residence required in freshman year. Options: coed, men-only, women-only housing available. F. Franklin Moon Library plus 1 other with 137,367 books, 204,150 microform titles, 2,000 serials, an OPAC, and a Web page. Operations spending for 2004 fiscal year: $986,625. 150 computers available on campus for general student use. A campuswide network can be accessed from student residence rooms and from off campus. Staffed computer lab on campus.

Community Environment: See Syracuse University.

■ **STATE UNIVERSITY OF NEW YORK COLLEGE OF ENVIRONMENTAL SCIENCE & FORESTRY, RANGER SCHOOL** *E-20*
PO Box 48, 257 Ranger School Rd.
Wanakena, NY 13695
Tel: (315)848-2566
Free: 800-777-7373
Admissions: (315)470-6600
Fax: (315)470-6933
E-mail: esfinfo@esf.edu
Web Site: http://www.esf.edu/

Description: State-supported, 2-year, coed. Part of State University of New York System. Awards transfer associate and terminal associate degrees. Founded 1912. Setting: 2,800-acre rural campus. Endowment: $524,891. Total enrollment: 43. Student-undergrad faculty ratio is 8:1. 72 applied, 76% were admitted. Full-time: 43 students, 12% women, 88% men. Students come from 4 states and territories, 6% from out-of-state, 0% Native American, 0% Hispanic, 0% black, 0% Asian American or Pacific Islander, 0% international, 20% 25 or older, 100% live on campus. Core. Calendar: semesters. Advanced placement, distance learning.

Entrance Requirements: Options: electronic application, deferred admission. Required: minimum 2.00 high school GPA, SAT or ACT. Recom-

mended: essay, high school transcript, minimum 2.50 high school GPA, interview. Entrance: minimally difficult. Application deadline: Rolling.

Costs Per Year: Application fee: $40. State resident tuition: $4350 full-time, $181 per credit hour part-time. Nonresident tuition: $10,610 full-time, $442 per credit hour part-time. Mandatory fees: $527. College room and board: $8400. College room only: $2450.

Collegiate Environment: Orientation program. Major annual events: Winter Weekend, Open House. Student services: legal services, health clinic, personal-psychological counseling. Option: coed housing available. Ranger School Library with 5,000 books, 60 serials, and an OPAC. 20 computers available on campus for general student use. from student residence rooms and from off campus

■ **STATE UNIVERSITY OF NEW YORK COLLEGE AT GENESEO** *K-10*
1 College Circle
Geneseo, NY 14454-1401
Tel: (585)245-5211; (866)245-5211
Admissions: (585)245-5571
Fax: (585)245-5005
E-mail: admissions@geneseo.edu
Web Site: http://www.geneseo.edu/

Description: State-supported, comprehensive, coed. Part of State University of New York System. Awards bachelor's and master's degrees. Founded 1871. Setting: 220-acre small town campus with easy access to Rochester. Endowment: $6 million. Research spending for 2004 fiscal year: $766,939. Educational spending for 2005 fiscal year: $5202 per student. Total enrollment: 5,484. Faculty: 330 (242 full-time, 88 part-time). Student-undergrad faculty ratio is 19:1. 10,448 applied, 41% were admitted. 51% from top 10% of their high school class, 89% from top quarter, 99% from top half. 32 valedictorians. Full-time: 5,174 students, 59% women, 41% men. Part-time: 132 students, 61% women, 39% men. Students come from 23 states and territories, 34 other countries, 1% from out-of-state, 0.3% Native American, 3% Hispanic, 2% black, 5% Asian American or Pacific Islander, 3% international, 4% 25 or older, 55% live on campus, 8% transferred in. Retention: 92% of full-time freshmen returned the following year. Academic areas with the most degrees conferred: education; business/marketing; social sciences. Core. Calendar: semesters. ESL program, services for LD students, advanced placement, honors program, independent study, double major, summer session for credit, part-time degree program, internships, graduate courses open to undergrads. Off campus study at Rochester Area Colleges. Study abroad program. ROTC: Army (c), Air Force (c).

Entrance Requirements: Options: electronic application, early admission, early decision, deferred admission. Required: essay, high school transcript, SAT or ACT. Recommended: recommendations, interview. Required for some: minimum X high school GPA. Entrance: very difficult. Application deadlines: 1/15, 11/15 for early decision. Notification: continuous until 3/15, 12/15 for early decision.

Costs Per Year: Application fee: $40. State resident tuition: $4350 full-time, $181 per credit hour part-time. Nonresident tuition: $10,610 full-time, $442 per credit hour part-time. Mandatory fees: $1170 full-time, $48.55 per credit hour part-time. College room and board: $7390.

Collegiate Environment: Orientation program. Drama-theater group, choral group, student-run newspaper, radio station. Social organizations: 164 open to all; national fraternities, national sororities, local fraternities, local sororities; 10% of eligible men and 12% of eligible women are members. Major annual events: homecoming, Parents' Weekend, Spring Weekend. Student services: legal services, health clinic, personal-psychological counseling, women's center. Campus security: 24-hour emergency response devices and patrols, student patrols, late night transport-escort service, controlled dormitory access. 3,026 college housing spaces available; 2,848 were occupied in 2003-04. Freshmen guaranteed college housing. On-campus residence required in freshman year. Option: coed housing available. Milne Library plus 1 other with 576,700 books, 764,317 microform titles, 1,758 serials, 15,248 audiovisual materials, an OPAC, and a Web page. Operations spending for 2004 fiscal year: $3.6 million. 900 computers available on campus for general student use. Computer purchase/lease plans available. A campuswide network can be accessed from student residence rooms and from off campus. Staffed computer lab on campus.

■ **STATE UNIVERSITY OF NEW YORK COLLEGE AT OLD WESTBURY** *E-43*
PO Box 210
Old Westbury, NY 11568-0210
Tel: (516)876-3000

Admissions: (516)876-3073

Fax: (516)876-3307

Web Site: http://www.oldwestbury.edu/

Description: State-supported, comprehensive, coed. Part of State University of New York System. Awards bachelor's and master's degrees. Founded 1965. Setting: 605-acre suburban campus with easy access to New York City. Total enrollment: 3,398. Faculty: 253 (129 full-time, 124 part-time). Student-undergrad faculty ratio is 17:1. 3,267 applied, 59% were admitted. 4% from top 10% of their high school class, 30% from top quarter, 60% from top half. Full-time: 2,717 students, 61% women, 39% men. Part-time: 656 students, 60% women, 40% men. Students come from 5 states and territories, 27 other countries, 1% from out-of-state, 0.2% Native American, 16% Hispanic, 28% black, 7% Asian American or Pacific Islander, 2% international, 34% 25 or older, 25% live on campus, 16% transferred in. Retention: 75% of full-time freshmen returned the following year. Academic areas with the most degrees conferred: business/marketing; education; social sciences. Core. Calendar: semesters. Academic remediation for entering students, ESL program, services for LD students, advanced placement, honors program, independent study, distance learning, double major, summer session for credit, part-time degree program, internships. Off campus study at other units of the State University of New York System, Long Island University, C.W. Post Campus, New York Institute of Technology. Study abroad program. ROTC: Army (c), Air Force (c).

Entrance Requirements: Options: electronic application, early admission, early decision, deferred admission. Required: essay, high school transcript, SAT or ACT. Required for some: 2 recommendations, interview. Entrance: moderately difficult. Application deadlines: Rolling, 11/1 for early decision plan 1. Notification: continuous, 12/15 for early decision plan 1.

Costs Per Year: Application fee: $40. State resident tuition: $4350 full-time, $181 per credit part-time. Nonresident tuition: $10,610 full-time, $442 per credit part-time. Mandatory fees: $722 full-time. College room and board: $8083. College room only: $5793.

Collegiate Environment: Orientation program. Drama-theater group, choral group, student-run newspaper, radio station. Social organizations: 55 open to all; national fraternities, national sororities, local fraternities, local sororities; 5% of eligible men and 5% of eligible women are members. Most popular organizations: Alianza Latina, Caribbean Student Association, Asian Club, Finance/Accounting Society. Major annual events: Welcome Back Old Westbury Day, Multicultural Festival, Spring Fling. Student services: health clinic, personal-psychological counseling, women's center. Campus security: 24-hour emergency response devices and patrols, student patrols, late night transport-escort service, controlled dormitory access. 850 college housing spaces available; 837 were occupied in 2003-04. Freshmen guaranteed college housing. Option: coed housing available. SUNY College at Old Westbury Library plus 1 other with 196,000 books, 21,695 microform titles, 803 serials, 2,057 audiovisual materials, an OPAC, and a Web page. 342 computers available on campus for general student use. A campuswide network can be accessed from student residence rooms and from off campus. Staffed computer lab on campus.

■ **STATE UNIVERSITY OF NEW YORK COLLEGE AT ONEONTA** *M-20*

Ravine Parkway

Oneonta, NY 13820-4015

Tel: (607)436-3500

Free: 800-SUNY-123

Admissions: (607)436-2524

Fax: (607)436-3074

Web Site: http://www.oneonta.edu/

Description: State-supported, comprehensive, coed. Part of State University of New York System. Awards bachelor's and master's degrees and post-master's certificates. Founded 1889. Setting: 250-acre small town campus. Endowment: $25.1 million. Research spending for 2004 fiscal year: $4.5 million. Educational spending for 2005 fiscal year: $4185 per student. Total enrollment: 5,860. Faculty: 467 (252 full-time, 215 part-time). Student-undergrad faculty ratio is 17:1. 10,900 applied, 45% were admitted. 11% from top 10% of their high school class, 48% from top quarter, 94% from top half. 8 valedictorians. Full-time: 5,488 students, 58% women, 42% men. Part-time: 161 students, 51% women, 49% men. Students come from 18 states and territories, 17 other countries, 2% from out-of-state, 0.1% Native American, 5% Hispanic, 3% black, 2% Asian American or Pacific Islander, 1% international, 6% 25 or older, 57% live on campus, 8% transferred in. Retention: 80% of full-time freshmen returned the following year. Academic areas with the most degrees conferred: education; visual and performing arts; communications/journalism. Core. Calendar: semesters. Academic

remediation for entering students, ESL program, services for LD students, advanced placement, honors program, independent study, distance learning, double major, summer session for credit, part-time degree program, adult/continuing education programs, internships, graduate courses open to undergrads. Off campus study at Hartwick College. Study abroad program.

Entrance Requirements: Options: electronic application, early admission, early action, deferred admission, international baccalaureate accepted. Required: essay, high school transcript, SAT or ACT. Recommended: minimum 3.0 high school GPA, 3 recommendations. Entrance: very difficult. Application deadlines: Rolling, 11/1 for early action. Notification: continuous, 11/15 for early action.

Costs Per Year: Application fee: $40. State resident tuition: $4350 full-time, $181 per semester hour part-time. Nonresident tuition: $10,610 full-time, $442 per semester hour part-time. Mandatory fees: $1017 full-time, $34.35 per semester hour part-time. College room and board: $7538. College room only: $4378.

Collegiate Environment: Orientation program. Drama-theater group, choral group, student-run newspaper, radio station. Social organizations: 70 open to all; national fraternities, national sororities, local fraternities, local sororities; 2% of eligible men and 5% of eligible women are members. Most popular organizations: Center for Social Responsibility and Community, Mask and Hammer, Terpsichorean, student government, WONY radio station. Major annual events: Homecoming and Family Weekend, Exploration Series, Spring Weekend. Student services: health clinic, personal-psychological counseling, women's center. Campus security: 24-hour emergency response devices and patrols, late night transport-escort service, controlled dormitory access. 3,219 college housing spaces available; 3,212 were occupied in 2003-04. Freshmen guaranteed college housing. On-campus residence required through sophomore year. Option: coed housing available. Milne Library with 552,389 books, 1.2 million microform titles, 18,506 serials, 30,320 audiovisual materials, an OPAC, and a Web page. Operations spending for 2004 fiscal year: $1.8 million. 700 computers available on campus for general student use. Computer purchase/lease plans available. A campuswide network can be accessed from student residence rooms and from off campus. Staffed computer lab on campus.

■ **STATE UNIVERSITY OF NEW YORK COLLEGE AT POTSDAM** *C-20*

44 Pierrepont Ave.

Potsdam, NY 13676

Tel: (315)267-2000; 877-POTSDAM

Admissions: (315)267-2180

Fax: (315)267-2163

E-mail: admissions@potsdam.edu

Web Site: http://www.potsdam.edu/

Description: State-supported, comprehensive, coed. Part of State University of New York System. Awards bachelor's and master's degrees. Founded 1816. Setting: 240-acre small town campus. Endowment: $13.6 million. Total enrollment: 4,329. Faculty: 366 (256 full-time, 110 part-time). Student-undergrad faculty ratio is 14:1. 3,423 applied, 73% were admitted. 12% from top 10% of their high school class, 36% from top quarter, 76% from top half. 1 valedictorian. Full-time: 3,465 students, 58% women, 42% men. Part-time: 154 students, 68% women, 32% men. Students come from 23 states and territories, 25 other countries, 2% from out-of-state, 2% Native American, 2% Hispanic, 2% black, 1% Asian American or Pacific Islander, 3% international, 11% 25 or older, 52% live on campus, 10% transferred in. Retention: 76% of full-time freshmen returned the following year. Academic areas with the most degrees conferred: education; social sciences; visual and performing arts. Core. Calendar: semesters. Services for LD students, advanced placement, self-designed majors, honors program, independent study, distance learning, double major, summer session for credit, part-time degree program, adult/continuing education programs, internships, graduate courses open to undergrads. Off campus study at Associated Colleges of the St. Lawrence Valley, National Student Exchange. Study abroad program. ROTC: Army (c), Air Force (c).

Entrance Requirements: Options: electronic application, early admission, deferred admission, international baccalaureate accepted. Required: high school transcript, minimum 2.5 high school GPA, SAT or ACT. Recommended: interview. Required for some: essay, recommendations, audition for music program. Entrance: moderately difficult. Application deadline: Rolling. Notification: continuous.

Costs Per Year: Application fee: $40. State resident tuition: $4350 full-time, $181 per credit hour part-time. Nonresident tuition: $10,610 full-time, $442 per credit hour part-time. Mandatory fees: $939 full-time, $43.95 per credit hour part-time. College room and board: $7670. College room only: $4420. Room and board charges vary according to board plan and housing facility.

Collegiate Environment: Orientation program. Drama-theater group, choral group, student-run newspaper, radio station. Social organizations: 100 open to all; national fraternities, national sororities, local fraternities, local sororities; 7% of eligible men and 11% of eligible women are members. Most popular organizations: Student Government Association, Crane Student Association, Student Entertainment Services (Programming Board), Caribbean-Latin American Student Society, The Racquette Student Newspaper. Major annual events: Springfest, Battle of The Bands, Holiday Candlelight Concert. Student services: legal services, health clinic, personal-psychological counseling, women's center. Campus security: 24-hour emergency response devices and patrols, late night transport-escort service, controlled dormitory access, self-defense education, pamphlets/posters/films. 2,500 college housing spaces available; 1,849 were occupied in 2003-04. Freshmen guaranteed college housing. On-campus residence required through sophomore year. Options: coed, women-only housing available. F. W. Crumb Memorial Library plus 1 other with 408,755 books, 770,007 microform titles, 933 serials, 15,570 audiovisual materials, an OPAC, and a Web page. 400 computers available on campus for general student use. Computer purchase/lease plans available. A campuswide network can be accessed from student residence rooms and from off campus. Staffed computer lab on campus.

■ **STATE UNIVERSITY OF NEW YORK COLLEGE OF TECHNOLOGY AT ALFRED** *N-11*
Alfred, NY 14802
Tel: (607)587-4111
Free: 800-4-ALFRED
Admissions: (607)587-4215
Fax: (607)587-4299
E-mail: admissions@alfredstate.edu
Web Site: http://www.alfredstate.edu/
Description: State-supported, primarily 2-year, coed. Part of State University of New York System. Awards certificates, transfer associate, terminal associate, and bachelor's degrees. Founded 1908. Setting: 175-acre rural campus. Endowment: $2.6 million. Research spending for 2004 fiscal year: $149,193. Total enrollment: 3,377. Student-undergrad faculty ratio is 20:1. 4,463 applied, 65% were admitted. 9% from top 10% of their high school class, 35% from top quarter, 58% from top half. Students come from 29 states and territories, 8% from out-of-state, 0.3% Native American, 3% Hispanic, 3% black, 1% Asian American or Pacific Islander, 23% 25 or older, 70% live on campus. Retention: 96% of full-time freshmen returned the following year. Academic areas with the most degrees conferred: engineering technologies; computer and information sciences; architecture. Core. Calendar: semesters. Academic remediation for entering students, services for LD students, advanced placement, self-designed majors, honors program, independent study, distance learning, summer session for credit, part-time degree program, external degree program, adult/continuing education programs, co-op programs and internships. Off campus study at Alfred University. Study abroad program. ROTC: Army (c).
Entrance Requirements: Options: Common Application, electronic application, deferred admission. Required: high school transcript. Recommended: essay, recommendations, interview, SAT or ACT. Required for some: minimum 2.0 high school GPA, SAT or ACT. Entrance: moderately difficult. Application deadline: Rolling. Notification: continuous.
Costs Per Year: Application fee: $40. State resident tuition: $4350 full-time. Nonresident tuition: $7210 full-time. College room and board: $6700. College room only: $3770.
Collegiate Environment: Orientation program. Drama-theater group, choral group, student-run newspaper, radio station. Social organizations: 60 open to all; local fraternities, local sororities; 3% of eligible men and 2% of eligible women are members. Most popular organizations: Outdoor Activity Club, BACCHUS, Sondai Society, Drama Club, choir. Major annual events: Freshman Carnival, Ag Day, homecoming. Student services: health clinic, personal-psychological counseling, ESL. Campus security: 24-hour emergency response devices and patrols, late night transport-escort service, residence hall entrance guards. 2,506 college housing spaces available; 2,094 were occupied in 2003-04. Freshmen guaranteed college housing. Option: coed housing available. Walter C. Hinkle Memorial Library plus 1 other with 71,243 books, 76,431 microform titles, 594 serials, 8,148 audiovisual materials, an OPAC, and a Web page. Operations spending for 2004 fiscal year: $420,400. 1,600 computers available on campus for general student use. Computer purchase/lease plans available. A campuswide network can be accessed from student residence rooms and from off campus. Staffed computer lab on campus.

■ **STATE UNIVERSITY OF NEW YORK COLLEGE OF TECHNOLOGY AT CANTON** *C-19*
Cornell Dr.
Canton, NY 13617
Tel: (315)386-7011
Free: 800-388-7123
Admissions: (315)386-7123
Fax: (315)386-7930
Web Site: http://www.canton.edu/
Description: State-supported, primarily 2-year, coed. Part of State University of New York System. Awards certificates, transfer associate, terminal associate, and bachelor's degrees. Founded 1906. Setting: 555-acre small town campus. Endowment: $5.6 million. Total enrollment: 2,518. 2,984 applied, 83% were admitted. Full-time: 2,055 students, 49% women, 51% men. Part-time: 463 students, 69% women, 31% men. Students come from 15 states and territories, 5 other countries, 3% from out-of-state, 2% Native American, 2% Hispanic, 8% black, 1% Asian American or Pacific Islander, 1% international, 21% 25 or older, 48% live on campus, 8% transferred in. Retention: 82% of full-time freshmen returned the following year. Core. Calendar: semesters. Academic remediation for entering students, services for LD students, advanced placement, self-designed majors, independent study, distance learning, summer session for credit, part-time degree program, adult/continuing education programs, internships. Off campus study at the Associated Colleges of the St. Lawrence Valley. ROTC: Army (c), Air Force (c).
Entrance Requirements: Options: electronic application, early admission, deferred admission. Required: high school transcript. Recommended: minimum 2.0 high school GPA. Required for some: interview. Entrance: minimally difficult. Application deadline: Rolling. Notification: continuous.
Costs Per Year: Application fee: $40. One-time mandatory fee: $20. State resident tuition: $4350 full-time, $181 per credit hour part-time. Nonresident tuition: $10,610 full-time, $442 per credit hour part-time. Mandatory fees: $1065 full-time, $39.30 per credit hour part-time, $5. Full-time tuition and fees vary according to degree level, location, and program. Part-time tuition and fees vary according to degree level, location, and program. College room and board: $7350. College room only: $4220. Room and board charges vary according to housing facility.
Collegiate Environment: Orientation program. Drama-theater group, choral group, student-run newspaper, radio station. Social organizations: 53 open to all; national fraternities, national sororities, local fraternities, local sororities; 2% of eligible men and 1% of eligible women are members. Most popular organizations: Karate Club, Automotive Club, Outing Club, WATC Radio, Afro-Latin Society. Major annual events: Family Weekend, Mardi Gras, Ghoul's Gala. Student services: health clinic, personal-psychological counseling. Campus security: 24-hour emergency response devices and patrols, late night transport-escort service, controlled dormitory access. 900 college housing spaces available; all were occupied in 2003-04. No special consideration for freshman housing applicants. On-campus residence required through sophomore year. Options: coed, men-only, women-only housing available. Southworth Library with 64,912 books, 5,922 microform titles, 303 serials, 1,569 audiovisual materials, an OPAC, and a Web page. 300 computers available on campus for general student use. Computer purchase/lease plans available. A campuswide network can be accessed. Staffed computer lab on campus.

■ **STATE UNIVERSITY OF NEW YORK COLLEGE OF TECHNOLOGY AT DELHI** *N-21*
Main St.
Delhi, NY 13753
Tel: (607)746-4000
Free: 800-96-DELHI
Fax: (607)746-4104
Web Site: http://www.delhi.edu/
Description: State-supported, primarily 2-year, coed. Part of State University of New York System. Awards certificates, transfer associate, terminal associate, and bachelor's degrees. Founded 1913. Setting: 405-acre rural campus. Endowment: $1.2 million. Educational spending for 2005 fiscal year: $4078 per student. Total enrollment: 2,557. Student-undergrad faculty ratio is 17:1. 3,650 applied, 61% were admitted. Students come from 7 states and territories, 3 other countries, 2% from out-of-state, 0.2% Native American, 6% Hispanic, 12% black, 2% Asian American or Pacific Islander, 2% international, 19% 25 or older, 61% live on campus. Core. Calendar: semesters. Academic remediation for entering students, ESL program, services for LD students, advanced placement, self-designed majors, honors

program, distance learning, summer session for credit, part-time degree program, adult/continuing education programs, internships.

Entrance Requirements: Options: electronic application, early admission, deferred admission. Required: high school transcript. Required for some: minimum 2.0 high school GPA. Entrance: moderately difficult. Application deadline: Rolling. Notification: continuous.

Costs Per Year: Application fee: $30. State resident tuition: $4350 full-time, $181 per credit hour part-time. Nonresident tuition: $7210 full-time, $300 per credit hour part-time. Mandatory fees: $1248 full-time, $42 per credit hour part-time, $5 per term part-time. College room and board: $7880.

Collegiate Environment: Orientation program. Drama-theater group, student-run newspaper, radio station. Social organizations: 40 open to all; national fraternities, local fraternities, local sororities; 10% of eligible men and 8% of eligible women are members. Most popular organizations: Latin American Student Organization, Hotel Sales Management Association, student radio station, Phi Theta Kappa, Student Programming Board. Major annual events: Fall Weekend, Winter Weekend, Spring Weekend. Student services: legal services, health clinic, personal-psychological counseling. Campus security: 24-hour emergency response devices and patrols. On-campus residence required through sophomore year. Option: coed housing available. Louis and Mildred Resnick Library with 47,909 books, 384 serials, and an OPAC. Operations spending for 2004 fiscal year: $97,865. 350 computers available on campus for general student use. A campuswide network can be accessed from off-campus. Staffed computer lab on campus.

■ STATE UNIVERSITY OF NEW YORK DOWNSTATE MEDICAL CENTER *O-34*

450 Clarkson Ave.
Brooklyn, NY 11203-2098
Tel: (718)270-1000
Fax: (718)270-7592
Web Site: http://www.downstate.edu/

Description: State-supported, upper-level, coed. Part of State University of New York System. Awards bachelor's, master's, doctoral, and first professional degrees and post-master's certificates. Founded 1858. Setting: urban campus. Total enrollment: 1,567. Full-time: 203 students, 77% women, 23% men. Part-time: 142 students, 89% women, 11% men. 1% from out-of-state, 0% Native American, 7% Hispanic, 50% black, 7% Asian American or Pacific Islander, 0.3% international, 45% transferred in. Academic area with the most degrees conferred: health professions and related sciences. Core. Calendar: semesters. Services for LD students, advanced placement, accelerated degree program, independent study, summer session for credit, part-time degree program, adult/continuing education programs, internships. Off campus study.

Costs Per Year: Application fee: $30. State resident tuition: $4350 full-time, $181 per credit part-time. Nonresident tuition: $10,610 full-time, $442 per credit part-time. College room and board: $11,774.

Collegiate Environment: Orientation program. Student services: health clinic, personal-psychological counseling. Campus security: late night transport-escort service. 406 college housing spaces available; 13 were occupied in 2003-04. Option: coed housing available. The Medical Research Library of Brooklyn with 357,209 books, 2,104 serials, 812 audiovisual materials, an OPAC, and a Web page. 183 computers available on campus for general student use. A campuswide network can be accessed from student residence rooms and from off campus. Staffed computer lab on campus.

■ STATE UNIVERSITY OF NEW YORK EMPIRE STATE COLLEGE *J-24*

1 Union Ave.
Saratoga Springs, NY 12866-4391
Tel: (518)587-2100
Free: 800-847-3000
Fax: (518)587-2100
E-mail: jennifer.riley@esc.edu
Web Site: http://www.esc.edu/

Description: State-supported, comprehensive, coed. Part of State University of New York System. Awards associate, bachelor's, and master's degrees (branch locations at 7 regional centers with 35 auxiliary units). Founded 1971. Setting: small town campus. Endowment: $10.1 million. Research spending for 2004 fiscal year: $96,900. Educational spending for 2005 fiscal year: $5500 per student. Total enrollment: 9,996. Faculty: 1,075 (154 full-time, 921 part-time). Student-undergrad faculty ratio is 11:1. 1,341 applied, 81% were admitted. Full-time: 3,189 students, 68% women, 32%

men. Part-time: 6,333 students, 55% women, 45% men. Students come from 52 states and territories, 24 other countries, 9% from out-of-state, 1% Native American, 6% Hispanic, 12% black, 1% Asian American or Pacific Islander, 7% international, 83% 25 or older, 22% transferred in. Retention: 43% of full-time freshmen returned the following year. Academic areas with the most degrees conferred: business/marketing; public administration and social services; English; psychology. Core. Calendar: continuous. Services for LD students, advanced placement, self-designed majors, independent study, distance learning, part-time degree program, external degree program, adult/continuing education programs, co-op programs. Off campus study at New York State Visiting Student Program. Study abroad program.

Entrance Requirements: Options: electronic application, early admission. Required: essay, high school transcript, possession of high school diploma or its equivalent. Required for some: interview. Entrance: minimally difficult. Application deadline: Rolling.

Costs Per Year: Application fee: $0. One-time mandatory fee: $300. State resident tuition: $4350 full-time, $181 per credit part-time. Nonresident tuition: $10,610 full-time, $442 per credit part-time. Mandatory fees: $225 full-time, $7.10 per credit part-time, $75 per term part-time.

Collegiate Environment: College housing not available. 11,000 books and 10,000 serials. Operations spending for 2004 fiscal year: $197,900. 100 computers available on campus for general student use. A campuswide network can be accessed from off-campus. Staffed computer lab on campus.

■ STATE UNIVERSITY OF NEW YORK, FREDONIA *M-5*

Fredonia, NY 14063-1136
Tel: (716)673-3111
Free: 800-252-1212
Admissions: (716)673-3251
Fax: (716)673-3249
E-mail: admissions.office@fredonia.edu
Web Site: http://www.fredonia.edu/

Description: State-supported, comprehensive, coed. Part of State University of New York System. Awards bachelor's and master's degrees. Founded 1826. Setting: 266-acre small town campus with easy access to Buffalo. Endowment: $10 million. Research spending for 2004 fiscal year: $1.4 million. Educational spending for 2005 fiscal year: $3060 per student. Total enrollment: 5,432. Faculty: 405 (245 full-time, 160 part-time). Student-undergrad faculty ratio is 18:1. 5,902 applied, 55% were admitted. 16% from top 10% of their high school class, 47% from top quarter, 89% from top half. 7 valedictorians. Full-time: 4,843 students, 57% women, 43% men. Students come from 27 states and territories, 9 other countries, 2% from out-of-state, 1% Native American, 3% Hispanic, 2% black, 2% Asian American or Pacific Islander, 0.2% international, 7% 25 or older, 53% live on campus, 9% transferred in. Retention: 81% of full-time freshmen returned the following year. Academic areas with the most degrees conferred: education; business/marketing; communications/journalism. Core. Calendar: semesters. Services for LD students, advanced placement, accelerated degree program, self-designed majors, honors program, independent study, distance learning, double major, summer session for credit, part-time degree program, adult/continuing education programs, internships, graduate courses open to undergrads. Off campus study at Western New York Consortium. Study abroad program.

Entrance Requirements: Options: electronic application, early admission, early decision, deferred admission, international baccalaureate accepted. Required: high school transcript, minimum 2.5 high school GPA, SAT or ACT. Recommended: recommendations. Required for some: essay, interview, audition for music and theater programs, portfolio for art and media arts program. Entrance: moderately difficult. Application deadlines: Rolling, 11/1 for early decision. Notification: continuous, 12/1 for early decision.

Costs Per Year: Application fee: $40. State resident tuition: $4350 full-time, $181 per credit hour part-time. Nonresident tuition: $10,610 full-time, $442 per credit hour part-time. Mandatory fees: $1091 full-time, $43.15 per credit hour part-time. College room and board: $6940. College room only: $4350. Room and board charges vary according to board plan and housing facility.

Collegiate Environment: Orientation program. Drama-theater group, choral group, student-run newspaper, radio station. Social organizations: 120 open to all; national fraternities, national sororities; 5% of eligible men and 3% of eligible women are members. Most popular organizations: Student Association, Undergraduate Alumni Council, Communication Club, ethnic organizations. Major annual events: Homecoming, Fredoniafest, Parents' Weekend. Student services: legal services, health clinic, personal-psychological counseling. Campus security: 24-hour emergency response devices and patrols, late night transport-escort service, controlled dormitory access.

2,600 college housing spaces available; 2,449 were occupied in 2003-04. Freshmen guaranteed college housing. On-campus residence required through sophomore year. Options: coed, men-only, women-only housing available. Reed Library with 396,000 books, 1.1 million microform titles, 2,270 serials, 17,607 audiovisual materials, an OPAC, and a Web page. Operations spending for 2004 fiscal year: $1.5 million. 500 computers available on campus for general student use. A campuswide network can be accessed from student residence rooms and from off campus. Staffed computer lab on campus.

■ STATE UNIVERSITY OF NEW YORK INSTITUTE OF TECHNOLOGY
J-19
PO Box 3050
Utica, NY 13504-3050
Tel: (315)792-7100
Free: 800-SUN-YTEC
Admissions: (315)792-7500
Fax: (315)792-7837
E-mail: admissions@sunyit.edu
Web Site: http://www.sunyit.edu/

Description: State-supported, comprehensive, coed. Part of State University of New York System. Awards bachelor's and master's degrees and post-master's certificates. Founded 1966. Setting: 850-acre suburban campus. Endowment: $1.7 million. Research spending for 2004 fiscal year: $812,000. Educational spending for 2005 fiscal year: $4020 per student. Total enrollment: 2,590. Faculty: 162 (95 full-time, 67 part-time). Student-undergrad faculty ratio is 17:1. 1,015 applied, 42% were admitted. Full-time: 1,241 students, 36% women, 64% men. Part-time: 778 students, 70% women, 30% men. Students come from 10 states and territories, 14 other countries, 1% Native American, 3% Hispanic, 7% black, 3% Asian American or Pacific Islander, 1% international, 56% 25 or older, 18% live on campus, 26% transferred in. Retention: 83% of full-time freshmen returned the following year. Academic areas with the most degrees conferred: business/marketing; engineering technologies; computer and information sciences. Core. Calendar: semesters. Academic remediation for entering students, ESL program, services for LD students, advanced placement, accelerated degree program, independent study, distance learning, double major, summer session for credit, part-time degree program, adult/continuing education programs, internships, graduate courses open to undergrads. ROTC: Army (c), Air Force (c).

Entrance Requirements: Options: electronic application, deferred admission, international baccalaureate accepted. Required: essay, high school transcript. Recommended: minimum 2.50 high school GPA, interview. Entrance: minimally difficult. Application deadlines: Rolling, 11/1 for early decision. Notification: continuous until 1/15, 12/15 for early decision.

Costs Per Year: Application fee: $40. State resident tuition: $4350 full-time, $181 per credit hour part-time. Nonresident tuition: $10,610 full-time, $442 per credit hour part-time. Mandatory fees: $935 full-time, $36.70 per credit hour part-time. College room and board: $7290.

Collegiate Environment: Orientation program. Student-run newspaper, radio station. Social organizations: 45 open to all. Most popular organizations: Telecommunications Club, Snowmobile Club, Phi Beta Lambda, Black Student Union, American Society of Mechanical Engineers. Major annual events: Fall Fest, Apocalypse, Children's Holiday Party. Student services: health clinic, personal-psychological counseling. Campus security: 24-hour emergency response devices and patrols, late night transport-escort service, controlled dormitory access, closed-circuit TV monitors. 398 undergraduates lived in college housing during 2003-04. Option: coed housing available. SUNY Institute of Technology at Utica/Rome Library with 193,682 books, 200,298 microform titles, 1,090 serials, 11,818 audiovisual materials, an OPAC, and a Web page. Operations spending for 2004 fiscal year: $868,992. 250 computers available on campus for general student use. A campuswide network can be accessed from student residence rooms and from off campus. Staffed computer lab on campus.

■ STATE UNIVERSITY OF NEW YORK MARITIME COLLEGE
6 Pennyfield Ave.
Throggs Neck, NY 10465-4198
Tel: (718)409-7200
Free: 800-642-1874
Admissions: (718)409-7220
Fax: (718)409-7392
E-mail: dwhitman@sunymaritime.edu
Web Site: http://www.sunymaritime.edu/

Description: State-supported, comprehensive, coed. Part of State University of New York System. Awards associate, bachelor's, and master's degrees. Founded 1874. Setting: 56-acre suburban campus. Endowment: $1 million. Educational spending for 2005 fiscal year: $4797 per student. Total enrollment: 1,294. Faculty: 75 (60 full-time, 15 part-time). Student-undergrad faculty ratio is 17:1. 1,097 applied, 70% were admitted. 6% from top 10% of their high school class, 23% from top quarter, 66% from top half. Students come from 15 states and territories, 28% from out-of-state, 0.1% Native American, 6% Hispanic, 6% black, 4% Asian American or Pacific Islander, 6% international, 7% 25 or older, 98% live on campus. Retention: 88% of full-time freshmen returned the following year. Core. Calendar: semesters plus 2-month summer sea term. Services for LD students, advanced placement, self-designed majors, independent study, summer session for credit, adult/continuing education programs, co-op programs and internships, graduate courses open to undergrads. Study abroad program. ROTC: Naval, Air Force (c).

Entrance Requirements: Options: electronic application, early admission, early decision, deferred admission. Required: high school transcript, minimum 2.5 high school GPA, medical history, SAT or ACT. Recommended: essay, 1 recommendation, interview, SAT Subject Tests. Entrance: moderately difficult. Application deadlines: Rolling, 12/1 for early decision. Notification: continuous, 12/15 for early decision.

Costs Per Year: Application fee: $40. State resident tuition: $4350 full-time, $181 per credit part-time. Nonresident tuition: $10,610 full-time, $442 per credit part-time. Mandatory fees: $3055 full-time, $27.53 per credit part-time. Full-time tuition and fees vary according to reciprocity agreements. Part-time tuition and fees vary according to reciprocity agreements. College room and board: $8000. College room only: $4900. Room and board charges vary according to board plan and housing facility.

Collegiate Environment: Orientation program. Marching band, student-run newspaper. Social organizations: 35 open to all. Most popular organizations: Propeller Club, Eagle Scout Fraternity, Society of Naval Architects and Marine Engineers, Culture Club, Society for Professional Hispanic Engineers. Major annual events: Admiral's Ball, Spring Formal, monthly mixers. Student services: health clinic, personal-psychological counseling. Campus security: 24-hour emergency response devices and patrols, student patrols, late night transport-escort service. On-campus residence required through senior year. Option: coed housing available. Stephen Luce Library with 69,637 books, 55,281 microform titles, 1,087 serials, 6,280 audiovisual materials, an OPAC, and a Web page. Operations spending for 2004 fiscal year: $420,800. 110 computers available on campus for general student use. A campuswide network can be accessed from student residence rooms and from off campus. Staffed computer lab on campus.

Community Environment: The College is located on the Throgs Neck Peninsula, a small waterfront community within New York City.

■ STATE UNIVERSITY OF NEW YORK AT NEW PALTZ *P-24*
75 South Manheim Blvd.
New Paltz, NY 12561
Tel: (845)257-2121
Admissions: (845)257-3210
Fax: (845)257-3209
E-mail: eatond@newpaltz.edu
Web Site: http://www.newpaltz.edu/

Description: State-supported, comprehensive, coed. Part of State University of New York System. Awards bachelor's and master's degrees and post-master's certificates. Founded 1828. Setting: 216-acre small town campus. Endowment: $7.4 million. Research spending for 2004 fiscal year: $3.6 million. Educational spending for 2005 fiscal year: $6187 per student. Total enrollment: 7,825. Faculty: 706 (294 full-time, 412 part-time). Student-undergrad faculty ratio is 16:1. 11,358 applied, 44% were admitted. 15% from top 10% of their high school class, 56% from top quarter, 94% from top half. 1 National Merit Scholar, 6 class presidents, 2 valedictorians, 49 student government officers. Full-time: 5,715 students, 67% women, 33% men. Part-time: 706 students, 68% women, 32% men. Students come from 23 states and territories, 40 other countries, 3% from out-of-state, 0.1% Native American, 10% Hispanic, 6% black, 3% Asian American or Pacific Islander, 3% international, 17% 25 or older, 52% live on campus, 11% transferred in. Academic areas with the most degrees conferred: education; business/marketing; English; visual and performing arts. Core. Calendar: semesters. Academic remediation for entering students, ESL program, services for LD students, advanced placement, self-designed majors, honors program, independent study, distance learning, double major, summer session for credit, part-time degree program, adult/continuing education programs, co-op programs and internships, graduate courses open to undergrads. Off campus study at Associated Colleges of the Mid-Hudson Area. Study abroad program.

Entrance Requirements: Options: electronic application, early admission, early action, deferred admission, international baccalaureate accepted. Required: high school transcript, SAT or ACT. Recommended: minimum 3.4 high school GPA. Required for some: portfolio for art program, audition for music and theater programs. Entrance: very difficult. Application deadlines: 4/1, 11/15 for early action. Notification: continuous, 1/1 for early action.

Costs Per Year: Application fee: $40. State resident tuition: $4350 full-time, $181 per credit part-time. Nonresident tuition: $10,610 full-time, $442 per credit part-time. Mandatory fees: $1010 full-time, $28.60 per credit part-time, $160 per term part-time. College room and board: $7230. College room only: $4500.

Collegiate Environment: Orientation program. Drama-theater group, choral group, student-run newspaper, radio station. Social organizations: 135 open to all; national fraternities, national sororities, local fraternities, local sororities; 3% of eligible men and 2% of eligible women are members. Most popular organizations: Outing Club, intramurals, Residence Hall Student Association, Student Art Alliance. Major annual events: Rainbow Month Semi-Formal, Spirit Weekend, Homecoming Weekend. Student services: legal services, health clinic, personal-psychological counseling. Campus security: 24-hour emergency response devices and patrols, late night transport-escort service, controlled dormitory access, safety seminars. 3,012 college housing spaces available; 2,970 were occupied in 2003-04. Freshmen guaranteed college housing. On-campus residence required in freshman year. Option: coed housing available. Sojourner Truth Library with 525,296 books, 1.2 million microform titles, 1,253 serials, 1,564 audiovisual materials, an OPAC, and a Web page. Operations spending for 2004 fiscal year: $2.2 million. 600 computers available on campus for general student use. A campuswide network can be accessed from student residence rooms and from off campus. Staffed computer lab on campus.

■ **STATE UNIVERSITY OF NEW YORK AT OSWEGO** *H-15*

7060 Route 104
Oswego, NY 13126
Tel: (315)312-2500
Admissions: (315)312-2250
Fax: (315)312-5799
E-mail: admiss@oswego.edu
Web Site: http://www.oswego.edu/

Description: State-supported, comprehensive, coed. Part of State University of New York System. Awards bachelor's and master's degrees and post-master's certificates. Founded 1861. Setting: 696-acre small town campus with easy access to Syracuse. Endowment: $6 million. Research spending for 2004 fiscal year: $1.8 million. Educational spending for 2005 fiscal year: $4796 per student. Total enrollment: 8,282. Faculty: 511 (317 full-time, 194 part-time). Student-undergrad faculty ratio is 18:1. 7,565 applied, 56% were admitted. 10% from top 10% of their high school class, 50% from top quarter, 84% from top half. Full-time: 6,620 students, 54% women, 46% men. Part-time: 518 students, 60% women, 40% men. Students come from 28 states and territories, 19 other countries, 1% from out-of-state, 1% Native American, 4% Hispanic, 4% black, 2% Asian American or Pacific Islander, 1% international, 12% 25 or older, 57% live on campus, 10% transferred in. Retention: 76% of full-time freshmen returned the following year. Academic areas with the most degrees conferred: education; business/marketing; communications/journalism. Core. Calendar: semesters. ESL program, services for LD students, advanced placement, accelerated degree program, self-designed majors, freshman honors college, honors program, independent study, distance learning, double major, summer session for credit, part-time degree program, adult/continuing education programs, co-op programs and internships, graduate courses open to undergrads. Off campus study at Bryant and Stratton North Campus, Finger Lakes Community College, Jefferson-Lewis Board of Cooperative Educational Services, Onondage-Cortland-Madison Board of Cooperative Educational Services. Study abroad program. ROTC: Army (c).

Entrance Requirements: Options: electronic application, early admission, early decision, deferred admission, international baccalaureate accepted. Required: high school transcript, SAT or ACT. Recommended: essay, interview. Required for some: recommendations. Entrance: moderately difficult. Application deadlines: Rolling, 11/15 for early decision. Notification: 1/15, 12/15 for early decision.

Costs Per Year: Application fee: $40. State resident tuition: $4350 full-time, $181 per credit hour part-time. Nonresident tuition: $10,610 full-time, $442

per credit hour part-time. Mandatory fees: $972 full-time, $30.18 per credit hour part-time. Part-time tuition and fees vary according to class time, course load, and location. College room and board: $8340. College room only: $5090. Room and board charges vary according to board plan and housing facility.

Collegiate Environment: Orientation program. Drama-theater group, choral group, student-run newspaper, radio station. Social organizations: 123 open to all; national fraternities, national sororities, local fraternities, local sororities; 6% of eligible men and 6% of eligible women are members. Most popular organizations: club/intramural sports, student radio/television stations, Outing/Recreation Club, student government, programming boards. Major annual events: Quest, May Day, Family and Friends Weekend. Student services: legal services, health clinic, personal-psychological counseling, women's center. Campus security: 24-hour emergency response devices and patrols, controlled dormitory access. 3,926 college housing spaces available; 3,700 were occupied in 2003-04. Freshmen guaranteed college housing. On-campus residence required through sophomore year. Option: coed housing available. Penfield Library plus 1 other with 477,930 books, 2.1 million microform titles, 959 serials, 32,179 audiovisual materials, an OPAC, and a Web page. Operations spending for 2004 fiscal year: $2.6 million. 600 computers available on campus for general student use. Computer purchase/lease plans available. A campuswide network can be accessed from student residence rooms and from off campus. Staffed computer lab on campus.

■ **STATE UNIVERSITY OF NEW YORK AT PLATTSBURGH** *C-25*

101 Broad Steet
Plattsburgh, NY 12901-2681
Tel: (518)564-2000
Admissions: (518)564-2040
Fax: (518)564-2045
E-mail: admissions@plattsburgh.edu
Web Site: http://www.plattsburgh.edu/

Description: State-supported, comprehensive, coed. Part of State University of New York System. Awards bachelor's and master's degrees and post-master's certificates. Founded 1889. Setting: 265-acre small town campus with easy access to Montreal. Endowment: $10.2 million. Research spending for 2004 fiscal year: $1.1 million. Educational spending for 2005 fiscal. year: $5471 per student. Total enrollment: 6,044. Faculty: 455 (252 full-time, 203 part-time). Student-undergrad faculty ratio is 17:1. 5,321 applied, 62% were admitted. 9% from top 10% of their high school class, 33% from top quarter, 78% from top half. Full-time: 5,024 students, 57% women, 43% men. Part-time: 370 students, 60% women, 40% men. Students come from 26 states and territories, 49 other countries, 4% from out-of-state, 0.5% Native American, 4% Hispanic, 5% black, 2% Asian American or Pacific Islander, 6% international, 18% 25 or older, 48% live on campus, 10% transferred in. Retention: 77% of full-time freshmen returned the following year. Academic areas with the most degrees conferred: business/marketing; education; social sciences. Core. Calendar: semesters plus 2 5-week summer sessions and 1 winter session. Academic remediation for entering students, ESL program, services for LD students, advanced placement, accelerated degree program, self-designed majors, honors program, independent study, distance learning, double major, summer session for credit, part-time degree program, adult/continuing education programs, co-op programs and internships, graduate courses open to undergrads. Off campus study at National Student Exchange, Clinton Community College, State University of New York Empire State College, Adirondack Community College. Study abroad program.

Entrance Requirements: Options: electronic application, early admission, early decision, deferred admission, international baccalaureate accepted. Required: high school transcript, minimum 2.5 high school GPA, SAT or ACT. Recommended: essay, minimum 3.4 high school GPA, recommendations, interview. Entrance: moderately difficult. Application deadlines: 8/1, 11/15 for early decision. Notification: continuous, 12/15 for early decision.

Costs Per Year: Application fee: $40. State resident tuition: $4350 full-time, $181 per credit hour part-time. Nonresident tuition: $10,610 full-time, $442 per credit hour part-time. Mandatory fees: $946 full-time, $39 per credit hour part-time. College room and board: $7066. College room only: $4400.

Collegiate Environment: Orientation program. Drama-theater group, choral group, student-run newspaper, radio station. Social organizations: 90 open to all; national fraternities, national sororities, local fraternities, local sororities; 7% of eligible men and 5% of eligible women are members. Most popular organizations: Student Association, honor societies, student media organizations, service/leadership organizations, intramural and recreational sports. Major annual events: concerts, Student Recognition Awards Ceremony, Family Weekend. Student services: legal services, health clinic, personal-psychological counseling, women's center. Campus security: 24-hour emergency response devices and patrols, late night transport-escort service, controlled dormitory access, enhanced 911 system. 2,777 college housing spaces available; 2,373 were occupied in 2003-04. Freshmen guaranteed college housing. On-campus residence required through sophomore year. Option: coed housing available. Feinberg Library with 378,020 books, 1.9 million microform titles, 1,412 serials, 36,749 audiovisual materials, an OPAC, and a Web page. Operations spending for 2004 fiscal year: $2.2 million. 475 computers available on campus for general student use. Computer purchase/lease plans available. A campuswide network can be accessed from student residence rooms and from off campus. Staffed computer lab on campus.

■ **STATE UNIVERSITY OF NEW YORK UPSTATE MEDICAL UNIVERSITY** *J-16*
750 East Adams St.
Syracuse, NY 13210-2334
Tel: (315)464-5540
Free: 800-736-2171
Admissions: (315)464-4816
Fax: (315)464-8823
Web Site: http://www.upstate.edu/
Description: State-supported, upper-level, coed. Part of State University of New York System. Awards bachelor's, master's, doctoral, and first professional degrees and post-master's certificates. Founded 1950. Setting: 25-acre urban campus. Total enrollment: 1,235. Faculty: 686 (477 full-time, 209 part-time). Student-undergrad faculty ratio is 2:1. 410 applied, 40% were admitted. Full-time: 150 students, 63% women, 37% men. Part-time: 93 students, 87% women, 13% men. Students come from 7 states and territories, 9 other countries, 1% from out-of-state, 0.4% Native American, 2% Hispanic, 3% black, 2% Asian American or Pacific Islander, 3% international, 50% live on campus, 45% transferred in. Academic area with the most degrees conferred: health professions and related sciences. Core. Calendar: semesters. Services for LD students, advanced placement, summer session for credit, part-time degree program, internships. Off campus study.
Costs Per Year: Application fee: $40. State resident tuition: $8700 full-time, $181 per credit part-time. Nonresident tuition: $21,200 full-time, $422 per credit part-time. Mandatory fees: $466 full-time. College room only: $3585.
Collegiate Environment: Orientation program. Most popular organizations: Undergraduate Student Council, Diversity in Allied Health. Major annual events: Elizabeth Blackwell Day, Black History Month. Student services: health clinic, personal-psychological counseling. Campus security: late night transport-escort service, controlled dormitory access. 240 college housing spaces available; 50 were occupied in 2003-04. Option: coed housing available. Weiskotten Library with 132,500 books, 1,800 serials, 29,515 audiovisual materials, an OPAC, and a Web page. 130 computers available on campus for general student use. A campuswide network can be accessed from student residence rooms and from off campus. Staffed computer lab on campus.
Community Environment: See Syracuse University.

■ **STONY BROOK UNIVERSITY, STATE UNIVERSITY OF NEW YORK** *B-52*
Nicolls Rd.
Stony Brook, NY 11794
Tel: (631)632-6000
Free: 800-872-7869
Admissions: (631)632-6868
E-mail: admiss@mail.upsa.sunysb.edu
Web Site: http://www.sunysb.edu/
Description: State-supported, university, coed. Part of State University of New York System. Awards bachelor's, master's, doctoral, and first professional degrees and post-master's and first professional certificates. Founded 1957. Setting: 1,100-acre small town campus with easy access to New York City. Endowment: $63.9 million. Research spending for 2004 fiscal year: $141.2 million. Total enrollment: 22,011. Faculty: 1,389 (909 full-time, 480 part-time). Student-undergrad faculty ratio is 16:1. 18,206 applied, 51% were admitted. 33% from top 10% of their high school class, 69% from top quarter, 97% from top half. 10 National Merit Scholars, 17 valedictorians. Full-time: 13,180 students, 49% women, 51% men. Part-time: 1,107 students, 51% women, 49% men. Students come from 42 states and territories, 72 other countries, 4% from out-of-state, 0.1% Native American, 9% Hispanic, 10%

black, 22% Asian American or Pacific Islander, 5% international, 12% 25 or older, 63% live on campus, 11% transferred in. Retention: 87% of full-time freshmen returned the following year. Academic areas with the most degrees conferred: social sciences; health professions and related sciences; psychology. Core. Calendar: semesters. Academic remediation for entering students, ESL program, services for LD students, advanced placement, self-designed majors, freshman honors college, honors program, independent study, distance learning, double major, summer session for credit, part-time degree program, adult/continuing education programs, internships, graduate courses open to undergrads. Off campus study at 17 members of the Long Island Regional Advisory Council for Higher Education and The National Student Exchange. Study abroad program. ROTC: Army (c), Air Force (c).
Entrance Requirements: Options: electronic application, early action, deferred admission, international baccalaureate accepted. Required: essay, high school transcript, minimum 3.0 high school GPA, SAT or ACT. Recommended: 2 recommendations, interview, SAT Subject Tests. Required for some: audition. Entrance: very difficult. Application deadlines: 3/1, 11/15 for early action. Notification: continuous, 1/1 for early action.
Costs Per Year: Application fee: $40. State resident tuition: $4350 full-time, $181 per credit part-time. Nonresident tuition: $10,610 full-time, $442 per credit part-time. Mandatory fees: $1225 full-time, $59.30 per credit part-time. College room and board: $8050. Room and board charges vary according to board plan and housing facility.
Collegiate Environment: Orientation program. Drama-theater group, choral group, student-run newspaper, radio station. Social organizations: 160 open to all; national fraternities, national sororities, local fraternities, local sororities; 2% of eligible men and 3% of eligible women are members. Most popular organizations: Caribbean Student Organization, Muslim Student Association, Commuter Student Association, Student Activities Board. Major annual events: Roth Pond Regatta, Latin Weekend, Black Women's Weekend. Student services: legal services, health clinic, personal-psychological counseling, women's center. Campus security: 24-hour emergency response devices and patrols, late night transport-escort service, controlled dormitory access. 7,913 undergraduates lived in college housing during 2003-04. Freshmen guaranteed college housing. Option: coed housing available. Frank Melville, Jr. Building Library plus 6 others with 2.2 million books, 3.8 million microform titles, 29,091 serials, 37,441 audiovisual materials, an OPAC, and a Web page. Operations spending for 2004 fiscal year: $10.6 million. 2,600 computers available on campus for general student use. A campuswide network can be accessed from student residence rooms and from off campus. Staffed computer lab on campus.

■ **SUFFOLK COUNTY COMMUNITY COLLEGE** *O-45*
533 College Rd.
Selden, NY 11784-2899
Tel: (631)451-4110
Web Site: http://www.sunysuffolk.edu/
Description: State and locally supported, 2-year, coed. Part of State University of New York System. Awards certificates, diplomas, transfer associate, and terminal associate degrees. Founded 1959. Setting: 500-acre small town campus with easy access to New York City. Total enrollment: 20,280. 6,095 applied, 90% were admitted. 2% from top 10% of their high school class, 19% from top quarter, 43% from top half. Full-time: 10,860 students, 54% women, 46% men. Part-time: 9,420 students, 66% women, 34% men. Students come from 14 states and territories, 1% from out-of-state, 0.4% Native American, 10% Hispanic, 7% black, 2% Asian American or Pacific Islander, 1% international, 33% 25 or older, 3% transferred in. Core. Calendar: semesters. Academic remediation for entering students, ESL program, services for LD students, advanced placement, honors program, independent study, distance learning, summer session for credit, part-time degree program, adult/continuing education programs, co-op programs and internships. Off campus study at members of the Long Island Regional Advisory Council for Higher Education. ROTC: Army (c).
Entrance Requirements: Open admission except for some programs. Option: deferred admission. Required: high school transcript. Placement: SAT or ACT recommended; SAT or ACT required for some. Entrance: noncompetitive. Application deadline: Rolling. Notification: continuous. Preference given to county residents.
Collegiate Environment: Orientation program. Drama-theater group, choral group, student-run newspaper. Student services: health clinic, personal-psychological counseling, women's center. Campus security: 24-hour

emergency response devices and patrols. College housing not available. 659 serials, an OPAC, and a Web page.

■ **SULLIVAN COUNTY COMMUNITY COLLEGE** *P-22*
112 College Rd.
Loch Sheldrake, NY 12759
Tel: (845)434-5750
Admissions: (914)434-5750
Fax: (845)434-4806
E-mail: sarir@sullivan.suny.edu
Web Site: http://www.sullivan.suny.edu/
Description: State and locally supported, 2-year, coed. Part of State University of New York System. Awards certificates, transfer associate, and terminal associate degrees. Founded 1962. Setting: 405-acre rural campus. Endowment: $657,688. Educational spending for 2005 fiscal year: $4117 per student. Total enrollment: 1,684. Student-undergrad faculty ratio is 18:1. 2,573 applied, 71% were admitted. Full-time: 1,067 students, 56% women, 44% men. Part-time: 617 students, 67% women, 33% men. Students come from 6 states and territories, 9 other countries, 1% from out-of-state, 0.4% Native American, 10% Hispanic, 18% black, 1% Asian American or Pacific Islander, 1% international, 31% 25 or older, 6% transferred in. Core. Calendar: 4-1-4. Academic remediation for entering students, services for LD students, advanced placement, honors program, distance learning, double major, summer session for credit, part-time degree program, adult/continuing education programs, internships.
Entrance Requirements: Open admission. Options: Common Application, electronic application, early admission, deferred admission. Required: high school transcript. Entrance: noncompetitive. Application deadline: Rolling. Notification: continuous.
Costs Per Year: Application fee: $0. State resident tuition: $3200 full-time, $125 per credit part-time. Nonresident tuition: $6400 full-time, $160 per credit part-time. Mandatory fees: $306 full-time, $12 per credit part-time. College room and board: $6500. College room only: $4080.
Collegiate Environment: Orientation program. Student-run radio station. Social organizations: 15 open to all. Most popular organizations: Science Alliance, Black Student Union, Drama Club, Baking Club, Honor Society. Major annual events: Talent Show, Kite Day. Student services: legal services, health clinic, personal-psychological counseling. Campus security: 24-hour emergency response devices and patrols. Hermann Memorial Library with 65,699 books, 363 microform titles, 400 serials, an OPAC, and a Web page. Operations spending for 2004 fiscal year: $605,516. 205 computers available on campus for general student use. A campuswide network can be accessed. Staffed computer lab on campus.

■ **SWEDISH INSTITUTE, COLLEGE OF HEALTH SCIENCES** *N-34*
226 West 26th St.
New York, NY 10001-6700
Tel: (212)924-5900
Fax: (212)924-7600
E-mail: leslie@swedishinstitute.org
Web Site: http://www.swedishinstitute.org/
Description: Proprietary, comprehensive, coed. Founded 1916. Calendar: trimesters.

■ **SYRACUSE UNIVERSITY** *J-16*
Syracuse, NY 13244
Tel: (315)443-1870
Admissions: (315)443-3611
E-mail: orange@syr.edu
Web Site: http://www.syracuse.edu/
Description: Independent, university, coed. Awards bachelor's, master's, doctoral, and first professional degrees and post-master's certificates. Founded 1870. Setting: 200-acre urban campus. Endowment: $835.9 million. Research spending for 2004 fiscal year: $47.1 million. Total enrollment: 17,266. Faculty: 1,391 (865 full-time, 526 part-time). Student-undergrad faculty ratio is 12:1. 16,260 applied, 65% were admitted. 43% from top 10% of their high school class, 80% from top quarter, 98% from top half. Full-time: 11,374 students, 56% women, 44% men. Part-time: 67 students, 37% women, 63% men. Students come from 52 states and territories, 59 other countries, 60% from out-of-state, 0.3% Native American, 5% Hispanic, 6% black, 6% Asian American or Pacific Islander, 3% international, 2% 25 or older, 73% live on campus, 3% transferred in. Retention: 92% of full-time freshmen returned the following year. Academic areas with the most degrees conferred: business/marketing; visual and performing arts; social sciences.

Core. Calendar: semesters. ESL program, services for LD students, advanced placement, accelerated degree program, self-designed majors, honors program, independent study, distance learning, double major, summer session for credit, part-time degree program, external degree program, adult/continuing education programs, co-op programs and internships, graduate courses open to undergrads. Off campus study at State University of New York College of Environmental Science and Forestry. Study abroad program. ROTC: Army, Air Force.
Entrance Requirements: Options: Common Application, electronic application, early admission, early decision, deferred admission, international baccalaureate accepted. Required: essay, high school transcript, 2 recommendations, interview, SAT or ACT. Required for some: audition for drama and music programs, portfolio for art and architecture programs. Entrance: very difficult. Application deadlines: 1/1, 11/15 for early decision. Notification: 3/15, 12/31 for early decision.
Costs Per Year: Application fee: $60. Comprehensive fee: $38,655 includes full-time tuition ($27,210), mandatory fees ($1075), and college room and board ($10,370). College room only: $5620. Room and board charges vary according to board plan and housing facility. Part-time tuition: $1120 per credit hour.
Collegiate Environment: Orientation program. Drama-theater group, choral group, marching band, student-run newspaper, radio station. Social organizations: 250 open to all; national fraternities, national sororities, local fraternities; 12% of eligible men and 16% of eligible women are members. Most popular organizations: Student Government Association, Programming Council, First Year Players, Student African-American Society. Major annual events: opening weekend activities, Homecoming/Parents' Weekend, Senior Celebration. Student services: legal services, health clinic, personal-psychological counseling, women's center. Campus security: 24-hour emergency response devices and patrols, late night transport-escort service, controlled dormitory access, crime prevention and neighborhood outreach programs. 7,381 college housing spaces available; 7,337 were occupied in 2003-04. Freshmen guaranteed college housing. On-campus residence required through sophomore year. Option: coed housing available. E. S. Bird Library plus 6 others with 3.1 million books, 6 million microform titles, 15,154 serials, 1.2 million audiovisual materials, an OPAC, and a Web page. Operations spending for 2004 fiscal year: $15.8 million. 1,200 computers available on campus for general student use. Computer purchase/lease plans available. A campuswide network can be accessed from student residence rooms and from off campus. Staffed computer lab on campus.
Community Environment: The city of Syracuse (metropolitan area population of 500,000) is the business, educational, and cultural hub of central New York. The city offers professional theater, symphony, opera, and visiting artists and performers. Highlights of the downtown area are the Everson Museum of Art, designed by I.M. Pei, the impressive Civic Center, and the popular Carousel Center shopping Mall. Central New York offers lakes, parks, mountains, and outstanding recreational opportunities. Syracuse is serviced by most major airlines, Amtrak, and Greyhound. Hancock International Airport is only a few miles from downtown and the University, and is served by taxis. The famous Finger Lakes region, offering excellent summer and winter activities, is easily accessible. Diversified industry includes medicine, education, manufacturing, banking, insurance, communications, engineering, and retailing. Part-time employment opportunities are available for students. A transportation network includes bus lines, airlines, and excellent highways and thruways. Parking is excellent in the downtown shopping and theatrical districts. Syracuse is home to 40 museums and galleries, 40 golf courses (more than any other area in the northeast), and has more than 50 parks and several n

■ **TALMUDICAL INSTITUTE OF UPSTATE NEW YORK** *J-11*
769 Park Ave.
Rochester, NY 14607-3046
Tel: (716)473-2810
Fax: (716)442-0417
Web Site: http://www.tiuny.org/
Description: Independent Jewish, 5-year, men only. Awards bachelor's degrees (also offers some graduate courses). Founded 1974. Setting: 1-acre urban campus. Total enrollment: 30. 5 applied, 100% were admitted. Full-time: 22 students. Students come from 6 states and territories, 0% 25 or older. Calendar: semesters. Self-designed majors.
Entrance Requirements: Open admission. Options: Common Application, early admission. Required: high school transcript. Required for some: interview. Entrance: noncompetitive. Application deadline: Rolling. Notification: continuous.

Collegiate Environment: Campus security: student patrols. Option: men-only housing available. Talmudical Library with 3,000 books and 5 serials. 14 computers available on campus for general student use.

■ **TALMUDICAL SEMINARY OHOLEI TORAH** *O-34*
667 Eastern Parkway
Brooklyn, NY 11213-3310
Tel: (718)774-5050
Admissions: (718)363-2034

Description: Independent religious, 4-year, men only. Awards bachelor's degrees. Founded 1956. Setting: urban campus. Total enrollment: 287. 0% 25 or older. Core. Calendar: semesters. Honors program.

Entrance Requirements: Option: deferred admission. Required: high school transcript, interview, Talmudic examination. Recommended: recommendations. Application deadline: 9/1. Notification: continuous.

Collegiate Environment: Student services: personal-psychological counseling. Campus security: late night transport-escort service.

■ **TAYLOR BUSINESS INSTITUTE** *N-34*
269 West 40th St.
New York, NY 10018
Tel: (212)643-2020
Admissions: (212)302-4000

Description: Proprietary, 2-year, coed. Part of Phillips Colleges, Inc. Awards transfer associate and terminal associate degrees. Founded 1961. Setting: urban campus. 20% 25 or older. Academic remediation for entering students, honors program, summer session for credit.

Entrance Requirements: Option: deferred admission. Required: high school transcript, CPAt. Entrance: minimally difficult. Application deadline: Rolling.

Collegiate Environment: Student services: personal-psychological counseling. Campus security: student patrols, 12-hour campus security. College housing not available. 2,873 books and 83 serials. 120 computers available on campus for general student use. Staffed computer lab on campus.

■ **TCI-THE COLLEGE OF TECHNOLOGY** *N-34*
320 West 31st St.
New York, NY 10001-2705
Tel: (212)594-4000
Fax: (212)629-3937
E-mail: admissions@tciedu.com
Web Site: http://www.tciedu.com/

Description: Proprietary, 2-year, coed. Awards certificates, diplomas, transfer associate, and terminal associate degrees. Founded 1909. Setting: urban campus. Total enrollment: 3,842. 2,138 applied, 79% were admitted. Students come from 3 states and territories, 102 other countries, 49% 25 or older. Calendar: semesters. Academic remediation for entering students, ESL program, services for LD students, advanced placement, independent study, double major, summer session for credit, part-time degree program, adult/continuing education programs, co-op programs and internships.

Entrance Requirements: Options: Common Application, deferred admission. Required: essay, high school transcript, interview. Entrance: minimally difficult. Application deadline: Rolling. Notification: continuous.

Collegiate Environment: Orientation program. Drama-theater group, choral group, student-run radio station. Social organizations: 18 open to all; international social clubs; 30% of eligible men and 35% of eligible women are members. Most popular organizations: Dare to Dream, ASHRAE, student government, IEEE. Major annual events: student Christmas parties, basketball games, Commencement. Student services: personal-psychological counseling. Campus security: 24-hour patrols. College housing not available. Technical Career Institutes Library plus 1 other with 8,000 books, 120 serials, and an OPAC. Operations spending for 2004 fiscal year: $88,325. 490 computers available on campus for general student use. A campuswide network can be accessed. Staffed computer lab on campus.

■ **TOMPKINS CORTLAND COMMUNITY COLLEGE** *D-9*
170 North St., PO Box 139
Dryden, NY 13053-0139
Tel: (607)844-8211
Admissions: (607)844-8222
Fax: (607)844-6538
Web Site: http://www.sunytccc.edu/

Description: State and locally supported, 2-year, coed. Part of State University of New York System. Awards certificates, transfer associate, and terminal associate degrees. Founded 1968. Setting: 250-acre rural campus with easy access to Syracuse. Endowment: $2.2 million. Educational spending for 2005 fiscal year: $3971 per student. Total enrollment: 3,174. Student-undergrad faculty ratio is 18:1. Full-time: 2,146 students, 55% women, 45% men. Part-time: 1,028 students, 69% women, 31% men. Students come from 22 states and territories, 43 other countries, 2% from out-of-state, 0.3% Native American, 3% Hispanic, 6% black, 2% Asian American or Pacific Islander, 3% international, 37% 25 or older, 4% live on campus, 10% transferred in. Core. Calendar: semesters. Academic remediation for entering students, ESL program, services for LD students, advanced placement, honors program, summer session for credit, part-time degree program, adult/continuing education programs, co-op programs and internships. Off campus study at State University of New York College at Cortland. ROTC: Army (c).

Entrance Requirements: Open admission except for nursing program. Options: Peterson's Universal Application, early admission, deferred admission. Required: high school transcript. Entrance: noncompetitive. Application deadline: Rolling. Notification: continuous.

Costs Per Year: Application fee: $15. State resident tuition: $3200 full-time, $124 per credit part-time. Nonresident tuition: $6700 full-time, $250 per credit part-time. Mandatory fees: $553 full-time, $15 per credit part-time. College room only: $5400.

Collegiate Environment: Drama-theater group, student-run newspaper. Social organizations: 15 open to all. Most popular organizations: Art Works, Accounting Club, Nurse's Association. Major annual event: Spring May Day. Student services: personal-psychological counseling. Campus security: 24-hour emergency response devices and patrols. 284 college housing spaces available; all were occupied in 2003-04. Option: coed housing available. Gerald A. Barry Memorial Library with 50,630 books, 5,497 microform titles, 489 serials, an OPAC, and a Web page. Operations spending for 2004 fiscal year: $550,435. 350 computers available on campus for general student use. A campuswide network can be accessed from student residence rooms. Staffed computer lab on campus.

■ **TORAH TEMIMAH TALMUDICAL SEMINARY** *O-34*
507 Ocean Parkway
Brooklyn, NY 11218-5913
Tel: (718)853-8500

Description: Independent Jewish, 4-year, men only. Awards bachelor's degrees. Founded 1978. Total enrollment: 248. Calendar: semesters.

■ **TOURO COLLEGE** *N-34*
27-33 West 23rd St.
New York, NY 10010
Tel: (212)463-0400
Fax: (212)779-2344
Web Site: http://www.touro.edu/

Description: Independent, comprehensive, coed. Awards associate, bachelor's, master's, doctoral, and first professional degrees and post-master's certificates. Founded 1971. Setting: urban campus. Total enrollment: 11,447. 71% from top 10% of their high school class, 90% from top quarter, 94% from top half. Full-time: 6,513 students, 70% women, 30% men. Part-time: 880 students, 66% women, 34% men. Students come from 33 states and territories, 30 other countries, 10% from out-of-state, 47% 25 or older. Core. Calendar: semesters. Academic remediation for entering students, ESL program, advanced placement, accelerated degree program, self-designed majors, honors program, independent study, distance learning, double major, summer session for credit, part-time degree program, external degree program, internships, graduate courses open to undergrads. Study abroad program.

Entrance Requirements: Open admission for Associate degree programs. Options: early admission, deferred admission. Required: high school transcript. Recommended: essay, 1 recommendation, SAT or ACT. Required for some: 2 recommendations, interview. Entrance: moderately difficult. Application deadline: Rolling. Notification: continuous.

Collegiate Environment: Orientation program. Drama-theater group, student-run newspaper. Student services: personal-psychological counseling. Campus security: 24-hour emergency response devices and patrols. Touro College Library plus 14 others with 302,700 books, 14,470 microform titles, 6,950 serials, 735 audiovisual materials, an OPAC, and a Web page. 350 computers available on campus for general student use. A campuswide network can be accessed from off-campus. Staffed computer lab on campus.

Community Environment: See New York University

■ **TROCAIRE COLLEGE** *K-7*
360 Choate Ave.
Buffalo, NY 14220-2094

Tel: (716)826-1200
Fax: (716)826-4704
Web Site: http://www.trocaire.edu/
Description: Independent, 2-year, coed. Awards certificates, transfer associate, and terminal associate degrees. Founded 1958. Setting: 1-acre urban campus. Endowment: $4.2 million. Educational spending for 2005 fiscal year: $4564 per student. Total enrollment: 780. 526 applied, 93% were admitted. 4% from top 10% of their high school class, 15% from top quarter, 40% from top half. Students come from 3 states and territories, 4 other countries, 1% from out-of-state, 0.4% Native American, 2% Hispanic, 23% black, 1% Asian American or Pacific Islander, 1% international, 51% 25 or older. Core. Calendar: semesters. Academic remediation for entering students, services for LD students, advanced placement, independent study, summer session for credit, part-time degree program, external degree program, adult/continuing education programs, internships. Off campus study at members of the Western New York Consortium.
Entrance Requirements: Option: deferred admission. Required: high school transcript. Recommended: interview. Required for some: SAT or ACT. Entrance: minimally difficult. Application deadline: Rolling.
Collegiate Environment: Orientation program. Student-run newspaper. Social organizations: 3 open to all; national fraternities. Most popular organizations: Student Government Association, student newspaper, Environmental Club, Ski Club. Major annual event: TGIO Picnic. Student services: health clinic, personal-psychological counseling. Campus security: 24-hour emergency response devices and patrols, late night transport-escort service. The Rachel R. Savarino Library with 15,403 books, 93 serials, an OPAC, and a Web page. Operations spending for 2004 fiscal year: $143,443. 55 computers available on campus for general student use. A campuswide network can be accessed. Staffed computer lab on campus.
Community Environment: Trocaire is located in a residential area of South Buffalo, adjacent to Mercy Hospital and Cazenovia Park, a quiet corner of the city. Three bus lines serve the city and within a short distance is the New York State Thruway and the Buffalo Skyway.

■ **ULSTER COUNTY COMMUNITY COLLEGE** *P-23*
Cottekill Rd.
Stone Ridge, NY 12484
Tel: (914)687-5000
Free: 800-724-0833
Admissions: (914)687-5027
Web Site: http://www.sunyulster.edu/
Description: State and locally supported, 2-year, coed. Part of State University of New York System. Awards certificates, diplomas, transfer associate, and terminal associate degrees. Founded 1961. Setting: 165-acre rural campus. Endowment: $2.4 million. Educational spending for 2005 fiscal year: $4462 per student. Total enrollment: 3,105. 22% from top 10% of their high school class, 34% from top quarter, 63% from top half. Students come from 3 states and territories, 1 other country, 0% from out-of-state, 1% Native American, 5% Hispanic, 4% black, 1% Asian American or Pacific Islander, 1% international, 40% 25 or older. Core. Calendar: semesters. Academic remediation for entering students, ESL program, services for LD students, advanced placement, self-designed majors, honors program, independent study, distance learning, double major, summer session for credit, part-time degree program, adult/continuing education programs, co-op programs and internships. Off campus study at State University of New York College at New Paltz.
Entrance Requirements: Open admission. Options: early admission, deferred admission. Placement: ACT ASSET, ACT COMPASS required for some. Entrance: noncompetitive. Application deadline: Rolling. Notification: continuous.
Collegiate Environment: Drama-theater group, choral group, student-run newspaper, radio station. Social organizations: 15 open to all. Most popular organizations: Ski Club, Basic Club, Biology Club, Nursing Club. Major annual events: Earth Day, annual dance, Welcome Back BBQ. Student services: health clinic, personal-psychological counseling. Campus security: 24-hour emergency response devices and patrols. College housing not available. McDonald Dewitt Library with 70,758 books, 21,144 microform titles, 481 serials, 3,880 audiovisual materials, an OPAC, and a Web page. Operations spending for 2004 fiscal year: $695,752. 250 computers available on campus for general student use. A campuswide network can be accessed. Staffed computer lab on campus.

■ **UNION COLLEGE** *K-24*
807 Union St.
Schenectady, NY 12308-2311

Tel: (518)388-6000
Admissions: (518)388-6112
Fax: (518)388-6986
E-mail: admissions@union.edu
Web Site: http://www.union.edu/
Description: Independent, 4-year, coed. Awards bachelor's degrees. Founded 1795. Setting: 100-acre suburban campus. Endowment: $298.3 million. Research spending for 2004 fiscal year: $2.1 million. Educational spending for 2005 fiscal year: $14,730 per student. Total enrollment: 2,252. Student-undergrad faculty ratio is 11:1. 4,230 applied, 47% were admitted. 62% from top 10% of their high school class, 87% from top quarter, 98% from top half. Full-time: 2,209 students, 45% women, 55% men. Part-time: 43 students, 56% women, 44% men. Students come from 36 states and territories, 18 other countries, 56% from out-of-state, 0.05% Native American, 5% Hispanic, 3% black, 7% Asian American or Pacific Islander, 2% international, 0% 25 or older, 88% live on campus, 1% transferred in. Retention: 91% of full-time freshmen returned the following year. Academic areas with the most degrees conferred: social sciences; engineering; biological/life sciences. Core. Calendar: trimesters. Advanced placement, accelerated degree program, self-designed majors, honors program, independent study, double major, summer session for credit, part-time degree program, co-op programs and internships. Off campus study at Hudson-Mohawk Association of Colleges and Universities. Study abroad program. ROTC: Army (c), Air Force (c).
Entrance Requirements: Options: Peterson's Universal Application, Common Application, electronic application, early admission, early decision, deferred admission, international baccalaureate accepted. Required: essay, high school transcript, 2 recommendations, SAT or ACT, or 2 SAT II Subject Tests. Recommended: interview. Required for some: SAT Subject Tests. Entrance: very difficult. Application deadlines: 1/15, 11/15 for early decision plan 1, 1/15 for early decision plan 2. Notification: 4/1, 12/15 for early decision plan 1, 2/1 for early decision plan 2.
Costs Per Year: Application fee: $50. Comprehensive fee: $41,595.
Collegiate Environment: Orientation program. Drama-theater group, choral group, student-run newspaper, radio station. Social organizations: 95 open to all; national fraternities, national sororities, local fraternities, local sororities, theme houses; 36% of eligible men and 37% of eligible women are members. Most popular organizations: U-Program (Programming Board), student radio station, student newspaper, Concert Committee. Major annual events: Spring Fest, Parents' Weekend, Party in the Garden. Student services: health clinic, personal-psychological counseling, women's center. Campus security: 24-hour emergency response devices and patrols, late night transport-escort service, controlled dormitory access, awareness programs, bicycle patrol, shuttle service. 1,944 college housing spaces available; 1,774 were occupied in 2003-04. Freshmen guaranteed college housing. On-campus residence required through senior year. Option: coed housing available. Schaffer Library with 571,508 books, 893,493 microform titles, 3,485 serials, 9,044 audiovisual materials, an OPAC, and a Web page. Operations spending for 2004 fiscal year: $3.5 million. 480 computers available on campus for general student use. Computer purchase/lease plans available. A campuswide network can be accessed from student residence rooms and from off campus. Staffed computer lab on campus.

■ **UNITED STATES MERCHANT MARINE ACADEMY** *M-36*
300 Steamboat Rd.
Kings Point, NY 11024-1699
Tel: (516)773-5000; (866)546-4778
Admissions: (516)773-5391
Fax: (516)773-5390
Web Site: http://www.usmma.edu/
Description: Federally supported, 4-year, coed. Awards bachelor's degrees. Founded 1943. Setting: 82-acre suburban campus with easy access to New York City. Total enrollment: 1,007. Student-undergrad faculty ratio is 11:1. 1,797 applied, 16% were admitted. 26% from top 10% of their high school class, 64% from top quarter, 96% from top half. 17 class presidents, 7 valedictorians. Full-time: 1,007 students, 14% women, 86% men. Students come from 49 states and territories, 3 other countries, 86% from out-of-state, 0% 25 or older, 100% live on campus, 0% transferred in. Retention: 92% of full-time freshmen returned the following year. Core. Calendar: trimesters. Honors program, internships.
Entrance Requirements: Options: electronic application, early decision. Required: essay, high school transcript, 3 recommendations, SAT or ACT. Recommended: interview. Entrance: very difficult. Application deadlines: 3/1, 11/1 for early decision. Notification: continuous until 4/1, 12/15 for early decision.

Costs Per Year: Application fee: $0.

Collegiate Environment: Orientation program. Drama-theater group, choral group, marching band, student-run newspaper. Social organizations: 45 open to all. Most popular organization: Regimental Band. Major annual events: homecoming, parent's weekend, Graduation/Commencement. Student services: health clinic, personal-psychological counseling. Campus security: 24-hour patrols. 1,007 undergraduates lived in college housing during 2003-04. On-campus residence required through senior year. Option: coed housing available. Schuyler Otis Bland Memorial Library with 185,000 books, 15,269 microform titles, 950 serials, 3,389 audiovisual materials, an OPAC, and a Web page. 1,200 computers available on campus for general student use. Computer purchase/lease plans available. A campuswide network can be accessed from student residence rooms. Staffed computer lab on campus.

■ **UNITED STATES MILITARY ACADEMY** *F-34*

600 Thayer Rd.
West Point, NY 10996
Tel: (845)938-4011
Admissions: (845)938-4041
Fax: (845)938-3021
E-mail: 8dad@sunams.usma.army.mil
Web Site: http://www.usma.edu/

Description: Federally supported, 4-year, coed. Awards bachelor's degrees. Founded 1802. Setting: 16,080-acre small town campus with easy access to New York City. Total enrollment: 4,231. Student-undergrad faculty ratio is 7:1. 10,958 applied, 14% were admitted. 50% from top 10% of their high school class, 81% from top quarter, 97% from top half. 226 National Merit Scholars, 225 class presidents, 85 valedictorians, 446 student government officers. Full-time: 4,231 students, 15% women, 85% men. Students come from 53 states and territories, 25 other countries, 92% from out-of-state, 1% Native American, 7% Hispanic, 6% black, 7% Asian American or Pacific Islander, 1% international, 0% 25 or older, 100% live on campus. Retention: 92% of full-time freshmen returned the following year. Academic areas with the most degrees conferred: engineering; area and ethnic studies; computer and information sciences; foreign languages and literature; law/legal studies; military science and technologies; psychology; history; social sciences; physical sciences; mathematics; science technologies; English; engineering technologies. Core. Calendar: semesters. Academic remediation for entering students, advanced placement, double major, summer session for credit. Off campus study at United States Naval Academy, United States Air Force Academy, United States Coast Guard Academy.

Entrance Requirements: Required: essay, high school transcript, 4 recommendations, medical examination, authorized nomination, SAT or ACT. Recommended: interview. Entrance: most difficult. Application deadline: 2/28. Notification: continuous until 6/1.

Costs Per Year: Application fee: $0.

Collegiate Environment: Drama-theater group, choral group, student-run radio station. Social organizations: 120 open to all. Most popular organizations: Rugby Club, chapel choirs, Big Brothers/Big Sisters, Orienteering Team, Spirit Support Group. Major annual events: Graduation Week, Homecoming/Ring Weekend, Army-Navy Football Week. Student services: legal services, health clinic, personal-psychological counseling. Campus security: 24-hour emergency response devices and patrols, student patrols, late night transport-escort service. 4,400 college housing spaces available; all were occupied in 2003-04. Freshmen guaranteed college housing. On-campus residence required through senior year. Option: coed housing available. United States Military Academy Library plus 1 other with 457,340 books, 1,200 microform titles, 2,220 serials, 8,000 audiovisual materials, an OPAC, and a Web page. 5,500 computers available on campus for general student use. Computer purchase/lease plans available. A campuswide network can be accessed from student residence rooms and from off campus. Staffed computer lab on campus.

■ **UNITED TALMUDICAL SEMINARY** *O-34*

82 Lee Ave.
Brooklyn, NY 11211-7900
Tel: (718)963-9260

Description: Independent Jewish, comprehensive, men only. Awards bachelor's and master's degrees. Founded 1949. Total enrollment: 1,670. Calendar: semesters.

■ **UNIVERSITY AT ALBANY, STATE UNIVERSITY OF NEW YORK** *L-25*

1400 Washington Ave.
Albany, NY 12222-0001

Tel: (518)442-3300
Admissions: (518)442-5435
E-mail: ugadmissions@albany.edu
Web Site: http://www.albany.edu/

Description: State-supported, university, coed. Part of State University of New York System. Awards bachelor's, master's, and doctoral degrees and post-master's certificates. Founded 1844. Setting: 560-acre suburban campus. Endowment: $20.2 million. Total enrollment: 17,040. Faculty: 1,161 (631 full-time, 530 part-time). Student-undergrad faculty ratio is 19:1. 16,725 applied, 63% were admitted. 15% from top 10% of their high school class, 47% from top quarter, 88% from top half. 2 National Merit Scholars, 42 class presidents, 15 valedictorians, 357 student government officers. Full-time: 11,211 students, 50% women, 50% men. Part-time: 802 students, 52% women, 48% men. Students come from 38 states and territories, 51 other countries, 6% from out-of-state, 0.2% Native American, 7% Hispanic, 8% black, 6% Asian American or Pacific Islander, 2% international, 7% 25 or older, 58% live on campus, 10% transferred in. Retention: 85% of full-time freshmen returned the following year. Academic areas with the most degrees conferred: social sciences; business/marketing; psychology. Core. Calendar: semesters. ESL program, services for LD students, advanced placement, self-designed majors, freshman honors college, honors program, independent study, double major, summer session for credit, internships, graduate courses open to undergrads. Off campus study at New York State Visiting Student Program, Hudson-Mohawk Association of Colleges and Universities. Study abroad program. ROTC: Army, Air Force (c).

Entrance Requirements: Options: Common Application, electronic application, early admission, early action, deferred admission, international baccalaureate accepted. Required: high school transcript, SAT or ACT. Recommended: essay, recommendations. Required for some: portfolio, audition. Entrance: moderately difficult. Application deadlines: 3/1, 11/15 for early action. Notification: continuous, 1/1 for early action.

Costs Per Year: Application fee: $40. State resident tuition: $4350 full-time, $181 per credit part-time. Nonresident tuition: $10,610 full-time, $442 per credit part-time. Mandatory fees: $1537 full-time. Part-time tuition varies according to course load. College room and board: $8050. College room only: $4834. Room and board charges vary according to board plan and housing facility.

Collegiate Environment: Orientation program. Drama-theater group, choral group, student-run newspaper, radio station. Social organizations: 160 open to all; national fraternities, national sororities, local fraternities, local sororities; 2% of eligible men and 5% of eligible women are members. Most popular organizations: intramural athletics, cultural organizations, political organizations, community service. Major annual events: Fountain Day, Purple Growl, Cultural Carnival. Student services: legal services, health clinic, personal-psychological counseling, Disabled Student Services. Campus security: 24-hour emergency response devices and patrols, late night transport-escort service, controlled dormitory access, crime prevention unit. On-campus residence required through sophomore year. Options: coed, men-only, women-only housing available. University Library plus 2 others with 2.1 million books, 2.9 million microform titles, 39,240 serials, 10,115 audiovisual materials, an OPAC, and a Web page. Operations spending for 2004 fiscal year: $12.2 million. 500 computers available on campus for general student use. A campuswide network can be accessed from student residence rooms and from off campus. Staffed computer lab on campus.

■ **UNIVERSITY OF ROCHESTER** *J-11*

Wilson Blvd.
Rochester, NY 14627-0250
Tel: (585)275-2121; 888-822-2256
Admissions: (585)275-3221
Fax: (585)273-1118
E-mail: admit@admissions.rochester.edu
Web Site: http://www.rochester.edu/

Description: Independent, university, coed. Awards bachelor's, master's, doctoral, and first professional degrees and post-master's and first professional certificates. Founded 1850. Setting: 534-acre suburban campus. Total enrollment: 8,588. Faculty: 768 (505 full-time, 263 part-time). 11,272 applied, 48% were admitted. 76% from top 10% of their high school class, 96% from top quarter, 98% from top half. Full-time: 4,435 students, 48% women, 52% men. Part-time: 261 students, 79% women, 21% men. Students come from 52 states and territories, 36 other countries, 0% from out-of-state, 0.2% Native American, 4% Hispanic, 5% black, 10% Asian American or Pacific Islander, 4% international, 87% live on campus, 2% transferred in. Retention: 95% of full-time freshmen returned the following year. Academic areas with the most degrees conferred: social sciences; psychology; biological/life sciences. Calendar: semesters plus optional summer term. ESL program, services for LD students, advanced placement, self-designed majors, honors program, independent study, double major, summer session for credit, part-time degree program, internships, graduate courses open to undergrads. Off campus study at Rochester Area Colleges. Study abroad program. ROTC: Naval, Air Force (c).

Entrance Requirements: Options: Peterson's Universal Application, Common Application, electronic application, early admission, early decision, deferred admission, international baccalaureate accepted. Required: essay, high school transcript, 1 recommendation, SAT or ACT. Recommended: 2 recommendations, interview, SAT Subject Tests. Required for some: audition, portfolio. Entrance: very difficult. Application deadline: 1/15. Notification: 4/1, 12/15 for early decision plan 1.

Costs Per Year: Application fee: $50. Comprehensive fee: $41,485 includes full-time tuition ($30,540), mandatory fees ($757), and college room and board ($10,188). College room only: $5710. Room and board charges vary according to board plan. Part-time tuition: $534 per credit hour. Part-time tuition varies according to course load.

Collegiate Environment: Orientation program. Drama-theater group, choral group, student-run newspaper, radio station. Social organizations: 200 open to all; national fraternities, national sororities; 25% of eligible men and 20% of eligible women are members. Most popular organizations: student radio station, cinema group, Debate Union, Campus Board Program. Major annual events: Yellowjacket Day, Dandelion Day, Winter Carnival. Student services: legal services, health clinic, personal-psychological counseling, women's center. Campus security: 24-hour emergency response devices and patrols, late night transport-escort service, controlled dormitory access. 3,631 college housing spaces available; 3,550 were occupied in 2003-04. Freshmen guaranteed college housing. On-campus residence required through sophomore year. Options: coed, men-only, women-only housing available. Rush Rhees Library plus 5 others with 3 million books, 4.1 million microform titles, 11,254 serials, 78,600 audiovisual materials, an OPAC, and a Web page. 260 computers available on campus for general student use. A campuswide network can be accessed from student residence rooms and from off campus. Staffed computer lab on campus.

Community Environment: With Lake Ontario on its northern border and the scenic Finger Lakes on the south, the Rochester community of about one million people is located in an attractive setting. It offers a wide range of cultural and recreational opportunities-from concerts by the Rochester Philharmonic Orchestra and Eastman School ensembles, performances by resident professional theater companies, and an unusual concentration of first-class museums (including the University's own Memorial Art Gallery), to professional baseball and ice hockey and nearby opportunities for recreational canoeing, sculling, ice-skating, and skiing.

■ **U.T.A. MESIVTA OF KIRYAS JOEL** *G-32*
33 Forest Rd., Ste. 101
Monroe, NY 10950
Tel: (845)873-9901
Fax: (845)782-3620
Description: Independent Jewish, 4-year.

■ **UTICA COLLEGE** *J-19*
1600 Burrstone Rd.
Utica, NY 13502-4892
Tel: (315)792-3111
Free: 800-782-8884
Admissions: (315)792-3006
Fax: (315)792-3003
Web Site: http://www.utica.edu/
Description: Independent, comprehensive, coed. Awards bachelor's, master's, and first professional degrees. Founded 1946. Setting: 128-acre suburban campus. Endowment: $15.7 million. Research spending for 2004 fiscal year: $203,868. Educational spending for 2005 fiscal year: $6306 per student. Total enrollment: 2,888. Faculty: 286 (119 full-time, 167 part-time). Student-undergrad faculty ratio is 17:1. 2,497 applied, 79% were admitted. 8% from top 10% of their high school class, 28% from top quarter, 66% from top half. 1 class president, 24 student government officers. Full-time: 2,030 students, 58% women, 42% men. Part-time: 383 students, 62% women, 38% men. Students come from 37 states and territories, 15 other countries, 15% from out-of-state, 1% Native American, 3% Hispanic, 9% black, 2% Asian American or Pacific Islander, 1% international, 16% 25 or older, 48% live on campus, 10% transferred in. Retention: 70% of full-time freshmen

returned the following year. Academic areas with the most degrees conferred: security and protective services; business/marketing; health professions and related sciences. Core. Calendar: semesters. Academic remediation for entering students, services for LD students, advanced placement, accelerated degree program, honors program, independent study, distance learning, double major, summer session for credit, part-time degree program, adult/continuing education programs, co-op programs and internships, graduate courses open to undergrads. Off campus study at members of the New York State Visiting Student Program. Study abroad program. ROTC: Army, Air Force (c).

Entrance Requirements: Options: Peterson's Universal Application, Common Application, electronic application, early admission, deferred admission, international baccalaureate accepted. Required: essay, high school transcript, minimum 2.0 high school GPA, 1 recommendation. Recommended: interview, SAT or ACT. Required for some: minimum 3.0 high school GPA, SAT or ACT. Entrance: moderately difficult. Application deadlines: Rolling, Rolling for nonresidents. Notification: 9/1, 9/1 for nonresidents.

Costs Per Year: Application fee: $40. Comprehensive fee: $31,396 includes full-time tuition ($22,030), mandatory fees ($310), and college room and board ($9056). College room only: $4750. Full-time tuition and fees vary according to class time and course load. Room and board charges vary according to board plan and housing facility. Part-time tuition: $750 per credit hour. Part-time mandatory fees: $50 per term. Part-time tuition and fees vary according to class time and course load.

Collegiate Environment: Orientation program. Drama-theater group, choral group, student-run newspaper, radio station. Social organizations: 67 open to all; national fraternities, national sororities, local fraternities, local sororities; 1% of eligible men and 1% of eligible women are members. Most popular organizations: honor association, Double Up, Outing Club, Student Senate, CJ Student Association. Major annual events: Air Band, Spring Fling, faculty-served dinner. Student services: health clinic, personal-psychological counseling, women's center. Campus security: 24-hour emergency response devices and patrols, late night transport-escort service, controlled dormitory access. College housing designed to accommodate 935 students; 967 undergraduates lived in college housing during 2003-04. Freshmen guaranteed college housing. On-campus residence required through sophomore year. Option: coed housing available. Frank E. Gannett Memorial Library with 183,559 books, 56,862 microform titles, 1,279 serials, 2,042 audiovisual materials, an OPAC, and a Web page. Operations spending for 2004 fiscal year: $1 million. 140 computers available on campus for general student use. A campuswide network can be accessed from student residence rooms. Staffed computer lab on campus.

Community Environment: Utica is an area rich in the history of the Iroquois Confederacy, the French and Indian Wars, the American Revolution, the great migration to the Midwest and the western expansion of American commerce via the Erie Canal. Historic treasures in the area include the Oriskany Battlefield, Revolutionary Fort Stanwix (restored as a national monument) in Rome, and the homes of Revolutionary War heroes General Nicholas Herkimer and Major General Friedrich Wilhelm Baron von Steuben. Within an hour's drive of Utica are Johnson Hall, home of Sir William Johnson, colonial superintendent of Indian Affairs, in Johnstown; the Mansion House of the Oneida Community in Oneida; and Cooperstown, birthplace of James Fenimore Cooper, site of the Baseball Museum and Hall of Fame, the Farmer's Museum, and the headquarters of the New York State Historical Association. Utica's cultural assets include Munson-Williams-Proctor Institute and School of Art, one of the finest small art institutions in the country; the Oneida Historical Society; the Utica Civic Symphony; the Broadway Theatre League; the Players Theater Company; the Great Artists Concert series; and the Utica Public Library.

■ **UTICA SCHOOL OF COMMERCE** *J-19*
201 Bleecker St.
Utica, NY 13501-2280
Tel: (315)733-2307
Free: 800-321-4USC
Admissions: (315)733-2300
Fax: (315)733-9281
Web Site: http://www.uscny.edu/
Description: Proprietary, 2-year, coed. Awards certificates, diplomas, transfer associate, and terminal associate degrees. Founded 1896. Setting: 2-acre urban campus. Endowment: $21,000. Total enrollment: 400. 6% from top 10% of their high school class, 37% from top quarter, 57% from top half. 0% from out-of-state, 57% 25 or older. Core. Academic remediation for

entering students, services for LD students, advanced placement, accelerated degree program, honors program, independent study, summer session for credit, part-time degree program, adult/continuing education programs, internships.

Entrance Requirements: Open admission. Options: electronic application, early admission, deferred admission. Required: high school transcript, interview. Recommended: essay, recommendations. Entrance: noncompetitive. Application deadline: Rolling.

Collegiate Environment: Orientation program. Student-run newspaper. Major annual events: Spring Fling, Winter Semi-Formal, Fall Picnic. Campus security: security during class hours. College housing not available. Utica School of Commerce Library plus 3 others with 2,000 books, 135 serials, an OPAC, and a Web page. Operations spending for 2004 fiscal year: $24,000. 212 computers available on campus for general student use. A campuswide network can be accessed. Staffed computer lab on campus.

■ **VASSAR COLLEGE** *P-24*
124 Raymond Ave.
Poughkeepsie, NY 12604
Tel: (845)437-7000
Free: 800-827-7270
Admissions: (845)437-7300
Fax: (845)437-7063
E-mail: admissions@vassar.edu
Web Site: http://www.vassar.edu/
Description: Independent, 4-year, coed. Awards bachelor's and master's degrees. Founded 1861. Setting: 1,000-acre suburban campus with easy access to New York City. Endowment: $671.4 million. Research spending for 2004 fiscal year: $3.6 million. Educational spending for 2005 fiscal year: $21,225 per student. Total enrollment: 2,378. Faculty: 306 (277 full-time, 29 part-time). Student-undergrad faculty ratio is 8:1. 6,314 applied, 29% were admitted. 67% from top 10% of their high school class, 94% from top quarter, 100% from top half. 28 class presidents, 30 valedictorians. Full-time: 2,326 students, 59% women, 41% men. Part-time: 52 students, 73% women, 27% men. Students come from 53 states and territories, 58 other countries, 73% from out-of-state, 0.3% Native American, 6% Hispanic, 5% black, 9% Asian American or Pacific Islander, 5% international, 1% 25 or older, 95% live on campus, 1% transferred in. Retention: 96% of full-time freshmen returned the following year. Academic areas with the most degrees conferred: social sciences; visual and performing arts; English. Calendar: semesters. Services for LD students, advanced placement, self-designed majors, independent study, double major, part-time degree program, co-op programs and internships. Off campus study at Howard University, Fisk University, Hampton University, Spelman College, Morehouse College, members of the Twelve College Exchange Program, Bard College. Study abroad program.
Entrance Requirements: Options: Common Application, electronic application, early decision, deferred admission, international baccalaureate accepted. Required: essay, high school transcript, 2 recommendations, SAT and SAT Subject Tests or ACT. Entrance: very difficult. Application deadlines: 1/1, 11/15 for early decision plan 1, 1/1 for early decision plan 2. Notification: 4/1, 12/15 for early decision plan 1, 2/1 for early decision plan 2.
Costs Per Year: Application fee: $60. Comprehensive fee: $41,700 includes full-time tuition ($33,310), mandatory fees ($490), and college room and board ($7900). College room only: $4190. Room and board charges vary according to board plan and housing facility. Part-time tuition: $3920 per course. Part-time mandatory fees: $240 per year. Part-time tuition and fees vary according to course load.
Collegiate Environment: Orientation program. Drama-theater group, choral group, student-run newspaper, radio station. Social organizations: 85 open to all. Most popular organizations: Student Association, Black Students Union, VICE (programming social events), Student Activists' Union, Poder Latino. Major annual events: Spring and Fall Convocation, Founders' Day, All-Parents' Weekend. Student services: health clinic, personal-psychological counseling, women's center. Campus security: 24-hour emergency response devices and patrols, student patrols, late night transport-escort service, controlled dormitory access. 2,480 college housing spaces available; 2,340 were occupied in 2003-04. Freshmen guaranteed college housing. On-campus residence required in freshman year. Options: coed, women-only housing available. Vassar College Libraries plus 1 other with 878,177 books, 610,130 microform titles, 5,302 serials, 22,345 audiovisual materials, an OPAC, and a Web page. Operations spending for 2004 fiscal year: $5.5 million. 300 computers available on campus for general student use. Computer purchase/lease plans available. A campuswide network can be accessed from student residence rooms and from off campus. Staffed computer lab on campus.

Community Environment: Poughkeepsie, area population 85,000, originally settled by the Dutch, was the capital of New York from 1778 to 1783. Situated on a plateau above the Hudson River, Poughkeepsie is about 75 miles north of New York City and is easily accessible by car, train, bus, and air. Community services include a library, YMCA, YWCA, churches, art galleries, the Mid-Hudson Civic Center (with an ice-skating rink), the Bardavon Opera House (1869), and a Jewish Community Center. The area offers facilities for recreation and places of historic interest such as the Franklin D. Roosevelt National Historic Site in Hyde Park, and the Vanderbilt Mansion. Industries within the area include IBM and the Fairchild Corporation.

■ **VAUGHN COLLEGE OF AERONAUTICS AND TECHNOLOGY**
8601 23rd Ave.
Flushing, NY 11369-1037
Tel: (718)429-6600
Fax: (718)429-0256
E-mail: pro@aero.edu
Web Site: http://www.vaughn.edu/
Description: Independent, 4-year, coed. Awards associate and bachelor's degrees. Founded 1932. Setting: 6-acre urban campus. Endowment: $22 million. Educational spending for 2005 fiscal year: $3900 per student. Total enrollment: 1,126. Student-undergrad faculty ratio is 11:1. 328 applied, 95% were admitted. 2 National Merit Scholars, 3 class presidents, 8 student government officers. Full-time: 842 students, 13% women, 87% men. Part-time: 284 students, 11% women, 89% men. Students come from 10 states and territories, 15 other countries, 6% from out-of-state, 0% Native American, 35% Hispanic, 19% black, 11% Asian American or Pacific Islander, 4% international, 28% 25 or older, 6% transferred in. Retention: 73% of full-time freshmen returned the following year. Academic areas with the most degrees conferred: mechanic and repair technologies; engineering technologies; transportation and materials moving. Core. Calendar: semesters. Academic remediation for entering students, services for LD students, advanced placement, independent study, distance learning, summer session for credit, part-time degree program, adult/continuing education programs, co-op programs and internships. ROTC: Army (c), Air Force (c).
Entrance Requirements: Open admission for all Associate degree programs; selective for certain Bachelor's degree programs. Options: Peterson's Universal Application, deferred admission. Required: essay, high school transcript, SAT or ACT. Recommended: interview. Required for some: interview. Entrance: minimally difficult. Application deadline: Rolling.
Costs Per Year: Application fee: $45. Tuition: $13,400 full-time, $450 per credit part-time. Mandatory fees: $280 full-time. Full-time tuition and fees vary according to course load, degree level, and program.
Collegiate Environment: Orientation program. Student-run newspaper. Social organizations: 10 open to all. Most popular organizations: Hispanic Society of Aeronautical Engineers, student government, Women in Aviation International, Society of Automotive Engineers, American Association of Airport Executives. Major annual events: Winter Fest, Spring Fest. Student services: personal-psychological counseling. Campus security: 24-hour emergency response devices and patrols. College housing not available. George A. Vaughn Memorial Library with 62,000 books, 400 serials, 1,849 audiovisual materials, an OPAC, and a Web page. Operations spending for 2004 fiscal year: $166,000. 85 computers available on campus for general student use. A campuswide network can be accessed from off-campus. Staffed computer lab on campus.
Community Environment: See Queens College of the City University of New York.

■ **VILLA MARIA COLLEGE OF BUFFALO** *K-7*
240 Pine Ridge Rd.
Buffalo, NY 14225-3999
Tel: (716)896-0700
Fax: (716)896-0705
Web Site: http://www.villa.edu/
Description: Independent, primarily 2-year, coed, affiliated with Roman Catholic Church. Awards transfer associate, terminal associate, and bachelor's degrees. Founded 1960. Setting: 9-acre suburban campus. Endowment: $386,940. Research spending for 2004 fiscal year: $27,690. Educational spending for 2005 fiscal year: $6500 per student. Total enrollment: 502. Student-undergrad faculty ratio is 11:1. 414 applied, 78% were admitted. 1% from top 10% of their high school class, 9% from top quarter, 45% from top half. Full-time: 396 students, 72% women, 28% men. Part-time: 106 students, 81% women, 19% men. Students come from 3 states

and territories, 5 other countries, 1% from out-of-state, 1% Native American, 1% Hispanic, 30% black, 1% Asian American or Pacific Islander, 0% international, 40% 25 or older, 11% transferred in. Core. Calendar: semesters. Academic remediation for entering students, services for LD students, advanced placement, independent study, double major, summer session for credit, part-time degree program, co-op programs and internships. Off campus study at members of the Western New York Consortium. Study abroad program.

Entrance Requirements: Options: electronic application, deferred admission. Required: essay, high school transcript, interview, writing sample. Entrance: minimally difficult. Application deadline: Rolling. Notification: continuous.

Costs Per Year: Tuition: $11,280 full-time, $420 per credit hour part-time. Mandatory fees: $430 full-time.

Collegiate Environment: Orientation program. Choral group, student-run newspaper. Social organizations: 19 open to all. Most popular organizations: Design and Beyond, Teachers Love Children, Multicultural Club, Phi Theta Kappa, Helping Adults New Dreams Succeed. Major annual events: Spring Arts Festival, formal dinner dance. Student services: health clinic, personal-psychological counseling. Campus security: late night transport-escort service. Villa Maria College Library with 37,000 books, 17,300 microform titles, 130 serials, 3,500 audiovisual materials, an OPAC, and a Web page. Operations spending for 2004 fiscal year: $122,450. 127 computers available on campus for general student use. A campuswide network can be accessed. Staffed computer lab on campus.

Community Environment: See Canisius College.

■ **WAGNER COLLEGE** *P-32*
1 Campus Rd.
Staten Island, NY 10301-4495
Tel: (718)390-3100
Free: 800-221-1010
Admissions: (718)390-3411
Fax: (718)390-3105
E-mail: adm@wagner.edu
Web Site: http://www.wagner.edu/

Description: Independent, comprehensive, coed. Awards bachelor's and master's degrees and post-master's certificates. Founded 1883. Setting: 105-acre urban campus with easy access to New York City. Endowment: $25.1 million. Educational spending for 2005 fiscal year: $6793 per student. Total enrollment: 2,287. Faculty: 229 (99 full-time, 130 part-time). Student-undergrad faculty ratio is 15:1. 2,858 applied, 61% were admitted. 17% from top 10% of their high school class, 64% from top quarter, 92% from top half. 24 class presidents, 7 valedictorians, 63 student government officers. Full-time: 1,892 students, 63% women, 37% men. Part-time: 70 students, 64% women, 36% men. Students come from 38 states and territories, 14 other countries, 56% from out-of-state, 0.3% Native American, 5% Hispanic, 5% black, 2% Asian American or Pacific Islander, 1% international, 2% 25 or older, 70% live on campus, 1% transferred in. Retention: 89% of full-time freshmen returned the following year. Academic areas with the most degrees conferred: business/marketing; visual and performing arts; health professions and related sciences. Core. Calendar: semesters. Services for LD students, honors program, double major, summer session for credit, part-time degree program, internships, graduate courses open to undergrads. Off campus study at California Lutheran University. Study abroad program.

Entrance Requirements: Options: Peterson's Universal Application, Common Application, electronic application, early admission, early decision, deferred admission, international baccalaureate accepted. Required: essay, high school transcript, minimum 2.7 high school GPA, 2 recommendations, SAT or ACT. Recommended: minimum 3.0 high school GPA, interview. Required for some: interview. Entrance: moderately difficult. Application deadlines: 2/15, 1/1 for early decision. Notification: 3/1, 2/1 for early decision.

Costs Per Year: Application fee: $50. Comprehensive fee: $33,300 includes full-time tuition ($25,350) and college room and board ($7950). Part-time tuition: $845 per credit hour.

Collegiate Environment: Orientation program. Drama-theater group, choral group, student-run newspaper, radio station. Social organizations: 66 open to all; national fraternities, national sororities, local fraternities, local sororities; 11% of eligible men and 9% of eligible women are members. Most popular organizations: Student Government Association, Student Activities Board, Wagner College Theatre, Wagner College Choir, student newspaper. Major annual events: homecoming, Songfest, Spring Fling. Student services: health clinic, personal-psychological counseling. Campus security: 24-hour

emergency response devices and patrols, late night transport-escort service, controlled dormitory access. 1,300 college housing spaces available; 1,280 were occupied in 2003-04. Freshmen guaranteed college housing. Option: coed housing available. August Horrmann Library with 310,000 books, 187 microform titles, 1,000 serials, 1,616 audiovisual materials, and a Web page. 150 computers available on campus for general student use. A campuswide network can be accessed from student residence rooms and from off campus. Staffed computer lab on campus.

■ **WEBB INSTITUTE** *M-37*
Crescent Beach Rd.
Glen Cove, NY 11542-1398
Tel: (516)671-2213
Fax: (516)674-9838
E-mail: admissions@webb-institute.edu
Web Site: http://www.webb-institute.edu/

Description: Independent, 4-year, coed. Awards bachelor's degrees. Founded 1889. Setting: 26-acre suburban campus with easy access to New York City. Endowment: $51.1 million. Research spending for 2004 fiscal year: $27,700. Educational spending for 2005 fiscal year: $27,099 per student. Total enrollment: 80. Student-undergrad faculty ratio is 8:1. 103 applied, 30% were admitted. 70% from top 10% of their high school class, 100% from top quarter. 1 valedictorian. Full-time: 80 students, 20% women, 80% men. Students come from 19 states and territories, 76% from out-of-state, 0% Native American, 1% Hispanic, 1% black, 3% Asian American or Pacific Islander, 0% international, 1% 25 or older, 100% live on campus, 0% transferred in. Retention: 92% of full-time freshmen returned the following year. Academic area with the most degrees conferred: engineering. Core. Calendar: semesters. Independent study, double major, co-op programs and internships. Off campus study at Hofstra University.

Entrance Requirements: Option: early decision. Required: high school transcript, minimum 3.5 high school GPA, 2 recommendations, interview, proof of US citizenship or permanent residency status, SAT, SAT Subject Tests, SAT Subject Tests in math and either physics or chemistry. Entrance: most difficult. Application deadlines: 2/15, 10/15 for early decision. Notification: continuous until 4/30, 12/15 for early decision.

Costs Per Year: Application fee: $25. Comprehensive fee: $8340 includes full-time tuition ($0) and college room and board ($8340).

Collegiate Environment: Orientation program. Drama-theater group, choral group. Social organizations: The Webb Women. Most popular organizations: Student Organization, Society of Naval Architects and Marine Engineers, American Society of Naval Engineers, Society of Women Engineers. Major annual events: Family Weekend, Webbstock, Casino Night. Student services: personal-psychological counseling. Campus security: 24-hour emergency response devices and patrols, controlled dormitory access. 110 college housing spaces available; 100 were occupied in 2003-04. Freshmen guaranteed college housing. On-campus residence required through senior year. Options: coed, men-only, women-only housing available. Livingston Library with 53,319 books, 1,656 microform titles, 270 serials, 885 audiovisual materials, an OPAC, and a Web page. Operations spending for 2004 fiscal year: $197,579. 76 computers available on campus for general student use. A campuswide network can be accessed from student residence rooms and from off campus.

Community Environment: Population 27,000, Glen Cove lies 22 miles from New York City on Long Island's historic North Shore. The Long Island Railroad furnishes commuter service to New York City. The area has excellent boating, swimming, horseback riding, and fishing facilities. Part-time employment is available.

■ **WELLS COLLEGE** *K-8*
170 Main St.
Aurora, NY 13026
Tel: (315)364-3266
Free: 800-952-9355
Admissions: (315)364-3264
Fax: (315)364-3227
E-mail: admissions@wells.edu
Web Site: http://www.wells.edu/

Description: Independent, 4-year, coed. Awards bachelor's degrees. Founded 1868. Setting: 365-acre rural campus with easy access to Syracuse. Endowment: $53.7 million. Research spending for 2004 fiscal year: $81,727. Educational spending for 2005 fiscal year: $12,256 per student. Total enrollment: 417. Student-undergrad faculty ratio is 8:1. 1,036 applied, 65% were admitted. 25% from top 10% of their high school class,

64% from top quarter, 93% from top half. 1 valedictorian. Full-time: 405 students, 91% women, 9% men. Part-time: 12 students, 92% women, 8% men. Students come from 31 states and territories, 5 other countries, 30% from out-of-state, 0.2% Native American, 4% Hispanic, 7% black, 3% Asian American or Pacific Islander, 2% international, 14% 25 or older, 80% live on campus, 6% transferred in. Retention: 71% of full-time freshmen returned the following year. Academic areas with the most degrees conferred: psychology; visual and performing arts; English. Core. Calendar: semesters. ESL program, services for LD students, advanced placement, accelerated degree program, self-designed majors, independent study, double major, part-time degree program, adult/continuing education programs, internships. Off campus study at members of the Association of Colleges and Universities of the State of New York, Cornell University, American University, Ithaca College. Study abroad program. ROTC: Air Force (c).

Entrance Requirements: Options: Peterson's Universal Application, Common Application, electronic application, early admission, early decision, early action, deferred admission, international baccalaureate accepted. Required: essay, high school transcript, 2 recommendations, SAT or ACT. Recommended: interview. Entrance: moderately difficult. Application deadlines: 3/1, 12/15 for early decision, 12/15 for early action. Notification: 4/1, 1/15 for early decision, 2/1 for early action.

Costs Per Year: Application fee: $40. Comprehensive fee: $24,180 includes full-time tuition ($15,580), mandatory fees ($1100), and college room and board ($7500). College room only: $3750.

Collegiate Environment: Orientation program. Drama-theater group, choral group, student-run newspaper. Social organizations: 35 open to all. Most popular organizations: creative and performing arts groups, POWER, Amnesty International, Athletic Association, choral groups. Major annual events: Spring Weekend, Fall Semi-Formal, Odd-Even Game/Weekend. Student services: health clinic, personal-psychological counseling, women's center. Campus security: 24-hour emergency response devices and patrols, late night transport-escort service, controlled dormitory access. 465 college housing spaces available; 302 were occupied in 2003-04. Freshmen guaranteed college housing. On-campus residence required through senior year. Options: coed, women-only housing available. Louis Jefferson Long Library with 253,458 books, 14,387 microform titles, 411 serials, 1,016 audiovisual materials, an OPAC, and a Web page. Operations spending for 2004 fiscal year: $215,819. 89 computers available on campus for general student use. A campuswide network can be accessed from student residence rooms and from off campus. Staffed computer lab on campus.

Community Environment: The college has always shared a close relationship with the small, picturesque village of Aurora, New York; which is noted on the National Historic Registry. Aurora is also home to the highly acclaimed Aurora Inn and the nationally known company Mackenzie-Childs.

■ **WESTCHESTER COMMUNITY COLLEGE** *J-36*
75 Grasslands Rd.
Valhalla, NY 10595-1698
Tel: (914)785-6600
Admissions: (914)606-6735
Web Site: http://www.sunywcc.edu/
Description: State and locally supported, 2-year, coed. Part of State University of New York System. Awards certificates, transfer associate, and terminal associate degrees. Founded 1946. Setting: 218-acre suburban campus with easy access to New York City. Endowment: $8.5 million. Educational spending for 2005 fiscal year: $4352 per student. Total enrollment: 11,564. Student-undergrad faculty ratio is 16:1. Students come from 14 states and territories, 70 other countries, 0.1% from out-of-state, 1% Native American, 18% Hispanic, 19% black, 5% Asian American or Pacific Islander, 2% international, 40% 25 or older. Core. Calendar: semesters. Academic remediation for entering students, ESL program, services for LD students, self-designed majors, honors program, independent study, distance learning, double major, summer session for credit, part-time degree program, adult/continuing education programs, co-op programs and internships. Off campus study. Study abroad program.
Entrance Requirements: Open admission except for nursing, radiological technology, respiratory care programs. Options: electronic application, early admission. Required: high school transcript. Recommended: interview. Entrance: noncompetitive. Application deadline: Rolling. Notification: continuous until 2/2.
Costs Per Year: Application fee: $25. State resident tuition: $3350 full-time, $140 per credit part-time. Nonresident tuition: $8376 full-time, $350 per credit part-time.
Collegiate Environment: Orientation program. Drama-theater group, choral group, student-run newspaper, radio station. Social organizations: 50 open

to all. Most popular organizations: Student Senate, African Culture Club, Italian Club, International Friendship Club, Alpha Beta Gamma. Major annual events: Graduation, end of the year BBQ, Spring Club Days. Student services: health clinic, personal-psychological counseling, women's center. Campus security: 24-hour emergency response devices and patrols, late night transport-escort service. College housing not available. Harold L. Drimmer Library with 96,419 books, 34,868 microform titles, 531 serials, 5,163 audiovisual materials, an OPAC, and a Web page. Operations spending for 2004 fiscal year: $1.8 million. 1,200 computers available on campus for general student use. A campuswide network can be accessed. Staffed computer lab on campus.

■ **WOOD TOBE-COBURN SCHOOL** *N-34*
8 East 40th St.
New York, NY 10016
Tel: (212)686-9040
Fax: (212)686-9171
Web Site: http://www.woodtobecoburn.com/
Description: Proprietary, 2-year, coed. Part of Bradford Schools, Inc. Awards diplomas and terminal associate degrees. Founded 1879. Setting: urban campus. Total enrollment: 269. Student-undergrad faculty ratio is 27:1. 899 applied, 86% were admitted. 5% from top 10% of their high school class, 26% from top quarter, 47% from top half. Full-time: 269 students, 77% women, 23% men. Students come from 3 states and territories, 5% from out-of-state, 0.4% Native American, 52% Hispanic, 27% black, 2% Asian American or Pacific Islander, 2% international, 1% 25 or older. Calendar: semesters. Academic remediation for entering students, summer session for credit, co-op programs and internships.
Entrance Requirements: Required: high school transcript, interview. Entrance: minimally difficult. Application deadline: Rolling.
Costs Per Year: Application fee: $50. Tuition: $14,400 full-time.
Collegiate Environment: Campus security: 24-hour emergency response devices and patrols. College housing not available. WTC Learning Resources Center with 698 books, 45 serials, and an OPAC. 134 computers available on campus for general student use. A campuswide network can be accessed. Staffed computer lab on campus.

■ **YESHIVA AND KOLLEL HARBOTZAS TORAH** *O-34*
1049 East 15th St.
Brooklyn, NY 11230
Tel: (718)692-0208
Description: Independent Jewish, 4-year.

■ **YESHIVA DERECH CHAIM** *O-34*
1573 39th St.
Brooklyn, NY 11218
Tel: (718)438-3070
Admissions: (718)438-5476
Description: Independent Jewish, comprehensive, men only. Awards bachelor's and master's degrees. Founded 1975. Total enrollment: 163. Calendar: semesters.

■ **YESHIVA D'MONSEY RABBINICAL COLLEGE** *J-33*
2 Roman Blvd.
Monsey, NY 10952
Tel: (914)352-5852
Fax: (914)362-3453
Description: Independent Jewish, 4-year.

■ **YESHIVA GEDOLAH IMREI YOSEF D'SPINKA** *O-34*
1466 56th St.
Brooklyn, NY 11219
Tel: (718)851-8721
Description: Independent Jewish, 4-year.

■ **YESHIVA KARLIN STOLIN RABBINICAL INSTITUTE** *O-34*
1818 Fifty-fourth St.
Brooklyn, NY 11204
Tel: (718)232-7800
Fax: (718)331-4833
Description: Independent Jewish, comprehensive, men only. Awards bachelor's and master's degrees. Founded 1948. Setting: urban campus. Research spending for 2004 fiscal year: $130,000. Total enrollment: 53. 33% from top 10% of their high school class, 75% from top quarter, 100% from

top half. Full-time: 38 students. Students come from 4 other countries, 8% transferred in. Retention: 70% of full-time freshmen returned the following year. Core. Calendar: semesters. Independent study, co-op programs. Study abroad program.

Entrance Requirements: Required: high school transcript, interview. Entrance: very difficult. Application deadline: Rolling. Preference given to students from Mesivta Karlin Stolin.

Collegiate Environment: Student services: personal-psychological counseling. Campus security: 24-hour emergency response devices. 6,000 books. Operations spending for 2004 fiscal year: $15,000. 2 computers available on campus for general student use.

■ **YESHIVA AND KOLEL BAIS MEDRASH ELYON** *J-33*
73 Main St.
Monsey, NY 10952
Tel: (845)356-7064
Description: Independent Jewish, 4-year.

■ **YESHIVA OF NITRA RABBINICAL COLLEGE** *H-36*
Pines Bridge Rd.
Mount Kisco, NY 10549
Tel: (718)384-5460
Description: Independent Jewish, comprehensive, men only. Awards bachelor's and master's degrees. Founded 1946. Setting: small town campus with easy access to New York City. Total enrollment: 241. Calendar: semesters.

■ **YESHIVA SHAAR HATORAH TALMUDIC RESEARCH INSTITUTE**
117-06 84th Ave.
Kew Gardens, NY 11418-1469
Tel: (718)846-1940
Description: Independent Jewish, comprehensive, men only. Awards bachelor's and master's degrees. Founded 1976. Calendar: semesters.

■ **YESHIVA SHAAREI TORAH OF ROCKLAND** *I-32*
91 West Carlton Rd.
Suffern, NY 10901
Tel: (845)352-3431
Description: Independent Jewish, 4-year.

■ **YESHIVA OF THE TELSHE ALUMNI**
4904 Independence Ave.
Riverdale, NY 10471
Tel: (718)601-3523
Description: Independent Jewish, 4-year.

■ **YESHIVA UNIVERSITY** *N-34*
500 West 185th St.
New York, NY 10033-3201
Tel: (212)960-5400
Admissions: (212)960-5277
Fax: (212)960-0086
Web Site: http://www.yu.edu/
Description: Independent, university, coed. Awards bachelor's, master's, doctoral, and first professional degrees (Yeshiva College and Stern College for Women are coordinate undergraduate colleges of arts and sciences for men and women, respectively. Sy Syms School of Business offers programs at both campuses). Founded 1886. Setting: urban campus. Endowment: $493 million. Research spending for 2004 fiscal year: $102.1 million. Total enrollment: 5,998. 1,768 applied, 78% were admitted. Full-time: 2,778 students, 44% women, 56% men. Part-time: 41 students, 37% women, 63% men. Students come from 31 states and territories, 30 other countries, 1% 25 or older, 1% transferred in. Retention: 85% of full-time freshmen returned the following year. Core. Calendar: semesters. ESL program, advanced placement, self-designed majors, honors program, double major, summer session for credit, internships, graduate courses open to undergrads. Off campus study at Fashion Institute of Technology (Stern College students only). Study abroad program.

Entrance Requirements: Options: early admission, deferred admission. Required: essay, high school transcript, 2 recommendations, interview, SAT or ACT. Recommended: SAT Subject Tests. Entrance: moderately difficult. Application deadline: 2/15. Notification: continuous.

Collegiate Environment: Orientation program. Drama-theater group, choral group, student-run newspaper, radio station. Most popular organizations:

dramatics societies, student newspapers, social action groups. Major annual events: Hanukkah Concert, Purim Chagiga, annual dramatics society's production. Student services: personal-psychological counseling. Campus security: 24-hour emergency response devices and patrols, late night transport-escort service. Mendel Gottesman Library plus 6 others with 995,312 books and 9,760 serials. 142 computers available on campus for general student use. Staffed computer lab on campus.

Community Environment: See New York University.

■ **YESHIVAS NOVOMINSK** *O-34*
1569 47th St.
Brooklyn, NY 11219
Tel: (718)438-2727
Description: Independent Jewish, 4-year.

■ **YESHIVAT MIKDASH MELECH** *O-34*
1326 Ocean Parkway
Brooklyn, NY 11230-5601
Tel: (718)339-1090
Description: Independent Jewish, 4-year, men only. Awards bachelor's degrees. Founded 1972. Total enrollment: 77. Calendar: continuous.

Entrance Requirements: Application deadline: Rolling. Notification: continuous.

■ **YESHIVATH VIZNITZ** *J-33*
Phyllis Terrace, PO Box 446
Monsey, NY 10952
Tel: (914)356-1010
Description: Independent Jewish, comprehensive, men only. Awards bachelor's and master's degrees. Founded 1946. Setting: small town campus with easy access to New York City. Total enrollment: 372. Calendar: semesters.

■ **YESHIVATH ZICHRON MOSHE** *P-22*
Laurel Park Rd.
South Fallsburg, NY 12779
Tel: (914)434-5240
Description: Independent Jewish, comprehensive, men only. Awards bachelor's and master's degrees. Founded 1969. Setting: 70-acre small town campus. Total enrollment: 130. 38 applied, 37% were admitted. Students come from 4 states and territories, 4 other countries. Core. Calendar: semesters.

Collegiate Environment: Student services: personal-psychological counseling. On-campus residence required through senior year.

■ **YORK COLLEGE OF THE CITY UNIVERSITY OF NEW YORK**
94-20 Guy R Brewer Blvd.
Jamaica, NY 11451-0001
Tel: (718)262-2000
Admissions: (718)262-2188
E-mail: warmsley@york.cuny.edu
Web Site: http://www.york.cuny.edu/
Description: State and locally supported, 4-year, coed. Part of City University of New York System. Awards bachelor's degrees. Founded 1967. Setting: 50-acre urban campus with easy access to New York City. Total enrollment: 5,900. Student-undergrad faculty ratio is 15:1. 6,945 applied, 46% were admitted. Full-time: 3,879 students, 66% women, 34% men. Part-time: 2,021 students, 72% women, 28% men. Students come from 4 states and territories, 100 other countries, 13% from out-of-state, 0.5% Native American, 15% Hispanic, 48% black, 10% Asian American or Pacific Islander, 53% 25 or older, 11% transferred in. Retention: 88% of full-time freshmen returned the following year. Academic areas with the most degrees conferred: business/marketing; psychology; engineering. Core. Calendar: semesters. ESL program, services for LD students, advanced placement, honors program, independent study, double major, summer session for credit, part-time degree program, adult/continuing education programs, co-op programs and internships. Off campus study at other units of the City University of New York System. ROTC: Army (c), Air Force (c).

Entrance Requirements: Options: electronic application, deferred admission, international baccalaureate accepted. Required: high school transcript, minimum 2.0 high school GPA, SAT or ACT. Recommended: minimum 3.0 high school GPA. Required for some: minimum 2.5 high school GPA. Entrance: moderately difficult. Application deadline: Rolling. Notification: continuous.

Costs Per Year: Application fee: $65. State resident tuition: $4000 full-time. Nonresident tuition: $8640 full-time.

Collegiate Environment: Drama-theater group, choral group, student-run newspaper. Most popular organizations: Haitian Students Association, Caribbean Students Association, Haitian Cultural Association, Latin Caucus. Major annual events: Club Fairs, talent shows, ethnic fairs. Student services: health clinic, personal-psychological counseling, women's center. Campus security: 24-hour emergency response devices and patrols, late night transport-escort service. College housing not available. York College Library plus 1 other with 179,022 books, 157,149 microform titles, 1,962 serials, an OPAC, and a Web page. 530 computers available on campus for general student use. A campuswide network can be accessed from off-campus. Staffed computer lab on campus.

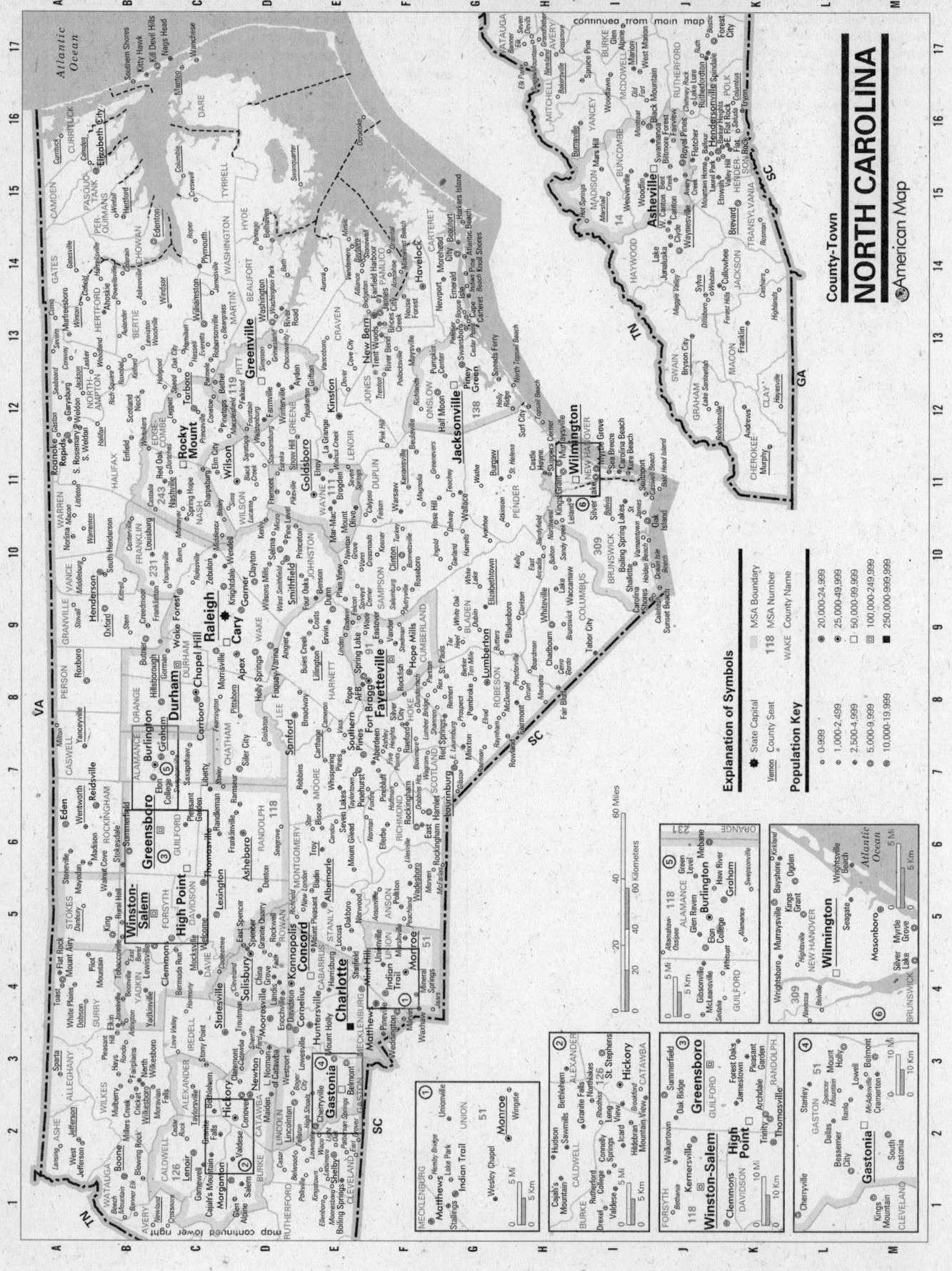

NORTH CAROLINA

County-Town

●American Map

■ **ALAMANCE COMMUNITY COLLEGE** *C-7*
PO Box 8000
Graham, NC 27253-8000
Tel: (336)578-2002
Fax: (336)578-1987
Web Site: http://www.alamance.cc.nc.us/
Description: State-supported, 2-year, coed. Part of North Carolina Community College System. Awards certificates, diplomas, transfer associate, and terminal associate degrees. Founded 1959. Setting: 48-acre small town campus. Endowment: $2.9 million. Educational spending for 2005 fiscal year: $2493 per student. Total enrollment: 4,285. Student-undergrad faculty ratio is 16:1. 982 applied, 100% were admitted. Full-time: 1,770 students, 66% women, 34% men. Part-time: 2,515 students, 66% women, 34% men. Students come from 23 states and territories, 3 other countries, 1% from out-of-state, 0.5% Native American, 2% Hispanic, 23% black, 1% Asian American or Pacific Islander, 2% international, 47% 25 or older, 10% transferred in. Calendar: semesters. Academic remediation for entering students, ESL program, services for LD students, independent study, distance learning, double major, summer session for credit, part-time degree program, adult/continuing education programs, co-op programs. Off campus study at University of North Carolina at Greensboro.
Entrance Requirements: Open admission except for nursing, allied health programs. Options: Common Application, deferred admission. Required: high school transcript. Entrance: noncompetitive. Application deadline: Rolling. Notification: continuous.
Costs Per Year: Application fee: $0. State resident tuition: $1264 full-time, $39.50 per credit hour part-time. Nonresident tuition: $7024 full-time, $219.50 per credit hour part-time. Mandatory fees: $30 full-time, $5 per term part-time.
Collegiate Environment: Social organizations: 5 open to all. Student services: personal-psychological counseling. Campus security: 24-hour emergency response devices and patrols, student patrols, late night transport-escort service. College housing not available. Learning Resources Center with 22,114 books, 25,837 microform titles, 185 serials, 3,033 audiovisual materials, an OPAC, and a Web page. Operations spending for 2004 fiscal year: $406,075. 56 computers available on campus for general student use. A campuswide network can be accessed. Staffed computer lab on campus.
Community Environment: The industrialized economy of Alamance County depends primarily upon textiles, hosiery, electronics, metal cutting and fabricating, packaging and plastics. The bulk of the industries are located here. Planes and buses serve the area. A library, museum, YMCA, hospitals and various civic and service organizations are a part of the community. Some part-time employment is available for students. Recreational facilities include a supervised city recreational program, and many lakes are available for winter sports and outdoor living.

■ **APEX SCHOOL OF THEOLOGY** *C-8*
5104 Revere Rd.
Durham, NC 27713
Tel: (919)572-1625
Fax: (919)572-1762
E-mail: info@apexsot.edu
Web Site: http://www.apexsot.org/
Description: Independent interdenominational, comprehensive, coed. Awards bachelor's and master's degrees. Founded 1995. Setting: suburban campus. Total enrollment: 44. Faculty: 15 (3 full-time, 12 part-time). Student-undergrad faculty ratio is 2:1. 8 applied, 75% were admitted. 0% from out-of-state, 97% black, 100% 25 or older. Retention: 100% of full-time freshmen returned the following year. Calendar: semesters.
Entrance Requirements: Open admission. Required: essay, high school transcript.
Costs Per Year: Application fee: $0. Tuition: $325 per course part-time.
Collegiate Environment: Choral group, student-run newspaper. Social organizations: ; 45% of eligible men and 55% of eligible women are members. College housing not available.

■ **APPALACHIAN STATE UNIVERSITY** *B-1*
Boone, NC 28608
Tel: (828)262-2000
Admissions: (828)262-2120
Fax: (828)262-3296
E-mail: admissions@conrad.appstate.edu
Web Site: http://www.appstate.edu/
Description: State-supported, comprehensive, coed. Part of University of North Carolina System. Awards bachelor's, master's, and doctoral degrees and post-master's certificates. Founded 1899. Setting: 340-acre small town campus. Endowment: $55 million. Research spending for 2004 fiscal year: $875,693. Educational spending for 2005 fiscal year: $5404 per student. Total enrollment: 14,653. Faculty: 998 (703 full-time, 295 part-time). Student-undergrad faculty ratio is 17:1. 9,923 applied, 69% were admitted. 16% from top 10% of their high school class, 50% from top quarter, 89% from top half. Full-time: 12,043 students, 49% women, 51% men. Part-time: 943 students, 64% women, 36% men. Students come from 48 states and territories, 23 other countries, 10% from out-of-state, 0.4% Native American, 2% Hispanic, 3% black, 1% Asian American or Pacific Islander, 0.4% international, 5% 25 or older, 42% live on campus, 6% transferred in. Retention: 86% of full-time freshmen returned the following year. Academic areas with the most degrees conferred: education; business/marketing; social sciences. Core. Calendar: semesters. Academic remediation for entering students, ESL program, services for LD students, advanced placement, accelerated degree program, self-designed majors, honors program, independent study, distance learning, double major, summer session for credit, part-time degree program, adult/continuing education programs, internships, graduate courses open to undergrads. Off campus study at Wake Forest University, North Carolina State University, University of North Carolina at Greensboro, The University of North Carolina at Chapel Hill. Study abroad program. ROTC: Army.
Entrance Requirements: Options: electronic application, early admission, deferred admission, international baccalaureate accepted. Required: high school transcript, SAT or ACT. Entrance: moderately difficult. Application deadline: Rolling. Notification: continuous.
Costs Per Year: Application fee: $45. State resident tuition: $2221 full-time, $80 per credit hour part-time. Nonresident tuition: $11,963 full-time, $425 per credit hour part-time. Mandatory fees: $1697 full-time. College room and board: $4960. College room only: $3100.
Collegiate Environment: Orientation program. Drama-theater group, choral group, marching band, student-run newspaper, radio station. Social organizations: 210 open to all; national fraternities, national sororities; 5% of eligible men and 5% of eligible women are members. Most popular organizations: Baptist Student Union, Inter-University Christian Fellowship, Campus Crusade for Christ, Circle K, Criminal Justice Association. Major annual events: First Night Celebration, Winter Wonderland Gala, homecoming.

Student services: legal services, health clinic, personal-psychological counseling, women's center. Campus security: 24-hour emergency response devices and patrols, late night transport-escort service, controlled dormitory access. 5,070 college housing spaces available; 4,756 were occupied in 2003-04. Freshmen guaranteed college housing. On-campus residence required in freshman year. Options: coed, men-only, women-only housing available. Carol Grotnes Belk Library plus 1 other with 904,597 books, 1.5 million microform titles, 5,306 serials, 92,558 audiovisual materials, an OPAC, and a Web page. Operations spending for 2004 fiscal year: $5.1 million. 500 computers available on campus for general student use. Computer purchase/lease plans available. A campuswide network can be accessed from student residence rooms and from off campus. Staffed computer lab on campus.

Community Environment: Located in Boone, North Carolina, Appalachian State University is in the middle of one of the most popular year-round recreation areas in the East. The campus is only a few miles from several major ski resorts, and Pisgah National Forest and the Appalachian Trail are easily accessible from Boone. Grandfather Mountain and"Tweetsie" railroad are famous tourist attractions."Horn in the West" is a historical drama portraying with music and dance the story of Daniel Boone and the struggle to establish freedom in the southern Appalachian Highlands. This is performed in an outdoor amphitheater in a lovely mountain setting during July and August. The climate in the area is temperate. The average summer temperature rarely climbs above 80 degrees, and when it does a brief, refreshing shower usually cools things off. Fall brings clear, brisk and color-splashed days and cool evenings. Winter means picturesque snowfalls and fireside nights. Besides skiing, the area offers ample opportunities for other outdoor recreation, including river canoeing, hiking and camping. Three highways, U.S. 421, reaching from the Great Lakes to the North Carolina coast, and U.S. 321 and 221, all come through Boone, providing easy travel in all directions. The scenic Blue Ridge Parkway is only six miles from campus. The area, both urban and rural, is rich in contrasts between a growing university town and traditional southern Appalachian Folkways.

■ THE ART INSTITUTE OF CHARLOTTE *E-3*

2110 Water Ridge Parkway
Charlotte, NC 28217
Tel: (704)357-8020
Fax: (704)357-1133
E-mail: guinane@aii.edu
Web Site: http://www.aich.artinstitutes.edu/

Description: Proprietary, primarily 2-year, coed. Part of Education Management Corporation. Awards certificates, terminal associate, and bachelor's degrees. Founded 1973. Setting: suburban campus. Educational spending for 2005 fiscal year: $24,000 per student. Total enrollment: 819. Student-undergrad faculty ratio is 19:1. 697 applied. 4% from top 10% of their high school class, 13% from top quarter, 38% from top half. Full-time: 564 students, 68% women, 32% men. Part-time: 255 students, 71% women, 29% men. 26% from out-of-state, 1% Native American, 3% Hispanic, 32% black, 2% Asian American or Pacific Islander, 0% international, 26% live on campus. Core. Academic remediation for entering students, services for LD students, advanced placement, accelerated degree program, independent study, distance learning, summer session for credit, part-time degree program, internships.

Entrance Requirements: Options: electronic application, deferred admission, international baccalaureate accepted. Required: essay, high school transcript. Recommended: SAT or ACT. Required for some: interview, SAT or ACT. Entrance: minimally difficult. Application deadline: Rolling. Notification: continuous.

Costs Per Year: Application fee: $50. Tuition: $23,232 full-time, $363 per credit part-time. Mandatory fees: $200 full-time. College room only: $5580.

Collegiate Environment: Orientation program. Student services: personal-psychological counseling. 186 college housing spaces available; all were occupied in 2003-04. Freshmen guaranteed college housing. The Art Institute of Charlotte Library with 15,000 books, 130 serials, 825 audiovisual materials, and an OPAC. 150 computers available on campus for general student use. A campuswide network can be accessed. Staffed computer lab on campus.

■ ASHEVILLE-BUNCOMBE TECHNICAL COMMUNITY COLLEGE *J-15*

340 Victoria Rd.
Asheville, NC 28801-4897
Tel: (828)254-1921
Fax: (828)251-6355
E-mail: lbush@abtech.edu
Web Site: http://www.abtech.edu/

Description: State-supported, 2-year, coed. Part of North Carolina Community College System. Awards certificates, diplomas, transfer associate, and terminal associate degrees. Founded 1959. Setting: 126-acre urban campus. Endowment: $98,442. Total enrollment: 5,627. 2,792 applied, 100% were admitted. Full-time: 2,042 students, 53% women, 47% men. Part-time: 3,585 students, 57% women, 43% men. 2% from out-of-state, 0.5% Native American, 1% Hispanic, 6% black, 0.5% Asian American or Pacific Islander, 1% international, 47% 25 or older. Core. Calendar: semesters. Academic remediation for entering students, services for LD students, advanced placement, independent study, distance learning, double major, summer session for credit, part-time degree program, adult/continuing education programs, co-op programs and internships.

Entrance Requirements: Open admission except for allied health programs. Option: deferred admission. Required: high school transcript. Required for some: recommendations, interview. Placement: CPT, SAT, or ACT required. Entrance: noncompetitive. Application deadline: Rolling. Notification: continuous.

Costs Per Year: Application fee: $0. State resident tuition: $1216 full-time, $38 per credit hour part-time. Nonresident tuition: $6752 full-time, $211 per credit hour part-time. Mandatory fees: $28 full-time, $11 per term part-time.

Collegiate Environment: Orientation program. Drama-theater group, student-run newspaper. Most popular organizations: Student Government Association, Phi Beta Lambda. Major annual events: Spring Fling, Welcome Freshmen Picnic, July 4th Ice Cream/Watermelon Cutting. Student services: personal-psychological counseling. Campus security: 24-hour emergency response devices and patrols. College housing not available. Holly Learning Resources Center with 37,439 books, 3,561 microform titles, 195 serials, and an OPAC. Operations spending for 2004 fiscal year: $437,688. 414 computers available on campus for general student use. A campuswide network can be accessed from off-campus. Staffed computer lab on campus.

Community Environment: The main campus is located on Victoria Road in Asheville, NC, a city repeatedly named as one of the most livable in America. Nestled between the Blue Ride and Great Smoky mountains, Asheville offers beautiful mountain scenery and an excellent quality of life. Recognized as an entrepreneurial hotspot, Asheville also enjoys a thriving business climate.

■ BARBER-SCOTIA COLLEGE *E-4*

145 Cabarrus Ave., West
Concord, NC 28025-5187
Tel: (704)789-2900
Free: 800-610-0778
Admissions: (704)789-2902
Fax: (704)784-3817
Web Site: http://www.b-sc.edu/

Description: Independent, 4-year, coed, affiliated with Presbyterian Church (U.S.A.). Awards bachelor's degrees. Founded 1867. Setting: 23-acre small town campus with easy access to Charlotte. Endowment: $4.3 million. Educational spending for 2005 fiscal year: $12,749 per student. Total enrollment: 742. 1,502 applied, 70% were admitted. 10% from top 10% of their high school class, 20% from top quarter, 30% from top half. Full-time: 737 students, 43% women, 57% men. Part-time: 5 students, 60% women, 40% men. Students come from 20 states and territories, 32% from out-of-state, 0.4% Hispanic, 86% black, 12% international, 20% 25 or older, 90% live on campus, 10% transferred in. Retention: 62% of full-time freshmen returned the following year. Core. Calendar: semesters. Academic remediation for entering students, advanced placement, honors program, double major, summer session for credit, co-op programs and internships. Off campus study at members of the Charlotte Area Educational Consortium. ROTC: Army (c), Air Force.

Entrance Requirements: Options: Common Application, electronic application, early admission. Required: high school transcript, recommendations, SAT or ACT. Recommended: essay, minimum 3.0 high school GPA, interview. Required for some: minimum 2.0 high school GPA. Entrance: minimally difficult. Application deadline: Rolling. Notification: continuous.

Collegiate Environment: Orientation program. Drama-theater group, choral group, student-run newspaper. Social organizations: 6 open to all; national fraternities, national sororities; 10% of eligible men and 12% of eligible women are members. Most popular organizations: SGA (Student Government Association), Student Christian Association, Pre-Alumni Council, Scotia Express, yearbook. Major annual events: Robing Ceremony, Homecoming, Honors Convocation. Student services: health clinic, personal-psychological counseling. Campus security: 24-hour emergency response devices and patrols. 350 college housing spaces available. On-campus residence required through senior year. Sage Memorial Library with 24,270 books and 193 serials. Operations spending for 2004 fiscal year: $210,925. 125 computers available on campus for general student use. A campuswide network can be accessed from off-campus. Staffed computer lab on campus.

■ **BARTON COLLEGE** *D-11*
PO Box 5000
Wilson, NC 27893-7000
Tel: (252)399-6300
Free: 800-345-4973
Admissions: (252)399-6314
Fax: (252)237-4957
E-mail: adenton@barton.edu
Web Site: http://www.barton.edu/
Description: Independent, 4-year, coed, affiliated with Christian Church (Disciples of Christ). Awards bachelor's degrees. Founded 1902. Setting: 62-acre small town campus with easy access to Raleigh-Durham, NC. Endowment: $21.1 million. Educational spending for 2005 fiscal year: $5094 per student. Total enrollment: 1,189. Student-undergrad faculty ratio is 13:1. 1,295 applied, 70% were admitted. 13% from top 10% of their high school class, 34% from top quarter, 61% from top half. 17 student government officers. Full-time: 917 students, 69% women, 31% men. Part-time: 272 students, 85% women, 15% men. Students come from 31 states and territories, 18 other countries, 20% from out-of-state, 0.2% Native American, 2% Hispanic, 23% black, 1% Asian American or Pacific Islander, 2% international, 26% 25 or older, 39% live on campus, 8% transferred in. Retention: 60% of full-time freshmen returned the following year. Academic areas with the most degrees conferred: business/marketing; health professions and related sciences; education. Core. Calendar: 4-1-4. Academic remediation for entering students, ESL program, services for LD students, advanced placement, honors program, independent study, double major, summer session for credit, part-time degree program, adult/continuing education programs, co-op programs and internships. Study abroad program.
Entrance Requirements: Options: electronic application, deferred admission, international baccalaureate accepted. Required: high school transcript, SAT or ACT. Recommended: interview. Entrance: minimally difficult. Application deadline: Rolling.
Costs Per Year: Application fee: $25. Comprehensive fee: $22,470 includes full-time tuition ($15,390), mandatory fees ($1280), and college room and board ($5800). College room only: $2774. Full-time tuition and fees vary according to course load and program. Room and board charges vary according to housing facility. Part-time tuition: $654 per credit hour. Part-time tuition varies according to course load and program.
Collegiate Environment: Orientation program. Drama-theater group, choral group, student-run newspaper. Social organizations: 39 open to all; national fraternities, national sororities; 14% of eligible men and 12% of eligible women are members. Most popular organizations: Barton College Association of Nurses, Students in Free Enterprise, Stage and Script, Campus Activities Board, College Habitat for Humanity. Major annual events: Fall Fling, Lighting of the Luminaries and Christmas Celebration, Pre-Exam Jam. Student services: health clinic, personal-psychological counseling. Campus security: 24-hour emergency response devices, late night transport-escort service, controlled dormitory access, city police substation on campus. 510 college housing spaces available; 481 were occupied in 2003-04. Freshmen guaranteed college housing. On-campus residence required through sophomore year. Options: coed, women-only housing available. Willis N. Hackney Library with 169,836 books, 301,132 microform titles, 13,437 serials, 3,581 audiovisual materials, an OPAC, and a Web page. Operations spending for 2004 fiscal year: $401,454. 125 computers available on campus for general student use. A campuswide network can be accessed from student residence rooms and from off campus. Staffed computer lab on campus.
Community Environment: Bus and train transportation are available. Community facilities include churches of all denominations, a hospital, library, shopping centers, numerous civic and service organizations, and a drama theater. Recreational parks with swimming pools, golf courses, and a large stadium are located here. Part-time jobs are available.

■ **BEAUFORT COUNTY COMMUNITY COLLEGE** *D-13*
PO Box 1069
Washington, NC 27889-1069

Tel: (252)946-6194
Admissions: (252)940-6233
Fax: (252)946-0271
Web Site: http://www.beaufortccc.edu/
Description: State-supported, 2-year, coed. Part of North Carolina Community College System. Awards certificates, diplomas, transfer associate, and terminal associate degrees. Founded 1967. Setting: 67-acre rural campus. Total enrollment: 1,424. 1% from out-of-state, 3% Hispanic, 34% black, 0.1% Asian American or Pacific Islander, 0% international, 58% 25 or older. Core. Calendar: semesters. Academic remediation for entering students, services for LD students, advanced placement, distance learning, summer session for credit, part-time degree program, co-op programs.
Entrance Requirements: Open admission except for nursing, medical laboratory technology programs. Option: electronic application. Required: high school transcript, CPT. Recommended: SAT and SAT Subject Tests or ACT. Required for some: essay, recommendations, interview. Entrance: noncompetitive. Application deadline: 8/18. Notification: continuous.
Costs Per Year: Application fee: $0. State resident tuition: $1264 full-time. Nonresident tuition: $7024 full-time. Mandatory fees: $64 full-time.
Collegiate Environment: Most popular organizations: Student Government Association, Gama Beta Phi, Phi Beta Lambda, Hope Club. Major annual events: Christmas celebration, Thanksgiving, Spring Fling. Student services: personal-psychological counseling. Campus security: 24-hour emergency response devices and patrols, late night transport-escort service. College housing not available. Beaufort Community College Library with 25,734 books, 214 serials, an OPAC, and a Web page. 60 computers available on campus for general student use. A campuswide network can be accessed from off-campus. Staffed computer lab on campus.
Community Environment: Washington, NC is located on the Pamlico River, which affords excellent fishing, boating, and water skiing. North Carolina's finest beach areas are only a short distance away. Year-round golf courses and tennis courts are also easily accessible. Other points of interest include the NC Estuarium, the Beaufort County Arts Council (located in the old Atlantic Coastal Railroad Depot), and the newly renovated Turnage Theater.

■ **BELMONT ABBEY COLLEGE** *E-3*
100 Belmont-Mt. Holly Rd.
Belmont, NC 28012-1802
Tel: (704)825-6700; 888-BAC-0110
Admissions: (704)825-6884
Fax: (704)825-6670
Web Site: http://www.belmontabbeycollege.edu/
Description: Independent Roman Catholic, 4-year, coed. Awards bachelor's degrees. Founded 1876. Setting: 650-acre small town campus with easy access to Charlotte. Endowment: $14.2 million. Educational spending for 2005 fiscal year: $3785 per student. Total enrollment: 800. 845 applied, 69% were admitted. 6% from top 10% of their high school class, 20% from top quarter, 52% from top half. Full-time: 712 students, 59% women, 41% men. Part-time: 88 students, 76% women, 24% men. Students come from 34 states and territories, 23 other countries, 51% from out-of-state, 0.3% Native American, 5% Hispanic, 12% black, 1% Asian American or Pacific Islander, 4% international, 30% 25 or older, 48% live on campus, 11% transferred in. Retention: 60% of full-time freshmen returned the following year. Core. Calendar: semesters. Services for LD students, advanced placement, accelerated degree program, freshman honors college, honors program, independent study, double major, summer session for credit, part-time degree program, external degree program, adult/continuing education programs, co-op programs and internships. Off campus study at Charlotte Area Educational Consortium. Study abroad program. ROTC: Army (c), Air Force (c).
Entrance Requirements: Options: Peterson's Universal Application, Common Application, electronic application, deferred admission, international baccalaureate accepted. Required: high school transcript, minimum 2.0 high school GPA, SAT or ACT. Recommended: interview. Required for some: essay, 2 recommendations. Entrance: moderately difficult. Application deadline: 8/1. Notification: continuous.
Costs Per Year: Application fee: $35. One-time mandatory fee: $672. Comprehensive fee: $25,310 includes full-time tuition ($15,910), mandatory fees ($814), and college room and board ($8586). College room only: $4829. Full-time tuition and fees vary according to class time, course level, course load, location, program, reciprocity agreements, and student level. Room and board charges vary according to board plan, housing facility, location, and student level. Part-time tuition: $499 per credit. Part-time manda-

tory fees: $201 per hour. Part-time tuition and fees vary according to class time, course level, course load, location, reciprocity agreements, and student level.

Collegiate Environment: Orientation program. Drama-theater group, choral group, student-run newspaper, radio station. Social organizations: 34 open to all; national fraternities, national sororities, local fraternities, local sororities; 35% of eligible men and 40% of eligible women are members. Most popular organizations: College Union, WABY (student radio station), Abbey Players. Major annual events: Homecoming, Parents' Weekend. Student services: health clinic, personal-psychological counseling. Campus security: 24-hour emergency response devices and patrols, late night transport-escort service. 750 college housing spaces available; 529 were occupied in 2003-04. Freshmen guaranteed college housing. On-campus residence required through senior year. Options: coed, men-only housing available. Abbot Vincent Taylor Library plus 1 other with 110,050 books, 59,000 microform titles, 630 serials, and an OPAC. Operations spending for 2004 fiscal year: $420,815. 125 computers available on campus for general student use. A campuswide network can be accessed from student residence rooms and from off campus. Staffed computer lab on campus.

Community Environment: In the southern Piedmont section of the state, Belmont is a growing textile center. Commercial transportation is available. The community facilities include churches of all denominations, hospitals and health services, a library, YMCA, and shopping centers. Numerous civic and service organizations are active. Hunting and fishing are popular sports in the area as well as all water sports, enjoyed at Lake Wylie.

■ **BENNETT COLLEGE FOR WOMEN** *C-6*

900 East Washington St.
Greensboro, NC 27401-3239
Tel: (336)273-4431
Admissions: (336)517-8624
Web Site: http://www.bennett.edu/

Description: Independent United Methodist, 4-year, women only. Awards bachelor's degrees. Founded 1873. Setting: 55-acre urban campus. Endowment: $8.7 million. Educational spending for 2005 fiscal year: $9892 per student. Total enrollment: 572. Student-undergrad faculty ratio is 10:1. 939 applied, 57% were admitted. 4% from top 10% of their high school class, 14% from top quarter, 38% from top half. Full-time: 566 students. Part-time: 6 students. Students come from 29 states and territories, 4 other countries, 72% from out-of-state, 0.4% Native American, 2% Hispanic, 95% black, 0% Asian American or Pacific Islander, 1% international, 5% 25 or older, 75% live on campus, 3% transferred in. Retention: 68% of full-time freshmen returned the following year. Academic areas with the most degrees conferred: biological/life sciences; communications/journalism; psychology. Core. Calendar: semesters. Academic remediation for entering students, services for LD students, self-designed majors, freshman honors college, honors program, summer session for credit, part-time degree program, adult/continuing education programs, co-op programs and internships. Off campus study at members of the Greensboro Regional Consortium, Piedmont Independent College Association of North Carolina, New York University, Union College (NY). ROTC: Army (c), Air Force (c).

Entrance Requirements: Option: deferred admission. Required: essay, high school transcript, minimum 2.0 high school GPA, recommendations, SAT or ACT. Required for some: interview. Entrance: moderately difficult. Application deadline: Rolling. Notification: continuous.

Costs Per Year: Application fee: $30. Comprehensive fee: $19,089 includes full-time tuition ($11,509), mandatory fees ($1730), and college room and board ($5850). College room only: $2937. Part-time tuition: $479 per credit hour. Part-time mandatory fees: $718 per term.

Collegiate Environment: Orientation program. Drama-theater group, choral group, student-run newspaper. Social organizations: 33 open to all; national sororities; 20% of eligible undergrads are members. Most popular organizations: Christian Fellowship, Pre-Alumnae Council, Belles of Harmony, NAACP, National Council of Negro Women. Major annual events: Convocatum Est, Founder's Day, Spring Festival. Student services: legal services, health clinic, personal-psychological counseling, women's center. Campus security: 24-hour patrols, late night transport-escort service. 578 college housing spaces available; 380 were occupied in 2003-04. On-campus residence required through sophomore year. Option: women-only housing available. Holgate Library plus 1 other with 119,191 books, 617 serials, 839 audiovisual materials, and an OPAC. Operations spending for 2004 fiscal year: $216,541. 115 computers available on campus for general student use.

Computer purchase/lease plans available. A campuswide network can be accessed from student residence rooms and from off campus. Staffed computer lab on campus.

Community Environment: See Greensboro College.

■ **BLADEN COMMUNITY COLLEGE**

PO Box 266
Dublin, NC 28332-0266
Tel: (910)879-5500
Admissions: (910)879-5574
Fax: (910)879-5508
Web Site: http://www.bladen.cc.nc.us/

Description: State and locally supported, 2-year, coed. Part of North Carolina Community College System. Awards certificates, diplomas, transfer associate, and terminal associate degrees. Founded 1967. Setting: 45-acre rural campus. Endowment: $72,151. Educational spending for 2005 fiscal year: $2997 per student. Total enrollment: 1,407. 10% from top 10% of their high school class, 20% from top quarter, 78% from top half. 2 class presidents, 6 student government officers. Full-time: 838 students, 78% women, 22% men. Part-time: 569 students, 76% women, 24% men. Students come from 3 states and territories, 0% from out-of-state, 10% Native American, 1% Hispanic, 48% black, 0.2% Asian American or Pacific Islander, 0% international, 62% 25 or older. Retention: 35% of full-time freshmen returned the following year. Core. Calendar: semesters. Academic remediation for entering students, services for LD students, advanced placement, independent study, distance learning, double major, summer session for credit, part-time degree program, adult/continuing education programs.

Entrance Requirements: Open admission. Options: Common Application, electronic application, deferred admission. Required: high school transcript, ACT COMPASS. Entrance: noncompetitive. Application deadline: 8/1. Notification: continuous until 8/15.

Costs Per Year: Application fee: $0. State resident tuition: $1264 full-time, $39.50 per hour part-time. Nonresident tuition: $7024 full-time, $219.50 per hour part-time. Mandatory fees: $66 full-time, $25.75 per term part-time.

Collegiate Environment: Orientation program. Major annual events: Spring Field Day, Christmas Dinner, fall Convocation. Student services: personal-psychological counseling. Campus security: 14-hour patrols. College housing not available. Learning Resource Center with 19,881 books, 36,052 microform titles, 52 serials, 2,364 audiovisual materials, an OPAC, and a Web page. Operations spending for 2004 fiscal year: $160,321. 150 computers available on campus for general student use. A campuswide network can be accessed from off-campus. Staffed computer lab on campus.

Community Environment: Dublin is located 30 miles south of Fayetteville. The principal business is agriculture. Community facilities include 15 churches of various denominations and a public library. Bladen Arts Council frequently sponsors cultural activities in the campus's 1,000-seat auditorium. A golf course, parks, state forest and several lakes provide facilities for excellent fishing and water sports.

■ **BLUE RIDGE COMMUNITY COLLEGE**

180 West Campus Dr.
Flat Rock, NC 28731-4728
Tel: (828)694-1700
Admissions: (828)694-1801
Fax: (828)694-1690
E-mail: frankb@blueridge.edu
Web Site: http://www.blueridge.edu/

Description: State and locally supported, 2-year, coed. Part of North Carolina Community College System. Awards certificates, diplomas, and transfer associate degrees. Founded 1969. Setting: 109-acre small town campus. Endowment: $51,500. Total enrollment: 1,959. 740 applied, 100% were admitted. Full-time: 787 students, 57% women, 43% men. Part-time: 1,172 students, 67% women, 33% men. Students come from 18 states and territories, 14 other countries, 0% from out-of-state, 0.2% Native American, 2% Hispanic, 5% black, 1% Asian American or Pacific Islander, 2% international, 69% 25 or older, 6% transferred in. Core. Calendar: semesters. Academic remediation for entering students, ESL program, services for LD students, advanced placement, distance learning, double major, summer session for credit, part-time degree program, adult/continuing education programs, co-op programs and internships.

Entrance Requirements: Open admission except for nursing, surgical technology, pharmacy technology programs. Options: Common Application, early admission. Required: high school transcript. Entrance: noncompetitive. Application deadline: Rolling. Notification: continuous.

Collegiate Environment: Orientation program. Drama-theater group, student-run newspaper. Social organizations: 10 open to all. Most popular organizations: Student Government Association, Phi Theta Kappa, Spanish Club, Rotaract. Major annual events: Christmas Celebration, Halloween Pizza Day, Summer Picnic. Student services: personal-psychological counseling. Campus security: sheriff's deputy during class hours. College housing not available. Blue Ridge Community College Library plus 1 other with 47,655 books, 19,025 microform titles, 3,875 serials, 1,692 audiovisual materials, and an OPAC. Operations spending for 2004 fiscal year: $175,505. 225 computers available on campus for general student use. A campuswide network can be accessed.

■ **BREVARD COLLEGE** *K-15*

400 North Broad St.
Brevard, NC 28712-3306
Tel: (828)883-8292
Free: 800-527-9090
Admissions: (828)884-8300
Fax: (828)884-3790
E-mail: admissions@brevard.edu
Web Site: http://www.brevard.edu/

Description: Independent United Methodist, 4-year, coed. Awards bachelor's degrees. Founded 1853. Setting: 120-acre small town campus. Endowment: $19.9 million. Educational spending for 2005 fiscal year: $10,217 per student. Total enrollment: 597. Student-undergrad faculty ratio is 9:1. 590 applied, 74% were admitted. 10% from top 10% of their high school class, 23% from top quarter, 54% from top half. Full-time: 572 students, 47% women, 53% men. Part-time: 25 students, 52% women, 48% men. Students come from 34 states and territories, 9 other countries, 53% from out-of-state, 1% Native American, 3% Hispanic, 4% black, 0.3% Asian American or Pacific Islander, 3% international, 7% 25 or older, 70% live on campus, 7% transferred in. Retention: 61% of full-time freshmen returned the following year. Academic areas with the most degrees conferred: parks and recreation; visual and performing arts; business/marketing. Core. Calendar: semesters. Academic remediation for entering students, services for LD students, advanced placement, self-designed majors, honors program, independent study, double major, part-time degree program, external degree program, adult/continuing education programs, internships. Study abroad program.

Entrance Requirements: Options: Peterson's Universal Application, Common Application, electronic application, deferred admission, international baccalaureate accepted. Required: essay, high school transcript, minimum 2.0 high school GPA, SAT or ACT. Recommended: 3 recommendations, interview. Required for some: students in music-auditions, music tests; students in art-portfolio. Entrance: minimally difficult. Application deadlines: Rolling, Rolling for nonresidents. Notification: continuous, continuous for nonresidents.

Costs Per Year: Application fee: $30. Comprehensive fee: $21,970 includes full-time tuition ($15,620), mandatory fees ($370), and college room and board ($5980). Full-time tuition and fees vary according to course load. Room and board charges vary according to board plan and housing facility. Part-time tuition: $620 per credit hour. Part-time mandatory fees: $20 per term. Part-time tuition and fees vary according to course load.

Collegiate Environment: Orientation program. Drama-theater group, choral group, student-run newspaper. Social organizations: 27 open to all. Most popular organizations: fine arts organizations, Omicron Delta Kappa, Fellowship of Christian Athletes, BC Recycles, Campus Coalition for Service. Major annual events: Earth Week Service and Celebration, Move-a-Mountain Day, Martin Luther King, Jr. Community Celebration. Student services: health clinic, personal-psychological counseling. Campus security: 24-hour emergency response devices and patrols. 603 college housing spaces available; 406 were occupied in 2003-04. Freshmen guaranteed college housing. On-campus residence required through sophomore year. Options: coed, men-only, women-only housing available. Jones Library plus 1 other with 57,281 books, 3,336 microform titles, 17,500 serials, 3,957 audiovisual materials, an OPAC, and a Web page. Operations spending for 2004 fiscal year: $288,553. 100 computers available on campus for general student use. A campuswide network can be accessed from student residence rooms. Staffed computer lab on campus.

Community Environment: Brevard, known as the "Land of Waterfalls" is 33 miles southwest of Asheville, NC. The area is the location of the Carl Sandburg home, the Thomas Wolfe Home, and the Brevard Music Center. This popular summer resort is at the entrance of Pisgah National Forest. Community facilities include churches of most major denominations, hospital

and many civic and service organizations. Part-time employment is available on and off campus. Recreational activities include camping, biking, backpacking, canoeing, snowskiing, kayaking, and mountain climbing.

■ **BRUNSWICK COMMUNITY COLLEGE**

PO Box 30
Supply, NC 28462-0030
Tel: (910)755-7300
Free: 800-754-1050
Admissions: (910)755-7321
Fax: (910)754-9609
Web Site: http://www.brunswick.cc.nc.us/

Description: State-supported, 2-year, coed. Part of North Carolina Community College System. Awards certificates, diplomas, transfer associate, and terminal associate degrees. Founded 1979. Setting: 266-acre rural campus. Endowment: $1.3 million. Total enrollment: 1,003. Full-time: 493 students, 67% women, 33% men. Part-time: 510 students, 74% women, 26% men. Students come from 5 states and territories, 1% from out-of-state, 0.2% Native American, 1% Hispanic, 21% black, 0.4% Asian American or Pacific Islander, 0% international, 46% 25 or older, 4% transferred in. Core. Calendar: semesters. Academic remediation for entering students, ESL program, services for LD students, advanced placement, independent study, distance learning, summer session for credit, part-time degree program, co-op programs and internships.

Entrance Requirements: Open admission except for allied health programs. Option: electronic application. Required: high school transcript. Required for some: recommendations, interview. Placement: ACT ASSET required. Entrance: noncompetitive. Application deadline: Rolling. Notification: continuous.

Costs Per Year: Application fee: $0. State resident tuition: $1185 full-time, $39.50 per semester hour part-time. Nonresident tuition: $6585 full-time, $219.50 per semester hour part-time. Mandatory fees: $73 full-time, $37 per term part-time. Part-time tuition and fees vary according to course load.

Collegiate Environment: Social organizations: 1 open to all. Most popular organizations: Student Government Association, Phi Theta Kappa Honor Society, National Vocational-Technical Honor Society. Major annual events: Spring Fling, Fall Festival, Diversity Luncheon. Student services: personal-psychological counseling. Campus security: late night transport-escort service, campus police. College housing not available. Brunswick Community College Library plus 1 other with 20,032 books, 35,076 microform titles, 69 serials, 986 audiovisual materials, and an OPAC. Operations spending for 2004 fiscal year: $194,445. 146 computers available on campus for general student use. A campuswide network can be accessed. Staffed computer lab on campus.

■ **CABARRUS COLLEGE OF HEALTH SCIENCES** *E-4*

401 Medical Park Dr.
Concord, NC 28025
Tel: (704)783-1555
Admissions: (704)783-1616
Fax: (704)783-1764
Web Site: http://www.cabarruscollege.edu/

Description: Independent, 4-year, coed. Awards associate and bachelor's degrees. Founded 1942. Setting: 5-acre suburban campus with easy access to Charlotte. Total enrollment: 308. Student-undergrad faculty ratio is 7:1. 36 applied, 69% were admitted. 11% from top 10% of their high school class, 47% from top quarter, 84% from top half. Full-time: 207 students, 89% women, 11% men. Part-time: 101 students, 89% women, 11% men. Students come from 2 states and territories, 2% from out-of-state, 0% Native American, 2% Hispanic, 7% black, 1% Asian American or Pacific Islander, 0% international, 59% 25 or older, 15% transferred in. Academic area with the most degrees conferred: health professions and related sciences. Core. Calendar: semesters. Advanced placement, independent study, distance learning, double major, part-time degree program.

Entrance Requirements: Option: electronic application. Required: essay, high school transcript, minimum 2.0 high school GPA, 2 recommendations, SAT or ACT. Recommended: minimum 3.0 high school GPA. Required for some: interview, ACT ASSET. Entrance: moderately difficult. Application deadline: 3/1. Notification: 4/15.

Costs Per Year: Application fee: $35. Tuition: $7300 full-time, $230 per hour part-time.

Collegiate Environment: Orientation program. Student-run newspaper. Most popular organizations: Student Nurse Association, Christian Student Union, student government, Honor Society, Allied Health Student Association. Major annual events: Welcome Picnic, Spring Family Day. Student services: health clinic, personal-psychological counseling. Campus security: 24-hour emergency response devices and patrols. College housing not available. Northeast Medical Center Library with 7,676 books, 2,127 serials, and 923 audiovisual materials. 30 computers available on campus for general student use. A campuswide network can be accessed from off-campus. Staffed computer lab on campus.

■ CALDWELL COMMUNITY COLLEGE AND TECHNICAL INSTITUTE
H-2
2855 Hickory Blvd.
Hudson, NC 28638-2397
Tel: (828)726-2200
Admissions: (828)726-2703
Fax: (828)726-2490
E-mail: cwoodard@cccti.edu
Web Site: http://www.cccti.edu/

Description: State-supported, 2-year, coed. Part of North Carolina Community College System. Awards certificates, diplomas, transfer associate, and terminal associate degrees. Founded 1964. Setting: 50-acre small town campus. Total enrollment: 3,744. 763 applied, 100% were admitted. Full-time: 1,281 students, 57% women, 43% men. Part-time: 2,463 students, 55% women, 45% men. Students come from 24 states and territories, 0.3% Native American, 1% Hispanic, 5% black, 1% Asian American or Pacific Islander, 0% international, 44% 25 or older, 9% transferred in. Core. Calendar: semesters. Academic remediation for entering students, services for LD students, advanced placement, independent study, distance learning, double major, summer session for credit, part-time degree program, adult/continuing education programs, co-op programs.

Entrance Requirements: Open admission except for allied health programs. Option: early admission. Required: high school transcript. Entrance: noncompetitive. Application deadline: Rolling. Notification: continuous.

Costs Per Year: Application fee: $0. State resident tuition: $1185 full-time, $39.50 per credit hour part-time. Nonresident tuition: $6585 full-time, $219.50 per credit hour part-time. Mandatory fees: $4.

Collegiate Environment: Orientation program. Drama-theater group, choral group. Campus security: trained security personnel during open hours. College housing not available. Broyhill Center for Learning Resources with 50,770 books, 251 serials, 5,352 audiovisual materials, an OPAC, and a Web page. 750 computers available on campus for general student use. A campuswide network can be accessed from off-campus. Staffed computer lab on campus.

Community Environment: Since more wood furniture is manufactured here than any other place in the South, Lenoir is known as "furniture land." Numerous parks and two recreation centers provide the facilities for relaxation. A number of churches are represented in the community.

■ CAMPBELL UNIVERSITY *E-9*
PO Box 97
Buies Creek, NC 27506
Tel: (910)893-1200
Free: 800-334-4111
Admissions: (910)893-1291
Fax: (910)893-1288
E-mail: kerner@mailcenter.campbell.edu
Web Site: http://www.campbell.edu/

Description: Independent, university, coed, affiliated with North Carolina Baptist State Convention. Awards associate, bachelor's, master's, doctoral, and first professional degrees. Founded 1887. Setting: 850-acre rural campus with easy access to Raleigh. Endowment: $91.7 million. Educational spending for 2005 fiscal year: $6309 per student. Total enrollment: 3,645. Faculty: 336 (188 full-time, 148 part-time). Student-undergrad faculty ratio is 12:1. 2,804 applied, 61% were admitted. 30% from top 10% of their high school class, 75% from top quarter, 85% from top half. 5 National Merit Scholars, 5 class presidents, 34 valedictorians, 94 student government officers. Full-time: 2,566 students, 57% women, 43% men. Part-time: 126 students, 52% women, 48% men. Students come from 50 states and territories, 50 other countries, 25% from out-of-state, 12% 25 or older, 50% live on campus, 28% transferred in. Retention: 87% of full-time freshmen returned the following year. Academic areas with the most degrees conferred: business/marketing; psychology; social sciences. Core. Calendar: semesters. Advanced placement, accelerated degree program, freshman honors college, honors program, independent study, distance learning,

double major, summer session for credit, part-time degree program, adult/continuing education programs, co-op programs and internships, graduate courses open to undergrads. Study abroad program. ROTC: Army.

Entrance Requirements: Options: Common Application, electronic application, early admission, deferred admission, international baccalaureate accepted. Required: high school transcript, minimum 2.7 high school GPA, SAT or ACT. Recommended: essay, interview. Required for some: 3 recommendations. Entrance: moderately difficult. Application deadline: Rolling. Notification: continuous.

Costs Per Year: Application fee: $35. Comprehensive fee: $22,835 includes full-time tuition ($17,027) and college room and board ($5808).

Collegiate Environment: Orientation program. Drama-theater group, choral group, student-run newspaper, radio station. Social organizations: 44 open to all. Most popular organizations: Student Government Association, Baptist Student Union, Campbell Catholic Community, Presidential Scholars Club, Pre-Pharmacy Club. Major annual events: Homecoming, Spring Fling, Parents' Day. Student services: health clinic, personal-psychological counseling. Campus security: 24-hour emergency response devices and patrols, late night transport-escort service, controlled dormitory access. 1,500 college housing spaces available; 1,347 were occupied in 2003-04. Freshmen guaranteed college housing. On-campus residence required through sophomore year. Options: men-only, women-only housing available. Carrie Rich Memorial Library plus 3 others with 218,000 books, 1.2 million microform titles, 12,645 serials, 4,507 audiovisual materials, an OPAC, and a Web page. Operations spending for 2004 fiscal year: $2.5 million. 256 computers available on campus for general student use. A campuswide network can be accessed from student residence rooms and from off campus. Staffed computer lab on campus.

Community Environment: Located 30 miles south of Raleigh where the climate is mild, and 30 miles north of Fayetteville, the community is served by Baptist and United Methodist churches, a community civic club and a full-time campus infirmary. There is a hospital seven miles away. Part-time employment for students is available.

■ CAPE FEAR COMMUNITY COLLEGE *I-11*
411 North Front St.
Wilmington, NC 28401-3993
Tel: (910)362-7000
Admissions: (910)362-7054
E-mail: lkasyan@cfcc.edu
Web Site: http://www.cfcc.edu/

Description: State-supported, 2-year, coed. Part of North Carolina Community College System. Awards certificates, diplomas, transfer associate, and terminal associate degrees. Founded 1959. Setting: 150-acre urban campus. Endowment: $1.8 million. Educational spending for 2005 fiscal year: $2869 per student. Total enrollment: 7,501. Student-undergrad faculty ratio is 13:1. Full-time: 3,160 students, 49% women, 51% men. Part-time: 4,341 students, 59% women, 41% men. Students come from 29 states and territories, 2 other countries, 7% from out-of-state, 1% Native American, 2% Hispanic, 14% black, 1% Asian American or Pacific Islander, 0% international, 11% 25 or older. Core. Calendar: semesters. Academic remediation for entering students, services for LD students, distance learning, part-time degree program, adult/continuing education programs, co-op programs.

Entrance Requirements: Open admission except for nursing, allied health programs. Options: electronic application, early admission, deferred admission. Required: high school transcript, placement testing. Entrance: noncompetitive. Application deadline: 8/19. Notification: continuous.

Costs Per Year: Application fee: $0. State resident tuition: $1264 full-time, $39.50 per credit part-time. Nonresident tuition: $7024 full-time, $219.50 per credit part-time. Mandatory fees: $70 full-time, $7 per credit part-time. Full-time tuition and fees vary according to course load. Part-time tuition and fees vary according to course load.

Collegiate Environment: Orientation program. Choral group, student-run newspaper. Social organizations: 25 open to all. Most popular organizations: Nursing Club, Dental Hygiene Club, Pineapple Guild. Major annual event: Spring Fling. Student services: personal-psychological counseling. Campus security: 24-hour emergency response devices and patrols, late night transport-escort service. College housing not available. Cape Fear Community College Library with 47,761 books, 28,400 microform titles, 936 serials, 6,317 audiovisual materials, an OPAC, and a Web page. Operations spending for 2004 fiscal year: $989,099. 80 computers available on campus for general student use. A campuswide network can be accessed from off-campus. Staffed computer lab on campus.

Community Environment: See University of North Carolina - Wilmington.

■ CAROLINAS COLLEGE OF HEALTH SCIENCES *E-3*

PO Box 32861, 1200 Blythe Blvd.

Charlotte, NC 28232-2861

Tel: (704)355-5043

Fax: (704)355-5967

Web Site: http://www.carolinascollege.edu/

Description: Independent, 2-year, coed. Part of Carolinas Healthcare System. Awards certificates, diplomas, and terminal associate degrees. Founded 1990. Setting: 3-acre urban campus. Endowment: $2 million. Total enrollment: 458. Full-time: 146 students, 84% women, 16% men. Part-time: 312 students, 87% women, 13% men. Students come from 3 states and territories, 6% from out-of-state, 0.4% Native American, 2% Hispanic, 15% black, 2% Asian American or Pacific Islander, 0% international, 46% 25 or older, 5% live on campus, 0% transferred in. Calendar: semesters. Advanced placement, independent study, distance learning, internships.

Entrance Requirements: Required: high school transcript. Recommended: minimum 2.5 high school GPA. Required for some: recommendations, interview, SAT or ACT. Entrance: moderately difficult. Application deadline: 2/6. Notification: 3/15. Preference given to county residents.

Costs Per Year: Application fee: $35. Tuition: $6145 full-time, $175 per credit part-time. Mandatory fees: $250 full-time. Full-time tuition and fees vary according to course load and program. Part-time tuition varies according to course load and program.

Collegiate Environment: Orientation program. Social organizations: 1 open to all. Most popular organization: Student Government Association. Major annual events: Spring Fling, Thanksgiving Covered Dish Luncheon, Holiday Mixer. Student services: legal services, health clinic, personal-psychological counseling. Campus security: 24-hour emergency response devices and patrols, student patrols, late night transport-escort service. 45 college housing spaces available; 25 were occupied in 2003-04. No special consideration for freshman housing applicants. AHEC Library with 9,810 books, 503 serials, and an OPAC. Operations spending for 2004 fiscal year: $60,000. 36 computers available on campus for general student use. A campuswide network can be accessed. Staffed computer lab on campus.

■ CARTERET COMMUNITY COLLEGE *G-14*

3505 Arendell St.

Morehead City, NC 28557-2989

Tel: (252)222-6000

Admissions: (252)222-6153

Fax: (252)222-6274

Web Site: http://www.carteret.edu/

Description: State-supported, 2-year, coed. Part of North Carolina Community College System. Awards certificates, diplomas, transfer associate, and terminal associate degrees. Founded 1963. Setting: 25-acre small town campus. Total enrollment: 1,659. Full-time: 181 students, 71% women, 29% men. Part-time: 192 students, 55% women, 45% men. Students come from 24 states and territories, 0.4% Native American, 3% Hispanic, 5% black, 0.2% Asian American or Pacific Islander, 53% 25 or older. Core. Calendar: semesters. Academic remediation for entering students, services for LD students, distance learning, double major, summer session for credit, part-time degree program, adult/continuing education programs, co-op programs and internships.

Entrance Requirements: Open admission except for allied health programs. Options: Common Application, electronic application, early admission. Required: high school transcript. Entrance: noncompetitive. Application deadline: Rolling. Notification: continuous.

Costs Per Year: Application fee: $0. State resident tuition: $1,314 full-time, $55.75 per credit hour part-time. Nonresident tuition: $7,074 full-time, $235.75 per credit hour part-time. Mandatory fees: $66 full-time, $15.25 per term part-time.

Collegiate Environment: Orientation program. Drama-theater group, student-run newspaper. College housing not available. Michael J. Smith Learning Resource Center with 22,000 books and 168 serials. 150 computers available on campus for general student use. A campuswide network can be accessed. Staffed computer lab on campus.

Community Environment: Morehead City is one of the most popular coastal resorts in the state. The $4 million Port Terminal with its 2,600-foot pier affords excellent facilities for oceangoing vessels. Fishing, particularly for menhaden, is an important industry. The Atlantic Beach across Bogue Sound is an excellent 24-mile beach. Recreational facilities are numerous for all kinds of ocean fishing, and for hunting wild ducks and geese.

■ CATAWBA COLLEGE *D-4*

2300 West Innes St.

Salisbury, NC 28144-2488

Tel: (704)637-4111

Free: 800-CAT-AWBA

E-mail: admissions@catawba.edu

Web Site: http://www.catawba.edu/

Description: Independent, comprehensive, coed, affiliated with United Church of Christ. Awards bachelor's and master's degrees. Founded 1851. Setting: 210-acre small town campus with easy access to Charlotte. Endowment: $33.3 million. Research spending for 2004 fiscal year: $101,750. Educational spending for 2005 fiscal year: $6100 per student. Total enrollment: 1,288. Faculty: 98 (72 full-time, 26 part-time). Student-undergrad faculty ratio is 15:1. 724 applied, 68% were admitted. 16% from top 10% of their high school class, 39% from top quarter, 75% from top half. Full-time: 1,222 students, 52% women, 48% men. Part-time: 34 students, 62% women, 38% men. Students come from 33 states and territories, 16 other countries, 30% from out-of-state, 1% Native American, 1% Hispanic, 16% black, 1% Asian American or Pacific Islander, 2% international, 29% 25 or older, 67% live on campus, 10% transferred in. Retention: 77% of full-time freshmen returned the following year. Academic areas with the most degrees conferred: business/marketing; computer and information sciences; education. Core. Calendar: semesters. Services for LD students, advanced placement, self-designed majors, honors program, independent study, double major, summer session for credit, part-time degree program, adult/continuing education programs, internships. Study abroad program. ROTC: Army (c).

Entrance Requirements: Options: Peterson's Universal Application, Common Application, electronic application, early admission, deferred admission, international baccalaureate accepted. Required: essay, high school transcript, minimum 2.0 high school GPA, recommendations, SAT or ACT. Recommended: interview. Entrance: moderately difficult. Application deadline: Rolling. Notification: continuous.

Costs Per Year: Application fee: $25. Comprehensive fee: $25,000 includes full-time tuition ($18,750) and college room and board ($6250). Full-time tuition varies according to class time. Part-time tuition: $500 per semester hour. Part-time tuition varies according to class time, course load, and degree level.

Collegiate Environment: Orientation program. Drama-theater group, choral group, student-run newspaper. Social organizations: 25 open to all. Most popular organizations: United In Service, Catawba Guides, Blue Masque (drama), L'il Chiefs, Wigwam Productions. Major annual events: homecoming, Parents' Weekend, Spring Fling. Student services: health clinic, personal-psychological counseling. Campus security: 24-hour emergency response devices and patrols, late night transport-escort service, controlled dormitory access. 768 college housing spaces available; 652 were occupied in 2003-04. Freshmen guaranteed college housing. On-campus residence required through sophomore year. Options: coed, men-only, women-only housing available. Corriher-Linn-Black Memorial Library plus 1 other with 112,447 books, 585,307 microform titles, 604 serials, 24,542 audiovisual materials, and an OPAC. Operations spending for 2004 fiscal year: $599,913. 97 computers available on campus for general student use. A campuswide network can be accessed from student residence rooms and from off campus. Staffed computer lab on campus.

Community Environment: Salisbury was founded in 1753 and during the year 1781 the city served, at different times, as headquarters for both Cornwallis and Greene, British and patriot generals. Community facilities include numerous churches, a public library, hospitals, and various civic and service organizations. Recreational activities include golf, swimming, fishing, and other sports. Part-time employment is available.

■ CATAWBA VALLEY COMMUNITY COLLEGE *D-2*

2550 Hwy. 70 SE

Hickory, NC 28602-9699

Tel: (828)327-7000

Fax: (828)327-7000

Web Site: http://www.cvcc.cc.nc.us/

Description: State and locally supported, 2-year, coed. Part of North Carolina Community College System. Awards certificates, diplomas, transfer associate, and terminal associate degrees. Founded 1960. Setting: 50-acre small town campus with easy access to Charlotte. Endowment: $591,181. Total enrollment: 3,943. Full-time: 1,524 students, 54% women, 46% men.

Part-time: 2,419 students, 58% women, 42% men. Students come from 3 states and territories, 2 other countries, 1% from out-of-state, 46% 25 or older, 24% transferred in. Core. Calendar: semesters. Academic remediation for entering students, ESL program, services for LD students, advanced placement, self-designed majors, independent study, distance learning, double major, summer session for credit, part-time degree program, adult/continuing education programs, co-op programs.

Entrance Requirements: Open admission except for allied health programs. Options: Common Application, early admission, deferred admission. Required: high school transcript. Placement: ACT ASSET required. Entrance: noncompetitive. Application deadline: Rolling. Notification: continuous.

Collegiate Environment: Choral group, student-run newspaper. Social organizations: 12 open to all. Most popular organizations: NCANS (Nursing), Phi Theta Kappa, Catawba Valley Outing Club, Respiratory Care Club, Rotoract. Major annual events: Fall Fling, Awards Day, Red Cross Bloodmobile. Student services: personal-psychological counseling. Campus security: 24-hour patrols. College housing not available. Learning Resource Center with 46,000 books, 49 microform titles, 274 serials, 3,644 audiovisual materials, and an OPAC. Operations spending for 2004 fiscal year: $362,606. 1,144 computers available on campus for general student use. A campuswide network can be accessed from off-campus. Staffed computer lab on campus.

Community Environment: See Lenoir-Rhyne College.

■ **CENTRAL CAROLINA COMMUNITY COLLEGE** *E-8*

1105 Kelly Dr.
Sanford, NC 27330-9000
Tel: (919)775-5401
Fax: (919)775-1221
Web Site: http://www.cccc.edu/

Description: State and locally supported, 2-year, coed. Part of North Carolina Community College System. Awards certificates, diplomas, transfer associate, and terminal associate degrees. Founded 1962. Setting: 41-acre small town campus. Endowment: $1 million. Educational spending for 2005 fiscal year: $2782 per student. Total enrollment: 4,857. 2,844 applied, 43% were admitted. Full-time: 1,845 students, 63% women, 37% men. Part-time: 3,012 students, 62% women, 38% men. Students come from 36 states and territories, 5 other countries, 6% from out-of-state, 1% Native American, 4% Hispanic, 25% black, 1% Asian American or Pacific Islander, 0.2% international, 50% 25 or older, 20% transferred in. Core. Calendar: semesters. Academic remediation for entering students, ESL program, services for LD students, advanced placement, independent study, distance learning, double major, summer session for credit, part-time degree program, adult/continuing education programs, internships.

Entrance Requirements: Open admission except for nursing, veterinary medical assistant programs. Options: electronic application, early admission, deferred admission. Required: high school transcript. Placement: CPT, ACCUPLACER, ACT COMPASS, ACT ASSET required; SAT or ACT recommended. Entrance: noncompetitive. Application deadline: Rolling. Notification: continuous. Preference given to residents of sponsoring counties.

Collegiate Environment: Orientation program. Student-run radio station. Major annual events: Activity Day, Miss CCCC Pageant, Spring Dance. Student services: personal-psychological counseling. Campus security: patrols by trained security personnel during operating hours. College housing not available. Library/Learning Resources Center plus 2 others with 50,479 books, 240 serials, 5,946 audiovisual materials, an OPAC, and a Web page. Operations spending for 2004 fiscal year: $408,437. 100 computers available on campus for general student use. A campuswide network can be accessed from off-campus. Staffed computer lab on campus.

Community Environment: Sanford, known as the brick capital of the nation, is nearly the exact center of North Carolina with all forms of commercial transportation available. Over 50 manufacturing and processing firms are located here. Modern shopping facilities and the privately owned hospital serve the community. Recreational opportunities are unparalleled at nearby Cape Fear and the resort areas of Pinehurst and Southern Pines.

■ **CENTRAL PIEDMONT COMMUNITY COLLEGE** *E-3*

PO Box 35009
Charlotte, NC 28235-5009
Tel: (704)330-2722
Admissions: (704)330-6784
Web Site: http://www.cpcc.edu/

Description: State and locally supported, 2-year, coed. Part of North Carolina Community College System. Awards certificates, diplomas, transfer associate, and terminal associate degrees. Founded 1963. Setting: 37-acre urban campus. Endowment: $16.1 million. Educational spending for 2005 fiscal year: $2896 per student. Total enrollment: 16,631. Student-undergrad faculty ratio is 16:1. 1,397 applied, 100% were admitted. Full-time: 6,115 students, 54% women, 46% men. Part-time: 10,516 students, 61% women, 39% men. Students come from 13 states and territories, 117 other countries, 3% from out-of-state, 1% Native American, 3% Hispanic, 32% black, 3% Asian American or Pacific Islander, 9% international, 50% 25 or older, 24% transferred in. Core. Calendar: semesters. Academic remediation for entering students, ESL program, services for LD students, advanced placement, accelerated degree program, self-designed majors, honors program, distance learning, summer session for credit, part-time degree program, co-op programs. Off campus study at members of the Charlotte Area Educational Consortium.

Entrance Requirements: Open admission. Option: Common Application. Required: high school transcript. Entrance: noncompetitive. Application deadlines: Rolling, Rolling for nonresidents. Notification: continuous, continuous for nonresidents.

Costs Per Year: Application fee: $0. State resident tuition: $1264 full-time, $39.50 per semester hour part-time. Nonresident tuition: $7024 full-time, $219.50 per semester hour part-time. Mandatory fees: $170 full-time, $56 per term part-time.

Collegiate Environment: Drama-theater group, choral group, student-run newspaper. Social organizations: 22 open to all; local fraternities. Most popular organizations: Phi Theta Kappa, Black Students Organization, Students for Environmental Sanity, Sierra Club, Nursing Club. Major annual events: Fall Fest, Spring Fling, World Games. Student services: personal-psychological counseling, women's center. Campus security: 24-hour emergency response devices and patrols. College housing not available. Hagemeyer Learning Center plus 5 others with 102,649 books, 125,462 microform titles, 750 serials, 17,802 audiovisual materials, an OPAC, and a Web page. Operations spending for 2004 fiscal year: $1.5 million.

Community Environment: See Queens College.

■ **CHOWAN UNIVERSITY** *A-13*

200 Jones Dr.
Murfreesboro, NC 27855
Tel: (252)398-6500
Free: 800-488-4101
Admissions: (252)398-6314
Fax: (252)398-1190
E-mail: admissions@chowan.edu
Web Site: http://www.chowan.edu

Description: Independent Baptist, 4-year, coed. Awards associate and bachelor's degrees. Founded 1848. Setting: 300-acre rural campus with easy access to Norfolk; Virginia and North Carolina Outer Banks. Endowment: $12 million. Educational spending for 2005 fiscal year: $5567 per student. Total enrollment: 800. 2,192 applied, 58% were admitted. 5% from top 10% of their high school class, 19% from top quarter, 55% from top half. Full-time: 800 students, 44% women, 56% men. Students come from 23 states and territories, 3 other countries, 51% from out-of-state, 1% Native American, 2% Hispanic, 29% black, 1% Asian American or Pacific Islander, 10% international, 2% 25 or older, 79% live on campus, 1% transferred in. Retention: 54% of full-time freshmen returned the following year. Core. Calendar: semesters. Advanced placement, self-designed majors, independent study, double major, summer session for credit, part-time degree program, internships. Study abroad program.

Entrance Requirements: Options: Peterson's Universal Application, electronic application, early admission, deferred admission, international baccalaureate accepted. Required: high school transcript, SAT or ACT. Recommended: minimum 2.0 high school GPA, 2 recommendations. Required for some: essay, interview. Entrance: minimally difficult. Application deadline: Rolling. Notification: continuous.

Costs Per Year: Application fee: $20. Comprehensive fee: $21,350 includes full-time tuition ($14,600), mandatory fees ($150), and college room and board ($6600). College room only: $3100. Room and board charges vary according to board plan. Part-time tuition: $230 per hour. Part-time tuition varies according to course load.

Collegiate Environment: Orientation program. Drama-theater group, choral group. Social organizations: 52 open to all; national fraternities, local sororities; 12% of eligible men and 13% of eligible women are members. Most popular organizations: Christian Student Union, Student Government Association, Habitat for Humanity, Phi Kappa Tau, SNCAE (Students of North Carolina Association of Educators). Major annual events: homecoming, Spring Fling, Family Day. Student services: health clinic, personal-psychological counseling. Campus security: 24-hour emergency response devices and patrols, late night transport-escort service; controlled dormitory access. 1,200 college housing spaces available. Freshmen guaranteed college housing. On-campus residence required through sophomore year. Options: men-only, women-only housing available. Whitaker Library plus 1 other with 93,676 books, 35,010 microform titles, 1,113 serials, 4,569 audiovisual materials, and an OPAC. Operations spending for 2004 fiscal year: $435,393. 100 computers available on campus for general student use. Computer purchase/lease plans available. A campuswide network can be accessed from student residence rooms and from off campus. Staffed computer lab on campus.

Community Environment: In the northeastern section of North Carolina, Murfreesboro is the location of several historical sites. Community facilities include several churches, museums and a library. A hospital and commercial transportation are available in nearby towns. Hunting, fishing, boating, jet skiing, and water skiing are some of the recreational activities.

■ **CLEVELAND COMMUNITY COLLEGE** *E-2*
137 South Post Rd.
Shelby, NC 28152
Tel: (704)484-4000
Admissions: (704)484-4073
Web Site: http://www.clevelandcommunitycollege.edu/

Description: State-supported, 2-year, coed. Part of North Carolina Community College System. Awards certificates, diplomas, transfer associate, and terminal associate degrees. Founded 1965. Setting: 43-acre small town campus with easy access to Charlotte. Endowment: $450,000. Educational spending for 2005 fiscal year: $3868 per student. Total enrollment: 3,047. 279 applied, 100% were admitted. Full-time: 1,241 students, 67% women, 33% men. Part-time: 1,806 students, 67% women, 33% men. Students come from 3 states and territories, 1% from out-of-state, 0.2% Native American, 1% Hispanic, 22% black, 1% Asian American or Pacific Islander, 0% international, 47% 25 or older, 1% transferred in. Core. Calendar: semesters. Academic remediation for entering students, ESL program, advanced placement, independent study, distance learning, double major, summer session for credit, part-time degree program, adult/continuing education programs. Off campus study at Foothills Nursing Consortium.

Entrance Requirements: Open admission except for allied health programs. Options: Common Application, electronic application, deferred admission. Required: high school transcript. Entrance: noncompetitive. Application deadline: Rolling. Notification: continuous.

Costs Per Year: Application fee: $0. State resident tuition: $1264 full-time, $39.50 per credit hour part-time. Nonresident tuition: $7024 full-time, $219.50 per credit hour part-time. Mandatory fees: $38 full-time. Full-time tuition and fees vary according to course load. Part-time tuition varies according to course load.

Collegiate Environment: Orientation program. Drama-theater group, choral group. Social organizations: 10 open to all. Most popular organizations: Gamma Beta Phi Honor Society, Student Government Association, Lamplighters, Mu Epsilon Delta, Black Awareness Club. Major annual events: Women's World, Spring Fling Welcome Back Students, Awards Night. Student services: personal-psychological counseling. Campus security: security personnel during open hours. College housing not available. Cleveland Community College Library with 34,000 books, 1,135 microform titles, 280 serials, 3,619 audiovisual materials, an OPAC, and a Web page. Operations spending for 2004 fiscal year: $420,550. 325 computers available on campus for general student use. A campuswide network can be accessed. Staffed computer lab on campus.

Community Environment: Shelby is the county seat for Cleveland County and is a diversified manufacturing area. The principal businesses are mercantile, textiles, and machine parts. A city park and a large lake provide the area with recreation facilities.

■ **COASTAL CAROLINA COMMUNITY COLLEGE** *G-12*
444 Western Blvd.
Jacksonville, NC 28546-6899
Tel: (910)455-1221
Admissions: (910)938-6254
Fax: (910)455-2767
E-mail: herringd@coastal.cc.nc.us
Web Site: http://www.coastalcarolina.edu/

Description: State and locally supported, 2-year, coed. Part of North Carolina Community College System. Awards certificates, diplomas, transfer associate, and terminal associate degrees. Founded 1964. Setting: 98-acre small town campus. Endowment: $1.9 million. Research spending for 2004 fiscal year: $37,912. Educational spending for 2005 fiscal year: $2768 per student. Total enrollment: 4,111. Student-undergrad faculty ratio is 16:1. 3,451 applied, 78% were admitted. Full-time: 2,072 students, 69% women, 31% men. Part-time: 2,039 students, 61% women, 39% men. Students come from 48 states and territories, 5 other countries, 31% from out-of-state, 1% Native American, 9% Hispanic, 19% black, 3% Asian American or Pacific Islander, 1% international, 45% 25 or older, 13% transferred in. Core. Calendar: semesters. Academic remediation for entering students, ESL program, services for LD students, advanced placement, independent study, distance learning, double major, summer session for credit, part-time degree program, adult/continuing education programs, internships.

Entrance Requirements: Open admission. Options: deferred admission, international baccalaureate accepted. Required: high school transcript. Required for some: 2 recommendations, interview. Entrance: noncompetitive. Application deadline: Rolling. Notification: continuous.

Costs Per Year: Application fee: $0. State resident tuition: $1264 full-time, $39.50 per credit hour part-time. Nonresident tuition: $7024 full-time, $219.50 per credit hour part-time. Mandatory fees: $30 full-time, $5 per term part-time.

Collegiate Environment: Orientation program. Drama-theater group. Social organizations: 7 open to all. Most popular organizations: SHELL (environmental group), SPYS (social sciences group), student government, Star of Life, Association of Nursing Students. Major annual events: Spring Fling, Winter Meltdown, Fall Festival. Student services: personal-psychological counseling. Campus security: 24-hour emergency response devices and patrols, late night transport-escort service. College housing not available. C. Louis Shields Learning Resources Center with 44,062 books, 738 microform titles, 266 serials, 10,460 audiovisual materials, and an OPAC. Operations spending for 2004 fiscal year: $366,476. 830 computers available on campus for general student use. A campuswide network can be accessed from off-campus. Staffed computer lab on campus.

Community Environment: The principal business of Jacksonville are marine-related industries, military support services, and wood products. Railroads serve the area. Thirty churches of various faiths, one library and numerous historical sites are within the community. Hunting and fishing are excellent, and there are also parks are in the area for other recreational activities.

■ **COLLEGE OF THE ALBEMARLE** *B-15*
PO Box 2327
Elizabeth City, NC 27906-2327
Tel: (252)335-0821
Fax: (252)335-2011
Web Site: http://www.albemarle.edu/

Description: State-supported, 2-year, coed. Part of North Carolina Community College System. Awards certificates, diplomas, transfer associate, and terminal associate degrees. Founded 1960. Setting: 40-acre small town campus. Total enrollment: 2,071. Full-time: 854 students, 63% women, 37% men. Part-time: 1,217 students, 68% women, 32% men. Students come from 17 states and territories, 4 other countries, 56% 25 or older. Calendar: semesters. Academic remediation for entering students, ESL program, services for LD students, advanced placement, summer session for credit, part-time degree program, adult/continuing education programs, co-op programs.

Entrance Requirements: Open admission except for nursing, allied health programs. Options: early admission, deferred admission. Required: high school transcript. Entrance: noncompetitive. Application deadline: Rolling. Notification: continuous.

Costs Per Year: Application fee: $0. State resident tuition: $1264 full-time, $39.50 per credit hour part-time. Nonresident tuition: $7024 full-time, $219.50 per credit hour part-time.

Collegiate Environment: Drama-theater group, choral group. Social organizations: 18 open to all. Most popular organizations: Phi Beta Lambda, Phi Theta Kappa. Major annual events: Welcome Back Day, Spring Fling, Career Day. Student services: personal-psychological counseling. Campus security: 24-hour patrols. College housing not available. Learning Resources Center with 48,400 books, 280 serials, an OPAC, and a Web page. 85 computers available on campus for general student use. Staffed computer lab on campus.

Community Environment: Elizabeth City is the home of a variety of manufacturing firms and serves as a shipping center for a large agricultural area producing corn, soybeans, potatoes, small grains, cabbage and other vegetables. All forms of commercial transportation are available. The Pasquotant River and nearby waterways provide for water sports, and deep sea and surf fishing on the Atlantic Ocean 40 miles away. The Dismal Swamp is a paradise for hunters, fishermen and naturalists. Big and small game include black bears, deer, foxes and many small mammals. Some of the historic points of interest are the Shiloh Baptist Church, the Old Brick House, Hall Creek Church, Winslow and Bayfield Home, the site of Culpepper's Rebellion in 1677-the first open rebellion against the king. Kitty Hawk, site of the Wright brothers' first powered flight, and Manteo, location of the first attempted English Colony, are nearby.

■ **CRAVEN COMMUNITY COLLEGE** *F-13*
800 College Ct.
New Bern, NC 28562-4984
Tel: (252)638-4131
Admissions: (252)638-7220
Fax: (252)638-4649
Web Site: http://www.craven.cc.nc.us/
Description: State-supported, 2-year, coed. Part of North Carolina Community College System. Awards certificates, diplomas, transfer associate, and terminal associate degrees. Founded 1965. Setting: 100-acre suburban campus. Endowment: $576,211. Total enrollment: 2,555. Students come from 25 states and territories, 2 other countries, 17% from out-of-state, 1% Native American, 3% Hispanic, 26% black, 2% Asian American or Pacific Islander, 0.2% international, 50% 25 or older. Core. Calendar: semesters. Academic remediation for entering students, services for LD students, advanced placement, self-designed majors, independent study, distance learning, double major, summer session for credit, part-time degree program, adult/continuing education programs, co-op programs and internships.
Entrance Requirements: Open admission except for nursing program. Required: high school transcript, interview. Placement: SAT or ACT recommended. Entrance: noncompetitive. Application deadline: Rolling.
Collegiate Environment: Orientation program. Drama-theater group, choral group. Social organizations: 15 open to all. Most popular organizations: Accounting Club, Alumni Association, Association of Information Technology Professionals, Criminal Justice Society, Phi Theta Kappa. Major annual events: Pizza Pizza , Diversity Fair, Job Fair. Student services: personal-psychological counseling. Campus security: 24-hour patrols. College housing not available. R. C. Godwin Memorial Library with 21,000 books, 301 serials, and an OPAC. Operations spending for 2004 fiscal year: $273,216. 350 computers available on campus for general student use. Staffed computer lab on campus.
Community Environment: New Bern, one of the oldest towns in the state, is interesting for its old buildings and many historical sites and markers. The first Provincial Congresses met here in 1774 and 1775. Some points of interest are the Christ Church, Federal Building, First Presbyterian Church and the Tryon Palace Restoration.

■ **DAVIDSON COLLEGE** *D-3*
Davidson, NC 28035
Tel: (704)894-2000
Free: 800-768-0380
Admissions: (704)894-2230
Fax: (704)894-2016
E-mail: admission@davidson.edu
Web Site: http://www.davidson.edu/
Description: Independent Presbyterian, 4-year, coed. Awards bachelor's degrees. Founded 1837. Setting: 556-acre small town campus with easy access to Charlotte. Endowment: $382.2 million. Research spending for 2004 fiscal year: $746,562. Educational spending for 2005 fiscal year: $13,455 per student. Total enrollment: 1,683. Student-undergrad faculty ratio is 10:1. 4,258 applied, 27% were admitted. 72% from top 10% of their high school class, 96% from top quarter, 99% from top half. Full-time: 1,683 students, 50% women, 50% men. Students come from 46 states and territories, 31 other countries, 82% from out-of-state, 0.4% Native American, 4% Hispanic, 6% black, 2% Asian American or Pacific Islander, 3% international, 0% 25 or older, 91% live on campus, 0.1% transferred in. Retention: 96% of full-time freshmen returned the following year. Academic areas with the most degrees conferred: social sciences; history; English. Core. Calendar: semesters. Services for LD students, advanced placement, self-designed majors, honors program, independent study, double major. Off campus study at 19 members of the Charlotte Area Educational Consortium. Study abroad program. ROTC: Army, Air Force (c).

Entrance Requirements: Options: Common Application, early admission, early decision, deferred admission. Required: essay, high school transcript, 3 recommendations, SAT or ACT. Recommended: interview, SAT Subject Tests. Entrance: very difficult. Application deadlines: 1/2, 11/15 for early decision plan 1, 1/2 for early decision plan 2. Notification: 4/1, 12/15 for early decision plan 1, 2/1 for early decision plan 2.
Costs Per Year: Application fee: $50. Comprehensive fee: $36,825 includes full-time tuition ($28,667) and college room and board ($8158). College room only: $4308.
Collegiate Environment: Orientation program. Drama-theater group, choral group, student-run newspaper, radio station. Social organizations: 162 open to all; national fraternities; 41% of eligible men and 73% of eligible women are members. Most popular organizations: Inter-Varsity Christian Fellowship, Dean Rusk Program Student Advisory Council, music organizations, Community Service Council, Student Government Association. Major annual events: homecoming, fall concert, spring concert. Student services: health clinic, personal-psychological counseling, women's center. Campus security: 24-hour emergency response devices and patrols, late night transport-escort service, controlled dormitory access. 1,536 college housing spaces available; 1,519 were occupied in 2003-04. Freshmen guaranteed college housing. On-campus residence required through senior year. Options: coed, men-only, women-only housing available. E. H. Little Library plus 1 other with 422,035 books, 475,798 microform titles, 2,767 serials, 9,497 audiovisual materials, an OPAC, and a Web page. Operations spending for 2004 fiscal year: $2.7 million. 142 computers available on campus for general student use. A campuswide network can be accessed from student residence rooms and from off campus. Staffed computer lab on campus.
Community Environment: The town of Davidson has grown around Davidson College. The cultural, social and religious life of the community revolves around the college. Davidson is twenty minutes north of Charlotte, NC, and offers students the advantages of that city's services, amenities, and recreational opportunities.

■ **DAVIDSON COUNTY COMMUNITY COLLEGE** *C-5*
PO Box 1287
Lexington, NC 27293-1287
Tel: (336)249-8186
Fax: (336)249-0379
E-mail: cottrell.judy@davidson.cc.nc.us
Web Site: http://www.davidson.cc.nc.us/
Description: State and locally supported, 2-year, coed. Part of North Carolina Community College System. Awards certificates, diplomas, transfer associate, and terminal associate degrees. Founded 1958. Setting: 83-acre rural campus. Endowment: $6.5 million. Educational spending for 2005 fiscal year: $2284 per student. Total enrollment: 2,303. 692 applied, 100% were admitted. Full-time: 829 students, 63% women, 37% men. Part-time: 1,474 students, 60% women, 40% men. Students come from 7 states and territories, 1% from out-of-state, 0.4% Native American, 1% Hispanic, 13% black, 1% Asian American or Pacific Islander, 0% international, 55% 25 or older. Core. Calendar: semesters. Academic remediation for entering students, services for LD students, advanced placement, double major, summer session for credit, part-time degree program, adult/continuing education programs, co-op programs and internships. Off campus study at Rowan-Cabarrus Community College, Forsyth Technical Community College, Guilford Technical Community College, Rockingham Community College.
Entrance Requirements: Open admission except for nursing, allied health programs. Options: early admission, deferred admission. Required: high school transcript. Required for some: interview. Entrance: noncompetitive. Application deadline: Rolling. Notification: continuous.
Costs Per Year: Application fee: $0. State resident tuition: $1140 full-time, $38 per credit hour part-time. Nonresident tuition: $6330 full-time, $211 per credit hour part-time. Mandatory fees: $1088 full-time, $27.25 per term part-time.
Collegiate Environment: Orientation program. Drama-theater group. Major annual events: Fall Fest, Spring Fling, G. E. Love Lecture Series. Campus security: late night transport-escort service, security guards. College housing not available. Grady E. Love Learning Resource Center plus 1 other with 56,445 books, 48,107 microform titles, 454 serials, 7,564 audiovisual materials, an OPAC, and a Web page. Operations spending for 2004 fiscal year: $386,215. 400 computers available on campus for general student use. A campuswide network can be accessed from off-campus. Staffed computer lab on campus.
Community Environment: Lexington is a suburban community located approximately 25 miles south of Greensboro, N.C. Industry here includes

furniture, textiles, apparel, electronics, and food processing. Bus and train transportation are available. A YMCA, churches of all major denominations, a library, hospital, and numerous civic and service organizations serve the community. For recreation, High Rock Lake, about 12 miles south of Lexington, offers boating, fishing, swimming and picnicking. There are job opportunities for students.

■ **DEVRY UNIVERSITY** *E-3*
4521 Sharon Rd., Ste. 145
Charlotte, NC 28211-3627
Tel: (704)362-2345; (866)923-3879
Fax: (704)362-2668
Web Site: http://www.devry.edu/
Description: Proprietary, comprehensive, coed. Part of DeVry University. Awards bachelor's and master's degrees. Total enrollment: 166. Faculty: 15 (4 full-time, 11 part-time). Student-undergrad faculty ratio is 6:1. Full-time: 32 students, 38% women, 63% men. Part-time: 35 students, 51% women, 49% men. 0% Native American, 4% Hispanic, 63% black, 6% Asian American or Pacific Islander, 1% international. Retention: 50% of full-time freshmen returned the following year. Academic area with the most degrees conferred: business/marketing. Calendar: semesters. Academic remediation for entering students, advanced placement, accelerated degree program, distance learning, summer session for credit, part-time degree program, adult/continuing education programs, co-op programs.
Entrance Requirements: Options: electronic application, deferred admission, international baccalaureate accepted. Required: high school transcript, interview. Entrance: minimally difficult. Application deadline: Rolling.
Costs Per Year: Application fee: $50. One-time mandatory fee: $40. Tuition: $11,790 full-time, $440 per credit part-time. Mandatory fees: $30 full-time, $30 per year part-time. Full-time tuition and fees vary according to course load. Part-time tuition and fees vary according to course load.
Collegiate Environment: Orientation program. College housing not available.

■ **DUKE UNIVERSITY** *C-8*
Durham, NC 27708-0586
Tel: (919)684-8111
Admissions: (919)684-3214
Fax: (919)681-8941
E-mail: askduke@admiss.duke.edu
Web Site: http://www.duke.edu/
Description: Independent, university, coed, affiliated with United Methodist Church. Awards bachelor's, master's, doctoral, and first professional degrees and post-master's certificates. Founded 1838. Setting: 8,500-acre suburban campus. Endowment: $3.8 billion. Research spending for 2004 fiscal year: $445.5 million. Total enrollment: 14,075. Faculty: (964 full-time). Student-undergrad faculty ratio is 8:1. 18,090 applied, 22% were admitted. 87% from top 10% of their high school class, 97% from top quarter, 100% from top half. 197 valedictorians. Full-time: 6,470 students, 48% women, 52% men. Part-time: 64 students, 59% women, 41% men. Students come from 53 states and territories, 89 other countries, 86% from out-of-state, 0.3% Native American, 7% Hispanic, 11% black, 14% Asian American or Pacific Islander, 5% international, 0.3% 25 or older, 82% live on campus, 1% transferred in. Retention: 96% of full-time freshmen returned the following year. Academic areas with the most degrees conferred: social sciences; engineering; psychology. Core. Calendar: semesters. ESL program, services for LD students, advanced placement, accelerated degree program, self-designed majors, honors program, independent study, distance learning, summer session for credit, part-time degree program, adult/continuing education programs, internships, graduate courses open to undergrads. Off campus study at University of North Carolina at Chapel Hill, North Carolina Central University, North Carolina State University, Howard University. Study abroad program. ROTC: Army, Air Force.
Entrance Requirements: Options: Common Application, electronic application, early admission, early decision, deferred admission, international baccalaureate accepted. Required: essay, high school transcript, 3 recommendations, SAT or ACT. Recommended: interview. Required for some: audition tape for dance, drama, or music; slides of work for art. Entrance: most difficult. Application deadlines: 1/2, 11/1 for early decision. Notification: 4/1, 12/15 for early decision. Preference given to children of alumni, minorities, state residents.
Costs Per Year: Application fee: $70. Comprehensive fee: $43,115 includes full-time tuition ($32,845), mandatory fees ($1118), and college room and board ($9152). College room only: $4950.

Collegiate Environment: Orientation program. Drama-theater group, choral group, marching band, student-run newspaper, radio station. Social organizations: 350 open to all; national fraternities, national sororities; 29% of eligible men and 42% of eligible women are members. Major annual events: homecoming, Parents' Weekend, Oktoberfest. Student services: legal services, health clinic, personal-psychological counseling, women's center. Campus security: 24-hour emergency response devices and patrols, late night transport-escort service, controlled dormitory access. 5,371 college housing spaces available; 5,017 were occupied in 2003-04. Freshmen guaranteed college housing. On-campus residence required through junior year. Options: coed, men-only, women-only housing available. Perkins Library plus 14 others with 5.5 million books, 4.2 million microform titles, 36,995 serials, 467,500 audiovisual materials, an OPAC, and a Web page. Operations spending for 2004 fiscal year: $30.3 million. 600 computers available on campus for general student use. Computer purchase/lease plans available. A campuswide network can be accessed from student residence rooms and from off campus. Staffed computer lab on campus.
Community Environment: Durham, North Carolina, a city of about 200,000 people, is approximately 250 miles south of Washington, D.C. Durham and nearby Raleigh and Chapel Hill constitute the three points of what is known as the Research Triangle, one of the nation's foremost centers for research-oriented industries and government, research, and regulatory agencies. The combined population of the Raleigh, Durham, and Chapel Hill area is one million. Two major interstates and the Raleigh-Durham International Airport (a 20-minute drive from campus) make Durham easily accessible from almost anywhere in the United States. Nationally known hospitals and clinics, including the Duke University Medical Center, make Durham a center for medicine. Other community facilities include numerous churches, museums, parks, shopping areas, an arts center, and major civic and service organizations. Both beaches and mountains are within a three-hour drive.

■ **DURHAM TECHNICAL COMMUNITY COLLEGE** *C-8*
1637 Lawson St.
Durham, NC 27703-5023
Tel: (919)686-3300
Admissions: (919)686-3619
Web Site: http://www.durhamtech.edu/
Description: State-supported, 2-year, coed. Part of North Carolina Community College System. Awards certificates, diplomas, transfer associate, and terminal associate degrees. Founded 1961. Setting: urban campus. Educational spending for 2005 fiscal year: $2751 per student. Total enrollment: 5,642. Full-time: 1,464 students, 58% women, 42% men. Part-time: 4,178 students, 65% women, 35% men. Students come from 50 states and territories, 1% from out-of-state, 0.2% Native American, 2% Hispanic, 41% black, 3% Asian American or Pacific Islander, 8% international, 63% 25 or older, 59% transferred in. Core. Calendar: semesters. Academic remediation for entering students, ESL program, services for LD students, advanced placement, accelerated degree program, self-designed majors, distance learning, summer session for credit, part-time degree program, adult/continuing education programs, co-op programs and internships. Off campus study at University of North Carolina at Chapel Hill, University of North Carolina at Greensboro, Wake Technical Community College, Asheville-Buncombe Community College, Central Piedmont Community College, Guilford Technical Community College, Piedmont Community College.
Entrance Requirements: Open admission. Option: deferred admission. Required: high school transcript. Recommended: interview. Placement: ACT ASSET or ACT COMPASS required. Entrance: noncompetitive. Application deadline: Rolling. Notification: continuous.
Collegiate Environment: Orientation program. Drama-theater group. Social organizations: 18 open to all. Most popular organizations: Amigos Unidos, Gamma Beta Phi, Student Senate, Student Nurses Association, Practical Nurses Students Club. Major annual events: Campus Fund Drive and Barbecue, Native American Festival, Pops on the Plaza summer concert. Student services: personal-psychological counseling. Campus security: 24-hour patrols, late night transport-escort service. College housing not available. Educational Resource Center with 36,388 books, 123,657 microform titles, 1,348 audiovisual materials, and an OPAC. Operations spending for 2004 fiscal year: $242,577. 664 computers available on campus for general student use. A campuswide network can be accessed from off-campus. Staffed computer lab on campus.
Community Environment: See Duke University.

■ **EAST CAROLINA UNIVERSITY** *D-12*
East 5th St.
Greenville, NC 27858-4353

Tel: (252)328-6131
Admissions: (252)328-6640
Fax: (252)328-6495
Web Site: http://www.ecu.edu/

Description: State-supported, university, coed. Part of The University of North Carolina. Awards bachelor's, master's, doctoral, and first professional degrees and post-master's certificates. Founded 1907. Setting: 1,000-acre urban campus. Endowment: $65.7 million. Research spending for 2004 fiscal year: $11.9 million. Educational spending for 2005 fiscal year: $8555 per student. Total enrollment: 23,164. Faculty: 1,292 (1,096 full-time, 196 part-time). Student-undergrad faculty ratio is 16:1. 11,633 applied, 74% were admitted. 14% from top 10% of their high school class, 42% from top quarter, 79% from top half. Full-time: 15,832 students, 59% women, 41% men. Part-time: 1,896 students, 63% women, 37% men. Students come from 42 states and territories, 28 other countries, 14% from out-of-state, 1% Native American, 2% Hispanic, 15% black, 2% Asian American or Pacific Islander, 0.5% international, 15% 25 or older, 28% live on campus, 8% transferred in. Retention: 76% of full-time freshmen returned the following year. Academic areas with the most degrees conferred: business/marketing; health professions and related sciences; education. Core. Calendar: semesters. Academic remediation for entering students, services for LD students, advanced placement, accelerated degree program, self-designed majors, honors program, independent study, distance learning, double major, summer session for credit, part-time degree program, adult/continuing education programs, co-op programs and internships, graduate courses open to undergrads. Off campus study. Study abroad program. ROTC: Army, Air Force.

Entrance Requirements: Options: electronic application, early admission, deferred admission, international baccalaureate accepted. Required: high school transcript, minimum 2.0 high school GPA, SAT or ACT. Entrance: moderately difficult. Application deadline: 3/15. Notification: continuous. Preference given to state residents.

Costs Per Year: Application fee: $50. State resident tuition: $2135 full-time. Nonresident tuition: $12,649 full-time. Mandatory fees: $1492 full-time. College room and board: $6840. College room only: $3790. Room and board charges vary according to board plan and housing facility.

Collegiate Environment: Orientation program. Drama-theater group, choral group, marching band, student-run newspaper, radio station. Social organizations: 244 open to all; national fraternities, national sororities; 4% of eligible men and 4% of eligible women are members. Most popular organizations: Student Government Association, Student Union, Residence Hall Association. Major annual events: Midnight Madness, Pirate Palooza, Barefoot on the Mall. Student services: legal services, health clinic, personal-psychological counseling. Campus security: 24-hour emergency response devices and patrols, student patrols, late night transport-escort service, controlled dormitory access, Operation ID, Staff and Faculty Eyes, Campus Community Watch program. 5,314 college housing spaces available; 4,936 were occupied in 2003-04. No special consideration for freshman housing applicants. Options: coed, men-only, women-only housing available. J. Y. Joyner Library plus 1 other with 4.2 million books, 34,276 serials, 24,610 audiovisual materials, an OPAC, and a Web page. Operations spending for 2004 fiscal year: $11.4 million. 1,692 computers available on campus for general student use. Computer purchase/lease plans available. A campuswide network can be accessed from student residence rooms and from off campus. Staffed computer lab on campus.

Community Environment: Greenville (population 60,000) is the largest medical, cultural and retailing center on eastern North Carolina. The climate is mild, the mean annual temperature being 61 degrees. There are churches of all major denominations, a major hospital, a community art center, one library, and various civic and service organizations in the community. Employment opportunities are good.

■ **ECPI TECHNICAL COLLEGE** *D-9*
4101 Doie Cope Rd.
Raleigh, NC 27613-7387
Tel: (919)571-0057
Free: 800-986-1200
Fax: (919)571-0780
E-mail: swells@ecpi.edu
Web Site: http://www.ecpi.net/

Description: Proprietary, 2-year, coed. Awards diplomas and terminal associate degrees. Founded 1990. Total enrollment: 550. Student-undergrad faculty ratio is 13:1. 0% from out-of-state, 1% Native American, 2% Hispanic, 60% black, 2% Asian American or Pacific Islander, 0% international, 51% 25

or older. Core. Calendar: trimesters. Academic remediation for entering students, accelerated degree program, independent study, distance learning, adult/continuing education programs, co-op programs and internships. Study abroad program.

Entrance Requirements: Options: Common Application, electronic application. Required: high school transcript, interview. Recommended: SAT, SAT or ACT, SAT Subject Tests. Entrance: moderately difficult. Application deadline: Rolling. Notification: continuous.

Costs Per Year: Tuition: $9750 full-time.

Collegiate Environment: Orientation program. Student-run newspaper. Social organizations: national fraternities, national sororities, local fraternities, local sororities; 25% of eligible men and 20% of eligible women are members. Student services: personal-psychological counseling. College housing not available. 200 computers available on campus for general student use. A campuswide network can be accessed from off-campus. Staffed computer lab on campus.

■ **EDGECOMBE COMMUNITY COLLEGE** *C-12*
2009 West Wilson St.
Tarboro, NC 27886-9399
Tel: (252)823-5166
Fax: (252)823-6817
Web Site: http://www.edgecombe.edu/

Description: State and locally supported, 2-year, coed. Part of North Carolina Community College System. Awards certificates, diplomas, transfer associate, and terminal associate degrees. Founded 1968. Setting: 90-acre small town campus. Endowment: $1 million. Research spending for 2004 fiscal year: $50,000. Educational spending for 2005 fiscal year: $4250 per student. Total enrollment: 2,553. 374 applied, 95% were admitted. Full-time: 947 students, 79% women, 21% men. Part-time: 1,606 students, 71% women, 29% men. Students come from 3 states and territories, 4 other countries, 1% from out-of-state, 1% Native American, 1% Hispanic, 62% black, 0.4% Asian American or Pacific Islander, 0.1% international, 47% 25 or older, 2% transferred in. Calendar: semesters. Academic remediation for entering students, ESL program, services for LD students, advanced placement, independent study, distance learning, double major, summer session for credit, part-time degree program, adult/continuing education programs, co-op programs. Off campus study.

Entrance Requirements: Open admission except for radiological technology, nursing, respiratory therapy, surgical technology, networking technology programs. Options: Common Application, electronic application. Required: high school transcript, minimum 2.0 high school GPA. Required for some: recommendations. Placement: SAT or ACT, MAPS recommended. Entrance: noncompetitive. Application deadline: Rolling. Notification: continuous.

Costs Per Year: Application fee: $0. State resident tuition: $1264 full-time, $39.50 per credit part-time. Nonresident tuition: $7024 full-time, $219.50 per credit part-time. Mandatory fees: $72 full-time, $2.75 per credit part-time.

Collegiate Environment: Orientation program. Social organizations: 1 open to all. Most popular organization: Student Government Association. Major annual events: Annual Dance, Spring Fling, Halloween Festival. College housing not available. 42,460 books, 54,841 microform titles, 239 serials, 2,527 audiovisual materials, an OPAC, and a Web page. Operations spending for 2004 fiscal year: $460,000. 180 computers available on campus for general student use. A campuswide network can be accessed from off-campus. Staffed computer lab on campus.

Community Environment: See North Carolina Wesleyan College.

■ **ELIZABETH CITY STATE UNIVERSITY** *B-15*
1704 Weeksville Rd.
Elizabeth City, NC 27909-7806
Tel: (252)335-3400
Free: 800-347-3278
Admissions: (252)335-3305
Fax: (252)335-3731
Web Site: http://www.ecsu.edu/

Description: State-supported, comprehensive, coed. Part of University of North Carolina System. Awards bachelor's and master's degrees. Founded 1891. Setting: 125-acre small town campus with easy access to Norfolk. Total enrollment: 2,470. 1,678 applied, 77% were admitted. 4% from top 10% of their high school class, 18% from top quarter, 53% from top half. Full-time: 2,118 students, 58% women, 42% men. Part-time: 319 students, 81% women, 19% men. Students come from 25 states and territories, 1 other country, 14% from out-of-state, 0.2% Native American, 0.5% Hispanic, 79% black, 1% Asian American or Pacific Islander, 0.04% international, 23%

25 or older, 49% live on campus, 9% transferred in. Retention: 75% of full-time freshmen returned the following year. Core. Calendar: semesters. Academic remediation for entering students, services for LD students, advanced placement, honors program, independent study, distance learning, double major, summer session for credit, part-time degree program, adult/continuing education programs, co-op programs and internships, graduate courses open to undergrads. Off campus study at North Carolina Model Teacher Education Consortium. Study abroad program. ROTC: Army.

Entrance Requirements: Options: electronic application, deferred admission. Required: high school transcript, minimum 2.0 high school GPA, SAT or ACT. Entrance: moderately difficult. Application deadline: Rolling. Notification: continuous. Preference given to state residents.

Costs Per Year: Application fee: $30. State resident tuition: $1399 full-time. Nonresident tuition: $9738 full-time. Mandatory fees: $1824 full-time. College room and board: $4709. College room only: $2867.

Collegiate Environment: Orientation program. Drama-theater group, choral group, marching band, student-run newspaper, radio station. Social organizations: 35 open to all; national fraternities, national sororities, local fraternities; 10% of eligible men and 10% of eligible women are members. Major annual events: homecoming, Scholarcade, Viking Feast. Student services: health clinic, personal-psychological counseling. Campus security: 24-hour emergency response devices and patrols. 1,624 college housing spaces available; 1,197 were occupied in 2003-04. Options: coed, men-only, women-only housing available. G. R. Little Library with 193,880 books, 487,832 microform titles, 1,785 serials, 488,718 audiovisual materials, an OPAC, and a Web page. 400 computers available on campus for general student use. A campuswide network can be accessed from student residence rooms. Staffed computer lab on campus.

Community Environment: See College of the Albemarle.

■ ELON UNIVERSITY

2700 Campus Box
Elon, NC 27244-2010
Tel: (336)278-2000
Free: 800-334-8448
Admissions: (336)278-3566
Fax: (336)538-3986
E-mail: admissions@elon.edu
Web Site: http://www.elon.edu/

Description: Independent, comprehensive, coed, affiliated with United Church of Christ. Awards bachelor's, master's, doctoral, and first professional degrees. Founded 1889. Setting: 580-acre suburban campus with easy access to Raleigh. Endowment: $57.5 million. Research spending for 2004 fiscal year: $829,326. Educational spending for 2005 fiscal year: $8617 per student. Total enrollment: 4,956. Faculty: 370 (279 full-time, 91 part-time). Student-undergrad faculty ratio is 15:1. 9,065 applied, 41% were admitted. 32% from top 10% of their high school class, 67% from top quarter, 93% from top half. 12 valedictorians. Full-time: 4,607 students, 61% women, 39% men. Part-time: 95 students, 51% women, 49% men. Students come from 48 states and territories, 40 other countries, 71% from out-of-state, 0.1% Native American, 1% Hispanic, 7% black, 1% Asian American or Pacific Islander, 2% international, 2% 25 or older, 59% live on campus, 2% transferred in. Retention: 89% of full-time freshmen returned the following year. Academic areas with the most degrees conferred: business/marketing; communications/journalism; education. Core. Calendar: 4-1-4. ESL program, services for LD students, advanced placement, accelerated degree program, self-designed majors, honors program, independent study, double major, summer session for credit, part-time degree program, internships. Off campus study at Augsburg College, Augustana College, Austin College, Birmingham-Southern College, Carthage College, Eckerd College, Erskine College, Gustavus Adolphus College, Linfield College, Pacific Lutheran College, St. Olaf College, Salem College, Tabor College, Washington and Jefferson College, Westminster College, Whitworth College, De Paul University. Study abroad program. ROTC: Army, Air Force (c).

Entrance Requirements: Options: Peterson's Universal Application, Common Application, electronic application, early admission, early decision, early action, deferred admission, international baccalaureate accepted. Required: essay, high school transcript, minimum 2.5 high school GPA, SAT or ACT. Entrance: moderately difficult. Application deadlines: 1/10, 11/1 for early decision, 11/10 for early action. Notification: 3/15, 12/1 for early decision, 12/20 for early action.

Costs Per Year: Application fee: $40. Comprehensive fee: $25,371 includes full-time tuition ($18,699), mandatory fees ($250), and college room and board ($6422). Room and board charges vary according to board plan and

housing facility. Part-time tuition: $588 per hour. Part-time mandatory fees: $125 per term. Part-time tuition and fees vary according to course load.

Collegiate Environment: Orientation program. Drama-theater group, choral group, marching band, student-run newspaper, radio station. Social organizations: 140 open to all; national fraternities, national sororities; 26% of eligible men and 43% of eligible women are members. Most popular organizations: Elon volunteers, student media, intramural athletics, religious life. Major annual events: Homecoming, Family Weekend, Fall Convocation. Student services: health clinic, personal-psychological counseling, women's center. Campus security: 24-hour emergency response devices and patrols, late night transport-escort service, controlled dormitory access. 2,800 college housing spaces available; 2,711 were occupied in 2003-04. Freshmen guaranteed college housing. On-campus residence required through sophomore year. Options: coed, men-only, women-only housing available. Carol Grotnes Belk with 240,058 books, 898,440 microform titles, 2,097 serials, 16,393 audiovisual materials, an OPAC, and a Web page. Operations spending for 2004 fiscal year: $2.3 million. 575 computers available on campus for general student use. Computer purchase/lease plans available. A campuswide network can be accessed from student residence rooms and from off campus. Staffed computer lab on campus.

Community Environment: See Alamance Community College.

■ FAYETTEVILLE STATE UNIVERSITY *F-8*

1200 Murchison Rd.
Fayetteville, NC 28301-4298
Tel: (910)672-1111
Free: 800-222-2594
Admissions: (910)486-1371
Fax: (910)672-1769
E-mail: rshabazz@uncfsu.edu
Web Site: http://www.uncfsu.edu/

Description: State-supported, comprehensive, coed. Part of University of North Carolina System. Awards bachelor's, master's, and doctoral degrees. Founded 1867. Setting: 156-acre urban campus with easy access to Raleigh. Endowment: $7.9 million. Research spending for 2004 fiscal year: $579,174. Total enrollment: 6,072. Faculty: 274 (200 full-time, 74 part-time). Student-undergrad faculty ratio is 22:1. 2,318 applied, 80% were admitted. 2% from top 10% of their high school class, 12% from top quarter, 32% from top half. Full-time: 4,119 students, 65% women, 35% men. Part-time: 910 students, 75% women, 25% men. Students come from 41 states and territories, 8 other countries, 12% from out-of-state, 1% Native American, 4% Hispanic, 77% black, 1% Asian American or Pacific Islander, 0.02% international, 8% transferred in. Retention: 75% of full-time freshmen returned the following year. Academic areas with the most degrees conferred: business/marketing; security and protective services; social sciences. Core. Calendar: semesters. Academic remediation for entering students, accelerated degree program, honors program, independent study, distance learning, double major, summer session for credit, part-time degree program, adult/continuing education programs, co-op programs and internships, graduate courses open to undergrads. ROTC: Army (c), Air Force.

Entrance Requirements: Options: electronic application, early admission, early decision, early action, deferred admission. Required: high school transcript, minimum 2.00 high school GPA, SAT or ACT. Recommended: essay, recommendations. Entrance: minimally difficult. Application deadline: 7/1. Notification: continuous.

Costs Per Year: Application fee: $25. State resident tuition: $1746 full-time. Nonresident tuition: $11,482 full-time. Mandatory fees: $1459 full-time. College room and board: $4570. College room only: $2570.

Collegiate Environment: Orientation program. Drama-theater group, choral group, marching band, student-run newspaper. Social organizations: national fraternities, national sororities, local fraternities, local sororities; 1% of eligible men and 1% of eligible women are members. Major annual events: Honor/Awards Program, Homecoming, Convocation. Student services: health clinic, personal-psychological counseling. Campus security: 24-hour emergency response devices and patrols, late night transport-escort service, controlled dormitory access. 1,100 college housing spaces available; 1,082 were occupied in 2003-04. Freshmen given priority for college housing. Options: coed, men-only, women-only housing available. Charles W. Chestnut Library with 311,016 books, 982,327 microform titles, 2,712 serials, 16,961 audiovisual materials, an OPAC, and a Web page. Operations spending for 2004 fiscal year: $112,404. 355 computers available on campus for general student use. A campuswide network can be accessed from student residence rooms and from off campus. Staffed computer lab on campus.

Community Environment: The"All-America City" of Fayetteville is located in Cumberland County with a metropolitan population of 285,299. It is near three of the most heavily traveled North-South Highways: US 301, US 401 and I-95. Fayetteville is the home of Pope Air Force Base and Fort Bragg, one of America's largest and most important military installations. It is the fourth largest urban population center in the state and one of the ten fastest growing counties in the southern states. Agriculture has contributed significantly to the area's economic growth and development.

■ **FAYETTEVILLE TECHNICAL COMMUNITY COLLEGE** *F-8*
PO Box 35236
Fayetteville, NC 28303-0236
Tel: (910)678-8400
Admissions: (910)678-8274
Fax: (910)678-8407
E-mail: kelleyj@faytechcc.edu
Web Site: http://www.faytechcc.edu/
Description: State-supported, 2-year, coed. Part of North Carolina Community College System. Awards certificates, diplomas, transfer associate, and terminal associate degrees. Founded 1961. Setting: 135-acre suburban campus with easy access to Raleigh. Endowment: $39,050. Educational spending for 2005 fiscal year: $4521 per student. Total enrollment: 9,950. Student-undergrad faculty ratio is 29:1. 4,471 applied, 100% were admitted. Full-time: 3,048 students, 69% women, 31% men. Part-time: 6,902 students, 70% women, 30% men. Students come from 50 states and territories, 9 other countries, 10% from out-of-state, 3% Native American, 7% Hispanic, 41% black, 2% Asian American or Pacific Islander, 0.01% international, 59% 25 or older, 21% transferred in. Core. Calendar: semesters. Academic remediation for entering students, ESL program, services for LD students, advanced placement, self-designed majors, independent study, distance learning, double major, summer session for credit, part-time degree program, adult/continuing education programs, co-op programs and internships. Off campus study at Pembroke State University online program.
Entrance Requirements: Open admission except for allied health programs. Options: electronic application, deferred admission. Required for some: high school transcript. Entrance: noncompetitive. Application deadline: Rolling. Notification: continuous.
Costs Per Year: Application fee: $0. State resident tuition: $1264 full-time, $39.50 per credit hour part-time. Nonresident tuition: $7024 full-time, $219.50 per credit hour part-time. Mandatory fees: $30 full-time, $30 per term part-time.
Collegiate Environment: Orientation program. Social organizations: 26 open to all. Most popular organizations: Criminal Justice Association, Early Childhood Club, Phi Beta Lambda, Student Nurses Club, Data Processing Management Association. Major annual events: Fall Fling, Spring Fling. Student services: health clinic, personal-psychological counseling. Campus security: 24-hour emergency response devices and patrols, late night transport-escort service. College housing not available. Paul H. Thompson Library with 61,580 books, 3,944 microform titles, 398 serials, 6,657 audiovisual materials, an OPAC, and a Web page. Operations spending for 2004 fiscal year: $1.1 million. 400 computers available on campus for general student use. A campuswide network can be accessed from off-campus. Staffed computer lab on campus.
Community Environment: See Fayetteville State University.

■ **FORSYTH TECHNICAL COMMUNITY COLLEGE** *C-5*
2100 Silas Creek Parkway
Winston-Salem, NC 27103-5197
Tel: (336)723-0371
Admissions: (336)734-7331
Fax: (336)761-2098
Web Site: http://www.forsythtech.edu/
Description: State-supported, 2-year, coed. Part of North Carolina Community College System. Awards certificates, diplomas, transfer associate, and terminal associate degrees. Founded 1964. Setting: 38-acre suburban campus. Endowment: $916,352. Educational spending for 2005 fiscal year: $4084 per student. Total enrollment: 6,978. Student-undergrad faculty ratio is 14:1. 932 applied, 100% were admitted. Full-time: 2,509 students, 60% women, 40% men. Part-time: 4,469 students, 66% women, 34% men. 1% Native American, 2% Hispanic, 23% black, 1% Asian American or Pacific Islander, 2% international, 51% 25 or older. Calendar: semesters. Academic remediation for entering students, ESL program, services for LD students, summer session for credit, part-time degree program, adult/continuing education programs.

Entrance Requirements: Open admission except for allied health, engineering technology programs. Option: Peterson's Universal Application. Required: high school transcript. Required for some: SAT or ACT, TEAS, CPT, ASSET, COMPASS. Entrance: noncompetitive. Application deadline: 8/25. Notification: continuous until 8/25.
Costs Per Year: State resident tuition: $948 full-time, $39.50 per credit hour part-time. Nonresident tuition: $5268 full-time, $219.50 per credit hour part-time. Mandatory fees: $35 full-time, $24 per term part-time.
Collegiate Environment: Student-run newspaper. Student services: personal-psychological counseling, women's center. Campus security: 24-hour patrols. College housing not available. Forsyth Technical Community College Library plus 1 other with 41,606 books and 358 serials. 450 computers available on campus for general student use. Staffed computer lab on campus.
Community Environment: See Wake Forest University.

■ **GARDNER-WEBB UNIVERSITY** *E-1*
PO Box 997
Boiling Springs, NC 28017
Tel: (704)406-2361
Free: 800-253-6472
Admissions: (704)406-4491
Fax: (704)434-4488
E-mail: admissions@gardner-webb.edu
Web Site: http://www.gardner-webb.edu/
Description: Independent Baptist, comprehensive, coed. Awards associate, bachelor's, master's, doctoral, and first professional degrees. Founded 1905. Setting: 250-acre small town campus with easy access to Charlotte. Endowment: $32.7 million. Total enrollment: 3,776. Faculty: 321 (133 full-time, 188 part-time). Student-undergrad faculty ratio is 15:1. 2,042 applied, 72% were admitted. 39% from top 10% of their high school class, 56% from top quarter, 90% from top half. 5 class presidents, 5 valedictorians, 75 student government officers. Full-time: 2,222 students, 64% women, 36% men. Part-time: 404 students, 75% women, 25% men. Students come from 36 states and territories, 31 other countries, 23% from out-of-state, 1% Native American, 1% Hispanic, 17% black, 1% Asian American or Pacific Islander, 0% international, 39% 25 or older, 71% live on campus, 19% transferred in. Retention: 73% of full-time freshmen returned the following year. Academic areas with the most degrees conferred: business/marketing; social sciences; health professions and related sciences. Core. Calendar: semesters. Academic remediation for entering students, ESL program, services for LD students, advanced placement, accelerated degree program, honors program, distance learning, double major, summer session for credit, part-time degree program, adult/continuing education programs, co-op programs and internships, graduate courses open to undergrads. Off campus study at Wake Forest University. Study abroad program. ROTC: Army.
Entrance Requirements: Options: Peterson's Universal Application, Common Application, electronic application, early admission, deferred admission, international baccalaureate accepted. Required: essay, high school transcript, minimum 2.4 high school GPA, SAT or ACT. Required for some: recommendations. Entrance: moderately difficult. Application deadline: Rolling.
Costs Per Year: Application fee: $40. Comprehensive fee: $21,850 includes full-time tuition ($15,960), mandatory fees ($350), and college room and board ($5540). College room only: $2840. Room and board charges vary according to board plan and housing facility. Part-time tuition: $295 per credit hour. Part-time tuition varies according to course load.
Collegiate Environment: Orientation program. Drama-theater group, choral group, marching band, student-run newspaper, radio station. Social organizations: 43 open to all. Most popular organizations: Student Volunteer Corps, The Verge, Fellowship of Christian Athletes, Student Government Association, Student Alumni Council. Major annual events: Homecoming, Parents' Weekend, Welcome Back events. Student services: personal-psychological counseling. Campus security: 24-hour patrols, student patrols, controlled dormitory access. 1,139 college housing spaces available; 1,101 were occupied in 2003-04. Freshmen guaranteed college housing. On-campus residence required in freshman year. Options: men-only, women-only housing available. Dover Memorial Library with 230,000 books, 645,000 microform titles, 12,500 serials, 10,000 audiovisual materials, an OPAC, and a Web page. Operations spending for 2004 fiscal year: $736,200. 150 computers available on campus for general student use. A campuswide network can be accessed from student residence rooms and from off campus. Staffed computer lab on campus.
Community Environment: Boiling Springs is located within the noted thermal belt; bus transportation is within five miles; three major railroad lines

are within 10 miles; nearest airport is Charlotte, N.C., 50 miles. The community has access to the indoor swimming pool at the college, observatory, theatre, football stadium, gymnasium and the many cultural arts and entertainment programs at the college. Shopping facilities are good, other community facilities include United Methodist and Baptist churches, and in nearby Shelby, churches of most major denominations, plus numerous civic and service organizations. Part-time employment opportunities are good.

■ **GASTON COLLEGE** *L-2*

201 Hwy. 321 South
Dallas, NC 28034-1499
Tel: (704)922-6200
Admissions: (704)922-6219
Web Site: http://www.gaston.edu/

Description: State and locally supported, 2-year, coed. Part of North Carolina Community College System. Awards certificates, diplomas, transfer associate, and terminal associate degrees. Founded 1963. Setting: 166-acre small town campus with easy access to Charlotte. Endowment: $716,546. Total enrollment: 5,048. Student-undergrad faculty ratio is 18:1. 5% from top 10% of their high school class, 39% from top quarter, 51% from top half. Full-time: 2,449 students, 65% women, 35% men. Part-time: 2,599 students, 70% women, 30% men. Students come from 10 states and territories, 0.4% Native American, 3% Hispanic, 15% black, 1% Asian American or Pacific Islander, 0% international, 52% 25 or older. Retention: 80% of full-time freshmen returned the following year. Core. Calendar: semesters. Academic remediation for entering students, ESL program, services for LD students, advanced placement, summer session for credit, part-time degree program, adult/continuing education programs, co-op programs. Off campus study at 10 members of the Charlotte Area Educational Consortium.

Entrance Requirements: Open admission except for nursing, allied health programs. Required for some: high school transcript. Entrance: noncompetitive. Application deadline: Rolling. Notification: continuous.

Costs Per Year: Application fee: $0. State resident tuition: $1264 full-time, $39.50 per credit hour part-time. Nonresident tuition: $7024 full-time, $219.50 per credit hour part-time. Mandatory fees: $80 full-time, $2.50 per credit hour part-time, $12 per term part-time.

Collegiate Environment: Orientation program. Student-run radio station. Social organizations: 15 open to all. Most popular organization: Student Government Association. Major annual events: Fall Week, Spring Week. Campus security: 24-hour patrols. College housing not available. Gaston College Library with 49,434 books, 45,163 microform titles, 561 serials, 3,343 audiovisual materials, and an OPAC. Operations spending for 2004 fiscal year: $506,470.

Community Environment: The 140 textile plants of Gaston County, 59 of which are in Gastonia, manufacture more than 80 percent of the fine combed cotton yarn made in the United States. Gastonia is an important industrial city of the South. Railroads serve the area with the Charlotte Airport 15 miles away. Community facilities include numerous churches, hospitals, a public library, and a number of civic and service organizations. Rankin Lake is the city's natural reservoir. Adjoining it is a public park that provides a museum and planetarium as well as facilities for golfing, swimming, boating, fishing, and tennis. The Atlantic Coast is within a five-hour drive.

■ **GREENSBORO COLLEGE** *C-6*

815 West Market St.
Greensboro, NC 27401-1875
Tel: (336)272-7102
Free: 800-346-8226
Fax: (336)271-6634
E-mail: admissions@gborocollege.edu
Web Site: http://www.gborocollege.edu/

Description: Independent United Methodist, comprehensive, coed. Awards bachelor's and master's degrees. Founded 1838. Setting: 75-acre urban campus with easy access to Charlotte. Endowment: $80.5 million. Educational spending for 2005 fiscal year: $7918 per student. Total enrollment: 1,226. 1,116 applied, 72% were admitted. 3% from top 10% of their high school class, 20% from top quarter, 48% from top half. Full-time: 923 students, 50% women, 50% men. Part-time: 242 students, 68% women, 32% men. Students come from 25 states and territories, 9 other countries, 26% from out-of-state, 0.3% Native American, 1% Hispanic, 19% black, 1% Asian American or Pacific Islander, 1% international, 23% 25 or older, 48% live on campus, 11% transferred in. Retention: 69% of full-time freshmen returned the following year. Core. Calendar: semesters. Academic

remediation for entering students, ESL program, services for LD students, advanced placement, accelerated degree program, self-designed majors, freshman honors college, honors program, independent study, double major, summer session for credit, part-time degree program, adult/continuing education programs, internships. Off campus study at 7 members of the Greater Greensboro Consortium. Study abroad program. ROTC: Army (c), Air Force (c).

Entrance Requirements: Options: Peterson's Universal Application, Common Application, electronic application, early admission, early action, deferred admission, international baccalaureate accepted. Required: high school transcript, SAT or ACT. Recommended: essay, interview. Required for some: 2 recommendations, interview. Entrance: moderately difficult. Application deadlines: Rolling, 12/15 for early action. Notification: continuous, 1/15 for early action.

Costs Per Year: Application fee: $35. Comprehensive fee: $25,040 includes full-time tuition ($17,850), mandatory fees ($270), and college room and board ($6920). Full-time tuition and fees vary according to course load. Room and board charges vary according to board plan and housing facility. Part-time tuition: $480 per hour. Part-time tuition varies according to course load.

Collegiate Environment: Orientation program. Drama-theater group, choral group, marching band, student-run newspaper. Social organizations: 52 open to all; national fraternities, local fraternities, local sororities; 3% of eligible men and 4% of eligible women are members. Most popular organizations: Student Christian Fellowship, Campus Activities Board, student government, Choir, United African American Society. Major annual events: homecoming, Spring Fling, lessons and carols. Student services: health clinic, personal-psychological counseling. Campus security: 24-hour patrols, late night transport-escort service, controlled dormitory access. 627 college housing spaces available; 574 were occupied in 2003-04. Freshmen guaranteed college housing. On-campus residence required through sophomore year. Options: coed, men-only, women-only housing available. James Addison Jones Library with 108,350 books, 2,970 microform titles, 290 serials, 2,686 audiovisual materials, an OPAC, and a Web page. Operations spending for 2004 fiscal year: $479,762. 120 computers available on campus for general student use. A campuswide network can be accessed from student residence rooms and from off campus. Staffed computer lab on campus.

Community Environment: Greensboro was named for General Nathanael Greene, hero of the Battle of Guilford Courthouse. Textiles are the predominant industry along with the manufacture of cigarettes. The War Memorial Auditorium and Coliseum provides one of the state's finest facilities for conventions, exhibitions, sports events, and shows. Recreation facilities include golf courses, swimming pools, and tennis courts. Part-time employment is available. Points of interest are the Greensboro Historical Museum and on the site of O. Henry's birthplace.

■ **GUILFORD COLLEGE** *C-6*

5800 West Friendly Ave.
Greensboro, NC 27410-4173
Tel: (336)316-2000
Free: 800-992-7759
Admissions: (336)316-2100
Fax: (336)316-2954
E-mail: admission@guilford.edu
Web Site: http://www.guilford.edu/

Description: Independent, 4-year, coed, affiliated with Society of Friends. Awards bachelor's degrees. Founded 1837. Setting: 340-acre suburban campus. Endowment: $51.4 million. Research spending for 2004 fiscal year: $47,000. Educational spending for 2005 fiscal year: $5064 per student. Total enrollment: 2,682. Student-undergrad faculty ratio is 17:1. 2,492 applied, 63% were admitted. 14% from top 10% of their high school class, 44% from top quarter, 78% from top half. 3 National Merit Scholars, 5 valedictorians, 49 student government officers. Full-time: 2,251 students, 61% women, 39% men. Part-time: 431 students, 70% women, 30% men. Students come from 45 states and territories, 18 other countries, 62% from out-of-state, 1% Native American, 2% Hispanic, 23% black, 1% Asian American or Pacific Islander, 1% international, 43% 25 or older, 80% live on campus, 15% transferred in. Retention: 72% of full-time freshmen returned the following year. Academic areas with the most degrees conferred: business/marketing; security and protective services; psychology. Core. Calendar: semesters. Academic remediation for entering students, ESL program, services for LD students, advanced placement, accelerated degree program, self-designed majors, honors program, independent study, double major, summer session for credit, part-time degree program, adult/continuing education programs, co-op programs and internships. Off campus study at Greater Greensboro Consortium, Duke University, Bowman Gray School of Medicine at Wake Forest University. Study abroad program.

Entrance Requirements: Options: Peterson's Universal Application, Common Application, electronic application, early admission, early action, deferred admission. Required: essay, high school transcript, minimum 2.0 high school GPA, SAT or ACT. Recommended: minimum 3.0 high school GPA, 2 recommendations, interview. Entrance: moderately difficult. Application deadlines: 2/15, 1/15 for early action. Notification: 4/1, 2/15 for early action. Preference given to Quakers.

Costs Per Year: Application fee: $25. Comprehensive fee: $29,710 includes full-time tuition ($22,690), mandatory fees ($330), and college room and board ($6690). Part-time tuition: $700 per credit hour. Part-time mandatory fees: $330 per year.

Collegiate Environment: Orientation program. Drama-theater group, choral group, student-run newspaper, radio station. Social organizations: 43 open to all. Most popular organizations: student government, student radio station, student newspaper, Project Community, African-American Cultural Society. Major annual events: Family Weekend, Binford Formal, Serendipity. Student services: health clinic, personal-psychological counseling, women's center. Campus security: 24-hour emergency response devices and patrols, student patrols, late night transport-escort service, controlled dormitory access. 925 college housing spaces available; 875 were occupied in 2003-04. Freshmen guaranteed college housing. On-campus residence required through junior year. Options: coed, men-only, women-only housing available. Hege Library with 157,054 books, 21,238 microform titles, 829 serials, 10,151 audiovisual materials, an OPAC, and a Web page. Operations spending for 2004 fiscal year: $794,855. 275 computers available on campus for general student use. A campuswide network can be accessed from student residence rooms and from off campus. Staffed computer lab on campus.

Community Environment: See Greensboro College.

■ **GUILFORD TECHNICAL COMMUNITY COLLEGE** *K-2*
PO Box 309
Jamestown, NC 27282-0309
Tel: (336)334-4822
Web Site: http://www.gtcc.edu/

Description: State and locally supported, 2-year, coed. Part of North Carolina Community College System. Awards certificates, diplomas, transfer associate, and terminal associate degrees. Founded 1958. Setting: 158-acre suburban campus. Total enrollment: 8,491. Full-time: 2,930 students, 53% women, 47% men. Part-time: 5,561 students, 59% women, 41% men. Students come from 21 states and territories, 1% Native American, 2% Hispanic, 34% black, 3% Asian American or Pacific Islander, 2% international, 44% 25 or older. Core. Calendar: semesters. Academic remediation for entering students, ESL program, services for LD students, advanced placement, self-designed majors, independent study, distance learning, summer session for credit, part-time degree program, external degree program, adult/continuing education programs, co-op programs and internships. Off campus study at members of the Greater Greensboro Consortium. ROTC: Army (c), Air Force (c).

Entrance Requirements: Open admission except for health-related, aviation maintenance programs. Options: early admission, deferred admission, international baccalaureate accepted. Required: high school transcript. Required for: interview. Placement: ACT COMPASS required. Entrance: noncompetitive. Application deadline: Rolling. Notification: continuous.

Costs Per Year: Application fee: $0. State resident tuition: $1216 full-time. Nonresident tuition: $6752 full-time. Mandatory fees: $75 full-time.

Collegiate Environment: Orientation program. Drama-theater group. Social organizations: 30 open to all. Major annual events: Clubs' Fair, Cultural Fling. College housing not available. M. W. Bell Library plus 2 others with 74,958 books, 32,483 microform titles, 381 serials, 7,286 audiovisual materials, an OPAC, and a Web page. 90 computers available on campus for general student use. A campuswide network can be accessed from off-campus. Staffed computer lab on campus.

Community Environment: Jamestown neighbors High Point and Greensboro. Primary businesses in Guilford County are textiles, furniture, and numerous other manufacturing concerns. Commercial transportation, one railroad, seven airlines, and recreational facilities are convenient in High Point and Greensboro.

■ **HALIFAX COMMUNITY COLLEGE** *A-12*
PO Drawer 809
Weldon, NC 27890-0809
Tel: (252)536-4221
Admissions: (252)536-7220
Fax: (252)536-4144
Web Site: http://www.hcc.cc.nc.us/

Description: State and locally supported, 2-year, coed. Part of North Carolina Community College System. Awards certificates, diplomas, transfer associate, and terminal associate degrees. Founded 1967. Setting: 109-acre rural campus. Total enrollment: 1,580. Students come from 2 states and territories. Core. Calendar: semesters. Academic remediation for entering students, summer session for credit, part-time degree program, adult/continuing education programs, co-op programs.

Entrance Requirements: Open admission. Option: deferred admission. Required: high school transcript. Entrance: noncompetitive. Application deadline: Rolling. Notification: continuous.

Costs Per Year: Application fee: $0. State resident tuition: $1216 full-time, $38 per credit part-time. Nonresident tuition: $6752 full-time, $211 per credit part-time. Mandatory fees: $80 full-time, $5 per credit part-time.

Collegiate Environment: Campus security: 12-hour patrols by trained security personnel. College housing not available. Halifax Community College Library with 26,527 books and 122 serials. 100 computers available on campus for general student use. Staffed computer lab on campus.

Community Environment: Located in the northeastern section of North Carolina, Weldon is in a good agricultural area where the main industries are in textiles and paper goods. Community facilities include churches, a library, historical sites, shopping centers, and medical facilities nearby. There are three convenient lakes, with miles of shoreline, known as the Rockfish Capital of the world.

■ **HAYWOOD COMMUNITY COLLEGE** *J-14*
185 Freedlander Dr.
Clyde, NC 28721-9453
Tel: (828)627-2821
Admissions: (828)627-4505
Fax: (828)627-4513
Web Site: http://www.haywood.edu/

Description: State and locally supported, 2-year, coed. Part of North Carolina Community College System. Awards certificates, diplomas, transfer associate, and terminal associate degrees. Founded 1964. Setting: 85-acre rural campus. Educational spending for 2005 fiscal year: $3100 per student. Total enrollment: 1,988. 1,018 applied, 67% were admitted. Full-time: 876 students, 54% women, 46% men. Part-time: 1,112 students, 57% women, 43% men. Students come from 7 states and territories, 1% from out-of-state, 1% Native American, 1% Hispanic, 1% black, 1% Asian American or Pacific Islander, 0% international, 43% 25 or older, 13% transferred in. Calendar: semesters. Academic remediation for entering students, ESL program, services for LD students, advanced placement, independent study, distance learning, double major, part-time degree program, adult/continuing education programs, co-op programs and internships.

Entrance Requirements: Open admission except for nursing, some technical programs. Required: high school transcript. Required for some: interview. Entrance: noncompetitive. Application deadline: Rolling.

Costs Per Year: Application fee: $0. State resident tuition: $1216 full-time, $38 per credit hour part-time. Nonresident tuition: $6752 full-time, $211 per credit hour part-time. Mandatory fees: $49 full-time, $13 per term part-time.

Collegiate Environment: Social organizations: 10 open to all. Most popular organizations: Student Government Association, Phi Theta Kappa, Phi Beta Lambda, Outdoor Club, Cosmetology Club. Major annual events: Ski Day, intramural sports. Student services: personal-psychological counseling. Campus security: 24-hour patrols. College housing not available. Freedlander Learning Resource Center with 26,788 books and 167 serials. 10 computers available on campus for general student use. A campuswide network can be accessed.

Community Environment: Haywood is a growing county of 47,000 people with an ever-expanding economy. Fine roads serve the county and new and expanding industry is experiencing a rapid increase. Agriculture is diversifying, and vegetable growing and truck farming share the market with cattle, corn, and tobacco. New and expanding tourist and recreational facilities are being developed. The county's proximity to the Great Smoky Mountains National Park and the world-famous Lake Junaluska Methodist Assembly Grounds make the area a natural tourist attraction. A large ski resort and the nearby lakes and forests have earned the area the distinction of being a winter and summer playground.

■ **HERITAGE BIBLE COLLEGE** *E-9*
PO Box 1628
Dunn, NC 28335-1628
Tel: (910)892-3178
Free: 800-297-6351
Fax: (910)892-1809
Web Site: http://www.heritagebiblecollege.org/
Description: Independent Pentecostal Free Will Baptist, 4-year, coed. Awards associate and bachelor's degrees. Founded 1971. Setting: 82-acre small town campus with easy access to Raleigh-Durham. Endowment: $27,000. Educational spending for 2005 fiscal year: $6000 per student. Total enrollment: 116. Student-undergrad faculty ratio is 17:1. 30 applied, 100% were admitted. Full-time: 84 students, 33% women, 67% men. Part-time: 32 students, 50% women, 50% men. Students come from 2 other countries, 5% from out-of-state, 2% Native American, 1% Hispanic, 27% black, 1% Asian American or Pacific Islander, 2% international, 69% 25 or older, 2% live on campus, 6% transferred in. Retention: 60% of full-time freshmen returned the following year. Academic area with the most degrees conferred: theology and religious vocations. Core. Calendar: semesters. Academic remediation for entering students, independent study, summer session for credit, external degree program, adult/continuing education programs, internships. Off campus study at Spring Lake extension program.
Entrance Requirements: Open admission. Options: Common Application, international baccalaureate accepted. Required: essay, high school transcript, recommendations. Entrance: minimally difficult. Application deadline: Rolling.
Costs Per Year: Application fee: $25. Comprehensive fee: $6600 includes full-time tuition ($3600), mandatory fees ($600), and college room and board ($2400). College room only: $1440. Part-time tuition: $150 per credit.
Collegiate Environment: Orientation program. Drama-theater group, choral group. Major annual events: Christian Drama, Arby-Carter Lectures. 60 college housing spaces available; 20 were occupied in 2003-04. No special consideration for freshman housing applicants. Option: coed housing available. Alphin Learning Center with 20,585 books, 95 serials, 1,338 audiovisual materials, an OPAC, and a Web page. Operations spending for 2004 fiscal year: $51,300. 25 computers available on campus for general student use. Staffed computer lab on campus.

■ **HIGH POINT UNIVERSITY** *C-6*
University Station, Montlieu Ave.
High Point, NC 27262-3598
Tel: (336)841-9000
Free: 800-345-6993
Admissions: (336)841-9216
Fax: (336)841-5123
E-mail: admiss@highpoint.edu
Web Site: http://www.highpoint.edu/
Description: Independent United Methodist, comprehensive, coed. Awards bachelor's and master's degrees. Founded 1924. Setting: 77-acre suburban campus with easy access to Charlotte. Endowment: $44.8 million. Educational spending for 2005 fiscal year: $8221 per student. Total enrollment: 2,760. Faculty: 227 (122 full-time, 105 part-time). Student-undergrad faculty ratio is 15:1. 2,184 applied, 67% were admitted. 14% from top 10% of their high school class, 36% from top quarter, 69% from top half. 9 class presidents, 10 valedictorians, 163 student government officers. Full-time: 2,325 students, 63% women, 37% men. Part-time: 199 students, 59% women, 41% men. Students come from 38 states and territories, 35% from out-of-state, 0.2% Native American, 2% Hispanic, 23% black, 2% Asian American or Pacific Islander, 3% international, 8% 25 or older, 60% live on campus, 11% transferred in. Retention: 74% of full-time freshmen returned the following year. Academic areas with the most degrees conferred: business/marketing; computer and information sciences; psychology. Core. Calendar: semesters. Academic remediation for entering students, ESL program, advanced placement, accelerated degree program, self-designed majors, honors program, independent study, double major, summer session for credit, part-time degree program, adult/continuing education programs, co-op programs and internships. Off campus study at 7 members of the Greater Greensboro Consortium. Study abroad program. ROTC: Army (c), Air Force (c).

Entrance Requirements: Options: Peterson's Universal Application, Common Application, electronic application, deferred admission, international baccalaureate accepted. Required: high school transcript, minimum 2.0 high school GPA, 2 recommendations, SAT or ACT. Recommended: essay, minimum 3.0 high school GPA, interview, SAT or ACT, SAT Subject Tests. Entrance: moderately difficult. Application deadlines: 8/15, 11/1 for early action. Notification: continuous until 8/15, 11/15 for early action.
Costs Per Year: Application fee: $25. Comprehensive fee: $26,000 includes full-time tuition ($16,760), mandatory fees ($1650), and college room and board ($7590). College room only: $3400. Part-time tuition: $263 per credit hour.
Collegiate Environment: Orientation program. Drama-theater group, choral group, student-run newspaper, radio station. Social organizations: 68 open to all; national fraternities, national sororities, local fraternities, local sororities; 15% of eligible men and 25% of eligible women are members. Most popular organizations: student government, Habitat for Humanity, International Club, Student Activities Board, Honors Club. Major annual events: Homecoming, Family Weekend, Spring Fling. Student services: health clinic, personal-psychological counseling. Campus security: 24-hour emergency response devices and patrols, student patrols, late night transport-escort service, controlled dormitory access. Options: coed, men-only, women-only housing available. Herman and Louise Smith Library with 205,000 books, 87,000 microform titles, 30,000 serials, 15,000 audiovisual materials, an OPAC, and a Web page. Operations spending for 2004 fiscal year: $706,668. 176 computers available on campus for general student use. A campuswide network can be accessed from student residence rooms and from off campus. Staffed computer lab on campus.
Community Environment: The city's name arose from the fact that the community was the highest point, on the original survey, for the old North Carolina Railroad between Goldsboro and Charlotte. Numerous diversified industries, including many furniture manufacturing plants and hosiery mills, are in High Point, the wood furniture manufacturing and hosiery production capital of the world. Parks, golf courses, and a lake provide the facilities for recreation.

■ **ISOTHERMAL COMMUNITY COLLEGE** *J-17*
PO Box 804
Spindale, NC 28160-0804
Tel: (828)286-3636
Fax: (828)286-8109
Web Site: http://www.isothermal.edu/
Description: State-supported, 2-year, coed. Part of North Carolina Community College System. Awards certificates, diplomas, transfer associate, and terminal associate degrees. Founded 1965. Setting: 120-acre rural campus. Total enrollment: 2,005. Full-time: 988 students, 64% women, 36% men. Part-time: 1,017 students, 65% women, 35% men. Students come from 40 states and territories, 3 other countries, 0.3% Native American, 1% Hispanic, 16% black, 0.3% Asian American or Pacific Islander, 0.3% international, 49% 25 or older. Retention: 33% of full-time freshmen returned the following year. Core. Calendar: semesters. Academic remediation for entering students, ESL program, services for LD students, advanced placement, self-designed majors, honors program, summer session for credit, part-time degree program, external degree program, adult/continuing education programs, co-op programs.
Entrance Requirements: Open admission. Options: early admission, deferred admission. Required: high school transcript. Placement: ACT ASSET required. Entrance: noncompetitive. Application deadline: Rolling. Notification: continuous.
Collegiate Environment: Orientation program. Choral group, student-run newspaper, radio station. Student services: personal-psychological counseling. College housing not available. 35,200 books, 289 serials, an OPAC, and a Web page.
Community Environment: Spindale is located 20 miles from Shelby, 28 miles from Hendersonville, and 35 miles from Asheville.

■ **JAMES SPRUNT COMMUNITY COLLEGE** *F-11*
PO Box 398
Kenansville, NC 28349-0398
Tel: (910)296-2400
Admissions: (910)296-2500
Fax: (910)296-1222
Web Site: http://www.sprunt.com/
Description: State-supported, 2-year, coed. Part of North Carolina Community College System. Awards certificates, diplomas, transfer associate,

and terminal associate degrees. Founded 1964. Setting: 51-acre rural campus. Endowment: $16,990. Educational spending for 2005 fiscal year: $3853 per student. Total enrollment: 1,370. Student-undergrad faculty ratio is 21:1. 247 applied, 83% were admitted. Full-time: 643 students, 72% women, 28% men. Part-time: 727 students, 70% women, 30% men. Students come from 2 states and territories, 1% from out-of-state, 0.1% Native American, 3% Hispanic, 42% black, 0% Asian American or Pacific Islander, 0.2% international, 51% 25 or older, 6% transferred in. Core. Calendar: semesters. Academic remediation for entering students, ESL program, advanced placement, accelerated degree program, independent study, distance learning, double major, summer session for credit, part-time degree program, external degree program, adult/continuing education programs, co-op programs and internships.

Entrance Requirements: Open admission except for allied health programs. Options: Peterson's Universal Application, Common Application, electronic application, early admission, deferred admission. Required: high school transcript. Entrance: noncompetitive. Application deadline: Rolling. Notification: continuous.

Costs Per Year: Application fee: $0. State resident tuition: $1264 full-time, $40 per semester hour part-time. Nonresident tuition: $7024 full-time, $220 per semester hour part-time. Mandatory fees: $70 full-time, $70 per term part-time.

Collegiate Environment: Orientation program. Student-run newspaper. Social organizations: 5 open to all; local fraternities. Most popular organizations: Student Nurses Association, Art Club, Alumni Association, National Technical-Vocational Honor Society, Phi Theta Kappa. Major annual events: Christmas Dance/Coronation, Activities Day, Halloween. Student services: personal-psychological counseling. Campus security: trained security personnel. College housing not available. James Sprunt Community College Library with 23,497 books, 26,000 microform titles, 235 serials, 1,392 audiovisual materials, and an OPAC. Operations spending for 2004 fiscal year: $141,170. 100 computers available on campus for general student use. A campuswide network can be accessed from off-campus. Staffed computer lab on campus.

Community Environment: Located 40 miles from the principal city of Goldsboro and 4 miles from Interstate 40, Kenansville is a rural community with three churches, a library, and good shopping areas for this size community. The primary businesses of the area are farming, textiles, poultry, and swine production. Good fishing and hunting are available in the area.

■ **JOHN WESLEY COLLEGE** *C-6*
2314 North Centennial St.
High Point, NC 27265-3197
Tel: (336)889-2262
E-mail: admissions@johnwesley.edu
Web Site: http://www.johnwesley.edu/

Description: Independent interdenominational, 4-year, coed. Awards associate and bachelor's degrees. Founded 1932. Setting: 24-acre urban campus. Educational spending for 2005 fiscal year: $1500 per student. Total enrollment: 130. Student-undergrad faculty ratio is 12:1. 23 applied, 52% were admitted. Full-time: 84 students, 44% women, 56% men. Part-time: 46 students, 43% women, 57% men. Students come from 8 states and territories, 5% from out-of-state, 2% Native American, 2% Hispanic, 24% black, 0% Asian American or Pacific Islander, 0% international, 71% 25 or older, 14% live on campus, 80% transferred in. Retention: 80% of full-time freshmen returned the following year. Core. Calendar: semesters. Academic remediation for entering students, advanced placement, independent study, distance learning, double major, summer session for credit, part-time degree program, external degree program, adult/continuing education programs, internships. Off campus study at High Point University.

Entrance Requirements: Options: electronic application, early admission, deferred admission. Required: high school transcript, 2 recommendations, interview. Recommended: minimum 2.0 high school GPA. Entrance: minimally difficult. Application deadline: 8/1. Notification: continuous until 8/10.

Costs Per Year: Application fee: $35. Tuition: $8512 full-time, $392 per semester hour part-time. Mandatory fees: $646 full-time, $323 per term part-time. Full-time tuition and fees vary according to course load. Part-time tuition and fees vary according to course load. College room only: $1990. Room charges vary according to housing facility.

Collegiate Environment: Orientation program. Choral group, student-run newspaper. Major annual events: Thanksgiving Banquet, Christmas Banquet, Valentine's Banquet. 48 college housing spaces available; 23 were occupied in 2003-04. No special consideration for freshman housing ap-

plicants. Temple Library with 43,305 books, 95 microform titles, 146 serials, 2,886 audiovisual materials, an OPAC, and a Web page. Operations spending for 2004 fiscal year: $75,546. 7 computers available on campus for general student use. Staffed computer lab on campus.

Community Environment: See High Point University.

■ **JOHNSON C. SMITH UNIVERSITY** *E-3*
100 Beatties Ford Rd.
Charlotte, NC 28216-5398
Tel: (704)378-1000
Free: 800-782-7303
Admissions: (704)378-1010
E-mail: admissions@jcsu.edu
Web Site: http://www.jcsu.edu/

Description: Independent, 4-year, coed. Awards bachelor's degrees. Founded 1867. Setting: 105-acre urban campus. Endowment: $44.4 million. Research spending for 2004 fiscal year: $61,395. Educational spending for 2005 fiscal year: $7692 per student. Total enrollment: 1,404. Student-undergrad faculty ratio is 14:1. 4,037 applied, 37% were admitted. 27% from top 10% of their high school class, 33% from top quarter, 40% from top half. 15 class presidents, 4 valedictorians, 92 student government officers. Full-time: 1,340 students, 61% women, 39% men. Part-time: 64 students, 53% women, 47% men. Students come from 21 states and territories, 72% from out-of-state, 0.1% Native American, 0.1% Hispanic, 99% black, 0.1% Asian American or Pacific Islander, 0% international, 4% 25 or older, 80% live on campus, 2% transferred in. Retention: 66% of full-time freshmen returned the following year. Academic areas with the most degrees conferred: business/marketing; computer and information sciences; communications/journalism. Core. Calendar: semesters. Services for LD students, advanced placement, freshman honors college, honors program, independent study, double major, summer session for credit, part-time degree program, adult/continuing education programs, co-op programs and internships. Off campus study at Charlotte Area Educational Consortium, Providence College. Study abroad program. ROTC: Army, Air Force (c).

Entrance Requirements: Options: Peterson's Universal Application, Common Application, electronic application, early admission, deferred admission, international baccalaureate accepted. Required: high school transcript, minimum 2.2 high school GPA, SAT or ACT. Recommended: essay, interview. Required for some: recommendations. Entrance: moderately difficult. Notification: continuous.

Costs Per Year: Application fee: $25. Comprehensive fee: $19,962 includes full-time tuition ($12,120), mandatory fees ($2279), and college room and board ($5563). College room only: $3201. Full-time tuition and fees vary according to course load. Room and board charges vary according to board plan and housing facility. Part-time tuition: $361 per credit hour. Part-time mandatory fees: $240 per term. Part-time tuition and fees vary according to course load.

Collegiate Environment: Orientation program. Drama-theater group, choral group, marching band, student-run newspaper. Social organizations: 48 open to all; national fraternities, national sororities, local fraternities, local sororities; 10% of eligible men and 8% of eligible women are members. Most popular organizations: Union Program Board, Royal Golden Bull Pep Squad, Health and Physical Education Club, Delta Sigma Theta, Alpha Kappa Alpha. Major annual events: Homecoming, Bullfest. Student services: health clinic, personal-psychological counseling. Campus security: 24-hour emergency response devices and patrols, late night transport-escort service, controlled dormitory access. 1,127 college housing spaces available; 994 were occupied in 2003-04. Freshmen guaranteed college housing. On-campus residence required in freshman year. Options: coed, men-only, women-only housing available. James B. Duke Library plus 1 other with 97,340 books, 173,636 microform titles, 290 serials, 1,276 audiovisual materials, an OPAC, and a Web page. Operations spending for 2004 fiscal year: $726,407. 250 computers available on campus for general student use. Computer purchase/lease plans available. A campuswide network can be accessed from off-campus. Staffed computer lab on campus.

Community Environment: Charlotte, the largest city of the Carolinas, with a population of more than 340,000, is a commercial and cultural center of the South. The city has tall buildings, huge warehouses, and numerous factories, but the residential sections are extensively gardened and beautifully landscaped. The area is rich in historical landmarks. Charlotte offers all the cultural and recreational facilities of any large city, including sports events, excellent shopping and dining facilities, rock and classical music, concerts, theater, and art. The area is served by Southern Railway and five major airlines. Major highways provide easy access to nearby beaches and mountains.

■ **JOHNSON & WALES UNIVERSITY** *E-3*
901 West Trade St., Ste. 175
Charlotte, NC 28202
Tel: (980)598-1000; (866)598-2427
E-mail: admissions.clt@jwu.edu
Web Site: http://www.jwucharlotte.org/
Description: Independent, 4-year, coed. Awards associate and bachelor's degrees. Founded 2004. Endowment: $168.3 million. Total enrollment: 2,156. Student-undergrad faculty ratio is 31:1. 6,226 applied, 74% were admitted. Full-time: 2,150 students, 52% women, 48% men. Part-time: 6 students, 50% women, 50% men. 62% from out-of-state, 0.5% Native American, 2% Hispanic, 27% black, 2% Asian American or Pacific Islander, 0.2% international.
Entrance Requirements: Required: high school transcript. Recommended: minimum 2.0 high school GPA, SAT or ACT. Required for some: recommendations, interview, SAT or ACT. Entrance: minimally difficult. Application deadline: Rolling. Notification: continuous.
Costs Per Year: Application fee: $0. Comprehensive fee: $29,126 includes full-time tuition ($19,875), mandatory fees ($951), and college room and board ($8300). Part-time tuition: $368 per quarter hour.
Collegiate Environment: Choral group. Student services: health clinic, personal-psychological counseling.

■ **JOHNSTON COMMUNITY COLLEGE** *D-10*
PO Box 2350
Smithfield, NC 27577-2350
Tel: (919)934-3051
Admissions: (919)209-2048
Fax: (919)934-2150
Web Site: http://www.johnston.cc.nc.us/
Description: State-supported, 2-year, coed. Part of North Carolina Community College System. Awards certificates, diplomas, transfer associate, and terminal associate degrees. Founded 1969. Setting: 100-acre rural campus. Endowment: $2.2 million. Educational spending for 2005 fiscal year: $2958 per student. Total enrollment: 4,095. Student-undergrad faculty ratio is 18:1. Full-time: 1,628 students, 57% women, 43% men. Part-time: 2,467 students, 69% women, 31% men. Students come from 10 states and territories, 1 other country, 1% from out-of-state, 0.5% Native American, 4% Hispanic, 20% black, 0.5% Asian American or Pacific Islander, 0.2% international, 43% 25 or older. Calendar: semesters. Academic remediation for entering students, services for LD students, advanced placement, honors program, independent study, distance learning, double major, summer session for credit, part-time degree program, adult/continuing education programs, co-op programs.
Entrance Requirements: Open admission except for nursing, radiological technology programs. Options: electronic application, international baccalaureate accepted. Required: high school transcript, interview. Entrance: noncompetitive. Application deadline: Rolling. Notification: continuous.
Costs Per Year: Application fee: $0. State resident tuition: $1264 full-time, $39.50 per credit hour part-time. Nonresident tuition: $7024 full-time, $219.50 per credit hour part-time. Mandatory fees: $70 full-time, $1 per credit hour part-time, $15 per term part-time.
Collegiate Environment: Choral group. Major annual events: Fall Festival, Spring Fling. Student services: personal-psychological counseling. Campus security: 24-hour patrols. College housing not available. Johnston Community College Library plus 1 other with 31,550 books, 2,297 microform titles, 348 serials, 4,445 audiovisual materials, an OPAC, and a Web page. Operations spending for 2004 fiscal year: $394,075. 186 computers available on campus for general student use. Staffed computer lab on campus.

■ **KING'S COLLEGE** *E-3*
322 Lamar Ave.
Charlotte, NC 28204-2436
Tel: (704)372-0266
Free: 800-768-2255
Admissions: (704)688-3613
Fax: (704)348-2029
E-mail: brockecharlie@kingscollege.org
Web Site: http://www.kingscollege.org/
Description: Proprietary, 2-year, coed. Awards transfer associate degrees. Founded 1901. Total enrollment: 519.
Costs Per Year: Comprehensive fee: $17,920 includes full-time tuition ($11,960) and college room and board ($5960).

■ **LEES-MCRAE COLLEGE**
PO Box 128
Banner Elk, NC 28604-0128
Tel: (828)898-5241
Free: 800-280-4562
Admissions: (828)898-8829
Fax: (828)898-8814
E-mail: crutchfield@lmc.edu
Web Site: http://www2.lmc.edu/
Description: Independent, 4-year, coed, affiliated with Presbyterian Church (U.S.A.). Awards bachelor's degrees. Founded 1900. Setting: 400-acre rural campus. Endowment: $19.3 million. Educational spending for 2005 fiscal year: $4711 per student. Total enrollment: 882. Student-undergrad faculty ratio is 15:1. 1,003 applied, 74% were admitted. 7% from top 10% of their high school class, 19% from top quarter, 54% from top half. Full-time: 866 students, 57% women, 43% men. Part-time: 16 students, 31% women, 69% men. Students come from 31 states and territories, 20 other countries, 33% from out-of-state, 1% Native American, 2% Hispanic, 6% black, 1% Asian American or Pacific Islander, 1% international, 18% 25 or older, 70% live on campus, 14% transferred in. Retention: 50% of full-time freshmen returned the following year. Academic areas with the most degrees conferred: education; business/marketing; health professions and related sciences. Core. Calendar: semesters. Academic remediation for entering students, services for LD students, advanced placement, self-designed majors, honors program, independent study, double major, summer session for credit, part-time degree program, external degree program, adult/continuing education programs, internships. Off campus study at Duke University. Study abroad program. ROTC: Army (c).
Entrance Requirements: Options: Peterson's Universal Application, Common Application, electronic application, early admission, deferred admission, international baccalaureate accepted. Required: high school transcript, minimum 2.0 high school GPA, SAT or ACT. Recommended: essay, recommendations. Required for some: interview. Entrance: minimally difficult. Application deadline: 8/1. Notification: continuous until 8/15.
Costs Per Year: Application fee: $25. Comprehensive fee: $24,000 includes full-time tuition ($18,000) and college room and board ($6000). Part-time tuition: $500 per semester hour.
Collegiate Environment: Orientation program. Drama-theater group, choral group. Social organizations: 19 open to all. Most popular organizations: Student Government Association, Students Against a Vanishing Environment, CATCH, Order of the Tower, Student Ambassadors. Major annual events: homecoming, Spring Fling, Mountain Day. Student services: health clinic, personal-psychological counseling. Campus security: 24-hour patrols. 560 college housing spaces available; 500 were occupied in 2003-04. On-campus residence required through sophomore year. Options: coed, men-only, women-only housing available. James H. Carson Library with 88,756 books and 429 serials. 60 computers available on campus for general student use. A campuswide network can be accessed from student residence rooms and from off campus. Staffed computer lab on campus.
Community Environment: Banner Elk is in the Blue Ridge Mountains of Western North Carolina, 100 miles from Charlotte and 83 miles northeast of Asheville. Elk River is nearby for trout fishing, and during the winter there is sufficient snow for outdoor winter sports.

■ **LENOIR COMMUNITY COLLEGE** *E-12*
PO Box 188
Kinston, NC 28502-0188
Tel: (252)527-6223
E-mail: tsb706@email.lenoir.cc.nc.us
Web Site: http://www.lenoircc.edu/
Description: State-supported, 2-year, coed. Part of North Carolina Community College System. Awards certificates, diplomas, transfer associate, and terminal associate degrees. Founded 1960. Setting: 86-acre small town campus. Total enrollment: 2,607. Core. Calendar: semesters. Academic remediation for entering students, ESL program, advanced placement, summer session for credit, part-time degree program, adult/continuing education programs, co-op programs.
Entrance Requirements: Open admission except for allied health programs. Option: early admission. Required: high school transcript. Placement: Assessment and Placement Services for Community Colleges required; SAT or ACT recommended. Entrance: noncompetitive. Application deadline: Rolling. Notification: continuous.
Collegiate Environment: Choral group, student-run newspaper. Social organizations: 19 open to all. Most popular organizations: Student Govern-

ment Association, Automotive Club, Electronics Club, Drafting Club, Cosmetology Club. Major annual events: Fall Festival, Spring Joust, Fall Get-Together. Student services: personal-psychological counseling. Campus security: 24-hour emergency response devices and patrols, student patrols. College housing not available. Learning Resources Center plus 1 other with 55,053 books and 381 serials. 116 computers available on campus for general student use. Staffed computer lab on campus.

Community Environment: Kinston is an important bright-leaf tobacco market as well as a grain and livestock producing region. Commercial transportation is convenient. The community facilities include a library with branches, churches representing 25 denominations, a museum, little theatre, arts council, hospitals, good shopping areas, and various civic and service organizations. Good part-time employment opportunities are available for students. Parks, swimming pools, and golf courses provide the recreational facilities for the community.

■ **LENOIR-RHYNE COLLEGE** *D-2*
625 7th Ave. NE
Hickory, NC 28603
Tel: (828)328-1741
Free: 800-277-5721
Admissions: (828)328-7300
Fax: (828)328-7338
Web Site: http://www.lrc.edu/

Description: Independent Lutheran, comprehensive, coed. Awards bachelor's and master's degrees. Founded 1891. Setting: 100-acre small town campus with easy access to Charlotte. Total enrollment: 1,579. 1,427 applied, 85% were admitted. 18% from top 10% of their high school class, 47% from top quarter, 78% from top half. Full-time: 1,273 students, 62% women, 38% men. Part-time: 134 students, 69% women, 31% men. Students come from 28 states and territories, 4 other countries, 26% from out-of-state, 0.4% Native American, 1% Hispanic, 8% black, 2% Asian American or Pacific Islander, 0.4% international, 18% 25 or older, 60% live on campus, 9% transferred in. Retention: 75% of full-time freshmen returned the following year. Core. Calendar: semesters. Academic remediation for entering students, ESL program, services for LD students, advanced placement, accelerated degree program, self-designed majors, honors program, independent study, distance learning, double major, summer session for credit, part-time degree program, adult/continuing education programs, co-op programs and internships. Study abroad program. ROTC: Army (c).

Entrance Requirements: Options: Peterson's Universal Application, electronic application, early action, deferred admission, international baccalaureate accepted. Required: high school transcript, minimum 2.5 high school GPA, SAT or ACT. Recommended: interview. Entrance: moderately difficult. Application deadline: Rolling. Notification: continuous, 9/1 for early action.

Costs Per Year: Application fee: $25. One-time mandatory fee: $200. Comprehensive fee: $25,600 includes full-time tuition ($18,150), mandatory fees ($770), and college room and board ($6680). Room and board charges vary according to board plan and housing facility. Part-time tuition: $455 per credit. Part-time mandatory fees: $10 per term. Part-time tuition and fees vary according to class time.

Collegiate Environment: Orientation program. Drama-theater group, choral group, student-run newspaper, radio station. Social organizations: 54 open to all; national fraternities, national sororities; 23% of eligible men and 27% of eligible women are members. Most popular organizations: Student Government Association, religious clubs, Outdoors and Service Club, Playmakers, Bear Trackers (student recruitment organization). Major annual events: Homecoming, Spring Fling, Greek Week. Student services: health clinic, personal-psychological counseling, women's center. Campus security: 24-hour emergency response devices and patrols, late night transport-escort service, controlled dormitory access. 779 college housing spaces available; 738 were occupied in 2003-04. Freshmen guaranteed college housing. On-campus residence required through junior year. Options: coed, men-only, women-only housing available. Carl Rudisill Library plus 3 others with 275,961 books, 462,878 microform titles, 445 serials, 40,379 audiovisual materials, an OPAC, and a Web page. Operations spending for 2004 fiscal year: $566,570. 100 computers available on campus for general student use. A campuswide network can be accessed from student residence rooms and from off campus. Staffed computer lab on campus.

Community Environment: Hickory, located in the western Piedmont section, is best known as one of North Carolina's major furniture manufacturing cities. All forms of commercial transportation are available. The community facilities include hospitals, numerous churches, a museum of art, a city

library, and various civic and service organizations. Nearby, Lake Hickory offers many recreational opportunities such as boating, fishing, and swimming, golf, and minor league baseball. Hickory is located 50 miles NW of Charlotte and just 40 miles from the Blue Ridge Mountains.

■ **LIVINGSTONE COLLEGE** *D-4*
701 West Monroe St.
Salisbury, NC 28144-5298
Tel: (704)216-6000
Free: 800-835-3435
Admissions: (704)216-6005
Fax: (704)216-6217
E-mail: rburney@livingstone.edu
Web Site: http://www.livingstone.edu/

Description: Independent, 4-year, coed, affiliated with African Methodist Episcopal Zion Church. Awards bachelor's degrees. Founded 1879. Setting: 272-acre small town campus. Endowment: $16.2 million. Educational spending for 2005 fiscal year: $5757 per student. Total enrollment: 895. Student-undergrad faculty ratio is 15:1. 1,526 applied, 93% were admitted. Full-time: 863 students, 46% women, 54% men. Part-time: 32 students, 22% women, 78% men. Students come from 26 states and territories, 5 other countries, 42% from out-of-state, 0.2% Native American, 1% Hispanic, 92% black, 0.2% Asian American or Pacific Islander, 2% international, 13% 25 or older, 65% live on campus, 9% transferred in. Retention: 61% of full-time freshmen returned the following year. Academic areas with the most degrees conferred: business/marketing; security and protective services; computer and information sciences. Core. Calendar: semesters. Academic remediation for entering students, advanced placement, honors program, double major, part-time degree program, adult/continuing education programs, co-op programs and internships. ROTC: Army (c).

Entrance Requirements: Option: deferred admission. Required: high school transcript, minimum 2.0 high school GPA, SAT or ACT. Recommended: essay, 3 recommendations, interview. Entrance: minimally difficult. Application deadline: 8/1. Notification: continuous.

Costs Per Year: Application fee: $25. Comprehensive fee: $17,815 includes full-time tuition ($10,279), mandatory fees ($1895), and college room and board ($5641). College room only: $2501. Part-time tuition: $428.30 per hour. Part-time mandatory fees: $79 per hour.

Collegiate Environment: Orientation program. Drama-theater group, choral group, marching band. Social organizations: 71 open to all; national fraternities, national sororities, local fraternities, local sororities; 30% of eligible men and 35% of eligible women are members. Major annual events: Homecoming, Greek Week. Student services: health clinic, personal-psychological counseling. Campus security: 24-hour emergency response devices and patrols, late night transport-escort service, controlled dormitory access. 710 college housing spaces available; 621 were occupied in 2003-04. Freshmen given priority for college housing. Carnegie Library plus 2 others with 135,000 books, 43,400 microform titles, 235 serials, and 1,003 audiovisual materials. Operations spending for 2004 fiscal year: $118,577. 62 computers available on campus for general student use. A campuswide network can be accessed from student residence rooms. Staffed computer lab on campus.

Community Environment: See Catawba College.

■ **LOUISBURG COLLEGE** *B-10*
501 North Main St.
Louisburg, NC 27549-2399
Tel: (919)496-2521
Free: 800-775-0208
Admissions: (919)497-3228
Fax: (919)496-1788
E-mail: admissions@earthlink.net
Web Site: http://www.louisburg.edu/

Description: Independent United Methodist, 2-year, coed. Awards transfer associate degrees. Founded 1787. Setting: 75-acre small town campus with easy access to Raleigh. Endowment: $6.8 million. Research spending for 2004 fiscal year: $20,300. Educational spending for 2005 fiscal year: $2265 per student. Total enrollment: 502. 725 applied, 99% were admitted. 2% from top 10% of their high school class, 5% from top quarter, 19% from top half. Full-time: 494 students, 43% women, 57% men. Part-time: 8 students, 100% men. Students come from 21 states and territories, 4 other countries, 19% from out-of-state, 0% Native American, 3% Hispanic, 46% black, 0.4% Asian American or Pacific Islander, 1% international, 12% 25 or older, 90% live on campus, 10% transferred in. Retention: 68% of full-time freshmen returned the following year. Core. Calendar: semesters. Academic remediation for entering students, ESL program, services for LD students, advanced placement, summer session for credit, part-time degree program, adult/continuing education programs.

Entrance Requirements: Options: Peterson's Universal Application, Common Application, deferred admission. Required: high school transcript, SAT or ACT. Required for some: recommendations, interview. Entrance: minimally difficult. Application deadline: Rolling. Notification: continuous.

Collegiate Environment: Orientation program. Drama-theater group, choral group, student-run newspaper, radio station. Social organizations: 12 open to all. Most popular organizations: Student Government Association, Workers Actively Volunteering Energetic Services, Drama Club, Christian Life Council, Ecological Concerns Club. Major annual events: Homecoming, Mud-Volleyball, Spring Dance. Student services: health clinic, personal-psychological counseling. Campus security: 24-hour emergency response devices and patrols, controlled dormitory access. On-campus residence required through sophomore year. Options: men-only, women-only housing available. Robbins Library with 64,000 books and 150 serials. Operations spending for 2004 fiscal year: $148,590. 30 computers available on campus for general student use. A campuswide network can be accessed from student residence rooms and from off campus. Staffed computer lab on campus.

Community Environment: Louisburg, a county seat, is 30 miles from Raleigh, the state capital, where all forms of transportation are available. A hospital, churches, good shopping facilities, and various civic and social organizations are found in the community. There are many part-time job opportunities.

■ **MARS HILL COLLEGE** *I-15*

PO Box 370
Mars Hill, NC 28754
Tel: (828)689-1307; (866)MHC-4-YOU
Admissions: (828)689-1201
Fax: (828)689-1474
E-mail: admissions@mhc.edu
Web Site: http://www.mhc.edu/

Description: Independent Baptist, 4-year, coed. Awards bachelor's degrees. Founded 1856. Setting: 194-acre small town campus. Endowment: $34 million. Educational spending for 2005 fiscal year: $5472 per student. Total enrollment: 1,378. Student-undergrad faculty ratio is 14:1. 1,006 applied, 85% were admitted. 10% from top 10% of their high school class, 23% from top quarter, 58% from top half. Full-time: 1,227 students, 57% women, 43% men. Part-time: 151 students, 77% women, 23% men. Students come from 29 states and territories, 16 other countries, 33% from out-of-state, 1% Native American, 2% Hispanic, 14% black, 1% Asian American or Pacific Islander, 3% international, 20% 25 or older, 25% live on campus, 10% transferred in. Retention: 73% of full-time freshmen returned the following year. Core. Calendar: semesters. Academic remediation for entering students, ESL program, services for LD students, advanced placement, accelerated degree program, self-designed majors, honors program, independent study, double major, summer session for credit, part-time degree program, adult/continuing education programs, co-op programs and internships. Study abroad program.

Entrance Requirements: Options: Peterson's Universal Application, early admission, deferred admission, international baccalaureate accepted. Required: high school transcript, minimum 2.0 high school GPA, SAT or ACT. Recommended: minimum 3.0 high school GPA. Required for some: interview. Entrance: moderately difficult. Application deadline: Rolling.

Costs Per Year: Application fee: $25. Comprehensive fee: $24,378 includes full-time tuition ($17,950) and college room and board ($6428). College room only: $3268. Part-time tuition: $500 per credit hour.

Collegiate Environment: Orientation program. Drama-theater group, choral group, marching band, student-run newspaper. Social organizations: 60 open to all; national fraternities, national sororities, local fraternities, local sororities; 15% of eligible men and 20% of eligible women are members. Most popular organizations: Student Government Association, Fellowship of Christian Athletes, Christian Student Movement, Student Union Board. Major annual events: Homecoming, Fall Fest, Spring Fling. Student services: health clinic, personal-psychological counseling. Campus security: 24-hour emergency response devices and patrols, late night transport-escort service, controlled dormitory access. On-campus residence required through sophomore year. Options: men-only, women-only housing available. Renfro Library plus 1 other with 98,150 books, 700 serials, an OPAC, and a Web page. Operations spending for 2004 fiscal year: $407,443. 188 computers

available on campus for general student use. A campuswide network can be accessed from student residence rooms and from off campus. Staffed computer lab on campus.

Community Environment: Mars Hill is located 17 miles north of Asheville and 10 miles from Marshall. Plane and bus transportation are available. Community facilities include a medical center and convenient shopping.

■ **MARTIN COMMUNITY COLLEGE** *C-13*

1161 Kehukee Park Rd.
Williamston, NC 27892
Tel: (252)792-1521
Fax: (252)792-0826
Web Site: http://www.martin.cc.nc.us/

Description: State-supported, 2-year, coed. Part of North Carolina Community College System. Awards certificates, diplomas, transfer associate, and terminal associate degrees. Founded 1968. Setting: 65-acre rural campus. Endowment: $32,015. Educational spending for 2005 fiscal year: $1577 per student. Total enrollment: 834. 134 applied, 100% were admitted. Full-time: 281 students, 75% women, 25% men. Part-time: 553 students, 71% women, 29% men. Students come from 1 other country, 1% from out-of-state, 0.2% Native American, 1% Hispanic, 54% black, 0% Asian American or Pacific Islander, 0% international, 37% 25 or older, 11% transferred in. Calendar: semesters. Academic remediation for entering students, ESL program, services for LD students, advanced placement, independent study, distance learning, summer session for credit, part-time degree program, internships. Off campus study.

Entrance Requirements: Open admission except for physical therapy assistant program. Required: high school transcript. Required for some: interview. Placement: ACT COMPASS required for some. Entrance: noncompetitive. Application deadline: Rolling. Notification: continuous until 8/17.

Collegiate Environment: Orientation program. Most popular organizations: Phi Theta Kappa, Student Government Association, Alpha Beta Gamma, Physical Therapy Club, Equine Club. Major annual events: Stampede in the Park, Spring Fling, Fall Festival. Student services: personal-psychological counseling. Campus security: 24-hour emergency response devices, part-time patrols by trained security personnel. College housing not available. Martin Community College Learning Resources Center with 36,443 books, 1,610 microform titles, 215 serials, 10,809 audiovisual materials, and an OPAC. Operations spending for 2004 fiscal year: $143,375. 215 computers available on campus for general student use. A campuswide network can be accessed from off-campus. Staffed computer lab on campus.

Community Environment: The college is located in the center of a prosperous agricultural area. Recreational facilities include tennis courts, parks, and several ball fields. The area is ideal for hunting, fishing, and camping. The Senator Bob Martin Eastern Agricultural Center attracts horse shows, rodeos, bull riding, concerts, and many other events.

■ **MAYLAND COMMUNITY COLLEGE** *I-17*

PO Box 547
Spruce Pine, NC 28777-0547
Tel: (828)765-7351
Fax: (828)765-0728
Web Site: http://www.mayland.edu

Description: State and locally supported, 2-year, coed. Part of North Carolina Community College System. Awards certificates, diplomas, transfer associate, and terminal associate degrees. Founded 1971. Setting: 38-acre rural campus. Research spending for 2004 fiscal year: $56,544. Educational spending for 2005 fiscal year: $2239 per student. Total enrollment: 1,019. 355 applied, 87% were admitted. Full-time: 487 students, 43% women, 57% men. Part-time: 532 students, 65% women, 35% men. Students come from 3 states and territories, 1% Native American, 1% Hispanic, 5% black, 0.5% Asian American or Pacific Islander, 0% international, 48% 25 or older, 3% transferred in. Retention: 0% of full-time freshmen returned the following year. Calendar: semesters. Academic remediation for entering students, services for LD students, advanced placement, independent study, distance learning, double major, summer session for credit, part-time degree program, adult/continuing education programs, co-op programs and internships.

Entrance Requirements: Open admission. Options: Common Application, electronic application, deferred admission. Required: high school transcript. Required for some: CPT required for all for placement, required for admission to nursing program. Entrance: noncompetitive. Application deadline: Rolling. Notification: continuous.

Collegiate Environment: Student services: personal-psychological counseling. College housing not available. Carolyn Munro Wilson Learning Resources Center plus 1 other with 19,041 books, 653 microform titles, 225 serials, 1,707 audiovisual materials, an OPAC, and a Web page. Operations spending for 2004 fiscal year: $222,723. 200 computers available on campus for general student use. A campuswide network can be accessed. Staffed computer lab on campus.

Community Environment: Mayland Community College is located in the Blue Ridge Mountains of Western North Carolina. The Main Campus is located on Highway 19E, two miles east of Spruce Pine.

■ MCDOWELL TECHNICAL COMMUNITY COLLEGE *I-17*

Route 1, Box 170
Marion, NC 28752-9724
Tel: (828)652-6021
Admissions: (828)652-6024
Fax: (828)652-1014
E-mail: lisab@mail.mcdowell.cc.nc.us
Web Site: http://www.mcdowelltech.cc.nc.us/

Description: State-supported, 2-year, coed. Part of North Carolina Community College System. Awards certificates, diplomas, transfer associate, and terminal associate degrees. Founded 1964. Setting: 31-acre rural campus. Total enrollment: 1,078. Students come from 2 other countries, 50% 25 or older. Core. Calendar: semesters. Academic remediation for entering students, ESL program, services for LD students, accelerated degree program, independent study, distance learning, summer session for credit, part-time degree program, adult/continuing education programs, co-op programs.

Entrance Requirements: Open admission except for registered nursing, licensed practical nursing programs. Options: Common Application, early admission, deferred admission. Required for some: high school transcript. Placement: CPT required for some. Entrance: noncompetitive. Application deadline: Rolling. Notification: continuous.

Collegiate Environment: Student services: personal-psychological counseling. Campus security: 24-hour emergency response devices. College housing not available. 18,055 books and 156 serials. 70 computers available on campus for general student use. Staffed computer lab on campus.

Community Environment: Located in the foothills of the Blue Ridge Mountains, Marion enjoys a temperate climate. Trains, buses, and airlines provide the commercial transportation. To serve the people of this community, there are 96 churches and medical facilities. 26 major industries are located here, furnishing part-time job opportunities for students. Outdoor recreational facilities include the Blue Ridge Parkway, Mt Mitchell State Park, Lake James and Lake Tahoma.

■ MEREDITH COLLEGE *D-9*

3800 Hillsborough St.
Raleigh, NC 27607-5298
Tel: (919)760-8600
Free: 800-MEREDITH
Admissions: (919)760-8581
Fax: (919)829-2348
E-mail: admissions@meredith.edu
Web Site: http://www.meredith.edu/

Description: Independent, comprehensive. Awards bachelor's and master's degrees. Founded 1891. Setting: 225-acre urban campus. Endowment: $67.6 million. Total enrollment: 2,168. Faculty: 250 (128 full-time, 122 part-time). Student-undergrad faculty ratio is 11:1. 1,132 applied, 95% were admitted. 19% from top 10% of their high school class, 47% from top quarter, 78% from top half. 4 valedictorians. Full-time: 1,645 students, 100% women. Part-time: 370 students, 96% women, 4% men. Students come from 33 states and territories, 20 other countries, 12% from out-of-state, 0.3% Native American, 2% Hispanic, 11% black, 2% Asian American or Pacific Islander, 1% international, 20% 25 or older, 46% live on campus, 8% transferred in. Retention: 75% of full-time freshmen returned the following year. Academic areas with the most degrees conferred: business/marketing; visual and performing arts; psychology. Core. Calendar: semesters. Academic remediation for entering students, services for LD students, advanced placement, accelerated degree program, self-designed majors, honors program, independent study, double major, summer session for credit, part-time degree program, adult/continuing education programs, co-op programs and internships, graduate courses open to undergrads. Off campus study at

Cooperating Raleigh Colleges, American University, Marymount College (NY), Drew University. Study abroad program. ROTC: Army (c), Air Force (c).

Entrance Requirements: Options: Common Application, electronic application, early admission, early decision, deferred admission, international baccalaureate accepted. Required: high school transcript, minimum 2.0 high school GPA, 2 recommendations, SAT or ACT. Required for some: essay, interview, SAT Subject Tests. Entrance: moderately difficult. Application deadlines: 2/15, 10/15 for early decision. Notification: continuous, 11/1 for early decision.

Costs Per Year: Application fee: $40. Comprehensive fee: $27,140 includes full-time tuition ($21,150), mandatory fees ($50), and college room and board ($5940). Part-time tuition: $555 per credit hour.

Collegiate Environment: Orientation program. Drama-theater group, choral group, student-run newspaper. Social organizations: 93 open to all. Most popular organizations: Student Government Association, Entertainment Association, Recreation Association, Class Organizations, choral groups. Major annual events: Cornhuskin', Day of Celebration, Spring Formal. Student services: health clinic, personal-psychological counseling. Campus security: 24-hour emergency response devices and patrols, late night transport-escort service, controlled dormitory access, self-defense instruction. 1,115 college housing spaces available; 825 were occupied in 2003-04. Freshmen guaranteed college housing. On-campus residence required through sophomore year. Option: women-only housing available. Carlyle Campbell Library plus 1 other with 186,100 books, 15,626 microform titles, 669 serials, 12,997 audiovisual materials, an OPAC, and a Web page. Operations spending for 2004 fiscal year: $1.2 million. 140 computers available on campus for general student use. Computer purchase/lease plans available. A campuswide network can be accessed from student residence rooms. Staffed computer lab on campus.

Community Environment: Meredith is located at the western edge of Raleigh, NC, the state capital and home of five other colleges and universities. The area is served by air, bus and rail. The campus is easily accessible from I-40, bordered by US 1 and Wade Avenue, with the front entrance facing Hillsborough Street. Raleigh is a part of the Research Triangle Area, which includes Durham and Chapel Hill, NC. It is a cultural center with the N.C. Museums of Art, History and Natural Science, the North Carolina Symphony and numerous theaters. Meredith itself is a center for many cultural events including the Fletcher School of the Performing Arts and the National Opera Company.

■ METHODIST COLLEGE *F-8*

5400 Ramsey St.
Fayetteville, NC 28311-1498
Tel: (910)630-7000
Free: 800-488-7110
Admissions: (910)630-7027
Fax: (910)630-7317
Web Site: http://www.methodist.edu/

Description: Independent United Methodist, comprehensive, coed. Awards associate, bachelor's, and master's degrees. Founded 1956. Setting: 600-acre suburban campus with easy access to Raleigh-Durham. Endowment: $10 million. Educational spending for 2005 fiscal year: $4858 per student. Total enrollment: 2,257. 2,288 applied, 77% were admitted. 11% from top 10% of their high school class, 35% from top quarter, 68% from top half. 4 valedictorians. Full-time: 1,722 students, 43% women, 57% men. Part-time: 473 students, 41% women, 59% men. Students come from 48 states and territories, 30 other countries, 48% from out-of-state, 1% Native American, 6% Hispanic, 21% black, 2% Asian American or Pacific Islander, 3% international, 24% 25 or older, 50% live on campus, 10% transferred in. Retention: 63% of full-time freshmen returned the following year. Core. Calendar: semesters. Academic remediation for entering students, ESL program, services for LD students, advanced placement, accelerated degree program, honors program, independent study, distance learning, double major, summer session for credit, part-time degree program, adult/continuing education programs, co-op programs and internships. Study abroad program. ROTC: Army, Air Force (c).

Entrance Requirements: Options: Peterson's Universal Application, Common Application, deferred admission, international baccalaureate accepted. Required: high school transcript, SAT or ACT. Recommended: 2 recommendations, interview. Required for some: essay, 2 recommendations, interview. Entrance: moderately difficult. Application deadline: Rolling. Notification: continuous until 8/15.

Costs Per Year: Application fee: $25. Comprehensive fee: $24,620 includes full-time tuition ($17,580), mandatory fees ($270), and college room and

board ($6770). Full-time tuition and fees vary according to class time. Room and board charges vary according to board plan and housing facility. Part-time tuition: $570 per semester hour. Part-time tuition varies according to class time.

Collegiate Environment: Orientation program. Drama-theater group, choral group, student-run newspaper. Social organizations: 76 open to all; national sororities, local fraternities, local sororities; 2% of eligible men and 5% of eligible women are members. Most popular organizations: Student Activities Committee, Student Government Association, Student Education Association, Fellowship of Christian Athletes, Residence Hall Association. Major annual events: homecoming, Spring Fling, Show You Care Day. Student services: health clinic, personal-psychological counseling. Campus security: 24-hour emergency response devices and patrols, late night transport-escort service, controlled dormitory access, regular patrol by county sheriff department. 850 college housing spaces available; all were occupied in 2003-04. Freshmen guaranteed college housing. On-campus residence required through sophomore year. Options: coed, men-only, women-only housing available. Davis Memorial Library plus 1 other with 86,259 books, 62,814 microform titles, 571 serials, 13,208 audiovisual materials, an OPAC, and a Web page. Operations spending for 2004 fiscal year: $526,906. 175 computers available on campus for general student use. Computer purchase/lease plans available. A campuswide network can be accessed from student residence rooms and from off campus. Staffed computer lab on campus.

Community Environment: Fayetteville, a community of 105,000, is part of the Carolina Sandhills region in the heart of golf country and two hours from the coast. It is accessible by air, rail, and highway. Its economy is based on agriculture, manufacturing and processing, distribution, and the government. The community has 4 hospitals, a public library with 8 branches, an art guild, theater, art museum, symphony, and brass band. There are 53 public and private golf courses within an hour's drive of the city. Popular sports include golf, tennis, archery, boating, and skating.

■ **MITCHELL COMMUNITY COLLEGE** *D-3*
500 West Broad
Statesville, NC 28677-5293
Tel: (704)878-3200
Admissions: (704)878-3281
Fax: (704)878-0872
Web Site: http://www.mitchell.cc.nc.us/

Description: State-supported, 2-year, coed. Part of North Carolina Community College System. Awards certificates, diplomas, transfer associate, and terminal associate degrees. Founded 1852. Setting: 8-acre small town campus with easy access to Charlotte. Research spending for 2004 fiscal year: $275,039. Educational spending for 2005 fiscal year: $2646 per student. Total enrollment: 2,243. Full-time: 993 students, 65% women, 35% men. Part-time: 1,250 students, 72% women, 28% men. Students come from 5 states and territories, 1 other country, 0.1% from out-of-state, 0.2% Native American, 2% Hispanic, 20% black, 2% Asian American or Pacific Islander, 0.1% international, 57% 25 or older, 4% transferred in. Retention: 61% of full-time freshmen returned the following year. Core. Calendar: semesters. Academic remediation for entering students, ESL program, services for LD students, advanced placement, distance learning, summer session for credit, part-time degree program, adult/continuing education programs. ROTC: Army (c).

Entrance Requirements: Open admission except for nursing program. Required: high school transcript. Entrance: noncompetitive. Application deadline: Rolling. Notification: continuous.

Collegiate Environment: Choral group. Social organizations: 10 open to all. Most popular organizations: Circle K, Phi Beta Lambda, Medical Assisting Club, Ebony Kinship. Major annual events: May (Spring) Week, Awards Day, Christmas activities. Student services: personal-psychological counseling. Campus security: day and evening security guards. College housing not available. Main library plus 1 other with 37,760 books, 33,426 microform titles, 218 serials, 2,225 audiovisual materials, and an OPAC. 40 computers available on campus for general student use. A campuswide network can be accessed. Staffed computer lab on campus.

Community Environment: On a plateau, surrounded by the foothills of the Blue Ridge Mountains, Statesville is in the heart of the Piedmont area. Industrial products and textiles, metal, and furniture are produced there. This is also a large milk-producing area. All forms of commercial transportation are available. There are churches of all denominations along with the various civic and service organizations. Excellent part-time job opportunities are available.

■ **MONTGOMERY COMMUNITY COLLEGE** *E-6*
1011 Page St.
Troy, NC 27371
Tel: (910)576-6222
Free: 800-839-6222
Web Site: http://www.montgomery.edu/

Description: State-supported, 2-year, coed. Part of North Carolina Community College System. Awards certificates, diplomas, transfer associate, and terminal associate degrees. Founded 1967. Setting: 159-acre rural campus. Total enrollment: 850. 152 applied, 100% were admitted. Full-time: 391 students, 67% women, 33% men. Part-time: 459 students, 71% women, 29% men. Students come from 4 states and territories, 1% from out-of-state, 1% Native American, 4% Hispanic, 24% black, 2% Asian American or Pacific Islander, 0.2% international, 57% 25 or older, 14% transferred in. Core. Calendar: semesters. Academic remediation for entering students, ESL program, services for LD students, advanced placement, distance learning, double major, summer session for credit, part-time degree program, co-op programs.

Entrance Requirements: Open admission except for nursing program. Options: early admission, deferred admission. Required: high school transcript. Entrance: noncompetitive. Application deadline: Rolling. Notification: continuous. Preference given to residents of Montgomery and adjacent counties.

Costs Per Year: Application fee: $0. State resident tuition: $1264 full-time, $39.50 per semester hour part-time. Nonresident tuition: $7024 full-time, $219.50 per semester hour part-time. Mandatory fees: $57 full-time, $28.25 per term part-time. Full-time tuition and fees vary according to course load. Part-time tuition and fees vary according to course load.

Collegiate Environment: Social organizations: 12 open to all. Most popular organizations: Gunsmithing Club, Student Government Association, Literary Club, Forestry Club. Major annual event: Spring Fling. Student services: personal-psychological counseling. College housing not available. 14,859 books, 99 serials, 500 audiovisual materials, and an OPAC. Operations spending for 2004 fiscal year: $133,525. 80 computers available on campus for general student use. Staffed computer lab on campus.

Community Environment: Troy is located 50 miles from Greensboro where the main industries are lumber and textiles. Train transportation is available with air travel convenient to Greensboro and Charlotte. The Pee Dee River is 12 miles away providing facilities for water skiing, fishing, and boating.

■ **MONTREAT COLLEGE**
PO Box 1267
Montreat, NC 28757-1267
Tel: (828)669-8012
Fax: (828)669-0120
E-mail: admissions@montreat.edu
Web Site: http://www.montreat.edu/

Description: Independent, comprehensive, coed, affiliated with Presbyterian Church (U.S.A.). Awards associate, bachelor's, and master's degrees. Founded 1916. Setting: 112-acre small town campus. Endowment: $9.7 million. Educational spending for 2005 fiscal year: $3140 per student. Total enrollment: 1,035. 409 applied, 78% were admitted. 8% from top 10% of their high school class, 34% from top quarter, 71% from top half. Full-time: 935 students, 62% women, 38% men. Part-time: 8 students, 50% women, 50% men. Students come from 28 states and territories, 8 other countries, 20% from out-of-state, 7% Native American, 1% Hispanic, 18% black, 1% Asian American or Pacific Islander, 1% international, 58% 25 or older, 34% live on campus, 6% transferred in. Retention: 66% of full-time freshmen returned the following year. Core. Calendar: semesters. Advanced placement, accelerated degree program, independent study, double major, part-time degree program, adult/continuing education programs, co-op programs and internships. Off campus study at Council for Christian Colleges and Universities. Study abroad program.

Entrance Requirements: Options: early admission, deferred admission, international baccalaureate accepted. Required: essay, high school transcript, minimum 2.25 high school GPA, 1 recommendation, SAT or ACT. Required for some: interview. Entrance: moderately difficult. Application deadline: 8/15. Notification: continuous.

Costs Per Year: Application fee: $15. Comprehensive fee: $20,568 includes full-time tuition ($15,560) and college room and board ($5008). Part-time tuition: $480 per credit hour.

Collegiate Environment: Orientation program. Drama-theater group, choral group, student-run newspaper. Social organizations: 14 open to all. Most popular organizations: student government, Student Christian Association, Inter-Varsity Missions Fellowship, Paintball Club, Business Club. Major annual events: Homecoming, Winter Dance, Spring Dance. Student services: health clinic, personal-psychological counseling. Campus security: 24-hour emergency response devices and patrols, controlled dormitory access. 385 college housing spaces available; 314 were occupied in 2003-04. Freshmen guaranteed college housing. On-campus residence required through sophomore year. Options: men-only, women-only housing available. L. Nelson Bell Library with 68,100 books, 426 serials, and an OPAC. Operations spending for 2004 fiscal year: $360,574. 60 computers available on campus for general student use. A campuswide network can be accessed from student residence rooms and from off campus. Staffed computer lab on campus.

Community Environment: Montreat is situated in the beautiful Blue Ridge Mountains, 17 miles from Asheville, and adjacent to the historic town of Black Mountain with picturesque avenues, stores, and restaurants. The climate is recognized as one of the world's finest and the region has long been a major vacation area. Montreat's recreational activities include golf, tennis, skiing, baseball, and basketball, as well as access to the Pisgah National Forest.

■ MOUNT OLIVE COLLEGE *E-11*

634 Henderson St.
Mount Olive, NC 28365
Tel: (919)658-2502
Fax: (919)658-8934
Web Site: http://www.moc.edu/

Description: Independent Free Will Baptist, 4-year, coed. Awards associate and bachelor's degrees. Founded 1951. Setting: 123-acre small town campus with easy access to Raleigh. Endowment: $7.3 million. Educational spending for 2005 fiscal year: $1732 per student. Total enrollment: 2,830. Student-undergrad faculty ratio is 17:1. 807 applied, 71% were admitted. 9% from top 10% of their high school class, 36% from top quarter, 69% from top half. Full-time: 1,946 students, 62% women, 38% men. Part-time: 884 students, 56% women, 44% men. Students come from 21 states and territories, 6% from out-of-state, 1% Native American, 2% Hispanic, 30% black, 1% Asian American or Pacific Islander, 0% international, 66% 25 or older, 13% live on campus, 6% transferred in. Retention: 60% of full-time freshmen returned the following year. Academic areas with the most degrees conferred: business/marketing; security and protective services; psychology. Core. Calendar: semester or continuous accelerated programs. Academic remediation for entering students, advanced placement, accelerated degree program, freshman honors college, honors program, independent study, double major, summer session for credit, part-time degree program, external degree program, adult/continuing education programs, co-op programs and internships. Off campus study at James Sprunt Community College, Wayne Community College, East Carolina University, Old Dominion University.

Entrance Requirements: Options: Peterson's Universal Application, Common Application, early admission, deferred admission, international baccalaureate accepted. Required: high school transcript, minimum 2.0 high school GPA, SAT or ACT. Recommended: 2 recommendations, interview, SAT. Entrance: minimally difficult. Application deadline: Rolling. Notification: continuous.

Costs Per Year: Application fee: $20. Comprehensive fee: $17,572 includes full-time tuition ($12,620) and college room and board ($4952). College room only: $2000. Part-time tuition: $215 per credit hour.

Collegiate Environment: Orientation program. Choral group, student-run newspaper. Social organizations: 20 open to all. Most popular organizations: Student Government Association, Phi Beta Lambda, commuters organization, Christian Student Fellowship, English Society. Major annual events: Pickle Classic Basketball Tournament, Mr. and Miss Mount Olive College, MOOS Day. Student services: health clinic, personal-psychological counseling. Campus security: overnight security patrols; weekend patrols. 41 undergraduates lived in college housing during 2003-04. On-campus residence required in freshman year. Options: men-only, women-only housing available. Moye Library plus 2 others with 65,413 books, 49,413 microform titles, 2,112 serials, 2,005 audiovisual materials, an OPAC, and a Web page. Operations spending for 2004 fiscal year: $216,883. 50 computers available on campus for general student use. Computer purchase/lease plans available. A campuswide network can be accessed from student residence rooms and from off campus. Staffed computer lab on campus.

Community Environment: Mount Olive is about 15 miles from the county seat, Goldsboro. Buses provide commercial transportation. Numerous civic

and service organizations, hospitals in separate towns 15 miles away, churches, and a library contribute to the community. The coast is a one-hour drive for swimming and fresh water fishing; other activities are tennis, softball, and golf.

■ NASH COMMUNITY COLLEGE *C-11*

PO Box 7488
Rocky Mount, NC 27804-0488
Tel: (252)443-4011
Fax: (252)443-0828
Web Site: http://www.nash.cc.nc.us/

Description: State-supported, 2-year, coed. Part of North Carolina Community College System. Awards certificates, diplomas, transfer associate, and terminal associate degrees. Founded 1967. Setting: 69-acre rural campus. Endowment: $147,220. Total enrollment: 2,567. 360 applied, 100% were admitted. Full-time: 904 students, 62% women, 38% men. Part-time: 1,663 students, 67% women, 33% men. Students come from 3 states and territories, 2% Native American, 1% Hispanic, 36% black, 0.3% Asian American or Pacific Islander, 0% international, 43% 25 or older, 1% transferred in. Calendar: semesters. Academic remediation for entering students, ESL program, services for LD students, advanced placement, independent study, distance learning, double major, summer session for credit, part-time degree program, adult/continuing education programs.

Entrance Requirements: Open admission except for nursing, physical therapy assistant, cosmetology, phlebotomy programs. Options: Common Application, deferred admission. Required: high school transcript. Recommended: interview. Required for some: SAT or ACT, SAT and SAT Subject Tests or ACT, ACT ASSET or ACT COMPASS. Entrance: noncompetitive. Application deadline: Rolling. Notification: continuous.

Collegiate Environment: Orientation program. Student-run newspaper. Social organizations: 4 open to all. Most popular organizations: Student Government Association, Gamma, Phi Beta Lambda, Student Nurses Organization/Physical Therapist Assistant Club, Criminal Justice Club. Campus security: 24-hour emergency response devices, late night transport-escort service. College housing not available. Nash Community College Library plus 1 other with 34,000 books, 110 serials, and an OPAC. Operations spending for 2004 fiscal year: $117,337. 110 computers available on campus for general student use. A campuswide network can be accessed. Staffed computer lab on campus.

Community Environment: See North Carolina Wesleyan College.

■ NEW LIFE THEOLOGICAL SEMINARY *E-3*

PO Box 790106
Charlotte, NC 28206-7901
Tel: (704)334-6882
Fax: (704)334-6885
Web Site: http://www.nlts.org/

Description: Independent religious, comprehensive, coed. Founded 1996.

■ NORTH CAROLINA AGRICULTURAL AND TECHNICAL STATE UNIVERSITY *C-6*

1601 East Market St.
Greensboro, NC 27411
Tel: (336)334-7500
Admissions: (336)334-7946
Fax: (336)334-7082
Web Site: http://www.ncat.edu/

Description: State-supported, university, coed. Part of University of North Carolina System. Awards bachelor's, master's, and doctoral degrees. Founded 1891. Setting: 800-acre urban campus. Endowment: $10.4 million. Research spending for 2004 fiscal year: $1.3 million. Educational spending for 2005 fiscal year: $5741 per student. Total enrollment: 11,103. Faculty: 458. Student-undergrad faculty ratio is 17:1. 6,502 applied, 84% were admitted. 1% from top 10% of their high school class, 11% from top quarter, 48% from top half. 7 National Merit Scholars. Full-time: 8,856 students, 52% women, 48% men. Part-time: 879 students, 54% women, 46% men. Students come from 42 states and territories, 23% from out-of-state, 0.3% Native American, 1% Hispanic, 93% black, 1% Asian American or Pacific Islander, 0.4% international, 21% 25 or older, 29% live on campus, 5% transferred in. Academic areas with the most degrees conferred: engineering; business/marketing; engineering technologies. Core. Calendar: semesters. Academic remediation for entering students, services for LD students, advanced placement, honors program, summer session for credit, part-time degree program, adult/continuing education programs, co-op programs and internships, graduate courses open to undergrads. Off campus study at University of North Carolina at Greensboro, Guilford College, Bennett College, High Point University, Greensboro College. Study abroad program. ROTC: Army, Air Force.

Entrance Requirements: Options: Peterson's Universal Application, early admission, deferred admission. Required: high school transcript, minimum 2.0 high school GPA. Recommended: SAT or ACT. Entrance: moderately difficult. Application deadline: Rolling. Notification: continuous.

Costs Per Year: Application fee: $45. State resident tuition: $1769 full-time. Nonresident tuition: $11,211 full-time. Mandatory fees: $1355 full-time. College room and board: $5254. College room only: $2954.

Collegiate Environment: Orientation program. Drama-theater group, choral group, marching band, student-run newspaper, radio station. Social organizations: national fraternities, national sororities, local fraternities, local sororities. Most popular organization: student government. Major annual events: Martin Luther King's Birthday, Homecoming, Commencement. Student services: health clinic, personal-psychological counseling. Campus security: 24-hour emergency response devices and patrols, late night transport-escort service, controlled dormitory access. Options: coed, men-only, women-only housing available. F. D. Bluford Library plus 1 other with 541,403 books, 1.1 million microform titles, 31,674 serials, and 35,735 audiovisual materials. Operations spending for 2004 fiscal year: $3.4 million. 250 computers available on campus for general student use. A campuswide network can be accessed from off-campus. Staffed computer lab on campus.

Community Environment: See Greensboro College.

■ NORTH CAROLINA CENTRAL UNIVERSITY *C-8*

1801 Fayetteville St.
Durham, NC 27707-3129
Tel: (919)560-6100; 877-667-7533
Admissions: (919)530-6298
Web Site: http://www.nccu.edu/

Description: State-supported, comprehensive, coed. Part of University of North Carolina System. Awards bachelor's, master's, and first professional degrees. Founded 1910. Setting: 103-acre urban campus. Endowment: $14.4 million. Research spending for 2004 fiscal year: $65,000. Educational spending for 2005 fiscal year: $62,229 per student. Total enrollment: 8,219. Faculty: 560 (325 full-time, 235 part-time). Student-undergrad faculty ratio is 17:1. 3,321 applied, 77% were admitted. 5% from top 10% of their high school class, 16% from top quarter, 51% from top half. 14 National Merit Scholars. Full-time: 5,005 students, 65% women, 35% men. Part-time: 1,348 students, 72% women, 28% men. Students come from 35 states and territories, 14 other countries, 9% from out-of-state, 0.4% Native American, 1% Hispanic, 86% black, 1% Asian American or Pacific Islander, 1% international, 28% 25 or older, 38% live on campus, 6% transferred in. Retention: 76% of full-time freshmen returned the following year. Academic areas with the most degrees conferred: business/marketing; social sciences; security and protective services. Core. Calendar: semesters. Academic remediation for entering students, ESL program, services for LD students, advanced placement, honors program, independent study, distance learning, double major, summer session for credit, part-time degree program, external degree program, adult/continuing education programs, co-op programs and internships, graduate courses open to undergrads. Off campus study. Study abroad program. ROTC: Army (c), Air Force (c).

Entrance Requirements: Open admission. Options: Common Application, electronic application, deferred admission, international baccalaureate accepted. Required: high school transcript, minimum 2.0 high school GPA, SAT or ACT. Entrance: minimally difficult. Application deadline: 8/1. Notification: continuous until 10/15. Preference given to qualified state residents.

Costs Per Year: Application fee: $30. State resident tuition: $1878 full-time, $235 per course part-time. Nonresident tuition: $11,622 full-time, $1453 per course part-time. Mandatory fees: $1218 full-time, $51 per course part-time. Part-time tuition and fees vary according to course load. College room and board: $4526. College room only: $2588. Room and board charges according to board plan and housing facility.

Collegiate Environment: Orientation program. Drama-theater group, choral group, marching band, student-run newspaper. Social organizations: national fraternities, national sororities, local fraternities, local sororities. Student services: health clinic, personal-psychological counseling. Campus security: 24-hour emergency response devices and patrols, controlled dormitory access. 2,092 undergraduates lived in college housing during 2003-04. Freshmen given priority for college housing. Option: coed housing available. Shepherd Library plus 4 others with 500,712 books, 510,384 microform titles, 1,934 serials, 7,600 audiovisual materials, an OPAC, and a Web page.

Operations spending for 2004 fiscal year: $5 million. 603 computers available on campus for general student use. Computer purchase/lease plans available. A campuswide network can be accessed from student residence rooms and from off campus. Staffed computer lab on campus.

Community Environment: See Duke University.

■ NORTH CAROLINA SCHOOL OF THE ARTS *C-5*

1533 South Main St.
PO Box 12189
Winston-Salem, NC 27127-2188
Tel: (336)770-3399
Admissions: (336)770-3290
Fax: (336)770-3370
Web Site: http://www.ncarts.edu/

Description: State-supported, comprehensive, coed. Part of University of North Carolina System. Awards bachelor's and master's degrees and post-master's certificates. Founded 1963. Setting: 57-acre urban campus. Endowment: $16.8 million. Total enrollment: 827. Faculty: 139 (135 full-time, 4 part-time). Student-undergrad faculty ratio is 8:1. 744 applied, 46% were admitted. 19% from top 10% of their high school class, 36% from top quarter. Full-time: 719 students, 39% women, 61% men. Part-time: 7 students, 43% women, 57% men. Students come from 44 states and territories, 52% from out-of-state, 0.4% Native American, 5% Hispanic, 9% black, 3% Asian American or Pacific Islander, 1% international, 5% 25 or older, 55% live on campus, 9% transferred in. Retention: 74% of full-time freshmen returned the following year. Academic area with the most degrees conferred: visual and performing arts. Core. Calendar: trimesters. Academic remediation for entering students, services for LD students.

Entrance Requirements: Options: electronic application, international baccalaureate accepted. Required: high school transcript, 2 recommendations, audition, SAT or ACT. Required for some: essay, interview. Entrance: very difficult. Application deadline: 3/1. Notification: continuous.

Costs Per Year: Application fee: $50. State resident tuition: $2755 full-time. Nonresident tuition: $14,035 full-time. Mandatory fees: $1551 full-time. Full-time tuition and fees vary according to program. College room and board: $5700. College room only: $3035. Room and board charges vary according to board plan and housing facility.

Collegiate Environment: Orientation program. Drama-theater group, choral group, student-run newspaper. Most popular organizations: Pride (gay/lesbian organization), Appreciation of Black Artists. Major annual events: Beaux Arts (spring festival), Resource Fair (career fair), Health Fair. Student services: health clinic, personal-psychological counseling. Campus security: 24-hour emergency response devices and patrols, controlled dormitory access. 400 college housing spaces available; all were occupied in 2003-04. Freshmen guaranteed college housing. On-campus residence required through sophomore year. Option: coed housing available. Semans Library plus 1 other with 87,917 books, 25,053 microform titles, 490 serials, 73,025 audiovisual materials, and an OPAC. Operations spending for 2004 fiscal year: $681,312. 60 computers available on campus for general student use. A campuswide network can be accessed from student residence rooms and from off campus. Staffed computer lab on campus.

Community Environment: See Wake Forest University.

■ NORTH CAROLINA STATE UNIVERSITY *D-9*

Raleigh, NC 27695
Tel: (919)515-2011
Admissions: (919)515-2434
Fax: (919)515-5039
E-mail: undergrad_admissions@ncsu.edu
Web Site: http://www.ncsu.edu/

Description: State-supported, university, coed. Part of University of North Carolina System. Awards associate, bachelor's, master's, doctoral, and first professional degrees and first professional certificates. Founded 1887. Setting: 1,623-acre suburban campus. Endowment: $380.5 million. Research spending for 2004 fiscal year: $176.8 million. Educational spending for 2005 fiscal year: $9894 per student. Total enrollment: 30,149. Faculty: 1,864 (1,671 full-time, 193 part-time). Student-undergrad faculty ratio is 16:1. 13,610 applied, 66% were admitted. 36% from top 10% of their high school class, 78% from top quarter, 98% from top half. 21 National Merit Scholars, 75 valedictorians. Full-time: 19,226 students, 43% women, 57% men. Part-time: 3,541 students, 42% women, 58% men. Students come from 52 states and territories, 54 other countries, 8% from out-of-state, 1% Native American, 2% Hispanic, 10% black, 5% Asian American or Pacific Islander, 1% international, 9% 25 or older, 33% live on campus, 5% transferred in.

Retention: 89% of full-time freshmen returned the following year. Academic areas with the most degrees conferred: engineering; business/marketing; biological/life sciences. Core. Calendar: semesters. Academic remediation for entering students, services for LD students, advanced placement, accelerated degree program, self-designed majors, honors program, independent study, distance learning, double major, summer session for credit, part-time degree program, adult/continuing education programs, co-op programs and internships, graduate courses open to undergrads. Off campus study at five members of the Cooperating Raleigh Colleges, Duke University, University of North Carolina at Chapel Hill. Study abroad program. ROTC: Army, Naval, Air Force.

Entrance Requirements: Options: Peterson's Universal Application, electronic application, early action, deferred admission, international baccalaureate accepted. Required: high school transcript, SAT or ACT. Recommended: essay, SAT Subject Tests. Required for some: interview. Entrance: very difficult. Application deadlines: 2/1, 11/1 for early action. Notification: continuous, 1/15 for early action. Preference given to state residents.

Costs Per Year: Application fee: $60. State resident tuition: $3530 full-time. Nonresident tuition: $15,728 full-time. Mandatory fees: $1254 full-time. College room and board: $7040. College room only: $4288.

Collegiate Environment: Orientation program. Drama-theater group, choral group, marching band, student-run newspaper, radio station. Social organizations: 300 open to all; national fraternities, national sororities, local sororities; 8% of eligible men and 10% of eligible women are members. Most popular organizations: student government, student media, student musical groups, intramural sports. Major annual events: homecoming, Wolfstock Concert Weekend, Pan-African Week. Student services: legal services, health clinic, personal-psychological counseling, women's center. Campus security: 24-hour emergency response devices and patrols, student patrols, late night transport-escort service, controlled dormitory access. 6,700 college housing spaces available; 6,164 were occupied in 2003-04. Freshmen given priority for college housing. Options: coed, men-only, women-only housing available. D. H. Hill Library plus 6 others with 3.4 million books, 5.4 million microform titles, 54,799 serials, 135,347 audiovisual materials, an OPAC, and a Web page. Operations spending for 2004 fiscal year: $22.8 million. 3,189 computers available on campus for general student use. Computer purchase/lease plans available. A campuswide network can be accessed from student residence rooms and from off campus. Staffed computer lab on campus.

■ **NORTH CAROLINA WESLEYAN COLLEGE** *C-11*
3400 North Wesleyan Blvd.
Rocky Mount, NC 27804-8677
Tel: (252)985-5100
Free: 800-488-6292
Fax: (252)985-5325
Web Site: http://www.ncwc.edu/

Description: Independent, 4-year, coed, affiliated with United Methodist Church. Awards bachelor's degrees (also offers adult part-time degree program with significant enrollment not reflected in profile). Founded 1956. Setting: 200-acre suburban campus. Endowment: $8.2 million. Educational spending for 2005 fiscal year: $4274 per student. Total enrollment: 1,752. Student-undergrad faculty ratio is 17:1. 1,169 applied, 81% were admitted. 8% from top 10% of their high school class, 18% from top quarter, 59% from top half. Full-time: 1,126 students, 46% women, 54% men. Part-time: 626 students, 54% women, 46% men. Students come from 22 states and territories, 15% from out-of-state, 1% Native American, 3% Hispanic, 45% black, 1% Asian American or Pacific Islander, 1% international, 56% 25 or older, 28% live on campus, 5% transferred in. Retention: 64% of full-time freshmen returned the following year. Academic areas with the most degrees conferred: business/marketing; computer and information sciences; law/legal studies. Core. Calendar: semesters. Academic remediation for entering students, services for LD students, advanced placement, accelerated degree program, honors program, independent study, distance learning, double major, summer session for credit, part-time degree program, adult/continuing education programs, co-op programs and internships.

Entrance Requirements: Options: Peterson's Universal Application, Common Application, electronic application, international baccalaureate accepted. Required: high school transcript, SAT or ACT. Recommended: minimum 2.0 high school GPA, 2 recommendations, interview. Entrance: moderately difficult. Application deadline: Rolling. Notification: continuous.

Costs Per Year: Application fee: $25. Comprehensive fee: $22,670 includes full-time tuition ($16,000) and college room and board ($6670). College room only: $3000. Full-time tuition varies according to location. Room and board

charges vary according to housing facility. Part-time tuition: $258 per credit hour. Part-time tuition varies according to location.

Collegiate Environment: Orientation program. Drama-theater group, choral group, student-run newspaper. Social organizations: 19 open to all; national fraternities, national sororities; 1% of eligible men and 1% of eligible women are members. Most popular organizations: Club Dramatica, Student Government Association, gospel choir, Wesleyan Singers, pep band. Major annual events: Homecoming week, Spring Fling, Wesleyan Symposium. Student services: health clinic, personal-psychological counseling. Campus security: 24-hour emergency response devices and patrols, student patrols, late night transport-escort service, controlled dormitory access. On-campus residence required through sophomore year. Options: coed, men-only housing available. Elizabeth Braswell Pearsall Library with 88,975 books, 30,720 microform titles, 11,245 serials, 1,810 audiovisual materials, an OPAC, and a Web page. Operations spending for 2004 fiscal year: $244,482. 43 computers available on campus for general student use. A campuswide network can be accessed. Staffed computer lab on campus.

Community Environment: Rocky Mount, population 55,000, is located three miles from Interstate 95 in the coastal plain region of the state. It is a progressive industrial and agricultural community, but still maintains its historic heritage. Nash General and Community Hospital are only 10 minutes from campus. Many recreational facilities are easily accessible.

■ **PAMLICO COMMUNITY COLLEGE**
PO Box 185
Grantsboro, NC 28529-0185
Tel: (252)249-1851
Fax: (252)249-2377
Web Site: http://www.pamlico.cc.nc.us/

Description: State-supported, 2-year, coed. Part of North Carolina Community College System. Awards certificates, diplomas, transfer associate, and terminal associate degrees. Founded 1963. Setting: 44-acre rural campus. Total enrollment: 300. 58% 25 or older. Core. Calendar: semesters. Academic remediation for entering students, services for LD students, summer session for credit, part-time degree program, adult/continuing education programs, co-op programs.

Entrance Requirements: Open admission. Options: early admission, deferred admission. Required: high school transcript. Placement: ACT ASSET required. Entrance: noncompetitive. Application deadline: Rolling. Notification: continuous.

Collegiate Environment: Student-run newspaper. Student services: personal-psychological counseling. Campus security: evening security guard. College housing not available. Pamlico Community College Library plus 1 other with 19,500 books and 202 serials. 68 computers available on campus for general student use.

■ **PEACE COLLEGE** *D-9*
15 East Peace St.
Raleigh, NC 27604-1194
Tel: (919)508-2000
Free: 800-PEACE-47
Admissions: (919)508-2016
Fax: (919)508-2328
E-mail: cchurch@peace.edu
Web Site: http://www.peace.edu/

Description: Independent, 4-year, women only, affiliated with Presbyterian Church (U.S.A.). Awards bachelor's degrees. Founded 1857. Setting: 20-acre urban campus. Endowment: $43.3 million. Educational spending for 2005 fiscal year: $5370 per student. Total enrollment: 701. Student-undergrad faculty ratio is 11:1. 717 applied, 35% were admitted. 10% from top 10% of their high school class, 20% from top quarter, 62% from top half. 4 valedictorians. Full-time: 668 students. Part-time: 33 students. 13% from out-of-state, 0.4% Native American, 3% Hispanic, 16% black, 2% Asian American or Pacific Islander, 1% international, 83% 25 or older, 82% live on campus, 5% transferred in. Retention: 65% of full-time freshmen returned the following year. Academic areas with the most degrees conferred: business/marketing; psychology; communications/journalism. Core. Calendar: semesters. Academic remediation for entering students, ESL program, services for LD students, advanced placement, freshman honors college, honors program, independent study, double major, adult/continuing education programs, internships. Off campus study at members of the Cooperating Raleigh Colleges Consortium. Study abroad program. ROTC: Army (c), Naval (c), Air Force (c).

Entrance Requirements: Options: Peterson's Universal Application, early admission, deferred admission. Required: essay, high school transcript, minimum 2.0 high school GPA, 2 recommendations, SAT or ACT. Recommended: interview. Entrance: moderately difficult. Application deadline: Rolling. Notification: continuous.

Costs Per Year: Application fee: $25. Comprehensive fee: $26,168 includes full-time tuition ($18,906), mandatory fees ($344), and college room and board ($6918). Part-time tuition: $400 per credit hour.

Collegiate Environment: Orientation program. Drama-theater group, choral group, student-run newspaper. Social organizations: 15 open to all. Most popular organizations: Student Government Association, Peace Student Christian Association, Human Resources Society, Psychology Club. Major annual events: Fall Festival, Spring Fling, Stunt Night. Student services: health clinic, personal-psychological counseling. Campus security: 24-hour emergency response devices and patrols, late night transport-escort service, controlled dormitory access. 500 college housing spaces available; 350 were occupied in 2003-04. Freshmen guaranteed college housing. On-campus residence required through sophomore year. Option: women-only housing available. Lucy Cooper Finch Library with 51,118 books, 2,000 microform titles, 3,900 serials, 1,200 audiovisual materials, an OPAC, and a Web page. Operations spending for 2004 fiscal year: $221,500. 45 computers available on campus for general student use. A campuswide network can be accessed. Staffed computer lab on campus.

Community Environment: Peace College is located in downtown Raleigh, NC, the state's political, education, and cultural center. The State Capitol, Legislative Building, State Library, and museums lie within a few blocks of campus. Shopping centers, restaurants, coffee shops and clubs are within a 10-block radius. Six other colleges and universities are located in the Raleigh area. The University of North Carolina at Chapel Hill and Duke University are within 25 miles of Peace. Numerous classical and popular concerts, dramatic presentations, and other cultural activities are available on campus, in the community, and in the surrounding Research Triangle Park area.

■ **PFEIFFER UNIVERSITY**
PO Box 960
Misenheimer, NC 28109-0960
Tel: (704)463-1360
Free: 800-338-2060
Fax: (704)463-1363
E-mail: scumming@pfeiffer.edu
Web Site: http://www.pfeiffer.edu/

Description: Independent United Methodist, comprehensive, coed. Awards bachelor's and master's degrees. Founded 1885. Setting: 300-acre rural campus with easy access to Charlotte. Endowment: $12.5 million. Educational spending for 2005 fiscal year: $4342 per student. Total enrollment: 2,150. Faculty: 143 (65 full-time, 78 part-time). Student-undergrad faculty ratio is 13:1. 629 applied, 77% were admitted. 13% from top 10% of their high school class, 34% from top quarter, 64% from top half. 1 valedictorian. Full-time: 1,055 students, 57% women, 43% men. Part-time: 147 students, 74% women, 26% men. Students come from 33 states and territories, 11 other countries, 17% from out-of-state, 1% Native American, 2% Hispanic, 22% black, 1% Asian American or Pacific Islander, 3% international, 41% 25 or older, 41% live on campus, 9% transferred in. Retention: 74% of full-time freshmen returned the following year. Academic areas with the most degrees conferred: business/marketing; security and protective services; education. Core. Calendar: semesters. Academic remediation for entering students, ESL program, services for LD students, advanced placement, accelerated degree program, honors program, independent study, double major, summer session for credit, part-time degree program, co-op programs and internships. Study abroad program. ROTC: Army (c).

Entrance Requirements: Options: Common Application, electronic application, early admission, deferred admission. Required: high school transcript, SAT or ACT. Recommended: minimum 2.0 high school GPA, interview. Required for some: 2 recommendations. Entrance: moderately difficult. Application deadline: Rolling. Notification: continuous.

Costs Per Year: Application fee: $25. Comprehensive fee: $21,900 includes full-time tuition ($15,590) and college room and board ($6310). College room only: $3710. Full-time tuition varies according to course load. Room and board charges vary according to housing facility. Part-time tuition: $355 per credit hour. Part-time tuition varies according to course load.

Collegiate Environment: Orientation program. Drama-theater group, choral group, student-run newspaper. Social organizations: 41 open to all. Most popular organizations: Student Government Association, Religious Life Council, Commuter Student Association, Programming Activities Council, Residence Hall Association. Major annual events: homecoming, Winterfest, Aprilfest. Student services: health clinic, personal-psychological counseling, women's center. Campus security: 24-hour emergency response devices and patrols, late night transport-escort service, controlled dormitory access. 717 college housing spaces available; 490 were occupied in 2003-04. Freshmen given priority for college housing. On-campus residence required through senior year. Options: coed, men-only, women-only housing available. Gustavus A. Pfeiffer Library with 117,000 books, 25,744 microform titles, 415 serials, 2,963 audiovisual materials, an OPAC, and a Web page. Operations spending for 2004 fiscal year: $531,192. 90 computers available on campus for general student use. A campuswide network can be accessed from student residence rooms and from off campus. Staffed computer lab on campus.

Community Environment: The setting for Misenheimer is a rural area with moderate mild climate. Commercial transportation is available at nearby Salisbury, and airlines at Charlotte. Recreational activities include swimming, boating, hunting and camping.

■ **PIEDMONT BAPTIST COLLEGE** *C-5*
716 Franklin St.
Winston-Salem, NC 27101-5197
Tel: (336)725-8344
Free: 800-937-5097
Fax: (336)725-5522
Web Site: http://www.pbc.edu/

Description: Independent Baptist, comprehensive, coed. Awards associate, bachelor's, and master's degrees. Founded 1947. Setting: 12-acre urban campus. Endowment: $288,000. Educational spending for 2005 fiscal year: $4380 per student. Total enrollment: 273. 73 applied, 79% were admitted. 13% from top 10% of their high school class, 33% from top quarter, 69% from top half. 46% from out-of-state, 0.4% Native American, 2% Hispanic, 2% black, 11% Asian American or Pacific Islander, 1% international, 29% 25 or older, 32% live on campus. Retention: 68% of full-time freshmen returned the following year. Core. Calendar: semesters. Academic remediation for entering students, advanced placement, summer session for credit, part-time degree program, adult/continuing education programs, internships, graduate courses open to undergrads. Study abroad program.

Entrance Requirements: Open admission. Options: Common Application, electronic application, early admission, early action, deferred admission. Required: essay, high school transcript, 2 recommendations, medical history, proof of immunization, ACT. Recommended: minimum 2.0 high school GPA, interview. Placement: ACT required. Entrance: noncompetitive. Application deadlines: Rolling, 11/1 for early action. Notification: 12/1 for early action.

Collegiate Environment: Orientation program. Choral group. Social organizations: 5 open to all. Most popular organizations: Piedmont Missions Fellowship, Piedmont Preachers Fellowship, Piedmont Educators' Fellowship, Piedmont Music Fellowship, Student Government Association. Major annual events: Annual Fall Missions Conference, Candlelight Carols, Mid-Winter Bible Conference. Campus security: student patrols, late night transport-escort service, controlled dormitory access, security guards on duty during evening hours. 156 college housing spaces available; 129 were occupied in 2003-04. On-campus residence required through senior year. Options: men-only, women-only housing available. George Manuel Memorial Library with 50,000 books and 204 serials. Operations spending for 2004 fiscal year: $105,725. 26 computers available on campus for general student use. A campuswide network can be accessed. Staffed computer lab on campus.

Community Environment: See Wake Forest University.

■ **PIEDMONT COMMUNITY COLLEGE** *B-8*
PO Box 1197
Roxboro, NC 27573-1197
Tel: (336)599-1181
Fax: (336)597-3817
Web Site: http://www.piedmont.cc.nc.us/

Description: State-supported, 2-year, coed. Part of North Carolina Community College System. Awards certificates, diplomas, transfer associate, and terminal associate degrees. Founded 1970. Setting: 178-acre small town campus. Endowment: $1.8 million. Research spending for 2004 fiscal year: $3902. Total enrollment: 2,189. 947 applied, 100% were admitted. Full-time: 826 students, 54% women, 46% men. Part-time: 1,363 students, 58% women, 42% men. Students come from 10 states and territories, 2 other countries, 1% from out-of-state, 1% Native American, 1% Hispanic, 42% black, 0.4% Asian American or Pacific Islander, 0.2% international, 47% 25 or older. Core. Calendar: semesters. Academic remediation for entering students, ESL program, advanced placement, summer session for credit, part-time degree program, adult/continuing education programs, co-op programs. Off campus study at other technical institutes and community colleges in North Carolina.

Entrance Requirements: Open admission except for nursing program. Options: early admission, deferred admission. Required for some: high school transcript. Placement: ACT ASSET required. Entrance: noncompetitive. Application deadline: Rolling. Notification: continuous until 9/29.

Collegiate Environment: Major annual events: Family Day, Valentine Dance, Blood Drive. Student services: personal-psychological counseling. Campus security: security guard during certain evening and weekend hours. College housing not available. Learning Resource Center with 24,166 books and 278 serials. Operations spending for 2004 fiscal year: $199,414. 75 computers available on campus for general student use. Staffed computer lab on campus.

■ **PITT COMMUNITY COLLEGE** *D-12*
Hwy. 11 South, PO Drawer 7007
Greenville, NC 27835-7007
Tel: (252)321-4200
Admissions: (252)321-4208
Fax: (252)321-4401
Web Site: http://www.pittcc.edu/

Description: State and locally supported, 2-year, coed. Part of North Carolina Community College System. Awards certificates, diplomas, transfer associate, and terminal associate degrees. Founded 1961. Setting: 172-acre small town campus. Endowment: $199,213. Educational spending for 2005 fiscal year: $2525 per student. Total enrollment: 5,980. 1,415 applied, 100% were admitted. Full-time: 3,200 students, 58% women, 42% men. Part-time: 2,780 students, 62% women, 38% men. Students come from 13 states and territories, 2% from out-of-state, 1% Native American, 1% Hispanic, 32% black, 1% Asian American or Pacific Islander, 0.4% international, 44% 25 or older, 27% transferred in. Retention: 57% of full-time freshmen returned the following year. Core. Calendar: semesters. Academic remediation for entering students, ESL program, services for LD students, advanced placement, independent study, distance learning, double major, summer session for credit, part-time degree program, external degree program, adult/continuing education programs, co-op programs and internships. ROTC: Army.

Entrance Requirements: Open admission except for health science programs. Options: electronic application, deferred admission. Required: high school transcript. Placement: ACT ASSET or ACT COMPASS required. Entrance: noncompetitive. Application deadline: Rolling.

Collegiate Environment: Orientation program. Student services: personal-psychological counseling. Campus security: 24-hour patrols, student patrols, late night transport-escort service. College housing not available. Learning Resources Center with 43,558 books, 1,433 microform titles, 275 serials, 5,225 audiovisual materials, an OPAC, and a Web page. Operations spending for 2004 fiscal year: $698,665. 60 computers available on campus for general student use. A campuswide network can be accessed from off-campus.

Community Environment: See East Carolina University.

■ **QUEENS UNIVERSITY OF CHARLOTTE** *E-3*
1900 Selwyn Ave.
Charlotte, NC 28274-0002
Tel: (704)337-2200
Free: 800-849-0202
Admissions: (704)337-2445
Fax: (704)337-2403
E-mail: ralphb@queens.edu
Web Site: http://www.queens.edu/

Description: Independent Presbyterian, comprehensive, coed. Awards associate, bachelor's, and master's degrees. Founded 1857. Setting: 25-acre suburban campus. Endowment: $49.7 million. Educational spending for 2005 fiscal year: $8418 per student. Total enrollment: 2,113. Faculty: 111 (68 full-time, 43 part-time). Student-undergrad faculty ratio is 15:1. 1,019 applied, 67% were admitted. 16% from top 10% of their high school class, 45% from top quarter, 80% from top half. Full-time: 1,016 students, 73% women, 27% men. Part-time: 607 students, 84% women, 16% men. Students come from 32 states and territories, 21 other countries, 0% from out-of-state, 1% Native American, 4% Hispanic, 17% black, 2% Asian American or Pacific

Islander, 5% international, 75% live on campus, 4% transferred in. Retention: 70% of full-time freshmen returned the following year. Academic areas with the most degrees conferred: business/marketing; communications/journalism; health professions and related sciences. Core. Calendar: semesters. Advanced placement, honors program, independent study, double major, summer session for credit, part-time degree program, adult/continuing education programs, internships, graduate courses open to undergrads. Off campus study at members of the Charlotte Area Educational Consortium. Study abroad program. ROTC: Army (c), Air Force (c).

Entrance Requirements: Options: Peterson's Universal Application, Common Application, electronic application, deferred admission, international baccalaureate accepted. Required: high school transcript, minimum 2.0 high school GPA, SAT or ACT. Recommended: interview. Required for some: essay, recommendations. Entrance: moderately difficult. Application deadline: Rolling. Notification: continuous.

Costs Per Year: Application fee: $40. Comprehensive fee: $26,430 includes full-time tuition ($19,450) and college room and board ($6980). Part-time tuition: $290 per credit hour.

Collegiate Environment: Orientation program. Drama-theater group, choral group, student-run newspaper. Social organizations: 40 open to all; national fraternities, national sororities; 17% of eligible men and 24% of eligible women are members. Most popular organizations: Senate, College Union Board, Admissions Ambassadors, Students for Black Awareness, International Club. Major annual events: Casino Night, Boar's Head/Yule Log, Mardi Gras. Student services: health clinic, personal-psychological counseling. Campus security: 24-hour emergency response devices and patrols, late night transport-escort service, controlled dormitory access. 604 college housing spaces available; 545 were occupied in 2003-04. Freshmen guaranteed college housing. On-campus residence required in freshman year. Options: coed, women-only housing available. Everett Library plus 1 other with 126,242 books, 1,452 microform titles, 592 serials, 2,251 audiovisual materials, an OPAC, and a Web page. Operations spending for 2004 fiscal year: $556,271. 125 computers available on campus for general student use. Computer purchase/lease plans available. A campuswide network can be accessed from student residence rooms and from off campus. Staffed computer lab on campus.

■ **RANDOLPH COMMUNITY COLLEGE** *D-6*
PO Box 1009
Asheboro, NC 27204-1009
Tel: (336)633-0200
Fax: (336)629-4695
Web Site: http://www.randolph.edu/

Description: State-supported, 2-year, coed. Part of North Carolina Community College System. Awards certificates, diplomas, transfer associate, and terminal associate degrees. Founded 1962. Setting: 27-acre small town campus. Endowment: $6.4 million. Educational spending for 2005 fiscal year: $2910 per student. Total enrollment: 2,291. 520 applied, 100% were admitted. Students come from 4 states and territories, 1 other country, 1% from out-of-state, 1% Native American, 2% Hispanic, 8% black, 1% Asian American or Pacific Islander, 0.1% international, 41% 25 or older. Core. Calendar: semesters. Academic remediation for entering students, ESL program, services for LD students, advanced placement, independent study, distance learning, double major, summer session for credit, part-time degree program, adult/continuing education programs, co-op programs and internships. Off campus study at other members of the North Carolina Community College System.

Entrance Requirements: Open admission. Options: Common Application, deferred admission, international baccalaureate accepted. Required: high school transcript. Placement: ACT ASSET or ACT COMPASS required for some. Entrance: noncompetitive. Application deadline: Rolling. Notification: continuous.

Collegiate Environment: Student-run newspaper. Most popular organization: Student Government Association. Major annual events: Fall Fling, Spring Fling. Student services: personal-psychological counseling. Campus security: security officer during open hours. College housing not available. R. Alton Cox Learning Resources Center with 36,776 books, 24,158 microform titles, 288 serials, 5,841 audiovisual materials, an OPAC, and a Web page. Operations spending for 2004 fiscal year: $271,184. 100 computers available on campus for general student use. A campuswide network can be accessed. Staffed computer lab on campus.

Community Environment: Asheboro is the county seat of Randolph County and is located near the geographical center of the state. The town has grown steadily with the surrounding area, which is mainly agricultural. Community facilities include numerous churches, a library, convenient shopping centers, and the North Carolina State Zoo. Several lakes nearby provide facilities for hunting, fishing, boating, and water skiing.

■ RICHMOND COMMUNITY COLLEGE F-6

PO Box 1189
Hamlet, NC 28345-1189
Tel: (910)582-7000
Admissions: (910)582-7113
Fax: (910)582-7102
Web Site: http://www.richmondcc.edu/

Description: State-supported, 2-year, coed. Part of North Carolina Community College System. Awards diplomas, transfer associate, and terminal associate degrees. Founded 1964. Setting: 163-acre rural campus. Endowment: $1 million. Educational spending for 2005 fiscal year: $7471 per student. Total enrollment: 1,472. Student-undergrad faculty ratio is 29:1. Full-time: 691 students, 71% women, 29% men. Part-time: 781 students, 75% women, 25% men. Students come from 3 states and territories, 1% from out-of-state, 9% Native American, 1% Hispanic, 32% black, 1% Asian American or Pacific Islander, 0% international, 57% 25 or older, 7% transferred in. Calendar: semesters. Academic remediation for entering students, ESL program, advanced placement, self-designed majors, independent study, distance learning, double major, summer session for credit, part-time degree program, adult/continuing education programs, co-op programs and internships.

Entrance Requirements: Open admission except for nursing program. Option: deferred admission. Required: high school transcript. Entrance: noncompetitive. Application deadline: Rolling. Notification: continuous until 8/1.

Costs Per Year: Application fee: $0. State resident tuition: $39.50 per credit hour part-time. Nonresident tuition: $219.50 per credit hour part-time. Mandatory fees: $12 per term part-time.

Collegiate Environment: Most popular organizations: Criminal Justice Club, Human Services Club, Native American Club. Major annual events: Native American Pow Wow, Field Day. Student services: personal-psychological counseling. Campus security: 24-hour emergency response devices, security guard during evening hours. College housing not available. Richmond Community College Library with 26,381 books, 99 microform titles, 192 serials, 1,676 audiovisual materials, and an OPAC. Operations spending for 2004 fiscal year: $242,876. 600 computers available on campus for general student use. A campuswide network can be accessed from off-campus. Staffed computer lab on campus.

Community Environment: Located 75 miles southeast of Charlotte, Hamlet is a town with a friendly atmosphere. Its primary businesses are manufacturing and textiles. Train and bus transportation is available. Community facilities include churches of various faiths, a library, shopping areas and good medical facilities. Recreational activities include swimming, boating, tennis, and fishing.

■ ROANOKE BIBLE COLLEGE B-15

715 North Poindexter St.
Elizabeth City, NC 27909-4054
Tel: (252)334-2070
Free: 800-RBC-8980
Admissions: (252)334-2028
Fax: (252)334-2071
E-mail: jaf@roanokebible.edu
Web Site: http://www.roanokebible.edu/

Description: Independent Christian, 4-year, coed. Awards associate and bachelor's degrees. Founded 1948. Setting: 19-acre small town campus with easy access to Norfolk. Endowment: $2.6 million. Total enrollment: 182. Student-undergrad faculty ratio is 10:1. 102 applied, 49% were admitted. 8% from top 10% of their high school class, 28% from top quarter, 72% from top half. Full-time: 158 students, 49% women, 51% men. Part-time: 24 students, 50% women, 50% men. Students come from 8 states and territories, 1 other country, 69% from out-of-state, 0% Native American, 2% Hispanic, 5% black, 0% Asian American or Pacific Islander, 1% international, 20% 25 or older, 65% live on campus, 12% transferred in. Retention: 67% of full-time freshmen returned the following year. Academic area with the most degrees conferred: theology and religious vocations. Core. Calendar: semesters. Academic remediation for entering students, advanced placement, part-time degree program, internships.

Entrance Requirements: Options: Peterson's Universal Application, electronic application, early admission, deferred admission, international baccalaureate accepted. Required: essay, high school transcript, minimum X high school GPA, recommendations, reference from church, SAT or ACT. Required for some: interview. Placement: SAT or ACT required. Entrance: minimally difficult. Application deadline: 8/1. Notification: continuous.

Costs Per Year: Application fee: $25. Comprehensive fee: $13,480 includes full-time tuition ($7840), mandatory fees ($680), and college room and board ($4960). College room only: $2780. Part-time tuition: $245 per credit hour.

Collegiate Environment: Orientation program. Choral group. Most popular organizations: Student Advisory Council, Counseling Club, Drama Club, choral group. Major annual events: Gospel Rally, Prime Time, High School Days. Student services: personal-psychological counseling. Campus security: 24-hour emergency response devices, controlled dormitory access. 224 college housing spaces available; 128 were occupied in 2003-04. On-campus residence required through senior year. Options: men-only, women-only housing available. Watson-Griffith Library with 28,552 books, 14 microform titles, 211 serials, 6,843 audiovisual materials, and an OPAC. Operations spending for 2004 fiscal year: $113,240. 24 computers available on campus for general student use. A campuswide network can be accessed from student residence rooms. Staffed computer lab on campus.

■ ROANOKE-CHOWAN COMMUNITY COLLEGE B-13

109 Community College Rd.
Ahoskie, NC 27910
Tel: (252)862-1200
Admissions: (252)862-1225
Fax: (252)862-1353
Web Site: http://www.roanokechowan.edu/

Description: State-supported, 2-year, coed. Part of North Carolina Community College System. Awards certificates, diplomas, transfer associate, and terminal associate degrees. Founded 1967. Setting: 39-acre rural campus. Endowment: $125,000. Total enrollment: 1,014. 327 applied, 100% were admitted. Full-time: 491 students, 85% women, 15% men. Part-time: 523 students, 73% women, 27% men. 1% Native American, 0.4% Hispanic, 67% black, 0.4% Asian American or Pacific Islander, 0% international, 48% 25 or older. Retention: 59% of full-time freshmen returned the following year. Core. Calendar: semesters. Academic remediation for entering students, distance learning, summer session for credit, part-time degree program, adult/continuing education programs, co-op programs.

Entrance Requirements: Open admission except for nursing program. Option: early admission. Required for some: interview. Placement: ACT ASSET required. Entrance: noncompetitive. Application deadline: Rolling. Notification: continuous.

Collegiate Environment: Orientation program. College housing not available. 29,268 books, 207 serials, an OPAC, and a Web page. 90 computers available on campus for general student use. A campuswide network can be accessed.

Community Environment: See Chowan College.

■ ROBESON COMMUNITY COLLEGE G-8

Hwy. 301 North, PO Box 1420
Lumberton, NC 28359-1420
Tel: (910)738-7101
Admissions: (910)618-5680
Fax: (910)671-4143
Web Site: http://www.robeson.cc.nc.us/

Description: State-supported, 2-year, coed. Part of North Carolina Community College System. Awards transfer associate and terminal associate degrees. Founded 1965. Setting: 78-acre small town campus. Total enrollment: 2,449. Calendar: semesters. Services for LD students, adult/continuing education programs.

Entrance Requirements: Open admission. Option: early admission. Placement: ACT ASSET, ACT COMPASS required. Entrance: noncompetitive. Application deadline: Rolling. Notification: continuous.

Collegiate Environment: Student services: personal-psychological counseling. College housing not available. 39,000 books and 225 serials. 100 computers available on campus for general student use. A campuswide network can be accessed from off-campus. Staffed computer lab on campus.

Community Environment: Located in a rural setting in Robeson County, this community is a short distance from Lumberton, the county seat, and has access to all the advantages of that city. Commercial transportation is available. Lumberton is also one of the major tobacco markets; other industries are here along with a number of churches and a library.

■ ROCKINGHAM COMMUNITY COLLEGE A-6

PO Box 38
Wentworth, NC 27375-0038

Tel: (336)342-4261

Web Site: http://www.rcc.cc.nc.us/

Description: State-supported, 2-year, coed. Part of North Carolina Community College System. Awards certificates, diplomas, transfer associate, and terminal associate degrees. Founded 1964. Setting: 257-acre rural campus. Total enrollment: 2,036. Student-undergrad faculty ratio is 18:1. Full-time: 604 students, 68% women, 32% men. Part-time: 1,432 students, 66% women, 34% men. Students come from 9 states and territories, 1 other country, 5% from out-of-state, 0.5% Native American, 1% Hispanic, 21% black, 1% Asian American or Pacific Islander, 0.4% international. Calendar: semesters. Academic remediation for entering students, advanced placement, self-designed majors, summer session for credit, part-time degree program, adult/continuing education programs, co-op programs.

Entrance Requirements: Open admission except for allied health programs. Options: early admission, deferred admission. Entrance: noncompetitive. Application deadline: Rolling. Notification: continuous.

Costs Per Year: Application fee: $0. State resident tuition: $1264 full-time, $39.50 per credit hour part-time. Nonresident tuition: $7061 full-time, $219.50 per credit hour part-time. Mandatory fees: $52 full-time.

Collegiate Environment: Student-run newspaper. Social organizations: 19 open to all. Most popular organizations: Phi Theta Kappa, Cultural Diversity Club, Paralegal Club. Major annual events: Rockingham County Folk Festival, Cultural Diversity Day. Student services: personal-psychological counseling. Campus security: late night transport-escort service. College housing not available. Gerald B. James Library with 43,044 books, 31,100 microform titles, 374 serials, 3,990 audiovisual materials, an OPAC, and a Web page. 150 computers available on campus for general student use. A campuswide network can be accessed. Staffed computer lab on campus.

Community Environment: Located near Reidsville and Eden in Rockingham County.

■ **ROWAN-CABARRUS COMMUNITY COLLEGE** *D-4*

PO Box 1595

Salisbury, NC 28145-1595

Tel: (704)637-0760

Fax: (704)633-6804

Web Site: http://www.rccc.cc.nc.us/

Description: State-supported, 2-year, coed. Part of North Carolina Community College System. Awards diplomas, transfer associate, and terminal associate degrees. Founded 1963. Setting: 100-acre small town campus. Total enrollment: 5,200. 1,909 applied, 100% were admitted. Full-time: 2,255 students, 65% women, 35% men. Part-time: 2,945 students, 69% women, 31% men. Students come from 2 other countries, 0.4% Native American, 2% Hispanic, 20% black, 1% Asian American or Pacific Islander, 0.02% international, 55% 25 or older. Calendar: semesters. Academic remediation for entering students, ESL program, services for LD students, advanced placement, distance learning, summer session for credit, part-time degree program, adult/continuing education programs, co-op programs and internships.

Entrance Requirements: Open admission. Option: Peterson's Universal Application. Required: high school transcript. Placement: ACT ASSET required. Entrance: noncompetitive. Application deadline: Rolling.

Collegiate Environment: Orientation program. Social organizations: 1 open to all. Major annual events: Field Day, holiday socials. Student services: personal-psychological counseling. Campus security: on-campus security during operating hours. College housing not available. Learning Resource Center with 23,005 books and 313 serials. 200 computers available on campus for general student use. Staffed computer lab on campus.

■ **ST. ANDREWS PRESBYTERIAN COLLEGE** *G-7*

1700 Dogwood Mile

Laurinburg, NC 28352-5598

Tel: (910)277-5000

Free: 800-763-0198

Admissions: (910)277-5555

Fax: (910)277-5087

E-mail: admission@sapc.edu

Web Site: http://www.sapc.edu/

Description: Independent Presbyterian, 4-year, coed. Awards bachelor's degrees. Founded 1958. Setting: 600-acre small town campus. Endowment: $12.8 million. Educational spending for 2005 fiscal year: $8077 per student. Total enrollment: 781. Student-undergrad faculty ratio is 14:1. 859 applied, 76% were admitted. Full-time: 706 students, 61% women, 39% men. Part-time: 75 students, 80% women, 20% men. Students come from 38 states

and territories, 16 other countries, 51% from out-of-state, 1% Native American, 3% Hispanic, 9% black, 1% Asian American or Pacific Islander, 4% international, 13% 25 or older, 76% live on campus, 8% transferred in. Retention: 67% of full-time freshmen returned the following year. Academic areas with the most degrees conferred: business/marketing; education; social sciences. Core. Calendar: semesters. Services for LD students, advanced placement, accelerated degree program, self-designed majors, honors program, independent study, double major, summer session for credit, part-time degree program, adult/continuing education programs, internships. Study abroad program.

Entrance Requirements: Options: Peterson's Universal Application, Common Application, electronic application, early admission, early decision, deferred admission, international baccalaureate accepted. Required: high school transcript, 1 recommendation, SAT or ACT. Recommended: minimum 2.0 high school GPA. Required for some: essay, interview. Entrance: moderately difficult. Application deadlines: Rolling, 12/1 for early decision. Notification: continuous, 1/1 for early decision.

Costs Per Year: Application fee: $30. Comprehensive fee: $24,756 includes full-time tuition ($17,162), mandatory fees ($900), and college room and board ($6694). College room only: $2748. Full-time tuition and fees vary according to location. Room and board charges vary according to housing facility. Part-time tuition: $410 per credit. Part-time tuition varies according to location.

Collegiate Environment: Orientation program. Drama-theater group, choral group, student-run newspaper. Social organizations: 33 open to all. Most popular organizations: Business Club, Breaking the Mirror (women's group), Writer's Forum, Student Activities Union, Eco-Action. Major annual events: Halloween Party, Senior Launching, Extravaganza Weekend. Student services: health clinic, personal-psychological counseling. Campus security: 24-hour emergency response devices and patrols, late night transport-escort service. 770 college housing spaces available; 567 were occupied in 2003-04. On-campus residence required through senior year. Options: coed, men-only, women-only housing available. DeTamble Library with 108,734 books, 26,330 microform titles, 436 serials, 4,405 audiovisual materials, an OPAC, and a Web page. Operations spending for 2004 fiscal year: $303,326. 100 computers available on campus for general student use. A campuswide network can be accessed from student residence rooms and from off campus. Staffed computer lab on campus.

■ **SAINT AUGUSTINE'S COLLEGE** *D-9*

1315 Oakwood Ave.

Raleigh, NC 27604-2298

Tel: (919)516-4000

Free: 800-948-1126

Admissions: (919)516-4012

Fax: (919)516-4415

Web Site: http://www.st-aug.edu/

Description: Independent Episcopal, 4-year, coed. Awards bachelor's degrees. Founded 1867. Setting: 105-acre urban campus. Endowment: $17.2 million. Educational spending for 2005 fiscal year: $4813 per student. Total enrollment: 1,395. 2,229 applied, 55% were admitted. 13% from top 10% of their high school class, 39% from top quarter, 74% from top half. Full-time: 1,333 students, 48% women, 52% men. Part-time: 62 students, 63% women, 37% men. Students come from 33 states and territories, 17 other countries, 1% Hispanic, 91% black, 7% international, 12% 25 or older, 62% live on campus, 3% transferred in. Retention: 62% of full-time freshmen returned the following year. Core. Calendar: semesters. Academic remediation for entering students, accelerated degree program, honors program, independent study, double major, summer session for credit, part-time degree program, adult/continuing education programs, co-op programs and internships. Off campus study at Meredith College, North Carolina State University, Peace College, Shaw University. ROTC: Army, Air Force (c).

Entrance Requirements: Options: Peterson's Universal Application, electronic application, deferred admission. Required: essay, high school transcript, 3 recommendations, medical history, SAT or ACT. Recommended: minimum 2.0 high school GPA. Entrance: moderately difficult. Application deadline: 7/1. Notification: continuous.

Costs Per Year: Application fee: $25. Comprehensive fee: $17,272 includes full-time tuition ($8952), mandatory fees ($2476), and college room and board ($5844). College room only: $3322. Full-time tuition and fees vary according to course load, program, and reciprocity agreements. Room and board charges vary according to board plan, housing facility, and location. Part-time tuition: $480 per credit. Part-time mandatory fees: $103 per credit. Part-time tuition and fees vary according to course load, program, and reciprocity agreements.

Collegiate Environment: Orientation program. Drama-theater group, choral group, student-run newspaper, radio station. Social organizations: 45 open to all; national fraternities, national sororities, local fraternities, local sororities; 6% of eligible men and 12% of eligible women are members. Most popular organizations: chorale group, jazz band, International Student Organization. Major annual events: Opening Convocation, CIAA Tournament, career/job fairs. Student services: health clinic, personal-psychological counseling. Campus security: 24-hour emergency response devices and patrols. 1,029 college housing spaces available; 856 were occupied in 2003-04. Freshmen guaranteed college housing. On-campus residence required in freshman year. Options: men-only, women-only housing available. Prezell R. Robinson Library with 76,000 books, 3 microform titles, 415 serials, 300 audiovisual materials, an OPAC, and a Web page. Operations spending for 2004 fiscal year: $374,162. 130 computers available on campus for general student use. A campuswide network can be accessed from student residence rooms. Staffed computer lab on campus.

■ **SALEM COLLEGE** *C-5*
PO Box 10548
Winston-Salem, NC 27108-0548
Tel: (336)721-2600
Free: 800-327-2536
Admissions: (336)721-2621
Fax: (336)724-7102
Web Site: http://www.salem.edu/

Description: Independent Moravian, comprehensive. Awards bachelor's and master's degrees (only students age 23 or over are eligible to enroll part-time; men may attend evening program only). Founded 1772. Setting: 57-acre urban campus. Endowment: $47.5 million. Educational spending for 2005 fiscal year: $4921 per student. Total enrollment: 1,109. Faculty: 91 (57 full-time, 34 part-time). Student-undergrad faculty ratio is 12:1. 387 applied, 69% were admitted. 33% from top 10% of their high school class, 58% from top quarter, 88% from top half. 4 valedictorians, 24 student government officers. Full-time: 702 students, 99% women, 1% men. Part-time: 166 students, 93% women, 7% men. Students come from 23 states and territories, 17 other countries, 41% from out-of-state, 0.2% Native American, 3% Hispanic, 19% black, 1% Asian American or Pacific Islander, 8% international, 36% 25 or older, 88% live on campus, 3% transferred in. Retention: 72% of full-time freshmen returned the following year. Academic areas with the most degrees conferred: communications/journalism; social sciences; business/marketing. Core. Calendar: 4-1-4. Advanced placement, self-designed majors, honors program, independent study, double major, summer session for credit, part-time degree program, external degree program, adult/continuing education programs, internships. Off campus study at Wake Forest University, American University, Drew University. Study abroad program. ROTC: Army (c).

Entrance Requirements: Options: Peterson's Universal Application, Common Application, electronic application, early admission, deferred admission, international baccalaureate accepted. Required: essay, high school transcript, 2 recommendations, SAT or ACT. Recommended: interview. Entrance: moderately difficult. Application deadline: Rolling. Notification: continuous.

Costs Per Year: Application fee: $30. Comprehensive fee: $26,441 includes full-time tuition ($16,975), mandatory fees ($215), and college room and board ($9251).

Collegiate Environment: Orientation program. Drama-theater group, choral group, marching band, student-run newspaper. Social organizations: 41 open to all. Most popular organizations: Student Government Association, Onua, Campus Activities Council, International Club, Ambassadors. Major annual events: Fall Fest, Dance Weekends, Candlelight Christmas Service. Student services: health clinic, personal-psychological counseling. Campus security: 24-hour emergency response devices and patrols, late night transport-escort service, controlled dormitory access. 488 college housing spaces available; 458 were occupied in 2003-04. Freshmen guaranteed college housing. On-campus residence required through senior year. Gramley Library plus 1 other with 132,510 books, 302,534 microform titles, 631 serials, 13,553 audiovisual materials, an OPAC, and a Web page. Operations spending for 2004 fiscal year: $502,126. 54 computers available on campus for general student use. A campuswide network can be accessed from student residence rooms and from off campus. Staffed computer lab on campus.

Community Environment: See Wake Forest University.

■ **SAMPSON COMMUNITY COLLEGE** *F-10*
PO Box 318
Clinton, NC 28329-0318
Tel: (910)592-8081
Admissions: (910)592-8084
Fax: (910)592-8048
Web Site: http://www.sampsoncc.edu/

Description: State and locally supported, 2-year, coed. Part of North Carolina Community College System. Awards certificates, diplomas, transfer associate, and terminal associate degrees. Founded 1965. Setting: 55-acre rural campus. Total enrollment: 1,579. 712 applied, 100% were admitted. Full-time: 679 students, 73% women, 27% men. Part-time: 900 students, 73% women, 27% men. Students come from 4 states and territories, 1% from out-of-state, 2% Native American, 3% Hispanic, 37% black, 0% international, 52% 25 or older, 1% transferred in. Core. Calendar: semesters. Academic remediation for entering students, services for LD students, advanced placement, independent study, summer session for credit, part-time degree program, adult/continuing education programs, co-op programs and internships.

Entrance Requirements: Open admission except for nursing program. Options: Common Application, deferred admission. Required: high school transcript, interview. Recommended: minimum 2.0 high school GPA. Placement: ACT ASSET required. Entrance: noncompetitive. Application deadline: Rolling. Notification: continuous.

Collegiate Environment: Orientation program. Social organizations: 7 open to all. Most popular organizations: Student Government Association, Criminal Justice Club, Nursing Student Association, Cosmetology Alliance Club, Phi Beta Lambda. Major annual event: Field Day. Student services: personal-psychological counseling. Campus security: local police patrol. College housing not available. Sampson Community College Library with 25,000 books, 250 serials, an OPAC, and a Web page. 78 computers available on campus for general student use. A campuswide network can be accessed. Staffed computer lab on campus.

Community Environment: The county seat of Sampson County, Clinton is in the coastal plain section of the state. Community facilities have grown as Clinton has grown in population. A complete shopping center is located here, along with churches representing most denominations. A county hospital and numerous civic and service organizations serve the community. 28 industrial firms are based here. Job opportunities are available. Recreational activities include golf, hunting, fishing, and swimming.

■ **SANDHILLS COMMUNITY COLLEGE** *E-7*
3395 Airport Rd.
Pinehurst, NC 28374-8299
Tel: (910)692-6185
Admissions: (910)695-3735
Fax: (910)695-1823
E-mail: offuttb@sandpiper.sandhills.cc.nc.us
Web Site: http://www.sandhills.edu/

Description: State and locally supported, 2-year, coed. Part of North Carolina Community College System. Awards certificates, diplomas, transfer associate, and terminal associate degrees. Founded 1963. Setting: small town campus. Endowment: $4.1 million. Educational spending for 2005 fiscal year: $4312 per student. Total enrollment: 3,502. Students come from 42 states and territories, 23 other countries, 1% from out-of-state, 6% Native American, 1% Hispanic, 28% black, 1% Asian American or Pacific Islander, 44% 25 or older. Core. Calendar: semesters. Academic remediation for entering students, services for LD students, advanced placement, honors program, independent study, distance learning, double major, summer session for credit, part-time degree program, co-op programs and internships.

Entrance Requirements: Open admission except for landscape gardening, turf management, medical programs. Options: Peterson's Universal Application, Common Application, deferred admission. Required: high school transcript. Placement: ACT ASSET or ACT COMPASS required. Entrance: minimally difficult. Application deadline: Rolling. Notification: continuous.

Collegiate Environment: Orientation program. Choral group, student-run newspaper. Social organizations: 6 open to all. Most popular organizations: Student Government Association, Minority Students for Academic and Cultural Enrichment, Circle K. Major annual events: Spring Fling, College Days, Health Career Day. Student services: personal-psychological counseling. Campus security: 24-hour emergency response devices, security on duty until 12 a.m. College housing not available. Boyd Library with 76,080 books, 107,190 microform titles, 286 serials, 2,317 audiovisual materials, an OPAC, and a Web page. Operations spending for 2004 fiscal year: $436,162. 300 computers available on campus for general student use. A campuswide network can be accessed from off-campus. Staffed computer lab on campus.

Community Environment: Pinehurst, established originally as a health resort, has a small town environment. The area of Southern Pines is famous for its dry and mild climate, its golf and tourism as well as for major horse stables. Community facilities include three libraries, a twenty-five acre garden, churches of all denominations, and various civic and service organizations. Recreational activities include golf, tennis, horseback riding, hunting, and fishing.

■ **SCHOOL OF COMMUNICATION ARTS** *D-9*
3000 Wakefield Crossing Dr.
Raleigh, NC 27614
Tel: (919)488-8500
Free: 800-288-7442
Web Site: http://www.higherdigital.com/
Description: Proprietary, 2-year, coed. Founded 1992.

■ **SHAW UNIVERSITY** *D-9*
118 East South St.
Raleigh, NC 27601-2399
Tel: (919)546-8200
Free: 800-214-6683
Admissions: (919)546-8275
Fax: (919)546-8271
E-mail: sclifton@shawu.edu
Web Site: http://www.shawuniversity.edu/
Description: Independent Baptist, comprehensive, coed. Awards associate, bachelor's, master's, and first professional degrees. Founded 1865. Setting: 30-acre urban campus. Research spending for 2004 fiscal year: $1.7 million. Educational spending for 2005 fiscal year: $3587 per student. Total enrollment: 2,762. Faculty: 290 (111 full-time, 179 part-time). Student-undergrad faculty ratio is 15:1. 4,226 applied, 65% were admitted. 1% from top 10% of their high school class, 8% from top quarter, 31% from top half. Full-time: 2,283 students, 62% women, 38% men. Part-time: 282 students, 67% women, 33% men. Students come from 32 states and territories, 11 other countries, 32% from out-of-state, 0.2% Native American, 0.2% Hispanic, 89% black, 0.1% Asian American or Pacific Islander, 1% international, 44% 25 or older, 39% live on campus, 10% transferred in. Retention: 66% of full-time freshmen returned the following year. Academic areas with the most degrees conferred: business/marketing; security and protective services; psychology. Core. Calendar: semesters. Academic remediation for entering students, services for LD students, advanced placement, accelerated degree program, self-designed majors, honors program, independent study, distance learning, double major, summer session for credit, part-time degree program, adult/continuing education programs, internships. Off campus study at Cooperating Raleigh Colleges. Study abroad program. ROTC: Army (c), Air Force (c).
Entrance Requirements: Options: Common Application, electronic application, early admission, deferred admission, international baccalaureate accepted. Required: essay, high school transcript, minimum 2.0 high school GPA, SAT or ACT. Entrance: minimally difficult. Application deadline: 7/30. Notification: continuous.
Costs Per Year: Application fee: $25. Comprehensive fee: $16,430 includes full-time tuition ($8280), mandatory fees ($1740), and college room and board ($6410). College room only: $3010. Part-time tuition: $345 per semester hour. Part-time mandatory fees: $29 per semester hour.
Collegiate Environment: Orientation program. Drama-theater group, choral group, marching band, student-run newspaper, radio station. Social organizations: 30 open to all; national fraternities, national sororities; 4% of eligible men and 5% of eligible women are members. Most popular organizations: Student Government Association, choir, University band, Shaw Players, academic clubs. Major annual events: University Convocation, Homecoming, Honors Convocation. Student services: health clinic, personal-psychological counseling. Campus security: 24-hour emergency response devices and patrols, late night transport-escort service, 24-hour electronic surveillance cameras. 1,292 college housing spaces available; 823 were occupied in 2003-04. No special consideration for freshman housing applicants. On-campus residence required in freshman year. Options: men-only, women-only housing available. James E. Cheek Learning Resources Center plus 1 other with 154,368 books, 99,700 microform titles, 15,500 seri-

als, 873 audiovisual materials, an OPAC, and a Web page. Operations spending for 2004 fiscal year: $624,700. 200 computers available on campus for general student use. A campuswide network can be accessed from student residence rooms and from off campus. Staffed computer lab on campus.

Community Environment: See Meredith College.

■ **SOUTH COLLEGE-ASHEVILLE** *J-15*
1567 Patton Ave.
Asheville, NC 28806
Tel: (828)252-2486
Web Site: http://www.southcollegenc.com/
Description: Proprietary, 2-year, coed. Awards certificates and terminal associate degrees. Founded 1905. Setting: 8-acre urban campus. Educational spending for 2005 fiscal year: $2205 per student. Total enrollment: 112. 19 applied, 100% were admitted. Full-time: 88 students, 85% women, 15% men. Part-time: 24 students, 92% women, 8% men. Students come from 2 states and territories, 0% from out-of-state, 0% Native American, 1% Hispanic, 15% black, 0% Asian American or Pacific Islander, 0% international, 64% 25 or older. Core. Independent study, double major, summer session for credit, part-time degree program, adult/continuing education programs, co-op programs and internships.
Entrance Requirements: Open admission. Option: deferred admission. Required: high school transcript, CPAt. Entrance: noncompetitive. Application deadline: Rolling.
Collegiate Environment: Orientation program. Social organizations: 3 open to all. Most popular organizations: C-Med, C-Cap, C-Com. Campus security: night security. College housing not available. Hilde V. Kopf with 4,550 books and 37 serials. Operations spending for 2004 fiscal year: $55,376. 28 computers available on campus for general student use. A campuswide network can be accessed. Staffed computer lab on campus.

■ **SOUTH PIEDMONT COMMUNITY COLLEGE** *F-5*
PO Box 126
Polkton, NC 28135-0126
Tel: (704)272-7635
Free: 800-766-0319
E-mail: abaucom@vnet.net
Web Site: http://www.spcc.edu/
Description: State-supported, 2-year, coed. Part of North Carolina Community College System. Awards certificates, diplomas, transfer associate, and terminal associate degrees. Founded 1962. Setting: 56-acre rural campus with easy access to Charlotte. Endowment: $27,818. Educational spending for 2005 fiscal year: $2802 per student. Total enrollment: 1,875. 740 applied, 84% were admitted. 2% from top 10% of their high school class, 5% from top quarter, 10% from top half. Full-time: 746 students, 64% women, 36% men. Part-time: 1,129 students, 63% women, 37% men. Students come from 3 states and territories, 1% from out-of-state, 1% Native American, 1% Hispanic, 50% black, 1% Asian American or Pacific Islander, 0.3% international, 62% 25 or older, 22% transferred in. Core. Calendar: semesters. Academic remediation for entering students, ESL program, services for LD students, accelerated degree program, independent study, summer session for credit, part-time degree program, adult/continuing education programs, co-op programs and internships. Off campus study.
Entrance Requirements: Open admission. Options: electronic application, early admission, deferred admission. Required: high school transcript. Placement: CAT, CPT recommended; CAT, CPT required for some. Entrance: noncompetitive. Application deadline: Rolling. Notification: continuous.
Collegiate Environment: Orientation program. Choral group. Social organizations: 5 open to all. Most popular organizations: student association, Phi Beta Lambda, Phi Theta Kappa, Social Services Club, Criminal Justice Club. Major annual events: Spring Fling, Career Day, Christmas Party. Student services: personal-psychological counseling, women's center. Campus security: 24-hour emergency response devices and patrols, evening security. Martin Learning Resource Center with 18,917 books, 170 serials, and an OPAC. Operations spending for 2004 fiscal year: $167,634. 150 computers available on campus for general student use. A campuswide network can be accessed from off-campus. Staffed computer lab on campus.
Community Environment: The college is located in the geographic center of the Carolinas and Southeast. Its location is equidistant from the Appalachian and Blue Ridge Mountains and the Grand Strand area of the Atlantic; and is situated halfway between Washington, D.C. and Atlanta,

Georgia. The average annual temperature is 61 degrees; the coldest month is January (42.5 degrees), the warmest month is July (78.9 degrees). Annual rainfall is 49 inches.

■ SOUTHEASTERN BAPTIST THEOLOGICAL SEMINARY *C-9*

PO Box 1889
Wake Forest, NC 27588-1889
Tel: (919)556-3101
Free: 800-284-6317
Admissions: (919)761-2280
Web Site: http://www.sebts.edu/

Description: Independent Southern Baptist, comprehensive, coed. Administratively affiliated with Southeastern Baptist Theological Seminary. Awards associate, bachelor's, master's, doctoral, and first professional degrees. Founded 1950. Setting: 450-acre small town campus with easy access to Raleigh. Total enrollment: 1,979. Full-time: 282 students, 27% women, 73% men. Part-time: 170 students, 21% women, 79% men. Students come from 27 states and territories, 14 other countries, 40% from out-of-state, 1% Native American, 1% Hispanic, 2% black, 0.2% Asian American or Pacific Islander, 5% international, 49% 25 or older, 30% live on campus. Core. Calendar: semesters. Academic remediation for entering students, summer session for credit, part-time degree program, internships.

Entrance Requirements: Open admission. Options: Common Application, international baccalaureate accepted. Required: essay, high school transcript, 3 recommendations. Required for some: interview. Entrance: noncompetitive. Application deadline: 7/20. Notification: continuous until 8/20.

Collegiate Environment: Drama-theater group, choral group, student-run newspaper. Student services: health clinic, personal-psychological counseling. Campus security: 24-hour emergency response devices and patrols, late night transport-escort service. 1,462 college housing spaces available; 195 were occupied in 2003-04. Options: men-only, women-only housing available. 167,044 books and 938 serials. 7 computers available on campus for general student use. A campuswide network can be accessed. Staffed computer lab on campus.

Community Environment: Wake Forest is located 15 miles north of Raleigh and 22 miles east of Durham on US 1 and NC 98. The seminary is only 25 miles from the Raleigh-Durham Airport. 12 churches, a hospital, a public library, and numerous civic and service organizations are found within the community. A full-time recreational program, supervised by a recreational director, swimming pools, lighted athletic fields, tennis courts, racquetball courts, weight rooms, and two golf courses provide the recreational facilities.

■ SOUTHEASTERN COMMUNITY COLLEGE *H-9*

PO Box 151
Whiteville, NC 28472-0151
Tel: (910)642-7141
E-mail: jfowler@sccnc.edu
Web Site: http://www.sccnc.edu/

Description: State-supported, 2-year, coed. Part of North Carolina Community College System. Awards certificates, diplomas, transfer associate, and terminal associate degrees. Founded 1964. Setting: 106-acre rural campus. Total enrollment: 1,825. Student-undergrad faculty ratio is 20:1. 845 applied, 100% were admitted. 10% from top 10% of their high school class, 25% from top quarter, 50% from top half. Students come from 2 states and territories, 1% from out-of-state, 4% Native American, 26% black, 0.1% international, 45% 25 or older. Core. Calendar: semesters. Academic remediation for entering students, ESL program, services for LD students, advanced placement, honors program, independent study, distance learning, double major, summer session for credit, part-time degree program, adult/continuing education programs, co-op programs and internships.

Entrance Requirements: Open admission except for nursing, phlebotomy, medical laboratory technology programs. Options: Common Application, electronic application, early admission, deferred admission. Required: high school transcript. Entrance: noncompetitive. Application deadline: Rolling.

Costs Per Year: Application fee: $0. State resident tuition: $948 full-time, $39.50 per credit part-time. Nonresident tuition: $5268 full-time, $219.50 per credit part-time. Mandatory fees: $64 full-time, $35 per term part-time.

Collegiate Environment: Orientation program. Drama-theater group, choral group. Social organizations: 6 open to all. Most popular organizations: Student Government Association, Forestry Club, Nursing Club, Environmental Club. Major annual events: High School Senior Day, 8th-Grader Day. Student services: personal-psychological counseling. Campus security: 24-hour emergency response devices. College housing not available.

Southeastern Community College Library with 50,297 books, 192 serials, and an OPAC. 80 computers available on campus for general student use. A campuswide network can be accessed. Staffed computer lab on campus.

Community Environment: A rural community with a mean annual temperature of 64 degrees. Bus transportation is convenient, and there is plane service at Wilmington and Fayetteville. Shopping facilities, 14 churches representing a number of denominations, and a hospital are part of the community. A nearby lake, beaches, a golf course, swimming pools, and tennis courts provide recreational opportunities. Part-time employment is limited.

■ SOUTHWESTERN COMMUNITY COLLEGE *J-14*

447 College Dr.
Sylva, NC 28779
Tel: (828)586-4091
Fax: (828)586-4093
E-mail: pweast@southwest.cc.nc.us
Web Site: http://www.southwest.cc.nc.us/

Description: State-supported, 2-year, coed. Part of North Carolina Community College System. Awards certificates, diplomas, transfer associate, and terminal associate degrees. Founded 1964. Setting: 55-acre small town campus. Educational spending for 2005 fiscal year: $2473 per student. Total enrollment: 2,014. Full-time: 899 students, 68% women, 32% men. Part-time: 1,115 students, 66% women, 34% men. Students come from 6 states and territories, 1 other country, 1% from out-of-state, 10% Native American, 1% Hispanic, 1% black, 0.3% Asian American or Pacific Islander, 0.3% international, 36% 25 or older, 8% transferred in. Core. Calendar: semesters. Academic remediation for entering students, ESL program, services for LD students, independent study, distance learning, double major, summer session for credit, part-time degree program, adult/continuing education programs, co-op programs. Off campus study at Haywood Community College.

Entrance Requirements: Open admission except for allied health programs. Options: Common Application, early admission, deferred admission. Required: high school transcript. Recommended: SAT or ACT. Required for some: minimum 2.0 high school GPA, recommendations, interview. Entrance: noncompetitive. Application deadline: Rolling. Notification: continuous.

Collegiate Environment: Social organizations: 19 open to all. Most popular organizations: Electronics Club, EMT Club, HIT Club, Cyber Crime Club, National Vocational-Technical Honor Society. Major annual events: Spring Fling, Fall Welcome Back, Hullabaloo. Student services: personal-psychological counseling. Campus security: security during hours college is open. College housing not available. Learning Resources Center with 27,428 books, 3,170 microform titles, 257 serials, 18,410 audiovisual materials, and an OPAC. Operations spending for 2004 fiscal year: $130,200. 400 computers available on campus for general student use. A campuswide network can be accessed from off-campus. Staffed computer lab on campus.

■ STANLY COMMUNITY COLLEGE *E-5*

141 College Dr.
Albemarle, NC 28001-7458
Tel: (704)982-0121
Fax: (704)982-0819
E-mail: hinsonre@stanly.cc.nc.us
Web Site: http://www.stanly.edu/

Description: State-supported, 2-year, coed. Part of North Carolina Community College System. Awards certificates, diplomas, transfer associate, and terminal associate degrees. Founded 1971. Setting: 150-acre small town campus with easy access to Charlotte. Total enrollment: 2,000. 642 applied, 100% were admitted. Students come from 13 states and territories, 3 other countries, 3% from out-of-state, 48% 25 or older. Calendar: semesters. Academic remediation for entering students, ESL program, services for LD students, advanced placement, independent study, distance learning, double major, summer session for credit, part-time degree program, adult/continuing education programs, co-op programs and internships.

Entrance Requirements: Open admission except for allied health programs. Options: early admission, deferred admission. Required: high school transcript. Placement: ACT ASSET required; SAT recommended. Entrance: noncompetitive. Application deadline: Rolling. Notification: continuous.

Collegiate Environment: Orientation program. Student-run newspaper. Student services: personal-psychological counseling. College housing not available. 23,966 books, 10,586 microform titles, 200 serials, 2,500 audiovisual materials, an OPAC, and a Web page. 100 computers available on campus for general student use. A campuswide network can be accessed. Staffed computer lab on campus.

■ SURRY COMMUNITY COLLEGE *A-4*

630 South Main St.
PO Box 304
Dobson, NC 27017-8432
Tel: (336)386-8121
Admissions: (336)386-3238
Fax: (336)386-8951
Web Site: http://www.surry.cc.nc.us/
Description: State-supported, 2-year, coed. Part of North Carolina Community College System. Awards certificates, diplomas, transfer associate, and terminal associate degrees. Founded 1965. Setting: 100-acre rural campus. Total enrollment: 3,600. Students come from 3 states and territories, 4% from out-of-state, 0.3% Native American, 2% Hispanic, 5% black, 0.3% Asian American or Pacific Islander, 0.2% international, 42% 25 or older. Core. Calendar: semesters. Academic remediation for entering students, ESL program, advanced placement, independent study, distance learning, summer session for credit, part-time degree program, adult/continuing education programs, co-op programs and internships. Off campus study at Forsyth Technical Community College, Guilford Technical Community College, Rockingham Community College.
Entrance Requirements: Open admission except for nursing program. Options: electronic application, early admission, deferred admission. Required: high school transcript. Placement: CPT required. Entrance: noncompetitive.
Collegiate Environment: Orientation program. Drama-theater group, choral group, student-run radio station. Social organizations: 7 open to all. Most popular organizations: Student Government Association, Phi Beta Lambda, Phi Theta Kappa, BSU. Major annual events: Student Appreciation Day, New Student Orientation. Campus security: security guard during day and evening hours. College housing not available. Resource Center with 47,526 books, 10,225 microform titles, 362 serials, 3,233 audiovisual materials, an OPAC, and a Web page. 200 computers available on campus for general student use. A campuswide network can be accessed. Staffed computer lab on campus.
Community Environment: A rural community with temperate climate, Dobson is the county seat. Community facilities include a library, United Methodist and Baptist churches, a hospital within 11 miles, some shopping, and several civic and service organizations. There are job opportunities in textile factories and with a poultry processing plant.

■ TRI-COUNTY COMMUNITY COLLEGE *K-11*

4600 East US 64
Murphy, NC 28906-7919
Tel: (828)837-6810
Fax: (828)837-3266
Web Site: http://www.tricountycc.edu
Description: State-supported, 2-year, coed. Awards certificates, diplomas, transfer associate, and terminal associate degrees. Founded 1964. Setting: 40-acre rural campus. Educational spending for 2005 fiscal year: $2655 per student. Total enrollment: 1,155. Student-undergrad faculty ratio is 21:1. 518 applied, 100% were admitted. 10% from top 10% of their high school class, 35% from top quarter, 55% from top half. Students come from 8 states and territories, 3% from out-of-state, 2% Native American, 1% Hispanic, 1% black, 0% Asian American or Pacific Islander, 0% international, 65% 25 or older. Core. Calendar: semesters. Academic remediation for entering students, services for LD students, distance learning, double major, summer session for credit, part-time degree program, adult/continuing education programs.
Entrance Requirements: Open admission except for nursing, medical assistant programs. Required: high school transcript. Entrance: noncompetitive. Application deadline: Rolling. Notification: continuous. Preference given to state residents.
Costs Per Year: Application fee: $0. State resident tuition: $970 full-time, $38 per credit hour part-time. Nonresident tuition: $5122 full-time, $211 per credit hour part-time. Mandatory fees: $60 full-time, $29.25 per term part-time.
Collegiate Environment: Orientation program. Student services: personal-psychological counseling. College housing not available. 16,224 books and 306 serials. 33 computers available on campus for general student use. A campuswide network can be accessed.

Community Environment: Located in a valley in the central part of Cherokee County, Murphy has available bus and train transportation; Andrews Airport is 11 miles away. Community facilities include seven church denominations, two hospitals, and a fully equipped clinic. Mountains, streams, lakes, and forests make Murphy a sports lover's paradise. Parks, playgrounds, and other recreational facilities are available, including a complex that offers swimming pools, an 18-hole golf course, and horseback riding.

■ THE UNIVERSITY OF NORTH CAROLINA AT ASHEVILLE *J-15*

One University Heights
Asheville, NC 28804-3299
Tel: (828)251-6600
Free: 800-531-9842
Admissions: (828)251-6481
Fax: (828)251-6385
E-mail: admissions@unca.edu
Web Site: http://www.unca.edu/
Description: State-supported, comprehensive, coed. Part of University of North Carolina System. Awards bachelor's and master's degrees. Founded 1927. Setting: 265-acre suburban campus. Endowment: $16.6 million. Research spending for 2004 fiscal year: $465,019. Educational spending for 2005 fiscal year: $6171 per student. Total enrollment: 3,513. Faculty: 309 (199 full-time, 110 part-time). Student-undergrad faculty ratio is 13:1. 2,362 applied, 63% were admitted. 25% from top 10% of their high school class, 68% from top quarter, 98% from top half. 1 National Merit Scholar, 4 valedictorians. Full-time: 2,820 students, 58% women, 42% men. Part-time: 656 students, 57% women, 43% men. Students come from 41 states and territories, 28 other countries, 14% from out-of-state, 0.3% Native American, 2% Hispanic, 2% black, 2% Asian American or Pacific Islander, 1% international, 16% 25 or older, 39% live on campus, 7% transferred in. Retention: 76% of full-time freshmen returned the following year. Academic areas with the most degrees conferred: business/marketing; psychology; visual and performing arts. Core. Calendar: semesters. Academic remediation for entering students, advanced placement, self-designed majors, honors program, independent study, distance learning, double major, summer session for credit, part-time degree program, adult/continuing education programs, internships, graduate courses open to undergrads. Off campus study at Asheville Area Educational Consortium. Study abroad program.
Entrance Requirements: Options: Peterson's Universal Application, early action, deferred admission. Required: high school transcript, SAT or ACT. Recommended: essay. Required for some: interview. Entrance: moderately difficult. Application deadlines: 2/16, 11/10 for early action. Notification: 3/23, 12/18 for early action.
Costs Per Year: Application fee: $50. State resident tuition: $1897 full-time. Nonresident tuition: $11,697 full-time. Mandatory fees: $1628 full-time. College room and board: $5712. College room only: $3122. Room and board charges vary according to housing facility.
Collegiate Environment: Orientation program. Drama-theater group, choral group, student-run newspaper, radio station. Social organizations: 66 open to all; national fraternities, national sororities; 3% of eligible men and 2% of eligible women are members. Most popular organizations: Student Government Association, Underdog Productions, Residence Hall Association, African-American Association, International Student Association. Major annual events: Chancellor's Campus Community Dinner, Lawn Party, Taste of the Holidays. Student services: health clinic, personal-psychological counseling, women's center. Campus security: 24-hour emergency response devices and patrols, late night transport-escort service, dorm entrances secured at night. College housing designed to accommodate 1,207 students; 1,277 undergraduates lived in college housing during 2003-04. Freshmen guaranteed college housing. On-campus residence required in freshman year. Options: coed, men-only, women-only housing available. D. Hidden Ramsey Library with 254,179 books, 822,833 microform titles, 2,014 serials, 9,816 audiovisual materials, an OPAC, and a Web page. Operations spending for 2004 fiscal year: $2 million. 376 computers available on campus for general student use. Computer purchase/lease plans available. A campuswide network can be accessed from student residence rooms and from off campus. Staffed computer lab on campus.

■ THE UNIVERSITY OF NORTH CAROLINA AT CHAPEL HILL *C-8*

Chapel Hill, NC 27599
Tel: (919)962-2211
Admissions: (919)966-3621

E-mail: uadm@email.unc.edu

Web Site: http://www.unc.edu/

Description: State-supported, university, coed. Part of University of North Carolina System. Awards bachelor's, master's, doctoral, and first professional degrees and post-master's certificates. Founded 1789. Setting: 729-acre suburban campus with easy access to Raleigh-Durham. Endowment: $1.4 billion. Research spending for 2004 fiscal year: $257.9 million. Educational spending for 2005 fiscal year: $24,233 per student. Total enrollment: 26,878. Faculty: 1,440 (1,318 full-time, 122 part-time). Student-undergrad faculty ratio is 14:1. 18,850 applied, 36% were admitted. 74% from top 10% of their high school class, 95% from top quarter, 99% from top half. 125 National Merit Scholars, 161 valedictorians. Full-time: 15,698 students, 58% women, 42% men. Part-time: 827 students, 53% women, 47% men. Students come from 52 states and territories, 102 other countries, 17% from out-of-state, 1% Native American, 3% Hispanic, 11% black, 6% Asian American or Pacific Islander, 1% international, 3% 25 or older, 43% live on campus, 5% transferred in. Retention: 95% of full-time freshmen returned the following year. Core. Calendar: semesters. Services for LD students, advanced placement, self-designed majors, freshman honors college, honors program, independent study, distance learning, double major, summer session for credit, internships, graduate courses open to undergrads. Off campus study at North Carolina Central University, Duke University, North Carolina State University, University of North Carolina at Greensboro, University of North Carolina at Charlotte. Study abroad program. ROTC: Army, Naval, Air Force.

Entrance Requirements: Options: Peterson's Universal Application, electronic application, early action, deferred admission, international baccalaureate accepted. Required: essay, high school transcript, 1 recommendation, counselor's statement, SAT or ACT. Entrance: very difficult. Application deadlines: 1/15, 11/1 for early action. Notification: 3/31, 1/31 for early action. Preference given to state residents.

Costs Per Year: Application fee: $60. State resident tuition: $3205 full-time. Nonresident tuition: $17,003 full-time. Mandatory fees: $1,408 full-time. Full-time tuition and fees vary according to program. College room and board: $6516. College room only: $3630. Room and board charges vary according to board plan, housing facility, and location.

Collegiate Environment: Orientation program. Drama-theater group, choral group, marching band, student-run newspaper, radio station. Social organizations: 565 open to all; national fraternities, national sororities, local fraternities, local sororities. Most popular organizations: Campus Y, Newman Catholic Student Center Parish, Friendship Association of Chinese Students and Scholars, Residence Hall Association, North Carolina Hillel. Major annual events: homecoming, student elections, Fall Fest. Student services: legal services, health clinic, personal-psychological counseling, women's center. Campus security: 24-hour emergency response devices and patrols, student patrols, late night transport-escort service, controlled dormitory access, crime prevention programs. 7,449 college housing spaces available; 7,401 were occupied in 2003-04. Freshmen given priority for college housing. Options: coed, men-only, women-only housing available. Davis Library plus 14 others with 5.5 million books, 4.8 million microform titles, 40,597 serials, 260,948 audiovisual materials, an OPAC, and a Web page. Operations spending for 2004 fiscal year: $34.6 million. 600 computers available on campus for general student use. Computer purchase/lease plans available. A campuswide network can be accessed from student residence rooms and from off campus. Staffed computer lab on campus.

■ **THE UNIVERSITY OF NORTH CAROLINA AT CHARLOTTE** *E-3*

9201 University City Blvd.

Charlotte, NC 28223-0001

Tel: (704)687-2000

Admissions: (704)687-2213

Fax: (704)510-6483

E-mail: unccadm@email.uncc.edu

Web Site: http://www.uncc.edu/

Description: State-supported, university, coed. Part of University of North Carolina System. Awards bachelor's, master's, and doctoral degrees and post-master's certificates. Founded 1946. Setting: 1,000-acre suburban campus. Endowment: $125.4 million. Research spending for 2004 fiscal year: $24.7 million. Educational spending for 2005 fiscal year: $6574 per student. Total enrollment: 20,772. Faculty: 1,245 (859 full-time, 386 part-time). Student-undergrad faculty ratio is 14:1. 8,665 applied, 78% were admitted. 11% from top 10% of their high school class, 37% from top quarter, 93% from top half. Full-time: 13,640 students, 53% women, 47% men. Part-time: 2,915 students, 56% women, 44% men. Students come from 48 states

and territories, 80 other countries, 9% from out-of-state, 0.4% Native American, 3% Hispanic, 15% black, 5% Asian American or Pacific Islander, 1% international, 22% 25 or older, 27% live on campus, 11% transferred in. Retention: 77% of full-time freshmen returned the following year. Academic areas with the most degrees conferred: business/marketing; psychology; social sciences. Core. Calendar: semesters. ESL program, services for LD students, advanced placement, freshman honors college, honors program, distance learning, double major, summer session for credit, part-time degree program, adult/continuing education programs, co-op programs and internships, graduate courses open to undergrads. Off campus study at 24 members of the Charlotte Area Educational Consortium. Study abroad program. ROTC: Army, Air Force.

Entrance Requirements: Options: Common Application, electronic application, early admission, deferred admission, international baccalaureate accepted. Required: high school transcript, minimum 2.0 high school GPA, medical history, no criminal record, SAT or ACT. Required for some: interview. Entrance: moderately difficult. Application deadlines: 7/1, 10/15 for early action. Notification: continuous. Preference given to state residents.

Costs Per Year: Application fee: $50. Area resident tuition: $148 per credit hour part-time. State resident tuition: $2129 full-time, $148 per credit hour part-time. Nonresident tuition: $12,541 full-time, $582 per credit hour part-time. Mandatory fees: $1420 full-time, $59 per credit hour part-time. Full-time tuition and fees vary according to course load. Part-time tuition and fees vary according to course load. College room and board: $5550. College room only: $2840. Room and board charges vary according to board plan and housing facility.

Collegiate Environment: Orientation program. Drama-theater group, choral group, student-run newspaper. Social organizations: 200 open to all; national fraternities, national sororities; 8% of eligible men and 6% of eligible women are members. Most popular organizations: University Program Board, Student Government Association, Resident Student Association, Black Student Union. Major annual events: Greek Week, International Festival, Homecoming Week. Student services: health clinic, personal-psychological counseling. Campus security: 24-hour emergency response devices and patrols, late night transport-escort service, controlled dormitory access. 4,386 college housing spaces available; 4,234 were occupied in 2003-04. No special consideration for freshman housing applicants. Options: coed, men-only, women-only housing available. J. Murrey Atkins Library with 916,218 books, 2.1 million microform titles, 10,599 serials, 52,096 audiovisual materials, an OPAC, and a Web page. Operations spending for 2004 fiscal year: $8 million. 1,400 computers available on campus for general student use. Computer purchase/lease plans available. A campuswide network can be accessed from student residence rooms and from off campus. Staffed computer lab on campus.

■ **THE UNIVERSITY OF NORTH CAROLINA AT GREENSBORO** *C-6*

1000 Spring Garden St.

Greensboro, NC 27412-5001

Tel: (336)334-5000

Admissions: (336)334-5243

Fax: (336)334-4180

E-mail: undergrad_admissions@uncg.edu

Web Site: http://www.uncg.edu/

Description: State-supported, university, coed. Part of University of North Carolina System. Awards bachelor's, master's, and doctoral degrees. Founded 1891. Setting: 200-acre urban campus. Research spending for 2004 fiscal year: $14.1 million. Educational spending for 2005 fiscal year: $7942 per student. Total enrollment: 16,060. Faculty: 989 (746 full-time, 243 part-time). Student-undergrad faculty ratio is 16:1. 8,987 applied, 60% were admitted. 14% from top 10% of their high school class, 45% from top quarter, 84% from top half. Full-time: 10,584 students, 68% women, 32% men. Part-time: 1,707 students, 66% women, 34% men. Students come from 41 states and territories, 55 other countries, 7% from out-of-state, 0.4% Native American, 2% Hispanic, 20% black, 3% Asian American or Pacific Islander, 1% international, 18% 25 or older, 34% live on campus, 8% transferred in. Retention: 78% of full-time freshmen returned the following year. Academic areas with the most degrees conferred: business/marketing; visual and performing arts; education. Core. Calendar: semesters. Academic remediation for entering students, ESL program, services for LD students, advanced placement, accelerated degree program, self-designed majors, freshman honors college, honors program, independent study, distance learning, double major, summer session for credit, part-time degree program, adult/continuing education programs, internships, graduate courses open to undergrads. Off campus study at Bennett College, Guilford

College, Greensboro College, High Point University, North Carolina Agricultural and Technical State University. Study abroad program. ROTC: Army (c), Air Force (c).

Entrance Requirements: Options: early admission, international bac-calaureate accepted. Required: high school transcript, minimum 2.0 high school GPA, SAT or ACT. Entrance: moderately difficult. Application deadline: 3/1. Notification: continuous.

Costs Per Year: Application fee: $45. State resident tuition: $2308 full-time. Nonresident tuition: $13,576 full-time. Mandatory fees: $1505 full-time. College room and board: $5706. College room only: $3232.

Collegiate Environment: Orientation program. Drama-theater group, choral group, student-run newspaper, radio station. Social organizations: 151 open to all; national fraternities, national sororities; 8% of eligible men and 6% of eligible women are members. Most popular organizations: Campus Activities Board, Neo-Black Society, religious organizations, International Students Association. Major annual events: homecoming, Fall Kick-Off, Spring Fling. Student services: health clinic, personal-psychological counseling. Campus security: 24-hour emergency response devices and patrols, late night transport-escort service, controlled dormitory access. Freshmen given priority for college housing. Options: coed, women-only housing available. Jackson Library plus 1 other with 844,448 books, 1.4 million microform titles, 8,714 serials, 59,027 audiovisual materials, an OPAC, and a Web page. Operations spending for 2004 fiscal year: $4.4 million. 500 computers available on campus for general student use. Computer purchase/lease plans available. A campuswide network can be accessed from student residence rooms and from off campus. Staffed computer lab on campus.

■ **THE UNIVERSITY OF NORTH CAROLINA AT PEMBROKE** *G-8*
One University Dr., PO Box 1510
Pembroke, NC 28372-1510
Tel: (910)521-6000
Free: 800-949-UNCP
Admissions: (910)521-6262
Web Site: http://www.uncp.edu/

Description: State-supported, comprehensive, coed. Part of University of North Carolina System. Awards bachelor's and master's degrees. Founded 1887. Setting: 152-acre rural campus. Endowment: $4.6 million. Research spending for 2004 fiscal year: $34,291. Educational spending for 2005 fiscal year: $13,200 per student. Total enrollment: 5,732. Faculty: 328 (238 full-time, 90 part-time). Student-undergrad faculty ratio is 16:1. 2,374 applied, 86% were admitted. 9% from top 10% of their high school class, 30% from top quarter, 64% from top half. Full-time: 3,702 students, 60% women, 40% men. Part-time: 1,361 students, 72% women, 28% men. Students come from 33 states and territories, 20 other countries, 5% from out-of-state, 22% Native American, 3% Hispanic, 24% black, 2% Asian American or Pacific Islander, 1% international, 37% 25 or older, 27% live on campus, 10% transferred in. Retention: 71% of full-time freshmen returned the following year. Academic areas with the most degrees conferred: education; business/marketing; social sciences. Core. Calendar: semesters. Academic remediation for entering students, ESL program, services for LD students, advanced placement, accelerated degree program, honors program, independent study, distance learning, double major, summer session for credit, part-time degree program, adult/continuing education programs, co-op programs and internships, graduate courses open to undergrads. Off campus study at Richmond Community College, Fayetteville State University, Sandhills Community College, Southeastern Community College, Fayetteville Technical College. Study abroad program. ROTC: Army, Air Force.

Entrance Requirements: Options: Peterson's Universal Application, Common Application, early admission, deferred admission. Required: high school transcript, SAT or ACT. Recommended: essay, minimum 2.0 high school GPA. Required for some: recommendations; interview. Entrance: moderately difficult. Application deadline: Rolling. Notification: continuous.

Costs Per Year: Application fee: $40. State resident tuition: $1689 full-time. Nonresident tuition: $11,129 full-time. Mandatory fees: $1291 full-time. Full-time tuition and fees vary according to course load and location. College room and board: $4890. College room only: $2700. Room and board charges vary according to board plan and housing facility.

Collegiate Environment: Orientation program. Drama-theater group, choral group, student-run newspaper. Social organizations: 70 open to all; national fraternities, national sororities, local fraternities, local sororities; 5% of eligible men and 8% of eligible women are members. Major annual events: homecoming, Pembroke Day, A Taste of Culture. Student services: health clinic, personal-psychological counseling. Campus security: 24-hour

emergency response devices and patrols, late night transport-escort service, controlled dormitory access. 1,344 college housing spaces available; 1,213 were occupied in 2003-04. Options: coed, men-only, women-only housing available. Sampson-Livermore Library with 325,499 books, 694,584 microform titles, 1,200 serials, 2,295 audiovisual materials, an OPAC, and a Web page. Operations spending for 2004 fiscal year: $2.3 million. 650 computers available on campus for general student use. A campuswide network can be accessed from student residence rooms and from off campus. Staffed computer lab on campus.

■ **THE UNIVERSITY OF NORTH CAROLINA WILMINGTON** *I-11*
601 South College Rd.
Wilmington, NC 28403-3297
Tel: (910)962-3000
Free: 800-228-5571
Admissions: (910)962-4198
Fax: (910)962-3038
E-mail: admissions@uncwil.edu
Web Site: http://www.uncw.edu/

Description: State-supported, comprehensive, coed. Part of University of North Carolina System. Awards bachelor's, master's, and doctoral degrees. Founded 1947. Setting: 650-acre urban campus. Endowment: $33.5 million. Research spending for 2004 fiscal year: $12.9 million. Educational spending for 2005 fiscal year: $5475 per student. Total enrollment: 11,653. Faculty: 776 (491 full-time, 285 part-time). Student-undergrad faculty ratio is 19:1. 8,820 applied, 61% were admitted. 21% from top 10% of their high school class, 60% from top quarter, 93% from top half. Full-time: 9,591 students, 58% women, 42% men. Part-time: 990 students, 66% women, 34% men. Students come from 49 states and territories, 28 other countries, 12% from out-of-state, 1% Native American, 2% Hispanic, 5% black, 2% Asian American or Pacific Islander, 0.5% international, 13% 25 or older, 23% live on campus, 12% transferred in. Retention: 83% of full-time freshmen returned the following year. Academic areas with the most degrees conferred: history; English; education. Core. Calendar: semesters. Academic remediation for entering students, ESL program, services for LD students, advanced placement, accelerated degree program, honors program, independent study, distance learning, double major, summer session for credit, part-time degree program, adult/continuing education programs, co-op programs and internships. Study abroad program.

Entrance Requirements: Options: Common Application, electronic application, early admission, deferred admission. Required: essay, high school transcript, SAT or ACT. Recommended: recommendations. Entrance: moderately difficult. Application deadlines: 2/1, 11/1 for early action. Notification: 4/1, 1/20 for early action.

Costs Per Year: Application fee: $45. State resident tuition: $1928 full-time. Nonresident tuition: $11,863 full-time. Mandatory fees: $1767 full-time. Full-time tuition and fees vary according to course load. College room and board: $6412. Room and board charges vary according to board plan and housing facility.

Collegiate Environment: Orientation program. Drama-theater group, choral group, student-run newspaper, radio station. Social organizations: 114 open to all; national fraternities, national sororities, local sororities; 7% of eligible men and 8% of eligible women are members. Most popular organizations: Student Government Association, Association of Campus Entertainment, Residence Hall Association, Sailing Club. Major annual events: Welcome Week, Midnight Madness, Homecoming. Student services: legal services, health clinic, personal-psychological counseling. Campus security: 24-hour emergency response devices and patrols, late night transport-escort service, controlled dormitory access, escort service. College housing designed to accommodate 2,364 students; 2,401 undergraduates lived in college housing during 2003-04. Freshmen given priority for college housing. Options: coed, women-only housing available. William M. Randall Library with 530,368 books, 1 million microform titles, 3,668 serials, 15,445 audiovisual materials, an OPAC, and a Web page. Operations spending for 2004 fiscal year: $4.4 million. 778 computers available on campus for general student use. Computer purchase/lease plans available. A campuswide network can be accessed from student residence rooms and from off campus. Staffed computer lab on campus.

■ **UNIVERSITY OF PHOENIX-CHARLOTTE CAMPUS** *E-3*
3800 Arco Corporate Dr., Ste. 100
Charlotte, NC 28273
Tel: (704)504-5409
Free: 800-228-7240

Admissions: (480)557-1712

Web Site: http://www.phoenix.edu/

Description: Proprietary, comprehensive, coed. Awards bachelor's and master's degrees. Founded 2003. Total enrollment: 1,301. Faculty: 230 (7 full-time, 223 part-time). Student-undergrad faculty ratio is 10:1. 39 applied. Full-time: 854 students, 63% women, 37% men. 0% Native American, 1% Hispanic, 10% black, 0.2% Asian American or Pacific Islander, 6% international, 95% 25 or older. Academic areas with the most degrees conferred: business/marketing; computer and information sciences. Core. Calendar: continuous. Advanced placement, accelerated degree program, independent study, distance learning, external degree program, adult/continuing education programs, graduate courses open to undergrads.

Entrance Requirements: Open admission. Option: deferred admission. Required: 1 recommendation. Required for some: high school transcript. Entrance: noncompetitive. Application deadline: Rolling.

Costs Per Year: Application fee: $110. Tuition: $10,170 full-time, $339 per credit part-time. Mandatory fees: $560 full-time, $70 per course part-time.

Collegiate Environment: College housing not available. University Library with 444 books, 666 serials, an OPAC, and a Web page. System-wide operations spending for 2004 fiscal year: $3.2 million.

■ **UNIVERSITY OF PHOENIX-RALEIGH CAMPUS** *D-9*

5511 Capital Center Dr.

Raleigh, NC 27606

Free: 800-228-7240

Admissions: (480)557-1712

Web Site: http://www.phoenix.edu/

Description: Proprietary, comprehensive, coed. Awards bachelor's and master's degrees. Total enrollment: 221. Faculty: 19 (3 full-time, 16 part-time). Student-undergrad faculty ratio is 5:1. Full-time: 134 students, 64% women, 36% men. 0% from out-of-state, 0% Native American, 1% Hispanic, 3% black, 0% Asian American or Pacific Islander, 3% international. Core. Advanced placement, accelerated degree program, independent study, distance learning, external degree program, adult/continuing education programs, graduate courses open to undergrads.

Entrance Requirements: Open admission. Option: deferred admission. Required: 1 recommendation. Required for some: high school transcript. Entrance: noncompetitive. Application deadline: Rolling.

Costs Per Year: Application fee: $110. Tuition: $10,170 full-time, $339 per credit part-time. Mandatory fees: $560 full-time, $70 per course part-time.

Collegiate Environment: College housing not available. University Library with 444 books, 666 serials, an OPAC, and a Web page. System-wide operations spending for 2004 fiscal year: $3.2 million.

■ **VANCE-GRANVILLE COMMUNITY COLLEGE** *B-10*

PO Box 917

Henderson, NC 27536-0917

Tel: (252)492-2061

Fax: (252)430-0460

Web Site: http://www.vgcc.cc.nc.us/

Description: State-supported, 2-year, coed. Part of North Carolina Community College System. Awards certificates, diplomas, transfer associate, and terminal associate degrees. Founded 1969. Setting: 83-acre rural campus with easy access to Raleigh. Endowment: $3 million. Total enrollment: 4,057. Student-undergrad faculty ratio is 9:1. 1,765 applied, 100% were admitted. 12% from top 10% of their high school class, 22% from top quarter, 40% from top half. 35 student government officers. Full-time: 1,718 students, 65% women, 35% men. Part-time: 2,339 students, 68% women, 32% men. Students come from 10 states and territories, 15 other countries, 2% from out-of-state, 1% Native American, 2% Hispanic, 43% black, 0.2% Asian American or Pacific Islander, 1% international, 53% 25 or older, 2% transferred in. Core. Calendar: semesters. Academic remediation for entering students, ESL program, services for LD students, advanced placement, accelerated degree program, distance learning, double major, summer session for credit, part-time degree program, adult/continuing education programs, co-op programs and internships.

Entrance Requirements: Open admission except for nursing, radiology programs, electronics engineering. Options: Common Application, early admission, deferred admission. Required: high school transcript. Entrance: noncompetitive. Application deadline: Rolling. Notification: continuous. Preference given to district, then state residents.

Costs Per Year: Application fee: $0. State resident tuition: $948 full-time, $39.50 per credit hour part-time. Nonresident tuition: $5592 full-time, $233.50 per credit hour part-time. Mandatory fees: $38 full-time, $14 per term part-time.

Collegiate Environment: Orientation program. Drama-theater group. Most popular organizations: Vocational Club, Phi Theta Kappa, Computer Club, Criminal Justice Club, Business Club. Major annual events: Spring Sports Day, College-Wide Olympic Games, Career Day. Student services: personal-psychological counseling. Campus security: 24-hour emergency response devices and patrols. College housing not available. Vance-Granville Community College Learning Resource Center plus 1 other with 38,720 books, 317 serials, an OPAC, and a Web page. 184 computers available on campus for general student use. A campuswide network can be accessed from off-campus. Staffed computer lab on campus.

■ **WAKE FOREST UNIVERSITY** *C-5*

Reynolda Station

Winston-Salem, NC 27109

Tel: (336)758-5000

Admissions: (336)758-5201

Fax: (336)758-6074

Web Site: http://www.wfu.edu/

Description: Independent, university, coed. Awards bachelor's, master's, doctoral, and first professional degrees. Founded 1834. Setting: 340-acre suburban campus. Endowment: $906.8 million. Research spending for 2004 fiscal year: $191.8 million. Total enrollment: 6,716. Faculty: 548 (450 full-time, 98 part-time). Student-undergrad faculty ratio is 10:1. 7,484 applied, 39% were admitted. 61% from top 10% of their high school class, 94% from top quarter, 98% from top half. 4 National Merit Scholars, 32 class presidents, 42 valedictorians, 32 student government officers. Full-time: 4,138 students, 51% women, 49% men. Part-time: 125 students, 43% women, 57% men. Students come from 50 states and territories, 25 other countries, 71% from out-of-state, 0.4% Native American, 2% Hispanic, 7% black, 4% Asian American or Pacific Islander, 1% international, 1% 25 or older, 78% live on campus, 1% transferred in. Retention: 93% of full-time freshmen returned the following year. Academic areas with the most degrees conferred: social sciences; business/marketing; communications/journalism. Core. Calendar: semesters. Services for LD students, advanced placement, accelerated degree program, honors program, independent study, double major, summer session for credit, part-time degree program, internships, graduate courses open to undergrads. Off campus study. Study abroad program. ROTC: Army.

Entrance Requirements: Options: Common Application, electronic application, early admission, early decision, deferred admission, international baccalaureate accepted. Required: essay, high school transcript, 1 recommendation, SAT or ACT. Entrance: very difficult. Application deadlines: 1/15, 11/15 for early decision. Notification: 4/1, 12/15 for early decision.

Costs Per Year: Application fee: $40. Comprehensive fee: $40,940 includes full-time tuition ($32,040), mandatory fees ($100), and college room and board ($8800). College room only: $5500. Part-time tuition: $1250 per credit hour.

Collegiate Environment: Orientation program. Drama-theater group, choral group, marching band, student-run newspaper, radio station. Social organizations: 135 open to all; national fraternities, national sororities; 33% of eligible men and 53% of eligible women are members. Most popular organizations: Student Union Network, Volunteer Service Corps, Inter-Varsity Christian Fellowship, student government. Major annual events: Brian Piccolo Cancer Fund Drive, Project Pumpkin, homecoming. Student services: health clinic, personal-psychological counseling. Campus security: 24-hour emergency response devices and patrols, late night transport-escort service, controlled dormitory access. 3,016 college housing spaces available. Freshmen guaranteed college housing. On-campus residence required through sophomore year. Option: coed housing available. Z. Smith Reynolds Library plus 3 others with 923,123 books, 2 million microform titles, 16,448 serials, 21,055 audiovisual materials, an OPAC, and a Web page. Operations spending for 2004 fiscal year: $11.4 million. 150 computers available on campus for general student use. Computer purchase/lease plans available. A campuswide network can be accessed from student residence rooms and from off campus. Staffed computer lab on campus.

Community Environment: Wake Forest is located in Piedmont North Carolina, an hour from the Blue Ridge mountains, in the northwestern suburb of Winston-Salem, a city of 150,000 dating from the 1700s. Wake Forest shares a close working relationship with Salem College, Winston-Salem State University, and the North Carolina School of the Arts. Winston-Salem is a city of colleges, business, recreation, and the arts. The numerous points of interest include Reynolda House and Gardens, Old Salem, Wachovia Museum, Southeastern Center of Contemporary Art, Museum of Early Southern Decorative Arts, Nature Science Museum, Tanglewood Estates Park, two annual craft fairs and numerous craft and art galleries.

■ WAKE TECHNICAL COMMUNITY COLLEGE *D-9*

9101 Fayetteville Rd.
Raleigh, NC 27603-5696
Tel: (919)662-3400
Admissions: (919)662-3357
Fax: (919)662-3529
Web Site: http://www.waketech.edu/

Description: State and locally supported, 2-year, coed. Part of North Carolina Community College System. Awards certificates, diplomas, transfer associate, and terminal associate degrees. Founded 1958. Setting: 79-acre suburban campus. Research spending for 2004 fiscal year: $77,047. Educational spending for 2005 fiscal year: $2547 per student. Total enrollment: 11,372. 4% from top 10% of their high school class, 22% from top quarter, 47% from top half. Full-time: 3,891 students, 55% women, 45% men. Part-time: 7,481 students, 55% women, 45% men. Students come from 15 states and territories, 41 other countries, 56% 25 or older, 15% transferred in. Core. Calendar: semesters. Academic remediation for entering students, ESL program, services for LD students, advanced placement, double major, summer session for credit, part-time degree program, adult/continuing education programs, co-op programs.

Entrance Requirements: Open admission except for nursing program. Options: Common Application, electronic application, early admission. Required: high school transcript. Placement: ACT ASSET or ACT COMPASS required; SAT or ACT recommended. Entrance: noncompetitive. Application deadline: Rolling.

Costs Per Year: Application fee: $0. State resident tuition: $1264 full-time, $39.50 per credit hour part-time. Nonresident tuition: $7024 full-time, $219.50 per credit hour part-time. Mandatory fees: $52 full-time, $1 per credit hour part-time, $10 per term part-time.

Collegiate Environment: Drama-theater group, choral group, student-run newspaper. Social organizations: 5 open to all. Most popular organizations: Science Club, History Club, Drama Club, Amateur Radio Club, Design and Garden Club. Major annual events: Spring Fling, graduation, International Day. Student services: personal-psychological counseling. Campus security: 24-hour patrols. College housing not available. Bruce M. Howell Library plus 1 other with 70,617 books, 52,779 microform titles, 474 serials, 6,141 audiovisual materials, an OPAC, and a Web page. Operations spending for 2004 fiscal year: $725,897. 23 computers available on campus for general student use. A campuswide network can be accessed. Staffed computer lab on campus.

Community Environment: See Meredith College.

■ WARREN WILSON COLLEGE *J-15*

PO Box 9000
Asheville, NC 28815-9000
Tel: (828)298-3325
Free: 800-934-3536
Admissions: (828)771-2073
Fax: (828)298-1440
E-mail: admit@warren-wilson.edu
Web Site: http://www.warren-wilson.edu/

Description: Independent, comprehensive, coed, affiliated with Presbyterian Church (U.S.A.). Awards bachelor's and master's degrees. Founded 1894. Setting: 1,135-acre small town campus. Endowment: $31.9 million. Educational spending for 2005 fiscal year: $9908 per student. Total enrollment: 901. Faculty: 75 (62 full-time, 13 part-time). Student-undergrad faculty ratio is 13:1. 857 applied, 77% were admitted. 11% from top 10% of their high school class, 25% from top quarter, 78% from top half. 7 valedictorians. Full-time: 820 students, 61% women, 39% men. Part-time: 12 students, 33% women, 67% men. Students come from 46 states and territories, 12 other countries, 81% from out-of-state, 0.1% Native American, 2% Hispanic, 1% black, 1% Asian American or Pacific Islander, 3% international, 4% 25 or older, 88% live on campus, 8% transferred in. Retention: 62% of full-time freshmen returned the following year. Academic areas with the most degrees conferred: social sciences; natural resources/environmental science; biological/life sciences. Core. Calendar: semesters. ESL program, services for LD students, advanced placement, self-designed majors, honors program, independent study, double major, part-time degree program, co-op programs and internships. Off campus study at Appalachian State University, Washington University, Duke University, University of North Carolina at Asheville, Mars Hill College. Study abroad program.

Entrance Requirements: Options: Peterson's Universal Application, Common Application, electronic application, early admission, early decision, deferred admission. Required: essay, high school transcript, minimum 2.5

high school GPA, 2 recommendations, SAT or ACT. Recommended: interview. Entrance: moderately difficult. Application deadlines: 3/15, 11/15 for early decision. Notification: continuous, 12/1 for early decision.

Costs Per Year: Application fee: $0. Comprehensive fee: $26,126 includes full-time tuition ($20,126) and college room and board ($6000).

Collegiate Environment: Orientation program. Drama-theater group, choral group, student-run newspaper, radio station. Social organizations: 20 open to all. Most popular organizations: Collective Conscience/Social Justice/Student Caucus, Resistance and Peacemaking (RAP), yoga, Outing Club, African Dance Club. Major annual events: coffee houses, Work Day, Winter Dinner and Dance. Student services: health clinic, personal-psychological counseling. Campus security: 24-hour emergency response devices and patrols, student patrols, late night transport-escort service, controlled dormitory access. 715 college housing spaces available; 652 were occupied in 2003-04. Freshmen guaranteed college housing. On-campus residence required in freshman year. Options: coed, men-only, women-only housing available. Pew Learning Center and Ellison Library with 106,837 books, 33,194 microform titles, 2,588 audiovisual materials, an OPAC, and a Web page. Operations spending for 2004 fiscal year: $54,034. 87 computers available on campus for general student use. A campuswide network can be accessed from student residence rooms and from off campus. Staffed computer lab on campus.

Community Environment: Situated in the Swannanoa Valley among the Blue Ridge Mountains of western North Carolina, the campus is ten miles east of Asheville. Inhabitants enjoy all the conveniences of the smaller local community, and all the advantages of the nearby city.

■ WAYNE COMMUNITY COLLEGE *E-11*

PO Box 8002
Goldsboro, NC 27533-8002
Tel: (919)735-5151
Fax: (919)736-3204
E-mail: msm@wayne.cc.nc.us
Web Site: http://www.waynecc.edu/

Description: State and locally supported, 2-year, coed. Part of North Carolina Community College System. Awards certificates, diplomas, transfer associate, and terminal associate degrees. Founded 1957. Setting: 125-acre small town campus. Endowment: $45,924. Total enrollment: 3,181. Students come from 47 states and territories, 16% from out-of-state, 2% Native American, 2% Hispanic, 31% black, 2% Asian American or Pacific Islander, 0% international, 33% 25 or older. Calendar: semesters. Academic remediation for entering students, ESL program, services for LD students, advanced placement, distance learning, double major, summer session for credit, part-time degree program, adult/continuing education programs, co-op programs.

Entrance Requirements: Open admission except for health occupations programs. Option: deferred admission. Required: high school transcript, interview. Placement: ACT ASSET required. Entrance: noncompetitive. Application deadline: Rolling. Notification: continuous.

Collegiate Environment: Choral group, student-run newspaper. Social organizations: 11 open to all; national fraternities; 10% of men are members. Most popular organizations: Student Government Association, Phi Beta Lambda, Agriculture Club, Multicultural Association for Enrichment, Student American Dental Hygienist Association. Major annual events: Spring Fling, Faculty Appreciation Day, Jail-A-Thon. Student services: health clinic, personal-psychological counseling. Campus security: 24-hour emergency response devices and patrols, student patrols. College housing not available. Wayne Community College Library with 42,133 books, 49,783 microform titles, 427 serials, 5,840 audiovisual materials, an OPAC, and a Web page. Operations spending for 2004 fiscal year: $644,681. 56 computers available on campus for general student use. A campuswide network can be accessed from off-campus. Staffed computer lab on campus.

Community Environment: 50% of the state's bright-leaf tobacco is produced within a radius of 60 miles of Goldsboro. The soil and climate also make livestock production and farming important. All forms of commercial transportation are available. Churches of all denominations, a hospital, and medical clinic are a part of the city's facilities. Job opportunities are plentiful. Recreational facilities are good for all outdoor sports.

■ WESTERN CAROLINA UNIVERSITY *K-14*

Cullowhee, NC 28723
Tel: (828)227-7211; 877-WCU4YOU
Admissions: (828)227-7317
E-mail: cauley@wcu.edu

Web Site: http://www.wcu.edu/

Description: State-supported, comprehensive, coed. Part of University of North Carolina System. Awards bachelor's, master's, and doctoral degrees and post-master's certificates. Founded 1889. Setting: 260-acre rural campus. Endowment: $24.5 million. Research spending for 2004 fiscal year: $3.5 million. Educational spending for 2005 fiscal year: $5962 per student. Total enrollment: 8,665. Faculty: 663 (433 full-time, 230 part-time). Student-undergrad faculty ratio is 14:1. 4,964 applied, 75% were admitted. 8% from top 10% of their high school class, 27% from top quarter, 61% from top half. 3 National Merit Scholars, 8 valedictorians. Full-time: 6,015 students, 51% women, 49% men. Part-time: 965 students, 62% women, 38% men. Students come from 46 states and territories, 43 other countries, 10% from out-of-state, 2% Native American, 1% Hispanic, 5% black, 1% Asian American or Pacific Islander, 3% international, 11% 25 or older, 50% live on campus, 9% transferred in. Retention: 69% of full-time freshmen returned the following year. Academic areas with the most degrees conferred: business/marketing; education; health professions and related sciences. Core. Calendar: semesters. Academic remediation for entering students, ESL program, services for LD students, advanced placement, accelerated degree program, self-designed majors, honors program, independent study, distance learning, double major, summer session for credit, part-time degree program, adult/continuing education programs, co-op programs and internships, graduate courses open to undergrads. Study abroad program.

Entrance Requirements: Options: electronic application, early admission. Required: high school transcript, minimum 2.5 high school GPA, SAT or ACT. Entrance: moderately difficult. Application deadline: 8/1. Notification: continuous.

Costs Per Year: Application fee: $40. State resident tuition: $278.03 per hour part-time. Nonresident tuition: $1,457.53 per hour part-time.

Collegiate Environment: Orientation program. Drama-theater group, choral group, marching band, student-run newspaper, radio station. Social organizations: 120 open to all; national fraternities, national sororities; 9% of eligible men and 8% of eligible women are members. Most popular organizations: Student Government Association, Organization of Ebony Students, Resident Student Association. Major annual events: Mountain Heritage Day, Valley Ballyhoo, Homecoming. Student services: health clinic, personal-psychological counseling, women's center. Campus security: 24-hour emergency response devices and patrols, controlled dormitory access. 3,750 college housing spaces available; 3,664 were occupied in 2003-04. Freshmen guaranteed college housing. On-campus residence required in freshman year. Options: coed, men-only, women-only housing available. Hunter Library with 694,530 books, 1.5 million microform titles, 3,330 serials, 25,657 audiovisual materials, an OPAC, and a Web page. Operations spending for 2004 fiscal year: $3.2 million. 823 computers available on campus for general student use. A campuswide network can be accessed from student residence rooms and from off campus. Staffed computer lab on campus.

Community Environment: Cullowhee is in an area containing several of the most scenic drives in western North Carolina. It is a rural area with bus transportation available. Asheville is nearby and provides an airport for air transportation. Student employment is available in clerical and cafeteria positions. Recreational activities include boating, fishing, water sports, mountain climbing and nature trails. Main shopping facilities are in Asheville.

■ **WESTERN PIEDMONT COMMUNITY COLLEGE** *D-1*

1001 Burkemont Ave.

Morganton, NC 28655-4511

Tel: (828)438-6000

Admissions: (828)438-6051

Fax: (828)438-6015

E-mail: swilliams@wpcc.edu

Web Site: http://www.wpcc.edu/

Description: State-supported, 2-year, coed. Part of North Carolina Community College System. Awards certificates, diplomas, transfer associate, and terminal associate degrees. Founded 1964. Setting: 130-acre small town campus. Total enrollment: 2,897. 827 applied, 100% were admitted. Students come from 5 states and territories, 0.4% Native American, 1% Hispanic, 9% black, 4% Asian American or Pacific Islander, 1% international. Core. Calendar: semesters. Academic remediation for entering students, advanced placement, summer session for credit, part-time degree program, adult/continuing education programs, co-op programs.

Entrance Requirements: Open admission. Required: high school transcript. Placement: ACT ASSET required. Entrance: noncompetitive. Application deadline: Rolling. Notification: continuous.

Collegiate Environment: Drama-theater group, student-run newspaper. Student services: personal-psychological counseling, women's center. College housing not available. 31,195 books and 200 serials. 60 computers available on campus for general student use.

Community Environment: Western Piedmont Community College, in Morganton (population 15,000), is situated in the Appalachian foothills of western North Carolina near the Catawba River. Burke County (population 76,000) was established in 1777 and named in honor of the third governor of North Carolina, Thomas Burke. Manufacturing is diversified and includes furniture, textiles, electronics, and assembly plants. The major employer is the State of North Carolina with services at Broughton Hospital, Western Carolina Center, Western Correctional Center, and the North Carolina School for the Deaf. Burke County is located in the fastest growing region of the state but as yet maintains its rural values.

■ **WILKES COMMUNITY COLLEGE** *B-3*

1328 Collegiate Dr., PO Box 120

Wilkesboro, NC 28697

Tel: (336)838-6100

Admissions: (336)838-6141

Fax: (336)838-6277

E-mail: mac.warren@wilkescc.edu

Web Site: http://www.wilkescc.edu/

Description: State-supported, 2-year, coed. Part of North Carolina Community College System. Awards certificates, diplomas, transfer associate, and terminal associate degrees. Founded 1965. Setting: 140-acre small town campus. Endowment: $2.7 million. Educational spending for 2005 fiscal year: $2929 per student. Total enrollment: 2,617. Student-undergrad faculty ratio is 10:1. 1,215 applied, 100% were admitted. Full-time: 1,347 students, 58% women, 42% men. Part-time: 1,270 students, 68% women, 32% men. Students come from 13 states and territories, 15 other countries, 1% from out-of-state, 0.5% Native American, 2% Hispanic, 5% black, 1% Asian American or Pacific Islander, 0% international, 44% 25 or older, 3% transferred in. Core. Calendar: semesters. Academic remediation for entering students, ESL program, services for LD students, advanced placement, accelerated degree program, independent study, distance learning, double major, summer session for credit, part-time degree program, adult/continuing education programs, co-op programs and internships.

Entrance Requirements: Open admission. Options: electronic application, deferred admission. Required: high school transcript. Entrance: noncompetitive. Application deadline: Rolling. Notification: continuous.

Costs Per Year: Application fee: $0. State resident tuition: $1264 full-time, $39.50 per credit hour part-time. Nonresident tuition: $7024 full-time, $219.50 per credit hour part-time. Mandatory fees: $58 full-time, $1.75 per credit hour part-time, $11.25 per term part-time.

Collegiate Environment: Drama-theater group, choral group, student-run newspaper, radio station. Social organizations: 21 open to all. Most popular organizations: Student Government Association, Phi Theta Kappa, Phi Beta Lambda, Rotaract, Baptist Student Union. Major annual events: Alcohol Awareness Week Activities, Welcome Back Week Activities, Fall Festival. Student services: personal-psychological counseling. Campus security: 24-hour emergency response devices, student patrols, late night transport-escort service. College housing not available. Learning Resources Center with 56,142 books, 1,040 microform titles, 127 serials, 6,867 audiovisual materials, an OPAC, and a Web page. Operations spending for 2004 fiscal year: $273,143. 255 computers available on campus for general student use. A campuswide network can be accessed. Staffed computer lab on campus.

Community Environment: Located 50 miles from Winston-Salem, Wilkesboro is the county seat of Wilkes County. The community offers churches of various faiths, shopping areas, and adequate medical facilities. The Kerr Scott Dam and Reservoir provides boating, fishing, water skiing, and swimming. The Blue Ridge Mountains around the Boone area provides winter time sports such as skiing and ice skating.

■ **WILSON TECHNICAL COMMUNITY COLLEGE** *D-11*

902 Herring Ave., PO Box 4305

Wilson, NC 27893-3310

Tel: (252)291-1195

Admissions: (252)246-1275

Fax: (252)243-7148

E-mail: dboyette@wilsontech.edu

Web Site: http://www.wilsontech.edu/

Description: State-supported, 2-year, coed. Part of North Carolina Community College System. Awards certificates, diplomas, transfer associate, and terminal associate degrees. Founded 1958. Setting: 35-acre small town campus. Endowment: $837,822. Educational spending for 2005 fiscal year: $3094 per student. Total enrollment: 1,925. Student-undergrad faculty ratio is 19:1. 507 applied, 97% were admitted. Full-time: 883 students, 73% women, 27% men. Part-time: 1,042 students, 74% women, 26% men. Students come from 4 states and territories, 4 other countries, 1% from out-of-state, 0.3% Native American, 2% Hispanic, 48% black, 0.3% Asian American or Pacific Islander, 0.1% international, 61% 25 or older, 16% transferred in. Core. Calendar: semesters. Academic remediation for entering students, ESL program, services for LD students, advanced placement, independent study, distance learning, double major, summer session for credit, part-time degree program, co-op programs and internships.
Entrance Requirements: Open admission except for health occupations programs. Options: Common Application, electronic application, deferred admission. Required: high school transcript. Entrance: noncompetitive. Application deadline: Rolling. Notification: continuous.
Costs Per Year: Application fee: $0. State resident tuition: $1264 full-time, $39.50 per credit hour part-time. Nonresident tuition: $7024 full-time, $219.50 per credit hour part-time. Mandatory fees: $38 full-time, $.75 per credit hour part-time, $7.
Collegiate Environment: Campus security: 11-hour patrols by trained security personnel. College housing not available. 38,466 books, 44,853 microform titles, 7,658 audiovisual materials, and an OPAC. Operations spending for 2004 fiscal year: $254,671. 33 computers available on campus for general student use. A campuswide network can be accessed. Staffed computer lab on campus.
Community Environment: The campus is located in Wilson, NC, a community of 37,000. Raleigh, the capital, is 45 miles west of Wilson.

■ **WINGATE UNIVERSITY** *H-3*
PO Box 159
Wingate, NC 28174-0159
Tel: (704)233-8000
Free: 800-755-5550
E-mail: admit@wingate.edu
Web Site: http://www.wingate.edu/
Description: Independent Baptist, comprehensive, coed. Awards bachelor's, master's, and first professional degrees. Founded 1896. Setting: 330-acre small town campus with easy access to Charlotte. Total enrollment: 1,632. Faculty: 152 (99 full-time, 53 part-time). Student-undergrad faculty ratio is 14:1. 1,247 applied, 84% were admitted. 19% from top 10% of their high school class, 41% from top quarter, 72% from top half. 6 class presidents, 6 valedictorians, 23 student government officers. Full-time: 1,311 students, 52% women, 48% men. Part-time: 30 students, 53% women, 47% men. Students come from 35 states and territories, 17 other countries, 39% from out-of-state, 1% Native American, 1% Hispanic, 11% black, 1% Asian American or Pacific Islander, 3% international, 3% 25 or older, 84% live on campus, 5% transferred in. Retention: 70% of full-time freshmen returned the following year. Academic areas with the most degrees conferred: business/marketing; communications/journalism; education. Core. Calendar: semesters. Services for LD students, advanced placement, accelerated degree program, honors program, independent study, double major, summer session for credit, part-time degree program, adult/continuing education programs, internships, graduate courses open to undergrads. Off campus study at members of the Charlotte Area Educational Consortium. Study abroad program. ROTC: Army (c), Air Force (c).
Entrance Requirements: Options: Peterson's Universal Application, Common Application, electronic application, early admission, early decision, deferred admission, international baccalaureate accepted. Required: high school transcript, minimum 2.0 high school GPA, SAT or ACT. Recommended: essay, minimum 3.0 high school GPA, SAT. Required for some: recommendations, interview. Entrance: moderately difficult. Application deadlines: Rolling, 12/1 for early decision. Notification: continuous, 12/15 for early decision.
Costs Per Year: Application fee: $30. Comprehensive fee: $23,300 includes full-time tuition ($15,800), mandatory fees ($1050), and college room and board ($6450). Part-time tuition: $525 per credit hour. Part-time mandatory fees: $175 per term.
Collegiate Environment: Orientation program. Drama-theater group, choral group, student-run newspaper. Social organizations: 30 open to all; national fraternities, national sororities; 20% of eligible men and 20% of eligible women are members. Most popular organizations: Student Community

Service Organization, Fellowship of Christian Athletes, Student Government Association, Christian Student Union. Major annual events: homecoming, fall/spring festivals, Parents' Weekend. Student services: health clinic, personal-psychological counseling. Campus security: 24-hour emergency response devices and patrols, late night transport-escort service, controlled dormitory access. 1,078 college housing spaces available; 1,054 were occupied in 2003-04. Freshmen guaranteed college housing. On-campus residence required through senior year. Options: men-only, women-only housing available. Ethel K. Smith Library with 107,187 books, 440,680 microform titles, 15,325 serials, 6,925 audiovisual materials, an OPAC, and a Web page. 75 computers available on campus for general student use. A campuswide network can be accessed from student residence rooms and from off campus. Staffed computer lab on campus.

■ **WINSTON-SALEM BIBLE COLLEGE** *C-5*
4117 Northampton Dr.
PO Box 777
Winston-Salem, NC 27102-0777
Tel: (336)744-0900
Fax: (336)744-0901
Web Site: http://www.wsbc.edu/
Description: Independent nondenominational, 4-year, coed. Awards associate and bachelor's degrees. Founded 1949. Total enrollment: 40. Calendar: semesters.

■ **WINSTON-SALEM STATE UNIVERSITY** *C-5*
601 Martin Luther King Jr Dr.
Winston-Salem, NC 27110-0003
Tel: (336)750-2000
Free: 800-257-4052
Admissions: (336)750-2070
Fax: (336)750-2079
E-mail: admissions@wssu.edu
Web Site: http://www.wssu.edu/
Description: State-supported, comprehensive, coed. Part of University of North Carolina System. Awards bachelor's and master's degrees. Founded 1892. Setting: 94-acre urban campus. Endowment: $16 million. Total enrollment: 5,566. Faculty: 315 (208 full-time, 107 part-time). Student-undergrad faculty ratio is 18:1. 2,889 applied, 79% were admitted. 4% from top 10% of their high school class, 19% from top quarter, 58% from top half. Full-time: 4,631 students, 70% women, 30% men. Part-time: 633 students, 72% women, 28% men. Students come from 34 states and territories, 8 other countries, 9% from out-of-state, 0.2% Native American, 1% Hispanic, 84% black, 1% Asian American or Pacific Islander, 0% international, 26% 25 or older, 46% live on campus, 10% transferred in. Retention: 68% of full-time freshmen returned the following year. Academic areas with the most degrees conferred: health professions and related sciences; business/marketing; computer and information sciences; social sciences. Core. Calendar: semesters. Academic remediation for entering students, services for LD students, advanced placement, accelerated degree program, freshman honors college, honors program, independent study, distance learning, double major, summer session for credit, part-time degree program, adult/continuing education programs, co-op programs and internships. ROTC: Army, Air Force.
Entrance Requirements: Options: Peterson's Universal Application, deferred admission. Required: high school transcript, SAT or ACT. Recommended: 1 recommendation. Entrance: minimally difficult. Application deadline: 7/15.
Costs Per Year: Application fee: $30. State resident tuition: $1451 full-time. Nonresident tuition: $10,090 full-time. Mandatory fees: $1354 full-time. Full-time tuition and fees vary according to degree level. College room and board: $5298. College room only: $3122. Room and board charges vary according to board plan and housing facility.
Collegiate Environment: Orientation program. Drama-theater group, choral group, marching band, student-run newspaper, radio station. Social organizations: 70 open to all; national fraternities, national sororities, local fraternities, local sororities; 5% of eligible men and 5% of eligible women are members. Major annual events: homecoming, Lyceum Series. Student services: health clinic, personal-psychological counseling, women's center. Campus security: 24-hour emergency response devices and patrols. 1,664 college housing spaces available; all were occupied in 2003-04. Freshmen given priority for college housing. Options: coed, men-only, women-only housing available. O'Kelly Library with 197,765 books, 196,000 microform titles, 1,010 serials, 2,198 audiovisual materials, an OPAC, and a Web page.

500 computers available on campus for general student use. A campuswide network can be accessed from student residence rooms and from off campus. Staffed computer lab on campus.
Community Environment: See Wake Forest University.

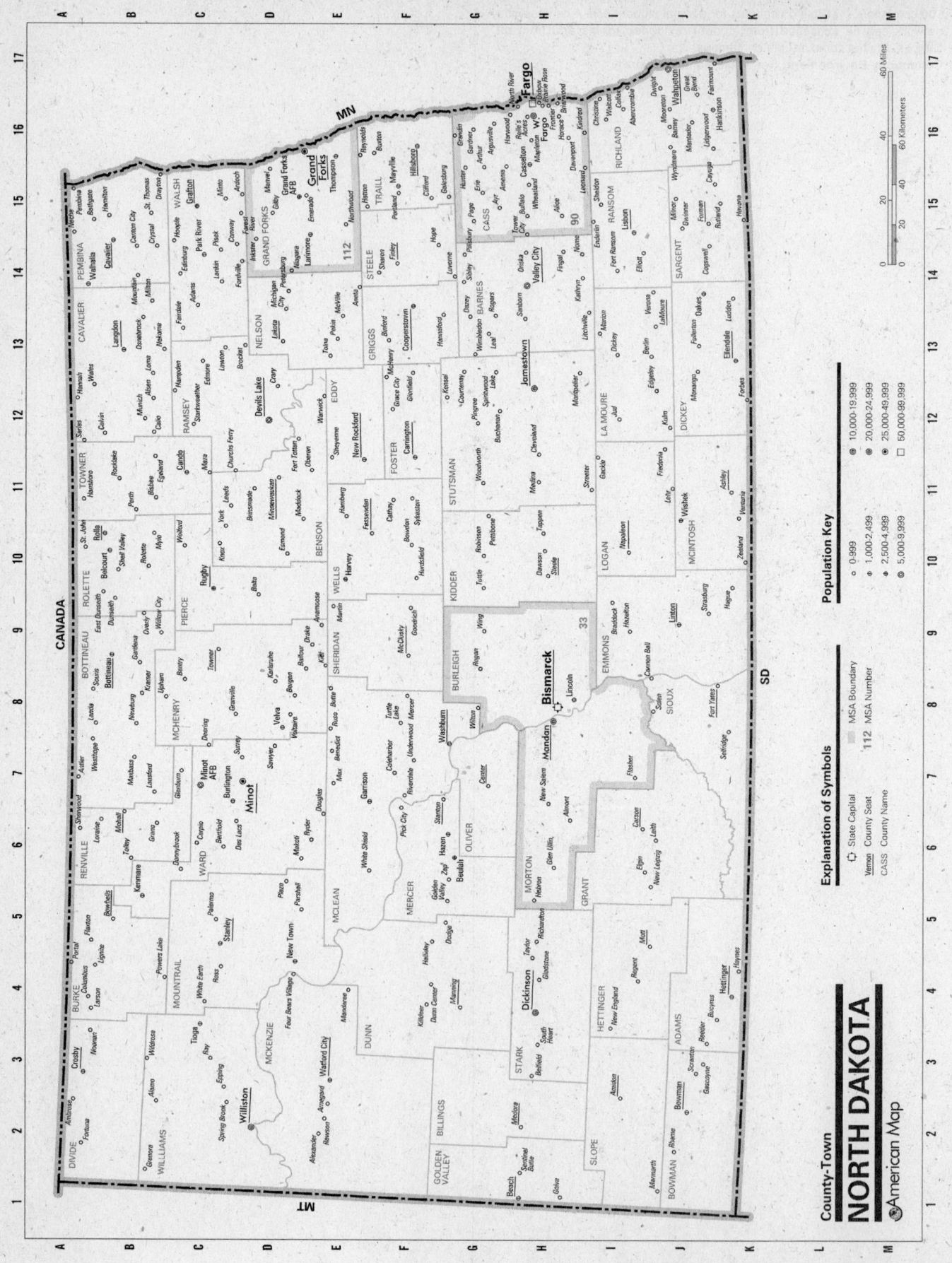

NORTH DAKOTA

County-Town

●American Map

Explanation of Symbols

⌂ State Capital

Vernon County Seat

CASS County Name

▬ MSA Boundary

112 MSA Number

Population Key

∘ 0-999

⌖ 1,000-2,499

⬤ 2,500-4,999

◉ 5,000-9,999

⊚ 10,000-19,999

⊛ 20,000-24,999

◍ 25,000-49,999

□ 50,000-99,999

■ **AAKERS BUSINESS COLLEGE** *H-16*
4012 19th Ave., SW
Fargo, ND 58103
Tel: (701)277-3889
Free: 800-817-0009
Fax: (701)277-5604
E-mail: blargent@aakers-college.com
Web Site: http://www.aakers-college.com/
Description: Proprietary, primarily 2-year, coed. Awards diplomas, transfer associate, terminal associate, and bachelor's degrees. Founded 1902. Total enrollment: 577. Student-undergrad faculty ratio is 13:1. Full-time: 320 students, 79% women, 21% men. Part-time: 257 students, 79% women, 21% men. 24% from out-of-state, 1% Native American, 1% Hispanic, 0.2% black, 1% Asian American or Pacific Islander.
Entrance Requirements: Required: high school transcript. Entrance: minimally difficult. Application deadlines: 10/3, 10/3 for nonresidents, 4/1 for early decision.
Costs Per Year: Application fee: $60. Tuition: $2535 full-time, $845 per course part-time.
Collegiate Environment: Student services: student support group, student senate.

■ **BISMARCK STATE COLLEGE** *H-8*
PO Box 5587
Bismarck, ND 58506-5587
Tel: (701)224-5400
Free: 800-445-5073
Admissions: (701)224-5426
Fax: (701)224-5643
Web Site: http://www.bismarckstate.edu/
Description: State-supported, 2-year, coed. Part of North Dakota University System. Awards certificates, diplomas, transfer associate, and terminal associate degrees. Founded 1939. Setting: 100-acre suburban campus. Total enrollment: 3,541. 1,050 applied, 100% were admitted. Full-time: 2,329 students, 44% women, 56% men. Part-time: 1,212 students, 54% women, 46% men. Students come from 18 states and territories, 11 other countries, 8% from out-of-state, 3% Native American, 1% Hispanic, 1% black, 0.4% Asian American or Pacific Islander, 0.3% international, 32% 25 or older, 8% live on campus, 11% transferred in. Core. Calendar: semesters. Academic remediation for entering students, services for LD students, advanced placement, distance learning, summer session for credit, part-time degree program, adult/continuing education programs, co-op programs. ROTC: Army (c), Air Force (c).
Entrance Requirements: Open admission. Options: Peterson's Universal Application, Common Application, electronic application. Required: high school transcript, SAT or ACT. Entrance: noncompetitive. Application deadline: Rolling. Notification: continuous.
Costs Per Year: Application fee: $35. State resident tuition: $3356 full-time, $92.89 per credit hour part-time. Nonresident tuition: $8009 full-time, $248.02 per credit hour part-time. Mandatory fees: $500 full-time, $22.40 per credit hour part-time. College room and board: $4288.
Collegiate Environment: Drama-theater group, choral group, student-run newspaper. Social organizations: 14 open to all. Most popular organizations: Phi Theta Kappa, Drama Club, Art Club, Anime Club. Major annual events: Fall Fantasy Week, Snow Fest Week. Campus security: 24-hour emergency response devices and patrols, controlled dormitory access. 212 college housing spaces available. No special consideration for freshman housing applicants. Options: men-only, women-only housing available. Bismarck State College Library with 69,142 books, 1,458 microform titles, 374 serials, 6,518 audiovisual materials, an OPAC, and a Web page. 420 computers available on campus for general student use. A campuswide network can be accessed from student residence rooms and from off campus. Staffed computer lab on campus.
Community Environment: Bismarck, North Dakota's capital city, is the second largest city with a population of 50,000. Because of its central location, modern shopping centers and Civic Center, the city hosts many state and national conventions. Bismarck is considered the cultural, business and educational center of western and central North Dakota. It is also the medical center for the region with two modern medical centers and clinics. Bismarck has a large city library, a State Historical Library, and numerous libraries related to state and federal offices; a city orchestra, civic chorus, and amateur drama club; and many churches representing various denominations. The city has many parks and recreation areas, a city zoo, three golf courses, and clubs for a variety of recreational activities. The Missouri River and nearby Lake Sakakawea offer boating, fishing and other water sports. Bismarck has transportation service from several major air carriers, commuter airlines, and bus lines. Interstate 94 and U.S. Highway 83 meet in Bismarck. The city has a pleasant summer climate and moderate to severe winters.

■ **CANKDESKA CIKANA COMMUNITY COLLEGE**
PO Box 269
Fort Totten, ND 58335-0269
Tel: (701)766-4415
Admissions: (701)766-1342
Fax: (701)766-4077
Web Site: http://www.littlehoop.edu/
Description: Federally supported, 2-year, coed. Awards certificates, transfer associate, and terminal associate degrees. Founded 1974. Setting: 1-acre small town campus. Total enrollment: 168. Students come from 5 states and territories, 30% 25 or older. Core. Calendar: semesters. Academic remediation for entering students, services for LD students, self-designed majors, summer session for credit, part-time degree program, adult/continuing education programs, co-op programs. Off campus study at members of the American Indian Higher Education Consortium.
Entrance Requirements: Open admission. Options: early admission, deferred admission. Placement: TABE required. Entrance: noncompetitive. Application deadline: 8/22. Notification: continuous.
Collegiate Environment: Drama-theater group. Student services: personal-psychological counseling. Campus security: late night transport-escort service. College housing not available. 7,500 books and 48 serials. 50 computers available on campus for general student use. Staffed computer lab on campus.

■ **DICKINSON STATE UNIVERSITY** *H-4*
291 Campus Dr.
Dickinson, ND 58601-4896
Tel: (701)483-2507
Free: 800-279-4295
Admissions: (701)483-2331
Fax: (701)483-2006

E-mail: dsuhawk@eagle.dsu.nodak.edu

Web Site: http://www.dsu.nodak.edu/

Description: State-supported, 4-year, coed. Part of North Dakota University System. Awards associate and bachelor's degrees. Founded 1918. Setting: 100-acre small town campus. Endowment: $4.8 million. Educational spending for 2005 fiscal year: $3586 per student. Total enrollment: 2,516. Student-undergrad faculty ratio is 19:1. 555 applied, 99% were admitted. 4% from top 10% of their high school class, 17% from top quarter, 50% from top half. Full-time: 1,755 students, 55% women, 45% men. Part-time: 761 students, 63% women, 37% men. Students come from 22 states and territories, 23 other countries, 29% from out-of-state, 2% Native American, 2% Hispanic, 2% black, 1% Asian American or Pacific Islander, 7% international, 22% 25 or older, 30% live on campus, 9% transferred in. Retention: 56% of full-time freshmen returned the following year. Academic areas with the most degrees conferred: business/marketing; education; liberal arts/general studies. Core. Calendar: semesters. Academic remediation for entering students, services for LD students, advanced placement, accelerated degree program, self-designed majors, honors program, independent study, distance learning, double major, summer session for credit, part-time degree program, external degree program, adult/continuing education programs, co-op programs and internships. Off campus study. Study abroad program.

Entrance Requirements: Open admission for all United States students. Options: electronic application, early admission, deferred admission. Required: high school transcript, medical history, proof of measles-rubella shot, SAT or ACT. Entrance: minimally difficult. Application deadline: Rolling. Notification: continuous.

Costs Per Year: Application fee: $35. State resident tuition: $4154 full-time. Nonresident tuition: $9712 full-time. Mandatory fees: $825 full-time. Full-time tuition and fees vary according to location, program, and reciprocity agreements. College room and board: $3694. Room and board charges vary according to board plan.

Collegiate Environment: Orientation program. Drama-theater group, choral group, marching band, student-run newspaper. Social organizations: 50 open to all; 5% of women are members. Most popular organizations: Rodeo Club, Blue Hawk Brigade, chorale, Business Club, Navigators. Major annual events: Homecoming Week, Sure Beats Winter Week, Back to School Week. Student services: health clinic. Campus security: late night transport-escort service. 592 college housing spaces available; 577 were occupied in 2003-04. Freshmen guaranteed college housing. On-campus residence required through sophomore year. Option: coed housing available. Stoxen Library with 105,713 books, 8,924 microform titles, 823 serials, 5,411 audiovisual materials, an OPAC, and a Web page. Operations spending for 2004 fiscal year: $446,251. 216 computers available on campus for general student use. A campuswide network can be accessed from student residence rooms and from off campus. Staffed computer lab on campus.

Community Environment: Dickinson, population 16,500, is approximately 95 miles from the state capital of Bismarck and is a shipping point for lignite coal, oil, grain, dairy products, meat products, and livestock. Nearby Patterson Lake and Recreational Area and Theodore Roosevelt National Park provide ample opportunities for outdoor sports and activities.

■ **FORT BERTHOLD COMMUNITY COLLEGE** *D-4*

PO Box 490

New Town, ND 58763-0490

Tel: (701)627-4738

Admissions: (701)627-3665

Fax: (701)627-3609

Web Site: http://www.fbcc.bia.edu/

Description: Independent, 2-year, coed. Awards certificates, transfer associate, and terminal associate degrees. Founded 1973. Setting: small town campus. Total enrollment: 416. 4% from top 10% of their high school class, 20% from top quarter, 50% from top half. 40% 25 or older. Core. Calendar: semesters. Academic remediation for entering students, summer session for credit, part-time degree program, co-op programs and internships. Off campus study at University of North Dakota, Minot State University.

Entrance Requirements: Open admission except for nursing program. Options: Common Application, deferred admission. Entrance: noncompetitive. Application deadline: Rolling.

Costs Per Year: Application fee: $10. Tuition: $2640 full-time, $110 per credit part-time. Mandatory fees: $600 full-time, $25 per term part-time.

Collegiate Environment: Drama-theater group, student-run newspaper. Student services: legal services, health clinic, personal-psychological counseling. College housing not available. 10,000 books and 300 serials. 100 computers available on campus for general student use.

■ **JAMESTOWN COLLEGE** *H-12*

6000 College Ln.

Jamestown, ND 58405

Tel: (701)252-3467

Free: 800-336-2554

Fax: (701)253-4318

E-mail: admissions@jc.edu

Web Site: http://www.jc.edu/

Description: Independent Presbyterian, 4-year, coed. Awards bachelor's degrees. Founded 1883. Setting: 107-acre small town campus. Endowment: $19.4 million. Educational spending for 2005 fiscal year: $4800 per student. Total enrollment: 1,026. Student-undergrad faculty ratio is 15:1. 1,026 applied, 98% were admitted. 16% from top 10% of their high school class, 40% from top quarter, 69% from top half. Full-time: 960 students, 55% women, 45% men. Part-time: 66 students, 68% women, 32% men. Students come from 30 states and territories, 16 other countries, 42% from out-of-state, 1% Native American, 1% Hispanic, 1% black, 1% Asian American or Pacific Islander, 4% international, 10% 25 or older, 61% live on campus, 6% transferred in. Retention: 68% of full-time freshmen returned the following year. Academic areas with the most degrees conferred: business/marketing; education; health professions and related sciences. Core. Calendar: semesters. Services for LD students, advanced placement, self-designed majors, honors program, independent study, double major, summer session for credit, part-time degree program, co-op programs and internships. Off campus study. Study abroad program.

Entrance Requirements: Options: Peterson's Universal Application, Common Application, electronic application, deferred admission, international baccalaureate accepted. Required: high school transcript. Recommended: minimum 2.5 high school GPA, minimum ACT score of 18 or minimum SAT score of 850, SAT or ACT. Required for some: recommendations, minimum ACT score of 18 or minimum SAT score of 850. Entrance: minimally difficult. Application deadline: Rolling.

Costs Per Year: Application fee: $20. Comprehensive fee: $14,890 includes full-time tuition ($10,550) and college room and board ($4340). College room only: $1850. Part-time tuition: $295 per credit.

Collegiate Environment: Orientation program. Drama-theater group, choral group, student-run newspaper. Social organizations: 34 open to all. Most popular organizations: Jimmie Ambassadors, Student Activities Committee, Nursing Students' Association, Students of Service, Student Senate. Major annual events: homecoming, Family Weekend, Jimmie Jive Week. Student services: personal-psychological counseling. Campus security: late night transport-escort service, controlled dormitory access. 714 college housing spaces available; 592 were occupied in 2003-04. Freshmen guaranteed college housing. On-campus residence required through sophomore year. Option: coed housing available. Raugust Library with 121,382 books, 9,380 microform titles, 630 serials, 6,137 audiovisual materials, an OPAC, and a Web page. Operations spending for 2004 fiscal year: $309,669. 440 computers available on campus for general student use. A campuswide network can be accessed from student residence rooms and from off campus. Staffed computer lab on campus.

Community Environment: In the valley of the James River, Jamestown (population 16,800) was originally the site of Fort Seward, which was established in 1872. Jamestown is located in southeastern North Dakota and is provided transportation by bus lines, air, and major highways. The community has churches, one hospital, a library, two radio stations, and two shopping centers. Parks in the general area provide outdoor recreation facilities. There are several active civic, fraternal, and veteran's organizations in Jamestown.

■ **LAKE REGION STATE COLLEGE** *D-12*

1801 College Dr. North

Devils Lake, ND 58301-1598

Tel: (701)662-1600

Free: 800-443-1313

Admissions: (701)662-1513

Fax: (701)662-1570

E-mail: laurel.goulding@lrsc.nodak.edu

Web Site: http://www.lrsc.nodak.edu/

Description: State-supported, 2-year, coed. Part of North Dakota University System. Awards certificates, diplomas, transfer associate, and terminal associate degrees. Founded 1941. Setting: 120-acre small town campus. Endowment: $2.2 million. Total enrollment: 1,471. Student-undergrad faculty ratio is 15:1. 164 applied, 100% were admitted. Full-time: 409 students, 59% women, 41% men. Part-time: 1,062 students, 57% women, 43% men.

Students come from 28 states and territories, 12 other countries, 10% from out-of-state, 8% Native American, 1% Hispanic, 2% black, 0.5% Asian American or Pacific Islander, 2% international, 21% 25 or older, 30% live on campus, 4% transferred in. Core. Calendar: semesters. Academic remediation for entering students, ESL program, freshman honors college, honors program, distance learning, double major, summer session for credit, part-time degree program, adult/continuing education programs, co-op programs and internships.

Entrance Requirements: Open admission. Options: Peterson's Universal Application, electronic application. Required: high school transcript, immunizations, SAT or ACT, COMPASS. Entrance: noncompetitive. Application deadline: Rolling. Notification: continuous.

Costs Per Year: Application fee: $35. State resident tuition: $2550 full-time, $133 per credit part-time. Nonresident tuition: $2550 full-time, $133 per credit part-time. Mandatory fees: $783 full-time. College room and board: $3790.

Collegiate Environment: Orientation program. Drama-theater group. Social organizations: 12 open to all. Most popular organizations: DECA, drama, SOTA (Students Other than Average), Student Senate, Computer Club. Major annual events: Orientation week, Snow Daze, Spring Blast. Student services: personal-psychological counseling. Campus security: 24-hour emergency response devices, controlled dormitory access. 200 college housing spaces available; 22 were occupied in 2003-04. No special consideration for freshman housing applicants. Options: men-only, women-only housing available. Paul Hoghaug Library plus 1 other with 42,000 books, 200 serials, 2,000 audiovisual materials, and an OPAC. Operations spending for 2004 fiscal year: $97,585. 275 computers available on campus for general student use. Computer purchase/lease plans available. A campuswide network can be accessed from student residence rooms and from off campus. Staffed computer lab on campus.

Community Environment: A center of scenic, historical and recreational attractions, Devils Lake (population 7,782) was named for the largest natural body of water in the state. There are scenic drives, a golf course, a skiway, and camping and recreation facilities at nearby Shelvers Grove, Roosevelt Park, and Lakewood Park. The area is noted for its abundance of ducks and geese. The city has churches of various denominations, hospitals and clinics, a library, six motels, and various civic, fraternal and veteran's organizations. Local recreational facilities include a theatre, baseball, golf, football, bowling alley, swimming pools, hockey, skating, curling, skiing, parks, and playgrounds. Part-time employment is available.

■ **MAYVILLE STATE UNIVERSITY** *F-15*
330 3rd St., NE
Mayville, ND 58257-1299
Tel: (701)786-2301
Free: 800-437-4104
Admissions: (701)788-5222
Fax: (701)786-4748
E-mail: c_heckman@mayvillestate.edu
Web Site: http://www.mayvillestate.edu/
Description: State-supported, 4-year, coed. Part of North Dakota University System. Awards associate and bachelor's degrees. Founded 1889. Setting: 60-acre rural campus. Endowment: $1.7 million. Educational spending for 2005 fiscal year: $4452 per student. Total enrollment: 912. Student-undergrad faculty ratio is 15:1. 307 applied, 68% were admitted. 31% from top quarter of their high school class, 57% from top half. Full-time: 625 students, 49% women, 51% men. Part-time: 287 students, 66% women, 34% men. Students come from 20 states and territories, 16 other countries, 28% from out-of-state, 3% Native American, 2% Hispanic, 3% black, 0.4% Asian American or Pacific Islander, 6% international, 5% 25 or older, 43% live on campus, 13% transferred in. Retention: 58% of full-time freshmen returned the following year. Academic areas with the most degrees conferred: education; business/marketing; computer and information sciences. Core. Calendar: semesters. Academic remediation for entering students, services for LD students, advanced placement, accelerated degree program, self-designed majors, distance learning, double major, summer session for credit, part-time degree program, adult/continuing education programs, co-op programs and internships. ROTC: Army (c), Air Force.

Entrance Requirements: Open admission. Options: Peterson's Universal Application, electronic application, deferred admission. Required: high school transcript, SAT or ACT. Recommended: interview. Entrance: noncompetitive. Application deadlines: Rolling, Rolling for nonresidents. Notification: 1/1, 1/1 for nonresidents.

Costs Per Year: Application fee: $35. State resident tuition: $3300 full-time, $137.50 per credit hour part-time. Nonresident tuition: $8811 full-time,

$367.14 per hour part-time. Mandatory fees: $1643 full-time, $68.45 per credit hour part-time. Full-time tuition and fees vary according to course load and reciprocity agreements. Part-time tuition and fees vary according to course load and reciprocity agreements. College room and board: $3724. College room only: $1524. Room and board charges vary according to board plan and housing facility.

Collegiate Environment: Orientation program. Drama-theater group, choral group, student-run newspaper. Social organizations: 17 open to all. Most popular organizations: Student Activities Council, Student Education Association, Health and Physical Education Club, Campus Crusade, Student Ambassadors. Major annual events: Homecoming, Spring Fling. Student services: health clinic, personal-psychological counseling. Campus security: controlled dormitory access. 400 college housing spaces available; 288 were occupied in 2003-04. Freshmen guaranteed college housing. On-campus residence required through sophomore year. Options: coed, men-only, women-only housing available. Byrnes-Quanbeck Library plus 1 other with 71,595 books, 12,530 microform titles, 599 serials, 20,679 audiovisual materials, and an OPAC. Operations spending for 2004 fiscal year: $226,691.

Community Environment: Mayville and its twin community, Portland, have a combined population of 4,000 in this rural farming area between Grand Forks and Fargo, North Dakota. The local community offers a city library, many churches, a modern hospital, medical clinic, and dental and optometry offices. A modern business district is also present with air transportation available at airports in Grand Forks and Fargo. A small airport is also located in the community. Housing off campus is abundant, with many choices of apartments, duplexes, and single-family dwellings. Recreational facilities are available for camping, hiking, fishing, golf, skiing, swimming, and horseshoes; a theatre and parks are also available.

■ **MEDCENTER ONE COLLEGE OF NURSING** *H-8*
512 North 7th St.
Bismarck, ND 58501-4494
Tel: (701)323-6271
E-mail: msmith@mohs.org
Web Site: http://medcenterone.com/college/nursing.htm
Description: Independent, upper-level, coed. Administratively affiliated with Medcenter One Health Systems. Awards bachelor's degrees. Founded 1988. Setting: 15-acre small town campus. Endowment: $119,113. Educational spending for 2005 fiscal year: $19,679 per student. Total enrollment: 88. 66 applied, 77% were admitted. Full-time: 86 students, 94% women, 6% men. Part-time: 2 students, 100% women. Students come from 6 states and territories, 6% from out-of-state, 6% Native American, 1% Hispanic, 1% Asian American or Pacific Islander, 0% international, 34% 25 or older, 11% live on campus, 52% transferred in. Retention: 81% of full-time entering class returned the following year. Core. Calendar: semesters. Honors program, independent study, internships.

Costs Per Year: Application fee: $40. Tuition: $8400 full-time, $350 per credit part-time. Mandatory fees: $751 full-time, $5.25 per credit part-time, $499 per term part-time. Part-time tuition and fees vary according to course load. College room only: $1800.

Collegiate Environment: Orientation program. Student-run newspaper. Social organizations: 2 open to all. Most popular organizations: Student Body Organization, Student Nurses Association. Major annual events: Christmas Party, Annual Picnic, Awards Banquet. Student services: health clinic, personal-psychological counseling. Campus security: late night transport-escort service. 29 college housing spaces available; 10 were occupied in 2003-04. Option: coed housing available. Q & R/Medcenter One Health Sciences Library plus 1 other with 28,470 books, 56 microform titles, 331 serials, 1,467 audiovisual materials, an OPAC, and a Web page. Operations spending for 2004 fiscal year: $139,026. 17 computers available on campus for general student use.

■ **MINOT STATE UNIVERSITY** *D-7*
500 University Ave. West
Minot, ND 58707-0002
Tel: (701)858-3000
Free: 800-777-0750
Admissions: (701)858-3822
Fax: (701)839-6933
E-mail: stephanie.witwer@minotstateu.edu
Web Site: http://www.minotstateu.edu/
Description: State-supported, comprehensive, coed. Part of North Dakota University System. Awards associate, bachelor's, and master's degrees and

post-master's certificates. Founded 1913. Setting: 103-acre small town campus. Endowment: $2.5 million. Research spending for 2004 fiscal year: $1.1 million. Total enrollment: 3,797. Faculty: 273 (172 full-time, 101 part-time). Student-undergrad faculty ratio is 15:1. 645 applied, 85% were admitted. Full-time: 2,473 students, 63% women, 37% men. Part-time: 1,074 students, 63% women, 37% men. Students come from 46 states and territories, 21 other countries, 11% from out-of-state, 3% Native American, 2% Hispanic, 2% black, 1% Asian American or Pacific Islander, 6% international, 22% 25 or older, 13% live on campus, 14% transferred in. Academic areas with the most degrees conferred: business/marketing; education; health professions and related sciences. Core. Calendar: semesters. Academic remediation for entering students, services for LD students, advanced placement, accelerated degree program, self-designed majors, honors program, independent study, distance learning, double major, summer session for credit, part-time degree program, adult/continuing education programs, co-op programs and internships, graduate courses open to undergrads. Study abroad program.

Entrance Requirements: Options: electronic application, deferred admission. Required: high school transcript, SAT or ACT. Required for some: minimum 2.75 high school GPA. Entrance: minimally difficult. Application deadline: Rolling. Notification: continuous.

Costs Per Year: Application fee: $35. State resident tuition: $3460 full-time, $144.17 per credit hour part-time. Nonresident tuition: $9238 full-time, $384.93 per credit hour part-time. Mandatory fees: $632 full-time. Full-time tuition and fees vary according to class time, course load, location, program, and reciprocity agreements. Part-time tuition varies according to class time, location, program, and reciprocity agreements. College room and board: $4460. College room only: $2240. Room and board charges vary according to board plan and housing facility.

Collegiate Environment: Orientation program. Drama-theater group, choral group, student-run newspaper, radio station. Social organizations: 60 open to all. Most popular organizations: Student ND Education Association, Minot State Club of Physical Education, Inter-Varsity Christian Fellowship, Residence Hall Association, National Student Speech and Hearing Association. Major annual events: Homecoming Week, Welcome Week, Final Frenzy Week. Student services: health clinic, personal-psychological counseling, women's center. Campus security: controlled dormitory access, patrols by trained security personnel. 643 college housing spaces available; 506 were occupied in 2003-04. Freshmen guaranteed college housing. Options: coed, men-only, women-only housing available. Gordon B. Olson Library with 420,971 books, 709,857 microform titles, 752 serials, 11,073 audiovisual materials, an OPAC, and a Web page. Operations spending for 2004 fiscal year: $1.2 million. 460 computers available on campus for general student use. A campuswide network can be accessed from student residence rooms and from off campus. Staffed computer lab on campus.

Community Environment: Minot, population 35,000, began as a tent town of the Great Northern Railroad and now contains the electronic freight classification Gavin Yard. It grew so rapidly that it was called the"Magic City." Today it is a trade center for an area including part of Canada and Montana, as well as northern North Dakota. The town lies within the eastern boundaries of oil-rich Williston Basin and is surrounded by a number of lignite strip mines. The area has good highways, rail, bus, and air lines. Minot has many churches and active civic and fraternal organizations. Part-time job opportunities are available for students.

■ **MINOT STATE UNIVERSITY-BOTTINEAU CAMPUS** *B-9*
105 Simrall Blvd.
Bottineau, ND 58318-1198
Tel: (701)228-2277
Free: 800-542-6866
Admissions: (701)228-5451
Fax: (701)228-5499
E-mail: bergpla@misu.nodak.edu
Web Site: http://www.misu-b.nodak.edu/
Description: State-supported, 2-year, coed. Part of North Dakota University System. Awards certificates, diplomas, transfer associate, and terminal associate degrees. Founded 1906. Setting: 35-acre rural campus. Endowment: $1 million. Total enrollment: 620. 298 applied, 100% were admitted. Full-time: 387 students, 41% women, 59% men. Part-time: 233 students, 59% women, 41% men. Students come from 26 states and territories, 1 other country, 13% from out-of-state, 5% Native American, 1% Hispanic, 2% black, 1% Asian American or Pacific Islander, 6% international, 14% 25 or older, 45% live on campus, 7% transferred in. Calendar: semesters. Academic remediation for entering students, services for LD students, distance learn-

ing, double major, summer session for credit, part-time degree program, co-op programs and internships. Off campus study at Minot State University, Minot Air Force Base.

Entrance Requirements: Open admission. Options: Common Application, electronic application, early admission, deferred admission. Required: high school transcript. Placement: SAT or ACT recommended. Entrance: noncompetitive. Application deadline: Rolling.

Collegiate Environment: Orientation program. Drama-theater group, choral group. Most popular organizations: Student Senate, Wildlife Club, Paul Bunyan Club, Horticulture Club, DECA. Major annual events: Smokey's Week, Luau Week. Student services: personal-psychological counseling. Campus security: controlled dormitory access. 293 college housing spaces available; 180 were occupied in 2003-04. Freshmen guaranteed college housing. On-campus residence required through sophomore year. Options: coed, men-only, women-only housing available. Minot State University-Bottineau Library plus 1 other with 45,000 books, 5,000 microform titles, 250 serials, 800 audiovisual materials, an OPAC, and a Web page. 60 computers available on campus for general student use. A campuswide network can be accessed from student residence rooms and from off campus. Staffed computer lab on campus.

■ **NORTH DAKOTA STATE COLLEGE OF SCIENCE** *J-17*
800 North Sixth St.
Wahpeton, ND 58076
Tel: (701)671-2401
Free: 800-342-4325
Admissions: (701)671-2189
Fax: (701)671-2332
Web Site: http://www.ndscs.nodak.edu/
Description: State-supported, 2-year, coed. Part of North Dakota University System. Awards certificates, diplomas, transfer associate, and terminal associate degrees. Founded 1903. Setting: 125-acre rural campus. Endowment: $4000. Educational spending for 2005 fiscal year: $3757 per student. Total enrollment: 2,468. Student-undergrad faculty ratio is 15:1. Full-time: 1,954 students, 33% women, 67% men. Part-time: 514 students, 54% women, 46% men. Students come from 54 states and territories, 11 other countries, 27% from out-of-state, 2% Native American, 1% Hispanic, 2% black, 0.4% Asian American or Pacific Islander, 1% international, 18% 25 or older, 56% live on campus, 9% transferred in. Core. Calendar: semesters. Academic remediation for entering students, ESL program, services for LD students, self-designed majors, independent study, distance learning, double major, summer session for credit, part-time degree program, adult/continuing education programs, co-op programs and internships.

Entrance Requirements: Open admission. Options: Common Application, electronic application, early admission. Required: high school transcript. Entrance: noncompetitive. Application deadline: Rolling. Notification: continuous.

Costs Per Year: Application fee: $35. State resident tuition: $3757 full-time. Nonresident tuition: $9197 full-time. College room and board: $4638.

Collegiate Environment: Orientation program. Drama-theater group, choral group, marching band. Social organizations: 3 open to all. Most popular organizations: Student Health Advisory Club, Drama Club, Inter-Varsity Christian Fellowship, Cultural Diversity, Habitat for Humanity. Major annual events: Homecoming, Agawasie Day. Student services: legal services, health clinic, personal-psychological counseling. Campus security: 24-hour emergency response devices and patrols, student patrols, late night transport-escort service, controlled dormitory access. 3,600 college housing spaces available; 1,052 were occupied in 2003-04. On-campus residence required in freshman year. Options: coed, men-only, women-only housing available. Mildred Johnson Library with 124,508 books, 61,787 microform titles, 852 serials, 4,178 audiovisual materials, an OPAC, and a Web page. Operations spending for 2004 fiscal year: $183,748. 450 computers available on campus for general student use. Computer purchase/lease plans available. A campuswide network can be accessed from student residence rooms and from off campus. Staffed computer lab on campus.

Community Environment: Wahpeton (population 9,300) is located at the origin of the Red River in southeastern North Dakota. The city is served by a bus line, and U.S. Highway 75, Interstates 29 and 94 and State Highways 13 & 81.

■ **NORTH DAKOTA STATE UNIVERSITY** *H-16*
1301 North University Ave.
Fargo, ND 58105
Tel: (701)231-8011

Free: 800-488-NDSU
Admissions: (701)231-8643
Fax: (701)231-8802
E-mail: ndsu.admission@ndsu.edu
Web Site: http://www.ndsu.edu/

Description: State-supported, university, coed. Part of North Dakota University System. Awards bachelor's, master's, doctoral, and first professional degrees and post-master's certificates. Founded 1890. Setting: 2,100-acre urban campus. Endowment: $369,573. Educational spending for 2005 fiscal year: $4998 per student. Total enrollment: 12,099. Faculty: 616 (525 full-time, 91 part-time). Student-undergrad faculty ratio is 19:1. 4,007 applied, 84% were admitted. 18% from top 10% of their high school class, 43% from top quarter, 75% from top half. 3 National Merit Scholars, 100 valedictorians. Full-time: 9,410 students, 45% women, 55% men. Part-time: 1,086 students, 49% women, 51% men. Students come from 44 states and territories, 67 other countries, 1% Native American, 1% Hispanic, 1% black, 1% Asian American or Pacific Islander, 1% international, 8% 25 or older, 29% live on campus, 7% transferred in. Retention: 77% of full-time freshmen returned the following year. Academic areas with the most degrees conferred: engineering; business/marketing; health professions and related sciences. Core. Calendar: semesters. Academic remediation for entering students, ESL program, services for LD students, advanced placement, self-designed majors, honors program, independent study, distance learning, double major, summer session for credit, part-time degree program, co-op programs and internships, graduate courses open to undergrads. Off campus study at members of the Tri-College University-Concordia College, Moorhead, MN, Minnesota State University Moorhead. Study abroad program. ROTC: Army, Air Force.

Entrance Requirements: Options: electronic application, international baccalaureate accepted. Required: high school transcript, minimum 2.5 high school GPA, SAT or ACT. Entrance: moderately difficult. Application deadline: 8/15. Notification: continuous.

Costs Per Year: Application fee: $35. One-time mandatory fee: $45. Area resident tuition: $4360 full-time, $181.67 per credit part-time. Nonresident tuition: $11,641 full-time, $485.04 per credit part-time. Mandatory fees: $904 full-time, $37.65 per credit part-time. Full-time tuition and fees vary according to reciprocity agreements. Part-time tuition and fees vary according to course load and reciprocity agreements. College room and board: $5130. College room only: $2070. Room and board charges vary according to board plan and housing facility.

Collegiate Environment: Orientation program. Drama-theater group, choral group, marching band, student-run newspaper, radio station. Social organizations: 218 open to all; national fraternities, national sororities; 4% of eligible men and 2% of eligible women are members. Most popular organizations: Saddle and Sirloin, Habitat for Humanity, Residence Hall Association, Juggling Club. Major annual events: Homecoming, International Students Week, Spring Blast. Student services: health clinic, personal-psychological counseling. Campus security: 24-hour emergency response devices and patrols, student patrols, late night transport-escort service, controlled dormitory access. College housing designed to accommodate 2,870 students; 3,052 undergraduates lived in college housing during 2003-04. Freshmen guaranteed college housing. On-campus residence required in freshman year. Options: coed, men-only, women-only housing available. North Dakota State University Library plus 3 others with 303,274 books, 168,008 microform titles, 4,497 serials, 2,757 audiovisual materials, an OPAC, and a Web page. Operations spending for 2004 fiscal year: $3.5 million. 500 computers available on campus for general student use. A campuswide network can be accessed from student residence rooms and from off campus. Staffed computer lab on campus.

Community Environment: North Dakota's largest city at 90,599, Fargo is the largest distribution point between Minneapolis and Spokane. Fargo-Moorhead as seen designated as one of the top ten All-American cities for 2000. The metropolitan area has over a hundred manufacturing plants producing agricultural machinery, feed, fertilizers, foodstuffs, and dairy products. In addition, the community contains the largest medical complex between Minneapolis and the West Coast. Recreation facilities in the city's 765-acre park system include three golf courses, a winter sports building, and four swimming pools. There are part-time employment opportunities for students.

■ **SITTING BULL COLLEGE** *K-8*
1341 92nd St.
Fort Yates, ND 58538-9701
Tel: (701)854-3861

Admissions: (701)854-3864
Fax: (701)854-3403
E-mail: melodys@sbcl.edu
Web Site: http://www.sittingbull.edu/

Description: Independent, 2-year, coed. Awards certificates, transfer associate, and terminal associate degrees. Founded 1973. Setting: rural campus. Endowment: $541,000. Educational spending for 2005 fiscal year: $2001 per student. Total enrollment: 214. 63 applied, 100% were admitted. 20% from top 10% of their high school class, 30% from top quarter, 50% from top half. 2 class presidents, 2 valedictorians, 10 student government officers. Students come from 2 states and territories, 35% 25 or older. Core. Calendar: semesters. Academic remediation for entering students, part-time degree program, adult/continuing education programs. Off campus study at members of the American Indian Higher Education Consortium.

Entrance Requirements: Open admission. Option: early admission. Required: high school transcript, medical questionnaire. Placement: TABE required. Entrance: noncompetitive. Application deadline: 9/6. Notification: continuous.

Collegiate Environment: Student-run newspaper. Most popular organizations: student government, Future Teachers, Ikce Oyate Culture Club, Phi Beta Lambda, Ski Club. Major annual events: homecoming, Thanksgiving Dinner, Student Awards Night. Student services: personal-psychological counseling. College housing not available. Sitting Bull College Library with 10,000 books, 130 serials, and an OPAC. 16 computers available on campus for general student use. Staffed computer lab on campus.

■ **TRINITY BIBLE COLLEGE** *K-13*
50 South 6th Ave.
Ellendale, ND 58436-7150
Tel: (701)349-3621; 888-TBC-2DAY
Fax: (701)349-5443
Web Site: http://www.trinitybiblecollege.edu/

Description: Independent Assemblies of God, 4-year, coed. Awards associate and bachelor's degrees. Founded 1948. Setting: 28-acre rural campus. Endowment: $539,057. Educational spending for 2005 fiscal year: $2793 per student. Total enrollment: 307. 234 applied, 50% were admitted. Full-time: 272 students, 53% women, 47% men. Part-time: 35 students, 66% women, 34% men. Students come from 29 states and territories, 77% from out-of-state, 3% Native American, 3% Hispanic, 2% black, 1% Asian American or Pacific Islander, 0% international, 18% 25 or older, 69% live on campus, 7% transferred in. Retention: 81% of full-time freshmen returned the following year. Core. Calendar: semesters. Academic remediation for entering students, advanced placement, accelerated degree program, distance learning, double major, summer session for credit, part-time degree program, internships.

Entrance Requirements: Options: Peterson's Universal Application, Common Application, deferred admission, international baccalaureate accepted. Required: essay, high school transcript, minimum 2.0 high school GPA, 2 recommendations, health form, evidence of Christian conversion, ACT. Required for some: interview, SAT. Entrance: noncompetitive. Application deadline: Rolling. Notification: continuous.

Collegiate Environment: Orientation program. Drama-theater group, choral group, student-run radio station. Social organizations: 30 open to all. Most popular organizations: GAP, Youth Ministry, Inner City Ministry, Fine Arts Club, Children's Ministry. Major annual events: College Days, Spring Missions Convention, Spiritual Emphasis Week. Student services: personal-psychological counseling. Campus security: 24-hour emergency response devices, student patrols, late night transport-escort service. 269 college housing spaces available; 185 were occupied in 2003-04. Freshmen guaranteed college housing. On-campus residence required through junior year. Options: men-only, women-only housing available. Graham Library with 67,868 books, 5,873 microform titles, 227 serials, and 2,258 audiovisual materials. Operations spending for 2004 fiscal year: $91,908. 40 computers available on campus for general student use. Staffed computer lab on campus.

Community Environment: Ellendale is a rural community (population 1,967) just north of the South Dakota border and 62 miles south of Jamestown on U.S. Highway 281.

■ **TURTLE MOUNTAIN COMMUNITY COLLEGE** *B-10*
Box 340
Belcourt, ND 58316-0340
Tel: (701)477-7862
Admissions: (701)477-5605

Fax: (701)477-7807
E-mail: jlafontaine@tm.edu
Web Site: http://www.turtle-mountain.cc.nd.us/
Description: Independent, 2-year, coed. Awards certificates, transfer associate, and terminal associate degrees. Founded 1972. Setting: 10-acre rural campus. Total enrollment: 579. 102 applied, 100% were admitted. Full-time: 378 students, 61% women, 39% men. Part-time: 201 students, 73% women, 27% men. 0% from out-of-state, 75% 25 or older. Core. Calendar: semesters. Academic remediation for entering students, part-time degree program, adult/continuing education programs.
Entrance Requirements: Open admission. Options: early admission, deferred admission. Required: high school transcript, ACT. Entrance: noncompetitive. Application deadline: Rolling.
Collegiate Environment: Most popular organization: student government. Major annual events: College Awareness Week, Student Picnic, Annual Pow-Wow. Student services: personal-psychological counseling. College housing not available. Turtle Mountain Community College Library with 20,500 books, 150 serials, and an OPAC. 147 computers available on campus for general student use. A campuswide network can be accessed from off-campus. Staffed computer lab on campus.

■ **UNITED TRIBES TECHNICAL COLLEGE** *H-8*
3315 University Dr.
Bismarck, ND 58504-7596
Tel: (701)255-3285
E-mail: vgillette@uttc.edu
Web Site: http://www.uttc.edu/
Description: Federally supported, 2-year, coed. Awards certificates, transfer associate, and terminal associate degrees. Founded 1969. Setting: 105-acre small town campus. Total enrollment: 885. Student-undergrad faculty ratio is 8:1. 179 applied, 84% were admitted. Full-time: 635 students, 70% women, 30% men. Part-time: 250 students, 73% women, 27% men. 75% Native American, 0.3% Hispanic, 0.2% black, 1% Asian American or Pacific Islander, 0% international. Calendar: semesters. Academic remediation for entering students, honors program, summer session for credit, part-time degree program, co-op programs and internships.
Entrance Requirements: Open admission. Required: high school transcript. Entrance: noncompetitive. Application deadline: Rolling.
Costs Per Year: Application fee: $0. One-time mandatory fee: $100. Comprehensive fee: $6580 includes full-time tuition ($2800), mandatory fees ($780), and college room and board ($3000). Part-time tuition: $87.50 per credit.
Collegiate Environment: Student-run newspaper. Major annual events: basketball games, Parent Breakfast. Student services: personal-psychological counseling. Campus security: 24-hour emergency response devices and patrols. Options: men-only, women-only housing available. United Tribes Technical College Library plus 1 other with 6,000 books, 86 serials, an OPAC, and a Web page. 210 computers available on campus for general student use. Staffed computer lab on campus.

■ **UNIVERSITY OF MARY** *H-8*
7500 University Dr.
Bismarck, ND 58504-9652
Tel: (701)255-7500
Free: 800-288-6279
Admissions: (701)355-8191
Fax: (701)255-7687
Web Site: http://www.umary.edu/
Description: Independent Roman Catholic, comprehensive, coed. Awards associate, bachelor's, master's, and doctoral degrees. Founded 1959. Setting: 107-acre suburban campus. Endowment: $13 million. Educational spending for 2005 fiscal year: $4378 per student. Total enrollment: 2,758. Faculty: 349 (100 full-time, 249 part-time). Student-undergrad faculty ratio is 16:1. 1,040 applied, 86% were admitted. 16% from top 10% of their high school class, 44% from top quarter, 80% from top half. 27 valedictorians. Full-time: 2,044 students, 61% women, 39% men. Part-time: 153 students, 63% women, 37% men. Students come from 27 states and territories, 19 other countries, 27% from out-of-state, 4% Native American, 2% Hispanic, 2% black, 1% Asian American or Pacific Islander, 1% international, 25% 25 or older, 35% live on campus, 12% transferred in. Retention: 71% of full-time freshmen returned the following year. Academic areas with the most degrees conferred: business/marketing; education; health professions and related sciences. Core. Calendar: 4-4-1. Academic remediation for entering students, services for LD students, advanced placement, accelerated degree

program, independent study, distance learning, double major, summer session for credit, part-time degree program, external degree program, adult/continuing education programs, co-op programs and internships, graduate courses open to undergrads. Off campus study. Study abroad program.
Entrance Requirements: Options: Peterson's Universal Application, Common Application, electronic application, early admission, deferred admission, international baccalaureate accepted. Required: high school transcript, 1 recommendation, SAT or ACT. Recommended: minimum 2.5 high school GPA. Required for some: essay, interview. Entrance: moderately difficult. Application deadline: Rolling.
Costs Per Year: Application fee: $25. Comprehensive fee: $15,374 includes full-time tuition ($11,100), mandatory fees ($224), and college room and board ($4050). College room only: $1750. Part-time tuition: $350 per credit. Part-time mandatory fees: $7 per credit.
Collegiate Environment: Orientation program. Drama-theater group, choral group, student-run newspaper, radio station. Social organizations: 15 open to all. Most popular organizations: Student Senate, Student Social Workers Association, Nursing Student Organization, Student Education Association, Fellowship of Christian Athletes. Major annual event: homecoming. Student services: health clinic, personal-psychological counseling. 776 college housing spaces available; 730 were occupied in 2003-04. Freshmen guaranteed college housing. On-campus residence required through sophomore year. Options: men-only, women-only housing available. University of Mary Library with 65,842 books, 1,040 microform titles, 584 serials, 6,849 audiovisual materials, and an OPAC. Operations spending for 2004 fiscal year: $421,669. 233 computers available on campus for general student use. A campuswide network can be accessed from student residence rooms and from off campus. Staffed computer lab on campus.
Community Environment: Bismarck, North Dakota's capital city, is the second largest city with a population of 48,000. Because of its central location, modern shopping centers and Civic Center, the city hosts many state and national conventions. Bismarck is considered the cultural, business and educational center of western and central North Dakota. It is also the medical center for the region with two modern medical centers and clinics. Bismarck has a large city library, a State Historical Library, and numerous libraries related to state and federal offices; a city orchestra, civic chorus, and amateur drama club; and many churches representing various denominations. The city has many parks and recreation areas, a city zoo, three golf courses, and clubs for a variety of recreational activities. The Missouri River and nearby Lake Sakakawea offer boating, fishing and other water sports. Bismarck has transportation service from several major air carriers, commuter airlines, and bus lines. Interstate 94 and U.S. Highway 83 meet in Bismarck. The city has a pleasant summer climate and moderate to severe winters.

■ **UNIVERSITY OF NORTH DAKOTA** *E-16*
Grand Forks, ND 58202
Tel: (701)777-2011
Free: 800-CALL UND
Admissions: (701)777-4463
Fax: (701)777-3650
E-mail: kenton_pauls@und.nodak.edu
Web Site: http://www.und.nodak.edu/
Description: State-supported, university, coed. Part of North Dakota University System. Awards bachelor's, master's, doctoral, and first professional degrees and post-master's certificates. Founded 1883. Setting: 543-acre small town campus. Endowment: $8.7 million. Research spending for 2004 fiscal year: $31.5 million. Educational spending for 2005 fiscal year: $9710 per student. Total enrollment: 12,954. Faculty: 825 (668 full-time, 157 part-time). Student-undergrad faculty ratio is 18:1. 3,749 applied, 73% were admitted. 16% from top 10% of their high school class, 38% from top quarter, 72% from top half. 3 National Merit Scholars, 65 valedictorians. Full-time: 9,364 students, 46% women, 54% men. Part-time: 1,134 students, 44% women, 56% men. Students come from 56 states and territories, 37 other countries, 47% from out-of-state, 3% Native American, 1% Hispanic, 1% black, 1% Asian American or Pacific Islander, 12% 25 or older, 31% live on campus, 7% transferred in. Retention: 75% of full-time freshmen returned the following year. Academic areas with the most degrees conferred: business/marketing; health professions and related sciences; education. Core. Calendar: semesters. ESL program, services for LD students, advanced placement, accelerated degree program, self-designed majors, honors program, independent study, distance learning, double major, summer session for credit, part-time degree program, adult/continuing education

programs, co-op programs and internships, graduate courses open to undergrads. Off campus study. Study abroad program. ROTC: Army, Air Force.

Entrance Requirements: Options: electronic application, deferred admission. Required: high school transcript, SAT or ACT. Recommended: minimum 2.5 high school GPA, ACT. Entrance: minimally difficult. Application deadline: 7/1. Notification: continuous.

Costs Per Year: Application fee: $35. State resident tuition: $4390 full-time. Nonresident tuition: $11,722 full-time. Mandatory fees: $937 full-time. Full-time tuition and fees vary according to degree level, program, and reciprocity agreements. College room and board: $4787. College room only: $1979. Room and board charges vary according to board plan and housing facility.

Collegiate Environment: Orientation program. Drama-theater group, choral group, marching band, student-run newspaper, radio station. Social organizations: 250 open to all; national fraternities, national sororities; 10% of eligible men and 8% of eligible women are members. Most popular organizations: student government, National Society of Collegiate Scholars, Association of Residence Halls, University of North Dakota Indian Association, Sioux Crew. Major annual events: Spring Fest, Homecoming, Feast of Nations. Student services: legal services, health clinic, personal-psychological counseling, women's center. Campus security: 24-hour emergency response devices and patrols, student patrols, late night transport-escort service, controlled dormitory access, emergency telephones. 3,311 college housing spaces available; 3,152 were occupied in 2003-04. Freshmen guaranteed college housing. Options: coed, men-only, women-only housing available. Chester Fritz Library plus 2 others with 925,367 books, 1.6 million microform titles, 18,955 serials, 19,048 audiovisual materials, an OPAC, and a Web page. Operations spending for 2004 fiscal year: $5.7 million. 1,100 computers available on campus for general student use. Computer purchase/lease plans available. A campuswide network can be accessed from student residence rooms and from off campus. Staffed computer lab on campus.

■ **VALLEY CITY STATE UNIVERSITY** *H-14*
101 College St., SW
Valley City, ND 58072
Tel: (701)845-7990
Free: 800-532-8641
Admissions: (701)845-7204
Fax: (701)845-7245
E-mail: dan.klein@vcsu.edu
Web Site: http://www.vcsu.edu/
Description: State-supported, 4-year, coed. Part of North Dakota University System. Awards bachelor's degrees. Founded 1890. Setting: 55-acre small town campus. Endowment: $593,346. Educational spending for 2005 fiscal year: $5402 per student. Total enrollment: 1,035. Student-undergrad faculty ratio is 18:1. 256 applied, 94% were admitted. 6% from top 10% of their high school class, 22% from top quarter, 53% from top half. Full-time: 783 students, 49% women, 51% men. Part-time: 230 students, 66% women, 34% men. Students come from 24 states and territories, 8 other countries, 25% from out-of-state, 2% Native American, 1% Hispanic, 2% black, 0.5% Asian American or Pacific Islander, 5% international, 22% 25 or older, 32% live on campus, 8% transferred in. Academic areas with the most degrees conferred: education; business/marketing; computer and information sciences. Core. Calendar: semesters. Academic remediation for entering students, services for LD students, self-designed majors, distance learning, double major, summer session for credit, part-time degree program, co-op programs and internships. Off campus study at North Dakota State University, Mayville State University.

Entrance Requirements: Open admission. Options: Peterson's Universal Application, electronic application, early admission, deferred admission. Required: high school transcript. Required for some: SAT or ACT. Entrance: noncompetitive. Application deadline: Rolling. Notification: continuous.

Costs Per Year: Application fee: $35. State resident tuition: $3656 full-time, $114.25 per semester hour part-time. Nonresident tuition: $9761 full-time, $305.05 per semester hour part-time. Mandatory fees: $1504 full-time. College room and board: $4694. College room only: $2080. Room and board charges vary according to board plan.

Collegiate Environment: Orientation program. Drama-theater group, choral group, student-run newspaper. Social organizations: 18 open to all; local fraternities, local sororities; 2% of eligible men and 3% of eligible women are members. Most popular organizations: departmental clubs, Fellowship of Christian Athletes. Major annual event: music and theater productions.

Student services: health clinic, personal-psychological counseling. Campus security: controlled dormitory access. 435 college housing spaces available; 297 were occupied in 2003-04. Freshmen guaranteed college housing. On-campus residence required through sophomore year. Options: coed, men-only, women-only housing available. Allen Memorial Library with 94,450 books, 59,000 microform titles, 7,500 serials, 15,300 audiovisual materials, an OPAC, and a Web page. Operations spending for 2004 fiscal year: $372,473. 925 computers available on campus for general student use. Computer purchase/lease plans available. A campuswide network can be accessed from student residence rooms and from off campus. Staffed computer lab on campus.

Community Environment: Valley City, in the Sheyenne River Valley, is the home of the North Dakota Winter Show, a statewide agricultural fair held in the first week in March. The area is served by buses, railroad, and Interstate Highways 94, 10, and 52.

■ **WILLISTON STATE COLLEGE** *D-2*
Box 1326
Williston, ND 58802-1326
Tel: (701)774-4200; 888-863-9455
Admissions: (701)774-4554
Fax: (701)774-4211
Web Site: http://www.wsc.nodak.edu/
Description: State-supported, 2-year, coed. Part of North Dakota University System. Awards certificates, diplomas, transfer associate, and terminal associate degrees. Founded 1957. Setting: 80-acre small town campus. Endowment: $52,200. Educational spending for 2005 fiscal year: $4642 per student. Total enrollment: 947. Student-undergrad faculty ratio is 14:1. 540 applied, 98% were admitted. Full-time: 557 students, 66% women, 34% men. Part-time: 390 students, 83% women, 17% men. Students come from 9 states and territories, 3 other countries, 14% from out-of-state, 5% Native American, 2% Hispanic, 1% black, 0.3% Asian American or Pacific Islander, 3% international, 28% 25 or older, 13% live on campus, 84% transferred in. Core. Calendar: semesters. Academic remediation for entering students, services for LD students, advanced placement, self-designed majors, honors program, independent study, distance learning, summer session for credit, part-time degree program, co-op programs. Off campus study at Lake Region State College.

Entrance Requirements: Open admission except for practical nursing and physical therapist assistant programs. Options: Common Application, electronic application. Required: high school transcript. Entrance: noncompetitive. Application deadline: Rolling. Notification: continuous.

Costs Per Year: Application fee: $35. State resident tuition: $2073 full-time, $79.76 per credit part-time. Nonresident tuition: $3111 full-time, $119.64 per credit part-time. Mandatory fees: $575 full-time, $22.11 per credit part-time. College room and board: $3500. College room only: $1000.

Collegiate Environment: Orientation program. Drama-theater group, choral group, student-run newspaper. Social organizations: 17 open to all; national sororities; 2% of women are members. Most popular organizations: PTK, PBL, Student Senate, VICA, Student Nurses Association. Major annual events: Winter Carnival, Graduation, Halloween Dance. Student services: personal-psychological counseling. Campus security: controlled dormitory access. 90 college housing spaces available; 20 were occupied in 2003-04. No special consideration for freshman housing applicants. Options: coed, men-only, women-only housing available. Williston State College Library with 16,218 books, 14 microform titles, 214 serials, 475 audiovisual materials, an OPAC, and a Web page. 70 computers available on campus for general student use. Computer purchase/lease plans available. A campuswide network can be accessed from student residence rooms and from off campus. Staffed computer lab on campus.

Community Environment: Midway between two dams, Fort Peck in Montana and Garrison in North Dakota, Williston has been a railroad and distributing center since its earliest days. In the farming and stock-raising region of the oil-rich Williston Basin, the city has more than 1,000 producing wells within its trade territory. This is a rural community with temperate climate. The area is served by bus, rail, and air lines. Good U.S. Highways intersect the city. Community services include 24 churches representing 18 denominations, a public library, museum, community concert association, modern hospital, and clinics. There are also various civic, fraternal, and veteran's organizations here. Local recreation includes theaters, a drive-in, golf clubs, bowling alley, tennis courts, baseball stadium, several softball complexes, and excellent fishing in Garrison Reservoir and the Missouri River.

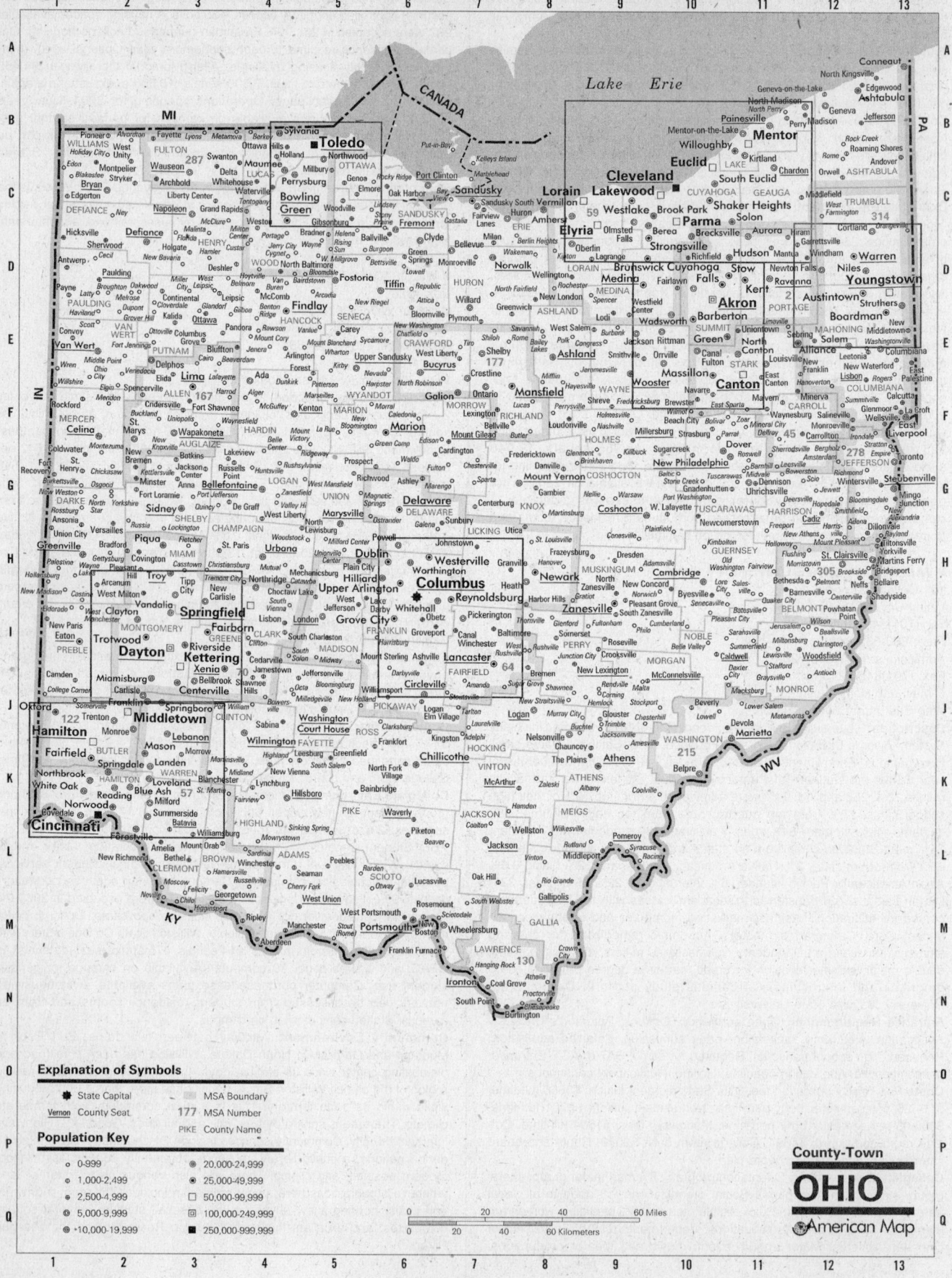

County-Town

OHIO

American Map

Explanation of Symbols

✳ State Capital
Vernon County Seat
177 MSA Number
PIKE County Name
▒ MSA Boundary

Population Key

○ 0-999
◎ 1,000-2,499
● 2,500-4,999
◉ 5,000-9,999
● 10,000-19,999
◉ 20,000-24,999
◉ 25,000-49,999
□ 50,000-99,999
▣ 100,000-249,999
■ 250,000-999,999

0   20   40   60 Miles
0   20   40   60 Kilometers

■ **ACADEMY OF COURT REPORTING** *C-10*
2044 Euclid Ave.
Cleveland, OH 44115
Tel: (216)861-3222
Fax: (216)861-4517
E-mail: admissionaocr@hotmail.com
Web Site: http://www.acr.edu/
Description: Proprietary, 2-year, coed. Founded 1970. Total enrollment: 100.

■ **ALLEGHENY WESLEYAN COLLEGE** *E-12*
2161 Woodsdale Rd.
Salem, OH 44460
Tel: (330)337-6403
Free: 800-292-3153
Fax: (330)337-6255
Web Site: http://www.awc.edu/
Description: Independent religious, 4-year, coed. Awards bachelor's degrees. Total enrollment: 70. Calendar: semesters.

■ **ANTIOCH COLLEGE** *I-18*
795 Livermore St.
Yellow Springs, OH 45387-1697
Tel: (937)769-1000
Free: 800-543-9436
Admissions: (937)769-1100
Fax: (937)769-1288
E-mail: admissions@college.antioch.edu
Web Site: http://www.antioch-college.edu/
Description: Independent, 4-year, coed. Part of Antioch University. Awards bachelor's degrees. Founded 1852. Setting: 100-acre small town campus with easy access to Dayton. Endowment: $28.4 million. Educational spending for 2005 fiscal year: $8369 per student. Total enrollment: 470. Student-undergrad faculty ratio is 11:1. 368 applied, 51% were admitted. 13% from top 10% of their high school class, 39% from top quarter, 70% from top half. Full-time: 460 students, 57% women, 43% men. Part-time: 4 students, 50% women, 50% men. Students come from 43 states and territories, 2 other countries, 68% from out-of-state, 1% Native American, 3% Hispanic, 4% black, 1% Asian American or Pacific Islander, 0.3% international, 7% 25 or older, 97% live on campus, 7% transferred in. Academic areas with the most degrees conferred: area and ethnic studies; interdisciplinary studies; liberal arts/general studies. Core. Calendar: trimesters. Academic remediation for entering students, services for LD students, advanced placement, self-designed majors, independent study, double major, summer session for credit, co-op programs and internships. Off campus study at members of the Great Lakes Colleges Association, Southwestern Ohio Council for Higher Education. Study abroad program.
Entrance Requirements: Options: Peterson's Universal Application, Common Application, electronic application, early action, deferred admission, international baccalaureate accepted. Required: essay, high school transcript, minimum 2.5 high school GPA, 2 recommendations. Recommended: interview. Entrance: moderately difficult. Application deadlines: 2/1, 1/1 for early action. Notification: continuous until 4/1, 2/1 for early action.
Costs Per Year: Application fee: $0. Comprehensive fee: $34,214 includes full-time tuition ($26,492), mandatory fees ($722), and college room and board ($7000). College room only: $3426. Part-time tuition: $435 per credit hour.

Collegiate Environment: Orientation program. Drama-theater group, choral group, student-run newspaper, radio station. Most popular organizations: Third World Alliance, Women's Center, Lesbian/Gay/Bisexual Center, Uni-Dad, Alternative Library. Major annual events: Camelot Race, Div Dance, Drag Ball. Student services: health clinic, personal-psychological counseling, women's center. Campus security: 24-hour emergency response devices and patrols, late night transport-escort service. 612 college housing spaces available; 581 were occupied in 2003-04. On-campus residence required through senior year. Options: coed, men-only, women-only housing available. Olive Kettering Memorial Library with 300,000 books, 48,320 microform titles, 10,504 serials, 6,259 audiovisual materials, an OPAC, and a Web page. Operations spending for 2004 fiscal year: $520,166. 68 computers available on campus for general student use. A campuswide network can be accessed from student residence rooms and from off campus. Staffed computer lab on campus.
Community Environment: Yellow Springs, Ohio, is a magnet for creative thinkers and doers. The residents are socially concerned, politically active, and intensely interested in the arts. Ingenious shops, natural food stores, unusual restaurants, and an array of art galleries line the village streets. Bookstores can be found with specialties ranging from science fiction to feminist literature. Local craft shops display items of clay, silver, wood, stained glass, unusual weavings, original clothing, oils, and essences. The Little Art Theatre offers top foreign and American arts films in three-day runs. A 1,000 Nature Preserve, Glen Helen, adjacent to campus, provides a maze of stone cliffs, waterfalls, forests, streams, wooded trails, and old bridges. It offers opportunities for hiking, horseback riding, cross-country skiing, canoeing, rock-climbing, rappelling and solitude.

■ **ANTIOCH UNIVERSITY MCGREGOR** *I-18*
800 Livermore St.
Yellow Springs, OH 45387-1609
Tel: (937)769-1800; (937)769-1818
Admissions: (937)769-1823
Fax: (937)769-1805
E-mail: orobinson@mcgregor.edu
Web Site: http://www.mcgregor.edu/
Description: Independent, upper-level, coed. Part of Antioch University. Awards bachelor's and master's degrees and post-master's certificates. Founded 1988. Setting: 100-acre small town campus with easy access to Dayton. Total enrollment: 695. Faculty: 90 (27 full-time, 63 part-time). Student-undergrad faculty ratio is 6:1. Full-time: 57 students, 74% women, 26% men. Part-time: 95 students, 65% women, 35% men. 0% from out-of-state, 1% Native American, 2% Hispanic, 20% black, 0% Asian American or Pacific Islander, 0% international, 99% 25 or older, 27% transferred in. Retention: 92% of full-time entering class returned the following year. Academic areas with the most degrees conferred: liberal arts/general studies; psychology; business/marketing. Core. Advanced placement, accelerated degree program, independent study, distance learning, double major, summer session for credit, part-time degree program, adult/continuing education programs, co-op programs and internships.
Costs Per Year: Application fee: $45. Tuition: $12,288 full-time, $256 per credit hour part-time. Mandatory fees: $225 full-time, $75 per term part-time.
Collegiate Environment: Student services: personal-psychological counseling. Campus security: 24-hour emergency response devices and patrols. College housing not available. Olive Kettering Library with 285,000 books, 1,000 serials, and a Web page. 49 computers available on campus

for general student use. A campuswide network can be accessed from off-campus. Staffed computer lab on campus.

■ ANTONELLI COLLEGE *L-2*
124 East Seventh St.
Cincinnati, OH 45202-2592
Tel: (513)241-4338
Free: 800-505-4338
Fax: (513)241-9396
Web Site: http://www.antonellic.com/

Description: Proprietary, 2-year, coed. Awards diplomas and terminal associate degrees. Founded 1947. Setting: urban campus. Total enrollment: 387. 130 applied, 91% were admitted. Students come from 6 states and territories, 20% from out-of-state, 1% Native American, 1% Hispanic, 12% black, 3% Asian American or Pacific Islander, 0% international, 30% 25 or older. Core. Honors program, summer session for credit, part-time degree program, internships.

Entrance Requirements: Open admission. Options: early admission, deferred admission. Required: high school transcript, interview. Required for some: art portfolio. Entrance: noncompetitive. Application deadline: Rolling.

Collegiate Environment: Student services: personal-psychological counseling. Campus security: 24-hour emergency response devices, security personnel while classes are in session. College housing not available. Main library plus 1 other with 2,000 books and 30 serials. 46 computers available on campus for general student use. Staffed computer lab on campus.

■ ART ACADEMY OF CINCINNATI *L-2*
1212 Jackson St.
Cincinnati, OH 45202
Tel: (513)562-6262
Admissions: (513)562-8744
Fax: (513)562-8778
E-mail: zumwalde@artacademy.edu
Web Site: http://www.artacademy.edu/

Description: Independent, comprehensive, coed. Awards associate, bachelor's, and master's degrees. Founded 1887. Setting: 184-acre urban campus. Endowment: $12.5 million. Total enrollment: 164. Faculty: 61 (16 full-time, 45 part-time). Student-undergrad faculty ratio is 12:1. 205 applied, 25% were admitted. 12% from top 10% of their high school class, 43% from top quarter, 45% from top half. Full-time: 155 students, 54% women, 46% men. Part-time: 8 students, 88% women, 13% men. Students come from 15 states and territories, 7 other countries, 35% from out-of-state, 0% Native American, 1% Hispanic, 2% black, 1% Asian American or Pacific Islander, 2% international, 17% 25 or older, 13% transferred in. Retention: 81% of full-time freshmen returned the following year. Academic area with the most degrees conferred: visual and performing arts. Core. Calendar: semesters. Services for LD students, advanced placement, self-designed majors, honors program, independent study, double major, summer session for credit, part-time degree program, adult/continuing education programs, co-op programs and internships, graduate courses open to undergrads. Off campus study at members of the Greater Cincinnati Consortium of Colleges and Universities, Association of Independent Colleges of Art and Design. Study abroad program.

Entrance Requirements: Options: electronic application, deferred admission. Required: essay, high school transcript, minimum 2.0 high school GPA, 1 recommendation, portfolio, SAT or ACT. Recommended: interview. Entrance: moderately difficult. Application deadline: 6/30. Notification: continuous.

Costs Per Year: Application fee: $25. Tuition: $19,250 full-time, $810 per credit hour part-time. Mandatory fees: $350 full-time, $175 per term part-time.

Collegiate Environment: Orientation program. Major annual events: annual field trips to art centers in Chicago and New York, Art Academy Awards Ceremony, End of the Year Party. Student services: health clinic, personal-psychological counseling. Campus security: 24-hour emergency response devices and patrols. College housing not available. Mary Schiff Library with 66,404 books, 150 microform titles, 150 serials, and 588 audiovisual materials. 40 computers available on campus for general student use. Staffed computer lab on campus.

Community Environment: The Art Academy is located in Eden Park, a metropolitan park of 184 acres that also contains the Cincinnati Historical Society. Mirror Lake, the Krohm Conservatory, two dramatic theaters, one outdoor theater and the Ohio River overlook the area.

■ THE ART INSTITUTE OF CINCINNATI *L-2*
1171 East Kemper Rd.
Cincinnati, OH 45246
Tel: (513)751-1206
Fax: (513)751-1209
Web Site: http://www.theartinstituteofcincinnati.com/

Description: Proprietary, 2-year, coed. Part of Education Management Corporation. Awards transfer associate degrees. Educational spending for 2005 fiscal year: $11,996 per student. Total enrollment: 74. 25% from top quarter of their high school class. Full-time: 74 students, 53% women, 47% men. 1% from out-of-state, 1% black, 5% 25 or older, 7% transferred in. Core.

Entrance Requirements: Option: Common Application. Required: high school transcript, recommendations, interview, portfolio. Entrance: moderately difficult. Application deadline: 9/8.

Collegiate Environment: Orientation program. Campus security: 24-hour emergency response devices. College housing not available. The Art Institute of Cincinnati Library with 1,500 books. 48 computers available on campus for general student use. Staffed computer lab on campus.

■ THE ART INSTITUTE OF OHIO-CINCINNATI *L-2*
1011 Glendale Milford Rd.
Cincinnati, OH 45215
Tel: (513)771-2821
Fax: 877-477-8486
E-mail: mlee@aii.edu
Web Site: http://www.aiohc.aii.edu

Description: Proprietary, 2-year, coed. Part of The Art Institutes. Awards transfer associate and terminal associate degrees. Total enrollment: 229. Student-undergrad faculty ratio is 25:1. Students come from 3 states and territories, 9% from out-of-state, 0.4% Native American, 0.4% Hispanic, 32% black, 2% Asian American or Pacific Islander, 0% international, 62% 25 or older. Core. Calendar: continuous. Services for LD students, accelerated degree program, distance learning, part-time degree program, co-op programs and internships.

Entrance Requirements: Open admission. Options: early admission, early decision, early action, deferred admission. Required: high school transcript, interview. Entrance: noncompetitive. Application deadline: Rolling. Notification: continuous.

Collegiate Environment: Orientation program. Library with 7,018 books, 75 serials, 493 audiovisual materials, and an OPAC. 229 computers available on campus for general student use. A campuswide network can be accessed. Staffed computer lab on campus.

■ ASHLAND UNIVERSITY *E-8*
401 College Ave.
Ashland, OH 44805-3702
Tel: (419)289-4142
Free: 800-882-1548
Admissions: (419)289-5052
Fax: (419)289-5999
E-mail: auadmsn@ashland.edu
Web Site: http://www.exploreashland.com

Description: Independent, comprehensive, coed, affiliated with Brethren Church. Awards associate, bachelor's, master's, doctoral, and first professional degrees. Founded 1878. Setting: 98-acre small town campus with easy access to Cleveland. Endowment: $30.2 million. Educational spending for 2005 fiscal year: $5000 per student. Total enrollment: 6,472. Faculty: 593 (231 full-time, 362 part-time). Student-undergrad faculty ratio is 13:1. 1,950 applied, 91% were admitted. 17% from top 10% of their high school class, 43% from top quarter, 71% from top half. 11 valedictorians. Full-time: 2,511 students, 58% women, 42% men. Part-time: 280 students, 68% women, 33% men. Students come from 31 states and territories, 23 other countries, 8% from out-of-state, 0.3% Native American, 2% Hispanic, 8% black, 0.5% Asian American or Pacific Islander, 1% international, 18% 25 or older, 71% live on campus, 5% transferred in. Retention: 73% of full-time freshmen returned the following year. Academic areas with the most degrees conferred: education; business/marketing; social sciences. Core. Calendar: semesters. Academic remediation for entering students, ESL program, services for LD students, advanced placement, self-designed majors, honors program, independent study, double major, summer session for credit, part-time degree program, adult/continuing education programs, internships. Off campus study at Case Western Reserve University, Art Institute of

Pittsburgh, Purdue University, Drew University, American University, Merrill-Palmer Institute, Hunter College of the City University of New York. Study abroad program.

Entrance Requirements: Options: Peterson's Universal Application, Common Application, electronic application, deferred admission, international baccalaureate accepted. Required: essay, high school transcript, minimum 2.5 high school GPA, SAT or ACT. Recommended: interview. Required for some: recommendations, interview. Entrance: moderately difficult. Application deadline: Rolling. Notification: continuous.

Costs Per Year: Application fee: $25. Comprehensive fee: $29,220 includes full-time tuition ($20,666), mandatory fees ($764), and college room and board ($7790). College room only: $4184. Part-time tuition: $635 per credit hour.

Collegiate Environment: Orientation program. Drama-theater group, choral group, marching band, student-run newspaper, radio station. Social organizations: 90 open to all; national fraternities, national sororities; 14% of eligible men and 22% of eligible women are members. Most popular organizations: Campus Activity Board, Fellowship of Christian Athletes, Hope Fellowship, intramurals, Community Care. Major annual events: homecoming, Parents' Weekend, Banana Split Contest. Student services: health clinic, personal-psychological counseling, women's center. Campus security: 24-hour emergency response devices and patrols, student patrols, late night transport-escort service, controlled dormitory access. 1,884 college housing spaces available; 1,525 were occupied in 2003-04. Freshmen guaranteed college housing. On-campus residence required through senior year. Options: coed, men-only, women-only housing available. Ashland Library plus 2 others with 205,200 books, 318,000 microform titles, 1,625 serials, 3,550 audiovisual materials, an OPAC, and a Web page. Operations spending for 2004 fiscal year: $744,378. 600 computers available on campus for general student use. Computer purchase/lease plans available. A campuswide network can be accessed from student residence rooms and from off campus. Staffed computer lab on campus.

Community Environment: Five rubber manufacturers in Ashland produce most of the world's toy balloons. Other industries produce spray equipment, hydraulic cylinders, and clothing. Bus transportation is available while Mansfield Airport and Cleveland Airport furnish air transportation. Recreational facilities within the city are good and nearby Mohican State Park provides additional opportunities for fishing and camping.

■ ATS INSTITUTE OF TECHNOLOGY *C-20*

230 Alpha Park
Highland Heights, OH 44143
Tel: (440)449-1700
Fax: (440)449-1389
Web Site: http://www.atsinstitute.com/
Description: Proprietary, 2-year, coed.

■ BALDWIN-WALLACE COLLEGE *D-9*

275 Eastland Rd.
Berea, OH 44017-2088
Tel: (440)826-2900
Admissions: (440)826-2222
Fax: (440)826-3830
E-mail: admission@baldwinw.edu
Web Site: http://www.bw.edu/
Description: Independent Methodist, comprehensive, coed. Awards bachelor's and master's degrees. Founded 1845. Setting: 100-acre suburban campus with easy access to Cleveland. Endowment: $122.3 million. Research spending for 2004 fiscal year: $116,163. Educational spending for 2005 fiscal year: $7929 per student. Total enrollment: 4,469. Faculty: 352 (162 full-time, 190 part-time). Student-undergrad faculty ratio is 17:1. 2,366 applied, 79% were admitted. 28% from top 10% of their high school class, 29% from top quarter, 87% from top half. 24 valedictorians, 23 student government officers. Full-time: 2,994 students, 58% women, 42% men. Part-time: 687 students, 68% women, 32% men. Students come from 36 states and territories, 15 other countries, 10% from out-of-state, 0.2% Native American, 1% Hispanic, 5% black, 1% Asian American or Pacific Islander, 1% international, 3% 25 or older, 58% live on campus, 6% transferred in. Retention: 82% of full-time freshmen returned the following year. Academic areas with the most degrees conferred: business/marketing; education; psychology. Core. Calendar: semesters. Academic remediation for entering students, ESL program, services for LD students, advanced placement, accelerated degree program, self-designed majors, honors program, independent study, distance learning, double major, summer session for

credit, part-time degree program, adult/continuing education programs, internships, graduate courses open to undergrads. Off campus study at Drew University, American University. Study abroad program. ROTC: Air Force (c).

Entrance Requirements: Options: Peterson's Universal Application, Common Application, electronic application, deferred admission. Required: essay, high school transcript, minimum 2.7 high school GPA, 1 recommendation, SAT or ACT. Recommended: minimum 3.2 high school GPA, interview. Entrance: moderately difficult. Application deadline: Rolling. Notification: continuous until 5/1.

Costs Per Year: Application fee: $25. Comprehensive fee: $28,210 includes full-time tuition ($21,236) and college room and board ($6974). College room only: $3406. Part-time tuition: $674 per semester hour.

Collegiate Environment: Orientation program. Drama-theater group, choral group, student-run newspaper, radio station. Social organizations: 100 open to all; national fraternities, national sororities; 7% of eligible men and 17% of eligible women are members. Most popular organizations: campus entertainment productions, Student Senate, Dance Marathon, Campus Crusade, Black Student Alliance. Major annual events: April Reign, Homecoming, Bach Festival. Student services: health clinic, personal-psychological counseling, women's center. Campus security: 24-hour emergency response devices and patrols, student patrols, late night transport-escort service, controlled dormitory access. 1,856 college housing spaces available; 1,745 were occupied in 2003-04. No special consideration for freshman housing applicants. Options: coed, men-only, women-only housing available. Ritter Library plus 2 others with 200,000 books, 885 serials, an OPAC, and a Web page. Operations spending for 2004 fiscal year: $1.7 million. 460 computers available on campus for general student use. Computer purchase/lease plans available. A campuswide network can be accessed from student residence rooms. Staffed computer lab on campus.

Community Environment: Berea, with its tree-lined streets and picturesque homes, is an ideal college town, yet it is only 20 minutes from the heart of Cleveland, home to many fortune 500 companies and recreational and cultural opportunities.

■ BELMONT TECHNICAL COLLEGE

120 Fox Shannon Place
St. Clairsville, OH 43950-9735
Tel: (740)695-9500
Fax: (740)695-2247
E-mail: gfehr@btc.edu
Web Site: http://www.btc.edu/
Description: State-supported, 2-year, coed. Part of Ohio Board of Regents. Awards diplomas and terminal associate degrees. Founded 1971. Setting: 55-acre rural campus. Educational spending for 2005 fiscal year: $5900 per student. Total enrollment: 1,740. Full-time: 1,180 students, 57% women, 43% men. Part-time: 560 students, 59% women, 41% men. Students come from 10 states and territories, 3% from out-of-state, 0.5% Native American, 0.1% Hispanic, 3% black, 0.2% Asian American or Pacific Islander, 0% international, 55% 25 or older. Retention: 56% of full-time freshmen returned the following year. Core. Academic remediation for entering students, independent study, distance learning, summer session for credit, part-time degree program.

Entrance Requirements: Open admission except for nursing, emergency medical technology programs. Option: early admission. Placement: ACT COMPASS required. Entrance: noncompetitive. Application deadline: Rolling.

Costs Per Year: State resident tuition: $2520 full-time, $56 per credit hour part-time. Nonresident tuition: $5220 full-time, $116 per credit hour part-time. Mandatory fees: $1050 full-time, $23 per credit hour part-time, $5 per term part-time.

Collegiate Environment: Orientation program. Student services: personal-psychological counseling. College housing not available. 5,612 books and 217 serials. Operations spending for 2004 fiscal year: $27,000. 85 computers available on campus for general student use. Staffed computer lab on campus.

Community Environment: Belmont Technical College is located in a rural area of Belmont County, Ohio, just 10 miles west of Wheeling, WV. The college is active in the community and exposes students to a variety of activities, including the fine arts.

■ BLUFFTON UNIVERSITY *E-4*

1 University Dr.
Bluffton, OH 45817

Tel: (419)358-3000
Free: 800-488-3257
Admissions: (419)358-3254
Fax: (419)358-3232
E-mail: admissions@bluffton.edu
Web Site: http://www.bluffton.edu/

Description: Independent Mennonite, comprehensive, coed. Awards bachelor's and master's degrees. Founded 1899. Setting: 65-acre small town campus with easy access to Toledo. Endowment: $18.3 million. Educational spending for 2005 fiscal year: $6054 per student. Total enrollment: 1,211. Faculty: 114 (67 full-time, 47 part-time). Student-undergrad faculty ratio is 14:1. 1,074 applied, 71% were admitted. 14% from top 10% of their high school class, 42% from top quarter, 80% from top half. 12 class presidents, 6 valedictorians, 50 student government officers. Full-time: 1,005 students, 58% women, 42% men. Part-time: 74 students, 59% women, 41% men. Students come from 21 states and territories, 13 other countries, 12% from out-of-state, 0.3% Native American, 2% Hispanic, 3% black, 1% Asian American or Pacific Islander, 2% international, 14% 25 or older, 85% live on campus, 8% transferred in. Retention: 70% of full-time freshmen returned the following year. Academic areas with the most degrees conferred: business/marketing; education; parks and recreation. Core. Calendar: semesters. Academic remediation for entering students, advanced placement, self-designed majors, honors program, independent study, double major, summer session for credit, part-time degree program, adult/continuing education programs, internships. Off campus study at Christian College Coalition, Council of Independent Colleges. Study abroad program.

Entrance Requirements: Options: Common Application, electronic application, deferred admission, international baccalaureate accepted. Required: high school transcript, 2 recommendations, rank in upper 50% of high school class or 2.3 high school GPA, SAT or ACT. Recommended: interview. Required for some: essay. Entrance: moderately difficult. Application deadline: 5/31. Notification: continuous.

Costs Per Year: Application fee: $20. Comprehensive fee: $27,652 includes full-time tuition ($20,170), mandatory fees ($400), and college room and board ($7082). College room only: $3260. Part-time tuition: $840 per credit hour.

Collegiate Environment: Orientation program. Drama-theater group, choral group, student-run newspaper, radio station. Social organizations: 40 open to all. Most popular organizations: Brothers and Sisters in Christ, Campus Government, Student Union Board, music groups/chorale, chapel service. Major annual events: homecoming, Christian Emphasis, May Day. Student services: health clinic, personal-psychological counseling, women's center. Campus security: late night transport-escort service, controlled dormitory access, night security guards. 840 college housing spaces available; 812 were occupied in 2003-04. Freshmen guaranteed college housing. On-campus residence required through senior year. Options: coed, men-only, women-only housing available. Musselman Library with 163,448 books, 135,213 microform titles, 385 serials, 1,259 audiovisual materials, an OPAC, and a Web page. Operations spending for 2004 fiscal year: $577,099. 150 computers available on campus for general student use. Computer purchase/lease plans available. A campuswide network can be accessed from student residence rooms and from off campus. Staffed computer lab on campus.

■ **BOHECKER'S BUSINESS COLLEGE** *D-11*
326 East Main St.
Ravenna, OH 44266
Tel: (330)297-7319
Fax: (330)297-7315
Web Site: http://www.boheckers.com/
Description: Independent, 2-year, coed. Total enrollment: 189.

■ **BOWLING GREEN STATE UNIVERSITY** *C-4*
Bowling Green, OH 43403
Tel: (419)372-2531
Admissions: (419)372-BGSU
E-mail: admissions@bgnet.bgsu.edu
Web Site: http://www.bgsu.edu/
Description: State-supported, university, coed. Awards bachelor's, master's, and doctoral degrees and post-master's certificates. Founded 1910. Setting: 1,230-acre small town campus with easy access to Toledo. Endowment: $113.8 million. Research spending for 2004 fiscal year: $5.9 million. Educational spending for 2005 fiscal year: $6083 per student. Total enrollment: 19,016. Faculty: 1,047 (851 full-time, 196 part-time). Student-undergrad faculty ratio is 19:1. 11,168 applied, 90% were admitted. 14%

from top 10% of their high school class, 71% from top half. 16 National Merit Scholars. Full-time: 15,014 students, 55% women, 45% men. Part-time: 1,065 students, 50% women, 50% men. Students come from 49 states and territories, 43 other countries, 8% from out-of-state, 1% Native American, 3% Hispanic, 8% black, 1% Asian American or Pacific Islander, 1% international, 5% 25 or older, 46% live on campus, 4% transferred in. Retention: 79% of full-time freshmen returned the following year. Academic areas with the most degrees conferred: education; business/marketing; visual and performing arts. Core. Calendar: semesters. Academic remediation for entering students, ESL program, services for LD students, advanced placement, accelerated degree program, self-designed majors, honors program, independent study, distance learning, double major, summer session for credit, part-time degree program, adult/continuing education programs, co-op programs and internships, graduate courses open to undergrads. Off campus study at University of Toledo, Medical College of Ohio. Study abroad program. ROTC: Army, Air Force.

Entrance Requirements: Options: Peterson's Universal Application, electronic application, deferred admission, international baccalaureate accepted. Required: high school transcript, minimum 2.5 high school GPA, SAT and SAT Subject Tests or ACT. Recommended: interview. Entrance: moderately difficult. Application deadline: 7/15. Notification: continuous.

Costs Per Year: Application fee: $35. State resident tuition: $7314 full-time, $357 per credit hour part-time. Nonresident tuition: $14,622 full-time, $706 per credit hour part-time. Mandatory fees: $1246 full-time, $62 per credit hour part-time. Part-time tuition and fees vary according to course load. College room and board: $6434. College room only: $3934. Room and board charges vary according to board plan and housing facility.

Collegiate Environment: Orientation program. Drama-theater group, choral group, marching band, student-run newspaper, radio station. Social organizations: 285 open to all; national fraternities, national sororities. Most popular organizations: University Activities Organization, Undergraduate Student Government, Latino Student Union, H20 (Religious/Spiritual Group). Major annual events: homecoming, Sibs and Kids Weekend, dance marathon. Student services: legal services, health clinic, personal-psychological counseling, women's center. Campus security: 24-hour emergency response devices and patrols, student patrols, late night transport-escort service, controlled dormitory access. 7,286 college housing spaces available; 7,129 were occupied in 2003-04. Freshmen guaranteed college housing. On-campus residence required through sophomore year. Option: coed housing available. Jerome Library plus 2 others with 2.5 million books, 2.4 million microform titles, 9,502 serials, 718,734 audiovisual materials, an OPAC, and a Web page. Operations spending for 2004 fiscal year: $5.4 million. 6,240 computers available on campus for general student use. A campuswide network can be accessed from student residence rooms and from off campus. Staffed computer lab on campus.

Community Environment: Bowling Green, the county seat of Wood County, is located 23 miles south of Toledo. Community facilities in this metropolitan area include libraries, many churches, a hospital, shopping areas, and major civic and service organizations. Lake Erie and the Maumee River provide facilities for recreation.

■ **BOWLING GREEN STATE UNIVERSITY-FIRELANDS COLLEGE** *C-7*
One University Dr.
Huron, OH 44839-9791
Tel: (419)433-5560
E-mail: ahazlet@bgnet.bgsu.edu
Web Site: http://www.firelands.bgsu.edu/
Description: State-supported, primarily 2-year, coed. Part of Bowling Green State University System. Awards certificates, transfer associate, terminal associate, and bachelor's degrees (also offers some upper-level and graduate courses). Founded 1968. Setting: 216-acre rural campus with easy access to Cleveland and Toledo. Endowment: $1.6 million. Educational spending for 2005 fiscal year: $3760 per student. Total enrollment: 1,986. 528 applied, 94% were admitted. 2% from top 10% of their high school class, 18% from top quarter, 49% from top half. Full-time: 1,042 students, 69% women, 31% men. Part-time: 876 students, 63% women, 37% men. Students come from 2 states and territories, 0% from out-of-state, 1% Native American, 3% Hispanic, 6% black, 0.2% Asian American or Pacific Islander, 42% 25 or older, 22% transferred in. Retention: 42% of full-time freshmen returned the following year. Core. Calendar: semesters. Academic remediation for entering students, services for LD students, advanced placement, self-designed majors, independent study, distance learning, double major, summer session for credit, part-time degree program, adult/continuing education programs, internships. ROTC: Army (c), Air Force (c).

Entrance Requirements: Open admission. Options: electronic application, early admission, deferred admission. Required: high school transcript. Placement: SAT or ACT required for some. Entrance: noncompetitive. Application deadline: 8/15. Notification: continuous until 8/15.

Collegiate Environment: Orientation program. Drama-theater group. Social organizations: 20 open to all. Most popular organizations: Speech Activities Organization, Allied Health Club, student government, Intramural Club, Campus Fellowship. Major annual events: Beggars Banquet, Welcome Back Cookout, Recognition Banquet. Campus security: 24-hour emergency response devices, late night transport-escort service, patrols by trained security personnel. College housing not available. Firelands College Library with 41,281 books, 2,663 microform titles, 241 serials, 2,331 audiovisual materials, an OPAC, and a Web page. Operations spending for 2004 fiscal year: $281,160. 300 computers available on campus for general student use. A campuswide network can be accessed from off-campus. Staffed computer lab on campus.

■ **BRADFORD SCHOOL** *I-6*
2469 Stelzer Rd.
Columbus, OH 43219
Tel: (614)416-6200
Free: 800-678-7981
Web Site: http://www.bradfordschoolcolumbus.edu/
Description: Proprietary, 2-year, coed. Awards diplomas, transfer associate, and terminal associate degrees. Founded 1911. Setting: suburban campus. Educational spending for 2005 fiscal year: $1650 per student. Total enrollment: 312. 613 applied, 89% were admitted. 3% from top 10% of their high school class, 11% from top quarter, 41% from top half. 1 valedictorian. Full-time: 312 students, 76% women, 24% men. Students come from 2 states and territories, 5 other countries, 0% from out-of-state, 3% Hispanic, 32% black, 2% Asian American or Pacific Islander, 8% 25 or older, 41% live on campus, 1% transferred in. Core. Calendar: semesters. Adult/continuing education programs, co-op programs and internships.
Entrance Requirements: Options: Common Application, electronic application. Required: high school transcript, interview. Entrance: minimally difficult. Application deadline: Rolling.
Collegiate Environment: Orientation program. Social organizations: 2 open to all. Most popular organization: International Association of Administrative Professionals. Major annual events: fall lunches and dinners, Halloween celebration, spirit week. Campus security: 24-hour patrols. 128 college housing spaces available; all were occupied in 2003-04. Freshmen given priority for college housing. Options: coed, women-only housing available. Resource Center with 2,000 books, 15 serials, 100 audiovisual materials, and an OPAC. Operations spending for 2004 fiscal year: $3500. 102 computers available on campus for general student use.

■ **BROWN MACKIE COLLEGE-AKRON** *E-10*
2791 Mogadore Rd.
Akron, OH 44312-1596
Tel: (330)733-8766
Fax: (330)733-5853
E-mail: tfoose@brownmackie.edu
Web Site: http://www.socaec.com/
Description: Proprietary, 2-year, coed. Administratively affiliated with Southern Ohio College. Awards certificates, diplomas, and terminal associate degrees. Founded 1968. Setting: 3-acre suburban campus with easy access to Cleveland. Total enrollment: 521. Student-undergrad faculty ratio is 18:1. 1% from top 10% of their high school class, 18% from top quarter, 65% from top half. Students come from 1 other country, 0% from out-of-state, 1% Native American, 1% Hispanic, 44% black, 0.4% Asian American or Pacific Islander, 0% international, 70% 25 or older. Core. Academic remediation for entering students, advanced placement, summer session for credit, co-op programs and internships.
Entrance Requirements: Options: early admission, deferred admission. Recommended: minimum 2.0 high school GPA. Entrance: minimally difficult. Application deadline: Rolling. Notification: continuous.
Costs Per Year: Application fee: $0. Tuition: $179 per credit part-time. Mandatory fees: $10 per credit part-time.
Collegiate Environment: Student-run newspaper. Social organizations: 3 open to all. Most popular organizations: Phi Beta Lambda, Student Advisory Board, Collegiate Secretaries International. Major annual events: National Medical Assisting Week, holiday food drives, Blood Drives. Student services: personal-psychological counseling. Campus security: late night transport-

escort service. College housing not available. 3,725 books and 56 serials. 51 computers available on campus for general student use. Staffed computer lab on campus.

■ **BROWN MACKIE COLLEGE-CINCINNATI** *L-2*
1011 Glendale-Milford Rd.
Cincinnati, OH 45215
Tel: (513)771-2424
Web Site: http://www.brownmackie.edu/locations.asp?locid=6
Description: Proprietary, 2-year, coed. Part of American Education Centers, Inc. Awards certificates, diplomas, and terminal associate degrees. Founded 1927. Setting: 3-acre suburban campus. Educational spending for 2005 fiscal year: $1500 per student. Total enrollment: 971. Student-undergrad faculty ratio is 16:1. 5% from top 10% of their high school class, 15% from top quarter, 50% from top half. Students come from 3 states and territories, 1% from out-of-state, 55% 25 or older. Core. Academic remediation for entering students, advanced placement, summer session for credit, adult/continuing education programs, internships.
Entrance Requirements: Open admission. Options: Common Application, early admission, deferred admission. Required: high school transcript, interview. Application deadline: Rolling.
Costs Per Year: Application fee: $20. Tuition: $6444 full-time. Mandatory fees: $360 full-time.
Collegiate Environment: Orientation program. Campus security: 24-hour emergency response devices, night security guard on-campus. College housing not available. 8,747 books, 80 serials, and 437 audiovisual materials. 125 computers available on campus for general student use.

■ **BROWN MACKIE COLLEGE-FINDLAY** *E-4*
1637 Tiffin Ave.
Findlay, OH 45840
Tel: (419)423-2211
Free: 800-842-3687
Fax: (419)423-0725
Web Site: http://www.brownmackie.edu
Description: Proprietary, 2-year, coed. Administratively affiliated with Education Management Corporation. Awards diplomas and terminal associate degrees. Founded 1929. Setting: 1-acre rural campus. Educational spending for 2005 fiscal year: $2541 per student. Total enrollment: 632. Student-undergrad faculty ratio is 19:1. Full-time: 459 students, 93% women, 7% men. Part-time: 173 students, 87% women, 13% men. Students come from 2 states and territories, 1% from out-of-state, 1% Native American, 6% Hispanic, 32% black, 1% Asian American or Pacific Islander, 0% international, 80% 25 or older, 3% transferred in. Core. Calendar: continuous. Advanced placement, independent study, double major, external degree program, co-op programs and internships.
Entrance Requirements: Open admission. Option: Common Application. Required: high school transcript, interview. Entrance: noncompetitive. Application deadline: Rolling. Notification: continuous.
Costs Per Year: Application fee: $0. Tuition: $11,500 full-time, $250 per credit hour part-time. Mandatory fees: $460 full-time, $10 per credit hour part-time.
Collegiate Environment: Orientation program. Campus security: 24-hour emergency response devices. College housing not available. 3,134 books, 41 serials, 26 audiovisual materials, an OPAC, and a Web page. Operations spending for 2004 fiscal year: $11,118. 74 computers available on campus for general student use. Computer purchase/lease plans available. A campuswide network can be accessed. Staffed computer lab on campus.

■ **BROWN MACKIE COLLEGE-NORTH CANTON** *E-11*
1320 West Maple St., NW
North Canton, OH 44720-2854
Tel: (330)494-1214
E-mail: elaudermilt@brownmackie.edu
Web Site: http://www.socaec.com/
Description: Proprietary, 2-year, coed. Part of Educational Management Corporation. Awards diplomas and terminal associate degrees. Founded 1929. Setting: suburban campus. Total enrollment: 1,131. Student-undergrad faculty ratio is 21:1. 631 applied, 98% were admitted. Full-time: 1,131 students, 80% women, 20% men. 0% from out-of-state, 0% Native American, 1% Hispanic, 25% black, 0% Asian American or Pacific Islander, 0% international, 0.4% transferred in. Advanced placement, independent study, adult/continuing education programs.

Entrance Requirements: Option: Common Application. Required: high school transcript, interview, ASSET Evaluation. Required for some: Transcript of GED record. Entrance: minimally difficult. Application deadline: Rolling. Notification: continuous.

Costs Per Year: Application fee: $0. Tuition: $8592 full-time, $179 per credit part-time. Mandatory fees: $480 full-time, $10 per credit part-time.

Collegiate Environment: Orientation program. Student-run newspaper. Student services: personal-psychological counseling. College housing not available. 65 computers available on campus for general student use.

■ **BRYANT AND STRATTON COLLEGE (CLEVELAND)** *C-10*
1700 East 13th St.
Cleveland, OH 44114-3203
Tel: (216)771-1700
Fax: (216)771-1700
E-mail: jploskonka@bryantstratton.edu
Web Site: http://www.bryantstratton.edu/
Description: Proprietary, 4-year, coed. Part of Bryant and Stratton Business Institute, Inc. Awards associate and bachelor's degrees. Founded 1929. Setting: urban campus. Total enrollment: 428. Student-undergrad faculty ratio is 10:1. Full-time: 282 students, 71% women, 29% men. Part-time: 146 students, 60% women, 40% men. Students come from 2 states and territories, 0% from out-of-state, 0% Native American, 3% Hispanic, 85% black, 0.2% Asian American or Pacific Islander, 0% international, 59% 25 or older, 10% live on campus. Academic area with the most degrees conferred: business/marketing. Core. Calendar: semesters. Academic remediation for entering students, services for LD students, independent study, distance learning, double major, summer session for credit, part-time degree program, adult/continuing education programs, co-op programs and internships.
Entrance Requirements: Options: Peterson's Universal Application, deferred admission. Required: high school transcript, interview, entrance evaluation and placement evaluation, TABE. Recommended: SAT or ACT. Entrance: minimally difficult. Application deadline: Rolling.
Costs Per Year: Tuition: $18,675 full-time, $415 per credit hour part-time. Mandatory fees: $25 full-time.
Collegiate Environment: Orientation program. Student-run newspaper. Most popular organization: student/staff softball. Major annual events: Summer Carnival, Team Spirit Day (hot dog sale). Campus security: controlled dormitory access. Option: coed housing available. 4,466 books, 80 serials, 159 audiovisual materials, and a Web page. 66 computers available on campus for general student use. Staffed computer lab on campus.

■ **BRYANT AND STRATTON COLLEGE (PARMA)** *C-10*
12955 Snow Rd.
Parma, OH 44130-1013
Tel: (216)265-3151
Fax: (216)265-0325
Web Site: http://www.bryantstratton.edu/
Description: Proprietary, primarily 2-year, coed. Part of Bryant and Stratton Business Institute, Inc. Awards terminal associate and bachelor's degrees. Founded 1981. Setting: 4-acre suburban campus with easy access to Cleveland. Research spending for 2004 fiscal year: $4000. Educational spending for 2005 fiscal year: $1335 per student. Total enrollment: 329. 2% from top 10% of their high school class, 4% from top quarter, 46% from top half. Full-time: 183 students, 74% women, 26% men. Part-time: 146 students, 75% women, 25% men. 0% from out-of-state, 0% Native American, 13% Hispanic, 25% black, 0.3% Asian American or Pacific Islander, 0% international, 51% 25 or older, 2% transferred in. Retention: 33% of full-time freshmen returned the following year. Academic area with the most degrees conferred: business/marketing. Core. Calendar: semesters. Academic remediation for entering students, independent study, distance learning, double major, summer session for credit, part-time degree program, co-op programs and internships.
Entrance Requirements: Option: deferred admission. Required: high school transcript, interview, entrance evaluation and placement evaluation, CPAt. Recommended: SAT or ACT. Required for some: recommendations. Entrance: minimally difficult. Application deadline: Rolling.
Costs Per Year: Tuition: $18,675 full-time, $415 per credit hour part-time. Mandatory fees: $25 full-time.
Collegiate Environment: Orientation program. Social organizations: 4 open to all. Most popular organizations: Business Professionals of America, Association for Computing Machinery, Baccus Gamma. Major annual events: Summer Carnival, International Potluck, Halloween Party. Campus security:

24-hour emergency response devices. College housing not available. Main library plus 1 other with 1,500 books, 20 serials, and an OPAC. Operations spending for 2004 fiscal year: $52,000. 96 computers available on campus for general student use.

■ **BRYANT AND STRATTON COLLEGE (WILLOUGHBY HILLS)** *C-20*
27557 Chardon Rd.
Willoughby Hills, OH 44092
Tel: (440)944-6800
Admissions: (440)444-6800
Web Site: http://www.bryantstratton.edu/
Description: Proprietary, 2-year, coed. Part of Bryant and Stratton Business Institute, Inc. Awards diplomas and terminal associate degrees. Founded 1987. Setting: suburban campus with easy access to Cleveland. Educational spending for 2005 fiscal year: $1680 per student. Total enrollment: 172. 95 applied, 100% were admitted. 0% from top 10% of their high school class, 12% from top quarter, 13% from top half. Full-time: 98 students, 66% women, 34% men. Part-time: 74 students, 73% women, 27% men. 0% from out-of-state, 0% Native American, 0% Hispanic, 66% black, 1% Asian American or Pacific Islander, 0% international, 84% 25 or older, 1% transferred in. Retention: 33% of full-time freshmen returned the following year. Core. Calendar: semesters. Academic remediation for entering students, advanced placement, independent study, distance learning, double major, summer session for credit, part-time degree program, internships.
Entrance Requirements: Option: deferred admission. Required: essay, high school transcript, interview, entrance evaluation and placement evaluation, CPAt. Recommended: minimum 2.0 high school GPA, SAT or ACT. Required for some: recommendations. Entrance: minimally difficult. Application deadline: Rolling.
Collegiate Environment: Orientation program. Choral group, student-run newspaper. Social organizations: 5 open to all. Most popular organizations: Student Council, Professional Secretaries International, Accounting Club, Information Technology Organization, Ambassador Society. Major annual events: Professional Dress Seminar, Professional Lunchtime Seminars, student success cook-outs and pizza parties. Student services: personal-psychological counseling. Campus security: 24-hour emergency response devices, late night transport-escort service. College housing not available. Main library plus 1 other with 1,500 books, 19 serials, and an OPAC. Operations spending for 2004 fiscal year: $34,805. 90 computers available on campus for general student use.

■ **CAPITAL UNIVERSITY** *I-6*
2199 East Main St.
Columbus, OH 43209-2394
Tel: (614)236-6011
Free: 800-289-6289
Admissions: (614)236-6101
Fax: (614)236-6820
E-mail: admissions@capital.edu
Web Site: http://www.capital.edu/
Description: Independent, comprehensive, coed, affiliated with Evangelical Lutheran Church in America. Awards bachelor's, master's, and first professional degrees. Founded 1830. Setting: 48-acre suburban campus. Endowment: $45.8 million. Educational spending for 2005 fiscal year: $8443 per student. Total enrollment: 3,901. Faculty: 460 (218 full-time, 242 part-time). Student-undergrad faculty ratio is 10:1. 3,023 applied, 78% were admitted. 29% from top 10% of their high school class, 55% from top quarter, 86% from top half. Full-time: 2,242 students, 61% women, 39% men. Part-time: 620 students, 74% women, 26% men. Students come from 23 states and territories, 15 other countries, 0% from out-of-state, 0.2% Native American, 1% Hispanic, 12% black, 2% Asian American or Pacific Islander, 1% international, 27% 25 or older, 36% live on campus, 4% transferred in. Retention: 76% of full-time freshmen returned the following year. Academic areas with the most degrees conferred: education; health professions and related sciences; interdisciplinary studies. Core. Calendar: semesters. ESL program, services for LD students, advanced placement, self-designed majors, freshman honors college, independent study, double major, summer session for credit, part-time degree program, adult/continuing education programs, internships. Off campus study at members of the Higher Education Council of Columbus. Study abroad program. ROTC: Army, Air Force (c).
Entrance Requirements: Options: Peterson's Universal Application, Common Application, early action, deferred admission. Required: high school transcript, minimum 2.6 high school GPA, SAT or ACT. Recommended:

interview. Required for some: 1 recommendation, audition. Entrance: moderately difficult. Application deadlines: 4/15, 9/22 for early action. Notification: 9/15, 10/2 for early action.

Costs Per Year: Application fee: $25. Comprehensive fee: $30,444 includes full-time tuition ($24,100) and college room and board ($6344). Full-time tuition varies according to course load, degree level, program, and student level. Room and board charges vary according to board plan and housing facility. Part-time tuition: $756 per credit hour. Part-time tuition varies according to course load, degree level, program, and student level.

Collegiate Environment: Orientation program. Drama-theater group, choral group, student-run newspaper, radio station. Social organizations: national fraternities, national sororities, local fraternities, local sororities. Student services: health clinic, personal-psychological counseling. Campus security: 24-hour patrols, late night transport-escort service, controlled dormitory access. 1,166 college housing spaces available; 1,009 were occupied in 2003-04. Freshmen guaranteed college housing. On-campus residence required through sophomore year. Option: coed housing available. Blackmore Library with 187,281 books, 138,244 microform titles, 3,741 serials, 6,048 audiovisual materials, and an OPAC. Operations spending for 2004 fiscal year: $2.7 million. 100 computers available on campus for general student use. A campuswide network can be accessed from student residence rooms and from off campus. Staffed computer lab on campus.

Community Environment: See Ohio State University - Columbus Campus.

■ **CASE WESTERN RESERVE UNIVERSITY** *C-10*
10900 Euclid Ave.
Cleveland, OH 44106
Tel: (216)368-2000
Admissions: (216)368-4450
Fax: (216)368-5111
E-mail: admission@case.edu
Web Site: http://www.case.edu/

Description: Independent, university, coed. Awards bachelor's, master's, doctoral, and first professional degrees. Founded 1826. Setting: 150-acre urban campus. Endowment: $1.5 billion. Research spending for 2004 fiscal year: $211.8 million. Total enrollment: 9,615. Faculty: 853 (687 full-time, 166 part-time). Student-undergrad faculty ratio is 9:1. 7,181 applied, 68% were admitted. 63% from top 10% of their high school class, 91% from top quarter, 99% from top half. 60 National Merit Scholars, 61 valedictorians. Full-time: 3,714 students, 40% women, 60% men. Part-time: 235 students, 44% women, 56% men. Students come from 50 states and territories, 28 other countries, 41% from out-of-state, 0.3% Native American, 2% Hispanic, 5% black, 15% Asian American or Pacific Islander, 4% international, 3% 25 or older, 75% live on campus, 2% transferred in. Retention: 92% of full-time freshmen returned the following year. Academic areas with the most degrees conferred: engineering; biological/life sciences; social sciences. Core. Calendar: semesters. ESL program, services for LD students, advanced placement, accelerated degree program, self-designed majors, honors program, independent study, double major, summer session for credit, part-time degree program, adult/continuing education programs, co-op programs and internships, graduate courses open to undergrads. Off campus study at Cleveland Institute of Art, Cleveland Institute of Music, 11 other Cleveland area institutions. Study abroad program. ROTC: Army (c), Air Force (c).

Entrance Requirements: Options: Peterson's Universal Application, Common Application, electronic application, early admission, early action, deferred admission, international baccalaureate accepted. Required: essay, high school transcript, 1 recommendation, SAT or ACT. Recommended: interview, SAT Subject Tests. Entrance: very difficult. Application deadlines: 1/15, 11/1 for early action. Notification: 4/1, 1/1 for early action.

Costs Per Year: Application fee: $35. Comprehensive fee: $40,968 includes full-time tuition ($31,090), mandatory fees ($598), and college room and board ($9280). College room only: $5440. Part-time tuition: $1296 per credit hour.

Collegiate Environment: Orientation program. Drama-theater group, choral group, marching band, student-run newspaper, radio station. Social organizations: 100 open to all; national fraternities, national sororities, local sororities; 34% of eligible men and 23% of eligible women are members. Most popular organizations: student radio station, Habitat for Humanity, international student groups, music/dance groups. Major annual events: Winter Carnival/Spring Olympics, Hudson Relays, Engineers' Week. Student services: legal services, health clinic, personal-psychological counseling, women's center. Campus security: 24-hour emergency response devices and patrols, student patrols, late night transport-escort service, controlled dormitory access, crime prevention programs. 2,711 college housing spaces

available; 2,435 were occupied in 2003-04. Freshmen guaranteed college housing. On-campus residence required through sophomore year. Option: coed housing available. University Library plus 6 others with 2.5 million books, 2.5 million microform titles, 20,678 serials, 47,491 audiovisual materials, an OPAC, and a Web page. Operations spending for 2004 fiscal year: $13.7 million. 280 computers available on campus for general student use. Computer purchase/lease plans available. A campuswide network can be accessed from student residence rooms and from off campus. Staffed computer lab on campus.

Community Environment: The university is located on the eastern edge of Cleveland in University Circle, a 500-acre area of parks, gardens, museums, schools, hospitals, churches and human service institutions. The Cleveland Museum of Art and the Cleveland Orchestra are within walking distance, and downtown Cleveland, offering restaurants, music, theatre, and professional sports, is only ten minutes away by RTA rapid transit. Students also have easy access to many facilities provided by the city of Cleveland and the outlying areas. Among these are Cleveland's well-known "Emerald Necklace" of parks, and Blossom Music Center, the summer home of the Cleveland Orchestra. CWRU also owns a 400-acre farm in Hunting Valley, about 10 miles east of the campus, that is open to students. Recreational facilities include a picnic area, fishing ponds, hiking and ski trails, and buildings for social events.

■ **CEDARVILLE UNIVERSITY** *I-4*
251 North Main St.
Cedarville, OH 45314-0601
Tel: (937)766-2211
Free: 800-CEDARVILLE
Admissions: (937)766-7700
Fax: (937)766-7575
E-mail: admiss@cedarville.edu
Web Site: http://www.cedarville.edu/

Description: Independent Baptist, comprehensive, coed. Awards bachelor's and master's degrees. Founded 1887. Setting: 400-acre rural campus with easy access to Columbus and Dayton. Endowment: $13.5 million. Educational spending for 2005 fiscal year: $8485 per student. Total enrollment: 3,113. Faculty: 259 (208 full-time, 51 part-time). Student-undergrad faculty ratio is 13:1. 2,017 applied, 83% were admitted. 34% from top 10% of their high school class, 63% from top quarter, 89% from top half. 13 National Merit Scholars, 61 valedictorians, 195 student government officers. Full-time: 2,930 students, 56% women, 44% men. Part-time: 160 students, 54% women, 46% men. Students come from 47 states and territories, 16 other countries, 63% from out-of-state, 0.1% Native American, 2% Hispanic, 2% black, 1% Asian American or Pacific Islander, 0.5% international, 3% 25 or older, 83% live on campus, 5% transferred in. Retention: 81% of full-time freshmen returned the following year. Academic areas with the most degrees conferred: education; business/marketing; theology and religious vocations. Core. Calendar: semesters. Academic remediation for entering students, services for LD students, advanced placement, accelerated degree program, honors program, independent study, distance learning, double major, summer session for credit, part-time degree program, internships. Off campus study at Au Sable Institute. Study abroad program. ROTC: Army (c), Air Force (c).

Entrance Requirements: Options: electronic application, early admission, deferred admission, international baccalaureate accepted. Required: essay, high school transcript, minimum 3.0 high school GPA, 2 recommendations, SAT or ACT. Required for some: interview. Entrance: moderately difficult. Application deadline: Rolling. Notification: continuous.

Costs Per Year: Application fee: $30. Comprehensive fee: $22,130 includes full-time tuition ($17,120) and college room and board ($5010). College room only: $2684. Part-time tuition: $535 per credit hour.

Collegiate Environment: Orientation program. Drama-theater group, choral group, student-run newspaper, radio station. Social organizations: 52 open to all. Most popular organizations: Student Government Association, College Republicans, ASME, Chi Theta Pi, MENC. Major annual events: homecoming, Junior/Senior Banquet, ELLIV. Student services: health clinic, personal-psychological counseling. Campus security: 24-hour emergency response devices and patrols, student patrols, late night transport-escort service, controlled dormitory access. 2,523 college housing spaces available; all were occupied in 2003-04. Freshmen guaranteed college housing. On-campus residence required through senior year. Options: men-only, women-only housing available. Centennial Library with 162,195 books, 21,392 microform titles, 5,250 serials, 15,788 audiovisual materials, an OPAC, and a Web page. Operations spending for 2004 fiscal year: $1.5 million. 30

computers available on campus for general student use. Computer purchase/lease plans available. A campuswide network can be accessed from student residence rooms and from off campus. Staffed computer lab on campus.

■ CENTRAL OHIO TECHNICAL COLLEGE *H-8*
1179 University Dr.
Newark, OH 43055-1767
Tel: (740)366-1351
Admissions: (740)366-9222
Fax: (740)366-5047
E-mail: lnelson@bigvax.newark.ohio-state.edu
Web Site: http://www.cotc.edu/

Description: State-supported, 2-year, coed. Part of Ohio Board of Regents. Awards certificates and terminal associate degrees. Founded 1971. Setting: 155-acre small town campus with easy access to Columbus. Total enrollment: 2,592. 1,171 applied, 100% were admitted. Full-time: 1,149 students, 71% women, 29% men. Part-time: 1,443 students, 72% women, 28% men. Students come from 3 states and territories, 1 other country, 1% from out-of-state, 1% Native American, 1% Hispanic, 5% black, 1% Asian American or Pacific Islander, 0% international, 76% 25 or older, 1% live on campus, 5% transferred in. Retention: 52% of full-time freshmen returned the following year. Core. Academic remediation for entering students, ESL program, services for LD students, advanced placement, accelerated degree program, double major, summer session for credit, part-time degree program, adult/continuing education programs, co-op programs and internships. Off campus study at Ohio State University-Newark Campus, Higher Education Council of Columbus.
Entrance Requirements: Open admission except for health programs. Options: Common Application, electronic application, early admission, deferred admission. Required: high school transcript. Placement: ACT ASSET or ACT COMPASS required. Entrance: noncompetitive. Application deadline: Rolling.
Collegiate Environment: Orientation program. Drama-theater group, choral group. Social organizations: 15 open to all. Most popular organizations: Student Senate, Phi Theta Kappa, Student Nurses Organization, Campus Chorus, Physical Therapy Assistants Organization. Major annual events: Spring Fling, Annual 'Blood Battle' Blood Drive, Campus Artists and Performers Series. Student services: personal-psychological counseling. Campus security: 24-hour emergency response devices, student patrols, late night transport-escort service. Option: coed housing available. Newark Campus Library with 45,000 books, 500 serials, and an OPAC. 300 computers available on campus for general student use. A campuswide network can be accessed from off-campus. Staffed computer lab on campus.

■ CENTRAL STATE UNIVERSITY *J-18*
1400 Brush Row Rd.
PO Box 1004
Wilberforce, OH 45384
Tel: (937)376-6011
Admissions: (937)376-6580
Fax: (937)376-6648
E-mail: rrucker@centralstate.edu
Web Site: http://www.centralstate.edu/

Description: State-supported, comprehensive, coed. Part of Ohio Board of Regents. Awards bachelor's and master's degrees. Founded 1887. Setting: 60-acre rural campus with easy access to Dayton. Research spending for 2004 fiscal year: $1.2 million. Educational spending for 2005 fiscal year: $4880 per student. Total enrollment: 1,623. Faculty: 162 (94 full-time, 68 part-time). Student-undergrad faculty ratio is 13:1. 4,563 applied, 38% were admitted. 1% from top 10% of their high school class, 5% from top quarter, 57% from top half. 2 valedictorians. Full-time: 1,450 students, 48% women, 52% men. Part-time: 167 students, 60% women, 40% men. Students come from 26 states and territories, 5 other countries, 30% from out-of-state, 0.1% Native American, 1% Hispanic, 87% black, 0.1% Asian American or Pacific Islander, 1% international, 12% 25 or older, 50% live on campus, 8% transferred in. Retention: 47% of full-time freshmen returned the following year. Academic areas with the most degrees conferred: business/marketing; education; communications/journalism; social sciences. Core. Calendar: semesters. Services for LD students, honors program, independent study, double major, summer session for credit, part-time degree program, adult/continuing education programs, co-op programs and internships. Off campus study at members of the Southwestern Ohio Council for Higher Education. Study abroad program. ROTC: Army.

Entrance Requirements: Open admission for state residents. Option: Common Application. Required: high school transcript, SAT or ACT. Recommended: interview, ACT. Required for some: minimum 2.0 high school GPA, 2 recommendations, 2.5 high school GPA for nonresidents. Entrance: minimally difficult. Application deadline: 6/15. Notification: continuous.
Costs Per Year: Application fee: $20. State resident tuition: $2726 full-time. Nonresident tuition: $8546 full-time. Mandatory fees: $2268 full-time. Full-time tuition and fees vary according to course load. College room and board: $6982. Room and board charges vary according to board plan.
Collegiate Environment: Orientation program. Drama-theater group, choral group, marching band, student-run newspaper, radio station. Social organizations: 115 open to all; national fraternities, national sororities, local fraternities, local sororities; 45% of eligible men and 65% of eligible women are members. Most popular organizations: Student Ambassadors, student government. Major annual events: homecoming, May Week. Student services: health clinic, personal-psychological counseling. Campus security: 24-hour emergency response devices and patrols, controlled dormitory access. 978 college housing spaces available; 926 were occupied in 2003-04. Freshmen guaranteed college housing. On-campus residence required in freshman year. Options: men-only, women-only housing available. Hallie Q. Brown Memorial Library plus 1 other with 280,470 books, 608,887 microform titles, 26,066 serials, 497 audiovisual materials, and an OPAC. Operations spending for 2004 fiscal year: $610,328. 338 computers available on campus for general student use. A campuswide network can be accessed. Staffed computer lab on campus.
Community Environment: A college community, Wilberforce was named after William Wilberforce, the English philanthropist who fought for the abolition of slave trade. The community is known as a noted African-American cultural center. Part-time employment opportunities are available for students.

■ CHATFIELD COLLEGE
20918 State Route 251
St. Martin, OH 45118-9705
Tel: (513)875-3344
Fax: (513)875-3912
E-mail: ajones@chatfield.edu
Web Site: http://www.chatfield.edu/

Description: Independent, 2-year, coed, affiliated with Roman Catholic Church. Awards transfer associate and terminal associate degrees. Founded 1970. Setting: 200-acre rural campus with easy access to Cincinnati and Dayton. Endowment: $700,000. Educational spending for 2005 fiscal year: $4388 per student. Total enrollment: 230. Student-undergrad faculty ratio is 12:1. 129 applied, 100% were admitted. 0% from out-of-state, 30% black, 50% 25 or older. Core. Calendar: semesters. Academic remediation for entering students, advanced placement, summer session for credit, part-time degree program, adult/continuing education programs, internships. Off campus study at 14 members of the Greater Cincinnati Consortium of Colleges and Universities.
Entrance Requirements: Open admission. Options: Common Application, early admission, deferred admission. Required: high school transcript. Entrance: noncompetitive. Application deadline: Rolling. Notification: continuous.
Costs Per Year: Application fee: $10. Tuition: $3360 full-time, $280 per credit hour part-time. Mandatory fees: $80 full-time.
Collegiate Environment: Orientation program. Drama-theater group, choral group, student-run newspaper. Major annual event: Quilt and Craft Show. Student services: personal-psychological counseling. Campus security: 12-hour night patrols by security. College housing not available. Chatfield College Library with 15,000 books, 30 serials, and an OPAC. Operations spending for 2004 fiscal year: $113,795. 16 computers available on campus for general student use. A campuswide network can be accessed from off-campus. Staffed computer lab on campus.

■ CINCINNATI CHRISTIAN UNIVERSITY *L-2*
2700 Glenway Ave.
PO Box 04320
Cincinnati, OH 45204-3200
Tel: (513)244-8100
Free: 800-949-4CBC
Admissions: 800-949-4222
Fax: (513)244-8140
Web Site: http://www.ccuniversity.edu/

Description: Independent, comprehensive, coed, affiliated with Church of Christ. Awards associate, bachelor's, master's, and first professional degrees. Founded 1924. Setting: 40-acre urban campus. Endowment: $988,063. Educational spending for 2005 fiscal year: $2700 per student. Total enrollment: 922. 227 applied, 99% were admitted. 22% from top 10% of their high school class, 37% from top quarter, 69% from top half. 9 National Merit Scholars, 6 class presidents, 5 valedictorians, 28 student government officers. Full-time: 501 students, 45% women, 55% men. Part-time: 125 students, 40% women, 60% men. Students come from 33 states and territories, 6 other countries, 33% from out-of-state, 20% 25 or older, 16% transferred in. Retention: 62% of full-time freshmen returned the following year. Core. Calendar: semesters. Academic remediation for entering students, advanced placement, independent study, double major, summer session for credit, part-time degree program, adult/continuing education programs, internships, graduate courses open to undergrads. Off campus study at College of Mount St. Joseph, Greater Cincinnati Consortium of Colleges and Universities.

Entrance Requirements: Options: early admission, deferred admission. Required: essay, high school transcript, 3 recommendations, SAT or ACT. Recommended: minimum 2.0 high school GPA, interview. Entrance: minimally difficult. Application deadline: 8/10. Notification: continuous.

Costs Per Year: Application fee: $35. Comprehensive fee: $15,080 includes full-time tuition ($9120), mandatory fees ($570), and college room and board ($5390). Part-time tuition: $285 per credit hour. Part-time mandatory fees: $75 per term.

Collegiate Environment: Orientation program. Drama-theater group, choral group, student-run newspaper. Social organizations: 12 open to all. Major annual events: Hearts Day, Fall Thing, Campus Picnic. Student services: health clinic, personal-psychological counseling. Campus security: 24-hour emergency response devices and patrols, student patrols. On-campus residence required through sophomore year. Options: men-only, women-only housing available. Cincinnati Bible College Library with 93,000 books, 656 serials, and an OPAC. Operations spending for 2004 fiscal year: $263,000. 32 computers available on campus for general student use. A campuswide network can be accessed from student residence rooms and from off campus. Staffed computer lab on campus.

■ CINCINNATI COLLEGE OF MORTUARY SCIENCE *L-2*

645 West North Bend Rd.
Cincinnati, OH 45224-1462
Tel: (513)761-2020
Fax: (513)761-3333
Web Site: http://www.ccms.edu/

Description: Independent, primarily 2-year, coed. Awards terminal associate and bachelor's degrees. Founded 1882. Setting: 10-acre urban campus. Educational spending for 2005 fiscal year: $13,500 per student. Total enrollment: 133. Student-undergrad faculty ratio is 5:1. 12 applied, 100% were admitted. Full-time: 133 students, 46% women, 54% men. Students come from 17 states and territories, 1% Hispanic, 7% black, 55% 25 or older, 68% transferred in. Core. Academic remediation for entering students, advanced placement, summer session for credit, adult/continuing education programs.

Entrance Requirements: Option: deferred admission. Required: high school transcript. Recommended: recommendations. Entrance: minimally difficult. Application deadline: Rolling.

Costs Per Year: Application fee: $25. Tuition: $13,500 full-time, $180 per credit hour part-time.

Collegiate Environment: Social organizations: local fraternities, local sororities; 50% of eligible men and 50% of eligible women are members. College housing not available. 5,000 books, 30 serials, and a Web page. 16 computers available on campus for general student use. Staffed computer lab on campus.

Community Environment: See University of Cincinnati.

■ CINCINNATI STATE TECHNICAL AND COMMUNITY COLLEGE *L-2*

3520 Central Parkway
Cincinnati, OH 45223-2690
Tel: (513)569-1500
Admissions: (513)569-1550
Fax: (513)569-1562
E-mail: gaby.boeckermann@cincinnatistate.edu
Web Site: http://www.cincinnatistate.edu/

Description: State-supported, 2-year, coed. Part of Ohio Board of Regents. Awards certificates, transfer associate, and terminal associate degrees. Founded 1966. Setting: 46-acre urban campus. Endowment: $1.4 million.

Educational spending for 2005 fiscal year: $6218 per student. Total enrollment: 8,470. Student-undergrad faculty ratio is 17:1. Full-time: 3,485 students, 54% women, 46% men. Part-time: 4,985 students, 58% women, 42% men. Students come from 9 states and territories, 62 other countries, 11% from out-of-state, 0.2% Native American, 1% Hispanic, 26% black, 1% Asian American or Pacific Islander, 3% international, 45% 25 or older. Retention: 48% of full-time freshmen returned the following year. Core. Calendar: 5 ten-week terms. Academic remediation for entering students, ESL program, services for LD students, advanced placement, self-designed majors, honors program, distance learning, double major, summer session for credit, part-time degree program, co-op programs and internships. Off campus study at 12 members of the Greater Cincinnati Consortium of Colleges and Universities.

Entrance Requirements: Open admission. Option: electronic application. Required: high school transcript. Entrance: noncompetitive. Application deadline: Rolling. Notification: continuous.

Costs Per Year: Application fee: $0. State resident tuition: $4411 full-time, $80.20 per credit hour part-time. Nonresident tuition: $8822 full-time, $160.40 per credit hour part-time. Mandatory fees: $344 full-time, $6 per credit hour part-time, $31 per term part-time.

Collegiate Environment: Orientation program. Drama-theater group. Social organizations: 12 open to all. Most popular organizations: student government, Nursing Student Association, Phi Theta Kappa, American Society of Civil Engineers, Students in Free Enterprise. Major annual events: homecoming, Student government Picnic, Spirit Week. Student services: personal-psychological counseling. Campus security: 24-hour emergency response devices and patrols, late night transport-escort service. College housing not available. Johnnie Mae Berry Library with 30,762 books, 268 serials, 3,428 audiovisual materials, an OPAC, and a Web page. 150 computers available on campus for general student use. A campuswide network can be accessed from off-campus. Staffed computer lab on campus.

Community Environment: See University of Cincinnati.

■ CIRCLEVILLE BIBLE COLLEGE *J-6*

1476 Lancaster Pike, PO Box 458
Circleville, OH 43113-9487
Tel: (740)474-8896
Free: 800-701-0222
Admissions: (740)477-7741
Fax: (740)477-7755
E-mail: sfaughn@biblecollege.edu
Web Site: http://www.biblecollege.edu/

Description: Independent, 4-year, coed, affiliated with Churches of Christ in Christian Union. Awards associate and bachelor's degrees. Founded 1948. Setting: 40-acre small town campus with easy access to Columbus. Educational spending for 2005 fiscal year: $2495 per student. Total enrollment: 317. 135 applied, 61% were admitted. 7% from top 10% of their high school class, 26% from top quarter, 55% from top half. Full-time: 284 students, 47% women, 53% men. Part-time: 33 students, 45% women, 55% men. Students come from 11 states and territories, 26% from out-of-state, 1% Native American, 1% Hispanic, 6% black, 1% Asian American or Pacific Islander, 42% 25 or older, 55% live on campus, 7% transferred in. Retention: 71% of full-time freshmen returned the following year. Core. Calendar: semesters. Academic remediation for entering students, services for LD students, advanced placement, self-designed majors, honors program, independent study, double major, summer session for credit, part-time degree program, adult/continuing education programs, internships. Off campus study at Columbus State Community College.

Entrance Requirements: Options: Common Application, electronic application, early admission. Required: essay, high school transcript, 4 recommendations, medical form. Recommended: SAT. Required for some: interview, ACT. Entrance: minimally difficult. Application deadline: Rolling. Notification: continuous.

Costs Per Year: Application fee: $25. Comprehensive fee: $16,436 includes full-time tuition ($9596), mandatory fees ($956), and college room and board ($5884). Part-time tuition: $370 per semester hour. Part-time mandatory fees: $345 per term.

Collegiate Environment: Orientation program. Drama-theater group, choral group. Social organizations: 10 open to all. Most popular organizations: Student Council, S.I., SHINE, prison ministries, choir. Major annual events: Mr. and Miss CBC, Youth Conference, Convocation. Student services: legal services, personal-psychological counseling. Campus security: security checks after midnight. On-campus residence required through senior year. Options: men-only, women-only housing available. Melvin Maxwell Memorial

Library with 37,521 books, 111 serials, 1,995 audiovisual materials, and an OPAC. Operations spending for 2004 fiscal year: $107,466. 25 computers available on campus for general student use. A campuswide network can be accessed from student residence rooms. Staffed computer lab on campus.

Community Environment: Circleville is situated in the central part of the state, 23 miles south of Columbus. A shopping center and a number of civic and service organizations serve the community. The annual Circleville Pumpkin Show features a 350-pound pumpkin pie, five feet in diameter, attracting over 500,000 visitors from throughout the world.

■ CLARK STATE COMMUNITY COLLEGE *I-4*

570 East Leffel Ln., PO Box 570
Springfield, OH 45501-0570
Tel: (937)325-0691
Admissions: (937)328-6027
E-mail: schaidja@clarkstate.edu
Web Site: http://www.clarkstate.edu/

Description: State-supported, 2-year, coed. Part of Ohio Board of Regents. Awards certificates, transfer associate, and terminal associate degrees. Founded 1962. Setting: 60-acre suburban campus with easy access to Columbus and Dayton. Total enrollment: 3,504. Student-undergrad faculty ratio is 16:1. 1,743 applied, 100% were admitted. Full-time: 1,583 students, 65% women, 35% men. Part-time: 1,921 students, 72% women, 28% men. 0.4% Native American, 1% Hispanic, 14% black, 1% Asian American or Pacific Islander, 0.03% international, 4% transferred in. Core. Academic remediation for entering students, services for LD students, advanced placement, distance learning, summer session for credit, part-time degree program, adult/continuing education programs, co-op programs. Off campus study at 17 members of the Southwestern Ohio Council for Higher Education. ROTC: Army (c).

Entrance Requirements: Open admission except for some programs. Options: Common Application, electronic application, early admission, deferred admission. Required: high school transcript. Entrance: noncompetitive. Application deadline: Rolling. Notification: continuous.

Costs Per Year: Application fee: $15. State resident tuition: $3720 full-time, $77.50 per credit hour part-time. Nonresident tuition: $7440 full-time, $155 per credit hour part-time. Mandatory fees: $1500 full-time.

Collegiate Environment: Drama-theater group, choral group, student-run newspaper. Social organizations: local fraternities, local sororities. Most popular organizations: Student Government Association, Minority Student Forum. Major annual event: Multicultural Day. Student services: health clinic, personal-psychological counseling. Campus security: late night transport-escort service. College housing not available. Clark State Community College Library with 31,988 books, 378 serials, an OPAC, and a Web page. 350 computers available on campus for general student use. A campuswide network can be accessed from off-campus. Staffed computer lab on campus.

Community Environment: See Wittenberg University.

■ THE CLEVELAND INSTITUTE OF ART *C-10*

11141 East Blvd.
Cleveland, OH 44106-1700
Tel: (216)421-7000
Free: 800-223-4700
Admissions: (216)421-7418
Fax: (216)421-7438
E-mail: 74527.17@compuserve.com
Web Site: http://www.cia.edu/

Description: Independent, comprehensive, coed. Awards bachelor's and master's degrees. Founded 1882. Setting: 488-acre urban campus. Endowment: $17.9 million. Educational spending for 2005 fiscal year: $23,385 per student. Total enrollment: 610. 531 applied, 76% were admitted. 6% from top 10% of their high school class, 29% from top quarter, 66% from top half. Full-time: 581 students, 51% women, 49% men. Part-time: 23 students, 91% women, 9% men. Students come from 26 states and territories, 16 other countries, 32% from out-of-state, 0.2% Native American, 2% Hispanic, 5% black, 4% Asian American or Pacific Islander, 3% international, 11% 25 or older, 20% live on campus, 9% transferred in. Retention: 82% of full-time freshmen returned the following year. Core. Calendar: semesters. Academic remediation for entering students, services for LD students, advanced placement, honors program, independent study, part-time degree program, internships. Off campus study at Case Western Reserve University, Northeast Ohio Commission on Higher Education, Association of Independent Colleges of Art and Design. Study abroad program.

Entrance Requirements: Options: Peterson's Universal Application, electronic application, deferred admission. Required: essay, high school transcript, minimum 2.0 high school GPA, 2 recommendations, portfolio, SAT or ACT. Recommended: interview. Entrance: moderately difficult. Application deadline: Rolling. Notification: continuous.

Costs Per Year: Application fee: $30. Comprehensive fee: $36,313 includes full-time tuition ($24,917), mandatory fees ($2260), and college room and board ($9136). College room only: $5480. Room and board charges vary according to board plan and housing facility. Part-time tuition: $1045 per credit. Part-time mandatory fees: $90 per credit. Part-time tuition and fees vary according to course load.

Collegiate Environment: Orientation program. Student-run newspaper. Social organizations: 10 open to all. Most popular organizations: Photo Club, PUMA, Artist for Christ, GIBT, Student Artist Association. Major annual events: Halloween Party, Student Independent Exhibition, Pink Pig year-end picnic and art auction. Student services: health clinic, personal-psychological counseling. Campus security: 24-hour emergency response devices and patrols, late night transport-escort service, controlled dormitory access. 132 college housing spaces available; 100 were occupied in 2003-04. Freshmen given priority for college housing. On-campus residence required in freshman year. Option: coed housing available. Jessica R. Gund Memorial Library with 42,000 books, 18,200 microform titles, 250 serials, 100,000 audiovisual materials, an OPAC, and a Web page. Operations spending for 2004 fiscal year: $350,511. 80 computers available on campus for general student use. Computer purchase/lease plans available. A campuswide network can be accessed from off-campus. Staffed computer lab on campus.

Community Environment: See Case Western Reserve University.

■ CLEVELAND INSTITUTE OF ELECTRONICS *C-10*

1776 East Seventeenth St.
Cleveland, OH 44114-3636
Tel: (216)781-9400
Free: 800-243-6446
Web Site: http://www.cie-wc.edu/

Description: Proprietary, 2-year, coed. Awards terminal associate degrees (offers only external degree programs conducted through home study). Founded 1934. Total enrollment: 2,602. Students come from 52 states and territories, 70 other countries, 97% from out-of-state, 85% 25 or older. Calendar: continuous. Part-time degree program, external degree program, adult/continuing education programs.

Entrance Requirements: Open admission. Options: Common Application, electronic application, early admission. Required: high school transcript. Entrance: noncompetitive. Application deadline: Rolling. Notification: continuous.

Costs Per Year: Tuition: $1770 per term part-time.

Collegiate Environment: College housing not available. 5,000 books and 38 serials.

■ CLEVELAND INSTITUTE OF MUSIC *C-10*

11021 East Blvd.
Cleveland, OH 44106-1776
Tel: (216)791-5000
Admissions: (216)795-3107
Fax: (216)791-1530
E-mail: cimadmission@po.cwru.edu
Web Site: http://www.cim.edu/

Description: Independent, comprehensive, coed. Awards bachelor's, master's, and doctoral degrees. Founded 1920. Setting: 488-acre urban campus. Endowment: $24 million. Educational spending for 2005 fiscal year: $16,700 per student. Total enrollment: 409. Faculty: 105 (33 full-time, 72 part-time). Student-undergrad faculty ratio is 7:1. 447 applied, 34% were admitted. Full-time: 243 students, 55% women, 45% men. Part-time: 1 student, 100% women. Students come from 41 states and territories, 16 other countries, 81% from out-of-state, 1% Native American, 5% Hispanic, 2% black, 10% Asian American or Pacific Islander, 11% international, 2% 25 or older, 40% live on campus, 4% transferred in. Retention: 95% of full-time freshmen returned the following year. Academic area with the most degrees conferred: visual and performing arts. Calendar: semesters. Academic remediation for entering students, ESL program, advanced placement, accelerated degree program, independent study, distance learning, double major, summer session for credit, internships, graduate courses open to undergrads. Off campus study at Case Western Reserve University. Study abroad program. ROTC: Army (c), Air Force (c).

Entrance Requirements: Options: early admission, deferred admission, international baccalaureate accepted. Required: essay, high school transcript, 2 recommendations, audition. Recommended: interview. Required for some: SAT or ACT. Entrance: very difficult. Application deadline: 12/1. Notification: 4/1.

Costs Per Year: Application fee: $100. Comprehensive fee: $35,596 includes full-time tuition ($25,870), mandatory fees ($1000), and college room and board ($8726). College room only: $5120. Room and board charges vary according to board plan. Part-time tuition: $1078 per credit hour.

Collegiate Environment: Orientation program. Choral group. Student services: health clinic, personal-psychological counseling. Campus security: 24-hour emergency response devices and patrols, late night transport-escort service, controlled dormitory access. 100 college housing spaces available; all were occupied in 2003-04. Freshmen guaranteed college housing. On-campus residence required through sophomore year. Option: coed housing available. Cleveland Institute of Music Library with 50,924 books, 115 serials, 22,312 audiovisual materials, an OPAC, and a Web page. Operations spending for 2004 fiscal year: $262,000. 25 computers available on campus for general student use. Computer purchase/lease plans available. A campuswide network can be accessed from student residence rooms and from off campus. Staffed computer lab on campus.

Community Environment: See Case Western Reserve University.

■ **CLEVELAND STATE UNIVERSITY** *C-10*
2121 Euclid Ave.
Cleveland, OH 44115
Tel: (216)687-2000; 888-CSU-OHIO
Fax: (216)687-9366
Web Site: http://www.csuohio.edu/

Description: State-supported, university, coed. Awards bachelor's, master's, doctoral, and first professional degrees and post-master's certificates. Founded 1964. Setting: 70-acre urban campus with easy access to Akron. Endowment: $21.4 million. Research spending for 2004 fiscal year: $15.2 million. Total enrollment: 15,722. Faculty: 997 (575 full-time, 422 part-time). Student-undergrad faculty ratio is 14:1. 3,153 applied, 80% were admitted. 9% from top 10% of their high school class, 29% from top quarter, 53% from top half. Full-time: 6,771 students, 54% women, 46% men. Part-time: 3,182 students, 57% women, 43% men. Students come from 21 states and territories, 63 other countries, 2% from out-of-state, 0.3% Native American, 3% Hispanic, 22% black, 3% Asian American or Pacific Islander, 2% international, 36% 25 or older, 4% live on campus, 10% transferred in. Retention: 61% of full-time freshmen returned the following year. Academic areas with the most degrees conferred: business/marketing; education; social sciences. Core. Calendar: semesters. Academic remediation for entering students, ESL program, advanced placement, accelerated degree program, self-designed majors, freshman honors college, honors program, independent study, summer session for credit, part-time degree program, adult/continuing education programs, co-op programs and internships, graduate courses open to undergrads. Off campus study at 7 members of the Cleveland Commission on Higher Education, University of Akron, Baldwin-Wallace College, University of Toledo. Study abroad program. ROTC: Army (c), Naval (c), Air Force (c).

Entrance Requirements: Open admission for state residents. Options: Peterson's Universal Application, Common Application, deferred admission. Required: high school transcript, SAT or ACT. Entrance: noncompetitive. Application deadline: Rolling. Notification: continuous.

Costs Per Year: Application fee: $30. State resident tuition: $6792 full-time, $283 per semester hour part-time. Nonresident tuition: $9216 full-time, $384 per semester hour part-time. Full-time tuition varies according to program and student level. Part-time tuition varies according to program and student level. College room and board: $6809. College room only: $4091. Room and board charges vary according to board plan and housing facility.

Collegiate Environment: Orientation program. Drama-theater group, choral group, student-run newspaper, radio station. Social organizations: 150 open to all; national fraternities, national sororities, local fraternities; 5% of eligible men and 5% of eligible women are members. Most popular organizations: honor societies, International Student Association, Chinese Student Association. Major annual events: Homecoming, Spring Fest, Black Aspirations Week. Student services: health clinic, personal-psychological counseling, women's center. Campus security: 24-hour emergency response devices and patrols, student patrols, late night transport-escort service, controlled dormitory access. 450 college housing spaces available; 390 were occupied in 2003-04. Freshmen guaranteed college housing. Option: coed housing

available. University Library plus 1 other with 484,914 books, 690,023 microform titles, 6,186 serials, 101,376 audiovisual materials, an OPAC, and a Web page. Operations spending for 2004 fiscal year: $8.2 million. 600 computers available on campus for general student use. Computer purchase/lease plans available. A campuswide network can be accessed. Staffed computer lab on campus.

■ **COLLEGE OF ART ADVERTISING** *L-2*
4343 Bridgetown Rd.
Cincinnati, OH 45211-4427
Tel: (513)574-1010
Admissions: (937)294-0592
Fax: (513)574-6116
E-mail: janet.bussberg@fuse.net
Web Site: http://www.collegeofartadvertising.com/
Description: Proprietary, 2-year.

■ **COLLEGE OF MOUNT ST. JOSEPH** *L-2*
5701 Delhi Rd.
Cincinnati, OH 45233-1670
Tel: (513)244-4200
Free: 800-654-9314
Admissions: (513)244-4531
Fax: (513)244-4629
E-mail: peggy_minnich@mail.msj.edu
Web Site: http://www.msj.edu/

Description: Independent Roman Catholic, comprehensive, coed. Awards associate, bachelor's, and master's degrees. Founded 1920. Setting: 88-acre suburban campus. Endowment: $20 million. Educational spending for 2005 fiscal year: $6659 per student. Total enrollment: 2,233. Faculty: 233 (124 full-time, 109 part-time). Student-undergrad faculty ratio is 11:1. 1,087 applied, 73% were admitted. 13% from top 10% of their high school class, 36% from top quarter, 69% from top half. 1 National Merit Scholar, 5 class presidents, 5 valedictorians, 50 student government officers. Full-time: 1,338 students, 63% women, 37% men. Part-time: 597 students, 82% women, 18% men. Students come from 21 states and territories, 12% from out-of-state, 0.2% Native American, 1% Hispanic, 10% black, 0.4% Asian American or Pacific Islander, 0.4% international, 34% 25 or older, 23% live on campus, 9% transferred in. Retention: 78% of full-time freshmen returned the following year. Academic areas with the most degrees conferred: health professions and related sciences; business/marketing; personal and culinary services. Core. Calendar: semesters. Academic remediation for entering students, services for LD students, advanced placement, accelerated degree program, honors program, independent study, distance learning, double major, summer session for credit, part-time degree program, adult/continuing education programs, co-op programs and internships, graduate courses open to undergrads. Off campus study at Greater Cincinnati Consortium of Colleges and Universities. Study abroad program. ROTC: Army (c), Air Force (c).

Entrance Requirements: Options: Common Application, electronic application, deferred admission, international baccalaureate accepted. Required: high school transcript, SAT or ACT. Recommended: minimum 2.5 high school GPA, minimum SAT score of 960 or ACT score of 19. Required for some: 1 recommendation, interview. Entrance: moderately difficult. Application deadline: 8/15. Notification: continuous.

Costs Per Year: Application fee: $25. Comprehensive fee: $24,860 includes full-time tuition ($18,400), mandatory fees ($390), and college room and board ($6070). College room only: $3000. Full-time tuition and fees vary according to course load, program, and reciprocity agreements. Room and board charges vary according to board plan and housing facility. Part-time tuition: $430 per semester hour. Part-time mandatory fees: $65 per term. Part-time tuition and fees vary according to course load, location, program, and reciprocity agreements.

Collegiate Environment: Orientation program. Drama-theater group, choral group, marching band, student-run newspaper. Social organizations: 40 open to all. Most popular organizations: Student Government Association, Black Student Union, peer educators, Campus Activities Board, Campus Ambassadors. Major annual events: Musicfest, Laughter on the Hill, MSJ Trick or Treat. Student services: health clinic, personal-psychological counseling, women's center. Campus security: 24-hour emergency response devices and patrols, late night transport-escort service. 450 college housing spaces available; 414 were occupied in 2003-04. Freshmen given priority for college housing. On-campus residence required through sophomore year. Option: coed housing available. Archbishop Alter Library with 97,576 books,

380,391 microform titles, 425 serials, 3,414 audiovisual materials, an OPAC, and a Web page. Operations spending for 2004 fiscal year: $591,295. 278 computers available on campus for general student use. Computer purchase/lease plans available. A campuswide network can be accessed from student residence rooms and from off campus. Staffed computer lab on campus.

Community Environment: See University of Cincinnati.

■ **THE COLLEGE OF WOOSTER** *F-9*
1189 Beall Ave.
Wooster, OH 44691-2363
Tel: (330)263-2000
Free: 800-877-9905
Admissions: (330)263-2270
Fax: (330)263-2621
E-mail: admissions@acs.wooster.edu
Web Site: http://www.wooster.edu/

Description: Independent, 4-year, coed, affiliated with Presbyterian Church (U.S.A.). Awards bachelor's degrees. Founded 1866. Setting: 240-acre small town campus with easy access to Cleveland. Endowment: $208.1 million. Research spending for 2004 fiscal year: $570,498. Educational spending for 2005 fiscal year: $10,907 per student. Total enrollment: 1,846. Student-undergrad faculty ratio is 12:1. 2,542 applied, 75% were admitted. 30% from top 10% of their high school class, 66% from top quarter, 92% from top half. Full-time: 1,813 students, 52% women, 48% men. Part-time: 33 students, 55% women, 45% men. Students come from 47 states and territories, 37 other countries, 48% from out-of-state, 0.2% Native American, 2% Hispanic, 4% black, 2% Asian American or Pacific Islander, 5% international, 1% 25 or older, 99% live on campus, 1% transferred in. Retention: 88% of full-time freshmen returned the following year. Academic areas with the most degrees conferred: social sciences; history; English. Core. Calendar: semesters. Services for LD students, advanced placement, self-designed majors, independent study, double major, summer session for credit, internships. Off campus study. Study abroad program.

Entrance Requirements: Options: Peterson's Universal Application, Common Application, electronic application, early admission, early decision, deferred admission, international baccalaureate accepted. Required: essay, high school transcript, 2 recommendations, SAT or ACT. Recommended: interview. Entrance: moderately difficult. Application deadlines: 2/15, 12/1 for early decision plan 1, 1/15 for early decision plan 2. Notification: 4/1, 12/15 for early decision plan 1, 2/1 for early decision plan 2.

Costs Per Year: Application fee: $40. Comprehensive fee: $35,290 includes full-time tuition ($28,230) and college room and board ($7060). College room only: $3210. Full-time tuition varies according to course load and reciprocity agreements.

Collegiate Environment: Orientation program. Drama-theater group, choral group, marching band, student-run newspaper, radio station. Social organizations: 102 open to all; local fraternities, local sororities, coed fraternity; 9% of eligible men and 10% of eligible women are members. Most popular organizations: Volunteer Network, Christian Fellowship, National Student Speech, Hearing, and Language Association, Gay, Lesbian, Bisexual, Transgendered and Allies, Let's Dance. Major annual events: Winter Gala, Party on the Green, Scot Spirit Day. Student services: health clinic, personal-psychological counseling, women's center. Campus security: 24-hour emergency response devices and patrols, student patrols, late night transport-escort service, controlled dormitory access. 1,860 college housing spaces available. Freshmen guaranteed college housing. On-campus residence required through senior year. Options: coed, women-only housing available. The College of Wooster Libraries plus 3 others with 581,518 books, 210,094 microform titles, 12,416 audiovisual materials, an OPAC, and a Web page. Operations spending for 2004 fiscal year: $2.4 million. 500 computers available on campus for general student use. Computer purchase/lease plans available. A campuswide network can be accessed from student residence rooms and from off campus. Staffed computer lab on campus.

Community Environment: City of Wooster population of 22,000, county seat of Wayne County, and leading agricultural region in the United States. In Ohio, Wayne County ranks first in cash receipts from dairy products, cattle and calves, and first in production of hay and oats. The Ohio Agricultural Research and Development Center is second largest in the United States. Companies in the city include Newell Rubbermaid Incorporated, Wooster Brush Company, the Gerstenslager Company, Bell and Howell, Frito-Lay, and others. Other educational institutions include Ohio State University's Agricultural Technical Institute and the Wayne General and Technical Col-

lege. Wooster has been designated "Tree City, U.S.A." Students have access to Cleveland, Columbus, Pittsburgh, Cincinnati, and Akron.

■ **COLUMBUS COLLEGE OF ART & DESIGN** *I-6*
107 North Ninth St.
Columbus, OH 43215-1758
Tel: (614)224-9101; 877-997-2223
Web Site: http://www.ccad.edu/

Description: Independent, 4-year, coed. Awards bachelor's degrees. Founded 1879. Setting: 10-acre urban campus. Endowment: $6.9 million. Educational spending for 2005 fiscal year: $5298 per student. Total enrollment: 1,455. Student-undergrad faculty ratio is 12:1. 487 applied, 72% were admitted. 3% from top 10% of their high school class, 27% from top quarter, 48% from top half. Full-time: 1,256 students, 51% women, 49% men. Part-time: 199 students, 62% women, 38% men. Students come from 37 states and territories, 18 other countries, 23% from out-of-state, 0.3% Native American, 3% Hispanic, 7% black, 2% Asian American or Pacific Islander, 7% international, 10% 25 or older, 20% live on campus, 4% transferred in. Retention: 82% of full-time freshmen returned the following year. Academic area with the most degrees conferred: visual and performing arts. Core. Calendar: semesters. Academic remediation for entering students, ESL program, services for LD students, advanced placement, independent study, double major, summer session for credit, part-time degree program, internships. Off campus study at members of the Higher Education Council of Columbus.

Entrance Requirements: Options: deferred admission, international baccalaureate accepted. Required: essay, high school transcript, minimum 2.0 high school GPA, 1 recommendation, portfolio, SAT or ACT. Recommended: interview. Entrance: moderately difficult. Application deadline: Rolling. Notification: continuous.

Costs Per Year: Application fee: $25. Comprehensive fee: $26,728 includes full-time tuition ($19,728), mandatory fees ($550), and college room and board ($6450). Room and board charges vary according to housing facility and student level. Part-time tuition: $822 per credit. Part-time mandatory fees: $275 per term. Part-time tuition and fees vary according to course load.

Collegiate Environment: Orientation program. Social organizations: 5 open to all. Most popular organizations: Student Government Interest Group, International Student Group, Student Art Critique, Anime Club, Environmental Awareness Society. Major annual events: Annual Student Art Exhibition, Bi-Annual Student Art Sales, Big Boo Halloween Party. Student services: legal services, personal-psychological counseling. Campus security: 24-hour emergency response devices and patrols, late night transport-escort service, controlled dormitory access. 312 college housing spaces available; 267 were occupied in 2003-04. Freshmen given priority for college housing. On-campus residence required in freshman year. Option: coed housing available. Packard Library with 49,330 books, 17,950 microform titles, 381 serials, 121,104 audiovisual materials, an OPAC, and a Web page. Operations spending for 2004 fiscal year: $673,427. 226 computers available on campus for general student use. A campuswide network can be accessed. Staffed computer lab on campus.

Community Environment: See Ohio State University - Columbus Campus.

■ **COLUMBUS STATE COMMUNITY COLLEGE** *I-6*
Box 1609
Columbus, OH 43216-1609
Tel: (614)287-2400
Free: 800-621-6407
Admissions: (614)287-2669
Fax: (614)287-5117
E-mail: kconner@cscc.edu
Web Site: http://www.cscc.edu/

Description: State-supported, 2-year, coed. Part of Ohio Board of Regents. Awards certificates, transfer associate, and terminal associate degrees. Founded 1963. Setting: 75-acre urban campus. Total enrollment: 21,872. 3,058 applied, 100% were admitted. Full-time: 8,530 students, 59% women, 41% men. Part-time: 13,342 students, 59% women, 41% men. Students come from 41 states and territories, 127 other countries, 1% from out-of-state, 1% Native American, 2% Hispanic, 23% black, 3% Asian American or Pacific Islander, 1% international, 57% 25 or older, 3% transferred in. Retention: 48% of full-time freshmen returned the following year. Core. Academic remediation for entering students, ESL program, services for LD students, advanced placement, self-designed majors, honors program, distance learning, summer session for credit, part-time degree program, adult/continuing education programs, co-op programs and internships. Off campus study at members of the Higher Education Council of Columbus. ROTC: Army, Air Force (c).

Entrance Requirements: Open admission. Options: Common Application, early admission, deferred admission. Recommended: high school transcript. Placement: ACT COMPASS required. Entrance: noncompetitive. Application deadline: Rolling. Notification: continuous.

Costs Per Year: Application fee: $10. One-time mandatory fee: $35. State resident tuition: $2736 full-time, $76 per credit part-time. Nonresident tuition: $6048 full-time, $168 per credit part-time.

Collegiate Environment: Choral group. Social organizations: 17 open to all. Most popular organizations: Phi Theta Kappa; Alpha Xi Tau, African-American Women's Support Group, Society of Manufacturing Engineers, Student Organization for Legal Assistants. Major annual events: Welcome Back, May Day, homecoming. Student services: health clinic, personal-psychological counseling. Campus security: 24-hour emergency response devices and patrols, late night transport-escort service. College housing not available. Educational Resources Center plus 1 other with 38,192 books, 489 serials, 7,903 audiovisual materials, an OPAC, and a Web page. Operations spending for 2004 fiscal year: $1 million. 960 computers available on campus for general student use. A campuswide network can be accessed from off-campus. Staffed computer lab on campus.

Community Environment: See Ohio State University Columbus Campus.

■ **CUYAHOGA COMMUNITY COLLEGE** *C-10*
700 Carnegie Ave.
Cleveland, OH 44115-2878
Tel: (216)987-6000
Free: 800-954-8742
Admissions: (216)987-4030
Fax: (216)987-5050
Web Site: http://www.tri-c.edu/

Description: State and locally supported, 2-year, coed. Awards certificates, transfer associate, and terminal associate degrees. Founded 1963. Setting: urban campus. Educational spending for 2005 fiscal year: $3709 per student. Total enrollment: 25,358. Student-undergrad faculty ratio is 18:1. 8,438 applied, 100% were admitted. Full-time: 10,326 students, 61% women, 39% men. Part-time: 15,032 students, 65% women, 35% men. Students come from 21 states and territories, 63 other countries, 0% from out-of-state, 1% Native American, 4% Hispanic, 30% black, 2% Asian American or Pacific Islander, 2% international, 42% 25 or older, 3% transferred in. Calendar: semesters. ESL program, services for LD students, advanced placement, independent study, distance learning, summer session for credit, part-time degree program, external degree program, adult/continuing education programs, co-op programs.

Entrance Requirements: Open admission. Options: early admission, deferred admission, international baccalaureate accepted. Required for some: high school transcript. Entrance: noncompetitive. Application deadline: Rolling. Notification: continuous.

Costs Per Year: Application fee: $0. Area resident tuition: $2416 full-time, $80.54 per credit hour part-time. State resident tuition: $3194 full-time, $106.48 per credit hour part-time. Nonresident tuition: $6541 full-time, $218.04 per credit hour part-time.

Collegiate Environment: Orientation program. Drama-theater group, choral group, student-run newspaper. Social organizations: 47 open to all. Most popular organizations: Student Senate, Student Nursing Organization, Business Focus, Phi Theta Kappa. Major annual events: Welcome Back, Diversity Day. Student services: health clinic, personal-psychological counseling. Campus security: 24-hour emergency response devices and patrols, late night transport-escort service. College housing not available. 177,767 books, 177,926 microform titles, 1,135 serials, an OPAC, and a Web page. 1,275 computers available on campus for general student use. A campuswide network can be accessed from off-campus. Staffed computer lab on campus.

■ **DAVID N. MYERS UNIVERSITY** *C-10*
112 Prospect Ave.
Cleveland, OH 44115
Tel: (216)696-9000
Free: 800-424-3953
Admissions: (216)523-3806
Fax: (216)523-3808
E-mail: mquinn@dnmyers.edu
Web Site: http://www.dnmyers.edu/

Description: Independent, comprehensive, coed. Awards associate, bachelor's, and master's degrees. Founded 1848. Setting: 1-acre urban campus. Endowment: $631,558. Educational spending for 2005 fiscal year: $4000 per student. Total enrollment: 1,177. 382 applied, 65% were admitted. Full-time: 573 students, 77% women, 23% men. Part-time: 523 students, 63% women, 37% men. 0% from out-of-state, 0% Native American, 3% Hispanic, 45% black, 0.3% Asian American or Pacific Islander, 0% international, 50% 25 or older, 13% transferred in. Core. Calendar: semesters. Academic remediation for entering students, advanced placement, accelerated degree program, self-designed majors, independent study, distance learning, double major, summer session for credit, part-time degree program, external degree program, adult/continuing education programs, co-op programs and internships. Off campus study at members of the Northeast Ohio Commission on Higher Education.

Entrance Requirements: Options: Common Application, early admission, deferred admission. Required: high school transcript, SAT or ACT. Recommended: recommendations. Required for some: essay, interview. Entrance: minimally difficult. Application deadline: Rolling. Notification: continuous.

Costs Per Year: Application fee: $25. Tuition: $9840 full-time.

Collegiate Environment: Orientation program. Student-run newspaper. Most popular organizations: Students in Free Enterprise, Accounting Association, Mock Trial Association, Delta Club. Major annual events: Orientation, Homecoming, Martin Luther King Day. Student services: personal-psychological counseling. Campus security: 24-hour patrols, late night transport-escort service. College housing not available. Library Resource Center with 15,027 books, 528 microform titles, 140 serials, 377 audiovisual materials, and a Web page. Operations spending for 2004 fiscal year: $159,382. 70 computers available on campus for general student use. A campuswide network can be accessed from off-campus. Staffed computer lab on campus.

■ **DAVIS COLLEGE** *B-5*
4747 Monroe St.
Toledo, OH 43623-4307
Tel: (419)473-2700
Free: 800-477-7021
Web Site: http://daviscollege.edu/

Description: Proprietary, 2-year, coed. Awards diplomas and terminal associate degrees. Founded 1858. Setting: 1-acre urban campus with easy access to Detroit. Educational spending for 2005 fiscal year: $10,196 per student. Total enrollment: 451. Student-undergrad faculty ratio is 14:1. 72 applied, 100% were admitted. Full-time: 225 students, 86% women, 14% men. Part-time: 226 students, 84% women, 16% men. Students come from 2 states and territories, 5% from out-of-state, 0.5% Native American, 2% Hispanic, 29% black, 0% Asian American or Pacific Islander, 0% international, 70% 25 or older, 26% transferred in. Core. Academic remediation for entering students, advanced placement, distance learning, summer session for credit, part-time degree program, adult/continuing education programs, internships.

Entrance Requirements: Options: Peterson's Universal Application, Common Application, electronic application, early admission, deferred admission. Required: high school transcript, interview, CPAt. Entrance: minimally difficult. Application deadline: Rolling. Notification: continuous.

Costs Per Year: Application fee: $30. Tuition: $8100 full-time, $225 per credit hour part-time. Mandatory fees: $480 full-time.

Collegiate Environment: Orientation program. Social organizations: 1 open to all. Most popular organization: Student Advisory Board. Major annual events: Spring Parking Lot Event, Christmas Party, Halloween Haunted House. Student services: personal-psychological counseling. Campus security: 24-hour emergency response devices, security cameras for parking lot. College housing not available. Davis College Resource Center with 3,207 books, 164 serials, 341 audiovisual materials, and an OPAC. 78 computers available on campus for general student use. Staffed computer lab on campus.

■ **DEFIANCE COLLEGE** *D-2*
701 North Clinton St.
Defiance, OH 43512-1610
Tel: (419)784-4010
Free: 800-520-4632
Admissions: (419)783-2361
Fax: (419)783-2468
Web Site: http://www.defiance.edu/

Description: Independent, comprehensive, coed, affiliated with United Church of Christ. Awards associate, bachelor's, and master's degrees. Founded 1850. Setting: 150-acre small town campus with easy access to Toledo. Endowment: $14.5 million. Educational spending for 2005 fiscal year: $4682 per student. Total enrollment: 930. Faculty: 88 (38 full-time, 50 part-time). Student-undergrad faculty ratio is 15:1. 845 applied, 72% were admitted. 15% from top 10% of their high school class, 34% from top quarter, 64% from top half. Full-time: 673 students, 53% women, 47% men. Part-time: 154 students, 66% women, 34% men. Students come from 16 states and territories, 4 other countries, 20% from out-of-state, 0.5% Native American, 3% Hispanic, 4% black, 0.1% Asian American or Pacific Islander, 0% international, 22% 25 or older, 55% live on campus, 9% transferred in. Retention: 65% of full-time freshmen returned the following year. Core. Calendar: semesters. Academic remediation for entering students, advanced placement, self-designed majors, honors program, independent study, distance learning, double major, summer session for credit, part-time degree program, external degree program, adult/continuing education programs, co-op programs and internships, graduate courses open to undergrads. Off campus study at Bowling Green State University. Study abroad program.

Entrance Requirements: Options: Common Application, electronic application, deferred admission, international baccalaureate accepted. Required: high school transcript, SAT or ACT. Recommended: recommendations, interview. Required for some: essay, interview. Entrance: moderately difficult. Application deadline: 8/15. Notification: continuous.

Costs Per Year: Application fee: $25. Comprehensive fee: $25,910 includes full-time tuition ($19,260), mandatory fees ($480), and college room and board ($6170). College room only: $3150. Part-time tuition: $325 per credit hour. Part-time mandatory fees: $65 per term.

Collegiate Environment: Orientation program. Drama-theater group, choral group, student-run newspaper. Social organizations: 30 open to all; national fraternities, national sororities, local fraternities, local sororities; 6% of eligible men and 8% of eligible women are members. Most popular organizations: Campus Activities Board, Criminal Justice Society, Student Senate, Fellowship of Christian Athletes. Major annual events: Homecoming, Family Weekend, Sibs Weekend. Student services: health clinic, personal-psychological counseling. Campus security: late night transport-escort service, controlled dormitory access. 517 college housing spaces available; 417 were occupied in 2003-04. Freshmen guaranteed college housing. On-campus residence required through junior year. Options: coed, men-only, women-only housing available. Pilgrim Library with 88,000 books, 25,000 microform titles, 424 serials, 25,000 audiovisual materials, and an OPAC. Operations spending for 2004 fiscal year: $508,184. 200 computers available on campus for general student use. A campuswide network can be accessed from student residence rooms and from off campus. Staffed computer lab on campus.

Community Environment: Defiance College is located in Defiance Ohio, site of Fort Defiance, and birthplace of the Indian Chief Pontiac. Today, Defiance is a community of over 18,000 residents and one of the fastest growing areas in Northwest Ohio. Highly diversified industry and some of the richest farmland in the nation contribute to the areas prosperity. A major shopping mall is 2 blocks north of the campus.

■ **DENISON UNIVERSITY** *H-7*
Granville, OH 43023
Tel: (740)587-0810
Free: 800-DEN-ISON
Admissions: (740)587-6276
Fax: (740)587-6306
E-mail: admissions@denison.edu
Web Site: http://www.denison.edu/

Description: Independent, 4-year, coed. Awards bachelor's degrees. Founded 1831. Setting: 1,200-acre small town campus with easy access to Columbus. Endowment: $477.5 million. Research spending for 2004 fiscal year: $457,975. Educational spending for 2005 fiscal year: $37,661 per student. Total enrollment: 2,329. Student-undergrad faculty ratio is 11:1. 5,144 applied, 39% were admitted. 54% from top 10% of their high school class, 80% from top quarter, 96% from top half. 16 National Merit Scholars, 27 class presidents, 35 valedictorians, 136 student government officers. Full-time: 2,292 students, 56% women, 44% men. Part-time: 37 students, 59% women, 41% men. Students come from 49 states and territories, 28 other countries, 59% from out-of-state, 0.3% Native American, 3% Hispanic, 5% black, 3% Asian American or Pacific Islander, 5% international, 1% 25 or older, 98% live on campus, 1% transferred in. Retention: 90% of full-time freshmen returned the following year. Academic areas with the most degrees

conferred: social sciences; communications/journalism; psychology. Calendar: semesters plus optional May term. Services for LD students, advanced placement, self-designed majors, honors program, independent study, double major, part-time degree program, co-op programs and internships. Off campus study at American University, Great Lakes Colleges Association, Marine Science Consortium. Study abroad program. ROTC: Army (c).

Entrance Requirements: Options: Peterson's Universal Application, Common Application, early admission, early decision, deferred admission. Required: essay, high school transcript, 2 recommendations, SAT or ACT. Recommended: interview. Entrance: very difficult. Application deadlines: 1/15, 11/1 for early decision plan 1, 12/1 for early decision plan 2. Notification: 4/1, 11/15 for early decision plan 1, 12/15 for early decision plan 2.

Costs Per Year: Application fee: $40. Comprehensive fee: $37,040 includes full-time tuition ($28,170), mandatory fees ($750), and college room and board ($8120). College room only: $4470. Room and board charges vary according to housing facility. Part-time tuition: $880 per semester hour. Part-time tuition varies according to course load.

Collegiate Environment: Orientation program. Drama-theater group, choral group, student-run newspaper, radio station. Social organizations: 147 open to all; national fraternities, national sororities; 25% of eligible men and 30% of eligible women are members. Most popular organizations: Community Association, Black Student Union, International Student Association, Student Activities Committee. Major annual events: All-Campus Gala, Academic Awards Convocation, Community Fair and Picnic on registration day. Student services: health clinic, personal-psychological counseling, women's center. Campus security: 24-hour emergency response devices and patrols, student patrols, late night transport-escort service, controlled dormitory access, security lighting, escort service. 2,130 college housing spaces available; 2,027 were occupied in 2003-04. Freshmen guaranteed college housing. On-campus residence required through senior year. Options: coed, men-only, women-only housing available. William Howard Doane Library with 784,189 books, 122,070 microform titles, 6,116 serials, 29,566 audiovisual materials, an OPAC, and a Web page. Operations spending for 2004 fiscal year: $2.5 million. 587 computers available on campus for general student use. Computer purchase/lease plans available. A campuswide network can be accessed from student residence rooms and from off campus. Staffed computer lab on campus.

Community Environment: Of interest are the many beautiful homes in Granville. The town was founded by settlers from the Massachusetts town of the same name in 1805. Granville is a delightful bit of New England tucked in the rolling hills of Central Ohio.

■ **DEVRY UNIVERSITY (CLEVELAND)** *C-10*
200 Public Square, Ste. 150
Cleveland, OH 44114-2301
Tel: (216)781-8000
Fax: (216)781-8001
Web Site: http://www.devry.edu/

Description: Proprietary, comprehensive, coed. Calendar: semesters.

Costs Per Year: One-time mandatory fee: $40. Tuition: $11,790 full-time, $440 per credit part-time. Mandatory fees: $60 full-time, $30 per year part-time. Full-time tuition and fees vary according to course load. Part-time tuition and fees vary according to course load.

■ **DEVRY UNIVERSITY (COLUMBUS)** *I-6*
1350 Alum Creek Dr.
Columbus, OH 43209-2705
Tel: (614)253-7291
Free: 800-426-2206
Web Site: http://www.devry.edu/

Description: Proprietary, comprehensive, coed. Part of DeVry University. Awards associate, bachelor's, and master's degrees. Founded 1952. Setting: 21-acre urban campus. Total enrollment: 2,643. Faculty: 116 (60 full-time, 56 part-time). Student-undergrad faculty ratio is 26:1. Full-time: 1,653 students, 35% women, 65% men. Part-time: 770 students, 45% women, 55% men. 0.5% Native American, 1% Hispanic, 21% black, 1% Asian American or Pacific Islander, 1% international, 42% 25 or older. Retention: 46% of full-time freshmen returned the following year. Academic areas with the most degrees conferred: computer and information sciences; business/marketing; engineering technologies. Calendar: semesters. Academic remediation for entering students, services for LD students, advanced placement, accelerated degree program, distance learning, summer session for credit, part-time degree program, adult/continuing education programs, co-op programs. ROTC: Army (c).

Entrance Requirements: Options: electronic application, deferred admission, international baccalaureate accepted. Required: high school transcript, interview. Entrance: minimally difficult. Application deadline: Rolling.

Costs Per Year: Application fee: $50. One-time mandatory fee: $40. Tuition: $11,790 full-time, $440 per credit part-time. Mandatory fees: $270 full-time, $160 per year part-time. Full-time tuition and fees vary according to course load. Part-time tuition and fees vary according to course load.

Collegiate Environment: Orientation program. Social organizations: 9 open to all. Most popular organizations: Institute for Electrical and Electronic Engineers, American Production and Inventory Control Society, Association of Information Technology Professionals, Tau Alpha Pi, Asian-American Association or Prism. Major annual events: Student Appreciation Week, Parents' Weekend, Honors Banquet. Campus security: late night transport-escort service, security at evening activities. College housing not available. Learning Resource Center with 30,000 books, 5,892 serials, 1,050 audiovisual materials, an OPAC, and a Web page. 408 computers available on campus for general student use. Computer purchase/lease plans available. A campuswide network can be accessed from off-campus. Staffed computer lab on campus.

■ DEVRY UNIVERSITY (SEVEN HILLS) E-18

The Genesis Bldg.
6000 Lombardo Center
Seven Hills, OH 44131-6907
Tel: (216)328-8754; (866)453-3879
Fax: (216)328-8764
Web Site: http://www.devry.edu/

Description: Proprietary, comprehensive, coed. Calendar: semesters.

Costs Per Year: One-time mandatory fee: $40. Tuition: $11,790 full-time, $440 per credit part-time. Mandatory fees: $60 full-time, $30 per year part-time. Full-time tuition and fees vary according to course load. Part-time tuition and fees vary according to course load.

■ EDISON STATE COMMUNITY COLLEGE H-2

1973 Edison Dr.
Piqua, OH 45356-9253
Tel: (937)778-8600
Fax: (937)778-1920
E-mail: info@edison.cc.oh.us
Web Site: http://www.edisonohio.edu/

Description: State-supported, 2-year, coed. Part of Ohio Board of Regents. Awards certificates, transfer associate, and terminal associate degrees. Founded 1973. Setting: 130-acre small town campus with easy access to Cincinnati and Dayton. Total enrollment: 3,000. 4% from top 10% of their high school class, 12% from top quarter, 24% from top half. Full-time: 1,028 students, 63% women, 37% men. Part-time: 1,972 students, 65% women, 35% men. Students come from 5 states and territories, 0.3% Native American, 1% Hispanic, 2% black, 1% Asian American or Pacific Islander, 49% 25 or older, 4% transferred in. Core. Calendar: semesters. Academic remediation for entering students, services for LD students, advanced placement, accelerated degree program, self-designed majors, independent study, distance learning, double major, summer session for credit, part-time degree program, adult/continuing education programs, internships. Off campus study at Southwestern Ohio Council for Higher Education. ROTC: Army (c), Air Force (c).

Entrance Requirements: Open admission except for nursing program. Options: electronic application, early admission, deferred admission. Required: high school transcript. Placement: ACT ASSET, ACT COMPASS recommended; SAT or ACT, ACT ASSET, ACT COMPASS required for some. Entrance: noncompetitive. Application deadline: Rolling.

Collegiate Environment: Orientation program. Drama-theater group. Student services: personal-psychological counseling. Campus security: late night transport-escort service, 18-hour patrols by trained security personnel. College housing not available. Edison Community College Library with 29,851 books, 86,834 microform titles, 542 serials, 2,424 audiovisual materials, an OPAC, and a Web page. 251 computers available on campus for general student use. Computer purchase/lease plans available. A campuswide network can be accessed from off-campus. Staffed computer lab on campus.

Community Environment: Located in Piqua, Ohio, Edison State Community College serves Darke, Miami, Shelby, and neighboring counties in west-central Ohio. The region, made up of small-sized and medium-sized towns, has an excellent balance among agricultural, industrial and residential areas.

■ ETI TECHNICAL COLLEGE OF NILES D-12

2076 Youngstown-Warren Rd.
Niles, OH 44446-4398
Tel: (330)652-9919
Fax: (330)652-4399
Web Site: http://www.eti-college.com/

Description: Proprietary, 2-year, coed. Awards diplomas and terminal associate degrees. Founded 1989. Setting: small town campus with easy access to Cleveland and Pittsburgh. Total enrollment: 222. 107 applied, 75% were admitted. 5% from top 10% of their high school class, 10% from top quarter, 50% from top half. Full-time: 186 students, 68% women, 32% men. Part-time: 36 students, 25% women, 75% men. Students come from 2 states and territories, 10% from out-of-state, 3% Hispanic, 22% black, 0.5% international, 60% 25 or older, 0% transferred in. Core. Calendar: semesters. Academic remediation for entering students, services for LD students, advanced placement, part-time degree program, adult/continuing education programs.

Entrance Requirements: Open admission. Options: Peterson's Universal Application, Common Application, early admission, deferred admission. Required: high school transcript, interview. Recommended: SAT, ACT. Entrance: moderately difficult. Application deadline: Rolling. Notification: continuous.

Collegiate Environment: Orientation program. Student-run newspaper. Social organizations: 1 open to all. Most popular organization: student government. Major annual events: Christmas Party, Halloween. Student services: personal-psychological counseling. Campus security: 24-hour emergency response devices. College housing not available. Main Library plus 3 others with a Web page. 45 computers available on campus for general student use. Staffed computer lab on campus.

■ FRANCISCAN UNIVERSITY OF STEUBENVILLE G-13

1235 University Blvd.
Steubenville, OH 43952-1763
Tel: (740)283-3771
Free: 800-783-6220
Admissions: (740)283-6226
Fax: (740)283-6472
E-mail: admissions@franciscan.edu
Web Site: http://www.franciscan.edu/

Description: Independent Roman Catholic, comprehensive, coed. Awards associate, bachelor's, and master's degrees. Founded 1946. Setting: 124-acre suburban campus with easy access to Pittsburgh. Endowment: $22 million. Total enrollment: 2,421. Faculty: 205 (104 full-time, 101 part-time). Student-undergrad faculty ratio is 15:1. 1,047 applied, 81% were admitted. 27% from top 10% of their high school class, 59% from top quarter, 85% from top half. 12 valedictorians. Full-time: 1,818 students, 61% women, 39% men. Part-time: 163 students, 61% women, 39% men. Students come from 52 states and territories, 24 other countries, 79% from out-of-state, 0.5% Native American, 3% Hispanic, 0.5% black, 1% Asian American or Pacific Islander, 1% international, 9% 25 or older, 56% live on campus, 10% transferred in. Retention: 85% of full-time freshmen returned the following year. Academic areas with the most degrees conferred: theology and religious vocations; health professions and related sciences; education. Core. Calendar: semesters. Services for LD students, advanced placement, accelerated degree program, honors program, independent study, distance learning, double major, summer session for credit, part-time degree program, adult/continuing education programs, internships, graduate courses open to undergrads. Study abroad program.

Entrance Requirements: Options: Common Application, early admission, deferred admission, international baccalaureate accepted. Required: essay, high school transcript, minimum 2.4 high school GPA, standardized test scores, SAT or ACT. Recommended: interview. Entrance: moderately difficult. Notification: continuous.

Costs Per Year: Application fee: $20. Comprehensive fee: $21,950 includes full-time tuition ($16,070), mandatory fees ($380), and college room and board ($5500). Room and board charges vary according to board plan. Part-time tuition: $535 per credit. Part-time mandatory fees: $10 per credit. Part-time tuition and fees vary according to course load.

Collegiate Environment: Orientation program. Drama-theater group, choral group, student-run newspaper, radio station. Social organizations: 8 open to all; national fraternities, national sororities. Most popular organizations: Franciscan University Student Association, Student Activities Board, Human Life Concerns, Works of Mercy, Troubadour. Major annual events: SAB Winter Formal, Campus Olympics and Music Fest, Opening Semester

Retreat. Student services: health clinic, personal-psychological counseling. Campus security: 24-hour emergency response devices and patrols, student patrols, late night transport-escort service. College housing designed to accommodate 1,041 students; 1,044 undergraduates lived in college housing during 2003-04. On-campus residence required through junior year. Options: men-only, women-only housing available. John Paul II Library with 231,176 books, 256,000 microform titles, 578 serials, 1,260 audiovisual materials, an OPAC, and a Web page. Operations spending for 2004 fiscal year: $655,140. 126 computers available on campus for general student use. A campuswide network can be accessed. Staffed computer lab on campus.

Community Environment: The county seat of Jefferson County, Steubenville is a city in eastern Ohio situated on the Ohio River. An unlimited supply of both deep-mine and strip coal is available in the Steubenville district. Because of the coal and the Ohio River, more steam electricity is generated within a 40-mile radius of the city than in any other area in the world. Steel, iron, and paper are some of the products of industries here.

■ **FRANKLIN UNIVERSITY** *I-6*
201 South Grant Ave.
Columbus, OH 43215-5399
Tel: (614)797-4700; 877-341-6300
Fax: (614)224-8027
E-mail: info@franklin.edu
Web Site: http://www.franklin.edu/
Description: Independent, comprehensive, coed. Awards associate, bachelor's, and master's degrees and post-master's certificates. Founded 1902. Setting: 14-acre urban campus. Endowment: $27.8 million. Educational spending for 2005 fiscal year: $2171 per student. Total enrollment: 6,823. 262 applied, 100% were admitted. Full-time: 1,979 students, 59% women, 41% men. Part-time: 3,841 students, 52% women, 48% men. Students come from 48 states and territories, 65 other countries, 26% from out-of-state, 0.4% Native American, 2% Hispanic, 19% black, 3% Asian American or Pacific Islander, 5% international, 78% 25 or older, 39% transferred in. Core. Calendar: trimesters. Academic remediation for entering students, ESL program, services for LD students, advanced placement, accelerated degree program, self-designed majors, independent study, distance learning, summer session for credit, part-time degree program, adult/continuing education programs, co-op programs and internships. Off campus study at members of the Higher Education Council of Columbus. Study abroad program. ROTC: Army (c), Air Force (c).
Entrance Requirements: Open admission except for international students. Option: deferred admission. Required for some: high school transcript. Entrance: noncompetitive. Application deadline: Rolling.
Costs Per Year: Application fee: $0. Tuition: $7320 full-time, $244 per credit hour part-time. Full-time tuition varies according to program. Part-time tuition varies according to program.
Collegiate Environment: Orientation program. Social organizations: 6 open to all. Most popular organizations: American Marketing Association, International Student Association, Human Resources Society, Accounting Association. Major annual events: New Student Orientation, Awards/ Scholarship Reception, Opening Week Activities. Campus security: security personnel during operating hours. College housing not available. Franklin University Library with 27,547 books, 15,290 serials, 246 audiovisual materials, an OPAC, and a Web page. Operations spending for 2004 fiscal year: $619,000. 341 computers available on campus for general student use. A campuswide network can be accessed. Staffed computer lab on campus.
Community Environment: See Ohio State University - Columbus Campus.

■ **GALLIPOLIS CAREER COLLEGE** *M-8*
1176 Jackson Pike, Ste. 312
Gallipolis, OH 45631
Tel: (740)446-4367
Free: 800-214-0452
Admissions: (740)446-4124
Fax: (740)446-4124
E-mail: admissions@gallipoliscareercollege.com
Web Site: http://www.gallipoliscareercollege.com/
Description: Independent, 2-year, coed. Awards certificates, diplomas, and terminal associate degrees. Founded 1962. Setting: small town campus. Total enrollment: 154. Student-undergrad faculty ratio is 22:1. Full-time: 145 students, 83% women, 17% men. Part-time: 9 students, 89% women, 11% men. Students come from 2 states and territories, 13% from out-of-state, 0% Native American, 0% Hispanic, 9% black, 0% Asian American or Pacific Islander, 0% international. Core. Academic remediation for entering

students, independent study, double major, summer session for credit, part-time degree program, adult/continuing education programs, internships.
Entrance Requirements: Required: high school transcript, interview, Wonderlic aptitude test. Application deadline: Rolling.
Costs Per Year: Application fee: $50. Tuition: $8640 full-time, $180 per credit hour part-time. Mandatory fees: $100 full-time. Tuition guaranteed not to increase for student's term of enrollment.
Collegiate Environment: Orientation program. College housing not available. Gallipolis Career College Library with 94 audiovisual materials. 28 computers available on campus for general student use. A campuswide network can be accessed. Staffed computer lab on campus.

■ **GOD'S BIBLE SCHOOL AND COLLEGE** *L-2*
1810 Young St.
Cincinnati, OH 45202-6838
Tel: (513)721-7944
Free: 800-486-4637
Fax: (513)721-3971
E-mail: lprofitt@gbs.edu
Web Site: http://www.gbs.edu/
Description: Independent interdenominational, 4-year, coed. Awards associate and bachelor's degrees. Founded 1900. Setting: 14-acre urban campus. Total enrollment: 271. Student-undergrad faculty ratio is 16:1. 60 applied, 88% were admitted. 44% from top quarter of their high school class, 72% from top half. Full-time: 226 students, 57% women, 43% men. Part-time: 45 students, 33% women, 67% men. Students come from 25 states and territories, 13 other countries, 58% from out-of-state, 1% Native American, 1% Hispanic, 3% black, 1% Asian American or Pacific Islander, 13% international, 19% 25 or older, 10% transferred in. Retention: 71% of full-time freshmen returned the following year. Academic areas with the most degrees conferred: theology and religious vocations; family and consumer sciences; education. Core. Calendar: semesters. Academic remediation for entering students, advanced placement, independent study, summer session for credit, part-time degree program, internships.
Entrance Requirements: Options: Peterson's Universal Application, Common Application. Required: high school transcript, 3 recommendations, interview, SAT or ACT. Recommended: SAT. Application deadline: 8/18.
Costs Per Year: Application fee: $25. Comprehensive fee: $8160 includes full-time tuition ($4200), mandatory fees ($660), and college room and board ($3300). College room only: $1350. Part-time tuition: $162 per credit hour. Part-time mandatory fees: $25 per credit hour.
Collegiate Environment: Orientation program. Choral group, student-run newspaper. Student services: health clinic. Campus security: 24-hour patrols. 200 college housing spaces available; 193 were occupied in 2003-04. On-campus residence required through senior year. Options: men-only, women-only housing available. R. G. Flexon Memorial Library with 28,452 books and 240 serials. 14 computers available on campus for general student use. Staffed computer lab on campus.

■ **HEIDELBERG COLLEGE** *D-6*
310 East Market St.
Tiffin, OH 44883-2462
Tel: (419)448-2000
Free: 800-434-3352
Admissions: (419)448-2330
Fax: (419)448-2334
E-mail: lsooy@heidelberg.edu
Web Site: http://www.heidelberg.edu/
Description: Independent, comprehensive, coed, affiliated with United Church of Christ. Awards bachelor's and master's degrees. Founded 1850. Setting: 110-acre small town campus. Endowment: $35.5 million. Research spending for 2004 fiscal year: $1.8 million. Educational spending for 2005 fiscal year: $7406 per student. Total enrollment: 1,435. 1,830 applied, 75% were admitted. 14% from top 10% of their high school class, 34% from top quarter, 68% from top half. Full-time: 1,179 students, 49% women, 51% men. Part-time: 51 students, 65% women, 35% men. Students come from 22 states and territories, 10 other countries, 5% from out-of-state, 0% Native American, 1% Hispanic, 4% black, 1% Asian American or Pacific Islander, 2% international, 10% 25 or older, 87% live on campus, 3% transferred in. Retention: 68% of full-time freshmen returned the following year. Academic areas with the most degrees conferred: business/marketing; education; communications/journalism. Core. Calendar: semesters. Academic remediation for entering students, ESL program, services for LD students, advanced

placement, accelerated degree program, honors program, double major, summer session for credit, part-time degree program, adult/continuing education programs, internships. Off campus study at members of the East Central College Consortium. Study abroad program. ROTC: Army (c), Air Force (c).

Entrance Requirements: Options: Peterson's Universal Application, Common Application, electronic application, deferred admission, international baccalaureate accepted. Required: high school transcript, minimum 2.5 high school GPA, SAT or ACT. Recommended: essay, interview. Required for some: recommendations. Entrance: moderately difficult. Notification: continuous until 8/1.

Costs Per Year: Application fee: $25. Comprehensive fee: $23,242 includes full-time tuition ($15,740), mandatory fees ($394), and college room and board ($7108). College room only: $3296. Full-time tuition and fees vary according to course load, degree level, and location. Room and board charges vary according to board plan and housing facility. Part-time tuition: $504 per semester hour. Part-time tuition varies according to degree level and location.

Collegiate Environment: Orientation program. Drama-theater group, choral group, student-run newspaper, radio station. Social organizations: 60 open to all; local fraternities, local sororities; 18% of eligible men and 24% of eligible women are members. Most popular organizations: Alpha Phi Omega, BERG Events Council, Student Senate, Campus Fellowship, Black Student Union/World Student Union. Major annual events: Activities Fair, Greek Sing, Late Night Breakfast. Student services: health clinic, personal-psychological counseling. Campus security: 24-hour emergency response devices and patrols, student patrols, late night transport-escort service. 850 college housing spaces available; 87 were occupied in 2003-04. Freshmen guaranteed college housing. On-campus residence required through junior year. Options: coed, women-only housing available. Beeghly Library plus 1 other with 268,702 books, 260,839 microform titles, 513 serials, an OPAC, and a Web page. Operations spending for 2004 fiscal year: $69,477. 125 computers available on campus for general student use. A campuswide network can be accessed from student residence rooms and from off campus. Staffed computer lab on campus.

Community Environment: The 110-acre campus is located in Tiffin, Ohio, at the intersection of U.S. route 224 and Ohio Route 53, 50 miles southeast of Toledo and 92 miles west of Cleveland. Amtrack stops in Sandusky, Toledo, Lima and Crestline. Churches, civic, service and social service agencies, and private enterprises offer many opportunities for volunteer and class-related experiences. Places of worship are available on campus and in the immediate community for Protestants and Catholics, and within 23 miles for Jewish students.

■ **HIRAM COLLEGE** *D-11*
Box 67
Hiram, OH 44234-0067
Tel: (330)569-3211
Free: 800-362-5280
Admissions: (330)569-5169
Fax: (330)569-5944
E-mail: admission@hiram.edu
Web Site: http://www.hiram.edu/

Description: Independent, 4-year, coed, affiliated with Christian Church (Disciples of Christ). Awards bachelor's and master's degrees. Founded 1850. Setting: 110-acre rural campus with easy access to Cleveland. Endowment: $62.7 million. Research spending for 2004 fiscal year: $74,803. Educational spending for 2005 fiscal year: $7056 per student. Total enrollment: 1,111. Faculty: 103 (64 full-time, 39 part-time). Student-undergrad faculty ratio is 12:1. 832 applied, 85% were admitted. 24% from top 10% of their high school class, 52% from top quarter, 83% from top half. 11 valedictorians. Full-time: 877 students, 54% women, 46% men. Part-time: 205 students, 67% women, 33% men. Students come from 31 states and territories, 20 other countries, 17% from out-of-state, 0.2% Native American, 1% Hispanic, 10% black, 1% Asian American or Pacific Islander, 4% international, 88% live on campus, 2% transferred in. Retention: 81% of full-time freshmen returned the following year. Academic areas with the most degrees conferred: business/marketing; social sciences; biological/life sciences. Core. Calendar: semesters. ESL program, services for LD students, advanced placement, self-designed majors, independent study, double major, summer session for credit, part-time degree program, adult/continuing education programs, internships. Off campus study. Study abroad program.

Entrance Requirements: Options: Peterson's Universal Application, Common Application, electronic application, early admission, deferred admission,

international baccalaureate accepted. Required: essay, high school transcript, 2 recommendations, SAT or ACT. Recommended: 3 recommendations, interview. Required for some: interview. Entrance: moderately difficult. Application deadline: 4/1. Notification: continuous.

Costs Per Year: Application fee: $35. Comprehensive fee: $31,790 includes full-time tuition ($23,510), mandatory fees ($670), and college room and board ($7610). College room only: $3590. Full-time tuition and fees vary according to student level. Room and board charges vary according to housing facility. Part-time tuition: $784 per credit hour. Tuition guaranteed not to increase for student's term of enrollment.

Collegiate Environment: Orientation program. Drama-theater group, choral group, student-run newspaper, radio station. Social organizations: 60 open to all; local fraternities, local sororities; 8% of eligible men and 12% of eligible women are members. Most popular organizations: Student Senate, African American Students United, Outdoors Club, Resident Student Association, Christian Outreach. Major annual events: Homecoming, Art and Music Festival, Campus Days. Student services: health clinic, personal-psychological counseling. Campus security: 24-hour emergency response devices and patrols, late night transport-escort service, controlled dormitory access. 1,100 college housing spaces available; 700 were occupied in 2003-04. Freshmen guaranteed college housing. On-campus residence required through junior year. Options: coed, women-only housing available. Hiram College Library with 187,451 books, 116,100 microform titles, 3,993 serials, 10,351 audiovisual materials, an OPAC, and a Web page. Operations spending for 2004 fiscal year: $723,089.

Community Environment: Located in a dairy and orchard growing area, Hiram is a rural community with numerous buildings in the Western Reserve style. This area has long been famous for the production of maple syrup. Air, bus and train transportation is available. Nearby lakes provide the facilities for boating, swimming, and fishing. Job opportunities are available mainly at the college.

■ **HOCKING COLLEGE** *J-8*
3301 Hocking Parkway
Nelsonville, OH 45764-9588
Tel: (740)753-3591
Fax: (740)753-1452
E-mail: hull_lyn@hocking.edu
Web Site: http://www.hocking.edu/

Description: State-supported, 2-year, coed. Part of Ohio Board of Regents. Awards certificates, diplomas, transfer associate, and terminal associate degrees. Founded 1968. Setting: 1,600-acre rural campus with easy access to Columbus. Endowment: $2.3 million. Educational spending for 2005 fiscal year: $4084 per student. Total enrollment: 5,250. Students come from 28 states and territories, 3% from out-of-state, 0.3% Native American, 1% Hispanic, 3% black, 1% Asian American or Pacific Islander, 0% international, 37% 25 or older, 9% live on campus. Core. Academic remediation for entering students, ESL program, services for LD students, advanced placement, accelerated degree program, self-designed majors, distance learning, double major, summer session for credit, part-time degree program, adult/continuing education programs, co-op programs and internships. ROTC: Army (c).

Entrance Requirements: Open admission except for nursing program. Options: Peterson's Universal Application, electronic application. Required: high school transcript. Placement: SAT or ACT recommended; nursing exam required for some. Entrance: noncompetitive. Application deadline: Rolling. Notification: continuous.

Collegiate Environment: Orientation program. Drama-theater group, choral group. Social organizations: 40 open to all. Most popular organizations: Phi Theta Kappa, Recycling Club, Unity Board, Alpha Beta Gamma, Native American Club. Major annual events: Paul Bunyan Show, Winterfest. Student services: health clinic, personal-psychological counseling, women's center. Campus security: 24-hour emergency response devices and patrols, student patrols, late night transport-escort service. 500 college housing spaces available; all were occupied in 2003-04. Option: coed housing available. Hocking College Learning Resources Center plus 1 other with 19,663 books, 38,766 microform titles, 223 serials, 8,327 audiovisual materials, an OPAC, and a Web page. Operations spending for 2004 fiscal year: $523,820. 280 computers available on campus for general student use. A campuswide network can be accessed from student residence rooms and from off campus. Staffed computer lab on campus.

Community Environment: Nelsonville is a small community on the Hocking River. It is easily accessible from all points north and south in Ohio via US route 33. It is 65 miles from Columbus and is serviced by Greyhound bus lines.

■ **HONDROS COLLEGE** *H-6*
4140 Executive Parkway
Westerville, OH 43081-3855
Tel: (614)508-7277
Free: 800-783-0095
Admissions: (614)508-7244
Fax: (614)508-7279
Web Site: http://www.hondroscollege.com/
Description: Proprietary, 2-year, coed. Awards certificates, transfer associ-
ate, and terminal associate degrees. Total enrollment: 100.
Entrance Requirements: Open admission. Entrance: noncompetitive.
Collegiate Environment: Campus security: 24-hour emergency response
devices. College housing not available.

■ **INTERNATIONAL COLLEGE OF BROADCASTING** *I-3*
6 South Smithville Rd.
Dayton, OH 45431-1833
Tel: (937)258-8251
Web Site: http://www.icbcollege.com/
Description: Private, 2-year, coed. Awards diplomas, transfer associate,
and terminal associate degrees. Setting: 1-acre urban campus. Total enroll-
ment: 87. 21 applied, 67% were admitted. Full-time: 87 students, 26%
women, 74% men. 0% Native American, 1% Hispanic, 31% black, 0% Asian
American or Pacific Islander, 0% international. Calendar: semesters.

■ **ITT TECHNICAL INSTITUTE (DAYTON)** *I-3*
3325 Stop 8 Rd.
Dayton, OH 45414-3425
Tel: (937)454-2267
Web Site: http://www.itt-tech.edu/
Description: Proprietary, 2-year, coed. Part of ITT Educational Services,
Inc. Awards terminal associate degrees. Founded 1935. Setting: 7-acre
suburban campus. Core.
Entrance Requirements: Option: deferred admission. Required: high
school transcript, interview, Wonderlic aptitude test. Recommended: recom-
mendations. Entrance: minimally difficult. Application deadline: Rolling.
Notification: continuous.
Costs Per Year: Application fee: $100.
Collegiate Environment: Orientation program. College housing not avail-
able.

■ **ITT TECHNICAL INSTITUTE (HILLIARD)** *H-6*
3781 Park Mill Run Dr.
Hilliard, OH 43026
Tel: (614)771-4888; 888-483-4888
Fax: (614)921-4179
Web Site: http://www.itt-tech.edu/
Description: Proprietary, 2-year, coed. Awards terminal associate degrees.
Founded 2003.
Entrance Requirements: Required: high school transcript, interview,
Wonderlic aptitude test. Recommended: recommendations. Application
deadline: Rolling. Notification: continuous.
Costs Per Year: Application fee: $100.

■ **ITT TECHNICAL INSTITUTE (NORWOOD)** *K-2*
4750 Wesley Ave.
Norwood, OH 45212
Tel: (513)531-8300
Free: 800-314-8324
Web Site: http://www.itt-tech.edu/
Description: Proprietary, 2-year, coed. Part of ITT Educational Services,
Inc. Awards transfer associate degrees. Core.
Entrance Requirements: Option: deferred admission. Required: high
school transcript, interview, Wonderlic aptitude test. Recommended: recom-
mendations. Entrance: minimally difficult. Application deadline: Rolling.
Notification: continuous.
Costs Per Year: Application fee: $100.
Collegiate Environment: Orientation program. College housing not avail-
able.

■ **ITT TECHNICAL INSTITUTE (STRONGSVILLE)** *D-9*
14955 Sprague Rd.
Strongsville, OH 44136
Tel: (440)234-9091

Free: 800-331-1488
Web Site: http://www.itt-tech.edu/
Description: Proprietary, 2-year, coed. Part of ITT Educational Services,
Inc. Awards terminal associate degrees. Core.
Entrance Requirements: Option: deferred admission. Required: high
school transcript, interview, Wonderlic aptitude test. Recommended: recom-
mendations. Entrance: minimally difficult. Application deadline: Rolling.
Notification: continuous.
Costs Per Year: Application fee: $100.
Collegiate Environment: Orientation program. College housing not avail-
able.

■ **ITT TECHNICAL INSTITUTE (WARRENSVILLE HEIGHTS)**
4700 Richmond Rd.
Warrensville Heights, OH 44128
Tel: (216)896-6500
Free: 800-741-3494
Web Site: http://www.itt-tech.edu/
Description: 2-year, coed. Awards terminal associate degrees.
Entrance Requirements: Required: high school transcript, interview,
Wonderlic aptitude test. Recommended: recommendations. Application
deadline: Rolling. Notification: continuous.
Costs Per Year: Application fee: $100.

■ **ITT TECHNICAL INSTITUTE (YOUNGSTOWN)** *D-13*
1030 North Meridian Rd.
Youngstown, OH 44509-4098
Tel: (330)270-1600
Free: 800-832-5001
Fax: (330)270-8333
Web Site: http://www.itt-tech.edu/
Description: Proprietary, 2-year, coed. Part of ITT Educational Services,
Inc. Awards terminal associate degrees. Founded 1967. Setting: suburban
campus with easy access to Cleveland and Pittsburgh. Core.
Entrance Requirements: Option: deferred admission. Required: high
school transcript, interview, Wonderlic aptitude test. Recommended: recom-
mendations. Entrance: minimally difficult. Application deadline: Rolling.
Notification: continuous.
Costs Per Year: Application fee: $100.
Collegiate Environment: Orientation program. Student-run newspaper.
College housing not available.

■ **JAMES A. RHODES STATE COLLEGE** *F-3*
4240 Campus Dr.
Lima, OH 45804-3597
Tel: (419)995-8000
Admissions: (419)995-8050
Fax: (419)995-8098
E-mail: lingrel.s@rhodesstate.edu
Web Site: http://www.rhodesstate.edu/
Description: State-supported, 2-year, coed. Awards certificates, transfer associate, and terminal associate degrees. Founded 1971. Setting: 565-acre
rural campus. Endowment: $849,362. Educational spending for 2005 fiscal
year: $4097 per student. Total enrollment: 2,842. 1,092 applied, 100% were
admitted. 5% from top 10% of their high school class, 22% from top quarter,
52% from top half. Full-time: 1,417 students, 67% women, 33% men. Part-
time: 1,425 students, 70% women, 30% men. Students come from 8 states
and territories, 0.3% from out-of-state, 0.2% Native American, 1% Hispanic,
7% black, 1% Asian American or Pacific Islander, 0% international, 48% 25
or older, 6% transferred in. Core. Academic remediation for entering
students, services for LD students, advanced placement, self-designed
majors, independent study, distance learning, summer session for credit,
part-time degree program, adult/continuing education programs, co-op
programs and internships. Off campus study.
Entrance Requirements: Open admission except for allied health
programs. Options: Common Application, early admission, deferred admission. Required: high school transcript. Placement: ACT, ACT ASSET and
ACT COMPASS required for some. Entrance: noncompetitive. Application
deadline: Rolling. Notification: continuous until 9/22.
Collegiate Environment: Orientation program. Drama-theater group, choral
group, student-run newspaper. Social organizations: 25 open to all. Most
popular organizations: Student Senate, Social Activities Board, Ski Club,
Society of Manufacturing Engineers, Psychology Club. Major annual events:
May Week, annual rock concert. Campus security: student patrols, late night

transport-escort service. College housing not available. Rhodes State/Ohio State Library/ with 80,000 books and an OPAC. Operations spending for 2004 fiscal year: $182,139. 150 computers available on campus for general student use. A campuswide network can be accessed from off-campus. Staffed computer lab on campus.

Community Environment: Lima, population 45,549, is an industrial city and the county seat of Allen County. It is 68 miles SSW of Toledo. Its major industries include motor vehicles, steel castings, aircraft parts, machine tools, and building machinery. It is also the center of a diversified agricultural region.

■ **JEFFERSON COMMUNITY COLLEGE** *G-13*
4000 Sunset Blvd.
Steubenville, OH 43952-3598
Tel: (740)264-5591
Fax: (740)266-2706
Web Site: http://www.jcc.edu/

Description: State and locally supported, 2-year, coed. Part of Ohio Board of Regents. Awards certificates, transfer associate, and terminal associate degrees. Founded 1966. Setting: 83-acre small town campus with easy access to Pittsburgh. Endowment: $197,077. Educational spending for 2005 fiscal year: $7268 per student. Total enrollment: 1,697. Student-undergrad faculty ratio is 16:1. 879 applied, 100% were admitted. Full-time: 911 students, 59% women, 41% men. Part-time: 786 students, 65% women, 35% men. Students come from 23 states and territories, 16% from out-of-state, 0.1% Native American, 1% Hispanic, 5% black, 1% Asian American or Pacific Islander, 0% international, 43% 25 or older, 28% transferred in. Core. Calendar: semesters. Academic remediation for entering students, services for LD students, summer session for credit, part-time degree program, adult/continuing education programs, internships. Off campus study at members of the Southeastern Ohio Technical Education Consortium.

Entrance Requirements: Open admission except for allied health programs. Options: early admission, deferred admission. Required for some: high school transcript, SAT or ACT. Entrance: noncompetitive. Application deadline: 8/20. Notification: continuous until 8/20.

Costs Per Year: Application fee: $20. Area resident tuition: $2550 full-time, $85 per credit part-time. State resident tuition: $2730 full-time, $91 per credit part-time. Nonresident tuition: $3450 full-time, $115 per credit part-time. Mandatory fees: $600 full-time. Full-time tuition and fees vary according to reciprocity agreements. Part-time tuition varies according to reciprocity agreements.

Collegiate Environment: Most popular organizations: Student Senate, SADD, AITP (Association for Information Technology Professionals), American Drafting and Design Association, Writers Club. Major annual events: Battle of the Bands, Blood Drive. Campus security: student patrols. College housing not available. Jefferson Community College Library with 12,500 books, 1,394 microform titles, 180 serials, 246 audiovisual materials, and an OPAC. Operations spending for 2004 fiscal year: $177,042. 325 computers available on campus for general student use. Staffed computer lab on campus.

■ **JOHN CARROLL UNIVERSITY** *D-19*
20700 North Park Blvd.
University Heights, OH 44118-4581
Tel: (216)397-1886
Admissions: (216)397-4294
Fax: (216)397-3098
E-mail: admission@jcvaxa.jcu.edu
Web Site: http://www.jcu.edu/

Description: Independent Roman Catholic (Jesuit), comprehensive, coed. Awards bachelor's and master's degrees. Founded 1886. Setting: 60-acre suburban campus with easy access to Cleveland. Endowment: $122.4 million. Research spending for 2004 fiscal year: $4.6 million. Educational spending for 2005 fiscal year: $5696 per student. Total enrollment: 4,101. 2,761 applied, 89% were admitted. 27% from top 10% of their high school class, 54% from top quarter, 85% from top half. 5 National Merit Scholars, 12 valedictorians. Full-time: 3,184 students, 54% women, 46% men. Part-time: 166 students, 49% women, 51% men. Students come from 35 states and territories, 27% from out-of-state, 0.1% Native American, 3% Hispanic, 4% black, 2% Asian American or Pacific Islander, 0% international, 4% 25 or older, 57% live on campus, 5% transferred in. Retention: 86% of full-time freshmen returned the following year. Core. Calendar: semesters. Advanced placement, accelerated degree program, self-designed majors, honors program, independent study, double major, summer session for credit, part-

time degree program, adult/continuing education programs, co-op programs and internships, graduate courses open to undergrads. Off campus study at Northeast Ohio Commission on Higher Education. Study abroad program. ROTC: Army.

Entrance Requirements: Options: Peterson's Universal Application, early admission, deferred admission. Required: high school transcript, 1 recommendation, SAT or ACT. Recommended: essay, interview. Required for some: interview. Entrance: moderately difficult. Application deadline: 2/1. Notification: continuous.

Costs Per Year: Application fee: $25. Comprehensive fee: $31,156 includes full-time tuition ($23,380), mandatory fees ($250), and college room and board ($7526). Part-time tuition: $708 per credit hour.

Collegiate Environment: Orientation program. Drama-theater group, choral group, student-run newspaper, radio station. Social organizations: 87 open to all; national fraternities, national sororities; 13% of eligible men and 18% of eligible women are members. Most popular organizations: Volunteer Service Organization, Student Union, Carroll News, band, University Concert Choir. Major annual events: homecoming, Parents' Weekend, Christmas Carroll Evening. Student services: health clinic, personal-psychological counseling. Campus security: 24-hour emergency response devices and patrols, late night transport-escort service. 1,900 college housing spaces available; 1,805 were occupied in 2003-04. On-campus residence required in freshman year. Options: coed, men-only, women-only housing available. Grasselli Library with 620,000 books, 692,005 microform titles, 2,198 serials, 5,820 audiovisual materials, an OPAC, and a Web page. Operations spending for 2004 fiscal year: $2.7 million. 210 computers available on campus for general student use. A campuswide network can be accessed from student residence rooms and from off campus. Staffed computer lab on campus.

■ **KENT STATE UNIVERSITY** *D-11*
PO Box 5190
Kent, OH 44242-0001
Tel: (330)672-3000
Free: 800-988-KENT
Admissions: (330)672-2444
Fax: (330)672-2499
E-mail: admissions@kent.edu
Web Site: http://www.kent.edu/

Description: State-supported, university, coed. Part of Kent State University System. Awards associate, bachelor's, master's, and doctoral degrees and post-master's certificates. Founded 1910. Setting: 1,347-acre suburban campus with easy access to Cleveland. Endowment: $71 million. Research spending for 2004 fiscal year: $16.4 million. Educational spending for 2005 fiscal year: $5752 per student. Total enrollment: 23,622. Faculty: 1,455 (841 full-time, 614 part-time). Student-undergrad faculty ratio is 19:1. 10,774 applied, 94% were admitted. 13% from top 10% of their high school class, 34% from top quarter, 70% from top half. 59 valedictorians. Full-time: 15,828 students, 60% women, 40% men. Part-time: 2,917 students, 59% women, 41% men. Students come from 47 states and territories, 60 other countries, 9% from out-of-state, 0.4% Native American, 1% Hispanic, 8% black, 1% Asian American or Pacific Islander, 1% international, 12% 25 or older, 35% live on campus, 5% transferred in. Retention: 72% of full-time freshmen returned the following year. Academic areas with the most degrees conferred: business/marketing; education; health professions and related sciences; English. Core. Calendar: semesters. Academic remediation for entering students, ESL program, services for LD students, advanced placement, accelerated degree program, self-designed majors, freshman honors college, honors program, independent study, distance learning, double major, summer session for credit, part-time degree program, external degree program, adult/continuing education programs, co-op programs and internships, graduate courses open to undergrads. Off campus study at Cuyahoga Community College, Lorain County Community College, Lakeland Community College. Study abroad program. ROTC: Army, Air Force.

Entrance Requirements: Options: Peterson's Universal Application, electronic application, early admission. Required: high school transcript, minimum 2.5 high school GPA, SAT or ACT. Entrance: moderately difficult. Application deadline: 5/1.

Costs Per Year: Application fee: $30. State resident tuition: $7954 full-time, $363 per credit hour part-time. Nonresident tuition: $15,386 full-time, $701 per credit hour part-time. Full-time tuition varies according to course level, course load, degree level, location, program, reciprocity agreements, and student level. Part-time tuition varies according to course level, course load, degree level, location, program, reciprocity agreements, and student level. College room and board: $6640. College room only: $4040. Room and board charges vary according to board plan and housing facility.

Collegiate Environment: Orientation program. Drama-theater group, choral group, marching band, student-run newspaper, radio station. Social organizations: 175 open to all; national fraternities, national sororities, local sororities; 7% of eligible men and 4% of eligible women are members. Most popular organizations: Kent Interhall Council, Black United Students, All Campus Programming Board, Delta Sigma PI, Late Night Christian Fellowship. Major annual events: FlashFest, Back to School Blastoff, Homecoming Week Celebration. Student services: legal services, health clinic, personal-psychological counseling, women's center. Campus security: 24-hour emergency response devices and patrols, student patrols, late night transport-escort service, controlled dormitory access, campus police and fire department, electronic locks on computer labs, studios and laboratory research areas. 6,546 college housing spaces available; all were occupied in 2003-04. Freshmen guaranteed college housing. On-campus residence required through sophomore year. Options: coed, men-only, women-only housing available. Kent State University Libraries & Media Services plus 6 others with 2.3 million books, 1.3 million microform titles, 11,139 serials, 10,266 audiovisual materials, an OPAC, and a Web page. Operations spending for 2004 fiscal year: $10.9 million. 1,690 computers available on campus for general student use. A campuswide network can be accessed from student residence rooms and from off campus. Staffed computer lab on campus.

Community Environment: Kent, a city of some 30,000, on the banks of the Cuyahoga River, in Portage County, is situated 11 miles east of Akron, 33 miles south of Cleveland, 40 miles west of Youngstown and 28 miles north of Canton. The community provides students with many places to shop and entertain themselves and places of worship for most major denominations. Recreational activities include fishing, boating, skiing, swimming, and golf. The university is located near two major jetports, Cleveland Hopkins International and Akron-Canton.

■ **KENT STATE UNIVERSITY, ASHTABULA CAMPUS** *B-12*
3325 West 13th St.
Ashtabula, OH 44004-2299
Tel: (440)964-3322
Admissions: (440)964-4217
Fax: (440)964-4269
E-mail: sanford@ashtabula.kent.edu
Web Site: http://www.ashtabula.kent.edu/

Description: State-supported, primarily 2-year, coed. Part of Kent State University System. Awards certificates, transfer associate, terminal associate, and bachelor's degrees (also offers some upper-level and graduate courses). Founded 1958. Setting: 120-acre small town campus with easy access to Cleveland. Research spending for 2004 fiscal year: $87,132. Total enrollment: 1,396. 3 class presidents, 1 valedictorian, 20 student government officers. 1% Native American, 2% Hispanic, 5% black, 1% Asian American or Pacific Islander, 0.4% international. Calendar: semesters. Academic remediation for entering students, advanced placement, self-designed majors, freshman honors college, honors program, summer session for credit, part-time degree program, internships. ROTC: Army (c).

Entrance Requirements: Open admission except for nursing program. Options: early admission, deferred admission. Placement: SAT or ACT recommended. Entrance: noncompetitive. Application deadlines: 8/1, 7/15 for nonresidents. Notification: continuous until 8/1, continuous until 7/15 for nonresidents.

Collegiate Environment: Drama-theater group, student-run newspaper. Most popular organizations: student government, student newspaper, Student Nurses Association. Campus security: 24-hour emergency response devices. College housing not available. 51,884 books and 225 serials. 25 computers available on campus for general student use. Staffed computer lab on campus.

Community Environment: This growing industrial city is on Lake Erie at the mouth of the Ashtabula River. Two municipal parks on Lake Erie have excellent facilities for swimming, boating, and fishing.

■ **KENT STATE UNIVERSITY, EAST LIVERPOOL CAMPUS** *F-13*
400 East 4th St.
East Liverpool, OH 43920-3497
Tel: (330)385-3805
Admissions: (330)382-7414
Fax: (330)385-6348
E-mail: admissions@eliv.kent.edu
Web Site: http://www.kenteliv.kent.edu/

Description: State-supported, 2-year, coed. Part of Kent State University System. Awards certificates, transfer associate, and terminal associate degrees (also offers some upper-level and graduate courses). Founded 1967. Setting: 4-acre small town campus with easy access to Pittsburgh. Educational spending for 2005 fiscal year: $3004 per student. Total enrollment: 657. 125 applied, 80% were admitted. Students come from 3 states and territories, 6% from out-of-state, 47% 25 or older. Core. Calendar: semesters. Academic remediation for entering students, services for LD students, advanced placement, accelerated degree program, self-designed majors, distance learning, summer session for credit, part-time degree program, adult/continuing education programs, internships. ROTC: Army (c), Naval (c), Air Force (c).

Entrance Requirements: Open admission except for nursing, physical therapy assistant, occupational therapy assistant programs. Options: early admission, deferred admission. Required: high school transcript. Placement: ACT recommended. Entrance: noncompetitive. Application deadline: Rolling. Notification: continuous until 9/1.

Collegiate Environment: Orientation program. Student-run newspaper. Social organizations: 9 open to all. Most popular organizations: Student Senate, Student Nurses Association, Alpha Beta Gamma, Occupational Therapist Assistant Club, Physical Therapist Assistant Club. Major annual events: Christmas on Campus, Ohio River Arts Festival, Welcome Back Fest. Campus security: student patrols, late night transport-escort service. College housing not available. East Liverpool Campus Library with 31,320 books, 135 serials, an OPAC, and a Web page. 72 computers available on campus for general student use. A campuswide network can be accessed. Staffed computer lab on campus.

Community Environment: East Liverpool is in one of the most scenic sections of the upper Ohio Valley and is a leading pottery center producing semivitreous porcelain ware. Train and bus transportation is available and a local airport is available for private planes. Community facilities include numerous churches, representing 18 denominations, and a library. Thompson park provides facilities for all outdoor sports including winter sports; Beaver Creek provides facilities for camping, fishing, and picnicking.

■ **KENT STATE UNIVERSITY, GEAUGA CAMPUS** *D-23*
14111 Claridon-Troy Rd.
Burton, OH 44021-9500
Tel: (440)834-4187
Fax: (440)834-0919
E-mail: hmohan1@kent.edu
Web Site: http://www.geauga.kent.edu/

Description: State-supported, primarily 2-year, coed. Part of Kent State University System. Awards certificates, diplomas, transfer associate, and bachelor's degrees. Founded 1964, Setting: 87-acre rural campus with easy access to Cleveland. Total enrollment: 918. Student-undergrad faculty ratio is 14:1. 172 applied, 100% were admitted. 18% from top 10% of their high school class, 30% from top quarter, 54% from top half. Full-time: 315 students, 51% women, 49% men. Part-time: 603 students, 59% women, 41% men. Students come from 6 states and territories, 2 other countries, 1% from out-of-state, 0.3% Native American, 1% Hispanic, 6% black, 1% Asian American or Pacific Islander, 0.4% international, 39% 25 or older, 1% transferred in. Core. Calendar: semesters. Academic remediation for entering students, services for LD students, advanced placement, self-designed majors, distance learning, double major, summer session for credit, part-time degree program, adult/continuing education programs, internships. ROTC: Army (c), Air Force (c).

Entrance Requirements: Open admission. Options: early admission, deferred admission. Required: high school transcript. Entrance: noncompetitive. Application deadline: Rolling.

Costs Per Year: Application fee: $30. State resident tuition: $4770 full-time, $217 per credit hour part-time. Nonresident tuition: $12,202 full-time, $555 per credit hour part-time.

Collegiate Environment: Student-run newspaper. Social organizations: 5 open to all. Most popular organizations: Computer Club, Student Senate, Accounting Club, student newspaper. Major annual events: Computer Software Fair, Faculty Colloquium. Campus security: 24-hour emergency response devices. College housing not available. Kent State University Library with 8,300 books, 6,600 serials, an OPAC, and a Web page. Operations spending for 2004 fiscal year: $84,426. 50 computers available on campus for general student use. Staffed computer lab on campus.

Community Environment: Burton located 30 miles from Cleveland, is primarily a residential area with a few small businesses. Planes and trains are within 18 miles. Community facilities include shopping facilities, churches, and civic and service organizations. Ski resort is nearby for all winter sports.

■ KENT STATE UNIVERSITY, SALEM CAMPUS *E-12*
2491 State Route 45 South
Salem, OH 44460-9412
Tel: (330)332-0361
Fax: (330)332-9256
E-mail: ask-us@salem.kent.edu
Web Site: http://www.salem.kent.edu/
Description: State-supported, primarily 2-year, coed. Part of Kent State University System. Awards transfer associate, terminal associate, and bachelor's degrees (also offers some upper-level and graduate courses). Founded 1966. Setting: 98-acre rural campus. Total enrollment: 1,332. 507 applied, 97% were admitted. 2% from top 10% of their high school class, 20% from top quarter, 30% from top half. Students come from 2 states and territories, 2 other countries, 0.1% Native American, 0.4% Hispanic, 3% black, 0.4% Asian American or Pacific Islander, 0% international, 55% 25 or older. Core. Calendar: semesters. Academic remediation for entering students, services for LD students, advanced placement, freshman honors college, honors program, distance learning, summer session for credit, part-time degree program, adult/continuing education programs, internships. ROTC: Army (c), Air Force (c).
Entrance Requirements: Open admission except for radiological technology, human services programs, and honors program. Options: early admission, deferred admission. Required: high school transcript. Required for some: essay, minimum X high school GPA, recommendations, ACT. Placement: SAT or ACT recommended; SAT or ACT required for some. Entrance: noncompetitive. Application deadline: Rolling.
Collegiate Environment: Orientation program. Drama-theater group. Social organizations: 11 open to all. Most popular organizations: student government, NEXUS, Ski Club, Art Club, Drama Club. Major annual events: Awards Banquet, movie nights, Career Days. Student services: personal-psychological counseling, women's center. Campus security: 24-hour emergency response devices, late night transport-escort service. College housing not available. 19,000 books, 2,415 microform titles, 163 serials, 158 audiovisual materials, an OPAC, and a Web page. 100 computers available on campus for general student use. A campuswide network can be accessed. Staffed computer lab on campus.
Community Environment: Known as the "Quaker City" because of its founders, Salem is one of the most productive dairy and fruit growing sections of Ohio. Salem is an area of thriving manufacturing and commercial establishments were full- and part-time employment is available. Centennial Park offers varied recreational facilities.

■ KENT STATE UNIVERSITY, STARK CAMPUS *F-11*
6000 Frank Ave., NW
Canton, OH 44720-7599
Tel: (330)499-9600
Admissions: (330)244-3259
Fax: (330)494-6121
E-mail: dspeck@stark.kent.edu
Web Site: http://www.stark.kent.edu/
Description: State-supported, primarily 2-year, coed. Part of Kent State University System. Awards transfer associate and bachelor's degrees (also offers some graduate courses). Founded 1967. Setting: 200-acre suburban campus with easy access to Cleveland. Total enrollment: 3,736. 1,510 applied, 100% were admitted. 5% from top 10% of their high school class, 18% from top quarter, 48% from top half. 2 valedictorians. Students come from 2 states and territories, 30% 25 or older. Core. Calendar: semesters. Academic remediation for entering students, ESL program, services for LD students, advanced placement, self-designed majors, freshman honors college, honors program, independent study, summer session for credit, part-time degree program, adult/continuing education programs, internships. Off campus study at Stark State College of Technology. Study abroad program. ROTC: Army (c), Air Force (c).
Entrance Requirements: Open admission. Options: early admission, deferred admission. Required: high school transcript. Required for some: interview, SAT or ACT. Entrance: noncompetitive. Application deadline: Rolling.
Collegiate Environment: Orientation program. Drama-theater group, choral group. Social organizations: 15 open to all. Most popular organizations: Psychology Club, Pan African Student Alliance, Criminal Justice Society,

Women's Studies Club, History Club. Major annual events: New Student Day, Featured Speaker Series. Campus security: 24-hour emergency response devices, late night transport-escort service. College housing not available. Kent State University Library with 72,807 books, 313 serials, an OPAC, and a Web page. 100 computers available on campus for general student use. A campuswide network can be accessed from off-campus. Staffed computer lab on campus.
Community Environment: The Kent State University Stark Campus is a commuter campus located Jackson Township in suburban Canton, Ohio.

■ KENT STATE UNIVERSITY, TRUMBULL CAMPUS *D-12*
4314 Mahoning Ave., NW
Warren, OH 44483-1998
Tel: (330)847-0571
E-mail: info@trumbull.kent.edu
Web Site: http://www.trumbull.kent.edu/
Description: State-supported, primarily 2-year, coed. Part of Kent State University System. Awards certificates, transfer associate, terminal associate, and bachelor's degrees (also offers some upper-level and graduate courses). Founded 1954. Setting: 200-acre suburban campus with easy access to Cleveland. Total enrollment: 2,036. Student-undergrad faculty ratio is 16:1. 432 applied, 100% were admitted. 7% from top 10% of their high school class, 18% from top quarter, 51% from top half. Full-time: 893 students, 61% women, 39% men. Part-time: 1,143 students, 64% women, 36% men. Students come from 4 states and territories, 1% from out-of-state, 0.3% Native American, 1% Hispanic, 12% black, 0.4% Asian American or Pacific Islander, 0.1% international, 54% 25 or older. Retention: 58% of full-time freshmen returned the following year. Core. Calendar: semesters. Academic remediation for entering students, services for LD students, advanced placement, self-designed majors, freshman honors college, honors program, independent study, distance learning, summer session for credit, part-time degree program, adult/continuing education programs, co-op programs and internships. ROTC: Army (c), Air Force (c).
Entrance Requirements: Open admission except for nursing program. Options: Peterson's Universal Application, early admission, deferred admission. Required: high school transcript. Entrance: noncompetitive. Application deadline: 7/30. Notification: continuous until 8/30.
Costs Per Year: Application fee: $30. State resident tuition: $4770 full-time, $217 per credit hour part-time. Nonresident tuition: $12,202 full-time, $555 per credit hour part-time.
Collegiate Environment: Orientation program. Drama-theater group, student-run newspaper. Social organizations: 10 open to all. Most popular organizations: Student Senate, Trumbull Environmental Club, Union Activities Board, Gamemasters, Kent Christian Fellowship. Campus security: 24-hour emergency response devices, late night transport-escort service, patrols by trained security personnel during open hours. College housing not available. Trumbull Campus Library with 65,951 books, 759 serials, an OPAC, and a Web page. Operations spending for 2004 fiscal year: $380,165. 300 computers available on campus for general student use. Staffed computer lab on campus.
Community Environment: Located in the northeastern part of Ohio, the New England influences brought here by early settlers are still strongly felt. Warren, an industrial city, is in the great Mahoning Valley steel district and also has an active electrical and automotive parts industry. Shopping facilities here are good. Mosquito State Park, located 10 miles north, provides facilities for fishing, boating, swimming and camping. Points of interest are the John Stark Edwards House and the Nelson and Kennedy Ledges State Park.

■ KENT STATE UNIVERSITY, TUSCARAWAS CAMPUS *G-11*
330 University Dr., NE
New Philadelphia, OH 44663-9403
Tel: (330)339-3391
Fax: (330)339-3321
Web Site: http://www.tusc.kent.edu/
Description: State-supported, primarily 2-year, coed. Part of Kent State University System. Awards certificates, diplomas, transfer associate, terminal associate, bachelor's, and master's degrees (also offers some upper-level and graduate courses). Founded 1962. Setting: 172-acre small town campus with easy access to Cleveland. Educational spending for 2005 fiscal year: $3417 per student. Total enrollment: 1,949. Faculty: 122 (48 full-time, 74 part-time). Student-undergrad faculty ratio is 18:1. 513 applied. Full-time: 935 students, 58% women, 42% men. Part-time: 970 students, 67% women, 33% men. 0% from out-of-state, 0.2% Native American, 1%

Hispanic, 1% black, 0.3% Asian American or Pacific Islander, 0.2% international, 29% 25 or older. Core. Calendar: semesters. Academic remediation for entering students, services for LD students, advanced placement, accelerated degree program, self-designed majors, freshman honors college, honors program, distance learning, double major, summer session for credit, part-time degree program, adult/continuing education programs, internships. ROTC: Army (c), Air Force (c).

Entrance Requirements: Open admission except for business administration, education, nursing, fine and performing arts programs. Options: Common Application, early admission, deferred admission. Required: high school transcript, SAT and SAT Subject Tests or ACT. Entrance: noncompetitive. Application deadline: 9/1. Notification: continuous.

Costs Per Year: Application fee: $30. State resident tuition: $2637 full-time. Nonresident tuition: $6353 full-time.

Collegiate Environment: Orientation program. Choral group. Social organizations: 14 open to all. Most popular organizations: Society of Mechanical Engineers, IEEE, Imagineers, Criminal Justice Club, Salt and Light. Major annual events: Spring Awards Banquet, Buck Lunches, Commencement. College housing not available. Tuscarawas Campus Library with 62,783 books, 2,120 microform titles, 250 serials, 800 audiovisual materials, an OPAC, and a Web page. Operations spending for 2004 fiscal year: $252,879. 194 computers available on campus for general student use. A campuswide network can be accessed from off-campus. Staffed computer lab on campus.

■ KENYON COLLEGE *G-8*

Gambier, OH 43022-9623
Tel: (740)427-5000
Free: 800-848-2468
Admissions: (740)427-5776
Fax: (740)427-2634
E-mail: admissions@kenyon.edu
Web Site: http://www.kenyon.edu/

Description: Independent, 4-year, coed. Awards bachelor's degrees. Founded 1824. Setting: 1,200-acre rural campus with easy access to Columbus. Endowment: $158.1 million. Research spending for 2004 fiscal year: $287,071. Educational spending for 2005 fiscal year: $15,036 per student. Total enrollment: 1,661. Student-undergrad faculty ratio is 10:1. 3,929 applied, 36% were admitted. 57% from top 10% of their high school class, 91% from top quarter, 100% from top half. 29 National Merit Scholars, 6 class presidents, 19 valedictorians, 28 student government officers. Full-time: 1,640 students, 53% women, 47% men. Part-time: 21 students, 62% women, 38% men. Students come from 46 states and territories, 28 other countries, 77% from out-of-state, 0.4% Native American, 3% Hispanic, 3% black, 4% Asian American or Pacific Islander, 3% international, 0% 25 or older, 98% live on campus, 1% transferred in. Retention: 92% of full-time freshmen returned the following year. Academic areas with the most degrees conferred: social sciences; English; visual and performing arts. Core. Calendar: semesters. Services for LD students, advanced placement, accelerated degree program, self-designed majors, honors program, independent study, double major, internships. Off campus study. Study abroad program.

Entrance Requirements: Options: Peterson's Universal Application, Common Application, electronic application, early admission, early decision, deferred admission, international baccalaureate accepted. Required: essay, high school transcript, 1 recommendation, counselor recommendation, SAT or ACT. Recommended: minimum 3.5 high school GPA, 2 recommendations, interview. Entrance: very difficult. Application deadlines: 1/15, 12/1 for early decision plan 1, 1/15 for early decision plan 2. Notification: 4/1, 12/15 for early decision plan 1, 2/1 for early decision plan 2.

Costs Per Year: Application fee: $50. Comprehensive fee: $39,500 includes full-time tuition ($32,980), mandatory fees ($950), and college room and board ($5570). College room only: $2620. Room and board charges vary according to housing facility. Part-time tuition: $825 per credit hour.

Collegiate Environment: Orientation program. Drama-theater group, choral group, student-run newspaper, radio station. Social organizations: 138 open to all; national fraternities, local fraternities, local sororities; 19% of eligible men and 7% of eligible women are members. Most popular organizations: music groups, Student Theater Organization, writing organizations, student radio station, Ballroom Dance Club. Major annual events: Summer Send-off, Philander's Phebruary Phling, Take Back the Night. Student services: health clinic, personal-psychological counseling, women's center. Campus security: 24-hour emergency response devices and patrols, student patrols, late night transport-escort service. College housing designed to accommodate 1,530

students; 1,574 undergraduates lived in college housing during 2003-04. Freshmen guaranteed college housing. On-campus residence required through senior year. Options: coed, women-only housing available. Olin Library plus 1 other with 826,059 books, 141,663 microform titles, 8,574 serials, 173,783 audiovisual materials, an OPAC, and a Web page. Operations spending for 2004 fiscal year: $2.1 million. 300 computers available on campus for general student use. A campuswide network can be accessed from student residence rooms and from off campus. Staffed computer lab on campus.

Community Environment: Gambier, a hamlet in central Ohio, is 47 miles northeast of Columbus, and just east of Mount Vernon. It is a village dating from pre-Civil War days and many buildings of that era still remain.

■ KETTERING COLLEGE OF MEDICAL ARTS *J-3*

3737 Southern Blvd.
Kettering, OH 45429-1299
Tel: (937)395-8601
Free: 800-433-5262
Admissions: (937)296-7228
Fax: (937)395-8333
Web Site: http://www.kcma.edu/

Description: Independent Seventh-day Adventist, primarily 2-year, primarily women. Awards certificates, transfer associate, terminal associate, and bachelor's degrees. Founded 1967. Setting: 35-acre suburban campus. Total enrollment: 653. 14% from top 10% of their high school class, 35% from top quarter, 70% from top half. Students come from 29 states and territories, 3 other countries, 0.3% Native American, 2% Hispanic, 7% black, 3% Asian American or Pacific Islander, 0.5% international, 51% 25 or older, 20% live on campus. Core. Calendar: semesters. Advanced placement, summer session for credit, part-time degree program, internships. Off campus study at members of the Southwestern Ohio Council for Higher Education.

Entrance Requirements: Option: early admission. Required: high school transcript, minimum 2.0 high school GPA, 3 recommendations, ACT. Recommended: minimum 3.0 high school GPA, interview, SAT. Entrance: moderately difficult. Application deadline: Rolling. Notification: continuous.

Collegiate Environment: Drama-theater group, choral group. Social organizations: 3 open to all. Most popular organizations: student association/student life, campus ministries. Major annual events: Weeks of Spiritual Emphasis, Nursing Dedication Ceremony, Christmas Party. Student services: health clinic, personal-psychological counseling. Campus security: 24-hour emergency response devices and patrols, late night transport-escort service. Option: coed housing available. Learning Resources Center plus 1 other with 29,390 books, 266 serials, an OPAC, and a Web page. 30 computers available on campus for general student use. Staffed computer lab on campus.

Community Environment: The city is surrounded by rolling, wooded hills and is a suburb of Dayton. The recreational, educational, and cultural advantages of Dayton are enjoyed by the citizens of Kettering also. Kettering is the home of the world's largest supply of electronic components. Community facilities include 37 churches of many denominations and many shopping centers and plazas. Nine golf courses are in the area.

■ LAKE ERIE COLLEGE *B-11*

391 West Washington St.
Painesville, OH 44077-3389
Tel: (440)296-1856
Free: 800-916-0904
Admissions: (440)375-7050
Fax: (440)352-3533
E-mail: jcalhoun@lec.edu
Web Site: http://www.lec.edu/

Description: Independent, comprehensive, coed. Awards bachelor's and master's degrees. Founded 1856. Setting: 57-acre small town campus with easy access to Cleveland. Endowment: $30 million. Educational spending for 2005 fiscal year: $3905 per student. Total enrollment: 952. Faculty: 93 (34 full-time, 59 part-time). Student-undergrad faculty ratio is 12:1. 532 applied, 76% were admitted. 15% from top 10% of their high school class, 29% from top quarter, 59% from top half. Full-time: 574 students, 73% women, 27% men. Part-time: 108 students, 76% women, 24% men. Students come from 22 states and territories, 5 other countries, 20% from out-of-state, 0.1% Native American, 2% Hispanic, 7% black, 1% Asian American or Pacific Islander, 0.4% international, 24% 25 or older, 47% live on campus, 12% transferred in. Retention: 64% of full-time freshmen returned the following year. Academic areas with the most degrees conferred: education; business/

marketing; agriculture; social sciences. Core. Calendar: semesters. Academic remediation for entering students, services for LD students, advanced placement, accelerated degree program, self-designed majors, freshman honors college, honors program, independent study, double major, summer session for credit, part-time degree program, external degree program, adult/continuing education programs, co-op programs and internships, graduate courses open to undergrads. Off campus study at Northeast Ohio Commission on Higher Education. Study abroad program.

Entrance Requirements: Options: Peterson's Universal Application, Common Application, electronic application, deferred admission, international baccalaureate accepted. Required: high school transcript, minimum 2.5 high school GPA, SAT or ACT. Recommended: interview. Required for some: essay. Entrance: minimally difficult. Notification: continuous.

Costs Per Year: Application fee: $25. Comprehensive fee: $27,724 includes full-time tuition ($20,500), mandatory fees ($890), and college room and board ($6334). Part-time tuition: $508 per hour. Part-time mandatory fees: $26 per hour.

Collegiate Environment: Orientation program. Drama-theater group, choral group, student-run newspaper, radio station. Social organizations: 28 open to all; national sororities; 8% of women are members. Most popular organizations: Delta Kappa Psi, Student Government Association, Mortar Board, IHSA, Activities Council. Major annual events: Spring Formal, Homecoming, movie nights. Campus security: 24-hour emergency response devices and patrols, late night transport-escort service. 285 college housing spaces available; 280 were occupied in 2003-04. Freshmen guaranteed college housing. On-campus residence required through sophomore year. Options: coed, men-only, women-only housing available. Lincoln Library plus 2 others with 87,000 books, 11,700 microform titles, 6,050 serials, 2,000 audiovisual materials, an OPAC, and a Web page. 104 computers available on campus for general student use. A campuswide network can be accessed from student residence rooms and from off campus. Staffed computer lab on campus.

Community Environment: Painesville is a city of 30,000 residents located 25 miles east of Cleveland and 3 miles from Lake Erie. The surrounding area boasts numerous fine commercial nurseries, the home of President Garfield, maple sugar industries, and the Holden Arboretum. Lake Erie College sponsors an ongoing series of cultural activities at the B. K. Smith Fine Arts Gallery and the C. K. Rickel Theater on the Lake Erie campus. Other community facilities include a variety of churches, the YMCA, and Morley Library, as well as various civic and service organizations.

■ **LAKELAND COMMUNITY COLLEGE** *C-11*

7700 Clocktower Dr.
Kirtland, OH 44094-5198
Tel: (440)525-7000
Admissions: (440)525-7230
Fax: (440)525-4330
Web Site: http://www.lakeland.cc.oh.us/

Description: State and locally supported, 2-year, coed. Part of Ohio Board of Regents. Awards certificates, transfer associate, and terminal associate degrees. Founded 1967. Setting: 380-acre suburban campus with easy access to Cleveland. Endowment: $1.4 million. Total enrollment: 8,635. Full-time: 3,098 students, 54% women, 46% men. Part-time: 5,537 students, 63% women, 37% men. Students come from 5 states and territories, 31 other countries, 1% from out-of-state, 0.2% Native American, 1% Hispanic, 8% black, 1% Asian American or Pacific Islander, 3% international, 43% 25 or older. Core. Calendar: semesters. Academic remediation for entering students, services for LD students, advanced placement, distance learning, summer session for credit, part-time degree program, external degree program, adult/continuing education programs, co-op programs and internships.

Entrance Requirements: Open admission except for allied health programs. Options: Peterson's Universal Application, Common Application, electronic application, early admission, deferred admission. Required: high school transcript. Placement: SAT or ACT recommended; SAT or ACT, ACT ASSET or ACT COMPASS required for some. Entrance: noncompetitive. Application deadline: 9/1. Notification: continuous until 9/1.

Collegiate Environment: Orientation program. Drama-theater group, choral group, student-run newspaper, radio station. Social organizations: 29 open to all. Most popular organizations: Campus Activities Board, Gamers Guild, Computers Users Group, Veterans Group, Aikido Club. Major annual events: Spring Fling, health educational programming, Student Activities Fair. Student services: health clinic, personal-psychological counseling, women's center. Campus security: 24-hour emergency response devices and patrols,

student patrols, late night transport-escort service. College housing not available. Lakeland Community College Library with 70,874 books, 2,205 serials, 3,453 audiovisual materials, an OPAC, and a Web page. 500 computers available on campus for general student use. A campuswide network can be accessed from off-campus. Staffed computer lab on campus.

Community Environment: Mentor is located in attractive Lake County, in the northeastern portion of the state along Lake Erie, 20 miles east of Cleveland. The land area amounts to 231 square miles with a total population of 212,800. The county itself consists of two distinctly different areas: a densely populated western end with approximately 68% of the population and a sparsely populated eastern end. The community offers exceptional opportunity for personal and professional growth.

■ **LAURA AND ALVIN SIEGAL COLLEGE OF JUDAIC STUDIES** *D-20*

26500 Shaker Blvd.
Beachwood, OH 44122-7116
Tel: (216)464-4050; 888-336-2257
Fax: (216)464-5827
Web Site: http://www.siegalcollege.edu/

Description: Independent, comprehensive, coed. Awards bachelor's and master's degrees. Founded 1963. Setting: 2-acre suburban campus with easy access to Cleveland. Total enrollment: 146. 5 applied, 20% were admitted. Full-time: 2 students, 50% women, 50% men. Part-time: 9 students, 78% women, 22% men. 0% from out-of-state, 0% Native American, 0% Hispanic, 0% black, 0% Asian American or Pacific Islander, 0% international, 85% 25 or older, 0% transferred in. Retention: 100% of full-time freshmen returned the following year. Core. Calendar: semesters. Independent study, distance learning, double major, summer session for credit, part-time degree program, external degree program, adult/continuing education programs, co-op programs and internships, graduate courses open to undergrads. Off campus study at John Carroll University, Ursuline College, Case Western Reserve University, Cleveland State University.

Entrance Requirements: Open admission. Options: Peterson's Universal Application, Common Application, deferred admission. Required: essay, high school transcript, 2 recommendations, interview. Entrance: noncompetitive. Application deadline: Rolling. Notification: continuous.

Costs Per Year: Application fee: $50. Tuition: $15,000 full-time, $500 per credit part-time. Mandatory fees: $25 full-time. Full-time tuition and fees vary according to course load. Part-time tuition varies according to course load.

Collegiate Environment: Orientation program. Social organizations: 1 open to all. Most popular organization: 'YES'-Young Educators and Scholars. Major annual events: Meet the Professors (fall opening event), Dinner for Degree Students. Campus security: 24-hour emergency response devices, 24-hour ID check at all doors. College housing not available. Aaron Garber Library with 28,000 books, 100 serials, and an OPAC. 8 computers available on campus for general student use.

■ **LORAIN COUNTY COMMUNITY COLLEGE** *D-9*

1005 Abbe Rd., North
Elyria, OH 44035
Tel: (440)365-5222
Free: 800-995-5222
Admissions: (440)366-7566
Fax: (440)365-6519
Web Site: http://www.lorainccc.edu/

Description: State and locally supported, 2-year, coed. Part of Ohio Board of Regents. Awards certificates, transfer associate, and terminal associate degrees. Founded 1963. Setting: 480-acre suburban campus with easy access to Cleveland. Total enrollment: 9,409. Full-time: 3,432 students, 61% women, 39% men. Part-time: 5,977 students, 70% women, 30% men. Students come from 20 states and territories, 7 other countries, 1% Native American, 6% Hispanic, 7% black, 1% Asian American or Pacific Islander, 1% international, 45% 25 or older. Core. Calendar: semesters. Academic remediation for entering students, ESL program, services for LD students, advanced placement, self-designed majors, honors program, independent study, distance learning, summer session for credit, part-time degree program, adult/continuing education programs, co-op programs.

Entrance Requirements: Open admission. Options: early admission, deferred admission. Required for some: high school transcript. Placement: SAT or ACT recommended; ACT ASSET, ACT COMPASS required for some. Entrance: noncompetitive. Application deadline: Rolling. Notification: continuous.

Collegiate Environment: Orientation program. Drama-theater group, choral group, student-run newspaper, radio station. Social organizations: national fraternities, national sororities. Most popular organizations: Phi Beta Kappa, Black Progressives, Hispanic Club. Major annual events: Fall Picnic, Spring Picnic, Family Fest. Student services: legal services, health clinic, personal-psychological counseling, women's center. Campus security: 24-hour emergency response devices and patrols, late night transport-escort service. College housing not available. Learning Resource Center with 198,984 books, 14,330 microform titles, 3,289 audiovisual materials, and an OPAC. 400 computers available on campus for general student use. A campuswide network can be accessed from off-campus. Staffed computer lab on campus.

Community Environment: Situated in the far northeast corner of the city of Elyria and 26 miles west of Cleveland, the campus is just four miles from downtown Elyria, a city of over 57,500 and the county seat; eight miles to the north lies Lorain, an industrial community on Lake Erie at the mouth of the Black River; its harbor is one of the best on the Great Lakes. One of Ford Motor Co.'s largest assembly plants is located here with Lake Shore Development. Community facilities include churches representing all denominations, YMCA, YWCA, six hospitals, and all leading civic and service organizations. Boating, fishing, swimming, golf, and tennis are some of the outdoor sports. Job opportunities are excellent. Lakeview Park is noted for its extensive rose garden and colorfully lighted fountain. Cascade Park is a favorite recreation area and is located in the city of Elyria. A rapidly expanding network of major state and interstate highways, including the nearby Ohio Turnpike, makes the college easily reached by automobile.

■ **LOURDES COLLEGE** *B-4*
6832 Convent Blvd.
Sylvania, OH 43560-2898
Tel: (419)885-3211
Free: 800-878-3210
Admissions: (419)885-5291
Fax: (419)882-3987
E-mail: lcadmits@lourdes.edu
Web Site: http://www.lourdes.edu/

Description: Independent Roman Catholic, comprehensive, coed. Awards associate, bachelor's, and master's degrees. Founded 1958. Setting: 90-acre suburban campus with easy access to Toledo. Endowment: $3.5 million. Educational spending for 2005 fiscal year: $5271 per student. Total enrollment: 1,460. 252 applied, 72% were admitted. Full-time: 676 students, 85% women, 15% men. Part-time: 714 students, 84% women, 16% men. Students come from 4 states and territories, 7% from out-of-state, 1% Native American, 2% Hispanic, 15% black, 0.3% Asian American or Pacific Islander, 0% international, 66% 25 or older, 21% transferred in. Retention: 56% of full-time freshmen returned the following year. Core. Calendar: semesters. Academic remediation for entering students, services for LD students, advanced placement, accelerated degree program, self-designed majors, independent study, distance learning, double major, summer session for credit, part-time degree program, adult/continuing education programs, co-op programs and internships, graduate courses open to undergrads. Study abroad program. ROTC: Army (c), Air Force (c).

Entrance Requirements: Options: Peterson's Universal Application, Common Application, electronic application, early admission, deferred admission. Required: high school transcript. Required for some: interview, SAT or ACT. Entrance: moderately difficult. Application deadline: Rolling. Notification: continuous.

Costs Per Year: Application fee: $25. Tuition: $11,070 full-time, $369 per credit hour part-time. Mandatory fees: $1200 full-time, $40 per credit hour part-time.

Collegiate Environment: Orientation program. Drama-theater group, choral group, student-run newspaper. Social organizations: 12 open to all. Most popular organizations: Future Educators Association, Student Leader Advisory Council, Lourdes College Chorus, Student Nurse Association, Campus Ministry Organization. Major annual events: Holiday Tree Lighting Ceremony and Dinner, All-Campus Spring Picnic, Spike the Spirit volleyball tournament. Student services: personal-psychological counseling. Campus security: 24-hour emergency response devices, late night transport-escort service, evening patrols by trained security personnel. College housing not available. Duns Scotus Library plus 1 other with 58,633 books, 10,187 microform titles, 448 serials, 1,429 audiovisual materials, an OPAC, and a Web page. Operations spending for 2004 fiscal year: $195,042. 129 computers available on campus for general student use. Computer purchase/lease plans available. A campuswide network can be accessed from off-campus. Staffed computer lab on campus.

Community Environment: Sylvania is a suburban area with a temperate climate; plane and bus transportation is available. Job opportunities are

good for students. Community facilities include a public library, adequate hospital services, churches, numerous major civic and service organizations, and shopping facilities.

■ **MALONE COLLEGE** *F-11*
515 25th St., NW
Canton, OH 44709-3897
Tel: (330)471-8100
Free: 800-521-1146
Admissions: (330)471-8145
Fax: (330)454-6977
Web Site: http://www.malone.edu/

Description: Independent, comprehensive, coed, affiliated with Evangelical Friends Church-Eastern Region. Awards bachelor's and master's degrees. Founded 1892. Setting: 78-acre suburban campus with easy access to Cleveland. Endowment: $16.8 million. Research spending for 2004 fiscal year: $45,419. Educational spending for 2005 fiscal year: $3670 per student. Total enrollment: 2,277. Faculty: 202 (104 full-time, 98 part-time). Student-undergrad faculty ratio is 14:1. 1,036 applied, 81% were admitted. 19% from top 10% of their high school class, 47% from top quarter, 76% from top half. 13 valedictorians. Full-time: 1,676 students, 60% women, 40% men. Part-time: 244 students, 69% women, 31% men. Students come from 24 states and territories, 12 other countries, 10% from out-of-state, 0.2% Native American, 1% Hispanic, 6% black, 0.4% Asian American or Pacific Islander, 1% international, 23% 25 or older, 51% live on campus, 4% transferred in. Retention: 75% of full-time freshmen returned the following year. Academic areas with the most degrees conferred: business/marketing; education; health professions and related sciences. Core. Calendar: semesters. Academic remediation for entering students, services for LD students, advanced placement, accelerated degree program, self-designed majors, honors program, independent study, distance learning, double major, summer session for credit, part-time degree program, adult/continuing education programs, co-op programs and internships, graduate courses open to undergrads. Off campus study at members of the Christian College Consortium, Council for Christian Colleges and Universities. Study abroad program. ROTC: Army (c), Air Force (c).

Entrance Requirements: Options: Peterson's Universal Application, Common Application, electronic application, early admission, deferred admission. Required: essay, high school transcript, minimum 2.5 high school GPA, SAT or ACT. Required for some: interview. Entrance: moderately difficult. Application deadline: 7/1. Notification: continuous.

Costs Per Year: Application fee: $20. Comprehensive fee: $24,190 includes full-time tuition ($17,520), mandatory fees ($270), and college room and board ($6400). College room only: $3300. Part-time tuition: $330 per semester hour. Part-time mandatory fees: $67.50 per term.

Collegiate Environment: Orientation program. Drama-theater group, choral group, marching band, student-run newspaper, radio station. Social organizations: 44 open to all. Most popular organizations: Spiritual Life Committee, Student Activities Council, Student Senate, Woolman-Whittier-Fox Hall Council, intramural athletics. Major annual events: homecoming, Christmas celebration, Nike Air Band. Student services: health clinic, personal-psychological counseling. Campus security: 24-hour emergency response devices and patrols, late night transport-escort service. 961 college housing spaces available; 945 were occupied in 2003-04. Freshmen given priority for college housing. On-campus residence required through junior year. Options: men-only, women-only housing available. Everett L. Cattell Library with 238,830 books, 652,263 microform titles, 1,385 serials, 12,756 audiovisual materials, an OPAC, and a Web page. Operations spending for 2004 fiscal year: $857,692. 200 computers available on campus for general student use. A campuswide network can be accessed from student residence rooms and from off campus. Staffed computer lab on campus.

Community Environment: Canton is an industrial, residential, and cultural city of 80,000. The city is the home of the Pro Football Hall of Fame, and birthplace of former president William McKinley. A beautiful Cultural Center for the Arts and an extensive park system enhances the city's beauty and provides many cultural and educational opportunities for the students.

■ **MARIETTA COLLEGE** *K-11*
215 Fifth St.
Marietta, OH 45750-4000
Tel: (740)376-4000
Free: 800-331-7896
Admissions: (740)376-4600

Fax: (740)376-4896

E-mail: admit@marietta.edu

Web Site: http://www.marietta.edu/

Description: Independent, comprehensive, coed. Awards associate, bachelor's, and master's degrees. Founded 1835. Setting: 120-acre small town campus. Endowment: $48.6 million. Educational spending for 2005 fiscal year: $10,775 per student. Total enrollment: 1,461. Faculty: 140 (91 full-time, 49 part-time). Student-undergrad faculty ratio is 12:1. 2,237 applied, 78% were admitted. 20% from top 10% of their high school class, 47% from top quarter, 76% from top half. Full-time: 1,274 students, 49% women, 51% men. Part-time: 70 students, 73% women, 27% men. Students come from 43 states and territories, 12 other countries, 50% from out-of-state, 0.4% Native American, 2% Hispanic, 4% black, 1% Asian American or Pacific Islander, 5% international, 3% 25 or older, 85% live on campus, 5% transferred in. Retention: 73% of full-time freshmen returned the following year. Academic areas with the most degrees conferred: business/marketing; liberal arts/general studies; communications/journalism; visual and performing arts. Core. Calendar: semesters. Academic remediation for entering students, ESL program, services for LD students, advanced placement, accelerated degree program, self-designed majors, honors program, independent study, double major, summer session for credit, part-time degree program, adult/continuing education programs, internships. Off campus study at American University, Stillman College, Central College, Institute of European Studies, Institute of Asian Studies. Study abroad program.

Entrance Requirements: Options: Peterson's Universal Application, Common Application, electronic application, early admission, deferred admission, international baccalaureate accepted. Required: essay, high school transcript, minimum 2.0 high school GPA, 2 recommendations, SAT or ACT. Recommended: minimum 3.0 high school GPA, interview, SAT Subject Tests. Entrance: moderately difficult. Application deadline: 4/15. Notification: continuous until 5/1.

Costs Per Year: Application fee: $25. Comprehensive fee: $29,100 includes full-time tuition ($22,070), mandatory fees ($585), and college room and board ($6445). College room only: $3445. Room and board charges vary according to board plan. Part-time tuition: $735 per credit. Part-time tuition varies according to class time.

Collegiate Environment: Orientation program. Drama-theater group, choral group, student-run newspaper, radio station. Social organizations: 100 open to all; national fraternities, national sororities; 22% of eligible men and 22% of eligible women are members. Most popular organizations: Student Programming Board, student government, Great Outdoors Club, Inter-Varsity Christian Fellowship, Arts and Humanities Council. Major annual events: Homecoming Weekend, Doo Dah Day, Family Weekend. Student services: health clinic, personal-psychological counseling. Campus security: 24-hour emergency response devices and patrols, student patrols, late night transport-escort service, controlled dormitory access. College housing designed to accommodate 1,034 students; 1,280 undergraduates lived in college housing during 2003-04. Freshmen guaranteed college housing. On-campus residence required through senior year. Options: coed, men-only, women-only housing available. Dawes Memorial Library with 250,000 books, 130,700 microform titles, 7,100 serials, 5,800 audiovisual materials, an OPAC, and a Web page. Operations spending for 2004 fiscal year: $669,504. 200 computers available on campus for general student use. A campuswide network can be accessed from student residence rooms and from off campus. Staffed computer lab on campus.

Community Environment: Founded in 1788, Marietta, has the distinction of being the first permanent settlement of America's Northwest Territory. The city is rich in history, with stately homes, brick paved streets, sternwheeler festivals, and an antique row of stores. Students have easy access to the town which is located 1 block from the campus. Large urban cities as Pittsburgh, PA and Columbus, OH are within a two-hour drive. Parkersburg, WV, with a population of 80,000, is 20 minutes away. Transportation is readily available. Part-time employment opportunities are available.

■ **MARION TECHNICAL COLLEGE** *F-6*

1467 Mount Vernon Ave.

Marion, OH 43302-5694

Tel: (740)389-4636

Fax: (740)389-6136

E-mail: mtc@on-ramp.net

Web Site: http://www.mtc.edu/

Description: State-supported, 2-year, coed. Part of Ohio Board of Regents. Awards certificates, transfer associate, and terminal associate degrees.

Founded 1971. Setting: 180-acre small town campus with easy access to Columbus. Total enrollment: 2,121. 850 applied, 98% were admitted. Full-time: 981 students, 55% women, 45% men. Part-time: 1,140 students, 67% women, 33% men. Students come from 4 states and territories, 0.4% Native American, 1% Hispanic, 7% black, 0.3% Asian American or Pacific Islander, 0% international, 51% 25 or older, 2% transferred in. Retention: 56% of full-time freshmen returned the following year. Academic remediation for entering students, services for LD students, self-designed majors, distance learning, summer session for credit, part-time degree program, adult/continuing education programs, co-op programs and internships.

Entrance Requirements: Open admission except for nursing, medical laboratory technology, paralegal, human services, radiological technology, physical therapist assisting programs. Options: early admission, deferred admission. Required: high school transcript. Placement: ACT required for some. Entrance: noncompetitive. Application deadline: Rolling. Notification: continuous.

Collegiate Environment: Orientation program. Most popular organization: Student Ambassadors. Major annual events: Fall Quarter Kickoff, Scarlet and Gray Week, Beach Party in Winter. Campus security: 24-hour emergency response devices. College housing not available. Marion Campus Library with 38,000 books, 200 serials, and an OPAC. 270 computers available on campus for general student use. A campuswide network can be accessed. Staffed computer lab on campus.

■ **MEDCENTRAL COLLEGE OF NURSING** *F-7*

335 Glessner Ave.

Mansfield, OH 44903

Tel: (419)520-2600; 877-656-4360

E-mail: charris@medcentral.edu

Web Site: http://www.medcentral.edu/

Description: Independent, 4-year, coed. Awards bachelor's degrees. Founded 1996. Total enrollment: 365. 54% from top 10% of their high school class, 86% from top quarter, 100% from top half. 2 class presidents, 1 valedictorian, 4 student government officers. Full-time: 318 students, 91% women, 9% men. Part-time: 47 students, 96% women, 4% men. Students come from 2 states and territories, 0% from out-of-state, 0.3% Native American, 0% Hispanic, 1% black, 0.3% Asian American or Pacific Islander, 0% international, 49% 25 or older, 18% live on campus. Core. Advanced placement, accelerated degree program, independent study, part-time degree program, adult/continuing education programs.

Entrance Requirements: Options: Common Application, electronic application, deferred admission, international baccalaureate accepted. Required: high school transcript, minimum 2.8 high school GPA, SAT or ACT. Recommended: minimum 3.0 high school GPA. Required for some: essay, interview. Entrance: moderately difficult. Application deadline: 8/1. Notification: continuous until 8/15.

Costs Per Year: Application fee: $40. Tuition: $9100 full-time, $260 per credit hour part-time. Mandatory fees: $150 full-time. Full-time tuition and fees vary according to course load. Part-time tuition varies according to course load. College room only: $4200.

Collegiate Environment: Orientation program. Social organizations: 2 open to all; 50% of eligible men and 30% of eligible women are members. Major annual events: Opening Convocation, Annual Dinner Dance, Graduation. Student services: health clinic. College housing designed to accommodate 20 students; 35 undergraduates lived in college housing during 2003-04. Freshmen given priority for college housing. On-campus residence required through sophomore year. Option: coed housing available. Bromfield Library with an OPAC and a Web page. 40 computers available on campus for general student use. A campuswide network can be accessed. Staffed computer lab on campus.

■ **MERCY COLLEGE OF NORTHWEST OHIO** *B-5*

2221 Madison Ave.

Toledo, OH 43624-1132

Tel: (419)251-1313; 888-80-Mercy

Fax: (419)251-4116

Web Site: http://www.mercycollege.edu/

Description: Independent, primarily 2-year, coed, affiliated with Roman Catholic Church. Awards certificates, transfer associate, and bachelor's degrees. Founded 1993. Setting: urban campus with easy access to Detroit. Endowment: $4.3 million. Educational spending for 2005 fiscal year: $6806 per student. Total enrollment: 756. Student-undergrad faculty ratio is 17:1. 343 applied, 57% were admitted. Full-time: 397 students, 87% women, 13% men. Part-time: 359 students, 83% women, 17% men. Students come from

5 states and territories, 12% from out-of-state, 1% Native American, 4% Hispanic, 7% black, 1% Asian American or Pacific Islander, 0% international, 51% 25 or older, 8% live on campus, 17% transferred in. Retention: 71% of full-time freshmen returned the following year. Academic area with the most degrees conferred: health professions and related sciences. Core. Calendar: semesters. Academic remediation for entering students, services for LD students, advanced placement, independent study, summer session for credit, part-time degree program, internships.

Entrance Requirements: Required: high school transcript. Recommended: SAT or ACT. Required for some: SAT or ACT. Entrance: moderately difficult. Application deadline: Rolling. Notification: continuous.

Costs Per Year: Application fee: $25. Tuition: $8640 full-time, $299 per credit hour part-time. Mandatory fees: $650 full-time, $5 per credit hour part-time, $650 per year part-time.

Collegiate Environment: Orientation program. Student-run newspaper. Social organizations: 4 open to all. Most popular organizations: Campus Ministry, Student Senate, Mercy College Musical Ensemble, Student Nurses Association, Stress Busters. Major annual events: Ahh Day, Creative Coffeehouse, Spring Fling. Student services: personal-psychological counseling. Campus security: 24-hour patrols, late night transport-escort service, controlled dormitory access. 60 college housing spaces available; 54 were occupied in 2003-04. No special consideration for freshman housing applicants. Option: coed housing available. Mercy College of Northwest Ohio Library with 6,400 books, 172 serials, 351 audiovisual materials, and an OPAC. Operations spending for 2004 fiscal year: $224,694. 40 computers available on campus for general student use. A campuswide network can be accessed from student residence rooms and from off campus. Staffed computer lab on campus.

■ **MIAMI-JACOBS COLLEGE** *I-3*
PO Box 1433
Dayton, OH 45401-1433
Tel: (937)461-5174
Fax: (937)461-3384
Web Site: http://www.miamijacobs.edu/
Description: Proprietary, 2-year, coed. Awards certificates, diplomas, and terminal associate degrees. Founded 1860. Setting: small town campus. Total enrollment: 317. Full-time: 317 students, 61% women, 39% men. 66% 25 or older. Core. Academic remediation for entering students, honors program, distance learning, summer session for credit, part-time degree program, internships. Off campus study at Southwestern Ohio Council for Higher Education.
Entrance Requirements: Options: Peterson's Universal Application, early admission, deferred admission. Required: essay, high school transcript, interview, Wonderlic aptitude test. Recommended: recommendations, SAT or ACT. Required for some: ACT. Entrance: minimally difficult. Application deadline: 8/15. Notification: continuous until 8/25.
Collegiate Environment: Social organizations: 5 open to all. Most popular organization: American Association of Medical Assistants. Major annual events: Spring Fling, Fall Party, Christmas Party. Student services: personal-psychological counseling. Campus security: late night transport-escort service. College housing not available. 130 computers available on campus for general student use. Staffed computer lab on campus.
Community Environment: See Wright State University.

■ **MIAMI UNIVERSITY** *J-1*
Oxford, OH 45056
Tel: (513)529-1809
Admissions: (513)529-5040
Fax: (513)529-1550
E-mail: admission@muohio.edu
Web Site: http://www.muohio.edu/
Description: State-related, university, coed. Part of Miami University System. Awards associate, bachelor's, master's, and doctoral degrees and post-master's certificates. Founded 1809. Setting: 2,000-acre small town campus with easy access to Cincinnati. Endowment: $265.9 million. Research spending for 2004 fiscal year: $7.9 million. Educational spending for 2005 fiscal year: $8556 per student. Total enrollment: 16,338. Faculty: 1,198 (842 full-time, 356 part-time). Student-undergrad faculty ratio is 16:1. 15,579 applied, 69% were admitted. 41% from top 10% of their high school class, 79% from top quarter, 99% from top half. 102 National Merit Scholars, 412 student government officers. Full-time: 14,312 students, 53% women, 47% men. Part-time: 331 students, 50% women, 50% men. Students come from 50 states and territories, 32 other countries, 28% from out-of-state, 1%

Native American, 2% Hispanic, 3% black, 3% Asian American or Pacific Islander, 1% international, 2% 25 or older, 45% live on campus, 1% transferred in. Retention: 89% of full-time freshmen returned the following year. Academic areas with the most degrees conferred: business/marketing; education; social sciences. Core. Calendar: semesters. Services for LD students, advanced placement, self-designed majors, honors program, independent study, double major, summer session for credit, adult/continuing education programs, co-op programs and internships, graduate courses open to undergrads. Off campus study at Greater Cincinnati Consortium of Colleges and Universities. Study abroad program. ROTC: Army (c), Naval, Air Force.

Entrance Requirements: Options: Common Application, electronic application, early decision, early action, deferred admission. Required: high school transcript, SAT or ACT. Recommended: essay, 1 recommendation. Entrance: moderately difficult. Application deadlines: 1/31, 11/1 for early decision, 12/1 for early action. Notification: 3/15, 12/15 for early decision, 2/1 for early action.

Costs Per Year: Application fee: $45. State resident tuition: $19,877 full-time. Nonresident tuition: $19,877 full-time. Mandatory fees: $1610 full-time. College room and board: $7610. College room only: $3860. Room and board charges vary according to board plan and housing facility. Ohio residents receive a minimum of $10,000 in resident scholarships.

Collegiate Environment: Orientation program. Drama-theater group, choral group, marching band, student-run newspaper, radio station. Social organizations: 350 open to all; national fraternities, national sororities; 22% of eligible men and 25% of eligible women are members. Most popular organizations: student government, Alpha Phi Omega, Miami Marketing Enterprises, Campus Crusade for Christ. Major annual events: Parents' Weekend, Kids' Fest Weekend, homecoming. Student services: health clinic, personal-psychological counseling, women's center. Campus security: 24-hour emergency response devices and patrols, student patrols, late night transport-escort service, controlled dormitory access. 6,970 college housing spaces available; all were occupied in 2003-04. Freshmen guaranteed college housing. On-campus residence required in freshman year. Options: coed, men-only, women-only housing available. King Library plus 3 others with 2.7 million books, 3 million microform titles, 14,089 serials, 143,868 audiovisual materials, an OPAC, and a Web page. Operations spending for 2004 fiscal year: $11.2 million. 1,000 computers available on campus for general student use. A campuswide network can be accessed from student residence rooms and from off campus. Staffed computer lab on campus.

Community Environment: A college town with many beautiful old homes, Oxford, the location of Miami University, is where Professor McGuffey compiled the first of his readers. Recreational facilities provide for tennis, bowling, golf, swimming. The Hueston Woods State Park also provides for swimming, boating, and picnicking.

■ **MIAMI UNIVERSITY HAMILTON** *K-2*
1601 Peck Blvd.
Hamilton, OH 45011-3399
Tel: (513)785-3000
Admissions: (513)785-3111
E-mail: nelsona3@muohio.edu
Web Site: http://www.ham.muohio.edu/
Description: State-supported, primarily 2-year, coed. Part of Miami University System. Awards certificates, transfer associate, terminal associate, bachelor's, and master's degrees (degrees awarded by Miami University main campus). Founded 1968. Setting: 78-acre suburban campus with easy access to Cincinnati. Total enrollment: 3,398. 947 applied, 89% were admitted. Full-time: 2,432 students, 55% women, 45% men. Part-time: 898 students, 61% women, 39% men. 0.2% Native American, 1% Hispanic, 6% black, 2% Asian American or Pacific Islander, 0% international, 25% 25 or older, 4% transferred in. Core. Calendar: semesters plus summer sessions. Academic remediation for entering students, ESL program, services for LD students, advanced placement, self-designed majors, honors program, double major, summer session for credit, part-time degree program, adult/continuing education programs, co-op programs and internships. Study abroad program. ROTC: Naval (c), Air Force (c).
Entrance Requirements: Open admission except for nursing program, transfer students. Option: electronic application. Required: high school transcript. Entrance: noncompetitive. Application deadline: Rolling. Notification: continuous.
Costs Per Year: Application fee: $25. State resident tuition: $3714 full-time, $154.75 per credit part-time. Nonresident tuition: $15,246 full-time, $650 per credit part-time. Mandatory fees: $390 full-time, $14.75 per credit part-time, $18 per term part-time.

Collegiate Environment: Orientation program. Drama-theater group, choral group. Social organizations: 11 open to all. Most popular organizations: student government, Campus Activities Committee, Ski Club, Student Nursing Association, Minority Action Committee. Major annual events: New Student Orientation, Spring Fest, Fall Picnic. Student services: personal-psychological counseling. Campus security: 24-hour emergency response devices and patrols, late night transport-escort service. College housing not available. Rentschler Library with 68,000 books, 400 serials, an OPAC, and a Web page. 300 computers available on campus for general student use. A campuswide network can be accessed from off-campus. Staffed computer lab on campus.

Community Environment: The town of Hamilton is easily accessible from most of northern and western Hamilton County via several state and interstate routes. Employment opportunities are good in this area.

■ **MIAMI UNIVERSITY-MIDDLETOWN CAMPUS** *J-2*

4200 East University Blvd.
Middletown, OH 45042-3497
Tel: (513)727-3200
Admissions: (513)727-3346
Fax: (513)727-3223
E-mail: flynnml@muohio.edu
Web Site: http://www.mid.muohio.edu/

Description: State-supported, primarily 2-year, coed. Part of Miami University System. Awards certificates, diplomas, transfer associate, terminal associate, and bachelor's degrees (also offers up to 2 years of most bachelor's degree programs offered at Miami University main campus). Founded 1966. Setting: 141-acre small town campus with easy access to Cincinnati and Dayton. Endowment: $779,742. Total enrollment: 2,660. 763 applied, 96% were admitted. 4% from top 10% of their high school class, 19% from top quarter, 50% from top half. 1% from out-of-state, 1% Native American, 1% Hispanic, 6% black, 1% Asian American or Pacific Islander, 28% 25 or older. Retention: 71% of full-time freshmen returned the following year. Core. Calendar: semesters. Academic remediation for entering students, services for LD students, advanced placement, self-designed majors, independent study, distance learning, double major, summer session for credit, part-time degree program, adult/continuing education programs, co-op programs and internships. Off campus study at members of the Greater Cincinnati Consortium of Colleges and Universities. Study abroad program. ROTC: Air Force (c).

Entrance Requirements: Open admission except for nursing program. Options: electronic application, early admission, deferred admission. Required: high school transcript. Placement: SAT or ACT recommended. Entrance: noncompetitive. Application deadline: Rolling. Notification: continuous.

Collegiate Environment: Orientation program. Drama-theater group, choral group, student-run newspaper, radio station. Social organizations: 28 open to all. Most popular organizations: student radio station, SEAL (Save Every Animal by Learning), Student Advisory Council, Model United Nations, Program Board. Major annual events: Haunted Trails, End of Year Picnic, MUMOXMUH. Student services: personal-psychological counseling, women's center. Campus security: 24-hour patrols, late night transport-escort service. College housing not available. Gardner-Harvey Library with 58,239 microform titles, 540 serials, 4,857 audiovisual materials, an OPAC, and a Web page. Operations spending for 2004 fiscal year: $479,848. 180 computers available on campus for general student use. A campuswide network can be accessed from off-campus. Staffed computer lab on campus.

Community Environment: Middletown, population 46,022, is an industrial city in Butler County, SW Ohio. Its industries include aircraft parts, steel, and paper products.

■ **MOUNT CARMEL COLLEGE OF NURSING** *I-6*

127 South Davis Ave.
Columbus, OH 43222
Tel: (614)234-5800
Admissions: (614)234-5144
Web Site: http://www.mccn.edu/

Description: Independent, comprehensive, coed. Awards bachelor's and master's degrees. Setting: urban campus. Total enrollment: 573. 150 applied, 59% were admitted. 20% from top 10% of their high school class, 40% from top quarter, 85% from top half. Full-time: 431 students, 93% women, 7% men. Part-time: 119 students, 91% women, 9% men. 0.2% Native American, 1% Hispanic, 9% black, 4% Asian American or Pacific Islander, 0% international. Retention: 75% of full-time freshmen returned the following year. Calendar: semesters.

Entrance Requirements: Entrance: moderately difficult. Application deadline: Rolling.

Costs Per Year: Application fee: $30. Tuition: $15,497 full-time. Mandatory fees: $312 full-time. College room only: $1870.

Collegiate Environment: 33 college housing spaces available; 32 were occupied in 2003-04.

■ **MOUNT UNION COLLEGE** *E-11*

1972 Clark Ave.
Alliance, OH 44601-3993
Tel: (330)821-5320
Free: 800-992-6682
Admissions: (330)823-2590
Fax: (330)821-0425
E-mail: admission@muc.edu
Web Site: http://www.muc.edu/

Description: Independent United Methodist, 4-year, coed. Awards bachelor's degrees. Founded 1846. Setting: 105-acre suburban campus with easy access to Cleveland. Endowment: $122 million. Educational spending for 2005 fiscal year: $7020 per student. Total enrollment: 2,205. Student-undergrad faculty ratio is 13:1. 1,768 applied, 80% were admitted. 14% from top 10% of their high school class, 41% from top quarter, 73% from top half. Full-time: 2,021 students, 51% women, 49% men. Part-time: 184 students, 76% women, 24% men. Students come from 31 states and territories, 9 other countries, 11% from out-of-state, 0.2% Native American, 1% Hispanic, 4% black, 0.4% Asian American or Pacific Islander, 2% international, 2% 25 or older, 67% live on campus, 9% transferred in. Retention: 75% of full-time freshmen returned the following year. Academic areas with the most degrees conferred: education; business/marketing; parks and recreation. Core. Calendar: semesters. ESL program, services for LD students, advanced placement, accelerated degree program, self-designed majors, honors program, independent study, double major, summer session for credit, part-time degree program, external degree program, adult/continuing education programs, co-op programs and internships. Off campus study at 6 members of the East Central College Consortium. Study abroad program. ROTC: Army (c), Air Force (c).

Entrance Requirements: Options: electronic application, early admission, deferred admission. Required: essay, high school transcript, minimum 2.0 high school GPA, 1 recommendation, SAT or ACT. Recommended: interview. Entrance: moderately difficult. Application deadline: Rolling. Notification: continuous.

Costs Per Year: Comprehensive fee: $25,840 includes full-time tuition ($19,600), mandatory fees ($250), and college room and board ($5990). College room only: $2650. Room and board charges vary according to board plan and housing facility. Part-time tuition: $820 per semester hour. Part-time mandatory fees: $50 per term.

Collegiate Environment: Orientation program. Drama-theater group, choral group, marching band, student-run newspaper, radio station. Social organizations: 74 open to all; national fraternities, national sororities, local sororities; 12% of eligible men and 20% of eligible women are members. Most popular organizations: Association of Women Students, Student Senate, Black Student Union, Student Activities Council, Association of International Students. Major annual events: homecoming, Black Student Union, Schooler Lecture Series. Student services: health clinic, personal-psychological counseling. Campus security: 24-hour emergency response devices and patrols, 24-hour locked residence hall entrances, outside phones. 1,475 college housing spaces available; 1,373 were occupied in 2003-04. Freshmen guaranteed college housing. On-campus residence required through sophomore year. Options: coed, men-only, women-only housing available. Mount Union College Library plus 2 others with 244,115 books, 49,096 microform titles, 949 serials, 5,148 audiovisual materials, an OPAC, and a Web page. Operations spending for 2004 fiscal year: $1272. 249 computers available on campus for general student use. Computer purchase/lease plans available. A campuswide network can be accessed from student residence rooms and from off campus. Staffed computer lab on campus.

Community Environment: Alliance, population 23,376, is an industrial city located within a circle of large cities, Cleveland, Akron, and Pittsburgh. Heavy steel equipment and forgings are among the products of its industry. Commercial transportation is available. Recreational activities include swimming, golfing, fishing, boating and tennis. The Carnation Festival is an annual event. Part-time employment is available.

■ MOUNT VERNON NAZARENE UNIVERSITY *G-8*

800 Martinsburg Rd.
Mount Vernon, OH 43050-9500
Tel: (740)392-6868; (866)462-6868
E-mail: admissions@mvnc.edu
Web Site: http://www.mvnu.edu/

Description: Independent Nazarene, comprehensive, coed. Awards associate, bachelor's, and master's degrees (Associate). Founded 1964. Setting: 401-acre small town campus with easy access to Columbus. Endowment: $9.9 million. Educational spending for 2005 fiscal year: $5594 per student. Total enrollment: 2,549. Faculty: 226 (88 full-time, 138 part-time). Student-undergrad faculty ratio is 17:1. 741 applied, 80% were admitted. 17% from top 10% of their high school class, 48% from top quarter, 81% from top half. 12 valedictorians. Full-time: 1,921 students, 59% women, 41% men. Part-time: 274 students, 50% women, 50% men. Students come from 24 states and territories, 11 other countries, 8% from out-of-state, 0.1% Native American, 1% Hispanic, 4% black, 1% Asian American or Pacific Islander, 1% international, 39% 25 or older, 74% live on campus, 2% transferred in. Retention: 78% of full-time freshmen returned the following year. Academic areas with the most degrees conferred: business/marketing; education; biological/life sciences. Core. Calendar: 4-1-4. Academic remediation for entering students, services for LD students, advanced placement, freshman honors college, honors program, independent study, double major, summer session for credit, part-time degree program, adult/continuing education programs, co-op programs and internships. Off campus study at Kenyon College, Capital University, Coalition for Christian Colleges and Universities. Study abroad program.

Entrance Requirements: Options: Peterson's Universal Application, electronic application, deferred admission. Required: essay, high school transcript, minimum 2.5 high school GPA, 2 recommendations, SAT or ACT. Entrance: moderately difficult. Application deadline: 5/1. Notification: continuous until 9/1.

Costs Per Year: Application fee: $25. Comprehensive fee: $21,816 includes full-time tuition ($16,216), mandatory fees ($510), and college room and board ($5090). College room only: $2840. Part-time tuition: $585 per semester hour. Part-time mandatory fees: $18 per semester hour.

Collegiate Environment: Orientation program. Drama-theater group, choral group, student-run newspaper, radio station. Social organizations: 37 open to all; 73% of eligible men and 77% of eligible women are members. Most popular organizations: campus ministry groups, Student Government Association, Student Education Association, Drama Club, music department ensembles. Major annual events: Homecoming, concerts, Lecture Artists Series. Student services: health clinic, personal-psychological counseling. Campus security: 24-hour emergency response devices and patrols, late night transport-escort service, controlled dormitory access. 1,138 college housing spaces available; 954 were occupied in 2003-04. Freshmen guaranteed college housing. On-campus residence required through senior year. Options: men-only, women-only housing available. Thorne Library/Learning Resource Center with 96,646 books, 11,269 microform titles, 544 serials, 3,863 audiovisual materials, an OPAC, and a Web page. Operations spending for 2004 fiscal year: $649,787. 217 computers available on campus for general student use. A campuswide network can be accessed from student residence rooms and from off campus. Staffed computer lab on campus.

■ MUSKINGUM COLLEGE *H-10*

163 Stormont St.
New Concord, OH 43762
Tel: (740)826-8211
Free: 800-752-6082
Admissions: (740)826-8137
Fax: (740)826-8404
E-mail: adminfo@muskingum.edu
Web Site: http://www.muskingum.edu/

Description: Independent, comprehensive, coed, affiliated with Presbyterian Church (U.S.A.). Awards bachelor's and master's degrees. Founded 1837. Setting: 215-acre small town campus with easy access to Columbus. Endowment: $55.7 million. Total enrollment: 2,142. 1,703 applied, 80% were admitted. 22% from top 10% of their high school class, 42% from top quarter, 74% from top half. Full-time: 1,547 students, 49% women, 51% men. Part-time: 75 students, 64% women, 36% men. Students come from 26 states

and territories, 19 other countries, 12% from out-of-state, 0.2% Native American, 0.5% Hispanic, 4% black, 1% Asian American or Pacific Islander, 2% international, 3% 25 or older, 88% live on campus, 3% transferred in. Retention: 71% of full-time freshmen returned the following year. Core. Calendar: semesters. ESL program, services for LD students, advanced placement, accelerated degree program, self-designed majors, independent study, double major, summer session for credit, part-time degree program, external degree program, internships. Off campus study at Case Western Reserve University. Study abroad program.

Entrance Requirements: Options: Peterson's Universal Application, electronic application, early admission, deferred admission, international baccalaureate accepted. Required: high school transcript, minimum 2.0 high school GPA, 1 recommendation, SAT or ACT. Recommended: essay, minimum 3.0 high school GPA, interview. Entrance: moderately difficult. Application deadline: 6/1. Notification: continuous.

Collegiate Environment: Orientation program. Drama-theater group, choral group, marching band, student-run newspaper, radio station. Social organizations: 40 open to all; national fraternities, national sororities, local fraternities, local sororities; 30% of eligible men and 40% of eligible women are members. Most popular organizations: Centerboard, student radio station, BACCHUS, Cable TV 8, Fellowship of Christian Students. Major annual events: homecoming, Pledge Weekend, Muskiepalooza. Student services: health clinic, personal-psychological counseling, women's center. Campus security: 24-hour emergency response devices and patrols, student patrols, late night transport-escort service. 1,300 college housing spaces available; 1,270 were occupied in 2003-04. Freshmen guaranteed college housing. On-campus residence required through sophomore year. Options: coed, men-only, women-only housing available. College Library with 233,000 books, 200,000 microform titles, 900 serials, 6,000 audiovisual materials, and a Web page. Operations spending for 2004 fiscal year: $451,000. 76 computers available on campus for general student use. A campuswide network can be accessed from student residence rooms and from off campus. Staffed computer lab on campus.

Community Environment: New Concord is the boyhood home of John H. Glenn, Jr., the first American astronaut to orbit the earth. Also of interest is the log cabin birthplace of William Rainey Harper, first president of the University of Chicago and an alumnus of Muskingum College. Recreational activities in the area include golf, boating, fishing, hunting, and skating.

■ NATIONAL INSTITUTE OF TECHNOLOGY *D-10*

2545 Bailey Rd.
Cuyahoga Falls, OH 44221
Tel: (330)923-9959
Fax: (330)923-0886
Web Site: http://www.nationalinstituteoftechnology.com/
Description: Proprietary, 2-year, coed.

■ NORTH CENTRAL STATE COLLEGE *F-7*

2441 Kenwood Circle, PO Box 698
Mansfield, OH 44901-0698
Tel: (419)755-4800
Admissions: (419)755-4813
Fax: (419)755-4750
E-mail: nfletcher@ncstatecollege.edu
Web Site: http://www.ncstatecollege.edu/

Description: State-supported, 2-year, coed. Part of Ohio Board of Regents. Awards certificates and terminal associate degrees. Founded 1961. Setting: 600-acre suburban campus with easy access to Cleveland and Columbus. Endowment: $624,998. Educational spending for 2005 fiscal year: $2859 per student. Total enrollment: 3,333. 1,056 applied, 100% were admitted. 0.4% Native American, 1% Hispanic, 5% black, 1% Asian American or Pacific Islander, 0% international, 49% 25 or older. Academic remediation for entering students, services for LD students, advanced placement, self-designed majors, independent study, distance learning, summer session for credit, part-time degree program, adult/continuing education programs, internships.

Entrance Requirements: Open admission. Options: early admission, deferred admission. Required for some: high school transcript. Placement: ACT COMPASS required; ACT required for some. Entrance: noncompetitive. Application deadline: Rolling. Notification: continuous.

Costs Per Year: State resident tuition: $3,431 full-time, $76.25 per credit hour part-time. Nonresident tuition: $6,862 full-time, $152.50 per credit hour part-time. Mandatory fees: $245 full-time, $11.80 per credit hour part-time. Full-time tuition and fees vary according to course load. Part-time tuition and fees vary according to course load.

Collegiate Environment: Orientation program. Choral group, student-run radio station. Social organizations: 2 open to all. Most popular organizations: Student Programming Board, choral group. Major annual event: May Daze. Student services: personal-psychological counseling. Campus security: 24-hour emergency response devices and patrols, late night transport-escort service. College housing not available. Bromfield Library plus 1 other with 52,700 books, 410 serials, and an OPAC. Operations spending for 2004 fiscal year: $201,334. 144 computers available on campus for general student use. A campuswide network can be accessed. Staffed computer lab on campus.

Community Environment: See Ohio State University Mansfield Campus.

■ **NORTHWEST STATE COMMUNITY COLLEGE** *C-2*
22-600 State Route 34
Archbold, OH 43502-9542
Tel: (419)267-5511
Admissions: (419)267-1213
Fax: (419)267-3688
Web Site: http://www.northweststate.edu

Description: State-supported, 2-year, coed. Part of Ohio Board of Regents. Awards certificates, transfer associate, and terminal associate degrees. Founded 1968. Setting: 80-acre rural campus with easy access to Toledo. Endowment: $529,395. Educational spending for 2005 fiscal year: $3463 per student. Total enrollment: 3,145. 649 applied, 100% were admitted. 6% from top 10% of their high school class, 22% from top quarter, 48% from top half. Full-time: 1,088 students, 60% women, 40% men. Part-time: 2,057 students, 57% women, 43% men. Students come from 6 states and territories, 2% from out-of-state, 0.4% Native American, 6% Hispanic, 1% black, 0.5% Asian American or Pacific Islander, 0.1% international, 50% 25 or older, 3% transferred in. Retention: 55% of full-time freshmen returned the following year. Core. Calendar: semesters. Academic remediation for entering students, services for LD students, advanced placement, self-designed majors, independent study, distance learning, double major, summer session for credit, part-time degree program, external degree program, adult/continuing education programs, co-op programs and internships. Off campus study.

Entrance Requirements: Open admission. Options: electronic application, early admission, deferred admission. Required: high school transcript. Entrance: noncompetitive. Application deadline: Rolling. Notification: continuous.

Costs Per Year: Application fee: $20. State resident tuition: $3660 full-time, $122 per credit part-time. Nonresident tuition: $6750 full-time, $225 per credit part-time. Mandatory fees: $180 full-time, $6 per credit part-time, $30 per term part-time. Full-time tuition and fees vary according to course load. Part-time tuition and fees vary according to course load.

Collegiate Environment: Orientation program. Social organizations: 3 open to all. Most popular organizations: Student Body Organization, Phi Theta Kappa, Campus Crusade for Christ. Major annual events: Spring Fling, student appreciation days, Chili Cook-Off. Student services: personal-psychological counseling. Campus security: security patrols. College housing not available. Northwest State Community College Library with 15,321 books, 90,497 microform titles, 1,680 serials, 1,913 audiovisual materials, an OPAC, and a Web page. Operations spending for 2004 fiscal year: $352,240. 425 computers available on campus for general student use. A campuswide network can be accessed. Staffed computer lab on campus.

Community Environment: The campus is in rural setting with a small town six miles to the north. The major metropolitan area of Toledo is 50 miles northeast, within easy access by major highways.

■ **NOTRE DAME COLLEGE** *C-10*
4545 College Rd.
South Euclid, OH 44121-4293
Tel: (216)381-1680
Free: 800-632-1680
Admissions: (216)373-5214
Fax: (216)381-3802
Web Site: http://www.notredamecollege.edu/

Description: Independent Roman Catholic, comprehensive, coed. Awards associate, bachelor's, and master's degrees. Founded 1922. Setting: 53-acre suburban campus with easy access to Cleveland. Endowment: $5.5 million. Educational spending for 2005 fiscal year: $4913 per student. Total enrollment: 1,299. 621 applied, 64% were admitted. 7% from top 10% of their high school class, 28% from top quarter, 63% from top half. Full-time: 505 students, 59% women, 41% men. Part-time: 494 students, 78% women,

22% men. Students come from 14 states and territories, 17 other countries, 10% from out-of-state, 0% Native American, 2% Hispanic, 25% black, 1% Asian American or Pacific Islander, 6% international, 51% 25 or older, 50% live on campus, 7% transferred in. Retention: 62% of full-time freshmen returned the following year. Core. Calendar: semesters. Academic remediation for entering students, advanced placement, accelerated degree program, self-designed majors, independent study, double major, summer session for credit, part-time degree program, adult/continuing education programs, co-op programs and internships. Off campus study at members of the Northeast Ohio Commission on Higher Education. Study abroad program.

Entrance Requirements: Options: Peterson's Universal Application, Common Application, electronic application, deferred admission. Required: essay, high school transcript, minimum 2.0 high school GPA, interview, SAT or ACT. Recommended: minimum 2.5 high school GPA, interview. Entrance: moderately difficult. Application deadline: Rolling. Notification: continuous.

Costs Per Year: Application fee: $30. Comprehensive fee: $25,868 includes full-time tuition ($18,670), mandatory fees ($550), and college room and board ($6648). College room only: $3300. Full-time tuition and fees vary according to class time, course load, and degree level. Room and board charges vary according to board plan. Part-time tuition: $405 per credit. Part-time tuition varies according to class time, course load, and degree level.

Collegiate Environment: Orientation program. Drama-theater group, choral group, student-run newspaper. Social organizations: 32 open to all. Most popular organizations: Undergraduate Student Senate, Resident Association Board, International Students/Multicultural Club, IHOP (I Help Other People), Bowling Club. Major annual events: Christmas Happening, Finals Week Stress Free Zone, All-Campus Picnic. Student services: personal-psychological counseling. Campus security: 24-hour emergency response devices and patrols, late night transport-escort service, controlled dormitory access. 336 college housing spaces available; 328 were occupied in 2003-04. Freshmen given priority for college housing. Options: coed, men-only, women-only housing available. Clara Fritzsche Library with 14,770 microform titles, 9,983 audiovisual materials, and an OPAC. Operations spending for 2004 fiscal year: $238,762. 65 computers available on campus for general student use. A campuswide network can be accessed. Staffed computer lab on campus.

■ **OBERLIN COLLEGE** *D-8*
173 West Lorain St.
Oberlin, OH 44074
Tel: (440)775-8121
Free: 800-622-OBIE
Admissions: (440)775-8411
Fax: (440)775-8886
Web Site: http://www.oberlin.edu/

Description: Independent, comprehensive, coed. Awards bachelor's and master's degrees. Founded 1833. Setting: 440-acre small town campus with easy access to Cleveland. Endowment: $550 million. Educational spending for 2005 fiscal year: $14,807 per student. Total enrollment: 2,864. Faculty: 288 (all full-time). Student-undergrad faculty ratio is 10:1. 6,587 applied, 34% were admitted. 65% from top 10% of their high school class, 90% from top quarter, 99% from top half. 36 National Merit Scholars, 47 valedictorians. Full-time: 2,755 students, 56% women, 44% men. Part-time: 90 students, 49% women, 51% men. Students come from 50 states and territories, 44 other countries, 90% from out-of-state, 1% Native American, 5% Hispanic, 5% black, 8% Asian American or Pacific Islander, 6% international, 1% 25 or older, 73% live on campus, 1% transferred in. Retention: 92% of full-time freshmen returned the following year. Core. Calendar: 4-1-4. ESL program, services for LD students, advanced placement, self-designed majors, honors program, independent study, double major, part-time degree program, internships. Off campus study at Great Lakes Colleges Association. Study abroad program.

Entrance Requirements: Options: Common Application, electronic application, early admission, early decision, deferred admission, international baccalaureate accepted. Required: essay, high school transcript, 2 recommendations, SAT or ACT. Recommended: SAT Subject Tests. Required for some: interview. Entrance: very difficult. Application deadlines: 1/15, 11/15 for early decision plan 1, 1/1 for early decision plan 2. Notification: 4/1, 12/10 for early decision plan 1, 1/20 for early decision plan 2.

Costs Per Year: Application fee: $35. Comprehensive fee: $40,904 includes full-time tuition ($32,524), mandatory fees ($200), and college room and board ($8180). College room only: $4300. Full-time tuition and fees vary according to course load. Room and board charges vary according to board plan and housing facility. Part-time tuition: $1350 per credit. Part-time tuition varies according to course load.

Collegiate Environment: Orientation program. Drama-theater group, choral group, marching band, student-run newspaper, radio station. Social organizations: 120 open to all. Most popular organizations: Experimental College, Community Outreach, Black Students Organization, Students Cooperative Association, student radio station. Major annual events: Artist Recital Series, Convocation, Commencement. Student services: health clinic, personal-psychological counseling, women's center. Campus security: 24-hour emergency response devices and patrols, student patrols, late night transport-escort service, controlled dormitory access, crime prevention programs. 2,200 college housing spaces available. Freshmen guaranteed college housing. On-campus residence required through sophomore year. Options: coed, women-only housing available. Mudd Center Library plus 3 others with 1.5 million books, 364,504 microform titles, 4,560 serials, 59,186 audiovisual materials, and an OPAC. Operations spending for 2004 fiscal year: $5.5 million. 340 computers available on campus for general student use. A campuswide network can be accessed from student residence rooms and from off campus. Staffed computer lab on campus.

Community Environment: Oberlin College is located 35 miles southwest of Cleveland in a small town.

■ **OHIO BUSINESS COLLEGE (LORAIN)** *C-8*
1907 North Ridge Rd.
Lorain, OH 44055
Tel: (440)277-0021; 888-514-3126
Fax: (440)277-7989
Web Site: http://www.ohiobusinesscollege.com/
Description: Proprietary, 2-year, coed. Part of Tri State Educational Systems. Awards diplomas and terminal associate degrees. Founded 1903. Total enrollment: 258. Full-time: 232 students, 84% women, 16% men. Part-time: 26 students, 81% women, 19% men. 0% from out-of-state, 0.4% Native American, 13% Hispanic, 28% black, 0% Asian American or Pacific Islander, 0% international, 40% 25 or older. Core. Academic remediation for entering students, advanced placement, accelerated degree program, independent study, double major, summer session for credit, part-time degree program, external degree program, adult/continuing education programs, internships.
Entrance Requirements: Open admission. Options: Common Application, electronic application. Required: high school transcript, interview. Placement: CPAt required. Entrance: noncompetitive. Application deadline: Rolling.
Collegiate Environment: Orientation program. College housing not available. Ohio Business College Library with 850 books and 20 serials. 66 computers available on campus for general student use. A campuswide network can be accessed. Staffed computer lab on campus.

■ **OHIO BUSINESS COLLEGE (SANDUSKY)** *C-7*
4020 Milan Rd.
Sandusky, OH 44870-5894
Tel: (419)627-8345; 888-627-8345
Fax: (419)627-1958
E-mail: sandusky@ohiobusinesscollege.edu
Web Site: http://www.ohiobusinesscollege.com/
Description: Proprietary, 2-year, coed. Awards diplomas and transfer associate degrees. Founded 1982. Setting: 1-acre suburban campus. Total enrollment: 192. Student-undergrad faculty ratio is 10:1. 38 applied, 100% were admitted. Full-time: 157 students, 82% women, 18% men. Part-time: 35 students, 83% women, 17% men.
Entrance Requirements: Required: high school transcript.
Costs Per Year: Application fee: $25. Tuition: $7380 full-time.

■ **OHIO COLLEGE OF MASSOTHERAPY** *E-10*
225 Heritage Woods Dr.
Akron, OH 44321
Tel: (330)665-1084
Fax: (330)665-5021
E-mail: johna@ocm.edu
Web Site: http://www.ocm.edu/
Description: Independent, 2-year, coed. Founded 1973. Calendar: semesters.

■ **OHIO DOMINICAN UNIVERSITY** *I-6*
1216 Sunbury Rd.
Columbus, OH 43219-2099

Tel: (614)253-2741
Free: 800-854-2670
Admissions: (614)251-4588
Fax: (614)252-0776
E-mail: admissions@odc.edu
Web Site: http://www.ohiodominican.edu/
Description: Independent Roman Catholic, comprehensive, coed. Awards associate, bachelor's, and master's degrees. Founded 1911. Setting: 62-acre urban campus. Endowment: $12.6 million. Educational spending for 2005 fiscal year: $3658 per student. Total enrollment: 2,942. Faculty: 201 (66 full-time, 135 part-time). Student-undergrad faculty ratio is 15:1. 1,902 applied, 72% were admitted. 13% from top 10% of their high school class, 33% from top quarter, 66% from top half. Full-time: 1,702 students, 60% women, 40% men. Part-time: 857 students, 69% women, 31% men. Students come from 19 states and territories, 11 other countries, 3% from out-of-state, 0.4% Native American, 1% Hispanic, 22% black, 1% Asian American or Pacific Islander, 0.4% international, 41% 25 or older, 29% live on campus, 8% transferred in. Retention: 62% of full-time freshmen returned the following year. Academic areas with the most degrees conferred: business/marketing; education; social sciences. Core. Calendar: semesters. Academic remediation for entering students, ESL program, advanced placement, self-designed majors, honors program, independent study, distance learning, summer session for credit, part-time degree program, adult/continuing education programs, internships, graduate courses open to undergrads. Off campus study at members of the Higher Education Council of Columbus. Study abroad program. ROTC: Army (c).
Entrance Requirements: Options: electronic application, deferred admission, international baccalaureate accepted. Required: high school transcript, minimum 2.0 high school GPA, interview, SAT or ACT. Required for some: essay, recommendations. Entrance: moderately difficult. Application deadline: Rolling. Notification: continuous.
Costs Per Year: Application fee: $25. One-time mandatory fee: $125. Comprehensive fee: $25,950 includes full-time tuition ($19,400), mandatory fees ($50), and college room and board ($6500). Room and board charges vary according to board plan and housing facility. Part-time tuition: $400 per credit hour. Part-time mandatory fees: $100 per term.
Collegiate Environment: Orientation program. Drama-theater group, choral group, student-run newspaper, radio station. Social organizations: 23 open to all. Most popular organizations: Campus Ministry, honors program, College Choir, Black Student Union, American-International Membership. Student services: health clinic, personal-psychological counseling. Campus security: 24-hour emergency response devices and patrols, late night transport-escort service, controlled dormitory access. 800 college housing spaces available; 681 were occupied in 2003-04. On-campus residence required through junior year. Option: coed housing available. Spangler Library with 105,722 books, 9,816 microform titles, 583 serials, 4,181 audiovisual materials, an OPAC, and a Web page. Operations spending for 2004 fiscal year: $716,154. 198 computers available on campus for general student use. A campuswide network can be accessed from student residence rooms and from off campus. Staffed computer lab on campus.
Community Environment: See Ohio State University Columbus Campus.

■ **OHIO INSTITUTE OF PHOTOGRAPHY AND TECHNOLOGY** *I-3*
2029 Edgefield Rd.
Dayton, OH 45439-1917
Tel: (937)294-6155
Free: 800-932-9698
Fax: (937)294-2259
Web Site: http://www.oipt.com/
Description: Proprietary, 2-year, coed. Part of Kaplan Higher Education. Awards diplomas and terminal associate degrees. Founded 1971. Setting: 2-acre urban campus with easy access to Cincinnati and Columbus. Total enrollment: 740. Student-undergrad faculty ratio is 25:1. 526 applied, 55% were admitted. Full-time: 740 students, 78% women, 22% men. Students come from 20 states and territories, 19% from out-of-state, 0.3% Native American, 1% Hispanic, 26% black, 0.1% Asian American or Pacific Islander, 0% international, 33% 25 or older. Core. Self-designed majors, summer session for credit, part-time degree program, co-op programs and internships.
Entrance Requirements: Options: Common Application, early admission, deferred admission. Required: high school transcript, interview, entrance exam. Entrance: moderately difficult. Application deadline: Rolling. Notification: continuous.
Costs Per Year: Application fee: $100. Tuition: $17,641 full-time. Mandatory fees: $1248 full-time.

Collegiate Environment: Major annual events: student/staff picnics, Just 'Shoot' Me, pet picture week. Campus security: 24-hour emergency response devices. College housing not available. Main Library with 640 books and 35 serials. 90 computers available on campus for general student use. Staffed computer lab on campus.

■ **OHIO NORTHERN UNIVERSITY** *F-4*
525 South Main
Ada, OH 45810-1599
Tel: (419)772-2000; 888-408-4ONU
Admissions: (419)772-2260
Fax: (419)772-2313
E-mail: admissions-ug@onu.edu
Web Site: http://www.onu.edu/
Description: Independent, comprehensive, coed, affiliated with United Methodist Church. Awards bachelor's, master's, and first professional degrees. Founded 1871. Setting: 285-acre small town campus. Endowment: $140.9 million. Total enrollment: 3,542. Faculty: 282 (205 full-time, 77 part-time). Student-undergrad faculty ratio is 14:1. 3,371 applied, 88% were admitted. 38% from top 10% of their high school class, 66% from top quarter, 87% from top half. Full-time: 2,525 students, 46% women, 54% men. Part-time: 72 students, 57% women, 43% men. Students come from 37 states and territories, 13% from out-of-state, 0.2% Native American, 1% Hispanic, 2% black, 1% Asian American or Pacific Islander, 0.4% international, 3% 25 or older, 79% live on campus, 2% transferred in. Retention: 82% of full-time freshmen returned the following year. Academic areas with the most degrees conferred: business/marketing; education; engineering. Core. Academic remediation for entering students, services for LD students, advanced placement, honors program, independent study, distance learning, double major, summer session for credit, part-time degree program, co-op programs and internships. Off campus study. Study abroad program. ROTC: Army (c), Air Force (c).
Entrance Requirements: Options: Peterson's Universal Application, Common Application, electronic application, deferred admission, international baccalaureate accepted. Required: high school transcript, SAT or ACT. Recommended: essay, minimum 2.5 high school GPA, interview. Required for some: 2 recommendations. Entrance: moderately difficult. Application deadline: 8/15. Notification: continuous.
Costs Per Year: Application fee: $30. Comprehensive fee: $35,340 includes full-time tuition ($28,050), mandatory fees ($210), and college room and board ($7080). College room only: $3540.
Collegiate Environment: Orientation program. Drama-theater group, choral group, marching band, student-run newspaper, radio station. Social organizations: 150 open to all; national fraternities, national sororities; 18% of eligible men and 20% of eligible women are members. Most popular organizations: Good News Bears, Student Planning Committee, Student Senate, President's Club. Major annual events: homecoming, Tunes on the Tundra, Winter Concert. Student services: legal services, health clinic, personal-psychological counseling. Campus security: 24-hour emergency response devices and patrols, late night transport-escort service, controlled dormitory access. College housing designed to accommodate 1,880 students; 1,901 undergraduates lived in college housing during 2003-04. Freshmen guaranteed college housing. On-campus residence required through junior year. Options: coed, men-only, women-only housing available. Heterick Memorial Library plus 1 other with 250,231 books, 280 microform titles, 9,220 serials, 9,776 audiovisual materials, an OPAC, and a Web page. 550 computers available on campus for general student use. A campuswide network can be accessed from student residence rooms and from off campus. Staffed computer lab on campus.
Community Environment: Ada, a community of nearly 5,000 people, is located 15 miles east of Lima, 22 miles south of Findlay, and only 8 miles from I-75. Health services are provided by the university. Some of the usual civic and service organizations are active.

■ **THE OHIO STATE UNIVERSITY** *I-6*
Enarson Hall, 154 W. 12th Ave.
Columbus, OH 43210
Tel: (614)292-6446
Admissions: (614)247-6281
Fax: (614)292-4818
Web Site: http://www.osu.edu/
Description: State-supported, university, coed. Awards associate, bachelor's, master's, doctoral, and first professional degrees and post-master's certificates. Founded 1870. Setting: 3,117-acre urban campus.

Endowment: $1.7 billion. Research spending for 2004 fiscal year: $446.8 million. Educational spending for 2005 fiscal year: $16,741 per student. Total enrollment: 50,504. Faculty: 3,895 (2,872 full-time, 1,023 part-time). Student-undergrad faculty ratio is 13:1. 17,566 applied, 74% were admitted. 39% from top 10% of their high school class, 76% from top quarter, 97% from top half. 98 National Merit Scholars, 223 valedictorians. Full-time: 33,817 students, 47% women, 53% men. Part-time: 3,594 students, 48% women, 52% men. Students come from 53 states and territories, 121 other countries, 10% from out-of-state, 0.4% Native American, 3% Hispanic, 8% black, 5% Asian American or Pacific Islander, 3% international, 9% 25 or older, 24% live on campus, 5% transferred in. Retention: 90% of full-time freshmen returned the following year. Academic areas with the most degrees conferred: business/marketing; social sciences; family and consumer sciences. Core. Academic remediation for entering students, ESL program, services for LD students, advanced placement, accelerated degree program, self-designed majors, freshman honors college, honors program, independent study, distance learning, double major, summer session for credit, part-time degree program, adult/continuing education programs, co-op programs and internships, graduate courses open to undergrads. Off campus study at Higher Education Council of Columbus. Study abroad program. ROTC: Army, Naval, Air Force.
Entrance Requirements: Options: Common Application, electronic application. Required: essay, high school transcript, SAT or ACT. Entrance: moderately difficult. Application deadline: 2/1. Notification: continuous.
Costs Per Year: Application fee: $40. State resident tuition: $7929 full-time. Nonresident tuition: $19,152 full-time. Mandatory fees: $153 full-time. Full-time tuition and fees vary according to course load, program, reciprocity agreements, and student level. College room and board: $7275. Room and board charges vary according to board plan and housing facility.
Collegiate Environment: Orientation program. Drama-theater group, choral group, marching band, student-run newspaper, radio station. Social organizations: 750 open to all; national fraternities, national sororities, local fraternities, local sororities; 6% of eligible men and 6% of eligible women are members. Most popular organizations: African Student Union, Bisexual, Gay and Lesbian Alliance, Campus Crusade for Christ, University Wide Council of Hispanic Organizations, Asian-American Association. Major annual events: Michigan Week festivities, Welcome Week, Homecoming. Student services: legal services, health clinic, personal-psychological counseling, women's center. Campus security: 24-hour emergency response devices and patrols, student patrols, late night transport-escort service, controlled dormitory access, dorm entrances locked after 9 p.m., lighted pathways and sidewalks, self-defense education. 8,886 college housing spaces available; all were occupied in 2003-04. Freshmen guaranteed college housing. On-campus residence required in freshman year. Option: coed housing available. Main Library plus 12 others with 5.6 million books, 5.6 million microform titles, 43,086 serials, 46,705 audiovisual materials, an OPAC, and a Web page. Operations spending for 2004 fiscal year: $27 million. 800 computers available on campus for general student use. A campuswide network can be accessed from student residence rooms and from off campus. Staffed computer lab on campus.

■ **THE OHIO STATE UNIVERSITY AGRICULTURAL TECHNICAL INSTITUTE** *F-9*
1328 Dover Rd.
Wooster, OH 44691
Tel: (330)264-3911
Web Site: http://www.ati.ohio-state.edu/
Description: State-supported, 2-year, coed. Part of Ohio State University. Awards certificates, diplomas, transfer associate, and terminal associate degrees. Founded 1971. Setting: small town campus with easy access to Cleveland and Columbus. Endowment: $2.1 million. Educational spending for 2005 fiscal year: $1847 per student. Total enrollment: 821. Student-undergrad faculty ratio is 16:1. 554 applied, 95% were admitted. 6% from top 10% of their high school class, 20% from top quarter, 52% from top half. Full-time: 721 students, 33% women, 67% men. Part-time: 100 students, 34% women, 66% men. Students come from 13 states and territories, 2 other countries, 2% from out-of-state, 0.4% Native American, 1% Hispanic, 1% black, 0.1% Asian American or Pacific Islander, 0.2% international, 10% 25 or older, 22% live on campus, 7% transferred in. Retention: 68% of full-time freshmen returned the following year. Core. Academic remediation for entering students, services for LD students, advanced placement, accelerated degree program, self-designed majors, honors program, summer session for credit, part-time degree program, adult/continuing education programs, co-op programs and internships. ROTC: Army (c), Naval (c), Air Force (c).

Entrance Requirements: Open admission for state residents. Option: early admission. Required: high school transcript. Required for some: SAT or ACT. Entrance: noncompetitive. Application deadline: 7/1. Notification: continuous until 9/15.

Costs Per Year: Application fee: $40. State resident tuition: $5478 full-time. Nonresident tuition: $16,701 full-time. Mandatory fees: $38 full-time. Full-time tuition and fees vary according to course load. College room and board: $5475. College room only: $4575. Room and board charges vary according to board plan.

Collegiate Environment: Orientation program. Social organizations: 19 open to all. Most popular organizations: Hoof-n-Hide Club, Horticulture Club, Campus Crusade for Christ, Phi Theta Kappa, Artist de Fleur Club. Major annual events: Welcome Days, Winter Blitz, Fall Barn Dance. Student services: health clinic, personal-psychological counseling. Campus security: 24-hour emergency response devices and patrols, controlled dormitory access. 533 college housing spaces available; 470 were occupied in 2003-04. No special consideration for freshman housing applicants. On-campus residence required in freshman year. Option: coed housing available. Agricultural Technical Institute Library with 19,009 books, 595 serials, and an OPAC. Operations spending for 2004 fiscal year: $217,716. 85 computers available on campus for general student use.

Community Environment: Wooster, population 26,000, is the county seat of Wayne County and is in a major agricultural area accessible from any area of the state. It is also home to the College of Wooster, and the corporate headquarters of Rubbermaid and other companies including Frito-Lay, Wooster Brush Company, Regal Ware, the Gerstenslager Company, and Bell and Howell. Students also have access to Cleveland, Columbus, Pittsburgh, Cincinnati, and Akron.

■ THE OHIO STATE UNIVERSITY AT LIMA *F-3*

4240 Campus Dr.
Lima, OH 45804
Tel: (419)995-8600
Admissions: (419)995-8434
Fax: (419)995-8483
E-mail: admissions@lima.ohio-state.edu
Web Site: http://www.lima.osu.edu/

Description: State-supported, comprehensive, coed. Part of Ohio State University. Awards associate, bachelor's, and master's degrees. Founded 1960. Setting: 565-acre small town campus. Research spending for 2004 fiscal year: $90,669. Educational spending for 2005 fiscal year: $8935 per student. Total enrollment: 1,145. Faculty: 77 (38 full-time, 39 part-time). Student-undergrad faculty ratio is 19:1. 720 applied, 99% were admitted. 5% from top 10% of their high school class, 31% from top quarter, 63% from top half. Full-time: 856 students, 54% women, 46% men. Part-time: 212 students, 66% women, 34% men. 0% from out-of-state, 0.4% Native American, 1% Hispanic, 3% black, 1% Asian American or Pacific Islander, 0.1% international, 20% 25 or older. Core. Academic remediation for entering students, ESL program, services for LD students, advanced placement, accelerated degree program, honors program, summer session for credit, part-time degree program, adult/continuing education programs, graduate courses open to undergrads. ROTC: Army (c), Naval (c), Air Force (c).

Entrance Requirements: Open admission for state residents. Option: early admission. Required: essay, high school transcript. Required for some: SAT or ACT. Entrance: noncompetitive. Application deadline: 7/1. Notification: continuous.

Costs Per Year: Application fee: $40. State resident tuition: $5310 full-time. Nonresident tuition: $16,533 full-time. Full-time tuition varies according to course load and student level. College room and board: $6264. Room and board charges vary according to housing facility.

Collegiate Environment: Orientation program. Drama-theater group, choral group, student-run newspaper, radio station. Social organizations: 14 open to all. Most popular organizations: chorus, Psychology Club, Buckeye Scholars, Bucks for Buckeyes, theatre. Major annual events: Welcome Back Picnic, movie nights, Spring Fling. Campus security: 24-hour emergency response devices and patrols, late night transport-escort service. Ohio State University-Lima Campus Library with 74,619 books, 592 serials, and an OPAC. 104 computers available on campus for general student use.

■ THE OHIO STATE UNIVERSITY-MANSFIELD CAMPUS *F-7*

1680 University Dr.
Mansfield, OH 44906-1599
Tel: (419)755-4011
Admissions: (419)755-4225

E-mail: admissions@mansfield.ohio-state.edu
Web Site: http://www.mansfield.osu.edu/

Description: State-supported, comprehensive, coed. Part of Ohio State University. Awards associate, bachelor's, and master's degrees. Founded 1958. Setting: 644-acre small town campus with easy access to Columbus and Cleveland. Research spending for 2004 fiscal year: $102,007. Educational spending for 2005 fiscal year: $7465 per student. Total enrollment: 1,610. Faculty: 89 (48 full-time, 41 part-time). Student-undergrad faculty ratio is 21:1. 979 applied, 99% were admitted. 9% from top 10% of their high school class, 26% from top quarter, 60% from top half. 8 valedictorians. Full-time: 1,050 students, 59% women, 41% men. Part-time: 463 students, 75% women, 25% men. Students come from 10 states and territories, 0% from out-of-state, 1% Native American, 1% Hispanic, 5% black, 2% Asian American or Pacific Islander, 0.1% international, 26% 25 or older. Core. Academic remediation for entering students, ESL program, services for LD students, advanced placement, accelerated degree program, honors program, summer session for credit, part-time degree program, adult/continuing education programs, graduate courses open to undergrads. ROTC: Army (c), Naval (c), Air Force (c).

Entrance Requirements: Open admission for state residents. Option: early admission. Required: essay, high school transcript. Required for some: SAT or ACT. Entrance: noncompetitive. Application deadline: 7/1. Notification: continuous.

Costs Per Year: Application fee: $40. State resident tuition: $5310 full-time. Nonresident tuition: $16,533 full-time. Full-time tuition varies according to course load and student level. College room and board: $6264. Room and board charges vary according to housing facility.

Collegiate Environment: Orientation program. Drama-theater group, choral group. Student services: personal-psychological counseling. Campus security: 24-hour emergency response devices and patrols, late night transport-escort service. Ohio State University-Mansfield Campus Library with 45,977 books, 453 serials, and an OPAC. 103 computers available on campus for general student use.

■ THE OHIO STATE UNIVERSITY AT MARION *F-6*

1465 Mount Vernon Ave.
Marion, OH 43302-5695
Tel: (740)389-6786
E-mail: moreau.1@osu.edu
Web Site: http://www.marion.ohio-state.edu/

Description: State-supported, comprehensive, coed. Part of Ohio State University. Awards associate, bachelor's, and master's degrees. Founded 1958. Setting: 180-acre small town campus with easy access to Columbus. Research spending for 2004 fiscal year: $12,826. Educational spending for 2005 fiscal year: $7180 per student. Total enrollment: 1,485. Faculty: 108 (35 full-time, 73 part-time). Student-undergrad faculty ratio is 22:1. 751 applied, 99% were admitted. 8% from top 10% of their high school class, 28% from top quarter, 65% from top half. Full-time: 1,159 students, 57% women, 43% men. Part-time: 247 students, 66% women, 34% men. Students come from 6 states and territories, 0% from out-of-state, 0.3% Native American, 2% Hispanic, 4% black, 3% Asian American or Pacific Islander, 0.3% international, 23% 25 or older. Core. Academic remediation for entering students, ESL program, services for LD students, advanced placement, accelerated degree program, honors program, summer session for credit, part-time degree program, adult/continuing education programs, graduate courses open to undergrads. ROTC: Army (c), Naval (c), Air Force (c).

Entrance Requirements: Open admission for state residents. Option: early admission. Required: essay, high school transcript. Entrance: noncompetitive. Application deadline: 7/1. Notification: continuous.

Costs Per Year: Application fee: $40. State resident tuition: $5310 full-time. Nonresident tuition: $16,533 full-time. Full-time tuition varies according to course load and student level.

Collegiate Environment: Orientation program. Choral group, student-run newspaper. Social organizations: 15 open to all. Student services: personal-psychological counseling. Campus security: 24-hour emergency response devices. Ohio State University-Marion Campus Library with 38,858 books, 413 serials, and an OPAC. 174 computers available on campus for general student use.

■ THE OHIO STATE UNIVERSITY-NEWARK CAMPUS *H-8*

1179 University Dr.
Newark, OH 43055-1797
Tel: (740)366-3321
Admissions: (614)366-9333

E-mail: vogelmeier.1@osu.edu

Web Site: http://www.newark.osu.edu/

Description: State-supported, comprehensive, coed. Part of Ohio State University. Awards associate, bachelor's, and master's degrees. Founded 1957. Setting: 101-acre small town campus with easy access to Columbus. Research spending for 2004 fiscal year: $41,671. Educational spending for 2005 fiscal year: $7113 per student. Total enrollment: 2,183. Faculty: 135 (50 full-time, 85 part-time). Student-undergrad faculty ratio is 25:1. 1,526 applied, 99% were admitted. 7% from top 10% of their high school class, 18% from top quarter, 55% from top half. 1 valedictorian. Full-time: 1,765 students, 54% women, 46% men. Part-time: 323 students, 60% women, 40% men. Students come from 14 states and territories, 1 other country, 0% from out-of-state, 1% Native American, 1% Hispanic, 7% black, 1% Asian American or Pacific Islander, 0.2% international, 18% 25 or older. Core. Academic remediation for entering students, ESL program, services for LD students, advanced placement, accelerated degree program, honors program, summer session for credit, part-time degree program, adult/continuing education programs, graduate courses open to undergrads. ROTC: Army (c), Naval (c), Air Force (c).

Entrance Requirements: Open admission for state residents. Option: early admission. Required: essay, high school transcript. Entrance: noncompetitive. Application deadline: 7/1. Notification: continuous.

Costs Per Year: Application fee: $40. State resident tuition: $5310 full-time. Nonresident tuition: $16,533 full-time. Full-time tuition varies according to course load and student level. College room and board: $6264. Room and board charges vary according to housing facility.

Collegiate Environment: Orientation program. Drama-theater group, choral group. Social organizations: 14 open to all. Student services: personal-psychological counseling. Campus security: 24-hour emergency response devices and patrols, late night transport-escort service, self-defense education. Ohio State University Newark Campus Library with 49,232 books, 423 serials, and an OPAC. Operations spending for 2004 fiscal year: $130,700. 36 computers available on campus for general student use.

■ **OHIO TECHNICAL COLLEGE** *C-10*

1374 East 51st St.

Cleveland, OH 44103

Tel: (216)881-1700

Free: 800-322-7000

Fax: (216)881-9145

E-mail: ohioauto@aol.com

Web Site: http://www.ohiotechnicalcollege.com/

Description: Proprietary, 2-year, coed. Founded 1969.

■ **OHIO UNIVERSITY** *K-9*

Athens, OH 45701-2979

Tel: (740)593-1000

Admissions: (740)593-4100

Fax: (740)593-4229

E-mail: uadmiss1@ohiou.edu

Web Site: http://www.ohio.edu/

Description: State-supported, university, coed. Part of Ohio Board of Regents. Awards associate, bachelor's, master's, doctoral, and first professional degrees. Founded 1804. Setting: 1,700-acre small town campus. Endowment: $195.7 million. Research spending for 2004 fiscal year: $30.4 million. Educational spending for 2005 fiscal year: $9575 per student. Total enrollment: 20,396. Faculty: 1,195 (875 full-time, 320 part-time). Student-undergrad faculty ratio is 18:1. 12,367 applied, 89% were admitted. 16% from top 10% of their high school class, 42% from top quarter, 80% from top half. 11 National Merit Scholars, 111 valedictorians. Full-time: 16,090 students, 52% women, 48% men. Part-time: 1,101 students, 58% women, 42% men. Students come from 52 states and territories, 109 other countries, 13% from out-of-state, 0.2% Native American, 1% Hispanic, 4% black, 1% Asian American or Pacific Islander, 2% international, 5% 25 or older, 43% live on campus, 3% transferred in. Retention: 81% of full-time freshmen returned the following year. Academic areas with the most degrees conferred: communications/journalism; business/marketing; education. Core. Academic remediation for entering students, ESL program, services for LD students, advanced placement, accelerated degree program, self-designed majors, honors program, independent study, distance learning, double major, summer session for credit, part-time degree program, external degree program, adult/continuing education programs, co-op programs and internships, graduate courses open to undergrads. Off campus study. Study abroad program. ROTC: Army, Air Force.

Entrance Requirements: Options: early admission, deferred admission, international baccalaureate accepted. Required: high school transcript, SAT or ACT. Recommended: 2 recommendations. Required for some: essay, interview. Entrance: moderately difficult. Application deadline: 2/1. Notification: continuous.

Costs Per Year: Application fee: $45. State resident tuition: $8235 full-time, $262 per quarter hour part-time. Nonresident tuition: $17,199 full-time, $557 per quarter hour part-time. College room and board: $7686. College room only: $3855. Room and board charges vary according to board plan.

Collegiate Environment: Orientation program. Drama-theater group, choral group, marching band, student-run newspaper, radio station. Social organizations: 372 open to all; national fraternities, national sororities; 12% of eligible men and 13% of eligible women are members. Most popular organizations: Gamma Pi Delta, Golden Key, International Student Union, Chinese Students and Visiting Scholars Club, Campus Crusade for Christ. Major annual events: Homecoming, International Week, Parents' Weekend. Student services: legal services, health clinic, personal-psychological counseling. Campus security: 24-hour emergency response devices and patrols, late night transport-escort service, controlled dormitory access, security lighting. 7,457 college housing spaces available; 7,000 were occupied in 2003-04. On-campus residence required through sophomore year. Options: coed, men-only, women-only housing available. Alden Library plus 1 other with 2.6 million books, 3.2 million microform titles, 25,557 serials, 86,574 audiovisual materials, an OPAC, and a Web page. Operations spending for 2004 fiscal year: $12.1 million. 1,500 computers available on campus for general student use. A campuswide network can be accessed from student residence rooms and from off campus. Staffed computer lab on campus.

Community Environment: Athens is a traditional college town with a nonstudent population of approximately 21,000. The city is located about 75 miles southeast of Columbus, the state capital, in the foothills of the Appalachian mountains and on the banks of the Hocking River. Several state parks and thousands of acres of national forests are within easy driving distance and provide ample facilities for swimming, hiking, camping, fishing, and picnicking.

■ **OHIO UNIVERSITY-CHILLICOTHE** *K-6*

571 West Fifth St., PO Box 629

Chillicothe, OH 45601-0629

Tel: (740)774-7200

Fax: (740)774-7295

Web Site: http://www.ohio.edu/chillicothe/

Description: State-supported, 4-year, coed. Part of Ohio Board of Regents. Awards associate, bachelor's, and master's degrees (offers first 2 years of most bachelor's degree programs available at the main campus in Athens; also offers several bachelor's degree programs that can be completed at this campus and several programs exclusive to this campus; also offers some graduate programs). Founded 1946. Setting: 124-acre small town campus with easy access to Columbus. Total enrollment: 2,000. 775 applied, 52% were admitted. Students come from 2 states and territories, 0.3% Native American, 0.4% Hispanic, 2% black, 0.3% Asian American or Pacific Islander, 0.2% international, 35% 25 or older. Retention: 55% of full-time freshmen returned the following year. Core. Academic remediation for entering students, services for LD students, advanced placement, accelerated degree program, self-designed majors, independent study, distance learning, double major, summer session for credit, part-time degree program, adult/continuing education programs, internships. ROTC: Army (c), Air Force (c).

Entrance Requirements: Open admission for state residents. Option: early admission. Required: high school transcript. Placement: SAT or ACT required. Entrance: noncompetitive. Application deadline: 9/1. Notification: continuous.

Costs Per Year: Application fee: $20. State resident tuition: $115 per credit hour part-time. Nonresident tuition: $131 per credit hour part-time. Mandatory fees: $16 per credit hour part-time.

Collegiate Environment: Orientation program. Drama-theater group. Social organizations: 8 open to all. Most popular organizations: Nursing Student Association, Students in Free Enterprise Club, Drama Club, Phi Theta Kappa, Gamma Phi Delta. Major annual event: G-Day. Student services: personal-psychological counseling. Campus security: 24-hour emergency response devices, patrols by city police. College housing not available. Quinn Library with 47,900 books and 418 serials. 215 computers available on campus for general student use. A campuswide network can be accessed from off-campus. Staffed computer lab on campus.

■ **OHIO UNIVERSITY-EASTERN**

45425 National Rd.
St. Clairsville, OH 43950-9724
Tel: (740)695-1720
Web Site: http://www.eastern.ohiou.edu/
Description: State-supported, 4-year, coed. Part of Ohio Board of Regents. Awards associate and bachelor's degrees (also offers some graduate courses). Founded 1957. Setting: 300-acre rural campus. Total enrollment: 1,118. 350 applied. Full-time: 681 students, 65% women, 35% men. Part-time: 250 students, 76% women, 24% men. Students come from 3 states and territories, 0% Native American, 0.1% Hispanic, 2% black, 0.1% Asian American or Pacific Islander, 0% international, 32% 25 or older. Core. Academic remediation for entering students, advanced placement, accelerated degree program, self-designed majors, summer session for credit, part-time degree program, external degree program, adult/continuing education programs.
Entrance Requirements: Open admission. Options: early admission, deferred admission. Required: high school transcript. Placement: SAT or ACT required. Entrance: noncompetitive. Application deadline: Rolling.
Costs Per Year: Application fee: $20. Area resident tuition: $115 per credit hour part-time. Nonresident tuition: $131 per credit hour part-time. Mandatory fees: $16 per credit hour part-time.
Collegiate Environment: Drama-theater group. Most popular organizations: Karate Club, Student Ambassadors, Student Literary Magazine. Major annual events: Spring Week, World Food Day, Black History/Women's History Month. College housing not available. 50,000 books, 625 serials, and an OPAC. 50 computers available on campus for general student use. A campuswide network can be accessed. Staffed computer lab on campus.

■ **OHIO UNIVERSITY-LANCASTER** *J-7*

1570 Granville Pike
Lancaster, OH 43130-1097
Tel: (740)654-6711; 888-446-4468
Fax: (740)687-9497
E-mail: shepherd@ohiou.edu
Web Site: http://www.ohiou.edu/lancaster/
Description: State-supported, comprehensive, coed. Part of Ohio Board of Regents. Awards associate, bachelor's, and master's degrees. Founded 1968. Setting: 360-acre small town campus with easy access to Columbus. Endowment: $75,000. Research spending for 2004 fiscal year: $8737. Educational spending for 2005 fiscal year: $1863 per student. Total enrollment: 1,744. 486 applied, 100% were admitted. 13% from top 10% of their high school class, 38% from top quarter, 64% from top half. Full-time: 880 students, 63% women, 37% men. Part-time: 737 students, 72% women, 28% men. Students come from 12 states and territories, 1 other country, 0.5% Native American, 0.4% Hispanic, 2% black, 0.5% Asian American or Pacific Islander, 0.2% international, 46% 25 or older. Core. Academic remediation for entering students, advanced placement, accelerated degree program, self-designed majors, independent study, distance learning, double major, summer session for credit, part-time degree program, external degree program, adult/continuing education programs, internships. ROTC: Army (c), Air Force (c).
Entrance Requirements: Open admission. Options: Common Application, electronic application, early admission, deferred admission. Required: high school transcript. Recommended: interview. Placement: SAT or ACT required. Entrance: noncompetitive. Application deadline: Rolling. Notification: continuous.
Costs Per Year: Application fee: $20. State resident tuition: $127 per credit hour part-time. Nonresident tuition: $144 per credit hour part-time. Mandatory fees: $17 per credit hour part-time.
Collegiate Environment: Orientation program. Drama-theater group. Most popular organization: Student Activities Association. Major annual events: Basketball Tournament, annual trips. College housing not available. Hannah V. McCauley Library with 94,688 books, 369,265 microform titles, 399 serials, 2,759 audiovisual materials, an OPAC, and a Web page. Operations spending for 2004 fiscal year: $417,213. 150 computers available on campus for general student use. A campuswide network can be accessed from off-campus. Staffed computer lab on campus.

■ **OHIO UNIVERSITY-SOUTHERN CAMPUS** *N-7*

1804 Liberty Ave.
Ironton, OH 45638-2214

Tel: (740)533-4600
Free: 800-626-0513
Admissions: (740)533-4612
Fax: (740)533-4632
Web Site: http://www.ohiou.edu/
Description: State-supported, comprehensive, coed. Part of Ohio Board of Regents. Awards associate, bachelor's, and master's degrees. Founded 1956. Setting: 9-acre small town campus. Total enrollment: 1,746. 482 applied, 100% were admitted. Full-time: 1,110 students, 61% women, 39% men. Part-time: 520 students, 69% women, 31% men. Students come from 4 states and territories, 14% from out-of-state, 1% Native American, 0.3% Hispanic, 3% black, 0.2% Asian American or Pacific Islander, 0.1% international, 48% 25 or older. Core. Academic remediation for entering students, self-designed majors, summer session for credit, part-time degree program, adult/continuing education programs.
Entrance Requirements: Open admission. Options: early admission, deferred admission. Required for some: high school transcript. Placement: SAT or ACT recommended. Entrance: noncompetitive. Application deadline: Rolling.
Costs Per Year: Application fee: $20. State resident tuition: $124 per credit hour part-time. Nonresident tuition: $165 per credit hour part-time. Mandatory fees: $12 per credit hour part-time. Part-time tuition and fees vary according to student level.
Collegiate Environment: Orientation program. Choral group. Student services: legal services. College housing not available. Ohio University-Southern Campus Library with 26,000 books, 19,198 microform titles, 275 serials, 524 audiovisual materials, an OPAC, and a Web page. 147 computers available on campus for general student use. A campuswide network can be accessed from off-campus. Staffed computer lab on campus.

■ **OHIO UNIVERSITY-ZANESVILLE** *I-9*

1425 Newark Rd.
Zanesville, OH 43701-2695
Tel: (740)453-0762
Admissions: (740)588-1439
Fax: (740)453-6161
Web Site: http://www.zanesville.ohiou.edu/
Description: State-supported, comprehensive, coed. Part of Ohio Board of Regents. Awards associate, bachelor's, and master's degrees (offers first 2 years of most bachelor's degree programs available at the main campus in Athens; also offers several bachelor's degree programs that can be completed at this campus; also offers some graduate courses). Founded 1946. Setting: 179-acre rural campus with easy access to Columbus. Total enrollment: 1,904. Faculty: 130 (31 full-time, 99 part-time). Student-undergrad faculty ratio is 23:1. 799 applied, 100% were admitted. 10% from top 10% of their high school class, 33% from top quarter, 65% from top half. Full-time: 1,139 students, 70% women, 30% men. Part-time: 710 students, 73% women, 27% men. Students come from 4 states and territories, 1% from out-of-state, 0.4% Native American, 0.5% Hispanic, 2% black, 0.4% Asian American or Pacific Islander, 0.1% international, 35% 25 or older. Retention: 62% of full-time freshmen returned the following year. Core. Academic remediation for entering students, services for LD students, advanced placement, self-designed majors, summer session for credit, part-time degree program, external degree program, adult/continuing education programs, graduate courses open to undergrads. Off campus study at Muskingum Area Technical College.
Entrance Requirements: Open admission except for nursing, engineering, business, communications programs, education. Options: Common Application, early admission, deferred admission. Required: high school transcript. Required for some: SAT or ACT. Entrance: noncompetitive. Application deadline: Rolling.
Costs Per Year: Application fee: $20. State resident tuition: $4596 full-time, $144 per credit hour part-time. Nonresident tuition: $8919 full-time, $275 per credit hour part-time. Full-time tuition varies according to course level. Part-time tuition varies according to course level.
Collegiate Environment: Orientation program. Drama-theater group, student-run newspaper, radio station. Most popular organizations: Student Senate, Student Nurses Association, Drama Club, Chess Club. Major annual events: Spring Fest, Fall Fest. Campus security: night security. College housing not available. Zanesville Campus Library plus 1 other with 64,227 books, 489 serials, and an OPAC. Operations spending for 2004 fiscal year: $247,287. 42 computers available on campus for general student use. A campuswide network can be accessed from off-campus. Staffed computer lab on campus.

■ OHIO VALLEY COLLEGE OF TECHNOLOGY F-13

16808 St. Clair Ave., PO Box 7000
East Liverpool, OH 43920
Tel: (330)385-1070
Web Site: http://www.ovct.edu/
Description: Proprietary, 2-year, coed. Awards diplomas and terminal associate degrees. Founded 1886. Setting: small town campus with easy access to Pittsburgh. Total enrollment: 126. Full-time: 121 students, 91% women, 9% men. Part-time: 5 students, 100% women. Students come from 3 states and territories, 10% from out-of-state, 1% Native American, 0% Hispanic, 3% black, 0% Asian American or Pacific Islander, 0% international, 69% 25 or older, 26% transferred in. Core. Calendar: semesters. Summer session for credit, part-time degree program, internships.
Entrance Requirements: Required: high school transcript, interview, CPAt. Entrance: minimally difficult. Application deadline: Rolling.
Collegiate Environment: Student services: personal-psychological counseling. College housing not available.

■ OHIO WESLEYAN UNIVERSITY G-6

61 South Sandusky St.
Delaware, OH 43015
Tel: (740)368-2000
Free: 800-922-8953
Admissions: (740)368-3025
Fax: (740)368-3314
E-mail: midrugov@owu.edu
Web Site: http://www.owu.edu/
Description: Independent United Methodist, 4-year, coed. Awards bachelor's degrees. Founded 1842. Setting: 200-acre small town campus with easy access to Columbus. Endowment: $144.4 million. Research spending for 2004 fiscal year: $531,056. Educational spending for 2005 fiscal year: $11,148 per student. Total enrollment: 1,976. Student-undergrad faculty ratio is 13:1. 2,929 applied, 75% were admitted. 30% from top 10% of their high school class, 52% from top quarter, 81% from top half. 17 National Merit Scholars, 22 valedictorians. Full-time: 1,941 students, 52% women, 48% men. Part-time: 35 students, 63% women, 37% men. Students come from 43 states and territories, 47 other countries, 41% from out-of-state, 0% Native American, 1% Hispanic, 5% black, 2% Asian American or Pacific Islander, 8% international, 0% 25 or older, 84% live on campus, 2% transferred in. Retention: 81% of full-time freshmen returned the following year. Academic areas with the most degrees conferred: social sciences; biological/life sciences; business/marketing. Core. Calendar: semesters. Services for LD students, advanced placement, self-designed majors, freshman honors college, honors program, independent study, double major, summer session for credit, part-time degree program, internships. Off campus study at Great Lakes Colleges Association, New York City Arts Program, Wesleyan in Washington, Philadelphia Center. Study abroad program. ROTC: Army (c).
Entrance Requirements: Options: Peterson's Universal Application, Common Application, electronic application, early admission, early decision, early action, deferred admission, international baccalaureate accepted. Required: essay, high school transcript, minimum 2.5 high school GPA, 1 recommendation, SAT or ACT. Recommended: 2 recommendations, interview, SAT Subject Tests. Entrance: very difficult. Application deadlines: 3/1, 12/1 for early decision, 12/15 for early action. Notification: continuous, 12/30 for early decision, 1/15 for early action.
Costs Per Year: Application fee: $35. Comprehensive fee: $35,830 includes full-time tuition ($27,920), mandatory fees ($360), and college room and board ($7550). College room only: $3750. Room and board charges vary according to board plan. Part-time tuition: $3040 per course.
Collegiate Environment: Orientation program. Drama-theater group, choral group, student-run newspaper, radio station. Social organizations: 85 open to all; national fraternities, national sororities; 39% of eligible men and 26% of eligible women are members. Most popular organizations: community services, student government, Campus Programming Board, religious organizations, ethnic organizations. Major annual events: homecoming, National Colloquium Day, Monnett Weekend. Student services: health clinic, personal-psychological counseling, women's center. Campus security: 24-hour emergency response devices and patrols, late night transport-escort service, controlled dormitory access. 1,732 college housing spaces available; 1,610 were occupied in 2003-04. Freshmen guaranteed college housing. On-campus residence required through senior year. Options: coed, men-only, women-only housing available. L. A. Beeghly Library plus 3 others with 441,912 books, 110,048 microform titles, 1,073 serials, 3,197

audiovisual materials, an OPAC, and a Web page. Operations spending for 2004 fiscal year: $2.2 million. 320 computers available on campus for general student use. A campuswide network can be accessed from student residence rooms and from off campus. Staffed computer lab on campus.
Community Environment: Delaware, a city of 23,000 and county seat of Delaware County, is a 25-minute drive from Columbus, with convenient access by air, highway or bus. The Delaware State Parks provide facilities for fishing, boating, camping, and swimming. An annual event is the Little Brown Jug, which is the largest pacing event in the United States. About half the faculty live within a ten minute walk of student halls and houses, in the architecturally historic northwest section of the city. Ohio Wesleyan is a national school; 50% of the students are from Ohio, while the other 50% represent 40 U.S. states and 54 countries.

■ OTTERBEIN COLLEGE H-6

1 Otterbein College
Westerville, OH 43081
Tel: (614)890-3000
Free: 800-488-8144
Admissions: (614)823-1500
Fax: (614)823-1200
E-mail: uotterb@otterbein.edu
Web Site: http://www.otterbein.edu/
Description: Independent United Methodist, comprehensive, coed. Awards bachelor's and master's degrees. Founded 1847. Setting: 142-acre suburban campus with easy access to Columbus. Endowment: $68.5 million. Total enrollment: 3,094. Faculty: 276 (157 full-time, 119 part-time). Student-undergrad faculty ratio is 13:1. 2,708 applied, 77% were admitted. 22% from top 10% of their high school class, 51% from top quarter, 77% from top half. 1 National Merit Scholar, 30 valedictorians. Full-time: 2,261 students, 64% women, 36% men. Students come from 35 states and territories, 34 other countries, 7% from out-of-state, 0% Native American, 2% Hispanic, 7% black, 2% Asian American or Pacific Islander, 24% 25 or older, 52% live on campus, 2% transferred in. Retention: 91% of full-time freshmen returned the following year. Core. Academic remediation for entering students, services for LD students, advanced placement, self-designed majors, honors program, double major, summer session for credit, part-time degree program, adult/continuing education programs, internships, graduate courses open to undergrads. Off campus study at American University, University of Pittsburgh (Semester at Sea), members of the Higher Education Council of Columbus. Study abroad program. ROTC: Army (c), Air Force (c).
Entrance Requirements: Options: Peterson's Universal Application, Common Application, electronic application, deferred admission. Required: high school transcript, SAT or ACT. Recommended: minimum 2.5 high school GPA, interview. Entrance: moderately difficult. Application deadline: 3/1. Notification: continuous.
Costs Per Year: Application fee: $25. Comprehensive fee: $28,986 includes full-time tuition ($22,518) and college room and board ($6468). College room only: $2994. Full-time tuition varies according to course load and program. Room and board charges vary according to housing facility. Part-time tuition: $270 per credit hour. Part-time tuition varies according to course load and program.
Collegiate Environment: Orientation program. Drama-theater group, choral group, marching band, student-run newspaper, radio station. Social organizations: 100 open to all; national fraternities, local fraternities, local sororities; 28% of eligible men and 28% of eligible women are members. Most popular organizations: musical groups, honoraries, academic interest clubs, Governance. Major annual events: Homecoming, Winterfest, Martin Luther King, Jr. Convocation. Student services: health clinic, personal-psychological counseling. Campus security: 24-hour emergency response devices and patrols, student patrols, late night transport-escort service, controlled dormitory access, 24-hour locked residence hall entrances. 1,103 undergraduates lived in college housing during 2003-04. Freshmen guaranteed college housing. On-campus residence required through sophomore year. Options: men-only, women-only housing available. Courtright Memorial Library with 182,629 books, 312,944 microform titles, 1,012 serials, 8,971 audiovisual materials, an OPAC, and a Web page. 146 computers available on campus for general student use. A campuswide network can be accessed from student residence rooms and from off campus. Staffed computer lab on campus.
Community Environment: Westerville was settled in 1813 by Connecticut, New York, and Virginia families, and Quakers from Pennsylvania. The community, seven miles north of Columbus, has excellent city and college librar-

ies, many churches, a modern medical center, and various civic and service organizations. A site of interest is the Hanby House. Hoover Reservoir is located about four miles east, and offers facilities for picnicking, fishing, and boating. Part-time employment is available.

■ OWENS COMMUNITY COLLEGE *B-5*

PO Box 10000
Toledo, OH 43699-1947
Tel: (419)661-7000
Free: 800-GO-OWENS
Admissions: (567)661-7225
E-mail: william_ivoska@owens.edu
Web Site: http://www.owens.edu/

Description: State-supported, 2-year, coed. Awards certificates, transfer associate, and terminal associate degrees. Founded 1966. Setting: 100-acre small town campus. Total enrollment: 20,244. Student-undergrad faculty ratio is 22:1. Full-time: 7,531 students, 57% women, 43% men. Part-time: 12,713 students, 41% women, 59% men. Students come from 15 states and territories, 49 other countries, 3% from out-of-state, 0.4% Native American, 4% Hispanic, 13% black, 1% Asian American or Pacific Islander, 1% international, 50% 25 or older. Core. Calendar: semesters. Academic remediation for entering students, ESL program, services for LD students, advanced placement, freshman honors college, honors program, independent study, distance learning, double major, summer session for credit, part-time degree program, external degree program, adult/continuing education programs, co-op programs and internships. ROTC: Army (c), Air Force.

Entrance Requirements: Open admission except for health technology, peace officer academy. Options: Common Application, early admission. Recommended: essay, high school transcript, recommendations. Required for some: minimum 2.0 high school GPA. Entrance: noncompetitive. Application deadline: Rolling. Notification: continuous.

Costs Per Year: Application fee: $0. State resident tuition: $2784 full-time, $116 per credit part-time. Nonresident tuition: $5208 full-time, $217 per credit part-time. Mandatory fees: $400 full-time, $15 per credit part-time, $10 per term part-time.

Collegiate Environment: Orientation program. Drama-theater group, choral group, student-run newspaper. Social organizations: 6 open to all. Most popular organizations: intramurals, Alpha Beta Gamma, Drama Club, Student Association for Young Children, Phi Theta Kappa. Major annual events: sporting events, spring break trip, Halloween Family Fun Night. Student services: health clinic, personal-psychological counseling. Campus security: 24-hour emergency response devices and patrols, student patrols. College housing not available. Owens Community College Library with 78,344 books, 71,720 microform titles, 6,230 serials, 9,021 audiovisual materials, an OPAC, and a Web page. 1,000 computers available on campus for general student use. A campuswide network can be accessed from off-campus. Staffed computer lab on campus.

Community Environment: See University of Toledo.

■ PONTIFICAL COLLEGE JOSEPHINUM *I-6*

7625 North High St.
Columbus, OH 43235-1498
Tel: (614)885-5585; 888-252-5812
E-mail: pcahall@pcj.edu
Web Site: http://www.pcj.edu/

Description: Independent Roman Catholic, comprehensive, coed. Awards bachelor's, master's, and first professional degrees. Founded 1888. Setting: 100-acre suburban campus. Endowment: $39.1 million. Educational spending for 2005 fiscal year: $14,542 per student. Total enrollment: 133. Faculty: 37 (18 full-time, 19 part-time). Student-undergrad faculty ratio is 6:1. 3 applied, 100% were admitted. Full-time: 76 students, 100% men. Students come from 15 states and territories, 1 other country, 85% from out-of-state, 3% Hispanic, 1% Asian American or Pacific Islander, 4% international, 35% 25 or older, 100% live on campus, 13% transferred in. Retention: 78% of full-time freshmen returned the following year. Academic areas with the most degrees conferred: English; area and ethnic studies; history. Core. Calendar: semesters. Academic remediation for entering students, ESL program, services for LD students, advanced placement, honors program, double major, internships, graduate courses open to undergrads. Off campus study at 2 members of the Theological Cluster.

Entrance Requirements: Option: deferred admission. Required: essay, high school transcript, 3 recommendations, interview, SAT and SAT Subject Tests or ACT. Entrance: minimally difficult. Application deadline: 7/31. Preference given to candidates for the priesthood.

Costs Per Year: Application fee: $25. Comprehensive fee: $21,635 includes full-time tuition ($14,000), mandatory fees ($635), and college room and board ($7000). Part-time tuition: $565 per credit hour.

Collegiate Environment: Orientation program. Drama-theater group, choral group. Student services: health clinic, personal-psychological counseling. Campus security: 24-hour emergency response devices, controlled dormitory access. 110 college housing spaces available; 81 were occupied in 2003-04. Freshmen guaranteed college housing. On-campus residence required through senior year. Option: men-only housing available. Wehrle Memorial Library with 137,883 books, 1,875 microform titles, 465 serials, 3,189 audiovisual materials, and a Web page. Operations spending for 2004 fiscal year: $303,425. 10 computers available on campus for general student use. A campuswide network can be accessed from student residence rooms. Staffed computer lab on campus.

Community Environment: See Ohio State University - Columbus Campus.

■ PROFESSIONAL SKILLS INSTITUTE *B-5*

20 Arco Dr.
Toledo, OH 43607
Tel: (419)531-9610
Fax: (419)531-4732
Web Site: http://www.proskills.com/

Description: Proprietary, 2-year, coed. Awards certificates, diplomas, and terminal associate degrees. Founded 1984. Setting: 2-acre urban campus with easy access to Detroit. Educational spending for 2005 fiscal year: $3800 per student. Total enrollment: 174. 57 applied, 93% were admitted. 48% from top half of their high school class. 1 National Merit Scholar, 2 student government officers. Full-time: 164 students, 77% women, 23% men. Part-time: 10 students, 80% women, 20% men. Students come from 5 states and territories, 60% 25 or older. Core. Services for LD students, part-time degree program, internships. Off campus study at Lourdes College.

Entrance Requirements: Required: high school transcript, minimum 2.0 high school GPA, recommendations, interview, Wonderlic aptitude test. Entrance: moderately difficult. Notification: 9/15.

Collegiate Environment: Student services: health clinic. Campus security: 24-hour emergency response devices, camera, alarm system. College housing not available. Professional Skills Institute Library plus 1 other with 2,200 books, 50 serials, and an OPAC. Operations spending for 2004 fiscal year: $7805. 28 computers available on campus for general student use. Staffed computer lab on campus.

■ RABBINICAL COLLEGE OF TELSHE *C-20*

28400 Euclid Ave.
Wickliffe, OH 44092-2523
Tel: (216)943-5300

Description: Independent religious, comprehensive.

■ REMINGTON COLLEGE-CLEVELAND CAMPUS *C-10*

14445 Broadway Ave.
Cleveland, OH 44125
Tel: (216)475-7520
Fax: (216)475-6055
Web Site: http://www.remingtoncollege.edu/

Description: Proprietary, 2-year, coed. Awards diplomas and transfer associate degrees. Setting: 2-acre urban campus. Total enrollment: 676. 369 applied, 76% were admitted. Full-time: 676 students, 85% women, 15% men. Core. Calendar: continuous. Co-op programs.

Entrance Requirements: Required: essay, high school transcript, interview. Entrance: moderately difficult.

Costs Per Year: Application fee: $50. Tuition: $15,745 full-time. Full-time tuition varies according to program.

Collegiate Environment: Orientation program. College housing not available.

■ REMINGTON COLLEGE-CLEVELAND WEST CAMPUS *E-16*

26350 Brookpark Rd.
North Olmsted, OH 44070
Tel: (440)777-2560
Fax: (440)777-3238
E-mail: gary.azotea@remingtoncollege.edu
Web Site: http://www.remingtoncollege.edu/

Description: Proprietary, 2-year, coed. Awards diplomas and terminal associate degrees. Founded 2003. Total enrollment: 399. Student-undergrad

faculty ratio is 23:1. Full-time: 399 students, 83% women, 17% men. 1% Native American, 8% Hispanic, 17% black, 1% Asian American or Pacific Islander.
Entrance Requirements: Required: Wonderlic.

■ **RETS TECH CENTER** *J-3*
555 East Alex Bell Rd.
Centerville, OH 45459
Tel: (937)433-3410
Free: 800-837-7387
Fax: (937)435-6516
Web Site: http://www.retstechcenter.com/
Description: Proprietary, 2-year, coed. Awards diplomas, transfer associate, and terminal associate degrees. Founded 1953. Setting: 4-acre suburban campus with easy access to Dayton. Educational spending for 2005 fiscal year: $4000 per student. Total enrollment: 556. Full-time: 556 students, 58% women, 42% men. Students come from 2 states and territories, 1% from out-of-state, 1% Hispanic, 22% black, 55% 25 or older, 1% transferred in. Core. Calendar: semesters. Advanced placement, summer session for credit, internships.
Entrance Requirements: Options: early admission, deferred admission. Required: high school transcript, interview. Entrance: noncompetitive. Application deadline: Rolling.
Collegiate Environment: Orientation program. Student services: personal-psychological counseling. Campus security: 24-hour emergency response devices. College housing not available. RETS Library with 2,200 books, 27 serials, and 66 audiovisual materials. Operations spending for 2004 fiscal year: $8900. 220 computers available on campus for general student use. A campuswide network can be accessed. Staffed computer lab on campus.

■ **ROSEDALE BIBLE COLLEGE**
2270 Rosedale Rd.
Irwin, OH 43029-9501
Tel: (740)857-1311
Fax: (740)857-1577
E-mail: pweber@rosedale.edu
Web Site: http://www.rosedalebible.org/
Description: Independent Mennonite, 2-year, coed. Founded 1952. Total enrollment: 49. Calendar: five six-week terms.

■ **SCHOOL OF ADVERTISING ART** *J-3*
1725 East David Rd.
Kettering, OH 45440-1612
Tel: (937)294-0592; 877-300-9866
Fax: (937)294-5869
E-mail: jayne@saacollege.com
Web Site: http://www.saacollege.com/
Description: Proprietary, 2-year, coed. Awards diplomas, transfer associate, and terminal associate degrees. Founded 1983. Setting: 5-acre suburban campus with easy access to Dayton, Ohio; Cincinnati, Ohio. Total enrollment: 146. Student-undergrad faculty ratio is 12:1. 10% from top 10% of their high school class, 35% from top quarter, 45% from top half. Full-time: 146 students, 51% women, 49% men. Students come from 4 states and territories, 2% from out-of-state, 1% Native American, 3% Hispanic, 5% black, 1% Asian American or Pacific Islander, 1% international, 3% 25 or older, 0% transferred in. Retention: 75% of full-time freshmen returned the following year. Calendar: trimesters.
Entrance Requirements: Required: high school transcript, interview. Recommended: minimum 2.5 high school GPA. Required for some: essay, minimum 2.0 high school GPA, 1 recommendation. Entrance: minimally difficult. Application deadlines: 7/1, 12/31 for early action. Notification: 7/1, 12/31 for early action.
Costs Per Year: Tuition: $17,775 full-time. Mandatory fees: $210 full-time.
Collegiate Environment: Social organizations: ; 7% of eligible men and 7% of eligible women are members. Major annual events: Portfolio Show, Picnic in the Park, holiday parties. Student services: personal-psychological counseling. College housing not available.

■ **SHAWNEE STATE UNIVERSITY** *M-6*
940 Second St.
Portsmouth, OH 45662-4344
Tel: (740)354-3205
Free: 800-959-2SSU
Admissions: (740)351-3610

Fax: (740)355-2470
E-mail: admsn@shawnee.edu
Web Site: http://www.shawnee.edu/
Description: State-supported, 4-year, coed. Part of Ohio Board of Regents. Awards associate and bachelor's degrees. Founded 1986. Setting: 52-acre small town campus. Endowment: $10.1 million. Educational spending for 2005 fiscal year: $13,782 per student. Total enrollment: 3,820. Student-undergrad faculty ratio is 18:1. 2,917 applied, 100% were admitted. 15% from top 10% of their high school class, 34% from top quarter, 67% from top half. Full-time: 3,197 students, 60% women, 40% men. Part-time: 623 students, 67% women, 33% men. Students come from 16 states and territories, 12 other countries, 9% from out-of-state, 1% Native American, 0.5% Hispanic, 3% black, 0.3% Asian American or Pacific Islander, 1% international, 28% 25 or older, 13% live on campus, 5% transferred in. Retention: 64% of full-time freshmen returned the following year. Academic areas with the most degrees conferred: business/marketing; social sciences; education. Core. Academic remediation for entering students, services for LD students, advanced placement, honors program, independent study, distance learning, double major, summer session for credit, part-time degree program, adult/continuing education programs, internships. Off campus study. Study abroad program.
Entrance Requirements: Open admission except for allied health programs, nonresident aliens. Options: electronic application, deferred admission. Required: high school transcript. Recommended: ACT. Required for some: recommendations, interview, ACT. Entrance: noncompetitive. Application deadline: Rolling. Notification: continuous.
Costs Per Year: Application fee: $0. State resident tuition: $4896 full-time, $153 per credit hour part-time. Nonresident tuition: $8784 full-time, $261 per credit hour part-time. Mandatory fees: $612 full-time, $17 per credit hour part-time. Full-time tuition and fees vary according to course load, reciprocity agreements, and student level. Part-time tuition and fees vary according to course load, reciprocity agreements, and student level. College room and board: $6729. College room only: $4281. Room and board charges vary according to board plan and housing facility.
Collegiate Environment: Orientation program. Drama-theater group, choral group, student-run newspaper. Social organizations: 31 open to all; national fraternities, local sororities; 5% of eligible men and 3% of eligible women are members. Most popular organizations: campus ministry, Health Executives and Administrators Learning Society, Student Programming Board, SGA. Major annual events: Homecoming, Springfest, Scare Week. Student services: health clinic, personal-psychological counseling. Campus security: 24-hour emergency response devices and patrols. 456 college housing spaces available; 453 were occupied in 2003-04. On-campus residence required through sophomore year. Option: coed housing available. Shawnee State University Library with 150,661 books, 59,957 microform titles, 13,820 serials, 39,046 audiovisual materials, an OPAC, and a Web page. Operations spending for 2004 fiscal year: $1.1 million. 400 computers available on campus for general student use. A campuswide network can be accessed from off-campus. Staffed computer lab on campus.
Community Environment: A quaint city of 23,000 residents, Portsmouth is Scioto County's largest retail center and a popular tourist area as well. Its Bonneyfiddle area, with its old-world charm, is a treasure trove for antique buffs, and the winding Ohio River offers opportunities for boating, waterskiing, and fishing. Shawnee State Park provides nature trails, as well as boating, fishing and golf.

■ **SINCLAIR COMMUNITY COLLEGE** *I-3*
444 West Third St.
Dayton, OH 45402-1460
Tel: (937)512-2500
Admissions: (937)512-3060
E-mail: ssmith@sinclair.edu
Web Site: http://www.sinclair.edu/
Description: State and locally supported, 2-year, coed. Part of Ohio Board of Regents. Awards certificates, transfer associate, and terminal associate degrees. Founded 1887. Setting: 50-acre urban campus with easy access to Cincinnati. Endowment: $25 million. Educational spending for 2005 fiscal year: $4386 per student. Total enrollment: 19,563. Student-undergrad faculty ratio is 19:1. 6,271 applied, 100% were admitted. Full-time: 7,550 students, 56% women, 44% men. Part-time: 12,013 students, 59% women, 41% men. Students come from 31 states and territories, 4% from out-of-state, 0.4% Native American, 1% Hispanic, 16% black, 1% Asian American or Pacific Islander, 1% international, 47% 25 or older, 6% transferred in. Retention: 56% of full-time freshmen returned the following year. Core. Academic

remediation for entering students, ESL program, services for LD students, self-designed majors, honors program, independent study, distance learning, summer session for credit, part-time degree program, external degree program, adult/continuing education programs, co-op programs and internships. Off campus study at 17 members of the Southwestern Ohio Council for Higher Education. ROTC: Army (c), Air Force (c).

Entrance Requirements: Open admission except for allied health programs. Options: electronic application, early admission, deferred admission. Required for some: high school transcript, interview. Entrance: noncompetitive. Application deadline: Rolling. Notification: continuous.

Costs Per Year: Application fee: $10. Area resident tuition: $1910 full-time, $42.25 per credit hour part-time. State resident tuition: $3121 full-time, $69.35 per credit hour part-time. Nonresident tuition: $5940 full-time, $132 per credit hour part-time. Full-time tuition varies according to course load. Part-time tuition varies according to course load.

Collegiate Environment: Orientation program. Drama-theater group, choral group, student-run newspaper. Social organizations: 55 open to all. Most popular organizations: African-American Men of the Future, Ohio Fellows, Phi Theta Kappa, student government, student newspaper. Major annual events: Welcome Week, Spring Fling, Student Health Fair. Student services: personal-psychological counseling. Campus security: 24-hour emergency response devices and patrols, student patrols, late night transport-escort service. College housing not available. Learning Resources Center with 147,613 books, 27,456 microform titles, 576 serials, 9,293 audiovisual materials, an OPAC, and a Web page. Operations spending for 2004 fiscal year: $1.8 million. 1,800 computers available on campus for general student use. A campuswide network can be accessed from off-campus. Staffed computer lab on campus.

■ **SOUTHEASTERN BUSINESS COLLEGE (CHILLICOTHE)** *K-6*
1855 Western Ave.
Chillicothe, OH 45601-1038
Tel: (740)774-6300
Fax: (740)774-2071
Web Site: http://www.careersohio.com/
Description: Proprietary, 2-year, coed. Awards terminal associate degrees. Founded 1976. Total enrollment: 100. 75 applied, 56% were admitted.

■ **SOUTHEASTERN BUSINESS COLLEGE (JACKSON)** *L-7*
504 McCarty Ln.
Jackson, OH 45640
Tel: (740)286-1554
Fax: (740)286-4476
E-mail: todd_sbc@yahoo.com
Web Site: http://www.careersohio.com/
Description: Proprietary, 2-year, coed. Founded 1976.

■ **SOUTHEASTERN BUSINESS COLLEGE (LANCASTER)** *J-7*
1522 Sheridan Dr.
Lancaster, OH 43130-1303
Tel: (740)687-6126
Fax: (740)687-0431
E-mail: rp_sbc@yahoo.com
Web Site: http://www.careersohio.com/
Description: Proprietary, 2-year, coed. Founded 1984.

■ **SOUTHEASTERN BUSINESS COLLEGE (NEW BOSTON)** *M-6*
3879 Rhodes Ave.
New Boston, OH 45662
Tel: (740)456-4124
Web Site: http://www.careersohio.com/
Description: Proprietary, 2-year, coed.

■ **SOUTHERN STATE COMMUNITY COLLEGE** *K-4*
100 Hobart Dr.
Hillsboro, OH 45133-9487
Tel: (937)393-3431
Fax: (937)393-9370
E-mail: wjohnson@sscc.edu
Web Site: http://www.sscc.edu/
Description: State-supported, 2-year, coed. Awards certificates, transfer associate, and terminal associate degrees. Founded 1975. Setting: 60-acre rural campus. Endowment: $443,111. Educational spending for 2005 fiscal year: $3213 per student. Total enrollment: 2,307. Student-undergrad faculty ratio is 21:1. 829 applied, 100% were admitted. 0.4% Native American, 0.3% Hispanic, 1% black, 0.5% Asian American or Pacific Islander, 0.04% international. Core. Academic remediation for entering students, services for LD students, advanced placement, self-designed majors, independent study, distance learning, double major, summer session for credit, part-time degree program, co-op programs and internships. Off campus study at 15 members of the Southwestern Ohio Council for Higher Education.

Entrance Requirements: Open admission. Options: Common Application, early admission, deferred admission. Recommended: high school transcript. Entrance: noncompetitive. Application deadline: Rolling. Notification: continuous.

Costs Per Year: Application fee: $0. State resident tuition: $3213 full-time. Nonresident tuition: $6189 full-time. Full-time tuition varies according to course load.

Collegiate Environment: Orientation program. Drama-theater group, choral group. Social organizations: 3 open to all. Most popular organizations: Student Leadership, Student Nurses Association, Drama Club, Association of Medical Assistants, Phi Theta Kappa. Major annual events: Spring Fling, Halloween Dance/Party, Fall Quarter Mixer. Student services: personal-psychological counseling. College housing not available. Learning Resources Center plus 3 others with 79,000 books, 552,000 microform titles, 1,107 serials, 7,428 audiovisual materials, an OPAC, and a Web page. Operations spending for 2004 fiscal year: $393,901. 300 computers available on campus for general student use. A campuswide network can be accessed from off-campus. Staffed computer lab on campus.

Community Environment: Hillsboro, approximately 40 miles east of Cincinnati, is in a primarily rural setting with small towns and villages.

■ **SOUTHWESTERN COLLEGE OF BUSINESS (CINCINNATI)** *L-2*
632 Vine St., Ste. 200
Cincinnati, OH 45202-4304
Tel: (513)421-3212
Web Site: http://www.swcollege.net/
Description: Proprietary, 2-year, coed. Awards diplomas, transfer associate, and terminal associate degrees. Founded 1972. Setting: urban campus. 162 applied, 90% were admitted. 41% 25 or older. Summer session for credit, part-time degree program, co-op programs and internships.

Entrance Requirements: Option: deferred admission. Required for some: CPAt. Entrance: minimally difficult. Application deadline: Rolling. Notification: continuous.

Collegiate Environment: College housing not available. 54 computers available on campus for general student use.

■ **SOUTHWESTERN COLLEGE OF BUSINESS (CINCINNATI)** *L-2*
149 Northland Blvd.
Cincinnati, OH 45246-1122
Tel: (513)874-0432
Web Site: http://www.swcollege.net/
Description: Proprietary, 2-year, coed. Awards diplomas and terminal associate degrees. Founded 1972. Setting: suburban campus. Total enrollment: 200. Core. Academic remediation for entering students, summer session for credit, external degree program, co-op programs.

Entrance Requirements: Option: deferred admission. Required for some: CPAt. Entrance: minimally difficult. Application deadline: Rolling. Notification: continuous.

Collegiate Environment: Student services: personal-psychological counseling. College housing not available. 50 computers available on campus for general student use. Staffed computer lab on campus.

■ **SOUTHWESTERN COLLEGE OF BUSINESS (DAYTON)** *I-3*
111 West First St.
Dayton, OH 45402-3003
Tel: (937)224-0061
Fax: (937)224-0065
Web Site: http://www.swcollege.net/
Description: Proprietary, 2-year, coed. Awards certificates, diplomas, and terminal associate degrees. Founded 1972. Setting: urban campus. Total enrollment: 214. 125 applied, 49% were admitted. Full-time: 214 students, 75% women, 25% men. 0% Native American, 0% Hispanic, 79% black, 0% Asian American or Pacific Islander, 0% international. Core. Academic remediation for entering students, summer session for credit, external degree program, co-op programs.

Entrance Requirements: Option: deferred admission. Entrance: minimally difficult. Application deadline: Rolling. Notification: continuous.

Collegiate Environment: Student services: personal-psychological counseling. College housing not available. 30 computers available on campus for general student use.

■ **SOUTHWESTERN COLLEGE OF BUSINESS (FRANKLIN)** *J-2*
201 East Second St.
Franklin, OH 45005
Tel: (937)746-6633
Web Site: http://www.swcollege.net/
Description: Proprietary, 2-year, coed. Awards certificates, diplomas, and terminal associate degrees. Founded 1981. Setting: suburban campus with easy access to Cincinnati and Dayton. Total enrollment: 150. 75% 25 or older. Core.
Entrance Requirements: Required: high school transcript, interview. Entrance: moderately difficult. Application deadline: Rolling. Notification: continuous.
Collegiate Environment: College housing not available. 33 computers available on campus for general student use.

■ **STARK STATE COLLEGE OF TECHNOLOGY** *E-11*
6200 Frank Ave., NW
North Canton, OH 44720-7299
Tel: (330)494-6170
Free: 800-797-8275
Admissions: (330)966-5450
Fax: (330)497-6313
Web Site: http://www.starkstate.edu/
Description: State and locally supported, 2-year, coed. Part of Ohio Board of Regents. Awards certificates, transfer associate, and terminal associate degrees. Founded 1970. Setting: 34-acre suburban campus with easy access to Cleveland. Endowment: $1.8 million. Total enrollment: 6,857. Student-undergrad faculty ratio is 19:1. 2,589 applied, 100% were admitted. Full-time: 2,297 students, 51% women, 49% men. Part-time: 4,560 students, 61% women, 39% men. Students come from 4 states and territories, 1% from out-of-state, 1% Native American, 1% Hispanic, 10% black, 1% Asian American or Pacific Islander, 0.2% international, 55% 25 or older, 11% transferred in. Core. Calendar: semesters. Academic remediation for entering students, services for LD students, self-designed majors, independent study, distance learning, summer session for credit, part-time degree program, external degree program, adult/continuing education programs. Off campus study at Malone College, University of Akron, Walsh College, Kent State University, Stark Campus.
Entrance Requirements: Open admission. Options: electronic application, early admission, deferred admission. Required: high school transcript. Entrance: noncompetitive. Application deadline: Rolling.
Costs Per Year: Application fee: $65. State resident tuition: $3810 full-time, $127 per credit hour part-time. Nonresident tuition: $5610 full-time, $187 per credit hour part-time.
Collegiate Environment: Orientation program. Student-run newspaper. Student services: personal-psychological counseling. Campus security: 24-hour emergency response devices, late night transport-escort service. College housing not available. Learning Resource Center with 70,000 books, 425 serials, and an OPAC. 500 computers available on campus for general student use. A campuswide network can be accessed from off-campus. Staffed computer lab on campus.
Community Environment: Set in small city environment - commuter campus only.

■ **STAUTZENBERGER COLLEGE** *B-5*
5355 Southwyck Blvd.
Toledo, OH 43614
Tel: (419)866-0261
Free: 800-552-5099
Fax: (419)867-9821
E-mail: klfitzgerald@stautzenberger.com
Web Site: http://www.sctoday.com/
Description: Proprietary, 2-year, coed. Awards certificates, diplomas, and terminal associate degrees. Setting: urban campus. Total enrollment: 792. 150 applied, 95% were admitted. 0.4% Native American, 3% Hispanic, 14% black, 1% Asian American or Pacific Islander, 0% international.

■ **TECHNOLOGY EDUCATION COLLEGE** *I-6*
288 South Hamilton Rd.
Columbus, OH 43213-2087

Tel: (614)759-7700
Free: 800-838-3233
Admissions: (614)456-4600
Fax: (614)759-7747
E-mail: mmontgomery@teceducation.com
Web Site: http://www.teceducation.com/
Description: Private, 2-year, coed. Awards certificates and terminal associate degrees. Total enrollment: 400. 55% black.

■ **TEMPLE BAPTIST COLLEGE** *L-2*
11965 Kenn Rd.
Cincinnati, OH 45240
Tel: (513)851-3800
Fax: (513)851-3800
Web Site: http://www.templebaptistcollege.com/
Description: Independent religious, 4-year, coed.

■ **TERRA STATE COMMUNITY COLLEGE** *D-6*
2830 Napoleon Rd.
Fremont, OH 43420-9670
Tel: (419)334-8400
Fax: (419)334-9035
E-mail: mmccue@terra.edu
Web Site: http://www.terra.edu/
Description: State-supported, 2-year, coed. Part of Ohio Board of Regents. Awards certificates, diplomas, transfer associate, and terminal associate degrees. Founded 1968. Setting: 100-acre small town campus with easy access to Toledo. Endowment: $907,000. Educational spending for 2005 fiscal year: $2835 per student. Total enrollment: 2,634. Full-time: 1,150 students, 52% women, 48% men. Part-time: 1,484 students, 48% women, 52% men. Students come from 5 states and territories, 0.1% from out-of-state, 0.2% Native American, 5% Hispanic, 4% black, 0.3% Asian American or Pacific Islander, 0% international, 41% 25 or older, 12% transferred in. Retention: 39% of full-time freshmen returned the following year. Core. Academic remediation for entering students, services for LD students, advanced placement, accelerated degree program, self-designed majors, honors program, independent study, distance learning, double major, summer session for credit, part-time degree program, adult/continuing education programs, co-op programs and internships.
Entrance Requirements: Open admission. Options: electronic application, early admission, deferred admission. Required: high school transcript. Placement: ACT COMPASS required; SAT or ACT recommended. Entrance: noncompetitive. Application deadline: Rolling.
Costs Per Year: Application fee: $15. State resident tuition: $3278 full-time, $68.30 per credit hour part-time. Nonresident tuition: $7067 full-time, $147.23 per credit hour part-time. Mandatory fees: $334 full-time, $6.95 per credit hour part-time. Full-time tuition and fees vary according to course load. Part-time tuition and fees vary according to course load.
Collegiate Environment: Orientation program. Choral group. Social organizations: 5 open to all; national fraternities; 4% of eligible men and 3% of eligible women are members. Most popular organizations: Phi Theta Kappa, Student Activities Club, Society of Plastic Engineers, Koinonia, Student Senate. Major annual events: Student Orientation, Commencement, Open House. Student services: personal-psychological counseling. Campus security: 24-hour emergency response devices, late night transport-escort service. College housing not available. Learning Resource Center with 22,675 books, 59,422 microform titles, 383 serials, 1,957 audiovisual materials, an OPAC, and a Web page. Operations spending for 2004 fiscal year: $220,047. 250 computers available on campus for general student use. A campuswide network can be accessed from off-campus. Staffed computer lab on campus.

■ **TIFFIN UNIVERSITY** *D-6*
155 Miami St.
Tiffin, OH 44883-2161
Tel: (419)447-6442
Free: 800-968-6446
Admissions: (419)448-3368
Fax: (419)447-9605
E-mail: admiss@tiffin.edu
Web Site: http://www.tiffin.edu/
Description: Independent, comprehensive, coed. Awards associate, bachelor's, and master's degrees. Founded 1888. Setting: 110-acre small town campus with easy access to Toledo. Endowment: $3.2 million.

Educational spending for 2005 fiscal year: $4872 per student. Total enrollment: 1,605. Faculty: 133 (51 full-time, 82 part-time). Student-undergrad faculty ratio is 16:1. 1,563 applied, 73% were admitted. 7% from top 10% of their high school class, 24% from top quarter, 62% from top half. Full-time: 1,097 students, 50% women, 50% men. Part-time: 138 students, 72% women, 28% men. Students come from 14 states and territories, 10 other countries, 6% from out-of-state, 0% Native American, 2% Hispanic, 15% black, 0.2% Asian American or Pacific Islander, 2% international, 27% 25 or older, 40% live on campus, 4% transferred in. Retention: 60% of full-time freshmen returned the following year. Core. Calendar: semesters. Advanced placement, accelerated degree program, independent study, distance learning, double major, summer session for credit, adult/continuing education programs, internships. Study abroad program. ROTC: Army (c), Air Force (c).

Entrance Requirements: Options: Peterson's Universal Application, Common Application, electronic application, deferred admission, international baccalaureate accepted. Required: high school transcript, SAT or ACT. Recommended: essay, minimum 3.00 high school GPA, interview, 19 on ACT or 890 on SAT. Required for some: essay, recommendations, interview. Entrance: minimally difficult. Application deadline: Rolling.

Costs Per Year: Application fee: $20. Comprehensive fee: $22,645 includes full-time tuition ($15,870) and college room and board ($6775). College room only: $3525. Part-time tuition: $529 per credit hour.

Collegiate Environment: Orientation program. Drama-theater group, choral group, marching band, student-run newspaper. Social organizations: 16 open to all; national fraternities, national sororities, local fraternities, local sororities; 16% of eligible men and 15% of eligible women are members. Most popular organizations: Student Government Association, Black United Students, International Student Association, Gay, Lesbian and Straight Supporters (GLASS). Major annual events: homecoming, Springfest, faculty vs. student basketball game. Student services: health clinic, personal-psychological counseling. Campus security: student patrols, late night transport-escort service. 422 college housing spaces available; 401 were occupied in 2003-04. Freshmen guaranteed college housing. On-campus residence required through sophomore year. Options: coed, men-only, women-only housing available. Pfeiffer Library with 29,779 books, 33,250 microform titles, 250 serials, 544 audiovisual materials, and an OPAC. Operations spending for 2004 fiscal year: $249,239. 60 computers available on campus for general student use. A campuswide network can be accessed from student residence rooms and from off campus. Staffed computer lab on campus.

Community Environment: See Heidelberg College.

■ **TRI-STATE BIBLE COLLEGE** *N-7*
506 Margaret St.
PO Box 445
South Point, OH 45680-8402
Tel: (740)377-2520
Fax: (740)377-0001
E-mail: tsbc@zoomnet.net
Web Site: http://www.tsbc.edu/
Description: Independent nondenominational, 4-year, coed. Founded 1970. Calendar: semesters.

■ **TRUMBULL BUSINESS COLLEGE** *D-12*
3200 Ridge Rd.
Warren, OH 44484
Tel: (330)369-3200
Fax: (330)369-6792
Web Site: http://www.tbc-trumbullbusiness.com/
Description: Proprietary, 2-year, coed. Awards diplomas and terminal associate degrees. Founded 1972. Setting: 6-acre small town campus. Educational spending for 2005 fiscal year: $1244 per student. Total enrollment: 411. 97 applied, 100% were admitted. Full-time: 347 students, 85% women, 15% men. Part-time: 64 students, 80% women, 20% men. Students come from 2 states and territories, 1% from out-of-state, 1% Hispanic, 19% black, 0.5% Asian American or Pacific Islander, 51% 25 or older, 0% transferred in.

Entrance Requirements: Required: high school transcript, interview. Entrance: noncompetitive. Application deadline: Rolling. Notification: continuous until 10/1.

Costs Per Year: Application fee: $70. One-time mandatory fee: $75. Tuition: $7560 full-time, $210 per credit hour part-time. Mandatory fees: $425 full-time. Full-time tuition and fees vary according to course load and program.

Part-time tuition varies according to course load and program. Tuition guaranteed not to increase for student's term of enrollment.

Collegiate Environment: Student-run newspaper. Social organizations: 2 open to all. Most popular organizations: Student Senate, MADD/SADD. College housing not available.

■ **UNION INSTITUTE & UNIVERSITY** *L-2*
440 East McMillan St.
Cincinnati, OH 45206-1925
Tel: (513)861-6400
Free: 800-486-3116
Fax: (513)861-0779
Web Site: http://www.tui.edu/
Description: Independent, university, coed. Awards bachelor's, master's, and doctoral degrees and post-master's certificates. Founded 1969. Setting: 5-acre urban campus. Endowment: $1.3 million. Educational spending for 2005 fiscal year: $7700 per student. Total enrollment: 2,379. Faculty: 169 (52 full-time, 117 part-time). Student-undergrad faculty ratio is 15:1. Full-time: 673 students, 74% women, 26% men. Part-time: 449 students, 59% women, 41% men. Students come from 45 states and territories, 6 other countries, 22% from out-of-state, 1% Native American, 8% Hispanic, 24% black, 1% Asian American or Pacific Islander, 0.1% international, 92% 25 or older. Retention: 67% of full-time freshmen returned the following year. Academic areas with the most degrees conferred: liberal arts/general studies; security and protective services; education. Core. Calendar: semesters. Services for LD students, advanced placement, accelerated degree program, self-designed majors, independent study, distance learning, double major, summer session for credit, part-time degree program, external degree program, adult/continuing education programs.

Entrance Requirements: Options: electronic application, deferred admission. Required: essay, high school transcript, 2 recommendations, interview. Entrance: moderately difficult. Application deadline: Rolling. Notification: continuous.

Costs Per Year: Application fee: $50. Tuition: $8830 full-time, $368 per credit part-time. Mandatory fees: $80 full-time, $20 per term part-time.

Collegiate Environment: Orientation program. Campus security: late night transport-escort service, security during class hours. College housing not available. Gary Library plus 1 other with 50,000 books, 300 audiovisual materials, an OPAC, and a Web page.

■ **THE UNIVERSITY OF AKRON** *E-10*
302 Buchtel Common
Akron, OH 44325
Tel: (330)972-7111
Free: 800-655-4884
Admissions: (330)972-7077
Fax: (330)972-7676
E-mail: admissions@uakron.edu
Web Site: http://www.uakron.edu/
Description: State-supported, university, coed. Awards bachelor's, master's, doctoral, and first professional degrees and first professional certificates (associate). Founded 1870. Setting: 170-acre urban campus with easy access to Cleveland. Endowment: $176.1 million. Research spending for 2004 fiscal year: $20.4 million. Educational spending for 2005 fiscal year: $5614 per student. Total enrollment: 21,049. Faculty: 1,474 (701 full-time, 773 part-time). Student-undergrad faculty ratio is 18:1. 8,810 applied, 82% were admitted. 12% from top 10% of their high school class, 18% from top quarter, 57% from top half. 4 National Merit Scholars, 52 valedictorians. Full-time: 12,635 students, 51% women, 49% men. Part-time: 4,505 students, 57% women, 43% men. Students come from 42 states and territories, 84 other countries, 2% from out-of-state, 0.3% Native American, 1% Hispanic, 15% black, 2% Asian American or Pacific Islander, 1% international, 30% 25 or older, 13% live on campus, 5% transferred in. Retention: 64% of full-time freshmen returned the following year. Academic areas with the most degrees conferred: business/marketing; education; health professions and related sciences. Core. Calendar: semesters. Academic remediation for entering students, ESL program, services for LD students, advanced placement, accelerated degree program, self-designed majors, honors program, independent study, distance learning, double major, summer session for credit, part-time degree program, adult/continuing education programs, co-op programs and internships, graduate courses open to undergrads. Study abroad program. ROTC: Army, Air Force.

Entrance Requirements: Options: Peterson's Universal Application, electronic application, early admission, early action, deferred admission, international baccalaureate accepted. Required: high school transcript, SAT or ACT. Required for some: essay, 3 recommendations, interview. Entrance: moderately difficult. Application deadlines: 8/1, 2/1 for early action. Notification: continuous.

Costs Per Year: Application fee: $30. State resident tuition: $6810 full-time, $284 per credit part-time. Nonresident tuition: $15,535 full-time, $575 per credit part-time. Mandatory fees: $1148 full-time, $47 per credit part-time. Full-time tuition and fees vary according to course load, degree level, and location. Part-time tuition and fees vary according to course load, degree level, and location. College room and board: $7208. College room only: $4494. Room and board charges vary according to board plan and housing facility.

Collegiate Environment: Orientation program. Drama-theater group, choral group, marching band, student-run newspaper, radio station. Social organizations: 200 open to all; national fraternities, national sororities, local fraternities; 2% of eligible men and 2% of eligible women are members. Most popular organizations: Associated Student Government, Residence Hall Program Board, American Society of Mechanical Engineers. Major annual events: Homecoming, May Day, Greek Week. Student services: legal services, health clinic, personal-psychological counseling, women's center. Campus security: 24-hour emergency response devices and patrols, student patrols, late night transport-escort service, controlled dormitory access. 2,064 college housing spaces available; 2,057 were occupied in 2003-04. Freshmen guaranteed college housing. On-campus residence required in freshman year. Options: coed, men-only, women-only housing available. Bierce Library plus 3 others with 1.2 million books, 1.7 million microform titles, 13,677 serials, 45,041 audiovisual materials, an OPAC, and a Web page. Operations spending for 2004 fiscal year: $8.8 million. 2,450 computers available on campus for general student use. Computer purchase/lease plans available. A campuswide network can be accessed from student residence rooms and from off campus. Staffed computer lab on campus.

Community Environment: The city is a merchandising center and a vital distribution gateway between the industrial East and the Midwest. The Portage Lakes district south of the city provides facilities for boating, swimming, fishing and ice skating. A number of parks provide additional facilities for skiing and other outdoor activities. A short distance to the north, are the New Gateway Complex, Jacobs Field, home of the Cleveland Indians, Gund Arena, of the Cleveland Cavaliers, and the Rock'n Roll Hall of Fame. To the South is The Pro Football Hall of Fame. Local points of interest are the Akron Art Museum, Blossom Music Center, Canal Park Baseball Stadium, Goodyear Aircraft Hanger, Inventure Place, Perkins Mansion, and the Stan Hywet Hall. Special events are the World Series of Golf, held at the Firestone Country Club, and the All-American Soap Box Derby.

■ THE UNIVERSITY OF AKRON-WAYNE COLLEGE *E-10*

1901 Smucker Rd.
Orrville, OH 44667-9192
Tel: (330)683-2010
Admissions: (330)684-8740
Fax: (330)684-8989
E-mail: gholly@uakron.edu
Web Site: http://www.wayne.uakron.edu/

Description: State-supported, 2-year, coed. Part of The University of Akron. Awards certificates, transfer associate, and terminal associate degrees. Founded 1972. Setting: 157-acre rural campus. Total enrollment: 1,737. Student-undergrad faculty ratio is 17:1. 647 applied, 93% were admitted. 7% from top 10% of their high school class, 24% from top quarter, 54% from top half. Full-time: 924 students, 60% women, 40% men. Part-time: 813 students, 67% women, 33% men. 0% from out-of-state, 0.4% Native American, 0.5% Hispanic, 3% black, 1% Asian American or Pacific Islander, 0% international, 41% 25 or older, 5% transferred in. Core. Calendar: semesters. Academic remediation for entering students, ESL program, services for LD students, advanced placement, honors program, independent study, distance learning, double major, summer session for credit, part-time degree program, adult/continuing education programs, co-op programs and internships. Off campus study at The University of Akron. ROTC: Army (c), Air Force (c).

Entrance Requirements: Open admission. Options: Common Application, electronic application, early admission, deferred admission. Recommended: SAT or ACT, ACT COMPASS. Required for some: high school transcript, SAT or ACT, ACT COMPASS. Entrance: noncompetitive. Application deadline: 8/30. Notification: continuous until 8/30.

Costs Per Year: Application fee: $30. State resident tuition: $4,884 full-time, $203.48 per credit hour part-time. Nonresident tuition: $13,202 full-time, $440.07 per credit hour part-time. Mandatory fees: $146 full-time, $6.07 per credit hour part-time.

Collegiate Environment: Orientation program. Student services: personal-psychological counseling. Campus security: late night transport-escort service. College housing not available. Wayne College Library with 23,450 books, 33,253 microform titles, 219 serials, 822 audiovisual materials, and an OPAC. Operations spending for 2004 fiscal year: $190,000. 240 computers available on campus for general student use. Computer purchase/lease plans available. A campuswide network can be accessed from off-campus. Staffed computer lab on campus.

Community Environment: Orrville is a thriving community with a diversified business and industry base, best known for being the home of The J. M. Smucker Company. Located 30 miles southwest of Akron and The University of Akron campus, and 50 miles south of Cleveland, the city of Orrville has a population of 7,800. Residents of this area have relatively easy access to metropolitan amenities while enjoying a more relaxed rural-suburban atmosphere. The community park provides many recreational facilities and the Rehm Performing Arts Pavilion is the setting for many musical and cultural events. There are also 26 churches of various denominations, a community library, and a 38 bed hospital in Orville.

■ UNIVERSITY OF CINCINNATI *L-2*

2624 Clifton Ave.
Cincinnati, OH 45221
Tel: (513)556-6000
Admissions: (513)556-1100
E-mail: admissions@uc.edu
Web Site: http://www.uc.edu/

Description: State-supported, university, coed. Part of University of Cincinnati System. Awards associate, bachelor's, master's, doctoral, and first professional degrees. Founded 1819. Setting: 137-acre urban campus. Endowment: $987 million. Research spending for 2004 fiscal year: $119.6 million. Educational spending for 2005 fiscal year: $10,552 per student. Total enrollment: 27,932. Faculty: 1,241 (1,200 full-time, 41 part-time). Student-undergrad faculty ratio is 14:1. 11,813 applied, 76% were admitted. 19% from top 10% of their high school class, 49% from top quarter, 82% from top half. Full-time: 16,098 students, 47% women, 53% men. Part-time: 3,414 students, 64% women, 36% men. Students come from 52 states and territories, 123 other countries, 10% from out-of-state, 0.3% Native American, 2% Hispanic, 14% black, 3% Asian American or Pacific Islander, 1% international, 17% 25 or older, 18% live on campus, 6% transferred in. Retention: 79% of full-time freshmen returned the following year. Academic areas with the most degrees conferred: business/marketing; engineering; visual and performing arts. Core. Academic remediation for entering students, ESL program, services for LD students, advanced placement, accelerated degree program, honors program, independent study, distance learning, double major, summer session for credit, part-time degree program, adult/continuing education programs, co-op programs and internships, graduate courses open to undergrads. Off campus study at Greater Cincinnati Consortium of Colleges and Universities. Study abroad program. ROTC: Army, Air Force.

Entrance Requirements: Options: Peterson's Universal Application, electronic application. Required: high school transcript, SAT or ACT. Recommended: interview. Required for some: 2 recommendations, audition. Entrance: moderately difficult. Application deadline: Rolling. Notification: continuous until 11/1. Preference given to state residents.

Costs Per Year: Application fee: $40. State resident tuition: $7458 full-time, $247 per credit hour part-time. Nonresident tuition: $21,210 full-time, $629 per credit hour part-time. Mandatory fees: $1425 full-time. Full-time tuition and fees vary according to course load, degree level, location, program, and reciprocity agreements. Part-time tuition varies according to course load, degree level, location, program, and reciprocity agreements. College room and board: $7890. College room only: $4680. Room and board charges vary according to board plan and housing facility.

Collegiate Environment: Orientation program. Drama-theater group, choral group, marching band, student-run newspaper, radio station. Social organizations: 50 open to all; national fraternities, national sororities, local sororities. Student services: legal services, health clinic, personal-psychological counseling, women's center. Campus security: 24-hour emergency response devices and patrols, late night transport-escort service, controlled dormitory access. College housing designed to accommodate 3,134 students; 3,257 undergraduates lived in college housing during 2003-

04. Freshmen guaranteed college housing. On-campus residence required in freshman year. Options: coed, men-only, women-only housing available. Langsam Library plus 7 others with 2.4 million microform titles, 16,560 serials, 51,224 audiovisual materials, an OPAC, and a Web page. Operations spending for 2004 fiscal year: $21.1 million. 325 computers available on campus for general student use. A campuswide network can be accessed from student residence rooms and from off campus. Staffed computer lab on campus.

Community Environment: Called by Longfellow,"The Queen City of the West," Cincinnati was founded in 1788 and was named Losantiville. The following year the name was changed to Cincinnati, after the Society of Cincinnati. The city is the third largest in Ohio and is situated on a series of plateaus above the Ohio River surrounded by hills. The altitude varies from 435 to 938 feet. Some of the industries located here are Proctor & Gamble Co., General Electric Co., Ford Motor Co., and the Kroger Co. The Cincinnati Convention-Exposition Center provides facilities for meetings as well as 95,000 square feet of exhibition space. Cultural facilities include the Cincinnati Symphony Orchestra, Art Academy of Cincinnati, and the University of Cincinnati College Conservatory of Music; Cincinnati is famous as a center of music and art. Recreational facilities are numerous. Among the points of interest are the Carew Tower Observatory, Cincinnati Art Museum, Cincinnati Museum of Natural History, King's Island which is a recreational facility, Hebrew Union College Museum, Mount Airy Forest, St. Peter in Chains Cathedral, Stowe House, and Taft Museum.

■ **UNIVERSITY OF CINCINNATI CLERMONT COLLEGE** *L-3*
4200 Clermont College Dr.
Batavia, OH 45103-1785.
Tel: (513)732-5200
Admissions: (513)732-5247
Web Site: http://www.clc.uc.edu/
Description: State-supported, 2-year, coed. Part of University of Cincinnati System. Awards certificates, transfer associate, and terminal associate degrees. Founded 1972. Setting: 65-acre rural campus with easy access to Cincinnati. Endowment: $338,141. Educational spending for 2005 fiscal year: $2724 per student. Total enrollment: 2,408. 8% from top 10% of their high school class, 28% from top quarter, 46% from top half. Students come from 3 states and territories, 50% 25 or older. Academic remediation for entering students, advanced placement, self-designed majors, summer session for credit, part-time degree program, adult/continuing education programs, co-op programs and internships. Off campus study at 11 members of the Greater Cincinnati Consortium of Colleges and Universities. ROTC: Air Force (c).
Entrance Requirements: Open admission. Option: deferred admission. Required: high school transcript. Placement: SAT or ACT recommended; SAT or ACT required for some. Entrance: noncompetitive. Application deadline: Rolling. Notification: continuous.
Collegiate Environment: Drama-theater group, student-run newspaper. Student services: personal-psychological counseling, women's center. Campus security: 12-hour patrols by trained security personnel. College housing not available. 19,235 books and 174 serials. Operations spending for 2004 fiscal year: $276,340. 118 computers available on campus for general student use.
Community Environment: Batavia, the Clermont County seat, is central to the entire county. Clermont County is recognized as the fastest growing county in Ohio. The completion of the Interstate Highway System and belt-freeway have made the Cincinnati metropolitan and Northern Kentucky areas easily accessible.

■ **UNIVERSITY OF CINCINNATI RAYMOND WALTERS COLLEGE** *L-2*
9555 Plainfield Rd.
Cincinnati, OH 45236-1007
Tel: (513)745-5600
Admissions: (513)745-5700
Fax: (513)745-5780
Web Site: http://www.rwc.uc.edu/
Description: State-supported, 2-year, coed. Part of University of Cincinnati System. Awards certificates, transfer associate, and terminal associate degrees. Founded 1967. Setting: 120-acre suburban campus. Endowment: $43,625. Educational spending for 2005 fiscal year: $8965 per student. Total enrollment: 4,421. 1,488 applied, 83% were admitted. 3% from top 10% of their high school class, 12% from top quarter, 35% from top half. Full-time: 2,177 students, 64% women, 36% men. Part-time: 2,244 students, 71% women, 29% men. Students come from 19 states and territories, 3% from

out-of-state, 0.3% Native American, 2% Hispanic, 15% black, 2% Asian American or Pacific Islander, 0.03% international, 41% 25 or older, 6% transferred in. Academic remediation for entering students, ESL program, services for LD students, advanced placement, accelerated degree program, self-designed majors, honors program, distance learning, double major, summer session for credit, part-time degree program, adult/continuing education programs, co-op programs and internships. Off campus study at 12 members of the Greater Cincinnati Consortium of Colleges and Universities. Study abroad program. ROTC: Army (c), Air Force (c).
Entrance Requirements: Open admission except for allied health programs. Options: electronic application, deferred admission, international baccalaureate accepted. Required: high school transcript. Entrance: noncompetitive. Application deadline: Rolling. Notification: continuous.
Costs Per Year: Application fee: $35. State resident tuition: $4938 full-time, $142 per quarter hour part-time. Nonresident tuition: $12,801 full-time, $336 per quarter hour part-time. Mandatory fees: $222 full-time.
Collegiate Environment: Orientation program. Drama-theater group, choral group, marching band, student-run newspaper. Social organizations: 15 open to all; national fraternities, national sororities, local fraternities, local sororities; 2% of eligible men and 2% of eligible women are members. Most popular organizations: student government, African-American Cultural Association, Phi Theta Kappa, College Secretaries International, American Dental Hygiene Students Association. Major annual events: Honors Ceremony, End of Year Picnic. Student services: health clinic, personal-psychological counseling, women's center. Campus security: 24-hour emergency response devices and patrols, student patrols, late night transport-escort service. College housing not available. Raymond Walters College Library with 48,226 books, 15,225 microform titles, 636 serials, 2,220 audiovisual materials, an OPAC, and a Web page. Operations spending for 2004 fiscal year: $666,479. 250 computers available on campus for general student use. A campuswide network can be accessed from off-campus. Staffed computer lab on campus.
Community Environment: See University of Cincinnati.

■ **UNIVERSITY OF DAYTON** *I-3*
300 College Park
Dayton, OH 45469-1300
Tel: (937)229-1000
Free: 800-837-7433
Admissions: (937)229-4411
Fax: (937)229-4545
E-mail: admission@udayton.edu
Web Site: http://www.udayton.edu/
Description: Independent Roman Catholic, university, coed. Awards bachelor's, master's, doctoral, and first professional degrees and post-master's certificates. Founded 1850. Setting: 110-acre suburban campus with easy access to Cincinnati. Endowment: $324.4 million. Research spending for 2004 fiscal year: $64.2 million. Educational spending for 2005 fiscal year: $8595 per student. Total enrollment: 10,572. Faculty: 896 (446 full-time, 450 part-time). Student-undergrad faculty ratio is 14:1. 8,675 applied, 80% were admitted. 24% from top 10% of their high school class, 50% from top quarter, 80% from top half. 17 National Merit Scholars, 49 valedictorians. Full-time: 6,913 students, 50% women, 50% men. Part-time: 513 students, 45% women, 55% men. Students come from 49 states and territories, 25 other countries, 33% from out-of-state, 0.2% Native American, 2% Hispanic, 4% black, 1% Asian American or Pacific Islander, 0.4% international, 3% 25 or older, 79% live on campus, 2% transferred in. Retention: 86% of full-time freshmen returned the following year. Academic areas with the most degrees conferred: business/marketing; education; engineering. Core. Calendar: semesters plus 2 6-week summer terms. Academic remediation for entering students, ESL program, services for LD students, advanced placement, accelerated degree program, self-designed majors, honors program, independent study, distance learning, double major, summer session for credit, part-time degree program, adult/continuing education programs, co-op programs and internships, graduate courses open to undergrads. Off campus study at Southwestern Ohio Council for Higher Education, Chaminade University of Honolulu, St. Mary's University. Study abroad program. ROTC: Army, Air Force (c).
Entrance Requirements: Options: electronic application, deferred admission, international baccalaureate accepted. Required: high school transcript, 1 recommendation, SAT or ACT. Recommended: essay, interview. Required for some: audition required for music, music therapy, music education programs. Entrance: moderately difficult. Application deadline: Rolling. Notification: continuous.

Costs Per Year: Application fee: $0. Comprehensive fee: $29,626 includes full-time tuition ($22,046), mandatory fees ($800), and college room and board ($6780). College room only: $4000. Full-time tuition and fees vary according to program. Room and board charges vary according to board plan, housing facility, and student level. Part-time tuition: $708 per credit hour. Part-time mandatory fees: $25 per term. Part-time tuition and fees vary according to course load and program.

Collegiate Environment: Orientation program. Drama-theater group, choral group, marching band, student-run newspaper, radio station. Social organizations: 200 open to all; national fraternities, national sororities, local fraternities, local sororities; 15% of eligible men and 19% of eligible women are members. Most popular organizations: Student Government Association, marching band, Red Scare (basketball student cheering section), Campus Connection, Chi Omega. Major annual events: Christmas on Campus, Parents' Weekend, graduation. Student services: health clinic, personal-psychological counseling, women's center. Campus security: 24-hour emergency response devices and patrols, student patrols, late night transport-escort service, controlled dormitory access. 5,904 college housing spaces available; 5,313 were occupied in 2003-04. Freshmen guaranteed college housing. On-campus residence required through sophomore year. Options: coed, men-only, women-only housing available. Roesch Library plus 2 others with 905,924 books, 795,807 microform titles, 7,554 serials, 3,030 audiovisual materials, an OPAC, and a Web page. Operations spending for 2004 fiscal year: $8.8 million. 8,000 computers available on campus for general student use. Computer purchase/lease plans available. A campuswide network can be accessed from student residence rooms and from off campus. Staffed computer lab on campus.

Community Environment: See Wright State University.

■ **THE UNIVERSITY OF FINDLAY** *E-4*
1000 North Main St.
Findlay, OH 45840-3653
Tel: (419)422-8313
Free: 800-548-0932
Admissions: (419)434-4732
Fax: (419)424-4822
Web Site: http://www.findlay.edu/

Description: Independent, comprehensive, coed, affiliated with Church of God. Awards associate, bachelor's, and master's degrees. Founded 1882. Setting: 200-acre small town campus with easy access to Toledo. Endowment: $18.5 million. Research spending for 2004 fiscal year: $245,379. Educational spending for 2005 fiscal year: $6294 per student. Total enrollment: 4,743. Faculty: 339 (175 full-time, 164 part-time). Student-undergrad faculty ratio is 15:1. 2,485 applied, 70% were admitted. 22% from top 10% of their high school class, 49% from top quarter, 80% from top half. 55 valedictorians. Full-time: 2,648 students, 60% women, 40% men. Part-time: 953 students, 61% women, 39% men. Students come from 45 states and territories, 34 other countries, 13% from out-of-state, 0.3% Native American, 1% Hispanic, 2% black, 1% Asian American or Pacific Islander, 4% international, 24% 25 or older, 41% live on campus, 4% transferred in. Retention: 74% of full-time freshmen returned the following year. Academic areas with the most degrees conferred: business/marketing; health professions and related sciences; education. Core. Calendar: semesters. Academic remediation for entering students, ESL program, services for LD students, advanced placement, accelerated degree program, self-designed majors, honors program, independent study, distance learning, double major, summer session for credit, part-time degree program, adult/continuing education programs, co-op programs and internships, graduate courses open to undergrads. Off campus study. Study abroad program. ROTC: Army (c), Air Force (c).

Entrance Requirements: Options: Peterson's Universal Application, Common Application, electronic application, deferred admission, international baccalaureate accepted. Required: essay, high school transcript, minimum 2.3 high school GPA, recommendations, SAT or ACT. Required for some: interview. Entrance: moderately difficult. Application deadline: Rolling. Notification: continuous.

Costs Per Year: Application fee: $0. Comprehensive fee: $29,238 includes full-time tuition ($20,796), mandatory fees ($950), and college room and board ($7492). College room only: $3756. Full-time tuition and fees vary according to location and program. Room and board charges vary according to housing facility. Part-time tuition: $458 per semester hour. Part-time mandatory fees: $125 per term. Part-time tuition and fees vary according to location and program.

Collegiate Environment: Orientation program. Drama-theater group, choral group, marching band, student-run newspaper, radio station. Social

organizations: 57 open to all; national fraternities, national sororities; 5% of eligible men and 2% of eligible women are members. Most popular organizations: Campus Program Board, Pre-Vet Club, Horse Club, Circle K, International Club. Major annual events: Homecoming, Family Weekend, Spring Bash. Student services: health clinic, personal-psychological counseling, women's center. Campus security: 24-hour emergency response devices and patrols, late night transport-escort service. 1,215 college housing spaces available; 1,146 were occupied in 2003-04. Freshmen guaranteed college housing. On-campus residence required through junior year. Options: coed, men-only, women-only housing available. Shafer Library with 132,052 books, 11,589 microform titles, 23,128 serials, 4,780 audiovisual materials, and an OPAC. Operations spending for 2004 fiscal year: $848,206. 200 computers available on campus for general student use. Computer purchase/lease plans available. A campuswide network can be accessed from student residence rooms and from off campus. Staffed computer lab on campus.

Community Environment: Findlay is located in the northwestern part of Ohio, which is both a rich agricultural and manufacturing region. Excellent internship and employment opportunities are available. Recreational activities include swimming, golf, boating, and fishing.

■ **UNIVERSITY OF NORTHWESTERN OHIO** *F-3*
1441 North Cable Rd.
Lima, OH 45805-1498
Tel: (419)227-3141
Fax: (419)229-6926
E-mail: info@nc.edu
Web Site: http://www.unoh.edu/

Description: Independent, primarily 2-year, coed. Awards certificates, diplomas, transfer associate, and bachelor's degrees. Founded 1920. Setting: 35-acre small town campus with easy access to Dayton and Toledo. Educational spending for 2005 fiscal year: $2300 per student. Total enrollment: 2,915. Student-undergrad faculty ratio is 20:1. 3,758 applied, 98% were admitted. Full-time: 2,629 students, 17% women, 83% men. Part-time: 286 students, 59% women, 41% men. Students come from 34 states and territories, 30% from out-of-state, 0% Native American, 0.1% Hispanic, 1% black, 0% Asian American or Pacific Islander, 0% international, 18% 25 or older, 45% live on campus, 2% transferred in. Retention: 70% of full-time freshmen returned the following year. Academic areas with the most degrees conferred: business/marketing; health professions and related sciences. Core. Academic remediation for entering students, advanced placement, accelerated degree program, distance learning, double major, summer session for credit, part-time degree program, adult/continuing education programs, co-op programs.

Entrance Requirements: Open admission. Options: electronic application, early admission, deferred admission. Required: high school transcript. Entrance: noncompetitive. Application deadline: Rolling.

Costs Per Year: Application fee: $50. Tuition: $11,400 full-time, $190 per credit hour part-time.

Collegiate Environment: Orientation program. Student-run newspaper. Social organizations: 1 open to all. Most popular organization: Students in Free Enterprise. Major annual events: Mud Volleyball, Car Show, Intramural Volleyball. Student services: personal-psychological counseling. Campus security: 24-hour emergency response devices and patrols, late night transport-escort service. 1,016 college housing spaces available; 705 were occupied in 2003-04. Freshmen guaranteed college housing. Options: men-only, women-only housing available. University of Northwestern Ohio Library with 4,553 books, 95 serials, an OPAC, and a Web page. Operations spending for 2004 fiscal year: $36,715. 149 computers available on campus for general student use. A campuswide network can be accessed from off-campus. Staffed computer lab on campus.

■ **UNIVERSITY OF PHOENIX-CINCINNATI CAMPUS**
9050 Centre Pointe Dr.
West Chester, OH 45069
Tel: (513)772-9600
Free: 800-228-7240
Admissions: (480)557-1712
Web Site: http://www.phoenix.edu/

Description: Proprietary, comprehensive, coed. Awards bachelor's and master's degrees. Founded 2003. Total enrollment: 619. Faculty: 97 (9 full-time, 88 part-time). Student-undergrad faculty ratio is 6:1. 29 applied. Full-time: 407 students, 60% women, 40% men. 0.2% Hispanic, 5% black, 9% international, 94% 25 or older. Academic area with the most degrees conferred: business/marketing. Core. Calendar: continuous. Advanced placement, accelerated degree program, independent study, distance learning, external degree program, adult/continuing education programs, graduate courses open to undergrads.

Entrance Requirements: Open admission. Option: deferred admission. Required: 1 recommendation. Required for some: high school transcript. Entrance: noncompetitive. Application deadline: Rolling.

Costs Per Year: Application fee: $110. Tuition: $11,550 full-time, $385 per credit part-time. Mandatory fees: $560 full-time, $70 per course part-time.

Collegiate Environment: College housing not available. University Library with 444 books, 666 serials, an OPAC, and a Web page. System-wide operations spending for 2004 fiscal year: $3.2 million.

■ UNIVERSITY OF PHOENIX-CLEVELAND CAMPUS *E-19*

5005 Rockside Rd., Ste. 325
Independence, OH 44131-2194
Tel: (216)447-8807
Free: 800-228-7240
Admissions: (480)557-1712
Web Site: http://www.phoenix.edu/

Description: Proprietary, comprehensive, coed. Awards bachelor's and master's degrees. Founded 2000. Setting: urban campus. Total enrollment: 882. Faculty: 166 (8 full-time, 158 part-time). Student-undergrad faculty ratio is 5:1. 29 applied. Full-time: 675 students, 68% women, 32% men. 1% Hispanic, 9% black, 0.3% Asian American or Pacific Islander, 17% international, 95% 25 or older. Academic areas with the most degrees conferred: business/marketing; computer and information sciences; health professions and related sciences. Core. Calendar: continuous. Advanced placement, accelerated degree program, independent study, distance learning, external degree program, adult/continuing education programs, graduate courses open to undergrads.

Entrance Requirements: Open admission. Option: deferred admission. Required: 1 recommendation. Required for some: high school transcript. Entrance: noncompetitive. Application deadline: Rolling.

Costs Per Year: Application fee: $110. Tuition: $11,550 full-time, $385 per credit part-time. Mandatory fees: $560 full-time, $70 per course part-time.

Collegiate Environment: College housing not available. University Library with 444 books, 666 serials, an OPAC, and a Web page. System-wide operations spending for 2004 fiscal year: $3.2 million.

■ UNIVERSITY OF PHOENIX-COLUMBUS OHIO CAMPUS *I-6*

8425 Pulsar Place
Columbus, OH 43240
Tel: (614)433-0095
Free: 800-228-7240
Admissions: (480)557-1712
Web Site: http://www.phoenix.edu/

Description: Proprietary, comprehensive, coed. Awards bachelor's and master's degrees. Founded 2003. Total enrollment: 493. Faculty: 66 (1 full-time, 65 part-time). Student-undergrad faculty ratio is 6:1. 16 applied. Full-time: 332 students, 59% women, 41% men. 0.3% Native American, 0.3% Hispanic, 6% black, 1% Asian American or Pacific Islander, 7% international, 87% 25 or older. Academic areas with the most degrees conferred: business/marketing; computer and information sciences. Core. Calendar: continuous. Advanced placement, accelerated degree program, independent study, distance learning, external degree program, adult/continuing education programs, graduate courses open to undergrads.

Entrance Requirements: Open admission. Option: deferred admission. Required: 1 recommendation. Required for some: high school transcript. Entrance: noncompetitive. Application deadline: Rolling.

Costs Per Year: Application fee: $110. Tuition: $11,550 full-time, $385 per credit part-time. Mandatory fees: $560 full-time, $70 per course part-time.

Collegiate Environment: College housing not available. 444 books, 666 serials, an OPAC, and a Web page. System-wide operations spending for 2004 fiscal year: $3.2 million.

■ UNIVERSITY OF RIO GRANDE

218 North College Ave.
Rio Grande, OH 45674
Tel: (740)245-5353
Admissions: (740)245-7208
Fax: (740)245-9220
E-mail: gsojka@rio.edu
Web Site: http://www.rio.edu/

Description: Independent, comprehensive, coed. Awards associate, bachelor's, and master's degrees. Founded 1876. Setting: 170-acre rural campus. Endowment: $19.5 million. Educational spending for 2005 fiscal year: $6646 per student. Total enrollment: 2,376. Faculty: 265 (81 full-time, 184 part-time). Student-undergrad faculty ratio is 18:1. 12% from top 10% of their high school class, 31% from top quarter, 65% from top half. Full-time: 1,699 students, 59% women, 41% men. Part-time: 442 students, 70% women, 30% men. Students come from 13 states and territories, 7 other countries, 5% from out-of-state, 0.2% Native American, 1% Hispanic, 3% black, 1% Asian American or Pacific Islander, 1% international, 34% 25 or older, 25% live on campus, 3% transferred in. Retention: 60% of full-time freshmen returned the following year. Academic areas with the most degrees conferred: business/marketing; education; health professions and related sciences. Core. Calendar: semesters. Academic remediation for entering students, ESL program, services for LD students, advanced placement, accelerated degree program, self-designed majors, freshman honors college, honors program, independent study, distance learning, summer session for credit, part-time degree program, adult/continuing education programs, co-op programs and internships. Study abroad program. ROTC: Army (c).

Entrance Requirements: Open admission except for nursing, red tech, education, social work. Options: Peterson's Universal Application, Common Application, electronic application. Required: high school transcript, medical history. Recommended: ACT. Entrance: noncompetitive. Application deadline: Rolling. Notification: continuous.

Costs Per Year: Application fee: $25. Area resident tuition: $12,540 full-time, $517 per semester hour part-time. State resident tuition: $12,750 full-time, $528 per semester hour part-time. Nonresident tuition: $13,132 full-time, $571 per semester hour part-time. Mandatory fees: $525 full-time, $13 per semester hour part-time, $91. Full-time tuition and fees vary according to course load, degree level, and program. Part-time tuition and fees vary according to course load, degree level, and program. College room and board: $6404. Room and board charges vary according to board plan.

Collegiate Environment: Orientation program. Drama-theater group, choral group, student-run newspaper, radio station. Social organizations: 41 open to all; national fraternities, local fraternities, local sororities; 5% of eligible men and 4% of eligible women are members. Most popular organizations: student government, Honoraries, Bible studies, Students in Free Enterprise. Major annual events: Community Service Day, Homecoming, Muscular Dystrophy Dance-a-thon. Student services: health clinic, personal-psychological counseling. Campus security: 24-hour emergency response devices and patrols, late night transport-escort service, controlled dormitory access. 630 college housing spaces available; 392 were occupied in 2003-04. No special consideration for freshman housing applicants. Options: coed, men-only, women-only housing available. Jeanette Albiez Davis Library plus 2 others with 96,731 books, 850 serials, an OPAC, and a Web page. Operations spending for 2004 fiscal year: $353,505. 300 computers available on campus for general student use. A campuswide network can be accessed from student residence rooms and from off campus. Staffed computer lab on campus.

Community Environment: Less than one mile from campus, the Bob Evans Farm offers canoe and horse rentals, trail rides, hiking, and fishing. A radio-controlled aircraft club meets monthly in good weather. The second weekend of October marks the annual Bob Evans Farm Festival, which brings visitors from surrounding states. Rio Grande students participate heavily in the Farm Festival as part of "Community Service Day" when most college classes are canceled. Annual campus-hosted events include World-Fest, Native American Pow Wow, and Celtic/Welsh festivals. Other recreational facilities within a reasonable driving distance include golf, boating, skiing, rock climbing, white-water rafting, camping, and fishing. A rural community, Rio Grande is located 90 miles southeast of Columbus, 130 miles east of Cincinnati, and 60 miles north of Charleston, WV. Local shopping is found in Jackson and Gallipolis, both within 20 miles. Lare malls are found in Charleston and Huntington, WV, both about 60 miles away. Gallipolis is a picturesque river town, settled on the banks of the Ohio River, one of the annual stops for the historic Delta Queen steamboat. The surrounding area includes active civic and service organizations, church groups, shopping facilities, the Holzer Medical Center, and Holzer Clinic. The Ohio Valley Symphony, the Valley Artist Series, and the French Art Colony provide music, theater, and fine arts cultural events and exhibits. Performances are held either on campus at the Merlyn Ross Fine Arts Center or in Gallipolis at the refurbished Victorian playhouse, the Ari

■ THE UNIVERSITY OF TOLEDO *B-5*

2801 West Bancroft
Toledo, OH 43606-3390

Tel: (419)530-4636
Admissions: (419)530-5737
Fax: (419)530-4940
E-mail: adm0017@uofT01.utoledo.edu
Web Site: http://www.utoledo.edu/

Description: State-supported, university, coed. Awards associate, bachelor's, master's, doctoral, and first professional degrees and post-master's certificates. Founded 1872. Setting: 407-acre suburban campus with easy access to Detroit. Endowment: $35.3 million. Research spending for 2004 fiscal year: $16.3 million. Educational spending for 2005 fiscal year: $7495 per student. Total enrollment: 19,480. 8,819 applied, 99% were admitted. 16% from top 10% of their high school class, 36% from top quarter, 63% from top half. Full-time: 13,146 students, 50% women, 50% men. Part-time: 3,220 students, 54% women, 46% men. Students come from 36 states and territories, 93 other countries, 8% from out-of-state, 0.2% Native American, 2% Hispanic, 12% black, 2% Asian American or Pacific Islander, 2% international, 17% 25 or older, 18% live on campus, 7% transferred in. Retention: 72% of full-time freshmen returned the following year. Core. Calendar: semesters. Academic remediation for entering students, services for LD students, advanced placement, self-designed majors, honors program, independent study, distance learning, double major, summer session for credit, part-time degree program, adult/continuing education programs, co-op programs and internships, graduate courses open to undergrads. Off campus study at Bowling Green State University, Medical College of Ohio, Consortium for Health Education, The Central States Universities, Inc. Study abroad program. ROTC: Army, Air Force (c).

Entrance Requirements: Open admission for state residents. Options: electronic application, deferred admission, international baccalaureate accepted. Required: high school transcript, SAT or ACT. Required for some: minimum 2.0 high school GPA. Entrance: noncompetitive. Application deadline: Rolling. Notification: continuous.

Costs Per Year: Application fee: $40. State resident tuition: $6430 full-time, $311 per semester hour part-time. Nonresident tuition: $15,241 full-time, $679 per semester hour part-time. Mandatory fees: $1064 full-time. Full-time tuition and fees vary according to course load, program, and reciprocity agreements. Part-time tuition varies according to course load, program, and reciprocity agreements. College room and board: $8312. Room and board charges vary according to board plan, housing facility, and location.

Collegiate Environment: Orientation program. Drama-theater group, choral group, marching band, student-run newspaper, radio station. Social organizations: 176 open to all; national fraternities, national sororities, local fraternities, local sororities; 6% of eligible men and 3% of eligible women are members. Most popular organizations: student government, University YMCA, Newman Club, International Student Association, Campus Activities and Programming. Major annual events: homecoming, Songfest, Carnival Royale and Activities Fair. Student services: legal services, health clinic, personal-psychological counseling, women's center. Campus security: 24-hour emergency response devices and patrols, student patrols, late night transport-escort service, controlled dormitory access, bicycle patrols by security staff, crime prevention officer. On-campus residence required in freshman year. Options: coed, women-only housing available. Carlson Library plus 4 others with 1.8 million books, 1.7 million microform titles, 6,500 serials, 6,350 audiovisual materials, an OPAC, and a Web page. Operations spending for 2004 fiscal year: $8.2 million. 2,800 computers available on campus for general student use. A campuswide network can be accessed from student residence rooms and from off campus. Staffed computer lab on campus.

Community Environment: Toledo's importance as a port stems from its location at the mouth of the Maumee River. It is the busiest freshwater port in the world. It ranks second on the Great Lakes, and ninth in the nation in tonnage handled.

■ **URBANA UNIVERSITY** *H-4*
579 College Way
Urbana, OH 43078-2091
Tel: (937)484-1400
Free: 800-7-URBANA
Admissions: (937)484-1356
Fax: (937)484-1389
Web Site: http://www.urbana.edu/

Description: Independent, comprehensive, coed, affiliated with Church of the New Jerusalem. Awards associate, bachelor's, and master's degrees. Founded 1850. Setting: 128-acre small town campus with easy access to Columbus and Dayton. Endowment: $415,000. Educational spending for 2005 fiscal year: $14,220 per student. Total enrollment: 1,551. Faculty: 120 (55 full-time, 65 part-time). Student-undergrad faculty ratio is 16:1. 495 applied, 65% were admitted. Full-time: 904 students, 46% women, 54% men. Part-time: 557 students, 64% women, 36% men. 4% from out-of-state, 0.4% Native American, 1% Hispanic, 12% black, 1% Asian American or Pacific Islander, 1% international, 6% transferred in. Retention: 70% of full-time freshmen returned the following year. Academic areas with the most degrees conferred: education; health professions and related sciences; security and protective services. Core. Calendar: semesters. Academic remediation for entering students, services for LD students, advanced placement, accelerated degree program, self-designed majors, freshman honors college, honors program, independent study, double major, summer session for credit, part-time degree program, adult/continuing education programs, co-op programs and internships. Off campus study at members of the Southwestern Ohio Council for Higher Education.

Entrance Requirements: Options: electronic application, deferred admission. Required: essay, high school transcript, minimum 2.0 high school GPA, SAT or ACT. Recommended: recommendations, interview. Required for some: 2 recommendations. Entrance: moderately difficult. Application deadline: Rolling. Notification: continuous.

Costs Per Year: Application fee: $25. Comprehensive fee: $22,866 includes full-time tuition ($16,254) and college room and board ($6612). College room only: $2234. Part-time tuition: $337 per semester hour.

Collegiate Environment: Orientation program. Drama-theater group, choral group, marching band, student-run newspaper, radio station. Social organizations: 20 open to all. Most popular organizations: Student Government Association, Business Club, Education Club, Drama Club, Student Activities Planning Committee. Major annual events: Homecoming, Spring Fling Week, Founders' Day. Student services: health clinic, personal-psychological counseling. Campus security: 24-hour emergency response devices and patrols, late night transport-escort service. 450 college housing spaces available. No special consideration for freshman housing applicants. On-campus residence required through junior year. Options: coed, men-only, women-only housing available. Swedenborg Memorial Library with 61,600 books, 10,000 microform titles, 800 serials, 22,036 audiovisual materials, an OPAC, and a Web page. 75 computers available on campus for general student use. A campuswide network can be accessed from student residence rooms. Staffed computer lab on campus.

Community Environment: Urbana is the county seat of Champaign county and has a population in excess of 12,000 residents. The community has become well known regionally for the restoration of the historic downtown business district. The community provides a modern small-town environment with easy access to major metropolitan areas, being located just 15 minutes from downtown Springfield and 45 minutes from Dayton and Columbus.

■ **URSULINE COLLEGE** *D-20*
2550 Lander Rd.
Pepper Pike, OH 44124-4398
Tel: (440)449-4200; 888-URSULINE
Admissions: (440)449-4203
Fax: (440)449-2235
Web Site: http://www.ursuline.edu/

Description: Independent Roman Catholic, comprehensive. Awards bachelor's and master's degrees and post-master's certificates (applications from men are also accepted). Founded 1871. Setting: 112-acre suburban campus with easy access to Cleveland. Endowment: $20.8 million. Educational spending for 2005 fiscal year: $7451 per student. Total enrollment: 1,494. Faculty: 212 (72 full-time, 140 part-time). Student-undergrad faculty ratio is 9:1. 439 applied, 65% were admitted. 40% from top 10% of their high school class, 51% from top quarter, 87% from top half. Full-time: 755 students, 95% women, 5% men. Part-time: 397 students, 88% women, 12% men. Students come from 6 states and territories, 6 other countries, 1% from out-of-state, 0.4% Native American, 2% Hispanic, 26% black, 1% Asian American or Pacific Islander, 1% international, 53% 25 or older, 14% live on campus, 14% transferred in. Retention: 65% of full-time freshmen returned the following year. Academic areas with the most degrees conferred: health professions and related sciences; business/marketing; education. Core. Calendar: semesters. Academic remediation for entering students, services for LD students, advanced placement, accelerated degree program, independent study, distance learning, double major, summer session for credit, part-time degree program, adult/continuing education programs, co-op programs and internships, graduate courses open to undergrads. Off campus study at Baldwin-Wallace College, Case Western Reserve University, Cleveland State University, Cuyahoga Community College, David N. Myers College, Notre Dame College of Ohio, John Carroll University.

Entrance Requirements: Options: Peterson's Universal Application, early action, deferred admission. Required: essay, high school transcript, SAT or ACT. Recommended: minimum 2.0 high school GPA, recommendations, interview. Entrance: minimally difficult. Application deadlines: Rolling, 11/15 for early action. Notification: continuous, 2/15 for early action.

Costs Per Year: Application fee: $25. Comprehensive fee: $25,456 includes full-time tuition ($18,900), mandatory fees ($190), and college room and board ($6366). College room only: $3252. Room and board charges vary according to board plan. Part-time tuition: $630 per credit hour. Part-time mandatory fees: $60 per term.

Collegiate Environment: Orientation program. Drama-theater group, choral group. Social organizations: 29 open to all. Most popular organizations: Student Government Association, Student Nurses of Ursuline College, Fashion Focus, Students United for Black Awareness, Drama Club. Major annual events: Founders' Day, All College Day, Fall Formal. Student services: personal-psychological counseling. Campus security: 24-hour emergency response devices and patrols, late night transport-escort service, controlled dormitory access. 164 college housing spaces available; all were occupied in 2003-04. Freshmen given priority for college housing. Ralph M. Besse Library with 108,699 books, 4,675 microform titles, 12,989 serials, 5,329 audiovisual materials, an OPAC, and a Web page. Operations spending for 2004 fiscal year: $537,581. 72 computers available on campus for general student use. A campuswide network can be accessed from student residence rooms. Staffed computer lab on campus.

Community Environment: See Case Western Reserve University.

■ **VATTEROTT COLLEGE** *F-18*

5025 East Royalton Rd.
Broadview Heights, OH 44147
Tel: (440)526-1660
Free: 800-864-5644
Fax: (440)526-1933
Web Site: http://www.vatterott-college.edu/

Description: Proprietary, 2-year, coed. Total enrollment: 143. Calendar: semesters.

■ **VIRGINIA MARTI COLLEGE OF ART AND DESIGN** *C-10*

11724 Detroit Ave., PO Box 580
Lakewood, OH 44107-3002
Tel: (216)221-8584
Web Site: http://www.vmcad.edu/

Description: Proprietary, 2-year, coed. Awards diplomas and terminal associate degrees. Founded 1966. Setting: urban campus with easy access to Cleveland. Total enrollment: 267. 56 applied, 59% were admitted. Students come from 2 states and territories, 60% 25 or older. Academic remediation for entering students, ESL program, self-designed majors, summer session for credit, part-time degree program, adult/continuing education programs, co-op programs and internships. Study abroad program.

Entrance Requirements: Options: early admission, deferred admission. Required: minimum 2.0 high school GPA, interview, CAPS. Entrance: minimally difficult. Application deadline: Rolling.

Collegiate Environment: Student-run newspaper. Student services: personal-psychological counseling. Campus security: 24-hour emergency response devices. College housing not available. 12 computers available on campus for general student use. Staffed computer lab on campus.

■ **WALSH UNIVERSITY** *E-11*

2020 East Maple St., NW
North Canton, OH 44720-3396
Tel: (330)499-7090
Free: 800-362-8846
Admissions: (330)490-7171
Fax: (330)490-7165
E-mail: admissions@walsh.edu
Web Site: http://www.walsh.edu/

Description: Independent Roman Catholic, comprehensive, coed. Awards associate, bachelor's, and master's degrees. Founded 1958. Setting: 107-acre small town campus with easy access to Cleveland. Endowment: $6.4 million. Educational spending for 2005 fiscal year: $5432 per student. Total enrollment: 2,183. Faculty: 189 (82 full-time, 107 part-time). Student-undergrad faculty ratio is 14:1. 1,179 applied, 80% were admitted. 15% from top 10% of their high school class, 42% from top quarter, 75% from top half. 4 valedictorians. Full-time: 1,415 students, 61% women, 39% men. Part-time: 444 students, 72% women, 28% men. Students come from 17 states and territories, 8 other countries, 3% from out-of-state, 0.4% Native American, 1% Hispanic, 6% black, 1% Asian American or Pacific Islander, 2% international, 28% 25 or older, 50% live on campus, 7% transferred in. Retention: 78% of full-time freshmen returned the following year. Academic areas with the most degrees conferred: business/marketing; education; health professions and related sciences. Core. Calendar: semesters. Academic remediation for entering students, ESL program, services for LD students, advanced placement, accelerated degree program, freshman honors college, honors program, independent study, double major, summer session for credit, part-time degree program, adult/continuing education programs, internships, graduate courses open to undergrads. Off campus study at University of Michigan, Case Western Reserve University, Stark State College of Technology, Cooperative Center for Study Abroad. Study abroad program.

Entrance Requirements: Options: Common Application, electronic application, early admission, deferred admission. Required: high school transcript, minimum 2.3 high school GPA, SAT or ACT. Recommended: interview. Required for some: essay, minimum 3.0 high school GPA, 2 recommendations. Entrance: moderately difficult. Application deadlines: Rolling, Rolling for nonresidents. Notification: continuous, continuous for nonresidents.

Costs Per Year: Application fee: $25. Comprehensive fee: $24,850 includes full-time tuition ($17,150), mandatory fees ($570), and college room and board ($7130). College room only: $4870. Part-time tuition: $570 per credit hour. Part-time mandatory fees: $19 per credit hour.

Collegiate Environment: Orientation program. Drama-theater group, choral group, student-run newspaper, radio station. Social organizations: 30 open to all; 25% of eligible men and 25% of eligible women are members. Most popular organizations: Walsh University Student Government, Circle K, Business and Communication Club, Behavioral Science Club, Education Club. Major annual events: Homecoming, Walshfest, Finals Week Late Night Breakfast. Student services: health clinic, personal-psychological counseling. Campus security: 24-hour emergency response devices and patrols, controlled dormitory access. 728 college housing spaces available; 613 were occupied in 2003-04. Freshmen guaranteed college housing. On-campus residence required through senior year. Options: coed, men-only, women-only housing available. Brother Edmond Drouin Library with 136,268 books, 8,586 microform titles, 605 serials, 1,749 audiovisual materials, an OPAC, and a Web page. Operations spending for 2004 fiscal year: $555,575. 262 computers available on campus for general student use. A campuswide network can be accessed from student residence rooms and from off campus. Staffed computer lab on campus.

Community Environment: Walsh University is conveniently located and easily accessible, near Ohio Interstate 77 in North Canton, a residential suburban area. The Walsh campus, near Canton, which city of about 84,000 with a wide array of cultural, recreational, and athletic activities. Home of the Professional Football Hall of Fame and the President McKinley National Memorial, the city boasts a symphony orchestra, art institute, civic opera, theater guild, and ballet. A number of major employers are headquartered in Stark County, including the Hoover Company, the Timken Company, and Diebold, Inc. 20 miles north of campus is Akron, and within an hour's drive is Cleveland. The Akron-Canton Regional Airport, is north of campus and serves the Canton-Stark County area, as do Amtrak trains and Greyhound buses.

■ **WASHINGTON STATE COMMUNITY COLLEGE** *K-11*

710 Colegate Dr.
Marietta, OH 45750-9225
Tel: (740)374-8716
Fax: (740)376-0257
Web Site: http://www.wscc.edu/

Description: State-supported, 2-year, coed. Part of Ohio Board of Regents. Awards certificates, transfer associate, and terminal associate degrees. Founded 1971. Setting: small town campus. Total enrollment: 2,086. Full-time: 1,174 students, 63% women, 37% men. Part-time: 912 students, 60% women, 40% men. Students come from 5 states and territories, 1% Native American, 1% Hispanic, 1% black, 0.4% Asian American or Pacific Islander, 0.05% international, 50% 25 or older. Retention: 52% of full-time freshmen returned the following year. Core. Academic remediation for entering students, services for LD students, self-designed majors, independent study, double major, summer session for credit, part-time degree program, adult/continuing education programs, internships.

Entrance Requirements: Open admission except for medical laboratory technology, nursing programs. Options: early admission, deferred admission. Recommended: high school transcript. Required for some: high school transcript. Placement: ACT ASSET required. Entrance: noncompetitive. Application deadline: Rolling. Notification: continuous.

Collegiate Environment: Choral group. Social organizations: 14 open to all. Most popular organizations: Student Senate, Phi Theta Kappa, Practical Nursing Club, Business Lunch Club, Beta Club. Student services: personal-psychological counseling. College housing not available. 15,000 books and 200 serials. 175 computers available on campus for general student use. Staffed computer lab on campus.

■ WILBERFORCE UNIVERSITY *J-18*

1055 North Bickett Rd.
Wilberforce, OH 45384
Tel: (937)376-2911
Free: 800-367-8568
Admissions: (937)708-5789
Fax: (937)376-4751
E-mail: admissions@shorter.wilberforce.edu
Web Site: http://www.wilberforce.edu/

Description: Independent, 4-year, coed, affiliated with African Methodist Episcopal Church. Awards bachelor's degrees. Founded 1856. Setting: 125-acre rural campus with easy access to Dayton. Endowment: $9.3 million. Total enrollment: 998. 2,405 applied, 22% were admitted. Full-time: 982 students, 61% women, 39% men. Part-time: 16 students, 44% women, 56% men. Students come from 30 states and territories, 3 other countries, 38% from out-of-state, 0.3% Native American, 1% Hispanic, 90% black, 0.2% Asian American or Pacific Islander, 1% international, 32% 25 or older, 85% live on campus, 3% transferred in. Retention: 62% of full-time freshmen returned the following year. Core. Calendar: semesters. Academic remediation for entering students, advanced placement, freshman honors college, honors program, external degree program, co-op programs. Off campus study at 18 members of the Southwestern Ohio Council for Higher Education. Study abroad program. ROTC: Army (c), Air Force (c).

Entrance Requirements: Options: Peterson's Universal Application, Common Application, electronic application, early admission, deferred admission. Required: essay, high school transcript, minimum 2.0 high school GPA, 2 recommendations, SAT or ACT. Recommended: interview. Entrance: minimally difficult. Application deadline: 7/1. Notification: continuous until 8/1.

Costs Per Year: Application fee: $20. Comprehensive fee: $16,100 includes full-time tuition ($9720), mandatory fees ($1060), and college room and board ($5320). Part-time tuition: $376 per credit hour.

Collegiate Environment: Orientation program. Drama-theater group, choral group, student-run newspaper, radio station. Social organizations: national fraternities, national sororities. Most popular organizations: yearbook staff, campus radio station, National Student Business League, Student Government Association. Major annual events: Homecoming/Parents' Weekend, Dawn Dance, Black History Month. Student services: health clinic, personal-psychological counseling. Campus security: 24-hour emergency response devices and patrols, controlled dormitory access. 787 college housing spaces available; 652 were occupied in 2003-04. On-campus residence required through junior year. Options: coed, men-only, women-only housing available. Rembert E. Stokes Library with 63,000 books, 10,000 microform titles, 650 serials, 500 audiovisual materials, an OPAC, and a Web page. 77 computers available on campus for general student use. A campuswide network can be accessed from student residence rooms and from off campus. Staffed computer lab on campus.

Community Environment: Located in rural village of Wilberforce with a history of significant activity in the underground railroad of pre-Civil War days. The city of Xenia, Ohio is nearby with a population of 25,000 and is a good shopping center. It provides a resource for field study, cultural and recreational activities plus the close urban centers of Dayton, Springfield, Columbus and Cincinnati.

■ WILMINGTON COLLEGE *J-4*

Pyle Center Box 1185
Wilmington, OH 45177
Tel: (937)382-6661
Free: 800-341-9318
Fax: (937)382-7077
E-mail: admission@wilmington.edu
Web Site: http://www.wilmington.edu/

Description: Independent Friends, comprehensive, coed. Awards bachelor's and master's degrees. Founded 1870. Setting: 1,465-acre small town campus with easy access to Cincinnati and Columbus. Endowment: $19 million. Total enrollment: 1,764. Faculty: 97 (71 full-time, 26 part-time). Student-

undergrad faculty ratio is 14:1. 1,409 applied, 98% were admitted. Full-time: 1,383 students, 53% women, 47% men. Part-time: 340 students, 57% women, 43% men. Students come from 15 states and territories, 6 other countries, 4% from out-of-state, 12% 25 or older, 62% live on campus, 4% transferred in. Retention: 73% of full-time freshmen returned the following year. Academic areas with the most degrees conferred: business/marketing; education; social sciences. Core. Calendar: semesters. Academic remediation for entering students, services for LD students, advanced placement, accelerated degree program, self-designed majors, honors program, double major, summer session for credit, part-time degree program, adult/continuing education programs, internships. Off campus study at members of the Southwestern Ohio Council for Higher Education, Greater Cincinnati Consortium of Colleges and Universities. Study abroad program.

Entrance Requirements: Options: Peterson's Universal Application, Common Application, deferred admission. Required: high school transcript, SAT or ACT. Recommended: minimum 2.5 high school GPA, 1 recommendation, interview. Entrance: moderately difficult. Application deadline: Rolling. Notification: continuous.

Costs Per Year: Comprehensive fee: $27,016 includes full-time tuition ($19,206), mandatory fees ($756), and college room and board ($7054). College room only: $3330. Room and board charges vary according to board plan and housing facility. Part-time tuition: $785 per credit. Part-time tuition varies according to course load.

Collegiate Environment: Orientation program. Drama-theater group, choral group, student-run newspaper. Social organizations: 49 open to all; national fraternities, local fraternities, local sororities; 7% of eligible men and 11% of eligible women are members. Most popular organizations: Aggie Club, Quest, student publications, Commuter Concerns. Major annual events: Homecoming, Community Day, Westheimer Peace Symposium. Student services: health clinic, personal-psychological counseling. Campus security: 24-hour emergency response devices and patrols, late night transport-escort service, controlled dormitory access. 833 college housing spaces available; 820 were occupied in 2003-04. On-campus residence required through senior year. Options: coed, women-only housing available. Watson Library plus 1 other with 103,706 books, 41,151 microform titles, 408 serials, 1,280 audiovisual materials, and an OPAC. 80 computers available on campus for general student use. A campuswide network can be accessed from student residence rooms and from off campus. Staffed computer lab on campus.

■ WITTENBERG UNIVERSITY *I-4*

PO Box 720
Springfield, OH 45501-0720
Tel: (937)327-6231
Free: 800-677-7558
Admissions: (937)327-6314
Fax: (937)327-6379
E-mail: admission@wittenberg.edu
Web Site: http://www.wittenberg.edu/

Description: Independent, comprehensive, coed, affiliated with Evangelical Lutheran Church. Awards bachelor's and master's degrees. Founded 1845. Setting: 71-acre suburban campus with easy access to Columbus and Dayton. Endowment: $107.4 million. Research spending for 2004 fiscal year: $116,510. Educational spending for 2005 fiscal year: $11,074 per student. Total enrollment: 2,093. Faculty: 202 (148 full-time, 54 part-time). Student-undergrad faculty ratio is 12:1. 2,479 applied, 85% were admitted. 27% from top 10% of their high school class, 56% from top quarter, 83% from top half. Full-time: 1,930 students, 57% women, 43% men. Part-time: 148 students, 66% women, 34% men. Students come from 38 states and territories, 14 other countries, 25% from out-of-state, 0.3% Native American, 1% Hispanic, 5% black, 1% Asian American or Pacific Islander, 2% international, 4% 25 or older, 86% live on campus, 2% transferred in. Retention: 78% of full-time freshmen returned the following year. Academic areas with the most degrees conferred: business/marketing; education; social sciences. Core. Calendar: semesters. Academic remediation for entering students, ESL program, advanced placement, accelerated degree program, self-designed majors, freshman honors college, honors program, independent study, double major, summer session for credit, part-time degree program, adult/continuing education programs, co-op programs and internships. Off campus study at 21 members of the Southwestern Ohio Council for Higher Education. Study abroad program. ROTC: Army (c), Air Force (c).

Entrance Requirements: Options: Peterson's Universal Application, Common Application, electronic application, early admission, early decision, early action, deferred admission, international baccalaureate accepted. Required: essay, high school transcript, minimum X high school GPA, interview, SAT or

ACT. Recommended: recommendations. Entrance: moderately difficult. Application deadlines: 11/15 for early decision, 12/1 for early action. Notification: continuous, 1/1 for early decision, 2/1 for early action. Preference given to Lutherans, children of alumni, county residents, minorities.

Costs Per Year: Application fee: $40. Comprehensive fee: $36,778 includes full-time tuition ($29,080), mandatory fees ($200), and college room and board ($7498). College room only: $3890. Part-time tuition: $969 per credit hour.

Collegiate Environment: Orientation program. Drama-theater group, choral group, student-run newspaper, radio station. Social organizations: 125 open to all; national fraternities, national sororities; 8% of eligible men and 18% of eligible women are members. Most popular organizations: Student Senate, Union Board, choirs, Weaver Chapel Association. Major annual events: New student Days, Wittfest, Activity Fair. Student services: health clinic, personal-psychological counseling, women's center. Campus security: 24-hour emergency response devices and patrols, student patrols, late night transport-escort service, controlled dormitory access, crime prevention programs. 1,755 college housing spaces available; 1,538 were occupied in 2003-04. Freshmen guaranteed college housing. On-campus residence required through sophomore year. Options: coed, women-only housing available. Thomas Library plus 2 others with 407,502 books, 82,109 microform titles, 958 serials, 22,274 audiovisual materials, an OPAC, and a Web page. Operations spending for 2004 fiscal year: $1.9 million. 750 computers available on campus for general student use. A campuswide network can be accessed from student residence rooms and from off campus. Staffed computer lab on campus.

Community Environment: Springfield is located 25 miles northeast of Dayton with all forms of commercial transportation available. Community facilities include houses of worship of all denominations, two hospitals, libraries, art and historical museums, Springfield Performing Arts Center, a symphony orchestra, and two theatre groups. Recreational activities include tennis and golf. Job opportunities are available.

■ WRIGHT STATE UNIVERSITY *I-3*

3640 Colonel Glenn Hwy.
Dayton, OH 45435
Tel: (937)775-3333
Free: 800-247-1770
Admissions: (937)775-5700
Fax: (937)775-5795
E-mail: admissions@wright.edu
Web Site: http://www.wright.edu/

Description: State-supported, university, coed. Awards associate, bachelor's, master's, doctoral, and first professional degrees and post-master's certificates. Founded 1964. Setting: 557-acre suburban campus with easy access to Cincinnati. Endowment: $6.1 million. Total enrollment: 16,207. Faculty: 835 (731 full-time, 104 part-time). Student-undergrad faculty ratio is 19:1. 5,497 applied, 87% were admitted. 15% from top 10% of their high school class, 35% from top quarter, 67% from top half. Full-time: 10,450 students, 57% women, 43% men. Part-time: 1,818 students, 53% women, 47% men. Students come from 49 states and territories, 66 other countries, 4% from out-of-state, 0.4% Native American, 1% Hispanic, 12% black, 2% Asian American or Pacific Islander, 2% international, 19% 25 or older, 22% live on campus, 7% transferred in. Retention: 73% of full-time freshmen returned the following year. Academic areas with the most degrees conferred: education; business/marketing; health professions and related sciences; psychology. Core. Academic remediation for entering students, ESL program, services for LD students, advanced placement, self-designed majors, honors program, summer session for credit, part-time degree program, adult/continuing education programs, co-op programs and internships, graduate courses open to undergrads. Off campus study at members of the Southwestern Ohio Council for Higher Education. Study abroad program. ROTC: Army, Air Force.

Entrance Requirements: Options: electronic application, early admission, deferred admission. Required: high school transcript, SAT or ACT. Recommended: minimum 2.0 high school GPA. Entrance: minimally difficult. Application deadline: Rolling. Notification: continuous.

Costs Per Year: Application fee: $30. State resident tuition: $7278 full-time, $219 per hour part-time. Nonresident tuition: $14,004 full-time, $425 per hour part-time. College room and board: $7180.

Collegiate Environment: Orientation program. Drama-theater group, choral group, student-run newspaper, radio station. Social organizations: 120 open to all; national fraternities, national sororities, local fraternities, local sororities; 2% of eligible men and 2% of eligible women are members. Major an-

nual events: May Daze, Fall Fest. Student services: legal services, health clinic, personal-psychological counseling, women's center. Campus security: 24-hour emergency response devices and patrols, student patrols, late night transport-escort service, controlled dormitory access. 2,832 undergraduates lived in college housing during 2003-04. Option: coed housing available. Paul Laurence Dunbar Library plus 2 others with 703,000 books, 1 million microform titles, 443,200 serials, 29,800 audiovisual materials, an OPAC, and a Web page. 450 computers available on campus for general student use. A campuswide network can be accessed from student residence rooms and from off campus. Staffed computer lab on campus.

Community Environment: Located in the Miami Valley at the junction of the Miami, Stillwater, and Mad Rivers in southwestern Ohio, Dayton is the state's fourth largest metropolitan area. Within a twenty-five mile radius, there is a population of over one million. The city lies fifty-four miles north of Cincinnati and seventy-two miles west of Columbus. Dayton International Airport, serviced by most major airlines, offers convenient access to almost any place in the Continental United States and abroad. The river corridor provides twenty-six scenic miles for walking, jogging, or cycling. Dayton also supports the arts, including a philharmonic orchestra, a ballet company, several art galleries and museums, and theater events for adults and children. The Opera Association presents fine productions with top stars on the bill each year.

■ WRIGHT STATE UNIVERSITY, LAKE CAMPUS *F-2*

7600 State Route 703
Celina, OH 45822-2921
Tel: (419)586-0300
Admissions: (419)586-0324
Fax: (419)586-0358
Web Site: http://www.wright.edu/lake/

Description: State-supported, 2-year, coed. Part of Ohio Board of Regents. Awards certificates, transfer associate, and terminal associate degrees. Founded 1969. Setting: 173-acre rural campus. Total enrollment: 10,061. 262 applied, 99% were admitted. Students come from 3 states and territories, 1 other country, 52% 25 or older. Core. Academic remediation for entering students, services for LD students, advanced placement, self-designed majors, honors program, summer session for credit, part-time degree program, adult/continuing education programs. Off campus study at members of the Southwestern Ohio Council for Higher Education.

Entrance Requirements: Open admission for state residents. Options: Peterson's Universal Application, early admission, deferred admission. Required: high school transcript. Recommended: minimum 2.0 high school GPA. Placement: SAT or ACT required. Entrance: noncompetitive. Application deadline: Rolling. Notification: continuous.

Collegiate Environment: Drama-theater group, student-run newspaper. Social organizations: 2 open to all. Most popular organizations: Business Professionals of America, Student Manufacturing Association. Student services: personal-psychological counseling. Campus security: 24-hour emergency response devices. College housing not available. Wright State University, Lake Campus Library with 26,000 books and 347 serials. 115 computers available on campus for general student use. A campuswide network can be accessed from off-campus. Staffed computer lab on campus.

■ XAVIER UNIVERSITY *L-2*

3800 Victory Parkway
Cincinnati, OH 45207
Tel: (513)745-3000
Free: 800-344-4698
Admissions: (513)745-3301
Fax: (513)745-4319
E-mail: xuadmit@admin.xu.edu
Web Site: http://www.xu.edu/

Description: Independent Roman Catholic, comprehensive, coed. Awards associate, bachelor's, master's, and doctoral degrees and post-master's certificates. Founded 1831. Setting: 130-acre suburban campus. Endowment: $100.3 million. Research spending for 2004 fiscal year: $157,000. Educational spending for 2005 fiscal year: $8447 per student. Total enrollment: 6,665. Faculty: 598 (294 full-time, 304 part-time). Student-undergrad faculty ratio is 13:1. 5,468 applied, 66% were admitted. 30% from top 10% of their high school class, 62% from top quarter, 89% from top half. 7 National Merit Scholars, 26 valedictorians. Full-time: 3,333 students, 55% women, 45% men. Part-time: 546 students, 62% women, 38% men. Students come from 50 states and territories, 40 other countries, 37% from out-of-state, 0.2% Native American, 2% Hispanic, 11% black, 2% Asian American or

Pacific Islander, 1% international, 14% 25 or older, 48% live on campus, 2% transferred in. Retention: 89% of full-time freshmen returned the following year. Academic areas with the most degrees conferred: business/marketing; liberal arts/general studies; communications/journalism. Core. Calendar: semesters. Academic remediation for entering students, ESL program, services for LD students, advanced placement, honors program, independent study, double major, summer session for credit, part-time degree program, adult/continuing education programs, co-op programs and internships, graduate courses open to undergrads. Off campus study at 13 members of the Greater Cincinnati Consortium of Colleges and Universities. Study abroad program. ROTC: Army, Air Force (c).

Entrance Requirements: Options: Peterson's Universal Application, Common Application, electronic application, early admission, early action, deferred admission, international baccalaureate accepted. Required: essay, high school transcript, 1 recommendation, SAT or ACT. Recommended: interview. Entrance: moderately difficult. Application deadlines: 2/1, 12/1 for early action. Notification: 3/15, 1/15 for early action.

Costs Per Year: Application fee: $35. Comprehensive fee: $31,070 includes full-time tuition ($21,850), mandatory fees ($580), and college room and board ($8640). College room only: $4860. Full-time tuition and fees vary according to program and student level. Room and board charges vary according to board plan and housing facility. Part-time tuition: $425 per credit hour. Part-time tuition varies according to course load.

Collegiate Environment: Orientation program. Drama-theater group, choral group, student-run newspaper, radio station. Social organizations: 100 open to all. Most popular organizations: Student Government Association, Student Activities Council, performing arts group, Xavier Action (service organization), Residence Hall Association. Major annual events: homecoming, Relay for Life, RSA Bingo. Student services: health clinic, personal-psychological counseling. Campus security: 24-hour emergency response devices and patrols, late night transport-escort service, campus-wide shuttle service. College housing designed to accommodate 1,774 students; 1,834 undergraduates lived in college housing during 2003-04. Freshmen guaranteed college housing. On-campus residence required through sophomore year. Option: coed housing available. McDonald Library plus 1 other with 222,331 books, 754,690 microform titles, 7,756 serials, 6,335 audiovisual materials, an OPAC, and a Web page. Operations spending for 2004 fiscal year: $2.5 million. 210 computers available on campus for general student use. A campuswide network can be accessed from student residence rooms and from off campus. Staffed computer lab on campus.

Community Environment: See University of Cincinnati.

■ **YOUNGSTOWN STATE UNIVERSITY** *D-13*
One University Plaza
Youngstown, OH 44555-0001
Tel: (330)941-3000; 877-468-6978
Admissions: (330)941-2000
Fax: (330)941-1998
E-mail: sedavis@ysu.edu
Web Site: http://www.ysu.edu/

Description: State-supported, comprehensive, coed. Awards associate, bachelor's, master's, and doctoral degrees. Founded 1908. Setting: 200-acre urban campus with easy access to Cleveland and Pittsburgh. Endowment: $141.7 million. Research spending for 2004 fiscal year: $2 million. Educational spending for 2005 fiscal year: $5992 per student. Total enrollment: 12,809. Faculty: 979 (427 full-time, 552 part-time). Student-undergrad faculty ratio is 17:1. 4,019 applied, 99% were admitted. 9% from top 10% of their high school class, 25% from top quarter, 52% from top half. Full-time: 9,241 students, 54% women, 46% men. Part-time: 2,459 students, 61% women, 39% men. Students come from 35 states and territories, 56 other countries, 9% from out-of-state, 0.4% Native American, 2% Hispanic, 12% black, 1% Asian American or Pacific Islander, 1% international, 28% 25 or older, 10% live on campus, 5% transferred in. Retention: 71% of full-time freshmen returned the following year. Academic areas with the most degrees conferred: education; business/marketing; health professions and related sciences. Core. Calendar: semesters. Academic remediation for entering students, ESL program, services for LD students, advanced placement, accelerated degree program, self-designed majors, honors program, distance learning, double major, summer session for credit, part-time degree program, adult/continuing education programs, co-op programs and internships, graduate courses open to undergrads. Off campus study at Lorain

County Community College, Cuyahoga Community College, North Central State. Study abroad program. ROTC: Army, Air Force (c).

Entrance Requirements: Open admission for state residents, students from Mercer and Lawrence Counties in Pennsylvania. Options: Peterson's Universal Application, Common Application, electronic application, early admission, early action, deferred admission, international baccalaureate accepted. Required: high school transcript, SAT or ACT. Required for some: interview. Entrance: noncompetitive. Application deadlines: 8/15, 2/15 for early action. Notification: continuous, 2/15 for early action.

Costs Per Year: Application fee: $30. State resident tuition: $6104 full-time, $254.33 per credit part-time. Nonresident tuition: $11,312 full-time, $471.33 per credit part-time. Mandatory fees: $229 full-time, $9.54 per credit part-time. Full-time tuition and fees vary according to course load. Part-time tuition and fees vary according to course load. College room and board: $6280. Room and board charges vary according to board plan and housing facility.

Collegiate Environment: Orientation program. Drama-theater group, choral group, marching band, student-run newspaper. Social organizations: 130 open to all; national fraternities, national sororities, local fraternities, local sororities; 3% of eligible men and 3% of eligible women are members. Most popular organizations: student government, Omicron Delta Kappa, Golden Key Society. Major annual events: Homecoming, Walk on Wick, Youngstown State University Annual Awards Banquet. Student services: health clinic, personal-psychological counseling, women's center. Campus security: 24-hour emergency response devices and patrols, student patrols, late night transport-escort service, controlled dormitory access, residence hall patrols. 1,222 college housing spaces available; 1,131 were occupied in 2003-04. No special consideration for freshman housing applicants. Options: coed, women-only housing available. Maag Library with 991,501 books, 90,023 microform titles, 2,908 serials, 16,976 audiovisual materials, an OPAC, and a Web page. Operations spending for 2004 fiscal year: $3.4 million. 1,619 computers available on campus for general student use. A campuswide network can be accessed from student residence rooms and from off campus. Staffed computer lab on campus.

Community Environment: The Youngstown area is a vibrant community, rich in heritage, natural and manmade resources, industry and business, and skilled responsible citizens. It is successfully undergoing a change from basic steelmaking to many diversified industries and businesses. Youngstown is located in bustling Northeast Ohio, five miles from the Pennsylvania line, equidistant between New York and Chicago, and 65 miles from both Pittsburgh and the Ohio River and the ports and beaches of Lake Erie. A network of interstate highways and Youngstown Airport have made it a major transportation center. Residents enjoy the areas lakes, fields, and forests, plus unusual 2,400-acre Mill Creek Park near the heart of the city. There are many churches, numerous fine teaching hospitals, a community playhouse, symphony orchestra, an outstanding public library system, excellent schools and many other cultural attractions, including the internationally famous Butler Institute of American Arts.

■ **ZANE STATE COLLEGE** *I-9*
1555 Newark Rd.
Zanesville, OH 43701-2626
Tel: (740)454-2501
Web Site: http://www.zanestate.edu/

Description: State and locally supported, 2-year, coed. Awards certificates, transfer associate, and terminal associate degrees. Founded 1969. Setting: 170-acre small town campus with easy access to Columbus. Total enrollment: 1,915. 722 applied, 82% were admitted. Students come from 2 other countries, 0.2% from out-of-state, 49% 25 or older. Core. Academic remediation for entering students, services for LD students, self-designed majors, honors program, summer session for credit, part-time degree program, adult/continuing education programs, co-op programs and internships. Off campus study at Ohio University-Zanesville.

Entrance Requirements: Open admission except for health technology programs. Option: early admission. Required: high school transcript. Recommended: SAT or ACT. Required for some: recommendations, interview. Entrance: noncompetitive. Application deadline: Rolling. Notification: continuous.

Collegiate Environment: Student-run newspaper. Major annual events: Fall Fest, Spring Fest. Student services: personal-psychological counseling. College housing not available. 110 computers available on campus for general student use. Staffed computer lab on campus.

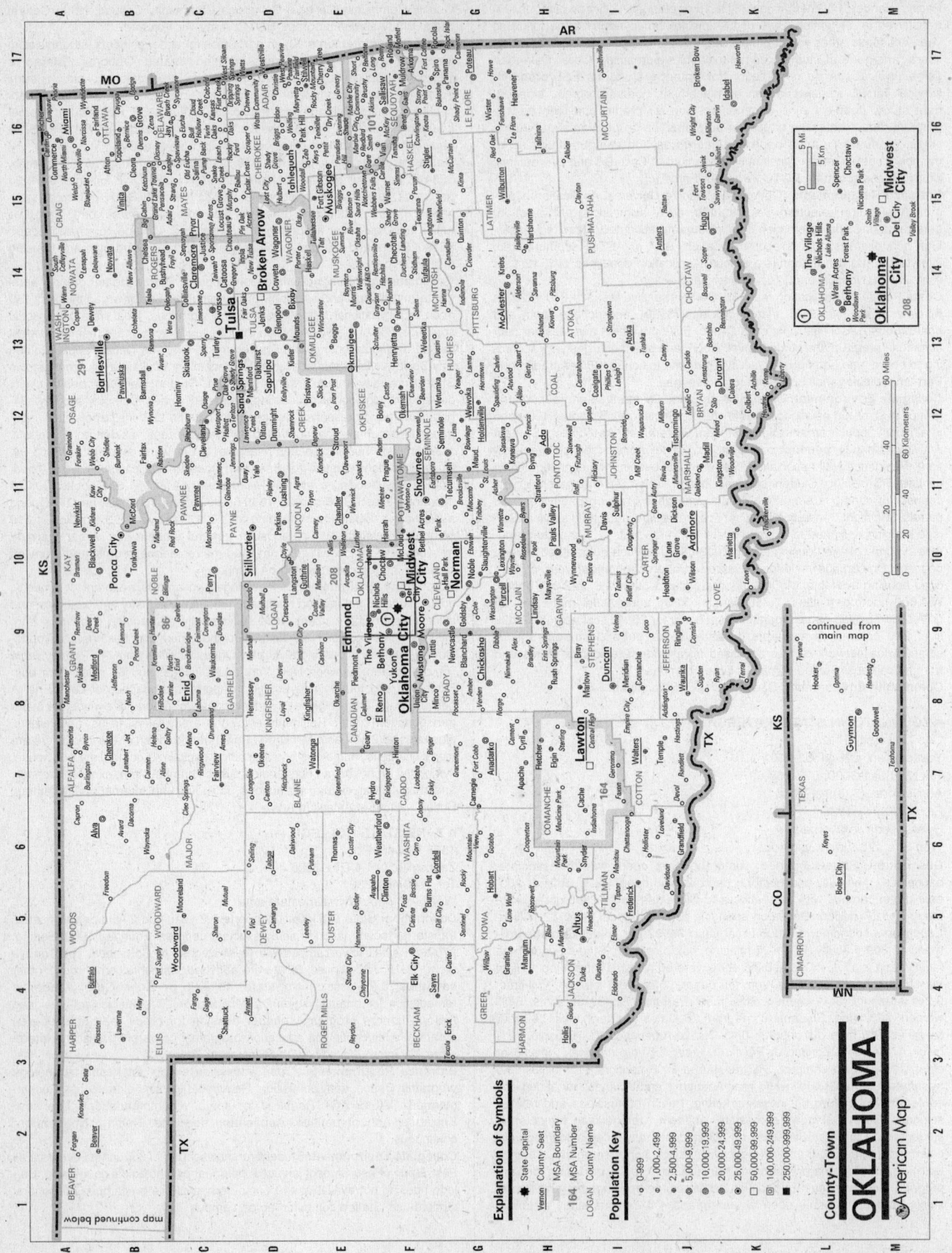

■ BACONE COLLEGE *E-15*
2299 Old Bacone Rd.
Muskogee, OK 74403-1597
Tel: (918)683-4581; 888-682-5514
Admissions: (918)781-7349
Fax: (918)682-5514
Web Site: http://www.bacone.edu/
Description: Independent, 4-year, coed, affiliated with American Baptist Churches in the U.S.A.. Awards associate and bachelor's degrees. Founded 1880. Setting: 220-acre small town campus with easy access to Tulsa. Endowment: $1.4 million. Total enrollment: 914. 819 applied, 58% were admitted. 6% from top 10% of their high school class, 17% from top quarter, 43% from top half. Full-time: 697 students, 43% women, 57% men. Part-time: 217 students, 88% women, 12% men. Students come from 24 states and territories, 10 other countries, 15% from out-of-state, 39% Native American, 4% Hispanic, 20% black, 3% international, 35% 25 or older, 48% live on campus, 10% transferred in. Retention: 50% of full-time freshmen returned the following year. Core. Calendar: semesters. Academic remediation for entering students, services for LD students, advanced placement, accelerated degree program, self-designed majors, summer session for credit, part-time degree program, adult/continuing education programs, co-op programs and internships.
Entrance Requirements: Options: Common Application, electronic application, early admission, deferred admission, international baccalaureate accepted. Required: high school transcript, minimum 2.0 high school GPA, minimum ACT score of 16, SAT or ACT. Recommended: ACT. Required for some: essay, recommendations, interview. Entrance: minimally difficult. Application deadline: Rolling. Notification: continuous.
Costs Per Year: Application fee: $25. Comprehensive fee: $14,467 includes full-time tuition ($8137), mandatory fees ($630), and college room and board ($5700). College room only: $3000. Part-time tuition: $350 per credit hour. Part-time mandatory fees: $240 per term. Part-time tuition and fees vary according to course load.
Collegiate Environment: Orientation program. Drama-theater group, choral group, student-run newspaper. Most popular organizations: Native American Club, Phi Beta Kappa, Christian Nurses Fellowship. Major annual event: Multicultural Day. Student services: health clinic, personal-psychological counseling. Campus security: 24-hour emergency response devices, controlled dormitory access, 8-hour patrols by trained security personnel. 425 college housing spaces available; 380 were occupied in 2003-04. Freshmen given priority for college housing. On-campus residence required through sophomore year. Options: men-only, women-only housing available. Bacone College Library with 34,564 books, 18,960 microform titles, 121 serials, 185 audiovisual materials, and an OPAC. 46 computers available on campus for general student use. A campuswide network can be accessed from off-campus. Staffed computer lab on campus.
Community Environment: Bacone is a suburban community, one mile from Muskogee, a town of 60,000. All the cultural, recreational, and community services are located in Muskogee.

■ CAMERON UNIVERSITY *I-7*
2800 West Gore Blvd.
Lawton, OK 73505-6377
Tel: (580)581-2200; 888-454-7600
Admissions: (580)581-2289
Fax: (580)581-5514

E-mail: admiss@cua.cameron.edu
Web Site: http://www.cameron.edu/
Description: State-supported, comprehensive, coed. Part of Oklahoma State Regents for Higher Education. Awards bachelor's and master's degrees. Founded 1908. Setting: 160-acre small town campus. Endowment: $11.6 million. Research spending for 2004 fiscal year: $269,443. Educational spending for 2005 fiscal year: $4602 per student. Total enrollment: 5,873. Faculty: 297 (180 full-time, 117 part-time). Student-undergrad faculty ratio is 17:1. 1,357 applied, 99.9% were admitted. 8% from top 10% of their high school class, 28% from top quarter, 62% from top half. Full-time: 3,173 students, 59% women, 41% men. Part-time: 2,266 students, 62% women, 38% men. Students come from 49 states and territories, 4% from out-of-state, 8% Native American, 9% Hispanic, 19% black, 3% Asian American or Pacific Islander, 3% international, 45% 25 or older, 4% live on campus, 8% transferred in. Retention: 56% of full-time freshmen returned the following year. Academic areas with the most degrees conferred: business/marketing; education; computer and information sciences. Core. Calendar: semesters. Academic remediation for entering students, services for LD students, advanced placement, accelerated degree program, honors program, independent study, distance learning, double major, summer session for credit, part-time degree program, adult/continuing education programs, graduate courses open to undergrads. Off campus study at University of Oklahoma, East Central University, Oklahoma State University. ROTC: Army.
Entrance Requirements: Open admission. Options: electronic application, early admission, deferred admission, international baccalaureate accepted. Required: high school transcript, minimum 2.7 high school GPA, SAT or ACT. Entrance: minimally difficult. Application deadline: Rolling. Notification: continuous until 8/10.
Costs Per Year: Application fee: $15. State resident tuition: $3240 full-time, $108 per semester hour part-time. Nonresident tuition: $7830 full-time, $261 per semester hour part-time. Mandatory fees: $200 full-time, $100 per term part-time. Full-time tuition and fees vary according to course load. Part-time tuition and fees vary according to course load. College room and board: $3014. Room and board charges vary according to board plan.
Collegiate Environment: Orientation program. Drama-theater group, choral group, student-run newspaper, radio station. Social organizations: 57 open to all; national fraternities, national sororities; 1% of eligible men and 2% of eligible women are members. Most popular organizations: Student Government Association, Aggie Club, Intramural Club, Baptist Student Union, Sociology Club. Major annual events: Comedy Club, Spring Fling, Diversity Week. Student services: personal-psychological counseling. Campus security: 24-hour emergency response devices and patrols, student patrols, late night transport-escort service. 512 college housing spaces available; 240 were occupied in 2003-04. No special consideration for freshman housing applicants. On-campus residence required in freshman year. Options: men-only, women-only housing available. Cameron University Library with 262,835 books, 507,461 microform titles, 4,272 serials, and 6,986 audiovisual materials. Operations spending for 2004 fiscal year: $1.3 million. 350 computers available on campus for general student use. A campuswide network can be accessed from student residence rooms and from off campus. Staffed computer lab on campus.
Community Environment: Lawton is a metropolitan area that enjoys a dry, temperate climate. The city is served by two airlines, two railroads for freight, bus service, and a turnpike. Community services include a public library, museum, churches of most denominations, two general and one public health hospital, major civic and fraternal organizations, and good shopping

facilities. Part-time employment is available for students. Local recreational facilities include camping, water sports, theaters, and bowling.

■ CARL ALBERT STATE COLLEGE *G-17*
1507 South McKenna
Poteau, OK 74953-5208
Tel: (918)647-1200
Admissions: (918)647-1301
Fax: (918)647-1306
E-mail: ddickerson@carlalbert.edu
Web Site: http://www.carlalbert.edu/
Description: State-supported, 2-year, coed. Part of Oklahoma State Regents for Higher Education. Awards certificates, transfer associate, and terminal associate degrees. Founded 1934. Setting: 78-acre small town campus. Educational spending for 2005 fiscal year: $7636 per student. Total enrollment: 2,501. Student-undergrad faculty ratio is 16:1. 996 applied, 79% were admitted. 5% from top 10% of their high school class, 30% from top half. Full-time: 1,484 students, 65% women, 35% men. Part-time: 1,017 students, 75% women, 25% men. 11% from out-of-state, 27% Native American, 2% Hispanic, 3% black, 1% Asian American or Pacific Islander, 1% international, 18% live on campus. Core. Calendar: semesters. Academic remediation for entering students, part-time degree program, adult/continuing education programs, co-op programs.
Entrance Requirements: Open admission. Required: high school transcript. Entrance: noncompetitive. Application deadline: 8/13. Notification: continuous.
Costs Per Year: Application fee: $0. State resident tuition: $1632 full-time, $68 per credit hour part-time. Nonresident tuition: $4004 full-time, $167 per credit hour part-time. Mandatory fees: $4 full-time, $2 per term part-time. College room and board: $1520. College room only: $1000.
Collegiate Environment: Orientation program. Drama-theater group, choral group, student-run newspaper, radio station. Social organizations: 25 open to all; local sororities; 5% of women are members. Most popular organizations: Student Government Association, Phi Theta Kappa, Baptist Student Union, BACCHUS, Student Physical Therapist Assistant Association. Major annual events: Welcome Week, Homecoming, graduation. Student services: health clinic, personal-psychological counseling. Campus security: security guards. 150 college housing spaces available; all were occupied in 2003-04. Options: men-only, women-only housing available. Joe E. White Library with 27,200 books, 1,350 serials, and an OPAC. 15 computers available on campus for general student use. A campuswide network can be accessed. Staffed computer lab on campus.
Community Environment: Poteau is located in central eastern Oklahoma in the Cavanal Mountain area. This is the county seat and may be reached by bus lines. Nearby Ouachita National Forest offers excellent recreational facilities.

■ COMMUNITY CARE COLLEGE *D-13*
4242 South Sheridan
Tulsa, OK 74145
Tel: (918)610-0027
Fax: (918)610-0029
E-mail: tknox@communitycarecollege.com
Web Site: http://www.communitycarecollege.com/
Description: Proprietary, 2-year, coed. Part of Dental Directions, Inc.. Awards certificates, diplomas, and terminal associate degrees. Founded 1995. Total enrollment: 525. Full-time: 512 students, 90% women, 10% men. Part-time: 13 students, 92% women, 8% men. 4% from out-of-state, 12% Native American, 3% Hispanic, 17% black, 1% Asian American or Pacific Islander, 0% international. Calendar: semesters.
Entrance Requirements: Required: high school transcript, interview, Assessment. Entrance: noncompetitive.
Costs Per Year: Application fee: $15. Tuition: $9000 full-time. Mandatory fees: $850 full-time.
Collegiate Environment: Student services: personal-psychological counseling.

■ CONNORS STATE COLLEGE *F-15*
Route 1 Box 1000
Warner, OK 74469-9700
Tel: (918)463-2931; (918)463-2931
Admissions: (918)463-6233
Web Site: http://www.connorsstate.edu/

Description: State-supported, 2-year, coed. Part of Oklahoma State Regents for Higher Education. Awards certificates, diplomas, transfer associate, and terminal associate degrees. Founded 1908. Setting: 1,658-acre rural campus. Endowment: $19,200. Educational spending for 2005 fiscal year: $1916 per student. Total enrollment: 2,335. 727 applied, 100% were admitted. 8% from top 10% of their high school class, 19% from top quarter, 35% from top half. 8 valedictorians. Students come from 36 states and territories, 4 other countries, 3% from out-of-state, 25% Native American, 2% Hispanic, 11% black, 1% Asian American or Pacific Islander, 1% international, 38% 25 or older, 12% live on campus. Core. Calendar: semesters. Academic remediation for entering students, advanced placement, accelerated degree program, summer session for credit, part-time degree program, adult/continuing education programs, internships.
Entrance Requirements: Open admission. Options: early admission, deferred admission. Required for some: high school transcript. Placement: SAT or ACT, ACT COMPASS required for some. Entrance: noncompetitive. Application deadline: Rolling.
Collegiate Environment: Drama-theater group, student-run newspaper. Social organizations: 21 open to all. Most popular organizations: Aggie Club, CD Club, Twilight Angels, McClarren Club, Library Club. Major annual events: Welcome Back Hamburger Cookout, Aggie Rodeo. Student services: health clinic. Campus security: late night transport-escort service, trained security personnel. 320 college housing spaces available; 198 were occupied in 2003-04. Freshmen guaranteed college housing. Options: coed, men-only, women-only housing available. Carl Westbrook Library with 63,728 books, 319 serials, and an OPAC. Operations spending for 2004 fiscal year: $223,165. 206 computers available on campus for general student use. Staffed computer lab on campus.
Community Environment: Warner is a rural community with mild winters and warm to hot summers. The area is provided transportation by bus lines, and U.S. Highways 64 and 266. There are several churches of various denominations, and civic and service clubs within the city. Recreational facilities within the area include theatres, restaurants, and nearby lakes. Within driving distance, there is the Five Civilized Tribes Museum.

■ EAST CENTRAL UNIVERSITY *H-11*
1100 East 14th St.
Ada, OK 74820-6899
Tel: (580)332-8000
Admissions: (580)310-5239
Fax: (580)436-5495
E-mail: parmstro@mailclerk.ecok.edu
Web Site: http://www.ecok.edu/
Description: State-supported, comprehensive, coed. Part of Oklahoma State Regents for Higher Education. Awards bachelor's and master's degrees. Founded 1909. Setting: 140-acre small town campus with easy access to Oklahoma City. Endowment: $1.6 million. Research spending for 2004 fiscal year: $381,950. Educational spending for 2005 fiscal year: $3947 per student. Total enrollment: 4,571. Faculty: 255 (156 full-time, 99 part-time). Student-undergrad faculty ratio is 20:1. 617 applied, 98% were admitted. 16% from top 10% of their high school class, 38% from top quarter, 74% from top half. Full-time: 3,172 students, 59% women, 41% men. Part-time: 631 students, 67% women, 33% men. Students come from 24 states and territories, 32 other countries, 5% from out-of-state, 20% Native American, 2% Hispanic, 5% black, 1% Asian American or Pacific Islander, 1% international, 39% 25 or older. Retention: 61% of full-time freshmen returned the following year. Academic areas with the most degrees conferred: education; business/marketing; public administration and social services. Core. Calendar: semesters. Academic remediation for entering students, services for LD students, advanced placement, honors program, independent study, distance learning, double major, summer session for credit, part-time degree program, adult/continuing education programs, internships, graduate courses open to undergrads. Off campus study at Ardmore Higher Education Center.
Entrance Requirements: Option: early admission. Required: high school transcript, SAT or ACT. Recommended: ACT. Required for some: minimum 2.7 high school GPA, rank in upper 50% of high school class. Entrance: moderately difficult. Notification: continuous.
Costs Per Year: Application fee: $20. State resident tuition: $2,722 full-time, $75.11 per semester hour part-time. Nonresident tuition: $5,739 full-time, $229.55 per semester hour part-time. Mandatory fees: $844 full-time, $31.80 per semester hour part-time, $23.50 per term part-time. Full-time tuition and fees vary according to course load. Part-time tuition and fees vary according to course load. College room and board: $3000. College room only: $1070. Room and board charges vary according to board plan and housing facility.

Collegiate Environment: Orientation program. Drama-theater group, choral group, marching band, student-run newspaper. Social organizations: 52 open to all; national fraternities, national sororities, local fraternities, local sororities; 3% of eligible men and 3% of eligible women are members. Most popular organizations: BACCHUS, Fellowship of Christian Athletes, Human Resources. Major annual events: Homecoming Week, concerts/plays, movie series. Student services: health clinic, personal-psychological counseling. Campus security: 24-hour patrols, controlled dormitory access. 1,009 college housing spaces available; 677 were occupied in 2003-04. No special consideration for freshman housing applicants. Options: coed, women-only housing available. Linscheid Library with 171,080 books, 8,308 microform titles, 1,221 serials, 8,955 audiovisual materials, an OPAC, and a Web page. Operations spending for 2004 fiscal year: $902,753. 500 computers available on campus for general student use. A campuswide network can be accessed. Staffed computer lab on campus.

Community Environment: Ada is the commercial, industrial, service, and medical center for this area. An EPA world-class groundwater research laboratory (Robert S. Kerr Environmental Research Laboratory) and the seat of government of the Chickasaw Indian Nation are located in Ada. Ada's primary commercial employers include a cement plant, a plastics molding operation, and petroleum and cattle industries. The climate is temperate with mild winters. The average temperature is 64 degrees. Ada is approximately 90 miles southeast of Oklahoma City. Community services include a major regional medical center, thirty churches, and many civic and fraternal organizations. Local recreational facilities include parks, swimming pools, picnic areas, hiking, golf, fishing, hunting, waterskiing, and tennis.

■ **EASTERN OKLAHOMA STATE COLLEGE** *H-15*
1301 West Main
Wilburton, OK 74578-4999
Tel: (918)465-2361
Fax: (918)465-2431
E-mail: lmiller@eosc.edu
Web Site: http://www.eosc.edu/

Description: State-supported, 2-year, coed. Part of Oklahoma State Regents for Higher Education. Awards certificates, transfer associate, and terminal associate degrees. Founded 1908. Setting: 4,000-acre rural campus. Total enrollment: 2,639. 12% from top 10% of their high school class, 18% from top quarter, 52% from top half. Students come from 8 states and territories, 2 other countries, 31% 25 or older, 20% live on campus. Core. Calendar: semesters. Academic remediation for entering students, advanced placement, honors program, double major, summer session for credit, part-time degree program, adult/continuing education programs, co-op programs and internships. Off campus study at E. T. Dunlap Higher Education Center, McAlester Higher Education Center.

Entrance Requirements: Open admission for state residents. Options: Common Application, early admission, deferred admission. Required: high school transcript. Placement: ACT required. Entrance: noncompetitive. Application deadline: Rolling.

Collegiate Environment: Orientation program. Drama-theater group, choral group, student-run newspaper. Most popular organizations: Student Senate, Aggie Club, Phi Beta Lambda. Major annual events: Homecoming Week, Mudbowl. Student services: personal-psychological counseling. On-campus residence required through sophomore year. Options: men-only, women-only housing available. Bill H. Hill Library with 41,639 books, 220 serials, and an OPAC. 250 computers available on campus for general student use. A campuswide network can be accessed from off-campus. Staffed computer lab on campus.

Community Environment: Wilburton is a small community located in the San Bois Mountains. The area is served by commercial bus lines, U.S. Route 270 and State Highway 2. A small municipal airport is located here, but commercial airlines are approximately 30 miles distant. Good recreational facilities for outdoor sports include nearby Robber's Cave State Park, and Kiamichi National Forest. The nearest large cities are Muskogee and Fort Smith, Arkansas.

■ **HERITAGE COLLEGE OF HAIR DESIGN** *F-9*
7100 I-35 Services Rd., Ste. 7118
Oklahoma City, OK 73149
Tel: (405)631-3399
Fax: (405)631-6711
Description: Proprietary, 2-year, coed.

■ **HILLSDALE FREE WILL BAPTIST COLLEGE** *F-9*
3701 South I-35 Service Rd.
PO Box 7208

Moore, OK 73160-1208
Tel: (405)912-9000
Admissions: (405)912-9006
Fax: (405)912-9050
E-mail: gosaints@flash.net
Web Site: http://www.hc.edu/

Description: Independent Free Will Baptist, comprehensive, coed. Awards associate, bachelor's, and master's degrees. Founded 1959. Setting: 41-acre suburban campus with easy access to Oklahoma City. Endowment: $277,141. Educational spending for 2005 fiscal year: $2587 per student. Total enrollment: 268. 88 applied, 100% were admitted. 4% from top 10% of their high school class, 24% from top quarter, 56% from top half. 1 valedictorian. Full-time: 203 students, 40% women, 60% men. Part-time: 51 students, 37% women, 63% men. 10% Native American, 5% Hispanic, 10% black, 0% Asian American or Pacific Islander, 7% international, 12% 25 or older, 45% live on campus, 14% transferred in. Retention: 47% of full-time freshmen returned the following year. Core. Calendar: semesters. Academic remediation for entering students, ESL program, advanced placement, accelerated degree program, independent study, double major, summer session for credit, part-time degree program, adult/continuing education programs, internships.

Entrance Requirements: Options: Common Application, early admission, deferred admission. Required: essay, high school transcript, 1 recommendation, Biblical foundation statement, student conduct pledge; medical form required for some. Recommended: minimum 2.0 high school GPA, 2 recommendations. Required for some: 1 recommendation, interview. Placement: SAT or ACT required. Entrance: noncompetitive. Application deadline: Rolling.

Costs Per Year: Application fee: $20. Comprehensive fee: $12,120 includes full-time tuition ($6800), mandatory fees ($1060), and college room and board ($4260). Full-time tuition and fees vary according to course load and program. Room and board charges vary according to board plan. Part-time tuition: $260 per credit hour. Part-time mandatory fees: $15 per credit hour, $150 per term. Part-time tuition and fees vary according to program.

Collegiate Environment: Orientation program. Drama-theater group, choral group. Social organizations: 11 open to all; local fraternities, local sororities; 48% of eligible men and 62% of eligible women are members. Most popular organizations: Student Mission Fellowship, Ironmen Fellowship, society organizations, Fellowship of Christian Athletes. Major annual events: Missions Emphasis Week, On-Campus Days, homecoming. Student services: personal-psychological counseling. Campus security: 24-hour emergency response devices, controlled dormitory access. 132 college housing spaces available; 116 were occupied in 2003-04. On-campus residence required through sophomore year. Options: men-only, women-only housing available. Geri Ann Hull Learning Resource Center with 20,102 books, 3,416 microform titles, 363 serials, 1,800 audiovisual materials, and an OPAC. Operations spending for 2004 fiscal year: $38,141. 22 computers available on campus for general student use. A campuswide network can be accessed. Staffed computer lab on campus.

Community Environment: Community transportation is provided by bus and rail. Will Rogers International Airport is 10 minutes away. The city has many churches, a library, and health facilities. Nearby Lake Draper offers water skiing and fishing. There are many businesses in town, and part-time employment is available for students.

■ **ITT TECHNICAL INSTITUTE** *D-13*
4943 South 78th East Ave.
Tulsa, OK 74145
Admissions: (918)619-8700
Web Site: http://www.itt-tech.edu/

Description: primarily 2-year, coed. Awards terminal associate and bachelor's degrees.

Entrance Requirements: Required: high school transcript, interview, Wonderlic aptitude test. Recommended: recommendations. Application deadline: Rolling. Notification: continuous.

Costs Per Year: Application fee: $100.

■ **LANGSTON UNIVERSITY** *D-10*
PO Box 907
Langston, OK 73050-0907
Tel: (405)466-2231
Admissions: (405)466-2980
Fax: (405)466-3381
Web Site: http://www.lunet.edu/

Description: State-supported, comprehensive, coed. Part of Oklahoma State Regents for Higher Education. Awards associate, bachelor's, and master's degrees. Founded 1897. Setting: 40-acre rural campus with easy access to Oklahoma City. Total enrollment: 3,010. 2,088 applied, 50% were admitted. Full-time: 2,230 students, 56% women, 44% men. Part-time: 668 students, 63% women, 37% men. Students come from 37 states and territories, 8 other countries, 2% Native American, 1% Hispanic, 75% black, 0.4% Asian American or Pacific Islander, 1% international, 20% 25 or older. Core. Calendar: semesters. Academic remediation for entering students, services for LD students, advanced placement, accelerated degree program, honors program, summer session for credit, part-time degree program, adult/continuing education programs, co-op programs and internships, graduate courses open to undergrads. ROTC: Army (c).

Entrance Requirements: Open admission. Option: electronic application. Required: high school transcript, minimum 2.70 high school GPA, SAT or ACT. Required for some: recommendations. Placement: SAT or ACT required. Entrance: minimally difficult. Application deadline: Rolling.

Collegiate Environment: Orientation program. Drama-theater group, student-run newspaper, radio station. Social organizations: national fraternities, national sororities. Student services: health clinic, personal-psychological counseling. 1,726 college housing spaces available; 1,384 were occupied in 2003-04. Freshmen guaranteed college housing. On-campus residence required through sophomore year. Main library plus 2 others with 97,565 books, 824,457 microform titles, 1,235 serials, 4,974 audiovisual materials, an OPAC, and a Web page. 200 computers available on campus for general student use. A campuswide network can be accessed from student residence rooms and from off campus. Staffed computer lab on campus.

Community Environment: Langston is a small rural community located 40 miles northeast of Oklahoma City and 90 miles west of Tulsa, OK.

■ **METROPOLITAN COLLEGE (OKLAHOMA CITY)** *F-9*
2901 North Classen Blvd., Ste. 200
Oklahoma City, OK 73106
Tel: (405)528-5000
Admissions: (405)843-1000
Fax: (405)528-0320
Web Site: http://www.metropolitancollege.edu/
Description: Proprietary, 4-year, coed. Part of Wyandotte Collegiate Systems. Awards associate and bachelor's degrees. Total enrollment: 140. 7% Native American, 1% Hispanic, 34% black, 1% international. Calendar: trimesters.
Entrance Requirements: Open admission. Required: high school transcript, interview, Wonderlic aptitude test. Entrance: minimally difficult.
Costs Per Year: Application fee: $50. Tuition: $7710 full-time.
Collegiate Environment: Orientation program.

■ **METROPOLITAN COLLEGE (TULSA)** *D-13*
4528 South Sheridan Rd., Ste. 105
Tulsa, OK 74145-1011
Tel: (918)627-9300
Fax: (918)627-2122
E-mail: admissions@metropolitancollege.edu
Web Site: http://www.metropolitancollege.edu/
Description: Proprietary, 4-year, coed. Awards associate and bachelor's degrees. Setting: urban campus. Total enrollment: 223. 2% from top 10% of their high school class, 10% from top quarter, 15% from top half. Full-time: 223 students, 91% women, 9% men. Students come from 3 states and territories, 1% from out-of-state, 3% Hispanic, 17% black, 5% Asian American or Pacific Islander, 71% 25 or older, 4% transferred in. Retention: 71% of full-time freshmen returned the following year. Calendar: trimesters. Academic remediation for entering students, accelerated degree program, part-time degree program, adult/continuing education programs, internships.
Entrance Requirements: Open admission. Option: international baccalaureate accepted. Required: high school transcript, interview, Wonderlic aptitude test. Entrance: minimally difficult.
Collegiate Environment: Orientation program. Student-run newspaper. College housing not available. 25 computers available on campus for general student use. A campuswide network can be accessed. Staffed computer lab on campus.

■ **MID-AMERICA CHRISTIAN UNIVERSITY** *F-9*
3500 Southwest 119th St.
Oklahoma City, OK 73170-4504

Tel: (405)691-3800
Admissions: (405)392-3241
Fax: (405)692-5165
Web Site: http://www.macu.edu/
Description: Independent, 4-year, coed, affiliated with Church of God. Awards associate and bachelor's degrees. Founded 1953. Setting: 145-acre suburban campus. Endowment: $421,051. Total enrollment: 613. 79 applied, 100% were admitted. Full-time: 547 students, 49% women, 51% men. Part-time: 66 students, 44% women, 56% men. Students come from 32 states and territories, 4 other countries, 29% from out-of-state, 3% Native American, 4% Hispanic, 10% black, 1% Asian American or Pacific Islander, 1% international, 53% 25 or older, 34% live on campus, 15% transferred in. Core. Calendar: semesters. Academic remediation for entering students, services for LD students, advanced placement, accelerated degree program, distance learning, double major, summer session for credit, part-time degree program, adult/continuing education programs, internships.
Entrance Requirements: Open admission. Options: Peterson's Universal Application, Common Application, early admission. Required: high school transcript. Required for some: 2 recommendations, interview. Placement: SAT or ACT required. Entrance: noncompetitive. Application deadline: Rolling.
Costs Per Year: Application fee: $20. Comprehensive fee: $14,360 includes full-time tuition ($9900) and college room and board ($4460). College room only: $2360. Full-time tuition varies according to course load. Part-time tuition: $420 per hour. Part-time tuition varies according to course load.
Collegiate Environment: Orientation program. Drama-theater group, choral group, student-run newspaper. Most popular organizations: Christian Women's Organization, Behavioral Science Club, Student Ministers' Fellowship, Drama Club, S.A.C.E. Major annual events: Howdy Party, Christmas Banquet, Spring Banquet. Student services: personal-psychological counseling. Campus security: 24-hour patrols, student patrols. On-campus residence required through senior year. Options: men-only, women-only housing available. Charles Ewing Brown Library with 60,000 books, 12,324 microform titles, 3,906 audiovisual materials, and a Web page. Operations spending for 2004 fiscal year: $101,656. 20 computers available on campus for general student use. Staffed computer lab on campus.
Community Environment: See Oklahoma City University.

■ **MURRAY STATE COLLEGE** *J-11*
One Murray Campus
Tishomingo, OK 73460-3130
Tel: (580)371-2371
Fax: (580)371-9844
Web Site: http://www.mscok.edu/
Description: State-supported, 2-year, coed. Part of Oklahoma State Regents for Higher Education. Awards transfer associate and terminal associate degrees. Founded 1908. Setting: 120-acre rural campus. Total enrollment: 1,958. Students come from 16 states and territories, 4 other countries, 3% from out-of-state, 15% Native American, 2% Hispanic, 6% black, 1% Asian American or Pacific Islander, 0.5% international, 6% live on campus. Core. Calendar: semesters. Academic remediation for entering students, services for LD students, advanced placement, honors program, distance learning, summer session for credit, part-time degree program, internships.
Entrance Requirements: Open admission. Options: Common Application, early admission, deferred admission. Required: high school transcript. Placement: ACT required. Entrance: noncompetitive. Application deadline: Rolling. Notification: continuous.
Collegiate Environment: Orientation program. Drama-theater group, choral group, student-run newspaper. Student services: personal-psychological counseling. Campus security: 24-hour patrols. 155 college housing spaces available; all were occupied in 2003-04. Option: coed housing available. Murray State College Library plus 1 other with 20,000 books and 160 serials. 100 computers available on campus for general student use. Staffed computer lab on campus.
Community Environment: Historically noted as the original capital of the Chickasaw Nation, Tishomingo is situated on the banks of Lake Texoma within a wildlife refuge. This is a rural area with a temperate climate. The city is served by five highways. Tishomingo has six churches, a hospital, and

major civic, fraternal and veteran's organizations. Local recreational facilities include water sports, hunting, fishing, and hiking.

■ NORTHEASTERN OKLAHOMA AGRICULTURAL AND MECHANI-CAL COLLEGE A-16

200 I St., NE
Miami, OK 74354-6434
Tel: (918)542-8441
Admissions: (918)540-6212
Fax: (918)542-9759
Web Site: http://www.neoam.cc.ok.us/

Description: State-supported, 2-year, coed. Part of Oklahoma State Regents for Higher Education. Awards certificates, transfer associate, and terminal associate degrees. Founded 1919. Setting: 340-acre small town campus. Total enrollment: 2,102. 5% from top 10% of their high school class, 80% from top half. Full-time: 1,473 students, 51% women, 49% men. Part-time: 629 students, 71% women, 29% men. Students come from 25 states and territories, 19 other countries, 15% from out-of-state, 35% 25 or older. Core. Calendar: semesters. Academic remediation for entering students, services for LD students, advanced placement, distance learning, double major, summer session for credit, part-time degree program, external degree program, adult/continuing education programs, internships.

Entrance Requirements: Open admission. Option: electronic application. Required: high school transcript. Placement: SAT or ACT required. Entrance: noncompetitive. Application deadline: Rolling.

Collegiate Environment: Drama-theater group, choral group, marching band, student-run newspaper. Social organizations: 50 open to all. Student services: legal services, health clinic, personal-psychological counseling, women's center. Campus security: 24-hour patrols. 500 college housing spaces available; 300 were occupied in 2003-04. Freshmen guaranteed college housing. On-campus residence required through sophomore year. Learning Resource Center with 74,000 books, 450 serials, an OPAC, and a Web page. 65 computers available on campus for general student use. Staffed computer lab on campus.

Community Environment: Miami is headquarters for the Grand Lake recreation area. Items produced by the city's manufacturers include automotive parts, tires and tubes, clothing, food products and boats and accessories. Part-time employment is available. The climate is temperate. There are dormitories and housing units on campus. Good health services are available.

■ NORTHEASTERN STATE UNIVERSITY D-16

600 North Grand
Tahlequah, OK 74464-2399
Tel: (918)456-5511
Fax: (918)458-2342
E-mail: nowlin@nsuok.edu
Web Site: http://www.nsuok.edu/

Description: State-supported, comprehensive, coed. Part of Oklahoma State Regents for Higher Education. Awards bachelor's, master's, and first professional degrees. Founded 1846. Setting: 160-acre small town campus with easy access to Tulsa. Endowment: $780,030. Research spending for 2004 fiscal year: $592,531. Educational spending for 2005 fiscal year: $3679 per student. Total enrollment: 9,562. 2,202 applied, 86% were admitted. 16% from top 10% of their high school class, 40% from top quarter, 73% from top half. Full-time: 6,677 students, 59% women, 41% men. Part-time: 1,866 students, 67% women, 33% men. Students come from 27 states and territories, 44 other countries, 0.1% from out-of-state, 29% Native American, 2% Hispanic, 6% black, 1% Asian American or Pacific Islander, 2% international, 35% 25 or older, 16% transferred in. Retention: 60% of full-time freshmen returned the following year. Core. Calendar: semesters. Academic remediation for entering students, ESL program, services for LD students, advanced placement, honors program, distance learning, double major, summer session for credit, part-time degree program, adult/continuing education programs, internships, graduate courses open to undergrads. ROTC: Army.

Entrance Requirements: Required: high school transcript, ACT. Required for some: recommendations, interview. Entrance: moderately difficult. Application deadline: 8/5. Notification: continuous.

Costs Per Year: Application fee: $0. State resident tuition: $3300 full-time. Nonresident tuition: $8100 full-time. Full-time tuition varies according to course level, course load, and location. College room and board: $3312. Room and board charges vary according to board plan and housing facility.

Collegiate Environment: Orientation program. Drama-theater group, choral group, marching band, student-run newspaper. Social organizations: 80 open to all; national fraternities, national sororities, local fraternities, local sororities; 3% of eligible men and 2% of eligible women are members. Major annual event: homecoming. Student services: health clinic, personal-psychological counseling. Campus security: 24-hour emergency response devices and patrols, late night transport-escort service, controlled dormitory access. 1,700 college housing spaces available; all were occupied in 2003-04. Freshmen given priority for college housing. On-campus residence required through sophomore year. Option: coed housing available. John Vaughn Library with 424,818 books, 742,695 microform titles, 3,983 serials, 6,804 audiovisual materials, an OPAC, and a Web page. Operations spending for 2004 fiscal year: $2.3 million. 534 computers available on campus for general student use. A campuswide network can be accessed from student residence rooms and from off campus. Staffed computer lab on campus.

Community Environment: In a region of lakes within the foothills of the Ozark Mountains, Tahlequah is the former capital city of the Cherokee Indian Nation. There are many historic sites and artifacts in the area. The city is accessible by five highways. Community services includes several churches of various denominations, two hospitals, two libraries, and a museum. Apartments provide student housing. There are various civic and fraternal organizations within the city. Limited part-time employment is available for students. Local recreational facilities include boating, fishing, hunting, water skiing, and swimming.

■ NORTHERN OKLAHOMA COLLEGE B-10

1220 East Grand Ave., PO Box 310
Tonkawa, OK 74653-0310
Tel: (580)628-6200
Free: 800-429-5715
Admissions: (580)628-6221
Fax: (580)628-6209
E-mail: wwebb@north-ok.edu
Web Site: http://www.north-ok.edu/

Description: State-supported, 2-year, coed. Part of Oklahoma State Regents for Higher Education. Awards transfer associate and terminal associate degrees. Founded 1901. Setting: 10-acre rural campus. Total enrollment: 3,050. Students come from 4 other countries, 40% 25 or older, 20% live on campus. Calendar: semesters. Academic remediation for entering students, services for LD students, advanced placement, summer session for credit, part-time degree program, adult/continuing education programs.

Entrance Requirements: Open admission except for nursing program. Options: Common Application, early admission. Required: high school transcript. Placement: ACT required. Entrance: noncompetitive. Application deadline: Rolling.

Collegiate Environment: Drama-theater group, choral group, student-run newspaper, radio station. Social organizations: 15 open to all. Most popular organizations: Phi Theta Kappa, Law Enforcement Club, Fellowship of Christian Athletes, Student Nurses Association, Young Republicans. Major annual events: homecoming, Drug Awareness Week. Student services: health clinic, personal-psychological counseling. Campus security: 24-hour emergency response devices and patrols. 550 college housing spaces available; 540 were occupied in 2003-04. On-campus residence required through sophomore year. Vineyard Library with 34,458 books and 211 serials. 150 computers available on campus for general student use. Staffed computer lab on campus.

Community Environment: Tonkawa is located 14 miles west of Ponca City and enjoys a mild climate. The city has a public library, churches representing 10 denominations, a nearby hospital, a Chamber of Commerce and other civic, fraternal and veteran's organizations. Housing for students is provided by dormitories and one hotel. There are limited job opportunities for students. Fishing in nearby rivers is considered excellent sport.

■ NORTHWESTERN OKLAHOMA STATE UNIVERSITY B-6

709 Oklahoma Blvd.
Alva, OK 73717-2799
Tel: (580)327-1700
Admissions: (580)327-8550
Fax: (580)327-1881
E-mail: smmurrow@nwosu.edu
Web Site: http://www.nwosu.edu/

Description: State-supported, comprehensive, coed. Part of Oklahoma State Regents for Higher Education. Awards bachelor's and master's degrees and post-master's certificates. Founded 1897. Setting: 70-acre small town campus. Endowment: $14.5 million. Research spending for 2004 fiscal year: $33,400. Educational spending for 2005 fiscal year: $4096 per student. Total enrollment: 2,102. Faculty: 145 (73 full-time, 72 part-time). Student-undergrad faculty ratio is 16:1. 438 applied, 99% were admitted. 12% from top 10% of their high school class, 28% from top quarter, 57% from top half. Full-time: 1,475 students, 57% women, 43% men. Part-time: 389 students, 64% women, 36% men. Students come from 31 states and territories, 30 other countries, 17% from out-of-state, 4% Native American, 3% Hispanic, 4% black, 1% Asian American or Pacific Islander, 3% international, 26% 25 or older, 20% live on campus, 12% transferred in. Retention: 62% of full-time freshmen returned the following year. Academic areas with the most degrees conferred: business/marketing; health professions and related sciences; education. Core. Calendar: semesters. Academic remediation for entering students, services for LD students, advanced placement, independent study, distance learning, double major, summer session for credit, part-time degree program, adult/continuing education programs, internships, graduate courses open to undergrads. Off campus study at Northern Oklahoma College, Southwestern Oklahoma State University. Study abroad program.

Entrance Requirements: Option: early admission. Required: high school transcript, SAT or ACT. Required for some: essay, minimum 2.7 high school GPA, 3 recommendations. Placement: SAT or ACT required. Entrance: moderately difficult. Application deadline: Rolling. Notification: continuous.

Costs Per Year: Application fee: $15. State resident tuition: $3270 full-time, $109 per credit hour part-time. Nonresident tuition: $8100 full-time, $270 per credit hour part-time. Full-time tuition varies according to course load, degree level, and location. Part-time tuition varies according to course load, degree level, and location. College room and board: $2980. College room only: $1000. Room and board charges vary according to board plan.

Collegiate Environment: Orientation program. Drama-theater group, choral group, marching band, student-run newspaper, radio station. Social organizations: 43 open to all; local fraternities, local sororities. Most popular organizations: Student Government Association, Aggie Club, Phi Beta Lambda, Baptist Student Union. Major annual events: Bahama Breakaway, Homecoming, Family Day. Student services: health clinic, personal-psychological counseling. Campus security: 24-hour emergency response devices and patrols, late night transport-escort service. 806 college housing spaces available; 396 were occupied in 2003-04. Freshmen guaranteed college housing. Options: men-only, women-only housing available. J. W. Martin Library plus 1 other with 344,640 books, 1 million microform titles, 3,990 serials, 3,609 audiovisual materials, an OPAC, and a Web page. Operations spending for 2004 fiscal year: $621,962. 131 computers available on campus for general student use. A campuswide network can be accessed from off-campus. Staffed computer lab on campus.

Community Environment: Alva is located in northwestern Oklahoma. The average mean temperature is 59.1 degrees. Rainfall averages 16 inches annually. Local public services include a hospital, many churches, five motels, and active civic and fraternal groups. A movie theatre, golf course, municipal swimming pool, park, picnic areas, lighted baseball fields, playgrounds, tennis courts, fishing, and hunting provide recreation and are all easily accessible. Little Sahara State Park and Alabaster Caverns are located approximately 25 miles distant.

■ **OKLAHOMA BAPTIST UNIVERSITY** *F-11*
500 West University
Shawnee, OK 74804
Tel: (405)275-2850
Free: 800-654-3285
Admissions: (405)878-2033
Fax: (405)878-2046
E-mail: admissions@mail.okbu.edu
Web Site: http://www.okbu.edu/

Description: Independent Southern Baptist, 4-year, coed. Awards bachelor's and master's degrees. Founded 1910. Setting: 125-acre small town campus with easy access to Oklahoma City. Endowment: $68.2 million. Educational spending for 2005 fiscal year: $5097 per student. Total enrollment: 1,883. 1,098 applied, 85% were admitted. 45% from top 10% of their high school class, 73% from top quarter, 92% from top half. 6 National Merit Scholars, 42 valedictorians. Full-time: 1,511 students, 61% women, 39% men. Part-time: 355 students, 34% women, 66% men. Students come from 42 states and territories, 17 other countries, 39% from out-of-state, 17% 25 or older, 72% live on campus, 5% transferred in. Retention: 74% of full-time freshmen returned the following year. Core. Calendar: 4-1-4. Academic remediation for entering students, services for LD students, advanced place-

ment, self-designed majors, honors program, independent study, double major, summer session for credit, part-time degree program, co-op programs and internships. Off campus study at St. Gregory's University. Study abroad program. ROTC: Air Force (c).

Entrance Requirements: Options: early admission, deferred admission, international baccalaureate accepted. Required: high school transcript, minimum 2.5 high school GPA, SAT or ACT. Required for some: essay, recommendations, interview. Entrance: moderately difficult. Application deadline: Rolling. Notification: continuous until 9/1.

Costs Per Year: Application fee: $25. Comprehensive fee: $17,986 includes full-time tuition ($12,924), mandatory fees ($922), and college room and board ($4140). College room only: $1840. Full-time tuition and fees vary according to course load. Room and board charges vary according to board plan and housing facility.

Collegiate Environment: Orientation program. Drama-theater group, choral group, student-run newspaper. Social organizations: 50 open to all; local fraternities, local sororities; 10% of eligible men and 10% of eligible women are members. Most popular organizations: Campus Activities Board, Student Ambassadors, Student Government Association, Baptist Student Union, University Concert Series. Major annual events: Stampede of Stars, Spring Affair, Welcome Week. Student services: health clinic, personal-psychological counseling. Campus security: 24-hour emergency response devices and patrols, late night transport-escort service, controlled dormitory access. On-campus residence required through junior year. Options: men-only, women-only housing available. Mabee Learning Center with 230,000 books, 315,000 microform titles, 1,800 serials, 1,600 audiovisual materials, an OPAC, and a Web page. Operations spending for 2004 fiscal year: $825,183. 170 computers available on campus for general student use. A campuswide network can be accessed from student residence rooms. Staffed computer lab on campus.

Community Environment: On the North Canadian River, Shawnee is in a rich agricultural and oil-producing area. The altitude of the city is 1,080 feet above sea level and the average temperature is 62.3 degrees. It is located near the geographical center of the state approximately 40 miles by interstate highway from Oklahoma City. The area is accessible via bus lines and a municipal airport. There are churches of most denominations and a YMCA in town. Local recreational facilities provide for golf, fishing, tennis, boating, hunting, bowling, and roller skating as well as picnic grounds, three swimming pools, parks, theatres, museums, and one drive-in. Events include horse shows and rodeo. There are various civic, fraternal and veterans' organizations here.

■ **OKLAHOMA CHRISTIAN UNIVERSITY** *F-9*
PO Box 11000
Oklahoma City, OK 73136-1100
Tel: (405)425-5000
Admissions: (405)425-5050
Fax: (405)425-5208
Web Site: http://www.oc.edu/

Description: Independent, comprehensive, coed, affiliated with Church of Christ. Awards bachelor's and master's degrees. Founded 1950. Setting: 200-acre suburban campus. Endowment: $45 million. Research spending for 2004 fiscal year: $25,000. Educational spending for 2005 fiscal year: $2946 per student. Total enrollment: 2,058. Faculty: 160 (85 full-time, 75 part-time). Student-undergrad faculty ratio is 15:1. 1,421 applied, 39% were admitted. 21% from top 10% of their high school class, 49% from top quarter, 77% from top half. 49% from out-of-state, 2% Native American, 3% Hispanic, 6% black, 1% Asian American or Pacific Islander, 66% live on campus. Retention: 66% of full-time freshmen returned the following year. Academic areas with the most degrees conferred: business/marketing; liberal arts/general studies; education. Core. Calendar: semesters. Academic remediation for entering students, ESL program, services for LD students, advanced placement, accelerated degree program, honors program, independent study, distance learning, double major, summer session for credit, internships. Off campus study at University of Central Oklahoma. Study abroad program. ROTC: Army (c), Air Force (c).

Entrance Requirements: Open admission. Options: early admission, deferred admission, international baccalaureate accepted. Required: high school transcript, SAT or ACT. Entrance: noncompetitive. Application deadline: Rolling. Notification: continuous.

Costs Per Year: Application fee: $25. Comprehensive fee: $20,416 includes full-time tuition ($13,422), mandatory fees ($1554), and college room and board ($5440). Part-time tuition: $559 per credit hour. Part-time mandatory fees: $747 per term.

Collegiate Environment: Orientation program. Drama-theater group, choral group, student-run newspaper, radio station. Social organizations: 19 open to all. Most popular organizations: Outreach, Agape, College Women for Christ, Young Republicans, College Democrats. Major annual events: Homecoming basketball game, Spring Sing, First Week Follies. Student services: health clinic, personal-psychological counseling. Campus security: 24-hour emergency response devices and patrols, late night transport-escort service. College housing designed to accommodate 1,183 students; 1,236 undergraduates lived in college housing during 2003-04. Freshmen guaranteed college housing. On-campus residence required through senior year. Options: men-only, women-only housing available. Tom and Ada Beam Library with 93,680 books, 700,019 microform titles, 1,171 serials, 5,083 audiovisual materials, an OPAC, and a Web page. Operations spending for 2004 fiscal year: $279,043. 101 computers available on campus for general student use. Computer purchase/lease plans available. A campuswide network can be accessed from student residence rooms and from off campus. Staffed computer lab on campus.

Community Environment: Oklahoma City has a metropolitan population of 958,000. Closer to the University is the smaller suburban community of Edmond, population 55,000. Air transportation is available at Will Rogers World Airport. Many cultural, entertainment, and job opportunities are readily available.

■ **OKLAHOMA CITY COMMUNITY COLLEGE** *F-9*

7777 South May Ave.
Oklahoma City, OK 73159-4419
Tel: (405)682-1611
Admissions: (405)682-7515
Web Site: http://www.okccc.edu/

Description: State-supported, 2-year, coed. Part of Oklahoma State Regents for Higher Education. Awards certificates, transfer associate, and terminal associate degrees. Founded 1969. Setting: 143-acre urban campus. Endowment: $91,544. Total enrollment: 12,048. Full-time: 4,863 students, 54% women, 46% men. Part-time: 7,185 students, 59% women, 41% men. Students come from 8 states and territories, 16 other countries, 5% Native American, 4% Hispanic, 8% black, 6% Asian American or Pacific Islander, 4% international, 6% transferred in. Core. Calendar: semesters. Academic remediation for entering students, ESL program, advanced placement, accelerated degree program, self-designed majors, honors program, independent study, distance learning, double major, summer session for credit, part-time degree program, external degree program, co-op programs.

Entrance Requirements: Open admission except for applicants under 19 or nursing, occupational therapy, physical therapy programs. Options: early admission, deferred admission. Required: high school transcript. Placement: ACT, ACT COMPASS required for some. Entrance: noncompetitive. Application deadline: Rolling.

Collegiate Environment: Orientation program. Drama-theater group, choral group, student-run newspaper. Social organizations: 20 open to all. Most popular organizations: Phi Theta Kappa, College Republicans, Future Teachers, Hispanic Organization to Promote Education, Student Activities Board. Major annual events: Arts Festival, Cultural Awareness Series, SAB Film Series. Student services: personal-psychological counseling. Campus security: 24-hour emergency response devices and patrols, late night transport-escort service. College housing not available.

Community Environment: Oklahoma City was born on April 22, 1889, when the population jumped from zero to 10,000 as a result of a unique land run. The city is one of the largest municipalities in the nation, covering a total of 621 square miles. The more than 970,000 residents enjoy temperatures ranging from the mid-80s in July to the mid-30s in January. The community is served by all major forms of transportation. Entertainment, cultural and sports related activities are numerous.

■ **OKLAHOMA CITY UNIVERSITY** *F-9*

2501 North Blackwelder
Oklahoma City, OK 73106-1402
Tel: (405)521-5000
Free: 800-633-7242
Admissions: (405)208-5050
E-mail: uadmissions@okcu.edu
Web Site: http://www.okcu.edu/

Description: Independent United Methodist, comprehensive, coed. Awards bachelor's, master's, and first professional degrees. Founded 1904. Setting: 68-acre urban campus. Endowment: $73.3 million. Educational spending for 2005 fiscal year: $7763 per student. Total enrollment: 3,688. Faculty: 285

(164 full-time, 121 part-time). Student-undergrad faculty ratio is 14:1. 1,044 applied, 81% were admitted. 30% from top 10% of their high school class, 65% from top quarter, 87% from top half. Full-time: 1,466 students, 61% women, 39% men. Part-time: 445 students, 67% women, 33% men. Students come from 49 states and territories, 65 other countries, 37% from out-of-state, 4% Native American, 4% Hispanic, 8% black, 2% Asian American or Pacific Islander, 20% international, 21% 25 or older, 39% live on campus, 6% transferred in. Retention: 72% of full-time freshmen returned the following year. Academic areas with the most degrees conferred: liberal arts/general studies; visual and performing arts; business/marketing. Core. Calendar: semesters. Academic remediation for entering students, ESL program, services for LD students, advanced placement, accelerated degree program, self-designed majors, honors program, independent study, double major, summer session for credit, part-time degree program, external degree program, adult/continuing education programs, co-op programs and internships, graduate courses open to undergrads. Off campus study at American University. Study abroad program. ROTC: Army (c), Air Force (c).

Entrance Requirements: Options: Common Application, electronic application, deferred admission, international baccalaureate accepted. Required: high school transcript, minimum 3.0 high school GPA, SAT or ACT. Required for some: interview, audition for music and dance programs. Entrance: moderately difficult. Application deadline: 8/20. Notification: continuous.

Costs Per Year: Application fee: $30. Comprehensive fee: $23,863 includes full-time tuition ($16,700), mandatory fees ($913), and college room and board ($6250). College room only: $3050. Full-time tuition and fees vary according to program. Room and board charges vary according to board plan and housing facility. Part-time tuition: $570 per semester hour. Part-time mandatory fees: $120 per term. Part-time tuition and fees vary according to program.

Collegiate Environment: Orientation program. Drama-theater group, choral group, student-run newspaper. Social organizations: 42 open to all; national fraternities, national sororities; 11% of eligible men and 15% of eligible women are members. Major annual events: homecoming, Spring Sing, Midnight Breakfast. Student services: health clinic, personal-psychological counseling. Campus security: 24-hour emergency response devices and patrols, student patrols, late night transport-escort service, Operation ID. 1,051 college housing spaces available. Freshmen given priority for college housing. On-campus residence required through senior year. Options: men-only, women-only housing available. Dulaney Browne Library plus 1 other with 440,374 books, 975,580 microform titles, 6,017 serials, 10,948 audiovisual materials, an OPAC, and a Web page. Operations spending for 2004 fiscal year: $2.6 million. 264 computers available on campus for general student use. A campuswide network can be accessed from student residence rooms and from off campus. Staffed computer lab on campus.

Community Environment: Oklahoma City, the capital City of Oklahoma, offers a wide variety of cultural, civic, religious, entertainment and sports events in the unique setting of modern facilities and old-fashioned Western hospitality. With more than 1,000,000 people in the metropolitan area, Oklahoma City is a dynamic, growing location with a wide range of opportunities to offer its students. From the State Capitol and the center of Oklahoma's political and governmental activity, to the cultural offerings the Oklahoma City Philharmonic, Lyric Theater, Ballet Oklahoma, Oklahoma Zoo, Omniplex, and more. Oklahoma City stands as a vibrant, growing metropolitan center offerings the Southwest. Out-of-state students are able to make use of the excellent transportation facilities available to the City. Oklahoma City is linked by interstate highways to other major cities in the region, and the City's Will Rogers International Airport, one offerings the busiest in the region, provides jet service coast-to-coast and international flights to Europe, Asia, and South America.

■ **OKLAHOMA PANHANDLE STATE UNIVERSITY** *M-7*

PO Box 430
Goodwell, OK 73939-0430
Tel: (580)349-2611
Free: 800-664-6778
Admissions: (580)349-1376
Fax: (580)349-2302
Web Site: http://www.opsu.edu/

Description: State-supported, 4-year, coed. Part of Oklahoma State Regents for Higher Education. Awards associate and bachelor's degrees. Founded 1909. Setting: 40-acre rural campus. Total enrollment: 1,144. Student-undergrad faculty ratio is 13:1. 257 applied, 100% were admitted. Full-time: 920 students, 51% women, 49% men. Part-time: 224 students, 71% women, 29% men. Students come from 34 states and territories, 19 other countries, 40% from out-of-state, 3% Native American, 12% Hispanic, 4% black, 0.3% Asian American or Pacific Islander, 3% international, 23% 25 or older, 17% live on campus, 16% transferred in. Academic areas with the most degrees conferred: agriculture; education; biological/life sciences. Core. Calendar: semesters. Academic remediation for entering students, ESL program, advanced placement, accelerated degree program, distance learning, double major, summer session for credit, part-time degree program, adult/continuing education programs, co-op programs and internships.

Entrance Requirements: Open admission. Options: Common Application, electronic application, international baccalaureate accepted. Required: high school transcript. Required for some: SAT or ACT. Entrance: noncompetitive. Application deadlines: Rolling, Rolling for nonresidents.

Costs Per Year: Application fee: $0. State resident tuition: $2274 full-time, $75.80 per hour part-time. Nonresident tuition: $4500 full-time, $150 per hour part-time. Mandatory fees: $1118 full-time, $34.50 per hour part-time, $62 per term part-time. Full-time tuition and fees vary according to course level and program. Part-time tuition and fees vary according to course level. College room and board: $4270. College room only: $2520. Room and board charges vary according to board plan, housing facility, and student level.

Collegiate Environment: Orientation program. Drama-theater group, choral group, marching band, student-run newspaper, radio station. Social organizations: 39 open to all. Major annual events: Fall Homecoming, Annual Rodeo. Student services: health clinic, personal-psychological counseling. Campus security: 24-hour emergency response devices and patrols, student patrols, safety bars over door latches. 450 college housing spaces available; 315 were occupied in 2003-04. Freshmen guaranteed college housing. On-campus residence required in freshman year. Option: coed housing available. McKee Library with 129,467 books, 10,064 microform titles, 5,295 serials, 6,132 audiovisual materials, an OPAC, and a Web page. Operations spending for 2004 fiscal year: $359,645. 50 computers available on campus for general student use. A campuswide network can be accessed from student residence rooms and from off campus. Staffed computer lab on campus.

Community Environment: Goodwell is located in the center of the Oklahoma Panhandle in Texas County. The climate is cool and arid. The area is served by railroad, and Highway 54. Goodwell has three churches, and various civic, fraternal and veteran's organizations.

■ **OKLAHOMA STATE UNIVERSITY** *D-10*
Stillwater, OK 74078
Tel: (405)744-5000
Free: 800-852-1255
Admissions: (405)744-5358
Fax: (405)744-5285
E-mail: paul.carney@okstate.edu
Web Site: http://osu.okstate.edu/

Description: State-supported, university, coed. Part of Oklahoma State University System. Awards bachelor's, master's, doctoral, and first professional degrees and post-master's certificates. Founded 1890. Setting: 840-acre small town campus with easy access to Oklahoma City and Tulsa. Endowment: $195.6 million. Research spending for 2004 fiscal year: $77.7 million. Educational spending for 2005 fiscal year: $6529 per student. Total enrollment: 23,461. Faculty: 1,237 (1,000 full-time, 237 part-time). Student-undergrad faculty ratio is 19:1. 6,533 applied, 88% were admitted. 27% from top 10% of their high school class, 55% from top quarter, 85% from top half. 7 National Merit Scholars, 621 valedictorians. Full-time: 16,731 students, 48% women, 52% men. Part-time: 2,178 students, 47% women, 53% men. Students come from 50 states and territories, 82 other countries, 15% from out-of-state, 9% Native American, 2% Hispanic, 4% black, 2% Asian American or Pacific Islander, 4% international, 12% 25 or older, 40% live on campus, 9% transferred in. Retention: 79% of full-time freshmen returned the following year. Academic areas with the most degrees conferred: business/marketing; engineering; education. Core. Calendar: semesters. Academic remediation for entering students, ESL program, services for LD students, advanced placement, accelerated degree program, self-designed majors, freshman honors college, honors program, independent study, distance learning, double major, summer session for credit, part-time degree program, adult/continuing education programs, co-op programs and internships, graduate courses open to undergrads. Off campus study at National Student Exchange. Study abroad program. ROTC: Army, Air Force.

Entrance Requirements: Options: electronic application, international baccalaureate accepted. Required: high school transcript, minimum 3.0 high

school GPA, class rank, SAT or ACT. Required for some: interview. Entrance: moderately difficult. Application deadline: Rolling. Notification: continuous.

Costs Per Year: Application fee: $40. State resident tuition: $3099 full-time, $103.30 per credit hour part-time. Nonresident tuition: $11,122 full-time, $370.75 per credit hour part-time. Mandatory fees: $1266 full-time, $42.21 per credit hour part-time. Full-time tuition and fees vary according to program and student level. Part-time tuition and fees vary according to program and student level. College room and board: $5848. College room only: $2848. Room and board charges vary according to board plan, housing facility, and location.

Collegiate Environment: Orientation program. Drama-theater group, choral group, marching band, student-run newspaper, radio station. Social organizations: 360 open to all; national fraternities, national sororities; 18% of eligible men and 24% of eligible women are members. Most popular organizations: Student Government Association, Campus Crusade for Christ, Flying Aggies, Block and Bridle Club, OSU Ski Club. Major annual events: Homecoming, Madrigal Dinner and Concert, Spring Sing. Student services: legal services, health clinic, personal-psychological counseling, women's center. Campus security: 24-hour emergency response devices and patrols, student patrols, controlled dormitory access. 6,052 college housing spaces available; 4,540 were occupied in 2003-04. Freshmen guaranteed college housing. On-campus residence required in freshman year. Options: coed, men-only, women-only housing available. Edmon Low Library plus 3 others with 2.5 million books, 4.5 million microform titles, 23,806 serials, 517,213 audiovisual materials, an OPAC, and a Web page. Operations spending for 2004 fiscal year: $12.8 million. 2,456 computers available on campus for general student use. A campuswide network can be accessed from student residence rooms and from off campus. Staffed computer lab on campus.

Community Environment: Stillwater is located in north central Oklahoma. The climate is mild with an average annual temperature of 59.8 degrees and average rainfall of 33.3 inches. The city is accessible by Highways 51 and 177, and nearby U.S. Highways 64 and Interstate 35. There are bus lines to the city. Stillwater has several churches of major denominations, a hospital, two clinics, and a health center. Local recreational facilities include 15 parks, three golf courses, fishing, camping, picnicking, hiking, hunting, boating, water-skiing, theatres, and a drive-in. Rooming houses, apartments and private homes provide housing for students. There is part-time employment available.

■ **OKLAHOMA STATE UNIVERSITY, OKLAHOMA CITY** *F-9*
900 North Portland
Oklahoma City, OK 73107-6120
Tel: (405)947-4421
Admissions: (405)945-3287
Fax: (405)945-3277
Web Site: http://www.osuokc.edu/

Description: State-supported, 2-year, coed. Part of Oklahoma State University. Awards certificates, transfer associate, and terminal associate degrees. Founded 1961. Setting: 80-acre urban campus. Total enrollment: 5,654. Students come from 18 states and territories, 15 other countries, 1% from out-of-state, 6% Native American, 3% Hispanic, 13% black, 3% Asian American or Pacific Islander, 1% international, 51% 25 or older. Core. Calendar: semesters. Academic remediation for entering students, services for LD students, advanced placement, honors program, independent study, distance learning, double major, summer session for credit, part-time degree program.

Entrance Requirements: Open admission except for nursing program. Option: early admission. Placement: SAT or ACT, ACT COMPASS required for some. Entrance: noncompetitive. Application deadline: Rolling. Notification: continuous.

Collegiate Environment: Social organizations: 20 open to all. Most popular organizations: Phi Theta Kappa, Deaf/Hearing Social Club, American Criminal Justice Association, Horticulture Club, Vet-Tech Club. Major annual events: Howdy Week, Spring Fling, Halloween Party. Campus security: 24-hour patrols, late night transport-escort service. College housing not available. Oklahoma State University-Oklahoma City Campus with 11,973 books, 244 serials, an OPAC, and a Web page. 75 computers available on campus for general student use. A campuswide network can be accessed from off-campus. Staffed computer lab on campus.

Community Environment: See Oklahoma City University.

■ **OKLAHOMA STATE UNIVERSITY, OKMULGEE** *E-13*
1801 East Fourth St.
Okmulgee, OK 74447-3901
Tel: (918)293-4678
Free: 800-722-4471
Admissions: (918)293-5298
Web Site: http://www.osu-okmulgee.edu/
Description: State-supported, 2-year, coed. Part of Oklahoma State University. Awards transfer associate and terminal associate degrees. Founded 1946. Setting: 160-acre small town campus with easy access to Tulsa. Total enrollment: 2,329. Full-time: 1,717 students, 33% women, 67% men. Part-time: 612 students, 58% women, 42% men. Students come from 22 states and territories, 3 other countries, 37% 25 or older, 25% live on campus. Core. Calendar: trimesters. Academic remediation for entering students, services for LD students, advanced placement, summer session for credit, part-time degree program, adult/continuing education programs, internships.
Entrance Requirements: Open admission. Options: Common Application, deferred admission. Required: high school transcript. Placement: SAT or ACT required. Entrance: noncompetitive. Application deadline: Rolling.
Collegiate Environment: Drama-theater group. Social organizations: 32 open to all. Most popular organizations: Student Senate, Junior Ambassadors, Phi Theta Kappa, departmental clubs, Drama Club. Major annual events: Super Weekend, Okmulgee College and Career Day, Auto Show. Student services: health clinic, personal-psychological counseling. Campus security: 24-hour emergency response devices and patrols, late night transport-escort service, controlled dormitory access. On-campus residence required in freshman year. Option: coed housing available. Learning Resource Center with 9,965 books, 484 serials, an OPAC, and a Web page. 360 computers available on campus for general student use. Staffed computer lab on campus.

■ **OKLAHOMA WESLEYAN UNIVERSITY** *B-13*
2201 Silver Lake Rd.
Bartlesville, OK 74006-6299
Tel: (918)335-6200
Admissions: (866)222-8226
Fax: (918)335-6229
E-mail: jweidman@okwu.edu
Web Site: http://www.okwu.edu/
Description: Independent, comprehensive, coed, affiliated with Wesleyan Church. Awards associate, bachelor's, and master's degrees. Founded 1909. Setting: 127-acre small town campus with easy access to Tulsa. Endowment: $2.9 million. Total enrollment: 887. 391 applied, 77% were admitted. 20% from top 10% of their high school class, 35% from top quarter, 80% from top half. 5 valedictorians. Full-time: 864 students, 54% women, 46% men. Part-time: 23 students, 61% women, 39% men. Students come from 31 states and territories, 13 other countries, 37% from out-of-state, 8% Native American, 2% Hispanic, 4% black, 1% Asian American or Pacific Islander, 2% international, 35% 25 or older, 70% live on campus, 6% transferred in. Retention: 70% of full-time freshmen returned the following year. Core. Calendar: semesters. Academic remediation for entering students, ESL program, advanced placement, accelerated degree program, self-designed majors, independent study, distance learning, double major, summer session for credit, part-time degree program, external degree program, adult/continuing education programs, co-op programs and internships. Off campus study at Tri-County Technical College, Coalition for Christian Colleges and Universities. Study abroad program.
Entrance Requirements: Options: Peterson's Universal Application, electronic application. Required: essay, high school transcript, minimum ACT of 18 or SAT 860, SAT or ACT. Recommended: minimum 2.0 high school GPA. Entrance: minimally difficult. Application deadline: Rolling.
Costs Per Year: Application fee: $25. Comprehensive fee: $18,950 includes full-time tuition ($12,900), mandatory fees ($850), and college room and board ($5200). College room only: $2625. Full-time tuition and fees vary according to course load. Room and board charges vary according to board plan and housing facility. Part-time tuition: $475 per credit. Part-time mandatory fees: $50 per credit.
Collegiate Environment: Orientation program. Choral group, student-run newspaper. Social organizations: 10 open to all. Most popular organizations: Forensics Club, Fellowship of Christian Athletes, Teachers Association, Theology Club, Education Club. Major annual events: Homecoming Festivi-

ties, seasonal banquets. Student services: health clinic, personal-psychological counseling. Campus security: 24-hour emergency response devices and patrols, controlled dormitory access. 300 college housing spaces available; 272 were occupied in 2003-04. No special consideration for freshman housing applicants. On-campus residence required through senior year. Options: men-only, women-only housing available. Oklahoma Wesleyan University Library with 124,722 books, 300 serials, an OPAC, and a Web page. Operations spending for 2004 fiscal year: $300,000. 30 computers available on campus for general student use. A campuswide network can be accessed from student residence rooms. Staffed computer lab on campus.

■ **ORAL ROBERTS UNIVERSITY** *D-13*
7777 South Lewis Ave.
Tulsa, OK 74171-0001
Tel: (918)495-6161
Free: 800-678-8876
Admissions: (918)495-6529
Fax: (918)495-6222
E-mail: admissions@oru.edu
Web Site: http://www.oru.edu/
Description: Independent interdenominational, comprehensive, coed. Awards bachelor's, master's, doctoral, and first professional degrees. Founded 1963. Setting: 263-acre urban campus. Endowment: $66.4 million. Research spending for 2004 fiscal year: $107,010. Educational spending for 2005 fiscal year: $2742 per student. Total enrollment: 4,086. Faculty: 235 (164 full-time, 71 part-time). Student-undergrad faculty ratio is 16:1. 1,244 applied, 70% were admitted. 6 National Merit Scholars. Students come from 41 other countries, 86% from out-of-state, 1% Native American, 5% Hispanic, 23% black, 3% Asian American or Pacific Islander, 5% international, 11% 25 or older, 71% live on campus. Core. Calendar: semesters. Academic remediation for entering students, ESL program, services for LD students, advanced placement, self-designed majors, freshman honors college, honors program, independent study, distance learning, double major, summer session for credit, part-time degree program, external degree program, adult/continuing education programs, internships, graduate courses open to undergrads. Off campus study at Christian College Coalition. Study abroad program. ROTC: Air Force (c).
Entrance Requirements: Options: early admission, early action, deferred admission, international baccalaureate accepted. Required: essay, high school transcript, minimum 2.0 high school GPA, 1 recommendation, proof of immunization, SAT or ACT. Required for some: interview. Entrance: moderately difficult. Application deadlines: Rolling, 9/1 for early action. Notification: continuous, 9/1 for early action.
Costs Per Year: Application fee: $35. Comprehensive fee: $22,650 includes full-time tuition ($15,400), mandatory fees ($480), and college room and board ($6770). College room only: $3280. Room and board charges vary according to board plan and housing facility. Part-time tuition: $642 per credit hour.
Collegiate Environment: Orientation program. Drama-theater group, choral group, student-run newspaper, radio station. Social organizations: 37 open to all. Most popular organizations: missions, Student Nurse Association, American Management Society, Accounting Society. Major annual events: homecoming, community outreach events, revivals. Student services: health clinic, personal-psychological counseling. Campus security: 24-hour emergency response devices and patrols, late night transport-escort service. On-campus residence required through senior year. Options: men-only, women-only housing available. John D. Messick Resources Center plus 1 other with 216,691 books, 49,936 microform titles, 600 serials, 25,445 audiovisual materials, an OPAC, and a Web page. Operations spending for 2004 fiscal year: $1.1 million. 253 computers available on campus for general student use. A campuswide network can be accessed from student residence rooms and from off campus. Staffed computer lab on campus.
Community Environment: Tulsa is located in northeast Oklahoma. The area has four distinct seasons, and is served by major airlines, bus lines, and U.S. highways. Tulsa is located on the fringe of the southwest's greatest inland vacation and recreation areas. Nearby lakes provide fishing, golf, boating, hunting, and other outdoor sports. Community services include many churches, an Opera Association, Philbrook and Gilcrease Museums, major health facilities, and civic organizations.

■ **PLATT COLLEGE (OKLAHOMA CITY)** *F-9*
309 South Ann Arbor Ave.
Oklahoma City, OK 73128

Tel: (405)946-7799
Fax: (405)943-2150
E-mail: janen@plattcollege.org
Web Site: http://www.plattcollege.org/
Description: Proprietary, 2-year, coed. Founded 1979. Calendar: continuous.

■ **PLATT COLLEGE (TULSA)** *D-13*
3801 South Sheridan Rd.
Tulsa, OK 74145
Tel: (918)663-9000
Fax: (918)622-1240
E-mail: susanr@plattcollege.org
Web Site: http://www.plattcollege.org/
Description: Proprietary, 2-year, coed. Founded 1979. Calendar: continuous.

■ **REDLANDS COMMUNITY COLLEGE** *F-8*
1300 South Country Club Rd.
El Reno, OK 73036-5304
Tel: (405)262-2552
Web Site: http://www.redlandscc.edu/
Description: State-supported, 2-year, coed. Part of Oklahoma State Regents for Higher Education. Awards certificates, transfer associate, and terminal associate degrees. Founded 1938. Setting: 55-acre suburban campus with easy access to Oklahoma City. Total enrollment: 2,323. Full-time: 583 students, 62% women, 38% men. Part-time: 1,740 students, 64% women, 36% men. Students come from 4 states and territories, 7 other countries, 8% Native American, 3% Hispanic, 6% black, 2% Asian American or Pacific Islander, 2% international, 36% 25 or older, 15% transferred in. Core. Calendar: semesters. Academic remediation for entering students, services for LD students, advanced placement, accelerated degree program, honors program, distance learning, double major, summer session for credit, part-time degree program, external degree program, adult/continuing education programs, co-op programs and internships.
Entrance Requirements: Open admission except for nursing, medical laboratory technology programs. Options: Common Application, electronic application, early admission, deferred admission. Required: high school transcript. Placement: ACT required. Entrance: noncompetitive. Application deadline: Rolling. Notification: continuous.
Costs Per Year: Application fee: $0. State resident tuition: $1380 full-time, $46 per credit hour part-time. Nonresident tuition: $3630 full-time, $121 per credit hour part-time. Mandatory fees: $930 full-time, $31 per credit hour part-time. Full-time tuition and fees vary according to location. Part-time tuition and fees vary according to location.
Collegiate Environment: Drama-theater group, choral group. Social organizations: 11 open to all. Most popular organizations: Nursing Club, Aggie Club, Baptist Student Union, Phi Theta Kappa, Outdoors Club. Major annual events: Back to School Bash, End of Year Party, Career Fair. Student services: personal-psychological counseling. Campus security: 24-hour patrols. College housing not available. Learning Resource Center with 14,810 books, 43,865 microform titles, 292 serials, 19,075 audiovisual materials, and an OPAC. 74 computers available on campus for general student use. A campuswide network can be accessed from off-campus. Staffed computer lab on campus.
Community Environment: El Reno is located on the south bank of the North Canadian River. The average annual temperature is 60 degrees. The city is served by bus lines, railroad, and an airport. Nearby lakes offer waterskiing, fishing, and boating. El Reno has many community service facilities including a hospital, hotel and many motels, a library, and various civic, service, and fraternal organizations. Part-time job opportunities are good. Local recreational facilities include two movie theatres, drive-ins, parks, tennis, golf, and a municipal swimming pool.

■ **ROGERS STATE UNIVERSITY** *C-14*
1701 West Will Rogers Blvd.
Claremore, OK 74017-3252
Tel: (918)343-7777
Free: 800-256-7511
Admissions: (918)343-7545
Fax: (918)343-7898
E-mail: bnoah@rsu.edu
Web Site: http://www.rsu.edu/

Description: State-supported, 4-year, coed. Part of Oklahoma State Regents for Higher Education. Awards associate and bachelor's degrees. Founded 1909. Setting: 40-acre small town campus with easy access to Tulsa. Endowment: $4 million. Research spending for 2004 fiscal year: $4500. Educational spending for 2005 fiscal year: $4478 per student. Total enrollment: 3,300. 1,001 applied, 89% were admitted. 8% from top 10% of their high school class, 26% from top quarter, 55% from top half. Full-time: 1,681 students, 61% women, 39% men. Part-time: 1,619 students, 65% women, 35% men. Students come from 16 other countries, 3% from out-of-state, 45% 25 or older, 10% live on campus, 28% transferred in. Retention: 51% of full-time freshmen returned the following year. Core. Calendar: semesters. Academic remediation for entering students, services for LD students, advanced placement, independent study, distance learning, double major, summer session for credit, part-time degree program, external degree program, adult/continuing education programs, co-op programs and internships. Off campus study at Northeast Technology Centers, Claremore and Pryor, OK; Tri-County Technology Center, Bartlesville, OK; University Learning Center of Northern Oklahoma; Central Technology Center, Drumright, OK. ROTC: Air Force (c).
Entrance Requirements: Open admission for applicants to the Associate's degree program or the Certificate program. Option: electronic application. Required: high school transcript. Required for some: minimum 2.7 high school GPA, ACT, ACT COMPASS (for students over 21). Entrance: noncompetitive. Application deadline: Rolling.
Costs Per Year: Application fee: $0. State resident tuition: $3300 full-time, $110 per credit hour part-time. Nonresident tuition: $7860 full-time, $262 per credit hour part-time. Mandatory fees: $30 full-time, $15 per term part-time. College room and board: $6210. College room only: $4050.
Collegiate Environment: Orientation program. Student-run newspaper, radio station. Social organizations: 22 open to all; 3% of eligible men and 5% of eligible women are members. Most popular organizations: Phi Theta Kappa, Adult Students Aspiring to Prosper, Horse and Ag Student Association, Native American Student Association, Criminal Justice Student Association. Major annual events: Welcome Week, Halloween Dance/Carnival, Spring Fling. Student services: personal-psychological counseling, women's center. Campus security: 24-hour patrols, late night transport-escort service. 256 college housing spaces available; 200 were occupied in 2003-04. No special consideration for freshman housing applicants. Option: coed housing available. Rogers State University Library with 57,283 books, 524 serials, 4,844 audiovisual materials, an OPAC, and a Web page. Operations spending for 2004 fiscal year: $468,500. 314 computers available on campus for general student use. A campuswide network can be accessed from student residence rooms and from off campus. Staffed computer lab on campus.

■ **ROSE STATE COLLEGE** *F-10*
6420 Southeast 15th St.
Midwest City, OK 73110-2799
Tel: (405)733-7673
Fax: (405)733-7399
E-mail: ekhutchings@ms.rose.cc.ok.us
Web Site: http://www.rose.edu/
Description: State and locally supported, 2-year, coed. Part of Oklahoma State Regents for Higher Education. Awards certificates, transfer associate, and terminal associate degrees. Founded 1968. Setting: 110-acre suburban campus with easy access to Oklahoma City. Total enrollment: 7,000. Students come from 18 states and territories, 33 other countries, 60% 25 or older. Core. Calendar: semesters. Academic remediation for entering students, services for LD students, advanced placement, accelerated degree program, honors program, independent study, distance learning, summer session for credit, part-time degree program, adult/continuing education programs, internships. Off campus study. ROTC: Army (c), Air Force (c).
Entrance Requirements: Open admission except for health occupations programs. Options: Common Application, electronic application, early admission, deferred admission. Required: high school transcript. Placement: SAT, ACT, or ACT COMPASS required. Entrance: noncompetitive. Application deadline: Rolling. Notification: continuous.
Collegiate Environment: Drama-theater group, choral group, student-run newspaper. Student services: health clinic, personal-psychological counseling, women's center. Campus security: 24-hour patrols. College housing not available. Rose State College Learning Resources Center with 90,000 books, 6,193 microform titles, 443 serials, 9,620 audiovisual materials, an OPAC, and a Web page. Operations spending for 2004 fiscal year: $1.3 million. 390 computers available on campus for general student use. A campuswide network can be accessed from off-campus. Staffed computer lab on campus.

Community Environment: See Oklahoma City University.

■ ST. GREGORY'S UNIVERSITY *F-11*

1900 West MacArthur Dr.
Shawnee, OK 74804-2499
Tel: (405)878-5100; 888-STGREGS
Fax: (405)878-5198
Web Site: http://www.stgregorys.edu/

Description: Independent Roman Catholic, 4-year, coed. Awards associate and bachelor's degrees. Founded 1875. Setting: 640-acre small town campus with easy access to Oklahoma City. Endowment: $9.5 million. Educational spending for 2005 fiscal year: $3314 per student. Total enrollment: 868. Student-undergrad faculty ratio is 15:1. 235 applied, 83% were admitted. 13% from top 10% of their high school class, 20% from top quarter, 26% from top half. Full-time: 476 students, 51% women, 49% men. Part-time: 392 students, 54% women, 46% men. Students come from 15 states and territories, 22 other countries, 13% from out-of-state, 8% Native American, 7% Hispanic, 6% black, 1% Asian American or Pacific Islander, 12% international, 30% 25 or older, 65% live on campus, 10% transferred in. Retention: 60% of full-time freshmen returned the following year. Academic areas with the most degrees conferred: business/marketing; social sciences; parks and recreation. Core. Calendar: semesters. ESL program, services for LD students, advanced placement, accelerated degree program, self-designed majors, honors program, independent study, distance learning, double major, summer session for credit, part-time degree program, external degree program, adult/continuing education programs, internships. Off campus study. Study abroad program. ROTC: Army (c), Air Force (c).

Entrance Requirements: Options: Peterson's Universal Application, Common Application, electronic application, deferred admission, international baccalaureate accepted. Required: high school transcript, minimum 2.0 high school GPA, SAT or ACT. Required for some: essay, recommendations, interview. Entrance: minimally difficult. Application deadline: Rolling. Notification: continuous.

Costs Per Year: Application fee: $25. Comprehensive fee: $19,408 includes full-time tuition ($12,922), mandatory fees ($850), and college room and board ($5636). College room only: $3200. Part-time tuition: $465 per hour. Part-time mandatory fees: $36 per hour.

Collegiate Environment: Orientation program. Drama-theater group, choral group, student-run newspaper. Social organizations: 27 open to all; local fraternities, local sororities; 25% of eligible men and 25% of eligible women are members. Most popular organizations: Student Government Association, Delta Epsilon Sigma Homer Society, Campus Ministry, ITEST-Institute for Theological Encounter with Science and Technology, Drama Club. Major annual events: Orientation, Dean's Activity Night, Winter/Spring Formals. Student services: personal-psychological counseling. Campus security: 24-hour emergency response devices and patrols, late night transport-escort service, controlled dormitory access. 400 college housing spaces available; 312 were occupied in 2003-04. Freshmen guaranteed college housing. On-campus residence required through senior year. Options: men-only, women-only housing available. James J. Kelly Library plus 1 other with 82,715 books, 3,000 microform titles, 2,060 serials, 267 audiovisual materials, an OPAC, and a Web page. Operations spending for 2004 fiscal year: $105,600. 60 computers available on campus for general student use. A campuswide network can be accessed from student residence rooms and from off campus.

■ SEMINOLE STATE COLLEGE *G-11*

PO Box 351
Seminole, OK 74818-0351
Tel: (405)382-9950
Admissions: (405)382-9272
Web Site: http://www.ssc.cc.ok.us/

Description: State-supported, 2-year, coed. Part of Oklahoma State Regents for Higher Education. Awards diplomas, transfer associate, and terminal associate degrees. Founded 1931. Setting: 40-acre small town campus with easy access to Oklahoma City. Educational spending for 2005 fiscal year: $2149 per student. Total enrollment: 2,584. 2,096 applied, 100% were admitted. Full-time: 2,096 students, 69% women, 31% men. Part-time: 488 students, 74% women, 26% men. Students come from 13 states and territories, 5 other countries, 2% from out-of-state, 23% Native American, 2% Hispanic, 6% black, 0.3% Asian American or Pacific Islander, 1% international, 47% 25 or older, 8% live on campus, 43% transferred in. Core. Calendar: semesters. Academic remediation for entering students, services for LD students, advanced placement, accelerated degree program, honors

program, independent study, distance learning, summer session for credit, part-time degree program, adult/continuing education programs, co-op programs. Off campus study at Gordon Cooper Technology Center, Wes Watkins Technology Center, Moore-Norman Technology Center.

Entrance Requirements: Open admission. Options: Common Application, early admission, deferred admission. Required: high school transcript. Entrance: noncompetitive. Application deadline: Rolling. Notification: continuous.

Costs Per Year: Application fee: $15. State resident tuition: $1116 full-time, $46.50 per credit hour part-time. Nonresident tuition: $3,589 full-time, $149.55 per credit hour part-time. Mandatory fees: $719 full-time, $29.95 per credit hour part-time. College room and board: $2470.

Collegiate Environment: Choral group, student-run newspaper. Social organizations: 21 open to all; local fraternities; 1% of eligible men and 1% of eligible women are members. Most popular organizations: Student Government Association, Native American Student Association, Psi Beta Honor Society, Student Nurses Association, Phi Theta Kappa. Major annual events: Trojan Olympics, SSC Coffee House, Mayfair. Student services: personal-psychological counseling. Campus security: 24-hour patrols. 125 college housing spaces available; all were occupied in 2003-04. Option: coed housing available. Boren Library with 27,507 books, 200 serials, and an OPAC. Operations spending for 2004 fiscal year: $205,958. 100 computers available on campus for general student use. A campuswide network can be accessed from off-campus. Staffed computer lab on campus.

Community Environment: Seminole is an urban community enjoying temperate climate. Local transportation services include railroad, bus, and airlines. The city has a public library, 30 churches of various denominations, a hospital, and three clinics. Some part-time employment is available for students. Recreational facilities in Seminole include a theater, a drive-in, bowling, and water sports. The major civic, fraternal and veteran's organizations are active within the immediate community. There are several historic sites located nearby.

■ SOUTHEASTERN OKLAHOMA STATE UNIVERSITY *K-12*

1405 North 4th Ave.
Durant, OK 74701-0609
Tel: (580)745-2000
Free: 800-435-1327
Admissions: (580)745-2060
Fax: (580)745-7490
E-mail: kstafford@sosu.edu
Web Site: http://www.sosu.edu/

Description: State-supported, comprehensive, coed. Part of Oklahoma State Regents for Higher Education. Awards bachelor's and master's degrees and post-master's certificates. Founded 1909. Setting: 177-acre small town campus. Endowment: $11.4 million. Research spending for 2004 fiscal year: $515,396. Educational spending for 2005 fiscal year: $7384 per student. Total enrollment: 4,075. Faculty: 237 (141 full-time, 96 part-time). Student-undergrad faculty ratio is 20:1. 1,067 applied, 80% were admitted. 11% from top 10% of their high school class, 20% from top quarter, 68% from top half. 26 valedictorians. Full-time: 2,994 students, 53% women, 47% men. Part-time: 669 students, 66% women, 34% men. Students come from 35 states and territories, 28 other countries, 21% from out-of-state, 29% Native American, 2% Hispanic, 5% black, 0.5% Asian American or Pacific Islander, 1% international, 24% 25 or older, 20% live on campus, 12% transferred in. Retention: 58% of full-time freshmen returned the following year. Academic areas with the most degrees conferred: education; business/marketing; engineering technologies. Core. Calendar: semesters. Academic remediation for entering students, services for LD students, advanced placement, accelerated degree program, honors program, independent study, distance learning, double major, summer session for credit, part-time degree program, adult/continuing education programs, internships, graduate courses open to undergrads. Off campus study at Ardmore Higher Education Center, E.T. Dunlap Higher Education Center, Tinker AFB, OKCCC.

Entrance Requirements: Open admission for adults over 21. Required: high school transcript, SAT or ACT. Required for some: interview. Entrance: moderately difficult. Application deadline: Rolling. Notification: continuous.

Costs Per Year: Application fee: $20. State resident tuition: $2195 full-time, $73.15 per credit hour part-time. Nonresident tuition: $7016 full-time, $233.85 per credit hour part-time. Mandatory fees: $1177 full-time, $34.70 per credit part-time, $68. Full-time tuition and fees vary according to course level. Part-time tuition and fees vary according to course level and course load. College room and board: $3910. College room only: $1875. Room and board charges vary according to board plan and housing facility.

Collegiate Environment: Orientation program. Drama-theater group, choral group, marching band, student-run newspaper, radio station. Social organizations: 40 open to all; national fraternities, national sororities; 1% of eligible men and 2% of eligible women are members. Most popular organizations: Baptist Collegiate Ministries, Fellowship of Christian Athletes, Wesley Foundation, Resident Hall Association. Major annual events: Springfest, Homecoming, Welcome Week. Student services: health clinic, personal-psychological counseling. Campus security: 24-hour patrols, late night transport-escort service. 636 college housing spaces available; 478 were occupied in 2003-04. No special consideration for freshman housing applicants. Options: coed, men-only, women-only housing available. Henry G. Bennett Memorial Library with 187,971 books, 457,438 microform titles, 671 serials, 5,291 audiovisual materials, an OPAC, and a Web page. Operations spending for 2004 fiscal year: $854,434. 425 computers available on campus for general student use. A campuswide network can be accessed from student residence rooms. Staffed computer lab on campus.

Community Environment: Durant is a rural community served by bus line and airport. The community has one hospital, Medical Center of Southeastern Oklahoma, and active civic, fraternal, and veteran's organizations. There are libraries, churches, and motels. Local recreational facilities include hunting, boating, fishing, golf and other sports.

■ **SOUTHERN NAZARENE UNIVERSITY** *F-9*
6729 Northwest 39th Expressway
Bethany, OK 73008
Tel: (405)789-6400
Free: 800-648-9899
Admissions: (405)491-6324
Fax: (405)491-6381
E-mail: lhess@snu.edu
Web Site: http://www.snu.edu/

Description: Independent Nazarene, comprehensive, coed. Awards associate, bachelor's, and master's degrees. Founded 1899. Setting: 40-acre suburban campus with easy access to Oklahoma City. Endowment: $15 million. Research spending for 2004 fiscal year: $2000. Educational spending for 2005 fiscal year: $6515 per student. Total enrollment: 2,218. Faculty: 176 (69 full-time, 107 part-time). Student-undergrad faculty ratio is 16:1. 529 applied, 54% were admitted. 25% from top 10% of their high school class, 45% from top quarter, 74% from top half. Full-time: 1,659 students, 50% women, 50% men. Part-time: 134 students, 63% women, 37% men. Students come from 34 states and territories, 28% from out-of-state, 4% Native American, 4% Hispanic, 9% black, 2% Asian American or Pacific Islander, 0.1% international, 32% 25 or older, 67% live on campus, 6% transferred in. Retention: 64% of full-time freshmen returned the following year. Academic areas with the most degrees conferred: business/marketing; health professions and related sciences; family and consumer sciences. Core. Calendar: semesters. Academic remediation for entering students, services for LD students, advanced placement, accelerated degree program, self-designed majors, honors program, double major, summer session for credit, part-time degree program, external degree program, adult/continuing education programs, internships, graduate courses open to undergrads. Off campus study at Christian College Coalition Council for Christian Colleges and Universities. Study abroad program. ROTC: Army (c), Air Force (c).

Entrance Requirements: Open admission. Options: Peterson's Universal Application, electronic application, deferred admission, international baccalaureate accepted. Required: high school transcript, 2 recommendations. Recommended: interview. Entrance: noncompetitive. Application deadline: 8/15. Notification: continuous.

Costs Per Year: Application fee: $25. One-time mandatory fee: $350. Comprehensive fee: $20,402 includes full-time tuition ($14,400), mandatory fees ($624), and college room and board ($5378). College room only: $2458. Part-time tuition: $507 per credit hour. Part-time mandatory fees: $23 per credit hour.

Collegiate Environment: Orientation program. Drama-theater group, choral group, student-run newspaper. Social organizations: 30 open to all. Most popular organizations: Business Gaming Team, Campus Social Life Committee, intramural sports societies, Choral Society, Inter-Club. Major annual events: Lip Sync Contest, Homecoming, Pow-Wow Weekend. Student services: health clinic, personal-psychological counseling. Campus security: 24-hour emergency response devices, student patrols, late night transport-escort service, controlled dormitory access. 964 college housing spaces available; 866 were occupied in 2003-04. Freshmen guaranteed college housing. On-campus residence required through senior year. Options: men-only, women-only housing available. R. T. Williams Learning Resources

Center with 95,535 books, 331,364 microform titles, 225 serials, 4,257 audiovisual materials, an OPAC, and a Web page. Operations spending for 2004 fiscal year: $327,732. 120 computers available on campus for general student use. A campuswide network can be accessed from student residence rooms and from off campus. Staffed computer lab on campus.

Community Environment: Bethany is a metropolitan community in central Oklahoma with a mild climate. Located on U.S. Highway 66, eight miles from Will Rogers Airport, the city also has train service. The community includes active churches, a Chamber of Commerce, nearby health centers and hospitals, and numerous motels. Unusual job opportunities are available for students.

■ **SOUTHWESTERN CHRISTIAN UNIVERSITY** *F-9*
PO Box 340
Bethany, OK 73008-0340
Tel: (405)789-7661
Web Site: http://www.swcu.edu/

Description: Independent, comprehensive, coed, affiliated with Pentecostal Holiness Church. Awards associate, bachelor's, and master's degrees. Founded 1946. Setting: 7-acre suburban campus with easy access to Oklahoma City. Total enrollment: 199. 2 class presidents, 4 valedictorians, 15 student government officers. Full-time: 121 students, 46% women, 54% men. Part-time: 7 students, 29% women, 71% men. Students come from 15 states and territories, 3 other countries, 30% from out-of-state, 5% Native American, 3% Hispanic, 9% black, 1% Asian American or Pacific Islander, 2% international, 20% 25 or older, 30% live on campus. Core. Calendar: semesters. Academic remediation for entering students, advanced placement, double major, summer session for credit, part-time degree program, internships, graduate courses open to undergrads. Off campus study at Southern Nazarene University.

Entrance Requirements: Options: Common Application, early admission, deferred admission. Required: essay, high school transcript, minimum 2.0 high school GPA, recommendations, minimum ACT score of 19 or SAT score of 910, ACT. Recommended: interview. Entrance: minimally difficult. Application deadline: Rolling. Notification: continuous.

Costs Per Year: Application fee: $25. Comprehensive fee: $12,250 includes full-time tuition ($8250) and college room and board ($4000). Part-time tuition: $295 per credit hour.

Collegiate Environment: Orientation program. Drama-theater group, choral group. Major annual events: Campus Revival, Feat of Ingathering, graduation. Student services: personal-psychological counseling. Campus security: 24-hour emergency response devices. On-campus residence required through senior year. Options: men-only, women-only housing available. Springer Learning Center with 38,900 books and 100 serials. 13 computers available on campus for general student use. A campuswide network can be accessed. Staffed computer lab on campus.

■ **SOUTHWESTERN OKLAHOMA STATE UNIVERSITY** *F-6*
100 Campus Dr.
Weatherford, OK 73096-3098
Tel: (580)772-6611
Admissions: (580)774-3782
Fax: (580)774-3795
Web Site: http://www.swosu.edu/

Description: State-supported, comprehensive, coed. Part of Southwestern Oklahoma State University. Awards bachelor's, master's, and first professional degrees. Founded 1901. Setting: 73-acre small town campus with easy access to Oklahoma City. Endowment: $9.1 million. Research spending for 2004 fiscal year: $396,532. Educational spending for 2005 fiscal year: $3713 per student. Total enrollment: 4,841. 1,451 applied, 94% were admitted. 18% from top 10% of their high school class, 42% from top quarter, 72% from top half. Full-time: 3,771 students, 54% women, 46% men. Part-time: 479 students, 65% women, 35% men. Students come from 32 states and territories, 32 other countries, 10% from out-of-state, 7% Native American, 4% Hispanic, 5% black, 1% Asian American or Pacific Islander, 3% international, 17% 25 or older, 27% live on campus, 7% transferred in. Retention: 69% of full-time freshmen returned the following year. Core. Calendar: semesters. Academic remediation for entering students, services for LD students, advanced placement, accelerated degree program, self-designed majors, independent study, distance learning, double major, summer session for credit, part-time degree program, adult/continuing education programs, co-op programs and internships, graduate courses open to undergrads. Off campus study at Academic Common Market.

Entrance Requirements: Option: deferred admission. Required: high school transcript, minimum 2.0 high school GPA, ACT. Entrance: minimally difficult. Notification: continuous. Preference given to state residents.

Collegiate Environment: Orientation program. Drama-theater group, choral group, marching band, student-run newspaper. Social organizations: 66 open to all; national fraternities, local fraternities, local sororities; 1% of eligible men and 2% of eligible women are members. Most popular organizations: Student Education Association, Baptist Student Union, Southwestern Pharmaceutical Association, Gamma Delta Kappa, Bible Chair Student Union. Major annual events: homecoming, Howdy Week, Panorama events. Student services: health clinic, personal-psychological counseling. Campus security: late night transport-escort service, controlled dormitory access, 20-hour campus emergency security. 1,255 college housing spaces available; 1,052 were occupied in 2003-04. Freshmen guaranteed college housing. Options: men-only, women-only housing available. Al Harris Library with 217,051 books, 1.2 million microform titles, 1,230 serials, 6,718 audiovisual materials, an OPAC, and a Web page. Operations spending for 2004 fiscal year: $1.5 million. 270 computers available on campus for general student use. A campuswide network can be accessed from student residence rooms and from off campus. Staffed computer lab on campus.

■ **SOUTHWESTERN OKLAHOMA STATE UNIVERSITY AT SAYRE** *F-4*
409 East Mississippi St.
Sayre, OK 73662-1236
Tel: (580)928-5533
Web Site: http://www.swosu.edu/sayre/

Description: State and locally supported, 2-year, coed. Part of Southwestern Oklahoma State University. Awards diplomas, transfer associate, and terminal associate degrees. Founded 1938. Setting: 6-acre rural campus. Total enrollment: 549. Student-undergrad faculty ratio is 18:1. 107 applied, 100% were admitted. 11% from top 10% of their high school class, 22% from top quarter, 55% from top half. Full-time: 328 students, 74% women, 26% men. Part-time: 221 students, 70% women, 30% men. Students come from 2 states and territories, 3% from out-of-state, 5% Native American, 5% Hispanic, 1% black, 0.4% Asian American or Pacific Islander, 0% international, 50% 25 or older. Core. Calendar: semesters. Academic remediation for entering students, services for LD students, advanced placement, independent study, distance learning, summer session for credit, part-time degree program, adult/continuing education programs, co-op programs.

Entrance Requirements: Open admission. Options: Common Application, early admission, deferred admission. Required: high school transcript. Required for some: ACT. Entrance: noncompetitive. Application deadline: Rolling.

Costs Per Year: Application fee: $15. State resident tuition: $3456 full-time, $108 per credit hour part-time.

Collegiate Environment: Student-run newspaper. College housing not available. Oscar McMahan Library with 9,975 books, 45 serials, an OPAC, and a Web page. 100 computers available on campus for general student use. A campuswide network can be accessed. Staffed computer lab on campus.

■ **SPARTAN COLLEGE OF AERONAUTICS AND TECHNOLOGY** *D-13*
8820 East Pine St., PO Box 582833
Tulsa, OK 74158-2833
Tel: (918)836-6886
Web Site: http://www.spartan.edu/

Description: Proprietary, primarily 2-year, coed. Awards certificates, terminal associate, and bachelor's degrees. Founded 1928. Setting: 26-acre urban campus. Total enrollment: 1,500. 5% from top 10% of their high school class, 30% from top quarter, 65% from top half. Students come from 52 states and territories, 40 other countries, 85% from out-of-state, 32% 25 or older. Calendar: calendar terms. Academic remediation for entering students, ESL program, advanced placement.

Entrance Requirements: Open admission. Option: deferred admission. Required: high school transcript. Recommended: interview. Placement: ACT ASSET required. Entrance: noncompetitive. Application deadline: Rolling.

Collegiate Environment: Most popular organizations: Aircraft Electronics Association, Model Club, Electronics Technician Association, NIFA Flight Team. Major annual event: Annual Barbecue. 18,000 books and 160 serials. 75 computers available on campus for general student use. Staffed computer lab on campus.

■ **TULSA COMMUNITY COLLEGE** *D-13*
6111 East Skelly Dr.
Tulsa, OK 74135-6198

Tel: (918)595-7000
Admissions: (918)595-7811
Fax: (918)595-7910
E-mail: lbrewer@tulsacc.edu
Web Site: http://www.tulsacc.edu/

Description: State-supported, 2-year, coed. Part of Oklahoma State Regents for Higher Education. Awards certificates, transfer associate, and terminal associate degrees. Founded 1968. Setting: 160-acre urban campus. Total enrollment: 16,803. Student-undergrad faculty ratio is 20:1. 15,911 applied, 100% were admitted. 3% from top 10% of their high school class, 10% from top quarter, 22% from top half. Full-time: 6,162 students, 61% women, 39% men. Part-time: 10,641 students, 64% women, 36% men. Students come from 16 states and territories, 1% from out-of-state, 8% Native American, 3% Hispanic, 9% black, 2% Asian American or Pacific Islander, 59% 25 or older, 18% transferred in. Core. Calendar: semesters. Academic remediation for entering students, ESL program, services for LD students, advanced placement, accelerated degree program, freshman honors college, honors program, distance learning, summer session for credit, part-time degree program, external degree program, adult/continuing education programs, co-op programs and internships.

Entrance Requirements: Open admission except for honors, allied health programs. Options: Common Application, early admission. Required: high school transcript. Entrance: noncompetitive. Application deadline: Rolling.

Costs Per Year: Application fee: $20. State resident tuition: $47.80 per semester hour part-time. Nonresident tuition: $172.20 per semester hour part-time. Mandatory fees: $25 per semester hour part-time.

Collegiate Environment: Orientation program. Drama-theater group, student-run newspaper. Social organizations: 50 open to all. Student services: health clinic, personal-psychological counseling, women's center. Campus security: 24-hour emergency response devices and patrols, student patrols, late night transport-escort service. College housing not available. Learning Resource Center plus 1 other with 110,000 books, 987 serials, and a Web page. 1,000 computers available on campus for general student use. A campuswide network can be accessed from off-campus. Staffed computer lab on campus.

■ **TULSA WELDING SCHOOL** *D-13*
2545 East 11th St.
Tulsa, OK 74104-3909
Tel: (918)587-6789
Free: 800-WELD-PRO
Admissions: 800-331-2934
Fax: (918)295-6821
Web Site: http://www.weldingschool.com/

Description: Proprietary, 2-year, coed. Administratively affiliated with Tulsa Welding School, Jacksonville Branch. Awards diplomas, transfer associate, and terminal associate degrees. Founded 1949. Setting: 5-acre urban campus. Total enrollment: 362. Student-undergrad faculty ratio is 16:1. Students come from 21 states and territories, 41% from out-of-state, 9% Native American, 3% Hispanic, 13% black, 1% Asian American or Pacific Islander, 0% international, 37% 25 or older. Core. Calendar: continuous (phased start every 3 weeks).

Entrance Requirements: Required: high school diploma, GED, or ATB test. Entrance: noncompetitive.

Costs Per Year: Tuition: $11,090 full-time. Mandatory fees: $1900 full-time.

Collegiate Environment: Orientation program. Student services: Student Advisor, Graduate Employment Assistance, Part-Time Job Assistance. Campus security: 24-hour emergency response devices. College housing not available. Technical Resource Center with 389 books, 2 serials, and a Web page. 3 computers available on campus for general student use. A campuswide network can be accessed.

■ **UNIVERSITY OF CENTRAL OKLAHOMA** *E-9*
100 North University Dr.
Edmond, OK 73034-5209
Tel: (405)974-2000
Free: 800-254-4215
Admissions: (405)974-2338
Fax: (405)974-4964
Web Site: http://www.ucok.edu/

Description: State-supported, comprehensive, coed. Part of Oklahoma State Regents for Higher Education. Awards bachelor's and master's degrees. Founded 1890. Setting: 200-acre suburban campus with easy access to Oklahoma City. Total enrollment: 15,953. Faculty: 812 (411 full-time,

401 part-time). Student-undergrad faculty ratio is 21:1. 4,020 applied. 14% from top 10% of their high school class, 36% from top quarter, 74% from top half. Full-time: 10,512 students, 58% women, 42% men. Part-time: 4,117 students, 60% women, 40% men. Students come from 48 states and territories, 81 other countries, 4% from out-of-state, 6% Native American, 3% Hispanic, 9% black, 3% Asian American or Pacific Islander, 7% international, 26% 25 or older, 9% live on campus, 11% transferred in. Retention: 72% of full-time freshmen returned the following year. Academic areas with the most degrees conferred: business/marketing; education; liberal arts/general studies. Core. Calendar: semesters. ESL program, services for LD students, advanced placement, accelerated degree program, honors program, independent study, distance learning, double major, summer session for credit, part-time degree program, adult/continuing education programs, internships. ROTC: Army.

Entrance Requirements: Option: deferred admission. Required: high school transcript, minimum 2.7 high school GPA, rank in upper 50% of high school class, SAT or ACT. Recommended: ACT. Entrance: minimally difficult. Application deadline: Rolling. Notification: continuous until 4/1.

Costs Per Year: Application fee: $25. State resident tuition: $2811 full-time, $93.70 per semester hour part-time. Nonresident tuition: $7821 full-time, $260.70 per semester hour part-time. Mandatory fees: $807 full-time, $26.90 per semester hour part-time. Full-time tuition and fees vary according to course load, degree level, program, and student level. Part-time tuition and fees vary according to course load, degree level, program, and student level. College room and board: $4476. College room only: $2166. Room and board charges vary according to board plan and housing facility.

Collegiate Environment: Orientation program. Drama-theater group, choral group, marching band, student-run newspaper, radio station. Social organizations: 160 open to all; national fraternities, national sororities; 5% of eligible men and 5% of eligible women are members. Most popular organizations: Malaysian Student Association, Baptist Student Union, Student Government Association, Association of Women Students, University Center Activities Board. Major annual events: homecoming, Earth Day, International Week. Student services: health clinic, personal-psychological counseling. Campus security: 24-hour emergency response devices and patrols, late night transport-escort service. 1,552 college housing spaces available; 1,350 were occupied in 2003-04. No special consideration for freshman housing applicants. Options: coed, men-only, women-only housing available. Max Chambers Library with 254,478 books, 966,565 microform titles, 3,707 serials, 37,484 audiovisual materials, an OPAC, and a Web page. 400 computers available on campus for general student use. A campuswide network can be accessed from student residence rooms and from off campus. Staffed computer lab on campus.

Community Environment: Edmond is a suburban city 12 miles north of Oklahoma City. All modes of transportation are available to the community. Edmond has churches of most denominations, a movie theatre, numerous parks, a swimming pool, and shopping centers. Part-time employment is plentiful.

■ **UNIVERSITY OF OKLAHOMA** *G-9*
660 Parrington Oval
Norman, OK 73019-0390
Tel: (405)325-0311
Free: 800-234-6868
Admissions: (405)325-4521
Fax: (405)325-7478
E-mail: admrec@ou.edu
Web Site: http://www.ou.edu/

Description: State-supported, university, coed. Awards bachelor's, master's, doctoral, and first professional degrees and post-master's certificates. Founded 1890. Setting: 3,500-acre suburban campus with easy access to Oklahoma City. Endowment: $560.1 million. Research spending for 2004 fiscal year: $60.4 million. Educational spending for 2005 fiscal year: $6370 per student. Total enrollment: 26,968. Faculty: 1,204 (976 full-time, 228 part-time). Student-undergrad faculty ratio is 22:1. 7,388 applied, 86% were admitted. 37% from top 10% of their high school class, 72% from top quarter, 93% from top half. 169 National Merit Scholars, 285 valedictorians. Full-time: 17,716 students, 49% women, 51% men. Part-time: 2,682 students, 48% women, 52% men. Students come from 50 states and territories, 74 other countries, 23% from out-of-state, 7% Native American, 4% Hispanic, 5% black, 5% Asian American or Pacific Islander, 3% international, 10% 25 or older, 20% live on campus, 7% transferred in. Retention: 85% of full-time freshmen returned the following year. Academic areas with the most degrees conferred: business/marketing; social sciences; communications/journalism.

Core. Calendar: semesters. Academic remediation for entering students, ESL program, services for LD students, advanced placement, accelerated degree program, self-designed majors, freshman honors college, honors program, independent study, distance learning, double major, summer session for credit, part-time degree program, external degree program, adult/continuing education programs, co-op programs and internships, graduate courses open to undergrads. Off campus study at Oklahoma State University, Langston University, Northeastern State University, Rose State College, Oklahoma City Community College, Rogers University, Cameron University. Study abroad program. ROTC: Army, Naval, Air Force.

Entrance Requirements: Option: international baccalaureate accepted. Required: high school transcript, minimum 3.0 high school GPA, SAT or ACT. Required for some: essay. Entrance: moderately difficult. Application deadline: 4/1. Notification: continuous.

Costs Per Year: Application fee: $40. State resident tuition: $2862 full-time, $95.40 per credit hour part-time. Nonresident tuition: $10,755 full-time, $358.50 per credit hour part-time. Mandatory fees: $1546 full-time, $44.10 per credit hour part-time, $111.50 per term part-time. Full-time tuition and fees vary according to course load, location, program, and reciprocity agreements. Part-time tuition and fees vary according to course load, location, program, and reciprocity agreements. College room and board: $6361. College room only: $3355. Room and board charges vary according to board plan and housing facility.

Collegiate Environment: Orientation program. Drama-theater group, choral group, marching band, student-run newspaper, radio station. Social organizations: 300 open to all; national fraternities, national sororities; 14% of eligible men and 23% of eligible women are members. Most popular organizations: Campus Activities Council, international student organizations, OU Cousins, American Indian Student Association, Black Student Association. Major annual events: The Big Event, Homecoming, Dad's Day/Mom's Day. Student services: legal services, health clinic, personal-psychological counseling, women's center. Campus security: 24-hour emergency response devices and patrols, student patrols, late night transport-escort service, controlled dormitory access, crime prevention programs, police bicycle patrols, self-defense classes. 4,368 college housing spaces available; 4,160 were occupied in 2003-04. Freshmen guaranteed college housing. On-campus residence required in freshman year. Options: coed, men-only, women-only housing available. Bizzell Memorial Library plus 8 others with 4.3 million books, 4.1 million microform titles, 24,292 serials, 9,743 audiovisual materials, an OPAC, and a Web page. Operations spending for 2004 fiscal year: $12.3 million. 2,356 computers available on campus for general student use. Computer purchase/lease plans available. A campuswide network can be accessed from student residence rooms and from off campus. Staffed computer lab on campus.

Community Environment: Norman is a mid-sized city in central Oklahoma with award-winning public schools; cultural offerings, such as theaters and museums; community services including churches, hospitals, a public library; and recreational facilities, including parks, golf courses and nearby Lake Thunderbird. The community is served by major highways, bus lines, and Will Rogers World Airport, located 18 miles north in Oklahoma City. The university operates Max Westheimer Airpark, a general aviation, reliever category airport in Norman.

■ **UNIVERSITY OF OKLAHOMA HEALTH SCIENCES CENTER** *F-9*
PO Box 26901
Oklahoma City, OK 73190
Tel: (405)271-4000
Admissions: (405)271-2359
Fax: (405)271-2480
Web Site: http://www.ouhsc.edu/

Description: State-supported, upper-level, coed. Part of University of Oklahoma. Awards bachelor's, master's, doctoral, and first professional degrees and post-master's and first professional certificates. Founded 1890. Setting: 200-acre urban campus with easy access to Oklahoma City. Endowment: $185.7 million. Research spending for 2004 fiscal year: $60.5 million. Educational spending for 2005 fiscal year: $42,433 per student. Total enrollment: 3,538. Faculty: 403 (273 full-time, 130 part-time). Student-undergrad faculty ratio is 3:1. Full-time: 777 students, 88% women, 12% men. Part-time: 104 students, 84% women, 16% men. Students come from 15 states and territories, 12 other countries, 7% from out-of-state, 9% Native American, 4% Hispanic, 5% black, 5% Asian American or Pacific Islander, 1% international, 38% 25 or older, 49% transferred in. Academic areas with the most degrees conferred: health professions and related sciences; biological/life sciences; interdisciplinary studies. Calendar: semesters.

Advanced placement, honors program, distance learning, summer session for credit, part-time degree program, internships, graduate courses open to undergrads. ROTC: Army (c), Air Force (c).

Costs Per Year: Application fee: $40. State resident tuition: $2862 full-time, $95.40 per credit hour part-time. Nonresident tuition: $10,755 full-time, $358.50 per credit hour part-time. Mandatory fees: $1382 full-time, $38.15 per credit hour part-time, $118.50 per term part-time.

Collegiate Environment: Orientation program. Student-run newspaper. Social organizations: 12 open to all. Most popular organizations: Student Government Association, Public Health Student Association, Student National Medical Association, Graduate Student Council, Student Medical Association. Student services: health clinic, personal-psychological counseling. Campus security: 24-hour emergency response devices and patrols, late night transport-escort service. College housing not available. Robert M. Bird Health Sciences Library plus 3 others with 300,260 books, 650 microform titles, 4,028 serials, 5,931 audiovisual materials, an OPAC, and a Web page. Operations spending for 2004 fiscal year: $3.1 million. 120 computers available on campus for general student use. A campuswide network can be accessed from off-campus. Staffed computer lab on campus.

Community Environment: See Oklahoma City University.

■ **UNIVERSITY OF PHOENIX-OKLAHOMA CITY CAMPUS** *F-9*

6501 North Broadway Extension, Ste. 100
Oklahoma City, OK 73116-8244
Tel: (405)842-8007
Free: 800-228-7240
Admissions: (480)557-1712
Web Site: http://www.phoenix.edu/

Description: Proprietary, comprehensive, coed. Awards bachelor's and master's degrees. Founded 1976. Setting: urban campus. Total enrollment: 1,051. Faculty: 187 (2 full-time, 185 part-time). Student-undergrad faculty ratio is 6:1. 31 applied. Full-time: 876 students, 60% women, 40% men. 1% Native American, 2% Hispanic, 7% black, 1% Asian American or Pacific Islander, 6% international, 92% 25 or older. Academic areas with the most degrees conferred: business/marketing; computer and information sciences; security and protective services. Core. Calendar: continuous. Advanced placement, accelerated degree program, independent study, distance learning, external degree program, adult/continuing education programs, graduate courses open to undergrads.

Entrance Requirements: Open admission. Option: deferred admission. Required: 1 recommendation. Required for some: high school transcript. Entrance: noncompetitive. Application deadline: Rolling.

Costs Per Year: Application fee: $110. Tuition: $9360 full-time, $312 per credit part-time. Mandatory fees: $560 full-time, $70 per course part-time.

Collegiate Environment: College housing not available. University Library with 444 books, 666 serials, an OPAC, and a Web page. System-wide operations spending for 2004 fiscal year: $3.2 million.

■ **UNIVERSITY OF PHOENIX-TULSA CAMPUS** *D-13*

10810 East 45th St., Ste. 103
Tulsa, OK 74146-3801
Tel: (918)622-4877
Free: 800-228-7240
Admissions: (480)557-1712
Web Site: http://www.phoenix.edu/

Description: Proprietary, comprehensive, coed. Awards bachelor's and master's degrees. Founded 1998. Setting: urban campus. Total enrollment: 1,302. Faculty: 161 (5 full-time, 156 part-time). Student-undergrad faculty ratio is 8:1. 52 applied. Full-time: 1,114 students, 60% women, 40% men. 0% from out-of-state, 2% Native American, 1% Hispanic, 2% black, 0.3% Asian American or Pacific Islander, 35% international, 89% 25 or older. Academic areas with the most degrees conferred: business/marketing; computer and information sciences; security and protective services. Core. Calendar: continuous. Advanced placement, accelerated degree program, independent study, distance learning, external degree program, adult/continuing education programs, graduate courses open to undergrads.

Entrance Requirements: Open admission. Option: deferred admission. Required: 1 recommendation. Required for some: high school transcript. Entrance: noncompetitive. Application deadline: Rolling.

Costs Per Year: Application fee: $110. Tuition: $9360 full-time, $312 per credit part-time. Mandatory fees: $560 full-time, $70 per course part-time.

Collegiate Environment: College housing not available. University Library with 444 books, 666 serials, an OPAC, and a Web page. System-wide operations spending for 2004 fiscal year: $3.2 million.

■ **UNIVERSITY OF SCIENCE AND ARTS OF OKLAHOMA** *G-8*

1727 West Alabama
Chickasha, OK 73018
Tel: (405)224-3140
Free: 800-933-8726
Admissions: (405)574-1204
Fax: (405)574-1220
E-mail: jwevans@usao.edu
Web Site: http://www.usao.edu/

Description: State-supported, 4-year, coed. Part of Oklahoma State Regents for Higher Education. Awards bachelor's degrees. Founded 1908. Setting: 75-acre small town campus with easy access to Oklahoma City. Endowment: $1.5 million. Research spending for 2004 fiscal year: $136,375. Educational spending for 2005 fiscal year: $3421 per student. Total enrollment: 1,430. Student-undergrad faculty ratio is 19:1. 448 applied, 89% were admitted. 13% from top 10% of their high school class, 42% from top quarter, 75% from top half. Full-time: 1,064 students, 60% women, 40% men. Part-time: 366 students, 74% women, 26% men. Students come from 20 states and territories, 13 other countries, 6% from out-of-state, 13% Native American, 3% Hispanic, 6% black, 1% Asian American or Pacific Islander, 2% international, 24% 25 or older, 36% live on campus, 9% transferred in. Retention: 61% of full-time freshmen returned the following year. Academic areas with the most degrees conferred: business/marketing; education; visual and performing arts. Core. Calendar: trimesters. Academic remediation for entering students, services for LD students, advanced placement, accelerated degree program, self-designed majors, independent study, distance learning, double major, summer session for credit, part-time degree program, adult/continuing education programs, internships. Off campus study.

Entrance Requirements: Options: Common Application, deferred admission. Recommended: graduated in top half of high school class. Required for some: high school transcript, minimum 2.85 high school GPA, graduated in top half of high school class. Entrance: moderately difficult. Application deadline: 9/6. Notification: 2/10.

Costs Per Year: Application fee: $15. State resident tuition: $2490 full-time, $83 per hour part-time. Nonresident tuition: $7230 full-time, $241 per hour part-time. Mandatory fees: $990 full-time, $33 per hour part-time. College room and board: $4170. College room only: $2180. Room and board charges vary according to board plan and housing facility.

Collegiate Environment: Orientation program. Drama-theater group, choral group, student-run newspaper. Social organizations: 24 open to all; national fraternities, local sororities; 2% of eligible men and 3% of eligible women are members. Most popular organizations: Student Activities Council, Volunteer Action Council, Baptist Student Union, Intertribal Heritage Club, Psychology Club. Major annual events: Montmartre Festival/Droverstock, Pow-Wow, Tinsel Ball. Student services: health clinic, personal-psychological counseling. Campus security: 24-hour emergency response devices and patrols, controlled dormitory access. 504 college housing spaces available; 423 were occupied in 2003-04. Freshmen guaranteed college housing. On-campus residence required in freshman year. Option: coed housing available. Nash Library with 79,780 books, 153,514 microform titles, 191 serials, 4,240 audiovisual materials, an OPAC, and a Web page. Operations spending for 2004 fiscal year: $144,649. 125 computers available on campus for general student use. A campuswide network can be accessed from student residence rooms and from off campus. Staffed computer lab on campus.

Community Environment: Chickasha is a suburban area southwest of Oklahoma City. Located in the fertile Washita River Valley, the city lies within one of the largest gas fields in the world. The community has rail, bus, and air service. The community includes Catholic and Protestant churches, a hospital, a public library, and major civic, fraternal, and veteran's organizations. Local recreational facilities include theatres and several good lakes within a few miles for boating, fishing and water sports. Some part-time employment is available for students.

■ **UNIVERSITY OF TULSA** *D-13*

600 South College Ave.
Tulsa, OK 74104-3189
Tel: (918)631-2000
Free: 800-331-3050
Admissions: (918)631-2307
Fax: (918)631-2247
E-mail: admission@utulsa.edu
Web Site: http://www.utulsa.edu/

Description: Independent, university, coed, affiliated with Presbyterian Church (U.S.A.). Awards bachelor's, master's, doctoral, and first professional degrees and first professional certificates. Founded 1894. Setting: 200-acre urban campus with easy access to Tulsa. Endowment: $770.5 million. Research spending for 2004 fiscal year: $14.6 million. Educational spending for 2005 fiscal year: $12,492 per student. Total enrollment: 4,084. Faculty: 422 (306 full-time, 116 part-time). Student-undergrad faculty ratio is 11:1. 2,687 applied, 75% were admitted. 63% from top 10% of their high school class, 81% from top quarter, 94% from top half. 66 National Merit Scholars, 30 valedictorians. Full-time: 2,635 students, 49% women, 51% men. Part-time: 161 students, 53% women, 47% men. Students come from 38 states and territories, 41 other countries, 34% from out-of-state, 5% Native American, 4% Hispanic, 7% black, 2% Asian American or Pacific Islander, 8% international, 10% 25 or older, 64% live on campus, 6% transferred in. Retention: 84% of full-time freshmen returned the following year. Academic areas with the most degrees conferred: business/marketing; engineering; visual and performing arts. Core. Calendar: semesters. ESL program, services for LD students, advanced placement, accelerated degree program, self-designed majors, honors program, independent study, double major, summer session for credit, part-time degree program, adult/continuing education programs, internships, graduate courses open to undergrads. Study abroad program. ROTC: Air Force (c).

Entrance Requirements: Options: Common Application, electronic application, early admission, deferred admission, international baccalaureate accepted. Required: high school transcript, 1 recommendation, SAT or ACT. Recommended: essay, minimum 3.0 high school GPA, interview. Entrance: very difficult. Application deadline: Rolling. Notification: continuous.

Costs Per Year: Application fee: $35. Comprehensive fee: $27,790 includes full-time tuition ($20,658), mandatory fees ($80), and college room and board ($7052). College room only: $3896. Part-time tuition: $741 per credit hour. Part-time mandatory fees: $3 per credit hour.

Collegiate Environment: Orientation program. Drama-theater group, choral group, marching band, student-run newspaper, radio station. Social organizations: 272 open to all; national fraternities, national sororities; 21% of eligible men and 23% of eligible women are members. Most popular organizations: Student Association, Residence Hall Association, honor societies, intramural sports, pre-professional clubs. Major annual events: Homecoming, Springfest, Parents' Weekend. Student services: health clinic, personal-psychological counseling, women's center. Campus security: 24-hour emergency response devices and patrols, late night transport-escort service, controlled dormitory access. 2,206 college housing spaces available; 1,752 were occupied in 2003-04. Freshmen guaranteed college housing. On-campus residence required through sophomore year. Options: coed, men-only, women-only housing available. McFarlin Library plus 1 other with 940,105 books, 3 million microform titles, 6,317 serials, 13,320 audiovisual materials, an OPAC, and a Web page. Operations spending for 2004 fiscal year: $5.5 million. 900 computers available on campus for general student use. Computer purchase/lease plans available. A campuswide network can be accessed from student residence rooms and from off campus. Staffed computer lab on campus.

Community Environment: The climate is temperate. The average year-round high temperature is 71 degrees. The population is 750,000 in the metropolitan area. The city features a professional opera company, a national ballet company, a symphony orchestra, museums, art galleries, community theatres, parks, minor league teams in hockey and baseball and recreation and shopping facilities. Public bus transportation is available.

■ **VATTEROTT COLLEGE (OKLAHOMA CITY)** *F-9*
4629 Northwest 23rd St.
Oklahoma City, OK 73127
Tel: (405)945-0088; 888-948-0088
Fax: (405)945-0788
Web Site: http://www.vatterott-college.edu/

Description: Proprietary, 2-year, coed. Awards diplomas, terminal associate, and first professional degrees. Setting: urban campus. Total enrollment: 284. 145 applied, 62% were admitted. 7% Native American, 5% Hispanic, 36% black, 2% Asian American or Pacific Islander, 0% international. Calendar: semesters.

Entrance Requirements: Required: essay, high school transcript, interview. Entrance: noncompetitive.

Costs Per Year: Tuition: $20,000 full-time. Mandatory fees: $900 full-time. Full-time tuition and fees vary according to degree level and program. Tuition guaranteed not to increase for student's term of enrollment.

■ **VATTEROTT COLLEGE (TULSA)** *D-13*
555 South Memorial Dr.
Tulsa, OK 74112
Tel: (918)835-8288; 888-857-4016
Admissions: (918)836-6656
Fax: (918)836-9698
Web Site: http://www.vatterott-college.edu/

Description: Proprietary, 2-year, coed. Awards diplomas and terminal associate degrees. Setting: 3-acre urban campus. Total enrollment: 226. Student-undergrad faculty ratio is 12:1. 117 applied, 78% were admitted. Full-time: 226 students, 29% women, 71% men. 11% Native American, 4% Hispanic, 28% black, 0% Asian American or Pacific Islander, 0% international. Retention: 71% of full-time freshmen returned the following year. Calendar: semesters.

■ **WESTERN OKLAHOMA STATE COLLEGE** *I-5*
2801 North Main St.
Altus, OK 73521-1397
Tel: (580)477-2000
Admissions: (580)477-7720
Fax: (580)477-7723
Web Site: http://www.wosc.edu/

Description: State-supported, 2-year, coed. Part of Oklahoma State Regents for Higher Education. Awards certificates, transfer associate, and terminal associate degrees. Founded 1926. Setting: 142-acre rural campus. Endowment: $2.5 million. Educational spending for 2005 fiscal year: $2376 per student. Total enrollment: 2,061. Student-undergrad faculty ratio is 20:1. 499 applied, 100% were admitted. 10% from top 10% of their high school class, 20% from top quarter, 50% from top half. 5 valedictorians. Full-time: 859 students, 55% women, 45% men. Part-time: 1,202 students, 60% women, 40% men. Students come from 30 states and territories, 1 other country, 4% Native American, 11% Hispanic, 13% black, 2% Asian American or Pacific Islander, 0% international, 65% 25 or older. Retention: 50% of full-time freshmen returned the following year. Core. Calendar: semesters. Academic remediation for entering students, services for LD students, advanced placement, self-designed majors, honors program, summer session for credit, part-time degree program, adult/continuing education programs. Off campus study at all state institutions in the Oklahoma Higher Education Televised Instructional System.

Entrance Requirements: Open admission. Options: electronic application, early admission. Required: high school transcript. Required for some: ACT. Entrance: noncompetitive. Application deadline: Rolling. Notification: continuous.

Costs Per Year: Application fee: $15. State resident tuition: $2213 full-time, $73.75 per semester hour part-time. Nonresident tuition: $5348 full-time, $178.25 per semester hour part-time. College room and board: $4400.

Collegiate Environment: Drama-theater group, choral group. Social organizations: national fraternities; 4% of men are members. Most popular organizations: Baptist Student Union, Phi Theta Kappa, Student Senate, Behavioral Science Club, Aggie Club. Major annual events: Homecoming, organizational competitions, basketball games. Student services: personal-psychological counseling. Campus security: 24-hour emergency response devices. 96 college housing spaces available; 83 were occupied in 2003-04. Option: coed housing available. Learning Resources Center with 33,000 books, 1,000 serials, an OPAC, and a Web page. Operations spending for 2004 fiscal year: $254,402. 50 computers available on campus for general student use. A campuswide network can be accessed from student residence rooms and from off campus. Staffed computer lab on campus.

Community Environment: Altus is an urban community served by bus, railroad, and major interstate highways. The climate is temperate. The community has one hospital, a public library, many churches, and recreational facilities.

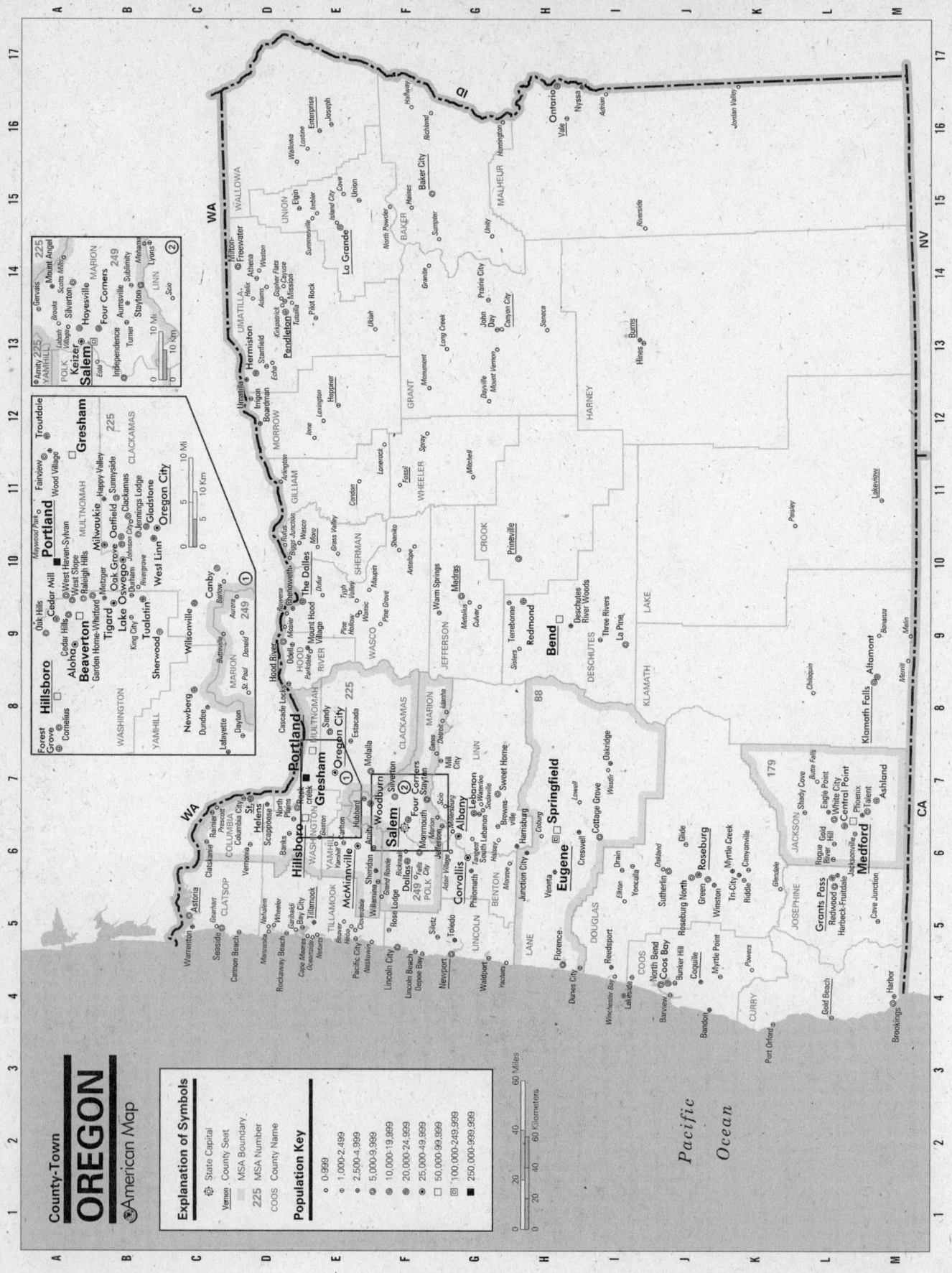

OREGON

County-Town

● American Map

Explanation of Symbols

⊛	State Capital
Vernon	County Seat
	MSA Boundary
225	MSA Number
COOS	County Name

Population Key

○	0-999
○	1,000-2,499
⊙	2,500-4,999
⊙	5,000-9,999
⊙	10,000-19,999
⊙	20,000-24,999
⊙	25,000-49,999
□	50,000-99,999
□	100,000-249,999
■	250,000-999,999

Pacific Ocean

■ **THE ART INSTITUTE OF PORTLAND** *E-7*

1122 NW Davis St.
Portland, OR 97209
Tel: (503)228-6528; 888-228-6528
Fax: (503)228-4227
E-mail: aipdadm@aii.edu
Web Site: http://www.aipd.artinstitutes.edu/

Description: Proprietary, 4-year, coed. Part of Education Management Corporation. Awards associate and bachelor's degrees. Founded 1963. Setting: 1-acre urban campus. Total enrollment: 1,583. Student-undergrad faculty ratio is 22:1. 437 applied, 59% were admitted. Full-time: 1,078 students, 51% women, 49% men. Part-time: 505 students, 51% women, 49% men. Students come from 20 states and territories, 11 other countries, 2% Native American, 5% Hispanic, 2% black, 6% Asian American or Pacific Islander, 0.1% international, 32% 25 or older, 10% live on campus. Retention: 50% of full-time freshmen returned the following year. Academic area with the most degrees conferred: visual and performing arts. Core. Academic remediation for entering students, services for LD students, advanced placement, independent study, summer session for credit, part-time degree program, internships. Study abroad program.

Entrance Requirements: Options: Peterson's Universal Application, electronic application, deferred admission. Required: essay, high school transcript, interview. Recommended: recommendations. Required for some: placement exam. Entrance: minimally difficult. Application deadline: Rolling. Notification: continuous.

Costs Per Year: Application fee: $50. Tuition: $17,460 full-time. College room only: $5625.

Collegiate Environment: Orientation program. Student-run newspaper. Social organizations: 3 open to all. Most popular organizations: Fashion Group International, Interior Design Student Chapter, International Student Group. Major annual events: Portfolio Review, Graduation Fashion Show, Animation Show. Student services: personal-psychological counseling. Campus security: 24-hour emergency response devices, security patrol from 4 p.m. to midnight, electronically operated building entrances. 140 college housing spaces available; all were occupied in 2003-04. No special consideration for freshman housing applicants. Option: coed housing available. AIPD Learning Resource Center with 24,231 books, 215 serials, 400 audiovisual materials, an OPAC, and a Web page. 160 computers available on campus for general student use. Staffed computer lab on campus.

■ **BIRTHINGWAY COLLEGE OF MIDWIFERY** *E-7*

12113 SE Foster Rd.
Portland, OR 97299
Tel: (503)760-3131
Web Site: http://www.birthingway.edu/

Description: Independent, upper-level, coed. Awards bachelor's degrees. Founded 1993. Calendar: 3 semesters.

■ **BLUE MOUNTAIN COMMUNITY COLLEGE** *D-13*

2411 Northwest Carden Ave.
PO Box 100
Pendleton, OR 97801-1000
Tel: (541)276-1260
Admissions: (541)278-5774
Fax: (541)278-5886

Web Site: http://www.bluecc.edu/

Description: State and locally supported, 2-year, coed. Awards certificates, transfer associate, and terminal associate degrees. Founded 1962. Setting: 170-acre rural campus. Endowment: $1.7 million. Educational spending for 2005 fiscal year: $2698 per student. Total enrollment: 1,878. Full-time: 872 students, 63% women, 37% men. Part-time: 1,006 students, 59% women, 41% men. Students come from 9 states and territories, 6 other countries, 2% from out-of-state, 4% Native American, 6% Hispanic, 1% black, 0.5% Asian American or Pacific Islander, 1% international, 16% 25 or older. Core. Academic remediation for entering students, ESL program, services for LD students, advanced placement, distance learning, summer session for credit, part-time degree program, adult/continuing education programs, co-op programs.

Entrance Requirements: Open admission. Option: electronic application. Required: high school transcript. Placement: ACT ASSET and ACT COMPASS required. Entrance: noncompetitive. Application deadline: Rolling. Notification: continuous.

Collegiate Environment: Orientation program. Drama-theater group, choral group. Social organizations: 2 open to all. Most popular organizations: Multicultural Club, Campus Crusade for Christ. Major annual events: Yippie Yahoo Day (Spring Term), Casino Night. Student services: personal-psychological counseling. College housing not available. Blue Mountain Community College Library with 39,026 books, 2,644 microform titles, 271 serials, 1,879 audiovisual materials, an OPAC, and a Web page. Operations spending for 2004 fiscal year: $314,649. 180 computers available on campus for general student use. A campuswide network can be accessed from off-campus. Staffed computer lab on campus.

Community Environment: Pendleton, pop. 16,000, is bordered by the Blue Mountains, the Columbia River, and rolling wheat fields with and agriculturally based economy. It is approximately 200 miles from Portland, OR, Spokane, WA, and Boise, ID. Community facilities include a public library, churches of major denominations, a hospital, shopping, and many services and civic organizations. Pendleton is known nationally for its annual event, The Pendleton Roundup. Other activities include a symphony, art shows, and many organized sports for children and adults. For the recreationist, the area offers a wide variety of seasonal sports, including skiing, fishing, hiking, and hunting.

■ **CASCADE COLLEGE** *E-7*

9101 East Burnside St.
Portland, OR 97216-1515
Tel: (503)255-7060
Free: 800-550-7678
Admissions: (503)257-1202
E-mail: jmurphy@cascade.edu
Web Site: http://www.cascade.edu/

Description: Independent, 4-year, coed, affiliated with Church of Christ. Administratively affiliated with Oklahoma Christian University. Awards bachelor's degrees. Founded 1994. Setting: 13-acre urban campus. Endowment: $358,467. Total enrollment: 292. Student-undergrad faculty ratio is 15:1. 227 applied, 60% were admitted. Full-time: 274 students, 54% women, 46% men. Part-time: 18 students, 39% women, 61% men. Students come from 23 states and territories, 6 other countries, 62% from out-of-state, 2% Native American, 6% Hispanic, 5% black, 3% Asian American or Pacific Islander, 4% international, 6% 25 or older, 66% live on campus, 13% transferred in. Retention: 60% of full-time freshmen returned the following year. Academic areas with the most degrees conferred: interdisciplinary studies; education; business/marketing; psychology. Core. Calendar: semesters. Academic remediation for entering students, services for LD students, advanced placement, accelerated degree program, independent study, double major, summer session for credit, internships. Off campus study at Mt. Hood Community College. Study abroad program. ROTC: Army (c), Air Force (c).

Entrance Requirements: Open admission. Options: Common Application, early admission, deferred admission, international baccalaureate accepted. Required: high school transcript, recommendations. Entrance: noncompetitive. Application deadline: Rolling.

Costs Per Year: Application fee: $25. Comprehensive fee: $18,920 includes full-time tuition ($12,200), mandatory fees ($600), and college room and board ($6120). Part-time tuition: $510 per semester hour.

Collegiate Environment: Orientation program. Drama-theater group, choral group. Social organizations: 16 open to all. Most popular organizations: choir, service clubs, student government. Major annual events: Campus Variety Show, Homecoming Week, Spiritual Emphasis Week. Student services: health clinic, personal-psychological counseling. Campus security: 24-hour emergency response devices, late night transport-escort service, controlled dormitory access, 12-hour patrols by trained security personnel. 236 college housing spaces available; 182 were occupied in 2003-04. Freshmen guaranteed college housing. On-campus residence required through senior year. Options: coed, men-only, women-only housing available. E.W. McMillan Library with 30,232 books, 62,045 microform titles, 86 serials, 1,218 audiovisual materials, an OPAC, and a Web page. Operations spending for 2004 fiscal year: $82,400. 26 computers available on campus for general student use. A campuswide network can be accessed from student residence rooms and from off campus. Staffed computer lab on campus.

Community Environment: See Portland State University.

■ CENTRAL OREGON COMMUNITY COLLEGE *H-9*

2600 Northwest College Way
Bend, OR 97701-5998
Tel: (541)383-7700
Admissions: (541)383-7211
Fax: (541)383-7506
E-mail: welcome@metolius.cocc.edu
Web Site: http://www.cocc.edu/

Description: District-supported, 2-year, coed. Part of Oregon Community College Association. Awards certificates, transfer associate, and terminal associate degrees. Founded 1949. Setting: 193-acre small town campus. Endowment: $5.5 million. Educational spending for 2005 fiscal year: $6146 per student. Total enrollment: 4,048. Student-undergrad faculty ratio is 23:1. 1,410 applied. Full-time: 1,536 students, 57% women, 43% men. Part-time: 2,512 students, 59% women, 41% men. Students come from 7 states and territories, 4% from out-of-state, 3% Native American, 4% Hispanic, 0.2% black, 1% Asian American or Pacific Islander, 0% international, 41% 25 or older, 3% live on campus. Core. Academic remediation for entering students, ESL program, self-designed majors, independent study, distance learning, double major, part-time degree program, co-op programs and internships. Study abroad program.

Entrance Requirements: Open admission except for nursing, emergency medical technology, geographic information systems, medical assistant, dental assistant, fire science programs. Option: electronic application. Entrance: noncompetitive. Application deadline: Rolling. Notification: continuous. Preference given to district residents for nursing program.

Costs Per Year: Application fee: $25. Area resident tuition: $2835 full-time, $63 per credit part-time. State resident tuition: $3870 full-time, $86 per credit part-time. Nonresident tuition: $7920 full-time, $176 per credit part-time. Mandatory fees: $114 full-time, $3.50 per credit part-time. College room and board: $6798.

Collegiate Environment: Orientation program. Choral group, student-run newspaper. Social organizations: 12 open to all. Most popular organizations: student government, club sports, Phi Theta Kappa, DEC, Science Learning Center. Major annual events: Earth Month, Salmon Bake, music series. Student services: health clinic, personal-psychological counseling. Campus security: 24-hour emergency response devices and patrols, late night transport-escort service. Option: coed housing available. COCC Library plus 1 other with 76,421 books, 114,539 microform titles, 329 serials, 3,570 audiovisual materials, an OPAC, and a Web page. 335 computers available on campus for general student use. A campuswide network can be accessed from student residence rooms and from off campus. Staffed computer lab on campus.

Community Environment: Bend is an extremely scenic town of some 60,000 people located at the foothills of the Oregon's Cascade Mountain range. The college serves a 10,000-square-mile district that includes part of Central Oregon's high desert country east of Bend. The area's primary industries are lumber and tourism. Bus lines connect Bend with other parts of the state. Two airlines serve the nearby town of Redmond, 14 miles distant, with jet air transport. Bend is 157 miles from Portland and 120 miles from Eugene, Oregon. Community facilities include a public library, churches of major denominations, three major shopping malls and many service and civic organizations. Bend is known nationally for its recreational environment. Bordering the 1.6 million-acre Deschutes National Forest, the town affords excellent hunting, fishing, hiking and camping opportunities. The full-facility Mt. Bachelor Ski Area, which is normally open from November through June, is 22 minutes from the college campus. Rain is rare in the area. Bend receives an average snowfall of three feet per year, although the mountainous areas receive considerably more.

■ CHEMEKETA COMMUNITY COLLEGE *F-6*

4000 Lancaster Dr. NE
P.O. Box 14007
Salem, OR 97309
Tel: (503)399-5000
Fax: (503)399-3918
Web Site: http://www.chemeketa.edu/

Description: State and locally supported, 2-year, coed. Awards certificates, diplomas, transfer associate, and terminal associate degrees. Founded 1955. Setting: 72-acre urban campus with easy access to Portland. Total enrollment: 15,000. Students come from 5 states and territories, 1% from out-of-state, 45% 25 or older. Academic remediation for entering students, ESL program, services for LD students, advanced placement, independent study, distance learning, double major, summer session for credit, part-time degree program, adult/continuing education programs, co-op programs and internships.

Entrance Requirements: Open admission except for nursing, allied health, fire science, building inspection, dental assisting, emergency medical technology, human services. Option: deferred admission. Required for some: high school transcript. Entrance: noncompetitive. Application deadline: Rolling. Notification: continuous.

Costs Per Year: Application fee: $0. State resident tuition: $2610 full-time, $58 per quarter hour part-time. Nonresident tuition: $8955 full-time, $199 per quarter hour part-time. Mandatory fees: $180 full-time, $4 per quarter hour part-time.

Collegiate Environment: Drama-theater group, choral group, student-run newspaper. Social organizations: 40 open to all. Most popular organizations: Health Occupations Students of America, International Conference of Building Officials, Ski Club, Christian Fellowship. Major annual events: International Food Fair, multicultural events, Career Expo. Student services: personal-psychological counseling, women's center. Campus security: 24-hour emergency response devices and patrols, late night transport-escort service. College housing not available. Chemeketa Community College Library plus 1 other with 7,145 microform titles, 801 audiovisual materials, an OPAC, and a Web page. Operations spending for 2004 fiscal year: $636,220.

Community Environment: See Willamette University.

■ CLACKAMAS COMMUNITY COLLEGE *E-7*

19600 South Molalla Ave.
Oregon City, OR 97045-7998
Tel: (503)657-6958
Fax: (503)650-6654
Web Site: http://www.clackamas.edu/

Description: District-supported, 2-year, coed. Awards certificates, diplomas, transfer associate, and terminal associate degrees. Founded 1966. Setting: 175-acre suburban campus with easy access to Portland. Endowment: $9.4 million. Educational spending for 2005 fiscal year: $3092 per student. Total enrollment: 7,329. Student-undergrad faculty ratio is 14:1. 2,149 applied, 100% were admitted. Full-time: 2,238 students, 52% women, 48% men. Part-time: 5,091 students, 52% women, 48% men. Students come from 38 states and territories, 16 other countries, 3% from out-of-state, 1% Native American, 11% Hispanic, 1% black, 4% Asian American or Pacific Islander, 0.2% international, 47% 25 or older, 29% transferred in. Core. Academic remediation for entering students, ESL program, services for LD students, advanced placement, accelerated degree program, honors program, independent study, distance learning, double major, summer session for credit, part-time degree program, adult/continuing education programs, co-op programs and internships. Study abroad program. ROTC: Air Force (c).

Entrance Requirements: Open admission except for nursing program, medical assistant, accelerated degree, PSU co-admit. Option: early admission. Entrance: noncompetitive. Application deadline: Rolling.

Costs Per Year: Application fee: $0. State resident tuition: $2520 full-time, $56 per credit hour part-time. Nonresident tuition: $8730 full-time, $194 per credit hour part-time. Mandatory fees: $180 full-time, $4 per credit hour part-time.

Collegiate Environment: Orientation program. Drama-theater group, choral group, student-run newspaper. Social organizations: 21 open to all; national fraternities. Most popular organizations: Ski Club, Spanish Club, Phi Theta Kappa, Horticulture Club, Speech Club. Major annual events: Club Fair, Fall Craft Fair, Environmental Week. Student services: personal-psychological counseling, women's center. Campus security: 24-hour emergency response devices and patrols, student patrols, late night transport-escort service. College housing not available. Dye Learning Resource Center plus 1 other with 41,263 books, 99,527 microform titles, 274 serials, 1,141 audiovisual materials, an OPAC, and a Web page. Operations spending for 2004 fiscal year: $408,101. 500 computers available on campus for general student use. A campuswide network can be accessed. Staffed computer lab on campus.

Community Environment: Oregon City was the capital of the Old Oregon Territory, founded in 1829. The city is on the bank of the Willamette River where there are 40-foot falls that provide waterpower for the production of paper, batteries, lumber and electric power. A municipal free elevator lifts pedestrians 90 feet up the steep face of a cliff to a residential business district. An observation deck at the top overlooks the downtown area and the falls. The Holly Knoll Museum is 7 miles southeast where antique furniture and harness and horsedrawn vehicles may be seen. The John McLoughlin House National Historic Site was built in 1846.

■ **CLATSOP COMMUNITY COLLEGE** *C-5*
1653 Jerome
Astoria, OR 97103-3698
Tel: (503)325-0910
Admissions: (503)338-2326
Fax: (503)325-5738
E-mail: klee@clatsopec.edu
Web Site: http://www.clatsopcc.edu/
Description: County-supported, 2-year, coed. Awards certificates, transfer associate, and terminal associate degrees. Founded 1958. Setting: 20-acre small town campus. Endowment: $2 million. Total enrollment: 1,824. Student-undergrad faculty ratio is 14:1. 340 applied, 81% were admitted. Full-time: 445 students, 61% women, 39% men. Part-time: 1,379 students, 44% women, 56% men. Students come from 28 states and territories, 1 other country, 15% from out-of-state, 3% Native American, 4% Hispanic, 1% black, 2% Asian American or Pacific Islander, 1% international, 50% 25 or older, 0.4% transferred in. Core. Academic remediation for entering students, ESL program, services for LD students, advanced placement, distance learning, summer session for credit, part-time degree program, external degree program, adult/continuing education programs, co-op programs and internships.

Entrance Requirements: Open admission. Option: early admission. Recommended: high school transcript. Entrance: noncompetitive. Application deadline: Rolling. Notification: continuous.

Costs Per Year: Application fee: $15. State resident tuition: $2700 full-time, $60 per credit part-time. Nonresident tuition: $5400 full-time, $120 per credit part-time.

Collegiate Environment: Orientation program. Most popular organizations: Lives in Transition, Phi Theta Kappa, Nursing Club, Spanish Club, Fine Arts Club. Major annual events: Blood Drive, Graduation Festival, End of Year Awards Ceremony. Student services: personal-psychological counseling. Campus security: 24-hour emergency response devices, late night transport-escort service. College housing not available. Dora Badollet Library plus 1 other with 48,517 books, 7,000 microform titles, 180 serials, 5,000 audiovisual materials, an OPAC, and a Web page. Operations spending for 2004 fiscal year: $444,678. 76 computers available on campus for general student use. A campuswide network can be accessed from off-campus. Staffed computer lab on campus.

Community Environment: Located on the Columbia River, about 10 miles from its mouth, Astoria is known principally for its salmon and tuna industries. Astoria's history dates from the winter of 1805 when the Lewis and Clark expedition camped at Fort Clatsop. Many plants here are in the fish canning, curing, and freezing business. At the larger docks, ocean liners load for world ports. Commercial transportation is available. There are a number of churches, a city-owned library, museums, hospitals, and many of the major civic and service organizations in the community. The opportunities are good for part-time employment. Recreational facilities are numerous; lakes, streams, rivers, and the ocean for fishing, swimming, boating, picnicking and digging for clams. During the fishing season, August 1 to September 10, more than 15,000 large fish are taken from the Columbia River near Astoria. Some of the points of interest are the Astoria Column, 125 feet high, which illustrates incidents in the early history of the region, Clatsop County Historical Museum, the Columbia River Maritime Museum, and Fort Astoria. The Astoria Regatta is an annual event.

■ **COLUMBIA GORGE COMMUNITY COLLEGE** *E-9*
400 East Scenic Dr.
The Dalles, OR 97058
Tel: (541)296-6182
Admissions: (541)298-3110
Fax: (541)298-3104
E-mail: kcarter@cgcc.cc.or.us
Web Site: http://www.cgcc.cc.or.us/
Description: State-supported, 2-year, coed. Awards certificates, diplomas, transfer associate, and terminal associate degrees. Founded 1977.

■ **CONCORDIA UNIVERSITY** *E-7*
2811 Northeast Holman
Portland, OR 97211-6099
Tel: (503)288-9371
Free: 800-321-9371
Admissions: (503)493-6526
Fax: (503)280-8531
Web Site: http://www.cu-portland.edu/
Description: Independent, comprehensive, coed, affiliated with Lutheran Church-Missouri Synod. Part of Concordia University System. Awards associate, bachelor's, and master's degrees. Founded 1905. Setting: 13-acre urban campus. Endowment: $5.3 million. Educational spending for 2005 fiscal year: $4620 per student. Total enrollment: 1,506. Faculty: 137 (42 full-time, 95 part-time). Student-undergrad faculty ratio is 17:1. 804 applied, 66% were admitted. 17% from top 10% of their high school class, 49% from top quarter, 77% from top half. 2 valedictorians. Full-time: 808 students, 62% women, 38% men. Part-time: 198 students, 63% women, 37% men. Students come from 19 states and territories, 12 other countries, 40% from out-of-state, 2% Native American, 4% Hispanic, 6% black, 4% Asian American or Pacific Islander, 1% international, 30% 25 or older, 44% live on campus, 15% transferred in. Retention: 68% of full-time freshmen returned the following year. Academic areas with the most degrees conferred: education; business/marketing; psychology. Core. Calendar: semesters. Academic remediation for entering students, ESL program, advanced placement, accelerated degree program, self-designed majors, double major, summer session for credit, part-time degree program, adult/continuing education programs, internships. Off campus study at Oregon Independent Colleges Association, Concordia University System. Study abroad program. ROTC: Air Force (c).

Entrance Requirements: Options: electronic application, deferred admission. Required: essay, high school transcript, minimum 2.5 high school GPA, 1 recommendation, SAT or ACT. Recommended: interview. Required for some: interview. Entrance: moderately difficult. Application deadline: Rolling. Notification: continuous.

Costs Per Year: Application fee: $20. Comprehensive fee: $26,000 includes full-time tuition ($19,900), mandatory fees ($200), and college room and board ($5900). College room only: $2800. Part-time tuition: $615 per credit.

Collegiate Environment: Orientation program. Drama-theater group, choral group, student-run newspaper, radio station. Social organizations: 10 open to all. Most popular organizations: Drama Club, Business Club, Christian Life Ministry, Service Organization, The Promethean. Major annual event: Graduation. Student services: health clinic, personal-psychological counseling. Campus security: 24-hour emergency response devices and patrols, student patrols, late night transport-escort service, controlled dormitory access. 417 college housing spaces available. Freshmen given priority for college housing. On-campus residence required through sophomore year. Option: coed housing available. Concordia Library plus 3 others with 65,000 books, 176,272 microform titles, 16,214 serials, 9,328 audiovisual materials, an OPAC, and a Web page. Operations spending for 2004 fiscal year: $324,292. 60 computers available on campus for general student use. A

campuswide network can be accessed from student residence rooms and from off campus. Staffed computer lab on campus.

■ CORBAN COLLEGE *F-6*
5000 Deer Park Dr., SE
Salem, OR 97301-9392
Tel: (503)581-8600
Free: 800-845-3005
Admissions: (503)375-7115
Fax: (503)585-4316
E-mail: mziesemer@corban.edu
Web Site: http://www.corban.edu/

Description: Independent religious, 4-year, coed. Awards associate, bachelor's, and master's degrees. Founded 1935. Setting: 107-acre suburban campus with easy access to Portland. Endowment: $1.5 million. Educational spending for 2005 fiscal year: $4138 per student. Total enrollment: 851. Faculty: 71 (34 full-time, 37 part-time). Student-undergrad faculty ratio is 16:1. 485 applied, 83% were admitted. 29% from top 10% of their high school class, 56% from top quarter, 75% from top half. Full-time: 653 students, 59% women, 41% men. Part-time: 151 students, 56% women, 44% men. Students come from 23 states and territories, 3 other countries, 32% from out-of-state, 1% Native American, 2% Hispanic, 1% black, 2% Asian American or Pacific Islander, 0.4% international, 18% 25 or older, 55% live on campus, 11% transferred in. Retention: 75% of full-time freshmen returned the following year. Academic areas with the most degrees conferred: business/marketing; family and consumer sciences; education. Core. Calendar: semesters. Services for LD students, advanced placement, accelerated degree program, freshman honors college, honors program, independent study, distance learning, double major, summer session for credit, adult/continuing education programs, internships. Off campus study at Oregon Independent Colleges Association, Council of Christian Colleges and Universities. Study abroad program. ROTC: Army (c), Air Force (c).

Entrance Requirements: Options: electronic application, early admission. Required: essay, high school transcript, minimum 2.5 high school GPA, 3 recommendations, SAT or ACT. Entrance: moderately difficult. Application deadline: 8/1.

Costs Per Year: Application fee: $40. Comprehensive fee: $26,378 includes full-time tuition ($19,084), mandatory fees ($210), and college room and board ($7084). Part-time tuition: $795 per credit.

Collegiate Environment: Orientation program. Drama-theater group, choral group, student-run newspaper. Social organizations: 6 open to all; 75% of eligible men and 75% of eligible women are members. Most popular organizations: Student Fellowship Groups, Poetry Club, Worship Teams, Drama Club, Westrek Hiking Club. Major annual events: homecoming, Christmas celebration, Western Weekends. Student services: health clinic, personal-psychological counseling. Campus security: 24-hour emergency response devices, student patrols, late night transport-escort service. 420 college housing spaces available; 378 were occupied in 2003-04. Freshmen guaranteed college housing. On-campus residence required through sophomore year. Options: men-only, women-only housing available. Western Baptist College Library with 98,700 books, 4,700 microform titles, 600 serials, 5,000 audiovisual materials, an OPAC, and a Web page. Operations spending for 2004 fiscal year: $228,170. 34 computers available on campus for general student use. A campuswide network can be accessed from student residence rooms and from off campus. Staffed computer lab on campus.

Community Environment: See Willamette University.

■ DEVRY UNIVERSITY *E-7*
Peterkort Center II
9755 SW Barnes Rd., Ste. 150
Portland, OR 97225-6651
Tel: (503)296-7468; (866)338-7934
Web Site: http://www.devry.edu/

Description: Proprietary, comprehensive, coed. Part of DeVry University. Awards bachelor's and master's degrees. Total enrollment: 166. Faculty: 6 (all part-time). Full-time: 81 students, 42% women, 58% men. Part-time: 50 students, 38% women, 62% men. 1% Native American, 34% Hispanic, 6% black, 18% Asian American or Pacific Islander, 0% international. Retention: 50% of full-time freshmen returned the following year. Academic area with the most degrees conferred: business/marketing. Calendar: semesters. Academic remediation for entering students, services for LD students, advanced placement, accelerated degree program, distance learning, summer session for credit, part-time degree program, adult/continuing education programs, co-op programs.

Entrance Requirements: Options: electronic application, deferred admission, international baccalaureate accepted. Required: high school transcript, interview. Entrance: minimally difficult. Application deadline: Rolling.

Costs Per Year: Application fee: $50. One-time mandatory fee: $40. Tuition: $11,790 full-time, $440 per credit part-time. Mandatory fees: $30 full-time, $30 per year part-time. Full-time tuition and fees vary according to course load. Part-time tuition and fees vary according to course load.

Collegiate Environment: Orientation program. College housing not available.

■ EASTERN OREGON UNIVERSITY *E-15*
1 University Blvd.
La Grande, OR 97850-2899
Tel: (541)962-3672
Free: 800-452-3393
Admissions: (541)962-3393
Fax: (541)962-3418
E-mail: admissions@eosc.osshe.edu
Web Site: http://www.eou.edu/

Description: State-supported, comprehensive, coed. Part of Oregon University System. Awards bachelor's and master's degrees. Founded 1929. Setting: 121-acre rural campus. Endowment: $1.7 million. Research spending for 2004 fiscal year: $223,000. Educational spending for 2005 fiscal year: $4611 per student. Total enrollment: 3,533. Faculty: 128 (97 full-time, 31 part-time). Student-undergrad faculty ratio is 24:1. 1,180 applied, 73% were admitted. 21% from top 10% of their high school class, 49% from top quarter, 81% from top half. Full-time: 2,029 students, 60% women, 40% men. Part-time: 1,168 students, 61% women, 39% men. Students come from 42 states and territories, 30 other countries, 31% from out-of-state, 3% Native American, 3% Hispanic, 2% black, 2% Asian American or Pacific Islander, 3% international, 39% 25 or older, 15% live on campus, 15% transferred in. Core. ESL program, services for LD students, advanced placement, self-designed majors, honors program, independent study, distance learning, double major, summer session for credit, part-time degree program, external degree program, adult/continuing education programs, co-op programs and internships. Off campus study at National Student Exchange. Study abroad program. ROTC: Army.

Entrance Requirements: Options: Peterson's Universal Application, electronic application, early action, deferred admission, international baccalaureate accepted. Required: high school transcript, minimum 3.0 high school GPA, SAT or ACT. Required for some: essay, 2 recommendations. Entrance: moderately difficult. Application deadlines: 9/1, 12/1 for early action. Notification: continuous, 1/15 for early action. Preference given to state residents.

Costs Per Year: Application fee: $50. State resident tuition: $4779 full-time. Nonresident tuition: $4779 full-time. Full-time tuition varies according to course load. College room and board: $7300. Room and board charges vary according to board plan and housing facility.

Collegiate Environment: Orientation program. Drama-theater group, choral group, student-run newspaper, radio station. Social organizations: 57 open to all. Most popular organizations: Outdoor Club, Island Magic, student radio station, intramurals, student government. Major annual events: Homecoming, Spring Symposium, Fall Honors Convocation. Student services: health clinic, personal-psychological counseling, women's center. Campus security: 24-hour emergency response devices and patrols, late night transport-escort service, controlled dormitory access. 548 college housing spaces available; 366 were occupied in 2003-04. On-campus residence required in freshman year. Options: coed, men-only, women-only housing available. Pierce Library plus 1 other with 329,942 books, 205,724 microform titles, 998 serials, 35,556 audiovisual materials, an OPAC, and a Web page. Operations spending for 2004 fiscal year: $1.1 million. 125 computers available on campus for general student use. Computer purchase/lease plans available. A campuswide network can be accessed from student residence rooms and from off campus. Staffed computer lab on campus.

■ EUGENE BIBLE COLLEGE *H-6*
2155 Bailey Hill Rd.
Eugene, OR 97405-1194
Tel: (541)485-1780
Free: 800-322-2638
Fax: (541)343-5801
E-mail: admissions@ebc.edu
Web Site: http://www.ebc.edu/

Description: Independent, 4-year, coed, affiliated with Open Bible Standard Churches. Awards bachelor's degrees. Founded 1925. Setting: 40-acre suburban campus. Endowment: $925,859. Educational spending for 2005 fiscal year: $3283 per student. Total enrollment: 203. Student-undergrad faculty ratio is 10:1. 217 applied, 47% were admitted. 12% from top 10% of their high school class, 38% from top quarter, 52% from top half. Full-time: 161 students, 43% women, 57% men. Part-time: 42 students, 38% women, 62% men. Students come from 15 states and territories, 4 other countries, 46% from out-of-state, 0% Native American, 2% Hispanic, 1% black, 1% Asian American or Pacific Islander, 1% international, 20% 25 or older, 56% live on campus. Retention: 68% of full-time freshmen returned the following year. Academic area with the most degrees conferred: theology and religious vocations. Core. Academic remediation for entering students, advanced placement, independent study, distance learning, double major, summer session for credit, part-time degree program, co-op programs and internships.

Entrance Requirements: Options: Common Application, electronic application. Required: essay, high school transcript, minimum 2.0 high school GPA, 2 recommendations, SAT or ACT. Entrance: minimally difficult. Application deadline: 9/1. Notification: continuous until 9/1.

Costs Per Year: Application fee: $30. Comprehensive fee: $12,875 includes full-time tuition ($7500), mandatory fees ($800), and college room and board ($4575). Part-time tuition: $220 per credit hour.

Collegiate Environment: Orientation program. Drama-theater group, choral group. Social organizations: 1 open to all. Most popular organization: Element X. Major annual events: Fall and Spring Flings, Memorial Day Picnic, Madrigal Dinner. Student services: personal-psychological counseling. Campus security: 24-hour emergency response devices, student patrols, controlled dormitory access. 120 college housing spaces available; 105 were occupied in 2003-04. Freshmen guaranteed college housing. On-campus residence required through junior year. Options: men-only, women-only housing available. Flint Memorial Library with 35,000 books, 2,174 microform titles, 251 serials, and 700 audiovisual materials. Operations spending for 2004 fiscal year: $59,863. 18 computers available on campus for general student use. A campuswide network can be accessed. Staffed computer lab on campus.

Community Environment: See University of Oregon.

■ **GEORGE FOX UNIVERSITY** C-8
414 North Meridian
Newberg, OR 97132-2697
Tel: (503)538-8383
Free: 800-765-4369
Admissions: (503)554-2240
Fax: (503)554-3830
E-mail: admissions@georgefox.edu
Web Site: http://www.georgefox.edu/

Description: Independent Friends, university, coed. Awards bachelor's, master's, doctoral, and first professional degrees. Founded 1891. Setting: 73-acre small town campus with easy access to Portland. Endowment: $20 million. Educational spending for 2005 fiscal year: $8254 per student. Total enrollment: 3,193. Faculty: 260 (144 full-time, 116 part-time). Student-undergrad faculty ratio is 12:1. 1,503 applied, 83% were admitted. 37% from top 10% of their high school class, 65% from top quarter, 86% from top half. Full-time: 1,541 students, 62% women, 38% men. Part-time: 301 students, 57% women, 43% men. Students come from 4 states and territories, 4 other countries, 32% from out-of-state, 1% Native American, 2% Hispanic, 1% black, 5% Asian American or Pacific Islander, 2% international, 21% 25 or older, 59% live on campus, 6% transferred in. Retention: 82% of full-time freshmen returned the following year. Academic areas with the most degrees conferred: business/marketing; interdisciplinary studies; history. Core. Calendar: semesters. Academic remediation for entering students, ESL program, services for LD students, advanced placement, accelerated degree program, self-designed majors, honors program, independent study, distance learning, double major, part-time degree program, external degree program, adult/continuing education programs, co-op programs and internships, graduate courses open to undergrads. Off campus study at members of the Christian College Consortium, Coalition for Christian Colleges and Universities, Oregon Independent Colleges Association. Study abroad program. ROTC: Air Force (c).

Entrance Requirements: Options: Peterson's Universal Application, Common Application, electronic application, early admission, deferred admission, international baccalaureate accepted. Required: essay, high school transcript, 2 recommendations, SAT or ACT. Recommended: interview.

Required for some: interview. Entrance: moderately difficult. Application deadlines: 2/1, 12/1 for early action. Notification: continuous until 10/1, 12/20 for early action.

Costs Per Year: Application fee: $40. Comprehensive fee: $29,780 includes full-time tuition ($22,250), mandatory fees ($320), and college room and board ($7210). College room only: $4050. Part-time tuition: $690 per hour.

Collegiate Environment: Orientation program. Drama-theater group, choral group, student-run newspaper, radio station. Social organizations: 18 open to all. Most popular organizations: student government, student activities, Christian ministries, Orientation Committee, Chaplain's Committee. Major annual events: Christmas Celebration, Quaker Heritage Week, Orientation. Student services: health clinic, personal-psychological counseling, women's center. Campus security: 24-hour emergency response devices and patrols, student patrols, late night transport-escort service, controlled dormitory access. 75 undergraduates lived in college housing during 2003-04. On-campus residence required through junior year. Options: men-only, women-only housing available. Murdock Learning Resource Center plus 1 other with 123,734 books, 207,180 microform titles, 1,323 serials, 2,687 audiovisual materials, an OPAC, and a Web page. Operations spending for 2004 fiscal year: $2 million. 1,300 computers available on campus for general student use. A campuswide network can be accessed from student residence rooms and from off campus. Staffed computer lab on campus.

Community Environment: Located 24 miles southwest of Portland, Newberg has a number of churches, a community hospital, and various civic and service organizations. Commercial transportation is easily accessible. Part-time employment is available.

■ **GUTENBERG COLLEGE** H-6
1883 University St.
Eugene, OR 97403
Tel: (541)683-5141
Admissions: (541)736-9071
Fax: (541)683-6997
Web Site: http://www.gutenberg.edu/

Description: Independent religious, 4-year, coed. Awards bachelor's degrees. Total enrollment: 44. 20 applied, 100% were admitted. Full-time: 38 students, 42% women, 58% men. Part-time: 6 students, 33% women, 67% men. Students come from 11 states and territories, 1 other country, 63% from out-of-state, 3% international, 5% 25 or older, 0% transferred in. Core.

Entrance Requirements: Open admission. Required: essay, high school transcript, 2 recommendations, SAT. Application deadline: 4/1. Notification: continuous until 9/10.

Costs Per Year: Application fee: $20. Comprehensive fee: $15,075 includes full-time tuition ($9970), mandatory fees ($650), and college room and board ($4455). Full-time tuition and fees vary according to student level. Room and board charges vary according to housing facility. Part-time tuition: $350 per quarter hour.

Collegiate Environment: Orientation program. Freshmen given priority for college housing. Option: men-only housing available. 2 computers available on campus for general student use. Staffed computer lab on campus.

■ **HEALD COLLEGE-PORTLAND** E-7
625 SW Broadway, 4th Floor
Portland, OR 97205
Tel: (503)229-0492
Fax: (503)229-0498
Web Site: http://www.heald.edu/

Description: Independent, 2-year, coed. Awards certificates, diplomas, transfer associate, and terminal associate degrees. Founded 1863. Total enrollment: 206. Student-undergrad faculty ratio is 10:1. Full-time: 149 students, 51% women, 49% men. Part-time: 57 students, 56% women, 44% men. 0% from out-of-state, 0.5% Native American, 5% Hispanic, 7% black, 4% Asian American or Pacific Islander, 0% international. Academic remediation for entering students, advanced placement, summer session for credit, part-time degree program, internships.

Entrance Requirements: Open admission. Options: electronic application, early admission, deferred admission. Required: high school transcript, interview, COMPASS. Entrance: minimally difficult. Application deadline: Rolling. Notification: continuous.

Collegiate Environment: Orientation program. Learning Resource Center with an OPAC.

■ **ITT TECHNICAL INSTITUTE** E-7
6035 Northeast 78th Ct.
Portland, OR 97218-2854

Tel: (503)255-6500
Free: 800-234-5488
Fax: (503)255-6135
Web Site: http://www.itt-tech.edu/
Description: Proprietary, primarily 2-year, coed. Part of ITT Educational Services, Inc. Awards terminal associate and bachelor's degrees. Founded 1971. Setting: 4-acre urban campus. Core.
Entrance Requirements: Option: deferred admission. Required: high school transcript, interview, Wonderlic aptitude test. Recommended: recommendations. Entrance: minimally difficult. Application deadline: Rolling. Notification: continuous.
Costs Per Year: Application fee: $100.
Collegiate Environment: Orientation program. Student-run newspaper. College housing not available.

■ **KLAMATH COMMUNITY COLLEGE** *M-8*
7390 South 6th St.
Klamath Falls, OR 97603
Tel: (541)882-3521
E-mail: browng@kcc.cc.or.us
Web Site: http://www.kcc.cc.or.us/
Description: State-supported, 2-year, coed. Awards certificates and terminal associate degrees. Founded 1996. Total enrollment: 3,000.
Collegiate Environment: College housing not available.

■ **LANE COMMUNITY COLLEGE** *H-6*
4000 East 30th Ave.
Eugene, OR 97405-0640
Tel: (541)747-4501
Fax: (541)744-3995
Web Site: http://www.lanecc.edu/
Description: State and locally supported, 2-year, coed. Awards certificates, transfer associate, and terminal associate degrees. Founded 1964. Setting: 240-acre suburban campus. Endowment: $6 million. Educational spending for 2005 fiscal year: $2832 per student. Total enrollment: 11,834. Students come from 28 states and territories, 27 other countries, 2% Native American, 4% Hispanic, 1% black, 2% Asian American or Pacific Islander, 2% international, 42% 25 or older. Retention: 62% of full-time freshmen returned the following year. Core. Academic remediation for entering students, ESL program, services for LD students, advanced placement, summer session for credit, part-time degree program, adult/continuing education programs, internships.
Entrance Requirements: Open admission. Options: Common Application, early admission. Entrance: noncompetitive. Application deadline: Rolling. Notification: continuous. Preference given to district residents.
Collegiate Environment: Orientation program. Drama-theater group, choral group, student-run newspaper, radio station. Social organizations: 15 open to all. Most popular organizations: Associated Students of Lane, Multicultural Club, Native American Club, Lane Writing Club, Forensics Club. Major annual events: Fall Welcome Week, Martin Luther King, Jr. Day. Student services: legal services, health clinic, personal-psychological counseling, women's center. Campus security: 24-hour emergency response devices and patrols, student patrols, late night transport-escort service. College housing not available. Lane Community College Library plus 1 other with 67,051 books, 513 serials, an OPAC, and a Web page. Operations spending for 2004 fiscal year: $1.2 million. 1,600 computers available on campus for general student use. A campuswide network can be accessed. Staffed computer lab on campus.
Community Environment: See University of Oregon.

■ **LEWIS & CLARK COLLEGE** *E-7*
0615 SW Palatine Hill Rd.
Portland, OR 97219-7899
Tel: (503)768-7000
Free: 800-444-4111
Admissions: (503)768-7040
Fax: (503)768-7055
E-mail: admissions@lclark.edu
Web Site: http://www.lclark.edu/
Description: Independent, comprehensive, coed. Awards bachelor's, master's, doctoral, and first professional degrees and post-master's certificates. Founded 1867. Setting: 137-acre suburban campus. Endowment: $180.5 million. Research spending for 2004 fiscal year: $1.4 million. Educational spending for 2005 fiscal year: $12,793 per student. Total enroll-

ment: 3,433. Faculty: 323 (205 full-time, 118 part-time). Student-undergrad faculty ratio is 13:1. 4,196 applied, 59% were admitted. 42% from top 10% of their high school class, 78% from top quarter, 98% from top half. 8 National Merit Scholars, 28 valedictorians. Full-time: 1,940 students, 61% women, 39% men. Part-time: 24 students, 58% women, 42% men. Students come from 49 states and territories, 44 other countries, 80% from out-of-state, 1% Native American, 4% Hispanic, 1% black, 6% Asian American or Pacific Islander, 4% international, 2% 25 or older, 64% live on campus, 4% transferred in. Retention: 86% of full-time freshmen returned the following year. Academic areas with the most degrees conferred: social sciences; psychology; biological/life sciences. Core. Calendar: semesters. ESL program, services for LD students, advanced placement, accelerated degree program, self-designed majors, honors program, independent study, double major, summer session for credit, part-time degree program, internships. Off campus study at Oregon Independent Colleges Association. Study abroad program.
Entrance Requirements: Options: Peterson's Universal Application, Common Application, electronic application, early admission, early action, deferred admission, international baccalaureate accepted. Required: essay, high school transcript, minimum 2.0 high school GPA, 2 recommendations, SAT, ACT, or academic portfolio. Recommended: minimum 3.0 high school GPA, interview. Required for some: 4 recommendations, portfolio applicants must submit samples of graded work, SAT or ACT. Entrance: very difficult. Application deadlines: 2/1, 11/15 for early action. Notification: 4/1, 1/15 for early action.
Costs Per Year: Application fee: $50. Comprehensive fee: $35,358 includes full-time tuition ($27,494), mandatory fees ($216), and college room and board ($7648). College room only: $3974. Room and board charges vary according to board plan and housing facility. Part-time tuition: $1386 per credit hour.
Collegiate Environment: Orientation program. Drama-theater group, choral group, student-run newspaper, radio station. Social organizations: 70 open to all. Most popular organizations: College Outdoors, Associated Students, Center for Service and Work, musical groups, student radio station. Major annual events: International Affairs Symposium, Gender Studies Symposium, Environmental Studies Symposium. Student services: health clinic, personal-psychological counseling, women's center. Campus security: 24-hour emergency response devices and patrols, student patrols, late night transport-escort service, controlled dormitory access. 1,202 college housing spaces available; all were occupied in 2003-04. Freshmen guaranteed college housing. On-campus residence required through sophomore year. Option: coed housing available. Aubrey Watzek Library plus 1 other with 227,609 books, 2 million microform titles, 7,477 serials, 11,586 audiovisual materials, an OPAC, and a Web page. Operations spending for 2004 fiscal year: $4.4 million. 158 computers available on campus for general student use. Computer purchase/lease plans available. A campuswide network can be accessed from student residence rooms and from off campus. Staffed computer lab on campus.
Community Environment: See Portland State University.

■ **LINFIELD COLLEGE** *E-6*
900 SE Baker St.
McMinnville, OR 97128-6894
Tel: (503)883-2200
Free: 800-640-2287
Admissions: (503)883-2213
Fax: (503)883-2472
E-mail: admission@linfield.edu
Web Site: http://www.linfield.edu/
Description: Independent American Baptist Churches in the USA, 4-year, coed. Awards bachelor's degrees. Founded 1849. Setting: 193-acre small town campus with easy access to Portland. Endowment: $53.2 million. Total enrollment: 1,750. Student-undergrad faculty ratio is 14:1. 2,131 applied, 73% were admitted. 38% from top 10% of their high school class, 68% from top quarter, 94% from top half. 10 class presidents, 26 valedictorians, 42 student government officers. Full-time: 1,708 students, 55% women, 45% men. Part-time: 42 students, 33% women, 67% men. Students come from 26 states and territories, 20 other countries, 44% from out-of-state, 1% Native American, 2% Hispanic, 1% black, 6% Asian American or Pacific Islander, 2% international, 1% 25 or older, 74% live on campus, 3% transferred in. Retention: 79% of full-time freshmen returned the following year. Academic areas with the most degrees conferred: business/marketing; education; social sciences. Core. Calendar: 4-1-4. ESL program, services for LD students, advanced placement, self-designed majors, independent study,

distance learning, double major, summer session for credit, part-time degree program, external degree program, adult/continuing education programs, internships. Off campus study at American Baptist Colleges and Universities. Study abroad program. ROTC: Air Force (c).

Entrance Requirements: Options: Peterson's Universal Application, Common Application, electronic application, early action, deferred admission, international baccalaureate accepted. Required: essay, high school transcript, 1 recommendation, SAT or ACT. Recommended: interview. Entrance: moderately difficult. Application deadlines: 2/15, 11/15 for early action. Notification: 4/1, 1/15 for early action.

Costs Per Year: Application fee: $40. Comprehensive fee: $29,632 includes full-time tuition ($22,790), mandatory fees ($232), and college room and board ($6610). College room only: $3540. Room and board charges vary according to board plan and housing facility. Part-time tuition: $710 per credit. Part-time mandatory fees: $68 per term. Part-time tuition and fees vary according to course load.

Collegiate Environment: Orientation program. Drama-theater group, choral group, student-run newspaper, radio station. Social organizations: 42 open to all; national fraternities, national sororities, local fraternities, local sororities; 26% of eligible men and 30% of eligible women are members. Most popular organizations: Fellowship of Christian Athletes, Linfield Ultimate Players Association, Hawaiian Club, International Club, Lacrosse Club. Major annual events: Luau, Wildstock, homecoming. Student services: health clinic, personal-psychological counseling. Campus security: 24-hour emergency response devices and patrols, late night transport-escort service, controlled dormitory access. 1,287 college housing spaces available; 1,283 were occupied in 2003-04. Freshmen guaranteed college housing. On-campus residence required through junior year. Options: coed, men-only, women-only housing available. Jereld R. Nicholson Library with 169,087 books, 17,609 microform titles, 1,278 serials, 27,286 audiovisual materials, an OPAC, and a Web page. 272 computers available on campus for general student use. Computer purchase/lease plans available. A campuswide network can be accessed from student residence rooms and from off campus. Staffed computer lab on campus.

Community Environment: Nestled in the heart of the Willamette Valley, McMinnville is a classic college town where students are quickly welcomed into the community. Downtown McMinnville boasts a charming historic shopping district, which includes art galleries, antique shops, coffeehouses, and nationally renowned restaurants like Nick's Italian Cafe, as well as a variety of job opportunities. Linfield students have many chances to get acquainted with their McMinnville neighbors while going to the Cinema 8 Multiplex or the Moonlight Theater and Pizzeria, attending community theatre productions or becoming members of one of the town's 28 churches.

■ LINN-BENTON COMMUNITY COLLEGE *G-6*

6500 Southwest Pacific Blvd.
Albany, OR 97321
Tel: (541)917-4999
Admissions: (541)917-4811
Fax: (541)917-4838
Web Site: http://www.linnbenton.edu/

Description: State and locally supported, 2-year, coed. Awards certificates, transfer associate, and terminal associate degrees. Founded 1966. Setting: 104-acre small town campus. Endowment: $2.1 million. Research spending for 2004 fiscal year: $114,328. Educational spending for 2005 fiscal year: $4215 per student. Total enrollment: 5,289. 2,896 applied, 100% were admitted. Full-time: 2,839 students, 52% women, 48% men. Part-time: 2,450 students, 57% women, 43% men. Students come from 5 states and territories, 10 other countries, 43% 25 or older. Core. Academic remediation for entering students, ESL program, services for LD students, advanced placement, self-designed majors, independent study, distance learning, summer session for credit, part-time degree program, adult/continuing education programs, co-op programs and internships. ROTC: Army (c), Air Force (c).

Entrance Requirements: Open admission. Option: deferred admission. Required for some: high school transcript. Entrance: noncompetitive. Application deadline: Rolling. Preference given to district residents.

Costs Per Year: Application fee: $25. State resident tuition: $2925 full-time. Nonresident tuition: $7470 full-time.

Collegiate Environment: Orientation program. Drama-theater group, choral group, student-run newspaper. Social organizations: 18 open to all. Most popular organizations: EBOP Club, Multicultural Club, Campus Family Co-op, Horticulture Club, Collegiate Secretary Club. Major annual events: Martin Luther King Celebration, Spring Daze, Children's Winter Festival. Student services: personal-psychological counseling. Campus security: 24-hour

emergency response devices and patrols, student patrols, late night transport-escort service. College housing not available. Linn-Benton Community College Library with 42,561 books, 1,172 microform titles, 91 serials, 8,758 audiovisual materials, an OPAC, and a Web page. Operations spending for 2004 fiscal year: $450,000. 500 computers available on campus for general student use. A campuswide network can be accessed from off-campus. Staffed computer lab on campus.

Community Environment: Noted for its rare metals industries, Albany is also in the fertile Willamette Valley, a rich timber area; the valley is one of the leading producers of rye grass seed and mint. The rare metals industries produce tantalum, tungsten, zirconium, hafnium, columbium, and molybdenum. Other manufactured products are plywood lumber, furniture, and mill machinery. The average rainfall is 39.7 inches. Community facilities include a number of churches, a YMCA, Boys Club, a hospital, and many clinics, excellent shopping areas, and a number of civic and service organizations. Part-time jobs are available. Recreational activities are swimming, tennis, and other sports. The World's Champion Timber Carnival in July draws loggers from all over to compete in log rolling, tree topping, axe throwing, and other events.

■ MARYLHURST UNIVERSITY

17600 Pacific Hwy., PO Box 261
Marylhurst, OR 97036-0261
Tel: (503)636-8141
Free: 800-634-9982
Fax: (503)636-9526
Web Site: http://www.marylhurst.edu/

Description: Independent Roman Catholic, comprehensive, coed. Awards bachelor's and master's degrees. Founded 1893. Setting: 73-acre suburban campus with easy access to Portland. Total enrollment: 1,268. Faculty: 209 (37 full-time, 172 part-time). Student-undergrad faculty ratio is 7:1. 34 applied, 44% were admitted. Full-time: 238 students, 73% women, 27% men. Part-time: 641 students, 75% women, 25% men. Students come from 9 states and territories, 22 other countries, 0.4% Native American, 1% Hispanic, 1% black, 1% Asian American or Pacific Islander, 2% international, 72% 25 or older, 62% transferred in. Academic areas with the most degrees conferred: business/marketing; visual and performing arts; communications/journalism. Core. ESL program, services for LD students, advanced placement, accelerated degree program, self-designed majors, independent study, distance learning, double major, summer session for credit, part-time degree program, adult/continuing education programs, internships, graduate courses open to undergrads. Off campus study at members of the Oregon Independent Colleges Association.

Entrance Requirements: Open admission except for some programs. Option: deferred admission. Required: high school transcript. Entrance: noncompetitive. Notification: continuous.

Costs Per Year: Application fee: $20. Tuition: $13,860 full-time, $308 per quarter hour part-time. Mandatory fees: $360 full-time, $8 per quarter hour part-time. Full-time tuition and fees vary according to course load. Part-time tuition and fees vary according to course load.

Collegiate Environment: Orientation program. Choral group. Social organizations: 6 open to all. Most popular organizations: Toastmasters, Environmental Science Club, Student Ambassadors, Bahia Club, student government. Major annual events: New Student Orientation, Graduation, Campus Ministries events. Student services: personal-psychological counseling. Campus security: 24-hour emergency response devices and patrols, late night transport-escort service, controlled dormitory access. Option: coed housing available. Shoen Library with 1,449 audiovisual materials, an OPAC, and a Web page. Operations spending for 2004 fiscal year: $562,411. 40 computers available on campus for general student use. A campuswide network can be accessed. Staffed computer lab on campus.

■ MOUNT ANGEL SEMINARY

St. Benedict, OR 97373
Tel: (503)845-3951
Web Site: http://www.mtangel.edu/Seminary/Seminary.htm

Description: Independent Roman Catholic, comprehensive. Awards bachelor's, master's, and first professional degrees (only candidates for the priesthood are admitted). Founded 1887. Setting: 75-acre rural campus with easy access to Portland. Total enrollment: 178. 15 applied, 73% were admitted. Students come from 14 states and territories, 10 other countries, 60% 25 or older. Retention: 88% of full-time freshmen returned the following year. Core. Calendar: semesters. Academic remediation for entering students, ESL program, advanced placement, part-time degree program, adult/

continuing education programs, graduate courses open to undergrads. Off campus study at Oregon Independent Colleges Association.

Entrance Requirements: Option: Common Application. Required: essay, high school transcript, minimum 2.0 high school GPA, 2 recommendations. Recommended: interview, SAT. Entrance: moderately difficult. Application deadline: 7/15. Notification: continuous. Preference given to Catholic seminarians.

Collegiate Environment: Orientation program. Choral group. Student services: health clinic, personal-psychological counseling. Campus security: 24-hour emergency response devices, patrols by police officers. On-campus residence required through senior year. Mount Angel Abbey Library with 240,000 books and 775 serials. 16 computers available on campus for general student use. Staffed computer lab on campus.

■ **MT. HOOD COMMUNITY COLLEGE** *E-7*
26000 Southeast Stark St.
Gresham, OR 97030-3300
Tel: (503)491-6422
Admissions: (503)491-7265
Fax: (503)491-7388
Web Site: http://www.mhcc.cc.or.us/

Description: State and locally supported, 2-year, coed. Awards certificates, diplomas, transfer associate, and terminal associate degrees. Founded 1966. Setting: 212-acre suburban campus with easy access to Portland. Research spending for 2004 fiscal year: $75,611. Total enrollment: 8,771. Full-time: 3,178 students, 53% women, 47% men. Part-time: 5,593 students, 57% women, 43% men. Students come from 16 states and territories, 6 other countries, 56% 25 or older. Core. Academic remediation for entering students, ESL program, services for LD students, advanced placement, summer session for credit, part-time degree program, adult/continuing education programs, co-op programs and internships. Study abroad program.

Entrance Requirements: Open admission except for allied health, some professional-technical programs. Options: early admission, deferred admission. Required for some: high school transcript, minimum 2.0 high school GPA. Placement: CPT required for some. Entrance: noncompetitive. Application deadline: Rolling. Notification: continuous. Preference given to state residents.

Collegiate Environment: Drama-theater group, choral group, student-run newspaper, radio station. Student services: health clinic, personal-psychological counseling, women's center. Campus security: 24-hour emergency response devices and patrols, student patrols, late night transport-escort service. College housing not available. Library Resource Center with 64,000 books and 412 serials. 100 computers available on campus for general student use. Staffed computer lab on campus.

■ **MULTNOMAH BIBLE COLLEGE AND BIBLICAL SEMINARY** *E-7*
8435 Northeast Glisan St.
Portland, OR 97220-5898
Tel: (503)255-0332
Free: 800-275-4672
Fax: (503)254-1268
Web Site: http://www.multnomah.edu/

Description: Independent interdenominational, comprehensive, coed. Awards bachelor's, master's, and first professional degrees. Founded 1936. Setting: 22-acre urban campus. Endowment: $5.9 million. Research spending for 2004 fiscal year: $12.5 million. Educational spending for 2005 fiscal year: $17,561 per student. Total enrollment: 803. Faculty: 57 (24 full-time, 33 part-time). Student-undergrad faculty ratio is 16:1. 185 applied, 89% were admitted. 12% from top 10% of their high school class, 34% from top quarter, 83% from top half. Full-time: 531 students, 47% women, 53% men. Part-time: 59 students, 46% women, 54% men. Students come from 30 states and territories, 55% from out-of-state, 1% Native American, 3% Hispanic, 2% black, 4% Asian American or Pacific Islander, 0.3% international, 21% 25 or older, 50% live on campus, 16% transferred in. Retention: 62% of full-time freshmen returned the following year. Academic area with the most degrees conferred: theology and religious vocations. Core. Calendar: early semesters. Academic remediation for entering students, services for LD students, advanced placement, double major, summer session for credit, part-time degree program, adult/continuing education programs, internships.

Entrance Requirements: Options: deferred admission, international baccalaureate accepted. Required: essay, high school transcript, minimum 2.5 high school GPA, 4 recommendations, SAT or ACT. Entrance: moderately difficult. Application deadline: 7/15. Notification: continuous.

Costs Per Year: Application fee: $40. Comprehensive fee: $16,810 includes full-time tuition ($11,750) and college room and board ($5060). Room and board charges vary according to board plan and housing facility. Part-time tuition: $486 per semester hour. Part-time tuition varies according to course load.

Collegiate Environment: Orientation program. Drama-theater group, choral group, student-run newspaper. Major annual events: Fall Retreat, Fall Banquet, Saturday in the Park. Student services: health clinic, personal-psychological counseling. Campus security: 24-hour emergency response devices and patrols, late night transport-escort service, controlled dormitory access. 386 college housing spaces available; 280 were occupied in 2003-04. Freshmen guaranteed college housing. On-campus residence required through senior year. Options: men-only, women-only housing available. John Mitchell Library with 84,535 books, 7,818 microform titles, 378 serials, 5,048 audiovisual materials, and an OPAC. Operations spending for 2004 fiscal year: $481,406. 42 computers available on campus for general student use. A campuswide network can be accessed from student residence rooms and from off campus. Staffed computer lab on campus.

Community Environment: See Portland State University.

■ **NORTHWEST CHRISTIAN COLLEGE** *H-6*
828 East 11th Ave.
Eugene, OR 97401-3745
Tel: (541)343-1641; 877-463-6622
Admissions: (541)684-7210
Fax: (541)684-7317
E-mail: randyj@nwcc.edu
Web Site: http://www.nwcc.edu/

Description: Independent Christian, comprehensive, coed. Awards associate, bachelor's, and master's degrees. Founded 1895. Setting: 8-acre urban campus with easy access to Portland. Endowment: $12.7 million. Total enrollment: 491. Faculty: 61 (19 full-time, 42 part-time). Student-undergrad faculty ratio is 11:1. 179 applied, 64% were admitted. 13% from top 10% of their high school class, 36% from top quarter, 67% from top half. Full-time: 377 students, 60% women, 40% men. Part-time: 25 students, 60% women, 40% men. Students come from 13 states and territories, 1 other country, 8% from out-of-state, 0.5% Native American, 1% Hispanic, 1% black, 1% Asian American or Pacific Islander, 0% international, 46% 25 or older, 11% transferred in. Retention: 62% of full-time freshmen returned the following year. Academic areas with the most degrees conferred: business/marketing; education; psychology. Core. Academic remediation for entering students, ESL program, services for LD students, advanced placement, accelerated degree program, self-designed majors, independent study, distance learning, double major, summer session for credit, part-time degree program, adult/continuing education programs, co-op programs and internships. Off campus study at University of Oregon, Lane Community College. Study abroad program. ROTC: Army (c).

Entrance Requirements: Options: Peterson's Universal Application, Common Application, electronic application, deferred admission, international baccalaureate accepted. Required: essay, high school transcript, minimum 2.5 high school GPA, 2 recommendations, SAT or ACT. Recommended: interview. Required for some: SAT Subject Tests. Entrance: moderately difficult. Application deadline: Rolling. Notification: continuous.

Costs Per Year: Application fee: $0. Comprehensive fee: $26,314 includes full-time tuition ($19,890) and college room and board ($6424). College room only: $2800. Part-time tuition: $663 per credit.

Collegiate Environment: Orientation program. Drama-theater group, choral group, student-run newspaper. Social organizations: 18 open to all. Most popular organizations: Praise Gathering, Spirit Club, Teachers for Tomorrow, Environmental Club, Drama Club. Major annual events: Spirit Week, Spring Formal, May Day Olympics. Student services: health clinic, personal-psychological counseling. Campus security: 24-hour emergency response devices, late night transport-escort service, controlled dormitory access, late-night patrols by trained security personnel. 213 college housing spaces available; 130 were occupied in 2003-04. Freshmen given priority for college housing. On-campus residence required in freshman year. Options: coed, men-only, women-only housing available. Kellenberger Library with 60,250 books, 766 microform titles, 261 serials, 10,367 audiovisual materials, an OPAC, and a Web page. 40 computers available on campus for general student use. A campuswide network can be accessed from student residence rooms and from off campus. Staffed computer lab on campus.

Community Environment: See University of Oregon.

■ OREGON COAST COMMUNITY COLLEGE *G-5*

332 SW Coast Hwy.
Newport, OR 97365
Tel: (541)265-2283
Admissions: (541)574-7125
E-mail: k.wimer@occc.cc.or.us
Web Site: http://www.occc.cc.or.us

Description: Public, 2-year, coed. Awards certificates and transfer associate degrees. Educational spending for 2005 fiscal year: $3887 per student. Total enrollment: 599. Student-undergrad faculty ratio is 14:1. 86 applied, 100% were admitted. Full-time: 73 students, 56% women, 44% men. Part-time: 526 students, 65% women, 35% men. Students come from 5 states and territories, 1% from out-of-state, 5% Native American, 4% Hispanic, 1% black, 2% Asian American or Pacific Islander, 0% international, 58% 25 or older, 43% transferred in. Core. Academic remediation for entering students, ESL program, services for LD students, honors program, distance learning, summer session for credit, part-time degree program, co-op programs and internships.

Entrance Requirements: Open admission. Option: Common Application. Entrance: noncompetitive.

Costs Per Year: State resident tuition: $2790 full-time, $62 per credit part-time. Nonresident tuition: $7740 full-time, $172 per credit part-time. Mandatory fees: $210 full-time, $5 per credit part-time.

Collegiate Environment: Orientation program. College housing not available. Oregon Coast Community College Library with 8,652 books, 51 serials, 1,210 audiovisual materials, an OPAC, and a Web page. Operations spending for 2004 fiscal year: $124,384. 40 computers available on campus for general student use. A campuswide network can be accessed. Staffed computer lab on campus.

■ OREGON COLLEGE OF ART & CRAFT *E-7*

8245 Southwest Barnes Rd.
Portland, OR 97225
Tel: (503)297-5544
Free: 800-390-0632
Fax: (503)297-3155
E-mail: bbeach@ocac.edu
Web Site: http://www.ocac.edu/

Description: Independent, 4-year, coed. Awards bachelor's degrees. Founded 1907. Setting: 11-acre urban campus. Endowment: $4.4 million. Educational spending for 2005 fiscal year: $8733 per student. Total enrollment: 153. Student-undergrad faculty ratio is 9:1. 42 applied, 95% were admitted. 12% from top 10% of their high school class, 30% from top quarter, 60% from top half. Full-time: 114 students, 59% women, 41% men. Part-time: 39 students, 62% women, 38% men. Students come from 26 states and territories, 2 other countries, 47% from out-of-state, 2% Native American, 5% Hispanic, 1% black, 2% Asian American or Pacific Islander, 0% international, 60% 25 or older, 3% live on campus, 30% transferred in. Retention: 80% of full-time freshmen returned the following year. Academic area with the most degrees conferred: visual and performing arts. Core. Calendar: semesters. Advanced placement, independent study, double major, part-time degree program, adult/continuing education programs, internships. Off campus study at AICAD Mobility Program.

Entrance Requirements: Options: Peterson's Universal Application, deferred admission, international baccalaureate accepted. Required: essay, high school transcript, minimum 2.5 high school GPA, 2 recommendations, portfolio. Recommended: SAT, ACT. Required for some: interview. Entrance: moderately difficult. Application deadline: Rolling. Notification: continuous.

Costs Per Year: Application fee: $35. Tuition: $16,900 full-time, $2214 per course part-time. Mandatory fees: $982 full-time, $50 per course part-time. College room only: $3600.

Collegiate Environment: Orientation program. Social organizations: 1 open to all. Most popular organization: Student Life Committee. Major annual events: Residents' Lectures, Juried Student Show, thesis presentations. Student services: personal-psychological counseling. Campus security: 24-hour emergency response devices, late night transport-escort service. 5 college housing spaces available; all were occupied in 2003-04. Freshmen given priority for college housing. On-campus residence required through junior year. Oregon College of Art and Craft Library plus 1 other with 9,000 books, 75 serials, 30,246 audiovisual materials, and an OPAC. Operations spending for 2004 fiscal year: $80,086. 14 computers available on campus

for general student use. A campuswide network can be accessed from off-campus. Staffed computer lab on campus.

■ OREGON HEALTH & SCIENCE UNIVERSITY *E-7*

3181 SW Sam Jackson Park Rd.
Portland, OR 97239-3098
Tel: (503)494-8311
Admissions: (503)494-7800
Fax: (503)494-5738
E-mail: honnellc@ohsu.edu
Web Site: http://www.ohsu.edu/

Description: State-related, upper-level, coed. Awards bachelor's, master's, doctoral, and first professional degrees and post-master's and first professional certificates. Founded 1974. Setting: 116-acre urban campus. Endowment: $316.5 million. Research spending for 2004 fiscal year: $62.2 million. Total enrollment: 2,511. Faculty: 836 (503 full-time, 333 part-time). Full-time: 474 students, 88% women, 12% men. Part-time: 175 students, 88% women, 12% men. Students come from 31 states and territories, 3 other countries, 8% from out-of-state, 1% Native American, 3% Hispanic, 1% black, 5% Asian American or Pacific Islander, 1% international, 64% 25 or older. Academic area with the most degrees conferred: health professions and related sciences. Core. Advanced placement, summer session for credit, part-time degree program, graduate courses open to undergrads. Off campus study at other members of the Oregon University System. ROTC: Army (c).

Costs Per Year: Application fee: $125. State resident tuition: $7920 full-time, $165 per credit part-time. Nonresident tuition: $18,480 full-time, $385 per credit part-time. Mandatory fees: $1193 full-time.

Collegiate Environment: Orientation program. Student services: health clinic, personal-psychological counseling. Campus security: 24-hour patrols. Option: coed housing available. Bic Bio-Informational Center plus 2 others with 200,771 books, 2,110 serials, an OPAC, and a Web page. 49 computers available on campus for general student use. A campuswide network can be accessed from student residence rooms and from off campus. Staffed computer lab on campus.

■ OREGON INSTITUTE OF TECHNOLOGY *M-8*

3201 Campus Dr.
Klamath Falls, OR 97601-8801
Tel: (541)885-1000
Free: 800-343-6653
Admissions: (541)885-1150
Fax: (541)885-1115
E-mail: oit@oit.edu
Web Site: http://www.oit.edu/

Description: State-supported, 4-year, coed. Part of Oregon University System. Awards associate, bachelor's, and master's degrees. Founded 1947. Setting: 173-acre small town campus. Endowment: $14.5 million. Research spending for 2004 fiscal year: $2.4 million. Educational spending for 2005 fiscal year: $11,229 per student. Total enrollment: 3,373. 735 applied, 90% were admitted. 21% from top 10% of their high school class, 54% from top quarter, 85% from top half. Full-time: 1,985 students, 44% women, 56% men. Part-time: 1,381 students, 51% women, 49% men. Students come from 37 states and territories, 13 other countries, 15% from out-of-state, 2% Native American, 4% Hispanic, 1% black, 5% Asian American or Pacific Islander, 1% international, 38% 25 or older, 15% live on campus, 12% transferred in. Retention: 72% of full-time freshmen returned the following year. Core. Academic remediation for entering students, services for LD students, advanced placement, distance learning, double major, summer session for credit, part-time degree program, external degree program, co-op programs and internships. Off campus study at Portland State University. Study abroad program. ROTC: Army (c).

Entrance Requirements: Options: Peterson's Universal Application, Common Application, electronic application, deferred admission. Required: high school transcript, minimum 3.0 high school GPA, SAT or ACT. Required for some: recommendations. Entrance: moderately difficult. Application deadline: 10/1. Notification: continuous until 8/1.

Costs Per Year: Application fee: $50. State resident tuition: $4101 full-time, $99 per credit part-time. Nonresident tuition: $14,310 full-time, $99 per credit part-time. Mandatory fees: $1,246 full-time. Full-time tuition and fees vary according to course load, location, and reciprocity agreements. College room and board: $6037. Room and board charges vary according to board plan.

Collegiate Environment: Orientation program. Choral group, student-run newspaper, radio station. Social organizations: 35 open to all; national fraternities. Most popular organizations: Phi Delta Theta, Christian Fellowship, International Club, Society of Women Engineers, Association of Student Mechanical Engineers. Major annual events: Super Club Sign-Up, Homecoming, Talent Show. Student services: health clinic, personal-psychological counseling. Campus security: 24-hour emergency response devices and patrols, late night transport-escort service. 500 college housing spaces available; 370 were occupied in 2003-04. Option: coed housing available. Center for Learning and Teaching plus 2 others with 90,389 books, 150,550 microform titles, 1,764 serials, 1,905 audiovisual materials, an OPAC, and a Web page. Operations spending for 2004 fiscal year: $1 million. 700 computers available on campus for general student use. A campuswide network can be accessed from off-campus. Staffed computer lab on campus.

Community Environment: Klamath Falls is located nearly equidistant from Portland, OR, San Francisco, CA, and Reno, NV. Bus, train and air transportation is available. A local phenomenon is a stratum of hot water underlying certain sections of the city, which is used to heat homes and offices. Numerous lakes are in Klamath County, including Crater Lake National Park. Outdoor recreation of all sorts is readily available and enjoyed year-round.

■ OREGON STATE UNIVERSITY *G-6*

Corvallis, OR 97331
Tel: (541)737-1000
Admissions: (541)737-4411
Fax: (541)737-6157
E-mail: osuadmit@ccmail.orst.edu
Web Site: http://oregonstate.edu/

Description: State-supported, university, coed. Part of Oregon University System. Awards bachelor's, master's, doctoral, and first professional degrees. Founded 1868. Setting: 422-acre small town campus with easy access to Portland. Endowment: $349.3 million. Total enrollment: 19,236. Faculty: 1,215 (760 full-time, 455 part-time). Student-undergrad faculty ratio is 19:1. 6,552 applied, 93% were admitted. 18% from top 10% of their high school class, 46% from top quarter, 79% from top half. Full-time: 13,862 students, 47% women, 53% men. Part-time: 1,885 students, 51% women, 49% men. Students come from 50 states and territories, 93 other countries, 10% from out-of-state, 1% Native American, 4% Hispanic, 1% black, 8% Asian American or Pacific Islander, 1% international, 7% 25 or older, 22% live on campus, 7% transferred in. Retention: 80% of full-time freshmen returned the following year. Academic areas with the most degrees conferred: business/marketing; engineering; family and consumer sciences. Core. Academic remediation for entering students, ESL program, services for LD students, advanced placement, self-designed majors, freshman honors college, honors program, distance learning, double major, summer session for credit, part-time degree program, external degree program, co-op programs and internships, graduate courses open to undergrads. Off campus study at members of the National Student Exchange, members of the Western Interstate Commission for Higher Education. Study abroad program. ROTC: Army, Naval, Air Force.

Entrance Requirements: Options: Peterson's Universal Application, Common Application, electronic application, early admission, early action, deferred admission. Required: high school transcript, minimum 3.0 high school GPA, SAT or ACT. Required for some: SAT Subject Tests. Entrance: moderately difficult. Application deadlines: 9/1, 11/1 for early action. Notification: continuous.

Costs Per Year: Application fee: $50. State resident tuition: $4176 full-time, $116 per credit part-time. Nonresident tuition: $16,236 full-time, $451 per credit part-time. Mandatory fees: $1,266 full-time. Part-time tuition varies according to course load. College room and board: $6930. Room and board charges vary according to board plan and housing facility.

Collegiate Environment: Orientation program. Drama-theater group, choral group, marching band, student-run newspaper, radio station. Social organizations: 300 open to all; national fraternities, national sororities; 9% of eligible men and 9% of eligible women are members. Most popular organizations: Associated Students of OSU, International Students of OSU, Graduate Students Organization, Campus Crusade, MECHA. Major annual events: Civil War Football Game, Homecoming, Parents' Weekend. Student services: legal services, health clinic, personal-psychological counseling, women's center. Campus security: 24-hour emergency response devices and patrols, student patrols, late night transport-escort service, controlled dormitory access, crime prevention office. Option: coed housing available.

Valley Library with 689,119 books, 1.8 million microform titles, 12,254 serials, 6,225 audiovisual materials, an OPAC, and a Web page. 2,251 computers available on campus for general student use. A campuswide network can be accessed from student residence rooms and from off campus. Staffed computer lab on campus.

Community Environment: Corvallis is situated in the Willamette Valley which is noted for crops and dairy goods. Air, rail and bus transportation is available. The community includes churches of major denominations, a hospital, library, shopping areas, and civic, fraternal, and veteran's organizations. The Willamette River is nearby for fishing and boating, and the Pacific Coast is a 50-mile drive. Part-time employment opportunities are fair.

■ OREGON STATE UNIVERSITY-CASCADES *H-9*

2600 NW College Way
Bend, OR 97701
Tel: (541)322-3100
Web Site: http://www.osucascades.edu
Description: State-supported, comprehensive, coed. Founded 2001.

■ PACIFIC NORTHWEST COLLEGE OF ART *E-7*

1241 NW Johnson St.
Portland, OR 97209
Tel: (503)226-4391
Admissions: (503)821-8972
Fax: (503)226-3587
E-mail: colin@pnca.edu
Web Site: http://www.pnca.edu/

Description: Independent, 4-year, coed. Awards bachelor's degrees. Founded 1909. Setting: 2-acre urban campus. Endowment: $4.4 million. Educational spending for 2005 fiscal year: $6721 per student. Total enrollment: 293. Student-undergrad faculty ratio is 11:1. 120 applied, 72% were admitted. 5% from top 10% of their high school class, 22% from top quarter, 67% from top half. Students come from 20 states and territories, 4 other countries, 2% from out-of-state, 1% Native American, 2% Hispanic, 0.3% black, 5% Asian American or Pacific Islander, 1% international, 40% 25 or older. Retention: 63% of full-time freshmen returned the following year. Core. Calendar: semesters. Services for LD students, advanced placement, self-designed majors, independent study, part-time degree program, adult/continuing education programs, internships. Off campus study at Reed College, Oregon Independent Colleges Association, Association of Independent Colleges of Art and Design. Study abroad program.

Entrance Requirements: Options: Common Application, electronic application, deferred admission. Required: essay, high school transcript, minimum 2.5 high school GPA, portfolio of artwork, 2 essays. Recommended: interview. Entrance: moderately difficult.

Costs Per Year: Application fee: $35. Tuition: $17,480 full-time, $728 per semester hour part-time. Mandatory fees: $692 full-time, $28 per semester hour part-time. College room only: $5200.

Collegiate Environment: Orientation program. Student services: personal-psychological counseling. Campus security: entrance security guards during open hours. Charles Vorhies Fine Arts Library plus 1 other with 14,650 books, 65 serials, 350 audiovisual materials, an OPAC, and a Web page. Operations spending for 2004 fiscal year: $102,169. 60 computers available on campus for general student use. A campuswide network can be accessed from off-campus. Staffed computer lab on campus.

Community Environment: See Portland State University.

■ PACIFIC UNIVERSITY *A-7*

2043 College Way
Forest Grove, OR 97116-1797
Tel: (503)357-6151; 877-722-8648
Admissions: (503)352-2218
Fax: (503)352-3191
E-mail: admissions@pacificu.edu
Web Site: http://www.pacificu.edu/

Description: Independent, comprehensive, coed. Awards bachelor's, master's, doctoral, and first professional degrees. Founded 1849. Setting: 55-acre small town campus with easy access to Portland. Endowment: $40 million. Research spending for 2004 fiscal year: $306,558. Educational spending for 2005 fiscal year: $7325 per student. Total enrollment: 2,563. Faculty: 128 (82 full-time, 46 part-time). Student-undergrad faculty ratio is 12:1. 1,324 applied, 87% were admitted. 28% from top 10% of their high school class, 59% from top quarter, 87% from top half. 11 valedictorians. Full-time: 1,173 students, 59% women, 41% men. Part-time: 59 students,

73% women, 27% men. Students come from 34 states and territories, 10 other countries, 51% from out-of-state, 1% Native American, 3% Hispanic, 1% black, 20% Asian American or Pacific Islander, 0.2% international, 8% 25 or older, 57% live on campus, 7% transferred in. Retention: 80% of full-time freshmen returned the following year. Academic areas with the most degrees conferred: biological/life sciences; business/marketing; education; parks and recreation. Core. Calendar: 4-1-4. ESL program, services for LD students, advanced placement, independent study, double major, summer session for credit, internships. Off campus study at United Church of Christ related colleges and universities. Study abroad program. ROTC: Army (c), Air Force (c).

Entrance Requirements: Options: Common Application, electronic application, deferred admission, international baccalaureate accepted. Required: essay, high school transcript, minimum 3.0 high school GPA, 1 recommendation, SAT or ACT. Recommended: interview. Entrance: moderately difficult. Application deadline: 8/15. Notification: continuous.

Costs Per Year: Application fee: $40. Comprehensive fee: $29,002 includes full-time tuition ($21,954), mandatory fees ($580), and college room and board ($6468). College room only: $3220. Part-time tuition: $916 per credit hour.

Collegiate Environment: Orientation program. Drama-theater group, choral group, student-run newspaper, radio station. Social organizations: 60 open to all; local fraternities, local sororities; 11% of eligible men and 10% of eligible women are members. Most popular organizations: Pacific Outback activities, Hawaiian Club, Big Buddy Program, Business and Economics Club, Exercise Science Club. Major annual events: Homecoming, Hawaiian Luau, Spring Fever (lip sync event). Student services: health clinic, personal-psychological counseling, women's center. Campus security: 24-hour emergency response devices and patrols, late night transport-escort service. 709 college housing spaces available; 695 were occupied in 2003-04. Freshmen guaranteed college housing. On-campus residence required through sophomore year. Option: coed housing available. Scott Memorial Library with 212,976 books, 82,893 microform titles, 1,908 serials, 6,385 audiovisual materials, an OPAC, and a Web page. Operations spending for 2004 fiscal year: $1.6 million. 150 computers available on campus for general student use. Computer purchase/lease plans available. A campuswide network can be accessed from student residence rooms and from off campus. Staffed computer lab on campus.

Community Environment: Located 30 miles west of Portland, Forest Grove (population 15,000) is the home of Pacific University, the first school to be chartered in the Oregon Territory. Part-time employment is available. Community facilities include 15 churches, 2 libraries, a hospital, and various civic and service organizations. Bus transportation is available. The Pacific Coast beaches are an hour's drive and skiing on Mt. Hood is 90 minutes away.

■ **PIONEER PACIFIC COLLEGE** *C-9*
27501 Southwest Parkway Ave.
Wilsonville, OR 97070
Tel: (503)682-3903
Admissions: (503)682-1862
Fax: (503)682-1514
E-mail: jrussell@pioneerpacific.edu
Web Site: http://www.pioneerpacific.edu/
Description: Proprietary, primarily 2-year, coed. Awards diplomas, transfer associate, and bachelor's degrees. Founded 1981. Setting: suburban campus with easy access to Portland. Educational spending for 2005 fiscal year: $3028 per student. Total enrollment: 1,132. Student-undergrad faculty ratio is 15:1. 752 applied, 84% were admitted. Full-time: 1,126 students, 77% women, 23% men. Part-time: 6 students, 50% women, 50% men. Students come from 2 states and territories, 1 other country, 6% from out-of-state, 0.4% Native American, 5% Hispanic, 2% black, 3% Asian American or Pacific Islander, 0.1% international, 64% 25 or older, 17% transferred in. Core. Calendar: continuous. Accelerated degree program, honors program, internships.

Entrance Requirements: Open admission. Option: international baccalaureate accepted. Required: high school transcript, interview, CPAt. Entrance: noncompetitive. Application deadline: Rolling.

Costs Per Year: Application fee: $50. Tuition: $8280 full-time, $188 per credit hour part-time. Mandatory fees: $150 full-time.

Collegiate Environment: Orientation program. Social organizations: 1 open to all. Most popular organization: Phi Beta Lambda. Major annual event: annual picnic. College housing not available. 2,500 books. Operations spending for 2004 fiscal year: $17,280. 300 computers available on campus for general student use. Computer purchase/lease plans available. A campuswide network can be accessed.

■ **PORTLAND COMMUNITY COLLEGE** *E-7*
PO Box 19000
Portland, OR 97280-0990
Tel: (503)244-6111
Admissions: (503)977-4519
Fax: (503)452-4988
Web Site: http://www.pcc.edu/
Description: State and locally supported, 2-year, coed. Awards certificates, diplomas, transfer associate, and terminal associate degrees. Founded 1961. Setting: 400-acre urban campus. Total enrollment: 96,764. 15,762 applied, 100% were admitted. 1 National Merit Scholar. Students come from 54 states and territories, 34 other countries, 12% from out-of-state, 1% Native American, 9% Hispanic, 4% black, 7% Asian American or Pacific Islander, 0.4% international, 55% 25 or older. Academic remediation for entering students, ESL program, services for LD students, advanced placement, independent study, distance learning, double major, summer session for credit, part-time degree program, external degree program, adult/continuing education programs, co-op programs and internships. Off campus study at Governors State University, Marylhurst University, members of the Oregon University System. Study abroad program.

Entrance Requirements: Open admission. Options: electronic application, international baccalaureate accepted. Entrance: noncompetitive. Application deadline: Rolling.

Costs Per Year: State resident tuition: $2880 full-time, $64 per credit part-time. Nonresident tuition: $9000 full-time, $200 per credit part-time. Mandatory fees: $240 full-time, $4.25 per credit part-time.

Collegiate Environment: Orientation program. Drama-theater group, choral group, student-run newspaper. Social organizations: 52 open to all. Major annual event: Art Beat. Student services: personal-psychological counseling, women's center. Campus security: 24-hour emergency response devices and patrols, late night transport-escort service. College housing not available. Main library plus 4 others with 91,472 books, 40 microform titles, 820 serials, 247 audiovisual materials, an OPAC, and a Web page. 1,572 computers available on campus for general student use. Computer purchase/lease plans available. A campuswide network can be accessed from off-campus. Staffed computer lab on campus.

Community Environment: See Portland State University.

■ **PORTLAND STATE UNIVERSITY** *E-7*
PO Box 751
Portland, OR 97207-0751
Tel: (503)725-3000
Free: 800-547-8887
Admissions: (503)725-3511
Fax: (503)725-5525
E-mail: askadm@ofa.pdx.edu
Web Site: http://www.pdx.edu/
Description: State-supported, university, coed. Part of Oregon University System. Awards bachelor's, master's, and doctoral degrees. Founded 1946. Setting: 49-acre urban campus. Research spending for 2004 fiscal year: $32.9 million. Total enrollment: 24,120. Faculty: 1,234 (737 full-time, 497 part-time). Student-undergrad faculty ratio is 17:1. 2,844 applied, 92% were admitted. Full-time: 10,851 students, 53% women, 47% men. Part-time: 7,120 students, 55% women, 45% men. Students come from 47 states and territories, 67 other countries, 13% from out-of-state, 1% Native American, 5% Hispanic, 3% black, 10% Asian American or Pacific Islander, 3% international, 38% 25 or older, 14% transferred in. Retention: 68% of full-time freshmen returned the following year. Academic areas with the most degrees conferred: business/marketing; social sciences; liberal arts/general studies; psychology. Core. Academic remediation for entering students, ESL program, services for LD students, advanced placement, accelerated degree program, self-designed majors, honors program, independent study, distance learning, double major, summer session for credit, part-time degree program, adult/continuing education programs, co-op programs and internships, graduate courses open to undergrads. Off campus study at other members of the Oregon University System. Study abroad program. ROTC: Army, Air Force (c).

Entrance Requirements: Options: electronic application, early admission, deferred admission. Required: high school transcript, minimum 3.0 high school GPA, SAT or ACT. Entrance: moderately difficult. Application deadline: Rolling. Notification: continuous.

Costs Per Year: Application fee: $50. State resident tuition: $3810 full-time, $93 per credit part-time. Nonresident tuition: $15,975 full-time, $93 per credit part-time. Mandatory fees: $1151 full-time, $18 per credit part-time, $48.50

per term part-time. Full-time tuition and fees vary according to program. College room and board: $8445. College room only: $6300. Room and board charges vary according to board plan and housing facility.

Collegiate Environment: Orientation program. Drama-theater group, choral group, student-run newspaper, radio station. Social organizations: 148 open to all; national fraternities, national sororities, local fraternities, local sororities; 4% of eligible men and 2% of eligible women are members. Most popular organizations: radio station, Women's Union, Association of African Students, Queers and Allies, OSPERG. Major annual events: PSU Weekend, Association of African Students Cultural Day, International Student Cultural Night. Student services: legal services, health clinic, personal-psychological counseling, women's center. Campus security: 24-hour emergency response devices and patrols, late night transport-escort service, controlled dormitory access, self-defense education. 2,200 college housing spaces available. Freshmen given priority for college housing. Option: coed housing available. Branford P. Millar Library plus 1 other with 1.8 million books, 2.4 million microform titles, 10,308 serials, 81,467 audiovisual materials, an OPAC, and a Web page. 800 computers available on campus for general student use. A campuswide network can be accessed from student residence rooms and from off campus. Staffed computer lab on campus.

Community Environment: Portland lies along both sides of the Willamette River at its juncture with the Columbia River, where there is a splendid port deep enough for the largest ships to dock. Portland has a beautiful background of snowcapped mountain peaks to the north and east, and because of the Japanese Current, enjoys a mild and equable climate. The Columbia River Highway is a beautiful drive, particularly through the Columbia River Gorge with cliffs 2,000 feet high. The Columbia and Willamette Rivers nearby offer year-round water sports, the ocean beach is also nearby, and skiing is available at nearby Mount Hood. Part-time employment and commercial transportation are available. Some of the points of interest are the Hoyt Arboretum, Oregon Art Institute, Oregon Historical Center, Oregon Museum of Science and Industry, Crystal Spring Rhododendron Garden, Washington Park Zoo, Japanese Gardens, World Forestry Center, and the Washington Park Rose Test Gardens.

■ **REED COLLEGE** *E-7*
3203 Southeast Woodstock Blvd.
Portland, OR 97202-8199
Tel: (503)771-1112
Free: 800-547-4750
Admissions: (503)777-7511
Fax: (503)777-7553
E-mail: admission@reed.edu
Web Site: http://www.reed.edu/

Description: Independent, comprehensive, coed. Awards bachelor's and master's degrees. Founded 1908. Setting: 98-acre suburban campus. Endowment: $352 million. Educational spending for 2005 fiscal year: $17,395 per student. Total enrollment: 1,340. Faculty: 131 (116 full-time, 15 part-time). Student-undergrad faculty ratio is 10:1. 2,646 applied, 45% were admitted. 57% from top 10% of their high school class, 86% from top quarter, 99% from top half. 9 National Merit Scholars, 25 valedictorians. Full-time: 1,272 students, 55% women, 45% men. Part-time: 37 students, 59% women, 41% men. Students come from 50 states and territories, 29 other countries, 86% from out-of-state, 1% Native American, 5% Hispanic, 2% black, 6% Asian American or Pacific Islander, 4% international, 3% 25 or older, 65% live on campus, 4% transferred in. Retention: 85% of full-time freshmen returned the following year. Academic areas with the most degrees conferred: social sciences; biological/life sciences; English. Core. Calendar: semesters. Services for LD students, advanced placement, independent study, double major, part-time degree program, co-op programs and internships, graduate courses open to undergrads. Off campus study at Oregon Independent Colleges Association, Pacific Northwest College of Art. Study abroad program.

Entrance Requirements: Options: Peterson's Universal Application, Common Application, electronic application, early admission, early decision, deferred admission, international baccalaureate accepted. Required: essay, high school transcript, 2 recommendations, SAT or ACT. Recommended: interview, SAT Subject Tests. Entrance: most difficult. Application deadlines: 1/15, 11/15 for early decision plan 1, 1/2 for early decision plan 2. Notification: 4/1, 12/15 for early decision plan 1, 2/1 for early decision plan 2.

Costs Per Year: Application fee: $40. Comprehensive fee: $41,106 includes full-time tuition ($32,360), mandatory fees ($230), and college room and board ($8516). College room only: $4470. Full-time tuition and fees vary ac-

cording to degree level. Room and board charges vary according to board plan and housing facility. Part-time tuition: $5400 per course. Part-time tuition varies according to course level and degree level.

Collegiate Environment: Orientation program. Drama-theater group, choral group, student-run newspaper, radio station. Social organizations: 41 open to all. Most popular organizations: Reed Recycling, Movie Board, Outdoor Club. Major annual events: Renaissance Faire, Paideia, Reed Arts Weekend. Student services: health clinic, personal-psychological counseling, women's center. Campus security: 24-hour emergency response devices and patrols, student patrols, late night transport-escort service, controlled dormitory access, 24-hour emergency dispatch. 838 college housing spaces available; all were occupied in 2003-04. Freshmen guaranteed college housing. On-campus residence required in freshman year. Options: coed, women-only housing available. Hauser Library with 528,000 books, 237,354 microform titles, 10,232 serials, 19,662 audiovisual materials, an OPAC, and a Web page. Operations spending for 2004 fiscal year: $3.3 million. 360 computers available on campus for general student use. Computer purchase/lease plans available. A campuswide network can be accessed from student residence rooms and from off campus. Staffed computer lab on campus.

Community Environment: See Portland State University.

■ **ROGUE COMMUNITY COLLEGE** *L-6*
3345 Redwood Hwy.
Grants Pass, OR 97527-9298
Tel: (541)956-7500
Admissions: (541)956-7176
E-mail: csullivan@roguecc.edu
Web Site: http://www.roguecc.edu/

Description: State and locally supported, 2-year, coed. Awards certificates, diplomas, transfer associate, and terminal associate degrees. Founded 1970. Setting: 90-acre rural campus. Endowment: $6.1 million. Educational spending for 2005 fiscal year: $2764 per student. Total enrollment: 4,224. Student-undergrad faculty ratio is 11:1. 367 applied, 100% were admitted. Full-time: 1,341 students, 53% women, 47% men. Part-time: 2,883 students, 57% women, 43% men. Students come from 5 states and territories, 5 other countries, 0.2% from out-of-state, 2% Native American, 6% Hispanic, 1% black, 2% Asian American or Pacific Islander, 0.2% international, 55% 25 or older, 25% transferred in. Core. Academic remediation for entering students, ESL program, services for LD students, advanced placement, distance learning, double major, summer session for credit, part-time degree program, adult/continuing education programs, co-op programs and internships.

Entrance Requirements: Open admission except for respiratory therapy, nursing, human services, emergency medical technology, mental health technician programs. Options: Peterson's Universal Application, early admission. Entrance: noncompetitive. Application deadline: Rolling. Preference given to local residents.

Costs Per Year: Application fee: $0. State resident tuition: $2304 full-time, $64 per credit hour part-time. Nonresident tuition: $2772 full-time, $77 per credit hour part-time. Mandatory fees: $294 full-time, $4 per credit hour part-time.

Collegiate Environment: Orientation program. Drama-theater group, choral group, student-run newspaper. Student services: personal-psychological counseling, women's center. Campus security: 24-hour patrols, late night transport-escort service. College housing not available. Rogue Community College Library with 33,000 books, 275 serials, and an OPAC. Operations spending for 2004 fiscal year: $697,930. 96 computers available on campus for general student use. A campuswide network can be accessed. Staffed computer lab on campus.

Community Environment: See Southern Oregon State College.

■ **SOUTHERN OREGON UNIVERSITY** *M-7*
1250 Siskiyou Blvd.
Ashland, OR 97520
Tel: (541)552-7672
Admissions: (541)552-6411
Fax: (541)552-6329
E-mail: admissions@sou.edu
Web Site: http://www.sou.edu/

Description: State-supported, comprehensive, coed. Part of Oregon University System. Awards bachelor's and master's degrees. Founded 1926. Setting: 175-acre small town campus. Endowment: $13 million. Research spending for 2004 fiscal year: $765,605. Educational spending for 2005 fiscal year: $8087 per student. Total enrollment: 4,977. Faculty: 289 (193 full-time, 96 part-time). Student-undergrad faculty ratio is 22:1. 2,157 applied, 80% were admitted. Full-time: 3,475 students, 56% women, 44% men. Part-time: 961 students, 59% women, 41% men. Students come from 45 states and territories, 33 other countries, 22% from out-of-state, 2% Native American, 4% Hispanic, 1% black, 3% Asian American or Pacific Islander, 2% international, 21% 25 or older, 24% live on campus, 10% transferred in. Retention: 65% of full-time freshmen returned the following year. Academic areas with the most degrees conferred: business/marketing; communications/journalism; social sciences. Core. Academic remediation for entering students, ESL program, services for LD students, advanced placement, accelerated degree program, self-designed majors, freshman honors college, honors program, independent study, distance learning, double major, summer session for credit, part-time degree program, adult/continuing education programs, co-op programs and internships. Off campus study at National Student Exchange, other members of the Oregon University System. Study abroad program.

Entrance Requirements: Options: Common Application, electronic application, early admission, deferred admission, international baccalaureate accepted. Required: high school transcript, 2.75 high school GPA or minimum SAT score of 1010, SAT or ACT. Required for some: essay, recommendations, SAT Subject Tests. Entrance: moderately difficult. Application deadline: Rolling. Notification: continuous.

Costs Per Year: Application fee: $50. State resident tuition: $4986 full-time, $108 per credit part-time. Nonresident tuition: $14,691 full-time, $108 per credit part-time. Mandatory fees: $25 per credit part-time. College room and board: $6468.

Collegiate Environment: Orientation program. Drama-theater group, choral group, student-run newspaper, radio station. Social organizations: 65 open to all. Most popular organizations: Native American Student Union, International Student Association, Impact (religious club), Ho'opa'a Hawaii Club, Omicron Delta Kappa. Major annual events: homecoming, International Week, One World (performing arts series). Student services: legal services, health clinic, personal-psychological counseling, women's center. Campus security: 24-hour emergency response devices and patrols, student patrols, late night transport-escort service. 1,100 college housing spaces available; 1,000 were occupied in 2003-04. Freshmen guaranteed college housing. On-campus residence required in freshman year. Option: coed housing available. Lenn and Dixie Hannon Library with 315,000 books, 797,000 microform titles, 1,949 serials, 7,800 audiovisual materials, an OPAC, and a Web page. Operations spending for 2004 fiscal year: $2.1 million. 750 computers available on campus for general student use. A campuswide network can be accessed from student residence rooms and from off campus. Staffed computer lab on campus.

Community Environment: Ashland, a town of 20,000 people, is nestled at the base of the Sikiyou Mountains in the Rogue Valley of Oregon. Culturally the community has gained national recognition through the Oregon Shakespearean festival and associated legitimate theatres, annually drawing over 300,000 patrons. The town is surrounded by natural forests, mountain lakes and rivers, spectacular for outdoor sports and ecological studies. For the skier, it's only 30 minutes to the 7,000 foot Mt. Ashland Ski Resort.

■ SOUTHWESTERN OREGON COMMUNITY COLLEGE *J-4*

1988 Newmark Ave.
Coos Bay, OR 97420-2912
Tel: (541)888-2525
Admissions: (541)888-7611
E-mail: tnicholls@socc.edu
Web Site: http://www.socc.edu/.

Description: State and locally supported, 2-year, coed. Awards certificates, diplomas, transfer associate, and terminal associate degrees. Founded 1961. Setting: 125-acre small town campus. Endowment: $769,894. Educational spending for 2005 fiscal year: $2340 per student. Total enrollment: 1,980. Student-undergrad faculty ratio is 10:1. 832 applied, 100% were admitted. Full-time: 976 students, 50% women, 50% men. Part-time: 1,004 students, 66% women, 34% men. Students come from 4 other countries, 15% from out-of-state, 5% Native American, 3% Hispanic, 2% black, 1% Asian American or Pacific Islander, 1% international, 45% 25 or older. Core. Academic remediation for entering students, ESL program, services for LD students, advanced placement, distance learning, summer session for credit, part-time degree program, adult/continuing education programs, co-op programs and internships.

Entrance Requirements: Open admission except for culinary institute, nursing, emergency medical technology programs, surgical technician,

pharmacy technician programs. Option: early admission. Required for some: high school transcript. Entrance: noncompetitive. Application deadline: Rolling. Notification: continuous.

Costs Per Year: Application fee: $30. State resident tuition: $3330 full-time, $62 per credit part-time. Nonresident tuition: $3330 full-time, $62 per credit part-time. Mandatory fees: $330 full-time, $12 per credit part-time, $22. College room and board: $6160.

Collegiate Environment: Orientation program. Drama-theater group, choral group, student-run newspaper. Major annual events: Orientation, Fall Funk Fest, Swocc Stock. Student services: crisis intervention counseling. Campus security: controlled dormitory access. 288 college housing spaces available. On-campus residence required in freshman year. Option: coed housing available. Southwestern Oregon Community College Library with 40,505 books, 1,836 microform titles, 218 serials, 3,673 audiovisual materials, an OPAC, and a Web page. Operations spending for 2004 fiscal year: $343,207. 65 computers available on campus for general student use. A campuswide network can be accessed. Staffed computer lab on campus.

Community Environment: Coos Bay is an important seaport and trading center as well as one of the world's largest lumber export points. Community facilities include a library, hospital, churches representing many major denominations, and civic and service organizations. Coos Bay and adjacent North Bend are the shopping centers for southwestern Oregon. The Golden and Silver Falls State Park is 24 miles away, offering facilities for picnicking, camping, and fishing, as do Millicoma-Myrtle Grove State Park and Shore Acres State Park. Opportunities for part-time employment are good.

■ TILLAMOOK BAY COMMUNITY COLLEGE *E-5*

2510 First St.
Tillamook, OR 97141
Tel: (503)842-8222
Fax: (503)842-2214
E-mail: om@tillamookbay.cc
Web Site: http://www.tbcc.cc.or.us/

Description: District-supported, 2-year, coed. Administratively affiliated with Portland Community College. Awards certificates, diplomas, transfer associate, and terminal associate degrees. Founded 1984. Total enrollment: 299. Student-undergrad faculty ratio is 8:1. 90 applied, 100% were admitted. Full-time: 73 students, 59% women, 41% men. Part-time: 226 students, 71% women, 29% men. Students come from 2 states and territories, 1 other country, 2% from out-of-state, 2% Native American, 1% Hispanic, 1% black, 2% Asian American or Pacific Islander, 0% international, 46% 25 or older, 4% transferred in.

Entrance Requirements: Recommended: high school transcript.

Costs Per Year: Application fee: $0. State resident tuition: $2976 full-time, $62 per credit part-time. Nonresident tuition: $3936 full-time, $82 per credit part-time. Mandatory fees: $530 full-time, $33 per course part-time.

Collegiate Environment: Campus security: Evening security guard. College housing not available.

■ TREASURE VALLEY COMMUNITY COLLEGE *H-17*

650 College Blvd.
Ontario, OR 97914-3423
Tel: (541)889-6493
Admissions: (541)881-8822
Fax: (541)881-2721
Web Site: http://www.tvcc.cc.or.us/

Description: State and locally supported, 2-year, coed. Awards certificates, transfer associate, and terminal associate degrees. Founded 1962. Setting: 95-acre small town campus. Total enrollment: 1,946. Student-undergrad faculty ratio is 11:1. Full-time: 1,056 students, 56% women, 44% men. Part-time: 890 students, 70% women, 30% men. Students come from 8 states and territories, 64% from out-of-state, 1% Native American, 17% Hispanic, 1% black, 2% Asian American or Pacific Islander, 0.1% international, 45% 25 or older, 6% live on campus. Core. Academic remediation for entering students, ESL program, services for LD students, advanced placement, accelerated degree program, honors program, independent study, distance learning, summer session for credit, part-time degree program, external degree program, adult/continuing education programs, co-op programs and internships. ROTC: Army (c).

Entrance Requirements: Open admission. Options: Common Application, early admission, deferred admission. Entrance: noncompetitive. Application deadline: Rolling. Notification: continuous.

Costs Per Year: Application fee: $10. State resident tuition: $2970 full-time, $66 per credit hour part-time. Nonresident tuition: $3420 full-time, $76 per credit hour part-time. Mandatory fees: $455 full-time, $10 per credit hour part-time. College room and board: $4470. College room only: $1680.

Collegiate Environment: Orientation program. Drama-theater group, choral group, marching band. Student services: health clinic, personal-psychological counseling. Campus security: student patrols, controlled dormitory access. Treasure Valley Community College Library with 28,000 books, 150 serials, and an OPAC. 70 computers available on campus for general student use. A campuswide network can be accessed from off-campus. Staffed computer lab on campus.

Community Environment: Ontario, one mile from the Oregon-Idaho state line, lies in an agricultural area that produces potatoes, onions, sugar beets, corn, and hay. All forms of commercial transportation are available. Community facilities include the Malheur County Library, a hospital, and several civic and service organizations. Mule, deer, and antelope hunting on the vast rangeland, and fishing on Owyhee Lake and the Malheur and Snake Rivers attract the sportsman. Semiprecious stones may be found in Malheur County. Skiing may be enjoyed at nearby ski resorts. Job opportunities are available.

■ **UMPQUA COMMUNITY COLLEGE** *J-6*
PO Box 967
Roseburg, OR 97470-0226
Tel: (541)440-4600
Admissions: (541)440-4616
Fax: (541)440-4612
Web Site: http://www.umpqua.edu/

Description: State and locally supported, 2-year, coed. Awards certificates, transfer associate, and terminal associate degrees. Founded 1964. Setting: 100-acre rural campus. Endowment: $2.9 million. Total enrollment: 2,141. Students come from 5 states and territories, 1% from out-of-state, 2% Native American, 2% Hispanic, 1% black, 1% Asian American or Pacific Islander, 60% 25 or older. Core. Academic remediation for entering students, ESL program, services for LD students, advanced placement, accelerated degree program, self-designed majors, honors program, distance learning, summer session for credit, part-time degree program, adult/continuing education programs, co-op programs.

Entrance Requirements: Open admission except for nursing, emergency medical technology programs. Options: Peterson's Universal Application, early admission, deferred admission. Recommended: high school transcript. Entrance: noncompetitive. Application deadline: Rolling.

Collegiate Environment: Orientation program. Drama-theater group, choral group, student-run newspaper. Social organizations: 10 open to all. Most popular organizations: Phi Theta Kappa, Computer Club, Phi Beta Lambda, Nursing Club, Umpqua Accounting Associates. Major annual events: Student Government Sponsored Quarterly BBQ, Transfer College Day. Student services: personal-psychological counseling. College housing not available. Umpqua Community College Library with 41,000 books, 350 serials, an OPAC, and a Web page. Operations spending for 2004 fiscal year: $282,325. 300 computers available on campus for general student use. Computer purchase/lease plans available. A campuswide network can be accessed from off-campus. Staffed computer lab on campus.

Community Environment: Roseburg is the county seat of Douglas County, one of the largest lumber centers in the country. Roseburg is also a noted sheep producing area. The town is the headquarters for the Umpqua National Forest, where good salmon and trout fishing may be enjoyed and in season, hunting of deer, elk, bear, and cougar is permitted.

■ **UNIVERSITY OF OREGON** *H-6*
Eugene, OR 97403
Tel: (541)346-3111
Admissions: (541)346-3201
Fax: (541)346-5815
E-mail: diradm@uoregon.edu
Web Site: http://www.uoregon.edu/

Description: State-supported, university, coed. Part of Oregon University System. Awards bachelor's, master's, doctoral, and first professional degrees and post-master's certificates. Founded 1872. Setting: 295-acre urban campus. Endowment: $304 million. Research spending for 2004 fiscal year: $85.4 million. Educational spending for 2005 fiscal year: $2857 per student. Total enrollment: 20,347. Faculty: 1,122 (785 full-time, 337 part-time). Student-undergrad faculty ratio is 18:1. 10,012 applied, 90% were admitted. 25% from top 10% of their high school class, 58% from top quarter, 91% from top half. 14 National Merit Scholars. Full-time: 14,996 students, 53% women, 47% men. Part-time: 1,477 students, 52% women, 48% men.

Students come from 56 states and territories, 87 other countries, 24% from out-of-state, 1% Native American, 3% Hispanic, 2% black, 6% Asian American or Pacific Islander, 4% international, 12% 25 or older, 21% live on campus, 9% transferred in. Retention: 84% of full-time freshmen returned the following year. Academic areas with the most degrees conferred: social sciences; business/marketing; communications/journalism. Core. Academic remediation for entering students, ESL program, services for LD students, advanced placement, accelerated degree program, self-designed majors, freshman honors college, honors program, independent study, distance learning, double major, summer session for credit, part-time degree program, adult/continuing education programs, internships, graduate courses open to undergrads. Off campus study at National Student Exchange. Study abroad program. ROTC: Army, Air Force (c).

Entrance Requirements: Options: electronic application, early admission, international baccalaureate accepted. Required: high school transcript, minimum 3 high school GPA, SAT or ACT. Required for some: essay, 2 recommendations. Entrance: moderately difficult. Application deadlines: 1/15, 11/1 for early action. Notification: 4/1, 12/15 for early action.

Costs Per Year: Application fee: $50. State resident tuition: $4164 full-time, $104 per credit hour part-time. Nonresident tuition: $15,996 full-time, $420 per credit hour part-time. Mandatory fees: $1449 full-time, $427 per term part-time. Full-time tuition and fees vary according to class time, course level, course load, degree level, program, and reciprocity agreements. Part-time tuition and fees vary according to class time, course level, course load, degree level, and program. College room and board: $7496. Room and board charges vary according to board plan and housing facility.

Collegiate Environment: Orientation program. Drama-theater group, choral group, marching band, student-run newspaper, radio station. Social organizations: 250 open to all; national fraternities, national sororities; 8% of eligible men and 8% of eligible women are members. Most popular organizations: Political and Environmental Action, cultural organizations, student newspaper, club sports. Major annual events: University Day, Homecoming, Family Weekend. Student services: legal services, health clinic, personal-psychological counseling, women's center. Campus security: 24-hour emergency response devices and patrols, student patrols, late night transport-escort service, controlled dormitory access. College housing designed to accommodate 3,197 students; 3,292 undergraduates lived in college housing during 2003-04. Freshmen given priority for college housing. Options: coed, men-only, women-only housing available. Knight Library plus 4 others with 2.6 million books, 2.9 million microform titles, 18,180 serials, 1.4 million audiovisual materials, an OPAC, and a Web page. Operations spending for 2004 fiscal year: $14.7 million. 1,600 computers available on campus for general student use. A campuswide network can be accessed from student residence rooms and from off campus. Staffed computer lab on campus.

Community Environment: Eugene, the center of a vast recreational area, is an important high-technology and software center. Bicycles are a major form of student transportation. Airline, bus and train transportation are available. Eugene's facilities include more than 80 churches, a large public library, a YMCA, YWCA, three hospitals, and a number of motels. Eugene is 60 miles east of the Pacific Ocean and 60 miles west of the Cascade Mountains. The Willamette National Forest nearby provides fine hunting and fishing opportunities and skiing is enjoyed at the Hoodoo Ski Bowl and Willamette Pass Ski area.

■ **UNIVERSITY OF PHOENIX-OREGON CAMPUS** *E-7*
13221 SW 68th Parkway, Ste. 500
Portland, OR 97223-8368
Tel: (503)670-0590
Free: 800-228-7240
Admissions: (480)557-1712
Fax: (503)670-0614
Web Site: http://www.phoenix.edu/

Description: Proprietary, comprehensive, coed. Awards bachelor's and master's degrees. Founded 1976. Setting: urban campus. Total enrollment: 2,053. Faculty: 283 (13 full-time, 270 part-time). Student-undergrad faculty ratio is 7:1. 28 applied. Full-time: 1,686 students, 51% women, 49% men. 0% from out-of-state, 0.2% Native American, 2% Hispanic, 2% black, 3% Asian American or Pacific Islander, 4% international, 92% 25 or older. Academic areas with the most degrees conferred: business/marketing; computer and information sciences; public administration and social services. Core. Calendar: continuous. Advanced placement, accelerated degree program, independent study, distance learning, external degree program, adult/continuing education programs, graduate courses open to undergrads.

Entrance Requirements: Open admission. Option: deferred admission. Required: 1 recommendation. Required for some: high school transcript. Entrance: noncompetitive. Application deadline: Rolling.

Costs Per Year: Application fee: $110. Tuition: $10,410 full-time, $347 per credit part-time. Mandatory fees: $560 full-time, $70 per course part-time.

Collegiate Environment: College housing not available. University Library with 444 books, 666 serials, an OPAC, and a Web page. System-wide operations spending for 2004 fiscal year: $3.2 million.

■ **UNIVERSITY OF PORTLAND** *E-7*

5000 North Willamette Blvd.
Portland, OR 97203-5798
Tel: (503)943-7911; 888-627-5601
Admissions: (503)943-7147
Fax: (503)943-7399
E-mail: admissions@uofport.edu
Web Site: http://www.up.edu/

Description: Independent Roman Catholic, comprehensive, coed. Awards bachelor's and master's degrees and post-master's certificates. Founded 1901. Setting: 125-acre urban campus. Endowment: $82.3 million. Research spending for 2004 fiscal year: $979,000. Educational spending for 2005 fiscal year: $7074 per student. Total enrollment: 3,413. Faculty: 279 (188 full-time, 91 part-time). Student-undergrad faculty ratio is 13:1. 3,026 applied, 81% were admitted. 44% from top 10% of their high school class, 76% from top quarter, 95% from top half. Full-time: 2,840 students, 62% women, 38% men. Part-time: 80 students, 50% women, 50% men. Students come from 40 states and territories, 19 other countries, 52% from out-of-state, 1% Native American, 4% Hispanic, 2% black, 9% Asian American or Pacific Islander, 1% international, 5% 25 or older, 54% live on campus, 4% transferred in. Retention: 86% of full-time freshmen returned the following year. Academic areas with the most degrees conferred: health professions and related sciences; business/marketing; engineering. Core. Calendar: semesters. Services for LD students, advanced placement, honors program, independent study, double major, summer session for credit, part-time degree program, adult/continuing education programs, internships, graduate courses open to undergrads. Off campus study. Study abroad program. ROTC: Army, Air Force.

Entrance Requirements: Options: Common Application, electronic application, deferred admission, international baccalaureate accepted. Required: essay, high school transcript, 1 recommendation, SAT or ACT. Entrance: moderately difficult. Application deadline: 6/1. Notification: continuous.

Costs Per Year: Application fee: $50. Comprehensive fee: $32,300 includes full-time tuition ($24,580), mandatory fees ($320), and college room and board ($7400). College room only: $3700. Full-time tuition and fees vary according to program. Room and board charges vary according to board plan and housing facility. Part-time tuition: $778 per credit hour. Part-time tuition varies according to program.

Collegiate Environment: Orientation program. Drama-theater group, choral group, student-run newspaper, radio station. Social organizations: 40 open to all. Most popular organizations: English Society, International Club, Hawaiian Club, Rugby Club, Social Science Club. Major annual events: Homecoming Dance, Blow-Out on the Bluff, Hawaiian Luau. Student services: health clinic, personal-psychological counseling. Campus security: 24-hour patrols, student patrols, late night transport-escort service, controlled dormitory access. 1,426 college housing spaces available; all were occupied in 2003-04. Freshmen guaranteed college housing. Options: coed, men-only, women-only housing available. Wilson M. Clark Library plus 1 other with 350,000 books, 540,073 microform titles, 1,400 serials, 11,044 audiovisual materials, an OPAC, and a Web page. 575 computers available on campus for general student use. A campuswide network can be accessed from student residence rooms and from off campus. Staffed computer lab on campus.

Community Environment: See Portland State University.

■ **WARNER PACIFIC COLLEGE** *E-7*

2219 Southeast 68th Ave.
Portland, OR 97215-4099
Tel: (503)517-1000
Free: 800-804-1510
Admissions: (503)517-1020
Fax: (503)788-7425
E-mail: admiss@warnerpacific.edu
Web Site: http://www.warnerpacific.edu/

Description: Independent, comprehensive, coed, affiliated with Church of God. Awards associate, bachelor's, and master's degrees. Founded 1937. Setting: 15-acre urban campus. Educational spending for 2005 fiscal year: $19,150 per student. Total enrollment: 575. Faculty: 35 (all full-time). Student-undergrad faculty ratio is 14:1. 820 applied, 57% were admitted. Students come from 20 states and territories, 29% from out-of-state, 1% Native American, 5% Hispanic, 7% black, 3% Asian American or Pacific Islander, 32% live on campus. Retention: 66% of full-time freshmen returned the following year. Core. Calendar: semesters. Academic remediation for entering students, services for LD students, advanced placement, self-designed majors, honors program, independent study, double major, summer session for credit, part-time degree program, adult/continuing education programs, co-op programs and internships, graduate courses open to undergrads. Off campus study at Mt. Hood Community College, Concordia College (OR), Oregon Independent Colleges Association. Study abroad program. ROTC: Army (c), Air Force (c).

Entrance Requirements: Options: electronic application, international baccalaureate accepted. Required: essay, high school transcript, minimum 2.5 high school GPA, SAT or ACT. Recommended: minimum 3.0 high school GPA, interview, SAT Subject Tests. Required for some: 1 recommendation, interview. Entrance: moderately difficult. Application deadline: Rolling. Notification: continuous.

Collegiate Environment: Orientation program. Drama-theater group, choral group, student-run newspaper. Social organizations: 10 open to all. Most popular organizations: Associated Students of Warner Pacific College, yearbook, College Activities Board, Fellowship of Christian Athletes. Major annual events: homecoming, spring and winter banquets, Midnight Barbecue and Breakfast. Student services: health clinic, personal-psychological counseling. Campus security: 24-hour emergency response devices and patrols, student patrols, late night transport-escort service, controlled dormitory access. On-campus residence required through sophomore year. Options: men-only, women-only housing available. Otto F. Linn Library with 54,000 books, 400 serials, and an OPAC. 30 computers available on campus for general student use. A campuswide network can be accessed from student residence rooms and from off campus.

Community Environment: See Portland State University.

■ **WESTERN BUSINESS COLLEGE** *E-7*

425 Southwest Washington
Portland, OR 97204
Tel: (503)222-3225
Fax: (503)228-6926
Web Site: http://www.western-college.com/

Description: Proprietary, 2-year, coed. Founded 1955.

■ **WESTERN CULINARY INSTITUTE** *E-7*

1235 Southwest 12th Ave., Ste. 100
Portland, OR 97201
Tel: (503)223-2245
Free: 800-666-0312
Fax: (503)223-0126
Web Site: http://www.westernculinary.com/

Description: Proprietary, 2-year, coed. Founded 1983. Calendar: continuous.

■ **WESTERN OREGON UNIVERSITY** *F-6*

345 North Monmouth Ave.
Monmouth, OR 97361-1394
Tel: (503)838-8000; 877-877-1593
Admissions: (503)838-8211
Fax: (503)838-8067
E-mail: wolfgram@wou.edu
Web Site: http://www.wou.edu/

Description: State-supported, comprehensive, coed. Part of Oregon University System. Awards associate, bachelor's, and master's degrees. Founded 1856. Setting: 157-acre rural campus with easy access to Portland. Endowment: $4 million. Research spending for 2004 fiscal year: $7.4 million. Educational spending for 2005 fiscal year: $9006 per student. Total enrollment: 4,520. Faculty: 354 (179 full-time, 175 part-time). Student-undergrad faculty ratio is 17:1. 1,881 applied, 55% were admitted. 9% from top 10% of their high school class, 27% from top quarter, 62% from top half. Full-time: 3,783 students, 59% women, 41% men. Part-time: 478 students, 51% women, 49% men. Students come from 23 states and territories, 19 other countries, 9% from out-of-state, 2% Native American, 6% Hispanic, 2%

black, 3% Asian American or Pacific Islander, 1% international, 14% 25 or older, 20% live on campus, 11% transferred in. Retention: 64% of full-time freshmen returned the following year. Academic areas with the most degrees conferred: education; social sciences; business/marketing. Core. Academic remediation for entering students, ESL program, services for LD students, advanced placement, self-designed majors, freshman honors college, honors program, independent study, distance learning, double major, summer session for credit, part-time degree program, adult/continuing education programs, internships, graduate courses open to undergrads. Off campus study at other members of the Oregon University System. Study abroad program. ROTC: Army, Air Force (c).

Entrance Requirements: Options: electronic application, deferred admission. Required: high school transcript, minimum 2.75 high school GPA, general college prep program completion, SAT or ACT. Recommended: SAT Subject Tests. Entrance: moderately difficult. Application deadline: Rolling. Notification: continuous.

Costs Per Year: Application fee: $50. State resident tuition: $3240 full-time, $90 per credit part-time. Nonresident tuition: $11,685 full-time, $325 per credit part-time. Mandatory fees: $1092 full-time. College room and board: $6276. Room and board charges vary according to board plan and housing facility.

Collegiate Environment: Orientation program. Drama-theater group, choral group, student-run newspaper. Social organizations: 50 open to all. Most popular organizations: Model United Nations, Multicultural Student Union, Oregon Student Association. Major annual events: homecoming, Holiday Tree Lighting, Alcohol Awareness Week. Student services: health clinic, personal-psychological counseling, women's center. Campus security: 24-hour emergency response devices and patrols, student patrols, late night transport-escort service, controlled dormitory access. 1,275 college housing spaces available; 1,139 were occupied in 2003-04. Freshmen given priority for college housing. On-campus residence required in freshman year. Option: coed housing available. Wayne and Lynn Hamersly Library with 157,186 books, 682,067 microform titles, 3,680 serials, 3,169 audiovisual materials, an OPAC, and a Web page. 411 computers available on campus for general student use. A campuswide network can be accessed from student residence rooms and from off campus. Staffed computer lab on campus.

Community Environment: Located in Monmouth, a town of 7,500, Western is 15 miles from Salem, the state capital, and is midway between the state's two largest cities, Portland and Eugene. Western is a short drive from the famed Oregon Coast to the west and the majestic Cascade Mountains to the east. Monmouth is located in the Willamette Valley. The University is the town's main employer and serves as the cultural and athletic center for the area.

■ **WILLAMETTE UNIVERSITY** *F-6*
900 State St.
Salem, OR 97301-3931
Tel: (503)370-6300; 877-542-2787
Admissions: (503)370-6303
Fax: (503)375-5363
E-mail: libarts@willamette.edu
Web Site: http://www.willamette.edu/
Description: Independent United Methodist, comprehensive, coed. Awards bachelor's, master's, and first professional degrees and first professional certificates. Founded 1842. Setting: 72-acre urban campus with easy access

to Portland. Endowment: $212.3 million. Research spending for 2004 fiscal year: $821,919. Educational spending for 2005 fiscal year: $9122 per student. Total enrollment: 2,642. Faculty: 301 (184 full-time, 117 part-time). Student-undergrad faculty ratio is 11:1. 2,790 applied, 74% were admitted. 40% from top 10% of their high school class, 73% from top quarter, 96% from top half. 18 National Merit Scholars, 18 class presidents, 48 valedictorians, 98 student government officers. Full-time: 1,823 students, 55% women, 45% men. Part-time: 131 students, 39% women, 61% men. Students come from 38 states and territories, 10 other countries, 60% from out-of-state, 1% Native American, 4% Hispanic, 2% black, 7% Asian American or Pacific Islander, 1% international, 2% 25 or older, 69% live on campus, 3% transferred in. Retention: 88% of full-time freshmen returned the following year. Academic areas with the most degrees conferred: social sciences; foreign languages and literature; biological/life sciences. Core. Calendar: semesters. Services for LD students, advanced placement, accelerated degree program, self-designed majors, independent study, double major, part-time degree program, co-op programs and internships, graduate courses open to undergrads. Off campus study at American University, Urban Life Center (Chicago). Study abroad program. ROTC: Air Force (c).

Entrance Requirements: Options: Common Application, electronic application, early action, deferred admission, international baccalaureate accepted. Required: essay, high school transcript, minimum 2.0 high school GPA, 1 recommendation, SAT or ACT. Recommended: interview. Required for some: interview. Entrance: very difficult. Application deadlines: 2/1, 12/1 for early action. Notification: 4/1, 1/15 for early action.

Costs Per Year: Application fee: $50. Comprehensive fee: $35,416 includes full-time tuition ($28,250), mandatory fees ($166), and college room and board ($7000). Full-time tuition and fees vary according to course load. Room and board charges vary according to board plan and housing facility. Part-time tuition: $3531 per course. Part-time tuition varies according to course load.

Collegiate Environment: Orientation program. Drama-theater group, choral group, student-run newspaper, radio station. Social organizations: 100 open to all; national fraternities, national sororities; 35% of eligible men and 29% of eligible women are members. Most popular organizations: Hawaii Club, Bush Mentor Program, Outdoors Club, Campus Ambassadors, Associated Students. Major annual events: Black Tie Affair, International Extravaganza, Hawaiian Luau. Student services: health clinic, personal-psychological counseling, women's center. Campus security: 24-hour emergency response devices and patrols, student patrols, late night transport-escort service, controlled dormitory access. 1,400 college housing spaces available; 1,385 were occupied in 2003-04. Freshmen guaranteed college housing. On-campus residence required through sophomore year. Option: coed housing available. Mark O. Hatfield Library plus 1 other with 317,000 books, 333,275 microform titles, 1,400 serials, 8,800 audiovisual materials, an OPAC, and a Web page. Operations spending for 2004 fiscal year: $2 million. 400 computers available on campus for general student use. A campuswide network can be accessed from student residence rooms and from off campus. Staffed computer lab on campus.

Community Environment: Salem, the capital city, has a population of 125,000. All forms of commercial transportation are available. Recreational activities include tennis, fishing, swimming, boating, riding, and hiking. Ski area facilities and the Pacific Ocean are nearby. Part-time employment is available. Points of interest are Bush Park, a large city park planted with rare trees and shrubs, Salem Art Center, Mission Mill Museum and the Oregon State Capitol.

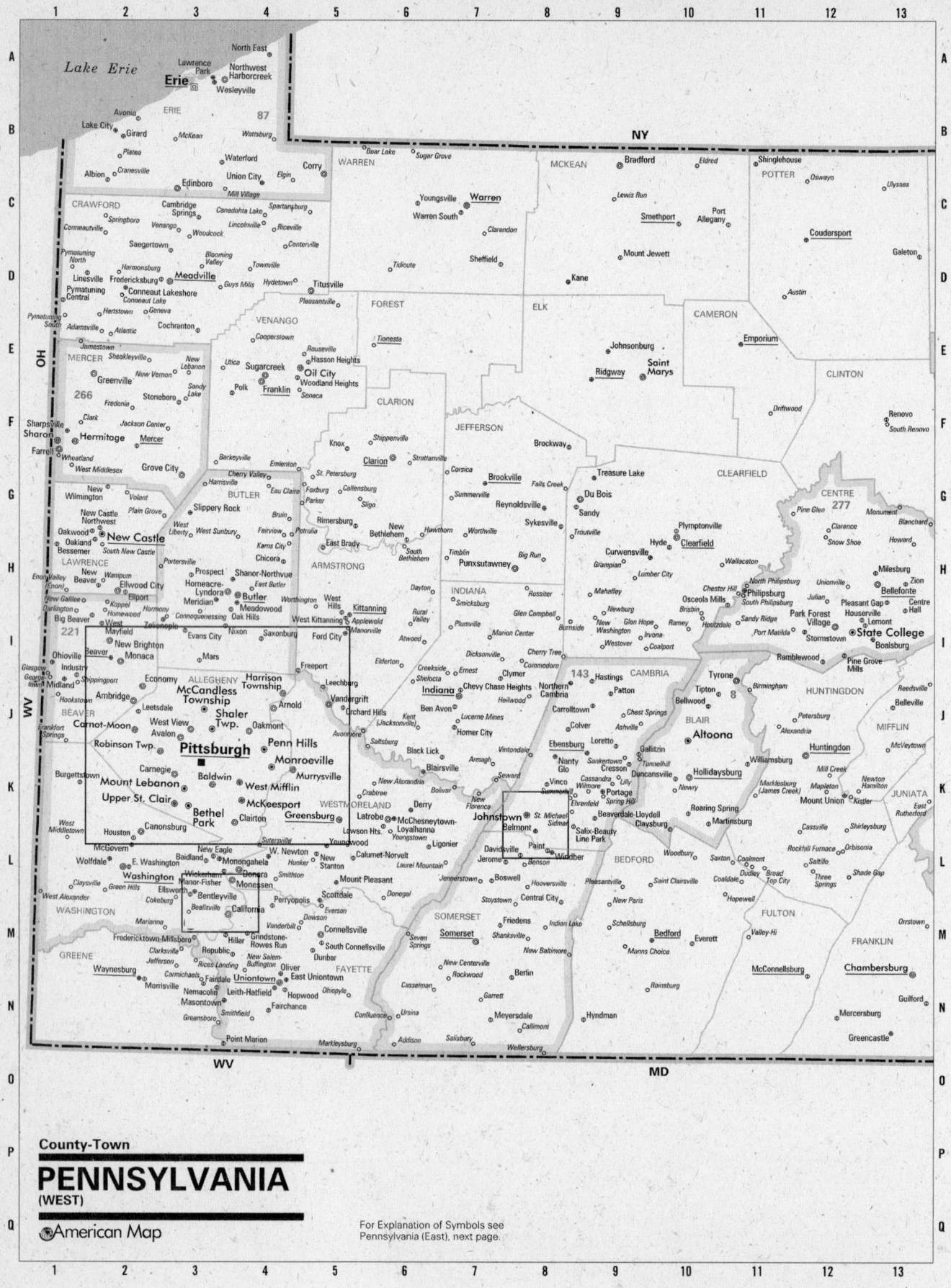

County-Town

PENNSYLVANIA
(WEST)

American Map

For Explanation of Symbols see Pennsylvania (East), next page.

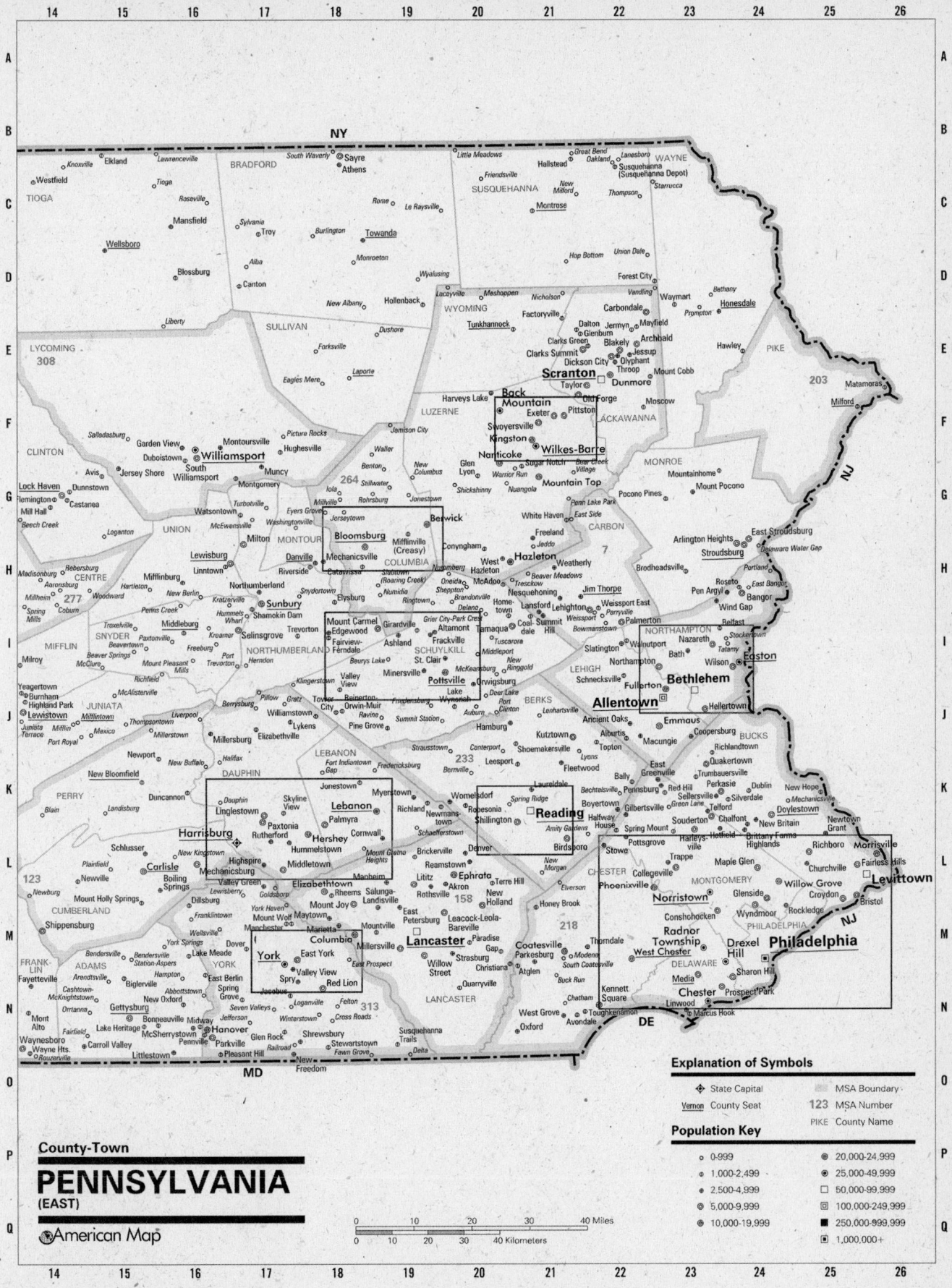

County-Town

PENNSYLVANIA
(EAST)

American Map

Explanation of Symbols

◈ State Capital   ▨ MSA Boundary
Vernon County Seat   **123** MSA Number
                          PIKE County Name

Population Key

○ 0-999   ◉ 20,000-24,999
○ 1,000-2,499   ◉ 25,000-49,999
• 2,500-4,999   ▫ 50,000-99,999
◉ 5,000-9,999   ▣ 100,000-249,999
◉ 10,000-19,999   ■ 250,000-999,999
                          ▣ 1,000,000+

0   10   20   30   40 Miles
0 10 20 30 40 Kilometers

■ **ACADEMY OF MEDICAL ARTS AND BUSINESS** *L-17*
2301 Academy Dr.
Harrisburg, PA 17112-1012
Tel: (717)545-4747
Fax: (717)901-9090
Web Site: http://www.acadcampus.com/
Description: Proprietary, 2-year, coed. Awards diplomas, transfer associate, and terminal associate degrees. Founded 1980. Setting: 8-acre suburban campus. Total enrollment: 491. 0% from out-of-state, 0% Native American, 6% Hispanic, 19% black, 2% Asian American or Pacific Islander, 0% international, 70% 25 or older. Retention: 74% of full-time freshmen returned the following year. Calendar: continuous. Advanced placement, internships.
Entrance Requirements: Open admission. Option: Common Application. Required: high school transcript, interview. Entrance: noncompetitive. Application deadline: Rolling.
Costs Per Year: Application fee: $150. Tuition: $9650 full-time. Mandatory fees: $1990 full-time.
Collegiate Environment: Orientation program. Student-run newspaper. Major annual events: American Red Cross Blood Drive, food drive for homeless shelter, March of Dimes Walkathon. College housing not available. Resource Center with 1,620 books, 30 serials, 30 audiovisual materials, and an OPAC. Operations spending for 2004 fiscal year: $10,650. 75 computers available on campus for general student use. Staffed computer lab on campus.

■ **ALBRIGHT COLLEGE** *K-21*
13th and Bern Sts., PO Box 15234
Reading, PA 19612-5234
Tel: (610)921-2381
Free: 800-252-1856
Admissions: (610)921-7260
Fax: (610)921-7530
E-mail: albright@joe.alb.edu
Web Site: http://www.albright.edu/
Description: Independent, 4-year, coed, affiliated with United Methodist Church. Awards bachelor's and master's degrees. Founded 1856. Setting: 118-acre suburban campus with easy access to Philadelphia. Endowment: $31.8 million. Research spending for 2004 fiscal year: $48,935. Educational spending for 2005 fiscal year: $6250 per student. Total enrollment: 2,180. Faculty: 155 (103 full-time, 52 part-time). Student-undergrad faculty ratio is 14:1. 3,058 applied, 69% were admitted. 23% from top 10% of their high school class, 48% from top quarter, 79% from top half. 1 class president, 2 valedictorians. Full-time: 2,066 students, 58% women, 42% men. Part-time: 46 students, 70% women, 30% men. Students come from 18 states and territories, 28 other countries, 37% from out-of-state, 0.3% Native American, 4% Hispanic, 9% black, 2% Asian American or Pacific Islander, 3% international, 1% 25 or older, 65% live on campus, 2% transferred in. Retention: 76% of full-time freshmen returned the following year. Academic areas with the most degrees conferred: business/marketing; social sciences; psychology. Core. Calendar: 4-1-4. Academic remediation for entering students, ESL program, services for LD students, advanced placement, accelerated degree program, self-designed majors, honors program, independent study, double major, summer session for credit, part-time degree program, internships. Off campus study at The Washington Center, Philadelphia Center, National Theatre Centre, Fashion Institute of Technology, Marine Science Consortium. Study abroad program.

Entrance Requirements: Options: Peterson's Universal Application, Common Application, electronic application, early admission, deferred admission, international baccalaureate accepted. Required: essay, high school transcript, 1 recommendation, secondary school report (guidance department), SAT or ACT. Recommended: interview. Entrance: moderately difficult. Application deadline: Rolling. Notification: continuous.
Costs Per Year: Application fee: $25. Comprehensive fee: $33,920 includes full-time tuition ($25,232), mandatory fees ($800), and college room and board ($7888). College room only: $4490. Full-time tuition and fees vary according to program. Room and board charges vary according to board plan and housing facility. Part-time tuition: $3154 per course. Part-time tuition varies according to class time.
Collegiate Environment: Orientation program. Drama-theater group, choral group, student-run newspaper, radio station. Social organizations: 70 open to all; national fraternities, national sororities. Most popular organizations: Campus Center Board, Student Government Association, yearbook, newspaper, radio station. Major annual events: homecoming, Spring Fever Weekend, Greek Weekend. Student services: health clinic, personal-psychological counseling, women's center. Campus security: 24-hour emergency response devices and patrols, student patrols, late night transport-escort service, controlled dormitory access. 1,097 college housing spaces available; 1,020 were occupied in 2003-04. Freshmen guaranteed college housing. On-campus residence required in freshman year. Options: coed, men-only, women-only housing available. F. W. Gingrich Library plus 1 other with 218,232 books, 73,734 microform titles, 8,190 serials, 8,166 audiovisual materials, an OPAC, and a Web page. Operations spending for 2004 fiscal year: $921,059. 800 computers available on campus for general student use. Computer purchase/lease plans available. A campuswide network can be accessed from student residence rooms and from off campus. Staffed computer lab on campus.
Community Environment: The Reading and Berks County area has a temperate climate. The community is served by U.S. air and several bus companies. Reading is world famous for its outlet shopping. The city has many churches representing major denominations, a symphony orchestra, two major hospitals, four museums, several theaters, and beautiful park and recreational facilities. It is within easy driving distance from major metropolitan areas such as Philadelphia, New York City, Washington, D.C., and Baltimore, MD.

■ **ALLEGHENY COLLEGE** *D-3*
520 North Main St.
Meadville, PA 16335
Tel: (814)332-3100
Free: 800-521-5293
Admissions: (814)332-4351
Fax: (814)337-0431
E-mail: admissions@allegheny.edu
Web Site: http://www.allegheny.edu/
Description: Independent, 4-year, coed. Awards bachelor's degrees. Founded 1815. Setting: 254-acre small town campus. Endowment: $119.9 million. Research spending for 2004 fiscal year: $1.1 million. Educational spending for 2005 fiscal year: $8788 per student. Total enrollment: 2,053. Student-undergrad faculty ratio is 14:1. 3,540 applied, 62% were admitted. 45% from top 10% of their high school class, 77% from top quarter, 97% from top half. 19 National Merit Scholars, 23 valedictorians, 21 student government officers. Full-time: 2,010 students, 53% women, 47% men. Part-

time: 43 students, 60% women, 40% men. Students come from 34 states and territories, 36% from out-of-state, 0.5% Native American, 1% Hispanic, 1% black, 3% Asian American or Pacific Islander, 1% international, 1% 25 or older, 75% live on campus, 1% transferred in. Retention: 90% of full-time freshmen returned the following year. Academic areas with the most degrees conferred: social sciences; psychology; biological/life sciences. Core. Calendar: semesters. Services for LD students, advanced placement, self-designed majors, independent study, double major, internships. Off campus study at American University, Duke University; Marine Biological Laboratory, NC and Bermuda; Ecosystems Center in Woods Hole Massachusetts. Study abroad program.

Entrance Requirements: Options: Peterson's Universal Application, Common Application, electronic application, early admission, early decision, deferred admission, international baccalaureate accepted. Required: essay, high school transcript, 2 recommendations, SAT or ACT. Recommended: interview. Entrance: very difficult. Application deadlines: 2/15, 11/15 for early decision. Notification: 4/1, 12/15 for early decision.

Costs Per Year: Application fee: $35. Comprehensive fee: $35,300 includes full-time tuition ($28,000), mandatory fees ($300), and college room and board ($7000). College room only: $3600. Part-time tuition: $1167 per credit hour. Part-time mandatory fees: $150 per term.

Collegiate Environment: Orientation program. Drama-theater group, choral group, student-run newspaper, radio station. Social organizations: 87 open to all; national fraternities, national sororities; 24% of eligible men and 26% of eligible women are members. Most popular organizations: student government, Gators Activity Programming, Orchesis Dance Company, Up'til Dawn. Major annual events: Make A Difference Day, Homecoming, Springfest. Student services: health clinic, personal-psychological counseling. Campus security: 24-hour emergency response devices and patrols, student patrols, late night transport-escort service, controlled dormitory access, local police patrol. 1,438 college housing spaces available; 1,078 were occupied in 2003-04. Freshmen guaranteed college housing. On-campus residence required through junior year. Options: coed, men-only, women-only housing available. Lawrence Lee Pelletier Library with 287,368 books, 519,232 microform titles, 3,802 serials, 7,790 audiovisual materials, an OPAC, and a Web page. Operations spending for 2004 fiscal year: $1.4 million. 308 computers available on campus for general student use. Computer purchase/lease plans available. A campuswide network can be accessed from student residence rooms and from off campus. Staffed computer lab on campus.

Community Environment: Population 14,000, Meadville, the seat of Crawford County, is in a rich agricultural and active vacation area. The community lies on the western Appalachian slope. The area is served by plane, bus and interstate highways. There are many churches, a public library, active arts organizations, and a large medical center within the community. Most civic, fraternal, and veteran's organizations are represented here. Local recreational facilities include five movie screens, a professional theater, parks, lakes, and picnic groves. Activities include fishing, boating, hunting, swimming, golf, tennis, a major summer jazz festival, hot-air balloon festival, and folk-art festival. Part-time employment is available.

■ **ALLIED MEDICAL AND TECHNICAL CAREERS** *N-45*
166 Slocum St.
Forty Fort, PA 18704-2936
Tel: (717)288-8400
Fax: (717)287-7936
Web Site: http://www.alliedteched.com/
Description: Proprietary, 2-year, coed.

■ **ALVERNIA COLLEGE** *K-21*
400 Saint Bernardine St.
Reading, PA 19607-1799
Tel: (610)796-8200
Admissions: (610)796-3005
Fax: (610)796-8336
Web Site: http://www.alvernia.edu/
Description: Independent Roman Catholic, comprehensive, coed. Awards associate, bachelor's, and master's degrees and post-master's certificates. Founded 1958. Setting: 85-acre suburban campus with easy access to Philadelphia. Endowment: $10.2 million. Educational spending for 2005 fiscal year: $3680 per student. Total enrollment: 2,735. Faculty: 235 (74 full-time, 161 part-time). Student-undergrad faculty ratio is 13:1. 922 applied, 76% were admitted. 8% from top 10% of their high school class, 27% from top quarter, 53% from top half. Full-time: 1,515 students, 67% women, 33%

men. Part-time: 481 students, 75% women, 25% men. Students come from 13 states and territories, 4 other countries, 14% from out-of-state, 0.5% Native American, 5% Hispanic, 13% black, 1% Asian American or Pacific Islander, 0.2% international, 40% 25 or older, 26% live on campus, 4% transferred in. Retention: 77% of full-time freshmen returned the following year. Academic areas with the most degrees conferred: health professions and related sciences; business/marketing; security and protective services. Core. Calendar: semesters. Academic remediation for entering students, services for LD students, advanced placement, accelerated degree program, honors program, independent study, double major, summer session for credit, part-time degree program, adult/continuing education programs, internships, graduate courses open to undergrads. Off campus study at Washington Center for Internships and Academic Seminars. ROTC: Army (c).

Entrance Requirements: Options: Peterson's Universal Application, Common Application, electronic application, deferred admission, international baccalaureate accepted. Required: essay, high school transcript, SAT or ACT. Recommended: minimum 2.0 high school GPA, 1 recommendation. Required for some: 2 recommendations, interview. Entrance: moderately difficult. Application deadline: Rolling. Notification: continuous.

Costs Per Year: Application fee: $25. Comprehensive fee: $26,388 includes full-time tuition ($18,900), mandatory fees ($189), and college room and board ($7299). College room only: $3477. Full-time tuition and fees vary according to class time and reciprocity agreements. Room and board charges vary according to board plan and housing facility. Part-time tuition: $555 per credit. Part-time tuition varies according to class time and course load.

Collegiate Environment: Orientation program. Drama-theater group, choral group, student-run newspaper. Social organizations: 32 open to all. Most popular organizations: Student Government Association, Ice Hockey Club, Science Association, Sigma Tau Delta, Criminal Justice Association. Major annual events: Christmas on Campus, Club Fair, Spring Fling. Student services: health clinic, personal-psychological counseling. Campus security: 24-hour patrols, late night transport-escort service, controlled dormitory access. 500 college housing spaces available; 493 were occupied in 2003-04. Freshmen given priority for college housing. Options: coed, women-only housing available. Franco Library with 89,399 books, 1,036 microform titles, 378 serials, 7,766 audiovisual materials, an OPAC, and a Web page. Operations spending for 2004 fiscal year: $647,039. 60 computers available on campus for general student use. A campuswide network can be accessed from student residence rooms. Staffed computer lab on campus.

Community Environment: Alvernia College is located in a tree-lined neighborhood three miles south of the city of Reading. The 85-acre campus adjoins Angelica Lake. Public transportation provides service to within walking distance of the campus. Alvernia is noted for its accessibility to metropolitan and historical areas of interest. Near enough to New York, Philadelphia, and Baltimore to share their cultural and educational opportunities, the college is only a short distance from the Amish country in nearby Lancaster and York counties.

■ **ANTONELLI INSTITUTE** *M-24*
300 Montgomery Ave.
Erdenheim, PA 19038
Tel: (215)836-2222
Free: 800-722-7871
Fax: (215)836-2794
Web Site: http://www.antonelli.edu/
Description: Proprietary, 2-year, coed. Awards terminal associate degrees. Founded 1938. Setting: 15-acre suburban campus with easy access to Philadelphia. Total enrollment: 189. Student-undergrad faculty ratio is 13:1. 182 applied, 65% were admitted. 7% from top 10% of their high school class, 28% from top quarter, 68% from top half. Full-time: 183 students, 64% women, 36% men. Part-time: 6 students, 83% women, 17% men. Students come from 9 states and territories, 22% from out-of-state, 0% Native American, 3% Hispanic, 5% black, 0% Asian American or Pacific Islander, 0% international, 8% 25 or older, 40% live on campus, 0% transferred in. Retention: 100% of full-time freshmen returned the following year. Core. Calendar: semesters. Part-time degree program, adult/continuing education programs.

Entrance Requirements: Open admission. Options: Peterson's Universal Application, Common Application, deferred admission. Required: high school transcript, interview. Entrance: noncompetitive. Application deadline: 9/1.

Costs Per Year: Application fee: $25. Tuition: $16,300 full-time, $545 per credit part-time. Mandatory fees: $25 full-time. College room only: $6200.

Collegiate Environment: Major annual events: Antonelli Day Barbecue, school trip, Halloween Party. Student services: personal-psychological counseling. Campus security: 24-hour emergency response devices. 80 college housing spaces available; 70 were occupied in 2003-04. Freshmen given priority for college housing. Option: coed housing available. Antonelli Institute Library with 4,000 books, 70 serials, and 50 audiovisual materials. 21 computers available on campus for general student use. Computer purchase/lease plans available. A campuswide network can be accessed. Staffed computer lab on campus.

■ **ARCADIA UNIVERSITY** *M-24*
450 South Easton Rd.
Glenside, PA 19038-3295
Tel: (215)572-2900; 877-ARCADIA
Admissions: (215)572-2910
Fax: (215)572-4049
E-mail: admiss@arcadia.edu
Web Site: http://www.arcadia.edu/

Description: Independent, comprehensive, coed, affiliated with Presbyterian Church (U.S.A.). Awards bachelor's, master's, and doctoral degrees. Founded 1853. Setting: 60-acre suburban campus with easy access to Philadelphia. Endowment: $38.3 million. Total enrollment: 3,403. Faculty: 329 (114 full-time, 215 part-time). Student-undergrad faculty ratio is 12:1. 2,693 applied, 79% were admitted. 32% from top 10% of their high school class, 65% from top quarter, 94% from top half. Full-time: 1,748 students, 72% women, 28% men. Part-time: 207 students, 66% women, 34% men. Students come from 27 states and territories, 15 other countries, 32% from out-of-state, 29% 25 or older, 68% live on campus, 5% transferred in. Retention: 78% of full-time freshmen returned the following year. Academic areas with the most degrees conferred: business/marketing; education; visual and performing arts. Core. Calendar: semesters. ESL program, services for LD students, advanced placement, self-designed majors, honors program, independent study, distance learning, double major, summer session for credit, part-time degree program, adult/continuing education programs, co-op programs and internships, graduate courses open to undergrads. Off campus study. Study abroad program. ROTC: Army (c).

Entrance Requirements: Options: Peterson's Universal Application, Common Application, electronic application, early admission, early decision, deferred admission, international baccalaureate accepted. Required: essay, high school transcript, 2 recommendations, SAT or ACT. Recommended: minimum 3.0 high school GPA, interview. Required for some: portfolio, acting audition. Entrance: moderately difficult. Application deadlines: Rolling, 11/1 for early decision. Notification: continuous until 9/1, 12/1 for early decision.

Costs Per Year: Application fee: $30. Comprehensive fee: $35,650 includes full-time tuition ($25,650), mandatory fees ($340), and college room and board ($9660). Part-time tuition: $442 per credit.

Collegiate Environment: Orientation program. Drama-theater group, choral group, student-run newspaper, radio station. Social organizations: 32 open to all. Most popular organizations: Student Program Board, Residence Hall Council, student government, Arcadia Christian Fellowship, Student Alumni Association. Major annual events: Mr. Beaver Contest, Woodstock, Spring Fling. Student services: health clinic, personal-psychological counseling. Campus security: 24-hour emergency response devices and patrols, student patrols, late night transport-escort service, controlled dormitory access. Freshmen guaranteed college housing. Options: coed, women-only housing available. Landman Library with 140,000 books, 251,507 microform titles, 798 serials, 2,861 audiovisual materials, an OPAC, and a Web page. 110 computers available on campus for general student use. Computer purchase/lease plans available. A campuswide network can be accessed from student residence rooms and from off campus. Staffed computer lab on campus.

Community Environment: Population 8,704. Glenside is a suburb of Philadelphia served by railroad, buses, and major highways. There are many churches in the immediate area as well as various civic and fraternal organizations. Local recreational facilities include golf courses, ice rinks, parks, and a swimming pool.

■ **THE ART INSTITUTE OF PHILADELPHIA** *M-24*
1622 Chestnut St.
Philadelphia, PA 19103-5198
Tel: (215)567-7080
Free: 800-275-2474
Admissions: (215)405-6777
E-mail: lmchugh@aii.edu
Web Site: http://www.aiph.artinstitutes.edu/

Description: Proprietary, primarily 2-year, coed. Part of Education Management Corporation. Awards terminal associate and bachelor's degrees. Founded 1966. Setting: urban campus. Total enrollment: 3,374. Student-undergrad faculty ratio is 22:1. 3,214 applied, 86% were admitted. 5% from top 10% of their high school class, 20% from top quarter, 60% from top half. Full-time: 600 students, 58% women, 42% men. Part-time: 217 students, 53% women, 47% men. Students come from 30 states and territories, 49% from out-of-state, 0.4% Native American, 5% Hispanic, 20% black, 4% Asian American or Pacific Islander, 0.2% international, 20% 25 or older, 27% live on campus, 1% transferred in. Core. Academic remediation for entering students, services for LD students, advanced placement, independent study, summer session for credit, part-time degree program, external degree program, adult/continuing education programs, co-op programs and internships. Off campus study at The Art Institutes.

Entrance Requirements: Options: Peterson's Universal Application, electronic application, early admission, early decision, deferred admission. Required: essay, high school transcript, interview. Recommended: minimum 2.5 high school GPA, recommendations. Entrance: moderately difficult. Application deadline: Rolling. Notification: continuous.

Costs Per Year: Application fee: $50. Tuition: $401 per quarter hour part-time. College room only: $2334.

Collegiate Environment: Orientation program. Major annual events: All School Picnic, Student Art Show, Portfolio Review of Graduates. Student services: personal-psychological counseling. Campus security: 24-hour patrols, controlled dormitory access. Freshmen guaranteed college housing. Option: coed housing available. The Art Institute of Philadelphia Library with 25,000 books, 150 serials, 2,000 audiovisual materials, an OPAC, and a Web page. 368 computers available on campus for general student use. Computer purchase/lease plans available. A campuswide network can be accessed. Staffed computer lab on campus.

■ **THE ART INSTITUTE OF PITTSBURGH** *K-3*
420 Blvd. of the Allies
Pittsburgh, PA 15219
Tel: (412)263-6600
Free: 800-275-2470
Fax: (412)263-6667
Web Site: http://www.aip.artinstitutes.edu/

Description: Proprietary, 4-year, coed. Part of Education Management Corporation. Awards associate and bachelor's degrees. Founded 1921. Setting: urban campus. Total enrollment: 4,872. 2,739 applied, 46% were admitted. 1% from top 10% of their high school class, 16% from top quarter, 60% from top half. Full-time: 2,590 students, 44% women, 56% men. Part-time: 2,282 students, 66% women, 34% men. Students come from 40 states and territories, 35 other countries, 48% from out-of-state, 0.2% Native American, 0.4% Hispanic, 6% black, 0.3% Asian American or Pacific Islander, 0.02% international, 30% live on campus, 5% transferred in. Core. Academic remediation for entering students, ESL program, services for LD students, advanced placement, distance learning, summer session for credit, part-time degree program, adult/continuing education programs, internships.

Entrance Requirements: Options: Common Application, deferred admission. Required: essay, high school transcript, minimum 2.0 high school GPA. Recommended: interview. Required for some: art portfolio. Placement: ACCUPLACER required; SAT or ACT recommended. Entrance: minimally difficult. Application deadline: Rolling. Notification: continuous.

Collegiate Environment: Orientation program. Drama-theater group, student-run newspaper, radio station. Social organizations: 11 open to all. Most popular organizations: American Society of Interior Designers, The Cel Group, AIPIK, Production Monsters, Video Visions. Major annual events: Health and Wellness Week, Welcome Week-Up All Night, School Tour Day. Student services: personal-psychological counseling. Campus security: 24-hour emergency response devices and patrols, student patrols, late night transport-escort service, controlled dormitory access. College housing designed to accommodate 560 students; 700 undergraduates lived in college housing during 2003-04. No special consideration for freshman housing applicants. Library with 6,997 books, 199 serials, an OPAC, and a Web page. Operations spending for 2004 fiscal year: $136,250. 400 computers available on campus for general student use. Computer purchase/lease plans available. A campuswide network can be accessed from student residence rooms and from off campus. Staffed computer lab on campus.

■ **BAPTIST BIBLE COLLEGE OF PENNSYLVANIA** *E-21*
538 Venard Rd.
Clarks Summit, PA 18411-1297

Tel: (570)586-2400
Free: 800-451-7664
Fax: (570)585-9400
E-mail: gamos@bbc.edu
Web Site: http://www.bbc.edu/

Description: Independent Baptist, comprehensive, coed. Awards associate, bachelor's, master's, doctoral, and first professional degrees. Founded 1932. Setting: 124-acre suburban campus. Endowment: $1.3 million. Educational spending for 2005 fiscal year: $3170 per student. Total enrollment: 917. Faculty: 32 (30 full-time, 2 part-time). Student-undergrad faculty ratio is 22:1. 335 applied, 77% were admitted. 35% from top 10% of their high school class, 50% from top quarter, 75% from top half. Full-time: 673 students, 58% women, 42% men. Part-time: 26 students, 46% women, 54% men. Students come from 30 states and territories, 4 other countries, 63% from out-of-state, 0.3% Native American, 2% Hispanic, 1% black, 1% Asian American or Pacific Islander, 2% international, 7% 25 or older, 80% live on campus, 11% transferred in. Retention: 73% of full-time freshmen returned the following year. Academic areas with the most degrees conferred: theology and religious vocations; education; communications/journalism. Core. Calendar: semesters. Academic remediation for entering students, advanced placement, summer session for credit, part-time degree program, internships, graduate courses open to undergrads. Study abroad program. ROTC: Army (c).

Entrance Requirements: Options: early admission, deferred admission, international baccalaureate accepted. Required: essay, high school transcript, 3 recommendations, Christian testimony, SAT or ACT. Required for some: interview. Entrance: minimally difficult. Application deadline: 8/15.

Costs Per Year: Application fee: $30. Comprehensive fee: $19,580 includes full-time tuition ($12,960), mandatory fees ($1020), and college room and board ($5600). College room only: $2500. Part-time tuition: $540 per credit. Part-time mandatory fees: $34 per credit.

Collegiate Environment: Orientation program. Drama-theater group, choral group. Social organizations: ; 25% of eligible men and 25% of eligible women are members. Major annual events: Homecoming Day, Winter Banquet, Spring Banquet. Student services: health clinic, personal-psychological counseling. Campus security: 24-hour patrols, student patrols. On-campus residence required through senior year. Options: men-only, women-only housing available. Murphy Memorial Library plus 1 other with 104,534 books, 9,756 microform titles, 502 serials, and 27,088 audiovisual materials. Operations spending for 2004 fiscal year: $309,147. 25 computers available on campus for general student use. A campuswide network can be accessed from student residence rooms. Staffed computer lab on campus.

Community Environment: Population of 15,000. Served by bus; major airport serves Scranton; train serves Harrisburg (100 miles). Public transportation serves campus. The community has a public library, nearby hospitals, recreational facilities, and many local parks. Part-time employment opportunities are excellent.

■ **BEREAN INSTITUTE** *M-24*
1901 West Girard Ave.
Philadelphia, PA 19130-1599
Tel: (215)763-4833
Web Site: http://www.bereaninstitute.org/

Description: Independent, 2-year, coed. Awards certificates, diplomas, transfer associate, and terminal associate degrees. Founded 1899. Setting: 3-acre urban campus. Endowment: $135,000. Educational spending for 2005 fiscal year: $2924 per student. Total enrollment: 208. 1% from top 10% of their high school class, 8% from top quarter, 15% from top half. Full-time: 171 students, 67% women, 33% men. Part-time: 37 students, 97% women, 3% men. Students come from 3 states and territories, 25% 25 or older. Academic remediation for entering students, advanced placement, honors program, part-time degree program, adult/continuing education programs, internships.

Entrance Requirements: Open admission. Options: Common Application, deferred admission. Required: high school transcript, interview. Entrance: noncompetitive. Application deadline: Rolling. Notification: continuous.

Collegiate Environment: Orientation program. Drama-theater group, choral group, student-run newspaper. Social organizations: 4 open to all; local fraternities; 40% of eligible men and 60% of eligible women are members. Most popular organizations: Berean Student Government, Berean Choir. Major annual events: Founder's Day Celebration, Thanksgiving Luncheon, Women's History Month Program. Student services: personal-psychological counseling. Campus security: 24-hour emergency response devices and patrols. College housing not available. 3,500 books, 48 serials, an OPAC,

and a Web page. Operations spending for 2004 fiscal year: $14,500. 30 computers available on campus for general student use. Staffed computer lab on campus.

■ **BERKS TECHNICAL INSTITUTE** *P-41*
2205 Ridgewood Rd.
Wyomissing, PA 19610-1168
Tel: (610)372-1722
Free: 800-821-4662
Fax: (610)376-4684
E-mail: jvokes@berks.edu
Web Site: http://www.berkstech.com/

Description: Proprietary, 2-year, coed. Part of Fore Front Education, Inc. Awards diplomas, transfer associate, and terminal associate degrees. Founded 1977. Setting: 8-acre small town campus. Educational spending for 2005 fiscal year: $294 per student. Total enrollment: 650. Student-undergrad faculty ratio is 12:1. 0% from out-of-state, 0.2% Native American, 10% Hispanic, 6% black, 1% Asian American or Pacific Islander, 25% 25 or older. Core. Calendar: semesters. Advanced placement, part-time degree program.

Entrance Requirements: Option: early admission. Required: high school transcript, recommendations, interview. Required for some: SAT and SAT Subject Tests or ACT, CPat and COMPAS. Entrance: noncompetitive.

Costs Per Year: Application fee: $50. Tuition: $23,405 full-time. Mandatory fees: $300 full-time.

Collegiate Environment: Orientation program. Campus security: 24-hour emergency response devices. College housing not available. Learning Resource Center with 450 books and 12 serials. Operations spending for 2004 fiscal year: $2500. 8 computers available on campus for general student use. A campuswide network can be accessed. Staffed computer lab on campus.

■ **BIDWELL TRAINING CENTER** *K-3*
1815 Metropolitan St.
Pittsburgh, PA 15233-2234
Tel: (412)323-4000
Fax: (412)321-2120
Web Site: http://www.bidwell-training.org/

Description: Independent, 2-year, coed. Founded 1968.

■ **BLOOMSBURG UNIVERSITY OF PENNSYLVANIA** *H-18*
400 East Second St.
Bloomsburg, PA 17815-1301
Tel: (570)389-4000
Admissions: (570)389-4316
Web Site: http://www.bloomu.edu/

Description: State-supported, comprehensive, coed. Part of Pennsylvania State System of Higher Education. Awards associate, bachelor's, master's, and doctoral degrees. Founded 1839. Setting: 282-acre small town campus. Research spending for 2004 fiscal year: $201,985. Educational spending for 2005 fiscal year: $5316 per student. Total enrollment: 8,570. Faculty: 400 (358 full-time, 42 part-time). Student-undergrad faculty ratio is 21:1. 8,237 applied, 68% were admitted. 9% from top 10% of their high school class, 35% from top quarter, 79% from top half. Full-time: 7,257 students, 60% women, 40% men. Part-time: 526 students, 64% women, 36% men. Students come from 26 states and territories, 33 other countries, 10% from out-of-state, 0.2% Native American, 2% Hispanic, 6% black, 1% Asian American or Pacific Islander, 1% international, 7% 25 or older, 42% live on campus, 5% transferred in. Retention: 82% of full-time freshmen returned the following year. Academic areas with the most degrees conferred: business/marketing; education; social sciences. Core. Calendar: semesters. Academic remediation for entering students, services for LD students, advanced placement, freshman honors college, honors program, independent study, distance learning, double major, summer session for credit, part-time degree program, adult/continuing education programs, co-op programs and internships, graduate courses open to undergrads. Off campus study at medical technology at several Pennsylvania medical centers. Study abroad program. ROTC: Army, Air Force (c).

Entrance Requirements: Options: electronic application, early admission, early decision, deferred admission. Required: high school transcript, recommendations, SAT or ACT. Entrance: moderately difficult. Application deadlines: Rolling, 11/15 for early decision, 10/31 for early action. Notification: 10/1, 12/1 for early decision. Preference given to state residents.

Costs Per Year: Application fee: $30. State resident tuition: $4906 full-time, $204 per credit part-time. Nonresident tuition: $12,266 full-time, $511 per credit part-time. Mandatory fees: $1320 full-time, $39 per credit part-time, $61. Full-time tuition and fees vary according to course load. Part-time tuition and fees vary according to course load. College room and board: $5376. College room only: $3126. Room and board charges vary according to board plan and housing facility.

Collegiate Environment: Orientation program. Drama-theater group, choral group, marching band, student-run newspaper, radio station. Social organizations: 160 open to all; national fraternities, national sororities, local fraternities, local sororities; 4% of eligible men and 6% of eligible women are members. Major annual events: homecoming, Renaissance Jamboree. Student services: legal services, health clinic, personal-psychological counseling, women's center. Campus security: 24-hour emergency response devices and patrols, late night transport-escort service, controlled dormitory access, monitored surveillance cameras. College housing designed to accommodate 2,980 students; 3,104 undergraduates lived in college housing during 2003-04. Freshmen guaranteed college housing. On-campus residence required in freshman year. Options: coed, women-only housing available. Andruss Library with 408,647 books, 2.1 million microform titles, 2,402 serials, 7,242 audiovisual materials, an OPAC, and a Web page. Operations spending for 2004 fiscal year: $3.2 million. 1,250 computers available on campus for general student use. A campuswide network can be accessed from student residence rooms and from off campus. Staffed computer lab on campus.

Community Environment: Population 12,350. Bloomsburg is located 40 miles southeast of Williamsport. Average winter temperature is 31 degrees; with a summer mean temperature of 70 degrees. The area is served by railroad, bus, and airlines. The community has multiple lodging accommodations, several churches of various denominations, a public library, and a hospital. There are numerous civic, fraternal and veteran's organizations in the area. Part-time employment is available.

■ **BRADFORD SCHOOL** *K-3*
707 Grant St., Gulf Tower
Pittsburgh, PA 15219
Tel: (412)391-6710
Fax: (412)471-6714
E-mail: info@bradfordpittsburgh.edu
Web Site: http://www.bradfordpittsburgh.edu/
Description: Private, 2-year. Founded 1968.

■ **BRADLEY ACADEMY FOR THE VISUAL ARTS** *M-17*
1409 Williams Rd.
York, PA 17402-9012
Tel: (717)755-2300
Free: 800-864-7725
Fax: (717)840-1951
E-mail: info@bradleyacademy.net
Web Site: http://www.bradleyacademy.net/
Description: Proprietary, 2-year, coed. Part of Education Management Corporation. Awards terminal associate degrees. Founded 1952. Setting: 7-acre suburban campus with easy access to Baltimore. Endowment: $500,000. Total enrollment: 596. Student-undergrad faculty ratio is 15:1. 302 applied, 65% were admitted. 5% from top 10% of their high school class, 20% from top quarter, 55% from top half. Full-time: 552 students, 60% women, 40% men. Part-time: 44 students, 61% women, 39% men. Students come from 9 states and territories, 16% from out-of-state, 0.2% Native American, 0% Hispanic, 4% black, 1% Asian American or Pacific Islander, 0% international, 11% 25 or older, 5% transferred in. Core. Academic remediation for entering students, summer session for credit, part-time degree program, adult/continuing education programs, internships.
Entrance Requirements: Option: deferred admission. Required: essay, high school transcript, interview. Recommended: minimum 2.5 high school GPA, SAT or ACT. Required for some: minimum 2.5 high school GPA, portfolio. Entrance: moderately difficult. Application deadline: Rolling. Notification: continuous.
Costs Per Year: Application fee: $50. Tuition: $15,840 full-time, $440 per credit part-time.
Collegiate Environment: Orientation program. Student-run newspaper. Social organizations: 3 open to all. Most popular organizations: ASID, Delta Epsilon Chi, AIGA. Major annual events: Senior Portfolio Exhibition, Annual Halloween Bash, Fall Open House. Student services: personal-psychological counseling. College housing not available. Bradley Academy Library with

1,900 books, 70 serials, an OPAC, and a Web page. Operations spending for 2004 fiscal year: $43,520. 175 computers available on campus for general student use. Computer purchase/lease plans available. A campuswide network can be accessed from off-campus. Staffed computer lab on campus.

■ **BRYN ATHYN COLLEGE OF THE NEW CHURCH** *C-48*
PO Box 717
Bryn Athyn, PA 19009-0717
Tel: (267)502-2543
Admissions: (267)502-2511
Fax: (267)502-2658
Web Site: http://www.brynathyn.edu/
Description: Independent Swedenborgian, comprehensive, coed. Part of The Academy of the New Church. Awards associate, bachelor's, master's, and first professional degrees and first professional certificates. Founded 1876. Setting: 130-acre suburban campus with easy access to Philadelphia. Endowment: $265.6 million. Research spending for 2004 fiscal year: $25,310. Educational spending for 2005 fiscal year: $12,042 per student. Total enrollment: 160. Faculty: 49 (20 full-time, 29 part-time). Student-undergrad faculty ratio is 7:1. 52 applied, 96% were admitted. 8 National Merit Scholars, 1 class president, 5 student government officers. Full-time: 134 students, 60% women, 40% men. Part-time: 8 students, 63% women, 38% men. Students come from 19 states and territories, 10 other countries, 19% from out-of-state, 0% Native American, 1% Hispanic, 0% black, 1% Asian American or Pacific Islander, 17% international, 10% 25 or older, 67% live on campus, 3% transferred in. Retention: 100% of full-time freshmen returned the following year. Academic areas with the most degrees conferred: interdisciplinary studies; education; history. Core. Calendar: trimesters. Academic remediation for entering students, ESL program, services for LD students, advanced placement, self-designed majors, independent study, part-time degree program, co-op programs and internships. Study abroad program.
Entrance Requirements: Options: electronic application, deferred admission. Required: essay, high school transcript, minimum 2.2 high school GPA, 1 recommendation, SAT or ACT. Required for some: interview. Entrance: minimally difficult. Application deadline: 7/1. Notification: continuous.
Costs Per Year: Application fee: $30. Comprehensive fee: $15,688 includes full-time tuition ($8264), mandatory fees ($1850), and college room and board ($5574). Part-time tuition: $319 per credit. Part-time mandatory fees: $70 per credit.
Collegiate Environment: Orientation program. Drama-theater group, choral group, student-run newspaper. Social organizations: 13 open to all; local sororities. Most popular organizations: C.A.R.E. Community Service, Business Club, International Student Organization, Peer Advisory Council, Outing Club. Major annual events: Charter Day, Service Day, College Alumni Weekend. Student services: health clinic, personal-psychological counseling. Campus security: 24-hour emergency response devices, controlled dormitory access, 18-hour patrols by trained personnel. 99 college housing spaces available; 91 were occupied in 2003-04. Freshmen guaranteed college housing. On-campus residence required in freshman year. Options: men-only, women-only housing available. Swedenborg Library plus 1 other with 103,911 books, 3,216 microform titles, 172 serials, 648 audiovisual materials, an OPAC, and a Web page. Operations spending for 2004 fiscal year: $339,035. 55 computers available on campus for general student use. A campuswide network can be accessed from student residence rooms. Staffed computer lab on campus.

■ **BRYN MAWR COLLEGE** *E-45*
101 North Merion Ave.
Bryn Mawr, PA 19010-2899
Tel: (610)526-5000
Free: 800-BMC-1885
Admissions: (610)526-5152
Fax: (610)526-7471
E-mail: admissions@brynmawr.edu
Web Site: http://www.brynmawr.edu/
Description: Independent, university. Awards bachelor's, master's, and doctoral degrees. Founded 1885. Setting: 135-acre suburban campus with easy access to Philadelphia. Endowment: $495.2 million. Research spending for 2004 fiscal year: $1.8 million. Educational spending for 2005 fiscal year: $25,000 per student. Total enrollment: 1,799. Faculty: 185 (150 full-time, 35 part-time). Student-undergrad faculty ratio is 8:1. 1,938 applied, 46% were admitted. 62% from top 10% of their high school class, 87% from

top quarter, 100% from top half. 3 National Merit Scholars, 11 valedictorians. Full-time: 1,307 students, 97% women, 3% men. Part-time: 39 students, 87% women, 13% men. Students come from 49 states and territories, 42 other countries, 83% from out-of-state, 0.1% Native American, 3% Hispanic, 5% black, 12% Asian American or Pacific Islander, 7% international, 5% 25 or older, 97% live on campus, 1% transferred in. Retention: 92% of full-time freshmen returned the following year. Academic areas with the most degrees conferred: social sciences; English; foreign languages and literature. Core. Calendar: semesters. Academic remediation for entering students, services for LD students, advanced placement, accelerated degree program, self-designed majors, honors program, independent study, double major, summer session for credit, adult/continuing education programs, graduate courses open to undergrads. Off campus study at Haverford College, Swarthmore College, University of Pennsylvania, Spelman College, Villanova University, Temple University. Study abroad program. ROTC: Air Force (c).

Entrance Requirements: Options: Common Application, electronic application, early admission, early decision, deferred admission, international baccalaureate accepted. Required: essay, high school transcript, 3 recommendations, SAT and SAT Subject Tests or ACT. Recommended: interview. Entrance: most difficult. Application deadlines: 1/15, 11/15 for early decision plan 1, 1/1 for early decision plan 2. Notification: 4/1, 12/15 for early decision plan 1, 2/1 for early decision plan 2.

Costs Per Year: Application fee: $50. Comprehensive fee: $42,780 includes full-time tuition ($32,230) and college room and board ($10,550). College room only: $6030. Part-time tuition: $3990 per course.

Collegiate Environment: Orientation program. Drama-theater group, choral group, student-run newspaper. Social organizations: 100 open to all. Most popular organizations: musical and theater groups, community service, Student Government Association, International Students Association, cultural groups. Major annual events: Fall Frolic, Lantern Night, May Day. Student services: health clinic, personal-psychological counseling, women's center. Campus security: 24-hour emergency response devices and patrols, late night transport-escort service, controlled dormitory access, shuttle bus service, awareness programs, bicycle registration, security Website. 1,200 college housing spaces available; 1,190 were occupied in 2003-04. Freshmen guaranteed college housing. On-campus residence required in freshman year. Options: coed, women-only housing available. Miriam Coffin Canaday Library plus 2 others with 1.1 million books, 157,522 microform titles, 4,400 serials, 3,100 audiovisual materials, an OPAC, and a Web page. Operations spending for 2004 fiscal year: $5.2 million. 200 computers available on campus for general student use. Computer purchase/lease plans available. A campuswide network can be accessed from student residence rooms and from off campus. Staffed computer lab on campus.

Community Environment: Population 5,737, Bryn Mawr is a suburban area 11 miles from Philadelphia. The immediate area has two clinics and a hospital, a public library, and churches of major denominations. Nearby Philadelphia offers all the facilities of a large city. Part-time employment opportunities are limited.

■ **BUCKNELL UNIVERSITY** *H-16*
Lewisburg, PA 17837
Tel: (570)577-2000
Admissions: (570)577-1101
Fax: (570)577-3760
E-mail: admissions@bucknell.edu
Web Site: http://www.bucknell.edu/

Description: Independent, comprehensive, coed. Awards bachelor's and master's degrees. Founded 1846. Setting: 445-acre small town campus. Endowment: $472.1 million. Research spending for 2004 fiscal year: $1.7 million. Educational spending for 2005 fiscal year: $13,489 per student. Total enrollment: 3,648. Faculty: 328 (299 full-time, 29 part-time). Student-undergrad faculty ratio is 11:1. 8,306 applied, 34% were admitted. 68% from top 10% of their high school class, 93% from top quarter, 100% from top half. Full-time: 3,469 students, 51% women, 49% men. Part-time: 36 students, 69% women, 31% men. Students come from 47 states and territories, 41 other countries, 72% from out-of-state, 0.3% Native American, 2% Hispanic, 3% black, 7% Asian American or Pacific Islander, 3% international, 1% 25 or older, 88% live on campus, 1% transferred in. Retention: 95% of full-time freshmen returned the following year. Academic areas with the most degrees conferred: social sciences; business/marketing; engineering. Calendar: semesters. Services for LD students, advanced placement, self-designed majors, honors program, independent study, double major, summer session for credit, part-time degree program, internships, graduate courses open to

undergrads. Off campus study at American University, Philadelphia Center, Woods Hole Marine Laboratories. Study abroad program. ROTC: Army.

Entrance Requirements: Options: Peterson's Universal Application, Common Application, electronic application, early decision, deferred admission, international baccalaureate accepted. Required: essay, high school transcript, 1 recommendation, SAT or ACT. Recommended: interview. Required for some: SAT Subject Tests. Entrance: most difficult. Application deadlines: 1/1, 11/15 for early decision plan 1, 1/1 for early decision plan 2. Notification: 4/1, 12/15 for early decision plan 1, 2/1 for early decision plan 2. Preference given to children of alumni.

Costs Per Year: Application fee: $60. Comprehensive fee: $43,368 includes full-time tuition ($35,802), mandatory fees ($200), and college room and board ($7366). College room only: $3972. Part-time tuition: $3930 per course.

Collegiate Environment: Orientation program. Drama-theater group, choral group, student-run newspaper, radio station. Social organizations: 135 open to all; national fraternities, national sororities; 48% of eligible men and 54% of eligible women are members. Most popular organizations: Alpha Phi Omega, Outing Club, C.A.L.V.I.N. & H.O.B.B.E.S., Activities Council, Catholic Campus Ministries. Major annual events: homecoming, Spring Greek Weekend, Parents' Weekend. Student services: health clinic, personal-psychological counseling, women's center. Campus security: 24-hour emergency response devices and patrols, student patrols, late night transport-escort service, well-lit pathways, self-defense education, safety/security orientation. College housing designed to accommodate 2,720 students; 2,792 undergraduates lived in college housing during 2003-04. Freshmen guaranteed college housing. On-campus residence required through senior year. Options: coed, women-only housing available. Ellen Clarke Bertrand Library plus 2 others with 793,936 books, 4,750 microform titles, 7,191 serials, 19,671 audiovisual materials, an OPAC, and a Web page. Operations spending for 2004 fiscal year: $4.7 million. 620 computers available on campus for general student use. A campuswide network can be accessed from student residence rooms and from off campus. Staffed computer lab on campus.

Community Environment: Lewisburg, population 8,100, is the county seat and the commercial center of a prosperous farming area. Some industries in the city produce textiles, furniture, business forms, and electronic materials. Some part-time employment is available.

■ **BUCKS COUNTY COMMUNITY COLLEGE** *L-25*
275 Swamp Rd.
Newtown, PA 18940-1525
Tel: (215)968-8000
Admissions: (215)968-8123
Fax: (215)968-8110
E-mail: kulicke@bucks.edu
Web Site: http://www.bucks.edu/

Description: County-supported, 2-year, coed. Awards certificates, transfer associate, and terminal associate degrees. Founded 1964. Setting: 200-acre suburban campus with easy access to Philadelphia. Endowment: $2.4 million. Research spending for 2004 fiscal year: $131,169. Educational spending for 2005 fiscal year: $2022 per student. Total enrollment: 9,596. Student-undergrad faculty ratio is 23:1. 5,003 applied, 99% were admitted. Full-time: 3,990 students, 49% women, 51% men. Part-time: 5,606 students, 65% women, 35% men. Students come from 5 states and territories, 15 other countries, 1% from out-of-state, 0.3% Native American, 2% Hispanic, 3% black, 2% Asian American or Pacific Islander, 6% international, 37% 25 or older, 4% transferred in. Core. Calendar: semesters. Academic remediation for entering students, ESL program, services for LD students, advanced placement, self-designed majors, independent study, distance learning, summer session for credit, part-time degree program, external degree program, adult/continuing education programs, co-op programs and internships.

Entrance Requirements: Open admission except for nursing, chef's apprentice, woodworking. Options: electronic application, early admission. Required: high school transcript. Required for some: essay, interview. Entrance: noncompetitive.

Costs Per Year: Application fee: $30. Area resident tuition: $2760 full-time, $92 per credit part-time. State resident tuition: $5520 full-time, $184 per credit part-time. Nonresident tuition: $8280 full-time, $276 per credit part-time. Mandatory fees: $584 full-time.

Collegiate Environment: Orientation program. Drama-theater group, choral group, student-run newspaper. Social organizations: 24 open to all; 2% of eligible men and 2% of eligible women are members. Most popular organizations: Phi Theta Kappa, Students in Free Enterprise, student council, The

Centurion (student newspaper). Major annual events: open house, Spring Fling, Career Day. Student services: personal-psychological counseling, women's center. Campus security: 24-hour emergency response devices and patrols, late night transport-escort service. College housing not available. Bucks County Community College Library with 155,779 books, 515 serials, an OPAC, and a Web page. Operations spending for 2004 fiscal year: $1.5 million. 1,600 computers available on campus for general student use. A campuswide network can be accessed from off-campus. Staffed computer lab on campus.

Community Environment: Population 4,238. Newtown is a suburb of Philadelphia located approximately 20 miles from the heart of the downtown area.

■ **BUSINESS INSTITUTE OF PENNSYLVANIA (MEADVILLE)** *D-3*

628 Arch St., Ste. B105
Meadville, PA 16335
Tel: (814)724-0700
Fax: (814)724-2777
Web Site: http://www.biop.edu/

Description: Proprietary, 2-year, coed. Awards certificates, diplomas, and terminal associate degrees. Founded 1987. Total enrollment: 68. Student-undergrad faculty ratio is 17:1. 38 applied, 82% were admitted. 11% from top 10% of their high school class, 30% from top quarter, 59% from top half. Full-time: 68 students, 88% women, 12% men. 0% from out-of-state, 0% Native American, 0% Hispanic, 6% black, 0% Asian American or Pacific Islander, 0% international.

Entrance Requirements: Required: high school transcript, interview, CPAt.

Costs Per Year: Application fee: $50. Tuition: $7500 full-time, $250 per credit part-time. Mandatory fees: $650 full-time.

Collegiate Environment: College housing not available.

■ **BUSINESS INSTITUTE OF PENNSYLVANIA (SHARON)** *F-1*

335 Boyd Dr.
Sharon, PA 16146
Tel: (724)983-0700
Free: 800-289-2069
Fax: (724)983-8355
Web Site: http://www.biop.edu/

Description: Proprietary, 2-year, coed. Awards certificates, diplomas, and terminal associate degrees. Founded 1926. Setting: 2-acre small town campus. Educational spending for 2005 fiscal year: $4300 per student. Total enrollment: 106. 49 applied, 80% were admitted. 14% from top 10% of their high school class, 27% from top quarter, 59% from top half. Full-time: 98 students, 93% women, 7% men. Part-time: 8 students, 100% women. 0% Native American, 0% Hispanic, 5% black, 0% Asian American or Pacific Islander, 0% international.

Entrance Requirements: Required: high school transcript, interview, ACT.

Costs Per Year: Tuition: $7500 full-time, $250 per credit part-time. Mandatory fees: $600 full-time.

Collegiate Environment: College housing not available.

■ **BUTLER COUNTY COMMUNITY COLLEGE** *H-4*

College Dr., PO Box 1203
Butler, PA 16003-1203
Tel: (724)287-8711; 888-826-2829
Fax: (724)285-6047
E-mail: pattie.bajoszik@bc3.edu
Web Site: http://www.bc3.edu/

Description: County-supported, 2-year, coed. Awards certificates, diplomas, transfer associate, and terminal associate degrees. Founded 1965. Setting: 300-acre rural campus with easy access to Pittsburgh. Educational spending for 2005 fiscal year: $1936 per student. Total enrollment: 3,809. Student-undergrad faculty ratio is 20:1. Full-time: 1,987 students, 56% women, 44% men. Part-time: 1,822 students, 65% women, 35% men. Students come from 8 states and territories, 1 other country, 1% from out-of-state, 0.1% Native American, 1% Hispanic, 2% black, 1% Asian American or Pacific Islander, 0.03% international, 40% 25 or older. Core. Calendar: semesters. Academic remediation for entering students, ESL program, services for LD students, advanced placement, summer session for credit, part-time degree program, adult/continuing education programs, co-op programs and internships.

Entrance Requirements: Open admission except for nursing, metrology, physical therapy, medical assistant technologies programs. Options: Common Application, early admission, deferred admission. Required: high school

transcript. Required for some: recommendations, interview. Entrance: noncompetitive. Application deadline: 8/15. Notification: continuous until 8/15.

Costs Per Year: Application fee: $25. Area resident tuition: $2130 full-time, $71 per credit part-time. State resident tuition: $4260 full-time, $142 per credit part-time. Nonresident tuition: $6390 full-time, $213 per credit part-time. Mandatory fees: $510 full-time, $17 per credit part-time.

Collegiate Environment: Orientation program. Drama-theater group, choral group, student-run newspaper. Social organizations: 35 open to all. Most popular organizations: student government, Ski Club, Drama Club, Outdoor Recreation Club. Major annual events: Spring Dinner Theatre, Spring Dinner Dance, Ice Cream Festival. Student services: personal-psychological counseling. Campus security: 24-hour emergency response devices, late night transport-escort service. College housing not available. John A. Beck, Jr. Library with 70,000 books and 305 serials. 350 computers available on campus for general student use. Staffed computer lab on campus.

Community Environment: In a region rich in coal, oil, natural gas and limestone, Butler's industries produce steel, cement, oil, glass, and metal products. The climate is temperate, and the average annual temperature is 50.6 degrees. The community has access to rail and air, and services include hospitals, churches, a library, YMCA, and YWCA. Local recreation includes boating, swimming, skiing, golf, parks, and movie theaters. Part-time employment is available.

■ **CABRINI COLLEGE** *M-23*

610 King of Prussia Rd.
Radnor, PA 19087-3698
Tel: (610)902-8100
Free: 800-848-1003
Admissions: (610)902-8552
Fax: (610)902-8309
E-mail: admit@cabrini.edu
Web Site: http://www.cabrini.edu/

Description: Independent Roman Catholic, comprehensive, coed. Awards bachelor's and master's degrees. Founded 1957. Setting: 112-acre suburban campus with easy access to Philadelphia. Endowment: $17.3 million. Educational spending for 2005 fiscal year: $6233 per student. Total enrollment: 2,318. Faculty: 237 (65 full-time, 172 part-time). Student-undergrad faculty ratio is 15:1. 2,535 applied, 87% were admitted. 8% from top 10% of their high school class, 27% from top quarter, 58% from top half. Full-time: 1,550 students, 69% women, 31% men. Part-time: 189 students, 61% women, 39% men. Students come from 20 states and territories, 12 other countries, 39% from out-of-state, 0.2% Native American, 2% Hispanic, 5% black, 2% Asian American or Pacific Islander, 1% international, 14% 25 or older, 61% live on campus, 4% transferred in. Retention: 72% of full-time freshmen returned the following year. Academic areas with the most degrees conferred: business/marketing; education; communications/journalism. Core. Calendar: semesters. Academic remediation for entering students, services for LD students, advanced placement, accelerated degree program, self-designed majors, honors program, independent study, double major, summer session for credit, part-time degree program, adult/continuing education programs, co-op programs and internships, graduate courses open to undergrads. Off campus study at Eastern College, Rosemont College, Valley Forge Military College, Southeastern Pennsylvania Consortium for Higher Education. Study abroad program. ROTC: Army (c).

Entrance Requirements: Options: Common Application, electronic application, early admission, deferred admission, international baccalaureate accepted. Required: high school transcript, minimum 2.0 high school GPA, SAT or ACT. Recommended: essay, minimum 3.0 high school GPA, 3 recommendations, interview. Entrance: moderately difficult. Application deadline: Rolling.

Costs Per Year: Application fee: $35. Comprehensive fee: $33,340 includes full-time tuition ($23,200), mandatory fees ($800), and college room and board ($9340). Full-time tuition and fees vary according to location. Room and board charges vary according to board plan and housing facility. Part-time tuition: $395 per credit hour. Part-time mandatory fees: $45 per term. Part-time tuition and fees vary according to course load.

Collegiate Environment: Orientation program. Drama-theater group, choral group, student-run newspaper, radio station. Social organizations: 25 open to all. Most popular organizations: Student Government Association, student newspaper, International Club, campus radio station, Council for Exceptional Children. Major annual events: Cabrini Day, Family Weekend, Yule Log. Student services: health clinic, personal-psychological counseling. Campus security: 24-hour emergency response devices and patrols, student patrols, late night transport-escort service, controlled dormitory access, resident assistants and directors on nightly duty. College housing designed to accommodate 804 students; 861 undergraduates lived in college housing during 2003-04. Freshmen given priority for college housing. Options: coed, women-only housing available. Holy Spirit Library with 82,865 books, 118,435 microform titles, 523 serials, 1,164 audiovisual materials, an OPAC, and a Web page. Operations spending for 2004 fiscal year: $785,111. 195 computers available on campus for general student use. A campuswide network can be accessed from student residence rooms. Staffed computer lab on campus.

Community Environment: See Villanova University.

■ **CALIFORNIA UNIVERSITY OF PENNSYLVANIA** *M-3*
250 University Ave.
California, PA 15419-1394
Tel: (724)938-4000
Admissions: (724)938-4404
Fax: (724)938-4138
E-mail: inquiry@cup.edu
Web Site: http://www.cup.edu/

Description: State-supported, comprehensive, coed. Part of Pennsylvania State System of Higher Education. Awards associate, bachelor's, and master's degrees. Founded 1852. Setting: 148-acre small town campus with easy access to Pittsburgh. Endowment: $9 million. Research spending for 2004 fiscal year: $75,960. Educational spending for 2005 fiscal year: $5520 per student. Total enrollment: 7,184. Faculty: 384 (289 full-time, 95 part-time). Student-undergrad faculty ratio is 20:1. 3,015 applied, 74% were admitted. 3% from top 10% of their high school class, 13% from top quarter, 40% from top half. 9 valedictorians. Full-time: 5,273 students, 51% women, 49% men. Part-time: 670 students, 63% women, 37% men. Students come from 22 states and territories, 15 other countries, 4% from out-of-state, 0.1% Native American, 1% Hispanic, 5% black, 0.5% Asian American or Pacific Islander, 1% international, 16% 25 or older, 25% live on campus, 34% transferred in. Retention: 77% of full-time freshmen returned the following year. Academic areas with the most degrees conferred: education; business/marketing; security and protective services. Core. Calendar: semesters. Academic remediation for entering students, services for LD students, advanced placement, accelerated degree program, honors program, independent study, distance learning, double major, summer session for credit, part-time degree program, adult/continuing education programs, co-op programs and internships, graduate courses open to undergrads. Off campus study at other members of the Pennsylvania State System of Higher Education, National Student Exchange. Study abroad program. ROTC: Army.

Entrance Requirements: Options: Common Application, electronic application, early admission, deferred admission. Required: high school transcript, minimum 2.0 high school GPA, SAT. Recommended: essay, minimum 3.0 high school GPA, ACT, SAT Subject Tests. Required for some: recommendations, interview. Entrance: moderately difficult. Application deadline: 8/15. Notification: continuous.

Costs Per Year: Application fee: $25. State resident tuition: $4906 full-time, $204 per credit part-time. Nonresident tuition: $7306 full-time, $307 per credit part-time. Mandatory fees: $1585 full-time, $217 per credit part-time. Full-time tuition and fees vary according to location. Part-time tuition and fees vary according to location. College room and board: $7788. College room only: $5140. Room and board charges vary according to board plan.

Collegiate Environment: Orientation program. Drama-theater group, choral group, marching band, student-run newspaper, radio station. Social organizations: 80 open to all; national fraternities, national sororities; 10% of eligible men and 10% of eligible women are members. Most popular organizations: student government, In-Res Hall Council, Graduate Student Association, Black Student Union, sports recreation. Student services: legal services, health clinic, personal-psychological counseling, women's center. Campus security: 24-hour emergency response devices and patrols, student patrols, late night transport-escort service. 1,873 college housing spaces available; 1,660 were occupied in 2003-04. Freshmen guaranteed college housing. On-campus residence required through sophomore year. Option: coed housing available. Manderino Library with 437,160 books, 819,891 microform titles, 881 serials, 59,703 audiovisual materials, an OPAC, and a Web page. Operations spending for 2004 fiscal year: $2 million. 1,220 computers available on campus for general student use. A campuswide network can be accessed from student residence rooms. Staffed computer lab on campus.

Community Environment: Population 6,635. California is located 35 miles

south of Pittsburgh on the Monogahela River. This is a coal mining region of the Appalachian Foothills. Some part-time employment is available.

■ **CAMBRIA-ROWE BUSINESS COLLEGE (INDIANA)** *J-7*
422 South 13th St.
Indiana, PA 15701
Tel: (724)463-0222
Fax: (724)463-7246
E-mail: rallen@crbc.net
Web Site: http://www.crbc.net/

Description: Proprietary, 2-year, coed. Awards diplomas, transfer associate, and terminal associate degrees. Founded 1959. Setting: 1-acre small town campus. Total enrollment: 118. 58 applied, 72% were admitted. 10% from top 10% of their high school class, 30% from top quarter, 70% from top half. Full-time: 111 students, 88% women, 12% men. Part-time: 7 students, 86% women, 14% men. 0% Native American, 0% Hispanic, 1% black, 0% Asian American or Pacific Islander, 0% international.

■ **CAMBRIA-ROWE BUSINESS COLLEGE (JOHNSTOWN)** *K-8*
221 Central Ave.
Johnstown, PA 15902-2494
Tel: (814)536-5168
Fax: (814)536-5160
Web Site: http://www.crbc.net/

Description: Proprietary, 2-year, coed. Awards diplomas, transfer associate, and terminal associate degrees. Founded 1891. Setting: small town campus with easy access to Pittsburgh. Total enrollment: 230. Student-undergrad faculty ratio is 20:1. Full-time: 230 students, 89% women, 11% men. 0% from out-of-state, 0% Native American, 0% Hispanic, 3% black, 0% Asian American or Pacific Islander, 0% international, 51% 25 or older, 4% transferred in. Core. Advanced placement, accelerated degree program, summer session for credit, part-time degree program, adult/continuing education programs.

Entrance Requirements: Options: Peterson's Universal Application, Common Application, electronic application, early admission. Required: high school transcript, entrance exam. Recommended: interview. Entrance: minimally difficult. Application deadline: Rolling. Notification: continuous.

Costs Per Year: Application fee: $15. Tuition: $15,600 full-time, $220 per credit part-time. Mandatory fees: $1875 full-time, $300 per term part-time.

Collegiate Environment: Orientation program. College housing not available. 105 computers available on campus for general student use. Computer purchase/lease plans available.

■ **CAREER TRAINING ACADEMY (MONROEVILLE)** *K-4*
105 Mall Blvd., Ste. 300 West
Expo Mart
Monroeville, PA 15146
Tel: (412)372-3900
Fax: (412)373-4262
Web Site: http://www.careerta.com/

Description: Proprietary, 2-year, coed. Founded 1986.

■ **CAREER TRAINING ACADEMY (NEW KENSINGTON)** *D-35*
950 Fifth Ave.
New Kensington, PA 15068-6301
Tel: (724)337-1000
Fax: (724)335-7140
E-mail: admissions@careeta.edu
Web Site: http://www.careerta.com/

Description: Proprietary, 2-year, coed. Awards diplomas, transfer associate, and terminal associate degrees (profile includes branch campuses in Monroeville and Pittsburgh, PA). Founded 1986. Student-undergrad faculty ratio is 20:1. 61 applied, 85% were admitted. 0% from out-of-state, 1% Native American, 0.3% Hispanic, 12% black, 0% Asian American or Pacific Islander, 0% international.

Entrance Requirements: Required: essay, high school transcript, minimum 1.5 high school GPA, interview. Application deadline: Rolling. Notification: continuous.

Costs Per Year: Application fee: $30. Tuition: $7000 full-time.

Collegiate Environment: Student services: personal-psychological counseling.

■ **CAREER TRAINING ACADEMY (PITTSBURGH)** *K-3*
1500 Northway Mall, Ste. 200
Pittsburgh, PA 15237

Tel: (412)367-4000
Web Site: http://www.careerta.com/
Description: Proprietary, 2-year, coed.

■ **CARLOW UNIVERSITY** *K-3*
3333 Fifth Ave.
Pittsburgh, PA 15213-3165
Tel: (412)578-6005
Free: 800-333-CARLOW
Admissions: (412)578-6059
Fax: (412)578-6668
E-mail: admissions@carlow.edu
Web Site: http://www.carlow.edu/
Description: Independent Roman Catholic, comprehensive, coed. Awards bachelor's and master's degrees and post-master's certificates. Founded 1929. Setting: 14-acre urban campus. Endowment: $5.3 million. Educational spending for 2005 fiscal year: $7187 per student. Total enrollment: 2,123. Faculty: 233 (79 full-time, 154 part-time). Student-undergrad faculty ratio is 12:1. 1,076 applied, 64% were admitted. 16% from top 10% of their high school class, 43% from top quarter, 84% from top half. Full-time: 1,167 students, 95% women, 5% men. Part-time: 456 students, 94% women, 6% men. Students come from 12 states and territories, 5 other countries, 4% from out-of-state, 1% Native American, 1% Hispanic, 18% black, 1% Asian American or Pacific Islander, 0.1% international, 46% 25 or older, 21% live on campus, 5% transferred in. Retention: 69% of full-time freshmen returned the following year. Academic areas with the most degrees conferred: health professions and related sciences; education; business/marketing. Core. Calendar: semesters. Academic remediation for entering students, services for LD students, advanced placement, accelerated degree program, self-designed majors, honors program, independent study, distance learning, double major, summer session for credit, part-time degree program, external degree program, adult/continuing education programs, co-op programs and internships, graduate courses open to undergrads. Off campus study at 9 members of the Pittsburgh Council on Higher Education. ROTC: Army (c), Naval (c), Air Force (c).
Entrance Requirements: Options: Peterson's Universal Application, Common Application, electronic application, early admission, early action, deferred admission, international baccalaureate accepted. Required: high school transcript, SAT or ACT. Recommended: minimum 3.0 high school GPA, interview, rank in upper two-fifths of high school class. Required for some: recommendations. Entrance: moderately difficult. Application deadlines: 4/1, 9/30 for early action. Notification: continuous, 10/30 for early action.
Costs Per Year: Application fee: $20. Comprehensive fee: $25,787 includes full-time tuition ($17,760), mandatory fees ($738), and college room and board ($7289). College room only: $3720. Part-time tuition: $583 per credit.
Collegiate Environment: Orientation program. Drama-theater group, choral group, student-run newspaper. Social organizations: 31 open to all. Most popular organizations: Commuter Student Association, Resident Student Association, Student Athletic Association, 'Blessed' (gospel choir), Student Government Association. Major annual events: Spring Fair, Wellness Fair, Homecoming. Student services: health clinic, personal-psychological counseling, women's center. Campus security: 24-hour emergency response devices and patrols, late night transport-escort service, controlled dormitory access. 342 college housing spaces available; 330 were occupied in 2003-04. No special consideration for freshman housing applicants. Option: women-only housing available. Grace Library with 81,532 books, 11,556 microform titles, 382 serials, 4,631 audiovisual materials, an OPAC, and a Web page. Operations spending for 2004 fiscal year: $399,844. 250 computers available on campus for general student use. A campuswide network can be accessed from student residence rooms and from off campus. Staffed computer lab on campus.
Community Environment: The campus occupies 14 acres in the Oakland section of Pittsburgh, which is the educational heart of the city. Carlow is within walking distance of several other colleges and universities, and students enjoy all the educational and social opportunities this collection of institutions offers. The school is just 10 minutes from downtown Pittsburgh. The metropolitan center of Western Pennsylvania and one of the country's largest corporate headquarters, Pittsburgh is rich in educational, medical, entertainment, cultural, and business activities. Pittsburgh is also noted for

its professional sports teams, ballet and theater companies, outdoor art festivals and river regattas, and multiple venues that attract a wide range of entertainment.

■ **CARNEGIE MELLON UNIVERSITY** *K-3*
5000 Forbes Ave.
Pittsburgh, PA 15213-3891
Tel: (412)268-2000
Admissions: (412)268-2082
Fax: (412)268-7838
E-mail: undergraduate-admissions@andrew.cmu.edu
Web Site: http://www.cmu.edu/
Description: Independent, university, coed. Awards bachelor's, master's, and doctoral degrees and post-master's certificates. Founded 1900. Setting: 103-acre urban campus. Endowment: $837.5 million. Research spending for 2004 fiscal year: $235.4 million. Educational spending for 2005 fiscal year: $26,809 per student. Total enrollment: 10,017. Faculty: 995 (822 full-time, 173 part-time). Student-undergrad faculty ratio is 10:1. 15,777 applied, 39% were admitted. 71% from top 10% of their high school class, 94% from top quarter, 99% from top half. 63 valedictorians. Full-time: 5,384 students, 40% women, 60% men. Part-time: 239 students, 41% women, 59% men. Students come from 52 states and territories, 47 other countries, 67% from out-of-state, 0.5% Native American, 5% Hispanic, 5% black, 24% Asian American or Pacific Islander, 12% international, 1% 25 or older, 84% live on campus, 1% transferred in. Retention: 94% of full-time freshmen returned the following year. Academic areas with the most degrees conferred: engineering; business/marketing; computer and information sciences; visual and performing arts. Core. Calendar: semesters. Services for LD students, advanced placement, self-designed majors, freshman honors college, independent study, distance learning, double major, summer session for credit, part-time degree program, adult/continuing education programs, co-op programs and internships, graduate courses open to undergrads. Off campus study at members of the Pittsburgh Council on Higher Education. Study abroad program. ROTC: Army, Naval, Air Force.
Entrance Requirements: Options: Peterson's Universal Application, Common Application, electronic application, early admission, early decision, deferred admission, international baccalaureate accepted. Required: essay, high school transcript, 1 recommendation, SAT or ACT. Recommended: interview. Required for some: portfolio, audition, SAT Subject Tests. Entrance: very difficult. Application deadlines: 1/1, 11/15 for early decision plan 1, 12/15 for early decision plan 2. Notification: 4/15, 12/15 for early decision plan 1, 1/15 for early decision plan 2.
Costs Per Year: Application fee: $60. Comprehensive fee: $43,858 includes full-time tuition ($34,180), mandatory fees ($398), and college room and board ($9280). College room only: $5440. Part-time tuition: $475 per unit. Part-time mandatory fees: $199 per term.
Collegiate Environment: Orientation program. Drama-theater group, choral group, marching band, student-run newspaper, radio station. Social organizations: 100 open to all; national fraternities, national sororities, local sororities; 13% of eligible men and 13% of eligible women are members. Most popular organizations: Student Senate, Alpha Phi Omega, Tartan Club, Spirit Club. Major annual events: carnival, Homecoming, drama performances. Student services: legal services, health clinic, personal-psychological counseling, women's center. Campus security: 24-hour emergency response devices and patrols, late night transport-escort service, controlled dormitory access. 3,943 college housing spaces available; 3,744 were occupied in 2003-04. Freshmen guaranteed college housing. On-campus residence required in freshman year. Options: coed, men-only, women-only housing available. Hunt Library plus 2 others with 1 million books, 958,462 microform titles, 19,048 serials, 226,146 audiovisual materials, an OPAC, and a Web page. Operations spending for 2004 fiscal year: $9.2 million. 402 computers available on campus for general student use. A campuswide network can be accessed from student residence rooms and from off campus. Staffed computer lab on campus.
Community Environment: See University of Pittsburgh.

■ **CEDAR CREST COLLEGE** *J-23*
100 College Dr.
Allentown, PA 18104-6196
Tel: (610)437-4471
Free: 800-360-1222
Admissions: (610)740-3780
Fax: (610)606-4647
E-mail: cccadmis@cedarcrest.edu

Web Site: http://www.cedarcrest.edu/

Description: Independent, comprehensive, women only, affiliated with United Church of Christ. Awards associate, bachelor's, and master's degrees. Founded 1867. Setting: 84-acre suburban campus with easy access to Philadelphia. Endowment: $13.5 million. Educational spending for 2005 fiscal year: $6607 per student. Total enrollment: 1,856. 1,424 applied, 71% were admitted. 29% from top 10% of their high school class, 57% from top quarter, 87% from top half. 2 class presidents, 2 valedictorians, 5 student government officers. Full-time: 887 students. Part-time: 897 students. Students come from 31 states and territories, 10 other countries, 18% from out-of-state, 0.2% Native American, 5% Hispanic, 5% black, 3% Asian American or Pacific Islander, 0.2% international, 54% 25 or older, 80% live on campus, 2% transferred in. Retention: 83% of full-time freshmen returned the following year. Core. Calendar: semesters. Academic remediation for entering students, ESL program, services for LD students, advanced placement, accelerated degree program, self-designed majors, freshman honors college, honors program, independent study, distance learning, double major, summer session for credit, part-time degree program, adult/continuing education programs, internships. Off campus study at 6 members of the Lehigh Valley Association of Independent Colleges, American University. Study abroad program. ROTC: Army (c).

Entrance Requirements: Options: Peterson's Universal Application, Common Application, electronic application, early admission, deferred admission, international baccalaureate accepted. Required: essay, high school transcript, SAT or ACT. Recommended: minimum 2.0 high school GPA, interview. Required for some: 2 recommendations. Entrance: moderately difficult. Application deadline: Rolling.

Costs Per Year: Application fee: $30. Comprehensive fee: $30,965 includes full-time tuition ($22,712), mandatory fees ($300), and college room and board ($7953). Full-time tuition and fees vary according to course load. Room and board charges vary according to board plan.

Collegiate Environment: Orientation program. Drama-theater group, choral group, student-run newspaper, radio station. Social organizations: 46 open to all; 70% of eligible undergrads are members. Most popular organizations: Alpha Phi Omega, Out There, Athletes Club, Student Activities Board, Student Government Association. Major annual events: Dink Donut Night, Junior Ring Ceremony, Midnight Breakfast. Student services: health clinic, personal-psychological counseling. Campus security: 24-hour emergency response devices and patrols, late night transport-escort service, controlled dormitory access, crime prevention programs. 550 college housing spaces available; 467 were occupied in 2003-04. Freshmen guaranteed college housing. On-campus residence required through junior year. Option: women-only housing available. Cressman Library with 133,763 books, 12,948 microform titles, 8,695 serials, 16,316 audiovisual materials, an OPAC, and a Web page. Operations spending for 2004 fiscal year: $663,000. 227 computers available on campus for general student use. A campuswide network can be accessed from student residence rooms and from off campus. Staffed computer lab on campus.

Community Environment: Population 110,000, Allentown is located on the Lehigh River within 55 miles of Philadelphia and 90 miles from New York City. It is Pennsylvania's third largest industrial market. Diversified manufacturing includes machinery and tools, trucks, electric appliances, electronic equipment, apparel, cement, and gas-generating equipment. The area has good transportation facilities including four railroad lines, air service, and bus lines. The community has many churches representing various denominations. Four hospitals, a dental hospital, a library system, a museum, and an Equity theatre company are located here. Local recreational facilities encompass volleyball, baseball, tennis, basketball, swimming, hiking, band concerts, opera, community theatre, five radio stations, and many movie theatres. Part-time employment is available for students.

■ **CENTER FOR ADVANCED MANUFACTURING & TECHNOLOGY**
B-3

5451 Merwin Ln.
Erie, PA 16510
Tel: (814)452-1122; 888-834-4226
Admissions: (814)897-0391
Fax: (814)452-1171
E-mail: lpeszel@gocamtech.com
Web Site: http://www.gocamtech.com/

Description: Independent, 2-year, coed. Founded 1991. Calendar: semesters.

■ **CENTRAL PENNSYLVANIA COLLEGE** *K-17*

College Hill & Valley Roads
Summerdale, PA 17093-0309
Tel: (717)732-0702
Free: 800-759-2727
Admissions: (717)728-2213
Fax: (717)732-5254
E-mail: admissions@centralpenn.edu
Web Site: http://www.centralpenn.edu/

Description: Proprietary, 4-year, coed. Awards associate and bachelor's degrees. Founded 1881. Setting: 35-acre small town campus. Total enrollment: 981. Student-undergrad faculty ratio is 16:1. 2,544 applied, 42% were admitted. Full-time: 701 students, 65% women, 35% men. Part-time: 280 students, 64% women, 36% men. Students come from 10 states and territories, 9% from out-of-state, 1% Native American, 5% Hispanic, 16% black, 1% Asian American or Pacific Islander, 0% international, 14% 25 or older, 40% live on campus. Academic areas with the most degrees conferred: business/marketing; computer and information sciences; security and protective services. Core. Calendar: trimesters. Academic remediation for entering students, advanced placement, honors program, independent study, distance learning, double major, summer session for credit, part-time degree program, adult/continuing education programs, internships. Study abroad program.

Entrance Requirements: Open admission. Options: Peterson's Universal Application, electronic application. Required: essay, high school transcript, minimum 2.0 high school GPA, interview. Entrance: minimally difficult. Application deadline: 9/20. Notification: continuous.

Costs Per Year: Application fee: $0. Comprehensive fee: $17,670 includes full-time tuition ($10,980), mandatory fees ($630), and college room and board ($6060). College room only: $4725. Full-time tuition and fees vary according to course load and program. Room and board charges vary according to board plan and housing facility. Part-time tuition: $305 per credit hour. Part-time mandatory fees: $210 per term. Part-time tuition and fees vary according to course load and program.

Collegiate Environment: Orientation program. Choral group, student-run newspaper. Social organizations: 14 open to all. Most popular organizations: Campus Christian Fellowship, College Council, Student Ambassadors, Phi Beta Lambda, Travel Club. Major annual events: Career Expo, Fashion Show, Formal. Student services: personal-psychological counseling. Campus security: 24-hour emergency response devices and patrols. 383 college housing spaces available; 367 were occupied in 2003-04. Option: coed housing available. Charles T Jones Leadership Library plus 1 other with 7,923 books, 4,850 serials, 356 audiovisual materials, and an OPAC. 150 computers available on campus for general student use. A campuswide network can be accessed from student residence rooms and from off campus. Staffed computer lab on campus.

Community Environment: Located in the small town of Summerdale, Pennsylvania, Central Penn is just across the river from Harrisburg. As the state capital, Harrisburg is home to a variety of recreational, cultural, historic, and sporting attractions.

■ **CHATHAM COLLEGE** *K-3*

Woodland Rd.
Pittsburgh, PA 15232-2826
Tel: (412)365-1100
Free: 800-837-1290
Fax: (412)365-1609
E-mail: mpoll@chatham.edu
Web Site: http://www.chatham.edu/

Description: Independent, comprehensive. Awards bachelor's, master's, and doctoral degrees and post-master's certificates. Founded 1869. Setting: 32-acre urban campus. Endowment: $60.9 million. Educational spending for 2005 fiscal year: $9000 per student. Total enrollment: 1,440. Faculty: 75 (70 full-time, 5 part-time). Student-undergrad faculty ratio is 13:1. 457 applied, 61% were admitted. 12% from top 10% of their high school class, 42% from top quarter, 84% from top half. 1 class president, 5 valedictorians, 22 student government officers. Full-time: 432 students, 100% women. Part-time: 362 students, 80% women, 20% men. Students come from 34 states and territories, 19 other countries, 26% from out-of-state, 0.5% Native American, 2% Hispanic, 10% black, 2% Asian American or Pacific Islander, 8% international, 20% 25 or older, 60% live on campus, 6% transferred in.

Retention: 73% of full-time freshmen returned the following year. Academic areas with the most degrees conferred: psychology; visual and performing arts; biological/life sciences. Core. Calendar: 4-4-1. ESL program, services for LD students, advanced placement, accelerated degree program, self-designed majors, independent study, distance learning, double major, summer session for credit, part-time degree program, adult/continuing education programs, co-op programs and internships, graduate courses open to undergrads. Off campus study at members of the Pittsburgh Council on Higher Education. Study abroad program. ROTC: Army (c), Air Force (c).

Entrance Requirements: Options: Peterson's Universal Application, Common Application, electronic application, early admission, deferred admission, international baccalaureate accepted. Required: essay, high school transcript, minimum 2.5 high school GPA, 1 recommendation. Recommended: minimum 2.5 high school GPA, 1 recommendation, interview. Required for some: SAT or ACT. Entrance: moderately difficult. Application deadline: Rolling. Notification: continuous until 9/1.

Costs Per Year: Application fee: $35. Comprehensive fee: $31,765 includes full-time tuition ($24,014), mandatory fees ($165), and college room and board ($7586). College room only: $3880.

Collegiate Environment: Orientation program. Drama-theater group, choral group, student-run newspaper. Social organizations: 28 open to all. Most popular organizations: Chatham Student Government, choir, Chatham Feminist Collective, Students of Community Service, Activities Board. Major annual events: Spring Fling, Fickes Eggnog, Battle of the Classes. Student services: health clinic, personal-psychological counseling. Campus security: 24-hour emergency response devices and patrols, late night transport-escort service, controlled dormitory access, self defense education; well lighted pathways and sidewalks. 406 college housing spaces available; 247 were occupied in 2003-04. Freshmen guaranteed college housing. On-campus residence required through sophomore year. Option: women-only housing available. Jennie King Mellon Library with 95,480 books, 7,748 microform titles, 392 serials, 354 audiovisual materials, an OPAC, and a Web page. Operations spending for 2004 fiscal year: $1.3 million. 265 computers available on campus for general student use. Computer purchase/lease plans available. A campuswide network can be accessed from student residence rooms and from off campus. Staffed computer lab on campus.

Community Environment: See University of Pittsburgh.

■ **CHESTNUT HILL COLLEGE** *M-24*
9601 Germantown Ave.
Philadelphia, PA 19118-2693
Tel: (215)248-7000
Free: 800-248-0052
Admissions: (215)248-7004
Fax: (215)248-7056
E-mail: kingj@chc.edu
Web Site: http://www.chc.edu/

Description: Independent Roman Catholic, comprehensive, coed. Awards associate, bachelor's, master's, and doctoral degrees and post-master's certificates (profile includes figures from both traditional and accelerated (part-time) programs). Founded 1924. Setting: 45-acre suburban campus. Endowment: $5.2 million. Educational spending for 2005 fiscal year: $7641 per student. Total enrollment: 1,719. Faculty: 255 (72 full-time, 183 part-time). Student-undergrad faculty ratio is 9:1. 1,255 applied, 73% were admitted. 13% from top 10% of their high school class, 30% from top quarter, 65% from top half. Full-time: 802 students, 72% women, 28% men. Part-time: 237 students, 83% women, 17% men. Students come from 16 states and territories, 9 other countries, 25% from out-of-state, 0% Native American, 6% Hispanic, 38% black, 3% Asian American or Pacific Islander, 1% international, 41% 25 or older, 67% live on campus, 15% transferred in. Retention: 74% of full-time freshmen returned the following year. Academic areas with the most degrees conferred: business/marketing; security and protective services; education. Core. Calendar: semesters. Academic remediation for entering students, ESL program, advanced placement, self-designed majors, honors program, independent study, double major, summer session for credit, part-time degree program, adult/continuing education programs, co-op programs and internships, graduate courses open to undergrads. Off campus study at La Salle University, Thomas Jefferson University, Sisters of St. Joseph College Consortium Student Exchange Program, Temple University. Study abroad program.

Entrance Requirements: Open admission for students in the Chestnut Hill College ACCELERATED program for working adults. Options: Peterson's Universal Application, Common Application, early admission, deferred admission, international baccalaureate accepted. Required: essay, high

school transcript, SAT or ACT. Recommended: minimum 2.0 high school GPA, 1 recommendation, interview. Required for some: interview. Entrance: moderately difficult. Application deadline: Rolling. Notification: continuous.

Costs Per Year: Application fee: $35. Comprehensive fee: $30,700 includes full-time tuition ($22,750) and college room and board ($7950). Part-time tuition: $500 per credit.

Collegiate Environment: Orientation program. Drama-theater group, choral group, student-run newspaper. Social organizations: 20 open to all. Most popular organizations: student government, Hispanics in Action, African American Awareness Society, Campus Ministry Community Service Group, Mosaic of Cultures Club. Major annual events: Fall Fest/Homecoming, Christmas celebrations, Spring Fling. Student services: health clinic, personal-psychological counseling. Campus security: 24-hour emergency response devices and patrols, late night transport-escort service, controlled dormitory access. 350 college housing spaces available; 314 were occupied in 2003-04. Freshmen guaranteed college housing. Options: men-only, women-only housing available. Logue Library with 128,489 books, 203,958 microform titles, 484 serials, 2,089 audiovisual materials, an OPAC, and a Web page. Operations spending for 2004 fiscal year: $499,465. 101 computers available on campus for general student use. Computer purchase/lease plans available. A campuswide network can be accessed from student residence rooms. Staffed computer lab on campus.

Community Environment: Chestnut Hill College is located in a 45-acre suburban setting of Philadelphia. Historic homes, a regional art museum, a well-respected arboretum, stables, and quaint specialty shops are within two miles of the campus, which is 30 minutes from Center-city Philadelphia. Villanova University, Saint Joseph's University, the University of Pennsylvania, Drexel University, and LaSalle University are nearby.

■ **CHEYNEY UNIVERSITY OF PENNSYLVANIA** *N-23*
1837 University Circle, PO Box 200
Cheyney, PA 19319-0200
Tel: (610)399-2000
Free: 800-CHE-YNEY
Admissions: (610)399-2275
Fax: (610)399-2099
E-mail: gstemley@cheyney.edu
Web Site: http://www.cheyney.edu/

Description: State-supported, comprehensive, coed. Part of Pennsylvania State System of Higher Education. Awards associate, bachelor's, and master's degrees. Founded 1837. Setting: 275-acre suburban campus with easy access to Philadelphia. Endowment: $1.3 million. Total enrollment: 1,560. Faculty: 127 (103 full-time, 24 part-time). Student-undergrad faculty ratio is 14:1. 2,751 applied, 56% were admitted. Full-time: 1,295 students, 53% women, 47% men. Part-time: 106 students, 63% women, 37% men. Students come from 19 states and territories, 6 other countries, 19% from out-of-state, 0% Native American, 1% Hispanic, 94% black, 0.1% Asian American or Pacific Islander, 1% international, 10% 25 or older, 76% live on campus, 5% transferred in. Academic areas with the most degrees conferred: social sciences; education; business/marketing. Core. Calendar: 4-1-4. Academic remediation for entering students, services for LD students, independent study, summer session for credit, part-time degree program, adult/continuing education programs, co-op programs and internships, graduate courses open to undergrads. Off campus study at West Chester University of Pennsylvania. Study abroad program. ROTC: Army, Air Force (c).

Entrance Requirements: Option: electronic application. Required: essay, high school transcript, SAT or ACT. Recommended: interview, SAT Subject Tests. Required for some: 3 recommendations. Entrance: minimally difficult. Application deadline: Rolling. Notification: continuous. Preference given to state residents.

Costs Per Year: Application fee: $20. State resident tuition: $4906 full-time, $204 per credit part-time. Nonresident tuition: $12,266 full-time, $511 per credit part-time. Mandatory fees: $912 full-time. Full-time tuition and fees vary according to reciprocity agreements. Part-time tuition varies according to reciprocity agreements. College room and board: $5679. College room only: $3106. Room and board charges vary according to board plan.

Collegiate Environment: Orientation program. Drama-theater group, choral group, marching band, student-run newspaper, radio station. Social organizations: 41 open to all; national fraternities, national sororities, local fraternities, local sororities; 5% of eligible men and 8% of eligible women are members. Major annual events: Founders' Day, Homecoming, commencement. Student services: health clinic, personal-psychological counseling. Campus security: 24-hour emergency response devices and patrols. 1,300 college housing spaces available; 1,051 were occupied in 2003-04. Freshmen given priority for college housing. Option: coed housing available. Leslie Pickney Hill Library with 361,539 books, 771,410 microform titles, 414 serials, 1,379 audiovisual materials, an OPAC, and a Web page. 250 computers available on campus for general student use. A campuswide network can be accessed from student residence rooms and from off campus. Staffed computer lab on campus.

Community Environment: Population of the Delaware Valley exceeds 4,716,000. Cheyney's campus looks out on open fields and wooded hills in one of Pennsylvania's most scenic areas, yet the campus is less than an hour from Philadelphia. The summer temperatures range from 70 to 90 degrees, with winter ranges from 20 to 50 degrees. The area is served by bus and railroad. All major religious denominations are represented in town. There are very few shopping facilities in the immediate area. Part-time employment is available in neighboring community.

■ **CHI INSTITUTE** *L-24*
520 St. Rd.
Southampton, PA 18966-3747
Tel: (215)357-5100
Free: 800-336-7696
Web Site: http://www.chitraining.com/
Description: Proprietary, 2-year, coed. Part of Quest Education. Awards certificates, diplomas, transfer associate, and terminal associate degrees. Founded 1981. Setting: 6-acre suburban campus with easy access to Philadelphia. Total enrollment: 700. 650 applied, 86% were admitted. 15% from top 10% of their high school class, 20% from top quarter, 50% from top half. Students come from 3 states and territories, 2 other countries, 22% from out-of-state, 7% Hispanic, 25% black, 3% Asian American or Pacific Islander, 1% international, 50% 25 or older. Core. Academic remediation for entering students, adult/continuing education programs.
Entrance Requirements: Options: Peterson's Universal Application, Common Application, deferred admission. Required: high school transcript, interview. Entrance: moderately difficult. Application deadline: Rolling.
Collegiate Environment: Student-run newspaper. Student services: personal-psychological counseling. College housing not available. 2,500 books and 25 serials. 70 computers available on campus for general student use.

■ **CHI INSTITUTE, RETS CAMPUS** *E-44*
Lawrence Park Shopping Center
Rt. 320 & Lawrence Rd.
Broomall, PA 19008
Tel: (610)353-7630
Web Site: http://www.chitraining.com/
Description: Proprietary, 2-year, coed. Awards diplomas and terminal associate degrees. Founded 1958. Setting: 10-acre small town campus with easy access to Philadelphia. Total enrollment: 650. 40% 25 or older. Advanced placement, honors program, adult/continuing education programs.
Entrance Requirements: Option: deferred admission. Required: high school transcript. Entrance: minimally difficult. Application deadline: Rolling.
Collegiate Environment: College housing not available. 75 computers available on campus for general student use. Staffed computer lab on campus.

■ **CLARION UNIVERSITY OF PENNSYLVANIA** *G-6*
890 Wood St.
Clarion, PA 16214
Tel: (814)393-2000
Free: 800-672-7171
Admissions: (814)393-2306
Fax: (814)393-2030
E-mail: mdunlap@clarion.edu
Web Site: http://www.clarion.edu/
Description: State-supported, comprehensive, coed. Part of Pennsylvania State System of Higher Education. Awards associate, bachelor's, and master's degrees and post-master's certificates. Founded 1867. Setting: 100-acre rural campus. Research spending for 2004 fiscal year: $124,845. Educational spending for 2005 fiscal year: $4978 per student. Total enrollment: 6,338. Faculty: 304 (254 full-time, 50 part-time). Student-undergrad faculty ratio is 19:1. 3,346 applied, 78% were admitted. 24% from top quarter of their high school class, 60% from top half. Full-time: 5,069 students, 60% women, 40% men. Part-time: 675 students, 71% women, 29% men. Students come from 29 states and territories, 40 other countries, 4% from

out-of-state, 0.3% Native American, 1% Hispanic, 5% black, 1% Asian American or Pacific Islander, 1% international, 16% 25 or older, 34% live on campus, 6% transferred in. Retention: 75% of full-time freshmen returned the following year. Academic areas with the most degrees conferred: education; business/marketing; communications/journalism. Core. Calendar: semesters. Academic remediation for entering students, services for LD students, advanced placement, accelerated degree program, honors program, distance learning, double major, summer session for credit, part-time degree program, adult/continuing education programs, internships, graduate courses open to undergrads. Study abroad program.
Entrance Requirements: Options: Peterson's Universal Application, deferred admission. Required: high school transcript, SAT or ACT. Recommended: essay, recommendations, interview. Required for some: essay, interview. Entrance: minimally difficult. Application deadline: Rolling.
Costs Per Year: Application fee: $30. State resident tuition: $4906 full-time, $204 per credit part-time. Nonresident tuition: $9814 full-time, $409 per credit part-time. Mandatory fees: $1561 full-time, $117 per credit part-time. College room and board: $5246. College room only: $3564. Room and board charges vary according to board plan.
Collegiate Environment: Orientation program. Drama-theater group, choral group, marching band, student-run newspaper, radio station. Social organizations: 125 open to all; national fraternities, national sororities, local fraternities, local sororities; 4% of eligible men and 7% of eligible women are members. Student services: health clinic, personal-psychological counseling, women's center. Campus security: 24-hour emergency response devices and patrols, student patrols. Options: coed, men-only, women-only housing available. Carlson Library with 429,800 books, 1.6 million microform titles, 750 serials, 23,444 audiovisual materials, an OPAC, and a Web page. Operations spending for 2004 fiscal year: $2.3 million. 400 computers available on campus for general student use. A campuswide network can be accessed from student residence rooms and from off campus. Staffed computer lab on campus.
Community Environment: Clarion is in a rural area located near Cook Forest State Park and Allegheny National Forest. The area offers excellent hunting and fishing. The city has a public library, historical museum, nine churches, a hospital, and good shopping facilities. Two airports with commercial commuter and charter service are located within easy driving distance.

■ **COLLEGE MISERICORDIA** *F-21*
301 Lake St.
Dallas, PA 18612-1098
Tel: (570)674-6400; (866)262-6363
Admissions: (570)675-4449
Fax: (570)675-2441
E-mail: jdessoye@misericordia.edu
Web Site: http://www.misericordia.edu/
Description: Independent Roman Catholic, comprehensive, coed. Awards bachelor's, master's, and doctoral degrees and post-master's certificates. Founded 1924. Setting: 100-acre small town campus. System endowment: $10.2 million. System-wide educational spending for 2005 fiscal year: $6737 per student. Total enrollment: 2,343. Faculty: 258 (90 full-time, 168 part-time). Student-undergrad faculty ratio is 11:1. 1,071 applied, 81% were admitted. 11% from top 10% of their high school class, 40% from top quarter, 72% from top half. Full-time: 1,428 students, 72% women, 28% men. Part-time: 644 students, 78% women, 22% men. Students come from 21 states and territories, 2 other countries, 17% from out-of-state, 0.4% Native American, 2% Hispanic, 2% black, 1% Asian American or Pacific Islander, 0.2% international, 26% 25 or older, 39% live on campus, 6% transferred in. Retention: 79% of full-time freshmen returned the following year. Academic areas with the most degrees conferred: health professions and related sciences; business/marketing; education. Core. Calendar: semesters. Academic remediation for entering students, ESL program, services for LD students, advanced placement, accelerated degree program, self-designed majors, honors program, independent study, distance learning, double major, summer session for credit, part-time degree program, adult/continuing education programs, co-op programs and internships, graduate courses open to undergrads. Off campus study at King's College (PA), Wilkes University. Study abroad program. ROTC: Army (c), Air Force (c).
Entrance Requirements: Options: Peterson's Universal Application, Common Application, electronic application, early admission, deferred admission, international baccalaureate accepted. Required: high school transcript, SAT or ACT. Recommended: interview. Required for some: essay, minimum 2.0 high school GPA, 2 recommendations, interview. Entrance: moderately difficult. Application deadline: Rolling. Notification: continuous.

Costs Per Year: Application fee: $25. Comprehensive fee: $27,950 includes full-time tuition ($18,700), mandatory fees ($1000), and college room and board ($8250). College room only: $4730. Room and board charges vary according to board plan and housing facility. Part-time tuition: $425 per credit. Part-time tuition varies according to location.

Collegiate Environment: Orientation program. Drama-theater group, choral group, student-run newspaper, radio station. Social organizations: 35 open to all. Most popular organizations: Circle K, SOAR Student Outdoor Adventure and Recreation, BACCHUS, Peer Advocates, Commuter Council. Major annual events: homecoming, Snowball Week, Harvest Ball. Student services: health clinic, personal-psychological counseling, women's center. Campus security: 24-hour emergency response devices and patrols, late night transport-escort service. College housing designed to accommodate 740 students; 756 undergraduates lived in college housing during 2003-04. Freshmen given priority for college housing. Option: coed housing available. Mary Kintz Bevevino Library with 90,000 books, 7,697 microform titles, 575 serials, 2,240 audiovisual materials, an OPAC, and a Web page. System-wide operations spending for 2004 fiscal year: $539,862. 75 computers available on campus for general student use. Computer purchase/lease plans available. A campuswide network can be accessed from student residence rooms and from off campus. Staffed computer lab on campus.

Community Environment: The community of Dallas surrounding College Misericordia has a suburban atmosphere. It is located just nine miles from the city of Wilkes-Barre. The area provides shopping centers, a mall, cinemas, sporting events and a variety of cultural activities. Also nearby are Pennsylvania's largest natural lake, two state parks, the ski resorts of the Poconos, and five other colleges. New York and Philadelphia are within a two-hour drive. Public transportation is available to and from the campus.

■ COMMONWEALTH TECHNICAL INSTITUTE *K-8*

727 Goucher St.
Johnstown, PA 15905-3092
Tel: (814)255-8200
E-mail: rhalza@state.pa.us
Web Site: http://www.hgac.org/

Description: State-supported, 2-year, coed. Awards certificates, diplomas, and terminal associate degrees. Total enrollment: 275. Student-undergrad faculty ratio is 10:1. 113 applied, 89% were admitted. Full-time: 275 students, 35% women, 65% men. 1% from out-of-state, 1% Native American, 1% Hispanic, 11% black, 1% Asian American or Pacific Islander, 0% international. Retention: 64% of full-time freshmen returned the following year. Calendar: trimesters.

Entrance Requirements: Open admission. Recommended: high school transcript. Required for some: high school transcript. Entrance: noncompetitive. Preference given to disabled students.

Costs Per Year: State resident tuition: $16,836 full-time, $323 per credit part-time. Mandatory fees: $75 full-time, $25 per term part-time. College room and board: $14,274.

Collegiate Environment: Choral group. Student services: health clinic, personal-psychological counseling. Campus security: 24-hour patrols.

■ COMMUNITY COLLEGE OF ALLEGHENY COUNTY *K-3*

800 Allegheny Ave.
Pittsburgh, PA 15233-1894
Tel: (412)323-2323
Web Site: http://www.ccac.edu/

Description: County-supported, 2-year, coed. Awards certificates, diplomas, transfer associate, and terminal associate degrees. Founded 1966. Setting: 242-acre urban campus. Total enrollment: 18,404. Student-undergrad faculty ratio is 15:1. 7,333 applied, 85% were admitted. Full-time: 7,580 students, 55% women, 45% men. Part-time: 10,824 students, 59% women, 41% men. Students come from 17 states and territories, 79 other countries, 1% from out-of-state, 1% Native American, 1% Hispanic, 16% black, 1% Asian American or Pacific Islander, 1% international, 48% 25 or older, 11% transferred in. Core. Calendar: semesters. Academic remediation for entering students, ESL program, services for LD students, advanced placement, honors program, independent study, distance learning, summer session for credit, part-time degree program, external degree program. Off campus study at members of the Pittsburgh Council on Higher Education. Study abroad program.

Entrance Requirements: Open admission except for automotive, culinary arts, health-related programs. Option: deferred admission. Recommended: high school transcript. Entrance: noncompetitive. Application deadline: Rolling. Notification: continuous.

Costs Per Year: Application fee: $0. Area resident tuition: $2400 full-time, $80 per credit part-time. State resident tuition: $4800 full-time, $160 per credit part-time. Nonresident tuition: $7200 full-time, $240 per credit part-time. Mandatory fees: $295 full-time, $10.70 per credit part-time.

Collegiate Environment: Drama-theater group, choral group, student-run newspaper. Social organizations: local fraternities. Most popular organization: Phi Theta Kappa. Student services: health clinic, personal-psychological counseling, women's center. Campus security: 24-hour emergency response devices and patrols, late night transport-escort service. College housing not available. Community College of Allegheny County Library plus 4 others with 272,697 books, 12,340 microform titles, 933 serials, 13,165 audiovisual materials, an OPAC, and a Web page. 3,100 computers available on campus for general student use. A campuswide network can be accessed from off-campus. Staffed computer lab on campus.

■ COMMUNITY COLLEGE OF BEAVER COUNTY *I-2*

One Campus Dr.
Monaca, PA 15061-2588
Tel: (724)775-8561
Free: 800-335-0222
Fax: (724)728-7599
E-mail: mike.macon@ccbc.edu
Web Site: http://www.ccbc.edu/

Description: State-supported, 2-year, coed. Awards certificates, diplomas, transfer associate, and terminal associate degrees. Founded 1966. Setting: 75-acre small town campus with easy access to Pittsburgh. Research spending for 2004 fiscal year: $102,575. Educational spending for 2005 fiscal year: $3345 per student. Total enrollment: 2,500. 920 applied, 100% were admitted. Students come from 7 states and territories, 2 other countries, 3% from out-of-state, 56% 25 or older. Core. Calendar: semesters. Academic remediation for entering students, services for LD students, advanced placement, independent study, distance learning, double major, summer session for credit, part-time degree program, adult/continuing education programs, co-op programs and internships. Off campus study at Geneva College, Pennsylvania State University Beaver Campus of the Commonwealth College, La Roche College, Robert Morris College.

Entrance Requirements: Open admission except for nursing, medical laboratory technology programs. Option: early admission. Recommended: high school transcript, interview. Placement: ACT ASSET, ACT, or nursing exam depending on program required. Entrance: noncompetitive. Application deadline: Rolling. Notification: continuous.

Costs Per Year: Application fee: $25. Area resident tuition: $2400 full-time, $80 per credit part-time. State resident tuition: $4800 full-time, $160 per credit part-time. Nonresident tuition: $7200 full-time, $240 per credit part-time. Mandatory fees: $525 full-time, $17.50 per credit part-time.

Collegiate Environment: Social organizations: local fraternities, local sororities; 1% of eligible men and 2% of eligible women are members. Campus security: 24-hour emergency response devices and patrols, late night transport-escort service. College housing not available. Community College of Beaver County Library with 52,857 books, 3,753 microform titles, and 300 serials. Operations spending for 2004 fiscal year: $274,618.

Community Environment: Beaver County covers 436 square miles of rolling hills and valleys in southwestern Pennsylvania. Professional sporting events, world-renowned museums, and numerous cultural events are within commuting distance in nearby Pittsburgh.

■ COMMUNITY COLLEGE OF PHILADELPHIA *M-24*

1700 Spring Garden St.
Philadelphia, PA 19130-3991
Tel: (215)751-8010
Admissions: (215)751-8199
Web Site: http://www.ccp.edu/

Description: State and locally supported, 2-year, coed. Awards certificates, diplomas, transfer associate, and terminal associate degrees. Founded 1964. Setting: 14-acre urban campus. Total enrollment: 22,671. 53% 25 or older. Core. Calendar: semesters. Academic remediation for entering students, ESL program, services for LD students, accelerated degree program, self-designed majors, honors program, summer session for credit, part-time degree program, adult/continuing education programs, internships.

Entrance Requirements: Open admission except for allied health, mental health/social service, engineering science programs. Options: Peterson's Universal Application, early admission, deferred admission. Required for some: high school transcript. Entrance: noncompetitive. Application deadline: Rolling. Notification: continuous. Preference given to city residents.

Costs Per Year: Application fee: $20. Area resident tuition: $104 per credit hour part-time. State resident tuition: $208 per credit hour part-time. Nonresident tuition: $312 per credit hour part-time.

Collegiate Environment: Orientation program. Drama-theater group, choral group, student-run newspaper, radio station. Social organizations: 40 open to all. Student services: health clinic, personal-psychological counseling, women's center. Campus security: 24-hour emergency response devices and patrols. College housing not available. 92,698 books, 376 serials, and a Web page. 350 computers available on campus for general student use. Staffed computer lab on campus.

Community Environment: See Temple University.

■ **CONSOLIDATED SCHOOL OF BUSINESS (LANCASTER)** *M-19*

2124 Ambassador Circle
Lancaster, PA 17603
Tel: (717)394-6211
Admissions: (717)764-9550
Fax: (717)394-6213
E-mail: bobjr@csb.edu
Web Site: http://www.csb.edu/

Description: Proprietary, 2-year, coed. Awards diplomas and terminal associate degrees. Founded 1986. Setting: suburban campus with easy access to Philadelphia. Total enrollment: 173. Student-undergrad faculty ratio is 15:1. 0% Native American, 19% Hispanic, 7% black, 0% Asian American or Pacific Islander, 0% international, 23% 25 or older. Core. Calendar: continuous. Services for LD students, accelerated degree program, self-designed majors, honors program, independent study, part-time degree program, internships.

Entrance Requirements: Open admission. Option: Common Application. Required: high school transcript, interview. Entrance: minimally difficult. Application deadline: Rolling.

Costs Per Year: Application fee: $25. Tuition: $3500 full-time.

Collegiate Environment: Orientation program. Social organizations: 1 open to all. Most popular organization: Community Service Club. Major annual events: Summer Picnic, Food Drive, Holiday Party. College housing not available. 120 computers available on campus for general student use. Staffed computer lab on campus.

■ **CONSOLIDATED SCHOOL OF BUSINESS (YORK)** *M-17*

1605 Clugston Rd.
York, PA 17404
Tel: (717)764-9550
Free: 800-520-0691
Fax: (717)764-9469
E-mail: bobjr@csb.edu
Web Site: http://www.csb.edu/

Description: Proprietary, 2-year, coed. Awards diplomas and terminal associate degrees. Founded 1981. Setting: 6-acre suburban campus with easy access to Baltimore. Total enrollment: 176. Student-undergrad faculty ratio is 15:1. 41% 25 or older. Core. Calendar: continuous. Services for LD students, accelerated degree program, self-designed majors, honors program, independent study, part-time degree program, internships.

Entrance Requirements: Open admission. Option: Common Application. Required: high school transcript, interview. Entrance: minimally difficult. Application deadline: Rolling.

Collegiate Environment: Orientation program. Social organizations: 1 open to all. Most popular organization: Community Service Club. Major annual events: Summer Picnic, Holiday Party, Food Drive. College housing not available. 120 computers available on campus for general student use. Staffed computer lab on campus.

■ **THE CURTIS INSTITUTE OF MUSIC** *M-24*

1726 Locust St.
Philadelphia, PA 19103-6107
Tel: (215)893-5252
Admissions: (215)893-5262
Fax: (215)893-7900
Web Site: http://www.curtis.edu/

Description: Independent, comprehensive, coed. Awards bachelor's and master's degrees. Founded 1924. Setting: urban campus. Total enrollment: 160. 787 applied, 5% were admitted. Students come from 24 states and territories, 22 other countries. Core. Calendar: semesters. ESL program, advanced placement, accelerated degree program. Off campus study.

Entrance Requirements: Options: Common Application, early admission. Required: essay, high school transcript, recommendations, audition. Placement: SAT required. Entrance: most difficult. Application deadline: 1/15. Notification: continuous.

Collegiate Environment: Orientation program. Student services: personal-psychological counseling. Campus security: 24-hour patrols. College housing not available. Curtis Institute of Music Library with 70,000 books.

Community Environment: See Temple University.

■ **DEAN INSTITUTE OF TECHNOLOGY** *K-3*

1501 West Liberty Ave.
Pittsburgh, PA 15226-1103
Tel: (412)531-4433
Fax: (412)531-4435
Web Site: http://home.earthlink.net/~deantech/

Description: Proprietary, 2-year, coed. Awards diplomas and terminal associate degrees. Founded 1947. Setting: 2-acre urban campus. Total enrollment: 228. 10% from top half of their high school class. Students come from 3 states and territories, 1 other country, 15% 25 or older. Core. Part-time degree program.

Entrance Requirements: Open admission. Options: early admission, deferred admission. Entrance: noncompetitive. Application deadline: Rolling.

Collegiate Environment: Campus security: 24-hour emergency response devices. College housing not available. 2,500 books and 25 serials. 18 computers available on campus for general student use.

■ **DELAWARE COUNTY COMMUNITY COLLEGE** *N-23*

901 South Media Line Rd.
Media, PA 19063-1094
Tel: (610)359-5000
Free: 800-543-0146
Admissions: (610)359-5333
E-mail: admiss@dccc.edu
Web Site: http://www.dccc.edu/

Description: State and locally supported, 2-year, coed. Awards certificates, transfer associate, and terminal associate degrees. Founded 1967. Setting: 123-acre suburban campus with easy access to Philadelphia. Endowment: $676,410. Educational spending for 2005 fiscal year: $2542 per student. Total enrollment: 10,608. 3,840 applied, 100% were admitted. Full-time: 4,263 students, 52% women, 48% men. Part-time: 6,345 students, 59% women, 41% men. Students come from 13 states and territories, 46 other countries, 1% from out-of-state, 0.2% Native American, 2% Hispanic, 15% black, 4% Asian American or Pacific Islander, 1% international, 42% 25 or older. Calendar: semesters. Academic remediation for entering students, ESL program, services for LD students, advanced placement, self-designed majors, independent study, distance learning, double major, summer session for credit, part-time degree program, adult/continuing education programs, co-op programs and internships.

Entrance Requirements: Open admission except for international students, nursing, respiratory therapy, surgical technology, plumbing apprentice, municipal police training programs. Options: early admission, deferred admission, international baccalaureate accepted. Required: high school transcript. Entrance: noncompetitive. Application deadline: Rolling. Notification: continuous. Preference given to residents of sponsoring school districts for nursing, respiratory therapy, surgical technology programs.

Costs Per Year: Application fee: $20. Area resident tuition: $1968 full-time, $82 per credit part-time. State resident tuition: $3936 full-time, $164 per credit part-time. Nonresident tuition: $5904 full-time, $246 per credit part-time. Mandatory fees: $544 full-time, $21 per credit part-time, $20 per term part-time.

Collegiate Environment: Orientation program. Drama-theater group, choral group, student-run newspaper, radio station. Social organizations: 23 open to all. Most popular organizations: student government, student radio station, Phi Theta Kappa, Business Society, Student Pennsylvania State Education Association. Major annual events: Springfest, Transfer Fairs, Career Fairs. Student services: health clinic, personal-psychological counseling. Campus security: 24-hour emergency response devices and patrols, late night transport-escort service. College housing not available. Delaware County Community College Library with 58,692 books, 7,922 microform titles, 421 serials, 3,251 audiovisual materials, an OPAC, and a Web page. Operations spending for 2004 fiscal year: $860,906. 1,200 computers available on campus for general student use. A campuswide network can be accessed from off-campus. Staffed computer lab on campus.

Community Environment: Maple Township, population 23,123, is in central Delaware County. The city is located 20 miles from Philadelphia with all its cultural, educational, and recreational opportunities.

■ **DELAWARE VALLEY COLLEGE** *K-24*

700 East Butler Ave.

Doylestown, PA 18901-2697

Tel: (215)345-1500

Admissions: (215)489-2211

Fax: (215)345-5277

E-mail: admitme@devalcol.edu

Web Site: http://www.devalcol.edu/

Description: Independent, comprehensive, coed. Awards associate, bachelor's, and master's degrees. Founded 1896. Setting: 600-acre suburban campus with easy access to Philadelphia. Endowment: $14.5 million. Research spending for 2004 fiscal year: $1 million. Educational spending for 2005 fiscal year: $5420 per student. Total enrollment: 2,070. Faculty: 192 (78 full-time, 114 part-time). Student-undergrad faculty ratio is 15:1. 1,476 applied, 79% were admitted. 15% from top 10% of their high school class, 41% from top quarter, 75% from top half. Full-time: 1,600 students, 56% women, 44% men. Part-time: 399 students, 48% women, 52% men. Students come from 16 states and territories, 7 other countries, 33% from out-of-state, 0.3% Native American, 1% Hispanic, 4% black, 1% Asian American or Pacific Islander, 0.1% international, 14% 25 or older, 55% live on campus, 4% transferred in. Retention: 75% of full-time freshmen returned the following year. Academic areas with the most degrees conferred: agriculture; business/marketing; security and protective services. Core. Calendar: semesters. Academic remediation for entering students, services for LD students, advanced placement, honors program, independent study, distance learning, double major, summer session for credit, part-time degree program, adult/continuing education programs, co-op programs and internships. Study abroad program.

Entrance Requirements: Options: Peterson's Universal Application, Common Application, electronic application, early admission, deferred admission. Required: high school transcript, 1 recommendation, SAT or ACT. Recommended: minimum 2.75 high school GPA, interview. Required for some: minimum 3.00 high school GPA. Entrance: moderately difficult. Application deadline: Rolling. Notification: continuous.

Costs Per Year: Application fee: $35. Comprehensive fee: $29,944 includes full-time tuition ($20,664), mandatory fees ($1150), and college room and board ($8130). College room only: $3686. Full-time tuition and fees vary according to program. Room and board charges vary according to board plan. Part-time tuition: $560 per credit.

Collegiate Environment: Orientation program. Drama-theater group, choral group, student-run newspaper, radio station. Social organizations: 40 open to all; local fraternities, local sororities; 4% of eligible men and 5% of eligible women are members. Most popular organizations: Block and Bridle Club, Community Service Corps, Student Government, Halloween Haunting. Major annual events: A-Day, Homecoming, Family Day. Student services: health clinic, personal-psychological counseling. Campus security: 24-hour patrols, late night transport-escort service, controlled dormitory access. College housing designed to accommodate 895 students; 915 undergraduates lived in college housing during 2003-04. Freshmen given priority for college housing. Option: coed housing available. Joseph Krauskopf Memorial Library with 56,347 books, 162,164 microform titles, 728 serials, an OPAC, and a Web page. Operations spending for 2004 fiscal year: $680,204. 210 computers available on campus for general student use. A campuswide network can be accessed. Staffed computer lab on campus.

Community Environment: Doylestown, population 25,000, and founded in 1745, is in Bucks County, one of the finest farming sections of the state. The city is located 30 miles north of Philadelphia, and can be reached by rail, bus, and good highways. There are several churches, a hospital, public library, historical society, and more than 50 civic, fraternal, and veteran's organizations in the community. Local recreational facilities include theaters, a swimming pool, bowling lanes, and a radio station. Part-time employment is available.

■ **DESALES UNIVERSITY** *J-23*

2755 Station Ave.

Center Valley, PA 18034-9568

Tel: (610)282-1100

Free: 800-228-5114

Fax: (610)282-2254

E-mail: peter.rautzhan@desales.edu

Web Site: http://www.desales.edu

Description: Independent Roman Catholic, comprehensive, coed. Awards bachelor's and master's degrees and post-master's certificates. Founded 1964. Setting: 350-acre suburban campus with easy access to Philadelphia and New York City. Endowment: $37.4 million. Research spending for 2004 fiscal year: $102,461. Educational spending for 2005 fiscal year: $7247 per student. Total enrollment: 3,282. Faculty: 163 (92 full-time, 71 part-time). Student-undergrad faculty ratio is 15:1. 1,728 applied, 79% were admitted. 20% from top 10% of their high school class, 48% from top quarter, 79% from top half. Full-time: 1,766 students, 56% women, 44% men. Part-time: 723 students, 62% women, 38% men. Students come from 10 states and territories, 29% from out-of-state, 0.1% Native American, 1% Hispanic, 1% black, 0.5% Asian American or Pacific Islander, 0.04% international, 34% 25 or older, 72% live on campus, 3% transferred in. Retention: 82% of full-time freshmen returned the following year. Academic areas with the most degrees conferred: business/marketing; visual and performing arts; education. Core. Calendar: semesters. Services for LD students, advanced placement, accelerated degree program, honors program, independent study, distance learning, double major, summer session for credit, part-time degree program, adult/continuing education programs, internships, graduate courses open to undergrads. Off campus study at Lehigh Valley Association of Independent Colleges. Study abroad program. ROTC: Army (c).

Entrance Requirements: Options: Peterson's Universal Application, Common Application, electronic application, early admission, deferred admission. Required: high school transcript, 2 recommendations, SAT or ACT. Recommended: essay, interview. Entrance: moderately difficult. Application deadline: 8/1. Notification: continuous.

Costs Per Year: Application fee: $30. Comprehensive fee: $28,580 includes full-time tuition ($20,000), mandatory fees ($700), and college room and board ($7880). Full-time tuition and fees vary according to class time, course load, and degree level. Room and board charges vary according to board plan and housing facility. Part-time tuition: $830 per credit. Part-time mandatory fees: $15 per course. Part-time tuition and fees vary according to class time, course load, and degree level.

Collegiate Environment: Orientation program. Drama-theater group, choral group, student-run newspaper, radio station. Social organizations: 32 open to all; local sororities; 1% of women are members. Most popular organizations: Sigma Alpha Omega, social outreach, Student Nursing Organization, Student Government Association, Business Club. Major annual events: Formal, Semi-Formal, Club McShea. Student services: health clinic, personal-psychological counseling. Campus security: 24-hour emergency response devices and patrols, late night transport-escort service, desk security in residence halls 24 hours per day. College housing designed to accommodate 833 students; 883 undergraduates lived in college housing during 2003-04. Freshmen guaranteed college housing. Options: coed, men-only, women-only housing available. Trexler Library with 138,151 books, 432,807 microform titles, 538 serials, 5,978 audiovisual materials, an OPAC, and a Web page. Operations spending for 2004 fiscal year: $825,726. 200 computers available on campus for general student use. Computer purchase/lease plans available. A campuswide network can be accessed from student residence rooms and from off campus. Staffed computer lab on campus.

Community Environment: Center Valley is a suburban area that enjoys a temperate climate. Lehigh Valley is accessible by air, bus, and car (Route 309), and the nearby towns are Allentown (population 110,000) and Bethlehem (population 73,000).

■ **DEVRY UNIVERSITY (CHESTERBROOK)** *D-43*

701 Lee Rd., Ste. 103

Chesterbrook, PA 19087-5612

Tel: (610)889-9980

Fax: (610)889-9918

Web Site: http://www.devry.edu/

Description: Proprietary, comprehensive, coed. Calendar: semesters.

Costs Per Year: One-time mandatory fee: $40. Tuition: $13,060 full-time, $475 per credit part-time. Mandatory fees: $60 full-time, $30 per year part-time. Full-time tuition and fees vary according to course load. Part-time tuition and fees vary according to course load.

■ **DEVRY UNIVERSITY (FORT WASHINGTON)** *C-46*

1140 Virginia Dr.

Fort Washington, PA 19034

Tel: (215)591-5700; (866)338-7934

Web Site: http://www.devry.edu/

Description: Proprietary, comprehensive, coed. Part of DeVry University. Awards associate, bachelor's, and master's degrees. Founded 2002. Total enrollment: 803. Faculty: 84 (44 full-time, 40 part-time). Student-undergrad faculty ratio is 11:1. Full-time: 507 students, 39% women, 61% men. Part-time: 204 students, 53% women, 47% men. 0.3% Native American, 4% Hispanic, 35% black, 4% Asian American or Pacific Islander, 1% international. Academic areas with the most degrees conferred: business/marketing; computer and information sciences; engineering technologies. Calendar: semesters. Academic remediation for entering students, services for LD students, advanced placement, accelerated degree program, distance learning, summer session for credit, part-time degree program, adult/continuing education programs, co-op programs.

Entrance Requirements: Options: electronic application, deferred admission, international baccalaureate accepted. Required: high school transcript, interview. Entrance: minimally difficult. Application deadline: Rolling.

Costs Per Year: Application fee: $50. One-time mandatory fee: $40. Tuition: $13,060 full-time, $475 per credit part-time. Mandatory fees: $270 full-time, $160. Full-time tuition and fees vary according to course load. Part-time tuition and fees vary according to course load.

Collegiate Environment: Orientation program. College housing not available. Learning Resource Center with 12,755 books, 69 serials, 427 audiovisual materials, an OPAC, and a Web page. 84 computers available on campus for general student use. Computer purchase/lease plans available. A campuswide network can be accessed from off-campus. Staffed computer lab on campus.

■ **DEVRY UNIVERSITY (PITTSBURGH)** *K-3*

FreeMarkets Center
210 Sixth Ave., Ste. 200
Pittsburgh, PA 15222-9123
Tel: (412)642-9072; (866)77D-EVRY
Web Site: http://www.devry.edu/

Description: Proprietary, comprehensive, coed. Calendar: semesters.

Costs Per Year: One-time mandatory fee: $40. Tuition: $11,890 full-time, $445 per credit part-time. Mandatory fees: $60 full-time, $30 per year part-time. Full-time tuition and fees vary according to course load. Part-time tuition and fees vary according to course load.

■ **DICKINSON COLLEGE** *L-15*

PO Box 1773
Carlisle, PA 17013-2896
Tel: (717)243-5121
Free: 800-644-1773
Fax: (717)245-1442
E-mail: admit@dickinson.edu
Web Site: http://www.dickinson.edu/

Description: Independent, 4-year, coed. Awards bachelor's degrees. Founded 1773. Setting: 115-acre suburban campus with easy access to Harrisburg. Endowment: $206.2 million. Research spending for 2004 fiscal year: $3.9 million. Educational spending for 2005 fiscal year: $12,687 per student. Total enrollment: 2,352. Student-undergrad faculty ratio is 12:1. 4,784 applied, 49% were admitted. 52% from top 10% of their high school class, 81% from top quarter, 98% from top half. Full-time: 2,311 students, 56% women, 44% men. Part-time: 41 students, 66% women, 34% men. Students come from 43 states and territories, 28 other countries, 72% from out-of-state, 0.5% Native American, 4% Hispanic, 4% black, 4% Asian American or Pacific Islander, 5% international, 1% 25 or older, 90% live on campus, 1% transferred in. Retention: 89% of full-time freshmen returned the following year. Academic areas with the most degrees conferred: social sciences; foreign languages and literature; biological/life sciences; psychology. Core. Calendar: semesters. ESL program, services for LD students, advanced placement, accelerated degree program, self-designed majors, independent study, double major, summer session for credit, part-time degree program, adult/continuing education programs, internships. Off campus study at The Washington Center, University of Pennsylvania, Woods Hole Oceanographic Institution, Consortium Exchange: Dickinson College, Franklin and Marshall College, Gettysburg College. Study abroad program. ROTC: Army.

Entrance Requirements: Options: Peterson's Universal Application, Common Application, electronic application, early decision, early action, deferred admission, international baccalaureate accepted. Required: essay, high school transcript, 2 recommendations. Recommended: minimum 3.0 high school GPA, interview, SAT or ACT. Entrance: very difficult. Application deadlines: 2/1, 11/15 for early decision plan 1, 1/15 for early decision plan 2,

12/1 for early action. Notification: 3/31, 12/15 for early decision plan 1, 2/15 for early decision plan 2, 1/31 for early action.

Costs Per Year: Application fee: $60. One-time mandatory fee: $25. Comprehensive fee: $40,170 includes full-time tuition ($31,800), mandatory fees ($320), and college room and board ($8050). College room only: $4150. Room and board charges vary according to housing facility. Part-time tuition: $3975 per course. Part-time mandatory fees: $40 per credit.

Collegiate Environment: Orientation program. Drama-theater group, choral group, student-run newspaper, radio station. Social organizations: 120 open to all; national fraternities, national sororities, local fraternities, local sororities; 19% of eligible men and 24% of eligible women are members. Most popular organizations: Student Senate, College Choir, Alpha Lambda Delta, Multi-Organization Board, Alpha Phi Omega. Major annual events: homecoming, Public Affairs Symposium, Springfest. Student services: health clinic, personal-psychological counseling, women's center. Campus security: 24-hour emergency response devices and patrols, student patrols, late night transport-escort service, controlled dormitory access. 1,909 college housing spaces available; 1,897 were occupied in 2003-04. Freshmen guaranteed college housing. On-campus residence required in freshman year. Option: coed housing available. Waidner-Spahr Library plus 6 others with 512,232 books, 166,352 microform titles, 1,600 serials, 16,736 audiovisual materials, an OPAC, and a Web page. Operations spending for 2004 fiscal year: $2.8 million. 536 computers available on campus for general student use. Computer purchase/lease plans available. A campuswide network can be accessed from student residence rooms and from off campus. Staffed computer lab on campus.

Community Environment: Carlisle, population 20,000, is in the Cumberland Valley located at the western edge of Harrisburg, the state capital. It is 3 miles from I-76 and I-81, and within 2-3 hours of Baltimore, Washington and Philadelphia. Founded in 1751, it was the focus of the Scotch-Irish colonists who settled in Pennsylvania in the pre-revolutionary period. Several historic figures made their homes in Carlisle during the revolutionary period. Numerous buildings of Colonial and Federal architecture, many of native limestone, have been restored in the historic district of Carlisle. The eastern most ranges of the Appalachian Mountains are within a few miles of the downtown area, and the Appalachian Trail passes within five miles. Four state parks provide opportunities for hiking, fishing, hunting, and water and winter sports. The Carlisle Hospital, a variety of theatres, restaurants, and churches, three amusement parks, and public golf courses are within easy reach.

■ **DOUGLAS EDUCATION CENTER** *L-3*

130 Seventh St.
Monessen, PA 15062
Tel: (724)684-3684
Fax: (724)684-7463
Web Site: http://www.douglas-school.com/

Description: Proprietary, 2-year, coed. Awards certificates, diplomas, transfer associate, and terminal associate degrees. Total enrollment: 140. 120 applied, 61% were admitted. 30% 25 or older.

Entrance Requirements: Required: high school transcript, interview, Wonderlic aptitude test. Entrance: minimally difficult. Application deadline: Rolling. Notification: continuous.

■ **DREXEL UNIVERSITY** *M-24*

3141 Chestnut St.
Philadelphia, PA 19104-2875
Tel: (215)895-2000
Free: 800-2-DREXEL
Admissions: (215)895-2400
Fax: (215)895-5939
E-mail: undergrad-admissions@post.drexel.edu
Web Site: http://www.drexel.edu/

Description: Independent, university, coed. Awards associate, bachelor's, master's, doctoral, and first professional degrees and post-master's and first professional certificates. Founded 1891. Setting: 42-acre urban campus. Endowment: $511.7 million. Research spending for 2004 fiscal year: $25.3 million. Educational spending for 2005 fiscal year: $11,326 per student. Total enrollment: 18,466. Faculty: (723 full-time). Student-undergrad faculty ratio is 10:1. 12,093 applied, 82% were admitted. 30% from top 10% of their high school class, 59% from top quarter, 86% from top half. Full-time: 10,158 students, 40% women, 60% men. Part-time: 2,199 students, 49% women, 51% men. Students come from 44 states and territories, 96 other countries, 44% from out-of-state, 0.2% Native American, 3% Hispanic, 9% black, 12%

Asian American or Pacific Islander, 6% international, 20% 25 or older, 37% live on campus, 9% transferred in. Retention: 80% of full-time freshmen returned the following year. Academic areas with the most degrees conferred: business/marketing; engineering; computer and information sciences. Academic remediation for entering students, ESL program, services for LD students, advanced placement, accelerated degree program, freshman honors college, honors program, independent study, distance learning, double major, summer session for credit, part-time degree program, adult/continuing education programs, co-op programs and internships, graduate courses open to undergrads. Study abroad program. ROTC: Army, Air Force (c).

Entrance Requirements: Options: Peterson's Universal Application, electronic application, deferred admission. Required: high school transcript, minimum 2.0 high school GPA, SAT or ACT. Recommended: 2 recommendations, interview, SAT. Required for some: essay. Entrance: moderately difficult. Application deadline: 3/1. Notification: continuous.

Costs Per Year: Application fee: $50. Comprehensive fee: $34,795 includes full-time tuition ($22,700), mandatory fees ($1580), and college room and board ($10,515). College room only: $6255. Full-time tuition and fees vary according to course load, program, and student level. Room and board charges vary according to board plan and housing facility. Part-time tuition: $500 per credit. Part-time mandatory fees: $100 per term. Part-time tuition and fees vary according to course load and program.

Collegiate Environment: Orientation program. Drama-theater group, choral group, student-run newspaper, radio station. Social organizations: 75 open to all; national fraternities, national sororities, local fraternities; 12% of eligible men and 8% of eligible women are members. Most popular organizations: student government, Black Student Union, Society of Hispanic Professional Engineers, Society of Minority Engineers and Scientists, Campus Activities Board. Major annual events: Spring Jam, Welcome Back, homecoming. Student services: health clinic, personal-psychological counseling. Campus security: 24-hour emergency response devices and patrols, late night transport-escort service, controlled dormitory access. 2,079 college housing spaces available. On-campus residence required in freshman year. Option: coed housing available. W. W. Hagerty Library with 570,335 books, 213,500 microform titles, 8,321 serials, 10,322 audiovisual materials, an OPAC, and a Web page. Operations spending for 2004 fiscal year: $3.6 million. 6,500 computers available on campus for general student use. A campuswide network can be accessed from student residence rooms and from off campus. Staffed computer lab on campus.

Community Environment: Philadelphia, a metropolitan city with historical significance, provides considerable cultural, social, and recreational resources, as well as excellent shopping and dining. Transportation includes public transit, major highways, Amtrak, and Philadelphia International Airport.

■ **DUBOIS BUSINESS COLLEGE** *G-9*

1 Beaver Dr.
DuBois, PA 15801-2401
Tel: (814)371-6920
E-mail: stanfordlj@dbcollege.com
Web Site: http://www.dbcollege.com/

Description: Proprietary, 2-year, coed. Awards diplomas and terminal associate degrees. Founded 1885. Setting: 4-acre rural campus. Total enrollment: 240. 141 applied, 64% were admitted. 20% from top 10% of their high school class, 40% from top half. Students come from 1 other country, 10% from out-of-state, 40% 25 or older, 7% live on campus. Core. Academic remediation for entering students, accelerated degree program, double major, summer session for credit, part-time degree program.

Entrance Requirements: Options: Common Application, electronic application, deferred admission. Required: high school transcript, interview. Recommended: recommendations. Entrance: moderately difficult. Application deadline: Rolling. Notification: continuous.

Collegiate Environment: Orientation program. Student-run newspaper. Social organizations: 4 open to all; national fraternities, national sororities; 50% of eligible men and 50% of eligible women are members. Most popular organizations: student association, Bible study. Major annual events: President's Day Picnic, Annual Christmas Party, Academic Field Trip Day. Student services: personal-psychological counseling. Campus security: late night transport-escort service, controlled dormitory access. 48 college housing spaces available; 46 were occupied in 2003-04. Option: coed housing available. DuBois Business College Main Campus Library with 2,100 books, 10 serials, and a Web page. 110 computers available on campus for general student use. Staffed computer lab on campus.

Community Environment: See Penn State University, DuBois Campus.

■ **DUFF'S BUSINESS INSTITUTE** *K-3*

100 Forbes Ave., Ste. 1200
Pittsburgh, PA 15222
Tel: (412)261-4520; 888-279-3314
Fax: (412)261-4546
Web Site: http://www.duffs-institute.com/

Description: Proprietary, 2-year, coed. Part of Phillips Colleges, Inc. Awards diplomas and transfer associate degrees. Founded 1840. Setting: urban campus. Total enrollment: 1,251. 126 applied, 78% were admitted. Students come from 3 states and territories, 0.2% Native American, 1% Hispanic, 59% black, 0.1% Asian American or Pacific Islander, 0% international, 40% 25 or older. Core. Academic remediation for entering students, advanced placement, summer session for credit, part-time degree program, adult/continuing education programs, co-op programs and internships.

Entrance Requirements: Option: deferred admission. Required: CPAt. Entrance: moderately difficult. Application deadline: Rolling.

Collegiate Environment: Orientation program. Student services: personal-psychological counseling. Campus security: 24-hour emergency response devices. College housing not available. Main library plus 1 other with 7,500 books and 30 serials. 80 computers available on campus for general student use.

■ **DUQUESNE UNIVERSITY** *K-3*

600 Forbes Ave.
Pittsburgh, PA 15282-0001
Tel: (412)396-6000
Free: 800-456-0590
Admissions: (412)396-5000
Fax: (412)396-5779
Web Site: http://www.duq.edu/

Description: Independent Roman Catholic, university, coed. Awards bachelor's, master's, doctoral, and first professional degrees and post-master's certificates. Founded 1878. Setting: 43-acre urban campus. Endowment: $123.3 million. Research spending for 2004 fiscal year: $10.1 million. Educational spending for 2005 fiscal year: $9049 per student. Total enrollment: 9,916. Faculty: 908 (429 full-time, 479 part-time). Student-undergrad faculty ratio is 15:1. 4,740 applied, 80% were admitted. 28% from top 10% of their high school class, 58% from top quarter, 88% from top half. 31 valedictorians. Full-time: 5,323 students, 59% women, 41% men. Part-time: 327 students, 57% women, 43% men. Students come from 46 states and territories, 57 other countries, 18% from out-of-state, 0.1% Native American, 1% Hispanic, 4% black, 2% Asian American or Pacific Islander, 2% international, 7% 25 or older, 54% live on campus, 4% transferred in. Retention: 89% of full-time freshmen returned the following year. Academic areas with the most degrees conferred: business/marketing; health professions and related sciences; education. Core. Calendar: semesters. ESL program, services for LD students, advanced placement, accelerated degree program, self-designed majors, freshman honors college, honors program, independent study, distance learning, double major, summer session for credit, part-time degree program, external degree program, adult/continuing education programs, internships, graduate courses open to undergrads. Off campus study at Harrisburg Campus, Westinghouse Electric in Monroeville, American Eagle Outfitter in Cranberry, US Steel Irwin Works/Plant in Braddock, Art Institute, Moon Township, Pittsburgh Technical Institute, St. Vincent. Study abroad program. ROTC: Army, Naval (c), Air Force (c).

Entrance Requirements: Options: Common Application, electronic application, early admission, early decision, early action, deferred admission, international baccalaureate accepted. Required: essay, high school transcript, 1 recommendation, SAT or ACT. Recommended: minimum 3.0 high school GPA, interview. Entrance: moderately difficult. Application deadlines: 7/1, 11/1 for early decision, 12/1 for early action. Notification: continuous, 12/15 for early decision, 1/15 for early action.

Costs Per Year: Application fee: $50. Comprehensive fee: $29,534 includes full-time tuition ($19,721), mandatory fees ($1759), and college room and board ($8054). College room only: $4394. Full-time tuition and fees vary according to program. Room and board charges vary according to board plan and housing facility. Part-time tuition: $641 per credit. Part-time mandatory fees: $69 per credit. Part-time tuition and fees vary according to program.

Collegiate Environment: Orientation program. Drama-theater group, choral group, marching band, student-run newspaper, radio station. Social organizations: 134 open to all; national fraternities, national sororities, local fraternities, local sororities; 16% of eligible men and 20% of eligible women are members. Most popular organizations: Student Government Association, University Volunteers, Program Council, Commuter Council, Black Student

Union. Major annual events: Orientation, Dance Marathon, Carnival. Student services: health clinic, personal-psychological counseling, women's center. Campus security: 24-hour emergency response devices and patrols, late night transport-escort service, controlled dormitory access, 24-hour front desk personnel, 24-hour video monitors at residence hall entrances, surveillance cameras throughout the campus. 3,340 college housing spaces available; 2,902 were occupied in 2003-04. Freshmen given priority for college housing. On-campus residence required through sophomore year. Options: coed, men-only, women-only housing available. Gumberg Library plus 1 other with 723,919 books, 328,312 microform titles, 1,124 serials, 49,175 audiovisual materials, an OPAC, and a Web page. Operations spending for 2004 fiscal year: $4.8 million. 800 computers available on campus for general student use. A campuswide network can be accessed from student residence rooms and from off campus. Staffed computer lab on campus.

Community Environment: Located adjacent to downtown Pittsburgh, Duquesne University's modern hilltop campus is readily accessible to the business, entertainment, and shopping centers of the city, while still offering students the privacy and peace of its own self-enclosed 43-acre site. Long noted as one of the world's great corporate centers, Pittsburgh combines the features of urban living with many of the charms and personal characteristics of a much smaller town. The world-renowned Pittsburgh Symphony Orchestra, Pittsburgh Opera, and Pittsburgh Ballet Theatre all perform regularly in the elegant Heinz Hall for the Performing Arts and the Benedum Center. The theatergoer can choose from productions of the Pittsburgh Public Theatre, local college drama departments and programs, and a wide variety of summer and after dinner club theatres. Duquesne student

■ EAST STROUDSBURG UNIVERSITY OF PENNSYLVANIA H-24

200 Prospect St.
East Stroudsburg, PA 18301-2999
Tel: (570)422-3211; 877-230-5547
Admissions: (570)422-3542
Fax: (570)422-3933
E-mail: jserowick@po-box.esu.edu
Web Site: http://www3.esu.edu/

Description: State-supported, comprehensive, coed. Part of Pennsylvania State System of Higher Education. Awards associate, bachelor's, and master's degrees. Founded 1893. Setting: 213-acre small town campus. Endowment: $10.8 million. Research spending for 2004 fiscal year: $289,240. Educational spending for 2005 fiscal year: $5360 per student. Total enrollment: 6,793. Faculty: 332 (259 full-time, 73 part-time). Student-undergrad faculty ratio is 19:1. 5,063 applied, 64% were admitted. 7% from top 10% of their high school class, 26% from top quarter, 71% from top half. Full-time: 5,056 students, 58% women, 42% men. Part-time: 540 students, 60% women, 40% men. Students come from 19 states and territories, 16 other countries, 22% from out-of-state, 0.2% Native American, 4% Hispanic, 4% black, 1% Asian American or Pacific Islander, 0.5% international, 11% 25 or older, 44% live on campus, 7% transferred in. Retention: 78% of full-time freshmen returned the following year. Academic areas with the most degrees conferred: education; business/marketing; social sciences. Core. Calendar: semesters. Academic remediation for entering students, services for LD students, advanced placement, self-designed majors, honors program, independent study, double major, summer session for credit, part-time degree program, adult/continuing education programs, internships, graduate courses open to undergrads. Off campus study at National Student Exchange, Wallops Island Consortium. Study abroad program. ROTC: Army (c), Air Force (c).

Entrance Requirements: Option: electronic application. Required: high school transcript, SAT or ACT. Entrance: moderately difficult. Application deadline: 4/1. Notification: continuous until 5/1. Preference given to state residents.

Costs Per Year: Application fee: $35. Area resident tuition: $204 per credit part-time. State resident tuition: $4906 full-time, $204 per credit part-time. Nonresident tuition: $12,266 full-time, $511 per credit part-time. Mandatory fees: $1556 full-time, $55 per credit part-time. Part-time tuition and fees vary according to course load. College room and board: $4794. College room only: $3098. Room and board charges vary according to board plan and housing facility.

Collegiate Environment: Orientation program. Drama-theater group, choral group, marching band, student-run newspaper, radio station. Social organizations: 90 open to all; national fraternities, national sororities; 5% of eligible men and 4% of eligible women are members. Most popular organizations: Student Senate, Stage II, Council for Exceptional Children, United Campus Ministry/ESU Christian Fellowship, University Band/Vocal Perform-

ing Choirs. Major annual events: Welcome Week, Homecoming, Greek Week. Student services: health clinic, personal-psychological counseling, women's center. Campus security: 24-hour emergency response devices and patrols, late night transport-escort service, controlled dormitory access. College housing designed to accommodate 2,200 students; 2,337 undergraduates lived in college housing during 2003-04. Freshmen guaranteed college housing. On-campus residence required in freshman year. Options: coed, men-only housing available. Kemp Library with 449,107 books, 1.4 million microform titles, 1,175 serials, 12,289 audiovisual materials, an OPAC, and a Web page. Operations spending for 2004 fiscal year: $2 million. 500 computers available on campus for general student use. A campuswide network can be accessed from student residence rooms and from off campus. Staffed computer lab on campus.

Community Environment: Population 7,894. East Stroudsburg is an urban area with temperate climate. The community is served by bus lines and Routes 611, 80 and 191. The community has a public library, YMCA, a hospital, good shopping facilities, and churches of major denominations. Part-time employment opportunities are excellent. The area offers good recreational facilities with nearby resorts.

■ EASTERN UNIVERSITY M-23

1300 Eagle Rd.
St. Davids, PA 19087-3696
Tel: (610)341-5800
Free: 800-452-0996
Admissions: (610)225-5005
Fax: (610)341-1723
E-mail: ugadm@eastern.edu
Web Site: http://www.eastern.edu/

Description: Independent American Baptist Churches in the USA, comprehensive, coed. Awards associate, bachelor's, and master's degrees. Founded 1952. Setting: 107-acre small town campus with easy access to Philadelphia. Total enrollment: 3,253. 1,193 applied, 78% were admitted. 19% from top 10% of their high school class, 51% from top quarter, 79% from top half. Full-time: 1,946 students, 66% women, 34% men. Part-time: 254 students, 65% women, 35% men. Students come from 38 states and territories, 26 other countries, 40% from out-of-state, 0.3% Native American, 5% Hispanic, 13% black, 2% Asian American or Pacific Islander, 1% international, 39% 25 or older, 74% live on campus, 3% transferred in. Retention: 78% of full-time freshmen returned the following year. Core. Calendar: semesters. Academic remediation for entering students, ESL program, advanced placement, accelerated degree program, self-designed majors, honors program, independent study, summer session for credit, part-time degree program, adult/continuing education programs, internships, graduate courses open to undergrads. Off campus study at all American Baptist-related colleges, Cabrini College, Rosemont College, Ursinus College. ROTC: Army (c), Air Force (c).

Entrance Requirements: Options: Peterson's Universal Application, electronic application, early admission, deferred admission. Required: essay, high school transcript, minimum 2.0 high school GPA, 1 recommendation, SAT or ACT. Recommended: minimum 3.0 high school GPA, 3 recommendations, interview. Entrance: moderately difficult. Application deadline: Rolling. Notification: continuous.

Costs Per Year: Application fee: $25. One-time mandatory fee: $45. Comprehensive fee: $26,670 includes full-time tuition ($18,830) and college room and board ($7840). College room only: $4280. Full-time tuition varies according to course load and program. Room and board charges vary according to board plan and housing facility. Part-time tuition: $420 per credit hour.

Collegiate Environment: Orientation program. Drama-theater group, choral group, student-run newspaper, radio station. Social organizations: 70 open to all. Most popular organizations: Habitat for Humanity, Y.A.C.H.T. Club, Angels of Harmony, Black Student League, Fellowship of Christian Athletes. Major annual events: Spring Banquet, Homecoming Dance, Christmas Party. Student services: health clinic, personal-psychological counseling, women's center. Campus security: 24-hour emergency response devices and patrols, late night transport-escort service, controlled dormitory access, emergency call boxes. College housing designed to accommodate 1,000 students; 1,074 undergraduates lived in college housing during 2003-04. On-campus residence required through senior year. Option: coed housing available. Warner Library plus 1 other with 143,815 books, 693,975 microform titles, 1,215 serials, 11,673 audiovisual materials, an OPAC, and a Web page. 60 computers available on campus for general student use. A campuswide network can be accessed from student residence rooms and from off campus. Staffed computer lab on campus.

■ EDINBORO UNIVERSITY OF PENNSYLVANIA *C-3*

Edinboro, PA 16444
Tel: (814)732-2000
Free: 800-626-2203
Admissions: (814)732-2761
Fax: (814)732-2420
Web Site: http://www.edinboro.edu/

Description: State-supported, comprehensive, coed. Part of Pennsylvania State System of Higher Education. Awards associate, bachelor's, and master's degrees and post-master's certificates. Founded 1857. Setting: 585-acre small town campus. Endowment: $7.5 million. Research spending for 2004 fiscal year: $85,727. Educational spending for 2005 fiscal year: $5037 per student. Total enrollment: 7,691. Faculty: 408 (363 full-time, 45 part-time). Student-undergrad faculty ratio is 17:1. 3,541 applied, 82% were admitted. 6% from top 10% of their high school class, 21% from top quarter, 55% from top half. Full-time: 5,722 students, 57% women, 43% men. Part-time: 801 students, 61% women, 39% men. Students come from 41 states and territories, 39 other countries, 11% from out-of-state, 0.2% Native American, 1% Hispanic, 8% black, 1% Asian American or Pacific Islander, 2% international, 18% 25 or older, 27% live on campus, 7% transferred in. Retention: 66% of full-time freshmen returned the following year. Academic areas with the most degrees conferred: visual and performing arts; education; health professions and related sciences. Core. Calendar: semesters. Academic remediation for entering students, services for LD students, advanced placement, self-designed majors, freshman honors college, honors program, independent study, distance learning, double major, summer session for credit, part-time degree program, adult/continuing education programs, internships, graduate courses open to undergrads. Off campus study at members of the Northwestern Pennsylvania Planning Council for Higher Education, Gannon University, Mercyhurst College, Hamot Medical Center, Pennsylvania State University at Erie, The Behrend College, Clarion University of Pennsylvania, Slippery Rock University of Pennsylvania, University of Pittsburgh, Case-Western University. Study abroad program. ROTC: Army.

Entrance Requirements: Options: Peterson's Universal Application, Common Application, electronic application, deferred admission. Required: high school transcript, SAT or ACT. Recommended: minimum 2.5 high school GPA. Required for some: essay, interview, music auditions, SAT, ACT. Entrance: moderately difficult. Application deadline: 4/1. Notification: 7/1.

Costs Per Year: Application fee: $30. State resident tuition: $4906 full-time, $204 per credit part-time. Nonresident tuition: $9814 full-time, $409 per credit part-time. Mandatory fees: $1384 full-time, $52.32 per credit part-time. Part-time tuition and fees vary according to course load. College room and board: $5518. College room only: $3400. Room and board charges vary according to board plan.

Collegiate Environment: Orientation program. Drama-theater group, choral group, marching band, student-run newspaper, radio station. Social organizations: 109 open to all; national fraternities, national sororities, local fraternities, local sororities. Most popular organizations: Student Government Association, AFRICA, Gamma Sigma Sigma, Health and Physical Education Majors Club. Major annual events: Homecoming, Greek Week, Black History Month. Student services: legal services, health clinic, personal-psychological counseling, women's center. Campus security: 24-hour emergency response devices and patrols, self-defense education. 2,500 college housing spaces available; 1,819 were occupied in 2003-04. Freshmen guaranteed college housing. On-campus residence required in freshman year. Options: coed, men-only, women-only housing available. Baron-Forness Library plus 1 other with 501,276 books, 1.4 million microform titles, 1,523 serials, an OPAC, and a Web page. Operations spending for 2004 fiscal year: $2.4 million. 818 computers available on campus for general student use. Computer purchase/lease plans available. A campuswide network can be accessed from student residence rooms and from off campus. Staffed computer lab on campus.

Community Environment: Population 7,736, Edinboro lies approximately 18 miles south of Erie, Pennsylvania. The community has several churches that represent various denominations. Bus and highway transportation is available. Local recreational facilities include hunting, boating, swimming, fishing, golf, and skiing. Edinboro Lake, which is one mile from the campus, has three beaches.

■ ELIZABETHTOWN COLLEGE *L-18*

1 Alpha Dr.
Elizabethtown, PA 17022-2298
Tel: (717)361-1000
Admissions: (717)361-1400
E-mail: admissions@etown.edu
Web Site: http://www.etown.edu/

Description: Independent, comprehensive, coed, affiliated with Church of the Brethren. Awards associate, bachelor's, and master's degrees. Founded 1899. Setting: 185-acre small town campus with easy access to Baltimore and Philadelphia. Endowment: $42.2 million. Research spending for 2004 fiscal year: $72,381. Educational spending for 2005 fiscal year: $9039 per student. Total enrollment: 2,248. Faculty: 207 (125 full-time, 82 part-time). Student-undergrad faculty ratio is 12:1. 2,709 applied, 62% were admitted. 29% from top 10% of their high school class, 63% from top quarter, 88% from top half. 86 class presidents, 12 valedictorians, 50 student government officers. Full-time: 1,895 students, 66% women, 34% men. Students come from 32 states and territories, 33 other countries, 32% from out-of-state, 0.1% Native American, 1% Hispanic, 1% black, 2% Asian American or Pacific Islander, 2% international, 1% 25 or older, 85% live on campus, 2% transferred in. Retention: 86% of full-time freshmen returned the following year. Academic areas with the most degrees conferred: business/marketing; education; health professions and related sciences. Core. Calendar: semesters. ESL program, services for LD students, advanced placement, honors program, independent study, double major, summer session for credit, part-time degree program, external degree program, adult/continuing education programs, internships. Off campus study at American University. Study abroad program.

Entrance Requirements: Options: Peterson's Universal Application, Common Application, electronic application, early admission, deferred admission, international baccalaureate accepted. Required: essay, high school transcript, minimum 2.0 high school GPA, 2 recommendations, SAT or ACT. Recommended: minimum 3.0 high school GPA, interview. Required for some: interview. Entrance: moderately difficult. Application deadline: Rolling.

Costs Per Year: Application fee: $30. Comprehensive fee: $34,250 includes full-time tuition ($26,950) and college room and board ($7300). College room only: $3650. Part-time tuition: $660 per credit hour.

Collegiate Environment: Orientation program. Drama-theater group, choral group, student-run newspaper, radio station. Social organizations: 85 open to all. Most popular organizations: Activities Planning Board, Student Senate, Residence Hall Association, student newspaper, Habitat for Humanity. Major annual events: Into the Streets Service Weekend, Thank God It's Spring Weekend, New Student Induction and Progressive Hike. Student services: health clinic, personal-psychological counseling. Campus security: 24-hour emergency response devices and patrols, student patrols, late night transport-escort service, self-defense workshops, crime prevention program. 1,495 college housing spaces available; all were occupied in 2003-04. Freshmen guaranteed college housing. On-campus residence required through senior year. Options: coed, women-only housing available. High Library plus 1 other with 190,261 books, 17,763 microform titles, 1,055 serials, 31,523 audiovisual materials, an OPAC, and a Web page. Operations spending for 2004 fiscal year: $955,725. 200 computers available on campus for general student use. Computer purchase/lease plans available. A campuswide network can be accessed from student residence rooms and from off campus. Staffed computer lab on campus.

Community Environment: Population 18,000. Located in Lancaster County, Elizabethtown enjoys the advantages of the neighboring communities' facilities. This suburb has a library, several churches, and major fraternal and civic organizations within the immediate locale. Some part-time employment is available.

■ ERIE BUSINESS CENTER, MAIN *B-3*

246 West Ninth St.
Erie, PA 16501-1392
Tel: (814)456-7504
Free: 800-352-3743
Fax: (814)456-4882
E-mail: welkera@eriebc.edu
Web Site: http://www.eriebc.edu/

Description: Proprietary, 2-year, coed. Awards certificates, diplomas, and terminal associate degrees. Founded 1884. Setting: 1-acre urban campus with easy access to Cleveland and Buffalo. Total enrollment: 393. Student-undergrad faculty ratio is 14:1. 261 applied, 90% were admitted. 1% from top 10% of their high school class, 10% from top quarter, 30% from top half. Full-time: 279 students, 71% women, 29% men. Part-time: 114 students, 76% women, 24% men. Students come from 3 states and territories, 2% from out-of-state, 0% Native American, 3% Hispanic, 25% black, 0% Asian American or Pacific Islander, 0% international, 38% 25 or older, 1% live on campus, 1% transferred in. Core. Calendar: trimesters. Advanced placement, independent study, summer session for credit, part-time degree program, adult/continuing education programs.

Entrance Requirements: Options: Peterson's Universal Application, Common Application, deferred admission. Required: essay, high school transcript, interview, Wonderlic aptitude test, Wonderlic aptitude test. Entrance: minimally difficult. Application deadline: Rolling. Notification: continuous.

Costs Per Year: Application fee: $25. Tuition: $7290 full-time, $243 per credit part-time. Mandatory fees: $850 full-time, $25 per credit part-time, $25 per term part-time.

Collegiate Environment: Orientation program. Drama-theater group. Most popular organizations: Student Ambassadors, Spring trip, Fall Festival, Holiday Dinner Dance, Flag football. Major annual events: pre-registration activities, Orientation, Christmas Dinner Dance. Campus security: 24-hour emergency response devices, security guard. 20 college housing spaces available; 19 were occupied in 2003-04. No special consideration for freshman housing applicants. Option: coed housing available. EBC Blackmer Library with 3,035 books, 84 serials, and an OPAC. Operations spending for 2004 fiscal year: $5000. 114 computers available on campus for general student use. A campuswide network can be accessed from off-campus. Staffed computer lab on campus.

■ ERIE BUSINESS CENTER SOUTH *H-2*

170 Cascade Galleria
New Castle, PA 16101-3950
Tel: (724)658-9066
Admissions: (724)658-3595
Fax: (724)658-3083
Web Site: http://www.eriebc.com/

Description: Proprietary, 2-year, coed. Awards diplomas, transfer associate, and terminal associate degrees. Founded 1894. Setting: 1-acre small town campus with easy access to Pittsburgh. Total enrollment: 100. 45 applied, 87% were admitted. 0% Native American, 0% Hispanic, 8% black, 0% Asian American or Pacific Islander, 0% international. Retention: 80% of full-time freshmen returned the following year. Core. Academic remediation for entering students, part-time degree program, adult/continuing education programs, internships.

Entrance Requirements: Options: Common Application, electronic application, deferred admission. Required: high school transcript. Recommended: interview, SAT and SAT Subject Tests or ACT. Entrance: moderately difficult. Application deadline: Rolling.

Collegiate Environment: Orientation program. Social organizations: 6 open to all. Most popular organizations: student government, Business Club, Medical Club, Travel Club, Ambassadors Club. Major annual events: Winter Formal, Christmas Party, Kennywood Park Fun Day. Student services: personal-psychological counseling. Campus security: 24-hour patrols. College housing not available. 1,725 books, 20 serials, and 8 audiovisual materials. 60 computers available on campus for general student use. A campuswide network can be accessed. Staffed computer lab on campus.

■ ERIE INSTITUTE OF TECHNOLOGY *B-3*

5539 Peach St.
Erie, PA 16509
Tel: (814)868-9900; (866)868-3743
Fax: (814)868-9977
Web Site: http://www.erieit.org/

Description: Proprietary, 2-year, coed. Awards diplomas and terminal associate degrees. Setting: suburban campus. Total enrollment: 173. 2% Hispanic, 2% black, 3% Asian American or Pacific Islander, 92% international. Calendar: 4 3-month terms.

Entrance Requirements: Entrance: minimally difficult. Application deadline: Rolling. Notification: continuous.

■ FRANKLIN AND MARSHALL COLLEGE *M-19*

PO Box 3003
Lancaster, PA 17604-3003
Tel: (717)291-3911
Admissions: (717)291-3953
Fax: (717)291-4389
E-mail: admission@fandm.edu
Web Site: http://www.fandm.edu/

Description: Independent, 4-year, coed. Awards bachelor's degrees. Founded 1787. Setting: 125-acre suburban campus with easy access to Philadelphia. Endowment: $327.4 million. Research spending for 2004 fiscal year: $215,600. Educational spending for 2005 fiscal year: $15,045 per student. Total enrollment: 2,025. Student-undergrad faculty ratio is 11:1. 4,227 applied, 45% were admitted. 54% from top 10% of their high school class, 83% from top quarter, 97% from top half. Full-time: 1,982 students, 47% women, 53% men. Part-time: 43 students, 30% women, 70% men. Students come from 40 states and territories, 40 other countries, 65% from out-of-state, 0.1% Native American, 4% Hispanic, 3% black, 4% Asian American or Pacific Islander, 7% international, 0% 25 or older, 66% live on campus, 1% transferred in. Retention: 92% of full-time freshmen returned the following year. Academic areas with the most degrees conferred: social sciences; health professions and related sciences; English. Core. Calendar: semesters. Advanced placement, accelerated degree program, self-designed majors, honors program, independent study, double major, summer session for credit, internships. Off campus study at National Theater Institute, School of Visual Arts, American University. Study abroad program.

Entrance Requirements: Options: Peterson's Universal Application, Common Application, electronic application, early admission, early decision, deferred admission, international baccalaureate accepted. Required: essay, high school transcript, 2 recommendations, SAT or ACT. Recommended: interview. Entrance: very difficult. Application deadlines: 2/1, 11/15 for early decision plan 1, 1/15 for early decision plan 2. Notification: 4/1, 12/15 for early decision plan 1, 2/15 for early decision plan 2.

Costs Per Year: Application fee: $50. Comprehensive fee: $40,590 includes full-time tuition ($32,480), mandatory fees ($50), and college room and board ($8060). College room only: $5250. Full-time tuition and fees vary according to reciprocity agreements. Room and board charges vary according to board plan and housing facility. Part-time tuition: $4060 per course. Part-time tuition varies according to course load.

Collegiate Environment: Orientation program. Drama-theater group, choral group, student-run newspaper, radio station. Social organizations: 120 open to all; national fraternities, national sororities; 35% of eligible men and 13% of eligible women are members. Most popular organizations: Women's Center, Ware Institute for Community Service, College Reporter, Ben's Underground, F&M Players. Major annual events: homecoming, Spring Arts, Fall Arts. Student services: health clinic, personal-psychological counseling, women's center. Campus security: 24-hour emergency response devices and patrols, late night transport-escort service, controlled dormitory access, residence hall security, campus security connected to city police and fire company. 1,270 college housing spaces available; all were occupied in 2003-04. Freshmen guaranteed college housing. On-campus residence required through sophomore year. Options: coed, men-only, women-only housing available. Shadek-Fackenthal Library plus 1 other with 479,127 books, 527,288 microform titles, 2,278 serials, 13,055 audiovisual materials, an OPAC, and a Web page. Operations spending for 2004 fiscal year: $3.1 million. 139 computers available on campus for general student use. Computer purchase/lease plans available. A campuswide network can be accessed from student residence rooms and from off campus. Staffed computer lab on campus.

Community Environment: Metropolitan area of 300,000; vital, historic city.

■ GANNON UNIVERSITY *B-3*

University Square
Erie, PA 16541-0001
Tel: (814)871-7000
Free: 800-GAN-NONU
Admissions: (814)871-7240
Fax: (814)871-5803
Web Site: http://www.gannon.edu/

Description: Independent Roman Catholic, comprehensive, coed. Awards bachelor's, master's, and doctoral degrees and post-master's certificates (associate). Founded 1925. Setting: 13-acre urban campus with easy access to Cleveland. Endowment: $25.2 million. Research spending for 2004 fiscal year: $1.1 million. Educational spending for 2005 fiscal year: $6530 per student. Total enrollment: 3,590. Faculty: 299 (180 full-time, 119 part-time). Student-undergrad faculty ratio is 11:1. 2,443 applied, 86% were admitted. 21% from top 10% of their high school class, 48% from top quarter, 76% from top half. 16 valedictorians. Full-time: 2,184 students, 59% women, 41% men. Part-time: 390 students, 62% women, 38% men. Students come from 30 states and territories, 11 other countries, 22% from out-of-state, 0.2% Native American, 1% Hispanic, 5% black, 1% Asian American or Pacific Islander, 1% international, 12% 25 or older, 54% live on campus, 3% transferred in. Retention: 83% of full-time freshmen returned the following year. Academic areas with the most degrees conferred: health professions and related sciences; business/marketing; education. Core. Calendar: semesters plus 2 summer sessions. Academic remediation for entering students, ESL program, services for LD students, advanced placement, accelerated degree program, honors program, independent study, distance learning, double major, summer session for credit, part-time degree program, external degree program, adult/continuing education programs, co-op programs and internships, graduate courses open to undergrads. Off campus study at Mercyhurst College and Edinboro University. Study abroad program. ROTC: Army.

Entrance Requirements: Options: Peterson's Universal Application, Common Application, electronic application, early admission, deferred admission, international baccalaureate accepted. Required: high school transcript, minimum 2.0 high school GPA, counselor's recommendation, SAT or ACT. Recommended: essay. Required for some: minimum 3.0 high school GPA, 3 recommendations, interview. Entrance: moderately difficult. Application deadline: Rolling.

Costs Per Year: Application fee: $25. Comprehensive fee: $26,100 includes full-time tuition ($18,220), mandatory fees ($470), and college room and board ($7410). College room only: $4020. Full-time tuition and fees vary according to class time and program. Room and board charges vary according to board plan and housing facility. Part-time tuition: $565 per credit hour. Part-time mandatory fees: $15 per credit hour. Part-time tuition and fees vary according to class time and program.

Collegiate Environment: Orientation program. Drama-theater group, student-run newspaper, radio station. Social organizations: 63 open to all; national fraternities, national sororities. Most popular organizations: Model United Nations, Vitality Through Exercise, Gannon University Residence Union. Major annual events: Homecoming, Distinguished Speaker Series, Family Weekend. Student services: health clinic, personal-psychological counseling. Campus security: 24-hour emergency response devices and patrols, student patrols, late night transport-escort service, controlled dormitory access, security cameras. 1,133 college housing spaces available; 1,121 were occupied in 2003-04. Freshmen guaranteed college housing. On-campus residence required through sophomore year. Option: coed housing available. Nash Library plus 1 other with 270,282 books, 186,581 microform titles, 6,292 serials, 3,028 audiovisual materials, an OPAC, and a Web page. Operations spending for 2004 fiscal year: $1.2 million. 175 computers available on campus for general student use. A campuswide network can be accessed from student residence rooms and from off campus. Staffed computer lab on campus.

Community Environment: Pennsylvania's third largest city and its only port on the Great Lakes, Erie is a city of widely diversified industry and commerce. A public library was built on the waterfront and an observation tower to celebrate the city's bicentennial. The area is served by rail, air, and bus lines. The community has many churches representing the major denominations, numerous civic and fraternal organizations, and community health clinics and hospitals. Local facilities include theatres, restaurants, shops, golf courses, city parks, Presque Isle State Park, fishing, ice fishing, boating, beach volleyball, and skating. Part-time employment opportunities are excellent.

■ **GENEVA COLLEGE** A-28
3200 College Ave.
Beaver Falls, PA 15010-3599
Tel: (724)846-5100
Free: 800-847-8255
Fax: (724)847-6687
Web Site: http://www.geneva.edu/
Description: Independent, comprehensive, coed, affiliated with Reformed Presbyterian Church of North America. Awards associate, bachelor's, and master's degrees. Founded 1848. Setting: 55-acre small town campus with easy access to Pittsburgh. Endowment: $28.6 million. Educational spending for 2005 fiscal year: $15,776 per student. Total enrollment: 2,141. 1,690 applied, 68% were admitted. 15% from top 10% of their high school class, 22% from top quarter, 24% from top half. 2 National Merit Scholars, 14 valedictorians. Students come from 33 states and territories, 17 other countries, 27% from out-of-state, 0.3% Native American, 1% Hispanic, 4% black, 1% Asian American or Pacific Islander, 1% international, 24% 25 or older, 69% live on campus. Retention: 77% of full-time freshmen returned the following year. Core. Calendar: semesters. Academic remediation for entering students, ESL program, services for LD students, advanced placement, accelerated degree program, self-designed majors, honors program, independent study, double major, summer session for credit, adult/continuing education programs, co-op programs and internships, graduate courses

open to undergrads. Off campus study at Coalition for Christian Colleges and Universities, Community College of Beaver County, University of Rochester. Study abroad program. ROTC: Army (c).

Entrance Requirements: Options: Peterson's Universal Application, Common Application, electronic application, early admission, deferred admission. Required: essay, high school transcript, minimum 2.0 high school GPA, recommendations, SAT and SAT Subject Tests or ACT. Recommended: minimum 3.0 high school GPA, interview. Required for some: interview. Entrance: moderately difficult. Application deadline: Rolling. Notification: continuous.

Costs Per Year: Application fee: $25. Comprehensive fee: $24,245 includes full-time tuition ($16,910), mandatory fees ($565), and college room and board ($6770). College room only: $3530. Full-time tuition and fees vary according to course load. Room and board charges vary according to board plan and housing facility. Part-time tuition: $565 per credit. Part-time tuition varies according to course load.

Collegiate Environment: Orientation program. Drama-theater group, choral group, marching band, student-run newspaper, radio station. Social organizations: 50 open to all. Most popular organizations: marching band, Genevans A Capella Choir, ministry groups, International Student Organization, discipleship. Major annual events: homecoming, The Big Event, Midnight Madness. Student services: health clinic, personal-psychological counseling. Campus security: 24-hour emergency response devices and patrols, late night transport-escort service, controlled dormitory access. 994 college housing spaces available; 970 were occupied in 2003-04. Freshmen guaranteed college housing. On-campus residence required through senior year. Options: men-only, women-only housing available. McCartney Library plus 5 others with 163,734 books, 223,044 microform titles, 857 serials, 13,767 audiovisual materials, an OPAC, and a Web page. Operations spending for 2004 fiscal year: $850,000. 150 computers available on campus for general student use. A campuswide network can be accessed from student residence rooms and from off campus. Staffed computer lab on campus.

Community Environment: Rich in natural resources and historical heritage, Beaver County supports commercial and industrial growth as well as a thriving agribusiness enterprise. 18,000 acres of park lands, excellent health care facilities, and numerous churches of various denominations help to meet needs of residents. Public transportation is accessible and proximity to Pittsburgh makes cultural and professional sports events available year-round. Part-time employment is available.

■ **GETTYSBURG COLLEGE** N-15
300 North Washington St.
Gettysburg, PA 17325-1483
Tel: (717)337-6000
Free: 800-431-0803
Admissions: (717)337-6100
Fax: (717)337-6008
E-mail: admiss@gettysburg.edu
Web Site: http://www.gettysburg.edu/
Description: Independent, 4-year, coed, affiliated with Evangelical Lutheran Church in America. Awards bachelor's degrees. Founded 1832. Setting: 230-acre suburban campus with easy access to Baltimore and Washington, DC. Endowment: $218.7 million. Total enrollment: 2,463. Student-undergrad faculty ratio is 11:1. 5,097 applied, 43% were admitted. 66% from top 10% of their high school class, 89% from top quarter, 100% from top half. Full-time: 2,454 students, 52% women, 48% men. Part-time: 9 students, 44% women, 56% men. Students come from 40 states and territories, 32 other countries, 72% from out-of-state, 0.1% Native American, 2% Hispanic, 4% black, 1% Asian American or Pacific Islander, 1% international, 1% 25 or older, 94% live on campus, 1% transferred in. Retention: 92% of full-time freshmen returned the following year. Academic areas with the most degrees conferred: business/marketing; social sciences; biological/life sciences. Core. Calendar: semesters. Advanced placement, self-designed majors, independent study, double major, adult/continuing education programs, internships. Off campus study at 2 members of the Central Pennsylvania Consortium. Study abroad program. ROTC: Army (c).

Entrance Requirements: Options: Common Application, electronic application, early admission, early decision, deferred admission, international baccalaureate accepted. Required: essay, high school transcript, 2 recommendations, SAT or ACT. Recommended: minimum 3.0 high school GPA, interview, extracurricular activities, SAT Subject Tests. Entrance: most difficult. Application deadlines: 2/15, 11/15 for early decision plan 1, 1/15 for early decision plan 2. Notification: 4/1, 12/15 for early decision plan 1, 2/15 for early decision plan 2.

Costs Per Year: Application fee: $45. Comprehensive fee: $39,864 includes full-time tuition ($31,790), mandatory fees ($280), and college room and board ($7794). College room only: $4134. Room and board charges vary according to board plan and housing facility. Part-time tuition: $3450 per course.

Collegiate Environment: Orientation program. Drama-theater group, choral group, marching band, student-run newspaper, radio station. Social organizations: 100 open to all; national fraternities, national sororities; 40% of eligible men and 26% of eligible women are members. Most popular organizations: community service, music; athletics, student government. Major annual events: family weekend programs, Common Hour programs, Snowball. Student services: health clinic, personal-psychological counseling, women's center. Campus security: 24-hour emergency response devices and patrols, late night transport-escort service, controlled dormitory access. 2,220 college housing spaces available; all were occupied in 2003-04. Freshmen guaranteed college housing. On-campus residence required in freshman year. Option: coed housing available. Mussleman Library with 351,848 books, 62,303 microform titles, 4,778 serials, 21,752 audiovisual materials, an OPAC, and a Web page.

Community Environment: Historic area of 20,000 with easy access to Harrisburg, PA, Washington, DC, and Baltimore, MD. The college borders the town and the 3800-acre National Park. A wide variety of recreational opportunities are available.

■ GRATZ COLLEGE *M-24*

7605 Old York Rd.
Melrose Park, PA 19027
Tel: (215)635-7300
Free: 800-475-4635
Fax: (215)635-7320
E-mail: admissions@gratz.edu
Web Site: http://www.gratzcollege.edu/

Description: Independent Jewish, comprehensive, coed. Awards bachelor's and master's degrees and post-master's certificates. Founded 1895. Setting: 28-acre suburban campus with easy access to Philadelphia. Total enrollment: 696. Faculty: 14 (8 full-time, 6 part-time). Student-undergrad faculty ratio is 12:1. 7 applied, 71% were admitted. Full-time: 6 students, 83% women, 17% men. Part-time: 10 students, 90% women, 10% men. Students come from 5 states and territories, 44% from out-of-state, 90% 25 or older, 31% transferred in. Retention: 100% of full-time freshmen returned the following year. Core. Calendar: semesters. Independent study, double major, summer session for credit, part-time degree program, adult/continuing education programs, internships, graduate courses open to undergrads. Study abroad program.

Entrance Requirements: Open admission. Options: electronic application, early admission, deferred admission. Required: essay, high school transcript, recommendations. Required for some: interview. Entrance: moderately difficult. Application deadline: Rolling. Notification: continuous.

Collegiate Environment: Orientation program. Choral group. Major annual events: College President's Annual Student Reception, Abramson Fellowship Concert. Campus security: 24-hour patrols. College housing not available. Tuttleman Library with 100,000 books, 175 serials, 380 audiovisual materials, and an OPAC. 2 computers available on campus for general student use. A campuswide network can be accessed from off-campus.

Community Environment: All the amenities of Greater Philadelphia's cultural and academic environment (museums, concert halls, colleges and universities, etc.) are available and accessible to Gratz's multifaceted student body by either private or public transportation. A large, diverse and well-organized Jewish community enables those interested in an active Jewish communal life to thrive.

■ GROVE CITY COLLEGE *G-3*

100 Campus Dr.
Grove City, PA 16127-2104
Tel: (724)458-2000
Admissions: (724)458-2100
Fax: (724)458-3395
E-mail: jcmincey@gcc.edu
Web Site: http://www.gcc.edu/

Description: Independent Presbyterian, 4-year, coed. Awards bachelor's degrees. Founded 1876. Setting: 150-acre small town campus with easy access to Pittsburgh. Total enrollment: 2,341. Student-undergrad faculty ratio is 16:1. 2,077 applied, 45% were admitted. 54% from top 10% of their high school class, 83% from top quarter, 95% from top half. 19 National Merit

Scholars, 2 class presidents, 53 valedictorians, 274 student government officers. Full-time: 2,308 students, 49% women, 51% men. Part-time: 33 students, 61% women, 39% men. Students come from 44 states and territories, 14 other countries, 49% from out-of-state, 0.1% Native American, 0.4% Hispanic, 0.3% black, 2% Asian American or Pacific Islander, 1% international, 0% 25 or older, 90% live on campus, 1% transferred in. Retention: 91% of full-time freshmen returned the following year. Academic areas with the most degrees conferred: business/marketing; education; biological/life sciences. Core. Calendar: semesters. Advanced placement, self-designed majors, independent study, double major, summer session for credit, internships. Study abroad program. ROTC: Army (c).

Entrance Requirements: Options: Peterson's Universal Application, electronic application, early admission, early decision, deferred admission, international baccalaureate accepted. Required: essay, high school transcript, 2 recommendations, SAT or ACT. Recommended: interview. Entrance: most difficult. Application deadlines: 2/1, 11/15 for early decision. Notification: 3/15, 12/15 for early decision.

Costs Per Year: Application fee: $50. Comprehensive fee: $15,984 includes full-time tuition ($10,440), mandatory fees ($200), and college room and board ($5344). Full-time tuition and fees vary according to course load. Part-time tuition: $334 per credit.

Collegiate Environment: Orientation program. Drama-theater group, choral group, marching band, student-run newspaper, radio station. Social organizations: 123 open to all; local fraternities, local sororities; 15% of eligible men and 17% of eligible women are members. Most popular organizations: Salt Company, Warriors for Christ, orientation board, Orchesis, touring choir. Major annual events: homecoming, Parents' Weekend, President's Gala. Student services: health clinic, personal-psychological counseling. Campus security: 24-hour emergency response devices and patrols, student patrols, late night transport-escort service, controlled dormitory access, monitored women's residence hall entrances. 2,030 college housing spaces available; all were occupied in 2003-04. Freshmen guaranteed college housing. On-campus residence required through senior year. Options: men-only, women-only housing available. Henry Buhl Library with 139,000 books, 263,000 microform titles, 550 serials, and an OPAC.

Community Environment: Grove City, population 8,000, is an urban community that produces compressors, gas and diesel engines, soldering equipment and linemen's supplies. The city has a hospital, several churches, a library, theatre, YMCA, and various civic and fraternal organizations. You can experience big-city shopping at the Grove City Factory Shops located just outside of town. Local recreation includes hunting, fishing, golf, football, baseball, swimming, tennis, basketball, bowling, boating, and ice and roller skating.

■ GWYNEDD-MERCY COLLEGE *L-23*

Sumneytown Pike
PO Box 901
Gwynedd Valley, PA 19437-0901
Tel: (215)646-7300
Fax: (215)641-5556
Web Site: http://www.gmc.edu/

Description: Independent Roman Catholic, comprehensive, coed. Awards associate, bachelor's, and master's degrees and post-master's certificates. Founded 1948. Setting: 170-acre suburban campus with easy access to Philadelphia. Endowment: $7.3 million. Educational spending for 2005 fiscal year: $6281 per student. Total enrollment: 2,723. Faculty: 274 (78 full-time, 196 part-time). Student-undergrad faculty ratio is 13:1. 1,622 applied, 65% were admitted. 4% from top 10% of their high school class, 20% from top quarter, 58% from top half. Full-time: 1,273 students, 75% women, 25% men. Part-time: 907 students, 75% women, 25% men. Students come from 8 states and territories, 49 other countries, 6% from out-of-state, 0.3% Native American, 2% Hispanic, 14% black, 3% Asian American or Pacific Islander, 1% international, 43% 25 or older, 20% live on campus, 10% transferred in. Retention: 79% of full-time freshmen returned the following year. Academic areas with the most degrees conferred: business/marketing; education; health professions and related sciences. Core. Calendar: semesters. Academic remediation for entering students, ESL program, advanced placement, accelerated degree program, freshman honors college, honors program, independent study, double major, summer session for credit, part-time degree program, adult/continuing education programs, co-op programs and internships, graduate courses open to undergrads.

Entrance Requirements: Options: Peterson's Universal Application, Common Application, electronic application, early admission, deferred admission.

Required: high school transcript, 1 recommendation, SAT or ACT. Recommended: interview. Required for some: interview. Entrance: moderately difficult. Application deadline: Rolling. Notification: continuous.

Costs Per Year: Application fee: $25. Comprehensive fee: $27,520 includes full-time tuition ($18,720), mandatory fees ($500), and college room and board ($8300). Part-time tuition: $415 per credit. Part-time mandatory fees: $10 per credit.

Collegiate Environment: Orientation program. Drama-theater group, choral group, student-run newspaper. Social organizations: 20 open to all. Most popular organizations: Voices of Gwynedd, Athletic Association, student government, Program Board, Peer Mentors. Major annual events: Family Day, Carol Night, International Night. Student services: health clinic, personal-psychological counseling. Campus security: 24-hour emergency response devices and patrols, late night transport-escort service. College housing designed to accommodate 387 students; 441 undergraduates lived in college housing during 2003-04. Freshmen given priority for college housing. Option: coed housing available. Lourdes Library plus 1 other with 99,493 books, 15,140 microform titles, 685 serials, 11,056 audiovisual materials, an OPAC, and a Web page. Operations spending for 2004 fiscal year: $617,668. 97 computers available on campus for general student use. Computer purchase/lease plans available. A campuswide network can be accessed from student residence rooms and from off campus. Staffed computer lab on campus.

Community Environment: Gwynedd Valley is a suburban location with the community located 20 miles from Center City, Philadelphia, which has cultural, recreational, and community service opportunities. The immediate locale has churches, recreational facilities, shopping malls, movies and restaurants.

■ **HARCUM COLLEGE** *E-45*

750 Montgomery Ave.
Bryn Mawr, PA 19010-3476
Tel: (610)525-4100
Free: 800-345-2600
Admissions: (610)526-6153
Fax: (610)526-6147
Web Site: http://www.harcum.edu/

Description: Independent, 2-year, coed. Awards certificates, transfer associate, and terminal associate degrees. Founded 1915. Setting: 12-acre suburban campus with easy access to Philadelphia. Endowment: $9 million. Educational spending for 2005 fiscal year: $1500 per student. Total enrollment: 573. Student-undergrad faculty ratio is 9:1. 1,086 applied, 2% were admitted. 40% from top half of their high school class. Full-time: 385 students, 92% women, 8% men. Part-time: 188 students, 80% women, 20% men. Students come from 8 states and territories, 6 other countries, 10% from out-of-state, 40% 25 or older, 23% live on campus, 21% transferred in. Retention: 90% of full-time freshmen returned the following year. Core. Calendar: semesters. Academic remediation for entering students, ESL program, services for LD students, advanced placement, honors program, independent study, distance learning, double major, summer session for credit, part-time degree program, adult/continuing education programs, internships. Off campus study.

Entrance Requirements: Options: Peterson's Universal Application, Common Application, electronic application, early admission, deferred admission. Required: essay, high school transcript, recommendations, SAT or ACT. Recommended: interview. Entrance: minimally difficult. Application deadline: Rolling. Notification: continuous.

Costs Per Year: Application fee: $25. Comprehensive fee: $22,596 includes full-time tuition ($15,250), mandatory fees ($100), and college room and board ($7246). Part-time tuition: $508 per credit.

Collegiate Environment: Orientation program. Choral group, student-run newspaper. Social organizations: 12 open to all. Most popular organizations: OATS (Organization for Animal Tech Students), Student Association of Dental Hygienist of America, Ebony Club, Dental Assisting Club, FLA International Club. Major annual events: College Transfer Fair, Student Leadership Banquet, Health and Wellness Fair. Student services: health clinic, personal-psychological counseling, women's center. Campus security: 24-hour emergency response devices and patrols, controlled dormitory access. 350 college housing spaces available; 110 were occupied in 2003-04. Freshmen guaranteed college housing. Options: coed, women-only housing available. Main library plus 1 other with 39,000 books, 300 serials, and 1,000 audiovisual materials. Operations spending for 2004 fiscal year: $235,319. 65 computers available on campus for general student use. Staffed computer lab on campus.

Community Environment: Located in Bryn Mawr, Harcum College is neighbor to Villanova University, St. Joseph's University, Bryn Mawr College, Cabrini College, Eastern College, among others. Historical and residential, the local community offers many shops, banks, and activities for students. The city of Philadelphia is just 25 minutes away by car or train.

■ **HARRISBURG AREA COMMUNITY COLLEGE** *L-17*

1 HACC Dr.
Harrisburg, PA 17110-2999
Tel: (717)780-2300
Fax: (717)231-7674
Web Site: http://www.hacc.edu/

Description: State and locally supported, 2-year, coed. Awards certificates, diplomas, transfer associate, and terminal associate degrees. Founded 1964. Setting: 212-acre urban campus. Endowment: $31.9 million. Research spending for 2004 fiscal year: $15,900. Educational spending for 2005 fiscal year: $4600 per student. Total enrollment: 16,899. Student-undergrad faculty ratio is 20:1. 7,655 applied, 98% were admitted. Full-time: 6,634 students, 58% women, 42% men. Part-time: 10,265 students, 70% women, 30% men. Students come from 14 states and territories, 8 other countries, 1% from out-of-state, 0.3% Native American, 5% Hispanic, 9% black, 3% Asian American or Pacific Islander, 1% international, 48% 25 or older, 29% transferred in. Core. Calendar: semesters. Academic remediation for entering students, ESL program, services for LD students, advanced placement, self-designed majors, honors program, independent study, distance learning, double major, summer session for credit, part-time degree program, adult/continuing education programs, internships. Study abroad program. ROTC: Army.

Entrance Requirements: Open admission except for allied health, chef's apprenticeship programs. Options: electronic application, early admission. Required: high school transcript. Entrance: noncompetitive. Application deadline: Rolling.

Costs Per Year: Application fee: $30. Area resident tuition: $2850 full-time, $95 per credit hour part-time. State resident tuition: $5250 full-time, $175 per credit hour part-time. Nonresident tuition: $7650 full-time, $255 per credit hour part-time. Mandatory fees: $510 full-time, $17 per credit hour part-time.

Collegiate Environment: Drama-theater group, student-run newspaper, radio station. Social organizations: 28 open to all. Most popular organizations: Student Government Association, Phi Theta Kappa, African American Student Association, Mosiaco Club, Fourth Estate. Student services: personal-psychological counseling. Campus security: 24-hour emergency response devices and patrols, late night transport-escort service. College housing not available. McCormick Library with 119,000 books, 10,742 microform titles, 873 serials, 12,733 audiovisual materials, an OPAC, and a Web page. Operations spending for 2004 fiscal year: $900,812. 974 computers available on campus for general student use. A campuswide network can be accessed from off-campus. Staffed computer lab on campus.

Community Environment: Population 68,061. On the Susquehanna River, Harrisburg lies between mountains which rise abruptly to the north and west and rolling hills which slope to the south and east. Extensive coal and iron mines in the vicinity furnish raw materials for the city's large steel plants. Part-time employment opportunities are good. Harrisburg is a metropolitan area served by airlines, railroad, and bus lines. The community has state and public libraries, a State Museum, several hospitals, and major civic, fraternal and veteran's organizations. Shopping facilities are excellent. Local recreational opportunities include theatres, summer theatres, parks, golf, professional hockey, and water sports.

■ **HAVERFORD COLLEGE** *M-23*

370 Lancaster Ave.
Haverford, PA 19041-1392
Tel: (610)896-1000
Admissions: (610)896-1350
Fax: (610)896-1338
E-mail: admitme@haverford.edu
Web Site: http://www.haverford.edu/

Description: Independent, 4-year, coed. Awards bachelor's degrees. Founded 1833. Setting: 200-acre suburban campus with easy access to Philadelphia. Endowment: $894.7 million. Total enrollment: 1,168. Student-undergrad faculty ratio is 8:1. 3,112 applied, 26% were admitted. 91% from top 10% of their high school class, 96% from top quarter, 100% from top half. Full-time: 1,168 students, 53% women, 47% men. Students come from 53 states and territories, 39 other countries, 85% from out-of-state, 1% Native American, 8% Hispanic, 7% black, 13% Asian American or Pacific Islander,

4% international, 0% 25 or older, 99% live on campus, 0% transferred in. Retention: 97% of full-time freshmen returned the following year. Academic areas with the most degrees conferred: social sciences; biological/life sciences; English; history; physical sciences. Core. Calendar: semesters. Services for LD students, advanced placement, accelerated degree program, self-designed majors, independent study, double major, internships. Off campus study at University of Pennsylvania, Swarthmore College, Bryn Mawr College. Study abroad program.

Entrance Requirements: Options: Common Application, electronic application, early admission, early decision, deferred admission, international baccalaureate accepted. Required: essay, 2 recommendations, SAT Reasoning Test or ACT and two SAT Subject Tests. Recommended: interview. Entrance: most difficult. Application deadlines: 1/15, 11/15 for early decision. Notification: 4/15, 12/15 for early decision. Preference given to children of alumni, to the extent possible.

Costs Per Year: Application fee: $60. Comprehensive fee: $41,600 includes full-time tuition ($31,466), mandatory fees ($294), and college room and board ($9840). College room only: $5540.

Collegiate Environment: Orientation program. Drama-theater group, choral group, student-run newspaper, radio station. Social organizations: 50 open to all. Most popular organizations: volunteer programs, student government, choral groups, multicultural groups, orientation team/residential life leaders. Major annual events: Haverfest/May Day, Snowball, athletic events against Swarthmore. Student services: health clinic, personal-psychological counseling, women's center. Campus security: 24-hour emergency response devices and patrols, late night transport-escort service. 1,156 undergraduates lived in college housing during 2003-04. Freshmen guaranteed college housing. On-campus residence required in freshman year. Options: coed, men-only, women-only housing available. Magill Library plus 4 others with 395,799 books, 88,828 microform titles, 3,240 serials, 10,716 audiovisual materials, an OPAC, and a Web page. 300 computers available on campus for general student use. A campuswide network can be accessed from student residence rooms and from off campus. Staffed computer lab on campus.

Community Environment: The school has cooperative arrangements with several colleges and universities (see Bryn Mawr College, Swarthmore College, University of Pennsylvania) and is located near many colleges and universities in metropolitan Philadelphia area.

■ **HOLY FAMILY UNIVERSITY** *M-24*
Grant and Frankford Avenues
Philadelphia, PA 19114-2094
Tel: (215)637-7700
Free: 800-637-1191
Admissions: (215)637-3050
Fax: (215)281-1022
Web Site: http://www.holyfamily.edu/

Description: Independent Roman Catholic, comprehensive, coed. Awards associate, bachelor's, and master's degrees. Founded 1954. Setting: 47-acre suburban campus. Endowment: $5.2 million. Educational spending for 2005 fiscal year: $4500 per student. Total enrollment: 2,670. 573 applied, 77% were admitted. 11% from top 10% of their high school class, 33% from top quarter, 73% from top half. Full-time: 1,086 students, 75% women, 25% men. Part-time: 696 students, 73% women, 27% men. Students come from 7 states and territories, 3 other countries, 12% from out-of-state, 0.1% Native American, 2% Hispanic, 3% black, 3% Asian American or Pacific Islander, 0.3% international, 36% 25 or older, 9% transferred in. Retention: 82% of full-time freshmen returned the following year. Core. Calendar: semesters. Academic remediation for entering students, services for LD students, advanced placement, accelerated degree program, freshman honors college, honors program, independent study, double major, summer session for credit, part-time degree program, adult/continuing education programs, co-op programs and internships, graduate courses open to undergrads. Study abroad program.

Entrance Requirements: Options: Common Application, deferred admission, international baccalaureate accepted. Required: essay, high school transcript, 1 recommendation, SAT or ACT. Recommended: interview. Entrance: moderately difficult. Application deadline: Rolling.

Costs Per Year: Application fee: $25. Comprehensive fee: $25,740 includes full-time tuition ($17,240), mandatory fees ($500), and college room and board ($8000). College room only: $4700. Full-time tuition and fees vary according to course load and program. Part-time tuition: $380 per credit hour. Part-time mandatory fees: $60 per term. Part-time tuition and fees vary according to program.

Collegiate Environment: Orientation program. Drama-theater group, student-run newspaper. Social organizations: 7 open to all. Most popular organizations: Students at Your Service (S.A.Y.S.), Rainbow Connections, Campus Ministry Team, Folio, Tri-lite. Major annual events: Christmas Rose, Charter Day, Buddy Day. Student services: health clinic, personal-psychological counseling. Campus security: 24-hour emergency response devices and patrols, student patrols, late night transport-escort service. Holy Family College Library plus 1 other with 126,780 books, 3,337 microform titles, 742 serials, 1,875 audiovisual materials, and an OPAC. Operations spending for 2004 fiscal year: $703,015. 148 computers available on campus for general student use. A campuswide network can be accessed. Staffed computer lab on campus.

Community Environment: The main campus of Holy Family College is located on 46 acres in the residential Torresdale section of northeast Philadelphia near the boundary with Bucks County, Pennsylvania. The main campus is easily reached by public transportation. The Newtown campus is located on 85 acres in the heart of suburban Bucks County, Pennsylvania. It is situated very close to the Newtown exit of Interstate-95.

■ **HUSSIAN SCHOOL OF ART** *M-24*
1118 Market St.
Philadelphia, PA 19107-3679
Tel: (215)981-0900
Fax: (215)864-9115
E-mail: info@hussianart.edu
Web Site: http://www.hussianart.edu/

Description: Proprietary, 4-year, coed. Awards associate degrees. Founded 1946. Setting: 1-acre urban campus. Total enrollment: 155. Student-undergrad faculty ratio is 18:1. 101 applied, 94% were admitted. Full-time: 155 students, 36% women, 64% men. Students come from 4 states and territories, 20% from out-of-state, 0% Native American, 3% Hispanic, 12% black, 2% Asian American or Pacific Islander, 0% international, 2% 25 or older, 0% transferred in. Retention: 90% of full-time freshmen returned the following year. Core. Calendar: semesters. Independent study, internships.

Entrance Requirements: Options: Common Application, deferred admission. Required: high school transcript, interview, art portfolio. Entrance: minimally difficult. Application deadline: Rolling. Notification: continuous.

Costs Per Year: Application fee: $25. Tuition: $10,000 full-time. Mandatory fees: $465 full-time.

Collegiate Environment: Campus security: security guard during open hours. College housing not available. Main library plus 1 other with 194,587 books. 58 computers available on campus for general student use. A campuswide network can be accessed. Staffed computer lab on campus.

■ **ICM SCHOOL OF BUSINESS & MEDICAL CAREERS** *K-3*
10 Wood St. at Fort Pitt Blvd.
Pittsburgh, PA 15222-1977
Tel: (412)261-2647
Free: 800-441-5222
E-mail: mrosenberg@icmschool.com
Web Site: http://www.icmschool.com/

Description: Proprietary, 2-year, coed. Awards diplomas, transfer associate, and terminal associate degrees. Founded 1963. Setting: urban campus. Total enrollment: 1,095. 496 applied, 63% were admitted. 1% from top 10% of their high school class, 20% from top quarter, 35% from top half. Full-time: 1,065 students, 69% women, 31% men. Part-time: 30 students, 100% women. Students come from 3 states and territories, 2% from out-of-state, 0.5% Native American, 1% Hispanic, 48% black, 0.3% Asian American or Pacific Islander, 0.1% international, 45% 25 or older. Core. Calendar: continuous. Academic remediation for entering students, advanced placement, independent study, summer session for credit, part-time degree program, co-op programs and internships.

Entrance Requirements: Option: Common Application. Required: essay, high school transcript, interview, Wonderlic aptitude test, CPAt. Required for some: SAT and SAT Subject Tests or ACT. Entrance: moderately difficult. Application deadline: Rolling. Notification: continuous.

Costs Per Year: Application fee: $30. Tuition: $24,400 full-time. Mandatory fees: $130 full-time.

Collegiate Environment: Orientation program. Most popular organizations: Association of Information Technology Professionals, American Association of Information Professionals, Student Activities Association, American Association of Medical Assistants, Travel and Tourism Club. Major annual events: Annual Picnic, Christmas Dance. Campus security: 24-hour emergency response devices, evening security personnel. College housing not available. ICM Learning Resource Center with 3,100 books and 48 serials. 120 computers available on campus for general student use. Staffed computer lab on campus.

■ IMMACULATA UNIVERSITY *M-22*

1145 King Rd.
Immaculata, PA 19345
Tel: (610)647-4400; 877-428-6328
Fax: (610)251-1668
E-mail: admiss@immaculata.edu
Web Site: http://www.immaculata.edu/

Description: Independent Roman Catholic, comprehensive, coed. Awards associate, bachelor's, master's, and doctoral degrees. Founded 1920. Setting: 400-acre suburban campus with easy access to Philadelphia. Endowment: $13.2 million. Educational spending for 2005 fiscal year: $11,463 per student. Total enrollment: 4,019. Faculty: 297 (87 full-time, 210 part-time). Student-undergrad faculty ratio is 12:1. 1,394 applied, 80% were admitted. Full-time: 691 students, 79% women, 21% men. Part-time: 2,326 students, 79% women, 21% men. 32% from out-of-state, 0.1% Native American, 2% Hispanic, 7% black, 1% Asian American or Pacific Islander, 1% international, 75% live on campus, 1% transferred in. Retention: 69% of full-time freshmen returned the following year. Academic areas with the most degrees conferred: health professions and related sciences; business/marketing; psychology. Core. Calendar: semesters. Academic remediation for entering students, ESL program, services for LD students, advanced placement, accelerated degree program, honors program, independent study, double major, summer session for credit, part-time degree program, external degree program, adult/continuing education programs, internships. Off campus study at South Eastern Pennsylvania Consortium for Higher Education. Multiple off campus Immaculata University locations. Study abroad program.
Entrance Requirements: Options: Peterson's Universal Application, Common Application, electronic application, early action, deferred admission. Required: high school transcript, minimum 2.0 high school GPA, SAT or ACT. Recommended: minimum 3.0 high school GPA, interview, SAT and SAT Subject Tests or ACT. Required for some: essay. Entrance: moderately difficult. Application deadline: 8/15. Notification: 8/15.
Costs Per Year: Application fee: $35. Comprehensive fee: $29,910 includes full-time tuition ($20,575) and college room and board ($9335). College room only: $5010. Part-time tuition: $355 per credit.
Collegiate Environment: Orientation program. Drama-theater group, choral group, student-run newspaper. Social organizations: 30 open to all; local fraternities, local sororities; 8% of eligible men and 30% of eligible women are members. Most popular organizations: Campus Ministry, Student Association, chorale, Honor Society, Cue and Curtain. Major annual events: Carol Night, Guardian Angel Dinner, Spring Fling. Student services: health clinic, personal-psychological counseling. Campus security: 24-hour emergency response devices and patrols, late night transport-escort service, controlled dormitory access. 350 college housing spaces available; 316 were occupied in 2003-04. Freshmen guaranteed college housing. Options: coed, women-only housing available. Gabriele Library with 143,145 books, 1,354 microform titles, 604 serials, 3,422 audiovisual materials, an OPAC, and a Web page. Operations spending for 2004 fiscal year: $494,401. 254 computers available on campus for general student use. A campuswide network can be accessed from student residence rooms. Staffed computer lab on campus.
Community Environment: Immaculata is a suburban area with a temperate climate. An airport, railroad, and bus lines serve the area. The school is located in Chester County, twenty miles west of Philadelphia, at the junction of routes 30 and 352. The community has a public library, churches of major denominations, two hospitals, and several large shopping centers. There are active civic and fraternal organizations within the area.

■ INDIANA UNIVERSITY OF PENNSYLVANIA *J-7*

Indiana, PA 15705-1087
Tel: (724)357-2100
Free: 800-442-6830
Admissions: (724)357-2230
Fax: (724)357-2685
E-mail: admissions-inquiry@iup.edu
Web Site: http://www.iup.edu/

Description: State-supported, university, coed. Part of Pennsylvania State System of Higher Education. Awards associate, bachelor's, master's, and doctoral degrees and post-master's certificates. Founded 1875. Setting: 350-acre small town campus with easy access to Pittsburgh. Endowment: $35.7

million. Research spending for 2004 fiscal year: $2.3 million. Educational spending for 2005 fiscal year: $6664 per student. Total enrollment: 14,081. Faculty: 711 (639 full-time, 72 part-time). Student-undergrad faculty ratio is 18:1. 8,293 applied, 55% were admitted. 13% from top 10% of their high school class, 32% from top quarter, 70% from top half. Full-time: 11,223 students, 55% women, 45% men. Part-time: 824 students, 54% women, 46% men. Students come from 38 states and territories, 74 other countries, 5% from out-of-state, 0.2% Native American, 1% Hispanic, 7% black, 1% Asian American or Pacific Islander, 2% international, 3% 25 or older, 32% live on campus, 5% transferred in. Retention: 77% of full-time freshmen returned the following year. Academic areas with the most degrees conferred: business/marketing; social sciences; education. Core. Calendar: semesters. Academic remediation for entering students, ESL program, services for LD students, advanced placement, accelerated degree program, freshman honors college, honors program, independent study, distance learning, double major, summer session for credit, part-time degree program, adult/continuing education programs, co-op programs and internships, graduate courses open to undergrads. Off campus study at 14 members of the Marine Science Consortium, The Art Institute of Pittsburgh, National Student Exchange. Study abroad program. ROTC: Army.
Entrance Requirements: Options: Peterson's Universal Application, Common Application, electronic application, early admission, deferred admission, international baccalaureate accepted. Required: high school transcript, SAT or ACT. Recommended: recommendations. Entrance: moderately difficult. Application deadline: Rolling. Notification: 9/1.
Costs Per Year: Application fee: $30. State resident tuition: $4810 full-time, $204 per credit hour part-time. Nonresident tuition: $12,026 full-time, $511 per credit hour part-time. Mandatory fees: $1275 full-time, $20.40 per credit hour part-time, $167 per term part-time. Full-time tuition and fees vary according to course load, location, and reciprocity agreements. Part-time tuition and fees vary according to course load, location, and reciprocity agreements. College room and board: $4866. College room only: $2740. Room and board charges vary according to board plan, housing facility, and location.
Collegiate Environment: Orientation program. Drama-theater group, choral group, marching band, student-run newspaper, radio station. Social organizations: 200 open to all; national fraternities, national sororities; 10% of eligible men and 11% of eligible women are members. Most popular organizations: NAACP, Student Congress, Alpha Phi Omega. Major annual events: International Day, Homecoming, Family Weekend. Student services: legal services, health clinic, personal-psychological counseling, women's center. Campus security: 24-hour emergency response devices and patrols, late night transport-escort service, controlled dormitory access. 4,000 college housing spaces available; 3,679 were occupied in 2003-04. Freshmen guaranteed college housing. On-campus residence required in freshman year. Options: coed, men-only, women-only housing available. Stapleton Library with 570,735 books, 2.4 million microform titles, 2,626 serials, 109,308 audiovisual materials, an OPAC, and a Web page. Operations spending for 2004 fiscal year: $5.3 million. 3,500 computers available on campus for general student use. Computer purchase/lease plans available. A campuswide network can be accessed from student residence rooms and from off campus. Staffed computer lab on campus.
Community Environment: Population 35,000. Indiana is known as the"Christmas Tree Capital of the World" and is the birthplace of actor Jimmy Stewart. The town is located 50 miles northeast of Pittsburgh in the foothills of the beautiful Allegheny Mountains. Indiana has churches of all denominations, a library, a recreation center, a hospital, and various civic, fraternal and veteran's organizations. Local recreational facilities include golf courses, theatres, swimming pool, ice skating rink, tennis, baseball fields, a grandstand and an outdoor stage. Some part-time employment is available.

■ INFORMATION COMPUTER SYSTEMS INSTITUTE *J-23*

2201 Hangar Place
Allentown, PA 18103-9504
Tel: (610)264-8029
E-mail: wbarber@ptd.net
Web Site: http://www.icsinstitute.com/
Description: Private, 2-year. Awards certificates, transfer associate, and terminal associate degrees. Founded 1978. Total enrollment: 125. 60% 25 or older.

■ INTERNATIONAL ACADEMY OF DESIGN & TECHNOLOGY *K-3*

555 Grant St.
Pittsburgh, PA 15219

Tel: (412)391-4197
Free: 800-447-8324
Fax: (412)391-4224
Web Site: http://www.iadtpitt.com/
Description: Proprietary, 2-year. Awards terminal associate degrees. Total enrollment: 954. 174 applied, 100% were admitted. Full-time: 840 students, 24% women, 76% men. Part-time: 114 students, 32% women, 68% men. 1% from out-of-state, 70% 25 or older.

■ **JNA INSTITUTE OF CULINARY ARTS** *M-24*

1212 South Broad St.
Philadelphia, PA 19146
Tel: (215)468-8880
Fax: (215)468-8838
Web Site: http://www.culinaryarts.com/
Description: Proprietary, 2-year, coed. Founded 1988. Calendar: continuous.

■ **JOHNSON COLLEGE** *F-22*

3427 North Main Ave.
Scranton, PA 18508-1495
Tel: (570)342-6404
Free: 800-2-WE-WORK
Fax: (570)348-2181
E-mail: admit@johnson.edu
Web Site: http://www.johnson.edu/
Description: Independent, 2-year, coed. Awards terminal associate degrees. Founded 1912. Setting: 65-acre urban campus. Total enrollment: 405. Student-undergrad faculty ratio is 17:1. 246 applied, 69% were admitted. 5% from top 10% of their high school class, 15% from top quarter, 65% from top half. Students come from 4 states and territories, 10% from out-of-state, 30% 25 or older, 17% live on campus. Core. Calendar: semesters. Academic remediation for entering students, services for LD students, summer session for credit, part-time degree program, adult/continuing education programs, internships.
Entrance Requirements: Options: Common Application, electronic application, deferred admission. Required: essay, high school transcript, recommendations, interview. Recommended: SAT. Required for some: SAT, ACCUPLACER. Entrance: minimally difficult. Application deadline: Rolling. Notification: 8/15.
Costs Per Year: Application fee: $30. Tuition: $12,267 full-time, $325 per credit part-time. Mandatory fees: $1000 full-time. College room only: $2975.
Collegiate Environment: Orientation program. Most popular organizations: student government, Social Force Club, trade/technical/clinical clubs. Major annual events: Activity Day, Career Day, Parents' Day. Student services: personal-psychological counseling. Campus security: 24-hour emergency response devices. Option: coed housing available. Johnson Technical Institute Library with 4,473 books, 118 serials, an OPAC, and a Web page. 75 computers available on campus for general student use. Staffed computer lab on campus.

■ **JUNIATA COLLEGE** *K-12*

1700 Moore St.
Huntingdon, PA 16652-2119
Tel: (814)641-3000; 877-JUNIATA
Admissions: (814)641-3432
Fax: (814)641-3100
Web Site: http://www.juniata.edu/
Description: Independent, 4-year, coed, affiliated with Church of the Brethren. Awards bachelor's degrees. Founded 1876. Setting: 110-acre small town campus. Endowment: $57.8 million. Research spending for 2004 fiscal year: $1 million. Educational spending for 2005 fiscal year: $7099 per student. Total enrollment: 1,449. Student-undergrad faculty ratio is 13:1. 1,745 applied, 68% were admitted. 43% from top 10% of their high school class, 79% from top quarter, 97% from top half. 10 National Merit Scholars, 16 valedictorians. Full-time: 1,389 students, 53% women, 47% men. Part-time: 60 students, 43% women, 57% men. Students come from 28 states and territories, 26 other countries, 28% from out-of-state, 0.3% Native American, 1% Hispanic, 2% black, 2% Asian American or Pacific Islander, 3% international, 4% 25 or older, 84% live on campus, 2% transferred in. Retention: 83% of full-time freshmen returned the following year. Academic areas with the most degrees conferred: biological/life sciences; business/marketing; education. Core. Calendar: semesters. ESL program, services for LD students, advanced placement, accelerated degree program, self-

designed majors, freshman honors college, honors program, independent study, distance learning, double major, summer session for credit, part-time degree program, adult/continuing education programs, internships. Off campus study at Duke University, American University, Philadelphia Urban Semester, Washington Center, Institute for Experiential Learning. Study abroad program.
Entrance Requirements: Options: Peterson's Universal Application, Common Application, electronic application, early admission, early decision, deferred admission, international baccalaureate accepted. Required: essay, high school transcript, minimum 3.0 high school GPA, 1 recommendation. Recommended: interview, SAT or ACT. Entrance: moderately difficult. Application deadlines: 3/1, 11/1 for early decision. Notification: continuous, 12/30 for early decision.
Costs Per Year: Application fee: $30. Comprehensive fee: $35,220 includes full-time tuition ($26,900), mandatory fees ($640), and college room and board ($7680). College room only: $4030.
Collegiate Environment: Orientation program. Drama-theater group, choral group, student-run newspaper, radio station. Social organizations: 86 open to all. Most popular organizations: student government, Activities Board, HOSA, International Club, Habitat for Humanity. Major annual events: Mountain Day, Springfest, All-Class Night. Student services: health clinic, personal-psychological counseling, women's center. Campus security: 24-hour emergency response devices and patrols, student patrols, late night transport-escort service, fire safety training, adopt-an-officer program, security website, weather/terror alerts, travel forecast, crime statistics. 1,175 college housing spaces available; 1,162 were occupied in 2003-04. Freshmen guaranteed college housing. On-campus residence required through senior year. Options: coed, women-only housing available. Beeghly Library with 275,000 books, 400 microform titles, 1,000 serials, 1,700 audiovisual materials, an OPAC, and a Web page. Operations spending for 2004 fiscal year: $759,140. 375 computers available on campus for general student use. A campuswide network can be accessed from student residence rooms and from off campus. Staffed computer lab on campus.
Community Environment: Huntingdon, population 8,000, on the Juniata River, is in one of the most scenic sections of the state. It was founded on the site of an Indian Village called Standing Stone. The city is the county seat and lies approximately 30 miles east of Altoona. The area is served by railroad. Penn State (32 miles away) offers cultural and social activities. Nearby state parks, forests, and the Raystown Lake recreation area provide excellent camping, fishing, canoeing, hunting, swimming, and boating opportunities. In winter ski slopes are less than 40 miles away.

■ **KATHARINE GIBBS SCHOOL** *M-23*

2501 Monroe Blvd.
Norristown, PA 19403
Tel: (610)676-0500; (866)PAG-IBBS
Fax: (610)676-0530
E-mail: jcarretta@pagibbs.com
Web Site: http://www.pagibbs.com/
Description: Proprietary, 2-year, coed.

■ **KEYSTONE COLLEGE** *E-21*

One College Green
La Plume, PA 18440
Tel: (570)945-5141; 877-4COLLEGE
Admissions: (570)945-8112
E-mail: admissions@keystone.edu
Web Site: http://www.keystone.edu/
Description: Independent, primarily 2-year, coed. Awards certificates, transfer associate, terminal associate, and bachelor's degrees. Founded 1868. Setting: 270-acre rural campus. Endowment: $8.9 million. Educational spending for 2005 fiscal year: $3699 per student. Total enrollment: 1,638. Student-undergrad faculty ratio is 12:1. 872 applied, 91% were admitted. 4% from top 10% of their high school class, 17% from top quarter, 49% from top half. 2 class presidents, 1 valedictorian. Full-time: 1,234 students, 57% women, 43% men. Part-time: 404 students, 74% women, 26% men. Students come from 12 states and territories, 7 other countries, 18% from out-of-state, 0.3% Native American, 1% Hispanic, 3% black, 1% Asian American or Pacific Islander, 1% international, 28% 25 or older, 24% live on campus, 10% transferred in. Retention: 63% of full-time freshmen returned the following year. Academic areas with the most degrees conferred: business/marketing; education; computer and information sciences; security and protective services. Core. Calendar: semesters. Academic remediation for entering students, services for LD students, advanced placement, self-

designed majors, freshman honors college, honors program, independent study, distance learning, summer session for credit, part-time degree program, external degree program, adult/continuing education programs, co-op programs and internships. ROTC: Army (c), Air Force (c).

Entrance Requirements: Options: Peterson's Universal Application, Common Application, electronic application, early admission, deferred admission, international baccalaureate accepted. Required: high school transcript, 1 recommendation. Recommended: essay, interview, SAT or ACT. Required for some: interview, art portfolio, SAT or ACT. Entrance: minimally difficult. Application deadline: 7/1.

Costs Per Year: Application fee: $25. Comprehensive fee: $24,026 includes full-time tuition ($14,946), mandatory fees ($970), and college room and board ($8110). College room only: $4300. Part-time tuition: $330 per credit. Part-time mandatory fees: $110 per term.

Collegiate Environment: Orientation program. Drama-theater group, choral group, student-run newspaper, radio station. Social organizations: 30 open to all. Most popular organizations: Campus Activity Board, Student Senate, Art Society, Inter-Hall Council, Commuter Council. Major annual events: Homecoming, Winterfest, Spring Fling. Student services: health clinic, personal-psychological counseling, women's center. Campus security: 24-hour emergency response devices and patrols, student patrols, late night transport-escort service, controlled dormitory access. 420 college housing spaces available; 400 were occupied in 2003-04. Freshmen guaranteed college housing. Options: coed, women-only housing available. Miller Library with 65,000 books, 39,000 microform titles, 309 serials, 10,000 audiovisual materials, an OPAC, and a Web page. Operations spending for 2004 fiscal year: $343,599. 120 computers available on campus for general student use. Computer purchase/lease plans available. A campuswide network can be accessed from student residence rooms and from off campus. Staffed computer lab on campus.

Community Environment: Population of Scranton is 103,564. The city is provided transportation by bus and air. Air facilities are located near Scranton. This is a semirural community with many churches and synagogues close at hand. There are service clubs active locally. Five modern hospitals are easily accessible. Local recreation includes movies, museum, art galleries, professional sports, lakes, streams, ski slopes, hunting, and fishing areas.

■ **KING'S COLLEGE** *F-21*

133 North River St.
Wilkes Barre, PA 18711-0801
Tel: (570)208-5900; 888-KINGSPA
Admissions: (570)208-5858
Fax: (570)208-5971
E-mail: admssions@kings.edu
Web Site: http://www.kings.edu/

Description: Independent Roman Catholic, comprehensive, coed. Awards associate, bachelor's, and master's degrees. Founded 1946. Setting: 48-acre suburban campus. Endowment: $47.2 million. Educational spending for 2005 fiscal year: $6959 per student. Total enrollment: 2,323. Faculty: 201 (110 full-time, 91 part-time). Student-undergrad faculty ratio is 14:1. 1,654 applied, 84% were admitted. 16% from top 10% of their high school class, 40% from top quarter, 71% from top half. 4 class presidents, 6 valedictorians, 3 student government officers. Full-time: 1,849 students, 45% women, 55% men. Part-time: 261 students, 63% women, 37% men. Students come from 21 states and territories, 6 other countries, 23% from out-of-state, 0.1% Native American, 2% Hispanic, 2% black, 1% Asian American or Pacific Islander, 0.4% international, 3% 25 or older, 45% live on campus, 4% transferred in. Retention: 80% of full-time freshmen returned the following year. Academic areas with the most degrees conferred: business/marketing; education; psychology. Core. Calendar: semesters. ESL program, services for LD students, advanced placement, accelerated degree program, self-designed majors, honors program, independent study, distance learning, double major, summer session for credit, part-time degree program, adult/continuing education programs, internships. Off campus study at College Misericordia, Wilkes University. Study abroad program. ROTC: Army, Air Force.

Entrance Requirements: Options: Common Application, electronic application, early admission, deferred admission. Required: essay, high school transcript, SAT or ACT. Recommended: 2 recommendations, interview. Entrance: moderately difficult. Application deadline: Rolling. Notification: continuous.

Costs Per Year: Application fee: $30. Comprehensive fee: $29,810 includes full-time tuition ($20,320), mandatory fees ($900), and college room and board ($8590). College room only: $3980. Room and board charges vary according to board plan and housing facility. Part-time tuition: $495 per credit hour.

Collegiate Environment: Orientation program. Drama-theater group, choral group, student-run newspaper, radio station. Social organizations: 51 open to all. Most popular organizations: Association of Campus Events, Student Government Association, Accounting Association, International/Multicultural Club, Biology Club. Major annual events: Homecoming, Friends and Family Weekend, Christmas Fair at King's. Student services: health clinic, personal-psychological counseling, women's center. Campus security: 24-hour emergency response devices and patrols, student patrols, late night transport-escort service, bicycle patrols. 860 college housing spaces available

Free: 800 were occupied in 2003-04. Freshmen guaranteed college housing. On-campus residence required through sophomore year. Options: men-only, women-only housing available. D. Leonard Corgan Library with 168,793 books, 562,747 microform titles, 791 serials, 2,586 audiovisual materials, an OPAC, and a Web page. Operations spending for 2004 fiscal year: $1.3 million. 318 computers available on campus for general student use. Computer purchase/lease plans available. A campuswide network can be accessed from student residence rooms and from off campus. Staffed computer lab on campus.

■ **KUTZTOWN UNIVERSITY OF PENNSYLVANIA** *J-21*

15200 Kutztown Rd.
Kutztown, PA 19530-0730
Tel: (610)683-4000; 877-628-1915
Admissions: (610)683-4060
Fax: (610)683-1375
Web Site: http://www.kutztown.edu/

Description: State-supported, comprehensive, coed. Part of Pennsylvania State System of Higher Education. Awards bachelor's and master's degrees. Founded 1866. Setting: 326-acre rural campus with easy access to Philadelphia. Endowment: $11.7 million. Research spending for 2004 fiscal year: $179,908. Educational spending for 2005 fiscal year: $4715 per student. Total enrollment: 9,864. Faculty: 461 (411 full-time, 50 part-time). Student-undergrad faculty ratio is 19:1. 8,603 applied, 65% were admitted. 6% from top 10% of their high school class, 22% from top quarter, 73% from top half. Full-time: 7,951 students, 58% women, 42% men. Part-time: 855 students, 70% women, 30% men. Students come from 21 states and territories, 29 other countries, 9% from out-of-state, 0.3% Native American, 4% Hispanic, 8% black, 1% Asian American or Pacific Islander, 1% international, 6% 25 or older, 52% live on campus, 7% transferred in. Retention: 76% of full-time freshmen returned the following year. Academic areas with the most degrees conferred: education; visual and performing arts; business/marketing. Core. Calendar: semesters. Academic remediation for entering students, services for LD students, advanced placement, accelerated degree program, self-designed majors, honors program, independent study, distance learning, double major, summer session for credit, part-time degree program, external degree program, adult/continuing education programs, internships. Off campus study at members of the Marine Science Consortium, Pennsylvania Consortium for International Education. Study abroad program. ROTC: Army (c), Air Force (c).

Entrance Requirements: Options: electronic application, early admission, deferred admission, international baccalaureate accepted. Required: high school transcript, minimum 2.0 high school GPA, SAT or ACT. Required for some: audition required for music program; portfolio and/or art test required for art education, communication design, crafts, and fine arts programs, SAT Subject Tests. Entrance: moderately difficult. Application deadline: 3/1. Notification: 4/15.

Costs Per Year: Application fee: $35. State resident tuition: $4906 full-time, $204 per credit part-time. Nonresident tuition: $12,266 full-time, $511 per credit part-time. Mandatory fees: $1519 full-time, $50.31 per credit part-time, $31 per term part-time. College room and board: $5480. College room only: $3900.

Collegiate Environment: Orientation program. Drama-theater group, choral group, marching band, student-run newspaper, radio station. Social organizations: 118 open to all; national fraternities, national sororities, local sororities; 3% of eligible men and 3% of eligible women are members. Most popular organizations: Student Government Board, Student Pennsylvania State Education Association, National Art Education Association, Residence Hall Association. Major annual events: Homecoming, Family Day, Bear Fest. Student services: health clinic, personal-psychological counseling, women's center. Campus security: 24-hour emergency response devices and patrols, student patrols, late night transport-escort service, secondary door electronic alarm system in residence halls, 24-hour student desk personnel at main entrance of residence halls. College housing designed to accommodate 3,948 students; 4,098 undergraduates lived in college housing during 2003-04. Freshmen guaranteed college housing. Options: coed, women-only housing available. Rohrbach Library with 500,484 books, 1.3 million microform titles, 15,600 serials, 15,981 audiovisual materials, an OPAC, and a Web page. Operations spending for 2004 fiscal year: $3 million. 650 computers available on campus for general student use. A campuswide network can be accessed from student residence rooms and from off campus. Staffed computer lab on campus.

Community Environment: Kutztown is a rural, small town located on U.S. Route 222, midway between Reading and Allentown, one and a half hours from Philadelphia, and three hours from New York City. Airports are located in Allentown and Reading, with bus transportation provided daily to Philadelphia and New York as well as to local destinations. The community has churches, civic organizations, and hospitals are located in nearby Reading and Allentown. Area recreation includes golf, bowling, tennis, hunting, fishing, swimming, basketball, football, theatre, nature study at Hawk Mountain Sanctuary, and the annual Kutztown Folk Festival.

■ **LA ROCHE COLLEGE** *K-3*
9000 Babcock Blvd.
Pittsburgh, PA 15237-5898
Tel: (412)367-9300
Free: 800-838-4LRC
Admissions: (412)536-1198
Fax: (412)536-1075
E-mail: schaeft1@laroche.edu
Web Site: http://www.laroche.edu/

Description: Independent, comprehensive, coed, affiliated with Roman Catholic Church. Awards associate, bachelor's, and master's degrees. Founded 1963. Setting: 80-acre suburban campus. Endowment: $3.9 million. Educational spending for 2005 fiscal year: $4658 per student. Total enrollment: 1,707. Faculty: 225 (62 full-time, 163 part-time). Student-undergrad faculty ratio is 12:1. 838 applied, 65% were admitted. 12% from top 10% of their high school class, 31% from top quarter, 63% from top half. Full-time: 1,202 students, 66% women, 34% men. Part-time: 298 students, 76% women, 24% men. Students come from 19 states and territories, 28 other countries, 5% from out-of-state, 1% Native American, 1% Hispanic, 4% black, 1% Asian American or Pacific Islander, 11% international, 26% 25 or older, 35% live on campus, 13% transferred in. Retention: 69% of full-time freshmen returned the following year. Academic areas with the most degrees conferred: business/marketing; education; computer and information sciences, Core. Calendar: semesters plus summer term. Academic remediation for entering students, ESL program, services for LD students, advanced placement, accelerated degree program, self-designed majors, independent study, distance learning, double major, summer session for credit, part-time degree program, adult/continuing education programs, internships, graduate courses open to undergrads. Study abroad program. ROTC: Army (c), Air Force (c).

Entrance Requirements: Options: electronic application, early admission, deferred admission, international baccalaureate accepted. Required: high school transcript, minimum 2.0 high school GPA, recommendations, SAT or ACT. Recommended: essay, minimum 3.0 high school GPA, interview. Entrance: minimally difficult. Application deadline: Rolling. Notification: 9/15.

Costs Per Year: Application fee: $50. Comprehensive fee: $24,724 includes full-time tuition ($16,780), mandatory fees ($600), and college room and board ($7344). College room only: $4600. Full-time tuition and fees vary according to program. Part-time tuition: $512 per credit. Part-time mandatory fees: $14 per credit, $50 per term. Part-time tuition and fees vary according to program.

Collegiate Environment: Orientation program. Drama-theater group, choral group, student-run newspaper, radio station. Social organizations: 28 open to all. Most popular organizations: American Society of Interior Design, student government, Visions (environmental club), Helping Hands, Project Achievement. Major annual events: International Fashion Show, The Spring Fling, Gateway Clipper Cruise. Student services: health clinic, personal-psychological counseling. Campus security: 24-hour emergency response devices and patrols, student patrols, late night transport-escort service, controlled dormitory access. 628 college housing spaces available; 499 were occupied in 2003-04. Freshmen guaranteed college housing. Option: coed housing available. John J. Wright Library with 108,432 books, 30,000 microform titles, 601 serials, 1,010 audiovisual materials, an OPAC, and a

Web page. Operations spending for 2004 fiscal year: $391,979. 200 computers available on campus for general student use. A campuswide network can be accessed from student residence rooms and from off campus. Staffed computer lab on campus.

Community Environment: The college is located just ten miles north of the center of Pittsburgh. The campus has an ideal combination of rural and urban life: within a five-mile radius of its own natural beauty are the recreational facilities and wooded expanse of North Park and the shops, restaurants and theaters of the McKnight Road malls.

■ **LA SALLE UNIVERSITY** *M-24*
1900 West Olney Ave.
Philadelphia, PA 19141-1199
Tel: (215)951-1000
Free: 800-328-1910
Admissions: (215)951-1500
Fax: (215)951-1656
E-mail: admiss@lasalle.edu
Web Site: http://www.lasalle.edu/

Description: Independent Roman Catholic, comprehensive, coed. Awards associate, bachelor's, master's, and doctoral degrees and post-master's certificates. Founded 1863. Setting: 100-acre urban campus. Endowment: $54.1 million. Educational spending for 2005 fiscal year: $6000 per student. Total enrollment: 6,138. Faculty: 396 (210 full-time, 186 part-time). Student-undergrad faculty ratio is 13:1. 4,562 applied, 70% were admitted. 18% from top 10% of their high school class, 47% from top quarter, 75% from top half. Full-time: 3,281 students, 55% women, 45% men. Part-time: 1,058 students, 75% women, 25% men. Students come from 36 states and territories, 36 other countries, 37% from out-of-state, 0.2% Native American, 8% Hispanic, 15% black, 3% Asian American or Pacific Islander, 1% international, 2% 25 or older, 63% live on campus, 9% transferred in. Retention: 85% of full-time freshmen returned the following year. Academic areas with the most degrees conferred: business/marketing; communications/journalism; health professions and related sciences. Core. Calendar: semesters. Services for LD students, advanced placement, accelerated degree program, self-designed majors, freshman honors college, honors program, independent study, double major, summer session for credit, part-time degree program, adult/continuing education programs, co-op programs and internships, graduate courses open to undergrads. Off campus study at Chestnut Hill College, Bucks County Center, Gwynedd-Mercy College. Study abroad program. ROTC: Army (c), Air Force (c).

Entrance Requirements: Options: Peterson's Universal Application, Common Application, electronic application, early admission, early action, deferred admission, international baccalaureate accepted. Required: essay, high school transcript, 1 recommendation, SAT or ACT. Recommended: interview. Entrance: moderately difficult. Application deadline: 11/15 for early action. Notification: continuous, 12/15 for early action.

Costs Per Year: Application fee: $35. Comprehensive fee: $38,110 includes full-time tuition ($27,500), mandatory fees ($310), and college room and board ($10,300). College room only: $5120. Part-time tuition: $395 per credit.

Collegiate Environment: Orientation program. Drama-theater group, choral group, student-run newspaper, radio station. Social organizations: 90 open to all; national fraternities, national sororities, local fraternities, local sororities; 10% of eligible men and 10% of eligible women are members. Most popular organizations: Student Government Association, community service organization, La Salle Entertainment Organization, The Explorer (yearbook), The Masque (theater group). Major annual events: Branch Out Day, Homecoming, Spring Fling. Student services: health clinic, personal-psychological counseling, women's center. Campus security: 24-hour emergency response devices and patrols, student patrols, late night transport-escort service, controlled dormitory access. 2,210 college housing spaces available; 2,061 were occupied in 2003-04. Freshmen guaranteed college housing. Option: coed housing available. Connelly Library with 400,000 books, 50,000 microform titles, 6,900 serials, 10,000 audiovisual materials, an OPAC, and a Web page. Operations spending for 2004 fiscal year: $1.7 million. 1,000 computers available on campus for general student use. A campuswide network can be accessed from student residence rooms and from off campus. Staffed computer lab on campus.

Community Environment: See Temple University.

■ **LACKAWANNA COLLEGE** *F-22*
501 Vine St.
Scranton, PA 18509

Tel: (570)961-7810

Admissions: (570)961-7852

Fax: (570)961-7858

E-mail: dudam@lackawanna.edu

Web Site: http://www.lackawanna.edu/

Description: Independent, 2-year, coed. Awards certificates, diplomas, transfer associate, and terminal associate degrees. Founded 1894. Setting: 4-acre urban campus. Endowment: $1.2 million. Research spending for 2004 fiscal year: $48,241. Total enrollment: 1,197. Student-undergrad faculty ratio is 13:1. Full-time: 758 students, 45% women, 55% men. Part-time: 439 students, 67% women, 33% men. Students come from 20 states and territories, 3% from out-of-state, 0.3% Native American, 2% Hispanic, 11% black, 1% Asian American or Pacific Islander, 0% international, 33% 25 or older, 12% live on campus, 11% transferred in. Core. Calendar: semesters. Academic remediation for entering students, ESL program, services for LD students, double major, summer session for credit, part-time degree program, adult/continuing education programs, co-op programs and internships. ROTC: Army (c), Air Force (c).

Entrance Requirements: Open admission. Options: electronic application, early admission, deferred admission. Required: high school transcript, interview. Recommended: SAT, ACT, SAT or ACT. Entrance: noncompetitive. Application deadline: Rolling.

Costs Per Year: Application fee: $30. Comprehensive fee: $15,770 includes full-time tuition ($9400), mandatory fees ($70), and college room and board ($6300). College room only: $4100. Full-time tuition and fees vary according to course load. Part-time tuition: $310 per credit. Part-time mandatory fees: $35 per term. Part-time tuition and fees vary according to course load.

Collegiate Environment: Orientation program. Drama-theater group, student-run newspaper. Social organizations: 5 open to all. Most popular organizations: student government, Student/Alumni Association, Diversity Club, student newspaper, Phi Beta Lambda. Major annual events: Breakfast with Santa, Graduation Dinner Dance, Homecoming activities. Student services: personal-psychological counseling. Campus security: 24-hour emergency response devices, late night transport-escort service, patrols by college liaison staff. 140 college housing spaces available; all were occupied in 2003-04. No special consideration for freshman housing applicants. On-campus residence required through sophomore year. Option: men-only housing available. Seeley Memorial Library with 15,276 books, 58 serials, 491 audiovisual materials, an OPAC, and a Web page. Operations spending for 2004 fiscal year: $110,012. 200 computers available on campus for general student use. A campuswide network can be accessed from student residence rooms and from off campus. Staffed computer lab on campus.

■ **LAFAYETTE COLLEGE** *I-24*

Easton, PA 18042-1798

Tel: (610)330-5000

Admissions: (610)330-5100

Fax: (610)330-5127

E-mail: rowlandc@lafayette.edu

Web Site: http://www.lafayette.edu/

Description: Independent, 4-year, coed, affiliated with Presbyterian Church (U.S.A.). Awards bachelor's degrees. Founded 1826. Setting: 340-acre suburban campus with easy access to New York City and Philadelphia. Endowment: $633.4 million. Research spending for 2004 fiscal year: $594,400. Educational spending for 2005 fiscal year: $27,516 per student. Total enrollment: 2,346. Student-undergrad faculty ratio is 11:1. 5,728 applied, 37% were admitted. 62% from top 10% of their high school class, 88% from top quarter, 99% from top half. 6 National Merit Scholars. Full-time: 2,281 students, 47% women, 53% men. Part-time: 65 students, 51% women, 49% men. Students come from 38 states and territories, 41 other countries, 70% from out-of-state, 0.2% Native American, 4% Hispanic, 5% black, 2% Asian American or Pacific Islander, 6% international, 0% 25 or older, 98% live on campus, 1% transferred in. Retention: 93% of full-time freshmen returned the following year. Academic areas with the most degrees conferred: social sciences; engineering; English. Core. Calendar: semesters plus interim January program. Academic remediation for entering students, services for LD students, advanced placement, accelerated degree program, self-designed majors, honors program, summer session for credit, part-time degree program, adult/continuing education programs, internships. Off campus study at 5 members of the Lehigh Valley Association of Independent Colleges, American University. Study abroad program. ROTC: Army (c).

Entrance Requirements: Options: Peterson's Universal Application, Common Application, electronic application, early admission, early decision, deferred admission, international baccalaureate accepted. Required: essay,

high school transcript, 1 recommendation. Recommended: interview. Entrance: most difficult. Application deadlines: 1/1, 12/1 for early decision. Notification: continuous until 4/1, 3/15 for early decision.

Costs Per Year: Application fee: $60. Comprehensive fee: $41,533 includes full-time tuition ($31,501), mandatory fees ($168), and college room and board ($9864). College room only: $5784.

Collegiate Environment: Orientation program. Drama-theater group, choral group, student-run newspaper, radio station. Social organizations: 250 open to all; national fraternities, national sororities, social dorms; 26% of eligible men and 45% of eligible women are members. Most popular organizations: Association of Biscer Collegians, International Student Association, Activities Forum. Major annual events: All College Day, Earth Day, Lafayette-Lehigh Weekend. Student services: health clinic, personal-psychological counseling, women's center. Campus security: 24-hour emergency response devices and patrols, student patrols, late night transport-escort service, controlled dormitory access. 2,200 college housing spaces available; 2,100 were occupied in 2003-04. Freshmen guaranteed college housing. On-campus residence required through senior year. Option: coed housing available. Skillman Library plus 1 other with 530,000 books, 3,500 serials, an OPAC, and a Web page. 480 computers available on campus for general student use. A campuswide network can be accessed from student residence rooms and from off campus. Staffed computer lab on campus.

Community Environment: Population 29,000, Easton is located at the confluence of the Lehigh and Delaware Rivers in the Lehigh Valley. The area is served by bus lines and a county airport. The valley has a YMCA, YWCA, nine hospitals, four public libraries, many churches and synagogues, a community concert association, and numerous civic and fraternal organizations. Recreational activities include baseball, softball, tennis, bowling, golf, boating, swimming, hunting, and fishing.

■ **LANCASTER BIBLE COLLEGE** *M-19*

901 Eden Rd., PO Box 83403

Lancaster, PA 17608-3403

Tel: (717)569-7071; (866)LBC-4YOU

Admissions: (717)560-8271

Fax: (717)560-8213

E-mail: jroper@lbc.edu

Web Site: http://www.lbc.edu/

Description: Independent nondenominational, comprehensive, coed. Awards associate, bachelor's, and master's degrees. Founded 1933. Setting: 100-acre suburban campus with easy access to Philadelphia. Endowment: $4.8 million. Educational spending for 2005 fiscal year: $5017 per student. Total enrollment: 1,001. Faculty: 86 (44 full-time, 42 part-time). Student-undergrad faculty ratio is 15:1. 223 applied, 57% were admitted. 15% from top 10% of their high school class, 32% from top quarter, 82% from top half. Full-time: 589 students, 53% women, 47% men. Part-time: 240 students, 51% women, 49% men. Students come from 24 states and territories, 4 other countries, 28% from out-of-state, 0.1% Native American, 2% Hispanic, 3% black, 1% Asian American or Pacific Islander, 1% international, 17% 25 or older, 54% live on campus, 8% transferred in. Retention: 73% of full-time freshmen returned the following year. Academic areas with the most degrees conferred: theology and religious vocations; education. Core. Calendar: semesters. Academic remediation for entering students, services for LD students, advanced placement, independent study, double major, summer session for credit, part-time degree program, adult/continuing education programs, internships, graduate courses open to undergrads. Study abroad program.

Entrance Requirements: Options: early admission, deferred admission. Required: essay, high school transcript, minimum 2.0 high school GPA, 3 recommendations, SAT or ACT. Required for some: interview. Entrance: minimally difficult. Application deadline: Rolling. Notification: continuous.

Costs Per Year: Application fee: $25. Comprehensive fee: $18,060 includes full-time tuition ($11,850), mandatory fees ($510), and college room and board ($5700). College room only: $2500. Part-time tuition: $417 per credit. Part-time mandatory fees: $19 per credit.

Collegiate Environment: Orientation program. Drama-theater group, choral group, student-run newspaper. Social organizations: 19 open to all. Most popular organizations: Student Government Association, Student Missionary Fellowship, International Student Fellowship, Resident Affairs Council, Student Intramural Association. Major annual events: homecoming, Missions Conference, Spiritual Life Week. Student services: health clinic, personal-psychological counseling. Campus security: student patrols, late night transport-escort service, controlled dormitory access. 405 college housing spaces available; all were occupied in 2003-04. Freshmen guaranteed college housing. On-campus residence required through senior year. Options: men-only, women-only housing available. Lancaster Bible College Library with 132,599 books, 30,248 microform titles, 6,852 serials, 6,654 audiovisual materials, and an OPAC. Operations spending for 2004 fiscal year: $361,437. 50 computers available on campus for general student use. A campuswide network can be accessed from student residence rooms. Staffed computer lab on campus.

■ **LANSDALE SCHOOL OF BUSINESS** *B-45*
201 Church Rd.
North Wales, PA 19454-4148
Tel: (215)699-5700
Fax: (215)699-8770
E-mail: mjohnson@lsb.edu
Web Site: http://www.lsbonline.com/
Description: Proprietary, 2-year, coed. Awards certificates, diplomas, transfer associate, and terminal associate degrees. Founded 1918. Setting: suburban campus with easy access to Philadelphia. Total enrollment: 410. 10% from top quarter of their high school class, 40% from top half. 50% 25 or older. Core. Calendar: semesters. Accelerated degree program, honors program, independent study, double major, summer session for credit, part-time degree program, adult/continuing education programs, internships. Off campus study.
Entrance Requirements: Option: Common Application. Required: high school transcript, interview. Required for some: recommendations. Entrance: minimally difficult. Application deadline: Rolling.
Collegiate Environment: Orientation program. Student-run newspaper. College housing not available. Lansdale School of Business Library with 2,000 books, 125 serials, an OPAC, and a Web page. 48 computers available on campus for general student use. Staffed computer lab on campus.

■ **LAUREL BUSINESS INSTITUTE** *N-4*
11-15 Penn St.
Uniontown, PA 15401
Tel: (724)439-4900
Fax: (724)439-3607
E-mail: ddecker@laurelbusiness.edu
Web Site: http://www.laurel.edu/
Description: Proprietary, 2-year, coed. Awards certificates, diplomas, transfer associate, and terminal associate degrees. Founded 1985. Setting: 10-acre small town campus with easy access to Pittsburgh. Educational spending for 2005 fiscal year: $1951 per student. Total enrollment: 297. Student-undergrad faculty ratio is 16:1. 415 applied, 59% were admitted. 10% from top 10% of their high school class, 15% from top quarter, 50% from top half. Students come from 2 states and territories, 1% from out-of-state, 0% Hispanic, 6% black, 0% international. Core. Calendar: trimesters. Academic remediation for entering students, services for LD students, advanced placement, freshman honors college, honors program, double major, part-time degree program, adult/continuing education programs, co-op programs and internships.
Entrance Requirements: Open admission. Options: Common Application, electronic application, deferred admission. Required: essay, high school transcript, interview, Wonderlic. Entrance: minimally difficult. Application deadline: Rolling. Notification: continuous.
Costs Per Year: Application fee: $55. Tuition: $10,125 full-time, $215 per credit part-time. Mandatory fees: $1828 full-time, $349 per term part-time.
Collegiate Environment: Orientation program. College housing not available. 75 computers available on campus for general student use. A campuswide network can be accessed from off-campus. Staffed computer lab on campus.

■ **LEBANON VALLEY COLLEGE** *K-32*
101 North College Ave.
Annville, PA 17003-1400
Tel: (717)867-6100; (866)LVC-4ADM
Admissions: (717)867-6181
Fax: (717)867-6124
E-mail: admiss@lvc.edu
Web Site: http://www.lvc.edu/
Description: Independent United Methodist, comprehensive, coed. Awards associate, bachelor's, master's, and first professional degrees. Founded 1866. Setting: 275-acre small town campus. Endowment: $37.8 million. Educational spending for 2005 fiscal year: $8231 per student. Total enrollment: 1,915. Faculty: 199 (100 full-time, 99 part-time). Student-undergrad

faculty ratio is 13:1. 2,006 applied, 77% were admitted. 36% from top 10% of their high school class, 70% from top quarter, 93% from top half. 2 class presidents, 4 valedictorians, 29 student government officers. Full-time: 1,614 students, 54% women, 46% men. Part-time: 160 students, 76% women, 24% men. Students come from 22 states and territories, 5 other countries, 21% from out-of-state, 0.2% Native American, 2% Hispanic, 2% black, 2% Asian American or Pacific Islander, 0.5% international, 7% 25 or older, 74% live on campus, 3% transferred in. Retention: 85% of full-time freshmen returned the following year. Academic areas with the most degrees conferred: education; business/marketing; psychology. Core. Calendar: semesters. Academic remediation for entering students, services for LD students, advanced placement, self-designed majors, independent study, double major, summer session for credit, part-time degree program, adult/continuing education programs, internships. Off campus study at George Washington University. Study abroad program. ROTC: Army (c).
Entrance Requirements: Options: electronic application, international baccalaureate accepted. Required: high school transcript, SAT or ACT. Recommended: 2 recommendations, interview. Required for some: essay, audition for music majors. Entrance: moderately difficult. Application deadline: Rolling. Notification: continuous.
Costs Per Year: Application fee: $30. Comprehensive fee: $31,700 includes full-time tuition ($24,210), mandatory fees ($650), and college room and board ($6840). College room only: $3340. Room and board charges vary according to board plan and housing facility. Part-time tuition: $440 per credit. Part-time tuition varies according to class time and degree level.
Collegiate Environment: Orientation program. Drama-theater group, choral group, marching band, student-run newspaper, radio station. Social organizations: 74 open to all; national fraternities, national sororities, local fraternities, local sororities; 14% of eligible men and 12% of eligible women are members. Most popular organizations: LVC PSEA, Council of Christian Organization, Tae Kwon Do Club, Phi Beta Lambda, Wig and Buckle (theatrical group). Major annual events: Cherry Blossom Festival, Homecoming, Christmas at the Valley. Student services: health clinic, personal-psychological counseling. Campus security: 24-hour emergency response devices and patrols, late night transport-escort service, controlled dormitory access, dormitory entrances locked at midnight. College housing designed to accommodate 1,151 students; 1,156 undergraduates lived in college housing during 2003-04. Freshmen guaranteed college housing. On-campus residence required through senior year. Options: coed, men-only, women-only housing available. Bishop Library with 181,445 books, 14,102 microform titles, 800 serials, 10,518 audiovisual materials, an OPAC, and a Web page. Operations spending for 2004 fiscal year: $1.1 million. 227 computers available on campus for general student use. A campuswide network can be accessed from student residence rooms and from off campus. Staffed computer lab on campus.
Community Environment: Population 5,000. Annville is located seven miles east of Hershey. The area has a temperate climate. The city has many churches that represent various denominations, a public library, three hospitals that are easily accessible, and major civic, fraternal, and veteran's organizations. Community recreational facilities include theaters and radio and TV stations. Community concerts are also available.

■ **LEHIGH CARBON COMMUNITY COLLEGE** *J-22*
4525 Education Park Dr.
Schnecksville, PA 18078-2598
Tel: (610)799-2121
Admissions: (610)799-1575
Fax: (610)799-1527
E-mail: tellme@lccc.edu
Web Site: http://www.lccc.edu/
Description: State and locally supported, 2-year, coed. Awards certificates, diplomas, transfer associate, and terminal associate degrees. Founded 1967. Setting: 153-acre suburban campus with easy access to Philadelphia. Endowment: $841,000. Educational spending for 2005 fiscal year: $1702 per student. Total enrollment: 6,674. 2,791 applied, 99% were admitted. Full-time: 2,607 students, 54% women, 46% men. Part-time: 4,067 students, 65% women, 35% men. Students come from 19 states and territories, 9 other countries, 1% from out-of-state, 0.2% Native American, 8% Hispanic, 5% black, 2% Asian American or Pacific Islander, 0.1% international, 33% 25 or older, 33% transferred in. Core. Calendar: semesters. Academic remediation for entering students, ESL program, services for LD students, advanced placement, independent study, distance learning, summer session for credit, part-time degree program, adult/continuing education programs, co-op programs and internships. ROTC: Army (c).

Entrance Requirements: Open admission except for allied health, aviation, veterinary technician programs. Required for some: essay, high school transcript, interview. Placement: ACT or ACT COMPASS required for some. Entrance: noncompetitive. Application deadline: Rolling. Notification: continuous.

Costs Per Year: Application fee: $25. Area resident tuition: $2700 full-time, $76 per credit part-time. State resident tuition: $5250 full-time, $152 per credit part-time. Nonresident tuition: $7800 full-time, $228 per credit part-time. Mandatory fees: $420 full-time, $14 per credit hour part-time. Full-time tuition and fees vary according to course load and reciprocity agreements. Part-time tuition and fees vary according to course load and reciprocity agreements.

Collegiate Environment: Orientation program. Student-run newspaper, radio station. Social organizations: 22 open to all. Most popular organizations: Phi Theta Kappa, STEP Student Association, student radio station, student government, College Activity Board. Major annual events: Spring Awards Program, Diversity Week programs. Student services: personal-psychological counseling. Campus security: 24-hour emergency response devices and patrols, student patrols, late night transport-escort service. College housing not available. Learning Resource Center with 99,734 books, 510 serials, 6,016 audiovisual materials, an OPAC, and a Web page. Operations spending for 2004 fiscal year: $795,061. 830 computers available on campus for general student use. Staffed computer lab on campus.

Community Environment: See Muhlenberg College.

■ **LEHIGH UNIVERSITY** *J-23*
27 Memorial Dr. West
Bethlehem, PA 18015-3094
Tel: (610)758-3000
Admissions: (610)758-3100
Fax: (610)758-4361
E-mail: admissions@lehigh.edu
Web Site: http://www.lehigh.edu/

Description: Independent, university, coed. Awards bachelor's, master's, and doctoral degrees and post-master's certificates. Founded 1865. Setting: 1,600-acre suburban campus with easy access to Philadelphia. Endowment: $844.7 million. Research spending for 2004 fiscal year: $38.2 million. Educational spending for 2005 fiscal year: $22,081 per student. Total enrollment: 6,748. Faculty: 621 (434 full-time, 187 part-time). Student-undergrad faculty ratio is 9:1. 10,501 applied, 41% were admitted. 78% from top 10% of their high school class, 95% from top quarter, 100% from top half. Full-time: 4,621 students, 41% women, 59% men. Part-time: 58 students, 31% women, 69% men. Students come from 52 states and territories, 43 other countries, 72% from out-of-state, 0.2% Native American, 2% Hispanic, 2% black, 5% Asian American or Pacific Islander, 3% international, 1% 25 or older, 67% live on campus, 2% transferred in. Retention: 95% of full-time freshmen returned the following year. Academic areas with the most degrees conferred: business/marketing; engineering; social sciences. Calendar: semesters. ESL program, services for LD students, advanced placement, accelerated degree program, honors program, independent study, distance learning, double major, summer session for credit, external degree program, adult/continuing education programs, co-op programs and internships, graduate courses open to undergrads. Off campus study at members of the Lehigh Valley Association of Independent Colleges, American University. Study abroad program. ROTC: Army.

Entrance Requirements: Options: Peterson's Universal Application, Common Application, electronic application, early admission, early decision, deferred admission. Required: high school transcript, 1 recommendation, graded writing sample, SAT or ACT. Recommended: essay, interview. Entrance: most difficult. Application deadlines: 1/1, 11/15 for early decision plan 1, 1/15 for early decision plan 2. Notification: 4/1, 12/15 for early decision plan 1, 2/15 for early decision plan 2.

Costs Per Year: Application fee: $60. Comprehensive fee: $39,980 includes full-time tuition ($31,180), mandatory fees ($240), and college room and board ($8560). College room only: $4890. Room and board charges vary according to board plan and student level. Part-time tuition: $1300 per credit.

Collegiate Environment: Orientation program. Drama-theater group, choral group, marching band, student-run newspaper, radio station. Social organizations: 130 open to all; national fraternities, national sororities; 41% of eligible men and 43% of eligible women are members. Most popular organizations: Student Senate, University Productions, Graduate Student Council, Residence Hall Association, Global Union. Major annual events: Greek Week/Sundaze, Lehigh/Lafayette Football Weekend, Student Organization and Cub Night. Student services: health clinic, personal-

psychological counseling, women's center. Campus security: 24-hour emergency response devices and patrols, student patrols, late night transport-escort service, controlled dormitory access. 2,259 college housing spaces available; 2,151 were occupied in 2003-04. Freshmen guaranteed college housing. Option: coed housing available. E. W. Fairchild-Martindale Library plus 1 other with 1.2 million books, 1.7 million microform titles, 6,271 serials, 8,415 audiovisual materials, an OPAC, and a Web page. 572 computers available on campus for general student use. A campuswide network can be accessed from student residence rooms and from off campus. Staffed computer lab on campus.

Community Environment: Population: 70,000. Bethlehem is famous for the Moravian Community, the Bach Choir, the corporate headquarters of Bethlehem Steel and Lehigh University. The historic area of Bethlehem has many 18th century buildings still in use; others are being restored by active community groups. The town contains 6 colonial and Victorian museums. The Bach Festival is held annually in May in Packer Chapel on the Lehigh campus.

■ **LEHIGH VALLEY COLLEGE** *J-23*
2809 East Saucon Valley Rd.
Center Valley, PA 18034
Tel: (610)791-5100
Free: 800-227-9109
Fax: (610)791-7810
E-mail: joshua.padron@lehighvalley.edu
Web Site: http://www.lehighvalley.edu/

Description: Proprietary, 2-year, coed. Part of Career Education Corporation. Awards terminal associate degrees. Founded 1869. Setting: 30-acre urban campus with easy access to Philadelphia. Endowment: $500,000. Educational spending for 2005 fiscal year: $10,000 per student. Total enrollment: 1,236. Student-undergrad faculty ratio is 26:1. 707 applied, 25% were admitted. 1% from top 10% of their high school class, 10% from top quarter, 45% from top half. Students come from 3 states and territories, 1% from out-of-state, 55% 25 or older, 0% live on campus. Retention: 63% of full-time freshmen returned the following year. Core. Academic remediation for entering students, services for LD students, advanced placement, independent study, adult/continuing education programs, co-op programs and internships.

Entrance Requirements: Open admission. Options: Common Application, electronic application, deferred admission. Required: high school transcript, ACCUPLACER. Recommended: interview. Entrance: noncompetitive. Application deadline: Rolling. Notification: continuous.

Costs Per Year: Application fee: $50. Tuition: $325 per credit hour part-time. Varies by program.

Collegiate Environment: Orientation program. Social organizations: 3 open to all. Most popular organizations: Student Government, Travel Club. Major annual events: ALS walk, SIFE. Campus security: evening security guard. College housing not available. Operations spending for 2004 fiscal year: $60,000. 100 computers available on campus for general student use. Computer purchase/lease plans available. A campuswide network can be accessed. Staffed computer lab on campus.

■ **LINCOLN TECHNICAL INSTITUTE (ALLENTOWN)** *J-23*
5151 Tilghman St.
Allentown, PA 18104-3298
Tel: (610)398-5300
Admissions: (610)398-5301
Web Site: http://www.lincolntech.com/

Description: Proprietary, 2-year, coed. Part of Lincoln Technical Institute, Inc. Awards diplomas and terminal associate degrees. Founded 1949. Setting: 10-acre suburban campus with easy access to Philadelphia. Total enrollment: 500. 325 applied, 77% were admitted. Core. Calendar: semesters. Summer session for credit.

Entrance Requirements: Open admission. Options: Common Application, early admission. Required: high school transcript, interview. Recommended: recommendations. Entrance: noncompetitive. Application deadline: Rolling.

Collegiate Environment: Orientation program. College housing not available. 60 computers available on campus for general student use.

■ **LINCOLN TECHNICAL INSTITUTE (PHILADELPHIA)** *M-24*
9191 Torresdale Ave.
Philadelphia, PA 19136-1595
Tel: (215)335-0800
Free: 800-238-8381
Fax: (215)335-1443

E-mail: jkuntz@lincolntech.com

Web Site: http://www.lincolntech.com/

Description: Proprietary, 2-year, coed. Part of Lincoln Technical Institute, Inc. Awards terminal associate degrees. Founded 1946. Setting: 3-acre suburban campus. Total enrollment: 400. Core. Calendar: modular. Part-time degree program, adult/continuing education programs, co-op programs.

Entrance Requirements: Open admission. Option: deferred admission. Required: high school transcript, minimum 2.0 high school GPA, interview. Entrance: noncompetitive. Application deadline: Rolling.

Collegiate Environment: Student-run newspaper. Campus security: 16-hour patrols by trained security personnel. College housing not available. 6 computers available on campus for general student use.

■ LINCOLN UNIVERSITY *N-21*

PO Box 179

Lincoln University, PA 19352

Tel: (610)932-8300

Free: 800-790-0191

E-mail: admiss@lincoln.edu

Web Site: http://www.lincoln.edu/

Description: State-related, comprehensive, coed. Awards bachelor's and master's degrees. Founded 1854. Setting: 422-acre rural campus with easy access to Philadelphia. Endowment: $18.9 million. Research spending for 2004 fiscal year: $3.2 million. Educational spending for 2005 fiscal year: $7174 per student. Total enrollment: 2,278. Faculty: 183 (93 full-time, 90 part-time). Student-undergrad faculty ratio is 16:1. 5,435 applied, 35% were admitted. 7% from top 10% of their high school class, 23% from top quarter, 45% from top half. Full-time: 1,652 students, 61% women, 39% men. Part-time: 62 students, 58% women, 42% men. Students come from 25 states and territories, 33 other countries, 53% from out-of-state, 0.1% Native American, 0.2% Hispanic, 93% black, 0% Asian American or Pacific Islander, 6% international, 7% 25 or older, 97% live on campus, 2% transferred in. Retention: 68% of full-time freshmen returned the following year. Academic areas with the most degrees conferred: business/marketing; education; communications/journalism. Core. Calendar: semesters. Academic remediation for entering students, advanced placement, accelerated degree program, self-designed majors, honors program, independent study, double major, summer session for credit, part-time degree program, adult/continuing education programs, co-op programs and internships, graduate courses open to undergrads. Off campus study at Lafayette College, Temple University, University of Delaware. Study abroad program. ROTC: Army (c), Air Force (c).

Entrance Requirements: Options: electronic application, early admission, deferred admission. Required: essay, high school transcript, minimum 2.0 high school GPA, 2 recommendations, SAT or ACT. Recommended: interview. Entrance: moderately difficult. Application deadline: Rolling. Notification: 2/15. Preference given to state residents.

Costs Per Year: Application fee: $20. State resident tuition: $5236 full-time, $284 per credit hour part-time. Nonresident tuition: $8912 full-time, $459 per credit hour part-time. Mandatory fees: $2382 full-time. Part-time tuition varies according to course load. College room and board: $6792. College room only: $3692. Room and board charges vary according to board plan.

Collegiate Environment: Orientation program. Drama-theater group, choral group, student-run newspaper, radio station. Social organizations: 65 open to all; national fraternities, national sororities; 2% of eligible men and 1% of eligible women are members. Most popular organizations: The Gospel Ensemble, Ziana Fashion Club, We R One, Council of Independent Organizations. Major annual events: Homecoming, Spring Fling, Pump Handle. Student services: health clinic, personal-psychological counseling, women's center. Campus security: 24-hour emergency response devices and patrols, late night transport-escort service. 1,500 college housing spaces available; 1,476 were occupied in 2003-04. Freshmen given priority for college housing. Options: coed, men-only, women-only housing available. Langston Hughes Memorial Library with 188,811 books, 10,257 microform titles, 605 serials, 2,643 audiovisual materials, and an OPAC. Operations spending for 2004 fiscal year: $1 million. 210 computers available on campus for general student use. Computer purchase/lease plans available. A campuswide network can be accessed from student residence rooms and from off campus. Staffed computer lab on campus.

■ LOCK HAVEN UNIVERSITY OF PENNSYLVANIA *G-14*

401 N. Fairview St.

Lock Haven, PA 17745-2390

Tel: (570)893-2011

Free: 800-233-8978

Admissions: (570)893-2027

Fax: (570)893-2201

E-mail: admissions@eagle.lhup.edu

Web Site: http://www.lhup.edu/

Description: State-supported, comprehensive, coed. Part of Pennsylvania State System of Higher Education. Awards associate, bachelor's, and master's degrees. Founded 1870. Setting: 165-acre rural campus. Endowment: $6.7 million. Educational spending for 2005 fiscal year: $4666 per student. Total enrollment: 5,283. Faculty: 273 (254 full-time, 19 part-time). Student-undergrad faculty ratio is 19:1. 4,182 applied, 77% were admitted. 7% from top 10% of their high school class, 25% from top quarter, 62% from top half. Full-time: 4,556 students, 57% women, 43% men. Part-time: 421 students, 68% women, 32% men. Students come from 32 states and territories, 39 other countries, 9% from out-of-state, 0.3% Native American, 2% Hispanic, 5% black, 1% Asian American or Pacific Islander, 1% international, 10% 25 or older, 36% live on campus, 5% transferred in. Retention: 73% of full-time freshmen returned the following year. Academic areas with the most degrees conferred: education; parks and recreation; health professions and related sciences. Core. Calendar: semesters. Academic remediation for entering students, ESL program, services for LD students, advanced placement, self-designed majors, honors program, independent study, distance learning, double major, summer session for credit, part-time degree program, adult/continuing education programs, co-op programs and internships, graduate courses open to undergrads. Off campus study at Pennsylvania Consortium for International Education. Study abroad program. ROTC: Army.

Entrance Requirements: Options: Peterson's Universal Application, electronic application, deferred admission. Required: SAT or ACT. Recommended: minimum 3.0 high school GPA. Required for some: essay, high school transcript, recommendations. Entrance: moderately difficult. Application deadline: Rolling. Notification: continuous.

Costs Per Year: Application fee: $25. State resident tuition: $4906 full-time, $204 per credit part-time. Nonresident tuition: $10,266 full-time, $428 per credit part-time. Mandatory fees: $1352 full-time, $38 per credit part-time, $98 per term part-time. Full-time tuition and fees vary according to course load and location. Part-time tuition and fees vary according to course load and location. College room and board: $5840. College room only: $3204. Room and board charges vary according to board plan and housing facility.

Collegiate Environment: Orientation program. Drama-theater group, choral group, marching band, student-run newspaper, radio station. Social organizations: 93 open to all; national fraternities, national sororities. Most popular organizations: student government, Residence Hall Association. Major annual events: Homecoming, Family Day, Spring Week. Student services: health clinic, personal-psychological counseling. Campus security: 24-hour emergency response devices and patrols. 1,764 college housing spaces available; all were occupied in 2003-04. Freshmen given priority for college housing. On-campus residence required through sophomore year. Options: coed, women-only housing available. Stevenson Library with 429,941 books, 741,692 microform titles, 935 serials, 8,861 audiovisual materials, an OPAC, and a Web page. Operations spending for 2004 fiscal year: $1.9 million. 290 computers available on campus for general student use. A campuswide network can be accessed from student residence rooms and from off campus. Staffed computer lab on campus.

Community Environment: Population 10,500, Loch Haven was laid out at the site of old Fort Reed, which was erected to protect the frontier settlers from the Indians. The fort was evacuated in the great runaway of 1778. Today, lumbering is a major industry and paper products are produced here. The city lies in a central mountainous region with a moderate climate. Local recreation includes hunting, fishing, boating, hang gliding, and skiing. Private homes provide supplemental student housing.

■ LUZERNE COUNTY COMMUNITY COLLEGE *G-20*

1333 South Prospect St.

Nanticoke, PA 18634-9804

Tel: (570)740-0300

Admissions: (570)740-0342

Web Site: http://www.luzerne.edu/

Description: County-supported, 2-year, coed. Awards certificates, diplomas, transfer associate, and terminal associate degrees. Founded 1966. Setting: 122-acre suburban campus with easy access to Philadelphia. Research spending for 2004 fiscal year: $91,428. Educational spending for 2005 fiscal year: $5350 per student. Total enrollment: 6,170. Student-undergrad faculty ratio is 19:1. 2,337 applied, 67% were admitted. Full-time: 2,940 students,

51% women, 49% men. Part-time: 3,230 students, 65% women, 35% men. Students come from 2 states and territories, 1 other country, 0% from out-of-state, 0.1% Native American, 1% Hispanic, 2% black, 1% Asian American or Pacific Islander, 0.1% international, 43% 25 or older, 6% transferred in. Core. Calendar: semesters. Academic remediation for entering students, services for LD students, advanced placement, accelerated degree program, distance learning, summer session for credit, part-time degree program, external degree program, internships. ROTC: Air Force (c).

Entrance Requirements: Open admission except for health sciences programs. Options: early admission, deferred admission. Recommended: high school transcript. Entrance: noncompetitive. Application deadline: Rolling.

Costs Per Year: Application fee: $40. Area resident tuition: $76 per credit part-time. State resident tuition: $152 per credit part-time. Nonresident tuition: $228 per credit part-time. Mandatory fees: $16 per credit part-time.

Collegiate Environment: Orientation program. Student-run newspaper, radio station. Social organizations: 25 open to all. Most popular organizations: student government, Circle K, Nursing Forum, Science Club, SADAH. Major annual events: Alumni Career Fair, College Night, Craft Festival. Campus security: 24-hour patrols. College housing not available. Learning Resources Center plus 1 other with 60,000 books, 35,500 microform titles, 744 serials, 3,000 audiovisual materials, an OPAC, and a Web page. Operations spending for 2004 fiscal year: $62,500. 150 computers available on campus for general student use. A campuswide network can be accessed. Staffed computer lab on campus.

■ **LYCOMING COLLEGE** *F-16*
700 College Place
Williamsport, PA 17701-5192
Tel: (570)321-4000
Free: 800-345-3920
Admissions: (570)321-4026
Fax: (570)321-4337
E-mail: admissions@lycoming.edu
Web Site: http://www.lycoming.edu/

Description: Independent United Methodist, 4-year, coed. Awards bachelor's degrees. Founded 1812. Setting: 35-acre small town campus. Endowment: $101.2 million. Research spending for 2004 fiscal year: $95,000. Educational spending for 2005 fiscal year: $7156 per student. Total enrollment: 1,467. Student-undergrad faculty ratio is 14:1. 1,511 applied, 77% were admitted. 19% from top 10% of their high school class, 45% from top quarter, 80% from top half. 21 class presidents, 23 valedictorians, 75 student government officers. Full-time: 1,450 students, 57% women, 43% men. Part-time: 17 students, 100% women. Students come from 24 states and territories, 13 other countries, 30% from out-of-state, 0.5% Native American, 1% Hispanic, 3% black, 1% Asian American or Pacific Islander, 1% international, 3% 25 or older, 83% live on campus, 3% transferred in. Retention: 84% of full-time freshmen returned the following year. Academic areas with the most degrees conferred: psychology; social sciences; business/marketing. Core. Calendar: semesters. Services for LD students, advanced placement, accelerated degree program, self-designed majors, honors program, independent study, double major, summer session for credit, part-time degree program, internships. Off campus study at members of the Student Enrichment Semester. Study abroad program. ROTC: Army (c).

Entrance Requirements: Options: Common Application, electronic application, early admission, deferred admission, international baccalaureate accepted. Required: essay, high school transcript, 2 recommendations, SAT or ACT. Recommended: minimum 2.3 high school GPA, interview. Entrance: moderately difficult. Application deadline: 6/1. Notification: continuous.

Costs Per Year: Application fee: $35. Comprehensive fee: $30,622 includes full-time tuition ($23,680), mandatory fees ($400), and college room and board ($6542). College room only: $3356. Full-time tuition and fees vary according to course load. Room and board charges vary according to housing facility. Part-time tuition: $740 per credit hour.

Collegiate Environment: Orientation program. Drama-theater group, choral group, student-run newspaper, radio station. Social organizations: 64 open to all; national fraternities, national sororities, local sororities; 14% of eligible men and 17% of eligible women are members. Most popular organizations: Radio Club (WRLC), Wilderness Club, student newspaper, campus ministry, Habitat for Humanity. Major annual events: Major Concert, Family Weekend, carnival. Student services: health clinic, personal-psychological counseling. Campus security: 24-hour emergency response devices and patrols, student patrols, late night transport-escort service, controlled dormitory access. College housing designed to accommodate 1,235 students; 1,242 undergraduates lived in college housing during 2003-04. Freshmen guaranteed college housing. On-campus residence required through senior year. Options: coed, women-only housing available. Snowden Library plus 1 other with 170,000 books, 950 serials, an OPAC, and a Web page. Operations spending for 2004 fiscal year: $867,000. 140 computers available on campus for general student use. Computer purchase/lease plans available. A campuswide network can be accessed from student residence rooms and from off campus. Staffed computer lab on campus.

Community Environment: Population 35,000. This town, in a scenic mountainous region on the west branch of the Susquehanna River, was known as a great lumber center until the 1890s. As the forests were depleted, it became a manufacturing city and now has a diversified production including steel wire rope, computer components, batteries, flashbulbs, radio tubes, power piping, chemicals, lumber and its byproducts, aircraft engines, textiles, furniture, leather, and mobile homes. The area is provided transportation by bus and air lines. The community has many churches representing various faiths. There are two hospitals, numerous health agencies, a library, a community cultural center, a museum, and various civic, fraternal and veteran's organizations in the immediate area. Part-time employment is available. Local recreation includes boating, golf, hiking, picnic areas, fishing, hunting, skiing, and cycling.

■ **MANOR COLLEGE** *D-47*
700 Fox Chase Rd.
Jenkintown, PA 19046
Tel: (215)885-2360
Admissions: (215)884-2216
E-mail: ftadmiss@manor.edu
Web Site: http://www.manor.edu/

Description: Independent Byzantine Catholic, 2-year, coed. Awards certificates, diplomas, transfer associate, and terminal associate degrees. Founded 1947. Setting: 35-acre small town campus with easy access to Philadelphia. Total enrollment: 865. Student-undergrad faculty ratio is 14:1. 536 applied, 50% were admitted. 4% from top 10% of their high school class, 19% from top quarter, 45% from top half. Full-time: 433 students, 75% women, 25% men. Part-time: 432 students, 87% women, 13% men. Students come from 5 states and territories, 8 other countries, 7% from out-of-state, 41% 25 or older, 27% transferred in. Core. Calendar: semesters. Academic remediation for entering students, ESL program, advanced placement, honors program, independent study, distance learning, double major, summer session for credit, part-time degree program, adult/continuing education programs, internships.

Entrance Requirements: Options: electronic application, deferred admission. Required: high school transcript, interview, SAT or ACT. Entrance: minimally difficult. Application deadline: Rolling. Notification: continuous.

Costs Per Year: Application fee: $20. Comprehensive fee: $16,514 includes full-time tuition ($10,868), mandatory fees ($350), and college room and board ($5296). Part-time tuition: $235 per credit hour. Part-time mandatory fees: $25 per term.

Collegiate Environment: Orientation program. Choral group. Student services: personal-psychological counseling. Campus security: 24-hour emergency response devices and patrols. Option: coed housing available. Basileiad Library with 42,000 books, 4,000 microform titles, 225 serials, 300 audiovisual materials, an OPAC, and a Web page. 35 computers available on campus for general student use. A campuswide network can be accessed from student residence rooms. Staffed computer lab on campus.

■ **MANSFIELD UNIVERSITY OF PENNSYLVANIA** *C-16*
Academy St.
Mansfield, PA 16933
Tel: (570)662-4000
Free: 800-577-6826
Admissions: (570)662-4813
Fax: (570)662-4121
E-mail: admissions@mnsfld.edu
Web Site: http://www.mansfield.edu/

Description: State-supported, comprehensive, coed. Part of Pennsylvania State System of Higher Education. Awards associate, bachelor's, and master's degrees. Founded 1857. Setting: 205-acre small town campus. Endowment: $6.2 million. Educational spending for 2005 fiscal year: $5065 per student. Total enrollment: 3,390. Faculty: 223 (165 full-time, 58 part-time). Student-undergrad faculty ratio is 16:1. 2,348 applied, 72% were admitted. 12% from top 10% of their high school class, 33% from top quarter,

64% from top half. 4 valedictorians. Full-time: 2,713 students, 61% women, 39% men. Part-time: 273 students, 71% women, 29% men. Students come from 17 states and territories, 23 other countries, 20% from out-of-state, 1% Native American, 1% Hispanic, 6% black, 1% Asian American or Pacific Islander, 1% international, 17% 25 or older, 50% live on campus, 8% transferred in. Retention: 64% of full-time freshmen returned the following year. Academic areas with the most degrees conferred: education; business/marketing; communications/journalism. Core. Calendar: semesters. Academic remediation for entering students, services for LD students, advanced placement, accelerated degree program, self-designed majors, freshman honors college, honors program, independent study, distance learning, double major, summer session for credit, part-time degree program, adult/continuing education programs, internships, graduate courses open to undergrads. Off campus study at other members of the Pennsylvania State System of Higher Education. Study abroad program.

Entrance Requirements: Options: Peterson's Universal Application, electronic application, early admission, deferred admission, international baccalaureate accepted. Required: high school transcript, SAT or ACT. Recommended: essay, minimum 2.5 high school GPA, recommendations. Required for some: interview. Entrance: moderately difficult. Application deadline: Rolling. Notification: continuous.

Costs Per Year: Application fee: $25. State resident tuition: $4906 full-time, $204 per credit part-time. Nonresident tuition: $12,266 full-time, $511 per credit part-time. Mandatory fees: $1502 full-time, $78 per credit part-time. Part-time tuition and fees vary according to course load. College room and board: $5868. Room and board charges vary according to board plan.

Collegiate Environment: Orientation program. Drama-theater group, choral group, marching band, student-run newspaper, radio station. Social organizations: 108 open to all; national fraternities, national sororities, local fraternities; 5% of eligible men and 5% of eligible women are members. Most popular organizations: Mansfield International Student Organization, P.R. Society, PSEA, Ski Club, Activities Council. Major annual events: Parents' Weekend, Homecoming, Greek Week. Student services: health clinic, personal-psychological counseling, women's center. Campus security: 24-hour emergency response devices and patrols, student patrols, late night transport-escort service, controlled dormitory access. 1,800 college housing spaces available; 1,400 were occupied in 2003-04. Freshmen guaranteed college housing. On-campus residence required through junior year. Option: coed housing available. North Hall Library with 246,141 books, 818,288 microform titles, 2,948 serials, 26,742 audiovisual materials, an OPAC, and a Web page. Operations spending for 2004 fiscal year: $1.7 million. 550 computers available on campus for general student use. Computer purchase/lease plans available. A campuswide network can be accessed from student residence rooms and from off campus. Staffed computer lab on campus.

Community Environment: Population 4,114, Mansfield is a rural town located on the north-central border of Pennsylvania at the intersection of U.S. Highways 6 and 15. It is mild in summer and often near freezing in winter. The community is served by bus lines. Ski slopes, camping areas, lakes, and hiking trails are all within an hours drive. Other recreational activities include river-rafting, cross-country skiing, fishing, and hunting.

■ **MARYWOOD UNIVERSITY** *F-22*

2300 Adams Ave.
Scranton, PA 18509-1598
Tel: (570)348-6211
Free: 800-346-5014
Admissions: (570)348-6234
Fax: (570)961-4763
E-mail: ugadm@ac.marywood.edu
Web Site: http://www.marywood.edu/

Description: Independent Roman Catholic, comprehensive, coed. Awards associate, bachelor's, master's, and doctoral degrees and post-master's certificates. Founded 1915. Setting: 115-acre suburban campus. Endowment: $22.2 million. Research spending for 2004 fiscal year: $46,778. Educational spending for 2005 fiscal year: $7785 per student. Total enrollment: 3,127. 1,377 applied, 76% were admitted. 16% from top 10% of their high school class, 38% from top quarter, 75% from top half. Full-time: 1,598 students, 74% women, 26% men. Part-time: 213 students, 69% women, 31% men. Students come from 28 states and territories, 18 other countries, 20% from out-of-state, 0.3% Native American, 2% Hispanic, 2% black, 1% Asian American or Pacific Islander, 2% international, 14% 25 or older, 38% live on campus, 7% transferred in. Retention: 81% of full-time freshmen returned the following year. Core. Calendar: semesters. Academic

remediation for entering students, ESL program, services for LD students, advanced placement, accelerated degree program, self-designed majors, honors program, independent study, distance learning, double major, summer session for credit, part-time degree program, external degree program, adult/continuing education programs, internships, graduate courses open to undergrads. Off campus study at University of Scranton. Study abroad program. ROTC: Army (c), Air Force (c).

Entrance Requirements: Options: Peterson's Universal Application, Common Application, electronic application, early admission, deferred admission. Required: high school transcript, 1 recommendation, SAT or ACT. Recommended: essay, interview, SAT. Required for some: essay, interview. Entrance: moderately difficult. Application deadline: Rolling. Notification: continuous.

Costs Per Year: Application fee: $30. Comprehensive fee: $30,740 includes full-time tuition ($20,700), mandatory fees ($940), and college room and board ($9100). College room only: $5152. Room and board charges vary according to board plan and housing facility. Part-time tuition: $643 per credit. Part-time mandatory fees: $190 per term. Part-time tuition and fees vary according to course load.

Collegiate Environment: Orientation program. Drama-theater group, choral group, student-run newspaper, radio station. Social organizations: 53 open to all; local sororities; 3% of women are members. Most popular organizations: Outdoor Adventure Club, Psi Chi, International Club, Peer Mediators, Speech and Hearing Club. Major annual events: Family Weekend, Orientation, Opening Day Ceremony and Picnic. Student services: health clinic, personal-psychological counseling. Campus security: 24-hour emergency response devices and patrols, late night transport-escort service, controlled dormitory access, apartments with deadbolts, self-defense education, lighted pathways, seminars on safety. 671 college housing spaces available; 618 were occupied in 2003-04. Freshmen guaranteed college housing. On-campus residence required through sophomore year. Options: coed, men-only, women-only housing available. Learning Resources Center plus 1 other with 220,205 books, 351,622 microform titles, 913 serials, 44,013 audiovisual materials, an OPAC, and a Web page. Operations spending for 2004 fiscal year: $1.1 million. 367 computers available on campus for general student use. A campuswide network can be accessed from student residence rooms and from off campus. Staffed computer lab on campus.

Community Environment: The city of Scranton is a regional center for business, health care, social services, and recreation in northeastern Pennsylvania. It is 120 miles west of New York City and 115 miles north of Philadelphia. Sports, special events, music, theater, and parks are available. The nearby Pocono Mountains region offers six major ski areas, resorts, campgrounds, snowmobiling, canoeing, whitewater rafting, and various other activities. The Scranton area is home to seven other colleges and universities in addition to Marywood.

■ **MCCANN SCHOOL OF BUSINESS & TECHNOLOGY** *J-19*

2650 Woodglen Rd.
Pottsville, PA 17901
Tel: (570)622-7622
Fax: (570)622-7770
Web Site: http://www.mccannschool.com/

Description: Proprietary, 2-year, coed. Awards certificates, diplomas, transfer associate, and terminal associate degrees. Founded 1897. Setting: small town campus. Total enrollment: 841. 4% from top 10% of their high school class, 23% from top quarter, 54% from top half. Full-time: 540 students, 79% women, 21% men. Part-time: 301 students, 74% women, 26% men. 0% from out-of-state, 0% Native American, 1% black, 0.1% Asian American or Pacific Islander, 0% international, 58% 25 or older, 4% transferred in. Core. Advanced placement, independent study, double major, summer session for credit, part-time degree program, internships.

Entrance Requirements: Open admission. Options: Common Application, electronic application. Required: high school transcript, minimum 2.0 high school GPA, interview, Wonderlic aptitude test. Entrance: minimally difficult. Application deadline: Rolling.

Collegiate Environment: Orientation program. Social organizations: 3 open to all. Most popular organizations: student council, Circle K, American Marketing Association. College housing not available. 1,850 books and 26 serials. 300 computers available on campus for general student use. A campuswide network can be accessed. Staffed computer lab on campus.

■ **MEDIAN SCHOOL OF ALLIED HEALTH CAREERS** *K-3*

125 7th St.
Pittsburgh, PA 15222-3400

Tel: (412)391-7021
Free: 800-570-0693
Fax: (412)232-4348
Web Site: http://www.medianschool.edu/
Description: Proprietary, 2-year, coed. Awards diplomas and terminal associate degrees. Founded 1958. Setting: urban campus. Total enrollment: 287. Students come from 11 states and territories, 2 other countries, 6% from out-of-state, 33% 25 or older. Internships.
Entrance Requirements: Open admission. Option: deferred admission. Required: essay, high school transcript, interview, Wonderlic aptitude test. Recommended: minimum 2.0 high school GPA. Entrance: minimally difficult. Application deadline: Rolling.
Collegiate Environment: Student services: personal-psychological counseling. Campus security: security during class hours. College housing not available. Median Resource Center with 1,485 books and 43 serials. 38 computers available on campus for general student use. Staffed computer lab on campus.

■ **MERCYHURST COLLEGE** *B-3*
501 East 38th St.
Erie, PA 16546
Tel: (814)824-2000
Free: 800-825-1926
Admissions: (814)824-2576
Fax: (814)824-2071
Web Site: http://www.mercyhurst.edu/
Description: Independent Roman Catholic, comprehensive, coed. Awards associate, bachelor's, and master's degrees. Founded 1926. Setting: 88-acre suburban campus with easy access to Buffalo. Endowment: $15.2 million. Educational spending for 2005 fiscal year: $4586 per student. Total enrollment: 4,120. Faculty: 248 (163 full-time, 85 part-time). Student-undergrad faculty ratio is 18:1. 2,711 applied, 78% were admitted. 18% from top 10% of their high school class, 43% from top quarter, 79% from top half. 17 valedictorians. Full-time: 3,378 students, 59% women, 41% men. Part-time: 462 students, 72% women, 28% men. Students come from 38 states and territories, 26 other countries, 38% from out-of-state, 0.2% Native American, 2% Hispanic, 4% black, 1% Asian American or Pacific Islander, 4% international, 16% 25 or older, 73% live on campus, 2% transferred in. Retention: 83% of full-time freshmen returned the following year. Academic areas with the most degrees conferred: business/marketing; education; family and consumer sciences; visual and performing arts. Core. Calendar: 4-3-3. Academic remediation for entering students, services for LD students, advanced placement, accelerated degree program, self-designed majors, honors program, independent study, double major, summer session for credit, part-time degree program, adult/continuing education programs, co-op programs and internships, graduate courses open to undergrads. Off campus study. Study abroad program. ROTC: Army (c), Air Force (c).
Entrance Requirements: Open admission. Options: Common Application, electronic application, deferred admission, international baccalaureate accepted. Required: high school transcript, SAT or ACT. Recommended: essay, interview. Required for some: recommendations. Entrance: moderately difficult. Application deadline: Rolling. Notification: continuous until 8/1.
Costs Per Year: Application fee: $30. Comprehensive fee: $26,187 includes full-time tuition ($17,760), mandatory fees ($1353), and college room and board ($7074). College room only: $3576. Room and board charges vary according to board plan and housing facility. Part-time tuition: $592 per credit. Part-time tuition varies according to course load and location.
Collegiate Environment: Orientation program. Drama-theater group, choral group, student-run newspaper, radio station. Social organizations: 44 open to all; 12% of eligible men and 16% of eligible women are members. Most popular organizations: student government, chorus, Admission Ambassadors, Amnesty International, The Merciad. Major annual events: Christmas on Campus, Homecoming, Parents' Weekend. Student services: health clinic, personal-psychological counseling. Campus security: 24-hour emergency response devices and patrols, campus-wide camera system. 1,950 college housing spaces available; 1,837 were occupied in 2003-04. Freshmen guaranteed college housing. On-campus residence required through sophomore year. Options: men-only, women-only housing available. Hammermill Library with 179,680 books, 53,026 microform titles, 1,013 serials, 10,669 audiovisual materials, an OPAC, and a Web page. Operations spending for 2004 fiscal year: $1 million. 330 computers available on campus for general student use. Computer purchase/lease plans available. A campuswide network can be accessed from student residence rooms and from off campus. Staffed computer lab on campus.

Community Environment: See Gannon University.

■ **MESSIAH COLLEGE** *L-17*
One College Ave.
Grantham, PA 17027
Tel: (717)766-2511
Free: 800-233-4220
Admissions: (717)691-6000
Fax: (717)796-5374
E-mail: admiss@messiah.edu
Web Site: http://www.messiah.edu/
Description: Independent interdenominational, 4-year, coed. Awards bachelor's degrees. Founded 1909. Setting: 400-acre small town campus. Endowment: $104 million. Educational spending for 2005 fiscal year: $9108 per student. Total enrollment: 2,916. Student-undergrad faculty ratio is 13:1. 2,730 applied, 75% were admitted. 39% from top 10% of their high school class, 71% from top quarter, 94% from top half. 15 National Merit Scholars, 41 valedictorians. Full-time: 2,864 students, 63% women, 37% men. Part-time: 52 students, 58% women, 42% men. Students come from 41 states and territories, 29 other countries, 48% from out-of-state, 0.03% Native American, 2% Hispanic, 2% black, 2% Asian American or Pacific Islander, 3% international, 2% 25 or older, 89% live on campus, 3% transferred in. Retention: 85% of full-time freshmen returned the following year. Academic areas with the most degrees conferred: education; business/marketing; health professions and related sciences. Core. Calendar: semesters. Academic remediation for entering students, ESL program, services for LD students, advanced placement, accelerated degree program, self-designed majors, honors program, independent study, double major, summer session for credit, part-time degree program, adult/continuing education programs, internships. Off campus study at Christian College Consortium, Council for Christian Colleges and Universities. Study abroad program.
Entrance Requirements: Options: Peterson's Universal Application, Common Application, electronic application, early admission, deferred admission, international baccalaureate accepted. Required: essay, high school transcript, 2 recommendations. Recommended: interview. Required for some: SAT or ACT. Entrance: moderately difficult. Application deadline: Rolling. Notification: continuous.
Costs Per Year: Application fee: $30. Comprehensive fee: $28,910 includes full-time tuition ($21,420), mandatory fees ($690), and college room and board ($6800). College room only: $3540. Room and board charges vary according to board plan, housing facility, and location. Part-time tuition: $890 per credit. Part-time mandatory fees: $28 per credit.
Collegiate Environment: Orientation program. Drama-theater group, choral group, student-run newspaper, radio station. Social organizations: 60 open to all. Most popular organizations: outreach teams, student government, music ensembles, Small Group Program, Outdoors Club. Major annual events: Family Weekend, Homecoming, Christmas Tradition Banquet. Student services: health clinic, personal-psychological counseling. Campus security: 24-hour emergency response devices and patrols, student patrols, late night transport-escort service, controlled dormitory access, bicycle patrols, security lighting, self-defense classes, prevention/awareness programs. College housing designed to accommodate 2,369 students; 2,497 undergraduates lived in college housing during 2003-04. Freshmen guaranteed college housing. On-campus residence required through senior year. Options: coed, men-only, women-only housing available. Murray Library with 290,838 books, 117,923 microform titles, 5,973 serials, 17,920 audiovisual materials, an OPAC, and a Web page. Operations spending for 2004 fiscal year: $1.4 million. 481 computers available on campus for general student use. A campuswide network can be accessed from student residence rooms and from off campus. Staffed computer lab on campus.
Community Environment: Population of Harrisburg 100,000. Grantham is a semirural community in south-central Pennsylvania located 12 miles southwest of the state capital, Harrisburg - providing easy access to urban centers such Harrisburg, Philadelphia, Baltimore, and Washington, D.C.

■ **METROPOLITAN CAREER CENTER** *M-24*
100 South Broad St.
Philadelphia, PA 19110
Tel: (215)568-9215
Admissions: (215)843-6615
Fax: (215)568-3511
E-mail: khuselton@mcc-btc.org
Web Site: http://www.metropolitancareercenter.org/

Description: Independent, 2-year, coed. Founded 1974. Calendar: semesters.

■ **MILLERSVILLE UNIVERSITY OF PENNSYLVANIA** *M-19*
PO Box 1002
Millersville, PA 17551-0302
Tel: (717)872-3011
Free: 800-MU-ADMIT
Admissions: (717)872-3371
E-mail: adm_info@mu3.millersv.edu
Web Site: http://www.millersville.edu/

Description: State-supported, comprehensive, coed. Part of Pennsylvania State System of Higher Education. Awards associate, bachelor's, and master's degrees and post-master's certificates. Founded 1855. Setting: 190-acre small town campus. Endowment: $2 million. Research spending for 2004 fiscal year: $374,262. Educational spending for 2005 fiscal year: $5917 per student. Total enrollment: 7,998. Faculty: 468 (320 full-time, 148 part-time). Student-undergrad faculty ratio is 18:1. 6,471 applied, 60% were admitted. 15% from top 10% of their high school class, 43% from top quarter, 82% from top half. Full-time: 6,378 students, 57% women, 43% men. Part-time: 613 students, 55% women, 45% men. Students come from 23 states and territories, 4% from out-of-state, 0.2% Native American, 3% Hispanic, 6% black, 2% Asian American or Pacific Islander, 0.4% international, 10% 25 or older, 37% live on campus, 5% transferred in. Retention: 81% of full-time freshmen returned the following year. Core. Calendar: 4-1-4. Academic remediation for entering students, services for LD students, advanced placement, accelerated degree program, honors program, independent study, distance learning, double major, summer session for credit, part-time degree program, adult/continuing education programs, co-op programs and internships, graduate courses open to undergrads. Off campus study at Franklin and Marshall College, Lancaster Theological Seminary, Marine Science Consortium. Study abroad program. ROTC: Army.
Entrance Requirements: Options: Common Application, electronic application, early admission, deferred admission. Required: high school transcript, minimum 2.0 high school GPA, SAT or ACT. Recommended: recommendations. Required for some: essay, recommendations, interview. Entrance: moderately difficult. Application deadline: Rolling. Notification: continuous.
Costs Per Year: Application fee: $35. State resident tuition: $4906 full-time, $204 per credit part-time. Nonresident tuition: $12,266 full-time, $511 per credit part-time. Mandatory fees: $1329 full-time, $81 per credit part-time. Part-time tuition and fees vary according to course load. College room and board: $5878. College room only: $3474. Room and board charges vary according to board plan.
Collegiate Environment: Orientation program. Drama-theater group, choral group, marching band, student-run newspaper, radio station. Social organizations: 109 open to all; national fraternities, national sororities, local fraternities, local sororities; 4% of eligible men and 6% of eligible women are members. Most popular organizations: Ocean Science Club, John Newman Association, United Campus Ministries, Resident Student Association, National Broadcasting Society. Major annual events: Superfest, Into the Streets, homecoming. Student services: health clinic, personal-psychological counseling, women's center. Campus security: 24-hour emergency response devices and patrols, student patrols, late night transport-escort service, controlled dormitory access, crime awareness programs, self-defense education, shuttle buses. College housing designed to accommodate 2,529 students; 2,640 undergraduates lived in college housing during 2003-04. Freshmen guaranteed college housing. On-campus residence required through sophomore year. Option: coed housing available. Helen A. Ganser Library with 503,145 books, 592,019 microform titles, 10,861 serials, 31,594 audiovisual materials, an OPAC, and a Web page. Operations spending for 2004 fiscal year: $3.1 million. 510 computers available on campus for general student use. Computer purchase/lease plans available. A campuswide network can be accessed from student residence rooms and from off campus. Staffed computer lab on campus.
Community Environment: Population 8,064, Millersville is a suburban community adjacent to Lancaster. The climate is temperate. There is air and train service, bus lines, and major highways are easily accessible. The community has churches, theatres, hospitals, and shopping facilities located in Lancaster. Major civic, fraternal and veteran's organizations are represented here.

■ **MONTGOMERY COUNTY COMMUNITY COLLEGE** *C-46*
340 DeKalb Pike
Blue Bell, PA 19422-0796

Tel: (215)641-6300
Admissions: (215)641-6551
Fax: (215)653-0585
E-mail: admrec@admin.mc3.edu
Web Site: http://www.mc3.edu

Description: County-supported, 2-year, coed. Awards certificates, transfer associate, and terminal associate degrees. Founded 1964. Setting: 186-acre suburban campus with easy access to Philadelphia. Educational spending for 2005 fiscal year: $2806 per student. Total enrollment: 10,874. Student-undergrad faculty ratio is 23:1. 4,184 applied, 100% were admitted. Full-time: 4,761 students, 51% women, 49% men. Part-time: 6,113 students, 65% women, 35% men. Students come from 10 states and territories, 41 other countries, 0.2% from out-of-state, 0.2% Native American, 3% Hispanic, 9% black, 6% Asian American or Pacific Islander, 1% international, 27% 25 or older. Retention: 61% of full-time freshmen returned the following year. Core. Calendar: semesters. Academic remediation for entering students, ESL program, services for LD students, advanced placement, self-designed majors, honors program, independent study, distance learning, summer session for credit, part-time degree program, adult/continuing education programs, internships. Study abroad program.
Entrance Requirements: Open admission except for dental hygiene, nursing, medical laboratory technology, automotive technology programs. Options: electronic application, early admission, deferred admission. Required for some: high school transcript, interview. Entrance: noncompetitive. Application deadline: 5/1. Notification: continuous. Preference given to county residents.
Costs Per Year: Application fee: $25. Area resident tuition: $2716 full-time, $83 per credit part-time. State resident tuition: $5348 full-time, $191 per credit part-time. Nonresident tuition: $7980 full-time, $285 per credit part-time. Mandatory fees: $14 per credit part-time.
Collegiate Environment: Orientation program. Drama-theater group, choral group, student-run newspaper, radio station. Social organizations: 20 open to all. Most popular organizations: student government, Meridians Non-traditional Age Club, student radio station. Major annual events: Volleyball Benefit, Spring Fling/Fun Day, Cultural Fair. Student services: health clinic, personal-psychological counseling. Campus security: 24-hour emergency response devices and patrols, late night transport-escort service. College housing not available. The Brendlinger Library plus 1 other with 201,174 books, 53,587 microform titles, 550 serials, 19,450 audiovisual materials, an OPAC, and a Web page. Operations spending for 2004 fiscal year: $243,809. 800 computers available on campus for general student use. A campuswide network can be accessed from off-campus. Staffed computer lab on campus.
Community Environment: Rural community (under 2,500). Suburban campus environment. 5 miles from (north) Norristown. Some bus transportation. Approximately 45 minute commute to Philadelphia. Surrounding industries include pharmaceutical and chemical-product companies; some farming.

■ **MOORE COLLEGE OF ART & DESIGN** *M-24*
20th and the Parkway
Philadelphia, PA 19103
Tel: (215)568-4515
Free: 800-523-2025
Fax: (215)568-3547
E-mail: hlee@moore.edu
Web Site: http://www.moore.edu/

Description: Independent, 4-year, women only. Awards bachelor's degrees. Founded 1848. Setting: 3-acre urban campus. Endowment: $7 million. Educational spending for 2005 fiscal year: $7603 per student. Total enrollment: 491. Student-undergrad faculty ratio is 8:1. 223 applied, 87% were admitted. Full-time: 421 students. Part-time: 70 students. Students come from 29 states and territories, 7 other countries, 45% from out-of-state, 0.4% Native American, 5% Hispanic, 10% black, 6% Asian American or Pacific Islander, 2% international, 15% 25 or older, 55% live on campus, 1% transferred in. Retention: 79% of full-time freshmen returned the following year. Academic areas with the most degrees conferred: visual and performing arts; education. Core. Calendar: semesters. Academic remediation for entering students, services for LD students, advanced placement, accelerated degree program, independent study, double major, summer session for credit, part-time degree program, adult/continuing education programs, internships. Study abroad program.
Entrance Requirements: Options: Peterson's Universal Application, Common Application, early admission, early decision, deferred admission.

Required: high school transcript, minimum 2.5 high school GPA, 1 recommendation, portfolio, SAT or ACT. Recommended: essay, interview. Required for some: minimum 3.0 high school GPA. Entrance: moderately difficult. Application deadlines: 8/15, 11/15 for early decision. Notification: continuous, 11/30 for early decision.

Costs Per Year: Application fee: $40. Comprehensive fee: $32,256 includes full-time tuition ($22,846), mandatory fees ($756), and college room and board ($8654). College room only: $5227. Part-time tuition: $920 per credit. Part-time mandatory fees: $189 per term.

Collegiate Environment: Orientation program. Student-run newspaper. Social organizations: 10 open to all. Most popular organizations: Student Government Association, Into the Streets, Moore Environment Action Now, Black Student Union, Asian Student Union. Major annual events: Family Day/Homecoming, Spring Fling Weekend, Student Show Month. Student services: health clinic, personal-psychological counseling, women's center. Campus security: 24-hour patrols, late night transport-escort service. 222 college housing spaces available; all were occupied in 2003-04. Freshmen guaranteed college housing. Option: women-only housing available. Moore College Library plus 1 other with 40,000 books and 124,804 audiovisual materials. Operations spending for 2004 fiscal year: $377,091. 150 computers available on campus for general student use. Staffed computer lab on campus.

Community Environment: See Temple University.

■ **MORAVIAN COLLEGE** *J-23*
1200 Main St.
Bethlehem, PA 18018-6650
Tel: (610)861-1300
Free: 800-441-3191
Admissions: (610)861-1320
Fax: (610)861-3956
E-mail: admissions@moravian.edu
Web Site: http://www.moravian.edu/

Description: Independent, comprehensive, coed, affiliated with Moravian Church. Awards bachelor's, master's, and first professional degrees. Founded 1742. Setting: 65-acre suburban campus with easy access to Philadelphia. Endowment: $61 million. Educational spending for 2005 fiscal year: $10,764 per student. Total enrollment: 2,030. Faculty: 190 (118 full-time, 72 part-time). Student-undergrad faculty ratio is 12:1. 1,890 applied, 65% were admitted. 31% from top 10% of their high school class, 64% from top quarter, 93% from top half. 2 class presidents, 4 valedictorians, 22 student government officers. Full-time: 1,543 students, 59% women, 41% men. Part-time: 249 students, 64% women, 36% men. Students come from 21 states and territories, 14 other countries, 41% from out-of-state, 0.1% Native American, 3% Hispanic, 2% black, 2% Asian American or Pacific Islander, 1% international, 69% live on campus, 3% transferred in. Retention: 86% of full-time freshmen returned the following year. Academic areas with the most degrees conferred: social sciences; business/marketing; psychology. Core. Calendar: semesters. Services for LD students, advanced placement, self-designed majors, honors program, independent study, double major, summer session for credit, part-time degree program, adult/continuing education programs, internships, graduate courses open to undergrads. Off campus study at Five other members of the Lehigh Valley Association of Independent Colleges, Washington Semester. Study abroad program. ROTC: Army (c).

Entrance Requirements: Options: Peterson's Universal Application, Common Application, electronic application, early admission, early decision, deferred admission, international baccalaureate accepted. Required: essay, high school transcript, 3 recommendations, SAT or ACT. Recommended: interview. Entrance: moderately difficult. Application deadlines: 2/15, 1/15 for early decision. Notification: 3/15, 12/15 for early decision.

Costs Per Year: Application fee: $40. One-time mandatory fee: $100. Comprehensive fee: $32,793 includes full-time tuition ($24,813), mandatory fees ($450), and college room and board ($7530). College room only: $4230. Room and board charges vary according to board plan and housing facility. Part-time tuition: $775 per credit. Part-time tuition varies according to class time.

Collegiate Environment: Orientation program. Drama-theater group, choral group, marching band, student-run newspaper, radio station. Social organizations: 77 open to all; national fraternities, national sororities; 15% of eligible men and 22% of eligible women are members. Most popular organizations: Student Alumni Association, United Student Government, Moravian College Choir, Twenty-six Points (student ambassador group), International Club. Major annual events: Mardi Gras, Christmas Vespers, an-

nual concert. Student services: health clinic, personal-psychological counseling. Campus security: 24-hour emergency response devices and patrols, late night transport-escort service, controlled dormitory access. 1,057 college housing spaces available; 1,052 were occupied in 2003-04. Freshmen guaranteed college housing. On-campus residence required in freshman year. Options: coed, men-only, women-only housing available. Reeves Library with 256,352 books, 11,414 microform titles, 1,318 serials, 1,950 audiovisual materials, an OPAC, and a Web page. Operations spending for 2004 fiscal year: $2 million. 236 computers available on campus for general student use. Computer purchase/lease plans available. A campuswide network can be accessed from student residence rooms and from off campus. Staffed computer lab on campus.

Community Environment: Town of about 75,000 residential neighborhood.

■ **MOUNT ALOYSIUS COLLEGE** *K-9*
7373 Admiral Peary Hwy.
Cresson, PA 16630-1999
Tel: (814)886-4131; 888-823-2220
Admissions: (814)886-6383
Fax: (814)886-2978
Web Site: http://www.mtaloy.edu/

Description: Independent Roman Catholic, comprehensive, coed. Awards associate, bachelor's, and master's degrees. Founded 1939. Setting: 165-acre rural campus. Endowment: $8.5 million. Educational spending for 2005 fiscal year: $10,564 per student. Total enrollment: 1,539. Faculty: 165 (62 full-time, 103 part-time). Student-undergrad faculty ratio is 14:1. 949 applied, 77% were admitted. 5 class presidents, 2 valedictorians, 100 student government officers. Full-time: 1,147 students, 71% women, 29% men. Part-time: 335 students, 75% women, 25% men. Students come from 10 states and territories, 12 other countries, 2% from out-of-state, 1% Native American, 1% Hispanic, 2% black, 0.2% Asian American or Pacific Islander, 2% international, 43% 25 or older, 22% live on campus, 16% transferred in. Retention: 69% of full-time freshmen returned the following year. Academic areas with the most degrees conferred: health professions and related sciences; business/marketing; security and protective services. Core. Calendar: semesters. Academic remediation for entering students, services for LD students, advanced placement, accelerated degree program, self-designed majors, honors program, independent study, distance learning, summer session for credit, part-time degree program, adult/continuing education programs, internships.

Entrance Requirements: Options: Common Application, electronic application, early admission, deferred admission, international baccalaureate accepted. Required: high school transcript, minimum 2.5 high school GPA, SAT or ACT. Recommended: interview. Required for some: essay, 3 recommendations, interview. Entrance: minimally difficult. Application deadline: Rolling. Notification: continuous.

Costs Per Year: Application fee: $30. Comprehensive fee: $20,840 includes full-time tuition ($14,220), mandatory fees ($430), and college room and board ($6190). College room only: $3130. Full-time tuition and fees vary according to class time, course load, and program. Room and board charges vary according to board plan. Part-time tuition: $450 per credit. Part-time tuition varies according to class time, course load, and program.

Collegiate Environment: Orientation program. Drama-theater group, choral group, student-run newspaper. Social organizations: 60 open to all. Most popular organizations: Phi Theta Kappa, Student Nursing Association, Student Government, Delta Epsilon Sigma, Residence Hall Association. Major annual events: Madrigal Dinner, Graduate Salute, Christmas at Mount Aloysius College. Student services: health clinic, personal-psychological counseling, women's center. Campus security: 24-hour emergency response devices and patrols, late night transport-escort service, controlled dormitory access. 234 college housing spaces available; 222 were occupied in 2003-04. Freshmen guaranteed college housing. Option: coed housing available. Mount Aloysius College Library plus 1 other with 84,174 books, 4,472 microform titles, 279 serials, 2,508 audiovisual materials, an OPAC, and a Web page. Operations spending for 2004 fiscal year: $456,798. 149 computers available on campus for general student use. Computer purchase/lease plans available. A campuswide network can be accessed from student residence rooms and from off campus. Staffed computer lab on campus.

Community Environment: Population 5,000. Cresson is a rural community with a moderately humid climate and relatively high temperatures in summer. The area is served by bus, highway, and an airport at Martinsburg 45 minutes away. The city has two Catholic, a Methodist, Presbyterian, Christian, and Missionary Alliance Churches. There are several civic, fraternal, and veteran's organizations within the area. Theatres, concerts, sport events, and other recreational facilities are located in nearby Altoona and Johnstown. There are part-time employment opportunities for students on campus.

■ MUHLENBERG COLLEGE *J-23*

2400 Chew St.
Allentown, PA 18104-5586
Tel: (484)664-3100
Admissions: (484)664-3245
Fax: (484)664-3234
E-mail: adm@muhlenberg.edu
Web Site: http://www.muhlenberg.edu/

Description: Independent, 4-year, coed, affiliated with Lutheran Church. Awards bachelor's degrees. Founded 1848. Setting: 75-acre suburban campus with easy access to Philadelphia. Endowment: $199.3 million. Research spending for 2004 fiscal year: $794,668. Educational spending for 2005 fiscal year: $9682 per student. Total enrollment: 2,457. Student-undergrad faculty ratio is 12:1. 4,219 applied, 43% were admitted. 42% from top 10% of their high school class, 82% from top quarter, 98% from top half. 18 class presidents, 6 valedictorians, 55 student government officers. Full-time: 2,267 students, 58% women, 42% men. Part-time: 190 students, 59% women, 41% men. Students come from 35 states and territories, 4 other countries, 74% from out-of-state, 0.2% Native American, 3% Hispanic, 2% black, 2% Asian American or Pacific Islander, 0.4% international, 0% 25 or older, 91% live on campus, 0.5% transferred in. Retention: 93% of full-time freshmen returned the following year. Academic areas with the most degrees conferred: business/marketing; social sciences; visual and performing arts. Core. Calendar: semesters. Services for LD students, advanced placement, accelerated degree program, self-designed majors, honors program, independent study, double major, summer session for credit, part-time degree program, adult/continuing education programs, internships. Off campus study at 6 members of the Lehigh Valley Association of Independent Colleges. Study abroad program. ROTC: Army (c).

Entrance Requirements: Options: Peterson's Universal Application, Common Application, electronic application, early admission, early decision, deferred admission, international baccalaureate accepted. Required: essay, high school transcript, 2 recommendations. Recommended: interview. Required for some: interview, SAT or ACT. Entrance: very difficult. Application deadlines: 2/15, 2/1 for early decision. Notification: 3/15.

Costs Per Year: Application fee: $45. Comprehensive fee: $37,890 includes full-time tuition ($30,260) and college room and board ($7630). College room only: $4420. Part-time tuition: $3528 per course.

Collegiate Environment: Orientation program. Drama-theater group, choral group, student-run newspaper, radio station. Social organizations: 109 open to all; national fraternities, national sororities; 14% of eligible men and 18% of eligible women are members. Most popular organizations: Theater Association, Environmental Action Team, Jefferson School Partnership, Select Choir, Habitat for Humanity. Major annual events: homecoming, Jefferson School Field Day, Family Weekend. Student services: health clinic, personal-psychological counseling. Campus security: 24-hour emergency response devices and patrols, late night transport-escort service, controlled dormitory access. 1,865 college housing spaces available; 1,855 were occupied in 2003-04. Freshmen guaranteed college housing. On-campus residence required in freshman year. Options: coed, women-only housing available. Trexler Library with 302,946 books, 329,805 microform titles, 865 serials, 13,848 audiovisual materials, an OPAC, and a Web page. Operations spending for 2004 fiscal year: $1.4 million. 486 computers available on campus for general student use. Computer purchase/lease plans available. A campuswide network can be accessed from student residence rooms and from off campus. Staffed computer lab on campus.

Community Environment: Population 110,000. Allentown is located on the Lehigh River. It is Pennsylvania's third largest industrial market. Diversified manufacturing includes machinery and tools, trucks, electrical appliances, electronic equipment, apparel, cement, and gas-generating equipment. Other industries manufacture metal products, batteries, foodstuffs, textiles, and shoes. The area has good transportation facilities including four railroad lines, air service, and bus lines. The community has many churches representing various denominations. Four hospitals, a dental hospital, a library system, a museum and an Equity theater company are located here. Local recreational facilities encompass volleyball, baseball, tennis, basketball, pools, hiking, band concerts, opera, community theatre, five radio stations, and many motion picture and drive-in theatres. Part-time employment is available for students.

■ NEUMANN COLLEGE *N-23*

One Neumann Dr.
Aston, PA 19014-1298
Tel: (610)459-0905
Free: 800-963-8626
Admissions: (610)361-2448
E-mail: murphyjd@neumann.edu
Web Site: http://www.neumann.edu/

Description: Independent Roman Catholic, comprehensive, coed. Awards associate, bachelor's, and master's degrees. Founded 1965. Setting: 50-acre suburban campus with easy access to Philadelphia. Endowment: $13.2 million. Educational spending for 2005 fiscal year: $4221 per student. Total enrollment: 2,810. Faculty: 215 (84 full-time, 131 part-time). Student-undergrad faculty ratio is 16:1. 2,080 applied, 96% were admitted. 10% from top 10% of their high school class, 35% from top quarter, 50% from top half. Full-time: 1,832 students, 64% women, 36% men. Part-time: 481 students, 76% women, 24% men. Students come from 18 states and territories, 8 other countries, 29% from out-of-state, 0.2% Native American, 2% Hispanic, 13% black, 1% Asian American or Pacific Islander, 1% international, 26% 25 or older, 46% live on campus, 3% transferred in. Retention: 77% of full-time freshmen returned the following year. Academic areas with the most degrees conferred: liberal arts/general studies; education; business/marketing; health professions and related sciences. Core. Calendar: semesters. Academic remediation for entering students, services for LD students, advanced placement, accelerated degree program, self-designed majors, freshman honors college, honors program, independent study, distance learning, double major, summer session for credit, part-time degree program, adult/continuing education programs, co-op programs and internships, graduate courses open to undergrads. Off campus study. Study abroad program. ROTC: Army (c).

Entrance Requirements: Options: early admission, deferred admission. Required: high school transcript, minimum 2.00 high school GPA, SAT or ACT. Recommended: interview. Entrance: moderately difficult. Application deadline: 4/1. Notification: continuous.

Costs Per Year: Application fee: $35. Comprehensive fee: $25,996 includes full-time tuition ($17,300), mandatory fees ($620), and college room and board ($8076). College room only: $4796. Part-time tuition: $395 per credit.

Collegiate Environment: Orientation program. Drama-theater group, choral group, student-run newspaper. Social organizations: 15 open to all. Most popular organizations: Professional Education Society, Student Nurses Association, theater ensemble, Environmental Club, community chorus. Major annual events: Homecoming, Halloween Carnival, Winter Formal. Student services: health clinic, personal-psychological counseling. Campus security: 24-hour emergency response devices and patrols, late night transport-escort service, controlled dormitory access. 760 college housing spaces available; all were occupied in 2003-04. Freshmen given priority for college housing. Option: coed housing available. Neumann College Library with 75,000 books, 99,758 microform titles, 400 serials, 30,000 audiovisual materials, and an OPAC. Operations spending for 2004 fiscal year: $494,208. 200 computers available on campus for general student use. A campuswide network can be accessed from student residence rooms and from off campus. Staffed computer lab on campus.

Community Environment: Population of Philadelphia 1,950,098. Aston is a suburban township serving a commuter population from the Tri-state area of Philadelphia, Wilmington and South Jersey. The city enjoys temperate climate. Local historical sites include Valley Forge National Park, Brandywine Battlefield, and many others. Nearby Philadelphia offers all the cultural, recreational, and community service facilities normally found in a metropolis. The immediate area is served by railroad and bus lines with an airport located 10 miles away. There are three hospitals and numerous shopping centers in the area. Part-time employment opportunities are good.

■ NEW CASTLE SCHOOL OF TRADES *G-1*

New Castle Youngstown Rd., Route 422 RD1
Pulaski, PA 16143-9721
Tel: (724)964-8811
Free: 800-837-8299
E-mail: ncstrades@aol.com
Web Site: http://www.ncstrades.com/

Description: Independent, 2-year, coed. Part of Educational Enterprises Incorporated. Awards diplomas and transfer associate degrees. Founded 1945. Setting: 20-acre rural campus with easy access to Youngstown. Total enrollment: 451. 87 applied, 97% were admitted. 5% from top 10% of their high school class, 25% from top quarter, 35% from top half. Students come from 3 states and territories, 40% from out-of-state, 0.4% Native American, 4% Hispanic, 14% black, 1% Asian American or Pacific Islander, 0% international, 35% 25 or older.

Entrance Requirements: Required: high school transcript, interview, Wonderlic aptitude test. Required for some: essay, recommendations.

Collegiate Environment: Student services: personal-psychological counseling. Campus security: 24-hour emergency response devices. College housing not available.

■ **NEWPORT BUSINESS INSTITUTE (LOWER BURRELL)** *D-36*
945 Greensburg Rd.
Lower Burrell, PA 15068-3929
Tel: (724)339-7542
Free: 800-752-7695
Fax: (724)339-2950
Web Site: http://www.nbi.edu
Description: Proprietary, 2-year, coed. Awards certificates, diplomas, and terminal associate degrees. Founded 1895. Setting: 4-acre small town campus with easy access to Pittsburgh. Research spending for 2004 fiscal year: $2000. Total enrollment: 79. Student-undergrad faculty ratio is 14:1. 32 applied, 100% were admitted. Full-time: 79 students, 80% women, 20% men. 0% from out-of-state, 0% Hispanic, 3% black, 0% international, 40% 25 or older, 4% transferred in. Advanced placement, self-designed majors, double major, internships.

Entrance Requirements: Open admission. Options: Peterson's Universal Application, Common Application, early admission. Required: high school transcript. Recommended: interview. Entrance: noncompetitive. Application deadline: Rolling. Notification: continuous.

Costs Per Year: Application fee: $25. Tuition: $7800 full-time, $655 per course part-time. Mandatory fees: $1575 full-time.

Collegiate Environment: Student-run newspaper. Social organizations: 6 open to all. Most popular organizations: student services, Returning Adults Club, new student mentoring, peer liaison. Major annual events: Blood Drive, Commencement, Bring-a-Friend Day. Student services: personal-psychological counseling. Campus security: security system. College housing not available. Jean H. Mullen Memorial Library with 962 books and 18 serials. 85 computers available on campus for general student use. Staffed computer lab on campus.

■ **NEWPORT BUSINESS INSTITUTE (WILLIAMSPORT)** *F-16*
941 West Third St.
Williamsport, PA 17701-5855
Tel: (570)326-2869
Free: 800-962-6971
Fax: (570)326-2136
E-mail: director_NBI@suscom.net
Web Site: http://www.newportbusiness.com/
Description: Proprietary, 2-year, coed. Awards terminal associate degrees. Founded 1955. Setting: small town campus. Total enrollment: 104. Student-undergrad faculty ratio is 15:1. 35 applied, 100% were admitted. Full-time: 103 students, 85% women, 15% men. Part-time: 1 student, 100% women. 0% from out-of-state, 7% black, 1% Asian American or Pacific Islander, 48% 25 or older, 15% transferred in. Summer session for credit, part-time degree program, internships.

Entrance Requirements: Option: deferred admission. Required: high school transcript, interview. Entrance: moderately difficult. Application deadline: Rolling.

Costs Per Year: Application fee: $25. Tuition: $8850 full-time, $737.50 per course part-time. Mandatory fees: $475 full-time.

Collegiate Environment: Most popular organization: Student Council. College housing not available. 64 computers available on campus for general student use. Staffed computer lab on campus.

■ **NORTH CENTRAL INDUSTRIAL TECHNICAL EDUCATION CENTER** *E-9*
651 Montmorenci Ave.
Ridgway, PA 15853
Tel: (814)772-1012
Free: 800-242-5872

Fax: (814)772-1554
E-mail: linzana@ncentral.com
Description: Proprietary, 2-year, coed. Calendar: trimesters.

■ **NORTHAMPTON COUNTY AREA COMMUNITY COLLEGE** *J-23*
3835 Green Pond Rd.
Bethlehem, PA 18020-7599
Tel: (610)861-5300
Admissions: (610)861-5506
E-mail: adminfo@northampton.edu
Web Site: http://www.northampton.edu/
Description: State and locally supported, 2-year, coed. Awards certificates, diplomas, transfer associate, and terminal associate degrees. Founded 1967. Setting: 165-acre suburban campus with easy access to Philadelphia. Endowment: $14.7 million. Educational spending for 2005 fiscal year: $2588 per student. Total enrollment: 8,754. Student-undergrad faculty ratio is 21:1. 3,386 applied, 100% were admitted. 1% from top 10% of their high school class, 8% from top quarter, 35% from top half. Full-time: 3,680 students, 53% women, 47% men. Part-time: 5,074 students, 70% women, 30% men. Students come from 22 states and territories, 39 other countries, 3% from out-of-state, 0.2% Native American, 10% Hispanic, 7% black, 2% Asian American or Pacific Islander, 1% international, 41% 25 or older, 3% live on campus, 33% transferred in. Retention: 58% of full-time freshmen returned the following year. Core. Calendar: semesters. Academic remediation for entering students, ESL program, services for LD students, advanced placement, accelerated degree program, self-designed majors, distance learning, double major, summer session for credit, part-time degree program, adult/continuing education programs, co-op programs and internships. Study abroad program.

Entrance Requirements: Open admission except for allied health, veterinary technician and culinary arts programs.. Options: Peterson's Universal Application, Common Application, electronic application, deferred admission. Required: high school transcript. Required for some: minimum X high school GPA, interview, interview required for radiography, veterinary technician, and diagnostic medical sonography programs; portfolio required for fine art programs; audition required for theatre program. Entrance: noncompetitive. Application deadline: Rolling. Notification: continuous.

Costs Per Year: Application fee: $25. Area resident tuition: $2100 full-time, $70 per credit hour part-time. State resident tuition: $4200 full-time, $140 per credit hour part-time. Nonresident tuition: $6300 full-time, $210 per credit hour part-time. Mandatory fees: $720 full-time, $24 per credit hour part-time. Full-time tuition and fees vary according to course load. Part-time tuition and fees vary according to course load. College room and board: $5944. College room only: $3434. Room and board charges vary according to board plan and housing facility.

Collegiate Environment: Orientation program. Drama-theater group, choral group, student-run newspaper, radio station. Social organizations: 51 open to all. Most popular organizations: Phi Theta Kappa, Nursing Student Organization, NAVTA (Veterinary Technology Club), Student American Dental Hygiene Association, Video Waves. Student services: health clinic, personal-psychological counseling. Campus security: 24-hour emergency response devices and patrols, controlled dormitory access. 250 college housing spaces available; all were occupied in 2003-04. No special consideration for freshman housing applicants. Option: coed housing available. Paul & Harriett Mack Library with 64,758 books, 10 microform titles, 355 serials, 9,169 audiovisual materials, an OPAC, and a Web page. Operations spending for 2004 fiscal year: $967,328. 1,400 computers available on campus for general student use. Computer purchase/lease plans available. A campuswide network can be accessed from student residence rooms and from off campus. Staffed computer lab on campus.

■ **OAKBRIDGE ACADEMY OF ARTS** *D-36*
1250 Greensburg Rd.
Lower Burrell, PA 15068
Tel: (724)335-5336
Free: 800-734-5601
Fax: (724)335-3367
Web Site: http://www.akvalley.com/oakbridge/
Description: Proprietary, 2-year, coed. Awards transfer associate and terminal associate degrees. Founded 1972. Setting: 2-acre small town campus with easy access to Pittsburgh. Total enrollment: 66. Student-undergrad faculty ratio is 16:1. 6% from top 10% of their high school class, 21% from top quarter, 39% from top half. Full-time: 66 students, 62% women, 38% men. Students come from 4 states and territories, 0.01% from

out-of-state, 0% Native American, 0% Hispanic, 0% black, 0% Asian American or Pacific Islander, 0% international, 28% 25 or older, 9% transferred in. Core. Academic remediation for entering students, advanced placement, internships.

Entrance Requirements: Options: Common Application, electronic application. Required: high school transcript, portfolio. Application deadline: 8/31.

Costs Per Year: Application fee: $50. One-time mandatory fee: $30. Tuition: $22,400 full-time, $600 per course part-time. Mandatory fees: $1750 full-time.

Collegiate Environment: Orientation program. Major annual events: graduation, art shows. Campus security: 24-hour emergency response devices. College housing not available. Robert J. Mullen Memorial Library plus 1 other with 3,000 books, 15 serials, 80 audiovisual materials, and a Web page. 40 computers available on campus for general student use. Staffed computer lab on campus.

■ ORLEANS TECHNICAL INSTITUTE-CENTER CITY CAMPUS *M-24*
1845 Walnut St., Ste. 700
Philadelphia, PA 19103-4707
Tel: (215)854-1853
Fax: (215)854-1880
Web Site: http://www.jevs.org/schools_svs.asp

Description: Proprietary, 2-year, coed. Awards transfer associate and terminal associate degrees. Setting: urban campus. Educational spending for 2005 fiscal year: $6593 per student. Total enrollment: 135. 45 applied, 76% were admitted. Full-time: 87 students, 94% women, 6% men. Part-time: 48 students, 94% women, 6% men. Students come from 3 states and territories, 1 other country, 60% from out-of-state, 1% Native American, 6% Hispanic, 24% black, 1% Asian American or Pacific Islander, 0% international, 73% 25 or older, 6% transferred in. Core. Calendar: trimesters. Academic remediation for entering students, summer session for credit, part-time degree program, internships.

Entrance Requirements: Open admission. Required: high school transcript, interview, CPAt. Application deadline: Rolling.

Costs Per Year: Application fee: $150. Tuition: $10,500 full-time, $7350 per year part-time. Mandatory fees: $150 full-time. Full-time tuition and fees vary according to program. Part-time tuition varies according to program.

Collegiate Environment: Orientation program. College housing not available. Library plus 1 other with 625 books and 14 serials. Operations spending for 2004 fiscal year: $500. 46 computers available on campus for general student use. Staffed computer lab on campus.

■ PACE INSTITUTE *K-21*
606 Ct. St.
Reading, PA 19601
Tel: (610)375-1212
Fax: (610)375-1924
Web Site: http://www.paceinstitute.com/

Description: Private, 2-year, coed. Awards diplomas, transfer associate, and terminal associate degrees. Total enrollment: 274. 95% 25 or older.

Collegiate Environment: College housing not available.

■ PEIRCE COLLEGE *M-24*
1420 Pine St.
Philadelphia, PA 19102-4699
Tel: (215)545-6400; 888-467-3472
Admissions: (215)670-9236
Fax: (215)546-5996
E-mail: nmmaher@peirce.edu
Web Site: http://www.peirce.edu/

Description: Independent, 4-year, coed. Awards associate and bachelor's degrees. Founded 1865. Setting: 1-acre urban campus. Endowment: $9.9 million. Educational spending for 2005 fiscal year: $5825 per student. Total enrollment: 1,971. Student-undergrad faculty ratio is 14:1. 659 applied, 45% were admitted. Full-time: 825 students, 75% women, 25% men. Part-time: 1,146 students, 72% women, 28% men. Students come from 38 states and territories, 31 other countries, 20% from out-of-state, 0.4% Native American, 5% Hispanic, 50% black, 1% Asian American or Pacific Islander, 3% international, 81% 25 or older, 44% transferred in. Retention: 74% of full-time freshmen returned the following year. Academic areas with the most degrees conferred: business/marketing; computer and information sciences; law/legal studies. Core. Calendar: continuous. Academic remediation for entering students, ESL program, services for LD students, advanced place-

ment, accelerated degree program, independent study, distance learning, summer session for credit, part-time degree program, co-op programs and internships.

Entrance Requirements: Open admission. Options: Peterson's Universal Application, electronic application. Required: high school transcript. Entrance: noncompetitive. Application deadline: Rolling. Notification: continuous.

Costs Per Year: Application fee: $50. Tuition: $11,760 full-time, $392 per credit hour part-time. Mandatory fees: $1000 full-time, $100 per course part-time. Full-time tuition and fees vary according to course load. Part-time tuition and fees vary according to course load.

Collegiate Environment: Orientation program. Major annual events: Academic Awards Ceremony, Commencement, Student Appreciation Day. Campus security: 24-hour emergency response devices and patrols, late night transport-escort service, 24-hour security cameras. College housing not available. Peirce College Library with 30,502 books, 1,620 microform titles, 70 serials, 399 audiovisual materials, an OPAC, and a Web page. Operations spending for 2004 fiscal year: $177,196. 230 computers available on campus for general student use. Computer purchase/lease plans available. A campuswide network can be accessed. Staffed computer lab on campus.

■ PENN COMMERCIAL BUSINESS AND TECHNICAL SCHOOL *L-2*
242 Oak Spring Rd.
Washington, PA 15301
Tel: (724)222-5330
Fax: (724)222-4722
E-mail: mjoyce@penn-commercial.com
Web Site: http://www.penncommercial.net/

Description: Proprietary, 2-year, coed. Awards certificates, diplomas, transfer associate, and terminal associate degrees. Founded 1929. Setting: 1-acre small town campus with easy access to Pittsburgh. Total enrollment: 304. 3% from top 10% of their high school class, 37% from top quarter, 60% from top half. Full-time: 304 students, 56% women, 44% men. Students come from 3 states and territories, 50% 25 or older. Academic remediation for entering students, summer session for credit, part-time degree program.

Entrance Requirements: Open admission. Options: early admission, deferred admission. Required: high school transcript. Entrance: noncompetitive. Application deadline: Rolling. Notification: continuous.

Collegiate Environment: Student-run newspaper. College housing not available. Main library plus 1 other with 400 books and 60 serials. 100 computers available on campus for general student use. Staffed computer lab on campus.

■ PENN FOSTER CAREER SCHOOL *F-22*
925 Oak St.
Scranton, PA 18515
Tel: (570)342-7701
Free: 800-233-4191
Web Site: http://www.pennfoster.edu/

Description: Proprietary, 2-year, coed. Awards terminal associate degrees (offers only external degree programs conducted through home study). Founded 1975. Total enrollment: 18,881. 18,941 applied, 99% were admitted. Students come from 52 states and territories, 15 other countries, 76% 25 or older. Core. Calendar: semesters. Academic remediation for entering students, independent study, distance learning, summer session for credit, part-time degree program, external degree program, adult/continuing education programs.

Entrance Requirements: Open admission. Required: high school transcript, Math/Reading. Entrance: noncompetitive. Application deadline: Rolling.

Costs Per Year: Tuition: $900 per term part-time. Mandatory fees: $60 per term part-time.

Collegiate Environment: Orientation program. College housing not available.

■ PENNCO TECH *L-25*
3815 Otter St.
Bristol, PA 19007-3696
Tel: (215)824-3200
E-mail: admissions@penncotech.com
Web Site: http://www.penncotech.com/

Description: Proprietary, 2-year, coed. Part of Pennco Institutes, Inc. Awards transfer associate and terminal associate degrees. Founded 1961. Setting: 7-acre suburban campus with easy access to Philadelphia. Total enrollment: 350. Students come from 3 states and territories, 51% 25 or older. Calendar: modular. Academic remediation for entering students, advanced placement, adult/continuing education programs.

Entrance Requirements: Option: Common Application. Required: recommendations, interview. Required for some: essay, IBM Aptitude Test. Entrance: minimally difficult. Application deadline: Rolling.

Collegiate Environment: Orientation program. Campus security: 24-hour emergency response devices, controlled dormitory access. Resource Center with 6,000 books and 10 serials. 75 computers available on campus for general student use. Staffed computer lab on campus.

■ **PENNSYLVANIA COLLEGE OF ART & DESIGN** *M-19*
204 North Prince St., PO Box 59
Lancaster, PA 17608-0059
Tel: (717)396-7833
Fax: (717)396-1339
E-mail: smatson@pcad.edu
Web Site: http://www.pcad.edu/

Description: Independent, 4-year, coed. Awards bachelor's degrees. Founded 1982. Setting: urban campus with easy access to Philadelphia and Wilmington. Total enrollment: 225. Student-undergrad faculty ratio is 9:1. 238 applied, 63% were admitted. 84% from top half of their high school class. Full-time: 203 students, 64% women, 36% men. Part-time: 22 students, 64% women, 36% men. 20% from out-of-state, 0.4% Native American, 2% Hispanic, 2% black, 2% Asian American or Pacific Islander, 0% international. Retention: 72% of full-time freshmen returned the following year. Academic area with the most degrees conferred: visual and performing arts. Core. Calendar: semesters. Advanced placement, part-time degree program, internships.

Entrance Requirements: Open admission. Option: deferred admission. Required: essay, high school transcript, interview, portfolio. Recommended: minimum 2.0 high school GPA. Required for some: 2 recommendations. Entrance: moderately difficult. Application deadline: 5/1.

Costs Per Year: Application fee: $40. Tuition: $13,607 full-time, $567 per credit part-time. Mandatory fees: $450 full-time, $80 per term part-time.

Collegiate Environment: Orientation program. Social organizations: 2 open to all. Most popular organizations: Student Council, yearbook. Major annual events: Halloween Party, Thanksgiving Feast, Spring Picnic. Campus security: trained evening/weekend security personnel. College housing not available. 10,000 books, 76 serials, 24,090 audiovisual materials, and an OPAC. 42 computers available on campus for general student use. Computer purchase/lease plans available. Staffed computer lab on campus.

■ **PENNSYLVANIA COLLEGE OF TECHNOLOGY** *F-16*
One College Ave.
Williamsport, PA 17701-5778
Tel: (570)326-3761
Admissions: (570)327-4761
Fax: (570)321-5551
E-mail: cschuman@pct.edu
Web Site: http://www.pct.edu/

Description: State-related, 4-year, coed. Administratively affiliated with Pennsylvania State University. Awards associate and bachelor's degrees. Founded 1965. Setting: 958-acre small town campus. Endowment: $602,752. Educational spending for 2005 fiscal year: $5048 per student. Total enrollment: 6,537. Student-undergrad faculty ratio is 19:1. 2,793 applied, 97% were admitted. 7% from top 10% of their high school class, 18% from top quarter, 44% from top half. Full-time: 5,515 students, 30% women, 70% men. Part-time: 1,022 students, 61% women, 39% men. Students come from 32 states and territories, 19 other countries, 9% from out-of-state, 1% Native American, 1% Hispanic, 3% black, 1% Asian American or Pacific Islander, 0.5% international, 19% 25 or older, 23% live on campus, 3% transferred in. Academic areas with the most degrees conferred: engineering technologies; computer and information sciences; business/marketing. Core. Calendar: semesters. Academic remediation for entering students, ESL program, services for LD students, advanced placement, self-designed majors, independent study, distance learning, double major, summer session for credit, part-time degree program, co-op programs and internships. Off campus study at Lycoming College, Pennsylvania State University. ROTC: Army (c).

Entrance Requirements: Open admission except for some programs. Options: Peterson's Universal Application, electronic application, early admission, deferred admission. Required: high school transcript. Required for some: SAT. Entrance: noncompetitive. Application deadline: 7/1.

Costs Per Year: Application fee: $50. State resident tuition: $8580 full-time, $286 per credit part-time. Nonresident tuition: $11,160 full-time, $372 per credit part-time. Mandatory fees: $1500 full-time. Full-time tuition and fees vary according to course load and program. Part-time tuition varies according to course load and program. College room and board: $6900. College room only: $4200. Room and board charges vary according to board plan, housing facility, and location.

Collegiate Environment: Orientation program. Student-run newspaper, radio station. Social organizations: 50 open to all; local fraternities. Most popular organizations: Student Government Association, Resident Hall Association (RHA), Wildcats Event Board (WEB), Phi Beta Lambda, Early Educators. Major annual events: Fall Visitation Days, Career Days, Welcome Day. Student services: personal-psychological counseling, women's center. Campus security: 24-hour emergency response devices and patrols, late night transport-escort service. 1,472 college housing spaces available; all were occupied in 2003-04. No special consideration for freshman housing applicants. Option: coed housing available. Penn College Library plus 1 other with 96,281 books, 12,631 microform titles, 9,118 serials, 13,625 audiovisual materials, an OPAC, and a Web page. Operations spending for 2004 fiscal year: $1.6 million. 1,400 computers available on campus for general student use. Computer purchase/lease plans available. A campuswide network can be accessed from student residence rooms and from off campus. Staffed computer lab on campus.

Community Environment: The main campus is in Williamsport, a city known internationally as the home of Little League Baseball. Williamsport (population 32,500) is the seat of Lycoming County (population 121,000); it offers the advantages of a city situated in a rural environment. The surrounding area is an outdoor-lovers' paradise, with hunting, fishing, hiking, camping, backpacking, and more, just minutes from downtown.

■ **PENNSYLVANIA CULINARY INSTITUTE** *K-3*
717 Liberty Ave.
Pittsburgh, PA 15222-3500
Tel: (412)566-2433
Free: 800-432-2433
Fax: (412)566-2434
Web Site: http://www.paculinary.com/

Description: Proprietary, 2-year, coed. Awards terminal associate degrees. Founded 1986. Setting: urban campus. Educational spending for 2005 fiscal year: $3206 per student. Total enrollment: 1,040. Students come from 31 states and territories, 10 other countries, 46% from out-of-state, 0.2% Native American, 2% Hispanic, 11% black, 1% Asian American or Pacific Islander, 32% 25 or older. Core. Calendar: semesters. Academic remediation for entering students, services for LD students, double major, internships.

Entrance Requirements: Options: Common Application, electronic application. Required: high school transcript, interview. Recommended: essay. Required for some: entrance examination (qualifying score on either SAT or ACT will exempt applicant from examination).

Costs Per Year: Application fee: $100. Comprehensive fee: $25,570 includes full-time tuition ($18,550) and college room and board ($7020). College room only: $4450. Room and board charges vary according to board plan and housing facility. Tuition guaranteed not to increase for student's term of enrollment.

Collegiate Environment: Orientation program. Freshmen given priority for college housing. Option: coed housing available. L. Edwin Brown Library and Resource Center with 5,000 books, 100 serials, 350 audiovisual materials, an OPAC, and a Web page. Operations spending for 2004 fiscal year: $182,955. 102 computers available on campus for general student use. A campuswide network can be accessed from student residence rooms and from off campus. Staffed computer lab on campus.

■ **PENNSYLVANIA HIGHLAND COMMUNITY COLLEGE** *K-8*
PO Box 68
Johnstown, PA 15907-0068
Tel: (814)532-5300
Admissions: (814)532-5327
Web Site: http://www.pennhighlands.edu/

Description: State and locally supported, 2-year, coed. Awards certificates, diplomas, transfer associate, and terminal associate degrees. Setting: small town campus. Total enrollment: 1,327. 459 applied, 100% were admitted. Full-time: 594 students, 57% women, 43% men. Part-time: 733 students, 66% women, 34% men. 66% 25 or older. Core. Calendar: semesters. Academic remediation for entering students, services for LD students, advanced placement, honors program, independent study, distance learning, part-time degree program, adult/continuing education programs, co-op programs and internships.

Entrance Requirements: Open admission. Option: Common Application. Recommended: high school transcript, interview. Entrance: noncompetitive. Application deadline: 8/20.

Costs Per Year: Application fee: $20. Area resident tuition: $1680 full-time, $70 per credit hour part-time. State resident tuition: $3360 full-time, $140 per credit hour part-time. Nonresident tuition: $5040 full-time, $210 per credit hour part-time. Mandatory fees: $390 full-time, $15 per credit hour part-time, $15 per term part-time.

Collegiate Environment: Orientation program. Cambria County Area Community College Main Library, plus 3 others with an OPAC. 100 computers available on campus for general student use. A campuswide network can be accessed. Staffed computer lab on campus.

■ **PENNSYLVANIA INSTITUTE OF TECHNOLOGY** *N-23*

800 Manchester Ave.
Media, PA 19063-4098
Tel: (610)892-1500
Free: 800-422-0025
Admissions: (610)892-1550
Fax: (610)892-1510
E-mail: info@pit.edu
Web Site: http://www.pit.edu/

Description: Independent, 2-year, coed. Awards certificates, transfer associate, and terminal associate degrees. Founded 1953. Setting: 12-acre small town campus with easy access to Philadelphia. Total enrollment: 384. Student-undergrad faculty ratio is 10:1. 224 applied, 100% were admitted. Full-time: 270 students, 56% women, 44% men. Part-time: 114 students, 41% women, 59% men. Students come from 3 states and territories, 3% from out-of-state, 2% Hispanic, 42% black, 2% Asian American or Pacific Islander, 51% 25 or older. Retention: 58% of full-time freshmen returned the following year. Core. Calendar: semesters. Academic remediation for entering students, advanced placement, summer session for credit, part-time degree program, adult/continuing education programs, co-op programs.

Entrance Requirements: Options: Peterson's Universal Application, Common Application, electronic application, deferred admission. Required: high school transcript, interview. Recommended: essay. Required for some: 2 recommendations. Entrance: noncompetitive. Application deadline: 9/19. Notification: continuous until 9/19.

Costs Per Year: Application fee: $25. Tuition: $9000 full-time, $300 per credit part-time. Mandatory fees: $330 full-time, $11 per credit part-time.

Collegiate Environment: Orientation program. Major annual events: Spring Open House, Holiday Party. Student services: personal-psychological counseling. Campus security: 24-hour emergency response devices. College housing not available. Pennsylvania Institute of Technology Library/ Learning Resource Center with 16,500 books, 217 serials, an OPAC, and a Web page. 85 computers available on campus for general student use. Staffed computer lab on campus.

■ **THE PENNSYLVANIA STATE UNIVERSITY ABINGTON COLLEGE** *L-24*

1600 Woodland Rd.
Abington, PA 19001
Tel: (215)881-7300
Admissions: (814)865-5471
E-mail: admissions@psu.edu
Web Site: http://www.abington.psu.edu/

Description: State-related, 4-year, coed. Part of Pennsylvania State University. Awards associate and bachelor's degrees. Founded 1950. Setting: 46-acre small town campus with easy access to Philadelphia. Endowment: $1.2 billion. Total enrollment: 3,142. Student-undergrad faculty ratio is 18:1. 2,694 applied, 78% were admitted. 10% from top 10% of their high school class, 29% from top quarter, 64% from top half. Full-time: 2,393 students, 47% women, 53% men. Part-time: 749 students, 60% women, 40% men. 4% from out-of-state, 0.1% Native American, 5% Hispanic, 12% black, 14% Asian American or Pacific Islander, 1% international, 12% 25 or older, 3% transferred in. Retention: 76% of full-time freshmen returned the following year. Academic areas with the most degrees conferred: business/ marketing; security and protective services; psychology. Core. Calendar: semesters. Academic remediation for entering students, ESL program, services for LD students, advanced placement, accelerated degree program, self-designed majors, honors program, independent study, distance learning,

double major, summer session for credit, external degree program, adult/ continuing education programs, co-op programs and internships. Study abroad program. ROTC: Army, Air Force (c).

Entrance Requirements: Options: electronic application, early admission, deferred admission. Required: high school transcript, SAT or ACT. Recommended: essay. Required for some: recommendations, interview. Entrance: very difficult. Application deadlines: Rolling, Rolling for nonresidents. Notification: continuous until 11/1.

Costs Per Year: Application fee: $50. State resident tuition: $9722 full-time, $393 per credit hour part-time. Nonresident tuition: $14,854 full-time, $619 per credit hour part-time. Mandatory fees: $468 full-time, $79 per term part-time. Full-time tuition and fees vary according to course level, location, program, and student level. Part-time tuition and fees vary according to course level, course load, location, program, and student level.

Collegiate Environment: Orientation program. Drama-theater group, choral group, marching band, student-run newspaper, radio station. Student services: legal services, health clinic, personal-psychological counseling, women's center. Campus security: 24-hour patrols. College housing not available. 65,866 books, 12,417 microform titles, 318 serials, and 4,046 audiovisual materials. 286 computers available on campus for general student use. Computer purchase/lease plans available. A campuswide network can be accessed from off-campus. Staffed computer lab on campus.

■ **THE PENNSYLVANIA STATE UNIVERSITY ALTOONA COLLEGE** *J-10*

3000 Ivyside Park
Altoona, PA 16601-3760
Tel: (814)949-5000
Free: 800-848-9843
Admissions: (814)865-5471
Fax: (814)949-5011
E-mail: admissions@psu.edu
Web Site: http://www.aa.psu.edu/

Description: State-related, 4-year, coed. Part of Pennsylvania State University. Awards associate and bachelor's degrees. Founded 1939. Setting: 106-acre suburban campus. Endowment: $1.2 billion. Total enrollment: 3,647. Student-undergrad faculty ratio is 16:1. 4,183 applied, 80% were admitted. 5% from top 10% of their high school class, 27% from top quarter, 70% from top half. Full-time: 3,338 students, 48% women, 52% men. Part-time: 309 students, 70% women, 30% men. 14% from out-of-state, 0.1% Native American, 2% Hispanic, 7% black, 2% Asian American or Pacific Islander, 1% international, 11% 25 or older, 24% live on campus, 2% transferred in. Retention: 85% of full-time freshmen returned the following year. Academic areas with the most degrees conferred: business/marketing; security and protective services; education. Core. Calendar: semesters. Academic remediation for entering students, ESL program, services for LD students, advanced placement, accelerated degree program, self-designed majors, honors program, independent study, distance learning, double major, summer session for credit, adult/continuing education programs, co-op programs and internships. Study abroad program. ROTC: Army, Air Force.

Entrance Requirements: Options: electronic application, early admission, deferred admission. Required: high school transcript, SAT or ACT. Recommended: essay. Required for some: recommendations, interview. Entrance: very difficult. Application deadlines: Rolling, Rolling for nonresidents. Notification: continuous until 11/1, continuous for nonresidents.

Costs Per Year: Application fee: $50. Area resident tuition: $423 per credit hour part-time. State resident tuition: $10,148 full-time, $423 per credit hour part-time. Nonresident tuition: $15,546 full-time, $648 per credit hour part-time. Mandatory fees: $478 full-time, $80 per term part-time. Full-time tuition and fees vary according to course level, location, program, and student level. Part-time tuition and fees vary according to course level, course load, location, program, and student level. College room and board: $6530. College room only: $3430. Room and board charges vary according to board plan and housing facility.

Collegiate Environment: Orientation program. Drama-theater group, choral group, marching band, student-run newspaper, radio station. Social organizations: national fraternities, national sororities; 4% of eligible men and 2% of eligible women are members. Student services: legal services, health clinic, personal-psychological counseling, women's center. Campus security: 24-hour emergency response devices and patrols, student patrols, late night transport-escort service, controlled dormitory access. 903 college housing spaces available; 898 were occupied in 2003-04. Freshmen guaranteed college housing. Option: coed housing available. 70,851 books, 58,596 microform titles, 308 serials, and 5,680 audiovisual materials. 167

computers available on campus for general student use. Computer purchase/lease plans available. A campuswide network can be accessed from student residence rooms and from off campus. Staffed computer lab on campus.

■ THE PENNSYLVANIA STATE UNIVERSITY BEAVER CAMPUS OF THE COMMONWEALTH COLLEGE *I-2*

100 University Dr.
Monaca, PA 15061
Tel: (724)773-3500; 877-564-6778
Admissions: (814)865-5471
Fax: (724)773-3557
E-mail: admissions@psu.edu
Web Site: http://www.br.psu.edu/

Description: State-related, primarily 2-year, coed. Part of Pennsylvania State University. Awards transfer associate, terminal associate, and bachelor's degrees. Founded 1964. Setting: 91-acre small town campus with easy access to Pittsburgh. System endowment: $1.2 billion. Total enrollment: 641. Student-undergrad faculty ratio is 15:1. 569 applied, 89% were admitted. 7% from top 10% of their high school class, 27% from top quarter, 61% from top half. Full-time: 546 students, 42% women, 58% men. Part-time: 86 students, 38% women, 62% men. 4% from out-of-state, 0% Native American, 1% Hispanic, 4% black, 2% Asian American or Pacific Islander, 0% international, 11% 25 or older, 25% live on campus, 4% transferred in. Retention: 71% of full-time freshmen returned the following year. Core. Calendar: semesters. Academic remediation for entering students, ESL program, services for LD students, advanced placement, accelerated degree program, honors program, independent study, distance learning, double major, summer session for credit, adult/continuing education programs, internships. Study abroad program.

Entrance Requirements: Options: electronic application, early admission, deferred admission. Required: high school transcript, SAT or ACT. Recommended: essay. Required for some: recommendations, interview. Entrance: moderately difficult. Application deadline: Rolling. Notification: continuous.

Costs Per Year: Application fee: $50. State resident tuition: $9722 full-time, $393 per credit hour part-time. Nonresident tuition: $14,854 full-time, $619 per credit hour part-time. Mandatory fees: $478 full-time. College room and board: $6530. College room only: $3430.

Collegiate Environment: Orientation program. Drama-theater group, student-run newspaper, radio station. Student services: health clinic, personal-psychological counseling. Campus security: 24-hour patrols, controlled dormitory access. 308 college housing spaces available; 192 were occupied in 2003-04. Freshmen guaranteed college housing. Option: coed housing available. 39,861 books, 9,506 microform titles, 222 serials, and 6,683 audiovisual materials. 106 computers available on campus for general student use. Computer purchase/lease plans available. A campuswide network can be accessed from student residence rooms and from off campus. Staffed computer lab on campus.

■ THE PENNSYLVANIA STATE UNIVERSITY BERKS CAMPUS OF THE BERKS-LEHIGH VALLEY COLLEGE *K-21*

Tulpehocken Rd., PO Box 7009
Reading, PA 19610-6009
Tel: (610)396-6000
Admissions: (814)865-5471
E-mail: admissions@psu.edu
Web Site: http://www.bk.psu.edu/

Description: State-related, 4-year, coed. Part of Pennsylvania State University. Awards associate and bachelor's degrees. Founded 1924. Setting: 240-acre suburban campus with easy access to Philadelphia. Endowment: $1.2 billion. Total enrollment: 2,488. Student-undergrad faculty ratio is 18:1. 2,747 applied, 78% were admitted. 5% from top 10% of their high school class, 21% from top quarter, 58% from top half. Full-time: 2,204 students, 41% women, 59% men. Part-time: 240 students, 39% women, 61% men. 8% from out-of-state, 0.1% Native American, 4% Hispanic, 7% black, 4% Asian American or Pacific Islander, 1% international, 9% 25 or older, 34% live on campus, 3% transferred in. Retention: 84% of full-time freshmen returned the following year. Academic areas with the most degrees conferred: business/marketing; computer and information sciences; psychology. Core. Calendar: semesters. Academic remediation for entering students, services for LD students, advanced placement, accelerated degree program, honors program, independent study, distance learning, summer session for credit, adult/continuing education programs, co-op programs and internships. Study abroad program.

Entrance Requirements: Options: electronic application, early admission, deferred admission. Required: high school transcript, SAT or ACT. Recommended: essay. Required for some: recommendations, interview. Entrance: very difficult. Application deadlines: Rolling, Rolling for nonresidents. Notification: continuous until 11/1, continuous for nonresidents.

Costs Per Year: Application fee: $50. State resident tuition: $10,148 full-time, $423 per credit hour part-time. Nonresident tuition: $15,546 full-time, $648 per credit hour part-time. Mandatory fees: $478 full-time, $80 per term part-time. Full-time tuition and fees vary according to course level, course load, and student level. Part-time tuition and fees vary according to course level and student level. College room and board: $7140. College room only: $4040. Room and board charges vary according to board plan and housing facility.

Collegiate Environment: Orientation program. Drama-theater group, choral group, marching band, student-run newspaper, radio station. Student services: legal services, health clinic, personal-psychological counseling, women's center. Campus security: 24-hour emergency response devices and patrols, controlled dormitory access. 805 college housing spaces available; 804 were occupied in 2003-04. Freshmen guaranteed college housing. Option: coed housing available. 49,520 books, 2,095 microform titles, 460 serials, and 2,336 audiovisual materials. 156 computers available on campus for general student use. Computer purchase/lease plans available. A campuswide network can be accessed from student residence rooms and from off campus. Staffed computer lab on campus.

■ THE PENNSYLVANIA STATE UNIVERSITY DELAWARE COUNTY CAMPUS OF THE COMMONWEALTH COLLEGE *N-23*

25 Yearsley Mill Rd.
Media, PA 19063-5596
Tel: (610)892-1350
Admissions: (814)865-5471
E-mail: admissions@psu.edu
Web Site: http://www.de.psu.edu/

Description: State-related, primarily 2-year, coed. Part of Pennsylvania State University. Awards terminal associate and bachelor's degrees. Founded 1966. Setting: 87-acre small town campus with easy access to Philadelphia. System endowment: $1.2 billion. Total enrollment: 1,589. Student-undergrad faculty ratio is 16:1. 1,402 applied, 77% were admitted. 8% from top 10% of their high school class, 21% from top quarter, 56% from top half. Full-time: 1,356 students, 43% women, 57% men. Part-time: 233 students, 44% women, 56% men. 3% from out-of-state, 0.1% Native American, 2% Hispanic, 15% black, 7% Asian American or Pacific Islander, 0.4% international, 10% 25 or older, 3% transferred in. Retention: 72% of full-time freshmen returned the following year. Core. Calendar: semesters. Academic remediation for entering students, ESL program, services for LD students, advanced placement, honors program, independent study, distance learning, double major, summer session for credit, adult/continuing education programs, internships. Study abroad program. ROTC: Air Force (c).

Entrance Requirements: Options: electronic application, early admission, deferred admission. Required: high school transcript, SAT or ACT. Recommended: essay. Required for some: recommendations, interview. Entrance: moderately difficult. Application deadline: Rolling. Notification: continuous.

Costs Per Year: Application fee: $50. State resident tuition: $9722 full-time, $393 per credit hour part-time. Nonresident tuition: $14,854 full-time, $619 per credit hour part-time. Mandatory fees: $478 full-time.

Collegiate Environment: Orientation program. Drama-theater group, choral group, student-run newspaper. Student services: health clinic, personal-psychological counseling, women's center. Campus security: late night transport-escort service, part-time trained security personnel. College housing not available. 59,930 books, 4,526 microform titles, 457 serials, and 3,987 audiovisual materials. 180 computers available on campus for general student use. Computer purchase/lease plans available. A campuswide network can be accessed from off-campus. Staffed computer lab on campus.

■ THE PENNSYLVANIA STATE UNIVERSITY DUBOIS CAMPUS OF THE COMMONWEALTH COLLEGE *G-9*

College Place
DuBois, PA 15801-3199
Tel: (814)375-4700
Free: 800-346-7627
Admissions: (814)865-5471
E-mail: admissions@psu.edu
Web Site: http://www.ds.psu.edu/

Description: State-related, primarily 2-year, coed. Part of Pennsylvania State University. Awards transfer associate, terminal associate, and bachelor's degrees. Founded 1935. Setting: 20-acre small town campus. System endowment: $1.2 billion. Total enrollment: 804. Student-undergrad faculty ratio is 12:1. 346 applied, 92% were admitted. 8% from top 10% of their high school class, 26% from top quarter, 59% from top half. Full-time: 595 students, 51% women, 49% men. Part-time: 209 students, 56% women, 44% men. 1% from out-of-state, 0.3% Native American, 0.3% Hispanic, 1% black, 0.5% Asian American or Pacific Islander, 0% international, 34% 25 or older, 2% transferred in. Retention: 75% of full-time freshmen returned the following year. Core. Calendar: semesters. Academic remediation for entering students, services for LD students, advanced placement, accelerated degree program, self-designed majors, honors program, independent study, distance learning, double major, summer session for credit, adult/continuing education programs, internships. Study abroad program.

Entrance Requirements: Options: electronic application, early admission, deferred admission. Required: high school transcript, SAT or ACT. Recommended: essay. Required for some: recommendations, interview. Entrance: moderately difficult. Application deadline: Rolling. Notification: continuous.

Costs Per Year: Application fee: $50. State resident tuition: $9722 full-time, $393 per credit hour part-time. Nonresident tuition: $14,854 full-time, $619 per credit hour part-time. Mandatory fees: $468 full-time.

Collegiate Environment: Orientation program. Drama-theater group, choral group, student-run newspaper. Student services: health clinic, personal-psychological counseling, women's center. College housing not available. 43,710 books, 17,158 microform titles, 224 serials, and 1,091 audiovisual materials. 126 computers available on campus for general student use. Computer purchase/lease plans available. A campuswide network can be accessed from off-campus. Staffed computer lab on campus.

■ **THE PENNSYLVANIA STATE UNIVERSITY AT ERIE, THE BEHREND COLLEGE** *B-3*

5091 Station Rd.
Erie, PA 16563-0001
Tel: (814)898-6000; (866)374-3378
Admissions: (814)865-5471
E-mail: admissions@psu.edu
Web Site: http://www.pserie.psu.edu/

Description: State-related, comprehensive, coed. Part of Pennsylvania State University. Awards associate, bachelor's, and master's degrees. Founded 1948. Setting: 727-acre suburban campus. Endowment: $1.2 billion. Total enrollment: 3,542. Faculty: 261 (200 full-time, 61 part-time). Student-undergrad faculty ratio is 15:1. 2,417 applied, 80% were admitted. 12% from top 10% of their high school class, 36% from top quarter, 76% from top half. Full-time: 3,160 students, 33% women, 67% men. Part-time: 222 students, 30% women, 70% men. 7% from out-of-state, 0.03% Native American, 2% Hispanic, 3% black, 2% Asian American or Pacific Islander, 1% international, 8% 25 or older, 48% live on campus, 3% transferred in. Retention: 83% of full-time freshmen returned the following year. Academic areas with the most degrees conferred: business/marketing; engineering; psychology. Core. Calendar: semesters. Academic remediation for entering students, services for LD students, advanced placement, accelerated degree program, honors program, independent study, distance learning, double major, summer session for credit, adult/continuing education programs, co-op programs and internships, graduate courses open to undergrads. Study abroad program. ROTC: Army (c).

Entrance Requirements: Options: electronic application, early admission, deferred admission. Required: high school transcript, SAT or ACT. Recommended: essay. Required for some: recommendations, interview. Entrance: very difficult. Application deadlines: Rolling, Rolling for nonresidents. Notification: continuous until 11/1, continuous for nonresidents.

Costs Per Year: Application fee: $50. Area resident tuition: $423 per credit hour part-time. State resident tuition: $10,148 full-time, $423 per credit hour part-time. Nonresident tuition: $15,546 full-time, $648 per credit hour part-time. Mandatory fees: $478 full-time, $80 per term part-time. Full-time tuition and fees vary according to course level and student level. Part-time tuition and fees vary according to course level, course load, and student level. College room and board: $6530. College room only: $3430. Room and board charges vary according to board plan and housing facility.

Collegiate Environment: Orientation program. Drama-theater group, choral group, marching band, student-run newspaper, radio station. Social organizations: national fraternities, national sororities; 4% of eligible men and 4% of eligible women are members. Most popular organization: Student Government Association. Student services: legal services, health clinic, personal-psychological counseling, women's center. Campus security: 24-hour emergency response devices and patrols, student patrols, late night transport-escort service, controlled dormitory access. College housing designed to accommodate 1,208 students; 1,242 undergraduates lived in college housing during 2003-04. Freshmen guaranteed college housing. Options: coed, men-only, women-only housing available. 103,524 books, 58,349 microform titles, 810 serials, and 3,180 audiovisual materials. 448 computers available on campus for general student use. Computer purchase/lease plans available. A campuswide network can be accessed from student residence rooms and from off campus. Staffed computer lab on campus.

■ **THE PENNSYLVANIA STATE UNIVERSITY FAYETTE CAMPUS OF THE COMMONWEALTH COLLEGE** *N-4*

1 University Dr., PO Box 519
Uniontown, PA 15401-0519
Tel: (724)430-4100; 877-568-4130
Admissions: (814)865-5471
Fax: (724)430-4184
E-mail: admissions@psu.edu
Web Site: http://www.fe.psu.edu/

Description: State-related, primarily 2-year, coed. Part of Pennsylvania State University. Awards transfer associate, terminal associate, and bachelor's degrees. Founded 1934. Setting: 92-acre small town campus. System endowment: $1.2 billion. Total enrollment: 995. Student-undergrad faculty ratio is 13:1. 382 applied, 86% were admitted. 7% from top 10% of their high school class, 29% from top quarter, 70% from top half. Full-time: 727 students, 57% women, 43% men. Part-time: 268 students, 76% women, 24% men. 1% from out-of-state, 0% Native American, 0.5% Hispanic, 7% black, 1% Asian American or Pacific Islander, 0% international, 39% 25 or older, 3% transferred in. Retention: 67% of full-time freshmen returned the following year. Core. Calendar: semesters. Academic remediation for entering students, services for LD students, advanced placement, accelerated degree program, self-designed majors, honors program, independent study, distance learning, double major, summer session for credit, adult/continuing education programs, internships. Study abroad program.

Entrance Requirements: Options: electronic application, early admission, deferred admission. Required: high school transcript, SAT or ACT. Recommended: essay. Required for some: recommendations, interview. Entrance: moderately difficult. Application deadline: Rolling. Notification: continuous.

Costs Per Year: Application fee: $50. State resident tuition: $9722 full-time, $393 per credit hour part-time. Nonresident tuition: $14,854 full-time, $619 per credit hour part-time. Mandatory fees: $468 full-time.

Collegiate Environment: Orientation program. Drama-theater group, choral group, student-run newspaper. Student services: health clinic, personal-psychological counseling. Campus security: student patrols, 8-hour patrols by trained security personnel. College housing not available. 54,610 books, 6,556 microform titles, 187 serials, and 6,721 audiovisual materials. 103 computers available on campus for general student use. Computer purchase/lease plans available. A campuswide network can be accessed from off-campus. Staffed computer lab on campus.

■ **THE PENNSYLVANIA STATE UNIVERSITY HARRISBURG CAMPUS** *L-17*

777 West Harrisburg Pike
Middletown, PA 17057-4898
Tel: (717)948-6000
Free: 800-222-2056
Admissions: (814)865-5471
E-mail: admissions@psu.edu
Web Site: http://www.hbg.psu.edu/

Description: State-related, comprehensive, coed. Part of Pennsylvania State University. Awards associate, bachelor's, master's, and doctoral degrees. Founded 1966. Setting: 218-acre small town campus. Endowment: $1.2 billion. Total enrollment: 3,736. Faculty: 273 (169 full-time, 104 part-time). Student-undergrad faculty ratio is 12:1. 1,616 applied, 64% were admitted. 10% from top 10% of their high school class, 43% from top quarter, 85% from top half. Full-time: 1,592 students, 47% women, 53% men. Part-time: 476 students, 57% women, 43% men. 7% from out-of-state, 0% Native American, 3% Hispanic, 8% black, 7% Asian American or Pacific Islander, 1% international, 33% 25 or older, 14% live on campus, 13% transferred in. Retention: 85% of full-time freshmen returned the following year. Academic areas with the most degrees conferred: business/marketing; engineering; education. Core. Calendar: semesters. Academic remediation for entering students, services for LD students, advanced placement, accelerated degree program, self-designed majors, honors program, independent study, distance learning, double major, summer session for credit, part-time degree program, adult/continuing education programs, co-op programs and internships, graduate courses open to undergrads. Study abroad program. ROTC: Army (c).

Entrance Requirements: Options: electronic application, early admission, deferred admission. Required: high school transcript, SAT or ACT. Recommended: essay. Required for some: recommendations, interview. Entrance: very difficult. Application deadlines: Rolling, Rolling for nonresidents. Notification: continuous until 11/1, continuous for nonresidents.

Costs Per Year: Application fee: $50. State resident tuition: $10,148 full-time, $423 per credit hour part-time. Nonresident tuition: $15,546 full-time, $648 per credit hour part-time. Mandatory fees: $468 full-time, $79 per term part-time. Full-time tuition and fees vary according to course level, location, program, and student level. Part-time tuition and fees vary according to course level, course load, location, program, and student level. College room and board: $8030. College room only: $4930. Room and board charges vary according to board plan and housing facility.

Collegiate Environment: Orientation program. Drama-theater group, choral group, marching band, student-run newspaper, radio station. Student services: legal services, health clinic, personal-psychological counseling, women's center. Campus security: 24-hour patrols, student patrols, late night transport-escort service. 292 college housing spaces available; 291 were occupied in 2003-04. Freshmen guaranteed college housing. 285,171 books, 1.1 million microform titles, 1,903 serials, and 5,144 audiovisual materials. 132 computers available on campus for general student use. Computer purchase/lease plans available. A campuswide network can be accessed from student residence rooms and from off campus. Staffed computer lab on campus.

■ THE PENNSYLVANIA STATE UNIVERSITY HAZLETON CAMPUS OF THE COMMONWEALTH COLLEGE *H-20*

Hazleton, PA 18202-1291
Tel: (570)450-3000
Free: 800-279-8495
Admissions: (814)865-5471
E-mail: admissions@psu.edu
Web Site: http://www.hn.psu.edu/

Description: State-related, primarily 2-year, coed. Part of Pennsylvania State University. Awards transfer associate, terminal associate, and bachelor's degrees. Founded 1934. Setting: 98-acre small town campus. System endowment: $1.2 billion. Total enrollment: 1,066. Student-undergrad faculty ratio is 16:1. 1,084 applied, 91% were admitted. 7% from top 10% of their high school class, 26% from top quarter, 62% from top half. Full-time: 1,011 students, 40% women, 60% men. Part-time: 54 students, 37% women, 63% men. 25% from out-of-state, 0.2% Native American, 7% Hispanic, 7% black, 6% Asian American or Pacific Islander, 0.2% international, 6% 25 or older, 43% live on campus, 3% transferred in. Retention: 80% of full-time freshmen returned the following year. Core. Calendar: semesters. Academic remediation for entering students, ESL program, services for LD students, advanced placement, accelerated degree program, self-designed majors, honors program, independent study, distance learning, double major, summer session for credit, adult/continuing education programs, internships. Study abroad program. ROTC: Army, Air Force (c).

Entrance Requirements: Options: electronic application, early admission, deferred admission. Required: high school transcript, SAT or ACT. Recommended: essay. Required for some: recommendations, interview. Entrance: moderately difficult. Application deadline: Rolling. Notification: continuous.

Costs Per Year: Application fee: $50. State resident tuition: $9722 full-time, $393 per credit hour part-time. Nonresident tuition: $14,854 full-time, $619 per credit hour part-time. Mandatory fees: $468 full-time. College room and board: $6530. College room only: $3430.

Collegiate Environment: Orientation program. Drama-theater group, choral group, student-run newspaper, radio station. Student services: legal services, health clinic, personal-psychological counseling, women's center. Campus security: 24-hour patrols, late night transport-escort service, controlled dormitory access. College housing designed to accommodate 456 students; 466 undergraduates lived in college housing during 2003-04. Freshmen guaranteed college housing. Option: coed housing available. 83,266 books, 8,991 microform titles, 996 serials, and 6,771 audiovisual materials. 131 computers available on campus for general student use. Computer purchase/lease plans available. A campuswide network can be accessed from student residence rooms and from off campus. Staffed computer lab on campus.

■ THE PENNSYLVANIA STATE UNIVERSITY, LEHIGH VALLEY CAMPUS OF THE BERKS-LEHIGH VALLEY COLLEGE *J-22*

8380 Mohr Ln.
Fogelsville, PA 18051-9999
Tel: (610)285-5000
Admissions: (814)865-5471
Web Site: http://www.lv.psu.edu/

Description: State-related, primarily 2-year, coed. Part of Pennsylvania State University. Awards terminal associate and bachelor's degrees. Founded 1912. Setting: 42-acre small town campus. Total enrollment: 680. 662 applied, 80% were admitted. 8% from top 10% of their high school class, 26% from top quarter, 62% from top half. Full-time: 491 students, 35% women, 65% men. Part-time: 153 students, 38% women, 62% men. 2% from out-of-state, 0% Native American, 6% Hispanic, 3% black, 8% Asian American or Pacific Islander, 1% international, 15% 25 or older, 5% transferred in. Retention: 82% of full-time freshmen returned the following year. Core. Calendar: semesters. Academic remediation for entering students, services for LD students, advanced placement, accelerated degree program, honors program, independent study, distance learning, summer session for credit, adult/continuing education programs, co-op programs and internships. Study abroad program.

Entrance Requirements: Options: electronic application, early admission, deferred admission. Required: high school transcript, SAT or ACT. Entrance: moderately difficult. Application deadline: Rolling. Notification: continuous.

Costs Per Year: Application fee: $50. State resident tuition: $9722 full-time. Nonresident tuition: $14,854 full-time. Mandatory fees: $478 full-time. Full-time tuition and fees vary according to course level.

Collegiate Environment: Orientation program. Drama-theater group. College housing not available. 36,641 books, 3,231 microform titles, 152 serials, and 6,579 audiovisual materials. 62 computers available on campus for general student use. Computer purchase/lease plans available. A campuswide network can be accessed from off-campus. Staffed computer lab on campus.

■ THE PENNSYLVANIA STATE UNIVERSITY MCKEESPORT CAMPUS OF THE COMMONWEALTH COLLEGE *K-4*

4000 University Dr.
McKeesport, PA 15132-7698
Tel: (412)675-9000
Admissions: (814)865-5471
E-mail: admissions@psu.edu
Web Site: http://www.mk.psu.edu/

Description: State-related, primarily 2-year, coed. Part of Pennsylvania State University. Awards terminal associate and bachelor's degrees. Founded 1947. Setting: 40-acre small town campus with easy access to Pittsburgh. System endowment: $1.2 billion. Total enrollment: 682. Student-undergrad faculty ratio is 13:1. 445 applied, 82% were admitted. 7% from top 10% of their high school class, 31% from top quarter, 67% from top half. Full-time: 593 students, 38% women, 62% men. Part-time: 89 students, 47% women, 53% men. 6% from out-of-state, 0% Native American, 1% Hispanic, 14% black, 3% Asian American or Pacific Islander, 0.2% international, 8% 25 or older, 14% live on campus, 4% transferred in. Retention: 79% of full-time freshmen returned the following year. Core. Calendar: semesters. Academic remediation for entering students, services for LD students, advanced placement, accelerated degree program, honors program, independent study, distance learning, double major, summer session for credit, adult/continuing education programs, internships. Study abroad program. ROTC: Air Force (c).

Entrance Requirements: Options: electronic application, early admission, deferred admission. Required: high school transcript, SAT or ACT. Recommended: essay. Required for some: recommendations, interview. Entrance: moderately difficult. Application deadline: Rolling. Notification: continuous.

Costs Per Year: Application fee: $50. State resident tuition: $9722 full-time, $393 per credit hour part-time. Nonresident tuition: $14,854 full-time, $619 per credit hour part-time. Mandatory fees: $458 full-time. College room and board: $6530. College room only: $3430.

Collegiate Environment: Orientation program. Drama-theater group, choral group, student-run newspaper, radio station. Student services: health clinic, personal-psychological counseling, women's center. Campus security: 24-hour patrols, controlled dormitory access. 210 college housing spaces available; 135 were occupied in 2003-04. Freshmen guaranteed college housing. Option: coed housing available. 40,851 books, 10,538 microform titles, 300 serials, and 2,783 audiovisual materials. 167 computers available on campus for general student use. Computer purchase/lease plans available.

A campuswide network can be accessed from student residence rooms and from off campus. Staffed computer lab on campus.

■ **THE PENNSYLVANIA STATE UNIVERSITY MONT ALTO CAMPUS OF THE COMMONWEALTH COLLEGE** *N-14*
Campus Dr.
Mont Alto, PA 17237-9703
Tel: (717)749-6000
Free: 800-392-6173
Admissions: (814)865-5471
E-mail: admissions@psu.edu
Web Site: http://www.ma.psu.edu/

Description: State-related, primarily 2-year, coed. Part of Pennsylvania State University. Awards terminal associate and bachelor's degrees. Founded 1929. Setting: 64-acre small town campus. System endowment: $1.2 billion. Total enrollment: 932. Student-undergrad faculty ratio is 12:1. 614 applied, 84% were admitted. 6% from top 10% of their high school class, 21% from top quarter, 66% from top half. Full-time: 674 students, 51% women, 49% men. Part-time: 258 students, 71% women, 29% men. 12% from out-of-state, 0.2% Native American, 3% Hispanic, 9% black, 2% Asian American or Pacific Islander, 0.4% international, 26% 25 or older, 33% live on campus, 7% transferred in. Retention: 78% of full-time freshmen returned the following year. Core. Calendar: semesters. Academic remediation for entering students, services for LD students, advanced placement, accelerated degree program, honors program, independent study, distance learning, double major, summer session for credit, adult/continuing education programs, internships. Study abroad program. ROTC: Army (c).

Entrance Requirements: Options: electronic application, early admission, deferred admission. Required: high school transcript, SAT or ACT. Recommended: essay. Required for some: recommendations, interview. Entrance: moderately difficult. Application deadline: Rolling. Notification: continuous.

Costs Per Year: Application fee: $50. State resident tuition: $9722 full-time, $393 per credit hour part-time. Nonresident tuition: $14,854 full-time, $619 per credit hour part-time. Mandatory fees: $478 full-time. College room and board: $6530. College room only: $3430.

Collegiate Environment: Orientation program. Drama-theater group, student-run newspaper, radio station. Student services: health clinic, women's center. Campus security: 24-hour patrols, controlled dormitory access. 438 college housing spaces available; 373 were occupied in 2003-04. Freshmen guaranteed college housing. Option: coed housing available. 38,962 books, 19,744 microform titles, 273 serials, and 1,418 audiovisual materials. 182 computers available on campus for general student use. Computer purchase/lease plans available. A campuswide network can be accessed from student residence rooms and from off campus. Staffed computer lab on campus.

■ **THE PENNSYLVANIA STATE UNIVERSITY NEW KENSINGTON CAMPUS OF THE COMMONWEALTH COLLEGE** *D-35*
3550 7th St. Rd., RT 780
New Kensington, PA 15068-1798
Tel: (724)334-5466; 888-968-7297
Admissions: (814)865-5471
Fax: (724)334-6111
E-mail: admissions@psu.edu
Web Site: http://www.nk.psu.edu/

Description: State-related, primarily 2-year, coed. Part of Pennsylvania State University. Awards transfer associate, terminal associate, and bachelor's degrees. Founded 1958. Setting: 71-acre small town campus with easy access to Pittsburgh. System endowment: $1.2 billion. Total enrollment: 882. Student-undergrad faculty ratio is 12:1. 376 applied, 86% were admitted. 3% from top 10% of their high school class, 22% from top quarter, 62% from top half. Full-time: 628 students, 40% women, 60% men. Part-time: 252 students, 54% women, 46% men. 2% from out-of-state, 0.1% Native American, 1% Hispanic, 2% black, 1% Asian American or Pacific Islander, 0% international, 23% 25 or older, 5% transferred in. Retention: 77% of full-time freshmen returned the following year. Core. Calendar: semesters. Academic remediation for entering students, services for LD students, advanced placement, accelerated degree program, honors program, independent study, distance learning, double major, summer session for credit, external degree program, adult/continuing education programs, internships.

Entrance Requirements: Options: electronic application, early admission, deferred admission. Required: high school transcript, SAT or ACT. Recom-

mended: essay. Required for some: recommendations, interview. Entrance: moderately difficult. Application deadline: Rolling. Notification: continuous.

Costs Per Year: Application fee: $50. State resident tuition: $9722 full-time, $393 per credit hour part-time. Nonresident tuition: $14,854 full-time, $619 per credit hour part-time. Mandatory fees: $478 full-time.

Collegiate Environment: Orientation program. Drama-theater group, choral group, marching band, student-run newspaper. Student services: health clinic, women's center. Campus security: part-time trained security personnel. College housing not available. 28,897 books, 4,506 microform titles, 404 serials, and 4,294 audiovisual materials. 264 computers available on campus for general student use. Computer purchase/lease plans available. A campuswide network can be accessed from off-campus. Staffed computer lab on campus.

■ **THE PENNSYLVANIA STATE UNIVERSITY SCHUYLKILL CAMPUS OF THE CAPITAL COLLEGE** *K-44*
200 University Dr.
Schuylkill Haven, PA 17972-2208
Tel: (570)385-6000
Admissions: (814)865-5471
E-mail: admissions@psu.edu
Web Site: http://www.sl.psu.edu/

Description: State-related, primarily 2-year, coed. Part of Pennsylvania State University. Awards transfer associate, terminal associate, and bachelor's degrees (bachelor's degree programs completed at the Harrisburg campus). Founded 1934. Setting: 42-acre small town campus. Total enrollment: 969. 675 applied, 87% were admitted. 5% from top 10% of their high school class, 26% from top quarter, 65% from top half. Full-time: 773 students, 52% women, 48% men. Part-time: 151 students, 65% women, 35% men. 15% from out-of-state, 0.3% Native American, 4% Hispanic, 17% black, 3% Asian American or Pacific Islander, 1% international, 15% 25 or older, 28% live on campus, 2% transferred in. Retention: 81% of full-time freshmen returned the following year. Core. Calendar: semesters. Academic remediation for entering students, services for LD students, advanced placement, accelerated degree program, self-designed majors, honors program, independent study, distance learning, double major, summer session for credit, adult/continuing education programs, co-op programs and internships. Study abroad program.

Entrance Requirements: Options: electronic application, early admission, deferred admission. Required: high school transcript, SAT or ACT. Entrance: moderately difficult. Application deadline: Rolling. Notification: continuous.

Costs Per Year: Application fee: $50. State resident tuition: $9722 full-time. Nonresident tuition: $14,854 full-time. Mandatory fees: $458 full-time. Full-time tuition and fees vary according to course level, location, program, and student level. College room and board: $7110. College room only: $3474. Room and board charges vary according to board plan and housing facility.

Collegiate Environment: Orientation program. Drama-theater group, choral group, student-run newspaper. Campus security: 24-hour patrols, controlled dormitory access. Freshmen guaranteed college housing. 39,289 books, 27,466 microform titles, 518 serials, and 930 audiovisual materials. 146 computers available on campus for general student use. Computer purchase/lease plans available. A campuswide network can be accessed from student residence rooms and from off campus. Staffed computer lab on campus.

■ **THE PENNSYLVANIA STATE UNIVERSITY SHENANGO CAMPUS OF THE COMMONWEALTH COLLEGE** *F-1*
147 Shenango Ave.
Sharon, PA 16146-1537
Tel: (724)983-2814
Admissions: (814)865-5471
Fax: (724)983-2820
E-mail: admissions@psu.edu
Web Site: http://www.shenango.psu.edu/

Description: State-related, primarily 2-year, coed. Part of Pennsylvania State University. Awards transfer associate, terminal associate, and bachelor's degrees. Founded 1965. Setting: 14-acre small town campus. System endowment: $1.2 billion. Total enrollment: 856. Student-undergrad faculty ratio is 14:1. 211 applied, 90% were admitted. 4% from top 10% of their high school class, 20% from top quarter, 52% from top half. Full-time: 508 students, 59% women, 41% men. Part-time: 347 students, 77% women, 23% men. 11% from out-of-state, 0.2% Native American, 1% Hispanic, 8% black, 0.3% Asian American or Pacific Islander, 0% international, 50% 25 or older, 4% transferred in. Retention: 74% of full-time freshmen returned the

following year. Core. Calendar: semesters. Academic remediation for entering students, services for LD students, advanced placement, accelerated degree program, self-designed majors, honors program, independent study, distance learning, double major, summer session for credit, adult/continuing education programs, internships. Study abroad program.

Entrance Requirements: Options: electronic application, early admission, deferred admission. Required: high school transcript, SAT or ACT. Recommended: essay. Required for some: recommendations, interview. Entrance: moderately difficult. Application deadline: Rolling. Notification: continuous.

Costs Per Year: Application fee: $50. State resident tuition: $9722 full-time, $393 per credit hour part-time. Nonresident tuition: $14,854 full-time, $619 per credit hour part-time. Mandatory fees: $478 full-time.

Collegiate Environment: Orientation program. Drama-theater group. Student services: health clinic, women's center. Campus security: part-time trained security personnel. College housing not available. 25,273 books, 3,581 microform titles, 346 serials, and 2,064 audiovisual materials. 102 computers available on campus for general student use. Computer purchase/lease plans available. A campuswide network can be accessed from off-campus. Staffed computer lab on campus.

■ **THE PENNSYLVANIA STATE UNIVERSITY UNIVERSITY PARK CAMPUS** *I-12*

201 Old Main
University Park, PA 16802-1503
Tel: (814)865-4700
Admissions: (814)865-5471
E-mail: admissions@psu.edu
Web Site: http://www.psu.edu/

Description: State-related, university, coed. Part of Pennsylvania State University. Awards associate, bachelor's, master's, and doctoral degrees. Founded 1855. Setting: 6,388-acre small town campus. Endowment: $1.2 billion. Total enrollment: 40,709. Faculty: 2,546 (2,233 full-time, 313 part-time). Student-undergrad faculty ratio is 16:1. 29,904 applied, 62% were admitted. 40% from top 10% of their high school class, 78% from top quarter, 98% from top half. Full-time: 33,208 students, 46% women, 54% men. Part-time: 1,429 students, 39% women, 61% men. Students come from 54 states and territories, 23% from out-of-state, 0.1% Native American, 3% Hispanic, 4% black, 6% Asian American or Pacific Islander, 2% international, 3% 25 or older, 38% live on campus, 1% transferred in. Retention: 93% of full-time freshmen returned the following year. Academic areas with the most degrees conferred: business/marketing; engineering; communications/journalism. Core. Calendar: semesters. Academic remediation for entering students, ESL program, services for LD students, advanced placement, accelerated degree program, self-designed majors, freshman honors college, honors program, independent study, distance learning, double major, summer session for credit, part-time degree program, external degree program, adult/continuing education programs, co-op programs and internships, graduate courses open to undergrads. Study abroad program. ROTC: Army, Naval, Air Force.

Entrance Requirements: Options: electronic application, early admission, deferred admission. Required: high school transcript, minimum 2.0 high school GPA, SAT or ACT. Recommended: essay. Required for some: recommendations, interview. Entrance: very difficult. Application deadlines: Rolling, Rolling for nonresidents. Notification: continuous until 11/1, continuous for nonresidents.

Costs Per Year: Application fee: $50. State resident tuition: $11,024 full-time, $459 per credit hour part-time. Nonresident tuition: $21,260 full-time, $886 per credit hour part-time. Mandatory fees: $484 full-time, $180 per term part-time. College room and board: $6530. College room only: $3430.

Collegiate Environment: Orientation program. Drama-theater group, choral group, marching band, student-run newspaper, radio station. Social organizations: 400 open to all; national fraternities, national sororities; 12% of eligible men and 10% of eligible women are members. Major annual events: homecoming, Four Diamonds Dance Marathon, Parents' Weekend. Student services: legal services, health clinic, personal-psychological counseling, women's center. Campus security: 24-hour emergency response devices and patrols, student patrols, late night transport-escort service, controlled dormitory access. College housing designed to accommodate 12,361 students; 12,782 undergraduates lived in college housing during 2003-04. Freshmen guaranteed college housing. On-campus residence required in freshman year. Options: coed, men-only, women-only housing available. Pattee Library plus 7 others with 3.1 million books, 2.5 million microform titles, 36,856 serials, 146,254 audiovisual materials, an OPAC, and a Web page. 3,589 computers available on campus for general student

use. A campuswide network can be accessed fro and from off campus. Staffed computer lab on ca

■ **THE PENNSYLVANIA STATE UNIVERSITY WIL CAMPUS OF THE COMMONWEALTH COLLEGE**

PO PSU
Lehman, PA 18627-0217
Tel: (570)675-2171
Free: 800-966-6613
Admissions: (814)865-5471
E-mail: admissions@psu.edu
Web Site: http://www.wb.psu.edu/

Description: State-related, primarily 2-year, coed. Part of P State University. Awards transfer associate, terminal asso bachelor's degrees. Founded 1916. Setting: 156-acre rural campu endowment: $1.2 billion. Total enrollment: 699. Student-undergra ratio is 13:1. 427 applied, 84% were admitted. 10% from top 10% high school class, 29% from top quarter, 67% from top half. Full-tim students, 30% women, 70% men. Part-time: 131 students, 50% wo 50% men. 4% from out-of-state, 0% Native American, 2% Hispanic, black, 1% Asian American or Pacific Islander, 0% international, 14% 25 older, 6% transferred in. Retention: 79% of full-time freshmen returned t following year. Core. Calendar: semesters. Academic remediation for enter ing students, services for LD students, advanced placement, accelerated degree program, self-designed majors, honors program, independent study, distance learning, double major, summer session for credit, adult/continuing education programs, internships. Study abroad program. ROTC: Air Force (c).

Entrance Requirements: Options: electronic application, early admission, deferred admission. Required: high school transcript, SAT or ACT. Recommended: essay. Required for some: recommendations, interview. Entrance: moderately difficult. Application deadline: Rolling. Notification: continuous.

Costs Per Year: Application fee: $50. State resident tuition: $9722 full-time, $393 per credit hour part-time. Nonresident tuition: $14,854 full-time, $619 per credit hour part-time. Mandatory fees: $478 full-time.

Collegiate Environment: Orientation program. Student-run newspaper, radio station. Student services: health clinic, personal-psychological counseling. Campus security: part-time trained security personnel. College housing not available. 35,697 books, 1,992 microform titles, 199 serials, and 394 audiovisual materials. 137 computers available on campus for general student use. Computer purchase/lease plans available. A campuswide network can be accessed from off-campus. Staffed computer lab on campus.

■ **THE PENNSYLVANIA STATE UNIVERSITY WORTHINGTON SCRANTON CAMPUS OF THE COMMONWEALTH COLLEGE** *E-22*

120 Ridge View Dr.
Dunmore, PA 18512-1699
Tel: (570)963-2500
Admissions: (814)865-5471
Fax: (570)963-2535
E-mail: admissions@psu.edu
Web Site: http://www.sn.psu.edu/

Description: State-related, primarily 2-year, coed. Part of Pennsylvania State University. Awards terminal associate and bachelor's degrees. Founded 1923. Setting: 43-acre small town campus. System endowment: $1.2 billion. Total enrollment: 1,262. Student-undergrad faculty ratio is 14:1. 580 applied, 84% were admitted. 6% from top 10% of their high school class, 23% from top quarter, 62% from top half. Full-time: 955 students, 46% women, 54% men. Part-time: 286 students, 65% women, 35% men. 1% from out-of-state, 0.1% Native American, 2% Hispanic, 2% black, 1% Asian American or Pacific Islander, 0.3% international, 26% 25 or older, 7% transferred in. Retention: 77% of full-time freshmen returned the following year. Core. Calendar: semesters. Academic remediation for entering students, services for LD students, advanced placement, accelerated degree program, honors program, independent study, distance learning, double major, summer session for credit, adult/continuing education programs, co-op programs and internships. Study abroad program. ROTC: Air Force (c).

Entrance Requirements: Options: electronic application, early admission, deferred admission. Required: high school transcript, SAT or ACT. Recommended: essay. Required for some: recommendations, interview. Entrance: moderately difficult. Application deadline: Rolling. Notification: continuous.

Costs Per Year: Application fee: $50. State resident tuition: $9722 full-time, $393 per credit hour part-time. Nonresident tuition: $14,854 full-time, $619 per credit hour part-time. Mandatory fees: $458 full-time.

legiate Environment: Orientation program. Drama-theater group, choral up, student-run newspaper. Student services: health clinic, personal-chological counseling, women's center. Campus security: part-time ined security personnel. College housing not available. 53,572 books, 3,130 microform titles, 102 serials, and 3,048 audiovisual materials. 104 omputers available on campus for general student use. Computer urchase/lease plans available. A campuswide network can be accessed from off-campus. Staffed computer lab on campus.

■ THE PENNSYLVANIA STATE UNIVERSITY YORK CAMPUS OF THE COMMONWEALTH COLLEGE *M-17*

1031 Edgecomb Ave.
York, PA 17403-3398
Tel: (717)771-4000
Free: 800-778-6227
Admissions: (814)865-5471
Fax: (717)771-4062
E-mail: admissions@psu.edu
Web Site: http://www.yk.psu.edu/

Description: State-related, primarily 2-year, coed. Part of Pennsylvania State University. Awards transfer associate, terminal associate, and bachelor's degrees (also offers up to 2 years of most bachelor's degree programs offered at University Park campus). Founded 1926. Setting: 53-acre suburban campus. System endowment: $1.2 billion. Total enrollment: 1,606. Student-undergrad faculty ratio is 13:1. 813 applied, 81% were admitted. 5% from top 10% of their high school class, 25% from top quarter, 50% from top half. Full-time: 822 students, 43% women, 57% men. Part-time: 593 students, 46% women, 54% men. 2% from out-of-state, 0.4% Native American, 4% Hispanic, 4% black, 6% Asian American or Pacific Islander, 0.2% international, 31% 25 or older, 2% transferred in. Retention: 74% of full-time freshmen returned the following year. Core. Calendar: semesters. Academic remediation for entering students, ESL program, services for LD students, advanced placement, accelerated degree program, self-designed majors, honors program, independent study, distance learning, double major, summer session for credit, adult/continuing education programs, internships. Study abroad program.
Entrance Requirements: Options: electronic application, early admission, deferred admission. Required: high school transcript, SAT or ACT. Recommended: essay. Required for some: recommendations, interview. Entrance: moderately difficult. Application deadline: Rolling. Notification: continuous.
Costs Per Year: Application fee: $50. State resident tuition: $9722 full-time, $393 per credit hour part-time. Nonresident tuition: $14,854 full-time, $619 per credit hour part-time. Mandatory fees: $458 full-time.
Collegiate Environment: Orientation program. Student-run newspaper. Student services: health clinic, personal-psychological counseling, women's center. Campus security: part-time trained security personnel. College housing not available. 49,996 books, 23,349 microform titles, 243 serials, and 3,567 audiovisual materials. 155 computers available on campus for general student use. Computer purchase/lease plans available. A campuswide network can be accessed from off-campus. Staffed computer lab on campus.

■ PHILADELPHIA BIBLICAL UNIVERSITY *B-50*

200 Manor Ave.
Langhorne, PA 19047-2990
Tel: (215)752-5800
Free: 800-366-0049
Admissions: (215)702-4550
Fax: (215)752-5812
E-mail: admissions@pcb.edu
Web Site: http://www.pbu.edu/

Description: Independent nondenominational, comprehensive, coed. Awards bachelor's, master's, and first professional degrees. Founded 1913. Setting: 105-acre suburban campus with easy access to Philadelphia. Endowment: $7.1 million. Educational spending for 2005 fiscal year: $5529 per student. Total enrollment: 1,439. Faculty: 156 (64 full-time, 92 part-time). Student-undergrad faculty ratio is 12:1. 307 applied, 94% were admitted. 17% from top 10% of their high school class, 45% from top quarter, 75% from top half. Full-time: 978 students, 57% women, 43% men. Part-time: 102 students, 44% women, 56% men. Students come from 38 states and territories, 49% from out-of-state, 0.1% Native American, 3% Hispanic, 11% black, 3% Asian American or Pacific Islander, 2% international, 20% 25 or older, 52% live on campus, 9% transferred in. Retention: 75% of full-time freshmen returned the following year. Academic areas with the most degrees conferred: education; public administration and social services; business/

marketing. Core. Calendar: semesters. Academic remediation for entering students, services for LD students, advanced placement, accelerated degree program, honors program, independent study, double major, summer session for credit, part-time degree program, adult/continuing education programs, internships, graduate courses open to undergrads. Off campus study at Bucks County Community College. Study abroad program. ROTC: Air Force (c).
Entrance Requirements: Options: Peterson's Universal Application, electronic application, early admission, deferred admission, international baccalaureate accepted. Required: minimum 2.0 high school GPA, SAT or ACT. Recommended: interview. Required for some: interview, SAT or ACT. Entrance: moderately difficult. Application deadline: Rolling. Notification: continuous.
Costs Per Year: Application fee: $25. Comprehensive fee: $22,425 includes full-time tuition ($15,555), mandatory fees ($320), and college room and board ($6550). College room only: $3400. Part-time tuition: $469 per credit.
Collegiate Environment: Orientation program. Drama-theater group, choral group, student-run newspaper. Social organizations: 17 open to all. Most popular organizations: Student Theological Society, Student Missionary Fellowship, Cultural Awareness Association, University Social Committee, Student Senate. Major annual events: homecoming, Spring Formal, Missions Conference. Student services: health clinic, personal-psychological counseling. Campus security: 24-hour emergency response devices and patrols, student patrols, late night transport-escort service, controlled dormitory access. 527 college housing spaces available; 517 were occupied in 2003-04. Freshmen guaranteed college housing. On-campus residence required through senior year. Options: men-only, women-only housing available. Masland Learning Resource Center with 96,988 books, 63,703 microform titles, 733 serials, 13,740 audiovisual materials, and an OPAC. Operations spending for 2004 fiscal year: $696,960. 85 computers available on campus for general student use. Computer purchase/lease plans available. A campuswide network can be accessed from student residence rooms and from off campus. Staffed computer lab on campus.

■ PHILADELPHIA UNIVERSITY *M-24*

School House Ln. and Henry Ave.
Philadelphia, PA 19144-5497
Tel: (215)951-2700
Admissions: (215)951-2800
Fax: (215)951-2907
Web Site: http://www.philau.edu/

Description: Independent, comprehensive, coed. Awards associate, bachelor's, master's, and doctoral degrees and post-master's certificates. Founded 1884. Setting: 100-acre suburban campus. Endowment: $21.8 million. Research spending for 2004 fiscal year: $1.9 million. Educational spending for 2005 fiscal year: $8574 per student. Total enrollment: 3,193. Faculty: 418 (104 full-time, 314 part-time). Student-undergrad faculty ratio is 12:1. 4,180 applied, 64% were admitted. 12% from top 10% of their high school class, 38% from top quarter, 80% from top half. Full-time: 2,432 students, 70% women, 30% men. Part-time: 275 students, 68% women, 32% men. Students come from 47 states and territories, 29 other countries, 50% from out-of-state, 0.1% Native American, 3% Hispanic, 9% black, 4% Asian American or Pacific Islander, 3% international, 14% 25 or older, 51% live on campus, 4% transferred in. Retention: 74% of full-time freshmen returned the following year. Academic areas with the most degrees conferred: business/marketing; architecture; visual and performing arts. Core. Calendar: semesters. Academic remediation for entering students, ESL program, services for LD students, advanced placement, accelerated degree program, freshman honors college, honors program, independent study, summer session for credit, part-time degree program, adult/continuing education programs, co-op programs and internships, graduate courses open to undergrads. Off campus study. Study abroad program.
Entrance Requirements: Options: Peterson's Universal Application, Common Application, electronic application, deferred admission. Required: high school transcript, SAT or ACT. Recommended: essay, 2 recommendations, interview. Entrance: moderately difficult. Application deadline: Rolling.
Costs Per Year: Application fee: $35. Comprehensive fee: $30,076 includes full-time tuition ($22,070), mandatory fees ($70), and college room and board ($7936). College room only: $3910. Full-time tuition and fees vary according to program. Room and board charges vary according to board plan and housing facility. Part-time tuition: $713 per credit. Part-time tuition varies according to class time and program.
Collegiate Environment: Orientation program. Drama-theater group, choral group, student-run newspaper. Social organizations: 30 open to all; national

fraternities, national sororities, local fraternities, local sororities; 1% of eligible men and 1% of eligible women are members. Most popular organizations: Gemini Theatre, Black Student Union, Cornerstone, Phila'cappella, Global Friends. Major annual events: Homecoming/Family Day, Welcome Week, Spring Weekend. Student services: health clinic, personal-psychological counseling. Campus security: 24-hour emergency response devices and patrols, late night transport-escort service, controlled dormitory access. College housing designed to accommodate 1,235 students; 1,265 undergraduates lived in college housing during 2003-04. Freshmen guaranteed college housing. Options: coed, women-only housing available. Paul J. Gutman Library plus 1 other with 108,141 books, 125,000 microform titles, 991 serials, 47,818 audiovisual materials, an OPAC, and a Web page. Operations spending for 2004 fiscal year: $1.2 million. 400 computers available on campus for general student use. A campuswide network can be accessed from student residence rooms and from off campus. Staffed computer lab on campus.

Community Environment: This suburban campus is 15 minutes from the heart of Philadelphia.

■ **PITTSBURGH INSTITUTE OF AERONAUTICS** K-3

PO Box 10897
Pittsburgh, PA 15236-0897
Tel: (412)462-9011
Free: 800-444-1440
Admissions: (412)346-2100
Fax: (412)466-0513
E-mail: admissions@piainfo.org
Web Site: http://www.pia.edu/

Description: Independent, 2-year, coed. Awards transfer associate degrees. Founded 1929. Setting: suburban campus. Total enrollment: 571. 85 applied, 100% were admitted. Full-time: 571 students, 4% women, 96% men. Students come from 12 states and territories, 4 other countries, 35% from out-of-state, 0.2% Native American, 0.2% Hispanic, 2% black, 0.4% Asian American or Pacific Islander, 2% international, 30% 25 or older. Core. Academic remediation for entering students, advanced placement.

Entrance Requirements: Open admission. Options: Peterson's Universal Application, deferred admission. Recommended: high school transcript, interview. Entrance: noncompetitive. Application deadline: Rolling. Notification: continuous.

Collegiate Environment: Student services: personal-psychological counseling. College housing not available. Technical Library with 15,000 books and 35 serials. 30 computers available on campus for general student use. Staffed computer lab on campus.

■ **PITTSBURGH INSTITUTE OF MORTUARY SCIENCE, INCORPORATED** K-3

5808 Baum Blvd.
Pittsburgh, PA 15206-3706
Tel: (412)362-8500
Free: 800-933-5808
Fax: (412)362-1684
E-mail: pims5808@aol.com
Web Site: http://www.pims.edu/

Description: Independent, 2-year, coed. Awards diplomas, transfer associate, and terminal associate degrees. Founded 1939. Setting: urban campus. Total enrollment: 192. Student-undergrad faculty ratio is 13:1. Full-time: 181 students, 43% women, 57% men. Part-time: 11 students, 45% women, 55% men. Students come from 10 states and territories, 23% from out-of-state, 1% Hispanic, 14% black, 48% 25 or older. Core. Calendar: trimesters. Academic remediation for entering students, services for LD students, part-time degree program, adult/continuing education programs, co-op programs and internships.

Entrance Requirements: Open admission. Option: international baccalaureate accepted. Required: high school transcript, 2 recommendations, interview, immunizations. Entrance: noncompetitive. Application deadline: Rolling. Notification: continuous.

Costs Per Year: Application fee: $40. Tuition: $8000 full-time, $240 per credit part-time. Mandatory fees: $170 full-time.

Collegiate Environment: Orientation program. Campus security: 24-hour emergency response devices. College housing not available. William J. Musmanno Memorial Library with 2,167 books, 48 serials, an OPAC, and a Web page. 10 computers available on campus for general student use. Staffed computer lab on campus.

■ **PITTSBURGH TECHNICAL INSTITUTE** G-29

1111 McKee Rd.
Oakdale, PA 15071
Tel: (412)809-5100
Free: 800-784-9675
Fax: (412)809-5388
Web Site: http://www.pti.edu/

Description: Proprietary, 2-year, coed. Founded 1946. Total enrollment: 1,975.

■ **THE PJA SCHOOL** M-23

7900 West Chester Pike
Upper Darby, PA 19082-1926
Tel: (610)789-6700
Free: 800-RING-PJA
E-mail: pjaschool@dvol.com
Web Site: http://www.pjaschool.com/

Description: Proprietary, 2-year, coed. Founded 1981.

■ **POINT PARK UNIVERSITY** K-3

201 Wood St.
Pittsburgh, PA 15222-1984
Tel: (412)391-4100
Free: 800-321-0129
Admissions: (412)392-3430
Fax: (412)391-1980
E-mail: jminford@pointpark.edu
Web Site: http://www.pointpark.edu/

Description: Independent, comprehensive, coed. Awards associate, bachelor's, and master's degrees and post-master's certificates. Founded 1960. Setting: urban campus. Endowment: $12.4 million. Educational spending for 2005 fiscal year: $6417 per student. Total enrollment: 3,407. Faculty: 390 (87 full-time, 303 part-time). Student-undergrad faculty ratio is 15:1. 2,453 applied, 76% were admitted. 12% from top 10% of their high school class, 38% from top quarter, 72% from top half. 25 class presidents, 117 student government officers. Full-time: 2,263 students, 60% women, 40% men. Part-time: 699 students, 54% women, 46% men. Students come from 45 states and territories, 34 other countries, 16% from out-of-state, 0.2% Native American, 2% Hispanic, 18% black, 1% Asian American or Pacific Islander, 1% international, 34% 25 or older, 22% live on campus, 16% transferred in. Retention: 71% of full-time freshmen returned the following year. Academic areas with the most degrees conferred: business/marketing; visual and performing arts; security and protective services. Core. Calendar: semesters. Academic remediation for entering students, services for LD students, advanced placement, accelerated degree program, self-designed majors, honors program, independent study, distance learning, double major, summer session for credit, part-time degree program, adult/continuing education programs, internships, graduate courses open to undergrads. Off campus study at 10 members of the Pittsburgh Council on Higher Education. Study abroad program. ROTC: Army (c), Air Force (c).

Entrance Requirements: Options: Peterson's Universal Application, Common Application, electronic application, early admission, deferred admission, international baccalaureate accepted. Required: high school transcript, SAT or ACT. Recommended: essay, minimum 2.0 high school GPA. Required for some: 2 recommendations, interview, audition. Entrance: moderately difficult. Application deadline: Rolling.

Costs Per Year: Application fee: $40. Comprehensive fee: $24,160 includes full-time tuition ($16,280), mandatory fees ($460), and college room and board ($7420). College room only: $3500. Full-time tuition and fees vary according to program. Room and board charges vary according to board plan. Part-time tuition: $447 per credit. Part-time mandatory fees: $10 per credit. Part-time tuition and fees vary according to program.

Collegiate Environment: Orientation program. Drama-theater group, choral group, student-run newspaper, radio station. Social organizations: 18 open to all. Most popular organizations: Black Student Union, student radio station, Dance Club, Alpha Phi Omega, College Students in Broadcasting. Major annual events: Welcome Back Riverboat Cruise, Labor Day Picnic, Spring Fling Riverboat Cruise. Student services: health clinic, personal-psychological counseling. Campus security: 24-hour emergency response devices and patrols, late night transport-escort service, 24-hour security desk, video security. College housing designed to accommodate 584 students; 617 undergraduates lived in college housing during 2003-04. Freshmen guaranteed college housing. Option: coed housing available. Point Park University Library with 125,000 books, 21,000 microform titles,

230 serials, 500 audiovisual materials, and an OPAC. Operations spending for 2004 fiscal year: $1 million. 170 computers available on campus for general student use. A campuswide network can be accessed from student residence rooms and from off campus. Staffed computer lab on campus.

Community Environment: The college is centrally located in the city of Pittsburgh, population 365,000. See also University of Pittsburgh, Pittsburgh Campus.

■ **READING AREA COMMUNITY COLLEGE** *K-21*
PO Box 1706
Reading, PA 19603-1706
Tel: (610)372-4721
Admissions: (610)607-6224
Fax: (610)375-8255
Web Site: http://www.racc.edu/
Description: County-supported, 2-year, coed. Awards certificates, diplomas, transfer associate, and terminal associate degrees. Founded 1971. Setting: 14-acre urban campus with easy access to Philadelphia. Endowment: $745,770. Total enrollment: 4,158. 2,318 applied, 100% were admitted. Full-time: 1,578 students, 63% women, 37% men. Part-time: 2,580 students, 70% women, 30% men. Students come from 10 other countries, 1% Native American, 13% Hispanic, 9% black, 2% Asian American or Pacific Islander, 1% international, 56% 25 or older. Core. Academic remediation for entering students, ESL program, services for LD students, self-designed majors, summer session for credit, part-time degree program, external degree program, adult/continuing education programs, co-op programs.
Entrance Requirements: Open admission. Options: electronic application, early admission, deferred admission. Entrance: noncompetitive. Application deadline: Rolling.
Collegiate Environment: Student-run newspaper. Student services: personal-psychological counseling, women's center. Campus security: 24-hour patrols. College housing not available. Yocum Library with 25,541 books, 284 serials, an OPAC, and a Web page. 80 computers available on campus for general student use. Staffed computer lab on campus.
Community Environment: Reading is located about 60 miles north of Philadelphia and approximately 2 1/2 hours by bus or car to New York City.

■ **THE RESTAURANT SCHOOL AT WALNUT HILL COLLEGE** *M-24*
4207 Walnut St.
Philadelphia, PA 19104-3518
Tel: (215)222-4200; 877-925-6884
Fax: (215)222-4219
Web Site: http://www.walnuthillcollege.edu/
Description: Proprietary, primarily 2-year, coed. Awards terminal associate and bachelor's degrees. Founded 1974. Setting: 2-acre urban campus. Total enrollment: 585. Students come from 10 states and territories, 5 other countries, 57% from out-of-state, 21% 25 or older, 20% live on campus. Calendar: semesters. Academic remediation for entering students, part-time degree program, internships.
Entrance Requirements: Open admission. Options: Common Application, early admission, early decision, deferred admission. Required: essay, high school transcript, 2 recommendations, interview. Recommended: minimum 2.0 high school GPA, SAT or ACT. Required for some: entrance exam. Application deadline: Rolling.
Collegiate Environment: Orientation program. Student-run newspaper. Most popular organizations: Community Action Society, Les Gastronome, Culinary Salon, Tastevin, Pastry Club. Major annual events: Welcome Tea, Friends and Family Day. Option: coed housing available. Alumni Resource Center with 5,000 books and 200 serials. 24 computers available on campus for general student use. Staffed computer lab on campus.

■ **ROBERT MORRIS UNIVERSITY** *J-3*
6001 University Blvd.
Moon Township, PA 15108-1189
Tel: (412)262-8200
Free: 800-762-0097
Admissions: (412)262-8412
Fax: (412)262-8619
E-mail: budziszewski@rmu.edu
Web Site: http://www.rmu.edu/
Description: Independent, university, coed. Awards bachelor's, master's, and doctoral degrees. Founded 1921. Setting: 230-acre suburban campus with easy access to Pittsburgh. Endowment: $17.2 million. Educational spending for 2005 fiscal year: $5496 per student. Total enrollment: 5,095.

Faculty: 384 (157 full-time, 227 part-time). Student-undergrad faculty ratio is 16:1. 2,584 applied, 78% were admitted. 8% from top 10% of their high school class, 27% from top quarter, 66% from top half. Full-time: 3,103 students, 43% women, 57% men. Part-time: 868 students, 54% women, 46% men. Students come from 31 states and territories, 23 other countries, 11% from out-of-state, 0.1% Native American, 1% Hispanic, 8% black, 1% Asian American or Pacific Islander, 2% international, 28% 25 or older, 30% live on campus, 11% transferred in. Retention: 78% of full-time freshmen returned the following year. Academic areas with the most degrees conferred: business/marketing; communications/journalism; computer and information sciences. Core. Calendar: semesters. Academic remediation for entering students, services for LD students, advanced placement, accelerated degree program, honors program, independent study, distance learning, double major, summer session for credit, part-time degree program, adult/continuing education programs, co-op programs and internships, graduate courses open to undergrads. Off campus study at Pittsburgh Council on Higher Education. Study abroad program. ROTC: Army (c), Air Force (c).
Entrance Requirements: Options: Common Application, electronic application, deferred admission. Required: high school transcript, minimum 2.5 high school GPA, SAT or ACT. Recommended: minimum 3.0 high school GPA, recommendations, interview. Required for some: interview. Entrance: moderately difficult. Application deadline: 7/1. Notification: continuous.
Costs Per Year: Application fee: $30. Comprehensive fee: $22,822 includes full-time tuition ($15,152) and college room and board ($7670). College room only: $4650. Room and board charges vary according to board plan and housing facility. Part-time tuition: $505 per credit. Part-time tuition varies according to course load.
Collegiate Environment: Orientation program. Drama-theater group, marching band, student-run newspaper. Social organizations: 50 open to all; national fraternities, national sororities; 5% of eligible men and 4% of eligible women are members. Most popular organizations: Student Government Association, Residence Hall Association, R-MOVE, National Society of Collegiate Scholars. Major annual events: Snowball, Homecoming, Spring Fest. Student services: health clinic, personal-psychological counseling. Campus security: 24-hour emergency response devices and patrols, late night transport-escort service, controlled dormitory access. 1,130 college housing spaces available; 1,129 were occupied in 2003-04. Freshmen given priority for college housing. Options: coed, men-only, women-only housing available. Robert Morris University Library with 197,034 books, 329,126 microform titles, 699 serials, 2,699 audiovisual materials, and an OPAC. Operations spending for 2004 fiscal year: $1.3 million. 300 computers available on campus for general student use. A campuswide network can be accessed from student residence rooms and from off campus. Staffed computer lab on campus.

■ **ROSEDALE TECHNICAL INSTITUTE** *K-3*
215 Beecham Dr.
Ste. 2
Pittsburgh, PA 15205-9791
Tel: (412)521-6200
Free: 800-521-6262
Fax: (412)521-9277
E-mail: admissions@rosedaletech.org
Web Site: http://www.rosedaletech.org/
Description: Independent, 2-year, coed. Awards diplomas and terminal associate degrees. Setting: 6-acre suburban campus. Total enrollment: 200. Student-undergrad faculty ratio is 13:1. 156 applied, 65% were admitted. Calendar: semesters.

■ **ROSEMONT COLLEGE** *M-23*
1400 Montgomery Ave.
Rosemont, PA 19010-1699
Tel: (610)527-0200
Free: 800-331-0708
Fax: (610)527-1041
E-mail: randrews@rosemont.edu
Web Site: http://www.rosemont.edu/
Description: Independent Roman Catholic, comprehensive. Awards bachelor's and master's degrees. Founded 1921. Setting: 56-acre suburban campus with easy access to Philadelphia. Endowment: $8.7 million. Educational spending for 2005 fiscal year: $18,200 per student. Total enrollment: 1,048. Faculty: 77 (32 full-time, 45 part-time). Student-undergrad faculty ratio is 8:1. 434 applied, 66% were admitted. 25% from top 10% of

their high school class, 45% from top quarter, 71% from top half. 2 class presidents, 1 valedictorian, 9 student government officers. Full-time: 425 students, 100% women. Part-time: 219 students, 76% women, 24% men. Students come from 14 states and territories, 13 other countries, 30% from out-of-state, 0% Native American, 7% Hispanic, 28% black, 7% Asian American or Pacific Islander, 4% international, 47% 25 or older, 70% live on campus, 4% transferred in. Retention: 78% of full-time freshmen returned the following year. Academic areas with the most degrees conferred: visual and performing arts; business/marketing; social sciences. Core. Calendar: semesters. ESL program, services for LD students, advanced placement, accelerated degree program, self-designed majors, honors program, independent study, double major, summer session for credit, part-time degree program, adult/continuing education programs, internships, graduate courses open to undergrads. Off campus study at Villanova University, Cabrini College, Eastern College, Sepche Consortium. Study abroad program. ROTC: Army (c).

Entrance Requirements: Options: Peterson's Universal Application, Common Application, electronic application, early admission, deferred admission, international baccalaureate accepted. Required: essay, high school transcript, 2 recommendations, SAT or ACT. Recommended: minimum 3.0 high school GPA, interview. Entrance: moderately difficult. Application deadline: Rolling. Notification: continuous until 8/1.

Costs Per Year: Application fee: $35. Comprehensive fee: $29,350 includes full-time tuition ($19,450), mandatory fees ($1100), and college room and board ($8800). Room and board charges vary according to housing facility. Part-time tuition: $750 per credit. Part-time mandatory fees: $310 per term.

Collegiate Environment: Orientation program. Drama-theater group, choral group, student-run newspaper. Social organizations: 11 open to all. Most popular organizations: student government, Triad, Jest and Gesture, Best Buddies, Political Science Club. Major annual events: Oktoberfest, Founders' Day/Spring Fling, Annual Concert. Student services: legal services, health clinic, personal-psychological counseling, women's center. Campus security: 24-hour emergency response devices and patrols, late night transport-escort service, controlled dormitory access. 335 college housing spaces available; 250 were occupied in 2003-04. Freshmen guaranteed college housing. On-campus residence required through junior year. Option: women-only housing available. Kistler Library with 161,374 books, 25,024 microform titles, 891 serials, 2,858 audiovisual materials, an OPAC, and a Web page. Operations spending for 2004 fiscal year: $730,600. 77 computers available on campus for general student use. A campuswide network can be accessed from student residence rooms and from off campus. Staffed computer lab on campus.

Community Environment: See Villanova University.

■ **ST. CHARLES BORROMEO SEMINARY, OVERBROOK** *M-23*
100 East Wynnewood Rd.
Wynnewood, PA 19096
Tel: (610)667-3394
Admissions: (610)785-6271
E-mail: cas@adphila.org
Web Site: http://www.scs.edu/
Description: Independent Roman Catholic, comprehensive. Awards bachelor's, master's, and first professional degrees (also offers coed part-time programs). Founded 1832. Setting: 77-acre suburban campus with easy access to Philadelphia. Endowment: $16.8 million. Total enrollment: 328. Faculty: 30 (22 full-time, 8 part-time). Student-undergrad faculty ratio is 7:1. 8 applied, 100% were admitted. 13% from top 10% of their high school class, 50% from top quarter, 63% from top half. Full-time: 82 students, 100% men. Part-time: 113 students, 81% women, 19% men. Students come from 9 states and territories, 1 other country, 35% from out-of-state, 0% Native American, 2% Hispanic, 0% black, 2% Asian American or Pacific Islander, 3% international, 12% 25 or older, 94% live on campus, 5% transferred in. Retention: 82% of full-time freshmen returned the following year. Core. Calendar: semesters. Academic remediation for entering students, ESL program, advanced placement, accelerated degree program, independent study, summer session for credit, adult/continuing education programs, graduate courses open to undergrads.

Entrance Requirements: Options: deferred admission, international baccalaureate accepted. Required: essay, high school transcript, minimum 2.0 high school GPA, 3 recommendations, interview, sponsorship by diocese or religious community. Recommended: SAT or ACT. Entrance: moderately difficult. Application deadline: 7/15. Notification: continuous.

Costs Per Year: Application fee: $0. Comprehensive fee: $19,850 includes full-time tuition ($12,350) and college room and board ($7500). Part-time tuition: $150 per credit.

Collegiate Environment: Orientation program. Drama-theater group, choral group, student-run newspaper. Most popular organizations: Seminarians for Life, student council. Student services: health clinic, personal-psychological counseling. Campus security: 24-hour emergency response devices and patrols. 250 college housing spaces available; 65 were occupied in 2003-04. Freshmen guaranteed college housing. On-campus residence required through senior year. Option: men-only housing available. Ryan Memorial Library with 113,761 books, 1,889 microform titles, 575 serials, 9,090 audiovisual materials, and a Web page. 60 computers available on campus for general student use. A campuswide network can be accessed. Staffed computer lab on campus.

■ **SAINT FRANCIS UNIVERSITY** *J-9*
PO Box 600, 117 Evergreen Dr.
Loretto, PA 15940-0600
Tel: (814)472-3000
Free: 800-342-5732
Admissions: (814)472-3100
Fax: (814)472-3044
Web Site: http://www.francis.edu/
Description: Independent Roman Catholic, comprehensive, coed. Awards associate, bachelor's, and master's degrees. Founded 1847. Setting: 600-acre rural campus. Endowment: $16.5 million. Research spending for 2004 fiscal year: $9.5 million. Educational spending for 2005 fiscal year: $7037 per student. Total enrollment: 2,065. Faculty: 164 (89 full-time, 75 part-time). Student-undergrad faculty ratio is 14:1. 1,246 applied, 91% were admitted. 22% from top 10% of their high school class, 52% from top quarter, 78% from top half. 14 National Merit Scholars, 10 class presidents, 7 valedictorians, 70 student government officers. Full-time: 1,255 students, 60% women, 40% men. Part-time: 206 students, 77% women, 23% men. Students come from 34 states and territories, 33 other countries, 27% from out-of-state, 0.2% Native American, 1% Hispanic, 7% black, 1% Asian American or Pacific Islander, 0.3% international, 5% 25 or older, 72% live on campus, 7% transferred in. Retention: 83% of full-time freshmen returned the following year. Core. Calendar: semesters. Academic remediation for entering students, advanced placement, accelerated degree program, self-designed majors, freshman honors college, honors program, distance learning, double major, summer session for credit, part-time degree program, external degree program, adult/continuing education programs, internships, graduate courses open to undergrads. Off campus study at Washington Center for Learning Alternatives. Study abroad program. ROTC: Army (c).

Entrance Requirements: Options: Peterson's Universal Application, electronic application, deferred admission, international baccalaureate accepted. Required: high school transcript, 1 recommendation, SAT or ACT. Recommended: essay, interview. Required for some: 3 recommendations, interview. Entrance: moderately difficult. Application deadline: Rolling.

Costs Per Year: Application fee: $30. Comprehensive fee: $28,978 includes full-time tuition ($20,360), mandatory fees ($1050), and college room and board ($7568). College room only: $3672. Full-time tuition and fees vary according to course load and program. Room and board charges vary according to board plan. Part-time tuition: $636 per credit. Part-time mandatory fees: $315 per credit hour.

Collegiate Environment: Orientation program. Drama-theater group, choral group, student-run newspaper, radio station. Social organizations: 54 open to all; national fraternities, national sororities, local sororities; 17% of eligible men and 12% of eligible women are members. Most popular organizations: Student Activities Organization, New Theatre, Student Government Association. Major annual events: Parents' Weekend, Winter Weekend, Spring Fest. Student services: health clinic, personal-psychological counseling. Campus security: 24-hour emergency response devices and patrols, late night transport-escort service, controlled dormitory access. 983 college housing spaces available; 870 were occupied in 2003-04. Freshmen guaranteed college housing. On-campus residence required through junior year. Options: men-only, women-only housing available. Pasquerella Library with 118,333 books, 8,055 microform titles, 7,202 serials, 3,735 audiovisual materials, an OPAC, and a Web page. Operations spending for 2004 fiscal year: $956,996. 60 computers available on campus for general student use. Computer purchase/lease plans available. A campuswide network can be accessed from student residence rooms and from off campus. Staffed computer lab on campus.

■ **SAINT JOSEPH'S UNIVERSITY** *M-24*
5600 City Ave.
Philadelphia, PA 19131-1395

Tel: (610)660-1000
Admissions: (610)660-1300
E-mail: admit@sju.edu
Web Site: http://www.sju.edu/

Description: Independent Roman Catholic (Jesuit), comprehensive, coed. Awards associate, bachelor's, master's, and doctoral degrees and post-master's certificates. Founded 1851. Setting: 65-acre suburban campus. Endowment: $97.9 million. Research spending for 2004 fiscal year: $4.3 million. Educational spending for 2005 fiscal year: $8077 per student. Total enrollment: 7,714. Faculty: 598 (269 full-time, 329 part-time). Student-undergrad faculty ratio is 15:1. 9,021 applied, 47% were admitted. 24% from top 10% of their high school class, 78% from top quarter, 87% from top half. Full-time: 4,247 students, 52% women, 48% men. Part-time: 896 students, 57% women, 43% men. Students come from 38 states and territories, 48 other countries, 46% from out-of-state, 0.2% Native American, 3% Hispanic, 8% black, 3% Asian American or Pacific Islander, 1% international, 0% 25 or older, 59% live on campus, 2% transferred in. Retention: 89% of full-time freshmen returned the following year. Academic areas with the most degrees conferred: business/marketing; social sciences; education. Core. Calendar: semesters. Academic remediation for entering students, ESL program, services for LD students, advanced placement, accelerated degree program, self-designed majors, honors program, independent study, distance learning, double major, summer session for credit, part-time degree program, adult/continuing education programs, co-op programs and internships, graduate courses open to undergrads. Off campus study at members of the Jesuit Student Exchange. Study abroad program. ROTC: Army (c), Naval (c), Air Force.

Entrance Requirements: Options: Peterson's Universal Application, Common Application, electronic application, early action, deferred admission. Required: essay, high school transcript, 1 recommendation, SAT or ACT. Recommended: minimum 3.0 high school GPA. Entrance: very difficult. Application deadlines: 2/1, 11/15 for early action. Notification: 3/15, 1/15 for early action.

Costs Per Year: Application fee: $55. Comprehensive fee: $37,428 includes full-time tuition ($27,320), mandatory fees ($135), and college room and board ($9973). Full-time tuition and fees vary according to student level. Room and board charges vary according to board plan and housing facility. Part-time tuition: $895 per credit.

Collegiate Environment: Orientation program. Drama-theater group, choral group, student-run newspaper, radio station. Social organizations: 70 open to all; national fraternities, national sororities; 8% of eligible men and 11% of eligible women are members. Most popular organizations: University Student Senate, Student Union Board, Cap and Bells Dramatic Arts Society, Hand-in-Hand, Up 'til Dawn. Major annual events: Midnight Madness, Hand-in-Hand Festival, Up 'til Dawn. Student services: health clinic, personal-psychological counseling. Campus security: 24-hour emergency response devices and patrols, late night transport-escort service, controlled dormitory access, 24-hour shuttle/escort service, bicycle patrols. College housing designed to accommodate 2,421 students; 2,446 undergraduates lived in college housing during 2003-04. Freshmen guaranteed college housing. On-campus residence required through sophomore year. Options: coed, men-only, women-only housing available. Francis A. Drexel Library plus 1 other with 353,101 books, 853,441 microform titles, 2,698 serials, 4,415 audiovisual materials, an OPAC, and a Web page. Operations spending for 2004 fiscal year: $2.5 million. 400 computers available on campus for general student use. Computer purchase/lease plans available. A campuswide network can be accessed from student residence rooms and from off campus. Staffed computer lab on campus.

■ **SAINT VINCENT COLLEGE** *L-6*
300 Fraser Purchase Rd.
Latrobe, PA 15650-2690
Tel: (724)532-6600
Free: 800-782-5549
Admissions: (724)532-5089
Fax: (724)537-4554
E-mail: admission@stvincent.edu
Web Site: http://www.stvincent.edu/

Description: Independent Roman Catholic, comprehensive, coed. Awards bachelor's and master's degrees. Founded 1846. Setting: 200-acre suburban campus with easy access to Pittsburgh. Endowment: $46.5 million. Research spending for 2004 fiscal year: $106,361. Educational spending for 2005 fiscal year: $6849 per student. Total enrollment: 1,687. Faculty: 167 (95 full-time, 72 part-time). Student-undergrad faculty ratio is 13:1. 1,488 ap-

plied, 73% were admitted. 21% from top 10% of their high school class, 53% from top quarter, 86% from top half. 1 class president, 6 valedictorians. Full-time: 1,471 students, 52% women, 48% men. Part-time: 105 students, 54% women, 46% men. Students come from 27 states and territories, 22 other countries, 14% from out-of-state, 0.3% Native American, 1% Hispanic, 2% black, 1% Asian American or Pacific Islander, 1% international, 7% 25 or older, 70% live on campus, 4% transferred in. Retention: 89% of full-time freshmen returned the following year. Academic areas with the most degrees conferred: business/marketing; psychology; communications/journalism. Core. Calendar: semesters. Advanced placement, accelerated degree program, honors program, independent study, summer session for credit, part-time degree program, adult/continuing education programs, co-op programs and internships, graduate courses open to undergrads. Off campus study at Duquesne University, Seton Hill University. Study abroad program. ROTC: Air Force (c).

Entrance Requirements: Options: Peterson's Universal Application, early admission, deferred admission, international baccalaureate accepted. Required: essay, high school transcript, minimum 2.5 high school GPA, SAT or ACT. Recommended: minimum 3.2 high school GPA, 3 recommendations, interview. Required for some: interview. Entrance: moderately difficult. Application deadline: 5/1. Notification: continuous.

Costs Per Year: Application fee: $25. Comprehensive fee: $28,553 includes full-time tuition ($21,104), mandatory fees ($575), and college room and board ($6874). College room only: $3500. Room and board charges vary according to board plan and student level. Part-time tuition: $660 per credit hour. Part-time mandatory fees: $45 per term.

Collegiate Environment: Orientation program. Drama-theater group, choral group, student-run newspaper, radio station. Social organizations: 54 open to all. Most popular organizations: The Company (student theatre group), Dreamkeepers Society (student multicultural organization), Student Orientation Program, student government, Alpha Lambda Delta Academic Honor Society. Major annual events: Founders' Day, Christmas Cotillion, Concert Series. Student services: health clinic, personal-psychological counseling. Campus security: 24-hour emergency response devices and patrols, late night transport-escort service, controlled dormitory access, limited access to residence halls on weekends. 1,074 college housing spaces available; 484 were occupied in 2003-04. Freshmen given priority for college housing. Option: coed housing available. Saint Vincent College Library with 271,481 books, 99,608 microform titles, 683 serials, 4,287 audiovisual materials, an OPAC, and a Web page. Operations spending for 2004 fiscal year: $592,601. 190 computers available on campus for general student use. A campuswide network can be accessed from student residence rooms and from off campus. Staffed computer lab on campus.

Community Environment: Population 8,994. Located in the Laurel Highlands region of the Allegheny Mountains, Latrobe is 35 miles east of Pittsburgh. The area is accessible by air, railroad and major highways. There is a county airport adjacent to campus. The community has a public library, churches and a synagogue and multiple shopping malls.

■ **SCHUYLKILL INSTITUTE OF BUSINESS AND TECHNOLOGY** *J-19*
171 Red Horse Rd.
Pottsville, PA 17901
Tel: (570)622-4835
Fax: (570)622-4835
E-mail: sseaman@sibt.edu
Web Site: http://www.sibt.edu/

Description: Proprietary, 2-year, coed. Part of Fore Front Education, Inc. Awards diplomas, transfer associate, and terminal associate degrees. Setting: rural campus. Educational spending for 2005 fiscal year: $492 per student. Total enrollment: 136. Student-undergrad faculty ratio is 6:1. 36 applied, 100% were admitted. 1% from top 10% of their high school class, 25% from top quarter, 50% from top half. Full-time: 136 students, 65% women, 35% men. 0% from out-of-state, 1% Native American, 1% Hispanic, 1% black, 45% 25 or older, 3% transferred in. Core. Academic remediation for entering students, services for LD students, advanced placement, independent study, co-op programs and internships.

Entrance Requirements: Open admission. Option: Common Application. Required: high school transcript, interview. Entrance: minimally difficult. Application deadline: 10/25.

Costs Per Year: Application fee: $50. Tuition: $10,000 full-time. Mandatory fees: $450 full-time. Full-time tuition and fees vary according to degree level and program. Tuition guaranteed not to increase for student's term of enrollment.

Collegiate Environment: Orientation program. College housing not available. Schuylkill Institute of Business and Technology Learning Resource

Cent with 920 books, 20 serials, 300 audiovisual materials, and an OPAC. Operations spending for 2004 fiscal year: $55,000. 41 computers available on campus for general student use. from off-campusStaffed computer lab on campus.

■ SETON HILL UNIVERSITY L-5

Seton Hill Dr.
Greensburg, PA 15601
Tel: (724)834-2200
Free: 800-826-6234
Admissions: (724)838-4255
Fax: (724)830-4611
E-mail: admit@setonhill.edu
Web Site: http://www.setonhill.edu/

Description: Independent Roman Catholic, comprehensive, coed. Awards bachelor's and master's degrees and post-master's certificates. Founded 1883. Setting: 200-acre small town campus with easy access to Pittsburgh. Endowment: $9.9 million. Educational spending for 2005 fiscal year: $5511 per student. Total enrollment: 1,863. Faculty: 185 (68 full-time, 117 part-time). Student-undergrad faculty ratio is 15:1. 2,133 applied, 70% were admitted. 14% from top 10% of their high school class, 39% from top quarter, 73% from top half. Full-time: 1,226 students, 61% women, 39% men. Part-time: 300 students, 77% women, 23% men. Students come from 28 states and territories, 12 other countries, 18% from out-of-state, 0.5% Native American, 2% Hispanic, 8% black, 1% Asian American or Pacific Islander, 2% international, 17% 25 or older, 60% live on campus, 5% transferred in. Retention: 78% of full-time freshmen returned the following year. Academic areas with the most degrees conferred: business/marketing; visual and performing arts; public administration and social services. Core. Calendar: semesters. Academic remediation for entering students, ESL program, advanced placement, accelerated degree program, self-designed majors, honors program, independent study, distance learning, double major, summer session for credit, part-time degree program, adult/continuing education programs, internships, graduate courses open to undergrads. Off campus study at Saint Vincent College, University of Pittsburgh at Greensburg, Westmoreland County Community College. Study abroad program. ROTC: Army (c).

Entrance Requirements: Options: Peterson's Universal Application, Common Application, electronic application, early admission, deferred admission, international baccalaureate accepted. Required: essay, high school transcript, minimum 2.0 high school GPA, recommendations, portfolio for art program, audition for music and theater programs, separate application process for physician assistant program. Recommended: interview, SAT or ACT. Entrance: moderately difficult. Application deadline: 8/15. Notification: continuous.

Costs Per Year: Application fee: $35. Comprehensive fee: $29,020 includes full-time tuition ($21,870), mandatory fees ($120), and college room and board ($7030). Room and board charges vary according to board plan and housing facility. Part-time tuition: $580 per credit. Part-time mandatory fees: $60 per term. Part-time tuition and fees vary according to course load.

Collegiate Environment: Orientation program. Drama-theater group, choral group, student-run newspaper. Social organizations: 28 open to all. Most popular organizations: Intercultural Student Organization, Biology/Environmental Club, Association of Black Collegians, Chemistry Club, Pennsylvania Student Education Association. Major annual events: Christmas on the Hill, Labor of Love, Washington, DC trip. Student services: health clinic, personal-psychological counseling. Campus security: 24-hour emergency response devices and patrols, late night transport-escort service, controlled dormitory access, student personnel at entrances during evening hours, 15-hour overnight patrols by trained police officers. 571 college housing spaces available; 569 were occupied in 2003-04. Freshmen guaranteed college housing. Options: coed, men-only, women-only housing available. Reeves Memorial Library with 116,974 books, 5,995 microform titles, 9,598 serials, 6,663 audiovisual materials, an OPAC, and a Web page. Operations spending for 2004 fiscal year: $375,019. 259 computers available on campus for general student use. A campuswide network can be accessed from student residence rooms and from off campus. Staffed computer lab on campus.

■ SHIPPENSBURG UNIVERSITY OF PENNSYLVANIA M-14

1871 Old Main Dr.
Shippensburg, PA 17257-2299
Tel: (717)477-7447
Admissions: (717)477-1231

Fax: (717)477-1273
E-mail: admiss@ship.edu
Web Site: http://www.ship.edu/

Description: State-supported, comprehensive, coed. Part of Pennsylvania State System of Higher Education. Awards bachelor's and master's degrees and post-master's certificates. Founded 1871. Setting: 200-acre rural campus. Endowment: $20.3 million. Research spending for 2004 fiscal year: $478,592. Educational spending for 2005 fiscal year: $5254 per student. Total enrollment: 7,485. Faculty: 371 (305 full-time, 66 part-time). Student-undergrad faculty ratio is 20:1. 6,281 applied, 66% were admitted. 10% from top 10% of their high school class, 30% from top quarter, 70% from top half. 21 class presidents, 141 student government officers. Full-time: 6,175 students, 52% women, 48% men. Part-time: 284 students, 58% women, 42% men. Students come from 28 states and territories, 21 other countries, 6% from out-of-state, 0.3% Native American, 2% Hispanic, 5% black, 1% Asian American or Pacific Islander, 0.2% international, 51% 25 or older, 34% live on campus, 5% transferred in. Retention: 76% of full-time freshmen returned the following year. Academic areas with the most degrees conferred: business/marketing; education; communications/journalism; security and protective services. Core. Calendar: semesters. Academic remediation for entering students, services for LD students, advanced placement, accelerated degree program, honors program, independent study, distance learning, double major, summer session for credit, part-time degree program, co-op programs and internships, graduate courses open to undergrads. Off campus study at Wilson College, Marine Science Consortium, Art Institutes International, Fashion Institute of Technology, HACC, Hagerstown CC, Carroll CC, Alleghany College, Co. Osmo, PJJHE Frederic CC, International Studies Consortium. Study abroad program. ROTC: Army.

Entrance Requirements: Options: Peterson's Universal Application, Common Application, electronic application, early admission, early action, deferred admission, international baccalaureate accepted. Required: high school transcript, SAT or ACT. Recommended: essay, recommendations, class rank. Required for some: interview. Entrance: moderately difficult. Application deadlines: Rolling, Rolling for nonresidents. Notification: continuous, continuous for nonresidents.

Costs Per Year: Application fee: $30. State resident tuition: $4906 full-time, $204 per credit hour part-time. Nonresident tuition: $12,266 full-time, $511 per credit hour part-time. Mandatory fees: $1269 full-time, $20 per credit hour part-time, $147 per term part-time. College room and board: $5710. College room only: $3290. Room and board charges vary according to board plan and housing facility.

Collegiate Environment: Orientation program. Drama-theater group, choral group, marching band, student-run newspaper, radio station. Social organizations: 247 open to all; national fraternities, national sororities, local sororities; 6% of eligible men and 8% of eligible women are members. Most popular organizations: band, Christian Fellowship, Residence Hall Association, United Campus Ministry, African-American Organization. Major annual events: homecoming, Parents' Days, Spring Fest. Student services: health clinic, personal-psychological counseling, women's center. Campus security: 24-hour emergency response devices and patrols, student patrols, late night transport-escort service, controlled dormitory access, surveillance cameras in certain parking lots and buildings, foot, vehicular and bicycle patrols by security officers. 2,650 college housing spaces available; 2,542 were occupied in 2003-04. Freshmen guaranteed college housing. On-campus residence required in freshman year. Options: coed, women-only housing available. Ezra Lehman Memorial Library with 447,016 books, 1.3 million microform titles, 1,255 serials, 76,846 audiovisual materials, an OPAC, and a Web page. Operations spending for 2004 fiscal year: $2.6 million. 800 computers available on campus for general student use. A campuswide network can be accessed from student residence rooms and from off campus. Staffed computer lab on campus.

Community Environment: Located in south-central Pennsylvania, Shippensburg, population 6,500, is a semirural community. The area has 32 churches of various denominations, a library, and many civic and fraternal organizations. Recreational activities include fishing, hunting, swimming, football, baseball, and bowling. Limited part-time employment opportunities are available.

■ SLIPPERY ROCK UNIVERSITY OF PENNSYLVANIA G-3

1 Morrow Way
Slippery Rock, PA 16057-1383
Tel: (724)738-9000
Free: 800-SRU-9111

Fax: (724)738-2098
Web Site: http://www.sru.edu/
Description: State-supported, comprehensive, coed. Awards bachelor's, master's, and doctoral degrees. Founded 1889. Setting: 600-acre rural campus with easy access to Pittsburgh. Endowment: $16.5 million. Research spending for 2004 fiscal year: $328,664. Educational spending for 2005 fiscal year: $6212 per student. Total enrollment: 8,105. Faculty: 401 (367 full-time, 34 part-time). Student-undergrad faculty ratio is 19:1. 4,360 applied, 41% were admitted. 8% from top 10% of their high school class, 28% from top quarter, 70% from top half. 14 valedictorians. Full-time: 6,883 students, 54% women, 46% men. Part-time: 531 students, 68% women, 32% men. Students come from 36 states and territories, 39 other countries, 6% from out-of-state, 0.4% Native American, 1% Hispanic, 4% black, 1% Asian American or Pacific Islander, 1% international, 11% 25 or older, 39% live on campus, 7% transferred in. Retention: 78% of full-time freshmen returned the following year. Core. Calendar: semesters. Academic remediation for entering students, services for LD students, advanced placement, honors program, independent study, distance learning, double major, summer session for credit, part-time degree program, adult/continuing education programs, internships, graduate courses open to undergrads. Off campus study at members of the Marine Science Consortium. Study abroad program. ROTC: Army.
Entrance Requirements: Options: Peterson's Universal Application, electronic application, deferred admission. Required: high school transcript, standardized test scores, SAT or ACT. Entrance: moderately difficult. Notification: 9/1. Preference given to state residents.
Costs Per Year: Application fee: $25. State resident tuition: $4906 full-time, $204 per credit hour part-time. Nonresident tuition: $7360 full-time, $511 per credit part-time. Mandatory fees: $1369 full-time, $47 per credit part-time, $53.25 per term part-time. College room and board: $4796. College room only: $2688.
Collegiate Environment: Orientation program. Drama-theater group, choral group, marching band, student-run newspaper, radio station. Social organizations: 112 open to all; national fraternities, national sororities; 4% of eligible men and 5% of eligible women are members. Most popular organizations: Association of Residence Hall Students, University Program Board, Student Union for Minority Affairs, Student Government Association. Major annual events: Homecoming, Family Day, concerts. Student services: legal services, health clinic, personal-psychological counseling, women's center. Campus security: 24-hour emergency response devices and patrols, late night transport-escort service, controlled dormitory access. 2,780 college housing spaces available; all were occupied in 2003-04. Freshmen guaranteed college housing. On-campus residence required in freshman year. Options: coed, women-only housing available. Bailey Library with 512,424 books, 1.5 million microform titles, 11,987 serials, 88,184 audiovisual materials, an OPAC, and a Web page. Operations spending for 2004 fiscal year: $2.2 million. 940 computers available on campus for general student use. Computer purchase/lease plans available. A campuswide network can be accessed from student residence rooms and from off campus. Staffed computer lab on campus.
Community Environment: Population 3,000, Slippery Rock is located approximately an hour's drive from Pittsburgh. The climate is pleasant both in winter and in summer. There are several Protestant and Catholic churches in the community. The area has good highways and bus service. Local recreation includes hunting, fishing, boating, swimming, golf, and theatres, all easily accessible. Rooms are available in private homes. Many special interest and veteran's clubs are active in the community.

■ **SOUTH HILLS SCHOOL OF BUSINESS & TECHNOLOGY (ALTOONA)** *J-10*
508 58th St.
Altoona, PA 16602
Tel: (814)944-6134
Admissions: (814)234-7755
Fax: (814)944-4684
Web Site: http://www.southhills.edu/
Description: Proprietary, 2-year, coed. Awards diplomas, transfer associate, and terminal associate degrees. Founded 2001. Total enrollment: 148. 106 applied, 80% were admitted. 10% from top 10% of their high school class, 15% from top quarter, 75% from top half. Full-time: 142 students, 74% women, 26% men. Part-time: 6 students, 83% women, 17% men. 0% from out-of-state, 45% 25 or older, 0% transferred in. Calendar: trimesters. Independent study, double major, summer session for credit, part-time degree program, internships.

Entrance Requirements: Open admission. Options: Common Application, electronic application. Required: high school transcript, minimum 1.5 high school GPA, interview. Recommended: minimum 3.0 high school GPA. Required for some: essay, CPAt. Application deadline: 9/1.
Collegiate Environment: Orientation program. College housing not available. 93 computers available on campus for general student use. A campuswide network can be accessed. Staffed computer lab on campus.

■ **SOUTH HILLS SCHOOL OF BUSINESS & TECHNOLOGY (STATE COLLEGE)** *I-12*
480 Waupelani Dr.
State College, PA 16801-4516
Tel: (814)234-7755; 888-282-7427
Fax: (814)234-0926
Web Site: http://www.southhills.edu/
Description: Proprietary, 2-year, coed. Awards certificates, diplomas, transfer associate, and terminal associate degrees (also includes Altoona campus). Founded 1970. Setting: 6-acre small town campus. Total enrollment: 663. Student-undergrad faculty ratio is 15:1. 619 applied, 77% were admitted. 10% from top 10% of their high school class, 15% from top quarter, 75% from top half. Full-time: 611 students, 69% women, 31% men. Part-time: 52 students, 69% women, 31% men. 1% from out-of-state, 0% Native American, 0.5% Hispanic, 1% black, 0.5% Asian American or Pacific Islander, 0% international, 39% 25 or older, 17% transferred in. Retention: 71% of full-time freshmen returned the following year. Advanced placement, independent study, distance learning, double major, part-time degree program, internships.
Entrance Requirements: Option: electronic application. Required: high school transcript, minimum 1.5 high school GPA, interview, CPAt. Recommended: minimum 3.0 high school GPA. Required for some: essay, 2 recommendations. Placement: CPAt required for some. Entrance: minimally difficult. Application deadline: 9/2.
Costs Per Year: Application fee: $25. Tuition: $11,637 full-time, $323 per credit part-time. Mandatory fees: $75 full-time, $25 per term part-time.
Collegiate Environment: Orientation program. Student-run newspaper. Social organizations: 6 open to all. Most popular organizations: Phi Beta Lambda, South Hills Executives, Student Forum, newspaper. Major annual events: school picnics, school trips. Campus security: 24-hour emergency response devices. College housing not available. 360 computers available on campus for general student use.

■ **SUSQUEHANNA UNIVERSITY** *I-17*
514 University Ave.
Selinsgrove, PA 17870
Tel: (570)374-0101
Free: 800-326-9672
Admissions: (570)372-4260
Fax: (570)372-2722
E-mail: suadmiss@susqu.edu
Web Site: http://www.susqu.edu/
Description: Independent, 4-year, coed, affiliated with Evangelical Lutheran Church in America. Awards bachelor's degrees (also offers evening associate degree program limited to local adult students). Founded 1858. Setting: 220-acre suburban campus with easy access to Harrisburg. Endowment: $99.8 million. Research spending for 2004 fiscal year: $279,508. Educational spending for 2005 fiscal year: $9591 per student. Total enrollment: 1,989. Student-undergrad faculty ratio is 13:1. 2,217 applied, 81% were admitted. 30% from top 10% of their high school class, 63% from top quarter, 92% from top half. 2 National Merit Scholars, 18 class presidents, 12 valedictorians, 112 student government officers. Full-time: 1,894 students, 55% women, 45% men. Part-time: 95 students, 66% women, 34% men. Students come from 25 states and territories, 10 other countries, 39% from out-of-state, 0.2% Native American, 2% Hispanic, 3% black, 2% Asian American or Pacific Islander, 1% international, 2% 25 or older, 80% live on campus, 1% transferred in. Retention: 85% of full-time freshmen returned the following year. Academic areas with the most degrees conferred: business/marketing; education; communications/journalism. Core. Calendar: semesters. Advanced placement, accelerated degree program, self-designed majors, honors program, independent study, distance learning, double major, summer session for credit, part-time degree program, adult/continuing education programs, internships. Off campus study at American University, Drew University, Bucknell University, The Washington Center, Lutheran College-Washington Consortium semester in Washington, Boston Semester, Philadelphia Center. Study abroad program. ROTC: Army (c).

Entrance Requirements: Options: Peterson's Universal Application, Common Application, electronic application, early admission, early decision, deferred admission, international baccalaureate accepted. Required: essay, high school transcript, minimum 2.5 high school GPA, 1 recommendation. Recommended: minimum 3.0 high school GPA, interview, SAT or ACT, SAT Subject Tests. Required for some: writing portfolio, auditions for music programs. Entrance: moderately difficult. Application deadlines: 3/1, 11/15 for early decision plan 1, 1/1 for early decision plan 2. Notification: 1/15, 12/1 for early decision plan 1, 1/15 for early decision plan 2.

Costs Per Year: Application fee: $35. Comprehensive fee: $33,465 includes full-time tuition ($26,265) and college room and board ($7200). Part-time tuition: $825 per semester hour.

Collegiate Environment: Orientation program. Drama-theater group, choral group, student-run newspaper, radio station. Social organizations: 100 open to all; national fraternities, national sororities; 16% of eligible men and 20% of eligible women are members. Most popular organizations: Student Government Association, community service organizations, music performance groups, theater performance groups, intramurals and outdoor recreation. Major annual events: Fall Musical, Spring Weekend, homecoming. Student services: health clinic, personal-psychological counseling, women's center. Campus security: 24-hour patrols, late night transport-escort service, controlled dormitory access. College housing designed to accommodate 1,366 students; 1,400 undergraduates lived in college housing during 2003-04. Freshmen guaranteed college housing. On-campus residence required through junior year. Option: coed housing available. Blough-Weis Library with 294,337 books, 123,134 microform titles, 15,766 serials, 13,974 audiovisual materials, an OPAC, and a Web page. Operations spending for 2004 fiscal year: $1.6 million. 440 computers available on campus for general student use. A campuswide network can be accessed from student residence rooms and from off campus. Staffed computer lab on campus.

Community Environment: Population 5,500. The beautiful Susquehanna River winds through this quiet town. Route 80 is one half hour north and the Pennsylvania Turnpike is one hour south of campus. Selinsgrove is 50 miles north of Harrisburg. Limited part-time employment is available.

■ **SWARTHMORE COLLEGE** *G-44*

500 College Ave.
Swarthmore, PA 19081-1397
Tel: (610)328-8000
Free: 800-667-3110
Admissions: (610)328-8300
Fax: (610)328-8673
E-mail: admissions@swarthmore.edu
Web Site: http://www.swarthmore.edu/

Description: Independent, 4-year, coed. Awards bachelor's degrees. Founded 1864. Setting: 357-acre suburban campus with easy access to Philadelphia. Endowment: $1.2 billion. Research spending for 2004 fiscal year: $2.8 million. Educational spending for 2005 fiscal year: $23,799 per student. Total enrollment: 1,479. Student-undergrad faculty ratio is 8:1. 4,085 applied, 22% were admitted. 88% from top 10% of their high school class, 95% from top quarter, 100% from top half. 26 National Merit Scholars, 38 valedictorians. Full-time: 1,472 students, 52% women, 48% men. Part-time: 7 students, 57% women, 43% men. Students come from 53 states and territories, 46 other countries, 84% from out-of-state, 1% Native American, 10% Hispanic, 7% black, 15% Asian American or Pacific Islander, 6% international, 0% 25 or older, 94% live on campus, 0.3% transferred in. Retention: 96% of full-time freshmen returned the following year. Academic areas with the most degrees conferred: social sciences; biological/life sciences; English. Core. Calendar: semesters. Services for LD students, advanced placement, self-designed majors, honors program, independent study, double major, internships. Off campus study at University of Pennsylvania, Haverford College, Bryn Mawr College, Tufts University, Pomona College, Rice University, Middlebury College, Harvey Mudd College, Mills College. Study abroad program. ROTC: Army (c), Air Force (c).

Entrance Requirements: Options: Peterson's Universal Application, Common Application, electronic application, early admission, early decision, deferred admission, international baccalaureate accepted. Required: essay, high school transcript, 3 recommendations, SAT and SAT Subject Tests or ACT. Recommended: interview. Entrance: most difficult. Application deadlines: 1/2, 11/15 for early decision plan 1, 1/2 for early decision plan 2. Notification: 4/1, 12/15 for early decision plan 1, 2/15 for early decision plan 2.

Costs Per Year: Application fee: $60. Comprehensive fee: $41,280 includes full-time tuition ($31,196), mandatory fees ($320), and college room and board ($9764). College room only: $5006. Room and board charges vary according to board plan.

Collegiate Environment: Orientation program. Drama-theater group, choral group, student-run newspaper, radio station. Social organizations: 100 open to all; national fraternities, local fraternities; 6% of men are members. Most popular organizations: community service and activist groups, club sports and intramurals, music/acapella groups, social/cultural clubs, political and debate clubs. Major annual events: Formal Dance, Spring Fling. Student services: health clinic, personal-psychological counseling, women's center. Campus security: 24-hour emergency response devices and patrols, student patrols, late night transport-escort service. 1,344 college housing spaces available; 1,301 were occupied in 2003-04. Freshmen guaranteed college housing. On-campus residence required in freshman year. Options: coed, men-only, women-only housing available. McCabe Library plus 3 others with 754,499 books, 70,556 microform titles, 7,811 serials, 20,786 audiovisual materials, an OPAC, and a Web page. Operations spending for 2004 fiscal year: $4.3 million. 110 computers available on campus for general student use. Computer purchase/lease plans available. A campuswide network can be accessed from student residence rooms and from off campus. Staffed computer lab on campus.

Community Environment: Swarthmore, population 6,500, is in a suburban area 11 miles from Philadelphia. The climate is temperate. There is bus and rail service to Philadelphia, New York and Washington. Philadelphia International Airport is 15 minutes from campus by car, with a college shuttle before and after breaks and public rail service year-round. The immediate community has a library and churches of various denominations. There are hospitals nearby. For civic services, recreation and cultural facilities, see Philadelphia.

■ **TALMUDICAL YESHIVA OF PHILADELPHIA** *M-24*

6063 Drexel Rd.
Philadelphia, PA 19131-1296
Tel: (215)473-1212
Fax: (215)477-5065

Description: Independent Jewish, 4-year, men only. Awards bachelor's degrees (also offers some graduate courses). Founded 1953. Setting: 3-acre urban campus. Educational spending for 2005 fiscal year: $7000 per student. Total enrollment: 85. 45 applied, 78% were admitted. 15% from top 10% of their high school class, 30% from top quarter, 60% from top half. Full-time: 85 students. Students come from 11 states and territories, 4 other countries, 85% from out-of-state, 0% Native American, 0% Hispanic, 0% black, 0% Asian American or Pacific Islander, 13% international, 0% 25 or older, 98% live on campus, 2% transferred in. Retention: 87% of full-time freshmen returned the following year. Core. Calendar: trimesters. Academic remediation for entering students, honors program, internships. Study abroad program.

Entrance Requirements: Options: Common Application, early admission, deferred admission. Required: high school transcript, 1 recommendation, interview, oral examination. Entrance: moderately difficult. Application deadline: 7/15. Notification: 8/5.

Costs Per Year: Comprehensive fee: $11,600 includes full-time tuition ($6500), mandatory fees ($100), and college room and board ($5000).

Collegiate Environment: Social organizations: 3 open to all. Most popular organizations: Pirchei, Mishmar, Bikur Cholim. Student services: health clinic, personal-psychological counseling. Campus security: controlled dormitory access, night security patrol. 120 college housing spaces available; 85 were occupied in 2003-04. Freshmen guaranteed college housing. On-campus residence required through senior year. Option: men-only housing available. 4,800 books and 300 serials.

■ **TEMPLE UNIVERSITY** *M-24*

1801 North Broad St.
Philadelphia, PA 19122-6096
Tel: (215)204-7000; 888-340-2222
Admissions: (215)204-8556
Fax: (215)204-5694
E-mail: tuadm@vm.temple.edu
Web Site: http://www.temple.edu/

Description: State-related, university, coed. Awards associate, bachelor's, master's, doctoral, and first professional degrees and post-master's and first professional certificates. Founded 1884. Setting: 110-acre urban campus. Endowment: $195.2 million. Research spending for 2004 fiscal year: $63.8 million. Educational spending for 2005 fiscal year: $10,678 per student. Total enrollment: 33,693. Faculty: 2,561 (1,206 full-time, 1,355 part-time). Student-undergrad faculty ratio is 17:1. 17,352 applied, 63% were admitted. 19% from top 10% of their high school class, 51% from top quarter, 89% from top half. 19 valedictorians. Full-time: 20,936 students, 56% women, 44% men. Part-time: 3,258 students, 58% women, 42% men. Students come from 46 states and territories, 105 other countries, 22% from out-of-state, 0.2% Native American, 3% Hispanic, 19% black, 9% Asian American or Pacific Islander, 3% international, 15% 25 or older, 26% live on campus, 11% transferred in. Retention: 84% of full-time freshmen returned the following year. Academic areas with the most degrees conferred: business/marketing; education; visual and performing arts. Core. Calendar: semesters. Academic remediation for entering students, ESL program, services for LD students, advanced placement, self-designed majors, honors program, independent study, distance learning, double major, summer session for credit, part-time degree program, adult/continuing education programs, co-op programs and internships, graduate courses open to undergrads. Off campus study at Messiah College, University of Puerto Rico, Consortium of East Coast Art Schools, Gratz College. Study abroad program. ROTC: Army, Naval (c), Air Force (c).

Entrance Requirements: Options: Peterson's Universal Application, electronic application, early admission, deferred admission. Required: essay, high school transcript, minimum 2.0 high school GPA, SAT or ACT. Required for some: recommendations, interview, portfolio, audition. Entrance: moderately difficult. Application deadline: 4/1. Notification: continuous.

Costs Per Year: Application fee: $35. State resident tuition: $9140 full-time, $354 per credit hour part-time. Nonresident tuition: $16,736 full-time, $596 per credit hour part-time. Mandatory fees: $500 full-time, $109 per term part-time. Full-time tuition and fees vary according to course load, location, program, and reciprocity agreements. Part-time tuition and fees vary according to course load, location, program, and reciprocity agreements. College room and board: $7794. College room only: $5054. Room and board charges vary according to board plan and housing facility.

Collegiate Environment: Orientation program. Drama-theater group, choral group, marching band, student-run newspaper, radio station. Social organizations: 150 open to all; national fraternities, national sororities, local fraternities; 1% of eligible men and 1% of eligible women are members. Most popular organizations: African Student Union, India Student Association at Temple, Student Organization for Caribbean Awareness. Major annual events: Spring Fling, Homecoming, Cherry and White Day. Student services: legal services, health clinic, personal-psychological counseling. Campus security: 24-hour emergency response devices and patrols, late night transport-escort service, controlled dormitory access. 5,314 college housing spaces available; 5,093 were occupied in 2003-04. Freshmen given priority for college housing. Option: coed housing available. Paley Library plus 11 others with 3.3 million books, 3 million microform titles, 20,980 serials, 25,244 audiovisual materials, an OPAC, and a Web page. Operations spending for 2004 fiscal year: $15.6 million. 2,000 computers available on campus for general student use. A campuswide network can be accessed from student residence rooms and from off campus. Staffed computer lab on campus.

Community Environment: "Birthplace of the Nation", Philadelphia has retained much of the charm of its colonial origins even while developing into one of the great industrial cities of the world. Population of the greater metropolitan area is over 2,000,000. Distinctive colonial characteristics such as the Liberty Bell and Independence Hall blend with evidence of vast manufacturing. Narrow cobblestone streets may be found within blocks of the business district. The city has museums, churches of all denominations, many libraries (including the first Free Library in the United States), Fairmon Park (the largest city park in the U.S.), a zoo, planetarium, major league and collegiate sports teams, numerous cultural and entertainment facilities, and all the fraternal, civic, and community service organizations of any large metropolis. Local recreation includes golf, tennis, horseback riding, hunting, boating, fishing, and swimming.

■ **THADDEUS STEVENS COLLEGE OF TECHNOLOGY** M-19
750 East King St.
Lancaster, PA 17602-3198
Tel: (717)299-7730
Admissions: (717)299-7772
Fax: (717)391-6929
Web Site: http://www.stevenscollege.edu/
Description: State-supported, 2-year, coed. Awards transfer associate and terminal associate degrees. Founded 1905. Setting: 33-acre urban campus with easy access to Philadelphia. Educational spending for 2005 fiscal year:

$6155 per student. Total enrollment: 660. 1,063 applied, 40% were admitted. 7% from top 10% of their high school class, 52% from top quarter, 77% from top half. 1 class president, 1 student government officer. 1% Native American, 6% Hispanic, 16% black, 1% Asian American or Pacific Islander, 0% international, 6% 25 or older, 48% live on campus. Retention: 60% of full-time freshmen returned the following year. Core. Calendar: semesters. Academic remediation for entering students, services for LD students, internships.

Entrance Requirements: Options: Common Application, electronic application, deferred admission. Required: essay, high school transcript, minimum 2.0 high school GPA, recommendations, ASSET Test, ACT ASSET. Required for some: interview. Entrance: moderately difficult. Application deadline: 6/30. Notification: continuous until 7/15. Preference given to needy students, indigent orphans.

Collegiate Environment: Orientation program. Student-run newspaper. Most popular organization: Tech Phi Tech. Student services: health clinic, personal-psychological counseling, women's center. Campus security: 24-hour emergency response devices. 310 college housing spaces available; all were occupied in 2003-04. Freshmen given priority for college housing. Options: coed, men-only housing available. K.W. Schuler Learning Resources Center plus 1 other with 26,000 books, 450 serials, an OPAC, and a Web page. Operations spending for 2004 fiscal year: $90,060. 100 computers available on campus for general student use. A campuswide network can be accessed. Staffed computer lab on campus.

■ **THIEL COLLEGE** E-2
75 College Ave.
Greenville, PA 16125-2181
Tel: (724)589-2000
Free: 800-248-4435
Admissions: (724)589-2226
Fax: (724)589-2013
Web Site: http://www.thiel.edu/
Description: Independent, 4-year, coed, affiliated with Evangelical Lutheran Church in America. Awards associate and bachelor's degrees. Founded 1866. Setting: 135-acre rural campus with easy access to Cleveland and Pittsburgh. Endowment: $20.9 million. Educational spending for 2005 fiscal year: $4035 per student. Total enrollment: 1,320. Student-undergrad faculty ratio is 17:1. 2,397 applied, 75% were admitted. 8% from top 10% of their high school class, 24% from top quarter, 57% from top half. Full-time: 1,253 students, 45% women, 55% men. Part-time: 67 students, 48% women, 52% men. Students come from 19 states and territories, 15 other countries, 25% from out-of-state, 0.1% Native American, 1% Hispanic, 6% black, 1% Asian American or Pacific Islander, 5% international, 1% 25 or older, 82% live on campus, 4% transferred in. Retention: 69% of full-time freshmen returned the following year. Academic areas with the most degrees conferred: business/marketing; psychology; social sciences. Core. Calendar: semesters. Academic remediation for entering students, ESL program, services for LD students, advanced placement, freshman honors college, honors program, double major, summer session for credit, part-time degree program, adult/continuing education programs, co-op programs and internships. Off campus study at American University, Art Institute of Pittsburgh, Bryant and Stratton Business Institute (Buffalo), Community College of Allegheny County, Drew University, Harrisburg Area Community College, Union College (KY). Study abroad program.

Entrance Requirements: Options: Peterson's Universal Application, Common Application, electronic application, early action, deferred admission, international baccalaureate accepted. Required: high school transcript, minimum 2.0 high school GPA, SAT or ACT. Recommended: essay, recommendations, interview. Required for some: recommendations, interview. Entrance: moderately difficult. Application deadline: 6/30. Notification: continuous.

Costs Per Year: Application fee: $25. Comprehensive fee: $24,580 includes full-time tuition ($16,200), mandatory fees ($1390), and college room and board ($6990). College room only: $3566. Full-time tuition and fees vary according to course load. Room and board charges vary according to board plan and housing facility. Part-time tuition: $400 per credit hour. Part-time mandatory fees: $21 per credit hour. Part-time tuition and fees vary according to course load.

Collegiate Environment: Orientation program. Drama-theater group, choral group, student-run newspaper, radio station. Social organizations: 40 open to all; national fraternities, national sororities, local fraternities; 15% of eligible men and 18% of eligible women are members. Most popular organizations: Thiel Players Theatre Group, student government, Thiel

Choir. Major annual events: Homecoming, theater productions, Greek Week. Student services: health clinic, personal-psychological counseling, women's center. Campus security: 24-hour emergency response devices and patrols, student patrols, late night transport-escort service, controlled dormitory access. 1,188 college housing spaces available; 975 were occupied in 2003-04. Freshmen guaranteed college housing. On-campus residence required through senior year. Option: coed housing available. Langenheim Library with 131,176 books, 39,970 microform titles, 532 serials, 6,463 audiovisual materials, an OPAC, and a Web page. Operations spending for 2004 fiscal year: $410,080. 220 computers available on campus for general student use. Computer purchase/lease plans available. A campuswide network can be accessed from student residence rooms. Staffed computer lab on campus.

Community Environment: Local industry is devoted principally to the manufacture of steel, cars, tanks, structural steel and other steel and aluminum products. Greenville is a small town of 10,000 situated halfway between Erie and Pittsburgh. Cleveland and Youngstown are also with 1 to 1 1/2 hours driving. The community is served by railroad, bus lines, and airlines located at nearby Youngstown airport. Greenville has numerous churches, public library, hospital, and excellent shopping and restaurants. Part-time employment is available. Local recreational facilities include a symphony orchestra, theatre and a number of civic parks. Nearby lakes provide boating, swimming, fishing, water skiing, and golf courses. There are various civic, fraternal, and veteran's organizations active in the community.

■ **THOMAS JEFFERSON UNIVERSITY** *M-24*
Eleventh and Walnut Sts.
Philadelphia, PA 19107
Tel: (215)955-6000; 877-533-3247
Admissions: (215)503-1040
Fax: (215)503-7241
Web Site: http://www.jefferson.edu/

Description: Independent, university, coed. Awards bachelor's, master's, and doctoral degrees. Founded 1824. Setting: 13-acre urban campus. Endowment: $18.2 million. Research spending for 2004 fiscal year: $4.1 million. Educational spending for 2005 fiscal year: $10,442 per student. Total enrollment: 2,681. Faculty: 266 (76 full-time, 190 part-time). Student-undergrad faculty ratio is 10:1. 1,198 applied, 14% were admitted. Full-time: 669 students, 81% women, 19% men. Part-time: 319 students, 85% women, 15% men. Students come from 19 states and territories, 6 other countries, 27% from out-of-state, 0.5% Native American, 3% Hispanic, 15% black, 8% Asian American or Pacific Islander, 0% international, 50% 25 or older, 30% live on campus, 41% transferred in. Core. Calendar: semesters. Academic remediation for entering students, services for LD students, advanced placement, accelerated degree program, honors program, independent study, distance learning, double major, part-time degree program, adult/continuing education programs, co-op programs, graduate courses open to undergrads. Off campus study. Study abroad program. ROTC: Air Force (c).

Entrance Requirements: Option: deferred admission. Required: essay, 2 recommendations. Recommended: SAT or ACT. Entrance: moderately difficult. Application deadline: Rolling. Notification: continuous.

Costs Per Year: Application fee: $50. Tuition: $21,975 full-time.

Collegiate Environment: Orientation program. Choral group. Social organizations: 30 open to all. Most popular organizations: Commons Board, student government, choir, Admission Ambassadors, Student Nurses Association of Pennsylvania. Major annual events: Winter Social, International Day, Orientation. Student services: health clinic, personal-psychological counseling. Campus security: 24-hour emergency response devices and patrols, late night transport-escort service, controlled dormitory access. 650 college housing spaces available; 211 were occupied in 2003-04. Freshmen guaranteed college housing. Options: coed, men-only, women-only housing available. Scott Memorial Library plus 1 other with 170,000 books, 2,290 serials, and a Web page. Operations spending for 2004 fiscal year: $3.2 million. 100 computers available on campus for general student use. A campuswide network can be accessed from off-campus. Staffed computer lab on campus.

■ **THOMPSON INSTITUTE** *L-17*
5650 Derry St.
Harrisburg, PA 17111-3518
Tel: (717)564-4112
Fax: (717)564-3779
Web Site: http://www.thompson.edu/

Description: Proprietary, primarily 2-year, coed. Part of Kaplan Higher Education Corporation. Awards certificates, diplomas, terminal associate, and bachelor's degrees. Founded 1918. Setting: 5-acre suburban campus. Educational spending for 2005 fiscal year: $421 per student. Total enrollment: 485. 165 applied, 88% were admitted. 1% from top 10% of their high school class, 5% from top quarter, 10% from top half. Full-time: 485 students, 53% women, 47% men. Students come from 2 states and territories, 2% from out-of-state, 0% Native American, 5% Hispanic, 14% black, 1% Asian American or Pacific Islander, 0% international, 60% 25 or older. Core. Academic remediation for entering students, services for LD students, advanced placement, summer session for credit, adult/continuing education programs, internships.

Entrance Requirements: Open admission. Options: Peterson's Universal Application, Common Application, electronic application, deferred admission. Required: high school transcript. Recommended: minimum 2.0 high school GPA. Entrance: noncompetitive. Application deadline: Rolling.

Costs Per Year: Application fee: $50. Tuition: $8600 full-time. College room only: $1600.

Collegiate Environment: Orientation program. Social organizations: 4 open to all; national sororities; 5% of women are members. Most popular organizations: Electronics Club, CAD Club, DPMA, Math Club. Major annual events: Thanksgiving Dinner, Spring Open House. Student services: personal-psychological counseling. Campus security: campus facilities manager. 62 college housing spaces available; 56 were occupied in 2003-04. No special consideration for freshman housing applicants. Option: coed housing available. 950 books, 20 serials, and an OPAC. Operations spending for 2004 fiscal year: $10,800. 113 computers available on campus for general student use. Computer purchase/lease plans available. A campuswide network can be accessed from off-campus. Staffed computer lab on campus.

■ **TRI-STATE BUSINESS INSTITUTE** *B-3*
5757 West 26th St.
Erie, PA 16506
Tel: (814)838-7673
Fax: (814)838-8642
E-mail: geuliano@tsbi.org
Web Site: http://www.tsbi.org/
Description: Private, 2-year.

■ **TRIANGLE TECH, INC.-DUBOIS SCHOOL** *G-9*
PO Box 551
DuBois, PA 15801-0551
Tel: (814)371-2090
Free: 800-874-8324
Admissions: (412)359-1000
Fax: (814)371-9227
Web Site: http://www.triangle-tech.edu/

Description: Proprietary, 2-year, coed. Part of Triangle Tech, Inc. Awards diplomas and terminal associate degrees. Founded 1944. Setting: 5-acre small town campus. Educational spending for 2005 fiscal year: $12,951 per student. Total enrollment: 246. Student-undergrad faculty ratio is 11:1. 142 applied, 96% were admitted. Full-time: 246 students, 9% women, 91% men. Students come from 3 states and territories, 0% from out-of-state, 0% Native American, 0% Hispanic, 0.4% black, 0% Asian American or Pacific Islander, 0% international, 40% 25 or older. Retention: 67% of full-time freshmen returned the following year. Core. Calendar: semesters. Academic remediation for entering students, advanced placement. Off campus study at all other campuses of Triangle Tech.

Entrance Requirements: Option: deferred admission. Required: high school transcript, minimum 2.0 high school GPA, interview. Entrance: minimally difficult. Application deadline: Rolling.

Costs Per Year: Application fee: $0. Tuition: $11,408 full-time.

Collegiate Environment: Social organizations: 1 open to all. 1,200 books and 15 serials. 40 computers available on campus for general student use. A campuswide network can be accessed from off-campus. Staffed computer lab on campus.

■ **TRIANGLE TECH, INC.-ERIE SCHOOL** *B-3*
2000 Liberty St.
Erie, PA 16502-2594
Tel: (814)453-6016
Free: 800-TRI-TECH
Fax: (814)454-2818

Web Site: http://www.triangle-tech.com/

Description: Proprietary, 2-year, coed. Part of Triangle Tech, Inc. Awards transfer associate and terminal associate degrees. Founded 1976. Setting: 1-acre urban campus. Total enrollment: 83. 61 applied, 100% were admitted. Students come from 3 states and territories, 10% from out-of-state, 65% 25 or older. Core. Calendar: semesters. Academic remediation for entering students, services for LD students, advanced placement.

Entrance Requirements: Option: deferred admission. Required: high school transcript, minimum 2.0 high school GPA, interview. Entrance: minimally difficult. Application deadline: Rolling.

Collegiate Environment: Orientation program. Social organizations: 1 open to all. Campus security: 24-hour emergency response devices. College housing not available. 1,000 books and 15 serials. 50 computers available on campus for general student use. Staffed computer lab on campus.

■ TRIANGLE TECH, INC.-GREENSBURG SCHOOL *L-5*

222 East Pittsburgh St., Ste. A
Greensburg, PA 15601-3304
Tel: (724)832-1050
Free: 800-874-8324
Admissions: (412)359-1000
Web Site: http://www.triangle-tech.com/

Description: Proprietary, 2-year, coed. Part of Triangle Tech, Inc. Awards diplomas and terminal associate degrees. Founded 1944. Setting: 1-acre small town campus with easy access to Pittsburgh. Total enrollment: 271. Student-undergrad faculty ratio is 12:1. 166 applied, 100% were admitted. Full-time: 271 students, 1% women, 99% men. Students come from 2 states and territories, 1% from out-of-state, 0.4% Native American, 0% Hispanic, 1% black, 0% Asian American or Pacific Islander, 0% international, 49% 25 or older. Core. Calendar: semesters. Academic remediation for entering students, advanced placement, summer session for credit, adult/continuing education programs.

Entrance Requirements: Options: Common Application, deferred admission. Required: high school transcript. Entrance: moderately difficult. Application deadline: Rolling.

Costs Per Year: Application fee: $75. Tuition: $11,408 full-time. Mandatory fees: $200 full-time.

Collegiate Environment: Orientation program. Student services: personal-psychological counseling. College housing not available. Triangle Tech Library plus 2 others with 550 books and 15 serials. 100 computers available on campus for general student use. A campuswide network can be accessed from off-campus. Staffed computer lab on campus.

■ TRIANGLE TECH, INC.-PITTSBURGH SCHOOL *K-3*

1940 Perrysville Ave.
Pittsburgh, PA 15214-3897
Tel: (412)359-1000
Free: 800-874-8324
Fax: (412)359-1012
Web Site: http://www.triangle-tech.edu/

Description: Proprietary, 2-year, coed. Part of Triangle Tech Group. Awards diplomas, transfer associate, and terminal associate degrees. Founded 1944. Setting: 5-acre urban campus. Total enrollment: 377. 121 applied, 99% were admitted. 9% from top 10% of their high school class, 55% from top half. Full-time: 377 students, 4% women, 96% men. Students come from 3 states and territories, 6% from out-of-state, 0% Native American, 0% Hispanic, 11% black, 0% Asian American or Pacific Islander, 0% international, 35% 25 or older, 0% transferred in. Core. Calendar: semesters. Academic remediation for entering students, advanced placement.

Entrance Requirements: Options: early admission, deferred admission. Required: high school transcript, minimum 2.0 high school GPA, interview. Entrance: moderately difficult. Application deadline: Rolling.

Costs Per Year: Tuition: $301.78 per credit part-time.

Collegiate Environment: Social organizations: 1 open to all. Most popular organization: student council. Major annual events: semi-annual blood drives, Trades Week, Drafting Week. Campus security: 16-hour patrols by trained security personnel. College housing not available. 2,000 books and 30 serials. Operations spending for 2004 fiscal year: $6029. 50 computers available on campus for general student use. from off-campusStaffed computer lab on campus.

■ TRIANGLE TECH, INC.-SUNBURY SCHOOL *I-17*

RR No. 1, Box 51
Sunbury, PA 17801

Tel: (570)988-0700
Web Site: http://www.triangle-tech.com/
Description: Proprietary, 2-year, coed. Calendar: semesters.

■ THE UNIVERSITY OF THE ARTS *M-24*

320 South Broad St.
Philadelphia, PA 19102-4944
Tel: (215)717-6000
Free: 800-616-ARTS
Admissions: (215)717-6039
Fax: (215)717-6045
E-mail: sgandy@uarts.edu
Web Site: http://www.uarts.edu/

Description: Independent, comprehensive, coed. Awards bachelor's and master's degrees. Founded 1870. Setting: 18-acre urban campus. Endowment: $17.1 million. Research spending for 2004 fiscal year: $86,280. Educational spending for 2005 fiscal year: $8357 per student. Total enrollment: 2,277. Faculty: 472 (118 full-time, 354 part-time). Student-undergrad faculty ratio is 9:1. 2,283 applied, 49% were admitted. 13% from top 10% of their high school class, 32% from top quarter, 66% from top half. Full-time: 2,035 students, 55% women, 45% men. Part-time: 44 students, 70% women, 30% men. Students come from 42 states and territories, 38 other countries, 61% from out-of-state, 0.2% Native American, 4% Hispanic, 10% black, 3% Asian American or Pacific Islander, 3% international, 4% 25 or older, 36% live on campus, 6% transferred in. Retention: 82% of full-time freshmen returned the following year. Academic areas with the most degrees conferred: visual and performing arts; communications/journalism; education. Core. Calendar: semesters. Academic remediation for entering students, ESL program, services for LD students, advanced placement, independent study, double major, part-time degree program, adult/continuing education programs, internships, graduate courses open to undergrads. Off campus study at Consortium of East Coast Art Schools, Philadelphia College of Textiles and Science, Vermont Studio School. Study abroad program.

Entrance Requirements: Options: Common Application, electronic application, early admission, deferred admission. Required: essay, high school transcript, minimum 2.0 high school GPA, 1 recommendation, portfolio or audition, SAT or ACT. Recommended: interview. Required for some: interview. Entrance: moderately difficult. Application deadline: Rolling. Notification: continuous.

Costs Per Year: Application fee: $60. Tuition: $24,730 full-time, $1070 per credit part-time. Mandatory fees: $950 full-time. College room only: $6300.

Collegiate Environment: Orientation program. Drama-theater group, choral group. Social organizations: 7 open to all. Most popular organizations: African-American Student Union, Gaming Society, Outreach, Multimedia Artist Society, Student Council. Major annual events: Fall Carnival, Black History Month Extravaganza, Art in the Park. Student services: health clinic, personal-psychological counseling. Campus security: 24-hour emergency response devices and patrols, late night transport-escort service, crime prevention workshops and seminars. 690 college housing spaces available; all were occupied in 2003-04. Freshmen guaranteed college housing. Option: coed housing available. Albert M. Greenfield Library plus 2 others with 123,175 books, 461 microform titles, 538 serials, 321,710 audiovisual materials, an OPAC, and a Web page. Operations spending for 2004 fiscal year: $706,308. 475 computers available on campus for general student use. Computer purchase/lease plans available. A campuswide network can be accessed from student residence rooms. Staffed computer lab on campus.

Community Environment: The campus is located in the heart of Philadelphia's cultural community. The area has theaters, museums, galleries, music and dance facilities, restaurants of many ethnic varieties, and major department stores and shops. Philadelphia offers a broad mix of experiences of historical importance. The city is also known as a supporter of the arts. Urban and sophisticated, it is at the same time a series of small, close-knit neighborhoods. Fairmount Park, the largest municipal park in the world, provides facilities for boating, fishing, hiking, biking, picnicking, and relaxing.

■ UNIVERSITY OF PENNSYLVANIA *M-24*

3451 Walnut St.
Philadelphia, PA 19104
Tel: (215)898-5000
Admissions: (215)898-7507
Web Site: http://www.upenn.edu/

Description: Independent, university, coed. Awards associate, bachelor's, master's, doctoral, and first professional degrees and post-master's and first professional certificates (also offers evening program with significant enrollment not reflected in profile). Founded 1740. Setting: 269-acre urban campus. Endowment: $4.4 billion. Research spending for 2004 fiscal year: $549.4 million. Educational spending for 2005 fiscal year: $79,579 per student. Total enrollment: 18,814. Faculty: 1,990 (1,388 full-time, 602 part-time). Student-undergrad faculty ratio is 6:1. 18,824 applied, 21% were admitted. 94% from top 10% of their high school class, 99% from top quarter, 100% from top half. 101 National Merit Scholars, 69 class presidents, 255 valedictorians, 565 student government officers. Full-time: 9,545 students, 50% women, 50% men. Part-time: 296 students, 43% women, 57% men. Students come from 54 states and territories, 101 other countries, 80% from out-of-state, 0.3% Native American, 6% Hispanic, 7% black, 18% Asian American or Pacific Islander, 9% international, 1% 25 or older, 64% live on campus, 2% transferred in. Retention: 98% of full-time freshmen returned the following year. Academic areas with the most degrees conferred: business/marketing; social sciences; engineering. Core. Calendar: semesters plus 2 5-week summer sessions. Academic remediation for entering students, ESL program, services for LD students, advanced placement, accelerated degree program, self-designed majors, honors program, independent study, distance learning, double major, summer session for credit, part-time degree program, adult/continuing education programs, internships, graduate courses open to undergrads. Off campus study at Bryn Mawr College, Haverford College, Swarthmore College. Study abroad program. ROTC: Army (c), Naval, Air Force (c).

Entrance Requirements: Options: electronic application, early admission, early decision, deferred admission, international baccalaureate accepted. Required: essay, high school transcript, 2 recommendations, SAT and SAT Subject Tests or ACT. Entrance: most difficult. Application deadlines: 1/1, 11/1 for early decision. Notification: 4/1, 12/15 for early decision.

Costs Per Year: Application fee: $70. Comprehensive fee: $41,766 includes full-time tuition ($29,030), mandatory fees ($3334), and college room and board ($9402). College room only: $5730. Room and board charges vary according to board plan and housing facility. Part-time tuition: $3708 per course. Part-time mandatory fees: $389 per course. Part-time tuition and fees vary according to course load.

Collegiate Environment: Orientation program. Drama-theater group, choral group, marching band, student-run newspaper, radio station. Social organizations: 384 open to all; national fraternities, national sororities; 24% of eligible men and 17% of eligible women are members. Most popular organizations: Kite and Key Society, Social Planning and Events Committee, Hillel at Penn, Sports Club Council. Major annual events: Homecoming, Spring Fling, Hey Day. Student services: health clinic, personal-psychological counseling, women's center. Campus security: 24-hour emergency response devices and patrols, student patrols, late night transport-escort service, controlled dormitory access. 6,500 college housing spaces available; 5,894 were occupied in 2003-04. Freshmen guaranteed college housing. Option: coed housing available. Van Pelt-Dietrich Library plus 13 others with 5.4 million books, 4 million microform titles, 39,426 serials, 68,568 audiovisual materials, an OPAC, and a Web page. Operations spending for 2004 fiscal year: $38.7 million. 975 computers available on campus for general student use. A campuswide network can be accessed from student residence rooms and from off campus. Staffed computer lab on campus.

Community Environment: Philadelphia is a large city with the feel of small villages; many with distinct characters. It is a center of history, culture and business, opera, symphony and ballet, museums, major sports teams and theater. The city is ideally located near both seashore and ski resorts.

■ **UNIVERSITY OF PHOENIX-PHILADELPHIA CAMPUS** *M-23*
170 South Warner Rd., Ste. 200
Wayne, PA 19087-2121
Tel: (610)989-0880
Free: 800-228-7240
Admissions: (480)557-1712
Fax: (610)989-0881
Web Site: http://www.phoenix.edu/
Description: Proprietary, comprehensive, coed. Awards bachelor's and master's degrees. Founded 1999. Setting: urban campus. Total enrollment: 1,694. Faculty: 187 (13 full-time, 174 part-time). Student-undergrad faculty ratio is 8:1. 68 applied. Full-time: 1,282 students, 62% women, 38% men. 0% from out-of-state, 0.2% Native American, 1% Hispanic, 12% black, 1% Asian American or Pacific Islander, 8% international, 93% 25 or older.

Academic areas with the most degrees conferred: business/marketing; computer and information sciences. Core. Calendar: continuous. Advanced placement, accelerated degree program, independent study, distance learning, external degree program, adult/continuing education programs, graduate courses open to undergrads.

Entrance Requirements: Open admission. Option: deferred admission. Required: 1 recommendation. Required for some: high school transcript. Entrance: noncompetitive. Application deadline: Rolling.

Costs Per Year: Application fee: $110. Tuition: $13,050 full-time, $435 per credit part-time. Mandatory fees: $560 full-time, $70 per course part-time.

Collegiate Environment: College housing not available. University Library with 444 books, 666 serials, an OPAC, and a Web page. System-wide operations spending for 2004 fiscal year: $3.2 million.

■ **UNIVERSITY OF PHOENIX-PITTSBURGH CAMPUS** *K-3*
Penn Center West Six, Ste. 100
Pittsburgh, PA 15276
Tel: (412)747-9000
Free: 800-228-7240
Admissions: (480)557-1712
Fax: (412)747-0676
Web Site: http://www.phoenix.edu/
Description: Proprietary, comprehensive, coed. Awards bachelor's and master's degrees. Founded 2001. Setting: urban campus. Total enrollment: 645. Faculty: 117 (11 full-time, 106 part-time). Student-undergrad faculty ratio is 5:1. 26 applied. Full-time: 497 students, 54% women, 46% men. 0% from out-of-state, 0.2% Native American, 1% Hispanic, 4% black, 0.4% Asian American or Pacific Islander, 2% international, 93% 25 or older. Academic areas with the most degrees conferred: business/marketing; computer and information sciences. Core. Calendar: continuous. Advanced placement, accelerated degree program, independent study, distance learning, external degree program, adult/continuing education programs, graduate courses open to undergrads.

Entrance Requirements: Open admission. Option: deferred admission. Required: 1 recommendation. Required for some: high school transcript. Entrance: noncompetitive. Application deadline: Rolling.

Costs Per Year: Application fee: $110. Tuition: $13,050 full-time, $435 per credit part-time. Mandatory fees: $560 full-time, $70 per course part-time.

Collegiate Environment: College housing not available. University Library with 444 books, 666 serials, an OPAC, and a Web page. System-wide operations spending for 2004 fiscal year: $3.2 million.

■ **UNIVERSITY OF PITTSBURGH** *K-3*
4200 Fifth Ave.
Pittsburgh, PA 15260
Tel: (412)624-4141
Admissions: (412)624-7488
Fax: (412)648-8815
E-mail: oafa@pitt.edu
Web Site: http://www.pitt.edu/
Description: State-related, university, coed. Part of Commonwealth System of Higher Education. Awards bachelor's, master's, doctoral, and first professional degrees and post-master's certificates. Founded 1787. Setting: 132-acre urban campus. Endowment: $1.5 billion. Research spending for 2004 fiscal year: $419.9 million. Total enrollment: 26,559. 18,153 applied, 53% were admitted. 43% from top 10% of their high school class, 80% from top quarter, 98% from top half. 29 National Merit Scholars, 93 valedictorians. Full-time: 15,100 students, 51% women, 49% men. Part-time: 1,924 students, 57% women, 43% men. Students come from 53 states and territories, 49 other countries, 15% from out-of-state, 0.2% Native American, 1% Hispanic, 9% black, 4% Asian American or Pacific Islander, 1% international, 6% 25 or older, 36% live on campus, 4% transferred in. Academic areas with the most degrees conferred: business/marketing; English; social sciences. Core. Calendar: semesters plus summer term. Academic remediation for entering students, ESL program, services for LD students, advanced placement, accelerated degree program, self-designed majors, freshman honors college, honors program, independent study, distance learning, double major, summer session for credit, part-time degree program, external degree program, adult/continuing education programs, co-op programs and internships, graduate courses open to undergrads. Off campus study at 10 other institutions in the surrounding area. Study abroad program. ROTC: Army, Naval (c), Air Force.

Entrance Requirements: Options: Peterson's Universal Application, Common Application, early admission, deferred admission, international baccalaureate accepted. Required: high school transcript, SAT or ACT. Recommended: essay, recommendations, interview. Entrance: moderately difficult. Application deadline: Rolling. Notification: continuous.

Costs Per Year: Application fee: $35. State resident tuition: $10,736 full-time, $412 per credit part-time. Nonresident tuition: $20,084 full-time, $772 per credit part-time. Mandatory fees: $700 full-time, $164 per term part-time. Full-time tuition and fees vary according to degree level and program. Part-time tuition and fees vary according to degree level and program. College room and board: $7430. College room only: $4510. Room and board charges vary according to board plan and housing facility.

Collegiate Environment: Orientation program. Drama-theater group, choral group, marching band, student-run newspaper, radio station. Social organizations: 300 open to all; national fraternities, national sororities. Most popular organizations: Pitt Program Council, Quo Vadis, Black Action Society, crew team, Blue and Gold Society. Major annual events: Laser and Fireworks Show, Fall Fest, Bigelow Bash. Student services: health clinic, personal-psychological counseling, women's center. Campus security: 24-hour emergency response devices and patrols, late night transport-escort service, controlled dormitory access, on-call van transportation. 6,178 college housing spaces available. Freshmen guaranteed college housing. Options: coed, women-only housing available. Hillman Library plus 25 others with 4.6 million books, 4.6 million microform titles, 3,767 serials, 804,470 audiovisual materials, an OPAC, and a Web page. Operations spending for 2004 fiscal year: $40.4 million. 600 computers available on campus for general student use. Computer purchase/lease plans available. A campuswide network can be accessed from student residence rooms and from off campus. Staffed computer lab on campus.

Community Environment: Pittsburgh is a city of hills, rivers, and bridges, and a mixture of traditional and contemporary lifestyles. Accessible by air, bus, and rail its attractions include concerts, folk festivals, the Pittsburgh Symphony, Phipps Conservatory, professional sports, museums, libraries, parks, and art galleries.

■ **UNIVERSITY OF PITTSBURGH AT BRADFORD** *B-9*
300 Campus Dr.
Bradford, PA 16701-2812
Tel: (814)362-7500
Free: 800-872-1787
Admissions: (814)362-7677
Fax: (814)362-7578
E-mail: nazemetz@upb.pitt.edu
Web Site: http://www.upb.pitt.edu/
Description: State-related, 4-year, coed. Part of University of Pittsburgh System. Awards associate and bachelor's degrees. Founded 1963. Setting: 170-acre small town campus with easy access to Buffalo. Endowment: $11.7 million. Research spending for 2004 fiscal year: $1.7 million. Educational spending for 2005 fiscal year: $2002 per student. Total enrollment: 1,301. Student-undergrad faculty ratio is 13:1. 592 applied, 76% were admitted. 11% from top 10% of their high school class, 32% from top quarter, 76% from top half. Full-time: 991 students, 56% women, 44% men. Part-time: 310 students, 72% women, 28% men. Students come from 16 states and territories, 10% from out-of-state, 1% Native American, 1% Hispanic, 4% black, 1% Asian American or Pacific Islander, 0.3% international, 22% 25 or older, 47% live on campus, 9% transferred in. Retention: 65% of full-time freshmen returned the following year. Academic areas with the most degrees conferred: business/marketing; social sciences; security and protective services. Core. Calendar: semesters. Academic remediation for entering students, services for LD students, advanced placement, accelerated degree program, independent study, distance learning, double major, summer session for credit, part-time degree program, adult/continuing education programs, internships. Off campus study at St. Bonaventure University, University of Pittsburgh. Study abroad program. ROTC: Army (c).
Entrance Requirements: Options: Peterson's Universal Application, Common Application, deferred admission, international baccalaureate accepted. Required: high school transcript, minimum 2.0 high school GPA, SAT or ACT. Recommended: essay, recommendations, interview. Required for some: minimum 3.0 high school GPA. Entrance: minimally difficult. Application deadline: Rolling.
Costs Per Year: Application fee: $35. State resident tuition: $9888 full-time, $380 per credit part-time. Nonresident tuition: $19,776 full-time, $760 per credit part-time. Mandatory fees: $650 full-time, $95 per term part-time. Full-time tuition and fees vary according to course load and program. Part-time tuition and fees vary according to course load and program. College room and board: $6470. Room and board charges vary according to board plan and housing facility.

Collegiate Environment: Orientation program. Drama-theater group, choral group, student-run newspaper, radio station. Social organizations: 38 open to all; local fraternities, local sororities. Most popular organizations: Student Government Association, Student Activities Board, The Source (student newspaper), Alpha Phi Omega (national service fraternity), WDRQ (student radio station). Major annual events: Alumni Weekend, Winter Weekend, Spring Fling. Student services: health clinic, personal-psychological counseling. Campus security: 24-hour emergency response devices and patrols, late night transport-escort service. College housing designed to accommodate 524 students; 586 undergraduates lived in college housing during 2003-04. Freshmen guaranteed college housing. On-campus residence required through sophomore year. Option: coed housing available. T. Edward and Tullah Hanley Library with 88,969 books, 14,471 microform titles, 342 serials, 4,167 audiovisual materials, an OPAC, and a Web page. Operations spending for 2004 fiscal year: $16,258. 150 computers available on campus for general student use. A campuswide network can be accessed from student residence rooms and from off campus. Staffed computer lab on campus.

■ **UNIVERSITY OF PITTSBURGH AT GREENSBURG** *L-5*
1150 Mount Pleasant Rd.
Greensburg, PA 15601-5860
Tel: (724)837-7040
Admissions: (724)836-9880
Fax: (724)836-9901
E-mail: upgadmit@pitt.edu
Web Site: http://www.upg.pitt.edu/
Description: State-related, 4-year, coed. Part of University of Pittsburgh System. Awards bachelor's degrees. Founded 1963. Setting: 219-acre small town campus with easy access to Pittsburgh. Endowment: $523,014. Educational spending for 2005 fiscal year: $2567 per student. Total enrollment: 1,796. Student-undergrad faculty ratio is 18:1. 1,580 applied, 89% were admitted. 10% from top 10% of their high school class, 33% from top quarter, 82% from top half. 1 National Merit Scholar, 2 class presidents, 3 valedictorians. Full-time: 1,641 students, 51% women, 49% men. Part-time: 155 students, 50% women, 50% men. Students come from 10 states and territories, 1 other country, 1% from out-of-state, 0.2% Native American, 1% Hispanic, 3% black, 2% Asian American or Pacific Islander, 0% international, 15% 25 or older, 35% live on campus, 7% transferred in. Retention: 75% of full-time freshmen returned the following year. Academic areas with the most degrees conferred: business/marketing; social sciences; psychology. Core. Calendar: semesters. Academic remediation for entering students, services for LD students, advanced placement, accelerated degree program, self-designed majors, independent study, distance learning, double major, summer session for credit, part-time degree program, adult/continuing education programs, internships. Off campus study at Seton Hill College, other units of the University of Pittsburgh, Westmoreland County Community College. Study abroad program. ROTC: Army (c), Air Force (c).
Entrance Requirements: Options: Peterson's Universal Application, Common Application, electronic application, early admission, deferred admission. Required: high school transcript, minimum 2.5 high school GPA, SAT or ACT. Recommended: essay, interview. Required for some: recommendations. Entrance: moderately difficult. Application deadline: 8/1. Notification: continuous.
Costs Per Year: Application fee: $45. State resident tuition: $9888 full-time, $380 per credit part-time. Nonresident tuition: $19,776 full-time, $760 per credit part-time. Mandatory fees: $674 full-time, $113 per term part-time. College room and board: $7210. College room only: $4910.
Collegiate Environment: Orientation program. Drama-theater group, choral group, student-run newspaper. Social organizations: 45 open to all. Most popular organizations: Student Government Association, Circle K, Freshmen Honor Society-Phi Eta Sigma, Senior Honor Society-Phi Kappa Phi, Student Activities Board. Major annual events: annual luau, Spring Weekend, volunteerism. Student services: health clinic, personal-psychological counseling. Campus security: 24-hour emergency response devices and patrols, late night transport-escort service, controlled dormitory access. 600 college housing spaces available; all were occupied in 2003-04. No special consideration for freshman housing applicants. Option: coed housing available. Millstein Library with 75,000 books, 418 serials, an OPAC, and a Web page. Operations spending for 2004 fiscal year: $350,800. 400 computers

available on campus for general student use. A campuswide network can be accessed from student residence rooms and from off campus. Staffed computer lab on campus.

■ UNIVERSITY OF PITTSBURGH AT JOHNSTOWN *K-8*

450 Schoolhouse Rd.
Johnstown, PA 15904-2990
Tel: (814)269-7000
Free: 800-765-4875
Admissions: (814)269-7050
Fax: (814)269-7044
E-mail: gyure@pitt.edu
Web Site: http://www.upj.pitt.edu/

Description: State-related, 4-year, coed. Part of University of Pittsburgh System. Awards associate and bachelor's degrees. Founded 1927. Setting: 650-acre suburban campus with easy access to Pittsburgh. Endowment: $14.8 million. Educational spending for 2005 fiscal year: $4746 per student. Total enrollment: 3,173. 2,589 applied, 85% were admitted. 22% from top 10% of their high school class, 67% from top quarter, 72% from top half. 8 valedictorians. Full-time: 2,915 students, 48% women, 52% men. Part-time: 258 students, 37% women, 63% men. Students come from 11 states and territories, 1 other country, 1% from out-of-state, 0.1% Native American, 0.5% Hispanic, 1% black, 1% Asian American or Pacific Islander, 0% international, 8% 25 or older, 76% live on campus, 3% transferred in. Academic areas with the most degrees conferred: business/marketing; education; social sciences. Core. Calendar: semesters. Services for LD students, advanced placement, accelerated degree program, self-designed majors, independent study, distance learning, double major, summer session for credit, part-time degree program, adult/continuing education programs, co-op programs and internships. Off campus study at members of the Pittsburgh Council on Higher Education. Study abroad program.

Entrance Requirements: Options: Peterson's Universal Application, electronic application, early admission, deferred admission. Required: high school transcript, minimum 2.0 high school GPA, SAT or ACT. Recommended: essay, 3 recommendations. Required for some: interview. Placement: SAT or ACT required for some. Entrance: moderately difficult. Application deadlines: Rolling, Rolling for nonresidents. Notification: continuous, continuous for nonresidents.

Costs Per Year: Application fee: $35. State resident tuition: $9888 full-time, $380 per credit part-time. Nonresident tuition: $19,776 full-time, $760 per credit part-time. Mandatory fees: $612 full-time, $77 per term part-time. Full-time tuition and fees vary according to program and student level. Part-time tuition and fees vary according to program and student level. College room and board: $6100. College room only: $3700. Room and board charges vary according to board plan and housing facility.

Collegiate Environment: Orientation program. Drama-theater group, choral group, student-run newspaper, radio station. Social organizations: 65 open to all; national fraternities, national sororities, local fraternities; 7% of eligible men and 6% of eligible women are members. Most popular organizations: student radio station, Student Senate, Programming Board, dance ensemble. Major annual events: Homecoming, Greek Week, Welcome Back Daze. Student services: health clinic, personal-psychological counseling. Campus security: 24-hour patrols, late night transport-escort service. College housing designed to accommodate 1,720 students; 1,963 undergraduates lived in college housing during 2003-04. Freshmen guaranteed college housing. Option: coed housing available. Owen Library with 145,507 books, 20,718 microform titles, 450 serials, 711 audiovisual materials, an OPAC, and a Web page. 150 computers available on campus for general student use. Computer purchase/lease plans available. A campuswide network can be accessed from student residence rooms and from off campus. Staffed computer lab on campus.

■ UNIVERSITY OF PITTSBURGH AT TITUSVILLE *D-5*

PO Box 287
Titusville, PA 16354
Tel: (814)827-4400; 888-878-0462
Admissions: (814)827-4409
Fax: (814)827-4448
E-mail: uptadm@pitt.edu
Web Site: http://www.upt.pitt.edu/

Description: State-related, 2-year, coed. Part of University of Pittsburgh System. Awards certificates, transfer associate, and terminal associate degrees. Founded 1963. Setting: 10-acre small town campus. Endowment: $825,000. Total enrollment: 547. Student-undergrad faculty ratio is 12:1. 281

applied, 86% were admitted. 4% from top 10% of their high school class, 20% from top quarter, 42% from top half. Full-time: 413 students, 60% women, 40% men. Part-time: 134 students, 80% women, 20% men. Students come from 15 states and territories, 8% from out-of-state, 0% Native American, 1% Hispanic, 16% black, 2% Asian American or Pacific Islander, 0% international, 48% live on campus, 6% transferred in. Core. Calendar: semesters. Academic remediation for entering students, advanced placement, independent study, distance learning, summer session for credit, part-time degree program, internships. Study abroad program.

Entrance Requirements: Options: Peterson's Universal Application, deferred admission. Required: high school transcript, minimum 2.0 high school GPA, SAT or ACT. Recommended: interview, SAT. Required for some: essay, 1 recommendation. Entrance: minimally difficult. Application deadline: Rolling. Notification: continuous.

Costs Per Year: Application fee: $35. State resident tuition: $8710 full-time, $335 per credit part-time. Nonresident tuition: $17,610 full-time, $677 per credit part-time. Mandatory fees: $780 full-time, $93 per term part-time. Part-time tuition and fees vary according to student level. College room and board: $7234. Room and board charges vary according to board plan.

Collegiate Environment: Orientation program. Drama-theater group, choral group. Social organizations: 20 open to all. Most popular organizations: Phi Theta Kappa, Weight Club, SAB, SIFE, Diversity Club. Major annual events: talent show, semi-formal dance, stress relief week. Student services: health clinic, personal-psychological counseling. Campus security: 24-hour emergency response devices and patrols, controlled dormitory access. 300 college housing spaces available; 270 were occupied in 2003-04. Freshmen guaranteed college housing. On-campus residence required through sophomore year. Option: coed housing available. Haskell Memorial Library with 49,256 books, 1,358 microform titles, 126 serials, 505 audiovisual materials, and an OPAC. 62 computers available on campus for general student use. A campuswide network can be accessed from student residence rooms and from off campus. Staffed computer lab on campus.

■ UNIVERSITY OF THE SCIENCES IN PHILADELPHIA *M-24*

600 South 43rd St.
Philadelphia, PA 19104-4495
Tel: (215)596-8800
Admissions: (215)596-8810
Fax: (215)895-1100
E-mail: admit@pcps.edu
Web Site: http://www.usip.edu/

Description: Independent, university, coed. Awards bachelor's, master's, doctoral, and first professional degrees. Founded 1821. Setting: 35-acre urban campus. Endowment: $97.2 million. Research spending for 2004 fiscal year: $1.7 million. Educational spending for 2005 fiscal year: $10,497 per student. Total enrollment: 2,808. Faculty: 249 (151 full-time, 98 part-time). Student-undergrad faculty ratio is 14:1. 2,897 applied, 65% were admitted. 35% from top 10% of their high school class, 74% from top quarter, 98% from top half. Full-time: 1,940 students, 61% women, 39% men. Part-time: 39 students, 82% women, 18% men. Students come from 31 states and territories, 16 other countries, 46% from out-of-state, 0.4% Native American, 2% Hispanic, 6% black, 32% Asian American or Pacific Islander, 1% international, 12% 25 or older, 29% live on campus, 3% transferred in. Retention: 83% of full-time freshmen returned the following year. Academic areas with the most degrees conferred: health professions and related sciences; biological/life sciences; business/marketing. Core. Calendar: semesters. Academic remediation for entering students, ESL program, services for LD students, advanced placement, honors program, distance learning, double major, summer session for credit, part-time degree program, adult/continuing education programs, co-op programs and internships, graduate courses open to undergrads. Off campus study at Drexel University. ROTC: Army (c), Air Force (c).

Entrance Requirements: Options: electronic application, deferred admission, international baccalaureate accepted. Required: high school transcript, SAT or ACT. Recommended: minimum 3.0 high school GPA, SAT. Entrance: moderately difficult. Application deadline: Rolling. Notification: continuous.

Costs Per Year: Application fee: $45. Comprehensive fee: $33,362 includes full-time tuition ($22,798), mandatory fees ($1184), and college room and board ($9380). College room only: $5730. Full-time tuition and fees vary according to degree level and program. Room and board charges vary according to board plan. Part-time tuition: $950 per credit. Part-time mandatory fees: $37 per credit. Part-time tuition and fees vary according to course load and degree level.

Collegiate Environment: Orientation program. Drama-theater group, choral group, student-run newspaper. Social organizations: 65 open to all; national fraternities, national sororities, local fraternities, local sororities. Most popular organizations: student government, Bharat, Academy of Students of Pharmacy, Student Physical Therapy Association, Asian Student Association. Major annual events: Greek Week, Student Appreciation Day, Parent's Weekend. Student services: health clinic, personal-psychological counseling. Campus security: 24-hour emergency response devices and patrols, late night transport-escort service, controlled dormitory access. 725 college housing spaces available. Freshmen guaranteed college housing. On-campus residence required in freshman year. Option: coed housing available. Joseph W. England Library plus 1 other with 87,125 books, 27,642 microform titles, 9,817 serials, 1,121 audiovisual materials, an OPAC, and a Web page. Operations spending for 2004 fiscal year: $1.9 million. 120 computers available on campus for general student use. A campuswide network can be accessed from student residence rooms and from off campus. Staffed computer lab on campus.

■ **THE UNIVERSITY OF SCRANTON** *F-22*
800 Linden St.
Scranton, PA 18510
Tel: (570)941-7400; 888-SCRANTON
Admissions: (570)941-7540
Fax: (570)941-5928
E-mail: admissions@uofs.edu
Web Site: http://www.scranton.edu/
Description: Independent Roman Catholic (Jesuit), comprehensive, coed. Awards associate, bachelor's, master's, and doctoral degrees and post-master's certificates. Founded 1888. Setting: 50-acre urban campus. Endowment: $95.2 million. Total enrollment: 5,160. Faculty: 424 (251 full-time, 173 part-time). Student-undergrad faculty ratio is 12:1. 6,343 applied, 75% were admitted. 26% from top 10% of their high school class, 57% from top quarter, 84% from top half. Full-time: 3,858 students, 58% women, 42% men. Part-time: 226 students, 58% women, 42% men. Students come from 30 states and territories, 12 other countries, 50% from out-of-state, 0.1% Native American, 5% Hispanic, 2% black, 2% Asian American or Pacific Islander, 0.4% international, 7% 25 or older, 52% live on campus, 1% transferred in. Retention: 88% of full-time freshmen returned the following year. Academic areas with the most degrees conferred: business/marketing; education; health professions and related sciences. Core. Calendar: 4-1-4. Academic remediation for entering students, services for LD students, advanced placement, accelerated degree program, self-designed majors, honors program, independent study, distance learning, double major, summer session for credit, part-time degree program, external degree program, adult/continuing education programs, internships, graduate courses open to undergrads. Off campus study at Marywood University. Study abroad program. ROTC: Army, Air Force (c).
Entrance Requirements: Options: Peterson's Universal Application, Common Application, electronic application, early admission, early action, deferred admission, international baccalaureate accepted. Required: essay, high school transcript, recommendations, SAT or ACT. Required for some: interview. Entrance: moderately difficult. Application deadlines: 3/1, 11/15 for early action. Notification: continuous until 5/1, 12/15 for early action.
Costs Per Year: Application fee: $40. Comprehensive fee: $33,934 includes full-time tuition ($23,750), mandatory fees ($280), and college room and board ($9904). College room only: $5786. Room and board charges vary according to board plan and housing facility. Part-time tuition: $660 per credit. Part-time mandatory fees: $25 per term.
Collegiate Environment: Orientation program. Drama-theater group, choral group, student-run newspaper, radio station. Social organizations: 80 open to all. Most popular organizations: Service-Oriented Students Club, United Colors, retreat program, Biology/Pre-Medicine Club, Pre-Law Society. Major annual events: Spring Fling, Senior Formal, President's Ball. Student services: health clinic, personal-psychological counseling, women's center. Campus security: 24-hour emergency response devices and patrols, student patrols, late night transport-escort service, controlled dormitory access. 2,183 college housing spaces available; 2,057 were occupied in 2003-04. Freshmen guaranteed college housing. On-campus residence required through sophomore year. Options: coed, men-only, women-only housing available. Harry and Jeanette Weinberg Memorial Library plus 1 other with 465,871 books, 1,714 serials, an OPAC, and a Web page. Operations spending for 2004 fiscal year: $3 million. 903 computers available on campus for general student use. A campuswide network can be accessed from student residence rooms and from off campus. Staffed computer lab on campus.
Community Environment: Settled in the late eighteenth century, Scranton is the commercial and industrial center of northeast Pennsylvania.

Scranton's manufactured items include textiles, clothing, electronic equipment, furniture, plastic, canvas, and metal products. Lying in the Appalachian Mountains on the Lackawana River, Scranton is 10 minutes from the Montage Ski and Recreation Area. Also of interest are the Everhart Museum of Natural History, Science, and Art, Steamtown, and McDade State Park and Coal Mine Tour.

■ **URSINUS COLLEGE** *L-23*
Box 1000, Main St.
Collegeville, PA 19426-1000
Tel: (610)409-3000
Admissions: (610)409-3200
Fax: (610)489-0627
E-mail: admissions@ursinus.edu
Web Site: http://www.ursinus.edu/
Description: Independent, 4-year, coed. Awards bachelor's degrees. Founded 1869. Setting: 168-acre suburban campus with easy access to Philadelphia. Endowment: $109.9 million. Research spending for 2004 fiscal year: $154,811. Educational spending for 2005 fiscal year: $11,245 per student. Total enrollment: 1,571. Student-undergrad faculty ratio is 12:1. 1,776 applied, 75% were admitted. 41% from top 10% of their high school class, 65% from top quarter, 93% from top half. 3 National Merit Scholars, 9 class presidents, 7 valedictorians, 73 student government officers. Full-time: 1,552 students, 52% women, 48% men. Part-time: 19 students, 79% women, 21% men. Students come from 28 states and territories, 14 other countries, 39% from out-of-state, 0.3% Native American, 3% Hispanic, 7% black, 4% Asian American or Pacific Islander, 1% international, 0% 25 or older, 91% live on campus, 0.3% transferred in. Retention: 91% of full-time freshmen returned the following year. Academic areas with the most degrees conferred: social sciences; biological/life sciences; psychology. Core. Calendar: semesters. ESL program, advanced placement, self-designed majors, honors program, independent study, double major, part-time degree program, adult/continuing education programs, internships. Off campus study at Howard University, American University, Butler University. Study abroad program.
Entrance Requirements: Options: Peterson's Universal Application, Common Application, electronic application, early admission, early decision, deferred admission, international baccalaureate accepted. Required: essay, high school transcript, 2 recommendations, graded paper. Recommended: interview, SAT Subject Tests. Required for some: SAT or ACT. Entrance: very difficult. Application deadlines: 2/15, 1/15 for early decision, 12/15 for early action. Notification: 4/1, 2/1 for early decision.
Costs Per Year: Application fee: $50. Comprehensive fee: $38,950 includes full-time tuition ($31,450), mandatory fees ($150), and college room and board ($7350). Part-time tuition: $1048 per credit.
Collegiate Environment: Orientation program. Drama-theater group, choral group, student-run newspaper, radio station. Social organizations: 105 open to all; national fraternities, national sororities, local fraternities, local sororities; 26% of eligible men and 38% of eligible women are members. Most popular organizations: Environmental Action Committee, Habitat for Humanity, Campus Activities Board, Christian Fellowship, Multicultural Student Union. Major annual events: homecoming, Air Band Competition, Spring Fling. Student services: health clinic, personal-psychological counseling. Campus security: 24-hour emergency response devices and patrols, late night transport-escort service, student EMT Corps for first aid/emergency first response. 1,329 college housing spaces available; all were occupied in 2003-04. Freshmen guaranteed college housing. Options: coed, men-only, women-only housing available. Myrin Library plus 2 others with 200,000 books, 155,000 microform titles, 900 serials, 17,500 audiovisual materials, an OPAC, and a Web page. Operations spending for 2004 fiscal year: $837,357. 350 computers available on campus for general student use. A campuswide network can be accessed from student residence rooms and from off campus. Staffed computer lab on campus.
Community Environment: Collegeville is 25 miles northwest of Philadelphia. Within a one-hour drive are museums, libraries, historical sights, educational institutions, recreational facilities, and theaters. Part-time employment is available.

■ **VALLEY FORGE CHRISTIAN COLLEGE** *L-22*
1401 Charlestown Rd.
Phoenixville, PA 19460
Tel: (610)935-0450
Free: 800-432-8322
E-mail: admissions@vfcc.edu

Web Site: http://www.vfcc.edu/

Description: Independent Assemblies of God, 4-year, coed. Awards associate and bachelor's degrees. Founded 1938. Setting: 77-acre small town campus with easy access to Philadelphia. Endowment: $779,981. Educational spending for 2005 fiscal year: $3178 per student. Total enrollment: 934. Student-undergrad faculty ratio is 20:1. 398 applied, 75% were admitted. Full-time: 847 students, 53% women, 47% men. Part-time: 87 students, 56% women, 44% men. Students come from 24 states and territories, 3 other countries, 46% from out-of-state, 0.2% Native American, 6% Hispanic, 5% black, 1% Asian American or Pacific Islander, 0.2% international, 12% 25 or older, 91% live on campus, 7% transferred in. Retention: 76% of full-time freshmen returned the following year. Academic areas with the most degrees conferred: theology and religious vocations; psychology; education. Core. Calendar: semesters. Academic remediation for entering students, ESL program, advanced placement, honors program, independent study, distance learning, double major, summer session for credit, adult/continuing education programs, internships. Study abroad program.

Entrance Requirements: Open admission. Options: electronic application, early admission, deferred admission. Required: essay, high school transcript, 1 recommendation, SAT or ACT. Required for some: interview. Entrance: minimally difficult. Application deadline: 8/1. Notification: continuous.

Costs Per Year: Application fee: $25. Comprehensive fee: $17,550 includes full-time tuition ($10,750), mandatory fees ($950), and college room and board ($5850). College room only: $2650. Part-time tuition: $414 per credit.

Collegiate Environment: Orientation program. Drama-theater group, choral group, student-run newspaper. Most popular organizations: Prison Ministries Organization, Homeless Outreach Ministry, J.C. Powerhouse. Major annual events: homecoming, Missions Convention, Spiritual Emphasis Week. Student services: health clinic, personal-psychological counseling. Campus security: late night transport-escort service, 16-hour patrols by trained security personnel. 857 college housing spaces available; 774 were occupied in 2003-04. Freshmen guaranteed college housing. On-campus residence required through senior year. Options: men-only, women-only housing available. Valley Forge Christian College Library with 61,887 books, 230 serials, 500 audiovisual materials, and an OPAC. Operations spending for 2004 fiscal year: $269,597. 30 computers available on campus for general student use. A campuswide network can be accessed from student residence rooms and from off campus. Staffed computer lab on campus.

Community Environment: Phoenixville is a quiet residential town on the boundary of Valley Forge State Park and is approximately 40 miles from Philadelphia. The climate is temperate. The immediate area provides an abundance of shopping areas and malls, as well as religious, medical and professional services. Recreational opportunities include picnicking, fishing, swimming, boating, camping, and tennis. There are considerable job opportunities available.

■ **VALLEY FORGE MILITARY COLLEGE** *M-23*
1001 Eagle Rd.
Wayne, PA 19087-3695
Tel: (610)989-1200
Free: 800-234-8362
Admissions: (610)989-1303
Fax: (610)688-1545
Web Site: http://www.vfmac.edu/

Description: Independent, 2-year, coed. Awards transfer associate degrees. Founded 1928. Setting: 120-acre suburban campus with easy access to Philadelphia. Endowment: $7.2 million. Educational spending for 2005 fiscal year: $6368 per student. Total enrollment: 165. Student-undergrad faculty ratio is 10:1. 256 applied, 89% were admitted. Full-time: 165 students, 100% men. Students come from 6 other countries, 85% from out-of-state, 0% Native American, 7% Hispanic, 13% black, 6% Asian American or Pacific Islander, 2% international, 100% live on campus, 73% transferred in. Core. Calendar: 4-1-4. Academic remediation for entering students, ESL program, advanced placement. ROTC: Army, Air Force (c).

Entrance Requirements: Options: Peterson's Universal Application, Common Application, early admission, deferred admission. Required: high school transcript, guidance counselor/teacher evaluation form, SAT or ACT. Recommended: minimum 2.0 high school GPA, interview. Entrance: moderately difficult. Application deadline: 8/2. Notification: continuous.

Costs Per Year: Application fee: $25. Comprehensive fee: $30,977 includes full-time tuition ($19,693) and college room and board ($11,284).

Collegiate Environment: Orientation program. Drama-theater group, choral group, marching band, student-run newspaper. Social organizations: 12

open to all; national fraternities; 20% of men are members. Most popular organizations: Rotoract, Young Republicans, Phi Theta Kappa, Business Club, Criminal Justice Club. Major annual events: class trip, Winter Ball, Field Day. Student services: health clinic, personal-psychological counseling. Campus security: 24-hour patrols, student patrols. On-campus residence required through sophomore year. Option: men-only housing available. Baker Library with 75,830 books, 70,220 microform titles, 189 serials, 326 audiovisual materials, and an OPAC. 44 computers available on campus for general student use. A campuswide network can be accessed from student residence rooms and from off campus. Staffed computer lab on campus.

■ **VILLANOVA UNIVERSITY** *M-23*
800 Lancaster Ave.
Villanova, PA 19085-1699
Tel: (610)519-4500
Admissions: (610)519-4000
Fax: (610)519-6450
E-mail: gotovu@villanova.edu
Web Site: http://www.villanova.edu/

Description: Independent Roman Catholic, comprehensive, coed. Awards associate, bachelor's, master's, doctoral, and first professional degrees. Founded 1842. Setting: 254-acre suburban campus with easy access to Philadelphia. Endowment: $241.2 million. Research spending for 2004 fiscal year: $3.9 million. Educational spending for 2005 fiscal year: $11,970 per student. Total enrollment: 10,450. Faculty: 898 (545 full-time, 353 part-time). Student-undergrad faculty ratio is 13:1. 10,394 applied, 51% were admitted. 47% from top 10% of their high school class, 83% from top quarter, 97% from top half. 23 valedictorians. Full-time: 6,541 students, 51% women, 49% men. Part-time: 667 students, 47% women, 53% men. Students come from 51 states and territories, 29 other countries, 67% from out-of-state, 0.3% Native American, 5% Hispanic, 4% black, 6% Asian American or Pacific Islander, 2% international, 4% 25 or older, 65% live on campus, 1% transferred in. Retention: 94% of full-time freshmen returned the following year. Academic areas with the most degrees conferred: business/marketing; social sciences; engineering. Core. Calendar: semesters. ESL program, services for LD students, advanced placement, accelerated degree program, honors program, independent study, distance learning, double major, summer session for credit, part-time degree program, adult/continuing education programs, internships, graduate courses open to undergrads. Off campus study at Rosemont College. Study abroad program. ROTC: Army (c), Naval, Air Force (c).

Entrance Requirements: Options: electronic application, early admission, early action, deferred admission, international baccalaureate accepted. Required: essay, high school transcript, activities resume, SAT or ACT. Entrance: very difficult. Application deadlines: 1/7, 11/1 for early action. Notification: 4/1, 12/20 for early action.

Costs Per Year: Application fee: $70. Comprehensive fee: $38,797 includes full-time tuition ($28,760), mandatory fees ($675), and college room and board ($9362). College room only: $4962. Full-time tuition and fees vary according to program and student level. Room and board charges vary according to board plan and housing facility. Part-time tuition: $624 per credit hour. Part-time mandatory fees: $280 per term. Part-time tuition and fees vary according to class time, course level, and program.

Collegiate Environment: Orientation program. Drama-theater group, choral group, marching band, student-run newspaper, radio station. Social organizations: 100 open to all; national fraternities, national sororities; 11% of eligible men and 31% of eligible women are members. Most popular organizations: Blue Key Society, orientation counselor program, Special Olympics, campus activities team. Major annual events: Balloon Day, Special Olympics, homecoming. Student services: legal services, health clinic, personal-psychological counseling. Campus security: 24-hour emergency response devices and patrols, student patrols, late night transport-escort service, controlled dormitory access. 4,300 college housing spaces available; all were occupied in 2003-04. Freshmen guaranteed college housing. Options: coed, men-only, women-only housing available. Falvey Library plus 2 others with 900,248 books, 1.8 million microform titles, 10,800 serials, 8,170 audiovisual materials, an OPAC, and a Web page. Operations spending for 2004 fiscal year: $10 million. 3,711 computers available on campus for general student use. Computer purchase/lease plans available. A campuswide network can be accessed from student residence rooms and from off campus. Staffed computer lab on campus.

Community Environment: The "Main Line" is a suburban residential area located 12 miles due west of downtown Philadelphia, which includes the towns of Radnor, Rosemont, Villanova, St. Davids, Wayne, Haverford, and

Merion Station. The mean temperature for the area is 54.3 degrees. The area is served by Amtrak and local commuter rail lines, regional bus lines, and the Schuylkill Expressway. The total locale has more than 200 civic, social, and church groups. There are art centers, theater groups, a symphony orchestra, several museums, many libraries, two hospitals, and good shopping facilities. Local recreation facilities include golf courses, swimming pools, skating rinks, parks, and playgrounds.

■ WASHINGTON & JEFFERSON COLLEGE L-2

60 South Lincoln St.
Washington, PA 15301
Tel: (724)222-4400; 888-WANDJAY
Admissions: (724)223-6025
Fax: (724)223-5271
E-mail: anewell@washjeff.edu
Web Site: http://www.washjeff.edu/

Description: Independent, 4-year, coed. Awards associate and bachelor's degrees. Founded 1781. Setting: 51-acre small town campus with easy access to Pittsburgh. Endowment: $81.8 million. Research spending for 2004 fiscal year: $249,114. Educational spending for 2005 fiscal year: $9745 per student. Total enrollment: 1,418. Student-undergrad faculty ratio is 12:1. 4,477 applied, 39% were admitted. 31% from top 10% of their high school class, 65% from top quarter, 94% from top half. 17 valedictorians. Full-time: 1,400 students, 48% women, 52% men. Part-time: 18 students, 61% women, 39% men. Students come from 31 states and territories, 24% from out-of-state, 0% Native American, 1% Hispanic, 2% black, 1% Asian American or Pacific Islander, 0% international, 0.5% 25 or older, 81% live on campus, 1% transferred in. Retention: 86% of full-time freshmen returned the following year. Academic areas with the most degrees conferred: business/marketing; social sciences; psychology. Core. Calendar: 4-1-4. Academic remediation for entering students, services for LD students, advanced placement, accelerated degree program, self-designed majors, honors program, independent study, double major, summer session for credit, part-time degree program, internships. Study abroad program. ROTC: Army (c), Air Force (c).

Entrance Requirements: Options: Peterson's Universal Application, Common Application, electronic application, early admission, early decision, early action, deferred admission. Required: essay, high school transcript, 1 recommendation, SAT or ACT. Recommended: interview. Required for some: interview. Entrance: very difficult. Application deadlines: 3/1, 12/1 for early decision, 1/15 for early action. Notification: 4/1, 12/15 for early decision, 2/15 for early action.

Costs Per Year: Application fee: $25. Comprehensive fee: $33,490 includes full-time tuition ($25,930), mandatory fees ($400), and college room and board ($7160). College room only: $4150. Room and board charges vary according to board plan and housing facility. Part-time tuition: $810 per credit hour.

Collegiate Environment: Orientation program. Drama-theater group, choral group, student-run newspaper, radio station. Social organizations: 88 open to all; national fraternities, national sororities; 43% of eligible men and 37% of eligible women are members. Most popular organizations: student government, Saturday Nite Life, George and Tom's, Pre-Health Society, Pre-Legal Society. Major annual events: Homecoming, student concert, Greek Week. Student services: health clinic, personal-psychological counseling. Campus security: 24-hour emergency response devices and patrols, late night transport-escort service, controlled dormitory access. 1,142 college housing spaces available; 1,092 were occupied in 2003-04. Freshmen guaranteed college housing. On-campus residence required through senior year. Options: coed, men-only, women-only housing available. U. Grant Miller Library with 157,665 books, 14,807 microform titles, 8,124 serials, 8,925 audiovisual materials, an OPAC, and a Web page. Operations spending for 2004 fiscal year: $909,686. 450 computers available on campus for general student use. Computer purchase/lease plans available. A campuswide network can be accessed from student residence rooms and from off campus. Staffed computer lab on campus.

■ WAYNESBURG COLLEGE N-2

51 West College St.
Waynesburg, PA 15370-1222
Tel: (724)627-8191
Free: 800-225-7393
Admissions: (724)852-3333
Fax: (724)627-8124
Web Site: http://www.waynesburg.edu/

Description: Independent, comprehensive, coed, affiliated with Presbyterian Church (U.S.A.). Awards associate, bachelor's, and master's degrees. Founded 1849. Setting: 30-acre small town campus with easy access to Pittsburgh. Endowment: $30.8 million. Research spending for 2004 fiscal year: $20,000. Educational spending for 2005 fiscal year: $6042 per student. Total enrollment: 2,159. Faculty: 135 (62 full-time, 73 part-time). Student-undergrad faculty ratio is 13:1. 1,518 applied, 74% were admitted. 14% from top 10% of their high school class, 40% from top quarter, 77% from top half. 4 class presidents, 7 valedictorians. Full-time: 1,332 students, 58% women, 42% men. Part-time: 284 students, 81% women, 19% men. Students come from 17 states and territories, 4 other countries, 0.1% Native American, 1% Hispanic, 3% black, 0.2% Asian American or Pacific Islander, 0% international, 19% 25 or older, 59% live on campus, 3% transferred in. Retention: 76% of full-time freshmen returned the following year. Academic areas with the most degrees conferred: business/marketing; health professions and related sciences; education. Core. Calendar: semesters. Academic remediation for entering students, advanced placement, accelerated degree program, honors program, independent study, distance learning, double major, adult/continuing education programs, internships. Study abroad program. ROTC: Army (c).

Entrance Requirements: Options: Peterson's Universal Application, Common Application, early admission. Required: high school transcript, minimum 2.75 high school GPA, SAT or ACT. Recommended: minimum 3.0 high school GPA, interview. Required for some: essay, recommendations. Entrance: moderately difficult. Application deadline: Rolling. Notification: continuous.

Costs Per Year: Application fee: $20. Comprehensive fee: $20,890 includes full-time tuition ($14,810) and college room and board ($6080). College room only: $3100. Full-time tuition varies according to class time. Room and board charges vary according to board plan. Part-time tuition: $620 per credit. Part-time mandatory fees: $15 per credit. Part-time tuition and fees vary according to class time, course load, and location.

Collegiate Environment: Orientation program. Drama-theater group, choral group, marching band, student-run newspaper, radio station. Social organizations: 35 open to all. Most popular organizations: Student Senate, Student Activities Board (SAB), Student Nurses Association, Christian Fellowship. Major annual events: homecoming, Spring Week, Charter Day. Student services: health clinic, personal-psychological counseling. Campus security: 24-hour emergency response devices and patrols, late night transport-escort service, controlled dormitory access. 814 college housing spaces available; 796 were occupied in 2003-04. Freshmen guaranteed college housing. On-campus residence required through junior year. Options: men-only, women-only housing available. Waynesburg College Library with 100,000 books, 5,183 microform titles, 1,189 serials, 2,932 audiovisual materials, an OPAC, and a Web page. Operations spending for 2004 fiscal year: $488,550. 150 computers available on campus for general student use. A campuswide network can be accessed from student residence rooms and from off campus. Staffed computer lab on campus.

Community Environment: Population 5299, Waynesburg is located 50 miles from Pittsburgh in southwestern Pennsylvania. The climate is moderate. Community service facilities include a library, several churches, a hospital, hotels, motels, and rooming houses. There is bus service available. Local recreation includes theatres, hunting, boating, fishing, golf, and movies. Many civic, fraternal and veteran's organizations are active in the community.

■ WEST CHESTER UNIVERSITY OF PENNSYLVANIA M-22

University Ave. and High St.
West Chester, PA 19383
Tel: (610)436-1000
Admissions: (610)436-3414
E-mail: ugadmiss@wcupa.edu
Web Site: http://www.wcupa.edu/

Description: State-supported, comprehensive, coed. Part of Pennsylvania State System of Higher Education. Awards bachelor's and master's degrees. Founded 1871. Setting: 547-acre suburban campus with easy access to Philadelphia. Endowment: $12.4 million. Research spending for 2004 fiscal year: $285,989. Educational spending for 2005 fiscal year: $3162 per student. Total enrollment: 12,988. Faculty: 797 (567 full-time, 230 part-time). Student-undergrad faculty ratio is 16:1. 11,013 applied, 49% were admitted. 9% from top 10% of their high school class, 31% from top quarter, 67% from top half. Full-time: 9,788 students, 62% women, 38% men. Part-time: 1,050 students, 58% women, 42% men. Students come from 35 states and territories, 12% from out-of-state, 0.3% Native American, 3% Hispanic, 9%

black, 2% Asian American or Pacific Islander, 0.4% international, 13% 25 or older, 30% live on campus, 9% transferred in. Retention: 84% of full-time freshmen returned the following year. Academic areas with the most degrees conferred: business/marketing; education; health professions and related sciences. Core. Calendar: semesters. Academic remediation for entering students, ESL program, services for LD students, advanced placement, accelerated degree program, self-designed majors, honors program, independent study, distance learning, double major, summer session for credit, part-time degree program, adult/continuing education programs, internships, graduate courses open to undergrads. Off campus study at members of the National Student Exchange. Study abroad program. ROTC: Army (c), Air Force (c).

Entrance Requirements: Options: electronic application, early admission, deferred admission. Required: essay, high school transcript, SAT or ACT. Recommended: minimum 3.0 high school GPA. Required for some: recommendations, interview. Entrance: moderately difficult. Application deadline: Rolling. Notification: continuous.

Costs Per Year: Application fee: $35. State resident tuition: $4906 full-time, $204 per credit part-time. Nonresident tuition: $12,266 full-time, $511 per credit part-time. Mandatory fees: $1241 full-time, $47 per credit part-time. College room and board: $6208. College room only: $4140.

Collegiate Environment: Orientation program. Drama-theater group, choral group, marching band, student-run newspaper, radio station. Social organizations: 205 open to all; national fraternities, national sororities; 8% of eligible men and 8% of eligible women are members. Most popular organizations: Off Campus and Commuter Association, Residence Hall Association, Student Government Association, Sports Club Council. Major annual events: Homecoming, Family Day, Alumni Weekend. Student services: legal services, health clinic, personal-psychological counseling, women's center. Campus security: 24-hour emergency response devices and patrols, late night transport-escort service. 3,880 college housing spaces available; 3,166 were occupied in 2003-04. Freshmen given priority for college housing. Options: coed, women-only housing available. Francis Harvey Green Library plus 1 other with 744,976 books, 879,548 microform titles, 4,593 serials, 72,486 audiovisual materials, an OPAC, and a Web page. Operations spending for 2004 fiscal year: $4 million. 700 computers available on campus for general student use. A campuswide network can be accessed from student residence rooms and from off campus. Staffed computer lab on campus.

Community Environment: Population 20,000. Essentially a residential and college community, West Chester is the county seat of a region rich in colonial history. Local industries include pharmaceuticals, firefighting foam, electrical appliances, air compressors, tags and labels, and refrigerated cabinets. The average January temperature is 31.5 degrees, and the average July temperature is 75 degrees. The community is provided transportation by railroad, bus lines, and an airport nearby. There are several churches, a YMCA, hospital, and public library serving the community. Local recreation includes swimming, bowling, volleyball, tennis, hunting, fishing, and golf. Civic and fraternal organizations are active within the area.

■ **WESTERN SCHOOL OF HEALTH AND BUSINESS CAREERS (MONROEVILLE)** *K-4*

1 Monroeville Center, Ste. 250, Route 22
3824 Northern Pike
Monroeville, PA 15146-2142
Tel: (412)373-6400
Fax: (412)373-2544
Web Site: http://www.westernschool.com/
Description: Proprietary, 2-year, coed. Founded 1980. Calendar: continuous.

■ **WESTERN SCHOOL OF HEALTH AND BUSINESS CAREERS (PITTSBURGH)** *K-3*

421 Seventh Ave.
Pittsburgh, PA 15219-1907
Tel: (412)281-2600
Free: 800-333-6607
Admissions: (412)281-7083
Fax: (412)281-0319
Web Site: http://www.westernschool.com/
Description: Proprietary, 2-year, coed. Awards terminal associate degrees. Founded 1980. Setting: urban campus. Total enrollment: 600. 2% from top 10% of their high school class, 8% from top quarter, 48% from top half. 20 student government officers. Students come from 6 states and territories, 2

other countries, 2% from out-of-state, 50% 25 or older. Core. Calendar: continuous. Academic remediation for entering students, ESL program, services for LD students, advanced placement, accelerated degree program, adult/continuing education programs, co-op programs and internships.

Entrance Requirements: Options: Common Application, electronic application, early admission, deferred admission. Required: high school transcript, interview. Recommended: recommendations, SAT or ACT, SAT Subject Tests. Required for some: recommendations. Entrance: minimally difficult.

Collegiate Environment: Orientation program. Social organizations: 2 open to all. Most popular organizations: basketball, newspaper. Major annual event: Mr. & Mrs. Valentine. Campus security: 24-hour emergency response devices, 14-hour security patrols Monday through Friday. College housing not available. Campus Library with 1,687 books and 1,403 serials.

■ **WESTMINSTER COLLEGE** *G-2*

319 South Market St.
New Wilmington, PA 16172-0001
Tel: (724)946-8761
Admissions: (724)946-7100
Fax: (724)946-7171
E-mail: swartzdl@westminster.edu
Web Site: http://www.westminster.edu/
Description: Independent, comprehensive, coed, affiliated with Presbyterian Church (U.S.A.). Awards bachelor's and master's degrees. Founded 1852. Setting: 350-acre small town campus with easy access to Pittsburgh. Endowment: $86.3 million. Educational spending for 2005 fiscal year: $7000 per student. Total enrollment: 1,593. Faculty: 149 (100 full-time, 49 part-time). Student-undergrad faculty ratio is 12:1. 1,302 applied, 77% were admitted. 20% from top 10% of their high school class, 55% from top quarter, 87% from top half. Full-time: 1,410 students, 64% women, 36% men. Part-time: 54 students, 63% women, 37% men. Students come from 22 states and territories, 3 other countries, 22% from out-of-state, 0.2% Native American, 0.4% Hispanic, 2% black, 0.2% Asian American or Pacific Islander, 0% international, 1% 25 or older, 2% transferred in. Retention: 83% of full-time freshmen returned the following year. Academic areas with the most degrees conferred: education; business/marketing; social sciences. Core. Calendar: semesters. Advanced placement, self-designed majors, honors program, independent study, double major, summer session for credit, part-time degree program, adult/continuing education programs, internships, graduate courses open to undergrads. Off campus study at members of the East Central College Consortium. Study abroad program. ROTC: Army (c).

Entrance Requirements: Options: Common Application, deferred admission. Required: essay, high school transcript, minimum 2.0 high school GPA, 2 recommendations, SAT or ACT. Recommended: minimum 3.0 high school GPA, interview. Entrance: moderately difficult. Application deadline: 5/1. Notification: continuous.

Costs Per Year: Application fee: $35. Comprehensive fee: $31,395 includes full-time tuition ($23,220), mandatory fees ($1105), and college room and board ($7070). Part-time tuition: $730 per semester hour.

Collegiate Environment: Orientation program. Drama-theater group, choral group, marching band, student-run newspaper, radio station. Social organizations: 85 open to all; national fraternities, national sororities; 33% of eligible men and 34% of eligible women are members. Most popular organizations: student government, Habitat for Humanity, established service teams. Major annual events: Homecoming, Christmas Vespers, Greek Week. Student services: health clinic, personal-psychological counseling, learning center, handicapped services. Campus security: 24-hour patrols, late night transport-escort service. 1,098 college housing spaces available; 1,057 were occupied in 2003-04. Freshmen guaranteed college housing. On-campus residence required through junior year. Options: men-only, women-only housing available. McGill Memorial Library plus 1 other with 283,070 books, 9,737 microform titles, 848 serials, 14,251 audiovisual materials, an OPAC, and a Web page. Operations spending for 2004 fiscal year: $983,562. 158 computers available on campus for general student use. A campuswide network can be accessed from student residence rooms and from off campus. Staffed computer lab on campus.

■ **WESTMORELAND COUNTY COMMUNITY COLLEGE** *L-5*

400 Armbrust Rd.
Youngwood, PA 15697-1898
Tel: (724)925-4000
Admissions: (724)925-4123
Fax: (724)925-1150

E-mail: admission@wccc-pa.edu
Web Site: http://www.wccc-pa.edu/
Description: County-supported, 2-year, coed. Awards certificates, diplomas, transfer associate, and terminal associate degrees. Founded 1970. Setting: 85-acre rural campus with easy access to Pittsburgh. Total enrollment: 6,133. Student-undergrad faculty ratio is 17:1. 3,539 applied, 100% were admitted. Full-time: 2,670 students, 60% women, 40% men. Part-time: 3,463 students, 68% women, 32% men. Students come from 5 states and territories, 9% from out-of-state, 0.2% Native American, 1% Hispanic, 2% black, 1% Asian American or Pacific Islander, 0% international, 45% 25 or older. Retention: 58% of full-time freshmen returned the following year. Core. Calendar: semesters. Academic remediation for entering students, ESL program, services for LD students, advanced placement, honors program, independent study, distance learning, double major, summer session for credit, part-time degree program, adult/continuing education programs, co-op programs and internships. Off campus study at Seton Hill College, University of Pittsburgh.
Entrance Requirements: Open admission except for nursing, dental services programs. Options: electronic application, early admission. Entrance: noncompetitive. Application deadline: Rolling. Notification: continuous.
Costs Per Year: Application fee: $10. Area resident tuition: $68 per credit part-time. State resident tuition: $136 per credit part-time. Nonresident tuition: $204 per credit part-time. Mandatory fees: $7 per credit part-time.
Collegiate Environment: Orientation program. Choral group, student-run newspaper, radio station. Social organizations: 25 open to all. Student services: personal-psychological counseling. Campus security: 24-hour emergency response devices and patrols. College housing not available. 34,522 books and 643 serials. 600 computers available on campus for general student use. A campuswide network can be accessed. Staffed computer lab on campus.

■ WIDENER UNIVERSITY N-23

One University Place
Chester, PA 19013-5792
Tel: (610)499-4000; 888-WIDENER
Admissions: (610)499-4126
Fax: (610)499-4676
E-mail: admissions.office@widener.edu
Web Site: http://www.widener.edu/
Description: Independent, comprehensive, coed. Awards associate, bachelor's, master's, doctoral, and first professional degrees. Founded 1821. Setting: 110-acre suburban campus with easy access to Philadelphia. Endowment: $46.7 million. Research spending for 2004 fiscal year: $333,711. Educational spending for 2005 fiscal year: $11,457 per student. Total enrollment: 5,793. Faculty: 398 (221 full-time, 177 part-time). Student-undergrad faculty ratio is 12:1. 2,963 applied, 81% were admitted. 12% from top 10% of their high school class, 33% from top quarter, 67% from top half. Full-time: 2,375 students, 49% women, 51% men. Part-time: 141 students, 48% women, 52% men. Students come from 26 states and territories, 38 other countries, 34% from out-of-state, 0.2% Native American, 2% Hispanic, 13% black, 2% Asian American or Pacific Islander, 2% international, 6% 25 or older, 61% live on campus, 5% transferred in. Retention: 67% of full-time freshmen returned the following year. Academic areas with the most degrees conferred: business/marketing; health professions and related sciences; engineering. Core. Calendar: semesters. Academic remediation for entering students, ESL program, services for LD students, advanced placement, accelerated degree program, self-designed majors, honors program, independent study, distance learning, double major, summer session for credit, part-time degree program, adult/continuing education programs, co-op programs and internships, graduate courses open to undergrads. Off campus study. Study abroad program. ROTC: Army, Naval (c), Air Force (c).
Entrance Requirements: Options: Peterson's Universal Application, Common Application, electronic application, early admission, early action, deferred admission, international baccalaureate accepted. Required: essay, high school transcript, recommendations, SAT or ACT. Recommended: interview. Required for some: minimum 2.85 high school GPA. Entrance: moderately difficult. Application deadlines: Rolling, Rolling for nonresidents. Notification: continuous, continuous for nonresidents.
Costs Per Year: Application fee: $35..Comprehensive fee: $33,490 includes full-time tuition ($24,620), mandatory fees ($350), and college room and board ($8520). College room only: $3900. Full-time tuition and fees vary according to class time, course load, and program. Room and board charges vary according to board plan and housing facility. Part-time tuition: $821 per credit. Part-time mandatory fees: $65.

Collegiate Environment: Orientation program. Drama-theater group, choral group, student-run newspaper, radio station. Social organizations: 62 open to all; national fraternities, national sororities; 20% of eligible men and 18% of eligible women are members. Most popular organizations: WDNR Radio, Black Student Union, volunteer services, Rugby Club, Theatre Widener. Major annual events: Spring Carnival, Greek Week, Homecoming. Student services: health clinic, personal-psychological counseling. Campus security: 24-hour emergency response devices and patrols, late night transport-escort service, controlled dormitory access, 'blue light' emergency phones located throughout campus. 1,480 college housing spaces available; 1,455 were occupied in 2003-04. Freshmen guaranteed college housing. On-campus residence required through sophomore year. Options: coed, men-only, women-only housing available. Wolfgram Memorial Library with 238,349 books, 175,116 microform titles, 1,974 serials, 6,179 audiovisual materials, an OPAC, and a Web page. Operations spending for 2004 fiscal year: $5.8 million. 345 computers available on campus for general student use. Computer purchase/lease plans available. A campuswide network can be accessed from student residence rooms and from off campus. Staffed computer lab on campus.

■ WILKES UNIVERSITY F-21

84 West South St.
Wilkes-Barre, PA 18766-0002
Tel: (570)408-5000
Free: 800-945-5378
Admissions: (570)408-4400
Fax: (570)408-7820
Web Site: http://www.wilkes.edu/
Description: Independent, comprehensive, coed. Awards bachelor's, master's, and first professional degrees. Founded 1933. Setting: 25-acre urban campus. Endowment: $35.8 million. Research spending for 2004 fiscal year: $463,269. Educational spending for 2005 fiscal year: $6449 per student. Total enrollment: 4,480. Faculty: 217 (131 full-time, 86 part-time). Student-undergrad faculty ratio is 15:1. 2,702 applied, 77% were admitted. 20% from top 10% of their high school class, 48% from top quarter, 82% from top half. Full-time: 1,968 students, 53% women, 47% men. Part-time: 220 students, 51% women, 49% men. Students come from 21 states and territories, 7 other countries, 19% from out-of-state, 0.1% Native American, 2% Hispanic, 2% black, 2% Asian American or Pacific Islander, 0.3% international, 9% 25 or older, 43% live on campus, 6% transferred in. Retention: 80% of full-time freshmen returned the following year. Academic areas with the most degrees conferred: business/marketing; liberal arts/general studies; education. Core. Calendar: semesters. Academic remediation for entering students, advanced placement, accelerated degree program, self-designed majors, honors program, independent study, distance learning, double major, summer session for credit, part-time degree program, adult/continuing education programs, co-op programs and internships, graduate courses open to undergrads. Study abroad program. ROTC: Army (c), Air Force.
Entrance Requirements: Options: electronic application, early admission, deferred admission. Required: high school transcript, SAT or ACT. Recommended: interview. Required for some: recommendations. Entrance: moderately difficult. Application deadline: Rolling. Notification: continuous until 8/30.
Costs Per Year: Application fee: $35. Comprehensive fee: $30,886 includes full-time tuition ($20,592), mandatory fees ($1054), and college room and board ($9240). College room only: $5600. Room and board charges vary according to board plan and housing facility. Part-time tuition: $569 per credit. Part-time mandatory fees: $43 per credit.
Collegiate Environment: Orientation program. Drama-theater group, choral group, student-run newspaper, radio station. Social organizations: 65 open to all. Student services: health clinic, personal-psychological counseling. Campus security: 24-hour emergency response devices and patrols, late night transport-escort service, controlled dormitory access. 872 college housing spaces available; 840 were occupied in 2003-04. On-campus residence required through sophomore year. Options: coed, men-only, women-only housing available. Eugene S. Farley Library with 236,942 books, 39,098 microform titles, 848 serials, 159 audiovisual materials, and an OPAC. 700 computers available on campus for general student use. A

campuswide network can be accessed from student residence rooms and from off campus. Staffed computer lab on campus.

■ THE WILLIAMSON FREE SCHOOL OF MECHANICAL TRADES
N-23

106 South New Middletown Rd.
Media, PA 19063
Tel: (610)566-1776
Fax: (610)566-6502
E-mail: ebailey@williamson.edu
Web Site: http://www.williamson.edu/

Description: Independent, 2-year, men only. Awards diplomas and terminal associate degrees. Founded 1888. Setting: 240-acre small town campus with easy access to Philadelphia. Educational spending for 2005 fiscal year: $2375 per student. Total enrollment: 251. Student-undergrad faculty ratio is 14:1. 349 applied, 26% were admitted. 5% from top 10% of their high school class, 20% from top quarter, 60% from top half. 12 class presidents, 27 student government officers. Full-time: 251 students. Students come from 5 states and territories, 0% Native American, 2% Hispanic, 13% black, 0% Asian American or Pacific Islander, 0% 25 or older, 100% live on campus. Core. Calendar: semesters. Academic remediation for entering students, internships. Off campus study at Delaware County Community College.

Entrance Requirements: Required: essay, high school transcript, minimum 2.0 high school GPA, interview, Armed Services Vocational Aptitude Battery. Required for some: 3 recommendations. Entrance: minimally difficult. Application deadline: 3/15. Preference given to needy students.

Collegiate Environment: Orientation program. Choral group, student-run newspaper. Most popular organizations: Campus Crusade for Christ, Vocational Industrial Clubs of America. Major annual events: Homecoming, Alumni Day, Founder's Day. Student services: health clinic, personal-psychological counseling. Campus security: evening patrols, gate security. 253 college housing spaces available; all were occupied in 2003-04. Shrigley Library plus 3 others with 1,600 books and 70 serials. 20 computers available on campus for general student use. Staffed computer lab on campus.

■ WILSON COLLEGE *N-13*

1015 Philadelphia Ave.
Chambersburg, PA 17201-1285
Tel: (717)264-4141
Free: 800-421-8402
Admissions: (717)262-2025
Fax: (717)264-1578
E-mail: kberard@wilson.edu
Web Site: http://www.wilson.edu/

Description: Independent, 4-year, women only, affiliated with Presbyterian Church (U.S.A.). Awards associate and bachelor's degrees. Founded 1869. Setting: 300-acre small town campus. Endowment: $39 million. Educational spending for 2005 fiscal year: $6155 per student. Total enrollment: 732. Student-undergrad faculty ratio is 10:1. 441 applied, 57% were admitted. 9% from top 10% of their high school class, 39% from top quarter, 84% from top half. 1 valedictorian. Full-time: 348 students. Part-time: 384 students. Students come from 18 states and territories, 10 other countries, 17% from out-of-state, 0.2% Native American, 3% Hispanic, 5% black, 1% Asian American or Pacific Islander, 5% international, 40% 25 or older, 32% live on campus, 3% transferred in. Retention: 63% of full-time freshmen returned the following year. Academic areas with the most degrees conferred: health professions and related sciences; business/marketing; education; social sciences. Core. Calendar: 4-1-4. Academic remediation for entering students, ESL program, services for LD students, advanced placement, self-designed majors, independent study, double major, summer session for credit, part-time degree program, external degree program, adult/continuing education programs, co-op programs and internships. Off campus study at Shippensburg University of Pennsylvania, Gettysburg College. Study abroad program. ROTC: Army (c).

Entrance Requirements: Options: Common Application, electronic application, early admission, deferred admission, international baccalaureate accepted. Required: essay, high school transcript, recommendations, interview, SAT or ACT. Recommended: minimum 2.7 high school GPA. Entrance: moderately difficult. Application deadlines: Rolling, Rolling for nonresidents. Notification: continuous, continuous for nonresidents.

Costs Per Year: Application fee: $35. Comprehensive fee: $27,660 includes full-time tuition ($19,570), mandatory fees ($480), and college room and board ($7610). College room only: $3920. Room and board charges vary according to board plan. Part-time tuition: $1960 per course. Part-time mandatory fees: $30 per course, $35 per term. Part-time tuition and fees vary according to course load.

Collegiate Environment: Orientation program. Drama-theater group, choral group, student-run newspaper, radio station. Social organizations: 23 open to all. Most popular organizations: Muhibbah Club, Orchesis Club, student newspaper, student government, Black Student Union. Major annual events: White Dinner, Mardi Gras, May Weekend/Fair. Student services: health clinic, personal-psychological counseling, women's center. Campus security: 24-hour emergency response devices and patrols, late night transport-escort service, controlled dormitory access. 414 college housing spaces available; 244 were occupied in 2003-04. Freshmen guaranteed college housing. On-campus residence required through junior year. Option: women-only housing available. Stewart Library with 172,205 books, 10,772 microform titles, 312 serials, 1,664 audiovisual materials, an OPAC, and a Web page. Operations spending for 2004 fiscal year: $154,423. 80 computers available on campus for general student use. A campuswide network can be accessed from student residence rooms and from off campus. Staffed computer lab on campus.

Community Environment: Population 20,000, Chambersburg was occupied three times during the Civil War and burned in 1864 when it refused to pay an indemnity of $100,000. Today, this diversified manufacturing community is also considered the state's largest producer of apples and peaches. The city has 2 libraries, a hospital, and many churches and historic sites. Part-time employment is available for students both on and off campus.

■ WINNER INSTITUTE OF ARTS & SCIENCES *F-1*

One Winner Place
Transfer, PA 16154
Tel: (724)646-2433; 888-414-2433
Fax: (724)646-0218
Web Site: http://www.winner-institute.edu/
Description: Independent, 2-year, coed.

■ WYOTECH *K-6*

500 Innovation Dr.
Blairsville, PA 15717
Tel: (724)459-9500
Free: 800-822-8253
Admissions: (724)459-3286
Fax: (724)459-6499
E-mail: whauser@wyotech.edu
Web Site: http://www.wyotech.com/

Description: Proprietary, 2-year, coed. Awards diplomas and terminal associate degrees. Total enrollment: 1,200. Calendar: 9-month program.

Entrance Requirements: Required: high school transcript. Entrance: moderately difficult.

Costs Per Year: Application fee: $100. Tuition: $23,300 full-time.

■ YESHIVA BETH MOSHE *F-22*

930 Hickory St., PO Box 1141
Scranton, PA 18505-2124
Tel: (717)346-1747
Description: Independent Jewish, comprehensive, men only. Awards bachelor's and master's degrees. Founded 1965. Students come from 1 other country. Calendar: semesters.

Entrance Requirements: Required: high school transcript, interview, oral examination.

Collegiate Environment: On-campus residence required through senior year.

■ YORK COLLEGE OF PENNSYLVANIA *M-17*

York, PA 17405-7199
Tel: (717)846-7788
Free: 800-455-8018
Admissions: (717)849-1600
Web Site: http://www.ycp.edu/

Description: Independent, comprehensive, coed. Awards associate, bachelor's, and master's degrees. Founded 1787. Setting: 118-acre suburban campus with easy access to Baltimore. Endowment: $56.1 million. Educational spending for 2005 fiscal year: $4886 per student. Total enrollment: 5,316. Faculty: 429 (134 full-time, 295 part-time). Student-undergrad faculty ratio is 21:1. 4,152 applied, 75% were admitted. 28% from top 10% of their high school class, 65% from top quarter, 93% from top half. 7 valedictorians. Full-time: 4,469 students, 57% women, 43% men. Part-time: 701 students, 70% women, 30% men. Students come from 36 states and territories, 45% from out-of-state, 0.1% Native American, 2% Hispanic, 2% black, 1% Asian American or Pacific Islander, 0.2% international, 6% 25 or older, 45% live on campus, 6% transferred in. Retention: 80% of full-time freshmen returned the following year. Academic areas with the most degrees conferred: business/marketing; education; communications/journalism; health professions and related sciences. Core. Calendar: semesters. Academic remediation for entering students, advanced placement, accelerated degree program, self-designed majors, honors program, independent study, distance learning, double major, summer session for credit, part-time degree program, adult/continuing education programs, co-op programs and internships, graduate courses open to undergrads. Study abroad program. ROTC: Army (c).

Entrance Requirements: Options: Peterson's Universal Application, Common Application, electronic application, early admission, deferred admission. Required: essay, high school transcript, SAT or ACT. Recommended: 1 recommendation. Required for some: interview. Entrance: moderately difficult. Application deadline: 8/1. Notification: continuous.

Costs Per Year: Application fee: $30. Comprehensive fee: $16,550 includes full-time tuition ($9350), mandatory fees ($700), and college room and board ($6500). College room only: $3625. Full-time tuition and fees vary according to course load and program. Room and board charges vary according to housing facility. Part-time tuition: $285 per credit hour. Part-time tuition varies according to course load and program.

Collegiate Environment: Orientation program. Drama-theater group, choral group, student-run newspaper, radio station. Social organizations: 80 open to all; national fraternities, national sororities, local fraternities, local sororities; 10% of eligible men and 10% of eligible women are members. Most popular organizations: Student Senate, Theater Company, Ski and Outdoor Club, Marketing Club, Student Education Association. Major annual events: Spring Weekend Campus Festival, Fall Fest, Family Weekend and Homecoming. Student services: health clinic, personal-psychological counseling. Campus security: 24-hour emergency response devices and patrols, late night transport-escort service. 1,870 college housing spaces available; all were occupied in 2003-04. Freshmen guaranteed college housing. On-campus residence required through junior year. Options: coed, women-only housing available. Schmidt Library plus 1 other with 300,000 books, 500,000 microform titles, 1,400 serials, 11,000 audiovisual materials, an OPAC, and a Web page. Operations spending for 2004 fiscal year: $1.3 million. 400 computers available on campus for general student use. A campuswide network can be accessed from student residence rooms and from off campus. Staffed computer lab on campus.

Community Environment: York College is located in the heart of one of the most naturally beautiful and historically rich sections of Pennsylvania. Traveling by car, York is just four hours from New York and Pittsburgh, less than two hours from Philadelphia and Washington, DC, and an hour from Baltimore. The area has much to offer, including great local food, interesting places to visit and shop, and parks, lakes, and miles of trails that afford opportunities for picnicking, hiking, and skiing. On the practical side, there is a shopping center, a bank, and York Hospital within walking distance of the campus. Culture is an important part of York's heritage as well. The York Symphony Orchestra, the York Little Theater, and the Strand-Capitol Performing Arts Center bring well-known performing artists to the area. Throughout the year, numerous galleries exhibit a wide variety of artwork.

■ **YORK TECHNICAL INSTITUTE** *M-17*
1405 Williams Rd.
York, PA 17402-9017
Tel: (717)757-1100
Free: 800-227-9675
Fax: (717)757-4964
Web Site: http://www.yti.edu/

Description: Private, 2-year, coed. Awards diplomas and terminal associate degrees. Setting: suburban campus. Total enrollment: 1,296. Full-time: 1,296 students, 30% women, 70% men. Students come from 5 states and territories, 10% from out-of-state, 15% 25 or older. Core. Calendar: continuous. Academic remediation for entering students, advanced placement, co-op programs and internships.

Entrance Requirements: Open admission. Required: high school transcript, minimum 2.0 high school GPA, interview. Required for some: essay. Entrance: noncompetitive.

Collegiate Environment: Orientation program. 250 computers available on campus for general student use. A campuswide network can be accessed. Staffed computer lab on campus.

■ **YORKTOWNE BUSINESS INSTITUTE** *M-17*
West Seventh Ave.
York, PA 17404
Tel: (717)846-5000
Free: 800-840-1004
Fax: (717)848-4584
Web Site: http://www.ybi.edu/

Description: Proprietary, 2-year, coed. Awards diplomas, transfer associate, and terminal associate degrees. Founded 1976. Setting: 1-acre small town campus with easy access to Baltimore. Total enrollment: 320. 180 applied, 90% were admitted. Students come from 2 states and territories, 10% from out-of-state, 60% 25 or older. Core. Calendar: semesters. Independent study, double major, part-time degree program, adult/continuing education programs, internships.

Entrance Requirements: Required: high school transcript, interview. Required for some: admissions test. Entrance: minimally difficult. Application deadline: Rolling.

Collegiate Environment: Orientation program. Major annual events: Student Appreciation Day, Graduation. College housing not available. 100 computers available on campus for general student use. Staffed computer lab on campus.

■ AMERICAN UNIVERSITY OF PUERTO RICO

PO Box 2037
Bayamon, PR 00960-2037
Tel: (787)620-2040
Admissions: (787)740-6410
Fax: (787)785-7377
Web Site: http://www.aupr.edu/

Description: Independent, 4-year, coed. Awards associate and bachelor's degrees. Founded 1963. Setting: 21-acre urban campus with easy access to San Juan. Research spending for 2004 fiscal year: $30,000. Total enrollment: 3,691. 568 applied, 100% were admitted. 3% from top 10% of their high school class, 15% from top quarter, 25% from top half. 0% Native American, 100% Hispanic, 0% black, 0% Asian American or Pacific Islander, 0% international, 20% 25 or older. Core. Calendar: semesters. Services for LD students, advanced placement, freshman honors college, honors program, summer session for credit, part-time degree program, adult/continuing education programs, co-op programs and internships. ROTC: Army (c).

Entrance Requirements: Option: deferred admission. Required: high school transcript. Placement: SAT, CEEB required. Entrance: noncompetitive. Application deadline: 8/1. Notification: continuous.

Collegiate Environment: Drama-theater group. Student services: health clinic. Campus security: 24-hour patrols. College housing not available. Loida Figueroa Meacado with 100,000 books, 231 serials, and 2,091 audiovisual materials. 150 computers available on campus for general student use. Staffed computer lab on campus.

■ ATLANTIC COLLEGE

PO Box 3918
Guaynabo, PR 00970
Tel: (787)720-1022
Fax: (787)720-1092
Web Site: http://www.atlanticcollege-pr.com/

Description: Independent, comprehensive. Awards associate and bachelor's degrees. Total enrollment: 656. 0% from out-of-commonwealth, 100% Hispanic, 29% 25 or older. Calendar: semesters. Part-time degree program, internships.

Entrance Requirements: Open admission. Option: Common Application. Required: high school transcript. Required for some: interview. Application deadline: 8/27. Notification: continuous.

Collegiate Environment: Orientation program. Resources Center with 8,663 books, 85 serials, and 412 audiovisual materials. 70 computers available on campus for general student use. Staffed computer lab on campus.

■ BAYAMON CENTRAL UNIVERSITY

PO Box 1725
Bayamon, PR 00960-1725
Tel: (787)786-3030
Web Site: http://www.ucb.edu.pr/

Description: Independent Roman Catholic, comprehensive, coed. Awards associate, bachelor's, and master's degrees. Founded 1970. Setting: 55-acre suburban campus with easy access to San Juan. Endowment: $7.3 million. Educational spending for 2005 fiscal year: $1950 per student. Total enrollment: 3,311. 551 applied, 57% were admitted. Full-time: 2,205 students, 71% women, 29% men. Part-time: 569 students, 71% women, 29% men. 0% from out-of-commonwealth, 100% Hispanic, 41% 25 or older, 6% transferred in. Retention: 70% of full-time freshmen returned the following year. Core. Calendar: semesters for undergraduate programs, trimesters for graduate programs. Academic remediation for entering students, ESL program, services for LD students, advanced placement, accelerated degree program, self-designed majors, honors program, independent study, summer session for credit, part-time degree program, adult/continuing education programs, internships. ROTC: Army (c), Air Force (c).

Entrance Requirements: Options: Common Application, international baccalaureate accepted. Required: high school transcript, medical history, College Examination Entrance Board Test. Recommended: minimum 2.0 high school GPA. Required for some: recommendations, interview. Entrance: moderately difficult. Application deadline: 8/15.

Costs Per Year: Application fee: $15. Tuition: $4080 full-time, $130 per credit part-time. Mandatory fees: $360 full-time, $180. Full-time tuition and fees vary according to course load, degree level, and program. Part-time tuition and fees vary according to course load, degree level, and program.

Collegiate Environment: Orientation program. Choral group, student-run newspaper. Social organizations: 21 open to all. Most popular organizations: Business Students' Association, Nursing Students' Association, Journalism Students' Association, Psychology Students' Association, Biology Students' Association. Major annual events: intercollegiate sports competitions, Commencement. Student services: legal services, health clinic, personal-psychological counseling. Campus security: 24-hour patrols. 10 college housing spaces available; all were occupied in 2003-04. No special consideration for freshman housing applicants. BCU Library plus 1 other with 51,011 books, 336 microform titles, 3,027 serials, 900 audiovisual materials, and an OPAC. Operations spending for 2004 fiscal year: $45,681. 130 computers available on campus for general student use. A campuswide network can be accessed. Staffed computer lab on campus.

■ CARIBBEAN UNIVERSITY

Box 493
Bayamon, PR 00960-0493
Tel: (787)780-0070
Fax: (787)785-0101
Web Site: http://www.caribbean.edu/

Description: Independent, comprehensive, coed. Awards associate, bachelor's, and master's degrees. Founded 1969. Setting: 16-acre campus with easy access to San Juan. Total enrollment: 1,786. 1,932 applied, 82% were admitted. 25% from top half of their high school class. 33% 25 or older. Core. Calendar: trimesters. Academic remediation for entering students, ESL program, services for LD students, accelerated degree program, summer session for credit, part-time degree program, adult/continuing education programs. ROTC: Army (c).

Entrance Requirements: Option: deferred admission. Required: high school transcript. Placement: SAT, SAT Subject Tests required. Entrance: minimally difficult. Application deadline: Rolling.

Collegiate Environment: Student services: health clinic, personal-psychological counseling. College housing not available. 17,632 books and 153 serials. 90 computers available on campus for general student use.

■ CARLOS ALBIZU UNIVERSITY

151 Tanca St.
San Juan, PR 00901

Tel: (787)725-6500
Fax: (787)721-7187
Web Site: http://www.albizu.edu/
Description: Independent, upper-level, coed. Awards bachelor's, master's, and doctoral degrees. Founded 1966. Total enrollment: 843. Calendar: semesters.

■ CENTRO DE ESTUDIOS MULTIDISCIPLINARIOS
Calle 13 No. 1206
Ext. San Agustin
San Juan, PR 00926
Tel: (787)765-4210
Web Site: http://www.cempr.edu/
Description: Independent, 2-year, coed. Awards certificates and terminal associate degrees. Founded 1980. Total enrollment: 1,290. 771 applied, 96% were admitted.

■ COLEGIO BIBLICO PENTECOSTAL
PO Box 901
St. Just, PR 00978-0901
Tel: (787)761-0640
Web Site: http://www.cbp.edu/
Description: Independent Pentecostal, 4-year, coed. Awards bachelor's degrees. Founded 1956. Setting: 4-acre suburban campus with easy access to San Juan. Total enrollment: 231. 65 applied, 86% were admitted. Calendar: semesters.

■ COLEGIO PENTECOSTAL MIZPA
Bo Caimito Rd. 199
Apartado 20966
Rio Piedras, PR 00928-0966
Tel: (787)720-4476
Fax: (787)720-2012
Description: Independent, 4-year, affiliated with Pentecostal Church. Awards associate and bachelor's degrees. Founded 1937. Total enrollment: 169. Calendar: semesters.
Entrance Requirements: Open admission.
Costs Per Year: Application fee: $35. Comprehensive fee: $5020 includes full-time tuition ($1200), mandatory fees ($220), and college room and board ($3600). College room only: $2000. Full-time tuition and fees vary according to course level. Room and board charges vary according to board plan and housing facility.

■ COLEGIO UNIVERSITARIO DE SAN JUAN
180 Jose Oliver Ave.,
Tres Monjitas Industrial Park
San Juan, PR 00918
Tel: (787)250-7111
Fax: (787)250-7395
Web Site: http://www.cunisanjuan.edu/
Description: City-supported, 2-year, coed.

■ COLUMBIA COLLEGE (CAGUAS)
PO Box 8517
Caguas, PR 00726
Tel: (787)743-4041
Fax: (787)744-7931
Web Site: http://www.columbiaco.edu/
Description: Proprietary, comprehensive, coed. Awards associate, bachelor's, and master's degrees. Founded 1966. Setting: 6-acre rural campus with easy access to San Juan. Total enrollment: 859. Faculty: 65 (15 full-time, 50 part-time). Student-undergrad faculty ratio is 17:1. 509 applied, 56% were admitted. Full-time: 506 students, 73% women, 27% men. Part-time: 304 students, 61% women, 39% men. 0% from out-of-commonwealth, 0% Native American, 100% Hispanic, 0% black, 0% Asian American or Pacific Islander, 0% international, 68% 25 or older. Academic areas with the most degrees conferred: business/marketing; health professions and related sciences. Core. Calendar: semesters. Accelerated degree program, independent study, part-time degree program, external degree program, adult/continuing education programs.
Entrance Requirements: Option: Common Application. Required: high school transcript. Required for some: essay, minimum 2.0 high school GPA, 3 recommendations, interview. Entrance: noncompetitive. Application deadline: Rolling. Notification: continuous.

Costs Per Year: Application fee: $50. Tuition: $4140 full-time, $140 per unit part-time. Mandatory fees: $300 full-time, $200 per term part-time.
Collegiate Environment: Student services: personal-psychological counseling. Campus security: 24-hour patrols. College housing not available. Efrain Sola Bezares Library with 10,200 books, 164 serials, and an OPAC. 55 computers available on campus for general student use. Staffed computer lab on campus.

■ COLUMBIA COLLEGE (YAUCO)
Box 3062
Yauco, PR 00698
Tel: (787)856-0945
Fax: (787)267-2335
Web Site: http://www.columbiaco.edu/
Description: Proprietary, primarily 2-year, coed. Awards terminal associate and bachelor's degrees. Founded 1976. Total enrollment: 330. Calendar: semesters.
Entrance Requirements: Open admission.

■ CONSERVATORY OF MUSIC OF PUERTO RICO
350 Rafael Lamar St at FDR Ave
San Juan, PR 00918
Tel: (787)751-0160
Web Site: http://www.cmpr.edu/
Description: Commonwealth-supported, 4-year, coed. Awards bachelor's degrees. Founded 1959. Setting: 6-acre urban campus. Endowment: $465,949. Total enrollment: 266. Full-time: 203 students, 33% women, 67% men. Part-time: 63 students, 25% women, 75% men. 98% from out-of-commonwealth, 100% Hispanic, 42% 25 or older, 8% transferred in. Core. Calendar: semesters. Academic remediation for entering students, advanced placement, summer session for credit, part-time degree program, co-op programs. Off campus study at Sacred Heart University. ROTC: Army (c).
Entrance Requirements: Options: Common Application, early admission. Required: high school transcript, minimum 2.0 high school GPA, interview, audition, music and theory examinations, SAT, SAT Subject Tests. Required for some: essay, minimum 2.50 high school GPA. Entrance: moderately difficult. Application deadline: 3/6.
Collegiate Environment: Student services: health clinic, personal-psychological counseling. Campus security: 24-hour patrols. College housing not available. Anaurg Veray Music Library plus 1 other with 24,865 books, 19 microform titles, 75 serials, 4,910 audiovisual materials, and an OPAC. Operations spending for 2004 fiscal year: $405,233. 12 computers available on campus for general student use. A campuswide network can be accessed.

■ ELECTRONIC DATA PROCESSING COLLEGE OF PUERTO RICO
560 Ave. Ponce de Leon
Hato Rey, PR 00919-2303
Tel: (787)765-3560
Web Site: http://www.edpcollege.edu/
Description: Proprietary, comprehensive, coed. Awards associate, bachelor's, and master's degrees. Founded 1968. Setting: 1-acre campus. Total enrollment: 929. 154 applied, 94% were admitted. Core. Calendar: semesters. Academic remediation for entering students, ESL program, part-time degree program. ROTC: Army (c), Air Force (c).
Entrance Requirements: Option: deferred admission. Required: high school transcript, interview. Placement: SAT, SAT Subject Tests recommended. Entrance: minimally difficult. Application deadline: Rolling.
Collegiate Environment: Student services: personal-psychological counseling. College housing not available. 10,005 books and 123 serials. 17 computers available on campus for general student use.

■ ELECTRONIC DATA PROCESSING COLLEGE OF PUERTO RICO-SAN SEBASTIAN
Ave. Betances No. 49
San Sebastian, PR 00685
Tel: (787)896-2137
Fax: (787)896-0066
Web Site: http://www.edpcollege.edu/
Description: Proprietary, 4-year, coed. Awards associate and bachelor's degrees. Founded 1976. Total enrollment: 730. 283 applied, 96% were admitted. Calendar: semesters.

■ ESCUELA DE ARTES PLASTICAS DE PUERTO RICO
PO Box 9021112
San Juan, PR 00902-1112

Tel: (787)725-8120

E-mail: marineslopez1974@aol.com

Web Site: http://www.eap.edu/

Description: Commonwealth-supported, 4-year, coed. Awards bachelor's degrees. Founded 1966. Setting: urban campus. Endowment: $323,000. Educational spending for 2005 fiscal year: $1996 per student. Total enrollment: 459. Student-undergrad faculty ratio is 11:1. 120 applied, 78% were admitted. Full-time: 368 students, 50% women, 50% men. Part-time: 91 students, 46% women, 54% men. 0% from out-of-commonwealth, 100% Hispanic, 29% 25 or older, 20% transferred in. Retention: 81% of full-time freshmen returned the following year. Core. Calendar: semesters. Services for LD students, summer session for credit, co-op programs. Off campus study at Sacred Heart University.

Entrance Requirements: Option: Common Application. Required: essay, high school transcript, minimum 2.0 high school GPA, interview, portfolio. Recommended: recommendations. Entrance: moderately difficult. Application deadline: 4/1. Notification: 5/1.

Costs Per Year: Application fee: $20. Area resident tuition: $75 per credit part-time. Mandatory fees: $70 per credit part-time, $212 per year part-time.

Collegiate Environment: Most popular organization: student government. Major annual events: Student Day, Health Fair, Halloween Costume Party. Campus security: 24-hour patrols, security cameras. College housing not available. Francisco Oller Library with 24,582 books, 111 serials, 34,082 audiovisual materials, and an OPAC. Operations spending for 2004 fiscal year: $157,776. 36 computers available on campus for general student use. Staffed computer lab on campus.

■ **HUERTAS JUNIOR COLLEGE**

PO Box 8429

Caguas, PR 00726

Tel: (787)743-2156

Admissions: (787)743-1242

E-mail: huertas@huertas.org

Web Site: http://www.huertasjrcollege.org/

Description: Proprietary, 2-year, coed. Awards terminal associate degrees. Founded 1945. Setting: 4-acre urban campus with easy access to San Juan. Educational spending for 2005 fiscal year: $570 per student. Total enrollment: 1,459. 100% Hispanic. Core. Calendar: trimesters. Academic remediation for entering students, ESL program, part-time degree program, internships.

Entrance Requirements: Open admission. Options: Common Application, deferred admission. Required for some: minimum 2.0 high school GPA. Application deadline: Rolling. Notification: continuous.

Collegiate Environment: Choral group. Social organizations: 1 open to all. Student services: health clinic. Campus security: 24-hour patrols. College housing not available. Learning Resources Center with 5,524 books and 1,144 serials. 100 computers available on campus for general student use. Staffed computer lab on campus.

■ **HUMACAO COMMUNITY COLLEGE**

PO Box 9139

Humacao, PR 00792

Tel: (787)852-1430

Admissions: (787)852-2525

Fax: (787)850-1760

Description: Independent, 2-year. Awards certificates, diplomas, and terminal associate degrees. Total enrollment: 387. 0% Native American, 100% Hispanic, 0% black, 0% Asian American or Pacific Islander, 0% international. Calendar: trimesters.

Entrance Requirements: Open admission. Option: early admission. Required: high school transcript. Entrance: noncompetitive.

■ **ICPR JUNIOR COLLEGE-HATO REY CAMPUS**

San Juan, PR

Web Site: http://www.icprjc.edu/

Description: Proprietary, 2-year, coed. Founded 1946.

■ **INSTITUTO COMERCIAL DE PUERTO RICO JUNIOR COLLEGE**

558 Munoz Rivera Ave., PO Box 190304

San Juan, PR 00919-0304

Tel: (787)753-6000

Fax: (787)763-7249

Web Site: http://www.icprjc.edu/

Description: Proprietary, 2-year, coed. Awards certificates, diplomas, and terminal associate degrees. Founded 1946. Setting: 1-acre urban campus. Total enrollment: 1,270. 1,429 applied, 49% were admitted. Full-time: 1,086 students, 63% women, 37% men. Part-time: 184 students, 64% women, 36% men. 1% from out-of-commonwealth, 100% Hispanic. Core. Calendar: trimesters. ESL program, independent study, double major, part-time degree program, adult/continuing education programs. ROTC: Army (c).

Entrance Requirements: Options: Common Application, early admission. Required: high school transcript, interview, proficiency in Spanish. Recommended: recommendations. Entrance: minimally difficult. Application deadline: 8/15. Notification: continuous.

Costs Per Year: Application fee: $25. Comprehensive fee: $7716 includes full-time tuition ($4680), mandatory fees ($180), and college room and board ($2856). College room only: $1142. Part-time tuition: $130 per credit.

Collegiate Environment: Student services: personal-psychological counseling. Campus security: 24-hour emergency response devices. Pedro Negron Library plus 1 other with 40,858 books, 173 serials, and 320 audiovisual materials. Operations spending for 2004 fiscal year: $176,910. 76 computers available on campus for general student use. Staffed computer lab on campus.

■ **INTER AMERICAN UNIVERSITY OF PUERTO RICO, AGUADILLA CAMPUS**

Call Box 20000

Aguadilla, PR 00605

Tel: (787)891-0925

Web Site: http://www.aguadilla.inter.edu/

Description: Independent, comprehensive, coed. Part of Inter American University of Puerto Rico. Awards associate, bachelor's, and master's degrees. Founded 1957. Setting: 50-acre small town campus. Endowment: $1.1 million. Educational spending for 2005 fiscal year: $1563 per student. Total enrollment: 4,129. Faculty: 254 (75 full-time, 179 part-time). Student-undergrad faculty ratio is 26:1. Full-time: 3,465 students, 58% women, 42% men. Part-time: 594 students, 60% women, 40% men. 0% from out-of-commonwealth, 100% Hispanic, 2% transferred in. Academic areas with the most degrees conferred: business/marketing; education; security and protective services. Core. Calendar: semesters. Academic remediation for entering students, services for LD students, advanced placement, honors program, independent study, distance learning, double major, summer session for credit, part-time degree program, external degree program, adult/continuing education programs, co-op programs and internships. ROTC: Army.

Entrance Requirements: Options: Common Application, electronic application, early admission, international baccalaureate accepted. Required: high school transcript, minimum 2.00 high school GPA, PAA. Required for some: SAT. Entrance: moderately difficult. Application deadline: Rolling.

Costs Per Year: Application fee: $0. Tuition: $3360 full-time, $140 per credit hour part-time. Mandatory fees: $364 full-time, $144 per term part-time.

Collegiate Environment: Orientation program. Drama-theater group, choral group, student-run radio station. Social organizations: 24 open to all. Most popular organizations: Criminal Justice Association, Secretarial Sciences Association, Future Teachers Association, Psychosocial Human Services Association, IPDAS (Drugs, Alcohol and Aids Prevention Institute). Major annual events: Justas Universitarias, Festival de Flora y Fauna, Noche de Logros. Student services: health clinic, personal-psychological counseling. Campus security: 24-hour emergency response devices and patrols. College housing not available. Manuel Mendez Ballester Information Access Center with 56,037 books, 2,628 microform titles, 437 serials, 24,918 audiovisual materials, an OPAC, and a Web page. Operations spending for 2004 fiscal year: $588,493. 485 computers available on campus for general student use. A campuswide network can be accessed from off-campus. Staffed computer lab on campus.

■ **INTER AMERICAN UNIVERSITY OF PUERTO RICO, ARECIBO CAMPUS**

PO Box 4050

Arecibo, PR 00614-4050

Tel: (787)878-5475

Fax: (787)880-1624

Web Site: http://www.arecibo.inter.edu/

Description: Independent, comprehensive, coed. Part of Inter American University of Puerto Rico. Awards associate, bachelor's, and master's degrees. Founded 1957. Setting: 20-acre urban campus with easy access to San Juan. Endowment: $40.5 million. Educational spending for 2005 fiscal year: $1460 per student. Total enrollment: 4,589. 1,641 applied, 61% were admitted. 0% from out-of-commonwealth, 100% Hispanic, 29% 25 or older. Retention: 80% of full-time freshmen returned the following year. Core. Calendar: semesters. Academic remediation for entering students, services for LD students, advanced placement, honors program, independent study, summer session for credit, part-time degree program, adult/continuing education programs, internships, graduate courses open to undergrads. ROTC: Army (c).

Entrance Requirements: Options: electronic application, early admission, deferred admission. Required: high school transcript, minimum 2.0 high school GPA, PAA, CEEB. Recommended: minimum 3.0 high school GPA. Required for some: interview. Entrance: moderately difficult. Application deadline: Rolling.

Collegiate Environment: Orientation program. Drama-theater group. Social organizations: 20 open to all; local fraternities, local sororities; 5% of eligible men and 5% of eligible women are members. Most popular organizations: theatrical group 'Ciclorama', Association of Student Advisers Youth Against Drugs, literary circle 'Rene Marques', Future Social Workers Association, Student Counseling Association. Major annual events: Congress of Scientific Research, Mycology Symposium. Student services: health clinic, personal-psychological counseling. Campus security: 24-hour emergency response devices and patrols. College housing not available. Rene Marques Library with 68,893 books, 81 microform titles, 315 serials, 29,146 audiovisual materials, an OPAC, and a Web page. Operations spending for 2004 fiscal year: $38,297. 295 computers available on campus for general student use. A campuswide network can be accessed from off-campus. Staffed computer lab on campus.

■ INTER AMERICAN UNIVERSITY OF PUERTO RICO, BARRANQUITAS CAMPUS

PO Box 517
Barranquitas, PR 00794
Tel: (787)857-3600
Fax: (787)857-2284
E-mail: mdiaz@br.inter.edu
Web Site: http://www.br.inter.edu/

Description: Independent, comprehensive, coed. Part of Inter American University of Puerto Rico. Awards associate and bachelor's degrees. Founded 1957. Setting: small town campus with easy access to San Juan. Endowment: $3 million. Educational spending for 2005 fiscal year: $3500 per student. Total enrollment: 2,324. 1,160 applied, 41% were admitted. 100% Hispanic, 17% 25 or older. Retention: 77% of full-time freshmen returned the following year. Academic areas with the most degrees conferred: education; business/marketing; health professions and related sciences. Core. Calendar: semesters. Academic remediation for entering students, ESL program, advanced placement, summer session for credit, part-time degree program, adult/continuing education programs. Study abroad program. ROTC: Army (c).

Entrance Requirements: Options: Common Application, deferred admission. Required: high school transcript, interview, CEEB. Required for some: SAT or ACT. Entrance: moderately difficult. Application deadline: 5/15.

Costs Per Year: Application fee: $0. Comprehensive fee: $12,071 includes full-time tuition ($3920), mandatory fees ($850), and college room and board ($7301). College room only: $4978. Part-time tuition: $140 per credit.

Collegiate Environment: Orientation program. Campus security: 24-hour patrols. Luis Munoz Marin with 32,863 books, 224 serials, an OPAC, and a Web page. Operations spending for 2004 fiscal year: $347,886. 365 computers available on campus for general student use. A campuswide network can be accessed from student residence rooms. Staffed computer lab on campus.

■ INTER AMERICAN UNIVERSITY OF PUERTO RICO, BAYAMÓN CAMPUS

500 Rd. 830
Bayamon, PR 00957
Tel: (787)279-1912
Fax: (787)279-2205
E-mail: calicea@bc.inter.edu
Web Site: http://bc.inter.edu/

Description: Independent, comprehensive, coed. Part of Inter American University of Puerto Rico. Awards associate, bachelor's, and master's degrees. Founded 1912. Setting: 51-acre urban campus with easy access to San Juan. Endowment: $2 million. Educational spending for 2005 fiscal year: $1759 per student. Total enrollment: 5,255. Faculty: 315 (99 full-time, 216

part-time). Student-undergrad faculty ratio is 24:1. 4,108 applied, 44% were admitted. Full-time: 4,301 students, 44% women, 56% men. Part-time: 901 students, 41% women, 59% men. Students come from 4 other countries, 0% from out-of-commonwealth, 100% Hispanic, 17% 25 or older, 2% transferred in. Retention: 64% of full-time freshmen returned the following year. Academic areas with the most degrees conferred: business/marketing; communication technologies; engineering. Core. Calendar: semesters. Academic remediation for entering students, ESL program, services for LD students, advanced placement, accelerated degree program, honors program, independent study, distance learning, double major, summer session for credit, part-time degree program, external degree program, adult/continuing education programs, co-op programs and internships. ROTC: Army (c).

Entrance Requirements: Options: Common Application, electronic application. Required: high school transcript, minimum 2.0 high school GPA, 2.50 GPA for engineering programs, CEEB. Required for some: SAT. Application deadline: 7/30. Notification: continuous.

Costs Per Year: Application fee: $0. Tuition: $3764 full-time, $140 per credit part-time.

Collegiate Environment: Orientation program. Choral group, student-run newspaper. Social organizations: 18 open to all. Most popular organizations: Associacion de Estudiantes de Administracion de Empresas, Estudiantes Unidos por la Ciencia, Associacion Estudiantes de Aviacion, Consejo de Estudiante, Asociacion Estudiantes de Ingenieria. Student services: health clinic, personal-psychological counseling. Campus security: 24-hour patrols. College housing not available. Centro de Acceso a la Informacion plus 1 other with 55,695 books, 1,848 microform titles, 196 serials, 2,231 audiovisual materials, an OPAC, and a Web page. Operations spending for 2004 fiscal year: $664,106. 700 computers available on campus for general student use. Computer purchase/lease plans available. A campuswide network can be accessed from student residence rooms and from off campus. Staffed computer lab on campus.

■ INTER AMERICAN UNIVERSITY OF PUERTO RICO, FAJARDO CAMPUS

Call Box 70003
Fajardo, PR 00738-7003
Tel: (787)863-2390
Admissions: (787)860-2390
E-mail: evrivera@ns.inter.edu
Web Site: http://fajardo.inter.edu/

Description: Independent, comprehensive, coed. Part of Inter American University of Puerto Rico. Awards associate, bachelor's, and master's degrees. Founded 1965. Setting: 11-acre small town campus with easy access to San Juan. Total enrollment: 2,245. 1,196 applied, 36% were admitted. Retention: 65% of full-time freshmen returned the following year. Core. Calendar: semesters. Academic remediation for entering students, ESL program, advanced placement, freshman honors college, honors program, summer session for credit, part-time degree program, adult/continuing education programs. Off campus study at other units of the Inter American University of Puerto Rico.

Entrance Requirements: Options: early admission, deferred admission. Required: high school transcript, minimum 2.0 high school GPA, SAT, PAA. Required for some: recommendations. Entrance: moderately difficult. Application deadline: Rolling. Notification: 5/1.

Collegiate Environment: Orientation program. Social organizations: 12 open to all. Most popular organizations: Future Teachers Association, Criminal Justice Student Association, Student Counseling Association, Practical Teaching Association. Major annual events: Graduation Services, Student Welcome Back, Achievement Night. Student services: personal-psychological counseling. Campus security: 24-hour patrols. College housing not available. Antonio S. Belaval Library with 39,951 books, 686 serials, and a Web page. 90 computers available on campus for general student use. Staffed computer lab on campus.

■ INTER AMERICAN UNIVERSITY OF PUERTO RICO, GUAYAMA CAMPUS

Call Box 10004
Guayama, PR 00785
Tel: (787)864-2222
Web Site: http://www.guayama.inter.edu/

Description: Independent, comprehensive, coed. Part of Inter American University of Puerto Rico. Awards associate, bachelor's, and master's degrees. Founded 1958. Setting: 50-acre small town campus. Research spending for 2004 fiscal year: $85 million. Total enrollment: 2,273. 849 applied, 71% were admitted. 5% from top 10% of their high school class, 15% from top quarter, 80% from top half. Students come from 6 other countries, 37% 25 or older. Core. Calendar: semesters. Academic remediation for entering students, ESL program, honors program, independent study, summer session for credit, part-time degree program, adult/continuing education programs. Off campus study at other units of the Inter American University of Puerto Rico. ROTC: Army (c).

Entrance Requirements: Options: Common Application, international baccalaureate accepted. Required: high school transcript, minimum 2.00 high school GPA, SAT, PAA. Required for some: essay, interview. Entrance: moderately difficult. Application deadline: 8/1.

Collegiate Environment: Orientation program. Drama-theater group, student-run newspaper. Most popular organizations: Nursing Club, CONFRA Inter, Sciences Club, AFPO Association. Student services: health clinic. College housing not available. Luis Pales Matos Center for Access to Information plus 1 other with 21,000 books, 212 serials, 2,100 audiovisual materials, an OPAC, and a Web page. Operations spending for 2004 fiscal year: $210,129. 120 computers available on campus for general student use. Staffed computer lab on campus.

■ INTER AMERICAN UNIVERSITY OF PUERTO RICO, METROPOLITAN CAMPUS

PO Box 191293
San Juan, PR 00919-1293
Tel: (787)250-1912
Web Site: http://metro.inter.edu/

Description: Independent, comprehensive, coed. Part of Inter American University of Puerto Rico. Awards associate, bachelor's, master's, and doctoral degrees and first professional certificates. Founded 1960. Total enrollment: 10,451. 2,691 applied, 49% were admitted. Students come from 2 other countries, 0.4% from out-of-commonwealth, 0% Native American, 99% Hispanic, 0% black, 0% Asian American or Pacific Islander, 0.3% international, 41% 25 or older. Core. Calendar: semesters. ESL program, services for LD students, accelerated degree program, honors program, independent study, distance learning, summer session for credit, part-time degree program, external degree program, adult/continuing education programs, co-op programs and internships, graduate courses open to undergrads. Study abroad program. ROTC: Army (c), Naval (c), Air Force (c).

Entrance Requirements: Option: international baccalaureate accepted. Required: high school transcript, minimum 2.0 high school GPA. Required for some: SAT. Placement: SAT required for some. Entrance: moderately difficult. Application deadline: 5/15.

Collegiate Environment: Orientation program. Drama-theater group, choral group, student-run newspaper. Social organizations: 23 open to all. Most popular organizations: The House of Commerce, American Marketing Association, Chemical Students Association, Association of Biology Students, Human Resources Management Association. Major annual events: Students Leadership Week, Open House, Initiation Ceremony. Student services: health clinic, personal-psychological counseling. Campus security: 24-hour emergency response devices and patrols, video security system. College housing not available. Centro de Acceso a la Informacion plus 1 other with 113,200 books, 638,275 microform titles, 2,771 serials, 5,078 audiovisual materials, an OPAC, and a Web page. 400 computers available on campus for general student use. A campuswide network can be accessed from student residence rooms and from off campus. Staffed computer lab on campus.

■ INTER AMERICAN UNIVERSITY OF PUERTO RICO, PONCE CAMPUS

104 Industrial Park Turpo RD 1
Mercedita, PR 00715-1602
Tel: (787)284-1912
E-mail: fldiaz@acpon1.ponce.inter.edu
Web Site: http://www.ponce.inter.edu/

Description: Independent, comprehensive, coed. Part of Inter American University of Puerto Rico. Awards associate, bachelor's, and master's degrees. Founded 1962. Setting: 50-acre urban campus with easy access to San Juan. Total enrollment: 5,327. Faculty: 257 (81 full-time, 176 part-time). 2,123 applied, 63% were admitted. Full-time: 4,269 students, 62% women, 38% men. Part-time: 877 students, 64% women, 36% men. 0% from out-of-commonwealth, 100% Hispanic, 31% 25 or older, 1% transferred in. Academic areas with the most degrees conferred: business/marketing; education; law/legal studies. Core. Calendar: semesters. Academic

remediation for entering students, ESL program, services for LD students, honors program, independent study, distance learning, summer session for credit, part-time degree program, adult/continuing education programs, co-op programs and internships. Off campus study at other units of the Inter American University of Puerto Rico. Study abroad program.

Entrance Requirements: Options: Common Application, deferred admission. Required: high school transcript, minimum 2.00 high school GPA, CEEB. Required for some: SAT. Entrance: moderately difficult. Application deadline: 8/1.

Costs Per Year: Application fee: $0. Tuition: $4350 full-time, $145 per credit part-time. Mandatory fees: $406 full-time, $177 per term part-time.

Collegiate Environment: Orientation program. Drama-theater group, choral group, marching band. Social organizations: 18 open to all. Most popular organizations: IKARUS 'Drama Association', American Marketing Associations, ABACUS, ECOS, Cheer-Leaders. Major annual events: Welcoming of New Students, Students Athletes, Techno Nights. Student services: health clinic, personal-psychological counseling. Campus security: 24-hour patrols. College housing not available. Centro de Acceso a la Informacion plus 1 other with 49,531 books, 211 serials, 3,496 audiovisual materials, an OPAC, and a Web page. Operations spending for 2004 fiscal year: $835,059. 700 computers available on campus for general student use. A campuswide network can be accessed from off-campus. Staffed computer lab on campus.

■ INTER AMERICAN UNIVERSITY OF PUERTO RICO, SAN GERMÁN CAMPUS

PO Box 5100
San German, PR 00683-5008
Tel: (787)264-1912
Fax: (787)892-6350
Web Site: http://www.sg.inter.edu/

Description: Independent, university, coed. Part of Inter American University of Puerto Rico. Awards associate, bachelor's, master's, and doctoral degrees. Founded 1912. Setting: 260-acre small town campus. Total enrollment: 5,764. Faculty: 337 (137 full-time, 200 part-time). Student-undergrad faculty ratio is 26:1. 2,721 applied, 61% were admitted. Full-time: 4,252 students, 53% women, 47% men. Part-time: 620 students, 54% women, 46% men. Students come from 15 states and territories, 1% from out-of-commonwealth, 100% Hispanic, 23% 25 or older, 10% live on campus, 2% transferred in. Academic areas with the most degrees conferred: business/marketing; education; biological/life sciences. Core. Calendar: semesters. Academic remediation for entering students, ESL program, services for LD students, advanced placement, accelerated degree program, honors program, independent study, distance learning, double major, summer session for credit, part-time degree program, external degree program, adult/continuing education programs, co-op programs and internships, graduate courses open to undergrads. Off campus study at other units of the Inter American University of Puerto Rico. ROTC: Army (c), Naval (c), Air Force (c).

Entrance Requirements: Options: early admission, international baccalaureate accepted. Required: high school transcript, medical history, CEEB. Recommended: essay, minimum 2.50 high school GPA. Required for some: 1 recommendation, interview. Entrance: moderately difficult. Application deadline: 5/13. Notification: continuous.

Costs Per Year: Application fee: $0. Comprehensive fee: $7016 includes full-time tuition ($4200), mandatory fees ($416), and college room and board ($2400). College room only: $922. Part-time tuition: $140 per credit. Part-time mandatory fees: $208 per term.

Collegiate Environment: Drama-theater group, choral group, student-run newspaper. Social organizations: 50 open to all; national fraternities, national sororities; 10% of eligible men and 9% of eligible women are members. Most popular organizations: Future Teachers Association, PolyNature, Association for Computer Machinery, International Association of Administrative Professionals, Biology Honor Society. Major annual events: End of Semester Dance, Freshmen Dance, Athletic Inter-University Match. Student services: personal-psychological counseling. Campus security: 24-hour emergency response devices and patrols. 600 college housing spaces available. No special consideration for freshman housing applicants. Options: men-only, women-only housing available. Juan Cancio Ortiz Library with 154,828 books, 561,790 microform titles, 5,034 serials, 30,831 audiovisual materials, an OPAC, and a Web page. 1,400 computers available on campus for general student use. A campuswide network can be accessed. Staffed computer lab on campus.

■ INTERNATIONAL JUNIOR COLLEGE

1254 Ave. Ponce de Leon
pda. 18 1/2
Santurce, PR 00908
Tel: (787)723-3333
Fax: (787)724-0281
Web Site: http://www.internationaljuniorcollege.com/
Description: Proprietary, 2-year. Awards terminal associate degrees. Total enrollment: 287.
Entrance Requirements: Open admission.

■ NATIONAL COLLEGE

PO Box 2036
Bayamon, PR 00960
Tel: (787)780-5134
Free: 800-780-5188
Fax: (787)740-7360
E-mail: desil@nationalcollegepr.edu
Web Site: http://www.nationalcollegepr.edu/
Description: Private, 2-year. Total enrollment: 2,289. 895 applied, 88% were admitted.

■ POLYTECHNIC UNIVERSITY OF PUERTO RICO

377 Ponce de Leon Ave.
Hato Rey, PR 00919
Tel: (787)754-8000
E-mail: tcardona@pupr.edu
Web Site: http://www.pupr.edu/
Description: Independent, comprehensive, coed. Awards bachelor's and master's degrees. Founded 1966. Setting: 10-acre urban campus with easy access to San Juan. Endowment: $2 million. Research spending for 2004 fiscal year: $116,832. Educational spending for 2005 fiscal year: $1804 per student. Total enrollment: 5,771. Faculty: 300 (169 full-time, 131 part-time). Student-undergrad faculty ratio is 19:1. 36 valedictorians. Full-time: 2,558 students, 24% women, 76% men. Part-time: 2,512 students, 22% women, 78% men. 0% from out-of-commonwealth, 0% Native American, 100% Hispanic, 0% black, 0% Asian American or Pacific Islander, 0% international, 34% 25 or older, 1% transferred in. Retention: 70% of full-time freshmen returned the following year. Academic areas with the most degrees conferred: engineering; business/marketing; architecture. Core. Calendar: trimesters. Academic remediation for entering students, ESL program, self-designed majors, summer session for credit, part-time degree program. ROTC: Army (c).
Entrance Requirements: Options: early admission, deferred admission. Required: high school transcript. Required for some: SAT. Entrance: minimally difficult. Application deadline: 8/15.
Costs Per Year: Application fee: $30. Tuition: $5472 full-time, $152 per credit part-time. Mandatory fees: $450 full-time, $150 per term part-time.
Collegiate Environment: Drama-theater group, choral group. Social organizations: 22 open to all; 10% of eligible men and 10% of eligible women are members. Most popular organizations: Society of Women Engineers, American Civil Engineering - Student Chapter, Society of Hispanic Professional Engineers, Society of Automotive Engineers, Capitulo Estuadiantil Ingenieros Electricos. Student services: health clinic, personal-psychological counseling. Campus security: 24-hour patrols. College housing not available. Main library plus 1 other with 95,029 books, 3,212 serials, 1,841 audiovisual materials, an OPAC, and a Web page. Operations spending for 2004 fiscal year: $1.1 million. 375 computers available on campus for general student use. A campuswide network can be accessed from student residence rooms and from off campus. Staffed computer lab on campus.

■ PONTIFICAL CATHOLIC UNIVERSITY OF PUERTO RICO

2250 Las Americas Ave., Ste. 564
Ponce, PR 00717-0777
Tel: (787)841-2000
Free: 800-981-5040
Fax: (787)840-4295
E-mail: abonilla@email.pucpr.edu
Web Site: http://www.pucpr.edu/

Description: Independent Roman Catholic, university, coed. Awards associate, bachelor's, master's, doctoral, and first professional degrees (branch locations in Arecibo, Guayana, Mayaguez). Founded 1948. Setting: 120-acre urban campus with easy access to San Juan. Endowment: $16.2 million. Research spending for 2004 fiscal year: $18,064. Educational spending for 2005 fiscal year: $3680 per student. Total enrollment: 7,474. Faculty: 352 (205 full-time, 147 part-time). Student-undergrad faculty ratio is 24:1. 1,741 applied, 79% were admitted. Full-time: 4,697 students, 65% women, 35% men. Part-time: 666 students, 66% women, 34% men. 0% from out-of-commonwealth, 99.9% Hispanic, 0.02% international, 9% 25 or older, 4% live on campus, 3% transferred in. Retention: 74% of full-time freshmen returned the following year. Academic areas with the most degrees conferred: business/marketing; education; health professions and related sciences. Core. Calendar: semesters. Academic remediation for entering students, ESL program, services for LD students, advanced placement, honors program, independent study, double major, summer session for credit, part-time degree program, adult/continuing education programs, co-op programs, graduate courses open to undergrads. Off campus study at Polytechnic University of Puerto Rico. ROTC: Army (c).
Entrance Requirements: Options: early admission, deferred admission. Required: high school transcript, minimum 2.0 high school GPA, SAT. Required for some: essay, minimum 3.0 high school GPA, 1 recommendation, interview. Entrance: moderately difficult. Application deadline: 3/15. Notification: continuous.
Costs Per Year: Application fee: $15. Comprehensive fee: $8078 includes full-time tuition ($4480), mandatory fees ($458), and college room and board ($3140). College room only: $1100. Full-time tuition and fees vary according to course load. Part-time tuition: $140 per credit. Part-time tuition varies according to course load.
Collegiate Environment: Orientation program. Drama-theater group, choral group, student-run newspaper, radio station. Social organizations: 50 open to all; national fraternities, national sororities, local fraternities, local sororities; 1% of eligible men and 1% of eligible women are members. Most popular organizations: Accounting Students Club, Foreign Students Club, Christ Heralds. Major annual events: Peace Day, Educational Professional Development Convention, Puerto Rican Heritage Week. Student services: health clinic, personal-psychological counseling. Campus security: 24-hour emergency response devices and patrols. 180 college housing spaces available; 147 were occupied in 2003-04. No special consideration for freshman housing applicants. Options: men-only, women-only housing available. Encarnacion Valdes Library plus 1 other with 495,667 microform titles, 58,185 serials, an OPAC, and a Web page. Operations spending for 2004 fiscal year: $2.4 million. 419 computers available on campus for general student use. A campuswide network can be accessed from off-campus. Staffed computer lab on campus.
Community Environment: Ponce is a metropolitan area. Mercedita Airport furnishes transportation to Mayaguez and San Juan. Bus transportation is available to all parts of the island. Community facilities include a public library, museums, churches of major denominations, hospitals, excellent shopping facilities and a number of the major civic, fraternal and service organizations. Part-time employment opportunities are limited. Carnival celebrations and Fiesta Patronales are special annual events.

■ PUERTO RICO TECHNICAL JUNIOR COLLEGE (MAYAGUEZ)

Calle Santiago R. Palmer No. 15 Est
Mayaguez, PR 00680
Tel: (787)832-2762
Description: Proprietary, 2-year, coed.

■ PUERTO RICO TECHNICAL JUNIOR COLLEGE (SAN JUAN)

703 Ponce De Leon Ave., Hato Rey
San Juan, PR 00917
Tel: (787)751-0133
Fax: (787)754-3431
Description: Proprietary, 2-year, coed. Awards terminal associate degrees. Total enrollment: 300.
Entrance Requirements: Open admission.

■ RAMÍREZ COLLEGE OF BUSINESS AND TECHNOLOGY

Ave. Ponce de Leon No. 70
San Juan, PR 00918
Tel: (787)763-3120
Description: Proprietary, 2-year, coed. Awards diplomas, transfer associate, and terminal associate degrees. Founded 1922. Setting: small town campus.

Total enrollment: 439. Students come from 5 other countries, 24% 25 or older. Calendar: trimesters. Academic remediation for entering students, adult/continuing education programs.

Entrance Requirements: Open admission. Required: minimum 2.0 high school GPA, interview. Entrance: noncompetitive. Application deadline: Rolling.

Collegiate Environment: Student services: health clinic, personal-psychological counseling. College housing not available.

■ **TECHNOLOGICAL COLLEGE OF SAN JUAN**
180 Jose R Oliver St.
Tres Monjitas Industrial Park
San Juan, PR 00918
Tel; (787)250-7111
Fax: (787)250-7395

Description: City-supported, 2-year, coed. Awards certificates, diplomas, transfer associate, and terminal associate degrees. Founded 1971. Setting: 5-acre urban campus. Endowment: $14 million. Total enrollment: 777. 257 applied, 99% were admitted. Full-time: 592 students, 49% women, 51% men. Part-time: 185 students, 44% women, 56% men. 100% Hispanic, 40% 25 or older, 4% transferred in. Core. Calendar: semesters. Academic remediation for entering students, ESL program, services for LD students, independent study, summer session for credit, part-time degree program, co-op programs and internships. Off campus study at Inter American University of Puerto Rico.

Entrance Requirements: Open admission. Option: Common Application. Required: high school transcript, minimum 2.0 high school GPA, medical history. Required for some: recommendations, interview, SAT, CEEB. Entrance: noncompetitive. Application deadline: 4/30. Notification: continuous until 7/31.

Collegiate Environment: Orientation program. Drama-theater group, student-run newspaper. Social organizations: 2 open to all. Most popular organization: student council. Major annual events: track and field championship, Student Day, Student Assembly. Student services: health clinic, personal-psychological counseling, women's center. Campus security: 24-hour patrols. College housing not available. Access to Information Center with 14,298 books, 39 serials, 199 audiovisual materials, an OPAC, and a Web page. Operations spending for 2004 fiscal year: $9572. 60 computers available on campus for general student use. A campuswide network can be accessed. Staffed computer lab on campus.

■ **UNIVERSIDAD ADVENTISTA DE LAS ANTILLAS**
PO Box 118
Mayaguez, PR 00681-0118
Tel: (787)834-9595
Fax: (787)834-9597
E-mail: admissions@uaa.edu
Web Site: http://www.uaa.edu/

Description: Independent Seventh-day Adventist, comprehensive, coed. Awards associate, bachelor's, and master's degrees. Founded 1957. Setting: 284-acre rural campus. Endowment: $10,000. Research spending for 2004 fiscal year: $8121. Educational spending for 2005 fiscal year: $4910 per student. Total enrollment: 831. Faculty: 63 (42 full-time, 21 part-time). Student-undergrad faculty ratio is 13:1. 446 applied, 90% were admitted. Full-time: 704 students, 59% women, 41% men. Part-time: 56 students, 66% women, 34% men. Students come from 11 states and territories, 20 other countries, 28% from out-of-commonwealth, 0% Native American, 92% Hispanic, 3% black, 0% Asian American or Pacific Islander, 5% international, 22% 25 or older, 27% live on campus, 7% transferred in. Retention: 60% of full-time freshmen returned the following year. Academic areas with the most degrees conferred: health professions and related sciences; business/marketing; education. Core. Calendar: semesters. Academic remediation for entering students, ESL program, services for LD students, advanced placement, double major, summer session for credit, part-time degree program, adult/continuing education programs, co-op programs and internships.

Entrance Requirements: Options: Peterson's Universal Application, Common Application, early admission. Required: high school transcript, minimum 2.0 high school GPA, recommendations. Recommended: SAT or ACT, PAA. Required for some: interview. Entrance: minimally difficult.

Costs Per Year: Application fee: $20. Comprehensive fee: $5590 includes full-time tuition ($3680), mandatory fees ($510), and college room and board ($1400). College room only: $800. Full-time tuition and fees vary according to course load. Room and board charges vary according to board plan. Part-

time tuition: $130 per credit. Part-time mandatory fees: $130 per credit. Part-time tuition and fees vary according to course load.

Collegiate Environment: Orientation program. Choral group, student-run newspaper. Social organizations: 4 open to all. Most popular organizations: Score Group, Gymnastic Club, student council, Group Life. Major annual events: Christmas Cantata, Olympic Games, International Fair. Student services: health clinic, personal-psychological counseling. Campus security: 24-hour emergency response devices and patrols, student patrols, controlled dormitory access. 200 college housing spaces available; 168 were occupied in 2003-04. Freshmen given priority for college housing. On-campus residence required in freshman year. Options: coed, men-only, women-only housing available. Biblioteca Dennis Soto plus 1 other with 86,465 books, 452 serials, 325 audiovisual materials, an OPAC, and a Web page. Operations spending for 2004 fiscal year: $287,390. 62 computers available on campus for general student use. Staffed computer lab on campus.

■ **UNIVERSIDAD CENTRAL DEL CARIBE**
PO Box 60-327
Bayamon, PR 00960-6032
Tel: (787)798-3001
Web Site: http://www.uccaribe.edu/

Description: Independent, 2-year, coed. Awards terminal associate, master's, and first professional degrees. Founded 1976. Total enrollment: 362. 22 applied, 91% were admitted. Calendar: semesters.

■ **UNIVERSIDAD DEL ESTE**
PO Box 2010
Carolina, PR 00983
Tel: (787)257-7373
Fax: (787)257-7373
E-mail: ue_nortiz@suagm.edu
Web Site: http://www.suagm.edu/une/

Description: Independent, comprehensive, coed. Part of Ana G. Mendez University System. Awards associate, bachelor's, and master's degrees. Founded 1949. Setting: small town campus with easy access to San Juan. Total enrollment: 10,330. 5,555 applied, 48% were admitted. 100% Hispanic, 36% 25 or older. Retention: 65% of full-time freshmen returned the following year. Calendar: semesters. Academic remediation for entering students, honors program, summer session for credit, part-time degree program, external degree program, adult/continuing education programs.

Entrance Requirements: Option: deferred admission. Required: high school transcript, CEEB. Required for some: interview. Entrance: noncompetitive. Application deadline: 3/15. Notification: continuous.

Collegiate Environment: Student services: health clinic, personal-psychological counseling. Campus security: 24-hour patrols. College housing not available. 13,856 books and 223 serials.

Community Environment: See University of Puerto Rico - Rio Piedras Campus.

■ **UNIVERSIDAD METROPOLITANA**
Apartado 21150
San Juan, PR 00928-1150
Tel: (787)766-1717
Free: 800-747-8362
Fax: (787)759-7663
E-mail: um_frivera@suagm1.suagm.edu
Web Site: http://www.suagm.edu/umet/

Description: Independent, comprehensive, coed. Part of Ana G. Mendez University System. Awards associate, bachelor's, and master's degrees. Founded 1980. Setting: small town campus with easy access to San Juan. Total enrollment: 10,195. 4,869 applied, 58% were admitted. 100% Hispanic, 33% 25 or older. Retention: 65% of full-time freshmen returned the following year. Core. Calendar: semesters. Academic remediation for entering students, advanced placement, freshman honors college, honors program, summer session for credit, part-time degree program, co-op programs. Off campus study.

Entrance Requirements: Option: Common Application. Required: high school transcript, PAA. Required for some: interview. Entrance: moderately difficult. Application deadline: 7/30.

Collegiate Environment: Drama-theater group, choral group. Social organizations: 10 open to all; national fraternities. Campus security: 24-hour patrols. College housing not available. 50 computers available on campus for general student use.

■ UNIVERSIDAD DEL TURABO
PO Box 3030
Gurabo, PR 00778-3030
Tel: (787)743-7979
E-mail: ac_msantana@suagm.edu
Web Site: http://www.suagm.edu/ut/

Description: Independent, comprehensive, coed. Part of Ana G. Mendez University System. Awards associate, bachelor's, and master's degrees. Founded 1972. Setting: 140-acre urban campus with easy access to San Juan. Total enrollment: 13,692. 4,429 applied, 64% were admitted. 100% Hispanic, 35% 25 or older. Retention: 69% of full-time freshmen returned the following year. Core. Calendar: semesters. Academic remediation for entering students, services for LD students, advanced placement, honors program, summer session for credit, part-time degree program. Off campus study at Jackson State University, University of California, Berkeley, Rensselaer Polytechnic Institute, Georgia Institute of Technology, University of New Mexico, New Mexico State University. ROTC: Army (c), Air Force (c).

Entrance Requirements: Option: deferred admission. Required: high school transcript. Placement: CEEB required. Entrance: minimally difficult. Application deadline: Rolling. Notification: continuous until 8/1.

Collegiate Environment: Drama-theater group, choral group, student-run newspaper. Most popular organizations: Social Work Students Association, Honor's Student Association, Drama Club, Chorus, Computerized Sciences Organization. Major annual event: New Students Reception. Student services: health clinic, personal-psychological counseling. Campus security: 24-hour patrols. College housing not available. 90,020 books and 655 serials.

■ UNIVERSITY COLLEGE OF CRIMINAL JUSTICE OF PUERTO RICO
HC 02 Box 12000
Gurabo, PR 00778-9601
Tel: (787)737-3351
Fax: (787)737-7619
Description: State-supported, 2-year, coed.

■ UNIVERSITY OF PHOENIX-PUERTO RICO CAMPUS
B7 Tabonuco St., Ste. 700 Santander Tower
PO Box 3870
Guaynabo, PR 00968
Tel: (787)731-5400
Free: 800-228-7240
Admissions: (480)557-1712
Fax: (787)731-1510
Web Site: http://www.phoenix.edu/

Description: Proprietary, comprehensive, coed. Awards bachelor's and master's degrees (courses conducted at 121 campuses and learning centers in 25 states). Founded 1995. Setting: urban campus. Total enrollment: 2,714. Faculty: 109 (7 full-time, 102 part-time). Student-undergrad faculty ratio is 16:1. 35 applied. Full-time: 832 students, 50% women, 50% men. 0% from out-of-commonwealth, 0% Native American, 25% Hispanic, 0.4% black, 0% Asian American or Pacific Islander, 3% international, 92% 25 or older. Academic area with the most degrees conferred: business/marketing. Core. Calendar: continuous. Advanced placement, accelerated degree program, independent study, distance learning, external degree program, adult/continuing education programs, graduate courses open to undergrads.

Entrance Requirements: Open admission. Option: deferred admission. Required: 1 recommendation. Required for some: high school transcript. Entrance: noncompetitive. Application deadline: Rolling.

Costs Per Year: Application fee: $110. Tuition: $5640 full-time, $188 per credit part-time. Mandatory fees: $560 full-time, $70 per course part-time.

Collegiate Environment: College housing not available. University Library with 444 books, 666 serials, an OPAC, and a Web page. System-wide operations spending for 2004 fiscal year: $3.2 million.

■ UNIVERSITY OF PUERTO RICO, AGUADILLA UNIVERSITY COLLEGE
PO Box 250-160
Aguadilla, PR 00604-0160
Tel: (787)890-2681
Web Site: http://www.uprag.edu/

Description: Commonwealth-supported, 4-year, coed. Part of University of Puerto Rico System. Awards associate and bachelor's degrees. Founded 1972. Setting: 32-acre suburban campus. Research spending for 2004 fiscal year: $54,752. Educational spending for 2005 fiscal year: $3900 per student.

Total enrollment: 3,393. 965 applied, 88% were admitted. 10% 25 or older. Retention: 83% of full-time freshmen returned the following year. Core. Calendar: semesters. Academic remediation for entering students, ESL program, advanced placement, honors program, summer session for credit, part-time degree program, adult/continuing education programs. ROTC: Army.

Entrance Requirements: Options: Common Application, early admission, deferred admission. Required: high school transcript, SAT, SAT Subject Tests, PAA. Entrance: moderately difficult. Application deadline: 3/29. Notification: continuous until 8/1.

Collegiate Environment: Orientation program. Choral group. Social organizations: local fraternities. Campus security: 24-hour patrols. College housing not available. 31,420 books and 242 serials.

■ UNIVERSITY OF PUERTO RICO AT ARECIBO
PO Box 4010
Arecibo, PR 00613
Tel: (787)878-2830
Web Site: http://www.upra.edu/

Description: Commonwealth-supported, 4-year, coed. Part of University of Puerto Rico System. Awards associate and bachelor's degrees. Founded 1967. Setting: 44-acre urban campus with easy access to San Juan. Research spending for 2004 fiscal year: $100,953. Total enrollment: 4,432. 1,371 applied, 77% were admitted. 100% Hispanic, 1% 25 or older. Retention: 89% of full-time freshmen returned the following year. Core. Calendar: semesters. Academic remediation for entering students, ESL program, services for LD students, advanced placement, honors program, distance learning, summer session for credit, adult/continuing education programs. ROTC: Army.

Entrance Requirements: Required: high school transcript, SAT Subject Tests, PAA or SAT, CEEB. Placement: SAT Subject Tests required. Entrance: very difficult. Application deadline: 12/8. Notification: 3/18.

Collegiate Environment: Orientation program. Drama-theater group, choral group, marching band. Social organizations: local fraternities, local sororities; 10% of eligible men and 17% of eligible women are members. Most popular organizations: Club Rotaract, CONFRA, Student Counselors, band/ATUC, ACTRE. Major annual events: Award Night, Anniversary Festival, Athletic Tournament. Student services: health clinic, personal-psychological counseling. Campus security: 24-hour emergency response devices and patrols. General Library with 65,000 books and 3,660 serials. Operations spending for 2004 fiscal year: $789,800. 243 computers available on campus for general student use. Staffed computer lab on campus.

■ UNIVERSITY OF PUERTO RICO AT BAYAMÓN
170 Carretera 174 Parque Industrial Minillas
Bayamon, PR 00959
Tel: (787)786-2885
E-mail: e_velez@cutb.upr.clu.edu
Web Site: http://www.uprb.edu/

Description: Commonwealth-supported, 4-year, coed. Part of University of Puerto Rico System. Awards associate and bachelor's degrees. Founded 1971. Setting: 78-acre urban campus with easy access to San Juan. Total enrollment: 4,852. 6,096 applied, 18% were admitted. Students come from 4 other countries. Retention: 78% of full-time freshmen returned the following year. Core. Calendar: semesters. Academic remediation for entering students, advanced placement, honors program, summer session for credit, part-time degree program, adult/continuing education programs, co-op programs. ROTC: Army, Air Force (c).

Entrance Requirements: Option: Common Application. Required: high school transcript, SAT, SAT Subject Tests. Entrance: very difficult. Application deadline: 12/15. Notification: 5/1.

Collegiate Environment: Orientation program. Drama-theater group. Social organizations: 13 open to all. Most popular organizations: American Marketing Association, Collegiate Secretaries International, Associacion de Estudiantes de Electronica, Associacion de Estudiantes de Gerenies de Materials, Society for Human Research Management. Major annual events: Torres de Baloncesto El Chicharion, Ceremonia de Letra Insiquia, Testas Interuniversitaries. Student services: health clinic. Campus security: 24-hour patrols. College housing not available. 60,815 books and 480 serials. 370 computers available on campus for general student use. Staffed computer lab on campus.

■ UNIVERSITY OF PUERTO RICO AT CAROLINA
PO Box 4800
Carolina, PR 00984-4800

Tel: (787)257-0000

Admissions: (787)757-1485

Web Site: http://uprc.edu/

Description: Commonwealth-supported, primarily 2-year, coed. Part of University of Puerto Rico System. Awards transfer associate, terminal associate, and bachelor's degrees. Founded 1974. Setting: 60-acre urban campus with easy access to San Juan. Total enrollment: 3,991. 2,025 applied, 51% were admitted. 5% 25 or older. Core. Academic remediation for entering students, ESL program, services for LD students, part-time degree program, adult/continuing education programs. ROTC: Army (c), Air Force (c).

Entrance Requirements: Required: PAA. Required for some: SAT, SAT Subject Tests. Entrance: moderately difficult. Application deadline: 12/6. Notification: continuous until 8/1.

Collegiate Environment: Orientation program. Drama-theater group. Student services: health clinic, personal-psychological counseling. College housing not available. 28,037 books and 264 serials. 20 computers available on campus for general student use.

■ **UNIVERSITY OF PUERTO RICO, CAYEY UNIVERSITY COLLEGE**

205 Ave. Antonio R. Barcelo

Cayey, PR 00736

Tel: (787)738-2161

Web Site: http://www.cayey.upr.edu/

Description: Commonwealth-supported, 4-year, coed. Part of University of Puerto Rico System. Awards associate and bachelor's degrees. Founded 1967. Setting: 177-acre urban campus with easy access to San Juan. Total enrollment: 3,987. 4,084 applied, 22% were admitted. Full-time: 3,595 students, 71% women, 29% men. Part-time: 392 students, 74% women, 26% men. 100% Hispanic, 2% transferred in. Retention: 89% of full-time freshmen returned the following year. Core. Calendar: semesters. Academic remediation for entering students, advanced placement, accelerated degree program, honors program, summer session for credit, part-time degree program. Off campus study at Inter-American University of Puerto Rico, Catholic University of Puerto Rico, Universidad del Turabo, Sacred Heart University, University of Massachusetts Amherst. Study abroad program. ROTC: Army.

Entrance Requirements: Options: Common Application, early admission. Required: high school transcript, minimum 2.0 high school GPA, CEEB. Required for some: SAT. Entrance: very difficult. Application deadline: 12/1. Notification: continuous until 5/5.

Collegiate Environment: Orientation program. Drama-theater group, choral group. Social organizations: national fraternities, national sororities; 1% of eligible men and 1% of eligible women are members. Most popular organizations: Business Administration Circle, Christian University Association. Major annual events: Student Day, Honors Program Day, Techno Chem. Student services: health clinic, personal-psychological counseling, women's center. Campus security: 24-hour emergency response devices and patrols, late night transport-escort service. College housing not available. Victor M. Pons Library with 109,776 books, 53 microform titles, 2,013 serials, 2,286 audiovisual materials, an OPAC, and a Web page. 265 computers available on campus for general student use. A campuswide network can be accessed from off-campus. Staffed computer lab on campus.

■ **UNIVERSITY OF PUERTO RICO AT HUMACAO**

HUC Station 100, Rd. 908

Humacao, PR 00791

Tel: (787)850-0000

Admissions: (787)850-9301

Fax: (787)852-4638

E-mail: i_ferrer@cuhac.upr.clu.edu

Web Site: http://www.uprh.edu/

Description: Commonwealth-supported, 4-year, coed. Part of University of Puerto Rico System. Awards associate and bachelor's degrees. Founded 1962. Setting: 62-acre suburban campus with easy access to San Juan. Research spending for 2004 fiscal year: $1.7 million. Educational spending for 2005 fiscal year: $4745 per student. Total enrollment: 4,462. 2,133 applied, 53% were admitted. Students come from 3 states and territories, 0.1% from out-of-commonwealth, 100% Hispanic, 13% 25 or older. Retention: 87% of full-time freshmen returned the following year. Core. Calendar: semesters. Academic remediation for entering students, ESL program, services for LD students, freshman honors college, honors program, summer session for credit, part-time degree program, internships. Off campus study at National Student Exchange. ROTC: Army.

Entrance Requirements: Option: deferred admission. Required: high school transcript, minimum 2.0 high school GPA, CEEB for Puerto Rican applicants, PAA and 3 achievement tests. Required for some: SAT, SAT Subject Tests. Entrance: moderately difficult. Application deadline: 11/15. Notification: continuous until 4/15.

Collegiate Environment: Orientation program. Drama-theater group, choral group, marching band, student-run radio station. Social organizations: 18 open to all; national fraternities. Most popular organizations: Recreational Organization, Accounting Students Association, Management Students Association, Microbiology Students Association, Human Resources Students Association. Major annual events: Student Day, Shakespeare Festival, Puerto Rican Culture Week. Student services: personal-psychological counseling. Campus security: 24-hour patrols, 24-hour gate security. College housing not available. 64,557 books, 10,221 microform titles, 2,526 serials, 752 audiovisual materials, an OPAC, and a Web page. Operations spending for 2004 fiscal year: $1.6 million. 166 computers available on campus for general student use. Computer purchase/lease plans available. A campuswide network can be accessed from off-campus. Staffed computer lab on campus.

■ **UNIVERSITY OF PUERTO RICO, MAYAGEZ CAMPUS**

PO Box 9000

Mayaguez, PR 00681-9000

Tel: (787)832-4040

Admissions: (787)265-3811

E-mail: af_delgado@rumaxp.rum.clu.edu

Web Site: http://www.uprm.edu

Description: Commonwealth-supported, university, coed. Part of University of Puerto Rico System. Awards bachelor's, master's, and doctoral degrees. Founded 1911. Setting: 315-acre urban campus. Research spending for 2004 fiscal year: $10.9 million. Educational spending for 2005 fiscal year: $3260 per student. Total enrollment: 12,108. 3,891 applied, 62% were admitted. Full-time: 10,010 students, 50% women, 50% men. Part-time: 1,022 students, 57% women, 43% men. Retention: 86% of full-time freshmen returned the following year. Core. Calendar: semesters. Advanced placement, honors program, distance learning, summer session for credit, adult/continuing education programs, co-op programs and internships, graduate courses open to undergrads. Off campus study at State University of New York College at Oswego, National Student Exchange. Study abroad program. ROTC: Army, Air Force.

Entrance Requirements: Options: Common Application, early action. Required: high school transcript, SAT, SAT Subject Tests, PEAU. Entrance: moderately difficult. Application deadlines: 12/15, 12/15 for early action. Notification: 3/15, 12/15 for early action.

Costs Per Year: Application fee: $15.

Collegiate Environment: Orientation program. Drama-theater group, choral group, marching band, student-run newspaper. Social organizations: 113 open to all; national fraternities, national sororities, local fraternities, local sororities. Major annual events: Intercollegiate Athletic Tournament, Back to School Ball, End of Semester Ball. Student services: health clinic, personal-psychological counseling. Campus security: 24-hour emergency response devices and patrols. General Library plus 1 other with 921,392 books, 606,868 microform titles, 590,716 serials, 40,735 audiovisual materials, and an OPAC. Operations spending for 2004 fiscal year: $1.7 million. 1,066 computers available on campus for general student use. A campuswide network can be accessed from off-campus. Staffed computer lab on campus.

■ **UNIVERSITY OF PUERTO RICO, MEDICAL SCIENCES CAMPUS**

PO Box 365067

San Juan, PR 00936-5067

Tel: (787)758-2525

Fax: (787)754-0474

E-mail: rvelez@rcm.upr.edu

Web Site: http://www.rcm.upr.edu/

Description: Commonwealth-supported, upper-level, coed. Part of University of Puerto Rico System. Awards associate, bachelor's, master's, doctoral, and first professional degrees and first professional certificates (bachelor's degree is upper-level). Founded 1950. Setting: 11-acre urban campus. Total enrollment: 2,334. 100% Hispanic. Calendar: semesters. Academic remediation for entering students, summer session for credit, adult/continuing education programs, internships. Off campus study at University of Puerto Rico, Rio Piedras.

Collegiate Environment: Orientation program. Drama-theater group, choral group. Social organizations: national fraternities, national sororities, local fraternities, local sororities. Most popular organizations: General Council of Students, Academy of Pharmacy Students, Council of Medicine Students, Council of Public Health Students, American Medical Association-Puerto Rico Chapter-Student Section. Major annual events: Freshman Orientation Week, job fair, AIDS Awareness Day. Student services: legal services, health clinic, personal-psychological counseling, women's center. Campus security: 24-hour emergency response devices. College housing not available. Medical Sciences Library plus 1 other with 46,679 books, 13 microform titles, 1,432 serials, 1,522 audiovisual materials, an OPAC, and a Web page.

Community Environment: San Juan juxtaposes the old and the new: Old San Juan and the moss-covered El Morro castle are contrasted with high-rise office buildings. Founded in 1521, San Juan is a metropolitan city with a mild climate. Museums (e.g. colonial architecture, rare books Puerto Rican art), outdoor sports (swimming, surfing, baseball, fishing, cock fighting), hospitals and excellent shopping are available to everyone. Special San Juan events include drama festivals, native carnivals, the International Theatrical Festival and the Casals Festival.

■ UNIVERSITY OF PUERTO RICO AT PONCE
PO Box 7186
Ponce, PR 00732-7186
Tel: (787)844-8181
Fax: (787)844-8679
Web Site: http://upr-ponce.upr.edu/
Description: Commonwealth-supported, 4-year, coed. Part of University of Puerto Rico System. Awards associate and bachelor's degrees. Founded 1970. Setting: 86-acre urban campus with easy access to San Juan. Educational spending for 2005 fiscal year: $1298 per student. Total enrollment: 3,661. 3,804 applied, 21% were admitted. 100% Hispanic, 3% 25 or older. Retention: 18% of full-time freshmen returned the following year. Core. Calendar: semesters. Academic remediation for entering students, ESL program, advanced placement, accelerated degree program, freshman honors college, honors program, summer session for credit, part-time degree program, adult/continuing education programs, internships. ROTC: Army.
Entrance Requirements: Options: Common Application, early admission. Required: high school transcript, SAT, PAA. Entrance: moderately difficult. Application deadlines: 11/15, 1/15 for early decision. Notification: 3/4, 1/20 for early decision.
Costs Per Year: Application fee: $15. Commonwealth resident tuition: $1360 full-time, $40 per credit hour part-time. Nonresident tuition: $2400 full-time, $100 per credit hour part-time. Mandatory fees: $814 full-time. Full-time tuition and fees vary according to class time. Part-time tuition varies according to class time.
Collegiate Environment: Orientation program. Drama-theater group, choral group. Most popular organizations: American Marketing Association, Secretarial Sciences Association, Drama Club, Alfa Computer Club. Major annual events: Athletic Intercollegiate Tournament, Voice Festival, Christmas Choir Concert. Student services: health clinic. Campus security: 24-hour patrols. College housing not available. 53,000 books, 1,643 serials, and an OPAC. Operations spending for 2004 fiscal year: $660,456. 231 computers available on campus for general student use. Staffed computer lab on campus.

■ UNIVERSITY OF PUERTO RICO, RÍO PIEDRAS
PO Box 23300
San Juan, PR 00931-3300
Tel: (787)764-0000
Web Site: http://www.uprrp.edu/
Description: Commonwealth-supported, university, coed. Part of University of Puerto Rico System. Awards bachelor's, master's, doctoral, and first professional degrees and post-master's certificates. Founded 1903. Setting: 281-acre urban campus. Research spending for 2004 fiscal year: $11.3 million. Total enrollment: 21,755. 5,613 applied, 67% were admitted. Students come from 4 states and territories, 9 other countries, 1% from out-of-commonwealth, 99% Hispanic, 0.2% international, 14% 25 or older. Core. Calendar: semesters. Academic remediation for entering students, ESL program, services for LD students, advanced placement, accelerated degree program, honors program, summer session for credit, part-time degree program, adult/continuing education programs, graduate courses open to undergrads. Study abroad program. ROTC: Army, Air Force.
Entrance Requirements: Options: Common Application, electronic application. Required: high school transcript, minimum 2.0 high school GPA, SAT, SAT Subject Tests, CEEB. Required for some: interview. Entrance: very difficult. Application deadline: 2/15. Notification: continuous.

Collegiate Environment: Orientation program. Drama-theater group, choral group, student-run newspaper, radio station. Social organizations: national fraternities, national sororities, local fraternities, local sororities. Student services: legal services, health clinic, personal-psychological counseling. Campus security: 24-hour emergency response devices, late night transport-escort service. 789 college housing spaces available. No special consideration for freshman housing applicants. Option: coed housing available. Jose M. Lazaro Library plus 10 others with 1.8 million books, 1.7 million microform titles, 5,599 serials, 5,599 audiovisual materials, and an OPAC. 170 computers available on campus for general student use. A campuswide network can be accessed from student residence rooms. Staffed computer lab on campus.

■ UNIVERSITY OF PUERTO RICO AT UTUADO
PO Box 2500
Utuado, PR 00641-2500
Tel: (787)894-2828
Web Site: http://upr-utuado.upr.clu.edu/
Description: Commonwealth-supported, 4-year, coed. Part of University of Puerto Rico System. Awards associate and bachelor's degrees. Founded 1979. Setting: 180-acre small town campus with easy access to San Juan. Research spending for 2004 fiscal year: $37,651. Educational spending for 2005 fiscal year: $6227 per student. Total enrollment: 1,654. 1,441 applied, 42% were admitted. 100% Hispanic, 16% 25 or older. Core. Calendar: semesters. Academic remediation for entering students, honors program, distance learning, summer session for credit, adult/continuing education programs, co-op programs.
Entrance Requirements: Options: Common Application, electronic application, early admission, deferred admission. Required: SAT and SAT Subject Tests or ACT, PAA. Entrance: moderately difficult. Application deadline: Rolling.
Collegiate Environment: Orientation program. Drama-theater group. Student services: health clinic. Campus security: 24-hour emergency response devices and patrols. College housing not available. Learning Resource Center with 22,482 books, 129,160 microform titles, 223 serials, and 40,110 audiovisual materials. Operations spending for 2004 fiscal year: $447,368. 40 computers available on campus for general student use. A campuswide network can be accessed. Staffed computer lab on campus.

■ UNIVERSITY OF THE SACRED HEART
PO Box 12383
San Juan, PR 00914-0383
Tel: (787)728-1515
Web Site: http://www.sagrado.edu/
Description: Independent Roman Catholic, comprehensive, coed. Awards associate, bachelor's, and master's degrees. Founded 1935. Setting: 33-acre urban campus. Endowment: $16 million. Educational spending for 2005 fiscal year: $2487 per student. Total enrollment: 5,206. 2,321 applied, 74% were admitted. Full-time: 3,279 students, 66% women, 34% men. Part-time: 1,144 students, 65% women, 35% men. 2% from out-of-commonwealth, 100% Hispanic, 19% 25 or older, 4% transferred in. Retention: 77% of full-time freshmen returned the following year. Core. Calendar: semesters. Academic remediation for entering students, services for LD students, advanced placement, accelerated degree program, honors program, summer session for credit, part-time degree program, adult/continuing education programs, co-op programs and internships. Study abroad program.
Entrance Requirements: Options: Common Application, early admission. Required: high school transcript, minimum 2.5 high school GPA, 1 recommendation, PAA, CEEB. Entrance: moderately difficult. Application deadline: 6/30.
Collegiate Environment: Orientation program. Drama-theater group, choral group, student-run newspaper. Social organizations: 18 open to all. Most popular organizations: La Red (personal development center), Student Council, Judo Club, Athletic Association. Major annual events: Welcome Party, Inter-University Athletic Competition. Student services: health clinic, personal-psychological counseling. Campus security: 24-hour patrols. 553 college housing spaces available; 385 were occupied in 2003-04. No special consideration for freshman housing applicants. Options: men-only, women-only housing available. Maria Teresa Guevara Library plus 1 other with 430,531 microform titles, 1,525 serials, 67,048 audiovisual materials, an OPAC, and a Web page. Operations spending for 2004 fiscal year: $697,331. 500 computers available on campus for general student use. A campuswide network can be accessed from off-campus. Staffed computer lab on campus.

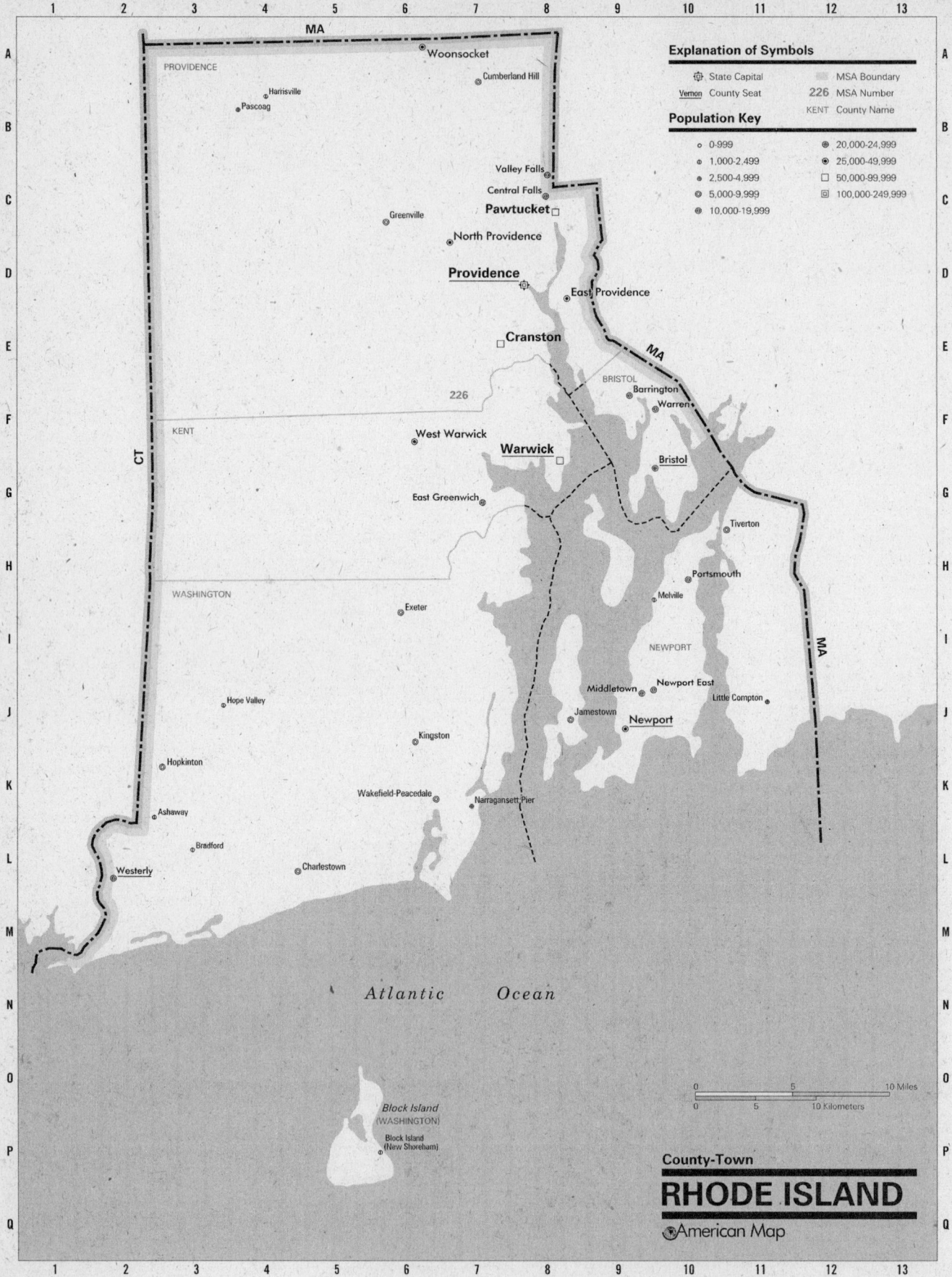

RHODE ISLAND

County-Town

American Map

Explanation of Symbols

⊕	State Capital		MSA Boundary
Vernon	County Seat	226	MSA Number
		KENT	County Name

Population Key

○	0-999	⊛	20,000-24,999
⊙	1,000-2,499	⊛	25,000-49,999
⊙	2,500-4,999	▢	50,000-99,999
⊚	5,000-9,999	▣	100,000-249,999
⊛	10,000-19,999		

MA

PROVIDENCE

Woonsocket

Cumberland Hill

Harrisville

Pascoag

Valley Falls

Central Falls

Pawtucket

Greenville

North Providence

Providence

East Providence

Cranston

226

BRISTOL

Barrington

Warren

KENT

West Warwick

Warwick

Bristol

East Greenwich

MA

CT

Tiverton

Portsmouth

Melville

WASHINGTON

Exeter

NEWPORT

Hope Valley

Middletown

Newport East

Little Compton

Jamestown

Kingston

Newport

MA

Hopkinton

Wakefield-Peacedale

Narragansett Pier

Ashaway

Bradford

Charlestown

Westerly

Atlantic Ocean

Block Island
(WASHINGTON)

Block Island
(New Shoreham)

0 — 5 — 10 Miles

0 — 5 — 10 Kilometers

■ **BROWN UNIVERSITY** *D-8*
Providence, RI 02912
Tel: (401)863-1000
Admissions: (401)863-2378
Fax: (401)863-9300
E-mail: admission_undergraduate@brown.edu
Web Site: http://www.brown.edu/

Description: Independent, university, coed. Awards bachelor's, master's, doctoral, and first professional degrees. Founded 1764. Setting: 140-acre urban campus with easy access to Boston. Total enrollment: 8,261. Faculty: 888 (630 full-time, 258 part-time). Student-undergrad faculty ratio is 9:1. 16,911 applied, 15% were admitted. 90% from top 10% of their high school class, 99% from top quarter, 100% from top half. 160 valedictorians. Full-time: 5,931 students, 53% women, 47% men. Part-time: 245 students, 64% women, 36% men. Students come from 52 states and territories, 72 other countries, 96% from out-of-state, 1% Native American, 7% Hispanic, 7% black, 14% Asian American or Pacific Islander, 6% international, 1% 25 or older, 85% live on campus, 2% transferred in. Retention: 97% of full-time freshmen returned the following year. Academic areas with the most degrees conferred: social sciences; biological/life sciences; physical sciences. Calendar: semesters. Services for LD students, advanced placement, accelerated degree program, self-designed majors, honors program, independent study, double major, summer session for credit, part-time degree program, adult/continuing education programs, internships, graduate courses open to undergrads. Off campus study at Rhode Island School of Design, Tougaloo College, Wheaton College (MA), Dartmouth Medical School. Study abroad program. ROTC: Army (c).

Entrance Requirements: Options: electronic application, early admission, early decision, deferred admission, international baccalaureate accepted. Required: essay, high school transcript, 2 recommendations, SAT and SAT Subject Tests or ACT. Required for some: 3 recommendations. Entrance: most difficult. Application deadlines: 1/1, 11/1 for early decision. Notification: 4/1, 12/15 for early decision.

Costs Per Year: Application fee: $70. Comprehensive fee: $42,020 includes full-time tuition ($32,264), mandatory fees ($960), and college room and board ($8796). College room only: $5498. Room and board charges vary according to board plan. Part-time tuition: $4033 per course. Tuition guaranteed not to increase for student's term of enrollment.

Collegiate Environment: Orientation program. Drama-theater group, choral group, marching band, student-run newspaper, radio station. Social organizations: 240 open to all; national fraternities, national sororities; 12% of eligible men and 2% of eligible women are members. Most popular organizations: Community Outreach, Bruin Club, Undergraduate Council of Students, orchestra and chorus, Daily Herald. Major annual events: Spring Weekend, Homecoming, Commencement. Student services: legal services, health clinic, personal-psychological counseling, women's center. Campus security: 24-hour emergency response devices and patrols, late night transport-escort service, controlled dormitory access. 4,350 college housing spaces available; all were occupied in 2003-04. Freshmen guaranteed college housing. On-campus residence required through junior year. Options: coed, women-only housing available. John D. Rockefeller Library plus 5 others with 3 million books, 17,000 serials, an OPAC, and a Web page. 500 computers available on campus for general student use. Computer purchase/lease plans available. A campuswide network can be accessed from student residence rooms and from off campus. Staffed computer lab on campus.

Community Environment: In its early days, Providence was a shipping and shipbuilding town, running the Triangular Trade route with slaves, rum, and molasses between Africa, the West Indies and the colonies. Providence, the second largest city in New England, is the industrial and commercial center in addition to being the capital of Rhode Island. The city is one of the largest manufacturing centers in the world and excels in several branches of the metal and rubber industries. Textile manufacturing is of first importance. Historical sites and points of interest include Cathedral of St. John, Cathedral of St. Peter and St. Paul, John Brown House, the Arcade (oldest shopping center in the U.S.), Museum of the Rhode Island School of Design, Waterplace Park, the Athenaeum (oldest library in the U.S.), the Rhode Island Historical Society, Round Top Church, and the State House.

■ **BRYANT UNIVERSITY** *C-6*
1150 Douglas Pike
Smithfield, RI 02917-1284
Tel: (401)232-6000
Free: 800-622-7001
Admissions: (401)232-6100
Fax: (401)232-6741
E-mail: admission@bryant.edu
Web Site: http://www.bryant.edu/

Description: Independent, comprehensive, coed. Awards bachelor's and master's degrees and post-master's certificates. Founded 1863. Setting: 392-acre suburban campus with easy access to Boston and Providence. Endowment: $159.1 million. Educational spending for 2005 fiscal year: $5861 per student. Total enrollment: 3,642. Faculty: 262 (133 full-time, 129 part-time). Student-undergrad faculty ratio is 16:1. 4,214 applied, 58% were admitted. 18% from top 10% of their high school class, 56% from top quarter, 90% from top half. 3 valedictorians. Full-time: 3,012 students, 40% women, 60% men. Part-time: 191 students, 50% women, 50% men. Students come from 30 states and territories, 28 other countries, 81% from out-of-state, 0.3% Native American, 4% Hispanic, 3% black, 2% Asian American or Pacific Islander, 2% international, 6% 25 or older, 78% live on campus, 4% transferred in. Retention: 88% of full-time freshmen returned the following year. Academic areas with the most degrees conferred: business/marketing; computer and information sciences; communications/journalism. Core. Calendar: semesters. Services for LD students, advanced placement, honors program, independent study, double major, summer session for credit, part-time degree program, adult/continuing education programs, internships. Study abroad program. ROTC: Army.

Entrance Requirements: Options: Common Application, electronic application, early admission, early decision, deferred admission, international baccalaureate accepted. Required: essay, high school transcript, 1 recommendation, senior year first-quarter grades, SAT or ACT. Recommended: minimum 3.3 high school GPA. Entrance: moderately difficult. Application deadlines: 2/15, 11/15 for early decision. Notification: 3/15, 12/15 for early decision.

Costs Per Year: Application fee: $50. Comprehensive fee: $34,330 includes full-time tuition ($24,762) and college room and board ($9568). College room only: $5550. Full-time tuition varies according to course load. Room and board charges vary according to board plan and housing facility. Part-time tuition: $891 per course. Part-time tuition varies according to course load. Full-time tuition includes cost of personal laptop computer.

Collegiate Environment: Orientation program. Drama-theater group, choral group, student-run newspaper, radio station. Social organizations: 60 open

to all; national fraternities, national sororities; 6% of eligible men and 4% of eligible women are members. Most popular organizations: Bryant Outdoor Activities Club, Student Programming Board, Rhythm and Pride Dance Team, radio station, Bryant Players (drama club). Major annual events: homecoming, Parents' and Family Weekend, Spring Weekend. Student services: health clinic, personal-psychological counseling, women's center. Campus security: 24-hour emergency response devices and patrols, late night transport-escort service, controlled dormitory access, bicycle patrols, video cameras, lighted pathways/sidewalks, monitored one point of access/egress. 2,484 college housing spaces available; 2,371 were occupied in 2003-04. Freshmen guaranteed college housing. Options: coed, women-only housing available. Douglas and Judith Krupp Library with 133,250 books, 14,500 microform titles, 970 audiovisual materials, an OPAC, and a Web page. Operations spending for 2004 fiscal year: $1 million. 467 computers available on campus for general student use. Computer purchase/lease plans available. A campuswide network can be accessed from student residence rooms and from off campus. Staffed computer lab on campus.

Community Environment: The college is located in the midst of the social, cultural, and recreational center that is southern New England. Its 392-acre campus offers the best of two worlds: the security of its suburban location with easy access to the excitement of the city. The setting, the campus, and the ultramodern facilities have been designed to maximize the interaction between faculty, students and administrators. This integrative atmosphere contributes to an individualistic approach to education and fosters an intimate relationship among all segments of the college community.

■ COMMUNITY COLLEGE OF RHODE ISLAND *G-8*

400 East Ave.
Warwick, RI 02886-1807
Tel: (401)825-1000
Admissions: (401)333-7302
Fax: (401)825-2418
Web Site: http://www.ccri.edu/

Description: State-supported, 2-year, coed. Awards certificates, transfer associate, and terminal associate degrees. Founded 1964. Setting: 205-acre suburban campus with easy access to Boston. Endowment: $1.2 million. Total enrollment: 16,293. 6,510 applied, 72% were admitted. Full-time: 5,731 students, 56% women, 44% men. Part-time: 10,562 students, 68% women, 32% men. Students come from 17 states and territories, 14 other countries, 1% Native American, 10% Hispanic, 7% black, 3% Asian American or Pacific Islander, 0.1% international, 3% transferred in. Core. Calendar: semesters. Academic remediation for entering students, ESL program, services for LD students, advanced placement, honors program, independent study, distance learning, double major, summer session for credit, part-time degree program, external degree program, adult/continuing education programs, co-op programs and internships. Off campus study at Rhode Island College, University of Rhode Island. Study abroad program. ROTC: Army (c).

Entrance Requirements: Open admission except for nursing, dental, radiography, physical therapist assistant, computer programming, engineering, cardio-respiratory care, medical laboratory technician, occupational therapy assistant. Options: Peterson's Universal Application, deferred admission. Entrance: noncompetitive. Application deadline: Rolling. Notification: continuous. Preference given to state residents, New England Regional Student Program applicants.

Costs Per Year: Application fee: $20. State resident tuition: $2180 full-time, $102 per credit hour part-time. Nonresident tuition: $6410 full-time, $307 per credit hour part-time. Mandatory fees: $290 full-time, $8 per credit hour part-time, $32 per term part-time. Part-time tuition and fees vary according to course load.

Collegiate Environment: Orientation program. Drama-theater group, choral group. Social organizations: 54 open to all. Most popular organizations: Distributive Education Clubs of America, theater group, ABLE, Phi Theta Kappa. Major annual events: Christmas Dinner Theater, Spring Fest, ABLE Handicapped Awareness Day. Student services: health clinic, personal-psychological counseling. Campus security: 24-hour emergency response devices and patrols. College housing not available. Community College of Rhode Island Learning Resources Center plus 3 others with 98,140 books, 81,340 microform titles, 872 serials, 20,231 audiovisual materials, an OPAC, and a Web page. 1,200 computers available on campus for general student use. A campuswide network can be accessed from off-campus. Staffed computer lab on campus.

■ JOHNSON & WALES UNIVERSITY *D-8*

8 Abbott Park Place
Providence, RI 02903-3703

Tel: (401)598-1000
Free: 800-342-5598
Admissions: (401)598-2310
Fax: (401)598-1835
E-mail: admissions.pvd@jwu.edu
Web Site: http://www.jwu.edu/

Description: Independent, comprehensive, coed. Awards associate, bachelor's, master's, and doctoral degrees (branch locations in Charleston, SC; Denver, CO; North Miami, FL; Norfolk, VA; Gothenberg, Sweden). Founded 1914. Setting: 47-acre urban campus with easy access to Boston. System endowment: $168.3 million. Total enrollment: 10,171. Faculty: 406 (279 full-time, 127 part-time). Student-undergrad faculty ratio is 27:1. 15,258 applied, 80% were admitted. Full-time: 8,400 students, 52% women, 48% men. Part-time: 937 students, 56% women, 44% men. Students come from 50 states and territories, 51 other countries, 78% from out-of-state, 0.2% Native American, 5% Hispanic, 8% black, 2% Asian American or Pacific Islander, 4% international, 4% transferred in. Academic areas with the most degrees conferred: business/marketing; personal and culinary services; foreign languages and literature. Core. Academic remediation for entering students, ESL program, services for LD students, advanced placement, accelerated degree program, freshman honors college, honors program, independent study, double major, summer session for credit, part-time degree program, adult/continuing education programs, co-op programs and internships, graduate courses open to undergrads. Study abroad program.

Entrance Requirements: Options: Peterson's Universal Application, Common Application, electronic application, early admission, deferred admission, international baccalaureate accepted. Required: high school transcript. Recommended: minimum 2.0 high school GPA. Required for some: essay, minimum 2.75 high school GPA, recommendations, interview, SAT or ACT. Entrance: minimally difficult. Application deadline: Rolling. Notification: continuous.

Costs Per Year: Application fee: $0. Comprehensive fee: $28,126 includes full-time tuition ($19,875), mandatory fees ($951), and college room and board ($7300). Part-time tuition: $368 per quarter hour.

Collegiate Environment: Orientation program. Drama-theater group, choral group, student-run newspaper. Social organizations: 77 open to all; national fraternities, national sororities, local fraternities, local sororities; 1% of eligible men and 2% of eligible women are members. Most popular organizations: Delta Epsilon Chi, Vocational Industrial Clubs of America, Phi Beta Lambda, FHA/HERO, FFA. Major annual events: Spring Weekend, Homecoming Weekend. Student services: health clinic, personal-psychological counseling, women's center. Campus security: 24-hour emergency response devices and patrols, student patrols, late night transport-escort service. 3,614 college housing spaces available. Freshmen guaranteed college housing. On-campus residence required in freshman year. Option: coed housing available. Johnson & Wales University Library plus 1 other with 91,180 books, 408,876 microform titles, 643 serials, 2,726 audiovisual materials, an OPAC, and a Web page. 400 computers available on campus for general student use. A campuswide network can be accessed from student residence rooms and from off campus. Staffed computer lab on campus.

■ NEW ENGLAND INSTITUTE OF TECHNOLOGY *G-8*

2500 Post Rd.
Warwick, RI 02886-2244
Tel: (401)739-5000
E-mail: neit@ids.net
Web Site: http://www.neit.edu/

Description: Independent, primarily 2-year, coed. Awards transfer associate, terminal associate, and bachelor's degrees. Founded 1940. Setting: 10-acre suburban campus with easy access to Boston. Total enrollment: 2,839. Students come from 10 states and territories, 22 other countries, 1% Native American, 6% Hispanic, 5% black, 2% Asian American or Pacific Islander, 6% international, 48% 25 or older. Core. Academic remediation for entering students, ESL program, services for LD students, advanced placement, distance learning, summer session for credit, part-time degree program, adult/continuing education programs, internships.

Entrance Requirements: Open admission. Options: early admission, deferred admission. Required: high school transcript, interview. Entrance: noncompetitive. Application deadline: Rolling.

Collegiate Environment: Student services: personal-psychological counseling. Campus security: security personnel during open hours. College housing not available. Library with 42,614 books, 3,961 serials, an OPAC, and a Web page. 325 computers available on campus for general student use. A campuswide network can be accessed from off-campus. Staffed computer lab on campus.

■ **PROVIDENCE COLLEGE** *D-8*
River Ave. and Eaton St.
Providence, RI 02918
Tel: (401)865-1000
Free: 800-721-6444
Admissions: (401)865-2535
Fax: (401)865-2826
E-mail: pcadmiss@providence.edu
Web Site: http://www.providence.edu/
Description: Independent Roman Catholic, comprehensive, coed. Awards associate, bachelor's, and master's degrees. Founded 1917. Setting: 105-acre suburban campus with easy access to Boston. Endowment: $115.3 million. Research spending for 2004 fiscal year: $325,578. Educational spending for 2005 fiscal year: $8698 per student. Total enrollment: 4,832. Faculty: 369 (287 full-time, 82 part-time). Student-undergrad faculty ratio is 12:1. 8,237 applied, 54% were admitted. 38% from top 10% of their high school class, 79% from top quarter, 98% from top half. 25 National Merit Scholars, 51 class presidents, 16 valedictorians, 311 student government officers. Full-time: 3,896 students, 57% women, 43% men. Part-time: 16 students, 63% women, 38% men. Students come from 43 states and territories, 78 other countries, 88% from out-of-state, 0.1% Native American, 2% Hispanic, 1% black, 2% Asian American or Pacific Islander, 1% international, 8% 25 or older, 75% live on campus, 2% transferred in. Retention: 93% of full-time freshmen returned the following year. Academic areas with the most degrees conferred: business/marketing; social sciences; education. Core. Calendar: semesters. Services for LD students, advanced placement, self-designed majors, honors program, independent study, double major, summer session for credit, part-time degree program, adult/continuing education programs, co-op programs and internships, graduate courses open to undergrads. Study abroad program. ROTC: Army.
Entrance Requirements: Options: Common Application, electronic application, early admission, early action, deferred admission, international baccalaureate accepted. Required: essay, high school transcript, 2 recommendations, SAT or ACT. Recommended: SAT Subject Tests. Entrance: very difficult. Application deadlines: 1/15, 11/1 for early action. Notification: 4/1, 1/1 for early action.
Costs Per Year: Application fee: $55. Comprehensive fee: $34,580 includes full-time tuition ($24,800), mandatory fees ($510), and college room and board ($9270). College room only: $4970. Room and board charges vary according to board plan and housing facility. Part-time tuition: $827 per credit.
Collegiate Environment: Orientation program. Drama-theater group, choral group, student-run newspaper, radio station. Social organizations: 94 open to all. Most popular organizations: Board of Programmers, Student Congress, student newspaper, Big Brothers/Big Sisters, Pastoral Council. Major annual events: Junior Ring Weekend, Mr. PC Pageant, Clam Jam. Student services: health clinic, personal-psychological counseling. Campus security: 24-hour emergency response devices and patrols, student patrols, late night transport-escort service, controlled dormitory access. 3,074 college housing spaces available; 3,063 were occupied in 2003-04. Freshmen guaranteed college housing. On-campus residence required through sophomore year. Options: coed, men-only, women-only housing available. Phillips Memorial Library with 563,289 books, 12,019 microform titles, 11,809 serials, an OPAC, and a Web page. Operations spending for 2004 fiscal year: $2.8 million. 164 computers available on campus for general student use. A campuswide network can be accessed from student residence rooms and from off campus. Staffed computer lab on campus.
Community Environment: See Brown University.

■ **RHODE ISLAND COLLEGE** *D-8*
600 Mount Pleasant Ave.
Providence, RI 02908-1991
Tel: (401)456-8000
Free: 800-669-5760
Admissions: (401)456-8234
Fax: (401)456-8379
Web Site: http://www.ric.edu/
Description: State-supported, comprehensive, coed. Awards bachelor's, master's, and doctoral degrees and post-master's certificates. Founded 1854. Setting: 180-acre suburban campus with easy access to Boston.

Endowment: $11.9 million. Research spending for 2004 fiscal year: $7.6 million. Educational spending for 2005 fiscal year: $10,905 per student. Total enrollment: 8,871. Faculty: 639 (306 full-time, 333 part-time). Student-undergrad faculty ratio is 16:1. 3,385 applied, 78% were admitted. 7% from top 10% of their high school class, 33% from top quarter, 75% from top half. Full-time: 5,310 students, 67% women, 33% men. Part-time: 2,167 students, 68% women, 32% men. Students come from 10 states and territories, 11% from out-of-state, 0.3% Native American, 5% Hispanic, 5% black, 2% Asian American or Pacific Islander, 0.5% international, 24% 25 or older, 12% live on campus, 9% transferred in. Retention: 78% of full-time freshmen returned the following year. Academic areas with the most degrees conferred: education; business/marketing; psychology. Core. Calendar: semesters. Academic remediation for entering students, services for LD students, advanced placement, self-designed majors, freshman honors college, honors program, independent study, double major, summer session for credit, part-time degree program, adult/continuing education programs, internships, graduate courses open to undergrads. Off campus study at Community College of Rhode Island, Providence College, University of Rhode Island. Study abroad program. ROTC: Army (c).
Entrance Requirements: Options: Common Application, early admission, deferred admission. Required: essay, high school transcript, recommendations, SAT or ACT. Required for some: interview. Application deadline: 5/1. Notification: continuous.
Costs Per Year: Application fee: $50. State resident tuition: $3888 full-time, $168 per credit part-time. Nonresident tuition: $11,200 full-time, $466 per credit part-time. Mandatory fees: $788 full-time, $21 per credit part-time, $60 per term part-time. Part-time tuition and fees vary according to course load. College room and board: $7010. College room only: $3740. Room and board charges vary according to board plan and housing facility.
Collegiate Environment: Orientation program. Drama-theater group, choral group, student-run newspaper, radio station. Social organizations: 60 open to all; local fraternities, local sororities; 10% of eligible men and 10% of eligible women are members. Most popular organizations: student government, newspaper, campus radio station (WXIN), OASPA (Organization of African Students and Professionals in the Americas), Asian Student Association. Major annual events: Midnight Madness, Spring RIC End, Spring Cotillion. Student services: health clinic, personal-psychological counseling, women's center. Campus security: 24-hour patrols, late night transport-escort service. 840 college housing spaces available; all were occupied in 2003-04. Options: coed, women-only housing available. Adams Library with 639,489 books, 1.4 million microform titles, 1,192 serials, 3,982 audiovisual materials, an OPAC, and a Web page. Operations spending for 2004 fiscal year: $2.8 million. 350 computers available on campus for general student use. Computer purchase/lease plans available. A campuswide network can be accessed from student residence rooms and from off campus. Staffed computer lab on campus.

■ **RHODE ISLAND SCHOOL OF DESIGN** *D-8*
2 College St.
Providence, RI 02903-2784
Tel: (401)454-6100
Free: 800-364-7473
Admissions: (401)454-6307
Fax: (401)454-6309
E-mail: admissions@risd.edu
Web Site: http://www.risd.edu/
Description: Independent, comprehensive, coed. Awards bachelor's, master's, and first professional degrees. Founded 1877. Setting: 13-acre urban campus with easy access to Boston. Endowment: $262.1 million. Research spending for 2004 fiscal year: $394,498. Educational spending for 2005 fiscal year: $13,445 per student. Total enrollment: 2,258. Faculty: 494 (139 full-time, 355 part-time). Student-undergrad faculty ratio is 9:1. 2,512 applied, 35% were admitted. 28% from top 10% of their high school class, 72% from top quarter, 94% from top half. Full-time: 1,878 students, 66% women, 34% men. Students come from 51 states and territories, 44 other countries, 94% from out-of-state, 1% Native American, 5% Hispanic, 2% black, 14% Asian American or Pacific Islander, 13% international, 4% 25 or older, 40% live on campus, 6% transferred in. Retention: 94% of full-time freshmen returned the following year. Core. Calendar: 4-1-4. Academic remediation for entering students, ESL program, services for LD students, advanced placement, independent study, internships. Off campus study at Brown University, Association of Independent Colleges of Art and Design. Study abroad program.
Entrance Requirements: Options: electronic application, early admission, early action, deferred admission. Required: essay, high school transcript,

portfolio, drawing assignments, SAT or ACT. Recommended: 3 recommendations. Entrance: very difficult. Application deadlines: 2/15, 12/15 for early action. Notification: 4/1, 1/25 for early action.

Costs Per Year: Application fee: $50. Comprehensive fee: $40,740 includes full-time tuition ($31,145), mandatory fees ($235), and college room and board ($9360). College room only: $5260.

Collegiate Environment: Orientation program. Drama-theater group, student-run newspaper. Social organizations: 60 open to all. Most popular organizations: athletic clubs, Industrial Design Club, Korean Students Association, Lesbian/Gay/Bisexual Alliance. Major annual events: Beaux Arts Ball, Artists' Ball, RISD Apparel Showcase. Student services: legal services, health clinic, personal-psychological counseling. Campus security: 24-hour emergency response devices and patrols, late night transport-escort service, controlled dormitory access. 790 college housing spaces available; all were occupied in 2003-04. Freshmen guaranteed college housing. On-campus residence required in freshman year. Option: coed housing available. RISD Library plus 1 other with 107,436 books, 1,855 microform titles, 420 serials, 683,580 audiovisual materials, an OPAC, and a Web page. Operations spending for 2004 fiscal year: $1.4 million. 400 computers available on campus for general student use. Computer purchase/lease plans available. A campuswide network can be accessed from student residence rooms and from off campus. Staffed computer lab on campus.

Community Environment: See Brown University.

■ ROGER WILLIAMS UNIVERSITY *G-9*

1 Old Ferry Rd.
Bristol, RI 02809
Tel: (401)253-1040
Free: 800-458-7144
Admissions: (401)254-3500
Fax: (401)254-3557
E-mail: admit@alpha.rwu.edu
Web Site: http://www.rwu.edu/

Description: Independent, comprehensive, coed. Awards associate, bachelor's, master's, and first professional degrees. Founded 1956. Setting: 140-acre small town campus with easy access to Boston. Endowment: $77.8 million. Research spending for 2004 fiscal year: $380,000. Educational spending for 2005 fiscal year: $8610 per student. Total enrollment: 5,214. Faculty: 398 (178 full-time, 220 part-time). Student-undergrad faculty ratio is 16:1. 6,658 applied, 78% were admitted. 11% from top 10% of their high school class, 35% from top quarter, 72% from top half. 1 National Merit Scholar, 1 valedictorian, 45 student government officers. Full-time: 3,741 students, 51% women, 49% men. Part-time: 618 students, 40% women, 60% men. Students come from 44 states and territories, 37 other countries, 87% from out-of-state, 0.2% Native American, 2% Hispanic, 1% black, 2% Asian American or Pacific Islander, 2% international, 2% 25 or older, 79% live on campus, 3% transferred in. Retention: 78% of full-time freshmen returned the following year. Academic areas with the most degrees conferred: business/marketing; security and protective services; psychology. Core. Calendar: semesters. ESL program, services for LD students, advanced placement, self-designed majors, freshman honors college, honors program, independent study, distance learning, double major, summer session for credit, part-time degree program, external degree program, adult/continuing education programs, co-op programs and internships, graduate courses open to undergrads. Study abroad program. ROTC: Army.

Entrance Requirements: Options: Common Application, electronic application, early decision, deferred admission, international baccalaureate accepted. Required: essay, high school transcript, minimum 2.0 high school GPA, recommendations, SAT or ACT. Recommended: interview. Required for some: portfolio/audition. Entrance: moderately difficult. Application deadlines: Rolling, 12/1 for early decision. Notification: continuous, 12/15 for early decision.

Costs Per Year: Application fee: $50. Comprehensive fee: $34,759 includes full-time tuition ($22,932), mandatory fees ($1134), and college room and board ($10,693). College room only: $5569. Part-time tuition: $956 per credit.

Collegiate Environment: Orientation program. Drama-theater group, choral group, student-run newspaper, radio station. Social organizations: 54 open to all. Most popular organizations: Entertainment Network, Student Senate, American Institute of Architects, John Jay Society, residence hall councils. Major annual events: Spring Week/Winter Weekend, Midnight Madness, Super Stars. Student services: health clinic, personal-psychological counseling, women's center. Campus security: 24-hour emergency response devices and patrols, student patrols, late night transport-escort service,

controlled dormitory access. 2,864 college housing spaces available; 2,845 were occupied in 2003-04. Freshmen guaranteed college housing. On-campus residence required through sophomore year. Option: coed housing available. Roger Williams University Library plus 2 others with 202,495 books, 138,579 microform titles, 2,132 serials, 70,859 audiovisual materials, an OPAC, and a Web page. Operations spending for 2004 fiscal year: $1.5 million. 410 computers available on campus for general student use. Computer purchase/lease plans available. A campuswide network can be accessed from student residence rooms and from off campus. Staffed computer lab on campus.

■ SALVE REGINA UNIVERSITY *J-9*

100 Ochre Point Ave.
Newport, RI 02840-4192
Tel: (401)847-6650; 888-GO SALVE
Fax: (401)848-2823
E-mail: sruadmis@salve.edu
Web Site: http://www.salve.edu/

Description: Independent Roman Catholic, comprehensive, coed. Awards associate, bachelor's, master's, and doctoral degrees and post-master's certificates. Founded 1934. Setting: 70-acre suburban campus with easy access to Boston and Providence. Endowment: $32.6 million. Educational spending for 2005 fiscal year: $5960 per student. Total enrollment: 2,499. Faculty: 240 (122 full-time, 118 part-time). Student-undergrad faculty ratio is 14:1. 4,555 applied, 60% were admitted. 16% from top 10% of their high school class, 54% from top quarter, 89% from top half. 152 National Merit Scholars, 4 class presidents, 59 student government officers. Full-time: 1,987 students, 71% women, 29% men. Part-time: 104 students, 76% women, 24% men. Students come from 31 states and territories, 11 other countries, 84% from out-of-state, 0.3% Native American, 2% Hispanic, 1% black, 1% Asian American or Pacific Islander, 1% international, 5% 25 or older, 60% live on campus, 3% transferred in. Retention: 81% of full-time freshmen returned the following year. Academic areas with the most degrees conferred: education; business/marketing; security and protective services. Core. Calendar: semesters. ESL program, services for LD students, advanced placement, accelerated degree program, freshman honors college, honors program, independent study, distance learning, double major, summer session for credit, part-time degree program, adult/continuing education programs, internships, graduate courses open to undergrads. Study abroad program. ROTC: Army (c).

Entrance Requirements: Options: Peterson's Universal Application, Common Application, electronic application, early action, deferred admission, international baccalaureate accepted. Required: essay, high school transcript, 2 recommendations, SAT or ACT. Recommended: minimum 2.7 high school GPA. Entrance: moderately difficult. Application deadlines: 3/1, 11/1 for early action. Notification: continuous, 12/15 for early action.

Costs Per Year: Application fee: $40. Comprehensive fee: $33,450 includes full-time tuition ($23,500), mandatory fees ($450), and college room and board ($9500). Room and board charges vary according to board plan. Part-time tuition: $783 per credit. Part-time mandatory fees: $40 per term. Part-time tuition and fees vary according to course load.

Collegiate Environment: Orientation program. Drama-theater group, choral group, student-run newspaper, radio station. Social organizations: 30 open to all. Most popular organizations: Orpheus Musical Society, Student Government Association, Student Outdoor Adventures, Student Nurse Organization, Stagefright Theatre Company. Major annual events: Family Weekend, Spring Weekend. Student services: health clinic, personal-psychological counseling. Campus security: 24-hour emergency response devices and patrols, late night transport-escort service, controlled dormitory access. 1,177 college housing spaces available; 1,170 were occupied in 2003-04. Freshmen given priority for college housing. On-campus residence required through sophomore year. Options: coed, men-only, women-only housing available. McKillop Library with 139,161 books, 44,553 microform titles, 1,221 serials, 19,098 audiovisual materials, an OPAC, and a Web page. Operations spending for 2004 fiscal year: $1.3 million. 163 computers available on campus for general student use. A campuswide network can be accessed from student residence rooms and from off campus. Staffed computer lab on campus.

Community Environment: Newport, RI, an island community and home of Salve Regina, was founded in 1639 and thrived as a Colonial seaport. Today, yachting and sailing regattas still fill its harbor and the Museum of Yachting displays America's Cup memorabilia. The Newport Historical Society and Newport Preservation Society support the City-by-the-Sea's bountiful historic and architectural legacy, including colonial structures,

Victorian cottages, and Gilded Age mansions. The Cliff Walk and Ocean Drive provide stirring ocean vistas. The Redwood Library is the oldest library building in the United States in continuous use. The Newport Art museum exhibitions focus on the art of Newport and New England. The Newport Casino, which contains the Tennis Hall of Fame, hosts international tennis matches on its grass courts. World-acclaimed musicians perform at the Newport Music Festival. Opportunities abound for students to participate in the rich historical and cultural aspects of the community through university-sponsored work-study, volunteer, and intern programs.

■ UNIVERSITY OF RHODE ISLAND *J-6*

Kingston, RI 02881
Tel: (401)874-1000
Admissions: (401)874-7100
Fax: (401)874-5523
E-mail: uriadmit@riacc.uri.edu
Web Site: http://www.uri.edu

Description: State-supported, university, coed. Part of Rhode Island State System of Higher Education. Awards bachelor's, master's, doctoral, and first professional degrees. Founded 1892. Setting: 1,200-acre small town campus. Endowment: $68 million. Research spending for 2004 fiscal year: $39.1 million. Total enrollment: 15,095. Faculty: 691 (668 full-time, 23 part-time). Student-undergrad faculty ratio is 19:1. 13,388 applied, 77% were admitted. 21% from top 10% of their high school class, 88% from top half. Full-time: 9,766 students, 56% women, 44% men. Part-time: 1,780 students, 62% women, 38% men. Students come from 38 states and territories, 39% from out-of-state, 0.3% Native American, 4% Hispanic, 4% black, 2% Asian American or Pacific Islander, 0.3% international, 14% 25 or older, 39% live on campus, 5% transferred in. Retention: 80% of full-time freshmen returned the following year. Academic areas with the most degrees conferred: business/marketing; communications/journalism; engineering. Core. Calendar: semesters. Academic remediation for entering students, services for LD students, advanced placement, honors program, independent study, distance learning, double major, summer session for credit, part-time degree program, adult/continuing education programs, co-op programs and internships, graduate courses open to undergrads. Off campus study at National Student Exchange, New England Land Grant University Exchange Program. Study abroad program. ROTC: Army.

Entrance Requirements: Options: Peterson's Universal Application, Common Application, electronic application, early admission, early action. Required: high school transcript, SAT or ACT. Recommended: minimum 3.0 high school GPA, recommendations, interview. Required for some: minimum 3.0 high school GPA. Entrance: moderately difficult. Application deadlines: 2/1, 12/15 for early action. Notification: continuous, 1/15 for early action. Preference given to state residents.

Costs Per Year: Application fee: $50. State resident tuition: $5258 full-time, $219 per credit part-time. Nonresident tuition: $17,900 full-time, $746 per credit part-time. Mandatory fees: $2026 full-time, $74 per credit part-time, $48 per term part-time. Full-time tuition and fees vary according to reciprocity agreements. Part-time tuition and fees vary according to reciprocity agreements. College room and board: $8114. College room only: $4620. Room and board charges vary according to board plan and housing facility.

Collegiate Environment: Orientation program. Drama-theater group, choral group, marching band, student-run newspaper, radio station. Social organizations: 85 open to all; national fraternities, national sororities, local sororities; 10% of eligible men and 10% of eligible women are members. Most popular organizations: Student Entertainment Committee, student radio station, intramural sport clubs, Student Alumni Association, student newspaper. Major annual events: Family Weekend, Homecoming, Spring Week. Student services: health clinic, personal-psychological counseling, women's center. Campus security: 24-hour emergency response devices and patrols, student patrols, late night transport-escort service, controlled dormitory access. Option: coed housing available. University Library plus 1 other with 1.2 million books, 1.7 million microform titles, 7,926 serials, 11,671 audiovisual materials, an OPAC, and a Web page. Operations spending for 2004 fiscal year: $5.8 million. 552 computers available on campus for general student use. A campuswide network can be accessed from off-campus. Staffed computer lab on campus.

Community Environment: The quiet village of Kingston was founded about 1700. Some of the many interesting houses here date from pre-Revolutionary days. Community facilities include churches of all faiths, a museum, art center, hospitals, and numerous major civic, fraternal and veteran's organizations. Recreational activities include boating, fishing, golf, skiing, and summer theatre. International and deep-sea yacht races are special events. Many part-time jobs are available.

■ ZION BIBLE INSTITUTE *F-9*

27 Middle Hwy.
Barrington, RI 02806
Tel: (401)246-0900
Free: 800-356-4014
Fax: (401)246-0906
Web Site: http://www.zbi.edu/

Description: Independent, 4-year, coed, affiliated with Assembly of God Church. Founded 1924. Calendar: semesters.

Costs Per Year: Application fee: $35. Comprehensive fee: $10,922 includes full-time tuition ($5842), mandatory fees ($480), and college room and board ($4600). College room only: $3200.

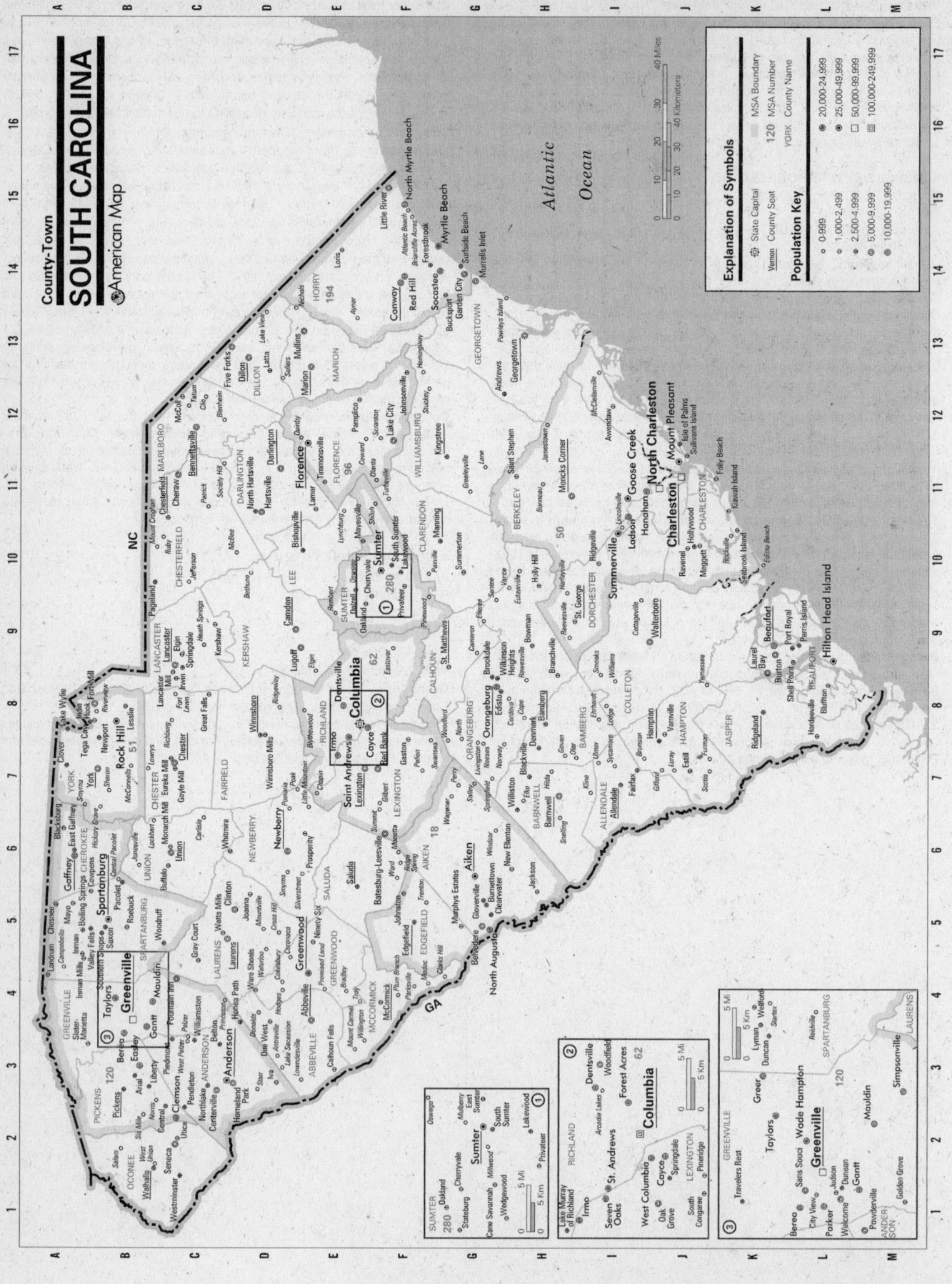

South Carolina

County-Town
SOUTH CAROLINA
American Map

South Carolina

■ **AIKEN TECHNICAL COLLEGE** *G-6*
PO Drawer 696
Aiken, SC 29802-0696
Tel: (803)593-9231
E-mail: pridepae@atc.edu
Web Site: http://www.aik.tec.sc.us/
Description: State and locally supported, 2-year, coed. Part of South Carolina State Board for Technical and Comprehensive Education. Awards certificates, diplomas, transfer associate, and terminal associate degrees. Founded 1972. Setting: 88-acre rural campus. Total enrollment: 2,516. 1,177 applied, 65% were admitted. 3% from top 10% of their high school class, 12% from top quarter, 39% from top half. Full-time: 1,397 students, 66% women, 34% men. Part-time: 1,119 students, 64% women, 36% men. Students come from 6 states and territories, 2 other countries, 10% from out-of-state, 3% Native American, 4% Hispanic, 2% black, 88% Asian American or Pacific Islander, 0% international, 40% 25 or older, 1% transferred in. Core. Calendar: semesters. Academic remediation for entering students, services for LD students, advanced placement, summer session for credit, part-time degree program, adult/continuing education programs, co-op programs and internships. Off campus study at University of South Carolina-Aiken.
Entrance Requirements: Open admission except for nursing program. Options: Common Application, deferred admission. Required: high school transcript. Required for some: essay. Entrance: noncompetitive. Application deadline: Rolling.
Costs Per Year: Application fee: $0. Area resident tuition: $2816 full-time, $117 per credit hour part-time. State resident tuition: $3176 full-time, $132 per credit hour part-time. Nonresident tuition: $8204 full-time, $337 per credit hour part-time. Mandatory fees: $120 full-time, $4.25 per credit hour part-time, $60 per term part-time.
Collegiate Environment: Student-run newspaper. Most popular organizations: student government, Phi Theta Kappa, student newspaper. Major annual events: Field Day, Health Fair, Orientation. Student services: personal-psychological counseling. Campus security: 24-hour patrols, late night transport-escort service. College housing not available. Aiken Technical College Library with 32,118 books, 425 serials, and an OPAC. Operations spending for 2004 fiscal year: $258,703. 200 computers available on campus for general student use. A campuswide network can be accessed. Staffed computer lab on campus.

■ **ALLEN UNIVERSITY** *E-8*
1530 Harden St.
Columbia, SC 29204
Tel: (803)254-4165
Admissions: (803)376-5789
Fax: (803)376-5731
Web Site: http://www.allenuniversity.edu/
Description: Independent African Methodist Episcopal, 4-year, coed. Awards bachelor's degrees. Founded 1870. Setting: suburban campus. Total enrollment: 565. 784 applied, 61% were admitted. Full-time: 552 students, 38% women, 62% men. Part-time: 13 students, 54% women, 46% men. Students come from 14 states and territories, 1 other country, 9% from out-of-state, 97% black, 3% international, 25% 25 or older, 80% live on campus, 12% transferred in. Retention: 41% of full-time freshmen returned the following year. Core. Calendar: semesters. Academic remediation for entering students, honors program, independent study, summer session for credit,

part-time degree program, adult/continuing education programs, co-op programs and internships. Study abroad program. ROTC: Army (c).
Entrance Requirements: Open admission. Options: Peterson's Universal Application, Common Application. Required: essay, high school transcript, 3 recommendations, SAT or ACT. Entrance: minimally difficult. Application deadline: 7/31.
Costs Per Year: Application fee: $20. Comprehensive fee: $6260 includes full-time tuition ($3609), mandatory fees ($546), and college room and board ($2105). College room only: $1230. Part-time tuition: $301 per credit hour.
Collegiate Environment: Orientation program. Choral group, student-run newspaper. Social organizations: 3 open to all; national fraternities, national sororities, local sororities; 7% of eligible men and 10% of eligible women are members. Most popular organizations: International Students Club, Social Science Club, Gospel Choir. Major annual events: Homecoming, Religious Emphasis Week, Black History Month observance. Student services: health clinic, personal-psychological counseling. Campus security: 24-hour patrols. 324 college housing spaces available; 275 were occupied in 2003-04. Freshmen guaranteed college housing. Options: men-only, women-only housing available. J. S. Flipper Library with 50,000 books and 175 serials. 130 computers available on campus for general student use. A campuswide network can be accessed. Staffed computer lab on campus.
Community Environment: See University of South Carolina.

■ **ANDERSON UNIVERSITY** *D-3*
316 Blvd.
Anderson, SC 29621-4035
Tel: (864)231-2000
Free: 800-542-3594
Admissions: (864)231-2030
Fax: (864)231-2004
E-mail: admissions@anderson-college.edu
Web Site: http://www.ac.edu/
Description: Independent Baptist, 4-year, coed. Awards bachelor's and master's degrees. Founded 1911. Setting: 44-acre suburban campus. Endowment: $17.2 million. Educational spending for 2005 fiscal year: $2942 per student. Total enrollment: 1,644. Faculty: 150 (68 full-time, 82 part-time). Student-undergrad faculty ratio is 15:1. 1,079 applied, 78% were admitted. 17% from top 10% of their high school class, 44% from top quarter, 81% from top half. Full-time: 1,277 students, 64% women, 36% men. Part-time: 367 students, 65% women, 35% men. Students come from 29 states and territories, 18 other countries, 11% from out-of-state, 0.4% Native American, 1% Hispanic, 10% black, 1% Asian American or Pacific Islander, 2% international, 17% 25 or older, 50% live on campus, 5% transferred in. Retention: 62% of full-time freshmen returned the following year. Academic areas with the most degrees conferred: business/marketing; education; visual and performing arts. Core. Calendar: semesters. Academic remediation for entering students, services for LD students, advanced placement, accelerated degree program, honors program, independent study, distance learning, double major, summer session for credit, part-time degree program, adult/continuing education programs, co-op programs and internships. Study abroad program. ROTC: Army (c), Air Force (c).
Entrance Requirements: Options: Peterson's Universal Application, electronic application, deferred admission. Required: high school transcript, SAT or ACT. Recommended: minimum 2.5 high school GPA. Required for some: essay, 2 recommendations, interview. Application deadline: 7/1. Notification: continuous.

Costs Per Year: Application fee: $25. Comprehensive fee: $22,950 includes full-time tuition ($15,400), mandatory fees ($1150), and college room and board ($6400). College room only: $3250. Part-time tuition: $410 per credit hour.

Collegiate Environment: Orientation program. Drama-theater group, choral group, student-run newspaper. Social organizations: 29 open to all. Most popular organizations: Baptist Campus Ministries, Fellowship of Christian Athletes, Student Government Association, Gamma Beta Phi, Student Alumni Council. Major annual events: CORE-Campus Organizations Recruitment Event, Christmas First Night, Founders' Day Convocation. Student services: health clinic, personal-psychological counseling. Campus security: 24-hour emergency response devices and patrols, late night transport-escort service, controlled dormitory access. 879 college housing spaces available; 830 were occupied in 2003-04. No special consideration for freshman housing applicants. On-campus residence required through sophomore year. Options: men-only, women-only housing available. Olin D. Johnston Library with 69,069 books, 7,200 microform titles, 314 serials, 4,868 audiovisual materials, an OPAC, and a Web page. 192 computers available on campus for general student use. A campuswide network can be accessed from student residence rooms and from off campus. Staffed computer lab on campus.

Community Environment: Located in the Piedmont Plateau section, Anderson enjoys moderate climate and is a busy manufacturing town with 32 textile plants and many other factories. The area is accessed by major highways, air, bus, and limited rail service. The community has a county-wide library system, churches of many denominations, hotel and motels, hospitals, shopping malls, and various civic and fraternal organizations. Local recreation includes theatres, bowling, tennis, excellent golf facilities, two large lakes, swimming, boating, fishing, hunting, and other outdoor sports. Part-time employment is available.

■ **BENEDICT COLLEGE** *E-8*

1600 Harden St.
Columbia, SC 29204
Tel: (803)256-4220
Admissions: (803)253-5275
Fax: (803)253-5167
Web Site: http://www.benedict.edu/

Description: Independent Baptist, 4-year, coed. Awards bachelor's degrees. Founded 1870. Setting: 20-acre urban campus. Endowment: $17 million. Total enrollment: 3,005. 4,039 applied, 71% were admitted. 7% from top 10% of their high school class, 14% from top quarter, 28% from top half. Full-time: 2,864 students, 50% women, 50% men. Part-time: 141 students, 58% women, 42% men. Students come from 32 states and territories, 20% from out-of-state, 0.1% Native American, 0.2% Hispanic, 99% black, 0.1% Asian American or Pacific Islander, 10% 25 or older, 66% live on campus, 6% transferred in. Core. Calendar: semesters. Advanced placement, honors program, summer session for credit, part-time degree program, adult/continuing education programs, internships. ROTC: Army, Air Force (c).

Entrance Requirements: Open admission. Options: Common Application, early admission, deferred admission. Required: high school transcript. Placement: SAT or ACT recommended. Entrance: minimally difficult. Application deadline: Rolling. Notification: continuous until 7/31.

Costs Per Year: Application fee: $25. Comprehensive fee: $18,912 includes full-time tuition ($11,574), mandatory fees ($1380), and college room and board ($5958). Part-time tuition: $388 per credit hour. Part-time mandatory fees: $45 per credit hour.

Collegiate Environment: Orientation program. Drama-theater group, choral group, student-run newspaper. Social organizations: 40 open to all; national fraternities, national sororities; 2% of eligible men and 5% of eligible women are members. Most popular organizations: NAACP, Student Education Association, African Awareness Student Union. Major annual events: Fall Convocation, Homecoming Week, Spring Fest Week. Student services: personal-psychological counseling. Campus security: 24-hour emergency response devices and patrols. 2,013 college housing spaces available; 1,850 were occupied in 2003-04. Freshmen guaranteed college housing. Option: coed housing available. Benjamin Payton Learning Resource Center with 114,770 books, 35,754 microform titles, 320 serials, 5,954 audiovisual materials, and a Web page. 500 computers available on campus for general student use. A campuswide network can be accessed from student residence rooms and from off campus. Staffed computer lab on campus.

Community Environment: See University of South Carolina.

■ **BOB JONES UNIVERSITY** *B-4*

1700 Wade Hampton Blvd.
Greenville, SC 29614
Tel: (803)242-5100
Free: 800-BJA-NDME
Admissions: (864)242-5100
E-mail: admissions@bju.edu
Web Site: http://www.bju.edu/

Description: Independent religious, university, coed. Awards associate, bachelor's, master's, doctoral, and first professional degrees. Founded 1927. Total enrollment: 4,099. Faculty: 302 (235 full-time, 67 part-time). Student-undergrad faculty ratio is 15:1. 1,773 applied, 82% were admitted. 7% from top 10% of their high school class, 37% from top quarter, 65% from top half. Full-time: 3,523 students, 55% women, 45% men. Part-time: 52 students, 37% women, 63% men. 77% from out-of-state. Retention: 76% of full-time freshmen returned the following year. Academic areas with the most degrees conferred: education; theology and religious vocations; business/marketing. Calendar: semesters.

Entrance Requirements: Required: high school transcript, 3 recommendations, ACT. Entrance: minimally difficult. Application deadline: 8/1.

Costs Per Year: Application fee: $45. Comprehensive fee: $14,750 includes full-time tuition ($9180), mandatory fees ($590), and college room and board ($4980). Part-time tuition: $459 per credit hour.

Collegiate Environment: Drama-theater group, choral group, student-run newspaper, radio station. Student services: health clinic.

■ **CENTRAL CAROLINA TECHNICAL COLLEGE** *F-10*

506 North Guignard Dr.
Sumter, SC 29150-2499
Tel: (803)778-1961
Free: 800-221-8711
Fax: (803)773-4859
E-mail: brackenlm@cctech.edu
Web Site: http://www.cctech.edu/

Description: State-supported, 2-year, coed. Part of South Carolina State Board for Technical and Comprehensive Education. Awards certificates, diplomas, transfer associate, and terminal associate degrees. Founded 1963. Setting: 70-acre small town campus. Total enrollment: 3,244. Student-undergrad faculty ratio is 19:1. Full-time: 945 students, 67% women, 33% men. Part-time: 2,299 students, 71% women, 29% men. Students come from 2 states and territories, 1% from out-of-state, 0.5% Native American, 1% Hispanic, 49% black, 1% Asian American or Pacific Islander, 0.2% international, 46% 25 or older, 13% transferred in. Core. Calendar: semesters. Academic remediation for entering students, advanced placement, independent study, distance learning, summer session for credit, part-time degree program, external degree program, adult/continuing education programs, co-op programs and internships.

Entrance Requirements: Open admission except for selected health science programs. Option: electronic application. Required: high school transcript. Entrance: noncompetitive. Application deadline: Rolling.

Costs Per Year: Application fee: $25. Area resident tuition: $2700 full-time, $112.50 per credit hour part-time. State resident tuition: $3168 full-time, $132.50 per credit hour part-time. Nonresident tuition: $4800 full-time, $200 per credit hour part-time.

Collegiate Environment: Orientation program. Social organizations: 11 open to all. Most popular organizations: Creative Arts Society, Phi Theta Kappa, Computer Club, National Student Nurses Association (local chapter), Natural Resources Management Club. Major annual events: Spring Fling, Student Appreciation Day. Student services: personal-psychological counseling. Campus security: 24-hour emergency response devices. College housing not available. Central Carolina Technical College Library with 20,356 books, 21,993 microform titles, 245 serials, 1,317 audiovisual materials, an OPAC, and a Web page. Operations spending for 2004 fiscal year: $256,334. 556 computers available on campus for general student use. A campuswide network can be accessed from off-campus. Staffed computer lab on campus.

Community Environment: See Morris College.

■ **CHARLESTON SOUTHERN UNIVERSITY** *J-11*

PO Box 118087
Charleston, SC 29423-8087
Tel: (843)863-7000

Free: 800-947-7474
Admissions: (843)863-7050
E-mail: enroll@csuniv.edu
Web Site: http://www.charlestonsouthern.edu/
Description: Independent Baptist, comprehensive, coed. Awards bachelor's and master's degrees. Founded 1964. Setting: 500-acre suburban campus. Endowment: $13.1 million. Educational spending for 2005 fiscal year: $4165 per student. Total enrollment: 3,022. Faculty: 178 (106 full-time, 72 part-time). Student-undergrad faculty ratio is 18:1. 2,744 applied, 71% were admitted. 12% from top 10% of their high school class, 34% from top quarter, 67% from top half. Full-time: 2,208 students, 61% women, 39% men. Part-time: 374 students, 61% women, 39% men. Students come from 42 states and territories, 25 other countries, 18% from out-of-state, 1% Native American, 1% Hispanic, 28% black, 2% Asian American or Pacific Islander, 2% international, 20% 25 or older, 46% live on campus, 10% transferred in. Retention: 63% of full-time freshmen returned the following year. Academic areas with the most degrees conferred: business/marketing; education; social sciences. Core. Calendar: 4-1-1. Academic remediation for entering students, services for LD students, advanced placement, accelerated degree program, honors program, double major, summer session for credit, part-time degree program, internships. Off campus study at Charleston Higher Education Consortium, University of North Carolina System, Clemson University. ROTC: Air Force.
Entrance Requirements: Option: international baccalaureate accepted. Required: high school transcript, minimum 2.0 high school GPA, SAT or ACT. Required for some: essay, 1 recommendation, interview. Entrance: moderately difficult. Application deadline: Rolling. Notification: continuous.
Costs Per Year: Application fee: $30. Comprehensive fee: $23,230 includes full-time tuition ($16,780) and college room and board ($6450). Part-time tuition: $271 per credit hour.
Collegiate Environment: Orientation program. Drama-theater group, choral group, marching band, student-run newspaper. Social organizations: 20 open to all; national fraternities, national sororities, local fraternities, local sororities. Most popular organizations: student government, Baptist Student Union, Fellowship of Christian Athletics. Major annual events: Convocation, Homecoming. Student services: personal-psychological counseling. Campus security: 24-hour emergency response devices and patrols, late night transport-escort service. 1,134 college housing spaces available; 1,080 were occupied in 2003-04. Freshmen given priority for college housing. On-campus residence required through sophomore year. Options: men-only, women-only housing available. L. Mendel Rivers Library with 192,600 books, 215,900 microform titles, 1,111 serials, 8,169 audiovisual materials, an OPAC, and a Web page. Operations spending for 2004 fiscal year: $883,948. 190 computers available on campus for general student use. A campuswide network can be accessed from student residence rooms and from off campus. Staffed computer lab on campus.
Community Environment: See The Citadel.

■ THE CITADEL, THE MILITARY COLLEGE OF SOUTH CAROLINA

J-11
171 Moultrie St.
Charleston, SC 29409
Tel: (843)953-5000
Free: 800-868-1842
Admissions: (843)953-5230
Fax: (843)953-7084
E-mail: john.powell@citadel.edu
Web Site: http://www.citadel.edu
Description: State-supported, comprehensive, coed. Awards bachelor's and master's degrees and post-master's certificates. Founded 1842. Setting: 130-acre urban campus. Endowment: $39.8 million. Research spending for 2004 fiscal year: $179,878. Educational spending for 2005 fiscal year: $5544 per student. Total enrollment: 3,386. Faculty: 232 (157 full-time, 75 part-time). Student-undergrad faculty ratio is 15:1. 1,913 applied, 78% were admitted. 9% from top 10% of their high school class, 31% from top quarter, 67% from top half. Full-time: 2,111 students, 6% women, 94% men. Part-time: 127 students, 47% women, 53% men. Students come from 48 states and territories, 29 other countries, 51% from out-of-state, 0.2% Native American, 4% Hispanic, 7% black, 2% Asian American or Pacific Islander, 2% international, 6% 25 or older, 100% live on campus, 4% transferred in. Retention: 82% of full-time freshmen returned the following year. Academic areas with the most degrees conferred: business/marketing; security and protective services; social sciences. Core. Calendar: semesters. ESL program, services for LD students, advanced placement, honors program,

independent study, double major, summer session for credit, part-time degree program, adult/continuing education programs, co-op programs and internships. Off campus study at 4 members of the Charleston Higher Education Consortium. Study abroad program. ROTC: Army, Naval, Air Force.
Entrance Requirements: Options: electronic application, international baccalaureate accepted. Required: high school transcript, minimum 2.0 high school GPA, SAT or ACT. Recommended: recommendations, interview. Entrance: moderately difficult. Application deadline: Rolling. Notification: 9/1. Preference given to state residents.
Costs Per Year: Application fee: $40. State resident tuition: $6522 full-time, $198 per credit hour part-time. Nonresident tuition: $15,918 full-time, $397 per credit hour part-time. Mandatory fees: $998 full-time, $15 per term part-time. College room and board: $4840.
Collegiate Environment: Orientation program. Drama-theater group, choral group, marching band, student-run newspaper. Social organizations: 37 open to all. Major annual events: Parents' Day, Homecoming, Corps Day. Student services: health clinic, personal-psychological counseling. Campus security: 24-hour patrols, student patrols, late night transport-escort service. 1,913 college housing spaces available. Freshmen guaranteed college housing. On-campus residence required through senior year. Option: coed housing available. Daniel Library with 233,745 books, 1.2 million microform titles, 583 serials, 2,868 audiovisual materials, an OPAC, and a Web page. Operations spending for 2004 fiscal year: $1.4 million. 350 computers available on campus for general student use. A campuswide network can be accessed from student residence rooms and from off campus. Staffed computer lab on campus.

■ CLAFLIN UNIVERSITY *G-8*

400 Magnolia St.
Orangeburg, SC 29115
Tel: (803)535-5097
Admissions: (803)535-5340
Fax: (803)531-2860
E-mail: mzeigler@claflin.edu
Web Site: http://www.claflin.edu/
Description: Independent United Methodist, comprehensive, coed. Awards bachelor's and master's degrees. Founded 1869. Setting: 32-acre small town campus with easy access to Columbia. Endowment: $14 million. Educational spending for 2005 fiscal year: $4456 per student. Total enrollment: 1,728. Faculty: 127 (93 full-time, 34 part-time). Student-undergrad faculty ratio is 14:1. 2,744 applied, 40% were admitted. 25% from top 10% of their high school class, 46% from top quarter, 75% from top half. Full-time: 1,598 students, 67% women, 33% men. Part-time: 80 students, 59% women, 41% men. Students come from 29 states and territories, 19 other countries, 15% from out-of-state, 0.1% Native American, 0.1% Hispanic, 93% black, 0.2% Asian American or Pacific Islander, 5% international, 15% 25 or older, 65% live on campus, 3% transferred in. Retention: 79% of full-time freshmen returned the following year. Academic areas with the most degrees conferred: business/marketing; security and protective services; social sciences. Core. Calendar: semesters. Academic remediation for entering students, advanced placement, freshman honors college, honors program, independent study, summer session for credit, part-time degree program, adult/continuing education programs, co-op programs and internships. Off campus study at South Carolina State University, Medical University of South Carolina, Orangeburg-Calhoun Technical College, Clemson University. Study abroad program. ROTC: Army (c).
Entrance Requirements: Options: Common Application, deferred admission. Required: essay, high school transcript, minimum 2.00 high school GPA, SAT or ACT. Recommended: recommendations, SAT Subject Tests. Entrance: minimally difficult. Application deadline: Rolling. Notification: continuous.
Costs Per Year: Application fee: $20. Comprehensive fee: $16,798 includes full-time tuition ($9206), mandatory fees ($1684), and college room and board ($5908). College room only: $2632. Room and board charges vary according to housing facility. Part-time tuition: $384 per credit hour. Part-time mandatory fees: $63 per credit hour.
Collegiate Environment: Orientation program. Drama-theater group, choral group, student-run newspaper, radio station. Social organizations: national fraternities, national sororities; 22% of eligible men and 26% of eligible women are members. Major annual events: graduation, Homecoming, Honors Convocation. Student services: health clinic, personal-psychological counseling. Campus security: 24-hour emergency response devices and patrols, student patrols. 1,003 college housing spaces available; 963 were

occupied in 2003-04. Options: men-only, women-only housing available. H. V. Manning Library with 158,108 books, 62,718 microform titles, 427 serials, 981 audiovisual materials, and an OPAC. Operations spending for 2004 fiscal year: $761,608. 500 computers available on campus for general student use. A campuswide network can be accessed from student residence rooms and from off campus. Staffed computer lab on campus.

■ CLEMSON UNIVERSITY C-2

Clemson, SC 29634
Tel: (864)656-3311
Admissions: (864)656-2287
Fax: (864)656-2464
Web Site: http://www.clemson.edu/

Description: State-supported, university, coed. Awards bachelor's, master's, and doctoral degrees. Founded 1889. Setting: 1,400-acre small town campus. Endowment: $264.9 million. Research spending for 2004 fiscal year: $104.5 million. Educational spending for 2005 fiscal year: $7729 per student. Total enrollment: 17,165. Faculty: 1,143 (1,015 full-time, 128 part-time). Student-undergrad faculty ratio is 16:1. 12,463 applied, 57% were admitted. 45% from top 10% of their high school class, 72% from top quarter, 97% from top half. 23 National Merit Scholars, 88 valedictorians. Full-time: 13,257 students, 46% women, 54% men. Part-time: 839 students, 41% women, 59% men. Students come from 53 states and territories, 62 other countries, 32% from out-of-state, 0.4% Native American, 1% Hispanic, 7% black, 2% Asian American or Pacific Islander, 1% international, 5% 25 or older, 47% live on campus, 5% transferred in. Retention: 89% of full-time freshmen returned the following year. Academic areas with the most degrees conferred: business/marketing; engineering; education. Core. Calendar: semesters. Academic remediation for entering students, services for LD students, advanced placement, accelerated degree program, honors program, distance learning, double major, summer session for credit, part-time degree program, co-op programs and internships, graduate courses open to undergrads. Study abroad program. ROTC: Army, Air Force.

Entrance Requirements: Options: Peterson's Universal Application, electronic application, international baccalaureate accepted. Required: high school transcript, SAT or ACT. Recommended: essay, recommendations. Entrance: moderately difficult. Application deadlines: 5/1, 12/1 for early action. Notification: continuous, 2/15 for early action. Preference given to state residents.

Costs Per Year: Application fee: $50. State resident tuition: $9016 full-time, $364 per hour part-time. Nonresident tuition: $18,640 full-time, $760 per hour part-time. Full-time tuition varies according to course load and program. Part-time tuition varies according to course load and program. College room and board: $5780. College room only: $3470. Room and board charges vary according to board plan and housing facility.

Collegiate Environment: Orientation program. Drama-theater group, choral group, marching band, student-run newspaper, radio station. Social organizations: 250 open to all; national fraternities, national sororities; 15% of eligible men and 22% of eligible women are members. Most popular organizations: student government, Fellowship of Christian Athletes, Tiger Band. Major annual events: Homecoming/Tigerama, Welcome Back Festival, Campus Sweep. Student services: legal services, health clinic, personal-psychological counseling. Campus security: 24-hour emergency response devices and patrols, late night transport-escort service, controlled dormitory access. College housing designed to accommodate 6,216 students; 6,329 undergraduates lived in college housing during 2003-04. Freshmen guaranteed college housing. On-campus residence required in freshman year. Options: coed, men-only, women-only housing available. Robert Muldrow Cooper Library plus 1 other with 1.2 million books, 1.2 million microform titles, 5,587 serials, 131,280 audiovisual materials, an OPAC, and a Web page. Operations spending for 2004 fiscal year: $10.4 million. 1,250 computers available on campus for general student use. Computer purchase/lease plans available. A campuswide network can be accessed from student residence rooms and from off campus. Staffed computer lab on campus.

Community Environment: Clemson is located in the foothills of the Blue Ridge Mountains approximately 135 miles from Charlotte and Atlanta. The average temperature is 61 degrees. The area is served by U.S. Highways 76 and 123, and air service is available nearby. Clemson has several churches of different denominations, a library, YMCA, concert series, and Little Theatre. Hotels, apartments, and rooming houses provide additional student

housing. Local recreational facilities include fishing, hunting, golf, tennis, swimming, sailing, and skiing. Job opportunities are available.

■ CLINTON JUNIOR COLLEGE B-8

PO Box 968, 1029 Crawford Rd.
Rock Hill, SC 29730
Tel: (803)327-7402
Fax: (803)327-3261
E-mail: ecopeland@clintonjrcollege.org
Web Site: http://www.clintonjuniorcollege.edu/

Description: Independent, 2-year, coed, affiliated with African Methodist Episcopal Zion Church. Founded 1894. Calendar: semesters.

■ COASTAL CAROLINA UNIVERSITY F-14

PO Box 261954
Conway, SC 29528-6054
Tel: (843)347-3161
Free: 800-277-7000
Admissions: (843)349-2037
Fax: (843)349-2127
E-mail: admissions@coastal.edu
Web Site: http://www.coastal.edu/

Description: State-supported, comprehensive, coed. Awards bachelor's and master's degrees. Founded 1954. Setting: 244-acre suburban campus. Endowment: $14.8 million. Research spending for 2004 fiscal year: $966,347. Educational spending for 2005 fiscal year: $4467 per student. Total enrollment: 7,613. Faculty: 414 (233 full-time, 181 part-time). Student-undergrad faculty ratio is 19:1. 5,427 applied, 74% were admitted. 11% from top 10% of their high school class, 43% from top quarter, 73% from top half. Full-time: 5,753 students, 52% women, 48% men. Part-time: 644 students, 61% women, 39% men. Students come from 45 states and territories, 41 other countries, 46% from out-of-state, 1% Native American, 2% Hispanic, 12% black, 1% Asian American or Pacific Islander, 2% international, 13% 25 or older, 35% live on campus, 9% transferred in. Retention: 64% of full-time freshmen returned the following year. Academic areas with the most degrees conferred: business/marketing; biological/life sciences; education. Core. Calendar: semesters. Services for LD students, advanced placement, accelerated degree program, self-designed majors, honors program, independent study, distance learning, double major, summer session for credit, part-time degree program, adult/continuing education programs, co-op programs and internships, graduate courses open to undergrads. Study abroad program.

Entrance Requirements: Options: Peterson's Universal Application, Common Application, electronic application, deferred admission. Required: high school transcript, minimum 2.0 high school GPA, SAT or ACT. Recommended: essay, 1 recommendation, interview. Entrance: moderately difficult. Application deadline: 8/15. Notification: continuous until 9/15. Preference given to state residents.

Costs Per Year: Application fee: $45. State resident tuition: $6780 full-time, $290 per credit hour part-time. Nonresident tuition: $15,020 full-time, $630 per credit hour part-time. Mandatory fees: $80 full-time. Full-time tuition and fees vary according to course load. Part-time tuition varies according to course load. College room and board: $6280. College room only: $4020. Room and board charges vary according to board plan and housing facility.

Collegiate Environment: Orientation program. Drama-theater group, choral group, marching band, student-run newspaper. Social organizations: 83 open to all; national fraternities, national sororities; 7% of eligible men and 6% of eligible women are members. Most popular organizations: Student Government Association, Coastal Productions Board, STAR (Students Taking Active Responsibility), FCA (Fellowship of Christian Athletes), Diversity of Programming. Major annual events: homecoming, Cino Day, Chanticleer Days. Student services: health clinic, personal-psychological counseling, women's center. Campus security: 24-hour emergency response devices and patrols, late night transport-escort service. 2,250 college housing spaces available; 2,093 were occupied in 2003-04. Option: coed housing available. Kimbel Library with 144,361 books, 17,804 microform titles, 8,638 serials, 4,003 audiovisual materials, an OPAC, and a Web page. Operations spending for 2004 fiscal year: $1.5 million. 600 computers available on campus for general student use. A campuswide network can be accessed from student residence rooms and from off campus. Staffed computer lab on campus.

Community Environment: Coastal Carolina University is located nine miles from the bustling resort area of Myrtle Beach, SC. Recreational and entertainment options provide many opportunities for internships for the

Professional Golf Management and Resort Tourism programs, as well as part-time employment opportunities. Brookgreen Gardens, one of the world's finest outdoor sculpture gardens, provides a tranquil setting for relaxation, while Broadway on the Beach provides entertainment, shopping, and dining attractions.

■ COKER COLLEGE D-11
300 East College Ave.
Hartsville, SC 29550
Tel: (843)383-8000
Free: 800-950-1908
Admissions: (843)383-8050
Fax: (843)383-8056
E-mail: admissions@coker.edu
Web Site: http://www.coker.edu/

Description: Independent, 4-year, coed. Awards bachelor's degrees (also offers evening program with significant enrollment not reflected in profile). Founded 1908. Setting: 30-acre small town campus with easy access to Charlotte. Total enrollment: 551. Student-undergrad faculty ratio is 9:1. 649 applied, 66% were admitted. 20% from top 10% of their high school class, 50% from top quarter, 82% from top half. 2 valedictorians. Full-time: 541 students, 59% women, 41% men. Part-time: 10 students, 50% women, 50% men. Students come from 28 states and territories, 6 other countries, 23% from out-of-state, 0.4% Native American, 2% Hispanic, 20% black, 1% Asian American or Pacific Islander, 2% international, 8% 25 or older, 70% live on campus, 8% transferred in. Retention: 74% of full-time freshmen returned the following year. Academic areas with the most degrees conferred: business/marketing; visual and performing arts; psychology. Core. Calendar: semesters. Academic remediation for entering students, ESL program, advanced placement, self-designed majors, honors program, independent study, double major, summer session for credit, part-time degree program, adult/continuing education programs, co-op programs and internships. Study abroad program.
Entrance Requirements: Options: Peterson's Universal Application, Common Application, electronic application, deferred admission, international baccalaureate accepted. Required: high school transcript, SAT or ACT. Required for some: essay. Entrance: moderately difficult. Application deadline: Rolling. Notification: 9/1.
Costs Per Year: Application fee: $15. Comprehensive fee: $23,728 includes full-time tuition ($17,472), mandatory fees ($480), and college room and board ($5776). College room only: $2740. Part-time tuition: $728 per semester hour.
Collegiate Environment: Orientation program. Drama-theater group, choral group, student-run newspaper. Social organizations: 27 open to all. Most popular organizations: Coker College Union, student government, Pan-African American Sisterhood Association, Sigma Alpha Chi, Commissioners. Major annual events: homecoming, C.O.W. Days, Bandfest. Student services: health clinic, personal-psychological counseling. Campus security: 24-hour patrols, late night transport-escort service, controlled dormitory access. 364 college housing spaces available; 338 were occupied in 2003-04. Freshmen guaranteed college housing. On-campus residence required through junior year. Options: coed, men-only, women-only housing available. James Lide Coker III Memorial Library plus 1 other with 78,706 books, 45,391 microform titles, 575 serials, 5,741 audiovisual materials, an OPAC, and a Web page. 40 computers available on campus for general student use. A campuswide network can be accessed from student residence rooms and from off campus. Staffed computer lab on campus.
Community Environment: Coker College is located in Hartsville, a community of approximately 20,000 people. It is located in the northeastern part of the state, 20 miles off I-95, and approximately a two-hour drive from South Carolina's beautiful beaches and mountains. The climate is temperate and mild year-round. There is a township library and many churches of various denominations. Florence airport is 24 miles away. Part-time employment is available for students. Local recreational facilities include two theaters, Lake Robinson, Prestwood Lake, golf, tennis, two city parks, and racing. There are various civic and fraternal organizations that are active within the community. Health service facilities are available.

■ COLLEGE OF CHARLESTON J-11
66 George St.
Charleston, SC 29424-0001
Tel: (843)953-5507
Admissions: (843)953-5670
E-mail: admissions@cofc.edu

Web Site: http://www.cofc.edu/
Description: State-supported, comprehensive, coed. Awards bachelor's and master's degrees (also offers graduate degree programs through University of Charleston, South Carolina). Founded 1770. Setting: 52-acre urban campus. Endowment: $36.6 million. Research spending for 2004 fiscal year: $4.4 million. Educational spending for 2005 fiscal year: $5153 per student. Total enrollment: 11,332. Faculty: 858 (515 full-time, 343 part-time). Student-undergrad faculty ratio is 13:1. 8,217 applied, 66% were admitted. 25% from top 10% of their high school class, 58% from top quarter, 91% from top half. 34 valedictorians. Full-time: 9,055 students, 64% women, 36% men. Part-time: 823 students, 57% women, 43% men. Students come from 52 states and territories, 76 other countries, 35% from out-of-state, 0.3% Native American, 2% Hispanic, 7% black, 2% Asian American or Pacific Islander, 2% international, 8% 25 or older, 29% live on campus, 5% transferred in. Retention: 83% of full-time freshmen returned the following year. Academic areas with the most degrees conferred: business/marketing; communications/journalism; social sciences. Core. Calendar: semesters. ESL program, services for LD students, advanced placement, accelerated degree program, honors program, independent study, distance learning, double major, summer session for credit, part-time degree program, adult/continuing education programs, co-op programs and internships, graduate courses open to undergrads. Off campus study at National Student Exchange, Medical University of South Carolina, Trident Technical College, The Citadel, Charleston Southern University. Study abroad program. ROTC: Air Force (c).
Entrance Requirements: Options: Peterson's Universal Application, Common Application, electronic application, early admission, early action, deferred admission, international baccalaureate accepted. Required: essay, high school transcript, recommendations, SAT or ACT. Recommended: interview. Entrance: moderately difficult. Application deadlines: 4/1, 4/1 for nonresidents, 11/1 for early action. Notification: 5/15, 5/15 for nonresidents, 12/15 for early action.
Costs Per Year: Application fee: $45. State resident tuition: $6668 full-time, $278 per semester hour part-time. Nonresident tuition: $15,342 full-time, $639 per semester hour part-time. Part-time tuition varies according to course load. College room and board: $6948. College room only: $4768. Room and board charges vary according to board plan and housing facility.
Collegiate Environment: Orientation program. Drama-theater group, choral group, student-run newspaper, radio station. Social organizations: 144 open to all; national fraternities, national sororities; 15% of eligible men and 20% of eligible women are members. Most popular organizations: Student Government Association, Cougar Productions, intramural basketball, Black Student Union. Major annual events: Cougar Walk, Pep Supper, Welcome Week. Student services: legal services, health clinic, personal-psychological counseling, women's center. Campus security: 24-hour emergency response devices and patrols, student patrols, late night transport-escort service. College housing designed to accommodate 2,644 students; 2,900 undergraduates lived in college housing during 2003-04. Freshmen guaranteed college housing. Options: coed, men-only, women-only housing available. Marlene and Nathan Addlestone Library plus 1 other with 476,108 books, 822,143 microform titles, 3,723 serials, 5,024 audiovisual materials, an OPAC, and a Web page. Operations spending for 2004 fiscal year: $4.5 million. 578 computers available on campus for general student use. Computer purchase/lease plans available. A campuswide network can be accessed from student residence rooms and from off campus. Staffed computer lab on campus.
Community Environment: See The Citadel.

■ COLUMBIA COLLEGE E-8
1301 Columbia College Dr.
Columbia, SC 29203-5998
Tel: (803)786-3012
Free: 800-277-1301
Admissions: (803)786-3091
Fax: (803)786-3674
E-mail: admissions@colacoll.edu
Web Site: http://www.columbiacollegesc.edu/

Description: Independent United Methodist, comprehensive. Awards bachelor's and master's degrees. Founded 1854. Setting: 33-acre suburban campus. Endowment: $19.4 million. Educational spending for 2005 fiscal year: $6653 per student. Total enrollment: 1,493. Faculty: 154 (82 full-time, 72 part-time). Student-undergrad faculty ratio is 10:1. 767 applied, 84% were admitted. 15% from top 10% of their high school class, 42% from top quarter, 71% from top half. Full-time: 867 students, 99% women, 1% men. Part-time:

241 students, 94% women, 6% men. Students come from 12 states and territories, 17 other countries, 6% from out-of-state, 0.3% Native American, 2% Hispanic, 43% black, 1% Asian American or Pacific Islander, 2% international, 30% 25 or older, 63% live on campus, 11% transferred in. Retention: 71% of full-time freshmen returned the following year. Academic areas with the most degrees conferred: business/marketing; education; public administration and social services. Core. Calendar: semesters. Academic remediation for entering students, advanced placement, self-designed majors, honors program, independent study, distance learning, double major, summer session for credit, part-time degree program, adult/continuing education programs, internships. Off campus study. Study abroad program. ROTC: Army (c), Naval (c), Air Force (c).

Entrance Requirements: Options: Peterson's Universal Application, Common Application, electronic application. Required: high school transcript, minimum 2.0 high school GPA, 1 recommendation, SAT or ACT. Recommended: essay. Required for some: interview. Entrance: moderately difficult. Application deadline: 8/1.

Costs Per Year: Application fee: $25. Comprehensive fee: $25,032 includes full-time tuition ($18,864), mandatory fees ($350), and college room and board ($5818). College room only: $3034. Full-time tuition and fees vary according to class time. Room and board charges vary according to board plan and housing facility. Part-time tuition: $506 per credit hour. Part-time tuition varies according to course load.

Collegiate Environment: Orientation program. Drama-theater group, choral group, student-run newspaper. Social organizations: 40 open to all. Most popular organizations: Student Government Association, African-American Student Association, Columbia College Activities Board, Heavenly Creations Gospel Choir, Student Christian Association. Major annual events: Ludy Bowl, Follies, Mom's Day/Dad's Night. Student services: health clinic, personal-psychological counseling, women's center. Campus security: 24-hour emergency response devices and patrols, late night transport-escort service, controlled dormitory access. 560 college housing spaces available; 539 were occupied in 2003-04. Freshmen guaranteed college housing. On-campus residence required through sophomore year. Option: women-only housing available. J. Drake Edens Library plus 1 other with 140,909 books, 12,060 microform titles, 513 serials, 18,144 audiovisual materials, an OPAC, and a Web page. Operations spending for 2004 fiscal year: $609,877. 150 computers available on campus for general student use. A campuswide network can be accessed. Staffed computer lab on campus.

■ **COLUMBIA INTERNATIONAL UNIVERSITY** *E-8*
PO Box 3122
Columbia, SC 29230-3122
Tel: (803)754-4100
Free: 800-777-2227
Fax: (803)786-4209
E-mail: yesciu@ciu.edu
Web Site: http://www.ciu.edu/

Description: Independent nondenominational, comprehensive, coed. Awards associate, bachelor's, master's, doctoral, and first professional degrees. Founded 1923. Setting: 450-acre suburban campus. Endowment: $3.4 million. Educational spending for 2005 fiscal year: $5874 per student. Total enrollment: 1,013. Faculty: 48 (23 full-time, 25 part-time). Student-undergrad faculty ratio is 18:1. 252 applied, 67% were admitted. 24% from top 10% of their high school class, 41% from top quarter, 71% from top half. 3 valedictorians. Full-time: 496 students, 58% women, 42% men. Part-time: 54 students, 57% women, 43% men. Students come from 38 states and territories, 10 other countries, 63% from out-of-state, 0.2% Native American, 1% Hispanic, 2% black, 1% Asian American or Pacific Islander, 3% international, 14% 25 or older, 59% live on campus, 12% transferred in. Retention: 69% of full-time freshmen returned the following year. Academic area with the most degrees conferred: theology and religious vocations. Core. Calendar: semesters. Academic remediation for entering students, advanced placement, accelerated degree program, independent study, distance learning, double major, summer session for credit, part-time degree program, co-op programs and internships, graduate courses open to undergrads. Off campus study at Midlands Technical College. Study abroad program.

Entrance Requirements: Options: Common Application, electronic application, deferred admission, international baccalaureate accepted. Required: essay, minimum 2.0 high school GPA, 4 recommendations, SAT or ACT. Required for some: high school transcript, interview. Entrance: minimally difficult. Application deadline: Rolling.

Costs Per Year: Application fee: $45. Comprehensive fee: $20,592 includes full-time tuition ($14,880) and college room and board ($5712). Part-time tuition: $600 per semester hour.

Collegiate Environment: Orientation program. Drama-theater group, choral group, student-run newspaper. Social organizations: 14 open to all. Most popular organizations: Student Union, Student Senate, Student Missions Connection. Major annual events: Spring Conference, Homecoming, World Christian Week. Student services: health clinic, personal-psychological counseling. Campus security: 24-hour emergency response devices and patrols, late night transport-escort service. 375 college housing spaces available; 339 were occupied in 2003-04. Freshmen guaranteed college housing. On-campus residence required through junior year. Options: men-only, women-only housing available. G. Allen Fleece Library with 118,752 books, 568,690 microform titles, 490 serials, 17,542 audiovisual materials, and an OPAC. Operations spending for 2004 fiscal year: $406,231. 42 computers available on campus for general student use. A campuswide network can be accessed. Staffed computer lab on campus.

Community Environment: See University of South Carolina.

■ **CONVERSE COLLEGE** *B-5*
580 East Main St.
Spartanburg, SC 29302-0006
Tel: (864)596-9000
Free: 800-766-1125
Admissions: (864)596-9040
Fax: (864)596-9158
E-mail: aaron.meis@converse.edu
Web Site: http://www.converse.edu/

Description: Independent, comprehensive. Awards bachelor's and master's degrees and post-master's certificates. Founded 1889. Setting: 70-acre urban campus. Endowment: $50 million. Research spending for 2004 fiscal year: $25,000. Educational spending for 2005 fiscal year: $6507 per student. Total enrollment: 2,176. Faculty: 173 (83 full-time, 90 part-time). Student-undergrad faculty ratio is 12:1. 423 applied, 84% were admitted. 29% from top 10% of their high school class, 62% from top quarter, 88% from top half. Full-time: 648 students, 100% women. Part-time: 128 students, 100% women. Students come from 30 states and territories, 8 other countries, 24% from out-of-state, 0.4% Native American, 1% Hispanic, 14% black, 1% Asian American or Pacific Islander, 4% international, 23% 25 or older, 90% live on campus, 3% transferred in. Retention: 75% of full-time freshmen returned the following year. Academic areas with the most degrees conferred: education; visual and performing arts; social sciences. Core. Calendar: 4-1-4. ESL program, advanced placement, accelerated degree program, honors program, independent study, distance learning, double major, summer session for credit, part-time degree program, adult/continuing education programs, internships, graduate courses open to undergrads. Off campus study at Wofford College. Study abroad program. ROTC: Army (c).

Entrance Requirements: Options: Peterson's Universal Application, electronic application, early admission, early decision, early action, deferred admission, international baccalaureate accepted. Required: high school transcript, 1 recommendation, SAT or ACT. Recommended: essay, minimum 3.0 high school GPA, interview. Entrance: moderately difficult. Application deadline: 4/1. Notification: continuous until 5/1.

Costs Per Year: Application fee: $40. Comprehensive fee: $29,082 includes full-time tuition ($22,234) and college room and board ($6848). Part-time tuition: $720 per credit hour. Part-time mandatory fees: $20 per term.

Collegiate Environment: Orientation program. Drama-theater group, choral group, student-run newspaper. Social organizations: 30 open to all. Most popular organizations: student government, student volunteer services, Student Christian Organization, Student Activities Committee, Athletic Association. Major annual events: 1889 Day, Founders' Day, Formal Opening. Student services: health clinic, personal-psychological counseling, women's center. Campus security: 24-hour emergency response devices and patrols, late night transport-escort service, controlled dormitory access. 600 college housing spaces available. Freshmen guaranteed college housing. On-campus residence required through senior year. Option: women-only housing available. Mickel Library with 129,411 books, 60,213 microform titles, 1,467 serials, 30,132 audiovisual materials, an OPAC, and a Web page. Operations spending for 2004 fiscal year: $546,000. 72 computers available on campus for general student use. A campuswide network can be accessed from student residence rooms and from off campus. Staffed computer lab on campus.

Community Environment: One of the leading textile manufacturing cities in the South, Spartanburg is also one of the largest peach shipping centers in the world. The city was named after the Spartan Regiment, which represented this community in the Revolutionary War. The community is located in the Piedmont section of South Carolina and has an average temperature of 60 degrees. Airlines, railroads, and bus lines serve the area. There are many churches representing various denominations, 3 hospitals, libraries, a YMCA Family Center, and various civic and fraternal groups serving the city. Motels, hotels, and rooming houses are available for guests. Local recreation includes football, basketball, baseball, golf, stock car racing, swimming, tennis, picnicking, water skiing, theater, and series of concerts. Part-time employment is available.

■ **DENMARK TECHNICAL COLLEGE** *H-7*
Solomon Blatt Blvd., Box 327
Denmark, SC 29042-0327
Tel: (803)793-5100
Admissions: (803)793-5176
Fax: (803)793-5942
Web Site: http://www.denmarktech.edu/
Description: State-supported, 2-year, coed. Part of South Carolina State Board for Technical and Comprehensive Education. Awards certificates, diplomas, transfer associate, and terminal associate degrees. Founded 1948. Setting: 53-acre rural campus. Total enrollment: 1,408. Student-undergrad faculty ratio is 19:1. 876 applied, 100% were admitted. Full-time: 969 students, 59% women, 41% men. Part-time: 439 students, 60% women, 40% men. Students come from 8 states and territories, 0% from out-of-state, 0.2% Native American, 0% Hispanic, 76% black, 0% Asian American or Pacific Islander, 0% international, 20% 25 or older. Calendar: semesters. Academic remediation for entering students, advanced placement, summer session for credit, part-time degree program, adult/continuing education programs, co-op programs and internships. Off campus study at Voorhees College, South Carolina State University. ROTC: Army (c).
Entrance Requirements: Open admission. Options: Peterson's Universal Application, early admission, deferred admission. Required: high school transcript, ACT ASSET. Entrance: noncompetitive. Application deadline: Rolling.
Costs Per Year: Application fee: $10. State resident tuition: $2088 full-time, $87 per credit hour part-time. Nonresident tuition: $4176 full-time, $174 per credit hour part-time. Mandatory fees: $190 full-time, $95 per term part-time. College room and board: $3096.
Collegiate Environment: Orientation program. Choral group, student-run newspaper. Social organizations: national fraternities, national sororities, local fraternities, local sororities; 25% of eligible men and 30% of eligible women are members. Most popular organizations: Phi Beta Lambda, Gospel Choir, Drama Club. Major annual events: Homecoming, Family Day, Annual Honors Day Convocation. Student services: health clinic, personal-psychological counseling. Campus security: 24-hour patrols. 330 college housing spaces available; all were occupied in 2003-04. Denmark Technical College Learning Resources Center with 15,437 books and 200 serials. 105 computers available on campus for general student use. Staffed computer lab on campus.

■ **ERSKINE COLLEGE** *D-4*
2 Washington St.
PO Box 338
Due West, SC 29639
Tel: (864)379-2131
Free: 800-241-8721
Admissions: (864)379-8830
Fax: (864)379-8759
E-mail: admissions@erskine.edu
Web Site: http://www.erskine.edu/
Description: Independent, 4-year, coed, affiliated with Associate Reformed Presbyterian Church. Administratively affiliated with Erskine Theological Seminary. Awards bachelor's, master's, doctoral, and first professional degrees. Founded 1839. Setting: 85-acre rural campus. Endowment: $45.6 million. Total enrollment: 890. Faculty: 68 (37 full-time, 31 part-time). Student-undergrad faculty ratio is 12:1. 854 applied, 70% were admitted. 31% from top 10% of their high school class, 58% from top quarter, 84% from top half. Full-time: 585 students, 55% women, 45% men. Part-time: 9 students, 56% women, 44% men. Students come from 24 states and territories, 12 other countries, 34% from out-of-state, 0.2% Native American, 1% Hispanic, 6% black, 1% Asian American or Pacific Islander, 2% international, 1% 25 or older, 88% live on campus, 2% transferred in. Retention: 77% of full-time freshmen returned the following year. Academic areas

with the most degrees conferred: business/marketing; education; biological/life sciences. Core. Calendar: 4-1-4. Advanced placement, independent study, double major, summer session for credit, part-time degree program, internships. Off campus study at other colleges having a 4-1-4 calendar. Study abroad program.
Entrance Requirements: Option: electronic application. Required: essay, high school transcript, 1 recommendation, SAT or ACT. Recommended: interview. Required for some: interview. Entrance: moderately difficult. Application deadline: Rolling. Notification: continuous. Preference given to members of Associate Reformed Presbyterian Church.
Costs Per Year: Application fee: $25. Comprehensive fee: $25,468 includes full-time tuition ($17,700), mandatory fees ($1342), and college room and board ($6426). Room and board charges vary according to board plan and housing facility.
Collegiate Environment: Orientation program. Drama-theater group, choral group, student-run newspaper, radio station. Social organizations: 49 open to all; local fraternities, local sororities; 14% of eligible men and 25% of eligible women are members. Most popular organizations: literary societies, religious organizations, Student Government Organization, publications, honor societies. Major annual events: Fall Fest, Spring Fling, homecoming. Student services: health clinic, personal-psychological counseling. Campus security: 24-hour patrols, late night transport-escort service, controlled dormitory access. 644 college housing spaces available; 535 were occupied in 2003-04. Freshmen guaranteed college housing. On-campus residence required through senior year. Options: men-only, women-only housing available. McCain Library with 233,541 books, 62,012 microform titles, 1,020 serials, 1,777 audiovisual materials, an OPAC, and a Web page. Operations spending for 2004 fiscal year: $463,693. 65 computers available on campus for general student use. Computer purchase/lease plans available. A campuswide network can be accessed from student residence rooms and from off campus. Staffed computer lab on campus.
Community Environment: Due West is a town of approximately 1,300 residents. It enjoys a temperate climate. There is easy access to Interstate Routes 26 and 85, and the cities of Anderson, Greenwood, and Greenville are nearby. The major metropolitan areas of Atlanta and Charlotte are within a 2.5-hour drive. The college arranges transportation to meet students arriving at these points by train, bus or plane. Local recreational facilities include tennis courts, a swimming pool, movies and a physical education/athletic center.

■ **FLORENCE-DARLINGTON TECHNICAL COLLEGE** *E-12*
2715 West Lucas St.
PO Box 100548
Florence, SC 29501-0548
Tel: (843)661-8324
Free: 800-228-5745
Admissions: (843)661-8153
Fax: (843)661-8306
E-mail: kirvenp@flo.tec.sc.us
Web Site: http://www.fdtc.edu/
Description: State-supported, 2-year, coed. Part of South Carolina State Board for Technical and Comprehensive Education. Awards certificates, diplomas, transfer associate, and terminal associate degrees. Founded 1963. Setting: 100-acre small town campus with easy access to Columbia. Endowment: $1000. Total enrollment: 4,041. Full-time: 2,147 students, 67% women, 33% men. Part-time: 1,894 students, 75% women, 25% men. Students come from 4 states and territories, 1% Native American, 0.4% Hispanic, 46% black, 0.4% Asian American or Pacific Islander, 0% international, 3% transferred in. Core. Calendar: semesters. Academic remediation for entering students, ESL program, advanced placement, summer session for credit, part-time degree program, adult/continuing education programs, internships. Study abroad program. ROTC: Army (c).
Entrance Requirements: Open admission. Options: Peterson's Universal Application, Common Application, deferred admission. Required for some: high school transcript, SAT or ACT, CPT. Entrance: noncompetitive. Application deadline: 8/1.
Collegiate Environment: Choral group, student-run newspaper. Social organizations: 3 open to all. Most popular organizations: International Club, FDTC Outreach Choir, Student Ambassadors. Major annual events: Spring Fling, Back to School Bash, Black History Month. Student services: personal-psychological counseling. Campus security: 24-hour emergency response devices and patrols, late night transport-escort service. College housing not available. Florence-Darlington Technical College Library with 34,814 books and 286 serials. Operations spending for 2004 fiscal year:

$341,742. 220 computers available on campus for general student use. A campuswide network can be accessed from off-campus. Staffed computer lab on campus.

Community Environment: Agriculture and industry support the economy of Florence. There are several diversified manufacturing companies within the area. Florence can be called an urban and a suburban community. It is located approximately 50 miles from the Atlantic Ocean resort areas. The city enjoys a temperate climate. Community services include public library, hospitals, museums, many churches of various denominations, and major civic, fraternal, and veteran's organizations. Local entertainment and recreation encompasses the Little Theatre group, movie theatres, a YMCA, a Civic Center, swimming, hunting, golf, tennis, and ice hockey.

■ **FORREST JUNIOR COLLEGE** *D-3*
601 East River St.
Anderson, SC 29624
Tel: (864)225-7653
Fax: (864)261-7471
Web Site: http://www.forrestcollege.com/

Description: Proprietary, 2-year, coed. Awards certificates, diplomas, transfer associate, and terminal associate degrees. Founded 1946. Setting: 3-acre small town campus. Educational spending for 2005 fiscal year: $7240 per student. Total enrollment: 165. 26 applied, 92% were admitted. Students come from 2 states and territories, 26% from out-of-state, 0% Native American, 0% Hispanic, 47% black, 0% Asian American or Pacific Islander, 0% international, 20% 25 or older. ESL program, advanced placement, accelerated degree program, freshman honors college, distance learning, double major, summer session for credit, part-time degree program, co-op programs and internships.

Entrance Requirements: Option: deferred admission. Required: essay, high school transcript, recommendations, interview. Entrance: minimally difficult. Application deadline: 9/30.

Costs Per Year: Application fee: $25. Tuition: $4950 full-time, $110 per quarter hour part-time. Mandatory fees: $450 full-time, $150 per term part-time. Full-time tuition and fees vary according to course load and program. Part-time tuition and fees vary according to course load and program.

Collegiate Environment: Student services: legal services, health clinic. Campus security: late night transport-escort service. College housing not available. Forrest Junior College Library plus 1 other with an OPAC. Operations spending for 2004 fiscal year: $12,000. 37 computers available on campus for general student use. A campuswide network can be accessed from off-campus. Staffed computer lab on campus.

■ **FRANCIS MARION UNIVERSITY** *E-12*
PO Box 100547
Florence, SC 29501-0547
Tel: (843)661-1362
Free: 800-368-7551
Admissions: (843)661-1231
Fax: (843)661-4635
Web Site: http://www.fmarion.edu/

Description: State-supported, comprehensive, coed. Awards bachelor's and master's degrees. Founded 1970. Setting: 309-acre rural campus. Endowment: $200,000. Research spending for 2004 fiscal year: $250,236. Educational spending for 2005 fiscal year: $4662 per student. Total enrollment: 4,008. Faculty: 281 (176 full-time, 105 part-time). Student-undergrad faculty ratio is 17:1. 2,524 applied, 71% were admitted. 14% from top 10% of their high school class, 39% from top quarter, 72% from top half. 7 valedictorians. Full-time: 3,058 students, 64% women, 36% men. Part-time: 442 students, 73% women, 27% men. Students come from 31 states and territories, 21 other countries, 4% from out-of-state, 0.4% Native American, 1% Hispanic, 42% black, 1% Asian American or Pacific Islander, 1% international, 11% 25 or older, 44% live on campus, 6% transferred in. Retention: 65% of full-time freshmen returned the following year. Academic areas with the most degrees conferred: business/marketing; biological/life sciences; education. Core. Calendar: semesters. Services for LD students, advanced placement, accelerated degree program, honors program, independent study, distance learning, double major, summer session for credit, part-time degree program, adult/continuing education programs, internships, graduate courses open to undergrads. Off campus study at University of South Carolina, Florence-Darlington Technical College, Clemson University. Study abroad program.

Entrance Requirements: Options: Peterson's Universal Application, Common Application, electronic application, early admission, deferred admission,

international baccalaureate accepted. Required: high school transcript, minimum 2.0 high school GPA, SAT or ACT. Entrance: moderately difficult. Application deadline: Rolling. Notification: continuous.

Costs Per Year: Application fee: $30. State resident tuition: $6327 full-time, $316.35 per credit hour part-time. Nonresident tuition: $12,654 full-time, $632.70 per credit hour part-time. Mandatory fees: $185 full-time, $4.75 per credit hour part-time. College room and board: $5430. College room only: $2960.

Collegiate Environment: Orientation program. Drama-theater group, choral group, student-run newspaper. Social organizations: 60 open to all; national fraternities, national sororities; 3% of eligible men and 4% of eligible women are members. Most popular organizations: Baptist Campus Ministries, Education Club, University Ambassadors, Psychology Club, Campus Outreach. Major annual events: Homecoming, Arts Alive, Springfest. Student services: health clinic, personal-psychological counseling. Campus security: 24-hour emergency response devices and patrols, late night transport-escort service, controlled dormitory access. 1,381 college housing spaces available; 1,358 were occupied in 2003-04. Freshmen given priority for college housing. Options: men-only, women-only housing available. James A. Rogers Library plus 1 other with 332,043 books, 351,613 microform titles, 1,559 serials, an OPAC, and a Web page. Operations spending for 2004 fiscal year: $1.6 million. 551 computers available on campus for general student use. A campuswide network can be accessed from student residence rooms and from off campus. Staffed computer lab on campus.

Community Environment: See Florence-Darlington Technical College.

■ **FURMAN UNIVERSITY** *B-4*
3300 Poinsett Hwy.
Greenville, SC 29613
Tel: (864)294-2000
Admissions: (864)294-2034
Fax: (864)294-3127
E-mail: admissions@furman.edu
Web Site: http://www.furman.edu/

Description: Independent, comprehensive, coed. Awards bachelor's and master's degrees. Founded 1826. Setting: 750-acre suburban campus. Endowment: $429.8 million. Research spending for 2004 fiscal year: $1.4 million. Educational spending for 2005 fiscal year: $13,967 per student. Total enrollment: 3,221. Faculty: 272 (220 full-time, 52 part-time). Student-undergrad faculty ratio is 11:1. 4,007 applied, 53% were admitted. 64% from top 10% of their high school class, 88% from top quarter, 98% from top half. 20 National Merit Scholars, 32 class presidents, 47 valedictorians, 176 student government officers. Full-time: 2,699 students, 56% women, 44% men. Part-time: 105 students, 49% women, 51% men. Students come from 45 states and territories, 24 other countries, 71% from out-of-state, 0.1% Native American, 1% Hispanic, 6% black, 2% Asian American or Pacific Islander, 1% international, 0% 25 or older, 91% live on campus, 1% transferred in. Retention: 93% of full-time freshmen returned the following year. Academic areas with the most degrees conferred: social sciences; visual and performing arts; business/marketing. Core. Calendar: 3-2-3. Services for LD students, advanced placement, accelerated degree program, self-designed majors, independent study, double major, summer session for credit, part-time degree program, adult/continuing education programs, internships, graduate courses open to undergrads. Study abroad program. ROTC: Army.

Entrance Requirements: Options: Peterson's Universal Application, Common Application, electronic application, early admission, early decision, international baccalaureate accepted. Required: essay, high school transcript, SAT or ACT. Recommended: minimum 3.0 high school GPA, 2 recommendations. Required for some: SAT Subject Tests. Entrance: very difficult. Application deadlines: 1/15, 11/15 for early decision. Notification: 3/15, 12/1 for early decision. Preference given to children of alumni.

Costs Per Year: Application fee: $40. Comprehensive fee: $33,264 includes full-time tuition ($25,888), mandatory fees ($464), and college room and board ($6912). College room only: $3712. Room and board charges vary according to board plan and housing facility. Part-time tuition: $809 per credit hour. Part-time tuition varies according to course load.

Collegiate Environment: Orientation program. Drama-theater group, choral group, marching band, student-run newspaper, radio station. Social organizations: 130 open to all; national fraternities, national sororities; 35% of eligible men and 40% of eligible women are members. Most popular organizations: Collegiate Educational Service Corps, Fellowship of Christian Athletes, Baptist Student Union, Student Activities Board, Furman Singers. Major annual events: Homecoming Spirit Competition, May Day-Play Day,

Beach Weekend. Student services: health clinic, personal-psychological counseling. Campus security: 24-hour emergency response devices and patrols, student patrols, late night transport-escort service, controlled dormitory access. 2,425 college housing spaces available; all were occupied in 2003-04. Freshmen guaranteed college housing. On-campus residence required through senior year. Options: coed, men-only, women-only housing available. James Buchanan Duke Library plus 2 others with 453,211 books, 811,000 microform titles, 2,052 serials, 5,644 audiovisual materials, an OPAC, and a Web page. Operations spending for 2004 fiscal year: $2.8 million. 340 computers available on campus for general student use. A campuswide network can be accessed from student residence rooms and from off campus. Staffed computer lab on campus.

Community Environment: An industrial city, Greenville is in an important manufacturing region with very diverse industry. It is a metropolitan community that enjoys a temperate climate. Part-time employment is available. The city is served by air, rail and bus lines. Community facilities include a performing arts center, 16,000 seat arena, public library, art museum, YMCA, YWCA, 5 general and 1 children's hospital, and over 400 churches that represent major denominations. Local recreation includes several community theatre groups, lakes and rivers for water sports, mountains for hiking and camping, and most major sports, including golf and minor league baseball and hockey teams.

■ **GREENVILLE TECHNICAL COLLEGE** *B-4*

PO Box 5616
Greenville, SC 29606-5616
Tel: (864)250-8000
Free: 800-723-0673
Admissions: (864)250-8109
Fax: (864)250-8534
Web Site: http://www.greenvilletech.com/

Description: State-supported, 2-year, coed. Part of South Carolina State Board for Technical and Comprehensive Education. Awards certificates, diplomas, transfer associate, and terminal associate degrees. Founded 1962. Setting: 407-acre urban campus. Total enrollment: 13,000. Students come from 6 other countries, 42% 25 or older. Core. Calendar: semesters. Academic remediation for entering students, advanced placement, summer session for credit, part-time degree program, adult/continuing education programs, co-op programs.

Entrance Requirements: Open admission except for allied health, nursing programs. Options: early admission, deferred admission. Required: high school transcript. Recommended: SAT, ACT ASSET, or ACT COMPASS. Entrance: noncompetitive. Application deadline: Rolling. Notification: continuous until 8/20.

Collegiate Environment: Social organizations: 12 open to all. Most popular organizations: Student Government Association, Phi Theta Kappa, Student Nurses Association, Christians on Campus, International and Friends Organization. Major annual events: Spring Picnic, Red Ribbon Week, Student Leadership Conference. Campus security: 24-hour emergency response devices and patrols, student patrols, late night transport-escort service. College housing not available. Verne Smith Library/Technical Resource Center with 49,500 books and 658 serials. 830 computers available on campus for general student use. Staffed computer lab on campus.

Community Environment: See Furman University.

■ **HORRY-GEORGETOWN TECHNICAL COLLEGE** *F-14*

2050 Hwy. 501, PO Box 261966
Conway, SC 29528-6066
Tel: (843)347-3186
Admissions: (843)349-5277
Fax: (843)347-4207
E-mail: george.swindoll@hgtc.edu
Web Site: http://www.hgtc.edu/

Description: State and locally supported, 2-year, coed. Part of South Carolina State Board for Technical and Comprehensive Education. Awards certificates, diplomas, transfer associate, and terminal associate degrees. Founded 1966. Setting: small town campus. Total enrollment: 5,362. Student-undergrad faculty ratio is 16:1. 5% from top 10% of their high school class, 5% from top quarter, 45% from top half. Full-time: 2,446 students, 61% women, 39% men. Part-time: 2,916 students, 71% women, 29% men. Students come from 10 states and territories, 22 other countries, 11% from out-of-state, 1% Native American, 1% Hispanic, 24% black, 1% Asian American or Pacific Islander, 2% international. Retention: 51% of full-time freshmen returned the following year. Core. Calendar: semesters. Academic

remediation for entering students, services for LD students, advanced placement, summer session for credit, part-time degree program, adult/continuing education programs, co-op programs and internships.

Entrance Requirements: Open admission. Option: early admission. Required for some: high school transcript. Application deadlines: Rolling, Rolling for nonresidents. Notification: continuous, continuous for nonresidents.

Costs Per Year: Application fee: $25. Area resident tuition: $2800 full-time, $117 per credit hour part-time. State resident tuition: $3544 full-time, $148 per credit hour part-time. Nonresident tuition: $4264 full-time, $178 per credit hour part-time. Mandatory fees: $144 full-time, $1 per credit hour part-time, $35 per term part-time.

Collegiate Environment: Orientation program. Student services: personal-psychological counseling. College housing not available. Conway Campus Learning Resource Center plus 2 others with a Web page. 300 computers available on campus for general student use. A campuswide network can be accessed from off-campus. Staffed computer lab on campus.

Community Environment: The college is located at the center of the largest tourist recreational environment along the Eastern Seaboard. Over 75 miles of white sand beaches as well as golf courses, restaurants, and hotels abound in the area. Air and bus service is available and Highway 17, the "Kings Highway", is the major coastal route in the area. Major arts and entertainment centers, libraries, churches, as well as numerous fraternal and civic organizations serve the community. There are extensive part-time employment opportunities for students, especially from March through September, the height of the tourist season.

■ **ITT TECHNICAL INSTITUTE** *B-4*

6 Independence Pointe
Greenville, SC 29615
Tel: (864)288-0777
Fax: (864)297-0053
Web Site: http://www.itt-tech.edu/

Description: Proprietary, primarily 2-year, coed. Part of ITT Educational Services, Inc. Awards terminal associate and bachelor's degrees. Founded 1992. Core.

Entrance Requirements: Option: deferred admission. Required: high school transcript, interview, Wonderlic aptitude test. Recommended: recommendations. Entrance: minimally difficult. Application deadline: Rolling. Notification: continuous.

Costs Per Year: Application fee: $100.

Collegiate Environment: Orientation program. College housing not available.

■ **LANDER UNIVERSITY** *E-4*

320 Stanley Ave.
Greenwood, SC 29649-2099
Tel: (864)388-8000; 888-452-6337
Admissions: (864)388-8307
Fax: (864)388-8125
E-mail: admissions@lander.edu
Web Site: http://www.lander.edu/

Description: State-supported, comprehensive, coed. Part of South Carolina Commission on Higher Education. Awards bachelor's and master's degrees. Founded 1872. Setting: 100-acre small town campus. Research spending for 2004 fiscal year: $11,187. Educational spending for 2005 fiscal year: $4586 per student. Total enrollment: 2,703. Faculty: 190 (126 full-time, 64 part-time). Student-undergrad faculty ratio is 19:1. 1,750 applied, 85% were admitted. 11% from top 10% of their high school class, 33% from top quarter, 72% from top half. Full-time: 2,373 students, 66% women, 34% men. Part-time: 239 students, 70% women, 30% men. Students come from 28 states and territories, 17 other countries, 3% from out-of-state, 1% Native American, 1% Hispanic, 24% black, 0.4% Asian American or Pacific Islander, 2% international, 13% 25 or older, 33% live on campus, 9% transferred in. Retention: 63% of full-time freshmen returned the following year. Academic areas with the most degrees conferred: history; business/marketing; education. Core. Calendar: semesters plus 3 summer sessions. Academic remediation for entering students, services for LD students, advanced placement, accelerated degree program, self-designed majors, honors program, independent study, distance learning, double major, summer session for credit, part-time degree program, adult/continuing education programs, co-op programs and internships, graduate courses open to undergrads. Off campus study at University Center of Greenville. Study abroad program. ROTC: Army.

Entrance Requirements: Options: Peterson's Universal Application, Common Application, electronic application, early admission, deferred admission, international baccalaureate accepted. Required: high school transcript, 1 recommendation, SAT or ACT. Recommended: interview. Entrance: moderately difficult. Application deadline: 8/1. Notification: continuous.

Costs Per Year: Application fee: $35. State resident tuition: $6108 full-time, $275 per semester hour part-time. Nonresident tuition: $13,528 full-time, $564 per semester hour part-time. Mandatory fees: $560 full-time. Full-time tuition and fees vary according to degree level. Part-time tuition varies according to degree level. College room and board: $5468. College room only: $3360. Room and board charges vary according to board plan and housing facility.

Collegiate Environment: Orientation program. Drama-theater group, choral group, student-run newspaper. Social organizations: 49 open to all; national fraternities, national sororities, local fraternities, local sororities; 11% of eligible men and 12% of eligible women are members. Most popular organizations: Students Promoting Intelligent Choices and Experiences (S.P.I.C.E.), Lander Association of Biological Science. Major annual events: Miss Lander Pageant, Homecoming, graduation. Student services: health clinic, personal-psychological counseling. Campus security: 24-hour emergency response devices and patrols, late night transport-escort service, controlled dormitory access. 1,032 college housing spaces available; 971 were occupied in 2003-04. Freshmen given priority for college housing. Options: coed, women-only housing available. Jackson Library with 175,366 books, 149,680 microform titles, 763 serials, 2,913 audiovisual materials, an OPAC, and a Web page. Operations spending for 2004 fiscal year: $798,827. 125 computers available on campus for general student use. Computer purchase/lease plans available. A campuswide network can be accessed from student residence rooms and from off campus. Staffed computer lab on campus.

Community Environment: Greenwood, an industrial city noted for its production of textiles, is located in west-central South Carolina. The climate is temperate and mild. Five rail lines, commercial air service, buses, and major highways serve the community. Public service facilities include one hospital and various health centers, an area mental health center, churches of all denominations, a library, and a YMCA. There are several motels, shopping, and various civic and fraternal organizations within the immediate area. Recreation includes several swimming pools, two recreation centers, 3 golf courses, baseball, football, tennis, basketball, and nearby Greenwood State Park, which provides water sports and picnic areas. Part-time employment is available.

■ **LIMESTONE COLLEGE** *A-6*
1115 College Dr.
Gaffney, SC 29340-3799
Tel: (864)489-7151
Free: 800-795-7151
Admissions: (864)488-4549
Fax: (864)487-8706
E-mail: cphenicie@limestone.edu
Web Site: http://www.limestone.edu/

Description: Independent, 4-year, coed. Awards associate and bachelor's degrees. Founded 1845. Setting: 115-acre suburban campus with easy access to Charlotte. Endowment: $8.7 million. Educational spending for 2005 fiscal year: $3711 per student. Total enrollment: 676. Student-undergrad faculty ratio is 10:1. 884 applied, 58% were admitted. 7% from top 10% of their high school class, 20% from top quarter, 54% from top half. 1 class president, 7 student government officers. Full-time: 660 students, 46% women, 54% men. Part-time: 16 students, 38% women, 63% men. Students come from 29 states and territories, 9 other countries, 41% from out-of-state, 1% Native American, 2% Hispanic, 18% black, 0.4% Asian American or Pacific Islander, 3% international, 9% 25 or older, 49% live on campus, 9% transferred in. Retention: 67% of full-time freshmen returned the following year. Academic areas with the most degrees conferred: education; business/marketing; psychology; parks and recreation. Core. Calendar: semesters. Academic remediation for entering students, services for LD students, advanced placement, accelerated degree program, self-designed majors, honors program, independent study, distance learning, double major, summer session for credit, part-time degree program, adult/continuing education programs, internships. ROTC: Army (c).

Entrance Requirements: Options: Peterson's Universal Application, Common Application, electronic application. Required: high school transcript, minimum 2.0 high school GPA, SAT or ACT. Recommended: 2 recommendations, interview. Entrance: moderately difficult. Application deadline: Rolling. Notification: continuous.

Costs Per Year: Application fee: $25. Comprehensive fee: $21,000 includes full-time tuition ($15,000) and college room and board ($6000). Part-time tuition: $625 per credit hour.

Collegiate Environment: Orientation program. Drama-theater group, choral group. Social organizations: 16 open to all; local sororities; 2% of women are members. Most popular organizations: Fellowship of Christian Athletes, Student Government Association, Gospel Choir, KDK, Student Ambassadors. Major annual events: Christmas On Campus, Mid-Term Madness, Earth Day. Student services: health clinic, personal-psychological counseling, women's center, student success center. Campus security: 24-hour emergency response devices and patrols, late night transport-escort service, controlled dormitory access. 345 college housing spaces available; 304 were occupied in 2003-04. Freshmen given priority for college housing. On-campus residence required through junior year. Options: men-only, women-only housing available. A. J. Eastwood Library with 104,582 books, 2,630 microform titles, 289 serials, 2,707 audiovisual materials, an OPAC, and a Web page. Operations spending for 2004 fiscal year: $221,973. 81 computers available on campus for general student use. A campuswide network can be accessed from student residence rooms and from off campus. Staffed computer lab on campus.

Community Environment: Once predominately a cotton-textile manufacturing city, Gaffney has many diversified industries today including the manufacture of frozen foods, roller bearings, clothes, gloves, rugs, clay and concrete products. The surrounding agricultural area is a major producer of peaches, and also grain and livestock. The city is located 2 miles from Interstate I-85. Approximately 45 miles north is the Charlotte International Airport, and 40 miles south is the Greenville-Spartanburg International Airport. The community has several churches representing many denominations, and many civic and service organizations.

■ **MEDICAL UNIVERSITY OF SOUTH CAROLINA** *J-11*
171 Ashley Ave.
Charleston, SC 29425-0002
Tel: (843)792-2300
Admissions: (843)792-3813
Fax: (843)792-3764
Web Site: http://www.musc.edu/

Description: State-supported, upper-level, coed. Awards bachelor's, master's, doctoral, and first professional degrees. Founded 1824. Setting: 61-acre urban campus. Endowment: $68.4 million. Research spending for 2004 fiscal year: $99.9 million. Educational spending for 2005 fiscal year: $55,776 per student. Total enrollment: 2,428. Faculty: 1,281. Student-undergrad faculty ratio is 12:1. Students come from 19 states and territories, 10% from out-of-state, 1% Native American, 0.3% Hispanic, 16% black, 2% Asian American or Pacific Islander, 0% international, 59% 25 or older. Retention: 87% of full-time entering class returned the following year. Calendar: semesters. Advanced placement, independent study, distance learning, part-time degree program, internships, graduate courses open to undergrads. Off campus study at Charleston Higher Education Consortium, University of South Carolina, University Center of Greenville, Francis Marion University.

Costs Per Year: Application fee: $75.

Collegiate Environment: Orientation program. Social organizations: 11 open to all. Most popular organizations: MUSC Student Government Association, Multicultural Group Advisory Board, Public Health Interest Group, International Association, Crisis Ministries. Major annual events: Alhambra, Back to School Party, Halloween Horror Cruise. Student services: health clinic, personal-psychological counseling. Campus security: 24-hour emergency response devices and patrols, late night transport-escort service. College housing not available. Medical University of South Carolina Library plus 1 other with 225,061 books, 3,088 microform titles, 3,746 serials, 1,570 audiovisual materials, an OPAC, and a Web page. Operations spending for 2004 fiscal year: $5.3 million. 200 computers available on campus for general student use. A campuswide network can be accessed from off-campus. Staffed computer lab on campus.

Community Environment: See The Citadel.

■ **MIDLANDS TECHNICAL COLLEGE** *E-8*
PO Box 2408
Columbia, SC 29202-2408
Tel: (803)738-1400
Admissions: (803)738-8324
Fax: (803)738-7784
E-mail: littlejohns@midlandstech.edu
Web Site: http://www.midlandstech.edu/

Description: State and locally supported, 2-year, coed. Part of South Carolina State Board for Technical and Comprehensive Education. Awards certificates, diplomas, transfer associate, and terminal associate degrees. Founded 1974. Setting: 113-acre suburban campus. Endowment: $2.5 million. Educational spending for 2005 fiscal year: $3594 per student. Total enrollment: 10,779. Student-undergrad faculty ratio is 21:1. 4,409 applied, 69% were admitted. Full-time: 4,743 students, 55% women, 45% men. Part-time: 6,036 students, 69% women, 31% men. Students come from 33 states and territories, 5% from out-of-state, 1% Native American, 2% Hispanic, 37% black, 2% Asian American or Pacific Islander, 0.4% international, 40% 25 or older. Calendar: semesters. Academic remediation for entering students, ESL program, services for LD students, advanced placement, self-designed majors, distance learning, double major, summer session for credit, part-time degree program, adult/continuing education programs, co-op programs and internships.

Entrance Requirements: Open admission except for nursing, radiology programs. Options: Common Application, electronic application, early admission, deferred admission. Required: ACT ASSET. Recommended: high school transcript, SAT or ACT. Entrance: minimally difficult. Application deadline: Rolling. Notification: continuous.

Costs Per Year: Area resident tuition: $2904 full-time, $121 per credit part-time. State resident tuition: $3676 full-time, $157 per credit part-time. Nonresident tuition: $8612 full-time, $363 per credit part-time. Mandatory fees: $100 full-time, $50 per term part-time. Full-time tuition and fees vary according to class time. Part-time tuition and fees vary according to class time.

Collegiate Environment: Orientation program. Student-run newspaper. Campus security: 24-hour emergency response devices and patrols. College housing not available. 89,618 books, 11,600 microform titles, 551 serials, 1,036 audiovisual materials, an OPAC, and a Web page. 125 computers available on campus for general student use. A campuswide network can be accessed from off-campus. Staffed computer lab on campus.

Community Environment: See University of South Carolina.

■ **MILLER-MOTTE TECHNICAL COLLEGE** *J-11*

8085 Rivers Ave., Ste. E
Charleston, SC 29418
Tel: (843)574-0101; 877-617-4740
Fax: (843)266-3434
E-mail: juliasc@miller-mott.net
Web Site: http://www.miller-motte.com/

Description: Proprietary, 2-year, coed. Awards diplomas degrees. Founded 2000. Setting: urban campus.

■ **MORRIS COLLEGE** *F-10*

100 West College St.
Sumter, SC 29150-3599
Tel: (803)934-3200; (866)853-1345
Admissions: (803)934-3225
Fax: (803)773-3687
E-mail: dcalhoun@morris.edu
Web Site: http://www.morris.edu/

Description: Independent, 4-year, coed, affiliated with Baptist Educational and Missionary Convention of South Carolina. Awards bachelor's degrees. Founded 1908. Setting: 34-acre small town campus. Endowment: $5.3 million. Educational spending for 2005 fiscal year: $4058 per student. Total enrollment: 863. Student-undergrad faculty ratio is 17:1. 892 applied, 85% were admitted. 0% from top 10% of their high school class, 9% from top quarter, 24% from top half. Full-time: 844 students, 64% women, 36% men. Part-time: 19 students, 63% women, 37% men. Students come from 21 states and territories, 16% from out-of-state, 99% black, 11% 25 or older, 72% live on campus, 3% transferred in. Retention: 55% of full-time freshmen returned the following year. Academic areas with the most degrees conferred: business/marketing; health professions and related sciences; security and protective services. Core. Calendar: semesters. Academic remediation for entering students, advanced placement, accelerated degree program, honors program, double major, summer session for credit, adult/ continuing education programs, co-op programs and internships. ROTC: Army.

Entrance Requirements: Open admission. Option: deferred admission. Required: high school transcript, minimum 2.0 high school GPA, medical examination. Required for some: interview, SAT or ACT. Entrance: noncompetitive. Application deadline: Rolling.

Costs Per Year: Application fee: $20. Comprehensive fee: $12,234 includes full-time tuition ($8163), mandatory fees ($235), and college room and board ($3836). Part-time tuition: $330 per credit hour. Part-time mandatory fees: $45 per term. Part-time tuition and fees vary according to class time.

Collegiate Environment: Orientation program. Drama-theater group, choral group, student-run newspaper, radio station. Social organizations: 50 open to all; national fraternities, national sororities; 12% of eligible men and 11% of eligible women are members. Most popular organizations: Student Government Association, New Emphasis on Nontraditional Students, Block 'M' Club, Students of South Carolina Educational Association, Baptist Student Union. Major annual events: Coronation of Miss Morris College, Thanksgiving Rally/Homecoming Parade, Homecoming Week. Student services: health clinic, personal-psychological counseling. Campus security: 24-hour patrols, controlled dormitory access. 696 college housing spaces available; 684 were occupied in 2003-04. Freshmen given priority for college housing. Options: men-only, women-only housing available. Richardson-Johnson Learning Resources Center with 102,206 books, 202,608 microform titles, 414 serials, 3,955 audiovisual materials, and an OPAC. Operations spending for 2004 fiscal year: $612,095. 210 computers available on campus for general student use. A campuswide network can be accessed from student residence rooms. Staffed computer lab on campus.

Community Environment: Sumter was named for General Thomas Sumter, "The Gamecock of the Revolution." The community is served by two bus lines and is 50 miles from an airport and 35 miles from rail service. The mean summer temperature is 90 degrees, and the mean winter temperature is 40 degrees. The city has many churches of various faiths, as well as a public library. Sumter offers both large natural parks and many lakes, and is famed for its Swan Lake Iris Gardens. Sports and recreation go hand-in-hand with the compatible climate and natural resources found in the community, and includes four theatres, a skating rink, bowling, and night-lit tennis courts.

■ **NEWBERRY COLLEGE** *D-6*

2100 College St.
Newberry, SC 29108-2197
Tel: (803)276-5010
Free: 800-845-4955
Admissions: (803)321-5129
E-mail: admissions@newberry.edu
Web Site: http://www.newberry.edu/

Description: Independent Evangelical Lutheran, 4-year, coed. Awards bachelor's degrees. Founded 1856. Setting: 60-acre small town campus. Endowment: $15.3 million. Educational spending for 2005 fiscal year: $3691 per student. Total enrollment: 841. Student-undergrad faculty ratio is 12:1. 1,102 applied, 59% were admitted. 3 class presidents, 6 valedictorians, 48 student government officers. Full-time: 841 students, 40% women, 60% men. Students come from 26 states and territories, 13 other countries, 0.4% Native American, 2% Hispanic, 26% black, 1% Asian American or Pacific Islander, 3% international, 4% 25 or older, 87% live on campus, 7% transferred in. Retention: 61% of full-time freshmen returned the following year. Academic areas with the most degrees conferred: business/marketing; biological/life sciences; communications/journalism. Core. Calendar: semesters. Advanced placement, self-designed majors, honors program, independent study, double major, summer session for credit, part-time degree program, adult/continuing education programs, co-op programs and internships. Study abroad program. ROTC: Army (c).

Entrance Requirements: Options: Peterson's Universal Application, Common Application, electronic application, early admission, deferred admission, international baccalaureate accepted. Required: high school transcript, minimum 2.0 high school GPA, SAT or ACT. Recommended: 1 recommendation, interview. Required for some: essay. Entrance: moderately difficult. Application deadline: Rolling. Notification: continuous.

Costs Per Year: Application fee: $30. Comprehensive fee: $26,511 includes full-time tuition ($18,900), mandatory fees ($731), and college room and board ($6880). College room only: $3230. Part-time tuition: $350 per hour. Part-time mandatory fees: $50 per term.

Collegiate Environment: Orientation program. Drama-theater group, choral group, marching band, student-run newspaper, radio station. Social organizations: 15 open to all; national fraternities, national sororities; 30% of eligible men and 31% of eligible women are members. Most popular organizations: Fellowship of Christian Athletes, Metoka Galeda (gospel choir and service group), Lutheran Student Movement, Baptist Student Union, Students Organized for Community Service. Major annual events: Homecoming, Fall Fling, Indian Princess event. Student services: health clinic, personal-psychological counseling. Campus security: 24-hour patrols. 630 college housing spaces available; 552 were occupied in 2003-04. Freshmen guaranteed college housing. On-campus residence required through junior year. Options: coed, men-only, women-only housing available. Wessels Library with 79,899 books, 7,212 microform titles, 499 serials, 1,389 audiovisual materials, an OPAC, and a Web page. Operations spending for 2004 fiscal year: $114,950. 78 computers available on campus for general student use. A campuswide network can be accessed from student residence rooms and from off campus. Staffed computer lab on campus.

Community Environment: Newberry is located in the Piedmont region of South Carolina between Lakes Murray and Greenwood. The city enjoys mild weather. Community services include churches of many denominations, a hospital, a county library, and various civic and fraternal organizations. Local recreation and facilities include a swimming pool, barbecue facilities, parks, theaters, fishing, boating, swimming, and camping on nearby lakes. Part-time employment is available for college students.

■ **NORTH GREENVILLE COLLEGE**

PO Box 1892
Tigerville, SC 29688-1892
Tel: (864)977-7000
Free: 800-468-6642
Admissions: (864)977-7052
Fax: (864)977-7177
E-mail: ngccwf@infoave.net
Web Site: http://www.ngc.edu/

Description: Independent Southern Baptist, 4-year, coed. Awards associate and bachelor's degrees. Founded 1892. Setting: 500-acre rural campus with easy access to Greenville. Endowment: $10.3 million. Educational spending for 2005 fiscal year: $3322 per student. Total enrollment: 1,766. 900 applied, 81% were admitted. 13% from top 10% of their high school class, 38% from top quarter, 68% from top half. Full-time: 1,559 students, 53% women, 47% men. Part-time: 207 students, 48% women, 52% men. Students come from 28 states and territories, 24 other countries, 21% from out-of-state, 0.3% Native American, 1% Hispanic, 9% black, 0.4% Asian American or Pacific Islander, 2% international, 7% 25 or older, 66% live on campus, 6% transferred in. Core. Calendar: semesters. Academic remediation for entering students, ESL program, services for LD students, advanced placement, accelerated degree program, self-designed majors, freshman honors college, honors program, independent study, double major, summer session for credit, part-time degree program, external degree program, internships. ROTC: Army (c).

Entrance Requirements: Options: electronic application, early admission, deferred admission, international baccalaureate accepted. Required: high school transcript, SAT or ACT. Recommended: minimum 2.0 high school GPA, CPT. Required for some: interview, CPT. Entrance: minimally difficult. Application deadline: 8/18. Notification: continuous. Preference given to Baptists.

Costs Per Year: Application fee: $25. Comprehensive fee: $16,300 includes full-time tuition ($10,350) and college room and board ($5950). Part-time tuition: $200 per hour. Part-time tuition varies according to course load.

Collegiate Environment: Orientation program. Drama-theater group, choral group, student-run newspaper, radio station. Most popular organizations: Baptist Student Union, Fellowship of Christians in Service, Fellowship of Christian Athletes, Black Student Fellowship, Education Club. Major annual events: Homecoming, Founders' Day, Miss NGC Pageant. Student services: health clinic, personal-psychological counseling. Campus security: 24-hour emergency response devices and patrols, controlled dormitory access. 1,200 college housing spaces available; 1,163 were occupied in 2003-04. Freshmen guaranteed college housing. On-campus residence required through sophomore year. Options: men-only, women-only housing available. Hester Memorial Library with 49,000 books, 2,930 microform titles, 536 serials, 5,644 audiovisual materials, an OPAC, and a Web page. Operations spending for 2004 fiscal year: $398,682. 72 computers available on campus for general student use. A campuswide network can be accessed from student residence rooms and from off campus. Staffed computer lab on campus.

Community Environment: Tigerville is a rural area adjacent to Greenville in the foothills of the Blue Ridge Mountains. The climate is temperate. There are several civic and fraternal organizations and a Baptist Church in the community. Part-time employment is available. Local recreation includes hunting, fishing, rafting, fine arts and the advantages of nearby Greenville.

■ **NORTHEASTERN TECHNICAL COLLEGE** *C-11*

PO Drawer 1007
Cheraw, SC 29520-1007
Tel: (843)921-6900
Admissions: (843)921-6935
Fax: (843)537-6148
E-mail: mnewton@netc.edu
Web Site: http://www.netc.edu/

Description: State and locally supported, 2-year, coed. Part of South Carolina State Board for Technical and Comprehensive Education. Awards certificates, diplomas, transfer associate, and terminal associate degrees. Founded 1967. Setting: 59-acre rural campus. Endowment: $27,621. Educational spending for 2005 fiscal year: $1445 per student. Total enrollment: 1,115. 468 applied, 100% were admitted. Students come from 2 states and territories, 1% from out-of-state, 2% Native American, 0.4% Hispanic, 46% black, 0.4% Asian American or Pacific Islander, 0% international, 45% 25 or older. Core. Calendar: semesters. Academic remediation for entering students, advanced placement, summer session for credit, part-time degree program, adult/continuing education programs.

Entrance Requirements: Open admission except for nursing program. Option: early admission. Required: high school transcript, interview. Required for some: SAT. Entrance: noncompetitive.

Costs Per Year: Application fee: $12.50. Area resident tuition: $2496 full-time, $104 per semester hour part-time. State resident tuition: $2688 full-time, $112 per semester hour part-time. Nonresident tuition: $4080 full-time, $170 per semester hour part-time. Mandatory fees: $30 full-time, $4 per semester hour part-time.

Collegiate Environment: Orientation program. Major annual event: Field Day. Student services: personal-psychological counseling. Campus security: 24-hour emergency response devices. College housing not available. Northeastern Technical College Library with 20,502 books, 261 serials, 690 audiovisual materials, an OPAC, and a Web page. Operations spending for 2004 fiscal year: $167,842. 125 computers available on campus for general student use. A campuswide network can be accessed from off-campus. Staffed computer lab on campus.

Community Environment: Cheraw is a small community enjoying mild climate year-round. The city has a public library, a shopping center, churches of many denominations, and good medical facilities. There are several service and civic organizations active in the area.

■ **ORANGEBURG-CALHOUN TECHNICAL COLLEGE** *G-8*

3250 St Matthews Rd., NE
Orangeburg, SC 29118-8299
Tel: (803)536-0311
Admissions: (803)535-1218
Fax: (803)535-1388
Web Site: http://www.octech.edu/

Description: State and locally supported, 2-year, coed. Part of State Board for Technical and Comprehensive Education, South Carolina. Awards certificates, diplomas, transfer associate, and terminal associate degrees. Founded 1968. Setting: 100-acre small town campus with easy access to Columbia. Endowment: $2.5 million. Total enrollment: 2,491. Full-time: 1,380 students, 68% women, 32% men. Part-time: 1,111 students, 77% women, 23% men. Students come from 5 states and territories, 1% from out-of-state, 1% Native American, 0.3% Hispanic, 58% black, 1% Asian American or Pacific Islander, 0% international, 35% 25 or older, 4% transferred in. Core. Calendar: semesters. Academic remediation for entering students, services for LD students, advanced placement, self-designed majors, independent study, distance learning, summer session for credit, part-time degree program, adult/continuing education programs, co-op programs and internships.

Entrance Requirements: Open admission. Options: Peterson's Universal Application, Common Application, early admission. Required: high school transcript. Required for some: interview. Placement: ACT ASSET required for some. Entrance: noncompetitive. Application deadline: Rolling. Notification: continuous.

Collegiate Environment: Orientation program. Most popular organization: Student Advisory Council. Major annual events: Get Acquainted Day, Awards Day. Student services: personal-psychological counseling. Campus security: 24-hour emergency response devices and patrols. College housing not available. Gressette Learning Center with 43,500 books, 143 serials, 2,253

audiovisual materials, and an OPAC. Operations spending for 2004 fiscal year: $357,362. 361 computers available on campus for general student use. A campuswide network can be accessed from off-campus.
Community Environment: See South Carolina State University.

■ **PIEDMONT TECHNICAL COLLEGE** *E-4*
620 North Emerald Rd.
PO Box 1467
Greenwood, SC 29648-1467
Tel: (864)941-8324
Admissions: (864)941-8603
Fax: (864)941-8555
Web Site: http://www.ptc.edu/
Description: State-supported, 2-year, coed. Part of South Carolina State Board for Technical and Comprehensive Education. Awards certificates, diplomas, transfer associate, and terminal associate degrees. Founded 1966. Setting: 60-acre small town campus. Endowment: $1.1 million. Research spending for 2004 fiscal year: $124,427. Educational spending for 2005 fiscal year: $2515 per student. Total enrollment: 4,911. 890 applied, 100% were admitted. Students come from 2 states and territories, 5 other countries, 1% from out-of-state, 38% 25 or older. Calendar: semesters. Academic remediation for entering students, services for LD students, advanced placement, independent study, distance learning, summer session for credit, part-time degree program, adult/continuing education programs, co-op programs and internships.
Entrance Requirements: Open admission except for nursing, health sciences programs. Options: electronic application, early admission, deferred admission. Required: high school transcript. Recommended: interview. Placement: ACT ACCESS, ACT COMPASS required; SAT recommended. Entrance: noncompetitive. Application deadline: Rolling. Notification: continuous until 8/20.
Collegiate Environment: Orientation program. Choral group. Social organizations: 18 open to all. Most popular organizations: National Honor Society, Career Peers (student volunteers), Student Nurses Association, Psychology Club, Ebony Club. Major annual events: Spring Activities Day, club fairs, Fall Convocation/Back to School Bash. Student services: personal-psychological counseling, women's center. Campus security: 24-hour emergency response devices and patrols, late night transport-escort service. College housing not available. Piedmont Technical College Library with 27,497 books, 4,497 microform titles, 345 serials, 1,501 audiovisual materials, an OPAC, and a Web page. Operations spending for 2004 fiscal year: $221,086. 320 computers available on campus for general student use. A campuswide network can be accessed from off-campus. Staffed computer lab on campus.
Community Environment: In additions to Greenwood county campus, Piedmont has 6 county center campuses serving students of the service area which includes Abbeville, Laurens, Edgefield, McCormick, Saluda, and Newberry.

■ **PRESBYTERIAN COLLEGE** *D-5*
503 South Broad St.
Clinton, SC 29325
Tel: (864)833-2820
Free: 800-476-7272
Admissions: (864)833-8229
Fax: (864)833-8481
E-mail: lpatters@presby.edu
Web Site: http://www.presby.edu/
Description: Independent, 4-year, coed, affiliated with Presbyterian Church (U.S.A.). Awards bachelor's degrees. Founded 1880. Setting: 215-acre small town campus with easy access to Greenville - Spartanburg. Endowment: $83.8 million. Research spending for 2004 fiscal year: $26.7 million. Educational spending for 2005 fiscal year: $7696 per student. Total enrollment: 1,196. Student-undergrad faculty ratio is 12:1. 1,110 applied, 76% were admitted. 31% from top 10% of their high school class, 62% from top quarter, 87% from top half. Full-time: 1,138 students, 51% women, 49% men. Part-time: 58 students, 64% women, 36% men. Students come from 30 states and territories, 13 other countries, 33% from out-of-state, 0.2% Native American, 1% Hispanic, 5% black, 1% Asian American or Pacific Islander, 0% international, 1% 25 or older, 94% live on campus, 1% transferred in. Retention: 83% of full-time freshmen returned the following year. Academic areas with the most degrees conferred: business/marketing; biological/life sciences; education. Core. Calendar: semesters. Services for LD students, advanced placement, accelerated degree program, freshman

honors college, honors program, independent study, double major, summer session for credit, internships. Off campus study at Gulf Coast Marine Laboratory, American University. Study abroad program. ROTC: Army.
Entrance Requirements: Options: Peterson's Universal Application, electronic application, early decision, deferred admission, international baccalaureate accepted. Required: essay, high school transcript, 1 recommendation, SAT or ACT. Recommended: interview. Entrance: very difficult. Application deadlines: 4/1, 12/5 for early decision. Notification: continuous until 6/1, 1/31 for early decision.
Costs Per Year: Application fee: $30. Comprehensive fee: $30,044 includes full-time tuition ($21,222), mandatory fees ($2022), and college room and board ($6800). College room only: $3340. Full-time tuition and fees vary according to program. Room and board charges vary according to board plan and housing facility. Part-time tuition: $885 per semester hour. Part-time tuition varies according to program.
Collegiate Environment: Orientation program. Drama-theater group, choral group, student-run newspaper, radio station. Social organizations: 60 open to all; national fraternities, national sororities; 80% of eligible men and 65% of eligible women are members. Most popular organizations: student volunteer services, intramurals, Student Union Board, Fellowship of Christian Athletes. Major annual events: homecoming, Special Olympics. Student services: health clinic, personal-psychological counseling. Campus security: 24-hour emergency response devices and patrols, late night transport-escort service, controlled dormitory access. 1,147 college housing spaces available; 1,099 were occupied in 2003-04. On-campus residence required through senior year. Options: coed, men-only, women-only housing available. James H. Thomason Library with 155,830 books, 13,376 microform titles, 740 serials, 9,037 audiovisual materials, an OPAC, and a Web page. Operations spending for 2004 fiscal year: $828,683. 130 computers available on campus for general student use. A campuswide network can be accessed from student residence rooms and from off campus. Staffed computer lab on campus.
Community Environment: Located in the Piedmont section of South Carolina, Clinton is approximately 64 miles northwest of Columbia. The annual mean January temperature is 43.6 degrees; July 79.9 degrees. The community has air and bus service and is adjacent to U.S. Highway 76, I-385; I-26. There are many churches of various denominations, a hospital, hotels and motels in town. Part-time employment is available. Local recreational facilities include tennis, golf, theatre and swimming; nearby Lake Greenwood provides boating, fishing and hunting. Various civic, fraternal and veteran's organizations are active in the community.

■ **SOUTH CAROLINA STATE UNIVERSITY** *G-8*
300 College St. Northeast
Orangeburg, SC 29117-0001
Tel: (803)536-7000
Free: 800-260-5956
Admissions: (803)536-8408
Fax: (803)536-8990
Web Site: http://www.scsu.edu/
Description: State-supported, comprehensive, coed. Part of South Carolina Commission on Higher Education. Awards bachelor's, master's, and doctoral degrees and post-master's certificates. Founded 1896. Setting: 160-acre small town campus. Endowment: $651,061. Research spending for 2004 fiscal year: $2.8 million. Total enrollment: 4,294. 4,364 applied, 53% were admitted. 6% from top 10% of their high school class, 22% from top quarter, 56% from top half. 35 student government officers. Full-time: 3,345 students, 57% women, 43% men. Part-time: 359 students, 64% women, 36% men. Students come from 36 states and territories, 26 other countries, 14% from out-of-state, 0.03% Native American, 0.2% Hispanic, 98% black, 0.3% Asian American or Pacific Islander, 0% international, 0.02% 25 or older, 58% live on campus, 7% transferred in. Retention: 76% of full-time freshmen returned the following year. Core. Calendar: semesters. Academic remediation for entering students, advanced placement, honors program, independent study, distance learning, summer session for credit, part-time degree program, adult/continuing education programs, co-op programs and internships. Off campus study at National Student Exchange. Study abroad program. ROTC: Army, Air Force (c).
Entrance Requirements: Options: Peterson's Universal Application, Common Application, deferred admission. Required: high school transcript, minimum 2.0 high school GPA, SAT or ACT. Recommended: SAT Subject Tests. Entrance: minimally difficult. Application deadline: 7/31. Notification: continuous.
Costs Per Year: Application fee: $25. State resident tuition: $6480 full-time, $270 per credit hour part-time. Nonresident tuition: $13,288 full-time, $554

per credit hour part-time. Mandatory fees: $185 full-time. Full-time tuition and fees vary according to course load, degree level, reciprocity agreements, and student level. Part-time tuition varies according to course load, degree level, reciprocity agreements, and student level. College room and board: $6028. College room only: $3642. Room and board charges vary according to board plan and housing facility.

Collegiate Environment: Orientation program. Drama-theater group, choral group, marching band, student-run newspaper. Social organizations: 89 open to all; national fraternities, national sororities, local fraternities, local sororities; 20% of eligible men and 20% of eligible women are members. Most popular organizations: student government, Student Union Board, NAACP. Major annual events: Spring Convocation, Smith-Hammond Middleton Memorial Program, Bulldog Fest. Student services: health clinic, personal-psychological counseling. Campus security: 24-hour emergency response devices and patrols, late night transport-escort service, controlled dormitory access. College housing designed to accommodate 2,049 students; 2,142 undergraduates lived in college housing during 2003-04. Freshmen given priority for college housing. Options: men-only, women-only housing available. Miller F. Whittaker Library plus 1 other with 273,264 books, 1,346 serials, and a Web page. Operations spending for 2004 fiscal year: $1.3 million. 300 computers available on campus for general student use. A campuswide network can be accessed. Staffed computer lab on campus.

Community Environment: Orangeburg is in an agricultural and dairying area. Its industries include textiles, wood products, meat packing, chemicals, and baking goods. This is a suburban community with a temperate climate. Airline service is available at nearby Columbia. Railroad and bus lines serve the immediate community. There is a public library, churches of major denominations, a hospital, and major civic and fraternal organizations. Some part-time employment is available. Local recreation includes four theatres, swimming, fishing and many sports.

■ **SOUTH UNIVERSITY** *E-8*

3810 Main St.

Columbia, SC 29203-6400

Tel: (803)799-9082; (866)629-3031

Fax: (803)799-9038

Web Site: http://www.southuniversity.edu/

Description: Proprietary, comprehensive, coed. Part of South University-Savannah. Awards associate, bachelor's, and master's degrees. Founded 1935. Setting: 2-acre urban campus. Educational spending for 2005 fiscal year: $528 per student. Total enrollment: 491. Faculty: 40 (18 full-time, 22 part-time). Student-undergrad faculty ratio is 15:1. 162 applied, 69% were admitted. 0% from top 10% of their high school class, 11% from top quarter, 77% from top half. Full-time: 289 students, 81% women, 19% men. Part-time: 137 students, 88% women, 12% men. 0% from out-of-state, 1% Native American, 1% Hispanic, 90% black, 0.5% Asian American or Pacific Islander, 0% international, 71% 25 or older, 19% transferred in. Retention: 42% of full-time freshmen returned the following year. Academic areas with the most degrees conferred: law/legal studies; business/marketing. Core. Academic remediation for entering students, services for LD students, advanced placement, accelerated degree program, distance learning, double major, summer session for credit, part-time degree program, adult/continuing education programs, co-op programs and internships.

Entrance Requirements: Options: electronic application, deferred admission, international baccalaureate accepted. Required: high school transcript, interview. Recommended: SAT and SAT Subject Tests or ACT. Entrance: minimally difficult. Application deadline: Rolling. Notification: continuous.

Costs Per Year: Application fee: $25. Tuition: $11,475 full-time.

Collegiate Environment: Orientation program. Social organizations: 2 open to all. Student services: personal-psychological counseling. Campus security: 24-hour emergency response devices. College housing not available. South University Library with 10,765 books, 100 serials, 250 audiovisual materials, and an OPAC. Operations spending for 2004 fiscal year: $184,505. 40 computers available on campus for general student use. A campuswide network can be accessed from off-campus.

■ **SOUTHERN METHODIST COLLEGE** *G-8*

541 Broughton Stret, PO Box 1027

Orangeburg, SC 29116-1027

Tel: (803)534-7826

Free: 800-360-1503

Web Site: http://www.smcollege.edu/

Description: Independent religious, 4-year, coed. Awards associate and bachelor's degrees. Founded 1956. Endowment: $397,606. Educational spending for 2005 fiscal year: $6815 per student. Total enrollment: 77. Full-time: 61 students, 62% women, 38% men. Part-time: 16 students, 75% women, 25% men. Students come from 7 states and territories, 1 other country, 15% from out-of-state, 0% Native American, 0% Hispanic, 52% black, 0% Asian American or Pacific Islander, 1% international, 69% 25 or older, 19% live on campus, 9% transferred in. Core. Academic remediation for entering students, services for LD students, advanced placement, accelerated degree program, honors program, independent study, double major, summer session for credit, part-time degree program, adult/continuing education programs, co-op programs and internships. Off campus study at Williamson Christian College.

Entrance Requirements: Options: Common Application, early admission, early action, deferred admission. Required: essay, high school transcript, 3 recommendations, interview, health certificate. Recommended: SAT or ACT. Entrance: minimally difficult. Application deadlines: 7/15, 7/15 for early action. Notification: continuous until 7/22.

Costs Per Year: Application fee: $25. Comprehensive fee: $9400 includes full-time tuition ($4600), mandatory fees ($600), and college room and board ($4200). Full-time tuition and fees vary according to class time and course load. Room and board charges vary according to housing facility. Part-time tuition: $192 per semester hour. Part-time mandatory fees: $25 per semester hour. Part-time tuition and fees vary according to class time and course load.

Collegiate Environment: Orientation program. 13 undergraduates lived in college housing during 2003-04. No special consideration for freshman housing applicants. Options: men-only, women-only housing available. Lynn Corbett Library with 21,743 books, 10,000 microform titles, 60 serials, and 171 audiovisual materials. 6 computers available on campus for general student use. Computer purchase/lease plans available. A campuswide network can be accessed. Staffed computer lab on campus.

Community Environment: See South Carolina State University.

■ **SOUTHERN WESLEYAN UNIVERSITY** *C-2*

907 Wesleyan Dr., PO Box 1020

Central, SC 29630-1020

Tel: (864)644-5000

Free: 800-289-1292

Admissions: (864)644-5550

Fax: (864)644-5900

Web Site: http://www.swu.edu/

Description: Independent, comprehensive, coed, affiliated with Wesleyan Church. Awards associate, bachelor's, and master's degrees. Founded 1906. Setting: 230-acre small town campus. Endowment: $2.4 million. Total enrollment: 2,632. Faculty: 228 (50 full-time, 178 part-time). Student-undergrad faculty ratio is 17:1. 401 applied, 66% were admitted. 13% from top 10% of their high school class, 23% from top quarter, 75% from top half. 1 National Merit Scholar, 2 valedictorians. Full-time: 1,909 students, 66% women, 34% men. Part-time: 86 students, 70% women, 30% men. Students come from 27 states and territories, 5 other countries, 15% from out-of-state, 1% Native American, 2% Hispanic, 36% black, 1% Asian American or Pacific Islander, 1% international, 16% live on campus, 3% transferred in. Retention: 64% of full-time freshmen returned the following year. Academic areas with the most degrees conferred: business/marketing; education; parks and recreation. Core. Calendar: semesters. Academic remediation for entering students, services for LD students, advanced placement, accelerated degree program, self-designed majors, freshman honors college, honors program, independent study, double major, summer session for credit, part-time degree program, adult/continuing education programs, co-op programs and internships. Off campus study at Clemson University, Tri-County Technical College, Council for Christian Colleges and Universities. Study abroad program. ROTC: Army (c), Air Force (c).

Entrance Requirements: Options: Peterson's Universal Application, electronic application, early admission, deferred admission. Required: high school transcript, minimum 2.3 high school GPA, 2 recommendations, lifestyle statement, SAT or ACT. Required for some: interview. Application deadline: 8/11. Notification: continuous.

Costs Per Year: Application fee: $25. Comprehensive fee: $20,900 includes full-time tuition ($15,000), mandatory fees ($450), and college room and board ($5450). College room only: $2050. Full-time tuition and fees vary according to course load, degree level, and program. Room and board charges vary according to board plan and housing facility. Part-time tuition: $460 per credit hour. Part-time mandatory fees: $225 per term. Part-time tuition and fees vary according to course load and degree level.

Collegiate Environment: Orientation program. Drama-theater group, choral group. Social organizations: 10 open to all. Most popular organizations: Student Government Association, Student Missions Fellowship, Ministry Teams, Music Club, Council for Exceptional Children. Major annual events: homecoming, Spiritual Emphasis Week, Christmas Banquet. Student services: health clinic, personal-psychological counseling. Campus security: 24-hour emergency response devices, late night security patrols. 362 college housing spaces available; 330 were occupied in 2003-04. Freshmen guaranteed college housing. On-campus residence required through senior year. Options: coed, men-only, women-only housing available. Rickman Library with 88,983 books, 975 microform titles, 525 serials, 3,502 audiovisual materials, and an OPAC. Operations spending for 2004 fiscal year: $535,189. 92 computers available on campus for general student use. A campuswide network can be accessed from student residence rooms and from off campus. Staffed computer lab on campus.

Community Environment: Central is located in the Piedmont section of South Carolina, between Atlanta, Georgia, and Charlotte, North Carolina. The community is five miles North of Clemson and is located near the metropolitan area of Greenville.

■ **SPARTANBURG METHODIST COLLEGE** *B-5*

1200 Textile Rd.
Spartanburg, SC 29301-0009
Tel: (864)587-4000
Free: 800-772-7286
Admissions: (864)587-4223
Fax: (864)587-4355
Web Site: http://www.smcsc.edu/

Description: Independent Methodist, 2-year, coed. Awards certificates, diplomas, transfer associate, and terminal associate degrees. Founded 1911. Setting: 111-acre urban campus with easy access to Charlotte, NC. Endowment: $14.3 million. Educational spending for 2005 fiscal year: $5200 per student. Total enrollment: 779. Student-undergrad faculty ratio is 23:1. 999 applied, 84% were admitted. 9% from top 10% of their high school class, 33% from top quarter, 65% from top half. 16 class presidents, 161 student government officers. Full-time: 716 students, 50% women, 50% men. Part-time: 63 students, 65% women, 35% men. Students come from 9 states and territories, 6 other countries, 6% from out-of-state, 0.3% Native American, 2% Hispanic, 32% black, 1% Asian American or Pacific Islander, 2% international, 6% 25 or older, 75% live on campus, 4% transferred in. Retention: 59% of full-time freshmen returned the following year. Core. Calendar: semesters. Academic remediation for entering students, ESL program, services for LD students, advanced placement, honors program, independent study, summer session for credit, part-time degree program. ROTC: Army (c).

Entrance Requirements: Options: Common Application, electronic application, deferred admission. Required: essay, high school transcript, minimum 2.0 high school GPA, rank in upper 75% of high school class, SAT or ACT. Recommended: interview. Required for some: recommendations, interview. Entrance: moderately difficult. Application deadline: Rolling. Notification: continuous.

Costs Per Year: Application fee: $20. Comprehensive fee: $15,476 includes full-time tuition ($9816), mandatory fees ($150), and college room and board ($5510). College room only: $2784. Room and board charges vary according to housing facility. Part-time tuition: $260 per credit. Part-time tuition varies according to course load.

Collegiate Environment: Orientation program. Drama-theater group, choral group, student-run newspaper. Social organizations: 14 open to all. Most popular organizations: College Christian Movement, Alpha Phi Omega, Campus Union, Fellowship of Christian Athletes, Kappa Sigma Alpha. Major annual events: College Wide Day of Service, Homecoming, Field Day. Student services: health clinic, personal-psychological counseling. Campus security: 24-hour emergency response devices and patrols, student patrols, late night transport-escort service, controlled dormitory access. 530 college housing spaces available; all were occupied in 2003-04. No special consideration for freshman housing applicants. On-campus residence required through sophomore year. Options: coed, men-only, women-only housing available. Marie Blair Burgess Learning Resource Center with 75,000 books, 2,900 microform titles, 5,000 serials, 3,150 audiovisual materials, an OPAC, and a Web page. Operations spending for 2004 fiscal year: $178,000. 48 computers available on campus for general student use. A campuswide network can be accessed from student residence rooms and from off campus. Staffed computer lab on campus.

Community Environment: See Converse College.

■ **SPARTANBURG TECHNICAL COLLEGE** *B-5*

PO Box 4386
Spartanburg, SC 29305-4386
Tel: (864)591-3600
Admissions: (864)592-4800
Web Site: http://www.stcsc.edu/

Description: State-supported, 2-year, coed. Part of South Carolina State Board for Technical and Comprehensive Education. Awards certificates, diplomas, transfer associate, and terminal associate degrees. Founded 1961. Setting: 104-acre suburban campus. Total enrollment: 4,409. 2% from out-of-state, 0.2% Native American, 2% Hispanic, 27% black, 3% Asian American or Pacific Islander, 43% 25 or older. Core. Calendar: semesters plus summer sessions. Academic remediation for entering students, services for LD students, advanced placement, distance learning, summer session for credit, part-time degree program, adult/continuing education programs, co-op programs.

Entrance Requirements: Open admission. Option: early admission. Required: high school transcript. Entrance: noncompetitive. Application deadline: Rolling. Notification: continuous.

Costs Per Year: Application fee: $0. Area resident tuition: $3094 full-time, $127 per hour part-time. State resident tuition: $3860 full-time, $159 per hour part-time. Nonresident tuition: $5490 full-time, $228 per hour part-time. Mandatory fees: $20 full-time.

Collegiate Environment: Orientation program. Drama-theater group, student-run newspaper. Social organizations: 5 open to all. Student services: personal-psychological counseling, women's center. Campus security: 24-hour patrols. College housing not available. Spartanburg Technical College Library with 36,173 books, 295 serials, 3,534 audiovisual materials, an OPAC, and a Web page. 360 computers available on campus for general student use. A campuswide network can be accessed from off-campus. Staffed computer lab on campus.

Community Environment: See Converse College.

■ **TECHNICAL COLLEGE OF THE LOWCOUNTRY** *K-9*

921 Ribaut Rd., PO Box 1288
Beaufort, SC 29901-1288
Tel: (843)525-8324
Admissions: (843)525-8307
E-mail: lbrediger@tcl.edu
Web Site: http://www.tclonline.org/

Description: State-supported, 2-year, coed. Part of South Carolina Technical and Comprehensive Education System. Awards certificates, diplomas, transfer associate, and terminal associate degrees. Founded 1972. Setting: 12-acre small town campus. Total enrollment: 1,765. 75% 25 or older. Calendar: semesters. Academic remediation for entering students, advanced placement, self-designed majors, summer session for credit, part-time degree program, adult/continuing education programs, internships.

Entrance Requirements: Open admission except for nursing program. Options: early admission, deferred admission. Required: ACT ASSET. Recommended: SAT and SAT Subject Tests or ACT. Entrance: noncompetitive. Application deadline: Rolling.

Collegiate Environment: Orientation program. Campus security: security during class hours. College housing not available. 25,226 books and 244 serials. 106 computers available on campus for general student use.

■ **TRI-COUNTY TECHNICAL COLLEGE** *C-2*

PO Box 587, 7900 Hwy. 76
Pendleton, SC 29670-0587
Tel: (864)646-8361
Admissions: (864)646-1500
E-mail: admstaff@tricty.tricounty.tec.sc.us
Web Site: http://www.tctc.edu/

Description: State-supported, 2-year, coed. Part of South Carolina State Board for Technical and Comprehensive Education. Awards certificates, diplomas, transfer associate, and terminal associate degrees. Founded 1962. Setting: 100-acre rural campus. Total enrollment: 4,100. Students come from 3 states and territories, 7 other countries, 0.3% Native American, 1% Hispanic, 11% black, 1% Asian American or Pacific Islander, 2% international, 38% 25 or older. Calendar: semesters. Academic remediation for entering students, ESL program, advanced placement, summer session for credit, part-time degree program, adult/continuing education programs, co-op programs and internships. ROTC: Army (c), Air Force (c).

Entrance Requirements: Open admission except for allied health programs. Option: early admission. Placement: SAT, National League of

Nursing Exam required for some. Entrance: noncompetitive. Application deadline: Rolling. Notification: continuous.

Collegiate Environment: Student-run newspaper. Social organizations: 14 open to all. Major annual events: Welcome Back Bash, Annual Talent Show. Campus security: 24-hour emergency response devices and patrols. College housing not available. Tri-County Technical College Library with 34,513 books, 356 serials, an OPAC, and a Web page. Operations spending for 2004 fiscal year: $380,152. 600 computers available on campus for general student use. Staffed computer lab on campus.

■ **TRIDENT TECHNICAL COLLEGE** *J-11*
PO Box 118067
Charleston, SC 29423-8067
Tel: (843)574-6111
Admissions: (843)574-6483
Fax: (843)574-6109
Web Site: http://www.tridenttech.edu/

Description: State and locally supported, 2-year, coed. Part of South Carolina State Board for Technical and Comprehensive Education. Awards certificates, diplomas, transfer associate, and terminal associate degrees. Founded 1964. Setting: urban campus. Educational spending for 2005 fiscal year: $3750 per student. Total enrollment: 11,795. Student-undergrad faculty ratio is 18:1. Full-time: 5,270 students, 61% women, 39% men. Part-time: 6,525 students, 65% women, 35% men. 1% from out-of-state, 1% Native American, 2% Hispanic, 28% black, 2% Asian American or Pacific Islander, 0% international, 47% 25 or older. Core. Calendar: semesters. Academic remediation for entering students, ESL program, services for LD students, advanced placement, summer session for credit, part-time degree program, co-op programs.

Entrance Requirements: Open admission except for nursing, allied health programs. Options: Common Application, early admission. Required for some: high school transcript. Entrance: noncompetitive. Application deadline: 8/4. Notification: continuous.

Costs Per Year: Application fee: $25. Area resident tuition: $2950 full-time, $120 per credit hour part-time. State resident tuition: $3276 full-time, $134 per credit hour part-time. Nonresident tuition: $5586 full-time, $230 per credit hour part-time. Mandatory fees: $50 full-time, $5 per credit hour part-time.

Collegiate Environment: Orientation program. Student-run newspaper. Social organizations: 33 open to all. Major annual events: Holiday Drop-in, Big Band Concert, Spring Week Carnival. Student services: personal-psychological counseling. Campus security: 24-hour emergency response devices and patrols, late night transport-escort service. College housing not available. Learning Resources Center plus 3 others with 68,462 books and 868 serials. 500 computers available on campus for general student use. Computer purchase/lease plans available. A campuswide network can be accessed. Staffed computer lab on campus.

Community Environment: North Charleston is a suburb located just eight miles from downtown Charleston. The community enjoys all the cultural, recreational and civic advantages of the nearby larger community, yet retains an air of the small town. There are good shopping areas, churches, parks and theatres.

■ **UNIVERSITY OF SOUTH CAROLINA** *E-8*
Columbia, SC 29208
Tel: (803)777-7000
Admissions: (803)777-7700
E-mail: admissions-ugrad@scarolina.edu
Web Site: http://www.sc.edu/

Description: State-supported, university, coed. Part of University of South Carolina System. Awards bachelor's, master's, doctoral, and first professional degrees and post-master's certificates. Founded 1801. Setting: 315-acre urban campus. Research spending for 2004 fiscal year: $78.2 million. Educational spending for 2005 fiscal year: $8011 per student. Total enrollment: 27,065. Faculty: 1,567 (1,190 full-time, 377 part-time). Student-undergrad faculty ratio is 18:1. 13,023 applied, 68% were admitted. 26% from top 10% of their high school class, 60% from top quarter, 91% from top half. 31 National Merit Scholars, 65 valedictorians. Full-time: 16,399 students, 55% women, 45% men. Part-time: 1,963 students, 50% women, 50% men. Students come from 54 states and territories, 66 other countries, 12% from out-of-state, 0.3% Native American, 2% Hispanic, 14% black, 3% Asian American or Pacific Islander, 1% international, 9% 25 or older, 46% live on campus, 6% transferred in. Retention: 83% of full-time freshmen returned the following year. Academic areas with the most degrees conferred: business/marketing; social sciences; communications/journalism.

Core. Calendar: semesters. ESL program, services for LD students, advanced placement, accelerated degree program, self-designed majors, freshman honors college, honors program, independent study, distance learning, double major, summer session for credit, part-time degree program, external degree program, adult/continuing education programs, co-op programs and internships, graduate courses open to undergrads. Study abroad program. ROTC: Army, Air Force.

Entrance Requirements: Options: electronic application, international baccalaureate accepted. Required: high school transcript, minimum 2.0 high school GPA, SAT or ACT. Entrance: moderately difficult. Application deadline: 12/1. Notification: continuous until 10/1.

Costs Per Year: Application fee: $50. State resident tuition: $6914 full-time, $324 per credit hour part-time. Nonresident tuition: $18,556 full-time, $844 per credit hour part-time. Full-time tuition varies according to program. College room and board: $6080. Room and board charges vary according to board plan, housing facility, and location.

Collegiate Environment: Orientation program. Drama-theater group, choral group, marching band, student-run newspaper, radio station. Social organizations: 270 open to all; national fraternities, national sororities; 14% of eligible men and 15% of eligible women are members. Most popular organizations: Fellowship of Christian Athletes, Association of African-American Students, Baptist Student Union, Garnet Circle/Student Alumni. Major annual events: Homecoming, Tigerburn, Greek Week. Student services: health clinic, personal-psychological counseling, women's center. Campus security: 24-hour emergency response devices and patrols, student patrols, late night transport-escort service, controlled dormitory access, Division of Law Enforcement and Safety. 6,937 college housing spaces available. Freshmen guaranteed college housing. On-campus residence required in freshman year. Options: coed, men-only, women-only housing available. Thomas Cooper Library plus 7 others with 3.4 million books, 5.1 million microform titles, 22,744 serials, 46,648 audiovisual materials, an OPAC, and a Web page. Operations spending for 2004 fiscal year: $15.5 million. 2,432 computers available on campus for general student use. A campuswide network can be accessed from student residence rooms and from off campus. Staffed computer lab on campus.

Community Environment: Columbia is located in the Midlands, halfway between the coast and the mountains - an easy two-and-a-half hour drive to some of the nicest beaches on the East Coast and some of the Carolinas' best hiking trails. A few blocks east of the university lies bustling Five Points, a longtime favorite of students for it boutiques, bookstores, restaurants, and bars. West of the university lies the Congaree Vista, a more upscale shopping and eating district. As the state's capital city, Columbia is home to the state government, as well as several other colleges and universities. Culture and entertainment abound. The city has several theatre groups, an art museum, and an art center that brings in major musical, dance, and theatre entertainment. For relaxation on Columbia's balmy spring-like days, downtown's Finlay Park is close by, and nearby Lake Murray offers swimming, camping, and fishing.

■ **UNIVERSITY OF SOUTH CAROLINA AIKEN** *G-6*
471 University Parkway
Aiken, SC 29801-6309
Tel: (803)648-6851; 888-WOW-USCA
Fax: (803)641-3727
E-mail: admit@aiken.sc.edu
Web Site: http://www.usca.edu/

Description: State-supported, comprehensive, coed. Part of University of South Carolina System. Awards bachelor's and master's degrees. Founded 1961. Setting: 453-acre suburban campus with easy access to Columbia. Endowment: $15.6 million. Research spending for 2004 fiscal year: $144,263. Educational spending for 2005 fiscal year: $4986 per student. Total enrollment: 3,303. Faculty: 246 (147 full-time, 99 part-time). Student-undergrad faculty ratio is 16:1. 2,064 applied, 48% were admitted. 15% from top 10% of their high school class, 39% from top quarter, 79% from top half. 10 valedictorians. Full-time: 2,270 students, 67% women, 33% men. Part-time: 880 students, 68% women, 32% men. Students come from 35 states and territories, 24 other countries, 11% from out-of-state, 0.2% Native American, 2% Hispanic, 26% black, 1% Asian American or Pacific Islander, 2% international, 26% 25 or older, 22% live on campus, 9% transferred in. Retention: 60% of full-time freshmen returned the following year. Academic areas with the most degrees conferred: business/marketing; education; social sciences. Core. Calendar: semesters. ESL program, services for LD students, advanced placement, accelerated degree program, self-designed majors, honors program, independent study, double major, summer session for credit, part-time degree program, adult/continuing education programs, co-op programs and internships. Off campus study at other units of the University of South Carolina System. Study abroad program.

Entrance Requirements: Options: Peterson's Universal Application, electronic application, early admission, deferred admission, international baccalaureate accepted. Required: high school transcript, minimum SAT of 800 or ACT of 17, SAT or ACT. Entrance: moderately difficult. Application deadline: 8/1. Notification: continuous.

Costs Per Year: Application fee: $35. State resident tuition: $5928 full-time, $258 per semester hour part-time. Nonresident tuition: $12,070 full-time, $520 per semester hour part-time. Mandatory fees: $230 full-time, $8 per semester hour part-time, $7 per term part-time. Full-time tuition and fees vary according to reciprocity agreements. Part-time tuition and fees vary according to course load and reciprocity agreements. College room and board: $5560. College room only: $3800. Room and board charges vary according to board plan and housing facility.

Collegiate Environment: Orientation program. Drama-theater group, choral group, student-run newspaper. Social organizations: 53 open to all; national fraternities, national sororities; 1% of eligible men and 1% of eligible women are members. Most popular organizations: student government, Pacesetters, Student Alumni Ambassadors, African-American Student Alliance, Pacer Union Board. Major annual events: Homecoming Week, leadership training events, Black History Month. Student services: health clinic, personal-psychological counseling. Campus security: 24-hour emergency response devices and patrols, late night transport-escort service. 680 college housing spaces available; 672 were occupied in 2003-04. Option: coed housing available. Gregg-Graniteville Library with 165,459 books, 26,566 microform titles, 745 serials, 915 audiovisual materials, an OPAC, and a Web page. Operations spending for 2004 fiscal year: $1 million. 450 computers available on campus for general student use. A campuswide network can be accessed from student residence rooms and from off campus. Staffed computer lab on campus.

Community Environment: Aiken, population c. 24,929, is the seat of Aiken County and is about 17 miles from Augusta, Georgia.

■ UNIVERSITY OF SOUTH CAROLINA BEAUFORT *K-9*

801 Carteret St.
Beaufort, SC 29902-4601
Tel: (843)521-4100
Web Site: http://www.sc.edu/beaufort/

Description: State-supported, 4-year, coed. Part of University of South Carolina System. Awards associate and bachelor's degrees. Founded 1959. Setting: 5-acre small town campus. Endowment: $832,000. Research spending for 2004 fiscal year: $107,353. Educational spending for 2005 fiscal year: $4642 per student. Total enrollment: 1,319. Student-undergrad faculty ratio is 15:1. 464 applied, 87% were admitted. 5% from top 10% of their high school class, 22% from top quarter, 52% from top half. Full-time: 676 students, 62% women, 38% men. Part-time: 643 students, 56% women, 44% men. Students come from 47 states and territories, 18 other countries, 19% from out-of-state, 1% Native American, 4% Hispanic, 16% black, 1% Asian American or Pacific Islander, 1% international, 33% 25 or older, 12% transferred in. Retention: 56% of full-time freshmen returned the following year. Academic areas with the most degrees conferred: education; business/marketing; social sciences. Core. Calendar: semesters. Services for LD students, advanced placement, independent study, distance learning, double major, summer session for credit, part-time degree program, adult/continuing education programs, internships. Off campus study. Study abroad program.

Entrance Requirements: Options: Common Application, electronic application, deferred admission, international baccalaureate accepted. Required: high school transcript, SAT or ACT. Recommended: minimum 2.0 high school GPA. Entrance: minimally difficult. Application deadline: Rolling. Notification: continuous.

Costs Per Year: Application fee: $40. State resident tuition: $4954 full-time, $207 per credit hour part-time. Nonresident tuition: $11,870 full-time, $495 per credit hour part-time. Mandatory fees: $330 full-time, $10 per credit hour part-time. College room only: $6900.

Collegiate Environment: Orientation program. Drama-theater group, student-run newspaper. Social organizations: 8 open to all. Most popular organizations: Student Government Association, Gamma Beta Phi, Black Student Organization, Business Club, Environmental Awareness Club. Major annual events: student cookouts, Christmas Party, Spring Fling. Campus security: 24-hour emergency response devices, evening security service. College housing not available. University of South Carolina at Beaufort Library plus 1 other with 50,000 books, 395 serials, an OPAC, and a Web

page. Operations spending for 2004 fiscal year: $449,830. 85 computers available on campus for general student use. A campuswide network can be accessed from off-campus. Staffed computer lab on campus.

■ UNIVERSITY OF SOUTH CAROLINA LANCASTER *C-8*

PO Box 889
Lancaster, SC 29721-0889
Tel: (803)313-7471
Admissions: (803)313-7000
Fax: (803)313-7106
E-mail: bparker@gwm.sc.edu
Web Site: http://usclancaster.sc.edu/

Description: State-supported, 2-year, coed. Part of University of South Carolina System. Awards transfer associate and terminal associate degrees. Founded 1959. Setting: 17-acre small town campus with easy access to Charlotte. Total enrollment: 943. 302 applied, 98% were admitted. 10% from top 10% of their high school class, 25% from top quarter, 50% from top half. Students come from 3 states and territories, 1 other country, 0.2% Native American, 0.3% Hispanic, 19% black, 1% Asian American or Pacific Islander, 37% 25 or older. Calendar: semesters. Academic remediation for entering students, advanced placement, honors program, part-time degree program, adult/continuing education programs.

Entrance Requirements: Open admission. Options: Common Application, early admission. Required: high school transcript. Placement: SAT or ACT required. Entrance: noncompetitive. Application deadline: Rolling. Notification: continuous.

Collegiate Environment: Orientation program. Choral group, student-run newspaper. Student services: personal-psychological counseling, women's center. College housing not available. Medford Library with 68,192 books and 454 serials. 25 computers available on campus for general student use.

■ UNIVERSITY OF SOUTH CAROLINA SALKEHATCHIE *I-7*

PO Box 617
Allendale, SC 29810-0617
Tel: (803)584-3446
Web Site: http://uscsalkehatchie.sc.edu/

Description: State-supported, 2-year, coed. Part of University of South Carolina System. Awards transfer associate degrees. Founded 1965. Setting: 95-acre rural campus. Educational spending for 2005 fiscal year: $2086 per student. Total enrollment: 777. 15% from top 10% of their high school class, 45% from top quarter, 75% from top half. 10 valedictorians. Students come from 3 states and territories, 1% from out-of-state, 41% black, 27% 25 or older. Core. Calendar: semesters. Academic remediation for entering students, services for LD students, advanced placement, accelerated degree program, self-designed majors, summer session for credit, part-time degree program, adult/continuing education programs, internships. ROTC: Army (c), Naval (c), Air Force (c).

Entrance Requirements: Open admission. Required: high school transcript, minimum 2.0 high school GPA, SAT or ACT. Entrance: noncompetitive. Application deadline: Rolling.

Collegiate Environment: Orientation program. Student-run newspaper. Major annual event: Feast Day. Campus security: 24-hour emergency response devices. College housing not available. Salkehatchie Learning Resource Center with 47,877 books, 11,477 microform titles, 832 audiovisual materials, an OPAC, and a Web page. Operations spending for 2004 fiscal year: $371,233. 70 computers available on campus for general student use. Staffed computer lab on campus.

■ UNIVERSITY OF SOUTH CAROLINA SUMTER *F-10*

200 Miller Rd.
Sumter, SC 29150-2498
Tel: (803)775-8727
Admissions: (803)938-3882
E-mail: kbritton@uscsumter.edu
Web Site: http://www.uscsumter.edu/

Description: State-supported, 2-year, coed. Part of University of South Carolina System. Awards transfer associate degrees. Founded 1966. Setting: 50-acre urban campus. Endowment: $1.8 million. Research spending for 2004 fiscal year: $25,459. Educational spending for 2005 fiscal year: $4064 per student. Total enrollment: 1,020. Student-undergrad faculty ratio is 19:1. 453 applied, 62% were admitted. 1 class president, 3 student government officers. Full-time: 580 students, 63% women, 37% men. Part-time: 440 students, 58% women, 42% men. Students come from 2 states and territories, 4 other countries, 1% from out-of-state, 1% Native American,

2% Hispanic, 26% black, 3% Asian American or Pacific Islander, 0.1% international, 30% 25 or older, 11% transferred in. Retention: 56% of full-time freshmen returned the following year. Core. Calendar: semesters. Services for LD students, advanced placement, honors program, independent study, distance learning, summer session for credit, part-time degree program, adult/continuing education programs. ROTC: Army (c), Air Force (c).

Entrance Requirements: Options: Common Application, electronic application, international baccalaureate accepted. Required: high school transcript, minimum 2.0 high school GPA, SAT or ACT. Entrance: moderately difficult. Application deadline: 8/8.

Costs Per Year: Application fee: $40. State resident tuition: $4064 full-time, $169 per semester hour part-time. Nonresident tuition: $10,124 full-time, $422 per semester hour part-time. Mandatory fees: $260 full-time. Full-time tuition and fees vary according to degree level.

Collegiate Environment: Orientation program. Drama-theater group, choral group. Social organizations: 16 open to all. Most popular organizations: Association of African-American Students, Baptist Student Union, Student Education Association, Gamecock Ambassadors, Environmental Club. Major annual events: Convocation, Alcohol Awareness Week Festival, Martin Luther King, Jr. Day festivities. Student services: personal-psychological counseling. Campus security: late night transport-escort service. College housing not available. University of South Carolina at Sumter Library with 81,114 books, 12,938 microform titles, 1,114 serials, 913 audiovisual materials, an OPAC, and a Web page. Operations spending for 2004 fiscal year: $302,089. 355 computers available on campus for general student use. A campuswide network can be accessed from off-campus. Staffed computer lab on campus.

■ **UNIVERSITY OF SOUTH CAROLINA UNION** *C-6*
PO Drawer 729
Union, SC 29379-0729
Tel: (864)427-3681
Admissions: (864)429-8728
Web Site: http://uscunion.sc.edu/

Description: State-supported, 2-year, coed. Part of University of South Carolina System. Awards transfer associate degrees. Founded 1965. Setting: small town campus with easy access to Charlotte. Total enrollment: 321. Student-undergrad faculty ratio is 14:1. 127 applied, 89% were admitted. 5% from top 10% of their high school class, 18% from top quarter, 41% from top half. Full-time: 161 students, 69% women, 31% men. Part-time: 160 students, 69% women, 31% men. Students come from 2 states and territories, 1% from out-of-state, 0.3% Native American, 1% Hispanic, 27% black, 1% Asian American or Pacific Islander, 0% international, 35% 25 or older, 12% transferred in. Calendar: semesters. Part-time degree program.

Entrance Requirements: Required: high school transcript, SAT or ACT. Entrance: minimally difficult. Application deadline: Rolling.

Costs Per Year: Application fee: $40. State resident tuition: $4064 full-time, $169 per credit hour part-time. Nonresident tuition: $10,124 full-time, $422 per credit hour part-time. Mandatory fees: $100 full-time, $10 per hour part-time.

Collegiate Environment: Drama-theater group, choral group, student-run newspaper. Social organizations: 12 open to all. College housing not available. 30 computers available on campus for general student use. A campuswide network can be accessed from off-campus.

■ **UNIVERSITY OF SOUTH CAROLINA UPSTATE** *B-5*
800 University Way
Spartanburg, SC 29303-4999
Tel: (864)503-5000
Free: 800-277-8727
Admissions: (864)503-5280
Fax: (864)503-5201
E-mail: dstewart@uscupstate.edu
Web Site: http://www.uscupstate.edu/

Description: State-supported, comprehensive, coed. Part of University of South Carolina System. Awards associate, bachelor's, and master's degrees. Founded 1967. Setting: 300-acre urban campus with easy access to Charlotte. Endowment: $2.6 million. Research spending for 2004 fiscal year: $354,813. Educational spending for 2005 fiscal year: $6436 per student. Total enrollment: 4,484. Faculty: 356 (207 full-time, 149 part-time). Student-undergrad faculty ratio is 15:1. 2,296 applied, 33% were admitted. 12% from top 10% of their high school class, 38% from top quarter, 71% from top half. 5 valedictorians. Full-time: 3,564 students, 66% women, 34% men. Part-time: 845 students, 67% women, 33% men. Students come from

37 states and territories, 42 other countries, 3% from out-of-state, 0.4% Native American, 2% Hispanic, 26% black, 3% Asian American or Pacific Islander, 2% international, 32% 25 or older, 15% live on campus, 13% transferred in. Retention: 61% of full-time freshmen returned the following year. Academic areas with the most degrees conferred: education; business/marketing; health professions and related sciences. Core. Calendar: semesters. Academic remediation for entering students, ESL program, services for LD students, advanced placement, accelerated degree program, self-designed majors, honors program, independent study, distance learning, double major, summer session for credit, part-time degree program, adult/continuing education programs, co-op programs and internships. Off campus study at Wofford College, Greenville Higher Education Consortium. Study abroad program. ROTC: Army (c).

Entrance Requirements: Options: Peterson's Universal Application, electronic application, deferred admission, international baccalaureate accepted. Required: high school transcript, minimum 2.0 high school GPA, college prep courses, SAT or ACT. Entrance: moderately difficult. Notification: continuous.

Costs Per Year: Application fee: $40. State resident tuition: $6436 full-time, $282 per hour part-time. Nonresident tuition: $13,274 full-time, $583 per hour part-time. Mandatory fees: $326 full-time, $11 per hour part-time, $25 per term part-time. Full-time tuition and fees vary according to course load. Part-time tuition and fees vary according to course load. College room and board: $5160. College room only: $3200. Room and board charges vary according to board plan and housing facility.

Collegiate Environment: Orientation program. Drama-theater group, choral group, student-run newspaper. Social organizations: 56 open to all; national fraternities, national sororities; 4% of eligible men and 4% of eligible women are members. Most popular organizations: African-American Association, Campus Activity Board, Student Nurses Association, Student Government Association, Association for the Education of Young Children. Major annual events: Premier Fall Kick-Off, Technology Fair, Angel Tree Program. Student services: health clinic, personal-psychological counseling, women's center. Campus security: 24-hour emergency response devices and patrols, late night transport-escort service, campus security cameras. 730 college housing spaces available; 400 were occupied in 2003-04. Option: coed housing available. University of South Carolina Upstate Library with 188,572 books, 55,051 microform titles, 14,953 serials, 7,640 audiovisual materials, an OPAC, and a Web page. Operations spending for 2004 fiscal year: $1.9 million. 320 computers available on campus for general student use. Computer purchase/lease plans available. A campuswide network can be accessed from student residence rooms. Staffed computer lab on campus.

Community Environment: Spartanburg, South Carolina, is one of the fastest-growing communities in the region, located on the thriving Interstate 85 corridor about three hours from Atlanta and an hour and a half from Charlotte, North Carolina. The Blue Ridge Mountains are less than an hour away; South Carolina's Grand Strand and historic Low Country are a four-hour drive in the other direction. The area has a growing international presence, and arts and cultural activities that would be the envy of many larger cities.

■ **VOORHEES COLLEGE** *H-7*
1411 Voorhees Rd., PO Box 678
Denmark, SC 29042
Tel: (803)793-3351
Free: 800-446-6250
Admissions: (803)703-7124
Fax: (803)793-5773
Web Site: http://www.voorhees.edu/

Description: Independent Episcopal, 4-year, coed. Awards bachelor's degrees. Founded 1897. Setting: 350-acre rural campus. Endowment: $5 million. Total enrollment: 847. 2,624 applied, 41% were admitted. 1% from top 10% of their high school class, 44% from top quarter, 50% from top half. Full-time: 807 students, 66% women, 34% men. Part-time: 40 students, 30% women, 70% men. Students come from 18 states and territories, 5 other countries, 0% Native American, 0% Hispanic, 95% black, 0% Asian American or Pacific Islander, 4% international, 26% 25 or older, 85% live on campus, 5% transferred in. Retention: 58% of full-time freshmen returned the following year. Core. Calendar: semesters. Academic remediation for entering students, advanced placement, honors program, double major, summer session for credit, part-time degree program, adult/continuing education programs, co-op programs and internships. ROTC: Army (c).

Entrance Requirements: Options: Common Application, electronic application, deferred admission. Required: high school transcript, minimum 2.0 high school GPA, SAT or ACT. Required for some: high school transcript, interview. Entrance: moderately difficult. Application deadline: Rolling.

Costs Per Year: Application fee: $25. Comprehensive fee: $11,848 includes full-time tuition ($7106), mandatory fees ($170), and college room and board ($4572). College room only: $1904. Room and board charges vary according to housing facility. Part-time tuition: $242 per semester hour. Part-time mandatory fees: $170 per term.

Collegiate Environment: Orientation program. Drama-theater group, choral group, student-run newspaper. Social organizations: 30 open to all; national fraternities, national sororities; 15% of eligible men and 10% of eligible women are members. Most popular organizations: White Rose, Elizabeth Evelyn Wright Culture Club. Major annual events: Founders' Day, Homecoming, Fall Convocation. Student services: health clinic, personal-psychological counseling. Campus security: 24-hour emergency response devices and patrols, student patrols, late night transport-escort service. 550 college housing spaces available; 404 were occupied in 2003-04. Freshmen guaranteed college housing. On-campus residence required through sophomore year. Wright-Potts Library with 107,260 books, 24,266 microform titles, 408 serials, 1,172 audiovisual materials, an OPAC, and a Web page. Operations spending for 2004 fiscal year: $213,167. 300 computers available on campus for general student use. A campuswide network can be accessed from student residence rooms and from off campus. Staffed computer lab on campus.

Community Environment: Denmark is a rural community located in south central South Carolina. The climate is temperate. There is a public library, local hospitals and several churches representing various denominations. The Lions Club, Masonic Lodge, and Woodmen of the World are active within the community. Recreation includes golf, swimming, boating, fishing and a local theatre.

■ **WILLIAMSBURG TECHNICAL COLLEGE** *G-11*
601 Martin Luther King, Jr Ave.
Kingstree, SC 29556-4197
Tel: (843)355-4110
Free: 800-768-2021
Fax: (843)355-4296
Web Site: http://www.wiltech.edu/
Description: State-supported, 2-year, coed. Part of South Carolina State Board for Technical and Comprehensive Education. Awards certificates, diplomas, transfer associate, and terminal associate degrees. Founded 1969. Setting: 41-acre rural campus. Endowment: $52,987. Educational spending for 2005 fiscal year: $1476 per student. Total enrollment: 595. 0% from out-of-state, 0% Native American, 0.2% Hispanic, 71% black, 0.3% Asian American or Pacific Islander, 0% international, 49% 25 or older. Core. Calendar: semesters. Academic remediation for entering students, services for LD students, advanced placement, independent study, distance learning, summer session for credit, part-time degree program, adult/continuing education programs, co-op programs and internships.
Entrance Requirements: Open admission. Options: Common Application, early admission, deferred admission. Required: high school transcript. Placement: ACT ASSET, ACT COMPASS required; SAT or ACT recommended. Entrance: noncompetitive. Application deadline: Rolling. Notification: continuous.
Collegiate Environment: Social organizations: 9 open to all; national fraternities, local fraternities, local sororities; 30% of eligible men and 30% of eligible women are members. Most popular organizations: Student Government Association, National Vocational-Technical Honor Society, Phi Theta Kappa International Honor Society, Computer Club. Major annual events: Tech Fest, Miss Tech Pageant, Christmas Party. Student services: personal-psychological counseling. Campus security: late night transport-escort service. College housing not available. Learning Resource Center with 25,456 books, 24,365 microform titles, 109 serials, 3,601 audiovisual materials, and an OPAC. Operations spending for 2004 fiscal year: $134,408. 100 computers available on campus for general student use. A campuswide network can be accessed. Staffed computer lab on campus.

■ **WINTHROP UNIVERSITY** *B-8*
701 Oakland Ave.
Rock Hill, SC 29733
Tel: (803)323-2211
Free: 800-763-0230
Admissions: (803)323-2191
Fax: (803)323-2137
E-mail: admissions@winthrop.edu

Web Site: http://www.winthrop.edu/
Description: State-supported, comprehensive, coed. Part of South Carolina Commission on Higher Education. Awards bachelor's and master's degrees. Founded 1886. Setting: 418-acre suburban campus with easy access to Charlotte. Endowment: $693,815. Research spending for 2004 fiscal year: $316,031. Educational spending for 2005 fiscal year: $4460 per student. Total enrollment: 6,480. Faculty: 542 (270 full-time, 272 part-time). Student-undergrad faculty ratio is 14:1. 4,304 applied, 69% were admitted. 22% from top 10% of their high school class, 56% from top quarter, 92% from top half. Full-time: 4,587 students, 69% women, 31% men. Part-time: 600 students, 72% women, 28% men. Students come from 41 states and territories, 30 other countries, 11% 25 or older, 43% live on campus, 7% transferred in. Retention: 72% of full-time freshmen returned the following year. Academic areas with the most degrees conferred: business/marketing; education; visual and performing arts. Core. Calendar: semesters. Services for LD students, advanced placement, honors program, independent study, distance learning, double major, summer session for credit, part-time degree program, adult/continuing education programs, co-op programs and internships, graduate courses open to undergrads. Off campus study at National Student Exchange, 19 members of the Charlotte Area Educational Consortium. Study abroad program.
Entrance Requirements: Options: Peterson's Universal Application, deferred admission, international baccalaureate accepted. Required: high school transcript, 1 recommendation, SAT or ACT. Recommended: essay. Entrance: moderately difficult. Application deadline: 5/1. Notification: continuous.
Costs Per Year: Application fee: $40. State resident tuition: $8756 full-time, $364 per semester hour part-time. Nonresident tuition: $16,150 full-time, $673 per semester hour part-time. Full-time tuition varies according to degree level. Part-time tuition varies according to degree level. College room and board: $5352. College room only: $3420. Room and board charges vary according to board plan and housing facility.
Collegiate Environment: Orientation program. Drama-theater group, choral group, student-run newspaper, radio station. Social organizations: 115 open to all; national fraternities, national sororities. Most popular organizations: Ebonites, campus ministries, Student Government Association, Dinkins Student Union. Major annual events: Homecoming, Greek Week, Convocation/Student Activities Fair. Student services: health clinic, personal-psychological counseling. Campus security: 24-hour emergency response devices and patrols, late night transport-escort service. Freshmen guaranteed college housing. Options: coed, men-only, women-only housing available. Dacus Library with 414,879 books, 1.2 million microform titles, 1,446 serials, 2,884 audiovisual materials, an OPAC, and a Web page. Operations spending for 2004 fiscal year: $2.2 million. 250 computers available on campus for general student use. A campuswide network can be accessed from student residence rooms and from off campus. Staffed computer lab on campus.
Community Environment: Rock Hill is a small progressive city of nearly 50,000 residents located 30 miles below Charlotte, North Carolina. The city is uniquely situated to offer the advantages of both small town living and big city amenities. Diversified industry fuels a growing local economy which produces textiles, wood, paper, concrete, plastic and chemical products. Rock Hill's facilities include the Museum of York County (featuring the world's largest collection of hooved African animals); Winthrop Galleries, host to local, national and international artists; Winthrop Coliseum, Glencairn Gardens, a six acre garden spot; and Cherry Park, a 68 acre recreation park featuring five major league baseball and softball diamonds, which attracts major tournaments from throughout the United States. Opportunities for recreation in the mild piedmont climate are plentiful. The city maintains a system of 28 parks that offer athletic fields and courts, play areas, fitness, walking and jogging trails, and amphitheaters. Lakes 20 minutes away are a convenient destination for water sports and sailing.

■ **WOFFORD COLLEGE** *B-5*
429 North Church St.
Spartanburg, SC 29303-3663
Tel: (864)597-4000
Admissions: (864)597-4130
Fax: (864)597-4149
E-mail: admissions@wofford.edu
Web Site: http://www.wofford.edu/
Description: Independent, 4-year, coed, affiliated with United Methodist Church. Awards bachelor's degrees. Founded 1854. Setting: 140-acre urban campus with easy access to Charlotte. Endowment: $123 million.

Educational spending for 2005 fiscal year: $6761 per student. Total enrollment: 1,173. Student-undergrad faculty ratio is 12:1. 1,871 applied, 66% were admitted. 58% from top 10% of their high school class, 83% from top quarter, 98% from top half. 1 National Merit Scholar, 8 class presidents, 19 valedictorians, 42 student government officers. Full-time: 1,158 students, 48% women, 52% men. Part-time: 15 students, 33% women, 67% men. Students come from 30 states and territories, 5 other countries, 35% from out-of-state, 0.3% Native American, 1% Hispanic, 6% black, 2% Asian American or Pacific Islander, 1% international, 0% 25 or older, 88% live on campus, 2% transferred in. Retention: 89% of full-time freshmen returned the following year. Academic areas with the most degrees conferred: business/marketing; biological/life sciences; social sciences. Core. Calendar: 4-1-4. Advanced placement, accelerated degree program, self-designed majors, independent study, double major, summer session for credit, part-time degree program, internships. Off campus study at Converse College, University of South Carolina-Spartanburg. Study abroad program. ROTC: Army.

Entrance Requirements: Options: Peterson's Universal Application, Common Application, electronic application, early admission, early decision, deferred admission. Required: essay, high school transcript, SAT or ACT. Recommended: 2 recommendations, interview. Entrance: very difficult. Application deadlines: 2/1, 11/15 for early decision. Notification: 3/15, 12/1 for early decision.

Costs Per Year: Application fee: $40. Comprehensive fee: $30,935 includes full-time tuition ($24,130) and college room and board ($6805). Part-time tuition: $875 per hour.

Collegiate Environment: Orientation program. Drama-theater group, choral group, student-run newspaper. Social organizations: 68 open to all; national fraternities, national sororities; 51% of eligible men and 59% of eligible women are members. Most popular organizations: performing arts groups, Twin Towers student volunteers, Fellowship of Christian Athletes. Major annual events: homecoming, Spring Weekend/Greek Games, Phi Beta Kappa Day. Student services: health clinic, personal-psychological counseling. Campus security: 24-hour emergency response devices and patrols, late night transport-escort service, controlled dormitory access. College housing designed to accommodate 966 students; 1,029 undergraduates lived in college housing during 2003-04. Freshmen given priority for college housing. On-campus residence required through senior year. Option: coed housing available. Sandor Teszler Library with 245,730 books, 37,005 microform titles, 10,046 serials, 2,796 audiovisual materials, an OPAC, and a Web page. 35 computers available on campus for general student use. Computer purchase/lease plans available. A campuswide network can be accessed from student residence rooms and from off campus. Staffed computer lab on campus.

Community Environment: Spartanburg County (population 250,000) is a thriving, rapidly growing Sunbelt business center that is particularly well known for its international community. Wofford students live in a downtown setting near restaurants, churches of all denominations, shopping districts, a busy arts center, and four other college campuses. Memorial Auditorium, Wofford's next-door neighbor, features concerts, touring Broadway plays, and other special attractions. Several major airlines serve the convenient Greenville-Spartanburg Airport, which is only twenty miles from the campus. Interstate highways 26 and 85 intersect at Spartanburg. Charlotte, Atlanta, historic Charleston, and South Carolina's world-famous coastal resorts are all within a pleasant afternoon drive.

■ YORK TECHNICAL COLLEGE *B-8*

452 South Anderson Rd.
Rock Hill, SC 29730-3395
Tel: (803)327-8000
Admissions: (803)981-7021
Fax: (803)327-8059
E-mail: kaldridge@yorktech.com
Web Site: http://www.yorktech.com/

Description: State-supported, 2-year, coed. Part of South Carolina State Board for Technical and Comprehensive Education. Awards certificates, diplomas, transfer associate, and terminal associate degrees. Founded 1961. Setting: 110-acre small town campus with easy access to Charlotte. Educational spending for 2005 fiscal year: $2900 per student. Total enrollment: 4,153. Full-time: 2,039 students, 60% women, 40% men. Part-time: 2,114 students, 67% women, 33% men. 2% from out-of-state, 2% Native American, 1% Hispanic, 24% black, 1% Asian American or Pacific Islander, 0.02% international, 39% 25 or older. Core. Calendar: semesters. Academic remediation for entering students, ESL program, services for LD students, advanced placement, honors program, distance learning, summer session for credit, part-time degree program, adult/continuing education programs, co-op programs and internships. Off campus study at Charlotte Area Educational Consortium.

Entrance Requirements: Open admission except for health and human services program. Option: electronic application. Required for some: high school transcript, SAT, ACT, or ACT ASSET, ACT COMPASS. Entrance: noncompetitive. Application deadline: Rolling. Notification: continuous.

Costs Per Year: Application fee: $0. Area resident tuition: $2900 full-time, $121 per credit hour part-time. State resident tuition: $3264 full-time, $136 per credit hour part-time. Nonresident tuition: $6528 full-time, $272 per credit hour part-time. Mandatory fees: $136 full-time, $4 per credit hour part-time, $68 per term part-time.

Collegiate Environment: Orientation program. Social organizations: 16 open to all. Most popular organizations: Jacobin Society, Phi Theta Kappa, Student Government Association, Phi Beta Lambda, Student Activities Board. Major annual events: Tech Fest, Welcome Back Blast, Health Fair. Campus security: 24-hour patrols. College housing not available. Anne Springs Close Library with 26,947 books, 50,574 microform titles, 475 serials, 1,813 audiovisual materials, an OPAC, and a Web page. 250 computers available on campus for general student use. A campuswide network can be accessed from off-campus. Staffed computer lab on campus.

Community Environment: See Winthrop University.

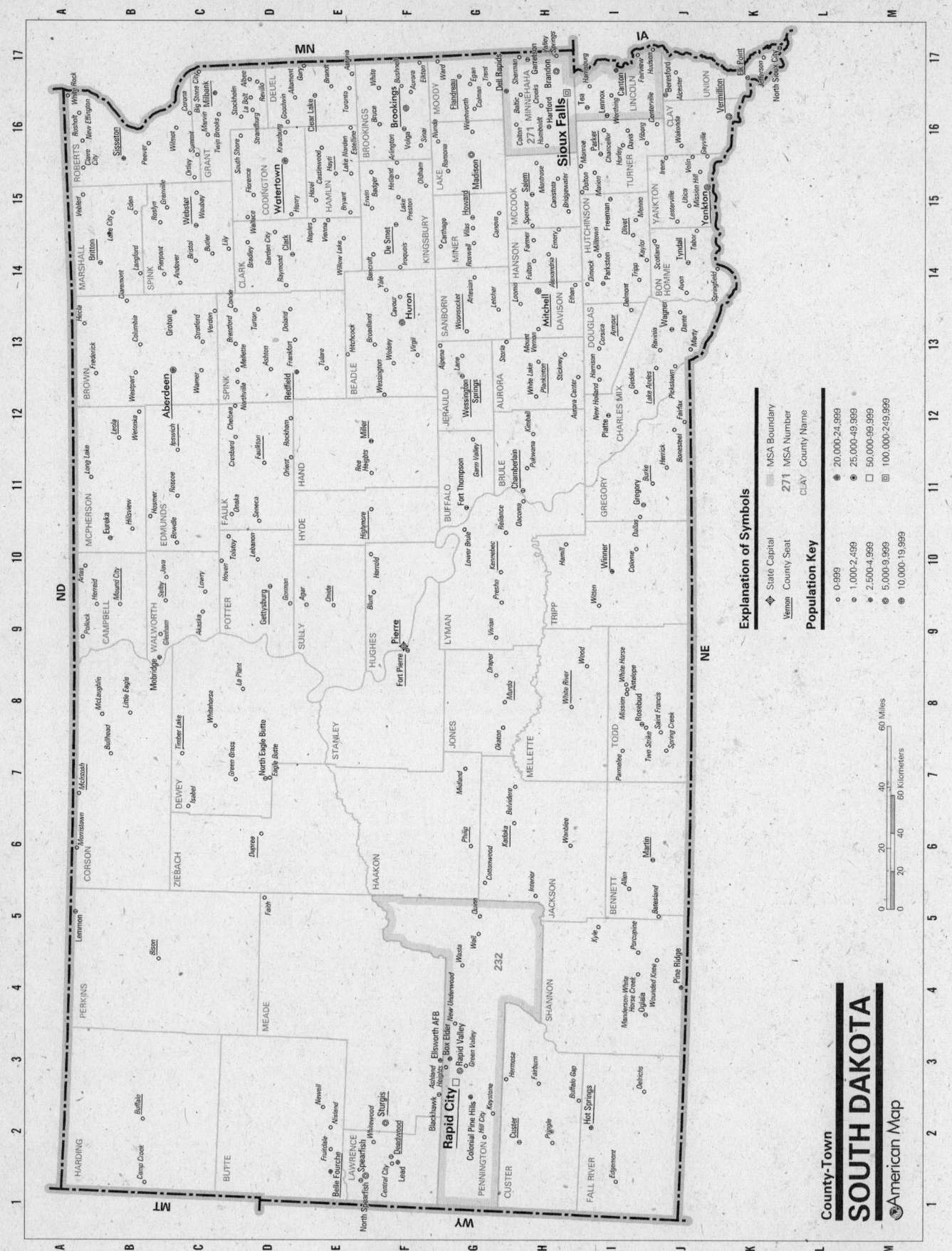

County-Town

SOUTH DAKOTA

American Map

■ AUGUSTANA COLLEGE *H-16*
2001 South Summit Ave.
Sioux Falls, SD 57197
Tel: (605)274-0770
Free: 800-727-2844
Admissions: (605)274-5516
Fax: (605)274-5518
Web Site: http://www.augie.edu/
Description: Independent, comprehensive, coed, affiliated with Evangelical Lutheran Church in America. Awards bachelor's and master's degrees. Founded 1860. Setting: 100-acre urban campus. Endowment: $40.4 million. Research spending for 2004 fiscal year: $849,485. Educational spending for 2005 fiscal year: $6910 per student. Total enrollment: 1,745. Faculty: 180 (108 full-time, 72 part-time). Student-undergrad faculty ratio is 13:1. 1,544 applied, 80% were admitted. 26% from top 10% of their high school class, 58% from top quarter, 86% from top half. 2 National Merit Scholars, 34 valedictorians. Full-time: 1,621 students, 62% women, 38% men. Part-time: 93 students, 66% women, 34% men. Students come from 32 states and territories, 10 other countries, 56% from out-of-state, 0.4% Native American, 0.3% Hispanic, 1% black, 1% Asian American or Pacific Islander, 2% international, 5% 25 or older, 67% live on campus, 5% transferred in. Retention: 79% of full-time freshmen returned the following year. Academic areas with the most degrees conferred: education; history; business/marketing. Core. Calendar: 4-1-4. Academic remediation for entering students, services for LD students, advanced placement, accelerated degree program, self-designed majors, honors program, independent study, double major, summer session for credit, part-time degree program, adult/continuing education programs, co-op programs and internships, graduate courses open to undergrads. Off campus study at 10 other colleges in the upper Midwest. Study abroad program.
Entrance Requirements: Options: Peterson's Universal Application, Common Application, electronic application, deferred admission, international baccalaureate accepted. Required: high school transcript, minimum 2.5 high school GPA, 1 recommendation, minimum ACT score of 20, SAT or ACT. Recommended: interview. Required for some: essay. Entrance: moderately difficult. Application deadline: 8/1. Notification: continuous.
Costs Per Year: Application fee: $0. Comprehensive fee: $25,458 includes full-time tuition ($19,750), mandatory fees ($236), and college room and board ($5472). College room only: $2700.
Collegiate Environment: Orientation program. Drama-theater group, choral group, student-run newspaper, radio station. Social organizations: 54 open to all. Most popular organizations: Fellowship of Christian Athletes, Circle K, Student Council for Exceptional Children, Habitat for Humanity, Spanish Club. Major annual events: Community Service Day, Vespers, Viking Days (Homecoming). Student services: legal services, health clinic, personal-psychological counseling. Campus security: 24-hour emergency response devices and patrols, late night transport-escort service, controlled dormitory access. 1,242 college housing spaces available; 1,107 were occupied in 2003-04. Freshmen guaranteed college housing. On-campus residence required through sophomore year. Option: coed housing available. Mikkelsen Library plus 1 other with 279,918 books, 31,345 microform titles, 595 serials, 8,515 audiovisual materials, an OPAC, and a Web page. Operations spending for 2004 fiscal year: $843,654. 360 computers available on campus for general student use. A campuswide network can be accessed from student residence rooms and from off campus. Staffed computer lab on campus.

Community Environment: See University of Sioux Falls.

■ BLACK HILLS STATE UNIVERSITY *F-1*
1200 University St.
Spearfish, SD 57799
Tel: (605)642-6011
Free: 800-255-2478
Admissions: (605)642-6343
E-mail: jberry@mystic.bhsu.edu
Web Site: http://www.bhsu.edu/
Description: State-supported, comprehensive, coed. Part of South Dakota University System. Awards associate, bachelor's, and master's degrees and post-master's certificates. Founded 1883. Setting: 123-acre small town campus. Endowment: $7.5 million. Research spending for 2004 fiscal year: $629,401. Educational spending for 2005 fiscal year: $3027 per student. Total enrollment: 3,846. 1,424 applied, 49% were admitted. 6% from top 10% of their high school class, 23% from top quarter, 55% from top half. Full-time: 2,533 students, 62% women, 38% men. Part-time: 1,120 students, 68% women, 32% men. Students come from 35 states and territories, 6 other countries, 19% from out-of-state, 3% Native American, 2% Hispanic, 1% black, 1% Asian American or Pacific Islander, 0.4% international, 28% 25 or older, 20% live on campus, 13% transferred in. Retention: 56% of full-time freshmen returned the following year. Core. Calendar: semesters. Academic remediation for entering students, services for LD students, advanced placement, accelerated degree program, honors program, independent study, distance learning, double major, summer session for credit, part-time degree program, co-op programs and internships, graduate courses open to undergrads. Off campus study at South Dakota State University. ROTC: Army.
Entrance Requirements: Options: Peterson's Universal Application, electronic application. Required: high school transcript, minimum 2.0 high school GPA in core curriculum, SAT or ACT. Entrance: minimally difficult. Application deadline: 7/18.
Costs Per Year: Application fee: $20. State resident tuition: $2444 full-time, $76.35 per credit part-time. Nonresident tuition: $7764 full-time, $242.60 per credit part-time. Mandatory fees: $2628 full-time, $82.10 per credit part-time. Full-time tuition and fees vary according to course load and reciprocity agreements. Part-time tuition and fees vary according to course load and reciprocity agreements. College room and board: $3663. College room only: $2078. Room and board charges vary according to board plan and housing facility.
Collegiate Environment: Orientation program. Drama-theater group, choral group, student-run newspaper, radio station. Social organizations: 60 open to all; national fraternities, national sororities; 1% of eligible men and 1% of eligible women are members. Most popular organizations: Student Activities Committee, student government. Major annual events: Swarm Days, Big 100 Week. Student services: health clinic, personal-psychological counseling. Campus security: 24-hour patrols, late night transport-escort service, controlled dormitory access. College housing designed to accommodate 788 students; 790 undergraduates lived in college housing during 2003-04. Freshmen given priority for college housing. On-campus residence required through sophomore year. Options: coed, men-only, women-only housing available. E. Y. Berry Library-Learning Center with 310,210 books, 370,738 microform titles, 485 serials, 751 audiovisual materials, an OPAC, and a Web page. Operations spending for 2004 fiscal year: $414,343. 220 comput-

ers available on campus for general student use. A campuswide network can be accessed from student residence rooms and from off campus. Staffed computer lab on campus.

Community Environment: Spearfish, population 10,000, is in a beautiful agricultural valley at the mouth of Spearfish Canyon. There are libraries, museums, churches, hospitals, and a number of civic and service organizations in the community and surrounding area. Recreational activities include hunting, fishing, hiking, skiing, golf, and boating. The Black Hills Passion Play is presented during the summer months in a specially constructed amphitheater. Part-time employment is available.

■ COLORADO TECHNICAL UNIVERSITY SIOUX FALLS CAMPUS
H-16
3901 West 59th St.
Sioux Falls, SD 57108
Tel: (605)361-0200
Fax: (605)361-5954
Web Site: http://www.ctu-siouxfalls.com/

Description: Proprietary, comprehensive, coed. Part of Colorado Technical University - Main Campus Colorado Springs, CO. Awards associate, bachelor's, and master's degrees. Founded 1965. Setting: 3-acre urban campus. Educational spending for 2005 fiscal year: $4950 per student. Total enrollment: 1,036. Full-time: 441 students, 61% women, 39% men. Part-time: 471 students, 58% women, 42% men. Students come from 3 states and territories, 5% from out-of-state, 1% Native American, 0.5% Hispanic, 2% black, 1% Asian American or Pacific Islander, 0% international, 18% 25 or older, 12% transferred in. Core. Accelerated degree program, distance learning, double major, summer session for credit, part-time degree program, adult/continuing education programs, co-op programs and internships, graduate courses open to undergrads. ROTC: Army (c).

Entrance Requirements: Open admission. Options: early admission, deferred admission, international baccalaureate accepted. Required: high school transcript, interview. Recommended: ACT. Entrance: minimally difficult. Application deadline: Rolling. Notification: continuous.

Collegiate Environment: Orientation program. Social organizations: 4 open to all. Most popular organizations: Phi Beta Lambda, AITP, CJ Honor Society, SHRM Student Chapter. College housing not available. Resource Center with 5,787 books, 25 serials, 280 audiovisual materials, an OPAC, and a Web page. Operations spending for 2004 fiscal year: $32,670. 55 computers available on campus for general student use. Computer purchase/lease plans available. A campuswide network can be accessed from off-campus. Staffed computer lab on campus.

■ DAKOTA STATE UNIVERSITY *G-16*
820 North Washington
Madison, SD 57042-1799
Tel: (605)256-5111; 888-DSU-9988
Admissions: (605)256-5696
Fax: (605)256-5316
E-mail: amy.crissinger@dsu.edu
Web Site: http://www.dsu.edu/

Description: State-supported, comprehensive, coed. Part of South Dakota Board of Regents. Awards associate, bachelor's, and master's degrees. Founded 1881. Setting: 40-acre rural campus with easy access to Sioux Falls. Research spending for 2004 fiscal year: $40,633. Educational spending for 2005 fiscal year: $2892 per student. Total enrollment: 2,319. Faculty: 108 (77 full-time, 31 part-time). Student-undergrad faculty ratio is 17:1. 594 applied, 97% were admitted. 6% from top 10% of their high school class, 20% from top quarter, 50% from top half. 7 valedictorians. Full-time: 1,162 students, 46% women, 54% men. Part-time: 919 students, 63% women, 37% men. Students come from 14 states and territories, 2 other countries, 21% from out-of-state, 1% Native American, 1% Hispanic, 1% black, 1% Asian American or Pacific Islander, 1% international, 18% 25 or older, 34% live on campus, 7% transferred in. Retention: 69% of full-time freshmen returned the following year. Academic areas with the most degrees conferred: computer and information sciences; business/marketing; education. Core. Calendar: semesters. Academic remediation for entering students, ESL program, services for LD students, advanced placement, honors program, independent study, distance learning, double major, summer session for credit, part-time degree program, external degree program, adult/continuing education programs, co-op programs and internships, graduate courses open to undergrads. Off campus study at South Dakota State University, University of Sioux Falls, University of South Dakota. Study abroad program. ROTC: Air Force (c).

Entrance Requirements: Options: electronic application, deferred admission. Required: high school transcript, minimum X high school GPA, rank in upper two-thirds of high school class, SAT or ACT. Entrance: minimally difficult. Application deadline: Rolling. Notification: continuous.

Costs Per Year: Application fee: $20. State resident tuition: $2382 full-time, $79 per credit hour part-time. Nonresident tuition: $3573 full-time, $119 per credit hour part-time. Mandatory fees: $3317 full-time, $89 per credit hour part-time. College room and board: $3927. College room only: $1924.

Collegiate Environment: Orientation program. Drama-theater group, choral group, marching band, student-run newspaper, radio station. Social organizations: 30 open to all. Most popular organizations: Business Club, band, Computer Club. Major annual events: Homecoming, Zimmfest Band Festival, Diversity Week. Student services: health clinic, personal-psychological counseling. Campus security: controlled dormitory access, night watchman. College housing designed to accommodate 700 students; 994 undergraduates lived in college housing during 2003-04. Freshmen guaranteed college housing. On-campus residence required through sophomore year. Options: coed, men-only, women-only housing available. Karl E. Mundt Library plus 1 other with 98,156 books, 3,111 microform titles, 350 serials, 2,435 audiovisual materials, an OPAC, and a Web page. Operations spending for 2004 fiscal year: $536,546. 398 computers available on campus for general student use. Computer purchase/lease plans available. A campuswide network can be accessed from student residence rooms and from off campus. Staffed computer lab on campus.

Community Environment: Dakota State University is located in the heart of the Midwest, in Madison, South Dakota, just minutes from Interstates 29 and 90, which are major highways. Two nearby lakes provide the best in outdoor recreation. In the summer, this includes water sports, fishing and camping, followed in the fall and winter by hunting, snowmobiling, cross-country skiing and more. One of South Dakota's finest state parks provides excellent facilities for all of these activities. Cultural events are provided by a local arts association, a summer theater group and through college-sponsored events. Madison is also located just an hour away from the state's largest city, Sioux Falls.

■ DAKOTA WESLEYAN UNIVERSITY *H-14*
1200 West University Ave.
Mitchell, SD 57301-4398
Tel: (605)995-2600
Free: 800-333-8506
Admissions: (605)995-2650
Fax: (605)995-2699
E-mail: admissions@cc.dwu.edu
Web Site: http://www.dwu.edu/

Description: Independent United Methodist, comprehensive, coed. Awards associate, bachelor's, and master's degrees. Founded 1885. Setting: 50-acre small town campus. Endowment: $19.1 million. Educational spending for 2005 fiscal year: $4124 per student. Total enrollment: 783. Faculty: 84 (50 full-time, 34 part-time). Student-undergrad faculty ratio is 12:1. 478 applied, 72% were admitted. 10% from top 10% of their high school class, 38% from top quarter, 78% from top half. Full-time: 730 students, 59% women, 41% men. Part-time: 28 students, 68% women, 32% men. Students come from 29 states and territories, 4 other countries, 25% from out-of-state, 4% Native American, 4% Hispanic, 5% black, 1% Asian American or Pacific Islander, 2% international, 20% 25 or older, 43% live on campus, 10% transferred in. Retention: 68% of full-time freshmen returned the following year. Academic areas with the most degrees conferred: business/marketing; education; law/legal studies. Core. Calendar: semesters. Academic remediation for entering students, ESL program, services for LD students, advanced placement, self-designed majors, honors program, independent study, distance learning, double major, summer session for credit, part-time degree program, adult/continuing education programs, internships. Off campus study. Study abroad program.

Entrance Requirements: Options: Peterson's Universal Application, electronic application. Required: high school transcript, SAT or ACT. Recommended: minimum 2.0 high school GPA. Entrance: moderately difficult. Application deadline: 8/28. Notification: continuous.

Costs Per Year: Application fee: $25. Comprehensive fee: $21,550 includes full-time tuition ($16,650) and college room and board ($4900). College room only: $2100. Part-time tuition: $350 per credit.

Collegiate Environment: Orientation program. Drama-theater group, choral group, student-run newspaper. Social organizations: 30 open to all. Most popular organizations: DWU Future Teachers Organization, Student Nurses Association, Culture Club, Human Services Club, Student Ministry Council.

Major annual events: Blue and White Days, Spring Week, Family Life Conference. Student services: health clinic, personal-psychological counseling. Campus security: 24-hour emergency response devices, student patrols, late night transport-escort service, controlled dormitory access, campus patrol from 2am to 6am by special request only. 380 college housing spaces available; 261 were occupied in 2003-04. Freshmen guaranteed college housing. On-campus residence required through sophomore year. Options: coed, men-only, women-only housing available. Layne Library with 63,000 books, 64,670 microform titles, 721 serials, 20,900 audiovisual materials, an OPAC, and a Web page. Operations spending for 2004 fiscal year: $367,080. 100 computers available on campus for general student use. A campuswide network can be accessed from student residence rooms and from off campus. Staffed computer lab on campus.

Community Environment: Located in the James River Valley, Mitchell (population 15,000) is one of the most fertile and diversified agricultural areas in the United States. Products are corn, sorghum, small grain, cattle and hogs. Mitchell is the trading center for the surrounding counties. Community facilities include shopping areas, churches, a library, YMCA, 2 hospitals and a number of the customary civic and service organizations. Recreational activities include boating, fishing, swimming and pheasant hunting.

■ **KILIAN COMMUNITY COLLEGE** *H-16*

300 East 6th St.
Sioux Falls, SD 57103
Tel: (605)221-3100
Free: 800-888-1147
Fax: (605)336-2606
E-mail: amodrell@kilian.edu
Web Site: http://www.kilian.edu/

Description: Independent, 2-year, coed. Awards certificates, transfer associate, and terminal associate degrees. Founded 1977. Setting: 2-acre urban campus. Total enrollment: 538. Student-undergrad faculty ratio is 8:1. 195 applied, 100% were admitted. Full-time: 108 students, 69% women, 31% men. Part-time: 430 students, 77% women, 23% men. Students come from 3 states and territories, 4% from out-of-state, 4% Native American, 3% Hispanic, 3% black, 0.2% Asian American or Pacific Islander, 0% international, 52% 25 or older, 6% transferred in. Core. Calendar: trimesters. Academic remediation for entering students, services for LD students, independent study, double major, summer session for credit, part-time degree program, co-op programs and internships.

Entrance Requirements: Open admission. Options: early admission, deferred admission. Required: high school transcript. Application deadline: Rolling.

Costs Per Year: Application fee: $25. Tuition: $7020 full-time, $195 per credit hour part-time. Mandatory fees: $150 full-time, $50 per term part-time.

Collegiate Environment: Student services: personal-psychological counseling. Campus security: late night transport-escort service. College housing not available. University of Sioux Falls Mears Library with 78,000 books, 395 serials, an OPAC, and a Web page. 37 computers available on campus for general student use. A campuswide network can be accessed. Staffed computer lab on campus.

■ **LAKE AREA TECHNICAL INSTITUTE** *D-15*

230 11th St. Northeast
Watertown, SD 57201
Tel: (605)882-5284
Free: 800-657-4344
E-mail: latiinfo@lati.tec.sd.us
Web Site: http://www.lati.tec.sd.us/

Description: State-supported, 2-year, coed. Awards diplomas and terminal associate degrees. Founded 1964. Setting: 16-acre small town campus. Total enrollment: 1,057. Core. Calendar: semesters. Academic remediation for entering students, services for LD students, internships.

Entrance Requirements: Option: electronic application. Required: high school transcript, ACT. Required for some: essay, 3 recommendations, interview. Entrance: minimally difficult.

Collegiate Environment: Orientation program. Social organizations: 10 open to all. Most popular organizations: PBL, VICA, Rodeo Club. College housing not available. Leonard H. Timmerman Library plus 1 other with 5,000 books and 128 serials. 650 computers available on campus for general student use. A campuswide network can be accessed from off-campus. Staffed computer lab on campus.

■ **MITCHELL TECHNICAL INSTITUTE** *H-14*

821 North Capital
Mitchell, SD 57301
Tel: (605)995-3024
Free: 800-952-0042
Admissions: (605)995-3025
Fax: (605)996-3299
Web Site: http://mti.tec.sd.us/

Description: District-supported, 2-year, coed. Awards diplomas, transfer associate, and terminal associate degrees. Founded 1968. Setting: 90-acre rural campus. Total enrollment: 832. Students come from 18 states and territories, 2 other countries, 2% Native American, 0.2% Hispanic, 1% Asian American or Pacific Islander, 24% 25 or older. Core. Calendar: semesters. Academic remediation for entering students, services for LD students, advanced placement, distance learning, summer session for credit, co-op programs and internships.

Entrance Requirements: Open admission except for some programs. Option: electronic application. Required: high school transcript. Recommended: minimum 2.0 high school GPA, ACT. Required for some: essay, interview, TABE. Entrance: minimally difficult. Application deadline: Rolling. Notification: continuous.

Collegiate Environment: Orientation program. Social organizations: 7 open to all. Most popular organizations: Student Representative Board, Vocational Industrial Clubs of America, Phi Beta Lambda, Post-Secondary Agricultural Students, Rodeo Club. Major annual events: Orientation Week, Christmas Party for Children, Winter Bowling Party. Student services: personal-psychological counseling. College housing not available. Instructional Services Center with 100 serials and an OPAC. Operations spending for 2004 fiscal year: $20,345. 110 computers available on campus for general student use. Computer purchase/lease plans available. A campuswide network can be accessed. Staffed computer lab on campus.

■ **MOUNT MARTY COLLEGE** *J-15*

1105 West 8th St.
Yankton, SD 57078-3724
Tel: (605)668-1011
Free: 800-658-4552
Admissions: (605)668-1545
Fax: (605)668-1607
E-mail: btschumper@mtmc.edu
Web Site: http://www.mtmc.edu/

Description: Independent Roman Catholic, comprehensive, coed. Awards associate, bachelor's, and master's degrees. Founded 1936. Setting: 80-acre small town campus. Endowment: $14.1 million. Educational spending for 2005 fiscal year: $4370 per student. Total enrollment: 1,189. Faculty: 113 (48 full-time, 65 part-time). Student-undergrad faculty ratio is 12:1. 317 applied, 85% were admitted. 14% from top 10% of their high school class, 34% from top quarter, 70% from top half. Full-time: 712 students, 71% women, 29% men. Part-time: 377 students, 58% women, 42% men. Students come from 11 states and territories, 3 other countries, 31% from out-of-state, 2% Native American, 2% Hispanic, 2% black, 0.2% Asian American or Pacific Islander, 0.3% international, 31% 25 or older, 9% transferred in. Retention: 78% of full-time freshmen returned the following year. Academic areas with the most degrees conferred: education; health professions and related sciences; business/marketing. Core. Calendar: semesters. Academic remediation for entering students, services for LD students, advanced placement, accelerated degree program, self-designed majors, honors program, independent study, double major, summer session for credit, part-time degree program, adult/continuing education programs, co-op programs and internships. Off campus study at members of the Colleges of Mid-America. ROTC: Army (c).

Entrance Requirements: Options: electronic application, early admission, deferred admission. Required: high school transcript, minimum 2.0 high school GPA, SAT or ACT. Recommended: interview, ACT. Required for some: recommendations. Entrance: moderately difficult. Application deadline: Rolling. Notification: continuous.

Costs Per Year: Application fee: $35. Comprehensive fee: $20,590 includes full-time tuition ($14,050), mandatory fees ($1680), and college room and board ($4860). Full-time tuition and fees vary according to course load and location. Part-time tuition: $228 per credit hour. Part-time mandatory fees: $20 per credit hour. Part-time tuition and fees vary according to course load and location.

Collegiate Environment: Orientation program. Drama-theater group, choral group, student-run newspaper. Social organizations: 40 open to all. Most

popular organizations: campus ministry, Student Government Association, Nursing Club, Education Club, Theater Club or SIFE (Students in Free Enterprise). Major annual events: Homecoming, October Service Blitz, Winterfest. Student services: health clinic, personal-psychological counseling. Campus security: 24-hour emergency response devices and patrols, controlled dormitory access. 360 college housing spaces available; 315 were occupied in 2003-04. Freshmen guaranteed college housing. On-campus residence required through senior year. Option: coed housing available. Mount Marty College Library with 76,571 books, 12,068 microform titles, 424 serials, 8,565 audiovisual materials, an OPAC, and a Web page. Operations spending for 2004 fiscal year: $185,193. 21 computers available on campus for general student use. Computer purchase/lease plans available. A campuswide network can be accessed from student residence rooms and from off campus. Staffed computer lab on campus.

Community Environment: Yankton is situated on the Missouri River, 60 miles northwest of Sioux City, Iowa, and 80 miles southwest of Sioux Falls, S.D. The city is located four miles downstream from Gavins Point Dam, and Lewis and Clark Lake, which provides some of the best fishing, swimming, boating, and picnicking areas in the Midwest. The All-American city served as the first capital of Dakota Territory and is known as the Mother City of the Dakotas. Its 14,000 friendly people take a deep interest in the activities of the college.

■ **NATIONAL AMERICAN UNIVERSITY (ELLSWORTH AFB)** *G-3*
2700 Doolittle Dr.
Ellsworth AFB, SD 57706
Tel: (605)923-5856
Web Site: http://www.national.edu/
Description: Proprietary, 2-year, coed.

■ **NATIONAL AMERICAN UNIVERSITY (RAPID CITY)** *G-3*
321 Kansas City St.
Rapid City, SD 57701
Tel: (605)394-4800
Free: 800-843-8892
Admissions: (605)394-4902
Fax: (605)394-4871
E-mail: abeck@national.edu
Web Site: http://www.national.edu/
Description: Proprietary, comprehensive, coed. Part of National College. Awards associate, bachelor's, and master's degrees. Founded 1941. Setting: 8-acre urban campus. Endowment: $30,000. Research spending for 2004 fiscal year: $35,000. Educational spending for 2005 fiscal year: $3320 per student. Total enrollment: 531. Faculty: 85 (70 full-time, 15 part-time). Student-undergrad faculty ratio is 26:1. 463 applied, 100% were admitted. Full-time: 311 students, 49% women, 51% men. Part-time: 152 students, 49% women, 51% men. Students come from 25 states and territories, 31% from out-of-state, 3% Native American, 1% Hispanic, 4% black, 2% Asian American or Pacific Islander, 13% international, 70% 25 or older, 21% live on campus. Retention: 57% of full-time freshmen returned the following year. Academic areas with the most degrees conferred: business/marketing; health professions and related sciences; computer and information sciences. Core. Academic remediation for entering students, ESL program, services for LD students, advanced placement, accelerated degree program, independent study, distance learning, summer session for credit, part-time degree program, external degree program, adult/continuing education programs, co-op programs and internships. ROTC: Army (c).
Entrance Requirements: Open admission. Options: Peterson's Universal Application, Common Application, electronic application, early admission, deferred admission. Required: high school transcript. Recommended: interview, ACT. Entrance: noncompetitive. Application deadline: Rolling. Notification: continuous.
Costs Per Year: Application fee: $25. Comprehensive fee: $15,423 includes full-time tuition ($11,520), mandatory fees ($50), and college room and board ($3853). College room only: $1938. Part-time tuition: $240 per credit hour. Part-time mandatory fees: $90 per credit hour.
Collegiate Environment: Orientation program. Social organizations: local fraternities, local sororities; 6% of eligible men and 7% of eligible women are members. Most popular organizations: Student Senate, Phi Beta Lambda, Dormitory Council, Student Association of Legal Assistants, President's Advisory Council. Major annual events: blood drives, Community Clean-Up. Student services: personal-psychological counseling. Campus security: part-time security personnel. 265 college housing spaces available; 97 were occupied in 2003-04. Freshmen guaranteed college housing. On-campus

residence required through sophomore year. Option: coed housing available. Jefferson Library with 31,018 books, 268 serials, and a Web page. 50 computers available on campus for general student use. A campuswide network can be accessed. Staffed computer lab on campus.

Community Environment: National College is located in a community of about 57,000 residents. Rapid City is a retail hub for several Midwestern states. Rapid City shops, entertainment facilities, and a wide array of dining establishments offer a"big city" feel. A strong Rapid City economy provides many part-time employment opportunities while students are in school. Only 20 minutes away lies one of the most popular tourist areas in the world-- Mount Rushmore--which is nestled in the majestic Black Hills. From Rushmore Mall and the Dahl Fine Arts Center to wilderness mountain biking and downhill skiing, Rapid City offers the social and cultural diversity that students desire.

■ **NATIONAL AMERICAN UNIVERSITY-SIOUX FALLS BRANCH** *H-16*
2801 South Kiwanis Ave.
Ste. 100
Sioux Falls, SD 57105-4293
Tel: (605)334-5430
Free: 800-388-5430
E-mail: lhoutsma@national.edu
Web Site: http://www.national.edu/
Description: Proprietary, 4-year, coed. Part of National College. Awards associate, bachelor's, and master's degrees. Founded 1941. Setting: urban campus. Total enrollment: 375. 9 applied, 100% were admitted. Students come from 6 states and territories, 1% Native American, 0% Hispanic, 1% black, 0% Asian American or Pacific Islander, 0% international, 76% 25 or older. Retention: 70% of full-time freshmen returned the following year. Core. Academic remediation for entering students, ESL program, advanced placement, accelerated degree program, distance learning, double major, summer session for credit, part-time degree program, adult/continuing education programs, co-op programs and internships.
Entrance Requirements: Open admission. Options: Common Application, electronic application, deferred admission. Required: high school transcript, interview. Entrance: noncompetitive. Application deadline: Rolling. Notification: continuous.
Collegiate Environment: Orientation program. Campus security: 24-hour emergency response devices. College housing not available. Main library plus 1 other with 1,580 books, 57 serials, and a Web page. 60 computers available on campus for general student use. A campuswide network can be accessed. Staffed computer lab on campus.

■ **NORTHERN STATE UNIVERSITY** *C-13*
1200 South Jay St.
Aberdeen, SD 57401-7198
Tel: (605)626-3011
Free: 800-678-5330
Admissions: (605)626-2544
Fax: (605)626-3022
E-mail: admissionl@wolf.northern.edu
Web Site: http://www.northern.edu/
Description: State-supported, comprehensive, coed. Part of South Dakota Board of Regents. Awards associate, bachelor's, and master's degrees. Founded 1901. Setting: 52-acre small town campus. Endowment: $9.2 million. Educational spending for 2005 fiscal year: $2300 per student. Total enrollment: 2,631. Faculty: 94 (all full-time). Student-undergrad faculty ratio is 20:1. 783 applied, 94% were admitted. 21% from top 10% of their high school class, 45% from top quarter, 68% from top half. Full-time: 1,595 students, 57% women, 43% men. Part-time: 830 students, 63% women, 37% men. Students come from 32 states and territories, 13 other countries, 19% from out-of-state, 3% Native American, 1% Hispanic, 1% black, 1% Asian American or Pacific Islander, 3% international, 19% 25 or older, 6% transferred in. Retention: 69% of full-time freshmen returned the following year. Academic areas with the most degrees conferred: business/marketing; education; social sciences. Core. Calendar: semesters. Academic remediation for entering students, ESL program, services for LD students, advanced placement, accelerated degree program, self-designed majors, honors program, distance learning, summer session for credit, part-time degree program, adult/continuing education programs, co-op programs and internships, graduate courses open to undergrads. Off campus study at National Student Exchange. Study abroad program.
Entrance Requirements: Options: Peterson's Universal Application, Common Application, early admission, deferred admission. Required: high school

transcript, minimum X high school GPA, SAT or ACT. Required for some: recommendations. Entrance: minimally difficult. Application deadline: 9/1. Notification: continuous.

Costs Per Year: Application fee: $15. State resident tuition: $2290 full-time, $76.35 per credit hour part-time. Nonresident tuition: $7278 full-time, $242.60 per credit hour part-time. Mandatory fees: $2409 full-time, $80.30 per credit hour part-time. Full-time tuition and fees vary according to course level, course load, and reciprocity agreements. Part-time tuition and fees vary according to course level, course load, and reciprocity agreements. College room and board: $3980. College room only: $2023. Room and board charges vary according to board plan.

Collegiate Environment: Orientation program. Drama-theater group, choral group, marching band, student-run newspaper. Social organizations: 100 open to all. Most popular organizations: Student Ambassadors, Choices, honor society, Native American Student Association. Major annual events: Homecoming-Gypsy Days, 'I Hate Winter', Commencement. Student services: health clinic, personal-psychological counseling. Campus security: 24-hour emergency response devices, controlled dormitory access, evening patrols. On-campus residence required through sophomore year. Option: coed housing available. Beulah Williams Library with 192,007 books, 367,763 microform titles, 882 serials, an OPAC, and a Web page. Operations spending for 2004 fiscal year: $364,407. 900 computers available on campus for general student use. A campuswide network can be accessed from student residence rooms and from off campus. Staffed computer lab on campus.

■ OGLALA LAKOTA COLLEGE

490 Piya Wiconi Rd.
Kyle, SD 57752-0490
Tel: (605)455-6000
Fax: (605)455-2787
Web Site: http://www.olc.edu/

Description: State and locally supported, comprehensive, coed. Awards associate, bachelor's, and master's degrees. Founded 1970. Setting: rural campus. Total enrollment: 1,000. Students come from 2 states and territories, 70% 25 or older. Core. Calendar: semesters. Academic remediation for entering students, accelerated degree program, summer session for credit, part-time degree program, adult/continuing education programs, co-op programs and internships. Off campus study at American Indian Higher Education Consortium.

Entrance Requirements: Open admission. Option: early admission. Required: high school transcript. Entrance: noncompetitive. Application deadline: Rolling. Notification: continuous. Preference given to Native Americans.

Collegiate Environment: Student-run newspaper. Social organizations: 10 open to all. College housing not available. Oglala Lakota College Learning Resource Center with 15,000 books and 150 serials. 65 computers available on campus for general student use.

■ PRESENTATION COLLEGE *C-13*

1500 North Main St.
Aberdeen, SD 57401-1299
Tel: (605)225-1634
Free: 800-437-6060
Admissions: (605)229-8492
Fax: (605)229-8518
E-mail: joellen.lindner@presentation.edu
Web Site: http://www.presentation.edu/

Description: Independent Roman Catholic, 4-year, coed. Awards associate and bachelor's degrees. Founded 1951. Setting: 100-acre small town campus. Endowment: $13.2 million. Educational spending for 2005 fiscal year: $5140 per student. Total enrollment: 758. Student-undergrad faculty ratio is 12:1. 315 applied, 99% were admitted. 13% from top 10% of their high school class, 28% from top quarter, 60% from top half. Full-time: 514 students, 81% women, 19% men. Part-time: 244 students, 82% women, 18% men. Students come from 1 other country, 34% from out-of-state, 6% Native American, 0.4% Hispanic, 1% black, 1% Asian American or Pacific Islander, 1% international, 21% 25 or older, 15% live on campus, 14% transferred in. Retention: 60% of full-time freshmen returned the following year. Academic areas with the most degrees conferred: health professions and related sciences; public administration and social services; business/marketing. Core. Calendar: semesters. Academic remediation for entering students, advanced placement, accelerated degree program, distance learn-

ing, double major, summer session for credit, part-time degree program, external degree program, adult/continuing education programs, co-op programs and internships.

Entrance Requirements: Open admission except for allied health programs, nursing. Option: electronic application. Required: high school transcript, ACT. Recommended: minimum 2.0 high school GPA. Required for some: 2 recommendations. Entrance: noncompetitive. Application deadline: Rolling. Notification: continuous.

Costs Per Year: Application fee: $0. Comprehensive fee: $17,075 includes full-time tuition ($12,300) and college room and board ($4775). College room only: $3975. Part-time tuition: $450 per credit.

Collegiate Environment: Orientation program. Drama-theater group, choral group, student-run newspaper. Social organizations: 41 open to all. Most popular organizations: Wellness, National Student Nursing Association, Social Work Organization. Major annual events: Snow Queen, Homecoming, Spring Fling. Student services: personal-psychological counseling. Campus security: 24-hour emergency response devices and patrols, late night transport-escort service, controlled dormitory access. 137 college housing spaces available; 115 were occupied in 2003-04. Freshmen guaranteed college housing. On-campus residence required in freshman year. Option: coed housing available. Presentation College Library plus 1 other with 40,000 books, 430 serials, 2,900 audiovisual materials, and an OPAC. Operations spending for 2004 fiscal year: $143,210. 30 computers available on campus for general student use. A campuswide network can be accessed from student residence rooms. Staffed computer lab on campus.

Community Environment: Aberdeen is a regional retail and market center with a population of 25,000. It is served by two major U.S. highways, and daily airline service.

■ SINTE GLESKA UNIVERSITY *I-8*

150 East 2nd St.
P.O. Box 105
Rosebud, SD 57570
Tel: (605)856-8100
Fax: (605)747-2098
Web Site: http://www.sinte.edu/

Description: Independent, comprehensive, coed. Awards associate, bachelor's, and master's degrees. Founded 1970. Setting: 52-acre rural campus. Total enrollment: 1,200. 168 applied, 100% were admitted. 73% 25 or older. Core. Calendar: semesters. Academic remediation for entering students, honors program, distance learning, double major, summer session for credit, part-time degree program, adult/continuing education programs, internships. Off campus study at American Indian Higher Education Consortium.

Entrance Requirements: Open admission. Required: high school transcript. Entrance: noncompetitive. Application deadline: 8/20. Notification: continuous until 8/30.

Collegiate Environment: Most popular organizations: Student Association, Lakota Club. Major annual events: Founders' Day, Student Awareness Week. Student services: personal-psychological counseling, women's center. Campus security: late night transport-escort service. College housing not available. Sinte Gleska University Library with 25,000 books, 80 serials, and an OPAC. 35 computers available on campus for general student use. A campuswide network can be accessed. Staffed computer lab on campus.

■ SISSETON-WAHPETON COMMUNITY COLLEGE *B-16*

Old Agency Box 689
Sisseton, SD 57262
Tel: (605)698-3966
Web Site: http://www.swc.tc/

Description: Federally supported, 2-year, coed. Awards certificates, transfer associate, and terminal associate degrees. Founded 1979. Setting: 2-acre rural campus. Endowment: $253,820. Educational spending for 2005 fiscal year: $1335 per student. Total enrollment: 274. 53 applied, 100% were admitted. Full-time: 147 students, 67% women, 33% men. Part-time: 127 students, 73% women, 27% men. Students come from 3 states and territories, 82% Native American, 0% Hispanic, 0% black, 0% Asian American or Pacific Islander, 0% international, 69% 25 or older, 5% transferred in. Core. Calendar: semesters. Academic remediation for entering students, double major, summer session for credit, part-time degree program, adult/continuing education programs, co-op programs and internships. Off campus study at members of the American Indian Higher Education Consortium.

Entrance Requirements: Open admission. Options: Common Application, deferred admission. Required: high school transcript. Recommended:

minimum 2.0 high school GPA, recommendations, interview. Placement: Assessment and Placement Services for Community Colleges required. Entrance: noncompetitive. Application deadline: Rolling.

Costs Per Year: Application fee: $0. State resident tuition: $2880 full-time. Mandatory fees: $490 full-time. Tuition guaranteed not to increase for student's term of enrollment.

Collegiate Environment: Orientation program. Social organizations: 1 open to all. Most popular organization: Student Senate. Major annual event: Native American Day. Student services: personal-psychological counseling. Campus security: 24-hour emergency response devices. College housing not available. Sisseton-Wahpeton Community College Library with 15,481 books, 8 microform titles, 162 serials, 885 audiovisual materials, an OPAC, and a Web page. Operations spending for 2004 fiscal year: $99,939. 28 computers available on campus for general student use. A campuswide network can be accessed from off-campus. Staffed computer lab on campus.

■ **SOUTH DAKOTA SCHOOL OF MINES AND TECHNOLOGY** *G-3*
501 East Saint Joseph
Rapid City, SD 57701-3995
Tel: (605)394-2511
Free: 800-544-8162
Admissions: (605)394-2414
Fax: (605)394-2914
E-mail: admissions@sdsmt.edu
Web Site: http://www.sdsmt.edu/

Description: State-supported, university, coed. Part of South Dakota State University System. Awards associate, bachelor's, master's, and doctoral degrees. Founded 1885. Setting: 120-acre suburban campus. Endowment: $25.6 million. Research spending for 2004 fiscal year: $6.6 million. Educational spending for 2005 fiscal year: $4749 per student. Total enrollment: 2,313. Faculty: 140 (107 full-time, 33 part-time). Student-undergrad faculty ratio is 16:1. 727 applied, 94% were admitted. 21% from top 10% of their high school class, 50% from top quarter, 81% from top half. Full-time: 1,592 students, 24% women, 76% men. Part-time: 465 students, 56% women, 44% men. Students come from 34 states and territories, 8 other countries, 31% from out-of-state, 3% Native American, 1% Hispanic, 1% black, 1% Asian American or Pacific Islander, 2% international, 16% 25 or older, 32% live on campus, 4% transferred in. Retention: 73% of full-time freshmen returned the following year. Academic areas with the most degrees conferred: engineering; interdisciplinary studies; computer and information sciences. Core. Calendar: semesters. Academic remediation for entering students, ESL program, services for LD students, advanced placement, independent study, distance learning, double major, summer session for credit, part-time degree program, adult/continuing education programs, co-op programs and internships, graduate courses open to undergrads. Study abroad program. ROTC: Army.

Entrance Requirements: Option: electronic application. Required: high school transcript, SAT or ACT. Recommended: minimum 2.6 high school GPA. Entrance: moderately difficult. Application deadline: Rolling. Notification: continuous.

Costs Per Year: Application fee: $20. State resident tuition: $2291 full-time, $76.35 per credit hour part-time. Nonresident tuition: $7278 full-time, $242.60 per credit hour part-time. Mandatory fees: $2466 full-time, $82.20 per credit hour part-time. Full-time tuition and fees vary according to course load, program, and reciprocity agreements. Part-time tuition and fees vary according to course load, program, and reciprocity agreements. College room and board: $2867. College room only: $1830. Room and board charges vary according to board plan and housing facility.

Collegiate Environment: Orientation program. Drama-theater group, choral group, student-run newspaper, radio station. Social organizations: national fraternities, national sororities; 22% of eligible men and 23% of eligible women are members. Most popular organizations: TONITE (Techs Outrageous New Initiative for Total Entertainment), SADD (Students Against Drunk Driving), ASCE (American Society of Civil Engineers), ASME (American Society of Mechanical Engineers), Ski Club. Major annual events: Homecoming/M Week, Engineers' Week, Fall Career Fair. Student services: health clinic, personal-psychological counseling. Campus security: 24-hour emergency response devices and patrols, student patrols, late night transport-escort service, controlled dormitory access. 571 college housing spaces available; 564 were occupied in 2003-04. Freshmen guaranteed college housing. On-campus residence required through sophomore year. Options: coed, men-only, women-only housing available. Devereaux Library with 273,243 books, 65,261 microform titles, 3,088 serials, 1,827 audiovisual materials, an OPAC, and a Web page. Operations spending for 2004 fiscal

year: $730,493. 210 computers available on campus for general student use. A campuswide network can be accessed from student residence rooms and from off campus. Staffed computer lab on campus.

Community Environment: Rapid City, founded in 1876, two years after gold was discovered in the Black Hills, is now a trading center and tourist headquarters of the Black Hills area. All commercial transportation is available. Community facilities include many churches, museums, hospitals, a library, radio stations, three TV stations, and a number of the major civic and service organizations.

■ **SOUTH DAKOTA STATE UNIVERSITY** *F-16*
PO Box 2201
Brookings, SD 57007
Tel: (605)688-4151
Free: 800-952-3541
Fax: (605)688-6384
Web Site: http://www.sdstate.edu/

Description: State-supported, university, coed. Awards associate, bachelor's, master's, doctoral and first professional degrees and post-master's certificates. Founded 1881. Setting: 272-acre small town campus. Endowment: $53 million. Research spending for 2004 fiscal year: $33.5 million. Educational spending for 2005 fiscal year: $8273 per student. Total enrollment: 10,938. Faculty: 584 (413 full-time, 171 part-time). Student-undergrad faculty ratio is 17:1. 3,641 applied, 93% were admitted. 15% from top 10% of their high school class, 37% from top quarter, 70% from top half. 2 National Merit Scholars. Full-time: 7,749 students, 48% women, 52% men. Part-time: 1,845 students, 69% women, 31% men. Students come from 33 states and territories, 21 other countries, 29% from out-of-state, 1% Native American, 1% Hispanic, 1% black, 1% Asian American or Pacific Islander, 0.2% international, 14% 25 or older, 28% live on campus, 8% transferred in. Retention: 74% of full-time freshmen returned the following year. Academic areas with the most degrees conferred: health professions and related sciences; agriculture; social sciences. Core. Calendar: semesters. Academic remediation for entering students, services for LD students, advanced placement, accelerated degree program, freshman honors college, honors program, independent study, distance learning, double major, summer session for credit, part-time degree program, adult/continuing education programs, co-op programs and internships, graduate courses open to undergrads. Off campus study at National Student Exchange. Study abroad program. ROTC: Army, Air Force.

Entrance Requirements: Options: Peterson's Universal Application, electronic application, deferred admission, international baccalaureate accepted. Required: high school transcript, minimum 2.6 high school GPA, minimum ACT score of 18, ACT. Entrance: minimally difficult. Application deadline: Rolling.

Costs Per Year: Application fee: $20. State resident tuition: $2291 full-time, $76.35 per credit part-time. Nonresident tuition: $7278 full-time, $242.60 per credit part-time. Mandatory fees: $2441 full-time, $81.35 per credit part-time. Full-time tuition and fees vary according to course load, program, and reciprocity agreements. Part-time tuition and fees vary according to course load, program, and reciprocity agreements. College room and board: $4769. College room only: $2113. Room and board charges vary according to board plan and housing facility.

Collegiate Environment: Orientation program. Drama-theater group, choral group, marching band, student-run newspaper, radio station. Social organizations: 200 open to all; national fraternities, national sororities; 4% of eligible men and 3% of eligible women are members. Most popular organizations: Student Association, University Programming Council, Block and Bridle Club. Major annual events: Hobo Day, Spring Fling, Festival of Cultures. Student services: legal services, health clinic, personal-psychological counseling, women's center. Campus security: 24-hour emergency response devices and patrols, student patrols, late night transport-escort service. 3,399 college housing spaces available; 3,345 were occupied in 2003-04. Freshmen guaranteed college housing. On-campus residence required through sophomore year. Option: coed housing available. H. M. Briggs Library with 927,701 books, 923,269 microform titles, 27,646 serials, 3,217 audiovisual materials, an OPAC, and a Web page. Operations spending for 2004 fiscal year: $3 million. 1,022 computers available on campus for general student use. A campuswide network can be accessed from student residence rooms and from off campus. Staffed computer lab on campus.

Community Environment: Brookings is located in the eastern part of the state, an agriculturally rich area with diversified farming influenced by research done at South Dakota State University. Located 55 miles from

Sioux Falls, the community facilities include a library, 23 churches, an hospital, and many civic and service clubs. Recreational activities include deer and pheasant hunting, golf, and water sports at the center lake region.

■ SOUTHEAST TECHNICAL INSTITUTE *H-16*

2320 N. Career Ave.
Sioux Falls, SD 57107-1301
Tel: (605)367-7624
E-mail: jim.rokusek@southeasttech.com
Web Site: http://www.southeasttech.com/

Description: State-supported, 2-year, coed. Awards certificates, diplomas, and terminal associate degrees. Founded 1968. Setting: 169-acre urban campus. Endowment: $238,427. Educational spending for 2005 fiscal year; $2996 per student. Total enrollment: 2,320. Student-undergrad faculty ratio is 19:1. 2,685 applied, 46% were admitted. Students come from 7 states and territories, 1 other country, 20% from out-of-state, 0.5% Native American, 0.2% Hispanic, 0.5% black, 0.5% Asian American or Pacific Islander, 0.04% international, 28% 25 or older, 1% live on campus. Retention: 83% of full-time freshmen returned the following year. Calendar: semesters. Academic remediation for entering students, services for LD students, advanced placement, accelerated degree program, independent study, double major, summer session for credit, part-time degree program, internships.

Entrance Requirements: Required: high school transcript, minimum 2.2 high school GPA. Recommended: ACT. Required for some: interview. Entrance: minimally difficult. Application deadline: Rolling. Notification: continuous.

Costs Per Year: Application fee: $0. State resident tuition: $2112 full-time, $66 per credit part-time. Nonresident tuition: $66 per credit part-time. Mandatory fees: $1408 full-time, $44 per credit part-time. College room only: $4200.

Collegiate Environment: Orientation program. Social organizations: 6 open to all. Most popular organizations: VICA, ICON, PBL, American Landscape Contractors Association, Silent Tones. Major annual event: Student Picnic. Student services: personal-psychological counseling. Campus security: 24-hour emergency response devices and patrols. 100 college housing spaces available; all were occupied in 2003-04. No special consideration for freshman housing applicants. Option: coed housing available. Southeast Library with 10,643 books, 1 microform title, 158 serials, 182 audiovisual materials, and an OPAC. Operations spending for 2004 fiscal year: $122,767. 400 computers available on campus for general student use. Computer purchase/lease plans available. A campuswide network can be accessed from off-campus. Staffed computer lab on campus.

■ UNIVERSITY OF SIOUX FALLS *H-16*

1101 West 22nd St.
Sioux Falls, SD 57105-1699
Tel: (605)331-5000
Free: 800-888-1047
Admissions: (605)331-6600
Fax: (605)331-6615
E-mail: admissions@usiouxfalls.edu
Web Site: http://www.usiouxfalls.edu/

Description: Independent American Baptist Churches in the USA, comprehensive, coed. Awards associate, bachelor's, master's, and doctoral degrees. Founded 1883. Setting: 22-acre suburban campus. Endowment: $12.1 million. Educational spending for 2005 fiscal year: $4328 per student. Total enrollment: 1,606. Faculty: 98 (62 full-time, 36 part-time). Student-undergrad faculty ratio is 18:1. 552 applied, 95% were admitted. 16% from top 10% of their high school class, 39% from top quarter, 69% from top half. Full-time: 1,026 students, 54% women, 46% men. Part-time: 236 students, 60% women, 40% men. Students come from 24 states and territories, 5 other countries, 31% from out-of-state, 0.5% Native American, 1% Hispanic, 2% black, 1% Asian American or Pacific Islander, 0.1% international, 11% 25 or older, 28% live on campus, 9% transferred in. Retention: 65% of full-time freshmen returned the following year. Academic areas with the most degrees conferred: business/marketing; education; health professions and related sciences. Core. Calendar: 4-1-4. Academic remediation for entering students, services for LD students, advanced placement, accelerated degree program, self-designed majors, honors program, independent study, distance learning, double major, summer session for credit, part-time degree program, external degree program, adult/continuing education programs, co-op programs and internships, graduate courses open to undergrads. Off campus study at Colleges of Mid-America, Augustana College (SD), North American Baptist Seminary, Christian College Coalition. Study abroad program.

Entrance Requirements: Options: electronic application, early admission, deferred admission. Required: high school transcript, SAT and SAT Subject Tests or ACT. Recommended: essay, minimum 2.5 high school GPA. Required for some: 2 recommendations, interview. Entrance: moderately difficult. Application deadline: Rolling. Notification: continuous.

Costs Per Year: Application fee: $25. Comprehensive fee: $21,920 includes full-time tuition ($16,400), mandatory fees ($320), and college room and board ($5200). College room only: $2300. Part-time tuition: $279 per semester hour.

Collegiate Environment: Orientation program. Drama-theater group, choral group, student-run newspaper, radio station. Social organizations: 12 open to all. Most popular organizations: Fellowship of Christian Athletes, Campus Ministry Outreach. Major annual events: homecoming, Madrigals, Spiritual Life Retreat. Student services: personal-psychological counseling, women's center. Campus security: late night transport-escort service, controlled dormitory access. 515 college housing spaces available; 505 were occupied in 2003-04. Freshmen given priority for college housing. On-campus residence required through sophomore year. Options: coed, men-only, women-only housing available. Norman B. Mears Library with 85,713 books, 3,665 microform titles, 378 serials, 5,291 audiovisual materials, an OPAC, and a Web page. Operations spending for 2004 fiscal year: $277,060. 150 computers available on campus for general student use. A campuswide network can be accessed from student residence rooms and from off campus. Staffed computer lab on campus.

Community Environment: Sioux Falls, population 130,000, is a commercial and industrial center. Credit card corporations, banking, retailing and meat packing are the leading industries of the community. Air and bus transportation are available. Community facilities include churches of many denominations, hospitals, an art center, and excellent shopping. Recreation includes all winter sports, water sports, hunting, and fishing. Part-time employment opportunities are excellent.

■ THE UNIVERSITY OF SOUTH DAKOTA *K-16*

414 East Clark St.
Vermillion, SD 57069-2390
Tel: (605)677-5011; 877-269-6837
Admissions: (605)677-5434
Fax: (605)677-6753
E-mail: cfoster@usd.edu
Web Site: http://www.usd.edu/

Description: State-supported, university, coed. Awards associate, bachelor's, master's, doctoral, and first professional degrees and post-master's certificates. Founded 1862. Setting: 216-acre small town campus. Endowment: $82.7 million. Research spending for 2004 fiscal year: $10.2 million. Educational spending for 2005 fiscal year: $7259 per student. Total enrollment: 8,641. Faculty: 406 (389 full-time, 17 part-time). Student-undergrad faculty ratio is 15:1. 2,829 applied, 86% were admitted. 13% from top 10% of their high school class, 35% from top quarter, 67% from top half. 2 National Merit Scholars, 83 valedictorians. Full-time: 4,274 students, 57% women, 43% men. Part-time: 2,134 students, 73% women, 27% men. Students come from 41 states and territories, 18 other countries, 26% from out-of-state, 2% Native American, 1% Hispanic, 1% black, 1% Asian American or Pacific Islander, 1% international, 21% 25 or older, 31% live on campus, 11% transferred in. Retention: 69% of full-time freshmen returned the following year. Academic areas with the most degrees conferred: business/marketing; education; health professions and related sciences; psychology. Core. Calendar: semesters. ESL program, services for LD students, advanced placement, honors program, independent study, distance learning, double major, summer session for credit, part-time degree program, internships. Off campus study at National Student Exchange. Study abroad program. ROTC: Army.

Entrance Requirements: Options: electronic application, early admission, deferred admission. Required: high school transcript, test scores, SAT or ACT. Recommended: minimum 2.0 high school GPA. Required for some: recommendations. Entrance: moderately difficult. Application deadline: 9/4. Notification: continuous.

Costs Per Year: Application fee: $20. State resident tuition: $2291 full-time, $76.35 per credit hour part-time. Nonresident tuition: $7278 full-time, $242.60 per credit hour part-time. Mandatory fees: $2538 full-time, $84.60 per credit hour part-time. Full-time tuition and fees vary according to course load and reciprocity agreements. Part-time tuition and fees vary according to course load and reciprocity agreements. College room and board: $4240. College room only: $2253. Room and board charges vary according to board plan and housing facility.

Collegiate Environment: Orientation program. Drama-theater group, choral group, marching band, student-run newspaper, radio station. Social organizations: 120 open to all; national fraternities, national sororities; 9% of eligible men and 8% of eligible women are members. Most popular organizations: Program Council, Residence Hall Association, Student Ambassadors, Delta Sigma Pi. Major annual events: Dakota Days, Strollers, Rockfest. Student services: legal services, health clinic, personal-psychological counseling. Campus security: 24-hour emergency response devices and patrols, student patrols, late night transport-escort service, controlled dormitory access. 1,975 college housing spaces available; 1,660 were occupied in 2003-04. Freshmen guaranteed college housing. On-campus residence required through sophomore year. Options: coed, men-only, women-only housing available. I. D. Weeks Library plus 2 others with 335,757 books, 673,116 microform titles, 2,852 serials, 30,885 audiovisual materials, and an OPAC. Operations spending for 2004 fiscal year: $4.1 million. 834 computers available on campus for general student use. A campuswide network can be accessed from student residence rooms and from off campus. Staffed computer lab on campus.

Community Environment: Vermillion is situated on a bluff overlooking the Missouri and Vermillion Rivers and was named for the red clay on the riverbanks. There is a public library, museums, churches of a number of denominations, a hospital, and major civic and service organizations. Shopping facilities are excellent. Part-time employment opportunities are good. There are a number of recreational activities, and hunting and fishing opportunities are excellent.

■ **WESTERN DAKOTA TECHNICAL INSTITUTE** *G-3*
800 Mickelson Dr.
Rapid City, SD 57703
Tel: (605)394-4034
Free: 800-544-8765
Web Site: http://www.westerndakotatech.org/

Description: State-supported, 2-year, coed. Awards certificates, diplomas, and terminal associate degrees. Founded 1968. Setting: 5-acre small town campus. Educational spending for 2005 fiscal year: $3116 per student. Total enrollment: 1,057. 901 applied, 74% were admitted. Full-time: 752 students, 44% women, 56% men. Part-time: 305 students, 66% women, 34% men. Students come from 20 states and territories, 13% from out-of-state, 33% 25 or older, 12% transferred in. Retention: 62% of full-time freshmen returned the following year. Core. Calendar: semesters. Academic remediation for entering students, services for LD students, advanced placement, independent study, summer session for credit, part-time degree program, internships.

Entrance Requirements: Open admission except for law enforcement program. Options: Peterson's Universal Application, Common Application, electronic application. Required: essay, high school transcript. Recommended: minimum 2.0 high school GPA. Required for some: recommendations, interview. Placement: TABE/NET for nursing applicants, HOBET for other medical programs required; ACT recommended. Entrance: noncompetitive. Application deadline: 8/1. Notification: continuous until 8/15.

Costs Per Year: Application fee: $10. State resident tuition: $2304 full-time, $64 per credit hour part-time. Nonresident tuition: $2304 full-time, $64 per credit hour part-time. Mandatory fees: $1688 full-time. Full-time tuition and fees vary according to program. Part-time tuition varies according to program.

Collegiate Environment: Orientation program. Social organizations: 2 open to all. Most popular organizations: student council, intercollegiate rodeo. Student services: personal-psychological counseling, women's center. College housing not available. Western Dakota Technical Institute Library with 10,000 books, 40 serials, 170 audiovisual materials, and an OPAC. Operations spending for 2004 fiscal year: $65,466. 140 computers available on campus for general student use. A campuswide network can be accessed. Staffed computer lab on campus.

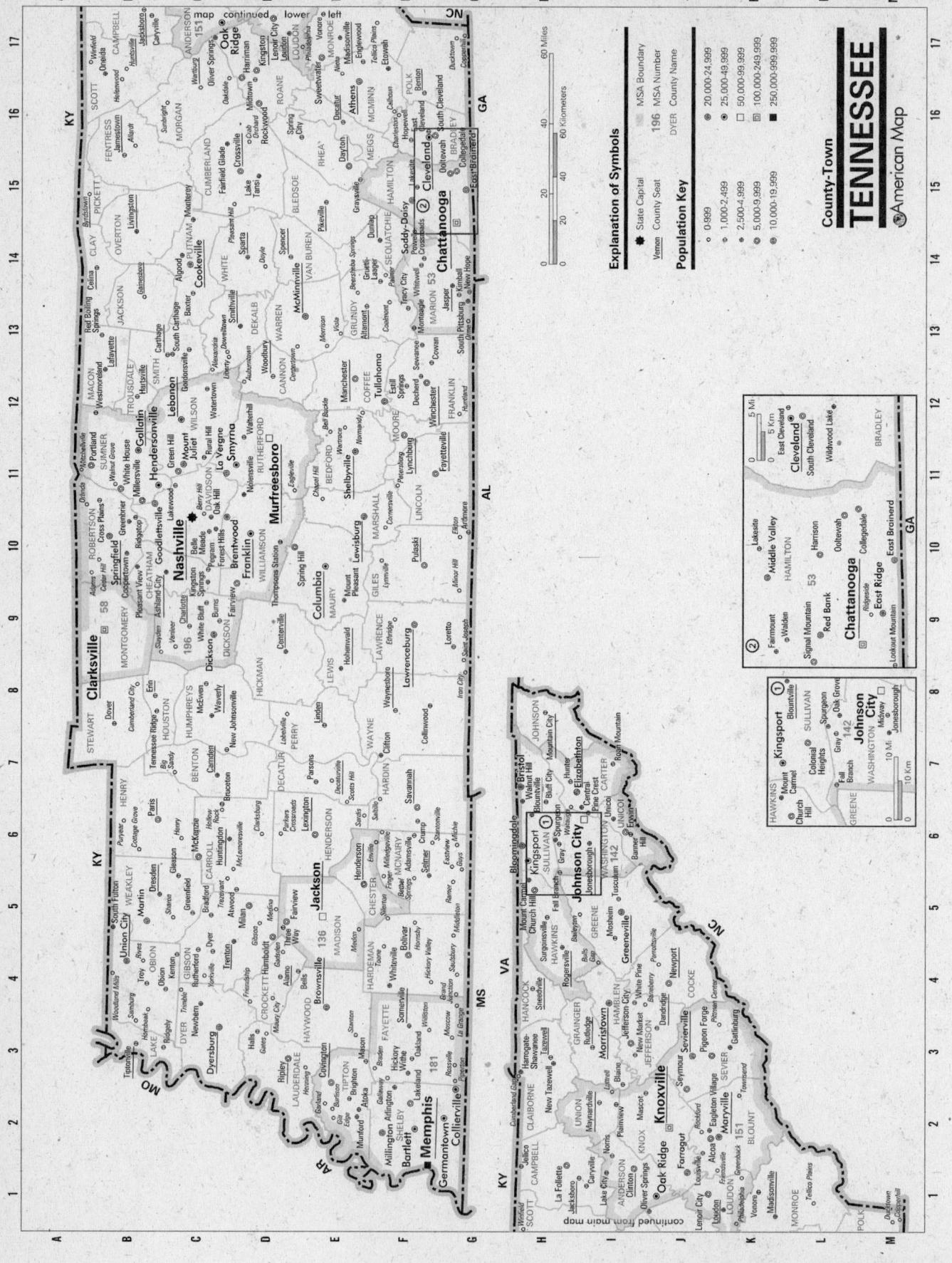

County-Town
TENNESSEE
American Map

■ AMERICAN ACADEMY OF NUTRITION, COLLEGE OF NUTRITION

J-2

1204 -D Kenesaw, Sequoyah Hills Center
Knoxville, TN 37919-7736
Tel: (865)524-8079
Free: 800-290-4226
Fax: (865)524-8339
E-mail: aantn@aol.com
Web Site: http://www.nutritioneducation.com/

Description: Proprietary, 2-year, coed. Awards certificates, diplomas, transfer associate, and terminal associate degrees (offers only external degree programs conducted through home study). Founded 1984. Setting: suburban campus. Research spending for 2004 fiscal year: $18,000. Total enrollment: 241. 33 applied, 100% were admitted. Students come from 49 states and territories, 15 other countries, 90% 25 or older. Core. Calendar: continuous. Academic remediation for entering students, self-designed majors, independent study, distance learning, summer session for credit, part-time degree program, external degree program, adult/continuing education programs.

Entrance Requirements: Open admission. Options: Peterson's Universal Application, Common Application, electronic application, deferred admission. Recommended: minimum 2.0 high school GPA. Required for some: high school transcript, interview. Entrance: noncompetitive. Application deadline: Rolling. Notification: continuous.

Costs Per Year: Tuition: $3950 full-time, $150 per credit hour part-time. Mandatory fees: $200 full-time. Full-time tuition and fees vary according to program. Part-time tuition varies according to program.

■ AMERICAN BAPTIST COLLEGE OF AMERICAN BAPTIST THEOLOGICAL SEMINARY *C-10*

1800 Baptist World Center Dr.
Nashville, TN 37207
Tel: (615)256-1463
E-mail: mlockhart@abcnash.edu
Web Site: http://www.abcnash.edu/

Description: Independent Baptist, 4-year, coed. Awards associate and bachelor's degrees. Founded 1924. Setting: 52-acre urban campus. Endowment: $1.6 million. Educational spending for 2005 fiscal year: $6767 per student. Total enrollment: 112. Student-undergrad faculty ratio is 14:1. 37 applied, 27% were admitted. Full-time: 64 students, 27% women, 73% men. Part-time: 48 students, 38% women, 63% men. Students come from 12 states and territories, 3 other countries, 35% from out-of-state, 0% Native American, 0% Hispanic, 96% black, 0% Asian American or Pacific Islander, 4% international, 90% 25 or older, 20% live on campus, 4% transferred in. Retention: 85% of full-time freshmen returned the following year. Academic area with the most degrees conferred: theology and religious vocations. Core. Calendar: semesters. Academic remediation for entering students, advanced placement, double major, summer session for credit, part-time degree program, adult/continuing education programs. Off campus study.

Entrance Requirements: Open admission. Options: Common Application, deferred admission. Required: essay, high school transcript, minimum 2.0 high school GPA, 3 recommendations, interview. Entrance: noncompetitive. Application deadline: 7/12. Notification: 8/15.

Costs Per Year: Application fee: $20. Tuition: $4032 full-time, $168 per credit hour part-time. Mandatory fees: $140 full-time, $140 per term part-time. Full-time tuition and fees vary according to course load. Part-time

tuition and fees vary according to course load. College room only: $1600. Room charges vary according to housing facility.

Collegiate Environment: Orientation program. Choral group. Social organizations: 2 open to all; national fraternities; 30% of men are members. Most popular organizations: Student Government Association, Vespers Service. Major annual events: Garnett-Nabritt Lectures, ABC Days, Presidential Scholarship Banquet. Campus security: student patrols, security patrols from 10 p.m. to 7 a.m. 100 college housing spaces available; 30 were occupied in 2003-04. No special consideration for freshman housing applicants. Options: coed, men-only, women-only housing available. T. L. Holcolm Library with 33,383 books, 179 serials, and 140 audiovisual materials. Operations spending for 2004 fiscal year: $100,385. 20 computers available on campus for general student use. A campuswide network can be accessed from off-campus. Staffed computer lab on campus.

■ AQUINAS COLLEGE *C-10*

4210 Harding Rd.
Nashville, TN 37205-2005
Tel: (615)297-7545
Free: 800-649-9956
Fax: (615)297-7970
Web Site: http://www.aquinas-tn.edu/

Description: Independent Roman Catholic, 4-year, coed. Administratively affiliated with The Dominican Sisters of the Saint Cecilia Congregation. Awards associate and bachelor's degrees. Founded 1961. Setting: 92-acre urban campus. Endowment: $6.9 million. Educational spending for 2005 fiscal year: $10,612 per student. Total enrollment: 902. Student-undergrad faculty ratio is 14:1. Students come from 10 states and territories, 9 other countries, 10% from out-of-state, 0.3% Native American, 3% Hispanic, 16% black, 3% Asian American or Pacific Islander, 0% international, 72% 25 or older. Retention: 70% of full-time freshmen returned the following year. Core. Calendar: semesters. Academic remediation for entering students, advanced placement, accelerated degree program, independent study, summer session for credit, part-time degree program, adult/continuing education programs, co-op programs and internships. ROTC: Army (c), Air Force (c).

Entrance Requirements: Open admission. Options: Common Application, electronic application, deferred admission. Required: high school transcript, minimum 2.0 high school GPA. Required for some: essay, SAT or ACT. Entrance: moderately difficult. Application deadline: Rolling. Notification: continuous.

Costs Per Year: Application fee: $25. Tuition: $13,620 full-time, $454 per credit hour part-time. Mandatory fees: $425 full-time, $150 per term part-time.

Collegiate Environment: Orientation program. Student-run newspaper. Social organizations: 1 open to all. Most popular organization: Student Council. Major annual events: homecoming, Cavalier Challenge, President's Council Barbecue. Campus security: 24-hour emergency response devices, patrols by security after class hours. 40 college housing spaces available; 18 were occupied in 2003-04. Option: coed housing available. Aquinas College Library plus 1 other with 46,549 books, 162,805 microform titles, 284 serials, 754 audiovisual materials, an OPAC, and a Web page. Operations spending for 2004 fiscal year: $403,500. 52 computers available on campus for general student use. A campuswide network can be accessed. Staffed computer lab on campus.

Community Environment: See Vanderbilt University.

■ **ARGOSY UNIVERSITY/NASHVILLE** *D-10*
341 Cool Springs Blvd., Ste. 210
Franklin, TN 37067-7226
Tel: (615)369-0616
Fax: (615)369-0601
Web Site: http://www.argosyu.edu/
Description: Proprietary, upper-level, coed. Founded 2001. Calendar: semesters.

■ **AUSTIN PEAY STATE UNIVERSITY** *B-9*
601 College St.
Clarksville, TN 37044-0001
Tel: (931)221-7011
Free: 800-844-2778
Admissions: (931)221-7661
Fax: (931)221-5994
E-mail: mcdonalds@apsu.edu
Web Site: http://www.apsu.edu/
Description: State-supported, comprehensive, coed. Part of Tennessee Board of Regents. Awards associate, bachelor's, and master's degrees and post-master's certificates. Founded 1927. Setting: 200-acre suburban campus with easy access to Nashville. Endowment: $5.6 million. Research spending for 2004 fiscal year: $1.3 million. Educational spending for 2005 fiscal year: $2095 per student. Total enrollment: 8,813. Faculty: 464 (290 full-time, 174 part-time). Student-undergrad faculty ratio is 21:1. 2,608 applied, 91% were admitted. 14% from top 10% of their high school class, 36% from top quarter, 68% from top half. Full-time: 6,348 students, 63% women, 37% men. Part-time: 1,868 students, 63% women, 37% men. Students come from 41 states and territories, 24 other countries, 8% from out-of-state, 1% Native American, 4% Hispanic, 18% black, 2% Asian American or Pacific Islander, 0.5% international, 42% 25 or older, 15% live on campus, 12% transferred in. Retention: 63% of full-time freshmen returned the following year. Academic areas with the most degrees conferred: business/marketing; health professions and related sciences; communications/journalism. Core. Calendar: semesters. Academic remediation for entering students, services for LD students, advanced placement, honors program, independent study, distance learning, double major, summer session for credit, part-time degree program, adult/continuing education programs, internships, graduate courses open to undergrads. Study abroad program. ROTC: Army.
Entrance Requirements: Options: early admission, deferred admission. Required: high school transcript, 2.75 high school GPA, minimum ACT composite score of 19. Required for some: SAT or ACT. Entrance: moderately difficult. Application deadline: 7/29. Notification: continuous.
Costs Per Year: Application fee: $15. State resident tuition: $3678 full-time, $161 per credit hour part-time. Nonresident tuition: $12,990 full-time, $565 per credit hour part-time. Mandatory fees: $957 full-time, $41 per credit hour part-time, $4 per term part-time. Part-time tuition and fees vary according to location. College room and board: $4800. College room only: $2900. Room and board charges vary according to board plan and housing facility.
Collegiate Environment: Orientation program. Drama-theater group, choral group, marching band, student-run newspaper, radio station. Social organizations: national fraternities, national sororities; 8% of eligible men and 4% of eligible women are members. Student services: health clinic, personal-psychological counseling. Campus security: 24-hour patrols, late night transport-escort service, controlled dormitory access. 1,500 college housing spaces available; 1,191 were occupied in 2003-04. Freshmen guaranteed college housing. On-campus residence required in freshman year. Options: coed, men-only, women-only housing available. Felix G. Woodward Library with 400,000 books, 663,000 microform titles, 1,754 serials, 4,700 audiovisual materials, an OPAC, and a Web page. Operations spending for 2004 fiscal year: $2 million. 650 computers available on campus for general student use. Computer purchase/lease plans available. A campuswide network can be accessed from student residence rooms and from off campus. Staffed computer lab on campus.
Community Environment: Clarksville, an urban area, was founded in 1784 and was named for General George Rogers Clark. Bus transportation is available. Community facilities include a number of churches, a hospital, a public library, and major civic and service organizations. Water sports are enjoyed on the Cumberland River and nearby lakes. Some part-time employment is available.

■ **BAPTIST COLLEGE OF HEALTH SCIENCES** *F-1*
1003 Monroe Ave.
Memphis, TN 38104

Tel: (901)227-4330; (866)575-2247
Admissions: (901)572-2465
Web Site: http://www.bchs.edu/
Description: Independent Southern Baptist, 4-year, coed. Administratively affiliated with Baptist Memorial Health Care Corporation. Awards bachelor's degrees. Founded 1994. Setting: urban campus. Total enrollment: 823. 260 applied. Students come from 9 states and territories, 0% Native American, 1% Hispanic, 34% black, 3% Asian American or Pacific Islander, 12% live on campus. Core. Calendar: semesters. Advanced placement, co-op programs.
Entrance Requirements: Options: Common Application, early admission. Required: high school transcript, minimum 2.75 high school GPA, 3 recommendations, ACT, Health Occupations Basic Entrance Test. Required for some: essay, interview. Application deadline: 6/1.
Collegiate Environment: Orientation program. Student-run newspaper. Most popular organizations: Student Government Association, Student Nursing Association, Allied Health Organization. Major annual events: Religious Emphasis Week, Convocation, Graduation. Campus security: 24-hour emergency response devices, late night transport-escort service, controlled dormitory access, 16 to 20-hour trained security personnel. 100 college housing spaces available; all were occupied in 2003-04. Health Sciences Library with an OPAC.

■ **BELMONT UNIVERSITY** *C-10*
1900 Belmont Blvd.
Nashville, TN 37212-3757
Tel: (615)460-6000
Free: 800-56E-NROL
Admissions: (615)460-6785
E-mail: buadmission@belmont.edu
Web Site: http://www.belmont.edu/
Description: Independent Baptist, comprehensive, coed. Awards bachelor's, master's, and doctoral degrees and post-master's certificates. Founded 1951. Setting: 34-acre urban campus. Endowment: $45.5 million. Educational spending for 2005 fiscal year: $17,815 per student. Total enrollment: 4,319. Faculty: 461 (214 full-time, 247 part-time). Student-undergrad faculty ratio is 13:1. 2,184 applied, 72% were admitted. 36% from top 10% of their high school class, 67% from top quarter, 91% from top half. 32 valedictorians. Full-time: 3,287 students, 61% women, 39% men. Part-time: 358 students, 65% women, 35% men. Students come from 48 states and territories, 27 other countries, 56% from out-of-state, 1% Native American, 2% Hispanic, 4% black, 1% Asian American or Pacific Islander, 1% international, 12% 25 or older, 57% live on campus, 9% transferred in. Retention: 79% of full-time freshmen returned the following year. Academic areas with the most degrees conferred: visual and performing arts; business/marketing; health professions and related sciences. Core. Calendar: semesters. Advanced placement, accelerated degree program, self-designed majors, honors program, independent study, distance learning, double major, summer session for credit, part-time degree program, adult/continuing education programs, co-op programs and internships. Off campus study at Cool Springs Center. Study abroad program. ROTC: Army (c), Naval (c).
Entrance Requirements: Options: Peterson's Universal Application, Common Application, early admission, deferred admission, international baccalaureate accepted. Required: essay, high school transcript, minimum 3.0 high school GPA, recommendations, resume of activities, SAT or ACT. Required for some: interview. Entrance: moderately difficult. Application deadline: 8/1. Notification: continuous.
Costs Per Year: Application fee: $35. Comprehensive fee: $25,910 includes full-time tuition ($16,360), mandatory fees ($900), and college room and board ($8650). College room only: $5300. Full-time tuition and fees vary according to class time and course load. Room and board charges vary according to board plan, housing facility, and location. Part-time tuition: $625 per credit hour. Part-time mandatory fees: $300 per term. Part-time tuition and fees vary according to course load.
Collegiate Environment: Orientation program. Drama-theater group, choral group, marching band, student-run newspaper, radio station. Social organizations: 54 open to all; national fraternities, national sororities; 6% of eligible men and 8% of eligible women are members. Major annual events: Fall Festival, Homecoming, Towering Traditions. Student services: health clinic, personal-psychological counseling, women's center. Campus security: 24-hour emergency response devices and patrols, late night transport-escort service, controlled dormitory access, bicycle patrol. 1,750 college housing spaces available; 1,700 were occupied in 2003-04. Freshmen given priority for college housing. On-campus residence required through sophomore year. Options: men-only, women-only housing available. Lila D. Bunch

Library with 184,835 books, 18,111 microform titles, 1,311 serials, 26,289 audiovisual materials, an OPAC, and a Web page. Operations spending for 2004 fiscal year: $1.7 million. 350 computers available on campus for general student use. A campuswide network can be accessed from student residence rooms and from off campus. Staffed computer lab on campus.
Community Environment: See Vanderbilt University.

■ **BETHEL COLLEGE** *C-6*
325 Cherry Ave.
McKenzie, TN 38201
Tel: (731)352-4000
Admissions: (731)352-4030
Fax: (731)352-4069
Web Site: http://www.bethel-college.edu/
Description: Independent Cumberland Presbyterian, comprehensive, coed. Awards bachelor's, master's, and first professional degrees. Founded 1842. Setting: 100-acre small town campus. Endowment: $7.9 million. Educational spending for 2005 fiscal year: $3125 per student. Total enrollment: 1,297. 685 applied, 59% were admitted. 11% from top 10% of their high school class, 20% from top quarter, 30% from top half. 1 valedictorian, 9 student government officers. Full-time: 915 students, 53% women, 47% men. Part-time: 219 students, 72% women, 28% men. Students come from 35 states and territories, 21 other countries, 39% from out-of-state, 0.2% Native American, 1% Hispanic, 23% black, 0% Asian American or Pacific Islander, 3% international, 53% 25 or older, 50% live on campus, 3% transferred in. Retention: 51% of full-time freshmen returned the following year. Core. Calendar: semesters. Academic remediation for entering students, services for LD students, advanced placement, accelerated degree program, self-designed majors, honors program, double major, summer session for credit, part-time degree program, adult/continuing education programs, internships, graduate courses open to undergrads. Off campus study at Tennessee Technological University, University of Memphis.
Entrance Requirements: Options: Peterson's Universal Application, electronic application, early admission, deferred admission. Required: high school transcript, minimum 2.25 high school GPA, SAT or ACT. Required for some: essay, 1 recommendation, interview. Entrance: minimally difficult. Application deadline: Rolling. Notification: continuous.
Collegiate Environment: Orientation program. Drama-theater group, choral group. Social organizations: 12 open to all; local fraternities, local sororities; 20% of eligible men and 15% of eligible women are members. Most popular organizations: FCA, SETA (Education), Black Student Union, Honor Club. Student services: personal-psychological counseling. Campus security: night patrols by trained security personnel. College housing designed to accommodate 291 students; 438 undergraduates lived in college housing during 2003-04. Freshmen guaranteed college housing. On-campus residence required through junior year. Options: coed, men-only, women-only housing available. Burroughs Learning Center with 83,919 books, 2,609 microform titles, 255 serials, 4,876 audiovisual materials, and a Web page. Operations spending for 2004 fiscal year: $442,252. 8 computers available on campus for general student use. Computer purchase/lease plans available. A campuswide network can be accessed from student residence rooms. Staffed computer lab on campus.

■ **BRYAN COLLEGE** *E-15*
PO Box 7000
Dayton, TN 37321-7000
Tel: (423)775-2041
Free: 800-277-9522
Fax: (423)775-7330
E-mail: admissions@bryan.edu
Web Site: http://www.bryan.edu/
Description: Independent interdenominational, 4-year, coed. Awards associate and bachelor's degrees. Founded 1930. Setting: 100-acre small town campus. Endowment: $2 million. Total enrollment: 775. Student-undergrad faculty ratio is 13:1. 460 applied, 76% were admitted. Full-time: 757 students, 57% women, 43% men. Part-time: 18 students, 61% women, 39% men. Students come from 33 states and territories, 7 other countries, 61% from out-of-state, 0% Native American, 1% Hispanic, 2% black, 0.1% Asian American or Pacific Islander, 1% international, 1% 25 or older, 74% live on campus, 4% transferred in. Retention: 74% of full-time freshmen returned the following year. Academic areas with the most degrees conferred: business/marketing; communications/journalism; education. Core. Calendar: semesters. Academic remediation for entering students, advanced placement, honors program, independent study, double major, summer ses-

sion for credit, part-time degree program, adult/continuing education programs, internships. Study abroad program.
Entrance Requirements: Options: electronic application, early admission, deferred admission. Required: essay, high school transcript, minimum 2.0 high school GPA, 3 recommendations, SAT or ACT. Required for some: interview. Entrance: moderately difficult. Application deadline: Rolling.
Costs Per Year: Application fee: $30. Comprehensive fee: $19,270 includes full-time tuition ($14,800) and college room and board ($4470). Part-time tuition: $625 per credit hour.
Collegiate Environment: Orientation program. Drama-theater group, choral group, student-run newspaper. Social organizations: 7 open to all. Most popular organizations: Practical Christian Involvement, Student Government Association, Fellowship of Christian Athletes, Hilltop Players, chorale. Major annual events: homecoming, Christmas Banquet, Junior/Senior Banquet. Student services: personal-psychological counseling. Campus security: student patrols, late night transport-escort service, controlled dormitory access, police patrols. 497 college housing spaces available; 454 were occupied in 2003-04. Freshmen guaranteed college housing. On-campus residence required through senior year. Options: men-only, women-only housing available. Ironside Memorial Library with 98,413 books, 59,986 microform titles, 4,212 serials, 1,396 audiovisual materials, an OPAC, and a Web page. 74 computers available on campus for general student use. A campuswide network can be accessed from student residence rooms. Staffed computer lab on campus.
Community Environment: Dayton is located 38 miles from Chattanooga, enjoying a very desirable climate the year round. Air and bus transportation are convenient. Community facilities include some 20 churches representing Protestant and Roman Catholic faiths, a public library, a hospital, and motels. TVA lakes provide fishing and water sports. Part-time employment is available for students. The East Tennessee Strawberry Festival is held in May.

■ **CARSON-NEWMAN COLLEGE** *I-3*
1646 Russell Ave., PO Box 557
Jefferson City, TN 37760
Tel: (865)471-2000
Free: 800-678-9061
Admissions: (865)471-3223
Fax: (865)471-3502
E-mail: cnadmiss@cn.edu
Web Site: http://www.cn.edu/
Description: Independent Southern Baptist, comprehensive, coed. Awards associate, bachelor's, and master's degrees. Founded 1851. Setting: 90-acre small town campus with easy access to Knoxville. Endowment: $30.1 million. Educational spending for 2005 fiscal year: $4967 per student. Total enrollment: 1,993. Faculty: 195 (128 full-time, 67 part-time). Student-undergrad faculty ratio is 13:1. 1,066 applied, 78% were admitted. 27% from top 10% of their high school class, 47% from top quarter, 73% from top half. Full-time: 1,759 students, 54% women, 46% men. Part-time: 92 students, 60% women, 40% men. Students come from 37 states and territories, 21 other countries, 31% from out-of-state, 0.2% Native American, 1% Hispanic, 9% black, 0% Asian American or Pacific Islander, 2% international, 13% 25 or older, 51% live on campus, 8% transferred in. Retention: 69% of full-time freshmen returned the following year. Academic areas with the most degrees conferred: education; business/marketing; social sciences. Core. Calendar: semesters. Academic remediation for entering students, ESL program, services for LD students, advanced placement, accelerated degree program, self-designed majors, honors program, summer session for credit, part-time degree program, adult/continuing education programs, internships, graduate courses open to undergrads. Off campus study. Study abroad program. ROTC: Army, Air Force (c).
Entrance Requirements: Options: Peterson's Universal Application, electronic application, deferred admission, international baccalaureate accepted. Required: high school transcript, minimum 2.25 high school GPA, medical history, SAT or ACT. Recommended: interview. Required for some: essay, recommendations, interview. Entrance: moderately difficult. Application deadline: 8/1. Notification: continuous.
Costs Per Year: Application fee: $25. Comprehensive fee: $21,260 includes full-time tuition ($15,300), mandatory fees ($760), and college room and board ($5200). College room only: $2250. Part-time tuition: $635 per semester hour.
Collegiate Environment: Orientation program. Drama-theater group, choral group, marching band, student-run newspaper. Social organizations: 63 open to all; national fraternities, national sororities, local fraternities, local

sororities; 5% of eligible men and 5% of eligible women are members. Most popular organizations: Baptist Student Union, Fellowship of Christian Athletes, Student Government Association, Student Ambassadors Association, Columbians. Major annual events: Welcome Week, Beach Fest, homecoming. Student services: health clinic, personal-psychological counseling. Campus security: 24-hour emergency response devices and patrols, late night transport-escort service, controlled dormitory access. 1,427 college housing spaces available. Freshmen guaranteed college housing. On-campus residence required through junior year. Options: men-only, women-only housing available. Stephens-Burnett Library plus 1 other with 218,371 books, 288,300 microform titles, 3,966 serials, 14,713 audiovisual materials, an OPAC, and a Web page. Operations spending for 2004 fiscal year: $668,990. 200 computers available on campus for general student use. A campuswide network can be accessed from student residence rooms and from off campus. Staffed computer lab on campus.

Community Environment: Jefferson City is located 27 miles from Knoxville, a city of approximately 400,000. Plane and bus transportation are available. Recreational activities include fishing, water skiing, swimming, and boating at Cherokee and Douglas Lakes, a short drive away. Skiing is available in the Great Smoky Mountains National Park. Part-time employment opportunities are available.

■ CHATTANOOGA STATE TECHNICAL COMMUNITY COLLEGE *G-14*

4501 Amnicola Hwy.
Chattanooga, TN 37406-1097
Tel: (423)697-4400
Admissions: (423)697-4401
Fax: (423)697-4709
E-mail: diane.norris@chattanoogastate.edu
Web Site: http://www.chattanoogastate.edu/

Description: State-supported, 2-year, coed. Part of Tennessee Board of Regents. Awards certificates, diplomas, transfer associate, and terminal associate degrees. Founded 1965. Setting: 100-acre urban campus. Total enrollment: 7,836. Student-undergrad faculty ratio is 22:1. 1,341 applied, 100% were admitted. Full-time: 3,533 students, 61% women, 39% men. Part-time: 4,303 students, 64% women, 36% men. Students come from 5 states and territories, 8% from out-of-state, 0.4% Native American, 2% Hispanic, 19% black, 2% Asian American or Pacific Islander, 0% international, 44% 25 or older, 23% transferred in. Core. Calendar: semesters. Academic remediation for entering students, ESL program, services for LD students, advanced placement, accelerated degree program, honors program, independent study, distance learning, summer session for credit, part-time degree program, adult/continuing education programs, co-op programs and internships.

Entrance Requirements: Open admission. Options: Peterson's Universal Application, early admission, deferred admission. Required: high school transcript. Entrance: noncompetitive. Application deadline: Rolling. Notification: continuous.

Costs Per Year: Application fee: $15. State resident tuition: $2142 full-time, $91 per semester hour part-time. Nonresident tuition: $8556 full-time, $369 per semester hour part-time.

Collegiate Environment: Orientation program. Choral group, student-run newspaper, radio station. Social organizations: 35 open to all. Most popular organizations: Black Student Association, Adult Connections, Human Services Specialists, Student Government Association, Student Nurses Association. Major annual events: Fun in the Sun, Oktoberfest, Wellness Festival. Student services: personal-psychological counseling, women's center. Campus security: 24-hour emergency response devices and patrols, late night transport-escort service. College housing not available. Augusta R. Kolwyck Library with 73,334 books, 803 serials, an OPAC, and a Web page. Operations spending for 2004 fiscal year: $875,000. 500 computers available on campus for general student use. A campuswide network can be accessed from off-campus. Staffed computer lab on campus.

Community Environment: Located in southeastern Tennessee on the Tennessee River, Chattanooga is an important industrial center with over 500 manufacturing plants. All forms of commercial transportation are convenient. Part-time employment is available. Recreational facilities are plentiful, Chickamauga Lake, formed by the TVA dam, provides a wonderful place for water sports, and fishing; also there are other lakes, rivers and streams, and Harrison Bay State Park and Hamilton County State Park for other activities. Chattanooga has a number of city parks, and five golf courses for activities within the city. Some points of interest are Lookout Mountain, Lookout Mountain Incline Railway, Rock City Gardens, the Ruby Falls-Lookout Mountain Caves, and the Chattanooga Choo-Choo.

■ CHRISTIAN BROTHERS UNIVERSITY *F-1*

650 East Parkway South
Memphis, TN 38104-5581
Tel: (901)321-3000
Free: 800-288-7576
Admissions: (901)321-3205
Fax: (901)321-3202
E-mail: tdysart@cbu.edu
Web Site: http://www.cbu.edu/

Description: Independent Roman Catholic, comprehensive, coed. Awards bachelor's and master's degrees. Founded 1871. Setting: 70-acre urban campus. Endowment: $25.3 million. Educational spending for 2005 fiscal year: $19,876 per student. Total enrollment: 1,778. Faculty: 154 (102 full-time, 52 part-time). Student-undergrad faculty ratio is 14:1. 963 applied, 72% were admitted. 35% from top 10% of their high school class, 60% from top quarter, 83% from top half. Full-time: 1,151 students, 52% women, 48% men. Part-time: 342 students, 65% women, 35% men. Students come from 31 states and territories, 22 other countries, 17% from out-of-state, 0% Native American, 2% Hispanic, 35% black, 5% Asian American or Pacific Islander, 2% international, 30% 25 or older, 31% live on campus, 3% transferred in. Retention: 78% of full-time freshmen returned the following year. Academic areas with the most degrees conferred: business/marketing; psychology; engineering. Core. Calendar: semesters. Advanced placement, accelerated degree program, honors program, double major, summer session for credit, part-time degree program, internships, graduate courses open to undergrads. Off campus study at Greater Memphis Consortium. Study abroad program. ROTC: Army (c), Naval (c), Air Force (c).

Entrance Requirements: Options: Peterson's Universal Application, Common Application, electronic application, early admission, deferred admission. Required: essay, high school transcript, minimum 2.5 high school GPA, SAT or ACT. Recommended: interview. Required for some: recommendations. Entrance: moderately difficult. Application deadline: 3/1. Notification: 8/1.

Costs Per Year: Application fee: $25. Comprehensive fee: $24,650 includes full-time tuition ($18,630), mandatory fees ($520), and college room and board ($5500). College room only: $2480. Full-time tuition and fees vary according to class time. Room and board charges vary according to board plan and housing facility. Part-time tuition: $585 per credit hour. Part-time tuition varies according to class time.

Collegiate Environment: Orientation program. Drama-theater group, choral group. Social organizations: 23 open to all; national fraternities, national sororities, local sororities; 30% of eligible men and 24% of eligible women are members. Most popular organizations: Black Student Association, BACCHUS Alcohol Awareness Group, Intercultural Club, College Republicans, Beta Beta Beta. Major annual events: Homecoming Week, Riverboat Dance, Las Vegas Night. Student services: health clinic, personal-psychological counseling. Campus security: 24-hour emergency response devices and patrols, student patrols, late night transport-escort service, controlled dormitory access. 550 college housing spaces available; 488 were occupied in 2003-04. Freshmen given priority for college housing. On-campus residence required in freshman year. Option: coed housing available. Plough Memorial Library and Media Center with 92,000 books, 51,000 microform titles, 520 serials, 1,100 audiovisual materials, an OPAC, and a Web page. Operations spending for 2004 fiscal year: $484,596. 300 computers available on campus for general student use. A campuswide network can be accessed from student residence rooms and from off campus. Staffed computer lab on campus.

Community Environment: See University of Memphis.

■ CLEVELAND STATE COMMUNITY COLLEGE *F-16*

PO Box 3570
Cleveland, TN 37320-3570
Tel: (423)472-7141
Admissions: (423)478-6212
Fax: (423)478-6255
E-mail: mburnette@clevelandstatecc.edu
Web Site: http://www.clevelandstatecc.edu/

Description: State-supported, 2-year, coed. Part of Tennessee Board of Regents. Awards certificates, transfer associate, and terminal associate degrees. Founded 1967. Setting: 105-acre small town campus. Endowment: $4.5 million. Educational spending for 2005 fiscal year: $3417 per student. Total enrollment: 3,027. Student-undergrad faculty ratio is 29:1. 920 applied, 61% were admitted. Full-time: 1,586 students, 60% women, 40% men. Part-time: 1,441 students, 63% women, 37% men. Students come from 9 states and territories, 1% from out-of-state, 1% Native American, 2% Hispanic, 5%

black, 1% Asian American or Pacific Islander, 0% international, 43% 25 or older, 5% transferred in. Core. Calendar: semesters. Academic remediation for entering students, ESL program, services for LD students, advanced placement, honors program, independent study, distance learning, double major, summer session for credit, part-time degree program, external degree program, adult/continuing education programs, co-op programs and internships. Off campus study at Chattanooga State Technical Community College.

Entrance Requirements: Open admission except for nursing, medical assistant programs. Options: early admission, deferred admission. Required: high school transcript. Entrance: noncompetitive. Application deadline: Rolling. Notification: continuous.

Costs Per Year: Application fee: $10. State resident tuition: $2142 full-time, $91 per credit hour part-time. Nonresident tuition: $8556 full-time, $369 per credit hour part-time. Mandatory fees: $263 full-time, $28.25 per credit hour part-time. Full-time tuition and fees vary according to course load.

Collegiate Environment: Orientation program. Choral group, student-run newspaper. Social organizations: 20 open to all. Most popular organizations: Student Senate, International Association of Administration Professionals, Phi Theta Kappa, Student Nursing Association. Major annual events: Career Fair, Octoberfest. Student services: personal-psychological counseling. Campus security: 24-hour emergency response devices and patrols, late night transport-escort service. College housing not available. Cleveland State Community College Library with 65,347 books, 80,007 microform titles, 368 serials, 10,116 audiovisual materials, an OPAC, and a Web page. Operations spending for 2004 fiscal year: $441,927. 450 computers available on campus for general student use. A campuswide network can be accessed from off-campus. Staffed computer lab on campus.

Community Environment: Cleveland was first settled in 1837 and served as headquarters for both General Grant and General Sherman during the Civil War. The city is in the heart of the great Tennessee Valley and is the gateway to the awe inspiring Cherokee National Forest. The climate is mild-temperate, long warm summers, and short mild winters. All forms of commercial transportation are available. The community facilities include a public library, many churches representing all denominations, YMCA, a hospital, community theatre, concert series, and a number of the usual civic and service organizations. Nearby, TVA lakes offer facilities for swimming, fishing, boating, and skiing; the city facilities provide for other activities such as tennis and golf. Part-time employment is available.

■ **COLUMBIA STATE COMMUNITY COLLEGE** *E-10*
PO Box 1315
Columbia, TN 38402-1315
Tel: (931)540-2722
Admissions: (931)540-2545
Fax: (931)540-2535
Web Site: http://www.columbiastate.edu/
Description: State-supported, 2-year, coed. Awards certificates, transfer associate, and terminal associate degrees. Founded 1966. Setting: 179-acre small town campus with easy access to Nashville. Endowment: $707,627. Educational spending for 2005 fiscal year: $2563 per student. Total enrollment: 4,613. 7% from top 10% of their high school class, 24% from top quarter, 55% from top half. Full-time: 2,423 students, 61% women, 39% men. Part-time: 2,190 students, 71% women, 29% men. Students come from 6 states and territories, 2 other countries, 0.4% Native American, 2% Hispanic, 8% black, 1% Asian American or Pacific Islander, 0.1% international, 28% 25 or older, 10% transferred in. Retention: 61% of full-time freshmen returned the following year. Core. Calendar: semesters. Academic remediation for entering students, services for LD students, advanced placement, honors program, double major, summer session for credit, part-time degree program, adult/continuing education programs.

Entrance Requirements: Open admission. Option: early admission. Required: high school transcript. Placement: SAT or ACT required for some. Entrance: noncompetitive. Application deadline: Rolling.

Collegiate Environment: Orientation program. Drama-theater group. Social organizations: 14 open to all. Most popular organizations: Student Government Association, Student Tennessee Education Association, Circle K, Gamma Beta Phi, Students in Free Enterprise. Major annual events: homecoming, Multicultural Festival, Drug Awareness Week. Student services: health clinic, personal-psychological counseling. Campus security: 24-hour patrols. College housing not available. John W. Finney Memorial Learning Resources Center with 61,200 books, 460 serials, and an OPAC. Operations spending for 2004 fiscal year: $271,790. 260 computers available on campus for general student use. A campuswide network can be accessed from off-campus. Staffed computer lab on campus.

Community Environment: A metropolitan community with temperate climate, Columbia is the boyhood home of James K. Polk. In Bluegrass country, it is noted for its diversified industry and agriculture. Particularly notable are the phosphate industry, and the Saturn automobile plant. Numerous civic and service organizations and excellent shopping facilities are part of the community. Outstanding recreational facilities include city parks, tennis courts, swimming pools, golf courses, and many TVA lakes for swimming, boating, fishing, and skiing. The National Tennessee Walking Horse Spring Jubilee is held each May in Maury County Park, three miles west. The Maury County Fair is an annual event. There are good opportunities for part-time employment.

■ **CONCORDE CAREER COLLEGE** *F-1*
5100 Poplar Ave., Ste. 132
Memphis, TN 38137
Tel: (901)761-9494
Fax: (901)761-3293
Web Site: http://www.concordecareercolleges.com/
Description: Proprietary, 2-year, coed. Founded 1969.

■ **CRICHTON COLLEGE** *F-1*
255 North Highland St.
Memphis, TN 38111
Tel: (901)320-9700
Free: 800-960-9777
Admissions: (901)320-9797
Fax: (901)320-9709
Web Site: http://www.crichton.edu/
Description: Independent, 4-year, coed. Awards bachelor's degrees. Founded 1941. Setting: 7-acre urban campus. Research spending for 2004 fiscal year: $105,379. Educational spending for 2005 fiscal year: $1534 per student. Total enrollment: 972. Student-undergrad faculty ratio is 15:1. Full-time: 503 students, 66% women, 34% men. Part-time: 469 students, 64% women, 36% men. Students come from 32 states and territories, 4 other countries, 17% from out-of-state, 0% Native American, 1% Hispanic, 60% black, 0% Asian American or Pacific Islander, 1% international, 70% 25 or older, 5% live on campus, 21% transferred in. Retention: 45% of full-time freshmen returned the following year. Core. Calendar: semesters. Academic remediation for entering students, advanced placement, accelerated degree program, self-designed majors, honors program, independent study, distance learning, double major, summer session for credit, part-time degree program, adult/continuing education programs, co-op programs and internships. Off campus study at Visible School, Memphis Center for Urban Theological Studies. Study abroad program.

Entrance Requirements: Options: electronic application, deferred admission, international baccalaureate accepted. Required: essay, high school transcript, minimum 2.0 high school GPA, 2 recommendations, minimum ACT score of 18, SAT or ACT. Recommended: interview. Entrance: minimally difficult. Application deadline: Rolling. Notification: continuous.

Costs Per Year: Application fee: $25. Tuition: $9960 full-time, $415 per credit hour part-time. Mandatory fees: $209 full-time, $12 per credit hour part-time. Full-time tuition and fees vary according to course load and program. Part-time tuition and fees vary according to program. College room only: $3600.

Collegiate Environment: Orientation program. Drama-theater group, choral group. Social organizations: 20 open to all. Most popular organizations: Student Government Association, orientation staff, Presidential Ambassadors, American Humanics, Alpha Sigma Lambda. Major annual events: Marriage and Family Conference, Missions Conference, Spring Awards Banquet. Student services: personal-psychological counseling. Campus security: 24-hour patrols, controlled dormitory access, security alarms in campus apartments. 56 college housing spaces available; 46 were occupied in 2003-04. Freshmen guaranteed college housing. Options: men-only, women-only housing available. J.W. and Dorothy Bell Library plus 1 other with 54,175 books, 75,929 microform titles, 3,655 serials, 1,658 audiovisual materials, and an OPAC. Operations spending for 2004 fiscal year: $267,167. 33 computers available on campus for general student use. Computer purchase/lease plans available. A campuswide network can be accessed from off-campus. Staffed computer lab on campus.

Community Environment: See University of Memphis.

■ **CUMBERLAND UNIVERSITY** *C-12*
One Cumberland Square
Lebanon, TN 37087-3408

Tel: (615)444-2562
Free: 800-467-0562
Fax: (615)444-2569
E-mail: epawlawski@cumberland.edu
Web Site: http://www.cumberland.edu/
Description: Independent, comprehensive, coed. Awards associate, bachelor's, and master's degrees. Founded 1842. Setting: 44-acre small town campus with easy access to Nashville. Endowment: $6.7 million. Educational spending for 2005 fiscal year: $5437 per student. Total enrollment: 1,508. Faculty: 98 (60 full-time, 38 part-time). Student-undergrad faculty ratio is 15:1. 1,038 applied, 69% were admitted. 10% from top 10% of their high school class, 40% from top quarter, 70% from top half. 2 class presidents, 2 valedictorians, 1 student government officer. Full-time: 937 students, 56% women, 44% men. Part-time: 146 students, 61% women, 39% men. Students come from 25 states and territories, 18 other countries, 13% from out-of-state, 1% Native American, 2% Hispanic, 10% black, 1% Asian American or Pacific Islander, 5% international, 19% 25 or older, 43% live on campus, 14% transferred in. Retention: 69% of full-time freshmen returned the following year. Academic areas with the most degrees conferred: health professions and related sciences; education; business/ marketing. Core. Calendar: semesters. Academic remediation for entering students, services for LD students, advanced placement, accelerated degree program, freshman honors college, honors program, double major, summer session for credit, part-time degree program, adult/continuing education programs, co-op programs and internships, graduate courses open to undergrads. ROTC: Army.
Entrance Requirements: Options: Peterson's Universal Application, electronic application, deferred admission, international baccalaureate accepted. Required: high school transcript, SAT or ACT. Recommended: essay, minimum 2.5 high school GPA, SAT. Required for some: 3 recommendations. Entrance: moderately difficult. Application deadline: Rolling. Notification: continuous.
Costs Per Year: Application fee: $25. Comprehensive fee: $18,564 includes full-time tuition ($13,344), mandatory fees ($400), and college room and board ($4820). Full-time tuition and fees vary according to course load. Room and board charges vary according to board plan and housing facility. Part-time tuition: $557 per semester hour.
Collegiate Environment: Orientation program. Drama-theater group, choral group, marching band. Social organizations: 15 open to all; national fraternities, national sororities; 17% of eligible men and 7% of eligible women are members. Most popular organizations: African-American Student Association, Baptist Collegiate Ministry, Law and Government Club, Student Government Association, Student Nurses' Association. Major annual events: homecoming, Spring Fling Week, Coming Home. Student services: personal-psychological counseling. Campus security: 24-hour patrols. 412 college housing spaces available; 350 were occupied in 2003-04. No special consideration for freshman housing applicants. On-campus residence required in freshman year. Options: men-only, women-only housing available. Doris and Harry Vise Library with 50,000 books, 130 serials, 250 audiovisual materials, an OPAC, and a Web page. Operations spending for 2004 fiscal year: $311,166. 150 computers available on campus for general student use. A campuswide network can be accessed from student residence rooms and from off campus. Staffed computer lab on campus.
Community Environment: Named for the Biblical Lebanon because of the tall cedars found in the area. There are TVA Lakes on three sides of the town, and the Cedars of Lebanon State Park is on the fourth side. Bus transportation is available. Nashville Airport is 25 miles away. Community facilities include three libraries, many churches of major denominations, hospitals and clinic, four major shopping areas and a number of the civic and service organizations. Recreational facilities are excellent for fishing, boating, hunting, swimming, and water skiing.

■ **DRAUGHONS JUNIOR COLLEGE (CLARKSVILLE)** *B-9*
1860 Wilma Rudolph Blvd.
Clarksville, TN 37040
Tel: (931)552-7600
Fax: (931)552-3624
Web Site: http://www.draughons.edu/
Description: Proprietary, 2-year, coed. Awards terminal associate degrees. Founded 1987. Total enrollment: 340. Core. Calendar: semesters. Part-time degree program.
Entrance Requirements: Open admission. Required: high school transcript, interview. Entrance: noncompetitive. Application deadline: Rolling. Notification: continuous.

■ **DRAUGHONS JUNIOR COLLEGE (NASHVILLE)** *C-10*
340 Plus Park Blvd.
Nashville, TN 37217
Tel: (615)361-7555
Web Site: http://www.draughons.edu/
Description: Proprietary, 2-year, coed. Awards transfer associate and terminal associate degrees. Founded 1884. Setting: 5-acre suburban campus. Total enrollment: 600. 5% from top 10% of their high school class, 30% from top half. Students come from 5 other countries, 50% 25 or older. Core. Calendar: semesters. Academic remediation for entering students, summer session for credit, part-time degree program, internships.
Entrance Requirements: Open admission. Option: deferred admission. Required: high school transcript. Entrance: noncompetitive. Application deadline: Rolling. Notification: continuous.
Collegiate Environment: Student-run newspaper. Student services: personal-psychological counseling. Campus security: 24-hour emergency response devices. College housing not available. 3,250 books, 20 serials, and a Web page. 75 computers available on campus for general student use. Staffed computer lab on campus.

■ **DYERSBURG STATE COMMUNITY COLLEGE** *C-3*
1510 Lake Rd.
Dyersburg, TN 38024
Tel: (731)286-3200
Admissions: (731)286-3327
Fax: (731)286-3325
E-mail: gullet@dscc.edu
Web Site: http://www.dscc.edu/
Description: State-supported, 2-year, coed. Part of Tennessee Board of Regents. Awards certificates, transfer associate, and terminal associate degrees. Founded 1969. Setting: 100-acre small town campus with easy access to Memphis. Endowment: $3.2 million. Total enrollment: 2,457. Student-undergrad faculty ratio is 24:1. 953 applied, 99% were admitted. 4% from top 10% of their high school class, 20% from top quarter, 47% from top half. Full-time: 1,428 students, 70% women, 30% men. Part-time: 1,029 students, 74% women, 26% men. Students come from 5 states and territories, 1% from out-of-state, 1% Native American, 1% Hispanic, 20% black, 1% Asian American or Pacific Islander, 0% international, 42% 25 or older, 7% transferred in. Retention: 44% of full-time freshmen returned the following year. Core. Calendar: semesters. Academic remediation for entering students, services for LD students, advanced placement, honors program, independent study, distance learning, double major, summer session for credit, part-time degree program, adult/continuing education programs.
Entrance Requirements: Open admission except for nursing program. Options: Common Application, early admission. Required: high school transcript. Entrance: noncompetitive. Application deadline: Rolling. Notification: continuous.
Costs Per Year: Application fee: $10. State resident tuition: $2142 full-time, $91 per hour part-time. Nonresident tuition: $8556 full-time, $369 per hour part-time. Mandatory fees: $251 full-time. Part-time tuition varies according to course load.
Collegiate Environment: Orientation program. Drama-theater group, choral group. Social organizations: 7 open to all. Most popular organizations: student government, Phi Theta Kappa, Minority Association for Successful Students, Video Club, Psychology Club. Major annual events: Spring Fling, Homecoming. Student services: personal-psychological counseling. Campus security: 24-hour patrols. College housing not available. Learning Resource Center with 44,033 books, 291 microform titles, 85 serials, 2,231 audiovisual materials, an OPAC, and a Web page. 501 computers available on campus for general student use. A campuswide network can be accessed from off-campus. Staffed computer lab on campus.

■ **EAST TENNESSEE STATE UNIVERSITY** *I-6*
807 University Parkway
Johnson City, TN 37614
Tel: (423)439-1000
Free: 800-462-3878
Admissions: (423)439-4213
Fax: (423)439-5770
E-mail: go2etsu@etsu.edu
Web Site: http://www.etsu.edu/
Description: State-supported, university, coed. Part of State University and Community College System of Tennessee, Tennessee Board of Regents. Awards associate, bachelor's, master's, doctoral, and first professional

degrees and post-master's certificates. Founded 1911. Setting: 366-acre small town campus. Endowment: $66.3 million. Research spending for 2004 fiscal year: $3.5 million. Educational spending for 2005 fiscal year: $5796 per student. Total enrollment: 11,894. Faculty: 789 (480 full-time, 309 part-time). Student-undergrad faculty ratio is 17:1. 3,601 applied, 81% were admitted. 18% from top 10% of their high school class, 38% from top quarter, 71% from top half. Full-time: 8,183 students, 57% women, 43% men. Part-time: 1,587 students, 58% women, 42% men. Students come from 44 states and territories, 52 other countries, 8% from out-of-state, 0.5% Native American, 1% Hispanic, 4% black, 1% Asian American or Pacific Islander, 1% international, 29% 25 or older, 21% live on campus, 9% transferred in. Retention: 69% of full-time freshmen returned the following year. Academic areas with the most degrees conferred: health professions and related sciences; business/marketing; liberal arts/general studies. Core. Calendar: semesters. Services for LD students, advanced placement, accelerated degree program, freshman honors college, honors program, independent study, distance learning, double major, summer session for credit, part-time degree program, adult/continuing education programs, co-op programs and internships, graduate courses open to undergrads. Off campus study at Milligan College, Emmanuel School of Religion. Study abroad program. ROTC: Army.

Entrance Requirements: Options: electronic application, early admission, international baccalaureate accepted. Required: high school transcript, minimum 2.3 high school GPA, SAT or ACT. Entrance: moderately difficult. Notification: continuous, continuous for nonresidents.

Costs Per Year: Application fee: $15. State resident tuition: $3678 full-time, $161 per hour part-time. Nonresident tuition: $12,990 full-time, $565 per hour part-time. Mandatory fees: $809 full-time. Full-time tuition and fees vary according to course load and program. College room and board: $4822. College room only: $2512. Room and board charges vary according to board plan and housing facility.

Collegiate Environment: Orientation program. Drama-theater group, choral group, student-run newspaper, radio station. Social organizations: 200 open to all; national fraternities, national sororities; 7% of eligible men and 7% of eligible women are members. Most popular organizations: honor societies, Volunteer ETSU, religious groups, residence hall councils. Major annual events: Homecoming, Greek Week, Winter Cruise. Student services: health clinic, personal-psychological counseling, women's center. Campus security: 24-hour emergency response devices and patrols, student patrols, late night transport-escort service, controlled dormitory access. 2,500 college housing spaces available; 2,000 were occupied in 2003-04. No special consideration for freshman housing applicants. Options: coed, men-only, women-only housing available. Sherrod Library plus 2 others with 1.1 million books, 1.7 million microform titles, 3,714 serials, 23,658 audiovisual materials, an OPAC, and a Web page. Operations spending for 2004 fiscal year: $3.1 million. 550 computers available on campus for general student use. Computer purchase/lease plans available. A campuswide network can be accessed. Staffed computer lab on campus.

Community Environment: Johnson City, Kingsport and Bristol compose the Tri-Cities area, which is Tennessee's fifth largest metropolitan area, having one million people living within a 50-mile radius. Johnson City, a progressive city with a population of approximately 50,000, is located close to the state lines of Virginia, Kentucky, West Virginia, North Carolina and South Carolina. Recreational opportunities abound and include boating and water skiing on major TVA lakes, a variety of snow skiing resorts featuring downhill and cross-country, mountain hiking trails including easy access to the Appalachian Trail, and white water rafting. Interstate highways I-40, I-81 and I-26 provide access by automobile, with Tri-Cities Regional Airport providing access by commercial airlines. All major religious denominations are represented.

■ ELECTRONIC COMPUTER PROGRAMMING COLLEGE *G-14*

3805 Brainerd Rd.
Chattanooga, TN 37411-3798
Tel: (423)624-0077
Web Site: http://www.ecpconline.com/
Description: Proprietary, 2-year. Awards transfer associate degrees. Total enrollment: 178. 100 applied, 45% were admitted. 0% Native American, 0% Hispanic, 31% black, 0% Asian American or Pacific Islander, 0% international, 60% 25 or older.

■ FISK UNIVERSITY *C-10*

1000 17th Ave. North
Nashville, TN 37208-3051

Tel: (615)329-8500
Free: 800-443-FISK
Admissions: (615)329-8819
Fax: (615)329-8576
E-mail: admit@fisk.edu
Web Site: http://www.fisk.edu/
Description: Independent, comprehensive, coed, affiliated with United Church of Christ. Awards bachelor's and master's degrees. Founded 1866. Setting: 40-acre urban campus. Endowment: $12.6 million. Research spending for 2004 fiscal year: $3.8 million. Educational spending for 2005 fiscal year: $6864 per student. Total enrollment: 890. Faculty: 91 (56 full-time, 35 part-time). Student-undergrad faculty ratio is 13:1. 1,643 applied, 80% were admitted. 17% from top 10% of their high school class, 40% from top quarter, 74% from top half. 27 class presidents, 3 valedictorians, 18 student government officers. Full-time: 788 students, 69% women, 31% men. Part-time: 46 students, 54% women, 46% men. Students come from 32 states and territories, 7 other countries, 69% from out-of-state, 0.1% Native American, 0.2% Hispanic, 92% black, 0.3% Asian American or Pacific Islander, 4% international, 4% 25 or older, 68% live on campus, 8% transferred in. Retention: 87% of full-time freshmen returned the following year. Academic areas with the most degrees conferred: psychology; business/marketing; social sciences. Core. Calendar: semesters. Advanced placement, self-designed majors, honors program, independent study, double major, co-op programs and internships, graduate courses open to undergrads. Off campus study at 4 members of the Nashville University Center, 17 other institutions. Study abroad program. ROTC: Army (c), Naval (c).

Entrance Requirements: Option: electronic application. Required: essay, high school transcript, minimum 2.5 high school GPA, 2 recommendations, SAT or ACT. Entrance: moderately difficult. Application deadlines: 3/1, 3/1 for nonresidents, 12/1 for early decision. Notification: continuous, continuous for nonresidents, 1/15 for early decision.

Costs Per Year: Application fee: $50. Comprehensive fee: $19,910 includes full-time tuition ($12,480), mandatory fees ($700), and college room and board ($6730). College room only: $3910. Full-time tuition and fees vary according to course load. Room and board charges vary according to board plan. Part-time tuition: $520 per credit hour. Part-time tuition varies according to course load.

Collegiate Environment: Orientation program. Drama-theater group, choral group, student-run newspaper, radio station. Social organizations: 55 open to all; national fraternities, national sororities; 25% of eligible men and 20% of eligible women are members. Most popular organizations: Student Government Association, state clubs. Major annual events: Homecoming, Arts Festival, Jubilee Day Convocation. Student services: personal-psychological counseling. Campus security: 24-hour patrols, late night transport-escort service. On-campus residence required through senior year. Options: coed, men-only, women-only housing available. Fisk University Main Library with 127,070 books, 111,224 microform titles, 221 serials, 3,880 audiovisual materials, an OPAC, and a Web page. Operations spending for 2004 fiscal year: $760,627. 40 computers available on campus for general student use. A campuswide network can be accessed from student residence rooms and from off campus. Staffed computer lab on campus.

Community Environment: See Vanderbilt University.

■ FOUNTAINHEAD COLLEGE OF TECHNOLOGY *J-2*

3203 Tazewell Pike
Knoxville, TN 37918-2530
Tel: (865)688-9422; 888-218-7335
Fax: (865)688-2419
Web Site: http://www.fountainheadcollege.edu/
Description: Proprietary, primarily 2-year, coed. Awards transfer associate, terminal associate, and bachelor's degrees. Founded 1947. Setting: 1-acre suburban campus. Total enrollment: 120. Student-undergrad faculty ratio is 13:1. 0% from out-of-state, 20% 25 or older. Core. Calendar: semesters. Summer session for credit.

Entrance Requirements: Open admission. Recommended: high school transcript. Entrance: noncompetitive. Application deadline: Rolling. Notification: continuous.

Collegiate Environment: Campus security: 24-hour emergency response devices. College housing not available. 1,200 books, 1,000 serials, and a Web page. Operations spending for 2004 fiscal year: $6000. 15 computers available on campus for general student use. A campuswide network can be accessed from off-campus. Staffed computer lab on campus.

■ **FREE WILL BAPTIST BIBLE COLLEGE** *C-10*
3606 West End Ave.
Nashville, TN 37205-2498
Tel: (615)844-5000
Free: 800-763-9222
Admissions: (615)844-1500
Fax: (615)269-6028
Web Site: http://www.fwbbc.edu/

Description: Independent Free Will Baptist, 4-year, coed. Awards associate and bachelor's degrees. Founded 1942. Setting: 10-acre suburban campus. Endowment: $821,571. Educational spending for 2005 fiscal year: $16,122 per student. Total enrollment: 377. Student-undergrad faculty ratio is 10:1. 127 applied, 67% were admitted. Students come from 25 states and territories, 6 other countries, 72% from out-of-state, 0.3% Native American, 1% Hispanic, 4% black, 0% Asian American or Pacific Islander, 2% international, 16% 25 or older, 71% live on campus. Retention: 61% of full-time freshmen returned the following year. Academic areas with the most degrees conferred: theology and religious vocations; psychology; education. Core. Calendar: semesters. Academic remediation for entering students, advanced placement, self-designed majors, distance learning, double major, summer session for credit, part-time degree program, internships. ROTC: Army (c), Air Force (c).

Entrance Requirements: Open admission. Options: Common Application, electronic application, early admission, deferred admission. Required: essay, high school transcript, 3 recommendations, medical history, ACT. Entrance: noncompetitive. Application deadline: Rolling. Preference given to Free Will Baptists.

Costs Per Year: Application fee: $35. Comprehensive fee: $15,874 includes full-time tuition ($10,470), mandatory fees ($696), and college room and board ($4708). Part-time tuition: $349 per semester hour.

Collegiate Environment: Orientation program. Drama-theater group, choral group. Campus security: 24-hour emergency response devices, student patrols, late night transport-escort service, controlled dormitory access. 265 undergraduates lived in college housing during 2003-04. Freshmen guaranteed college housing. On-campus residence required through senior year. Options: men-only, women-only housing available. Welch Library with 131,200 books, 71,232 microform titles, 388 serials, and 3,835 audiovisual materials. Operations spending for 2004 fiscal year: $193,468. 27 computers available on campus for general student use. A campuswide network can be accessed.

Community Environment: See Vanderbilt University.

■ **FREED-HARDEMAN UNIVERSITY** *F-5*
158 East Main St.
Henderson, TN 38340-2399
Tel: (731)989-6000
Free: 800-630-3480
Admissions: (731)989-6651
Fax: (731)989-6047
E-mail: admissions@fhu.edu
Web Site: http://www.fhu.edu/

Description: Independent, comprehensive, coed, affiliated with Church of Christ. Awards bachelor's and master's degrees and post-master's certificates. Founded 1869. Setting: 96-acre small town campus. Endowment: $24.8 million. Educational spending for 2005 fiscal year: $6472 per student. Total enrollment: 2,030. Faculty: 147 (106 full-time, 41 part-time). Student-undergrad faculty ratio is 14:1. 1,230 applied, 99% were admitted. 15 valedictorians. Full-time: 1,402 students, 54% women, 46% men. Part-time: 98 students, 51% women, 49% men. Students come from 35 states and territories, 18 other countries, 1% Native American, 0.5% Hispanic, 4% black, 1% Asian American or Pacific Islander, 2% international, 6% 25 or older, 81% live on campus, 4% transferred in. Retention: 80% of full-time freshmen returned the following year. Academic areas with the most degrees conferred: theology and religious vocations; business/marketing; interdisciplinary studies. Core. Calendar: semesters. Academic remediation for entering students, services for LD students, advanced placement, accelerated degree program, self-designed majors, honors program, independent study, double major, summer session for credit, part-time degree program, co-op programs and internships, graduate courses open to undergrads. Off campus study at Lambuth University, Union University. Study abroad program.

Entrance Requirements: Options: early admission, deferred admission, international baccalaureate accepted. Required: high school transcript, minimum 2.25 high school GPA, SAT or ACT. Recommended: essay, recommendations. Required for some: interview. Entrance: moderately difficult. Application deadline: Rolling. Notification: continuous.

Costs Per Year: Application fee: $0. Tuition: $11,000 full-time. Mandatory fees: $2092 full-time. College room only: $3700.

Collegiate Environment: Orientation program. Drama-theater group, choral group, student-run newspaper, radio station. Social organizations: 35 open to all; coed social clubs; 48% of eligible men and 48% of eligible women are members. Most popular organizations: Student Alumni Association, University Program Council, University Student Ambassadors, Evangelism Forum. Major annual events: Spring Weekend/Makin' Music, Homecoming, Annual Bible Lectureship. Student services: health clinic, personal-psychological counseling. Campus security: 24-hour emergency response devices and patrols, late night transport-escort service, controlled dormitory access. 1,414 college housing spaces available; 1,173 were occupied in 2003-04. Freshmen guaranteed college housing. On-campus residence required through senior year. Options: men-only, women-only housing available. Loden-Daniel Library with 154,689 books, 255,909 microform titles, 1,715 serials, 42,735 audiovisual materials, an OPAC, and a Web page. Operations spending for 2004 fiscal year: $670,746. 250 computers available on campus for general student use. Computer purchase/lease plans available. A campuswide network can be accessed from student residence rooms and from off campus. Staffed computer lab on campus.

Community Environment: Henderson is a rural town of 5,500 with an airport within 25 miles. A metropolitan area, Jackson, (population 55,000) is located within 15 miles and Memphis is only 80 miles away. The community facilities include churches, good shopping facilities, and some major civic and service organizations. The Tennessee River, Kentucky Lake, Chickasaw State Park, and Pickwick Dam provide a number of facilities for all kinds of water sports and other recreation. Some part-time employment is available.

■ **HIGH-TECH INSTITUTE (MEMPHIS)** *F-1*
5865 Shelby Oaks Circle
Memphis, TN 38134
Tel: (901)387-4555
Web Site: http://www.high-techinstitute.com/
Description: Proprietary, 2-year, coed. Founded 2003. Calendar: semesters.

■ **HIGH-TECH INSTITUTE (NASHVILLE)** *C-10*
2710 Old Lebanon Rd., Ste. 12
Nashville, TN 37214
Tel: (615)902-9705
Free: 800-987-0110
Fax: (615)902-9766
E-mail: dmartinez@hightechschools.com
Web Site: http://www.high-techinstitute.com/
Description: Proprietary, 2-year, coed. Founded 1999. Calendar: semesters.

■ **ITT TECHNICAL INSTITUTE (KNOXVILLE)** *J-2*
10208 Technology Dr.
Knoxville, TN 37932
Tel: (865)671-2800
Fax: (865)691-0337
Web Site: http://www.itt-tech.edu/
Description: Proprietary, primarily 2-year, coed. Part of ITT Educational Services, Inc. Awards terminal associate and bachelor's degrees. Founded 1988. Setting: 5-acre suburban campus. Core.

Entrance Requirements: Option: deferred admission. Required: high school transcript, interview, Wonderlic aptitude test. Recommended: recommendations. Entrance: minimally difficult. Application deadline: Rolling. Notification: continuous.

Costs Per Year: Application fee: $100.

Collegiate Environment: Orientation program. College housing not available.

■ **ITT TECHNICAL INSTITUTE (MEMPHIS)** *F-1*
1255 Lynnfield Rd., Ste. 92
Memphis, TN 38119
Tel: (901)762-0556
Admissions: (901)381-0200
Web Site: http://www.itt-tech.edu/

Description: Proprietary, primarily 2-year, coed. Part of ITT Educational Services, Inc. Awards terminal associate and bachelor's degrees. Founded 1994. Setting: 1-acre suburban campus. Core.

Entrance Requirements: Option: deferred admission. Required: high school transcript, interview, Wonderlic aptitude test. Recommended: recommendations. Entrance: minimally difficult. Application deadline: Rolling. Notification: continuous.

Costs Per Year: Application fee: $100.

Collegiate Environment: Orientation program. Student-run newspaper. College housing not available.

■ **ITT TECHNICAL INSTITUTE (NASHVILLE)** *C-10*

2845 Elm Hill Pike
Nashville, TN 37214-3717
Tel: (615)889-8700
Fax: (615)872-7209
Web Site: http://www.itt-tech.edu/ .

Description: Proprietary, primarily 2-year, coed. Part of ITT Educational Services, Inc. Awards terminal associate and bachelor's degrees. Founded 1984. Setting: 21-acre urban campus. Core.

Entrance Requirements: Option: deferred admission. Required: high school transcript, interview, Wonderlic aptitude test. Recommended: recommendations. Entrance: minimally difficult. Application deadline: Rolling. Notification: continuous.

Costs Per Year: Application fee: $100.

Collegiate Environment: Orientation program. College housing not available.

■ **JACKSON STATE COMMUNITY COLLEGE** *E-5*

2046 North Parkway
Jackson, TN 38301-3797
Tel: (731)424-3520
Admissions: (731)425-2644
Fax: (731)425-2647
E-mail: mray@jscc.edu
Web Site: http://www.jscc.edu/

Description: State-supported, 2-year, coed. Part of Tennessee Board of Regents. Awards certificates, transfer associate, and terminal associate degrees. Founded 1967. Setting: 104-acre small town campus. Endowment: $672,925. Educational spending for 2005 fiscal year: $3694 per student. Total enrollment: 3,866. Student-undergrad faculty ratio is 22:1. 1,273 applied, 84% were admitted. Full-time: 2,048 students, 62% women, 38% men. Part-time: 1,818 students, 69% women, 31% men. Students come from 9 states and territories, 0.2% from out-of-state, 0.2% Native American, 1% Hispanic, 18% black, 0.4% Asian American or Pacific Islander, 0.1% international, 43% 25 or older, 18% transferred in. Retention: 56% of full-time freshmen returned the following year. Core. Calendar: semesters. Academic remediation for entering students, advanced placement, honors program, distance learning, summer session for credit, part-time degree program, adult/continuing education programs, co-op programs and internships.

Entrance Requirements: Open admission except for allied health programs. Options: electronic application, early admission, deferred admission. Required: ACT, COMPASS. Required for some: high school transcript. Entrance: noncompetitive. Application deadline: 8/29. Notification: continuous. Preference given to state residents.

Costs Per Year: Application fee: $10. State resident tuition: $2142 full-time, $91 per credit hour part-time. Nonresident tuition: $8556 full-time, $369 per credit hour part-time. Mandatory fees: $253 full-time, $9 per credit hour part-time, $14 per term part-time.

Collegiate Environment: Drama-theater group, choral group. Social organizations: 10 open to all. Most popular organizations: Student Government Organization, Spanish Club, Biology Club, Art Club, Black Student Association. Major annual events: Welcome Back Cookout, Health Fair, Career and College Fair. Student services: health clinic, personal-psychological counseling. Campus security: 24-hour patrols. College housing not available. Jackson State Community College Library with 63,620 books, 118,535 microform titles, 225 serials, 2,000 audiovisual materials, an OPAC, and a Web page. Operations spending for 2004 fiscal year: $598,002. 725 computers available on campus for general student use. Computer purchase/lease plans available. A campuswide network can be accessed from off-campus. Staffed computer lab on campus.

Community Environment: Jackson, at one time a small cotton port, is now a trading and shipping center. All forms of commercial transportation are available. Because of direct access to major thoroughfares, Jackson is one of the fastest growing cities in Tennessee and is the trade center for a large populated area. Its facilities include hospitals, clinics, many churches, an art association, and symphony orchestra. The city is known as the home and burial place of John Luther "Casey" Jones, who became a part of American folklore and a legend of early railroading. The Casey Jones Railroad Museum may be seen here.

■ **JOHN A. GUPTON COLLEGE** *C-10*

1616 Church St.
Nashville, TN 37203-2920
Tel: (615)327-3927
Web Site: http://www.guptoncollege.edu/

Description: Independent, 2-year, coed. Awards diplomas and transfer associate degrees. Founded 1946. Setting: 1-acre urban campus. Endowment: $60,000. Educational spending for 2005 fiscal year: $2837 per student. Total enrollment: 97. 93 applied, 55% were admitted. Full-time: 91 students, 46% women, 54% men. Part-time: 6 students, 17% women, 83% men. Students come from 8 states and territories, 25% from out-of-state, 27% black, 22% 25 or older, 11% transferred in. Calendar: semesters. Part-time degree program.

Entrance Requirements: Options: Common Application, deferred admission. Required: essay, high school transcript, 2 recommendations, health forms, ACT. Entrance: minimally difficult. Application deadline: Rolling.

Collegiate Environment: Orientation program. Campus security: controlled dormitory access, day patrols. Option: coed housing available. Memorial Library with 4,000 books, 54 serials, and a Web page. 6 computers available on campus for general student use. Staffed computer lab on campus.

■ **JOHNSON BIBLE COLLEGE** *J-2*

7900 Johnson Dr.
Knoxville, TN 37998-1001
Tel: (865)573-4517
Free: 800-827-2122
Admissions: (865)251-2346
Fax: (865)251-2337
E-mail: twingfield@jbc.edu
Web Site: http://www.jbc.edu/

Description: Independent, comprehensive, coed, affiliated with Christian Churches and Churches of Christ. Awards associate, bachelor's, and master's degrees. Founded 1893. Setting: 75-acre rural campus. Educational spending for 2005 fiscal year: $3702 per student. Total enrollment: 889. 239 applied, 62% were admitted. 18% from top 10% of their high school class, 41% from top quarter, 68% from top half. Full-time: 728 students, 49% women, 51% men. Part-time: 28 students, 54% women, 46% men. Students come from 34 states and territories, 14 other countries, 77% from out-of-state, 0.3% Native American, 1% Hispanic, 2% black, 1% Asian American or Pacific Islander, 3% international, 15% 25 or older, 88% live on campus, 12% transferred in. Retention: 68% of full-time freshmen returned the following year. Core. Calendar: semesters. Academic remediation for entering students, ESL program, services for LD students, advanced placement, accelerated degree program, honors program, independent study, distance learning, double major, summer session for credit, part-time degree program, adult/continuing education programs, co-op programs and internships, graduate courses open to undergrads.

Entrance Requirements: Options: deferred admission, international baccalaureate accepted. Required: essay, high school transcript, 3 recommendations, SAT or ACT. Required for some: interview, ACT. Entrance: minimally difficult. Application deadline: 7/1. Notification: continuous.

Costs Per Year: Application fee: $35. Comprehensive fee: $10,580 includes full-time tuition ($5800), mandatory fees ($690), and college room and board ($4090). College room only: $2595. Room and board charges vary according to board plan and housing facility. Part-time tuition: $242 per semester hour. Part-time mandatory fees: $20.42 per semester hour. Part-time tuition and fees vary according to course load.

Collegiate Environment: Orientation program. Choral group, student-run radio station. Social organizations: 3 open to all. Most popular organizations: Quest, Timothy Club, International Harvesters. Major annual events: homecoming, Founders' Day, Miller-Scott Christmas Banquet. Student services: health clinic, personal-psychological counseling. Campus security: 24-hour emergency response devices, student patrols, controlled dormitory access. 720 college housing spaces available; 642 were occupied in 2003-04. No special consideration for freshman housing applicants. On-campus residence required through senior year. Options: men-only, women-only housing available. Glass Memorial Library plus 1 other with 104,808 books, 16,934 microform titles, 397 serials, 13,057 audiovisual materials, an OPAC, and a Web page. Operations spending for 2004 fiscal year: $370,721. 34 computers available on campus for general student use. A campuswide network can be accessed from student residence rooms and from off campus. Staffed computer lab on campus.

Community Environment: The college is located in the rural community of Kimberlin Heights within a 20-minute drive of Knoxville where shopping, jobs, recreation, hospitals, churches, and civic cultural, and service organizations are abundant.

■ **KING COLLEGE** *H-7*
1350 King College Rd.
Bristol, TN 37620-2699
Tel: (423)968-1187
Free: 800-362-0014
Admissions: (423)652-4861
Fax: (423)968-4456
E-mail: admissions@king.edu
Web Site: http://www.king.edu/

Description: Independent, comprehensive, coed, affiliated with Presbyterian Church (U.S.A.). Awards bachelor's and master's degrees. Founded 1867. Setting: 135-acre suburban campus. Endowment: $27.4 million. Educational spending for 2005 fiscal year: $5172 per student. Total enrollment: 970. Faculty: 94 (50 full-time, 44 part-time). Student-undergrad faculty ratio is 13:1. 550 applied, 95% were admitted. 19% from top 10% of their high school class, 43% from top quarter, 78% from top half. Full-time: 803 students, 61% women, 39% men. Part-time: 70 students, 56% women, 44% men. Students come from 27 states and territories, 16 other countries, 31% from out-of-state, 0.5% Native American, 1% Hispanic, 3% black, 1% Asian American or Pacific Islander, 4% international, 11% 25 or older, 56% live on campus, 9% transferred in. Retention: 67% of full-time freshmen returned the following year. Academic areas with the most degrees conferred: business/marketing; health professions and related sciences; English. Core. Calendar: semesters. ESL program, services for LD students, advanced placement, self-designed majors, freshman honors college, honors program, independent study, double major, summer session for credit, part-time degree program, adult/continuing education programs, internships. Off campus study at Virginia Intermont College. Study abroad program.

Entrance Requirements: Options: Peterson's Universal Application, Common Application, electronic application, early admission, deferred admission, international baccalaureate accepted. Required: high school transcript, minimum 2.4 high school GPA, minimum ACT score of 19 or SAT score of 980, SAT or ACT. Recommended: interview. Required for some: essay. Entrance: moderately difficult. Application deadline: Rolling. Notification: continuous.

Costs Per Year: Application fee: $20. Comprehensive fee: $24,545 includes full-time tuition ($17,291), mandatory fees ($1054), and college room and board ($6200). College room only: $3100. Part-time tuition: $575 per credit hour.

Collegiate Environment: Orientation program. Drama-theater group, choral group, student-run newspaper. Social organizations: 29 open to all. Most popular organizations: Student Government Association, Campus Life Committee, World Christian Fellowship, Fellowship of Christian Athletes, Drama Club. Major annual events: Fall Ball and Fall Play, Dogwood/Alumni Weekend, Parents' Weekend. Student services: personal-psychological counseling. Campus security: late night transport-escort service. 485 college housing spaces available; 377 were occupied in 2003-04. Freshmen guaranteed college housing. On-campus residence required through junior year. Options: men-only, women-only housing available. E. W. King Library with 80,888 books, 33,051 microform titles, 1,539 serials, 5,074 audiovisual materials, an OPAC, and a Web page. Operations spending for 2004 fiscal year: $351,945. 90 computers available on campus for general student use. Computer purchase/lease plans available. A campuswide network can be accessed from student residence rooms and from off campus. Staffed computer lab on campus.

Community Environment: Located in the beautiful Southern Highlands, Bristol is a twin city on the Tennessee-Virginia state line. Four distinct seasons offer year-round recreation. With three access points to the Appalachian trail within an hour's drive from campus, students can quickly escape to a wilderness playground. Nearby Cherokee and Jefferson National Forests provide more than 250,000 acres of unspoiled woodlands for hiking and camping. More than 40 square miles of inland lakes and freshwater streams await water enthusiasts, including South Holston Lake,

site of the world's third largest earthen dam. Several major ski resorts are located within an hour's drive. NASCAR fans enjoy the world's fastest half-mile track at the Bristol Motor Speedway, and Bristol's Viking Hall Civic Center serves as a stop for top-name concerts, sporting events and community-sponsored shows and bazaars.

■ **LAMBUTH UNIVERSITY** *E-5*
705 Lambuth Blvd.
Jackson, TN 38301
Tel: (731)425-2500
Free: 800-526-2884
Admissions: (731)425-3288
Fax: (731)988-4600
E-mail: burnley@lambuth.edu
Web Site: http://www.lambuth.edu/

Description: Independent United Methodist, 4-year, coed. Awards bachelor's degrees. Founded 1843. Setting: 50-acre urban campus with easy access to Memphis. Endowment: $6.4 million. Educational spending for 2005 fiscal year: $6097 per student. Total enrollment: 805. Student-undergrad faculty ratio is 14:1. 1,333 applied, 65% were admitted. 29% from top 10% of their high school class, 52% from top quarter, 79% from top half. 15 class presidents, 6 valedictorians, 33 student government officers. Full-time: 766 students, 54% women, 46% men. Part-time: 39 students, 46% women, 54% men. Students come from 25 states and territories, 12 other countries, 25% from out-of-state, 0.4% Native American, 3% Hispanic, 16% black, 1% Asian American or Pacific Islander, 3% international, 10% 25 or older, 59% live on campus, 11% transferred in. Retention: 58% of full-time freshmen returned the following year. Academic areas with the most degrees conferred: business/marketing; visual and performing arts; education. Core. Calendar: semesters. Academic remediation for entering students, ESL program, services for LD students, advanced placement, accelerated degree program, self-designed majors, honors program, independent study, double major, summer session for credit, part-time degree program, adult/continuing education programs, internships. Off campus study at Union University, Freed-Hardeman University. Study abroad program.

Entrance Requirements: Options: Common Application, electronic application, early admission, deferred admission. Required: essay, high school transcript, minimum 2.0 high school GPA, SAT or ACT. Recommended: interview. Required for some: 3 recommendations. Entrance: moderately difficult. Application deadline: Rolling. Notification: continuous.

Costs Per Year: Application fee: $25. Comprehensive fee: $23,090 includes full-time tuition ($15,980), mandatory fees ($400), and college room and board ($6710). College room only: $3195. Part-time tuition: $665 per credit hour. Part-time mandatory fees: $200 per term.

Collegiate Environment: Orientation program. Drama-theater group, choral group, student-run newspaper. Social organizations: 28 open to all; national fraternities, national sororities; 27% of eligible men and 32% of eligible women are members. Most popular organizations: student government, Student Activities Committee, Black Student Union, Religious Life Council, International Students Organization. Major annual events: All Sing, Homecoming activities/football game, Lambuth Palooza. Student services: health clinic, personal-psychological counseling. Campus security: 24-hour emergency response devices and patrols, late night transport-escort service, controlled dormitory access. 611 college housing spaces available; 454 were occupied in 2003-04. Freshmen guaranteed college housing. On-campus residence required through senior year. Options: coed, men-only, women-only housing available. Luther L. Gobbel Library with 272,435 books, 203,130 microform titles, 139,999 serials, 2,296 audiovisual materials, an OPAC, and a Web page. Operations spending for 2004 fiscal year: $328,607. 100 computers available on campus for general student use. A campuswide network can be accessed from student residence rooms and from off campus. Staffed computer lab on campus.

Community Environment: See Jackson State Community College.

■ **LANE COLLEGE** *E-5*
545 Ln. Ave.
Jackson, TN 38301-4598
Tel: (731)426-7500
Free: 800-960-7533
Admissions: (731)426-7533
Fax: (731)426-7559
Web Site: http://www.lanecollege.edu/

Description: Independent, 4-year, coed, affiliated with Christian Methodist Episcopal Church. Awards bachelor's degrees. Founded 1882. Setting: 25-

acre suburban campus with easy access to Memphis. Endowment: $2.8 million. Educational spending for 2005 fiscal year: $3255 per student. Total enrollment: 1,045. 3,189 applied, 28% were admitted. 30% from top 10% of their high school class, 58% from top quarter, 75% from top half. 18 class presidents, 15 valedictorians, 32 student government officers. Full-time: 1,035 students, 47% women, 53% men. Part-time: 10 students, 70% women, 30% men. Students come from 27 states and territories, 40% from out-of-state, 0% Native American, 0.2% Hispanic, 99% black, 0% Asian American or Pacific Islander, 0% international, 12% 25 or older, 60% live on campus, 5% transferred in. Retention: 74% of full-time freshmen returned the following year. Core. Calendar: semesters. Academic remediation for entering students, advanced placement, accelerated degree program, honors program, independent study, double major, summer session for credit, part-time degree program, co-op programs and internships. Study abroad program.

Entrance Requirements: Options: Common Application, electronic application, early admission, early decision. Required: high school transcript, minimum 2.0 high school GPA, 2 recommendations, SAT or ACT. Entrance: minimally difficult. Application deadlines: Rolling, 1/15 for early decision. Notification: continuous.

Costs Per Year: Application fee: $0. Comprehensive fee: $11,710 includes full-time tuition ($6576), mandatory fees ($600), and college room and board ($4534). Full-time tuition and fees vary according to course load. Part-time tuition: $292 per hour. Part-time tuition varies according to course load.

Collegiate Environment: Orientation program. Drama-theater group, choral group, marching band, student-run newspaper. Social organizations: 36 open to all; national fraternities, national sororities; 1% of eligible men and 5% of eligible women are members. Most popular organizations: Student Government Association, Pre-Law Club, Student Christian Association, Drama Club. Major annual events: Homecoming, Founder's Day, Religious Emphasis Week. Student services: health clinic, personal-psychological counseling. Campus security: 24-hour emergency response devices and patrols, surveillance cameras, lighted parking areas. 681 college housing spaces available; 629 were occupied in 2003-04. Freshmen given priority for college housing. Options: men-only, women-only housing available. Chambers-McClure Academic Center with 143,940 books, 53,276 microform titles, 240 serials, 860 audiovisual materials, an OPAC, and a Web page. Operations spending for 2004 fiscal year: $294,363. 520 computers available on campus for general student use. A campuswide network can be accessed from student residence rooms and from off campus. Staffed computer lab on campus.

Community Environment: See Jackson State Community College.

■ **LEE UNIVERSITY** *F-16*
PO Box 3450
Cleveland, TN 37320-3450
Tel: (423)614-8000
Free: 800-533-9930
Admissions: (423)614-8500
Fax: (423)614-8533
Web Site: http://www.leeuniversity.edu/

Description: Independent, comprehensive, coed, affiliated with Church of God. Awards bachelor's and master's degrees. Founded 1918. Setting: 115-acre small town campus. Endowment: $7.8 million. Educational spending for 2005 fiscal year: $4471 per student. Total enrollment: 3,930. Faculty: 312 (148 full-time, 164 part-time). Student-undergrad faculty ratio is 18:1. 1,465 applied, 61% were admitted. 19% from top 10% of their high school class, 43% from top quarter, 69% from top half. Full-time: 3,316 students, 58% women, 42% men. Part-time: 332 students, 55% women, 45% men. Students come from 50 states and territories, 47 other countries, 62% from out-of-state, 1% Native American, 3% Hispanic, 4% black, 1% Asian American or Pacific Islander, 5% international, 13% 25 or older, 44% live on campus, 8% transferred in. Retention: 73% of full-time freshmen returned the following year. Academic areas with the most degrees conferred: education; communication technologies; psychology. Core. Calendar: semesters. Academic remediation for entering students, ESL program, services for LD students, advanced placement, honors program, independent study, distance learning, double major, summer session for credit, part-time degree program, external degree program, adult/continuing education programs, internships. Study abroad program.

Entrance Requirements: Options: Peterson's Universal Application, Common Application, electronic application, early admission, deferred admission. Required: high school transcript, minimum 2.0 high school GPA, MMR immunization record, SAT or ACT. Recommended: 3 recommendations, ACT.

Required for some: 1 recommendation. Entrance: minimally difficult. Application deadline: 9/1. Notification: continuous.

Costs Per Year: Application fee: $25. Comprehensive fee: $14,780 includes full-time tuition ($9400), mandatory fees ($210), and college room and board ($5170). College room only: $2680. Full-time tuition and fees vary according to program. Room and board charges vary according to board plan and housing facility. Part-time tuition: $392 per credit hour. Part-time mandatory fees: $30 per term. Part-time tuition and fees vary according to program.

Collegiate Environment: Orientation program. Drama-theater group, choral group, student-run newspaper. Social organizations: 55 open to all; local fraternities, local sororities; 12% of eligible men and 10% of eligible women are members. Most popular organizations: Student Leadership Council, Pioneers for Christ, International Student Fellowship, Umoja, Back Yard Ministry. Major annual events: Sadie Hawkins, Dorm Wars, Luau. Student services: health clinic, personal-psychological counseling. Campus security: 24-hour emergency response devices and patrols, late night transport-escort service. 1,840 college housing spaces available; 1,698 were occupied in 2003-04. Freshmen guaranteed college housing. On-campus residence required through sophomore year. Options: men-only, women-only housing available. William G. Squires Library with 145,435 books, 55,000 microform titles, 14,611 serials, 15,150 audiovisual materials, an OPAC, and a Web page. Operations spending for 2004 fiscal year: $1.1 million.

Community Environment: See Cleveland State Community College.

■ **LEMOYNE-OWEN COLLEGE** *F-1*
807 Walker Ave.
Memphis, TN 38126-6595
Tel: (901)774-9090
Admissions: (901)435-1550
Fax: (901)942-6272
E-mail: mark_green@loc.edu
Web Site: http://www.loc.edu/

Description: Independent, 4-year, coed, affiliated with United Church of Christ. Awards bachelor's degrees. Founded 1862. Setting: 15-acre urban campus. Endowment: $11.9 million. Research spending for 2004 fiscal year: $100,000. Total enrollment: 809. Student-undergrad faculty ratio is 14:1. 1,562 applied, 38% were admitted. Full-time: 684 students, 69% women, 31% men. Part-time: 125 students, 68% women, 32% men. Students come from 20 states and territories, 7 other countries, 14% from out-of-state, 0% Native American, 0.1% Hispanic, 97% black, 0.2% Asian American or Pacific Islander, 1% international, 39% 25 or older, 20% live on campus, 14% transferred in. Retention: 47% of full-time freshmen returned the following year. Academic areas with the most degrees conferred: business/marketing; social sciences; biological/life sciences. Core. Calendar: semesters. Academic remediation for entering students; services for LD students, advanced placement, accelerated degree program, honors program, independent study, double major, summer session for credit, adult/continuing education programs, co-op programs and internships. Off campus study at Greater Memphis Consortium. Study abroad program. ROTC: Army (c), Air Force (c).

Entrance Requirements: Open admission. Options: Common Application, international baccalaureate accepted. Required: essay, high school transcript, minimum 2.0 high school GPA, 2 recommendations, interview, SAT or ACT. Entrance: minimally difficult. Application deadline: 4/1.

Costs Per Year: Application fee: $25. Comprehensive fee: $19,278 includes full-time tuition ($14,458), mandatory fees ($200), and college room and board ($4620). College room only: $2420. Room and board charges vary according to board plan.

Collegiate Environment: Orientation program. Drama-theater group, choral group, student-run newspaper. Social organizations: 26 open to all; national fraternities, national sororities; 35% of eligible men and 65% of eligible women are members. Most popular organizations: Students in Free Enterprise, National Black Student Accountant Club, gospel choir, pre-alumni organization. Major annual events: Homecoming, Honors Week, Black History Month. Student services: health clinic, personal-psychological counseling. Campus security: 24-hour patrols, late night transport-escort service, controlled dormitory access. 173 college housing spaces available; 169 were occupied in 2003-04. No special consideration for freshman housing applicants. Options: men-only, women-only housing available. Hollis F. Price Library with 1,495 microform titles and 90,000 serials. Operations spending for 2004 fiscal year: $162,000. 223 computers available on campus for general student use. A campuswide network can be accessed from off-campus. Staffed computer lab on campus.

Community Environment: See University of Memphis.

■ LINCOLN MEMORIAL UNIVERSITY

6965 Cumberland Gap Parkway
Harrogate, TN 37752-1901
Tel: (423)869-3611
Free: 800-325-0900
Admissions: (423)869-6280
Fax: (423)869-6250
E-mail: admissions@lmunet.edu
Web Site: http://www.lmunet.edu/

Description: Independent, comprehensive, coed. Awards associate, bachelor's, and master's degrees and post-master's certificates. Founded 1897. Setting: 1,000-acre small town campus. Endowment: $26.2 million. Educational spending for 2005 fiscal year: $3385 per student. Total enrollment: 2,802. Faculty: 152 (86 full-time, 66 part-time). Student-undergrad faculty ratio is 9:1. 1,350 applied, 37% were admitted. 36% from top 10% of their high school class, 58% from top quarter, 94% from top half. Full-time: 1,012 students, 72% women, 28% men. Part-time: 304 students, 72% women, 28% men. Students come from 30 states and territories, 15 other countries, 35% from out-of-state, 0.2% Native American, 0.5% Hispanic, 3% black, 0.2% Asian American or Pacific Islander, 4% international, 28% 25 or older, 32% live on campus, 10% transferred in. Retention: 54% of full-time freshmen returned the following year. Academic areas with the most degrees conferred: business/marketing; education; health professions and related sciences. Core. Calendar: semesters. ESL program, advanced placement, accelerated degree program, self-designed majors, honors program, independent study, double major, summer session for credit, part-time degree program, adult/continuing education programs, graduate courses open to undergrads.

Entrance Requirements: Options: Peterson's Universal Application, Common Application. Required: high school transcript, minimum 2.3 high school GPA, SAT or ACT. Recommended: interview. Required for some: essay. Entrance: moderately difficult. Application deadline: Rolling.

Costs Per Year: Application fee: $25. Comprehensive fee: $18,982 includes full-time tuition ($13,750) and college room and board ($5232). Part-time tuition: $573 per credit.

Collegiate Environment: Orientation program. Drama-theater group, choral group, student-run newspaper, radio station. Social organizations: 26 open to all; local fraternities, local sororities; 5% of eligible men and 10% of eligible women are members. Most popular organizations: Baptist Student Association, Wesleyan Association, Student Nurses Association, Student National Education Association, Student Alumni Association. Major annual events: musical concerts, conference and lecture series, homecoming. Student services: personal-psychological counseling. Campus security: 24-hour emergency response devices and patrols. 450 college housing spaces available; 350 were occupied in 2003-04. No special consideration for freshman housing applicants. Options: coed, men-only, women-only housing available. Carnegie Library with 145,537 books, 100,289 microform titles, 251 serials, 3,369 audiovisual materials, an OPAC, and a Web page. Operations spending for 2004 fiscal year: $506,277. 150 computers available on campus for general student use. A campuswide network can be accessed from student residence rooms. Staffed computer lab on campus.

■ LIPSCOMB UNIVERSITY *C-10*

3901 Granny White Pike
Nashville, TN 37204-3951
Tel: (615)269-1000; 877-582-4766
Fax: (615)269-1804
E-mail: admissions@lipscomb.edu
Web Site: http://www.lipscomb.edu/

Description: Independent, comprehensive, coed, affiliated with Church of Christ. Awards bachelor's, master's, and first professional degrees. Founded 1891. Setting: 65-acre urban campus. Endowment: $60.9 million. Total enrollment: 2,518. Faculty: 196 (119 full-time, 77 part-time). Student-undergrad faculty ratio is 15:1. 1,599 applied, 76% were admitted. 25% from top 10% of their high school class, 51% from top quarter, 82% from top half. Full-time: 2,070 students, 57% women, 43% men. Part-time: 227 students, 57% women, 43% men. 34% from out-of-state, 0.2% Native American, 2% Hispanic, 5% black, 1% Asian American or Pacific Islander, 1% international. Retention: 71% of full-time freshmen returned the following year. Academic areas with the most degrees conferred: business/marketing; education; biological/life sciences. Core. Calendar: semesters. Academic remediation for entering students, services for LD students, advanced placement, accelerated degree program, honors program, independent study, distance learning, double major, summer session for credit, part-time degree

program, adult/continuing education programs, internships, graduate courses open to undergrads. Study abroad program. ROTC: Army (c), Air Force (c).

Entrance Requirements: Options: Peterson's Universal Application, electronic application, early admission, international baccalaureate accepted. Required: high school transcript, minimum 2.25 high school GPA, 2 recommendations, SAT or ACT. Recommended: essay, interview. Entrance: moderately difficult. Application deadline: Rolling. Notification: continuous.

Costs Per Year: Application fee: $50. Comprehensive fee: $20,967 includes full-time tuition ($13,928), mandatory fees ($629), and college room and board ($6410). Full-time tuition and fees vary according to class time and degree level. Room and board charges vary according to board plan and housing facility. Part-time tuition: $525 per hour. Part-time mandatory fees: $629 per year. Part-time tuition and fees vary according to class time and degree level.

Collegiate Environment: Orientation program. Drama-theater group, choral group, student-run newspaper, radio station. Social organizations: 60 open to all; 15% of eligible men and 20% of eligible women are members. Most popular organizations: social clubs, Sigma Pi Beta, Circle K, business fraternities, intramural program. Major annual events: homecoming, Singarama, Convocation. Student services: health clinic, personal-psychological counseling. Campus security: 24-hour emergency response devices and patrols, late night transport-escort service, controlled dormitory access. 1,408 college housing spaces available; 1,185 were occupied in 2003-04. Freshmen given priority for college housing. On-campus residence required through senior year. Options: men-only, women-only housing available. Beaman Library plus 1 other with 202,378 books, 39,539 microform titles, 900 serials, 726 audiovisual materials, an OPAC, and a Web page. Operations spending for 2004 fiscal year: $868,832. 245 computers available on campus for general student use. A campuswide network can be accessed from student residence rooms and from off campus. Staffed computer lab on campus.

Community Environment: Lipscomb University is a vital part of Nashville, the capital of Tennessee, and a regional and national center for education, business, and culture. Nashville is centrally located and easy to reach. Half the population of the United States is within 600 miles of its borders. There are 3 major interstates in addition to Nashville International Airport. Nashville abounds in history and culture. From antebellum mansions like the Hermitage, home of President Andrew Jackson, to Cheekwood Botanical Gardens, the Parthenon, and the Tennessee State Museum, Nashville offers abundant resources to strengthen and complement student education.

■ MARTIN METHODIST COLLEGE *F-10*

433 West Madison St.
Pulaski, TN 38478-2716
Tel: (931)363-9868
Free: 800-467-1273
Admissions: (931)363-9804
Fax: (931)363-9818
Web Site: http://www.martinmethodist.edu/

Description: Independent United Methodist, 4-year, coed. Awards bachelor's degrees. Founded 1870. Setting: 6-acre small town campus with easy access to Nashville. Endowment: $9.3 million. Educational spending for 2005 fiscal year: $4392 per student. Total enrollment: 714. 525 applied, 97% were admitted. 12% from top 10% of their high school class, 37% from top quarter, 75% from top half. 8 class presidents, 4 valedictorians, 40 student government officers. Full-time: 483 students, 58% women, 42% men. Part-time: 231 students, 75% women, 25% men. Students come from 27 states and territories, 2 other countries, 23% from out-of-state, 0.4% Native American, 1% Hispanic, 12% black, 0.4% Asian American or Pacific Islander, 10% international, 39% 25 or older, 26% live on campus, 11% transferred in. Retention: 29% of full-time freshmen returned the following year. Core. Calendar: semesters. Academic remediation for entering students, ESL program, services for LD students, advanced placement, honors program, independent study, double major, summer session for credit, part-time degree program, adult/continuing education programs, internships.

Entrance Requirements: Options: Peterson's Universal Application, Common Application, electronic application, early admission, deferred admission. Required: high school transcript, minimum 2.0 high school GPA, SAT or ACT. Recommended: essay, interview. Entrance: minimally difficult. Application deadline: 8/26. Notification: continuous.

Collegiate Environment: Orientation program. Drama-theater group, choral group. Social organizations: 8 open to all. Most popular organizations: Student Christian Association, Fellowship of Christian Athletes, Drama Club,

International Club, Students for Environment Awareness. Major annual events: Luau, Boo-Out, exam breakfasts. Campus security: controlled dormitory access. 402 college housing spaces available; 186 were occupied in 2003-04. Freshmen guaranteed college housing. On-campus residence required through sophomore year. Options: coed, men-only, women-only housing available. Warden Memorial Library with 84,000 books, 19,000 microform titles, 664 serials, 996 audiovisual materials, an OPAC, and a Web page. Operations spending for 2004 fiscal year: $211,044. 61 computers available on campus for general student use. A campuswide network can be accessed from student residence rooms and from off campus. Staffed computer lab on campus.

Community Environment: Located in south-central Tennessee where the climate is mild, Pulaski, between Nashville, Tennessee, and Huntsville, Alabama, is a small, friendly town with much civic pride.

■ MARYVILLE COLLEGE *K-2*

502 East Lamar Alexander Parkway
Maryville, TN 37804-5907
Tel: (865)981-8000
Free: 800-597-2687
Admissions: (865)981-8206
Fax: (865)983-0581
E-mail: admissions@maryvillecollege.edu
Web Site: http://www.maryvillecollege.edu/

Description: Independent Presbyterian, 4-year, coed. Awards bachelor's degrees. Founded 1819. Setting: 350-acre suburban campus with easy access to Knoxville. Endowment: $28.3 million. Educational spending for 2005 fiscal year: $5817 per student. Total enrollment: 1,146. Student-undergrad faculty ratio is 14:1. 1,496 applied, 79% were admitted. 27% from top 10% of their high school class, 57% from top quarter, 84% from top half. 9 valedictorians. Full-time: 1,120 students, 54% women, 46% men. Part-time: 26 students, 38% women, 62% men. Students come from 29 states and territories, 19 other countries, 22% from out-of-state, 0.4% Native American, 1% Hispanic, 6% black, 1% Asian American or Pacific Islander, 4% international, 6% 25 or older, 70% live on campus, 5% transferred in. Retention: 72% of full-time freshmen returned the following year. Academic areas with the most degrees conferred: business/marketing; education; psychology. Core. Calendar: 4-1-4. ESL program, services for LD students, advanced placement, self-designed majors, honors program, independent study, double major, summer session for credit, part-time degree program, adult/continuing education programs, internships. Off campus study at Argonne National Laboratory, Oak Ridge National Laboratories, Woods Hole Oceanographic Institute. Study abroad program.

Entrance Requirements: Options: Peterson's Universal Application, Common Application, electronic application, early admission, early decision, early action, deferred admission, international baccalaureate accepted. Required: high school transcript, minimum 2.5 high school GPA, SAT or ACT. Recommended: minimum 3.0 high school GPA. Required for some: essay, recommendations, interview. Entrance: moderately difficult. Application deadlines: 3/1, 11/15 for early decision, 9/15 for early action. Notification: 4/1, 12/1 for early decision, 10/1 for early action.

Costs Per Year: Application fee: $25. Comprehensive fee: $29,224 includes full-time tuition ($21,624), mandatory fees ($600), and college room and board ($7000). College room only: $3500. Full-time tuition and fees vary according to course load. Room and board charges vary according to board plan, housing facility, and location. Part-time tuition: $901 per hour. Part-time mandatory fees: $13.50 per hour. Part-time tuition and fees vary according to course load.

Collegiate Environment: Orientation program. Drama-theater group, choral group, student-run newspaper, radio station. Social organizations: 47 open to all. Most popular organizations: Voices of Praise, student government, Student Programming Board, Equestrian Club, peer mentors. Major annual events: Homecoming, Blister in the Sun, Spring Fling. Student services: health clinic, personal-psychological counseling. Campus security: 24-hour emergency response devices and patrols, late night transport-escort service, controlled dormitory access. 777 college housing spaces available; 742 were occupied in 2003-04. Freshmen guaranteed college housing. On-campus residence required through senior year. Options: coed, men-only, women-only housing available. Lamar Memorial Library plus 1 other with 128,022 books, 7,507 microform titles, 16,000 serials, 24,566 audiovisual materials, an OPAC, and a Web page. Operations spending for 2004 fiscal year: $577,875. 96 computers available on campus for general student use. A campuswide network can be accessed from student residence rooms and from off campus. Staffed computer lab on campus.

Community Environment: Maryville was founded in 1819 and named for Mary Blount, wife of Governor William Blount. The town is located near the entrance of the Great Smoky Mountains National Park. Bus and air transportation is available. Fishing, boating, water skiing, golfing, and hiking are favorite sports in the county. Maryville is a suburban community located 15 miles from Knoxville in a metropolitan area of half a million.

■ MEDVANCE INSTITUTE *C-14*

1065 East 10th St.
Cookeville, TN 38501-1907
Tel: (931)526-3660
Free: 800-256-9085
Fax: (931)372-2603
Web Site: http://www.medvance.org/

Description: Proprietary, 2-year, coed. Awards certificates, diplomas, and terminal associate degrees. Founded 1970. Setting: 4-acre small town campus. Total enrollment: 231. Students come from 4 states and territories, 10% from out-of-state, 0% Native American, 0% Hispanic, 0% black, 0% Asian American or Pacific Islander, 0% international, 46% 25 or older. Core. Internships.

Entrance Requirements: Option: Common Application. Required: high school transcript, interview, Wonderlic aptitude test. Recommended: minimum 2.0 high school GPA, 2 recommendations. Entrance: noncompetitive. Application deadline: Rolling. Notification: continuous.

Collegiate Environment: Orientation program. Major annual events: National Medical Laboratory Technician Week, National Secretaries Week, Founder's Day Picnic. College housing not available. 40 computers available on campus for general student use. Staffed computer lab on campus.

■ MEMPHIS COLLEGE OF ART *F-1*

Overton Park, 1930 Poplar Ave.
Memphis, TN 38104-2764
Tel: (901)272-5100
Free: 800-727-1088
Admissions: (901)272-5153
Fax: (901)272-5104
E-mail: amoore@mca.edu
Web Site: http://www.mca.edu/

Description: Independent, comprehensive, coed. Awards bachelor's and master's degrees. Founded 1936. Setting: 200-acre urban campus. Endowment: $5.1 million. Educational spending for 2005 fiscal year: $5868 per student. Total enrollment: 326. Faculty: 45 (21 full-time, 24 part-time). Student-undergrad faculty ratio is 11:1. 614 applied, 51% were admitted. Full-time: 270 students, 52% women, 48% men. Part-time: 44 students, 36% women, 64% men. Students come from 26 states and territories, 5 other countries, 47% from out-of-state, 0.3% Native American, 4% Hispanic, 15% black, 2% Asian American or Pacific Islander, 2% international, 17% 25 or older, 37% live on campus, 14% transferred in. Retention: 70% of full-time freshmen returned the following year. Academic area with the most degrees conferred: visual and performing arts. Core. Calendar: semesters. Academic remediation for entering students, advanced placement, independent study, double major, summer session for credit, part-time degree program, adult/continuing education programs, internships, graduate courses open to undergrads. Off campus study at Greater Memphis Consortium, Association of Independent Colleges of Art and Design.

Entrance Requirements: Options: Peterson's Universal Application, Common Application, electronic application, early admission, deferred admission, international baccalaureate accepted. Required: high school transcript, SAT or ACT. Recommended: essay, interview. Required for some: portfolio. Entrance: moderately difficult. Application deadline: Rolling. Notification: continuous.

Costs Per Year: Application fee: $25. Tuition: $17,400 full-time, $2225 per course part-time. Mandatory fees: $60 full-time.

Collegiate Environment: Orientation program. Student-run newspaper. Most popular organization: student government. Major annual events: Holiday Bazaar, Horn Island Show Opening, Student Day. Student services: personal-psychological counseling. Campus security: late night transport-escort service, late night security patrols by trained personnel. 108 college housing spaces available; all were occupied in 2003-04. Freshmen guaranteed college housing. On-campus residence required in freshman year. Option: coed housing available. G. Pillow Lewis Library plus 1 other with 14,500 books and 102 serials. Operations spending for 2004 fiscal year: $98,631. 70 computers available on campus for general student use. Computer purchase/lease plans available. Staffed computer lab on campus.

Community Environment: Memphis is a friendly city. It's large enough to support a cultural life of high quality, but small enough not to overwhelm. The cost of living is low. The school is located in midtown, near the Mississippi River.

■ MID-AMERICA BAPTIST THEOLOGICAL SEMINARY *G-2*
PO Box 381528
Germantown, TN 38183-1528
Tel: (901)751-8453
Web Site: http://www.mabts.edu/

Description: Independent Southern Baptist, 2-year, coed. Awards terminal associate, master's, doctoral, and first professional degrees. Founded 1972. Setting: suburban campus with easy access to Memphis. Endowment: $3.6 million. Educational spending for 2005 fiscal year: $3500 per student. Total enrollment: 417. Faculty: 27 (all full-time). Student-undergrad faculty ratio is 15:1. Full-time: 37 students, 100% men. Part-time: 25 students, 100% men. Students come from 26 states and territories, 0% Native American, 0% Hispanic, 5% black, 0% Asian American or Pacific Islander. Core. Calendar: semesters. Summer session for credit, graduate courses open to undergrads.

Entrance Requirements: Open admission. Option: Common Application. Required: 2 recommendations. Required for some: high school transcript. Entrance: noncompetitive. Application deadline: 8/4.

Costs Per Year: Application fee: $25. Tuition: $3600 full-time.

Collegiate Environment: Campus security: 24-hour emergency response devices. Ora Byram Allison Memorial Library with 119,000 books, 931 serials, an OPAC, and a Web page. Operations spending for 2004 fiscal year: $217,748. 10 computers available on campus for general student use. Staffed computer lab on campus.

■ MIDDLE TENNESSEE STATE UNIVERSITY *D-11*
1301 East Main St.
Murfreesboro, TN 37132
Tel: (615)898-2300
Free: 800-433-MTSU
Admissions: (615)898-2111
E-mail: admissions@mtsu.edu
Web Site: http://www.mtsu.edu/

Description: State-supported, university, coed. Part of Tennessee Board of Regents. Awards bachelor's, master's, and doctoral degrees and post-master's certificates. Founded 1911. Setting: 500-acre urban campus with easy access to Nashville. Endowment: $23.8 million. Research spending for 2004 fiscal year: $3.6 million. Educational spending for 2005 fiscal year: $4856 per student. Total enrollment: 22,554. Faculty: (881 full-time). Student-undergrad faculty ratio is 22:1. 6,392 applied, 85% were admitted. 13% from top 10% of their high school class, 33% from top quarter, 59% from top half. 2 National Merit Scholars, 31 valedictorians. Full-time: 17,291 students, 52% women, 48% men. Part-time: 3,098 students, 55% women, 45% men. Students come from 47 states and territories, 0.4% Native American, 2% Hispanic, 12% black, 3% Asian American or Pacific Islander, 21% 25 or older, 20% live on campus, 10% transferred in. Academic areas with the most degrees conferred: business/marketing; visual and performing arts; communications/journalism. Core. Calendar: semesters. Academic remediation for entering students, ESL program, services for LD students, advanced placement, accelerated degree program, self-designed majors, freshman honors college, honors program, independent study, distance learning, double major, summer session for credit, part-time degree program, adult/continuing education programs, co-op programs and internships, graduate courses open to undergrads. Off campus study at Tennessee State University. Study abroad program. ROTC: Army, Air Force (c).

Entrance Requirements: Options: electronic application, early admission, deferred admission, international baccalaureate accepted. Required: high school transcript, minimum 3.0 high school GPA, SAT or ACT. Required for some: essay. Entrance: moderately difficult. Application deadline: 7/1. Notification: continuous.

Costs Per Year: Application fee: $25. State resident tuition: $3678 full-time, $161 per semester hour part-time. Nonresident tuition: $12,990 full-time, $565 per semester hour part-time. Mandatory fees: $922 full-time. Part-time tuition varies according to course load. College room and board: $5626. College room only: $3478. Room and board charges vary according to board plan and housing facility.

Collegiate Environment: Orientation program. Drama-theater group, choral group, marching band, student-run newspaper, radio station. Social organizations: 153 open to all; national fraternities, national sororities, local

sororities; 7% of eligible men and 8% of eligible women are members. Most popular organizations: African-American Student Association, Student Tennessee Education Association, Gamma Beta Phi, Golden Key National Honor Society. Major annual events: Homecoming, Welcome Week, African-American History Month activities. Student services: legal services, health clinic, personal-psychological counseling, women's center. Campus security: 24-hour emergency response devices and patrols, student patrols, late night transport-escort service, controlled dormitory access. 3,210 college housing spaces available; 3,108 were occupied in 2003-04. No special consideration for freshman housing applicants. Options: men-only, women-only housing available. James E. Walker Library with 748,888 books, 1.3 million microform titles, 4,144 serials, an OPAC, and a Web page. Operations spending for 2004 fiscal year: $7.6 million. 2,300 computers available on campus for general student use. A campuswide network can be accessed from student residence rooms and from off campus. Staffed computer lab on campus.

Community Environment: Murfreesboro is a small city of about 60,000 that is 32 miles southeast of the state capital, Nashville. Capital of the state from 1819 to 1825, Murfreesboro is a city proud of its history, but one that is changing with the times. Community and area facilities include historical landmarks such as Stones River Battlefield and Old Fort Park. Facilities range from an amphitheater to tennis courts, growing industries, charming old homes, new apartment complexes, churches, numerous recreational areas including many for water sports, the Veteran's Hospital. Because of its geographic location in the center of the state, MTSU is easily accessible from any direction.

■ MILLER-MOTTE TECHNICAL COLLEGE *B-9*
1820 Business Park Dr.
Clarksville, TN 37040
Tel: (931)553-0071
Admissions: 800-558-0071
Fax: (931)552-2916
E-mail: lisateague@hotmail.com
Web Site: http://www.miller-motte.com/

Description: Proprietary, 2-year, coed. Founded 1916.

■ MILLIGAN COLLEGE
PO Box 500
Milligan College, TN 37682
Tel: (423)461-8700
Admissions: (423)461-8730
Fax: (423)461-8960
E-mail: admissions@milligan.edu
Web Site: http://www.milligan.edu/

Description: Independent Christian, comprehensive, coed. Awards bachelor's and master's degrees. Founded 1866. Setting: 145-acre suburban campus. Endowment: $8.5 million. Educational spending for 2005 fiscal year: $5539 per student. Total enrollment: 954. Faculty: 108 (69 full-time, 39 part-time). Student-undergrad faculty ratio is 11:1. 686 applied, 78% were admitted. Full-time: 730 students, 61% women, 39% men. Part-time: 23 students, 74% women, 26% men. Students come from 33 states and territories, 10 other countries, 55% from out-of-state, 1% Native American, 1% Hispanic, 1% black, 1% Asian American or Pacific Islander, 2% international, 12% 25 or older, 78% live on campus, 6% transferred in. Retention: 73% of full-time freshmen returned the following year. Academic areas with the most degrees conferred: business/marketing; communications/journalism; psychology. Core. Calendar: semesters. Academic remediation for entering students, advanced placement, independent study, double major, summer session for credit, part-time degree program, adult/continuing education programs, co-op programs and internships, graduate courses open to undergrads. Off campus study at East Tennessee State University. Study abroad program. ROTC: Army (c).

Entrance Requirements: Options: Peterson's Universal Application, electronic application, deferred admission, international baccalaureate accepted. Required: essay, high school transcript, minimum 2.0 high school GPA, 2 recommendations, SAT or ACT. Recommended: minimum 3.0 high school GPA. Required for some: interview. Entrance: moderately difficult. Application deadline: 8/1. Notification: continuous.

Costs Per Year: Application fee: $30. Comprehensive fee: $21,990 includes full-time tuition ($16,730), mandatory fees ($510), and college room and board ($4750). College room only: $2350. Room and board charges vary according to board plan and housing facility. Part-time tuition: $290 per credit. Part-time tuition varies according to course load.

Collegiate Environment: Orientation program. Drama-theater group, choral group, student-run newspaper, radio station. Social organizations: 31 open to all. Most popular organizations: Social Affairs Committee, Buffalo Ramblers, Concert Council, Volunteer Milligan, Students for Life. Major annual events: Wonderful Wednesday, Spirit Week, SUB7 Coffeehouse. Student services: health clinic, personal-psychological counseling. Campus security: 24-hour patrols, late night transport-escort service. 636 college housing spaces available; 588 were occupied in 2003-04. Freshmen guaranteed college housing. On-campus residence required through senior year. Options: men-only, women-only housing available. P. H. Welshimer Memorial Library with 147,491 books, 493,520 microform titles, 11,946 serials, 4,057 audiovisual materials, an OPAC, and a Web page. Operations spending for 2004 fiscal year: $381,062. 122 computers available on campus for general student use. Computer purchase/lease plans available. A campuswide network can be accessed from student residence rooms and from off campus. Staffed computer lab on campus.

■ **MOTLOW STATE COMMUNITY COLLEGE** *F-12*
PO Box 8500
Lynchburg, TN 37352-8500
Tel: (931)393-1500
Fax: (931)393-1681
E-mail: galsup@mscc.edu
Web Site: http://www.mscc.cc.tn.us/
Description: State-supported, 2-year, coed. Part of Tennessee Board of Regents. Awards certificates, transfer associate, and terminal associate degrees. Founded 1969. Setting: 187-acre small town campus with easy access to Nashville. Endowment: $3.2 million. Educational spending for 2005 fiscal year: $1879 per student. Total enrollment: 3,407. Student-undergrad faculty ratio is 16:1. 1,239 applied. 5% from top 10% of their high school class, 18% from top quarter, 48% from top half. Full-time: 2,015 students, 62% women, 38% men. Part-time: 1,392 students, 67% women, 33% men. Students come from 11 states and territories, 8 other countries, 1% from out-of-state, 0.3% Native American, 2% Hispanic, 8% black, 1% Asian American or Pacific Islander, 0.4% international, 31% 25 or older, 7% transferred in. Retention: 0% of full-time freshmen returned the following year. Core. Calendar: semesters. Academic remediation for entering students, services for LD students, advanced placement, honors program, independent study, distance learning, double major, summer session for credit, part-time degree program, adult/continuing education programs, co-op programs.
Entrance Requirements: Open admission except for nursing program. Options: electronic application, early admission, deferred admission. Required: high school transcript. Entrance: noncompetitive. Application deadlines: 8/13, 8/13 for nonresidents. Notification: continuous.
Costs Per Year: Application fee: $10. State resident tuition: $2142 full-time, $91 per credit part-time. Nonresident tuition: $6414 full-time, $278 per credit part-time. Mandatory fees: $247 full-time, $40 per credit part-time. Full-time tuition and fees vary according to program. Part-time tuition and fees vary according to course load and program.
Collegiate Environment: Orientation program. Drama-theater group, choral group, student-run newspaper. Social organizations: 9 open to all. Most popular organizations: Photography Club, Psychology Club, Student Government Association, Outing Club, Baptist Student Union. Major annual events: Buck Barbecue, a play for children, basketball homecoming. Student services: health clinic, personal-psychological counseling. Campus security: 24-hour patrols, late night transport-escort service. College housing not available. Crouch Library with 54,968 books, 9,502 microform titles, 211 serials, 4,464 audiovisual materials, an OPAC, and a Web page. Operations spending for 2004 fiscal year: $645,755. 600 computers available on campus for general student use. A campuswide network can be accessed from off-campus. Staffed computer lab on campus.
Community Environment: Tullahoma is located in the southwest corner of Coffee County, not far from Shelbyville. See University of Tennessee - Space Institute.

■ **NASHVILLE AUTO DIESEL COLLEGE** *C-10*
1524 Gallatin Rd.
Nashville, TN 37206-3298
Tel: (615)226-3990
Free: 800-228-NADC
Fax: (615)262-8488
Web Site: http://www.nadcedu.com/

Description: Proprietary, 2-year, coed. Awards diplomas and terminal associate degrees. Founded 1919. Setting: 13-acre urban campus. Total enrollment: 1,306. Student-undergrad faculty ratio is 30:1. 2,924 applied, 89% were admitted. Full-time: 1,306 students, 0.4% women, 99% men. Students come from 50 states and territories, 83% from out-of-state, 1% Native American, 1% Hispanic, 30% black, 1% Asian American or Pacific Islander, 0% international, 5% 25 or older, 21% live on campus. Calendar: continuous. Advanced placement, honors program, co-op programs.
Entrance Requirements: Option: deferred admission. Required: high school transcript. Recommended: SAT or ACT. Required for some: interview. Entrance: minimally difficult. Application deadline: Rolling.
Costs Per Year: Application fee: $100. Tuition: $20,500 full-time. Mandatory fees: $100 full-time.
Collegiate Environment: Orientation program. Campus security: 24-hour emergency response devices and patrols. 703 college housing spaces available; 314 were occupied in 2003-04. Option: men-only housing available. NADC Library with 1,309 books and 69 serials. 40 computers available on campus for general student use. A campuswide network can be accessed. Staffed computer lab on campus.

■ **NASHVILLE STATE TECHNICAL COMMUNITY COLLEGE** *C-10*
120 White Bridge Rd.
Nashville, TN 37209-4515
Tel: (615)353-3333
Free: 800-272-7363
Admissions: (615)353-3217
Fax: (615)353-3243
Web Site: http://www.nscc.edu/
Description: State-supported, 2-year, coed. Part of Tennessee Board of Regents. Awards certificates, transfer associate, and terminal associate degrees. Founded 1970. Setting: 85-acre urban campus. Educational spending for 2005 fiscal year: $3020 per student. Total enrollment: 7,021. Full-time: 2,421 students, 54% women, 46% men. Part-time: 4,600 students, 60% women, 40% men. Students come from 36 states and territories, 55 other countries, 2% from out-of-state, 0.4% Native American, 2% Hispanic, 26% black, 4% Asian American or Pacific Islander, 3% international, 55% 25 or older, 3% transferred in. Core. Calendar: semesters. Academic remediation for entering students, ESL program, services for LD students, advanced placement, distance learning, summer session for credit, part-time degree program, adult/continuing education programs, co-op programs. Off campus study.
Entrance Requirements: Open admission except for occupational therapy, automotive services technology, surgical technology programs. Options: electronic application, deferred admission. Required: high school transcript. Placement: SAT or ACT required for some. Entrance: noncompetitive. Application deadline: Rolling. Notification: continuous. Preference given to state residents.
Costs Per Year: Application fee: $5. State resident tuition: $2367 full-time, $91 per credit hour part-time. Nonresident tuition: $8781 full-time, $369 per credit hour part-time. Mandatory fees: $235 full-time, $10 per credit hour part-time, $5 per term part-time. Part-time tuition and fees vary according to course load.
Collegiate Environment: Orientation program. Student-run newspaper. Social organizations: 7 open to all. Most popular organizations: Data Processing Management Association, Occupational Therapy Club, Phi Theta Kappa, Student Government Association, Black Student Association. Major annual events: Fall Festival, Spring Fling, Diversity Day. Student services: personal-psychological counseling. Campus security: 24-hour emergency response devices and patrols, late night transport-escort service. College housing not available. Jane G. Kisber Memorial Library with 38,502 books, 275 serials, an OPAC, and a Web page. Operations spending for 2004 fiscal year: $405,872. 518 computers available on campus for general student use. A campuswide network can be accessed from off-campus.
Community Environment: See Vanderbilt University.

■ **NATIONAL COLLEGE OF BUSINESS & TECHNOLOGY (BRISTOL)** *H-7*
1328 Hwy. 11 West
Bristol, TN 37620
Tel: (423)878-4440
E-mail: adm@educorp.edu
Web Site: http://www.ncbt.edu/
Description: Proprietary, 2-year, coed. Part of National College of Business and Technology. Awards diplomas and terminal associate degrees. Founded

1992. Setting: small town campus. Total enrollment: 319. Core. Services for LD students, advanced placement, honors program, double major, summer session for credit, part-time degree program, internships.

Entrance Requirements: Open admission. Option: electronic application. Required: high school transcript. Recommended: interview. Entrance: noncompetitive. Application deadline: Rolling.

Costs Per Year: Application fee: $30. Tuition: $6408 full-time, $178 per credit hour part-time. Mandatory fees: $75 full-time, $15 per term part-time.

Collegiate Environment: Orientation program. College housing not available. 35 computers available on campus for general student use. A campuswide network can be accessed. Staffed computer lab on campus.

■ **NATIONAL COLLEGE OF BUSINESS & TECHNOLOGY (KNOXVILLE)** *J-2*
8415 Kingston Pike
Knoxville, TN 37919
Tel: (865)539-2011
Free: 800-664-1886
Fax: (865)539-2049
E-mail: awills@ncbt.edu
Web Site: http://www.ncbt.edu/

Description: Proprietary, 2-year, coed. Part of National College of Business and Technology. Awards diplomas and terminal associate degrees. Founded 2003. Setting: 2-acre suburban campus. Total enrollment: 209.

Collegiate Environment: 55 computers available on campus for general student use. Staffed computer lab on campus.

■ **NATIONAL COLLEGE OF BUSINESS & TECHNOLOGY (NASHVILLE)** *C-10*
Ste. 200, 5042 Linbar Dr.
Nashville, TN 37211
Tel: (615)333-3344
Free: 800-664-1886
Web Site: http://www.ncbt.edu/

Description: Proprietary, 2-year, coed. Part of National College of Business and Technology. Awards diplomas and terminal associate degrees. Founded 1915. Setting: 1-acre urban campus. Total enrollment: 466. Core. Services for LD students, honors program, double major, summer session for credit, part-time degree program.

Entrance Requirements: Open admission. Option: electronic application. Recommended: interview. Entrance: noncompetitive. Application deadline: Rolling. Notification: continuous.

Costs Per Year: Application fee: $30. Tuition: $6408 full-time, $178 per credit hour part-time. Mandatory fees: $75 full-time, $15 per term part-time.

Collegiate Environment: Orientation program. College housing not available. 35 computers available on campus for general student use. Staffed computer lab on campus.

■ **NORTH CENTRAL INSTITUTE** *B-9*
168 Jack Miller Blvd.
Clarksville, TN 37042
Tel: (931)431-9700
Fax: (931)431-9771
E-mail: admissions@nci.edu
Web Site: http://www.nci.edu/

Description: Proprietary, 2-year, coed. Awards terminal associate degrees. Founded 1988. Setting: 14-acre suburban campus. Educational spending for 2005 fiscal year: $7400 per student. Total enrollment: 130. Student-undergrad faculty ratio is 8:1. 25 applied, 100% were admitted. 6% from top 10% of their high school class, 20% from top quarter, 74% from top half. 1 class president, 1 valedictorian. Full-time: 52 students, 2% women, 98% men. Part-time: 78 students, 17% women, 83% men. Students come from 50 states and territories, 90% from out-of-state, 7% Native American, 10% Hispanic, 24% black, 3% Asian American or Pacific Islander, 0% international, 50% 25 or older. Core. Calendar: continuous. Advanced placement, independent study, summer session for credit, part-time degree program, external degree program.

Entrance Requirements: Open admission. Options: Common Application, electronic application, early admission. Required: proof of high school. Recommended: high school transcript. Entrance: noncompetitive. Application deadline: Rolling. Notification: continuous.

Costs Per Year: Application fee: $35. Tuition: $14,800 full-time, $60 per semester hour part-time. Mandatory fees: $800 full-time.

Collegiate Environment: Social organizations: national fraternities; 12% of men are members. Most popular organization: Alpha Eta Rho (aviation fraternity). Major annual event: Career Day Open House. Campus security: 24-hour emergency response devices. College housing not available. Media Resource Center plus 1 other with 200 books, 12 serials, and 20 audiovisual materials. Operations spending for 2004 fiscal year: $1040.

■ **NORTHEAST STATE TECHNICAL COMMUNITY COLLEGE** *H-6*
PO Box 246
Blountville, TN 37617-0246
Tel: (423)323-3191
Admissions: (423)354-2589
Fax: (423)323-0215
E-mail: phsweeney@northeaststate.edu
Web Site: http://www.northeaststate.edu/

Description: State-supported, 2-year, coed. Part of Tennessee Board of Regents. Awards certificates, transfer associate, and terminal associate degrees. Founded 1966. Setting: 100-acre small town campus. Endowment: $3.5 million. Educational spending for 2005 fiscal year: $3211 per student. Total enrollment: 4,860. Student-undergrad faculty ratio is 22:1. 2,878 applied, 100% were admitted. 10% from top 10% of their high school class, 20% from top quarter, 40% from top half. Full-time: 2,610 students, 55% women, 45% men. Part-time: 2,250 students, 51% women, 49% men. Students come from 3 states and territories, 3% from out-of-state, 0.4% Native American, 1% Hispanic, 3% black, 1% Asian American or Pacific Islander, 0% international, 47% 25 or older, 5% transferred in. Retention: 58% of full-time freshmen returned the following year. Core. Calendar: semesters. Academic remediation for entering students, services for LD students, advanced placement, honors program, distance learning, double major, summer session for credit, part-time degree program, co-op programs.

Entrance Requirements: Open admission. Option: electronic application. Required: high school transcript, minimum 2.0 high school GPA. Entrance: noncompetitive. Application deadline: Rolling. Notification: continuous. Preference given to state residents.

Costs Per Year: Application fee: $10. State resident tuition: $2404 full-time, $91 per hour part-time. Nonresident tuition: $6414 full-time, $278 per hour part-time. Mandatory fees: $262 full-time, $12 per hour part-time, $18 per term part-time.

Collegiate Environment: Orientation program. Drama-theater group, student-run radio station. Social organizations: 23 open to all. Most popular organizations: Phi Theta Kappa, Student Government Association, Student Tennessee Education Association, Students in Free Enterprise, Student Ambassadors. Major annual events: Spring Fling, Club Fair, Fall Finale. Student services: health clinic, personal-psychological counseling. Campus security: 24-hour patrols, late night transport-escort service. College housing not available. Wayne G. Basler Library plus 1 other with 44,997 books, 54,217 microform titles, 438 serials, 8,591 audiovisual materials, an OPAC, and a Web page. Operations spending for 2004 fiscal year: $657,380. 910 computers available on campus for general student use. A campuswide network can be accessed from off-campus. Staffed computer lab on campus.

Community Environment: Blountville is located in the center of the Tri-Cities triangle of Bristol-Kingsport-Johnson City, approximately 15 miles from each city. Chemical, defense, manufacturing, and banking industries are numerous. The medical industry is a growing part of the economy. The Northeast Tennessee area is bordered by Virginia and North Carolina and is less than a day's drive to both East Coast recreation areas and large metropolitan areas such as Atlanta, GA, and Washington, DC. A system of TVA lakes offer warm weather recreation and snow skiing is a short drive away in the winter. Part-time employment is available.

■ **NOSSI COLLEGE OF ART** *B-11*
907 Two Mile Parkway, Ste. E-6
Goodlettsville, TN 37072-2319
Tel: (615)851-1088
Fax: (615)851-1087
E-mail: cyrus@nossi.com
Web Site: http://www.nossi.com/

Description: Independent, 2-year, coed. Awards terminal associate degrees. Total enrollment: 250. 70% 25 or older. Calendar: semesters.

Entrance Requirements: Required: portfolio.

■ **O'MORE COLLEGE OF DESIGN** *D-10*
423 South Margin St.
Franklin, TN 37064-2816

Tel: (615)794-4254
Fax: (615)790-1662
Web Site: http://www.omorecollege.edu/
Description: Independent, 4-year, coed. Awards bachelor's degrees. Founded 1970. Setting: 6-acre small town campus with easy access to Nashville. Total enrollment: 127. 90 applied, 72% were admitted. Full-time: 90 students, 84% women, 16% men. Part-time: 37 students, 86% women, 14% men. Students come from 18 states and territories, 5 other countries, 0% from out-of-state, 40% 25 or older, 27% transferred in. Retention: 85% of full-time freshmen returned the following year. Core. Calendar: semesters. Academic remediation for entering students, advanced placement, independent study, double major, summer session for credit, part-time degree program, adult/continuing education programs, co-op programs and internships.
Entrance Requirements: Options: Peterson's Universal Application, deferred admission. Required: high school transcript, minimum 2.1 high school GPA, SAT or ACT. Required for some: essay, interview, portfolio. Entrance: moderately difficult. Application deadline: 8/1. Notification: continuous until 8/1.
Collegiate Environment: Orientation program. Campus security: 24-hour emergency response devices. College housing not available. Fleming-Farrar Hall with 4,000 books and 60 serials. 20 computers available on campus for general student use. Staffed computer lab on campus.

■ **PELLISSIPPI STATE TECHNICAL COMMUNITY COLLEGE** *J-2*
PO Box 22990
Knoxville, TN 37933-0990
Tel: (865)694-6400
Admissions: (865)539-7013
E-mail: latouzeau@pstcc.cc.tn.us
Web Site: http://www.pstcc.edu/
Description: State-supported, 2-year, coed. Part of Tennessee Board of Regents. Awards certificates, transfer associate, and terminal associate degrees. Founded 1974. Setting: 144-acre suburban campus. Endowment: $2.8 million. Educational spending for 2005 fiscal year: $2978 per student. Total enrollment: 7,686. Student-undergrad faculty ratio is 21:1. Full-time: 3,882 students, 51% women, 49% men. Part-time: 3,804 students, 57% women, 43% men. Students come from 23 states and territories, 1% Native American, 2% Hispanic, 7% black, 2% Asian American or Pacific Islander, 1% international, 40% 25 or older. Core. Calendar: semesters. Academic remediation for entering students, ESL program, services for LD students, advanced placement, self-designed majors, freshman honors college, honors program, distance learning, double major, summer session for credit, part-time degree program, adult/continuing education programs, co-op programs and internships.
Entrance Requirements: Open admission. Options: Common Application, electronic application, early admission, deferred admission. Required: high school transcript. Entrance: noncompetitive. Application deadline: Rolling. Notification: continuous.
Costs Per Year: Application fee: $5. Area resident tuition: $100 per credit hour part-time. State resident tuition: $1227 full-time. Nonresident tuition: $4563 full-time, $397 per credit hour part-time. Mandatory fees: $2500 full-time.
Collegiate Environment: Orientation program. Drama-theater group, choral group, student-run newspaper. Social organizations: 27 open to all. Most popular organizations: Student Government Association, Active Black Students Association, Phi Theta Kappa, Baptist Student Union, Vision. Major annual events: Spring Fling, Octoberfest, Breakfast With Santa. Student services: personal-psychological counseling. Campus security: 24-hour patrols. College housing not available. Educational Resources Center plus 1 other with 43,000 books, 527 serials, an OPAC, and a Web page. Operations spending for 2004 fiscal year: $745,407. 1,200 computers available on campus for general student use. A campuswide network can be accessed from off-campus. Staffed computer lab on campus.
Community Environment: Located in Tennessee's third largest metropolitan area, Pellissippi State comprehensively serves the greater Knox and Blount County area and extends its engineering technology offerings to Anderson, Loudon, Roane, Cumberland, Campbell, Fentress, Scott, and Morgan Counties. The main campus is located west of Knoxville in Knox County. The city of Knoxville lies on the Tennessee River, about 40 miles from the Great Smoky Mountains National Park. Knoxville's population approaches 170,000, with approximately 640,000 in the metropolitan area. The city supports a wide variety of cultural and sports activities. The city is a business center in the East Tennessee Valley with markets in tobacco,

livestock, marble, and zinc. It is home to the state's flagship higher education institution: the University of Tennessee. The headquarters of the Tennessee Valley Authority are also located in the city.

■ **REMINGTON COLLEGE-MEMPHIS CAMPUS** *F-1*
2731 Nonconnah Blvd.
Memphis, TN 38132-2131
Tel: (901)291-4200
Admissions: (901)291-4225
Fax: (901)396-8310
E-mail: lori.may@remingtoncollege.edu
Web Site: http://www.remingtoncollege.edu/
Description: Proprietary, primarily 2-year. Awards transfer associate and bachelor's degrees. Total enrollment: 600. 700 applied, 71% were admitted. 1% Native American, 5% Hispanic, 66% black, 2% Asian American or Pacific Islander, 1% international, 35% 25 or older.

■ **REMINGTON COLLEGE-NASHVILLE CAMPUS** *C-10*
441 Donnelson Pike, Ste. 150
Nashville, TN 37214
Tel: (615)889-5520
Fax: (615)889-5528
E-mail: frank.vivelo@remingtoncollege.edu
Web Site: http://www.remingtoncollege.edu/
Description: Proprietary, 2-year, coed. Founded 2003.

■ **RHODES COLLEGE** *F-1*
2000 North Parkway
Memphis, TN 38112-1690
Tel: (901)843-3000
Free: 800-844-5969
Admissions: (901)843-3700
Fax: (901)843-3719
E-mail: adminfo@rhodes.edu
Web Site: http://www.rhodes.edu/
Description: Independent Presbyterian, comprehensive, coed. Awards bachelor's and master's degrees (master's degree in accounting only). Founded 1848. Setting: 100-acre suburban campus. Endowment: $222.9 million. Research spending for 2004 fiscal year: $586,000. Educational spending for 2005 fiscal year: $12,520 per student. Total enrollment: 1,692. Faculty: 184 (141 full-time, 43 part-time). Student-undergrad faculty ratio is 9:1. 3,695 applied, 49% were admitted. 50% from top 10% of their high school class, 79% from top quarter, 96% from top half. 6 National Merit Scholars, 11 class presidents, 21 valedictorians, 25 student government officers. Full-time: 1,641 students, 58% women, 42% men. Part-time: 36 students, 36% women, 64% men. Students come from 44 states and territories, 11 other countries, 73% from out-of-state, 0.4% Native American, 1% Hispanic, 5% black, 3% Asian American or Pacific Islander, 0.2% international, 0.1% 25 or older, 76% live on campus, 1% transferred in. Retention: 88% of full-time freshmen returned the following year. Core. Calendar: semesters. Services for LD students, advanced placement, self-designed majors, honors program, independent study, double major, part-time degree program, internships, graduate courses open to undergrads. Off campus study at Memphis College of Art, Gulf Coast Research Laboratory, Oak Ridge National Laboratory, University of the South, American University. Study abroad program. ROTC: Army (c), Air Force (c).
Entrance Requirements: Options: Peterson's Universal Application, Common Application, electronic application, early admission, early decision, deferred admission, international baccalaureate accepted. Required: essay, high school transcript, 2 recommendations, SAT or ACT. Recommended: interview. Entrance: very difficult. Application deadlines: Rolling, 11/1 for early decision plan 1, 1/1 for early decision plan 2. Notification: 4/1, 12/1 for early decision plan 1, 2/1 for early decision plan 2.
Costs Per Year: Application fee: $45. Comprehensive fee: $34,760 includes full-time tuition ($27,546), mandatory fees ($310), and college room and board ($6904). Full-time tuition and fees vary according to student level. Room and board charges vary according to board plan. Part-time tuition: $1000 per credit hour.
Collegiate Environment: Orientation program. Drama-theater group, choral group, student-run newspaper. Social organizations: 44 open to all; national fraternities, national sororities; 48% of eligible men and 53% of eligible women are members. Most popular organizations: Kinney Volunteer Program, Habitat for Humanity, Adopt A Friend, Foster. Major annual events: homecoming, Rites of Spring, Winter Formal. Student services: health clinic,

personal-psychological counseling. Campus security: 24-hour emergency response devices and patrols, student patrols, late night transport-escort service, 24-hour monitored security cameras in parking areas, fenced campus with monitored access at night. College housing designed to accommodate 1,212 students; 1,215 undergraduates lived in college housing during 2003-04. Freshmen guaranteed college housing. On-campus residence required through sophomore year. Options: coed, men-only, women-only housing available. Burrow Library plus 3 others with 274,886 books, 90,720 microform titles, 1,183 serials, 10,755 audiovisual materials, an OPAC, and a Web page. Operations spending for 2004 fiscal year: $1.3 million. 220 computers available on campus for general student use. A campuswide network can be accessed from student residence rooms and from off campus. Staffed computer lab on campus.

Community Environment: See University of Memphis.

■ ROANE STATE COMMUNITY COLLEGE D-16

276 Patton Ln.
Harriman, TN 37748-5011
Tel: (865)354-3000
Admissions: (865)882-4523
Fax: (865)882-4562
Web Site: http://www.roanestate.edu/

Description: State-supported, 2-year, coed. Part of Tennessee Board of Regents. Awards certificates, transfer associate, and terminal associate degrees. Founded 1971. Setting: 104-acre rural campus with easy access to Knoxville. Endowment: $18,123. Educational spending for 2005 fiscal year: $3586 per student. Total enrollment: 5,155. Student-undergrad faculty ratio is 17:1. 2,240 applied, 100% were admitted. Full-time: 2,873 students; 65% women, 35% men. Part-time: 2,282 students, 71% women, 29% men. Students come from 6 states and territories, 5 other countries, 1% from out-of-state, 0.3% Native American, 1% Hispanic, 2% black, 1% Asian American or Pacific Islander, 0.3% international, 45% 25 or older, 5% transferred in. Retention: 57% of full-time freshmen returned the following year. Core. Calendar: semesters. Academic remediation for entering students, services for LD students, advanced placement, accelerated degree program, freshman honors college, honors program, independent study, distance learning, double major, summer session for credit, part-time degree program, external degree program, adult/continuing education programs, co-op programs and internships. Off campus study. ROTC: Army (c), Air Force (c).

Entrance Requirements: Open admission except for allied health, nursing, computer technology programs. Options: Common Application, electronic application, early admission, deferred admission. Required: high school transcript. Entrance: noncompetitive. Application deadline: Rolling. Notification: continuous. Preference given to state residents.

Costs Per Year: Application fee: $10. State resident tuition: $1952 full-time, $83 per semester hour part-time. Nonresident tuition: $7798 full-time, $346 per semester hour part-time. Mandatory fees: $265 full-time, $15 per semester hour part-time. Full-time tuition and fees vary according to course load and program. Part-time tuition and fees vary according to program.

Collegiate Environment: Orientation program. Drama-theater group, choral group, student-run newspaper. Social organizations: 21 open to all. Most popular organizations: Baptist Student Union, American Chemical Society, Physical Therapy Student Association, Student Artists At Roane State (S.T. A.R.S.), Phi Theta Kappa. Major annual events: Thanksgiving Feast, Spring Fling, Children's Egg Hunt. Student services: health clinic, personal-psychological counseling. Campus security: 24-hour patrols. College housing not available. Roane State Community College Library plus 1 other with 66,024 books, 7,543 microform titles, 595 serials, 8,808 audiovisual materials, an OPAC, and a Web page. Operations spending for 2004 fiscal year: $523,386. 750 computers available on campus for general student use. A campuswide network can be accessed. Staffed computer lab on campus.

Community Environment: Harriman is located near the cities of Kingston and Rockwood and is easily accessible via U.S. highways.

■ SEWANEE: THE UNIVERSITY OF THE SOUTH F-13

735 University Ave.
Sewanee, TN 37383-1000
Tel: (931)598-1000
Free: 800-522-2234
Admissions: (931)598-1238
Fax: (931)598-1145
E-mail: admiss@sewanee.edu
Web Site: http://www.sewanee.edu/

Description: Independent Episcopal, comprehensive, coed. Awards bachelor's, master's, doctoral, and first professional degrees and post-master's and first professional certificates. Founded 1857. Setting: 10,000-acre small town campus. Endowment: $232.9 million. Research spending for 2004 fiscal year: $60,235. Educational spending for 2005 fiscal year: $10,930 per student. Total enrollment: 1,528. Faculty: 174 (130 full-time, 44 part-time). Student-undergrad faculty ratio is 12:1. 2,027 applied, 67% were admitted. 40% from top 10% of their high school class, 78% from top quarter, 94% from top half. 13 National Merit Scholars. Full-time: 1,410 students, 55% women, 45% men. Part-time: 22 students, 55% women, 45% men. Students come from 44 states and territories, 79% from out-of-state, 0.4% Native American, 2% Hispanic, 4% black, 2% Asian American or Pacific Islander, 2% international, 1% 25 or older, 92% live on campus, 1% transferred in. Retention: 88% of full-time freshmen returned the following year. Academic areas with the most degrees conferred: English; social sciences; history. Core. Calendar: semesters. Services for LD students, advanced placement, self-designed majors, independent study, double major, summer session for credit, internships, graduate courses open to undergrads. Study abroad program.

Entrance Requirements: Options: Common Application, electronic application, early admission, early decision, deferred admission. Required: essay, high school transcript, 2 recommendations, SAT or ACT. Recommended: interview. Entrance: very difficult. Application deadlines: 2/1, 11/15 for early decision. Notification: 4/1, 12/15 for early decision.

Costs Per Year: Application fee: $45. Comprehensive fee: $34,645 includes full-time tuition ($26,874), mandatory fees ($221), and college room and board ($7550). College room only: $3860. Part-time tuition: $975 per credit hour.

Collegiate Environment: Orientation program. Drama-theater group, choral group, student-run newspaper, radio station. Social organizations: 110 open to all; national fraternities, local sororities; 65% of eligible men and 55% of eligible women are members. Most popular organizations: Sewanee Outing Program, Community Service Council, Student Activities Programming Board, student radio station, BACCHUS (alcohol and drug education). Major annual events: homecoming, Parents' Weekend, Fall and Spring Party weekends. Student services: legal services, health clinic, personal-psychological counseling, women's center. Campus security: 24-hour emergency response devices and patrols, late night transport-escort service, security lighting. On-campus residence required through senior year. Options: coed, men-only, women-only housing available. Jessie Ball duPont Library with 648,459 books, 328,090 microform titles, 3,444 serials, 72,964 audiovisual materials, an OPAC, and a Web page. Operations spending for 2004 fiscal year: $2 million. 92 computers available on campus for general student use. A campuswide network can be accessed from student residence rooms and from off campus. Staffed computer lab on campus.

Community Environment: Sewanee is located on the Cuberland Plateau. It has an average temperature of 57 degrees and an average rainfall of 58 inches. Summer nights are cool and there is some snow in the winter. Churches, a hospital and clinic, and several civic and service organizations are a part of the community. Job opportunities are limited. Seventeen lakes in the surrounding area provide facilities for a number of sports, swimming, boating, fishing, and skating. Other activities are hunting, camping, mountain climbing, golf and tennis. There are many tourist attractions in this area.

■ SOUTH COLLEGE J-2

720 North Fifth Ave.
Knoxville, TN 37917
Tel: (865)524-3043
Fax: (865)673-8019
Web Site: http://www.southcollegetn.edu/

Description: Proprietary, primarily 2-year, coed. Awards certificates, terminal associate, and bachelor's degrees. Founded 1882. Setting: 2-acre urban campus. Total enrollment: 443. Students come from 2 states and territories, 0% from out-of-state, 0.2% Native American, 1% Hispanic, 14% black, 0.5% Asian American or Pacific Islander, 0.5% international, 50% 25 or older. Core. Advanced placement, double major, summer session for credit, part-time degree program, adult/continuing education programs, internships.

Entrance Requirements: Options: Common Application, early admission, deferred admission. Required: high school transcript, interview. Placement: SAT, ACT, or CPT recommended. Entrance: moderately difficult. Application deadline: 10/1.

Collegiate Environment: Orientation program. Social organizations: 4 open to all. Most popular organizations: Collegiate Secretaries International,

Paralegal Club, Students of Medical Assisting, Empowerment. Major annual events: College Picnic, Theme Day, Christmas Party. Student services: personal-psychological counseling. Campus security: evening and morning security patrols. College housing not available. Knoxville Business College Library with 6,500 books, 3,069 microform titles, 127 serials, 16 audiovisual materials, and a Web page. 50 computers available on campus for general student use. Staffed computer lab on campus.

■ SOUTHEASTERN CAREER COLLEGE *C-10*

2416 South 21st Ave., Ste. 300
Nashville, TN 37212
Tel: (615)269-9900
Free: 800-336-4457
Fax: (615)297-6678
Web Site: http://www.southeasterncareercollege.com/
Description: Proprietary, 2-year, coed. Founded 1981.

■ SOUTHERN ADVENTIST UNIVERSITY *G-15*

PO Box 370
Collegedale, TN 37315-0370
Tel: (423)236-2000
Free: 800-768-8437
Admissions: (423)236-2844
Fax: (423)236-1000
E-mail: admissions@southern.edu
Web Site: http://www.southern.edu/
Description: Independent Seventh-day Adventist, comprehensive, coed. Awards associate, bachelor's, and master's degrees. Founded 1892. Setting: 1,000-acre small town campus with easy access to Chattanooga. Endowment: $21.1 million. Research spending for 2004 fiscal year: $23,040. Educational spending for 2005 fiscal year: $7733 per student. Total enrollment: 2,522. Faculty: 217 (131 full-time, 86 part-time). Student-undergrad faculty ratio is 15:1. 1,471 applied, 69% were admitted. 4 National Merit Scholars. Full-time: 2,083 students, 54% women, 46% men. Part-time: 307 students, 55% women, 45% men. Students come from 48 states and territories, 50 other countries, 70% from out-of-state, 0.4% Native American, 12% Hispanic, 11% black, 5% Asian American or Pacific Islander, 5% international, 10% 25 or older, 59% live on campus, 10% transferred in. Retention: 73% of full-time freshmen returned the following year. Academic areas with the most degrees conferred: business/marketing; health professions and related sciences; visual and performing arts. Core. Calendar: semesters. ESL program, services for LD students, advanced placement, honors program, independent study, double major, summer session for credit, part-time degree program, internships, graduate courses open to undergrads. Off campus study. Study abroad program.
Entrance Requirements: Options: deferred admission, international baccalaureate accepted. Required: high school transcript, minimum 2.0 high school GPA, SAT and SAT Subject Tests or ACT. Required for some: essay. Entrance: moderately difficult. Application deadline: Rolling. Notification: continuous.
Costs Per Year: Application fee: $25. Comprehensive fee: $19,388 includes full-time tuition ($14,300), mandatory fees ($484), and college room and board ($4604). College room only: $2604. Part-time tuition: $604 per semester hour.
Collegiate Environment: Orientation program. Drama-theater group, choral group, student-run newspaper, radio station. Social organizations: 8 open to all. Most popular organizations: Student Association, Black Christian Union, Campus Ministries. Major annual events: SA Welcome-Back Party, SA Mid-Winter Party, Strawberry Festival. Student services: health clinic, personal-psychological counseling. Campus security: 24-hour patrols, late night transport-escort service, controlled dormitory access. 1,543 college housing spaces available; 1,331 were occupied in 2003-04. Freshmen guaranteed college housing. On-campus residence required through senior year. Options: men-only, women-only housing available. McKee Library with 139,200 books, 469,929 microform titles, 10,479 serials, 7,169 audiovisual materials, an OPAC, and a Web page. Operations spending for 2004 fiscal year: $1.1 million. 200 computers available on campus for general student use. A campuswide network can be accessed from student residence rooms and from off campus. Staffed computer lab on campus.
Community Environment: Collegedale is located 18 miles east of Chattanooga where the recreation areas of the TVA lake system are within 10 miles. There are residence halls for the students; part-time employment opportunities are available.

■ SOUTHWEST TENNESSEE COMMUNITY COLLEGE *F-1*

PO Box 780
Memphis, TN 38101-0780
Tel: (901)333-5000; 877-717-STCC
Admissions: (901)333-4221
Fax: (901)333-4273
E-mail: bwells@southwest.tn.edu
Web Site: http://www.southwest.tn.edu/
Description: State-supported, 2-year, coed. Part of Tennessee Board of Regents. Awards certificates, transfer associate, and terminal associate degrees. Setting: 100-acre urban campus. Endowment: $641,526. Educational spending for 2005 fiscal year: $3966 per student. Total enrollment: 11,556. 1,901 applied, 100% were admitted. 1 valedictorian. Full-time: 5,656 students, 63% women, 37% men. Part-time: 5,900 students, 67% women, 33% men. Students come from 14 states and territories, 2% from out-of-state, 1% Native American, 2% Hispanic, 59% black, 1% Asian American or Pacific Islander, 1% international, 50% 25 or older, 4% transferred in. Core. Calendar: semesters. Academic remediation for entering students, ESL program, services for LD students, advanced placement, accelerated degree program, self-designed majors, distance learning, double major, summer session for credit, part-time degree program, adult/continuing education programs, co-op programs and internships. ROTC: Army (c), Air Force (c).
Entrance Requirements: Open admission. Options: Common Application, early admission, deferred admission. Required: high school transcript. Entrance: noncompetitive. Application deadline: 9/1. Notification: continuous until 9/1.
Costs Per Year: Application fee: $5. State resident tuition: $2184 full-time, $91 per credit hour part-time. Nonresident tuition: $8856 full-time, $369 per credit hour part-time. Mandatory fees: $213 full-time, $28 per credit hour part-time.
Collegiate Environment: Orientation program. Drama-theater group, choral group, student-run newspaper. Social organizations: 18 open to all. Most popular organizations: Human Key Society, NAACP, Black Student Association, Honor Society, Collegiate Secretaries. Major annual events: College Transfer Day, International Night, Career Day. Student services: personal-psychological counseling. Campus security: 24-hour emergency response devices and patrols, late night transport-escort service. College housing not available. Infonet Library plus 4 others with 87,280 books, 10,066 microform titles, 522 serials, 10,588 audiovisual materials, an OPAC, and a Web page. Operations spending for 2004 fiscal year: $1.3 million. 800 computers available on campus for general student use. A campuswide network can be accessed from off-campus. Staffed computer lab on campus.
Community Environment: See University of Memphis.

■ TENNESSEE STATE UNIVERSITY *C-10*

3500 John A Merritt Blvd.
Nashville, TN 37209-1561
Tel: (615)963-5000
Admissions: (615)963-5101
Fax: (615)963-5108
E-mail: jcade@picard.tnstate.edu
Web Site: http://www.tnstate.edu/
Description: State-supported, comprehensive, coed. Part of Tennessee Board of Regents. Awards associate, bachelor's, master's, and doctoral degrees. Founded 1912. Setting: 450-acre urban campus. Research spending for 2004 fiscal year: $2 million. Total enrollment: 8,880. Faculty: 604 (431 full-time, 173 part-time). Student-undergrad faculty ratio is 14:1. 8,160 applied, 36% were admitted. Full-time: 5,873 students, 64% women, 36% men. Part-time: 1,163 students, 68% women, 32% men. Students come from 48 states and territories, 34 other countries, 33% from out-of-state, 0.05% Native American, 1% Hispanic, 81% black, 1% Asian American or Pacific Islander, 1% international, 30% 25 or older, 39% live on campus, 6% transferred in. Retention: 73% of full-time freshmen returned the following year. Core. Calendar: semesters. Academic remediation for entering students, services for LD students, accelerated degree program, freshman honors college, honors program, independent study, summer session for credit, part-time degree program, external degree program, adult/continuing education programs, co-op programs and internships. Off campus study at Volunteer State Community College, Meharry Medical College. ROTC: Army (c), Naval (c), Air Force.
Entrance Requirements: Option: electronic application. Required: high school transcript, SAT or ACT. Required for some: 3 recommendations.

Entrance: minimally difficult. Application deadline: 8/1. Notification: continuous until 8/15. Preference given to state residents.

Costs Per Year: Application fee: $15. State resident tuition: $4414 full-time, $336 per hour part-time. Nonresident tuition: $13,726 full-time, $740 per hour part-time. Mandatory fees: $225 full-time. Full-time tuition and fees vary according to course load and program. Part-time tuition varies according to course load. College room and board: $4270. College room only: $2460. Room and board charges vary according to board plan and housing facility.

Collegiate Environment: Orientation program. Drama-theater group, choral group, marching band, student-run newspaper, radio station. Social organizations: 103 open to all; national fraternities, national sororities; 12% of eligible men and 12% of eligible women are members. Most popular organizations: SADD, Pre-Alumni Council, Baptist Student Union, T. E. Poag Players. Major annual events: Homecoming, Greek shows, student elections. Student services: health clinic, personal-psychological counseling, women's center. Campus security: 24-hour patrols, controlled dormitory access. College housing designed to accommodate 3,500 students; 3,725 undergraduates lived in college housing during 2003-04. Freshmen given priority for college housing. Options: coed, men-only, women-only housing available. Martha M. Brown/Lois H. Daniel Library plus 1 other with 580,650 books, 899,731 microform titles, 23,668 audiovisual materials, an OPAC, and a Web page. Operations spending for 2004 fiscal year: $3.1 million. 705 computers available on campus for general student use. A campuswide network can be accessed from student residence rooms and from off campus. Staffed computer lab on campus.

Community Environment: See Vanderbilt University.

■ **TENNESSEE TECHNOLOGICAL UNIVERSITY** *C-14*

North Dixie Ave.
Cookeville, TN 38505
Tel: (931)372-3101
Free: 800-255-8881
Admissions: (931)372-3888
Fax: (931)372-6250
E-mail: admissions@tntech.edu
Web Site: http://www.tntech.edu/

Description: State-supported, university, coed. Part of Tennessee Board of Regents. Awards bachelor's, master's, and doctoral degrees. Founded 1915. Setting: 235-acre small town campus. Endowment: $45.3 million. Research spending for 2004 fiscal year: $12.3 million. Educational spending for 2005 fiscal year: $5827 per student. Total enrollment: 9,313. Faculty: 560 (380 full-time, 180 part-time). Student-undergrad faculty ratio is 18:1. 3,292 applied, 75% were admitted. 24% from top 10% of their high school class, 53% from top quarter, 84% from top half. 4 National Merit Scholars. Full-time: 6,453 students, 46% women, 54% men. Part-time: 802 students, 49% women, 51% men. Students come from 38 states and territories, 45 other countries, 4% from out-of-state, 0.3% Native American, 1% Hispanic, 4% black, 1% Asian American or Pacific Islander, 1% international, 15% 25 or older, 28% live on campus, 9% transferred in. Retention: 73% of full-time freshmen returned the following year. Academic areas with the most degrees conferred: business/marketing; engineering; interdisciplinary studies. Core. Calendar: semesters. Academic remediation for entering students, ESL program, services for LD students, advanced placement, accelerated degree program, honors program, independent study, distance learning, double major, summer session for credit, part-time degree program, adult/continuing education programs, co-op programs and internships. Off campus study at Roane State Community College-Oak Ridge, TN and Pellissippi State Community College-Knoxville, TN. Study abroad program. ROTC: Army, Air Force (c).

Entrance Requirements: Options: electronic application, early admission, deferred admission, international baccalaureate accepted. Required: high school transcript, minimum 2.5 high school GPA, ACT composite score of 19, SAT or ACT. Recommended: interview, ACT. Entrance: moderately difficult. Application deadline: 8/1. Notification: continuous. Preference given to state residents.

Costs Per Year: Application fee: $15. State resident tuition: $4660 full-time. Nonresident tuition: $14,620 full-time. College room and board: $6650. College room only: $3096.

Collegiate Environment: Orientation program. Drama-theater group, choral group, marching band, student-run newspaper, radio station. Social organizations: 178 open to all; national fraternities, national sororities; 18% of eligible men and 12% of eligible women are members. Most popular organizations: Baptist Collegiate Center, Fellowship of Christian Athletes, University Christian Student Center, Residence Hall Association. Major an-

nual events: Homecoming, Greek Week, Career Day. Student services: health clinic, personal-psychological counseling, women's center. Campus security: 24-hour emergency response devices and patrols, late night transport-escort service, student safety organization, lighted pathways. 2,321 college housing spaces available; 1,777 were occupied in 2003-04. Freshmen guaranteed college housing. On-campus residence required through sophomore year. Options: coed, men-only, women-only housing available. Angelo and Jennette Volpe Library and Media Center with 640,056 books, 1.5 million microform titles, 4,847 serials, 19,170 audiovisual materials, an OPAC, and a Web page. Operations spending for 2004 fiscal year: $2.4 million. 620 computers available on campus for general student use. A campuswide network can be accessed from student residence rooms and from off campus. Staffed computer lab on campus.

Community Environment: Cookeville, located in middle Tennessee, is predominantly an agricultural area. Bus transportation is available. Churches of most denominations, libraries, a hospital, and various civic and service organizations serve the community. Recreational activities include swimming, softball, baseball, tennis, and golf. Center Hill Dam and Reservoir are nearby for many other sports, such as boating, water sports, fishing, and camping.

■ **TENNESSEE TEMPLE UNIVERSITY** *G-14*

1815 Union Ave.
Chattanooga, TN 37404-3587
Tel: (423)493-4100
Free: 800-553-4050
Admissions: (423)493-4371
Fax: (423)493-4497
Web Site: http://www.tntemple.edu/

Description: Independent Baptist, comprehensive, coed. Awards associate, bachelor's, and master's degrees. Founded 1946. Setting: 55-acre urban campus. Endowment: $600,000. Total enrollment: 427. 177 applied, 96% were admitted. Full-time: 137 students, 52% women, 48% men. Students come from 38 states and territories, 11 other countries, 66% from out-of-state, 0.5% Native American, 3% Hispanic, 3% black, 2% Asian American or Pacific Islander, 3% international, 10% 25 or older, 64% live on campus, 22% transferred in. Retention: 58% of full-time freshmen returned the following year. Core. Calendar: semesters. Academic remediation for entering students, advanced placement, independent study, distance learning, double major, summer session for credit, part-time degree program, internships, graduate courses open to undergrads.

Entrance Requirements: Options: electronic application, deferred admission, international baccalaureate accepted. Required: high school transcript, minimum 2.0 high school GPA, 3 recommendations, interview, health and immunization report, SAT or ACT. Required for some: essay. Entrance: minimally difficult. Application deadline: 8/20. Notification: continuous.

Costs Per Year: Application fee: $30. Comprehensive fee: $13,430 includes full-time tuition ($7000), mandatory fees ($1000), and college room and board ($5430). Room and board charges vary according to board plan. Part-time tuition: $300 per semester hour. Part-time mandatory fees: $200 per term.

Collegiate Environment: Orientation program. Drama-theater group, choral group, student-run newspaper, radio station. Social organizations: societies for men and women. Most popular organizations: yearbook, music ensembles. Major annual events: Judgement Day, Homecoming Parade and Carnival, Singing Christmas Tree. Student services: health clinic, personal-psychological counseling. Campus security: 24-hour emergency response devices and patrols, late night transport-escort service. 1,800 college housing spaces available; 273 were occupied in 2003-04. On-campus residence required through senior year. Options: men-only, women-only housing available. Cierpke Memorial Library with 150,711 books and 76 serials. 105 computers available on campus for general student use. A campuswide network can be accessed from student residence rooms and from off campus. Staffed computer lab on campus.

Community Environment: The university is located near downtown Chattanooga, which sits in the valley of Lookout Mountain. The campus is only minutes from all of the downtown attractions and two malls.

■ **TENNESSEE WESLEYAN COLLEGE** *E-16*

PO Box 40
Athens, TN 37371-0040
Tel: (423)745-7504
Free: 800-PICK-TWC
Admissions: (423)746-5203

Fax: (423)744-9968

Web Site: http://www.twcnet.edu/

Description: Independent United Methodist, 4-year, coed. Awards bachelor's degrees (profile includes information for both the main and branch campuses). Founded 1857. Setting: 40-acre small town campus with easy access to Knoxville and Chattanooga. Total enrollment: 815. 430 applied, 84% were admitted. 21% from top 10% of their high school class, 39% from top quarter, 75% from top half. 2 valedictorians. Full-time: 687 students, 67% women, 33% men. Part-time: 128 students, 72% women, 28% men. Students come from 21 states and territories, 10 other countries, 7% from out-of-state, 0.2% Native American, 2% Hispanic, 2% black, 1% Asian American or Pacific Islander, 3% international, 26% 25 or older, 27% live on campus, 18% transferred in. Retention: 58% of full-time freshmen returned the following year. Core. Calendar: semesters. Academic remediation for entering students, ESL program, advanced placement, accelerated degree program, self-designed majors, freshman honors college, honors program, independent study, double major, summer session for credit, part-time degree program, adult/continuing education programs, co-op programs and internships. Off campus study. Study abroad program.

Entrance Requirements: Options: Peterson's Universal Application, electronic application, early admission, deferred admission, international baccalaureate accepted. Required: high school transcript, minimum 2.0 high school GPA, 1 recommendation, SAT or ACT. Recommended: essay. Required for some: interview. Entrance: moderately difficult. Application deadline: Rolling. Notification: continuous.

Costs Per Year: Application fee: $25. Comprehensive fee: $18,650 includes full-time tuition ($13,000), mandatory fees ($550), and college room and board ($5100). Full-time tuition and fees vary according to location. Room and board charges vary according to housing facility. Part-time tuition: $375 per semester hour. Part-time mandatory fees: $180 per term. Part-time tuition and fees vary according to class time and location.

Collegiate Environment: Orientation program. Drama-theater group, choral group, student-run newspaper. Social organizations: 16 open to all; national sororities, local sororities; 5% of women are members. Most popular organizations: Wesleyan Christian Fellowship, Circle K, Baptist Student Union, Student Government Association, choir. Major annual events: homecoming, Spring Fling Week, ski trip. Student services: health clinic, personal-psychological counseling. Campus security: controlled dormitory access, night patrols by trained security personnel. 287 college housing spaces available; 189 were occupied in 2003-04. Freshmen guaranteed college housing. On-campus residence required through senior year. Options: men-only, women-only housing available. Merner-Pfeiffer Library with 79,328 books, 8,932 microform titles, 825 serials, 3,610 audiovisual materials, an OPAC, and a Web page. 92 computers available on campus for general student use. A campuswide network can be accessed from student residence rooms. Staffed computer lab on campus.

Community Environment: Athens is the county seat of McMinn County, located between Chattanooga and Knoxville. The town is an industrial community providing jobs for approximately 13,000 people and serving as a shopping center for 50,000 rural residents. Recreational activities in the beautiful mountainous area include big game hunting, fresh water fishing, rafting, kayaking, hiking, and many other sports.

■ **TREVECCA NAZARENE UNIVERSITY** C-10

333 Murfreesboro Rd.

Nashville, TN 37210-2877

Tel: (615)248-1200; 888-210-4TNU

Admissions: (615)248-1320

Fax: (615)248-7728

E-mail: admissions_und@trevecca.edu

Web Site: http://www.trevecca.edu/

Description: Independent Nazarene, comprehensive, coed. Awards associate, bachelor's, master's, and doctoral degrees and post-master's certificates. Founded 1901. Setting: 65-acre urban campus. Endowment: $14 million. Educational spending for 2005 fiscal year: $5109 per student. Total enrollment: 2,196. Faculty: 217 (73 full-time, 144 part-time). Student-undergrad faculty ratio is 16:1. 762 applied, 69% were admitted. 20% from top 10% of their high school class, 48% from top quarter, 71% from top half. 1 National Merit Scholar, 3 valedictorians, 19 student government officers. Full-time: 987 students, 54% women, 46% men. Part-time: 258 students, 59% women, 41% men. 43% from out-of-state, 0.2% Native American, 2% Hispanic, 8% black, 1% Asian American or Pacific Islander, 2% international, 31% 25 or older, 57% live on campus, 4% transferred in. Retention: 68% of full-time freshmen returned the following year. Academic areas with the most

degrees conferred: business/marketing; education; visual and performing arts. Core. Calendar: semesters. Academic remediation for entering students, services for LD students, advanced placement, double major, summer session for credit, adult/continuing education programs, internships. Study abroad program. ROTC: Army (c).

Entrance Requirements: Options: Peterson's Universal Application, early admission, deferred admission. Required: high school transcript, minimum 2.5 high school GPA, medical history and immunization records, SAT or ACT. Recommended: recommendations. Entrance: moderately difficult. Application deadline: 7/1. Notification: continuous.

Costs Per Year: Application fee: $25. Comprehensive fee: $21,244 includes full-time tuition ($14,774) and college room and board ($6470). College room only: $2920. Part-time tuition: $569 per semester hour.

Collegiate Environment: Orientation program. Drama-theater group, choral group, marching band, student-run newspaper, radio station. Major annual events: Homecoming Week, Welcome Week-Back to School Bash, Friday Night Live. Student services: health clinic, personal-psychological counseling. Campus security: 24-hour patrols, student patrols, late night transport-escort service. 717 college housing spaces available; 689 were occupied in 2003-04. On-campus residence required through junior year. Options: men-only, women-only housing available. Mackey Library with 106,802 books, 307,122 microform titles, 482 serials, 3,910 audiovisual materials, an OPAC, and a Web page. Operations spending for 2004 fiscal year: $919,687. 200 computers available on campus for general student use. A campuswide network can be accessed from student residence rooms and from off campus. Staffed computer lab on campus.

Community Environment: See Vanderbilt University.

■ **TUSCULUM COLLEGE** I-5

60 Shiloh Rd.

Greeneville, TN 37743-9997

Tel: (423)636-7300

Free: 800-729-0256

Fax: (423)638-7166

Web Site: http://www.tusculum.edu/

Description: Independent Presbyterian, comprehensive, coed. Awards bachelor's and master's degrees. Founded 1794. Setting: 140-acre small town campus. Endowment: $12.9 million. Educational spending for 2005 fiscal year: $3170 per student. Total enrollment: 2,656. Faculty: 150 (80 full-time, 70 part-time). Student-undergrad faculty ratio is 17:1. 1,953 applied, 67% were admitted. 10% from top 10% of their high school class, 26% from top quarter, 61% from top half. Full-time: 2,240 students, 56% women, 44% men. Part-time: 49 students, 53% women, 47% men. Students come from 36 states and territories, 21 other countries, 48% from out-of-state, 0.3% Native American, 1% Hispanic, 12% black, 1% Asian American or Pacific Islander, 3% international, 9% 25 or older, 65% live on campus, 4% transferred in. Retention: 60% of full-time freshmen returned the following year. Academic areas with the most degrees conferred: business/marketing; education; parks and recreation. Core. Calendar: semesters. Academic remediation for entering students, ESL program, advanced placement, self-designed majors, independent study, double major, summer session for credit, part-time degree program, adult/continuing education programs, internships. Study abroad program.

Entrance Requirements: Options: Peterson's Universal Application, early admission, deferred admission. Required: essay, high school transcript, minimum 2.0 high school GPA, recommendations, SAT or ACT. Recommended: interview. Entrance: moderately difficult. Application deadline: Rolling.

Costs Per Year: Application fee: $0. Comprehensive fee: $22,715 includes full-time tuition ($15,900), mandatory fees ($315), and college room and board ($6500). Part-time tuition: $695 per semester hour.

Collegiate Environment: Orientation program. Drama-theater group, choral group, student-run newspaper, radio station. Social organizations: 21 open to all; national fraternities, national sororities; 1% of eligible men and 1% of eligible women are members. Most popular organizations: Pioneer Newspaper, Bonwondi, Campus Activities Board, Fellowship of Christian Athletes, 'Tusculana' (yearbook). Major annual events: Opening Convocation, Honors Convocation, Lantern Festival. Student services: health clinic, personal-psychological counseling, women's center. Campus security: 24-hour emergency response devices and patrols, student patrols, late night transport-escort service, controlled dormitory access, trained security personnel on duty. College housing designed to accommodate 594 students; 632 undergraduates lived in college housing during 2003-04. Freshmen guaranteed college housing. On-campus residence required through senior year. Options: coed, men-only, women-only housing available. Albert Columbus Tate Library plus 2 others with 49,905 books, 17,771 microform titles, 1,000 serials, 832 audiovisual materials, an OPAC, and a Web page. Operations spending for 2004 fiscal year: $444,207. 200 computers available on campus for general student use. A campuswide network can be accessed from student residence rooms and from off campus. Staffed computer lab on campus.

Community Environment: Greeneville, in Greene County, the birthplace of Davy Crockett, is accessible by bus and rail. The city has a full-time recreational director who supervises a year-round program in addition to the hunting, boating, fishing, golf, whitewater rafting, and cycling available in the area. Nearby is the Andrew Johnson Wildlife Management Area.

■ **UNION UNIVERSITY** *E-5*

1050 Union University Dr.
Jackson, TN 38305-3697
Tel: (731)668-1818
Free: 800-33-UNION
Admissions: (731)661-5102
Fax: (731)661-5187
E-mail: rgrimm@uu.edu
Web Site: http://www.uu.edu/

Description: Independent Southern Baptist, comprehensive, coed. Awards associate, bachelor's, master's, and doctoral degrees and post-master's certificates. Founded 1823. Setting: 290-acre small town campus with easy access to Memphis. Endowment: $24.3 million. Research spending for 2004 fiscal year: $150,000. Educational spending for 2005 fiscal year: $6094 per student. Total enrollment: 2,866. Faculty: 278 (152 full-time, 126 part-time). Student-undergrad faculty ratio is 12:1. 1,090 applied, 86% were admitted. 37% from top 10% of their high school class, 66% from top quarter, 89% from top half. 6 National Merit Scholars, 44 valedictorians. Full-time: 1,611 students, 60% women, 40% men. Part-time: 475 students, 61% women, 39% men. Students come from 44 states and territories, 36 other countries, 32% from out-of-state, 0.1% Native American, 1% Hispanic, 8% black, 1% Asian American or Pacific Islander, 2% international, 20% 25 or older, 56% live on campus, 6% transferred in. Retention: 67% of full-time freshmen returned the following year. Academic areas with the most degrees conferred: health professions and related sciences; business/marketing; education. Core. Calendar: 4-1-4. Academic remediation for entering students, ESL program, services for LD students, advanced placement, accelerated degree program, honors program, independent study, distance learning, double major, summer session for credit, part-time degree program, adult/continuing education programs, co-op programs and internships, graduate courses open to undergrads. Off campus study at Lambuth University, Freed-Hardeman University, Council for Christian Colleges and Universities. Study abroad program.

Entrance Requirements: Options: Peterson's Universal Application, Common Application, electronic application, early admission, early action, deferred admission, international baccalaureate accepted. Required: high school transcript, minimum 2.5 high school GPA, SAT or ACT. Recommended: essay, interview, SAT Subject Tests. Required for some: recommendations. Entrance: moderately difficult. Application deadlines: Rolling, 12/1 for early action. Notification: continuous until 8/1, 12/15 for early action.

Costs Per Year: Application fee: $25. Comprehensive fee: $21,920 includes full-time tuition ($15,900), mandatory fees ($550), and college room and board ($5470). College room only: $3290. Full-time tuition and fees vary according to class time, course load, location, and program. Room and board charges vary according to board plan and location. Part-time tuition: $530 per credit hour.

Collegiate Environment: Orientation program. Drama-theater group, choral group, student-run newspaper. Social organizations: 52 open to all; national fraternities, national sororities; 7% of eligible men and 12% of eligible women are members. Most popular organizations: campus ministries, Student Government Association, Student Activities Council, SIFE. Major annual events: Campus Day, All-Sing Contest, homecoming. Student services: health clinic, personal-psychological counseling. Campus security: 24-hour emergency response devices and patrols, student patrols, late night transport-escort service. 1,180 college housing spaces available; 1,100 were occupied in 2003-04. Freshmen given priority for college housing. On-campus residence required through junior year. Options: men-only, women-only housing available. Emma Waters Summar Library plus 1 other with 135,877 books, 466,987 microform titles, 4,655 serials, 11,526 audiovisual materials, an OPAC, and a Web page. Operations spending for 2004 fiscal year: $857,628. 236 computers available on campus for general student

use. A campuswide network can be accessed from student residence rooms and from off campus. Staffed computer lab on campus.

Community Environment: Jackson is a city of 55,000 that is 75 miles from Memphis and 125 miles from Nashville. There are 3 other colleges located in the same town.

■ **UNIVERSITY OF MEMPHIS** *F-1*

Memphis, TN 38152
Tel: (901)678-2000
Free: 800-669-2678
Admissions: (901)678-2101
Fax: (901)678-3053
E-mail: dwallace@memphis.edu
Web Site: http://www.memphis.edu/

Description: State-supported, university, coed. Part of Tennessee Board of Regents. Awards bachelor's, master's, doctoral, and first professional degrees and post-master's and first professional certificates. Founded 1912. Setting: 1,100-acre urban campus. Endowment: $166.6 million. Research spending for 2004 fiscal year: $44.2 million. Educational spending for 2005 fiscal year: $5757 per student. Total enrollment: 20,465. Faculty: 1,285 (743 full-time, 542 part-time). Student-undergrad faculty ratio is 17:1. 5,131 applied, 71% were admitted. 18% from top 10% of their high school class, 45% from top quarter, 81% from top half. Full-time: 11,568 students, 60% women, 40% men. Part-time: 4,197 students, 63% women, 37% men. Students come from 44 states and territories, 83 other countries, 6% from out-of-state, 0.3% Native American, 1% Hispanic, 38% black, 2% Asian American or Pacific Islander, 2% international, 31% 25 or older, 16% live on campus, 11% transferred in. Retention: 72% of full-time freshmen returned the following year. Academic areas with the most degrees conferred: business/marketing; interdisciplinary studies; communications/journalism; education. Core. Calendar: semesters. Academic remediation for entering students, ESL program, services for LD students, advanced placement, accelerated degree program, self-designed majors, honors program, independent study, distance learning, double major, summer session for credit, part-time degree program, external degree program, adult/continuing education programs, co-op programs and internships, graduate courses open to undergrads. Off campus study. Study abroad program. ROTC: Army, Naval, Air Force.

Entrance Requirements: Options: early admission, international baccalaureate accepted. Required: high school transcript, SAT or ACT. Required for some: minimum 2.0 high school GPA, 2 recommendations, interview. Entrance: moderately difficult. Application deadline: 7/1. Notification: continuous.

Costs Per Year: Application fee: $25. State resident tuition: $4216 full-time, $178 per credit hour part-time. Nonresident tuition: $14,030 full-time, $588 per credit hour part-time. Mandatory fees: $868 full-time, $62 per credit hour part-time. Full-time tuition and fees vary according to program and reciprocity agreements. Part-time tuition and fees vary according to course load and program. College room and board: $6069. College room only: $2950. Room and board charges vary according to housing facility.

Collegiate Environment: Orientation program. Drama-theater group, choral group, marching band, student-run newspaper, radio station. Social organizations: 45 open to all; national fraternities, national sororities, local sororities; 7% of eligible men and 5% of eligible women are members. Major annual events: homecoming, Springfest, Black History Month. Student services: health clinic, personal-psychological counseling, women's center, career counseling; employment service; daycare; minority services. Campus security: 24-hour emergency response devices and patrols, student patrols, late night transport-escort service. 2,080 undergraduates lived in college housing during 2003-04. Options: coed, men-only, women-only housing available. University of Memphis Libraries: McWherter Libraries plus 6 others with 1.1 million books, 3.5 million microform titles, 15,643 serials, 37,824 audiovisual materials, an OPAC, and a Web page. Operations spending for 2004 fiscal year: $9.2 million. 2,000 computers available on campus for general student use. A campuswide network can be accessed from off-campus. Staffed computer lab on campus.

Community Environment: Memphis, with a metropolitan area population of over one million, is one of the South's largest and most attractive cities. As a primary medical, educational, communication, distribution, and transportation center, Memphis offers a rich and full range of research opportunities and cultural experiences. The city, known worldwide for its musical heritage, has many fine restaurants, museums, and theaters, as well as one of the nation's largest urban park systems. All forms of commercial transportation are available. Opportunities are numerous for part-time employment. Annual events include the St. Jude Liberty Bowl Football Classic, the Memphis in

May International Festival, the Great River Carnival, and the Mid-South Fair. Some of the points of interest are the Brooks Memorial Art Gallery, Chuclissa Indian Villiage and Museum, Elvis Presley's Graceland, Mud Island, Libertyland, and the Great American Pyramid.

■ UNIVERSITY OF PHOENIX-NASHVILLE CAMPUS C-10

616 Marriott Dr., Ste. 150
Nashville, TN 37214
Tel: (615)872-0188
Free: 800-228-7240
Admissions: (480)557-1712
Web Site: http://www.phoenix.edu/

Description: Proprietary, comprehensive, coed. Awards bachelor's and master's degrees. Founded 2003. Total enrollment: 1,291. Faculty: 129 (6 full-time, 123 part-time). Student-undergrad faculty ratio is 8:1. 47 applied. Full-time: 909 students, 60% women, 40% men. 0.3% Native American, 1% Hispanic, 7% black, 1% Asian American or Pacific Islander, 3% international, 92% 25 or older. Academic areas with the most degrees conferred: business/marketing; computer and information sciences. Core. Calendar: continuous. Advanced placement, accelerated degree program, independent study, distance learning, external degree program, adult/continuing education programs, graduate courses open to undergrads.

Entrance Requirements: Open admission. Option: deferred admission. Required: 1 recommendation. Required for some: high school transcript. Entrance: noncompetitive. Application deadline: Rolling.

Costs Per Year: Application fee: $110. Tuition: $10,170 full-time, $339 per credit part-time. Mandatory fees: $560 full-time, $70 per course part-time.

Collegiate Environment: University Library with 444 books, 666 serials, an OPAC, and a Web page. System-wide operations spending for 2004 fiscal year: $3.2 million.

■ THE UNIVERSITY OF TENNESSEE J-2

Knoxville, TN 37996
Tel: (865)974-1000
Admissions: (865)974-2184
Web Site: http://www.tennessee.edu/

Description: State-supported, university, coed. Part of University of Tennessee System. Awards bachelor's, master's, doctoral, and first professional degrees and post-master's and first professional certificates. Founded 1794. Setting: 533-acre urban campus. Research spending for 2004 fiscal year: $182.5 million. Educational spending for 2005 fiscal year: $24,907 per student. Total enrollment: 31,157. Faculty: 1,386 (1,356 full-time, 30 part-time). Student-undergrad faculty ratio is 15:1. 12,251 applied, 74% were admitted. 34% from top 10% of their high school class, 63% from top quarter, 86% from top half. Full-time: 18,739 students, 51% women, 49% men. Part-time: 1,493 students, 53% women, 47% men. Students come from 56 states and territories, 101 other countries, 14% from out-of-state, 0.4% Native American, 2% Hispanic, 9% black, 3% Asian American or Pacific Islander, 1% international, 12% 25 or older, 37% live on campus, 6% transferred in. Retention: 80% of full-time freshmen returned the following year. Calendar: semesters. ESL program, services for LD students, advanced placement, accelerated degree program, self-designed majors, honors program, independent study, distance learning, double major, summer session for credit, part-time degree program, adult/continuing education programs, co-op programs and internships, graduate courses open to undergrads. Off campus study at Knoxville College, Academic Common Market. Study abroad program. ROTC: Army, Air Force.

Entrance Requirements: Options: electronic application, early admission, early action, deferred admission, international baccalaureate accepted. Required: essay, minimum 2.0 high school GPA, specific high school units, SAT or ACT. Entrance: moderately difficult. Application deadlines: 2/1, 11/1 for early action. Notification: continuous, 1/15 for early action. Preference given to state residents, children of alumni.

Costs Per Year: Application fee: $30. State resident tuition: $5290 full-time, $193 per hour part-time. Nonresident tuition: $16,360 full-time, $642 per hour part-time. Mandatory fees: $336 full-time, $30 per hour part-time. Full-time tuition and fees vary according to location and program. Part-time tuition and fees vary according to location and program. College room and board: $5560. College room only: $2890. Room and board charges vary according to board plan and housing facility.

Collegiate Environment: Orientation program. Drama-theater group, choral group, marching band, student-run newspaper, radio station. Social organizations: 350 open to all; national fraternities, national sororities; 15% of eligible men and 19% of eligible women are members. Most popular

organizations: Central Program Council, religious organizations, Volunteer Outreach for Leadership and Service, Student Government Association, dance marathon. Major annual events: homecoming, All-Sing, International Fair. Student services: legal services, health clinic, personal-psychological counseling, women's center. Campus security: 24-hour emergency response devices and patrols, late night transport-escort service. 7,337 college housing spaces available; 6,310 were occupied in 2003-04. Freshmen guaranteed college housing. On-campus residence required in freshman year. Option: coed housing available. John C. Hodges Library plus 6 others with 24.4 million books, 3.8 million microform titles, 17,628 serials, 175,541 audiovisual materials, an OPAC, and a Web page. Operations spending for 2004 fiscal year: $17 million. 1,500 computers available on campus for general student use. Computer purchase/lease plans available. A campuswide network can be accessed from student residence rooms and from off campus. Staffed computer lab on campus.

■ THE UNIVERSITY OF TENNESSEE AT CHATTANOOGA G-14

615 McCallie Ave.
Chattanooga, TN 37403-2598
Tel: (423)425-4111
Admissions: (423)425-4662
Fax: (423)425-4157
Web Site: http://www.utc.edu/

Description: State-supported, comprehensive, coed. Part of University of Tennessee System. Awards bachelor's, master's, doctoral, and first professional degrees and post-master's certificates. Founded 1886. Setting: 117-acre urban campus with easy access to Atlanta. Endowment: $103.7 million. Research spending for 2004 fiscal year: $6.3 million. Educational spending for 2005 fiscal year: $5088 per student. Total enrollment: 8,656. Faculty: 623 (371 full-time, 252 part-time). Student-undergrad faculty ratio is 16:1. 3,580 applied, 84% were admitted. Full-time: 6,190 students, 58% women, 42% men. Part-time: 1,087 students, 53% women, 47% men. Students come from 40 states and territories, 52 other countries, 8% from out-of-state, 0.5% Native American, 1% Hispanic, 22% black, 3% Asian American or Pacific Islander, 1% international, 20% 25 or older, 33% live on campus, 8% transferred in. Retention: 64% of full-time freshmen returned the following year. Academic areas with the most degrees conferred: business/marketing; family and consumer sciences; education. Core. Calendar: semesters. Academic remediation for entering students, ESL program, services for LD students, advanced placement, honors program, independent study, distance learning, double major, summer session for credit, part-time degree program, adult/continuing education programs, co-op programs and internships, graduate courses open to undergrads. Off campus study. Study abroad program.

Entrance Requirements: Option: deferred admission. Required: high school transcript, 1 recommendation, SAT or ACT. Recommended: essay. Required for some: SAT Subject Tests. Entrance: moderately difficult. Notification: continuous.

Costs Per Year: Application fee: $25. State resident tuition: $4500 full-time, $236 per hour part-time. Nonresident tuition: $14,024 full-time, $614 per hour part-time. Mandatory fees: $900 full-time. College room and board: $6238. College room only: $3790. Room and board charges vary according to housing facility.

Collegiate Environment: Orientation program. Drama-theater group, choral group, marching band, student-run newspaper, radio station. Social organizations: 130 open to all; national fraternities, national sororities; 6% of eligible men and 5% of eligible women are members. Most popular organizations: Student Government Association, Black Student Association, Association for Campus Entertainment, International Student Association, Baptist Student Union. Major annual event: Homecoming Week. Student services: health clinic, personal-psychological counseling. Campus security: 24-hour emergency response devices and patrols, late night transport-escort service. 2,975 college housing spaces available; 2,471 were occupied in 2003-04. Freshmen given priority for college housing. Option: coed housing available. Lupton Library with 491,179 books, 1.4 million microform titles, 1,847 serials, 19,522 audiovisual materials, an OPAC, and a Web page. Operations spending for 2004 fiscal year: $1 million. 300 computers available on campus for general student use. A campuswide network can be accessed from student residence rooms and from off campus. Staffed computer lab on campus.

■ THE UNIVERSITY OF TENNESSEE AT MARTIN B-5

University St.
Martin, TN 38238-1000

Tel: (731)881-7000
Free: 800-829-8861
Admissions: (731)881-7032
Fax: (731)881-7029
E-mail: jrayburn@utm.edu
Web Site: http://www.utm.edu/
Description: State-supported, comprehensive, coed. Part of University of Tennessee System. Awards bachelor's and master's degrees. Founded 1900. Setting: 250-acre small town campus. Endowment: $17.8 million. Research spending for 2004 fiscal year: $2 million. Educational spending for 2005 fiscal year: $5402 per student. Total enrollment: 6,484. Faculty: 416 (245 full-time, 171 part-time). Student-undergrad faculty ratio is 19:1. 2,803 applied, 78% were admitted. 20% from top 10% of their high school class, 50% from top quarter, 83% from top half. 1 National Merit Scholar, 30 valedictorians, 55 student government officers. Full-time: 5,016 students, 56% women, 44% men. Part-time: 926 students, 60% women, 40% men. Students come from 41 states and territories, 28 other countries, 6% from out-of-state, 0.5% Native American, 1% Hispanic, 15% black, 0.5% Asian American or Pacific Islander, 2% international, 17% 25 or older, 37% live on campus, 7% transferred in. Retention: 71% of full-time freshmen returned the following year. Academic areas with the most degrees conferred: business/marketing; interdisciplinary studies; agriculture. Calendar: semesters. Academic remediation for entering students, ESL program, services for LD students, advanced placement, accelerated degree program, self-designed majors, honors program, independent study, distance learning, double major, summer session for credit, part-time degree program, adult/continuing education programs, co-op programs and internships, graduate courses open to undergrads. Off campus study at Gulf Coast Research Laboratory. Study abroad program. ROTC: Army.
Entrance Requirements: Options: Peterson's Universal Application, Common Application, electronic application, deferred admission. Required: high school transcript, minimum 2.40 high school GPA, SAT or ACT. Entrance: moderately difficult. Application deadline: Rolling. Notification: continuous until 8/1.
Costs Per Year: Application fee: $25. State resident tuition: $3744 full-time, $156 per credit hour part-time. Nonresident tuition: $12,798 full-time, $534 per credit hour part-time. Mandatory fees: $749 full-time, $33 per credit hour part-time. College room and board: $4220. College room only: $2000. Room and board charges vary according to board plan and housing facility.
Collegiate Environment: Orientation program. Drama-theater group, choral group, marching band, student-run newspaper, radio station. Social organizations: 121 open to all; national fraternities, national sororities, local sororities; 7% of eligible men and 5% of eligible women are members. Most popular organizations: Student Government Association, religion-affiliated groups, Student Activities Council, Black Student Association (BSA). Major annual events: All-Niter, All Sing, Homecoming. Student services: health clinic, personal-psychological counseling. Campus security: 24-hour emergency response devices and patrols, student patrols, late night transport-escort service, controlled dormitory access. 2,090 college housing spaces available; 2,052 were occupied in 2003-04. Freshmen guaranteed college housing. On-campus residence required through sophomore year. Options: coed, men-only, women-only housing available. Paul Meek Library plus 1 other with 621,025 books, 703,690 microform titles, 1,994 serials, 12,374 audiovisual materials, an OPAC, and a Web page. Operations spending for 2004 fiscal year: $1.9 million. 836 computers available on campus for general student use. A campuswide network can be accessed from student residence rooms and from off campus. Staffed computer lab on campus.

■ **VANDERBILT UNIVERSITY** *C-10*
Nashville, TN 37240-1001
Tel: (615)322-7311
Free: 800-288-0432
Admissions: (615)322-2561
Fax: (615)343-7765
E-mail: admissions@vanderbilt.edu
Web Site: http://www.vanderbilt.edu/
Description: Independent, university, coed. Awards bachelor's, master's, doctoral, and first professional degrees. Founded 1873. Setting: 330-acre urban campus. Endowment: $2.6 billion. Total enrollment: 11,481. Faculty: (785 full-time). Student-undergrad faculty ratio is 9:1. 11,663 applied, 35% were admitted. 77% from top 10% of their high school class, 93% from top quarter, 99% from top half. 85 National Merit Scholars, 30 class presidents, 101 valedictorians. Full-time: 6,295 students, 52% women, 48% men. Part-

time: 107 students, 45% women, 55% men. Students come from 54 states and territories, 36 other countries, 83% from out-of-state, 0.3% Native American, 5% Hispanic, 8% black, 6% Asian American or Pacific Islander, 2% international, 1% 25 or older, 83% live on campus, 1% transferred in. Retention: 95% of full-time freshmen returned the following year. Academic areas with the most degrees conferred: social sciences; engineering; psychology. Core. Calendar: semesters. ESL program, services for LD students, advanced placement, accelerated degree program, self-designed majors, honors program, independent study, distance learning, double major, summer session for credit, co-op programs and internships, graduate courses open to undergrads. Off campus study at Fisk University, Howard University, Meharry Medical College. Study abroad program. ROTC: Army, Naval, Air Force (c).
Entrance Requirements: Options: Common Application, electronic application, early admission, early decision, deferred admission, international baccalaureate accepted. Required: essay, high school transcript, 2 recommendations, SAT or ACT. Recommended: SAT Subject Tests. Entrance: very difficult. Application deadlines: 1/3, 11/1 for early decision plan 1, 1/3 for early decision plan 2. Notification: 4/1, 12/15 for early decision plan 1, 2/15 for early decision plan 2.
Costs Per Year: Application fee: $50. Comprehensive fee: $41,986 includes full-time tuition ($30,920), mandatory fees ($780), and college room and board ($10,286). College room only: $6760.
Collegiate Environment: Orientation program. Drama-theater group, choral group, marching band, student-run newspaper, radio station. Social organizations: 264 open to all; national fraternities, national sororities; 34% of eligible men and 50% of eligible women are members. Major annual events: Rites of Spring, Impact Speaker Symposium, Accolade Homecoming Ball. Student services: health clinic, personal-psychological counseling, women's center. Campus security: 24-hour emergency response devices and patrols, student patrols, late night transport-escort service, controlled dormitory access. On-campus residence required through senior year. Options: coed, men-only, women-only housing available. Jean and Alexander Heard Library plus 7 others with 1.8 million books, 2.9 million microform titles, 26,885 serials, and 153,450 audiovisual materials. 400 computers available on campus for general student use. A campuswide network can be accessed from student residence rooms and from off campus. Staffed computer lab on campus.
Community Environment: Nashville, Tennessee's capital city, is one of the South's foremost centers for insurance, publishing, healthcare, and music. Ranking high among American cities in"quality of life" surveys, it offers four-star restaurants, sprawling shopping complexes, and entertainment to suit all tastes. The Tennessee Repertory Theatre, Community Concerts, Broadway touring companies, classical ensembles and the Nashville Symphony Orchestra, and the Circle Players perform regularly. The Tennessee Performing Arts Center continually hosts major orchestral and theatrical groups from throughout the nation. Among the attractions that bring visitors to Nashville each year are the Cheekwood Botanical Gardens and Fine Arts Center, the Cumberland Museum and Science Center, the Nashville Arena, and the Tennessee State Museum. Nashville is also home of an NFL team, the Tennessee Titans, and a NHS team, the Nashville Predators.

■ **VATTEROTT COLLEGE** *F-1*
6152 Macon Rd.
Memphis, TN 38134
Tel: (901)761-5730
Fax: (901)761-5730
Web Site: http://www.vatterott-college.edu/
Description: Proprietary, 2-year, coed. Founded 2004. Calendar: semesters.

■ **VOLUNTEER STATE COMMUNITY COLLEGE** *B-11*
1480 Nashville Pike
Gallatin, TN 37066-3188
Tel: (615)452-8600; 888-335-8722
Fax: (615)230-3577
Web Site: http://www.volstate.edu/
Description: State-supported, 2-year, coed. Part of Tennessee Board of Regents. Awards certificates, transfer associate, and terminal associate degrees. Founded 1970. Setting: 100-acre small town campus with easy access to Nashville. Total enrollment: 7,150. Student-undergrad faculty ratio is 20:1. 2,026 applied, 100% were admitted. Full-time: 3,503 students, 59% women, 41% men. Part-time: 3,647 students, 67% women, 33% men. Students come from 8 states and territories, 24 other countries, 1% from out-of-state, 0.3% Native American, 2% Hispanic, 10% black, 2% Asian

American or Pacific Islander, 39% 25 or older, 9% transferred in. Retention: 54% of full-time freshmen returned the following year. Core. Calendar: semesters. Academic remediation for entering students, ESL program, services for LD students, advanced placement, accelerated degree program, honors program, independent study, distance learning, double major, summer session for credit, part-time degree program, adult/continuing education programs.

Entrance Requirements: Open admission. Options: electronic application, early admission, deferred admission. Required: high school transcript. Required for some: essay, minimum 2.0 high school GPA, SAT or ACT. Entrance: noncompetitive. Application deadline: 9/1. Notification: continuous.

Costs Per Year: Application fee: $10. State resident tuition: $2142 full-time, $91 per credit hour part-time. Nonresident tuition: $8556 full-time, $369 per credit hour part-time. Mandatory fees: $241 full-time, $9 per credit hour part-time, $8 per term part-time. Full-time tuition and fees vary according to course load. Part-time tuition and fees vary according to course load.

Collegiate Environment: Orientation program. Drama-theater group, choral group, student-run newspaper, radio station. Social organizations: 18 open to all. Most popular organizations: Gamma Beta Phi, Returning Women's Organization, Phi Theta Kappa, Student Government Association, The Settler. Major annual events: Homecoming, Pioneer Field Day, Fall Fling. Student services: health clinic, personal-psychological counseling. Campus security: 24-hour emergency response devices and patrols, late night transport-escort service. College housing not available. Thigpen Learning Resource Center with 52,571 books, 66,387 microform titles, 274 serials, 3,212 audiovisual materials, an OPAC, and a Web page. Operations spending for 2004 fiscal year: $897,921. 600 computers available on campus for general student use. A campuswide network can be accessed from off-campus. Staffed computer lab on campus.

Community Environment: See Vanderbilt University.

■ **WALTERS STATE COMMUNITY COLLEGE** *I-4*
500 South Davy Crockett Parkway
Morristown, TN 37813-6899
Tel: (423)585-2600
Admissions: (423)585-2680
E-mail: pam.goodman@ws.edu
Web Site: http://www.ws.edu/

Description: State-supported, 2-year, coed. Part of Tennessee Board of Regents. Awards certificates, transfer associate, and terminal associate degrees. Founded 1970. Setting: 100-acre small town campus. Endowment: $6.9 million. Educational spending for 2005 fiscal year: $2500 per student. Total enrollment: 5,964. 1,698 applied, 100% were admitted. 10% from top 10% of their high school class, 25% from top quarter, 65% from top half. Full-time: 3,101 students, 60% women, 40% men. Part-time: 2,863 students, 70% women, 30% men. Students come from 8 states and territories, 6 other countries, 1% from out-of-state, 0.2% Native American, 1% Hispanic, 4% black, 1% Asian American or Pacific Islander, 0.1% international, 26% 25 or older, 4% transferred in. Core. Calendar: semesters. Academic remediation for entering students, advanced placement, accelerated degree program, freshman honors college, honors program, distance learning, summer session for credit, part-time degree program, adult/continuing education programs. ROTC: Army (c).

Entrance Requirements: Open admission. Option: early admission. Required: high school transcript, SAT or ACT. Entrance: noncompetitive. Application deadline: Rolling. Notification: continuous.

Costs Per Year: Application fee: $10. State resident tuition: $2142 full-time, $91 per hour part-time. Nonresident tuition: $8556 full-time, $391 per hour part-time. Mandatory fees: $239 full-time, $15 per hour part-time, $7 per term part-time.

Collegiate Environment: Choral group, student-run newspaper. Student services: health clinic. Campus security: 24-hour emergency response devices. College housing not available. Walters State Library with 47,559 books, 189 serials, 22,677 audiovisual materials, an OPAC, and a Web page. Operations spending for 2004 fiscal year: $591,184. 686 computers available on campus for general student use. A campuswide network can be accessed from off-campus. Staffed computer lab on campus.

Community Environment: Known as the City Between the Lakes, Morristown is centrally located in the college's 10-county service area. It has become a market center for the region with the establishment of a shopping mall as well as a growing industrial center. Farming remains an important part of the local economy with primary crops of light burley tobacco, corn,

hay, and wheat. The lakes provide for fishing, swimming, hunting, and picnicking. Scenic drives lead to the nearby Great Smoky Mountains, Clinch Mountain, and the larger urban areas to both the north and south.

■ **WATKINS COLLEGE OF ART AND DESIGN** *C-10*
2298 MetroCenter Blvd.
Nashville, TN 37228
Tel: (615)383-4848
Fax: (615)383-4849
Web Site: http://www.watkins.edu/

Description: Independent, 4-year, coed. Awards bachelor's degrees. Founded 1885. Setting: 13-acre urban campus. Total enrollment: 393. Student-undergrad faculty ratio is 11:1. 160 applied, 79% were admitted. 100% from top half of their high school class. Full-time: 214 students, 54% women, 46% men. Part-time: 161 students, 76% women, 24% men. Students come from 29 states and territories, 3 other countries, 9% from out-of-state, 0% Native American, 3% Hispanic, 5% black, 2% Asian American or Pacific Islander, 9% international, 41% 25 or older, 12% live on campus, 19% transferred in. Retention: 58% of full-time freshmen returned the following year. Academic area with the most degrees conferred: visual and performing arts. Core. Calendar: semesters. Double major, summer session for credit, part-time degree program, adult/continuing education programs, co-op programs and internships. Study abroad program.

Entrance Requirements: Option: deferred admission. Required: essay, high school transcript, minimum 2.0 high school GPA, recommendations, statement of good standing from prior institution(s); portfolio and home exercises, SAT or ACT. Required for some: statement of good standing from prior institution(s); portfolio and home exercises. Entrance: moderately difficult. Application deadline: 6/1.

Costs Per Year: Application fee: $50. Tuition: $12,000 full-time, $500 per hour part-time. Mandatory fees: $720 full-time, $30 per hour part-time. College room only: $5600.

Collegiate Environment: Orientation program. Student-run newspaper. Student services: personal-psychological counseling. Campus security: 24-hour patrols. 48 college housing spaces available; 26 were occupied in 2003-04. Freshmen given priority for college housing. On-campus residence required in freshman year. Options: coed, men-only, women-only housing available. The George B. Allen Library with 5,000 books and 42 serials. 50 computers available on campus for general student use. Staffed computer lab on campus.

■ **WILLIAMSON CHRISTIAN COLLEGE** *D-10*
200 Seaboard Ln.
Franklin, TN 37067
Tel: (615)771-7821
Fax: (615)771-7810
Web Site: http://www.williamsoncc.edu/

Description: Independent interdenominational, 4-year, coed. Awards associate and bachelor's degrees. Founded 1997. Setting: 1-acre suburban campus with easy access to Nashville. Endowment: $12,022. Educational spending for 2005 fiscal year: $1133 per student. Total enrollment: 70. Full-time: 60 students, 48% women, 52% men. Part-time: 10 students, 20% women, 80% men. Students come from 2 states and territories, 1% from out-of-state, 0% Native American, 0% Hispanic, 3% black, 0% Asian American or Pacific Islander, 0% international, 82% 25 or older, 24% transferred in. Core. Calendar: semesters. Accelerated degree program, independent study, distance learning, double major, part-time degree program, external degree program, adult/continuing education programs, internships.

Entrance Requirements: Open admission. Options: early admission, deferred admission, international baccalaureate accepted. Required: high school transcript. Required for some: interview, ACT, SAT Subject Tests. Entrance: noncompetitive. Application deadline: 9/1. Notification: continuous until 10/1.

Costs Per Year: Application fee: $25. Tuition: $7560 full-time, $295 per credit part-time. Mandatory fees: $50 full-time, $15 per course part-time. Part-time tuition and fees vary according to course load. Tuition guaranteed not to increase for student's term of enrollment.

Collegiate Environment: Orientation program. Major annual event: semi-professional baseball game. Student services: health clinic, personal-psychological counseling. College housing not available. John W. Neth, Jr. Library with 16,000 books and an OPAC. 3 computers available on campus for general student use.

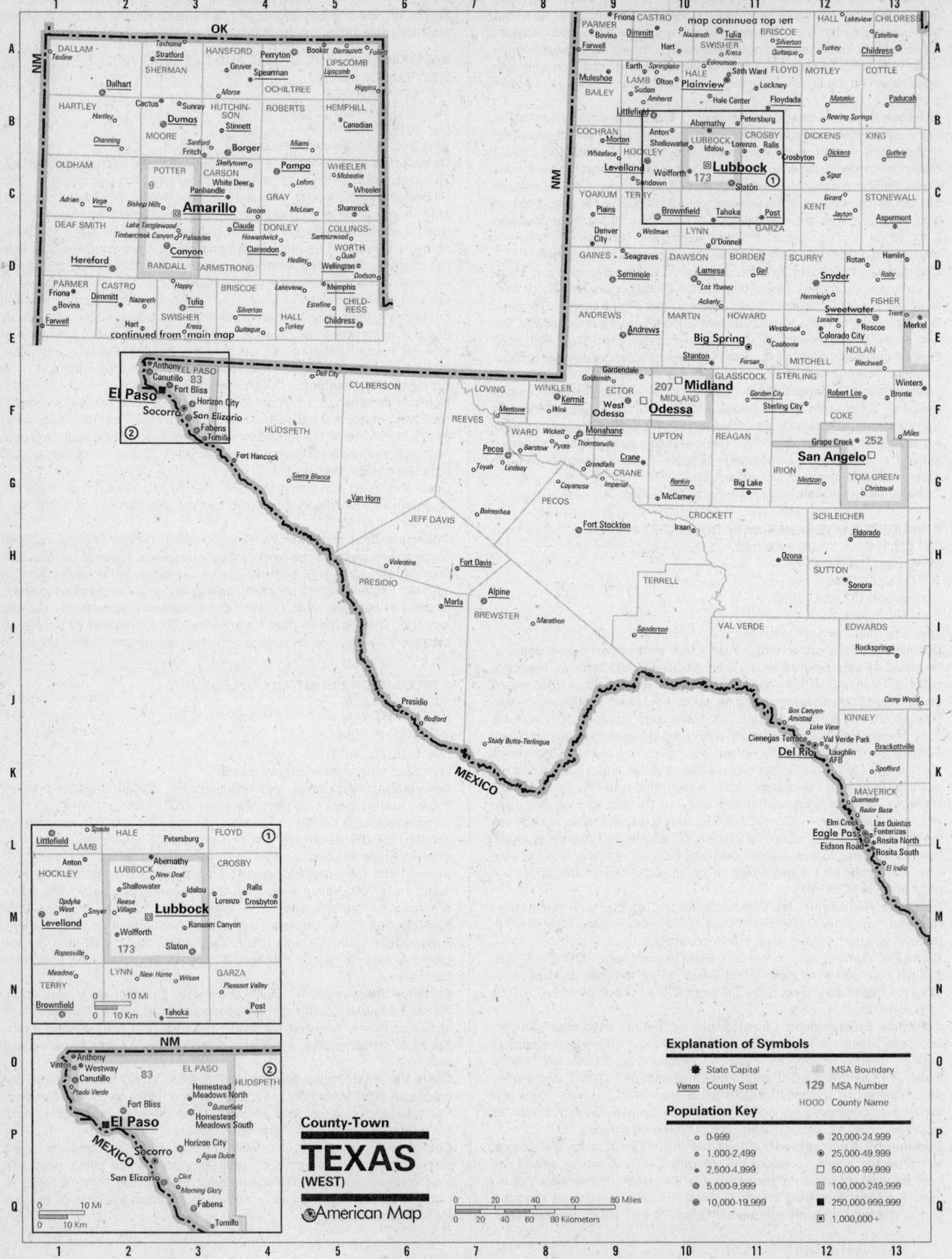

County-Town

TEXAS
(WEST)

American Map

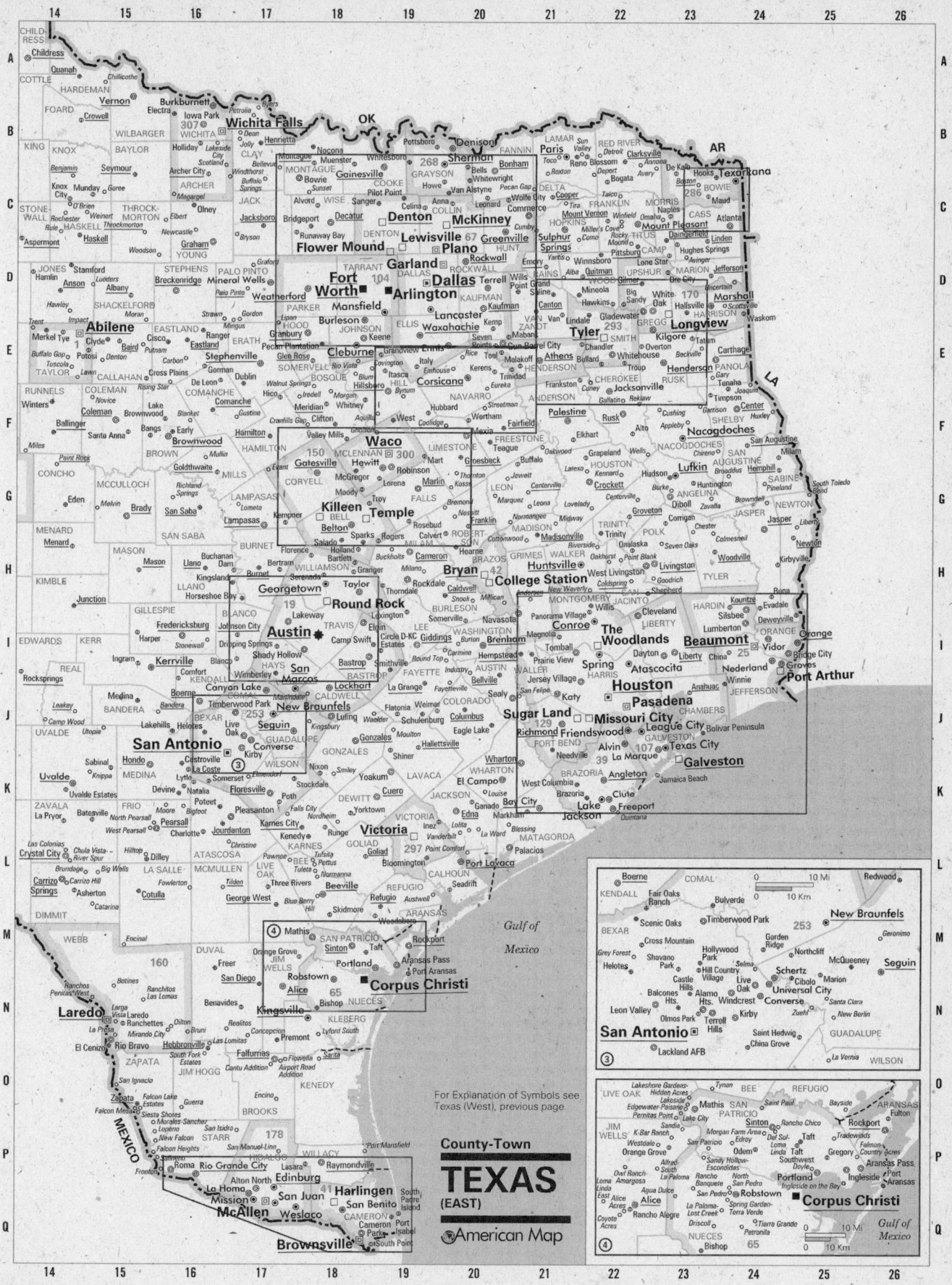

County-Town

TEXAS
(EAST)

American Map

■ **ABILENE CHRISTIAN UNIVERSITY** *E-14*
ACU Box 29100
Abilene, TX 79699-9100
Tel: (325)674-2000
Free: 800-460-6228
Admissions: (325)674-2765
Web Site: http://www.acu.edu/
Description: Independent, comprehensive, coed, affiliated with Church of Christ. Awards associate, bachelor's, master's, doctoral, and first professional degrees and post-master's certificates. Founded 1906. Setting: 208-acre urban campus. Endowment: $189.8 million. Research spending for 2004 fiscal year: $255,370. Educational spending for 2005 fiscal year: $5346 per student. Total enrollment: 4,685. Faculty: 359 (218 full-time, 141 part-time). Student-undergrad faculty ratio is 16:1. 3,825 applied, 55% were admitted. 21% from top 10% of their high school class, 49% from top quarter, 78% from top half. 8 National Merit Scholars, 31 valedictorians. Full-time: 3,929 students, 54% women, 46% men. Part-time: 191 students, 65% women, 35% men. Students come from 48 states and territories, 50 other countries, 22% from out-of-state, 1% Native American, 7% Hispanic, 7% black, 1% Asian American or Pacific Islander, 4% international, 7% 25 or older, 42% live on campus, 6% transferred in. Retention: 73% of full-time freshmen returned the following year. Academic areas with the most degrees conferred: business/marketing; education; interdisciplinary studies. Core. Calendar: semesters. ESL program, services for LD students, advanced placement, self-designed majors, honors program, independent study, distance learning, double major, summer session for credit, part-time degree program, external degree program, adult/continuing education programs, internships, graduate courses open to undergrads. Off campus study at McMurry University, Hardin-Simmons University, Texas Tech University, The University of Texas at Dallas, The University of Texas at Arlington. Study abroad program.
Entrance Requirements: Options: Common Application, electronic application, early admission. Required: high school transcript, 2 recommendations, SAT or ACT. Recommended: minimum 2.0 high school GPA, interview. Entrance: moderately difficult. Application deadline: 8/1. Notification: continuous until 9/1.
Costs Per Year: Application fee: $25. Comprehensive fee: $20,830 includes full-time tuition ($14,610), mandatory fees ($550), and college room and board ($5670). College room only: $2750. Full-time tuition and fees vary according to course load. Room and board charges vary according to board plan and housing facility. Part-time tuition: $487 per semester hour. Part-time mandatory fees: $26.50 per semester hour, $10 per term. Part-time tuition and fees vary according to course load.
Collegiate Environment: Orientation program. Drama-theater group, choral group, marching band, student-run newspaper, radio station. Social organizations: 104 open to all; local fraternities, local sororities; 18% of eligible men and 22% of eligible women are members. Most popular organizations: Student Association, Alpha Phi Omega, 'W' Club, Spring Break Campaign, Student Alumni Association. Major annual events: homecoming, Sing Song, Welcome Week. Student services: health clinic, personal-psychological counseling. Campus security: 24-hour emergency response devices and patrols, late night transport-escort service. 1,866 college housing spaces available; 1,780 were occupied in 2003-04. Freshmen guaranteed college housing. On-campus residence required through sophomore year. Options: men-only, women-only housing available. Brown Library with 490,973 books, 1,2 million microform titles, 2,435 serials, 64,131

audiovisual materials, an OPAC, and a Web page. Operations spending for 2004 fiscal year: $1.6 million. 700 computers available on campus for general student use. A campuswide network can be accessed from student residence rooms and from off campus. Staffed computer lab on campus.
Community Environment: Abilene, Texas, has the reputation of being a friendly and caring community. USA Today's annual "Make a Difference Day" issue has recognized Abilene's community efforts in each of the past three years. Abilene is located 150 miles west of the Dallas/Ft. Worth metroplex and has a population of about 110,000. Its climate is warm and sunny, with an occasional light snow some winters. Residents of Abilene are served by shopping malls, major restaurant chains, specialty shops, two hospitals, and a regional airport. Abilene is the home of Dyess Air Force Base. The city is second only to Houston in cultural events per capita in Texas, and has one of the lowest crime rates in the state. Part-time employment is available.

■ **THE ACADEMY OF HEALTH CARE PROFESSIONS** *J-22*
1900 North Loop West, Ste. 100
Houston, TX 77018
Tel: (713)862-2633
Admissions: (713)425-3111
Fax: (713)746-5466
E-mail: wfederick@academyofhealth.com
Web Site: http://www.academyofhealth.com/
Description: Proprietary, 2-year, coed. Awards terminal associate degrees. Founded 1988. Total enrollment: 224. Calendar: semesters.

■ **ALVIN COMMUNITY COLLEGE** *J-22*
3110 Mustang Rd.
Alvin, TX 77511-4898
Tel: (281)756-3500
Admissions: (281)756-3531
Fax: (281)756-3854
E-mail: admiss.rec.acc@flipper.alvin.cc.tx.us
Web Site: http://www.alvincollege.edu/
Description: State and locally supported, 2-year, coed. Awards certificates, diplomas, transfer associate, and terminal associate degrees. Founded 1949. Setting: 114-acre small town campus with easy access to Houston. Educational spending for 2005 fiscal year: $1211 per student. Total enrollment: 3,932. 590 applied, 100% were admitted. Full-time: 1,611 students, 57% women, 43% men. Part-time: 2,321 students, 56% women, 44% men. Students come from 17 states and territories, 5 other countries, 1% from out-of-state, 1% Native American, 20% Hispanic, 8% black, 2% Asian American or Pacific Islander, 0.3% international, 38% 25 or older, 6% transferred in. Core. Calendar: semesters. Academic remediation for entering students, ESL program, services for LD students, advanced placement, accelerated degree program, self-designed majors, honors program, independent study, distance learning, double major, summer session for credit, part-time degree program, adult/continuing education programs, internships. Study abroad program.
Entrance Requirements: Open admission. Required for some: high school transcript. Placement: THEA, ACCUPLACER required. Entrance: noncompetitive. Application deadline: Rolling.
Collegiate Environment: Orientation program. Drama-theater group, choral group, student-run radio station. Social organizations: 33 open to all. Most popular organizations: Student Government Association, Baptist Student

Union, Pan American College Forum, Catholic Newman Association, Phi Theta Kappa. Major annual events: Fall Festival and Carnival, Festival of Lights, Cinco de Mayo. Student services: personal-psychological counseling. Campus security: 24-hour patrols, late night transport-escort service. College housing not available. Alvin Community College Library with 28,361 books, 176 microform titles, 146 serials, 5 audiovisual materials, an OPAC, and a Web page. Operations spending for 2004 fiscal year: $238,452. 622 computers available on campus for general student use. A campuswide network can be accessed from off-campus. Staffed computer lab on campus.

Community Environment: Population 22,000, Alvin is a suburban community located 30 minutes from Houston, Galveston, and NASA. The city is served by a private airport, railroad, bus line, and State Routes 6 and 35. There are churches of major denominations, a public library, and hospital. Public recreation includes a theatre, bowling, fishing, and boating. Major civic, fraternal, and veteran's organizations are active in Alvin.

■ **AMARILLO COLLEGE** C-3
PO Box 447
Amarillo, TX 79178-0001
Tel: (806)371-5000
Admissions: (806)371-5024
Fax: (806)371-5370
E-mail: austin-rc@actx.edu
Web Site: http://www.actx.edu/
Description: State and locally supported, 2-year, coed. Awards certificates, transfer associate, and terminal associate degrees. Founded 1929. Setting: 58-acre suburban campus. Endowment: $13.6 million. Research spending for 2004 fiscal year: $17,000. Total enrollment: 10,196. Students come from 9 states and territories, 1% from out-of-state, 1% Native American, 22% Hispanic, 3% black, 3% Asian American or Pacific Islander, 43% 25 or older. Core. Calendar: semesters. Academic remediation for entering students, ESL program, services for LD students, advanced placement, honors program, distance learning, summer session for credit, part-time degree program, adult/continuing education programs.
Entrance Requirements: Open admission. Options: early admission, deferred admission. Required: high school transcript. Placement: THEA, MAPS required. Entrance: noncompetitive. Notification: continuous.
Costs Per Year: Application fee: $0. Area resident tuition: $1278 full-time, $53.25 per credit part-time. State resident tuition: $1638 full-time, $68.25 per credit part-time. Nonresident tuition: $5478 full-time, $228.25 per credit part-time.
Collegiate Environment: Drama-theater group, choral group, student-run newspaper, radio station. Most popular organizations: Student Government Association, College Republicans. Major annual events: Fall Fest, Badgerama, Spring Fling. Student services: personal-psychological counseling. Campus security: 24-hour patrols, late night transport-escort service. College housing not available. Lynn Library Learning Center plus 1 other with 75,200 books, 325 serials, and an OPAC. Operations spending for 2004 fiscal year: $745,000. 450 computers available on campus for general student use. A campuswide network can be accessed. Staffed computer lab on campus.
Community Environment: Population 165,425. Situated on the high plains of the Texas Panhandle, Amarillo is the capital of the oil and as industry. Pipelines from adjacent fields extend as far as the east coast. The average temperature ranges from 37.4 degrees in winter to 76 degrees in summer. The community is provided transportation by bus, and airlines, as well as five interstate highways and one state highway. Amarillo has many churches representing various faiths, public libraries, museums, several hospitals, a YMCA, and various civic, fraternal, and veteran's organizations. Part-time employment is available. Off-campus housing is plentiful.

■ **AMBERTON UNIVERSITY** D-19
1700 Eastgate Dr.
Garland, TX 75041-5595
Tel: (972)279-6511
Fax: (972)279-9773
Web Site: http://www.amberton.edu/
Description: Independent nondenominational, upper-level, coed. Awards bachelor's and master's degrees. Founded 1971. Setting: 5-acre suburban campus with easy access to Dallas-Fort Worth. Endowment: $10 million. Educational spending for 2005 fiscal year: $7400 per student. Total enrollment: 1,648. Faculty: 39 (14 full-time, 25 part-time). Student-undergrad faculty ratio is 25:1. Full-time: 126 students, 67% women, 33% men. Part-time: 507 students, 67% women, 33% men. 0% from out-of-state, 1% Native

American, 6% Hispanic, 31% black, 1% Asian American or Pacific Islander, 0% international, 98% 25 or older. Core. Calendar: 4 10-week terms. Self-designed majors, summer session for credit, part-time degree program, external degree program, adult/continuing education programs, internships, graduate courses open to undergrads.
Costs Per Year: Application fee: $0. Tuition: $6000 full-time, $200 per hour part-time.
Collegiate Environment: Campus security: 24-hour emergency response devices and patrols. College housing not available. Library Resource Center plus 1 other with 21,000 books, 120 serials, an OPAC, and a Web page. Operations spending for 2004 fiscal year: $100,000. 30 computers available on campus for general student use. Staffed computer lab on campus.

■ **AMERICAN INTERCONTINENTAL UNIVERSITY** J-22
9999 Richmond Ave.
Houston, TX 77042
Tel: (832)242-5788
Admissions: (832)201-3600
Fax: (832)242-5775
Web Site: http://www.aiuhouston.com/
Description: Proprietary, 4-year, coed. Awards associate, bachelor's, and master's degrees. Founded 2003. Total enrollment: 349. Faculty: 31 (14 full-time, 17 part-time). Student-undergrad faculty ratio is 11:1. Calendar: five 10-week terms.
Entrance Requirements: Required: high school transcript. Application deadline: Rolling. Notification: continuous.
Costs Per Year: Application fee: $50. Tuition: $18,420 full-time. Mandatory fees: $520 full-time.

■ **ANGELINA COLLEGE** G-23
PO Box 1768
Lufkin, TX 75902-1768
Tel: (409)639-1301
Admissions: (936)633-5201
Fax: (409)639-4299
Web Site: http://www.angelina.cc.tx.us/
Description: State and locally supported, 2-year, coed. Awards certificates, diplomas, transfer associate, and terminal associate degrees. Founded 1968. Setting: 140-acre small town campus. Endowment: $2.6 million. Total enrollment: 4,976. 6% from top 10% of their high school class, 20% from top quarter, 40% from top half. Students come from 15 states and territories, 2% from out-of-state, 33% 25 or older, 1% live on campus. Core. Calendar: semesters. Academic remediation for entering students, services for LD students, advanced placement, self-designed majors, honors program, distance learning, double major, summer session for credit, part-time degree program, adult/continuing education programs, co-op programs and internships. Off campus study. ROTC: Army (c).
Entrance Requirements: Open admission. Options: Peterson's Universal Application, Common Application, electronic application, early admission, deferred admission. Required: high school transcript. Placement: ACT COMPASS, THEA required. Entrance: noncompetitive. Application deadline: Rolling. Notification: continuous.
Collegiate Environment: Orientation program. Drama-theater group, choral group, student-run newspaper. Social organizations: local fraternities, local sororities; 6% of eligible men and 8% of eligible women are members. Most popular organizations: Students in Free Enterprise, Phi Theta Kappa, Student Nurses Association, Rodeo Club. Major annual events: Red Ribbon Week, Smokeout, School Spring Picnic. Student services: personal-psychological counseling. Campus security: 24-hour patrols. Option: coed housing available. Angelina College Library with 37,000 books, 270 serials, and an OPAC. Operations spending for 2004 fiscal year: $295,174. 200 computers available on campus for general student use. A campuswide network can be accessed from off-campus. Staffed computer lab on campus.
Community Environment: Population 33,000. Lufkin derives most of its income from the lumber and paper-making industries, two iron foundries and one chromium corporation. This urban community is headquarters for four national forests. The climate is temperate and mild. Lufkin is served by three railroad lines, airlines, and U.S. Routes 59 and 69. The community has a public library, 20 churches, three hospitals, and many civic, fraternal, and veteran's organizations. Part-time employment opportunities are unlimited. Local recreation includes theatres, hunting, fishing, boating, nearby Rayburn Lake, baseball, and swimming pools.

■ **ANGELO STATE UNIVERSITY** G-13
2601 West Ave. N
San Angelo, TX 76909

Tel: (325)942-2555
Admissions: (325)942-2185
Fax: (325)942-2038
E-mail: admissions@angelo.edu
Web Site: http://www.angelo.edu/
Description: State-supported, comprehensive, coed. Part of Texas State University System. Awards associate, bachelor's, and master's degrees. Founded 1928. Setting: 268-acre urban campus. Endowment: $83.1 million. Research spending for 2004 fiscal year: $734,307. Educational spending for 2005 fiscal year: $1901 per student. Total enrollment: 6,156. Faculty: 350 (233 full-time, 117 part-time). Student-undergrad faculty ratio is 20:1. 2,224 applied, 99% were admitted. 12% from top 10% of their high school class, 40% from top quarter, 75% from top half. 20 valedictorians. Full-time: 4,840 students, 53% women, 47% men. Part-time: 869 students, 58% women, 42% men. Students come from 40 states and territories, 25 other countries, 2% from out-of-state, 0.5% Native American, 23% Hispanic, 6% black, 1% Asian American or Pacific Islander, 1% international, 20% 25 or older, 25% live on campus, 8% transferred in. Retention: 61% of full-time freshmen returned the following year. Academic areas with the most degrees conferred: business/marketing; interdisciplinary studies; parks and recreation. Core. Calendar: semesters. Academic remediation for entering students, services for LD students, advanced placement, accelerated degree program, honors program, independent study, distance learning, double major, summer session for credit, part-time degree program, adult/continuing education programs, internships, graduate courses open to undergrads. Off campus study. Study abroad program. ROTC: Air Force.
Entrance Requirements: Options: Peterson's Universal Application, Common Application, electronic application, early admission, deferred admission. Required: high school transcript, high school class rank, SAT or ACT. Entrance: moderately difficult. Application deadline: 8/1. Notification: continuous.
Costs Per Year: Application fee: $20. State resident tuition: $3180 full-time, $156 per credit hour part-time. Nonresident tuition: $11,460 full-time, $432 per credit hour part-time. Mandatory fees: $1110 full-time. College room and board: $5314. College room only: $3147.
Collegiate Environment: Orientation program. Drama-theater group, choral group, marching band, student-run newspaper, radio station. Social organizations: 75 open to all; national fraternities, national sororities, local fraternities, local sororities; 3% of eligible men and 4% of eligible women are members. Most popular organizations: Block and Bridle Club, Baptist Student Union, Delta Sigma Pi, Air Force ROTC, Association of Mexican-American Students. Major annual events: homecoming, Parents' Day, Fish Splash. Student services: health clinic, personal-psychological counseling. Campus security: 24-hour emergency response devices and patrols, student patrols, late night transport-escort service, controlled dormitory access. 1,536 college housing spaces available. Freshmen given priority for college housing. On-campus residence required through sophomore year. Options: coed, women-only housing available. Porter Henderson Library plus 1 other with 481,826 books, 949,295 microform titles, 1,628 serials, 30,648 audiovisual materials, an OPAC, and a Web page. Operations spending for 2004 fiscal year: $1.5 million. 600 computers available on campus for general student use. A campuswide network can be accessed from student residence rooms and from off campus. Staffed computer lab on campus.
Community Environment: Population approx 100,000. San Angelo is an attractive city located in the heart of West Texas ranch country. San Angelo and the surrounding area provide a readily accessible social and physical environment for cultural and recreational activities so essential to the university community. Three nearby lakes make water sports a popular attraction among students and those living in San Angelo.

■ **ARGOSY UNIVERSITY/DALLAS** *D-19*
8950 North Central Expressway
Dallas, TX 75231
Tel: (214)890-9900; (866)954-9900
Fax: (214)656-3900
Web Site: http://www.argosyu.edu/
Description: Proprietary, upper-level, coed. Part of Argosy University System. Awards bachelor's, master's, and doctoral degrees. Founded 2002. Setting: urban campus. Total enrollment: 330. Full-time: 18 students, 67% women, 33% men. Part-time: 12 students, 83% women, 17% men. 27% transferred in. Core. Calendar: semesters. Accelerated degree program, distance learning, summer session for credit, part-time degree program, adult/continuing education programs.
Collegiate Environment: Campus security: late night transport-escort service. College housing not available.

■ **ARLINGTON BAPTIST COLLEGE** *D-19*
3001 West Division
Arlington, TX 76012-3425
Tel: (817)461-8741
Fax: (817)274-1138
E-mail: jhall@abconline.org
Web Site: http://www.abconline.edu/
Description: Independent Baptist, 4-year, coed. Awards bachelor's degrees. Founded 1939. Setting: 32-acre urban campus with easy access to Dallas-Fort Worth. Endowment: $72,008. Educational spending for 2005 fiscal year: $12,915 per student. Total enrollment: 181. Student-undergrad faculty ratio is 14:1. 72 applied, 100% were admitted. 0% from top 10% of their high school class, 24% from top quarter, 65% from top half. Full-time: 143 students, 49% women, 51% men. Part-time: 38 students, 50% women, 50% men. Students come from 18 states and territories, 7 other countries, 22% from out-of-state, 1% Native American, 4% Hispanic, 2% black, 1% Asian American or Pacific Islander, 6% international, 28% 25 or older, 48% live on campus, 38% transferred in. Retention: 46% of full-time freshmen returned the following year. Academic area with the most degrees conferred: education. Core. Calendar: semesters. Academic remediation for entering students, advanced placement, independent study, distance learning, double major, summer session for credit, part-time degree program, internships.
Entrance Requirements: Options: early admission, deferred admission, international baccalaureate accepted. Required: essay, high school transcript, 1 recommendation, pastoral recommendation, medical examination. Required for some: interview. Entrance: noncompetitive. Application deadline: Rolling. Notification: continuous. Preference given to professing Christians.
Costs Per Year: Application fee: $15. Comprehensive fee: $9250 includes full-time tuition ($4950), mandatory fees ($500), and college room and board ($3800). Part-time tuition: $165 per hour.
Collegiate Environment: Orientation program. Choral group, student-run newspaper. Social organizations: 5 open to all. Most popular organizations: Preachers Fellowship, Student Missionary Association, L.I.F.T., International Students Association, 4-12 Group. Major annual events: 'First Saturday Night Back', Homecoming Weekend, Fellowship Week. Student services: personal-psychological counseling. Campus security: student patrols, controlled dormitory access, night security guards. 160 college housing spaces available; 93 were occupied in 2003-04. Freshmen guaranteed college housing. On-campus residence required through senior year. Options: men-only, women-only housing available. Dr. Earl K. Oldham Library with 27,486 books, 399 microform titles, 701 serials, and 412 audiovisual materials. Operations spending for 2004 fiscal year: $76,799. 21 computers available on campus for general student use. A campuswide network can be accessed. Staffed computer lab on campus.
Community Environment: See University of Texas at Arlington.

■ **THE ART INSTITUTE OF DALLAS** *D-19*
Two NorthPark, 8080 Park Ln., Ste. 100
Dallas, TX 75231-9959
Tel: (214)692-8080
Free: 800-275-4243
Fax: (214)750-9460
Web Site: http://www.aid.edu/
Description: Proprietary, 4-year, coed. Part of Education Management Corporation. Awards associate and bachelor's degrees. Founded 1978. Setting: 2-acre urban campus. Total enrollment: 1,304. Student-undergrad faculty ratio is 18:1. Full-time: 997 students, 53% women, 47% men. Part-time: 307 students, 52% women, 48% men. Students come from 21 states and territories, 2 other countries, 16% from out-of-state, 1% Native American, 20% Hispanic, 9% black, 5% Asian American or Pacific Islander, 2% international, 20% live on campus. Retention: 94% of full-time freshmen returned the following year. Academic area with the most degrees conferred: visual and performing arts. Core. Academic remediation for entering students, summer session for credit, internships.
Entrance Requirements: Open admission. Option: deferred admission. Required: essay, high school transcript, interview. Entrance: noncompetitive. Application deadline: Rolling. Notification: continuous.
Costs Per Year: Application fee: $50. Tuition: $17,542 full-time, $390 per credit hour part-time. College room only: $4896.
Collegiate Environment: Student-run newspaper. Social organizations: 6 open to all. Most popular organizations: Young Chef Society, Multimedia Users Group, American Society of Interior Designers, Student Ambassadors, Web Girls. Major annual events: charity fund raisers, Fall Picnic, fashion

show. Student services: personal-psychological counseling. Campus security: 24-hour emergency response devices and patrols, late night transport-escort service. 205 undergraduates lived in college housing during 2003-04. Freshmen guaranteed college housing. Option: coed housing available. Mildred M. Kelley Library and Learning Resource Center plus 1 other with 24,000 books, 4,200 serials, 1,850 audiovisual materials, an OPAC, and a Web page. 96 computers available on campus for general student use. Computer purchase/lease plans available. A campuswide network can be accessed. Staffed computer lab on campus.

■ THE ART INSTITUTE OF HOUSTON *J-22*

1900 Yorktown
Houston, TX 77056-4115
Tel: (713)623-2040
Free: 800-275-4244
Fax: (713)966-2797
E-mail: sbehrens@aii.edu
Web Site: http://www.aih.artinstitutes.edu/

Description: Proprietary, 4-year, coed. Part of Education Management Corporation. Awards associate and bachelor's degrees. Founded 1978. Setting: urban campus. Total enrollment: 1,657. Student-undergrad faculty ratio is 20:1. 1,382 applied, 37% were admitted. Full-time: 1,066 students, 47% women, 53% men. Part-time: 591 students, 45% women, 55% men. Students come from 19 other countries, 0% from out-of-state, 0.4% Native American, 20% Hispanic, 10% black, 4% Asian American or Pacific Islander, 0% international, 33% 25 or older, 15% live on campus. Retention: 57% of full-time freshmen returned the following year. Academic area with the most degrees conferred: visual and performing arts. Core. Academic remediation for entering students, advanced placement, distance learning, adult/continuing education programs, co-op programs and internships. Off campus study at other members of The Art Institutes International.

Entrance Requirements: Options: Peterson's Universal Application, Common Application, electronic application. Required: essay, high school transcript, recommendations. Recommended: minimum 2.1 high school GPA, SAT or ACT. Required for some: minimum 2.5 high school GPA, portfolio. Entrance: moderately difficult. Application deadline: Rolling. Notification: continuous.

Costs Per Year: Application fee: $50. Tuition: $23,580 full-time, $393 per credit part-time. College room only: $3082.

Collegiate Environment: Orientation program. Most popular organizations: Texas Chef's Association, Association of Interior Designers, Computer Animation Society, Houston Ad Federation, International Television Association. Major annual events: Student Success Day, Faculty of the Quarter Project. Student services: personal-psychological counseling. Campus security: 24-hour emergency response devices. 100 college housing spaces available; all were occupied in 2003-04. No special consideration for freshman housing applicants. Options: coed, men-only, women-only housing available. Resource Center with 10,000 books, 188 serials, and an OPAC. Operations spending for 2004 fiscal year: $198,770. 194 computers available on campus for general student use. A campuswide network can be accessed from student residence rooms and from off campus. Staffed computer lab on campus.

■ ATI TECHNICAL TRAINING CENTER *D-19*

6627 Maple Ave.
Dallas, TX 75235
Tel: (214)263-4284
Admissions: (214)352-2222
Fax: (214)358-7500
E-mail: bdelozier@atienterprises.edu
Web Site: http://www.aticareertraining.com/
Description: Proprietary, 2-year, coed.

■ AUSTIN BUSINESS COLLEGE *I-18*

2101 IH-35 South, Third Floor
Austin, TX 78741
Tel: (512)447-9415
Fax: (512)447-0194
E-mail: pambinns@austinbusinesscollege.org
Web Site: http://www.austinbusinesscollege.org/
Description: Proprietary, 2-year, coed. Awards certificates and terminal associate degrees. Educational spending for 2005 fiscal year: $12,000 per student. Total enrollment: 252. 300 applied, 92% were admitted. 5% from top 10% of their high school class, 25% from top quarter, 50% from top half.

Full-time: 201 students, 80% women, 20% men. Part-time: 51 students, 78% women, 22% men. Students come from 5 states and territories, 2 other countries, 5% from out-of-state, 70% 25 or older. Core. Academic remediation for entering students, honors program, independent study, external degree program, adult/continuing education programs, co-op programs and internships.

Entrance Requirements: Open admission. Required: essay, high school transcript, interview, Wonderlic aptitude test. Entrance: noncompetitive. Application deadline: Rolling.

Collegiate Environment: Orientation program. Learning Resource Center with 1,000 books, 15 serials, and 50 audiovisual materials. Operations spending for 2004 fiscal year: $7500. 200 computers available on campus for general student use. A campuswide network can be accessed. Staffed computer lab on campus.

■ AUSTIN COLLEGE *C-19*

900 North Grand Ave.
Sherman, TX 75090-4400
Tel: (903)813-2000
Free: 800-442-5363
Admissions: (903)813-3000
Fax: (903)813-3198
E-mail: admission@austincollege.edu
Web Site: http://www.austincollege.edu/

Description: Independent Presbyterian, comprehensive, coed. Awards bachelor's and master's degrees. Founded 1849. Setting: 60-acre suburban campus with easy access to Dallas-Fort Worth. Endowment: $107.9 million. Research spending for 2004 fiscal year: $97,314. Educational spending for 2005 fiscal year: $9317 per student. Total enrollment: 1,327. Faculty: 131 (91 full-time, 40 part-time). Student-undergrad faculty ratio is 12:1. 1,530 applied, 67% were admitted. 44% from top 10% of their high school class, 75% from top quarter, 97% from top half. 5 National Merit Scholars, 10 valedictorians. Full-time: 1,286 students, 55% women, 45% men. Part-time: 12 students, 50% women, 50% men. Students come from 29 states and territories, 21 other countries, 9% from out-of-state, 1% Native American, 9% Hispanic, 4% black, 12% Asian American or Pacific Islander, 1% international, 1% 25 or older, 72% live on campus, 3% transferred in. Retention: 88% of full-time freshmen returned the following year. Academic areas with the most degrees conferred: social sciences; psychology; business/marketing. Core. Calendar: 4-1-4. Advanced placement, self-designed majors, honors program, independent study, double major, summer session for credit, part-time degree program, adult/continuing education programs, internships, graduate courses open to undergrads. Off campus study. Study abroad program.

Entrance Requirements: Options: Common Application, electronic application, early admission, early decision, early action, deferred admission, international baccalaureate accepted. Required: essay, high school transcript, 2 recommendations, SAT or ACT. Recommended: minimum 3.0 high school GPA, interview. Required for some: interview. Entrance: very difficult. Application deadlines: 5/1, 12/1 for early decision, 1/15 for early action. Notification: 1/10 for early decision, 3/1 for early action.

Costs Per Year: Application fee: $35. Comprehensive fee: $31,281 includes full-time tuition ($23,355), mandatory fees ($185), and college room and board ($7741). College room only: $3554. Part-time tuition: $3385 per course.

Collegiate Environment: Orientation program. Drama-theater group, choral group, student-run newspaper. Social organizations: 50 open to all; local fraternities, local sororities; 29% of eligible men and 28% of eligible women are members. Most popular organizations: Fellowship of Christian Athletes, Campus Activity Board, Indian Cultural Association, Student Development Board, International Relations Club. Major annual events: Homecoming, Earth Day, Spring Fest. Student services: health clinic, personal-psychological counseling. Campus security: 24-hour emergency response devices and patrols, late night transport-escort service, controlled dormitory access. 951 college housing spaces available; 913 were occupied in 2003-04. Freshmen guaranteed college housing. On-campus residence required through junior year. Options: coed, men-only, women-only housing available. Abell Library with 240,944 books, 113,834 microform titles, 2,181 serials, 7,917 audiovisual materials, an OPAC, and a Web page. Operations spending for 2004 fiscal year: $1.1 million. 165 computers available on campus for general student use. A campuswide network can be accessed from student residence rooms and from off campus. Staffed computer lab on campus.

Community Environment: Sherman, population 35,000, is a retail trade and industrial center located in north central Texas 60 miles north of Dallas.

The climate is mild and temperate. The average annual temperature is 64 degrees. Two bus lines, and U.S. Highways 82 and 75 serve the area. The community has a library, two hospitals, a shopping mall, two theatres, and various civic and fraternal organizations. Local recreation includes golf, bowling, skating, hunting, and on Lake Texoma with a 1,250 mile shoreline, fishing, swimming, water skiing, and boating. Part-time employment is available.

■ AUSTIN COMMUNITY COLLEGE *I-18*

5930 Middle Fiskville Rd.
Austin, TX 78752-4390
Tel: (512)223-7000
Admissions: (512)223-7766
Fax: (512)223-7665
E-mail: lkluck@austincc.edu
Web Site: http://www.austincc.edu/
Description: District-supported, 2-year, coed. Awards certificates, transfer associate, and terminal associate degrees. Founded 1972. Setting: urban campus. Total enrollment: 31,908. Student-undergrad faculty ratio is 20:1. 5,718 applied, 100% were admitted. Full-time: 8,829 students, 51% women, 49% men. Part-time: 23,079 students, 59% women, 41% men. Students come from 93 other countries, 2% from out-of-state, 1% Native American, 23% Hispanic, 7% black, 5% Asian American or Pacific Islander, 2% international, 39% 25 or older. Core. Calendar: semesters. Academic remediation for entering students, ESL program, services for LD students, advanced placement, accelerated degree program, honors program, independent study, distance learning, summer session for credit, part-time degree program, external degree program, adult/continuing education programs, co-op programs and internships. ROTC: Army (c), Air Force (c).
Entrance Requirements: Open admission. Option: electronic application. Entrance: noncompetitive. Application deadline: Rolling.
Costs Per Year: Application fee: $0. Area resident tuition: $1170 full-time, $39 per credit hour part-time. State resident tuition: $3060 full-time, $102 per credit hour part-time. Nonresident tuition: $5670 full-time, $189 per credit hour part-time. Mandatory fees: $420 full-time, $14 per credit hour part-time.
Collegiate Environment: Orientation program. Drama-theater group, student-run newspaper. Student services: personal-psychological counseling. College housing not available. Main library plus 6 others with 115,567 books, 62,574 microform titles, 1,974 serials, 14,044 audiovisual materials, an OPAC, and a Web page. 225 computers available on campus for general student use. A campuswide network can be accessed from off-campus. Staffed computer lab on campus.
Community Environment: See University of Texas at Austin.

■ AUSTIN GRADUATE SCHOOL OF THEOLOGY *I-18*

1909 University Ave.
Austin, TX 78705-5610
Tel: (512)476-2772; (866)AUS-GRAD
Fax: (512)476-3919
E-mail: keason@austingrad.edu
Web Site: http://www.austingrad.edu/
Description: Independent, upper-level, coed, affiliated with Church of Christ. Awards bachelor's and master's degrees. Founded 1917. Setting: urban campus. Endowment: $4 million. Research spending for 2004 fiscal year: $10,925. Educational spending for 2005 fiscal year: $5096 per student. Total enrollment: 61. Faculty: 10 (4 full-time, 6 part-time). Student-undergrad faculty ratio is 2:1. Full-time: 3 students, 67% women, 33% men. Part-time: 24 students, 38% women, 63% men. Students come from 3 states and territories, 3% from out-of-state, 11% Hispanic, 30% black, 87% 25 or older, 44% transferred in. Core. Calendar: semesters. Summer session for credit, part-time degree program, adult/continuing education programs.
Costs Per Year: Application fee: $0. Tuition: $5700 full-time, $570 per course part-time. Full-time tuition varies according to course load. Part-time tuition varies according to course load.
Collegiate Environment: Orientation program. Social organizations: 1 open to all. Most popular organization: student government. Major annual events: Christmas Party, Spring Picnic. Campus security: 24-hour emergency response devices. College housing not available. Austin Graduate School Library plus 1 other with 25,000 books, 120 serials, an OPAC, and a Web page. Operations spending for 2004 fiscal year: $92,030. 8 computers available on campus for general student use. A campuswide network can be accessed from off-campus. Staffed computer lab on campus.

■ BAPTIST MISSIONARY ASSOCIATION THEOLOGICAL SEMINARY *F-22*

1530 East Pine St.
Jacksonville, TX 75766-5407
Tel: (903)586-2501
Web Site: http://www.bmats.edu/
Description: Independent Baptist, comprehensive, coed. Awards associate, bachelor's, master's, and first professional degrees. Founded 1955. Setting: 17-acre small town campus. Endowment: $613,239. Educational spending for 2005 fiscal year: $3230 per student. Total enrollment: 94. 20 applied, 90% were admitted. Full-time: 14 students, 7% women, 93% men. Part-time: 34 students, 9% women, 91% men. Students come from 7 states and territories, 29% from out-of-state, 2% Native American, 2% Hispanic, 25% black, 0% Asian American or Pacific Islander, 6% international, 79% 25 or older, 36% live on campus, 4% transferred in. Retention: 100% of full-time freshmen returned the following year. Core. Calendar: semesters. Independent study, summer session for credit, part-time degree program, adult/continuing education programs, internships, graduate courses open to undergrads.
Entrance Requirements: Open admission. Required: 3 recommendations, interview. Entrance: noncompetitive. Application deadline: 7/25. Notification: continuous.
Costs Per Year: Application fee: $20. Tuition: $2880 full-time, $80 per hour part-time. Mandatory fees: $160 full-time, $40 per term part-time. College room only: $2400.
Collegiate Environment: Student services: personal-psychological counseling. 9 undergraduates lived in college housing during 2003-04. No special consideration for freshman housing applicants. Kellar Library with 63,603 books, 947 microform titles, 453 serials, 5,886 audiovisual materials, and an OPAC. Operations spending for 2004 fiscal year: $112,000. 5 computers available on campus for general student use.

■ BAPTIST UNIVERSITY OF THE AMERICAS *K-16*

8019 South Pan Am Expressway
San Antonio, TX 78224-2701
Tel: (210)924-4338
Free: 800-721-1396
Fax: (210)924-2701
E-mail: mranjel@bua.edu
Web Site: http://www.bua.edu/
Description: Independent Baptist, 4-year, coed. Awards bachelor's degrees (associate degree in Cross-Cultural Studies). Founded 1947. Endowment: $2.2 million. Educational spending for 2005 fiscal year: $3367 per student. Total enrollment: 171. Student-undergrad faculty ratio is 14:1. 124 applied, 50% were admitted. Full-time: 131 students, 34% women, 66% men. Part-time: 40 students, 33% women, 68% men. 0% from out-of-state, 59% Hispanic, 2% black, 2% Asian American or Pacific Islander, 30% international. Academic area with the most degrees conferred: theology and religious vocations. Calendar: semesters.
Entrance Requirements: Required: essay, high school transcript, 2 recommendations. Required for some: interview, ACCUPLACER, THEA (TEXAS HIGHER EDUCATION ASSESSMENT), TOEFL (TEST OF ENGLISH AS A SECOND LANGUAGE). Application deadlines: 2/15, 2/15 for nonresidents, 12/15 for early decision.
Costs Per Year: Application fee: $25. Comprehensive fee: $3037 includes full-time tuition ($1500) and college room and board ($1537). College room only: $500. Part-time tuition: $125 per hour. Part-time mandatory fees: $125 per term.
Collegiate Environment: Drama-theater group, choral group. Social organizations: ; 15% of eligible men and 11% of eligible women are members. Student services: health clinic. 88 college housing spaces available; 84 were occupied in 2003-04.

■ BAYLOR UNIVERSITY *G-19*

Waco, TX 76798
Tel: (254)710-1011
Free: 800-BAYLOR U
Admissions: (254)710-3435
E-mail: admissions_office@baylor.edu
Web Site: http://www.baylor.edu/

Description: Independent Baptist, university, coed. Awards bachelor's, master's, doctoral, and first professional degrees and post-master's certificates. Founded 1845. Setting: 432-acre urban campus with easy access to Dallas-Fort Worth. Endowment: $745.8 million. Total enrollment: 13,975. Faculty: 910 (755 full-time, 155 part-time). Student-undergrad faculty ratio is 16:1. 15,443 applied, 66% were admitted. 38% from top 10% of their high school class, 68% from top quarter, 91% from top half. 44 National Merit Scholars. Full-time: 11,465 students, 59% women, 41% men. Part-time: 360 students, 56% women, 44% men. Students come from 50 states and territories, 90 other countries, 17% from out-of-state, 1% Native American, 10% Hispanic, 8% black, 7% Asian American or Pacific Islander, 1% international, 3% 25 or older, 34% live on campus, 4% transferred in. Retention: 83% of full-time freshmen returned the following year. Academic areas with the most degrees conferred: business/marketing; communications/journalism; education. Core. Calendar: semesters. Services for LD students, advanced placement, accelerated degree program, self-designed majors, honors program, double major, summer session for credit, part-time degree program, internships, graduate courses open to undergrads. Study abroad program. ROTC: Air Force.

Entrance Requirements: Options: Common Application, electronic application, early admission, international baccalaureate accepted. Required: high school transcript, SAT or ACT, ACT essay. Recommended: interview. Required for some: essay. Entrance: moderately difficult. Application deadline: Rolling. Notification: continuous.

Costs Per Year: Application fee: $50. Comprehensive fee: $29,939 includes full-time tuition ($20,574), mandatory fees ($2240), and college room and board ($7125). College room only: $3600. Part-time tuition: $857 per semester hour. Part-time mandatory fees: $82 per semester hour.

Collegiate Environment: Orientation program. Drama-theater group, choral group, marching band, student-run newspaper, radio station. Social organizations: 289 open to all; national fraternities, national sororities, local fraternities, local sororities; 15% of eligible men and 17% of eligible women are members. Most popular organizations: Alpha Phi Omega, College Republicans, Gamma Beta Phi, student government. Major annual events: Diadeloso (Student Day of Fun), Homecoming, All-University Sing. Student services: legal services, health clinic, personal-psychological counseling. Campus security: 24-hour emergency response devices and patrols, late night transport-escort service, controlled dormitory access, bicycle patrols. 4,140 college housing spaces available; 3,976 were occupied in 2003-04. Freshmen guaranteed college housing. On-campus residence required in freshman year. Options: men-only, women-only housing available. Moody Memorial Library plus 8 others with 2.3 million books, 2.2 million microform titles, 8,429 serials, 73,228 audiovisual materials, an OPAC, and a Web page. 1,500 computers available on campus for general student use. Computer purchase/lease plans available. A campuswide network can be accessed from student residence rooms and from off campus. Staffed computer lab on campus.

Community Environment: The campus adjoins the historic Brazos River in Waco, a Central Texas city of 110,000 people. The climate is temperate with a mean annual temperature of 67.4 degrees, and an average rainfall of 35 inches. Waco is reached by interstate, airlines, railroad, and bus lines. There are almost 200 churches of various faiths, public hospitals and a veteran's hospital, excellent libraries, and convenient shopping facilities in the area. Nineteen civic clubs and many fraternal organizations are active in Waco. Local recreation includes boating, swimming, fishing, picnicking, bowling, biking, golfing, hiking, tennis, parks, a zoo, and Lake Waco. Part-time employment is available for students.

■ **BLINN COLLEGE** *I-20*
902 College Ave.
Brenham, TX 77833-4049
Tel: (979)830-4000
Admissions: (979)830-4140
Web Site: http://www.blinn.edu/

Description: State and locally supported, 2-year, coed. Awards certificates, diplomas, transfer associate, and terminal associate degrees. Founded 1883. Setting: 100-acre small town campus with easy access to Houston. Endowment: $29.8 million. Educational spending for 2005 fiscal year: $1692 per student. Total enrollment: 14,057. 4,561 applied, 100% were admitted. Students come from 36 states and territories, 42 other countries, 1% from out-of-state, 0.4% Native American, 10% Hispanic, 8% black, 2% Asian American or Pacific Islander, 1% international, 14% 25 or older, 9% live on campus. Core. Calendar: semesters. Academic remediation for entering students, ESL program, services for LD students, advanced placement,

freshman honors college, honors program, distance learning, double major, summer session for credit, part-time degree program, adult/continuing education programs.

Entrance Requirements: Open admission. Options: Common Application, electronic application, early admission, deferred admission. Required: high school transcript. Placement: THEA required. Entrance: noncompetitive. Application deadline: Rolling.

Costs Per Year: Application fee: $0. State resident tuition: $1968 full-time, $82 per hour part-time. Nonresident tuition: $3912 full-time, $163 per hour part-time. College room and board: $3700. Room and board charges vary according to board plan, gender, and housing facility.

Collegiate Environment: Orientation program. Drama-theater group, choral group, marching band, student-run newspaper. Social organizations: 42 open to all. Most popular organizations: Student Government Association, Phi Theta Kappa, Baptist student ministries, Blinn Ethnic Student Organization, Circle K. Major annual events: Homecoming, Blinnfest, Transfer Day. Student services: personal-psychological counseling. Campus security: 24-hour emergency response devices and patrols, controlled dormitory access. 950 college housing spaces available; all were occupied in 2003-04. No special consideration for freshman housing applicants. On-campus residence required through sophomore year. Options: men-only, women-only housing available. W. L. Moody, Jr. Library plus 1 other with 130,000 books, 700 serials, an OPAC, and a Web page. Operations spending for 2004 fiscal year: $745,933. 1,200 computers available on campus for general student use. A campuswide network can be accessed from student residence rooms and from off campus. Staffed computer lab on campus.

Community Environment: Population 10,900. Brenham is a suburban community enjoying temperate climate. The city has libraries, and churches of various denominations. Railroad, bus lines, and major highways serve the area. Part-time employment is available for students. There are motels and apartment houses available for student housing. Brenham has hospitals, and civic and fraternal organizations are active within the area. Local recreation includes theaters, hunting, fishing, golf, and sports.

■ **BORDER INSTITUTE OF TECHNOLOGY** *F-2*
9611 Acer Ave.
El Paso, TX 79925-6744
Tel: (915)593-7328
Fax: (915)595-2507
Web Site: http://bitelp.edu/

Description: Proprietary, 2-year, coed. Awards certificates, diplomas, transfer associate, and terminal associate degrees. Setting: suburban campus. Total enrollment: 250. 40% 25 or older.

■ **BRAZOSPORT COLLEGE** *K-22*
500 College Dr.
Lake Jackson, TX 77566-3199
Tel: (979)230-3000
Admissions: (979)230-3217
Fax: (979)230-3443
E-mail: pleyende@brazosport.edu
Web Site: http://www.brazosport.edu/

Description: State and locally supported, 2-year, coed. Awards certificates, transfer associate, and terminal associate degrees. Founded 1968. Setting: 160-acre small town campus with easy access to Houston. Endowment: $3.3 million. Educational spending for 2005 fiscal year: $3396 per student. Total enrollment: 3,503. Student-undergrad faculty ratio is 18:1. 10% from top 10% of their high school class, 25% from top quarter, 62% from top half. Full-time: 1,670 students, 55% women, 45% men. Part-time: 1,833 students, 54% women, 46% men. Students come from 12 states and territories, 11 other countries, 1% from out-of-state, 0.4% Native American, 24% Hispanic, 6% black, 1% Asian American or Pacific Islander, 1% international, 42% 25 or older, 4% transferred in. Calendar: semesters. Academic remediation for entering students, advanced placement, honors program, distance learning, summer session for credit, part-time degree program, adult/continuing education programs, co-op programs and internships.

Entrance Requirements: Open admission. Options: early admission, deferred admission. Required for some: high school transcript. Placement: THEA, ACT, COMPASS required for some. Entrance: noncompetitive. Application deadline: 8/15.

Costs Per Year: Application fee: $0. Area resident tuition: $840 full-time, $28 per hour part-time. State resident tuition: $1470 full-time, $49 per hour part-time. Nonresident tuition: $2880 full-time, $96 per hour part-time. Mandatory fees: $300 full-time, $9 per hour part-time, $15 per term part-time. Full-time tuition and fees vary according to course load. Part-time tuition and fees vary according to course load.

Collegiate Environment: Orientation program. Drama-theater group, choral group, student-run newspaper. Social organizations: 4 open to all. Most popular organizations: Phi Theta Kappa, Baptist Student Ministry, Student Senate, Fencing Club. Major annual events: Gator Day, Senior College Day, Movie Night. Campus security: 24-hour patrols. College housing not available. Brazosport College Library with 85,425 books, 154,281 microform titles, 339 serials, 397 audiovisual materials, an OPAC, and a Web page. Operations spending for 2004 fiscal year: $514,205. 420 computers available on campus for general student use. A campuswide network can be accessed from off-campus. Staffed computer lab on campus.

Community Environment: Population 25,000, Lake Jackson is located 50 miles south of Houston. Major cities in the district are Lake Jackson and Freeport (population 17,000), located on a stretch of beach on the Gulf Coast. The area is serviced by rail, four major highways, commuter planes, and good local bus service. Recreation in the area includes fishing, surfing, swimming, and other water sports in the Gulf of Mexico.

■ **BROOKHAVEN COLLEGE** *F-33*
3939 Valley View Ln.
Farmers Branch, TX 75244-4997
Tel: (972)860-4700
Admissions: (972)860-4604
Fax: (972)860-4897
Web Site: http://www.brookhavencollege.edu/
Description: County-supported, 2-year, coed. Part of Dallas County Community College District System. Awards certificates, transfer associate, and terminal associate degrees. Founded 1978. Setting: 200-acre suburban campus with easy access to Dallas-Fort Worth. Educational spending for 2005 fiscal year: $1014 per student. Total enrollment: 10,119. Full-time: 2,472 students, 55% women, 45% men. Part-time: 7,647 students, 62% women, 38% men. Students come from 26 states and territories, 58 other countries, 3% from out-of-state, 1% Native American, 16% Hispanic, 18% black, 8% Asian American or Pacific Islander, 6% international, 55% 25 or older. Core. Calendar: semesters. Academic remediation for entering students, ESL program, services for LD students, advanced placement, self-designed majors, honors program, summer session for credit, part-time degree program, adult/continuing education programs, internships. ROTC: Army (c).
Entrance Requirements: Open admission. Options: Common Application, early admission, deferred admission. Placement: THEA required; SAT or ACT recommended. Entrance: noncompetitive. Application deadline: Rolling.
Collegiate Environment: Drama-theater group, choral group, student-run newspaper. Social organizations: 20 open to all. Most popular organizations: Brookhaven Nursing Students Association, Phi Theta Kappa, International Clubs, Brookhaven Student Government, Latin American Student Association. Student services: health clinic, personal-psychological counseling. Campus security: 24-hour emergency response devices and patrols, late night transport-escort service. College housing not available. Brookhaven College Learning Resources Center with 45,000 books, 197 serials, and an OPAC. Operations spending for 2004 fiscal year: $985,272. 250 computers available on campus for general student use. A campuswide network can be accessed. Staffed computer lab on campus.

■ **BROWN MACKIE COLLEGE-DALLAS** *D-19*
1500 Eastgate Dr.
Garland, TX 75041
Tel: (972)279-4446; 888-699-4446
Web Site: http://www.brownmackie.edu/locations.asp?locid=5
Description: Proprietary, 2-year, coed.

■ **BROWN MACKIE COLLEGE-FORT WORTH**
301 Northeast Loop 820
Hurst, TX 76053
Tel: (817)589-0505; 888-906-0505
Web Site: http://www.brownmackie.edu/locations.asp?locid=10
Description: Proprietary, 2-year, coed.

■ **CEDAR VALLEY COLLEGE** *E-19*
3030 North Dallas Ave.
Lancaster, TX 75134-3799
Tel: (972)860-8201

E-mail: cboswell-ward@dcccd.edu
Web Site: http://www.cedarvalleycollege.edu/cvc.htm
Description: State-supported, 2-year, coed. Part of Dallas County Community College District System. Awards certificates, transfer associate, and terminal associate degrees. Founded 1977. Setting: 353-acre suburban campus with easy access to Dallas-Fort Worth. Endowment: $17.2 million. Educational spending for 2005 fiscal year: $3227 per student. Total enrollment: 4,290. Student-undergrad faculty ratio is 26:1. 1,956 applied, 100% were admitted. Full-time: 1,447 students, 54% women, 46% men. Part-time: 2,843 students, 66% women, 34% men. Students come from 5 other countries, 2% from out-of-state, 0.3% Native American, 12% Hispanic, 57% black, 1% Asian American or Pacific Islander, 0.3% international, 42% 25 or older, 74% transferred in. Core. Calendar: semesters. Academic remediation for entering students, ESL program, services for LD students, advanced placement, distance learning, summer session for credit, part-time degree program, co-op programs. ROTC: Army (c).
Entrance Requirements: Open admission. Options: electronic application, early admission. Required: THEA. Recommended: high school transcript, SAT or ACT. Required for some: recommendations, interview. Entrance: noncompetitive. Application deadline: Rolling. Notification: continuous.
Costs Per Year: Application fee: $0. Area resident tuition: $1080 full-time, $36 per credit part-time. State resident tuition: $1980 full-time, $66 per credit part-time. Nonresident tuition: $3180 full-time, $200 per credit part-time.
Collegiate Environment: Orientation program. Drama-theater group, choral group. Social organizations: 10 open to all. Most popular organizations: African-American Student Organization, Latin-American Student Organization, Veterinary Technology Club, Phi Theta Kappa, Police Academy Club. Major annual events: Convocation, Welcome Back Party, International Holiday Festival. Student services: health clinic, personal-psychological counseling. Campus security: 24-hour emergency response devices and patrols. College housing not available. Cedar Valley College Library with 43,788 books, 95,794 microform titles, 217 serials, 16,460 audiovisual materials, an OPAC, and a Web page. Operations spending for 2004 fiscal year: $301,887. 675 computers available on campus for general student use. A campuswide network can be accessed from off-campus. Staffed computer lab on campus.

■ **CENTER FOR ADVANCED LEGAL STUDIES** *J-22*
3910 Kirby Dr., Ste. 200
Houston, TX 77098-4151
Tel: (713)529-2778
Fax: (713)523-2715
Web Site: http://www.paralegal.edu/
Description: Proprietary, 2-year.

■ **CENTRAL TEXAS COLLEGE** *G-18*
PO Box 1800
Killeen, TX 76540-1800
Tel: (254)526-7161
Free: 800-792-3348
Admissions: (254)526-1452
Web Site: http://www.ctcd.edu/
Description: State and locally supported, 2-year, coed. Awards certificates, transfer associate, and terminal associate degrees. Founded 1967. Setting: 500-acre suburban campus with easy access to Austin. Endowment: $1.5 million. Educational spending for 2005 fiscal year: $7206 per student. Total enrollment: 18,351. Full-time: 2,986 students, 62% women, 38% men. Part-time: 15,365 students, 40% women, 60% men. Students come from 48 states and territories, 19 other countries, 1% Native American, 15% Hispanic, 28% black, 4% Asian American or Pacific Islander, 0.2% international, 55% 25 or older, 1% live on campus. Core. Calendar: semesters. Academic remediation for entering students, ESL program, services for LD students, advanced placement, accelerated degree program, self-designed majors, distance learning, summer session for credit, part-time degree program, external degree program, adult/continuing education programs, internships. ROTC: Army.
Entrance Requirements: Open admission. Options: electronic application, early admission, deferred admission. Required: high school transcript, minimum 2.0 high school GPA. Placement: THEA required; SAT or ACT, SAT Subject Tests recommended. Entrance: noncompetitive. Application deadline: Rolling.
Costs Per Year: Application fee: $0. Area resident tuition: $912 full-time, $38 per hour part-time. State resident tuition: $1104 full-time, $46 per hour part-time. Nonresident tuition: $2880 full-time, $60 per hour part-time. Mandatory

fees: $390 full-time, $8 per hour part-time. Full-time tuition and fees vary according to course load and location. Part-time tuition and fees vary according to course load and location. College room and board: $2990.

Collegiate Environment: Drama-theater group, student-run newspaper. Social organizations: 18 open to all. Most popular organizations: International Student Association, We Can Do It Club, Students in Free Enterprise, Student Nurses Association, NAACP. Major annual events: graduation, Annual Job Fair. Campus security: 24-hour emergency response devices and patrols. Option: coed housing available. Oveta Culp Hobby Memorial Library with 80,381 books, 173,023 microform titles, 467 serials, 2,590 audiovisual materials, an OPAC, and a Web page. Operations spending for 2004 fiscal year: $495,978. 130 computers available on campus for general student use. A campuswide network can be accessed from student residence rooms and from off campus. Staffed computer lab on campus.

Community Environment: Population 135,000. Killeen is considered an outstanding recreation area with beautiful lakes and streams located nearby. The climate is temperate. All types of transportation are accessible. The community has shopping centers, medical facilities, and churches of many different faiths. Part-time employment is available.

■ CISCO JUNIOR COLLEGE *E-16*

101 College Heights
Cisco, TX 76437-9321
Tel: (254)442-5000
Admissions: (254)442-2567
Fax: (254)442-5100
Web Site: http://www.cisco.cc.tx.us/

Description: State and locally supported, 2-year, coed. Awards certificates, transfer associate, and terminal associate degrees. Founded 1940. Setting: 40-acre rural campus. Total enrollment: 3,250. 1,227 applied, 100% were admitted. Students come from 21 states and territories, 1% Native American, 17% Hispanic, 10% black, 1% Asian American or Pacific Islander, 1% international, 45% 25 or older, 12% live on campus. Core. Calendar: semesters. Academic remediation for entering students, advanced placement, summer session for credit, part-time degree program. ROTC: Army (c).

Entrance Requirements: Open admission. Option: early admission. Placement: THEA required. Entrance: noncompetitive. Application deadline: Rolling.

Costs Per Year: Application fee: $0. Area resident tuition: $1564 full-time, $111 per hour part-time. State resident tuition: $1756 full-time, $119 per hour part-time. Nonresident tuition: $2062 full-time, $272 per hour part-time. Full-time tuition varies according to course load and location. Part-time tuition varies according to course load and location. College room and board: $3100. College room only: $900. Room and board charges vary according to board plan and housing facility.

Collegiate Environment: Orientation program. Drama-theater group, marching band. Most popular organizations: Christian Athletes Association, Agricultural Club. Major annual events: homecoming, Ranch Day. Campus security: late night transport-escort service. 325 college housing spaces available; all were occupied in 2003-04. On-campus residence required through sophomore year. Maner Library with 34,000 books, 173 serials, an OPAC, and a Web page. 36 computers available on campus for general student use. Staffed computer lab on campus.

Community Environment: Population 4,160. Cisco is a rural community that enjoys a temperate climate. The community is served by railroad, bus lines, and highways 80, 380, 183, 206 and Interstate-20. Local service facilities include a hospital, Rotary Club, Lions Club, and Veterans of Foreign Wars and Veterans of World War I. Merchants in the community provide jobs for many students. Recreation includes nearby Lake Cisco for boating, fishing, and water sports.

■ CLARENDON COLLEGE *D-4*

PO Box 968
Clarendon, TX 79226-0968
Tel: (806)874-3571
Web Site: http://www.clarendoncollege.edu/

Description: State and locally supported, 2-year, coed. Awards certificates, transfer associate, and terminal associate degrees. Founded 1898. Setting: 88-acre rural campus. Endowment: $2.6 million. Educational spending for 2005 fiscal year: $2370 per student. Total enrollment: 1,123. Student-undergrad faculty ratio is 17:1. 586 applied, 100% were admitted. Full-time: 557 students, 46% women, 54% men. Part-time: 566 students, 45% women, 55% men. Students come from 14 states and territories, 3 other countries,

8% from out-of-state, 1% Native American, 17% Hispanic, 12% black, 1% Asian American or Pacific Islander, 0.4% international. Core. Calendar: semesters. Academic remediation for entering students, services for LD students, advanced placement, independent study, distance learning, double major, summer session for credit, part-time degree program, adult/continuing education programs.

Entrance Requirements: Open admission. Options: early admission, deferred admission. Required: high school transcript. Required for some: recommendations, interview. Entrance: noncompetitive. Application deadline: Rolling. Notification: continuous.

Costs Per Year: Application fee: $0. Area resident tuition: $1140 full-time, $38 per credit hour part-time. State resident tuition: $1650 full-time, $55 per credit hour part-time. Nonresident tuition: $2100 full-time, $70 per credit hour part-time. Mandatory fees: $930 full-time, $24 per credit hour part-time, $72 per term part-time. College room and board: $3100. College room only: $1000.

Collegiate Environment: Orientation program. Drama-theater group, choral group. Campus security: 8-hour patrols by trained security personnel. 296 college housing spaces available; all were occupied in 2003-04. On-campus residence required through sophomore year. Vera Dial Dickey Library plus 1 other with 22,000 books, 15,000 microform titles, 89 serials, 350 audiovisual materials, an OPAC, and a Web page. 57 computers available on campus for general student use. Computer purchase/lease plans available. A campuswide network can be accessed from student residence rooms and from off campus. Staffed computer lab on campus.

Community Environment: Population 2,300. A rural community, Clarendon is the center of a ranching and farming area 54 miles southwest of Amarillo. The climate is temperate with an average temperature of 61 degrees, and rainfall average of 23 inches. The area is served by railroad, bus lines, and Highways 70 and U.S. 287. The community has many churches, a hospital and clinic, museum, and adequate shopping facilities. Local recreation includes a city park, theatres, a Youth Center, golf course, hunting and fishing, all sports, and Greenbelt Lake with a 35-mile shoreline. Part-time employment is available.

■ COASTAL BEND COLLEGE *M-18*

3800 Charco Rd.
Beeville, TX 78102-2197
Tel: (361)358-2838
Admissions: (361)354-2251
Fax: (361)354-2254
Web Site: http://www.cbc.cc.tx.us/

Description: County-supported, 2-year, coed. Awards certificates, transfer associate, and terminal associate degrees. Founded 1965. Setting: 100-acre rural campus. Endowment: $676,564. Educational spending for 2005 fiscal year: $1593 per student. Total enrollment: 3,366. Student-undergrad faculty ratio is 17:1. 1,193 applied, 100% were admitted. Full-time: 1,380 students, 64% women, 36% men. Part-time: 1,986 students, 60% women, 40% men. Students come from 15 states and territories, 3 other countries, 1% from out-of-state, 0.4% Native American, 64% Hispanic, 3% black, 1% Asian American or Pacific Islander, 1% international, 42% 25 or older, 5% live on campus, 65% transferred in. Retention: 62% of full-time freshmen returned the following year. Core. Calendar: semesters. Academic remediation for entering students, services for LD students, advanced placement, distance learning, summer session for credit, part-time degree program, adult/continuing education programs, co-op programs and internships. ROTC: Army (c), Air Force (c).

Entrance Requirements: Open admission. Option: deferred admission. Required: high school transcript. Entrance: noncompetitive. Application deadline: Rolling. Notification: continuous.

Costs Per Year: Application fee: $0.

Collegiate Environment: Orientation program. Social organizations: 15 open to all. Most popular organizations: student government, Computer Science Club, Creative Writing Club, Drama Club, Art Club. Major annual events: Transfer Day, Job Fair, CBC Day. Student services: personal-psychological counseling. Campus security: 24-hour emergency response devices. 147 college housing spaces available; all were occupied in 2003-04. No special consideration for freshman housing applicants. Options: coed, men-only, women-only housing available. Grady C. Hogue Learning Resource Center with 37,971 books, 3,270 microform titles, 268 serials, 2,974 audiovisual materials, and an OPAC. Operations spending for 2004 fiscal year: $541,128. 970 computers available on campus for general student use. A campuswide network can be accessed from off-campus. Staffed computer lab on campus.

■ **COLLEGE OF BIBLICAL STUDIES-HOUSTON** *J-22*
6000 Dale Carnegie Dr.
Houston, TX 77036
Tel: (713)785-5995
Admissions: (832)252-4638
Fax: (713)785-5998
E-mail: dlopez@cbshouston.edu
Web Site: http://www.cbshouston.edu/
Description: Independent nondenominational, 4-year, coed. Awards associate and bachelor's degrees. Founded 1979. Setting: 10-acre urban campus. Endowment: $26,686. Educational spending for 2005 fiscal year: $7316 per student. Total enrollment: 1,492. Full-time: 370 students, 44% women, 56% men. Part-time: 1,122 students, 46% women, 54% men. 0% from out-of-state, 0.2% Native American, 18% Hispanic, 55% black, 2% Asian American or Pacific Islander. Core. Calendar: semesters. Academic remediation for entering students, ESL program, accelerated degree program, honors program, independent study, summer session for credit, part-time degree program, adult/continuing education programs.
Entrance Requirements: Open admission for non-degree seeking students. Required: essay, high school transcript. Recommended: SAT and SAT Subject Tests or ACT, TAAS, THEA. Required for some: interview. Entrance: noncompetitive. Application deadline: Rolling. Preference given to Christians.
Costs Per Year: Application fee: $20. One-time mandatory fee: $50. Tuition: $4250 full-time, $90 per credit part-time. Mandatory fees: $60 full-time, $6 per credit part-time, $20 per term part-time. Full-time tuition and fees vary according to course level. Part-time tuition and fees vary according to course load. Tuition guaranteed not to increase for student's term of enrollment.
Collegiate Environment: Orientation program. Most popular organization: Student Development Committee. Major annual event: Student Appreciation/Development Week. Student services: personal-psychological counseling. Campus security: hourly patrols by trained security guards and police. College housing not available. College of Biblical Studies Library with 35,580 books, 359 microform titles, 609 serials, and 515 audiovisual materials. Operations spending for 2004 fiscal year: $165,228. 18 computers available on campus for general student use. Staffed computer lab on campus.

■ **COLLEGE OF THE MAINLAND** *K-23*
1200 Amburn Rd.
Texas City, TX 77591-2499
Tel: (409)938-1211
Fax: (409)938-1306
E-mail: kmusick@com.edu
Web Site: http://www.com.edu/
Description: State and locally supported, 2-year, coed. Awards certificates, diplomas, transfer associate, and terminal associate degrees. Founded 1967. Setting: 120-acre suburban campus with easy access to Houston. Educational spending for 2005 fiscal year: $1003 per student. Total enrollment: 3,999. Student-undergrad faculty ratio is 17:1. Full-time: 1,382 students, 57% women, 43% men. Part-time: 2,617 students, 60% women, 40% men. Students come from 8 states and territories, 0.4% from out-of-state, 1% Native American, 20% Hispanic, 16% black, 2% Asian American or Pacific Islander, 0.1% international, 41% 25 or older, 8% transferred in. Retention: 48% of full-time freshmen returned the following year. Core. Calendar: semesters. Academic remediation for entering students, ESL program, services for LD students, honors program, distance learning, summer session for credit, part-time degree program, adult/continuing education programs, co-op programs.
Entrance Requirements: Open admission. Options: electronic application, early admission, deferred admission. Required for some: high school transcript. Entrance: noncompetitive. Application deadline: Rolling. Notification: continuous.
Costs Per Year: Application fee: $0. Area resident tuition: $863 full-time, $26 per credit part-time. State resident tuition: $1655 full-time, $59 per credit part-time. Nonresident tuition: $2423 full-time, $89 per credit part-time. Mandatory fees: $167 full-time, $10.66 per credit part-time, $64 per term part-time.
Collegiate Environment: Orientation program. Drama-theater group, choral group. Social organizations: 19 open to all. Most popular organizations: Student Activities Board, Student Government Association, COM Amigos, COM Soccer Club, Phi Theta Kappa. Major annual events: Cinco de Mayo, Robert Burns Irish Celebration, International Festival. Student services: personal-psychological counseling, women's center. Campus security: 24-hour emergency response devices and patrols, student patrols. College housing not available. Com Library plus 1 other with 84,128 books, 19,000 serials, 492 audiovisual materials, an OPAC, and a Web page. Operations spending for 2004 fiscal year: $416,255. 307 computers available on campus for general student use. A campuswide network can be accessed from off-campus. Staffed computer lab on campus.
Community Environment: Population 70,000 Texas City is a suburban community located approximately 40 miles from the center of Houston.

■ **THE COLLEGE OF SAINT THOMAS MORE** *D-18*
3020 Lubbock St.
Fort Worth, TX 76109-2323
Tel: (817)923-8459
Free: 800-583-6489
Fax: (817)924-3206
E-mail: jpatrick@cstm.edu
Web Site: http://www.cstm.edu/
Description: Independent, 4-year, coed, affiliated with Roman Catholic Church. Awards associate and bachelor's degrees. Founded 1981. Setting: 1-acre urban campus with easy access to Dallas. Educational spending for 2005 fiscal year: $9096 per student. Total enrollment: 53. Student-undergrad faculty ratio is 4:1. 25 applied, 68% were admitted. Full-time: 21 students, 29% women, 71% men. Part-time: 32 students, 56% women, 44% men. Students come from 5 states and territories, 24% from out-of-state, 0% Native American, 8% Hispanic, 3% black, 0% Asian American or Pacific Islander, 0% international, 6% 25 or older, 51% live on campus, 6% transferred in. Academic area with the most degrees conferred: liberal arts/general studies. Core. Calendar: semesters. Academic remediation for entering students, summer session for credit, part-time degree program, co-op programs. Study abroad program.
Entrance Requirements: Options: Peterson's Universal Application, early admission, deferred admission, international baccalaureate accepted. Required: essay, high school transcript, minimum 2.0 high school GPA, 1 recommendation, SAT or ACT. Recommended: interview. Entrance: moderately difficult. Application deadline: Rolling.
Costs Per Year: Application fee: $35. Tuition: $12,000 full-time, $2000 per course part-time.
Collegiate Environment: Orientation program. Social organizations: 3 open to all. Major annual events: C. S. Lewis Lecture, Evening Enrichment, Cowan Lectures. Student services: personal-psychological counseling. Campus security: 24-hour patrols, student patrols, late night transport-escort service. 25 college housing spaces available; 15 were occupied in 2003-04. The College of Saint Thomas More Library with 12,000 books, 50 serials, and an OPAC. Operations spending for 2004 fiscal year: $2628. 7 computers available on campus for general student use. Staffed computer lab on campus.

■ **COLLIN COUNTY COMMUNITY COLLEGE DISTRICT** *D-19*
4800 Preston Park Blvd.
Plano, TX 75093-8309
Tel: (972)758-3800
Admissions: (972)881-5174
Fax: (972)758-5468
Web Site: http://www.ccccd.edu/
Description: State and locally supported, 2-year, coed. Awards certificates, transfer associate, and terminal associate degrees. Founded 1985. Setting: 333-acre suburban campus with easy access to Dallas-Fort Worth. Endowment: $2 million. Educational spending for 2005 fiscal year: $2699 per student. Total enrollment: 18,457. Student-undergrad faculty ratio is 21:1. Full-time: 7,226 students, 52% women, 48% men. Part-time: 11,231 students, 60% women, 40% men. Students come from 44 states and territories, 86 other countries, 3% from out-of-state, 1% Native American, 10% Hispanic, 8% black, 8% Asian American or Pacific Islander, 3% international, 37% 25 or older, 10% transferred in. Retention: 55% of full-time freshmen returned the following year. Core. Calendar: semesters. Academic remediation for entering students, ESL program, services for LD students, advanced placement, honors program, distance learning, summer session for credit, part-time degree program, adult/continuing education programs, co-op programs and internships. Study abroad program.
Entrance Requirements: Open admission except for selective admissions to some programs. Options: electronic application, international baccalaureate accepted. Required: THEA. Entrance: noncompetitive. Application deadline: Rolling. Notification: continuous.
Costs Per Year: Application fee: $0. Area resident tuition: $810 full-time, $27 per credit hour part-time. State resident tuition: $1020 full-time, $33 per

credit hour part-time. Nonresident tuition: $2550 full-time, $80 per credit hour part-time. Mandatory fees: $306 full-time, $10 per credit hour part-time, $2 per term part-time.

Collegiate Environment: Orientation program. Drama-theater group, choral group. Social organizations: 26 open to all. Most popular organizations: Phi Theta Kappa, LULAC/BSN, Baptist Student Ministry, Psi Beta, Collin Nursing Student Association. Major annual events: Welcome Week events, Get the Scoop on Student Groups, Safe Break activities. Student services: personal-psychological counseling. Campus security: 24-hour emergency response devices and patrols, late night transport-escort service, controlled dormitory access. College housing not available. Main library plus 3 others with 129,032 books, 4,000 microform titles, 940 serials, 17,342 audiovisual materials, an OPAC, and a Web page. Operations spending for 2004 fiscal year: $2.6 million. 1,858 computers available on campus for general student use. Computer purchase/lease plans available. A campuswide network can be accessed from student residence rooms. Staffed computer lab on campus.

■ **COMMONWEALTH INSTITUTE OF FUNERAL SERVICE** *J-22*
415 Barren Springs Dr.
Houston, TX 77090
Tel: (281)873-0262
Free: 800-628-1580
Fax: (281)873-5232
Web Site: http://www.commonwealthinst.org/
Description: Independent, 2-year, coed. Awards certificates and terminal associate degrees. Founded 1988. Setting: urban campus. Total enrollment: 164. Full-time: 157 students, 52% women, 48% men. Part-time: 7 students, 71% women, 29% men. Students come from 11 states and territories, 20% from out-of-state, 0% Native American, 17% Hispanic, 30% black, 1% Asian American or Pacific Islander, 0% international, 48% 25 or older, 7% transferred in. Core. External degree program, adult/continuing education programs.
Entrance Requirements: Option: Common Application. Required: high school transcript. Recommended: SAT or ACT. Required for some: Wonderlic aptitude test or THEA. Entrance: moderately difficult. Application deadline: Rolling. Notification: continuous.
Costs Per Year: Application fee: $50. Tuition: $9400 full-time, $13 per contact hour part-time. Mandatory fees: $100 full-time. Full-time tuition and fees vary according to course load and program. Part-time tuition varies according to course load and program.
Collegiate Environment: Social organizations: 1 open to all; local fraternities; 15% of eligible men and 15% of eligible women are members. Most popular organization: student council. Major annual events: Blood Drive, Food Drive, Toys for Tots. Campus security: 24-hour emergency response devices. College housing not available. Commonwealth Institute Library and York Learning Resource Center with 1,500 books and 12 serials. 15 computers available on campus for general student use. Staffed computer lab on campus.

■ **COMPUTER CAREER CENTER** *F-2*
6101 Montana Ave.
El Paso, TX 79925
Tel: (915)779-8031
Web Site: http://www.computercareercenter.com/
Description: Proprietary, 2-year, coed. Awards certificates, diplomas, transfer associate, and terminal associate degrees. Setting: urban campus. Total enrollment: 300. Calendar: 8 six-week terms.
Entrance Requirements: Open admission. Entrance: noncompetitive.
Collegiate Environment: 100 computers available on campus for general student use.

■ **CONCORDIA UNIVERSITY AT AUSTIN** *I-18*
3400 Interstate 35 North
Austin, TX 78705-2799
Tel: (512)486-2000
Free: 800-285-4252
Fax: (512)459-8517
E-mail: kristi.kirk@concordia.edu
Web Site: http://www.concordia.edu/
Description: Independent, comprehensive, coed, affiliated with Lutheran Church-Missouri Synod. Part of Concordia University System. Awards associate, bachelor's, and master's degrees. Founded 1926. Setting: 20-acre urban campus with easy access to San Antonio. Endowment: $11.7 million.

Educational spending for 2005 fiscal year: $6483 per student. Total enrollment: 1,219. Faculty: 135 (35 full-time, 100 part-time). Student-undergrad faculty ratio is 13:1. 728 applied, 73% were admitted. 10% from top 10% of their high school class, 36% from top quarter, 74% from top half. Full-time: 756 students, 54% women, 46% men. Part-time: 373 students, 63% women, 37% men. Students come from 21 states and territories, 7% from out-of-state, 0.1% Native American, 16% Hispanic, 9% black, 1% Asian American or Pacific Islander, 0.1% international, 39% 25 or older, 32% live on campus, 9% transferred in. Retention: 60% of full-time freshmen returned the following year. Academic areas with the most degrees conferred: business/marketing; education; social sciences. Core. Calendar: semesters. Academic remediation for entering students, services for LD students, advanced placement, accelerated degree program, honors program, independent study, distance learning, double major, summer session for credit, part-time degree program, external degree program, adult/continuing education programs, internships. Study abroad program. ROTC: Army (c), Air Force (c).
Entrance Requirements: Options: early admission, deferred admission, international baccalaureate accepted. Required: high school transcript, minimum 2.5 high school GPA, SAT or ACT. Required for some: essay, recommendations, interview. Entrance: moderately difficult. Application deadline: Rolling. Notification: continuous.
Costs Per Year: Application fee: $25. Comprehensive fee: $23,750 includes full-time tuition ($16,850) and college room and board ($6900). Full-time tuition varies according to course load and location. Room and board charges vary according to board plan.
Collegiate Environment: Orientation program. Drama-theater group, choral group. Social organizations: 9 open to all. Most popular organizations: student government, Education Club, Lutheran Student Fellowship, Students Active for the Environment, Accounting Club. Major annual events: Fall Festival, Homecoming, Parents' Day. Student services: personal-psychological counseling. Campus security: 24-hour emergency response devices, student patrols, late night transport-escort service, controlled dormitory access. On-campus residence required in freshman year. Options: coed, men-only, women-only housing available. Founders Library with 50,756 books, 29,057 microform titles, 814 serials, 3,859 audiovisual materials, an OPAC, and a Web page. 40 computers available on campus for general student use. Staffed computer lab on campus.

■ **COURT REPORTING INSTITUTE OF DALLAS** *D-19*
8585 North Stemmons Freeway, Ste. 200 North
Dallas, TX 75247
Tel: (214)350-9722
Free: 800-880-9722
Fax: (214)631-0143
Web Site: http://www.crid.com/
Description: Proprietary, 2-year, coed. Awards transfer associate and terminal associate degrees. Founded 1978. Setting: urban campus. Total enrollment: 526. Full-time: 526 students, 97% women, 3% men. Students come from 15 states and territories, 10% from out-of-state, 0.4% Native American, 22% Hispanic, 28% black, 1% Asian American or Pacific Islander, 0.2% international, 68% 25 or older, 19% transferred in.
Entrance Requirements: Option: early decision. Required: high school transcript, interview. Entrance: noncompetitive.
Collegiate Environment: Student-run newspaper. Campus security: 24-hour patrols, late night transport-escort service. College housing not available.

■ **COURT REPORTING INSTITUTE OF HOUSTON** *J-22*
13101 Northwest Freeway, Ste. 100
Houston, TX 77040
Tel: (713)996-8300; (866)996-8300
Web Site: http://www.crid.com/
Description: Proprietary, 2-year, coed.

■ **THE CRISWELL COLLEGE** *D-19*
4010 Gaston Ave.
Dallas, TX 75246-1537
Tel: (214)821-5433
Free: 800-899-0012
Admissions: (214)818-1305
Fax: (214)818-1310
E-mail: wdblair@criswell.edu
Web Site: http://www.criswell.edu/

Description: Independent, comprehensive, coed, affiliated with Southern Baptist Convention. Awards associate, bachelor's, master's, and first professional degrees. Founded 1970. Setting: 1-acre urban campus. Endowment: $6 million. Educational spending for 2005 fiscal year: $2054 per student. Total enrollment: 451. Students come from 34 states and territories, 31% from out-of-state. Retention: 87% of full-time freshmen returned the following year. Core. Calendar: semesters. Academic remediation for entering students, advanced placement, independent study, double major, summer session for credit, part-time degree program, internships, graduate courses open to undergrads.

Entrance Requirements: Options: early admission, deferred admission. Required: essay, high school transcript, 2 recommendations, church recommendation, SAT or ACT. Recommended: minimum 2.0 high school GPA, interview. Entrance: minimally difficult. Application deadline: 8/15. Notification: continuous.

Collegiate Environment: Orientation program. Student-run newspaper. Social organizations: 6 open to all. Most popular organizations: International Student Ministry, Women's Fellowship, Mission Awareness Fellowship, The Torchbearer, Student Life Cabinet. Major annual events: Spiritual Awakening Week, World Missions Conference, Criswell Theological Lectures. Student services: personal-psychological counseling. Campus security: 24-hour emergency response devices and patrols, late night transport-escort service. College housing not available. Wallace Library with 95,000 books and 500 serials. Operations spending for 2004 fiscal year: $196,000. 25 computers available on campus for general student use. Staffed computer lab on campus.

■ CY-FAIR COLLEGE *J-22*

14955 NW Freeway
Houston, TX 77040
Tel: (832)782-5000
Admissions: (281)290-3950
Web Site: http://www.cy-faircollege.com/

Description: State and locally supported, 2-year, coed. Part of North Harris Montgomery Community Course District. Awards certificates, diplomas, transfer associate, and terminal associate degrees. Founded 2002. Setting: 200-acre suburban campus. Total enrollment: 8,540. Full-time: 1,895 students, 52% women, 48% men. Part-time: 6,645 students, 62% women, 38% men. Students come from 36 other countries, 0.4% Native American, 21% Hispanic, 9% black, 8% Asian American or Pacific Islander, 3% international. Core. Calendar: semesters. Academic remediation for entering students, ESL program, services for LD students, advanced placement, honors program, independent study, distance learning, part-time degree program, external degree program, adult/continuing education programs, co-op programs and internships.

Entrance Requirements: Open admission. Option: electronic application. Placement: SAT or ACT required for some. Entrance: noncompetitive.

Costs Per Year: Area resident tuition: $768 full-time, $32 per credit hour part-time. State resident tuition: $1728 full-time, $72 per credit hour part-time. Nonresident tuition: $2088 full-time, $87 per credit hour part-time. Mandatory fees: $216 full-time, $8 per credit hour part-time, $12 per term part-time.

Collegiate Environment: Orientation program. College housing not available.

■ DALLAS BAPTIST UNIVERSITY *D-19*

3000 Mountain Creek Parkway
Dallas, TX 75211-9299
Tel: (214)333-7100
Free: 800-460-1328
Admissions: (214)333-5360
Fax: (214)333-5447
E-mail: admiss@dbu.edu
Web Site: http://www.dbu.edu/

Description: Independent, comprehensive, coed, affiliated with Baptist General Convention of Texas. Awards associate, bachelor's, and master's degrees. Founded 1965. Setting: 293-acre urban campus. Endowment: $27.8 million. Educational spending for 2005 fiscal year: $4659 per student. Total enrollment: 4,988. Faculty: 456 (100 full-time, 356 part-time). Student-undergrad faculty ratio is 17:1. 937 applied, 64% were admitted. 23% from top 10% of their high school class, 53% from top quarter, 83% from top half. 8 valedictorians. Full-time: 2,100 students, 58% women, 42% men. Part-time: 1,467 students, 62% women, 38% men. Students come from 40 states and territories, 42 other countries, 5% from out-of-state, 1% Native

American, 10% Hispanic, 17% black, 1% Asian American or Pacific Islander, 7% international, 51% 25 or older, 32% live on campus, 8% transferred in. Retention: 68% of full-time freshmen returned the following year. Core. Calendar: 4-1-4. ESL program, services for LD students, advanced placement, honors program, independent study, distance learning, double major, summer session for credit, part-time degree program, adult/continuing education programs, internships, graduate courses open to undergrads. Off campus study at Council for Christian Colleges and Universities. Study abroad program. ROTC: Army (c), Air Force (c).

Entrance Requirements: Options: Peterson's Universal Application, Common Application, electronic application. Required: essay, high school transcript, minimum 2.5 high school GPA, rank in upper 50% of high school class, minimum ACT score of 21, combined SAT score of 1,000, SAT or ACT. Recommended: recommendations, interview. Entrance: moderately difficult. Application deadline: Rolling. Notification: continuous.

Costs Per Year: Application fee: $25. Comprehensive fee: $17,040 includes full-time tuition ($12,270) and college room and board ($4770). College room only: $1900. Room and board charges vary according to board plan and housing facility. Part-time tuition: $409 per credit hour.

Collegiate Environment: Orientation program. Drama-theater group, choral group. Social organizations: 34 open to all. Most popular organizations: Student Activities Board, Baptist Student Ministry, Student Government Association, Student Education Association, International Student Organization. Major annual events: homecoming, Freshman Orientation/Student Welcome and Transition Week (SWAT), Spiritual Rush Weekend. Student services: health clinic, personal-psychological counseling. Campus security: 24-hour emergency response devices and patrols, late night transport-escort service, controlled dormitory access. 1,211 college housing spaces available; 1,135 were occupied in 2003-04. Freshmen given priority for college housing. On-campus residence required through senior year. Options: men-only, women-only housing available. Vance Memorial Library with 235,931 books, 517,334 microform titles, 561 serials, 6,171 audiovisual materials, an OPAC, and a Web page. Operations spending for 2004 fiscal year: $872,343. 182 computers available on campus for general student use. Computer purchase/lease plans available. A campuswide network can be accessed from student residence rooms and from off campus. Staffed computer lab on campus.

Community Environment: See University of Texas at Dallas.

■ DALLAS CHRISTIAN COLLEGE *D-19*

2700 Christian Parkway
Dallas, TX 75234-7299
Tel: (972)241-3371
Fax: (972)241-8021
Web Site: http://www.dallas.edu/

Description: Independent, 4-year, coed, affiliated with Christian Churches and Churches of Christ. Awards bachelor's degrees. Founded 1950. Setting: 22-acre urban campus with easy access to Fort Worth. Endowment: $146,707. Educational spending for 2005 fiscal year: $11,553 per student. Total enrollment: 366. 182 applied, 49% were admitted. 2% from top 10% of their high school class, 14% from top quarter, 44% from top half. 1 valedictorian. Full-time: 273 students, 43% women, 57% men. Part-time: 93 students, 40% women, 60% men. Students come from 26 states and territories, 16% from out-of-state, 1% Native American, 8% Hispanic, 17% black, 1% Asian American or Pacific Islander, 0% international, 54% 25 or older, 36% live on campus, 35% transferred in. Retention: 69% of full-time freshmen returned the following year. Core. Calendar: semesters. Academic remediation for entering students, advanced placement, accelerated degree program, independent study, distance learning, double major, summer session for credit, part-time degree program, adult/continuing education programs, internships.

Entrance Requirements: Option: deferred admission. Required: high school transcript, 2 recommendations, SAT or ACT. Required for some: essay, interview. Entrance: minimally difficult. Application deadline: Rolling. Preference given to Christians.

Collegiate Environment: Orientation program. Choral group. Major annual events: See You at the Pole, National Missionary Convention. Student services: personal-psychological counseling. Campus security: controlled dormitory access. 136 college housing spaces available; 132 were occupied in 2003-04. Freshmen guaranteed college housing. On-campus residence required through senior year. Options: men-only, women-only housing available. C. C. Crawford Memorial Library plus 1 other with 36,616 books, 84 microform titles, 3,514 serials, 1,972 audiovisual materials, an OPAC, and a Web page. Operations spending for 2004 fiscal year: $107,651. 16 computers available on campus for general student use. A campuswide network can be accessed from student residence rooms. Staffed computer lab on campus.

Community Environment: A manufacturing, financial and distributing center, Dallas is a center for scientifically oriented industry in the electronics and aerospace fields and ranks high in cotton, oil and consumer goods production. The city also houses a principal banking and insurance complex. Dallas is a transportation hub for rail, bus and airlines.

■ **DALLAS INSTITUTE OF FUNERAL SERVICE** *D-19*
3909 South Buckner Blvd.
Dallas, TX 75227
Tel: (214)388-5466
Free: 800-235-5444
Fax: (214)388-0316
E-mail: difs@dallasinstitute.edu
Web Site: http://www.dallasinstitute.edu/
Description: Independent, 2-year, coed. Awards certificates, transfer associate, and terminal associate degrees. Founded 1945. Setting: 8-acre urban campus with easy access to Dallas/Ft. Worth. Total enrollment: 247. Student-undergrad faculty ratio is 32:1. Full-time: 247 students, 48% women, 52% men. Students come from 12 states and territories, 10% from out-of-state, 0.4% Native American, 9% Hispanic, 26% black, 1% Asian American or Pacific Islander, 0% international, 52% 25 or older, 10% transferred in.
Entrance Requirements: Open admission. Required: high school transcript. Entrance: noncompetitive.
Costs Per Year: Application fee: $50. Tuition: $10,000 full-time, $200 per hour part-time. Mandatory fees: $50 full-time.
Collegiate Environment: Major annual event: college-wide picnics. Campus security: 24-hour emergency response devices. College housing not available.

■ **DEL MAR COLLEGE** *N-18*
101 Baldwin Blvd.
Corpus Christi, TX 78404-3897
Tel: (361)698-1200
Admissions: (361)698-1248
Fax: (361)698-1559
Web Site: http://www.delmar.edu/
Description: State and locally supported, 2-year, coed. Awards certificates, transfer associate, and terminal associate degrees. Founded 1935. Setting: 159-acre urban campus. Endowment: $29.1 million. Total enrollment: 11,338. 1,770 applied, 100% were admitted. Students come from 46 states and territories, 57 other countries, 1% from out-of-state, 0.1% Native American, 57% Hispanic, 2% black, 1% Asian American or Pacific Islander, 1% international, 41% 25 or older. Core. Calendar: semesters. Academic remediation for entering students, ESL program, services for LD students, advanced placement, accelerated degree program, freshman honors college, honors program, distance learning, summer session for credit, part-time degree program, adult/continuing education programs, co-op programs and internships. ROTC: Army.
Entrance Requirements: Open admission except for allied health programs. Options: early admission, deferred admission. Required: high school transcript. Placement: THEA or ACT ASSET required. Entrance: noncompetitive. Application deadline: Rolling.
Collegiate Environment: Orientation program. Drama-theater group, student-run newspaper, radio station. Campus security: 24-hour emergency response devices and patrols. College housing not available. White Library plus 1 other with 127,717 books, 739 serials, and an OPAC. Operations spending for 2004 fiscal year: $2.4 million. 450 computers available on campus for general student use. Staffed computer lab on campus.
Community Environment: See Texas A&M University Corpus Christi.

■ **DEVRY UNIVERSITY (HOUSTON)** *J-22*
11125 Equity Dr.
Houston, TX 77041
Tel: (713)850-0888; (866)338-7934
Fax: (713)850-0858
Web Site: http://www.devry.edu/
Description: Proprietary, comprehensive, coed. Awards associate, bachelor's, and master's degrees. Total enrollment: 695. Faculty: 97 (1 full-time, 96 part-time). Student-undergrad faculty ratio is 16:1. Full-time: 379 students, 35% women, 65% men. Part-time: 233 students, 42% women, 58% men. 0.3% Native American, 28% Hispanic, 35% black, 6% Asian

American or Pacific Islander, 1% international. Academic areas with the most degrees conferred: business/marketing; computer and information sciences. Calendar: semesters.
Entrance Requirements: Application deadline: Rolling. Notification: continuous.
Costs Per Year: Application fee: $50. One-time mandatory fee: $40. Tuition: $11,790 full-time, $440 per credit part-time. Mandatory fees: $270 full-time, $160 per year part-time. Full-time tuition and fees vary according to course load. Part-time tuition and fees vary according to course load.

■ **DEVRY UNIVERSITY (IRVING)** *G-33*
4800 Regent Blvd.
Irving, TX 75063-2439
Tel: (972)929-6777; (866)338-7934
Web Site: http://www.devry.edu/
Description: Proprietary, comprehensive, coed. Part of DeVry University. Awards associate, bachelor's, and master's degrees. Founded 1969. Setting: 13-acre suburban campus with easy access to Dallas. Total enrollment: 1,818. Faculty: 127 (59 full-time, 68 part-time). Student-undergrad faculty ratio is 17:1. Full-time: 1,102 students, 57% women, 43% men. Part-time: 498 students, 66% women, 34% men. 0.2% Native American, 19% Hispanic, 33% black, 4% Asian American or Pacific Islander, 1% international, 58% 25 or older. Academic areas with the most degrees conferred: business/marketing; computer and information sciences; engineering technologies. Calendar: semesters. Academic remediation for entering students, services for LD students, advanced placement, accelerated degree program, distance learning, summer session for credit, part-time degree program, adult/continuing education programs, co-op programs.
Entrance Requirements: Options: electronic application, deferred admission, international baccalaureate accepted. Required: high school transcript, interview. Entrance: minimally difficult. Application deadline: Rolling.
Costs Per Year: Application fee: $50. One-time mandatory fee: $40. Tuition: $11,790 full-time, $440 per credit part-time. Mandatory fees: $270 full-time, $160 per year part-time.
Collegiate Environment: Orientation program. Social organizations: 15 open to all. Most popular organizations: Association of Information Technology Professionals, Gamers, Business Information Systems, Toastmasters, Telecommunications Management and Associations. Major annual events: Thanksgiving Dinner, Club Fair Day, Block Party. Campus security: 24-hour emergency response devices, student patrols, late night transport-escort service, lighted pathways/sidewalks. College housing not available. Learning Resource Center with 21,500 books, 6,365 serials, 1,472 audiovisual materials, an OPAC, and a Web page. 442 computers available on campus for general student use. Computer purchase/lease plans available. A campuswide network can be accessed from off-campus. Staffed computer lab on campus.

■ **DEVRY UNIVERSITY (PLANO)** *D-19*
Plano Corporate Center II
2301 West Plano Parkway, Ste. 101
Plano, TX 75075-8435
Tel: (972)943-8041
Fax: (972)943-8061
Web Site: http://www.devry.edu/
Description: Proprietary, comprehensive, coed. Calendar: semesters.
Costs Per Year: One-time mandatory fee: $40. Tuition: $11,790 full-time, $440 per credit part-time. Mandatory fees: $60 full-time, $30 per year part-time. Full-time tuition and fees vary according to course load. Part-time tuition and fees vary according to course load.

■ **EAST TEXAS BAPTIST UNIVERSITY** *D-23*
1209 North Grove
Marshall, TX 75670-1498
Tel: (903)935-7963
Free: 800-804-ETBU
Admissions: (903)923-2000
Fax: (903)938-1705
E-mail: admissions@etbu.edu
Web Site: http://www.etbu.edu/
Description: Independent Baptist, 4-year, coed. Awards associate and bachelor's degrees. Founded 1912. Setting: 200-acre small town campus. Endowment: $51.3 million. Educational spending for 2005 fiscal year: $4897 per student. Total enrollment: 1,326. Student-undergrad faculty ratio is 15:1. 851 applied, 72% were admitted. 16% from top 10% of their high school

class, 44% from top quarter, 78% from top half. 9 valedictorians. Full-time: 1,176 students, 56% women, 44% men. Part-time: 150 students, 46% women, 54% men. Students come from 29 states and territories, 9 other countries, 13% from out-of-state, 1% Native American, 4% Hispanic, 15% black, 5% Asian American or Pacific Islander, 1% international, 11% 25 or older, 73% live on campus, 10% transferred in. Retention: 53% of full-time freshmen returned the following year. Academic areas with the most degrees conferred: education; business/marketing; theology and religious vocations. Core. Calendar: 4-4-1. Academic remediation for entering students, advanced placement, accelerated degree program, honors program, independent study, double major, summer session for credit, part-time degree program, external degree program, adult/continuing education programs, internships. Off campus study at Brooks Veteran's Administration Medical Center School of Medical Technology. Study abroad program.

Entrance Requirements: Options: Peterson's Universal Application, Common Application, electronic application, deferred admission. Required: high school transcript, minimum 2.0 high school GPA, SAT or ACT. Required for some: interview. Entrance: moderately difficult. Application deadlines: 8/17, 8/17 for nonresidents. Notification: continuous, continuous for nonresidents.

Costs Per Year: Application fee: $25. Comprehensive fee: $16,713 includes full-time tuition ($12,840) and college room and board ($3873). Room and board charges vary according to board plan and housing facility. Part-time tuition: $400 per semester hour. Tuition guaranteed not to increase for student's term of enrollment.

Collegiate Environment: Orientation program. Drama-theater group, choral group, marching band, student-run newspaper. Social organizations: 19 open to all; local fraternities, local sororities; 2% of eligible men and 3% of eligible women are members. Most popular organizations: Baptist Student Ministry, Residence Hall Councils, Student Government Association, REACT, Student Foundation Association. Major annual events: homecoming, Fabulous Feagin Fry Fun Frenzy, Welcome Back Party. Student services: personal-psychological counseling. Campus security: 24-hour emergency response devices, controlled dormitory access. 1,063 college housing spaces available; 1,037 were occupied in 2003-04. Freshmen guaranteed college housing. On-campus residence required through senior year. Options: men-only, women-only housing available. Mamye Jarrett Library with 116,895 books, 59,150 microform titles, 668 serials, and an OPAC. Operations spending for 2004 fiscal year: $460,134. 203 computers available on campus for general student use. A campuswide network can be accessed from student residence rooms and from off campus. Staffed computer lab on campus.

Community Environment: See Wiley College.

■ **EASTFIELD COLLEGE** *G-35*
3737 Motley Dr.
Mesquite, TX 75150-2099
Tel: (972)860-7100
Admissions: (972)860-7105
Fax: (972)860-8373
Web Site: http://www.efc.dcccd.edu/
Description: State and locally supported, 2-year, coed. Part of Dallas County Community College District System. Awards certificates, transfer associate, and terminal associate degrees. Founded 1970. Setting: 244-acre suburban campus with easy access to Dallas-Fort Worth. Educational spending for 2005 fiscal year: $4091 per student. Total enrollment: 12,111. Student-undergrad faculty ratio is 23:1. 1,466 applied, 100% were admitted. Full-time: 2,322 students, 53% women, 47% men. Part-time: 9,789 students, 61% women, 39% men. Students come from 18 states and territories, 1% from out-of-state, 1% Native American, 23% Hispanic, 21% black, 4% Asian American or Pacific Islander, 1% international, 35% 25 or older, 3% transferred in. Retention: 39% of full-time freshmen returned the following year. Core. Calendar: semesters. Academic remediation for entering students, ESL program, services for LD students, advanced placement, honors program, distance learning, summer session for credit, part-time degree program, adult/continuing education programs, co-op programs.

Entrance Requirements: Open admission. Options: early admission, deferred admission. Recommended: high school transcript. Entrance: noncompetitive. Application deadline: Rolling. Notification: continuous.

Costs Per Year: Application fee: $0. Area resident tuition: $1080 full-time, $36 per credit part-time. State resident tuition: $1980 full-time, $66 per credit part-time. Nonresident tuition: $3180 full-time, $106 per credit part-time.

Collegiate Environment: Drama-theater group, choral group, student-run newspaper. Social organizations: ; 4% of eligible men and 5% of eligible women are members. Most popular organizations: LULAC, Rodeo Club,

PTK, Rising Star, Communications Club. Major annual events: Student Leadership Academy, back to school parties, performing artists and speakers series. Student services: health clinic, personal-psychological counseling, women's center. Campus security: 24-hour emergency response devices and patrols. College housing not available. Eastfield College Learning Resource Center with 66,988 books, 48,976 microform titles, 415 serials, 2,620 audiovisual materials, an OPAC, and a Web page. Operations spending for 2004 fiscal year: $580,478. 50 computers available on campus for general student use. A campuswide network can be accessed from off-campus. Staffed computer lab on campus.

Community Environment: See University of Texas at Dallas.

■ **EL CENTRO COLLEGE** *D-19*
801 Main St.
Dallas, TX 75202-3604
Tel: (214)860-2037
Admissions: (214)860-2618
Fax: (214)860-2335
E-mail: rcb@dcccd.edu
Web Site: http://www.ecc.dcccd.edu/
Description: County-supported, 2-year, coed. Part of Dallas County Community College District System. Awards certificates, transfer associate, and terminal associate degrees. Founded 1966. Setting: 2-acre urban campus. Total enrollment: 6,089. Student-undergrad faculty ratio is 16:1. 1,253 applied, 100% were admitted. Full-time: 1,546 students, 66% women, 34% men. Part-time: 4,543 students, 70% women, 30% men. Students come from 20 states and territories, 40 other countries, 1% from out-of-state, 0.5% Native American, 25% Hispanic, 36% black, 5% Asian American or Pacific Islander, 3% international, 51% 25 or older, 16% transferred in. Core. Calendar: semesters. Academic remediation for entering students, ESL program, services for LD students, advanced placement, freshman honors college, honors program, distance learning, double major, summer session for credit, part-time degree program, adult/continuing education programs, co-op programs and internships. ROTC: Army (c).

Entrance Requirements: Open admission except for allied health, culinary arts programs. Options: electronic application, early admission. Required for some: high school transcript, 1 recommendation. Entrance: noncompetitive. Application deadline: Rolling.

Costs Per Year: Application fee: $0. Area resident tuition: $33 per credit part-time. State resident tuition: $60 per credit part-time. Nonresident tuition: $96 per credit part-time.

Collegiate Environment: Orientation program. Choral group. Most popular organizations: Phi Theta Kappa, Radiology Club, SPAR (Student Programs and Resources Office), Organization of Latin American Students. Student services: health clinic, personal-psychological counseling. Campus security: 24-hour emergency response devices and patrols, late night transport-escort service. College housing not available. El Centro College Library with 72,176 books, 6,494 microform titles, 371 serials, 5,463 audiovisual materials, an OPAC, and a Web page. 832 computers available on campus for general student use. A campuswide network can be accessed from off-campus. Staffed computer lab on campus.

Community Environment: See University of Texas at Dallas.

■ **EL PASO COMMUNITY COLLEGE** *F-2*
PO Box 20500
El Paso, TX 79998-0500
Tel: (915)831-2000
Admissions: (915)831-2580
Fax: (915)831-6145
E-mail: daryleh@epcc.edu
Web Site: http://www.epcc.edu/
Description: County-supported, 2-year, coed. Awards certificates, transfer associate, and terminal associate degrees. Founded 1969. Setting: urban campus. Endowment: $24,000. Total enrollment: 19,953. 3,672 applied, 100% were admitted. Students come from 47 states and territories, 40 other countries, 5% from out-of-state, 45% 25 or older. Core. Calendar: semesters. Academic remediation for entering students, ESL program, services for LD students, advanced placement, honors program, distance learning, summer session for credit, part-time degree program, external degree program, adult/continuing education programs, co-op programs and internships. Off campus study at University of Texas at El Paso. ROTC: Army (c).

Entrance Requirements: Open admission. Options: early admission, deferred admission. Placement: THEA required. Entrance: noncompetitive. Application deadline: 8/3.

Collegiate Environment: Drama-theater group, choral group, student-run newspaper, radio station. Social organizations: 52 open to all. Most popular organizations: African-American Coalition, Art Student Society, Phi Theta Kappa, Architecture Club, Social Science Club. Major annual events: National Alcohol Prevention Awareness Week, Intramural Sports Festival, Hispanic Heritage Month. Student services: personal-psychological counseling. Campus security: 24-hour patrols, late night transport-escort service. College housing not available. El Paso Community College Learning Resource Center plus 4 others with 442,879 books, 240,891 microform titles, 938 serials, 12,035 audiovisual materials, an OPAC, and a Web page. Operations spending for 2004 fiscal year: $2 million. 1,200 computers available on campus for general student use. A campuswide network can be accessed from off-campus. Staffed computer lab on campus.

Community Environment: See University of Texas - El Paso.

■ **EVEREST COLLEGE (ARLINGTON)** *D-19*
2801 East Division St., Ste. 250
Arlington, TX 76011
Tel: (817)652-7790
Fax: (817)649-6033
Web Site: http://www.everest-college.com/
Description: Proprietary, 2-year, coed. Founded 2003. Calendar: 6 or 12 week terms.

■ **EVEREST COLLEGE (DALLAS)** *D-19*
6060 North Central Expressway, Ste. 101
Dallas, TX 75206-5209
Tel: (214)234-4850
Fax: (214)696-6208
Web Site: http://www.everest-college.com/
Description: Proprietary, 2-year, coed. Founded 2003. Calendar: 6 or 12 week terms.

■ **EVEREST COLLEGE (FORT WORTH)** *D-18*
5237 North Riverside Dr.
Ste. G101
Fort Worth, TX 76137
Web Site: http://www.everest-college.com/
Description: Proprietary, 2-year, coed.

■ **FRANK PHILLIPS COLLEGE** *C-3*
Box 5118
Borger, TX 79008-5118
Tel: (806)274-5311
Free: 800-687-2056
Admissions: (806)457-4200
Fax: (806)274-6835
Web Site: http://www.fpc.cc.tx.us/
Description: State and locally supported, 2-year, coed. Awards certificates, transfer associate, and terminal associate degrees. Founded 1948. Setting: 60-acre small town campus. Endowment: $402,582. Total enrollment: 1,100. Students come from 11 states and territories, 12 other countries, 26% 25 or older. Core. Calendar: semesters. Academic remediation for entering students, services for LD students, advanced placement, accelerated degree program, honors program, distance learning, summer session for credit, part-time degree program, adult/continuing education programs, co-op programs and internships.
Entrance Requirements: Open admission. Options: Peterson's Universal Application, Common Application, early admission, deferred admission. Required: high school transcript. Placement: THEA required. Entrance: noncompetitive. Application deadline: 8/25. Notification: continuous until 8/25.
Costs Per Year: Application fee: $0. Area resident tuition: $720 full-time, $30 per semester hour part-time. State resident tuition: $1128 full-time, $47 per semester hour part-time. Nonresident tuition: $1296 full-time, $54 per semester hour part-time. Mandatory fees: $914 full-time, $36 per semester hour part-time, $50 per term part-time.
Collegiate Environment: Orientation program. Choral group. Social organizations: 10 open to all. Most popular organizations: Rodeo Club, Music Club, Computer Club, Phi Theta Kappa, student government. Major annual events: College Day, Career Fair, Honors Banquet. Student services: personal-psychological counseling. Campus security: 24-hour emergency response devices and patrols, controlled dormitory access. 200 college housing spaces available; 180 were occupied in 2003-04. Options: men-only, women-only housing available. Frank Phillips College Learning Resource Center with 35,700 books, 138 serials, and an OPAC. Operations spending for 2004 fiscal year: $126,467. 29 computers available on campus for general student use. A campuswide network can be accessed. Staffed computer lab on campus.

Community Environment: Population 14,195, one of the youngest towns in Texas, Borger was born as an oil boomtown in 1926. Today it is the center of the Panhandle gas reservoir, which produces more natural gas and allied products than any other field in the world. The community enjoys temperate climate. Air, rail, and bus service is available. Community services include a public library, churches of major denominations, a hospital, major civic, fraternal, and veteran's organizations, and shopping facilities. Local recreation includes theaters, golf, and other sports. Lake Meredith also offers recreational opportunities. The Oil Show, Rodeo, and Art Show are held annually. Part-time employment is available.

■ **GALVESTON COLLEGE** *K-23*
4015 Ave. Q
Galveston, TX 77550-7496
Tel: (409)763-6551
Admissions: (409)944-1234
Fax: (409)762-9367
E-mail: blowery@gc.edu
Web Site: http://www.gc.edu/
Description: State and locally supported, 2-year, coed. Awards certificates, transfer associate, and terminal associate degrees. Founded 1967. Setting: 11-acre urban campus with easy access to Houston. Total enrollment: 2,230. Student-undergrad faculty ratio is 16:1. 300 applied, 100% were admitted. Full-time: 851 students, 61% women, 39% men. Part-time: 1,379 students, 67% women, 33% men. Students come from 29 states and territories, 19 other countries, 4% from out-of-state, 0.3% Native American, 24% Hispanic, 19% black, 3% Asian American or Pacific Islander, 1% international, 45% 25 or older, 14% transferred in. Core. Calendar: semesters. Academic remediation for entering students, ESL program, services for LD students, advanced placement, distance learning, summer session for credit, part-time degree program, adult/continuing education programs, co-op programs and internships. Off campus study at Brazosport College, College of the Mainland.
Entrance Requirements: Open admission except for allied health programs. Option: Common Application. Required for some: high school transcript. Entrance: noncompetitive. Application deadline: Rolling. Notification: continuous.
Costs Per Year: Application fee: $0. State resident tuition: $900 full-time, $30 per hour part-time. Nonresident tuition: $1800 full-time, $60 per hour part-time. Mandatory fees: $430 full-time, $12 per hour part-time, $30 per term part-time.
Collegiate Environment: Drama-theater group, choral group. Social organizations: 17 open to all. Most popular organizations: student government, Phi Theta Kappa, Student Nurses Association, ATTC, Hispanic Student Organization. Major annual events: College Night, back to school activity, Business Symposium. Student services: personal-psychological counseling. Campus security: 24-hour emergency response devices, late night transport-escort service. College housing not available. David Glenn Hunt Memorial Library with 45,193 books, 54 microform titles, 4,000 serials, 1,500 audiovisual materials, an OPAC, and a Web page. Operations spending for 2004 fiscal year: $231,797. 173 computers available on campus for general student use. A campuswide network can be accessed. Staffed computer lab on campus.

Community Environment: Galveston is a port and recreational city. Major business activities include the tourist, maritime, and banking industries. Known as the "playground of the Southwest," Galveston has an average maximum temperature of 74.9 degrees, and an average minimum of 65.2 degrees. The climate is semitropical. The community is reached by rail, bus, and air. There are churches of various faiths, a library, YMCA, YWCA, medical facilities, a civic orchestra, Little Theatre, civic music association, an art league, and various fraternal, civic, and veteran's organizations in the community. Local recreation includes 32 miles of hard sand beaches, bathing, motoring, water sports, boating, deep-sea fishing, golf, and horseback riding. Part-time employment is abundant.

■ **GRAYSON COUNTY COLLEGE** *B-20*
6101 Grayson Dr.
Denison, TX 75020-8299
Tel: (903)465-6030

Fax: (903)463-5284

Web Site: http://www.grayson.edu/

Description: State and locally supported, 2-year, coed. Awards certificates, diplomas, transfer associate, and terminal associate degrees. Founded 1964. Setting: 500-acre rural campus. Total enrollment: 3,344. 3,344 applied, 100% were admitted. Students come from 3 states and territories, 2 other countries, 53% 25 or older. Retention: 54% of full-time freshmen returned the following year. Core. Calendar: semesters. Academic remediation for entering students, ESL program, advanced placement, honors program, summer session for credit, part-time degree program, adult/continuing education programs.

Entrance Requirements: Open admission. Options: early admission, deferred admission. Placement: THEA required; SAT or ACT recommended. Entrance: noncompetitive. Application deadline: 8/31. Notification: continuous.

Collegiate Environment: Drama-theater group. 318 college housing spaces available; 175 were occupied in 2003-04. No special consideration for freshman housing applicants. 51,500 books and 310 serials. 25 computers available on campus for general student use. Staffed computer lab on campus.

Community Environment: Population 94,965. Principal industries in this manufacturing city include railroad cars, furniture, fishing lures, wigs, pickup campers, mattresses, venetian blinds, food processing and pipes. This is a metropolitan community served by railway transite and bus lines. The community has a library, over 40 churches representing most denominations, four hospitals, and various civic, fraternal and veteran's organizations. Some part-time job opportunities are available. Local recreation includes nearby lakes featuring all water sports, and three downtown theater complexes.

■ **HALLMARK INSTITUTE OF AERONAUTICS** *K-16*

8901 Wetmore Rd.

San Antonio, TX 78216

Tel: (210)826-1000

Free: 800-683-3600

Admissions: (210)690-9000

Fax: (210)826-3707

Description: Private, 2-year, coed. Awards diplomas and terminal associate degrees. Calendar: continuous.

Entrance Requirements: Open admission.

■ **HALLMARK INSTITUTE OF TECHNOLOGY** *K-16*

10401 IH 10 West

San Antonio, TX 78230-1737

Tel: (210)690-9000

Free: 800-880-6600

Fax: (210)697-8225

Web Site: http://www.hallmarkinstitute.edu/

Description: Proprietary, 2-year, coed. Awards diplomas and terminal associate degrees. Founded 1969. Setting: suburban campus. Total enrollment: 462. 0% from out-of-state, 2% Native American, 41% Hispanic, 9% black, 3% Asian American or Pacific Islander, 0% international, 85% 25 or older. Calendar: continuous. Accelerated degree program.

Entrance Requirements: Required: high school transcript, interview, Wonderlic aptitude test. Application deadline: Rolling. Notification: continuous.

Collegiate Environment: Orientation program. Most popular organization: Student Appreciation Day. College housing not available. 30 computers available on campus for general student use. A campuswide network can be accessed. Staffed computer lab on campus.

■ **HARDIN-SIMMONS UNIVERSITY** *E-14*

2200 Hickory St.

Abilene, TX 79698-0001

Tel: (325)670-1000; 877-464-7889

Admissions: (325)670-1206

Fax: (325)677-8351

E-mail: jdsd@hsutx.edu

Web Site: http://www.hsutx.edu/

Description: Independent Baptist, comprehensive, coed. Awards bachelor's, master's, doctoral, and first professional degrees. Founded 1891. Setting: 120-acre urban campus. Endowment: $87.1 million. Educational spending for 2005 fiscal year: $6572 per student. Total enrollment: 2,435. Faculty: 179 (131 full-time, 48 part-time). Student-undergrad faculty ratio is 15:1. 1,179 applied, 66% were admitted. 21% from top 10% of their high school class, 45% from top quarter, 77% from top half. 8 valedictorians. Full-time: 1,779

students, 54% women, 46% men. Part-time: 212 students, 59% women, 41% men. Students come from 27 states and territories, 4% from out-of-state, 1% Native American, 10% Hispanic, 5% black, 1% Asian American or Pacific Islander, 0.5% international, 11% 25 or older, 44% live on campus, 10% transferred in. Retention: 69% of full-time freshmen returned the following year. Academic areas with the most degrees conferred: education; business/marketing; health professions and related sciences. Core. Calendar: semesters. Academic remediation for entering students, services for LD students, advanced placement, accelerated degree program, honors program, independent study, distance learning, double major, summer session for credit, part-time degree program, adult/continuing education programs, internships, graduate courses open to undergrads. Off campus study at Abilene Christian University, McMurry University. Study abroad program.

Entrance Requirements: Options: electronic application, deferred admission, international baccalaureate accepted. Required: high school transcript, minimum 2.0 high school GPA, ACT or SAT scores. Entrance: moderately difficult. Application deadline: Rolling. Notification: continuous.

Costs Per Year: Application fee: $50. Comprehensive fee: $20,206 includes full-time tuition ($14,850), mandatory fees ($776), and college room and board ($4580). College room only: $2365. Part-time tuition: $495 per semester hour. Part-time mandatory fees: $96 per term.

Collegiate Environment: Orientation program. Drama-theater group, choral group, marching band, student-run newspaper. Social organizations: 55 open to all; local fraternities, local sororities; 8% of eligible men and 11% of eligible women are members. Most popular organizations: Baptist Student Union, Student Foundation, Student Congress, Fellowship Christian Athletes. Major annual events: homecoming, Sing, All-School Christmas Party. Student services: health clinic, personal-psychological counseling. Campus security: 24-hour patrols, controlled dormitory access. 984 college housing spaces available; 784 were occupied in 2003-04. Freshmen guaranteed college housing. On-campus residence required through sophomore year. Options: men-only, women-only housing available. Richardson Library plus 1 other with 226,755 books, 20,827 microform titles, 28,911 serials, 11,351 audiovisual materials, an OPAC, and a Web page. Operations spending for 2004 fiscal year: $1 million. 224 computers available on campus for general student use. A campuswide network can be accessed from student residence rooms and from off campus. Staffed computer lab on campus.

Community Environment: See Abilene Christian University.

■ **HIGH-TECH INSTITUTE** *G-33*

4250 North Belt Line Rd.

Irving, TX 75038

Tel: (972)871-2824

Free: 800-987-0110

E-mail: clewellen@hightechschools.com

Web Site: http://www.high-techinstitute.com/

Description: Proprietary, 2-year, coed. Founded 2000. Calendar: semesters.

■ **HILL COLLEGE OF THE HILL JUNIOR COLLEGE DISTRICT** *F-19*

PO Box 619

Hillsboro, TX 76645-0619

Tel: (254)582-2555

E-mail: diharvey@hill-college.cc.tx.us

Web Site: http://www.hillcollege.edu/

Description: District-supported, 2-year, coed. Awards certificates, transfer associate, and terminal associate degrees. Founded 1923. Setting: 80-acre small town campus with easy access to Dallas-Fort Worth. Endowment: $416,886. Total enrollment: 3,236. Full-time: 1,569 students, 58% women, 42% men. Part-time: 1,667 students, 62% women, 38% men. Students come from 8 states and territories, 28 other countries, 6% from out-of-state, 1% Native American, 11% Hispanic, 6% black, 1% Asian American or Pacific Islander, 2% international, 20% 25 or older, 14% live on campus, 6% transferred in. Retention: 90% of full-time freshmen returned the following year. Core. Calendar: semesters. Academic remediation for entering students, ESL program, services for LD students, advanced placement, honors program, distance learning, double major, summer session for credit, part-time degree program, adult/continuing education programs, co-op programs and internships.

Entrance Requirements: Open admission. Options: early admission, deferred admission. Required: high school transcript. Placement: THEA required; SAT or ACT recommended. Entrance: noncompetitive. Application deadline: Rolling.

Collegiate Environment: Orientation program. Drama-theater group, choral group. Social organizations: 14 open to all. Most popular organizations: International Club, Sigma Phi Omega, Phi Theta Kappa, Fellowship of Christian Athletes, Psi Beta. Major annual events: Western Day, Career Day, Job Fair. Campus security: late night transport-escort service, controlled dormitory access, security officers. On-campus residence required through sophomore year. Options: men-only, women-only housing available. Hill College Library plus 1 other with 40,000 books, 3,161 microform titles, 300 serials, 500 audiovisual materials, an OPAC, and a Web page. Operations spending for 2004 fiscal year: $159,328. 250 computers available on campus for general student use. A campuswide network can be accessed from off-campus. Staffed computer lab on campus.

■ HOUSTON BAPTIST UNIVERSITY *J-22*

7502 Fondren Rd.
Houston, TX 77074-3298
Tel: (281)649-3000
Free: 800-696-3210
Fax: (281)649-3209
E-mail: unadm@hbu.edu
Web Site: http://www.hbu.edu/

Description: Independent Baptist, comprehensive, coed. Awards associate, bachelor's, and master's degrees and post-master's certificates. Founded 1960. Setting: 100-acre urban campus. Endowment: $84.6 million. Educational spending for 2005 fiscal year: $6311 per student. Total enrollment: 2,294. Faculty: 169 (103 full-time, 66 part-time). Student-undergrad faculty ratio is 15:1. 867 applied, 65% were admitted. 24% from top 10% of their high school class, 44% from top quarter, 79% from top half. Full-time: 1,653 students, 66% women, 34% men. Part-time: 279 students, 72% women, 28% men. Students come from 22 states and territories, 30 other countries, 3% from out-of-state, 0.3% Native American, 14% Hispanic, 20% black, 13% Asian American or Pacific Islander, 6% international, 18% 25 or older, 30% live on campus, 12% transferred in. Retention: 74% of full-time freshmen returned the following year. Core. Academic remediation for entering students, ESL program, advanced placement, accelerated degree program, honors program, independent study, double major, summer session for credit, part-time degree program, adult/continuing education programs, internships, graduate courses open to undergrads. Study abroad program. ROTC: Army (c).

Entrance Requirements: Options: early admission, deferred admission, international baccalaureate accepted. Required: essay, high school transcript, 2 recommendations, SAT or ACT. Recommended: interview. Entrance: moderately difficult. Application deadline: Rolling. Notification: continuous.

Costs Per Year: Application fee: $25. Comprehensive fee: $21,000 includes full-time tuition ($16,500) and college room and board ($4500). College room only: $2355. Part-time tuition: $550 per semester hour.

Collegiate Environment: Orientation program. Drama-theater group, choral group, student-run newspaper. Social organizations: 47 open to all; national fraternities, national sororities, local fraternities, local sororities; 11% of eligible men and 1% of eligible women are members. Most popular organizations: Alpha Epsilon Delta, Alpha Phi Omega, Association of Student Educators, Alpha Kappa Psi, Phi Mu. Major annual events: homecoming, Spring Fling. Student services: health clinic, personal-psychological counseling. Campus security: 24-hour emergency response devices and patrols, late night transport-escort service. 698 college housing spaces available; 539 were occupied in 2003-04. Freshmen guaranteed college housing. On-campus residence required in freshman year. Options: men-only, women-only housing available. Moody Library with 209,366 books, 105,280 microform titles, 21,000 serials, 9,255 audiovisual materials, an OPAC, and a Web page. Operations spending for 2004 fiscal year: $1.1 million. 95 computers available on campus for general student use. A campuswide network can be accessed from student residence rooms. Staffed computer lab on campus.

Community Environment: See University of Houston.

■ HOUSTON COMMUNITY COLLEGE SYSTEM *J-22*

3100 Main St.
PO Box 667517
Houston, TX 77266-7517
Tel: (713)718-2000
Admissions: (713)718-8500
Fax: (713)718-2111
Web Site: http://www.hccs.edu/

Description: State and locally supported, 2-year, coed. Awards certificates, transfer associate, and terminal associate degrees. Founded 1971. Setting: urban campus. Total enrollment: 39,516. Student-undergrad faculty ratio is 20:1. Full-time: 12,198 students, 55% women, 45% men. Part-time: 27,318 students, 60% women, 40% men. 0.2% Native American, 27% Hispanic, 25% black, 12% Asian American or Pacific Islander, 8% international. Core. Calendar: semesters. Academic remediation for entering students, ESL program, services for LD students, advanced placement, honors program, independent study, distance learning, summer session for credit, part-time degree program, adult/continuing education programs, co-op programs and internships. Study abroad program. ROTC: Army (c).

Entrance Requirements: Open admission except for allied health programs. Required for some: high school transcript, interview. Entrance: noncompetitive. Application deadline: Rolling.

Costs Per Year: Application fee: $0. Area resident tuition: $1176 full-time. State resident tuition: $2472 full-time. Nonresident tuition: $2952 full-time.

Collegiate Environment: Drama-theater group, student-run newspaper. Social organizations: 57 open to all. Most popular organizations: Phi Theta Kappa, Eastwood Student Association, Eagle's Club, Society of Hispanic Professional Engineers, International Student Association. Major annual events: Chancellor's Food/Toy Drive, Cinco de Mayo, Black History Month. Student services: personal-psychological counseling. Campus security: 24-hour emergency response devices and patrols, late night transport-escort service. College housing not available. Main library plus 19 others with 140,674 books, 671 microform titles, 2,012 serials, 16,334 audiovisual materials, an OPAC, and a Web page. 3,200 computers available on campus for general student use. A campuswide network can be accessed from off-campus. Staffed computer lab on campus.

■ HOWARD COLLEGE *E-11*

1001 Birdwell Ln.
Big Spring, TX 79720
Tel: (915)264-5000; (866)HC-HAWKS
Admissions: (432)264-5105
Fax: (915)264-5082
Web Site: http://www.howardcollege.edu/

Description: State and locally supported, 2-year, coed. Part of Howard County Junior College District System. Awards certificates, transfer associate, and terminal associate degrees. Founded 1945. Setting: 120-acre small town campus. Endowment: $1.2 million. Educational spending for 2005 fiscal year: $3421 per student. Total enrollment: 2,725. Student-undergrad faculty ratio is 11:1. 1,027 applied, 100% were admitted. Full-time: 1,174 students, 57% women, 43% men. Part-time: 1,551 students, 66% women, 34% men. Students come from 10 states and territories, 2 other countries, 2% from out-of-state, 0.5% Native American, 31% Hispanic, 5% black, 1% Asian American or Pacific Islander, 0.2% international, 58% 25 or older, 18% live on campus, 0.4% transferred in. Core. Calendar: semesters. Academic remediation for entering students, ESL program, services for LD students, advanced placement, independent study, distance learning, summer session for credit, part-time degree program, adult/continuing education programs, co-op programs and internships.

Entrance Requirements: Open admission. Option: early admission. Required: high school transcript. Entrance: noncompetitive. Application deadline: Rolling. Notification: continuous until 8/31.

Costs Per Year: Application fee: $0. Area resident tuition: $1140 full-time, $30 per credit hour part-time. State resident tuition: $1500 full-time, $40 per credit hour part-time. Nonresident tuition: $2160 full-time, $60 per credit hour part-time. Mandatory fees: $66 full-time, $50 per term part-time. Full-time tuition and fees vary according to course load, location, and program. Part-time tuition and fees vary according to course load, location, and program. College room and board: $3140.

Collegiate Environment: Orientation program. Drama-theater group, choral group. Most popular organizations: Phi Theta Kappa, Student Government Association, Mexican-American Student Association, Baptist Student Ministries. Major annual events: Awards Convocation, Battle of the Bulge, dances. Student services: personal-psychological counseling. Campus security: 24-hour patrols. 250 college housing spaces available; 180 were occupied in 2003-04. Freshmen given priority for college housing. On-campus residence required in freshman year. Options: men-only, women-only housing available. Howard College Library with 30,921 books, 47,555 microform titles, 16,006 serials, 1,710 audiovisual materials, an OPAC, and a Web page. Operations spending for 2004 fiscal year: $263,459. 300 computers available on campus for general student use. A campuswide network can be accessed from student residence rooms. Staffed computer lab on campus.

Community Environment: Big Spring, population 26,000, is an urban community noted for its varied industries, which include oil refining and production, petrochemical manufacturing, one carbon black plants, two bottling plants, and an ammonia plant. The climate is temperate and dry. The community is served by air, rail, and bus lines. There is a public library, YMCA, many churches of various faiths, three general and one Veteran's hospital, a crippled children's rehabilitation center, three theatres, good shopping facilities, and various civic, fraternal, and veteran's organizations in the area. Local recreation includes skating, bowling, and water sports on nearby lakes. Part-time employment opportunities are limited.

■ **HOWARD PAYNE UNIVERSITY** *F-16*
1000 Fisk St.
Brownwood, TX 76801-2715
Tel: (325)646-2502
Free: 800-880-4478
Admissions: (325)649-8027
Fax: (325)649-8905
E-mail: admissions@hputx.edu
Web Site: http://www.hputx.edu/
Description: Independent, 4-year, coed, affiliated with Baptist General Convention of Texas. Awards associate and bachelor's degrees. Founded 1889. Setting: 30-acre small town campus. Endowment: $39.3 million. Total enrollment: 1,319. 640 applied, 78% were admitted. 15% from top 10% of their high school class, 39% from top quarter, 71% from top half. 5 valedictorians. Full-time: 1,019 students, 51% women, 49% men. Part-time: 300 students, 48% women, 52% men. Students come from 34 states and territories, 7 other countries, 3% from out-of-state, 1% Native American, 13% Hispanic, 8% black, 1% Asian American or Pacific Islander, 1% international, 22% 25 or older, 48% live on campus, 5% transferred in. Retention: 58% of full-time freshmen returned the following year. Core. Calendar: semesters. Academic remediation for entering students, ESL program, services for LD students, advanced placement, honors program, independent study, double major, summer session for credit, part-time degree program, adult/continuing education programs, internships. Study abroad program.
Entrance Requirements: Options: Peterson's Universal Application, Common Application, early admission. Required: high school transcript, minimum 3.0 high school GPA, SAT or ACT. Required for some: recommendations, interview. Entrance: minimally difficult. Application deadline: 8/1.
Collegiate Environment: Orientation program. Drama-theater group, choral group, marching band, student-run newspaper, radio station. Social organizations: 38 open to all; local fraternities, local sororities; 15% of eligible men and 20% of eligible women are members. Most popular organizations: Baptist Student Ministry, Zeta Zeta Zeta, Delta Chi Ro, Student Foundation, Iota Chi Alpha. Major annual events: Parents' Weekend, Homecoming, Stinger Daze. Student services: health clinic, personal-psychological counseling. Campus security: 24-hour emergency response devices, controlled dormitory access, 12-hour patrols by trained security personnel. 751 college housing spaces available; 682 were occupied in 2003-04. Freshmen guaranteed college housing. On-campus residence required through junior year. Options: men-only, women-only housing available. Walker Memorial Library with 78,825 books, 279,911 microform titles, 1,017 serials, an OPAC, and a Web page. Operations spending for 2004 fiscal year: $270,333. 228 computers available on campus for general student use. A campuswide network can be accessed from student residence rooms and from off campus. Staffed computer lab on campus.
Community Environment: Population 20,000. Brownwood is located 26 miles from the geographic center of the state, which designates the community "deep in the heart of Texas." The annual average temperature is 66.7 degrees, with an average annual rainfall of 27.4 inches. Railroad, airlines, and bus lines serve the area. The community has many churches of various faiths, a public library, two hospitals, and various civic, fraternal and veteran's organizations. Recreation includes Lake Brownwood with fishing, hunting, boating, water skiing, bathing, and picnicking; many city parks, golf course, municipal swimming pool, tennis courts, and five ball parks.

■ **HUSTON-TILLOTSON UNIVERSITY** *I-18*
900 Chicon St.
Austin, TX 78702-2795
Tel: (512)505-3000
Admissions: (512)505-3029
Fax: (512)505-3190
E-mail: dfprice@htu.edu

Web Site: http://www.htu.edu/
Description: Independent interdenominational, 4-year, coed. Awards bachelor's degrees. Founded 1875. Setting: 23-acre urban campus. Endowment: $6.6 million. Educational spending for 2005 fiscal year: $7928 per student. Total enrollment: 706. Student-undergrad faculty ratio is 11:1. 409 applied, 56% were admitted. 1% from top 10% of their high school class, 17% from top quarter, 55% from top half. Full-time: 625 students, 53% women, 47% men. Part-time: 81 students, 62% women, 38% men. Students come from 13 states and territories, 13 other countries, 5% from out-of-state, 13% Hispanic, 75% black, 1% Asian American or Pacific Islander, 2% international, 17% 25 or older, 42% live on campus, 8% transferred in. Retention: 42% of full-time freshmen returned the following year. Academic areas with the most degrees conferred: business/marketing; computer and information sciences; physical sciences. Core. Calendar: semesters. Academic remediation for entering students, ESL program, services for LD students, advanced placement, accelerated degree program, double major, summer session for credit, part-time degree program, co-op programs and internships. ROTC: Army (c), Naval (c).
Entrance Requirements: Option: Common Application. Required: essay, high school transcript, minimum 2.0 high school GPA. Required for some: interview. Entrance: moderately difficult. Application deadline: 3/1.
Costs Per Year: Application fee: $25. Comprehensive fee: $14,018 includes full-time tuition ($7740), mandatory fees ($735), and college room and board ($5543). College room only: $2250. Part-time tuition: $258 per credit hour.
Collegiate Environment: Orientation program. Choral group. Social organizations: 17 open to all; national fraternities, national sororities, local fraternities, local sororities; 5% of eligible men and 5% of eligible women are members. Most popular organizations: Student Government Association, Campus Pals. Major annual events: Coronation, Charter Day, Graduation Day. Student services: health clinic, personal-psychological counseling, women's center. Campus security: 24-hour patrols. 439 college housing spaces available; 242 were occupied in 2003-04. Freshmen guaranteed college housing. Options: men-only, women-only housing available. Downs-Jones Library with 88,455 books, 69,216 microform titles, 330 serials, and 8,753 audiovisual materials. Operations spending for 2004 fiscal year: $309,189. 400 computers available on campus for general student use. A campuswide network can be accessed. Staffed computer lab on campus.
Community Environment: See University of Texas at Austin.

■ **ITT TECHNICAL INSTITUTE (ARLINGTON)** *D-19*
551 Ryan Plaza Dr.
Arlington, TX 76011
Tel: (817)794-5100
Fax: (817)275-8446
Web Site: http://www.itt-tech.edu/
Description: Proprietary, 2-year, coed. Part of ITT Educational Services, Inc. Awards terminal associate degrees. Founded 1982. Setting: suburban campus with easy access to Dallas-Fort Worth. Core.
Entrance Requirements: Option: deferred admission. Required: high school transcript, interview, Wonderlic aptitude test. Recommended: recommendations. Entrance: minimally difficult. Application deadline: Rolling. Notification: continuous.
Costs Per Year: Application fee: $100.
Collegiate Environment: Orientation program. College housing not available.

■ **ITT TECHNICAL INSTITUTE (AUSTIN)** *I-18*
6330 East Hwy. 290, Ste. 150
Austin, TX 78723-1061
Tel: (512)467-6800
Free: 800-431-0677
Web Site: http://www.itt-tech.edu/
Description: Proprietary, 2-year, coed. Part of ITT Educational Services, Inc. Awards terminal associate degrees. Founded 1985. Setting: urban campus. Core.
Entrance Requirements: Option: deferred admission. Required: high school transcript, interview, Wonderlic aptitude test. Recommended: recommendations. Entrance: minimally difficult. Application deadline: Rolling. Notification: continuous.
Costs Per Year: Application fee: $100.
Collegiate Environment: Orientation program. College housing not available.

■ **ITT TECHNICAL INSTITUTE (HOUSTON)** *J-22*
2222 Bay Area Blvd.
Houston, TX 77058

Tel: (281)486-2630

Web Site: http://www.itt-tech.edu/

Description: Proprietary, 2-year, coed. Part of ITT Educational Services, Inc. Awards terminal associate degrees. Founded 1995. Core.

Entrance Requirements: Option: deferred admission. Required: high school transcript, interview, Wonderlic aptitude test. Recommended: recommendations. Entrance: minimally difficult. Application deadline: Rolling. Notification: continuous.

Costs Per Year: Application fee: $100.

Collegiate Environment: Orientation program. College housing not available.

■ **ITT TECHNICAL INSTITUTE (HOUSTON)** *J-22*

2950 South Gessner

Houston, TX 77063-3751

Tel: (713)952-2294

Web Site: http://www.itt-tech.edu/

Description: Proprietary, 2-year, coed. Part of ITT Educational Services, Inc. Awards terminal associate degrees. Founded 1983. Setting: 4-acre urban campus. Total enrollment: 585. Core.

Entrance Requirements: Option: deferred admission. Required: high school transcript, interview, Wonderlic aptitude test. Recommended: recommendations. Entrance: minimally difficult. Application deadline: Rolling. Notification: continuous.

Costs Per Year: Application fee: $100.

Collegiate Environment: Orientation program. Student-run newspaper. College housing not available.

■ **ITT TECHNICAL INSTITUTE (HOUSTON)** *J-22*

15621 Blue Ash Dr., Ste. 160

Houston, TX 77090-5821

Tel: (281)873-0512

Fax: (281)873-0518

Web Site: http://www.itt-tech.edu/

Description: Proprietary, 2-year, coed. Part of ITT Educational Services, Inc. Awards terminal associate degrees. Founded 1985. Setting: 1-acre suburban campus. Core.

Entrance Requirements: Option: deferred admission. Required: high school transcript, interview, Wonderlic aptitude test. Recommended: recommendations. Entrance: minimally difficult. Application deadline: Rolling. Notification: continuous.

Costs Per Year: Application fee: $100.

Collegiate Environment: Orientation program. College housing not available.

■ **ITT TECHNICAL INSTITUTE (RICHARDSON)** *F-34*

2101 Waterview Parkway

Richardson, TX 75080

Tel: (972)690-9100; 888-488-5761

Web Site: http://www.itt-tech.edu/

Description: Proprietary, 2-year, coed. Part of ITT Educational Services, Inc. Awards terminal associate degrees. Founded 1989. Setting: suburban campus with easy access to Dallas-Fort Worth. Core.

Entrance Requirements: Option: deferred admission. Required: high school transcript, interview, Wonderlic aptitude test. Recommended: recommendations. Entrance: minimally difficult. Application deadline: Rolling. Notification: continuous.

Costs Per Year: Application fee: $100.

Collegiate Environment: Orientation program. College housing not available.

■ **ITT TECHNICAL INSTITUTE (SAN ANTONIO)** *K-16*

5700 Northwest Parkway

San Antonio, TX 78249-3303

Tel: (210)694-4612

Free: 800-880-0570

Fax: (210)694-4651

Web Site: http://www.itt-tech.edu/

Description: Proprietary, 2-year, coed. Part of ITT Educational Services, Inc. Awards terminal associate degrees. Founded 1988. Setting: urban campus. Core.

Entrance Requirements: Options: Peterson's Universal Application, deferred admission. Required: high school transcript, interview, Wonderlic

aptitude test. Recommended: recommendations. Entrance: minimally difficult. Application deadline: Rolling. Notification: continuous.

Costs Per Year: Application fee: $100.

Collegiate Environment: Orientation program. Student-run newspaper. College housing not available.

■ **JACKSONVILLE COLLEGE** *F-22*

105 B J Albritton Dr.

Jacksonville, TX 75766-4759

Tel: (903)586-2518

Free: 800-256-8522

E-mail: admissions@jacksonville-college.edu

Web Site: http://www.jacksonville-college.edu/

Description: Independent Baptist, 2-year, coed. Awards diplomas, transfer associate, and terminal associate degrees. Founded 1899. Setting: 20-acre small town campus. Total enrollment: 300. Student-undergrad faculty ratio is 16:1. 223 applied, 41% were admitted. Full-time: 220 students, 62% women, 38% men. Part-time: 80 students, 53% women, 48% men. Students come from 16 states and territories, 15 other countries, 3% from out-of-state, 0% Native American, 12% Hispanic, 16% black, 0.3% Asian American or Pacific Islander, 3% international, 12% 25 or older, 39% live on campus. Core. Calendar: semesters. Academic remediation for entering students, advanced placement, summer session for credit, part-time degree program, adult/continuing education programs.

Entrance Requirements: Open admission. Options: electronic application, early admission. Required for some: SAT, ACT, THEA. Entrance: noncompetitive. Application deadline: 8/15. Notification: continuous until 7/1.

Costs Per Year: Application fee: $15. Comprehensive fee: $4480 includes full-time tuition ($2800), mandatory fees ($307), and college room and board ($1373). Part-time tuition: $175 per credit hour.

Collegiate Environment: Drama-theater group, choral group. Social organizations: 3 open to all. Most popular organizations: Drama Club, Ministerial Alliance, Mission Band. Major annual events: Homecoming, College Preview Day, Spring Banquet. Student services: health clinic, personal-psychological counseling. Campus security: 24-hour emergency response devices, evening security personnel. On-campus residence required through sophomore year. Weatherby Memorial Building plus 1 other with 22,000 books and 170 serials. 20 computers available on campus for general student use. A campuswide network can be accessed. Staffed computer lab on campus.

Community Environment: Population 12,000, Jacksonville is a small community enjoying temperate climate. The average annual rainfall is approximately 45 inches. The community is reached by way of railroad, major airlines, bus lines and highways. Community service facilities include many churches, two hospitals, a public library, and a local radio station. There are parks and facilities for golf, hunting, fishing, rodeos, and swimming. Various civic and fraternal organizations are active in the area. Part-time employment is available.

■ **JARVIS CHRISTIAN COLLEGE** *D-22*

PO Box 1470

Hawkins, TX 75765-1470

Tel: (903)769-5700

Admissions: (903)769-5802

Fax: (903)769-4842

Web Site: http://www.jarvis.edu/

Description: Independent, 4-year, coed, affiliated with Christian Church (Disciples of Christ). Awards bachelor's degrees. Founded 1912. Setting: 465-acre rural campus. Endowment: $10.8 million. Educational spending for 2005 fiscal year: $5208 per student. Total enrollment: 572. Student-undergrad faculty ratio is 15:1. 170 applied, 58% were admitted. 3% from top 10% of their high school class, 10% from top quarter, 26% from top half. Full-time: 559 students, 54% women, 46% men. Part-time: 13 students, 46% women, 54% men. Students come from 21 states and territories, 2 other countries, 14% from out-of-state, 0% Native American, 1% Hispanic, 97% black, 0% Asian American or Pacific Islander, 0.2% international, 1% 25 or older, 87% live on campus, 5% transferred in. Retention: 57% of full-time freshmen returned the following year. Academic areas with the most degrees conferred: business/marketing; social sciences; computer and information sciences. Core. Calendar: semesters. Academic remediation for entering students, advanced placement, honors program, distance learning, summer session for credit, part-time degree program, co-op programs and internships. Off campus study at University of Texas at Arlington, University of Texas at Tyler, University of North Texas.

Entrance Requirements: Open admission. Option: Common Application. Required: high school transcript. Recommended: minimum 2.0 high school GPA, ACT, SAT or ACT. Entrance: minimally difficult. Application deadline: 8/1.

Costs Per Year: Application fee: $25. Comprehensive fee: $11,136 includes full-time tuition ($6280), mandatory fees ($700), and college room and board ($4156). College room only: $2056. Part-time tuition: $262 per hour. Part-time mandatory fees: $350 per term.

Collegiate Environment: Orientation program. Drama-theater group, choral group, student-run newspaper. Social organizations: 20 open to all; national fraternities, national sororities; 5% of eligible men and 10% of eligible women are members. Most popular organizations: Student Government Association, SIFE, Student Ministers' Association, SNEA, Residence Hall Councils. Major annual events: Homecoming/Founders' Week, Miss Jarvis Coronation, Open House/Parents' Weekend. Student services: health clinic, personal-psychological counseling. Campus security: 24-hour patrols. 750 college housing spaces available; 460 were occupied in 2003-04. No special consideration for freshman housing applicants. Options: men-only, women-only housing available. Olin Library with 54,291 books, 135 microform titles, 152 serials, 163 audiovisual materials, and an OPAC. Operations spending for 2004 fiscal year: $122,181. 318 computers available on campus for general student use. A campuswide network can be accessed from student residence rooms and from off campus. Staffed computer lab on campus.

Community Environment: Hawkins is located in southwestern Wood County, population 18,589. The area enjoys moderate, temperate climate. Serviced by U.S. Highway 80 and bus lines, there are churches of many denominations, a hospital and clinic, and various civic, fraternal, and veteran's organizations. Local recreation includes camping and hunting, with rivers, creeks, springs and lakes furnishing opportunities for fishing and boating.

■ **KD STUDIO** *D-19*
2600 Stemmons Freeway, No. 117
Dallas, TX 75207
Tel: (214)638-0484
Fax: (214)630-5140
E-mail: acting@onramp.net
Web Site: http://www.kdstudio.com/

Description: Proprietary, 2-year, coed. Awards terminal associate degrees. Founded 1979. Setting: urban campus. Educational spending for 2005 fiscal year: $2405 per student. Total enrollment: 152. Student-undergrad faculty ratio is 7:1. 67 applied, 91% were admitted. Full-time: 152 students, 51% women, 49% men. Students come from 10 states and territories, 4% from out-of-state, 0% Native American, 13% Hispanic, 36% black, 0% Asian American or Pacific Islander, 20% 25 or older. Core. Calendar: semesters. Co-op programs.

Entrance Requirements: Open admission. Options: Common Application, deferred admission. Required: essay, high school transcript, interview, audition. Required for some: recommendations. Entrance: noncompetitive. Application deadline: Rolling.

Collegiate Environment: Drama-theater group. Social organizations: 1 open to all. Most popular organization: Student Council. Major annual events: in-house plays/productions, Halloween Costume contest, monthly movie nights. Campus security: 24-hour emergency response devices and patrols. College housing not available. KD Studio Library with 800 books and 15 serials. Operations spending for 2004 fiscal year: $20,693. 1 computer on campus for general student use. Staffed computer lab on campus.

■ **KILGORE COLLEGE** *E-22*
1100 Broadway Blvd.
Kilgore, TX 75662-3299
Tel: (903)984-8531
Admissions: (903)983-8200
Fax: (903)983-8607
Web Site: http://www.kilgore.edu/

Description: State and locally supported, 2-year, coed. Awards certificates, transfer associate, and terminal associate degrees. Founded 1935. Setting: 35-acre small town campus with easy access to Dallas-Fort Worth. Endowment: $5.2 million. Educational spending for 2005 fiscal year: $3411 per student. Total enrollment: 4,957. 1,706 applied, 63% were admitted. Full-time: 2,749 students, 60% women, 40% men. Part-time: 2,208 students, 65% women, 35% men. Students come from 21 states and territories, 36 other countries, 1% from out-of-state, 0.1% Native American, 4% Hispanic, 15% black, 0.5% Asian American or Pacific Islander, 2% international, 30%

25 or older, 12% live on campus, 6% transferred in. Retention: 45% of full-time freshmen returned the following year. Core. Calendar: semesters. Academic remediation for entering students, ESL program, services for LD students, advanced placement, self-designed majors, summer session for credit, part-time degree program, adult/continuing education programs, co-op programs and internships. ROTC: Army (c).

Entrance Requirements: Open admission. Option: early admission. Required: high school transcript. Required for some: interview. Placement: THEA required; SAT or ACT recommended. Entrance: noncompetitive. Application deadline: Rolling.

Costs Per Year: Application fee: $0. Area resident tuition: $540 full-time, $18 per hour part-time. State resident tuition: $1680 full-time, $56 per hour part-time. Nonresident tuition: $2520 full-time, $84 per hour part-time. Mandatory fees: $510 full-time. College room and board: $3580. College room only: $1580.

Collegiate Environment: Orientation program. Drama-theater group, choral group, marching band. Social organizations: 27 open to all. Most popular organizations: Phi Theta Kappa, Student Government Association, Ambucs. Major annual events: KC Kickoff, Homecoming, Blood Drive. Campus security: 24-hour emergency response devices and patrols. 450 college housing spaces available; 393 were occupied in 2003-04. No special consideration for freshman housing applicants. On-campus residence required in freshman year. Options: coed, men-only, women-only housing available. Randolph C. Watson Library plus 1 other with 65,000 books, 394 microform titles, 6,679 serials, 13,351 audiovisual materials, an OPAC, and a Web page. Operations spending for 2004 fiscal year: $396,828. 302 computers available on campus for general student use. Staffed computer lab on campus.

Community Environment: Kilgore, population 10,000, is a suburban area enjoying temperate climate and four distinct seasons. The area is reached by bus, rail, air, and Interstate Highway 20, U.S. 259, and State 31. The community has over 40 churches representing various faiths, a library, medical facilities, and many civic, fraternal, and veteran's organizations. There are apartments available for student housing. Local recreation facilities include a swimming pool, tennis courts, picnic areas, bowling alleys, theatres, go-cart track, golf course, as well as water skiing, fishing, camping, and hunting. Part-time employment is available.

■ **KINGWOOD COLLEGE** *I-22*
20000 Kingwood Dr.
Kingwood, TX 77339-3801
Tel: (281)312-1600
Admissions: (281)312-1562
Fax: (281)312-1477
Web Site: http://kcweb.nhmccd.edu/

Description: State and locally supported, 2-year, coed. Part of North Harris Montgomery Community College District. Awards certificates, transfer associate, and terminal associate degrees. Founded 1984. Setting: 264-acre suburban campus with easy access to Houston. Total enrollment: 6,842. Student-undergrad faculty ratio is 16:1. 3,898 applied, 100% were admitted. Full-time: 1,308 students, 56% women, 44% men. Part-time: 5,534 students, 65% women, 35% men. Students come from 44 other countries, 1% from out-of-state, 0.4% Native American, 14% Hispanic, 8% black, 3% Asian American or Pacific Islander, 2% international, 35% 25 or older, 4% transferred in. Core. Calendar: semesters. Academic remediation for entering students, ESL program, services for LD students, advanced placement, accelerated degree program, honors program, independent study, distance learning, double major, summer session for credit, part-time degree program, external degree program, co-op programs and internships.

Entrance Requirements: Open admission. Options: Common Application, early admission. Required: high school transcript. Required for some: essay. Entrance: noncompetitive. Application deadline: Rolling.

Costs Per Year: Application fee: $0. Area resident tuition: $984 full-time, $52 per credit part-time. State resident tuition: $1944 full-time, $92 per credit part-time. Nonresident tuition: $2304 full-time, $220 per credit part-time.

Collegiate Environment: Orientation program. Drama-theater group, choral group. Social organizations: 13 open to all. Most popular organizations: Phi Theta Kappa, Office Administration Club, African American Student Association, Student Government Association, Delta Epsilon Chi. Major annual events: Fall Festival, Spring Fling, Commencement. Student services: personal-psychological counseling. Campus security: 24-hour emergency response devices and patrols, late night transport-escort service. College housing not available. Kingwood College Library with 38,000 books, 14,642 microform titles, 262 serials, 3,177 audiovisual materials, an OPAC, and a

Web page. 540 computers available on campus for general student use. A campuswide network can be accessed from off-campus. Staffed computer lab on campus.

■ **LAMAR INSTITUTE OF TECHNOLOGY** *I-24*

PO Box 10043
Beaumont, TX 77710
Tel: (409)880-8321
Free: 800-950-8321
Admissions: (409)880-8354
E-mail: rushjc@hal.lamar.edu
Web Site: http://theinstitute.lamar.edu/

Description: State-supported, 2-year, coed. Founded 1995. Calendar: semesters.

■ **LAMAR STATE COLLEGE-ORANGE** *I-25*

410 Front St.
Orange, TX 77630-5802
Tel: (409)883-7750
Admissions: (409)882-3362
Fax: (409)882-3374
Web Site: http://www.lsco.edu/

Description: State-supported, 2-year, coed. Part of The Texas State University System. Awards certificates, transfer associate, and terminal associate degrees. Founded 1969. Setting: 21-acre small town campus. Endowment: $5524. Research spending for 2004 fiscal year: $83,258. Educational spending for 2005 fiscal year: $1602 per student. Total enrollment: 2,143. Student-undergrad faculty ratio is 19:1. 447 applied, 70% were admitted. 5% from top 10% of their high school class. Full-time: 920 students, 70% women, 30% men. Part-time: 1,223 students, 73% women, 27% men. 10% from out-of-state, 1% Native American, 3% Hispanic, 19% black, 1% Asian American or Pacific Islander, 0% international, 38% 25 or older, 6% transferred in. Core. Calendar: semesters. Academic remediation for entering students, distance learning, double major, summer session for credit, part-time degree program, internships.

Entrance Requirements: Open admission except for some programs. Options: Common Application, early admission, deferred admission. Required: high school transcript. Entrance: noncompetitive. Application deadline: Rolling. Notification: continuous.

Costs Per Year: Application fee: $0. State resident tuition: $1824 full-time. Nonresident tuition: $8448 full-time. Mandatory fees: $736 full-time.

Collegiate Environment: Orientation program. Student-run newspaper. Social organizations: local fraternities. Major annual event: Spring Day. Campus security: 24-hour emergency response devices, late night transport-escort service. College housing not available. Lamar State College-Orange Library plus 1 other with 71,092 books, 1,306 serials, 288 audiovisual materials, and an OPAC. Operations spending for 2004 fiscal year: $168,687. 70 computers available on campus for general student use. A campuswide network can be accessed from off-campus. Staffed computer lab on campus.

■ **LAMAR STATE COLLEGE-PORT ARTHUR** *I-24*

PO Box 310
Port Arthur, TX 77641-0310
Tel: (409)983-4921
Free: 800-477-5872
Admissions: (409)984-6165
Fax: (409)984-6032
E-mail: connie.nicholas@lamarpa.edu
Web Site: http://www.lamarpa.edu/

Description: State-supported, 2-year, coed. Part of The Texas State University System. Awards certificates, transfer associate, and terminal associate degrees. Founded 1909. Setting: 34-acre suburban campus with easy access to Houston. Total enrollment: 2,530. Student-undergrad faculty ratio is 13:1. 836 applied, 61% were admitted. Full-time: 980 students, 68% women, 32% men. Part-time: 1,550 students, 60% women, 40% men. 1% from out-of-state, 0.4% Native American, 12% Hispanic, 28% black, 6% Asian American or Pacific Islander, 0.3% international, 41% 25 or older, 9% transferred in. Core. Calendar: semesters. Academic remediation for entering students, ESL program, services for LD students, advanced placement, accelerated degree program, honors program, independent study, distance learning, double major, summer session for credit, part-time degree

program, adult/continuing education programs, co-op programs and internships. Off campus study at Lamar University-Beaumont, Lamar University-Orange. ROTC: Army (c).

Entrance Requirements: Open admission. Options: Common Application, early admission, deferred admission. Required: high school transcript. Required for some: interview. Entrance: noncompetitive. Application deadline: Rolling. Notification: continuous.

Costs Per Year: Application fee: $0. One-time mandatory fee: $10. State resident tuition: $2340 full-time. Nonresident tuition: $10,590 full-time. Mandatory fees: $824 full-time.

Collegiate Environment: Orientation program. Drama-theater group, choral group. Social organizations: 9 open to all; local fraternities, local sororities; 2% of eligible men and 2% of eligible women are members. Most popular organizations: Historical Society, Chi Alpha, tennis, Student Government Association, Baptist Student Ministry. Major annual events: highway clean-up, Annual Talent Show, Food Drive. Student services: personal-psychological counseling. Campus security: 24-hour emergency response devices, student patrols, late night transport-escort service. College housing not available. Gates Memorial Library with 43,726 books, 15,992 microform titles, 3,400 serials, 1,493 audiovisual materials, an OPAC, and a Web page. Operations spending for 2004 fiscal year: $409,575.

■ **LAMAR UNIVERSITY** *I-24*

4400 Martin Luther King Parkway
Beaumont, TX 77710
Tel: (409)880-7011
Admissions: (409)880-8354
Fax: (409)880-8463
Web Site: http://www.lamar.edu/

Description: State-supported, university, coed. Part of Texas State University System. Awards associate, bachelor's, master's, and doctoral degrees. Founded 1923. Setting: 200-acre suburban campus with easy access to Houston. Total enrollment: 10,595. Faculty: 542 (372 full-time, 170 part-time). Student-undergrad faculty ratio is 20:1. 5,213 applied, 67% were admitted. 12% from top 10% of their high school class, 34% from top quarter, 75% from top half. 3 valedictorians. Full-time: 6,708 students, 58% women, 42% men. Part-time: 2,976 students, 64% women, 36% men. Students come from 30 states and territories, 27 other countries, 1% from out-of-state, 1% Native American, 6% Hispanic, 26% black, 3% Asian American or Pacific Islander, 1% international, 26% 25 or older, 7% transferred in. Retention: 61% of full-time freshmen returned the following year. Core. Calendar: semesters. Academic remediation for entering students, ESL program, services for LD students, advanced placement, accelerated degree program, self-designed majors, honors program, summer session for credit, part-time degree program, adult/continuing education programs, co-op programs and internships, graduate courses open to undergrads. Off campus study at Texas A&M University. Study abroad program.

Entrance Requirements: Options: electronic application, early admission. Required: high school transcript, SAT or ACT. Required for some: essay, SAT Subject Tests. Entrance: minimally difficult. Application deadline: 8/1. Notification: continuous.

Costs Per Year: Application fee: $0. Area resident tuition: $1262 per term part-time. State resident tuition: $2880 full-time. Nonresident tuition: $9504 full-time, $4813 per term part-time. Mandatory fees: $512 per term part-time. Part-time tuition and fees vary according to course load. College room and board: $5254. College room only: $3600. Room and board charges vary according to board plan and housing facility.

Collegiate Environment: Orientation program. Drama-theater group, choral group, student-run newspaper. Social organizations: national fraternities, national sororities; 5% of eligible men and 5% of eligible women are members. Major annual events: Midnight Madness, Homecoming, Springfest. Student services: health clinic, personal-psychological counseling. Campus security: 24-hour emergency response devices and patrols, student patrols, late night transport-escort service. Option: coed housing available. Mary and John Gray Library with 698,285 books, 268,825 microform titles, 2,900 serials, 6,572 audiovisual materials, an OPAC, and a Web page. 120 computers available on campus for general student use. A campuswide network can be accessed from student residence rooms and from off campus. Staffed computer lab on campus.

Community Environment: Beaumont and the surrounding area form one of the largest concentrations of petroleum refineries in the nation. Top manufactures of the area include deep sea and dry-land oil-drilling equipment and oil-processing apparatus. The city is located on the Neches River approximately 20 miles north of the Gulf of Mexico. The climate is mild the year round. Airlines, railroad, and bus lines serve the community. The community has many churches representing various faiths, three libraries, YMCA, and YWCA, several hospitals, and various civic and fraternal organizations. Part-time employment is available.

■ LAREDO COMMUNITY COLLEGE N-15

West End Washington St.
Laredo, TX 78040-4395
Tel: (956)722-0521
Admissions: (956)721-5109
Fax: (956)721-5493
Web Site: http://www.laredo.edu/

Description: State and locally supported, 2-year, coed. Awards certificates, transfer associate, and terminal associate degrees. Founded 1946. Setting: 186-acre urban campus. Endowment: $1.9 million. Educational spending for 2005 fiscal year: $4725 per student. Total enrollment: 8,298. Student-undergrad faculty ratio is 18:1. 1,245 applied, 100% were admitted. Full-time: 3,200 students, 56% women, 44% men. Part-time: 5,098 students, 59% women, 41% men. Students come from 4 states and territories, 5 other countries, 0.1% from out-of-state, 0.02% Native American, 94% Hispanic, 0.2% black, 0.3% Asian American or Pacific Islander, 4% international, 35% 25 or older. Retention: 83% of full-time freshmen returned the following year. Core. Calendar: semesters. Academic remediation for entering students, ESL program, services for LD students, advanced placement, freshman honors college, honors program, independent study, distance learning, double major, summer session for credit, part-time degree program, adult/continuing education programs, internships.

Entrance Requirements: Open admission. Options: Common Application, early admission, deferred admission. Required: high school transcript. Entrance: noncompetitive. Application deadline: Rolling.

Costs Per Year: Application fee: $0. Area resident tuition: $840 full-time, $35 per credit hour part-time. State resident tuition: $1680 full-time, $70 per credit hour part-time. Nonresident tuition: $2520 full-time, $105 per credit hour part-time. Mandatory fees: $270 full-time, $24 per credit hour part-time, $28 per term part-time. College room and board: $4229.

Collegiate Environment: Drama-theater group, choral group, student-run newspaper. Student services: personal-psychological counseling, women's center. Campus security: 24-hour emergency response devices and patrols, student patrols. 120 college housing spaces available; all were occupied in 2003-04. Option: coed housing available. Yeary Library with 88,006 books, 555 serials, and an OPAC.

Community Environment: Population approximately 100,000. A chief port of entry into Mexico, Laredo is separated from Nuevo Laredo, Mexico, by the Rio Grande. This is a metropolitan community located in the center of a rich cattle, oil, gas and agricultural district. It is a major import-export center. The city is reached by airlines, railroad, and bus service. The climate is temperate and dry. Laredo has a public library, churches of major denominations, two hospitals, and various civic and fraternal organizations. Shopping facilities are good. Part-time employment is available for students. Local recreation includes theaters, water sports, and most major sports.

■ LEE COLLEGE E-46

PO Box 818
Baytown, TX 77522-0818
Tel: (281)427-5611
Free: 800-621-8724
Admissions: (281)425-6399
Fax: (281)425-6831
E-mail: bgriffit@lee.edu
Web Site: http://www.lee.edu/

Description: District-supported, 2-year, coed. Awards certificates, transfer associate, and terminal associate degrees. Founded 1934. Setting: 35-acre suburban campus with easy access to Houston. Total enrollment: 5,906. 1,613 applied, 100% were admitted. Full-time: 1,624 students, 63% women, 37% men. Part-time: 4,282 students, 37% women, 63% men. Students come from 10 other countries, 0.2% Native American, 22% Hispanic, 12% black, 1% Asian American or Pacific Islander, 1% international, 52% 25 or older. Core. Calendar: semesters. Academic remediation for entering students, ESL program, advanced placement, honors program, independent study, distance learning, summer session for credit, part-time degree program, adult/continuing education programs, co-op programs and internships. ROTC: Army (c).

Entrance Requirements: Open admission except for nursing program. Options: early admission, deferred admission. Required for some: high school

transcript. Placement: THEA required. Entrance: noncompetitive. Application deadline: Rolling. Notification: continuous.

Collegiate Environment: Orientation program. Drama-theater group, choral group, student-run newspaper. Social organizations: 27 open to all. Most popular organizations: Student Congress, Health Information Student Association, Lee College Awareness, Digital Information Society, ASHRAE - Air Conditioning Society of Heat and Refrigeration Engineers. Major annual events: Fall Fiesta, Spring Fling, Annual Blood Drive. Student services: personal-psychological counseling. Campus security: 24-hour patrols, late night transport-escort service, emergency telephones. College housing not available. Erma Wood Carlson Learning Resource Center with 100,000 books, 660 serials, an OPAC, and a Web page. 800 computers available on campus for general student use. A campuswide network can be accessed. Staffed computer lab on campus.

Community Environment: Population 60,000. Baytown is located midway between Houston and the open sea on the Houston Ship Channel. The city is a consolidation of three towns: Baytown, Goose Creek, and Pelly. There are many churches in the immediate area, and four hospitals are easily accessible.

■ LETOURNEAU UNIVERSITY E-23

PO Box 7001
Longview, TX 75607-7001
Tel: (903)233-3000
Free: 800-759-8811
Admissions: (903)233-3400
Fax: (903)233-3411
E-mail: admissions@james.letu.edu
Web Site: http://www.letu.edu/

Description: Independent nondenominational, comprehensive, coed. Awards associate, bachelor's, and master's degrees. Founded 1946. Setting: 162-acre suburban campus. Endowment: $4.4 million. Research spending for 2004 fiscal year: $142,079. Educational spending for 2005 fiscal year: $4582 per student. Total enrollment: 3,980. Faculty: 315 (72 full-time, 243 part-time). Student-undergrad faculty ratio is 14:1. 920 applied, 76% were admitted. 32% from top 10% of their high school class, 60% from top quarter, 86% from top half. Full-time: 1,405 students, 32% women, 68% men. Part-time: 2,201 students, 71% women, 29% men. Students come from 50 states and territories, 27 other countries, 53% from out-of-state, 0.4% Native American, 8% Hispanic, 22% black, 1% Asian American or Pacific Islander, 1% international, 7% 25 or older, 76% live on campus, 3% transferred in. Retention: 72% of full-time freshmen returned the following year. Academic areas with the most degrees conferred: business/marketing; engineering; transportation and materials moving. Core. Calendar: semesters. Academic remediation for entering students, services for LD students, advanced placement, honors program, independent study, distance learning, double major, summer session for credit, part-time degree program, adult/continuing education programs, co-op programs and internships. Off campus study at Council for Christian Colleges and Universities. Study abroad program.

Entrance Requirements: Options: Peterson's Universal Application, electronic application, deferred admission. Required: SAT or ACT. Application deadline: 8/1. Notification: continuous.

Costs Per Year: Application fee: $25. Comprehensive fee: $22,176 includes full-time tuition ($15,710), mandatory fees ($180), and college room and board ($6286). Room and board charges vary according to board plan. Part-time tuition: $280 per hour. Part-time tuition varies according to course load.

Collegiate Environment: Orientation program. Drama-theater group, choral group, student-run newspaper. Social organizations: 22 open to all; 3 societies for men, 1 society for women. Most popular organizations: student ministries, Themelios, Student Foundation, Student Senate, Roller Hockey Club. Major annual events: Hootenanny, Fall Fest, Longview Blitz. Student services: health clinic, personal-psychological counseling. Campus security: 24-hour emergency response devices and patrols, late night transport-escort service, controlled dormitory access. 981 college housing spaces available; 879 were occupied in 2003-04. Freshmen guaranteed college housing. On-campus residence required through junior year. Options: men-only, women-only housing available. Margaret Estes Resource Center with 84,779 books, 50,481 microform titles, 383 serials, and 3,144 audiovisual materials. Operations spending for 2004 fiscal year: $393,203. 191 computers available on campus for general student use. Computer purchase/lease plans available. A campuswide network can be accessed from student residence rooms and from off campus. Staffed computer lab on campus.

Community Environment: Population 70,000. Oil is the major source of economy for this community. Longview has a city library, community center, two hospitals, and a number of medical clinics. Major civic and fraternal clubs are active in the area. Longview is reached by airlines, railroad, and bus lines. Residence halls and apartments furnish student housing. Local recreation includes theatres, symphony, parks, swimming, hunting, fishing, golf, and water skiing. Part-time employment is available.

■ LON MORRIS COLLEGE *F-22*

800 College Ave.
Jacksonville, TX 75766-2923
Tel: (903)589-4000
Free: 800-259-5753
Fax: (903)586-8562
Web Site: http://www.lonmorris.edu/

Description: Independent United Methodist, 2-year, coed. Awards transfer associate and terminal associate degrees. Founded 1854. Setting: 76-acre small town campus. Endowment: $20.1 million. Educational spending for 2005 fiscal year: $4251 per student. Total enrollment: 432. 261 applied, 86% were admitted. 3% from top 10% of their high school class, 18% from top quarter, 47% from top half. Full-time: 394 students, 48% women, 52% men. Part-time: 38 students, 68% women, 32% men. Students come from 5 states and territories, 5% from out-of-state, 1% Native American, 11% Hispanic, 21% black, 0.5% Asian American or Pacific Islander, 5% international, 1% 25 or older, 90% live on campus. Retention: 53% of full-time freshmen returned the following year. Core. Calendar: semesters. Academic remediation for entering students, ESL program, services for LD students, advanced placement, independent study, summer session for credit, part-time degree program. Study abroad program.

Entrance Requirements: Options: Common Application, electronic application, deferred admission. Required: high school transcript, SAT or ACT. Entrance: noncompetitive. Application deadline: Rolling.

Collegiate Environment: Orientation program. Drama-theater group, choral group, student-run newspaper. Social organizations: local fraternities, local sororities; 19% of eligible men and 29% of eligible women are members. Student services: personal-psychological counseling. Campus security: late night transport-escort service, controlled dormitory access. 260 college housing spaces available; 250 were occupied in 2003-04. Freshmen given priority for college housing. On-campus residence required through sophomore year. Options: men-only, women-only housing available. Henderson Library with 26,000 books, 265 serials, an OPAC, and a Web page. Operations spending for 2004 fiscal year: $170,661. 28 computers available on campus for general student use. Staffed computer lab on campus.

Community Environment: See Jacksonville College.

■ LUBBOCK CHRISTIAN UNIVERSITY *C-10*

5601 19th St.
Lubbock, TX 79407-2099
Tel: (806)796-8800
Free: 800-933-7601
Admissions: (806)720-7803
Fax: (806)796-8917
E-mail: mondy.brewer@lcu.edu
Web Site: http://www.lcu.edu/

Description: Independent, comprehensive, coed, affiliated with Church of Christ. Awards bachelor's, master's, and first professional degrees. Founded 1957. Setting: 120-acre suburban campus. Endowment: $11.1 million. Research spending for 2004 fiscal year: $44,480. Educational spending for 2005 fiscal year: $5274 per student. Total enrollment: 2,076. Faculty: 154 (81 full-time, 73 part-time). Student-undergrad faculty ratio is 15:1. 912 applied, 74% were admitted. 14% from top 10% of their high school class, 41% from top quarter, 71% from top half. 1 National Merit Scholar, 5 valedictorians. Full-time: 1,383 students, 57% women, 43% men. Part-time: 449 students, 57% women, 43% men. Students come from 33 states and territories, 13 other countries, 9% from out-of-state, 0.2% Native American, 14% Hispanic, 6% black, 1% Asian American or Pacific Islander, 1% international, 30% 25 or older, 30% live on campus, 15% transferred in. Retention: 69% of full-time freshmen returned the following year. Academic areas with the most degrees conferred: business/marketing; education; public administration and social services. Core. Calendar: semesters. Academic remediation for entering students, services for LD students, advanced placement, accelerated degree program, self-designed majors, honors program, distance learning, double major, summer session for credit, part-time degree program, adult/continuing education programs, internships, graduate courses open to undergrads. Study abroad program. ROTC: Army (c), Air Force (c).

Entrance Requirements: Options: Common Application, electronic application. Required: high school transcript, SAT or ACT. Entrance: moderately difficult. Application deadline: 8/1. Notification: continuous.

Costs Per Year: Application fee: $25. Comprehensive fee: $16,810 includes full-time tuition ($11,644), mandatory fees ($916), and college room and board ($4250). Full-time tuition and fees vary according to program. Room and board charges vary according to board plan and housing facility. Part-time tuition: $375 per semester hour. Part-time mandatory fees: $402 per term. Part-time tuition and fees vary according to course load and program.

Collegiate Environment: Orientation program. Drama-theater group, choral group, student-run newspaper. Social organizations: 24 open to all; local fraternities, local sororities; 29% of eligible men and 45% of eligible women are members. Major annual events: Masterfollies, Homecoming, LCU Lectureships. Student services: health clinic, personal-psychological counseling. Campus security: 24-hour patrols. 620 college housing spaces available; 497 were occupied in 2003-04. Freshmen guaranteed college housing. On-campus residence required through sophomore year. Options: men-only, women-only housing available. University Library with 113,556 books, 96,662 microform titles, 545 serials, an OPAC, and a Web page. Operations spending for 2004 fiscal year: $491,608. 159 computers available on campus for general student use. A campuswide network can be accessed from student residence rooms and from off campus. Staffed computer lab on campus.

Community Environment: Population 180,000. The industrial, agricultural and educational center of the South Plains of Texas, Lubbock is the third largest inland cotton market in the Nation. There are also many oil wells in the community. This metropolitan center is called "The Hub of the Plains." The climate is mild and arid. Community service facilities include over 200 churches, county libraries, hospitals, a planetarium, museum, and municipal auditorium. There are four TV stations, seven radio stations, four golf courses, movie theaters, drive-ins, hunting, water skiing, horseback riding, and many other forms of recreation available in the area. Part-time employment is available. The city is served by railroad, airlines, and a bus line.

■ MCLENNAN COMMUNITY COLLEGE *G-19*

1400 College Dr.
Waco, TX 76708-1499
Tel: (254)299-8622
Admissions: (254)299-8689
E-mail: vjefferson@mclennan.edu
Web Site: http://www.mclennan.edu/

Description: County-supported, 2-year, coed. Awards certificates, transfer associate, and terminal associate degrees. Founded 1965. Setting: 200-acre urban campus. Total enrollment: 7,562. 2,646 applied, 100% were admitted. Full-time: 3,354 students, 63% women, 37% men. Part-time: 4,208 students, 72% women, 28% men. Students come from 10 other countries, 0.3% Native American, 15% Hispanic, 17% black, 1% Asian American or Pacific Islander, 0.4% international, 42% 25 or older. Core. Calendar: semesters. Academic remediation for entering students, services for LD students, advanced placement, self-designed majors, honors program, distance learning, summer session for credit, part-time degree program, adult/continuing education programs, co-op programs and internships. Off campus study at Baylor University. Study abroad program. ROTC: Air Force.

Entrance Requirements: Open admission except for health careers programs. Option: early admission. Required: high school transcript. Placement: THEA required. Entrance: noncompetitive. Application deadline: Rolling. Notification: continuous until 9/2.

Costs Per Year: Area resident tuition: $1272 full-time. State resident tuition: $1560 full-time. Nonresident tuition: $2712 full-time. Mandatory fees: $216 full-time.

Collegiate Environment: Orientation program. Drama-theater group, choral group, student-run newspaper. Major annual event: Highland Games. Student services: personal-psychological counseling. Campus security: 24-hour emergency response devices and patrols. College housing not available. McLennan Community College Library with 93,000 books, 130,000 microform titles, 400 serials, an OPAC, and a Web page. 425 computers available on campus for general student use. A campuswide network can be accessed from off-campus. Staffed computer lab on campus.

Community Environment: See Baylor University.

■ MCMURRY UNIVERSITY *E-14*

South 14th and Sayles
Abilene, TX 79697
Tel: (325)793-3800

Free: 800-477-0077
Admissions: (325)793-4720
Fax: (325)691-6599
E-mail: dvoskuil@mcm.edu
Web Site: http://www.mcm.edu/

Description: Independent United Methodist, 4-year, coed. Awards bachelor's degrees. Founded 1923. Setting: 41-acre urban campus. Endowment: $49.5 million. Educational spending for 2005 fiscal year: $5866 per student. Total enrollment: 1,430. Student-undergrad faculty ratio is 14:1. 917 applied, 86% were admitted. 17% from top 10% of their high school class, 41% from top quarter, 74% from top half. 5 valedictorians. Full-time: 1,187 students, 50% women, 50% men. Part-time: 243 students, 52% women, 48% men. Students come from 16 states and territories, 10 other countries, 4% from out-of-state, 1% Native American, 14% Hispanic, 11% black, 1% Asian American or Pacific Islander, 1% international, 18% 25 or older, 51% live on campus, 13% transferred in. Retention: 65% of full-time freshmen returned the following year. Academic areas with the most degrees conferred: education; business/marketing; health professions and related sciences. Core. Calendar: semesters plus May term. Academic remediation for entering students, services for LD students, advanced placement, accelerated degree program, honors program, independent study, double major, summer session for credit, part-time degree program, internships. Study abroad program. ROTC: Air Force (c).

Entrance Requirements: Options: Peterson's Universal Application, Common Application, electronic application, deferred admission. Required: high school transcript, minimum 2.0 high school GPA, SAT or ACT. Required for some: essay, 3 recommendations. Entrance: moderately difficult. Application deadline: 8/15. Notification: continuous.

Costs Per Year: Application fee: $20. Comprehensive fee: $21,002 includes full-time tuition ($15,100), mandatory fees ($50), and college room and board ($5852). College room only: $2898. Part-time tuition: $475 per semester hour.

Collegiate Environment: Orientation program. Drama-theater group, choral group, marching band, student-run newspaper. Social organizations: 35 open to all; local fraternities, local sororities; 15% of eligible men and 20% of eligible women are members. Most popular organizations: Alpha Phi Omega, McMurry Christian Ministries, Indian Insight Service Club, Campus Activity Board, Servant Leadership Mentors. Major annual events: homecoming, Spring Thing, Spring McMadness. Student services: health clinic, personal-psychological counseling. Campus security: 24-hour emergency response devices and patrols, late night transport-escort service, controlled dormitory access. 667 college housing spaces available; 558 were occupied in 2003-04. Freshmen guaranteed college housing. On-campus residence required through junior year. Options: men-only, women-only housing available. Jay-Rollins Library with 153,954 books, 4,468 microform titles, 683 serials, 4,856 audiovisual materials, an OPAC, and a Web page. Operations spending for 2004 fiscal year: $360,952. 165 computers available on campus for general student use. A campuswide network can be accessed from student residence rooms. Staffed computer lab on campus.

■ **MIDLAND COLLEGE** *F-10*
3600 North Garfield
Midland, TX 79705-6399
Tel: (432)685-4500
Admissions: (432)685-5502
Fax: (432)685-4714
E-mail: twetendorf@midland.edu
Web Site: http://www.midland.edu/

Description: State and locally supported, primarily 2-year, coed. Awards certificates, transfer associate, terminal associate, and bachelor's degrees. Founded 1969. Setting: 163-acre suburban campus. Endowment: $3.3 million. Educational spending for 2005 fiscal year: $3739 per student. Total enrollment: 5,531. Student-undergrad faculty ratio is 18:1. 2,457 applied, 100% were admitted. Full-time: 2,027 students, 56% women, 44% men. Part-time: 3,504 students, 58% women, 42% men. Students come from 22 states and territories, 31 other countries, 2% from out-of-state, 1% Native American, 29% Hispanic, 5% black, 1% Asian American or Pacific Islander, 1% international, 16% 25 or older, 5% live on campus, 5% transferred in. Core. Calendar: semesters. Academic remediation for entering students, services for LD students, advanced placement, honors program, distance learning, adult/continuing education programs.

Entrance Requirements: Open admission except for nursing, respiratory therapy, radiological technology programs. Option: Common Application. Required: high school transcript. Entrance: noncompetitive. Application deadline: Rolling. Notification: continuous.

Costs Per Year: Application fee: $0. Area resident tuition: $1204 full-time, $93 per credit hour part-time. State resident tuition: $1540 full-time, $105 per credit hour part-time. Nonresident tuition: $2352 full-time, $470 per credit hour part-time. Mandatory fees: $350 full-time. College room and board: $3600.

Collegiate Environment: Orientation program. Drama-theater group, choral group, student-run newspaper. Social organizations: 20 open to all. Most popular organizations: OIKOS, Midland College Latin American Student Society, Student Government Association, Student Nurses Association, Baptist Student Ministries. Major annual events: Homecoming Night, Chappapalooza, Club Fair. Student services: personal-psychological counseling. Campus security: 24-hour patrols. 296 college housing spaces available; 280 were occupied in 2003-04. No special consideration for freshman housing applicants. Options: coed, men-only, women-only housing available. Murray Fasken Learning Resource Center plus 1 other with 65,760 books, 91,046 microform titles, 285 serials, 359 audiovisual materials, an OPAC, and a Web page. Operations spending for 2004 fiscal year: $373,296. 1,200 computers available on campus for general student use. A campuswide network can be accessed from student residence rooms and from off campus. Staffed computer lab on campus.

■ **MIDWESTERN STATE UNIVERSITY** *B-16*
3410 Taft Blvd.
Wichita Falls, TX 76308
Tel: (940)397-4000
Free: 800-842-1922
Admissions: (940)397-4334
Fax: (940)397-4302
E-mail: school.relations@mwsu.edu
Web Site: http://www.mwsu.edu/

Description: State-supported, comprehensive, coed. Awards associate, bachelor's, and master's degrees. Founded 1922. Setting: 172-acre urban campus. Endowment: $34.6 million. Research spending for 2004 fiscal year: $129,387. Educational spending for 2005 fiscal year: $4545 per student. Total enrollment: 6,279. Faculty: 320 (208 full-time, 112 part-time). Student-undergrad faculty ratio is 20:1. 1,561 applied, 83% were admitted. 12% from top 10% of their high school class, 33% from top quarter, 68% from top half. Full-time: 4,013 students, 57% women, 43% men. Part-time: 1,531 students, 59% women, 41% men. Students come from 42 states and territories, 37 other countries, 5% from out-of-state, 1% Native American, 9% Hispanic, 13% black, 3% Asian American or Pacific Islander, 5% international, 30% 25 or older, 14% live on campus, 11% transferred in. Retention: 60% of full-time freshmen returned the following year. Academic areas with the most degrees conferred: business/marketing; interdisciplinary studies; health professions and related sciences. Core. Calendar: semesters. Academic remediation for entering students, ESL program, services for LD students, advanced placement, accelerated degree program, honors program, distance learning, summer session for credit, part-time degree program, adult/continuing education programs, internships, graduate courses open to undergrads. Study abroad program. ROTC: Air Force (c).

Entrance Requirements: Options: Peterson's Universal Application, Common Application, early admission, deferred admission. Required: high school transcript, SAT or ACT. Entrance: minimally difficult. Application deadline: 8/7. Notification: continuous until 8/31.

Costs Per Year: Application fee: $25. State resident tuition: $1500 full-time, $50 per credit hour part-time. Nonresident tuition: $9750 full-time, $325 per credit hour part-time. Mandatory fees: $3066 full-time. College room and board: $5220. College room only: $2660.

Collegiate Environment: Orientation program. Drama-theater group, choral group, marching band, student-run newspaper. Social organizations: 100 open to all; national fraternities, national sororities; 13% of eligible men and 11% of eligible women are members. Most popular organizations: honor societies, political groups. Major annual events: Homecoming, Parents' Day, Honors Recognition Banquet. Student services: health clinic, personal-psychological counseling. Campus security: 24-hour emergency response devices and patrols, controlled dormitory access. College housing designed to accommodate 824 students; 856 undergraduates lived in college housing during 2003-04. Freshmen given priority for college housing. On-campus residence required through sophomore year. Option: coed housing available. Moffett Library with 484,106 books, 26,789 microform titles, 1,582 serials, 29,964 audiovisual materials, an OPAC, and a Web page. Operations spending for 2004 fiscal year: $1.6 million. 402 computers available on campus for general student use. A campuswide network can be accessed from student residence rooms and from off campus. Staffed computer lab on campus.

Community Environment: Population 100,000. A distributing point for both southern Oklahoma and northwestern Texas, Wichita Falls is one of the important trade centers of the Southwest. The community has a library, museum, two hospitals, 3 YMCA's and YWCA. Various civic, fraternal and veteran's organizations serve the city. Part-time employment is available. Local recreational facilities include theatres, nightclubs, bowling, skating, boating, fishing, municipal golf course, and two country club golf courses.

■ MONTGOMERY COLLEGE *I-22*

3200 College Park Dr.
Conroe, TX 77384
Tel: (936)273-7000
Admissions: (936)273-7236
Fax: (936)273-7234
E-mail: jade.e.borne@nhmccd.edu
Web Site: http://www.woodstock.edu/

Description: State and locally supported, 2-year, coed. Part of North Harris Montgomery Community College District. Awards certificates, transfer associate, and terminal associate degrees. Founded 1995. Setting: 200-acre suburban campus with easy access to Houston. Endowment: $500,000. Total enrollment: 8,306. Student-undergrad faculty ratio is 20:1. 1,677 applied, 100% were admitted. Full-time: 2,970 students, 55% women, 45% men. Part-time: 5,336 students, 65% women, 35% men. 1% from out-of-state, 1% Native American, 12% Hispanic, 6% black, 2% Asian American or Pacific Islander, 1% international, 30% 25 or older, 4% transferred in. Core. Calendar: semesters. Academic remediation for entering students, ESL program, services for LD students, advanced placement, summer session for credit, part-time degree program, adult/continuing education programs, internships.

Entrance Requirements: Open admission. Options: Common Application, early admission. Entrance: noncompetitive. Application deadline: Rolling.

Costs Per Year: Area resident tuition: $984 full-time, $32 per credit hour part-time. State resident tuition: $1944 full-time, $72 per credit hour part-time. Nonresident tuition: $2304 full-time, $87 per credit hour part-time. Mandatory fees: $20 full-time, $8 per credit hour part-time, $12 per term part-time.

Collegiate Environment: Orientation program. Drama-theater group, choral group, student-run newspaper. Most popular organizations: Campus Crusade for Christ, Criminal Justice Club, Phi Theta Kappa, Latino-American Student Association, African-American Cultural Awareness. Major annual events: Career Day, College/University Transfer Day. Student services: personal-psychological counseling. Campus security: 24-hour emergency response devices and patrols, late night transport-escort service. College housing not available. Library/Learning Resources Center with 4,000 books and 375 serials. 600 computers available on campus for general student use. A campuswide network can be accessed. Staffed computer lab on campus.

■ MOUNTAIN VIEW COLLEGE *D-19*

4849 West Illinois Ave.
Dallas, TX 75211-6599
Tel: (214)860-8600
Admissions: (214)860-8666
Fax: (214)860-8570
E-mail: ghall@dccd.edu
Web Site: http://www.mvc.dcccd.edu/

Description: State and locally supported, 2-year, coed. Part of Dallas County Community College District System. Awards certificates, transfer associate, and terminal associate degrees. Founded 1970. Setting: 200-acre urban campus. Total enrollment: 6,496. Students come from 9 states and territories, 36 other countries, 1% from out-of-state, 1% Native American, 44% Hispanic, 29% black, 3% Asian American or Pacific Islander, 1% international, 41% 25 or older. Core. Calendar: semesters. Academic remediation for entering students, ESL program, services for LD students, advanced placement, freshman honors college, honors program, independent study, distance learning, double major, summer session for credit, part-time degree program, external degree program, adult/continuing education programs, co-op programs and internships. ROTC: Army (c).

Entrance Requirements: Open admission. Options: Common Application, electronic application, early admission, deferred admission. Required: high school transcript. Entrance: noncompetitive. Application deadline: Rolling. Notification: continuous.

Costs Per Year: Application fee: $0. Area resident tuition: $1008 full-time. State resident tuition: $1848 full-time. Nonresident tuition: $2968 full-time.

Collegiate Environment: Orientation program. Drama-theater group, choral group. Student services: personal-psychological counseling. Campus security: 24-hour patrols, late night transport-escort service. College housing not available. 200 computers available on campus for general student use. Staffed computer lab on campus.

Community Environment: See University of Texas at Dallas.

■ MTI COLLEGE OF BUSINESS AND TECHNOLOGY (HOUSTON) *J-22*

7277 Regency Square Blvd.
Houston, TX 77036-3163
Tel: (713)974-7181
Free: 800-344-1990
Fax: (713)974-2090
E-mail: davidw@mti.edu
Web Site: http://www.mti.com/

Description: Proprietary, 2-year. Awards certificates, diplomas, and terminal associate degrees. Setting: 6-acre urban campus with easy access to Houston. Total enrollment: 718. Full-time: 718 students, 45% women, 55% men. 0% from out-of-state, 59% 25 or older. Calendar: semesters.

Collegiate Environment: Campus security: late night transport-escort service. College housing not available.

■ MTI COLLEGE OF BUSINESS AND TECHNOLOGY (HOUSTON) *J-22*

11420 E. Freeway
Houston, TX 77029
Tel: (281)333-3363; 888-532-7675
Fax: (281)333-4118
E-mail: derrell@mti-tex.com
Web Site: http://www.mti.edu/

Description: Proprietary, 2-year, coed. Awards certificates, diplomas, and terminal associate degrees. Founded 1984. Setting: 3-acre suburban campus. Total enrollment: 217. 0% from out-of-state, 0% Native American, 48% Hispanic, 12% black, 1% Asian American or Pacific Islander, 0% international, 55% 25 or older. Calendar: semesters. ESL program, advanced placement, co-op programs.

Entrance Requirements: Option: electronic application. Required: high school transcript, interview. Entrance: minimally difficult. Application deadline: Rolling.

Collegiate Environment: Orientation program. Major annual event: MTI Job Fair. College housing not available. 120 computers available on campus for general student use. Staffed computer lab on campus.

■ NAVARRO COLLEGE *E-20*

3200 West 7th Ave.
Corsicana, TX 75110-4899
Tel: (903)874-6501
Free: 800-628-2776
Web Site: http://www.nav.cc.tx.us/

Description: State and locally supported, 2-year, coed. Awards certificates, diplomas, transfer associate, and terminal associate degrees. Founded 1946. Setting: 275-acre small town campus with easy access to Dallas-Fort Worth. Total enrollment: 4,411. 4,411 applied, 100% were admitted. 10% from top 10% of their high school class, 40% from top half. Full-time: 2,516 students, 51% women, 49% men. Part-time: 1,895 students, 66% women, 34% men. Students come from 22 states and territories, 30 other countries, 35% 25 or older, 25% live on campus. Retention: 100% of full-time freshmen returned the following year. Core. Calendar: semesters. Academic remediation for entering students, services for LD students, advanced placement, self-designed majors, honors program, summer session for credit, part-time degree program, adult/continuing education programs, co-op programs.

Entrance Requirements: Open admission. Option: early admission. Required: high school transcript. Placement: THEA required; SAT or ACT recommended. Entrance: noncompetitive. Application deadline: 9/1. Notification: continuous until 9/1.

Collegiate Environment: Drama-theater group, choral group, marching band. Social organizations: 35 open to all; local sororities. Most popular organizations: Student Government Association, Phi Theta Kappa, Ebony Club, Que Pasa. Major annual events: Homecoming, Bulldog Bash, Mr. NC contest. Student services: personal-psychological counseling. Campus security: 24-hour patrols. Gaston T. Gooch Learning Resource Center with

40,000 books and 250 serials. 80 computers available on campus for general student use. Staffed computer lab on campus.

Community Environment: Navarro College is located in historic Corsicana, Texas. The economy is diversified and part-time jobs are available for students. The local climate is moderate to mild. The area is served by bus and major highways. There are several churches, a library, YMCA, and outstanding medical facilities. Residents can enjoy restaurants, shopping, and local fine arts events as well as excellent recreational facilities for boating, water skiing, fishing, golf, and hunting. Annual events include rodeo finals, bicycle races, and food festivals.

■ NORTH CENTRAL TEXAS COLLEGE *C-19*

1525 West California St.
Gainesville, TX 76240-4699
Tel: (940)668-7731
Admissions: (940)668-4222
Fax: (940)668-6049
Web Site: http://www.nctc.cc.tx.us/

Description: County-supported, 2-year, coed. Awards certificates, diplomas, transfer associate, and terminal associate degrees. Founded 1924. Setting: 132-acre rural campus with easy access to Dallas-Fort Worth. Endowment: $2.4 million. Research spending for 2004 fiscal year: $54,097. Educational spending for 2005 fiscal year: $2032 per student. Total enrollment: 6,183. 1,964 applied, 100% were admitted. Students come from 14 states and territories, 21 other countries, 5% from out-of-state, 1% Native American, 7% Hispanic, 6% black, 2% Asian American or Pacific Islander, 3% international, 33% 25 or older, 2% live on campus. Retention: 68% of full-time freshmen returned the following year. Core. Calendar: semesters. Academic remediation for entering students, services for LD students, advanced placement, distance learning, summer session for credit, part-time degree program, adult/continuing education programs, co-op programs and internships.

Entrance Requirements: Open admission except for allied health, legal assistant, equine technology, occupational therapy assistant programs. Option: early admission. Required: high school transcript. Placement: THEA required; SAT or ACT recommended. Entrance: noncompetitive. Application deadline: Rolling.

Collegiate Environment: Orientation program. Drama-theater group, choral group. Social organizations: 12 open to all; 2% of eligible men and 2% of eligible women are members. Most popular organizations: Baptist Student Ministry, Phi Theta Kappa, Nursing Student Association, Collegiate FFA. Major annual events: Sports Day, bowling party. Student services: personal-psychological counseling. Campus security: late night transport-escort service, late night security. Option: coed housing available. North Central Texas College Library plus 1 other with 44,861 books, 273 serials, and an OPAC. Operations spending for 2004 fiscal year: $215,410. 60 computers available on campus for general student use. A campuswide network can be accessed from off-campus. Staffed computer lab on campus.

Community Environment: Population 13,830. Gainesville is a rural community that enjoys a temperate climate. The area is reached by bus lines. There is a public library, churches of major denominations, a local hospital, and over 80 civic, fraternal and veteran's organizations in the city. Part-time employment is limited. Local recreation includes boating, tennis, fishing, and golf.

■ NORTH HARRIS COLLEGE *J-22*

2700 W. W. Thorne Dr.
Houston, TX 77073-3499
Tel: (281)618-5400
Admissions: (281)618-5794
Web Site: http://www.nhmccd.edu/

Description: State and locally supported, 2-year, coed. Part of North Harris Montgomery Community College District. Awards certificates, transfer associate, and terminal associate degrees. Founded 1972. Setting: 185-acre suburban campus. Total enrollment: 10,591. 1,641 applied, 100% were admitted. 1% from out-of-state, 0.3% Native American, 23% Hispanic, 21% black, 7% Asian American or Pacific Islander, 4% international, 41% 25 or older. Core. Calendar: semesters. Academic remediation for entering students, ESL program, services for LD students, advanced placement, honors program, independent study, distance learning, double major, summer session for credit, part-time degree program, external degree program, adult/continuing education programs, co-op programs and internships. Off campus study. ROTC: Army (c).

Entrance Requirements: Open admission except for nursing, respiratory therapy programs. Options: electronic application, early admission. Required for some: high school transcript, interview. Placement: SAT or ACT, ACT ASSET/THEA/ACCUPLACER/MAPS/ACT COMPASS required for some. Entrance: noncompetitive. Application deadline: Rolling.

Collegiate Environment: Orientation program. Drama-theater group, choral group, student-run newspaper. Social organizations: 33 open to all; local fraternities. Most popular organizations: Phi Theta Kappa, Student Ambassadors, Hispanic Student Forum, Vietnamese Student Association, Earth Alliance. Major annual events: Oktoberfest, Spring Fling. Student services: personal-psychological counseling, women's center. Campus security: 24-hour emergency response devices and patrols, late night transport-escort service. Marion M. Donaldson Memorial Library with 131,851 books, 247,253 microform titles, 1,203 serials, 11,869 audiovisual materials, an OPAC, and a Web page. 300 computers available on campus for general student use. A campuswide network can be accessed from student residence rooms and from off campus. Staffed computer lab on campus.

■ NORTH LAKE COLLEGE *G-33*

5001 North MacArthur Blvd.
Irving, TX 75038-3899
Tel: (972)273-3000
Admissions: (972)273-3109
Web Site: http://www.northlakecollege.edu/

Description: County-supported, 2-year, coed. Part of Dallas County Community College District System. Awards certificates, diplomas, transfer associate, and terminal associate degrees. Founded 1977. Setting: 250-acre suburban campus with easy access to Dallas-Fort Worth. Total enrollment: 8,779. Full-time: 2,925 students, 49% women, 51% men. Part-time: 5,854 students, 54% women, 46% men. Students come from 14 other countries, 1% Native American, 20% Hispanic, 16% black, 13% Asian American or Pacific Islander, 6% international, 51% 25 or older. Core. Calendar: semesters. Academic remediation for entering students, ESL program, services for LD students, advanced placement, distance learning, summer session for credit, part-time degree program, co-op programs.

Entrance Requirements: Open admission. Option: early admission. Recommended: high school transcript. Entrance: noncompetitive. Application deadline: 8/24. Notification: continuous.

Collegiate Environment: Orientation program. Drama-theater group, choral group, student-run newspaper. Student services: health clinic, personal-psychological counseling, women's center. Campus security: late night transport-escort service. College housing not available. North Lake College Library with 34,000 books, 400 serials, and a Web page. 65 computers available on campus for general student use. A campuswide network can be accessed. Staffed computer lab on campus.

■ NORTHEAST TEXAS COMMUNITY COLLEGE *C-22*

PO Box 1307
Mount Pleasant, TX 75456-1307
Tel: (903)572-1911
Fax: (903)572-6712
Web Site: http://www.ntcc.edu/

Description: State and locally supported, 2-year, coed. Awards certificates, transfer associate, and terminal associate degrees. Founded 1985. Setting: 175-acre rural campus. Total enrollment: 2,512. 872 applied, 100% were admitted. Full-time: 1,351 students, 64% women, 36% men. Part-time: 1,161 students, 67% women, 33% men. Students come from 21 states and territories, 6 other countries, 2% from out-of-state, 1% Native American, 10% Hispanic, 11% black, 0.4% Asian American or Pacific Islander, 1% international, 36% 25 or older, 3% live on campus, 7% transferred in. Retention: 54% of full-time freshmen returned the following year. Core. Calendar: semesters. Academic remediation for entering students, ESL program, services for LD students, advanced placement, independent study, distance learning, summer session for credit, part-time degree program, adult/continuing education programs, co-op programs.

Entrance Requirements: Open admission. Option: early admission. Required: high school transcript. Placement: SAT or ACT required for some. Entrance: noncompetitive. Application deadline: Rolling.

Collegiate Environment: Orientation program. Drama-theater group, choral group, student-run newspaper. Social organizations: 31 open to all. Most popular organizations: Phi Theta Kappa, Student Government, Psi Beta, Chemistry Club, Hispanic Culture Organization. Major annual events: Intercollegiate Rodeo, Welcome Back Lunch, Y'All Come Back Lunch. Student services: personal-psychological counseling, women's center.

Campus security: 24-hour patrols. No special consideration for freshman housing applicants. Learning Resource Center with 24,501 books and 325 serials. Operations spending for 2004 fiscal year: $263,296. 126 computers available on campus for general student use. Staffed computer lab on campus.

■ NORTHWEST VISTA COLLEGE *K-16*

3535 North Ellison Dr.
San Antonio, TX 78251
Tel: (210)348-2000
Admissions: (210)348-2016
E-mail: elang@accd.edu
Web Site: http://www.accd.edu/nvc/

Description: State and locally supported, 2-year, coed. Awards transfer associate and terminal associate degrees. Founded 1995. Total enrollment: 8,463. Student-undergrad faculty ratio is 12:1. 1% Native American, 44% Hispanic, 6% black, 3% Asian American or Pacific Islander, 0.2% international. Calendar: semesters.

Costs Per Year: Area resident tuition: $1008 full-time. State resident tuition: $2016 full-time. Nonresident tuition: $4032 full-time. Mandatory fees: $288 full-time.

Collegiate Environment: Drama-theater group, student-run newspaper. Student services: health clinic, personal-psychological counseling.

■ NORTHWOOD UNIVERSITY, TEXAS CAMPUS *H-33*

1114 West FM 1382
Cedar Hill, TX 75104-1204
Tel: (972)291-1541
Free: 800-927-9663
Admissions: (989)837-4367
Fax: (972)291-3824
E-mail: admissions@northwood.edu
Web Site: http://www.northwood.edu/

Description: Independent, 4-year, coed. Administratively affiliated with Northwood University (MI). Awards associate and bachelor's degrees. Founded 1966. Setting: 360-acre small town campus with easy access to Dallas. System endowment: $58.2 million. Educational spending for 2005 fiscal year: $2982 per student. Total enrollment: 1,061. Student-undergrad faculty ratio is 22:1. 635 applied, 54% were admitted. 9% from top 10% of their high school class, 23% from top quarter, 63% from top half. Full-time: 815 students, 58% women, 42% men. Part-time: 246 students, 66% women, 34% men. Students come from 16 states and territories, 18 other countries, 7% from out-of-state, 0.3% Native American, 26% Hispanic, 18% black, 3% Asian American or Pacific Islander, 4% international, 4% 25 or older, 28% live on campus, 4% transferred in. Retention: 60% of full-time freshmen returned the following year. Academic areas with the most degrees conferred: business/marketing; parks and recreation; communications/journalism. Core. Academic remediation for entering students, advanced placement, accelerated degree program, honors program, independent study, distance learning, double major, summer session for credit, part-time degree program, external degree program, adult/continuing education programs, internships. Off campus study. Study abroad program.

Entrance Requirements: Options: Peterson's Universal Application, Common Application, electronic application, early admission, deferred admission, international baccalaureate accepted. Required: essay, high school transcript, SAT or ACT. Recommended: minimum 2.0 high school GPA, 1 recommendation, interview. Entrance: moderately difficult. Application deadline: Rolling. Notification: continuous.

Costs Per Year: Application fee: $25. Comprehensive fee: $22,437 includes full-time tuition ($15,216), mandatory fees ($585), and college room and board ($6636). College room only: $3567. Part-time tuition: $317 per credit hour.

Collegiate Environment: Orientation program. Drama-theater group, choral group, student-run newspaper. Social organizations: 17 open to all; local fraternities, local sororities. Most popular organizations: Association of Entertainment and Sports Management, In-Line Hockey Club, Alpha Nu Omega, Alpha Omega, Delta Epsilon Chi. Major annual events: Haunted Forest, International Fest, Sanity Inn. Student services: health clinic, personal-psychological counseling. Campus security: 24-hour emergency response devices and patrols, student patrols. 248 college housing spaces available; 176 were occupied in 2003-04. Freshmen guaranteed college housing. On-campus residence required in freshman year. Options: men-only, women-only housing available. Hach Library with 12,000 books, 164 serials, 230 audiovisual materials, and an OPAC. Operations spending for

2004 fiscal year: $193,491. 73 computers available on campus for general student use. A campuswide network can be accessed from student residence rooms and from off campus. Staffed computer lab on campus.

■ ODESSA COLLEGE *F-9*

201 West University Ave.
Odessa, TX 79764-7127
Tel: (432)335-6400
Admissions: (432)335-6815
Fax: (432)335-6860
E-mail: regrs@odessa.edu
Web Site: http://www.odessa.edu/

Description: State and locally supported, 2-year, coed. Awards certificates, transfer associate, and terminal associate degrees. Founded 1946. Setting: 87-acre urban campus. Endowment: $2.5 million. Educational spending for 2005 fiscal year: $1353 per student. Total enrollment: 4,569. 1,101 applied, 100% were admitted. Full-time: 1,799 students, 60% women, 40% men. Part-time: 2,770 students, 60% women, 40% men. Students come from 32 states and territories, 1% from out-of-state, 1% Native American, 44% Hispanic, 4% black, 1% Asian American or Pacific Islander, 0.2% international, 40% 25 or older, 3% live on campus, 0.1% transferred in. Core. Calendar: semesters. Academic remediation for entering students, services for LD students, advanced placement, self-designed majors, summer session for credit, part-time degree program, adult/continuing education programs, co-op programs and internships.

Entrance Requirements: Open admission except for allied health programs. Options: Common Application, electronic application, early admission, deferred admission. Entrance: noncompetitive. Application deadline: Rolling. Notification: continuous.

Costs Per Year: Application fee: $0. Area resident tuition: $1110 full-time. State resident tuition: $1410 full-time. Nonresident tuition: $1860 full-time. Mandatory fees: $330 full-time. Full-time tuition and fees vary according to course load. College room and board: $4948. College room only: $3500. Room and board charges vary according to board plan and housing facility.

Collegiate Environment: Choral group. Social organizations: 13 open to all. Most popular organizations: Baptist Student Union, Student Government Association, Rodeo Club, Physical Therapy Assistant Club, American Chemical Society. Major annual events: Back-to-School Picnic, Homecoming, Spring Fest. Student services: personal-psychological counseling. Campus security: 24-hour emergency response devices and patrols, late night transport-escort service. 400 college housing spaces available; 230 were occupied in 2003-04. No special consideration for freshman housing applicants. Option: coed housing available. Murray H. Fly Learning Resource Center with 79,882 books and 496 serials. Operations spending for 2004 fiscal year: $451,500. 300 computers available on campus for general student use. A campuswide network can be accessed from off-campus. Staffed computer lab on campus.

Community Environment: Population of Odessa 100,000; of Midland 87,000. Odessa is one of the largest domestic oilfield supply centers in Texas. The community enjoys a mild climate. The city is reached by airlines, two bus lines, and railroad. Churches representing all denominations, two hospitals, a library, and many civic and fraternal organizations serve the area. Part-time employment is available. Local recreation includes theatres, bowling alleys, hunting, ice skating, and sports.

■ OUR LADY OF THE LAKE UNIVERSITY OF SAN ANTONIO *K-16*

411 Southwest 24th St.
San Antonio, TX 78207-4689
Tel: (210)434-6711
Free: 800-436-6558
Fax: (210)436-0824
E-mail: boatner@lake.occusa.edu
Web Site: http://www.ollusa.edu/

Description: Independent Roman Catholic, comprehensive, coed. Awards bachelor's, master's, and doctoral degrees. Founded 1895. Setting: 75-acre urban campus. Endowment: $22.3 million. Total enrollment: 2,872. Faculty: 225 (118 full-time, 107 part-time). Student-undergrad faculty ratio is 13:1. 2,214 applied, 53% were admitted. 22% from top 10% of their high school class, 47% from top quarter, 76% from top half. Full-time: 1,242 students, 76% women, 24% men. Part-time: 550 students, 76% women, 24% men. Students come from 11 states and territories, 5 other countries, 1% from out-of-state, 0.4% Native American, 71% Hispanic, 8% black, 1% Asian American or Pacific Islander, 1% international, 44% 25 or older, 41% live on campus, 8% transferred in. Retention: 62% of full-time freshmen returned the following year. Academic areas with the most degrees conferred: business/marketing; science technologies; education; liberal arts/general studies; public administration and social services. Core. Calendar: semesters plus 2 summer sessions. Academic remediation for entering students, ESL program, services for LD students, advanced placement, independent study, distance learning, double major, summer session for credit, part-time degree program, adult/continuing education programs, internships. Off campus study at United Colleges of San Antonio. ROTC: Army (c), Air Force (c).

Entrance Requirements: Options: Peterson's Universal Application, Common Application, electronic application, deferred admission, international baccalaureate accepted. Required: high school transcript, SAT or ACT. Required for some: interview. Entrance: moderately difficult. Application deadline: 7/15. Notification: continuous.

Costs Per Year: Application fee: $25. Comprehensive fee: $22,928 includes full-time tuition ($17,048), mandatory fees ($498), and college room and board ($5382). College room only: $3226. Full-time tuition and fees vary according to class time and degree level. Room and board charges vary according to board plan. Part-time tuition: $553 per credit hour. Part-time mandatory fees: $12 per credit hour, $48 per term. Part-time tuition and fees vary according to class time and degree level.

Collegiate Environment: Orientation program. Drama-theater group, choral group, student-run newspaper. Social organizations: 20 open to all. Major annual events: Spirit Day, Lake Fest, Spring Jam. Student services: health clinic, personal-psychological counseling, women's center. Campus security: 24-hour emergency response devices and patrols, late night transport-escort service, controlled dormitory access. 639 college housing spaces available; 524 were occupied in 2003-04. Freshmen given priority for college housing. Options: coed, men-only, women-only housing available. The Sueltenfuss Library plus 2 others with 162,154 books, 153,201 microform titles, 38,900 serials, 7,438 audiovisual materials, an OPAC, and a Web page. Operations spending for 2004 fiscal year: $1.1 million. 230 computers available on campus for general student use. Computer purchase/lease plans available. A campuswide network can be accessed from student residence rooms and from off campus. Staffed computer lab on campus.

Community Environment: See San Antonio College.

■ **PALO ALTO COLLEGE** *K-16*
1400 West Villaret
San Antonio, TX 78224-2499
Tel: (210)921-5000
Admissions: (210)921-5279
Web Site: http://www.accd.edu/pac/htm/

Description: State and locally supported, 2-year, coed. Part of Alamo Community College District System. Awards certificates, transfer associate, and terminal associate degrees. Founded 1987. Setting: urban campus. Total enrollment: 8,070. Student-undergrad faculty ratio is 17:1. 1,044 applied, 100% were admitted. Students come from 50 states and territories, 1% from out-of-state, 0.3% Native American, 64% Hispanic, 2% black, 1% Asian American or Pacific Islander, 0.4% international, 35% 25 or older. Core. Calendar: semesters. Academic remediation for entering students, ESL program, summer session for credit, part-time degree program, adult/continuing education programs, co-op programs.

Entrance Requirements: Open admission. Option: early admission. Required: high school transcript. Entrance: noncompetitive. Application deadline: Rolling.

Costs Per Year: Application fee: $0. Area resident tuition: $1546 full-time, $252 per credit hour part-time. State resident tuition: $2806 full-time, $504 per credit hour part-time. Nonresident tuition: $5318 full-time, $1008 per credit hour part-time. Mandatory fees: $280 full-time, $1 per credit hour part-time, $138 per term part-time.

Collegiate Environment: Drama-theater group, student-run newspaper. Social organizations: 20 open to all. Most popular organizations: Catholic Campus Ministries, International Club, Veterinary Technician Association, Movimiento Estudiantil Chicano De Aztlan, Phi Theta Kappa. Major annual events: PACFest, PAChanga. Student services: health clinic, personal-psychological counseling. Campus security: 24-hour emergency response devices and patrols. College housing not available. Operations spending for 2004 fiscal year: $1 million. 300 computers available on campus for general student use. A campuswide network can be accessed from off-campus. Staffed computer lab on campus.

■ **PANOLA COLLEGE** *E-23*
1109 West Panola St.
Carthage, TX 75633-2397

Tel: (903)693-2000
Admissions: (903)693-2034
E-mail: ezoellner@panola.edu
Web Site: http://www.panola.edu/

Description: State and locally supported, 2-year, coed. Awards certificates, transfer associate, and terminal associate degrees. Founded 1947. Setting: 35-acre small town campus. Endowment: $1.5 million. Educational spending for 2005 fiscal year: $2120 per student. Total enrollment: 1,927. Student-undergrad faculty ratio is 23:1. 360 applied, 100% were admitted. Full-time: 946 students, 62% women, 38% men. Part-time: 981 students, 70% women, 30% men. Students come from 15 states and territories, 5 other countries, 8% from out-of-state, 1% Native American, 4% Hispanic, 17% black, 1% Asian American or Pacific Islander, 1% international, 30% 25 or older, 12% live on campus. Retention: 42% of full-time freshmen returned the following year. Core. Calendar: semesters. Academic remediation for entering students, ESL program, services for LD students, advanced placement, distance learning, summer session for credit, part-time degree program, adult/continuing education programs, co-op programs.

Entrance Requirements: Open admission except for nursing, occupational therapy assisting, vocational nursing programs. Options: Common Application, electronic application, early admission. Recommended: high school transcript. Required for some: high school transcript. Entrance: noncompetitive. Application deadlines: Rolling, Rolling for nonresidents. Notification: continuous, continuous for nonresidents.

Costs Per Year: Area resident tuition: $630 full-time, $45 per semester hour part-time. State resident tuition: $1320 full-time, $68 per semester hour part-time. Nonresident tuition: $1710 full-time, $81 per semester hour part-time. Mandatory fees: $720 full-time. College room and board: $3300.

Collegiate Environment: Orientation program. Drama-theater group, choral group, marching band, student-run newspaper. Social organizations: 13 open to all. Most popular organizations: Student Senate, Excel Club, Baptist Student Union, Panola Pipers, Phi Theta Kappa. Major annual events: Welcome Back Dance, Fall Frolic, Spring Fling. Campus security: controlled dormitory access. 191 college housing spaces available; all were occupied in 2003-04. No special consideration for freshman housing applicants. On-campus residence required through sophomore year. Options: coed, men-only, women-only housing available. M. P. Baker Library with 88,897 books, 25,913 microform titles, 347 serials, 4,133 audiovisual materials, an OPAC, and a Web page. Operations spending for 2004 fiscal year: $373,455. 500 computers available on campus for general student use. A campuswide network can be accessed from off-campus. Staffed computer lab on campus.

Community Environment: Population 6400, Carthage is in a rural area with a temperate climate. The community is served by rail, bus, and U.S. Routes 59 and 79. Facilities include a public library, hospital, churches of eight denominations, theatres, a 35-mile lake shoreline for all water sports, a swimming pool, bowling alley, golf courses. Several rodeos and livestock shows are held annually. Part-time employment is somewhat limited.

■ **PARIS JUNIOR COLLEGE** *B-21*
2400 Clarksville St.
Paris, TX 75460-6298
Tel: (903)785-7661
Free: 800-232-5804
Admissions: (903)782-0425
E-mail: sreece@parisjc.edu
Web Site: http://www.parisjc.edu/

Description: State and locally supported, 2-year, coed. Awards certificates, diplomas, transfer associate, and terminal associate degrees. Founded 1924. Setting: 54-acre rural campus. Endowment: $7.4 million. Educational spending for 2005 fiscal year: $1197 per student. Total enrollment: 4,118. Student-undergrad faculty ratio is 24:1. 1,463 applied, 100% were admitted. Full-time: 1,457 students, 63% women, 37% men. Part-time: 2,661 students, 65% women, 35% men. Students come from 16 states and territories, 2% Native American, 6% Hispanic, 11% black, 1% Asian American or Pacific Islander, 0.2% international, 41% 25 or older. Calendar: semesters. Academic remediation for entering students, ESL program, summer session for credit, part-time degree program, external degree program, adult/continuing education programs.

Entrance Requirements: Open admission except for nursing program. Option: early admission. Required: high school transcript. Entrance: noncompetitive. Application deadline: Rolling.

Costs Per Year: Application fee: $0. Area resident tuition: $840 full-time, $35 per hour part-time. State resident tuition: $1560 full-time, $65 per hour part-time. Nonresident tuition: $2520 full-time, $105 per hour part-time. Mandatory fees: $228 full-time. College room and board: $1882. College room only: $690.

Collegiate Environment: Drama-theater group, choral group. Student services: personal-psychological counseling, women's center. Campus security: 24-hour emergency response devices and patrols, late night transport-escort service. On-campus residence required in freshman year. 38,150 books and 404 serials. 82 computers available on campus for general student use. Staffed computer lab on campus.

Community Environment: Population 25,000, Paris, a farming and industrial center, has a modern attractiveness which is the result of planned reconstruction following a fire that swept the town in 1916. Today the local industries produce furniture, light bulb parts, clothing, and food items. Located in the heart of Red River Valley, the area has a mean annual temperature of 63.9 degrees. There are four rail lines, two bus lines, five main highways, and an airport approximately seven miles away to serve the community. A public library, theatres, two hospitals, and civic and fraternal organizations are active in the city. Local recreation includes the parks, bowling, golf, and nearby Pat Mayse Lake providing boating, swimming, and fishing.

■ **PAUL QUINN COLLEGE** *D-19*

3837 Simpson-Stuart Rd.
Dallas, TX 75241-4331
Tel: (214)376-1000
Free: 800-237-2648
Admissions: (214)302-3575
Fax: (214)302-3559
Web Site: http://www.pqc.edu/

Description: Independent African Methodist Episcopal, 4-year, coed. Awards bachelor's degrees. Founded 1872. Setting: 132-acre suburban campus. Endowment: $1.5 million. Total enrollment: 871. 3,221 applied, 27% were admitted. 49% from top quarter of their high school class, 50% from top half. 3 National Merit Scholars, 10 class presidents, 5 valedictorians, 50 student government officers. Full-time: 732 students, 50% women, 50% men. Part-time: 139 students, 60% women, 40% men. Students come from 9 states and territories, 0.3% Native American, 3% Hispanic, 94% black, 0.1% Asian American or Pacific Islander, 2% international, 20% 25 or older, 35% live on campus. Retention: 42% of full-time freshmen returned the following year. Core. Calendar: semesters. Academic remediation for entering students, advanced placement, accelerated degree program, honors program, summer session for credit, part-time degree program, external degree program, adult/continuing education programs, co-op programs and internships. Off campus study at Texas State Technical Institute-Waco Campus.

Entrance Requirements: Options: Peterson's Universal Application, electronic application. Required: high school transcript, minimum 2.0 high school GPA. Required for some: recommendations, interview. Placement: SAT or ACT required. Entrance: moderately difficult. Application deadline: 6/1. Notification: continuous.

Collegiate Environment: Orientation program. Drama-theater group, choral group, student-run newspaper. Social organizations: 5 open to all; national fraternities, national sororities, local fraternities, local sororities; 40% of eligible men and 45% of eligible women are members. Most popular organizations: Student Ambassadors, NAACP. Major annual events: Homecoming, Seniorfest. Student services: health clinic. Campus security: 24-hour patrols. 450 college housing spaces available; 372 were occupied in 2003-04. On-campus residence required through sophomore year. Zale Library with 87,000 books and 167 serials. 50 computers available on campus for general student use. Staffed computer lab on campus.

Community Environment: See University of Texas at Dallas.

■ **PRAIRIE VIEW A&M UNIVERSITY** *I-21*

PO Box 519
Prairie View, TX 77446-0519
Tel: (936)857-3311
Admissions: (936)857-2626
Fax: (936)857-2699
Web Site: http://www.pvamu.edu/

Description: State-supported, comprehensive, coed. Part of Texas A&M University System. Awards bachelor's, master's, and doctoral degrees. Founded 1878. Setting: 1,440-acre small town campus with easy access to Houston. Endowment: $33.9 million. Research spending for 2004 fiscal year: $11.2 million. Total enrollment: 7,912. Faculty: 485 (366 full-time, 119 part-

time). Student-undergrad faculty ratio is 15:1. 4,325 applied, 60% were admitted. 5% from top 10% of their high school class, 18% from top quarter, 50% from top half. Full-time: 5,151 students, 56% women, 44% men. Part-time: 551 students, 70% women, 30% men. Students come from 21 states and territories, 21 other countries, 6% from out-of-state, 0.1% Native American, 3% Hispanic, 90% black, 1% Asian American or Pacific Islander, 2% international, 28% 25 or older, 52% live on campus, 6% transferred in. Retention: 63% of full-time freshmen returned the following year. Academic areas with the most degrees conferred: business/marketing; health professions and related sciences; engineering. Core. Calendar: semesters. Academic remediation for entering students, ESL program, services for LD students, advanced placement, accelerated degree program, honors program, independent study, distance learning, double major, summer session for credit, part-time degree program, co-op programs and internships, graduate courses open to undergrads. Off campus study. Study abroad program. ROTC: Army, Naval.

Entrance Requirements: Options: Common Application, electronic application, deferred admission. Required: high school transcript, minimum 2.5 high school GPA, recommendations, SAT or ACT. Entrance: moderately difficult. Application deadline: 6/1. Notification: continuous.

Costs Per Year: Application fee: $25. State resident tuition: $1500 full-time, $50 per credit hour part-time. Nonresident tuition: $9780 full-time, $326 per credit hour part-time. Mandatory fees: $3406 full-time, $113.53 per credit hour part-time. Full-time tuition and fees vary according to course load and degree level. Part-time tuition and fees vary according to course load and degree level. College room and board: $6204. Room and board charges vary according to board plan and housing facility.

Collegiate Environment: Orientation program. Drama-theater group, choral group, marching band, student-run newspaper, radio station. Social organizations: 30 open to all; national fraternities, national sororities, local fraternities, local sororities; 5% of eligible men and 5% of eligible women are members. Most popular organizations: National Society of Black Engineers, National Association of Black Accountants, National Organization of Black Chemists and Chemical Engineers, Toastmasters International, Baptist Student Movement. Major annual events: homecoming, The Yard Show, Miss Prairie View. Student services: health clinic, personal-psychological counseling. Campus security: 24-hour emergency response devices and patrols. 3,291 college housing spaces available; all were occupied in 2003-04. On-campus residence required in freshman year. Options: coed, men-only, women-only housing available. John B. Coleman Library with 347,477 books, 710,429 microform titles, 25,911 serials, 3,836 audiovisual materials, an OPAC, and a Web page. Operations spending for 2004 fiscal year: $2.2 million. 500 computers available on campus for general student use. Computer purchase/lease plans available. A campuswide network can be accessed from student residence rooms and from off campus. Staffed computer lab on campus.

■ **RANGER COLLEGE** *E-16*

College Circle
Ranger, TX 76470
Tel: (254)647-3234
Web Site: http://www.ranger.cc.tx.us/

Description: State-related, 2-year, coed. Awards transfer associate and terminal associate degrees. Founded 1926. Setting: 100-acre rural campus with easy access to Dallas-Fort Worth. Total enrollment: 843. 15% from top 10% of their high school class, 75% from top half. Students come from 7 states and territories, 4 other countries, 45% live on campus. Core. Calendar: semesters. Academic remediation for entering students, advanced placement, self-designed majors, freshman honors college, honors program, summer session for credit, part-time degree program, adult/continuing education programs.

Entrance Requirements: Open admission. Options: Peterson's Universal Application, early admission. Entrance: noncompetitive. Application deadline: Rolling. Notification: continuous.

Collegiate Environment: Choral group, marching band. Student services: health clinic, personal-psychological counseling. Campus security: controlled dormitory access. Golemon Library with 24,211 books and 133 serials. 42 computers available on campus for general student use. Staffed computer lab on campus.

Community Environment: Population 3,094. Ranger's name was derived from a camp of Texas Rangers, organized near here to protect settlers from marauding Indians. In 1917, oil was discovered and the community expanded. Today, there are several churches representing the major denominations. The community is reached by railroad and interstate highway. Local recreation includes fishing, swimming, boating, water skiing, a municipally owned swimming pool, hunting for deer, duck, dove, squirrel, and rabbit. Part-time employment is limited.

■ **REMINGTON COLLEGE-DALLAS CAMPUS** *D-19*

1800 East Gate Dr.
Garland, TX 75041-5513
Tel: (972)686-7878
Fax: (972)686-5116
E-mail: skip.walls@remingtoncollege.edu
Web Site: http://www.remingtoncollege.edu/
Description: Proprietary, 2-year. Founded 1987.

■ **REMINGTON COLLEGE-FORT WORTH CAMPUS** *D-18*

300 East Loop 820
Fort Worth, TX 76112
Tel: (817)451-0017
Fax: (817)496-1257
E-mail: lynn.wey@remingtoncollege.edu
Web Site: http://www.remingtoncollege.edu/
Description: Proprietary, 2-year, coed.

■ **REMINGTON COLLEGE-HOUSTON CAMPUS** *J-22*

3110 Hayes Rd., Ste. 380
Houston, TX 77082
Tel: (281)899-1240
Fax: (281)597-8466
Web Site: http://www.remingtoncollege.edu/houston/
Description: Proprietary, 2-year, coed. Awards certificates and terminal associate degrees. Total enrollment: 250.

■ **RICE UNIVERSITY** *J-22*

6100 Main St.
PO Box 1892
Houston, TX 77251-1892
Tel: (713)348-0000
Free: 800-527-OWLS
Admissions: (713)348-RICE
Fax: (713)348-5323
E-mail: admi@rice.edu
Web Site: http://www.rice.edu/
Description: Independent, university, coed. Awards bachelor's, master's, and doctoral degrees. Founded 1912. Setting: 300-acre urban campus. Endowment: $3.6 billion. Research spending for 2004 fiscal year: $56.7 million. Educational spending for 2005 fiscal year: $32,039 per student. Total enrollment: 5,258. Faculty: 710 (567 full-time, 143 part-time). Student-undergrad faculty ratio is 5:1. 7,890 applied, 25% were admitted. 88% from top 10% of their high school class, 96% from top quarter, 99% from top half. 192 National Merit Scholars, 17 class presidents, 94 valedictorians, 164 student government officers. Full-time: 3,057 students, 48% women, 52% men. Part-time: 128 students, 70% women, 30% men. Students come from 53 states and territories, 29 other countries, 47% from out-of-state, 1% Native American, 12% Hispanic, 7% black, 16% Asian American or Pacific Islander, 3% international, 1% 25 or older, 71% live on campus, 2% transferred in. Retention: 96% of full-time freshmen returned the following year. Academic areas with the most degrees conferred: social sciences; engineering; biological/life sciences. Core. Calendar: semesters. Services for LD students, advanced placement, accelerated degree program, self-designed majors, honors program, independent study, double major, summer session for credit, internships, graduate courses open to undergrads. Off campus study. Study abroad program. ROTC: Army (c), Naval, Air Force (c).
Entrance Requirements: Options: Peterson's Universal Application, Common Application, electronic application, early admission, early decision, early action, deferred admission, international baccalaureate accepted. Required: essay, high school transcript, 2 recommendations, portfolio required for architecture students; audition required for music students, SAT and SAT Subject Tests or ACT. Recommended: interview. Entrance: most difficult. Application deadlines: 1/10, 11/1 for early decision, 12/1 for early action. Notification: 4/1, 12/15 for early decision, 2/10 for early action.
Costs Per Year: Application fee: $50. Comprehensive fee: $32,726 includes full-time tuition ($23,310), mandatory fees ($436), and college room and

board ($8980). College room only: $5700. Full-time tuition and fees vary according to student level. Room and board charges vary according to board plan.
Collegiate Environment: Orientation program. Drama-theater group, choral group, marching band, student-run newspaper, radio station. Social organizations: 204 open to all. Most popular organizations: Drama Club, volunteer program, intramural sports, college government, Marching Owl Band. Major annual events: Beer-Bike Relay Race, campus-wide formals, Homecoming. Student services: health clinic, personal-psychological counseling, women's center. Campus security: 24-hour emergency response devices and patrols, late night transport-escort service, controlled dormitory access. 76 college housing spaces available; 71 were occupied in 2003-04. Freshmen guaranteed college housing. Option: coed housing available. Fondren Library with 2.4 million books, 3.1 million microform titles, 16,013 serials, 48,385 audiovisual materials, an OPAC, and a Web page. Operations spending for 2004 fiscal year: $20.9 million. 523 computers available on campus for general student use. A campuswide network can be accessed from student residence rooms and from off campus. Staffed computer lab on campus.

■ **RICHLAND COLLEGE** *D-19*

12800 Abrams Rd.
Dallas, TX 75243-2199
Tel: (972)238-6106
Admissions: (972)238-6123
Fax: (972)238-6957
Web Site: http://www.rlc.dcccd.edu/
Description: State and locally supported, 2-year, coed. Part of Dallas County Community College District System. Awards transfer associate and terminal associate degrees. Founded 1972. Setting: 250-acre suburban campus. Total enrollment: 14,128. Students come from 24 states and territories, 21 other countries, 47% 25 or older. Core. Calendar: semesters. Academic remediation for entering students, ESL program, services for LD students, advanced placement, freshman honors college, honors program, summer session for credit, part-time degree program, adult/continuing education programs, co-op programs. Study abroad program.
Entrance Requirements: Open admission. Option: early admission. Required for some: high school transcript. Placement: SAT or ACT recommended. Entrance: noncompetitive. Application deadline: Rolling. Notification: continuous.
Collegiate Environment: Drama-theater group, choral group, student-run newspaper. Student services: health clinic, personal-psychological counseling, women's center. Campus security: 24-hour emergency response devices and patrols, late night transport-escort service, emergency call boxes. College housing not available. Richland College Library with 63,000 books and 350 serials. 400 computers available on campus for general student use.

■ **ST. EDWARD'S UNIVERSITY** *I-18*

3001 South Congress Ave.
Austin, TX 78704
Tel: (512)448-8400
Free: 800-555-0164
Admissions: (512)448-8602
Fax: (512)448-8492
E-mail: seu.admit@admin.stedwards.edu
Web Site: http://www.stedwards.edu/
Description: Independent Roman Catholic, comprehensive, coed. Awards bachelor's and master's degrees. Founded 1885. Setting: 160-acre urban campus. Endowment: $48.7 million. Educational spending for 2005 fiscal year: $6445 per student. Total enrollment: 4,947. Faculty: 440 (155 full-time, 285 part-time). Student-undergrad faculty ratio is 14:1. 2,217 applied, 69% were admitted. 15% from top 10% of their high school class, 45% from top quarter, 80% from top half. 4 valedictorians. Full-time: 2,997 students, 58% women, 42% men. Part-time: 967 students, 58% women, 42% men. Students come from 40 states and territories, 39 other countries, 6% from out-of-state, 1% Native American, 30% Hispanic, 5% black, 2% Asian American or Pacific Islander, 2% international, 7% 25 or older, 39% live on campus, 6% transferred in. Retention: 84% of full-time freshmen returned the following year. Academic areas with the most degrees conferred: business/marketing; communications/journalism; construction trades; psychology. Core. Calendar: semesters. Academic remediation for entering students, services for LD students, advanced placement, honors program,

double major, summer session for credit, part-time degree program, adult/continuing education programs, internships. Study abroad program. ROTC: Army (c), Air Force (c).

Entrance Requirements: Options: Peterson's Universal Application, Common Application, electronic application, deferred admission. Required: essay, high school transcript, SAT or ACT. Recommended: 2 recommendations, interview. Entrance: moderately difficult. Application deadline: 5/1. Notification: continuous.

Costs Per Year: Application fee: $45. Comprehensive fee: $25,700 includes full-time tuition ($18,800) and college room and board ($6900). College room only: $3900. Part-time tuition: $628 per hour.

Collegiate Environment: Orientation program. Drama-theater group, choral group, student-run newspaper. Social organizations: 50 open to all. Most popular organizations: Student Government Association, University Programming Board, SEUTV, Alpha Phi Omega, Emerging Leaders. Major annual events: Hillfest, Midnight Breakfast, Welcome Week. Student services: health clinic, personal-psychological counseling. Campus security: 24-hour emergency response devices and patrols, late night transport-escort service, controlled dormitory access, self-defense educations, informal discussions, pamphlets, posters, films, lighted pathways and sidewalks. College housing designed to accommodate 1,056 students; 1,069 undergraduates lived in college housing during 2003-04. Freshmen guaranteed college housing. On-campus residence required in freshman year. Options: coed, women-only housing available. Scarborough-Phillips Library with 189,080 books, 102,415 microform titles, 3,531 audiovisual materials, an OPAC, and a Web page. Operations spending for 2004 fiscal year: $1.4 million. 475 computers available on campus for general student use. A campuswide network can be accessed from student residence rooms and from off campus. Staffed computer lab on campus.

■ **ST. MARY'S UNIVERSITY OF SAN ANTONIO** *K-16*
1 Camino Santa Maria
San Antonio, TX 78228-8507
Tel: (210)436-3011
Free: 800-FOR-STMU
Admissions: (210)436-3126
Fax: (210)431-6742
E-mail: uadm@stmarytx.edu
Web Site: http://www.stmarytx.edu/

Description: Independent Roman Catholic, comprehensive, coed. Awards bachelor's, master's, doctoral, and first professional degrees. Founded 1852. Setting: 135-acre urban campus. Endowment: $94.1 million. Research spending for 2004 fiscal year: $467,972. Educational spending for 2005 fiscal year: $6970 per student. Total enrollment: 3,963. Faculty: 333 (184 full-time, 149 part-time). Student-undergrad faculty ratio is 13:1. 1,942 applied, 72% were admitted. 32% from top 10% of their high school class, 63% from top quarter, 89% from top half. 14 valedictorians. Full-time: 2,185 students, 60% women, 40% men. Part-time: 238 students, 54% women, 46% men. Students come from 33 states and territories, 31 other countries, 4% from out-of-state, 0.1% Native American, 70% Hispanic, 4% black, 3% Asian American or Pacific Islander, 4% international, 13% 25 or older, 41% live on campus, 6% transferred in. Retention: 78% of full-time freshmen returned the following year. Academic areas with the most degrees conferred: business/marketing; social sciences; biological/life sciences. Core. Calendar: semesters. Academic remediation for entering students, ESL program, advanced placement, honors program, independent study, distance learning, double major, summer session for credit, part-time degree program, adult/continuing education programs, co-op programs and internships, graduate courses open to undergrads. Off campus study at University of the Incarnate Word, Our Lady of the Lake University of San Antonio, Oblate School of Theology, University of Dayton, Chaminade University, University of Notre Dame. Study abroad program. ROTC: Army.

Entrance Requirements: Options: Peterson's Universal Application, Common Application, early admission, deferred admission. Required: essay, high school transcript, SAT or ACT. Recommended: interview. Required for some: recommendations. Entrance: moderately difficult. Application deadline: Rolling. Notification: continuous.

Costs Per Year: Application fee: $30. Comprehensive fee: $26,162 includes full-time tuition ($18,274), mandatory fees ($1200), and college room and board ($6688). College room only: $3916. Full-time tuition and fees vary according to course load. Room and board charges vary according to board plan, housing facility, and student level. Part-time tuition: $548 per credit hour. Part-time mandatory fees: $250 per term. Part-time tuition and fees vary according to course load.

Collegiate Environment: Orientation program. Drama-theater group, choral group, student-run newspaper. Social organizations: 60 open to all; national fraternities, national sororities, local fraternities; 14% of eligible men and 11% of eligible women are members. Most popular organizations: Beta Beta Beta Biology Society, Emerging Leaders, Student Government Association, Mexican Student Organization, Delta Zeta. Major annual events: Fiesta Oyster Bake, President Peace Commission Symposia, Hunger Awareness Week. Student services: health clinic, personal-psychological counseling. Campus security: 24-hour emergency response devices and patrols, late night transport-escort service, controlled dormitory access. 1,213 college housing spaces available; 1,044 were occupied in 2003-04. Freshmen given priority for college housing. On-campus residence required in freshman year. Options: coed, men-only, women-only housing available. Louis J. Blume Library plus 1 other with 481,137 books, 253,621 microform titles, 1,213 serials, 4,203 audiovisual materials, an OPAC, and a Web page. Operations spending for 2004 fiscal year: $3.2 million. 100 computers available on campus for general student use. Computer purchase/lease plans available. A campuswide network can be accessed from student residence rooms and from off campus. Staffed computer lab on campus.

■ **ST. PHILIP'S COLLEGE** *K-16*
1801 Martin Luther King Dr.
San Antonio, TX 78203-2098
Tel: (210)531-3200
Admissions: (210)531-3290
Fax: (210)531-4831
E-mail: bcrow@accd.edu
Web Site: http://www.accd.edu/spc/

Description: District-supported, 2-year, coed. Part of Alamo Community College District System. Awards certificates, diplomas, transfer associate, and terminal associate degrees. Founded 1898. Setting: 16-acre urban campus. Total enrollment: 9,792. Student-undergrad faculty ratio is 18:1. Full-time: 4,209 students, 58% women, 42% men. Part-time: 5,583 students, 57% women, 43% men. Students come from 35 states and territories, 8 other countries, 1% Native American, 48% Hispanic, 16% black, 2% Asian American or Pacific Islander, 0.2% international, 48% 25 or older, 11% transferred in. Core. Calendar: semesters. Academic remediation for entering students, ESL program, services for LD students, advanced placement, honors program, independent study, distance learning, double major, summer session for credit, part-time degree program, adult/continuing education programs, co-op programs and internships. Off campus study. ROTC: Army (c).

Entrance Requirements: Open admission. Options: Common Application, electronic application, early admission. Required: high school transcript. Entrance: noncompetitive. Application deadline: Rolling. Notification: continuous.

Costs Per Year: Application fee: $0. Area resident tuition: $1200 full-time, $40 per hour part-time. State resident tuition: $2400 full-time, $80 per hour part-time. Nonresident tuition: $4800 full-time, $160 per hour part-time. Mandatory fees: $272 full-time, $136 per term part-time.

Collegiate Environment: Drama-theater group, choral group, student-run newspaper. Social organizations: 25 open to all. Most popular organizations: student government, Delta Epsilon Chi, Radiography Club, Respiratory Therapy Club, Diagnostic Imaging Club. Major annual events: Culture Fest, Hispanic Heritage Month, Black Heritage Month. Student services: health clinic, women's center. Campus security: 24-hour emergency response devices and patrols, late night transport-escort service. College housing not available. St. Philip's College Learning Resource Center plus 1 other with 112,197 books, 910,880 microform titles, 577 serials, 11,300 audiovisual materials, an OPAC, and a Web page. 885 computers available on campus for general student use. A campuswide network can be accessed from off-campus. Staffed computer lab on campus.

■ **SAM HOUSTON STATE UNIVERSITY** *H-21*
Huntsville, TX 77341
Tel: (936)294-1111; (866)232-7528
Admissions: (936)294-1828
Web Site: http://www.shsu.edu/

Description: State-supported, university, coed. Part of The Texas State University System. Awards bachelor's, master's, and doctoral degrees. Founded 1879. Setting: 1,256-acre small town campus with easy access to Houston. Endowment: $23.2 million. Research spending for 2004 fiscal year: $2.6 million. Educational spending for 2005 fiscal year: $1583 per student. Total enrollment: 15,000. Faculty: 681 (471 full-time, 210 part-time). Student-undergrad faculty ratio is 21:1. 13% from top 10% of their high school class, 43% from top quarter, 81% from top half. Full-time: 11,120 students, 58% women, 42% men. Part-time: 1,893 students, 60% women, 40% men. Students come from 45 states and territories, 47 other countries, 2% from out-of-state, 1% Native American, 11% Hispanic, 15% black, 1% Asian American or Pacific Islander, 0.5% international, 17% 25 or older, 27% live on campus, 13% transferred in. Retention: 69% of full-time freshmen returned the following year. Core. Calendar: semesters. Academic remediation for entering students, ESL program, services for LD students, advanced placement, honors program, independent study, distance learning, double major, summer session for credit, part-time degree program, adult/ continuing education programs, internships, graduate courses open to undergrads. Off campus study at The University Center, American Institute for Foreign Study. Study abroad program. ROTC: Army.

Entrance Requirements: Options: Common Application, early admission. Required: high school transcript, minimum 2.0 high school GPA, SAT or ACT. Entrance: moderately difficult. Application deadline: 8/1. Notification: continuous.

Costs Per Year: Application fee: $35. State resident tuition: $3822 full-time. Nonresident tuition: $9728 full-time. Full-time tuition varies according to course load. College room and board: $5002. College room only: $2826. Room and board charges vary according to board plan and housing facility.

Collegiate Environment: Orientation program. Drama-theater group, choral group, marching band, student-run newspaper, radio station. Social organizations: 147 open to all; national fraternities, national sororities, local fraternities, local sororities; 9% of eligible men and 8% of eligible women are members. Most popular organizations: Residence Hall Association, NAACP, Baptist Student Ministry. Major annual events: Bonfire, Block Party, Sam Jam. Student services: legal services, health clinic, personal-psychological counseling. Campus security: 24-hour emergency response devices and patrols, student patrols, late night transport-escort service. 3,500 college housing spaces available; 3,297 were occupied in 2003-04. Freshmen guaranteed college housing. On-campus residence required in freshman year. Options: coed, men-only, women-only housing available. Newton Gresham Library with 1.2 million books, 1.2 million microform titles, 4,521 serials, 21,848 audiovisual materials, an OPAC, and a Web page. Operations spending for 2004 fiscal year: $3.8 million. 552 computers available on campus for general student use. A campuswide network can be accessed from student residence rooms and from off campus. Staffed computer lab on campus.

Community Environment: Huntsville, population 35,222, is located in the pine belt 70 miles north of Houston. This was the home of General Sam Houston, and local museums commemorate his honor. The average temperatures are 51.1 degrees in winter and 82.6 degrees in summer. The community has a hospital, various fraternal, civic, and veteran's organizations, and is served by bus and U.S. Highway I-45. A nearby state park offers fishing, boating, swimming, picnicking, and camping. Part-time employment is available.

■ **SAN ANTONIO COLLEGE** *K-16*
1300 San Pedro Ave.
San Antonio, TX 78212-4299
Tel: (210)733-2000
Free: 800-944-7575
Admissions: (210)733-2582
Fax: (210)733-2200
Web Site: http://www.accd.edu/

Description: State and locally supported, 2-year, coed. Part of Alamo Community College District System. Awards certificates, transfer associate, and terminal associate degrees. Founded 1925. Setting: 45-acre urban campus. Total enrollment: 22,226. Full-time: 8,587 students, 56% women, 44% men. Part-time: 13,639 students, 62% women, 38% men. Students come from 54 states and territories, 112 other countries, 2% from out-of-state, 1% Native American, 49% Hispanic, 5% black, 2% Asian American or Pacific Islander, 2% international, 40% 25 or older, 8% transferred in. Core. Calendar: semesters. Academic remediation for entering students, ESL program, services for LD students, advanced placement, honors program, independent study, distance learning, double major, summer session for credit, part-time degree program, adult/continuing education programs, co-op programs and internships. ROTC: Army, Air Force (c).

Entrance Requirements: Open admission. Option: early admission. Required: minimum 2.0 high school GPA. Recommended: high school transcript. Required for some: high school transcript. Placement: SAT or

ACT, ACT ASSET, THEA, ACCUPLACER recommended; ACT ASSET, THEA, ACCUPLACER required for some. Entrance: noncompetitive. Application deadline: Rolling.

Costs Per Year: Application fee: $0. Area resident tuition: $960 full-time, $40 per semester hour part-time. State resident tuition: $1920 full-time, $80 per semester hour part-time. Nonresident tuition: $3840 full-time, $160 per semester hour part-time. Mandatory fees: $272 full-time, $136 per term part-time.

Collegiate Environment: Orientation program. Drama-theater group, choral group, student-run newspaper, radio station. Student services: health clinic, personal-psychological counseling, women's center. Campus security: 24-hour patrols, late night transport-escort service. College housing not available. San Antonio College Library and Media Services with 233,714 books, 9,765 microform titles, 1,498 serials, 6,082 audiovisual materials, an OPAC, and a Web page. 1,700 computers available on campus for general student use. A campuswide network can be accessed from off-campus. Staffed computer lab on campus.

Community Environment: Population 975,000. Called the cradle of Texas liberty because of its history, San Antonio is the birthplace of the rough riders and the home of the Alamo. San Antonio is a mixture of its early Spanish background and a modern metropolis. Skyscrapers exist alongside 18th-century adobe restorations. There are many historic sites to be seen in the area. The transportation to and within the city is excellent. There are local and transcontinental bus lines. More than 500 churches representing most denominations, many civic and fraternal organizations, hospitals and museums serve the community. San Antonio has a symphony orchestra and an art museum. The annual Fiesta San Jacinto, Everett Colborn World's Championship Rodeo, and Grand Opera Festival are held here. Local recreation includes 56 parks, sunken garden theater, golf courses, polo fields, baseball diamonds, tennis courts, bridle paths, picnic grounds, swimming pools, hunting, fishing, and boating. Part-time employment is available.

■ **SAN JACINTO COLLEGE DISTRICT** *J-22*
4624 Fairmont Parkway
Pasadena, TX 77504-3323
Tel: (281)998-6100
Web Site: http://www.sjcd.cc.tx.us/

Description: State and locally supported, 2-year, coed. Founded 1961. Endowment: $1.2 million. Educational spending for 2005 fiscal year: $2182 per student. 25% from top quarter of their high school class, 58% from top half. Students come from 17 states and territories, 12 other countries, 24% 25 or older. Calendar: semesters.

■ **SCHREINER UNIVERSITY** *I-15*
2100 Memorial Blvd.
Kerrville, TX 78028-5697
Tel: (830)896-5411
Free: 800-343-4919
Admissions: (830)792-7277
Fax: (830)792-7226
Web Site: http://www.schreiner.edu/

Description: Independent Presbyterian, comprehensive, coed. Awards associate, bachelor's, and master's degrees. Founded 1923. Setting: 175-acre small town campus with easy access to San Antonio and Austin. Endowment: $31.4 million. Educational spending for 2005 fiscal year: $5130 per student. Total enrollment: 842. 785 applied, 50% were admitted. 17% from top 10% of their high school class, 40% from top quarter, 69% from top half. Full-time: 717 students, 59% women, 41% men. Part-time: 76 students, 74% women, 26% men. Students come from 8 states and territories, 2 other countries, 1% from out-of-state, 1% Native American, 17% Hispanic, 3% black, 1% Asian American or Pacific Islander, 1% international, 26% 25 or older, 58% live on campus, 12% transferred in. Retention: 63% of full-time freshmen returned the following year. Core. Calendar: semesters. Academic remediation for entering students, services for LD students, advanced placement, accelerated degree program, self-designed majors, honors program, independent study, double major, summer session for credit, part-time degree program, co-op programs and internships, graduate courses open to undergrads. Study abroad program.

Entrance Requirements: Options: Peterson's Universal Application, Common Application, deferred admission, international baccalaureate accepted. Required: high school transcript, SAT or ACT. Recommended: essay, minimum 2.0 high school GPA, interview. Required for some: essay, 1 recommendation. Entrance: moderately difficult. Application deadline: 8/1. Notification: continuous.

Costs Per Year: Application fee: $25. Comprehensive fee: $22,474 includes full-time tuition ($14,742), mandatory fees ($400), and college room and board ($7332). College room only: $3900. Room and board charges vary according to board plan and housing facility. Part-time tuition: $629 per credit.

Collegiate Environment: Orientation program. Drama-theater group, choral group, student-run newspaper. Social organizations: 35 open to all; national fraternities, national sororities; 10% of eligible men and 13% of eligible women are members. Most popular organizations: Student Senate, Back on Campus Again (non-traditional student organization), Campus Ministry, International Club, Best Buddies. Major annual events: Spring Fling/Fall Ball, Convocation, Parents' Weekend. Student services: health clinic, personal-psychological counseling. Campus security: 24-hour emergency response devices and patrols, late night transport-escort service. 485 college housing spaces available; 380 were occupied in 2003-04. Freshmen guaranteed college housing. On-campus residence required through junior year. Option: coed housing available. W. M. Logan Library with 69,873 books, 593 microform titles, 225 serials, 477 audiovisual materials, an OPAC, and a Web page. Operations spending for 2004 fiscal year: $406,595. 106 computers available on campus for general student use. A campuswide network can be accessed from student residence rooms and from off campus. Staffed computer lab on campus.

Community Environment: Population 24,000. In the rugged hill region by the Guadalupe River, Kerrville is a popular summer and winter resort area. The hill country is famous for fishing and hunting. The city is located 65 miles northwest of San Antonio and enjoys moderate climate. The community has churches of major denominations, a hospital, and various civic, fraternal, and veteran's organizations. Local recreation includes theatres, boating, fishing, water skiing, and deer and turkey hunting. Job opportunities are available.

■ **SOUTH PLAINS COLLEGE** *C-9*
1401 South College Ave.
Levelland, TX 79336-6595
Tel: (806)894-9611
Fax: (806)897-3167
Web Site: http://www.southplainscollege.edu/
Description: State and locally supported, 2-year, coed. Awards certificates, transfer associate, and terminal associate degrees. Founded 1958. Setting: 177-acre small town campus. Endowment: $3 million. Educational spending for 2005 fiscal year: $2471 per student. Total enrollment: 9,273. Student-undergrad faculty ratio is 20:1. 10% from top 10% of their high school class, 32% from top quarter, 60% from top half. 8 valedictorians. Full-time: 4,774 students, 52% women, 48% men. Part-time: 4,499 students, 55% women, 45% men. Students come from 21 states and territories, 8 other countries, 4% from out-of-state, 1% Native American, 25% Hispanic, 4% black, 1% Asian American or Pacific Islander, 1% international, 39% 25 or older, 10% live on campus. Core. Calendar: semesters. Academic remediation for entering students, services for LD students, advanced placement, accelerated degree program, self-designed majors, distance learning, summer session for credit, part-time degree program, adult/continuing education programs. ROTC: Army (c), Air Force (c).
Entrance Requirements: Open admission. Option: early admission. Required: high school transcript. Recommended: ACT, SAT Subject Tests. Entrance: noncompetitive. Application deadline: Rolling.
Costs Per Year: Application fee: $0. Area resident tuition: $1394 full-time, $26 per hour part-time. State resident tuition: $1922 full-time, $48 per hour part-time. Nonresident tuition: $2306 full-time, $64 per hour part-time. College room and board: $3300.
Collegiate Environment: Orientation program. Drama-theater group, choral group, student-run newspaper. Most popular organizations: student government, Phi Beta Kappa, Bleacher Bums, Law Enforcement Association. Major annual events: homecoming, Spring Fling, Miss Cap Rock Pageant. Student services: health clinic. Campus security: 24-hour emergency response devices and patrols. 590 college housing spaces available; all were occupied in 2003-04. On-campus residence required through sophomore year. Options: men-only, women-only housing available. 70,000 books, 310 serials, and an OPAC. 130 computers available on campus for general student use. A campuswide network can be accessed. Staffed computer lab on campus.
Community Environment: Levelland, population 14,500, is a rural community enjoying a temperate climate. The area is served by bus, an airport, and Routes 114 and 385. The city has a public library, hospital, churches of major denominations, theatres, and active civic, fraternal, and veteran's organizations. Local recreation includes outdoor sports and rodeo. Part-time employment is available.

■ **SOUTH TEXAS COLLEGE** *Q-17*
3201 West Pecan
McAllen, TX 78501
Tel: (956)618-8323
Free: 800-742-7822
Admissions: (956)872-2147
Fax: (956)928-4445
E-mail: mshebbar@southtexascollege.edu
Web Site: http://www.southtexascollege.edu/
Description: District-supported, primarily 2-year, coed. Awards certificates, transfer associate, terminal associate, and bachelor's degrees. Founded 1993. Setting: 20-acre suburban campus. Endowment: $17,971. Total enrollment: 16,225. Student-undergrad faculty ratio is 22:1. 24% from top quarter of their high school class, 32% from top half. Full-time: 6,194 students, 57% women, 43% men. Part-time: 10,031 students, 61% women, 39% men. 0% from out-of-state, 0.04% Native American, 95% Hispanic, 0.2% black, 1% Asian American or Pacific Islander, 0.4% international, 35% 25 or older. Retention: 56% of full-time freshmen returned the following year. Calendar: semesters. Academic remediation for entering students, services for LD students, accelerated degree program, summer session for credit, part-time degree program, adult/continuing education programs, co-op programs. Off campus study at University of Texas-Pan American. ROTC: Army (c).
Entrance Requirements: Open admission. Options: Common Application, early admission, deferred admission. Required: high school transcript. Required for some: SAT and SAT Subject Tests or ACT, THEA. Entrance: noncompetitive. Application deadline: Rolling.
Costs Per Year: Application fee: $0. One-time mandatory fee: $75. Area resident tuition: $1416 full-time, $127 per credit hour part-time. State resident tuition: $1826 full-time, $164.50 per credit hour part-time. Nonresident tuition: $4848 full-time, $202 per credit hour part-time. Mandatory fees: $400 full-time, $6 per credit hour part-time, $85 per term part-time.
Collegiate Environment: Orientation program. Most popular organizations: Beta Epsilon Mu Honor Society, Automotive Technology Club, Child Care and Development Association Club, Heating, Air Conditioning, and Ventilation Club, Writing in Literary Discussion Club. Major annual events: Career Day, Cinco de Mayo, Thanksgiving Food Drive. Student services: personal-psychological counseling. Campus security: 24-hour emergency response devices and patrols, late night transport-escort service. College housing not available. Learning Resources Center with 12,611 books, 177 serials, an OPAC, and a Web page. Operations spending for 2004 fiscal year: $144,832. 240 computers available on campus for general student use. A campuswide network can be accessed from off-campus. Staffed computer lab on campus.

■ **SOUTHEASTERN CAREER INSTITUTE** *D-19*
5440 Harvest Hill, Ste. 200
Dallas, TX 75230-1600
Tel: (972)385-1446
Free: 800-525-1446
Fax: (972)385-0641
Web Site: http://www.southeasterncareerinstitute.com/
Description: Proprietary, 2-year, coed. Founded 1987.

■ **SOUTHERN METHODIST UNIVERSITY** *D-19*
6425 Boaz
Dallas, TX 75275
Tel: (214)768-2000
Free: 800-323-0672
Admissions: (214)768-1101
E-mail: ugadmission@smu.edu
Web Site: http://www.smu.edu/
Description: Independent, university, coed, affiliated with United Methodist Church. Awards bachelor's, master's, doctoral, and first professional degrees. Founded 1911. Setting: 165-acre suburban campus. Endowment: $1 billion. Total enrollment: 11,152. Faculty: 933 (604 full-time, 329 part-time). Student-undergrad faculty ratio is 12:1. 6,981 applied, 58% were admitted. 35% from top 10% of their high school class, 64% from top quarter, 92% from top half. Full-time: 6,126 students, 54% women, 46% men. Part-time: 363 students, 63% women, 37% men. Students come from 50 states and territories, 66 other countries, 38% from out-of-state, 1% Native American, 8% Hispanic, 6% black, 6% Asian American or Pacific Islander, 5% international, 5% 25 or older, 40% live on campus, 5% transferred in. Retention: 87% of full-time freshmen returned the following year. Academic areas with the most degrees conferred: business/marketing; social sciences;

communications/journalism. Core. Calendar: semesters. Academic remediation for entering students, ESL program, services for LD students, advanced placement, accelerated degree program, self-designed majors, honors program, independent study, distance learning, double major, summer session for credit, part-time degree program, adult/continuing education programs, internships, graduate courses open to undergrads. Study abroad program. ROTC: Army, Air Force (c).

Entrance Requirements: Options: Peterson's Universal Application, Common Application, early admission, early action, deferred admission, international baccalaureate accepted. Required: essay, high school transcript, 1 recommendation, SAT or ACT. Required for some: SAT Subject Tests. Entrance: moderately difficult. Application deadlines: 1/15, 11/1 for early action. Notification: continuous, 12/31 for early action.

Costs Per Year: Application fee: $50. Comprehensive fee: $38,325 includes full-time tuition ($25,400), mandatory fees ($3230), and college room and board ($9695). College room only: $5775. Part-time tuition: $1058 per credit hour. Part-time mandatory fees: $135 per credit hour.

Collegiate Environment: Orientation program. Drama-theater group, choral group, marching band, student-run newspaper, radio station. Social organizations: 152 open to all; national fraternities, national sororities; 29% of eligible men and 35% of eligible women are members. Most popular organizations: Program Council, Student Senate, Student Foundation, Residence Hall Association, United Methodist Campus Ministries. Major annual events: homecoming, Sing Song, All-School Block Party. Student services: health clinic, personal-psychological counseling, women's center. Campus security: 24-hour emergency response devices and patrols, late night transport-escort service, controlled dormitory access. 2,713 college housing spaces available; 2,491 were occupied in 2003-04. Freshmen guaranteed college housing. On-campus residence required in freshman year. Option: coed housing available. Central University Library plus 7 others with 2.8 million books, 1.7 million microform titles, 10,540 serials, 44,103 audiovisual materials, an OPAC, and a Web page. 758 computers available on campus for general student use. Computer purchase/lease plans available. A campuswide network can be accessed from student residence rooms and from off campus. Staffed computer lab on campus.

Community Environment: See University of Texas at Dallas.

■ **SOUTHWEST INSTITUTE OF TECHNOLOGY** *I-18*
5424 Hwy. 290 West, Ste. 200
Austin, TX 78735-8800
Tel: (512)892-2640
Fax: (512)892-1045
Web Site: http://www.swse.net/
Description: Proprietary, 2-year, coed. Awards diplomas, transfer associate, and terminal associate degrees. Setting: 1-acre urban campus. Total enrollment: 63. 77 applied, 82% were admitted. Full-time: 63 students, 14% women, 86% men. 27% Hispanic, 24% black, 14% Asian American or Pacific Islander. Calendar: continuous.

■ **SOUTHWEST TEXAS JUNIOR COLLEGE** *K-14*
2401 Garner Field Rd.
Uvalde, TX 78801-6297
Tel: (830)278-4401
Web Site: http://www.swtjc.net/
Description: State and locally supported, 2-year, coed. Awards certificates, transfer associate, and terminal associate degrees. Founded 1946. Setting: 97-acre small town campus with easy access to San Antonio. Total enrollment: 4,350. Students come from 2 states and territories, 4 other countries, 0% Native American, 75% Hispanic, 1% black, 1% Asian American or Pacific Islander, 0.2% international, 34% 25 or older, 9% live on campus. Core. Calendar: semesters. Academic remediation for entering students, ESL program, advanced placement, honors program, summer session for credit, part-time degree program, external degree program, adult/continuing education programs.

Entrance Requirements: Open admission. Options: electronic application, early admission, deferred admission. Required: high school transcript. Placement: THEA required; SAT or ACT recommended. Entrance: noncompetitive. Application deadline: Rolling. Notification: continuous. Preference given to local residents.

Collegiate Environment: Orientation program. Drama-theater group, student-run newspaper. Social organizations: 25 open to all. Most popular organizations: Catholic Students Club, Business Administration Club. Major annual event: Spring Palms Festival. Student services: health clinic, personal-psychological counseling. Campus security: 24-hour patrols,

controlled dormitory access. Options: coed, women-only housing available. Will C. Miller Memorial Library with 30,890 books and 285 serials. 300 computers available on campus for general student use. Staffed computer lab on campus.

Community Environment: Population 15,000. Uvalde is located at the base of the Texas Hill Country 75 miles west of San Antonio and is known for its agriculture production; hunting for deer, wild turkey, quail and doves; and fishing. The climate is moderate. City services include a memorial hospital, public library, community theatre in the historic Grand Opera House, U.S. Vice-President John Nance Garner Memorial Museum, and churches of various denominations. Uvalde is reached by buslines, major highways and a private airport. Dormitories, apartments and rental houses provide student housing. Local recreation includes six screen theater complex, 18-hole golf course, parks, two rivers, private clubs, various community celebrations.

■ **SOUTHWESTERN ADVENTIST UNIVERSITY** *E-18*
100 Hillcrest Dr.
Keene, TX 76059
Tel: (817)645-3921
Free: 800-433-2240
Fax: (817)556-4744
E-mail: bbaldwin@swau.edu
Web Site: http://www.swau.edu/
Description: Independent Seventh-day Adventist, comprehensive, coed. Awards associate, bachelor's, and master's degrees. Founded 1894. Setting: 150-acre rural campus with easy access to Dallas-Fort Worth. Endowment: $7.6 million. Educational spending for 2005 fiscal year: $3651 per student. Total enrollment: 1,191. 657 applied, 64% were admitted. 13% from top 10% of their high school class, 33% from top quarter, 74% from top half. 1 National Merit Scholar. Full-time: 821 students, 56% women, 44% men. Part-time: 342 students, 70% women, 30% men. Students come from 50 states and territories, 53 other countries, 39% from out-of-state, 1% Native American, 15% Hispanic, 14% black, 6% Asian American or Pacific Islander, 13% international, 36% 25 or older, 31% live on campus, 21% transferred in. Retention: 61% of full-time freshmen returned the following year. Core. Calendar: semesters. Academic remediation for entering students, ESL program, accelerated degree program, self-designed majors, honors program, independent study, summer session for credit, part-time degree program, external degree program, co-op programs and internships. Off campus study at Tarleton State University, Florida Hospital College of Health Sciences, Andrews University. Study abroad program.

Entrance Requirements: Option: deferred admission. Required: high school transcript, minimum 2.0 high school GPA, SAT or ACT. Required for some: essay, 1 recommendation, interview. Entrance: minimally difficult. Application deadline: 8/31. Notification: 9/1.

Costs Per Year: Application fee: $0. Comprehensive fee: $18,290 includes full-time tuition ($12,144), mandatory fees ($340), and college room and board ($5806). Full-time tuition and fees vary according to course load and program. Room and board charges vary according to board plan. Part-time mandatory fees: $170. Part-time fees vary according to course load and program.

Collegiate Environment: Orientation program. Drama-theater group, choral group, student-run newspaper, radio station. Social organizations: 10 open to all. Most popular organizations: Student Association, SIFE, Education/Psychology Club, Theology Club, Nursing Club. Major annual events: Mimosa Memories, Student Appreciation Weekend. Student services: health clinic, personal-psychological counseling. Campus security: 24-hour emergency response devices, student patrols. On-campus residence required in freshman year. Options: men-only, women-only housing available. Chan Shun Centennial Library with 108,481 books, 457 serials, an OPAC, and a Web page. Operations spending for 2004 fiscal year: $439,467. 50 computers available on campus for general student use. A campuswide network can be accessed from student residence rooms and from off campus. Staffed computer lab on campus.

Community Environment: Population 5,019. Keene is a small community in a rural area. The climate is temperate. The city is reached by bus lines and U.S. Route 67. There is a local Seventh Day Adventist Church. A shopping center is located seven miles distant. Part-time employment is available.

■ **SOUTHWESTERN ASSEMBLIES OF GOD UNIVERSITY** *E-19*
1200 Sycamore St.
Waxahachie, TX 75165-5735
Tel: (972)937-4010; 888-937-7248

Web Site: http://www.sagu.edu/

Description: Independent, comprehensive, coed, affiliated with Assemblies of God. Awards associate, bachelor's, and master's degrees. Founded 1927. Setting: 70-acre small town campus with easy access to Dallas. Endowment: $853,777. Educational spending for 2005 fiscal year: $1485 per student. Total enrollment: 1,676. 1,676 applied, 34% were admitted. 9% from top 10% of their high school class, 19% from top quarter, 40% from top half. Students come from 42 states and territories, 35% from out-of-state, 2% Native American, 16% Hispanic, 5% black, 1% Asian American or Pacific Islander, 1% international, 24% 25 or older, 55% live on campus. Retention: 61% of full-time freshmen returned the following year. Core. Calendar: semesters. Academic remediation for entering students, services for LD students, advanced placement, independent study, distance learning, double major, summer session for credit, part-time degree program, external degree program, adult/continuing education programs, internships, graduate courses open to undergrads. ROTC: Air Force (c).

Entrance Requirements: Options: early admission, deferred admission. Required: essay, high school transcript, 2 recommendations, medical history, evidence of approved Christian character, SAT or ACT. Entrance: noncompetitive. Application deadline: Rolling.

Collegiate Environment: Orientation program. Drama-theater group, choral group, student-run newspaper. Most popular organizations: Gold Jackets/ Blazers, intramurals, Mission Association, Student Congress, SOCS. Major annual events: homecoming, Class Night, All-School Picnic. Student services: health clinic, personal-psychological counseling. Campus security: student patrols, late night transport-escort service. On-campus residence required through senior year. Option: coed housing available. P. C. Nelson Memorial Library plus 1 other with 110,000 books, 600 serials, and a Web page. Operations spending for 2004 fiscal year: $110,773. 45 computers available on campus for general student use. A campuswide network can be accessed from off-campus. Staffed computer lab on campus.

Community Environment: Population 20,000, Waxahachie is the capital of Ellis County. It is located 28 miles south of Dallas and 40 miles southeast of Fort Worth. The area can be reached by rail, bus, and major highways. Community facilities include a medical center, a hospital and health clinic, many churches of various denominations, and several civic and fraternal organizations. Local recreation includes baseball, bowling, golf, hunting, boating, and fishing. Apartments and part-time employment are available.

■ **SOUTHWESTERN CHRISTIAN COLLEGE** *D-20*

Box 10
200 Bowser St.
Terrell, TX 75160
Tel: (972)524-3341
Admissions: (214)524-3341
Web Site: http://www.swcc.edu/

Description: Independent, 4-year, coed, affiliated with Church of Christ. Awards associate and bachelor's degrees. Founded 1949. Setting: 25-acre small town campus with easy access to Dallas-Fort Worth. Total enrollment: 186. 389 applied, 90% were admitted. 5% from top 10% of their high school class, 12% from top half. Students come from 26 states and territories, 5 other countries, 14% 25 or older, 80% live on campus. Retention: 92% of full-time freshmen returned the following year. Core. Calendar: semesters. Academic remediation for entering students, part-time degree program.

Entrance Requirements: Open admission. Options: Peterson's Universal Application, Common Application, early admission, deferred admission. Required: high school transcript, 2 recommendations. Placement: SAT or ACT recommended. Entrance: noncompetitive. Application deadline: 8/1.

Collegiate Environment: Orientation program. Choral group, student-run newspaper. Social organizations: national fraternities, national sororities, local fraternities, local sororities; 41% of eligible men and 33% of eligible women are members. Campus security: 24-hour patrols. Hogan Stewart Learning Center with 25,687 books and 158 serials. 40 computers available on campus for general student use.

Community Environment: Terrell is a suburban community enjoying dry, temperate climate. The city is reached by bus, railroad, and major highways. Community services include many churches representing most major denominations, hospitals, a public library, YMCA, and YWCA. There are theatres, parks, and nearby lakes for water sports. Part-time employment opportunities are limited. Various civic, fraternal and veteran's organizations are active in Terrell. Small city and all necessary items are within walking distance.

■ **SOUTHWESTERN UNIVERSITY** *H-18*

1001 East University Ave.
Georgetown, TX 78626
Tel: (512)863-6511
Free: 800-252-3166
Admissions: (512)863-1200
Fax: (512)863-6511
E-mail: admission@southwestern.edu
Web Site: http://www.southwestern.edu/

Description: Independent Methodist, 4-year, coed. Awards bachelor's degrees. Founded 1840. Setting: 700-acre suburban campus with easy access to Austin. Endowment: $279.3 million. Research spending for 2004 fiscal year: $481,092. Educational spending for 2005 fiscal year: $16,016 per student. Total enrollment: 1,309. Student-undergrad faculty ratio is 10:1. 1,760 applied, 67% were admitted. 49% from top 10% of their high school class, 82% from top quarter, 97% from top half. 2 National Merit Scholars, 13 valedictorians. Full-time: 1,286 students, 59% women, 41% men. Part-time: 23 students, 70% women, 30% men. Students come from 31 states and territories, 8 other countries, 7% from out-of-state, 1% Native American, 14% Hispanic, 3% black, 5% Asian American or Pacific Islander, 0.3% international, 2% 25 or older, 83% live on campus, 2% transferred in. Retention: 89% of full-time freshmen returned the following year. Academic areas with the most degrees conferred: social sciences; communications/journalism; business/marketing. Core. Calendar: semesters. Services for LD students, advanced placement, self-designed majors, independent study, double major, summer session for credit, part-time degree program, internships. Off campus study at GLCA Arts Program in New York; Washington Semester at American University. Study abroad program.

Entrance Requirements: Options: Peterson's Universal Application, Common Application, electronic application, early decision, deferred admission, international baccalaureate accepted. Required: essay, high school transcript, 1 recommendation. Recommended: interview. Required for some: interview. Entrance: very difficult. Application deadlines: 2/15, 11/1 for early decision. Notification: 4/1, 12/1 for early decision.

Costs Per Year: Application fee: $40. Comprehensive fee: $28,447 includes full-time tuition ($21,900) and college room and board ($6547). College room only: $3143. Room and board charges vary according to board plan, housing facility, and student level. Part-time tuition: $920 per semester hour.

Collegiate Environment: Orientation program. Drama-theater group, choral group, student-run newspaper. Social organizations: 105 open to all; national fraternities, national sororities; 29% of eligible men and 31% of eligible women are members. Most popular organizations: Alpha Phi Omega, International Club, Latinos Unidos. Major annual events: Homecoming, Brown Symposium, Parents' and Grandparents' Weekend. Student services: health clinic, personal-psychological counseling. Campus security: 24-hour emergency response devices and patrols, student patrols, late night transport-escort service, controlled dormitory access. 1,042 college housing spaces available; 1,038 were occupied in 2003-04. Freshmen guaranteed college housing. On-campus residence required in freshman year. Options: coed, men-only, women-only housing available. A. Frank Smith Jr. Library Center with 323,000 books, 58,813 microform titles, 2,598 serials, 12,858 audiovisual materials, an OPAC, and a Web page. Operations spending for 2004 fiscal year: $2.1 million. 223 computers available on campus for general student use. A campuswide network can be accessed from student residence rooms and from off campus. Staffed computer lab on campus.

Community Environment: Population 25,000, Georgetown enjoys the advantage of being a small town yet is only 26 miles from the state capital, Austin. The climate is moderate, both in winter and summer. The community is served by rail, bus lines, Austin-Bergstrom International Airport, and Interstate Highway 35 and has a modern hospital and clinic. Located in the heart of the highland lakes region, recreational opportunities include fishing, boating, and water sports. Part-time employment is available.

■ **STEPHEN F. AUSTIN STATE UNIVERSITY** *F-23*

1936 North St.
Nacogdoches, TX 75962
Tel: (936)468-2011
Free: 800-731-2902
Admissions: (936)468-2504
Fax: (936)468-3849

E-mail: mbsmith@sfasu.edu

Web Site: http://www.sfasu.edu/

Description: State-supported, comprehensive, coed. Awards bachelor's, master's, and doctoral degrees. Founded 1923. Setting: 400-acre small town campus. Research spending for 2004 fiscal year: $4.6 million. Total enrollment: 11,435. Faculty: 582 (434 full-time, 148 part-time). Student-undergrad faculty ratio is 19:1. 6,506 applied, 74% were admitted. 14% from top 10% of their high school class, 42% from top quarter, 81% from top half. Full-time: 8,490 students, 60% women, 40% men. Part-time: 1,316 students, 61% women, 39% men. Students come from 34 states and territories, 42 other countries, 2% from out-of-state, 1% Native American, 8% Hispanic, 17% black, 1% Asian American or Pacific Islander, 1% international, 23% 25 or older, 38% live on campus, 8% transferred in. Retention: 67% of full-time freshmen returned the following year. Academic areas with the most degrees conferred: business/marketing; interdisciplinary studies; health professions and related sciences. Core. Calendar: semesters. Academic remediation for entering students, services for LD students, advanced placement, accelerated degree program, self-designed majors, freshman honors college, honors program, independent study, distance learning, double major, summer session for credit, part-time degree program, adult/continuing education programs, internships, graduate courses open to undergrads. Off campus study. Study abroad program. ROTC: Army.

Entrance Requirements: Options: Common Application, international baccalaureate accepted. Required: high school transcript, SAT or ACT. Entrance: moderately difficult. Application deadline: Rolling. Notification: continuous.

Costs Per Year: Application fee: $25. State resident tuition: $4718 full-time, $126 per credit hour part-time. Nonresident tuition: $12,998 full-time, $402 per credit hour part-time. Mandatory fees: $60.50 per credit hour part-time, $9 per term part-time. Full-time tuition varies according to course load. Part-time tuition and fees vary according to course load. College room and board: $5459. Room and board charges vary according to board plan and housing facility.

Collegiate Environment: Orientation program. Drama-theater group, choral group, marching band, student-run newspaper, radio station. Social organizations: 180 open to all; national fraternities, national sororities; 13% of eligible men and 10% of eligible women are members. Most popular organizations: Texas Student Education Association, American Marketing Association, Baptist Student Union. Major annual events: homecoming, Parents' Day, Legislators' Day. Student services: legal services, health clinic, personal-psychological counseling. Campus security: 24-hour emergency response devices and patrols, student patrols, late night transport-escort service, controlled dormitory access. 3,963 college housing spaces available; 3,353 were occupied in 2003-04. Freshmen guaranteed college housing. On-campus residence required through sophomore year. Options: coed, men-only, women-only housing available. Ralph W. Steen Library with 2,791 serials, an OPAC, and a Web page. 1,000 computers available on campus for general student use. A campuswide network can be accessed from student residence rooms and from off campus. Staffed computer lab on campus.

Community Environment: Population 35,000. Nacogdoches is one of the oldest settlements in Texas. This is a rural community enjoying temperate climate. There are more than 30 churches representing 15 different denominations, a library, museums, two hospitals, garden clubs, and major civic and fraternal organizations within the community. Nacogdoches is reached by railroad, bus lines, and Highways 59, 259, 7 and 21. Part-time employment is available. Local recreation includes movie theatres, several lakes for boating, swimming, and other water sports, and national forests for hiking, picnicking and hunting.

■ **SUL ROSS STATE UNIVERSITY** *I-7*

East Hwy. 90

Alpine, TX 79832

Tel: (432)837-8011; 888-722-7778

Admissions: (432)837-8050

Fax: (432)837-8334

E-mail: njenkins@sulross-.edu

Web Site: http://www.sulross.edu/

Description: State-supported, comprehensive, coed. Part of Texas State University System. Awards associate, bachelor's, and master's degrees. Founded 1920. Setting: 640-acre small town campus. Endowment: $5.9 million. Research spending for 2004 fiscal year: $629,607. Educational spending for 2005 fiscal year: $4267 per student. Total enrollment: 1,954. 1,021 applied, 73% were admitted. 5% from top 10% of their high school class,

18% from top quarter, 55% from top half. Full-time: 1,236 students, 47% women, 53% men. Part-time: 166 students, 61% women, 39% men. Students come from 12 states and territories, 2 other countries, 2% from out-of-state, 1% Native American, 48% Hispanic, 4% black, 1% Asian American or Pacific Islander, 0.5% international, 23% 25 or older, 10% transferred in. Retention: 50% of full-time freshmen returned the following year. Core. Calendar: semesters. Academic remediation for entering students, advanced placement, honors program, distance learning, summer session for credit, part-time degree program, internships, graduate courses open to undergrads.

Entrance Requirements: Options: Peterson's Universal Application, deferred admission. Required: high school transcript, SAT or ACT. Recommended: interview. Entrance: noncompetitive. Application deadline: Rolling. Notification: continuous.

Collegiate Environment: Orientation program. Drama-theater group, choral group, student-run newspaper, radio station. Social organizations: 35 open to all. Most popular organizations: Baptist Student Union, Wesley Center, Rodeo Club, Wildlife Society, MECHA. Major annual events: Homecoming, Spring Blast, Sul Ross Rodeo. Student services: health clinic, personal-psychological counseling. Campus security: 24-hour patrols, late night transport-escort service. 717 college housing spaces available; 505 were occupied in 2003-04. Freshmen guaranteed college housing. On-campus residence required through sophomore year. Option: coed housing available. Bryan Wildenthal Memorial Library with 245,567 books, 549,490 microform titles, 1,350 serials, 7,011 audiovisual materials, an OPAC, and a Web page. Operations spending for 2004 fiscal year: $1.2 million. 200 computers available on campus for general student use. A campuswide network can be accessed from student residence rooms and from off campus. Staffed computer lab on campus.

Community Environment: Population 7,000, Alpine, located between El Paso on the west and Del Rio on the east, is known for its Highland Hereford breed of cattle. The city is also the gateway to travel to Big Bend National Park, Fort Davis National Historic Sites, Davis Mountains State Park, and McDonald Observatory. The climate in the area is mild. Railroad, commuter airline, and three bus lines serve the community. Local recreation includes baseball, hunting, golf, fishing, a theatre, and Summer Theatre during July and August. There is a hospital, library, and churches of various denominations within the city. Part-time employment is available.

■ **TARLETON STATE UNIVERSITY** *E-17*

Box T-0001

Tarleton Station

Stephenville, TX 76402

Tel: (254)968-9000

Admissions: (254)968-9125

Fax: (254)968-9920

Web Site: http://www.tarleton.edu/

Description: State-supported, comprehensive, coed. Part of Texas A&M University System. Awards associate, bachelor's, master's, and doctoral degrees. Founded 1899. Setting: 125-acre small town campus with easy access to Fort Worth. Endowment: $26.4 million. Research spending for 2004 fiscal year: $5.6 million. Educational spending for 2005 fiscal year: $9373 per student. Total enrollment: 9,144. Faculty: 534 (292 full-time, 242 part-time). Student-undergrad faculty ratio is 19:1. 2,247 applied, 84% were admitted. 10% from top 10% of their high school class, 33% from top quarter, 72% from top half. Full-time: 6,081 students, 56% women, 44% men. Part-time: 1,532 students, 60% women, 40% men. Students come from 32 states and territories, 9 other countries, 5% from out-of-state, 1% Native American, 8% Hispanic, 8% black, 1% Asian American or Pacific Islander, 1% international, 26% 25 or older, 19% live on campus, 12% transferred in. Retention: 65% of full-time freshmen returned the following year. Academic areas with the most degrees conferred: business/marketing; agriculture; interdisciplinary studies. Core. Calendar: semesters. Academic remediation for entering students, services for LD students, advanced placement, accelerated degree program, honors program, distance learning, double major, summer session for credit, part-time degree program, adult/continuing education programs, co-op programs and internships, graduate courses open to undergrads. Off campus study. Study abroad program. ROTC: Army.

Entrance Requirements: Options: electronic application, early admission, deferred admission. Required: high school transcript, SAT or ACT. Required for some: interview. Entrance: moderately difficult. Application deadlines: 4/28, 11/30 for early action.

Costs Per Year: Application fee: $25. State resident tuition: $3300 full-time, $110 per credit hour part-time. Nonresident tuition: $11,580 full-time, $386

per credit hour part-time. Mandatory fees: $870 full-time, $53 per credit hour part-time. Full-time tuition and fees vary according to course load. Part-time tuition and fees vary according to course load. College room and board: $5514. College room only: $2970. Room and board charges vary according to board plan and housing facility.

Collegiate Environment: Orientation program. Drama-theater group, choral group, marching band, student-run newspaper, radio station. Social organizations: 95 open to all; national fraternities, national sororities; 8% of eligible men and 7% of eligible women are members. Most popular organizations: Student Government Association, Student Programming Association, Plowboys Association, Student Organizational Forum, Tarleton Association of Student Leaders. Major annual events: homecoming, Halloween Carnival/Haunted House, Vegas Night. Student services: legal services, health clinic, personal-psychological counseling. Campus security: 24-hour emergency response devices and patrols, student patrols, late night transport-escort service, controlled dormitory access. 1,600 college housing spaces available; 1,462 were occupied in 2003-04. Freshmen guaranteed college housing. On-campus residence required through sophomore year. Options: coed, men-only, women-only housing available. Dick Smith Library plus 1 other with 320,302 books, 911,519 microform titles, 1,150 serials, 8,687 audiovisual materials, an OPAC, and a Web page. Operations spending for 2004 fiscal year: $2 million. 600 computers available on campus for general student use. A campuswide network can be accessed from student residence rooms and from off campus. Staffed computer lab on campus.

Community Environment: Stephenville, Texas, with a population of 15,000 is located in west central Texas, approximately 60 miles from the Ft. Worth/Dallas metroplex. With a typically mild climate average rainfall of 32 inches yearly, the region is commonly known as the Cross Timbers area, a term that refers to the many varieties of oak trees, including a heavy concentration of the live oak tree. Community services include churches of all denominations, a full-service hospital, including a new emergency wing and 24 hour care flight service, libraries and dozens of restaurants and shopping options. Railroad, bus, and a local airport are available. In addition, the Dallas/Ft. Worth International Airport is within a one and one-half hour drive.

■ **TARRANT COUNTY COLLEGE DISTRICT** *D-18*
1500 Houston St.
Fort Worth, TX 76102-6599
Tel: (817)515-5100
Admissions: (817)515-5291
Fax: (817)515-5295
Web Site: http://web.tccd.net/

Description: County-supported, 2-year, coed. Awards certificates, transfer associate, and terminal associate degrees. Founded 1967. Setting: 667-acre urban campus. Endowment: $1.5 million. Educational spending for 2005 fiscal year: $6600 per student. Total enrollment: 34,892. Student-undergrad faculty ratio is 19:1. 7,181 applied, 100% were admitted. Full-time: 12,259 students, 55% women, 45% men. Part-time: 22,633 students, 60% women, 40% men. Students come from 6 states and territories, 0% from out-of-state, 1% Native American, 17% Hispanic, 14% black, 5% Asian American or Pacific Islander, 1% international, 38% 25 or older. Core. Calendar: semesters. Academic remediation for entering students, ESL program, services for LD students, advanced placement, honors program, distance learning, summer session for credit, part-time degree program, adult/continuing education programs. ROTC: Army (c), Air Force (c).

Entrance Requirements: Open admission except for nursing, allied health programs. Option: early admission. Entrance: noncompetitive. Application deadline: Rolling.

Costs Per Year: Application fee: $0. Area resident tuition: $1200 full-time, $50 per credit hour part-time. State resident tuition: $1512 full-time, $63 per credit hour part-time. Nonresident tuition: $3600 full-time, $150 per credit hour part-time.

Collegiate Environment: Orientation program. Drama-theater group, choral group, student-run newspaper. Social organizations: 48 open to all. Student services: health clinic, personal-psychological counseling. Campus security: 24-hour emergency response devices and patrols. College housing not available. 197,352 books, 14,681 microform titles, 1,649 serials, 18,833 audiovisual materials, an OPAC, and a Web page. 2,000 computers available on campus for general student use. Staffed computer lab on campus.

■ **TEMPLE COLLEGE** *G-18*
2600 South First St.
Temple, TX 76504-7435
Tel: (254)298-8282

Admissions: (254)298-8308
Web Site: http://www.templejc.edu/

Description: District-supported, 2-year, coed. Awards certificates, transfer associate, and terminal associate degrees. Founded 1926. Setting: 114-acre suburban campus. Educational spending for 2005 fiscal year: $6900 per student. Total enrollment: 4,068. 753 applied, 100% were admitted. Full-time: 1,533 students, 61% women, 39% men. Part-time: 2,535 students, 65% women, 35% men. Students come from 20 states and territories, 8 other countries, 1% from out-of-state, 1% Native American, 15% Hispanic, 14% black, 2% Asian American or Pacific Islander, 0.2% international, 31% 25 or older, 1% live on campus, 7% transferred in. Retention: 51% of full-time freshmen returned the following year. Calendar: semesters. Academic remediation for entering students, ESL program, distance learning, summer session for credit, part-time degree program, adult/continuing education programs, internships. Off campus study at Temple College at Taylor, Cameron Education Center, McClenan Community College.

Entrance Requirements: Open admission. Option: early admission. Required for some: high school transcript. Placement: THEA required; ACT recommended. Entrance: noncompetitive. Application deadline: 8/19.

Costs Per Year: Application fee: $0. Area resident tuition: $1860 full-time, $62 per hour part-time. State resident tuition: $2850 full-time, $95 per hour part-time. Nonresident tuition: $4500 full-time, $150 per hour part-time. Mandatory fees: $65 full-time.

Collegiate Environment: Drama-theater group. Student services: personal-psychological counseling. Campus security: 24-hour emergency response devices and patrols. No special consideration for freshman housing applicants. Hubert Dawson Library with 55,536 books, 40,114 microform titles, 391 serials, 2,170 audiovisual materials, an OPAC, and a Web page. Operations spending for 2004 fiscal year: $400,882. 100 computers available on campus for general student use. A campuswide network can be accessed from student residence rooms and from off campus. Staffed computer lab on campus.

Community Environment: Population 53,733. Temple today is a medical center visited annually by thousands of patients. Located in central Texas, the city enjoys a temperate climate. The community has air, rail, and bus service available. Community service facilities include four excellent hospitals, many churches representing all major denominations, a library, and several hotels and motels. There are various civic, fraternal, and veteran's organizations active in the area. Local recreation includes hunting, fishing, boating, water skiing, and most water sports at nearby Lake Belton. Part-time employment is available.

■ **TEXARKANA COLLEGE** *C-24*
2500 North Robison Rd.
Texarkana, TX 75599-0001
Tel: (903)838-4541
Fax: (903)832-5030
E-mail: vmiller@texarkanacollege.edu
Web Site: http://www.texarkanacollege.edu/

Description: State and locally supported, 2-year, coed. Awards certificates, transfer associate, and terminal associate degrees. Founded 1927. Setting: 88-acre urban campus. Educational spending for 2005 fiscal year: $1880 per student. Total enrollment: 3,895. Full-time: 1,550 students, 61% women, 39% men. Part-time: 2,345 students, 63% women, 37% men. Students come from 7 states and territories, 5 other countries, 0.2% Native American, 1% Hispanic, 16% black, 0.3% Asian American or Pacific Islander, 0.2% international, 42% 25 or older. Core. Calendar: semesters. Academic remediation for entering students, services for LD students, advanced placement, summer session for credit, part-time degree program, adult/continuing education programs, co-op programs.

Entrance Requirements: Open admission. Option: early admission. Required: high school transcript. Placement: THEA required. Entrance: noncompetitive. Application deadline: Rolling.

Collegiate Environment: Orientation program. Drama-theater group, choral group, student-run newspaper, radio station. Social organizations: 16 open to all. Most popular organizations: Black Student Association, Earth Club. Major annual events: Octoberfest, Spring Fest. Student services: personal-psychological counseling. Campus security: 24-hour patrols. 75 college housing spaces available; 40 were occupied in 2003-04. No special consideration for freshman housing applicants. Palmer Memorial Library with 46,700 books and 646 serials. 105 computers available on campus for general student use. A campuswide network can be accessed. Staffed computer lab on campus.

Community Environment: Texarkana is located on the Arkansas-Texas border which runs approximately through the center of town. A trading center, there are many railroad lines coming into the area. The community has two hospitals, motels and hotels, and various civic, fraternal and veteran's organizations. Local recreation includes golf, hunting, fishing, boating, and water skiing. Part-time employment is available.

■ **TEXAS A&M INTERNATIONAL UNIVERSITY** *N-15*
5201 University Blvd.
Laredo, TX 78041-1900
Tel: (956)326-2001; 888-489-2648
Admissions: (956)326-2200
Fax: (956)326-2348
E-mail: adms@tamiu.edu
Web Site: http://www.tamiu.edu/
Description: State-supported, comprehensive, coed. Part of Texas A&M University System. Awards bachelor's, master's, and doctoral degrees. Founded 1969. Setting: 300-acre urban campus. Endowment: $21 million. Research spending for 2004 fiscal year: $396,428. Educational spending for 2005 fiscal year: $5154 per student. Total enrollment: 4,298. Faculty: 273 (161 full-time, 112 part-time). Student-undergrad faculty ratio is 15:1. 1,566 applied, 51% were admitted. 26% from top 10% of their high school class, 56% from top quarter, 90% from top half. Full-time: 2,236 students, 62% women, 38% men. Part-time: 1,098 students, 65% women, 35% men. Students come from 30 states and territories, 9 other countries, 1% from out-of-state, 0.03% Native American, 92% Hispanic, 0.5% black, 1% Asian American or Pacific Islander, 4% international, 37% 25 or older, 7% transferred in. Retention: 68% of full-time freshmen returned the following year. Academic areas with the most degrees conferred: business/marketing; interdisciplinary studies; security and protective services. Core. Calendar: semesters. Academic remediation for entering students, ESL program, services for LD students, advanced placement, honors program, summer session for credit, part-time degree program, internships, graduate courses open to undergrads. Study abroad program.
Entrance Requirements: Options: Common Application, electronic application, early admission, deferred admission, international baccalaureate accepted. Required: high school transcript, SAT or ACT. Entrance: moderately difficult. Application deadline: 7/1. Notification: 7/15.
Costs Per Year: Application fee: $0. State resident tuition: $3150 full-time. Nonresident tuition: $11,430 full-time. Mandatory fees: $1068 full-time. Full-time tuition and fees vary according to course load. College room and board: $6390. College room only: $4000. Room and board charges vary according to board plan and housing facility.
Collegiate Environment: Orientation program. Choral group, student-run newspaper. Social organizations: 35 open to all; national fraternities, local fraternities, local sororities. Most popular organizations: TAMIU Ambassadors, Electronic Commerce Association, Rainbow Education Association of Laredo, Student Finance Society, Psychology Club. Major annual events: Halloween Fest, Thanksgiving Festival, International Day. Student services: health clinic, personal-psychological counseling. Campus security: 24-hour emergency response devices and patrols. 250 college housing spaces available; all were occupied in 2003-04. Freshmen given priority for college housing. Sue and Radcliff Killam Library with 166,951 books, 148,825 microform titles, 8,492 serials, 1,040 audiovisual materials, an OPAC, and a Web page. Operations spending for 2004 fiscal year: $3.1 million. 200 computers available on campus for general student use. A campuswide network can be accessed from off-campus. Staffed computer lab on campus.

■ **TEXAS A&M UNIVERSITY** *H-20*
College Station, TX 77843
Tel: (979)845-3211
Admissions: (979)845-3741
E-mail: adminfo@tamu.edu
Web Site: http://www.tamu.edu/
Description: State-supported, university, coed. Part of Texas A&M University System. Awards bachelor's, master's, doctoral, and first professional degrees. Founded 1876. Setting: 5,200-acre suburban campus with easy access to Houston. System endowment: $5 billion. Research spending for 2004 fiscal year: $394.5 million. Educational spending for 2005 fiscal year: $8627 per student. Total enrollment: 44,910. Faculty: 2,232 (1,898 full-time, 334 part-time). Student-undergrad faculty ratio is 20:1. 17,871 applied, 70% were admitted. 50% from top 10% of their high school class, 79% from top quarter, 91% from top half. 137 National Merit Scholars, 216 valedictorians. Full-time: 33,085 students, 49% women, 51% men. Part-time: 3,283 students, 46% women, 54% men. Students come from 52 states and territories, 128 other countries, 4% from out-of-state, 0.5% Native American,

11% Hispanic, 3% black, 4% Asian American or Pacific Islander, 2% international, 4% 25 or older, 25% live on campus, 4% transferred in. Retention: 92% of full-time freshmen returned the following year. Academic areas with the most degrees conferred: business/marketing; agriculture; engineering. Core. Calendar: semesters. Academic remediation for entering students, ESL program, services for LD students, advanced placement, accelerated degree program, honors program, independent study, distance learning, double major, summer session for credit, part-time degree program, co-op programs and internships, graduate courses open to undergrads. Off campus study at Texas A&M University at Galveston. Study abroad program. ROTC: Army, Naval, Air Force.
Entrance Requirements: Options: electronic application, international baccalaureate accepted. Required: essay, high school transcript, SAT or ACT. Entrance: moderately difficult. Application deadline: 2/1. Notification: continuous. Preference given to students graduating in the top 10% of Texas high schools.
Costs Per Year: Application fee: $50. State resident tuition: $4110 full-time, $137 per semester hour part-time. Nonresident tuition: $12,390 full-time, $413 per semester hour part-time. Mandatory fees: $2289 full-time. Full-time tuition and fees vary according to course load, location, and program. College room and board: $6952. College room only: $3704. Room and board charges vary according to board plan, housing facility, and location.
Collegiate Environment: Orientation program. Drama-theater group, choral group, marching band, student-run newspaper, radio station. Social organizations: 700 open to all; national fraternities, national sororities, local fraternities, local sororities; 6% of eligible men and 12% of eligible women are members. Most popular organizations: Memorial Student Center, Corps of Cadets, Fish Camp, student government. Major annual events: Big Event, Parents' Weekend, Aggie Muster. Student services: legal services, health clinic, personal-psychological counseling, women's center. Campus security: 24-hour emergency response devices and patrols, late night transport-escort service, controlled dormitory access, student escorts. 10,000 college housing spaces available; 9,091 were occupied in 2003-04. No special consideration for freshman housing applicants. Options: coed, men-only, women-only housing available. Sterling C. Evans Library plus 4 others with 3 million books, 5.4 million microform titles, 45,710 serials, 323,023 audiovisual materials, an OPAC, and a Web page. Operations spending for 2004 fiscal year: $25.8 million. 1,300 computers available on campus for general student use. A campuswide network can be accessed from student residence rooms and from off campus. Staffed computer lab on campus.

■ **TEXAS A&M UNIVERSITY-COMMERCE** *C-21*
PO Box 3011
Commerce, TX 75429-3011
Tel: (903)886-5081
Free: 800-331-3878
Admissions: (903)886-5103
Fax: (903)886-5888
Web Site: http://www.tamu-commerce.edu/
Description: State-supported, university, coed. Part of Texas A&M University System. Awards bachelor's, master's, and doctoral degrees. Founded 1889. Setting: 140-acre small town campus with easy access to Dallas-Fort Worth. Endowment: $9.1 million. Research spending for 2004 fiscal year: $609,864. Educational spending for 2005 fiscal year: $6149 per student. Total enrollment: 8,787. Faculty: 500 (295 full-time, 205 part-time). Student-undergrad faculty ratio is 17:1. 16% from top 10% of their high school class, 42% from top quarter, 72% from top half. Students come from 27 states and territories, 31 other countries, 2% from out-of-state, 1% Native American, 7% Hispanic, 19% black, 2% Asian American or Pacific Islander, 1% international, 28% 25 or older, 24% live on campus. Retention: 66% of full-time freshmen returned the following year. Academic areas with the most degrees conferred: interdisciplinary studies; business/marketing; visual and performing arts. Core. Calendar: semesters. Academic remediation for entering students, services for LD students, advanced placement, honors program, independent study, distance learning, double major, summer session for credit, part-time degree program, adult/continuing education programs, co-op programs and internships. Off campus study at Federation of North Texas Area Universities. Study abroad program.
Entrance Requirements: Options: Common Application, electronic application, early admission. Required: high school transcript, SAT or ACT. Entrance: moderately difficult. Application deadline: 8/11. Notification: continuous.
Costs Per Year: Application fee: $25. State resident tuition: $3834 full-time, $278.50 per credit part-time. Nonresident tuition: $11,574 full-time, $554.50

per credit part-time. Mandatory fees: $990 full-time. Full-time tuition and fees vary according to course load. Part-time tuition varies according to course load. College room and board: $5740. Room and board charges vary according to board plan and housing facility.

Collegiate Environment: Orientation program. Drama-theater group, choral group, marching band, student-run newspaper, radio station. Social organizations: 100 open to all; national fraternities, national sororities. Major annual events: homecoming, Family Day, Sam Rayburn Leadership Institute. Student services: legal services, health clinic, personal-psychological counseling. Campus security: 24-hour emergency response devices and patrols, controlled dormitory access. 2,300 college housing spaces available; 1,563 were occupied in 2003-04. Freshmen guaranteed college housing. On-campus residence required in freshman year. Options: coed, men-only, women-only housing available. Gee Library with 112,601 books, 1.2 million microform titles, 7,918 serials, 50,283 audiovisual materials, an OPAC, and a Web page. Operations spending for 2004 fiscal year: $2.1 million. 405 computers available on campus for general student use. A campuswide network can be accessed from student residence rooms and from off campus. Staffed computer lab on campus.

■ **TEXAS A&M UNIVERSITY-CORPUS CHRISTI** *N-18*
6300 Ocean Dr.
Corpus Christi, TX 78412-5503
Tel: (361)825-5700
Free: 800-482-6822
Admissions: (361)825-2414
Fax: (361)825-5810
E-mail: jmorgan@falcon.tamucc.edu
Web Site: http://www.tamucc.edu/

Description: State-supported, comprehensive, coed. Part of Texas A&M University System. Awards bachelor's, master's, and doctoral degrees. Founded 1947. Setting: 240-acre suburban campus. Endowment: $2.3 million. Research spending for 2004 fiscal year: $5.4 million. Educational spending for 2005 fiscal year: $4984 per student. Total enrollment: 8,227. 3,273 applied, 85% were admitted. 17% from top 10% of their high school class, 50% from top quarter, 85% from top half. Full-time: 5,255 students, 61% women, 39% men. Part-time: 1,326 students, 59% women, 41% men. Students come from 37 states and territories, 23 other countries, 2% from out-of-state, 1% Native American, 37% Hispanic, 3% black, 2% Asian American or Pacific Islander, 1% international, 17% 25 or older, 16% live on campus, 20% transferred in. Retention: 64% of full-time freshmen returned the following year. Core. Calendar: semesters. Academic remediation for entering students, services for LD students, advanced placement, independent study, distance learning, double major, summer session for credit, part-time degree program, co-op programs and internships. Off campus study at Texas A&M University-Kingsville. ROTC: Army.

Entrance Requirements: Required: high school transcript, minimum 2.0 high school GPA, SAT or ACT. Entrance: moderately difficult. Application deadline: 7/1.

Costs Per Year: Application fee: $20. State resident tuition: $3348 full-time, $116 per semester hour part-time. Nonresident tuition: $11,628 full-time, $326 per semester hour part-time. Mandatory fees: $1168 full-time, $35 per semester hour part-time, $92.50. Full-time tuition and fees vary according to course load. Part-time tuition and fees vary according to course load. College room and board: $7800. College room only: $5400. Room and board charges vary according to housing facility.

Collegiate Environment: Orientation program. Drama-theater group, choral group, marching band, student-run newspaper. Social organizations: 75 open to all; national fraternities, national sororities, local fraternities, local sororities. Most popular organizations: Student Accounting Society, Student Art Association, science clubs. Major annual events: Fall Fest, Splash Day, Island Day. Student services: health clinic, personal-psychological counseling, women's center. Campus security: 24-hour emergency response devices and patrols, late night transport-escort service, security gate access with card after 10 p.m. 1,340 college housing spaces available; 1,160 were occupied in 2003-04. No special consideration for freshman housing applicants. Options: coed, men-only, women-only housing available. Mary and Jeff Bell Library with 731,586 books, 536,059 microform titles, 1,901 serials, 6,012 audiovisual materials, an OPAC, and a Web page. Operations spending for 2004 fiscal year: $1.9 million. 500 computers available on campus for

general student use. A campuswide network can be accessed from student residence rooms and from off campus. Staffed computer lab on campus.

■ **TEXAS A&M UNIVERSITY AT GALVESTON** *K-23*
PO Box 1675
Galveston, TX 77553-1675
Tel: (409)740-4400; 877-322-4443
Admissions: (409)740-4414
Fax: (409)740-4709
E-mail: seaaggie@tamug.edu
Web Site: http://www.tamug.edu/

Description: State-supported, comprehensive, coed. Part of Texas A&M University System. Awards bachelor's and master's degrees. Founded 1962. Setting: 122-acre suburban campus with easy access to Houston. Endowment: $1.6 million. Research spending for 2004 fiscal year: $2.9 million. Educational spending for 2005 fiscal year: $5669 per student. Total enrollment: 1,677. Faculty: 170 (68 full-time, 102 part-time). Student-undergrad faculty ratio is 13:1. 1,171 applied, 96% were admitted. 10% from top 10% of their high school class, 45% from top quarter, 75% from top half. Full-time: 1,488 students, 42% women, 58% men. Part-time: 148 students, 47% women, 53% men. Students come from 50 states and territories, 13 other countries, 18% from out-of-state, 1% Native American, 10% Hispanic, 3% black, 2% Asian American or Pacific Islander, 0.5% international, 11% 25 or older, 54% live on campus, 17% transferred in. Retention: 72% of full-time freshmen returned the following year. Academic areas with the most degrees conferred: business/marketing; biological/life sciences; transportation and materials moving. Core. Calendar: semesters. Academic remediation for entering students, ESL program, advanced placement, accelerated degree program, independent study, double major, summer session for credit, part-time degree program, co-op programs and internships, graduate courses open to undergrads. Study abroad program. ROTC: Naval.

Entrance Requirements: Options: Common Application, electronic application, early admission, deferred admission. Required: essay, high school transcript, SAT or ACT, THEA. Recommended: essay, recommendations, community involvement, SAT Subject Tests. Required for some: interview. Entrance: moderately difficult. Application deadline: Rolling. Notification: continuous.

Costs Per Year: Application fee: $35. State resident tuition: $4110 full-time, $137 per hour part-time. Nonresident tuition: $12,390 full-time, $413 per hour part-time. Mandatory fees: $1008 full-time, $504 per term part-time. Full-time tuition and fees vary according to course load and program. Part-time tuition and fees vary according to course load and program. College room and board: $4870. College room only: $1958. Room and board charges vary according to board plan and housing facility.

Collegiate Environment: Orientation program. Drama-theater group, choral group, student-run newspaper. Social organizations: 37 open to all. Most popular organizations: Sail Club, Caving Club, Dive Club, Rowing Club, Rifle Drill Team. Major annual events: Aggie Muster, Spring Fest, Maritime Ball. Student services: health clinic, personal-psychological counseling. Campus security: 24-hour emergency response devices and patrols. 650 college housing spaces available; all were occupied in 2003-04. Freshmen given priority for college housing. On-campus residence required through sophomore year. Options: coed, men-only, women-only housing available. Jack K. Williams Library with 56,589 books, 54,187 microform titles, 640 serials, 2,822 audiovisual materials, an OPAC, and a Web page. Operations spending for 2004 fiscal year: $1.1 million. 122 computers available on campus for general student use. A campuswide network can be accessed from student residence rooms and from off campus. Staffed computer lab on campus.

■ **TEXAS A&M UNIVERSITY-KINGSVILLE** *N-18*
West Santa Gertrudis
Kingsville, TX 78363
Tel: (361)593-2111
Free: 800-687-6000
Admissions: (361)593-2811
Web Site: http://www.tamuk.edu/

Description: State-supported, university, coed. Part of Texas A&M University System. Awards bachelor's, master's, and doctoral degrees. Founded 1925. Setting: 255-acre small town campus. Research spending for 2004 fiscal year: $5.8 million. Total enrollment: 7,126. 2,335 applied, 98% were admitted. 10% from top 10% of their high school class, 33% from top quarter, 65% from top half. Full-time: 3,910 students, 48% women, 52% men. Part-time: 1,735 students, 61% women, 39% men. Students come from 39 states and territories, 61 other countries, 2% from out-of-state, 0.2% Native American, 66% Hispanic, 6% black, 1% Asian American or Pacific Islander, 1% international, 28% 25 or older, 30% live on campus. Retention: 55% of full-time freshmen returned the following year. Core. Calendar: semesters. Academic remediation for entering students, ESL program, services for LD students, advanced placement, accelerated degree program, freshman honors college, honors program, distance learning, double major, summer session for credit, part-time degree program, external degree program, adult/continuing education programs, co-op programs and internships, graduate courses open to undergrads. Study abroad program. ROTC: Army.

Entrance Requirements: Open admission for the college of arts and sciences. Options: Common Application, early admission, deferred admission. Required: high school transcript. Recommended: minimum 2.0 high school GPA. Required for some: interview, SAT or ACT. Entrance: moderately difficult. Application deadline: Rolling. Notification: continuous.

Costs Per Year: Application fee: $15. State resident tuition: $3060 full-time. Nonresident tuition: $11,340 full-time. Mandatory fees: $1266 full-time.

Collegiate Environment: Orientation program. Drama-theater group, choral group, marching band, student-run newspaper, radio station. Social organizations: 100 open to all; national fraternities, national sororities, local sororities; 2% of eligible men and 2% of eligible women are members. Most popular organizations: Aggie Club, Rodeo Club, Educational Association, Child Development Club, Resident's Hall Club. Major annual events: Fall Carnival, Homecoming activities, Pageant. Student services: health clinic, personal-psychological counseling, women's center. Campus security: 24-hour emergency response devices and patrols, late night transport-escort service. On-campus residence required through sophomore year. Options: coed, men-only, women-only housing available. James C. Jernigan Library with 358,466 books, 183,416 microform titles, 2,304 serials, 3,224 audiovisual materials, and an OPAC. Operations spending for 2004 fiscal year: $1 million. 600 computers available on campus for general student use. A campuswide network can be accessed from student residence rooms and from off campus. Staffed computer lab on campus.

■ **TEXAS A&M UNIVERSITY SYSTEM HEALTH SCIENCE CENTER** *H-20*
301 Tarrow St.
7th Floor
College Station, TX 77840
Tel: (979)458-7200
Admissions: (214)828-8230
Fax: (979)458-7202
Web Site: http://www.tamhsc.edu/

Description: State-supported, upper-level, coed. Part of Texas A&M University System Health Science Center. Awards bachelor's, master's, doctoral, and first professional degrees and post-master's and first professional certificates. Founded 1999. Setting: urban campus. Total enrollment: 529. Faculty: 255 (137 full-time, 118 part-time). Full-time: 59 students, 100% women. Students come from 2 states and territories, 0% from out-of-state, 0% Native American, 7% Hispanic, 2% black, 14% Asian American or Pacific Islander, 0% international, 30% 25 or older, 51% transferred in. Retention: 0% of full-time entering class returned the following year. Academic area with the most degrees conferred: health professions and related sciences. Calendar: semesters. Services for LD students.

Costs Per Year: Application fee: $35. State resident tuition: $3752 full-time. Nonresident tuition: $13,342 full-time. Mandatory fees: $1,075 full-time.

Collegiate Environment: Orientation program. Student services: health clinic, personal-psychological counseling. Campus security: 24-hour emergency response devices and patrols, late night transport-escort service, electronically operated building access. College housing not available.

■ **TEXAS A&M UNIVERSITY-TEXARKANA** *C-24*
PO Box 5518
Texarkana, TX 75505-5518
Tel: (903)223-3000
Admissions: (903)223-3068
Fax: (903)832-8890
E-mail: patblack@etsu.edu
Web Site: http://www.tamut.edu/

Description: State-supported, upper-level, coed. Part of Texas A&M University System. Awards bachelor's and master's degrees. Founded 1971. Setting: 1-acre small town campus. Endowment: $1.2 million. Research spending for 2004 fiscal year: $4759. Total enrollment: 1,653. Faculty: 100.

Student-undergrad faculty ratio is 14:1. Students come from 6 states and territories, 1 other country, 24% from out-of-state, 2% Native American, 4% Hispanic, 14% black, 1% Asian American or Pacific Islander, 0.2% international. Academic areas with the most degrees conferred: interdisciplinary studies; business/marketing; liberal arts/general studies; psychology. Core. Calendar: semesters. Services for LD students, advanced placement, self-designed majors, independent study, distance learning, summer session for credit, part-time degree program, internships, graduate courses open to undergrads.

Costs Per Year: Application fee: $0. State resident tuition: $2160 full-time, $90 per credit hour part-time. Nonresident tuition: $8784 full-time, $366 per credit hour part-time. Mandatory fees: $390 full-time, $15.75 per credit hour part-time, $6 per term part-time. Full-time tuition and fees vary according to course level, course load, and student level. Part-time tuition and fees vary according to course level, course load, and student level.

Collegiate Environment: Orientation program. Student-run newspaper. Social organizations: 17 open to all. Most popular organizations: Education Club, Psychology Club, Science Club, Multicultural Association, Reading Club. Major annual events: Summer Fest, Fall Fest, Spring Fest. Campus security: 24-hour patrols, late night transport-escort service. College housing not available. John F. Moss Library plus 1 other with 125,991 books, 1.7 million microform titles, 5,709 serials, 3,720 audiovisual materials, an OPAC, and a Web page. Operations spending for 2004 fiscal year: $780,342. 133 computers available on campus for general student use. A campuswide network can be accessed from off-campus. Staffed computer lab on campus.

■ **TEXAS CHIROPRACTIC COLLEGE** *J-22*
5912 Spencer Hwy.
Pasadena, TX 77505-1699
Tel: (281)487-1170
Free: 800-468-6839
Admissions: (281)998-6017
E-mail: shughes@txchiro.edu
Web Site: http://www.txchiro.edu/

Description: Independent, upper-level, coed. Awards incidental bachelor's and first professional degrees. Founded 1908. Setting: 18-acre suburban campus with easy access to Houston. Total enrollment: 458. Faculty: 31 (28 full-time, 3 part-time). Student-undergrad faculty ratio is 15:1. Full-time: 27 students, 41% women, 59% men. Part-time: 26 students, 58% women, 42% men. Students come from 7 other countries, 0% from out-of-state. Core. Calendar: trimesters. Internships. Off campus study.

Costs Per Year: Application fee: $50. Tuition: $18,285 full-time, $508 per hour part-time. Mandatory fees: $315 full-time.

Collegiate Environment: Social organizations: local women's organization. Student services: health clinic, personal-psychological counseling. College housing not available. Mae Hilty Memorial Library with 10,500 books and 160 serials.

Community Environment: See San Jacinto College - Central Campus.

■ **TEXAS CHRISTIAN UNIVERSITY** *D-18*
2800 South University Dr.
Fort Worth, TX 76129-0002
Tel: (817)257-7000
Free: 800-828-3764
Admissions: (817)257-7490
E-mail: frogmail@tcu.edu
Web Site: http://www.tcu.edu/

Description: Independent, university, coed, affiliated with Christian Church (Disciples of Christ). Awards bachelor's, master's, doctoral, and first professional degrees and first professional certificates. Founded 1873. Setting: 260-acre suburban campus. Endowment: $950 million. Total enrollment: 8,749. Faculty: 810 (465 full-time, 345 part-time). Student-undergrad faculty ratio is 14:1. 8,155 applied, 67% were admitted. 28% from top 10% of their high school class, 61% from top quarter, 94% from top half. Full-time: 6,718 students, 60% women, 40% men. Part-time: 453 students, 56% women, 44% men. Students come from 50 states and territories, 75 other countries, 20% from out-of-state, 1% Native American, 6% Hispanic, 5% black, 2% Asian American or Pacific Islander, 4% international, 6% 25 or older, 44% live on campus, 6% transferred in. Retention: 84% of full-time freshmen returned the following year. Academic areas with the most degrees conferred: business/marketing; communications/journalism; education. Core. Calendar: semesters. ESL program, services for LD students, advanced placement, honors program, independent study, distance learning, double major, summer session for credit, part-time degree program, adult/continuing education programs, internships, graduate courses open to undergrads. Study abroad program. ROTC: Army, Air Force.

Entrance Requirements: Options: Peterson's Universal Application, Common Application, electronic application, early action, deferred admission, international baccalaureate accepted. Required: essay, high school transcript, minimum 2.0 high school GPA, 2 recommendations, SAT or ACT. Recommended: minimum 3.0 high school GPA, interview. Entrance: moderately difficult. Application deadlines: 2/15, 11/15 for early action. Notification: 4/1, 1/1 for early action.

Costs Per Year: Application fee: $40. Comprehensive fee: $28,300 includes full-time tuition ($21,280), mandatory fees ($40), and college room and board ($6980). College room only: $4180. Room and board charges vary according to board plan and housing facility.

Collegiate Environment: Orientation program. Drama-theater group, choral group, marching band, student-run newspaper, radio station. Social organizations: 195 open to all; national fraternities, national sororities, local fraternities, local sororities, local coed music fraternities; 34% of eligible men and 36% of eligible women are members. Major annual events: Family Weekend, Christmas tree lighting, Frog Fest/Frog Follies. Student services: legal services, health clinic, personal-psychological counseling, women's center. Campus security: 24-hour emergency response devices and patrols, student patrols, late night transport-escort service, controlled dormitory access, emergency call boxes, video camera surveillance in parking lots. 3,200 college housing spaces available; 3,116 were occupied in 2003-04. Freshmen guaranteed college housing. On-campus residence required in freshman year. Options: coed, men-only, women-only housing available. Mary Couts Burnett Library with 1.3 million books, 641,174 microform titles, 6,229 serials, 62,376 audiovisual materials, an OPAC, and a Web page.

Community Environment: The University is easily accessible to a variety of recreational, educational, and professional opportunities in the Fort Worth/Dallas metroplex. Major museums, parks, theatres, churches, and restaurants are within a few miles from the campus.

■ **TEXAS COLLEGE** *E-22*
2404 North Grand Ave.
PO Box 4500
Tyler, TX 75712-4500
Tel: (903)593-8311
Free: 800-306-6299
Web Site: http://www.texascollege.edu/

Description: Independent, 4-year, coed, affiliated with Christian Methodist Episcopal Church. Awards bachelor's degrees. Founded 1894. Total enrollment: 757. 1,243 applied, 25% were admitted. 3% from top 10% of their high school class, 10% from top quarter, 37% from top half. Full-time: 694 students, 45% women, 55% men. Part-time: 58 students, 59% women, 41% men. 0.1% Native American, 2% Hispanic, 97% black, 0% Asian American or Pacific Islander, 0% international, 75% live on campus. Retention: 32% of full-time freshmen returned the following year. Core. Calendar: semesters. Academic remediation for entering students, distance learning, summer session for credit, part-time degree program, adult/continuing education programs, internships.

Entrance Requirements: Open admission. Option: Common Application. Required: high school transcript. Entrance: noncompetitive. Application deadline: Rolling. Notification: continuous.

Costs Per Year: Application fee: $20. Comprehensive fee: $12,410 includes full-time tuition ($7680) and college room and board ($4730). College room only: $3000. Part-time tuition: $320 per semester hour.

Collegiate Environment: Orientation program. 435 college housing spaces available; all were occupied in 2003-04. D. R. Glass Library plus 1 other with 73,329 books, 201 microform titles, 122 serials, 1,268 audiovisual materials, and an OPAC. 75 computers available on campus for general student use. Computer purchase/lease plans available. A campuswide network can be accessed from off-campus. Staffed computer lab on campus.

■ **TEXAS CULINARY ACADEMY** *I-18*
11400 Burnet Rd., Ste. 2100
Austin, TX 78758
Tel: (512)323-2511; 888-553-2433
Admissions: (512)837-2665
Fax: (512)323-2126
E-mail: ppaulette@txca.com
Web Site: http://www.txca.com/

Description: Independent, 2-year, coed. Awards certificates, diplomas, transfer associate, and terminal associate degrees. Setting: urban campus. Total enrollment: 200. Calendar: continuous.

Entrance Requirements: Required: essay, high school transcript. Application deadline: Rolling.

Collegiate Environment: Campus security: 24-hour emergency response devices.

■ **TEXAS LUTHERAN UNIVERSITY** *J-17*
1000 West Ct. St.
Seguin, TX 78155-5999
Tel: (830)372-8000
Free: 800-771-8521
Admissions: (830)372-8050
Fax: (830)372-8096
E-mail: admissions@txlutheran.edu
Web Site: http://www.tlu.edu/

Description: Independent, 4-year, coed, affiliated with Evangelical Lutheran Church. Awards bachelor's degrees. Founded 1891. Setting: 196-acre suburban campus with easy access to San Antonio. Endowment: $52.4 million. Research spending for 2004 fiscal year: $39,892. Educational spending for 2005 fiscal year: $4644 per student. Total enrollment: 1,435. Student-undergrad faculty ratio is 16:1. 1,150 applied, 72% were admitted. 24% from top 10% of their high school class, 57% from top quarter, 90% from top half. 5 valedictorians. Full-time: 1,328 students, 53% women, 47% men. Part-time: 107 students, 60% women, 40% men. Students come from 24 states and territories, 12 other countries, 3% from out-of-state, 0.5% Native American, 16% Hispanic, 8% black, 2% Asian American or Pacific Islander, 1% international, 8% 25 or older, 66% live on campus, 4% transferred in. Retention: 67% of full-time freshmen returned the following year. Academic areas with the most degrees conferred: business/marketing; biological/life sciences; education; visual and performing arts; psychology. Core. Calendar: semesters. Services for LD students, advanced placement, honors program, independent study, double major, summer session for credit, part-time degree program, adult/continuing education programs, internships. Study abroad program. ROTC: Army (c), Air Force (c).

Entrance Requirements: Options: Peterson's Universal Application, Common Application, electronic application, deferred admission, international baccalaureate accepted. Required: essay, high school transcript, SAT or ACT. Recommended: interview. Required for some: minimum 2.0 high school GPA, 2 recommendations. Entrance: moderately difficult. Application deadline: Rolling. Notification: continuous until 8/1.

Costs Per Year: Application fee: $25. Comprehensive fee: $24,440 includes full-time tuition ($18,720), mandatory fees ($120), and college room and board ($5600). College room only: $2600. Part-time tuition: $630 per credit hour. Part-time mandatory fees: $60 per term.

Collegiate Environment: Orientation program. Drama-theater group, choral group, student-run newspaper. Social organizations: 57 open to all; local fraternities, local sororities; 15% of eligible men and 14% of eligible women are members. Most popular organizations: Campus Ministry, Mexican American Student Association, Student Government Association. Major annual events: KROST Symposium, Christmas Vespers, Spring Fling. Student services: health clinic, personal-psychological counseling, women's center. Campus security: 24-hour emergency response devices and patrols, late night transport-escort service, controlled dormitory access. 999 college housing spaces available; 902 were occupied in 2003-04. Freshmen guaranteed college housing. On-campus residence required through senior year. Options: coed, men-only, women-only housing available. Blumberg Memorial Library with 171,029 books, 118,592 microform titles, 566 serials, 4,297 audiovisual materials, an OPAC, and a Web page. Operations spending for 2004 fiscal year: $360,584. 48 computers available on campus for general student use. A campuswide network can be accessed from student residence rooms and from off campus. Staffed computer lab on campus.

Community Environment: Population 27,000, Seguin is a suburban community enjoying temperate climate. The city is reached by Interstate 10. There is a library, a museum, churches representing 10 different denominations, and a hospital serving the community. Various job opportunities are available here. Various civic, fraternal and veteran's organizations are active in Seguin. Nearby Lake McQueeney offers water skiing.

■ **TEXAS SOUTHERN UNIVERSITY** *J-22*
3100 Cleburne
Houston, TX 77004-4584
Tel: (713)313-7011
Admissions: (713)313-7472
Fax: (713)527-7842
Web Site: http://www.tsu.edu/

Description: State-supported, university, coed. Part of Texas Higher Education Coordinating Board. Awards bachelor's, master's, doctoral, and first professional degrees. Founded 1947. Setting: 147-acre urban campus. Endowment: $15.3 million. Research spending for 2004 fiscal year: $4.6 million. Total enrollment: 11,903. Faculty: 569. Student-undergrad faculty ratio is 25:1. 6,596 applied, 30% were admitted. Full-time: 7,739 students, 58% women, 42% men. Part-time: 2,021 students, 59% women, 41% men. Students come from 36 states and territories, 42 other countries, 12% from out-of-state, 0.1% Native American, 3% Hispanic, 90% black, 2% Asian American or Pacific Islander, 3% international, 23% 25 or older, 15% live on campus, 9% transferred in. Retention: 65% of full-time freshmen returned the following year. Academic areas with the most degrees conferred: business/marketing; biological/life sciences; health professions and related sciences. Core. Calendar: semesters. Academic remediation for entering students, ESL program, services for LD students, accelerated degree program, honors program, distance learning, summer session for credit, part-time degree program, adult/continuing education programs, co-op programs and internships, graduate courses open to undergrads. Off campus study at Houston Community College Pinemont Center, North Harris College Career Center. ROTC: Army (c), Naval (c).

Entrance Requirements: Open admission. Options: Common Application, electronic application. Required: high school transcript, SAT or ACT. Entrance: noncompetitive. Application deadline: 8/10. Notification: continuous until 8/28.

Costs Per Year: Application fee: $42. State resident tuition: $1200 full-time, $50 per hour part-time. Nonresident tuition: $7824 full-time, $326 per hour part-time. Mandatory fees: $2572 full-time, $817 per term part-time. Full-time tuition and fees vary according to course load and program. Part-time tuition and fees vary according to course load and program. College room and board: $6056. Room and board charges vary according to board plan and housing facility.

Collegiate Environment: Orientation program. Drama-theater group, choral group, marching band, student-run newspaper, radio station. Social organizations: 58 open to all; national fraternities, national sororities, local fraternities, local sororities; 1% of eligible men and 3% of eligible women are members. Most popular organizations: Debate Team, University Program Council, Student Government Association, Band. Major annual events: Homecoming Festival, Labor Day Classic Game, Spring Festival. Student services: legal services, health clinic, personal-psychological counseling. Campus security: 24-hour emergency response devices and patrols, student patrols, late night transport-escort service. College housing designed to accommodate 1,363 students; 1,462 undergraduates lived in college housing during 2003-04. Freshmen guaranteed college housing. On-campus residence required in freshman year. Options: men-only, women-only housing available. Robert J. Terry Library plus 2 others with 266,888 books, 462,135 microform titles, 1,750 serials, 4,016 audiovisual materials, and an OPAC. Operations spending for 2004 fiscal year: $1.8 million. 500 computers available on campus for general student use. A campuswide network can be accessed. Staffed computer lab on campus.

Community Environment: See University of Houston.

■ **TEXAS SOUTHMOST COLLEGE** *Q-18*

80 Fort Brown
Brownsville, TX 78520-4991
Tel: (956)544-8200
Admissions: (956)544-8992
E-mail: rvillarreal@utb.edu
Web Site: http://www.utb.edu/

Description: District-supported, 2-year, coed. Part of University of Texas System. Awards certificates, transfer associate, and terminal associate degrees. Founded 1926. Setting: 65-acre urban campus. Total enrollment: 9,973. 32% 25 or older. Core. Calendar: semesters. Academic remediation for entering students, ESL program, advanced placement, honors program, summer session for credit, part-time degree program, adult/continuing education programs, co-op programs.

Entrance Requirements: Open admission. Options: Common Application, early admission, deferred admission. Placement: THEA required. Entrance: noncompetitive. Application deadline: 8/1.

Collegiate Environment: Drama-theater group, student-run newspaper. Student services: health clinic, personal-psychological counseling. Campus security: 24-hour emergency response devices and patrols. College housing not available. Arnulfo L. Oliveira Library with 147,216 books, 710,820 microform titles, 4,447 serials, 1,000 audiovisual materials, an OPAC, and a Web page. 580 computers available on campus for general student use.

■ **TEXAS STATE TECHNICAL COLLEGE HARLINGEN** *Q-18*

1902 North Loop 499
Harlingen, TX 78550-3697
Tel: (956)364-4000
Admissions: (956)364-4100
Fax: (956)364-5140
Web Site: http://www.harlingen.tstc.edu/

Description: State-supported, 2-year, coed. Part of Texas State Technical College System. Awards certificates, transfer associate, and terminal associate degrees. Founded 1967. Setting: 125-acre small town campus. Research spending for 2004 fiscal year: $96,603. Educational spending for 2005 fiscal year: $4686 per student. Total enrollment: 4,028. 1,492 applied, 100% were admitted. Full-time: 1,729 students, 44% women, 56% men. Part-time: 2,299 students, 57% women, 43% men. Students come from 10 states and territories, 0.01% from out-of-state, 0.1% Native American, 85% Hispanic, 0.5% black, 0.3% Asian American or Pacific Islander, 4% international, 31% 25 or older, 8% live on campus, 12% transferred in. Core. Calendar: semesters. Academic remediation for entering students, ESL program, services for LD students, distance learning, double major, summer session for credit, part-time degree program, adult/continuing education programs, co-op programs and internships.

Entrance Requirements: Open admission except for dental hygiene, dental assistant, health information technology programs. Options: Common Application, early admission, deferred admission. Required: high school transcript. Placement: THEA required. SAT or ACT recommended. Entrance: noncompetitive. Application deadline: Rolling. Notification: continuous.

Collegiate Environment: Orientation program. Student-run newspaper. Most popular organizations: Student Congress, Vocational Industrial Clubs of America, Business Professionals of America. Major annual events: Oktoberfest, Miss TSTC Pageant, Techsan Day. Student services: health clinic, personal-psychological counseling, women's center. Campus security: 24-hour emergency response devices and patrols, late night transport-escort service, night watchman for housing area. Options: men-only, women-only housing available. Texas State Technical College Learning Resource Center with 25,000 books, 41 microform titles, 413 serials, an OPAC, and a Web page. Operations spending for 2004 fiscal year: $380,122. 250 computers available on campus for general student use. A campuswide network can be accessed. Staffed computer lab on campus.

■ **TEXAS STATE TECHNICAL COLLEGE-MARSHALL** *D-23*

2400 East End Blvd. S
Marshall, TX 75671
Tel: (903)935-1010
Web Site: http://www.marshall.tstc.edu
Description: State-supported, 2-year. Calendar: semesters.

■ **TEXAS STATE TECHNICAL COLLEGE WACO** *G-19*

3801 Campus Dr.
Waco, TX 76705-1695
Tel: (254)799-3611
Admissions: (254)867-2366
E-mail: dkhoury@tstc.edu
Web Site: http://waco.tstc.edu/

Description: State-supported, 2-year, coed. Part of Texas State Technical College System. Awards certificates, transfer associate, and terminal associate degrees. Founded 1965. Setting: 200-acre suburban campus. Total enrollment: 4,452. Student-undergrad faculty ratio is 16:1. 3,151 applied, 100% were admitted. Full-time: 2,989 students, 20% women, 80% men. Part-time: 1,463 students, 28% women, 72% men. Students come from 30 states and territories, 5 other countries, 2% from out-of-state, 0.4% Native American, 16% Hispanic, 16% black, 1% Asian American or Pacific Islander, 2% international, 18% 25 or older. Calendar: trimesters. Academic remediation for entering students, services for LD students, distance learning, summer session for credit, part-time degree program, adult/continuing education programs, co-op programs and internships.

Entrance Requirements: Open admission. Options: Common Application, electronic application, early admission. Required: high school transcript, ACCUPLACER. Required for some: interview. Entrance: noncompetitive. Application deadline: Rolling. Notification: continuous.

Costs Per Year: Application fee: $0. State resident tuition: $1950 full-time, $65 per credit hour part-time. Nonresident tuition: $5460 full-time, $182 per credit hour part-time. Mandatory fees: $2000 full-time, $21 per credit hour part-time. College room and board: $4100. College room only: $1860.

Collegiate Environment: Student-run newspaper. Social organizations: 25 open to all. Most popular organizations: Automotive VICA, Society of Mexican-American Engineers and Scientists, Texas Association of Black Persons In Higher Education, Phi Theta Kappa. Major annual events: DIA Techsana, Systems Olympics, Halloween Festival. Student services: health clinic, personal-psychological counseling, women's center. Campus security: 24-hour emergency response devices and patrols, late night transport-escort service, controlled dormitory access. On-campus residence required in freshman year. Options: coed, men-only, women-only housing available. Texas State Technical College-Waco Campus Library with 60,000 books, 791,104 microform titles, 400 serials, 2,324 audiovisual materials, an OPAC, and a Web page. 900 computers available on campus for general student use. A campuswide network can be accessed from student residence rooms. Staffed computer lab on campus.

■ **TEXAS STATE TECHNICAL COLLEGE WEST TEXAS** *E-13*
300 College Dr.
Sweetwater, TX 79556-4108
Tel: (915)235-7300
Free: 800-592-8784
Admissions: (915)235-7374
Fax: (915)235-7359
Web Site: http://www.sweetwater.tstc.edu/
Description: State-supported, 2-year, coed. Part of Texas State Technical College System. Awards certificates and terminal associate degrees. Founded 1970. Setting: 115-acre small town campus. Endowment: $50,000. Research spending for 2004 fiscal year: $149,343. Educational spending for 2005 fiscal year: $4260 per student. Total enrollment: 1,628. Students come from 5 states and territories, 2 other countries, 1% from out-of-state, 1% Native American, 24% Hispanic, 5% black, 0.5% Asian American or Pacific Islander, 0.1% international, 53% 25 or older, 29% live on campus. Core. Calendar: semesters. Academic remediation for entering students, services for LD students, advanced placement, distance learning, summer session for credit, part-time degree program, adult/continuing education programs, co-op programs and internships.
Entrance Requirements: Open admission. Options: early admission, deferred admission. Required: high school transcript, THEA. Entrance: noncompetitive. Application deadline: Rolling. Notification: continuous.
Collegiate Environment: Orientation program. Social organizations: 16 open to all. Most popular organizations: Student Government Association, Vocational Industrial Clubs of America, Mexican-American Student Club, Auto Tech 2000, Vocational Nursing Club. Major annual events: Techsan Day, Valentine's Dinner and Dance, Halloween Party. Student services: health clinic, personal-psychological counseling. Campus security: 24-hour patrols. College housing designed to accommodate 212 students; 213 undergraduates lived in college housing during 2003-04. Freshmen guaranteed college housing. Option: coed housing available. Texas State Technical College Library with 12,449 books, 36,467 microform titles, 6,102 serials, 102,316 audiovisual materials, an OPAC, and a Web page. Operations spending for 2004 fiscal year: $189,409. 500 computers available on campus for general student use. Computer purchase/lease plans available. A campuswide network can be accessed from student residence rooms and from off campus. Staffed computer lab on campus.

■ **TEXAS STATE UNIVERSITY-SAN MARCOS** *J-17*
601 University Dr.
San Marcos, TX 78666
Tel: (512)245-2111
Admissions: (512)245-2364
Fax: (512)245-8044
E-mail: admissions@txstate.edu
Web Site: http://www.txstate.edu/
Description: State-supported, university, coed. Part of Texas State University System. Awards bachelor's, master's, and doctoral degrees. Founded 1899. Setting: 423-acre suburban campus with easy access to San Antonio and Austin. Endowment: $37.5 million. Research spending for 2004 fiscal year: $9.1 million. Educational spending for 2005 fiscal year: $4302 per student. Total enrollment: 27,129. Faculty: 1,297 (775 full-time, 522 part-time). Student-undergrad faculty ratio is 24:1. 9,284 applied, 76% were admitted. 13% from top 10% of their high school class, 50% from top quarter, 94% from top half. 14 valedictorians. Full-time: 18,472 students, 55% women, 45% men. Part-time: 4,514 students, 57% women, 43% men. Students come from 46 states and territories, 55 other countries, 1% from out-of-state, 1% Native American, 20% Hispanic, 5% black, 2% Asian

American or Pacific Islander, 1% international, 18% 25 or older, 22% live on campus, 13% transferred in. Retention: 75% of full-time freshmen returned the following year. Academic areas with the most degrees conferred: business/marketing; parks and recreation; visual and performing arts. Core. Calendar: semesters. Academic remediation for entering students, ESL program, services for LD students, advanced placement, accelerated degree program, honors program, independent study, distance learning, double major, summer session for credit, part-time degree program, adult/continuing education programs, internships, graduate courses open to undergrads. Off campus study at The University of Texas at San Antonio, Austin Multi Institutional Teaching Center. Study abroad program. ROTC: Army, Air Force.
Entrance Requirements: Options: electronic application, early admission, deferred admission. Required: essay, high school transcript, SAT or ACT. Required for some: interview. Entrance: moderately difficult. Application deadline: 5/1. Notification: continuous.
Costs Per Year: Application fee: $40. State resident tuition: $3780 full-time, $126 per semester hour part-time. Nonresident tuition: $12,060 full-time, $402 per semester hour part-time. Mandatory fees: $1472 full-time, $37 per semester hour part-time, $267 per term part-time. Full-time tuition and fees vary according to course load. Part-time tuition and fees vary according to course load. College room and board: $5610. College room only: $3524. Room and board charges vary according to board plan and housing facility.
Collegiate Environment: Orientation program. Drama-theater group, choral group, marching band, student-run newspaper, radio station. Social organizations: 242 open to all; national fraternities, national sororities, local sororities; 5% of eligible men and 5% of eligible women are members. Most popular organizations: Non-traditional Students Association, Student Association for Campus Activities, Association Student Government. Major annual events: Homecoming, Springfest, Cricket Fest. Student services: legal services, health clinic, personal-psychological counseling. Campus security: 24-hour emergency response devices and patrols, late night transport-escort service, controlled dormitory access. 5,427 college housing spaces available; 5,185 were occupied in 2003-04. Freshmen guaranteed college housing. On-campus residence required through sophomore year. Options: coed, men-only, women-only housing available. Alkek Library with 1.3 million books, 1.9 million microform titles, 8,195 serials, 283,142 audiovisual materials, an OPAC, and a Web page. Operations spending for 2004 fiscal year: $4.1 million. 1,200 computers available on campus for general student use. Computer purchase/lease plans available. A campuswide network can be accessed from student residence rooms and from off campus. Staffed computer lab on campus.
Community Environment: The university is located in San Marcos, a historic community of 37,000 on I-35 located between San Antonio, 45 miles to the south, and Austin, 30 miles to the north. Both cities are within commuting distance of San Marcos and have major airports. San Marcos has a municipal airport. The central Texas climate offers sunshine most of the year with moderate to cool winters and warm to hot summers. The area enjoys a healthy economy bolstered by clean, light industry, active tourism, and well-preserved historic districts. It is the home to churches of many denominations and various civic organizations. Local recreation includes golfing, fishing, hunting, swimming,"tubing," canoeing and other outdoor activities. Annual celebrations include Chilympiad, Sights and Sounds of Christmas, Summerfest, Cinco de Mayo, and weekly summer concerts in the park.

■ **TEXAS TECH UNIVERSITY** *C-10*
Lubbock, TX 79409
Tel: (806)742-2011
Admissions: (806)742-1480
Fax: (806)742-3055
Web Site: http://www.ttu.edu/
Description: State-supported, university, coed. Part of Texas Tech University System. Awards bachelor's, master's, doctoral, and first professional degrees. Founded 1923. Setting: 1,839-acre urban campus. Endowment: $294.8 million. Research spending for 2004 fiscal year: $40.2 million. Educational spending for 2005 fiscal year: $6198 per student. Total enrollment: 28,001. Faculty: 1,123 (1,046 full-time, 77 part-time). Student-undergrad faculty ratio is 19:1. 12,583 applied, 71% were admitted. 22% from top 10% of their high school class, 55% from top quarter, 88% from top half. 9 National Merit Scholars, 79 valedictorians. Full-time: 20,821 students, 45% women, 55% men. Part-time: 2,181 students, 41% women, 59% men. Students come from 52 states and territories, 87 other countries, 4% from out-of-state, 1% Native American, 11% Hispanic, 3% black, 2% Asian American or Pacific Islander, 1% international, 7% 25 or older, 22% live on

campus, 9% transferred in. Retention: 84% of full-time freshmen returned the following year. Academic areas with the most degrees conferred: business/marketing; family and consumer sciences; engineering. Core. Calendar: semesters. Academic remediation for entering students, ESL program, services for LD students, advanced placement, accelerated degree program, self-designed majors, freshman honors college, honors program, independent study, distance learning, double major, summer session for credit, part-time degree program, external degree program, co-op programs and internships, graduate courses open to undergrads. Off campus study at South Plains College. Study abroad program. ROTC: Army, Air Force.

Entrance Requirements: Options: electronic application, early admission. Required: high school transcript, SAT or ACT. Required for some: essay. Entrance: moderately difficult. Application deadline: 5/1. Notification: continuous.

Costs Per Year: Application fee: $50. State resident tuition: $3870 full-time, $129 per credit hour part-time. Nonresident tuition: $12,150 full-time, $405 per credit hour part-time. Mandatory fees: $2282 full-time, $58.75 per credit hour part-time, $291. Full-time tuition and fees vary according to course load, program, and reciprocity agreements. Part-time tuition and fees vary according to course load, program, and reciprocity agreements. College room and board: $6875. College room only: $3663. Room and board charges vary according to board plan and housing facility.

Collegiate Environment: Orientation program. Drama-theater group, choral group, marching band, student-run newspaper, radio station. Social organizations: 459 open to all; national fraternities, national sororities, local fraternities, local sororities; 10% of eligible men and 14% of eligible women are members. Major annual events: homecoming, Carol of Lights, Spirit of Sharing. Student services: legal services, health clinic, personal-psychological counseling. Campus security: 24-hour emergency response devices and patrols, late night transport-escort service, controlled dormitory access. 6,354 college housing spaces available; 5,217 were occupied in 2003-04. Freshmen guaranteed college housing. On-campus residence required in freshman year. Options: coed, men-only, women-only housing available. Texas Tech Library plus 3 others with 2.4 million books, 222,858 microform titles, 30,823 serials, 85,969 audiovisual materials, an OPAC, and a Web page. Operations spending for 2004 fiscal year: $13.9 million. 3,000 computers available on campus for general student use. Computer purchase/lease plans available. A campuswide network can be accessed from student residence rooms and from off campus. Staffed computer lab on campus.

Community Environment: Lubbock, with a population of nearly 200,000, is located on top of the caprock on the South Plains of Texas. Its climate is excellent, with over 3,550 hours of sunshine every year. Summers are dry and not extremely hot, while winters are dry and moderate (average rainfall is only 18 inches). An average annual temperature of 60 degrees coupled with the average noon humidity of 46 percent combine to make Lubbock comfortable year-round. The city lies 320 miles west of Dallas, and an equal distance 320 miles south east of Albuquerque, New Mexico. Several airlines and an interstate bus line serve the city, as well as four U.S. highways, including an interstate highway.

■ **TEXAS WESLEYAN UNIVERSITY** *D-18*
1201 Wesleyan St.
Fort Worth, TX 76105-1536
Tel: (817)531-4444
Admissions: (817)531-4405
Fax: (817)531-7515
Web Site: http://www.txwesleyan.edu/

Description: Independent United Methodist, comprehensive, coed. Awards bachelor's, master's, and first professional degrees. Founded 1890. Setting: 74-acre urban campus. Endowment: $39.2 million. Research spending for 2004 fiscal year: $224,098. Educational spending for 2005 fiscal year: $6797 per student. Total enrollment: 2,742. 384 applied, 61% were admitted. Full-time: 974 students, 60% women, 40% men. Part-time: 517 students, 60% women, 40% men. Students come from 20 states and territories, 4% from out-of-state, 0.1% Native American, 14% Hispanic, 12% black, 2% Asian American or Pacific Islander, 3% international, 35% 25 or older, 10% live on campus, 15% transferred in. Retention: 67% of full-time freshmen returned the following year. Core. Calendar: semesters. Academic remediation for entering students, ESL program, services for LD students, advanced placement, distance learning, summer session for credit, part-time degree program, adult/continuing education programs, internships, graduate courses open to undergrads. Study abroad program. ROTC: Army (c), Air Force (c).

Entrance Requirements: Options: Peterson's Universal Application, Common Application, deferred admission, international baccalaureate accepted. Required: essay, high school transcript, minimum 2.5 high school GPA, SAT or ACT. Required for some: interview. Entrance: moderately difficult. Application deadline: Rolling. Notification: continuous.

Costs Per Year: Application fee: $25. Comprehensive fee: $19,500 includes full-time tuition ($12,950), mandatory fees ($1050), and college room and board ($5500). College room only: $1875. Full-time tuition and fees vary according to program. Room and board charges vary according to board plan and student level. Part-time tuition: $435 per credit. Part-time mandatory fees: $50 per credit. Part-time tuition and fees vary according to program.

Collegiate Environment: Orientation program. Drama-theater group, choral group, student-run newspaper. Social organizations: 57 open to all; national fraternities, national sororities, local fraternities, local sororities; 5% of eligible men and 5% of eligible women are members. Major annual events: Greek Week, Spring Musical, Reunion Weekend. Student services: health clinic, personal-psychological counseling. Campus security: 24-hour emergency response devices and patrols, student patrols, late night transport-escort service, controlled dormitory access. College housing designed to accommodate 375 students; 380 undergraduates lived in college housing during 2003-04. Options: coed, men-only, women-only housing available. Eunice and James L. West Library plus 1 other with 192,044 books, 883,274 microform titles, 632 serials, 5,302 audiovisual materials, and an OPAC. Operations spending for 2004 fiscal year: $2.5 million. 77 computers available on campus for general student use. A campuswide network can be accessed. Staffed computer lab on campus.

Community Environment: The campus is located in the Dallas/Fort Worth metropolitan area. Local public transportation is available in close proximity to the regional international airport, trains and buses. There are world-famous museums, cultural events, and professional football, basketball, baseball, and soccer teams in the area. The economy is widely diverse.

■ **TEXAS WOMAN'S UNIVERSITY** *C-19*
304 Administration Dr.
Denton, TX 76201
Tel: (940)898-2000; 888-948-9984
Admissions: (940)898-3040
Fax: (940)898-3198
Web Site: http://www.twu.edu/

Description: State-supported, university, coed. Awards bachelor's, master's, and doctoral degrees and post-master's certificates. Founded 1901. Setting: 270-acre suburban campus with easy access to Dallas-Fort Worth. Endowment: $8.1 million. Research spending for 2004 fiscal year: $2.6 million. Educational spending for 2005 fiscal year: $4715 per student. Total enrollment: 11,344. Faculty: 692 (426 full-time, 266 part-time). Student-undergrad faculty ratio is 15:1. 2,796 applied, 64% were admitted. 17% from top 10% of their high school class, 31% from top quarter, 76% from top half. 17 valedictorians. Full-time: 4,554 students, 94% women, 6% men. Part-time: 1,712 students, 92% women, 8% men. Students come from 19 states and territories, 47 other countries, 1% from out-of-state, 1% Native American, 14% Hispanic, 21% black, 6% Asian American or Pacific Islander, 3% international, 38% 25 or older, 25% live on campus, 13% transferred in. Retention: 75% of full-time freshmen returned the following year. Academic areas with the most degrees conferred: health professions and related sciences; interdisciplinary studies; business/marketing. Core. Calendar: semesters. Academic remediation for entering students, services for LD students, advanced placement, accelerated degree program, honors program, independent study, distance learning, double major, summer session for credit, part-time degree program, adult/continuing education programs, co-op programs and internships, graduate courses open to undergrads. Off campus study at Federation of North Texas Area Universities. Study abroad program. ROTC: Army (c), Air Force (c).

Entrance Requirements: Options: electronic application, early admission, deferred admission. Required: high school transcript, minimum 2.0 high school GPA, SAT or ACT. Entrance: minimally difficult. Application deadline: 7/15. Notification: continuous until 8/15.

Costs Per Year: Application fee: $30. State resident tuition: $3690 full-time, $123 per hour part-time. Nonresident tuition: $11,970 full-time, $399 per hour part-time. Mandatory fees: $1320 full-time. College room and board: $5598. College room only: $2804.

Collegiate Environment: Orientation program. Drama-theater group, choral group, student-run newspaper. Social organizations: 100 open to all; national sororities, local sororities; 6% of women are members. Most popular organizations: Campus Activities Board, Helping Hands, Gandsys, Trailblazers, Delta Phi Delta. Major annual events: Fiesta, parent and family days, Old Time Picnic. Student services: health clinic, personal-psychological counseling. Campus security: 24-hour emergency response devices and patrols, late night transport-escort service, controlled dormitory access. 1,477 college housing spaces available; 1,437 were occupied in 2003-04. Freshmen guaranteed college housing. On-campus residence required through sophomore year. Options: coed, women-only housing available. Blagg-Huey Library with 572,500 books, 1.6 million microform titles, 2,537 serials, 24,562 audiovisual materials, an OPAC, and a Web page. Operations spending for 2004 fiscal year: $2.9 million. 700 computers available on campus for general student use. A campuswide network can be accessed from student residence rooms and from off campus. Staffed computer lab on campus.

■ **TOMBALL COLLEGE** *I-21*
30555 Tomball Parkway
Tomball, TX 77375-4036
Tel: (281)351-3300
Admissions: (281)351-3334
Fax: (281)351-3384
E-mail: tc.advisors@nhmccd.edu
Web Site: http://wwwtc.nhmccd.edu/

Description: State and locally supported, 2-year, coed. Part of North Harris Montgomery Community College District. Awards certificates, transfer associate, and terminal associate degrees. Founded 1988. Setting: 210-acre suburban campus with easy access to Houston. Total enrollment: 7,647. Student-undergrad faculty ratio is 8:1. Full-time: 1,463 students, 52% women, 48% men. Part-time: 6,184 students, 62% women, 38% men. 1% from out-of-state, 0.4% Native American, 13% Hispanic, 7% black, 5% Asian American or Pacific Islander, 3% international, 32% 25 or older, 6% transferred in. Core. Calendar: semesters. Academic remediation for entering students, ESL program, services for LD students, advanced placement, honors program, summer session for credit, part-time degree program, adult/continuing education programs, co-op programs and internships.
Entrance Requirements: Open admission. Options: Common Application, early admission. Recommended: SAT or ACT, THEA, ACT COMPASS. Entrance: noncompetitive.
Costs Per Year: Application fee: $0. Area resident tuition: $1080 full-time, $56 per credit hour part-time. State resident tuition: $2040 full-time, $96 per credit hour part-time. Nonresident tuition: $2400 full-time, $220 per credit hour part-time.
Collegiate Environment: Orientation program. Drama-theater group, student-run newspaper. Social organizations: 15 open to all. Most popular organizations: Phi Theta Kappa, Culture Club, Veterinary Technicians Student Organization, Human Services Club, Student Nurses Association. Major annual events: We Cater to Students, Bluebonnet DAZE, Lighting of the Commons. Student services: personal-psychological counseling. Campus security: 24-hour emergency response devices, late night transport-escort service, trained security personnel during open hours. College housing not available. Learning Resource Center with 24,063 books, 385 serials, an OPAC, and a Web page. 92 computers available on campus for general student use. A campuswide network can be accessed from off-campus. Staffed computer lab on campus.

■ **TRINITY UNIVERSITY** *K-16*
One Trinity Place
San Antonio, TX 78212-7200
Tel: (210)999-7011
Free: 800-TRI-NITY
Admissions: (210)999-7207
Fax: (210)999-8164
Web Site: http://www.trinity.edu/

Description: Independent, comprehensive, coed, affiliated with Presbyterian Church. Awards bachelor's and master's degrees. Founded 1869. Setting: 113-acre urban campus. Endowment: $733.3 million. Research spending for 2004 fiscal year: $1.4 million. Educational spending for 2005 fiscal year: $17,609 per student. Total enrollment: 2,756. Faculty: 280 (219 full-time, 61 part-time). Student-undergrad faculty ratio is 10:1. 3,864 applied, 63% were admitted. 47% from top 10% of their high school class, 81% from top quarter, 98% from top half. 16 National Merit Scholars. Full-time: 2,485 students, 54% women, 46% men. Part-time: 39 students, 51% women, 49% men. Students come from 49 states and territories, 49 other countries, 28% from out-of-state, 1% Native American, 11% Hispanic, 3% black, 6% Asian American or Pacific Islander, 3% international, 1% 25 or older, 77% live on

campus, 1% transferred in. Retention: 89% of full-time freshmen returned the following year. Academic areas with the most degrees conferred: health professions and related sciences; social sciences; foreign languages and literature. Core. Calendar: semesters. Services for LD students, advanced placement, accelerated degree program, honors program, independent study, double major, summer session for credit, part-time degree program, internships. Study abroad program. ROTC: Air Force (c).
Entrance Requirements: Options: Peterson's Universal Application, Common Application, electronic application, early decision, early action, deferred admission, international baccalaureate accepted. Required: essay, high school transcript, 2 recommendations, SAT or ACT. Recommended: interview. Entrance: very difficult. Application deadlines: 2/1, 11/1 for early decision, 11/1 for early action. Notification: 4/1, 12/15 for early decision, 12/15 for early action.
Costs Per Year: Application fee: $50. Comprehensive fee: $30,307 includes full-time tuition ($21,432), mandatory fees ($150), and college room and board ($8725). College room only: $5815. Full-time tuition and fees vary according to course load. Room and board charges vary according to board plan. Part-time tuition: $893 per semester hour. Part-time tuition varies according to course load.
Collegiate Environment: Orientation program. Drama-theater group, choral group, student-run newspaper, radio station. Social organizations: local fraternities, local sororities; 26% of eligible men and 28% of eligible women are members. Most popular organizations: Voluntary Action Center, Alpha Phi Omega, Association of Student Representatives, Activities Council, Multicultural Network. Major annual events: homecoming, Trinity Night at the San Antonio Spurs game, Tower Party. Student services: health clinic, personal-psychological counseling. Campus security: 24-hour emergency response devices and patrols, late night transport-escort service, controlled dormitory access. On-campus residence required through junior year. Option: coed housing available. Elizabeth Huth Coates Library with 917,781 books, 298,508 microform titles, 2,188 serials, 25,862 audiovisual materials, an OPAC, and a Web page. Operations spending for 2004 fiscal year: $3266. 450 computers available on campus for general student use. A campuswide network can be accessed from student residence rooms and from off campus. Staffed computer lab on campus.
Community Environment: San Antonio, population of more than one million, is the 8th largest city in the United States and is rich in history. It has a healthy economy and supports many cultural, and recreational activities. An international airport provides wide access.

■ **TRINITY VALLEY COMMUNITY COLLEGE** *E-21*
100 Cardinal Dr.
Athens, TX 75751-2765
Tel: (903)677-TVCC
Admissions: (903)675-6209
E-mail: tvccinfo@tvcc.edu
Web Site: http://www.tvcc.edu/

Description: State and locally supported, 2-year, coed. Awards certificates, diplomas, transfer associate, and terminal associate degrees. Founded 1946. Setting: 65-acre small town campus with easy access to Dallas-Fort Worth. Endowment: $1.9 million. Educational spending for 2005 fiscal year: $3334 per student. Total enrollment: 5,821. Student-undergrad faculty ratio is 20:1. Full-time: 2,442 students, 61% women, 39% men. Part-time: 3,379 students, 53% women, 47% men. Students come from 48 states and territories, 1% from out-of-state, 0.3% Native American, 6% Hispanic, 13% black, 0.3% Asian American or Pacific Islander, 1% international, 48% 25 or older. Core. Calendar: semesters. Academic remediation for entering students, services for LD students, advanced placement, honors program, distance learning, summer session for credit, part-time degree program, adult/continuing education programs, co-op programs and internships.
Entrance Requirements: Open admission. Option: early admission. Required: high school transcript. Entrance: noncompetitive. Application deadline: Rolling. Notification: continuous.
Costs Per Year: State resident tuition: $1200 full-time, $20 per semester hour part-time. Nonresident tuition: $3900 full-time, $65 per semester hour part-time. Mandatory fees: $900 full-time, $15 per semester hour part-time. College room and board: $3470.
Collegiate Environment: Orientation program. Drama-theater group, choral group, marching band, student-run newspaper. Most popular organizations: Student Senate, Phi Theta Kappa, Delta Epsilon Chi. Major annual events: Homecoming, Cardinal Beauty Pageant, Cardette Spring Show. Student services: personal-psychological counseling. Campus security: 24-hour emergency response devices and patrols, controlled dormitory access. 300

college housing spaces available; 225 were occupied in 2003-04. Options: coed, men-only, women-only housing available. Ginger Murchison Learning Resource Center plus 3 others with 54,940 books, 7,051 microform titles, 257 serials, 1,954 audiovisual materials, an OPAC, and a Web page. Operations spending for 2004 fiscal year: $534,420. 66 computers available on campus for general student use. A campuswide network can be accessed. Staffed computer lab on campus.

Community Environment: Population 10,680, Athens is a rural community located approximately 70 miles from Dallas. The climate is unusually mild and dry. The average high temperature is 95 degrees, and the low temperature range is 18 to 30 degrees, with an annual rainfall of 25 inches. Airport facilities, bus lines, and six major highways provide transportation for the city. There is a hospital, libraries, churches of various denominations, and various civic and fraternal organizations. Recreation includes theaters, drive-ins, hunting, fishing, golf, boating, tennis, parks, and swimming pools. Part-time employment is available.

■ **TYLER JUNIOR COLLEGE** *E-22*
PO Box 9020
Tyler, TX 75711-9020
Tel: (903)510-2200
Free: 800-687-5680
Admissions: (903)510-2399
Web Site: http://www.tjc.edu/

Description: State and locally supported, 2-year, coed. Awards certificates, transfer associate, and terminal associate degrees. Founded 1926. Setting: 85-acre suburban campus. Total enrollment: 9,591. 10% from top 10% of their high school class, 50% from top half. 22 valedictorians. Students come from 30 states and territories, 25 other countries, 1% from out-of-state, 1% Native American, 8% Hispanic, 19% black, 1% Asian American or Pacific Islander, 1% international, 50% 25 or older, 8% live on campus. Core. Calendar: semesters. Academic remediation for entering students, ESL program, services for LD students, advanced placement, accelerated degree program, freshman honors college, honors program, distance learning, summer session for credit, part-time degree program, adult/continuing education programs.

Entrance Requirements: Open admission. Options: Common Application, early admission, international baccalaureate accepted. Required: high school transcript. Placement: THEA required. Entrance: noncompetitive. Application deadline: Rolling. Preference given to district residents.

Collegiate Environment: Orientation program. Drama-theater group, choral group, marching band, student-run newspaper. Social organizations: national fraternities, national sororities, local fraternities, local sororities; 5% of eligible men and 5% of eligible women are members. Most popular organizations: student government, religious affiliation clubs, Phi Theta Kappa. Major annual events: Homecoming, Annual Career Day, Fall Preview. Student services: health clinic, personal-psychological counseling. Campus security: 24-hour patrols, controlled dormitory access. Options: men-only, women-only housing available. Vaughn Library and Learning Resource Center with 2,668 microform titles, 569 serials, 64,776 audiovisual materials, and an OPAC. 60 computers available on campus for general student use. A campuswide network can be accessed. Staffed computer lab on campus.

Community Environment: Tyler, population 80,454, was incorporated in 1846 and named for President John Tyler who was responsible for bringing Texas into the Union. Industry is varied with production of fieldgrown rose bushes for shipment throughout the United States, an economic mainstay. Located in the Pine region of East Texas, the community is reached by rail, bus, and air, as well as eight major highways. Community facilities include a symphony orchestra, a library system, hospitals, and medical facilities with Tyler being the medical center for East Texas. Local recreation includes golf courses, parks, and nearby Tyler State Park and Lake Tyler. Part-time employment is available.

■ **UNIVERSAL TECHNICAL INSTITUTE** *J-22*
721 Lockhaven Dr.
Houston, TX 77073-5598
Tel: (281)443-6262
Web Site: http://www.uticorp.com/

Description: Private, 2-year. Awards diplomas, transfer associate, and terminal associate degrees. Total enrollment: 1,400. 15% 25 or older.

■ **UNIVERSITY OF DALLAS** *G-33*
1845 East Northgate Dr.
Irving, TX 75062-4736

Tel: (972)721-5000
Free: 800-628-6999
Admissions: (972)721-5266
Fax: (972)721-5017
Web Site: http://www.udallas.edu/

Description: Independent Roman Catholic, university, coed. Awards bachelor's, master's, and doctoral degrees and post-master's certificates. Founded 1955. Setting: 750-acre suburban campus with easy access to Dallas-Fort Worth. Endowment: $42.8 million. Research spending for 2004 fiscal year: $69,836. Educational spending for 2005 fiscal year: $7362 per student. Total enrollment: 3,021. Faculty: 221 (116 full-time, 105 part-time). Student-undergrad faculty ratio is 12:1. 817 applied, 81% were admitted. 31% from top 10% of their high school class, 55% from top quarter, 78% from top half. 6 National Merit Scholars, 6 valedictorians. Full-time: 1,070 students, 58% women, 42% men. Part-time: 96 students, 40% women, 60% men. Students come from 46 states and territories, 13 other countries, 44% from out-of-state, 0.4% Native American, 16% Hispanic, 1% black, 5% Asian American or Pacific Islander, 1% international, 2% 25 or older, 61% live on campus, 4% transferred in. Retention: 85% of full-time freshmen returned the following year. Academic areas with the most degrees conferred: social sciences; English; biological/life sciences. Core. Calendar: semesters. ESL program, services for LD students, advanced placement, accelerated degree program, self-designed majors, independent study, double major, summer session for credit, part-time degree program, internships, graduate courses open to undergrads. Off campus study. Study abroad program. ROTC: Army (c), Air Force (c).

Entrance Requirements: Options: Peterson's Universal Application, Common Application, electronic application, early admission, early action, deferred admission, international baccalaureate accepted. Required: essay, high school transcript, 2 recommendations, SAT or ACT. Recommended: interview. Required for some: interview. Entrance: moderately difficult. Application deadlines: 8/1, 11/1 for early action. Notification: continuous, 1/15 for early action.

Costs Per Year: Application fee: $40. Comprehensive fee: $29,137 includes full-time tuition ($20,780), mandatory fees ($1025), and college room and board ($7332). College room only: $4116. Part-time tuition: $900 per credit hour. Part-time mandatory fees: $1025 per year.

Collegiate Environment: Orientation program. Drama-theater group, choral group, student-run newspaper, radio station. Social organizations: 42 open to all. Most popular organizations: SPUD (Programming Board), Residence Hall Association, student government, Best Buddies, Alpha Phi Omega. Major annual events: Charity Week, Groundhog, Mallapalooza. Student services: health clinic, personal-psychological counseling. Campus security: 24-hour emergency response devices and patrols, late night transport-escort service, controlled dormitory access. 740 college housing spaces available; 650 were occupied in 2003-04. Freshmen guaranteed college housing. On-campus residence required through junior year. Options: coed, men-only, women-only housing available. William A. Blakley Library with 223,350 books, 75,554 microform titles, 583 serials, 1,636 audiovisual materials, an OPAC, and a Web page. Operations spending for 2004 fiscal year: $1.1 million. 125 computers available on campus for general student use. Computer purchase/lease plans available. A campuswide network can be accessed from student residence rooms and from off campus. Staffed computer lab on campus.

Community Environment: Population 150,000. Irving is a suburb of Dallas. The community enjoys a temperate climate. Transportation facilities in the community include a railroad, bus lines, excellent highways, and air lines at nearby Dallas and Fort Worth airports. The city has a public library, YMCA, many churches of various faiths, and hospital facilities. Some part-time employment is available. Local recreation includes four theaters, water sports on nearby lakes, and athletic facilities of neighboring communities. There are major civic, fraternal and veteran's organizations active in the area. The Dallas-Ft. Worth area has a population of nearly 3,000,000.

■ **UNIVERSITY OF HOUSTON** *J-22*
4800 Calhoun Rd.
Houston, TX 77204
Tel: (713)743-1000
Admissions: (713)743-7542
Fax: (713)743-9633
E-mail: admissions@uh.edu
Web Site: http://www.uh.edu/

Description: State-supported, university, coed. Part of University of Houston System. Awards bachelor's, master's, doctoral, and first professional degrees. Founded 1927. Setting: 550-acre urban campus. Endowment: $417.1 million. Research spending for 2004 fiscal year: $71.9 million. Educational spending for 2005 fiscal year: $5454 per student. Total enrollment: 35,344. Faculty: 1,645 (1,218 full-time, 427 part-time). Student-undergrad faculty ratio is 21:1. 8,875 applied, 80% were admitted. 21% from top 10% of their high school class, 50% from top quarter, 80% from top half. Full-time: 19,866 students, 53% women, 47% men. Part-time: 8,320 students, 51% women, 49% men. Students come from 52 states and territories, 130 other countries, 2% from out-of-state, 0.4% Native American, 21% Hispanic, 16% black, 21% Asian American or Pacific Islander, 5% international, 21% 25 or older, 10% live on campus, 10% transferred in. Retention: 78% of full-time freshmen returned the following year. Academic areas with the most degrees conferred: business/marketing; psychology; social sciences. Core. Calendar: semesters. Academic remediation for entering students, ESL program, services for LD students, advanced placement, accelerated degree program, freshman honors college, honors program, independent study, distance learning, double major, summer session for credit, part-time degree program, adult/continuing education programs, co-op programs and internships, graduate courses open to undergrads. Off campus study at University of Texas, Baylor College of Medicine, University of St. Thomas, Rice University, Texas Southern University, Houston Baptist University. Study abroad program. ROTC: Army, Naval (c).

Entrance Requirements: Options: Common Application, electronic application, early admission, deferred admission. Required: high school transcript, minimum 2.0 high school GPA, SAT or ACT. Recommended: recommendations, SAT Subject Tests. Entrance: moderately difficult. Application deadline: 4/1. Notification: continuous.

Costs Per Year: Application fee: $50. State resident tuition: $3920 full-time, $131 per credit hour part-time. Nonresident tuition: $12,200 full-time, $407 per credit hour part-time. Mandatory fees: $2566 full-time. Full-time tuition and fees vary according to course level, course load, degree level, location, program, reciprocity agreements, and student level. Part-time tuition varies according to course level, course load, degree level, location, program, reciprocity agreements, and student level. College room and board: $6058. College room only: $3492. Room and board charges vary according to board plan and housing facility.

Collegiate Environment: Orientation program. Drama-theater group, choral group, marching band, student-run newspaper, radio station. Social organizations: 300 open to all; national fraternities, national sororities; 34% of eligible men and 36% of eligible women are members. Most popular organizations: Council of Ethnic Organizations, Frontier Fiesta Association, intramural sports, Golden Key National Honor Society. Major annual events: Homecoming, International Student Organization Food Festival, Frontier Fiesta. Student services: legal services, health clinic, personal-psychological counseling, women's center. Campus security: 24-hour emergency response devices and patrols, student patrols, late night transport-escort service, controlled dormitory access, vehicle assistance. No special consideration for freshman housing applicants. Option: coed housing available. M.D. Anderson Library plus 5 others with 2.2 million books, 4.4 million microform titles, 22,052 serials, 10,059 audiovisual materials, an OPAC, and a Web page. Operations spending for 2004 fiscal year: $15.1 million. 825 computers available on campus for general student use. A campuswide network can be accessed from student residence rooms and from off campus. Staffed computer lab on campus.

Community Environment: Population 1,630,533. Although Houston lies 50 miles inland, it is a major seaport due to the conversion of Buffalo Bayou into the Houston Ship Channel. The city was named in honor of Sam Houston, hero of the Battle of San Jacinto. The community has excellent air, bus, and railroad facilities. Many points of interest in the city include L. B. Johnson Manned Spacecraft Center, Texas Medical Center, Jones Hall, Wortham Theatre, Enron Baseball Field, Burke Barker Planetarium, Museum of Fine Arts, Contemporary Arts Museum, Zoological Gardens, and the San Jacinto Battleground and Monument, the Astrodome and Battleship U.S.S. Texas. There are over one thousand churches representing all the major denominations, excellent medical facilities, ample shopping centers, and good student housing in the area. Full- and part-time employment is available.

■ **UNIVERSITY OF HOUSTON-CLEAR LAKE** *J-22*
2700 Bay Area Blvd.
Houston, TX 77058-1098
Tel: (281)283-7600
Admissions: (281)283-2518
Fax: (281)283-2530
E-mail: admissions@cl.uh.edu

Web Site: http://www.uhcl.edu/

Description: State-supported, upper-level, coed. Part of University of Houston System. Awards bachelor's and master's degrees. Founded 1971. Setting: 487-acre suburban campus. Endowment: $10.6 million. Research spending for 2004 fiscal year: $1.6 million. Educational spending for 2005 fiscal year: $6063 per student. Total enrollment: 7,853. Faculty: 524 (230 full-time, 294 part-time). Student-undergrad faculty ratio is 18:1. 1,957 applied, 64% were admitted. Full-time: 2,096 students, 69% women, 31% men. Part-time: 2,055 students, 67% women, 33% men. Students come from 16 states and territories, 84 other countries, 1% from out-of-state, 0.4% Native American, 17% Hispanic, 7% black, 6% Asian American or Pacific Islander, 1% international, 54% 25 or older, 3% live on campus, 88% transferred in. Academic areas with the most degrees conferred: business/marketing; interdisciplinary studies; psychology. Core. Calendar: semesters. ESL program, services for LD students, accelerated degree program, self-designed majors, independent study, distance learning, double major, summer session for credit, part-time degree program, co-op programs and internships, graduate courses open to undergrads.

Costs Per Year: Application fee: $35. State resident tuition: $2010 full-time, $120 per credit hour part-time. Nonresident tuition: $10,952 full-time, $326 per credit hour part-time. Mandatory fees: $2643 full-time, $986 per term part-time.

Collegiate Environment: Orientation program. Student-run newspaper. Social organizations: 70 open to all. Most popular organizations: Beta Alpha Psi, The Indian Student Association, The Management Association, Texas Student Education Association, Accounting Association. Major annual events: Student Life Fair, Chili Cook-Off, International Festival. Student services: health clinic, personal-psychological counseling, women's center. Campus security: 24-hour emergency response devices and patrols, late night transport-escort service. 288 college housing spaces available. Neumann Library with 650,000 books, 1.9 million microform titles, 984 serials, 795 audiovisual materials, and an OPAC. Operations spending for 2004 fiscal year: $2.5 million. 383 computers available on campus for general student use. A campuswide network can be accessed from off-campus. Staffed computer lab on campus.

Community Environment: A planned community 20 miles south of Houston, and 35 miles from Galveston, Texas. Mixture of education and space related employers. Many cultural activities available, both in the Clear Lake area, and within easy access of Houston. Abundance of outdoor recreational opportunities.

■ **UNIVERSITY OF HOUSTON-DOWNTOWN** *J-22*
One Main St.
Houston, TX 77002-1001
Tel: (713)221-8000
Admissions: (713)221-5337
Fax: (713)221-8157
E-mail: uhdadmit@dt.uh.edu
Web Site: http://www.uhd.edu/

Description: State-supported, comprehensive, coed. Part of University of Houston System. Awards bachelor's and master's degrees. Founded 1974. Setting: 20-acre urban campus. Endowment: $14.3 million. Research spending for 2004 fiscal year: $669,019. Educational spending for 2005 fiscal year: $2622 per student. Total enrollment: 11,484. Faculty: 573 (277 full-time, 296 part-time). Student-undergrad faculty ratio is 22:1. 1,754 applied, 98% were admitted. Full-time: 5,904 students, 59% women, 41% men. Part-time: 5,455 students, 59% women, 41% men. Students come from 17 states and territories, 76 other countries, 1% from out-of-state, 0.2% Native American, 37% Hispanic, 26% black, 10% Asian American or Pacific Islander, 4% international, 49% 25 or older, 12% transferred in. Retention: 61% of full-time freshmen returned the following year. Academic areas with the most degrees conferred: business/marketing; liberal arts/general studies; interdisciplinary studies; psychology; security and protective services. Core. Calendar: semesters. Academic remediation for entering students, ESL program, services for LD students, advanced placement, accelerated degree program, self-designed majors, honors program, independent study, distance learning, double major, summer session for credit, part-time degree program, adult/continuing education programs, co-op programs and internships. Off campus study. Study abroad program. ROTC: Army (c).

Entrance Requirements: Open admission. Options: Peterson's Universal Application, Common Application, electronic application, deferred admission, international baccalaureate accepted. Required: high school transcript. Entrance: noncompetitive. Application deadline: 7/1. Notification: continuous until 8/15.

Costs Per Year: Application fee: $25. State resident tuition: $3525 full-time. Nonresident tuition: $11,805 full-time. Mandatory fees: $694 full-time.

Collegiate Environment: Orientation program. Drama-theater group, student-run newspaper. Social organizations: 50 open to all; national fraternities, national sororities. Most popular organizations: Latin American Student Services Organization, Chinese Student Association, Indo-Pakistan Student Association, Professional Accounting Society, Student Government Association. Major annual events: One Main Event, Cross Roads, Culture on the Bayou. Student services: health clinic, personal-psychological counseling. Campus security: 24-hour emergency response devices and patrols, late night transport-escort service. College housing not available. W. I. Dykes Library with an OPAC and a Web page. Operations spending for 2004 fiscal year: $1.8 million. 1,200 computers available on campus for general student use. A campuswide network can be accessed from off-campus. Staffed computer lab on campus.

■ **UNIVERSITY OF HOUSTON-VICTORIA** *L-19*

3007 North Ben Wilson St.
Victoria, TX 77901-4450
Tel: (361)570-4848; 877-970-4848
Admissions: (361)570-4110
Fax: (361)572-9377
Web Site: http://www.vic.uh.edu/

Description: State-supported, upper-level, coed. Part of University of Houston System. Awards bachelor's and master's degrees and post-master's certificates. Founded 1973. Setting: 20-acre small town campus. Endowment: $4.3 million. Total enrollment: 2,491. Faculty: 130 (74 full-time, 56 part-time). Student-undergrad faculty ratio is 16:1. Full-time: 460 students, 78% women, 22% men. Part-time: 769 students, 72% women, 28% men. 0% from out-of-state, 1% Native American, 23% Hispanic, 7% black, 3% Asian American or Pacific Islander, 0.4% international, 62% 25 or older, 23% transferred in. Core. Calendar: semesters. Services for LD students, independent study, distance learning, double major, summer session for credit, part-time degree program, external degree program, adult/continuing education programs, internships, graduate courses open to undergrads. Off campus study. Study abroad program.

Costs Per Year: State resident tuition: $150 per semester hour part-time. Nonresident tuition: $426 per semester hour part-time.

Collegiate Environment: Orientation program. Student-run newspaper. Most popular organization: Texas Student Education Association. Major annual events: Mexican-American University Day, Annual Scholarship Reception, Annual Award Banquet. Campus security: 24-hour emergency response devices and patrols. College housing not available. VC/UHV Library plus 1 other with 227,800 books, 528,423 microform titles, 10,652 serials, 7,553 audiovisual materials, an OPAC, and a Web page. 150 computers available on campus for general student use. A campuswide network can be accessed from off-campus. Staffed computer lab on campus.

Community Environment: The campus is located in Victoria, a city of 58,000 inhabitants at the center of the South Texas Crossroads in the heart of the Golden Gulf Coast. This expanding city on the banks of the Guadalupe River is more than 150 years old, and is one of the first three towns chartered by The Republic of Texas. The city is near the Gulf of Mexico and is a popular coastal route between Houston and Mexico. The home of many petrochemical companies, such as DuPont, Alcoa, and Union Carbide, it is surrounded by vast expanses of ranchland.

■ **UNIVERSITY OF THE INCARNATE WORD** *K-16*

4301 Broadway
San Antonio, TX 78209-6397
Tel: (210)829-6000
Free: 800-749-WORD
Admissions: (210)829-6005
Fax: (210)829-3921
E-mail: admis@uiwtx.edu
Web Site: http://www.uiw.edu/

Description: Independent Roman Catholic, comprehensive, coed. Awards associate, bachelor's, master's, doctoral, and first professional degrees. Founded 1881. Setting: 200-acre urban campus. Endowment: $33.3 million. Research spending for 2004 fiscal year: $177,768. Educational spending for 2005 fiscal year: $5833 per student. Total enrollment: 5,217. Faculty: 444 (160 full-time, 284 part-time). Student-undergrad faculty ratio is 14:1. 2,070 applied, 75% were admitted. 17% from top 10% of their high school class, 42% from top quarter, 72% from top half. Full-time: 2,597 students, 68% women, 32% men. Part-time: 1,773 students, 63% women, 37% men.

Students come from 29 states and territories, 23 other countries, 2% from out-of-state, 1% Native American, 56% Hispanic, 7% black, 2% Asian American or Pacific Islander, 3% international, 35% 25 or older, 20% live on campus, 14% transferred in. Retention: 70% of full-time freshmen returned the following year. Academic areas with the most degrees conferred: business/marketing; health professions and related sciences; liberal arts/general studies. Core. Calendar: semesters. Academic remediation for entering students, ESL program, services for LD students, advanced placement, accelerated degree program, independent study, double major, summer session for credit, part-time degree program, external degree program, adult/continuing education programs, internships, graduate courses open to undergrads. Off campus study at Our Lady of the Lake University of San Antonio, St. Mary's University of San Antonio, Oblate School of Theology. Study abroad program. ROTC: Army (c), Air Force (c).

Entrance Requirements: Options: Peterson's Universal Application, electronic application, early admission, deferred admission. Required: high school transcript, SAT or ACT. Recommended: minimum 2.0 high school GPA, 1 recommendation. Required for some: essay, interview. Entrance: moderately difficult. Application deadline: Rolling.

Costs Per Year: Application fee: $20. One-time mandatory fee: $1500. Comprehensive fee: $24,747 includes full-time tuition ($17,400), mandatory fees ($872), and college room and board ($6475). College room only: $3800. Part-time tuition: $555 per semester hour. Part-time mandatory fees: $300 per term.

Collegiate Environment: Orientation program. Drama-theater group, choral group, student-run newspaper, radio station. Social organizations: 27 open to all; national fraternities, national sororities, local sororities; 2% of eligible men and 2% of eligible women are members. Most popular organizations: Alpha Phi Omega, Business Club, Red Alert Dance Team, cheerleading, Black Student Association. Major annual events: Golden Harvest Food Drive, Light the Way, First Francis Sport Pep Rally. Student services: health clinic, personal-psychological counseling. Campus security: 24-hour emergency response devices and patrols, late night transport-escort service, controlled dormitory access. 800 college housing spaces available; 654 were occupied in 2003-04. Freshmen given priority for college housing. Options: coed, men-only, women-only housing available. J.E. and L.E. Mabee Library plus 1 other with 257,651 books, 273,017 microform titles, 19,100 serials, 12,457 audiovisual materials, an OPAC, and a Web page. Operations spending for 2004 fiscal year: $1.3 million. 200 computers available on campus for general student use. Computer purchase/lease plans available. A campuswide network can be accessed from student residence rooms and from off campus. Staffed computer lab on campus.

Community Environment: See San Antonio College.

■ **UNIVERSITY OF MARY HARDIN-BAYLOR** *G-18*

900 College St.
Belton, TX 76513
Tel: (254)295-8642
Free: 800-727-8642
Admissions: (254)295-4520
Fax: (254)295-4535
E-mail: admissions@umhb.edu
Web Site: http://www.umhb.edu/

Description: Independent Southern Baptist, comprehensive, coed. Awards bachelor's and master's degrees. Founded 1845. Setting: 100-acre small town campus with easy access to Austin. Endowment: $49.4 million. Educational spending for 2005 fiscal year: $3833 per student. Total enrollment: 2,727. Faculty: 227 (133 full-time, 94 part-time). Student-undergrad faculty ratio is 14:1. 1,261 applied, 75% were admitted. 19% from top 10% of their high school class, 46% from top quarter, 79% from top half. Full-time: 2,270 students, 63% women, 37% men. Part-time: 321 students, 68% women, 32% men. Students come from 26 states and territories, 9 other countries, 1% from out-of-state, 0.5% Native American, 11% Hispanic, 11% black, 1% Asian American or Pacific Islander, 1% international, 21% 25 or older, 48% live on campus, 13% transferred in. Retention: 71% of full-time freshmen returned the following year. Academic areas with the most degrees conferred: education; health professions and related sciences; business/marketing. Core. Calendar: semesters. Academic remediation for entering students, ESL program, services for LD students, advanced placement, accelerated degree program, honors program, independent study, distance learning, double major, summer session for credit, part-time degree program, adult/continuing education programs, internships, graduate courses open to undergrads. ROTC: Air Force (c).

Entrance Requirements: Options: Common Application, electronic application, early admission, deferred admission. Required: high school transcript,

SAT or ACT. Required for some: essay, recommendations, interview. Entrance: moderately difficult. Application deadline: Rolling. Notification: continuous.

Costs Per Year: Application fee: $35. Comprehensive fee: $19,910 includes full-time tuition ($14,250), mandatory fees ($1460), and college room and board ($4200). Part-time tuition: $475 per semester hour. Part-time mandatory fees: $47 per semester hour, $30 per term.

Collegiate Environment: Orientation program. Drama-theater group, choral group, marching band, student-run newspaper. Social organizations: 40 open to all. Most popular organizations: Baptist Student Ministry, Student Government Association, Residence Hall Association, Campus Activities Board, Crusaders for Christ. Major annual events: homecoming, Easter Pageant, Play Day. Student services: health clinic, personal-psychological counseling. Campus security: 24-hour emergency response devices and patrols, late night transport-escort service, controlled dormitory access, campus police force, lighted pathways and sidewalks. 1,075 college housing spaces available; all were occupied in 2003-04. Freshmen given priority for college housing. On-campus residence required through junior year. Options: men-only, women-only housing available. Townsend Memorial Library with 153,120 books, 47,044 microform titles, 1,541 serials, 6,782 audiovisual materials, an OPAC, and a Web page. Operations spending for 2004 fiscal year: $1.2 million. 262 computers available on campus for general student use. Computer purchase/lease plans available. A campuswide network can be accessed from student residence rooms. Staffed computer lab on campus.

Community Environment: Belton, population 13,000, located in central Texas, has a mild climate. The community is served by railroad lines, bus lines, U.S. Highway I-35 and Texas State 317. There is an airport 15 miles away. Local community services include a library, museum, several churches, a hospital, and various civic, fraternal and veteran's organizations. The city is a one-hour drive from Waco and Austin for out-of-town entertainment. Belton has nearby Lake Belton for fishing, water skiing, swimming, and speed boat races. Part-time employment is available.

■ **UNIVERSITY OF NORTH TEXAS** *C-19*
PO Box 311277
Denton, TX 76203
Tel: (940)565-2000
Admissions: (940)565-3921
Fax: (940)565-2408
E-mail: undergrad@abn.unt.edu
Web Site: http://www.unt.edu/

Description: State-supported, university, coed. Awards bachelor's, master's, and doctoral degrees. Founded 1890. Setting: 744-acre suburban campus with easy access to Dallas-Fort Worth. Endowment: $37.3 million. Research spending for 2004 fiscal year: $15.6 million. Educational spending for 2005 fiscal year: $2490 per student. Total enrollment: 32,047. Faculty: 1,413 (936 full-time, 477 part-time). Student-undergrad faculty ratio is 18:1. 11,282 applied, 69% were admitted. 19% from top 10% of their high school class, 48% from top quarter, 86% from top half. 11 National Merit Scholars. Full-time: 19,830 students, 56% women, 44% men. Part-time: 5,478 students, 54% women, 46% men. 26% from out-of-state, 1% Native American, 11% Hispanic, 12% black, 5% Asian American or Pacific Islander, 3% international, 23% live on campus, 12% transferred in. Retention: 75% of full-time freshmen returned the following year. Academic areas with the most degrees conferred: business/marketing; visual and performing arts; education. Core. Calendar: semesters. Academic remediation for entering students, ESL program, services for LD students, advanced placement, accelerated degree program, freshman honors college, honors program, distance learning, double major, summer session for credit, part-time degree program, external degree program, co-op programs and internships, graduate courses open to undergrads. Study abroad program. ROTC: Army (c), Naval.

Entrance Requirements: Options: Common Application, electronic application, early admission, deferred admission, international baccalaureate accepted. Required: high school transcript, SAT or ACT. Required for some: essay, 3 recommendations, interview. Entrance: moderately difficult. Application deadline: 6/15. Notification: continuous.

Costs Per Year: Application fee: $40. State resident tuition: $3930 full-time, $131 per credit hour part-time. Nonresident tuition: $12,210 full-time, $407 per credit hour part-time. Mandatory fees: $1880 full-time, $488 per term part-time. Full-time tuition and fees vary according to course load. Part-time tuition and fees vary according to course load. College room and board: $5364. Room and board charges vary according to board plan and housing facility.

Collegiate Environment: Orientation program. Drama-theater group, choral group, marching band, student-run newspaper, radio station. Social organizations: 254 open to all; national fraternities, national sororities; 8% of eligible men and 7% of eligible women are members. Most popular organizations: Student Government Association, Residence Hall Association, Coalition of Black Student Organizations. Major annual events: Homecoming, Union Day, MLK Candlelight Vigil. Student services: legal services, health clinic, personal-psychological counseling, women's center. Campus security: 24-hour emergency response devices and patrols, late night transport-escort service, controlled dormitory access. College housing designed to accommodate 4,911 students; 5,588 undergraduates lived in college housing during 2003-04. Freshmen given priority for college housing. On-campus residence required in freshman year. Options: coed, women-only housing available. Willis Library plus 4 others with 2.1 million books, 3.3 million microform titles, 17,080 serials, 745 audiovisual materials, an OPAC, and a Web page. Operations spending for 2004 fiscal year: $5.6 million. 2,006 computers available on campus for general student use. A campuswide network can be accessed from student residence rooms and from off campus. Staffed computer lab on campus.

Community Environment: Denton is a community of approximately 73,050. Texas' largest and most modern airport, Dallas - Fort Worth International, is only a short drive from Denton.

■ **UNIVERSITY OF PHOENIX-DALLAS CAMPUS** *D-19*
Churchill Tower
12400 Coit Rd., Ste. 100
Dallas, TX 75251
Tel: (972)385-1055
Free: 800-228-7240
Admissions: (480)557-1712
Fax: (972)385-1700
Web Site: http://www.phoenix.edu/

Description: Proprietary, comprehensive, coed. Awards bachelor's and master's degrees. Founded 2001. Setting: urban campus. Total enrollment: 2,972. Faculty: 243 (5 full-time, 238 part-time). Student-undergrad faculty ratio is 12:1. 94 applied. Full-time: 2,303 students, 62% women, 38% men. 0.2% Native American, 3% Hispanic, 8% black, 1% Asian American or Pacific Islander, 26% international, 93% 25 or older. Academic area with the most degrees conferred: business/marketing. Core. Calendar: continuous. Advanced placement, accelerated degree program, independent study, distance learning, external degree program, adult/continuing education programs, graduate courses open to undergrads.

Entrance Requirements: Open admission. Option: deferred admission. Required: 1 recommendation. Required for some: high school transcript. Entrance: noncompetitive. Application deadline: Rolling.

Costs Per Year: Application fee: $110. Tuition: $10,785 full-time, $359.50 per credit part-time. Mandatory fees: $560 full-time, $70 per course part-time.

Collegiate Environment: College housing not available.

■ **UNIVERSITY OF PHOENIX-HOUSTON CAMPUS** *J-22*
11451 Katy Freeway, Ste. 100
Houston, TX 77079-2004
Tel: (281)596-0363
Free: 800-228-7240
Admissions: (480)557-1712
Fax: (281)596-0336
Web Site: http://www.phoenix.edu/

Description: Proprietary, comprehensive, coed. Awards bachelor's and master's degrees. Founded 2001. Setting: urban campus. Total enrollment: 4,808. Faculty: 442 (7 full-time, 435 part-time). Student-undergrad faculty ratio is 13:1. 145 applied. Full-time: 3,914 students, 68% women, 32% men. 0.1% Native American, 4% Hispanic, 12% black, 1% Asian American or Pacific Islander, 24% international, 93% 25 or older. Academic areas with the most degrees conferred: business/marketing; communication technologies; security and protective services. Core. Calendar: continuous. Advanced placement, accelerated degree program, independent study, distance learning, external degree program, adult/continuing education programs, graduate courses open to undergrads.

Entrance Requirements: Open admission. Option: deferred admission. Required: 1 recommendation. Required for some: high school transcript. Entrance: noncompetitive. Application deadline: Rolling.

Costs Per Year: Application fee: $110. Tuition: $10,785 full-time, $359.50 per credit part-time. Mandatory fees: $560 full-time, $70 per course part-time.

Collegiate Environment: College housing not available. University Library with an OPAC and a Web page. System-wide operations spending for 2004 fiscal year: $3.2 million.

■ **UNIVERSITY OF ST. THOMAS** *J-22*

3800 Montrose Blvd.
Houston, TX 77006-4696
Tel: (713)522-7911
Free: 800-856-8565
Admissions: (713)525-3500
Fax: (713)525-3558
E-mail: admissions@basil.stthom.edu
Web Site: http://www.stthom.edu/

Description: Independent Roman Catholic, comprehensive, coed. Awards bachelor's, master's, doctoral, and first professional degrees. Founded 1947. Setting: 21-acre urban campus. Endowment: $41 million. Educational spending for 2005 fiscal year: $7377 per student. Total enrollment: 3,776. Faculty: 272 (121 full-time, 151 part-time). Student-undergrad faculty ratio is 14:1. 807 applied, 92% were admitted. 29% from top 10% of their high school class, 58% from top quarter, 82% from top half. Full-time: 1,365 students, 63% women, 37% men. Part-time: 519 students, 57% women, 43% men. Students come from 29 states and territories, 40 other countries, 4% from out-of-state, 1% Native American, 29% Hispanic, 6% black, 12% Asian American or Pacific Islander, 3% international, 25% 25 or older, 15% live on campus, 9% transferred in. Retention: 71% of full-time freshmen returned the following year. Academic areas with the most degrees conferred: business/marketing; liberal arts/general studies; social sciences. Core. Calendar: semesters. Academic remediation for entering students, services for LD students, advanced placement, honors program, independent study, distance learning, double major, summer session for credit, part-time degree program, adult/continuing education programs, internships, graduate courses open to undergrads. Off campus study at University of Houston, Glassell School of Art. Study abroad program. ROTC: Army (c).

Entrance Requirements: Options: Peterson's Universal Application, Common Application, electronic application, deferred admission, international baccalaureate accepted. Required: essay, high school transcript, minimum 2.50 high school GPA, SAT or ACT. Entrance: moderately difficult. Application deadline: Rolling. Notification: continuous.

Costs Per Year: Application fee: $35. Comprehensive fee: $23,810 includes full-time tuition ($16,950), mandatory fees ($160), and college room and board ($6700). College room only: $4000. Full-time tuition and fees vary according to course load. Room and board charges vary according to board plan and housing facility. Part-time tuition: $565 per credit hour. Part-time mandatory fees: $80 per term. Part-time tuition and fees vary according to course load.

Collegiate Environment: Orientation program. Drama-theater group, choral group, student-run newspaper. Social organizations: 58 open to all; 40% of eligible men and 60% of eligible women are members. Major annual events: Welcome Back Week Activities, Council of Clubs activities on Academic Mall. Student services: personal-psychological counseling. Campus security: 24-hour emergency response devices and patrols, late night transport-escort service, controlled dormitory access. 383 college housing spaces available; 271 were occupied in 2003-04. Freshmen given priority for college housing. Option: coed housing available. Doherty Library plus 1 other with 248,606 books, 570,407 microform titles, 15,150 serials, 1,374 audiovisual materials, an OPAC, and a Web page. Operations spending for 2004 fiscal year: $1.5 million. 156 computers available on campus for general student use. A campuswide network can be accessed from student residence rooms and from off campus. Staffed computer lab on campus.

■ **THE UNIVERSITY OF TEXAS AT ARLINGTON** *D-19*

701 South Nedderman Dr.
Arlington, TX 76019
Tel: (817)272-2011
Admissions: (817)272-6287
Fax: (817)272-5656
E-mail: admissions@uta.edu
Web Site: http://www.uta.edu/

Description: State-supported, university, coed. Part of University of Texas System. Awards bachelor's, master's, and doctoral degrees and post-master's certificates. Founded 1895. Setting: 395-acre urban campus with easy access to Dallas-Fort Worth. Endowment: $47.1 million. Research spending for 2004 fiscal year: $16.9 million. Educational spending for 2005 fiscal year: $2328 per student. Total enrollment: 25,432. Faculty: 1,113 (781 full-time, 332 part-time). Student-undergrad faculty ratio is 22:1. 5,465 applied, 79% were admitted. 20% from top 10% of their high school class, 60% from top quarter, 89% from top half. 3 National Merit Scholars. Full-time: 13,995 students, 53% women, 47% men. Part-time: 5,654 students, 54% women, 46% men. Students come from 45 states and territories, 139 other countries, 2% from out-of-state, 1% Native American, 15% Hispanic, 14% black, 11% Asian American or Pacific Islander, 5% international, 28% 25 or older, 14% live on campus, 17% transferred in. Retention: 69% of full-time freshmen returned the following year. Academic areas with the most degrees conferred: business/marketing; engineering; health professions and related sciences; interdisciplinary studies. Core. Calendar: semesters. Academic remediation for entering students, ESL program, services for LD students, advanced placement, self-designed majors, freshman honors college, honors program, independent study, distance learning, double major, summer session for credit, part-time degree program, adult/continuing education programs, co-op programs and internships, graduate courses open to undergrads. Study abroad program. ROTC: Army, Air Force (c).

Entrance Requirements: Options: Peterson's Universal Application, early admission, deferred admission. Required: high school transcript, class rank, SAT or ACT. Entrance: moderately difficult. Application deadline: 6/1. Notification: continuous.

Costs Per Year: Application fee: $35. State resident tuition: $3893 full-time, $134.50 per credit hour part-time. Nonresident tuition: $12,173 full-time, $410.50 per credit hour part-time. Mandatory fees: $1670 full-time, $59.58 per credit hour part-time, $102.50 per term part-time. Full-time tuition and fees vary according to course level, course load, and program. Part-time tuition and fees vary according to course level, course load, and program. College room and board: $5345. Room and board charges vary according to board plan and housing facility.

Collegiate Environment: Orientation program. Drama-theater group, choral group, marching band, student-run newspaper, radio station. Social organizations: 423 open to all; national fraternities, national sororities, local fraternities, local sororities; 4% of eligible men and 3% of eligible women are members. Most popular organizations: Medical/Dental Preparatory Association, Institute of Electronic and Electrical Engineers, Tai Wanese Students Association, Accounting Society, Upsilon Pi Epsilon. Major annual events: homecoming, International Week, Activity Fair Days. Student services: legal services, health clinic, personal-psychological counseling. Campus security: 24-hour emergency response devices and patrols, late night transport-escort service, controlled dormitory access, remote emergency telephones, bicycle patrols, crime prevention program, student shuttle service from 7:30 a.m. to 4:30 p.m. 5,083 college housing spaces available; 2,741 were occupied in 2003-04. No special consideration for freshman housing applicants. Options: coed, men-only, women-only housing available. Central Library plus 2 others with 1.1 million books, 1.5 million microform titles, 16,053 serials, 8,784 audiovisual materials, an OPAC, and a Web page. Operations spending for 2004 fiscal year: $6.6 million. 1,000 computers available on campus for general student use. A campuswide network can be accessed from student residence rooms and from off campus. Staffed computer lab on campus.

■ **THE UNIVERSITY OF TEXAS AT AUSTIN** *I-18*

Austin, TX 78712-1111
Tel: (512)471-3434
Admissions: (512)475-7399
Fax: (512)475-7475
Web Site: http://www.utexas.edu/

Description: State-supported, university, coed. Part of University of Texas System. Awards bachelor's, master's, doctoral, and first professional degrees. Founded 1883. Setting: 350-acre urban campus with easy access to San Antonio. Endowment: $2.2 billion. Research spending for 2004 fiscal year: $320.9 million. Educational spending for 2005 fiscal year: $10,105 per student. Total enrollment: 49,696. Faculty: 2,734 (2,482 full-time, 252 part-time). Student-undergrad faculty ratio is 18:1. 23,925 applied, 51% were admitted. 68% from top 10% of their high school class, 92% from top quarter, 99% from top half. 242 National Merit Scholars. Full-time: 33,682 students, 53% women, 47% men. Part-time: 3,196 students, 46% women, 54% men. Students come from 52 states and territories, 121 other countries, 5% from out-of-state, 0.4% Native American, 16% Hispanic, 4% black, 17% Asian American or Pacific Islander, 4% international, 6% 25 or older, 18% live on campus, 5% transferred in. Retention: 93% of full-time freshmen returned the following year. Academic areas with the most degrees conferred: social sciences; business/marketing; communications/journalism. Core. Calendar: semesters. Academic remediation for entering students, ESL program, services for LD students, advanced placement, accelerated degree program, self-designed majors, honors program, independent study, distance learning, double major, summer session for credit, part-time degree program, adult/continuing education programs, co-op programs and internships, graduate courses open to undergrads. Study abroad program. ROTC: Army, Naval, Air Force.

Entrance Requirements: Options: Common Application, electronic application, deferred admission, international baccalaureate accepted. Required: essay, high school transcript, SAT or ACT. Required for some: SAT Subject Tests. Entrance: very difficult. Application deadline: 2/1. Notification: continuous. Preference given to Texas high school graduates in the top 10% of their graduating class are automatically admitted upon meeting all other enrollment requirements..

Costs Per Year: Application fee: $60. State resident tuition: $6972 full-time. Nonresident tuition: $16,310 full-time. Full-time tuition varies according to course load and program. College room and board: $7638. Room and board charges vary according to board plan, housing facility, and location.

Collegiate Environment: Orientation program. Drama-theater group, choral group, marching band, student-run newspaper, radio station. Social organizations: 900 open to all; national fraternities, national sororities; 9% of eligible men and 13% of eligible women are members. Most popular organizations: Alpha Phi Omega, Student Events Center, Texas Exes-Student Chapter, Longhorn Band Student Organization, Student Volunteer Board. Major annual events: Gone to Texas (freshman welcome), 40 Acres Fest, Commencement. Student services: legal services, health clinic, personal-psychological counseling. Campus security: 24-hour emergency response devices and patrols, student patrols, late night transport-escort service, controlled dormitory access. 6,698 college housing spaces available; all were occupied in 2003-04. Freshmen given priority for college housing. Options: coed, men-only, women-only housing available. Perry-Castaneda Library plus 16 others with an OPAC and a Web page. Operations spending for 2004 fiscal year: $27.2 million. 4,000 computers available on campus for general student use. A campuswide network can be accessed from student residence rooms and from off campus. Staffed computer lab on campus.

■ THE UNIVERSITY OF TEXAS AT BROWNSVILLE *Q-18*
80 Fort Brown
Brownsville, TX 78520-4991
Tel: (956)544-8200
Admissions: (956)882-8295
Fax: (956)544-8832
E-mail: admissions@utb.edu
Web Site: http://www.utb.edu/

Description: State-supported, upper-level, coed. Part of University of Texas System. Awards associate, bachelor's, and master's degrees. Founded 1973. Setting: 380-acre urban campus. Total enrollment: 13,316. Faculty: 659 (344 full-time, 315 part-time). Student-undergrad faculty ratio is 18:1. 3,197 applied, 100% were admitted. Full-time: 5,560 students, 59% women, 41% men. Part-time: 6,907 students, 62% women, 38% men. Students come from 6 states and territories, 18 other countries, 0.3% from out-of-state, 0.1% Native American, 91% Hispanic, 0.3% black, 0.5% Asian American or Pacific Islander, 3% international, 35% 25 or older, 1% live on campus, 4% transferred in. Retention: 64% of full-time entering class returned the following year. Academic areas with the most degrees conferred: business/marketing; interdisciplinary studies; security and protective services. Core. Calendar: semesters. Academic remediation for entering students, ESL program, services for LD students, advanced placement, independent study, distance learning, double major, summer session for credit, part-time degree program, co-op programs and internships, graduate courses open to undergrads. Off campus study.

Costs Per Year: Application fee: $0. State resident tuition: $2256 full-time. Nonresident tuition: $8880 full-time. Mandatory fees: $943 full-time. College room only: $2300.

Collegiate Environment: Choral group, student-run newspaper. Social organizations: 65 open to all; local fraternities, local sororities; 4% of eligible men and 4% of eligible women are members. Most popular organizations: Student Activities Programming Board, Criminal Justice Club, Gorgas Science Club, Club Cultural Latinoamericano. Major annual events: Scorpion Rush (club/organization recruitment day), La Posadea and Pastorela (cultural event), Bouganvillea Ball. Student services: health clinic, personal-psychological counseling. Campus security: 24-hour emergency response devices and patrols. 230 college housing spaces available; 144 were occupied in 2003-04. Option: coed housing available. Arnulfo L. Oliveira Library with 174,660 books, 710,820 microform titles, 4,447 serials, 1,000

audiovisual materials, an OPAC, and a Web page. 650 computers available on campus for general student use. Computer purchase/lease plans available. A campuswide network can be accessed from off-campus.

■ THE UNIVERSITY OF TEXAS AT DALLAS *F-34*
PO Box 830688
Richardson, TX 75083-0688
Tel: (972)883-2111
Free: 800-889-2443
Admissions: (972)883-2270
Fax: (972)883-6803
E-mail: admissions-status@utdallas.edu
Web Site: http://www.utdallas.edu/

Description: State-supported, university, coed. Part of University of Texas System. Awards bachelor's, master's, and doctoral degrees. Founded 1969. Setting: 455-acre suburban campus with easy access to Dallas. Endowment: $222.4 million. Research spending for 2004 fiscal year: $32.3 million. Educational spending for 2005 fiscal year: $12,847 per student. Total enrollment: 14,480. Faculty: 696 (457 full-time, 239 part-time). Student-undergrad faculty ratio is 20:1. 5,584 applied, 51% were admitted. 42% from top 10% of their high school class, 75% from top quarter, 96% from top half. 38 National Merit Scholars, 49 valedictorians. Full-time: 6,613 students, 45% women, 55% men. Part-time: 2,799 students, 50% women, 50% men. Students come from 48 states and territories, 156 other countries, 3% from out-of-state, 1% Native American, 10% Hispanic, 7% black, 20% Asian American or Pacific Islander, 5% international, 30% 25 or older, 21% live on campus, 15% transferred in. Retention: 82% of full-time freshmen returned the following year. Academic areas with the most degrees conferred: business/marketing; interdisciplinary studies; computer and information sciences. Core. Calendar: semesters. Academic remediation for entering students, services for LD students, advanced placement, accelerated degree program, self-designed majors, freshman honors college, honors program, independent study, distance learning, double major, summer session for credit, part-time degree program, adult/continuing education programs, co-op programs and internships, graduate courses open to undergrads. Study abroad program. ROTC: Army (c), Air Force (c).

Entrance Requirements: Options: Peterson's Universal Application, electronic application, deferred admission, international baccalaureate accepted. Required: essay, high school transcript, SAT or ACT. Recommended: 3 recommendations. Required for some: interview, THEA. Entrance: very difficult. Application deadline: 7/1. Notification: continuous.

Costs Per Year: Application fee: $50. State resident tuition: $6831 full-time, $198 per credit part-time. Nonresident tuition: $15,111 full-time, $474 per credit part-time. Full-time tuition varies according to course load, degree level, and program. Part-time tuition varies according to course load, degree level, and program. College room and board: $6244. Room and board charges vary according to board plan and housing facility.

Collegiate Environment: Orientation program. Drama-theater group, student-run newspaper, radio station. Social organizations: 115 open to all; national fraternities, national sororities, local sororities; 5% of eligible men and 3% of eligible women are members. Most popular organizations: Student Government Association, Golden Key National Honor Society, Muslim Students Association, Indian Student Association, Friendship Association of Chinese Students and Scholars. Major annual events: Jazz Concert, Homecoming Dance, Holiday Sing. Student services: legal services, health clinic, personal-psychological counseling, women's center. Campus security: 24-hour emergency response devices and patrols, late night transport-escort service. 3,000 college housing spaces available; 2,959 were occupied in 2003-04. Freshmen given priority for college housing. Option: coed housing available. Eugene McDermott Library plus 2 others with 797,719 books, 175,988 microform titles, 20,812 serials, 4,158 audiovisual materials, an OPAC, and a Web page. Operations spending for 2004 fiscal year: $5.9 million. 630 computers available on campus for general student use. A campuswide network can be accessed from student residence rooms and from off campus. Staffed computer lab on campus.

■ THE UNIVERSITY OF TEXAS AT EL PASO *F-2*
500 West University Ave.
El Paso, TX 79968-0001
Tel: (915)747-5000; 877-746-4636
Admissions: (915)747-5588
Fax: (915)747-5122
Web Site: http://www.utep.edu/

Description: State-supported, university, coed. Awards bachelor's, master's, and doctoral degrees. Founded 1913. Setting: 360-acre urban campus. Research spending for 2004 fiscal year: $13.6 million. Total enrollment: 19,268. Faculty: 1,059 (680 full-time, 379 part-time). Student-undergrad faculty ratio is 19:1. 4,012 applied, 99% were admitted. 17% from top 10% of their high school class, 41% from top quarter, 71% from top half. Full-time: 10,975 students, 54% women, 46% men. Part-time: 5,062 students, 57% women, 43% men. Students come from 47 states and territories, 67 other countries, 3% from out-of-state, 0.2% Native American, 76% Hispanic, 2% black, 1% Asian American or Pacific Islander, 10% international, 26% 25 or older, 3% live on campus, 7% transferred in. Retention: 69% of full-time freshmen returned the following year. Core. Calendar: semesters. Academic remediation for entering students, ESL program, services for LD students, advanced placement, accelerated degree program, honors program, independent study, distance learning, summer session for credit, part-time degree program, adult/continuing education programs, co-op programs and internships, graduate courses open to undergrads. Off campus study at National Student Exchange. ROTC: Army, Air Force.

Entrance Requirements: Option: deferred admission. Required: high school transcript. Required for some: SAT or ACT, PAA. Entrance: minimally difficult. Application deadline: 7/31.

Costs Per Year: Application fee: $0. State resident tuition: $3930 full-time, $131 per credit hour part-time. Nonresident tuition: $12,210 full-time. Mandatory fees: $1134 full-time. Part-time tuition varies according to course load. College room only: $4095. Room charges vary according to housing facility.

Collegiate Environment: Orientation program. Drama-theater group, choral group, marching band, student-run newspaper, radio station. Social organizations: national fraternities, national sororities. Student services: legal services, health clinic, personal-psychological counseling, women's center. Campus security: 24-hour emergency response devices and patrols, late night transport-escort service. 428 college housing spaces available; 337 were occupied in 2003-04. Option: coed housing available. University Library with 961,247 books, 1.7 million microform titles, and 3,005 serials.

■ THE UNIVERSITY OF TEXAS HEALTH SCIENCE CENTER AT HOUSTON *J-22*

PO Box 20036
Houston, TX 77225-0036
Tel: (713)500-3333
Admissions: (713)500-3361
Fax: (713)500-3026
E-mail: registrar@uth.tmc.edu
Web Site: http://www.uth.tmc.edu/

Description: State-supported, upper-level, coed. Part of University of Texas System. Awards bachelor's, master's, doctoral, and first professional degrees and post-master's certificates. Founded 1972. Setting: urban campus. Endowment: $113.5 million. Research spending for 2004 fiscal year: $151 million. Educational spending for 2005 fiscal year: $84,360 per student. Total enrollment: 3,399. 1% Native American, 15% Hispanic, 7% black, 17% Asian American or Pacific Islander, 2% international. Calendar: semesters. Accelerated degree program, independent study, distance learning, double major, part-time degree program, internships, graduate courses open to undergrads. ROTC: Army (c).

Costs Per Year: Application fee: $30. State resident tuition: $4905 full-time, $105 per hour part-time. Nonresident tuition: $16,571 full-time, $364.50 per hour part-time. Mandatory fees: $697 full-time. Part-time tuition varies according to course load.

Collegiate Environment: Orientation program. Student-run newspaper. Major annual event: UT Medics Community Projects. Student services: health clinic, personal-psychological counseling. Campus security: 24-hour emergency response devices and patrols, late night transport-escort service, controlled access to all buildings. Houston Academy of Medicine-Texas Medical Center Library plus 3 others with 339,062 books, 5,581 serials, 885 audiovisual materials, an OPAC, and a Web page. Operations spending for 2004 fiscal year: $2.7 million.

■ THE UNIVERSITY OF TEXAS HEALTH SCIENCE CENTER AT SAN ANTONIO *K-16*

7703 Floyd Curl Dr.
San Antonio, TX 78229-3900
Tel: (210)567-7000
Admissions: (210)567-2629
Fax: (210)567-2685
E-mail: peak@uthscsa.edu

Web Site: http://www.uthscsa.edu/

Description: State-supported, upper-level, coed. Part of University of Texas System. Awards bachelor's, master's, doctoral, and first professional degrees. Founded 1976. Setting: 100-acre suburban campus. Total enrollment: 2,754. 2,440 applied. Students come from 41 states and territories, 6 other countries, 75% 25 or older. Core. Calendar: semesters. Academic remediation for entering students, summer session for credit, part-time degree program, adult/continuing education programs. ROTC: Army (c), Air Force (c).

Collegiate Environment: Student services: health clinic, personal-psychological counseling. Campus security: 24-hour emergency response devices and patrols, late night transport-escort service. College housing not available. Dolph Briso Library with 192,576 books and 2,501 serials. 1,000 computers available on campus for general student use. A campuswide network can be accessed from off-campus.

■ THE UNIVERSITY OF TEXAS MEDICAL BRANCH *K-23*

301 University Blvd.
Galveston, TX 77555
Tel: (409)772-1011
Admissions: (409)772-1215
Fax: (409)772-5056
E-mail: student.admissions@utmb.edu
Web Site: http://www.utmb.edu/

Description: State-supported, upper-level, coed. Part of University of Texas System. Awards bachelor's, master's, doctoral, and first professional degrees. Founded 1891. Setting: 85-acre small town campus with easy access to Houston. Endowment: $397.1 million. Research spending for 2004 fiscal year: $120.7 million. Total enrollment: 2,198. Faculty: 102 (94 full-time, 8 part-time). Student-undergrad faculty ratio is 8:1. Full-time: 269 students, 73% women, 27% men. Part-time: 230 students, 83% women, 17% men. Students come from 3 states and territories, 7 other countries, 0.4% from out-of-state, 1% Native American, 13% Hispanic, 10% black, 15% Asian American or Pacific Islander, 3% international, 58% 25 or older, 46% transferred in. Academic area with the most degrees conferred: health professions and related sciences. Calendar: semesters (early semester). Services for LD students, advanced placement, independent study, distance learning, summer session for credit, part-time degree program, internships.

Costs Per Year: Application fee: $25. State resident tuition: $2160 full-time, $90 per credit hour part-time. Nonresident tuition: $8784 full-time, $366 per credit hour part-time. Mandatory fees: $530 full-time. College room only: $2322.

Collegiate Environment: Orientation program. Student-run newspaper. Social organizations: 40 open to all; national fraternities, local fraternities. Most popular organizations: Texas Medical Association, American Medical Student Association, American Medical Women's Association, Texas Association Latin American Medical Students, National Medical Student Association. Major annual events: Quest and Orientation, All Sports Day, Primary Care Day. Student services: legal services, health clinic, personal-psychological counseling. Campus security: 24-hour emergency response devices and patrols, late night transport-escort service. Option: coed housing available. Moody Medical Library with 248,370 books, 1,980 serials, 960 audiovisual materials, an OPAC, and a Web page. 200 computers available on campus for general student use. A campuswide network can be accessed from student residence rooms and from off campus. Staffed computer lab on campus.

■ THE UNIVERSITY OF TEXAS-PAN AMERICAN *Q-17*

1201 West University Dr.
Edinburg, TX 78541-2999
Tel: (956)381-2011
Admissions: (956)381-2481
E-mail: admissions@panam.edu
Web Site: http://www.utpa.edu/

Description: State-supported, comprehensive, coed. Part of University of Texas System. Awards bachelor's, master's, and doctoral degrees and post-master's certificates. Founded 1927. Setting: 238-acre small town campus with easy access to McAllen-Edinburg-Mission MSA. Endowment: $54.3 million. Research spending for 2004 fiscal year: $4.3 million. Educational spending for 2005 fiscal year: $3500 per student. Total enrollment: 17,048. Faculty: 706 (587 full-time, 119 part-time). Student-undergrad faculty ratio is 21:1. 19% from top 10% of their high school class, 46% from top quarter, 79% from top half. Full-time: 10,617 students, 58% women, 42% men. Part-time: 4,325 students, 60% women, 40% men. Students come from 25 states and territories, 27 other countries, 0% from out-of-state, 0.05% Native American, 88% Hispanic, 0.3% black, 1% Asian American or Pacific Islander, 4% international, 23% 25 or older, 1% live on campus, 6% transferred in. Retention: 68% of full-time freshmen returned the following year. Academic areas with the most degrees conferred: interdisciplinary studies; business/marketing; health professions and related sciences. Core. Calendar: semesters. Academic remediation for entering students, services for LD students, advanced placement, honors program, independent study, distance learning, double major, summer session for credit, part-time degree program, adult/continuing education programs, co-op programs and internships, graduate courses open to undergrads. Study abroad program. ROTC: Army.

Entrance Requirements: Options: Common Application, electronic application, early admission. Required: high school transcript, minimum 2.0 high school GPA, SAT or ACT. Required for some: recommendations, interview. Entrance: noncompetitive. Application deadline: 8/11. Notification: continuous.

Costs Per Year: Application fee: $0. State resident tuition: $3348 full-time, $116 per semester hour part-time. Nonresident tuition: $11,598 full-time, $391 per semester hour part-time. Mandatory fees: $812 full-time, $98 per semester hour part-time. College room and board: $4333. College room only: $2406.

Collegiate Environment: Orientation program. Drama-theater group, choral group, student-run newspaper. Social organizations: 119 open to all; national fraternities, national sororities, local sororities; 1% of eligible men and 1% of eligible women are members. Most popular organizations: Accounting Society, American Marketing Association, Pre-Medical/Bio Medical Society, Association of Texas Professional Educators, Financial Management Association. Major annual events: Carnival of the Great Pumpkin, Bronc Olympics, Cinco de Mayo. Student services: health clinic, personal-psychological counseling. Campus security: 24-hour emergency response devices and patrols, late night transport-escort service. 592 college housing spaces available; 585 were occupied in 2003-04. No special consideration for freshman housing applicants. Options: men-only, women-only housing available. University Library with 572,162 books, 1.1 million microform titles, 8,135 serials, 26,436 audiovisual materials, an OPAC, and a Web page. Operations spending for 2004 fiscal year: $4 million. 500 computers available on campus for general student use. A campuswide network can be accessed from off-campus. Staffed computer lab on campus.

Community Environment: Population 30,000. Edinburg is located in the subtropical lower Rio Grande Valley of Texas and enjoys a mild year-round climate. The average summer maximum temperature is about 90 degrees, with winter average of 70 degrees. The community is served by bus lines and U.S. Highway 281. Edinburg has a hospital and major civic, fraternal and veteran's organizations. Part-time employment is available. Local recreation includes hunting, fishing, golf, and swimming in the Gulf of Mexico approximately 70 miles away.

■ **THE UNIVERSITY OF TEXAS OF THE PERMIAN BASIN** *F-9*

4901 East University Blvd.
Odessa, TX 79762-0001
Tel: (432)552-2020; (866)552-UTPB
Admissions: (432)552-2605
Fax: (432)552-2109
E-mail: gomez-v@gusher.pb.utexas.edu
Web Site: http://www.utpb.edu/
Description: State-supported, comprehensive, coed. Part of University of Texas System. Awards bachelor's and master's degrees. Founded 1969. Setting: 600-acre urban campus. Total enrollment: 2,695. 453 applied, 88% were admitted. 21% from top 10% of their high school class, 46% from top quarter, 83% from top half. 2 valedictorians. Full-time: 1,393 students, 64% women, 36% men. Part-time: 619 students, 66% women, 34% men. Students come from 13 states and territories, 2% from out-of-state, 0.5% Native American, 36% Hispanic, 4% black, 1% Asian American or Pacific Islander, 0.3% international, 41% 25 or older, 17% transferred in. Retention: 59% of full-time freshmen returned the following year. Core. Calendar: semesters. Academic remediation for entering students, advanced placement, accelerated degree program, independent study, distance learning, double major, summer session for credit, part-time degree program, internships, graduate courses open to undergrads.

Entrance Requirements: Options: electronic application, deferred admission. Required: high school transcript, SAT or ACT. Required for some: recommendations, interview. Entrance: moderately difficult. Application deadline: 8/15. Notification: continuous.

Collegiate Environment: Orientation program. Student-run newspaper. Student services: personal-psychological counseling. Campus security: 24-hour patrols, late night transport-escort service. 168 college housing spaces available; 167 were occupied in 2003-04. No special consideration for freshman housing applicants. J. Conrad Dunagan Library with 257,531 books, 1.1 million microform titles, 723 serials, 6,322 audiovisual materials, an OPAC, and a Web page. 170 computers available on campus for general student use. Computer purchase/lease plans available. A campuswide network can be accessed from student residence rooms and from off campus. Staffed computer lab on campus.

Community Environment: Metropolitan area of Odessa-Midland, population 200,000. International Airport and Interstate Highway 20 access to campus.

■ **THE UNIVERSITY OF TEXAS AT SAN ANTONIO** *K-16*

6900 North Loop 1604 West
San Antonio, TX 78249-0617
Tel: (210)458-4011
Free: 800-669-0919
Admissions: (210)458-4530
Web Site: http://www.utsa.edu/
Description: State-supported, university, coed. Part of University of Texas System. Awards bachelor's, master's, and doctoral degrees. Founded 1969. Setting: 600-acre suburban campus with easy access to San Antonio, Texas. Endowment: $35.1 million. Research spending for 2004 fiscal year: $12.9 million. Educational spending for 2005 fiscal year: $3801 per student. Total enrollment: 27,337. Faculty: 1,083 (860 full-time, 223 part-time). Student-undergrad faculty ratio is 23:1. 9,144 applied, 99% were admitted. 9% from top 10% of their high school class, 32% from top quarter, 65% from top half. Full-time: 17,554 students, 52% women, 48% men. Part-time: 5,877 students, 56% women, 44% men. Students come from 50 states and territories, 72 other countries, 4% from out-of-state, 1% Native American, 46% Hispanic, 7% black, 5% Asian American or Pacific Islander, 2% international, 29% 25 or older, 10% transferred in. Retention: 58% of full-time freshmen returned the following year. Academic areas with the most degrees conferred: business/marketing; interdisciplinary studies; biological/life sciences. Core. Calendar: semesters. Academic remediation for entering students, ESL program, services for LD students, advanced placement, accelerated degree program, freshman honors college, honors program, independent study, distance learning, double major, summer session for credit, part-time degree program, adult/continuing education programs, co-op programs and internships, graduate courses open to undergrads. Study abroad program. ROTC: Army, Air Force.

Entrance Requirements: Options: Common Application, electronic application, international baccalaureate accepted. Required: high school transcript, SAT or ACT. Entrance: moderately difficult. Application deadline: 7/1. Notification: 11/1.

Costs Per Year: Application fee: $30. State resident tuition: $3,968 full-time, $132.25 per hour part-time. Nonresident tuition: $12,248 full-time, $408.25 per hour part-time. Mandatory fees: $1890 full-time. College room and board: $7190. College room only: $4770.

Collegiate Environment: Orientation program. Drama-theater group, choral group, student-run newspaper. Social organizations: national fraternities, national sororities; 4% of eligible men and 2% of eligible women are members. Student services: health clinic, personal-psychological counseling. Campus security: 24-hour emergency response devices and patrols. Option: coed housing available. UTSA Library plus 1 other with 622,333 books, 3 million microform titles, 10,484 serials, 33,464 audiovisual materials, an OPAC, and a Web page. Operations spending for 2004 fiscal year: $4.4 million. 800 computers available on campus for general student use. A campuswide network can be accessed from student residence rooms. Staffed computer lab on campus.

■ **THE UNIVERSITY OF TEXAS SOUTHWESTERN MEDICAL CENTER AT DALLAS** *D-19*

5323 Harry Hines Blvd.
Dallas, TX 75390
Tel: (214)648-3111
Admissions: (214)648-5617
Fax: (214)648-3289
Web Site: http://www.utsouthwestern.edu/
Description: State-supported, upper-level, coed. Part of University of Texas System. Awards bachelor's, master's, doctoral, and first professional degrees. Founded 1943. Setting: 98-acre urban campus. Research spend-

ing for 2004 fiscal year: $178 million. Total enrollment: 2,393. Faculty: 103 (76 full-time, 27 part-time). 72 applied, 53% were admitted. Full-time: 97 students, 62% women, 38% men. Part-time: 24 students, 88% women, 13% men. Students come from 5 states and territories, 10% from out-of-state, 75% 25 or older, 34% transferred in. Academic area with the most degrees conferred: health professions and related sciences. Calendar: semesters. Advanced placement, independent study, part-time degree program, internships.

Costs Per Year: Application fee: $10. State resident tuition: $2820 full-time, $48 per credit hour part-time. Nonresident tuition: $11,880 full-time, $350 per credit hour part-time. Full-time tuition varies according to course load. Part-time tuition varies according to course load.

Collegiate Environment: Student services: health clinic. Campus security: 24-hour patrols, late night transport-escort service. College housing not available. University of Texas Southwestern Library with 257,782 books, 2,865 serials, an OPAC, and a Web page. 150 computers available on campus for general student use. A campuswide network can be accessed from off-campus. Staffed computer lab on campus.

■ **THE UNIVERSITY OF TEXAS AT TYLER** *E-22*
3900 University Blvd.
Tyler, TX 75799-0001
Tel: (903)566-7000
Admissions: (903)566-7195
Fax: (903)566-7068
Web Site: http://www.uttyler.edu/
Description: State-supported, comprehensive, coed. Part of University of Texas System. Awards bachelor's and master's degrees. Founded 1971. Setting: 200-acre urban campus. Endowment: $49.6 million. Research spending for 2004 fiscal year: $850,696. Educational spending for 2005 fiscal year: $6725 per student. Total enrollment: 5,748. Faculty: 360 (218 full-time, 142 part-time). Student-undergrad faculty ratio is 17:1. 1,497 applied, 75% were admitted. 22% from top 10% of their high school class, 42% from top quarter. Full-time: 3,580 students, 59% women, 41% men. Part-time: 1,077 students, 60% women, 40% men. Students come from 31 states and territories, 41 other countries, 2% from out-of-state, 1% Native American, 6% Hispanic, 10% black, 2% Asian American or Pacific Islander, 1% international, 33% 25 or older, 10% live on campus, 19% transferred in. Retention: 60% of full-time freshmen returned the following year. Academic areas with the most degrees conferred: business/marketing; health professions and related sciences; interdisciplinary studies. Core. Calendar: semesters. ESL program, services for LD students, advanced placement, self-designed majors, independent study, distance learning, double major, summer session for credit, part-time degree program, adult/continuing education programs, co-op programs and internships, graduate courses open to undergrads. Study abroad program.

Entrance Requirements: Options: Peterson's Universal Application, Common Application, electronic application, deferred admission, international baccalaureate accepted. Required: high school transcript, SAT or ACT. Entrance: moderately difficult. Notification: continuous.

Costs Per Year: Application fee: $0. State resident tuition: $3450 full-time, $115 per semester hour part-time. Nonresident tuition: $11,730 full-time, $391 per semester hour part-time. Mandatory fees: $800 full-time. Full-time tuition and fees vary according to course load and degree level. College room and board: $7010. Room and board charges vary according to housing facility.

Collegiate Environment: Orientation program. Drama-theater group, choral group, student-run newspaper. Social organizations: 45 open to all; national sororities. Most popular organizations: Student Government Association, Pre-Med/Pre-Dental Club, American Chemistry Society, Press Club, Latin Club. Major annual events: Patriot Days, New Student Orientation, TennisTournament. Student services: health clinic, personal-psychological counseling. Campus security: 24-hour emergency response devices and patrols, late night transport-escort service, controlled dormitory access. 584 college housing spaces available; 461 were occupied in 2003-04. Freshmen given priority for college housing. Option: coed housing available. Robert Muntz Library with 216,622 books, 689,081 microform titles, 929 serials, 6,973 audiovisual materials, an OPAC, and a Web page. Operations spending for 2004 fiscal year: $892,167. 177 computers available on campus for general student use. A campuswide network can be accessed from student residence rooms and from off campus. Staffed computer lab on campus.

■ **VERNON COLLEGE** *B-15*
4400 College Dr.
Vernon, TX 76384-4092

Tel: (940)552-6291
Fax: (940)553-1753
Web Site: http://www.vernoncollege.edu/
Description: State and locally supported, 2-year, coed. Awards certificates, transfer associate, and terminal associate degrees. Founded 1970. Setting: 100-acre small town campus. Total enrollment: 2,270. Students come from 32 states and territories, 4 other countries, 0.1% from out-of-state, 1% Native American, 12% Hispanic, 7% black, 1% Asian American or Pacific Islander, 1% international, 47% 25 or older. Core. Calendar: semesters. Academic remediation for entering students, services for LD students, advanced placement, distance learning, double major, summer session for credit, part-time degree program, adult/continuing education programs, co-op programs and internships.

Entrance Requirements: Open admission. Options: electronic application, early admission. Placement: THEA required. Entrance: noncompetitive. Application deadline: Rolling.

Collegiate Environment: Drama-theater group, choral group. Social organizations: 3 open to all. Most popular organizations: Student Government Association, Baptist Student Union. Major annual event: Sports Day. Student services: health clinic, personal-psychological counseling. Campus security: 24-hour patrols. Options: men-only, women-only housing available. Wright Library with 29,000 books, 200 serials, an OPAC, and a Web page. 100 computers available on campus for general student use. A campuswide network can be accessed. Staffed computer lab on campus.

■ **VICTORIA COLLEGE** *L-19*
2200 East Red River
Victoria, TX 77901-4494
Tel: (361)573-3291
Fax: (361)572-3850
Web Site: http://www.victoriacollege.edu/
Description: County-supported, 2-year, coed. Awards certificates, transfer associate, and terminal associate degrees. Founded 1925. Setting: 80-acre urban campus. Total enrollment: 4,244. Students come from 4 states and territories, 2 other countries, 0.2% Native American, 29% Hispanic, 5% black, 1% Asian American or Pacific Islander, 0.2% international, 49% 25 or older. Core. Calendar: semesters. Academic remediation for entering students, services for LD students, advanced placement, distance learning, summer session for credit, part-time degree program, adult/continuing education programs.

Entrance Requirements: Open admission. Required: high school transcript. Placement: THEA required; SAT or ACT required for some. Entrance: noncompetitive. Application deadline: Rolling.

Collegiate Environment: Orientation program. Drama-theater group, choral group. Most popular organization: Student Senate. Student services: personal-psychological counseling. Campus security: 24-hour emergency response devices. College housing not available. Victoria College Library with 150,000 books and 1,500 serials. Operations spending for 2004 fiscal year: $466,045. 225 computers available on campus for general student use. Staffed computer lab on campus.

Community Environment: Population 50,000. After the battle of San Jacinto, the first military capital of the new republic was established here in Victoria. Today, the area is known for its cattle raising. The city is located 25 miles from the Gulf of Mexico. Local industries include chemicals, sand and gravel mining, and oil and gas production. Part-time employment is limited. The climate is mild. Victoria is reached by bus and airline connections. The community has several churches. Local recreation includes salt water fishing, boating, swimming and water skiing in the Gulf of Mexico, a municipal park and golf courses.

■ **VIRGINIA COLLEGE AT AUSTIN** *I-18*
6301 East Hwy. 290
Austin, TX 78723
Tel: (512)371-3500
Fax: (512)371-3502
Web Site: http://www.vc.edu/
Description: Proprietary, 2-year, coed. Founded 2002.

■ **WADE COLLEGE** *D-19*
Ste. M5120, International Apparel Mart
PO Box 586343
Dallas, TX 75258-6343
Tel: (214)637-3530
Free: 800-624-4850

Fax: (214)637-0827

Web Site: http://www.wadecollege.edu/

Description: Proprietary, 2-year, coed. Awards transfer associate and terminal associate degrees. Founded 1965. Setting: 175-acre urban campus. Educational spending for 2005 fiscal year: $10,000 per student. Total enrollment: 177. 116 applied, 96% were admitted. 10% from top 10% of their high school class, 15% from top quarter, 60% from top half. Full-time: 87 students, 91% women, 9% men. 40% from out-of-state, 14% 25 or older, 45% live on campus, 34% transferred in. Retention: 65% of full-time freshmen returned the following year. Core. Calendar: trimesters. Academic remediation for entering students, services for LD students, double major, summer session for credit, part-time degree program.

Entrance Requirements: Open admission. Options: Peterson's Universal Application, Common Application, electronic application. Required: high school transcript, interview. Entrance: minimally difficult. Application deadline: Rolling.

Collegiate Environment: Orientation program. Social organizations: 4 open to all; local fraternities, local sororities; 20% of eligible men and 20% of eligible women are members. Most popular organizations: Fashion Group, Phi Theta Kappa, Phi Beta Lambda, Interior Design Student Group. Major annual events: Annual Banquet, Women's Apparel Market, Men's Apparel Market. Student services: personal-psychological counseling, women's center. Campus security: 24-hour emergency response devices and patrols, late night transport-escort service, controlled dormitory access. Options: coed, men-only, women-only housing available. College Library with 7,000 books, 150 serials, 400 audiovisual materials, and an OPAC. Operations spending for 2004 fiscal year: $150,000. 50 computers available on campus for general student use. A campuswide network can be accessed. Staffed computer lab on campus.

■ **WAYLAND BAPTIST UNIVERSITY** *B-11*

1900 West Seventh St.

Plainview, TX 79072-6998

Tel: (806)291-1000

Free: 800-588-1928

Admissions: (806)291-3500

Fax: (806)291-1960

E-mail: admityou@wbu.edu

Web Site: http://www.wbu.edu/

Description: Independent Baptist, comprehensive, coed. Awards associate, bachelor's, and master's degrees (branch locations in Anchorage, AK; Amarillo, TX; Luke Airforce Base, AZ; Glorieta, NM; Aiea, HI; Lubbock, TX; San Antonio, TX; Wichita Falls, TX). Founded 1908. Setting: 80-acre small town campus. Endowment: $46.3 million. Educational spending for 2005 fiscal year: $5411 per student. Total enrollment: 1,124. Faculty: 102 (67 full-time, 35 part-time). Student-undergrad faculty ratio is 12:1. 511 applied, 65% were admitted. 23% from top 10% of their high school class, 53% from top quarter, 83% from top half. 5 valedictorians. Full-time: 840 students, 56% women, 44% men. Part-time: 164 students, 65% women, 35% men. Students come from 30 states and territories, 16 other countries, 14% from out-of-state, 1% Native American, 23% Hispanic, 4% black, 1% Asian American or Pacific Islander, 2% international, 20% 25 or older, 55% live on campus, 6% transferred in. Retention: 69% of full-time freshmen returned the following year. Academic areas with the most degrees conferred: education; business/marketing; security and protective services; theology and religious vocations. Core. Calendar: semesters. Academic remediation for entering students, advanced placement, accelerated degree program, honors program, distance learning, double major, summer session for credit, part-time degree program, external degree program, adult/continuing education programs, internships, graduate courses open to undergrads. ROTC: Army (c), Air Force (c).

Entrance Requirements: Required: high school transcript, SAT or ACT. Recommended: interview, ACT. Entrance: minimally difficult. Application deadline: 8/1. Notification: continuous.

Costs Per Year: Application fee: $35. Comprehensive fee: $13,484 includes full-time tuition ($9450), mandatory fees ($450), and college room and board ($3584). College room only: $1276. Full-time tuition and fees vary according to course load and location. Room and board charges vary according to board plan and housing facility. Part-time tuition: $315 per credit hour. Part-time mandatory fees: $50 per term. Part-time tuition and fees vary according to course load and location.

Collegiate Environment: Orientation program. Drama-theater group, choral group, marching band, student-run newspaper, radio station. Social organizations: 37 open to all; national fraternities, national sororities; 3% of

eligible men and 4% of eligible women are members. Most popular organization: student government. Major annual events: homecoming, Big Weekend, Pioneer Pride Week. Student services: health clinic, personal-psychological counseling. Campus security: 24-hour emergency response devices and patrols, security lighting. 535 college housing spaces available; 485 were occupied in 2003-04. Freshmen guaranteed college housing. On-campus residence required through junior year. Options: men-only, women-only housing available. J.E. and L.E. Mabee Learning Resource Center with 117,287 books, 277,407 microform titles, 538 serials, 11,383 audiovisual materials, an OPAC, and a Web page. Operations spending for 2004 fiscal year: $559,881. 123 computers available on campus for general student use. A campuswide network can be accessed from student residence rooms and from off campus. Staffed computer lab on campus.

Community Environment: Population 22,000. Plainview is an agricultural and industrial community located on the High Plains of Northwest Texas. The area is served by railroad, bus, and U.S. Highway 70 and Interstate 27; State Highways 194 and FM400. The city has many churches, a municipal airport, a memorial library, YMCA, and one hospital as well as several clinics to serve the community. Local recreation includes five swimming pools, summer baseball programs, golf courses, theatres, miniature golf, bowling facilities, and boating facilities. There are a great many civic and fraternal groups active in the area. Part-time employment is available.

■ **WEATHERFORD COLLEGE** *D-18*

225 College Park Ave.

Weatherford, TX 76086-5699

Tel: (817)594-5471

Free: 800-287-5471

Admissions: (817)598-6240

Fax: (817)598-6205

E-mail: durrett@wc.edu

Web Site: http://www.wc.edu/

Description: State and locally supported, 2-year, coed. Awards certificates, diplomas, transfer associate, and terminal associate degrees. Founded 1869. Setting: 94-acre small town campus with easy access to Dallas-Fort Worth. Endowment: $42.5 million. Research spending for 2004 fiscal year: $2.7 million. Educational spending for 2005 fiscal year: $13,251 per student. Total enrollment: 4,552. Student-undergrad faculty ratio is 22:1. 8% from out-of-state, 1% Native American, 8% Hispanic, 2% black, 1% Asian American or Pacific Islander, 1% international, 7% live on campus. Core. Calendar: semesters. Academic remediation for entering students, services for LD students, self-designed majors, freshman honors college, honors program, distance learning, summer session for credit, part-time degree program, adult/continuing education programs, co-op programs and internships. ROTC: Air Force (c).

Entrance Requirements: Open admission. Options: Peterson's Universal Application, early admission. Entrance: noncompetitive. Application deadline: Rolling. Notification: continuous.

Costs Per Year: Application fee: $0. Area resident tuition: $1456 full-time, $52 per hour part-time. State resident tuition: $1960 full-time, $70 per hour part-time. Nonresident tuition: $3164 full-time, $113 per hour part-time. College room and board: $6500.

Collegiate Environment: Orientation program. Drama-theater group, choral group. Social organizations: 21 open to all. Most popular organizations: Black Awareness Student Organization, Criminal Justice Club, Phi Theta Kappa. Major annual events: Homecoming, Halloween Dance, Family Weekend. Student services: personal-psychological counseling. Campus security: 24-hour emergency response devices and patrols, late night transport-escort service. College housing designed to accommodate 192 students; 200 undergraduates lived in college housing during 2003-04. Option: coed housing available. Weatherford College Library with 59,499 books, 362 serials, an OPAC, and a Web page. Operations spending for 2004 fiscal year: $3.5 million. 85 computers available on campus for general student use. A campuswide network can be accessed from off-campus. Staffed computer lab on campus.

Community Environment: Weatherford, population 18,000, is the county seat of Parker County. In a diversified crop and livestock market, watermelons are their best known product. Cutting horse ranches are a major market. It can be reached by rail, bus, and air lines, and Interstate 20. The climate is mild with a mean average temperature of 64 degrees and an average rainfall of 31.6 inches. There is a city library, a local hospital, several churches representing the major denominations, and various civic and fraternal organizations. The Parker Plaza Shopping Center and College Park Shopping Center serve the surrounding area. Local recreation includes

Weatherford Lake with boating, fishing, and swimming, a local picnic grounds, golf, and three public parks. Part-time employment opportunities are very limited.

■ WEST TEXAS A&M UNIVERSITY D-3
2501 4th Ave.
Canyon, TX 79016-0001
Tel: (806)651-2000
Free: 800-99-WTAMU
Admissions: (806)651-2020
Fax: (806)651-2126
E-mail: admissions@mail.wtamu.edu
Web Site: http://www.wtamu.edu/
Description: State-supported, comprehensive, coed. Part of Texas A&M University System. Awards bachelor's, master's, and doctoral degrees. Founded 1909. Setting: 128-acre small town campus. Endowment: $14.4 million. Research spending for 2004 fiscal year: $4.7 million. Educational spending for 2005 fiscal year: $4305 per student. Total enrollment: 8,667. Faculty: 321 (246 full-time, 75 part-time). Student-undergrad faculty ratio is 24:1. 1,903 applied, 73% were admitted. 14% from top 10% of their high school class, 42% from top quarter, 78% from top half. 19 valedictorians. Full-time: 4,461 students, 58% women, 42% men. Part-time: 1,334 students, 58% women, 42% men. Students come from 32 states and territories, 30 other countries, 1% Native American, 16% Hispanic, 4% black, 1% Asian American or Pacific Islander, 1% international, 26% 25 or older, 19% live on campus, 13% transferred in. Retention: 66% of full-time freshmen returned the following year. Academic areas with the most degrees conferred: business/marketing; interdisciplinary studies; liberal arts/general studies. Core. Calendar: semesters. Academic remediation for entering students, ESL program, services for LD students, advanced placement, honors program, independent study, distance learning, double major, summer session for credit, part-time degree program, adult/continuing education programs, co-op programs and internships.
Entrance Requirements: Options: Common Application, electronic application. Required: high school transcript, class rank + Texas high school curriculum or equivalent, SAT or ACT. Entrance: moderately difficult. Application deadline: Rolling. Notification: continuous.
Costs Per Year: Application fee: $25. State resident tuition: $2760 full-time. Nonresident tuition: $11,040 full-time. Mandatory fees: $996 full-time. College room and board: $4916. College room only: $2300.
Collegiate Environment: Orientation program. Drama-theater group, choral group, marching band, student-run newspaper, radio station. Social organizations: 100 open to all; national fraternities, national sororities, local fraternities, local sororities; 6% of eligible men and 4% of eligible women are members. Most popular organizations: Residence Hall Association, Student Organizations' Roundtable, student government, Students in Free Enterprise. Major annual events: Buffalo Branding, Workathon, Homecoming. Student services: health clinic, personal-psychological counseling. Campus security: 24-hour emergency response devices and patrols, late night transport-escort service, controlled dormitory access. 1,500 college housing spaces available; 1,260 were occupied in 2003-04. Freshmen guaranteed college housing. On-campus residence required through sophomore year. Options: coed, men-only, women-only housing available. Cornette Library with 1.1 million books, 1.3 million microform titles, 5,464 serials, 1,572 audiovisual materials, an OPAC, and a Web page. Operations spending for 2004 fiscal year: $954,631. 1,200 computers available on campus for general student use. A campuswide network can be accessed from student residence rooms and from off campus. Staffed computer lab on campus.

■ WESTERN TECHNICAL COLLEGE F-2
1000 Texas Ave.
El Paso, TX 79901-1536
Tel: (915)532-3737
Web Site: http://www.wtc-ep.edu/
Description: Private, 2-year, coed. Awards certificates, transfer associate, and terminal associate degrees. Total enrollment: 825. Student-undergrad faculty ratio is 18:1. 85% Hispanic, 3% black. Calendar: continuous.
Entrance Requirements: Open admission. Options: early admission, deferred admission.
Collegiate Environment: College housing not available. 25 computers available on campus for general student use. Computer purchase/lease plans available. A campuswide network can be accessed from off-campus. Staffed computer lab on campus.

■ WESTERN TECHNICAL INSTITUTE F-2
9451 Diana
El Paso, TX 79930-2610
Tel: (915)566-9621
Admissions: 800-225-5984
Web Site: http://www.wti-ep.com/
Description: Private, 2-year. Total enrollment: 925.

■ WESTERN TEXAS COLLEGE D-12
6200 College Ave.
Snyder, TX 79549-6105
Tel: (325)573-8511; 888-GO-TO-WTC
E-mail: jclifton@wtc.cc.tx.us
Web Site: http://www.wtc.edu/
Description: State and locally supported, 2-year, coed. Awards certificates, transfer associate, and terminal associate degrees. Founded 1969. Setting: 165-acre small town campus. Endowment: $653,379. Research spending for 2004 fiscal year: $27,127. Educational spending for 2005 fiscal year: $2575 per student. Total enrollment: 1,685. 1,775 applied, 95% were admitted. 15% from top 10% of their high school class, 35% from top quarter, 55% from top half. 39% 25 or older, 20% live on campus. Core. Calendar: semesters. Academic remediation for entering students, services for LD students, advanced placement, self-designed majors, summer session for credit, part-time degree program, adult/continuing education programs, internships.
Entrance Requirements: Open admission. Options: early admission, deferred admission. Required: high school transcript. Placement: THEA required; ACT required for some. Entrance: noncompetitive. Application deadline: Rolling. Notification: continuous.
Collegiate Environment: Drama-theater group, choral group, student-run newspaper. Student services: personal-psychological counseling. Campus security: 24-hour emergency response devices and patrols. 224 college housing spaces available; 190 were occupied in 2003-04. On-campus residence required in freshman year. Option: coed housing available. Western Texas College Resource Center with 43,000 books, 127 serials, and a Web page. 40 computers available on campus for general student use. Staffed computer lab on campus.
Community Environment: Snyder is a small rural city, population 12,000. Agriculture and oil are important industries.

■ WESTWOOD COLLEGE-DALLAS D-19
Executive Plaza I, Ste. 100
Dallas, TX 75243
Tel: (214)570-0100
Free: 800-281-2978
Admissions: 800-803-3140
Fax: (214)570-8502
Web Site: http://www.westwood.edu/
Description: Proprietary, 2-year, coed. Awards terminal associate degrees. Founded 2002. Setting: urban campus with easy access to Dallas. Total enrollment: 404. 468 applied. Full-time: 397 students, 34% women, 66% men. Part-time: 7 students, 43% women, 57% men. 0.5% Native American, 31% Hispanic, 30% black, 4% Asian American or Pacific Islander, 0.2% international, 32% 25 or older. Calendar: continuous.
Entrance Requirements: Required: interview, high school diploma or GED, and passing score on ACT/SAT or Accuplacer test..

■ WESTWOOD COLLEGE-FORT WORTH F-32
1331 Airport Freeway, Ste. 402
Euless, TX 76040
Tel: (817)605-8111
Admissions: (817)685-9994
Fax: (817)605-6972
Web Site: http://www.westwood.edu/
Description: Proprietary, 2-year, coed. Awards terminal associate degrees. Setting: urban campus with easy access to Dallas, TX. Total enrollment: 472. 478 applied. Full-time: 375 students, 31% women, 69% men. Part-time: 97 students, 39% women, 61% men. 1% Native American, 26% Hispanic, 13% black, 2% Asian American or Pacific Islander, 0% international, 33% 25 or older. Calendar: continuous.
Entrance Requirements: Required: interview, high school diploma/GED and passing scores on ACT/SAT or Accuplacer exam.

■ WESTWOOD COLLEGE-HOUSTON SOUTH CAMPUS J-22
One Arena Place, 7322 Southwest Freeway, Ste. 1900
Houston, TX 77074

Tel: (713)777-4433
Free: 800-281-2978
Fax: (713)219-2088
Web Site: http://www.westwood.edu/
Description: Proprietary, 2-year, coed. Awards terminal associate degrees. Founded 2003. Setting: urban campus with easy access to Houston, TX. Total enrollment: 16. 29 applied, 66% were admitted. Full-time: 16 students, 31% women, 69% men. 0% Native American, 13% Hispanic, 56% black, 0% Asian American or Pacific Islander, 0% international, 50% 25 or older. Calendar: continuous.
Entrance Requirements: Required: interview, high school diploma/GED and passing ACT/SAT or Accuplacer scores.

■ **WHARTON COUNTY JUNIOR COLLEGE** *K-21*
911 Boling Hwy.
Wharton, TX 77488-3298
Tel: (979)532-4560
Admissions: (979)532-6381
Web Site: http://www.wcjc.edu/
Description: State and locally supported, 2-year, coed. Awards certificates, transfer associate, and terminal associate degrees. Founded 1946. Setting: 90-acre rural campus with easy access to Houston. Total enrollment: 6,029. Student-undergrad faculty ratio is 22:1. 5% from top 10% of their high school class, 50% from top half. Students come from 8 states and territories, 5 other countries, 0.2% Native American, 24% Hispanic, 9% black, 4% Asian American or Pacific Islander, 4% international, 30% 25 or older, 5% live on campus. Core. Calendar: semesters. Academic remediation for entering students, advanced placement, self-designed majors, summer session for credit, part-time degree program, adult/continuing education programs.
Entrance Requirements: Open admission. Required: high school transcript, minimum 2.0 high school GPA. Entrance: noncompetitive. Application deadline: 8/14.
Costs Per Year: Application fee: $10. Area resident tuition: $1296 full-time, $54 per semester hour part-time. State resident tuition: $2160 full-time, $90 per semester hour part-time. Nonresident tuition: $2928 full-time, $122 per semester hour part-time. College room and board: $2500. College room only: $600.
Collegiate Environment: Drama-theater group. Student services: personal-psychological counseling. Campus security: 24-hour patrols. 160 college housing spaces available; 140 were occupied in 2003-04. J. M. Hodges Library with 51,478 books and 536 serials. 350 computers available on campus for general student use. Staffed computer lab on campus.
Community Environment: Population 9,881, Wharton is situated on the banks of the Colorado River, 45 miles from the Gulf of Mexico. The community is served by bus lines, a municipal airport, and U.S. Highway 59. Community facilities include a county library, hospital and clinic, several

churches of various faiths, and many civic and fraternal organizations. It also has a museum, theatre, concert series, health club, municipal swimming pool, hunting, and fishing. An annual Wharton County Youth Rodeo is held here. Part-time employment is available.

■ **WILEY COLLEGE** *D-23*
711 Wiley Ave.
Marshall, TX 75670-5199
Tel: (903)927-3300
Free: 800-658-6889
Admissions: (903)927-3356
Fax: (903)938-8100
Web Site: http://www.wileyc.edu/
Description: Independent, 4-year, coed, affiliated with United Methodist Church. Awards associate and bachelor's degrees. Founded 1873. Setting: 58-acre small town campus. Endowment: $5.1 million. Educational spending for 2005 fiscal year: $3220 per student. Total enrollment: 666. 725 applied, 44% were admitted. 10% from top quarter of their high school class, 33% from top half. Full-time: 648 students, 56% women, 44% men. Part-time: 18 students, 44% women, 56% men. Students come from 16 states and territories, 7 other countries, 35% from out-of-state, 0.3% Native American, 1% Hispanic, 87% black, 8% international, 34% 25 or older, 82% transferred in. Retention: 100% of full-time freshmen returned the following year. Core. Calendar: semesters. Academic remediation for entering students, self-designed majors, summer session for credit, part-time degree program, adult/continuing education programs. Off campus study at Howard University. Study abroad program.
Entrance Requirements: Options: early admission, deferred admission. Required: high school transcript, 1 recommendation. Recommended: SAT or ACT. Entrance: minimally difficult. Application deadline: 8/1. Notification: continuous until 8/10.
Collegiate Environment: Orientation program. Drama-theater group, student-run newspaper. Social organizations: national fraternities, national sororities. Student services: health clinic, personal-psychological counseling. 386 college housing spaces available; 339 were occupied in 2003-04. T. Winston Cole, Sr. Library with 24,000 books, 40,000 microform titles, 23,000 serials, and 8,000 audiovisual materials. Operations spending for 2004 fiscal year: $52,832. 30 computers available on campus for general student use.
Community Environment: Population 25,000. Marshall is located at the junction of Highways U.S. 59 and 80 and Interstate 20, approximately 40 miles west of Shreveport, and 150 miles east of Dallas. The climate is temperate and mild. Natural gas fields surround the city. Railroad and bus lines serve the community, and Harrison County Memorial Airport located three miles east offers airline facilities. There are many churches of various faiths, hospitals, radio stations, and public library serving the area. Skilled and unskilled employment opportunities are available. Local recreation includes camping, fishing, and hunting.

■ **UNIVERSITY OF THE VIRGIN ISLANDS**
2 John Brewers Bay
St. Thomas, VI 00802-9990
Tel: (340)776-9200
Admissions: (340)693-1224
E-mail: cooke@adminen.uvi.edu
Web Site: http://www.uvi.edu/

Description: Territory-supported, comprehensive, coed. Awards associate, bachelor's, and master's degrees. Founded 1962. Setting: 175-acre small town campus. Endowment: $6.3 million. Research spending for 2004 fiscal year: $6.3 million. Total enrollment: 2,392. Faculty: 259 (107 full-time, 152 part-time). Student-undergrad faculty ratio is 13:1. 802 applied, 72% were admitted. Full-time: 1,227 students, 73% women, 27% men. Part-time: 958 students, 80% women, 20% men. Students come from 29 states and territories, 10 other countries, 3% from out-of-territory, 0.4% Native American, 6% Hispanic, 77% black, 1% Asian American or Pacific Islander, 6% international, 48% 25 or older, 3% transferred in. Retention: 72% of full-time freshmen returned the following year. Academic areas with the most degrees conferred: business/marketing; education; biological/life sciences. Core. Calendar: semesters. Academic remediation for entering students, advanced placement, independent study, distance learning, summer session for credit, part-time degree program, external degree program, adult/continuing education programs, internships, graduate courses open to undergrads. Off campus study at National Student Exchange. ROTC: Army.

Entrance Requirements: Options: early admission, early action, deferred admission. Required: essay, high school transcript, 2 recommendations, SAT or ACT. Entrance: minimally difficult. Application deadline: 4/30. Notification: continuous.

Costs Per Year: Application fee: $25. Territory resident tuition: $3300 full-time, $110 per credit part-time. Nonresident tuition: $9900 full-time, $330 per credit part-time. Mandatory fees: $426 full-time, $276 per year part-time. Full-time tuition and fees vary according to course load, degree level, and program. Part-time tuition and fees vary according to course load, degree level, and program. College room and board: $7550. College room only: $1100. Room and board charges vary according to board plan and housing facility.

Collegiate Environment: Orientation program. Drama-theater group, choral group, student-run newspaper. Social organizations: 33 open to all; national sororities; 1% of women are members. Most popular organizations: The Squad, Predators, Golden Key Honor Society, National Student Exchange Club, St. Kitts and Nevis. Major annual events: Welcome Kontiki Boat Ride, Afternoon on the Green, Miss University of the Virgin Islands. Student services: health clinic, personal-psychological counseling. Campus security: 24-hour patrols. 250 college housing spaces available; 208 were occupied in 2003-04. No special consideration for freshman housing applicants. Options: men-only, women-only housing available. Ralph M. Paiewonsky Library with 106,361 books, 1.2 million microform titles, 136,790 serials, 1,065 audiovisual materials, an OPAC, and a Web page. Operations spending for 2004 fiscal year: $781,229. 100 computers available on campus for general student use. A campuswide network can be accessed from off-campus. Staffed computer lab on campus.

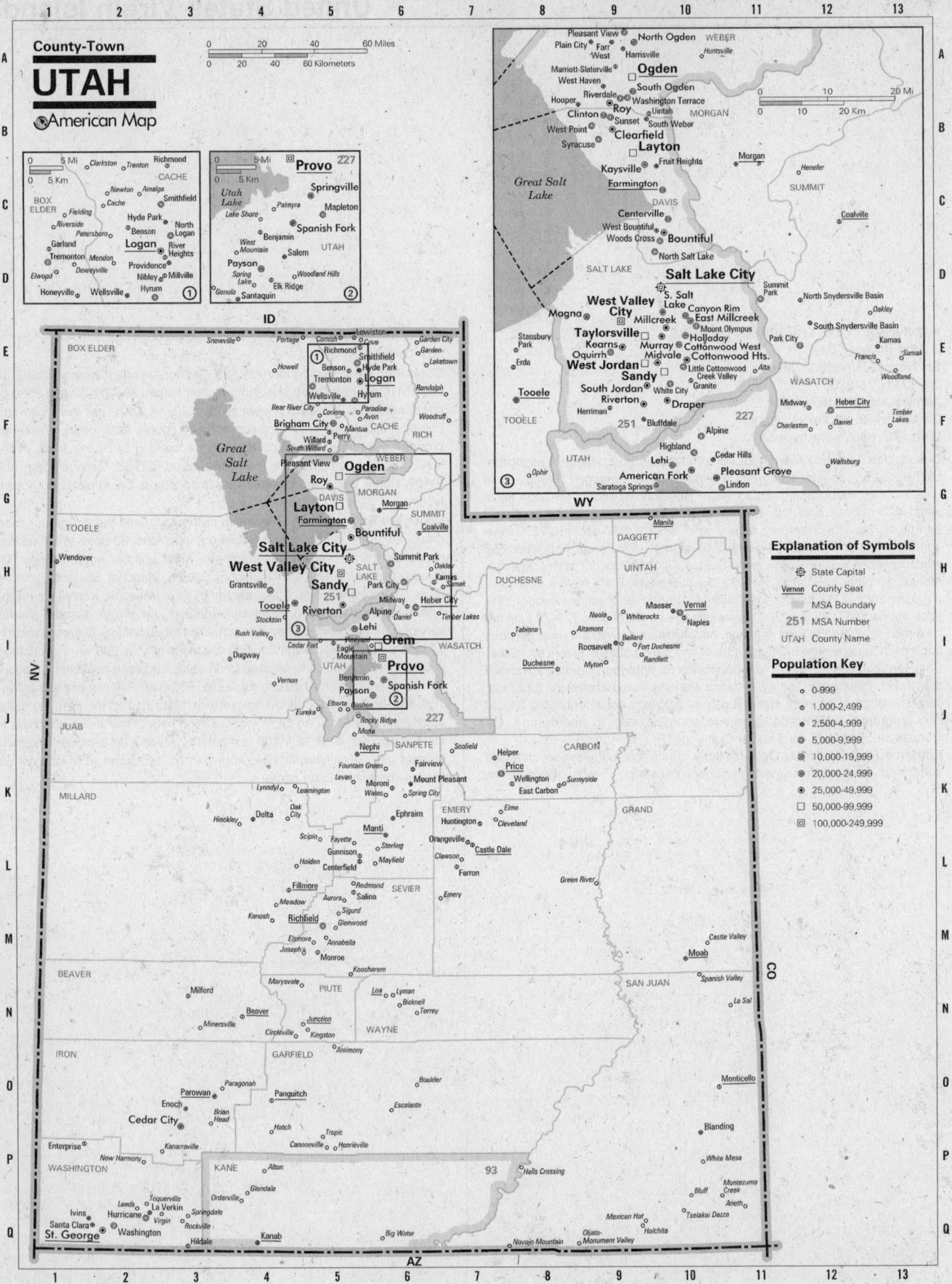

Utah

County-Town

UTAH

American Map

Explanation of Symbols

- ⊕ State Capital
- *Vernon* County Seat
- MSA Boundary
- 251 MSA Number
- UTAH County Name

Population Key

- ○ 0-999
- ◔ 1,000-2,499
- ◑ 2,500-4,999
- ◎ 5,000-9,999
- ◉ 10,000-19,999
- ◉ 20,000-24,999
- ⊕ 25,000-49,999
- □ 50,000-99,999
- ▣ 100,000-249,999

■ **BRIGHAM YOUNG UNIVERSITY** *I-6*
Provo, UT 84602-1001
Tel: (801)422-1211
Admissions: (801)422-2507
Fax: (801)422-5278
E-mail: admissions@byu.edu
Web Site: http://www.byu.edu/
Description: Independent, university, coed, affiliated with The Church of Jesus Christ of Latter-day Saints. Part of Church Education System (CES) of The Church of Jesus Christ of Latter-day Saints. Awards bachelor's, master's, doctoral, and first professional degrees. Founded 1875. Setting: 557-acre suburban campus with easy access to Salt Lake City. Total enrollment: 34,067. Faculty: 1,762 (1,321 full-time, 441 part-time). Student-undergrad faculty ratio is 21:1. 8,696 applied, 78% were admitted. 49% from top 10% of their high school class, 84% from top quarter, 99% from top half. 118 National Merit Scholars. Full-time: 27,460 students, 50% women, 50% men. Part-time: 3,338 students, 48% women, 52% men. Students come from 56 states and territories, 125 other countries, 72% from out-of-state, 1% Native American, 4% Hispanic, 1% black, 4% Asian American or Pacific Islander, 3% international, 10% 25 or older, 20% live on campus, 5% transferred in. Retention: 95% of full-time freshmen returned the following year. Academic areas with the most degrees conferred: business/marketing; education; visual and performing arts. Core. Calendar: semesters. Academic remediation for entering students, ESL program, services for LD students, advanced placement, accelerated degree program, freshman honors college, honors program, independent study, distance learning, double major, summer session for credit, part-time degree program, external degree program, adult/continuing education programs, co-op programs and internships, graduate courses open to undergrads. Off campus study at BYU Salt Lake Center. Study abroad program. ROTC: Army, Air Force.
Entrance Requirements: Options: electronic application, early admission, deferred admission. Required: essay, high school transcript, 1 recommendation, interview, ACT. Required for some: SAT or ACT. Entrance: moderately difficult. Application deadline: 2/15. Notification: continuous.
Costs Per Year: Application fee: $30. Comprehensive fee: $10,906 includes full-time tuition ($5116) and college room and board ($5790). Full-time tuition varies according to reciprocity agreements. Room and board charges vary according to board plan and housing facility.
Collegiate Environment: Orientation program. Drama-theater group, choral group, marching band, student-run newspaper, radio station. Social organizations: 390 open to all. Major annual events: homecoming, Handicap Awareness Week, Involvement Week. Student services: legal services, health clinic, personal-psychological counseling, women's center, legal services. Campus security: 24-hour emergency response devices and patrols, late night transport-escort service, controlled dormitory access. 7,812 college housing spaces available. No special consideration for freshman housing applicants. Options: men-only, women-only housing available. Main library plus 2 others with 3.5 million books, 3.4 million microform titles, 27,161 serials, 182,663 audiovisual materials, an OPAC, and a Web page. 2,000 computers available on campus for general student use. Computer purchase/lease plans available. A campuswide network can be accessed from student residence rooms and from off campus. Staffed computer lab on campus.
Community Environment: Located 45 miles from Salt Lake City. Local industries also produce steel, computer software, pig iron, and foundry products. The community may be reached by air, railroad, bus lines, and Highways 6, 91, 89, 50, and Interstate 15. The community has hospitals, shopping centers, and national monuments nearby. Part-time employment is available. Local recreation includes hunting, fishing, picnicking, hiking, swimming, boating, water-skiing, horseback riding, golf, tennis, ice skating, bobsledding, and snow skiing.

■ **CALIFORNIA COLLEGE FOR HEALTH SCIENCES** *H-5*
5295 South Commerce Dr.
Salt Lake City, UT 84107
Tel: 800-221-7374
Free: 800-791-7353
Fax: (801)263-0345
E-mail: admissions@cchs.edu
Web Site: http://www.cchs.edu/
Description: Proprietary, comprehensive, coed. Awards associate, bachelor's, and master's degrees (offers primarily external degree programs). Founded 1978. Setting: 2-acre urban campus with easy access to San Diego. Total enrollment: 5,458. Students come from 52 states and territories, 15 other countries, 95% from out-of-state, 85% 25 or older. Retention: 85% of full-time freshmen returned the following year. Calendar: continuous. Distance learning, part-time degree program, external degree program.
Entrance Requirements: Open admission. Option: deferred admission. Required: high school transcript. Recommended: employment in a health science field. Required for some: employment in a health science field. Entrance: noncompetitive. Application deadline: Rolling.
Costs Per Year: Application fee: $100. Tuition guaranteed not to increase for student's term of enrollment.
Collegiate Environment: College housing not available.

■ **COLLEGE OF EASTERN UTAH** *K-7*
451 East 400 North
Price, UT 84501-2699
Tel: (435)637-2120
Admissions: (435)613-5217
Fax: (435)637-4102
E-mail: todd.olson@ceu.edu
Web Site: http://www.ceu.edu/
Description: State-supported, 2-year, coed. Part of Utah System of Higher Education. Awards certificates, transfer associate, and terminal associate degrees. Founded 1937. Setting: 15-acre small town campus. Total enrollment: 2,294. Student-undergrad faculty ratio is 15:1. 477 applied, 100% were admitted. 10% from top 10% of their high school class, 29% from top quarter, 63% from top half. Full-time: 1,317 students, 54% women, 46% men. Part-time: 977 students, 55% women, 45% men. Students come from 21 states and territories, 9% from out-of-state, 15% Native American, 3% Hispanic, 1% black, 1% Asian American or Pacific Islander, 1% international, 26% 25 or older, 15% live on campus, 10% transferred in. Core. Calendar: semesters. Academic remediation for entering students, ESL program, services for LD students, advanced placement, independent study, distance learning, summer session for credit, part-time degree program, adult/continuing education programs, co-op programs.
Entrance Requirements: Open admission except for nursing program. Options: Peterson's Universal Application, electronic application, early admission. Recommended: high school transcript, ACT. Entrance: noncompetitive. Application deadline: Rolling.

Costs Per Year: Application fee: $25. State resident tuition: $2090 full-time, $88 per credit hour part-time. Nonresident tuition: $7122 full-time, $339 per credit hour part-time. Mandatory fees: $17.08 per credit hour part-time. College room and board: $3392.

Collegiate Environment: Orientation program. Drama-theater group, choral group, student-run newspaper. Social organizations: 25 open to all. Major annual event: Convocation. Student services: health clinic, personal-psychological counseling, women's center. Campus security: 24-hour emergency response devices and patrols, late night transport-escort service. 478 college housing spaces available; 400 were occupied in 2003-04. Option: coed housing available. College of Eastern Utah Library with 44,490 books, 31,308 microform titles, 1,464 audiovisual materials, an OPAC, and a Web page. 200 computers available on campus for general student use. A campuswide network can be accessed from student residence rooms and from off campus. Staffed computer lab on campus.

Community Environment: A trade center, Price is in a large coal mining and farming district. Natural gas deposits have also been found in the surrounding areas. The city is located at the base of Wasatch Mountain Range and has a temperate climate. There are churches of most denominations in the community. Several clinics, a hospital, library, and various civic and fraternal organizations serve the area. Price houses the College of Eastern Utah World renowned Prehistoric Museum. Part-time employment is available for students. Hotels, motels, rooming houses, and furnished apartments are available for student housing. Local recreation includes skiing, sledding, snowshoe hiking, movies, boating, water country skiing, mountain biking, hiking, fishing, hunting, rodeos, and baseball.

■ DIXIE STATE COLLEGE OF UTAH

225 South 700 East
St. George, UT 84770-3876
Tel: (435)652-7500; 888-GO2DIXIE
Admissions: (435)652-7704
Fax: (435)656-4005
Web Site: http://www.dixie.edu/

Description: State-supported, primarily 2-year, coed. Part of Utah System of Higher Education. Awards certificates, diplomas, transfer associate, terminal associate, and bachelor's degrees. Founded 1911. Setting: 60-acre small town campus. Endowment: $9.9 million. Educational spending for 2005 fiscal year: $2292 per student. Total enrollment: 8,992. Student-undergrad faculty ratio is 19:1. 2,745 applied, 85% were admitted. 12% from top 10% of their high school class, 35% from top quarter, 64% from top half. Full-time: 3,395 students, 53% women, 47% men. Part-time: 5,597 students, 51% women, 49% men. Students come from 44 states and territories, 19 other countries, 13% from out-of-state, 2% Native American, 3% Hispanic, 1% black, 2% Asian American or Pacific Islander, 1% international, 21% 25 or older, 2% live on campus, 5% transferred in. Retention: 48% of full-time freshmen returned the following year. Core. Calendar: semesters. Academic remediation for entering students, ESL program, services for LD students, advanced placement, honors program, distance learning, summer session for credit, part-time degree program, adult/continuing education programs, co-op programs. Off campus study.

Entrance Requirements: Open admission. Options: electronic application, early admission, deferred admission. Required: high school transcript. Entrance: noncompetitive. Application deadline: Rolling.

Costs Per Year: Application fee: $25. State resident tuition: $2100 full-time, $88 per credit part-time. Nonresident tuition: $8664 full-time, $361 per credit part-time. Mandatory fees: $392 full-time.

Collegiate Environment: Orientation program. Drama-theater group, choral group, student-run newspaper, radio station. Most popular organizations: Dixie Spirit, Outdoor Club, Association of Women Students. Major annual events: homecoming, D-Week, Student Orientation Week. Student services: health clinic, personal-psychological counseling. Campus security: 24-hour emergency response devices and patrols. 252 college housing spaces available. Options: coed, men-only housing available. Val A. Browning Library with 94,747 books, 34,538 microform titles, 263 serials, 13,411 audiovisual materials, an OPAC, and a Web page. Operations spending for 2004 fiscal year: $777,768.

■ ITT TECHNICAL INSTITUTE *E-10*

920 West Levoy Dr.
Murray, UT 84123-2500
Tel: (801)263-3313
Free: 800-365-2136
Web Site: http://www.itt-tech.edu/

Description: Proprietary, primarily 2-year, coed. Part of ITT Educational Services, Inc. Awards terminal associate and bachelor's degrees. Founded 1984. Setting: 3-acre suburban campus with easy access to Salt Lake City. Core.

Entrance Requirements: Option: deferred admission. Required: high school transcript, interview, Wonderlic aptitude test. Recommended: recommendations. Entrance: minimally difficult. Application deadline: Rolling. Notification: continuous.

Costs Per Year: Application fee: $100.

Collegiate Environment: Orientation program. College housing not available.

■ LDS BUSINESS COLLEGE *H-5*

411 East South Temple St.
Salt Lake City, UT 84111-1392
Tel: (801)524-8100
Free: 800-999-5767
Admissions: (801)524-8144
Fax: (801)524-1900
E-mail: renae@ldsbc.edu
Web Site: http://www.ldsbc.edu/

Description: Independent, 2-year, coed, affiliated with The Church of Jesus Christ of Latter-day Saints. Part of Latter-day Saints Church Educational System. Awards certificates, transfer associate, and terminal associate degrees. Founded 1886. Setting: urban campus. Total enrollment: 1,282. 630 applied, 82% were admitted. Full-time: 960 students, 61% women, 39% men. Part-time: 322 students, 59% women, 41% men. Students come from 40 states and territories, 45 other countries, 53% from out-of-state, 0.2% Native American, 4% Hispanic, 1% black, 2% Asian American or Pacific Islander, 22% international, 29% 25 or older, 13% live on campus, 11% transferred in. Core. Calendar: semesters. Academic remediation for entering students, advanced placement, summer session for credit, part-time degree program, adult/continuing education programs, co-op programs and internships.

Entrance Requirements: Open admission. Options: electronic application, early admission, deferred admission. Required: high school transcript, interview. Placement: ACT recommended. Entrance: noncompetitive. Application deadline: Rolling.

Costs Per Year: Application fee: $25. Tuition: $2480 full-time. Full-time tuition varies according to course load. College room only: $2236.

Collegiate Environment: Orientation program. Choral group, student-run newspaper. Social organizations: local sororities. Most popular organizations: Institute Women's Association, Institute Men's Association. Major annual event: Service-Learning Day. Campus security: 24-hour emergency response devices, controlled dormitory access. 112 college housing spaces available; 13 were occupied in 2003-04. Option: women-only housing available. LDS Business College Library with 24,000 books, 130 serials, 300 audiovisual materials, an OPAC, and a Web page. 350 computers available on campus for general student use. A campuswide network can be accessed from student residence rooms. Staffed computer lab on campus.

■ MIDWIVES COLLEGE OF UTAH *I-6*

560 South State St., Ste. B2
Orem, UT 84058
Tel: (801)764-9068; (866)764-9068
Fax: (801)434-8704
Web Site: http://www.midwifery.edu/

Description: Independent, comprehensive, women only. Awards bachelor's and master's degrees. Founded 1980. Setting: urban campus. Total enrollment: 73. Faculty: 8. Student-undergrad faculty ratio is 1:1. 32 applied, 100% were admitted. Part-time: 66 students. Retention: 93% of full-time freshmen returned the following year. Calendar: semesters.

■ MOUNTAIN WEST COLLEGE *H-5*

3280 West 3500 South
West Valley City, UT 84119
Tel: (801)840-4800
Fax: (801)969-0828
E-mail: jasonp@cci.edu
Web Site: http://www.mwcollege.com/

Description: Proprietary, 2-year, coed. Part of Corinthian Colleges, Inc. Awards diplomas, transfer associate, and terminal associate degrees. Founded 1982. Setting: suburban campus. Total enrollment: 773. 169 applied, 88% were admitted. 42% 25 or older. Core. Academic remediation for entering students, ESL program, accelerated degree program, independent study, summer session for credit, part-time degree program, internships.

Entrance Requirements: Option: deferred admission. Required: high school transcript, interview, CPAt. Recommended: SAT or ACT. Entrance: noncompetitive. Application deadline: Rolling.

Collegiate Environment: Orientation program. Social organizations: 1 open to all. Most popular organization: Student Activity Committee. Major annual events: Christmas Service Project, Christmas Social, Halloween Social. College housing not available. Learning Resource Center with 5,250 books and 41 serials. Operations spending for 2004 fiscal year: $30,000. 76 computers available on campus for general student use. A campuswide network can be accessed. Staffed computer lab on campus.

■ **NEUMONT UNIVERSITY** *H-5*
2755 East Cottonwood Parkway, Ste. 600
Salt Lake City, UT 84121
Tel: (801)438-1100; (866)622-3448
Admissions: (801)733-2833
Fax: (801)438-1111
E-mail: jamie.wyse@northface.edu
Web Site: http://www.neumont.edu/

Description: Proprietary, 4-year, coed. Administratively affiliated with Morrison University. Awards bachelor's degrees. Founded 2002. Setting: suburban campus. Total enrollment: 140. 300 applied, 83% were admitted. Students come from 25 states and territories, 32% from out-of-state, 30% live on campus. Retention: 96% of full-time freshmen returned the following year. Core. Accelerated degree program.

Entrance Requirements: Option: electronic application. Required: essay, high school transcript, 2 recommendations, interview. Recommended: SAT and SAT Subject Tests or ACT.

Collegiate Environment: Orientation program. Student services: health clinic, personal-psychological counseling. 200 college housing spaces available; 40 were occupied in 2003-04. Freshmen given priority for college housing. Option: coed housing available.

■ **PROVO COLLEGE** *I-6*
1450 West 820 North
Provo, UT 84601
Tel: (801)375-1861
Free: 800-748-4834
Fax: (801)375-9728
E-mail: gordonp@provocollege.org
Web Site: http://www.provocollege.com/
Description: Proprietary, 2-year, coed.

■ **SALT LAKE COMMUNITY COLLEGE** *H-5*
PO Box 30808
Salt Lake City, UT 84130-0808
Tel: (801)957-4111
Admissions: (801)957-4186
Fax: (801)957-4958
E-mail: janet.felker@slcc.edu
Web Site: http://www.slcc.edu/

Description: State-supported, 2-year, coed. Part of Utah System of Higher Education. Awards certificates, diplomas, transfer associate, and terminal associate degrees. Founded 1948. Setting: 114-acre urban campus. Endowment: $5.8 million. Educational spending for 2005 fiscal year: $2356 per student. Total enrollment: 24,111. Student-undergrad faculty ratio is 18:1. 9,271 applied, 100% were admitted. Full-time: 8,165 students, 48% women, 52% men. Part-time: 15,946 students, 50% women, 50% men. 4% from out-of-state, 1% Native American, 7% Hispanic, 1% black, 4% Asian American or Pacific Islander, 1% international, 37% 25 or older, 6% transferred in. Core. Calendar: semesters. Academic remediation for entering students, ESL program, services for LD students, advanced placement, self-designed majors, distance learning, double major, summer session for credit, part-time degree program, co-op programs and internships. Study abroad program. ROTC: Army (c), Air Force (c).

Entrance Requirements: Open admission except for health science programs. Options: electronic application, early admission, deferred admission. Entrance: noncompetitive. Application deadline: Rolling.

Costs Per Year: Application fee: $35. State resident tuition: $2046 full-time. Nonresident tuition: $7161 full-time. Mandatory fees: $358 full-time.

Collegiate Environment: Orientation program. Drama-theater group, choral group, student-run newspaper, radio station. Social organizations: 50 open

to all; local fraternities, local sororities; 6% of eligible men and 7% of eligible women are members. Most popular organizations: LDSSA, VICA, Phi Theta Kappa, PBL, Student Nurse Alliance. Major annual events: Rush Week, Monster Mash. Student services: health clinic, personal-psychological counseling. Campus security: 24-hour emergency response devices and patrols, late night transport-escort service. College housing not available. Markosian Library plus 2 others with 96,470 books, 51,342 microform titles, 781 serials, 29,810 audiovisual materials, an OPAC, and a Web page. Operations spending for 2004 fiscal year: $1.5 million. 2,905 computers available on campus for general student use. A campuswide network can be accessed from off-campus. Staffed computer lab on campus.

Community Environment: The capital of the state, Salt Lake City, is located at the foot of the beautiful Wasatch Mountains. The Great Salt Lake is northwest of the city was founded by Brigham Young and his followers, and many of the original buildings may still be seen. The city is a metropolis today enjoying excellent transportation facilities. There are five libraries, a law library, many churches of various denominations, hospitals, and clinics to serve the community. Some part-time employment is available. Local recreation facilities includes 23 parks, golf courses, fishing, hunting, bowling, skiing, several theatres, and outdoor sports. There are excellent shopping facilities located here. The Utah State Fair is held annually as well as the Music Festival.

■ **SNOW COLLEGE** *K-6*
150 East College Ave.
Ephraim, UT 84627-1203
Tel: (435)283-7000
Admissions: (435)283-7321
Fax: (435)283-6879
Web Site: http://www.snow.edu/

Description: State-supported, 2-year, coed. Part of Utah System of Higher Education. Awards certificates, diplomas, transfer associate, and terminal associate degrees. Founded 1888. Setting: 50-acre rural campus. Endowment: $5.8 million. Research spending for 2004 fiscal year: $21,046. Educational spending for 2005 fiscal year: $3194 per student. Total enrollment: 3,333. Student-undergrad faculty ratio is 13:1. 1,764 applied, 75% were admitted. Full-time: 2,463 students, 55% women, 45% men. Part-time: 870 students, 48% women, 52% men. Students come from 34 states and territories, 15 other countries, 8% from out-of-state, 1% Native American, 2% Hispanic, 0.4% black, 2% Asian American or Pacific Islander, 2% international, 14% 25 or older, 10% live on campus, 1% transferred in. Retention: 92% of full-time freshmen returned the following year. Core. Calendar: semesters. Academic remediation for entering students, ESL program, services for LD students, advanced placement, honors program, independent study, summer session for credit, part-time degree program, external degree program, adult/continuing education programs, co-op programs.

Entrance Requirements: Open admission. Option: early admission. Required: high school transcript. Entrance: noncompetitive. Application deadline: 6/15. Notification: continuous.

Costs Per Year: Application fee: $30. State resident tuition: $1784 full-time, $60 per credit hour part-time. Nonresident tuition: $7118 full-time, $237 per credit hour part-time. Mandatory fees: $380 full-time, $380 per term part-time. College room and board: $4500.

Collegiate Environment: Orientation program. Drama-theater group, choral group, student-run newspaper, radio station. Most popular organizations: Drama Club, Latter-Day Saints Singers, Dead Cats Society, Associated Women Students, Associated Men Students. Major annual events: homecoming, Snow King/Miss Snow, Earth Day. Student services: personal-psychological counseling. Campus security: student patrols. 250 undergraduates lived in college housing during 2003-04. Option: coed housing available. Lucy Phillips Library with 31,911 books, 53,351 microform titles, 1,870 audiovisual materials, an OPAC, and a Web page. Operations spending for 2004 fiscal year: $633,709. 220 computers available on campus for general student use. A campuswide network can be accessed from off-campus. Staffed computer lab on campus.

Community Environment: Ephraim is a small, rural, college town located in central Utah. The area has a moderate climate with four definite seasons. The community is reached by bus lines and Highway 89. The city has four churches in the immediate vicinity and others in the surrounding area, a hospital 13 miles distant, and a clinic in the town. Public restaurants, motels, and limited entertainment facilities are available. Student housing and part-time employments opportunities are available in the community. Local recreation includes boating, fishing, hunting, cross-country skiing, golf, and winter sports. The county fairs and local festivities highlight the heritages of local communities.

■ SOUTHERN UTAH UNIVERSITY *P-3*

351 West University Blvd.
Cedar City, UT 84720-2498
Tel: (435)586-7700
Admissions: (801)586-7740
Fax: (435)586-5475
E-mail: adminfo@suu.edu
Web Site: http://www.suu.edu/

Description: State-supported, comprehensive, coed. Part of Utah System of Higher Education. Awards associate, bachelor's, and master's degrees. Founded 1897. Setting: 113-acre small town campus. Endowment: $5.1 million. Educational spending for 2005 fiscal year: $2976 per student. Total enrollment: 6,859. Faculty: 274 (211 full-time, 63 part-time). Student-undergrad faculty ratio is 23:1. 2,492 applied, 80% were admitted. 28% from top 10% of their high school class, 51% from top quarter, 81% from top half. Full-time: 4,599 students, 55% women, 45% men. Part-time: 1,866 students, 64% women, 36% men. Students come from 40 states and territories, 14 other countries, 14% from out-of-state, 2% Native American, 2% Hispanic, 1% black, 2% Asian American or Pacific Islander, 1% international, 22% 25 or older, 13% live on campus, 8% transferred in. Retention: 59% of full-time freshmen returned the following year. Academic areas with the most degrees conferred: education; business/marketing; communications/journalism. Core. Calendar: semesters. Academic remediation for entering students, ESL program, services for LD students, advanced placement, honors program, independent study, distance learning, double major, summer session for credit, part-time degree program, adult/continuing education programs, co-op programs and internships, graduate courses open to undergrads. ROTC: Army.

Entrance Requirements: Options: Peterson's Universal Application, electronic application, early admission, deferred admission. Required: high school transcript, minimum 2.0 high school GPA, SAT or ACT. Entrance: moderately difficult. Application deadline: 8/1. Notification: continuous.

Costs Per Year: Application fee: $35. State resident tuition: $2834 full-time, $139 per credit hour part-time. Nonresident tuition: $9354 full-time, $461 per credit hour part-time. Mandatory fees: $524 full-time, $23 per credit hour part-time. Part-time tuition and fees vary according to course load. College room and board: $5400. College room only: $2400. Room and board charges vary according to board plan and housing facility.

Collegiate Environment: Orientation program. Drama-theater group, choral group, marching band, student-run newspaper, radio station. Social organizations: 45 open to all; national fraternities, national sororities, local sororities; 4% of eligible men and 3% of eligible women are members. Most popular organizations: Outdoor Club, Intertribal Club, Latter Day Saints Student Association, Ski Club, Residence Halls Association. Major annual events: Homecoming Parade, Thunderbird Awards, Miss SUU Pageant. Student services: health clinic, personal-psychological counseling, women's center. Campus security: 24-hour emergency response devices, student patrols, late night transport-escort service, controlled dormitory access. Options: coed, men-only, women-only housing available. Southern Utah University Library with 180,424 books, 629,897 microform titles, 6,165 serials, 13,352 audiovisual materials, an OPAC, and a Web page. Operations spending for 2004 fiscal year: $1.1 million. 300 computers available on campus for general student use. A campuswide network can be accessed from student residence rooms and from off campus. Staffed computer lab on campus.

Community Environment: Cedar City is located within a few hours of the Grand Canyon, Lake Powell, Cedar Breaks National Monument, Bryce Canyon, Zion National Park and other scenic wonders. It is 2 1/2 hours from Las Vegas. Cedar City is accessible by airlines, railroad, bus lines, and major highways. The community has churches representing most denominations, a hospital, public library, and a museum. Student housing is available in the community. Various civic, fraternal, and veteran's organizations are active in the area. Local recreation includes indoor and outdoor theatres, hunting, fishing, skiing, golf, and boating. There is a shopping center in the area.

■ STEVENS-HENAGER COLLEGE *G-5*

1890 West 1350 St.
Ogden, UT 84401-0251
Tel: (801)394-7791
Free: 800-371-7791
Fax: (801)393-1745
Web Site: http://www.stevenshenager.edu/

Description: Proprietary, primarily 2-year, coed. Part of CollegeAmerica, Inc. Awards terminal associate and bachelor's degrees. Founded 1891. Setting: 1-acre urban campus with easy access to Salt Lake City. Total enrollment: 479. 500 applied, 65% were admitted. 2% from top 10% of their high school class, 10% from top quarter, 68% from top half. Full-time: 479 students, 58% women, 42% men. Students come from 12 states and territories, 3 other countries, 27% from out-of-state, 50% 25 or older, 21% transferred in. Core. Academic remediation for entering students, part-time degree program, adult/continuing education programs.

Entrance Requirements: Open admission. Options: Common Application, early admission, deferred admission. Required: high school transcript, Wonderlic aptitude test. Recommended: SAT or ACT. Entrance: noncompetitive. Application deadline: Rolling. Notification: continuous.

Collegiate Environment: No special consideration for freshman housing applicants. 6,500 books, 35 serials, 377 audiovisual materials, and an OPAC. Operations spending for 2004 fiscal year: $1.6 million. 200 computers available on campus for general student use. A campuswide network can be accessed from off-campus. Staffed computer lab on campus.

■ UNIVERSITY OF PHOENIX-UTAH CAMPUS *H-5*

5373 South Green St.
Salt Lake City, UT 84123-4617
Tel: (801)263-1444
Free: 800-228-7240
Admissions: (480)557-1712
Fax: (801)269-9766
Web Site: http://www.phoenix.edu/

Description: Proprietary, comprehensive, coed. Awards bachelor's and master's degrees. Founded 1984. Setting: urban campus. Total enrollment: 4,135. Faculty: 388 (8 full-time, 380 part-time). Student-undergrad faculty ratio is 9:1. 187 applied, 98% were admitted. Full-time: 2,663 students, 44% women, 56% men. 0% from out-of-state, 0.4% Native American, 2% Hispanic, 0.5% black, 1% Asian American or Pacific Islander, 2% international, 92% 25 or older. Academic areas with the most degrees conferred: business/marketing; computer and information sciences; public administration and social services. Core. Calendar: continuous. Advanced placement, accelerated degree program, independent study, distance learning, external degree program, adult/continuing education programs, graduate courses open to undergrads.

Entrance Requirements: Open admission. Option: deferred admission. Required for some: high school transcript. Entrance: noncompetitive. Application deadline: Rolling.

Costs Per Year: Application fee: $110. Tuition: $10,020 full-time, $344 per credit part-time. Mandatory fees: $560 full-time, $70 per course part-time.

Collegiate Environment: College housing not available. University Library with 444 books, 666 serials, an OPAC, and a Web page. System-wide operations spending for 2004 fiscal year: $3.2 million.

■ UNIVERSITY OF UTAH *H-5*

201 South University St.
Salt Lake City, UT 84112-1107
Tel: (801)581-7200
Free: 800-444-8638
Admissions: (801)581-7281
Fax: (801)585-3034
Web Site: http://www.utah.edu/

Description: State-supported, university, coed. Part of Utah System of Higher Education. Awards bachelor's, master's, doctoral, and first professional degrees and post-master's certificates. Founded 1850. Setting: 1,500-acre urban campus. Endowment: $353.7 million. Research spending for 2004 fiscal year: $200.3 million. Educational spending for 2005 fiscal year: $10,000 per student. Total enrollment: 29,012. Faculty: 1,687 (1,175 full-time, 512 part-time). Student-undergrad faculty ratio is 15:1. 6,687 applied, 85% were admitted. 27% from top 10% of their high school class, 51% from top quarter, 82% from top half. Full-time: 15,551 students, 44% women, 56% men. Part-time: 7,110 students, 45% women, 55% men. Students come from 55 states and territories, 96 other countries, 7% from out-of-state, 1% Native American, 4% Hispanic, 1% black, 5% Asian American or Pacific Islander, 2% international, 32% 25 or older, 7% live on campus, 9% transferred in. Retention: 83% of full-time freshmen returned the following year. Academic areas with the most degrees conferred: social sciences; business/marketing; communications/journalism. Core. Calendar: semesters. Academic remediation for entering students, ESL program, services for LD students, advanced placement, accelerated degree program, self-designed majors, honors program, independent study, distance learning, double major, summer session for credit, part-time degree program, co-op programs and internships, graduate courses open to undergrads. Off campus study at members of the National Student Exchange. Study abroad program. ROTC: Army, Naval, Air Force.

Entrance Requirements: Options: electronic application, international baccalaureate accepted. Required: high school transcript, minimum 2.0 high school GPA, SAT or ACT. Recommended: minimum 3.0 high school GPA, ACT. Entrance: moderately difficult. Application deadline: 4/1.

Costs Per Year: Application fee: $35. State resident tuition: $3672 full-time, $102 per credit part-time. Nonresident tuition: $12,860 full-time, $351 per credit part-time. Mandatory fees: $670 full-time. Full-time tuition and fees vary according to course level, course load, degree level, and student level. Part-time tuition varies according to course level, course load, degree level, and student level. College room and board: $5422. College room only: $2704. Room and board charges vary according to board plan and housing facility.

Collegiate Environment: Orientation program. Drama-theater group, choral group, marching band, student-run newspaper, radio station. Social organizations: 170 open to all; national fraternities, national sororities, local fraternities, local sororities; 5% of eligible men and 5% of eligible women are members. Most popular organizations: Bennion Center, Latter-Day Saints Student Association, Newman Center, Center for Ethnic Student Affairs. Major annual events: First Week, Redfest, Homecoming. Student services: legal services, health clinic, personal-psychological counseling, women's center. Campus security: 24-hour emergency response devices and patrols, student patrols, late night transport-escort service, controlled dormitory access. 3,000 college housing spaces available; 2,500 were occupied in 2003-04. No special consideration for freshman housing applicants. Option: coed housing available. Marriott Library plus 3 others with 3 million books, 3.5 million microform titles, 33,517 serials, 62,356 audiovisual materials, an OPAC, and a Web page. Operations spending for 2004 fiscal year: $20.2 million. 8,000 computers available on campus for general student use. A campuswide network can be accessed from student residence rooms and from off campus. Staffed computer lab on campus.

Community Environment: The capital of the state, Salt Lake City, is located at the foot of the beautiful Wasatch Mountains. The Great Salt Lake is northwest of the city, and the desert is only a few miles away to the west. The city was founded by Brigham Young and his followers, and many of the original buildings may still be seen. The city is a metropolis today enjoying excellent transportation facilities. There are five libraries, a law library, many churches of various denominations, hospitals, and clinics to serve the community. Salt Lake City is the headquarters of the Church of Jesus Christ of Latter Day Saints, and is noted for Temple Square and the Mormon Temple and Tabernacle. Part-time employment is available. Local recreation facilities includes parks, golf courses, fishing, hunting, bowling, skiing, theatres, and outdoor sports. There are excellent shopping facilities located here. The Utah State Fair is held annually.

■ UTAH CAREER COLLEGE *E-9*

1902 West 7800 South
West Jordan, UT 84088
Tel: (801)304-4224; (866)304-4224
Fax: (801)304-4229
E-mail: kcooper@utahcollege.edu
Web Site: http://www.utahcollege.edu/

Description: Proprietary, 2-year, coed. Awards certificates, diplomas, and transfer associate degrees. Setting: 1-acre suburban campus with easy access to Salt Lake City. Educational spending for 2005 fiscal year: $9200 per student. Total enrollment: 570. Student-undergrad faculty ratio is 12:1. 95 applied, 100% were admitted. Full-time: 152 students, 82% women, 18% men. Part-time: 418 students, 79% women, 21% men. Students come from 2 states and territories, 1% from out-of-state, 1% Native American, 6% Hispanic, 0% black, 1% Asian American or Pacific Islander, 0% international, 53% 25 or older, 0% transferred in.

Entrance Requirements: Required: high school transcript, interview. Application deadline: 10/1.

Costs Per Year: Tuition: $12,060 full-time, $335 per credit part-time.

Collegiate Environment: Major annual event: Quarterly Student Appreciation Days. College housing not available.

■ UTAH STATE UNIVERSITY *F-5*

Old Main Hill
Logan, UT 84322

Tel: (435)797-1000
Free: 800-488-8108
Admissions: (435)797-1079
Fax: (435)797-3900
E-mail: admit@usu.edu
Web Site: http://www.usu.edu/

Description: State-supported, university, coed. Part of Utah System of Higher Education. Awards associate, bachelor's, master's, and doctoral degrees and post-master's certificates. Founded 1888. Setting: 456-acre urban campus. Endowment: $74.4 million. Research spending for 2004 fiscal year: $106.6 million. Educational spending for 2005 fiscal year: $4933 per student. Total enrollment: 14,458. Faculty: 764 (727 full-time, 37 part-time). Student-undergrad faculty ratio is 19:1. 25% from top 10% of their high school class, 51% from top quarter, 81% from top half. 14 National Merit Scholars. Full-time: 10,728 students, 49% women, 51% men. Part-time: 2,009 students, 47% women, 53% men. Students come from 53 states and territories, 52 other countries, 27% from out-of-state, 0.4% Native American, 2% Hispanic, 1% black, 1% Asian American or Pacific Islander, 3% international, 20% 25 or older, 8% transferred in. Retention: 73% of full-time freshmen returned the following year. Academic areas with the most degrees conferred: business/marketing; education; engineering. Core. Calendar: semesters. Academic remediation for entering students, ESL program, services for LD students, advanced placement, accelerated degree program, self-designed majors, freshman honors college, honors program, independent study, distance learning, double major, summer session for credit, part-time degree program, adult/continuing education programs, co-op programs and internships, graduate courses open to undergrads. Off campus study at Weber State University. Study abroad program. ROTC: Army, Air Force.

Entrance Requirements: Options: electronic application, early admission, deferred admission, international baccalaureate accepted. Required: high school transcript, SAT or ACT. Recommended: minimum 2.75 high school GPA. Entrance: moderately difficult. Application deadline: Rolling. Notification: continuous.

Costs Per Year: Application fee: $40. State resident tuition: $3128 full-time. Nonresident tuition: $10,072 full-time. Mandatory fees: $544 full-time. Full-time tuition and fees vary according to course load and student level. College room and board: $4330. College room only: $1550. Room and board charges vary according to board plan and housing facility.

Collegiate Environment: Orientation program. Drama-theater group, choral group, marching band, student-run newspaper. Social organizations: 250 open to all; national fraternities, national sororities; 2% of eligible men and 2% of eligible women are members. Most popular organizations: Latter-Day Saints Student Association, multicultural clubs, volunteer groups, college councils. Major annual events: homecoming, Halloween Howl. Student services: legal services, health clinic, personal-psychological counseling, women's center. Campus security: 24-hour emergency response devices and patrols, student patrols, late night transport-escort service, video monitors in pedestrian tunnels. No special consideration for freshman housing applicants. Options: coed, men-only, women-only housing available. Merrill Library plus 4 others with 1.5 million books, 2.6 million microform titles, 12,759 serials, 14,926 audiovisual materials, an OPAC, and a Web page. Operations spending for 2004 fiscal year: $7.4 million. 875 computers available on campus for general student use. Computer purchase/lease plans available. A campuswide network can be accessed from student residence rooms and from off campus. Staffed computer lab on campus.

Community Environment: Located in the fertile Cache Valley, Logan is the headquarters for the adjacent Cache National Forest. The Cache Valley was originally an ancient lakebed 500 feet deep, and shorelines of the lake are still visible along the foothills. Today, the community has excellent transportation with airlines, railroad, and bus connections. Major highways enter the city from four directions. Dairying is an important economic feature of the community, and the city has one of the largest Swiss cheese factories in the world. Some part-time employment is available. Local recreation includes hunting, fishing, skiing, and all the water sports.

■ UTAH VALLEY STATE COLLEGE *I-6*

800 West 1200 South St.
Orem, UT 84058-5999
Tel: (801)222-8000
Admissions: (801)863-8460
Fax: (801)225-4677
E-mail: info@uvsc.edu
Web Site: http://www.uvsc.edu/

Description: State-supported, 4-year, coed. Part of Utah System of Higher Education. Awards associate and bachelor's degrees. Founded 1941. Setting: 200-acre suburban campus with easy access to Salt Lake City. Endowment: $7.7 million. Educational spending for 2005 fiscal year: $2805 per student. Total enrollment: 24,487. Student-undergrad faculty ratio is 22:1. 4,573 applied, 100% were admitted. 5% from top 10% of their high school class, 20% from top quarter, 50% from top half. Full-time: 11,565 students, 42% women, 58% men. Part-time: 12,922 students, 46% women, 54% men. Students come from 50 states and territories, 78 other countries, 14% from out-of-state, 1% Native American, 4% Hispanic, 1% black, 2% Asian American or Pacific Islander, 1% international, 35% 25 or older, 9% transferred in. Retention: 43% of full-time freshmen returned the following year. Academic areas with the most degrees conferred: liberal arts/general studies; business/marketing; health professions and related sciences. Core. Calendar: semesters. Academic remediation for entering students, ESL program, services for LD students, advanced placement, accelerated degree program, self-designed majors, honors program, independent study, distance learning, summer session for credit, part-time degree program, co-op programs and internships. Off campus study at UVSC Wasatch Campus; Heber City, University Mall, North Lehi Valley Ed Center, Spanish Fork Ed. Center. Study abroad program. ROTC: Army, Air Force (c).

Entrance Requirements: Open admission. Options: electronic application, deferred admission, international baccalaureate accepted. Required: SAT or ACT, or in-house tests. Recommended: high school transcript. Entrance: noncompetitive. Application deadline: 8/15. Notification: continuous.

Costs Per Year: Application fee: $30. State resident tuition: $2580 full-time, $86 per credit part-time. Nonresident tuition: $9030 full-time, $301 per credit part-time. Mandatory fees: $442 full-time, $221 per term part-time. Part-time tuition and fees vary according to course load.

Collegiate Environment: Orientation program. Drama-theater group, choral group, student-run newspaper. Social organizations: 98 open to all. Major annual event: homecoming. Student services: legal services, health clinic, personal-psychological counseling, women's center. Campus security: 24-hour patrols. College housing not available. Utah Valley State College Library with 173,000 books, 6,000 serials, 9,000 audiovisual materials, an OPAC, and a Web page. Operations spending for 2004 fiscal year: $1.8 million. 1,000 computers available on campus for general student use. A campuswide network can be accessed from off-campus. Staffed computer lab on campus.

Community Environment: See Brigham Young University.

■ **WEBER STATE UNIVERSITY** *G-5*
1001 University Circle
Ogden, UT 84408-1001
Tel: (801)626-6000
Free: 800-848-7770
Admissions: (801)626-6046
Fax: (801)626-6747
E-mail: ccrivera@weber.edu
Web Site: http://weber.edu/

Description: State-supported, comprehensive, coed. Part of Utah System of Higher Education. Awards associate, bachelor's, and master's degrees. Founded 1889. Setting: 526-acre urban campus with easy access to Salt Lake City. Endowment: $23.8 million. Research spending for 2004 fiscal year: $348,517. Educational spending for 2005 fiscal year: $3173 per student. Total enrollment: 18,142. Faculty: 670 (465 full-time, 205 part-time). Student-undergrad faculty ratio is 22:1. 5,196 applied, 100% were admitted. 63% from top quarter of their high school class, 93% from top half. Full-time: 10,250 students, 48% women, 52% men. Part-time: 7,488 students, 53% women, 47% men. Students come from 52 states and territories, 37 other countries, 4% from out-of-state, 1% Native American, 4% Hispanic, 1% black, 2% Asian American or Pacific Islander, 1% international, 41% 25 or older, 3% live on campus, 9% transferred in. Retention: 71% of full-time freshmen returned the following year. Academic areas with the most degrees conferred: business/marketing; health professions and related sciences; education. Core. Calendar: semesters. Academic remediation for entering students, ESL program, services for LD students, advanced placement, accelerated degree program, self-designed majors, freshman honors college, honors program, independent study, distance learning, double major, summer session for credit, part-time degree program, external degree program, adult/continuing education programs, co-op programs and internships, graduate courses open to undergrads. Off campus study at Utah State University, Southern Utah University, Dixie College, Utah Valley State College, Salt Lake Community College. Study abroad program. ROTC: Army, Naval, Air Force.

Entrance Requirements: Open admission. Options: electronic application, early admission, deferred admission, international baccalaureate accepted.

Required: high school transcript. Required for some: SAT or ACT. Entrance: noncompetitive. Application deadline: 8/22. Notification: continuous.

Costs Per Year: Application fee: $30. State resident tuition: $2547 full-time. Nonresident tuition: $9008 full-time. Mandatory fees: $591 full-time. College room and board: $6500. College room only: $3300. Room and board charges vary according to board plan and housing facility.

Collegiate Environment: Orientation program. Drama-theater group, choral group, marching band, student-run newspaper, radio station. Social organizations: 116 open to all; national fraternities, national sororities, local fraternities, local sororities; 1% of eligible men and 1% of eligible women are members. Most popular organizations: LDSSA, Mountaineering Club, Rodeo Club, Beta Alpha Psi, student nurses organization. Major annual events: Homecoming, Graduation, student elections. Student services: legal services, health clinic, personal-psychological counseling, women's center. Campus security: 24-hour emergency response devices and patrols, student patrols, late night transport-escort service, controlled dormitory access. 644 college housing spaces available; all were occupied in 2003-04. No special consideration for freshman housing applicants. Options: men-only, women-only housing available. Stewart Library plus 1 other with 734,487 books, 595,534 microform titles, 26,735 audiovisual materials, an OPAC, and a Web page. Operations spending for 2004 fiscal year: $3.7 million. 558 computers available on campus for general student use. Computer purchase/lease plans available. A campuswide network can be accessed from student residence rooms and from off campus. Staffed computer lab on campus.

Community Environment: Located at the confluence of the Weber and Ogden Rivers, this community is an important railroad distribution center for products directed to west coast markets. Mormon pioneers settled the community. The climate is temperate with four distinct seasons. Ogden is reached by railroad, airlines, and highways. The community has many churches representing over 30 denominations. There are two hospitals, four health centers, a library and branch, 2 major shopping malls, and various civic and fraternal organizations serving the area. There are also five TV stations and a radio station. Part-time employment is available. Local recreation includes fishing, hunting, swimming, skiing, boating, picnicking, camping, golfing, and horseback riding.

■ **WESTERN GOVERNORS UNIVERSITY** *H-5*
4001 South 700 East, Ste. 700
Salt Lake City, UT 84107
Tel: (801)274-3280; 877-435-7948
Fax: (801)274-3305
Web Site: http://www.wgu.edu/

Description: Independent, comprehensive, coed. Awards bachelor's and master's degrees. Founded 1998. Total enrollment: 2,821. Full-time: 1,843 students, 71% women, 29% men. Students come from 37 states and territories, 92% 25 or older. Core. Calendar: continuous. Services for LD students, accelerated degree program, independent study, distance learning, double major, part-time degree program, external degree program, adult/continuing education programs.

Entrance Requirements: Open admission. Option: electronic application. Required for some: high school transcript. Entrance: minimally difficult.

Costs Per Year: Application fee: $100. Tuition: $5580 full-time. Mandatory fees: $155 full-time. Full-time tuition and fees vary according to program.

Collegiate Environment: Orientation program. College housing not available. WGU Central Library (online) with a Web page. Operations spending for 2004 fiscal year: $62,200.

■ **WESTMINSTER COLLEGE** *H-5*
1840 South 1300 East
Salt Lake City, UT 84105-3697
Tel: (801)484-7651
Free: 800-748-4753
Admissions: (801)832-2200
Fax: (801)484-3252
E-mail: admission@westminstercollege.edu
Web Site: http://www.westminstercollege.edu

Description: Independent, comprehensive, coed. Awards bachelor's and master's degrees. Founded 1875. Setting: 27-acre suburban campus. Endowment: $51.9 million. Research spending for 2004 fiscal year: $49,693. Educational spending for 2005 fiscal year: $8600 per student. Total enrollment: 2,455. Faculty: 259 (121 full-time, 138 part-time). Student-undergrad faculty ratio is 10:1. 897 applied, 89% were admitted. 30% from top 10% of their high school class, 57% from top quarter, 86% from top half. 2 National Merit Scholars, 14 valedictorians. Full-time: 1,633 students, 59% women,

41% men. Part-time: 245 students, 50% women, 50% men. Students come from 35 states and territories, 18 other countries, 9% from out-of-state, 0.4% Native American, 6% Hispanic, 1% black, 3% Asian American or Pacific Islander, 2% international, 29% 25 or older, 26% live on campus, 12% transferred in. Retention: 74% of full-time freshmen returned the following year. Academic areas with the most degrees conferred: business/marketing; health professions and related sciences; psychology. Core. Calendar: 4-4-1. Academic remediation for entering students, ESL program, services for LD students, advanced placement, accelerated degree program, self-designed majors, honors program, independent study, double major, summer session for credit, part-time degree program, external degree program, co-op programs and internships. Study abroad program. ROTC: Army (c), Naval (c), Air Force (c).

Entrance Requirements: Options: Peterson's Universal Application, Common Application, electronic application, deferred admission, international baccalaureate accepted. Required: essay, high school transcript, minimum 2.5 high school GPA, 1 recommendation, SAT or ACT. Recommended: essay, interview. Entrance: moderately difficult. Application deadline: 4/15. Notification: 10/1.

Costs Per Year: Application fee: $40. Comprehensive fee: $25,656 includes full-time tuition ($19,440), mandatory fees ($284), and college room and board ($5932). Full-time tuition and fees vary according to course load. Room and board charges vary according to board plan. Part-time tuition: $810 per credit hour. Part-time mandatory fees: $107 per term.

Collegiate Environment: Orientation program. Drama-theater group, choral group, student-run newspaper. Social organizations: 41 open to all; 3% of eligible men and 2% of eligible women are members. Most popular organizations: Outdoor Club, Pre-Med Society, English Club, Theatre Society, Students Educators Association. Major annual events: President's Ball, Cosmic Bowling, Movie Night. Student services: personal-psychological counseling. Campus security: 24-hour emergency response devices and patrols, student patrols, late night transport-escort service, controlled dormitory access. 500 college housing spaces available; 491 were occupied in 2003-04. Freshmen guaranteed college housing. On-campus residence required in freshman year. Option: coed housing available. Giovale Library plus 1 other with 119,410 books, 243,548 microform titles, 689 serials, 6,481 audiovisual materials, an OPAC, and a Web page. Operations spending for 2004 fiscal year: $960,285. 400 computers available on campus for general student use. A campuswide network can be accessed from student residence rooms and from off campus. Staffed computer lab on campus.

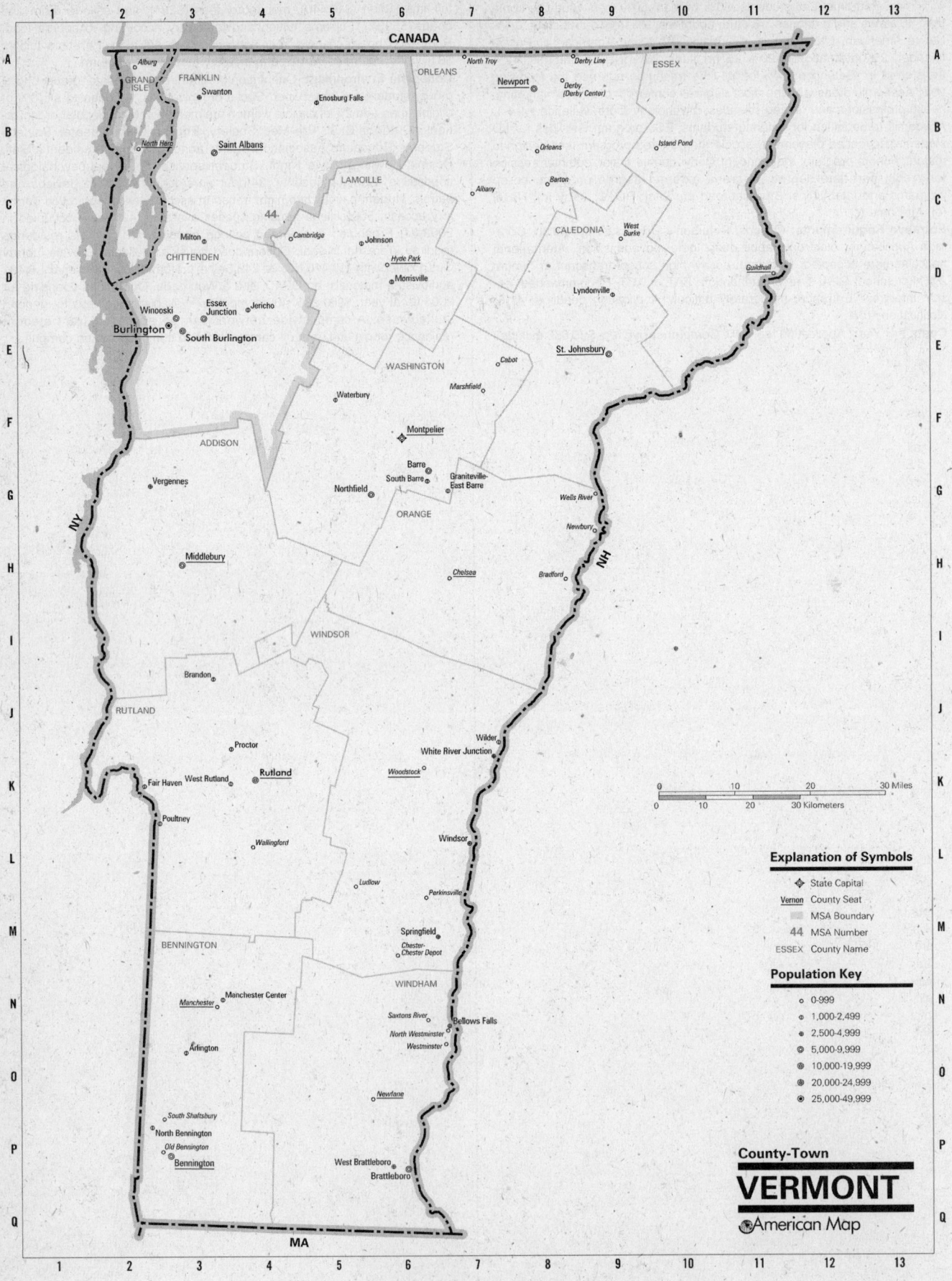

County-Town

VERMONT

American Map

■ **BENNINGTON COLLEGE** *P-3*

One College Dr.
Bennington, VT 05201
Tel: (802)442-5401
Free: 800-833-6845
Admissions: (802)440-4312
Fax: (802)447-4269
E-mail: admissions@bennington.edu
Web Site: http://www.bennington.edu/

Description: Independent, comprehensive, coed. Awards bachelor's and master's degrees. Founded 1932. Setting: 550-acre small town campus with easy access to Albany. Endowment: $11.8 million. Educational spending for 2005 fiscal year: $15,258 per student. Total enrollment: 725. Faculty: 90 (66 full-time, 24 part-time). Student-undergrad faculty ratio is 7:1. 723 applied, 62% were admitted. 30% from top 10% of their high school class, 74% from top quarter, 99% from top half. Full-time: 567 students, 66% women, 34% men. Part-time: 4 students, 50% women, 50% men. Students come from 43 states and territories, 18 other countries, 98% from out-of-state, 0.2% Native American, 3% Hispanic, 2% black, 2% Asian American or Pacific Islander, 3% international, 0% 25 or older, 98% live on campus, 3% transferred in. Retention: 87% of full-time freshmen returned the following year. Academic areas with the most degrees conferred: visual and performing arts; English; social sciences. Calendar: semesters plus winter work term in January and February. ESL program, services for LD students, accelerated degree program, self-designed majors, independent study, distance learning, double major, part-time degree program, co-op programs and internships. Study abroad program.

Entrance Requirements: Options: Peterson's Universal Application, Common Application, early admission, early decision, deferred admission, international baccalaureate accepted. Required: essay, high school transcript, 2 recommendations, graded analytic paper. Recommended: interview. Entrance: very difficult. Application deadlines: 1/3, 11/15 for early decision plan 1, 1/3 for early decision plan 2. Notification: 4/1, 12/15 for early decision plan 1, 2/15 for early decision plan 2.

Costs Per Year: Application fee: $60. Comprehensive fee: $41,890 includes full-time tuition ($32,700), mandatory fees ($870), and college room and board ($8320). College room only: $4460. Part-time tuition: $1050 per credit.

Collegiate Environment: Orientation program. Drama-theater group, choral group, student-run newspaper, radio station. Social organizations: 26 open to all. Most popular organizations: literary magazine, Amnesty International, Campus Activities Board, film society, student newspaper. Major annual events: Ben Belitt Lecture, Sunfest, Spring Ball. Student services: health clinic, personal-psychological counseling. Campus security: 24-hour emergency response devices and patrols, late night transport-escort service. 610 college housing spaces available; 602 were occupied in 2003-04. Freshmen guaranteed college housing. On-campus residence required through senior year. Option: coed housing available. Crossett Library plus 2 others with 128,413 books, 6,155 microform titles, 250 serials, 40,219 audiovisual materials, an OPAC, and a Web page. Operations spending for 2004 fiscal year: $534,376. 61 computers available on campus for general student use. A campuswide network can be accessed from student residence rooms and from off campus. Staffed computer lab on campus.

Community Environment: Situated on 550 acres in the foothills of Vermont's Green Mountains, Bennington College is a short drive from some of the region's top ski resorts. The College is four miles from the village of Bennington and one mile from North Bennington. Twenty miles to the south is Williamstown, MA, and the Berkshires, home to the nationally renowned museums The Clark Institute and MASSMoCA, while featuring such esteemed performing arts venues as the Williamstown Theatre Festival, Jacob's Pillow, and Tanglewood. Twenty miles north is Manchester, VT, and its fine restaurants and shopping, as well as a state-of-the-art ice skating rink. Approximately 40 miles to the west is Albany, NY, which provides numerous amenities as well as rail transportation to Boston, New York City, and elsewhere. Local historical sites include the Bennington Museum, Bennington Battle Monument, and Old First Church, where poet Robert Frost is buried.

■ **BURLINGTON COLLEGE** *E-3*

95 North Ave.
Burlington, VT 05401-2998
Tel: (802)862-9616
Free: 800-862-9616
Fax: (802)658-0071
Web Site: http://www.burlcol.edu/

Description: Independent, 4-year, coed. Awards associate and bachelor's degrees. Founded 1972. Setting: 1-acre urban campus. Endowment: $76,000. Total enrollment: 241. 46 applied, 72% were admitted. Full-time: 117 students, 56% women, 44% men. Part-time: 124 students, 58% women, 42% men. Students come from 23 states and territories, 1 other country, 45% from out-of-state, 46% 25 or older, 6% live on campus, 23% transferred in. Retention: 60% of full-time freshmen returned the following year. Core. Calendar: semesters. Academic remediation for entering students, services for LD students, accelerated degree program, self-designed majors, independent study, distance learning, double major, summer session for credit, part-time degree program, external degree program, adult/continuing education programs, co-op programs and internships. Off campus study at University of Vermont, Champlain College, Saint Michael's College, Community College of Vermont, Institute for Social Ecology. Study abroad program.

Entrance Requirements: Open admission for Associate degree only. Options: Peterson's Universal Application, Common Application, electronic application, deferred admission. Required: essay, high school transcript, 2 recommendations, interview. Entrance: noncompetitive. Application deadline: 8/1. Notification: continuous.

Costs Per Year: Application fee: $35. Tuition: $15,600 full-time, $515 per credit hour part-time. College room only: $4500.

Collegiate Environment: Orientation program. Student-run newspaper. Social organizations: 1 open to all. Most popular organization: Student Association. Major annual event: graduation. Student services: personal-psychological counseling. Campus security: 24-hour emergency response devices. 16 college housing spaces available; 15 were occupied in 2003-04. Freshmen given priority for college housing. Option: coed housing available. Burlington College Library with 5,700 books, 80 serials, 1,050 audiovisual materials, an OPAC, and a Web page. Operations spending for 2004 fiscal year: $95,702. 21 computers available on campus for general student use. A campuswide network can be accessed. Staffed computer lab on campus.

Community Environment: With five other colleges in the area, Burlington offers a wealth of cultural, economic and recreational opportunities, but still offers a friendly, small-city ambiance. Human-scale neighborhoods, and the college's governance structure itself, give students the chance to get involved, and make a difference.

■ **CASTLETON STATE COLLEGE** *K-3*

Castleton, VT 05735

Tel: (802)468-5611

Free: 800-639-8521

Admissions: (802)468-1213

Fax: (802)468-1476

Web Site: http://www.castleton.edu/

Description: State-supported, comprehensive, coed. Part of Vermont State Colleges System. Awards associate, bachelor's, and master's degrees and post-master's certificates. Founded 1787. Setting: 160-acre rural campus. Endowment: $4.5 million. Research spending for 2004 fiscal year: $17,206. Educational spending for 2005 fiscal year: $4566 per student. Total enrollment: 2,392. Faculty: 201 (89 full-time, 112 part-time). Student-undergrad faculty ratio is 14:1. 1,715 applied, 79% were admitted. 5% from top 10% of their high school class, 20% from top quarter, 57% from top half. Full-time: 1,684 students, 56% women, 44% men. Part-time: 207 students, 78% women, 22% men. Students come from 29 states and territories, 34% from out-of-state, 1% Native American, 1% Hispanic, 1% black, 1% Asian American or Pacific Islander, 0.4% international, 16% 25 or older, 50% live on campus, 9% transferred in. Retention: 66% of full-time freshmen returned the following year. Academic areas with the most degrees conferred: business/marketing; visual and performing arts; parks and recreation. Core. Calendar: semesters. Academic remediation for entering students, services for LD students, advanced placement, self-designed majors, honors program, independent study, double major, summer session for credit, part-time degree program, co-op programs and internships. Off campus study at Green Mountain College, other Vermont state colleges. Study abroad program. ROTC: Army (c).

Entrance Requirements: Options: Common Application, electronic application, deferred admission. Required: essay, high school transcript, minimum 2.5 high school GPA, recommendations, SAT or ACT. Recommended: interview. Entrance: moderately difficult. Application deadline: Rolling. Notification: continuous.

Costs Per Year: Application fee: $35. One-time mandatory fee: $195. State resident tuition: $6648 full-time, $277 per credit part-time. Nonresident tuition: $14,376 full-time, $599 per credit part-time. Mandatory fees: $180 full-time. College room and board: $6942.

Collegiate Environment: Orientation program. Drama-theater group, choral group, student-run newspaper, radio station. Social organizations: 40 open to all. Most popular organizations: student radio station, community service, women's issues organization, rugby, snowboarding. Major annual events: Soundings, Spring Weekend, Fall Festival. Student services: health clinic, personal-psychological counseling. Campus security: 24-hour emergency response devices and patrols, student patrols, late night transport-escort service, controlled dormitory access. 800 college housing spaces available; all were occupied in 2003-04. Freshmen guaranteed college housing. On-campus residence required in freshman year. Option: coed housing available. Calvin Coolidge Library with 166,011 books, 545,361 microform titles, 739 serials, 3,420 audiovisual materials, an OPAC, and a Web page. Operations spending for 2004 fiscal year: $771,318. 225 computers available on campus for general student use. Computer purchase/lease plans available. A campuswide network can be accessed from student residence rooms. Staffed computer lab on campus.

Community Environment: Adjacent to outstanding ski and summer resorts, the area is rural and surrounded by Vermont's beautiful lakes and mountains.

■ **CHAMPLAIN COLLEGE** *E-3*

PO Box 670

Burlington, VT 05402-0670

Tel: (802)860-2700

Free: 800-570-5858

Admissions: (802)860-2727

Fax: (802)862-2772

E-mail: admission@champlain.edu

Web Site: http://www.champlain.edu/

Description: Independent, comprehensive, coed. Awards associate, bachelor's, and master's degrees. Founded 1878. Setting: 21-acre suburban campus with easy access to Montreal, Canada. Endowment: $7 million. Educational spending for 2005 fiscal year: $6303 per student. Total enrollment: 2,529. Faculty: 258 (68 full-time, 190 part-time). Student-undergrad faculty ratio is 16:1. 1,850 applied, 64% were admitted. 15% from top 10% of their high school class, 35% from top quarter, 85% from top half. Full-time: 1,757 students, 46% women, 54% men. Part-time: 715 students, 54%

women, 46% men. Students come from 28 states and territories, 26 other countries, 70% from out-of-state, 1% Native American, 1% Hispanic, 1% black, 2% Asian American or Pacific Islander, 0.4% international, 5% 25 or older, 41% live on campus, 6% transferred in. Retention: 82% of full-time freshmen returned the following year. Academic areas with the most degrees conferred: business/marketing; computer and information sciences; education. Core. Calendar: semesters. Services for LD students, advanced placement, freshman honors college, honors program, distance learning, double major, summer session for credit, part-time degree program, co-op programs and internships. Off campus study. Study abroad program. ROTC: Army (c).

Entrance Requirements: Options: Peterson's Universal Application, Common Application, electronic application, international baccalaureate accepted. Required: essay, high school transcript, SAT or ACT. Recommended: minimum 2.0 high school GPA, 1 recommendation, interview. Required for some: SAT Subject Tests. Entrance: moderately difficult. Application deadline: Rolling. Notification: continuous.

Costs Per Year: Application fee: $40. Comprehensive fee: $24,605 includes full-time tuition ($14,660), mandatory fees ($250), and college room and board ($9695). College room only: $5855. Full-time tuition and fees vary according to course load. Room and board charges vary according to board plan and housing facility. Part-time tuition: $420 per credit hour. Part-time tuition varies according to course load.

Collegiate Environment: Orientation program. Drama-theater group, choral group, student-run newspaper. Social organizations: 25 open to all. Most popular organizations: Diversity Champlain, International Club, community service organization, Champlain Players (theater group), Outing Club/Skiing Snowboarding Club. Major annual events: Parents' Weekend, Halloween Masquerade Dance, Spring Meltdown. Student services: health clinic, personal-psychological counseling. Campus security: 24-hour emergency response devices and patrols, late night transport-escort service, controlled dormitory access. College housing designed to accommodate 680 students; 780 undergraduates lived in college housing during 2003-04. Freshmen guaranteed college housing. Options: coed, women-only housing available. Miller Information Commons with 60,000 books, 19,200 microform titles, 270 audiovisual materials, an OPAC, and a Web page. Operations spending for 2004 fiscal year: $486,244. 260 computers available on campus for general student use. A campuswide network can be accessed from student residence rooms and from off campus. Staffed computer lab on campus.

Community Environment: Burlington offers the best of both worlds: the excitement of life in the city and the tranquility and recreational splendor of the northern Vermont countryside. Three blocks from the Champlain campus, the Church Street Marketplace provides an exciting collection of more than 100 shops, services, and restaurants. Within one hour's drive are five major ski resorts: Stowe, Sugarbush, Bolton Valley, Mad River Glen, and Smugglers' Notch.

■ **COLLEGE OF ST. JOSEPH** *K-4*

71 Clement Rd.

Rutland, VT 05701-3899

Tel: (802)773-5900

Web Site: http://www.csj.edu/

Description: Independent Roman Catholic, comprehensive, coed. Awards associate, bachelor's, and master's degrees. Founded 1950. Setting: 90-acre small town campus. Endowment: $1.7 million. Educational spending for 2005 fiscal year: $3592 per student. Total enrollment: 450. Faculty: 68 (11 full-time, 57 part-time). Student-undergrad faculty ratio is 11:1. 157 applied, 68% were admitted. 5% from top 10% of their high school class, 29% from top quarter, 34% from top half. Students come from 12 states and territories, 44% from out-of-state, 0% Native American, 2% Hispanic, 4% black, 0.4% Asian American or Pacific Islander, 1% international, 46% 25 or older, 31% live on campus. Retention: 61% of full-time freshmen returned the following year. Academic areas with the most degrees conferred: business/marketing; education; liberal arts/general studies. Core. Calendar: semesters. Academic remediation for entering students, ESL program, services for LD students, advanced placement, accelerated degree program, double major, summer session for credit, part-time degree program, adult/continuing education programs, internships, graduate courses open to undergrads. Study abroad program.

Entrance Requirements: Options: Peterson's Universal Application, early admission, deferred admission, international baccalaureate accepted. Required: essay, high school transcript, minimum 2.0 high school GPA, 2 recommendations, SAT or ACT. Recommended: interview. Entrance: minimally difficult. Application deadline: Rolling. Notification: continuous.

Costs Per Year: Application fee: $25. Comprehensive fee: $22,050 includes full-time tuition ($14,650), mandatory fees ($250), and college room and board ($7150). Part-time tuition: $245 per credit. Part-time mandatory fees: $45 per term.

Collegiate Environment: Orientation program. Drama-theater group, choral group. Social organizations: 15 open to all; 20% of eligible men and 25% of eligible women are members. Most popular organizations: Human Services Club, Campus Ministry Club, Psi Chi, Ambassadors, chorus. Major annual events: Spring Fling, Fall Formal, Oktoberfest. Student services: personal-psychological counseling. Campus security: 24-hour emergency response devices. 150 college housing spaces available; 82 were occupied in 2003-04. Freshmen guaranteed college housing. On-campus residence required through sophomore year. Options: men-only, women-only housing available. St. Joseph Library plus 1 other with 75,000 books, 19,600 microform titles, 3,000 serials, 5,800 audiovisual materials, and an OPAC. Operations spending for 2004 fiscal year: $131,748. 30 computers available on campus for general student use. Computer purchase/lease plans available. A campuswide network can be accessed from student residence rooms and from off campus. Staffed computer lab on campus.

Community Environment: Rutland, though a small city of 30,000, is the third largest city in Vermont. All forms of commercial transportation are available. The community includes churches, a hospital, library, museum, community concert series, and a number of civic and service organizations. Recreational areas provide facilities for boating, swimming, fishing, camping, horseback riding, hunting, mountain climbing, and cross-country and alpine skiing at nearby Pico and Killington Ski areas. Rutland is the headquarters for the Green Mountain National Forest.

■ COMMUNITY COLLEGE OF VERMONT *E-5*

PO Box 120
Waterbury, VT 05676-0120
Tel: (802)241-3535
Admissions: (802)865-4422
Web Site: http://www.ccv.edu/

Description: State-supported, 2-year, coed. Part of Vermont State Colleges System. Awards certificates, diplomas, transfer associate, and terminal associate degrees. Founded 1970. Setting: rural campus. Total enrollment: 5,801. 602 applied, 100% were admitted. Students come from 16 states and territories, 3% from out-of-state, 1% Native American, 1% Hispanic, 2% black, 1% Asian American or Pacific Islander, 0.2% international, 60% 25 or older. Core. Calendar: semesters. Academic remediation for entering students, ESL program, services for LD students, accelerated degree program, self-designed majors, independent study, distance learning, double major, summer session for credit, part-time degree program, external degree program, adult/continuing education programs, co-op programs and internships.

Entrance Requirements: Open admission. Placement: ACCUPLACER required. Entrance: noncompetitive. Application deadline: Rolling.

Costs Per Year: State resident tuition: $3912 full-time, $163 per credit part-time. Nonresident tuition: $7824 full-time, $326 per credit part-time. Mandatory fees: $100 full-time, $50 per term part-time.

Collegiate Environment: College housing not available. Vermont Community and Technical College Library with an OPAC. 200 computers available on campus for general student use. A campuswide network can be accessed from off-campus. Staffed computer lab on campus.

■ GODDARD COLLEGE *F-7*

123 Pitkin Rd.
Plainfield, VT 05667-9432
Tel: (802)454-8311
Free: 800-906-8312
Fax: (802)454-1029
Web Site: http://www.goddard.edu/

Description: Independent, comprehensive, coed. Awards bachelor's and master's degrees. Founded 1938. Setting: 250-acre rural campus. Endowment: $932,377. Research spending for 2004 fiscal year: $120,000. Total enrollment: 560. Faculty: 74 (2 full-time, 72 part-time). Student-undergrad faculty ratio is 11:1. 13 applied, 92% were admitted. Full-time: 165 students, 61% women, 39% men. Students come from 33 states and territories, 1 other country, 82% from out-of-state, 2% Native American, 2% Hispanic, 2% black, 1% Asian American or Pacific Islander, 0% international, 68% 25 or older, 27% transferred in. Calendar: semesters. Services for LD students, advanced placement, self-designed majors, independent study, distance learning, double major, external degree program, adult/continuing education programs, internships. Off campus study at Council of Independent Colleges.

Entrance Requirements: Options: Peterson's Universal Application, electronic application, deferred admission. Required: essay, high school transcript, 2 recommendations, interview. Entrance: moderately difficult. Application deadline: Rolling. Notification: continuous.

Costs Per Year: Application fee: $40. Tuition: $9806 full-time. Mandatory fees: $900 full-time.

Collegiate Environment: Orientation program. Major annual events: senior presentations, Work Day. Student services: personal-psychological counseling. Campus security: 24-hour patrols, patrols by trained security personnel 9 p.m. to 6 a.m. College housing not available. Eliot Pratt Center with 70,000 books, 17 serials, 300 audiovisual materials, an OPAC, and a Web page. Operations spending for 2004 fiscal year: $206,452. 27 computers available on campus for general student use. A campuswide network can be accessed from student residence rooms and from off campus. Staffed computer lab on campus.

Community Environment: Located in the Upper Valley of Winooski River, this rural setting has the typical beauty of northern New England surrounded by the lower ranges of the Green Mountains. Winters are cold with heavy snow for good skiing. Opportunities are few for part-time employment.

■ GREEN MOUNTAIN COLLEGE *L-2*

One College Circle
Poultney, VT 05764-1199
Tel: (802)287-8000
Free: 800-776-6675
Admissions: (802)287-8207
Fax: (802)287-8099
E-mail: admiss@greenmtn.edu
Web Site: http://www.greenmtn.edu/

Description: Independent, 4-year, coed, affiliated with United Methodist Church. Awards bachelor's and master's degrees. Founded 1834. Setting: 155-acre small town campus. Endowment: $2.4 million. Research spending for 2004 fiscal year: $71,905. Educational spending for 2005 fiscal year: $5000 per student. Total enrollment: 696. Faculty: 65 (41 full-time, 24 part-time). Student-undergrad faculty ratio is 14:1. 927 applied, 91% were admitted. 9% from top 10% of their high school class, 24% from top quarter, 50% from top half. Full-time: 665 students, 48% women, 52% men. Part-time: 31 students, 42% women, 58% men. Students come from 37 states and territories, 14 other countries, 87% from out-of-state, 1% Native American, 3% Hispanic, 3% black, 1% Asian American or Pacific Islander, 1% international, 26% 25 or older, 85% live on campus, 6% transferred in. Retention: 72% of full-time freshmen returned the following year. Academic areas with the most degrees conferred: education; liberal arts/general studies; natural resources/environmental science; parks and recreation. Core. Calendar: semesters. ESL program, services for LD students, advanced placement, accelerated degree program, self-designed majors, honors program, independent study, double major, summer session for credit, part-time degree program, adult/continuing education programs, co-op programs and internships. Off campus study at Castleton State College. Study abroad program.

Entrance Requirements: Options: Common Application, electronic application, deferred admission, international baccalaureate accepted. Required: essay, high school transcript, 1 recommendation, SAT or ACT. Recommended: minimum 2.5 high school GPA, interview. Required for some: interview. Entrance: moderately difficult. Application deadline: Rolling. Notification: continuous until 8/1.

Costs Per Year: Application fee: $30. Comprehensive fee: $29,894 includes full-time tuition ($21,604), mandatory fees ($600), and college room and board ($7690). College room only: $4700. Full-time tuition and fees vary according to course load. Room and board charges vary according to housing facility. Part-time tuition: $720 per credit hour. Part-time tuition varies according to course load.

Collegiate Environment: Orientation program. Drama-theater group, choral group, student-run newspaper. Social organizations: 32 open to all. Most popular organizations: Student National Education Association, Student Government Association, Outing Club, Inter-Cultural Club, Peer Majors Club. Major annual events: Parents' Weekend, Annual Holiday Party, Earth Day. Student services: health clinic, personal-psychological counseling. Campus security: 24-hour emergency response devices and patrols, student patrols, late night transport-escort service, controlled dormitory access. 600 college housing spaces available; 483 were occupied in 2003-04. Freshmen guaranteed college housing. On-campus residence required through senior year. Option: coed housing available. Griswold Library with 73,400 books, 58,725 microform titles, 273 serials, 4,600 audiovisual materials, an OPAC, and a Web page. Operations spending for 2004 fiscal year: $316,960. 80

computers available on campus for general student use. A campuswide network can be accessed from student residence rooms and from off campus. Staffed computer lab on campus.

Community Environment: Poultney is in a small town community with a typical New England climate. Train and bus stations and airport are within 20 minutes. Lake Saint Catherine provides facilities for water sports, and other facilities in nearby areas offer winter sports. Pico and Killington Ski resorts, as well as 4 other major ski resorts.

■ **JOHNSON STATE COLLEGE** *D-5*

337 College Hill
Johnson, VT 05656-9405
Tel: (802)635-2356
Free: 800-635-2356
Admissions: (802)635-1219
Fax: (802)635-1230
E-mail: jscapply@badger.jsc.vsc.edu
Web Site: http://www.johnsonstatecollege.edu/

Description: State-supported, comprehensive, coed. Part of Vermont State Colleges System. Awards associate, bachelor's, and master's degrees. Founded 1828. Setting: 350-acre rural campus with easy access to Montreal. Endowment: $769,100. Total enrollment: 1,866. Faculty: 143 (54 full-time, 89 part-time). Student-undergrad faculty ratio is 17:1. 770 applied, 95% were admitted. 1% from top 10% of their high school class, 8% from top quarter, 41% from top half. Full-time: 1,022 students, 53% women, 47% men. Part-time: 544 students, 77% women, 23% men. Students come from 22 states and territories, 4 other countries, 26% from out-of-state, 1% Native American, 1% Hispanic, 2% black, 1% Asian American or Pacific Islander, 0.2% international, 33% 25 or older, 57% live on campus, 12% transferred in. Retention: 64% of full-time freshmen returned the following year. Academic areas with the most degrees conferred: education; psychology; liberal arts/general studies. Core. Calendar: semesters. ESL program, services for LD students, advanced placement, accelerated degree program, honors program, independent study, distance learning, double major, summer session for credit, part-time degree program, external degree program, co-op programs and internships, graduate courses open to undergrads. Off campus study at Vermont State Colleges System, National Student Exchange. ROTC: Army (c).

Entrance Requirements: Options: Peterson's Universal Application, electronic application, deferred admission. Required: essay, high school transcript, minimum 2.0 high school GPA, 1 recommendation, SAT. Recommended: minimum 2.5 high school GPA, interview. Entrance: moderately difficult. Application deadline: Rolling. Notification: continuous.

Costs Per Year: Application fee: $35. State resident tuition: $6722 full-time, $280 per credit part-time. Nonresident tuition: $14,524 full-time, $605 per credit part-time. Mandatory fees: $184 full-time, $8 per credit part-time. College room and board: $6910. College room only: $6132.

Collegiate Environment: Orientation program. Drama-theater group, choral group, student-run newspaper, radio station. Social organizations: 35 open to all. Most popular organizations: SERVE (Break Away, Habitat for Humanity), Outing Club, snowboarding, Earth Action Club, Gay-Straight Alliance. Major annual events: Fall Fest, major concerts, May Day/Spring Fling. Student services: health clinic, personal-psychological counseling, women's center. Campus security: 24-hour emergency response devices and patrols, student patrols, late night transport-escort service, controlled dormitory access. 516 college housing spaces available; 425 were occupied in 2003-04. No special consideration for freshman housing applicants. On-campus residence required through sophomore year. Option: coed housing available. Library and Learning Center with 100,053 books, 180,158 microform titles, 522 serials, 7,200 audiovisual materials, and an OPAC. 131 computers available on campus for general student use. A campuswide network can be accessed from student residence rooms and from off campus. Staffed computer lab on campus.

Community Environment: The 350-acre hilltop campus of Johnson State is home for more than 1,500 students. Its location, in the heart of the Green Mountains, places it just minutes away from some of the East's finest skiing and snowboarding at Stowe and Smuggler's Notch. Students have access to our on-campus snowboard park. Its modern facilities include one of the finest performing arts centers in northern New England.

■ **LANDMARK COLLEGE** *P-6*

River Rd. South
Putney, VT 05346
Tel: (802)387-4767

Admissions: (802)387-6716
Fax: (802)387-4779
Web Site: http://www.landmark.edu/

Description: Independent, 2-year, coed. Awards transfer associate and terminal associate degrees. Founded 1983. Setting: 125-acre rural campus. Endowment: $3.2 million. Research spending for 2004 fiscal year: $406,865. Educational spending for 2005 fiscal year: $15,396 per student. Total enrollment: 371. Student-undergrad faculty ratio is 4:1. 339 applied, 72% were admitted. Full-time: 233 students, 21% women, 79% men. Part-time: 138 students, 31% women, 69% men. Students come from 37 states and territories, 11 other countries, 92% from out-of-state, 0% Native American, 2% Hispanic, 5% black, 3% Asian American or Pacific Islander, 3% international, 7% 25 or older, 94% live on campus, 9% transferred in. Retention: 48% of full-time freshmen returned the following year. Core. Calendar: semesters. Academic remediation for entering students, services for LD students, advanced placement, summer session for credit, adult/continuing education programs. Study abroad program.

Entrance Requirements: Option: deferred admission. Required: essay, high school transcript, 2 recommendations, interview, diagnosis of LD and/or AD/HD, Wechsler Adult Intelligence Scale III and Nelson Denny Reading Test. Entrance: moderately difficult. Application deadline: Rolling. Notification: continuous.

Costs Per Year: Application fee: $75. One-time mandatory fee: $1850. Comprehensive fee: $46,470 includes full-time tuition ($38,500), mandatory fees ($770), and college room and board ($7200). College room only: $3600.

Collegiate Environment: Orientation program. Drama-theater group, choral group. Social organizations: 22 open to all. Most popular organizations: Student Government Association, Campus Activities Board, Phi Theta Kappa Honor Society, Jazz Band Club, Cultural Diversity Club. Major annual events: Charity Casino Night, Spring Fest, Dorm Wars. Student services: health clinic, personal-psychological counseling, women's center. Campus security: 24-hour emergency response devices and patrols, controlled dormitory access. 424 college housing spaces available; 360 were occupied in 2003-04. Freshmen guaranteed college housing. On-campus residence required in freshman year. Option: coed housing available. Landmark College Library with 30,066 books, 20 microform titles, 135 serials, and 1,555 audiovisual materials. Operations spending for 2004 fiscal year: $315,935. 50 computers available on campus for general student use. Computer purchase/lease plans available. A campuswide network can be accessed from student residence rooms and from off campus. Staffed computer lab on campus.

■ **LYNDON STATE COLLEGE** *D-9*

PO Box 919
Lyndonville, VT 05851-0919
Tel: (802)626-6200
Free: 800-225-1998
Admissions: (802)626-6413
Fax: (802)626-6335
E-mail: admissions@lyndonstate.edu
Web Site: http://www.lyndonstate.edu/

Description: State-supported, comprehensive, coed. Part of Vermont State Colleges System. Awards associate, bachelor's, and master's degrees. Founded 1911. Setting: 175-acre rural campus. Endowment: $1.8 million. Total enrollment: 1,319. Faculty: 145 (59 full-time, 86 part-time). Student-undergrad faculty ratio is 21:1. 994 applied, 94% were admitted. 12% from top 10% of their high school class, 22% from top quarter, 69% from top half. Full-time: 1,140 students, 46% women, 54% men. Part-time: 133 students, 67% women, 33% men. Students come from 26 states and territories, 15 other countries, 40% from out-of-state, 1% Native American, 1% Hispanic, 1% black, 1% Asian American or Pacific Islander, 0.1% international, 18% 25 or older, 50% live on campus, 6% transferred in. Retention: 66% of full-time freshmen returned the following year. Academic areas with the most degrees conferred: business/marketing; liberal arts/general studies; education. Core. Calendar: semesters. Academic remediation for entering students, services for LD students, advanced placement, accelerated degree program, self-designed majors, honors program, independent study, double major, summer session for credit, part-time degree program, adult/continuing education programs, co-op programs and internships. Study abroad program. ROTC: Air Force (c).

Entrance Requirements: Options: Peterson's Universal Application, Common Application, electronic application, early admission, deferred admission. Required: essay, high school transcript, minimum 2.0 high school GPA, 1 recommendation, SAT or ACT. Recommended: minimum 3.0 high school GPA, interview. Required for some: minimum 3.0 high school GPA. Entrance: moderately difficult. Application deadline: Rolling. Notification: continuous.

Costs Per Year: Application fee: $35. State resident tuition: $6312 full-time, $263 per credit hour part-time. Nonresident tuition: $13,632 full-time, $568 per credit hour part-time. Mandatory fees: $172 full-time, $8 per credit hour part-time. Full-time tuition and fees vary according to course load. Part-time tuition and fees vary according to course load. College room and board: $6674. College room only: $3974. Room and board charges vary according to board plan and housing facility.

Collegiate Environment: Orientation program. Drama-theater group, choral group, student-run newspaper, radio station. Social organizations: 22 open to all. Most popular organizations: American Meteorological Society, ASSIST (A Society of Students in Service Together), Student Senate, Campus Activities Board, Outing Club. Major annual events: Winter Weekend, Spring Weekend, Winter Ball. Student services: health clinic, personal-psychological counseling. Campus security: 24-hour emergency response devices, student patrols, late night transport-escort service, controlled dormitory access. 550 college housing spaces available; 540 were occupied in 2003-04. Freshmen given priority for college housing. On-campus residence required through sophomore year. Options: coed, women-only housing available. Samuel Read Hall Library with 109,629 books, 32,327 microform titles, 16,468 serials, 4,541 audiovisual materials, an OPAC, and a Web page. 125 computers available on campus for general student use. Computer purchase/lease plans available. A campuswide network can be accessed from student residence rooms and from off campus. Staffed computer lab on campus.

Community Environment: Lyndon is a rural community in the northeastern part of Vermont with community facilities that include churches of major denominations, civic and service organizations, a library, two hospitals, and good shopping areas. A ski resort at Burke Mountain and Jay Peak provide facilities for skiing and other winter sports.

■ **MARLBORO COLLEGE** *P-5*
PO Box A, South Rd.
Marlboro, VT 05344
Tel: (802)257-4333
Free: 800-343-0049
Admissions: (802)258-9261
E-mail: admissions@marlboro.edu
Web Site: http://www.marlboro.edu/

Description: Independent, comprehensive, coed. Awards bachelor's, master's, and first professional degrees. Founded 1946. Setting: 350-acre rural campus. Endowment: $19.2 million. Educational spending for 2005 fiscal year: $11,890 per student. Total enrollment: 387. Faculty: 50 (36 full-time, 14 part-time). Student-undergrad faculty ratio is 7:1. 497 applied, 58% were admitted. 24% from top 10% of their high school class, 58% from top quarter, 95% from top half. Full-time: 327 students, 61% women, 39% men. Part-time: 13 students, 46% women, 54% men. Students come from 39 states and territories, 5 other countries, 88% from out-of-state, 1% Native American, 4% Hispanic, 1% black, 1% Asian American or Pacific Islander, 1% international, 10% 25 or older, 82% live on campus, 7% transferred in. Retention: 78% of full-time freshmen returned the following year. Academic areas with the most degrees conferred: visual and performing arts; English; biological/life sciences. Calendar: semesters. Services for LD students, advanced placement, accelerated degree program, self-designed majors, independent study, double major, part-time degree program, internships. Off campus study at Brattleboro School of Music, School for International Training. Study abroad program.

Entrance Requirements: Options: Peterson's Universal Application, Common Application, electronic application, early admission, early decision, early action, deferred admission, international baccalaureate accepted. Required: essay, high school transcript, 2 recommendations, graded expository essay, SAT or ACT. Recommended: minimum 3.0 high school GPA. Required for some: interview. Entrance: moderately difficult. Application deadlines: 2/15, 11/15 for early decision, 1/15 for early action. Notification: 4/1, 12/15 for early decision, 2/1 for early action.

Costs Per Year: Application fee: $50. Comprehensive fee: $35,980 includes full-time tuition ($26,940), mandatory fees ($850), and college room and board ($8190). College room only: $4540. Part-time tuition: $890 per credit.

Collegiate Environment: Orientation program. Drama-theater group, choral group, student-run newspaper. Social organizations: 25 open to all. Most popular organizations: Theater Club, outdoor program, Fencing Club, Gay/Lesbian/Bisexual Alliance, women's chorus. Major annual events: Fall Rites

Cabaret, Broomball Tournament, Convocation. Student services: health clinic, personal-psychological counseling. Campus security: 24-hour emergency response devices. 264 college housing spaces available; all were occupied in 2003-04. Freshmen guaranteed college housing. On-campus residence required in freshman year. Options: coed, women-only housing available. Rice Memorial Library with 65,000 books, 5,519 microform titles, 275 serials, 778 audiovisual materials, an OPAC, and a Web page. Operations spending for 2004 fiscal year: $226,000. 47 computers available on campus for general student use. A campuswide network can be accessed from student residence rooms and from off campus. Staffed computer lab on campus.

Community Environment: Marlboro is located on the scenic Molly Stark Trail near Hogback Mountain which offers a panoramic view of the area. Recreational activities include canoeing, kayaking, cross country skiing, hiking, rock climbing, and biking. The Marlboro Summer Music Festival is an annual event.

■ **MIDDLEBURY COLLEGE** *H-3*
Middlebury, VT 05753-6002
Tel: (802)443-5000
Admissions: (802)443-3000
Fax: (802)443-2056
E-mail: admissions@middlebury.edu
Web Site: http://www.middlebury.edu/

Description: Independent, comprehensive, coed. Awards bachelor's, master's, and doctoral degrees. Founded 1800. Setting: 350-acre small town campus. Endowment: $664.8 million. Research spending for 2004 fiscal year: $3.5 million. Total enrollment: 2,455. Faculty: 300 (254 full-time, 46 part-time). Student-undergrad faculty ratio is 9:1. 5,254 applied, 24% were admitted. 84% from top 10% of their high school class, 96% from top quarter, 99% from top half. 57 class presidents. Full-time: 2,420 students, 51% women, 49% men. Part-time: 35 students, 49% women, 51% men. Students come from 52 states and territories, 67 other countries, 93% from out-of-state, 1% Native American, 5% Hispanic, 3% black, 7% Asian American or Pacific Islander, 9% international, 0% 25 or older, 97% live on campus, 0.1% transferred in. Retention: 94% of full-time freshmen returned the following year. Academic areas with the most degrees conferred: social sciences; family and consumer sciences; interdisciplinary studies. Core. Calendar: 4-1-4. Services for LD students, advanced placement, accelerated degree program, self-designed majors, honors program, independent study, double major, summer session for credit, internships, graduate courses open to undergrads. Off campus study at Swarthmore College, Berea College, Bucknell University, Eckerd College, St. Olaf College, American University, Williams College (Mystic Seaport Program), Institute for Architecture and Urban Studies. Study abroad program. ROTC: Army (c).

Entrance Requirements: Options: Peterson's Universal Application, Common Application, electronic application, early admission, early decision, deferred admission, international baccalaureate accepted. Required: essay, high school transcript, 3 recommendations, SAT and SAT Subject Tests or ACT, three tests to include: a writing test, a quantitative test, and an area of the applicant's choice. Recommended: interview. Entrance: most difficult. Application deadlines: 1/1, 11/15 for early decision plan 1, 12/15 for early decision plan 2. Notification: 4/1, 12/15 for early decision plan 1, 2/15 for early decision plan 2.

Costs Per Year: Application fee: $55. Comprehensive fee: $42,120.

Collegiate Environment: Orientation program. Drama-theater group, choral group, student-run newspaper, radio station. Social organizations: 95 open to all. Most popular organizations: Volunteer Service Organization, International Students Organization, Mountain Club, Activities Board, WRMC radio. Major annual events: Senior Week, Winter Carnival, Student Concert Series. Student services: health clinic, personal-psychological counseling, women's center. Campus security: 24-hour patrols, student patrols, late night transport-escort service, controlled dormitory access. 2,350 college housing spaces available; 2,290 were occupied in 2003-04. Freshmen guaranteed college housing. On-campus residence required through junior year. Option: coed housing available. Main Library plus 3 others with 853,000 books, 386,576 microform titles, 2,908 serials, 33,288 audiovisual materials, an OPAC, and a Web page. Operations spending for 2004 fiscal year: $5.6 million. 494 computers available on campus for general student use. Computer purchase/lease plans available. A campuswide network can be accessed from student residence rooms and from off campus. Staffed computer lab on campus.

Community Environment: Middlebury, population 8,000, is located between Burlington and Rutland. Churches, libraries, and various civic and service organizations serve the community. The college's Bread Loaf Mountain is nearby and has facilities for skiing and other winter sports. The College owns and operates an 18-hole golf course, an alpine ski area, and 2 cross-country ski areas. Other sports facilities in the area provide for tennis and horseback riding. Lake Champlain and Green Mountain National Forest are nearby and provide numerous additional facilities.

■ **NEW ENGLAND CULINARY INSTITUTE** *F-6*
250 Main St.
Montpelier, VT 05602-9720
Tel: (802)223-6324; 877-223-6324
Fax: (802)223-0634
E-mail: admissions@neci.edu
Web Site: http://www.neci.edu/

Description: Proprietary, primarily 2-year, coed. Awards certificates, terminal associate, and bachelor's degrees. Founded 1980. Setting: small town campus. Endowment: $291,550. Educational spending for 2005 fiscal year: $5000 per student. Total enrollment: 606. 426 applied, 24% were admitted. Full-time: 606 students, 26% women, 74% men. Students come from 49 states and territories, 93% from out-of-state, 0.2% Native American, 3% Hispanic, 2% black, 2% Asian American or Pacific Islander, 0.5% international, 32% 25 or older, 80% live on campus. Core. Services for LD students, advanced placement, accelerated degree program, honors program, co-op programs and internships.

Entrance Requirements: Options: Peterson's Universal Application, Common Application, electronic application, early admission, deferred admission. Required: essay, high school transcript, 1 recommendation, interview. Required for some: minimum TOEFL scores for foreign students. Placement: SAT recommended. Entrance: moderately difficult. Application deadline: Rolling.

Costs Per Year: Application fee: $0. Comprehensive fee: $28,365 includes full-time tuition ($21,500), mandatory fees ($450), and college room and board ($6415). Full-time tuition and fees vary according to degree level, program, and student level.

Collegiate Environment: Orientation program. Student-run newspaper. Social organizations: 10 open to all; 75% of eligible men and 25% of eligible women are members. Most popular organizations: American Culinary Federation, Toastmasters, Ice Carving Club. Major annual events: skiing trips, annual chef vs. student softball games and bbq, talent show. Student services: personal-psychological counseling. Campus security: 24-hour emergency response devices, student patrols, Mod patrols in the evening. 270 college housing spaces available; 260 were occupied in 2003-04. No special consideration for freshman housing applicants. Options: coed, men-only, women-only housing available. New England Culinary Institute Library with 2,400 books, 30 serials, 35 audiovisual materials, and an OPAC. Operations spending for 2004 fiscal year: $12,000. 14 computers available on campus for general student use. Computer purchase/lease plans available. A campuswide network can be accessed from student residence rooms. Staffed computer lab on campus.

■ **NEW ENGLAND CULINARY INSTITUTE AT ESSEX** *E-3*
48 1/2 Park St.
Essex Junction, VT 05452
Tel: (802)872-3400
Admissions: (802)223-6324
E-mail: sherrigilmore@neci.edu
Web Site: http://www.neci.edu/

Description: Proprietary, primarily 2-year, coed. Awards certificates, diplomas, transfer associate, terminal associate, and bachelor's degrees. Endowment: $336,943. Educational spending for 2005 fiscal year: $6000 per student. Total enrollment: 501. 229 applied, 78% were admitted. Full-time: 501 students, 32% women, 68% men. 72% from out-of-state, 1% Native American, 2% Hispanic, 2% black, 3% Asian American or Pacific Islander, 0% international.

Entrance Requirements: Required: essay, high school transcript, 1 recommendation, interview, minimum TOEFL scores for foreign students. Required for some: 2 recommendations.

Costs Per Year: Application fee: $0. Comprehensive fee: $33,830 includes full-time tuition ($23,835), mandatory fees ($3430), and college room and board ($6565).

Collegiate Environment: Student-run newspaper. Student services: personal-psychological counseling.

■ **NORWICH UNIVERSITY** *G-5*
158 Harmon Dr.
Northfield, VT 05663

Tel: (802)485-2000
Free: 800-468-6679
Admissions: (802)485-2013
Fax: (802)485-2580
E-mail: nuadm@norwich.edu
Web Site: http://www.norwich.edu/

Description: Independent, comprehensive, coed. Awards bachelor's and master's degrees. Founded 1819. Setting: 1,125-acre small town campus with easy access to Burlington. Endowment: $110.9 million. Research spending for 2004 fiscal year: $53,956. Educational spending for 2005 fiscal year: $4912 per student. Total enrollment: 2,707. Faculty: 272 (139 full-time, 133 part-time). Student-undergrad faculty ratio is 14:1. 1,472 applied, 91% were admitted. 8% from top 10% of their high school class, 20% from top quarter, 43% from top half. Students come from 41 states and territories, 10 other countries, 74% from out-of-state, 23% 25 or older, 84% live on campus. Retention: 71% of full-time freshmen returned the following year. Calendar: semesters. Academic remediation for entering students, ESL program, services for LD students, advanced placement, independent study, distance learning, double major, summer session for credit, part-time degree program, external degree program, adult/continuing education programs, co-op programs and internships, graduate courses open to undergrads. Study abroad program. ROTC: Army, Naval, Air Force.

Entrance Requirements: Options: Peterson's Universal Application, electronic application, early admission, early decision, deferred admission. Required: high school transcript, SAT or ACT. Recommended: essay, minimum 2.0 high school GPA, 2 recommendations, interview, SAT Subject Tests. Required for some: essay, portfolio. Entrance: moderately difficult. Application deadlines: Rolling, 11/15 for early decision. Notification: continuous, 12/15 for early decision.

Collegiate Environment: Orientation program. Drama-theater group, choral group, marching band, student-run newspaper, radio station. Social organizations: 45 open to all. Most popular organizations: Rugby Club, National Eagle Scout Association, Mountain and Cold Weather Company, Outing Club, band. Major annual events: Regimental Ball Weekend, Junior Weekend, Homecoming/Alumni Weekend. Student services: health clinic, personal-psychological counseling. Campus security: 24-hour emergency response devices and patrols, late night transport-escort service. On-campus residence required through senior year. Option: coed housing available. Kreitzberg Library with 280,000 books, 99,100 microform titles, 904 serials, 1,501 audiovisual materials, an OPAC, and a Web page. Operations spending for 2004 fiscal year: $837,080. 142 computers available on campus for general student use. A campuswide network can be accessed from student residence rooms and from off campus. Staffed computer lab on campus.

Community Environment: A rural community in the central section of Vermont, Northfield is 11 miles south of Montpelier, the state capital. Rail, bus and air transportation is available. Recreational activities include skiing, hiking, bicycling, fishing, and hunting.

■ **SAINT MICHAEL'S COLLEGE** *D-3*
One Winooski Park
Colchester, VT 05439
Tel: (802)654-2000
Free: 800-762-8000
Admissions: (802)654-3000
Fax: (802)654-2242
E-mail: admission@smcvt.edu
Web Site: http://www.smcvt.edu/

Description: Independent Roman Catholic, comprehensive, coed. Awards bachelor's and master's degrees and post-master's certificates. Founded 1904. Setting: 440-acre small town campus with easy access to Montreal. Endowment: $60.1 million. Research spending for 2004 fiscal year: $176,209. Educational spending for 2005 fiscal year: $9018 per student. Total enrollment: 2,474. Faculty: 217 (150 full-time, 67 part-time). Student-undergrad faculty ratio is 12:1. 2,924 applied, 72% were admitted. 26% from top 10% of their high school class, 58% from top quarter, 88% from top half. 5 valedictorians. Full-time: 1,945 students, 54% women, 46% men. Part-time: 61 students, 59% women, 41% men. Students come from 27 states and territories, 14 other countries, 77% from out-of-state, 0.2% Native American, 1% Hispanic, 1% black, 1% Asian American or Pacific Islander, 2% international, 2% 25 or older, 93% live on campus, 2% transferred in. Retention: 88% of full-time freshmen returned the following year. Academic areas with the most degrees conferred: business/marketing; psychology; social sciences. Core. Calendar: semesters. ESL program, advanced placement, self-designed majors, honors program, independent study, double major, summer session for credit, part-time degree program, internships. Off campus study at Washington Semester. Study abroad program. ROTC: Army (c), Air Force (c).

Entrance Requirements: Options: Peterson's Universal Application, Common Application, electronic application, early action, deferred admission, international baccalaureate accepted. Required: essay, high school transcript, SAT or ACT. Recommended: minimum 3.0 high school GPA, recommendations, interview. Entrance: moderately difficult. Application deadlines: 2/1, 11/1 for early action. Notification: 4/1, 12/31 for early action.

Costs Per Year: Application fee: $45. Comprehensive fee: $35,505 includes full-time tuition ($28,280), mandatory fees ($235), and college room and board ($6990). Part-time tuition: $945 per credit hour.

Collegiate Environment: Orientation program. Drama-theater group, choral group, student-run newspaper, radio station. Social organizations: 50 open to all. Most popular organizations: Student Association, Mobilization of Volunteer Efforts (MOVE), student radio station, wilderness program, student newspaper. Major annual events: Family Weekend, Martin Luther King, Jr. Convocation, Spring Weekend. Student services: health clinic, personal-psychological counseling, women's center. Campus security: 24-hour emergency response devices and patrols, student patrols, late night transport-escort service, bicycle patrols. 1,827 college housing spaces available; 1,755 were occupied in 2003-04. Freshmen guaranteed college housing. On-campus residence required through senior year. Options: coed, men-only, women-only housing available. Durick Library with 210,811 books, 123,970 microform titles, 1,533 serials, 8,044 audiovisual materials, an OPAC, and a Web page. Operations spending for 2004 fiscal year: $1.4 million. 233 computers available on campus for general student use. A campuswide network can be accessed from student residence rooms and from off campus. Staffed computer lab on campus.

■ **SOUTHERN VERMONT COLLEGE** *P-3*
982 Mansion Dr.
Bennington, VT 05201-6002
Tel: (802)442-5427
Free: 800-378-2782
Admissions: (802)447-6304
Fax: (802)447-4695
E-mail: admis@svc.edu
Web Site: http://www.svc.edu/

Description: Independent, 4-year, coed. Awards associate and bachelor's degrees. Founded 1926. Setting: 371-acre small town campus with easy access to Albany. Endowment: $1.2 million. Educational spending for 2005 fiscal year: $2920 per student. Total enrollment: 390. Student-undergrad faculty ratio is 11:1. 373 applied, 71% were admitted. 0% from top 10% of their high school class, 5% from top quarter, 35% from top half. Full-time: 323 students, 68% women, 32% men. Part-time: 67 students, 76% women, 24% men. Students come from 3 other countries, 58% from out-of-state, 0% Native American, 2% Hispanic, 4% black, 1% Asian American or Pacific Islander, 1% international, 29% 25 or older, 50% live on campus, 10% transferred in. Retention: 65% of full-time freshmen returned the following year. Academic areas with the most degrees conferred: business/marketing; security and protective services; psychology. Core. Calendar: semesters. Academic remediation for entering students, services for LD students, advanced placement, accelerated degree program, self-designed majors, honors program, independent study, distance learning, double major, summer session for credit, part-time degree program, external degree program, adult/continuing education programs, co-op programs and internships. Study abroad program.

Entrance Requirements: Options: Peterson's Universal Application, Common Application, electronic application, early admission, deferred admission, international baccalaureate accepted. Required: essay, high school transcript, 2 recommendations, SAT or ACT. Recommended: minimum 2.0 high school GPA, interview. Required for some: interview. Entrance: minimally difficult. Application deadline: Rolling. Notification: continuous.

Costs Per Year: Application fee: $30. Comprehensive fee: $21,317 includes full-time tuition ($14,373) and college room and board ($6944). College room only: $3230. Part-time tuition: $399 per credit.

Collegiate Environment: Orientation program. Drama-theater group, student-run newspaper, radio station. Social organizations: 13 open to all. Most popular organizations: Student Government Association, Men's and Women's Rugby Club, Community Action Club, Mountaineer Cheerleaders, Madhatters Club (drama). Major annual events: Family Weekend, Holiday Dance, Awards Banquet. Student services: health clinic, personal-

psychological counseling. Campus security: 24-hour patrols, late night transport-escort service, controlled dormitory access. 237 college housing spaces available; 208 were occupied in 2003-04. Freshmen guaranteed college housing. On-campus residence required in freshman year. Option: coed housing available. Southern Vermont College Library with 26,000 books, 80 microform titles, 250 serials, 500 audiovisual materials, and a Web page. Operations spending for 2004 fiscal year: $132,878. 35 computers available on campus for general student use. A campuswide network can be accessed from student residence rooms and from off campus. Staffed computer lab on campus.

Community Environment: See Bennington College.

■ **STERLING COLLEGE** *D-7*
PO Box 72
Craftsbury Common, VT 05827-0072
Tel: (802)586-7711
Free: 800-648-3591
E-mail: admissions@sterlingcollege.edu
Web Site: http://www.sterlingcollege.edu/

Description: Independent, 4-year, coed. Awards associate and bachelor's degrees. Founded 1958. Setting: 430-acre rural campus. Endowment: $640,859. Research spending for 2004 fiscal year: $41,038. Educational spending for 2005 fiscal year: $9235 per student. Total enrollment: 98. Student-undergrad faculty ratio is 4:1. 55 applied, 65% were admitted. 0% from top 10% of their high school class, 0% from top quarter, 29% from top half. Full-time: 90 students, 32% women, 68% men. Part-time: 8 students, 50% women, 50% men. Students come from 20 states and territories, 86% from out-of-state, 1% Native American, 1% Hispanic, 0% black, 2% Asian American or Pacific Islander, 0% international, 12% 25 or older, 77% live on campus, 13% transferred in. Retention: 83% of full-time freshmen returned the following year. Academic areas with the most degrees conferred: natural resources/environmental science; agriculture; parks and recreation. Core. Calendar: semesters. Services for LD students, self-designed majors, honors program, independent study, summer session for credit, part-time degree program, internships. Off campus study. Study abroad program.

Entrance Requirements: Options: Peterson's Universal Application, Common Application, electronic application, deferred admission, international baccalaureate accepted. Required: essay, high school transcript, 2 recommendations. Recommended: minimum 2.0 high school GPA, interview. Entrance: moderately difficult. Application deadlines: Rolling, 12/15 for early action. Notification: continuous until 8/30, 1/15 for early action.

Costs Per Year: Application fee: $35. Comprehensive fee: $28,286 includes full-time tuition ($16,600), mandatory fees ($350), and college room and board ($6336). College room only: $2860. Full-time tuition and fees vary according to course load. Room and board charges vary according to board plan. Part-time tuition: $520 per credit. Part-time tuition varies according to course load.

Collegiate Environment: Orientation program. Most popular organizations: Outing Club, Timbersports Team, Student Life Organization, Art Club. Major annual events: Contra Dances, Harvest Barbeque, May Day Festival. Student services: health clinic, personal-psychological counseling. Campus security: student patrols. 100 college housing spaces available; 71 were occupied in 2003-04. Freshmen guaranteed college housing. On-campus residence required in freshman year. Options: coed, men-only, women-only housing available. Brown Library plus 1 other with 10,000 books, 397 serials, 520 audiovisual materials, an OPAC, and a Web page. Operations spending for 2004 fiscal year: $80,996. 15 computers available on campus for general student use. A campuswide network can be accessed. Staffed computer lab on campus.

■ **UNIVERSITY OF VERMONT** *E-3*
Burlington, VT 05405
Tel: (802)656-3131
Admissions: (802)656-3370
E-mail: admissions@uvm.edu
Web Site: http://www.uvm.edu/

Description: State-supported, university, coed. Awards bachelor's, master's, doctoral, and first professional degrees and post-master's certificates. Founded 1791. Setting: 425-acre suburban campus. Endowment: $261.5 million. Research spending for 2004 fiscal year: $101.8 million. Educational spending for 2005 fiscal year: $18,670 per student. Total enrollment: 11,597. Faculty: 723 (560 full-time, 163 part-time). Student-undergrad faculty ratio is 15:1. 13,015 applied, 80% were admitted. 21% from top 10% of their high school class, 55% from top quarter, 91% from top half. 27 valedictorians.

Full-time: 8,652 students, 54% women, 46% men. Part-time: 1,207 students, 61% women, 39% men. Students come from 50 states and territories, 30 other countries, 63% from out-of-state, 0.3% Native American, 2% Hispanic, 1% black, 2% Asian American or Pacific Islander, 1% international, 5% 25 or older, 52% live on campus, 4% transferred in. Retention: 88% of full-time freshmen returned the following year. Academic areas with the most degrees conferred: social sciences; business/marketing; psychology. Calendar: semesters. ESL program, services for LD students, advanced placement, self-designed majors, freshman honors college, honors program, independent study, distance learning, double major, summer session for credit, part-time degree program, co-op programs and internships, graduate courses open to undergrads. Off campus study. Study abroad program. ROTC: Army.

Entrance Requirements: Options: Common Application, electronic application, early action, deferred admission, international baccalaureate accepted. Required: essay, high school transcript, 1 recommendation, SAT or ACT. Recommended: 2 recommendations. Entrance: moderately difficult. Application deadlines: 1/15, 11/1 for early action. Notification: 3/31, 12/15 for early action. Preference given to state residents.

Costs Per Year: Application fee: $45. State resident tuition: $9452 full-time, $394 per credit part-time. Nonresident tuition: $23,638 full-time, $985 per credit part-time. Mandatory fees: $1296 full-time. Part-time tuition varies according to course load. College room and board: $7332. College room only: $4936. Room and board charges vary according to board plan.

Collegiate Environment: Orientation program. Drama-theater group, choral group, student-run newspaper, radio station. Social organizations: 100 open to all; national fraternities, national sororities, local fraternities; 7% of eligible men and 5% of eligible women are members. Most popular organizations: Volunteers in Action, Outing Club, club sports. Major annual events: Springfest, Homecoming. Student services: legal services, health clinic, personal-psychological counseling, women's center. Campus security: 24-hour emergency response devices and patrols, late night transport-escort service, controlled dormitory access. 3,977 college housing spaces available; 3,900 were occupied in 2003-04. Freshmen guaranteed college housing. On-campus residence required through sophomore year. Option: coed housing available. Bailey-Howe Library plus 3 others with 2.4 million books, 1.9 million microform titles, 20,216 serials, 36,531 audiovisual materials, an OPAC, and a Web page. Operations spending for 2004 fiscal year: $10.3 million. 685 computers available on campus for general student use. Computer purchase/lease plans available. A campuswide network can be accessed from student residence rooms and from off campus. Staffed computer lab on campus.

Community Environment: Burlington is Vermont's largest city and, while the University is a significant resource, the city has many cultural, recreational, and social offerings. Burlington is a tourist and business center with a rich history and significant business development.

■ **VERMONT TECHNICAL COLLEGE** *H-6*
PO Box 500
Randolph Center, VT 05061-0500
Tel: (802)728-1000
Free: 800-442-VTC1
Admissions: (802)728-1244
Fax: (802)728-1390
E-mail: admissions@vtc.vsc.edu
Web Site: http://www.vtc.edu/

Description: State-supported, 4-year, coed. Part of Vermont State Colleges System. Awards associate and bachelor's degrees. Founded 1866. Setting: 544-acre rural campus. Endowment: $4.3 million. Research spending for 2004 fiscal year: $130,612. Educational spending for 2005 fiscal year: $7268 per student. Total enrollment: 1,356. Student-undergrad faculty ratio is 13:1. 742 applied, 70% were admitted. 10% from top 10% of their high school class, 25% from top quarter, 75% from top half. 1 National Merit Scholar, 3 class presidents, 6 valedictorians, 40 student government officers. Full-time: 1,033 students, 37% women, 63% men. Part-time: 323 students, 49% women, 51% men. Students come from 12 states and territories, 20% from out-of-state, 1% Native American, 1% Hispanic, 1% black, 2% Asian American or Pacific Islander, 0% international, 32% 25 or older, 66% live on campus, 14% transferred in. Retention: 72% of full-time freshmen returned

the following year. Academic areas with the most degrees conferred: engineering technologies; business/marketing; architecture. Core. Calendar: semesters. Academic remediation for entering students, ESL program, services for LD students, advanced placement, accelerated degree program, honors program, independent study, distance learning, double major, summer session for credit, part-time degree program, co-op programs and internships. ROTC: Army (c).

Entrance Requirements: Options: Peterson's Universal Application, Common Application, electronic application. Required: high school transcript. Recommended: minimum 3.0 high school GPA, recommendations, interview, SAT or ACT. Required for some: essay, recommendations, interview, SAT, SAT or ACT, nursing exam. Entrance: minimally difficult. Application deadline: Rolling. Notification: continuous until 9/1.

Costs Per Year: Application fee: $35. Area resident tuition: $7680 full-time. State resident tuition: $11,544 full-time, $320 per credit part-time. Nonresident tuition: $14,640 full-time, $610 per credit part-time. Mandatory fees: $246 full-time, $50 per term part-time. Full-time tuition and fees vary according to course load and program. Part-time tuition and fees vary according to program. College room and board: $6674. College room only: $3974. Room and board charges vary according to board plan.

Collegiate Environment: Orientation program. Drama-theater group, student-run radio station. Social organizations: 30 open to all. Most popular organizations: ASVTC (student government), Hockey Club, student radio station, American Institute of Architecture Students, Golf Club. Major annual events: Fall Festival, Winter Carnival, Spring Fling. Student services: health clinic, personal-psychological counseling. Campus security: 24-hour emergency response devices and patrols, late night transport-escort service, controlled dormitory access. 550 college housing spaces available; 540 were occupied in 2003-04. Freshmen guaranteed college housing. On-campus residence required through senior year. Options: coed, men-only, women-only housing available. Hartness Library with 59,480 books, 5,920 microform titles, 1,156 serials, 4,122 audiovisual materials, an OPAC, and a Web page. Operations spending for 2004 fiscal year: $663,127. 350 computers available on campus for general student use. A campuswide network can be accessed from student residence rooms and from off campus. Staffed computer lab on campus.

Community Environment: Randolph Center is a rural area, four miles from Randolph. A library, hospital, churches, shopping facilities, and several civic and service organizations serve the town. Outdoor sports include golf, fishing, hunting, skiing, ice skating, and tennis.

■ **WOODBURY COLLEGE** *F-6*
660 Elm St.
Montpelier, VT 05602
Tel: (802)229-0516
Fax: (802)229-2141
E-mail: admiss@woodbury-college.edu
Web Site: http://www.woodbury-college.edu/

Description: Independent, 4-year, coed. Awards associate and bachelor's degrees. Founded 1975. Setting: 8-acre small town campus. Endowment: $71,024. Educational spending for 2005 fiscal year: $4700 per student. Total enrollment: 138. Full-time: 99 students, 82% women, 18% men. Part-time: 39 students, 87% women, 13% men. 0% from out-of-state, 1% Native American, 0% Hispanic, 2% black, 0% Asian American or Pacific Islander, 0% international, 90% 25 or older, 10% transferred in. Core. Calendar: trimesters. Academic remediation for entering students, services for LD students, self-designed majors, independent study, distance learning, double major, part-time degree program, adult/continuing education programs, internships.

Entrance Requirements: Open admission except for mediation/conflict management program. Option: electronic application. Required: essay, interview. Required for some: high school transcript. Entrance: noncompetitive. Application deadline: Rolling.

Collegiate Environment: Orientation program. Major annual event: Community Meeting. Student services: personal-psychological counseling. College housing not available. Woodbury College Library with 2,782 books and 2 serials. Operations spending for 2004 fiscal year: $12,000. 10 computers available on campus for general student use. Staffed computer lab on campus.

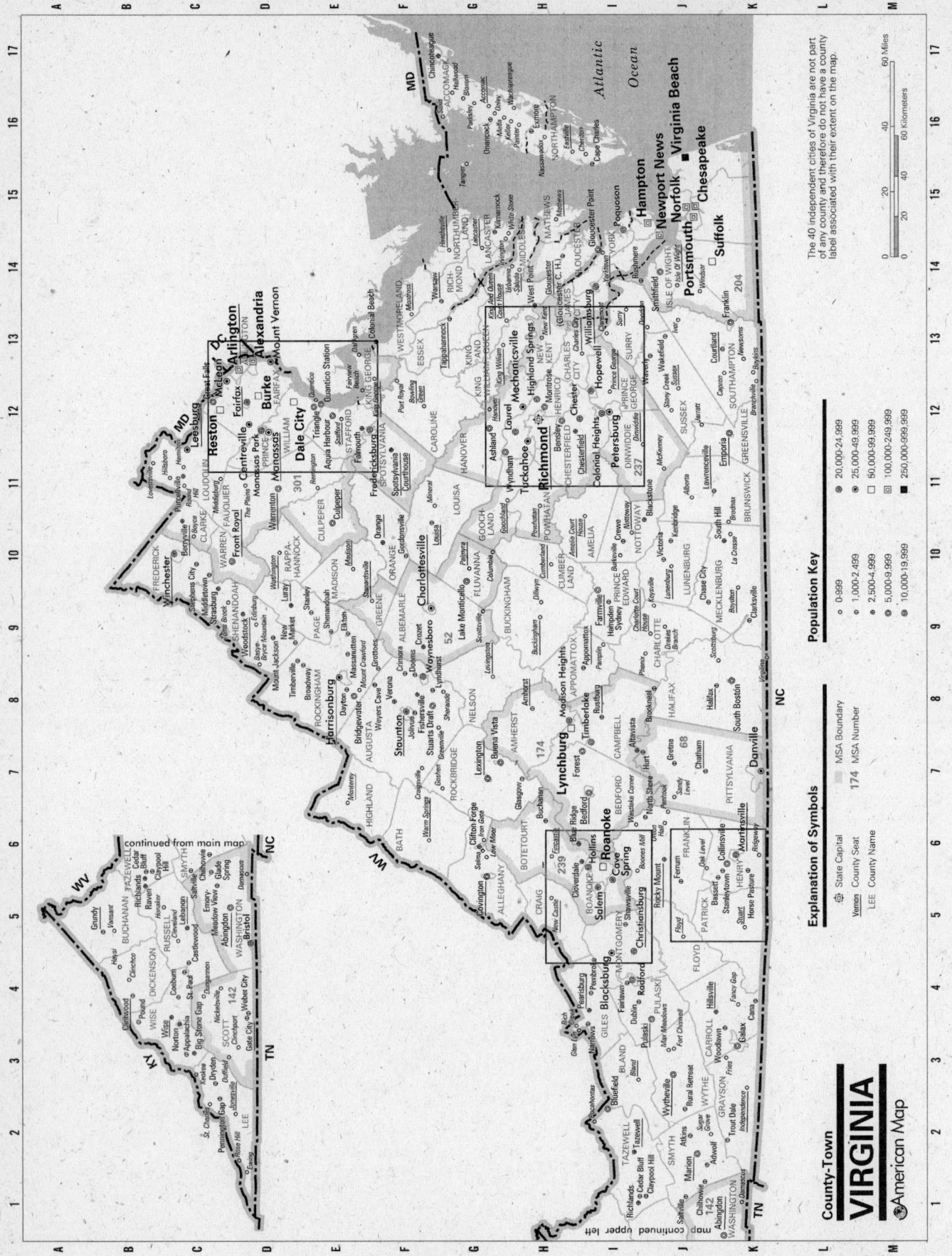

County-Town

VIRGINIA

American Map

Explanation of Symbols

State Capital

Vernon — County Seat

LEE — County Name

MSA Boundary

174 — MSA Number

Population Key

○ 0-999	◎ 20,000-24,999
● 1,000-2,499	◉ 25,000-49,999
● 2,500-4,999	□ 50,000-99,999
◎ 5,000-9,999	▣ 100,000-249,999
◉ 10,000-19,999	■ 250,000-999,999

The 40 independent cities of Virginia are not part of any county and therefore do not have a county label associated with their extent on the map.

■ **ACT COLLEGE** *D-13*
1100 Wilson Blvd.
Arlington, VA 22209
Web Site: http://www.healthtraining.com
Description: Proprietary, 2-year, coed.

■ **ADVANCED TECHNOLOGY INSTITUTE** *J-15*
5700 Southern Blvd.
Virginia Beach, VA 23462
Web Site: http://www.aticareers.com
Description: Proprietary, 2-year, coed.

■ **ARGOSY UNIVERSITY/WASHINGTON D.C.** *D-13*
1550 Wilson Blvd., Ste. 600
Arlington, VA 22209
Tel: (703)526-5800; (866)703-2777
Fax: (703)243-8973
Web Site: http://www.argosyu.edu/
Description: Proprietary, upper-level, coed. Part of Argosy Education Group. Awards bachelor's, master's, and doctoral degrees. Founded 1994. Setting: urban campus with easy access to Washington D.C.. Total enrollment: 13. Full-time: 13 students, 62% women, 38% men. 0% Native American, 8% Hispanic, 15% black, 8% Asian American or Pacific Islander, 0% international. Calendar: semesters.
Collegiate Environment: Social organizations: 1 open to all. Most popular organization: Student Government Association. Major annual event: Common Hours. College housing not available.

■ **THE ART INSTITUTE OF WASHINGTON** *D-13*
1820 North Fort Meyer Dr., Ground Floor
Arlington, VA 22209
Tel: (703)358-9550; 877-303-3771
Admissions: (703)247-6857
Fax: (703)358-9759
Web Site: http://www.artinstitutes.edu/arlington/
Description: Proprietary, 4-year, coed. Part of Education Management Corporation. Awards associate and bachelor's degrees. Founded 2000. Setting: urban campus. Total enrollment: 1,200. Student-undergrad faculty ratio is 20:1. Academic remediation for entering students, services for LD students, advanced placement, accelerated degree program, honors program, independent study, distance learning, part-time degree program, co-op programs and internships. Study abroad program.
Entrance Requirements: Option: electronic application. Required: essay, high school transcript, interview. Application deadline: Rolling. Notification: continuous.
Costs Per Year: Application fee: $50. Tuition: $385 per quarter hour part-time. College room only: $9500. Tuition guaranteed not to increase for student's term of enrollment.
Collegiate Environment: Orientation program. Student services: personal-psychological counseling.

■ **AVERETT UNIVERSITY** *K-7*
420 West Main St.
Danville, VA 24541-3692
Tel: (434)791-5600

Free: 800-AVE-RETT
Admissions: (434)791-7301
Fax: (434)791-5637
E-mail: ktune@averett.edu
Web Site: http://www.averett.edu/
Description: Independent, comprehensive, coed, affiliated with Baptist General Association of Virginia. Awards associate, bachelor's, and master's degrees. Founded 1859. Setting: 19-acre small town campus with easy access to Greensboro and Raleigh. Endowment: $22 million. Educational spending for 2005 fiscal year: $5708 per student. Total enrollment: 1,487. Faculty: 102 (56 full-time, 46 part-time). Student-undergrad faculty ratio is 13:1. 1,745 applied, 56% were admitted. 9% from top 10% of their high school class, 34% from top quarter, 67% from top half. Full-time: 230 students, 37% women, 63% men. Part-time: 11 students, 64% women, 36% men. Students come from 29 states and territories, 20 other countries, 30% from out-of-state, 0.5% Native American, 2% Hispanic, 23% black, 1% Asian American or Pacific Islander, 2% international, 9% 25 or older, 56% live on campus, 82% transferred in. Retention: 48% of full-time freshmen returned the following year. Academic areas with the most degrees conferred: business/marketing; liberal arts/general studies; security and protective services. Core. Calendar: semesters. Academic remediation for entering students, services for LD students, advanced placement, accelerated degree program, self-designed majors, honors program, independent study, double major, summer session for credit, part-time degree program, adult/continuing education programs, internships, graduate courses open to undergrads. Off campus study at Hong Kong Baptist University, Consortium for Global Education, American University. Study abroad program.
Entrance Requirements: Options: Peterson's Universal Application, Common Application, electronic application, early admission, deferred admission, international baccalaureate accepted. Required: high school transcript, minimum 2.2 high school GPA, College Prep curriculum, SAT or ACT, SAT and SAT Subject Tests or ACT, TOEFL for international students; nontraditional students are not required to submit ACT or SAT scores.. Recommended: essay, 1 recommendation, interview. Entrance: moderately difficult. Application deadline: 7/1.
Costs Per Year: Application fee: $0. Comprehensive fee: $25,600 includes full-time tuition ($18,040), mandatory fees ($1000), and college room and board ($6560). College room only: $4800. Room and board charges vary according to board plan and housing facility. Part-time tuition: $305 per credit. Part-time mandatory fees: $250 per term. Part-time tuition and fees vary according to course load, location, and program.
Collegiate Environment: Orientation program. Drama-theater group, choral group, student-run newspaper. Social organizations: 30 open to all; national fraternities, national sororities; 3% of eligible men and 2% of eligible women are members. Most popular organizations: Student Government Association, Baptist Student Union, Phi Sigma Sigma, Pi Kappa Phi, Averett Gospel Choir. Major annual events: homecoming, Spring Formal, President's Lunch on the Lawn. Student services: personal-psychological counseling. Campus security: 24-hour emergency response devices and patrols, late night transport-escort service, controlled dormitory access. 521 college housing spaces available; 453 were occupied in 2003-04. Freshmen guaranteed college housing. On-campus residence required through junior year. Options: coed, men-only, women-only housing available. Mary B. Blount Library with 103,193 books, 243,938 microform titles, 11,358 serials, 291 audiovisual materials, an OPAC, and a Web page. Operations spending for 2004 fiscal

year: $585,099. 100 computers available on campus for general student use. A campuswide network can be accessed. Staffed computer lab on campus.

■ AVIATION INSTITUTE OF MAINTENANCE-MANASSAS *D-12*
9821 Godwin Dr.
Manassas, VA 20110
Tel: (703)257-5515; 877-604-2121
Fax: (703)257-5523
E-mail: directoramm@aviationmaintenance.edu
Web Site: http://www.aviationmaintenance.edu/aviation-washington-dc.asp
Description: Proprietary, 2-year. Awards certificates and terminal associate degrees.
Entrance Requirements: Required: High School Diploma or GED.
Costs Per Year: Application fee: $25.

■ AVIATION INSTITUTE OF MAINTENANCE-VIRGINIA BEACH *J-15*
1429 Miller Store Ro
Virginia Beach, VA 23455
; 888-349-5387
Admissions: (757)363-2121
E-mail: directoramn@aviationmaintenance.edu
Web Site: http://www.aviationmaintenance.edu/aviation-norfolk.asp
Description: Proprietary, 2-year. Awards certificates and terminal associate degrees.
Entrance Requirements: Required: High school diploma or GED.
Costs Per Year: Application fee: $25. Tuition: $10,260 full-time, $220 per credit hour part-time.

■ BETA TECH *H-12*
1610 Forest Ave. - Ste214
Richmond, VA 23229
Tel: (804)673-7110
Description: Proprietary, 2-year.

■ BLUE RIDGE COMMUNITY COLLEGE *F-8*
PO Box 80
Weyers Cave, VA 24486-0080
Tel: (540)234-9261
Admissions: (540)453-2332
E-mail: waylandm@brcc.edu
Web Site: http://www.brcc.edu/
Description: State-supported, 2-year, coed. Part of Virginia Community College System. Awards certificates, diplomas, transfer associate, and terminal associate degrees. Founded 1967. Setting: 65-acre rural campus. Endowment: $2.1 million. Educational spending for 2005 fiscal year: $1491 per student. Total enrollment: 3,804. Student-undergrad faculty ratio is 22:1. 681 applied, 100% were admitted. Full-time: 1,513 students, 49% women, 51% men. Part-time: 2,291 students, 64% women, 36% men. Students come from 29 states and territories, 2 other countries, 2% from out-of-state, 0.4% Native American, 2% Hispanic, 4% black, 2% Asian American or Pacific Islander, 36% 25 or older, 42% transferred in. Retention: 41% of full-time freshmen returned the following year. Calendar: semesters. Academic remediation for entering students, ESL program, services for LD students, advanced placement, honors program, distance learning, double major, summer session for credit, part-time degree program, adult/continuing education programs, co-op programs and internships. Off campus study, Study abroad program.
Entrance Requirements: Open admission except for veterinary technology, nursing programs. Options: electronic application, early admission. Required for some: high school transcript, interview. Entrance: noncompetitive. Application deadline: Rolling. Notification: continuous.
Costs Per Year: Application fee: $0. State resident tuition: $2040 full-time, $68 per credit hour part-time. Nonresident tuition: $6420 full-time, $214 per credit hour part-time. Mandatory fees: $146 full-time, $4.85 per credit hour part-time.
Collegiate Environment: Orientation program. Most popular organizations: Student Government Association, Phi Theta Kappa, Christian Fellowship, intramural athletics, special interest groups. Major annual event: Folk Arts Festival. Student services: personal-psychological counseling, women's center. Campus security: 24-hour emergency response devices and patrols, late night transport-escort service. College housing not available. Houff Library with 59,735 books, 206 serials, 1,646 audiovisual materials, an

OPAC, and a Web page. Operations spending for 2004 fiscal year: $414,447. 285 computers available on campus for general student use. A campuswide network can be accessed. Staffed computer lab on campus.
Community Environment: Weyers Cave is a rural community located near Staunton and Harrisonburg.

■ BLUEFIELD COLLEGE *I-2*
3000 College Dr.
Bluefield, VA 24605-1799
Tel: (276)326-3682
Free: 800-872-0175
Admissions: (276)326-4217
Fax: (276)326-4288
Web Site: http://www.bluefield.edu/
Description: Independent Southern Baptist, 4-year, coed. Awards bachelor's degrees. Founded 1922. Setting: 85-acre small town campus. Endowment: $4.2 million. Educational spending for 2005 fiscal year: $3179 per student. Total enrollment: 776. Student-undergrad faculty ratio is 12:1. 537 applied, 50% were admitted. 23% from top 10% of their high school class, 44% from top quarter, 83% from top half. 3 valedictorians. Full-time: 692 students, 59% women, 41% men. Part-time: 84 students, 68% women, 32% men. Students come from 14 states and territories, 3 other countries, 37% from out-of-state, 0.4% Native American, 1% Hispanic, 18% black, 1% Asian American or Pacific Islander, 0.4% international, 45% 25 or older, 48% live on campus, 16% transferred in. Retention: 58% of full-time freshmen returned the following year. Academic areas with the most degrees conferred: business/marketing; law/legal studies; psychology. Core. Calendar: semesters. Academic remediation for entering students, services for LD students, advanced placement, accelerated degree program, self-designed majors, freshman honors college, honors program, double major, summer session for credit, part-time degree program, external degree program, adult/continuing education programs, internships. Study abroad program.
Entrance Requirements: Options: electronic application, deferred admission, international baccalaureate accepted. Required: high school transcript, minimum 2.0 high school GPA, SAT or ACT. Recommended: interview. Required for some: recommendations, interview. Entrance: minimally difficult. Application deadline: Rolling. Notification: continuous.
Costs Per Year: Application fee: $30. Comprehensive fee: $18,337 includes full-time tuition ($11,675), mandatory fees ($630), and college room and board ($6032). College room only: $2371. Part-time tuition: $382 per hour. Part-time mandatory fees: $155 per term.
Collegiate Environment: Orientation program. Drama-theater group, choral group, student-run newspaper. Social organizations: 6 open to all; local fraternities, local sororities; 2% of eligible men and 2% of eligible women are members. Most popular organizations: Baptist Student Union, Fellowship of Christian Athletes, Student Union Board, Student Government Association, Bluefield Singers. Major annual events: Homecoming Parade and Dance, Spring Formal, Mud Pig Day. Student services: health clinic, personal-psychological counseling. Campus security: controlled dormitory access, night security patrols. 240 college housing spaces available; 209 were occupied in 2003-04. Freshmen given priority for college housing. On-campus residence required through junior year. Options: coed, men-only, women-only housing available. Easley Library with 74,150 books, 14,000 serials, 2,210 audiovisual materials, an OPAC, and a Web page. Operations spending for 2004 fiscal year: $247,602. 100 computers available on campus for general student use. A campuswide network can be accessed from student residence rooms. Staffed computer lab on campus.
Community Environment: A suburban area in the Virginia Highlands, Bluefield is a center of diversified industry. Products of its industries are fabric dyes, mattresses, hardwood flooring, textiles, and mining equipment. All commercial transportation is available. Public libraries, churches, hospitals, and a number of civic and service organizations are a part of the community. Nearby mountains provide opportunities for numerous recreational activities. Some part-time employment is available.

■ BRIDGEWATER COLLEGE *E-8*
402 East College St.
Bridgewater, VA 22812-1599
Tel: (540)828-8000
Free: 800-759-8328
Admissions: (540)828-5375
Fax: (540)828-5481
E-mail: admissions@bridgewater.edu

Web Site: http://www.bridgewater.edu/

Description: Independent, 4-year, coed, affiliated with Church of the Brethren. Awards bachelor's degrees. Founded 1880. Setting: 190-acre small town campus. Endowment: $48.8 million. Educational spending for 2005 fiscal year: $5770 per student. Total enrollment: 1,506. Student-undergrad faculty ratio is 14:1. 1,502 applied, 86% were admitted. 17% from top 10% of their high school class, 44% from top quarter, 85% from top half. 12 valedictorians, 146 student government officers. Full-time: 1,495 students, 57% women, 43% men. Part-time: 11 students, 64% women, 36% men. Students come from 22 states and territories, 9 other countries, 23% from out-of-state, 0.5% Native American, 1% Hispanic, 8% black, 1% Asian American or Pacific Islander, 1% international, 1% 25 or older, 83% live on campus, 4% transferred in. Retention: 77% of full-time freshmen returned the following year. Academic areas with the most degrees conferred: business/marketing; education; biological/life sciences. Core. Calendar: 4-1-4. Advanced placement, honors program, independent study, double major, summer session for credit, part-time degree program, adult/continuing education programs, internships. Off campus study. Study abroad program.

Entrance Requirements: Options: Common Application, electronic application, deferred admission, international baccalaureate accepted. Required: high school transcript, minimum 2.0 high school GPA, 2 recommendations, SAT or ACT. Recommended: minimum 3.0 high school GPA, interview. Required for some: interview. Entrance: moderately difficult. Application deadline: Rolling. Notification: continuous.

Costs Per Year: Application fee: $30. Comprehensive fee: $29,250 includes full-time tuition ($20,190) and college room and board ($9060). College room only: $4595. Part-time tuition: $650 per credit hour. Part-time mandatory fees: $30.

Collegiate Environment: Orientation program. Drama-theater group, choral group, student-run newspaper, radio station. Social organizations: 42 open to all. Most popular organizations: Eagle Productions, pep band, Oratorio Choir, Baptist Student Union, Brethren Student Fellowship. Major annual events: Spring Carnival, Homecoming, May Day. Student services: health clinic, personal-psychological counseling. Campus security: 24-hour emergency response devices and patrols, controlled dormitory access. 1,308 college housing spaces available; 1,256 were occupied in 2003-04. Freshmen guaranteed college housing. On-campus residence required through senior year. Options: coed, men-only, women-only housing available. Alexander Mack Memorial Library with 138,020 books, 411,972 microform titles, 650 serials, 9,188 audiovisual materials, an OPAC, and a Web page. Operations spending for 2004 fiscal year: $716,165. 160 computers available on campus for general student use. Computer purchase/lease plans available. A campuswide network can be accessed from student residence rooms and from off campus. Staffed computer lab on campus.

Community Environment: Bridgewater is located in the Shenandoah Valley, seven miles south of Harrisonburg. The community facilities include churches, banks, restaurants, parks, museums, and shops. The city, its suburbs and the surrounding area offer entertainment, fine dining experiences, a shopping mall, libraries, a hospital, historic towns, civil war battlefields, the George Washington National Forest, the Massanutten Four Seasons Resort, the Shenandoah Regional Airport, various civic organizations, and events at James Madison University Convocation Center. The College is conveniently located 10 minutes from Harrisonburg, 50 minutes from Charlottesville, an hour and 40 minutes from Roanoke and approximately 2 hours from Richmond or Washington, D.C.

■ **BRYANT AND STRATTON COLLEGE, RICHMOND** *H-12*

8141 Hull St. Rd.
Richmond, VA 23235-6411
Tel: (804)745-2444
Fax: (804)499-7799
E-mail: tlawson@bryanstratton.edu
Web Site: http://www.bryanstratton.edu/

Description: Proprietary, primarily 2-year, coed. Part of Bryant and Stratton Business Institute, Inc. Awards terminal associate and bachelor's degrees. Founded 1952. Setting: suburban campus. Total enrollment: 421. Student-undergrad faculty ratio is 10:1. 0% from top 10% of their high school class, 0% from top quarter, 0% from top half. Full-time: 137 students, 88% women, 12% men. Part-time: 284 students, 82% women, 18% men. 0% from out-of-state, 1% Native American, 3% Hispanic, 71% black, 0.5% Asian American or Pacific Islander, 0% international, 75% 25 or older. Academic area with the most degrees conferred: business/marketing. Core. Calendar: semesters. Academic remediation for entering students, advanced place-

ment, independent study, distance learning, double major, summer session for credit, part-time degree program, adult/continuing education programs, internships.

Entrance Requirements: Option: deferred admission. Required: high school transcript, interview, entrance evaluation and placement evaluation, TABE, CPAt. Recommended: SAT or ACT. Required for some: recommendations. Entrance: minimally difficult. Application deadline: Rolling.

Costs Per Year: Tuition: $18,675 full-time, $415 per credit hour part-time. Mandatory fees: $25 full-time.

Collegiate Environment: Orientation program. Social organizations: 7 open to all. Most popular organizations: Phi Beta Lambda, Alpha Beta Gamma, Student Council, Medical Assisting Club, Paralegal Club. Campus security: late night transport-escort service. College housing not available. Bryant and Stratton Library with 3,176 books and 84 serials. 50 computers available on campus for general student use. A campuswide network can be accessed. Staffed computer lab on campus.

■ **BRYANT AND STRATTON COLLEGE, VIRGINIA BEACH** *J-15*

301 Centre Pointe Dr.
Virginia Beach, VA 23462-4417
Tel: (757)499-7900
Fax: (757)499-7799
Web Site: http://www.bryantstratton.edu/

Description: Proprietary, primarily 2-year, coed. Part of Bryant and Stratton Business Institute, Inc. Awards terminal associate and bachelor's degrees. Founded 1952. Setting: suburban campus. Educational spending for 2005 fiscal year: $1050 per student. Total enrollment: 340. 268 applied, 84% were admitted. Full-time: 238 students, 81% women, 19% men. Part-time: 102 students, 84% women, 16% men. 0% from out-of-state, 1% Native American, 4% Hispanic, 61% black, 1% Asian American or Pacific Islander, 0% international, 60% 25 or older, 12% transferred in. Retention: 85% of full-time freshmen returned the following year. Core. Calendar: semesters. Academic remediation for entering students, services for LD students, advanced placement, independent study, double major, summer session for credit, part-time degree program, adult/continuing education programs, internships.

Entrance Requirements: Open admission. Options: Peterson's Universal Application, Common Application, electronic application. Required: interview, CPAt. Required for some: high school transcript. Entrance: minimally difficult. Application deadline: Rolling.

Collegiate Environment: Orientation program. Student-run newspaper. Social organizations: 7 open to all. Most popular organizations: Phi Beta Lambda, Alpha Beta Gamma, Student Government Association, Medical Club, Law Society. Major annual events: Toy Drive, Red Cross Blood Drive, Southeastern Virginia Food Bank Drive. Campus security: late night transport-escort service. College housing not available. campus library with 9,646 books, 8,271 microform titles, 126 serials, and 359 audiovisual materials. Operations spending for 2004 fiscal year: $40,000. 61 computers available on campus for general student use. A campuswide network can be accessed. Staffed computer lab on campus.

■ **CENTRAL VIRGINIA COMMUNITY COLLEGE** *I-8*

3506 Wards Rd.
Lynchburg, VA 24502-2498
Tel: (434)832-7600
Admissions: (434)832-7630
Fax: (434)386-4700
Web Site: http://www.cvcc.vccs.edu/

Description: State-supported, 2-year, coed. Part of Virginia Community College System. Awards certificates, diplomas, transfer associate, and terminal associate degrees. Founded 1966. Setting: 104-acre suburban campus. Endowment: $1.7 million. Total enrollment: 4,741. Students come from 11 states and territories, 1% from out-of-state, 42% 25 or older. Core. Calendar: semesters. Academic remediation for entering students, services for LD students, advanced placement, independent study, distance learning, summer session for credit, part-time degree program, co-op programs and internships.

Entrance Requirements: Open admission. Options: early admission, deferred admission. Required for some: high school transcript, interview. Placement: ACT ASSET or ACT COMPASS required. Entrance: noncompetitive. Application deadline: Rolling. Notification: continuous.

Collegiate Environment: Orientation program. Drama-theater group, student-run newspaper. Social organizations: 12 open to all. Most popular organizations: Black Student Union, Data Processing Management Association, Radiology Club, Phi Theta Kappa, Respiratory Club. Major annual events: Semi-Annual Picnic, graduation. Student services: personal-psychological counseling. Campus security: 24-hour emergency response devices. College housing not available. Bedford Learning Resources Center with 37,000 books, 230 serials, an OPAC, and a Web page. 130 computers available on campus for general student use. Staffed computer lab on campus.

Community Environment: See Lynchburg College.

■ **CHRISTENDOM COLLEGE** *D-10*
134 Christendom Dr.
Front Royal, VA 22630-5103
Tel: (540)636-2900
Free: 800-877-5456
Fax: (540)636-1655
E-mail: admissions@christendom.edu
Web Site: http://www.christendom.edu/

Description: Independent Roman Catholic, comprehensive, coed. Awards associate, bachelor's, and master's degrees. Founded 1977. Setting: 100-acre rural campus with easy access to Washington, DC. Endowment: $3.1 million. Educational spending for 2005 fiscal year: $5077 per student. Total enrollment: 435. Faculty: 39 (23 full-time, 16 part-time). Student-undergrad faculty ratio is 12:1. 249 applied, 76% were admitted. 60% from top 10% of their high school class, 86% from top quarter, 100% from top half. 2 National Merit Scholars, 2 class presidents, 2 valedictorians, 16 student government officers. Full-time: 372 students, 57% women, 43% men. Part-time: 7 students, 71% women, 29% men. Students come from 43 states and territories, 2 other countries, 75% from out-of-state, 0% Native American, 3% Hispanic, 1% black, 2% Asian American or Pacific Islander, 2% international, 3% 25 or older, 95% live on campus, 4% transferred in. Retention: 88% of full-time freshmen returned the following year. Academic areas with the most degrees conferred: history; theology and religious vocations; social sciences. Core. Calendar: semesters. Academic remediation for entering students, services for LD students, advanced placement, accelerated degree program, independent study, double major, summer session for credit, co-op programs and internships, graduate courses open to undergrads. Study abroad program.

Entrance Requirements: Options: Common Application, electronic application, early admission, early action. Required: essay, high school transcript, 2 recommendations, SAT or ACT. Recommended: minimum 3.0 high school GPA, interview. Entrance: very difficult. Application deadlines: 3/1, 12/1 for early action. Notification: 4/1, 12/15 for early action.

Costs Per Year: Application fee: $25. Comprehensive fee: $22,806 includes full-time tuition ($16,290), mandatory fees ($450), and college room and board ($6066).

Collegiate Environment: Orientation program. Drama-theater group, choral group, student-run newspaper. Social organizations: 15 open to all. Most popular organizations: drama, choir, Shield of Roses, Legion of Mary, debate team. Major annual events: Christmas Dinner Dance, St. Patrick's Day, Spring Formal. Student services: health clinic, personal-psychological counseling. Campus security: 24-hour emergency response devices, late night transport-escort service, night patrols by trained security personnel. 339 college housing spaces available; all were occupied in 2003-04. Freshmen guaranteed college housing. On-campus residence required through senior year. Options: men-only, women-only housing available. O'Reilly Memorial Library with 64,265 books, 851 microform titles, 249 serials, 1,302 audiovisual materials, and an OPAC. Operations spending for 2004 fiscal year: $271,069. 60 computers available on campus for general student use. Staffed computer lab on campus.

Community Environment: Located in northwestern Virginia, the College community offers a wide variety of attractions. Visitors can choose from a wide variety of facilities and activities: fine restaurants, historic Bed & Breakfasts, Civil War battlefields, countless hiking trails, numerous golf courses, and tours of Skyline Drive and Skyline Caverns.

■ **CHRISTOPHER NEWPORT UNIVERSITY** *J-14*
1 University Place
Newport News, VA 23606-2998
Tel: (757)594-7000
Free: 800-333-4268
Admissions: (757)594-7015
Fax: (757)594-7333
E-mail: admit@cnu.edu
Web Site: http://www.cnu.edu/

Description: State-supported, comprehensive, coed. Awards bachelor's and master's degrees. Founded 1960. Setting: 175-acre suburban campus with easy access to Norfolk. Endowment: $3 million. Educational spending for 2005 fiscal year: $4358 per student. Total enrollment: 4,699. Faculty: 239 (218 full-time, 21 part-time). Student-undergrad faculty ratio is 19:1. 5,104 applied, 62% were admitted. 15% from top 10% of their high school class, 48% from top quarter, 90% from top half. Full-time: 4,204 students, 54% women, 46% men. Part-time: 332 students, 55% women, 45% men. Students come from 28 states and territories, 10 other countries, 3% from out-of-state, 1% Native American, 2% Hispanic, 8% black, 2% Asian American or Pacific Islander, 0.02% international, 16% 25 or older, 30% live on campus, 5% transferred in. Retention: 75% of full-time freshmen returned the following year. Academic areas with the most degrees conferred: business/marketing; social sciences; psychology. Core. Calendar: semesters. Academic remediation for entering students, services for LD students, advanced placement, accelerated degree program, self-designed majors, honors program, independent study, distance learning, double major, summer session for credit, part-time degree program, adult/continuing education programs, co-op programs and internships. Off campus study at Thomas Nelson Community College, Hampton University, Old Dominion University, College of William and Mary. Study abroad program. ROTC: Army.

Entrance Requirements: Options: Peterson's Universal Application, Common Application, electronic application, early admission, early action, deferred admission, international baccalaureate accepted. Required: high school transcript, minimum 3.0 high school GPA, SAT or ACT. Required for some: essay, 3 recommendations, interview. Application deadlines: 3/1, 12/1 for early action. Notification: continuous.

Costs Per Year: Application fee: $35. State resident tuition: $3442 full-time, $143 per credit hour part-time. Nonresident tuition: $10,464 full-time, $436 per credit hour part-time. Mandatory fees: $2384 full-time, $99. Full-time tuition and fees vary according to course load. Part-time tuition and fees vary according to course load. College room and board: $7500. Room and board charges vary according to housing facility.

Collegiate Environment: Orientation program. Drama-theater group, choral group, marching band, student-run newspaper, radio station. Social organizations: 50 open to all; national fraternities, national sororities; 8% of eligible men and 12% of eligible women are members. Most popular organizations: Student Virginia Education Association, Student Government Association. Major annual events: Homecoming, Fall Fest, Spring Fest. Student services: health clinic, personal-psychological counseling. Campus security: 24-hour emergency response devices and patrols, late night transport-escort service, controlled dormitory access, campus police. College housing designed to accommodate 2,333 students; 2,400 undergraduates lived in college housing during 2003-04. On-campus residence required in freshman year. Option: coed housing available. Captain John Smith Library with 328,319 books, 765,028 microform titles, 1,695 serials, 10,238 audiovisual materials, an OPAC, and a Web page. 1,000 computers available on campus for general student use. A campuswide network can be accessed from student residence rooms and from off campus. Staffed computer lab on campus.

Community Environment: The 125-acre campus located in Newport News, VA, is easily accessible to residents of that city. The campus is centrally located between recreational centers at Colonial Williamsburg and the Norfolk/Virginia Beach resorts.

■ **THE COLLEGE OF WILLIAM AND MARY** *I-14*
PO Box 8795
Williamsburg, VA 23187-8795
Tel: (757)221-4000
Admissions: (757)221-4223
Fax: (757)221-1242
E-mail: admiss@facstaff.wm.edu
Web Site: http://www.wm.edu/

Description: State-supported, university, coed. Awards bachelor's, master's, doctoral, and first professional degrees and post-master's certificates. Founded 1693. Setting: 1,200-acre small town campus with easy access to Richmond. Endowment: $409.9 million. Research spending for 2004 fiscal year: $34.4 million. Educational spending for 2005 fiscal year: $8778 per student. Total enrollment: 7,544. Faculty: 763 (596 full-time, 167 part-time). Student-undergrad faculty ratio is 11:1. 10,610 applied, 31% were admitted. 79% from top 10% of their high school class, 97% from top quarter, 100% from top half. 15 National Merit Scholars, 29 class presidents, 121 valedictorians, 564 student government officers. Full-time: 5,527 students, 54% women, 46% men. Part-time: 67 students, 73% women, 27% men.

Students come from 50 states and territories, 52 other countries, 33% from out-of-state, 1% Native American, 5% Hispanic, 6% black, 7% Asian American or Pacific Islander, 1% international, 1% 25 or older, 75% live on campus, 2% transferred in. Retention: 95% of full-time freshmen returned the following year. Academic areas with the most degrees conferred: social sciences; business/marketing; psychology. Core. Calendar: semesters. Services for LD students, advanced placement, accelerated degree program, self-designed majors, honors program, independent study, double major, summer session for credit, graduate courses open to undergrads. Study abroad program. ROTC: Army.

Entrance Requirements: Options: Peterson's Universal Application, Common Application, electronic application, early admission, early decision, deferred admission, international baccalaureate accepted. Required: essay, high school transcript, SAT or ACT. Recommended: 1 recommendation, SAT Subject Tests. Entrance: very difficult. Application deadlines: 1/1, 11/1 for early decision. Notification: 4/1, 12/1 for early decision. Preference given to state residents.

Costs Per Year: Application fee: $60. State resident tuition: $4730 full-time, $180 per credit hour part-time. Nonresident tuition: $20,000 full-time, $710 per credit hour part-time. Mandatory fees: $3048 full-time. Full-time tuition and fees vary according to program. Part-time tuition varies according to program. College room and board: $6417. College room only: $3856. Room and board charges vary according to board plan and housing facility.

Collegiate Environment: Orientation program. Drama-theater group, choral group, student-run newspaper, radio station. Social organizations: 300 open to all; national fraternities, national sororities. Most popular organizations: Alpha Phi Omega, College Partnership for Kids, student assembly, Flat Hat (student newspaper), Resident Housing Association. Major annual events: Yule Log Ceremony, King and Queen Ball, Opening Convocation Exercises. Student services: legal services, health clinic, personal-psychological counseling. Campus security: 24-hour emergency response devices and patrols, student patrols, late night transport-escort service, controlled dormitory access. 4,206 college housing spaces available; 4,189 were occupied in 2003-04. Freshmen guaranteed college housing. On-campus residence required in freshman year. Options: coed, women-only housing available. Swem Library plus 9 others with 2 million books, 2.2 million microform titles, 11,688 serials, 29,316 audiovisual materials, an OPAC, and a Web page. Operations spending for 2004 fiscal year: $8.9 million. 225 computers available on campus for general student use. A campuswide network can be accessed from student residence rooms and from off campus. Staffed computer lab on campus.

Community Environment: Williamsburg, the historic capital of Colonial Virginia, has been restored as nearly as possible to its 18th-century appearance. The Colonial Williamsburg project has been made possible by the generous provisions of the late John D. Rockefeller, Jr. The restored town offers excellent facilities, and the colonial shops on Merchant's Square provide historical interest. Williamsburg is a popular tourist center and has recreational activities such as fishing, boating, golf, and hunting. Major historic points of interest include William and Mary's Sir Christopher Wren Building (1695), the Bruton Parish Church, the Capitol, Governor's Palace, Peyton Randolph House, Raleigh Tavern, and the Wythe House.

■ **DABNEY S. LANCASTER COMMUNITY COLLEGE** *G-6*
100 Dabney Dr., PO Box 1000
Clifton Forge, VA 24422
Tel: (540)863-2800
Admissions: (540)863-2815
Fax: (540)863-2915
Web Site: http://www.dl.vccs.edu/
Description: State-supported, 2-year, coed. Part of Virginia Community College System. Awards certificates, diplomas, transfer associate, and terminal associate degrees. Founded 1964. Setting: 117-acre rural campus. Total enrollment: 1,453. Students come from 5 states and territories, 0.3% Native American, 1% Hispanic, 5% black, 0.5% Asian American or Pacific Islander, 0% international, 59% 25 or older. Calendar: semesters. Academic remediation for entering students, services for LD students, advanced placement, honors program, summer session for credit, part-time degree program, adult/continuing education programs, co-op programs and internships.
Entrance Requirements: Open admission except for nursing program. Options: early admission, deferred admission. Entrance: noncompetitive. Application deadline: Rolling. Notification: continuous.
Costs Per Year: Application fee: $0. State resident tuition: $1740 full-time, $72.50 per credit part-time. Nonresident tuition: $5648 full-time, $235.35 per credit part-time. Mandatory fees: $157 full-time, $6.55 per credit part-time.

Collegiate Environment: Drama-theater group. Student services: personal-psychological counseling. College housing not available. 37,716 books and 376 serials.
Community Environment: A rural community, Clifton Forge is served by limited modes of transportation. Libraries, churches of major denominations, a hospital, and various civic and service organizations are part of the community. Some part-time job opportunities are available. A state park, lakes and streams provide facilities for fishing and outdoor sports; other activities include baseball, basketball, football, tennis, canoeing, backpacking and skiing.

■ **DANVILLE COMMUNITY COLLEGE** *K-7*
1008 South Main St.
Danville, VA 24541-4088
Tel: (434)797-2222
Free: 800-560-4291
Admissions: (434)797-8490
Fax: (434)797-8541
Web Site: http://www.dcc.vccs.edu/
Description: State-supported, 2-year, coed. Part of Virginia Community College System. Awards certificates, diplomas, transfer associate, and terminal associate degrees. Founded 1967. Setting: 76-acre urban campus. Total enrollment: 4,089. Full-time: 1,366 students, 60% women, 40% men. Part-time: 2,723 students, 61% women, 39% men. Students come from 9 states and territories, 3 other countries, 2% from out-of-state, 0.1% Native American, 0.5% Hispanic, 34% black, 0.3% Asian American or Pacific Islander, 0.02% international, 58% 25 or older. Retention: 100% of full-time freshmen returned the following year. Core. Calendar: semesters. Academic remediation for entering students, advanced placement, honors program, distance learning, summer session for credit, part-time degree program, adult/continuing education programs, co-op programs.
Entrance Requirements: Open admission. Options: early admission, deferred admission. Required: high school transcript. Placement: ACT ASSET required for some. Entrance: noncompetitive. Application deadline: Rolling. Notification: continuous. Preference given to district residents.
Costs Per Year: Application fee: $0. State resident tuition: $2150 full-time, $71.65 per credit hour part-time. Nonresident tuition: $6596 full-time, $219.85 per credit hour part-time. Mandatory fees: $111 full-time, $3.65 per credit hour part-time.
Collegiate Environment: Campus security: 24-hour patrols. College housing not available. Learning Resource Center with 41,600 books, 345 serials, an OPAC, and a Web page. 265 computers available on campus for general student use. Staffed computer lab on campus.
Community Environment: See Averett College.

■ **DEVRY UNIVERSITY (ARLINGTON)** *D-13*
2450 Crystal Dr.
Arlington, VA 22202
Tel: (703)414-4000; (866)563-3900
Fax: (703)414-4040
Web Site: http://www.devry.edu/
Description: Proprietary, comprehensive, coed. Part of DeVry University. Awards associate, bachelor's, and master's degrees. Founded 2001. Total enrollment: 585. Faculty: 62 (20 full-time, 42 part-time). Student-undergrad faculty ratio is 13:1. Full-time: 310 students, 45% women, 55% men. Part-time: 153 students, 54% women, 46% men. 0% Native American, 10% Hispanic, 63% black, 7% Asian American or Pacific Islander, 2% international. Retention: 28% of full-time freshmen returned the following year. Academic areas with the most degrees conferred: computer and information sciences; business/marketing; engineering technologies. Calendar: semesters. Academic remediation for entering students, services for LD students, advanced placement, accelerated degree program, distance learning, summer session for credit, part-time degree program, adult/continuing education programs, co-op programs.
Entrance Requirements: Options: electronic application, deferred admission, international baccalaureate accepted. Required: high school transcript, interview. Entrance: minimally difficult. Application deadline: Rolling.
Costs Per Year: Application fee: $50. One-time mandatory fee: $40. Tuition: $13,060 full-time, $475 per credit part-time. Mandatory fees: $270 full-time, $160 per year part-time. Full-time tuition and fees vary according to course load. Part-time tuition and fees vary according to course load.
Collegiate Environment: Orientation program. College housing not available. Learning Resource Center with 7,800 books, 6,500 serials, 210 audiovisual materials, an OPAC, and a Web page. 380 computers available

on campus for general student use. Computer purchase/lease plans available. A campuswide network can be accessed from off-campus. Staffed computer lab on campus.

■ DEVRY UNIVERSITY (MCLEAN) *D-12*
1751 Pinnacle Dr., Ste. 250
McLean, VA 22102-3832
Tel: (703)556-9669
Fax: (703)556-9420
Web Site: http://www.devry.edu/
Description: Proprietary, comprehensive, coed. Calendar: semesters.
Costs Per Year: One-time mandatory fee: $40. Tuition: $13,060 full-time, $475 per credit part-time. Mandatory fees: $60 full-time, $30 per year part-time.

■ EASTERN MENNONITE UNIVERSITY *E-8*
1200 Park Rd.
Harrisonburg, VA 22802-2462
Tel: (540)432-4000
Free: 800-368-2665
Admissions: (540)432-4118
Fax: (540)432-4444
E-mail: admiss@emu.edu
Web Site: http://www.emu.edu/
Description: Independent Mennonite, comprehensive, coed. Awards associate, bachelor's, master's, and first professional degrees. Founded 1917. Setting: 93-acre small town campus. Endowment: $17.5 million. Research spending for 2004 fiscal year: $26,553. Educational spending for 2005 fiscal year: $10,246 per student. Total enrollment: 1,301. Faculty: 163 (116 full-time, 47 part-time). Student-undergrad faculty ratio is 9:1. 636 applied, 77% were admitted. 21% from top 10% of their high school class, 44% from top quarter, 77% from top half. 9 valedictorians. Full-time: 970 students, 62% women, 38% men. Part-time: 42 students, 74% women, 26% men. Students come from 35 states and territories, 20 other countries, 54% from out-of-state, 0.2% Native American, 3% Hispanic, 7% black, 2% Asian American or Pacific Islander, 4% international, 9% 25 or older, 66% live on campus, 8% transferred in. Retention: 74% of full-time freshmen returned the following year. Academic areas with the most degrees conferred: business/marketing; liberal arts/general studies; health professions and related sciences. Core. Calendar: semesters. Academic remediation for entering students, ESL program, services for LD students, advanced placement, honors program, independent study, distance learning, double major, summer session for credit, part-time degree program, adult/continuing education programs, internships, graduate courses open to undergrads. Off campus study at Council for Christian Colleges and Universities, James Madison University, The Catholic University of America, Brethren College Abroad, Howard University, Bridgewater College. Study abroad program.
Entrance Requirements: Options: Peterson's Universal Application, Common Application, electronic application, early admission, deferred admission, international baccalaureate accepted. Required: high school transcript, minimum 2.2 high school GPA, statement of commitment, SAT or ACT. Recommended: interview. Required for some: 2 recommendations. Entrance: moderately difficult. Application deadline: Rolling. Notification: continuous.
Costs Per Year: Application fee: $25. Comprehensive fee: $27,220 includes full-time tuition ($20,612), mandatory fees ($58), and college room and board ($6550). College room only: $3550. Part-time tuition: $862 per credit hour. Part-time mandatory fees: $2 per credit hour.
Collegiate Environment: Orientation program. Drama-theater group, choral group, student-run newspaper, radio station. Social organizations: 47 open to all. Most popular organizations: YPCA, Students in Free Enterprise, Student Government Association, Student Education Association, International Student Organization. Major annual events: Fall Festival, Multicultural Week, Spring Fling. Student services: health clinic, personal-psychological counseling. Campus security: 24-hour emergency response devices, controlled dormitory access, night watchman. 684 college housing spaces available; 517 were occupied in 2003-04. Freshmen guaranteed college housing. On-campus residence required through junior year. Options: coed, men-only, women-only housing available. Sadie Hartzler Library with 163,932 books, 89,094 microform titles, 1,112 serials, 3,570 audiovisual materials, an OPAC, and a Web page. Operations spending for 2004 fiscal year: $681,288. 110 computers available on campus for general student use. A campuswide network can be accessed from student residence rooms and from off campus.

Community Environment: The college is located in the heart of Virginia's beautiful Shenandoah Valley, near a national park.

■ EASTERN SHORE COMMUNITY COLLEGE
29300 Lankford Hwy.
Melfa, VA 23410-3000
Tel: (757)789-1789; 877-871-8455
Admissions: (757)789-1731
Fax: (757)789-1739
E-mail: eswilss@es.cc.va.us
Web Site: http://www.es.cc.va.us/
Description: State-supported, 2-year, coed. Part of Virginia Community College System. Awards certificates, transfer associate, and terminal associate degrees. Founded 1971. Setting: 117-acre rural campus. Total enrollment: 807. 390 applied, 83% were admitted. 0% Native American, 1% Hispanic, 44% black, 1% Asian American or Pacific Islander, 45% 25 or older. Retention: 36% of full-time freshmen returned the following year. Core. Calendar: semesters. Academic remediation for entering students, ESL program, services for LD students, advanced placement, distance learning, summer session for credit, part-time degree program, adult/continuing education programs, co-op programs. Off campus study at members of the Virginia Tidewater Consortium for Continuing Higher Education.
Entrance Requirements: Open admission. Required: high school transcript. Entrance: noncompetitive. Application deadline: Rolling. Notification: continuous. Preference given to county residents.
Costs Per Year: Application fee: $0. State resident tuition: $2040 full-time, $68 per credit part-time. Nonresident tuition: $6420 full-time, $214 per credit part-time. Mandatory fees: $110 full-time, $3.65 per credit part-time.
Collegiate Environment: Orientation program. Student services: personal-psychological counseling. Campus security: night security guard. College housing not available. Learning Resources Center with 20,479 books, 95 serials, an OPAC, and a Web page. 53 computers available on campus for general student use. A campuswide network can be accessed. Staffed computer lab on campus.
Community Environment: Located midway down the Delmarva Peninsula, which separates Chesapeake Bay from the Atlantic Ocean, Melfa has a population of 450. The area is known for vegetables, poultry, oysters, fish, sailing, and swimming.

■ ECPI COLLEGE OF TECHNOLOGY (NEWPORT NEWS) *J-14*
1001 Omni Blvd., No. 100
Newport News, VA 23606
Tel: (757)838-9191
Fax: (757)827-5351
Web Site: http://www.ecpi.edu/
Description: Proprietary, primarily 2-year, coed. Awards certificates, diplomas, terminal associate, and bachelor's degrees. Founded 1966. Setting: suburban campus. Total enrollment: 556. Student-undergrad faculty ratio is 16:1. Full-time: 556 students, 39% women, 61% men. Students come from 34 states and territories, 2% from out-of-state, 0.2% Native American, 6% Hispanic, 45% black, 2% Asian American or Pacific Islander, 0% international, 64% 25 or older, 77% transferred in. Core. Calendar: trimesters. Advanced placement, freshman honors college, honors program, summer session for credit, part-time degree program, adult/continuing education programs, internships.
Entrance Requirements: Options: Common Application, deferred admission. Required: high school transcript, minimum 2.0 high school GPA, interview. Recommended: SAT, SAT or ACT, SAT Subject Tests. Entrance: moderately difficult. Notification: continuous.
Costs Per Year: Application fee: $100.
Collegiate Environment: Orientation program. Social organizations: 6 open to all. Most popular organizations: SETA, IEEE, NVTHS, Accounting Society, CSI. Major annual events: Commencement, picnic. Student services: personal-psychological counseling. Campus security: building and parking lot security. College housing not available. ECPI-Virginia Beach Library with 13,014 books, 168 serials, an OPAC, and a Web page. 100 computers available on campus for general student use. A campuswide network can be accessed from off-campus. Staffed computer lab on campus.

■ ECPI COLLEGE OF TECHNOLOGY (VIRGINIA BEACH) *J-15*
5555 Greenwich Rd.
Virginia Beach, VA 23462
Tel: (757)671-7171
Free: 800-986-1200

E-mail: rballance@ecpi.edu

Web Site: http://www.ecpi.edu/

Description: Proprietary, primarily 2-year, coed. Awards certificates, diplomas, terminal associate, and bachelor's degrees. Founded 1966. Setting: 8-acre suburban campus. Total enrollment: 4,391. 1,433 applied, 69% were admitted. Full-time: 4,312 students, 47% women, 53% men. Part-time: 79 students, 43% women, 57% men. Students come from 6 states and territories, 10% from out-of-state, 0.4% Native American, 4% Hispanic, 43% black, 3% Asian American or Pacific Islander, 0% international, 50% 25 or older. Core. Calendar: trimesters. Advanced placement, freshman honors college, distance learning, summer session for credit, part-time degree program, adult/continuing education programs, internships.

Entrance Requirements: Options: Peterson's Universal Application, Common Application, electronic application, deferred admission. Required: high school transcript, interview. Recommended: SAT, SAT or ACT, SAT Subject Tests. Entrance: moderately difficult. Notification: continuous.

Costs Per Year: Application fee: $100. Tuition: $9750 full-time.

Collegiate Environment: Orientation program. Social organizations: 6 open to all; national fraternities, national sororities, local fraternities, local sororities; 25% of eligible men and 20% of eligible women are members. Most popular organizations: SETA, IEEE, NVTHS, ITE, Accounting Society. Major annual event: picnic. Student services: personal-psychological counseling. Campus security: building and parking lot security. No special consideration for freshman housing applicants. ECPI-Virginia Beach Library with an OPAC and a Web page. 600 computers available on campus for general student use. A campuswide network can be accessed from off-campus. Staffed computer lab on campus.

■ **ECPI TECHNICAL COLLEGE (GLEN ALLEN)** *O-9*

4305 Cox Rd.

Glen Allen, VA 23060

Tel: (804)934-0100

Free: 800-986-1200

Fax: (804)934-0054

E-mail: jpope@ecpi.edu

Web Site: http://www.ecpitech.edu/

Description: Proprietary, primarily 2-year, coed. Awards certificates, diplomas, terminal associate, and bachelor's degrees. Setting: urban campus with easy access to Richmond. Total enrollment: 473. Student-undergrad faculty ratio is 15:1. 148 applied, 82% were admitted. Full-time: 473 students, 38% women, 62% men. Students come from 2 states and territories, 1% from out-of-state, 1% Native American, 2% Hispanic, 36% black, 4% Asian American or Pacific Islander, 0% international, 48% 25 or older. Calendar: semesters.

Entrance Requirements: Required: high school transcript, interview. Recommended: SAT, SAT and SAT Subject Tests or ACT, SAT Subject Tests. Entrance: moderately difficult. Application deadline: Rolling. Notification: continuous.

Costs Per Year: Application fee: $100.

Collegiate Environment: Most popular organizations: CSI, OPMA, SETA, NVTHS, ITE. Campus security: building and parking lot security. College housing not available.

■ **ECPI TECHNICAL COLLEGE (RICHMOND)** *H-12*

800 Moorefield Park Dr.

Richmond, VA 23236

Tel: (804)330-5533

Free: 800-986-1200

E-mail: agerard@ecpi.edu

Web Site: http://www.ecpitech.edu/

Description: Proprietary, primarily 2-year, coed. Awards certificates, diplomas, terminal associate, and bachelor's degrees. Founded 1966. Setting: urban campus. Total enrollment: 400. Student-undergrad faculty ratio is 15:1. 176 applied, 75% were admitted. Students come from 2 states and territories, 1% from out-of-state, 46% 25 or older. Core. Calendar: semesters. Advanced placement, freshman honors college, honors program, summer session for credit, part-time degree program, adult/continuing education programs, internships.

Entrance Requirements: Options: Common Application, deferred admission. Required: high school transcript, interview. Recommended: SAT, SAT and SAT Subject Tests or ACT, SAT Subject Tests. Entrance: moderately difficult. Application deadline: Rolling. Notification: continuous.

Costs Per Year: Application fee: $100. Tuition: $9750 full-time.

Collegiate Environment: Orientation program. Most popular organizations: Collegiate Secretaries International, Data Processing Management Association, Student Electronics Technicians Association, Future Office Assistants, National Vocational-Technical Honor Society. Major annual event: picnics. Campus security: building and parking lot security. College housing not available. ECPI-Richmond Library with 3,165 books, 81 serials, an OPAC, and a Web page. 190 computers available on campus for general student use. A campuswide network can be accessed from off-campus. Staffed computer lab on campus.

■ **ECPI TECHNICAL COLLEGE (ROANOKE)** *I-6*

5234 Airport Rd.

Roanoke, VA 24012

Tel: (540)563-8080

Free: 800-986-1200

Fax: (540)362-5400

E-mail: ehass@ecpi.edu

Web Site: http://www.ecpi.net/

Description: Proprietary, primarily 2-year, coed. Awards certificates, diplomas, terminal associate, and bachelor's degrees. Founded 1966. Setting: 3-acre suburban campus. Total enrollment: 300. Student-undergrad faculty ratio is 15:1. 159 applied, 65% were admitted. Students come from 4 states and territories, 1% from out-of-state, 47% 25 or older. Core. Calendar: semesters. Advanced placement, accelerated degree program, distance learning, summer session for credit, part-time degree program, adult/continuing education programs, internships.

Entrance Requirements: Options: Common Application, electronic application, deferred admission. Required: high school transcript, interview. Recommended: SAT, SAT Subject Tests. Entrance: moderately difficult. Application deadline: Rolling. Notification: continuous.

Costs Per Year: Application fee: $100. Tuition: $9750 full-time.

Collegiate Environment: Orientation program. Most popular organizations: SETA, NVTHS, SAFA, FOAMA, ITE. Major annual events: picnic, Christmas Lunch. Campus security: building and parking lot security. College housing not available. ECPI-Roanoke Library plus 1 other with 1,703 books, 43 serials, and a Web page. 80 computers available on campus for general student use. A campuswide network can be accessed from off-campus. Staffed computer lab on campus.

■ **EMORY & HENRY COLLEGE**

PO Box 947

Emory, VA 24327-0947

Tel: (276)944-4121

Free: 800-848-5493

Admissions: (276)944-6133

Fax: (276)944-6934

E-mail: ehadmiss@ehc.edu

Web Site: http://www.ehc.edu/

Description: Independent United Methodist, comprehensive, coed. Awards bachelor's and master's degrees. Founded 1836. Setting: 331-acre rural campus. Endowment: $72.5 million. Research spending for 2004 fiscal year: $389,118. Educational spending for 2005 fiscal year: $6140 per student. Total enrollment: 1,101. Faculty: 95 (68 full-time, 27 part-time). Student-undergrad faculty ratio is 13:1. 1,329 applied, 76% were admitted. 18% from top 10% of their high school class, 44% from top quarter, 82% from top half. 9 valedictorians. Full-time: 999 students, 50% women, 50% men. Part-time: 28 students, 39% women, 61% men. Students come from 23 states and territories, 2 other countries, 29% from out-of-state, 0.4% Native American, 1% Hispanic, 4% black, 1% Asian American or Pacific Islander, 0.3% international, 5% 25 or older, 66% live on campus, 5% transferred in. Retention: 72% of full-time freshmen returned the following year. Academic areas with the most degrees conferred: social sciences; education; business/marketing. Core. Calendar: semesters. Services for LD students, advanced placement, self-designed majors, honors program, independent study, double major, summer session for credit, co-op programs and internships. Study abroad program.

Entrance Requirements: Options: Peterson's Universal Application, Common Application, electronic application, early admission, early decision, deferred admission, international baccalaureate accepted. Required: essay, high school transcript, SAT or ACT. Recommended: interview. Required for some: 2 recommendations. Entrance: moderately difficult. Application deadlines: Rolling, 11/1 for early decision. Notification: continuous until 8/1, 12/15 for early decision.

Costs Per Year: Application fee: $30. Comprehensive fee: $26,570 includes full-time tuition ($19,530) and college room and board ($7040). College room only: $3500. Full-time tuition varies according to course load. Room and board charges vary according to board plan. Part-time tuition: $815 per hour. Part-time tuition varies according to course load.

Collegiate Environment: Orientation program. Drama-theater group, choral group, student-run newspaper, radio station. Social organizations: 50 open to all; local fraternities, local sororities; 11% of eligible men and 26% of eligible women are members. Most popular organizations: Alpha Phi Omega, Student Virginia Education Association, student radio station, Campus Christian Fellowship. Major annual events: Winter Forum, Homecoming, Opening Street Dance. Student services: health clinic, personal-psychological counseling. Campus security: 24-hour emergency response devices and patrols, late night transport-escort service. 691 college housing spaces available; 612 were occupied in 2003-04. Freshmen guaranteed college housing. On-campus residence required through senior year. Options: men-only, women-only housing available. Kelly Library with 337,290 books, 42,359 microform titles, 9,946 serials, 4,577 audiovisual materials, an OPAC, and a Web page. Operations spending for 2004 fiscal year: $726,232. 250 computers available on campus for general student use. A campuswide network can be accessed from student residence rooms and from off campus. Staffed computer lab on campus.

Community Environment: Emory, in the Virginia Highlands, is approximately 20 miles north of Bristol, VA, just off exit 26 of I-81. The area is known for its scenic beauty, recreational opportunities, and abundance of talented craftspeople. In Abingdon, an historic town dating from the middle 1700's, the annual Virginia Highlands Festival brings together artists and craftspeople from throughout the eastern U.S. Just twenty minutes from the college campus is Mt. Rogers National Recreational Area, featuring numerous campgrounds, mountain streams, and miles of the Appalachian Trail.

■ **FERRUM COLLEGE** *J-5*
PO Box 1000
Ferrum, VA 24088-9001
Tel: (540)365-2121
Free: 800-868-9797
Admissions: (540)365-4290
Fax: (540)365-4266
E-mail: admissions@ferrum.edu
Web Site: http://www.ferrum.edu/

Description: Independent United Methodist, 4-year, coed. Awards bachelor's degrees. Founded 1913. Setting: 720-acre rural campus. Endowment: $39.6 million. Educational spending for 2005 fiscal year: $5427 per student. Total enrollment: 991. Student-undergrad faculty ratio is 14:1. 1,248 applied, 72% were admitted. 1% from top 10% of their high school class, 13% from top quarter, 39% from top half. 1 valedictorian. Full-time: 962 students, 41% women, 59% men. Part-time: 29 students, 76% women, 24% men. Students come from 24 states and territories, 8 other countries, 15% from out-of-state, 1% Native American, 2% Hispanic, 20% black, 1% Asian American or Pacific Islander, 1% international, 9% 25 or older, 70% live on campus, 8% transferred in. Retention: 55% of full-time freshmen returned the following year. Academic areas with the most degrees conferred: business/marketing; liberal arts/general studies; computer and information sciences; psychology. Core. Calendar: semesters. Services for LD students, advanced placement, self-designed majors, independent study, distance learning, double major, summer session for credit, part-time degree program, adult/continuing education programs, co-op programs and internships. Study abroad program.

Entrance Requirements: Options: Common Application, electronic application, early admission, deferred admission, international baccalaureate accepted. Required: high school transcript, SAT or ACT. Recommended: essay, minimum 2.0 high school GPA, 2 recommendations, interview. Required for some: interview. Entrance: minimally difficult. Application deadline: Rolling. Notification: continuous.

Costs Per Year: Application fee: $25. Comprehensive fee: $24,320 includes full-time tuition ($17,990), mandatory fees ($30), and college room and board ($6300). Room and board charges vary according to housing facility. Part-time tuition: $360 per hour. Part-time tuition varies according to course load.

Collegiate Environment: Orientation program. Drama-theater group, choral group, student-run newspaper, radio station. Social organizations: 60 open to all. Most popular organizations: Student Government Association, Agriculture Club, BACCHUS, Panther Productions, African American Student Association, Students in Free Enterprise. Major annual events:

Homecoming, Folklife Festival, Spring Fling. Student services: health clinic, personal-psychological counseling. Campus security: 24-hour emergency response devices and patrols, student patrols, late night transport-escort service, controlled dormitory access. 840 college housing spaces available; 640 were occupied in 2003-04. Freshmen guaranteed college housing. On-campus residence required through senior year. Options: coed, women-only housing available. Stanley Library with 154,370 books, 7,733 microform titles, 10,618 serials, 2,094 audiovisual materials, an OPAC, and a Web page. Operations spending for 2004 fiscal year: $486,586. 470 computers available on campus for general student use. A campuswide network can be accessed from student residence rooms and from off campus. Staffed computer lab on campus.

Community Environment: Located in the Blue Ridge Mountains of Virginia, Ferrum has an ideal environment for study and cultural enrichment. The College's proximity to the mountains and lakes enables students to enjoy outdoor activities such as hiking, camping, fishing, boating, swimming and skiing. Ferrum is 35 miles south of Roanoke, Virginia, which has excellent shopping, living, cultural and recreational facilities. Bus service and air transportation are available in Roanoke.

■ **GEORGE MASON UNIVERSITY** *D-12*
4400 University Dr.
Fairfax, VA 22030
Tel: (703)993-1000
Admissions: (703)993-2400
E-mail: admissions@gmu.edu
Web Site: http://www.gmu.edu/

Description: State-supported, university, coed. Awards bachelor's, master's, doctoral, and first professional degrees. Founded 1957. Setting: 677-acre suburban campus with easy access to Washington, DC. Endowment: $38 million. Research spending for 2004 fiscal year: $43.5 million. Educational spending for 2005 fiscal year: $6274 per student. Total enrollment: 29,728. Faculty: 1,955 (997 full-time, 958 part-time). Student-undergrad faculty ratio is 16:1. 10,344 applied, 69% were admitted. 14% from top 10% of their high school class, 44% from top quarter, 90% from top half. Full-time: 13,578 students, 54% women, 46% men. Part-time: 4,513 students, 53% women, 47% men. Students come from 52 states and territories, 129 other countries, 8% from out-of-state, 0.4% Native American, 8% Hispanic, 8% black, 17% Asian American or Pacific Islander, 4% international, 22% 25 or older, 23% live on campus, 12% transferred in. Retention: 84% of full-time freshmen returned the following year. Academic areas with the most degrees conferred: business/marketing; social sciences; health professions and related sciences. Core. Calendar: semesters. ESL program, services for LD students, advanced placement, accelerated degree program, self-designed majors, honors program, independent study, distance learning, double major, summer session for credit, part-time degree program, external degree program, adult/continuing education programs, co-op programs and internships, graduate courses open to undergrads. Off campus study at members of the Consortium of Universities of the Washington Metropolitan Area, Shenandoah University. Study abroad program. ROTC: Army, Air Force (c).

Entrance Requirements: Options: Common Application, electronic application, early admission, deferred admission, international baccalaureate accepted. Required: essay, high school transcript, minimum 2.0 high school GPA, interview, SAT or ACT. Recommended: minimum 3.0 high school GPA, recommendations. Entrance: moderately difficult. Application deadline: 1/15. Notification: 4/1.

Costs Per Year: Application fee: $60. State resident tuition: $4356 full-time, $181.50 per credit part-time. Nonresident tuition: $15,636 full-time, $651.50 per credit part-time. Mandatory fees: $1524 full-time, $63.50 per credit part-time. Full-time tuition and fees vary according to course load. Part-time tuition and fees vary according to course load. College room and board: $6480. College room only: $3700. Room and board charges vary according to board plan and housing facility.

Collegiate Environment: Orientation program. Drama-theater group, choral group, student-run newspaper, radio station. Social organizations: 255 open to all; national fraternities, national sororities; 5% of eligible men and 5% of eligible women are members. Most popular organizations: intramurals, student government, club sports, volunteer and community service. Major annual events: homecoming, Patriots' Day, Mason Day. Student services: health clinic, personal-psychological counseling, women's center. Campus security: 24-hour emergency response devices and patrols, student patrols, late night transport-escort service, controlled dormitory access. 3,500 college housing spaces available; 3,000 were occupied in 2003-04. Freshmen guaranteed college housing. Options: coed, men-only, women-only housing available. Fenwick Library plus 1 other with 1.5 million books, 2.7 million microform titles, 27,708 serials, 27,344 audiovisual materials, an OPAC, and a Web page. Operations spending for 2004 fiscal year: $12.8 million. 1,500 computers available on campus for general student use. A campuswide network can be accessed from student residence rooms and from off campus. Staffed computer lab on campus.

Community Environment: Fairfax is a rapidly growing residential area on the western fringes of Washington, DC. Shopping facilities, commercial transportation, recreation activities, part-time employment and moderate-to-expensive rental apartments are available nearby.

■ GERMANNA COMMUNITY COLLEGE

2130 Germanna Hwy.
Locust Grove, VA 22508-2102
Tel: (540)727-3000
Admissions: (540)891-3016
Fax: (540)727-3207
Web Site: http://www.gcc.vccs.edu/

Description: State-supported, 2-year, coed. Part of Virginia Community College System. Awards certificates, transfer associate, and terminal associate degrees. Founded 1970. Setting: 100-acre rural campus with easy access to Washington, DC. Total enrollment: 4,799. Student-undergrad faculty ratio is 20:1. 838 applied, 100% were admitted. Full-time: 1,359 students, 61% women, 39% men. Part-time: 3,440 students, 68% women, 32% men. Students come from 5 states and territories, 1 other country, 1% Native American, 3% Hispanic, 13% black, 3% Asian American or Pacific Islander, 0.04% international, 53% 25 or older. Core. Calendar: semesters. Academic remediation for entering students, summer session for credit, part-time degree program, adult/continuing education programs. Off campus study at Mary Washington College, other members of the Virginia Community College System.

Entrance Requirements: Open admission except for nursing program. Option: early admission. Required for some: high school transcript. Entrance: noncompetitive. Application deadline: Rolling. Notification: continuous.

Costs Per Year: Application fee: $0. State resident tuition: $1632 full-time, $68 per credit part-time. Nonresident tuition: $5136 full-time, $214 per credit part-time. Mandatory fees: $118 full-time, $4.90 per credit part-time. Full-time tuition and fees vary according to course load. Part-time tuition and fees vary according to course load.

Collegiate Environment: Orientation program. Student-run newspaper. Social organizations: 11 open to all. Most popular organizations: Student Nurses Association, Student Government Association, Phi Theta Kappa, Students Against Substance Abuse. Major annual events: Germanna Day, graduation. Student services: personal-psychological counseling. Campus security: 24-hour patrols. College housing not available. 22,412 books and 160 serials. 55 computers available on campus for general student use. Staffed computer lab on campus.

■ HAMPDEN-SYDNEY COLLEGE

PO Box 667
Hampden-Sydney, VA 23943
Tel: (434)223-6000
Free: 800-755-0733
Admissions: (434)223-6120
Fax: (434)223-6346
E-mail: agarland@hsc.edu
Web Site: http://www.hsc.edu/

Description: Independent, 4-year, men only, affiliated with Presbyterian Church (U.S.A.). Awards bachelor's degrees. Founded 1776. Setting: 660-acre rural campus with easy access to Richmond. Endowment: $113.3 million. Research spending for 2004 fiscal year: $13,119. Educational spending for 2005 fiscal year: $9522 per student. Total enrollment: 1,060. Student-undergrad faculty ratio is 10:1. 1,376 applied, 67% were admitted. 12% from top 10% of their high school class, 25% from top quarter, 75% from top half. 6 class presidents, 6 valedictorians, 64 student government officers. Full-time: 1,060 students. Students come from 36 states and territories, 6 other countries, 33% from out-of-state, 0.4% Native American, 1% Hispanic, 4% black, 1% Asian American or Pacific Islander, 1% international, 0.4% 25 or older, 93% live on campus, 2% transferred in. Retention: 83% of full-time freshmen returned the following year. Academic areas with the most degrees conferred: social sciences; history; business/marketing. Core. Calendar: semesters. Academic remediation for entering students, advanced placement, accelerated degree program, honors program, independent study, double major, summer session for credit, internships. Off campus study at

Seven-College Exchange Program, Longwood College Cooperative Program. Study abroad program. ROTC: Army (c).

Entrance Requirements: Options: Peterson's Universal Application, Common Application, electronic application, early admission, early decision, early action, international baccalaureate accepted. Required: essay, high school transcript, minimum 2.0 high school GPA, 2 recommendations, SAT or ACT. Recommended: minimum 3.0 high school GPA, interview, SAT Subject Tests. Entrance: moderately difficult. Application deadlines: 3/1, 11/15 for early decision, 1/15 for early action. Notification: continuous until 4/15, 12/15 for early decision, 2/15 for early action.

Costs Per Year: Application fee: $30. Comprehensive fee: $34,295 includes full-time tuition ($25,166), mandatory fees ($1004), and college room and board ($8125). College room only: $3436. Part-time tuition: $748 per credit hour.

Collegiate Environment: Orientation program. Drama-theater group, choral group, student-run newspaper, radio station. Social organizations: 45 open to all; national fraternities; 24% of eligible undergrads are members. Most popular organizations: Republican Society, Pre-Health Society, Outsiders Club, Tiger Athletic Club, Pre-Law Society. Major annual events: homecoming, Greek Weekend, Macon Week/Midwinters. Student services: health clinic, personal-psychological counseling. Campus security: 24-hour emergency response devices and patrols. 1,060 college housing spaces available; 1,000 were occupied in 2003-04. Freshmen guaranteed college housing. On-campus residence required through senior year. Option: men-only housing available. Eggleston Library with 219,221 books, 948 serials, an OPAC, and a Web page. Operations spending for 2004 fiscal year: $994,875. 140 computers available on campus for general student use. Computer purchase/lease plans available. A campuswide network can be accessed from student residence rooms and from off campus. Staffed computer lab on campus.

■ HAMPTON UNIVERSITY *J-15*

Hampton, VA 23668
Tel: (757)727-5000
Free: 800-624-3328
Admissions: (757)727-5328
Fax: (757)727-5084
E-mail: angela.boyd@hamptonu.edu
Web Site: http://www.hamptonu.edu/

Description: Independent, university, coed. Awards associate, bachelor's, master's, doctoral, and first professional degrees. Founded 1868. Setting: 210-acre urban campus with easy access to Norfolk. Endowment: $185.8 million. Total enrollment: 6,209. Faculty: 447 (323 full-time, 124 part-time). Student-undergrad faculty ratio is 16:1. 5,401 applied, 77% were admitted. 20% from top 10% of their high school class, 45% from top quarter, 90% from top half. Full-time: 4,913 students, 65% women, 35% men. Part-time: 412 students, 47% women, 53% men. Students come from 38 states and territories, 85% from out-of-state, 0.2% Native American, 1% Hispanic, 94% black, 1% Asian American or Pacific Islander, 11% 25 or older, 59% live on campus, 8% transferred in. Retention: 85% of full-time freshmen returned the following year. Academic areas with the most degrees conferred: business/marketing; health professions and related sciences; psychology. Core. Calendar: semesters. Academic remediation for entering students, services for LD students, advanced placement, accelerated degree program, honors program, independent study, distance learning, double major, summer session for credit, part-time degree program, adult/continuing education programs, co-op programs and internships, graduate courses open to undergrads. Off campus study at 11 members of the Virginia Tidewater Consortium for Continuing Higher Education. Study abroad program. ROTC: Army, Naval.

Entrance Requirements: Options: Common Application, electronic application, early admission, deferred admission, international baccalaureate accepted. Required: essay, high school transcript, minimum 2.0 high school GPA, 1 recommendation, SAT or ACT. Entrance: moderately difficult. Application deadlines: 3/1, 12/1 for early decision. Notification: continuous until 7/31, 12/15 for early decision.

Costs Per Year: Application fee: $25. Comprehensive fee: $20,928 includes full-time tuition ($12,722), mandatory fees ($1460), and college room and board ($6746). College room only: $3580. Full-time tuition and fees vary according to degree level. Room and board charges vary according to board plan and housing facility. Part-time tuition: $320 per credit.

Collegiate Environment: Orientation program. Drama-theater group, choral group, marching band, student-run newspaper, radio station. Social organizations: 80 open to all; national fraternities, national sororities; 5% of eligible men and 4% of eligible women are members. Most popular organizations: student government, student leaders, Student Union Board, student recruitment team, resident assistants. Major annual events: Homecoming, Commencement, Convocation. Student services: health clinic, personal-psychological counseling, women's center. Campus security: 24-hour emergency response devices and patrols, controlled dormitory access, emergency call boxes. 3,066 college housing spaces available; 2,692 were occupied in 2003-04. Freshmen given priority for college housing. Options: coed, men-only, women-only housing available. William R. and Norma B. Harvey Library plus 3 others with 336,092 books, 711,759 microform titles, 1,414 serials, 2,286 audiovisual materials, an OPAC, and a Web page. 1,300 computers available on campus for general student use. Computer purchase/lease plans available. A campuswide network can be accessed from student residence rooms and from off campus. Staffed computer lab on campus.

Community Environment: Hampton is the oldest English settlement still in existence in the nation; the city was settled in 1610. Hampton is the center of the fishing industry of Virginia. All modes of transportation are available. The Syms-Eaton Academy, first free school of America, and Hampton University, of which Booker T. Washington was an alumnus, are only two of the area's important sites. St. John's Church, which survived a partial burning during the Civil War, is another historic point of interest. Its most precious relic is communion silver made in 1618. The window dedicated to Pocahontas was donated by Indian students at Hampton Institute.

■ **HOLLINS UNIVERSITY** *I-6*
PO Box 9603
Roanoke, VA 24020-1603
Tel: (540)362-6000
Free: 800-456-9595
Admissions: (540)362-6401
Fax: (540)362-6218
E-mail: huadm@hollins.edu
Web Site: http://www.hollins.edu/
Description: Independent, comprehensive. Awards bachelor's and master's degrees and post-master's certificates. Founded 1842. Setting: 475-acre suburban campus. Endowment: $101.2 million. Research spending for 2004 fiscal year: $42,952. Educational spending for 2005 fiscal year: $14,084 per student. Total enrollment: 1,123. Faculty: 109 (68 full-time, 41 part-time). Student-undergrad faculty ratio is 10:1. 686 applied, 86% were admitted. 19% from top 10% of their high school class, 55% from top quarter, 87% from top half. Full-time: 790 students, 99% women, 0.3% men. Part-time: 58 students, 93% women, 7% men. Students come from 46 states and territories, 9 other countries, 48% from out-of-state, 1% Native American, 2% Hispanic, 8% black, 1% Asian American or Pacific Islander, 2% international, 12% 25 or older, 79% live on campus, 4% transferred in. Retention: 79% of full-time freshmen returned the following year. Academic areas with the most degrees conferred: English; visual and performing arts; social sciences. Core. Calendar: 4-1-4. Advanced placement, accelerated degree program, self-designed majors, independent study, double major, part-time degree program, adult/continuing education programs, internships, graduate courses open to undergrads. Off campus study at member of the Seven-College Exchange Program. Study abroad program.
Entrance Requirements: Options: Peterson's Universal Application, Common Application, electronic application, early admission, early decision, deferred admission, international baccalaureate accepted. Required: essay, high school transcript, 3 recommendations, SAT or ACT. Recommended: interview. Entrance: moderately difficult. Application deadline: 11/15 for early decision. Notification: continuous, 12/15 for early decision.
Costs Per Year: Application fee: $35. Comprehensive fee: $31,105 includes full-time tuition ($22,470), mandatory fees ($475), and college room and board ($8160). College room only: $4880. Part-time tuition: $702 per credit.
Collegiate Environment: Orientation program. Drama-theater group, choral group, student-run newspaper. Social organizations: 45 open to all. Most popular organizations: Student Government Association, SHARE (volunteer group), Religious Life Association, Student Athletic Association, campus political organizations. Major annual events: Literary Festival, Founders' Day, Tinker Day. Student services: health clinic, personal-psychological counseling, women's center. Campus security: 24-hour emergency response devices and patrols, late night transport-escort service, controlled dormitory access, emergency call boxes. 925 college housing spaces available; 637 were occupied in 2003-04. Freshmen guaranteed college housing. On-campus residence required through senior year. Option: women-only housing available. Wyndham Robertson Library plus 1 other with an OPAC and a

Web page. Operations spending for 2004 fiscal year: $870,150. 100 computers available on campus for general student use. A campuswide network can be accessed from student residence rooms and from off campus. Staffed computer lab on campus.

Community Environment: In this suburban area, the city of Roanoke is the business, cultural, and commercial center of Southwest Virginia. Air and bus transportation are available in Roanoke. Other community facilities of Roanoke are accessible to the students. There is also a symphony, opera company, ballet company, theatre company, art and science museums, and a farmers' market.

■ **ITT TECHNICAL INSTITUTE (CHANTILLY)** *O-3*
14420 Abermarle Point Place, Ste. 100
Chantilly, VA 20151
Tel: (703)263-2541; 888-895-8324
Web Site: http://www.itt-tech.edu/
Description: Proprietary, primarily 2-year, coed. Part of ITT Educational Services, Inc. Awards terminal associate and bachelor's degrees. Founded 2002. Core.
Entrance Requirements: Option: deferred admission. Required: high school transcript, interview. Recommended: recommendations. Entrance: minimally difficult. Application deadline: Rolling. Notification: continuous.
Costs Per Year: Application fee: $100.
Collegiate Environment: Orientation program. College housing not available.

■ **ITT TECHNICAL INSTITUTE (NORFOLK)** *J-15*
863 Glenrock Rd., Ste. 100
Norfolk, VA 23502-3701
Tel: (757)466-1260
Web Site: http://www.itt-tech.edu/
Description: Proprietary, primarily 2-year, coed. Part of ITT Educational Services, Inc. Awards terminal associate and bachelor's degrees. Founded 1988. Setting: 2-acre suburban campus. Core.
Entrance Requirements: Option: deferred admission. Required: high school transcript, interview, Wonderlic aptitude test. Recommended: recommendations. Entrance: minimally difficult. Application deadline: Rolling. Notification: continuous.
Costs Per Year: Application fee: $100.
Collegiate Environment: Orientation program. Student-run newspaper. College housing not available.

■ **ITT TECHNICAL INSTITUTE (RICHMOND)** *H-12*
300 Gateway Centre Parkway
Richmond, VA 23235
Tel: (804)330-4992
Web Site: http://www.itt-tech.edu/
Description: Proprietary, primarily 2-year, coed. Part of ITT Educational Services, Inc. Awards terminal associate and bachelor's degrees. Core.
Entrance Requirements: Option: deferred admission. Required: high school transcript, interview, Wonderlic aptitude test. Recommended: recommendations. Entrance: minimally difficult. Application deadline: Rolling. Notification: continuous.
Costs Per Year: Application fee: $100.
Collegiate Environment: Orientation program. College housing not available.

■ **ITT TECHNICAL INSTITUTE (SPRINGFIELD)** *Q-6*
7300 Boston Blvd.
Springfield, VA 22153
Tel: (703)440-9535; (866)817-8324
Fax: (703)440-9561
Web Site: http://www.itt-tech.edu/
Description: Proprietary, primarily 2-year, coed. Part of ITT Educational Services, Inc. Awards terminal associate and bachelor's degrees. Founded 2002. Core.
Entrance Requirements: Option: deferred admission. Required: high school transcript, interview, Wonderlic aptitude test. Recommended: recommendations. Entrance: minimally difficult. Application deadline: Rolling. Notification: continuous.
Costs Per Year: Application fee: $100.
Collegiate Environment: Orientation program. College housing not available.

■ **J. SARGEANT REYNOLDS COMMUNITY COLLEGE** *H-12*
PO Box 85622
Richmond, VA 23285-5622

Tel: (804)371-3000

Admissions: (804)371-3029

Fax: (804)371-3650

E-mail: srmarss@jsr.cc.va.us

Web Site: http://www.reynolds.edu

Description: State-supported, 2-year, coed. Part of Virginia Community College System. Awards certificates, transfer associate, and terminal associate degrees. Founded 1972. Setting: 207-acre suburban campus. Endowment: $2.3 million. Educational spending for 2005 fiscal year: $2508 per student. Total enrollment: 11,678. Full-time: 2,871 students, 58% women, 42% men. Part-time: 8,807 students, 62% women, 38% men. 1% Native American, 2% Hispanic, 36% black, 3% Asian American or Pacific Islander, 0.4% international. Calendar: semesters. Academic remediation for entering students, ESL program, services for LD students, advanced placement, independent study, distance learning, summer session for credit, part-time degree program, adult/continuing education programs, internships. Off campus study at Rappahannock Community College, Southside Virginia Community College.

Entrance Requirements: Open admission. Option: electronic application. Required: high school transcript. Required for some: interview. Entrance: noncompetitive. Application deadline: Rolling. Notification: continuous.

Costs Per Year: Application fee: $0. State resident tuition: $2282 full-time, $76.05 per credit hour part-time. Nonresident tuition: $6728 full-time, $224.25 per credit hour part-time.

Collegiate Environment: Orientation program. Drama-theater group, choral group. Social organizations: 20 open to all. Most popular organizations: Phi Theta Kappa, Student Nurses Association, SGA, Phi Beta Lambda. Major annual events: Semester Kick Off, Spring Fest, Graduation reception. Student services: personal-psychological counseling. Campus security: security during open hours. College housing not available. Learning Resource Center plus 2 others with 80,736 books, 11,173 microform titles, 465 serials, 1,575 audiovisual materials, an OPAC, and a Web page. Operations spending for 2004 fiscal year: $1.1 million. 1,069 computers available on campus for general student use. A campuswide network can be accessed from off-campus. Staffed computer lab on campus.

Community Environment: See University of Richmond.

■ **JAMES MADISON UNIVERSITY** *E-8*

800 South Main St.

Harrisonburg, VA 22807

Tel: (540)568-6211

Admissions: (540)568-5681

Fax: (540)568-3332

E-mail: gotojmu@jmu.edu

Web Site: http://www.jmu.edu/

Description: State-supported, comprehensive, coed. Awards bachelor's, master's, and doctoral degrees (also offers specialist in education degree). Founded 1908. Setting: 605-acre small town campus. Endowment: $23.7 million. Research spending for 2004 fiscal year: $5.5 million. Educational spending for 2005 fiscal year: $5115 per student. Total enrollment: 16,938. Faculty: 1,164 (795 full-time, 369 part-time). Student-undergrad faculty ratio is 17:1. 16,388 applied, 68% were admitted. 28% from top 10% of their high school class, 74% from top quarter, 98% from top half. Full-time: 14,885 students, 61% women, 39% men. Part-time: 733 students, 49% women, 51% men. Students come from 47 states and territories, 47 other countries, 30% from out-of-state, 0.2% Native American, 2% Hispanic, 3% black, 5% Asian American or Pacific Islander, 1% international, 2% 25 or older, 39% live on campus, 4% transferred in. Retention: 91% of full-time freshmen returned the following year. Academic areas with the most degrees conferred: business/marketing; social sciences; health professions and related sciences. Core. Calendar: semesters. Services for LD students, advanced placement, accelerated degree program, freshman honors college, honors program, independent study, distance learning, double major, summer session for credit, part-time degree program, adult/continuing education programs, internships, graduate courses open to undergrads. Study abroad program. ROTC: Army, Air Force (c).

Entrance Requirements: Options: electronic application, early action, deferred admission, international baccalaureate accepted. Required: high school transcript, SAT or ACT. Recommended: minimum 3.0 high school GPA. Entrance: very difficult. Application deadlines: 1/15, 11/1 for early action. Notification: 4/1, 1/15 for early action. Preference given to state residents.

Costs Per Year: Application fee: $40. State resident tuition: $5886 full-time.

Nonresident tuition: $15,322 full-time. College room and board: $6372. College room only: $3278. Room and board charges vary according to board plan and housing facility.

Collegiate Environment: Orientation program. Drama-theater group, choral group, marching band, student-run newspaper, radio station. Social organizations: 286 open to all; national fraternities, national sororities; 9% of eligible men and 11% of eligible women are members. Most popular organizations: Student Ambassadors, sports clubs, service organizations, special interest groups. Major annual events: Homecoming, Parents' Weekend, Commencement. Student services: health clinic, personal-psychological counseling. Campus security: 24-hour emergency response devices and patrols, student patrols, late night transport-escort service, controlled dormitory access, lighted pathways. 5,500 college housing spaces available; 5,474 were occupied in 2003-04. Freshmen guaranteed college housing. On-campus residence required in freshman year. Option: coed housing available. Carrier Library plus 2 others with an OPAC and a Web page. Operations spending for 2004 fiscal year: $5.6 million. 600 computers available on campus for general student use. Computer purchase/lease plans available. A campuswide network can be accessed from student residence rooms and from off campus. Staffed computer lab on campus.

Community Environment: Located in the geographic center of Shenandoah Valley, Harrisonburg is an attractive city of 30,000 people. The Shenandoah National Park and the George Washington National Forest are here. All forms of commercial transportation are available. Community facilities include a number of churches, a library, hospital, and various civic and service organizations. Recreational facilities are available for camping, fishing, and picnicking. A snow skiing resort is also nearby.

■ **JEFFERSON COLLEGE OF HEALTH SCIENCES** *I-6*

PO Box 13186

Roanoke, VA 24031-3186

Tel: (540)985-8483; 888-985-8483

Admissions: (540)985-9083

Fax: (540)985-9773

E-mail: jmckeon@jchs.edu

Web Site: http://www.jchs.edu/

Description: Independent, 4-year, coed. Awards associate and bachelor's degrees. Founded 1982. Setting: 1-acre urban campus. Endowment: $3.8 million. Educational spending for 2005 fiscal year: $5912 per student. Total enrollment: 697. 303 applied, 35% were admitted. Full-time: 423 students, 73% women, 27% men. Part-time: 274 students, 87% women, 13% men. Students come from 7 states and territories, 7% from out-of-state, 0.3% Native American, 1% Hispanic, 11% black, 2% Asian American or Pacific Islander, 0% international, 56% 25 or older, 15% live on campus, 27% transferred in. Retention: 51% of full-time freshmen returned the following year. Core. Calendar: semesters. Academic remediation for entering students, services for LD students, advanced placement, accelerated degree program, distance learning, summer session for credit, part-time degree program, adult/continuing education programs, internships.

Entrance Requirements: Option: early decision. Required: essay, high school transcript, minimum 2.0 high school GPA. Recommended: SAT. Required for some: recommendations, interview, volunteer experience, SAT or ACT, ACT ASSET. Entrance: moderately difficult. Application deadlines: 7/31, 10/15 for early decision. Notification: continuous until 7/31, 12/1 for early decision.

Collegiate Environment: Orientation program. Most popular organizations: Student Government Association, Student Nurse Association, Student Occupational Therapy Association, Student Physical Therapist Assistant Assembly, Crossroads. Major annual events: Health Care Futures, Orientation Picnic, Back to School Party. Student services: health clinic, personal-psychological counseling. Campus security: 24-hour emergency response devices and patrols, late night transport-escort service, controlled dormitory access. 100 college housing spaces available; all were occupied in 2003-04. No special consideration for freshman housing applicants. Option: coed housing available. Learning Resource Center with 10,533 books, 16 microform titles, 376 serials, 1,071 audiovisual materials, an OPAC, and a Web page. Operations spending for 2004 fiscal year: $218,456. 56 computers available on campus for general student use. Computer purchase/lease plans available. A campuswide network can be accessed from off-campus. Staffed computer lab on campus.

■ **JOHN TYLER COMMUNITY COLLEGE** *I-12*

13101 Jefferson Davis Hwy.

Chester, VA 23831-5316

Tel: (804)796-4000
Admissions: (804)796-4150
Fax: (804)796-4163
Web Site: http://www.jtcc.edu/

Description: State-supported, 2-year, coed. Part of Virginia Community College System. Awards certificates, transfer associate, and terminal associate degrees. Founded 1967. Setting: 160-acre suburban campus with easy access to Richmond. Endowment: $399,044. Educational spending for 2005 fiscal year: $3226 per student. Total enrollment: 6,314. Student-undergrad faculty ratio is 27:1. 470 applied, 100% were admitted. Full-time: 1,607 students, 60% women, 40% men. Part-time: 4,707 students, 64% women, 36% men. Students come from 38 states and territories, 1% from out-of-state, 0.5% Native American, 3% Hispanic, 25% black, 3% Asian American or Pacific Islander, 0.05% international, 51% 25 or older, 14% transferred in. Core. Calendar: semesters. Academic remediation for entering students, services for LD students, advanced placement, honors program, distance learning, summer session for credit, part-time degree program, external degree program, adult/continuing education programs. Off campus study. Study abroad program. ROTC: Army (c).

Entrance Requirements: Open admission. Options: Common Application, early admission, deferred admission. Recommended: high school transcript. Entrance: noncompetitive. Application deadline: Rolling. Notification: continuous. Preference given to district residents.

Costs Per Year: Application fee: $0. State resident tuition: $1708 full-time, $71.15 per credit part-time. Nonresident tuition: $5264 full-time, $219.35 per credit part-time. Mandatory fees: $50 full-time, $25 per term part-time.

Collegiate Environment: Campus security: 24-hour patrols. College housing not available. John Tyler Community College Learning Resource and Technology Center with 49,393 books, 47,469 microform titles, 179 serials, 1,544 audiovisual materials, an OPAC, and a Web page. Operations spending for 2004 fiscal year: $607,093. 465 computers available on campus for general student use. A campuswide network can be accessed from off-campus. Staffed computer lab on campus.

Community Environment: Located 10 miles from Richmond, the state capital, and Petersburg.

■ LIBERTY UNIVERSITY *I-8*

1971 University Blvd.
Lynchburg, VA 24502
Tel: (434)582-2000
Free: 800-543-5317
Admissions: (434)592-3015
Fax: (434)582-2304
Web Site: http://www.liberty.edu/

Description: Independent nondenominational, comprehensive, coed. Awards associate, bachelor's, master's, doctoral, and first professional degrees and post-master's certificates (also offers external degree program with significant enrollment not reflected in profile). Founded 1971. Setting: 230-acre suburban campus. Endowment: $6.2 million. Research spending for 2004 fiscal year: $155,613. Educational spending for 2005 fiscal year: $2489 per student. Total enrollment: 12,458. Faculty: 501 (336 full-time, 165 part-time). Student-undergrad faculty ratio is 27:1. 6,504 applied, 67% were admitted. 4% from top 10% of their high school class, 14% from top quarter, 41% from top half. 7 National Merit Scholars. Full-time: 8,427 students, 53% women, 47% men. Part-time: 1,548 students, 47% women, 53% men. Students come from 52 states and territories, 63 other countries, 64% from out-of-state, 1% Native American, 3% Hispanic, 10% black, 2% Asian American or Pacific Islander, 4% international, 29% 25 or older, 53% live on campus, 6% transferred in. Retention: 73% of full-time freshmen returned the following year. Academic areas with the most degrees conferred: psychology; business/marketing; interdisciplinary studies. Core. Calendar: semesters. Academic remediation for entering students, ESL program, services for LD students, advanced placement, accelerated degree program, self-designed majors, honors program, independent study, distance learning, double major, summer session for credit, part-time degree program, external degree program, internships, graduate courses open to undergrads. ROTC: Army, Air Force (c).

Entrance Requirements: Options: electronic application, early admission, deferred admission, international baccalaureate accepted. Required: essay, high school transcript, SAT or ACT. Recommended: minimum 2.0 high school GPA, recommendations. Required for some: recommendations, interview. Entrance: minimally difficult. Application deadline: 6/30. Notification: continuous until 8/15.

Costs Per Year: Application fee: $35. Comprehensive fee: $20,750 includes

full-time tuition ($14,400), mandatory fees ($950), and college room and board ($5400). Part-time tuition: $480 per semester hour. Part-time mandatory fees: $425 per term.

Collegiate Environment: Orientation program. Drama-theater group, choral group, marching band, student-run newspaper, radio station. Social organizations: 32 open to all. Most popular organizations: College Republicans, Youthquest, Circle K. Major annual events: SuperConference, Homecoming, Block Party. Student services: health clinic, personal-psychological counseling. Campus security: 24-hour patrols, late night transport-escort service, 24-hour emergency dispatch. 5,332 college housing spaces available; 4,645 were occupied in 2003-04. Freshmen guaranteed college housing. On-campus residence required through junior year. Options: men-only, women-only housing available. A. Pierre Guillermin Integrated Learning Resource Center plus 1 other with 199,150 books, 558,483 microform titles, 12,426 serials, 5,856 audiovisual materials, an OPAC, and a Web page. Operations spending for 2004 fiscal year: $2 million. 406 computers available on campus for general student use. Computer purchase/lease plans available. A campuswide network can be accessed from student residence rooms and from off campus. Staffed computer lab on campus.

Community Environment: Lynchburg, with a population of 70,000, is in the heart of Virginia on the south bank of the historic James River, with the scenic Blue Ridge Mountains nearby. The city is over 200 years old and is noted for its culture, beauty and educational advantages. It is at the crossroads of U.S. highways 29 and 460 and has adequate transportation facilities by bus, railway and air.

■ LONGWOOD UNIVERSITY *I-9*

201 High St.
Farmville, VA 23909
Tel: (434)395-2000
Free: 800-281-4677
Admissions: (434)395-2060
Fax: (434)395-2332
E-mail: lcadmit@longwood.lwc.edu
Web Site: http://www.longwood.edu/

Description: State-supported, comprehensive, coed. Part of The State Council of Higher Education for Virginia (SCHEV). Awards bachelor's and master's degrees. Founded 1839. Setting: 160-acre small town campus with easy access to Richmond. Endowment: $31.2 million. Research spending for 2004 fiscal year: $20,578. Educational spending for 2005 fiscal year: $3913 per student. Total enrollment: 4,289. 3,401 applied, 76% were admitted. 9% from top 10% of their high school class, 38% from top quarter, 85% from top half. Full-time: 3,604 students, 67% women, 33% men. Part-time: 135 students, 53% women, 47% men. Students come from 25 states and territories, 11 other countries, 10% from out-of-state, 0.4% Native American, 2% Hispanic, 6% black, 2% Asian American or Pacific Islander, 0.5% international, 2% 25 or older, 67% live on campus, 4% transferred in. Retention: 80% of full-time freshmen returned the following year. Core. Calendar: semesters. Services for LD students, advanced placement, accelerated degree program, honors program, independent study, distance learning, double major, summer session for credit, part-time degree program, internships, graduate courses open to undergrads. Off campus study at Hampden-Sydney College. Study abroad program. ROTC: Army.

Entrance Requirements: Options: Peterson's Universal Application, Common Application, electronic application, early admission, early action, deferred admission, international baccalaureate accepted. Required: essay, high school transcript, SAT or ACT. Recommended: minimum 2.7 high school GPA. Required for some: recommendations, interview. Entrance: moderately difficult. Application deadlines: 3/1, 12/1 for early action. Notification: continuous until 6/1, 1/1 for early action.

Costs Per Year: Application fee: $40. State resident tuition: $3586 full-time, $150 per credit hour part-time. Nonresident tuition: $10,270 full-time, $428 per credit hour part-time. Mandatory fees: $3434 full-time. College room and board: $5586. College room only: $3288. Room and board charges vary according to board plan.

Collegiate Environment: Orientation program. Drama-theater group, choral group, student-run newspaper, radio station. Social organizations: 125 open to all; national fraternities, national sororities; 14% of eligible men and 19% of eligible women are members. Most popular organizations: Student Government Association, Alpha Phi Omega, Inter-Varsity Christian Fellowship, Longwood Ambassadors, Wellness Advocates. Major annual events: Oktoberfest, Spring Weekend, Battle of the Bands. Student services: health clinic, personal-psychological counseling. Campus security: 24-hour emergency response devices and patrols, late night transport-escort service, controlled dormitory access, security lighting. 2,444 college housing spaces available; all were occupied in 2003-04. Freshmen guaranteed college housing. On-campus residence required through junior year. Options: coed, women-only housing available. The Janet D. Greenwood Library with 325,290 books, 720,205 microform titles, 5,018 serials, 18,771 audiovisual materials, an OPAC, and a Web page. Operations spending for 2004 fiscal year: $1.9 million. 270 computers available on campus for general student use. Computer purchase/lease plans available. A campuswide network can be accessed from student residence rooms and from off campus. Staffed computer lab on campus.

Community Environment: Farmville is a small residential town. Bus transportation is available. Most major religious denominations are represented, and a community hospital is 5 blocks from campus. Nearby state parks provide swimming, boating, camping and hiking facilities.

■ **LORD FAIRFAX COMMUNITY COLLEGE** *C-10*

173 Skirmisher Ln.
Middletown, VA 22645
Tel: (540)868-7000
Free: 800-906-5322
Admissions: (540)868-7105
Fax: (540)868-7100
Web Site: http://www.lfcc.edu/

Description: State-supported, 2-year, coed. Part of Virginia Community College System. Awards certificates, transfer associate, and terminal associate degrees. Founded 1969. Setting: 100-acre rural campus with easy access to Washington, DC. Total enrollment: 5,492. Full-time: 1,535 students, 58% women, 42% men. Part-time: 3,957 students, 63% women, 37% men. 2% from out-of-state, 0.4% Native American, 2% Hispanic, 5% black, 1% Asian American or Pacific Islander, 0% international, 49% 25 or older. Retention: 52% of full-time freshmen returned the following year. Core. Calendar: semesters. Academic remediation for entering students, services for LD students, advanced placement, honors program, distance learning, summer session for credit, part-time degree program, adult/continuing education programs, co-op programs.

Entrance Requirements: Open admission. Option: early admission. Recommended: high school transcript. Entrance: noncompetitive. Application deadline: Rolling. Notification: continuous.

Costs Per Year: Application fee: $0. State resident tuition: $1740 full-time, $72.50 per credit hour part-time. Nonresident tuition: $5748 full-time, $235.35 per credit hour part-time. Mandatory fees: $117 full-time, $4.30 per credit hour part-time.

Collegiate Environment: Drama-theater group. Social organizations: 11 open to all. Most popular organizations: Phi Theta Kappa, Phi Beta Lambda, Performing Arts Club, Scientific Society, Ambassadors Club. Major annual events: Honors Convocation, Fall Activities Day, Spring Fling. Student services: personal-psychological counseling, women's center. Campus security: late night transport-escort service. College housing not available. Learning Resources Center with 41,000 books, 300 serials, and an OPAC. 450 computers available on campus for general student use. A campuswide network can be accessed from off-campus. Staffed computer lab on campus.

Community Environment: The area is rural and does not offer public transportation. There is medium industry and seasonal employment in the apple industry.

■ **LYNCHBURG COLLEGE** *I-8*

1501 Lakeside Dr.
Lynchburg, VA 24501-3199
Tel: (434)544-8100
Free: 800-426-8101
Admissions: (434)544-8300
Fax: (434)544-8653
E-mail: admissions@lynchburg.edu
Web Site: http://www.lynchburg.edu/

Description: Independent, comprehensive, coed, affiliated with Christian Church (Disciples of Christ). Awards bachelor's and master's degrees. Founded 1903. Setting: 214-acre suburban campus. Endowment: $70.3 million. Educational spending for 2005 fiscal year: $7747 per student. Total enrollment: 2,428. Faculty: 237 (142 full-time, 95 part-time). Student-undergrad faculty ratio is 12:1. 4,009 applied, 72% were admitted. 13% from top 10% of their high school class, 26% from top quarter, 72% from top half. Full-time: 1,924 students, 59% women, 41% men. Part-time: 125 students, 62% women, 38% men. Students come from 36 states and territories, 13

other countries, 36% from out-of-state, 1% Native American, 3% Hispanic, 8% black, 2% Asian American or Pacific Islander, 0.4% international, 19% 25 or older, 81% live on campus, 3% transferred in. Retention: 74% of full-time freshmen returned the following year. Academic areas with the most degrees conferred: business/marketing; communications/journalism; education. Core. Calendar: semesters. Services for LD students, advanced placement, accelerated degree program, honors program, independent study, double major, summer session for credit, part-time degree program, adult/continuing education programs, internships, graduate courses open to undergrads. Off campus study at members of the Tri-College Consortium. Study abroad program.

Entrance Requirements: Options: Peterson's Universal Application, Common Application, electronic application, early admission, early decision, deferred admission. Required: high school transcript, SAT or ACT. Recommended: essay, 2 recommendations, interview. Entrance: moderately difficult. Application deadlines: Rolling, 11/15 for early decision. Notification: continuous, 12/15 for early decision.

Costs Per Year: Application fee: $30. Comprehensive fee: $30,645 includes full-time tuition ($23,700), mandatory fees ($545), and college room and board ($6400). College room only: $3200. Part-time tuition: $335 per credit hour.

Collegiate Environment: Orientation program. Drama-theater group, choral group, student-run newspaper. Social organizations: 56 open to all; national fraternities, national sororities; 10% of eligible men and 11% of eligible women are members. Most popular organizations: Association of Commuter Students, Omicron Delta Kappa, Ski and Snowboarding Club, Kappa Delta, Baptist Student Union. Major annual events: homecoming, Turkey Bowl, Sibs-n-Kids Weekend. Student services: health clinic, personal-psychological counseling. Campus security: 24-hour emergency response devices and patrols, late night transport-escort service, controlled dormitory access. 1,496 college housing spaces available; all were occupied in 2003-04. Freshmen guaranteed college housing. On-campus residence required through junior year. Option: coed housing available. Knight-Capron Library with 287,601 books, 12,909 microform titles, 636 serials, 9,360 audiovisual materials, an OPAC, and a Web page. Operations spending for 2004 fiscal year: $711,329. 217 computers available on campus for general student use. A campuswide network can be accessed from student residence rooms. Staffed computer lab on campus.

Community Environment: Founded in 1786, Lynchburg is rich in history. It is a modern community with diversified industry in a traditional, handsome setting. Although it has a metropolitan area population of 150,000, Lynchburg maintains intimate contact with the countryside since it is very near the Blue Ridge Mountains and is in the center of perhaps the most historic of states. Washington, D.C., is less than 4 hours away, Williamsburg approximately 3, and Richmond about 2 1/2. The area provides excellent climate, convenient shopping, and many cultural opportunities. There is an active Lynchburg Fine Arts Center, and professional musical and theatrical groups visit. Some of the 7 colleges in the area also present fine arts programs.

■ **MARY BALDWIN COLLEGE** *F-8*

201 East Frederick St.
Staunton, VA 24401-3610
Tel: (540)887-7000
Free: 800-468-2262
Admissions: (540)887-7019
Fax: (540)886-6634
E-mail: bbryant@mbc.edu
Web Site: http://www.mbc.edu/

Description: Independent, comprehensive, coed. Awards bachelor's and master's degrees. Founded 1842. Setting: 54-acre small town campus. Endowment: $37.1 million. Educational spending for 2005 fiscal year: $8925 per student. Total enrollment: 1,740. Faculty: 134 (76 full-time, 58 part-time). Student-undergrad faculty ratio is 10:1. 1,307 applied, 75% were admitted. 14% from top 10% of their high school class, 29% from top quarter, 72% from top half. Full-time: 1,002 students, 96% women, 4% men. Part-time: 533 students, 83% women, 17% men. Students come from 36 states and territories, 5 other countries, 38% from out-of-state, 1% Native American, 4% Hispanic, 21% black, 3% Asian American or Pacific Islander, 2% international, 1% 25 or older, 81% live on campus, 2% transferred in. Retention: 65% of full-time freshmen returned the following year. Academic areas with the most degrees conferred: social sciences; psychology; business/marketing; visual and performing arts. Core. Calendar: 4-4-1. Academic remediation for entering students, ESL program, services for LD students, advanced placement, accelerated degree program, self-designed majors, freshman honors college, honors program, independent study, double major, part-time degree program, external degree program, adult/continuing education programs, internships, graduate courses open to undergrads. Off campus study at members of the Seven-College Exchange Program. Study abroad program. ROTC: Army, Naval (c), Air Force (c).

Entrance Requirements: Options: Peterson's Universal Application, Common Application, electronic application, early admission, early decision, deferred admission, international baccalaureate accepted. Required: high school transcript, minimum 2.0 high school GPA, 1 recommendation, SAT or ACT. Recommended: interview. Entrance: moderately difficult. Application deadlines: Rolling, 11/15 for early decision. Notification: continuous, 12/1 for early decision.

Costs Per Year: Application fee: $35. Comprehensive fee: $26,465 includes full-time tuition ($20,405), mandatory fees ($200), and college room and board ($5860). College room only: $3738. Full-time tuition and fees vary according to degree level. Room and board charges vary according to housing facility. Part-time tuition: $345 per credit hour. Part-time tuition varies according to degree level.

Collegiate Environment: Orientation program. Drama-theater group, choral group, marching band, student-run newspaper, radio station. Social organizations: 48 open to all. Most popular organizations: Student Senate, Baldwin Program Board, President's Society, Black Student Alliance, Stars. Major annual events: Apple Day, Junior Dads Weekend, Christmas Cheer. Student services: health clinic, personal-psychological counseling. Campus security: 24-hour emergency response devices and patrols, late night transport-escort service, controlled dormitory access. 760 college housing spaces available; 658 were occupied in 2003-04. Freshmen guaranteed college housing. On-campus residence required through senior year. Option: women-only housing available. Grafton Library with 140,466 books, 69,644 microform titles, 11,889 serials, 6,668 audiovisual materials, an OPAC, and a Web page. Operations spending for 2004 fiscal year: $153,195. 227 computers available on campus for general student use. A campuswide network can be accessed from student residence rooms and from off campus. Staffed computer lab on campus.

Community Environment: Staunton, one of the oldest cities west of the Blue Ridge Mountains, originated the city manager form of government. Annual snowfall here is 16 inches. All modes of commercial transportation are available. Community facilities include a public library, YMCA, hospital, many churches, shopping areas, and civic and service organizations. Recreational activities include golf, tennis, skiing, horseback riding, bowling, swimming, fishing, and hunting. Some of the points of interest are the birthplace of Woodrow Wilson, the Old Trinity Church, and American Frontier Museum. Opportunities for part-time work are available.

■ **MARYMOUNT UNIVERSITY** *D-13*
2807 North Glebe Rd.
Arlington, VA 22207-4299
Tel: (703)522-5600
Free: 800-548-7638
Admissions: (703)284-1500
Fax: (703)522-0349
E-mail: admissions@marymount.edu
Web Site: http://www.marymount.edu/
Description: Independent, comprehensive, coed, affiliated with Roman Catholic Church. Awards bachelor's, master's, and doctoral degrees and post-master's certificates (Associate). Founded 1950. Setting: 21-acre suburban campus with easy access to Washington, DC. Endowment: $20.2 million. Educational spending for 2005 fiscal year: $6247 per student. Total enrollment: 3,684. Faculty: 352 (134 full-time, 218 part-time). Student-undergrad faculty ratio is 13:1. 1,802 applied, 86% were admitted. 12% from top 10% of their high school class, 30% from top quarter, 72% from top half. Full-time: 1,871 students, 74% women, 26% men. Part-time: 456 students, 79% women, 21% men. Students come from 42 states and territories, 62 other countries, 43% from out-of-state, 0.4% Native American, 11% Hispanic, 14% black, 9% Asian American or Pacific Islander, 7% international, 25% 25 or older, 30% live on campus, 14% transferred in. Retention: 73% of full-time freshmen returned the following year. Academic areas with the most degrees conferred: visual and performing arts; business/marketing; psychology. Core. Calendar: semesters plus 2 summer terms. Academic remediation for entering students, ESL program, services for LD students, advanced placement, self-designed majors, honors program, independent study, double major, summer session for credit, part-time degree program,

internships, graduate courses open to undergrads. Off campus study at Consortium of Universities of the Washington Metropolitan Area. Study abroad program. ROTC: Army (c).

Entrance Requirements: Options: Common Application, electronic application, deferred admission, international baccalaureate accepted. Required: high school transcript, minimum 2.5 high school GPA, 1 recommendation, SAT or ACT. Recommended: essay, interview. Entrance: moderately difficult. Application deadlines: Rolling, Rolling for nonresidents. Notification: continuous, continuous for nonresidents.

Costs Per Year: Application fee: $35. Comprehensive fee: $25,934 includes full-time tuition ($17,970), mandatory fees ($144), and college room and board ($7820). Part-time tuition: $582 per credit hour. Part-time mandatory fees: $6 per credit hour.

Collegiate Environment: Orientation program. Drama-theater group, choral group, student-run newspaper. Social organizations: 30 open to all. Most popular organizations: American Society of Interior Design, Student Nurses Association, Fashion Club, International Club, One 2 One (drama club). Major annual events: Portfolio in Motion, Snowball, International Week. Student services: health clinic, personal-psychological counseling. Campus security: 24-hour emergency response devices and patrols, late night transport-escort service, controlled dormitory access. 670 college housing spaces available; 667 were occupied in 2003-04. Freshmen given priority for college housing. On-campus residence required through sophomore year. Options: coed, men-only, women-only housing available. Emerson C. Reinsch Library plus 1 other with 187,097 books, 315,786 microform titles, 1,048 serials, 908 audiovisual materials, an OPAC, and a Web page. Operations spending for 2004 fiscal year: $2.3 million. 177 computers available on campus for general student use. Computer purchase/lease plans available. A campuswide network can be accessed from off-campus. Staffed computer lab on campus.

Community Environment: Located in Arlington, Virginia, just minutes from Washington, DC, Marymount provides students with an easy access to the resources of the nation's capital, including the Library of Congress, the National Archives, the Smithsonian Institution, the John F. Kennedy Center for the Performing Arts, and the Capitol. The University location offers both professional and scholarly opportunities for faculty; the opportunity to bring leaders from government, commerce, and the professions to the University campus; resources for instruction and research; internships placements for students; and employment opportunities for graduates.

■ **MEDICAL CAREERS INSTITUTE (NEWPORT NEWS)** *J-14*
1001 Omni Blvd., Ste. 200
Newport News, VA 23606
Tel: (757)873-2423
Fax: (757)873-2472
Web Site: http://www.medicalcareersinstitute.com/
Description: Proprietary, 2-year, coed. Founded 1978. Calendar: semesters.

■ **MEDICAL CAREERS INSTITUTE (RICHMOND)** *H-12*
800 Moorefield Park Dr., Ste. 302
Richmond, VA 23236-3659
Tel: (804)521-0400
Fax: (804)521-0406
E-mail: dmayle@medical.edu
Web Site: http://www.medicalcareersinstitute.com/
Description: Proprietary, 2-year, coed. Calendar: semesters.

■ **MEDICAL CAREERS INSTITUTE (VIRGINIA BEACH)** *J-15*
5501 Greenwich Rd.
Virginia Beach, VA 23462
Tel: (757)497-8400
Web Site: http://www.medical.edu
Description: Proprietary, 2-year, coed. Awards certificates, diplomas, and terminal associate degrees. Calendar: semesters.

■ **MOUNTAIN EMPIRE COMMUNITY COLLEGE** *C-3*
PO Drawer 700
Big Stone Gap, VA 24219-0700
Tel: (540)523-2400
Admissions: (276)523-2400
Web Site: http://www.me.vccs.edu/
Description: State-supported, 2-year, coed. Part of Virginia Community College System. Awards certificates, diplomas, transfer associate, and terminal associate degrees. Founded 1972. Setting: small town campus with easy

access to Kingsport. Total enrollment: 2,885. 3 valedictorians. Students come from 3 states and territories, 1 other country, 1% from out-of-state, 30% 25 or older. Calendar: semesters. Academic remediation for entering students, advanced placement, self-designed majors, distance learning, summer session for credit, part-time degree program, adult/continuing education programs, co-op programs and internships.
Entrance Requirements: Open admission except for nursing, respiratory care programs. Options: Peterson's Universal Application, early admission, deferred admission. Required: high school transcript. Required for some: minimum 2.0 high school GPA. Placement: ACT ASSET, ACT COMPASS required. Entrance: noncompetitive. Application deadline: Rolling. Notification: continuous. Preference given to state residents.
Collegiate Environment: Drama-theater group. Social organizations: 8 open to all. Most popular organizations: Phi Theta Kappa, Lambda Alpha Epsilon, MECC Group Artists, Phi Beta Lambda, Players on the Mountain. Major annual events: Spring Fest, Home Crafts Day, humanities series. Student services: personal-psychological counseling. Campus security: 24-hour emergency response devices and patrols. College housing not available. Robb Hall with 21,600 books, 100 microform titles, 105 serials, 200 audiovisual materials, and an OPAC. 400 computers available on campus for general student use. A campuswide network can be accessed from off-campus. Staffed computer lab on campus.
Community Environment: Big Stone Gap is a rural community in the southwest corner of Virginia, situated in the Cumberland Mountains. It has a population of 4,847. Many state parks and recreational areas are within an easy drive of the campus. Kingsport, Tennessee is approximately 30 miles south of the campus.

■ **NATIONAL COLLEGE OF BUSINESS & TECHNOLOGY (BLUEFIELD)** *I-2*
100 Logan St.
PO Box 629
Bluefield, VA 24605-1405
Tel: (276)326-3621
Free: 800-664-1886
Fax: (276)322-5731
Web Site: http://www.ncbt.edu/
Description: Proprietary, 2-year, coed. Part of National College of Business and Technology. Awards diplomas and terminal associate degrees. Founded 1886. Setting: small town campus. Total enrollment: 203. Core. Services for LD students, advanced placement, honors program, double major, summer session for credit, part-time degree program, internships.
Entrance Requirements: Open admission. Option: electronic application. Recommended: interview. Entrance: noncompetitive. Application deadline: Rolling.
Costs Per Year: Application fee: $30. Tuition: $6408 full-time, $178 per credit hour part-time. Mandatory fees: $75 full-time, $15 per term part-time. Full-time tuition and fees vary according to course load. Part-time tuition and fees vary according to course load.
Collegiate Environment: Orientation program. College housing not available. 35 computers available on campus for general student use. A campuswide network can be accessed. Staffed computer lab on campus.

■ **NATIONAL COLLEGE OF BUSINESS & TECHNOLOGY (CHARLOTTESVILLE)** *F-9*
1819 Emmet St.
Charlottesville, VA 22901
Tel: (434)295-0136
Free: 800-664-1886
Fax: (434)986-1344
Web Site: http://www.ncbt.edu/
Description: Proprietary, 2-year, coed. Part of National College of Business and Technology. Awards certificates, diplomas, and terminal associate degrees. Founded 1975. Setting: small town campus with easy access to Richmond. Total enrollment: 163. Core. Services for LD students, advanced placement, honors program, double major, summer session for credit, part-time degree program, internships.
Entrance Requirements: Open admission. Option: electronic application. Recommended: interview. Required for some: high school transcript. Entrance: noncompetitive. Application deadline: Rolling.
Costs Per Year: Application fee: $30. Tuition: $6408 full-time, $178 per credit hour part-time. Mandatory fees: $75 full-time, $15 per term part-time. Full-time tuition and fees vary according to course load. Part-time tuition and fees vary according to course load.

Collegiate Environment: Orientation program. College housing not available. 35 computers available on campus for general student use. A campuswide network can be accessed. Staffed computer lab on campus.

■ **NATIONAL COLLEGE OF BUSINESS & TECHNOLOGY (DANVILLE)** *K-7*
734 Main St.
Danville, VA 24541-1819
Tel: (434)793-6822
Free: 800-664-1886
Fax: (434)793-3634
Web Site: http://www.ncbt.edu/
Description: Proprietary, 2-year, coed. Part of National College of Business and Technology. Awards diplomas and terminal associate degrees. Founded 1975. Setting: small town campus. Core. Academic remediation for entering students, advanced placement, honors program, double major, summer session for credit, part-time degree program, internships.
Entrance Requirements: Open admission. Option: electronic application. Recommended: interview. Required for some: high school transcript. Entrance: noncompetitive. Application deadline: Rolling.
Collegiate Environment: Orientation program. 3,010 books and 12 serials. 35 computers available on campus for general student use. A campuswide network can be accessed. Staffed computer lab on campus.

■ **NATIONAL COLLEGE OF BUSINESS & TECHNOLOGY (HARRISONBURG)** *E-8*
51 B Burgess Rd.
Harrisonburg, VA 22801-9709
Tel: (540)432-0943
Free: 800-664-1886
Fax: (540)986-1344
Web Site: http://www.ncbt.edu/
Description: Proprietary, 2-year, coed. Part of National College of Business and Technology. Awards diplomas and terminal associate degrees. Founded 1988. Setting: small town campus. Total enrollment: 233. Core. Services for LD students, advanced placement, honors program, double major, summer session for credit, part-time degree program, internships.
Entrance Requirements: Open admission. Option: electronic application. Recommended: interview. Required for some: high school transcript. Entrance: noncompetitive. Application deadline: Rolling. Notification: continuous.
Costs Per Year: Application fee: $30. Tuition: $6408 full-time, $178 per credit hour part-time. Mandatory fees: $75 full-time, $15 per term part-time. Full-time tuition and fees vary according to course load. Part-time tuition and fees vary according to course load.
Collegiate Environment: Orientation program. College housing not available. 35 computers available on campus for general student use. A campuswide network can be accessed. Staffed computer lab on campus.

■ **NATIONAL COLLEGE OF BUSINESS & TECHNOLOGY (LYNCHBURG)** *I-8*
104 Candlewood Ct.
Lynchburg, VA 24502-2653
Tel: (434)239-3500
Free: 800-664-1886
Fax: (434)986-1344
Web Site: http://www.ncbt.edu/
Description: Proprietary, 2-year, coed. Part of National College of Business and Technology. Awards diplomas and terminal associate degrees. Founded 1979. Setting: 2-acre small town campus. Total enrollment: 383. Students come from 15 other countries, 24% 25 or older. Core. Services for LD students, advanced placement, honors program, double major, summer session for credit, part-time degree program, internships.
Entrance Requirements: Open admission. Option: electronic application. Recommended: interview. Required for some: high school transcript. Entrance: noncompetitive. Application deadline: Rolling.
Costs Per Year: Application fee: $30. Tuition: $6408 full-time, $178 per credit hour part-time. Mandatory fees: $75 full-time, $15 per term part-time. Full-time tuition and fees vary according to course load. Part-time tuition and fees vary according to course load.
Collegiate Environment: Orientation program. College housing not available. 10 serials. 35 computers available on campus for general student use. A campuswide network can be accessed. Staffed computer lab on campus.

■ NATIONAL COLLEGE OF BUSINESS & TECHNOLOGY (MARTINSVILLE) *K-6*

10 Church St., PO Box 232
Martinsville, VA 24114
Tel: (276)632-5621
Free: 800-664-1866
Fax: (276)986-1344
Web Site: http://www.ncbt.edu/

Description: Proprietary, 2-year, coed. Part of National College of Business and Technology. Awards diplomas and terminal associate degrees. Founded 1975. Setting: small town campus. Total enrollment: 383. Core. Services for LD students, advanced placement, honors program, double major, summer session for credit, part-time degree program, internships.

Entrance Requirements: Open admission. Option: electronic application. Recommended: interview. Required for some: high school transcript. Entrance: noncompetitive. Application deadline: Rolling.

Costs Per Year: Application fee: $30. Tuition: $6408 full-time, $178 per credit hour part-time. Mandatory fees: $75 full-time, $15 per term part-time.

Collegiate Environment: Orientation program. College housing not available. 35 computers available on campus for general student use. A campuswide network can be accessed. Staffed computer lab on campus.

■ NATIONAL COLLEGE OF BUSINESS & TECHNOLOGY (SALEM) *I-5*

1813 East Main St.
Salem, VA 24153
Tel: (540)986-1800
Free: 800-664-1886
Fax: (540)986-1344
Web Site: http://www.ncbt.edu/

Description: Proprietary, primarily 2-year, coed. Part of National College of Business and Technology. Awards certificates, diplomas, transfer associate, terminal associate, bachelor's, and master's degrees. Founded 1886. Setting: 3-acre urban campus. Total enrollment: 756. 346 applied, 100% were admitted. Students come from 15 other countries, 24% from out-of-state. Retention: 70% of full-time freshmen returned the following year. Core. Academic remediation for entering students, advanced placement, double major, summer session for credit, part-time degree program, internships.

Entrance Requirements: Open admission. Option: Peterson's Universal Application. Required: high school transcript. Recommended: interview. Entrance: noncompetitive. Application deadline: Rolling. Notification: continuous.

Costs Per Year: Application fee: $30. Tuition: $6408 full-time, $178 per credit hour part-time. Mandatory fees: $75 full-time, $15 per term part-time.

Collegiate Environment: Orientation program. College housing not available. Main library plus 1 other with 25,867 books and 40 serials. 35 computers available on campus for general student use. A campuswide network can be accessed. Staffed computer lab on campus.

■ NEW RIVER COMMUNITY COLLEGE *I-4*

PO Box 1127
Dublin, VA 24084-1127
Tel: (540)674-3600
Fax: (540)674-3644
Web Site: http://www.nr.cc.va.us/

Description: State-supported, 2-year, coed. Part of Virginia Community College System. Awards certificates, diplomas, transfer associate, and terminal associate degrees. Founded 1969. Setting: 100-acre rural campus. Endowment: $1.9 million. Total enrollment: 4,345. Full-time: 2,008 students, 49% women, 51% men. Part-time: 2,337 students, 56% women, 44% men. Students come from 22 states and territories, 21 other countries, 3% from out-of-state, 0.2% Native American, 1% Hispanic, 5% black, 1% Asian American or Pacific Islander, 0% international, 40% 25 or older, 5% transferred in. Calendar: semesters. Academic remediation for entering students, services for LD students, advanced placement, distance learning, double major, summer session for credit, part-time degree program, external degree program, adult/continuing education programs, co-op programs and internships.

Entrance Requirements: Open admission. Options: early admission, deferred admission. Required for some: high school transcript. Entrance: noncompetitive. Application deadline: Rolling. Notification: continuous. Preference given to local residents.

Collegiate Environment: Most popular organizations: Student Government Association, Phi Beta Lambda, Instrument Society of America, Human

Service Organization, Sign Language Club. Major annual events: Fall Bash, Freaky Friday, Spring Fling. Student services: personal-psychological counseling. Campus security: 24-hour patrols. College housing not available. New River Community College Library with 33,993 books, 258 serials, and an OPAC. Operations spending for 2004 fiscal year: $551,572. 120 computers available on campus for general student use. A campuswide network can be accessed. Staffed computer lab on campus.

■ NORFOLK STATE UNIVERSITY *J-15*

700 Park Ave.
Norfolk, VA 23504
Tel: (757)823-8600
Admissions: (757)823-8396
Fax: (757)823-9435
Web Site: http://www.nsu.edu/

Description: State-supported, comprehensive, coed. Part of State Council of Higher Education for Virginia. Awards associate, bachelor's, master's, and doctoral degrees. Founded 1935. Setting: 134-acre urban campus. Endowment: $4.8 million. Research spending for 2004 fiscal year: $5.4 million. Educational spending for 2005 fiscal year: $5082 per student. Total enrollment: 6,096. Faculty: 386 (280 full-time, 106 part-time). Student-undergrad faculty ratio is 21:1. 4,696 applied, 71% were admitted. 5% from top 10% of their high school class, 20% from top quarter, 56% from top half. Full-time: 4,420 students, 61% women, 39% men. Part-time: 917 students, 66% women, 34% men. Students come from 43 states and territories, 38 other countries, 27% from out-of-state, 0.3% Native American, 2% Hispanic, 89% black, 1% Asian American or Pacific Islander, 1% international, 23% 25 or older, 32% live on campus, 8% transferred in. Retention: 65% of full-time freshmen returned the following year. Academic areas with the most degrees conferred: interdisciplinary studies; business/marketing; social sciences. Core. Calendar: semesters. Services for LD students, advanced placement, accelerated degree program, self-designed majors, freshman honors college, honors program, independent study, distance learning, double major, summer session for credit, part-time degree program, adult/continuing education programs, co-op programs and internships, graduate courses open to undergrads. Off campus study at Old Dominion University, Virginia Wesleyan College, Christopher Newport University, Tidewater Community College, Paul D. Camp Community College, Eastern Shore Community College, Thomas Nelson Community College. Study abroad program. ROTC: Army, Naval.

Entrance Requirements: Options: Peterson's Universal Application, electronic application, deferred admission. Required: high school transcript, minimum 2.3 high school GPA, 2 recommendations, minimum SAT score of 800 or ACT score of 17, SAT or ACT. Entrance: moderately difficult. Application deadline: 5/31.

Costs Per Year: Application fee: $25. State resident tuition: $4670 full-time, $204 per credit hour part-time. Nonresident tuition: $14,480 full-time, $531 per credit hour part-time. Mandatory fees: $125 per credit hour part-time. College room and board: $6474. College room only: $4110.

Collegiate Environment: Orientation program. Drama-theater group, choral group, marching band, student-run newspaper, radio station. Social organizations: 112 open to all; national fraternities, national sororities, local fraternities, local sororities; 30% of eligible men and 30% of eligible women are members. Most popular organizations: Alpha Kappa Alpha, Alpha Phi Alpha, Kappa Alpha Psi, Omega Phi Psi, Sigma Gamma Rho. Major annual events: Martin Luther King Commemorative Activity, Black History Month activities, Homecoming events. Student services: health clinic, personal-psychological counseling. Campus security: 24-hour emergency response devices and patrols, late night transport-escort service, controlled dormitory access, campus call boxes. 1,944 college housing spaces available; 1,893 were occupied in 2003-04. Freshmen given priority for college housing. Options: men-only, women-only housing available. Lymon Beecher Brooks Library with 378,323 books, 18,919 microform titles, 124,460 serials, an OPAC, and a Web page. Operations spending for 2004 fiscal year: $1.8 million. 512 computers available on campus for general student use. Computer purchase/lease plans available. A campuswide network can be accessed. Staffed computer lab on campus.

Community Environment: See Old Dominion University.

■ NORTHERN VIRGINIA COMMUNITY COLLEGE *P-6*

4001 Wakefield Chapel Rd.
Annandale, VA 22003-3796
Tel: (703)323-3000
Admissions: (703)323-3195

Web Site: http://www.nv.cc.va.us/

Description: State-supported, 2-year, coed. Part of Virginia Community College System. Awards certificates, transfer associate, and terminal associate degrees. Founded 1965. Setting: 435-acre suburban campus with easy access to Washington, DC. Endowment: $1.1 million. Educational spending for 2005 fiscal year: $2301 per student. Total enrollment: 39,353. 2% from out-of-state, 2% Native American, 10% Hispanic, 15% black, 12% Asian American or Pacific Islander, 4% international, 57% 25 or older. Core. Calendar: semesters. Academic remediation for entering students, ESL program, services for LD students, advanced placement, honors program, distance learning, double major, summer session for credit, part-time degree program, external degree program, adult/continuing education programs, co-op programs. Study abroad program.

Entrance Requirements: Open admission except for veterinary technology, dental hygiene, other health-related programs. Options: Common Application, early admission, deferred admission. Required for some: high school transcript. Entrance: noncompetitive. Application deadline: Rolling. Notification: continuous.

Collegiate Environment: Student-run newspaper. Social organizations: 65 open to all. Campus security: 24-hour emergency response devices, campus police. College housing not available. 228,009 books, 132,449 microform titles, 1,949 serials, 12,227 audiovisual materials, an OPAC, and a Web page. Operations spending for 2004 fiscal year: $3.3 million. 2,000 computers available on campus for general student use. A campuswide network can be accessed. Staffed computer lab on campus.

Community Environment: Northern Virginia Community College is a five campus college located in the suburban communities of Northern Virginia, just outside Washington, D.C. The Northern Virginia region is rapidly growing, provides excellent job opportunities and has high quality public schools and community services. Part-time job opportunities are excellent for students and graduates of the occupational and technical programs and career placements attractive. Students seeking transfer to a university to earn a Bachelor's degree can enroll in appropriate programs that parallel most university programs.

■ **OLD DOMINION UNIVERSITY** *J-15*

5215 Hampton Blvd.
Norfolk, VA 23529
Tel: (757)683-3000
Free: 800-348-7926
Admissions: (757)683-3648
Fax: (757)683-5357
E-mail: amcadory@odu.edu
Web Site: http://www.odu.edu/

Description: State-supported, university, coed. Awards bachelor's, master's, and doctoral degrees and post-master's certificates. Founded 1930. Setting: 188-acre urban campus with easy access to Virginia Beach. Endowment: $138.9 million. Research spending for 2004 fiscal year: $34.1 million. Educational spending for 2005 fiscal year: $5996 per student. Total enrollment: 21,274. Faculty: 900 (617 full-time, 283 part-time). Student-undergrad faculty ratio is 17:1. 7,067 applied, 69% were admitted. 15% from top 10% of their high school class, 44% from top quarter, 88% from top half. 20 valedictorians. Full-time: 10,828 students, 58% women, 42% men. Part-time: 4,447 students, 60% women, 40% men. Students come from 37 states and territories, 79 other countries, 8% from out-of-state, 1% Native American, 3% Hispanic, 23% black, 6% Asian American or Pacific Islander, 2% international, 29% 25 or older, 24% live on campus, 10% transferred in. Retention: 77% of full-time freshmen returned the following year. Academic areas with the most degrees conferred: business/marketing; health professions and related sciences; English. Core. Calendar: semesters. ESL program, services for LD students, advanced placement, accelerated degree program, self-designed majors, freshman honors college, honors program, independent study, distance learning, double major, summer session for credit, part-time degree program, adult/continuing education programs, co-op programs and internships, graduate courses open to undergrads. Off campus study at 6 members of the Virginia Tidewater Consortium for Continuing Higher Education, Academic Common Market. Study abroad program. ROTC: Army, Naval.

Entrance Requirements: Options: Peterson's Universal Application, Common Application, electronic application, early admission, early action, deferred admission, international baccalaureate accepted. Required: essay, high school transcript, minimum 2.7 high school GPA, 1 recommendation, SAT or ACT. Required for some: interview. Application deadlines: 3/15, 12/15 for early action. Notification: continuous, 1/15 for early action.

Costs Per Year: Application fee: $40. State resident tuition: $5430 full-time, $181 per credit hour part-time. Nonresident tuition: $15,394 full-time, $507 per credit hour part-time. Mandatory fees: $181 full-time, $39 per term part-time. College room and board: $6292. College room only: $3442.

Collegiate Environment: Orientation program. Drama-theater group, choral group, student-run newspaper, radio station. Social organizations: 220 open to all; national fraternities, national sororities; 4% of eligible men and 3% of eligible women are members. Most popular organizations: Black Student Alliance, Council of International Student Organizations, Student Activities Council, Filipino-American Student Association. Major annual events: Mainstreet, Homecoming, Monarch Spring Fest. Student services: health clinic, personal-psychological counseling, women's center, career, veteran's, and financial aid counseling, campus ministries. Campus security: 24-hour emergency response devices and patrols, late night transport-escort service, controlled dormitory access. College housing designed to accommodate 2,380 students; 3,167 undergraduates lived in college housing during 2003-04. No special consideration for freshman housing applicants. Option: coed housing available. Douglas and Patricia Perry Library plus 3 others with 985,801 books, 1.8 million microform titles, 10,579 serials, 40,628 audiovisual materials, an OPAC, and a Web page. Operations spending for 2004 fiscal year: $6 million. 800 computers available on campus for general student use. A campuswide network can be accessed from student residence rooms and from off campus. Staffed computer lab on campus.

Community Environment: See Virginia Wesleyan College.

■ **PARKS COLLEGE** *D-13*

801 North Quincy St., Ste. 501
Arlington, VA 22203
Tel: (703)248-8887
Fax: (703)351-2202
E-mail: lgreen@cci.edu
Web Site: http://www.parks-college.com/

Description: Proprietary, 2-year, coed. Awards certificates and terminal associate degrees. Founded 2001. Setting: urban campus. 0% Native American, 7% Hispanic, 75% black, 2% Asian American or Pacific Islander, 0% international.

■ **PATRICK HENRY COLLEGE** *C-11*

One Patrick Henry Circle
Purcellville, VA 20132
Tel: (540)338-1776
Fax: (540)338-8707
E-mail: admissions@phc.edu
Web Site: http://www.phc.edu/

Description: Independent nondenominational, 4-year, coed. Awards bachelor's degrees. Founded 1999. Setting: 106-acre small town campus with easy access to Washington, DC. Total enrollment: 348. Student-undergrad faculty ratio is 16:1. 3 National Merit Scholars, 1 valedictorian. Full-time: 325 students, 50% women, 50% men. Part-time: 23 students, 57% women, 43% men. Students come from 43 states and territories, 88% from out-of-state, 0% Native American, 4% Hispanic, 0% black, 3% Asian American or Pacific Islander, 0% international, 2% 25 or older, 94% live on campus, 0.3% transferred in. Retention: 85% of full-time freshmen returned the following year. Calendar: semesters.

Entrance Requirements: Required: essay, high school transcript, 2 recommendations, interview, SAT or ACT. Entrance: very difficult. Application deadline: 4/1. Notification: 5/1.

Costs Per Year: Comprehensive fee: $21,730 includes full-time tuition ($16,000) and college room and board ($5730).

Collegiate Environment: Drama-theater group, choral group, student-run newspaper. Social organizations: 13 open to all. Most popular organizations: student government, intramural athletics, debate, intercollegiate soccer, drama troupe. Major annual events: Town Hall, drama presentations, Serve America. Student services: personal-psychological counseling. Campus security: 24-hour emergency response devices, student patrols, late night transport-escort service, controlled dormitory access, after hours patrols by trained security personnel. 312 college housing spaces available; 230 were occupied in 2003-04. Freshmen guaranteed college housing. On-campus residence required through senior year. Options: men-only, women-only housing available.

■ **PATRICK HENRY COMMUNITY COLLEGE** *K-6*

PO Box 5311
Martinsville, VA 24115-5311

Tel: (276)638-8777
Admissions: (276)656-0315
Fax: (276)656-0247
Web Site: http://www.ph.vccs.edu/
Description: State-supported, 2-year, coed. Part of Virginia Community College System. Awards transfer associate and terminal associate degrees. Founded 1962. Setting: 137-acre rural campus. Educational spending for 2005 fiscal year: $2723 per student. Total enrollment: 3,456. Students come from 3 states and territories, 58% 25 or older. Retention: 48% of full-time freshmen returned the following year. Calendar: semesters. Academic remediation for entering students, ESL program, services for LD students, advanced placement, summer session for credit, part-time degree program, adult/continuing education programs, co-op programs and internships.
Entrance Requirements: Open admission except for nursing program. Options: early admission, deferred admission. Required: high school transcript. Placement: ACT ASSET required. Entrance: noncompetitive. Application deadline: Rolling. Notification: continuous. Preference given to district residents.
Costs Per Year: Application fee: $0. State resident tuition: $1632 full-time, $68 per credit hour part-time. Nonresident tuition: $5136 full-time, $214 per credit hour part-time. Mandatory fees: $81 full-time, $3.15 per credit hour part-time, $5 per term part-time.
Collegiate Environment: Orientation program. Drama-theater group. Most popular organizations: Student Government Association, Student Support Services, Phi Theta Kappa, Gospel Choir, Black Student Association. Major annual events: Fall Festival, Spring Play Day, Awards Banquet. Campus security: 24-hour emergency response devices and patrols, late night transport-escort service. College housing not available. Lester Library with 26,160 books, 259 serials, an OPAC, and a Web page. Operations spending for 2004 fiscal year: $84,738. 505 computers available on campus for general student use. A campuswide network can be accessed from off-campus. Staffed computer lab on campus.
Community Environment: Martinsville is an important textile and furniture market as well as an industrial city with a wide range of products. It provides all forms of commercial transportation. Job opportunities are excellent and shopping is good. Philpott Reservoir, about 19 miles northwest of Martinsville, is a popular spot for fishing, boating, water skiing, and swimming. Other facilities within the city provide for swimming, baseball, and football.

■ **PAUL D. CAMP COMMUNITY COLLEGE** *K-13*
PO Box 737, 100 North College Dr.
Franklin, VA 23851-0737
Tel: (757)569-6700
Admissions: (757)569-6725
E-mail: vccscent@pc.vccs.edu
Web Site: http://www.pc.vccs.edu/
Description: State-supported, 2-year, coed. Part of Virginia Community College System. Awards certificates, transfer associate, and terminal associate degrees. Founded 1971. Setting: 99-acre small town campus. Endowment: $16,121. Total enrollment: 1,636. 410 applied, 100% were admitted. 5% from top 10% of their high school class, 20% from top quarter, 45% from top half. Full-time: 391 students, 68% women, 32% men. Part-time: 1,245 students, 65% women, 35% men. Students come from 2 states and territories, 2 other countries, 1% from out-of-state, 1% Native American, 1% Hispanic, 41% black, 1% Asian American or Pacific Islander, 0.1% international, 55% 25 or older, 3% transferred in. Core. Calendar: semesters. Academic remediation for entering students, advanced placement, honors program, independent study, distance learning, summer session for credit, part-time degree program, adult/continuing education programs, co-op programs and internships. Off campus study at members of the Virginia Consortium for Continuing Higher Education.
Entrance Requirements: Open admission. Option: deferred admission. Required: high school transcript. Placement: ACT COMPASS required. Entrance: noncompetitive. Application deadline: Rolling. Notification: continuous. Preference given to state residents.
Collegiate Environment: Student-run newspaper. Most popular organizations: African-American History Club, Phi Beta Lambda, Phi Theta Kappa, Student Government Association. Major annual events: Fall Festival, Christmas Parade, Spring Fling. Campus security: security staff until 7 p.m. College housing not available. Paul D. Camp Community College Library with 22,000 books, 200 serials, and an OPAC. Operations spending for 2004 fiscal year: $258,883. 90 computers available on campus for general student use. A campuswide network can be accessed. Staffed computer lab on campus.

Community Environment: Franklin is in a rural setting with a population of 96,000 in the area.

■ **PIEDMONT VIRGINIA COMMUNITY COLLEGE** *F-9*
501 College Dr.
Charlottesville, VA 22902-7589
Tel: (434)977-3900
Admissions: (434)961-5400
Fax: (434)971-8232
Web Site: http://www.pvcc.edu/
Description: State-supported, 2-year, coed. Part of Virginia Community College System. Awards certificates, transfer associate, and terminal associate degrees. Founded 1972. Setting: 114-acre suburban campus with easy access to Richmond. Educational spending for 2005 fiscal year: $2990 per student. Total enrollment: 4,163. Student-undergrad faculty ratio is 20:1. Full-time: 1,079 students, 51% women, 49% men. Part-time: 3,084 students, 62% women, 38% men. Students come from 12 states and territories, 1% from out-of-state, 0.3% Native American, 2% Hispanic, 13% black, 3% Asian American or Pacific Islander, 0.4% international, 44% 25 or older, 48% transferred in. Core. Calendar: semesters. Academic remediation for entering students, ESL program, services for LD students, advanced placement, honors program, independent study, distance learning, summer session for credit, part-time degree program, adult/continuing education programs, co-op programs and internships. ROTC: Army (c).
Entrance Requirements: Open admission except for nursing program. Options: Common Application, electronic application, early admission. Required for some: high school transcript, for nursing program: completion of any developmental studies; grade 'C' or better in high school or college developmental chemistry course; high school diploma/GED; and completion of nursing program application.. Entrance: noncompetitive. Application deadline: Rolling. Notification: continuous.
Costs Per Year: Application fee: $0. State resident tuition: $2175 full-time, $72.50 per credit hour part-time. Nonresident tuition: $7126 full-time, $237.55 per credit hour part-time. Mandatory fees: $159 full-time, $5.30 per credit hour part-time.
Collegiate Environment: Orientation program. Drama-theater group, choral group, student-run newspaper. Social organizations: 10 open to all. Most popular organizations: Phi Theta Kappa, Black Student Alliance, Science Club, Masquers, Christian Fellowship Club. Major annual events: plays and concerts, fall/spring picnics. Campus security: 24-hour patrols. College housing not available. Jessup Library with 72,574 books, 25,713 microform titles, 209 serials, 10,254 audiovisual materials, an OPAC, and a Web page. Operations spending for 2004 fiscal year: $251,877. 60 computers available on campus for general student use. A campuswide network can be accessed from off-campus. Staffed computer lab on campus.
Community Environment: Charlottesville is situated in the foothills of the Blue Ridge Mountains. The area has many old homes and estates. Albemarle County is renown for its horses, dogs and fruit orchards. Outdoor activities available include: golf, tennis, hunting, fishing and hiking. Points of interest are the Lewis and Clark Memorial, Monticello, and the University of Virginia. Commercial transportation and part-time employment are available.

■ **RADFORD UNIVERSITY** *I-4*
PO Box 6890, RU Station
Radford, VA 24142
Tel: (540)831-5000
Free: 800-890-4265
Admissions: (540)831-5371
Fax: (540)831-5138
E-mail: dwkraus@radford.edu
Web Site: http://www.radford.edu/
Description: State-supported, comprehensive, coed. Awards bachelor's and master's degrees and post-master's certificates. Founded 1910. Setting: 177-acre small town campus. Endowment: $41.7 million. Research spending for 2004 fiscal year: $220,767. Educational spending for 2005 fiscal year: $5501 per student. Total enrollment: 9,552. Faculty: 570 (377 full-time, 193 part-time). Student-undergrad faculty ratio is 20:1. 5,792 applied, 81% were admitted. 4% from top 10% of their high school class, 22% from top quarter, 69% from top half. Full-time: 8,028 students, 58% women, 42% men. Part-time: 454 students, 61% women, 39% men. Students come from 39 states and territories, 43 other countries, 8% from out-of-state, 0.3% Native American, 3% Hispanic, 6% black, 2% Asian American or Pacific Islander, 1% international, 6% 25 or older, 39% live on campus, 9% transferred in. Retention: 79% of full-time freshmen returned the following year. Academic

areas with the most degrees conferred: business/marketing; interdisciplinary studies; security and protective services. Core. Calendar: semesters. ESL program, services for LD students, advanced placement, accelerated degree program, self-designed majors, honors program, independent study, distance learning, double major, summer session for credit, part-time degree program, adult/continuing education programs, internships, graduate courses open to undergrads. Off campus study at Virginia Western Community College, Southwest Virginia Higher Education Center, Roanoke Higher Education Center. Study abroad program. ROTC: Army, Naval (c).

Entrance Requirements: Options: Common Application, electronic application, international baccalaureate accepted. Required: SAT or ACT. Recommended: essay. Required for some: high school transcript. Entrance: moderately difficult. Application deadlines: 2/1, 12/15 for early action. Notification: 3/20, 1/9 for early action.

Costs Per Year: Application fee: $35. State resident tuition: $3235 full-time, $214 per credit hour part-time. Nonresident tuition: $10,473 full-time, $515 per credit hour part-time. Mandatory fees: $1895 full-time, $78.90 per credit hour part-time. College room and board: $6120. College room only: $3300. Room and board charges vary according to board plan and housing facility.

Collegiate Environment: Orientation program. Drama-theater group, choral group, student-run newspaper, radio station. Social organizations: 159 open to all; national fraternities, national sororities; 6% of eligible men and 8% of eligible women are members. Most popular organizations: Student Government Association, Student Education Association, International Club, Ski Club, Student Life Committee. Major annual events: Club Fair, Family Weekend, Highlander Homecoming. Student services: health clinic, personal-psychological counseling. Campus security: 24-hour emergency response devices and patrols, student patrols, late night transport-escort service, controlled dormitory access. 3,360 college housing spaces available; 3,081 were occupied in 2003-04. On-campus residence required in freshman year. Option: coed housing available. McConnell Library plus 1 other with 395,643 books, 1.5 million microform titles, 4,162 serials, 15,656 audiovisual materials, an OPAC, and a Web page. Operations spending for 2004 fiscal year: $2.9 million. 500 computers available on campus for general student use. A campuswide network can be accessed from student residence rooms and from off campus. Staffed computer lab on campus.

Community Environment: Located on the banks of the scenic New River in the foothills of the beautiful Blue Ridge Mountains, the city of Radford, Virginia (population 16,000), is 45 miles southwest of Roanoke. First settled in 1756, the city features a number of churches, a public library, hospital, and many civic and service organizations. The city is clean and the weather is moderate. Outdoor sports enthusiasts can enjoy nearby Claytor Lake, the New River, the Appalachian Trail and many other streams, lakes and trails in close proximity.

■ **RANDOLPH-MACON COLLEGE** *G-12*
PO Box 5005
Ashland, VA 23005-5505
Tel: (804)752-7200
Free: 800-888-1762
Admissions: (804)752-7305
Fax: (804)752-4707
E-mail: admissions@rmc.edu
Web Site: http://www.rmc.edu/

Description: Independent United Methodist, 4-year, coed. Awards bachelor's degrees. Founded 1830. Setting: 110-acre suburban campus with easy access to Richmond. Endowment: $102.3 million. Research spending for 2004 fiscal year: $245,333. Educational spending for 2005 fiscal year: $9291 per student. Total enrollment: 1,125. Student-undergrad faculty ratio is 10:1. 1,727 applied, 79% were admitted. 20% from top 10% of their high school class, 43% from top quarter, 82% from top half. 7 class presidents, 1 valedictorian, 57 student government officers. Full-time: 1,102 students, 51% women, 49% men. Part-time: 23 students, 61% women, 39% men. Students come from 30 states and territories, 17 other countries, 32% from out-of-state, 0.5% Native American, 1% Hispanic, 7% black, 1% Asian American or Pacific Islander, 1% international, 0% 25 or older, 84% live on campus, 2% transferred in. Retention: 76% of full-time freshmen returned the following year. Academic areas with the most degrees conferred: social sciences; business/marketing; psychology. Core. Calendar: 4-1-4. Academic remediation for entering students, services for LD students, advanced placement, accelerated degree program, honors program, independent study, double major, summer session for credit, part-time degree program, internships. Off campus study at members of the Seven-College Exchange Program. Study abroad program. ROTC: Army (c).

Entrance Requirements: Options: Peterson's Universal Application, Common Application, electronic application, early decision, deferred admission, international baccalaureate accepted. Required: essay, high school transcript, minimum 2.0 high school GPA, 1 recommendation, SAT or ACT. Recommended: interview, SAT Subject Tests. Placement: SAT Subject Tests recommended. Entrance: moderately difficult. Application deadlines: 3/1, 11/15 for early decision, 12/1 for early action. Notification: 4/1, 12/1 for early decision, 1/1 for early action.

Costs Per Year: Application fee: $30. Comprehensive fee: $31,250 includes full-time tuition ($23,310), mandatory fees ($635), and college room and board ($7305). College room only: $4000. Room and board charges vary according to board plan and housing facility. Part-time tuition: $863 per credit hour.

Collegiate Environment: Orientation program. Drama-theater group, choral group, student-run newspaper, radio station. Social organizations: 76 open to all; national fraternities, national sororities; 33% of eligible men and 33% of eligible women are members. Most popular organizations: Macon Outdoors Club, Campus Activities Board/Student Government Association, Drama Guild, intramural sports, Student Honors Association. Major annual events: Dance Marathon, football game against Hampden-Sydney College, Springfest. Student services: health clinic, personal-psychological counseling, women's center. Campus security: 24-hour emergency response devices and patrols, late night transport-escort service, controlled dormitory access. 950 college housing spaces available; all were occupied in 2003-04. Freshmen guaranteed college housing. On-campus residence required through junior year. Options: coed, men-only, women-only housing available. McGraw-Page Library with 182,368 books, 209,300 microform titles, 1,455 serials, 5,116 audiovisual materials, an OPAC, and a Web page. Operations spending for 2004 fiscal year: $733,347. 350 computers available on campus for general student use. Computer purchase/lease plans available. A campuswide network can be accessed from student residence rooms and from off campus. Staffed computer lab on campus.

Community Environment: Ashland is a suburban area 15 miles from Richmond, and 90 miles south of Washington DC. Community facilities include a public library, six churches, 2 medical centers, and a number of civic and service organizations.

■ **RANDOLPH-MACON WOMAN'S COLLEGE** *I-8*
2500 Rivermont Ave.
Lynchburg, VA 24503-1526
Tel: (434)947-8000
Free: 800-745-7692
Admissions: (434)947-8100
Fax: (434)947-8996
E-mail: admissions@rmwc.edu
Web Site: http://www.rmwc.edu/

Description: Independent Methodist, 4-year, women only. Awards bachelor's degrees. Founded 1891. Setting: 100-acre suburban campus. Endowment: $133.4 million. Educational spending for 2005 fiscal year: $12,867 per student. Total enrollment: 712. Student-undergrad faculty ratio is 9:1. 774 applied, 87% were admitted. 36% from top 10% of their high school class, 70% from top quarter, 93% from top half. 2 National Merit Scholars, 3 class presidents, 10 valedictorians, 40 student government officers. Full-time: 685 students. Part-time: 27 students. Students come from 46 states and territories, 39 other countries, 61% from out-of-state, 1% Native American, 4% Hispanic, 9% black, 3% Asian American or Pacific Islander, 10% international, 8% 25 or older, 89% live on campus, 4% transferred in. Retention: 78% of full-time freshmen returned the following year. Academic areas with the most degrees conferred: social sciences; biological/life sciences; visual and performing arts. Core. Calendar: semesters. Services for LD students, advanced placement, accelerated degree program, self-designed majors, honors program, independent study, double major, part-time degree program, adult/continuing education programs, internships. Off campus study at members of the Tri-College Consortium, Seven-College Exchange Program, American University Washington Semester Programs, Woods Hole, Marine Biological Laboratory Consortium. Study abroad program.

Entrance Requirements: Options: Peterson's Universal Application, Common Application, electronic application, early admission, early decision, deferred admission, international baccalaureate accepted. Required: essay, high school transcript, 2 recommendations, SAT or ACT. Recommended: interview. Entrance: moderately difficult. Application deadlines: 3/1, 11/15 for early decision. Notification: 10/1, 12/15 for early decision.

Costs Per Year: Application fee: $35. Comprehensive fee: $31,540 includes full-time tuition ($22,550), mandatory fees ($380), and college room and

board ($8610). Part-time tuition: $940 per semester hour. Part-time mandatory fees: $45 per term. Part-time tuition and fees vary according to course load.

Collegiate Environment: Orientation program. Drama-theater group, choral group, student-run newspaper, radio station. Social organizations: 41 open to all. Most popular organizations: Pan World Club, Macon Activities Council, Model United Nations, BIONIC (Believe It or Not, I Care volunteer organization), Black Woman's Alliance. Major annual events: Tacky Party/Never Ending Weekend, Pumpkin Parade, Ring Night. Student services: health clinic, personal-psychological counseling. Campus security: 24-hour emergency response devices and patrols, late night transport-escort service. 700 college housing spaces available; 633 were occupied in 2003-04. Freshmen guaranteed college housing. On-campus residence required through senior year. Option: women-only housing available. Lipscomb Library with 197,332 books, 187,000 microform titles, 618 serials, 3,600 audiovisual materials, an OPAC, and a Web page. Operations spending for 2004 fiscal year: $692,589. 154 computers available on campus for general student use. Computer purchase/lease plans available. A campuswide network can be accessed from student residence rooms and from off campus. Staffed computer lab on campus.

■ RAPPAHANNOCK COMMUNITY COLLEGE

12745 College Dr.
Glenns, VA 23149-2616
Tel: (804)758-6700
Admissions: (804)758-6742
Fax: (804)758-3852
Web Site: http://www.rcc.vccs.edu/

Description: State-related, 2-year, coed. Part of Virginia Community College System. Awards certificates, diplomas, transfer associate, and terminal associate degrees. Founded 1970. Setting: 217-acre rural campus. Total enrollment: 2,824. Students come from 1 other country, 0.5% Native American, 1% Hispanic, 18% black, 1% Asian American or Pacific Islander, 0% international, 36% 25 or older. Calendar: semesters. Academic remediation for entering students, distance learning, summer session for credit, part-time degree program, adult/continuing education programs, internships. Off campus study at J. Sargeant Reynolds Community College.

Entrance Requirements: Open admission. Option: early admission. Placement: CPT required. Entrance: noncompetitive. Application deadline: Rolling. Notification: continuous.

Collegiate Environment: Student-run newspaper. Social organizations: 21 open to all. Most popular organizations: Phi Theta Kappa, Culture Club, Poetry Club, student government. Student services: personal-psychological counseling, women's center. Campus security: 24-hour emergency response devices. College housing not available. The College Library with 46,000 books, 85 serials, and an OPAC. 195 computers available on campus for general student use.

Community Environment: Glenns is centrally located in the Rappahannock River Tidewaters serving a 13-county region.

■ REGENT UNIVERSITY *J-15*

1000 Regent University Dr.
Virginia Beach, VA 23464-9800
Tel: (757)226-4000
Free: 800-373-5504
Admissions: (757)226-4826
E-mail: jerrfis@regent.edu
Web Site: http://www.regent.edu/

Description: Independent, comprehensive, coed. Awards bachelor's, master's, doctoral, and first professional degrees and post-master's certificates. Founded 1977. Endowment: $267.6 million. Total enrollment: 3,919. Faculty: 99 (10 full-time, 89 part-time). Student-undergrad faculty ratio is 20:1. 1,416 applied. Full-time: 490 students, 69% women, 31% men. Part-time: 444 students, 66% women, 34% men. 45% from out-of-state, 1% Native American, 3% Hispanic, 25% black, 2% Asian American or Pacific Islander, 1% international. Calendar: trimesters.

Entrance Requirements: Required: essay. Required for some: high school transcript, minimum 3.0 high school GPA, SAT, ACT. Entrance: minimally difficult.

Costs Per Year: Application fee: $40. Tuition: $11,850 full-time, $375 per credit hour part-time.

Collegiate Environment: Student services: personal-psychological counseling. 49 college housing spaces available; 10 were occupied in 2003-04.

■ RICHARD BLAND COLLEGE OF THE COLLEGE OF WILLIAM AND MARY *I-12*

11301 Johnson Rd.
Petersburg, VA 23805-7100
Tel: (804)862-6100
Admissions: (804)862-6225
Fax: (804)862-6189
E-mail: admit@rbc.edu
Web Site: http://www.rbc.edu/

Description: State-supported, 2-year, coed. Part of College of William and Mary. Awards transfer associate degrees. Founded 1961. Setting: 712-acre rural campus with easy access to Richmond. Total enrollment: 1,437. Student-undergrad faculty ratio is 23:1. 528 applied, 88% were admitted. 6% from top 10% of their high school class, 27% from top quarter, 63% from top half. Full-time: 814 students, 62% women, 38% men. Part-time: 623 students, 72% women, 28% men. Students come from 8 states and territories, 1% from out-of-state, 0.5% Native American, 2% Hispanic, 19% black, 2% Asian American or Pacific Islander, 0% international, 18% 25 or older, 7% transferred in. Retention: 61% of full-time freshmen returned the following year. Core. Calendar: semesters. Academic-remediation for entering students, services for LD students, advanced placement, accelerated degree program, summer session for credit, part-time degree program. ROTC: Army (c).

Entrance Requirements: Option: Peterson's Universal Application. Required: essay, high school transcript, minimum 2.0 high school GPA, In-State Residency Form, ACT COMPASS. Recommended: SAT or ACT. Required for some: recommendations, interview. Entrance: noncompetitive. Application deadline: 8/15. Notification: continuous.

Costs Per Year: Application fee: $20. State resident tuition: $2350 full-time, $91 per credit hour part-time. Nonresident tuition: $9608 full-time, $398 per credit hour part-time. Mandatory fees: $170 full-time, $4 per credit hour part-time. Full-time tuition and fees vary according to course load and location. Part-time tuition and fees vary according to course load and location.

Collegiate Environment: Orientation program. Drama-theater group, choral group, student-run newspaper. Social organizations: 13 open to all; local fraternities. Most popular organizations: RBC Newspaper, Multicultural Alliance, student government, Spanish Club, Biology Club. Major annual events: Spring Fling, Fall Orientation, International Forum. Campus security: 24-hour patrols. College housing not available. Richard Bland College Library with 91,000 books, 33,000 microform titles, 9,000 serials, 2,400 audiovisual materials, an OPAC, and a Web page. Operations spending for 2004 fiscal year: $319,682. 128 computers available on campus for general student use. A campuswide network can be accessed from off-campus. Staffed computer lab on campus.

■ ROANOKE COLLEGE *I-5*

221 College Ln.
Salem, VA 24153-3794
Tel: (540)375-2500
Free: 800-388-2276
Admissions: (540)375-2270
Fax: (540)375-2267
E-mail: admissions@roanoke.edu
Web Site: http://www.roanoke.edu/

Description: Independent, 4-year, coed, affiliated with Evangelical Lutheran Church in America. Awards bachelor's degrees. Founded 1842. Setting: 68-acre suburban campus. Endowment: $102 million. Research spending for 2004 fiscal year: $279,847. Educational spending for 2005 fiscal year: $8785 per student. Total enrollment: 1,936. Student-undergrad faculty ratio is 14:1. 3,016 applied, 74% were admitted. 23% from top 10% of their high school class, 50% from top quarter, 85% from top half. 7 class presidents, 9 valedictorians, 75 student government officers. Full-time: 1,833 students, 56% women, 44% men. Part-time: 103 students, 51% women, 49% men. Students come from 40 states and territories, 25 other countries, 41% from out-of-state, 1% Native American, 2% Hispanic, 4% black, 2% Asian American or Pacific Islander, 1% international, 5% 25 or older, 60% live on campus, 4% transferred in. Retention: 85% of full-time freshmen returned the following year. Academic areas with the most degrees conferred: business/marketing; social sciences; English. Core. Calendar: semesters. ESL program, services for LD students, advanced placement, accelerated degree program, honors program, independent study, double major, summer session for credit, part-time degree program, adult/continuing education programs, internships. Off campus study at Hollins College. Study abroad program.

Entrance Requirements: Options: Peterson's Universal Application, Common Application, electronic application, early admission, early decision, early action, deferred admission, international baccalaureate accepted. Required: high school transcript, SAT or ACT. Recommended: essay, 3 recommendations, interview. Entrance: moderately difficult. Application deadline: 3/15. Notification: 4/1.

Costs Per Year: Application fee: $30. Comprehensive fee: $30,748 includes full-time tuition ($22,848), mandatory fees ($605), and college room and board ($7295). College room only: $3526. Room and board charges vary according to housing facility. Part-time tuition: $1084 per course.

Collegiate Environment: Orientation program. Drama-theater group, choral group, student-run newspaper, radio station. Social organizations: 84 open to all; national fraternities, national sororities, local fraternities, local sororities. Most popular organizations: Outdoor Adventures, Habitat for Humanity, Honors Association, Campus Activities Board, Inter-Varsity Christian Fellowship. Major annual events: Founders' Ball, Alumni Weekend, Winterfest. Student services: health clinic, personal-psychological counseling. Campus security: 24-hour emergency response devices and patrols, late night transport-escort service, controlled dormitory access. 1,150 college housing spaces available; 1,106 were occupied in 2003-04. Freshmen guaranteed college housing. Options: coed, men-only, women-only housing available. Fintel Library plus 1 other with 134,035 books, 307,716 microform titles, 719 serials, 7,635 audiovisual materials, an OPAC, and a Web page. Operations spending for 2004 fiscal year: $987,663. 170 computers available on campus for general student use. Computer purchase/lease plans available. A campuswide network can be accessed from student residence rooms and from off campus. Staffed computer lab on campus.

Community Environment: Salem is located in the heart of the Roanoke Valley between the Blue Ridge Mountains to the east, and the Allegheny Mountains to the west. Many national manufacturing companies contribute to the diversified industry of Salem. Plane and bus transportation are available. Part-time employment opportunities are excellent. The Dixie Caverns subterranean wonderland is seven miles away. State parks, the Blue Ridge Parkway & the Appalachian Trail provide outdoor activities, and facilities within the city provide for tennis, skating, and golf.

■ **SAINT PAUL'S COLLEGE** *K-11*
115 College Dr.
Lawrenceville, VA 23868-1202
Tel: (434)848-3111
Free: 800-678-7071
Admissions: (434)848-6493
Fax: (434)848-0403
E-mail: rlewis@saintpauls.edu
Web Site: http://www.saintpauls.edu/

Description: Independent Episcopal, 4-year, coed. Awards bachelor's degrees. Founded 1888. Setting: 75-acre small town campus with easy access to Richmond. Total enrollment: 531. 408 applied, 88% were admitted. Students come from 12 states and territories, 0% Native American, 0% Hispanic, 97% black, 0% Asian American or Pacific Islander, 0% international, 1% 25 or older. Retention: 57% of full-time freshmen returned the following year. Core. Calendar: semesters. Academic remediation for entering students, services for LD students, honors program, summer session for credit, part-time degree program, adult/continuing education programs, co-op programs and internships. ROTC: Army.

Entrance Requirements: Options: Common Application, deferred admission. Required: high school transcript, 1 recommendation. Recommended: essay, interview. Placement: SAT or ACT required. Entrance: minimally difficult. Notification: continuous until 8/15.

Collegiate Environment: Orientation program. Drama-theater group, choral group, student-run newspaper. Social organizations: 28 open to all; national fraternities, national sororities; 2% of eligible men and 2% of eligible women are members. Most popular organizations: Dance Troupe, Literary Society, College Choir, Drama Club. Major annual events: Homecoming, Founders' Day Celebration, MLK Celebration. Student services: health clinic, personal-psychological counseling. Campus security: 24-hour emergency response devices and patrols, late night transport-escort service, alarms on doors. On-campus residence required through senior year. Options: men-only, women-only housing available. 100,000 books and 275 serials. 34 computers available on campus for general student use. Staffed computer lab on campus.

■ **SHENANDOAH UNIVERSITY** *C-10*
1460 University Dr.
Winchester, VA 22601-5195

Tel: (540)665-4500
Free: 800-432-2266
Admissions: (540)665-4581
Fax: (540)665-4627
E-mail: admit@su.edu
Web Site: http://www.su.edu/

Description: Independent United Methodist, comprehensive, coed. Awards associate, bachelor's, master's, doctoral, and first professional degrees and post-master's certificates. Founded 1875. Setting: 100-acre small town campus with easy access to Baltimore and Washington, DC. Endowment: $44.2 million. Educational spending for 2005 fiscal year: $10,452 per student. Total enrollment: 2,998. Faculty: 351 (181 full-time, 170 part-time). Student-undergrad faculty ratio is 9:1. 1,479 applied, 70% were admitted. 15% from top 10% of their high school class, 37% from top quarter, 68% from top half. Full-time: 1,530 students, 60% women, 40% men. Part-time: 76 students, 62% women, 38% men. Students come from 33 states and territories, 25 other countries, 45% from out-of-state, 0.1% Native American, 0.4% Hispanic, 2% black, 1% Asian American or Pacific Islander, 4% international, 16% 25 or older, 44% live on campus, 14% transferred in. Retention: 75% of full-time freshmen returned the following year. Academic areas with the most degrees conferred: visual and performing arts; business/marketing; education. Core. Calendar: semesters. ESL program, services for LD students, advanced placement, accelerated degree program, self-designed majors, independent study, distance learning, double major, summer session for credit, part-time degree program, adult/continuing education programs, internships, graduate courses open to undergrads. Off campus study. Study abroad program.

Entrance Requirements: Options: Peterson's Universal Application, Common Application, electronic application, deferred admission, international baccalaureate accepted. Required: high school transcript, SAT or ACT. Recommended: minimum 2.4 high school GPA. Required for some: essay, interview, audition. Entrance: moderately difficult. Application deadline: Rolling.

Costs Per Year: Application fee: $30. Comprehensive fee: $27,600 includes full-time tuition ($19,900), mandatory fees ($150), and college room and board ($7550). Full-time tuition and fees vary according to course load and program. Room and board charges vary according to board plan. Part-time tuition: $610 per credit hour. Part-time tuition varies according to course load and program.

Collegiate Environment: Orientation program. Drama-theater group, choral group, student-run newspaper, radio station. Social organizations: 50 open to all; national fraternities, national sororities; 2% of eligible men and 1% of eligible women are members. Most popular organizations: Harambee Singers, Alpha Psi Omega, Phi Mu Alpha, Student Government Association, Inter-Varsity Student Council. Major annual events: homecoming, Spring Fling Weekend, Sun Block Party. Student services: health clinic, personal-psychological counseling. Campus security: 24-hour emergency response devices and patrols, late night transport-escort service, controlled dormitory access, side door alarms, guard gate house, bike patrols. 674 college housing spaces available; all were occupied in 2003-04. Freshmen guaranteed college housing. On-campus residence required through senior year. Option: coed housing available. Alson H. Smith Jr. Library plus 1 other with 126,097 books, 134,500 microform titles, 1,340 serials, 18,299 audiovisual materials, an OPAC, and a Web page. Operations spending for 2004 fiscal year: $1.1 million. 175 computers available on campus for general student use. Computer purchase/lease plans available. A campuswide network can be accessed from student residence rooms and from off campus. Staffed computer lab on campus.

Community Environment: Winchester/Frederick County, a community of approximately 70,000 persons, is located 72 miles from Washington, D.C. near the northern end of the historic Shenandoah Valley. Winchester was founded in 1732 and played an important part in the French and Indian War and the Civil War. Bus transportation is available. Community facilities include a public library, museums, churches of major denominations, a medical center, excellent shopping areas, and a number of various civic and service organizations. Winchester is the host to the Shenandoah Apple Blossom Festival. George Washington began his career in Winchester in 1748 as surveyor to Lord Fairfax. Some of the historical points of interest are Abram's Delight (the Hollingsworth Home), Sheridan's Headquarters, "Stonewall" Jackson's Headquarters, Glen Burnie (home of James Wood), and Washington's Office.

■ **SOUTHERN VIRGINIA UNIVERSITY** *G-7*
One College Hill Dr.
Buena Vista, VA 24416

Tel: (540)261-8400
Free: 800-229-8420
Admissions: (540)261-2756
Fax: (540)261-8559
E-mail: tcaputo@southernvirginia.edu
Web Site: http://www.southernvirginia.edu/

Description: Independent Latter-day Saints, 4-year, coed. Awards bachelor's degrees. Founded 1867. Setting: 155-acre small town campus. Educational spending for 2005 fiscal year: $4954 per student. Total enrollment: 685. Student-undergrad faculty ratio is 15:1. 2,098 applied, 41% were admitted. 5% from top 10% of their high school class, 20% from top quarter, 45% from top half. Full-time: 648 students, 55% women, 45% men. Part-time: 37 students, 49% women, 51% men. Students come from 12 other countries, 81% from out-of-state, 1% Native American, 2% Hispanic, 3% black, 2% Asian American or Pacific Islander, 2% international, 4% 25 or older, 85% live on campus, 13% transferred in. Retention: 37% of full-time freshmen returned the following year. Academic areas with the most degrees conferred: business/marketing; parks and recreation; visual and performing arts. Core. Calendar: semesters. Summer session for credit, co-op programs. Study abroad program. ROTC: Army (c).

Entrance Requirements: Option: Common Application. Required: high school transcript, ecclesiastical endorsement, SAT or ACT. Recommended: minimum 2.0 high school GPA. Required for some: essay, interview. Entrance: moderately difficult. Application deadlines: 7/31, 7/31 for nonresidents.

Costs Per Year: Application fee: $35. Comprehensive fee: $20,126 includes full-time tuition ($15,826) and college room and board ($4300). College room only: $2800. Part-time tuition: $525 per hour.

Collegiate Environment: Orientation program. Drama-theater group, choral group. Social organizations: ; 45% of eligible men and 55% of eligible women are members. Most popular organizations: student association, LDS Institute of Religion. Student services: health clinic, personal-psychological counseling. Campus security: 24-hour emergency response devices and patrols. 400 college housing spaces available. Freshmen given priority for college housing. On-campus residence required through sophomore year. Options: men-only, women-only housing available. Von Canon Library with 107,630 books, 37,000 serials, 4,350 audiovisual materials, and an OPAC.

■ **SOUTHSIDE VIRGINIA COMMUNITY COLLEGE**
109 Campus Dr.
Alberta, VA 23821-9719
Tel: (804)949-1000
Admissions: (434)949-1012
Fax: (804)949-7863
Web Site: http://www.sv.vccs.edu/

Description: State-supported, 2-year, coed. Part of Virginia Community College System. Awards certificates, diplomas, transfer associate, and terminal associate degrees. Founded 1970. Setting: 207-acre rural campus. Endowment: $527,455. Educational spending for 2005 fiscal year: $3767 per student. Total enrollment: 4,686. Student-undergrad faculty ratio is 17:1. Full-time: 1,359 students, 66% women, 34% men. Part-time: 3,327 students, 64% women, 36% men. Students come from 3 states and territories, 2 other countries, 1% from out-of-state, 0.2% Native American, 1% Hispanic, 46% black, 1% Asian American or Pacific Islander, 0.04% international, 46% 25 or older. Core. Calendar: semesters. Academic remediation for entering students, services for LD students, advanced placement, honors program, distance learning, summer session for credit, part-time degree program. Off campus study at Hampden-Sydney College, Saint Paul's College, Longwood College. Study abroad program. ROTC: Army (c).

Entrance Requirements: Open admission except for nursing program. Options: Peterson's Universal Application, Common Application, electronic application, deferred admission. Required: high school transcript, interview. Entrance: noncompetitive. Application deadline: Rolling. Notification: continuous. Preference given to district residents.

Costs Per Year: Application fee: $0. State resident tuition: $2040 full-time, $68 per credit part-time. Nonresident tuition: $6420 full-time, $214 per credit part-time. Mandatory fees: $155 full-time, $5.15 per credit part-time. Full-time tuition and fees vary according to course load. Part-time tuition and fees vary according to course load.

Collegiate Environment: Orientation program. Choral group. Most popular organizations: Student Forum, Phi Theta Kappa, Phi Beta Lambda, Alpha Delta Omega. Major annual events: women's festivals, cultural events, Kwanza celebration. College housing not available. Julian M. Howell Library plus 1 other with 27,691 books, 164 serials, 1,307 audiovisual materials, an

OPAC, and a Web page. Operations spending for 2004 fiscal year: $260,114. 200 computers available on campus for general student use. A campuswide network can be accessed. Staffed computer lab on campus.
Community Environment: See Hampden-Sydney College.

■ **SOUTHWEST VIRGINIA COMMUNITY COLLEGE** *B-5*
PO Box SVCC
Richlands, VA 24641-1101
Tel: (276)964-2555
Admissions: (276)964-7300
Fax: (276)964-9307
Web Site: http://www.sw.edu/

Description: State-supported, 2-year, coed. Part of Virginia Community College System. Awards certificates, diplomas, transfer associate, and terminal associate degrees. Founded 1968. Setting: 100-acre rural campus. Total enrollment: 3,666. Student-undergrad faculty ratio is 17:1. 14% from top 10% of their high school class. Full-time: 1,514 students, 63% women, 37% men. Part-time: 2,152 students, 57% women, 43% men. Students come from 6 other countries, 0.1% Native American, 0.2% Hispanic, 2% black, 0.4% Asian American or Pacific Islander, 0% international, 57% 25 or older, 4% transferred in. Retention: 91% of full-time freshmen returned the following year. Core. Calendar: semesters. Academic remediation for entering students, advanced placement, honors program, distance learning, double major, summer session for credit, part-time degree program, adult/continuing education programs, internships.

Entrance Requirements: Open admission except for allied health, engineering programs. Options: early admission, deferred admission. Required: high school transcript, interview. Entrance: noncompetitive. Application deadline: Rolling. Preference given to district residents.

Costs Per Year: Application fee: $0. State resident tuition: $1904 full-time, $68 per credit hour part-time. Nonresident tuition: $5992 full-time, $214 per credit hour part-time. Mandatory fees: $130 full-time, $4.65 per credit hour part-time. Full-time tuition and fees vary according to course load. Part-time tuition and fees vary according to course load.

Collegiate Environment: Drama-theater group, student-run newspaper, radio station. Most popular organizations: PTK, PBL, Intervoice, Black Student Union, Service Club. Student services: personal-psychological counseling, women's center. Campus security: 24-hour emergency response devices and patrols, student patrols. College housing not available. 58,000 books, 225 serials, an OPAC, and a Web page. 150 computers available on campus for general student use. A campuswide network can be accessed from off-campus. Staffed computer lab on campus.

Community Environment: Richlands is a rural community in the Appalachian Mountain region. Bus and plane transportation are available. The main industries of the area are agriculture, mining, and manufacturing.

■ **STRATFORD UNIVERSITY** *O-6*
7777 Leesburg Pike, Ste. 100 South
Falls Church, VA 22043
Tel: (703)821-8570
Free: 800-444-0804
Fax: (703)556-9892
E-mail: skamarah@stratford.edu
Web Site: http://www.stratford.edu/

Description: Proprietary, comprehensive, coed. Awards associate, bachelor's, and master's degrees. Founded 1976. Setting: suburban campus. Educational spending for 2005 fiscal year: $8379 per student. Total enrollment: 486. Faculty: 61 (20 full-time, 41 part-time). Student-undergrad faculty ratio is 20:1. Full-time: 189 students, 42% women, 58% men. Part-time: 256 students, 52% women, 48% men. Students come from 9 states and territories, 40% from out-of-state, 0.4% Native American, 9% Hispanic, 43% black, 9% Asian American or Pacific Islander, 4% international, 61% 25 or older, 7% transferred in. Retention: 73% of full-time freshmen returned the following year. Academic areas with the most degrees conferred: business/marketing; personal and culinary services; computer and information sciences. Core. Advanced placement, accelerated degree program, distance learning, co-op programs and internships.

Entrance Requirements: Options: Common Application, electronic application, early decision. Required: high school transcript, minimum 2.0 high school GPA, interview. Recommended: SAT. Entrance: minimally difficult. Application deadlines: 7/30, 4/29 for early decision. Notification: continuous until 8/6, 6/15 for early decision.

Costs Per Year: Application fee: $50. Comprehensive fee: $15,750 includes full-time tuition ($10,260), mandatory fees ($50), and college room and board ($5440). Part-time tuition: $285 per credit hour.

Collegiate Environment: Orientation program. Campus security: 24-hour emergency response devices. College housing not available. Stratford University Library with 1,800 books, 75 serials, and 283 audiovisual materials. Operations spending for 2004 fiscal year: $58,630. 7 computers available on campus for general student use. A campuswide network can be accessed. Staffed computer lab on campus.

■ SWEET BRIAR COLLEGE
Sweet Briar, VA 24595
Tel: (434)381-6100
Free: 800-381-6142
Admissions: (434)381-6142
Fax: (434)381-6173
E-mail: admissions@sbc.edu
Web Site: http://www.sbc.edu/
Description: Independent, comprehensive, women only. Awards bachelor's and master's degrees. Founded 1901. Setting: 3,250-acre rural campus. Endowment: $91.8 million. Research spending for 2004 fiscal year: $576,625. Educational spending for 2005 fiscal year: $17,254 per student. Total enrollment: 752. Faculty: 99 (64 full-time, 35 part-time). Student-undergrad faculty ratio is 8:1. 623 applied, 79% were admitted. 25% from top 10% of their high school class, 64% from top quarter, 94% from top half. 3 class presidents, 1 valedictorian, 7 student government officers. Full-time: 703 students. Part-time: 36 students. Students come from 44 states and territories, 14 other countries, 54% from out-of-state, 1% Native American, 2% Hispanic, 3% black, 2% Asian American or Pacific Islander, 2% international, 4% 25 or older, 90% live on campus, 2% transferred in. Retention: 75% of full-time freshmen returned the following year. Academic areas with the most degrees conferred: social sciences; psychology; visual and performing arts. Core. Calendar: semesters. Services for LD students, advanced placement, accelerated degree program, self-designed majors, honors program, independent study, double major, summer session for credit, part-time degree program, adult/continuing education programs, internships. Off campus study at Seven-College Exchange Program, Tri-College Exchange Program, American University. Study abroad program.
Entrance Requirements: Options: Peterson's Universal Application, Common Application, electronic application, early admission, early decision, deferred admission, international baccalaureate accepted. Required: essay, high school transcript, 2 recommendations, SAT or ACT. Recommended: interview, SAT Subject Tests. Required for some: portfolio with courses taken, list of texts covered, essay about homeschooling, campus visit, interview for homeschooled applicants. Entrance: moderately difficult. Application deadlines: 2/1, 12/1 for early decision. Notification: 3/1, 12/15 for early decision.
Costs Per Year: Application fee: $40. Comprehensive fee: $32,820 includes full-time tuition ($23,340) and college room and board ($9480). College room only: $3810. Part-time tuition: $775 per credit hour.
Collegiate Environment: Orientation program. Drama-theater group, choral group, student-run newspaper, radio station. Social organizations: 43 open to all. Most popular organizations: WNRS radio station, American Chemical Society, cheerleading, Sweet Tones, Student Government Association/ Campus Events Organization. Major annual events: Fall Weekend, Singer/ Songwriter Festival, Parents' Weekend. Student services: health clinic, personal-psychological counseling. Campus security: 24-hour emergency response devices and patrols, late night transport-escort service, controlled dormitory access, front gate security. 551 college housing spaces available; 498 were occupied in 2003-04. Freshmen guaranteed college housing. On-campus residence required through senior year. Option: women-only housing available. Mary Helen Cochran Library plus 3 others with 255,175 books, 450,838 microform titles, 12,464 serials, 10,826 audiovisual materials, an OPAC, and a Web page. Operations spending for 2004 fiscal year: $1 million. 117 computers available on campus for general student use. A campuswide network can be accessed from student residence rooms and from off campus. Staffed computer lab on campus.
Community Environment: Sweet Briar is located on U.S. 29, 165 miles southwest of Washington, D.C., 50 miles south of Charlottesville, VA., and 100 miles west of Richmond. The nearest shopping area is in the town of Amherst, two miles north of Sweet Briar. Lynchburg, home of three other colleges, is 12 miles south of Sweet Briar. The Blue Ridge Mountains, visible a few miles to the west, offer numerous recreational possibilities, including the ski slopes at Wintergreen.

■ TESST COLLEGE OF TECHNOLOGY *D-13*
6315 Bren Mar Dr.
Alexandria, VA 22312-6342

Tel: (703)354-1005
Free: 800-48-TESST
Admissions: (703)548-4800
Fax: (703)354-3661
E-mail: tesstal@erols.com
Web Site: http://www.tesst.com/
Description: Proprietary, 2-year, coed. Founded 1986.

■ THOMAS NELSON COMMUNITY COLLEGE *J-15*
PO Box 9407
Hampton, VA 23670-0407
Tel: (757)825-2700
Admissions: (757)825-2800
Web Site: http://www.tncc.edu/
Description: State-supported, 2-year, coed. Part of Virginia Community College System. Awards certificates, diplomas, transfer associate, and terminal associate degrees. Founded 1968. Setting: 85-acre suburban campus with easy access to Virginia Beach. Total enrollment: 8,595. Full-time: 2,658 students, 60% women, 40% men. Part-time: 5,937 students, 59% women, 41% men. 1% Native American, 4% Hispanic, 34% black, 4% Asian American or Pacific Islander, 0.05% international. Calendar: semesters. Academic remediation for entering students, ESL program, services for LD students, advanced placement, honors program, summer session for credit, part-time degree program, external degree program, adult/continuing education programs, co-op programs and internships. Off campus study at Hampton University, Old Dominion University, Christopher Newport University.
Entrance Requirements: Open admission. Options: early admission, deferred admission. Required: high school transcript. Entrance: noncompetitive. Application deadline: Rolling. Notification: continuous. Preference given to state residents.
Costs Per Year: Application fee: $0. State resident tuition: $2175 full-time, $72.50 per credit hour part-time. Nonresident tuition: $7061 full-time, $235.35 per credit hour part-time. Mandatory fees: $116 full-time, $3.15 per credit hour part-time, $10.50 per term part-time.
Collegiate Environment: Orientation program. Choral group, student-run newspaper. Social organizations: 19 open to all. Most popular organizations: Phi Theta Kappa, Future Nurses Association, Human Services Education Club, Student Government Association, Health Care Advocates. Major annual events: Fall Festival, Spring Fest, Literature Circles. Student services: personal-psychological counseling. Campus security: 24-hour patrols. Learning Resource Center with 66,281 books and 467 serials. 80 computers available on campus for general student use. A campuswide network can be accessed. Staffed computer lab on campus.
Community Environment: See Hampton University.

■ TIDEWATER COMMUNITY COLLEGE *J-15*
121 College Place
Norfolk, VA 23510
Tel: (757)822-1122
Admissions: (757)822-1068
Fax: (757)822-1060
Web Site: http://www.tcc.edu/
Description: State-supported, 2-year, coed. Part of Virginia Community College System. Awards certificates, diplomas, transfer associate, and terminal associate degrees. Founded 1968. Setting: 520-acre suburban campus. Educational spending for 2005 fiscal year: $3674 per student. Total enrollment: 23,718. Student-undergrad faculty ratio is 15:1. Students come from 53 states and territories, 12% from out-of-state, 1% Native American, 4% Hispanic, 32% black, 5% Asian American or Pacific Islander, 53% 25 or older. Core. Calendar: semesters. Academic remediation for entering students, ESL program, services for LD students, advanced placement, accelerated degree program, honors program, independent study, distance learning, summer session for credit, part-time degree program, adult/continuing education programs, co-op programs and internships. Off campus study at members of the Virginia Tidewater Consortium for Continuing Higher Education.
Entrance Requirements: Open admission. Options: early admission, deferred admission. Entrance: noncompetitive. Application deadline: Rolling. Notification: continuous.
Costs Per Year: Application fee: $0. State resident tuition: $1944 full-time, $72.50 per credit part-time. Nonresident tuition: $5,905 full-time, $246.05 per credit part-time. Mandatory fees: $8.50 per credit part-time.

Collegiate Environment: Orientation program. Drama-theater group, student-run newspaper. Student services: personal-psychological counseling, women's center. Campus security: 24-hour patrols. College housing not available. 147,126 books and 913 serials. Operations spending for 2004 fiscal year: $535,000.

Community Environment: A metropolitan area, Tidewater is located on the Chesapeake Bay, and has been a strategic military location in this country's conflicts because of its shipbuilding and ship repair. All forms of commercial transportation are available. Recreational activities are numerous, all water sports are enjoyed on nearby beaches. There is excellent hunting and fishing in the area also. Part-time employment opportunities are limited.

■ **TIDEWATER TECH** *J-15*

2697 Dean Dr., Ste. 100
Virginia Beach, VA 23452
Tel: (757)340-2121
Fax: (757)340-9704
Web Site: http://www.tidetech.com/
Description: Proprietary, 2-year, coed. Founded 1969.

■ **UNIVERSITY OF MANAGEMENT AND TECHNOLOGY** *D-13*

1901 North Fort Myers Dr.
Arlington, VA 22209
Tel: (703)516-0035
Fax: (703)516-0985
Web Site: http://www.umtweb.edu/
Description: Proprietary, comprehensive, coed. Awards associate, bachelor's, master's, and doctoral degrees and post-master's certificates. Founded 1998. Setting: urban campus with easy access to Washington, D.C.. 0% from out-of-state. Calendar: continuous.
Costs Per Year: Tuition: $10,800 full-time, $390 per credit hour part-time. Mandatory fees: $90 full-time, $30 per term part-time. Tuition guaranteed not to increase for student's term of enrollment.
Collegiate Environment: College housing not available.

■ **UNIVERSITY OF MARY WASHINGTON** *F-12*

1301 College Ave.
Fredericksburg, VA 22401-5358
Tel: (540)654-1000
Free: 800-468-5614
Admissions: (540)654-2000
Fax: (540)654-1073
E-mail: admit@umw.edu
Web Site: http://www.umw.edu/
Description: State-supported, comprehensive, coed. Awards bachelor's and master's degrees. Founded 1908. Setting: 176-acre small town campus with easy access to Richmond and Washington, DC. Endowment: $25.3 million. Research spending for 2004 fiscal year: $279,049. Educational spending for 2005 fiscal year: $5095 per student. Total enrollment: 4,734. Faculty: 338 (231 full-time, 107 part-time). Student-undergrad faculty ratio is 17:1. 4,635 applied, 64% were admitted. 38% from top 10% of their high school class, 83% from top quarter, 97% from top half. 1 National Merit Scholar, 150 class presidents, 7 valedictorians, 350 student government officers. Full-time: 3,519 students, 66% women, 34% men. Part-time: 566 students, 66% women, 34% men. Students come from 44 states and territories, 15 other countries, 35% from out-of-state, 0.3% Native American, 3% Hispanic, 4% black, 4% Asian American or Pacific Islander, 0.3% international, 11% 25 or older, 70% live on campus, 4% transferred in. Retention: 85% of full-time freshmen returned the following year. Academic areas with the most degrees conferred: social sciences; business/marketing; English. Core. Calendar: semesters. Services for LD students, advanced placement, accelerated degree program, self-designed majors, independent study, double major, summer session for credit, part-time degree program, adult/continuing education programs, co-op programs and internships, graduate courses open to undergrads. Study abroad program.
Entrance Requirements: Options: Peterson's Universal Application, Common Application, electronic application, deferred admission, international baccalaureate accepted. Required: essay, high school transcript, SAT or ACT. Recommended: SAT Subject Tests. Entrance: very difficult. Application deadline: 2/1. Notification: 4/1. Preference given to state residents.
Costs Per Year: Application fee: $45. State resident tuition: $5634 full-time, $199 per credit part-time. Nonresident tuition: $14,776 full-time, $579 per credit part-time. Part-time tuition varies according to course load. College

room and board: $6002. College room only: $3484. Room and board charges vary according to board plan and housing facility.
Collegiate Environment: Orientation program. Drama-theater group, choral group, student-run newspaper, radio station. Social organizations: 96 open to all. Most popular organizations: Community Outreach, debate team, Washington Guides, Trek Club, entertainment committee. Major annual events: Fall Homecoming, Junior Ring Week, Multicultural International Festival. Student services: health clinic, personal-psychological counseling, women's center. Campus security: 24-hour emergency response devices and patrols, student patrols, late night transport-escort service, controlled dormitory access, self-defense and safety classes. 2,500 college housing spaces available; all were occupied in 2003-04. Freshmen guaranteed college housing. Options: coed, men-only, women-only housing available. Simpson Library with 355,478 books, 559,809 microform titles, 2,419 serials, 1,079 audiovisual materials, an OPAC, and a Web page. Operations spending for 2004 fiscal year: $1.9 million. 244 computers available on campus for general student use. A campuswide network can be accessed from student residence rooms and from off campus. Staffed computer lab on campus.
Community Environment: Fredericksburg is located an hour south of Washington, DC and an hour north of Richmond, in one of the fastest growing regions in the state. One of the most historic cities in the country, Fredericksburg was the childhood home of George Washington and was the site of several major battles of the Civil War. Today the surrounding metropolitan population reaches upwards of 150,000 people yet still maintains the charm of a small town. The 40-block Historic District is located within easy walking distance of the campus and includes fine shopping, restaurants, movie theaters as well as historic attractions. Located on I-95, Fredericksburg offers access to both Washington and Richmond by Amtrak, various bus lines, and transportation service to National Airport in Washington and Richmond International. Fredericksburg is on the regularly scheduled commuter rail to Washington.

■ **UNIVERSITY OF NORTHERN VIRGINIA**

10021 Balls Ford Rd.
Manassas, VA 20109
Tel: (703)392-0771
Fax: (703)392-6368
E-mail: bfrantz@unva.edu
Web Site: http://www.unva.edu/
Description: Proprietary, comprehensive, coed. Awards bachelor's and master's degrees. Founded 1998.

■ **UNIVERSITY OF PHOENIX-NORTHERN VIRGINIA CAMPUS** *C-12*

11730 Plaza American Dr., Ste. 2000
Reston, VA 20190
Tel: (703)435-4402
Free: 800-228-7240
Admissions: (480)557-1712
Web Site: http://www.phoenix.edu/
Description: Proprietary, comprehensive, coed. Awards bachelor's and master's degrees. Total enrollment: 1,377. Faculty: 154 (5 full-time, 149 part-time). Student-undergrad faculty ratio is 7:1. 53 applied. Full-time: 1,020 students, 50% women, 50% men. 0.3% Native American, 3% Hispanic, 9% black, 1% Asian American or Pacific Islander, 11% international, 94% 25 or older. Core. Advanced placement, accelerated degree program, independent study, distance learning, external degree program, adult/continuing education programs, graduate courses open to undergrads.
Entrance Requirements: Open admission. Option: deferred admission. Required: 1 recommendation. Required for some: high school transcript. Entrance: noncompetitive. Application deadline: Rolling.
Costs Per Year: Application fee: $110. Tuition: $11,805 full-time, $393.50 per credit part-time. Mandatory fees: $560 full-time, $70 per course part-time.
Collegiate Environment: College housing not available. University Library with 444 books, 666 serials, an OPAC, and a Web page. System-wide operations spending for 2004 fiscal year: $3.2 million.

■ **UNIVERSITY OF PHOENIX-RICHMOND CAMPUS** *H-12*

6802 Paragon Place, Ste. 420
Richmond, VA 23230
Tel: (804)288-3390
Free: 800-228-7240
Admissions: (480)557-1712
Web Site: http://www.phoenix.edu/

Description: Proprietary, comprehensive, coed. Awards bachelor's and master's degrees. Total enrollment: 383. Faculty: 38 (4 full-time, 34 part-time). Student-undergrad faculty ratio is 7:1. 45 applied. Full-time: 301 students, 66% women, 34% men. 0% from out-of-state, 0% Native American, 0% Hispanic, 2% black, 0.3% Asian American or Pacific Islander, 1% international. Academic area with the most degrees conferred: business/marketing. Core. Advanced placement, accelerated degree program, independent study, distance learning, external degree program, adult/continuing education programs, graduate courses open to undergrads.

Entrance Requirements: Open admission. Option: deferred admission. Required: 1 recommendation. Required for some: high school transcript. Entrance: noncompetitive. Application deadline: Rolling.

Costs Per Year: Application fee: $110. Tuition: $11,370 full-time, $379 per credit part-time. Mandatory fees: $560 full-time, $70 per course part-time.

Collegiate Environment: University Library with 444 books, 666 serials, an OPAC, and a Web page. System-wide operations spending for 2004 fiscal year: $3.2 million.

■ UNIVERSITY OF RICHMOND

28 Westhampton Way
University of Richmond, VA 23173
Tel: (804)289-8000
Free: 800-700-1662
Admissions: (804)289-8640
Fax: (804)287-6003
E-mail: admissions@richmond.edu
Web Site: http://www.richmond.edu/

Description: Independent, comprehensive, coed. Awards associate, bachelor's, master's, and first professional degrees. Founded 1830. Setting: 350-acre suburban campus. Endowment: $1.2 billion. Research spending for 2004 fiscal year: $2.2 million. Educational spending for 2005 fiscal year: $21,282 per student. Total enrollment: 3,685. Faculty: 320 (262 full-time, 58 part-time). Student-undergrad faculty ratio is 10:1. 5,778 applied, 47% were admitted. 58% from top 10% of their high school class, 88% from top quarter, 98% from top half. 101 National Merit Scholars, 81 class presidents, 9 valedictorians, 217 student government officers. Full-time: 2,881 students, 51% women, 49% men. Part-time: 39 students, 41% women, 59% men. Students come from 48 states and territories, 88 other countries, 85% from out-of-state, 0.2% Native American, 2% Hispanic, 4% black, 3% Asian American or Pacific Islander, 4% international, 0% 25 or older, 92% live on campus, 2% transferred in. Retention: 93% of full-time freshmen returned the following year. Academic areas with the most degrees conferred: business/marketing; social sciences; English. Core. Calendar: semesters. ESL program, services for LD students, advanced placement, accelerated degree program, self-designed majors, honors program, independent study, distance learning, double major, summer session for credit, part-time degree program, adult/continuing education programs, co-op programs and internships, graduate courses open to undergrads. Off campus study at American University, Duke University. Study abroad program. ROTC: Army.

Entrance Requirements: Options: Peterson's Universal Application, Common Application, electronic application, early admission, early decision, deferred admission, international baccalaureate accepted. Required: essay, high school transcript, minimum 2.0 high school GPA, 1 recommendation, signed character statement, SAT or ACT. Entrance: very difficult. Application deadlines: 1/15, 11/15 for early decision plan 1, 1/15 for early decision plan 2. Notification: 4/1, 12/15 for early decision plan 1, 2/15 for early decision plan 2.

Costs Per Year: Application fee: $50. Comprehensive fee: $42,610 includes full-time tuition ($36,550) and college room and board ($6060). College room only: $2710. Part-time tuition: $1460 per semester hour.

Collegiate Environment: Orientation program. Drama-theater group, choral group, student-run newspaper, radio station. Social organizations: 225 open to all; national fraternities, national sororities; 29% of eligible men and 65% of eligible women are members. Most popular organizations: Volunteer Action Council, Student Government Association, Campus Activities Board, Multicultural Student Union, intramurals. Major annual events: UR Century Bike Race, Homecoming, Greek Week. Student services: health clinic, personal-psychological counseling, women's center. Campus security: 24-hour emergency response devices and patrols, late night transport-escort service, controlled dormitory access, campus police. College housing designed to accommodate 2,686 students; 2,769 undergraduates lived in college housing during 2003-04. Freshmen given priority for college housing. Options: coed, men-only, women-only housing available. Boatwright Memorial Library plus 2 others with 1.1 million books, 85,336 microform titles,

20,831 serials, 17,684 audiovisual materials, an OPAC, and a Web page. Operations spending for 2004 fiscal year: $9.5 million. 650 computers available on campus for general student use. Computer purchase/lease plans available. A campuswide network can be accessed from student residence rooms and from off campus. Staffed computer lab on campus.

■ UNIVERSITY OF VIRGINIA *F-9*

Charlottesville, VA 22903
Tel: (434)924-0311
Admissions: (434)982-3200
Fax: (434)924-3587
E-mail: undergrad-admission@virginia.edu
Web Site: http://www.virginia.edu/

Description: State-supported, university, coed. Awards bachelor's, master's, doctoral, and first professional degrees and post-master's certificates. Founded 1819. Setting: 1,160-acre suburban campus with easy access to Richmond. Endowment: $2.2 billion. Research spending for 2004 fiscal year: $258.8 million. Educational spending for 2005 fiscal year: $10,108 per student. Total enrollment: 23,765. Faculty: 1,330 (1,193 full-time, 137 part-time). Student-undergrad faculty ratio is 15:1. 15,657 applied, 38% were admitted. 86% from top 10% of their high school class, 97% from top quarter, 99% from top half. 152 valedictorians. Full-time: 13,395 students, 54% women, 46% men. Part-time: 818 students, 54% women, 46% men. Students come from 52 states and territories, 102 other countries, 28% from out-of-state, 0.2% Native American, 4% Hispanic, 9% black, 11% Asian American or Pacific Islander, 4% international, 2% 25 or older, 46% live on campus, 4% transferred in. Retention: 97% of full-time freshmen returned the following year. Academic areas with the most degrees conferred: social sciences; engineering; business/marketing; psychology. Calendar: semesters. ESL program, services for LD students, advanced placement, accelerated degree program, self-designed majors, honors program, independent study, double major, summer session for credit, part-time degree program, adult/continuing education programs, co-op programs and internships, graduate courses open to undergrads. Study abroad program. ROTC: Army, Naval, Air Force.

Entrance Requirements: Options: electronic application, early decision, deferred admission. Required: essay, high school transcript, 1 recommendation, SAT and SAT Subject Tests or ACT, two SAT subject tests (student's choice). Entrance: most difficult. Application deadlines: 1/2, 11/1 for early decision. Notification: 4/1, 12/1 for early decision. Preference given to state residents, children of alumni.

Costs Per Year: Application fee: $60. State resident tuition: $5602 full-time. Nonresident tuition: $22,346 full-time. Mandatory fees: $1768 full-time. College room and board: $6389. College room only: $3289. Room and board charges vary according to board plan and housing facility.

Collegiate Environment: Orientation program. Drama-theater group, choral group, marching band, student-run newspaper, radio station. Social organizations: 300 open to all; national fraternities, national sororities, local fraternities; 30% of eligible men and 30% of eligible women are members. Most popular organizations: Madison House, student government, University guides, University Union, The Cavalier Daily. Major annual events: Family Weekend, Homecoming, Finals Weekend. Student services: legal services, health clinic, personal-psychological counseling, women's center, transfer student advising. Campus security: 24-hour emergency response devices and patrols, late night transport-escort service, controlled dormitory access. 6,779 college housing spaces available; 6,294 were occupied in 2003-04. Freshmen guaranteed college housing. On-campus residence required in freshman year. Option: coed housing available. Alderman Library plus 14 others with 4.9 million books, 5.5 million microform titles, 53,015 serials, 534,662 audiovisual materials, an OPAC, and a Web page. Operations spending for 2004 fiscal year: $29.4 million. 1,645 computers available on campus for general student use. Computer purchase/lease plans available. A campuswide network can be accessed from student residence rooms and from off campus. Staffed computer lab on campus.

Community Environment: Charlottesville, situated in the foothills of the Blue Ridge Mountains, was the home of Thomas Jefferson and James Monroe. Numerous old homes and estates in Charlottesville and the surrounding areas, reveal Jefferson's architectural influence. All forms of commercial transportation are available. Albemarle County is known for its horses, dogs, fox hunting, and for its peach and apple orchards. The many outdoor activities include golf, tennis, hunting, fishing, and hiking. Some part-time employment is available for students. Points of interest include the Lewis and Clark Memorial, Monticello, the home of Thomas Jefferson, Old Courthouse, and the University of Virginia-founded by Thomas Jefferson.

■ THE UNIVERSITY OF VIRGINIA'S COLLEGE AT WISE *C-4*

1 College Ave.
Wise, VA 24293
Tel: (276)328-0100; 888-282-9324
Admissions: (276)328-0322
Fax: (276)328-0251
Web Site: http://www.uvawise.edu/

Description: State-supported, 4-year, coed. Part of University of Virginia. Awards bachelor's degrees. Founded 1954. Setting: 396-acre small town campus. Endowment: $20.6 million. Educational spending for 2005 fiscal year: $4029 per student. Total enrollment: 1,836. 1,019 applied, 79% were admitted. 25% from top 10% of their high school class, 50% from top quarter, 86% from top half. Full-time: 1,432 students, 50% women, 50% men. Part-time: 404 students, 71% women, 29% men. Students come from 9 states and territories, 9 other countries, 6% from out-of-state, 0.2% Native American, 1% Hispanic, 5% black, 1% Asian American or Pacific Islander, 0.3% international, 23% 25 or older, 30% live on campus, 8% transferred in. Retention: 73% of full-time freshmen returned the following year. Core. Calendar: semesters. Academic remediation for entering students, services for LD students, advanced placement, accelerated degree program, self-designed majors, honors program, independent study, distance learning, double major, summer session for credit, part-time degree program, adult/continuing education programs, co-op programs and internships. Study abroad program.

Entrance Requirements: Options: early admission, early action, international baccalaureate accepted. Required: high school transcript, minimum 2.3 high school GPA, SAT or ACT. Recommended: 2 recommendations. Required for some: interview. Entrance: moderately difficult. Application deadlines: 8/1, 2/1 for early action. Notification: continuous until 8/20, 2/15 for early action.

Costs Per Year: Application fee: $25. State resident tuition: $2984 full-time, $123 per semester hour part-time. Nonresident tuition: $13,062 full-time, $539 per semester hour part-time. Mandatory fees: $2097 full-time, $38 per semester hour part-time, $14.25 per term part-time. College room and board: $6200. College room only: $3488.

Collegiate Environment: Orientation program. Drama-theater group, choral group, student-run newspaper, radio station. Social organizations: 50 open to all; national fraternities, national sororities, local fraternities, local sororities; 39% of eligible men and 32% of eligible women are members. Most popular organizations: student government, Student Activities Board, Multicultural Association, Residence Hall Association. Major annual events: Holly Ball, Homecoming, Jam for Man. Student services: health clinic, personal-psychological counseling. Campus security: 24-hour emergency response devices and patrols, student patrols, late night transport-escort service, self-defense, informal discussions, pamphlets/posters/films, and crime prevention office. 550 college housing spaces available; all were occupied in 2003-04. No special consideration for freshman housing applicants. Options: coed, men-only, women-only housing available. Wyllie Library with 95,861 books, 62,155 microform titles, 1,029 serials, 11,582 audiovisual materials, an OPAC, and a Web page. Operations spending for 2004 fiscal year: $683,647. 130 computers available on campus for general student use. A campuswide network can be accessed from student residence rooms and from off campus. Staffed computer lab on campus.

■ VIRGINIA COMMONWEALTH UNIVERSITY *H-12*

901 West Franklin St.
Richmond, VA 23284-9005
Tel: (804)828-0100
Free: 800-841-3638
Admissions: (804)828-1222
Fax: (804)828-1899
E-mail: vcuinfo@vcu.edu
Web Site: http://www.vcu.edu/

Description: State-supported, university, coed. Awards bachelor's, master's, doctoral, and first professional degrees and post-master's and first professional certificates. Founded 1838. Setting: 126-acre urban campus. Endowment: $235.3 million. Research spending for 2004 fiscal year: $145.8 million. Total enrollment: 29,349. Faculty: 2,813 (1,744 full-time, 1,069 part-time). Student-undergrad faculty ratio is 19:1. 11,764 applied, 68% were admitted. 16% from top 10% of their high school class, 44% from top quarter, 82% from top half. 11 valedictorians. Full-time: 16,109 students, 60% women, 40% men. Part-time: 4,399 students, 59% women, 41% men. Students come from 48 states and territories, 75 other countries, 5% from out-of-state, 1% Native American, 3% Hispanic, 20% black, 9% Asian American or Pacific Islander, 2% international, 17% 25 or older, 22% live on campus, 9% transferred in. Retention: 80% of full-time freshmen returned the following year. Academic areas with the most degrees conferred: visual and performing arts; business/marketing; health professions and related sciences. Core. Calendar: semesters. Academic remediation for entering students, ESL program, services for LD students, advanced placement, accelerated degree program, self-designed majors, honors program, independent study, distance learning, double major, summer session for credit, part-time degree program, adult/continuing education programs, co-op programs and internships, graduate courses open to undergrads. Off campus study. Study abroad program. ROTC: Army (c).

Entrance Requirements: Options: Common Application, electronic application, early admission, deferred admission, international baccalaureate accepted. Required: high school transcript, SAT or ACT. Required for some: essay. Application deadline: 2/1. Notification: continuous until 4/1. Preference given to state residents for some health science programs.

Costs Per Year: Application fee: $30. State resident tuition: $5385 full-time, $165.40 per credit part-time. Nonresident tuition: $17,440 full-time, $668 per credit part-time. Mandatory fees: $52.05 per credit part-time. College room and board: $7042. College room only: $4102. Room and board charges vary according to board plan.

Collegiate Environment: Orientation program. Drama-theater group, choral group, marching band, student-run newspaper, radio station. Social organizations: national fraternities, national sororities, local fraternities, local sororities. Most popular organizations: Student Government Organization, Activities Programming Board, Muslim Student Association, Black Caucus. Major annual events: Homecoming, Annual Fall Step Show, Spring Fest. Student services: health clinic, personal-psychological counseling. Campus security: 24-hour emergency response devices and patrols, student patrols, late night transport-escort service, controlled dormitory access, security personnel in residence halls. 4,706 college housing spaces available; 3,703 were occupied in 2003-04. Options: coed, men-only, women-only housing available. Virginia Commonwealth University Libraries plus 6 others with 1.8 million books, 3.1 million microform titles, 12,973 serials, 44,434 audiovisual materials, an OPAC, and a Web page. Operations spending for 2004 fiscal year: $9.9 million. 400 computers available on campus for general student use. A campuswide network can be accessed from student residence rooms and from off campus. Staffed computer lab on campus.

Community Environment: See University of Richmond.

■ VIRGINIA HIGHLANDS COMMUNITY COLLEGE *K-1*

PO Box 828
Abingdon, VA 24212-0828
Tel: (276)739-2400; 877-207-6115
Admissions: (276)739-2414
Fax: (276)739-2590
Web Site: http://www.vhcc.edu/

Description: State-supported, 2-year, coed. Part of Virginia Community College System. Awards certificates, diplomas, transfer associate, and terminal associate degrees. Founded 1967. Setting: 100-acre small town campus. Total enrollment: 3,867. 15% from top 10% of their high school class, 35% from top quarter, 65% from top half. Students come from 7 states and territories, 52% 25 or older. Calendar: semesters. Academic remediation for entering students, services for LD students, advanced placement, summer session for credit, part-time degree program, adult/continuing education programs, co-op programs.

Entrance Requirements: Open admission except for nursing, radiology, physical therapy programs. Options: early admission, deferred admission. Required: high school transcript. Placement: SCAT, ACT ASSET recommended; SCAT, ACT ASSET required for some. Entrance: noncompetitive. Application deadline: Rolling. Notification: continuous. Preference given to district, then state residents.

Collegiate Environment: Orientation program. Drama-theater group, choral group. Student services: personal-psychological counseling. College housing not available. 29,683 books and 174 serials. 240 computers available on campus for general student use. A campuswide network can be accessed from off-campus. Staffed computer lab on campus.

Community Environment: Abingdon is known as a handicraft center as well as being the largest burley tobacco market and the largest livestock auction in Virginia. Commercial transportation is available. The Blue Ridge and Holston Mountains are nearby providing facilities for many outdoor activities.

■ **VIRGINIA INTERMONT COLLEGE** *D-5*
1013 Moore St.
Bristol, VA 24201-4298
Tel: (276)669-6101
Free: 800-451-1842
Admissions: (276)466-7856
Fax: (276)669-5763
E-mail: viadmit@vic.edu
Web Site: http://www.vic.edu/
Description: Independent, 4-year, coed, affiliated with Baptist Church. Awards associate and bachelor's degrees. Founded 1884. Setting: 13-acre small town campus. Endowment: $2.8 million. Educational spending for 2005 fiscal year: $3859 per student. Total enrollment: 1,138. Student-undergrad faculty ratio is 11:1. 802 applied, 63% were admitted. 11% from top 10% of their high school class, 24% from top quarter, 70% from top half. 2 valedictorians. Full-time: 986 students, 71% women, 29% men. Part-time: 152 students, 63% women, 38% men. Students come from 36 states and territories, 36 other countries, 45% from out-of-state, 1% Native American, 2% Hispanic, 7% black, 1% Asian American or Pacific Islander, 1% international, 43% 25 or older, 56% live on campus, 9% transferred in. Retention: 72% of full-time freshmen returned the following year. Academic areas with the most degrees conferred: education; business/marketing; visual and performing arts. Core. Calendar: semesters. Academic remediation for entering students, ESL program, services for LD students, advanced placement, accelerated degree program, honors program, independent study, distance learning, double major, summer session for credit, part-time degree program, adult/continuing education programs, internships. Off campus study at King College. Study abroad program.
Entrance Requirements: Options: Peterson's Universal Application, Common Application, electronic application, early admission, deferred admission, international baccalaureate accepted. Required: essay, high school transcript, minimum 2.0 high school GPA, SAT or ACT. Required for some: interview. Entrance: minimally difficult. Application deadline: Rolling. Notification: continuous.
Costs Per Year: Application fee: $15. Comprehensive fee: $22,200 includes full-time tuition ($15,500), mandatory fees ($950), and college room and board ($5750). College room only: $2750. Full-time tuition and fees vary according to class time and program. Room and board charges vary according to housing facility. Part-time tuition: $220 per credit. Part-time mandatory fees: $50 per credit. Part-time tuition and fees vary according to class time, course level, course load, and program.
Collegiate Environment: Orientation program. Drama-theater group, choral group. Social organizations: 21 open to all. Most popular organizations: Student Government Association, Student Activities Committee, Christian Student Union, Equestrian Club, Business Organization for Student Success. Major annual events: Family Weekend, Homecoming, Christmas at VI. Student services: health clinic, personal-psychological counseling, women's center. Campus security: 24-hour patrols, late night transport-escort service. 490 college housing spaces available; 434 were occupied in 2003-04. Freshmen guaranteed college housing. On-campus residence required through junior year. Options: coed, men-only, women-only housing available. J. F. Hicks Library with 93,382 books, 9,350 microform titles, 76 serials, 2,247 audiovisual materials, an OPAC, and a Web page. Operations spending for 2004 fiscal year: $154,390. 80 computers available on campus for general student use. Computer purchase/lease plans available. A campuswide network can be accessed from student residence rooms and from off campus. Staffed computer lab on campus.
Community Environment: The name "Intermont" meaning "among the mountains," is descriptive of the College's setting. Virginia Intermont is located in Bristol, VA, off Exit 5 of Interstate 81, almost halfway between Roanoke, VA and Knoxville, TN. The campus is situated only eight blocks from the city's downtown district and two miles from the Bristol Mall.

■ **VIRGINIA MILITARY INSTITUTE** *G-7*
Lexington, VA 24450
Tel: (540)464-7207
Free: 800-767-4207
Admissions: (540)464-7211
Fax: (540)464-7746
E-mail: admissions@vmi.edu

Web Site: http://www.vmi.edu/
Description: State-supported, 4-year, coed. Awards bachelor's degrees. Founded 1839. Setting: 134-acre small town campus. Endowment: $281.4 million. Research spending for 2004 fiscal year: $622,851. Educational spending for 2005 fiscal year: $6827 per student. Total enrollment: 1,362. 1,579 applied, 50% were admitted. 13% from top 10% of their high school class, 54% from top quarter, 89% from top half. 82 student government officers. Full-time: 1,362 students, 6% women, 94% men. Students come from 45 states and territories, 17 other countries, 48% from out-of-state, 0.4% Native American, 3% Hispanic, 5% black, 3% Asian American or Pacific Islander, 2% international, 1% 25 or older, 100% live on campus, 2% transferred in. Retention: 87% of full-time freshmen returned the following year. Core. Calendar: semesters. Services for LD students, advanced placement, accelerated degree program, honors program, independent study, double major, summer session for credit, internships. Study abroad program. ROTC: Army, Naval, Air Force.
Entrance Requirements: Options: electronic application, early admission, early decision, international baccalaureate accepted. Required: high school transcript, SAT or ACT. Recommended: essay, 2 recommendations, interview. Entrance: moderately difficult. Application deadlines: 3/1, 11/15 for early decision. Notification: continuous, 12/15 for early decision.
Costs Per Year: Application fee: $35. One-time mandatory fee: $1678. State resident tuition: $4382 full-time. Nonresident tuition: $18,582 full-time. Mandatory fees: $2606 full-time. College room and board: $5666.
Collegiate Environment: Orientation program. Drama-theater group, choral group, marching band, student-run newspaper. Social organizations: 47 open to all. Most popular organizations: Newman Club, Officers Christian Fellowship, strength and fitness organizations, Promaji, Pre-Law Society. Major annual events: New Market Day, Parents' Weekend, Founders' Day. Student services: health clinic, personal-psychological counseling. Campus security: 24-hour emergency response devices and patrols, student patrols. 1,362 college housing spaces available; all were occupied in 2003-04. Freshmen guaranteed college housing. On-campus residence required through senior year. Option: coed housing available. Preston Library plus 1 other with 162,053 books, 18,137 microform titles, 785 serials, 4,896 audiovisual materials, an OPAC, and a Web page. Operations spending for 2004 fiscal year: $1.2 million. 200 computers available on campus for general student use. A campuswide network can be accessed from student residence rooms and from off campus. Staffed computer lab on campus.
Community Environment: VMI offers a small town flavor, with a hallowed history and breathtaking scenery.

■ **VIRGINIA POLYTECHNIC INSTITUTE AND STATE UNIVERSITY** *I-4*
Blacksburg, VA 24061
Tel: (540)231-6000
Fax: (540)231-3242
Web Site: http://www.vt.edu/
Description: State-supported, university, coed. Awards associate, bachelor's, master's, doctoral, and first professional degrees. Founded 1872. Setting: 2,600-acre small town campus. Educational spending for 2005 fiscal year: $7979 per student. Total enrollment: 27,979. Faculty: 1,532 (1,304 full-time, 228 part-time). Student-undergrad faculty ratio is 16:1. 17,619 applied, 70% were admitted. 35% from top 10% of their high school class, 79% from top quarter, 97% from top half. Full-time: 21,087 students, 41% women, 59% men. Part-time: 540 students, 37% women, 63% men. Students come from 52 states and territories, 104 other countries, 28% from out-of-state, 0.2% Native American, 2% Hispanic, 5% black, 7% Asian American or Pacific Islander, 2% international, 41% live on campus, 3% transferred in. Retention: 88% of full-time freshmen returned the following year. Academic areas with the most degrees conferred: business/marketing; engineering; family and consumer sciences. Core. Calendar: semesters. ESL program, services for LD students, advanced placement, accelerated degree program, honors program, independent study, distance learning, double major, summer session for credit, part-time degree program, adult/continuing education programs, co-op programs and internships, graduate courses open to undergrads. Study abroad program. ROTC: Army, Naval, Air Force.
Entrance Requirements: Options: electronic application, early admission, early decision, deferred admission, international baccalaureate accepted. Required: high school transcript, SAT or ACT. Recommended: minimum 3.0 high school GPA. Entrance: moderately difficult. Application deadlines: 1/15, 11/1 for early decision. Notification: 4/1, 12/15 for early decision.
Costs Per Year: Application fee: $40. State resident tuition: $4959 full-time, $206.75 per credit hour part-time. Nonresident tuition: $16,298 full-time, $679 per credit hour part-time. Mandatory fees: $1419 full-time, $169 per

term part-time. College room and board: $4400. College room only: $2346. Room and board charges vary according to board plan and location.

Collegiate Environment: Orientation program. Drama-theater group, choral group, marching band, student-run newspaper, radio station. Social organizations: 524 open to all; national fraternities, national sororities, local fraternities; 13% of eligible men and 15% of eligible women are members. Most popular organizations: Virginia Tech Union, Student Government Association, international student organizations. Major annual events: Military Ball, International Street Fair, Homecoming Week. Student services: legal services, health clinic, personal-psychological counseling, women's center. Campus security: 24-hour emergency response devices and patrols, student patrols, late night transport-escort service, controlled dormitory access. 8,900 college housing spaces available; all were occupied in 2003-04. Freshmen guaranteed college housing. On-campus residence required in freshman year. Options: coed, men-only, women-only housing available. Newman Library plus 4 others with 2.2 million books, 6.3 million microform titles, 28,596 serials, 23,420 audiovisual materials, an OPAC, and a Web page. Operations spending for 2004 fiscal year: $12.8 million. 8,000 computers available on campus for general student use. Computer purchase/lease plans available. A campuswide network can be accessed from student residence rooms and from off campus. Staffed computer lab on campus.

Community Environment: Blacksburg is a town with a population of 35,000 located on a plateau between the Blue Ridge and Allegheny Mountains, 38 miles southwest of Roanoke. Bus service is convenient and free to the university community. Civic and service organizations are active and welcome student participation. Outdoor recreation opportunities include hiking, horseback riding, fishing, swimming, boating, water skiing, and camping. Nearby are the Jefferson National Forest, the Appalachian Trail, the New River, and other parks and lakes.

■ **VIRGINIA STATE UNIVERSITY** *I-12*

1 Hayden St.

Petersburg, VA 23806-0001

Tel: (804)524-5000

Free: 800-871-7611

Admissions: (804)524-5902

Fax: (804)524-5055

E-mail: ilogan@vsu.edu

Web Site: http://www.vsu.edu/

Description: State-supported, comprehensive, coed. Part of State Council of Higher Education for Virginia. Awards associate, bachelor's, master's, and doctoral degrees and post-master's certificates. Founded 1882. Setting: 236-acre suburban campus with easy access to Richmond. Research spending for 2004 fiscal year: $3.4 million. Total enrollment: 5,055. Faculty: 327 (226 full-time, 101 part-time). Student-undergrad faculty ratio is 17:1. 4,000 applied, 79% were admitted. 4% from top 10% of their high school class, 19% from top quarter, 59% from top half. Full-time: 4,060 students, 60% women, 40% men. Part-time: 272 students, 64% women, 36% men. Students come from 35 states and territories, 32% from out-of-state, 0.1% Native American, 1% Hispanic, 96% black, 0.3% Asian American or Pacific Islander, 0% international, 10% 25 or older, 58% live on campus, 5% transferred in. Academic areas with the most degrees conferred: business/marketing; education; liberal arts/general studies. Core. Calendar: semesters. Services for LD students, advanced placement, self-designed majors, honors program, independent study, double major, summer session for credit, part-time degree program, adult/continuing education programs, co-op programs and internships, graduate courses open to undergrads. ROTC: Army.

Entrance Requirements: Options: Common Application, electronic application. Required: high school transcript, minimum 2.2 high school GPA, 2 recommendations, SAT or ACT. Entrance: minimally difficult. Application deadline: 5/1. Notification: continuous.

Costs Per Year: Application fee: $25. State resident tuition: $2317 full-time, $161 per credit part-time. Nonresident tuition: $9668 full-time, $402 per credit part-time. Mandatory fees: $2575 full-time. Full-time tuition and fees vary according to course load. Part-time tuition varies according to course load. College room and board: $6484. College room only: $3760. Room and board charges vary according to housing facility.

Collegiate Environment: Orientation program. Drama-theater group, choral group, marching band, student-run newspaper. Social organizations: 44 open to all; national fraternities, national sororities, local fraternities, local sororities; 10% of eligible men and 10% of eligible women are members. Most popular organizations: NAACP, Betterment of Brothers/Sisters, Student Government Association, dormitory cabinets, pre-alumni associations. Major annual events: Homecoming, Spring Fling, Commencement. Student

services: health clinic, personal-psychological counseling. Campus security: 24-hour emergency response devices and patrols, late night transport-escort service. 2,530 college housing spaces available; 2,418 were occupied in 2003-04. Freshmen given priority for college housing. On-campus residence required in freshman year. Options: coed, men-only, women-only housing available. Johnston Memorial Library with 284,213 books, 740,888 microform titles, 2,381 serials, 26,492 audiovisual materials, an OPAC, and a Web page. Operations spending for 2004 fiscal year: $3.3 million. 750 computers available on campus for general student use. A campuswide network can be accessed from student residence rooms and from off campus. Staffed computer lab on campus.

Community Environment: The immediate environs of the university offer an exciting atmosphere involving a variety of interesting sites and events for leisure-time activities. The Petersburg National Battlefield and Old Blandford Church are historical landmarks that are recognized in the National Historical Register. Other popular attractions include museums, art exhibits, parks, the Petersburg Symphony, and theatrical groups. The close proximity of Virginia's capital, Richmond, 25 minutes north, enhances the "VSU experience." Colonial Williamsburg and nearby Busch Gardens; Norfolk, home of one of America's busiest seaports; Virginia Beach, the top tourist attraction in the state; and the Blue Ridge Mountains are within easy driving distance.

■ **VIRGINIA UNION UNIVERSITY** *H-12*

1500 North Lombardy St.

Richmond, VA 23220-1170

Tel: (804)257-5600

Free: 800-368-3227

Admissions: (804)257-5881

Web Site: http://www.vuu.edu/

Description: Independent Baptist, comprehensive, coed. Awards bachelor's, master's, doctoral, and first professional degrees. Founded 1865. Setting: 72-acre urban campus. Total enrollment: 1,700. Faculty: 140 (84 full-time, 56 part-time). Student-undergrad faculty ratio is 15:1. 3,933 applied, 58% were admitted. 4% from top 10% of their high school class, 8% from top quarter, 36% from top half. Full-time: 1,309 students, 58% women, 42% men. Part-time: 35 students, 63% women, 37% men. Students come from 29 states and territories, 50% from out-of-state, 0% Native American, 1% Hispanic, 96% black, 0.3% Asian American or Pacific Islander, 0% international, 6% 25 or older, 4% transferred in. Retention: 69% of full-time freshmen returned the following year. Academic areas with the most degrees conferred: law/legal studies; business/marketing; social sciences. Core. Calendar: semesters. Academic remediation for entering students, ESL program, advanced placement, honors program, summer session for credit, adult/continuing education programs, co-op programs and internships. Off campus study at University of Richmond, Virginia Commonwealth University, Virginia State University. ROTC: Army (c).

Entrance Requirements: Options: Peterson's Universal Application, Common Application, early admission, deferred admission. Required: high school transcript, SAT or ACT. Recommended: essay, 3 recommendations. Entrance: moderately difficult. Application deadline: Rolling. Notification: continuous.

Costs Per Year: Application fee: $25. Comprehensive fee: $18,432 includes full-time tuition ($11,600), mandatory fees ($1170), and college room and board ($5662). College room only: $2662. Full-time tuition and fees vary according to course level and course load. Part-time tuition: $483 per credit hour. Part-time mandatory fees: $370 per term. Part-time tuition and fees vary according to course level and course load.

Collegiate Environment: Orientation program. Drama-theater group, choral group, marching band, student-run newspaper. Social organizations: national fraternities, national sororities; 10% of eligible men and 10% of eligible women are members. Student services: health clinic, personal-psychological counseling. Campus security: 24-hour emergency response devices and patrols, controlled dormitory access. 710 college housing spaces available; 619 were occupied in 2003-04. Freshmen given priority for college housing. Option: coed housing available. L. Douglas Wilder Learning Resource Center and Library with 147,611 books, 311 serials, and an OPAC. 128 computers available on campus for general student use. Staffed computer lab on campus.

Community Environment: See University of Richmond.

■ **VIRGINIA UNIVERSITY OF LYNCHBURG** *I-8*

2058 Garfield Ave.

Lynchburg, VA 24501-6417

Tel: (804)528-5276

Fax: (804)528-4257
Web Site: http://www.vulonline.org/
Description: Independent religious, comprehensive, coed. Founded 1886.
Calendar: semesters.

■ **VIRGINIA WESLEYAN COLLEGE** *J-15*
1584 Wesleyan Dr.
Norfolk, VA 23502-5599
Tel: (757)455-3200
Free: 800-737-8684
Admissions: (757)455-3208
Fax: (757)461-5238
E-mail: admissions@vwc.edu
Web Site: http://www.vwc.edu/
Description: Independent United Methodist, 4-year, coed. Awards
bachelor's degrees. Founded 1961. Setting: 300-acre urban campus with
easy access to Norfolk/Virginia Beach. Endowment: $43.5 million. Total
enrollment: 1,392. Student-undergrad faculty ratio is 12:1. 1,357 applied,
81% were admitted. 13% from top 10% of their high school class, 31% from
top quarter, 66% from top half. Full-time: 1,121 students, 61% women, 39%
men. Part-time: 271 students, 77% women, 23% men. Students come from
32 states and territories, 10 other countries, 22% from out-of-state, 0.5%
Native American, 3% Hispanic, 15% black, 2% Asian American or Pacific
Islander, 1% international, 21% 25 or older, 42% live on campus, 9%
transferred in. Retention: 66% of full-time freshmen returned the following
year. Academic areas with the most degrees conferred: business/marketing;
social sciences; communications/journalism. Core. Calendar: 4-1-4.
Academic remediation for entering students, services for LD students,
advanced placement, self-designed majors, freshman honors college,
honors program, independent study, distance learning, double major, summer session for credit, part-time degree program, adult/continuing education
programs, internships. Off campus study at Old Dominion University, Norfolk
State University, Virginia Tidewater Consortium for Higher Education. Study
abroad program. ROTC: Army (c).
Entrance Requirements: Options: Common Application, electronic application, international baccalaureate accepted. Required: essay, high school
transcript, minimum 2.5 high school GPA, SAT or ACT. Required for some:
interview. Entrance: moderately difficult. Application deadline: Rolling.
Notification: continuous.
Costs Per Year: Application fee: $40. Comprehensive fee: $29,986 includes
full-time tuition ($22,976), mandatory fees ($160), and college room and
board ($6850). Part-time tuition: $957 per semester hour.
Collegiate Environment: Orientation program. Drama-theater group, choral
group, student-run newspaper, radio station. Social organizations: 60 open
to all; national fraternities, national sororities; 10% of eligible men and 15%
of eligible women are members. Most popular organizations: student government, student radio station, student newspaper, Black Student Union,
Leadership Council. Major annual events: homecoming, Lake Taylor Music
Festival, Seafood Party in the Dell. Student services: health clinic, personal-
psychological counseling, women's center. Campus security: 24-hour
emergency response devices and patrols, late night transport-escort service,
controlled dormitory access, well-lit pathways. 633 college housing spaces
available; 609 were occupied in 2003-04. Freshmen guaranteed college
housing. On-campus residence required through senior year. Option: coed
housing available. H. C. Hofheimer II Library with 140,400 books, 15,844
microform titles, 923 serials, 3,810 audiovisual materials, an OPAC, and a
Web page. 100 computers available on campus for general student use.
Computer purchase/lease plans available. A campuswide network can be
accessed from student residence rooms. Staffed computer lab on campus.
Community Environment: Tidewater, Virginia, is the cultural center of the
Commonwealth. Norfolk features the Chrysler Museum, MacArthur Memo-
rial, Scope Arena, Chrysler Hall for professional theatre, an opera house,
and is headquarters of the Virginia Orchestra Group, Feldman String
Quartet, and the Tidewater Ballet Association. Virginia Beach, in addition to
its world-famous beaches, is proud of Seashore State Park, the Little
Theater, Edgar Cayce's Association for Research and Enlightenment, the
Virginia Beach Pops and other groups. Within one hour's driving time are
Colonial Williamsburg, Yorktown and Jamestown, several nationally known
museums including the Mariners Museum, and Busch Gardens.

■ **VIRGINIA WESTERN COMMUNITY COLLEGE** *I-6*
PO Box 14007
Roanoke, VA 24038
Tel: (540)857-7311

Admissions: (540)857-7231
Fax: (540)857-7204
Web Site: http://www.virginiawestern.edu/
Description: State-supported, 2-year, coed. Part of Virginia Community College System. Awards certificates, transfer associate, and terminal associate
degrees. Founded 1966. Setting: 70-acre suburban campus. Educational
spending for 2005 fiscal year: $5940 per student. Total enrollment: 8,124.
Full-time: 2,128 students, 58% women, 42% men. Part-time: 5,996 students,
59% women, 41% men. 1% from out-of-state, 0.3% Native American, 1%
Hispanic, 10% black, 2% Asian American or Pacific Islander, 0% international, 46% 25 or older, 16% transferred in. Core. Calendar: semesters.
Academic remediation for entering students, ESL program, services for LD
students, advanced placement, independent study, distance learning, double
major, summer session for credit, part-time degree program, adult/continuing
education programs, co-op programs and internships.
Entrance Requirements: Open admission except for health technology
programs. Options: Common Application, early admission, deferred admission. Required: high school transcript. Placement: SAT or ACT recommended. Entrance: noncompetitive. Application deadline: Rolling. Notification: continuous. Preference given to local residents.
Collegiate Environment: Drama-theater group, student-run newspaper.
Student services: personal-psychological counseling. College housing not
available. Brown Library with 67,129 books, 402 serials, an OPAC, and a
Web page. Operations spending for 2004 fiscal year: $344,730. 200 comput-
ers available on campus for general student use. A campuswide network can
be accessed from off-campus. Staffed computer lab on campus.
Community Environment: Roanoke is a manufacturing, regional service
and trading center, and a metropolitan area with all modes of transportation
available. Community facilities include libraries, YMCA, YWCA, many
churches, hospitals, and a number of the civic and service organizations.
Part-time employment opportunities are available to certain students.
Roanoke is headquarters for the Norfolk and Western Railway System and
the Blue Ridge Parkway. Smith Mountain Lake is a favorite water recreation
area. Carvin's Cove Lake nine and one-half miles north offers fishing, boating, and picnicking. Some of the points of interest are the Crystal Spring, Mill
Mountain, and Transportation Museum.

■ **WASHINGTON AND LEE UNIVERSITY** *G-7*
Lexington, VA 24450-0303
Tel: (540)458-8400
Admissions: (540)458-8710
Fax: (540)463-8062
E-mail: admissions@wlu.edu
Web Site: http://www.wlu.edu/
Description: Independent, comprehensive, coed. Awards bachelor's,
master's, and first professional degrees. Founded 1749. Setting: 322-acre
small town campus. Endowment: $532 million. Research spending for 2004
fiscal year: $1.6 million. Educational spending for 2005 fiscal year: $19,722
per student. Total enrollment: 2,179. Faculty: 217 (215 full-time, 2 part-time).
Student-undergrad faculty ratio is 10:1. 3,950 applied, 29% were admitted.
76% from top 10% of their high school class, 96% from top quarter, 100%
from top half. 32 National Merit Scholars, 39 valedictorians. Full-time: 1,766
students, 50% women, 50% men. Part-time: 4 students, 25% women, 75%
men. Students come from 47 states and territories, 35 other countries, 85%
from out-of-state, 0.3% Native American, 1% Hispanic, 4% black, 3% Asian
American or Pacific Islander, 4% international, 0% 25 or older, 61% live on
campus, 0.2% transferred in. Retention: 95% of full-time freshmen returned
the following year. Academic areas with the most degrees conferred: social
sciences; business/marketing; history. Core. Calendar: 4-4-2. Services for
LD students, advanced placement, accelerated degree program, self-
designed majors, honors program, independent study, double major, internships. Off campus study at 6 members of the Seven-College Exchange
Program, Bates College, Duke University, Virginia Military Institute. Study
abroad program. ROTC: Army (c).
Entrance Requirements: Options: Peterson's Universal Application, Common Application, electronic application, early decision, deferred admission,
international baccalaureate accepted. Required: essay, high school
transcript, 3 recommendations, SAT or ACT, 2 unrelated SAT Subject Tests.
Recommended: interview. Entrance: most difficult. Application deadlines:
1/15, 11/15 for early decision plan 1, 1/3 for early decision plan 2. Notification: 4/1, 12/22 for early decision plan 1, 2/1 for early decision plan 2.
Costs Per Year: Application fee: $50. Comprehensive fee: $35,860 includes
full-time tuition ($27,960), mandatory fees ($675), and college room and

board ($7225). College room only: $3425. Room and board charges vary according to housing facility and student level. Part-time tuition: $935 per credit.

Collegiate Environment: Orientation program. Drama-theater group, choral group, student-run newspaper, radio station. Social organizations: 127 open to all; national fraternities, national sororities; 78% of eligible men and 76% of eligible women are members. Most popular organizations: Outing Club, Student Activities Board, Nabors Service League, Mock Convention, College Republicans. Major annual events: Fancy Dress Ball, Homecoming, Alumni Weekend. Student services: health clinic, personal-psychological counseling, women's center. Campus security: 24-hour emergency response devices and patrols, late night transport-escort service, controlled dormitory access. 1,272 college housing spaces available; 1,081 were occupied in 2003-04. Freshmen guaranteed college housing. On-campus residence required through sophomore year. Options: coed, men-only, women-only housing available. James G. Leyburn Library plus 4 others with 907,325 books, 1 million microform titles, 8,027 serials, 16,079 audiovisual materials, an OPAC, and a Web page. Operations spending for 2004 fiscal year: $4.4 million. 297 computers available on campus for general student use. Computer purchase/lease plans available. A campuswide network can be accessed from student residence rooms and from off campus. Staffed computer lab on campus.

Community Environment: Lexington is located in the Shenandoah Valley of Virginia between the Blue Ridge and Allegheny Mountains. Two of the greatest Confederate heroes, Robert E. Lee and Thomas J. "Stonewall" Jackson, lived and are buried in Lexington, the "Shrine of the South." Bus transportation is available. Some of the points of interest are the Natural Bridge, Lee Chapel, Home of "Stonewall" Jackson, Virginia Military Institute, and Washington and Lee University. Cyrus McCormick, inventor of the reaper, lived nearby. Lexington is also the home of the Virginia Horse Center.

■ **WESTWOOD COLLEGE-ANNANDALE CAMPUS**

7611 Little River Turnpike, 3rd Floor
Annandale, VA 22003
Tel: (703)642-3770
Free: 800-281-2978
Web Site: http://www.westwood.edu/locations/virginia-colleges/annandale-college.asp

Description: Proprietary, primarily 2-year, coed. Awards transfer associate, terminal associate, and bachelor's degrees.

■ **WESTWOOD COLLEGE-ARLINGTON BALLSTON CAMPUS** *D-13*

1901 North Ft. Myer Dr.
Arlington, VA 22209
Tel: 800-281-2978
Admissions: 877-268-5218
E-mail: twilliams1@westwood.edu
Web Site: http://www.westwood.edu

Description: Proprietary, 4-year, coed. Awards associate and bachelor's degrees.

Entrance Requirements: Required: interview, Accuplacer Test. Entrance: minimally difficult.

Costs Per Year: Application fee: $100. Tuition: $12,300 full-time, $467 per credit part-time.

Collegiate Environment: Student services: personal-psychological counseling.

■ **WORLD COLLEGE** *J-15*

5193 Shore Dr., Ste. 105
Virginia Beach, VA 23455-2500
Tel: (757)464-4600
Free: 800-696-7532
Web Site: http://www.worldcollege.edu/

Description: Proprietary, 4-year, coed. Awards bachelor's degrees (offers only external degree programs). Founded 1992. Setting: suburban campus. Total enrollment: 281. Students come from 50 states and territories, 25 other countries, 94% 25 or older. Academic area with the most degrees conferred: engineering technologies. Core. Calendar: semesters. Academic remediation for entering students, accelerated degree program, distance learning, part-time degree program, external degree program, adult/continuing education programs.

Entrance Requirements: Open admission. Options: Common Application, early admission. Required: high school transcript. Entrance: noncompetitive. Application deadline: Rolling. Notification: continuous.

Costs Per Year: Tuition: $3540 per year part-time.

Collegiate Environment: College housing not available.

■ **WYTHEVILLE COMMUNITY COLLEGE** *J-3*

1000 East Main St.
Wytheville, VA 24382-3308
Tel: (276)223-4700
Admissions: (276)223-4755
Fax: (276)223-4860
E-mail: wcdixxs@wcc.vccs.edu
Web Site: http://www.wcc.vccs.edu/

Description: State-supported, 2-year, coed. Part of Virginia Community College System. Awards certificates, transfer associate, and terminal associate degrees. Founded 1967. Setting: 141-acre rural campus. Total enrollment: 2,450. 794 applied, 100% were admitted. Students come from 22 states and territories, 1 other country, 54% 25 or older. Core. Calendar: semesters. Academic remediation for entering students, services for LD students, advanced placement, distance learning, summer session for credit, part-time degree program, external degree program, adult/continuing education programs.

Entrance Requirements: Open admission. Option: early admission. Required: high school transcript. Required for some: interview. Entrance: noncompetitive. Application deadline: Rolling. Notification: continuous. Preference given to service region residents for allied health programs.

Collegiate Environment: Drama-theater group, student-run newspaper. Social organizations: national fraternities. Campus security: 24-hour emergency response devices and patrols. College housing not available. Wytheville Community College Library with 29,000 books and 261 serials. 105 computers available on campus for general student use. A campuswide network can be accessed. Staffed computer lab on campus.

Community Environment: Wytheville is located in a rich agricultural and cattle-raising area with most forms of commercial transportation available. A growing number of industries are located in the area, providing good part-time employment opportunities. Community facilities include a public library, churches, Jewish Synagogues in the neighboring towns of Bluefield and Bristol, a hospital, shopping areas, and a number of the civic and service organizations. Claytor Lake and the Jefferson National Forest provide opportunities for hunting, fishing, camping, and picnicking; other facilities within the city offer swimming and golf.

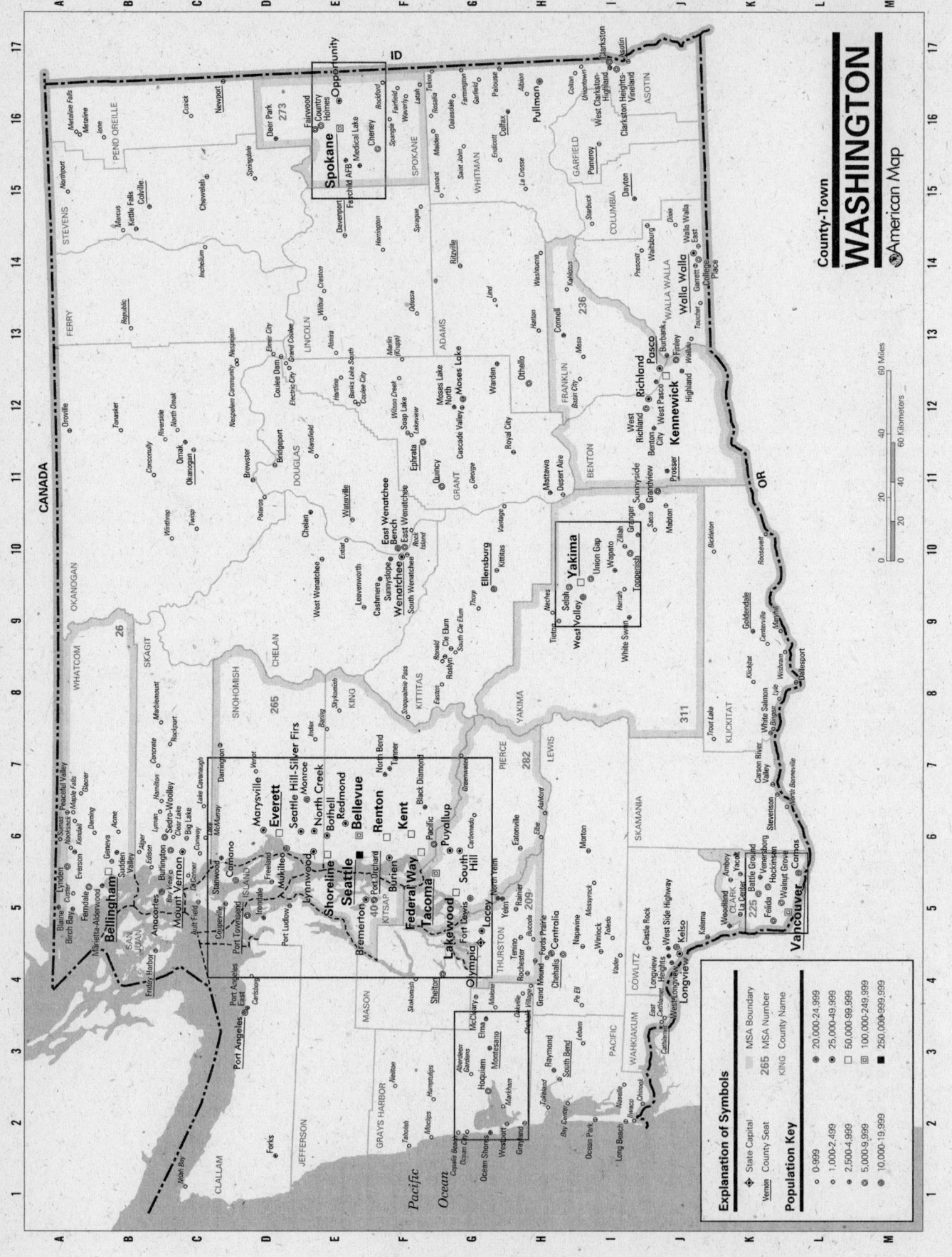

WASHINGTON
County-Town
American Map

Explanation of Symbols

◆ State Capital
<u>Vernon</u> County Seat
▓ MSA Boundary
265 MSA Number
<u>KING</u> County Name

Population Key

○ 0-999	◉ 20,000-24,999
○ 1,000-2,499	◉ 25,000-49,999
○ 2,500-4,999	□ 50,000-99,999
◉ 5,000-9,999	▣ 100,000-249,999
○ 10,000-19,999	■ 250,000-999,999

Scale: 0 20 40 60 Miles / 0 20 40 60 Kilometers

■ **ANTIOCH UNIVERSITY SEATTLE** *E-6*
2326 Sixth Ave.
Seattle, WA 98121-1814
Tel: (206)441-5352
Web Site: http://www.antiochsea.edu/
Description: Independent, upper-level, coed. Part of Antioch University. Awards bachelor's, master's, and doctoral degrees. Founded 1975. Setting: urban campus with easy access to Seattle. Total enrollment: 950. Students come from 3 states and territories, 2 other countries, 1% from out-of-state, 4% Native American, 3% Hispanic, 8% black, 3% Asian American or Pacific Islander, 1% international, 92% 25 or older. Core. Academic remediation for entering students, advanced placement, accelerated degree program, self-designed majors, summer session for credit, part-time degree program, external degree program, adult/continuing education programs, graduate courses open to undergrads. Study abroad program.
Collegiate Environment: Student-run newspaper. College housing not available. Antioch Seattle Library with 4,750 books, 85 serials, an OPAC, and a Web page. 8 computers available on campus for general student use. A campuswide network can be accessed from off-campus. Staffed computer lab on campus.

■ **APOLLO COLLEGE** *E-16*
1101 North Francher Rd.
Spokane, WA 99212
Tel: (509)532-8888
Fax: (509)533-5983
Web Site: http://www.apollocollege.com/
Description: Proprietary, 2-year, coed. Founded 1976.

■ **ARGOSY UNIVERSITY/SEATTLE** *E-6*
1019 Eighth Ave. North
Seattle, WA 98109
Tel: (206)283-4500; (866)283-2777
Fax: (206)283-5777
Web Site: http://www.argosyu.edu/
Description: Proprietary, upper-level, coed. Awards bachelor's, master's, and doctoral degrees. Founded 1995. Setting: urban campus with easy access to Seattle. Educational spending for 2005 fiscal year: $955 per student. Total enrollment: 293. 28 applied, 64% were admitted. Students come from 23 states and territories, 4% from out-of-state, 10% Hispanic, 5% black, 7% Asian American or Pacific Islander. Retention: 100% of full-time entering class returned the following year. Calendar: semesters.
Collegiate Environment: College housing not available.

■ **THE ART INSTITUTE OF SEATTLE** *E-6*
2323 Elliott Ave.
Seattle, WA 98121-1642
Tel: (206)448-0900
Free: 800-275-2471
Fax: (206)269-0275
E-mail: adm@ais.edu
Web Site: http://www.ais.artinstitutes.edu/
Description: Proprietary, 4-year, coed. Part of Education Management Corporation. Awards associate and bachelor's degrees. Founded 1982. Setting: urban campus. Total enrollment: 2,492. Student-undergrad faculty ratio

is 19:1. 693 applied, 67% were admitted. 8% from top 10% of their high school class, 18% from top quarter, 52% from top half. Full-time: 1,298 students, 48% women, 52% men. Part-time: 1,194 students, 49% women, 51% men. Students come from 49 states and territories, 21 other countries, 17% from out-of-state, 1% Native American, 3% Hispanic, 3% black, 8% Asian American or Pacific Islander, 6% international, 52% 25 or older, 2% transferred in. Retention: 66% of full-time freshmen returned the following year. Core. Academic remediation for entering students, services for LD students, honors program, summer session for credit, part-time degree program, adult/continuing education programs, internships. Off campus study at other members of The Art Institutes International, City University.
Entrance Requirements: Options: electronic application, deferred admission. Required: essay, high school transcript, minimum 2.0 high school GPA, interview. Recommended: 3 recommendations. Required for some: 2.5 GPA required for Bachelor degree applicants. Entrance: moderately difficult. Application deadline: Rolling. Notification: continuous.
Costs Per Year: Application fee: $50. Tuition: $17,550 full-time, $390 per credit part-time. College room only: $6867.
Collegiate Environment: Orientation program. Most popular organizations: Multicultural Affairs Organization, American Society of Interior Designers, DECA, Student Advisory Board. Major annual events: Student Art Show, Fashion Show, Holiday Dinner. Student services: personal-psychological counseling. Campus security: 24-hour emergency response devices and patrols, controlled dormitory access, patrols by trained security personnel for 17 hours. 524 college housing spaces available; 487 were occupied in 2003-04. Freshmen guaranteed college housing. Option: coed housing available. AIS Library plus 1 other with 17,164 books, 303 serials, 5,416 audiovisual materials, an OPAC, and a Web page. Operations spending for 2004 fiscal year: $272,500. 552 computers available on campus for general student use. A campuswide network can be accessed. Staffed computer lab on campus.

■ **BASTYR UNIVERSITY** *S-6*
14500 Juanita Dr., NE
Kenmore, WA 98028-4966
Tel: (425)823-1300
Admissions: (425)602-3014
Fax: (425)823-6222
Web Site: http://www.bastyr.edu/
Description: Independent, upper-level, coed. Awards bachelor's, master's, and first professional degrees and post-master's and first professional certificates. Founded 1978. Setting: 50-acre suburban campus with easy access to Seattle. Total enrollment: 1,098. Faculty: 148 (41 full-time, 107 part-time). Student-undergrad faculty ratio is 15:1. 723 applied, 77% were admitted. Full-time: 213 students, 84% women, 16% men. Part-time: 51 students, 82% women, 18% men. Students come from 21 states and territories, 8 other countries, 50% from out-of-state, 1% Native American, 5% Hispanic, 2% black, 5% Asian American or Pacific Islander, 5% international, 60% 25 or older, 7% live on campus, 50% transferred in. Academic areas with the most degrees conferred: interdisciplinary studies; health professions and related sciences; psychology. Independent study, double major, summer session for credit, part-time degree program, co-op programs and internships, graduate courses open to undergrads.
Costs Per Year: Application fee: $60. Tuition: $13,770 full-time, $306 per credit part-time. Mandatory fees: $1611 full-time. Full-time tuition and fees

vary according to course load and program. Part-time tuition varies according to course load and program. College room only: $2460. Room charges vary according to housing facility.

Collegiate Environment: Orientation program. Student-run newspaper. Most popular organizations: Parent Resource Center, Nature Club, Spirituality in Focus, Environmental Action Team, Toastmasters. Major annual events: Community Day, Talent Show, Graduation Party and Dance. Student services: health clinic, personal-psychological counseling. Campus security: student patrols, late night transport-escort service. Option: coed housing available. Bastyr University Library with 14,000 books, 265 serials, 6,000 audiovisual materials, an OPAC, and a Web page. Operations spending for 2004 fiscal year: $321,269. 28 computers available on campus for general student use. A campuswide network can be accessed from student residence rooms and from off campus. Staffed computer lab on campus.

■ **BATES TECHNICAL COLLEGE** G-5
1101 South Yakima Ave.
Tacoma, WA 98405-4895
Tel: (253)596-1500
Admissions: (253)680-7000
Web Site: http://www.bates.ctc.edu/
Description: State-supported, 2-year, coed. Part of Washington State Board for Community and Technical Colleges. Awards certificates, diplomas, and terminal associate degrees. Setting: urban campus with easy access to Seattle. Educational spending for 2005 fiscal year: $2977 per student. Total enrollment: 16,162.
Entrance Requirements: Placement: ACT ASSET required. Application deadline: Rolling. Notification: continuous.
Collegiate Environment: Student-run newspaper, radio station. Most popular organization: Associated Student Government. Major annual events: graduation, Martin Luther King, Jr. Celebration, Global Heritage Celebration. Campus security: 24-hour emergency response devices, on-campus weekday security to 10 p.m. College housing not available.

■ **BELLEVUE COMMUNITY COLLEGE** E-6
3000 Landerholm Circle, SE
Bellevue, WA 98007-6484
Tel: (425)564-1000
Admissions: (425)564-2222
Fax: (425)564-2261
Web Site: http://www.bcc.ctc.edu/
Description: State-supported, 2-year, coed. Part of Washington State Board for Community and Technical Colleges. Awards certificates, transfer associate, and terminal associate degrees. Founded 1966. Setting: 96-acre suburban campus with easy access to Seattle. Educational spending for 2005 fiscal year: $2722 per student. Total enrollment: 13,716. Students come from 32 states and territories, 64 other countries, 1% from out-of-state, 1% Native American, 1% Hispanic, 4% black, 14% Asian American or Pacific Islander, 2% international, 68% 25 or older. Core. Academic remediation for entering students, ESL program, services for LD students, advanced placement, honors program, independent study, distance learning, summer session for credit, part-time degree program, co-op programs and internships.
Entrance Requirements: Open admission. Option: electronic application. Entrance: noncompetitive. Application deadline: Rolling.
Costs Per Year: Application fee: $0. State resident tuition: $2655 full-time, $78.80 per credit part-time. Nonresident tuition: $7863 full-time, $250.50 per credit part-time.
Collegiate Environment: Orientation program. Drama-theater group, student-run newspaper, radio station. Student services: health clinic, personal-psychological counseling, women's center. College housing not available. Bellevue Community College Library with 42,000 books, 485 serials, an OPAC, and a Web page. Operations spending for 2004 fiscal year: $1.2 million. 600 computers available on campus for general student use. A campuswide network can be accessed from off-campus. Staffed computer lab on campus.
Community Environment: Bellevue is a suburban community of Seattle and enjoys temperate climate with an average rainfall of 33.5 inches. The city has churches of most denominations, a hospital, good shopping facilities, and major civic and fraternal organizations serving the area.

■ **BELLINGHAM TECHNICAL COLLEGE** B-5
3028 Lindbergh Ave.
Bellingham, WA 98225
Tel: (360)738-0221

Admissions: (360)738-3105
Fax: (360)676-2798
Web Site: http://www.btc.ctc.edu/
Description: State-supported, 2-year. Awards certificates and terminal associate degrees. Total enrollment: 4,159. 656 applied, 88% were admitted. 1 class president, 1 valedictorian. 2% Native American, 4% Hispanic, 1% black, 2% Asian American or Pacific Islander, 0.3% international, 52% 25 or older. Core. Academic remediation for entering students, ESL program, services for LD students, independent study, distance learning, summer session for credit, part-time degree program, co-op programs and internships.
Entrance Requirements: Open admission. Options: early admission, deferred admission. Entrance: noncompetitive. Application deadline: Rolling.
Collegiate Environment: Orientation program. Information Technology Resource Center with 9,537 books, 5,023 serials, 823 audiovisual materials, an OPAC, and a Web page. Operations spending for 2004 fiscal year: $220,000. 14 computers available on campus for general student use. A campuswide network can be accessed. Staffed computer lab on campus.

■ **BIG BEND COMMUNITY COLLEGE** G-12
7662 Chanute St., NE
Moses Lake, WA 98837-3299
Tel: (509)762-5351
Admissions: (509)793-2061
Fax: (509)762-6243
E-mail: candyl@bigbend.edu
Web Site: http://www.bigbend.edu/
Description: State-supported, 2-year, coed. Awards certificates, transfer associate, and terminal associate degrees. Founded 1962. Setting: 159-acre small town campus. Endowment: $1.1 million. Educational spending for 2005 fiscal year: $3191 per student. Total enrollment: 1,800. Student-undergrad faculty ratio is 20:1. 519 applied, 100% were admitted. Full-time: 1,194 students, 53% women, 47% men. Part-time: 606 students, 66% women, 34% men. Students come from 4 states and territories, 2 other countries, 5% from out-of-state, 1% Native American, 22% Hispanic, 1% black, 2% Asian American or Pacific Islander, 0.3% international, 30% 25 or older, 5% live on campus, 7% transferred in. Core. Academic remediation for entering students, services for LD students, advanced placement, distance learning, summer session for credit, part-time degree program, co-op programs.
Entrance Requirements: Open admission except for aviation, nursing programs. Options: early admission, deferred admission. Required for some: high school transcript. Entrance: noncompetitive. Application deadline: Rolling. Notification: continuous.
Costs Per Year: Application fee: $30. State resident tuition: $2586 full-time, $77.30 per credit part-time. Nonresident tuition: $2986 full-time, $90.50 per credit part-time. College room and board: $5200.
Collegiate Environment: Orientation program. Choral group. Student services: personal-psychological counseling. Campus security: 24-hour emergency response devices, student patrols. 150 college housing spaces available; 95 were occupied in 2003-04. No special consideration for freshman housing applicants. Option: coed housing available. Big Bend Community College Library with 41,900 books, 6,450 microform titles, 3,700 serials, 3,150 audiovisual materials, an OPAC, and a Web page. Operations spending for 2004 fiscal year: $305,584. 430 computers available on campus for general student use. A campuswide network can be accessed from off-campus. Staffed computer lab on campus.
Community Environment: Moses Lake is an important agricultural processing and shipping center for the Columbia Basin. This is a rural area with dry climate. The community has a library, many churches, a museum, a hospital and clinics, and modern shopping facilities. Local recreation includes lakes for fishing, swimming, boating, water skiing, and hydroplane boat races, as well as picnic areas and hunting areas for geese and pheasant. The community has major civic, fraternal and veteran's organizations. Grant County Fair, and a rodeo and parade are held here annually. Part-time employment is available.

■ **CASCADIA COMMUNITY COLLEGE** E-6
19017 120th Ave., NE, Ste. 102
Bothell, WA 98011
Tel: (425)398-5400
Admissions: (425)352-8000
Fax: (425)398-5730
Web Site: http://www.cascadia.ctc.edu/

Description: State-supported, 2-year, coed. Awards certificates, transfer associate, and terminal associate degrees. Founded 1999. Setting: 128-acre suburban campus. Total enrollment: 1,889. Full-time: 952 students, 46% women, 54% men. Part-time: 937 students, 52% women, 48% men. 0.2% Native American, 4% Hispanic, 2% black, 6% Asian American or Pacific Islander, 0% international. Retention: 60% of full-time freshmen returned the following year. Core. Academic remediation for entering students, ESL program, services for LD students, advanced placement, accelerated degree program, independent study, distance learning, part-time degree program, external degree program, adult/continuing education programs, co-op programs and internships. Off campus study. Study abroad program.

Entrance Requirements: Open admission.

Costs Per Year: State resident tuition: $2230 full-time, $74 per credit part-time. Nonresident tuition: $7738 full-time, $258 per credit part-time. Mandatory fees: $75 full-time, $4 per credit part-time.

Collegiate Environment: Campus security: 24-hour emergency response devices, late night transport-escort service. College housing not available. UWB/CCC Campus Library with 67,943 books, 10,799 microform titles, 979 serials, 6,100 audiovisual materials, an OPAC, and a Web page. 75 computers available on campus for general student use. Computer purchase/lease plans available. A campuswide network can be accessed from off-campus. Staffed computer lab on campus.

■ **CENTRAL WASHINGTON UNIVERSITY** *G-9*

400 East University Way
Ellensburg, WA 98926
Tel: (509)963-1111; (866)298-4968
Admissions: (509)963-1211
Fax: (509)963-3022
E-mail: cwuadmis@cwu.edu
Web Site: http://www.cwu.edu/

Description: State-supported, comprehensive, coed. Awards bachelor's and master's degrees. Founded 1891. Setting: 380-acre small town campus. Endowment: $9.1 million. Research spending for 2004 fiscal year: $2 million. Educational spending for 2005 fiscal year: $5208 per student. Total enrollment: 10,190. Faculty: 535 (364 full-time, 171 part-time). Student-undergrad faculty ratio is 22:1. 4,656 applied, 76% were admitted. 15% from top 10% of their high school class, 36% from top quarter, 77% from top half. Full-time: 8,530 students, 52% women, 48% men. Part-time: 1,087 students, 56% women, 44% men. Students come from 33 states and territories, 27 other countries, 3% from out-of-state, 1% Native American, 6% Hispanic, 2% black, 5% Asian American or Pacific Islander, 1% international, 22% 25 or older, 34% live on campus, 13% transferred in. Retention: 78% of full-time freshmen returned the following year. Academic areas with the most degrees conferred: business/marketing; education; security and protective services. Core. Academic remediation for entering students, ESL program, services for LD students, advanced placement, self-designed majors, honors program, independent study, distance learning, double major, summer session for credit, part-time degree program, adult/continuing education programs, co-op programs and internships, graduate courses open to undergrads. Off campus study at National Student Exchange. Study abroad program. ROTC: Army, Air Force.

Entrance Requirements: Options: Peterson's Universal Application, electronic application, international baccalaureate accepted. Required: high school transcript, minimum 2.0 high school GPA, SAT or ACT. Required for some: essay, recommendations, interview. Entrance: moderately difficult. Application deadline: 4/1. Notification: continuous.

Costs Per Year: Application fee: $50. State resident tuition: $4182 full-time. Nonresident tuition: $12,477 full-time. Mandatory fees: $624 full-time. College room and board: $6924.

Collegiate Environment: Orientation program. Drama-theater group, choral group, marching band, student-run newspaper, radio station. Social organizations: 50 open to all. Most popular organizations: International Business Club, Marketing Club, Associated Students of CWU. Major annual events: Homecoming, Parents' Weekend, Drug Awareness Week. Student services: health clinic, personal-psychological counseling. Campus security: 24-hour emergency response devices and patrols, late night transport-escort service, controlled dormitory access. 3,140 college housing spaces available; 2,194 were occupied in 2003-04. Freshmen guaranteed college housing. On-campus residence required in freshman year. Options: coed, women-only housing available. Central Washington University Library with 434,424 books, 1.1 million microform titles, 1,469 serials, 9,230 audiovisual materials, an OPAC, and a Web page. 720 computers available on campus

for general student use. A campuswide network can be accessed from student residence rooms and from off campus. Staffed computer lab on campus.

Community Environment: Ellensburg is a small university town in central Washington. The climate is mild and dry. The community has several churches, three libraries, a hospital and infirmary. Ellensburg may be reached by railroad, bus lines, and Interstate 90 and 82. Local recreation includes camping, hiking, river rafting, rodeo, snow sports, fishing, hunting, boating, skiing and golf. There are many job opportunities available at the university. Various civic and fraternal organizations are active in the community.

■ **CENTRALIA COLLEGE** *H-4*

600 West Locust
Centralia, WA 98531-4099
Tel: (360)736-9391
E-mail: scopeland@centralia.edu
Web Site: http://www.centralia.ctc.edu/

Description: State-supported, 2-year, coed. Part of Washington State Board for Community and Technical Colleges. Awards certificates, transfer associate, and terminal associate degrees. Founded 1925. Setting: 31-acre small town campus. Endowment: $4 million. Educational spending for 2005 fiscal year: $2740 per student. Total enrollment: 3,827. Student-undergrad faculty ratio is 24:1. 2,428 applied, 96% were admitted. Students come from 4 states and territories, 1% from out-of-state, 2% Native American, 10% Hispanic, 1% black, 2% Asian American or Pacific Islander, 1% international, 55% 25 or older. Retention: 72% of full-time freshmen returned the following year. Core. Academic remediation for entering students, ESL program, services for LD students, advanced placement, freshman honors college, honors program, independent study, distance learning, summer session for credit, part-time degree program, external degree program, adult/continuing education programs, co-op programs. Study abroad program.

Entrance Requirements: Open admission except for nursing program. Options: electronic application, international baccalaureate accepted. Required: high school transcript. Entrance: noncompetitive. Application deadline: Rolling. Notification: continuous until 9/15.

Costs Per Year: Application fee: $0. State resident tuition: $2586 full-time, $74 per credit part-time. Nonresident tuition: $2946 full-time, $86 per credit part-time. Mandatory fees: $274 full-time, $8 per credit part-time, $5 per term part-time.

Collegiate Environment: Orientation program. Drama-theater group, choral group, marching band, student-run newspaper, radio station. Social organizations: 22 open to all. Most popular organizations: Phi Theta Kappa, Diesel Tech Club, Business Management Association, Student Activities/Admissions Team, International Club. Major annual events: CC 101 Orientation, Graduation, Spring Fest. Student services: personal-psychological counseling. Campus security: 24-hour patrols, late night transport-escort service. College housing not available. Kirk Library with 38,000 books, 225 serials, an OPAC, and a Web page. Operations spending for 2004 fiscal year: $372,726. 125 computers available on campus for general student use. Computer purchase/lease plans available. A campuswide network can be accessed from off-campus. Staffed computer lab on campus.

■ **CITY UNIVERSITY** *E-6*

11900 NE First St.
Bellevue, WA 98005
Tel: (425)637-1010; 888-42-CITYU
Admissions: 800-426-5596
Fax: (425)277-2437
E-mail: info@cityu.edu
Web Site: http://www.cityu.edu/

Description: Independent, comprehensive, coed. Awards associate, bachelor's, and master's degrees. Founded 1973. Setting: suburban campus with easy access to Seattle. Endowment: $195,000. Educational spending for 2005 fiscal year: $1359 per student. Total enrollment: 4,020. Faculty: 1,241 (52 full-time, 1,189 part-time). Student-undergrad faculty ratio is 7:1. Full-time: 1,007 students, 58% women, 42% men. Part-time: 787 students, 54% women, 46% men. Students come from 47 states and territories, 33 other countries, 11% from out-of-state, 1% Native American, 3% Hispanic, 4% black, 6% Asian American or Pacific Islander, 6% international, 88% 25 or older. Academic areas with the most degrees conferred: business/marketing; computer and information sciences; education. Core. ESL program, services for LD students, advanced placement, accelerated degree program, self-designed majors, distance learning, double major, summer session for credit, part-time degree program, external degree program, adult/continuing education programs, internships, graduate courses open to undergrads.

Entrance Requirements: Open admission. Options: Common Application, electronic application, deferred admission. Recommended: high school transcript. Entrance: noncompetitive. Application deadline: Rolling. Notification: continuous.

Costs Per Year: Application fee: $80. Tuition: $8040 full-time, $268 per credit hour part-time. Mandatory fees: $120 full-time, $40 per term part-time.

Collegiate Environment: Campus security: 24-hour emergency response devices. College housing not available. City University Library with 32,329 books, 405,350 microform titles, 1,518 serials, 5,184 audiovisual materials, an OPAC, and a Web page. Operations spending for 2004 fiscal year: $774,136. 145 computers available on campus for general student use. A campuswide network can be accessed from off-campus. Staffed computer lab on campus.

■ **CLARK COLLEGE** *L-5*
1800 East McLoughlin Blvd.
Vancouver, WA 98663-3598
Tel: (360)992-2000
Admissions: (360)992-2308
Web Site: http://www.clark.edu/

Description: State-supported, 2-year, coed. Part of Washington State Board for Community and Technical Colleges. Awards certificates, diplomas, transfer associate, and terminal associate degrees. Founded 1933. Setting: 80-acre urban campus with easy access to Portland. Endowment: $43 million. Educational spending for 2005 fiscal year: $3194 per student. Total enrollment: 9,820. Student-undergrad faculty ratio is 23:1. 2,812 applied, 100% were admitted. Full-time: 4,255 students, 56% women, 44% men. Part-time: 5,565 students, 62% women, 38% men. Students come from 6 states and territories, 16 other countries, 4% from out-of-state, 36% 25 or older, 9% transferred in. Core. Academic remediation for entering students, ESL program, services for LD students, advanced placement, accelerated degree program, independent study, distance learning, summer session for credit, part-time degree program, adult/continuing education programs, co-op programs and internships. Study abroad program. ROTC: Army (c), Air Force (c).

Entrance Requirements: Open admission. Options: early admission, deferred admission. Required for some: high school transcript, interview. Entrance: noncompetitive. Application deadline: 8/3. Notification: continuous.

Costs Per Year: Application fee: $0. State resident tuition: $2704 full-time, $78 per credit hour part-time. Nonresident tuition: $3093 full-time, $91 per credit hour part-time. Full-time tuition varies according to course load and reciprocity agreements. Part-time tuition varies according to course load and reciprocity agreements.

Collegiate Environment: Orientation program. Drama-theater group, choral group, student-run newspaper. Social organizations: 25 open to all. Most popular organizations: Phi Theta Kappa, Baptist Student Ministries, Multicultural Students United, Peace Project, Students for Political Activism Now (SPAN). Major annual events: Earth Night/Week, International Night, Spring Thing. Student services: legal services, health clinic, personal-psychological counseling. Campus security: 24-hour patrols, late night transport-escort service, security staff during hours of operation. College housing not available. Lewis D. Cannell Library with 63,525 books, 9,645 microform titles, 417 serials, 2,147 audiovisual materials, an OPAC, and a Web page. Operations spending for 2004 fiscal year: $1 million. 750 computers available on campus for general student use. A campuswide network can be accessed from off-campus. Staffed computer lab on campus.

Community Environment: The oldest city in the state, Vancouver is located at the head of the deep-water navigation of the Columbia River. This is an industrial city with job opportunities for students. The city is served by rail, bus and major highways. Local recreation includes fishing, hunting, boating, skiing, and nearby beaches.

■ **CLOVER PARK TECHNICAL COLLEGE** *D-6*
4500 Steilacoom Blvd., SW
Lakewood, WA 98499
Tel: (253)589-5678
Admissions: (253)589-5570
Web Site: http://www.cptc.edu/

Description: State-supported, 2-year, coed. Part of Washington State Community and Technical College System. Awards certificates and terminal associate degrees. Founded 1942. Educational spending for 2005 fiscal year:

$2813 per student. Total enrollment: 8,488. Full-time: 1,848 students, 57% women, 43% men. Part-time: 6,640 students, 62% women, 38% men. Students come from 3 states and territories, 0% from out-of-state, 1% Native American, 3% Hispanic, 12% black, 7% Asian American or Pacific Islander, 1% international, 61% 25 or older. Core. Academic remediation for entering students, ESL program, services for LD students, accelerated degree program, distance learning, part-time degree program, co-op programs and internships.

Entrance Requirements: Open admission. Options: Common Application, electronic application, international baccalaureate accepted. Required for some: high school transcript, interview. Placement: ACT COMPASS required. Entrance: noncompetitive. Application deadline: 9/27. Notification: continuous until 9/27.

Costs Per Year: Application fee: $36. State resident tuition: $2529 full-time, $51 per credit hour part-time. Mandatory fees: $579 full-time.

Collegiate Environment: Orientation program. Student-run newspaper. Most popular organizations: Accounting Numbers Club, Auto Tech Club, Computer Users Club, Social Services Club. Major annual events: Veteran's Day Celebration, Martin Luther King, Jr. Celebration, car show. Student services: personal-psychological counseling. Campus security: 24-hour patrols, late night transport-escort service. College housing not available. CPTC Library with 11,219 books, 97 serials, 2,322 audiovisual materials, an OPAC, and a Web page. Operations spending for 2004 fiscal year: $355,014. 1,510 computers available on campus for general student use. A campuswide network can be accessed from off-campus. Staffed computer lab on campus.

■ **COLUMBIA BASIN COLLEGE** *J-12*
2600 North 20th Ave.
Pasco, WA 99301-3397
Tel: (509)547-0511
Fax: (509)546-0401
Web Site: http://www.columbiabasin.edu

Description: State-supported, 2-year, coed. Part of Washington State Board for Community and Technical Colleges. Awards transfer associate and terminal associate degrees. Founded 1955. Setting: 156-acre small town campus. Educational spending for 2005 fiscal year: $2378 per student. Total enrollment: 5,837. Full-time: 2,425 students, 51% women, 49% men. Part-time: 3,412 students, 55% women, 45% men. Students come from 17 states and territories, 2 other countries, 2% from out-of-state, 1% Native American, 11% Hispanic, 2% black, 3% Asian American or Pacific Islander, 0.3% international, 57% 25 or older, 1% transferred in. Core. Academic remediation for entering students, ESL program, services for LD students, advanced placement, accelerated degree program, distance learning, summer session for credit, part-time degree program, adult/continuing education programs, co-op programs and internships.

Entrance Requirements: Open admission except for nursing program. Options: Common Application, electronic application, international baccalaureate accepted. Required: high school transcript. Recommended: high school transcript. Placement: ACT ASSET required. Entrance: noncompetitive. Application deadline: Rolling. Notification: continuous.

Collegiate Environment: Orientation program. Drama-theater group, choral group, student-run newspaper. Social organizations: 20 open to all. Most popular organizations: Phi Theta Kappa, Men's Athletic Club, Band Club, Women's Athletic Club, Drama Club. Major annual events: drama productions, Student Center entertainment. Student services: personal-psychological counseling, women's center. Campus security: 24-hour patrols. College housing not available. Columbia Basin College Library with 54,331 books, 77,764 microform titles, 363 serials, 6,365 audiovisual materials, an OPAC, and a Web page. Operations spending for 2004 fiscal year: $543,409. 520 computers available on campus for general student use. A campuswide network can be accessed. Staffed computer lab on campus.

■ **CORNISH COLLEGE OF THE ARTS** *E-6*
1000 Lenora St.
Seattle, WA 98121
Tel: (206)726-5151
Free: 800-726-ARTS
Admissions: (206)726-5018
Fax: (206)720-1011
E-mail: epedersen@comish.edu
Web Site: http://www.cornish.edu/

Description: Independent, 4-year, coed. Awards bachelor's degrees. Founded 1914. Setting: 4-acre urban campus. Endowment: $636,870.

Educational spending for 2005 fiscal year: $6346 per student. Total enrollment: 768. Student-undergrad faculty ratio is 8:1. 1,135 applied, 51% were admitted. Full-time: 739 students, 64% women, 36% men. Part-time: 29 students, 76% women, 24% men. Students come from 27 states and territories, 14 other countries, 40% from out-of-state, 1% Native American, 5% Hispanic, 2% black, 4% Asian American or Pacific Islander, 3% international, 22% 25 or older, 5% transferred in. Retention: 71% of full-time freshmen returned the following year. Academic area with the most degrees conferred: visual and performing arts. Core. Calendar: semesters. Academic remediation for entering students, services for LD students, advanced placement, independent study, summer session for credit, internships. Study abroad program.

Entrance Requirements: Options: electronic application, deferred admission. Required: essay, high school transcript, minimum 2.0 high school GPA, portfolio or audition. Recommended: 2 recommendations, interview. Required for some: 2 recommendations. Entrance: moderately difficult. Application deadline: 8/15. Notification: continuous.

Costs Per Year: Application fee: $35. Tuition: $21,200 full-time, $875 per credit part-time. Mandatory fees: $300 full-time.

Collegiate Environment: Orientation program. Drama-theater group, choral group, student-run newspaper. Social organizations: 11 open to all. Most popular organizations: Birds and Whistles (Arts Magazine), film society, Black Student Alliance, Student Leadership Council, intramural club sports. Major annual events: Spring Festival, Cabaret, BFA Show. Student services: personal-psychological counseling. Campus security: 24-hour emergency response devices and patrols, late night transport-escort service. College housing not available. Cornish College of the Arts Library plus 2 others with 12,000 books, 3,000 serials, and an OPAC. Operations spending for 2004 fiscal year: $100,000. 20 computers available on campus for general student use. from off-campusStaffed computer lab on campus.

Community Environment: Urban.

■ **CROWN COLLEGE** *G-5*

8739 South Hosmer
Tacoma, WA 98444-1836
Tel: (253)531-3123; 888-689-3688
Fax: (253)531-3521
Web Site: http://www.crowncollege.edu/

Description: Proprietary, primarily 2-year, coed. Administratively affiliated with Killebrew Dalton, Inc. Awards transfer associate, terminal associate, and bachelor's degrees (bachelor's degree in public administration only). Founded 1969. Setting: urban campus with easy access to Seattle. Total enrollment: 218. Student-undergrad faculty ratio is 20:1. Students come from 39 states and territories, 1 other country, 82% from out-of-state, 59% 25 or older. Core. Calendar: continuous. Academic remediation for entering students, honors program, distance learning, double major, co-op programs and internships. Off campus study. Study abroad program.

Entrance Requirements: Options: Common Application, electronic application. Required: high school transcript, interview. Required for some: essay. Notification: continuous.

Costs Per Year: Application fee: $135. Tuition: $7500 full-time. Mandatory fees: $385 full-time.

Collegiate Environment: Orientation program. Campus security: 24-hour emergency response devices. College housing not available. Crown College Library plus 1 other with 9,500 books, 37 serials, 70 audiovisual materials, an OPAC, and a Web page. 12 computers available on campus for general student use. A campuswide network can be accessed from student residence rooms and from off campus. Staffed computer lab on campus.

■ **DEVRY UNIVERSITY (BELLEVUE)** *E-6*

500 108th Ave. NE, Ste. 320
Bellevue, WA 98004-5519
Tel: (425)455-2242
Fax: (425)455-2322
Web Site: http://www.devry.edu/

Description: Proprietary, comprehensive, coed. Calendar: semesters.

Costs Per Year: One-time mandatory fee: $40. Tuition: $13,060 full-time, $475 per credit part-time. Mandatory fees: $60 full-time, $30 per year part-time. Full-time tuition and fees vary according to course load. Part-time tuition and fees vary according to course load.

■ **DEVRY UNIVERSITY (FEDERAL WAY)** *F-6*

3600 South 344th Way
Federal Way, WA 98001

Tel: (253)943-2800; (866)338-7934
Web Site: http://www.devry.edu/

Description: Proprietary, comprehensive, coed. Part of DeVry University. Awards associate, bachelor's, and master's degrees. Founded 2001. Setting: 12-acre suburban campus. Total enrollment: 877. Faculty: 50 (32 full-time, 18 part-time). Student-undergrad faculty ratio is 18:1. Full-time: 549 students, 27% women, 73% men. Part-time: 225 students, 35% women, 65% men. 2% Native American, 7% Hispanic, 13% black, 11% Asian American or Pacific Islander, 1% international, 41% 25 or older. Academic areas with the most degrees conferred: computer and information sciences; business/marketing; engineering technologies. Calendar: semesters. Academic remediation for entering students, services for LD students, advanced placement, accelerated degree program, distance learning, summer session for credit, part-time degree program, adult/continuing education programs, co-op programs.

Entrance Requirements: Options: electronic application, deferred admission, international baccalaureate accepted. Required: high school transcript, interview. Entrance: minimally difficult. Application deadline: Rolling.

Costs Per Year: Application fee: $50. One-time mandatory fee: $40. Tuition: $13,060 full-time, $475 per credit part-time. Mandatory fees: $270 full-time, $160 per year part-time. Full-time tuition and fees vary according to course load. Part-time tuition and fees vary according to course load.

Collegiate Environment: Orientation program. Social organizations: 4 open to all. Most popular organizations: Associated Student Body (ASB), Ski Club, Computer Information Club, Basketball Club. Major annual events: Summer BBQ, Holiday Banquet, Stress Breaks. Campus security: 24-hour emergency response devices and patrols, lighted pathways, emergency response team. College housing not available. Learning Resource Center with 6,021 books, 6,807 serials, 61 audiovisual materials, an OPAC, and a Web page. 150 computers available on campus for general student use. Computer purchase/lease plans available. A campuswide network can be accessed from off-campus. Staffed computer lab on campus.

■ **DIGIPEN INSTITUTE OF TECHNOLOGY** *E-6*

5001 150th Ave., NE
Redmond, WA 98052
Tel: (425)558-0299
Fax: (425)558-0299
Web Site: http://www.digipen.edu/

Description: Proprietary, primarily 2-year, coed. Awards certificates, terminal associate, bachelor's, and master's degrees. Founded 1988. Total enrollment: 677. Faculty: 51. Student-undergrad faculty ratio is 13:1. Full-time: 617 students, 6% women, 94% men. Part-time: 40 students, 100% men. 0.3% Native American, 4% Hispanic, 2% black, 4% Asian American or Pacific Islander, 3% international. Calendar: semesters.

Entrance Requirements: Required: essay, high school transcript, minimum 2.5 high school GPA, 2 recommendations, SAT or ACT. Recommended: SAT/ACT art portfolio. Required for some: SAT/ACT art portfolio. Entrance: moderately difficult.

Costs Per Year: Application fee: $75. One-time mandatory fee: $150. Tuition: $15,200 full-time, $380 per credit part-time. Mandatory fees: $160 full-time, $80.

Collegiate Environment: Student services: personal-psychological counseling.

■ **EASTERN WASHINGTON UNIVERSITY** *F-16*

526 5th St.
Cheney, WA 99004-2431
Tel: (509)359-6200
Admissions: (509)359-6582
Fax: (509)359-4330
E-mail: admissions@ewu.edu
Web Site: http://www.ewu.edu/

Description: State-supported, comprehensive, coed. Awards bachelor's, master's, and doctoral degrees. Founded 1882. Setting: 335-acre small town campus. Endowment: $4.5 million. Research spending for 2004 fiscal year: $14.3 million. Educational spending for 2005 fiscal year: $3383 per student. Total enrollment: 10,908. Faculty: 575 (411 full-time, 164 part-time). Student-undergrad faculty ratio is 21:1. 4,365 applied, 83% were admitted. Full-time: 8,174 students, 58% women, 42% men. Part-time: 1,429 students, 56% women, 44% men. Students come from 46 states and territories, 34 other countries, 8% from out-of-state, 2% Native American, 6% Hispanic, 3% black, 4% Asian American or Pacific Islander, 1% international, 23% 25 or older, 20% live on campus, 12% transferred in. Retention: 77% of full-time freshmen returned the following year. Academic areas with the most degrees conferred: business/marketing; education; health professions and related sciences. Core. Academic remediation for entering students, ESL program, services for LD students, advanced placement, self-designed majors, honors program, independent study, distance learning, double major, summer session for credit, part-time degree program, co-op programs and internships. Off campus study at Intercollegiate Center for Nursing. Study abroad program. ROTC: Army.

Entrance Requirements: Options: Peterson's Universal Application, Common Application, electronic application, early admission, deferred admission, international baccalaureate accepted. Required: high school transcript, minimum 2.0 high school GPA, SAT or ACT. Recommended: minimum 3.0 high school GPA. Required for some: essay, recommendations, interview. Entrance: moderately difficult. Application deadline: 9/15. Notification: continuous.

Costs Per Year: Application fee: $50. State resident tuition: $4044 full-time, $135 per credit part-time. Nonresident tuition: $17,756 full-time, $444 per credit part-time. Mandatory fees: $237 full-time, $79 per term part-time. Full-time tuition and fees vary according to course load. Part-time tuition and fees vary according to course load. College room and board: $5733. Room and board charges vary according to board plan and housing facility.

Collegiate Environment: Orientation program. Drama-theater group, choral group, marching band, student-run newspaper, radio station. Social organizations: 93 open to all; national fraternities, national sororities; 10% of eligible men and 10% of eligible women are members. Most popular organizations: International Student Association, cultural heritage groups, Eagle Ambassadors, business/honor fraternities, religious organizations. Major annual events: homecoming, Club Vegas, World Party. Student services: health clinic, personal-psychological counseling, women's center. Campus security: 24-hour emergency response devices and patrols, student patrols, late night transport-escort service, controlled dormitory access, emergency call boxes. 2,000 college housing spaces available; 1,930 were occupied in 2003-04. No special consideration for freshman housing applicants. Options: coed, men-only, women-only housing available. John F. Kennedy Library plus 1 other with 852,186 books, 1.4 million microform titles, 6,429 serials, 31,832 audiovisual materials, an OPAC, and a Web page. Operations spending for 2004 fiscal year: $4 million. 200 computers available on campus for general student use. Computer purchase/lease plans available. A campuswide network can be accessed from student residence rooms and from off campus. Staffed computer lab on campus.

Community Environment: Cheney is located 16 miles southwest of Spokane. The community is reached by major highways, rail, bus, and air lines with Spokane Airport approximately 11 miles away. The city has many churches and various civic, fraternal, and veteran's organizations. Local recreation includes hunting, fishing, skiing, and swimming on nearby lakes. Part-time employment is available.

■ **EDMONDS COMMUNITY COLLEGE** *E-6*
20000 68th Ave. West
Lynnwood, WA 98036-5999
Tel: (425)640-1500
Admissions: (425)640-1401
Fax: (425)640-1159
E-mail: raeellen.reas@edcc.edu
Web Site: http://www.edcc.edu/

Description: State and locally supported, 2-year, coed. Part of Washington State Board for Community and Technical Colleges. Awards certificates, transfer associate, and terminal associate degrees. Founded 1967. Setting: 115-acre suburban campus with easy access to Seattle. Endowment: $2.7 million. Educational spending for 2005 fiscal year: $3600 per student. Total enrollment: 7,581. Student-undergrad faculty ratio is 21:1. 1,770 applied, 100% were admitted. Full-time: 3,398 students, 51% women, 49% men. Part-time: 4,183 students, 61% women, 39% men. Students come from 55 other countries, 2% from out-of-state, 2% Native American, 4% Hispanic, 5% black, 10% Asian American or Pacific Islander, 11% international, 11% 25 or older, 1% transferred in. Core. Academic remediation for entering students, ESL program, services for LD students, advanced placement, self-designed majors, honors program, distance learning, summer session for credit, part-time degree program, adult/continuing education programs, co-op programs and internships. Off campus study at other community colleges in Washington. Study abroad program.

Entrance Requirements: Open admission. Options: Common Application, electronic application, early admission, deferred admission. Entrance: noncompetitive. Application deadline: Rolling. Notification: continuous.

Costs Per Year: Application fee: $17. State resident tuition: $2436 full-time, $71.80 per credit hour part-time. Nonresident tuition: $7610 full-time, $251 per credit hour part-time. Mandatory fees: $166 full-time, $4.25 per credit hour part-time. Full-time tuition and fees vary according to course load. Part-time tuition and fees vary according to course load. College room only: $4500.

Collegiate Environment: Orientation program. Drama-theater group, choral group, student-run newspaper. Social organizations: 40 open to all. Most popular organizations: Phi Theta Kappa, AITP, AAWCC, International Club, Pottery/Art Club. Major annual events: Commencement, campus barbecues, music performances. Student services: personal-psychological counseling, women's center. Campus security: 24-hour emergency response devices and patrols, student patrols, late night transport-escort service. College housing not available. Edmonds Community College Library with 47,947 books, 51 microform titles, 312 serials, 7,735 audiovisual materials, an OPAC, and a Web page. Operations spending for 2004 fiscal year: $915,656. 1,129 computers available on campus for general student use. A campuswide network can be accessed from off-campus. Staffed computer lab on campus.

Community Environment: Lynnwood overlooks the Puget Sound and the Olympic Mountains, and is connected with the Olympic Peninsula by ferry. This is a large, rapidly growing suburban community. The city has a large public marina, good shopping facilities, and good recreation areas. There is a public library, churches, and theatres. Good skiing and winter sports may be found within an hour's drive.

■ **EVERETT COMMUNITY COLLEGE** *D-6*
2000 Tower St.
Everett, WA 98201-1327
Tel: (425)388-9100
Admissions: (425)388-9204
Fax: (425)388-9173
Web Site: http://www.evcc.ctc.edu/

Description: State-supported, 2-year, coed. Part of Washington State Board for Community and Technical Colleges. Awards certificates, diplomas, transfer associate, and terminal associate degrees. Founded 1941. Setting: 25-acre suburban campus with easy access to Seattle. Endowment: $1.5 million. Educational spending for 2005 fiscal year: $2213 per student. Total enrollment: 7,188. Full-time: 3,262 students, 60% women, 40% men. Part-time: 3,926 students, 63% women, 37% men. Students come from 17 states and territories, 13 other countries, 3% from out-of-state, 2% Native American, 4% Hispanic, 2% black, 5% Asian American or Pacific Islander, 0.4% international, 46% 25 or older, 3% transferred in. Retention: 59% of full-time freshmen returned the following year. Core. Academic remediation for entering students, ESL program, services for LD students, advanced placement, independent study, distance learning, summer session for credit, part-time degree program, adult/continuing education programs, co-op programs and internships. Study abroad program.

Entrance Requirements: Open admission except for some programs such as cosmetology, aviation, criminal justice, fire science, nursing, and medical assisting. Options: Common Application, electronic application, early admission, deferred admission. Recommended: high school transcript. Placement: ACT ASSET, ACT COMPASS recommended. Entrance: noncompetitive. Application deadline: Rolling. Notification: continuous.

Costs Per Year: Application fee: $0. State resident tuition: $2313 full-time, $69.35 per credit part-time. Nonresident tuition: $7521 full-time, $241.05 per credit part-time. Full-time tuition varies according to course load. Part-time tuition varies according to course load.

Collegiate Environment: Orientation program. Drama-theater group, choral group, student-run newspaper. Social organizations: 25 open to all. Most popular organizations: United Native American Council, Nippon Friendship Club, Student Nurses Association, International Students Club, Math, Engineering and Science Student Organization. Major annual events: Student Activities Kick-off, Campus Awareness Days, Artist and Lecture Series. Student services: personal-psychological counseling, women's center. Campus security: 24-hour emergency response devices and patrols, late night transport-escort service. College housing not available. John Terrey Library/Media Center with 49,600 books, 69,964 microform titles, 279 serials, 5,997 audiovisual materials, an OPAC, and a Web page. Operations spending for 2004 fiscal year: $1.1 million. 600 computers available on campus for general student use. A campuswide network can be accessed from off-campus. Staffed computer lab on campus.

Community Environment: Located on a natural landlocked harbor at the mouth of the Snohomish River, Everett looks across the Sound at the snowy crags of the Olympic Range. The chief industries of the area are lumbering and the manufacture of airplanes. Railroad lines, bus lines, and Interstate 5 serve the community. More than 60 churches of major denominations, two hospitals, and a library are within the immediate community. Local recreation includes a civic auditorium and stadium, ballfields, tennis courts, roller rinks, bowling alleys, golf courses, outdoor theaters, hunting, fishing, and boating. Skiing areas are a few hours away. Part-time employment is available for students.

■ **THE EVERGREEN STATE COLLEGE** *G-4*
2700 Evergreen Parkway, NW
Olympia, WA 98505
Tel: (360)867-6000
Admissions: (360)867-6170
Fax: (360)867-6577
E-mail: admissions@evergreen.edu
Web Site: http://www.evergreen.edu/
Description: State-supported, comprehensive, coed. Part of Washington State Public Institution. Awards bachelor's and master's degrees. Founded 1967. Setting: 1,000-acre small town campus with easy access to Seattle. Endowment: $2.3 million. Research spending for 2004 fiscal year: $1.1 million. Educational spending for 2005 fiscal year: $4701 per student. Total enrollment: 4,470. Faculty: 221 (158 full-time, 63 part-time). Student-undergrad faculty ratio is 21:1. 1,657 applied, 97% were admitted. 8% from top 10% of their high school class, 24% from top quarter, 60% from top half. Full-time: 3,655 students, 55% women, 45% men. Part-time: 516 students, 59% women, 41% men. Students come from 53 states and territories, 10 other countries, 22% from out-of-state, 4% Native American, 4% Hispanic, 5% black, 5% Asian American or Pacific Islander, 0.4% international, 35% 25 or older, 21% live on campus, 22% transferred in. Retention: 70% of full-time freshmen returned the following year. Academic area with the most degrees conferred: liberal arts/general studies. Services for LD students, advanced placement, accelerated degree program, self-designed majors, independent study, distance learning, double major, summer session for credit, part-time degree program, co-op programs and internships, graduate courses open to undergrads. Off campus study at University of Washington. Study abroad program.
Entrance Requirements: Options: electronic application, early admission, international baccalaureate accepted. Required: high school transcript, minimum 2.0 high school GPA, SAT or ACT. Recommended: essay. Entrance: moderately difficult. Application deadline: Rolling. Notification: 12/1. Preference given to Vietnam veterans, adults 25 and older, first-generation college students.
Costs Per Year: Application fee: $50. State resident tuition: $4128 full-time, $137.60 per quarter hour part-time. Nonresident tuition: $14,538 full-time, $484.60 per quarter hour part-time. Mandatory fees: $209 full-time, $2.05 per quarter hour part-time, $41 per term part-time. Full-time tuition and fees vary according to course load and degree level. Part-time tuition and fees vary according to course load and degree level. College room and board: $6924. College room only: $4482. Room and board charges vary according to board plan, housing facility, and student level.
Collegiate Environment: Orientation program. Drama-theater group, choral group, student-run newspaper, radio station. Social organizations: 70 open to all. Most popular organizations: Environmental Resource Center, Women's Resource Center, Evergreen Queer Alliance, Evergreen Political Information Center. Major annual events: Super Saturday, Expressions Performing Arts Series, Day of Absence/Day of Presence. Student services: health clinic, personal-psychological counseling, women's center. Campus security: 24-hour emergency response devices and patrols, student patrols, late night transport-escort service, controlled dormitory access. 870 college housing spaces available; 829 were occupied in 2003-04. Freshmen guaranteed college housing. Option: coed housing available. Daniel J. Evans Library with 476,500 books, 492,853 microform titles, 2,731 serials, 91,314 audiovisual materials, an OPAC, and a Web page. Operations spending for 2004 fiscal year: $2.9 million. 300 computers available on campus for general student use. A campuswide network can be accessed from student residence rooms and from off campus. Staffed computer lab on campus.
Community Environment: Olympia is a seaport community of 37,000, located at the southernmost tip of Puget Sound. The Pacific Ocean is about an hour's drive west of the campus. The rain forests of the Olympic Peninsula lie to the northwest, and the Cascade mountain range is a few hours east of the campus. Seattle, 60 miles from campus, offers all the cultural and recreational activities typically found in a large city.

■ **GONZAGA UNIVERSITY** *E-16*
502 East Boone Ave.
Spokane, WA 99258
Tel: (509)328-4220
Free: 800-322-2584
Admissions: (509)323-6591
Fax: (509)324-5780
E-mail: admissions@gonzaga.edu
Web Site: http://www.gonzaga.edu/
Description: Independent Roman Catholic, comprehensive, coed. Awards bachelor's, master's, doctoral, and first professional degrees and post-master's certificates. Founded 1887. Setting: 94-acre urban campus. Endowment: $116.4 million. Research spending for 2004 fiscal year: $316,734. Educational spending for 2005 fiscal year: $16,814 per student. Total enrollment: 6,377. Faculty: 335 (325 full-time, 10 part-time). Student-undergrad faculty ratio is 12:1. 4,328 applied, 73% were admitted. 40% from top 10% of their high school class, 71% from top quarter, 94% from top half. 10 National Merit Scholars, 24 class presidents, 308 student government officers. Full-time: 3,986 students, 53% women, 47% men. Part-time: 166 students, 58% women, 42% men. Students come from 50 states and territories, 36 other countries, 49% from out-of-state, 1% Native American, 4% Hispanic, 1% black, 5% Asian American or Pacific Islander, 1% international, 0.1% 25 or older, 56% live on campus, 4% transferred in. Retention: 90% of full-time freshmen returned the following year. Academic areas with the most degrees conferred: business/marketing; social sciences; engineering. Core. Calendar: semesters. ESL program, services for LD students, advanced placement, accelerated degree program, honors program, independent study, double major, summer session for credit, part-time degree program, adult/continuing education programs, internships. Off campus study at American University. Study abroad program. ROTC: Army.
Entrance Requirements: Options: Peterson's Universal Application, Common Application, electronic application, early action, deferred admission, international baccalaureate accepted. Required: essay, high school transcript, minimum 3.0 high school GPA, 1 recommendation, SAT or ACT. Recommended: interview. Entrance: moderately difficult. Application deadlines: 2/1, 11/15 for early action. Notification: 3/15, 1/15 for early action.
Costs Per Year: Application fee: $45. Comprehensive fee: $30,278 includes full-time tuition ($23,140), mandatory fees ($438), and college room and board ($6700). College room only: $3400. Room and board charges vary according to board plan and housing facility. Part-time tuition: $670 per credit. Part-time mandatory fees: $45 per term.
Collegiate Environment: Orientation program. Drama-theater group, choral group, student-run newspaper, radio station. Social organizations: 69 open to all. Most popular organizations: Student Body Association, Search, Circle K, Encore, Knights and Setons. Major annual events: new student orientation events, Spring Formal, Aprilfest. Student services: health clinic, personal-psychological counseling. Campus security: 24-hour emergency response devices and patrols, late night transport-escort service, controlled dormitory access. 2,130 college housing spaces available; all were occupied in 2003-04. Freshmen guaranteed college housing. On-campus residence required through sophomore year. Options: coed, men-only, women-only housing available. Ralph E. and Helen Higgins Foley Center plus 1 other with 228,622 books, 562,255 microform titles, 1,435 serials, 2,617 audiovisual materials, an OPAC, and a Web page. Operations spending for 2004 fiscal year: $4.2 million. 350 computers available on campus for general student use. Computer purchase/lease plans available. A campuswide network can be accessed from student residence rooms and from off campus. Staffed computer lab on campus.
Community Environment: See Spokane Falls Community College.

■ **GRAYS HARBOR COLLEGE** *R-12*
1620 Edward P Smith Dr.
Aberdeen, WA 98520-7599
Tel: (360)532-9020
Admissions: (360)538-4030
Fax: (360)538-4293
Web Site: http://www.ghc.ctc.edu/
Description: State-supported, 2-year, coed. Part of Washington State Board for Community and Technical Colleges. Awards certificates, diplomas, transfer associate, and terminal associate degrees. Founded 1930. Setting: 125-acre small town campus. Endowment: $927,238. Educational spending for 2005 fiscal year: $2463 per student. Total enrollment: 2,181. Full-time: 1,156 students, 50% women, 50% men. Part-time: 1,025 students, 49% women, 51% men. 6% Native American, 3% Hispanic, 1% black, 3% Asian

American or Pacific Islander, 0.1% international. Core. Academic remediation for entering students, ESL program, services for LD students, advanced placement, accelerated degree program, honors program, independent study, distance learning, double major, summer session for credit, part-time degree program, external degree program, adult/continuing education programs, co-op programs and internships.

Entrance Requirements: Open admission. Options: Common Application, electronic application, early admission. Recommended: high school transcript. Placement: ACT ASSET, CPT required. Entrance: noncompetitive. Application deadline: Rolling. Notification: continuous.

Collegiate Environment: Drama-theater group, choral group, student-run newspaper. Social organizations: 14 open to all. Most popular organizations: PTK, TYEE, Student Nurses Association, Human Services Student Association, student council. Major annual events: sporting events, Bishop Center, drama events. Student services: personal-psychological counseling, women's center. Campus security: 24-hour emergency response devices, late night transport-escort service. College housing not available. Spellman Library with 39,220 books, 2,309 audiovisual materials, an OPAC, and a Web page. Operations spending for 2004 fiscal year: $342,859. 145 computers available on campus for general student use. A campuswide network can be accessed. Staffed computer lab on campus.

Community Environment: Aberdeen is located in a heavily wooded area and is known chiefly for its lumbering and fishing. The area has good harbors where the fishing fleet anchors. The city has mild winters and cool summers, with up to 75 inches of rainfall per year. Aberdeen may be reached by bus and state highways. There is a public library, YMCA, two hospitals, churches of major denominations, theatres, public parks, and civic, fraternal, and veteran's organizations serving the community. Local recreation includes hunting, fishing, golf, swimming, tennis, and skiing three hours drive away. Part-time employment is available.

■ **GREEN RIVER COMMUNITY COLLEGE** *W-6*
12401 Southeast 320th St.
Auburn, WA 98092-3699
Tel: (253)833-9111
Fax: (253)288-3454
Web Site: http://www.greenriver.edu/

Description: State-supported, 2-year, coed. Part of Washington State Board for Community and Technical Colleges. Awards certificates, diplomas, transfer associate, and terminal associate degrees. Founded 1965. Setting: 168-acre rural campus with easy access to Seattle. Educational spending for 2005 fiscal year: $2345 per student. Total enrollment: 6,621. Full-time: 3,883 students, 51% women, 49% men. Part-time: 2,738 students, 62% women, 38% men. Students come from 30 other countries, 1% from out-of-state, 1% Native American, 5% Hispanic, 3% black, 7% Asian American or Pacific Islander, 4% international, 31% 25 or older. Core. Academic remediation for entering students, ESL program, services for LD students, advanced placement, distance learning, summer session for credit, part-time degree program, adult/continuing education programs, co-op programs and internships. Off campus study.

Entrance Requirements: Open admission except for nursing, physical therapy, occupational therapy, waste water technology programs. Options: Peterson's Universal Application, electronic application, early admission, deferred admission. Required for some: high school transcript. Placement: ACT ASSET or ACT COMPASS required. Entrance: noncompetitive. Application deadline: Rolling. Notification: continuous.

Collegiate Environment: Drama-theater group, choral group, student-run newspaper, radio station. Social organizations: 35 open to all. Most popular organizations: Phi Theta Kappa, Green River Active Christian Encounter, Vocational and Industrial Clubs of America (VICA), Multicultural Student Alliance. Major annual events: noon-hour lecture series, noon-hour entertainment programs. Student services: health clinic, personal-psychological counseling, women's center. Campus security: 24-hour emergency response devices and patrols, student patrols, late night transport-escort service. Holman Library with 32,500 books, 2,100 serials, 4,471 audiovisual materials, an OPAC, and a Web page. Operations spending for 2004 fiscal year: $791,736. 104 computers available on campus for general student use. A campuswide network can be accessed. Staffed computer lab on campus.

Community Environment: Auburn is a suburban community in the Seattle area. It is located approximately 30 miles from the heart of downtown Seattle. The climate is mild. Auburn may be reached by railroad, the Seattle airport, and major highways. One library, several churches, a museum, YMCA, general hospital, and clinics serve the community. Local recreation includes a city park, a golf club, community theater, a nearby beach and

rivers, hunting for deer, bear, birds and elk, lake fishing, water sports, skiing and mountain climbing. Some part-time employment is available. Various civic and fraternal organizations are active in the community. There are good shopping facilities.

■ **HENRY COGSWELL COLLEGE** *D-6*
3002 Colby Ave.
Everett, WA 98201
Tel: (425)258-3351; (866)411-4221
E-mail: jbuckman@henrycogswell.edu
Web Site: http://www.henrycogswell.edu/

Description: Independent, 4-year, coed. Administratively affiliated with Foundation for Educational Achievement. Awards bachelor's degrees. Founded 1979. Setting: 1-acre urban campus with easy access to Seattle. Endowment: $196,281. Educational spending for 2005 fiscal year: $3683 per student. Total enrollment: 200. Student-undergrad faculty ratio is 7:1. 86 applied, 84% were admitted. Full-time: 118 students, 29% women, 71% men. Part-time: 82 students, 21% women, 79% men. Students come from 3 states and territories, 0% from out-of-state, 1% Native American, 7% Hispanic, 3% black, 8% Asian American or Pacific Islander, 50% 25 or older, 18% transferred in. Retention: 64% of full-time freshmen returned the following year. Academic areas with the most degrees conferred: visual and performing arts; engineering; business/marketing. Core. Calendar: trimesters. Academic remediation for entering students, advanced placement, accelerated degree program, double major, summer session for credit, part-time degree program, adult/continuing education programs, co-op programs.

Entrance Requirements: Options: Peterson's Universal Application, Common Application, electronic application, deferred admission. Required: essay, high school transcript. Recommended: interview. Required for some: 3 recommendations, portfolio, SAT or ACT. Entrance: noncompetitive. Application deadline: Rolling. Notification: continuous.

Costs Per Year: Application fee: $50. Tuition: $17,520 full-time, $730 per credit part-time.

Collegiate Environment: Orientation program. Social organizations: 4 open to all. Most popular organizations: Leadership Council, IEEE, ASME, ACM, Sigma Iota Epsilon. Major annual events: Winter Holiday Party, Summer Picnic, Spring Easter Egg Hunt. Campus security: controlled dormitory access. College housing not available. Robert W. Phinney Library with 12,100 books, 60 serials, 249 audiovisual materials, and an OPAC. Operations spending for 2004 fiscal year: $100,744. 125 computers available on campus for general student use. A campuswide network can be accessed from off-campus. Staffed computer lab on campus.

■ **HERITAGE UNIVERSITY** *I-10*
3240 Fort Rd.
Toppenish, WA 98948-9599
Tel: (509)865-8500
Admissions: (509)865-8508
Fax: (509)865-4469
E-mail: garcia_l@heritage.edu
Web Site: http://www.heritage.edu/

Description: Independent, comprehensive, coed. Awards associate, bachelor's, and master's degrees. Founded 1982. Setting: 10-acre rural campus. Endowment: $4.5 million. Research spending for 2004 fiscal year: $237,491. Educational spending for 2005 fiscal year: $9600 per student. Total enrollment: 1,311. Faculty: 187 (47 full-time, 140 part-time). Student-undergrad faculty ratio is 11:1. 475 applied, 60% were admitted. Full-time: 568 students, 73% women, 27% men. Part-time: 238 students, 71% women, 29% men. 0% from out-of-state, 10% Native American, 53% Hispanic, 1% black, 1% Asian American or Pacific Islander, 0% international, 62% 25 or older, 15% transferred in. Retention: 67% of full-time freshmen returned the following year. Academic areas with the most degrees conferred: education; psychology; business/marketing. Core. Calendar: semesters. Academic remediation for entering students, ESL program, services for LD students, advanced placement, self-designed majors, honors program, independent study, double major, summer session for credit, part-time degree program, adult/continuing education programs, co-op programs and internships, graduate courses open to undergrads.

Entrance Requirements: Open admission. Options: Common Application, early admission, early decision, deferred admission. Required: high school transcript. Required for some: interview, SAT or ACT. Entrance: noncompetitive. Application deadline: Rolling. Notification: continuous.

Costs Per Year: Application fee: $0. Tuition: $9600 full-time, $320 per credit hour part-time. Mandatory fees: $45 full-time.

Collegiate Environment: Orientation program. Student-run newspaper. Student services: personal-psychological counseling. Campus security: 24-hour emergency response devices. College housing not available. Library and Resource Center with 47,500 books, 90,000 microform titles, 15,000 serials, 400 audiovisual materials, an OPAC, and a Web page. Operations spending for 2004 fiscal year: $297,729. 158 computers available on campus for general student use. A campuswide network can be accessed from off-campus. Staffed computer lab on campus.

Community Environment: Toppenish is located twenty miles south of Yakima, in the fertile lower Yakima Valley which produces fruit and hops and supports agricultural related industries. The climate is mild and dry. Toppenish has churches representing most denominations, a hospital, symphony, civic theatre, community concert series, and arts events. Local recreation includes swimming, skiing, boating, fishing, hunting, and golf. Local events include the Toppenish Rodeo and Pow-Wow, the Cinco de Mayo celebrations, and Yakima Indian Nation Cultural Center events.

■ HIGHLINE COMMUNITY COLLEGE *V-6*

2400 S. 240th St.
PO Box 98000
Des Moines, WA 98198-9800
Tel: (206)878-3710
Fax: (206)870-3782
Web Site: http://www.highline.edu/

Description: State-supported, 2-year, coed. Part of Washington State Board for Community and Technical Colleges. Awards certificates, diplomas, transfer associate, and terminal associate degrees. Founded 1961. Setting: 81-acre suburban campus with easy access to Seattle. Total enrollment: 6,372. 9,938 applied, 100% were admitted. Full-time: 3,229 students, 60% women, 40% men. Part-time: 3,143 students, 69% women, 31% men. 1% Native American, 5% Hispanic, 11% black, 17% Asian American or Pacific Islander, 0.2% international, 52% 25 or older. Retention: 60% of full-time freshmen returned the following year. Core. Academic remediation for entering students, ESL program, services for LD students, advanced placement, self-designed majors, freshman honors college, honors program, summer session for credit, part-time degree program, co-op programs and internships. Study abroad program. ROTC: Army (c), Air Force (c).

Entrance Requirements: Open admission except for allied health, nursing programs. Placement: ACT COMPASS recommended. Entrance: noncompetitive. Application deadline: Rolling.

Costs Per Year: Application fee: $21.15. State resident tuition: $2445 full-time, $71.80 per credit part-time. Nonresident tuition: $2835 full-time, $85 per credit part-time. Mandatory fees: $75 full-time, $2.50 per credit part-time.

Collegiate Environment: Drama-theater group, choral group, student-run newspaper. Social organizations: 18 open to all. Most popular organizations: Campus Crusade for Christ, Phi Theta Kappa, International Club, Respiratory Care. Student services: health clinic, personal-psychological counseling, women's center. Campus security: 24-hour patrols. College housing not available. Highline Community College Library with 57,678 books, 585 serials, and an OPAC. 300 computers available on campus for general student use. A campuswide network can be accessed. Staffed computer lab on campus.

Community Environment: Overlooking the Puget Sound, Des Moines is a suburb of Seattle, approximately 15 miles from the heart of downtown. (See Seattle University.) The community has all the advantages of a small town, and yet is easily accessible to all the cultural, recreational, and civic opportunities of the neighboring community.

■ ITT TECHNICAL INSTITUTE (BOTHELL) *E-6*

2525 223rd St., SE, Canyon Park East
Bothell, WA 98021
Tel: (425)485-0303
Admissions: (425)583-0200
Web Site: http://www.itt-tech.edu/

Description: Proprietary, primarily 2-year, coed. Part of ITT Educational Services, Inc. Awards terminal associate and bachelor's degrees. Founded 1993. Core.

Entrance Requirements: Option: deferred admission. Required: high school transcript, interview, Wonderlic aptitude test. Recommended: recommendations. Entrance: minimally difficult. Application deadline: Rolling. Notification: continuous.

Costs Per Year: Application fee: $100.

Collegiate Environment: Orientation program. College housing not available.

■ ITT TECHNICAL INSTITUTE (SEATTLE) *E-6*

12720 Gateway Dr., Ste. 100
Seattle, WA 98168-3333
Tel: (206)244-3300
Free: 800-422-2029
Web Site: http://www.itt-tech.edu/

Description: Proprietary, primarily 2-year, coed. Part of ITT Educational Services, Inc. Awards terminal associate and bachelor's degrees. Founded 1932. Setting: urban campus. Core.

Entrance Requirements: Option: deferred admission. Required: high school transcript, interview, Wonderlic aptitude test. Recommended: recommendations. Entrance: minimally difficult. Application deadline: Rolling. Notification: continuous.

Costs Per Year: Application fee: $100.

Collegiate Environment: Orientation program. College housing not available.

■ ITT TECHNICAL INSTITUTE (SPOKANE) *E-16*

1050 North Argonne Rd.
Spokane, WA 99212-2682
Tel: (509)926-2900
Free: 800-777-8324
Web Site: http://www.itt-tech.edu/

Description: Proprietary, primarily 2-year, coed. Part of ITT Educational Services, Inc. Awards terminal associate and bachelor's degrees. Founded 1985. Setting: 3-acre suburban campus. Core.

Entrance Requirements: Option: deferred admission. Required: high school transcript, interview, Wonderlic aptitude test. Recommended: recommendations. Entrance: minimally difficult. Application deadline: Rolling. Notification: continuous.

Costs Per Year: Application fee: $100.

Collegiate Environment: Orientation program. College housing not available.

■ LAKE WASHINGTON TECHNICAL COLLEGE *T-6*

11605 132nd Ave. NE
Kirkland, WA 98034-8506
Tel: (425)739-8100
Admissions: (425)739-8233
Web Site: http://www.lwtc.ctc.edu/

Description: District-supported, 2-year, coed. Part of Washington State Board for Community and Technical Colleges. Awards certificates, transfer associate, and terminal associate degrees. Founded 1949. Setting: 57-acre suburban campus with easy access to Seattle. Endowment: $198,295. Educational spending for 2005 fiscal year: $3465 per student. Total enrollment: 4,860. 3,256 applied. Full-time: 2,020 students, 48% women, 52% men. Part-time: 2,840 students, 62% women, 38% men. Students come from 4 states and territories, 12 other countries, 1% Native American, 9% Hispanic, 3% black, 13% Asian American or Pacific Islander, 1% international, 70% 25 or older. Academic remediation for entering students, ESL program, services for LD students, advanced placement, summer session for credit, co-op programs and internships.

Entrance Requirements: Open admission except for allied health programs. Options: Common Application, early admission. Required for some: high school transcript. Placement: ACT ASSET required. Entrance: noncompetitive. Application deadline: Rolling. Notification: continuous.

Collegiate Environment: Major annual events: Summer Party, Christmas Party. Student services: personal-psychological counseling, women's center. Campus security: 24-hour emergency response devices, late night transport-escort service, parking lot security, security cameras. College housing not available. Lake Washington Technical College Library/Media Center with 18,300 books, 770 serials, an OPAC, and a Web page. Operations spending for 2004 fiscal year: $230,389. 400 computers available on campus for general student use. A campuswide network can be accessed from off-campus. Staffed computer lab on campus.

■ LOWER COLUMBIA COLLEGE *J-4*

PO Box 3010
Longview, WA 98632-0310
Tel: (360)442-2000
Admissions: (360)442-2300
Fax: (360)442-2109
E-mail: mharding@lcc.ctc.edu
Web Site: http://www.lcc.ctc.edu/

Description: State-supported, 2-year, coed. Part of Washington State Board for Community and Technical Colleges. Awards certificates, diplomas, transfer associate, and terminal associate degrees. Founded 1934. Setting: 30-acre small town campus with easy access to Portland. Endowment: $2.3 million. Educational spending for 2005 fiscal year: $3354 per student. Total enrollment: 3,073. Student-undergrad faculty ratio is 21:1. 316 applied, 100% were admitted. Full-time: 1,755 students, 60% women, 40% men. Part-time: 1,318 students, 69% women, 31% men. Students come from 5 states and territories, 9% from out-of-state, 1% Native American, 3% Hispanic, 1% black, 2% Asian American or Pacific Islander, 0.1% international, 36% 25 or older, 12% transferred in. Retention: 55% of full-time freshmen returned the following year. Core. Academic remediation for entering students, ESL program, services for LD students, honors program, summer session for credit, part-time degree program, adult/continuing education programs, co-op programs. Study abroad program.
Entrance Requirements: Open admission. Options: early admission, deferred admission. Recommended: high school transcript. Entrance: noncompetitive. Application deadline: Rolling. Notification: continuous.
Costs Per Year: Application fee: $12.50. State resident tuition: $2465 full-time, $77.65 per credit part-time. Nonresident tuition: $3161 full-time, $83.40 per credit part-time. Mandatory fees: $6.10 per credit part-time.
Collegiate Environment: Drama-theater group, choral group, student-run newspaper. Social organizations: 8 open to all. Most popular organizations: Campus Entertainment, Phi Theta Kappa, Services and Relations Club, Multicultural Students Club, Theater Club. Major annual events: Red Devil Days, Open House. Student services: health clinic, personal-psychological counseling. Campus security: 24-hour emergency response devices and patrols. College housing not available. Allan Thompson Library plus 1 other with 41,991 books, 5,887 microform titles, 217 serials, 3,376 audiovisual materials, and an OPAC. Operations spending for 2004 fiscal year: $349,791. 250 computers available on campus for general student use. A campuswide network can be accessed. Staffed computer lab on campus.
Community Environment: Longview is a planned city located on the banks of the Columbia and Cowlitz Rivers. The city is 50 miles north of Portland, Oregon, and has a mild climate. There are several churches, a public library, YMCA and two hospitals accessible. Longview may be reached by five railroad lines, and an airport. Local recreation includes theatres, boating, fishing, golf, hunting, skiing, and other sports. Part-time employment is available for students. Hotels, motels, and apartments are available for student housing. The community has several large shopping centers.

■ **NORTH SEATTLE COMMUNITY COLLEGE** *E-6*
9600 College Way North
Seattle, WA 98103-3599
Tel: (206)527-3600
Admissions: (206)527-3663
Fax: (206)527-3635
Web Site: http://www.northseattle.edu/
Description: State-supported, 2-year, coed. Part of Seattle Community College District System. Awards certificates, diplomas, transfer associate, and terminal associate degrees. Founded 1970. Setting: 65-acre urban campus. Total enrollment: 5,959. Student-undergrad faculty ratio is 23:1. 5,726 applied, 100% were admitted. Full-time: 2,833 students, 56% women, 44% men. Part-time: 3,126 students, 69% women, 31% men. Students come from 50 states and territories, 1% from out-of-state, 2% Native American, 6% Hispanic, 8% black, 16% Asian American or Pacific Islander, 0.1% international, 55% 25 or older, 39% transferred in. Core. Academic remediation for entering students, ESL program, services for LD students, advanced placement, independent study, distance learning, summer session for credit, part-time degree program, external degree program, adult/continuing education programs, co-op programs and internships. ROTC: Army (c).
Entrance Requirements: Open admission. Options: Common Application, electronic application, early admission, deferred admission. Required: high school transcript. Required for some: essay. Entrance: noncompetitive. Application deadline: Rolling. Notification: continuous until 9/24.
Costs Per Year: Application fee: $0. State resident tuition: $3213 full-time, $71.40 per credit part-time. Nonresident tuition: $10,940 full-time, $243.10 per credit part-time. Mandatory fees: $346 full-time, $115.20 per term part-time. Full-time tuition and fees vary according to course load. Part-time tuition and fees vary according to course load.
Collegiate Environment: Orientation program. Drama-theater group, choral group, student-run newspaper. Social organizations: 25 open to all. Most popular organizations: Muslim Students Association, Indonesian Community

Club, Literary Guild, Phi Theta Kappa, Vietnamese Student Association. Major annual events: Cinco de Mayo, Welcome Back BBQ and Success Fair, Spring Fest. Student services: personal-psychological counseling, women's center. Campus security: 24-hour emergency response devices and patrols, student patrols, late night transport-escort service, patrols by security. College housing not available. North Seattle Community College Library with 52,496 books, 152,522 microform titles, 594 serials, 2,957 audiovisual materials, an OPAC, and a Web page. 1,600 computers available on campus for general student use. A campuswide network can be accessed from off-campus. Staffed computer lab on campus.
Community Environment: See Seattle University.

■ **NORTHWEST AVIATION COLLEGE** *W-6*
506 23rd, NE
Auburn, WA 98002
Tel: (253)854-4960
Fax: (253)931-0768
E-mail: spratt@afsnac.com
Web Site: http://www.afsnac.com/
Description: Private, 2-year, coed. Awards certificates and transfer associate degrees. Setting: urban campus. Total enrollment: 50. Core. Summer session for credit.
Entrance Requirements: Required: high school transcript. Application deadline: Rolling.
Collegiate Environment: Orientation program.

■ **NORTHWEST COLLEGE OF ART** *S-4*
16464 State Hwy. 305
Poulsbo, WA 98370
Tel: (360)779-9993
Free: 800-769-ARTS
Fax: (360)779-9933
Web Site: http://www.nca.edu/
Description: Proprietary, 4-year, coed. Awards bachelor's degrees. Founded 1982. Setting: 26-acre small town campus with easy access to Seattle. Core. Calendar: semesters. Double major, summer session for credit, internships.
Entrance Requirements: Option: deferred admission. Required: essay, high school transcript, minimum 2.0 high school GPA, 3 recommendations, interview, portfolio. Entrance: moderately difficult. Application deadline: 6/1. Notification: continuous.
Costs Per Year: Application fee: $50. Tuition: $14,300 full-time, $625 per credit part-time. Mandatory fees: $100 full-time. Part-time tuition varies according to course load. Tuition guaranteed not to increase for student's term of enrollment.
Collegiate Environment: Orientation program. Major annual events: Student Art Shows, Open House. College housing not available. 28 computers available on campus for general student use. Staffed computer lab on campus.

■ **NORTHWEST INDIAN COLLEGE** *B-5*
2522 Kwina Rd.
Bellingham, WA 98226
Tel: (360)676-2772
Fax: (360)738-0136
E-mail: lignacio@nwic.edu
Web Site: http://www.nwic.edu/
Description: Federally supported, 2-year, coed. Awards certificates, transfer associate, and terminal associate degrees (also offers bachelor's degree in elementary education in conjunction with Washington State University). Founded 1978. Setting: 5-acre rural campus. Endowment: $3 million. Total enrollment: 1,189. Students come from 6 states and territories, 2 other countries, 78% Native American, 1% Hispanic, 1% black, 1% Asian American or Pacific Islander, 75% 25 or older. Core. Academic remediation for entering students, self-designed majors, summer session for credit, part-time degree program, external degree program, adult/continuing education programs, co-op programs and internships. Study abroad program.
Entrance Requirements: Open admission. Required: high school transcript. Entrance: noncompetitive. Notification: continuous. Preference given to Native Americans.
Costs Per Year: Application fee: $25. State resident tuition: $2646 full-time, $73.50 per credit part-time. Nonresident tuition: $7182 full-time, $199.50 per credit part-time.

Collegiate Environment: Drama-theater group, choral group, student-run newspaper. Student services: personal-psychological counseling, career services, transfer advising, wellness center. College housing not available. 22 computers available on campus for general student use.

■ **NORTHWEST SCHOOL OF WOODEN BOATBUILDING** *D-5*
251 Otto St.
Port Townsend, WA 98368
Tel: (360)385-4948
Fax: (360)385-5089
E-mail: info@nwboatschool.org
Web Site: http://www.nwboatschool.org/
Description: Independent, 2-year, coed. Awards terminal associate degrees. Founded 1980. Calendar: semesters.

■ **NORTHWEST UNIVERSITY** *T-6*
5520 108th Ave. NE
Kirkland, WA 98033
Tel: (425)822-8266
Free: 800-669-3781
Admissions: (425)889-5209
Fax: (425)425-0148
E-mail: admissions@northwestu.edu
Web Site: http://www.northwestu.edu/
Description: Independent, comprehensive, coed, affiliated with Assemblies of God. Awards associate, bachelor's, and master's degrees. Founded 1934. Setting: 56-acre suburban campus with easy access to Seattle. Endowment: $8.4 million. Educational spending for 2005 fiscal year: $3756 per student. Total enrollment: 1,260. Faculty: 94 (52 full-time, 42 part-time). Student-undergrad faculty ratio is 17:1. 427 applied, 83% were admitted. Full-time: 1,051 students, 64% women, 36% men. Part-time: 102 students, 53% women, 47% men. Students come from 26 states and territories, 6 other countries, 16% from out-of-state, 1% Native American, 3% Hispanic, 3% black, 5% Asian American or Pacific Islander, 1% international, 26% 25 or older, 61% live on campus, 19% transferred in. Retention: 74% of full-time freshmen returned the following year. Academic areas with the most degrees conferred: business/marketing; theology and religious vocations; psychology. Core. Calendar: semesters. Academic remediation for entering students, ESL program, advanced placement, accelerated degree program, self-designed majors, independent study, double major, summer session for credit, part-time degree program, adult/continuing education programs, co-op programs and internships. Study abroad program. ROTC: Army (c).
Entrance Requirements: Options: electronic application, early decision, deferred admission, international baccalaureate accepted. Required: essay, high school transcript, minimum 2.3 high school GPA, 2 recommendations, SAT or ACT. Required for some: interview. Entrance: moderately difficult. Application deadline: 8/1. Notification: continuous.
Costs Per Year: Application fee: $30. Comprehensive fee: $24,594 includes full-time tuition ($17,920), mandatory fees ($224), and college room and board ($6450). Part-time tuition: $750 per credit. Part-time mandatory fees: $224 per year.
Collegiate Environment: Orientation program. Drama-theater group, choral group, student-run newspaper, radio station. Social organizations: 10 open to all. Most popular organizations: Environmental Club, Psychology Club, Association of Business Students, Drama Club, student ministries. Major annual events: Christmas Party, Homecoming/Family Weekend, All-School Banquet. Student services: health clinic, personal-psychological counseling. Campus security: 24-hour emergency response devices and patrols, late night transport-escort service, controlled dormitory access. 655 college housing spaces available; 509 were occupied in 2003-04. Freshmen guaranteed college housing. On-campus residence required through sophomore year. Options: men-only, women-only housing available. D. V. Hurst Library with 141,427 books, 41,320 microform titles, 905 serials, 5,021 audiovisual materials, an OPAC, and a Web page. Operations spending for 2004 fiscal year: $387,437. 88 computers available on campus for general student use. A campuswide network can be accessed from student residence rooms and from off campus. Staffed computer lab on campus.

■ **OLYMPIC COLLEGE** *F-5*
1600 Chester Ave.
Bremerton, WA 98337-1699
Tel: (360)792-6050
Free: 800-259-6718
Admissions: (360)475-7126

Fax: (360)792-2135
E-mail: gstamm@ctc.edu
Web Site: http://www.oc.ctc.edu/~oc/
Description: State-supported, 2-year, coed. Part of Washington State Board for Community and Technical Colleges. Awards certificates, diplomas, transfer associate, and terminal associate degrees. Founded 1946. Setting: 32-acre suburban campus with easy access to Seattle. Endowment: $3.9 million. Educational spending for 2005 fiscal year: $3012 per student. Total enrollment: 6,390. Student-undergrad faculty ratio is 25:1. 6,830 applied, 100% were admitted. Full-time: 3,253 students, 52% women, 48% men. Part-time: 3,137 students, 59% women, 41% men. Students come from 50 states and territories, 4 other countries, 2% Native American, 5% Hispanic, 3% black, 9% Asian American or Pacific Islander, 0.1% international, 49% 25 or older, 1% transferred in. Core. Academic remediation for entering students, ESL program, services for LD students, advanced placement, honors program, independent study, distance learning, summer session for credit, part-time degree program, adult/continuing education programs, co-op programs. Off campus study at other community colleges in Washington.
Entrance Requirements: Open admission except for nursing, medical office assistant program. Option: early admission. Required for some: high school transcript. Entrance: noncompetitive. Application deadline: Rolling. Notification: continuous.
Costs Per Year: Application fee: $0. State resident tuition: $71.80 per credit part-time. Nonresident tuition: $115.90 per credit part-time. Mandatory fees: $60 per term part-time.
Collegiate Environment: Orientation program. Drama-theater group, choral group, student-run newspaper. Most popular organizations: Phi Theta Kappa, Aware, Oceans (Nursing), ASOC, ASAD. Major annual events: Commencement, Student Appreciation Day, open mic talent competitions. Student services: personal-psychological counseling, women's center. Campus security: 24-hour emergency response devices and patrols, student patrols, late night transport-escort service. College housing not available. Haselwood Library with 51,443 books, 8,126 microform titles, 541 serials, 3,007 audiovisual materials, an OPAC, and a Web page. Operations spending for 2004 fiscal year: $994,375. 634 computers available on campus for general student use. A campuswide network can be accessed from off-campus. Staffed computer lab on campus.
Community Environment: Bremerton is a metropolitan community enjoying mild summer and winter temperatures. The major local industry is shipbuilding. The community has a library, hospital, churches of most denominations, and active civic, fraternal, and veteran's organizations. Rooming and boarding houses and small apartments are available for student housing. Local recreation includes sports, cultural events, boating, skiing, and snow boarding, all within a 3 hr. drive. Job opportunities are available for students.

■ **PACIFIC LUTHERAN UNIVERSITY** *G-5*
Tacoma, WA 98447
Tel: (253)531-6900
Free: 800-274-6758
Admissions: (253)535-7151
Fax: (253)536-5136
E-mail: admissions@plu.edu
Web Site: http://www.plu.edu/
Description: Independent, comprehensive, coed, affiliated with Evangelical Lutheran Church in America. Awards bachelor's and master's degrees and post-master's certificates. Founded 1890. Setting: 126-acre suburban campus with easy access to Seattle. Endowment: $57.4 million. Research spending for 2004 fiscal year: $275,834. Educational spending for 2005 fiscal year: $9131 per student. Total enrollment: 3,680. Faculty: 260 (236 full-time, 24 part-time). Student-undergrad faculty ratio is 15:1. 2,112 applied, 76% were admitted. 33% from top 10% of their high school class, 65% from top quarter, 89% from top half. 1 National Merit Scholar, 21 valedictorians. Full-time: 3,171 students, 64% women, 36% men. Part-time: 198 students, 56% women, 44% men. Students come from 42 states and territories, 24 other countries, 21% from out-of-state, 1% Native American, 2% Hispanic, 2% black, 6% Asian American or Pacific Islander, 6% international, 14% 25 or older, 51% live on campus, 9% transferred in. Retention: 82% of full-time freshmen returned the following year. Academic areas with the most degrees conferred: education; business/marketing; social sciences. Core. Calendar: 4-1-4. ESL program, services for LD students, advanced placement, self-designed majors, independent study, double major, summer session for credit, part-time degree program, adult/continuing education programs, co-op programs and internships, graduate courses open to undergrads. Study abroad program. ROTC: Army.

Entrance Requirements: Options: Peterson's Universal Application, Common Application, early admission, deferred admission, international baccalaureate accepted. Required: essay, high school transcript, minimum 2.5 high school GPA, 1 recommendation, SAT or ACT. Required for some: interview. Entrance: moderately difficult. Application deadline: Rolling. Notification: continuous.

Costs Per Year: Application fee: $40. Comprehensive fee: $28,805 includes full-time tuition ($22,040) and college room and board ($6765). College room only: $3330. Full-time tuition varies according to course load. Room and board charges vary according to board plan and housing facility. Part-time tuition: $687 per semester hour. Part-time tuition varies according to course load.

Collegiate Environment: Orientation program. Drama-theater group, choral group, student-run newspaper, radio station. Social organizations: 45 open to all. Most popular organizations: Rejoice, Circle K, Adult Students Club, Residence Hall Government, Inter-Varsity Fellowship. Major annual events: Homecoming, Convocation, All-Campus Picnics. Student services: health clinic, personal-psychological counseling, women's center. Campus security: 24-hour emergency response devices and patrols, student patrols, late night transport-escort service. 1,650 college housing spaces available; 1,600 were occupied in 2003-04. Freshmen guaranteed college housing. On-campus residence required through sophomore year. Options: coed, women-only housing available. Mortvedt Library with 340,842 books, 235,931 microform titles, 3,370 serials, 12,210 audiovisual materials, an OPAC, and a Web page. Operations spending for 2004 fiscal year: $2.2 million. 200 computers available on campus for general student use. Computer purchase/lease plans available. A campuswide network can be accessed from student residence rooms and from off campus. Staffed computer lab on campus.

Community Environment: The third largest city in Washington, Tacoma is a shipping, industrial, and distribution center located in the Puget Sound region. The city has diversified industries including electrochemicals, food and beverage processing, clothing manufacturing, iron and steel works, and shipyards. The city has several parks, a public library system, museums, hospitals, and many civic and fraternal organizations serving the community. Transportation is provided by railroads, airlines, twelve bus lines, and major highways. Its residents enjoy easy access to ocean beaches, the many waterways of Puget Sound, and Mt. Rainier, Olympic, and North Cascades National Parks. Nearby lakes and streams offer excellent fishing and numerous water sports.

■ **PENINSULA COLLEGE** *D-3*
1502 East Lauridsen Blvd.
Port Angeles, WA 98362-2779
Tel: (360)452-9277
Admissions: (360)417-6225
Fax: (360)457-8100
E-mail: jackh@pcadmin.ctc.edu
Web Site: http://www.pc.ctc.edu/
Description: State-supported, 2-year, coed. Awards certificates, transfer associate, and terminal associate degrees. Founded 1961. Setting: 75-acre small town campus. Endowment: $1.1 million. Educational spending for 2005 fiscal year: $3325 per student. Total enrollment: 4,256. Student-undergrad faculty ratio is 19:1. 173 applied, 100% were admitted. Full-time: 1,412 students, 51% women, 49% men. Part-time: 2,844 students, 63% women, 37% men. Students come from 5 other countries, 1% from out-of-state, 3% Native American, 2% Hispanic, 3% black, 2% Asian American or Pacific Islander, 1% international, 66% 25 or older. Core. Academic remediation for entering students, ESL program, services for LD students, advanced placement, honors program, distance learning, summer session for credit, part-time degree program, adult/continuing education programs, internships.

Entrance Requirements: Open admission except for nursing, industrial electronics, business computer systems programs, massage therapy. Options: Common Application, electronic application, deferred admission. Required for some: high school transcript. Entrance: noncompetitive. Application deadline: Rolling. Notification: continuous.

Costs Per Year: Application fee: $0. State resident tuition: $3325 full-time, $74.70 per credit part-time. Nonresident tuition: $3715 full-time, $87.90 per credit part-time. Mandatory fees: $135 full-time, $2.90 per credit part-time, $13.25 per term part-time.

Collegiate Environment: Orientation program. Drama-theater group, choral group, student-run newspaper. Social organizations: 5 open to all. Most popular organizations: Phi Theta Kappa, SAGE (Students Advocating Global Environmentalism). Student services: women's center. Campus security:

8-hour patrols by trained security personnel. 86 college housing spaces available. Option: coed housing available. 33,736 books and 383 serials. 38 computers available on campus for general student use. A campuswide network can be accessed from student residence rooms and from off campus. Staffed computer lab on campus.

Community Environment: Called the gateway to Olympic National Park, Port Angeles is a popular resort and tourist area located between the Olympic Mountains and Strait of Juan de Fuca. The area enjoys temperate climate with temperature ranges from 30 to 80 degrees. Average rainfall is 22.8 inches. The city may be reached by airlines and highways. There are libraries, churches representing many denominations, a YMCA, and a modern hospital. Local recreation includes theatres, parks, concerts, plays, swimming, golf, skiing, bowling, hiking, crabbing, fishing, sailing and other sports. The community has many civic organizations, a symphony orchestra, choral and theater groups.

■ **PIERCE COLLEGE** *G-6*
1601 39th Ave. SE
Puyallup, WA 98374-2222
Tel: (253)840-8400
Admissions: (253)964-6686
Fax: (253)840-8423
Web Site: http://www.pierce.ctc.edu/
Description: State-supported, 2-year, coed. Part of Washington State Board for Community and Technical Colleges. Awards certificates, diplomas, transfer associate, and terminal associate degrees. Founded 1967. Setting: 140-acre suburban campus with easy access to Seattle. Endowment: $4540. Educational spending for 2005 fiscal year: $6524 per student. Total enrollment: 13,294. Students come from 12 other countries, 56% 25 or older. Core. Academic remediation for entering students, ESL program, services for LD students, advanced placement, summer session for credit, part-time degree program, adult/continuing education programs, co-op programs and internships. Off campus study at Green River Community College, Tacoma Community College, Highline Community College, South Puget Sound Community College. ROTC: Army (c).

Entrance Requirements: Open admission except for international students or veterinary technology, dental hygiene programs. Option: early admission. Placement: ACT ASSET recommended; ACT ASSET required for some. Entrance: noncompetitive. Application deadline: Rolling. Notification: continuous.

Costs Per Year: Application fee: $0. Tuition: $392 per credit hour part-time. Mandatory fees: $1000 full-time, $100 per course part-time. Full-time fees vary according to course load. Part-time tuition and fees vary according to course load. Nonresident tuition: $11,760 full-time. Mandatory fees: $1000 full-time, $100 per course part-time. Full-time tuition and fees vary according to course load. Part-time fees vary according to course load.

Collegiate Environment: Drama-theater group, choral group, student-run newspaper. Social organizations: 26 open to all. Most popular organizations: Black Student Union, Phi Theta Kappa, Dental Hygiene Association, Veterinary Technology Association, Latino Student Union. Student services: women's center. Campus security: 24-hour emergency response devices and patrols, late night transport-escort service. College housing not available. 55,000 books and 425 serials. Operations spending for 2004 fiscal year: $732,414. 350 computers available on campus for general student use. Staffed computer lab on campus.

■ **PIMA MEDICAL INSTITUTE** *E-6*
1627 Eastlake Ave., East
Seattle, WA 98102
Tel: (206)322-6100; 888-898-9048
Fax: (206)324-1985
Web Site: http://www.pmi.edu
Description: Proprietary, 2-year, coed. Part of Vocational Training Institutes, Inc. Awards certificates and terminal associate degrees. Founded 1989. Setting: urban campus. Total enrollment: 289. 109 applied, 61% were admitted. Full-time: 289 students, 74% women, 26% men. Calendar: modular.
Entrance Requirements: Required: interview, Wonderlic aptitude test. Required for some: high school transcript. Entrance: minimally difficult.
Collegiate Environment: College housing not available.

■ **PUGET SOUND CHRISTIAN COLLEGE** *D-6*
1618 Hewitt Ave., PO Box 13108
Everett, WA 98201
Tel: (425)257-3090; 888-775-8699

Admissions: (425)775-8686
Fax: (425)258-1488
Web Site: http://www.pscc.edu/
Description: Independent Christian, 4-year, coed. Awards associate and bachelor's degrees. Founded 1950. Setting: 4-acre suburban campus with easy access to Seattle. Endowment: $321,391. Educational spending for 2005 fiscal year: $3663 per student. Total enrollment: 227. 59 applied, 71% were admitted. 25% from top 10% of their high school class, 38% from top quarter, 71% from top half. Full-time: 191 students, 54% women, 46% men. Part-time: 36 students, 42% women, 58% men. Students come from 8 states and territories, 1 other country, 35% from out-of-state, 37% 25 or older, 34% live on campus, 8% transferred in. Retention: 59% of full-time freshmen returned the following year. Core. Calendar: semesters. Academic remediation for entering students, advanced placement, independent study, double major, summer session for credit, part-time degree program, external degree program, adult/continuing education programs, internships.
Entrance Requirements: Option: deferred admission. Required: essay, high school transcript, minimum 2.0 high school GPA, recommendations. Required for some: interview. Entrance: minimally difficult. Application deadline: 8/1. Notification: continuous until 8/15. Preference given to members of Christian Church or Church of Christ.
Collegiate Environment: Orientation program. Choral group, student-run newspaper. Social organizations: 2 open to all. Most popular organizations: Team Macedonia, ASB Outreach Committee. Major annual events: High School Days, Gospel Festival, C. H. Phillips Lectureship. Student services: personal-psychological counseling. Campus security: 24-hour emergency response devices, student patrols. On-campus residence required in freshman year. Options: men-only, women-only housing available. C. H. Phillips Library with 37,500 books and 130 serials. Operations spending for 2004 fiscal year: $105,879. 8 computers available on campus for general student use. Staffed computer lab on campus.

■ **RENTON TECHNICAL COLLEGE** *F-6*
3000 NE Fourth St.
Renton, WA 98056-4195
Tel: (425)235-2352
Admissions: (425)235-2463
Fax: (425)235-7832
Web Site: http://www.rtc.edu/
Description: State-supported, 2-year, coed. Part of Washington State Board for Community and Technical Colleges. Awards certificates, diplomas, and terminal associate degrees. Founded 1942. Setting: 30-acre suburban campus with easy access to Seattle. Research spending for 2004 fiscal year: $59,756. Educational spending for 2005 fiscal year: $3093 per student. Total enrollment: 9,301. Students come from 9 states and territories, 13 other countries, 1% Native American, 5% Hispanic, 8% black, 12% Asian American or Pacific Islander, 0.4% international, 71% 25 or older. Academic remediation for entering students, ESL program, services for LD students, advanced placement, self-designed majors, distance learning, summer session for credit, part-time degree program, adult/continuing education programs, co-op programs and internships.
Entrance Requirements: Open admission. Option: early admission. Recommended: interview. Required for some: high school transcript. Placement: ACT ASSET, SLEP, COMPASS required. Entrance: noncompetitive. Application deadline: Rolling. Notification: continuous.
Collegiate Environment: Orientation program. Major annual events: Graduation, Orientation. Campus security: patrols by security, security system. College housing not available. Renton Technical College Library with 12,876 books, 684 microform titles, 2,316 serials, 321 audiovisual materials, and an OPAC. Operations spending for 2004 fiscal year: $169,650. 96 computers available on campus for general student use. A campuswide network can be accessed. Staffed computer lab on campus.

■ **SAINT MARTIN'S UNIVERSITY** *G-5*
5300 Pacific Ave., SE
Lacey, WA 98503-1297
Tel: (360)491-4700
Free: 800-368-8803
Admissions: (360)438-4590
Fax: (360)459-4124
E-mail: admissions@stmartin.edu
Web Site: http://www.stmartin.edu/
Description: Independent Roman Catholic, comprehensive, coed. Awards bachelor's and master's degrees. Founded 1895. Setting: 300-acre

suburban campus with easy access to Tacoma. Endowment: $11.3 million. Research spending for 2004 fiscal year: $830,484. Educational spending for 2005 fiscal year: $7114 per student. Total enrollment: 1,463. Faculty: 162 (66 full-time, 96 part-time). Student-undergrad faculty ratio is 11:1. 522 applied, 73% were admitted. 18% from top 10% of their high school class, 42% from top quarter, 82% from top half. 8 valedictorians. Full-time: 936 students, 58% women, 42% men. Part-time: 244 students, 55% women, 45% men. Students come from 8 states and territories, 11 other countries, 7% from out-of-state, 1% Native American, 6% Hispanic, 7% black, 10% Asian American or Pacific Islander, 7% international, 37% 25 or older, 29% live on campus, 15% transferred in. Retention: 75% of full-time freshmen returned the following year. Academic areas with the most degrees conferred: business/marketing; social sciences; psychology. Core. Calendar: semesters. Academic remediation for entering students, ESL program, services for LD students, advanced placement, accelerated degree program, independent study, double major, summer session for credit, part-time degree program, adult/continuing education programs, co-op programs and internships, graduate courses open to undergrads. Off campus study at American University. Study abroad program. ROTC: Army (c).
Entrance Requirements: Options: Peterson's Universal Application, Common Application, electronic application. Required: essay, high school transcript, minimum 2.8 high school GPA, 1 recommendation, minimum combined score of 900 in SAT, SAT or ACT. Required for some: interview. Entrance: moderately difficult. Notification: continuous until 8/15.
Costs Per Year: Application fee: $35. Comprehensive fee: $27,365 includes full-time tuition ($20,675), mandatory fees ($290), and college room and board ($6400). College room only: $3000. Part-time tuition: $689 per credit. Part-time mandatory fees: $145 per term.
Collegiate Environment: Orientation program. Drama-theater group, choral group, student-run newspaper. Social organizations: 22 open to all. Most popular organizations: Mexico Service Club, Education Club, Campus Ministry, SWE, Soccer Club. Major annual events: Luau, Homecoming, Career Fair. Student services: personal-psychological counseling. Campus security: 24-hour emergency response devices and patrols, late night transport-escort service, night patrols by security personnel. 415 college housing spaces available; 251 were occupied in 2003-04. Freshmen guaranteed college housing. On-campus residence required through sophomore year. Option: coed housing available. Saint Martin's College Library with 86,461 books, 132,768 microform titles, 824 serials, 1,487 audiovisual materials, an OPAC, and a Web page. Operations spending for 2004 fiscal year: $761,720. 153 computers available on campus for general student use. A campuswide network can be accessed from student residence rooms. Staffed computer lab on campus.

■ **SEATTLE CENTRAL COMMUNITY COLLEGE** *E-6*
1701 Broadway
Seattle, WA 98122-2400
Tel: (206)587-3800
Admissions: (206)587-3898
Web Site: http://www.seattlecentral.edu/
Description: State-supported, 2-year, coed. Part of Seattle Community College District System. Awards certificates, transfer associate, and terminal associate degrees. Founded 1966. Setting: 15-acre urban campus. Total enrollment: 9,418. 1% Native American, 5% Hispanic, 10% black, 14% Asian American or Pacific Islander, 6% international, 63% 25 or older. Core. Academic remediation for entering students, ESL program, services for LD students, summer session for credit, part-time degree program, external degree program, adult/continuing education programs, co-op programs and internships. ROTC: Army (c), Naval (c), Air Force (c).
Entrance Requirements: Open admission except for nursing program. Entrance: noncompetitive. Application deadline: Rolling.
Collegiate Environment: Orientation program. Drama-theater group, choral group, student-run newspaper. Social organizations: 30 open to all. Most popular organizations: Triangle Club, African Brothers of Unity, MECHA, Asian/Pacific Islander Student Union, Sea-King Club for the Deaf. Major annual events: Student Studies Institute, Student Leadership. Student services: personal-psychological counseling, women's center. Campus security: 24-hour emergency response devices. College housing not available. Main Library with 56,338 books and 425 serials. 366 computers available on campus for general student use. Staffed computer lab on campus.
Community Environment: See Seattle University.

■ **SEATTLE PACIFIC UNIVERSITY** *E-6*
3307 Third Ave. West
Seattle, WA 98119-1997

Tel: (206)281-2000
Free: 800-366-3344
Admissions: (206)281-2517
E-mail: admissions@spu.edu
Web Site: http://www.spu.edu/

Description: Independent Free Methodist, comprehensive, coed. Awards bachelor's, master's, and doctoral degrees and post-master's certificates. Founded 1891. Setting: 35-acre urban campus. Endowment: $26.6 million. Research spending for 2004 fiscal year: $657,000. Educational spending for 2005 fiscal year: $7855 per student. Total enrollment: 3,873. Faculty: 333 (181 full-time, 152 part-time): Student-undergrad faculty ratio is 14:1. 1,858 applied, 85% were admitted. 39% from top 10% of their high school class, 67% from top quarter, 91% from top half. 12 National Merit Scholars. Full-time: 2,880 students, 67% women, 33% men. Part-time: 142 students, 65% women, 35% men. Students come from 47 states and territories, 15 other countries, 68% from out-of-state, 1% Native American, 3% Hispanic, 2% black, 6% Asian American or Pacific Islander, 1% international, 7% 25 or older, 58% live on campus, 9% transferred in. Retention: 85% of full-time freshmen returned the following year. Academic areas with the most degrees conferred: business/marketing; health professions and related sciences; family and consumer sciences; social sciences. Core. Academic remediation for entering students, ESL program, services for LD students, advanced placement, self-designed majors, honors program, independent study, distance learning, double major, summer session for credit, part-time degree program, external degree program, adult/continuing education programs, co-op programs and internships, graduate courses open to undergrads. Off campus study at 13 members of the Coalition for Christian Colleges and Universities. Study abroad program. ROTC: Army (c), Naval (c), Air Force (c).

Entrance Requirements: Options: Common Application, electronic application, early admission, early action, deferred admission, international baccalaureate accepted. Required: essay, high school transcript, minimum 2.5 high school GPA, 2 recommendations, SAT or ACT. Recommended: SAT. Entrance: moderately difficult. Application deadlines: 3/1, 11/15 for early action. Notification: continuous until 3/1, 1/6 for early action.

Costs Per Year: Application fee: $45. Comprehensive fee: $29,355 includes full-time tuition ($21,447), mandatory fees ($336), and college room and board ($7572). College room only: $4071. Room and board charges vary according to board plan and housing facility. Part-time tuition: $596 per credit. Part-time tuition varies according to course load.

Collegiate Environment: Orientation program. Drama-theater group, choral group, student-run newspaper, radio station. Social organizations: 50 open to all. Most popular organizations: Centurions, Falconettes, forensics organization, Amnesty International, University Players. Major annual events: Homecoming, spring picnic, ivy cutting event. Student services: health clinic, personal-psychological counseling. Campus security: 24-hour emergency response devices and patrols, student patrols, late night transport-escort service, closed-circuit TV monitors. 1,712 college housing spaces available; 1,686 were occupied in 2003-04. Freshmen guaranteed college housing. On-campus residence required through senior year. Options: coed, women-only housing available. Seattle Pacific University Library with 191,807 books, 501,851 microform titles, 1,230 serials, 4,408 audiovisual materials, an OPAC, and a Web page. Operations spending for 2004 fiscal year: $1.7 million. 150 computers available on campus for general student use. A campuswide network can be accessed from student residence rooms and from off campus. Staffed computer lab on campus.

Community Environment: See Seattle University.

■ **SEATTLE UNIVERSITY** *E-6*
902 12th Ave., PO Box 222000
Seattle, WA 98122-1090
Tel: (206)296-6000
Free: 800-426-7123
Admissions: (206)296-2000
Fax: (206)296-5656
E-mail: admissions@seattleu.edu
Web Site: http://www.seattleu.edu/

Description: Independent Roman Catholic, comprehensive, coed. Awards bachelor's, master's, doctoral, and first professional degrees and post-master's and first professional certificates. Founded 1891. Setting: 46-acre urban campus. Endowment: $147.5 million. Educational spending for 2005 fiscal year: $5018 per student. Total enrollment: 7,109. Faculty: 582 (387 full-time, 195 part-time). Student-undergrad faculty ratio is 13:1. 4,339 applied, 68% were admitted. 32% from top 10% of their high school class, 60%

from top quarter, 88% from top half. Full-time: 3,877 students, 61% women, 39% men. Part-time: 305 students, 60% women, 40% men. Students come from 47 states and territories, 76 other countries, 40% from out-of-state, 1% Native American, 7% Hispanic, 5% black, 20% Asian American or Pacific Islander, 7% international, 13% 25 or older, 38% live on campus, 10% transferred in. Retention: 87% of full-time freshmen returned the following year. Academic areas with the most degrees conferred: business/marketing; health professions and related sciences; psychology. Core. ESL program, services for LD students, advanced placement, accelerated degree program, self-designed majors, freshman honors college, honors program, independent study, double major, summer session for credit, part-time degree program, adult/continuing education programs, internships, graduate courses open to undergrads. Off campus study at Photographic Center Northwest. Study abroad program. ROTC: Army, Air Force (c).

Entrance Requirements: Options: Peterson's Universal Application, Common Application, electronic application, early admission, deferred admission, international baccalaureate accepted. Required: essay, high school transcript, minimum 2.5 high school GPA, 2 recommendations, SAT or ACT. Entrance: moderately difficult. Application deadline: Rolling. Notification: continuous.

Costs Per Year: Application fee: $45. Comprehensive fee: $30,063 includes full-time tuition ($22,905) and college room and board ($7158). College room only: $4653. Full-time tuition varies according to course load. Room and board charges vary according to board plan. Part-time tuition: $509 per credit. Part-time tuition varies according to course load.

Collegiate Environment: Orientation program. Drama-theater group, choral group, student-run newspaper, radio station. Social organizations: 78 open to all. Most popular organizations: student government, Volunteer Center, Hawaiian Club, International Student Club. Major annual events: International Student Dinner, Luau, Quadstock. Student services: health clinic, personal-psychological counseling, women's center. Campus security: 24-hour emergency response devices and patrols, late night transport-escort service, controlled dormitory access, bicycle patrols. 1,600 college housing spaces available; 1,420 were occupied in 2003-04. Freshmen guaranteed college housing. On-campus residence required through sophomore year. Option: coed housing available. Lemieux Library plus 1 other with 141,478 books, 555,909 microform titles, 2,701 serials, 5,649 audiovisual materials, an OPAC, and a Web page. Operations spending for 2004 fiscal year: $2 million. 401 computers available on campus for general student use. A campuswide network can be accessed from student residence rooms and from off campus. Staffed computer lab on campus.

Community Environment: Built upon the hills between Lake Washington and Puget Sound, Seattle is the metropolis of the Pacific Northwest. A fine protected harbor makes the city one of the world's great seaports. The community has a prosperous fishing industry, and is important for shipping of fir, red cedar and salmon. Other industries in the area include software and computer-related industries, aerospace and related fields, foundries, electronics, marine science firms and the processing of food and forest products. The summer average temperature is 63 degrees, and the winter average is 42 degrees. Mountains surround the city and 193 miles of waterfront accommodate oceangoing vessels. The community has 45 parks, art galleries, museums, year-round theater, and opera. There are churches representing all major denominations, and civic, fraternal and veteran's organizations active in the area. Part-time employment is available. Professional sport teams include the Seahawks (football), Mariners (baseball), and Sonics (basketball).

■ **SHORELINE COMMUNITY COLLEGE** *S-6*
16101 Greenwood Ave. North
Shoreline, WA 98133-5696
Tel: (206)546-4101
Admissions: (206)546-4581
Fax: (206)546-4599
Web Site: http://www.shore.ctc.edu/

Description: State-supported, 2-year, coed. Part of Washington State Board for Community and Technical Colleges. Awards certificates, diplomas, and transfer associate degrees. Founded 1964. Setting: 80-acre suburban campus. Educational spending for 2005 fiscal year: $2457 per student. Total enrollment: 8,591. 45% 25 or older. Core. Academic remediation for entering students, ESL program, services for LD students, advanced placement, summer session for credit, part-time degree program, adult/continuing education programs, co-op programs and internships. Study abroad program.

Entrance Requirements: Open admission. Option: early admission.

Required: high school transcript. Placement: SAT or ACT, ACT ASSET or ACT COMPASS required for some. Entrance: noncompetitive. Application deadline: Rolling.

Collegiate Environment: Drama-theater group, choral group, student-run newspaper. Social organizations: 60 open to all. Most popular organizations: Arts and Entertainment Board, International Club, music groups. Major annual events: Robert E. Colbert Lecture Series, The Soulful Sounds of Christmas, Multicultural Week and Martin Luther King, Jr. Day. Student services: personal-psychological counseling, women's center. Campus security: 24-hour emergency response devices and patrols. College housing not available. Ray W. Howard Library/Media Center with 79,554 books, 1,735 serials, an OPAC, and a Web page. Operations spending for 2004 fiscal year: $1.2 million. 385 computers available on campus for general student use. Staffed computer lab on campus.

Community Environment: See Seattle University.

■ **SKAGIT VALLEY COLLEGE** *C-6*

2405 College Way
Mount Vernon, WA 98273-5899
Tel: (360)416-7600
Fax: (360)416-7890
Web Site: http://www.skagit.edu/

Description: State-supported, 2-year, coed. Part of Washington State Board for Community and Technical Colleges. Awards certificates, diplomas, transfer associate, and terminal associate degrees. Founded 1926. Setting: 85-acre small town campus with easy access to Seattle. Endowment: $3.2 million. Total enrollment: 6,858. 3,321 applied, 60% were admitted. Students come from 4 states and territories, 23 other countries, 3% from out-of-state, 68% 25 or older, 1% live on campus. Core. Academic remediation for entering students, ESL program, services for LD students, advanced placement, accelerated degree program, self-designed majors, independent study, distance learning, summer session for credit, part-time degree program, external degree program, adult/continuing education programs, co-op programs and internships. Study abroad program.

Entrance Requirements: Open admission except for some programs. Options: Common Application, electronic application, deferred admission. Required for some: high school transcript, interview. Entrance: noncompetitive. Application deadline: Rolling.

Collegiate Environment: Orientation program. Drama-theater group, choral group, student-run newspaper, radio station. Social organizations: 42 open to all. Most popular organizations: Phi Theta Kappa, Calling All Colors, Business Management Training, Human Services, Paralegal Club. Major annual events: Cardinal Day, Honors Banquet, Commencement. Student services: personal-psychological counseling, women's center. Campus security: 24-hour patrols, late night transport-escort service, telephone/pager system. Options: men-only, women-only housing available. Norwood Cole Library with 78,631 books, 46,186 microform titles, 359 serials, 2,599 audiovisual materials, an OPAC, and a Web page. 200 computers available on campus for general student use. A campuswide network can be accessed from off-campus. Staffed computer lab on campus.

Community Environment: Agriculture, mixed industries and tourism are the principal industries in this city located on the Skagit River. The climate here is moderate with neither cold nor hot extremes. Mount Vernon is accessible by railroad, bus lines and major highways and is 90 minutes from the Seattle Pacific Airport by automobile. The community has several churches, two hospitals and YMCA serving the residents. Local recreation includes hunting, fishing, skiing, golfing, boating, swimming, salt water or fresh water sports and nearby mountains and forests recreation areas. Various fraternal and civic organizations are found within the community.

■ **SOUTH PUGET SOUND COMMUNITY COLLEGE** *G-4*

2011 Mottman Rd., SW
Olympia, WA 98512-6292
Tel: (360)754-7711
Fax: (360)664-9407
Web Site: http://www.spscc.ctc.edu/

Description: State-supported, 2-year, coed. Part of Washington State Board for Community and Technical Colleges. Awards certificates, diplomas, transfer associate, and terminal associate degrees. Founded 1970. Setting: 86-acre suburban campus with easy access to Seattle. Total enrollment: 6,351. 3,732 applied, 100% were admitted. Students come from 19 other countries, 49% 25 or older. Core. Academic remediation for entering students, ESL program, services for LD students, advanced placement,

summer session for credit, part-time degree program, adult/continuing education programs, co-op programs and internships. Study abroad program. ROTC: Army (c).

Entrance Requirements: Open admission except for nursing, fire protection, dental assisting programs. Options: electronic application, early admission, deferred admission. Placement: CPT, ACCUPLACER required; SAT or ACT recommended. Entrance: noncompetitive. Application deadline: Rolling. Notification: continuous.

Collegiate Environment: Orientation program. Drama-theater group, student-run newspaper. Social organizations: 12 open to all. Student services: personal-psychological counseling. Campus security: 24-hour emergency response devices and patrols, late night transport-escort service. College housing not available. Media Center plus 1 other with 30,000 books, 340 serials, and an OPAC. 450 computers available on campus for general student use. A campuswide network can be accessed from off-campus. Staffed computer lab on campus.

■ **SOUTH SEATTLE COMMUNITY COLLEGE** *E-6*

6000 16th Ave., SW
Seattle, WA 98106-1499
Tel: (206)764-5300
Admissions: (206)764-5378
E-mail: kimmanderb@sccd.ctc.edu
Web Site: http://www.sccd.ctc.edu/

Description: State-supported, 2-year, coed. Part of Seattle Community College District System. Awards certificates, diplomas, and transfer associate degrees. Founded 1970. Setting: 65-acre urban campus. Students come from 24 other countries, 54% 25 or older. Academic remediation for entering students, ESL program, services for LD students, advanced placement, summer session for credit, part-time degree program, adult/continuing education programs. Off campus study at 9 community colleges in the Seattle metropolitan area.

Entrance Requirements: Open admission except for international students. Option: early admission. Placement: ACT ASSET required for some. Entrance: noncompetitive. Application deadline: Rolling.

Collegiate Environment: Drama-theater group, choral group, student-run newspaper. Most popular organizations: Phi Theta, Vietnamese Club, Afro-American Club, Delta Epsilon Chi, International Student Clubs. Major annual events: Rainbow Festival, Holiday Dinner. Student services: personal-psychological counseling, women's center. Campus security: 24-hour emergency response devices and patrols. College housing not available. South Seattle Community College Instructional Resource Center with 34,000 books, 350 serials, an OPAC, and a Web page. 300 computers available on campus for general student use. A campuswide network can be accessed. Staffed computer lab on campus.

■ **SPOKANE COMMUNITY COLLEGE** *E-16*

1810 North Greene St.
Spokane, WA 99217-5399
Tel: (509)533-7000
Admissions: (509)533-7075
Fax: (509)533-8839
E-mail: jdunlap@scc.spokane.edu
Web Site: http://www.scc.spokane.edu/

Description: State-supported, 2-year, coed. Part of Washington State Board for Community and Technical Colleges. Awards certificates, diplomas, transfer associate, and terminal associate degrees. Founded 1963. Setting: 108-acre urban campus. Endowment: $33,508. Educational spending for 2005 fiscal year: $3087 per student. Total enrollment: 6,152. Student-undergrad faculty ratio is 20:1. Full-time: 5,223 students, 56% women, 44% men. Part-time: 929 students, 67% women, 33% men. Students come from 5 states and territories, 20 other countries, 17% from out-of-state, 3% Native American, 2% Hispanic, 2% black, 3% Asian American or Pacific Islander, 0.1% international, 40% 25 or older, 4% transferred in. Retention: 35% of full-time freshmen returned the following year. Core. Academic remediation for entering students, ESL program, services for LD students, advanced placement, self-designed majors, independent study, distance learning, summer session for credit, part-time degree program, adult/continuing education programs, co-op programs and internships. ROTC: Army (c).

Entrance Requirements: Open admission. Options: early admission, deferred admission. Recommended: high school transcript. Entrance: noncompetitive. Application deadline: Rolling. Notification: continuous.

Costs Per Year: Application fee: $15. Tuition: $71.60 per credit part-time. Area resident tuition: $813 full-time. Nonresident tuition: $1392 full-time, $133.75 per credit part-time.

Collegiate Environment: Orientation program. Drama-theater group, student-run newspaper. Social organizations: 25 open to all. Most popular organizations: VICA, Delta Epsilon Chi, Intercultural Student Organization, Rho Beta Psi, Student Awareness League. Major annual events: Spring Fling, Celebration of Cultures, Job Fair. Campus security: 24-hour emergency response devices and patrols, student patrols, late night transport-escort service. College housing not available. Learning Resources Center plus 1 other with 38,967 books, 466 serials, and an OPAC. Operations spending for 2004 fiscal year: $786,010. 700 computers available on campus for general student use. A campuswide network can be accessed. Staffed computer lab on campus.

Community Environment: See Spokane Falls Community College.

■ **SPOKANE FALLS COMMUNITY COLLEGE** *E-16*

3410 West Fort George Wright Dr.
Spokane, WA 99224-5288
Tel: (509)533-3500; 888-509-7944
Admissions: (509)533-3682
Fax: (509)533-3433
Web Site: http://www.sfcc.spokane.cc.wa.us/

Description: State-supported, 2-year, coed. Part of State Board for Washington Community and Technical Colleges. Awards certificates, diplomas, transfer associate, and terminal associate degrees. Founded 1967. Setting: 125-acre urban campus. Endowment: $33,407. Educational spending for 2005 fiscal year: $3204 per student. Total enrollment: 5,649. Student-undergrad faculty ratio is 22:1. Students come from 6 states and territories, 14 other countries, 5% from out-of-state, 2% Native American, 0.4% Hispanic, 2% black, 4% Asian American or Pacific Islander, 0.1% international, 28% 25 or older. Retention: 29% of full-time freshmen returned the following year. Core. Academic remediation for entering students, ESL program, services for LD students, advanced placement, self-designed majors, summer session for credit, part-time degree program, adult/continuing education programs, co-op programs and internships. ROTC: Army (c).

Entrance Requirements: Open admission. Options: early admission, deferred admission. Recommended: high school transcript. Entrance: noncompetitive. Application deadline: Rolling. Notification: continuous.

Costs Per Year: Application fee: $15. Area resident tuition: $813 full-time, $71.60 per credit part-time. Nonresident tuition: $1392 full-time, $133.75 per credit part-time.

Collegiate Environment: Drama-theater group, choral group, student-run newspaper, radio station. Social organizations: 30 open to all. Most popular organizations: DECA, Associated Men Students, Associated Women Students, chorale, Forensics Club. Major annual events: Spring Fling, Winter Fest, Club Orientation Week. Student services: personal-psychological counseling, women's center. Campus security: late night transport-escort service, 24-hour emergency dispatch. College housing not available. Learning Resources Center plus 1 other with 58,000 books, 705 serials, and an OPAC. Operations spending for 2004 fiscal year: $1.1 million. 400 computers available on campus for general student use. A campuswide network can be accessed. Staffed computer lab on campus.

Community Environment: The second largest city in the state, Spokane has diversified natural resources including timber lands, tremendous waterpower, and mineral wealth. There are many industries in the area, and part-time work is available. The city is considered the economic and cultural capital of the region between the Rockies and the Cascades. The mean temperature is 47 degrees. Two airports, and several private fields, railroads, and bus lines serve the area. Over 200 churches of all denominations, a public library system, several hospitals, and many civic and fraternal organizations are active here. There are military establishments representing all the services within the area. The community has many fine cultural and recreational facilities as well as excellent shopping facilities.

■ **TACOMA COMMUNITY COLLEGE** *G-5*

6501 South 19th St.
Tacoma, WA 98466
Tel: (253)566-5000
Admissions: (253)566-5116
Fax: (253)566-5376
E-mail: ahayward@tcc.ctc.edu
Web Site: http://www.tacomacc.edu/

Description: State-supported, 2-year, coed. Part of Washington State Board for Community and Technical Colleges. Awards certificates, diplomas, transfer associate, and terminal associate degrees. Founded 1965. Setting:

150-acre urban campus with easy access to Seattle. Educational spending for 2005 fiscal year: $4562 per student. Total enrollment: 6,056. 5,295 applied, 100% were admitted. Students come from 20 other countries, 4% from out-of-state, 2% Native American, 7% Hispanic, 12% black, 10% Asian American or Pacific Islander, 3% international, 46% 25 or older. Core. Academic remediation for entering students, ESL program, services for LD students, advanced placement, accelerated degree program, self-designed majors, honors program, independent study, distance learning, summer session for credit, part-time degree program, adult/continuing education programs, internships. Off campus study at members of the Concurrent Enrollment Program. ROTC: Army (c).

Entrance Requirements: Open admission except for some vocational programs. Option: early admission. Placement: ACCUPLACER required. Entrance: noncompetitive. Application deadline: Rolling.

Costs Per Year: Application fee: $0. State resident tuition: $2,542 full-time. Nonresident tuition: $2,932 full-time. Mandatory fees: $68 full-time.

Collegiate Environment: Orientation program. Drama-theater group, choral group, student-run newspaper. Social organizations: 20 open to all. Major annual event: College Transfer Day. Student services: personal-psychological counseling, women's center. Campus security: Sonitrol electronic system. College housing not available. Pearl Wanamaker Library with 90,192 books, 5,237 microform titles, 269 serials, 5,281 audiovisual materials, an OPAC, and a Web page. Operations spending for 2004 fiscal year: $611,523. 310 computers available on campus for general student use. A campuswide network can be accessed. Staffed computer lab on campus.

Community Environment: The third largest city in Washington, Tacoma is a shipping, industrial and distributing center located in the Puget Sound region. The city has diversified industries including electrochemicals, food and beverage processing, clothing manufacturing, iron, steel, and shipyards. The area is provided transportation by rail, air, bus, and major highways. The city has many parks, a public library system, museums, hospitals, and many civic and fraternal organizations to serve the community. Tacoma is near Mt. Rainier National park and its residents enjoy easy access to ocean beaches, the many waterways of Puget Sound, and Olympic and North Cascades National Parks. Nearby lakes and streams offer excellent fishing.

■ **TRINITY LUTHERAN COLLEGE** *U-8*

4221 228th Ave., SE
Issaquah, WA 98029-9299
Tel: (425)392-0400
Free: 800-843-5659
Admissions: (425)961-5516
Fax: (425)392-0404
E-mail: admissn@lbi.edu
Web Site: http://www.tlc.edu/

Description: Independent Lutheran, 4-year, coed. Awards associate and bachelor's degrees. Founded 1944. Setting: 46-acre suburban campus with easy access to Seattle. Endowment: $1.2 million. Educational spending for 2005 fiscal year: $6812 per student. Total enrollment: 156. 50 applied, 70% were admitted. 0% from top 10% of their high school class, 14% from top quarter, 57% from top half. Full-time: 115 students, 58% women, 42% men. Part-time: 41 students, 80% women, 20% men. Students come from 13 states and territories, 6 other countries, 43% from out-of-state, 22% 25 or older, 13% transferred in. Retention: 88% of full-time freshmen returned the following year. Core. Academic remediation for entering students, ESL program, services for LD students, advanced placement, independent study, double major, part-time degree program, internships. Off campus study at Concordia University (OR). Study abroad program.

Entrance Requirements: Options: Peterson's Universal Application, early admission, deferred admission. Required: high school transcript, minimum 2.0 high school GPA, 2 recommendations, SAT or ACT. Required for some: interview. Entrance: minimally difficult. Application deadline: 9/15.

Costs Per Year: Application fee: $30. Comprehensive fee: $30,307 includes full-time tuition ($21,432), mandatory fees ($150), and college room and board ($8725). College room only: $5815. Full-time tuition and fees vary according to course load. Room and board charges vary according to board plan. Part-time tuition: $893 per semester hour. Part-time tuition varies according to course load.

Collegiate Environment: Orientation program. Drama-theater group, choral group. Social organizations: 8 open to all. Most popular organizations: Environmental Commission, Student government, Worship Commission, Global Concerns, Activities Commission. Major annual events: Day of Jubilee, Spring Retreat, Insanity Night. Student services: health clinic, personal-psychological counseling. Campus security: 24-hour emergency response devices, student patrols, controlled dormitory access. 250 college housing spaces available; 100 were occupied in 2003-04. Freshmen guaranteed college housing. Option: coed housing available. Trinity Lutheran College with 31,000 books and 217 serials. Operations spending for 2004 fiscal year: $147,806. 15 computers available on campus for general student use. Staffed computer lab on campus.

■ **UNIVERSITY OF PHOENIX-SPOKANE CAMPUS** *E-16*
8775 E. Mission Ave.
Spokane Valley, WA 99212
Tel: (509)327-2443
Free: 800-228-7240
Admissions: (480)557-1712
Web Site: http://www.phoenix.edu/
Description: Proprietary, comprehensive, coed. Awards bachelor's and master's degrees. Founded 2003. Total enrollment: 343. Faculty: 67 (2 full-time, 65 part-time). Student-undergrad faculty ratio is 4:1. 10 applied. Full-time: 284 students, 59% women, 41% men. 0% from out-of-state, 0.4% Native American, 0.4% Hispanic, 0.4% black, 36% international, 88% 25 or older. Academic area with the most degrees conferred: business/marketing. Core. Calendar: continuous. Advanced placement, accelerated degree program, independent study, distance learning, external degree program, adult/continuing education programs, graduate courses open to undergrads.
Entrance Requirements: Open admission. Option: deferred admission. Required: 1 recommendation. Required for some: high school transcript. Entrance: noncompetitive. Application deadline: Rolling.
Costs Per Year: Application fee: $110. Tuition: $9750 full-time, $325 per credit part-time. Mandatory fees: $560 full-time, $70 per course part-time.
Collegiate Environment: College housing not available. University Library with 444 books, 666 serials, an OPAC, and a Web page. System-wide operations spending for 2004 fiscal year: $3.2 million.

■ **UNIVERSITY OF PHOENIX-WASHINGTON CAMPUS** *E-6*
7100 Fort Dent Way, Ste. 100
Seattle, WA 98188-7500
Tel: (206)268-5800
Free: 800-228-7240
Admissions: (480)557-1712
Fax: (206)241-8848
Web Site: http://www.phoenix.edu/
Description: Proprietary, comprehensive, coed. Awards bachelor's and master's degrees. Founded 1997. Total enrollment: 2,172. Faculty: 258 (16 full-time, 242 part-time). Student-undergrad faculty ratio is 9:1. 34 applied. Full-time: 1,678 students, 56% women, 44% men. 0% from out-of-state, 1% Native American, 2% Hispanic, 5% black, 3% Asian American or Pacific Islander, 4% international, 93% 25 or older. Academic areas with the most degrees conferred: business/marketing; computer and information sciences; public administration and social services. Core. Calendar: continuous. Advanced placement, accelerated degree program, independent study, distance learning, external degree program, adult/continuing education programs, graduate courses open to undergrads.
Entrance Requirements: Open admission. Option: deferred admission. Required: 1 recommendation. Required for some: high school transcript. Entrance: noncompetitive. Application deadline: Rolling.
Costs Per Year: Application fee: $110. Tuition: $11,055 full-time, $368.50 per credit part-time. Mandatory fees: $560 full-time, $70 per course part-time.
Collegiate Environment: College housing not available. University Library with 444 books, 666 serials, an OPAC, and a Web page. System-wide operations spending for 2004 fiscal year: $3.2 million.

■ **UNIVERSITY OF PUGET SOUND** *G-5*
1500 North Warner St.
Tacoma, WA 98416
Tel: (253)879-3100
Free: 800-396-7191
Admissions: (253)879-3211
Fax: (253)879-3500
E-mail: admission@ups.edu
Web Site: http://www.ups.edu/
Description: Independent, comprehensive, coed. Awards bachelor's, master's, and first professional degrees and post-master's certificates. Founded 1888. Setting: 97-acre suburban campus with easy access to Seattle. Endowment: $201.8 million. Research spending for 2004 fiscal year:

$695,000. Educational spending for 2005 fiscal year: $12,000 per student. Total enrollment: 2,887. Faculty: 283 (224 full-time, 59 part-time). Student-undergrad faculty ratio is 11:1. 4,711 applied, 71% were admitted. 38% from top 10% of their high school class, 68% from top quarter, 93% from top half. 34 National Merit Scholars, 41 valedictorians. Full-time: 2,571 students, 58% women, 42% men. Part-time: 33 students, 45% women, 55% men. Students come from 46 states and territories, 14 other countries, 70% from out-of-state, 1% Native American, 4% Hispanic, 2% black, 9% Asian American or Pacific Islander, 0.4% international, 2% 25 or older, 59% live on campus, 4% transferred in. Retention: 87% of full-time freshmen returned the following year. Academic areas with the most degrees conferred: social sciences; business/marketing; visual and performing arts. Core. Calendar: semesters. Advanced placement, self-designed majors, honors program, independent study, double major, summer session for credit, part-time degree program, co-op programs and internships. Study abroad program. ROTC: Army (c).
Entrance Requirements: Options: Peterson's Universal Application, Common Application, electronic application, early admission, early decision, deferred admission, international baccalaureate accepted. Required: essay, high school transcript, 2 recommendations, SAT or ACT. Recommended: minimum 3.0 high school GPA, interview. Entrance: moderately difficult. Application deadlines: 2/1, 11/15 for early decision plan 1, 12/15 for early decision plan 2. Notification: 4/1, 12/15 for early decision plan 1, 1/15 for early decision plan 2.
Costs Per Year: Application fee: $40. Comprehensive fee: $35,600 includes full-time tuition ($28,270), mandatory fees ($190), and college room and board ($7140). College room only: $3900. Full-time tuition and fees vary according to course load. Room and board charges vary according to board plan and housing facility. Part-time tuition: $3570 per unit. Part-time tuition varies according to course load.
Collegiate Environment: Orientation program. Drama-theater group, choral group, student-run newspaper, radio station. Social organizations: 65 open to all; national fraternities, national sororities; 22% of eligible men and 23% of eligible women are members. Most popular organizations: Hui-O-Hawaii, Repertory Dance Group, Film and Theatre Society, outdoor programs, Lighthouse. Major annual events: Homecoming/Reunion/Songfest Weekend, Hui-O-Hawaii Luau/Spring Family Weekend, Mistletoast Holiday Festival. Student services: legal services, health clinic, personal-psychological counseling. Campus security: 24-hour emergency response devices and patrols, student patrols, late night transport-escort service, controlled dormitory access, 24-hour locked residence hall entrances. 1,651 college housing spaces available; 1,550 were occupied in 2003-04. Freshmen given priority for college housing. Options: coed, women-only housing available. Collins Memorial Library with 349,088 books, 356,705 microform titles, 10,169 serials, 24,850 audiovisual materials, an OPAC, and a Web page. Operations spending for 2004 fiscal year: $4.8 million. 314 computers available on campus for general student use. A campuswide network can be accessed from student residence rooms and from off campus. Staffed computer lab on campus.
Community Environment: Founded in 1888, the campus is located in residential North Tacoma. Thirty miles south of Seattle and easily accessible from Interstate 5, Tacoma is a dynamic city of 187,200 people. The university occupies 38 buildings on a 97 acre park-like campus; architecture is Tudor Gothic with its distinctive red-brick pattern arches and porticoes. Located close to the shores of Puget Sound and a short distance from ski slopes and the Pacific Ocean, the University is also the center for much of Tacoma's cultural life. Tacoma also features Point Defiance Zoo and Aquarium, many parks, a public library system, museums and hospitals.

■ **UNIVERSITY OF WASHINGTON** *E-6*
Seattle, WA 98195
Tel: (206)543-2100
Admissions: (206)543-9686
Web Site: http://www.washington.edu/
Description: State-supported, university, coed. Awards bachelor's, master's, doctoral, and first professional degrees and first professional certificates. Founded 1861. Setting: 703-acre urban campus. Endowment: $963 million. Research spending for 2004 fiscal year: $544.6 million. Educational spending for 2005 fiscal year: $10,259 per student. Total enrollment: 39,251. Faculty: 3,518 (2,879 full-time, 639 part-time). Student-undergrad faculty ratio is 11:1. 15,923 applied, 67% were admitted. 82% from top 10% of their high school class, 96% from top quarter, 100% from top half. 37 National Merit Scholars. Full-time: 23,216 students, 52% women, 48% men. Part-time: 4,272 students, 51% women, 49% men. Students come from 52 states and territories, 59 other countries, 14% from out-of-state, 1% Native

American, 4% Hispanic, 3% black, 27% Asian American or Pacific Islander, 3% international, 12% 25 or older, 17% live on campus, 6% transferred in. Retention: 93% of full-time freshmen returned the following year. Academic areas with the most degrees conferred: social sciences; business/marketing; education. Core. Academic remediation for entering students, ESL program, services for LD students, advanced placement, accelerated degree program, self-designed majors, honors program, independent study, distance learning, double major, summer session for credit, part-time degree program, external degree program, adult/continuing education programs, co-op programs and internships, graduate courses open to undergrads. Study abroad program. ROTC: Army, Naval, Air Force.

Entrance Requirements: Options: electronic application, early admission, international baccalaureate accepted. Required: essay, minimum 2.0 high school GPA, SAT or ACT. Required for some: high school transcript. Entrance: moderately difficult. Application deadline: 1/15. Notification: continuous. Preference given to state residents, children of alumni.

Costs Per Year: Application fee: $50. State resident tuition: $5532 full-time. Nonresident tuition: $19,830 full-time.

Collegiate Environment: Orientation program. Drama-theater group, choral group, marching band, student-run newspaper, radio station. Social organizations: 300 open to all; national fraternities, national sororities; 12% of eligible men and 11% of eligible women are members. Major annual events: homecoming, Earth Day, Tolo. Student services: legal services, health clinic, personal-psychological counseling, women's center. Campus security: 24-hour emergency response devices and patrols, late night transport-escort service, controlled dormitory access. 5,000 college housing spaces available. No special consideration for freshman housing applicants. Option: coed housing available. Suzzallo/Allen Library plus 21 others with 5.8 million books, 50,245 serials, 1.4 million audiovisual materials, and a Web page. Operations spending for 2004 fiscal year: $26.5 million. 285 computers available on campus for general student use. A campuswide network can be accessed from student residence rooms and from off campus. Staffed computer lab on campus.

■ **UNIVERSITY OF WASHINGTON, BOTHELL** *E-6*
18115 Campus Way NE
Bothell, WA 98011-8246
Tel: (425)352-5000
Admissions: (425)352-5305
Web Site: http://www.uwb.edu

Description: State-supported, upper-level, coed. Awards bachelor's and master's degrees. Endowment: $2.3 million. Educational spending for 2005 fiscal year: $6390 per student. Total enrollment: 1,537. Faculty: 103 (73 full-time, 30 part-time). Student-undergrad faculty ratio is 14:1. 660 applied, 72% were admitted. Full-time: 800 students, 56% women, 45% men. Part-time: 515 students, 55% women, 45% men. 1% from out-of-state, 0.5% Native American, 2% Hispanic, 2% black, 14% Asian American or Pacific Islander, 2% international. Academic areas with the most degrees conferred: interdisciplinary studies; business/marketing; health professions and related sciences.

Costs Per Year: Application fee: $0. State resident tuition: $5496 full-time. Nonresident tuition: $19,794 full-time.

Collegiate Environment: Student-run newspaper.

■ **UNIVERSITY OF WASHINGTON, TACOMA** *G-5*
1900 Commerce St.
Tacoma, WA 98402-3100
Tel: (253)692-4000
Free: 800-736-7750
Admissions: (253)692-4400
E-mail: wandaec@u.washington.edu
Web Site: http://www.tacoma.washington.edu/

Description: State-supported, upper-level, coed. Awards bachelor's, master's, and first professional degrees. Founded 1990. Setting: 48-acre urban campus. Endowment: $9.1 million. Educational spending for 2005 fiscal year: $5720 per student. Total enrollment: 2,113. Faculty: 142 (104 full-time, 38 part-time). Student-undergrad faculty ratio is 16:1. Full-time: 1,188 students, 60% women, 40% men. Part-time: 530 students, 60% women, 40% men. 3% from out-of-state, 2% Native American, 2% Hispanic, 6% black, 13% Asian American or Pacific Islander, 1% international. Academic areas with the most degrees conferred: interdisciplinary studies; business/marketing; health professions and related sciences.

Costs Per Year: Application fee: $50. State resident tuition: $5532 full-time, $923 per course part-time. Nonresident tuition: $19,830 full-time, $3305 per

course part-time. Mandatory fees: $90 full-time, $30 per course part-time, $30 per term part-time. College room and board: $10,125.

Collegiate Environment: Student-run newspaper. Social organizations: ; 1% of eligible men and 1% of eligible women are members. Student services: personal-psychological counseling.

■ **WALLA WALLA COLLEGE** *J-14*
204 South College Ave.
College Place, WA 99324-1198
Tel: (509)527-2615
Free: 800-541-8900
Admissions: (509)527-2327
Fax: (509)527-2397
E-mail: weisda@wwc.edu
Web Site: http://www.wwc.edu/

Description: Independent Seventh-day Adventist, comprehensive, coed. Awards associate, bachelor's, and master's degrees. Founded 1892. Setting: 77-acre small town campus. Endowment: $11.6 million. Research spending for 2004 fiscal year: $36,362. Total enrollment: 1,942. Faculty: 194 (122 full-time, 72 part-time). Student-undergrad faculty ratio is 12:1. 1,059 applied, 28% were admitted. 14% from top 10% of their high school class, 34% from top quarter, 63% from top half. Full-time: 1,528 students, 48% women, 52% men. Part-time: 142 students, 48% women, 52% men. Students come from 45 states and territories, 59% from out-of-state, 1% Native American, 7% Hispanic, 3% black, 5% Asian American or Pacific Islander, 8% 25 or older, 44% live on campus, 9% transferred in. Retention: 72% of full-time freshmen returned the following year. Core. Academic remediation for entering students, ESL program, services for LD students, advanced placement, freshman honors college, honors program, independent study, double major, summer session for credit, part-time degree program, co-op programs and internships, graduate courses open to undergrads. Study abroad program.

Entrance Requirements: Options: Common Application, electronic application, deferred admission. Required: high school transcript, minimum 2.0 high school GPA, 3 recommendations, SAT or ACT. Recommended: ACT. Entrance: moderately difficult. Application deadline: Rolling. Notification: continuous.

Costs Per Year: Application fee: $40. Comprehensive fee: $24,489 includes full-time tuition ($19,725), mandatory fees ($192), and college room and board ($4572). College room only: $2472. Part-time tuition: $516 per credit.

Collegiate Environment: Orientation program. Drama-theater group, choral group, student-run newspaper, radio station. Social organizations: 50 open to all. Most popular organizations: Associated Students of Walla Walla College (ASWWC), Village Singles' Club, Aleph Gimel Ain (women's club), Amnesty International, Omicron Pi Sigma (men's club). Major annual events: OPS Weekend, AGA Weekend, Sonnenberg Series. Student services: health clinic, personal-psychological counseling. Campus security: 24-hour emergency response devices and patrols, student patrols, late night transport-escort service, controlled dormitory access. 928 college housing spaces available; 779 were occupied in 2003-04. Freshmen guaranteed college housing. On-campus residence required through junior year. Options: men-only, women-only housing available. Peterson Memorial Library plus 3 others with 178,450 books, 17,500 microform titles, 1,105 serials, 3,431 audiovisual materials, an OPAC, and a Web page. Operations spending for 2004 fiscal year: $1.4 million. 118 computers available on campus for general student use. A campuswide network can be accessed from student residence rooms and from off campus. Staffed computer lab on campus.

Community Environment: College Place is a residential community adjacent to Walla Walla. The climate is temperate. Three miles away, all major forms of transportation are available. The immediate community has four churches and two hospitals. Part-time employment opportunities are fair.

■ **WALLA WALLA COMMUNITY COLLEGE** *J-14*
500 Tausick Way
Walla Walla, WA 99362-9267
Tel: (509)522-2500; 877-992-9292
Admissions: (509)527-4283
Fax: (509)527-3361
E-mail: admissions@mail.ww.cc.wa.us
Web Site: http://www.wwcc.edu/home/

Description: State-supported, 2-year, coed. Part of Washington State Board for Community and Technical Colleges. Awards certificates, diplomas, transfer associate, and terminal associate degrees. Founded 1967. Setting:

125-acre small town campus. Endowment: $4 million. Educational spending for 2005 fiscal year: $3150 per student. Total enrollment: 4,440. 1,256 applied, 91% were admitted. Full-time: 2,164 students, 49% women, 51% men. Part-time: 2,276 students, 52% women, 48% men. Students come from 5 other countries, 12% from out-of-state, 1% Native American, 6% Hispanic, 4% black, 1% Asian American or Pacific Islander, 0.2% international, 57% 25 or older. Core. Academic remediation for entering students, ESL program, services for LD students, advanced placement, honors program, independent study, distance learning, double major, summer session for credit, part-time degree program, external degree program, adult/continuing education programs, co-op programs and internships. Off campus study at other members of the Washington State Board for Community and Technical Colleges.

Entrance Requirements: Open admission. Options: Peterson's Universal Application, Common Application, electronic application. Recommended: high school transcript. Required for some: interview. Placement: ACT ASSET and ACT COMPASS required. Entrance: noncompetitive. Application deadline: Rolling.

Collegiate Environment: Orientation program. Drama-theater group, choral group. Social organizations: 30 open to all. Most popular organizations: Drama Club, Computer Club, intramurals, Nursing Club, Business Leadership Club. Major annual events: Spring Week, Celebration of Cultures, New Student Day. Student services: personal-psychological counseling. Campus security: student patrols, late night transport-escort service. College housing not available. Walla Walla Community College Library with 45,814 books, 19,767 microform titles, 428 serials, 3,715 audiovisual materials, and an OPAC. Operations spending for 2004 fiscal year: $813,154. 180 computers available on campus for general student use. A campuswide network can be accessed from off-campus. Staffed computer lab on campus.

Community Environment: Walla Walla is rich agricultural area in southern Washington near the Oregon State line. The chief crop is wheat. The area has excellent highways, a commuter airline and buslines serving the community. The climate is mild. Local recreation includes hunting, boating, fishing, camping and skiing in the nearby mountains. There are churches representing most denominations, health facilities and shopping centers in the area. All major lodges and service clubs are active here. Frontier days and a rodeo are held annually in September.

■ **WASHINGTON STATE UNIVERSITY** *H-16*
Pullman, WA 99164
Tel: (509)335-3564; 888-468-6978
Admissions: (509)335-5586
E-mail: admiss@wsu.edu
Web Site: http://www.wsu.edu/

Description: State-supported, university, coed. Awards bachelor's, master's, doctoral, and first professional degrees and post-master's certificates. Founded 1890. Setting: 620-acre rural campus. Endowment: $553.9 million. Research spending for 2004 fiscal year: $109.6 million. Educational spending for 2005 fiscal year: $8324 per student. Total enrollment: 23,544. Faculty: 1,449 (1,057 full-time, 392 part-time). Student-undergrad faculty ratio is 15:1. 9,193 applied, 74% were admitted. 37% from top 10% of their high school class, 57% from top quarter, 90% from top half. Full-time: 16,786 students, 51% women, 49% men. Part-time: 2,799 students, 61% women, 39% men. Students come from 53 states and territories, 65 other countries, 9% from out-of-state, 1% Native American, 4% Hispanic, 3% black, 6% Asian American or Pacific Islander, 3% international, 20% 25 or older, 37% live on campus, 13% transferred in. Retention: 84% of full-time freshmen returned the following year. Academic areas with the most degrees conferred: business/marketing; social sciences; communications/journalism. Core. Calendar: semesters. Academic remediation for entering students, ESL program, services for LD students, advanced placement, self-designed majors, honors program, independent study, distance learning, double major, summer session for credit, part-time degree program, external degree program, adult/continuing education programs, co-op programs and internships, graduate courses open to undergrads. Off campus study at University of Idaho, Education Abroad, National Student Exchange. Study abroad program. ROTC: Army, Naval, Air Force.

Entrance Requirements: Options: electronic application, early admission, international baccalaureate accepted. Required: essay, high school transcript, minimum 2.0 high school GPA, SAT or ACT. Required for some: 3 recommendations. Entrance: moderately difficult. Notification: 12/1.

Costs Per Year: Application fee: $50. State resident tuition: $5432 full-time. Nonresident tuition: $15,072 full-time.

Collegiate Environment: Orientation program. Drama-theater group, choral group, marching band, student-run newspaper, radio station. Social

organizations: 225 open to all; national fraternities, national sororities; 14% of eligible men and 18% of eligible women are members. Most popular organizations: Sigma Iota Hospitality Association, Student Alumni Connection, K-House, Fellowship for Student Athletes, Black Woman's Caucus. Major annual events: Up All Night, Homecoming, Cougfest. Student services: legal services, health clinic, personal-psychological counseling, women's center. Campus security: 24-hour emergency response devices and patrols, student patrols, late night transport-escort service, controlled dormitory access. 6,021 college housing spaces available; 5,777 were occupied in 2003-04. Freshmen given priority for college housing. On-campus residence required in freshman year. Options: coed, men-only, women-only housing available. Holland Library plus 5 others with 2.2 million books, 3.9 million microform titles, 30,789 serials, 365,812 audiovisual materials, an OPAC, and a Web page. Operations spending for 2004 fiscal year: $13.4 million. 2,400 computers available on campus for general student use. A campuswide network can be accessed from student residence rooms and from off campus. Staffed computer lab on campus.

Community Environment: Pullman is located 7 miles west of the Idaho border. The summer temperature averages in the 80s and the winter temperature averages around 30 degrees. The area is accessible by airlines and bus lines. There are 30 churches, a public library, and various civic, fraternal, and veteran's organizations serving the community. Local recreation includes four parks, baseball diamonds, swimming pools, theaters, bowling alleys, a golf course, tennis courts and nearby lakes and rivers offering swimming, boating and skating.

■ **WENATCHEE VALLEY COLLEGE** *F-10*
1300 Fifth St.
Wenatchee, WA 98801-1799
Tel: (509)662-1651
Admissions: (509)682-6800
Fax: (509)664-2511
Web Site: http://wvc.ctc.edu/

Description: State and locally supported, 2-year, coed. Part of Washington State Board for Community and Technical Colleges. Awards certificates, diplomas, transfer associate, and terminal associate degrees. Founded 1939. Setting: 56-acre rural campus. Endowment: $358,000. Total enrollment: 4,046. 843 applied, 100% were admitted. Students come from 6 other countries, 54% 25 or older. Core. Academic remediation for entering students, ESL program, services for LD students, advanced placement, honors program, independent study, distance learning, summer session for credit, part-time degree program, external degree program, adult/continuing education programs, co-op programs.

Entrance Requirements: Open admission except for allied health programs. Options: Common Application, electronic application, early admission, deferred admission. Required for some: high school transcript. Placement: ACT ASSET required. Entrance: noncompetitive. Application deadline: Rolling.

Collegiate Environment: Drama-theater group, choral group, student-run newspaper. Social organizations: 16 open to all. Major annual event: Cinco de Mayo. Campus security: evening and late night security patrols. Option: coed housing available. John Brown Library plus 1 other with 32,000 books, 220 serials, an OPAC, and a Web page. 54 computers available on campus for general student use. Staffed computer lab on campus.

Community Environment: Situated at the confluence of the Wenatchee and Columbia Rivers, Wenatchee is known as the apple capital of the world. In the eastern foothills of the Cascade Mountains, the city has a temperate climate with four definite seasons. The average maximum temperature is 75 degrees, with an average minimum of 28 degrees, with an average rainfall of 9.58 inches. The community is accessible by bus, air, and major highways. There are almost 40 churches representing various denominations, a YMCA, YWCA, library, museum, theatres, medical facilities, motels, hotels, good shopping, and many civic and fraternal organizations. Local recreation includes hunting, boating, fishing, golf, and skiing. A state apple blossom festival is held annually. Part-time employment is available.

■ **WESTERN BUSINESS COLLEGE** *L-5*
120 Northeast 136th Ave., Ste. 130
Vancouver, WA 98684
Tel: (360)254-3282
Web Site: http://www.western-college.com/

Description: Proprietary, 2-year, coed. Awards diplomas and terminal associate degrees. Founded 1979. Total enrollment: 555.

Entrance Requirements: Recommended: interview. Entrance: moderately difficult. Application deadline: Rolling.
Collegiate Environment: College housing not available.

■ **WESTERN WASHINGTON UNIVERSITY** *B-5*
516 High St.
Bellingham, WA 98225-5996
Tel: (360)650-3000
Admissions: (360)650-3440
E-mail: admit@wwu.edu
Web Site: http://www.wwu.edu/
Description: State-supported, comprehensive, coed. Awards bachelor's and master's degrees. Founded 1893. Setting: 223-acre small town campus with easy access to Seattle and Vancouver. Endowment: $4.3 million. Research spending for 2004 fiscal year: $10.7 million. Educational spending for 2005 fiscal year: $4760 per student. Total enrollment: 14,247. Faculty: 628 (472 full-time, 156 part-time). Student-undergrad faculty ratio is 20:1. 7,922 applied, 75% were admitted. 31% from top 10% of their high school class, 64% from top quarter, 95% from top half. 8 National Merit Scholars, 50 valedictorians. Full-time: 11,943 students, 56% women, 44% men. Part-time: 1,059 students, 55% women, 45% men. Students come from 44 states and territories, 29 other countries, 6% from out-of-state, 2% Native American, 3% Hispanic, 2% black, 8% Asian American or Pacific Islander, 0.4% international, 8% 25 or older, 30% live on campus, 8% transferred in. Retention: 84% of full-time freshmen returned the following year. Academic areas with the most degrees conferred: business/marketing; social sciences; English; psychology. Core. ESL program, services for LD students, advanced placement, accelerated degree program, self-designed majors, honors program, independent study, distance learning, double major, summer session for credit, co-op programs and internships, graduate courses open to undergrads. Off campus study at National Student Exchange. Study abroad program.
Entrance Requirements: Options: Common Application, electronic application, international baccalaureate accepted. Required: high school transcript, minimum 2.5 high school GPA, SAT or ACT, TOEFL for International Students. Recommended: essay. Entrance: moderately difficult. Application deadline: 3/1. Notification: continuous until 4/15.
Costs Per Year: Application fee: $50. State resident tuition: $3673 full-time, $137 per credit part-time. Nonresident tuition: $13,623 full-time, $469 per credit part-time. Mandatory fees: $1065 full-time. Full-time tuition and fees vary according to location. Part-time tuition varies according to location. College room and board: $6524. College room only: $4209. Room and board charges vary according to board plan and housing facility.
Collegiate Environment: Orientation program. Drama-theater group, choral group, student-run newspaper, radio station. Social organizations: 140 open to all. Most popular organizations: intramurals, Residence Hall Association, Associated Students, Outdoor Center, Ethnic Student Center. Major annual events: Fall New Student Convocation, Information Faire, Earth Day. Student services: legal services, health clinic, personal-psychological counseling, women's center. Campus security: 24-hour emergency response devices and patrols, student patrols, late night transport-escort service, controlled dormitory access. 3,943 college housing spaces available; 3,813 were occupied in 2003-04. Freshmen guaranteed college housing. Option: coed housing available. Wilson Library plus 1 other with 1.3 million books, 1.9 million microform titles, 5,236 serials, 28,289 audiovisual materials, an OPAC, and a Web page. Operations spending for 2004 fiscal year: $7.1 million. 1,874 computers available on campus for general student use. A campuswide network can be accessed from student residence rooms and from off campus. Staffed computer lab on campus.
Community Environment: Bellingham overlooks Puget Sound and the San Juan Islands. The city enjoys a temperate climate with a summer temperature seldom exceeding 73 degrees, and winter temperatures range from 28 to 55 degrees. There are frequently winters without snow, and the average rainfall is 34 inches. County industries include shipbuilding, food processing, oil refining, and manufacturing of aluminum, cement, plywood, and paper products. There is also a commercial fishing fleet. The community has hospitals, theatres, and major civic and fraternal organizations. Local recreation includes hiking, fishing, sailing, golf, baseball, softball, and bowling. Mt. Baker for skiing and climbing is 50 miles away. Part-time employment is available.

■ **WHATCOM COMMUNITY COLLEGE** *B-5*
237 West Kellogg Rd.
Bellingham, WA 98226-8003

Tel: (360)676-2170
Fax: (360)676-2171
Web Site: http://www.whatcom.ctc.edu/
Description: State-supported, 2-year, coed. Part of Washington State Board for Community and Technical Colleges. Awards certificates, diplomas, transfer associate, and terminal associate degrees. Founded 1970. Setting: 52-acre small town campus with easy access to Vancouver. Endowment: $2 million. Total enrollment: 4,173. 5% from out-of-state, 30% 25 or older. Core. Academic remediation for entering students, ESL program, services for LD students, advanced placement, accelerated degree program, self-designed majors, honors program, independent study, distance learning, summer session for credit, part-time degree program, external degree program, adult/continuing education programs, co-op programs and internships. Study abroad program.
Entrance Requirements: Open admission. Option: electronic application. Entrance: noncompetitive. Application deadline: Rolling. Notification: continuous.
Costs Per Year: Application fee: $0. State resident tuition: $2484 full-time, $73.10 per credit part-time. Nonresident tuition: $7692 full-time, $244.80 per credit part-time. Full-time tuition varies according to course load and reciprocity agreements. Part-time tuition varies according to course load and reciprocity agreements.
Collegiate Environment: Orientation program. Drama-theater group, choral group, student-run newspaper. Social organizations: 13 open to all. Most popular organizations: Anime Anonymous, Deaf Student Fellowship Club, Health and Wellness Club, Phi Theta Kappa, International Friendship Club. Major annual events: Commencement, Spring BBQ, Fall Welcome. Student services: personal-psychological counseling. Campus security: 24-hour emergency response devices. College housing not available. Whatcom Community College Library with 14,680 books, 41,682 microform titles, 193 serials, 3,653 audiovisual materials, an OPAC, and a Web page. 79 computers available on campus for general student use. A campuswide network can be accessed from off-campus. Staffed computer lab on campus.

■ **WHITMAN COLLEGE** *J-14*
345 Boyer Ave.
Walla Walla, WA 99362-2083
Tel: (509)527-5111; 877-462-9448
Admissions: (509)527-5176
Fax: (509)527-4967
E-mail: admission@whitman.edu
Web Site: http://www.whitman.edu/
Description: Independent, 4-year, coed. Awards bachelor's degrees. Founded 1859. Setting: 117-acre small town campus. Endowment: $311.8 million. Research spending for 2004 fiscal year: $426,727. Educational spending for 2005 fiscal year: $12,429 per student. Total enrollment: 1,512. Student-undergrad faculty ratio is 10:1. 2,544 applied, 49% were admitted. 60% from top 10% of their high school class, 91% from top quarter, 98% from top half. 36 National Merit Scholars, 57 valedictorians. Full-time: 1,480 students, 54% women, 46% men. Part-time: 32 students, 59% women, 41% men. Students come from 44 states and territories, 26 other countries, 58% from out-of-state, 1% Native American, 4% Hispanic, 2% black, 9% Asian American or Pacific Islander, 3% international, 1% 25 or older, 56% live on campus, 1% transferred in. Retention: 95% of full-time freshmen returned the following year. Academic areas with the most degrees conferred: social sciences; biological/life sciences; visual and performing arts. Core. Calendar: semesters. Services for LD students, advanced placement, accelerated degree program, self-designed majors, honors program, independent study, double major, co-op programs. Off campus study at American University, Associated Colleges of the Midwest, Great Lakes Colleges Association, Columbia University. Study abroad program.
Entrance Requirements: Options: Peterson's Universal Application, Common Application, electronic application, early decision, deferred admission, international baccalaureate accepted. Required: essay, high school transcript, 1 recommendation, SAT or ACT. Recommended: interview. Entrance: very difficult. Application deadlines: 1/15, 11/15 for early decision plan 1, 1/1 for early decision plan 2. Notification: 4/1, 12/15 for early decision plan 1, 1/23 for early decision plan 2.
Costs Per Year: Application fee: $45. Comprehensive fee: $36,110 includes full-time tuition ($28,400), mandatory fees ($240), and college room and board ($7470). College room only: $3430. Room and board charges vary according to board plan and housing facility. Part-time tuition: $1190 per credit.
Collegiate Environment: Orientation program. Drama-theater group, choral group, student-run newspaper, radio station. Social organizations: 60 open

to all; national fraternities, national sororities; 34% of eligible men and 26% of eligible women are members. Most popular organizations: Associated Students, outdoor program, Center for Community Service. Major annual events: Renaissance Faire, Choral Contest, Interest House Block Party. Student services: health clinic, personal-psychological counseling, women's center. Campus security: 24-hour emergency response devices and patrols, student patrols, late night transport-escort service, controlled dormitory access. 882 college housing spaces available; 830 were occupied in 2003-04. Freshmen guaranteed college housing. On-campus residence required through sophomore year. Options: coed, women-only housing available. Penrose Library plus 1 other with 356,731 books, 20,000 microform titles, 2,000 serials, 6,548 audiovisual materials, an OPAC, and a Web page. Operations spending for 2004 fiscal year: $1.4 million. 397 computers available on campus for general student use. A campuswide network can be accessed from student residence rooms and from off campus. Staffed computer lab on campus.

■ **WHITWORTH COLLEGE** *E-16*
300 West Hawthorne Rd.
Spokane, WA 99251-0001
Tel: (509)777-1000
Free: 800-533-4668
Admissions: (509)777-4348
Fax: (509)777-3773
E-mail: admissions@whitworth.edu
Web Site: http://www.whitworth.edu/
Description: Independent Presbyterian, comprehensive, coed. Awards bachelor's and master's degrees. Founded 1890. Setting: 200-acre suburban campus. Endowment: $72 million. Research spending for 2004 fiscal year: $310,000. Educational spending for 2005 fiscal year: $6509 per student. Total enrollment: 2,441. Faculty: 291 (120 full-time, 171 part-time). Student-undergrad faculty ratio is 13:1. 2,062 applied, 67% were admitted. 42% from top 10% of their high school class, 72% from top quarter, 96% from top half. 40 valedictorians. Full-time: 2,065 students, 60% women, 40% men. Part-time: 114 students, 68% women, 32% men. Students come from 31 states and territories, 25 other countries, 42% from out-of-state, 1% Native American, 2% Hispanic, 2% black, 4% Asian American or Pacific Islander, 1% international, 3% 25 or older, 65% live on campus, 5% transferred in. Retention: 87% of full-time freshmen returned the following year. Academic areas with the most degrees conferred: business/marketing; education; visual and performing arts. Core. Calendar: 4-1-4. ESL program, services for LD students, advanced placement, self-designed majors, independent study, double major, summer session for credit, part-time degree program, adult/continuing education programs, co-op programs and internships. Off campus study at 3 members of the Intercollegiate Center for Nursing, 2 members of the Intercollegiate Language Study Consortium. Study abroad program. ROTC: Army (c).
Entrance Requirements: Options: Peterson's Universal Application, Common Application, electronic application, early admission, early action, deferred admission. Required: essay, high school transcript, recommendations, SAT or ACT. Required for some: interview. Entrance: very difficult. Application deadlines: 3/1, 11/30 for early action. Notification: 12/20 for early action.
Costs Per Year: Application fee: $0. Comprehensive fee: $31,184 includes full-time tuition ($23,850), mandatory fees ($304), and college room and board ($7030). Part-time tuition: $994 per credit.
Collegiate Environment: Orientation program. Drama-theater group, choral group, student-run newspaper, radio station. Social organizations: 80 open to all. Most popular organizations: International Club, Young Life, En Christo, Hawaiian Club, intramural sports. Major annual events: Homecoming, Community Building Day, Spring Fest. Student services: health clinic, personal-psychological counseling. Campus security: 24-hour emergency response

devices and patrols, late night transport-escort service. 1,150 college housing spaces available; 1,078 were occupied in 2003-04. Freshmen guaranteed college housing. On-campus residence required through sophomore year. Option: coed housing available. Harriet Cheney Cowles Library plus 2 others with 17,982 books, 773 serials, an OPAC, and a Web page. Operations spending for 2004 fiscal year: $788,594. 200 computers available on campus for general student use. Computer purchase/lease plans available. A campuswide network can be accessed from student residence rooms and from off campus. Staffed computer lab on campus.
Community Environment: See Spokane Community College.

■ **YAKIMA VALLEY COMMUNITY COLLEGE** *I-9*
PO Box 22520
Yakima, WA 98907-2520
Tel: (509)574-4600
Admissions: (509)574-6806
Fax: (509)574-6860
Web Site: http://www.yvcc.edu/
Description: State-supported, 2-year, coed. Part of Washington State Board for Community and Technical Colleges. Awards certificates, transfer associate, and terminal associate degrees. Founded 1928. Setting: 20-acre small town campus. Endowment: $5.4 million. Educational spending for 2005 fiscal year: $4416 per student. Total enrollment: 6,225. Student-undergrad faculty ratio is 20:1. 1,354 applied, 100% were admitted. Students come from 10 other countries, 2% from out-of-state, 3% Native American, 37% Hispanic, 1% black, 2% Asian American or Pacific Islander, 46% 25 or older, 1% live on campus. Core. Academic remediation for entering students, ESL program, services for LD students, advanced placement, distance learning, summer session for credit, part-time degree program, adult/continuing education programs, co-op programs and internships.
Entrance Requirements: Open admission except for nursing, dental hygiene, radiological technology, allied health programs. Options: Peterson's Universal Application, Common Application, electronic application, deferred admission. Recommended: high school transcript. Required for some: high school transcript, recommendations, interview. Entrance: noncompetitive. Application deadline: 9/16. Notification: continuous until 9/16.
Costs Per Year: Application fee: $20. State resident tuition: $2550 full-time, $72 per credit part-time. Nonresident tuition: $2939 full-time. Mandatory fees: $3.50 per credit part-time. Full-time tuition varies according to course load. Part-time tuition and fees vary according to course load. College room only: $2400.
Collegiate Environment: Orientation program. Choral group. Social organizations: 31 open to all. Most popular organizations: Veterans with Supporters, Business Management/Marketing Club, Image Makers, Agri-Business Club. Major annual events: Casino Night, Annual Student/Staff Barbecue, Multicultural Week. Student services: health clinic, personal-psychological counseling. Campus security: 24-hour emergency response devices, student patrols, late night transport-escort service, controlled dormitory access. No special consideration for freshman housing applicants. Option: coed housing available. Raymond Library with 31,716 books, 860 serials, and an OPAC. Operations spending for 2004 fiscal year: $576,262. 369 computers available on campus for general student use. A campuswide network can be accessed. Staffed computer lab on campus.
Community Environment: Located in the fertile Yakima Valley known as the "Fruit Bowl of the Nation," the area produces cherries, peaches, pears, apples, and other small fruit. The climate is mild and dry with an average of 302 days of sun per year. The community is served by railroad, air, and main arterial highways. Local recreation includes swimming, skiing, boating, fishing, hunting and golf. Part-time employment is available for students. There are churches representing most of the religious denominations, as well as many civic and fraternal organizations serving the community. Many "western" type celebrations are held in the area. Yakima was named an "All-American City" in 1994.

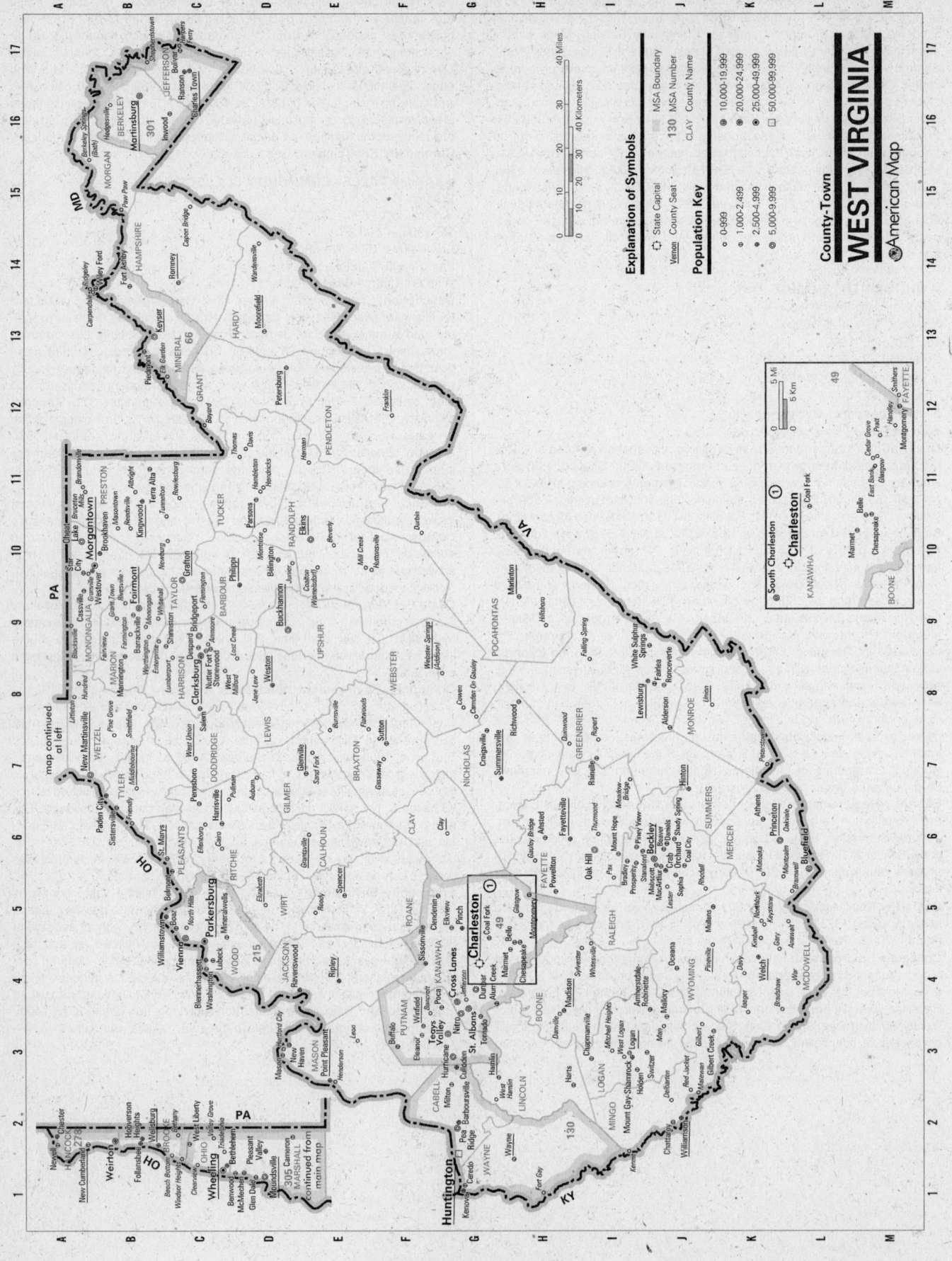

WEST VIRGINIA

County-Town

American Map

Explanation of Symbols

- State Capital
- County Seat — *Vernon*
- MSA Boundary
- MSA Number — 130
- County Name — CLAY

Population Key

- 0-999
- 1,000-2,499
- 2,500-4,999
- 5,000-9,999
- 10,000-19,999
- 20,000-24,999
- 25,000-49,999
- 50,000-99,999

■ **ALDERSON-BROADDUS COLLEGE** *D-9*
1 College Hill Dr.
Philippi, WV 26416
Tel: (304)457-1700
Free: 800-263-1549
Fax: (304)457-6239
E-mail: admissions@ab.wvnet.edu
Web Site: http://www.ab.edu/
Description: Independent, comprehensive, coed, affiliated with American Baptist Churches in the U.S.A.. Awards associate, bachelor's, and master's degrees. Founded 1871. Setting: 170-acre rural campus. Endowment: $12.7 million. Research spending for 2004 fiscal year: $38,284. Educational spending for 2005 fiscal year: $7240 per student. Total enrollment: 779. Faculty: 87 (58 full-time, 29 part-time). Student-undergrad faculty ratio is 11:1. 480 applied, 75% were admitted. 19% from top 10% of their high school class, 45% from top quarter, 79% from top half. 27 student government officers. Full-time: 592 students, 67% women, 33% men. Part-time: 56 students, 86% women, 14% men. Students come from 22 states and territories, 5 other countries, 20% from out-of-state, 0.3% Native American, 1% Hispanic, 2% black, 1% Asian American or Pacific Islander, 2% international, 27% 25 or older, 41% live on campus, 11% transferred in. Retention: 69% of full-time freshmen returned the following year. Academic areas with the most degrees conferred: health professions and related sciences; biological/life sciences; education. Core. Calendar: semesters. Academic remediation for entering students, advanced placement, accelerated degree program, honors program, independent study, double major, summer session for credit, part-time degree program, internships. Off campus study at Mountain State Association of Colleges. Study abroad program.
Entrance Requirements: Options: electronic application, deferred admission. Required: high school transcript, minimum 2.0 high school GPA, SAT or ACT. Required for some: 3 recommendations, interview. Entrance: moderately difficult. Application deadline: Rolling. Notification: continuous until 8/31.
Costs Per Year: Application fee: $10. Comprehensive fee: $24,006 includes full-time tuition ($17,970), mandatory fees ($166), and college room and board ($5870). College room only: $2860. Full-time tuition and fees vary according to degree level. Room and board charges vary according to housing facility. Part-time tuition: $598 per credit hour. Part-time mandatory fees: $41.50 per term. Part-time tuition and fees vary according to degree level.
Collegiate Environment: Orientation program. Drama-theater group, choral group, student-run newspaper, radio station. Social organizations: 50 open to all; local fraternities, local sororities; 10% of eligible men and 12% of eligible women are members. Most popular organizations: Baptist Campus Ministry, Collegiate 4-H, American Academy of Physician Assistants, S.L.I.C.E. (Students Learning in Community Education), Association of Women Students. Major annual events: homecoming, Spring Festival, Opening Convocation. Student services: health clinic, personal-psychological counseling. Campus security: 24-hour patrols, late night transport-escort service, controlled dormitory access. 758 college housing spaces available; 283 were occupied in 2003-04. On-campus residence required through senior year. Options: coed, women-only housing available. Pickett Library with 100,000 books, 9,000 serials, 700 audiovisual materials, an OPAC, and a Web page. Operations spending for 2004 fiscal year: $313,203. 75 computers available on campus for general student use. A campuswide network can be accessed from student residence rooms and from off campus. Staffed computer lab on campus.

Community Environment: Philippi is a rural community enjoying a moderate climate ranging from balmy summers to snowy winters. There are churches of major denominations, a hospital, clinic, and more than 50 civic, fraternal, and veteran's organizations active in the community. Local recreation includes swimming, bowling, theater, and major outdoor sports. Skiing and whitewater rafting are within minutes of the campus. Some part-time employment is available.

■ **AMERICAN PUBLIC UNIVERSITY SYSTEM** *C-17*
111 West Congress St.
Charles Town, WV 25414
Tel: (304)724-6857; 877-468-6268
Admissions: (703)330-5398
Fax: (304)724-6863
Web Site: http://www.apus.edu/
Description: Proprietary, comprehensive, coed. Awards associate, bachelor's, and master's degrees (profile includes American Public University, American Military University and American Community College). Founded 1991. Total enrollment: 13,477. Faculty: 362 (47 full-time, 315 part-time). Student-undergrad faculty ratio is 12:1. 3,489 applied, 81% were admitted. Full-time: 473 students, 27% women, 73% men. Part-time: 8,557 students, 19% women, 81% men. Students come from 52 states and territories, 23 other countries, 96% from out-of-state, 83% 25 or older. Retention: 68% of full-time freshmen returned the following year. Academic areas with the most degrees conferred: military science and technologies; security and protective services; liberal arts/general studies. Core. Calendar: trimesters. Independent study, distance learning, part-time degree program, external degree program, adult/continuing education programs.
Entrance Requirements: Open admission. Options: Peterson's Universal Application, electronic application, deferred admission, international baccalaureate accepted. Required: high school transcript, complete no-fee orientation. Entrance: noncompetitive. Application deadline: Rolling.
Costs Per Year: Application fee: $0. One-time mandatory fee: $75. Tuition: $6000 full-time, $250 per semester hour part-time.
Collegiate Environment: College housing not available.

■ **APPALACHIAN BIBLE COLLEGE** *I-6*
PO Box ABC
Bradley, WV 25818
Tel: (304)877-6428
Free: 800-678-9ABC
Web Site: http://www.abc.edu/
Description: Independent nondenominational, 4-year, coed. Awards associate and bachelor's degrees. Founded 1950. Setting: 110-acre small town campus. Endowment: $242,376. Total enrollment: 304. 105 applied, 69% were admitted. Full-time: 238 students, 52% women, 48% men. Part-time: 66 students, 65% women, 35% men. Students come from 31 states and territories, 8 other countries, 0% Native American, 1% Hispanic, 2% black, 1% Asian American or Pacific Islander, 2% international, 33% 25 or older, 12% transferred in. Core. Calendar: semesters. Academic remediation for entering students, advanced placement, honors program, independent study, summer session for credit, part-time degree program, adult/continuing education programs, internships.
Entrance Requirements: Required: essay, high school transcript, 3 recommendations, SAT or ACT. Recommended: minimum 2.5 high school GPA, interview. Entrance: minimally difficult. Application deadline: Rolling.

Costs Per Year: Application fee: $10. Comprehensive fee: $12,808 includes full-time tuition ($7140), mandatory fees ($1268), and college room and board ($4400). Part-time tuition: $297 per credit hour. Part-time mandatory fees: $32 per credit hour.

Collegiate Environment: Orientation program. Drama-theater group, choral group. Social organizations: 1 open to all. Most popular organization: Campus Missionary Fellowship. Major annual events: Spring Music Festival, Christmas Concert, Bible Conference. Student services: health clinic, personal-psychological counseling. Campus security: 24-hour emergency response devices, patrols by trained security personnel. 236 college housing spaces available; 191 were occupied in 2003-04. Freshmen given priority for college housing. On-campus residence required through senior year. Options: men-only, women-only housing available. John Van Pufflen Library with 44,944 books, 985 microform titles, 347 serials, 4,268 audiovisual materials, and an OPAC. 7 computers available on campus for general student use. A campuswide network can be accessed from student residence rooms and from off campus. Staffed computer lab on campus.

Community Environment: Bradley is a rural community enjoying temperate climate. There is a railroad line 15 miles distant, an airline 14 miles away, buses, and Highways I-77, I-64, 19, 21, and 16 to serve the community. The city has 5 churches and a Lions Club. Within walking distance is Crossroads Mall. The community provides numerous part-time employment opportunities, and enjoys all the cultural, recreational, and medical facilities of nearby Beckley.

■ **BETHANY COLLEGE**
Main St.
Bethany, WV 26032
Tel: (304)829-7000
Free: 800-922-7611
Admissions: (304)829-7611
Fax: (304)829-7142
E-mail: wblair@bethanywv.edu
Web Site: http://www.bethanywv.edu/
Description: Independent, 4-year, coed, affiliated with Christian Church (Disciples of Christ). Awards bachelor's degrees. Founded 1840. Setting: 1,600-acre rural campus with easy access to Pittsburgh. Endowment: $42 million. Educational spending for 2005 fiscal year: $4873 per student. Total enrollment: 902. Student-undergrad faculty ratio is 14:1. 859 applied, 75% were admitted. 11% from top 10% of their high school class, 28% from top quarter, 58% from top half. 1 National Merit Scholar, 17 class presidents, 13 valedictorians, 67 student government officers. Full-time: 895 students, 54% women, 46% men. Part-time: 7 students, 86% women, 14% men. Students come from 26 states and territories, 20 other countries, 73% from out-of-state, 0.1% Native American, 1% Hispanic, 4% black, 0.2% Asian American or Pacific Islander, 3% international, 2% 25 or older, 88% live on campus, 6% transferred in. Retention: 75% of full-time freshmen returned the following year. Academic areas with the most degrees conferred: education; business/marketing; psychology. Core. Calendar: 4-1-4. Academic remediation for entering students, ESL program, services for LD students, advanced placement, self-designed majors, independent study, double major, internships. Off campus study at members of the East Central College Consortium. Study abroad program.
Entrance Requirements: Options: Peterson's Universal Application, Common Application, electronic application, deferred admission, international baccalaureate accepted. Required: essay, high school transcript, minimum 2.5 high school GPA, 1 recommendation, documentation of student involvement, SAT or ACT. Recommended: interview. Required for some: interview. Entrance: moderately difficult. Application deadline: Rolling. Notification: continuous until 8/15.
Costs Per Year: Application fee: $25. Comprehensive fee: $23,520 includes full-time tuition ($15,750) and college room and board ($7770). College room only: $4000.
Collegiate Environment: Orientation program. Drama-theater group, choral group, student-run newspaper, radio station. Social organizations: 38 open to all; national fraternities, national sororities; 40% of eligible men and 45% of eligible women are members. Most popular organizations: Student Board of Governors, Outdoor Club, Model United Nations, Public Relations Society, International Student Association. Major annual events: Homecoming, Mardi Gras, Spring Weekend. Student services: health clinic, personal-psychological counseling. Campus security: 24-hour emergency response devices and patrols, late night transport-escort service. Freshmen guaranteed college housing. On-campus residence required through senior year. Options: coed, men-only, women-only housing available. T. W. Phillips

Memorial Library with 130,696 books, 116,065 microform titles, 785 serials, 3,101 audiovisual materials, an OPAC, and a Web page. Operations spending for 2004 fiscal year: $449,182. 136 computers available on campus for general student use. A campuswide network can be accessed from student residence rooms and from off campus. Staffed computer lab on campus.

■ **BLUEFIELD STATE COLLEGE** *L-6*
219 Rock St.
Bluefield, WV 24701-2198
Tel: (304)327-4000
Free: 800-654-7798
Admissions: (304)327-4567
Fax: (304)327-7747
E-mail: jcardwell@bscvax.wvnet.edu
Web Site: http://www.bluefieldstate.edu/
Description: State-supported, 4-year, coed. Part of Higher Education Policy Commission System. Awards associate and bachelor's degrees. Founded 1895. Setting: 45-acre small town campus. Endowment: $7.6 million. Educational spending for 2005 fiscal year: $3498 per student. Total enrollment: 1,708. Student-undergrad faculty ratio is 17:1. 615 applied, 96% were admitted. 10% from top 10% of their high school class, 27% from top quarter, 71% from top half. 38 class presidents, 3 valedictorians, 3 student government officers. Full-time: 1,400 students, 59% women, 41% men. Part-time: 308 students, 62% women, 38% men. Students come from 21 states and territories, 11 other countries, 8% from out-of-state, 0.2% Native American, 1% Hispanic, 11% black, 0.4% Asian American or Pacific Islander, 1% international, 46% 25 or older, 13% transferred in. Retention: 58% of full-time freshmen returned the following year. Academic areas with the most degrees conferred: education; health professions and related sciences; liberal arts/general studies. Core. Calendar: semesters. Academic remediation for entering students, advanced placement, self-designed majors, honors program, distance learning, double major, summer session for credit, part-time degree program, external degree program, adult/continuing education programs, internships.
Entrance Requirements: Open admission except for allied health programs. Options: Peterson's Universal Application, Common Application, electronic application, deferred admission. Required: high school transcript, minimum 2.0 high school GPA. Recommended: SAT or ACT. Entrance: noncompetitive. Application deadline: Rolling. Notification: continuous.
Costs Per Year: Application fee: $0. State resident tuition: $3410 full-time, $142 per credit part-time. Nonresident tuition: $7014 full-time, $292 per credit part-time. Full-time tuition varies according to degree level, program, and reciprocity agreements. Part-time tuition varies according to course load, program, and reciprocity agreements.
Collegiate Environment: Orientation program. Drama-theater group, choral group, marching band, student-run newspaper. Social organizations: 35 open to all; national fraternities, national sororities, local fraternities, local sororities; 5% of eligible men and 8% of eligible women are members. Most popular organizations: Phi Eta Sigma, Student Nurses Association, Student Government Association, Minorities on the Move. Major annual events: homecoming, Greek Week, Black History Month. Student services: health clinic, personal-psychological counseling. Campus security: 24-hour emergency response devices and patrols, student patrols. College housing not available. Hardway Library with 76,391 books, 706,413 microform titles, 2,453 serials, 341 audiovisual materials, an OPAC, and a Web page. Operations spending for 2004 fiscal year: $283,454. 358 computers available on campus for general student use. A campuswide network can be accessed from off-campus. Staffed computer lab on campus.
Community Environment: At the foot of the East River Mountain, high in the Appalachian chain, Bluefield is situated at the southern tip of West Virginia, bordering on the Virginia state line. The city is the commercial and industrial center for the surrounding area. The climate is temperate with a mean annual temperature of 53.7 degrees and an average rainfall of 38.52 inches. Due to a high altitude and low humidity, the city known as "Nature's Air Conditioned City." Bluefield is accessible by airlines, bus lines, and major highways. There are many churches representing most denominations, community health facilities, and major civic, fraternal, and veteran's organizations to serve the community. Local recreation includes nearby Bluestone Reservoir and lakes for fishing, swimming, and boating; municipal swimming pools, golf, a football stadium, tennis courts, softball, and Little Theatre group.

■ **COMMUNITY AND TECHNICAL COLLEGE OF SHEPHERD** *B-16*
400 West Stephen St.
Martinsburg, WV 25401

Tel: (304)260-4380
Fax: (304)260-4376
E-mail: lseectc@shepherd.edu
Web Site: http://www.shepherd.edu/ctcweb/
Description: County-supported, 2-year, coed. Awards certificates, transfer associate, and terminal associate degrees. Total enrollment: 1,711. Student-undergrad faculty ratio is 29:1. 333 applied, 99% were admitted. Full-time: 427 students, 55% women, 45% men. Part-time: 1,284 students, 62% women, 38% men. 40% from out-of-state, 1% Native American, 2% Hispanic, 8% black, 1% Asian American or Pacific Islander, 0.2% international.
Entrance Requirements: Required: high school transcript. Recommended: SAT and SAT Subject Tests or ACT. Required for some: interview. Entrance: noncompetitive.
Costs Per Year: Application fee: $35. State resident tuition: $2944 full-time, $123 per credit part-time. Nonresident tuition: $8542 full-time, $355 per credit part-time.
Collegiate Environment: Social organizations: national fraternities.

■ **COMMUNITY & TECHNICAL COLLEGE AT WEST VIRGINIA UNIVERSITY INSTITUTE OF TECHNOLOGY** *H-5*
Montgomery, WV 25136
Tel: (304)442-3149; 888-554-8324
Admissions: (304)442-3167
Web Site: http://ctc.wvutech.edu/.
Description: County-supported, 2-year, coed. Awards certificates and terminal associate degrees. Total enrollment: 645.

■ **CONCORD UNIVERSITY** *K-6*
Vermillion St., PO Box 1000
Athens, WV 24712-1000
Tel: (304)384-3115; 888-384-5249
Admissions: (304)384-5248
Fax: (304)384-9044
E-mail: addsm@ccvms.wvnet.edu
Web Site: http://www.concord.edu/
Description: State-supported, 4-year, coed. Part of State College System of West Virginia. Awards associate, bachelor's, and master's degrees. Founded 1872. Setting: 100-acre rural campus. Endowment: $19.1 million. Educational spending for 2005 fiscal year: $6397 per student. Total enrollment: 3,015. Faculty: 185 (97 full-time, 88 part-time). Student-undergrad faculty ratio is 22:1. 2,227 applied, 67% were admitted. 20% from top 10% of their high school class, 43% from top quarter, 74% from top half. 12 valedictorians, 127 student government officers. Full-time: 2,444 students, 57% women, 43% men. Part-time: 508 students, 68% women, 32% men. Students come from 27 states and territories, 15 other countries, 15% from out-of-state, 0.2% Native American, 1% Hispanic, 5% black, 1% Asian American or Pacific Islander, 0% international, 18% 25 or older, 39% live on campus, 5% transferred in. Retention: 65% of full-time freshmen returned the following year. Academic areas with the most degrees conferred: education; business/marketing; social sciences. Core. Calendar: semesters. Academic remediation for entering students, ESL program, services for LD students, advanced placement, accelerated degree program, self-designed majors, honors program, independent study, distance learning, double major, summer session for credit, part-time degree program, external degree program, internships. Off campus study. Study abroad program.
Entrance Requirements: Options: Peterson's Universal Application, Common Application, electronic application, early admission, early decision, international baccalaureate accepted. Required: high school transcript, minimum 2.0 high school GPA, SAT or ACT. Recommended: interview, ACT. Required for some: essay, interview. Entrance: minimally difficult. Application deadlines: Rolling, 1/15 for nonresidents. Notification: continuous, 3/1 for nonresidents.
Costs Per Year: Application fee: $0. State resident tuition: $3872 full-time, $160 per credit hour part-time. Nonresident tuition: $8646 full-time, $359 per credit hour part-time. Full-time tuition varies according to course load. Part-time tuition varies according to course load. College room and board: $5796. College room only: $2966.
Collegiate Environment: Orientation program. Drama-theater group, choral group, student-run newspaper, radio station. Social organizations: 13 open to all; national fraternities, national sororities, local fraternities, local sororities; 20% of eligible men and 25% of eligible women are members. Most popular organizations: Student Board, student government, student-run publications, music groups, student union activities board. Major annual

events: Homecoming, Mt. Lion Festival, Graduation. Student services: health clinic. Campus security: 24-hour emergency response devices and patrols, late night transport-escort service, controlled dormitory access. 1,163 college housing spaces available; 1,018 were occupied in 2003-04. Freshmen guaranteed college housing. On-campus residence required through senior year. Options: coed, men-only, women-only housing available. J. Frank Marsh Library with 150,151 books, 268,451 microform titles, 227 serials, 4,060 audiovisual materials, an OPAC, and a Web page. Operations spending for 2004 fiscal year: $490,196. 250 computers available on campus for general student use. A campuswide network can be accessed from student residence rooms and from off campus. Staffed computer lab on campus.
Community Environment: Located in the mountains in a quiet rural area, this is an excellent atmosphere for students. The climate is moderate with cool summers. Local recreation includes good hunting and fishing. Pipestem State Park and Winterplace Ski Resort are located nearby.

■ **DAVIS & ELKINS COLLEGE** *E-10*
100 Campus Dr.
Elkins, WV 26241-3996
Tel: (304)637-1900
Free: 800-624-3157
Admissions: (304)637-1974
Fax: (304)637-1800
E-mail: admiss@davisandelkins.edu
Web Site: http://www.davisandelkins.edu/
Description: Independent Presbyterian, 4-year, coed. Awards associate and bachelor's degrees. Founded 1904. Setting: 170-acre small town campus. Endowment: $16.6 million. Educational spending for 2005 fiscal year: $5629 per student. Total enrollment: 624. Student-undergrad faculty ratio is 11:1. 840 applied, 55% were admitted. 10% from top 10% of their high school class, 25% from top quarter, 59% from top half. 7 class presidents, 1 valedictorian, 26 student government officers. Full-time: 560 students, 63% women, 37% men. Part-time: 64 students, 64% women, 36% men. Students come from 20 states and territories, 15 other countries, 31% from out-of-state, 1% Native American, 1% Hispanic, 3% black, 1% Asian American or Pacific Islander, 4% international, 44% live on campus, 11% transferred in. Retention: 77% of full-time freshmen returned the following year. Academic areas with the most degrees conferred: business/marketing; education; social sciences. Core. Calendar: 4-1-4. ESL program, services for LD students, advanced placement, accelerated degree program, self-designed majors, honors program, independent study, double major, summer session for credit, part-time degree program, external degree program, adult/continuing education programs, co-op programs and internships. Study abroad program.
Entrance Requirements: Options: Common Application, electronic application, early admission, deferred admission, international baccalaureate accepted. Required: high school transcript, minimum 2.0 high school GPA, SAT or ACT. Recommended: essay, interview. Required for some: essay, 2 recommendations, interview. Entrance: moderately difficult. Application deadline: Rolling. Notification: continuous.
Costs Per Year: Application fee: $35. Comprehensive fee: $22,936 includes full-time tuition ($16,312), mandatory fees ($520), and college room and board ($6104). Full-time tuition and fees vary according to course load. Room and board charges vary according to board plan. Part-time tuition: $525 per credit hour. Part-time tuition varies according to course load.
Collegiate Environment: Orientation program. Drama-theater group, choral group, student-run newspaper, radio station. Social organizations: 42 open to all; national fraternities, national sororities; 14% of eligible men and 14% of eligible women are members. Most popular organizations: Beta Alpha Beta, campus radio station, Student Nurses Association, Student Education Association, International Student Organization. Major annual events: Parents' Weekend, Homecoming, Alumni Weekend. Student services: health clinic, personal-psychological counseling. Campus security: late night transport-escort service, controlled dormitory access, late night security personnel. 572 college housing spaces available; 320 were occupied in 2003-04. Freshmen guaranteed college housing. On-campus residence required through senior year. Options: coed, men-only, women-only housing available. Booth Library with 225,816 books, 219,947 microform titles, 2,339 serials, 6,240 audiovisual materials, an OPAC, and a Web page. Operations spending for 2004 fiscal year: $277,103. 101 computers available on campus for general student use. Computer purchase/lease plans available. A campuswide network can be accessed from student residence rooms and from off campus. Staffed computer lab on campus.
Community Environment: Elkins is located in the foothills of the Alleghenies and is the headquarters for the nearby Monongahela National

Forest. The community is accessible by auto and airline. The climate is temperate. Elkins has several churches of various denominations, a hospital, YMCA, and major civic and fraternal organizations. The nearby national forest offers excellent trout streams, hunting, camping, 4 modern ski resorts, and bathing beaches. An annual autumn State Forest Festival is held here. Part-time employment is limited.

■ EASTERN WEST VIRGINIA COMMUNITY AND TECHNICAL COLLEGE D-13

HC 65 Box 402
Moorefield, WV 26836
Tel: (304)434-8000; 877-982-2322
E-mail: sbungard@eastern.wvnet.edu
Web Site: http://www.eastern.wvnet.edu/

Description: State-supported, 2-year, coed. Awards certificates, transfer associate, and terminal associate degrees. Founded 1999. Setting: rural campus. Total enrollment: 882. Student-undergrad faculty ratio is 21:1. 104 applied, 100% were admitted. Full-time: 68 students, 81% women, 19% men. Part-time: 814 students, 66% women, 34% men. 0.4% Native American, 0% Hispanic, 3% black, 0% Asian American or Pacific Islander, 0% international. Calendar: semesters.

Costs Per Year: State resident tuition: $1704 full-time. Nonresident tuition: $6822 full-time.

Collegiate Environment: College housing not available.

■ FAIRMONT STATE COMMUNITY & TECHNICAL COLLEGE B-9

1201 Locust Ave.
Fairmont, WV 26554
Tel: (304)367-4892
Free: 800-641-5678
Fax: (304)367-4692
Web Site: http://www.fscwv.edu/fsctc/

Description: State-supported, 2-year, coed. Administratively affiliated with Fairmont State College. Awards certificates, transfer associate, and terminal associate degrees. Setting: 90-acre small town campus. Endowment: $91,000. Research spending for 2004 fiscal year: $1834. Total enrollment: 3,355. 1,267 applied, 88% were admitted. Full-time: 1,878 students, 54% women, 46% men. Part-time: 1,477 students, 61% women, 39% men. Students come from 11 states and territories, 1% Native American, 1% Hispanic, 5% black, 1% Asian American or Pacific Islander, 0% international, 15% 25 or older. Calendar: semesters. Summer session for credit, part-time degree program, external degree program, adult/continuing education programs.

Entrance Requirements: Open admission except for health career programs. Options: Common Application, electronic application, deferred admission, international baccalaureate accepted. Required: SAT or ACT. Recommended: high school transcript, minimum 2.25 high school GPA. Required for some: ACT COMPASS. Entrance: minimally difficult. Application deadline: Rolling. Notification: continuous.

Collegiate Environment: Orientation program. Drama-theater group, choral group, marching band, student-run newspaper. Social organizations: national fraternities, national sororities. Student services: health clinic, personal-psychological counseling. 600 college housing spaces available; all were occupied in 2003-04.

■ FAIRMONT STATE UNIVERSITY B-9

1201 Locust Ave.
Fairmont, WV 26554
Tel: (304)367-4000
Free: 800-641-5678
Admissions: (304)367-4702
Fax: (304)367-4789
E-mail: admit@fairmontstate.edu
Web Site: http://www.fairmontstate.edu/

Description: State-supported, comprehensive, coed. Part of State College System of West Virginia. Awards associate, bachelor's, and master's degrees. Founded 1865. Setting: 80-acre small town campus. Endowment: $8.6 million. Research spending for 2004 fiscal year: $27,016. Educational spending for 2005 fiscal year: $2837 per student. Total enrollment: 7,759. Faculty: 535 (220 full-time, 315 part-time). Student-undergrad faculty ratio is 17:1. 3,008 applied, 75% were admitted. 12% from top 10% of their high school class, 25% from top quarter, 66% from top half. 7 valedictorians. Full-time: 5,534 students, 55% women, 45% men. Part-time: 1,986 students, 56% women, 44% men. Students come from 22 states and territories, 23

other countries, 6% from out-of-state, 0.4% Native American, 1% Hispanic, 4% black, 1% Asian American or Pacific Islander, 0% international, 26% 25 or older, 6% live on campus, 4% transferred in. Retention: 70% of full-time freshmen returned the following year. Core. Calendar: semesters. Academic remediation for entering students, ESL program, services for LD students, advanced placement, accelerated degree program, honors program, double major, summer session for credit, part-time degree program, adult/continuing education programs, internships. ROTC: Army.

Entrance Requirements: Open admission. Options: Common Application, electronic application, early admission. Required: high school transcript, SAT and SAT Subject Tests or ACT. Recommended: minimum 2.0 high school GPA. Entrance: minimally difficult. Application deadline: 6/15.

Costs Per Year: Application fee: $0. State resident tuition: $4218 full-time, $155 per hour part-time. Nonresident tuition: $8808 full-time, $331 per hour part-time. Mandatory fees: $194 full-time, $177 per credit hour part-time. College room and board: $5674. College room only: $2814.

Collegiate Environment: Orientation program. Drama-theater group, choral group, marching band, student-run newspaper. Social organizations: 46 open to all; national fraternities, national sororities, local fraternities; 1% of eligible men and 2% of eligible women are members. Most popular organizations: Alpha Phi Omega, Circle K, Society for Non-traditional Students, Criminal Justice Club, Honors Association. Major annual events: Homecoming, Student Leadership Conference, Alcohol Awareness Week. Student services: legal services, health clinic, personal-psychological counseling. Campus security: 24-hour emergency response devices and patrols, student patrols, controlled dormitory access. 1,183 college housing spaces available; 983 were occupied in 2003-04. Options: coed, men-only, women-only housing available. Musick Library with 276,722 books, 27,211 microform titles, 883 serials, 2,066 audiovisual materials, an OPAC, and a Web page. Operations spending for 2004 fiscal year: $936,519. 1,300 computers available on campus for general student use. A campuswide network can be accessed from off-campus. Staffed computer lab on campus.

Community Environment: The College's 80-acre campus, with its twelve major buildings, is attractively located in Fairmont, West Virginia. Approximately ninety miles south of Pittsburgh on Interstate 79, Fairmont, with a population of about 20,000, is the county seat of Marion County.

■ GLENVILLE STATE COLLEGE E-7

200 High St.
Glenville, WV 26351-1200
Tel: (304)462-7361
Admissions: (304)462-4128
Fax: (304)462-8619
Web Site: http://www.glenville.edu/

Description: State-supported, 4-year, coed. Part of West Virginia Higher Education Policy Commission. Awards associate and bachelor's degrees. Founded 1872. Setting: 331-acre rural campus. Endowment: $5 million. Research spending for 2004 fiscal year: $5241. Educational spending for 2005 fiscal year: $7895 per student. Total enrollment: 1,392. 1,154 applied, 100% were admitted. 10% from top 10% of their high school class, 27% from top quarter, 66% from top half. Students come from 21 states and territories, 4 other countries, 9% from out-of-state, 0.3% Native American, 0.3% Hispanic, 5% black, 1% Asian American or Pacific Islander, 0% international, 18% 25 or older, 33% live on campus. Core. Calendar: semesters. Academic remediation for entering students, ESL program, services for LD students, advanced placement, accelerated degree program, self-designed majors, honors program, distance learning, double major, summer session for credit, part-time degree program, adult/continuing education programs, co-op programs and internships.

Entrance Requirements: Open admission. Options: Peterson's Universal Application, Common Application, electronic application, deferred admission. Required: high school transcript, minimum 2.0 high school GPA, completion of college-preparatory program, SAT or ACT. Entrance: noncompetitive. Application deadline: Rolling. Notification: continuous.

Costs Per Year: Application fee: $0. State resident tuition: $3628 full-time, $151.17 per credit hour part-time. Nonresident tuition: $8640 full-time, $360 per credit hour part-time. College room and board: $5150. College room only: $2500. Room and board charges vary according to housing facility.

Collegiate Environment: Orientation program. Drama-theater group, choral group, marching band. Social organizations: 25 open to all; national fraternities, local fraternities, local sororities; 2% of eligible men and 2% of eligible women are members. Most popular organizations: Student Government Association, Percussion Ensemble, Band, Choir, Fellowship of Christian Athletes. Major annual events: homecoming, GSC Week, Convocation.

Student services: health clinic, personal-psychological counseling. Campus security: 24-hour emergency response devices, student patrols, late night transport-escort service, controlled dormitory access. 596 college housing spaces available; 430 were occupied in 2003-04. Freshmen guaranteed college housing. On-campus residence required through sophomore year. Options: coed, men-only, women-only housing available. Robert F. Kidd Library with 125,240 books, 605,783 microform titles, 11,676 serials, 2,677 audiovisual materials, an OPAC, and a Web page. Operations spending for 2004 fiscal year: $361,793. 232 computers available on campus for general student use. A campuswide network can be accessed from student residence rooms and from off campus. Staffed computer lab on campus.

Community Environment: Glenville is located in the approximate geographical center of the state. Interstate 79 passes within 15 miles of the campus. Glenville has 5 churches, a modern clinic, motel, and several civic and fraternal organizations. Within the area there are facilities for hunting, fishing, golf, baseball, softball. A state park is located 6 miles away. Job opportunities are available. An annual West Virginia Folk Festival is held each year in June.

■ **HUNTINGTON JUNIOR COLLEGE** *G-2*

900 Fifth Ave.
Huntington, WV 25701-2004
Tel: (304)697-7550
Fax: (304)697-7554
Web Site: http://www.huntingtonjuniorcollege.com/
Description: Proprietary, 2-year, coed. Awards terminal associate degrees. Founded 1936. Setting: urban campus. Total enrollment: 700. 40% 25 or older. Core. Academic remediation for entering students, services for LD students, summer session for credit, part-time degree program.
Entrance Requirements: Open admission. Required: high school transcript. Entrance: minimally difficult. Application deadline: Rolling.
Collegiate Environment: Orientation program. College housing not available. 1,900 books and 35 serials. 60 computers available on campus for general student use. Staffed computer lab on campus.

■ **INTERNATIONAL ACADEMY OF DESIGN & TECHNOLOGY** *B-9*

2000 Green River Dr.
Fairmont, WV 26554-9790
Tel: (304)534-5677; 888-406-8324
Fax: (304)534-5669
E-mail: dhirsh@iadtwv.com
Web Site: http://iadtwv.com/
Description: Proprietary, 2-year, coed. Founded 1971.

■ **MARSHALL COMMUNITY AND TECHNICAL COLLEGE** *G-2*

One John Marshall Dr.
Huntington, WV 25755
Tel: (304)696-6282
Admissions: (304)696-3160
Web Site: http://www.marshall.edu/ctc/
Description: County-supported, 2-year, coed. Part of Community and Technical College System of West Virginia. Administratively affiliated with Marshall University. Awards certificates and terminal associate degrees. Endowment: $142,700. Educational spending for 2005 fiscal year: $2749 per student. Total enrollment: 2,589. Student-undergrad faculty ratio is 27:1. 695 applied, 99% were admitted. Full-time: 1,305 students, 49% women, 51% men. Part-time: 1,284 students, 28% women, 72% men. Students come from 24 states and territories, 3 other countries, 19% from out-of-state, 0.3% Native American, 1% Hispanic, 6% black, 1% Asian American or Pacific Islander, 0.1% international, 55% 25 or older, 7% transferred in. Core. Calendar: semesters. Academic remediation for entering students, ESL program, services for LD students, accelerated degree program, independent study, distance learning, double major, summer session for credit, part-time degree program, co-op programs and internships. Off campus study. ROTC: Army.
Entrance Requirements: Open admission. Options: Common Application, electronic application, early admission, international baccalaureate accepted. Required: high school transcript, minimum 2.0 high school GPA. Recommended: SAT, ACT. Entrance: noncompetitive. Application deadline: Rolling. Notification: continuous.
Costs Per Year: Application fee: $25. State resident tuition: $2814 full-time, $118 per credit hour part-time. Nonresident tuition: $8142 full-time, $340 per credit hour part-time. College room and board: $6272. College room only: $3496.

Collegiate Environment: Orientation program. Drama-theater group, choral group, marching band, student-run newspaper, radio station. Social organizations: national fraternities, national sororities, local fraternities, local sororities. Student services: legal services, health clinic, personal-psychological counseling, women's center. 2,200 college housing spaces available. Freshmen guaranteed college housing. On-campus residence required in freshman year. Options: coed, men-only, women-only housing available. John Deaver Drinko Library plus 2 others with 478,274 books, 972,106 microform titles, 5,314 serials, 24,759 audiovisual materials, an OPAC, and a Web page. 1,854 computers available on campus for general student use. A campuswide network can be accessed from student residence rooms and from off campus. Staffed computer lab on campus.

■ **MARSHALL UNIVERSITY** *G-2*

One John Marshall Dr.
Huntington, WV 25755
Tel: (304)696-3170
Admissions: (304)696-3160
Fax: (304)696-3135
E-mail: admissions@marshall.edu
Web Site: http://www.marshall.edu/
Description: State-supported, university, coed. Part of University System of West Virginia. Awards associate, bachelor's, master's, doctoral, and first professional degrees and post-master's certificates. Founded 1837. Setting: 70-acre urban campus. Research spending for 2004 fiscal year: $14.6 million. Total enrollment: 13,988. Faculty: 722 (469 full-time, 253 part-time). Student-undergrad faculty ratio is 20:1. 2,412 applied, 82% were admitted. Full-time: 8,190 students, 56% women, 44% men. Part-time: 1,651 students, 60% women, 40% men. Students come from 41 states and territories, 29 other countries, 18% from out-of-state, 0.3% Native American, 1% Hispanic, 5% black, 1% Asian American or Pacific Islander, 1% international, 18% 25 or older, 20% live on campus, 5% transferred in. Retention: 72% of full-time freshmen returned the following year. Academic areas with the most degrees conferred: business/marketing; education; liberal arts/general studies. Core. Calendar: semesters. Academic remediation for entering students, ESL program, services for LD students, advanced placement, accelerated degree program, honors program, independent study, distance learning, double major, summer session for credit, part-time degree program, adult/continuing education programs, co-op programs and internships, graduate courses open to undergrads. Off campus study at National Student Exchange. Study abroad program. ROTC: Army.
Entrance Requirements: Options: Common Application, electronic application, early admission, deferred admission, international baccalaureate accepted. Required: minimum 2.0 high school GPA, SAT or ACT. Required for some: high school transcript. Entrance: moderately difficult. Application deadline: Rolling. Notification: continuous.
Costs Per Year: Application fee: $25. State resident tuition: $3932 full-time, $155.75 per credit hour part-time. Nonresident tuition: $10,634 full-time, $423.25 per credit hour part-time. Full-time tuition varies according to degree level, location, program, and reciprocity agreements. Part-time tuition varies according to course load, degree level, location, program, and reciprocity agreements. College room and board: $6272. College room only: $3496. Room and board charges vary according to board plan and housing facility.
Collegiate Environment: Orientation program. Drama-theater group, choral group, marching band, student-run newspaper, radio station. Social organizations: 75 open to all; national fraternities, national sororities; 8% of eligible men and 4% of eligible women are members. Most popular organizations: Campus Crusade for Christ, Gamma Beta Phi, The International Students' Organization, Newman Association, Phi Alpha Theta. Major annual events: homecoming, Spring Fest, Independence Daze. Student services: legal services, health clinic, personal-psychological counseling, women's center. Campus security: 24-hour emergency response devices and patrols, student patrols, late night transport-escort service, controlled dormitory access. 2,200 college housing spaces available. Freshmen guaranteed college housing. On-campus residence required through sophomore year. Options: coed, men-only, women-only housing available. John Deaver Drinko Library plus 2 others with 478,274 books, 972,106 microform titles, 5,314 serials, 24,759 audiovisual materials, an OPAC, and a Web page. Operations spending for 2004 fiscal year: $2.4 million. 1,854 computers available on campus for general student use. A campuswide network can be accessed from student residence rooms and from off campus. Staffed computer lab on campus.
Community Environment: Huntington is a busy river terminal and serves as the shipping point for millions of tons of coal mined annually from the

great bituminous fields to the south of the city. It is also the center of a large natural gas and oil-producing area. The annual mean temperature is 56.6 degrees with an annual rainfall of 41.8 inches. The community is accessed by bus, rail, and air. There are medical facilities, a public library, YMCA, YWCA, and over 140 churches of various denominations serving the area. Recreation includes municipal swimming pools, roller skating rinks, golf, tennis, bowling, boating, the Memorial Field House, theatres, and the Huntington Civic Center which attracts top entertainment. Part-time employment is available.

■ **MOUNTAIN STATE COLLEGE** *C-4*
1508 Spring St.
Parkersburg, WV 26101-3993
Tel: (304)485-5487
Free: 800-841-0201
Fax: (304)485-3524
Web Site: http://www.mountainstate.org/
Description: Proprietary, 2-year, coed. Awards diplomas and terminal associate degrees. Founded 1888. Setting: small town campus. Educational spending for 2005 fiscal year: $7765 per student. Total enrollment: 166. Student-undergrad faculty ratio is 17:1. Full-time: 166 students, 83% women, 17% men. 0% Native American, 1% Hispanic, 1% black, 1% Asian American or Pacific Islander, 0% international, 55% 25 or older. Retention: 70% of full-time freshmen returned the following year.
Entrance Requirements: Required: interview, CPAt. Entrance: minimally difficult.
Costs Per Year: Tuition: $7050 full-time. Mandatory fees: $115 full-time.
Collegiate Environment: College housing not available.

■ **MOUNTAIN STATE UNIVERSITY** *J-6*
Box 9003
Beckley, WV 25802-9003
Tel: (304)253-7351
Free: 800-766-6067
Admissions: (304)929-1358
Fax: (304)253-5072
E-mail: astone@mountainstate.edu
Web Site: http://www.mountainstate.edu/
Description: Independent, comprehensive, coed. Awards associate, bachelor's, and master's degrees and post-master's certificates. Founded 1933. Setting: 7-acre small town campus. Endowment: $8.2 million. Educational spending for 2005 fiscal year: $2705 per student. Total enrollment: 4,404. Faculty: 316 (79 full-time, 237 part-time). Student-undergrad faculty ratio is 23:1. 1,224 applied, 100% were admitted. 2% from top 10% of their high school class, 13% from top quarter, 40% from top half. Full-time: 2,954 students, 64% women, 36% men. Part-time: 1,024 students, 71% women, 29% men. Students come from 47 states and territories, 24 other countries, 25% from out-of-state, 1% Native American, 2% Hispanic, 10% black, 1% Asian American or Pacific Islander, 2% international, 67% 25 or older, 4% live on campus, 17% transferred in. Retention: 51% of full-time freshmen returned the following year. Academic areas with the most degrees conferred: business/marketing; health professions and related sciences; security and protective services. Core. Calendar: semesters. Academic remediation for entering students, ESL program, advanced placement, accelerated degree program, self-designed majors, independent study, distance learning, double major, summer session for credit, part-time degree program, external degree program, adult/continuing education programs, co-op programs and internships, graduate courses open to undergrads.
Entrance Requirements: Open admission except for allied health programs. Options: Common Application, electronic application, early admission, deferred admission. Required: high school transcript. Recommended: SAT and SAT Subject Tests or ACT. Required for some: essay, recommendations, interview, SAT and SAT Subject Tests or ACT. Entrance: noncompetitive. Application deadline: Rolling.
Costs Per Year: Application fee: $25. Comprehensive fee: $12,876 includes full-time tuition ($5700), mandatory fees ($1650), and college room and board ($5526). College room only: $2810. Full-time tuition and fees vary according to program. Room and board charges vary according to board plan. Part-time tuition: $190 per credit. Part-time mandatory fees: $55 per credit. Part-time tuition and fees vary according to program.
Collegiate Environment: Orientation program. Drama-theater group, choral group, student-run newspaper. Social organizations: 15 open to all; local fraternities; 5% of eligible men and 5% of eligible women are members. Most popular organizations: Student Christian Organization, Astronomy Club,

creative writing group, Gay, Lesbian, and Bisexual Student Support Group, Student Government Association. Major annual events: Halloween Party, Black History Month, Super Bowl Party. Student services: health clinic. Campus security: 24-hour emergency response devices, late night transport-escort service, controlled dormitory access, night patrols by security. 192 college housing spaces available; 160 were occupied in 2003-04. No special consideration for freshman housing applicants. On-campus residence required through sophomore year. Option: coed housing available. Mountain State University Library with 93,527 books, 1,416 microform titles, 7,030 serials, 1,931 audiovisual materials, and an OPAC. Operations spending for 2004 fiscal year: $401,657. 97 computers available on campus for general student use. A campuswide network can be accessed from student residence rooms and from off campus. Staffed computer lab on campus.

■ **NATIONAL INSTITUTE OF TECHNOLOGY** *G-4*
5514 Big Tyler Rd.
Cross Lanes, WV 25313-1390
Tel: (304)776-6290; 888-741-4271
Web Site: http://www.nitschools.com/
Description: Proprietary, 2-year, coed. Part of Corinthian Schools, Inc. Awards certificates, diplomas, and transfer associate degrees. Founded 1938. Setting: small town campus. Total enrollment: 520. Students come from 4 states and territories, 2% from out-of-state, 0% Native American, 2% Hispanic, 2% black, 1% Asian American or Pacific Islander, 0% international, 30% 25 or older. Core. Advanced placement, internships.
Entrance Requirements: Option: deferred admission. Required: high school transcript, interview. Entrance: moderately difficult. Application deadline: Rolling. Notification: continuous.
Collegiate Environment: Orientation program. Student-run newspaper. College housing not available. 140 computers available on campus for general student use. Computer purchase/lease plans available. Staffed computer lab on campus.

■ **NEW RIVER COMMUNITY AND TECHNICAL COLLEGE** *J-6*
167 Dye Dr.
Beckley, WV 25801
Tel: (304)255-5821
Admissions: (304)647-6564
Web Site: http://www.nrctc.org/
Description: County-supported, 2-year, coed. Awards certificates, transfer associate, and terminal associate degrees. Total enrollment: 1,600.

■ **OHIO VALLEY UNIVERSITY** *C-5*
One Campus View Dr.
Vienna, WV 26105-8000
Tel: (304)865-6000; 877-446-8668
Admissions: (304)865-6203
Fax: (304)865-6001
E-mail: admissions@ovu.edu
Web Site: http://www.ovu.edu/
Description: Independent, 4-year, coed, affiliated with Church of Christ. Awards associate and bachelor's degrees. Founded 1960. Setting: 299-acre small town campus. Endowment: $965,736. Educational spending for 2005 fiscal year: $12,743 per student. Total enrollment: 542. Student-undergrad faculty ratio is 12:1. 512 applied, 48% were admitted. 10% from top 10% of their high school class, 32% from top quarter, 57% from top half. 2 valedictorians, 21 student government officers. Full-time: 508 students, 52% women, 48% men. Part-time: 34 students, 65% women, 35% men. Students come from 26 states and territories, 12 other countries, 35% from out-of-state, 1% Native American, 1% Hispanic, 4% black, 0.4% Asian American or Pacific Islander, 6% international, 77% 25 or older, 60% live on campus, 8% transferred in. Retention: 74% of full-time freshmen returned the following year. Academic areas with the most degrees conferred: business/marketing; education; psychology. Core. Calendar: semesters. Academic remediation for entering students, ESL program, advanced placement, honors program, double major, summer session for credit, part-time degree program, external degree program, adult/continuing education programs, internships. Study abroad program. ROTC: Air Force (c).
Entrance Requirements: Options: Common Application, electronic application, early admission, early action, deferred admission. Required: high school transcript, SAT and SAT Subject Tests or ACT. Recommended: recommendations. Required for some: essay, interview. Entrance: minimally difficult. Application deadlines: 8/15, 9/1 for early action. Notification: continuous, 10/1 for early action.

Costs Per Year: Application fee: $20. Comprehensive fee: $18,972 includes full-time tuition ($11,700), mandatory fees ($1392), and college room and board ($5880). College room only: $3080. Full-time tuition and fees vary according to course load. Room and board charges vary according to board plan. Part-time tuition: $400 per credit hour. Part-time mandatory fees: $58 per credit hour. Part-time tuition and fees vary according to course load.

Collegiate Environment: Orientation program. Drama-theater group, choral group, student-run newspaper. Social organizations: 15 open to all; local fraternities, local sororities; 76% of eligible men and 75% of eligible women are members. Most popular organizations: Mission Club, Women for Christ, SIFE, Ambassadors, Black Student Union. Major annual events: Expressions, Winter Banquet, Spring Banquet. Student services: health clinic, personal-psychological counseling. Campus security: 24-hour emergency response devices, late night transport-escort service. 400 college housing spaces available; 247 were occupied in 2003-04. Freshmen guaranteed college housing. On-campus residence required through sophomore year. Options: men-only, women-only housing available. Icy Belle Library with 34,000 books, 48,279 microform titles, 455 serials, 6,303 audiovisual materials, and an OPAC. Operations spending for 2004 fiscal year: $157,799. 34 computers available on campus for general student use. A campuswide network can be accessed from student residence rooms. Staffed computer lab on campus.

■ **POTOMAC STATE COLLEGE OF WEST VIRGINIA UNIVERSITY**
B-13
Fort Ave.
Keyser, WV 26726-2698
Tel: (304)788-6800
Free: 800-262-7332
Admissions: (304)788-6820
Fax: (304)788-6939
Web Site: http://www.potomacstatecollege.edu/

Description: State-supported, 2-year, coed. Part of West Virginia Higher Education Policy Commission. Awards certificates, transfer associate, and terminal associate degrees. Founded 1901. Setting: 616-acre small town campus. Endowment: $1.8 million. Educational spending for 2005 fiscal year: $7443 per student. Total enrollment: 1,330. 5% from top 10% of their high school class, 8% from top quarter, 54% from top half. Students come from 17 states and territories, 2 other countries, 14% from out-of-state, 13% 25 or older, 35% live on campus. Core. Calendar: semesters. Academic remediation for entering students, services for LD students, advanced placement, honors program, summer session for credit, part-time degree program, adult/continuing education programs.

Entrance Requirements: Open admission for state residents. Options: electronic application, early admission, deferred admission. Required: high school transcript. Required for some: SAT or ACT. Entrance: noncompetitive. Application deadline: Rolling.

Costs Per Year: Application fee: $0. State resident tuition: $2328 full-time, $98 per credit hour part-time. Nonresident tuition: $7872 full-time, $329 per credit hour part-time. Part-time tuition varies according to course load. College room and board: $4914. College room only: $2340. Room and board charges vary according to board plan and location.

Collegiate Environment: Orientation program. Drama-theater group, choral group, student-run newspaper. Social organizations: 17 open to all. Most popular organizations: student newspaper, Circle K Club, Agriculture and Forestry Club, Business Club, Community Chorus. Major annual events: Homecoming, multicultural festival, Heritage Days. Student services: health clinic, personal-psychological counseling. Campus security: 24-hour emergency response devices and patrols, controlled dormitory access. On-campus residence required through sophomore year. Options: men-only, women-only housing available. Shipper Library with 44,197 books, 51,796 microform titles, 304 serials, 23,395 audiovisual materials, an OPAC, and a Web page. Operations spending for 2004 fiscal year: $209,933. 113 computers available on campus for general student use. A campuswide network can be accessed from off-campus. Staffed computer lab on campus.

Community Environment: During the Civil War, the country around Keyser was a frequent battleground. The community was a supply point for, alternately, the Union Army and the Confederate forces. It changed hands 14 times in 4 years of war. The climate is temperate. There are churches of many denominations, libraries, a hospital and various civic, fraternal, and veteran's organizations serving the area. The city has good shopping facilities and is accessible by railroad, buses, and U.S. Highways 48,50 and 220. Residence Halls provide student housing. Part-time employment is available. Local recreation includes hunting, boating, fishing, golf, swimming, skiing, and tennis.

■ **SALEM INTERNATIONAL UNIVERSITY** *C-8*
223 West Main St., PO Box 500
Salem, WV 26426-0500
Tel: (304)782-5011
Free: 800-283-4562
Admissions: (304)782-5336
E-mail: admissions@salemiu.edu
Web Site: http://www.salemiu.edu/

Description: Independent, comprehensive, coed. Awards associate, bachelor's, and master's degrees. Founded 1888. Setting: 300-acre rural campus. Total enrollment: 568. 251 applied, 99% were admitted. 11% from top 10% of their high school class, 33% from top quarter, 59% from top half. 1 valedictorian. Full-time: 359 students, 48% women, 52% men. Part-time: 84 students, 40% women, 60% men. Students come from 33 states and territories, 17 other countries, 56% from out-of-state, 1% Native American, 2% Hispanic, 8% black, 1% Asian American or Pacific Islander, 39% international, 11% 25 or older, 64% live on campus, 9% transferred in. Retention: 68% of full-time freshmen returned the following year. Core. Calendar: modular. Academic remediation for entering students, ESL program, services for LD students, advanced placement, accelerated degree program, independent study, double major, part-time degree program, internships, graduate courses open to undergrads. Off campus study at West Virginia Association of Independent Colleges and Universities. Study abroad program.

Entrance Requirements: Options: Peterson's Universal Application, electronic application, deferred admission, international baccalaureate accepted. Required: high school transcript, minimum 2.00 high school GPA, SAT or ACT. Recommended: essay, interview. Required for some: interview. Entrance: minimally difficult. Application deadline: Rolling.

Collegiate Environment: Orientation program. Choral group, student-run newspaper, radio station. Social organizations: 25 open to all; national fraternities, national sororities, local fraternities, local sororities; 30% of eligible men and 30% of eligible women are members. Most popular organizations: National Honor Society, Humanics Student Association, Equestrian Club, Alpha Phi Omega Service Fraternity, LIGHT. Major annual events: Homecoming, Spring Fling, Winterfest. Student services: health clinic, personal-psychological counseling. Campus security: 24-hour emergency response devices and patrols, late night transport-escort service, controlled dormitory access. 644 college housing spaces available; 244 were occupied in 2003-04. No special consideration for freshman housing applicants. On-campus residence required through junior year. Options: coed, men-only, women-only housing available. Benedum Library with 179,918 books, 278,224 microform titles, 398 serials, 827 audiovisual materials, an OPAC, and a Web page. Operations spending for 2004 fiscal year: $179,788. 50 computers available on campus for general student use. A campuswide network can be accessed from off-campus. Staffed computer lab on campus.

Community Environment: Tucked into a quiet valley, Salem-Teikyo University is surrounded by the scenic mountains for which West Virginia is known. Nearby parks provide excellent hiking, biking, white water rafting, skiing and fishing locations. Although the atmosphere is rural, students are within minutes of shopping malls, cinemas, fine restaurants, and the Benedum Airport. There is easy access to metropolitan areas such as Pittsburgh, Washington, D.C., and New York.

■ **SHEPHERD UNIVERSITY**
PO Box 3210
Shepherdstown, WV 25443-3210
Tel: (304)876-5000
Free: 800-344-5231
Admissions: (304)876-5212
Fax: (304)876-5165
E-mail: admissions@shepherd.edu
Web Site: http://www.shepherd.edu/

Description: State-supported, comprehensive, coed. Part of West Virginia Higher Education Policy Commission. Awards bachelor's and master's degrees. Founded 1871. Setting: 320-acre small town campus with easy access to Washington, DC. Endowment: $20.4 million. Educational spending for 2005 fiscal year: $3201 per student. Total enrollment: 3,901. Faculty: 253 (109 full-time, 144 part-time). Student-undergrad faculty ratio is 21:1. 1,593 applied, 93% were admitted. Full-time: 2,949 students, 56% women, 44% men. Part-time: 860 students, 61% women, 39% men. Students come from 49 states and territories, 21 other countries, 36% from out-of-state, 0.5% Native American, 2% Hispanic, 5% black, 1% Asian American or Pacific

Islander, 1% international, 26% 25 or older, 25% live on campus, 10% transferred in. Retention: 69% of full-time freshmen returned the following year. Academic areas with the most degrees conferred: liberal arts/general studies; education; business/marketing. Core. Calendar: semesters. Academic remediation for entering students, services for LD students, advanced placement, accelerated degree program, honors program, independent study, double major, summer session for credit, part-time degree program, adult/continuing education programs, co-op programs and internships, graduate courses open to undergrads. Study abroad program.

Entrance Requirements: Options: Common Application, electronic application, early admission, early action, deferred admission, international baccalaureate accepted. Required: high school transcript, minimum 2.0 high school GPA, SAT or ACT. Recommended: essay, minimum 3.0 high school GPA, 3 recommendations. Entrance: moderately difficult. Application deadlines: Rolling, 11/15 for early action. Notification: continuous until 8/15, 12/15 for early action.

Costs Per Year: Application fee: $35. State resident tuition: $4046 full-time. Nonresident tuition: $10,618 full-time. Full-time tuition varies according to degree level, program, and reciprocity agreements. College room and board: $6020. Room and board charges vary according to board plan and housing facility.

Collegiate Environment: Orientation program. Drama-theater group, choral group, marching band, student-run newspaper, radio station. Social organizations: 42 open to all; national fraternities, national sororities; 6% of eligible men and 5% of eligible women are members. Most popular organizations: Student Government Association, Program Board, Student Community Services, United Brothers, Common Ground. Major annual events: homecoming, Shepfest, Midnight Breakfast. Student services: health clinic, personal-psychological counseling. Campus security: 24-hour emergency response devices and patrols, late night transport-escort service, controlled dormitory access. 1,019 college housing spaces available; 1,000 were occupied in 2003-04. Freshmen given priority for college housing. On-campus residence required through senior year. Option: coed housing available. Ruth Scarborough Library with 183,197 books, 245,794 microform titles, 918 serials, 11,393 audiovisual materials, an OPAC, and a Web page. Operations spending for 2004 fiscal year: $1.3 million. 350 computers available on campus for general student use. A campuswide network can be accessed from student residence rooms and from off campus. Staffed computer lab on campus.

Community Environment: Shepherdstown is a small town of about 5,000 located near Martinsburg, Charles Town and Harpers Ferry, West Virginia, and Hagerstown, Maryland. The town was established by English and German farmers who had crossed the river from Maryland before 1730. There are many historic sites in the area. The climate is temperate and the community is reached by State Route 45. There are 10 churches, 4 libraries, and 4 hospitals nearby. Some part-time employment is available in the surrounding area.

■ **SOUTHERN WEST VIRGINIA COMMUNITY AND TECHNICAL COLLEGE**

Dempsey Branch Rd., PO Box 2900
Mount Gay, WV 25637-2900
Tel: (304)792-7160
Fax: (304)792-7096
E-mail: admissions@southern.wvnet.edu
Web Site: http://www.southern.wvnet.edu/

Description: State-supported, 2-year, coed. Part of State College System of West Virginia. Awards certificates, transfer associate, and terminal associate degrees. Founded 1971. Setting: 23-acre rural campus. Total enrollment: 1,982. Student-undergrad faculty ratio is 20:1. 875 applied, 100% were admitted. 3% from top 10% of their high school class, 10% from top quarter, 28% from top half. Full-time: 1,257 students, 66% women, 34% men. Part-time: 725 students, 75% women, 25% men. Students come from 2 states and territories, 12% from out-of-state, 0.2% Native American, 0.2% Hispanic, 2% black, 0.3% Asian American or Pacific Islander, 38% 25 or older, 7% transferred in. Retention: 0% of full-time freshmen returned the following year. Core. Calendar: semesters. Academic remediation for entering students, services for LD students, advanced placement, summer session for credit, part-time degree program, external degree program, adult/continuing education programs, co-op programs.

Entrance Requirements: Open admission except for nursing, medical laboratory technology, radiological technology programs. Options: early admission, deferred admission. Required: high school transcript. Entrance: noncompetitive. Application deadline: Rolling. Notification: continuous.

Costs Per Year: Application fee: $0. State resident tuition: $1634 full-time, $68 per credit hour part-time. Nonresident tuition: $6486 full-time, $270 per credit hour part-time.

Collegiate Environment: Drama-theater group. Student services: personal-psychological counseling. College housing not available. 70,576 books and 233 serials. 92 computers available on campus for general student use. A campuswide network can be accessed from off-campus. Staffed computer lab on campus.

■ **UNIVERSITY OF CHARLESTON** *G-4*

2300 MacCorkle Ave., SE
Charleston, WV 25304-1099
Tel: (304)357-4800
Free: 800-995-GOUC
Admissions: (304)357-4750
Fax: (304)357-4781
E-mail: admissions@ucwv.edu
Web Site: http://www.ucwv.edu/

Description: Independent, comprehensive, coed. Awards associate, bachelor's, and master's degrees. Founded 1888. Setting: 40-acre urban campus. Endowment: $27.6 million. Educational spending for 2005 fiscal year: $5669 per student. Total enrollment: 1,006. Faculty: 99 (60 full-time, 39 part-time). Student-undergrad faculty ratio is 13:1. 1,124 applied, 96% were admitted. 25% from top 10% of their high school class, 50% from top quarter, 76% from top half. Full-time: 852 students, 59% women, 41% men. Part-time: 135 students, 65% women, 35% men. Students come from 40 states and territories, 24 other countries, 32% from out-of-state, 0.1% Native American, 1% Hispanic, 6% black, 1% Asian American or Pacific Islander, 8% international, 25% 25 or older, 50% live on campus, 17% transferred in. Retention: 68% of full-time freshmen returned the following year. Academic areas with the most degrees conferred: health professions and related sciences; business/marketing; education. Core. Calendar: semesters. Academic remediation for entering students, advanced placement, accelerated degree program, self-designed majors, independent study, distance learning, double major, summer session for credit, part-time degree program, adult/continuing education programs, internships, graduate courses open to undergrads. Study abroad program. ROTC: Army.

Entrance Requirements: Options: Peterson's Universal Application, electronic application, early admission, deferred admission, international baccalaureate accepted. Required: high school transcript, minimum 2.25 high school GPA, minimum scores ACT 19; SAT 900, SAT or ACT. Recommended: essay, recommendations. Required for some: interview. Entrance: moderately difficult. Application deadlines: Rolling, Rolling for nonresidents. Notification: continuous, continuous for nonresidents.

Costs Per Year: Application fee: $25. Comprehensive fee: $27,600 includes full-time tuition ($20,200) and college room and board ($7400). College room only: $4175. Room and board charges vary according to board plan and housing facility. Part-time tuition: $380 per credit. Part-time mandatory fees: $75 per term. Part-time tuition and fees vary according to course load and program.

Collegiate Environment: Orientation program. Drama-theater group, choral group, student-run newspaper. Social organizations: 46 open to all; national fraternities, local sororities; 4% of eligible men and 4% of eligible women are members. Most popular organizations: Student Activities Board, American Society of Interior Designers, Student Government Association, Capitol Association of Nursing Students, International Student Organization. Major annual events: Governor's Cup Regatta, Homecoming, Family Weekend. Student services: personal-psychological counseling. Campus security: 24-hour emergency response devices and patrols, student patrols, late night transport-escort service, controlled dormitory access, radio connection to city police and ambulance. 515 college housing spaces available; 422 were occupied in 2003-04. Freshmen guaranteed college housing. On-campus residence required through sophomore year. Option: coed housing available. Schoenbaum Library with 111,264 books, 144,984 microform titles, 2,011 serials, 2,505 audiovisual materials, an OPAC, and a Web page. Operations spending for 2004 fiscal year: $351,066. 200 computers available on campus for general student use. A campuswide network can be accessed from student residence rooms and from off campus. Staffed computer lab on campus.

Community Environment: Charleston, with a metropolitan population of 280,000, is the state capital, as well as the cultural, social, political, and economic center of West Virginia. Located in the Kanawha Valley, near the foothills of the Appalachian Mountains, it offers scenic tranquility as well as the convenience and excitement of a modern city. Downtown Charleston, just a 5-minute drive from campus, offers social and cultural opportunities that can be found only in a large city.

■ VALLEY COLLEGE B-16

287 Aikens Center
Martinsburg, WV 25401
Tel: (304)263-0979
Fax: (304)263-2413
E-mail: gkennedy@vct.edu
Web Site: http://www.valleycollege.com/

Description: Proprietary, 2-year, coed. Awards certificates and terminal associate degrees. Founded 1983. Setting: suburban campus. Total enrollment: 47. Student-undergrad faculty ratio is 14:1. Full-time: 47 students, 94% women, 6% men. 4% Native American, 2% Hispanic, 13% black. Calendar: continuous.

Entrance Requirements: Required: high school transcript, interview.

Costs Per Year: Tuition: $7200 full-time, $225 per credit part-time.

■ WEST LIBERTY STATE COLLEGE C-2

PO Box 295
West Liberty, WV 26074
Tel: (304)336-5000
Free: 800-732-6204
Admissions: (304)336-8076
Fax: (304)336-8285
E-mail: wladmsn1@wlsvax.wvnet.edu
Web Site: http://www.wlsc.edu/

Description: State-supported, 4-year, coed. Part of West Virginia Higher Education Policy Commission. Awards associate and bachelor's degrees. Founded 1837. Setting: 290-acre rural campus with easy access to Pittsburgh. Endowment: $6.3 million. Research spending for 2004 fiscal year: $95,308. Educational spending for 2005 fiscal year: $3734 per student. Total enrollment: 2,246. Student-undergrad faculty ratio is 17:1. 1,202 applied, 98% were admitted. 6% from top 10% of their high school class, 33% from top quarter, 58% from top half. Full-time: 1,974 students, 57% women, 43% men. Part-time: 267 students, 61% women, 39% men. Students come from 24 states and territories, 5 other countries, 30% from out-of-state, 0.1% Native American, 1% Hispanic, 3% black, 0.2% Asian American or Pacific Islander, 0.5% international, 16% 25 or older, 45% live on campus, 9% transferred in. Retention: 72% of full-time freshmen returned the following year. Academic areas with the most degrees conferred: business/marketing; education; health professions and related sciences. Core. Calendar: semesters. Academic remediation for entering students, advanced placement, accelerated degree program, self-designed majors, honors program, independent study, double major, summer session for credit, part-time degree program, external degree program, adult/continuing education programs, internships. Off campus study at Warwood Center, Wheeling WV.

Entrance Requirements: Options: Peterson's Universal Application, electronic application. Required: high school transcript, minimum 2.0 high school GPA, SAT or ACT. Recommended: interview. Entrance: minimally difficult. Notification: continuous.

Costs Per Year: Application fee: $0. State resident tuition: $3686 full-time. Nonresident tuition: $9054 full-time. Mandatory fees: $50 full-time. College room and board: $5456. Room and board charges vary according to board plan and housing facility.

Collegiate Environment: Orientation program. Drama-theater group, choral group, marching band, student-run newspaper, radio station. Social organizations: national fraternities, national sororities, local fraternities, local sororities; 6% of eligible men and 10% of eligible women are members. Most popular organizations: Delta Sigma Pi, Student Senate, Drama Club, Students in Free Enterprise. Major annual events: Homecoming, Greek Week, Spring Concert. Student services: health clinic, personal-psychological counseling. Campus security: 24-hour emergency response devices and patrols, late night transport-escort service. 1,300 college housing spaces available; 938 were occupied in 2003-04. No special consideration for freshman housing applicants. Options: coed, men-only, women-only housing available. Paul N. Elbin Library plus 1 other with 194,715 books, 124,000 microform titles, 485 serials, an OPAC, and a Web page. Operations spending for 2004 fiscal year: $376,993. 300 computers available on campus for general student use. A campuswide network can be accessed from student residence rooms and from off campus. Staffed computer lab on campus.

Community Environment: West Liberty is located 10 miles from the city limits of Wheeling. There are 2 Protestant churches and a visiting priest for Catholic students. Famous Oglebay Park, 6 miles from the campus, is used for recreation. Job opportunities are good in the area. There are dormitories, campus health services, and an infirmary for students. Fraternities and sororities are prominent here.

■ WEST VIRGINIA BUSINESS COLLEGE (NUTTER FORT) C-9

116 Pennsylvania Ave.
Nutter Fort, WV 26301
Tel: (304)624-7695
Fax: (304)622-2149
Web Site: http://www.stratuswave.com/~wvbc/

Description: Proprietary, 2-year, coed.

■ WEST VIRGINIA BUSINESS COLLEGE (WHEELING) C-1

1052 Main St.
Wheeling, WV 26003
Tel: (304)232-0361
Fax: (304)232-0363
Web Site: http://www.stratuswave.com/~wvbc/

Description: Proprietary, 2-year, coed. Awards diplomas and terminal associate degrees. Founded 1881. Setting: 5-acre urban campus. Total enrollment: 78. Student-undergrad faculty ratio is 6:1. 12 applied, 100% were admitted. 0% from out-of-state, 50% 25 or older.

Costs Per Year: Tuition: $15,500 per degree program.

■ WEST VIRGINIA JUNIOR COLLEGE (BRIDGEPORT) C-9

176 Thompson Dr.
Bridgeport, WV 26330
Tel: (304)363-8824
Web Site: http://www.wvjc.com/

Description: Proprietary, 2-year, coed. Awards transfer associate and terminal associate degrees. Founded 1922. Setting: 3-acre small town campus. 60 applied, 100% were admitted. 20% from top 10% of their high school class, 40% from top quarter, 70% from top half. 40% 25 or older. Core. Academic remediation for entering students, honors program, summer session for credit, part-time degree program, external degree program, adult/continuing education programs.

Entrance Requirements: Open admission. Option: deferred admission. Entrance: noncompetitive. Application deadline: Rolling. Notification: continuous.

Collegiate Environment: Student services: personal-psychological counseling. College housing not available. 550 books and 3 serials. 18 computers available on campus for general student use.

■ WEST VIRGINIA JUNIOR COLLEGE (CHARLESTON) G-4

1000 Virginia St. East
Charleston, WV 25301-2817
Tel: (304)345-2820
Web Site: http://www.wvjc.com/

Description: Proprietary, 2-year, coed. Awards terminal associate degrees. Founded 1892. Setting: urban campus. Total enrollment: 230. 130 applied, 100% were admitted. 5% from top 10% of their high school class, 10% from top quarter, 20% from top half. Students come from 6 states and territories, 40% 25 or older. Advanced placement, summer session for credit, part-time degree program, adult/continuing education programs.

Entrance Requirements: Open admission. Options: Common Application, early admission, deferred admission. Entrance: noncompetitive. Application deadline: Rolling.

Collegiate Environment: Student services: personal-psychological counseling. College housing not available. 1,300 books and 40 serials. 75 computers available on campus for general student use. Staffed computer lab on campus.

■ WEST VIRGINIA JUNIOR COLLEGE (MORGANTOWN) B-10

148 Willey St.
Morgantown, WV 26505-5521
Tel: (304)296-8282
Web Site: http://www.wvjc.com/

Description: Proprietary, 2-year, coed. Awards terminal associate degrees (also offers non-degree programs with significant enrollment not reflected in profile). Founded 1922. Setting: small town campus with easy access to

Pittsburgh. Students come from 2 states and territories, 1 other country, 70% 25 or older. Core. Adult/continuing education programs.

Entrance Requirements: Open admission. Required: high school transcript, interview. Recommended: recommendations. Entrance: noncompetitive. Application deadline: Rolling. Notification: continuous.

Collegiate Environment: Student services: personal-psychological counseling. College housing not available. 12 computers available on campus for general student use. Staffed computer lab on campus.

■ WEST VIRGINIA NORTHERN COMMUNITY COLLEGE C-1

1704 Market St.
Wheeling, WV 26003-3699
Tel: (304)233-5900
Fax: (304)233-5900
Web Site: http://www.northern.wvnet.edu/

Description: State-supported, 2-year, coed. Awards certificates, transfer associate, and terminal associate degrees. Founded 1972. Setting: small town campus with easy access to Pittsburgh. Endowment: $700,706. Educational spending for 2005 fiscal year: $3021 per student. Total enrollment: 2,842. Student-undergrad faculty ratio is 19:1. 788 applied, 53% were admitted. 2% from top 10% of their high school class, 11% from top quarter, 40% from top half. Full-time: 1,421 students, 68% women, 32% men. Part-time: 1,421 students, 71% women, 29% men. Students come from 5 states and territories, 17% from out-of-state, 0.2% Native American, 0.3% Hispanic, 3% black, 0.4% Asian American or Pacific Islander, 0.1% international, 94% 25 or older, 8% transferred in. Retention: 51% of full-time freshmen returned the following year. Core. Calendar: semesters. Academic remediation for entering students, advanced placement, accelerated degree program, self-designed majors, honors program, distance learning, double major, summer session for credit, part-time degree program, adult/continuing education programs, internships.

Entrance Requirements: Open admission except for health science programs. Options: Peterson's Universal Application, Common Application, electronic application, early admission, deferred admission. Required for some: high school transcript. Entrance: noncompetitive. Application deadline: Rolling.

Costs Per Year: State resident tuition: $1752 full-time, $73 per credit part-time. Nonresident tuition: $5592 full-time, $233 per credit part-time. Full-time tuition varies according to course load and reciprocity agreements. Part-time tuition varies according to course load and reciprocity agreements.

Collegiate Environment: Orientation program. Student-run newspaper. Social organizations: 1 open to all. Student services: personal-psychological counseling. Campus security: security personnel during evening and night classes. College housing not available. Wheeling B and O Campus Library plus 2 others with 36,650 books, 8 microform titles, 188 serials, 3,495 audiovisual materials, an OPAC, and a Web page. Operations spending for 2004 fiscal year: $83,294. 250 computers available on campus for general student use. A campuswide network can be accessed from off-campus. Staffed computer lab on campus.

Community Environment: Wheeling, one of the country's most liveable small cities, is a one-hour drive from Pittsburgh, PA, and a two-hour drive from Columbus, OH. It is in a central area of approximately 150,000 people. Many cultural and recreational facilities are available, including 1,500-acre Oglebay Park and 250-acre Wheeling Park. Excellent local recreation areas provide opportunities for camping, hiking, skiing, swimming, golf, and other such activities.

■ WEST VIRGINIA STATE COMMUNITY AND TECHNICAL COLLEGE

Thomas W. Cole, Jr., Complex
PO Box 1000
Institute, WV 25112
Tel: (304)766-3118
Free: 800-987-2112
Admissions: (304)766-3033
Web Site: http://fozzy.wvsc.edu/ctc/index.html

Description: County-supported, 2-year, coed. Awards certificates, transfer associate, and terminal associate degrees. Total enrollment: 1,609. 7% from out-of-state.

Costs Per Year: State resident tuition: $3222 full-time, $110 per credit hour part-time. Nonresident tuition: $7400 full-time, $294 per credit hour part-time. Full-time tuition varies according to class time, course level, and program. College room and board: $4720. College room only: $2200. Room and board charges vary according to board plan and housing facility.

■ WEST VIRGINIA STATE UNIVERSITY

Post Office Box 1000
Institute, WV 25112-1000
Tel: (304)766-3000
Free: 800-987-2112
Admissions: (304)766-3221
Fax: (304)766-4158
E-mail: sowell@wvstateu.edu
Web Site: http://www.wvstateu.edu/

Description: State-supported, comprehensive, coed. Part of State College System of West Virginia. Awards bachelor's and master's degrees. Founded 1891. Setting: 90-acre suburban campus. Total enrollment: 3,491. Faculty: 194 (120 full-time, 74 part-time). Student-undergrad faculty ratio is 23:1. 862 applied, 50% were admitted. Full-time: 2,396 students, 56% women, 44% men. Part-time: 1,059 students, 64% women, 36% men. Students come from 32 states and territories, 4 other countries, 9% from out-of-state, 0.4% Native American, 1% Hispanic, 15% black, 1% Asian American or Pacific Islander, 0% international, 37% 25 or older, 7% live on campus, 5% transferred in. Core. Calendar: semesters. Academic remediation for entering students, services for LD students, advanced placement, accelerated degree program, summer session for credit, part-time degree program, external degree program, adult/continuing education programs, co-op programs and internships. ROTC: Army.

Entrance Requirements: Options: Peterson's Universal Application, Common Application, electronic application, early admission. Required: high school transcript, SAT or ACT. Recommended: SAT. Required for some: SAT or ACT. Placement: SAT or ACT required. Entrance: minimally difficult. Application deadline: 8/11. Notification: continuous.

Costs Per Year: Application fee: $0. State resident tuition: $3528 full-time, $147 per credit hour part-time. Nonresident tuition: $8104 full-time, $338 per credit hour part-time. Full-time tuition varies according to program. Part-time tuition varies according to course load and program. College room and board: $4850. College room only: $2200. Room and board charges vary according to board plan and housing facility.

Collegiate Environment: Orientation program. Choral group, marching band, student-run newspaper. Social organizations: 22 open to all; national fraternities, national sororities; 1% of eligible men and 1% of eligible women are members. Major annual event: homecoming. Student services: health clinic, personal-psychological counseling. Campus security: 24-hour emergency response devices and patrols, late night transport-escort service. On-campus residence required in freshman year. Options: men-only, women-only housing available. Drain-Jordan Library with 228,026 books, 63,047 microform titles, 513 serials, 4,468 audiovisual materials, and an OPAC.

Community Environment: Institute is a suburb of Charleston and is reached by railroad, bus lines, feeder airlines, and a local transit system. There are churches of major denominations and community services in the easily accessible neighboring community. Part-time employment is available.

■ WEST VIRGINIA UNIVERSITY B-10

University Ave.
Morgantown, WV 26506
Tel: (304)293-0111
Free: 800-344-9881
Admissions: (304)293-2121
Fax: (304)293-3080
E-mail: wvuinfo@wvnvm.wvnet.edu
Web Site: http://www.wvu.edu/

Description: State-supported, university, coed. Part of West Virginia Higher Education Policy Commission. Awards bachelor's, master's, doctoral, and first professional degrees. Founded 1867. Setting: 913-acre small town campus with easy access to Pittsburgh. Endowment: $386.1 million. Research spending for 2004 fiscal year: $81.1 million. Total enrollment: 26,051. Faculty: 1,120 (785 full-time, 335 part-time). Student-undergrad faculty ratio is 22:1. 10,957 applied, 92% were admitted. 17% from top 10% of their high school class, 43% from top quarter, 74% from top half. Full-time: 18,449 students, 46% women, 54% men. Part-time: 1,061 students, 55% women, 45% men. Students come from 51 states and territories, 59 other countries, 42% from out-of-state, 0.4% Native American, 2% Hispanic, 4% black, 2% Asian American or Pacific Islander, 2% international, 7% 25 or older, 27% live on campus, 4% transferred in. Retention: 81% of full-time freshmen returned the following year. Academic areas with the most degrees conferred: business/marketing; liberal arts/general studies; communications/journalism. Core. Calendar: semesters. Academic remediation for entering students, ESL program, services for LD students, advanced placement, accelerated degree program, self-designed majors, honors program, independent study, distance learning, double major, summer session for credit, part-time degree program, external degree program, adult/continuing education programs, internships, graduate courses open to undergrads. Off campus study at Academic Common Market, Garrett County Community College. Study abroad program. ROTC: Army, Air Force.

Entrance Requirements: Options: Common Application, electronic application, early admission, deferred admission, international baccalaureate accepted. Required: high school transcript, minimum 2.0 high school GPA, SAT or ACT. Required for some: essay, minimum 2.25 high school GPA. Entrance: moderately difficult. Application deadline: 8/1. Preference given to state residents.

Costs Per Year: Application fee: $25. State resident tuition: $4164 full-time, $176 per credit hour part-time. Nonresident tuition: $12,874 full-time, $538 per credit hour part-time. Full-time tuition varies according to location, program, and reciprocity agreements. Part-time tuition varies according to course load, location, program, and reciprocity agreements. College room and board: $6342. College room only: $3348. Room and board charges vary according to board plan, housing facility, and location.

Collegiate Environment: Orientation program. Drama-theater group, choral group, marching band, student-run newspaper, radio station. Social organizations: 270 open to all; national fraternities, national sororities; 5% of eligible men and 5% of eligible women are members. Most popular organizations: Residential Hall Association, Gamma Beta Phi, Alpha Beta Phi. Major annual events: Mountaineer Week, Fall Fest, Parents' Weekend. Student services: legal services, health clinic, personal-psychological counseling, women's center. Campus security: 24-hour emergency response devices and patrols, student patrols, late night transport-escort service. 4,876 college housing spaces available; 4,639 were occupied in 2003-04. Freshmen guaranteed college housing. On-campus residence required in freshman year. Options: coed, men-only, women-only housing available. Wise Library plus 9 others with 1.7 million books, 2.9 million microform titles, 9,107 serials, 46,488 audiovisual materials, an OPAC, and a Web page. Operations spending for 2004 fiscal year: $11.9 million. 2,500 computers available on campus for general student use. Computer purchase/lease plans available. A campuswide network can be accessed from student residence rooms and from off campus. Staffed computer lab on campus.

Community Environment: West Virginia University's main campus is located in Morgantown, a small city of 30,000 in the Appalachian Mountains on West Virginia's northern border. Although the state is rural and the community quiet, Greater Morgantown is within easy traveling distance, on modern interstate highways, of the metropolitan areas of Pittsburgh, about 70 miles north, and Baltimore and Washington, D.C., about 200 miles to the east. The community has churches of various denominations, two hospitals, a city library, and various civic and fraternal organizations. Local recreation is available through the city's park system which includes several municipal pools and an ice skating rink. The area has golf courses, 1,800-acre Cheat Lake, whitewater rafting, and nearby Cooper's Rock State Forest. A half dozen snow skiing areas are within easy driving distance, as are some of the best remaining wilderness areas in the eastern United States.

■ WEST VIRGINIA UNIVERSITY INSTITUTE OF TECHNOLOGY *H-5*

405 Fayette Pike
Montgomery, WV 25136
Tel: (304)442-3071; 888-554-8324
Admissions: (304)442-3167
Fax: (304)442-3097
E-mail: wvutech@wvit.wvnet.edu
Web Site: http://www.wvutech.edu/

Description: State-supported, comprehensive, coed. Part of University System of West Virginia. Awards associate, bachelor's, and master's degrees. Founded 1895. Setting: 200-acre small town campus with easy access to Charleston. Endowment: $5.2 million. Educational spending for 2005 fiscal year: $6688 per student. Total enrollment: 2,468. 1,191 applied, 74% were admitted. 10% from top 10% of their high school class, 21% from top quarter, 58% from top half. 8 valedictorians. Full-time: 1,702 students, 37% women, 63% men. Part-time: 733 students, 46% women, 54% men. Students come from 26 states and territories, 23 other countries, 6% from out-of-state, 0.3% Native American, 1% Hispanic, 8% black, 1% Asian American or Pacific Islander, 4% international, 28% 25 or older, 26% live on campus, 8% transferred in. Retention: 60% of full-time freshmen returned the following year. Core. Calendar: semesters. Academic remediation for entering students, ESL program, services for LD students, advanced place-

ment, accelerated degree program, self-designed majors, summer session for credit, part-time degree program, external degree program, adult/continuing education programs, co-op programs and internships, graduate courses open to undergrads. ROTC: Army.

Entrance Requirements: Open admission for state residents. Options: Peterson's Universal Application, Common Application, electronic application, early admission. Required: high school transcript, SAT or ACT. Required for some: minimum 2.0 high school GPA. Entrance: noncompetitive. Application deadline: Rolling. Notification: continuous until 8/15.

Collegiate Environment: Orientation program. Drama-theater group, choral group, marching band, student-run newspaper. Social organizations: 42 open to all; national fraternities, national sororities; 9% of eligible men and 8% of eligible women are members. Most popular organizations: Student Government Association, Christian Student Union, Alpha Phi Omega. Major annual events: homecoming, open house, Family Day. Student services: health clinic, personal-psychological counseling, women's center. Campus security: 24-hour emergency response devices and patrols, late night transport-escort service. 776 college housing spaces available; 433 were occupied in 2003-04. On-campus residence required through sophomore year. Option: coed housing available. Vining Library plus 1 other with 166,292 books, 431,948 microform titles, 605 serials, an OPAC, and a Web page. Operations spending for 2004 fiscal year: $654,628. 625 computers available on campus for general student use. A campuswide network can be accessed from student residence rooms and from off campus. Staffed computer lab on campus.

Community Environment: The community has nearby plants that include the world's largest producer of ferro alloys for steel and a steam-produced electric power plant. Montgomery may be reached by bus lines and Amtrak.

■ WEST VIRGINIA UNIVERSITY AT PARKERSBURG *C-4*

300 Campus Dr.
Parkersburg, WV 26104-8647
Tel: (304)424-8000
Admissions: (304)424-8222
Web Site: http://www.wvup.edu/

Description: State-supported, primarily 2-year, coed. Administratively affiliated with West Virginia University. Awards certificates, transfer associate, terminal associate, and bachelor's degrees. Founded 1961. Setting: 140-acre small town campus. Educational spending for 2005 fiscal year: $2958 per student. Total enrollment: 3,722. 663 applied, 100% were admitted. Full-time: 2,148 students, 61% women, 39% men. Part-time: 1,574 students, 64% women, 36% men. Students come from 5 states and territories, 2% from out-of-state, 0.3% Native American, 0.3% Hispanic, 0.5% black, 1% Asian American or Pacific Islander, 0.03% international, 44% 25 or older, 5% transferred in. Retention: 56% of full-time freshmen returned the following year. Core. Calendar: semesters. Academic remediation for entering students, ESL program, services for LD students, advanced placement, independent study, distance learning, summer session for credit, part-time degree program, adult/continuing education programs, co-op programs and internships. Study abroad program. ROTC: Army. (c).

Entrance Requirements: Open admission except for nursing, bachelor of science degree programs, surgical technology, paramedic science. Options: Peterson's Universal Application, Common Application, electronic application, early admission, deferred admission. Required for some: high school transcript. Placement: ACT required. Entrance: noncompetitive. Application deadline: Rolling. Notification: continuous.

Costs Per Year: Application fee: $0. State resident tuition: $2280 full-time, $95 per credit hour part-time. Nonresident tuition: $6024 full-time, $251 per credit hour part-time. Full-time tuition varies according to degree level and reciprocity agreements. Part-time tuition varies according to degree level and reciprocity agreements.

Collegiate Environment: Orientation program. Drama-theater group, student-run newspaper. Student services: health clinic, personal-psychological counseling. College housing not available. WVUP Library plus 1 other with 41,300 books, 248 serials, an OPAC, and a Web page. Operations spending for 2004 fiscal year: $317,256. 200 computers available on campus for general student use. A campuswide network can be accessed from off-campus. Staffed computer lab on campus.

■ WEST VIRGINIA WESLEYAN COLLEGE *D-9*

59 College Ave.
Buckhannon, WV 26201
Tel: (304)473-8000
Free: 800-722-9933

Fax: (304)472-2571
Web Site: http://www.wvwc.edu/
Description: Independent, comprehensive, coed, affiliated with United Methodist Church. Awards bachelor's and master's degrees. Founded 1890. Setting: 80-acre small town campus. Endowment: $40.4 million. Educational spending for 2005 fiscal year: $4615 per student. Total enrollment: 1,408. Faculty: 160 (80 full-time, 80 part-time). Student-undergrad faculty ratio is 13:1. 1,268 applied, 77% were admitted. 23% from top 10% of their high school class, 53% from top quarter, 81% from top half. 17 valedictorians. Full-time: 1,332 students, 54% women, 46% men. Part-time: 34 students, 53% women, 47% men. Students come from 36 states and territories, 14 other countries, 45% from out-of-state, 0.2% Native American, 1% Hispanic, 5% black, 1% Asian American or Pacific Islander, 3% international, 2% 25 or older, 80% live on campus, 2% transferred in. Retention: 72% of full-time freshmen returned the following year. Academic areas with the most degrees conferred: business/marketing; education; visual and performing arts. Core. Calendar: semesters. Academic remediation for entering students, ESL program, services for LD students, advanced placement, self-designed majors, honors program, independent study, double major, summer session for credit, part-time degree program, adult/continuing education programs, internships. Off campus study at Mountain State Association of Colleges. Study abroad program.
Entrance Requirements: Options: Peterson's Universal Application, Common Application, electronic application, early decision, early action, deferred admission. Required: high school transcript, SAT or ACT. Recommended: essay, recommendations, interview. Required for some: SAT Subject Tests. Placement: SAT or ACT required for some. Entrance: moderately difficult. Application deadlines: 7/1, 12/1 for early decision, 10/1 for early action. Notification: continuous, 1/31 for early decision, 10/20 for early action.
Costs Per Year: Application fee: $35. Comprehensive fee: $26,800 includes full-time tuition ($20,250), mandatory fees ($1000), and college room and board ($5550). Full-time tuition and fees vary according to course load. Room and board charges vary according to board plan and housing facility.
Collegiate Environment: Orientation program. Drama-theater group, choral group, student-run newspaper, radio station. Social organizations: 75 open to all; national fraternities, national sororities; 26% of eligible men and 25% of eligible women are members. Most popular organizations: Campus Activities Board, Environmental Club, American Marketing Club, Wesleyan Ambassadors. Major annual events: Founders' Day/Homecoming, Festival of Lessons and Carols, Spring Weekend. Student services: health clinic, personal-psychological counseling. Campus security: 24-hour emergency response devices and patrols, student patrols, late night transport-escort service, controlled dormitory access. 1,160 undergraduates lived in college housing during 2003-04. Freshmen guaranteed college housing. On-campus residence required through senior year. Options: coed, men-only, women-only housing available. A. M. Pfeiffer Library with 91,061 books, 23,142 microform titles, 2,462 serials, 7,605 audiovisual materials, an OPAC, and a Web page.
Community Environment: Buckhannon is a rural community supported by agriculture, coal, natural gas, and local industries. The climate is temperate with an average annual temperature of 53 degrees. Bus and airlines are accessible 25 miles distant at Clarksburg. The community has a public library, restaurants, hotels, churches of most denominations, 1 hospital, and a YWCA. Part-time employment is available. Buckhannon is the home of the West Virginia Strawberry Festival. Local recreation includes hunting, fishing, boating, skiing, white-water rafting, and most outdoor sports. Civic, fraternal, and veterans' organizations are active in the area.

■ **WHEELING JESUIT UNIVERSITY** *C-1*
316 Washington Ave.
Wheeling, WV 26003-6295

Tel: (304)243-2000
Free: 800-624-6992
Fax: (304)243-2397
E-mail: admis@wju.edu
Web Site: http://www.wju.edu/
Description: Independent Roman Catholic (Jesuit), comprehensive, coed. Awards bachelor's, master's, and doctoral degrees. Founded 1954. Setting: 65-acre suburban campus with easy access to Pittsburgh, PA. Endowment: $15.5 million. Educational spending for 2005 fiscal year: $9477 per student. Total enrollment: 1,699. 1,157 applied, 75% were admitted. 26% from top 10% of their high school class, 29% from top quarter, 90% from top half. Full-time: 1,049 students, 60% women, 40% men. Part-time: 183 students, 79% women, 21% men. Students come from 33 states and territories, 17 other countries, 62% from out-of-state, 0.2% Native American, 2% Hispanic, 2% black, 1% Asian American or Pacific Islander, 3% international, 21% 25 or older, 78% live on campus, 7% transferred in. Retention: 72% of full-time freshmen returned the following year. Core. Calendar: semesters. Academic remediation for entering students, ESL program, services for LD students, advanced placement, accelerated degree program, self-designed majors, honors program, independent study, distance learning, double major, summer session for credit, part-time degree program, external degree program, adult/continuing education programs, internships, graduate courses open to undergrads. Off campus study at Bethany College, Belmont Technical College, members of the Jesuit Student Exchange. Study abroad program.
Entrance Requirements: Options: Peterson's Universal Application, Common Application, electronic application, early admission, deferred admission, international baccalaureate accepted. Required: high school transcript, SAT or ACT. Recommended: essay, minimum 2.5 high school GPA, 2 recommendations, interview. Required for some: interview. Entrance: moderately difficult. Application deadline: Rolling. Notification: continuous.
Costs Per Year: Application fee: $25. Comprehensive fee: $27,800 includes full-time tuition ($20,890), mandatory fees ($460), and college room and board ($6450). College room only: $3070. Full-time tuition and fees vary according to course load and program. Room and board charges vary according to board plan, gender, and housing facility. Part-time tuition: $540 per credit hour. Part-time mandatory fees: $465 per term. Part-time tuition and fees vary according to class time and program.
Collegiate Environment: Orientation program. Drama-theater group, choral group, student-run newspaper. Social organizations: 50 open to all; 25% of eligible men and 40% of eligible women are members. Most popular organizations: Student Government, Student Senate, Campus Activity Board, Inter Hall Council, Campus Ministry. Major annual events: play production, Fall/Spring Formal. Student services: health clinic, personal-psychological counseling, women's center. Campus security: 24-hour emergency response devices and patrols, student patrols, late night transport-escort service, controlled dormitory access. 1,000 college housing spaces available; 700 were occupied in 2003-04. Freshmen guaranteed college housing. On-campus residence required through senior year. Options: coed, men-only, women-only housing available. Bishop Hodges Library plus 1 other with 153,590 books, 127,773 microform titles, 512 serials, an OPAC, and a Web page. Operations spending for 2004 fiscal year: $455,897. 125 computers available on campus for general student use. A campuswide network can be accessed from student residence rooms and from off campus. Staffed computer lab on campus.
Community Environment: Wheeling, one of the country's most liveable small cities, is a one-hour drive from Pittsburgh, PA and a two-hour drive from Columbus, OH. In a central area of approximately 150,000 people, many cultural and recreational facilities are available for golf, camping, hiking, skiing, and swimming, including 1,500-acre Oglebay Park and 250-acre Wheeling Park.

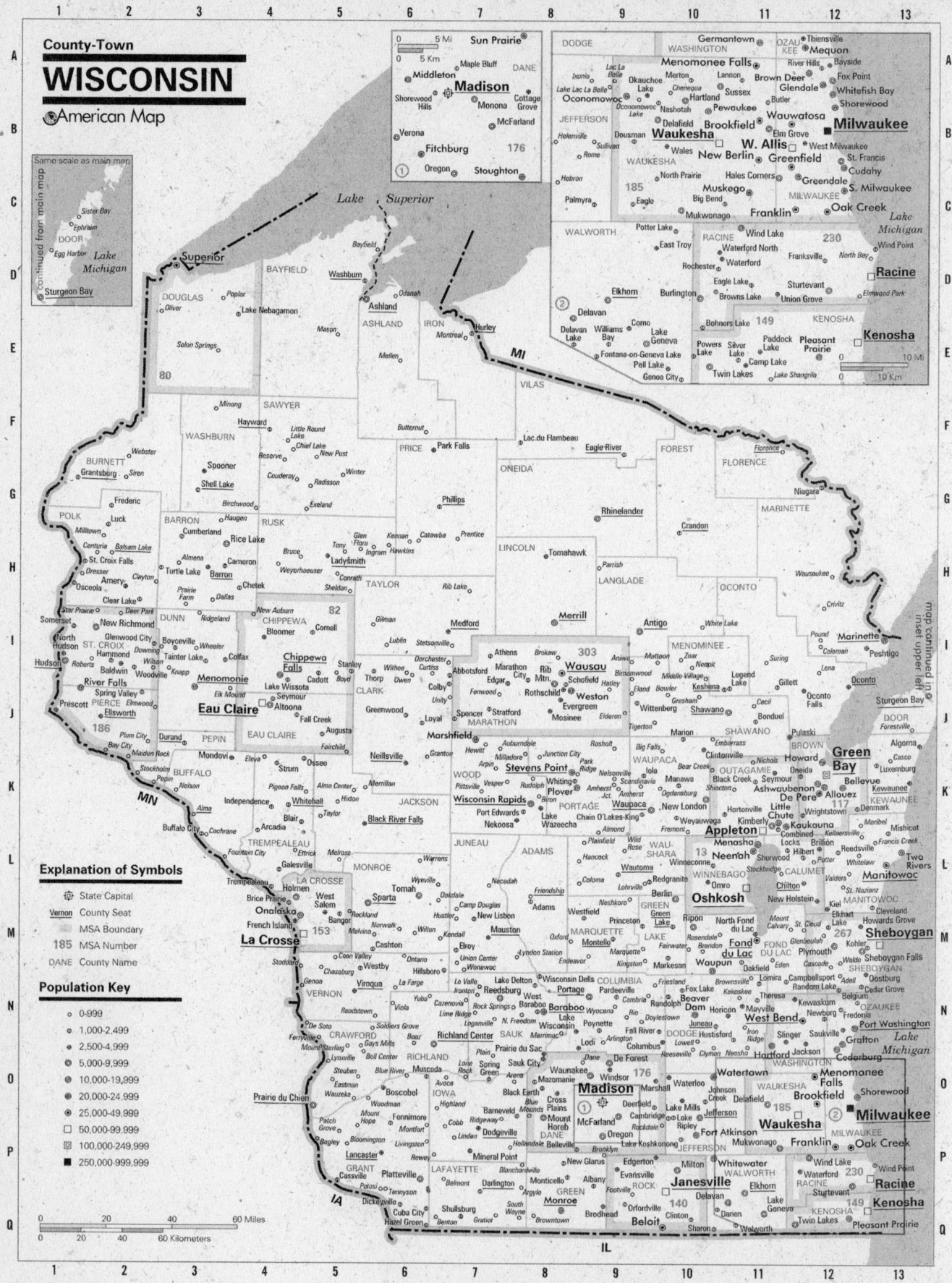

County-Town
WISCONSIN
American Map

■ **ALVERNO COLLEGE** *O-12*

3400 South 43rd St., PO Box 343922

Milwaukee, WI 53234-3922

Tel: (414)382-6000

Free: 800-933-3401

Admissions: (414)382-6031

Fax: (414)382-6354

E-mail: admissions@alverno.edu

Web Site: http://www.alverno.edu/

Description: Independent Roman Catholic, comprehensive. Awards associate, bachelor's, and master's degrees (also offers weekend program with significant enrollment not reflected in profile). Founded 1887. Setting: 46-acre suburban campus. Endowment: $24.1 million. Research spending for 2004 fiscal year: $455,619. Educational spending for 2005 fiscal year: $4390 per student. Total enrollment: 2,372. Faculty: 225 (104 full-time, 121 part-time). Student-undergrad faculty ratio is 12:1. 789 applied, 56% were admitted. Full-time: 1,515 students, 100% women. Part-time: 661 students, 98% women, 2% men. Students come from 56 states and territories, 11 other countries, 2% from out-of-state, 1% Native American, 11% Hispanic, 20% black, 5% Asian American or Pacific Islander, 1% international, 48% 25 or older, 10% live on campus, 9% transferred in. Retention: 76% of full-time freshmen returned the following year. Academic areas with the most degrees conferred: business/marketing; health professions and related sciences; education. Core. Calendar: semesters. Academic remediation for entering students, advanced placement, self-designed majors, independent study, double major, summer session for credit, part-time degree program, adult/continuing education programs, internships. Study abroad program. ROTC: Army (c), Air Force (c).

Entrance Requirements: Options: Peterson's Universal Application, Common Application, electronic application, deferred admission, international baccalaureate accepted. Required: essay, high school transcript, SAT or ACT. Recommended: interview. Entrance: moderately difficult. Application deadline: Rolling. Notification: continuous.

Costs Per Year: Application fee: $20. Comprehensive fee: $21,628 includes full-time tuition ($15,168), mandatory fees ($250), and college room and board ($6210). College room only: $2100. Full-time tuition and fees vary according to class time and program. Room and board charges vary according to board plan and housing facility. Part-time tuition: $632 per credit. Part-time mandatory fees: $125 per term. Part-time tuition and fees vary according to class time and program.

Collegiate Environment: Orientation program. Drama-theater group, choral group, student-run newspaper. Social organizations: 35 open to all. Most popular organizations: Student Nurses Association, Women in Communication, Pi Sigma Epsilon, Students in Free Enterprise, Alverno Student Educators Organization. Major annual events: Convocation, Student Group Open House, Community Day. Student services: health clinic. Campus security: 24-hour emergency response devices and patrols, late night transport-escort service, controlled dormitory access, well-lit parking lots and pathways, emergency first-aid and CPR, crisis intervention team and plan in place. 205 college housing spaces available; all were occupied in 2003-04. Freshmen guaranteed college housing. On-campus residence required in freshman year. Option: women-only housing available. Alverno College Library with 82,416 books, 287,726 microform titles, 1,382 serials, 15,728 audiovisual materials, an OPAC, and a Web page. Operations spending for 2004 fiscal year: $951,405. 400 computers available on campus for general student use. A campuswide network can be accessed from student residence rooms and from off campus. Staffed computer lab on campus.

Community Environment: See Milwaukee Area Technical College.

■ **BELLIN COLLEGE OF NURSING** *K-12*

725 South Webster Ave, PO Box 23400

Green Bay, WI 54305-3400

Tel: (920)433-3560

Free: 800-236-8707

Admissions: (920)433-5803

Fax: (920)433-7416

Web Site: http://www.bcon.edu/

Description: Independent, 4-year, coed. Administratively affiliated with Bellin Health System. Awards bachelor's and master's degrees. Founded 1909. Setting: urban campus. Endowment: $7.4 million. Educational spending for 2005 fiscal year: $6804 per student. Total enrollment: 239. 214 applied, 37% were admitted. Full-time: 181 students, 95% women, 5% men. Part-time: 35 students, 89% women, 11% men. Students come from 2 states and territories, 0.04% from out-of-state, 1% Native American, 1% Hispanic, 0% black, 2% Asian American or Pacific Islander, 0% international, 21% 25 or older, 19% transferred in. Retention: 90% of full-time freshmen returned the following year. Core. Calendar: semesters. Advanced placement, accelerated degree program, independent study, distance learning, summer session for credit, part-time degree program. Off campus study at University of Wisconsin-Green Bay. ROTC: Army (c).

Entrance Requirements: Options: Peterson's Universal Application, electronic application. Required: high school transcript, minimum 3.25 high school GPA, 3 recommendations, interview, ACT score 23 composite, ACT. Recommended: minimum 3.25 high school GPA. Entrance: moderately difficult. Application deadline: Rolling. Notification: continuous.

Costs Per Year: Application fee: $30. Tuition: $14,500 full-time, $684 per credit part-time. Mandatory fees: $268 full-time. Full-time tuition and fees vary according to course level. Part-time tuition varies according to course load.

Collegiate Environment: Orientation program. Social organizations: 2 open to all. Most popular organizations: Student Senate, Student Nurses Association. Major annual events: Dinner Dance, Spring Picnic, Pizza Party. Student services: health clinic, personal-psychological counseling. Campus security: 24-hour patrols, late night transport-escort service, electronically operated building access after hours. College housing not available. Meredith B. and John M. Rose Library with 7,000 books, 225 serials, and 600 audiovisual materials. Operations spending for 2004 fiscal year: $121,350. 18 computers available on campus for general student use. A campuswide network can be accessed. Staffed computer lab on campus.

■ **BELOIT COLLEGE** *Q-10*

700 College St.

Beloit, WI 53511-5596

Tel: (608)363-2000

Free: 800-9-BELOIT

Admissions: (608)363-2380

Fax: (608)363-2075

E-mail: admiss@beloit.edu

Web Site: http://www.beloit.edu/

Description: Independent, 4-year, coed. Awards bachelor's degrees. Founded 1846. Setting: 65-acre small town campus with easy access to Chicago and Milwaukee. Endowment: $106.1 million. Research spending for 2004 fiscal year: $15,847. Educational spending for 2005 fiscal year: $14,688 per student. Total enrollment: 1,385. Student-undergrad faculty ratio is 11:1. 2,054 applied, 64% were admitted. 37% from top 10% of their high school class, 64% from top quarter, 94% from top half. 6 National Merit Scholars, 11 valedictorians. Full-time: 1,330 students, 59% women, 41% men. Part-time: 55 students, 64% women, 36% men. Students come from 49 states and territories, 50 other countries, 82% from out-of-state, 1% Native American, 2% Hispanic, 3% black, 4% Asian American or Pacific Islander, 5% international, 2% 25 or older, 93% live on campus, 3% transferred in. Retention: 89% of full-time freshmen returned the following year. Academic areas with the most degrees conferred: social sciences; visual and performing arts; English; psychology. Core. Calendar: semesters. ESL program, services for LD students, advanced placement, self-designed majors, independent study, double major, summer session for credit, adult/continuing education programs, internships. Off campus study at University of Wisconsin-Madison, University of Chicago, Spelman College, Morehouse College, Associated Colleges of the Midwest. Study abroad program.

Entrance Requirements: Options: Peterson's Universal Application, Common Application, electronic application, early admission, early action, deferred admission, international baccalaureate accepted. Required: essay, high school transcript, 1 recommendation, SAT or ACT. Recommended: interview. Required for some: interview. Entrance: very difficult. Application deadlines: 1/15, 12/15 for early action. Notification: 4/1, 1/15 for early action.

Costs Per Year: Application fee: $35. Comprehensive fee: $32,808 includes full-time tuition ($26,664), mandatory fees ($220), and college room and board ($5924). College room only: $2890. Room and board charges vary according to board plan. Part-time tuition: $3334 per course.

Collegiate Environment: Orientation program. Drama-theater group, choral group, student-run newspaper, radio station. Social organizations: 85 open to all; national fraternities, local fraternities, local sororities; 15% of eligible men and 5% of eligible women are members. Most popular organizations: Science Fiction and Fantasy Association, Black Student's Union, International Club, Alliance, Ballroom Dancing Club. Major annual events: Folk 'n' Blues Festival, Spring Day, International Symposium. Student services: health clinic, personal-psychological counseling, women's center. Campus security: 24-hour emergency response devices and patrols, late night transport-escort service, controlled dormitory access. 1,081 college housing spaces available; 1,079 were occupied in 2003-04. Freshmen guaranteed college housing. On-campus residence required through junior year. Options: coed, men-only, women-only housing available. Morse Library and Black Information Center with 183,736 books, 139,248 microform titles, 946 serials, 7,285 audiovisual materials, an OPAC, and a Web page. Operations spending for 2004 fiscal year: $1.1 million. 152 computers available on campus for general student use. A campuswide network can be accessed from student residence rooms and from off campus. Staffed computer lab on campus.

Community Environment: Beloit College is located in Beloit, Wisconsin (population 36,000), 90 miles northwest of Chicago, 50 miles south of Madison, and 70 miles southwest of Milwaukee. Students take advantage of the varied resources offered by these three major metropolitan areas, as well as those offered by the city of Beloit itself. Beloit's hospital, clinics, manufacturers, and various civic and service organizations provide numerous internship, job shadowing, enrichment, and community outreach opportunities. Year-round sports and recreation areas are available in southern Wisconsin and northern Illinois. There is direct bus service from O'Hare International Airport, and the same bus continues on to the University of Wisconsin in Madison.

■ **BLACKHAWK TECHNICAL COLLEGE** Q-10
PO Box 5009
Janesville, WI 53547-5009
Tel: (608)758-6900
Free: 800-472-0024
Admissions: (608)757-7713
Fax: (608)757-9407
Web Site: http://www.blackhawk.edu/
Description: District-supported, 2-year, coed. Part of Wisconsin Technical College System. Awards transfer associate and terminal associate degrees. Founded 1968. Setting: 84-acre rural campus. Total enrollment: 2,627. Full-time: 1,015 students, 55% women, 45% men. Part-time: 1,612 students, 61% women, 39% men. Students come from 4 states and territories, 0.4%

Native American, 3% Hispanic, 6% black, 1% Asian American or Pacific Islander, 60% 25 or older. Core. Calendar: semesters. Academic remediation for entering students, ESL program, services for LD students, advanced placement, accelerated degree program, self-designed majors, independent study, distance learning, summer session for credit, part-time degree program, external degree program, adult/continuing education programs, co-op programs and internships.

Entrance Requirements: Open admission. Options: Common Application, electronic application. Required: high school transcript. Entrance: noncompetitive. Application deadline: Rolling. Notification: continuous. Preference given to district residents.

Collegiate Environment: Orientation program. Student-run newspaper. Major annual events: Fall Social, Spring Social. Student services: personal-psychological counseling, women's center. College housing not available. Blackhawk Technical College Library with 25,000 books, 435 serials, and an OPAC. 180 computers available on campus for general student use. A campuswide network can be accessed. Staffed computer lab on campus.

■ **BRYANT AND STRATTON COLLEGE** O-12
1300 North Jackson St.
Milwaukee, WI 53202-2608
Tel: (414)276-5200
Web Site: http://www.bryantstratton.edu/
Description: Proprietary, primarily 2-year, coed. Part of Bryant and Stratton Business Institute, Inc. Awards terminal associate and bachelor's degrees. Founded 1863. Setting: 2-acre urban campus. Total enrollment: 488. Student-undergrad faculty ratio is 10:1. 403 applied, 83% were admitted. 0% from out-of-state, 0.2% Native American, 4% Hispanic, 84% black, 1% Asian American or Pacific Islander, 0% international. Retention: 70% of full-time freshmen returned the following year. Academic area with the most degrees conferred: business/marketing. Core. Calendar: semesters. Academic remediation for entering students, advanced placement, independent study, distance learning, double major, summer session for credit, part-time degree program, adult/continuing education programs, co-op programs and internships.

Entrance Requirements: Option: Peterson's Universal Application. Required: high school transcript, interview, entrance and placement evaluations, TABE. Recommended: SAT or ACT. Required for some: recommendations. Entrance: minimally difficult. Application deadline: Rolling.

Costs Per Year: Tuition: $18,675 full-time, $415 per credit hour part-time. Mandatory fees: $25 full-time.

Collegiate Environment: Orientation program. Student-run newspaper. Most popular organizations: Phi Beta Lambda, Association of Information Technology Professionals, Allied Health Association, Institute of Management Accountants, Student Advisory Board. Major annual events: Professional Day, Career Fair, All-School Picnic. Campus security: 24-hour emergency response devices and patrols. College housing not available. Bryant and Stratton College Library with 120 serials and 100 audiovisual materials. 130 computers available on campus for general student use. A campuswide network can be accessed. Staffed computer lab on campus.

■ **BRYANT AND STRATTON COLLEGE, WAUWATOSA CAMPUS** B-11
10950 W. Potter Rd.
Wauwatosa, WI 53226
Tel: (414)302-7000
Web Site: http://www.byrantstratton.edu/
Description: Proprietary, 4-year, coed. Awards associate and bachelor's degrees. Total enrollment: 374. Student-undergrad faculty ratio is 10:1. Calendar: semesters.
Entrance Requirements: Required: high school transcript, interview, entrance and placement evaluation, TABE. Recommended: SAT or ACT. Application deadline: Rolling. Notification: continuous.
Costs Per Year: Tuition: $18,675 full-time, $415 per credit hour part-time. Mandatory fees: $25 full-time.

■ **CARDINAL STRITCH UNIVERSITY** O-12
6801 North Yates Rd.
Milwaukee, WI 53217-3985
Tel: (414)410-4000
Free: 800-347-8822
Admissions: (414)410-4040
Fax: (414)410-4239
Web Site: http://www.stritch.edu/

Description: Independent Roman Catholic, comprehensive, coed. Awards associate, bachelor's, master's, and doctoral degrees. Founded 1937. Setting: 40-acre suburban campus. Endowment: $17.7 million. Educational spending for 2005 fiscal year: $2612 per student. Total enrollment: 6,785. 617 applied, 93% were admitted. 12% from top 10% of their high school class, 27% from top quarter, 69% from top half. Full-time: 2,936 students, 67% women, 33% men. Part-time: 315 students, 81% women, 19% men. Students come from 16 states and territories, 27 other countries, 1% Native American, 4% Hispanic, 18% black, 2% Asian American or Pacific Islander, 2% international, 73% 25 or older, 5% live on campus, 5% transferred in. Retention: 73% of full-time freshmen returned the following year. Core. Calendar: semesters. Academic remediation for entering students, ESL program, services for LD students, advanced placement, accelerated degree program, self-designed majors, honors program, independent study, distance learning, double major, summer session for credit, part-time degree program, external degree program, adult/continuing education programs, co-op programs and internships, graduate courses open to undergrads. Off campus study at Concordia University Wisconsin, Saint Francis Seminary, Sacred Heart School of Theology.

Entrance Requirements: Options: Peterson's Universal Application, Common Application, electronic application, deferred admission, international baccalaureate accepted. Required: essay, high school transcript, minimum 2.0 high school GPA, SAT or ACT. Recommended: interview, ACT. Required for some: recommendations. Entrance: moderately difficult. Application deadline: Rolling.

Costs Per Year: Application fee: $25. Comprehensive fee: $22,260 includes full-time tuition ($16,480), mandatory fees ($350), and college room and board ($5430). Part-time tuition: $515 per credit. Part-time mandatory fees: $125 per term.

Collegiate Environment: Orientation program. Drama-theater group, choral group, student-run newspaper, radio station. Social organizations: 35 open to all. Most popular organizations: Residence Hall Association, Student Government Association, Student Activities Board. Major annual events: Christmas Dinner/Dance, Homecoming, Spring Semi-formal Dance. Student services: health clinic, personal-psychological counseling. Campus security: 24-hour emergency response devices and patrols, late night transport-escort service. Option: coed housing available. Cardinal Stritch University Library with 124,897 books, 180,550 microform titles, 667 serials, 6,250 audiovisual materials, an OPAC, and a Web page. Operations spending for 2004 fiscal year: $729,000. 236 computers available on campus for general student use. A campuswide network can be accessed from student residence rooms and from off campus. Staffed computer lab on campus.

Community Environment: See Milwaukee Area Technical College.

■ **CARROLL COLLEGE** *P-12*
100 North East Ave.
Waukesha, WI 53186-5593
Tel: (262)547-1211
Free: 800-CAR-ROLL
Admissions: (262)524-7221
Fax: (262)524-7139
E-mail: cc.info@ccadmin.cc.edu
Web Site: http://www.cc.edu/

Description: Independent Presbyterian, comprehensive, coed. Awards bachelor's and master's degrees. Founded 1846. Setting: 52-acre suburban campus with easy access to Milwaukee. Endowment: $34.3 million. Research spending for 2004 fiscal year: $12,831. Educational spending for 2005 fiscal year: $5093 per student. Total enrollment: 3,123. Faculty: 243 (103 full-time, 140 part-time). Student-undergrad faculty ratio is 17:1. 2,429 applied, 79% were admitted. 15% from top 10% of their high school class, 50% from top quarter, 76% from top half. Full-time: 2,314 students, 66% women, 34% men. Part-time: 568 students, 66% women, 34% men. Students come from 28 states and territories, 30 other countries, 18% from out-of-state, 0.5% Native American, 3% Hispanic, 2% black, 1% Asian American or Pacific Islander, 2% international, 23% 25 or older, 54% live on campus, 7% transferred in. Retention: 76% of full-time freshmen returned the following year. Academic areas with the most degrees conferred: education; business/marketing; health professions and related sciences. Core. Calendar: semesters. Academic remediation for entering students, services for LD students, advanced placement, self-designed majors, honors program, independent study, distance learning, double major, summer session for credit, part-time degree program, adult/continuing education programs, internships, graduate courses open to undergrads. Study abroad program. ROTC: Air Force (c).

Entrance Requirements: Options: Peterson's Universal Application, Common Application, electronic application, early admission, deferred admission, international baccalaureate accepted. Required: high school transcript, minimum 2.0 high school GPA, 1 recommendation, SAT and SAT Subject Tests or ACT. Recommended: interview. Required for some: essay. Entrance: moderately difficult. Application deadline: Rolling. Notification: continuous until 8/20.

Costs Per Year: Application fee: $0. Comprehensive fee: $25,980 includes full-time tuition ($19,500), mandatory fees ($410), and college room and board ($6070). College room only: $3300. Part-time tuition: $235 per credit.

Collegiate Environment: Orientation program. Drama-theater group, choral group, student-run newspaper, radio station. Social organizations: 50 open to all; national sororities, local fraternities; 10% of eligible men and 11% of eligible women are members. Most popular organizations: College Activities Board, Student Senate, Black Student Union, Carroll College Christian Fellowship, Residence Hall Association. Major annual events: homecoming, Parents' Weekend, Spring Fling. Student services: health clinic, personal-psychological counseling. Campus security: 24-hour emergency response devices and patrols, student patrols, late night transport-escort service, controlled dormitory access. 1,202 college housing spaces available; 1,170 were occupied in 2003-04. Freshmen guaranteed college housing. On-campus residence required in freshman year. Options: coed, women-only housing available. Todd Wehr Memorial Library with 200,000 books, 24,324 microform titles, 11,000 serials, 362 audiovisual materials, an OPAC, and a Web page. Operations spending for 2004 fiscal year: $841,660. 250 computers available on campus for general student use. A campuswide network can be accessed from student residence rooms and from off campus. Staffed computer lab on campus.

■ **CARTHAGE COLLEGE** *Q-13*
2001 Alford Park Dr.
Kenosha, WI 53140
Tel: (262)551-8500
Free: 800-351-4058
Admissions: (262)551-5850
Fax: (262)551-5762
E-mail: admissions@carthage.edu
Web Site: http://www.carthage.edu/

Description: Independent, comprehensive, coed, affiliated with Evangelical Lutheran Church in America. Awards bachelor's and master's degrees. Founded 1847. Setting: 72-acre suburban campus with easy access to Chicago and Milwaukee. Total enrollment: 2,699. Faculty: 210 (125 full-time, 85 part-time). Student-undergrad faculty ratio is 15:1. 4,000 applied, 76% were admitted. 18% from top 10% of their high school class, 43% from top quarter, 76% from top half. Full-time: 2,145 students, 56% women, 44% men. Part-time: 449 students, 73% women, 27% men. Students come from 31 states and territories, 11 other countries, 68% from out-of-state, 0.4% Native American, 4% Hispanic, 5% black, 1% Asian American or Pacific Islander, 1% international, 12% 25 or older, 68% live on campus, 3% transferred in. Retention: 75% of full-time freshmen returned the following year. Academic areas with the most degrees conferred: business/marketing; education; psychology. Core. Calendar: 4-1-4. Services for LD students, advanced placement, accelerated degree program, self-designed majors, honors program, independent study, double major, summer session for credit, part-time degree program, adult/continuing education programs, co-op programs and internships. Off campus study at University of Wisconsin-Parkside, Marquette University. Study abroad program. ROTC: Army (c), Air Force (c).

Entrance Requirements: Options: Peterson's Universal Application, Common Application, electronic application, early admission, early action, deferred admission, international baccalaureate accepted. Required: high school transcript, minimum 2.0 high school GPA, SAT or ACT. Recommended: essay, minimum 2.75 high school GPA, interview. Required for some: essay, 2 recommendations, interview. Entrance: moderately difficult. Application deadlines: Rolling, 7/1 for early action. Notification: continuous, 7/15 for early action.

Costs Per Year: Application fee: $25. Comprehensive fee: $30,450 includes full-time tuition ($23,650) and college room and board ($6800). Part-time tuition: $345 per credit hour.

Collegiate Environment: Orientation program. Drama-theater group, choral group, student-run newspaper, radio station. Social organizations: 80 open to all; national fraternities, national sororities, local fraternities, local sororities; 22% of eligible men and 25% of eligible women are members. Most popular organizations: Residence Life Council, Alpha Lambda Delta, Circle

K, Inter-Varsity Christian Fellowship, Pals-n-Partners. Major annual events: homecoming, May Madness, Casino Night. Student services: health clinic, personal-psychological counseling. Campus security: 24-hour emergency response devices and patrols, student patrols, late night transport-escort service, controlled dormitory access. 1,359 college housing spaces available; all were occupied in 2003-04. Freshmen guaranteed college housing. On-campus residence required through senior year. Options: coed, men-only, women-only housing available. Hedberg Library with 128,551 books, 7,149 microform titles, 425 serials, 4,361 audiovisual materials, an OPAC, and a Web page. Operations spending for 2004 fiscal year: $1 million. 200 computers available on campus for general student use. Computer purchase/lease plans available. A campuswide network can be accessed from student residence rooms and from off campus. Staffed computer lab on campus.

Community Environment: See Gateway Technical College.

■ CHIPPEWA VALLEY TECHNICAL COLLEGE *J-4*

620 West Clairemont Ave.
Eau Claire, WI 54701-6162
Tel: (715)833-6200
Free: 800-547-2882
Admissions: (715)833-6245
Fax: (715)833-6470
Web Site: http://www.cvtc.edu/

Description: District-supported, 2-year, coed. Part of Wisconsin Technical College System. Awards certificates, diplomas, and terminal associate degrees. Founded 1912. Setting: 160-acre urban campus. Total enrollment: 16,100. 10% from top 10% of their high school class, 15% from top quarter, 25% from top half. Students come from 10 states and territories, 4 other countries, 5% from out-of-state, 50% 25 or older. Calendar: semesters. Academic remediation for entering students, ESL program, services for LD students, distance learning, double major, summer session for credit, part-time degree program, adult/continuing education programs, internships.

Entrance Requirements: Open admission except for allied health, nursing, trade, industrial programs. Options: Common Application, early admission, deferred admission. Required: high school transcript. Required for some: interview. Placement: ACT COMPASS required; ACT required for some. Entrance: noncompetitive. Application deadline: Rolling. Notification: continuous.

Collegiate Environment: Student-run newspaper. Social organizations: 20 open to all. Student services: personal-psychological counseling. Campus security: 24-hour emergency response devices, late night transport-escort service. College housing not available. Technical Resource Center with 34,000 books, 750 serials, and an OPAC. 600 computers available on campus for general student use. A campuswide network can be accessed. Staffed computer lab on campus.

Community Environment: See University of Wisconsin Eau Claire.

■ COLLEGE OF MENOMINEE NATION *J-10*

PO Box 1179
Keshena, WI 54135
Tel: (715)799-5600
Fax: (715)799-1308
Web Site: http://www.menominee.edu/

Description: Independent, 2-year, coed. Awards certificates, transfer associate, and terminal associate degrees. Total enrollment: 499. 77% Native American, 0.2% Hispanic, 0.4% black, 1% Asian American or Pacific Islander. Calendar: semesters.

Entrance Requirements: Open admission. Placement: TABE required. Entrance: noncompetitive. Application deadline: 8/14.

Collegiate Environment: College housing not available.

■ COLUMBIA COLLEGE OF NURSING *O-12*

2121 East Newport Ave.
Milwaukee, WI 53211-2952
Tel: (414)961-3530
Free: 800-321-6265
Admissions: (414)256-1219
Web Site: http://www.ccon.edu/

Description: Independent, 4-year, coed. Awards bachelor's degrees (nursing degree is awarded in conjunction with Mount Mary College). Founded 1901. Setting: urban campus. Endowment: $900,000. Research spending for 2004 fiscal year: $42,000. Educational spending for 2005 fiscal year: $4969 per student. Total enrollment: 260. 123 applied, 46% were admitted. 13%

from top 10% of their high school class, 65% from top quarter, 91% from top half. Full-time: 243 students, 97% women, 3% men. Part-time: 17 students, 94% women, 6% men. Students come from 2 states and territories, 5% out-of-state, 0% Native American, 2% Hispanic, 13% black, 3% Asian American or Pacific Islander, 0% international, 2% live on campus. Retention: 63% of full-time freshmen returned the following year. Core. Calendar: semesters. Advanced placement, honors program, independent study, double major, summer session for credit, part-time degree program. Off campus study at Mount Mary College, Milwaukee, WI.

Entrance Requirements: Options: Common Application, electronic application. Required: high school transcript, SAT or ACT. Recommended: essay, 1 recommendation, interview. Required for some: essay. Entrance: moderately difficult. Application deadline: 8/1.

Costs Per Year: Application fee: $25. Comprehensive fee: $21,375 includes full-time tuition ($15,975), mandatory fees ($1200), and college room and board ($4200). College room only: $3200. Room and board charges vary according to board plan, housing facility, location, and student level. Part-time tuition: $466 per credit hour. Part-time tuition varies according to program.

Collegiate Environment: Social organizations: 2 open to all. Most popular organizations: Student Senate, Student Nurses Association. Major annual events: holiday party, Spring Banquet, homecoming. Student services: health clinic, personal-psychological counseling. Campus security: 24-hour emergency response devices and patrols, student patrols, late night transport-escort service, controlled dormitory access. 100 college housing spaces available; 4 were occupied in 2003-04. No special consideration for freshman housing applicants. Option: coed housing available. Ellen Bacon Library plus 2 others with 9,060 books, 253 serials, 508 audiovisual materials, and an OPAC. Operations spending for 2004 fiscal year: $111,752. 18 computers available on campus for general student use. A campuswide network can be accessed. Staffed computer lab on campus.

■ CONCORDIA UNIVERSITY WISCONSIN *A-12*

12800 North Lake Shore Dr.
Mequon, WI 53097-2402
Tel: (262)243-5700; 888-628-9472
Admissions: (262)243-4305
Fax: (262)243-4351
E-mail: kgaschk@cuw.edu
Web Site: http://www.cuw.edu/

Description: Independent, comprehensive, coed, affiliated with Lutheran Church-Missouri Synod. Awards associate, bachelor's, master's, and doctoral degrees. Founded 1881. Setting: 155-acre suburban campus with easy access to Milwaukee. Endowment: $40 million. Educational spending for 2005 fiscal year: $4651 per student. Total enrollment: 5,418. Faculty: 199 (89 full-time, 110 part-time). Student-undergrad faculty ratio is 18:1. 1,274 applied, 84% were admitted. 19% from top 10% of their high school class, 38% from top quarter, 68% from top half. Full-time: 2,007 students, 61% women, 39% men. Part-time: 1,975 students, 64% women, 36% men. Students come from 35 states and territories, 21 other countries, 30% from out-of-state, 1% Native American, 3% Hispanic, 13% black, 1% Asian American or Pacific Islander, 1% international, 59% 25 or older, 78% live on campus, 2% transferred in. Retention: 80% of full-time freshmen returned the following year. Academic areas with the most degrees conferred: business/marketing; education; health professions and related sciences. Core. Calendar: 4-1-4. Academic remediation for entering students, ESL program, services for LD students, advanced placement, accelerated degree program, self-designed majors, honors program, independent study, distance learning, double major, summer session for credit, part-time degree program, adult/continuing education programs, internships. Off campus study at Milwaukee Area Technical College, Milwaukee Institute of Art and Design, Cardinal Stritch University, Mount Mary College. Study abroad program.

Entrance Requirements: Options: deferred admission, international baccalaureate accepted. Required: high school transcript, minimum 2.0 high school GPA, ACT. Recommended: interview. Required for some: essay, minimum 3.0 high school GPA, 3 recommendations. Entrance: moderately difficult. Application deadline: 8/15. Notification: continuous.

Costs Per Year: Application fee: $35. Comprehensive fee: $23,820 includes full-time tuition ($17,190), mandatory fees ($90), and college room and board ($6540). Full-time tuition and fees vary according to program. Room and board charges vary according to board plan. Part-time tuition: $716 per credit hour. Part-time tuition varies according to class time and program. Tuition guaranteed not to increase for student's term of enrollment.

Collegiate Environment: Orientation program. Drama-theater group, choral group, student-run newspaper, radio station. Most popular organizations: Fellowship of Christian Athletes, Kammerchor, Youth Ministry, band. Major annual events: Homecoming Week, Winterfest, Springfest. Student services: health clinic, personal-psychological counseling. Campus security: student patrols, controlled dormitory access. 1,000 college housing spaces available; all were occupied in 2003-04. Freshmen given priority for college housing. Options: men-only, women-only housing available. Rinker Memorial Library plus 1 other with 365,314 books, 292,737 microform titles, 4,440 serials, 3,122 audiovisual materials, and an OPAC. Operations spending for 2004 fiscal year: $935,000. 100 computers available on campus for general student use. A campuswide network can be accessed from student residence rooms and from off campus. Staffed computer lab on campus.

Community Environment: See Milwaukee Area Technical College.

■ **DEVRY UNIVERSITY (MILWAUKEE)** *O-12*
100 East Wisconsin Ave., Ste. 2550
Milwaukee, WI 53202-4107
Tel: (414)278-7677; (866)683-3879
Fax: (414)278-0137
Web Site: http://www.devry.edu/
Description: Proprietary, comprehensive, coed. Part of DeVry University. Awards bachelor's and master's degrees. Total enrollment: 216. Faculty: 17 (1 full-time, 16 part-time). Student-undergrad faculty ratio is 7:1. Full-time: 28 students, 71% women, 29% men. Part-time: 46 students, 63% women, 37% men. 1% Native American, 7% Hispanic, 55% black, 1% Asian American or Pacific Islander, 0% international. Calendar: semesters. Academic remediation for entering students, services for LD students, advanced placement, accelerated degree program, distance learning, summer session for credit, part-time degree program, adult/continuing education programs, co-op programs.
Entrance Requirements: Options: electronic application, deferred admission, international baccalaureate accepted. Required: high school transcript, interview. Entrance: minimally difficult. Application deadline: Rolling.
Costs Per Year: Application fee: $50. One-time mandatory fee: $40. Tuition: $11,890 full-time, $445 per credit part-time. Mandatory fees: $30 full-time, $30 per year part-time.
Collegiate Environment: Orientation program. College housing not available.

■ **DEVRY UNIVERSITY (WAUKESHA)** *P-12*
20935 Swenson Dr., Ste. 450
Waukesha, WI 53186-4047
Tel: (262)798-9889
Fax: (262)798-9912
Web Site: http://www.devry.edu/
Description: Proprietary, comprehensive, coed. Calendar: semesters.

■ **EDGEWOOD COLLEGE** *B-6*
1000 Edgewood College Dr.
Madison, WI 53711-1997
Tel: (608)663-4861
Free: 800-444-4861
Admissions: (608)663-2254
Fax: (608)663-3291
E-mail: admissions@edgewood.edu
Web Site: http://www.edgewood.edu/
Description: Independent Roman Catholic, comprehensive, coed. Awards associate, bachelor's, master's, and doctoral degrees. Founded 1927. Setting: 55-acre urban campus. Endowment: $10.2 million. Educational spending for 2005 fiscal year: $4545 per student. Total enrollment: 2,646. Faculty: 220 (86 full-time, 134 part-time). Student-undergrad faculty ratio is 13:1. 1,035 applied, 81% were admitted. 11% from top 10% of their high school class, 34% from top quarter, 73% from top half. Full-time: 1,517 students, 74% women, 26% men. Part-time: 506 students, 71% women, 29% men. Students come from 16 states and territories, 22 other countries, 6% from out-of-state, 0.4% Native American, 2% Hispanic, 2% black, 2% Asian American or Pacific Islander, 1% international, 24% 25 or older, 20% live on campus, 9% transferred in. Retention: 74% of full-time freshmen returned the following year. Academic areas with the most degrees conferred: business/marketing; health professions and related sciences; education. Calendar: 4-1-4. Academic remediation for entering students, services for LD students, advanced placement, independent study, summer session for

credit, part-time degree program, adult/continuing education programs. Off campus study at University of Wisconsin-Madison.
Entrance Requirements: Options: Peterson's Universal Application, deferred admission. Required: high school transcript, minimum 2.5 high school GPA, SAT or ACT. Recommended: interview. Required for some: essay, 2 recommendations, interview. Entrance: moderately difficult. Application deadline: Rolling. Notification: continuous.
Costs Per Year: Application fee: $25. Comprehensive fee: $22,862 includes full-time tuition ($17,000) and college room and board ($5862). College room only: $2700. Part-time tuition: $534 per credit.
Collegiate Environment: Orientation program. Drama-theater group, choral group, student-run newspaper. Social organizations: 24 open to all. Most popular organizations: Student Government Association, Student Programming Board, Resident Life Association, Chalk Talk, Student Nurses Association. Major annual events: Mazzachelli Fest, Family Day, Spring Fest. Student services: health clinic, personal-psychological counseling. Campus security: 24-hour emergency response devices and patrols, student patrols, late night transport-escort service, controlled dormitory access. 354 college housing spaces available; 340 were occupied in 2003-04. Freshmen given priority for college housing. Options: coed, women-only housing available. Oscar Rennebohm Library with 90,253 books, 96,072 microform titles, 447 serials, 4,359 audiovisual materials, an OPAC, and a Web page. Operations spending for 2004 fiscal year: $511,124. 140 computers available on campus for general student use. Computer purchase/lease plans available. A campuswide network can be accessed from student residence rooms and from off campus. Staffed computer lab on campus.
Community Environment: See University of Wisconsin - Madison.

■ **FOX VALLEY TECHNICAL COLLEGE** *L-11*
1825 North Bluemound, PO Box 2277
Appleton, WI 54912-2277
Tel: (920)735-5600
Free: 800-735-3882
Admissions: (920)735-5643
Fax: (920)735-2582
Web Site: http://www.fvtc.edu/
Description: State and locally supported, 2-year, coed. Part of Wisconsin Technical College System. Awards certificates, diplomas, transfer associate, and terminal associate degrees. Founded 1967. Setting: 100-acre suburban campus. Educational spending for 2005 fiscal year: $9497 per student. Total enrollment: 7,855. Student-undergrad faculty ratio is 18:1. 4,586 applied, 70% were admitted. Full-time: 1,624 students, 38% women, 62% men. Part-time: 6,231 students, 56% women, 44% men. Students come from 11 states and territories, 1% from out-of-state, 1% Native American, 2% Hispanic, 1% black, 3% Asian American or Pacific Islander, 0% international, 51% 25 or older. Core. Calendar: semesters. Academic remediation for entering students, ESL program, services for LD students, advanced placement, accelerated degree program, self-designed majors, honors program, independent study, distance learning, double major, summer session for credit, part-time degree program, adult/continuing education programs, co-op programs and internships. Off campus study at Georgetown University and other institutions. Study abroad program.
Entrance Requirements: Open admission. Options: Common Application, electronic application, early admission, deferred admission. Required: high school transcript. Entrance: noncompetitive. Application deadline: Rolling.
Costs Per Year: Application fee: $30. State resident tuition: $2610 full-time, $87 per credit part-time. Nonresident tuition: $16,089 full-time, $536.30 per credit part-time. Mandatory fees: $550 full-time.
Collegiate Environment: Student-run newspaper. Social organizations: 26 open to all. Most popular organizations: Business Professionals of America, Delta Epsilon Chi, Vocational Industrial Clubs of America. Student services: health clinic, personal-psychological counseling, women's center. Campus security: late night transport-escort service, 16-hour patrols by trained security personnel. College housing not available. William Sirek Educational Resource Center with 45,139 books, 297 serials, 7,953 audiovisual materials, an OPAC, and a Web page. Operations spending for 2004 fiscal year: $673,002. 300 computers available on campus for general student use. A campuswide network can be accessed from off-campus. Staffed computer lab on campus.

■ **GATEWAY TECHNICAL COLLEGE** *Q-13*
3520 30th Ave.
Kenosha, WI 53144-1690
Tel: (262)564-2200

Admissions: (262)564-3224
Fax: (262)564-2201
Web Site: http://www.gtc.edu/
Description: State and locally supported, 2-year, coed. Part of Wisconsin Technical College System. Awards certificates, diplomas, and terminal associate degrees. Founded 1911. Setting: 10-acre urban campus with easy access to Chicago and Milwaukee. Educational spending for 2005 fiscal year: $12,625 per student. Total enrollment: 6,816. 4,489 applied, 85% were admitted. Full-time: 1,304 students, 55% women, 45% men. Part-time: 5,512 students, 63% women, 37% men. Students come from 7 states and territories, 0.3% Native American, 7% Hispanic, 10% black, 1% Asian American or Pacific Islander, 0% international, 50% 25 or older. Core. Calendar: semesters. Academic remediation for entering students, ESL program, services for LD students, advanced placement, self-designed majors, independent study, distance learning, double major, summer session for credit, part-time degree program, co-op programs and internships.
Entrance Requirements: Open admission except for health occupations programs. Options: electronic application, early admission, deferred admission. Required for some: high school transcript, minimum 2.0 high school GPA, interview. Placement: ACT ASSET or ACT COMPASS required; ACT recommended. Entrance: noncompetitive. Application deadline: Rolling. Notification: continuous.
Collegiate Environment: Student-run newspaper, radio station. Student services: personal-psychological counseling. Campus security: 24-hour emergency response devices and patrols, late night transport-escort service. College housing not available. Library/Learning Resources Center with 45,433 books, 1,537 microform titles, 409 serials, 12,400 audiovisual materials, and an OPAC. Operations spending for 2004 fiscal year: $1 million. 840 computers available on campus for general student use. A campuswide network can be accessed from off-campus. Staffed computer lab on campus.
Community Environment: Located on the shore of Lake Michigan, Kenosha (population 79,000) has an excellent harbor with 83% of its shoreline providing recreation. It is surrounded by a prosperous agricultural area and is one of the chief industrial centers of the state. Both Chicago and Milwaukee are an hour away. Points of interest are the Hall of Fame, Art Museum, County Historical Society, and Petrifying Springs Park.

■ **HERZING COLLEGE** *B-6*
5218 East Terrace Dr.
Madison, WI 53718
Tel: (608)249-6611
Free: 800-582-1227
Fax: (608)249-8593
E-mail: info@msn.herzing.edu
Web Site: http://www.herzing.edu/madison
Description: Proprietary, primarily 2-year, coed. Part of Herzing Institutes, Inc. Awards diplomas, transfer associate, terminal associate, and bachelor's degrees. Founded 1948. Setting: suburban campus with easy access to Milwaukee. Total enrollment: 650. 80% from top half of their high school class. Students come from 5 states and territories, 2 other countries, 33% from out-of-state. Core. Calendar: semesters. Academic remediation for entering students, services for LD students, advanced placement, accelerated degree program, honors program, independent study, distance learning, double major, part-time degree program, adult/continuing education programs, co-op programs and internships.
Entrance Requirements: Open admission. Options: Common Application, electronic application, early admission. Required: high school transcript, interview, college entrance examination. Entrance: moderately difficult. Application deadline: Rolling.
Costs Per Year: Application fee: $0. Tuition: $10,000 full-time, $290 per credit part-time. Mandatory fees: $25 full-time. Full-time tuition and fees vary according to course load, location, and program. Part-time tuition varies according to course load, location, and program.
Collegiate Environment: Orientation program. Campus security: 24-hour emergency response devices. College housing not available. Herzing College Library with 1,500 books, 15 serials, an OPAC, and a Web page. 210 computers available on campus for general student use. Computer purchase/lease plans available. A campuswide network can be accessed from off-campus. Staffed computer lab on campus.

■ **ITT TECHNICAL INSTITUTE (GREEN BAY)** *K-12*
470 Security Blvd.
Green Bay, WI 54313
Tel: (920)662-9000; 888-884-3626

Web Site: http://www.itt-tech.edu/
Description: Proprietary, primarily 2-year, coed. Part of ITT Educational Services, Inc. Awards terminal associate and bachelor's degrees. Founded 2000. Core.
Entrance Requirements: Option: deferred admission. Required: high school transcript, interview, Wonderlic aptitude test. Recommended: recommendations. Entrance: minimally difficult. Application deadline: Rolling. Notification: continuous.
Costs Per Year: Application fee: $100.
Collegiate Environment: Orientation program. College housing not available.

■ **ITT TECHNICAL INSTITUTE (GREENFIELD)** *C-11*
6300 West Layton Ave.
Greenfield, WI 53220-4612
Tel: (414)282-9494
Web Site: http://www.itt-tech.edu/
Description: Proprietary, primarily 2-year, coed. Part of ITT Educational Services, Inc. Awards terminal associate and bachelor's degrees. Founded 1968. Setting: suburban campus with easy access to Milwaukee. Total enrollment: 548. Core.
Entrance Requirements: Option: deferred admission. Required: high school transcript, interview, Wonderlic aptitude test. Recommended: recommendations. Entrance: minimally difficult. Application deadline: Rolling. Notification: continuous.
Costs Per Year: Application fee: $100.
Collegiate Environment: Orientation program. College housing not available.

■ **LAC COURTE OREILLES OJIBWA COMMUNITY COLLEGE** *F-4*
13466 West Trepania Rd.
Hayward, WI 54843-2181
Tel: (715)634-4790; 888-526-6221
Web Site: http://www.lco-college.edu/
Description: Federally supported, 2-year, coed. Awards certificates, transfer associate, and terminal associate degrees. Founded 1982. Setting: 2-acre rural campus. Endowment: $950,616. Total enrollment: 505. Student-undergrad faculty ratio is 10:1. 151 applied, 100% were admitted. Full-time: 294 students, 73% women, 27% men. Part-time: 211 students, 71% women, 29% men. 3% from out-of-state, 77% Native American, 1% Hispanic, 1% black, 0% Asian American or Pacific Islander, 0% international, 75% 25 or older. Core. Calendar: semesters. Academic remediation for entering students, honors program, independent study, distance learning, double major, part-time degree program, external degree program, adult/continuing education programs.
Entrance Requirements: Open admission. Options: Common Application, early admission. Required: high school transcript, ACT COMPASS. Entrance: noncompetitive. Application deadline: Rolling.
Costs Per Year: Application fee: $10. Area resident tuition: $4050 full-time, $135 per credit part-time. Mandatory fees: $25 full-time.
Collegiate Environment: Orientation program. Drama-theater group. Most popular organization: student association. Major annual events: Welcome Feast, Thanksgiving Feast, graduation. Campus security: 24-hour emergency response devices. College housing not available. Lac Courte Oreilles Ojibwa Community College Library with 13,800 books, 100 serials, and an OPAC. Operations spending for 2004 fiscal year: $115,580. 25 computers available on campus for general student use. A campuswide network can be accessed. Staffed computer lab on campus.

■ **LAKELAND COLLEGE** *M-13*
PO Box 359
Sheboygan, WI 53082-0359
Tel: (920)565-1000
Admissions: (920)565-1588
Fax: (920)565-1206
E-mail: admissions@lakeland.edu
Web Site: http://www.lakeland.edu/
Description: Independent, comprehensive, coed, affiliated with United Church of Christ. Awards bachelor's and master's degrees. Founded 1862. Setting: 240-acre rural campus with easy access to Milwaukee. Endowment: $10.2 million. Educational spending for 2005 fiscal year: $3565 per student. Total enrollment: 4,021. Faculty: 69 (54 full-time, 15 part-time). Student-undergrad faculty ratio is 17:1. 872 applied, 71% were admitted. 7% from top 10% of their high school class, 21% from top quarter, 64% from top half. 3

valedictorians. Full-time: 1,400 students, 53% women, 47% men. Part-time: 1,973 students, 67% women, 33% men. Students come from 42 states and territories, 40 other countries, 12% from out-of-state, 1% Native American, 2% Hispanic, 6% black, 2% Asian American or Pacific Islander, 5% international, 18% 25 or older, 60% live on campus, 11% transferred in. Retention: 67% of full-time freshmen returned the following year. Academic areas with the most degrees conferred: business/marketing; computer and information sciences; education. Core. Calendar: 4-4-1. Academic remediation for entering students, ESL program, services for LD students, advanced placement, honors program, independent study, distance learning, summer session for credit, part-time degree program, adult/continuing education programs, internships, graduate courses open to undergrads. Off campus study. Study abroad program.

Entrance Requirements: Options: Peterson's Universal Application, Common Application, electronic application, deferred admission, international baccalaureate accepted. Required: essay, high school transcript, minimum 2.0 high school GPA, SAT or ACT. Recommended: recommendations. Required for some: interview. Entrance: minimally difficult. Application deadline: 9/1. Notification: continuous until 9/1.

Costs Per Year: Application fee: $20. Comprehensive fee: $22,216 includes full-time tuition ($16,080), mandatory fees ($716), and college room and board ($5420). College room only: $3882. Part-time tuition: $1608 per course.

Collegiate Environment: Orientation program. Drama-theater group, choral group, student-run newspaper. Social organizations: 32 open to all; local fraternities, local sororities; 20% of eligible men and 15% of eligible women are members. Most popular organizations: Lakeland College Campus Activities Board, Student Association, Black Student Union, Mortar Board, Global Students Association. Major annual events: homecoming, Essence of Heritage (Celebration of African American history and culture), Spring Fling. Student services: health clinic, personal-psychological counseling. Campus security: 24-hour emergency response devices, student patrols, late night transport-escort service, controlled dormitory access. 517 college housing spaces available; all were occupied in 2003-04. Freshmen guaranteed college housing. On-campus residence required through senior year. Options: coed; men-only, women-only housing available. Esch Memorial Library with 64,970 books, 35,350 microform titles, 317 serials, 647 audiovisual materials, and a Web page. Operations spending for 2004 fiscal year: $282,986. 100 computers available on campus for general student use. Computer purchase/lease plans available. A campuswide network can be accessed from student residence rooms and from off campus. Staffed computer lab on campus.

Community Environment: The college is located 12 miles northwest of Sheboygan, Wisconsin, 60 miles north of Milwaukee and 60 miles south of Green Bay. Sheboygan has a population of 50,000 and offers students off-campus opportunities for work and recreation. Sheboygan's county airport, the bus depot, and Interstate 43 offer easy access to Lakeland.

■ **LAKESHORE TECHNICAL COLLEGE** *M-13*

1290 North Ave.

Cleveland, WI 53015-1414

Tel: (920)693-1000; 888-GO TO LTC

Admissions: (920)693-1102

Fax: (920)693-1363

Web Site: http://www.gotoltc.com/

Description: State and locally supported, 2-year, coed. Part of Wisconsin Technical College System. Awards certificates, diplomas, transfer associate, and terminal associate degrees. Founded 1967. Setting: 160-acre rural campus with easy access to Milwaukee. Research spending for 2004 fiscal year: $147,565. Educational spending for 2005 fiscal year: $12,044 per student. Total enrollment: 2,939. Student-undergrad faculty ratio is 14:1. 1,667 applied, 68% were admitted. Full-time: 772 students, 59% women, 41% men. Part-time: 2,167 students, 60% women, 40% men. Students come from 3 states and territories, 1% from out-of-state, 0.4% Native American, 2% Hispanic, 0.4% black, 2% Asian American or Pacific Islander, 0% international, 55% 25 or older. Core. Calendar: semesters. Academic remediation for entering students, ESL program, services for LD students, advanced placement, accelerated degree program, self-designed majors, independent study, distance learning, double major, summer session for credit, part-time degree program, external degree program, adult/continuing education programs, co-op programs and internships.

Entrance Requirements: Open admission. Options: Common Application, electronic application, early admission, deferred admission. Recommended:

ACT, SAT or ACT, ACCUPLACER/ACT ASSET. Required for some: high school transcript, interview. Entrance: noncompetitive. Application deadline: Rolling. Notification: continuous.

Costs Per Year: Application fee: $30. Area resident tuition: $2610 full-time. State resident tuition: $16,089 full-time, $87 per credit part-time. Nonresident tuition: $536.30 per credit part-time.

Collegiate Environment: Orientation program. Social organizations: 14 open to all. Most popular organizations: student government, Business Professionals of America, Police Science Club, Lakeshore Student Nurse Association, Dairy Herd Club. Major annual events: Hypnotist, Fun Flicks, Virtual Reality. Student services: health clinic, personal-psychological counseling. Campus security: 24-hour patrols. College housing not available. 15,749 books, 220 serials, 9,931 audiovisual materials, and an OPAC. Operations spending for 2004 fiscal year: $280,669. 720 computers available on campus for general student use. A campuswide network can be accessed. Staffed computer lab on campus.

Community Environment: See Lakeland College.

■ **LAWRENCE UNIVERSITY** *L-11*

PO Box 599

Appleton, WI 54912-0599

Tel: (920)832-7000

Free: 800-227-0982

Admissions: (920)832-6500

Fax: (920)832-6606

Web Site: http://www.lawrence.edu/

Description: Independent, 4-year, coed. Awards bachelor's degrees. Founded 1847. Setting: 84-acre small town campus. Endowment: $188.1 million. Research spending for 2004 fiscal year: $722,677. Educational spending for 2005 fiscal year: $9616 per student. Total enrollment: 1,450. Student-undergrad faculty ratio is 9:1. 2,060 applied, 68% were admitted. 41% from top 10% of their high school class, 72% from top quarter, 97% from top half. 10 National Merit Scholars, 12 valedictorians. Full-time: 1,383 students, 54% women, 46% men. Part-time: 67 students, 37% women, 63% men. Students come from 49 states and territories, 51 other countries, 56% from out-of-state, 0.3% Native American, 3% Hispanic, 2% black, 3% Asian American or Pacific Islander, 8% international, 3% 25 or older, 98% live on campus, 2% transferred in. Retention: 87% of full-time freshmen returned the following year. Academic areas with the most degrees conferred: visual and performing arts; social sciences; foreign languages and literature. Core. Calendar: trimesters. ESL program, services for LD students, advanced placement, self-designed majors, independent study, double major, internships. Off campus study at Associated Colleges of the Midwest, Great Lakes Colleges Association. Study abroad program.

Entrance Requirements: Options: Peterson's Universal Application, Common Application, electronic application, early admission, early decision, early action, deferred admission, international baccalaureate accepted. Required: essay, high school transcript, 2 recommendations, audition for music program. Recommended: minimum 3.0 high school GPA, interview. Required for some: SAT or ACT. Entrance: very difficult. Application deadlines: 1/15, 11/15 for early decision, 12/1 for early action. Notification: 4/1, 12/1 for early decision, 1/15 for early action.

Costs Per Year: Application fee: $40. Comprehensive fee: $35,979 includes full-time tuition ($29,376), mandatory fees ($222), and college room and board ($6381). College room only: $2934.

Collegiate Environment: Orientation program. Drama-theater group, choral group, student-run newspaper, radio station. Social organizations: 130 open to all; national fraternities, national sororities; 23% of eligible men and 10% of eligible women are members. Most popular organizations: Lawrence Swing Dancers, Lawrence International, Outdoor Recreation Club, Lawrence Christian Fellowship, Lambda Sigma. Major annual events: Fall Festival, Jazz Celebration Weekend, Midwest Trivia Contest. Student services: health clinic, personal-psychological counseling. Campus security: 24-hour emergency response devices, student patrols, late night transport-escort service, controlled dormitory access, evening patrols by trained security personnel. 1,400 college housing spaces available; 1,360 were occupied in 2003-04. Freshmen guaranteed college housing. On-campus residence required through senior year. Options: coed, men-only, women-only housing available. Seeley G. Mudd Library with 389,262 books, 104,081 microform titles, 1,744 serials, 19,598 audiovisual materials, an OPAC, and a Web page. Operations spending for 2004 fiscal year: $1.7 million. 175 computers available on campus for general student use. A campuswide network can be accessed from student residence rooms and from off campus. Staffed computer lab on campus.

Community Environment: Appleton is a thriving and dynamic small city (pop. 65,000), located in the papermaking center of the country and rated among the best communities in the United States for quality of life. The city is accessible by car, bus, and plane.

■ MADISON AREA TECHNICAL COLLEGE *B-6*

3550 Anderson St.
Madison, WI 53704-2599
Tel: (608)246-6100
Admissions: (608)246-6212
Web Site: http://www.matcmadison.edu/matc/

Description: District-supported, 2-year, coed. Part of Wisconsin Technical College System. Awards certificates, diplomas, transfer associate, and terminal associate degrees. Founded 1911. Setting: 150-acre urban campus. Research spending for 2004 fiscal year: $195,238. Total enrollment: 13,479. 1% from top 10% of their high school class, 31% from top half. Students come from 9 states and territories, 50% 25 or older. Core. Calendar: semesters. Academic remediation for entering students, ESL program, services for LD students, summer session for credit, part-time degree program, adult/continuing education programs, co-op programs and internships. Off campus study at University of Wisconsin-Baraboo/Sauk County.

Entrance Requirements: Open admission except for data processing, technology, health occupations, quota programs. Option: early admission. Required for some: high school transcript, ACT. Entrance: noncompetitive. Application deadline: 7/1. Notification: continuous. Preference given to state residents.

Collegiate Environment: Drama-theater group, choral group, student-run newspaper. Social organizations: 45 open to all. Most popular organizations: Marketing Club, Minority Networking Groups, Data Processing Management Association, Student Nurses Association, Business Professionals of America. Major annual events: spring picnic, Celebrate Diversity Series, service-learning activities. Student services: health clinic, personal-psychological counseling, women's center. Campus security: 24-hour emergency response devices and patrols, late night transport-escort service. College housing not available. Truax-Information Resource Center with 66,000 books, 657 serials, an OPAC, and a Web page. Operations spending for 2004 fiscal year: $921,250. 1,500 computers available on campus for general student use. Staffed computer lab on campus.

Community Environment: Home of the state capital and the University of Wisconsin, Madison is a lovely city situated between two lakes. Four campuses are in smaller cities with growing industrial bases.

■ MADISON MEDIA INSTITUTE *B-6*

2702 Agriculture Dr., Ste. 1
Madison, WI 53718
Tel: (608)829-2728
Free: 800-236-4997
Admissions: (608)663-2000
Fax: (608)829-2661
E-mail: chutch@madisonmedia.com
Web Site: http://www.madisonmedia.com/

Description: Proprietary, 2-year, coed. Awards diplomas and terminal associate degrees. Founded 1969.

■ MARANATHA BAPTIST BIBLE COLLEGE *O-10*

745 West Main St.
Watertown, WI 53094
Tel: (920)261-9300
Free: 800-622-2947
Admissions: (920)206-2327
Fax: (920)261-9109
E-mail: admissions@mbbc.edu
Web Site: http://www.mbbc.edu/

Description: Independent Baptist, comprehensive, coed. Awards associate, bachelor's, and master's degrees. Founded 1968. Setting: 60-acre small town campus with easy access to Milwaukee. Endowment: $55,884. Educational spending for 2005 fiscal year: $2705 per student. Total enrollment: 904. 364 applied, 68% were admitted. Full-time: 850 students, 54% women, 46% men. Students come from 42 states and territories, 10 other countries, 68% from out-of-state, 0.2% Native American, 1% Hispanic, 1% black, 1% Asian American or Pacific Islander, 0.5% international, 4% 25 or older, 71% live on campus, 0.5% transferred in. Retention: 64% of full-time freshmen returned the following year. Core. Calendar: semesters. Academic remediation for entering students, accelerated degree program, independent

study, distance learning, double major, summer session for credit, part-time degree program, internships, graduate courses open to undergrads. Off campus study at Madison Area Technical College. ROTC: Air Force.

Entrance Requirements: Open admission. Options: Common Application, early admission, deferred admission. Required: essay, high school transcript, 4 recommendations. Recommended: ACT. Placement: ACT required. Entrance: noncompetitive. Application deadline: Rolling. Preference given to Christians.

Costs Per Year: Application fee: $40. Comprehensive fee: $13,510 includes full-time tuition ($7680), mandatory fees ($830), and college room and board ($5000). Full-time tuition and fees vary according to course level. Part-time tuition: $240 per semester hour. Part-time tuition varies according to course level.

Collegiate Environment: Orientation program. Drama-theater group, choral group. Social organizations: ; 100% of eligible men and 100% of eligible women are members. Major annual events: Christmas Festival of Music, semi-annual college play, Commencement. Student services: health clinic, personal-psychological counseling. Campus security: student patrols, late night transport-escort service, controlled dormitory access. 715 college housing spaces available; 480 were occupied in 2003-04. Freshmen guaranteed college housing. On-campus residence required through senior year. Options: men-only, women-only housing available. Cedarholm Library and Resource Center with 122,251 books, 146,438 microform titles, 502 serials, 5,550 audiovisual materials, and an OPAC. Operations spending for 2004 fiscal year: $244,615. 61 computers available on campus for general student use. A campuswide network can be accessed from student residence rooms and from off campus. Staffed computer lab on campus.

■ MARIAN COLLEGE OF FOND DU LAC *M-11*

45 South National Ave.
Fond du Lac, WI 54935-4699
Tel: (920)923-7600
Admissions: (920)923-7650
Fax: (920)923-8755
E-mail: admit@mariancoll.edu
Web Site: http://www.mariancollege.edu/

Description: Independent Roman Catholic, comprehensive, coed. Awards bachelor's, master's, and doctoral degrees. Founded 1936. Setting: 77-acre small town campus with easy access to Milwaukee. Endowment: $6.3 million. Educational spending for 2005 fiscal year: $4104 per student. Total enrollment: 2,975. Faculty: 285 (78 full-time, 207 part-time). Student-undergrad faculty ratio is 13:1. 766 applied, 86% were admitted. 11% from top 10% of their high school class, 31% from top quarter, 62% from top half. Full-time: 1,361 students, 74% women, 26% men. Part-time: 716 students, 71% women, 29% men. Students come from 18 states and territories, 7 other countries, 5% from out-of-state, 1% Native American, 2% Hispanic, 5% black, 1% Asian American or Pacific Islander, 1% international, 41% 25 or older, 33% live on campus, 10% transferred in. Retention: 72% of full-time freshmen returned the following year. Academic areas with the most degrees conferred: business/marketing; health professions and related sciences; education. Core. Calendar: semesters. Academic remediation for entering students, services for LD students, advanced placement, accelerated degree program, self-designed majors, honors program, independent study, distance learning, double major, summer session for credit, part-time degree program, external degree program, adult/continuing education programs, co-op programs and internships. Study abroad program. ROTC: Army.

Entrance Requirements: Options: Peterson's Universal Application, Common Application, electronic application, deferred admission. Required: high school transcript, SAT or ACT. Recommended: minimum 2.0 high school GPA, recommendations. Required for some: interview. Entrance: moderately difficult. Application deadline: Rolling. Notification: continuous until 8/15.

Costs Per Year: Application fee: $20. Comprehensive fee: $21,775 includes full-time tuition ($16,380), mandatory fees ($325), and college room and board ($5070). College room only: $3350. Full-time tuition and fees vary according to class time and program. Room and board charges vary according to board plan and housing facility. Part-time tuition: $280 per credit. Part-time mandatory fees: $80 per term. Part-time tuition and fees vary according to class time, course load, and program.

Collegiate Environment: Orientation program. Drama-theater group, choral group, student-run newspaper. Social organizations: 30 open to all; national fraternities, national sororities; 13% of eligible men and 11% of eligible women are members. Most popular organizations: Student Senate, Student Nurses Association, Student Education Association, Arts and Humanities Club, Music Performance Organization. Major annual events: Family

Weekend, Mardi Gras, Homecoming. Student services: health clinic, personal-psychological counseling. Campus security: 24-hour emergency response devices and patrols, student patrols, late night transport-escort service, controlled dormitory access. 445 college housing spaces available; 429 were occupied in 2003-04. Freshmen guaranteed college housing. On-campus residence required in freshman year. Option: coed housing available. Cardinal Meyer Library with 90,327 books, 14,978 microform titles, 737 serials, 913 audiovisual materials, an OPAC, and a Web page. Operations spending for 2004 fiscal year: $432,890. 225 computers available on campus for general student use. A campuswide network can be accessed from student residence rooms. Staffed computer lab on campus.

Community Environment: Marian College of Fond du Lac, Wisconsin (population 38,000) is located on the edge of the scenic Kettle Moraine region, the dominant glacial formation of Wisconsin. It is less than a mile from beautiful Lake Winnebago. The campus is easily reached by U.S. Highways 41, 45, and 151. There is efficient bus service from other cities and airports. Fond du Lac offers its own cultural attractions: a modern public library, churches, local community theaters, and the Civic Music Center. Students who wish to expand their cultural horizons may easily travel to the nearby cities of Green Bay, Madison, Milwaukee, or Oshkosh.

■ **MARQUETTE UNIVERSITY** *O-12*
PO Box 1881
Milwaukee, WI 53201-1881
Tel: (414)288-7250
Free: 800-222-6544
Admissions: (414)288-7004
E-mail: roby.blust@marquette.edu
Web Site: http://www.marquette.edu/

Description: Independent Roman Catholic (Jesuit), university, coed. Awards associate, bachelor's, master's, doctoral, and first professional degrees and post-master's certificates. Founded 1881. Setting: 80-acre urban campus. Endowment: $266.8 million. Research spending for 2004 fiscal year: $20.9 million. Total enrollment: 11,594. Faculty: 1,046 (592 full-time, 454 part-time). Student-undergrad faculty ratio is 15:1. 10,359 applied, 70% were admitted. 34% from top 10% of their high school class, 65% from top quarter, 94% from top half. 16 National Merit Scholars. Full-time: 7,530 students, 55% women, 45% men. Part-time: 480 students, 54% women, 46% men. Students come from 50 states and territories, 82 other countries, 52% from out-of-state, 0.3% Native American, 4% Hispanic, 5% black, 4% Asian American or Pacific Islander, 2% international, 6% 25 or older, 50% live on campus, 2% transferred in. Retention: 90% of full-time freshmen returned the following year. Academic areas with the most degrees conferred: business/marketing; communications/journalism; engineering. Core. Calendar: semesters. ESL program, services for LD students, advanced placement, honors program, double major, summer session for credit, part-time degree program, adult/continuing education programs, co-op programs and internships, graduate courses open to undergrads. Off campus study at Milwaukee Institute of Art and Design, Les Aspin Center for Government, Washington, DC. Study abroad program. ROTC: Army, Naval, Air Force.

Entrance Requirements: Options: Peterson's Universal Application, Common Application, electronic application, early admission, deferred admission, international baccalaureate accepted. Required: essay, high school transcript, minimum 2.5 high school GPA, 1 recommendation, SAT or ACT. Recommended: minimum 3.4 high school GPA. Entrance: moderately difficult. Application deadline: 12/1. Notification: 1/31.

Costs Per Year: Application fee: $30. Comprehensive fee: $33,234 includes full-time tuition ($24,670), mandatory fees ($404), and college room and board ($8160). College room only: $5304. Part-time tuition: $725 per credit. Part-time mandatory fees: $465 per credit.

Collegiate Environment: Orientation program. Drama-theater group, choral group, student-run newspaper, radio station. Social organizations: 180 open to all; national fraternities, national sororities; 5% of eligible men and 7% of eligible women are members. Most popular organizations: student government, club sports, community service organizations, band/jazz/orchestra, Residence Hall Association. Major annual events: Winter Flurry, Hunger Clean-Up, Midnight Madness Basketball Kick-Off. Student services: health clinic, personal-psychological counseling. Campus security: 24-hour emergency response devices and patrols, student patrols, late night transport-escort service, 24-hour desk attendants in residence halls. 4,404 college housing spaces available; 3,920 were occupied in 2003-04. On-campus residence required through sophomore year. Options: coed, men-only, women-only housing available. Raynor Memorial Libraries plus 1 other with 1.1 million books, 575,652 microform titles, 5,894 serials, 9,332

audiovisual materials, an OPAC, and a Web page. Operations spending for 2004 fiscal year: $13.8 million. 1,200 computers available on campus for general student use. Computer purchase/lease plans available. A campuswide network can be accessed from student residence rooms and from off campus. Staffed computer lab on campus.

Community Environment: Located in the heart of the city, students have access to a multitude of social, educational and cultural opportunities. Marquette's mission statement comes alive with the countless opportunities to volunteer. Whether it's tutoring elementary school students or building homes through Habitat for Humanity, Marquette students put the "community" in community service and have been nationally recognized for their efforts. The Milwaukee business district provides students with an excellent chance to network with professionals in their field, or to gain valuable experience through internships or part-time work. Theaters, concerts, and museums offer a fun and relaxing way to expand the college experience and the lakefront recreational area and downtown shopping provide students with a way to unwind after a week of classes.

■ **MID-STATE TECHNICAL COLLEGE** *K-8*
500 32nd St. North
Wisconsin Rapids, WI 54494-5599
Tel: (715)422-5300; 888-575-6782
Admissions: (715)422-5446
Fax: (715)422-5440
Web Site: http://www.mstc.edu/

Description: State and locally supported, 2-year, coed. Part of Wisconsin Technical College System. Awards certificates, diplomas, transfer associate, and terminal associate degrees. Founded 1917. Setting: 155-acre small town campus. Endowment: $1.2 million. Educational spending for 2005 fiscal year: $5646 per student. Total enrollment: 10,737. 1,100 applied, 95% were admitted. Students come from 2 states and territories, 1% out-of-state, 51% 25 or older. Core. Calendar: semesters. Academic remediation for entering students, ESL program, services for LD students, independent study, distance learning, double major, summer session for credit, part-time degree program, adult/continuing education programs, co-op programs and internships.

Entrance Requirements: Open admission. Options: electronic application, early admission, deferred admission. Required: high school transcript. Placement: ACT ASSET required; SAT or ACT recommended. Entrance: noncompetitive. Application deadline: Rolling. Notification: continuous.

Collegiate Environment: Student-run newspaper. Most popular organizations: Business Professionals of America, Civil Tech Club, Barber and Cosmetology Club, Society of Hosteurs, UICA. Major annual events: Tech Fest, Winter Fest. Student services: health clinic, personal-psychological counseling, women's center. College housing not available. Mid-State Technical College Library with 20,148 books, 910 microform titles, 539 serials, 2,685 audiovisual materials, and an OPAC. Operations spending for 2004 fiscal year: $274,887. 120 computers available on campus for general student use. A campuswide network can be accessed from off-campus. Staffed computer lab on campus.

Community Environment: The college serves the area which includes Mansfield (population 18,200), Stevens Point (population 23,996), and Wisconsin Rapids (population 18,587), the county seat of Wood, near the geographical center of the state of Wisconsin.

■ **MILWAUKEE AREA TECHNICAL COLLEGE** *O-12*
700 West State St.
Milwaukee, WI 53233-1443
Tel: (414)297-6600
Admissions: (414)297-6274
Fax: (414)297-7990
Web Site: http://matc.edu

Description: District-supported, 2-year, coed. Part of Wisconsin Technical College System. Awards certificates, diplomas, transfer associate, and terminal associate degrees. Founded 1912. Setting: urban campus. Total enrollment: 55,992. 10,500 applied, 100% were admitted. Core. Calendar: semesters. Academic remediation for entering students, ESL program, services for LD students, advanced placement, accelerated degree program, self-designed majors, freshman honors college, honors program, independent study, distance learning, double major, summer session for credit, part-time degree program, external degree program, adult/continuing education programs, co-op programs and internships. Off campus study.

Entrance Requirements: Open admission for students satisfying minimum degree requirements (students not meeting these requirements are placed in pre-program curricula). Options: Common Application, electronic application. Required: high school transcript, ACCUPLACER. Entrance: noncompetitive. Application deadline: Rolling. Notification: continuous until 8/20. Preference given to district residents.

Costs Per Year: Application fee: $30. State resident tuition: $2609 full-time. Nonresident tuition: $15,503 full-time. Mandatory fees: $262 full-time, $10 per credit part-time. Full-time tuition and fees vary according to course level and program. Part-time fees vary according to course level and program.

Collegiate Environment: Orientation program. Choral group, student-run newspaper. Student services: legal services, personal-psychological counseling, women's center. Campus security: 24-hour emergency response devices and patrols, student patrols, late night transport-escort service. College housing not available. William F. Rasche Library plus 4 others with 60,847 books, 856 serials, an OPAC, and a Web page. 1,000 computers available on campus for general student use. A campuswide network can be accessed. Staffed computer lab on campus.

Community Environment: Located on the west shore of Lake Michigan, Milwaukee (population 640,000) is the largest city in Wisconsin with all major forms of commercial transportation available. Milwaukee is the nation's brewing center, also a major grain market and manufacturing center. Products of industry are metal, machinery, food, leather, chemicals, textiles, electrical machinery, and other items. The city is headquarters of the Lake States National Forest Region. The county has a park system and many of the units contain public golf courses, tennis courts, and other recreational facilities. Milwaukee's State Fair is held each year in August.

■ **MILWAUKEE INSTITUTE OF ART AND DESIGN** *O-12*
273 East Erie St.
Milwaukee, WI 53202-6003
Tel: (414)276-7889; 888-749-MIAD
Admissions: (414)847-3259
Fax: (414)291-8077
Web Site: http://www.miad.edu/

Description: Independent, 4-year, coed. Awards bachelor's degrees. Founded 1974. Setting: urban campus. Endowment: $2.6 million. Educational spending for 2005 fiscal year: $7500 per student. Total enrollment: 645. Student-undergrad faculty ratio is 10:1. 308 applied, 82% were admitted. 8% from top 10% of their high school class, 21% from top quarter, 48% from top half. Full-time: 606 students, 47% women, 53% men. Part-time: 39 students, 49% women, 51% men. Students come from 17 states and territories, 6 other countries, 35% from out-of-state, 1% Native American, 7% Hispanic, 3% black, 6% Asian American or Pacific Islander, 0.2% international, 10% 25 or older, 23% live on campus, 8% transferred in. Retention: 73% of full-time freshmen returned the following year. Academic area with the most degrees conferred: visual and performing arts. Core. Calendar: semesters. Academic remediation for entering students, services for LD students, advanced placement, independent study, double major, summer session for credit, adult/continuing education programs, co-op programs and internships. Off campus study at Marquette University, Association of Independent Colleges of Art and Design. Study abroad program.

Entrance Requirements: Options: Common Application, electronic application, deferred admission. Required: essay, high school transcript, interview, portfolio. Recommended: minimum 2.0 high school GPA. Required for some: recommendations. Entrance: moderately difficult. Application deadline: Rolling.

Costs Per Year: Application fee: $25. Comprehensive fee: $30,400 includes full-time tuition ($23,100), mandatory fees ($300), and college room and board ($7000). Part-time tuition: $770 per credit hour.

Collegiate Environment: Orientation program. Drama-theater group. Social organizations: 6 open to all. Most popular organizations: student government, Student Gallery Committee, Student Activities Committee, Minority Student Organization, community service. Major annual events: All Student Show-Exhibition, Senior Exhibition, Scholarship Show. Student services: health clinic, personal-psychological counseling. Campus security: 24-hour emergency response devices, late night transport-escort service. 165 college housing spaces available; all were occupied in 2003-04. Freshmen given priority for college housing. On-campus residence required in freshman year. Option: coed housing available. 23,000 books, 84 serials, 360 audiovisual materials, an OPAC, and a Web page. Operations spending for

2004 fiscal year: $145,227. 130 computers available on campus for general student use. A campuswide network can be accessed. Staffed computer lab on campus.

■ **MILWAUKEE SCHOOL OF ENGINEERING** *O-12*
1025 North Broadway
Milwaukee, WI 53202-3109
Tel: (414)277-7300
Free: 800-332-6763
Admissions: (414)277-6765
Fax: (414)277-7475
E-mail: explore@msoe.edu
Web Site: http://www.msoe.edu/

Description: Independent, comprehensive, coed. Awards bachelor's and master's degrees. Founded 1903. Setting: 15-acre urban campus. Endowment: $54.6 million. Research spending for 2004 fiscal year: $2.9 million. Educational spending for 2005 fiscal year: $11,152 per student. Total enrollment: 2,315. Faculty: 214 (120 full-time, 94 part-time). Student-undergrad faculty ratio is 12:1. 1,742 applied, 69% were admitted. Full-time: 1,819 students, 18% women, 82% men. Part-time: 273 students, 15% women, 85% men. Students come from 27 states and territories, 19 other countries, 29% from out-of-state, 1% Native American, 3% Hispanic, 4% black, 3% Asian American or Pacific Islander, 2% international, 10% 25 or older, 52% live on campus, 7% transferred in. Retention: 81% of full-time freshmen returned the following year. Academic areas with the most degrees conferred: engineering; business/marketing; engineering technologies. Core. Academic remediation for entering students, ESL program, services for LD students, advanced placement, accelerated degree program, independent study, distance learning, double major, summer session for credit, part-time degree program, adult/continuing education programs, internships, graduate courses open to undergrads. Study abroad program. ROTC: Army (c), Naval (c), Air Force (c).

Entrance Requirements: Options: Peterson's Universal Application, Common Application, electronic application, deferred admission. Required: high school transcript, minimum 2.5 high school GPA, SAT or ACT. Required for some: essay, interview. Entrance: moderately difficult. Application deadline: Rolling. Notification: continuous.

Costs Per Year: Application fee: $25. Comprehensive fee: $31,149 includes full-time tuition ($24,960) and college room and board ($6189). College room only: $3969. Part-time tuition: $432 per quarter hour.

Collegiate Environment: Orientation program. Drama-theater group, choral group, student-run newspaper, radio station. Social organizations: 61 open to all; national fraternities, national sororities, local fraternities, local sororities; 3% of eligible men and 5% of eligible women are members. Most popular organizations: Architectural Engineering and Construction Management Societies, Student Athletic Advisory Committee, MAGE, Student Government. Major annual events: Homecoming Week, St. Patrick's Week, Greek Week. Student services: health clinic, personal-psychological counseling. Campus security: 24-hour emergency response devices and patrols, late night transport-escort service, controlled dormitory access. 927 college housing spaces available; 827 were occupied in 2003-04. Freshmen guaranteed college housing. On-campus residence required through sophomore year. Option: coed housing available. Walter Schroeder Library with 59,564 books, 79,054 microform titles, 585 serials, 1,428 audiovisual materials, an OPAC, and a Web page. Operations spending for 2004 fiscal year: $548,207. 125 computers available on campus for general student use. Computer purchase/lease plans available. A campuswide network can be accessed from student residence rooms and from off campus. Staffed computer lab on campus.

Community Environment: See Milwaukee Area Technical College.

■ **MORAINE PARK TECHNICAL COLLEGE** *M-11*
235 North National Ave, PO Box 1940
Fond du Lac, WI 54936-1940
Tel: (920)922-8611
Admissions: (920)929-2126
Fax: (920)924-2471
Web Site: http://www.morainepark.edu/

Description: State and locally supported, 2-year, coed. Part of Wisconsin Technical College System. Awards certificates, diplomas, transfer associate, and terminal associate degrees. Founded 1967. Setting: 40-acre small town campus with easy access to Milwaukee. Educational spending for 2005 fiscal year: $6948 per student. Total enrollment: 7,509. Full-time: 1,197 students, 62% women, 38% men. Part-time: 6,312 students, 55% women,

45% men. Students come from 5 states and territories, 1% from out-of-state, 1% Native American, 2% Hispanic, 4% black, 1% Asian American or Pacific Islander, 0% international, 51% 25 or older, 0.4% transferred in. Core. Calendar: semesters. Academic remediation for entering students, ESL program, advanced placement, accelerated degree program, independent study, distance learning, summer session for credit, part-time degree program, external degree program, adult/continuing education programs, internships.

Entrance Requirements: Open admission. Options: electronic application, deferred admission. Required: interview, ACT ASSET, ACCUPLACER. Recommended: high school transcript. Required for some: ACT. Entrance: noncompetitive. Application deadline: Rolling. Notification: continuous.

Costs Per Year: Application fee: $30. State resident tuition: $2610 full-time, $87 per credit part-time. Nonresident tuition: $16,089 full-time, $536.30 per credit part-time. Mandatory fees: $250 full-time, $8.35 per credit part-time.

Collegiate Environment: Orientation program. Social organizations: 24 open to all. Most popular organizations: Student Programming Board, student government, Corrections Club, HVAC Club, Food Service Executives. Major annual events: student and staff welcome back picnic, Spring Fling. Student services: personal-psychological counseling. Campus security: 24-hour emergency response devices. College housing not available. Moraine Park Technical College Library/Learning Resource Center with 32,166 books, 630 serials, 13,330 audiovisual materials, an OPAC, and a Web page. Operations spending for 2004 fiscal year: $560,730.

Community Environment: See Marian College of Fond du Lac.

■ **MOUNT MARY COLLEGE** *O-12*
2900 North Menomonee River Parkway
Milwaukee, WI 53222-4597
Tel: (414)258-4810
Fax: (414)256-1224
E-mail: admiss@mtmary.edu
Web Site: http://www.mtmary.edu/

Description: Independent Roman Catholic, comprehensive. Awards bachelor's and master's degrees. Founded 1913. Setting: 80-acre urban campus. Endowment: $10.1 million. Educational spending for 2005 fiscal year: $5057 per student. Total enrollment: 1,722. Faculty: 198 (64 full-time, 134 part-time). Student-undergrad faculty ratio is 9:1. 438 applied. 22% from top 10% of their high school class, 50% from top quarter, 80% from top half. Students come from 8 states and territories, 9 other countries, 3% from out-of-state, 1% Native American, 6% Hispanic, 18% black, 4% Asian American or Pacific Islander, 1% international, 43% 25 or older, 10% live on campus. Retention: 65% of full-time freshmen returned the following year. Academic areas with the most degrees conferred: health professions and related sciences; visual and performing arts; business/marketing. Core. Calendar: semesters. Academic remediation for entering students, services for LD students, advanced placement, accelerated degree program, self-designed majors, honors program, independent study, double major, summer session for credit, part-time degree program, adult/continuing education programs, internships, graduate courses open to undergrads. Study abroad program. ROTC: Army (c).

Entrance Requirements: Options: Peterson's Universal Application, Common Application, electronic application, deferred admission, international baccalaureate accepted. Required: high school transcript, minimum 2.5 high school GPA, SAT or ACT. Recommended: interview. Required for some: essay, 2 recommendations. Entrance: moderately difficult. Application deadline: Rolling. Notification: continuous.

Costs Per Year: Application fee: $25. Comprehensive fee: $22,895 includes full-time tuition ($16,925), mandatory fees ($180), and college room and board ($5790). Room and board charges vary according to board plan. Part-time tuition: $466 per credit. Part-time mandatory fees: $45 per term. Part-time tuition and fees vary according to course load.

Collegiate Environment: Orientation program. Drama-theater group, choral group, student-run newspaper. Social organizations: 38 open to all. Most popular organizations: department-affiliated clubs, Campus Ministry, student athletics, student government. Major annual events: Investiture, Christmas Madrigal Dinner, All-School Picnic. Student services: health clinic, personal-psychological counseling, women's center. Campus security: 24-hour patrols, late night transport-escort service, controlled dormitory access. 200 college housing spaces available; 145 were occupied in 2003-04. Freshmen guaranteed college housing. Option: women-only housing available. Haggerty Library with 654,128 books, 4,000 microform titles, 165 serials, 8,262 audiovisual materials, an OPAC, and a Web page. Operations spending for 2004 fiscal year: $502,954. 170 computers available on campus for

general student use. A campuswide network can be accessed from student residence rooms and from off campus. Staffed computer lab on campus.

Community Environment: Mount Mary is one of 5 private colleges in Milwaukee. The campus is located on the northwest side of the city, about 15 minutes from the downtown area. It is within walking distance of a shopping mall and restaurants. The city of Milwaukee boasts a major symphony, well-respected dance companies, a beautiful lakefront art museum, and a fine natural history museum. Three professional sports divide the Milwaukee seasons. It is also the ideal site in which to explore various career options.

■ **NICOLET AREA TECHNICAL COLLEGE** *G-9*
Box 518
Rhinelander, WI 54501-0518
Tel: (715)365-4410
Admissions: (715)365-4451
Fax: (715)365-4445
E-mail: inquire@nicolet.tec.wi.us
Web Site: http://www.nicoletcollege.edu/

Description: State and locally supported, 2-year, coed. Part of Wisconsin Technical College System. Awards certificates, diplomas, transfer associate, and terminal associate degrees. Founded 1968. Setting: 280-acre rural campus. Total enrollment: 1,945. Students come from 8 states and territories, 2 other countries, 64% 25 or older. Core. Calendar: semesters. Academic remediation for entering students, ESL program, services for LD students, advanced placement, self-designed majors, independent study, distance learning, summer session for credit, part-time degree program, adult/continuing education programs, co-op programs and internships. Study abroad program.

Entrance Requirements: Open admission except for nursing program. Options: electronic application, early admission. Required: essay, high school transcript, minimum 2.0 high school GPA. Recommended: ACT. Entrance: noncompetitive. Application deadline: Rolling. Notification: continuous. Preference given to district residents.

Costs Per Year: Application fee: $25. State resident tuition: $3491 full-time, $109.10 per credit part-time. Nonresident tuition: $9995 full-time, $312.35 per credit part-time. Full-time tuition varies according to course level, degree level, and reciprocity agreements. Part-time tuition varies according to course level, degree level, and reciprocity agreements.

Collegiate Environment: Orientation program. Drama-theater group, student-run newspaper. Student services: personal-psychological counseling, women's center. Campus security: 24-hour emergency response devices. College housing not available. Richard Brown Library with 38,369 books, 598 serials, and an OPAC. 100 computers available on campus for general student use. A campuswide network can be accessed from off-campus. Staffed computer lab on campus.

Community Environment: The county seat for Oneida County, Rhinelander (population 8,218) is a summer and winter resort, located in the most concentrated lake area of the Middle West. Rhinelander has one of the largest paper mills under one roof in America. All commercial transportation is available. Parks and many lakes and trout streams and rivers provide facilities for all water sports and fishing. The Logging Museum is a reproduction of a logging camp with living quarters. Also on display is a narrow gauge engine built in 1879.

■ **NORTHCENTRAL TECHNICAL COLLEGE** *J-8*
1000 West Campus Dr.
Wausau, WI 54401-1899
Tel: (715)675-3331
Fax: (715)675-9776
Web Site: http://www.ntc.edu/

Description: District-supported, 2-year, coed. Part of Wisconsin Technical College System. Awards certificates, diplomas, transfer associate, and terminal associate degrees. Founded 1912. Setting: 96-acre rural campus. Endowment: $1.4 million. Research spending for 2004 fiscal year: $93,000. Educational spending for 2005 fiscal year: $5126 per student. Total enrollment: 3,734. Full-time: 1,276 students, 54% women, 46% men. Part-time: 2,458 students, 64% women, 36% men. Students come from 3 states and territories, 2 other countries, 1% from out-of-state, 1% Native American, 1% Hispanic, 0.1% black, 2% Asian American or Pacific Islander, 1% international, 65% 25 or older, 4% transferred in. Calendar: semesters. Academic remediation for entering students, ESL program, services for LD students, advanced placement, self-designed majors, independent study, distance learning, double major, summer session for credit, part-time degree program, adult/continuing education programs, internships.

Entrance Requirements: Open admission except for technical nursing, dental hygiene programs. Options: Common Application, electronic application, early admission, deferred admission. Required: high school transcript. Required for some: interview. Placement: ACCUPLACER required for some. Entrance: noncompetitive. Application deadline: Rolling. Notification: continuous. Preference given to district residents.

Costs Per Year: Application fee: $25. State resident tuition: $2415 full-time, $80.50 per credit part-time. Nonresident tuition: $15,309 full-time, $510.30 per credit part-time. Mandatory fees: $392 full-time, $8.20 per credit part-time. Full-time tuition and fees vary according to course level, course load, and program. Part-time tuition and fees vary according to course level, course load, and program. College room and board: $3952. Room and board charges vary according to board plan.

Collegiate Environment: Student-run newspaper. Social organizations: 3 open to all. Most popular organizations: Student Governing Board, International Club, Habitat for Humanity, Nursing Club, Delta Epsilon Chi (marketing club). Major annual events: Sno-Fest (winter carnival), Career Week, Spring Fling. Student services: health clinic, personal-psychological counseling, women's center. Campus security: 24-hour emergency response devices, late night transport-escort service. Northcentral Technical College, Wausau Campus plus 1 other with 30,000 books, 400 serials, an OPAC, and a Web page. Operations spending for 2004 fiscal year: $260,878. 1,200 computers available on campus for general student use. A campuswide network can be accessed from off-campus. Staffed computer lab on campus.

Community Environment: The Wausau area (population 70,000) is one of the major industrial centers in the state. Over 70 highly diversified industries are located here, producing over 40 different products. The area is one of the nation's leading producers of cheddar cheese, and it is a major center of dairy farming in both the state and nation and a leading exporter of ginseng. The community offers many cultural and recreational programs plus an excellent public school system. The school works closely with the branch campus of the University of Wisconsin to maximize use of facilities and programs and to eliminate duplication.

■ **NORTHEAST WISCONSIN TECHNICAL COLLEGE** *K-12*

2740 W Mason St., PO Box 19042

Green Bay, WI 54307-9042

Tel: (920)498-5400

Free: 800-422-6982

Admissions: (920)498-5425

Web Site: http://www.nwtc.edu/

Description: State and locally supported, 2-year, coed. Part of Wisconsin Technical College System. Awards certificates, diplomas, and terminal associate degrees. Founded 1913. Setting: 192-acre suburban campus. Educational spending for 2005 fiscal year: $7150 per student. Total enrollment: 8,760. 4,258 applied, 46% were admitted. Full-time: 3,001 students, 53% women, 47% men. Part-time: 5,759 students, 63% women, 37% men. Students come from 3 states and territories, 89% from out-of-state, 3% Native American, 1% Hispanic, 1% black, 1% Asian American or Pacific Islander, 0% international, 55% 25 or older. Core. Calendar: semesters. Academic remediation for entering students, ESL program, services for LD students, advanced placement, accelerated degree program, self-designed majors, distance learning, summer session for credit, part-time degree program, adult/continuing education programs.

Entrance Requirements: Option: early admission. Required for some: high school transcript. Entrance: minimally difficult. Application deadline: Rolling. Preference given to state residents.

Collegiate Environment: Social organizations: 33 open to all. Most popular organizations: Skills USA, Wisconsin Marketing Management Association, Business Professionals of America, Auto Club, Architectural Club. Major annual events: graduation ceremonies, academic awards, on-campus entertainment. Student services: health clinic, personal-psychological counseling. Campus security: 24-hour emergency response devices, late night transport-escort service. College housing not available. 22,250 books and 450 serials. Operations spending for 2004 fiscal year: $547,150. 395 computers available on campus for general student use. Staffed computer lab on campus.

Community Environment: Green Bay, population 92,000 and the oldest permanent settlement in Wisconsin, is in an important harbor for the Great Lakes-St. Lawrence Seaway System. Industries in the area include shipping, cheese producing, paper, and jobbers wholesale and distribution. Points of interest are the Bay Beach Park, Heritage Hill Park, Neville Public Museum, Cotton House, Fort Howard Hospital Museum, Lambeau Stadium, National Railroad Museum, Tank Cottage, and the Green Bay Packer Hall of Fame.

■ **NORTHLAND COLLEGE** *D-5*

1411 Ellis Ave.

Ashland, WI 54806-3925

Tel: (715)682-1699

Free: 800-753-1040

Admissions: (715)682-1224

Fax: (715)682-1258

E-mail: admit@wakefield.northland.edu

Web Site: http://www.northland.edu/

Description: Independent, 4-year, coed, affiliated with United Church of Christ. Awards bachelor's degrees. Founded 1892. Setting: 130-acre small town campus. Endowment: $19 million. Educational spending for 2005 fiscal year: $5533 per student. Total enrollment: 739. Student-undergrad faculty ratio is 13:1. 804 applied, 75% were admitted. 26% from top 10% of their high school class, 50% from top quarter, 78% from top half. 1 valedictorian. Full-time: 649 students, 56% women, 44% men. Part-time: 90 students, 70% women, 30% men. Students come from 44 states and territories, 7 other countries, 67% from out-of-state, 3% Native American, 2% Hispanic, 2% black, 1% Asian American or Pacific Islander, 1% international, 12% 25 or older, 60% live on campus, 8% transferred in. Retention: 86% of full-time freshmen returned the following year. Academic areas with the most degrees conferred: education; natural resources/environmental science; business/marketing. Core. Calendar: 4-4-1. Services for LD students, advanced placement, accelerated degree program, self-designed majors, honors program, independent study, distance learning, double major, summer session for credit, part-time degree program, adult/continuing education programs, co-op programs and internships. Off campus study at members of the May Term Consortium, Allegheny College, Beloit College, Ecoleaglue. Study abroad program.

Entrance Requirements: Options: Common Application, electronic application, early admission, deferred admission, international baccalaureate accepted. Required: essay, high school transcript, 1 recommendation, SAT or ACT. Recommended: minimum 2.0 high school GPA, interview. Entrance: moderately difficult. Application deadline: 5/1. Notification: continuous.

Costs Per Year: Application fee: $0. Comprehensive fee: $26,680 includes full-time tuition ($20,188), mandatory fees ($601), and college room and board ($5891). College room only: $2384. Part-time tuition: $390 per credit.

Collegiate Environment: Orientation program. Drama-theater group, choral group, student-run newspaper, radio station. Social organizations: 36 open to all; local sororities. Most popular organizations: Psi Chi, the National Honor Society in Psychology, Northland College Student Association, Native American Student Association, Northland Greens, 'N' Club. Major annual events: Book Across the Bay, Snow Fest, Spring Fling. Student services: health clinic, personal-psychological counseling, women's center. Campus security: 24-hour emergency response devices, controlled dormitory access. 580 college housing spaces available; 436 were occupied in 2003-04. Freshmen guaranteed college housing. On-campus residence required through sophomore year. Options: coed, men-only, women-only housing available. Dexter Library with 75,000 books, 260 serials, and an OPAC. Operations spending for 2004 fiscal year: $250,842. 120 computers available on campus for general student use. A campuswide network can be accessed from student residence rooms and from off campus. Staffed computer lab on campus.

Community Environment: Ashland (population 9,615) is located on Lake Superior near the Chequamegon National Forest.

■ **RIPON COLLEGE** *M-10*

300 Seward St., PO Box 248

Ripon, WI 54971

Tel: (920)748-8115

Free: 800-947-4766

Admissions: (920)748-8185

Fax: (920)748-7243

E-mail: adminfo@ripon.edu

Web Site: http://www.ripon.edu/

Description: Independent, 4-year, coed. Awards bachelor's degrees. Founded 1851. Setting: 250-acre small town campus with easy access to Milwaukee. Endowment: $46.6 million. Research spending for 2004 fiscal year: $61,659. Educational spending for 2005 fiscal year: $9249 per student. Total enrollment: 979. Student-undergrad faculty ratio is 13:1. 976 applied, 81% were admitted. 23% from top 10% of their high school class, 50% from top quarter, 87% from top half. Full-time: 953 students, 50% women, 50% men. Part-time: 26 students, 65% women, 35% men. Students come from 35 states and territories, 13 other countries, 25% from out-of-state, 1% Native American, 2% Hispanic, 3% black, 2% Asian American or Pacific Islander, 2% international, 1% 25 or older, 90% live on campus, 3% transferred in. Retention: 84% of full-time freshmen returned the following year. Academic areas with the most degrees conferred: education; social sciences; biological/life sciences. Core. Calendar: semesters. Services for LD students, advanced placement, accelerated degree program, self-designed majors, double major, part-time degree program, internships. Off campus study at American University, Newberry Library, Oak Ridge National Laboratory, University of Chicago, Associated Colleges of the Midwest Wilderness Field Station. Study abroad program. ROTC: Army.

Entrance Requirements: Options: Peterson's Universal Application, Common Application, electronic application, deferred admission. Required: essay, high school transcript, minimum 2.0 high school GPA, 1 recommendation, SAT or ACT. Recommended: interview. Entrance: moderately difficult. Application deadline: Rolling. Notification: continuous.

Costs Per Year: Application fee: $30. Comprehensive fee: $28,497 includes full-time tuition ($22,162), mandatory fees ($275), and college room and board ($6060). College room only: $3030. Part-time tuition: $890 per credit.

Collegiate Environment: Orientation program. Drama-theater group, choral group, student-run newspaper, radio station. Social organizations: 45 open to all; national fraternities, national sororities, local fraternities, local sororities; 27% of eligible men and 16% of eligible women are members. Most popular organizations: Environmental Group, Student Senate, Community Service Coalition, SMAC (Student Media and Activities Committee). Major annual events: Springfest, Winterfest, Frisbee Golf Tournament. Student services: health clinic, personal-psychological counseling. Campus security: 24-hour emergency response devices and patrols, student patrols, late night transport-escort service, controlled dormitory access. 944 college housing spaces available; 740 were occupied in 2003-04. Freshmen guaranteed college housing. On-campus residence required through senior year. Options: coed, men-only, women-only housing available. Lane Library with 163,615 books, 23,820 microform titles, 939 serials, 376 audiovisual materials, an OPAC, and a Web page. Operations spending for 2004 fiscal year: $356,195. 150 computers available on campus for general student use. A campuswide network can be accessed from student residence rooms and from off campus. Staffed computer lab on campus.

Community Environment: Students who select Ripon seek a small-town community and enjoy the recreational opportunities of Green Lake. In east central Wisconsin, the town is a one and one-half hour drive to Madison and Milwaukee, and 3 hours from Chicago. Various community groups encourage student participation in service-oriented activities.

■ **ST. NORBERT COLLEGE** *K-12*
100 Grant St.
De Pere, WI 54115-2099
Tel: (920)337-3181
Free: 800-236-4878
Admissions: (920)403-3005
Fax: (920)403-4088
E-mail: admit@snc.edu
Web Site: http://www.snc.edu/

Description: Independent Roman Catholic, comprehensive, coed. Awards bachelor's and master's degrees. Founded 1898. Setting: 92-acre suburban campus. Endowment: $52.6 million. Research spending for 2004 fiscal year: $588,974. Educational spending for 2005 fiscal year: $6601 per student. Total enrollment: 2,050. Faculty: 177 (109 full-time, 68 part-time). Student-undergrad faculty ratio is 14:1. 1,683 applied, 86% were admitted. 27% from top 10% of their high school class, 56% from top quarter, 90% from top half. 4 National Merit Scholars, 15 class presidents, 14 valedictorians. Full-time: 1,922 students, 57% women, 43% men. Part-time: 65 students, 54% women, 46% men. Students come from 26 states and territories, 21 other countries, 27% from out-of-state, 1% Native American, 2% Hispanic, 1% black, 1% Asian American or Pacific Islander, 2% international, 4% 25 or older, 75% live on campus, 2% transferred in. Retention: 88% of full-time freshmen returned the following year. Academic areas with the most degrees conferred: business/marketing; education; communications/journalism. Core. Calendar: semesters. Academic remediation for entering students, ESL program, services for LD students, advanced placement, self-designed majors, honors program, independent study, distance learning, double major, summer session for credit, part-time degree program, internships. Off campus study at Higher Education Consortium for Urban Affairs, American University. Study abroad program. ROTC: Army.

Entrance Requirements: Options: Peterson's Universal Application, Common Application, electronic application, early admission, early decision,

deferred admission, international baccalaureate accepted. Required: essay, high school transcript, 1 recommendation, SAT or ACT. Required for some: interview. Entrance: moderately difficult. Application deadlines: Rolling, 12/1 for early decision. Notification: continuous, 12/15 for early decision. Preference given to children of alumni, siblings of current or former students, dependents of employees.

Costs Per Year: Application fee: $25. Comprehensive fee: $28,577 includes full-time tuition ($22,209), mandatory fees ($300), and college room and board ($6068). College room only: $3212. Full-time tuition and fees vary according to course load. Room and board charges vary according to board plan, housing facility, and student level. Part-time tuition: $694 per credit. Part-time tuition varies according to course load.

Collegiate Environment: Orientation program. Drama-theater group, choral group, student-run newspaper, radio station. Social organizations: 70 open to all; national fraternities, national sororities, local fraternities, local sororities; 9% of eligible men and 13% of eligible women are members. Most popular organizations: Yes Your Entertainment Service, Student Government Association, Residence Hall Association. Major annual events: Homecoming, Family Weekend/Fall Fest, holiday dinner in dining room. Student services: health clinic, personal-psychological counseling, women's center. Campus security: 24-hour emergency response devices and patrols, student patrols, late night transport-escort service, controlled dormitory access, crime prevention programs. 1,525 college housing spaces available; 1,488 were occupied in 2003-04. Freshmen guaranteed college housing. On-campus residence required through senior year. Options: coed, women-only housing available. Todd Wehr Library with 217,248 books, 29,318 microform titles, 648 serials, 6,411 audiovisual materials, an OPAC, and a Web page. Operations spending for 2004 fiscal year: $917,276. 219 computers available on campus for general student use. Computer purchase/lease plans available. A campuswide network can be accessed from student residence rooms and from off campus. Staffed computer lab on campus.

■ **SILVER LAKE COLLEGE** *L-13*
2406 South Alverno Rd.
Manitowoc, WI 54220-9319
Tel: (920)684-6691
Admissions: (920)686-6208
Fax: (920)684-7082
E-mail: admslc@sl.edu
Web Site: http://www.sl.edu/

Description: Independent Roman Catholic, comprehensive, coed. Awards associate, bachelor's, and master's degrees. Founded 1869. Setting: 30-acre rural campus with easy access to Milwaukee. Endowment: $5.1 million. Educational spending for 2005 fiscal year: $5109 per student. Total enrollment: 913. Faculty: 168 (42 full-time, 126 part-time). Student-undergrad faculty ratio is 9:1. 102 applied, 83% were admitted. 3% from top 10% of their high school class, 23% from top quarter, 24% from top half. Full-time: 214 students, 80% women, 20% men. Part-time: 415 students, 70% women, 30% men. Students come from 4 states and territories, 1 other country, 4% from out-of-state, 4% Native American, 1% Hispanic, 0.2% black, 0.5% Asian American or Pacific Islander, 0.2% international, 65% 25 or older, 3% live on campus, 10% transferred in. Retention: 66% of full-time freshmen returned the following year. Academic areas with the most degrees conferred: business/marketing; education; psychology. Core. Calendar: semesters. Academic remediation for entering students, ESL program, advanced placement, accelerated degree program, self-designed majors, independent study, distance learning, double major, summer session for credit, part-time degree program, adult/continuing education programs, co-op programs and internships, graduate courses open to undergrads.

Entrance Requirements: Options: electronic application, early admission, deferred admission. Required: high school transcript, minimum 2.0 high school GPA, SAT or ACT. Required for some: interview, audition. Entrance: minimally difficult. Application deadline: 8/31. Notification: continuous.

Costs Per Year: Application fee: $35. Tuition: $17,108 full-time, $525 per credit part-time. College room only: $4400.

Collegiate Environment: Orientation program. Choral group, student-run newspaper. Social organizations: 12 open to all. Most popular organizations: Campus Ministry projects, education-related clubs. Major annual events: Martin Luther King Day events, School liturgies, Student Forum meetings. Student services: personal-psychological counseling. Campus security: 24-hour emergency response devices. 32 college housing spaces available; 28 were occupied in 2003-04. Freshmen given priority for college housing. On-campus residence required in freshman year. Options: men-only, women-only housing available. The Erma M. and Theodore M. Zigmunt Library with

60,466 books, 2,161 microform titles, 301 serials, 11,501 audiovisual materials, and an OPAC. Operations spending for 2004 fiscal year: $156,307. 50 computers available on campus for general student use. A campuswide network can be accessed from off-campus. Staffed computer lab on campus.
Community Environment: The communities of Manitowoc and Two Rivers were founded in 1838 and are located on the shore of Lake Michigan with convenient access to major Wisconsin cities. This industrial and tourism-based community has 37 churches, 3 modern hospitals, museums, and numerous parks and recreation areas.

■ **SOUTHWEST WISCONSIN TECHNICAL COLLEGE** *P-6*
1800 Bronson Blvd.
Fennimore, WI 53809-9778
Tel: (608)822-3262
Fax: (608)822-6019
Web Site: http://www.swtc.edu/
Description: State and locally supported, 2-year, coed. Part of Wisconsin Technical College System. Awards certificates, diplomas, and terminal associate degrees. Founded 1967. Setting: 53-acre rural campus. Endowment: $935,000. Research spending for 2004 fiscal year: $112,925. Educational spending for 2005 fiscal year: $7055 per student. Total enrollment: 1,861. Full-time: 778 students, 49% women, 51% men. Part-time: 1,083 students, 54% women, 46% men. Students come from 4 states and territories, 1% from out-of-state, 0.3% Native American, 1% Hispanic, 1% black, 1% Asian American or Pacific Islander, 0% international, 29% 25 or older, 3% live on campus. Calendar: semesters. Academic remediation for entering students, ESL program, services for LD students, advanced placement, self-designed majors, distance learning, double major, summer session for credit, part-time degree program, adult/continuing education programs, internships.
Entrance Requirements: Open admission except for nursing program. Options: electronic application, early admission. Required: high school transcript, interview. Placement: TABE required. Entrance: noncompetitive. Application deadline: Rolling. Preference given to district residents.
Collegiate Environment: Orientation program. Student-run newspaper. Social organizations: 7 open to all. Most popular organizations: Business Professionals of America, Vocational Industrial Clubs of America, Health Occupations Students of America, Marketing and Management Association. Student services: health clinic, personal-psychological counseling, women's center. 62 college housing spaces available; all were occupied in 2003-04. Option: coed housing available. Southwest Technical College Library plus 1 other with 25,000 books, 60 microform titles, 307 serials, 5,000 audiovisual materials, and an OPAC. Operations spending for 2004 fiscal year: $141,025. 250 computers available on campus for general student use. A campuswide network can be accessed from off-campus. Staffed computer lab on campus.

■ **UNIVERSITY OF PHOENIX-WISCONSIN CAMPUS** *O-12*
20075 Watertower Blvd.
Brookfield, WI 53045-6608
Tel: (262)785-0608
Free: 800-228-7240
Admissions: (480)557-1712
Fax: (262)785-0608
Web Site: http://www.phoenix.edu/
Description: Proprietary, comprehensive, coed. Awards bachelor's and master's degrees. Founded 2001. Setting: urban campus. Total enrollment: 1,357. Faculty: 217 (8 full-time, 209 part-time). Student-undergrad faculty ratio is 5:1. 59 applied. Full-time: 1,067 students, 59% women, 41% men. 0% from out-of-state, 0.4% Native American, 1% Hispanic, 5% black, 0.4% Asian American or Pacific Islander, 5% international, 90% 25 or older. Academic areas with the most degrees conferred: business/marketing; computer and information sciences. Core. Calendar: continuous. Advanced placement, accelerated degree program, independent study, distance learning, external degree program, adult/continuing education programs, graduate courses open to undergrads.
Entrance Requirements: Open admission. Option: deferred admission. Required: 1 recommendation. Required for some: high school transcript. Entrance: noncompetitive. Application deadline: Rolling.
Costs Per Year: Application fee: $110. Tuition: $10,785 full-time, $359.50 per credit part-time. Mandatory fees: $560 full-time, $70 per course part-time.
Collegiate Environment: College housing not available. University Library with 444 books, 666 serials, an OPAC, and a Web page. System-wide operations spending for 2004 fiscal year: $3.2 million.

■ **UNIVERSITY OF WISCONSIN-BARABOO/SAUK COUNTY** *N-8*
1006 Connie Rd.
Baraboo, WI 53913-1015
Tel: (608)356-8351
Admissions: (608)355-5255
Fax: (608)356-4074
E-mail: booinfo@uwc.edu
Web Site: http://www.baraboo.uwc.edu/
Description: State-supported, 2-year, coed. Part of University of Wisconsin System. Awards certificates, transfer associate, and terminal associate degrees. Founded 1968. Setting: 68-acre small town campus. Total enrollment: 548. Student-undergrad faculty ratio is 16:1. 8% from top 10% of their high school class, 31% from top quarter, 67% from top half. Students come from 3 states and territories, 3 other countries, 1% from out-of-state, 1% Native American, 2% Hispanic, 0.4% black, 1% Asian American or Pacific Islander, 0% international, 19% 25 or older. Core. Calendar: semesters. Academic remediation for entering students, services for LD students, advanced placement, self-designed majors, honors program, independent study, distance learning, summer session for credit, part-time degree program, external degree program, internships. Off campus study at other units of the University of Wisconsin Colleges, four-year campuses of the University of Wisconsin and University of Wisconsin Extension, also UW Colleges distance learning, University of Plymouth Colleges, England. Study abroad program.
Entrance Requirements: Options: electronic application, early admission, deferred admission. Required: high school transcript, SAT or ACT. Recommended: ACT. Required for some: interview. Entrance: moderately difficult. Application deadline: Rolling. Notification: continuous until 8/31. Preference given to racial minorities.
Costs Per Year: Application fee: $35. State resident tuition: $4296 full-time, $180.85 per credit part-time. Nonresident tuition: $12,992 full-time, $543.35 per credit part-time. Part-time tuition varies according to course load.
Collegiate Environment: Orientation program. Drama-theater group, choral group, student-run newspaper. Social organizations: 10 open to all. Most popular organizations: Student Government Association, chorus and band, dance team, Gaming Club, Business Club. Major annual events: Boo Bash, Welcome Picnic, Packer parties/bonfires. Student services: personal-psychological counseling. College housing not available. T. N. Savides Library with 45,000 books, 52 microform titles, 300 serials, 940 audiovisual materials, and an OPAC. Operations spending for 2004 fiscal year: $120,000. 50 computers available on campus for general student use. A campuswide network can be accessed from off-campus. Staffed computer lab on campus.

■ **UNIVERSITY OF WISCONSIN-BARRON COUNTY** *H-3*
1800 College Dr.
Rice Lake, WI 54868-2497
Tel: (715)234-8176
Admissions: (715)234-8024
Web Site: http://www.barron.uwc.edu/
Description: State-supported, 2-year, coed. Part of University of Wisconsin System. Awards transfer associate degrees. Founded 1966. Setting: 142-acre small town campus. Total enrollment: 616. 300 applied, 99% were admitted. 4% from top 10% of their high school class, 14% from top quarter, 44% from top half. Students come from 2 states and territories, 20% 25 or older. Core. Calendar: semesters. Academic remediation for entering students, services for LD students, advanced placement, independent study, distance learning, summer session for credit, part-time degree program, adult/continuing education programs, internships. Off campus study at other units of the University of Wisconsin Colleges, four-year campuses of the University of Wisconsin. Study abroad program.
Entrance Requirements: Options: electronic application, deferred admission. Required: high school transcript, ACT. Required for some: essay, 1 recommendation. Placement: SAT or ACT required. Entrance: minimally difficult. Application deadline: 9/15. Notification: continuous.
Costs Per Year: Application fee: $35. State resident tuition: $3996 full-time, $165 per credit part-time. Nonresident tuition: $12,676 full-time, $528 per credit part-time. Mandatory fees: $373 full-time, $16 per credit part-time. Full-time tuition and fees vary according to reciprocity agreements. Part-time tuition and fees vary according to reciprocity agreements.
Collegiate Environment: Orientation program. Drama-theater group, choral group, student-run newspaper. Most popular organizations: Phi Theta Kappa, student government, Encore, Delta Psi Omega, Sociology Club. Major annual events: Humanities Day, Spring Fling. Student services: health

clinic. College housing not available. Main library plus 1 other with 39,479 books, 233 serials, and an OPAC. 50 computers available on campus for general student use. Computer purchase/lease plans available. A campuswide network can be accessed from off-campus. Staffed computer lab on campus.

■ **UNIVERSITY OF WISCONSIN-EAU CLAIRE** *J-4*
PO Box 4004
Eau Claire, WI 54702-4004
Tel: (715)836-2637
Admissions: (715)836-5415
Fax: (715)836-2380
E-mail: admissions@uwec.edu
Web Site: http://www.uwec.edu/
Description: State-supported, comprehensive, coed. Part of University of Wisconsin System. Awards associate, bachelor's, and master's degrees and post-master's certificates. Founded 1916. Setting: 333-acre urban campus. Endowment: $25 million. Research spending for 2004 fiscal year: $984,000. Educational spending for 2005 fiscal year: $5021 per student. Total enrollment: 10,566. Faculty: 508 (401 full-time, 107 part-time). Student-undergrad faculty ratio is 20:1. 7,134 applied, 70% were admitted. 23% from top 10% of their high school class, 60% from top quarter, 95% from top half. 4 National Merit Scholars, 63 valedictorians. Full-time: 9,374 students, 59% women, 41% men. Part-time: 689 students, 62% women, 38% men. Students come from 21 states and territories, 45 other countries, 22% from out-of-state, 1% Native American, 1% Hispanic, 0.5% black, 3% Asian American or Pacific Islander, 1% international, 8% 25 or older, 38% live on campus, 5% transferred in. Retention: 83% of full-time freshmen returned the following year. Academic areas with the most degrees conferred: business/marketing; education; health professions and related sciences. Core. Calendar: semesters. Academic remediation for entering students, ESL program, services for LD students, advanced placement, honors program, independent study, distance learning, double major, summer session for credit, part-time degree program, adult/continuing education programs, co-op programs and internships, graduate courses open to undergrads. Off campus study at National Student Exchange. Study abroad program.
Entrance Requirements: Options: electronic application, early admission. Required: high school transcript, rank in upper 50% of high school class, SAT or ACT. Entrance: moderately difficult. Application deadline: Rolling. Notification: continuous.
Costs Per Year: Application fee: $35. State resident tuition: $5178 full-time, $215.59 per credit part-time. Nonresident tuition: $15,224 full-time, $634.18 per credit part-time. Full-time tuition varies according to reciprocity agreements. Part-time tuition varies according to reciprocity agreements. College room and board: $4737. College room only: $2540. Room and board charges vary according to board plan.
Collegiate Environment: Orientation program. Drama-theater group, choral group, marching band, student-run newspaper, radio station. Social organizations: 150 open to all; national fraternities, national sororities; 1% of eligible men and 1% of eligible women are members. Most popular organizations: American Marketing Association, Beta Upsilon Sigma, International Greek Association, Student Information Management Society, Hobnailers. Major annual events: Viennese Ball, Homecoming, Winter Carnival. Student services: legal services, health clinic, personal-psychological counseling. Campus security: 24-hour emergency response devices and patrols, late night transport-escort service, controlled dormitory access. 3,924 college housing spaces available; 3,855 were occupied in 2003-04. Freshmen guaranteed college housing. On-campus residence required in freshman year. Options: coed, men-only, women-only housing available. William D. McIntyre Library plus 1 other with 764,275 books, 1.4 million microform titles, 2,448 serials, 17,676 audiovisual materials, an OPAC; and a Web page. Operations spending for 2004 fiscal year: $2.9 million. 1,150 computers available on campus for general student use. A campuswide network can be accessed from student residence rooms and from off campus. Staffed computer lab on campus.
Community Environment: Eau Claire is a cultural, commercial, educational, and medical center in west-central Wisconsin. The city, which is located at the confluence of the Eau Claire and Chippewa Rivers, is served by air and bus lines. Community facilities and services include numerous hotels, motels, hospitals, churches, restaurants, shopping areas, a public library and YMCA, as well as numerous civic organizations and clubs. The city and the surrounding area abound in colorful, natural beauty and offers numerous year-round recreational activities. Local lakes and parks provide opportunities to enjoy aquatic sports, golf, skiing, skating, tennis, baseball, and many other sports.

■ **UNIVERSITY OF WISCONSIN-FOND DU LAC** *M-11*
400 University Dr.
Fond du Lac, WI 54935
Tel: (920)929-3600
Admissions: (920)929-3606
E-mail: bstrande@uwcmail.uwc.edu
Web Site: http://www.fdl.uwc.edu/
Description: State-supported, 2-year, coed. Part of University of Wisconsin System. Awards transfer associate degrees. Founded 1968. Setting: 182-acre small town campus with easy access to Milwaukee. Total enrollment: 716. 6% from top 10% of their high school class, 23% from top quarter, 46% from top half. Full-time: 454 students, 57% women, 43% men. Part-time: 262 students, 61% women, 39% men. Students come from 3 states and territories, 1% from out-of-state, 1% Native American, 1% Hispanic, 1% black, 2% Asian American or Pacific Islander, 0% international, 16% 25 or older. Retention: 58% of full-time freshmen returned the following year. Core. Calendar: semesters. Academic remediation for entering students, advanced placement, summer session for credit, part-time degree program, adult/continuing education programs. Off campus study at other units of the University of Wisconsin Colleges, four-year campuses of the University of Wisconsin. ROTC: Army (c).
Entrance Requirements: Options: electronic application, deferred admission. Required: high school transcript, ACT. Entrance: moderately difficult. Application deadline: Rolling.
Collegiate Environment: Orientation program. Drama-theater group, choral group. Social organizations: 8 open to all. Most popular organizations: student government, Campus Ambassadors, Phi Theta Kappa, drama. Student services: personal-psychological counseling. Campus security: 24-hour emergency response devices. College housing not available. 41,891 books and 160 serials. 50 computers available on campus for general student use. Staffed computer lab on campus.

■ **UNIVERSITY OF WISCONSIN-FOX VALLEY** *L-11*
1478 Midway Rd.
Menasha, WI 54952
Tel: (920)832-2600; 888-INFOUWC
Admissions: (920)832-2620
Fax: (920)832-2647
E-mail: foxinfo@uwc.edu
Web Site: http://www.uwfoxvalley.uwc.edu/
Description: State-supported, 2-year, coed. Part of University of Wisconsin System. Awards transfer associate degrees. Founded 1933. Setting: 33-acre urban campus. Total enrollment: 1,797. 569 applied, 80% were admitted. 3% from top 10% of their high school class, 15% from top quarter, 43% from top half. 2 valedictorians. Students come from 3 states and territories, 4 other countries, 1% from out-of-state, 1% Native American, 2% Hispanic, 1% black, 3% Asian American or Pacific Islander, 1% international. Core. Calendar: semesters. Academic remediation for entering students, services for LD students, advanced placement, honors program, independent study, distance learning, summer session for credit, part-time degree program, adult/continuing education programs, co-op programs. Off campus study at other units of the University of Wisconsin Colleges, four-year campuses of the University of Wisconsin.
Entrance Requirements: Options: Common Application, early admission. Required: high school transcript, ACT. Entrance: minimally difficult. Notification: continuous.
Costs Per Year: State resident tuition: $4196 full-time, $177 per credit part-time. Nonresident tuition: $12,896 full-time, $528.21 per credit part-time. Full-time tuition varies according to course load. Part-time tuition varies according to course load.
Collegiate Environment: Drama-theater group, choral group, student-run newspaper, radio station. Social organizations: 29 open to all. Most popular organizations: Business Club, Education Club, Earth Science Club, Computer Science Club, Political Science Club. Major annual events: Honors Convocation and Commencement, Campus Picnic. Student services: personal-psychological counseling. College housing not available. 29,000 books, 230 serials, an OPAC, and a Web page. 52 computers available on campus for general student use. A campuswide network can be accessed from off-campus. Staffed computer lab on campus.

■ **UNIVERSITY OF WISCONSIN-GREEN BAY** *K-12*
2420 Nicolet Dr.
Green Bay, WI 54311-7001
Tel: (920)465-2000; 888-367-8942

Admissions: (920)465-2111
Fax: (920)465-2032
Web Site: http://www.uwgb.edu/
Description: State-supported, comprehensive, coed. Part of University of Wisconsin System. Awards associate, bachelor's, and master's degrees. Founded 1968. Setting: 700-acre suburban campus. Endowment: $7.7 million. Research spending for 2004 fiscal year: $957,426. Educational spending for 2005 fiscal year: $4448 per student. Total enrollment: 5,826. Faculty: 279 (179 full-time, 100 part-time). Student-undergrad faculty ratio is 23:1. 3,350 applied, 66% were admitted. Full-time: 4,519 students, 65% women, 35% men. Part-time: 1,103 students, 70% women, 30% men. Students come from 34 states and territories, 29 other countries, 5% from out-of-state, 1% Native American, 1% Hispanic, 1% black, 3% Asian American or Pacific Islander, 1% international, 17% 25 or older, 34% live on campus, 9% transferred in. Retention: 76% of full-time freshmen returned the following year. Academic areas with the most degrees conferred: business/marketing; psychology; biological/life sciences. Core. Calendar: semesters. Academic remediation for entering students, services for LD students, advanced placement, self-designed majors, independent study, distance learning, double major, summer session for credit, part-time degree program, external degree program, adult/continuing education programs, co-op programs and internships, graduate courses open to undergrads. Off campus study at National Student Exchange. Study abroad program. ROTC: Army.
Entrance Requirements: Options: electronic application, deferred admission, international baccalaureate accepted. Required: high school transcript, minimum 2.25 high school GPA, minimum ACT score of 17, SAT or ACT. Recommended: essay. Required for some: recommendations, interview. Entrance: moderately difficult. Notification: continuous until 8/15.
Costs Per Year: Application fee: $35. State resident tuition: $4277 full-time, $178 per credit hour part-time. Nonresident tuition: $14,323 full-time, $597 per credit hour part-time. Mandatory fees: $1148 full-time, $38 per credit hour part-time. Full-time tuition and fees vary according to reciprocity agreements. Part-time tuition and fees vary according to reciprocity agreements. College room and board: $4698. College room only: $2772. Room and board charges vary according to board plan and housing facility.
Collegiate Environment: Orientation program. Drama-theater group, choral group, marching band, student-run newspaper, radio station. Social organizations: 80 open to all; national fraternities, national sororities, local fraternities, local sororities; 1% of eligible men and 1% of eligible women are members. Most popular organizations: Good Times, Psychology and Human Development Club, Ambassadors, Residence Hall Apartment Association, Student Government Association. Major annual events: Welcome Week, Frost Fest, Senior Celebration. Student services: health clinic, personal-psychological counseling. Campus security: 24-hour emergency response devices and patrols, late night transport-escort service, controlled dormitory access. 1,900 college housing spaces available; 1,883 were occupied in 2003-04. Freshmen given priority for college housing. Option: coed housing available. Cofrin Library with 333,482 books, 714,166 microform titles, 5,512 serials, 45,396 audiovisual materials, an OPAC, and a Web page. Operations spending for 2004 fiscal year: $1.3 million. 550 computers available on campus for general student use. A campuswide network can be accessed from student residence rooms and from off campus. Staffed computer lab on campus.
Community Environment: Green Bay, a trading and transportation center in Northeastern Wisconsin, is a city of approximately 90,000 inhabitants located in Wisconsin's third largest population area. The city has an outstanding regional museum, an excellent public library system and many parks. A community symphony orchestra, community chorus and several theater groups provide cultural enrichment and added opportunities for participation and performance by qualified students. Nearby resort areas provide a variety of recreational opportunities and summer jobs for students. The university is easy to reach by air, bus or interstate highway.

■ **UNIVERSITY OF WISCONSIN-LA CROSSE** *M-4*
1725 State St.
La Crosse, WI 54601-3742
Tel: (608)785-8000
Admissions: (608)785-8939
Fax: (608)785-6695
E-mail: admissions@post.uwlax.edu
Web Site: http://www.uwlax.edu
Description: State-supported, comprehensive, coed. Part of University of Wisconsin System. Awards associate, bachelor's, and master's degrees. Founded 1909. Setting: 121-acre suburban campus. Endowment: $12.7 mil-

lion. Research spending for 2004 fiscal year: $3.9 million. Educational spending for 2005 fiscal year: $4435 per student. Total enrollment: 9,397. Faculty: 448 (339 full-time, 109 part-time). Student-undergrad faculty ratio is 22:1. 6,347 applied, 67% were admitted. 30% from top 10% of their high school class, 80% from top quarter, 97% from top half. 59 valedictorians. Full-time: 7,720 students, 59% women, 41% men. Part-time: 413 students, 58% women, 42% men. Students come from 35 states and territories, 42 other countries, 16% from out-of-state, 1% Native American, 1% Hispanic, 1% black, 3% Asian American or Pacific Islander, 1% international, 5% 25 or older, 36% live on campus, 4% transferred in. Retention: 90% of full-time freshmen returned the following year. Academic areas with the most degrees conferred: business/marketing; parks and recreation; social sciences. Core. Calendar: semesters. Academic remediation for entering students, ESL program, services for LD students, advanced placement, freshman honors college, honors program, distance learning, double major, summer session for credit, part-time degree program, adult/continuing education programs, co-op programs and internships, graduate courses open to undergrads. Off campus study at Viterbo College. Study abroad program. ROTC: Army.
Entrance Requirements: Options: electronic application, early admission, international baccalaureate accepted. Required: high school transcript, SAT or ACT. Recommended: essay, ACT. Required for some: interview. Entrance: moderately difficult. Application deadline: Rolling. Notification: continuous.
Costs Per Year: Application fee: $35. State resident tuition: $5225 full-time, $230 per credit hour part-time. Nonresident tuition: $15,271 full-time, $649 per credit hour part-time. Full-time tuition varies according to program and reciprocity agreements. Part-time tuition varies according to course load, program, and reciprocity agreements. College room and board: $4820. College room only: $2720. Room and board charges vary according to board plan.
Collegiate Environment: Orientation program. Drama-theater group, choral group, marching band, student-run newspaper, radio station. Social organizations: 140 open to all; national fraternities, national sororities; 1% of eligible men and 1% of eligible women are members. Most popular organizations: Sports and Activities Club, Residential Hall Council. Major annual events: Homecoming, Parents' Weekend, Air Band. Student services: legal services, health clinic, personal-psychological counseling, women's center. Campus security: 24-hour emergency response devices and patrols, late night transport-escort service, controlled dormitory access. 2,889 college housing spaces available; 2,733 were occupied in 2003-04. Freshmen given priority for college housing. On-campus residence required in freshman year. Options: coed, women-only housing available. Murphy Library with 673,060 books, 1.2 million microform titles, 1,750 serials, 2,384 audiovisual materials, an OPAC, and a Web page. Operations spending for 2004 fiscal year: $2.3 million. 600 computers available on campus for general student use. A campuswide network can be accessed from student residence rooms and from off campus. Staffed computer lab on campus.
Community Environment: Founded in 1842 as an Indian trading post, La Crosse is situated on the east bank of the Mississippi River in southern Wisconsin. It is approximately midway between Minneapolis-St. Paul and Chicago. Noted for its exceptional natural beauty and outstanding recreational opportunities, the city is the industrial, commercial and medical center of Wisconsin's famous"Coulee Country." The population is approximately 50,000. All commercial transportation is convenient.

■ **UNIVERSITY OF WISCONSIN-MADISON** *B-6*
500 Lincoln Dr.
Madison, WI 53706-1380
Tel: (608)262-1234
Admissions: (608)262-3961
Fax: (608)262-1429
E-mail: onwisconsin@admissions.wisc.edu
Web Site: http://www.wisc.edu/
Description: State-supported, university, coed. Part of University of Wisconsin System. Awards bachelor's, master's, doctoral, and first professional degrees and post-master's and first professional certificates. Founded 1848. Setting: 1,050-acre urban campus with easy access to Milwaukee. Endowment: $1 billion. Research spending for 2004 fiscal year: $645.1 million. Total enrollment: 41,480. Faculty: 2,975 (2,365 full-time, 610 part-time). Student-undergrad faculty ratio is 13:1. 21,682 applied, 68% were admitted. 56% from top 10% of their high school class, 91% from top quarter, 99% from top half. Full-time: 27,441 students, 54% women, 46% men. Part-time: 2,665 students, 53% women, 47% men. Students come from 54 states and territories, 110 other countries, 30% from out-of-state, 1% Native American, 3% Hispanic, 3% black, 5% Asian American or Pacific Islander, 3%

international, 5% 25 or older, 24% live on campus, 4% transferred in. Retention: 94% of full-time freshmen returned the following year. Academic areas with the most degrees conferred: social sciences; biological/life sciences; engineering. Calendar: semesters. ESL program, services for LD students, advanced placement, accelerated degree program, self-designed majors, honors program, independent study, distance learning, double major, summer session for credit, part-time degree program, adult/continuing education programs, co-op programs and internships, graduate courses open to undergrads. Study abroad program. ROTC: Army, Naval, Air Force.

Entrance Requirements: Options: electronic application, deferred admission, international baccalaureate accepted. Required: essay, high school transcript, SAT or ACT. Entrance: very difficult. Application deadline: 2/1. Notification: continuous.

Costs Per Year: Application fee: $35. State resident tuition: $6284 full-time, $264 per credit part-time. Nonresident tuition: $20,284 full-time, $847 per credit part-time. Mandatory fees: $333 full-time, $30 per credit part-time. Full-time tuition and fees vary according to degree level and reciprocity agreements. Part-time tuition and fees vary according to course load, degree level, and reciprocity agreements. College room and board: $6500. Room and board charges vary according to board plan, housing facility, and location.

Collegiate Environment: Orientation program. Drama-theater group, choral group, marching band, student-run newspaper, radio station. Social organizations: 690 open to all; national fraternities, national sororities; 9% of eligible men and 8% of eligible women are members. Student services: health clinic, personal-psychological counseling, women's center. Campus security: 24-hour emergency response devices and patrols, late night transport-escort service, controlled dormitory access, free cab rides throughout the city. 6,600 college housing spaces available; all were occupied in 2003-04. Freshmen given priority for college housing. Options: coed, men-only, women-only housing available. Memorial Library plus 40 others with an OPAC and a Web page.

Community Environment: Founded in 1836, the city was named for James Madison, the fourth President of the United States, and is the capital of Wisconsin. Madison is the center of one of the richest dairy regions in America and has over 200 industries. The city is also important as a medical center with its 12 hospitals and its manufacturing of precision surgical instruments. Recreational facilities include 10 golf courses, 3 of which are public, tennis courts, and a number of beaches for water sports. Fishing boats are for hire. Points of interest are the Henry Vilas Park Zoo, Nevin Fish Hatchery, U.S. Forest Products Laboratory, State Historical Society Museum, and the Wisconsin State Capitol which is one of the most impressive in the United States.

■ UNIVERSITY OF WISCONSIN-MANITOWOC *L-13*

705 Viebahn St.
Manitowoc, WI 54220-6699
Tel: (920)683-4700
Admissions: (920)683-4708
Fax: (920)683-4776
E-mail: christopher.lewis@uwc.edu
Web Site: http://www.manitowoc.uwc.edu/

Description: State-supported, 2-year, coed. Part of University of Wisconsin System. Awards certificates, transfer associate, and terminal associate degrees. Founded 1935. Setting: 50-acre small town campus with easy access to Milwaukee. Total enrollment: 643. Student-undergrad faculty ratio is 24:1. 320 applied, 91% were admitted. 2% from top 10% of their high school class, 11% from top quarter, 25% from top half. Students come from 3 states and territories, 1% Native American, 1% Hispanic, 0.2% black, 3% Asian American or Pacific Islander, 1% international, 23% 25 or older. Core. Calendar: semesters. Academic remediation for entering students, services for LD students, advanced placement, self-designed majors, distance learning, summer session for credit, part-time degree program, adult/continuing education programs. Off campus study at other units of the University of Wisconsin Colleges, four-year campuses of the University of Wisconsin.

Entrance Requirements: Options: electronic application, early admission. Required: high school transcript, minimum X high school GPA, ACT, SAT or ACT. Required for some: essay, interview. Entrance: minimally difficult. Notification: continuous until 7/1, continuous until 7/1 for nonresidents.

Costs Per Year: Application fee: $35. Area resident tuition: $165.71 per credit part-time. State resident tuition: $3,977 full-time, $528.21 per credit part-time. Nonresident tuition: $12,677 full-time, $528.21 per credit part-time. Mandatory fees: $211 full-time, $8.64 per credit part-time, $8.64.

Collegiate Environment: Orientation program. Drama-theater group, choral group, student-run newspaper. Social organizations: 4 open to all. Most

popular organizations: Business Club, Drama Club, Music Club, Phi Kappa Theta, Environmental Awareness. College housing not available. 25,750 books, 150 serials, and an OPAC. Operations spending for 2004 fiscal year: $80,000. 50 computers available on campus for general student use. A campuswide network can be accessed from off-campus. Staffed computer lab on campus.

■ UNIVERSITY OF WISCONSIN-MARATHON COUNTY *J-8*

518 South Seventh Ave.
Wausau, WI 54401-5396
Tel: (715)261-6100; 888-367-8962
Admissions: (715)261-6238
Fax: (715)261-6333
Web Site: http://www.uwmc.uwc.edu/

Description: State-supported, 2-year, coed. Part of University of Wisconsin System. Awards transfer associate degrees. Founded 1933. Setting: 7-acre small town campus. Educational spending for 2005 fiscal year: $2600 per student. Total enrollment: 1,303. 6% from top 10% of their high school class, 20% from top quarter, 52% from top half. Full-time: 883 students, 51% women, 49% men. Part-time: 420 students, 60% women, 40% men. 0.5% Native American, 1% Hispanic, 1% black, 7% Asian American or Pacific Islander, 0% international, 21% 25 or older, 16% live on campus. Retention: 100% of full-time freshmen returned the following year. Core. Calendar: semesters. Academic remediation for entering students, advanced placement, self-designed majors, honors program, summer session for credit, part-time degree program, adult/continuing education programs. Off campus study at other units of the University of Wisconsin Colleges, four-year campuses of the University of Wisconsin. Study abroad program. ROTC: Army (c).

Entrance Requirements: Options: Common Application, electronic application, early admission, deferred admission. Required: ACT. Recommended: minimum 2.0 high school GPA. Required for some: interview. Entrance: minimally difficult.

Costs Per Year: Application fee: $35. State resident tuition: $4000 full-time, $175 per credit part-time. Nonresident tuition: $13,000 full-time, $545 per credit part-time. College room and board: $3800. Room and board charges vary according to board plan.

Collegiate Environment: Orientation program. Drama-theater group, choral group, student-run newspaper. Social organizations: 12 open to all. Most popular organizations: Fiercely Independent Theatre, Ski Club, Ten Percent Society, Unity, Tempo. Major annual events: chorale/swing choir concerts, Educational Assistance Through Scholarships (EATS), Student-Faculty Basketball Game. Student services: personal-psychological counseling. Campus security: 24-hour emergency response devices, controlled dormitory access. 160 college housing spaces available; all were occupied in 2003-04. Option: coed housing available. University of Wisconsin-Marathon Library with 37,000 books, 150 serials, an OPAC, and a Web page. 50 computers available on campus for general student use. A campuswide network can be accessed. Staffed computer lab on campus.

■ UNIVERSITY OF WISCONSIN-MARINETTE *I-13*

750 West Bay Shore
Marinette, WI 54143-4299
Tel: (715)735-4300
Admissions: (715)735-4301
E-mail: cbailey@uwc.edu
Web Site: http://www.uwc.edu/

Description: State-supported, 2-year, coed. Part of University of Wisconsin System. Awards transfer associate degrees. Founded 1965. Setting: 36-acre small town campus. Endowment: $200,000. Total enrollment: 486. 6% from top 10% of their high school class, 21% from top quarter, 50% from top half. Students come from 2 states and territories, 16 other countries, 1% Native American, 2% Hispanic, 0% black, 1% Asian American or Pacific Islander, 6% international, 31% 25 or older. Core. Calendar: semesters. Academic remediation for entering students, ESL program, services for LD students, advanced placement, independent study, distance learning, summer session for credit, part-time degree program, adult/continuing education programs, co-op programs and internships. Off campus study at other units of the University of Wisconsin Colleges, four-year campuses of the University of Wisconsin.

Entrance Requirements: Open admission. Option: electronic application. Required: high school transcript. Recommended: SAT or ACT. Entrance: noncompetitive. Application deadline: Rolling. Notification: continuous.

Collegiate Environment: Orientation program. Drama-theater group, choral group, student-run newspaper. Social organizations: 5 open to all. Most popular organizations: Student Senate, Writers Club/Literature Club, Phi Theta Kappa, Student Ambassadors. Major annual events: Spring Banquet, End of Year Party, Commencement. Student services: personal-psychological counseling. College housing not available. Main library plus 1 other with 23,000 books and 135 serials. 48 computers available on campus for general student use. A campuswide network can be accessed. Staffed computer lab on campus.

■ **UNIVERSITY OF WISCONSIN-MARSHFIELD/WOOD COUNTY** *J-7*
2000 West 5th St.
Marshfield, WI 54449
Tel: (715)389-6500
Web Site: http://marshfield.uwc.edu/
Description: State-supported, 2-year, coed. Part of University of Wisconsin System. Awards transfer associate degrees. Founded 1964. Setting: 71-acre small town campus. Endowment: $500,000. Total enrollment: 643. 322 applied, 93% were admitted. 8% from top 10% of their high school class, 17% from top quarter, 55% from top half. 2 National Merit Scholars, 1 class president, 10 student government officers. Students come from 2 states and territories, 1 other country, 1% from out-of-state, 2% Native American, 0.2% Hispanic, 1% black, 1% Asian American or Pacific Islander, 0.2% international, 25% 25 or older. Retention: 99% of full-time freshmen returned the following year..Core. Calendar: semesters. Academic remediation for entering students, services for LD students, advanced placement, accelerated degree program, independent study, distance learning, summer session for credit, part-time degree program, external degree program, adult/continuing education programs. Off campus study at other units of the University of Wisconsin Colleges, four-year campuses of the University of Wisconsin. Study abroad program. ROTC: Army (c).
Entrance Requirements: Options: Common Application, electronic application, early admission, deferred admission. Required: high school transcript, SAT or ACT. Required for some: essay, recommendations, interview. Entrance: moderately difficult. Application deadline: Rolling.
Collegiate Environment: Orientation program. Drama-theater group, choral group, student-run newspaper. Social organizations: 10 open to all. Most popular organizations: Student Nurses Association, student newspaper, literary magazine, Student Education Association, Inter-Varsity Christian Fellowship. Major annual events: Fall Picnic, campus plays, Spring Picnic. Campus security: 24-hour patrols, patrols by city police. College housing not available. Learning Resource Center with 35,000 books, 185 serials, an OPAC, and a Web page. Operations spending for 2004 fiscal year: $80,151. 60 computers available on campus for general student use. A campuswide network can be accessed. Staffed computer lab on campus.

■ **UNIVERSITY OF WISCONSIN-MILWAUKEE** *O-12*
PO Box 413
Milwaukee, WI 53201-0413
Tel: (414)229-1122
Admissions: (414)229-3800
Fax: (414)229-6940
E-mail: deswcb@des.uwm.edu
Web Site: http://www.uwm.edu/
Description: State-supported, university, coed. Part of University of Wisconsin System. Awards bachelor's, master's, and doctoral degrees and post-master's certificates. Founded 1956. Setting: 90-acre urban campus. Total enrollment: 27,502. 11,238 applied, 81% were admitted. 7% from top 10% of their high school class, 26% from top quarter, 67% from top half. Full-time: 18,856 students, 53% women, 47% men. Part-time: 4,060 students, 56% women, 44% men. Students come from 53 states and territories, 2% from out-of-state, 1% Native American, 4% Hispanic, 7% black, 4% Asian American or Pacific Islander, 1% international, 19% 25 or older, 13% live on campus, 7% transferred in. Retention: 71% of full-time freshmen returned the following year. Academic areas with the most degrees conferred: business/marketing; education; health professions and related sciences. Core. Calendar: semesters. Academic remediation for entering students, ESL program, services for LD students, advanced placement, accelerated degree program, self-designed majors, honors program, independent study, distance learning, double major, summer session for credit, part-time degree program, adult/continuing education programs, co-op programs and internships, graduate courses open to undergrads. Off campus study at University of Wisconsin-Parkside. Study abroad program. ROTC: Army (c), Air Force (c).

Entrance Requirements: Option: deferred admission. Required: high school transcript, SAT or ACT, ACT for state residents. Entrance: moderately difficult. Application deadline: continuous.
Costs Per Year: Application fee: $35. State resident tuition: $5494 full-time, $228.93 per credit part-time. Nonresident tuition: $18,246 full-time, $760.26 per credit part-time. Mandatory fees: $730 full-time. Full-time tuition and fees vary according to location, program, and reciprocity agreements. Part-time tuition varies according to course load, location, program, and reciprocity agreements. College room and board: $4922. College room only: $2988. Room and board charges vary according to board plan and housing facility.
Collegiate Environment: Orientation program. Drama-theater group, choral group, marching band, student-run newspaper, radio station. Social organizations: national fraternities, national sororities, local fraternities. Major annual event: homecoming. Student services: legal services, health clinic, personal-psychological counseling, women's center. Campus security: 24-hour emergency response devices, late night transport-escort service. Option: coed housing available. Golda Meir Library with 1.4 million books, 1.7 million microform titles, 8,240 serials, 37,376 audiovisual materials, an OPAC, and a Web page. 310 computers available on campus for general student use. A campuswide network can be accessed from off-campus. Staffed computer lab on campus.
Community Environment: Located on the west shore of Lake Michigan, Milwaukee (population 640,000) is the largest city in Wisconsin. All major forms of commercial transportation are available. Milwaukee is the nation's brewing center, as well as a major grain market and manufacturing center. Products of industry are metal, machinery, food, leather, chemicals, textiles, electrical machinery, and other items. The city is the headquarters of the Lake States National Forest Region. The county has a park system and many of the units contain public golf courses, tennis courts, and other recreational facilities. Wisconsin's State Fair is held each year in August.

■ **UNIVERSITY OF WISCONSIN-OSHKOSH** *L-11*
800 Algoma Blvd.
Oshkosh, WI 54901
Tel: (920)424-1234
Admissions: (920)424-0202
Fax: (920)424-1098
E-mail: oshadmuw@uwosh.edu
Web Site: http://www.uwosh.edu/
Description: State-supported, comprehensive, coed. Part of University of Wisconsin System. Awards associate, bachelor's, and master's degrees. Founded 1871. Setting: 192-acre suburban campus with easy access to Milwaukee. Endowment: $350,000. Research spending for 2004 fiscal year: $750,000. Educational spending for 2005 fiscal year: $9100 per student. Total enrollment: 10,997. Faculty: 566 (381 full-time, 185 part-time). Student-undergrad faculty ratio is 20:1. 4,777 applied, 79% were admitted. 11% from top 10% of their high school class, 38% from top quarter, 89% from top half. Full-time: 8,538 students, 59% women, 41% men. Part-time: 1,202 students, 64% women, 36% men. Students come from 30 states and territories, 32 other countries, 3% from out-of-state, 1% Native American, 1% Hispanic, 1% black, 3% Asian American or Pacific Islander, 1% international, 16% 25 or older, 34% live on campus, 10% transferred in. Retention: 76% of full-time freshmen returned the following year. Academic areas with the most degrees conferred: business/marketing; education; health professions and related sciences. Core. Calendar: semesters. Academic remediation for entering students, ESL program, services for LD students, advanced placement, accelerated degree program, self-designed majors, honors program, independent study, distance learning, double major, summer session for credit, part-time degree program, adult/continuing education programs, co-op programs and internships, graduate courses open to undergrads. Study abroad program. ROTC: Army.
Entrance Requirements: Options: electronic application, deferred admission, international baccalaureate accepted. Required: high school transcript, rank in upper 50% of high school class or ACT composite score of 23 or above, SAT or ACT, ACT required for state residents. Recommended: essay. Entrance: moderately difficult. Application deadline: Rolling. Notification: continuous.
Costs Per Year: Application fee: $35. State resident tuition: $4,981 full-time, $209 per credit hour part-time. Nonresident tuition: $15,027 full-time, $628 per credit hour part-time. Full-time tuition varies according to reciprocity agreements. Part-time tuition varies according to reciprocity agreements. College room and board: $4884. College room only: $2784. Room and board charges vary according to board plan and housing facility.
Collegiate Environment: Orientation program. Drama-theater group, choral group, student-run newspaper, radio station. Social organizations: 175 open

to all; national fraternities, national sororities; 3% of eligible men and 3% of eligible women are members. Most popular organizations: USRH, Model UN, Pi Sigma Epsilon, Human Services Organization. Major annual events: Homecoming, Winter Carnival, Taste of UW Oshkosh. Student services: legal services, health clinic, personal-psychological counseling, women's center. Campus security: 24-hour emergency response devices and patrols, student patrols, late night transport-escort service, controlled dormitory access. 3,571 college housing spaces available. Freshmen guaranteed college housing. On-campus residence required through sophomore year. Options: coed, women-only housing available. Forrest R. Polk Library with 446,774 books, 1.3 million microform titles, 5,219 serials, 9,102 audiovisual materials, an OPAC, and a Web page. Operations spending for 2004 fiscal year: $3.4 million. 475 computers available on campus for general student use. A campuswide network can be accessed from student residence rooms and from off campus. Staffed computer lab on campus.

Community Environment: A city of 60,000, Oshkosh is situated between Lake Winnebago and Lake Butte des Morts. The Fox River runs through the city with parks and marinas dotting its shores. At historic Wittman Field, the Experimental Aircraft Association's annual international convention is the world's largest.

■ **UNIVERSITY OF WISCONSIN-PARKSIDE** *Q-13*

900 Wood Rd., Box 2000

Kenosha, WI 53141-2000

Tel: (262)595-2345

Admissions: (262)595-2784

Fax: (262)595-2630

E-mail: matthew.jensen@uwp.edu

Web Site: http://www.uwp.edu/

Description: State-supported, comprehensive, coed. Part of University of Wisconsin System. Awards bachelor's and master's degrees. Founded 1968. Setting: 700-acre suburban campus with easy access to Chicago and Milwaukee. Endowment: $949,351. Research spending for 2004 fiscal year: $829,600. Total enrollment: 4,944. Faculty: 313 (181 full-time, 132 part-time). Student-undergrad faculty ratio is 18:1. 1,868 applied, 92% were admitted. 5% from top 10% of their high school class, 23% from top quarter, 56% from top half. Full-time: 3,545 students, 55% women, 45% men. Part-time: 1,308 students, 61% women, 39% men. Students come from 24 states and territories, 27 other countries, 7% from out-of-state, 1% Native American, 6% Hispanic, 10% black, 3% Asian American or Pacific Islander, 1% international, 22% 25 or older, 16% live on campus, 8% transferred in. Retention: 65% of full-time freshmen returned the following year. Academic areas with the most degrees conferred: business/marketing; social sciences; security and protective services. Core. Calendar: semesters. Academic remediation for entering students, ESL program, services for LD students, advanced placement, accelerated degree program, honors program, independent study, distance learning, double major, summer session for credit, part-time degree program, external degree program, internships, graduate courses open to undergrads. Off campus study at Carthage College. Study abroad program. ROTC: Army (c).

Entrance Requirements: Options: electronic application, deferred admission, international baccalaureate accepted. Required: high school transcript, minimum of 17 high school units distributed as specified in the UW-Parkside catalog. Required for some: SAT or ACT. Entrance: moderately difficult. Application deadline: 8/1. Notification: continuous.

Costs Per Year: Application fee: $35. State resident tuition: $5001 full-time. Nonresident tuition: $15,047 full-time. Full-time tuition varies according to course load and reciprocity agreements. College room and board: $5500. College room only: $3250. Room and board charges vary according to board plan and housing facility.

Collegiate Environment: Orientation program. Drama-theater group, choral group, student-run newspaper, radio station. Social organizations: 73 open to all; national fraternities, national sororities, local fraternities, local sororities; 1% of eligible men and 1% of eligible women are members. Most popular organizations: Black Student Union, Latinos Unidos, Parkside Student Government Association, Asian-American Club, Parkside Adult Student Alliance. Major annual events: Welcome Week, Hypnotist Show, Casino Night. Student services: health clinic, personal-psychological counseling, women's center. Campus security: 24-hour emergency response devices and patrols, late night transport-escort service, controlled dormitory access. 765 college housing spaces available; 740 were occupied in 2003-04. No special consideration for freshman housing applicants. Option: coed housing available. Library-Learning Center with 400,000 books, 981,400 microform titles, 1,590 serials, 21,220 audiovisual materials, an OPAC, and

a Web page. Operations spending for 2004 fiscal year: $1.4 million. 225 computers available on campus for general student use. A campuswide network can be accessed from student residence rooms and from off campus. Staffed computer lab on campus.

Community Environment: See Gateway Technical College.

■ **UNIVERSITY OF WISCONSIN-PLATTEVILLE** *P-6*

1 University Plaza

Platteville, WI 53818-3099

Tel: (608)342-1491

Free: 800-362-5515

Admissions: (608)342-1125

E-mail: admit@uwplatt.edu

Web Site: http://www.uwplatt.edu/

Description: State-supported, comprehensive, coed. Part of University of Wisconsin System. Awards associate, bachelor's, and master's degrees. Founded 1866. Setting: 380-acre small town campus. Endowment: $2.7 million. Research spending for 2004 fiscal year: $193,101. Educational spending for 2005 fiscal year: $5150 per student. Total enrollment: 6,431. Faculty: 348 (249 full-time, 99 part-time). Student-undergrad faculty ratio is 20:1. 3,075 applied, 85% were admitted. 12% from top 10% of their high school class, 35% from top quarter, 77% from top half. Full-time: 5,180 students, 37% women, 63% men. Part-time: 595 students, 48% women, 52% men. Students come from 31 states and territories, 7 other countries, 10% from out-of-state, 0.4% Native American, 1% Hispanic, 1% black, 1% Asian American or Pacific Islander, 0.4% international, 7% 25 or older, 44% live on campus, 6% transferred in. Retention: 76% of full-time freshmen returned the following year. Academic areas with the most degrees conferred: engineering; business/marketing; education. Core. Calendar: semesters. Academic remediation for entering students, ESL program, services for LD students, advanced placement, self-designed majors, honors program, independent study, distance learning, double major, summer session for credit, part-time degree program, external degree program, adult/continuing education programs, co-op programs and internships, graduate courses open to undergrads. Off campus study at Westfield State College. Study abroad program. ROTC: Army (c).

Entrance Requirements: Option: electronic application. Required: high school transcript, SAT or ACT. Recommended: essay. Required for some: recommendations, interview. Entrance: moderately difficult. Application deadline: Rolling. Preference given to Illinois and Iowa students as part of a cost recovery pilot program..

Costs Per Year: Application fee: $35. State resident tuition: $4277 full-time, $178.21 per credit part-time. Nonresident tuition: $14,323 full-time, $596.80 per credit part-time. Mandatory fees: $848 full-time, $35.17 per credit part-time, $2 per term part-time. Full-time tuition and fees vary according to course load, degree level, and reciprocity agreements. Part-time tuition and fees vary according to course load, degree level, and reciprocity agreements. College room and board: $4654. College room only: $2494. Room and board charges vary according to board plan.

Collegiate Environment: Orientation program. Drama-theater group, choral group, marching band, student-run newspaper, radio station. Social organizations: 120 open to all; national fraternities, national sororities, local fraternities, local sororities; 3% of eligible men and 2% of eligible women are members. Major annual events: homecoming, Pioneer Distinguished Lecture Program. Student services: health clinic, personal-psychological counseling, women's center. Campus security: 24-hour emergency response devices and patrols, student patrols, late night transport-escort service. 2,329 college housing spaces available; 2,312 were occupied in 2003-04. Freshmen guaranteed college housing. On-campus residence required through sophomore year. Options: coed, men-only, women-only housing available. Karrmann Library with 362,247 books, 1 million microform titles, 2,116 serials, 14,325 audiovisual materials, an OPAC, and a Web page. Operations spending for 2004 fiscal year: $1.6 million. 1,000 computers available on campus for general student use. A campuswide network can be accessed from student residence rooms and from off campus. Staffed computer lab on campus.

Community Environment: Located in the heart of Wisconsin's dairyland and lead and zinc mining district, Platteville (population 9,950) was settled in 1827. Scheduled air transportation is available from Dubuque, Iowa, 20 miles away. Community facilities include a hospital, library, churches, mining museum, other historical sites, and various civic and service organizations. Recreational activities are golf, hunting, fishing, swimming, tennis, bowling, and horseback riding.

■ UNIVERSITY OF WISCONSIN-RICHLAND *O-6*

1200 Hwy. 14 West
Richland Center, WI 53581
Tel: (608)647-6186
Admissions: (608)647-8422
Fax: (608)647-6225
E-mail: jpoole@uwc.edu
Web Site: http://richland.uwc.edu/

Description: State-supported, 2-year, coed. Part of University of Wisconsin System. Awards transfer associate degrees. Founded 1967. Setting: 135-acre rural campus. Total enrollment: 464. Student-undergrad faculty ratio is 18:1. 3% from top 10% of their high school class, 13% from top quarter, 43% from top half. Full-time: 313 students, 55% women, 45% men. Part-time: 151 students, 62% women, 38% men. Students come from 4 states and territories, 15 other countries, 1% from out-of-state, 0.2% Native American, 0.2% Hispanic, 0.2% black, 0.4% Asian American or Pacific Islander, 4% international, 16% 25 or older, 35% live on campus, 6% transferred in. Retention: 55% of full-time freshmen returned the following year. Core. Calendar: semesters. Academic remediation for entering students, services for LD students, advanced placement, independent study, distance learning, summer session for credit, part-time degree program, external degree program, adult/continuing education programs. Off campus study at four-year campuses of the University of Wisconsin, other units of the University of Wisconsin Colleges. Study abroad program.

Entrance Requirements: Options: electronic application, early admission, international baccalaureate accepted. Required: high school transcript, SAT or ACT. Recommended: ACT. Required for some: recommendations, interview. Entrance: moderately difficult. Application deadline: Rolling. Notification: continuous until 9/1.

Costs Per Year: Application fee: $35. State resident tuition: $4372 full-time, $182 per credit part-time. Nonresident tuition: $13,072 full-time, $545 per credit part-time. Mandatory fees: $395 full-time, $16.47 per credit part-time. College room and board: $4730. College room only: $2990. Room and board charges vary according to board plan.

Collegiate Environment: Orientation program. Drama-theater group, choral group, student-run newspaper. Social organizations: 15 open to all. Major annual events: Burlap Olympic Games, Roadrunner Road Rally. Student services: personal-psychological counseling. 120 college housing spaces available; 106 were occupied in 2003-04. Option: coed housing available. Miller Memorial Library with 45,000 books, 200 serials, an OPAC, and a Web page. 45 computers available on campus for general student use. A campuswide network can be accessed from off-campus. Staffed computer lab on campus.

■ UNIVERSITY OF WISCONSIN-RIVER FALLS *J-1*

410 South Third St.
River Falls, WI 54022-5001
Tel: (715)425-3911
Admissions: (715)425-3500
Fax: (715)425-0678
Web Site: http://www.uwrf.edu/

Description: State-supported, comprehensive, coed. Part of University of Wisconsin System. Awards bachelor's and master's degrees and post-master's certificates. Founded 1874. Setting: 225-acre suburban campus with easy access to Minneapolis-St. Paul. Total enrollment: 5,950. 2,786 applied, 76% were admitted. 17% from top 10% of their high school class, 42% from top quarter, 83% from top half. Full-time: 5,132 students, 61% women, 39% men. Part-time: 372 students, 62% women, 38% men. Students come from 26 states and territories, 12 other countries, 48% from out-of-state, 1% Native American, 1% Hispanic, 1% black, 3% Asian American or Pacific Islander, 1% international, 6% 25 or older, 38% live on campus, 7% transferred in. Retention: 75% of full-time freshmen returned the following year. Core. Calendar: semesters. Academic remediation for entering students, services for LD students, advanced placement, accelerated degree program, self-designed majors, honors program, independent study, distance learning, double major, summer session for credit, part-time degree program, external degree program, adult/continuing education programs, co-op programs and internships, graduate courses open to undergrads. Off campus study at National Student Exchange. Study abroad program.

Entrance Requirements: Options: Common Application, electronic application, deferred admission, international baccalaureate accepted. Required: high school transcript, ACT. Recommended: rank in upper 40% of high school class. Entrance: moderately difficult. Application deadline: Rolling. Notification: continuous.

Costs Per Year: Application fee: $35. State resident tuition: $4968 full-time. Nonresident tuition: $15,014 full-time. Full-time tuition varies according to course load.

Collegiate Environment: Orientation program. Drama-theater group, choral group, student-run newspaper, radio station. Social organizations: 120 open to all; national fraternities, national sororities; 5% of eligible men and 3% of eligible women are members. Most popular organizations: Bushwackers (high adventure club), Habitat for Humanity, Agricultural Education Society, Dairy Club, Rodeo Club. Major annual events: Homecoming, Unity in the Community, Winter Carnival. Student services: health clinic, personal-psychological counseling, women's center. Campus security: 24-hour emergency response devices and patrols, student patrols, late night transport-escort service, controlled dormitory access. 2,200 college housing spaces available; 2,150 were occupied in 2003-04. On-campus residence required through sophomore year. Options: coed, women-only housing available. Chalmer Davee Library with 448,088 books, 471,621 microform titles, 1,660 serials, 7,500 audiovisual materials, an OPAC, and a Web page. 387 computers available on campus for general student use. A campuswide network can be accessed from student residence rooms and from off campus. Staffed computer lab on campus.

Community Environment: Location is an important asset to the learning environment of the university. At UW-River Falls, students are exposed to the quiet charm of a friendly community nestled in the scenic St. Croix River Valley. Balanced against that setting is the opportunity and excitement of the metropolitan area of the Twin Cities of Minneapolis and St. Paul, located 20 minutes away. This unique region offers access to internationally renowned theater and cultural resources, major league sports, and an industrial and business complex that provides opportunities for internships and cooperative education experiences as well as employment.

■ UNIVERSITY OF WISCONSIN-ROCK COUNTY *Q-10*

2909 Kellogg Ave.
Janesville, WI 53546-5699
Tel: (608)758-6565; 888-INFO-UWC
Admissions: (608)758-6523
Fax: (608)758-6564
E-mail: gsmith@mail.uwc.edu
Web Site: http://rock.uwc.edu/

Description: State-supported, 2-year, coed. Part of University of Wisconsin System. Awards certificates and transfer associate degrees. Founded 1966. Setting: 50-acre suburban campus with easy access to Milwaukee. Total enrollment: 880. 371 applied, 97% were admitted. 3% from top 10% of their high school class, 17% from top quarter, 41% from top half. Full-time: 751 students, 56% women, 44% men. Part-time: 129 students, 47% women, 53% men. Students come from 10 states and territories, 4 other countries, 1% from out-of-state, 34% 25 or older, 11% transferred in. Core. Calendar: semesters. Academic remediation for entering students, services for LD students, advanced placement, distance learning, summer session for credit, part-time degree program, adult/continuing education programs. Off campus study at other units of the University of Wisconsin Colleges, four-year campuses of the University of Wisconsin.

Entrance Requirements: Options: electronic application, deferred admission. Required: high school transcript, ACT. Entrance: minimally difficult. Application deadline: Rolling. Notification: continuous.

Collegiate Environment: Orientation program. Drama-theater group, choral group. Social organizations: 10 open to all. Most popular organizations: Student Government Association, Multicultural Student Union, U-Rock Players, Education Club, Adult Student Club. Major annual events: Non-Traditional Student Week, Fall Fest, May Fest. College housing not available. University of Wisconsin-Rock County Library with 79,972 books, 4,466 audiovisual materials, an OPAC, and a Web page. Operations spending for 2004 fiscal year: $78,000. 50 computers available on campus for general student use. A campuswide network can be accessed. Staffed computer lab on campus.

■ UNIVERSITY OF WISCONSIN-SHEBOYGAN *M-13*

One University Dr.
Sheboygan, WI 53081-4789
Tel: (920)459-6600

Admissions: (920)459-6633

Fax: (920)459-6602

Web Site: http://www.sheboygan.uwc.edu/

Description: State-supported, 2-year, coed. Part of University of Wisconsin System. Awards transfer associate degrees. Founded 1933. Setting: 75-acre small town campus with easy access to Milwaukee. Total enrollment: 731. 6% from top 10% of their high school class, 18% from top quarter, 48% from top half. Students come from 5 other countries, 1% Native American, 3% Hispanic, 1% black, 6% Asian American or Pacific Islander, 0.1% international, 24% 25 or older. Calendar: semesters. Core. Academic remediation for entering students, ESL program, services for LD students, advanced placement, independent study, distance learning, summer session for credit, part-time degree program, adult/continuing education programs. Off campus study at other units of the University of Wisconsin Colleges, four-year campuses of the University of Wisconsin.

Entrance Requirements: Open admission. Options: Common Application, electronic application. Required: high school transcript. Required for some: interview. Placement: ACT required. Entrance: noncompetitive. Application deadline: Rolling.

Collegiate Environment: Orientation program. Drama-theater group, choral group, student-run newspaper. Social organizations: 26 open to all; coed fraternity; 4% of eligible men and 5% of eligible women are members. Most popular organizations: Student Ambassadors, Phi Theta Kappa, student government, Circle K, Zoomers (nontraditional students). Major annual events: Fall Kick-off, Spring Kick-Off, Spring Picnic. Campus security: 24-hour patrols by city police. College housing not available. Battig Memorial Library with 40,100 books, 160 serials, an OPAC, and a Web page. Operations spending for 2004 fiscal year: $86,430. 60 computers available on campus for general student use. A campuswide network can be accessed. Staffed computer lab on campus.

■ **UNIVERSITY OF WISCONSIN-STEVENS POINT** *K-8*

2100 Main St.

Stevens Point, WI 54481-3897

Tel: (715)346-0123

Admissions: (715)346-2441

Fax: (715)346-2561

E-mail: admiss@uwsp.edu

Web Site: http://www.uwsp.edu/

Description: State-supported, comprehensive, coed. Part of University of Wisconsin System. Awards associate, bachelor's, and master's degrees. Founded 1894. Setting: 335-acre small town campus. Endowment: $12 million. Research spending for 2004 fiscal year: $1.5 million. Educational spending for 2005 fiscal year: $5776 per student. Total enrollment: 8,577. Faculty: 437 (357 full-time, 80 part-time). Student-undergrad faculty ratio is 21:1. 4,583 applied, 80% were admitted. 14% from top 10% of their high school class, 42% from top quarter, 91% from top half. 28 valedictorians. Full-time: 7,746 students, 54% women, 46% men. Part-time: 607 students, 55% women, 45% men. Students come from 29 states and territories, 28 other countries, 6% from out-of-state, 1% Native American, 1% Hispanic, 1% black, 2% Asian American or Pacific Islander, 1% international, 11% 25 or older, 36% live on campus, 8% transferred in. Retention: 76% of full-time freshmen returned the following year. Academic areas with the most degrees conferred: natural resources/environmental science; business/marketing; social sciences. Core. Calendar: semesters. Academic remediation for entering students, ESL program, services for LD students, advanced placement, accelerated degree program, self-designed majors, independent study, distance learning, double major, summer session for credit, part-time degree program, adult/continuing education programs, co-op programs and internships, graduate courses open to undergrads. Off campus study at University of Wisconsin campuses at Oshkosh, Eau Claire, Fond du Lac, Marinette, Marshfield, and Marathon. Study abroad program. ROTC: Army.

Entrance Requirements: Options: electronic application, deferred admission. Required: high school transcript, SAT or ACT. Recommended: campus visit. Entrance: moderately difficult. Application deadline: Rolling. Notification: continuous.

Costs Per Year: Application fee: $35. State resident tuition: $4277 full-time, $178 per credit part-time. Nonresident tuition: $14,323 full-time, $596 per credit part-time. Mandatory fees: $785 full-time, $70 per credit part-time. Full-time tuition and fees vary according to course load and reciprocity agreements. Part-time tuition and fees vary according to course load and reciprocity agreements. College room and board: $4322. College room only: $2574. Room and board charges vary according to housing facility.

Collegiate Environment: Orientation program. Drama-theater group, choral group, student-run newspaper, radio station. Social organizations: 151 open

to all; national fraternities, national sororities; 1% of eligible men and 1% of eligible women are members. Student services: health clinic, personal-psychological counseling, women's center. Campus security: 24-hour emergency response devices and patrols, student patrols, late night transport-escort service, controlled dormitory access. 3,316 college housing spaces available; 3,118 were occupied in 2003-04. Freshmen guaranteed college housing. On-campus residence required through sophomore year. Options: coed, men-only, women-only housing available. Learning Resources Center with an OPAC and a Web page. Operations spending for 2004 fiscal year: $2.4 million. 880 computers available on campus for general student use. A campuswide network can be accessed from student residence rooms and from off campus. Staffed computer lab on campus.

Community Environment: Stevens Point is located in the very center of the state on the Wisconsin River. It lies midway between Milwaukee and Minneapolis and is approximately 250 miles from Chicago. Air service is available through the Central Wisconsin Airport. Stevens Point is a city of about 25,000 and is the "Gateway to Wisconsin's Vacationland." A wide range of cultural and year-around recreational opportunities are available. The area is known for insurance, agribusiness, paper production, finance, and light industry.

■ **UNIVERSITY OF WISCONSIN-STOUT** *J-3*

Menomonie, WI 54751

Tel: (715)232-1122

Admissions: (715)232-2639

Fax: (715)232-1667

E-mail: gilbertsc@uwstout.edu

Web Site: http://www.uwstout.edu/

Description: State-supported, comprehensive, coed. Part of University of Wisconsin System. Awards bachelor's and master's degrees and post-master's certificates. Founded 1891. Setting: 120-acre small town campus with easy access to Minneapolis-St. Paul. Research spending for 2004 fiscal year: $1.1 million. Total enrollment: 7,891. Faculty: 394 (289 full-time, 105 part-time). Student-undergrad faculty ratio is 20:1. 3,953 applied, 81% were admitted. 6% from top 10% of their high school class, 28% from top quarter, 73% from top half. Full-time: 6,605 students, 50% women, 50% men. Part-time: 732 students, 43% women, 57% men. Students come from 26 states and territories, 31% from out-of-state, 1% Native American, 1% Hispanic, 1% black, 2% Asian American or Pacific Islander, 1% international, 12% 25 or older, 38% live on campus, 8% transferred in. Retention: 73% of full-time freshmen returned the following year. Academic areas with the most degrees conferred: business/marketing; education; visual and performing arts. Core. Calendar: 4-1-4. Academic remediation for entering students, services for LD students, advanced placement, accelerated degree program, honors program, independent study, distance learning, double major, summer session for credit, part-time degree program, external degree program, adult/continuing education programs, co-op programs and internships, graduate courses open to undergrads. Off campus study at Fashion Institute of Technology, University of Wisconsin-Eau Claire. Study abroad program.

Entrance Requirements: Option: electronic application. Required: high school transcript, SAT or ACT. Recommended: minimum 2.50 high school GPA. Required for some: minimum 2.75 high school GPA. Entrance: moderately difficult. Application deadline: Rolling. Notification: continuous.

Costs Per Year: Application fee: $35. State resident tuition: $4745 full-time, $158 per credit part-time. Nonresident tuition: $15,078 full-time, $503 per credit part-time. Mandatory fees: $1847 full-time, $62 per credit part-time. Full-time tuition and fees vary according to reciprocity agreements. Part-time tuition and fees vary according to reciprocity agreements. College room and board: $4572. College room only: $2814. Room and board charges vary according to board plan and housing facility.

Collegiate Environment: Orientation program. Drama-theater group, choral group, marching band, student-run newspaper, radio station. Social organizations: 117 open to all; national fraternities, national sororities, local fraternities, local sororities; 2% of eligible men and 4% of eligible women are members. Most popular organizations: Hotel/Motel Management Association, DECA-District Educational Clubs of America, Recreation Commission, OASIS. Major annual events: Homecoming, Family Weekend, Bash on the Grass (spring festival). Student services: legal services, health clinic, personal-psychological counseling. Campus security: 24-hour patrols, student patrols, controlled dormitory access. 2,936 college housing spaces available; 2,650 were occupied in 2003-04. Freshmen guaranteed college housing. On-campus residence required through sophomore year. Option: coed housing available. Library Learning Center with 229,986 books, 1.2 million microform titles, 1,784 serials, 16,142 audiovisual materials, an OPAC, and a Web page. Operations spending for 2004 fiscal year: $3.3 million. 590 computers available on campus for general student use. Computer purchase/lease plans available. A campuswide network can be accessed from student residence rooms and from off campus. Staffed computer lab on campus.

Community Environment: Menomonie, population 14,000, is located on the Red Cedar River and Lake Menomin, and is accessible by all commercial transportation.

■ **UNIVERSITY OF WISCONSIN-SUPERIOR** *D-3*

Belknap and Catlin
PO Box 2000
Superior, WI 54880-4500
Tel: (715)394-8101
Admissions: (715)394-8396
Fax: (715)394-8407
E-mail: admissions@uwsuper.edu
Web Site: http://www.uwsuper.edu/

Description: State-supported, comprehensive, coed. Part of University of Wisconsin System. Awards bachelor's and master's degrees (associate, educational specialist). Founded 1893. Setting: 230-acre small town campus. Endowment: $6.4 million. Research spending for 2004 fiscal year: $991,820. Educational spending for 2005 fiscal year: $5256 per student. Total enrollment: 2,872. Faculty: 170 (118 full-time, 52 part-time). Student-undergrad faculty ratio is 17:1. 918 applied, 74% were admitted. 14% from top 10% of their high school class, 44% from top quarter, 82% from top half. 3 valedictorians. Full-time: 2,133 students, 59% women, 41% men. Part-time: 450 students, 64% women, 36% men. Students come from 17 states and territories, 32 other countries, 42% from out-of-state, 3% Native American, 1% Hispanic, 1% black, 1% Asian American or Pacific Islander, 5% international, 26% 25 or older, 22% live on campus, 0% transferred in. Retention: 71% of full-time freshmen returned the following year. Academic areas with the most degrees conferred: business/marketing; education; communications/journalism. Core. Calendar: semesters. Academic remediation for entering students, ESL program, services for LD students, advanced placement, self-designed majors, freshman honors college, honors program, independent study, distance learning, double major, summer session for credit, part-time degree program, external degree program, adult/continuing education programs, co-op programs and internships, graduate courses open to undergrads. Off campus study at College of St. Scholastica, Northland College, University of Minnesota, Duluth. Study abroad program. ROTC: Air Force (c).

Entrance Requirements: Options: electronic application, early admission, deferred admission. Required: high school transcript, SAT or ACT. Recommended: interview. Required for some: essay, recommendations. Entrance: moderately difficult. Application deadline: Rolling. Notification: continuous.

Costs Per Year: Application fee: $35. State resident tuition: $4,427 full-time, $184.46 per credit part-time. Nonresident tuition: $14,473 full-time, $603.05 per credit part-time. Mandatory fees: $761 full-time, $242.28 per unit part-time. College room and board: $4422. College room only: $2552.

Collegiate Environment: Orientation program. Drama-theater group, choral group, student-run newspaper, radio station. Social organizations: 45 open to all. Most popular organizations: Student Senate, Student Activities Board, Residence Hall Association, Inter-Varsity Christian Fellowship. Major annual events: Student Activities Board Comedy Shop, New Student Orientation, Family Weekend Orientation. Student services: health clinic, personal-psychological counseling, women's center. Campus security: 24-hour emergency response devices and patrols, student patrols, late night transport-escort service, controlled dormitory access. 600 college housing spaces available; 550 were occupied in 2003-04. Freshmen guaranteed college housing. On-campus residence required in freshman year. Options: coed, women-only housing available. Jim Dan Hill Library with 467,700 books, 105,398 microform titles, 753 serials, 5,467 audiovisual materials, an OPAC, and a Web page. Operations spending for 2004 fiscal year: $843,024. 161 computers available on campus for general student use. Computer purchase/lease plans available. A campuswide network can be accessed from student residence rooms and from off campus. Staffed computer lab on campus.

Community Environment: Superior is Wisconsin's leading port of entry and is located at the head of Lake Superior at the northwest corner of the state. The largest iron ore dock, grain elevator and briquette plant in the world are here at Superior. The area is a leading summer and winter recreation resort. Along with neighbor city Duluth, MN, the area offers a wide range of music, theater, shopping, and recreational opportunities.

■ **UNIVERSITY OF WISCONSIN-WASHINGTON COUNTY** *N-12*

400 University Dr.
West Bend, WI 53095-3699
Tel: (262)335-5200
Admissions: (262)335-5201
Fax: (262)335-5257
E-mail: www.mnelson@uwc.edu
Web Site: http://www.washington.uwc.edu/

Description: State-supported, 2-year, coed. Part of University of Wisconsin System. Awards transfer associate degrees. Founded 1968. Setting: 87-acre small town campus with easy access to Milwaukee. Educational spending for 2005 fiscal year: $3977 per student. Total enrollment: 951. Student-undergrad faculty ratio is 21:1. 708 applied, 67% were admitted. 3% from top 10% of their high school class, 15% from top quarter, 51% from top half. Full-time: 663 students, 53% women, 47% men. Part-time: 288 students, 63% women, 37% men. Students come from 2 states and territories, 2 other countries, 1% from out-of-state, 1% Native American, 1% Hispanic, 0.2% black, 0% Asian American or Pacific Islander, 0% international, 16% 25 or older, 7% transferred in. Core. Calendar: semesters. Academic remediation for entering students, services for LD students, advanced placement, honors program, independent study, distance learning, double major, summer session for credit, part-time degree program. Off campus study at other units of the University of Wisconsin Colleges, four-year campuses of the University of Wisconsin.

Entrance Requirements: Options: electronic application, deferred admission. Required: high school transcript, SAT and SAT Subject Tests or ACT. Recommended: ACT. Required for some: essay, recommendations, interview. Entrance: noncompetitive. Application deadline: Rolling.

Costs Per Year: Application fee: $35. State resident tuition: $4520 full-time, $190 per credit part-time. Nonresident tuition: $11,700 full-time, $488 per credit part-time. Mandatory fees: $268 full-time, $11 per credit part-time, $132 per term part-time.

Collegiate Environment: Orientation program. Drama-theater group, choral group, student-run newspaper. Social organizations: 6 open to all. Most popular organizations: Student Government Association, Business Club, Phi Theta Kappa, Writers' Guild, Student Impact. Major annual events: Summer Send-Off Picnic, United Way Fund Drive, Convocation/Commencement. Student services: personal-psychological counseling. College housing not available. University of Wisconsin-Washington County Library with 46,429 books, 22 microform titles, 247 serials, 4,998 audiovisual materials, an OPAC, and a Web page. 78 computers available on campus for general student use. A campuswide network can be accessed from off-campus. Staffed computer lab on campus.

■ **UNIVERSITY OF WISCONSIN-WAUKESHA** *P-12*

1500 University Dr.
Waukesha, WI 53188-2799
Tel: (414)521-5200
Fax: (414)521-5491
Web Site: http://www.waukesha.uwc.edu/

Description: State-supported, 2-year, coed. Part of University of Wisconsin System. Awards transfer associate degrees. Founded 1966. Setting: 86-acre suburban campus with easy access to Milwaukee. Educational spending for 2005 fiscal year: $4200 per student. Total enrollment: 2,064. 1,886 applied, 66% were admitted. 2% from top 10% of their high school class, 8% from top quarter, 23% from top half. Students come from 5 states and territories, 1% from out-of-state, 1% Native American, 4% Hispanic, 2% black, 3% Asian American or Pacific Islander, 0.1% international, 16% 25 or older. Core. Calendar: semesters. Academic remediation for entering students, services for LD students, advanced placement, self-designed majors, honors program, summer session for credit, part-time degree program, adult/continuing education programs. Off campus study at Carroll College, other units of the University of Wisconsin Colleges and 4-year campuses of the University of Wisconsin.

Entrance Requirements: Options: early admission, deferred admission. Required: high school transcript, SAT or ACT. Recommended: interview. Required for some: recommendations, SAT. Entrance: minimally difficult. Application deadline: Rolling. Notification: continuous.

Costs Per Year: Application fee: $35. State resident tuition: $4210 full-time, $177.25 per credit part-time. Nonresident tuition: $12,910 full-time, $539.75 per credit part-time.

Collegiate Environment: Orientation program. Drama-theater group, choral group, student-run newspaper, radio station. Social organizations: 32 open to all. Most popular organizations: student government, Student Activities

Committee, Campus Crusade, Phi Theta Kappa, Circle K. Major annual events: Fall Fest, Spring Carnival, Honors and Degree Ceremony. Campus security: late night transport-escort service, part-time patrols by trained security personnel. College housing not available. University of Wisconsin-Waukesha Library plus 1 other with 41,000 books and 300 serials. 90 computers available on campus for general student use. A campuswide network can be accessed. Staffed computer lab on campus.

■ UNIVERSITY OF WISCONSIN-WHITEWATER *P-10*

800 West Main St.
Whitewater, WI 53190-1790
Tel: (262)472-1234
Admissions: (262)472-1440
Fax: (262)472-1515
E-mail: mckellis@uww.edu
Web Site: http://www.uww.edu/

Description: State-supported, comprehensive, coed. Part of University of Wisconsin System. Awards associate, bachelor's, and master's degrees. Founded 1868. Setting: 385-acre small town campus with easy access to Milwaukee. Endowment: $10.3 million. Research spending for 2004 fiscal year: $541,733. Educational spending for 2005 fiscal year: $4305 per student. Total enrollment: 10,750. Faculty: 497 (399 full-time, 98 part-time). Student-undergrad faculty ratio is 21:1. 5,403 applied, 55% were admitted. 8% from top 10% of their high school class, 32% from top quarter, 79% from top half. Full-time: 8,572 students, 51% women, 49% men. Part-time: 815 students, 57% women, 43% men. Students come from 29 states and territories, 26 other countries, 4% from out-of-state, 1% Native American, 2% Hispanic, 4% black, 2% Asian American or Pacific Islander, 1% international, 10% 25 or older, 40% live on campus, 7% transferred in. Retention: 76% of full-time freshmen returned the following year. Academic areas with the most degrees conferred: business/marketing; education; communications/journalism. Core. Calendar: semesters. Academic remediation for entering students, ESL program, services for LD students, advanced placement, accelerated degree program, self-designed majors, honors program, independent study, distance learning, double major, summer session for credit, part-time degree program, external degree program, adult/continuing education programs, co-op programs and internships, graduate courses open to undergrads. Study abroad program. ROTC: Army, Air Force.
Entrance Requirements: Options: Common Application, electronic application, early admission, deferred admission, international baccalaureate accepted. Required: high school transcript. Recommended: SAT or ACT. Required for some: recommendations, SAT or ACT. Entrance: moderately difficult. Application deadline: Rolling.
Costs Per Year: Application fee: $35. One-time mandatory fee: $100. State resident tuition: $4370 full-time, $186 per credit part-time. Nonresident tuition: $14,965 full-time, $663 per credit part-time. Mandatory fees: $710 full-time, $28.75 per credit part-time. Full-time tuition and fees vary according to degree level and reciprocity agreements. College room and board: $4210. College room only: $2460. Room and board charges vary according to board plan.
Collegiate Environment: Drama-theater group, choral group, marching band, student-run newspaper, radio station. Social organizations: 125 open to all; national fraternities, national sororities, local fraternities, local sororities; 4% of eligible men and 3% of eligible women are members. Most popular organizations: Finance Association, American Marketing Association, Black Student Union, Golden Key, Wisconsin Education Association. Major annual events: Homecoming Week, Student Open Education Fair. Student services: legal services, health clinic, personal-psychological counseling, women's center. Campus security: 24-hour emergency response devices, late night transport-escort service. 3,800 college housing spaces available; 3,694 were occupied in 2003-04. Freshmen guaranteed college housing. On-campus residence required through sophomore year. Options: coed, women-only housing available. Andersen Library with 683,564 books, 1.2 million microform titles, 4,164 serials, 18,277 audiovisual materials, an OPAC, and a Web page. Operations spending for 2004 fiscal year: $2.2 million. 1,300 computers available on campus for general student use. A campuswide network can be accessed from student residence rooms and from off campus. Staffed computer lab on campus.
Community Environment: UW-Whitewater is located in a city of 12,000 near the scenic beauty of the Southern Kettle Moraine State Forest. It is a one-hour drive from Madison and Milwaukee, and a two-hour drive from Chicago. The area around Whitewater offers lakes, recreation, cross country skiing, backpacking, hiking, and other forms of outdoor activity. The campus is within walking distance of 2 shopping areas and a city park is adjacent to the campus.

■ VITERBO UNIVERSITY *M-4*

900 Viterbo Dr.
La Crosse, WI 54601-4797
Tel: (608)796-3000
Free: 800-VIT-ERBO
Admissions: (608)796-3010
Fax: (608)796-3050
E-mail: admission@viterbo.edu
Web Site: http://www.viterbo.edu/

Description: Independent Roman Catholic, comprehensive, coed. Awards bachelor's and master's degrees. Founded 1890. Setting: 72-acre suburban campus. Endowment: $13.6 million. Educational spending for 2005 fiscal year: $6961 per student. Total enrollment: 2,534. Faculty: 224 (119 full-time, 105 part-time). Student-undergrad faculty ratio is 11:1. 1,098 applied, 86% were admitted. 12% from top 10% of their high school class, 35% from top quarter, 69% from top half. Full-time: 1,429 students, 72% women, 28% men. Part-time: 415 students, 73% women, 27% men. Students come from 19 states and territories, 14 other countries, 20% from out-of-state, 0.4% Native American, 1% Hispanic, 1% black, 2% Asian American or Pacific Islander, 1% international, 28% 25 or older, 35% live on campus, 12% transferred in. Retention: 68% of full-time freshmen returned the following year. Academic areas with the most degrees conferred: health professions and related sciences; business/marketing; education. Core. Calendar: semesters. Academic remediation for entering students, services for LD students, advanced placement, accelerated degree program, self-designed majors, independent study, distance learning, double major, summer session for credit, part-time degree program, adult/continuing education programs, internships, graduate courses open to undergrads. Off campus study at University of Wisconsin-La Crosse, Western Wisconsin Technical College, Viterbo Centers: West Demoine, West Allis, WI. Study abroad program. ROTC: Army (c).
Entrance Requirements: Options: Peterson's Universal Application, Common Application, electronic application, deferred admission, international baccalaureate accepted. Required: high school transcript, minimum 2.0 high school GPA, ACT. Required for some: essay, 1 recommendation, interview, audition for theater and music; portfolio for art. Entrance: moderately difficult. Application deadlines: Rolling, Rolling for nonresidents. Notification: continuous until 8/15, continuous until 8/15 for nonresidents.
Costs Per Year: Application fee: $25. Comprehensive fee: $23,700 includes full-time tuition ($17,640), mandatory fees ($420), and college room and board ($5640). College room only: $2430. Part-time tuition: $505 per credit. Part-time mandatory fees: $10 per credit, $30.
Collegiate Environment: Orientation program. Drama-theater group, choral group, student-run newspaper. Social organizations: 22 open to all. Most popular organizations: Viterbo Student Nurses Association, Viterbo Education Students Club, Connect (AODA peer counselors), campus ministry (volunteer services and service trips), Sigma Pi Delta. Major annual events: Homecoming, Hypnotist show, Courtyard Carni. Student services: health clinic, personal-psychological counseling. Campus security: 24-hour emergency response devices, late night transport-escort service, controlled dormitory access, security officers on campus 5:00 p.m. to 7:00 a.m, lighted pathways, emergency evacuation plan, self-defense education programs. 561 college housing spaces available; 521 were occupied in 2003-04. Freshmen guaranteed college housing. On-campus residence required through sophomore year. Options: coed, men-only, women-only housing available. Todd Wehr Memorial Library with 92,591 books, 233,467 microform titles, 491 serials, 6,229 audiovisual materials, an OPAC, and a Web page. Operations spending for 2004 fiscal year: $609,318. 278 computers available on campus for general student use. A campuswide network can be accessed from student residence rooms and from off campus. Staffed computer lab on campus.

■ WAUKESHA COUNTY TECHNICAL COLLEGE *B-10*

800 Main St.
Pewaukee, WI 53072-4601
Tel: (262)691-5566; 888-892-WCTC
Admissions: (262)691-5464
Fax: (262)691-5693
E-mail: lfrederick@wctc.edu
Web Site: http://www.wctc.edu/

Description: State and locally supported, 2-year, coed. Part of Wisconsin Technical College System. Awards certificates, diplomas, and terminal associate degrees. Founded 1923. Setting: 137-acre small town campus with easy access to Milwaukee. Educational spending for 2005 fiscal year:

$11,982 per student. Total enrollment: 6,386. Student-undergrad faculty ratio is 8:1. Full-time: 1,614 students, 44% women, 56% men. Part-time: 4,772 students, 58% women, 42% men. Students come from 4 other countries, 0% from out-of-state, 0.4% Native American, 4% Hispanic, 4% black, 2% Asian American or Pacific Islander, 0% international, 90% 25 or older. Calendar: semesters. Academic remediation for entering students, ESL program, services for LD students, advanced placement, summer session for credit, part-time degree program, external degree program, adult/continuing education programs, co-op programs.

Entrance Requirements: Open admission. Option: early admission. Required: high school transcript. Required for some: interview, varies. Entrance: noncompetitive. Application deadline: Rolling.

Costs Per Year: Application fee: $30. State resident tuition: $2610 full-time, $87 per credit part-time. Nonresident tuition: $16,089 full-time, $536 per credit part-time.

Collegiate Environment: Student services: health clinic. Campus security: patrols by police officers 8 a.m. to 10 p.m. College housing not available. 50 computers available on campus for general student use.

■ WESTERN TECHNICAL COLLEGE *M-4*

304 6th St. North
PO Box C-908
La Crosse, WI 54602-0908
Tel: (608)785-9200
Free: 800-248-9982
Admissions: (608)785-9158
Fax: (608)785-9205
E-mail: wellsj@wwtc.edu
Web Site: http://www.wwtc.edu/

Description: District-supported, 2-year, coed. Part of Wisconsin Technical College System. Awards certificates, diplomas, transfer associate, and terminal associate degrees. Founded 1911. Setting: 10-acre urban campus. Research spending for 2004 fiscal year: $227,769. Educational spending for 2005 fiscal year: $9793 per student. Total enrollment: 4,765. Student-undergrad faculty ratio is 7:1. 3,443 applied, 35% were admitted. Students come from 4 states and territories, 7% from out-of-state, 1% Native American, 1% Hispanic, 2% black, 3% Asian American or Pacific Islander, 0% international, 16% 25 or older, 2% live on campus. Core. Calendar: semesters. Academic remediation for entering students, ESL program, services for LD students, advanced placement, accelerated degree program, self-designed majors, distance learning, summer session for credit, part-time degree program, external degree program, adult/continuing education programs, co-op programs and internships. Off campus study.

Entrance Requirements: Open admission except for health occupations programs. Options: Common Application, electronic application, early admission. Required: high school transcript. Recommended: interview, ACT. Required for some: ACT ASSET. Entrance: noncompetitive. Application deadline: Rolling.

Costs Per Year: Application fee: $30. State resident tuition: $2610 full-time, $87 per credit part-time. Nonresident tuition: $16,089 full-time, $536.30 per credit part-time. Mandatory fees: $185 full-time, $185 per term part-time. College room only: $2312.

Collegiate Environment: Orientation program. Student-run newspaper. Social organizations: 28 open to all. Most popular organizations: Wisconsin Marketing Management Association (WMMA), Air Conditioning, Refrigeration Organization (ACRO), Multicultural Club, Business Professionals of America (BPA), Advertising Club. Major annual event: Orientation. Student services: personal-psychological counseling. Campus security: 24-hour emergency response devices and patrols, student patrols, late night transport-escort service, controlled dormitory access. 100 college housing spaces available; all were occupied in 2003-04. Option: coed available. Western Wisconsin Technical College Library plus 1 other with 31,243 books, 397 microform titles, 313 serials, 3,750 audiovisual materials, and an OPAC. Operations spending for 2004 fiscal year: $303,682. 800 computers available on campus for general student use. A campuswide network can be accessed from student residence rooms and from off campus. Staffed computer lab on campus.

Community Environment: See University of Wisconsin - La Crosse.

■ WISCONSIN INDIANHEAD TECHNICAL COLLEGE *G-3*

505 Pine Ridge Dr.
Shell Lake, WI 54871
Tel: (715)468-2815
Free: 800-243-9482
Fax: (715)468-2819
Web Site: http://www.witc.edu/

Description: District-supported, 2-year, coed. Part of Wisconsin Technical College System. Awards certificates, diplomas, and terminal associate degrees. Founded 1912. Setting: 113-acre urban campus. System endowment: $1.8 million. System-wide educational spending for 2005 fiscal year: $7343 per student. Total enrollment: 3,533. Student-undergrad faculty ratio is 6:1. Full-time: 1,561 students, 53% women, 47% men. Part-time: 1,972 students, 67% women, 33% men. 3% Native American, 1% Hispanic, 0.3% black, 1% Asian American or Pacific Islander, 45% 25 or older. Calendar: semesters.

Entrance Requirements: Application deadline: Rolling.

■ WISCONSIN LUTHERAN COLLEGE *O-12*

8800 West Bluemound Rd.
Milwaukee, WI 53226-9942
Tel: (414)443-8800; 888-WIS LUTH
Admissions: (414)443-8811
Fax: (414)443-8514
E-mail: craig_swiontek@wlc.edu
Web Site: http://www.wlc.edu/

Description: Independent, 4-year, coed, affiliated with Wisconsin Evangelical Lutheran Synod. Awards bachelor's degrees. Founded 1973. Setting: 21-acre suburban campus. Endowment: $10.3 million. Research spending for 2004 fiscal year: $38,210. Educational spending for 2005 fiscal year: $7362 per student. Total enrollment: 706. 531 applied, 84% were admitted. 23% from top 10% of their high school class, 53% from top quarter, 83% from top half. 10 valedictorians. Full-time: 672 students, 61% women, 39% men. Part-time: 34 students, 44% women, 56% men. Students come from 28 states and territories, 6 other countries, 19% from out-of-state, 0% Native American, 1% Hispanic, 1% black, 1% Asian American or Pacific Islander, 1% international, 1% 25 or older, 78% live on campus, 3% transferred in. Retention: 80% of full-time freshmen returned the following year. Core. Calendar: semesters. Services for LD students, advanced placement, self-designed majors, independent study, double major, summer session for credit, part-time degree program, internships. Study abroad program. ROTC: Army (c), Naval (c), Air Force (c).

Entrance Requirements: Options: Peterson's Universal Application, Common Application, electronic application. Required: high school transcript, minimum 2.70 high school GPA, 1 recommendation, minimum ACT score of 21, SAT or ACT. Required for some: interview. Entrance: moderately difficult. Notification: continuous.

Costs Per Year: Application fee: $20. Comprehensive fee: $23,510 includes full-time tuition ($17,340), mandatory fees ($130), and college room and board ($6040).

Collegiate Environment: Orientation program. Drama-theater group, choral group, student-run newspaper. Social organizations: 31 open to all. Major annual events: Commencement Weekend, Opening Weekend (Orientation), Christmas Week activities and events. Student services: health clinic, personal-psychological counseling. Campus security: 24-hour emergency response devices and patrols, late night transport-escort service, controlled dormitory access, closed-circuit TV monitors. 600 college housing spaces available; 539 were occupied in 2003-04. Freshmen guaranteed college housing. On-campus residence required through senior year. Options: men-only, women-only housing available. Marvin M. Schwan Library with 71,731 books, 9,211 microform titles, 614 serials, 4,409 audiovisual materials, an OPAC, and a Web page. Operations spending for 2004 fiscal year: $366,354. 200 computers available on campus for general student use. A campuswide network can be accessed from student residence rooms and from off campus. Staffed computer lab on campus.

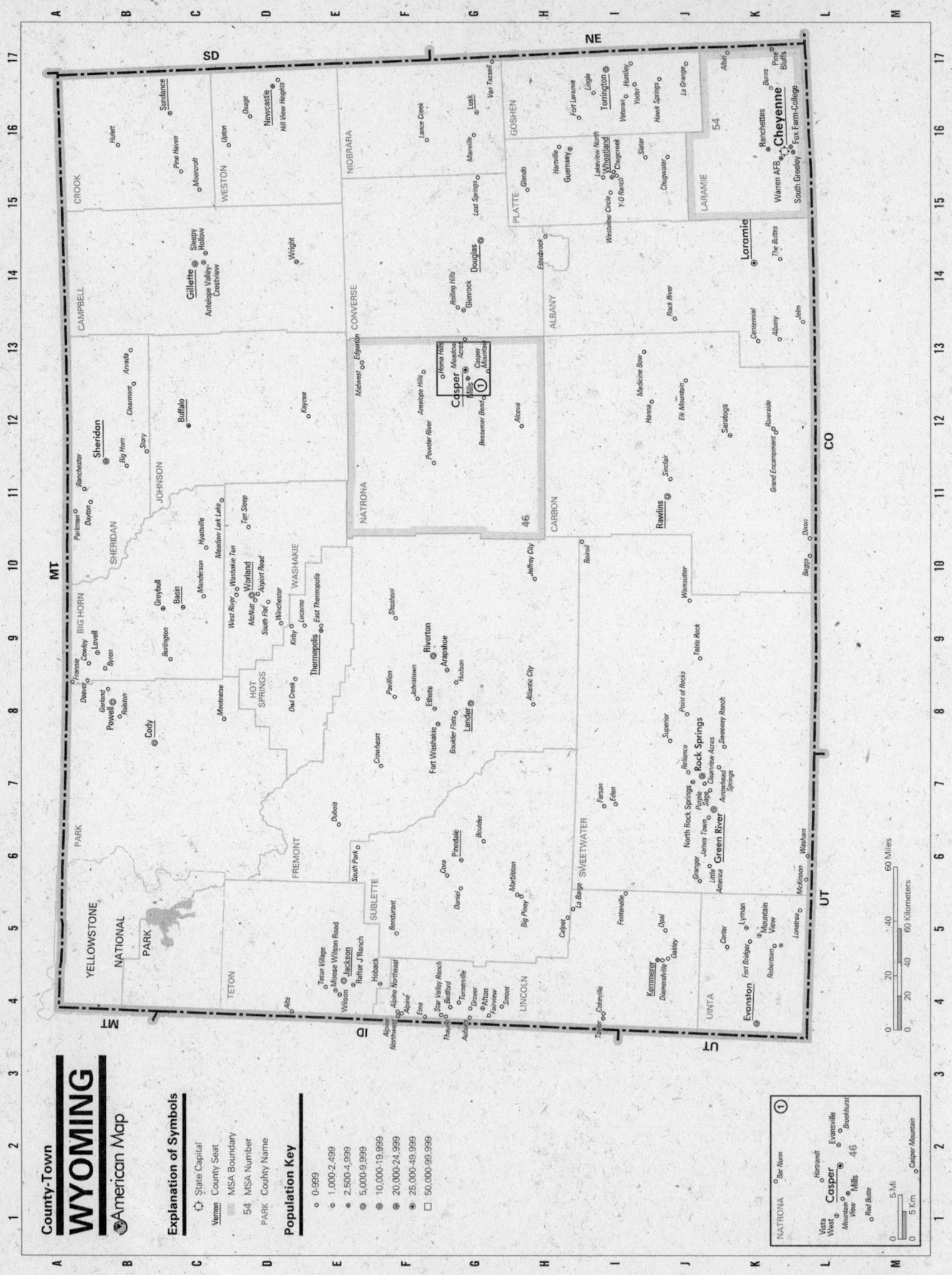

County-Town
WYOMING

● American Map

Explanation of Symbols

⚙ State Capital
Vernon ● County Seat
▬ MSA Boundary
54 MSA Number
PARK County Name

Population Key

○ 0-999
● 1,000-2,499
● 2,500-4,999
◉ 5,000-9,999
◉ 10,000-19,999
◉ 20,000-24,999
◉ 25,000-49,999
☐ 50,000-99,999

■ CASPER COLLEGE *G-13*

125 College Dr.
Casper, WY 82601-4699
Tel: (307)268-2110
Free: 800-442-2963
Admissions: (307)268-2220
Fax: (307)268-2682
E-mail: amcnulty@caspercollege.edu
Web Site: http://www.caspercollege.edu/

Description: District-supported, 2-year, coed. Part of Wyoming Community College Commission. Awards certificates, transfer associate, and terminal associate degrees. Founded 1945. Setting: 125-acre small town campus. Total enrollment: 4,285. Student-undergrad faculty ratio is 14:1. 1,046 applied, 100% were admitted. Full-time: 1,896 students, 60% women, 40% men. Part-time: 2,389 students, 60% women, 40% men. Students come from 40 states and territories, 15 other countries, 8% from out-of-state, 1% Native American, 3% Hispanic, 1% black, 0.4% Asian American or Pacific Islander, 1% international, 45% 25 or older, 15% live on campus, 6% transferred in. Retention: 61% of full-time freshmen returned the following year. Core. Calendar: semesters. Academic remediation for entering students, ESL program, services for LD students, advanced placement, accelerated degree program, independent study, distance learning, summer session for credit, part-time degree program, adult/continuing education programs, co-op programs and internships. Off campus study at Great Falls University, University of Wyoming-Casper Campus, University of North Dakota, University of Maryland. ROTC: Army (c).

Entrance Requirements: Open admission for state residents. Options: electronic application, early admission, international baccalaureate accepted. Required: high school transcript. Entrance: noncompetitive. Application deadline: 8/15. Notification: continuous until 8/15.

Costs Per Year: Application fee: $0. State resident tuition: $1416 full-time, $59 per credit part-time. Nonresident tuition: $4272 full-time, $178 per credit part-time. Mandatory fees: $168 full-time, $7 per credit part-time. College room and board: $3590.

Collegiate Environment: Orientation program. Drama-theater group, choral group, student-run newspaper. Most popular organizations: Student Senate, Student Activities Board, Agriculture Club, Theater Club, Phi Theta Kappa. Major annual events: Casino Night, Back to School Dance, Weekend of Welcome. Student services: health clinic, personal-psychological counseling, women's center. Campus security: 24-hour patrols, late night transport-escort service. 400 college housing spaces available; 359 were occupied in 2003-04. Option: coed housing available. Goodstein Library with 118,000 books, 500 serials, an OPAC, and a Web page. 130 computers available on campus for general student use. A campuswide network can be accessed from student residence rooms. Staffed computer lab on campus.

Community Environment: Rich in oil and uranium, Casper is Wyoming's leading industrial city. Cattle and sheep ranches in the surrounding area provide the basis for the city's wool and livestock markets. Situated at the foot of Casper Mountain in the approximate geographic center of Wyoming, the climate is invigorating with 300 days of sunshine each year. The community has 70 churches, a hospital, library, symphony orchestra, theatre group, a mall, 11 theatres and a community concert series. Local recreation includes tennis, golf, trap shooting, a multipurpose event center, swimming pools, bowling alleys, excellent fishing and hunting, city and mountain parks, archery and rifle ranges, and a ski area. Several rodeos are held here each year, as well as skiing and mountain climbing events.

■ CENTRAL WYOMING COLLEGE *G-9*

2660 Peck Ave.
Riverton, WY 82501-2273
Tel: (307)855-2000
Free: 800-735-8418
Admissions: (307)855-2231
Fax: (307)855-2092
E-mail: tshultz@cwc.edu
Web Site: http://www.cwc.edu/

Description: State and locally supported, 2-year, coed. Part of Wyoming Community College Commission. Awards certificates, transfer associate, and terminal associate degrees. Founded 1966. Setting: 200-acre small town campus. Endowment: $3.9 million. Educational spending for 2005 fiscal year: $3705 per student. Total enrollment: 1,637. Student-undergrad faculty ratio is 14:1. 346 applied, 100% were admitted. 8% from top 10% of their high school class, 24% from top quarter, 55% from top half. 2 valedictorians. Full-time: 696 students, 65% women, 35% men. Part-time: 941 students, 65% women, 35% men. Students come from 39 states and territories, 6 other countries, 4% from out-of-state, 19% Native American, 4% Hispanic, 0.5% black, 0.2% Asian American or Pacific Islander, 2% international, 41% 25 or older, 9% live on campus, 12% transferred in. Retention: 51% of full-time freshmen returned the following year. Core. Calendar: semesters. Academic remediation for entering students, ESL program, services for LD students, advanced placement, self-designed majors, honors program, independent study, distance learning, summer session for credit, part-time degree program, adult/continuing education programs, co-op programs. Off campus study.

Entrance Requirements: Open admission except for nursing program. Options: Peterson's Universal Application, early admission, deferred admission. Recommended: high school transcript. Entrance: noncompetitive. Application deadline: Rolling.

Costs Per Year: Application fee: $0. State resident tuition: $1416 full-time, $59 per credit part-time. Nonresident tuition: $4272 full-time, $178 per credit part-time. Mandatory fees: $528 full-time, $22 per credit part-time. College room and board: $3060. College room only: $1460.

Collegiate Environment: Orientation program. Drama-theater group, choral group, student-run newspaper, radio station. Social organizations: 18 open to all. Most popular organizations: Multi-Cultural Club, La Vida Nueva Club, Fellowship of College Christians, Quality Leaders, Science Club. Major annual events: I Hate Winter Dance, theater and music productions, Final Feed. Student services: personal-psychological counseling. Campus security: 24-hour patrols. 180 college housing spaces available; 163 were occupied in 2003-04. No special consideration for freshman housing applicants. Option: coed housing available. Central Wyoming College Library with 78,167 books, 33,700 microform titles, 183 serials, 1,256 audiovisual materials, an OPAC, and a Web page. Operations spending for 2004 fiscal year: $177,656. 323 computers available on campus for general student use. A campuswide network can be accessed from student residence rooms and from off campus. Staffed computer lab on campus.

Community Environment: Located in the lower Wind River Basin, Riverton (population 10,000) is the center of a large farming, lumbering and livestock producing region. The area has a stimulating climate with a summer average temperature of 66 degrees and a winter average of 35 degrees. There are less than 10 inches of rainfall annually. The community is accessed by bus and air lines. There are 25 churches, a modern library, 2 hospitals, 3 clinics, and good shopping available. Local recreation facilities include an Olympic-size swimming pool, and provide for golf, baseball, bowling, hunting, fishing, boating, water skiing, snow skiing, rock hunting, and hiking. An Antique Museum, the Wind River Indian Reservation, and many national and state parks are of interest. Part-time employment is available for students.

■ EASTERN WYOMING COLLEGE *I-17*

3200 West C St.
Torrington, WY 82240-1699
Tel: (307)532-8200
Free: 800-658-3195
Admissions: (307)532-8257
Fax: (307)532-8222
E-mail: mcotant@ewc.wy.edu
Web Site: http://www.ewc.wy.edu/

Description: State and locally supported, 2-year, coed. Part of Wyoming Community College Commission. Awards certificates, diplomas, transfer associate, and terminal associate degrees. Founded 1948. Setting: 40-acre rural campus. Total enrollment: 1,346. Student-undergrad faculty ratio is 13:1. 4% from top 10% of their high school class, 16% from top quarter, 45% from top half. Full-time: 522 students, 60% women, 40% men. Part-time: 824 students, 72% women, 28% men. Students come from 23 states and territories, 3 other countries, 26% from out-of-state, 1% Native American, 7% Hispanic, 1% black, 0% Asian American or Pacific Islander, 1% international, 32% 25 or older, 26% live on campus, 4% transferred in. Core. Calendar: semesters. Academic remediation for entering students, ESL program, services for LD students, advanced placement, accelerated degree program, self-designed majors, independent study, distance learning, summer session for credit, part-time degree program, adult/continuing education programs, co-op programs and internships.

Entrance Requirements: Open admission. Options: Peterson's Universal Application, electronic application, early admission. Recommended: high school transcript. Entrance: noncompetitive. Application deadline: Rolling. Preference given to state residents.

Costs Per Year: Application fee: $0. State resident tuition: $1416 full-time, $59 per credit hour part-time. Nonresident tuition: $4272 full-time, $178 per credit hour part-time. Mandatory fees: $384 full-time, $16 per credit hour part-time. College room and board: $3220. College room only: $1364.

Collegiate Environment: Orientation program. Drama-theater group, choral group, student-run newspaper. Social organizations: 17 open to all. Most popular organizations: Criminal Justice Club, Veterinary Technology Club, Student Senate, Music Club, Rodeo Club. Major annual events: school dances, Night of Elegance (dinner/formal dance), fall Welcome Back picnic. Student services: personal-psychological counseling. Campus security: 24-hour emergency response devices, controlled dormitory access. 160 college housing spaces available. Options: coed, men-only, women-only housing available. Eastern Wyoming College Library with an OPAC and a Web page. 124 computers available on campus for general student use. A campuswide network can be accessed. Staffed computer lab on campus.

Community Environment: Torrington is located in the southeastern part of the state, and is a small western town in a rural environment. The climate is invigorating, but relatively mild.

■ LARAMIE COUNTY COMMUNITY COLLEGE *L-16*

1400 East College Dr.
Cheyenne, WY 82007-3299
Tel: (307)778-5222
Admissions: (307)778-1242
Fax: (307)778-1399
Web Site: http://www.lccc.wy.edu/

Description: State-supported, 2-year, coed. Part of Wyoming Community College Commission. Awards certificates, transfer associate, and terminal associate degrees. Founded 1968. Setting: 270-acre small town campus. Endowment: $5.8 million. Total enrollment: 4,603. Student-undergrad faculty ratio is 18:1. 1,561 applied, 100% were admitted. Full-time: 1,704 students, 58% women, 42% men. Part-time: 2,899 students, 62% women, 38% men. Students come from 40 states and territories, 14 other countries, 7% from out-of-state, 1% Native American, 7% Hispanic, 2% black, 1% Asian American or Pacific Islander, 0.4% international, 45% 25 or older, 2% live on campus, 4% transferred in. Core. Calendar: semesters. Academic remediation for entering students, ESL program, services for LD students, advanced placement, honors program, independent study, distance learning, double major, summer session for credit, part-time degree program, adult/continuing education programs, co-op programs and internships. Off campus study at Albany County Campus, Eastern Laramie County Campus. ROTC: Air Force (c).

Entrance Requirements: Open admission except for nursing, radiological technology, equine studies, dental hygiene programs. Options: electronic application, early admission. Required: high school transcript. Required for some: interview. Entrance: noncompetitive. Application deadline: Rolling. Notification: continuous until 8/31.

Costs Per Year: Application fee: $20. State resident tuition: $2004 full-time, $83.50 per credit hour part-time. Nonresident tuition: $4860 full-time, $202.50 per credit hour part-time. Mandatory fees: $24.50 per credit hour part-time. College room and board: $5024.

Collegiate Environment: Orientation program. Drama-theater group, choral group, student-run newspaper. Social organizations: 35 open to all. Most popular organizations: Block and Bridle Club, Phi Theta Kappa, music, Student Nurses Association, STAR Club. Major annual events: Orientation, Fall All-Campus Barbeque, Homecoming Week. Student services: personal-psychological counseling. Campus security: 24-hour patrols, controlled dormitory access. 84 college housing spaces available; all were occupied in 2003-04. No special consideration for freshman housing applicants. Option: coed housing available. Laramie County Community College Library with 51,872 books, 187,739 microform titles, 323 serials, 31,514 audiovisual materials, an OPAC, and a Web page. Operations spending for 2004 fiscal year: $622,708. 720 computers available on campus for general student use. A campuswide network can be accessed from off-campus. Staffed computer lab on campus.

Community Environment: Founded in 1867, Cheyenne is the capital of Wyoming. It is located on a rolling plain at the foothills of the Rocky Mountains and has a population of 52,000. The town keeps the spirit of the "Wild West" with its well-known annual Cheyenne Frontier Days celebration held in July. The State Capitol, State Museum, and Cheyenne Art Center are features of the city.

■ NORTHWEST COLLEGE *B-8*

231 West 6th St.
Powell, WY 82435-1898
Tel: (307)754-6000
Free: 800-560-4692
Admissions: (307)754-6043
Fax: (307)754-6700
E-mail: beark@adm.nwc.whecn.edu
Web Site: http://www.northwestcollege.edu/

Description: State and locally supported, 2-year, coed. Part of Wyoming Community College Commission. Awards certificates, transfer associate, and terminal associate degrees. Founded 1946. Setting: 75-acre rural campus. Endowment: $6.1 million. Educational spending for 2005 fiscal year: $3802 per student. Total enrollment: 1,711. 1,160 applied, 83% were admitted. 8% from top 10% of their high school class, 14% from top quarter, 36% from top half. Full-time: 1,121 students, 57% women, 43% men. Part-time: 590 students, 69% women, 31% men. Students come from 23 states and territories, 27% from out-of-state, 1% Native American, 4% Hispanic, 1% black, 1% Asian American or Pacific Islander, 0.4% international, 23% 25 or older, 46% live on campus, 6% transferred in. Core. Calendar: semesters. Academic remediation for entering students, ESL program, services for LD students, advanced placement, honors program, distance learning, double major, summer session for credit, part-time degree program, external degree program, adult/continuing education programs, co-op programs and internships. Study abroad program.

Entrance Requirements: Open admission for state residents, except for nursing program. Options: Common Application, electronic application, early admission, deferred admission. Required: high school transcript. Recommended: minimum 2.0 high school GPA. Required for some: SAT or ACT, ACT COMPASS. Entrance: noncompetitive. Application deadline: 8/15. Notification: continuous.

Collegiate Environment: Orientation program. Drama-theater group, choral group, student-run newspaper. Social organizations: 40 open to all. Major annual event: homecoming/Alumni Reunion. Student services: health clinic, personal-psychological counseling. Campus security: 24-hour emergency response devices and patrols, late night transport-escort service, controlled dormitory access. 560 college housing spaces available; 374 were occupied in 2003-04. Freshmen guaranteed college housing. On-campus residence required in freshman year. Options: coed, women-only housing available. John Taggart Hinckley Library plus 1 other with 55,330 books, 79,002 microform titles, 1,738 serials, 741 audiovisual materials, an OPAC, and a Web page. Operations spending for 2004 fiscal year: $255,907. 300 computers available on campus for general student use. Computer purchase/lease plans available. A campuswide network can be accessed from student residence rooms. Staffed computer lab on campus.

■ **SHERIDAN COLLEGE-GILLETTE CAMPUS** *C-14*
300 West Sinclair St.
Gillette, WY 82718
Tel: (307)686-0254
Web Site: http://www.sheridan.edu/index_live.asp?id=2
Description: State and locally supported, 2-year, coed. Founded 2003.
Calendar: semesters.

■ **SHERIDAN COLLEGE-SHERIDAN AND GILLETTE** *B-11*
PO Box 1500
Sheridan, WY 82801-1500
Tel: (307)674-6446
Free: 800-913-9139
Fax: (307)674-7205
E-mail: admissions@sheridan.edu
Web Site: http://www.sheridan.edu/
Description: State and locally supported, 2-year, coed. Part of Wyoming Community College Commission. Awards certificates, transfer associate, and terminal associate degrees. Founded 1948. Setting: 124-acre small town campus. Educational spending for 2005 fiscal year: $3973 per student. Total enrollment: 2,895. Student-undergrad faculty ratio is 14:1. Full-time: 1,047 students, 61% women, 39% men. Part-time: 1,848 students, 55% women, 45% men. Students come from 31 states and territories, 3 other countries, 9% from out-of-state, 2% Native American, 2% Hispanic, 1% black, 1% Asian American or Pacific Islander, 1% international, 38% 25 or older, 20% live on campus, 3% transferred in. Core. Calendar: semesters. Academic remediation for entering students, ESL program, services for LD students, advanced placement, self-designed majors, independent study, distance learning, double major, summer session for credit, part-time degree program, adult/continuing education programs, co-op programs and internships. Off campus study at Western Wyoming Community College.
Entrance Requirements: Open admission except for dental hygiene, nursing programs. Options: Peterson's Universal Application, electronic application, early admission, deferred admission. Recommended: high school transcript. Required for some: high school transcript. Entrance: noncompetitive. Application deadline: Rolling. Notification: continuous.
Costs Per Year: Application fee: $0. State resident tuition: $1416 full-time, $59 per credit hour part-time. Nonresident tuition: $4248 full-time, $177 per credit hour part-time. Mandatory fees: $480 full-time, $20 per credit hour part-time. College room and board: $3920.
Collegiate Environment: Orientation program. Drama-theater group, choral group. Social organizations: 20 open to all. Most popular organizations: student government, Phi Theta Kappa, Art Club, Nursing Club, Police Science Club. Major annual events: Homecoming, Campus Craze, Christmas Dance. Student services: personal-psychological counseling. Campus security: 24-hour emergency response devices, student patrols, controlled dormitory access, night patrols by certified officers. 260 college housing spaces available; 200 were occupied in 2003-04. No special consideration for freshman housing applicants. Options: coed, women-only housing available. Griffith Memorial Library plus 1 other with 46,589 books, 52,511 microform titles, 545 serials, 17,122 audiovisual materials, an OPAC, and a Web page. Operations spending for 2004 fiscal year: $433,040. 200 computers available on campus for general student use. A campuswide network can be accessed from student residence rooms and from off campus. Staffed computer lab on campus.
Community Environment: The town of Sheridan is located in northeastern Wyoming at the foot of the scenic Big Horn Mountains. The Big Horns rise to 13,165 feet above Sheridan's 3,745-foot elevation and provide year-round opportunities for outdoor recreation from wilderness hiking to rock climbing, skiing, camping, hunting and fishing. With a population of about 16,000, Sheridan retains an atmosphere of small-town friendliness while offering its citizens many fine services. The YMCA, Sheridan Recreation District, and other organizations provide activities for all ages. The community also supports a number of high-quality programs for the visual and performing arts.

■ **UNIVERSITY OF WYOMING** *K-14*
Laramie, WY 82070
Tel: (307)766-1121
Free: 800-342-5996
Admissions: (307)766-4272
Fax: (307)766-2271
E-mail: undergraduate.admissions@uwyo.edu
Web Site: http://www.uwyo.edu/

Description: State-supported, university, coed. Awards bachelor's, master's, doctoral, and first professional degrees and post-master's certificates. Founded 1886. Setting: 785-acre small town campus. Endowment: $190 million. Research spending for 2004 fiscal year: $37.6 million. Educational spending for 2005 fiscal year: $9198 per student. Total enrollment: 13,126. Faculty: 704 (651 full-time, 53 part-time). Student-undergrad faculty ratio is 15:1. 3,155 applied, 95% were admitted. 20% from top 10% of their high school class, 48% from top quarter, 80% from top half. Full-time: 7,699 students, 50% women, 50% men. Part-time: 1,811 students, 68% women, 32% men. Students come from 53 states and territories, 46 other countries, 30% from out-of-state, 1% Native American, 4% Hispanic, 1% black, 1% Asian American or Pacific Islander, 1% international, 20% 25 or older, 20% live on campus, 11% transferred in. Retention: 74% of full-time freshmen returned the following year. Academic areas with the most degrees conferred: business/marketing; education; engineering. Core. Calendar: semesters. ESL program, services for LD students, advanced placement, accelerated degree program, self-designed majors, honors program, independent study, distance learning, double major, summer session for credit, part-time degree program, external degree program, internships, graduate courses open to undergrads. Off campus study. Study abroad program. ROTC: Army, Air Force.
Entrance Requirements: Options: Peterson's Universal Application, Common Application, electronic application, deferred admission, international baccalaureate accepted. Required: minimum 2.75 high school GPA. Required for some: high school transcript, minimum 3.0 high school GPA, SAT or ACT. Application deadline: 8/10. Notification: continuous. Preference given to qualified graduates of Wyoming high schools.
Costs Per Year: Application fee: $30. State resident tuition: $2760 full-time, $92 per credit hour part-time. Nonresident tuition: $9150 full-time, $305 per credit hour part-time. Mandatory fees: $666 full-time, $162 per term part-time. Full-time tuition and fees vary according to course load, location, program, and reciprocity agreements. Part-time tuition and fees vary according to course load, location, program, and reciprocity agreements. College room and board: $6240. College room only: $2709. Room and board charges vary according to board plan and housing facility.
Collegiate Environment: Orientation program. Drama-theater group, choral group, marching band, student-run newspaper, radio station. Social organizations: 180 open to all; national fraternities, national sororities. Most popular organizations: Golden Key, SPURS, Fellowship of Christian Athletes, MECHA. Major annual events: homecoming, Resource Fair, Club Day. Student services: legal services, health clinic, personal-psychological counseling, women's center. Campus security: 24-hour emergency response devices and patrols, student patrols, late night transport-escort service, controlled dormitory access. 1,860 college housing spaces available; 1,839 were occupied in 2003-04. Freshmen guaranteed college housing. On-campus residence required in freshman year. Option: coed housing available. William Robertson Coe Library plus 8 others with 1.3 million books, 3 million microform titles, 12,632 serials, 4,641 audiovisual materials, an OPAC, and a Web page. Operations spending for 2004 fiscal year: $7.8 million. 950 computers available on campus for general student use. Computer purchase/lease plans available. A campuswide network can be accessed from student residence rooms and from off campus. Staffed computer lab on campus.
Community Environment: Named for Jacques LaRamie, an early trapper for the American Fur Company, Laramie was established in 1868. Today, the community is known as the "Gem City of the Plains." The mean annual temperature is 42 degrees. The city is accessible by air and bus lines. There are 24 churches in the area, representing 20 different religious denominations, a full-service hospital, library, and civic and fraternal organizations serving the community. Local recreation includes 2 movie theaters, bowling, golf, hunting, fishing, and nearby Snowy Range ski area. An annual rodeo and jubilee are held in July.

■ **WESTERN WYOMING COMMUNITY COLLEGE** *J-7*
PO Box 428
Rock Springs, WY 82902-0428
Tel: (307)382-1600
Free: 800-226-1181
Admissions: (307)382-1647
Fax: (307)382-1636
E-mail: lwatkins@wwcc.cc.wy.us
Web Site: http://www.wwcc.wy.edu
Description: State and locally supported, 2-year, coed. Awards certificates, diplomas, transfer associate, and terminal associate degrees. Founded

1959. Setting: 10-acre small town campus. Endowment: $6 million. Total enrollment: 2,654. 1,137 applied, 79% were admitted. Full-time: 1,099 students, 60% women, 40% men. Part-time: 1,555 students, 65% women, 35% men. Students come from 12 states and territories, 17 other countries, 7% from out-of-state, 1% Native American, 7% Hispanic, 1% black, 1% Asian American or Pacific Islander, 3% international, 47% 25 or older, 13% live on campus, 3% transferred in. Retention: 47% of full-time freshmen returned the following year. Core. Calendar: semesters. Academic remediation for entering students, ESL program, services for LD students, advanced placement, freshman honors college, honors program, independent study, distance learning, summer session for credit, part-time degree program, adult/continuing education programs, co-op programs and internships.

Entrance Requirements: Open admission except nursing program. Options: Common Application, electronic application, early admission, deferred admission. Required: high school transcript. Placement: ACT COMPASS required; SAT or ACT recommended. Entrance: noncompetitive. Application deadline: Rolling.

Costs Per Year: Application fee: $0. State resident tuition: $1658 full-time, $70 per credit hour part-time. Nonresident tuition: $4418 full-time, $185 per credit hour part-time. Full-time tuition varies according to reciprocity agreements. Part-time tuition varies according to course load and reciprocity agreements. College room and board: $3033. College room only: $1474. Room and board charges vary according to board plan and housing facility.

Collegiate Environment: Orientation program. Drama-theater group, choral group, student-run newspaper. Social organizations: 20 open to all. Most popular organizations: Phi Theta Kappa, Students Without Borders (international club), Residence Hall Association, Associated Student Government, LDSSA. Major annual events: Campusfest, Kick-off Day, ASG Awards Event. Student services: personal-psychological counseling. Campus security: 24-hour emergency response devices, late night transport-escort service, controlled dormitory access, patrols by trained security personnel from 4 p.m. to 8 a.m., 24-hour patrols on weekends and holidays. 350 college housing spaces available; all were occupied in 2003-04. No special consideration for freshman housing applicants. Option: coed housing available. Hay Library with 115,000 books, 25,000 microform titles, 175 serials, 3,500 audiovisual materials, an OPAC, and a Web page. Operations spending for 2004 fiscal year: $332,260. 350 computers available on campus for general student use. A campuswide network can be accessed from student residence rooms and from off campus. Staffed computer lab on campus.

Community Environment: This is a rural area with a cold, dry climate. Airlines, the railroad, bus lines, and Routes 30, 1-80, and 191 make the city accessible. There are a public library, churches of major denominations, a hospital, a mental health clinic and major civic and fraternal organizations are active in the community. The city has adequate shopping facilities. Local recreation includes theatres, a drive-in, bowling, hunting, fishing, and hiking. Nearby attractions include Yellowstone and Grand Teton National Parks, Flaming Gorge National Recreation Area, the Wind River Mountains and the Bridger Wilderness. A county fair is held annually. Some part-time work is available.

■ **WYOTECH** *K-14*
4373 North Third St.
Laramie, WY 82072-9519
Tel: (307)742-3776
Free: 800-521-7158
Web Site: http://www.wyotech.com/

Description: Proprietary, 2-year, coed. Awards diplomas and terminal associate degrees. Founded 1966. Setting: rural campus. Total enrollment: 2,011. 784 applied, 100% were admitted. Full-time: 2,011 students, 2% women, 98% men. 2% Native American, 7% Hispanic, 1% black, 1% Asian American or Pacific Islander. Core. Calendar: 9-month program. Services for LD students.

Entrance Requirements: Open admission. Option: Common Application. Required: high school transcript. Entrance: noncompetitive. Application deadline: Rolling.

Collegiate Environment: Student services: personal-psychological counseling. 1,214 college housing spaces available; 930 were occupied in 2003-04. 42 computers available on campus for general student use. Staffed computer lab on campus.

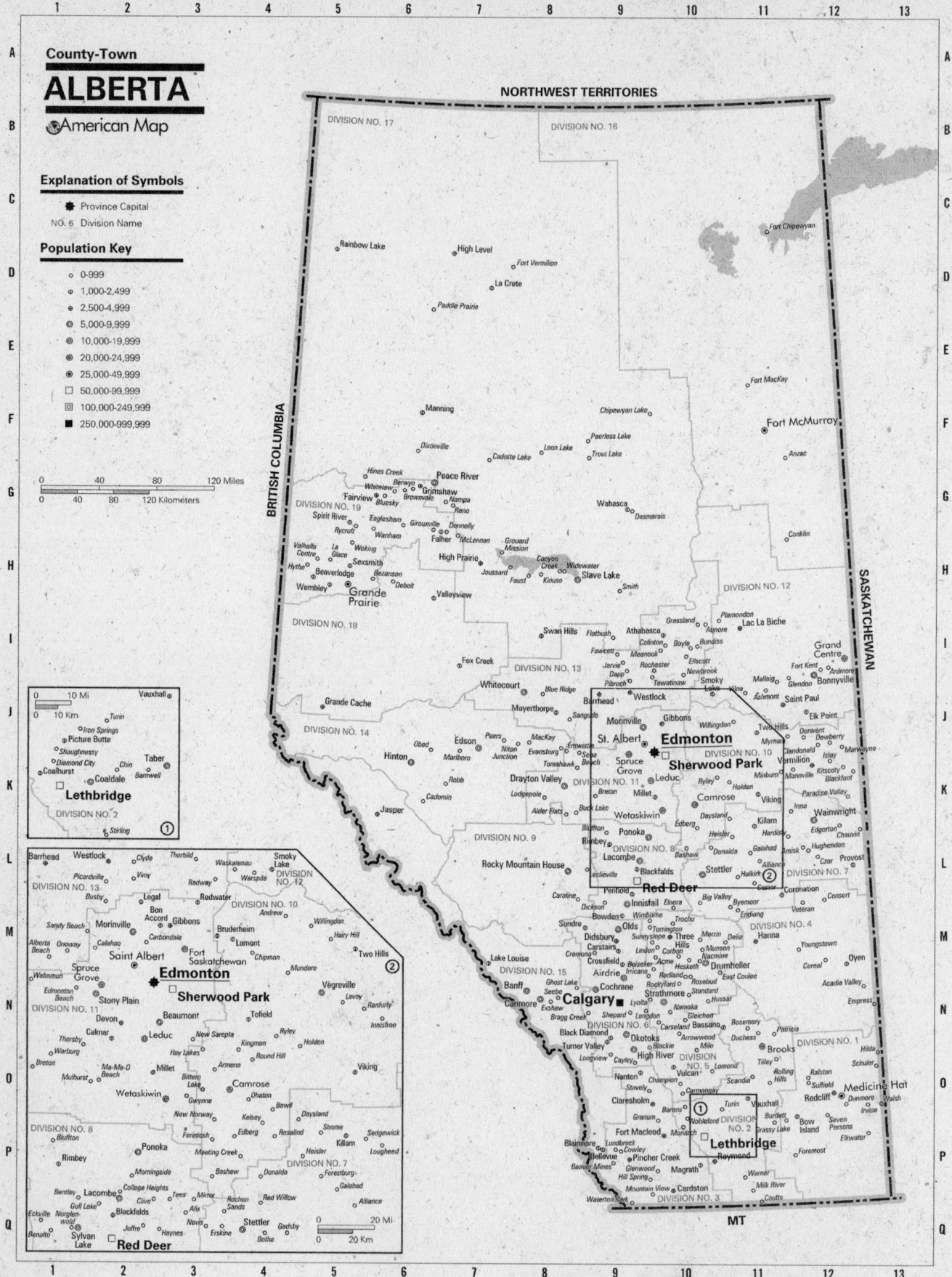

County-Town
ALBERTA
American Map

Explanation of Symbols

✱ Province Capital

NO. 6 Division Name

Population Key

○ 0-999
◎ 1,000-2,499
◉ 2,500-4,999
● 5,000-9,999
◉ 10,000-19,999
● 20,000-24,999
● 25,000-49,999
□ 50,000-99,999
◉ 100,000-249,999
■ 250,000-999,999

0   40   80   120 Miles
0   40   80   120 Kilometers

NORTHWEST TERRITORIES

DIVISION NO. 17   DIVISION NO. 16

BRITISH COLUMBIA

SASKATCHEWAN

Fort Chipewyan

Rainbow Lake   High Level
                          Fort Vermilion
                      La Crete

Paddle Prairie

Fort MacKay

Manning   Chipewyan Lake   Fort McMurray

Dixonville   Peerless Lake   Anzac
          Cadotte Lake   Loon Lake   Trout Lake

Hines Creek   Berwyn Peace River   Wabasca
Fairview Whitelaw Grimshaw   Desmarais
Bluesky Brownvale Nampa
Spirit River Eaglesham Girouxville Reno   Conklin
  Rycroft Wanham Donnelly
Valhalla La Woking Falher McLennan Grouard
Centre Glace   Mission
Hythe Sexsmith Bezanson   Canyon Widewater
Beaverlodge   Debolt High Prairie Creek
Wembley Grande   Joussard Widewater Slave Lake
          Prairie Valleyview Faust Kinuso Smith

DIVISION NO. 19   DIVISION NO. 12

DIVISION NO. 18   Swan Hills Flatbush Grassland Plamondon
          Athabasca Colinton Boyle Lac La Biche
Fox Creek Fawcett Meanook Bundiss Grand
  DIVISION NO. 13 Jarvie Rochester Ellscott Centre
          Dapp Pibroch Newbrook Fort Kent Ardmore
Whitecourt Blue Ridge Tawatinaw Smoky Mallaig Bonnyville
          Mayerthorpe Barrhead Westlock Vilna Glendon
Grande Cache Obed   Sangudo Morinville Gibbons Willingdon Two Hills Saint Paul
  DIVISION NO. 14   St. Albert Edmonton   Elk Point
          Edson MacKay Evansburg Spruce Sherwood Park Myrnam Derwent
  Hinton Marlboro Niton Sexa Grove   Clandonald Dewberry
          Junction Tomahawk Leduc Ryley Holden Vermilion Marwayne
          Robb Drayton Valley DIVISION NO. 11 Millet   Islay Blackfoot
Jasper Cadomin   Breton Camrose Viking Minburn Paradise Valley
          Lodgepole Buck Lake Wetaskiwin Edberg Daysland Mannville Kitscoty
          Alder Flats   Bluffton Ponoka Heisler Hardisty Irma Wainwright
          DIVISION NO. 9 Rimbey DIVISION NO. 8 Donalda Galahad Amisk Edgerton Chauvin
Rocky Mountain House   Lacombe Blackfalds Stettler Halkirk Alliance Hughenden
          Eslieville   Penhold Red Deer Big Valley DIVISION NO. 7 Provost
          Caroline Innisfail Elnora   Byemoor Coronation Consort
          Dickson Bowden Trochu Veteran
          Sundre Didsbury Olds Torrington Merrin Delia Hanna Youngstown
          Carstairs Linden Carbon Munson Nacmine DIVISION NO. 4
Lake Louise Crossfield Irricana Beiseker Hesketh Drumheller Cereal Oyen
          DIVISION NO. 15 Airdrie Redland Rosebud East Coulee Acadia Valley
Banff Cochrane Strathmore Rockyford Standard
          Seebe Calgary Shepard Langdon Namaka Hussar Duchess Empress
Canmore Exshaw   Carseland Bassano Bleichen Rosemary Patricia
          Bragg Creek DIVISION NO. 6 Gleichen Standard Brooks DIVISION NO. 1
Black Diamond Okotoks High River Blackie Mossleigh Milo Rolling Duchess Hilda
Turner Valley Cayley Arrowwood DIVISION Lomond Tilley Hills Ralston
          Longview Nanton Champion NO. 5 Rainier Redcliff Schuler
          Stavely Vulcan Scandia Suffield Medicine Hat
          Claresholm Barons Carmangay Lomond Vauxhall Burdett Walsh
          Granum Lomond Turin DIVISION Grassy Lake Seven
          Fort Macleod Nobleford Monarch NO. 2 Bow Persons
Blairmore Lundbreck Coalhurst Lethbridge Island Irvine
          Bellevue Cowley Raymond Warner Ellwater
Beaver Mines Pincher Creek Magrath Milk River Foremost
          Glenwood Hill Spring Cardston Coutts
          Mountain View
Waterton Park   DIVISION NO. 3

MT

Inset 1 (Lethbridge area)

0   10 Mi
0   10 Km

Vauxhall

Turin
Iron Springs
Picture Butte
Shaughnessy   Taber
Diamond City Chin
Coalhurst Coaldale Barnwell

Lethbridge

DIVISION NO. 2

Stirling

①

Inset 2 (Edmonton / Red Deer area)

Barrhead Westlock Clyde Thorhild   Smoky
          Vimy   Waskatenau Lake
          Picardville Legal Radway Warspite DIVISION
DIVISION NO. 13 Busby Radway   NO. 12
          Sandy Beach Morinville Legal Redwater
          Bon Gibbons DIVISION NO. 10 Andrew
          Accord   Bruderheim Willingdon
Alberta Onoway Calahoo   Lamont Hairy Hill
Beach   Carbondale Chipman   Two Hills
Webaman Spruce Saint Albert Fort   Mundare   ②
          Grove   Saskatchewan   Vegreville
Edmonton   Edmonton   Lavoy Ranfurly
Beach   Stony Plain Sherwood Park Tofield   Innisfree
DIVISION NO. 11 Devon   Beaumont   Ryley
Thorsby   Calmar Leduc New Sarepta Kingman   Holden
          Warburg Ma-Me-O Hay Lakes Armena Round Hill Viking
Breton   Beach Millet Bittern
Mulhurst   Wetaskiwin Gwynne Lake Camrose
          New Norway Kelsey Bawlf Ohaton
DIVISION NO. 8 Bluffton Ferintosh Edberg Daysland
          Rimbey   Meeting Creek Rosalind Strome Sedgewick
          Morningside Bashaw Heisler Killam Lougheed
Bentley Lacombe College Heights Tees Mirror Donalda Forestburg Galahad
Eckville Norglenwold Clive Alix Rochon Red Willow Alliance
Benalto Sylvan Blackfalds Nevis Erskine Sands Stettler Gadsby
          Lake Joffre Haynes   Botha

0   20 Mi
0   20 Km

Red Deer

ALBERTA COLLEGE OF ART & DESIGN *N-9*

1407 14 Ave. NW
Calgary, AB, Canada T2N 4R3
Tel: (403)284-7600
Free: 800-251-8290
Admissions: (403)284-7689
Web Site: http://www.acad.ca/

Description: Province-supported, 4-year, coed. Awards bachelor's degrees. Founded 1926. Setting: 1-acre urban campus. Endowment: $2 million. Educational spending for 2005 fiscal year: $6345 per student. Total enrollment: 1,093. Student-undergrad faculty ratio is 9:1. 692 applied, 51% were admitted. Full-time: 974 students, 69% women, 31% men. Part-time: 119 students, 72% women, 28% men. Students come from 11 provinces and territories, 16 other countries, 0% from out-of province, 9% transferred in. Retention: 72% of full-time freshmen returned the following year. Academic area with the most degrees conferred: visual and performing arts. Core. Calendar: semesters. Academic remediation for entering students, services for LD students, advanced placement, independent study, summer session for credit, part-time degree program, external degree program, adult/continuing education programs, internships. Study abroad program.

Entrance Requirements: Options: electronic application, early admission, early decision, early action, international baccalaureate accepted. Required: essay, high school transcript, portfolio of artwork. Recommended: minimum 2.0 high school GPA. Entrance: moderately difficult. Application deadlines: 4/1, 3/1 for early action. Notification: 6/15, 4/30 for early action.

Costs Per Year: Application fee: $50 Canadian dollars. Tuition, fee, and room and board charges are reported in Canadian dollars. Province resident tuition: $4,490 full-time, $575.35 per course part-time. Canadian resident tuition: $1,321 per course part-time. Mandatory fees: $674 full-time, $306.50 per year part-time. Full-time tuition and fees vary according to course load. Part-time tuition and fees vary according to course load. College room and board: $7000. College room only: $4000. International student tuition: $11,943 full-time. Room and board is available at the Southern Alberta Institute of Technology.

Collegiate Environment: Orientation program. Major annual events: Christmas Show and Sale, Open House, Graduating Exhibition. Student services: health clinic, personal-psychological counseling. Campus security: 24-hour emergency response devices and patrols, late night transport-escort service, controlled dormitory access. College housing not available. Luke Lindoe Library with 25,000 books, 66 serials, an OPAC, and a Web page. 65 computers available on campus for general student use. A campuswide network can be accessed. Staffed computer lab on campus.

ALLIANCE UNIVERSITY COLLEGE *N-9*

630, 833-4th Ave. SW
Calgary, AB, Canada T2P 3T5
Tel: (403)410-2000
Free: 800-461-1222
Web Site: http://www.auc-nuc.ca/

Description: Independent, comprehensive, coed, affiliated with The Christian and Missionary Alliance. Awards bachelor's degrees (graduate and professional degrees are offered by Canadian Theological Seminary). Founded 1941. Setting: 16-acre urban campus. Endowment: $1.2 million. Educational spending for 2005 fiscal year: $1759 per student. Total enrollment: 329. 129 applied, 100% were admitted. Full-time: 245 students, 44% women, 56% men. Part-time: 84 students, 56% women, 44% men. Students

come from 11 provinces and territories, 36% from out-of-province, 2% Native American, 1% Hispanic, 1% black, 4% Asian Canadian, 2% international, 9% 25 or older, 66% live on campus. Retention: 64% of full-time freshmen returned the following year. Core. Calendar: semesters. Academic remediation for entering students, ESL program, services for LD students, advanced placement, accelerated degree program, honors program, independent study, distance learning, double major, summer session for credit, part-time degree program, external degree program, adult/continuing education programs, co-op programs and internships. Off campus study at University of Regina. Study abroad program.

Entrance Requirements: Open admission. Options: Peterson's Universal Application, Common Application, electronic application, early admission, deferred admission, international baccalaureate accepted. Required: essay, high school transcript, 2 recommendations. Recommended: medical history. Required for some: interview. Entrance: noncompetitive. Application deadline: Rolling. Notification: continuous until 9/1.

Collegiate Environment: Orientation program. Drama-theater group, choral group, student-run newspaper. Social organizations: 6 open to all. Most popular organizations: International Students Fellowship, Missions Group. Major annual events: Youth Conference, Regina Romp, Christmas Concert/Spring Musical. Student services: health clinic, personal-psychological counseling, women's center. Campus security: 24-hour emergency response devices, controlled dormitory access. On-campus residence required through sophomore year. Options: men-only, women-only housing available. Archibald Foundation Library with 65,000 books, 546 serials, and an OPAC. Operations spending for 2004 fiscal year: $264,500. 14 computers available on campus for general student use. A campuswide network can be accessed.

ATHABASCA UNIVERSITY *I-10*

1 University Dr.
Athabasca, AB, Canada T9S 3A3
Tel: (780)675-6100
Free: 800-788-9041
Admissions: (780)675-6302
Fax: (780)675-6437
E-mail: reginfo@cs.athabascau.ca
Web Site: http://www.athabascau.ca/

Description: Province-supported, comprehensive, coed. Awards bachelor's and master's degrees (offers only external degree programs). Founded 1970. Setting: 480-acre small town campus. Endowment: $1.2 million. Research spending for 2004 fiscal year: $1.7 million. Educational spending for 2005 fiscal year: $5270 per student. Total enrollment: 33,437. Faculty: 509 (125 full-time, 384 part-time). Part-time: 30,311 students, 68% women, 32% men. Students come from 13 provinces and territories, 73 other countries, 42% from out-of-province, 73% 25 or older. Core. Calendar: continuous. Academic remediation for entering students, ESL program, services for LD students, advanced placement, accelerated degree program, self-designed majors, distance learning, summer session for credit, part-time degree program, external degree program, adult/continuing education programs, co-op programs, graduate courses open to undergrads. Off campus study at see website for list of collaborative agreements with educational institutions: www.athabascau.ca/collab/collab.php. Study abroad program.

Entrance Requirements: Open admission. Options: Common Application, electronic application, international baccalaureate accepted. Required: high school transcript. Entrance: noncompetitive. Application deadline: Rolling. Notification: continuous.

Costs Per Year: Application fee: $60 Canadian dollars. Tuition and fee charges are reported in Canadian dollars. Area resident tuition: $418 per course part-time. Province resident tuition: $4180 full-time, $473 per course part-time. Canadian resident tuition: $4730 full-time, $696 per course part-time. International student tuition: $6960 full-time.

Collegiate Environment: Student-run newspaper. Campus security: 24-hour emergency response devices. College housing not available. Athabasca University Library plus 1 other with 143,000 books, 1,500 microform titles, 12,000 serials, 3,400 audiovisual materials, an OPAC, and a Web page. Operations spending for 2004 fiscal year: $1.3 million. 28 computers available on campus for general student use. A campuswide network can be accessed from off-campus. Staffed computer lab on campus.

Community Environment: The central campus is located in a small rural town (population 2,800) in the northern section of the province. Learning Centers are located in larger urban centres.

■ **CONCORDIA UNIVERSITY COLLEGE OF ALBERTA** *K-9*

7128 Ada Blvd., NW

Edmonton, AB, Canada T5B 4E4

Tel: (780)479-8481; (866)479-5200

Admissions: (780)479-9224

Fax: (780)474-1933

Web Site: http://www.concordia.ab.ca/

Description: Independent Lutheran, 4-year, coed. Awards bachelor's degrees. Founded 1921. Setting: 15-acre urban campus. Educational spending for 2005 fiscal year: $5372 per student. Total enrollment: 1,794. 1,856 applied, 37% were admitted. Students come from 7 provinces and territories, 3% live on campus. Core. Calendar: semesters. Services for LD students, advanced placement, honors program, independent study, double major, summer session for credit, part-time degree program, external degree program, internships. Study abroad program.

Entrance Requirements: Options: Common Application, electronic application, early admission, international baccalaureate accepted. Required: high school transcript, minimum 2.0 high school GPA. Required for some: essay, 2 recommendations, interview. Entrance: moderately difficult. Application deadlines: 6/30, 5/1 for nonresidents. Notification: 9/5, 8/15 for nonresidents.

Costs Per Year: Application fee: $0 Canadian dollars, $75 Canadian dollars for nonresidents. Tuition, fee, and room and board charges are reported in Canadian dollars. Comprehensive fee: $10,588 includes full-time tuition ($5810), mandatory fees ($348), and college room and board ($4430). College room only: $2450. Full-time tuition and fees vary according to class time, course load, and program. Room and board charges vary according to board plan and student level. Part-time tuition: $726.25 per course. Part-time mandatory fees: $242.08 per credit. Part-time tuition and fees vary according to class time, course load, and program. International student tuition: $8435 full-time.

Collegiate Environment: Orientation program. Drama-theater group, choral group, student-run newspaper. Social organizations: 3 open to all. Most popular organizations: orchestra, community chorus, Toastmasters. Major annual events: Orientation, Oktoberfest, Valentine Social and Christmas formal. Student services: personal-psychological counseling. Campus security: 24-hour patrols, late night transport-escort service. 90 college housing spaces available; 80 were occupied in 2003-04. No special consideration for freshman housing applicants. Options: men-only, women-only housing available. Arnold Guebert Memorial Library plus 1 other with 89,380 books, 27 microform titles, 8,565 serials, an OPAC, and a Web page. 250 computers available on campus for general student use. A campuswide network can be accessed from student residence rooms and from off campus. Staffed computer lab on campus.

■ **THE KING'S UNIVERSITY COLLEGE** *K-9*

9125 50th St.

Edmonton, AB, Canada T6B 2H3

Tel: (780)465-3500

Free: 800-661-8582

Fax: (780)465-3534

E-mail: registrar@kingsu.ca

Web Site: http://www.kingsu.ca/

Description: Independent interdenominational, 4-year, coed. Awards bachelor's degrees. Founded 1979. Setting: 20-acre suburban campus. Endowment: $915,730. Research spending for 2004 fiscal year: $126,530.

Educational spending for 2005 fiscal year: $4527 per student. Total enrollment: 631. Student-undergrad faculty ratio is 9:1. 453 applied, 82% were admitted. Full-time: 511 students, 58% women, 42% men. Part-time: 53 students, 47% women, 53% men. Students come from 5 provinces and territories, 33 other countries, 19% from out-of-province, 16% 25 or older, 28% live on campus, 13% transferred in. Retention: 67% of full-time freshmen returned the following year. Academic areas with the most degrees conferred: education; psychology; biological/life sciences. Core. Calendar: Canadian standard year. ESL program, services for LD students, advanced placement, independent study, double major, summer session for credit, part-time degree program, adult/continuing education programs, internships. Off campus study. Study abroad program.

Entrance Requirements: Options: electronic application, international baccalaureate accepted. Required: high school transcript, minimum 2.0 high school GPA, 1 recommendation. Required for some: essay, interview. Entrance: moderately difficult. Application deadline: Rolling. Notification: 8/15.

Costs Per Year: Application fee: $50 Canadian dollars. Tuition, fee, and room and board charges are reported in Canadian dollars. Comprehensive fee: $12,320 includes full-time tuition ($7595), mandatory fees ($325), and college room and board ($4400). College room only: $2400. Part-time tuition: $245 per credit. Part-time mandatory fees: $81.25 per term. International student tuition: $9095 full-time.

Collegiate Environment: Orientation program. Drama-theater group, choral group, student-run newspaper. Social organizations: 15 open to all. Most popular organizations: Action and Awareness, The King's Players (drama club), chamber and concert choirs, King's Science Society, Hockey Club. Major annual events: Student Association Barbecue, Students' Association Dance, Christmas Banquet. Student services: personal-psychological counseling. Campus security: 24-hour emergency response devices, student patrols, controlled dormitory access. 260 college housing spaces available; 185 were occupied in 2003-04. Freshmen given priority for college housing. Options: coed, women-only housing available. Simona Maaskant with 75,295 books, 33,276 microform titles, 4,263 serials, 4,691 audiovisual materials, an OPAC, and a Web page. Operations spending for 2004 fiscal year: $371,774. 37 computers available on campus for general student use. A campuswide network can be accessed. Staffed computer lab on campus.

■ **NEWMAN THEOLOGICAL COLLEGE** *K-9*

15611 Saint Albert Trail NW

Edmonton, AB, Canada T6V 1H3

Tel: (780)447-2993

Free: 800-386-7531

Web Site: http://www.newman.edu/

Description: Independent Roman Catholic, comprehensive, coed. Founded 1969. Calendar: semesters.

■ **PRAIRIE BIBLE INSTITUTE** *M-10*

330 Sixth Ave. North, PO Box 4000

Three Hills, AB, Canada T0M 2N0

Tel: (403)443-5511

Free: 800-661-2425

Fax: (403)443-5540

Web Site: http://www.pbi.ab.ca/

Description: Independent interdenominational, 4-year, coed. Awards bachelor's degrees. Founded 1922. Setting: 130-acre small town campus with easy access to Calgary. Research spending for 2004 fiscal year: $5681. Total enrollment: 457. Full-time: 371 students, 43% women, 57% men. Part-time: 86 students, 30% women, 70% men. Students come from 7 other countries, 78% live on campus. Retention: 43% of full-time freshmen returned the following year. Core. Calendar: semesters. ESL program, advanced placement, accelerated degree program, part-time degree program, adult/continuing education programs, internships. Study abroad program.

Entrance Requirements: Options: Common Application, electronic application. Required: essay, high school transcript, 2 recommendations. Recommended: minimum 2.0 high school GPA. Required for some: minimum 3.0 high school GPA. Entrance: minimally difficult. Application deadlines: 8/15, 3/1 for early decision.

Collegiate Environment: Orientation program. Drama-theater group, choral group, student-run newspaper, radio station. Social organizations: 8 open to all. Most popular organizations: WIN, SMF, student government, Off-Campus. Major annual events: Youth Quest, Missions Conference, Music Night. Student services: health clinic, personal-psychological counseling.

Campus security: 24-hour emergency response devices and patrols, late night transport-escort service, controlled dormitory access. 540 college housing spaces available; 400 were occupied in 2003-04. Freshmen guaranteed college housing. On-campus residence required in freshman year. Options: men-only, women-only housing available. T. S. Rendall Library with 60,745 books and 458 serials. Operations spending for 2004 fiscal year: $177,886. 30 computers available on campus for general student use. Staffed computer lab on campus.

■ ROCKY MOUNTAIN COLLEGE N-9
4039 Brentwood Rd., NW
Calgary, AB, Canada T2L 1L1
Tel: (403)284-5100
E-mail: enrolment@rockymountaincollege.ca
Web Site: http://www.rockymountaincollege.ca/
Description: Independent, 4-year, coed, affiliated with Missionary Church. Awards bachelor's degrees. Founded 1992. Setting: 1-acre suburban campus. Endowment: $343,200. Educational spending for 2005 fiscal year: $2330 per student. Total enrollment: 342. 169 applied, 96% were admitted. Students come from 8 provinces and territories, 13 other countries, 20% live on campus. Core. Calendar: semesters. Academic remediation for entering students, advanced placement, summer session for credit, part-time degree program, adult/continuing education programs, internships.
Entrance Requirements: Options: deferred admission, international baccalaureate accepted. Required: essay, high school transcript, 2 recommendations. Required for some: interview. Entrance: noncompetitive. Application deadline: Rolling.
Collegiate Environment: Drama-theater group, choral group. Most popular organization: Missions Fellowship. Major annual events: Rocky Mountain trip, Christmas Celebration Banquet, Spring Banquet. Student services: personal-psychological counseling. Campus security: 24-hour emergency response devices. Option: coed housing available. Main library plus 1 other with 25,280 books and 135 serials. Operations spending for 2004 fiscal year: $101,240. 5 computers available on campus for general student use. Staffed computer lab on campus.

■ SOUTHERN ALBERTA INSTITUTE OF TECHNOLOGY N-9
1301 16th Ave. NW
Calgary, AB, Canada T2M 0L4
Tel: (403)284-8110; 877-284-SAIT
Admissions: (403)284-7248
Fax: (403)284-7112
Web Site: http://www.sait.ca/
Description: Province-supported, 4-year, coed. Awards bachelor's degrees. Founded 1916. Calendar: trimesters.
Entrance Requirements: Option: electronic application. Application deadline: 2/28.
Costs Per Year: Application fee: $25. Province resident tuition: $81.33 per credit part-time. Canadian resident tuition: $3738 full-time. Mandatory fees: $498 full-time. Full-time tuition and fees vary according to course load, degree level, and program. Part-time tuition varies according to class time. College room only: $664. International student tuition: $8306 full-time.
Collegiate Environment: 950 college housing spaces available.

■ TAYLOR UNIVERSITY COLLEGE AND SEMINARY K-9
11525-23 Ave.
Edmonton, AB, Canada T6J 4T3
Tel: (780)431-5200
Free: 800-567-4988
Fax: (780)436-9416
Web Site: http://www.taylor-edu.ca/
Description: Independent North American Baptist, comprehensive, coed. Awards associate, bachelor's, and master's degrees. Founded 1940. Setting: 27-acre urban campus. Endowment: $1.6 million. Educational spending for 2005 fiscal year: $1795 per student. Total enrollment: 269. 152 applied, 78% were admitted. Full-time: 202 students, 50% women, 50% men. Part-time: 67 students, 40% women, 60% men. Students come from 4 provinces and territories, 4 other countries, 28% from out-of-province, 10% 25 or older, 55% live on campus, 5% transferred in. Retention: 88% of full-time freshmen returned the following year. Core. Calendar: semesters. Academic remediation for entering students, ESL program, advanced placement, self-designed majors, part-time degree program, adult/continuing education programs, co-op programs and internships. Off campus study at University of Alberta, Grant MacEwan Community College.

Entrance Requirements: Options: Common Application, deferred admission, international baccalaureate accepted. Required: essay, high school transcript, 3 recommendations. Recommended: SAT or ACT. Required for some: minimum 3.0 high school GPA, interview. Entrance: minimally difficult. Application deadline: 8/1. Notification: continuous until 8/31.
Collegiate Environment: Orientation program. Drama-theater group, choral group, student-run newspaper. Social organizations: 20 open to all. Most popular organizations: Choristers (choral group), Student Union, prayer groups, Sacrifice of Praise (band). Major annual events: Discovery Days, Missions Week, Spiritual Emphasis Days. Student services: personal-psychological counseling. Campus security: evening and late night patrols by security. On-campus residence required in freshman year. Option: coed housing available. Schalm Library with 50,083 books, 303 serials, and an OPAC. Operations spending for 2004 fiscal year: $120,594. 16 computers available on campus for general student use. A campuswide network can be accessed. Staffed computer lab on campus.

■ UNIVERSITY OF ALBERTA K-9
Edmonton, AB, Canada T6G 2E1
Tel: (780)492-3111
Admissions: (780)492-3113
Fax: (780)492-7172
E-mail: registrar@ualberta.ca
Web Site: http://www.ualberta.ca/
Description: Province-supported, university, coed. Awards bachelor's, master's, and doctoral degrees. Founded 1906. Setting: 154-acre urban campus. Endowment: $564 million. Research spending for 2004 fiscal year: $274.4 million. Total enrollment: 35,443. Faculty: 1,676. Student-undergrad faculty ratio is 21:1. 9,551 applied. Full-time: 27,145 students, 57% women, 43% men. Part-time: 2,225 students, 62% women, 38% men. Students come from 13 provinces and territories, 110 other countries, 14% from out-of-province, 21% 25 or older, 15% live on campus, 12% transferred in. Calendar: Canadian standard year. Academic remediation for entering students, ESL program, services for LD students, advanced placement, self-designed majors, honors program, distance learning, double major, summer session for credit, part-time degree program, adult/continuing education programs, co-op programs and internships, graduate courses open to undergrads. Off campus study. Study abroad program.
Entrance Requirements: Options: electronic application, deferred admission, international baccalaureate accepted. Required: high school transcript. Recommended: minimum 2.0 high school GPA. Required for some: essay, recommendations, interview. Entrance: moderately difficult. Application deadline: 5/1. Notification: continuous until 9/1. Preference given to province residents.
Costs Per Year: Application fee: $100 Canadian dollars. Tuition, fee, and room and board charges are reported in Canadian dollars. Province resident tuition: $479.76 per course part-time. Canadian resident tuition: $4,537 full-time, $1,509.12 per course part-time. Mandatory fees: $498 full-time, $272.20 per term part-time. College room and board: $4712. College room only: $2032. International student tuition: $15,091 full-time.
Collegiate Environment: Orientation program. Drama-theater group, choral group, student-run newspaper, radio station. Social organizations: 200 open to all; national fraternities, national sororities, local fraternities, local sororities. Major annual events: Week of Welcome, Anti-Freeze (January week of welcome). Student services: legal services, health clinic, personal-psychological counseling, women's center. Campus security: 24-hour emergency response devices, student patrols, late night transport-escort service. 4,153 college housing spaces available; 3,500 were occupied in 2003-04. Freshmen given priority for college housing. On-campus residence required through senior year. Option: coed housing available. Cameron Library plus 10 others with 9.7 million books, an OPAC, and a Web page. Operations spending for 2004 fiscal year: $32.4 million. 721 computers available on campus for general student use. Computer purchase/lease plans available. A campuswide network can be accessed from student residence rooms and from off campus. Staffed computer lab on campus.
Community Environment: Edmonton is the provincial capital and largest city of Alberta, with a population of 850,000. It takes its name from Fort Edmonton, an early trading post of the Hudson Bay Company. The city, center of an important farming region, is also an oil and gas exploration and manufacturing center. Major industries include pipeline construction, chemical plants, meat packing, construction, oilfield construction and servicing, and food processing. The city was the first to establish a municipal airport and has long been the Gateway to the North. It is easily accessible by air, rail, bus and car. It is also home to the Alberta Research Council and Edmonton Research Park.

■ **UNIVERSITY OF CALGARY** *N-9*
2500 University Dr., NW
Calgary, AB, Canada T2N 1N4
Tel: (403)220-5110
Fax: (403)289-1253
Web Site: http://www.ucalgary.ca/

Description: Province-supported, university, coed. Awards bachelor's, master's, and doctoral degrees. Founded 1945. Setting: 213-hectare urban campus. Total enrollment: 27,928. 6,928 applied, 58% were admitted. Students come from 12 provinces and territories, 78 other countries, 20% 25 or older. Calendar: semesters. ESL program, services for LD students, advanced placement, honors program, distance learning, double major, summer session for credit, part-time degree program, adult/continuing education programs, co-op programs and internships, graduate courses open to undergrads. Study abroad program.

Entrance Requirements: Options: electronic application, early admission, international baccalaureate accepted. Required: high school transcript. Required for some: SAT, SAT Subject Tests. Entrance: moderately difficult. Application deadline: 4/1. Notification: continuous.

Costs Per Year: Application fee: $130 Canadian dollars. Tuition and fee charges are reported in Canadian dollars. Area resident tuition: $486 per course part-time.

Collegiate Environment: Orientation program. Choral group, student-run newspaper, radio station. Major annual events: Frosh Week, Bermuda Shorts Day. Student services: legal services, health clinic, personal-psychological counseling. Campus security: 24-hour emergency response devices and patrols, late night transport-escort service, controlled dormitory access. 1,860 college housing spaces available; all were occupied in 2003-04. Freshmen given priority for college housing. Option: coed housing available. MacKimmie Library plus 4 others with 2.4 million books, 3.5 million microform titles, 20,237 serials, 138,759 audiovisual materials, an OPAC, and a Web page. 800 computers available on campus for general student use. A campuswide network can be accessed from student residence rooms and from off campus. Staffed computer lab on campus.

Community Environment: Situated centrally in western Canada, Calgary is located at the convergence of the Bow and Elbow Rivers, As Canada's energy capital and western Canada's business capital, Calgary is home to the second largest concentration of corporate head offices in the country. Within an hour's drive are the Rocky Mountains, Kananaskis Valley and Banff National Park where hiking, skiing, canoeing, mountain climbing, and mountain biking can be enjoyed. Calgary is home to more than 820,000 people, which makes it Canada's fifth largest city. Cultural activities abound with a philharmonic orchestra, as well as theater and dance companies, museums, art galleries, libraries, and a planetarium.

■ **UNIVERSITY OF LETHBRIDGE** *P-10*
4401 University Dr.
Lethbridge, AB, Canada T1K 3M4
Tel: (403)329-2111
Admissions: (403)382-7134
E-mail: reg_admoo@hg.uleth.ca
Web Site: http://www.uleth.ca/

Description: Province-supported, university, coed. Awards bachelor's, master's, and doctoral degrees. Founded 1967. Setting: 576-acre urban campus. Endowment: $15 million. Research spending for 2004 fiscal year: $5.7 million. Educational spending for 2005 fiscal year: $5019 per student. Total enrollment: 7,986. Faculty: 379. 2,415 applied, 55% were admitted. Students come from 11 provinces and territories, 50 other countries, 17% from out-of province, 22% 25 or older, 10% live on campus. Retention: 74% of full-time freshmen returned the following year. Academic areas with the most degrees conferred: business/marketing; visual and performing arts; education. Core. Calendar: semesters. Academic remediation for entering

students, ESL program, accelerated degree program, self-designed majors, independent study, distance learning, double major, summer session for credit, part-time degree program, co-op programs and internships, graduate courses open to undergrads. Off campus study at Southern Alberta Institute of Technology. Study abroad program.

Entrance Requirements: Options: Common Application, electronic application, early admission, early decision, deferred admission, international baccalaureate accepted. Required: high school transcript, minimum 2.0 high school GPA. Required for some: minimum 3.0 high school GPA, recommendations, interview. Entrance: moderately difficult. Application deadlines: 6/1, 4/1 for early decision. Notification: continuous, 4/22 for early decision.

Costs Per Year: Application fee: $60. Canadian resident tuition: $4560 full-time, $456 per course part-time. Mandatory fees: $830 full-time, $97.34. College room and board: $5892. College room only: $3592. International student tuition: $9120 full-time.

Collegiate Environment: Orientation program. Drama-theater group, choral group, student-run newspaper, radio station. Social organizations: 25 open to all. Most popular organizations: Management Students Society, Inter-Varsity Christian Fellowship, Organization of Residence Students, The University of Lethbridge Geography Club, Education Undergraduate Society. Major annual events: Campus Fest, Imaginus, Student Union Cabarets. Student services: health clinic, personal-psychological counseling, women's center. Campus security: 24-hour emergency response devices and patrols, student patrols, late night transport-escort service, controlled dormitory access, video camera monitored entrances, hallways. 806 college housing spaces available; all were occupied in 2003-04. No special consideration for freshman housing applicants. Option: coed housing available. The University of Lethbridge Library with 539,154 books, 866,066 microform titles, 1,614 serials, 7,156 audiovisual materials, an OPAC, and a Web page. Operations spending for 2004 fiscal year: $3.2 million. 600 computers available on campus for general student use. Computer purchase/lease plans available. A campuswide network can be accessed from student residence rooms and from off campus. Staffed computer lab on campus.

Community Environment: The centre of a prosperous farming and ranching area, Lethbridge is characterized by its many green areas and parks, and its abundant cultural and recreational facilities. It is located in southern Alberta, approximately 145 kilometres (90 miles) east of the Canadian Rockies and 95 kilometres (60 miles) north of the United States border.

■ **VANGUARD COLLEGE** *K-9*
11617 106 Ave., NW
Edmonton, AB, Canada T5H 0S1
Tel: (780)452-0808
Fax: (780)452-5803
Web Site: http://www.vanguardcollege.com/

Description: Independent, 4-year, coed, affiliated with Pentecostal Assemblies of Canada. Administratively affiliated with Pentecostal Assemblies of Canada (PAOC). Awards bachelor's degrees. Founded 1946. Setting: 1-hectare urban campus. Total enrollment: 208. 95 applied, 100% were admitted. Students come from 10 provinces and territories, 5 other countries, 27% from out-of-province. Retention: 55% of full-time freshmen returned the following year. Core. Calendar: semesters. Services for LD students, advanced placement, accelerated degree program, independent study, distance learning, double major, summer session for credit, part-time degree program, internships. Off campus study.

Entrance Requirements: Options: Common Application, early decision. Required: essay, high school transcript, recommendations. Application deadlines: 8/19, 4/15 for early decision.

Collegiate Environment: Choral group, student-run newspaper. College housing not available. Vanguard College Library with 23,698 books, 282,055 serials, 1,350 audiovisual materials, and an OPAC. 20 computers available on campus for general student use. A campuswide network can be accessed from off-campus. Staffed computer lab on campus.

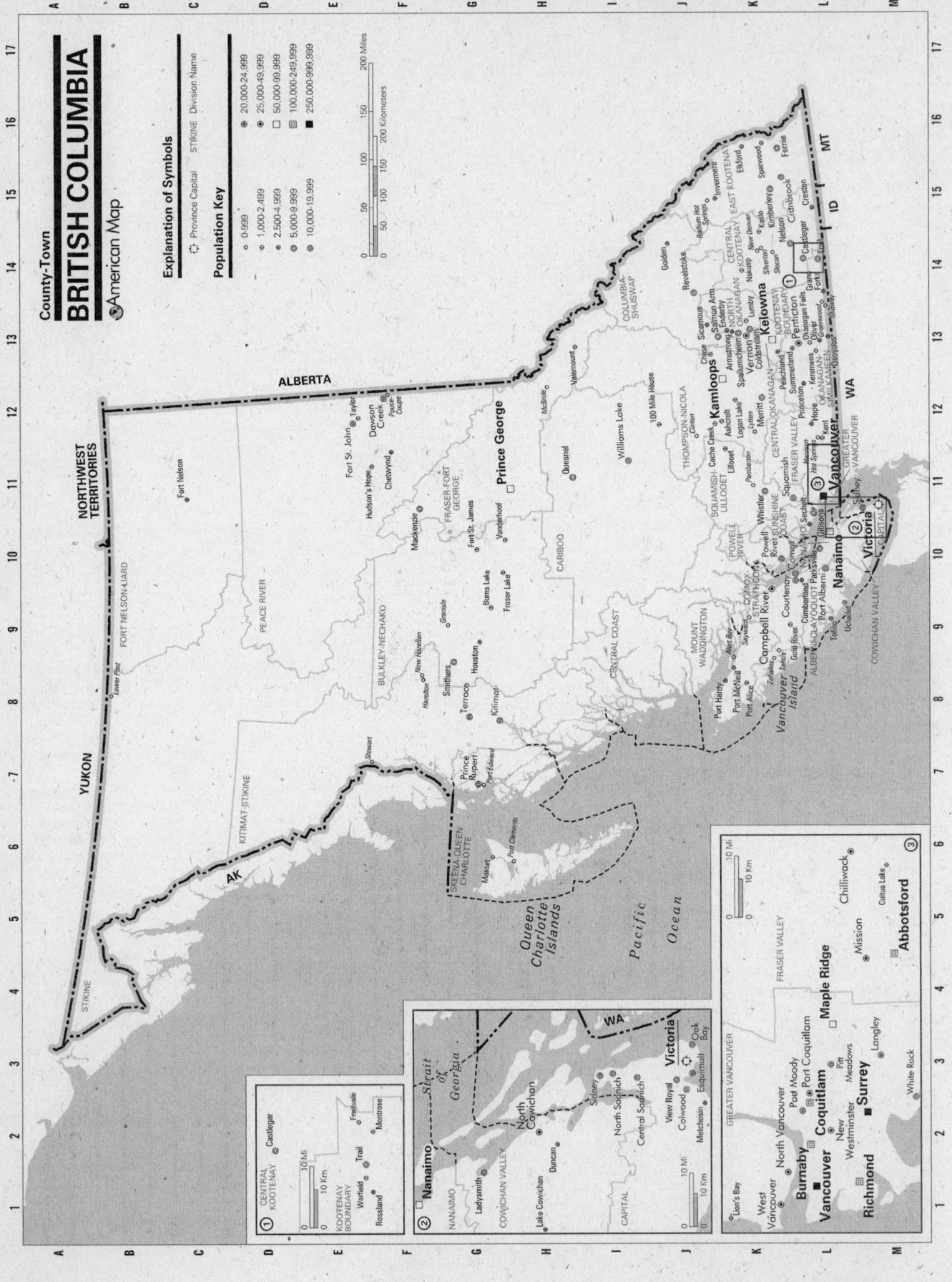

County-Town
BRITISH COLUMBIA
American Map

Explanation of Symbols

⬡ Province Capital   STIKINE   Division Name

Population Key

- ◦ 0-999
- ⊙ 1,000-2,499
- ⊚ 2,500-4,999
- ⊡ 5,000-9,999
- ⊞ 10,000-19,999
- ◉ 20,000-24,999
- ⊛ 25,000-49,999
- ◻ 50,000-99,999
- ⊡ 100,000-249,999
- ■ 250,000-999,999

0   50   100   150   200 Miles
0   50   100   150   200 Kilometers

■ **BRITISH COLUMBIA INSTITUTE OF TECHNOLOGY** *L-2*
3700 Willingdon Ave.
Burnaby, BC, Canada V5G 3H2
Tel: (604)434-5734
Admissions: (604)432-8215
Fax: (604)278-5363
Web Site: http://www.bcit.ca/
Description: Province-supported, 4-year, coed. Awards bachelor's degrees. Founded 1964. Setting: 103-acre urban campus with easy access to Vancouver. Total enrollment: 22,670. 7,700 applied, 33% were admitted. 5% live on campus.
Entrance Requirements: Option: electronic application. Required: high school transcript. Required for some: essay, 2 recommendations, interview. Entrance: moderately difficult.
Costs Per Year: Application fee: $60 Canadian dollars. Tuition, fee, and room only charges are reported in Canadian dollars. Province resident tuition: $4390 full-time. College room only: $3735. International student tuition: $15,071 full-time. Tuition guaranteed not to increase for student's term of enrollment.
Collegiate Environment: Student-run newspaper, radio station. Student services: health clinic, personal-psychological counseling. Campus security: 24-hour emergency response devices and patrols, student patrols, late night transport-escort service. 343 college housing spaces available; all were occupied in 2003-04. Freshmen given priority for college housing. Options: coed, men-only, women-only housing available. British Columbia Institute of Technology Library plus 1 other with 169,404 books, 39,295 microform titles, 1,080 serials, 4,627 audiovisual materials, an OPAC, and a Web page. Operations spending for 2004 fiscal year: $2.9 million.

■ **COLUMBIA BIBLE COLLEGE** *M-4*
2940 Clearbrook Rd.
Abbotsford, BC, Canada V2T 2Z8
Tel: (604)853-3358
Free: 800-283-0881
Fax: (604)853-3063
E-mail: ron.penner@columbiabc.edu
Web Site: http://www.columbiabc.edu/
Description: Independent Mennonite Brethren, 4-year, coed. Awards bachelor's degrees. Founded 1936. Setting: 9-acre urban campus with easy access to Vancouver. Endowment: $176,885. Educational spending for 2005 fiscal year: $2982 per student. Total enrollment: 491. Student-undergrad faculty ratio is 21:1. 320 applied, 72% were admitted. Students come from 5 provinces and territories, 11 other countries, 15% 25 or older, 65% live on campus. Academic area with the most degrees conferred: theology and religious vocations. Core. Calendar: semesters. Academic remediation for entering students, ESL program, services for LD students, advanced placement, independent study, distance learning, double major, part-time degree program, co-op programs and internships.
Entrance Requirements: Open admission. Required: essay, high school transcript, minimum X high school GPA, recommendations. Required for some: interview. Entrance: noncompetitive. Application deadline: 8/15. Notification: continuous.
Costs Per Year: Application fee: $50. Comprehensive fee: $12,140 includes full-time tuition ($7320) and college room and board ($4820). Full-time tuition varies according to program. Room and board charges vary according to board plan.

Collegiate Environment: Orientation program. Drama-theater group, choral group, student-run newspaper. Student services: personal-psychological counseling. Campus security: late night transport-escort service, night watchman 11 p.m. to 6 a.m. College housing designed to accommodate 200 students; 239 undergraduates lived in college housing during 2003-04. On-campus residence required through sophomore year. Options: men-only, women-only housing available. Columbia Resource Center plus 1 other with 44,000 books, 100 serials, and a Web page. 20 computers available on campus for general student use. A campuswide network can be accessed. Staffed computer lab on campus.

■ **KWANTLEN UNIVERSITY COLLEGE** *M-2*
1266 72nd Ave.
Surrey, BC, Canada V3W 2M8
Tel: (604)599-2100
Admissions: (604)599-2018
Fax: (604)555-2068
Web Site: http://www.kwantlen.ca/
Description: Province-supported, 4-year, coed. Awards associate and bachelor's degrees (profile includes information from Langley, Richmond, Newton and Surrey campuses). Setting: urban campus with easy access to Vancouver. Endowment: $6.4 million. Educational spending for 2005 fiscal year: $7700 per student. Total enrollment: 10,383. Student-undergrad faculty ratio is 35:1. 9,107 applied, 97% were admitted. Full-time: 7,291 students, 58% women, 42% men. Part-time: 3,092 students, 60% women, 40% men. Students come from 41 other countries, 2% Native American, 1% black, 22% Asian Canadian, 26% 25 or older, 28% transferred in. Retention: 90% of full-time freshmen returned the following year. Academic areas with the most degrees conferred: business/marketing; health professions and related sciences; computer and information sciences. Core. Calendar: semesters. Academic remediation for entering students, ESL program, services for LD students, advanced placement, accelerated degree program, independent study, distance learning, double major, summer session for credit, part-time degree program, adult/continuing education programs, co-op programs and internships. Study abroad program.
Entrance Requirements: Open admission. Options: electronic application, early admission, early decision, early action, international baccalaureate accepted. Required: high school transcript. Recommended: high school transcript. Required for some: essay, minimum 2.0 high school GPA, recommendations, interview, portfolio, external testing, certain levels of certification (i.e. - first aid). Application deadlines: 6/30, 5/30 for nonresidents, 2/28 for early decision. Notification: continuous until 6/30, 5/30 for nonresidents, 3/31 for early decision. Preference given to students residing in all catchment area and apply for Bachelor in science for nursing.
Costs Per Year: Application fee: $40 Canadian dollars. Tuition and fee charges are reported in Canadian dollars. Province resident tuition: $3360 full-time, $112 per credit part-time. Canadian resident tuition: $3360 full-time, $112 per credit part-time. International student tuition: $11,400 full-time.
Collegiate Environment: Orientation program. Choral group, student-run newspaper. Social organizations: 15 open to all. Most popular organizations: academic clubs, Rowing Club, Cultural Diversity Club, Buddy Language Club. Major annual events: Welcome to Kwantlen Days, Kwantlen Eagles basketball games and tournaments, Majors Fair. Student services: health clinic, personal-psychological counseling, women's center. Campus security: 24-hour emergency response devices and patrols. College housing not available. Kwantlen University College Library - Surrey Campus plus 2 oth-

ers with an OPAC and a Web page. Operations spending for 2004 fiscal year: $4.4 million. 100 computers available on campus for general student use. A campuswide network can be accessed from off-campus. Staffed computer lab on campus.

■ MALASPINA UNIVERSITY-COLLEGE *F-1*
900 Fifth St.
Nanaimo, BC, Canada V9R 5S5
Tel: (250)753-3245
Admissions: (250)740-6356
Web Site: http://www.mala.bc.ca/
Description: Province-supported, comprehensive, coed. Awards associate, bachelor's, and master's degrees. Founded 1969. Setting: 110-acre campus. Total enrollment: 20,679. Students come from 52 other countries. Calendar: semesters.
Costs Per Year: Application fee: $30 Canadian dollars. Tuition and fee charges are reported in Canadian dollars. Area resident tuition: $3489 full-time, $116.30 per credit hour part-time. Mandatory fees: $279 full-time.
Community Environment: Nanaimo is situated on Vancouver Island, across the Strait of Georgia from the city of Vancouver. The island is the largest on the Pacific Coast, both in North and South America. Nanaimo is the second largest community (95,000) on the island, being outranked by Victoria (250,000), the provincial capital located at the southern tip of the island. There are many excellent recreational facilities in the nearby mountains, forests, and lakes. Attractions include the Bastion, and the Centennial-Polk Theatre Museum. There is direct and frequent ferry service to Vancouver as well as rail, bus, and road connections to Victoria.

■ OPEN LEARNING AGENCY *L-2*
4355 Mathissi Place
Burnaby, BC, Canada V5G 4S8
Tel: (604)431-3000
Free: 800-663-9711
Fax: (604)431-3381
E-mail: edinfo@ola.bc.ca
Web Site: http://www.ola.ca/
Description: Province-supported, 4-year, coed. Part of Province of British Columbia, Canada public post-secondary system. Awards bachelor's degrees (offers only distance learning degree programs). Founded 1978. Setting: suburban campus with easy access to Vancouver. Total enrollment: 13,950. Core. Calendar: continuous. Academic remediation for entering students, ESL program, services for LD students, self-designed majors, honors program, independent study, distance learning, double major, part-time degree program, external degree program, adult/continuing education programs. Off campus study at members of the Open University Consortium of British Columbia and Canada Virtual University Consortium.
Entrance Requirements: Open admission. Options: Common Application, electronic application, deferred admission, international baccalaureate accepted. Required for some: program specific. Entrance: noncompetitive. Application deadline: Rolling.
Collegiate Environment: College housing not available. Open Learning Agency Library plus 1 other with an OPAC and a Web page.

■ ROYAL ROADS UNIVERSITY *M-11*
2005 Sooke Rd.
Victoria, BC, Canada V9B 5Y2
Tel: (250)391-2511
Free: 800-788-8028
Admissions: (250)391-2552
Fax: (250)391-2522
Web Site: http://www.royalroads.ca/
Description: Province-supported, upper-level, coed. Awards bachelor's and master's degrees. Founded 1996. Setting: 125-acre suburban campus. Endowment: $2 million. Research spending for 2004 fiscal year: $577,000. Educational spending for 2005 fiscal year: $4900 per student. Total enrollment: 2,984. Full-time: 199 students, 36% women, 64% men. Part-time: 211 students, 51% women, 49% men. Students come from 10 provinces and territories, 3 other countries, 15% from out-of province, 1% international, 76% 25 or older, 0% live on campus, 58% transferred in. Calendar: continuous. Advanced placement, accelerated degree program, distance learning, summer session for credit, part-time degree program, adult/continuing education programs. Off campus study.
Collegiate Environment: Student-run newspaper. Most popular organizations: rowing, mountain biking, Recycling Club. Major annual events: rowing

orientation, Garden City 10K run, Christmas Dance. Student services: personal-psychological counseling. Campus security: 24-hour emergency response devices and patrols, late night transport-escort service, controlled dormitory access. Learning Resource Centre plus 1 other with 40,000 books, 164 microform titles, 609 audiovisual materials, an OPAC, and a Web page. Operations spending for 2004 fiscal year: $700,000. 100 computers available on campus for general student use. A campuswide network can be accessed from student residence rooms and from off campus. Staffed computer lab on campus.

■ SIMON FRASER UNIVERSITY *L-2*
8888 University Dr.
Burnaby, BC, Canada V5A 1S6
Tel: (604)291-3111
Admissions: (604)291-3224
Fax: (604)291-4969
E-mail: undergraduate-admissions@sfu.ca
Web Site: http://www.sfu.ca/
Description: Province-supported, university, coed. Awards bachelor's, master's, and doctoral degrees and post-master's certificates. Founded 1965. Setting: suburban campus with easy access to Vancouver. Endowment: $88.4 million. Educational spending for 2005 fiscal year: $7279 per student. Total enrollment: 20,187. Faculty: 698 (all full-time). Student-undergrad faculty ratio is 25:1. Students come from 11 provinces and territories, 78 other countries, 5% from out-of province, 24% 25 or older, 4% live on campus. Retention: 73% of full-time freshmen returned the following year. Academic areas with the most degrees conferred: social sciences; business/marketing; education. Calendar: trimesters. Advanced placement, self-designed majors, honors program, independent study, distance learning, double major, summer session for credit, part-time degree program, adult/continuing education programs, co-op programs, graduate courses open to undergrads. Off campus study. Study abroad program.
Entrance Requirements: Options: electronic application, early admission, early decision, international baccalaureate accepted. Required: high school transcript, minimum 3.2 high school GPA, SAT or ACT. Required for some: essay, recommendations, interview. Entrance: moderately difficult. Application deadlines: 4/30, 4/1 for early decision. Notification: 6/30, 4/15 for early decision.
Costs Per Year: Application fee: $100 Canadian dollars. Tuition and fee charges are reported in Canadian dollars. Province resident tuition: $148.10 per credit hour part-time.
Collegiate Environment: Orientation program. Drama-theater group, student-run newspaper, radio station. Social organizations: 60 open to all. Most popular organizations: The Peak Newspaper, orientation leaders, crisis line, Women's Centre, Simon Fraser Public Interest Research Group. Major annual events: Convocation, Clubs' Day, United Way Campaign. Student services: legal services, health clinic, personal-psychological counseling, women's center. Campus security: 24-hour emergency response devices and patrols, student patrols, late night transport-escort service, controlled dormitory access, safe-walk stations, 24-hour safe study area. 1,117 college housing spaces available. Freshmen guaranteed college housing. Options: coed, women-only housing available. W. A. C. Bennett Library with 1.4 million books, 1.2 million microform titles, 26,413 serials, 149,361 audiovisual materials, an OPAC, and a Web page. Operations spending for 2004 fiscal year: $11.9 million. 900 computers available on campus for general student use. A campuswide network can be accessed from off-campus. Staffed computer lab on campus.
Community Environment: The 1,200 acre campus is situated atop Burnaby Mountain, making Simon Fraser a striking campus with spectacular views of the coastal mountains and the cities of the Lower Mainland. The outstanding architecture has won many awards. Services on campus include day care centres, Health Services (including physicians, a psychiatrist, nurses and physiotherapists), Athletic and Recreational Services (two full gymnasia, swimming and diving pools, tennis, squash and racquetball courts, sauna, and weight rooms), a campus radio station, printshop, legal advice clinic, ecumenical chaplaincy, women's centre, bookstores and student Pub. Simon Fraser University is wheelchair accessible.

■ SUMMIT PACIFIC COLLEGE *M-4*
Box 1700
Abbotsford, BC, Canada V2S 7E7
Tel: (604)853-7491
Free: 800-976-8388
Fax: (604)853-8951

Web Site: http://www.summitpacific.ca/

Description: Independent, 4-year, coed, affiliated with Pentecostal Assemblies of Canada. Awards bachelor's degrees. Founded 1941. Setting: 101-acre suburban campus with easy access to Vancouver. Total enrollment: 197. Students come from 9 provinces and territories, 4 other countries, 27% 25 or older, 68% live on campus. Core. Calendar: semesters. Academic remediation for entering students, summer session for credit, part-time degree program, internships. Off campus study at Fraser Valley College, Trinity Western University.

Entrance Requirements: Options: Common Application, deferred admission. Required: essay, high school transcript, 3 recommendations. Required for some: interview. Entrance: moderately difficult. Application deadline: Rolling.

Collegiate Environment: Drama-theater group, choral group. Student services: personal-psychological counseling. Campus security: student patrols, campus gate locked after 11 p.m. On-campus residence required through senior year. Lorne Hudson Philip Memorial Library with 35,409 books and 132 serials. 4 computers available on campus for general student use. Staffed computer lab on campus.

■ **THOMPSON RIVERS UNIVERSITY** *K-12*
PO Box 3010, Station Terminal
Kamloops, BC, Canada V2C 5N3
Tel: (250)828-5000
Admissions: (250)828-5043
Fax: (250)828-5086
E-mail: admissions@tru.ca
Web Site: http://www.tru.ca

Description: Province-supported, 4-year, coed. Awards associate, bachelor's, and master's degrees. Founded 1970. Setting: 100-acre small town campus. Endowment: $6.7 million. Educational spending for 2005 fiscal year: $6900 per student. Total enrollment: 9,662. Faculty: 623 (469 full-time, 154 part-time). Student-undergrad faculty ratio is 13:1. 2,390 applied, 59% were admitted. Students come from 10 provinces and territories, 48 other countries, 7% from out-of-province, 27% 25 or older, 9% live on campus. Calendar: semesters. ESL program, services for LD students, advanced placement, honors program, independent study, distance learning, double major, summer session for credit, part-time degree program, adult/continuing education programs, co-op programs and internships. Off campus study. Study abroad program.

Entrance Requirements: Open admission for first-year university: arts, science, business, tourism. Options: electronic application, international baccalaureate accepted. Required: high school transcript. Required for some: recommendations, interview. Application deadline: 3/1. Notification: continuous until 3/1.

Costs Per Year: Application fee: $25 Canadian dollars. Tuition, fee, and room only charges are reported in Canadian dollars. Province resident tuition: $3335 full-time, $111 per credit part-time. Canadian resident tuition: $3335 full-time, $111 per credit part-time. Mandatory fees: $600 full-time. College room only: $3000. International student tuition: $12,000 full-time.

Collegiate Environment: Orientation program. Choral group, student-run newspaper, radio station. Major annual events: Welcome Back BBQ, Orientation, Open House and Career Day. Student services: health clinic, personal-psychological counseling. Campus security: 24-hour emergency response devices and patrols, student patrols, late night transport-escort service. 600 college housing spaces available; all were occupied in 2003-04. No special consideration for freshman housing applicants. Option: coed housing available. University College of the Cariboo Library with 223,300 books, 920 serials, 10,300 audiovisual materials, an OPAC, and a Web page. Operations spending for 2004 fiscal year: $2.3 million. 300 computers available on campus for general student use. A campuswide network can be accessed from student residence rooms and from off campus. Staffed computer lab on campus.

■ **TRINITY WESTERN UNIVERSITY** *M-3*
7600 Glover Rd.
Langley, BC, Canada V2Y 1Y1
Tel: (604)888-7511; 888-468-6898
Fax: (604)513-2061
E-mail: admissions@twu.ca
Web Site: http://www.twu.ca/

Description: Independent, comprehensive, coed, affiliated with Evangelical Free Church of America. Awards bachelor's, master's, and doctoral degrees. Founded 1962. Setting: 150-acre suburban campus with easy access to

Vancouver. Endowment: $4.5 million. Total enrollment: 3,520. 1,759 applied, 77% were admitted. Students come from 10 provinces and territories, 29 other countries, 33% from out-of-province, 15% 25 or older, 40% live on campus. Retention: 79% of full-time freshmen returned the following year. Core. Calendar: semesters. ESL program, advanced placement, honors program, independent study, distance learning, double major, summer session for credit, part-time degree program, co-op programs and internships. Off campus study. Study abroad program.

Entrance Requirements: Options: Peterson's Universal Application, Common Application, electronic application, deferred admission, international baccalaureate accepted. Required: essay, high school transcript, minimum 2.5 high school GPA, 2 recommendations, community standards document. Required for some: interview, SAT or ACT. Entrance: moderately difficult. Application deadline: 6/15. Notification: continuous.

Costs Per Year: Application fee: $40 Canadian dollars. Tuition, fee, and room and board charges are reported in Canadian dollars. Comprehensive fee: $22,960 includes full-time tuition ($14,520), mandatory fees ($220), and college room and board ($8220). Full-time tuition and fees vary according to program. Room and board charges vary according to board plan, housing facility, and student level. Part-time tuition: $484 per semester hour. Part-time tuition varies according to program.

Collegiate Environment: Orientation program. Drama-theater group, choral group, student-run newspaper. Social organizations: 33 open to all. Most popular organizations: Campus Ministries, choir, student newspaper, discipleship program. Major annual events: The 'Challenge', Christmas Banquet, Harvestfest. Student services: health clinic, personal-psychological counseling. Campus security: 24-hour emergency response devices and patrols, late night transport-escort service, controlled dormitory access. 950 college housing spaces available; 880 were occupied in 2003-04. Freshmen given priority for college housing. On-campus residence required through sophomore year. Options: men-only, women-only housing available. Norma Marion Alloway Library with 190,565 books, 324,902 microform titles, 11,000 serials, 2,974 audiovisual materials, an OPAC, and a Web page. 50 computers available on campus for general student use. A campuswide network can be accessed from student residence rooms and from off campus. Staffed computer lab on campus.

Community Environment: Trinity Western is set on a wooded 100-acre campus, adjacent to the Trans Canada Highway No. 1, between Langley and Fort Langley. Students enjoy the solitude of a rural environment and have easy access to the beautiful urban center of Vancouver, just 45 minutes away. Public transportation is available off University Lane.

■ **THE UNIVERSITY OF BRITISH COLUMBIA** *L-11*
2075 Wesbrook Mall
Vancouver, BC, Canada V6T 1Z1
Tel: (604)822-2211
Admissions: (604)822-3014
Fax: (604)822-3599
E-mail: registrar.admissions@ubc.ca
Web Site: http://www.ubc.ca/

Description: Province-supported, university, coed. Awards bachelor's, master's, doctoral, and first professional degrees. Founded 1915. Setting: 1,000-acre urban campus. Endowment: $697.3 million. Research spending for 2004 fiscal year: $275 million. Educational spending for 2005 fiscal year: $7762 per student. Total enrollment: 42,427. Faculty: (2,048 full-time). Student-undergrad faculty ratio is 15:1. 17,001 applied, 57% were admitted. 39% from top 10% of their high school class, 100% from top quarter, 100% from top half. Full-time: 19,961 students, 55% women, 45% men. Part-time: 9,950 students, 58% women, 42% men. Students come from 10 provinces and territories, 100 other countries, 24% 25 or older, 23% live on campus, 6% transferred in. Retention: 91% of full-time freshmen returned the following year. Calendar: Canadian standard year. Academic remediation for entering students, ESL program, services for LD students, advanced placement, self-designed majors, freshman honors college, honors program, distance learning, double major, summer session for credit, part-time degree program, external degree program, adult/continuing education programs, co-op programs and internships. Off campus study at Ecole Polytechnique de Montreal, Canadian University Student Exchange Consortium. Study abroad program. ROTC: Army (c), Air Force (c).

Entrance Requirements: Options: electronic application, early admission, international baccalaureate accepted. Required: high school transcript, minimum 2.6 high school GPA. Recommended: SAT and SAT Subject Tests or ACT. Required for some: essay, recommendations. Entrance: very difficult. Application deadline: 2/28. Notification: continuous until 8/31.

Collegiate Environment: Orientation program. Drama-theater group, choral group, student-run newspaper, radio station. Social organizations: 200 open to all; national fraternities, national sororities, local fraternities, local sororities; 3% of eligible men and 2% of eligible women are members. Most popular organizations: Ski and Board Club, Dance Club, AIESEC Club, UBC Film Society, Varsity Outdoors Club. Major annual events: Storm the Wall, Dragon Boat Racing, Arts County Fair. Student services: legal services, health clinic, personal-psychological counseling, women's center, academic advising, international orientation, international house. Campus security: 24-hour emergency response devices and patrols, student patrols, late night transport-escort service, 24-hour desk attendants in residence halls. 5,500 college housing spaces available; all were occupied in 2003-04. Freshmen given priority for college housing. Options: coed, men-only, women-only housing available. Walter C. Koerner Library plus 9 others with 4.7 million books, 5 million microform titles, 44,722 serials, 93,059 audiovisual materials, an OPAC, and a Web page. Operations spending for 2004 fiscal year: $28,600. 1,500 computers available on campus for general student use. A campuswide network can be accessed from student residence rooms and from off campus. Staffed computer lab on campus.

■ UNIVERSITY COLLEGE OF THE FRASER VALLEY *M-4*

33844 King Rd.

Abbotsford, BC, Canada V2S 7M8

Tel: (604)853-7441

Admissions: (604)864-4645

Fax: (604)853-9990

Web Site: http://www.ucfv.bc.ca/

Description: Province-supported, comprehensive, coed. Part of B.C. provincial education. Awards associate, bachelor's, and master's degrees. Founded 1974. Setting: urban campus with easy access to Vancouver. Endowment: $1.1 million. Research spending for 2004 fiscal year: $18,592. Educational spending for 2005 fiscal year: $4567 per student. Total enrollment: 5,987. Calendar: semesters. Academic remediation for entering students, ESL program, services for LD students, advanced placement, independent study, distance learning, double major, summer session for credit, part-time degree program, adult/continuing education programs, co-op programs and internships.

Entrance Requirements: Open admission for general studies programs. Options: Common Application, electronic application, deferred admission, international baccalaureate accepted. Required for some: essay, high school transcript, 2 recommendations, interview, minimum GPA of 2.0 to 2.67 for specific undergraduate programs. Application deadline: 1/31. Notification: continuous until 9/1.

Collegiate Environment: Orientation program. Drama-theater group, student-run newspaper. Major annual event: Welcome Barbecue. Student services: personal-psychological counseling. Campus security: late night transport-escort service. College housing not available. Peter Jones Library plus 3 others with an OPAC and a Web page. Operations spending for 2004 fiscal year: $1.3 million. 850 computers available on campus for general student use. Staffed computer lab on campus.

■ UNIVERSITY OF NORTHERN BRITISH COLUMBIA *H-11*

3333 University Way

Prince George, BC, Canada V2N 4Z9

Tel: (250)960-5555

Admissions: (250)960-6347

Fax: (250)960-5791

Web Site: http://www.unbc.ca/

Description: Province-supported, university, coed. Awards bachelor's, master's, doctoral, and first professional degrees. Endowment: $30.5 million. Research spending for 2004 fiscal year: $6.8 million. Educational spending for 2005 fiscal year: $7439 per student. Total enrollment: 3,561. Faculty: 182. Student-undergrad faculty ratio is 15:1. 1,082 applied, 83% were admitted. Full-time: 2,145 students, 59% women, 41% men. Part-time: 942 students, 62% women, 38% men. Students come from 11 provinces and territories, 17 other countries, 31% 25 or older, 16% live on campus, 15% transferred in. Academic areas with the most degrees conferred: business/marketing; natural resources/environmental science; health professions and related sciences. Core. Calendar: semesters. Services for LD students, advanced placement, self-designed majors, honors program, independent study, distance learning, double major, part-time degree program, co-op programs and internships, graduate courses open to undergrads. Study abroad program.

Entrance Requirements: Options: Common Application, early admission, early decision, international baccalaureate accepted. Required: high school transcript, minimum 2.00 high school GPA. Required for some: essay. Application deadline: 3/1.

Costs Per Year: Application fee: $25 Canadian dollars. Tuition, fee, and room only charges are reported in Canadian dollars. Area resident tuition: $4110 full-time, $137 per credit hour part-time. Mandatory fees: $648 full-time, $4.50 per credit hour part-time, $129 per term part-time. Full-time tuition and fees vary according to location and program. Part-time tuition and fees vary according to location and program. College room only: $3926. Room charges vary according to housing facility. International student tuition: $14,386 full-time.

Collegiate Environment: Orientation program. Student-run newspaper, radio station. Student services: health clinic, personal-psychological counseling, women's center. 542 college housing spaces available; 541 were occupied in 2003-04. No special consideration for freshman housing applicants. Option: coed housing available. Geoffrey Weller Library with 617,236 books, 406,004 microform titles, 7,854 serials, 2,879 audiovisual materials, an OPAC, and a Web page. Operations spending for 2004 fiscal year: $2.8 million. 300 computers available on campus for general student use. A campuswide network can be accessed from student residence rooms and from off campus. Staffed computer lab on campus.

■ UNIVERSITY OF PHOENIX-VANCOUVER CAMPUS *L-2*

4401 Still Creek Dr., Ste. 200

Burnaby, BC, Canada V5C 6G9

Tel: (604)205-6999

Free: 800-228-7240

Admissions: (480)557-1712

Web Site: http://www.phoenix.edu/

Description: Proprietary, comprehensive, coed. Awards bachelor's and master's degrees. Founded 1998. Setting: urban campus. Total enrollment: 645. Faculty: 6 (all part-time). Student-undergrad faculty ratio is 6:1. Full-time: 256 students, 42% women, 58% men. 0% from out-of-province, 1% Native American, 2% Hispanic, 2% black, 18% Asian Canadian, 82% 25 or older. Academic area with the most degrees conferred: business/marketing. Core. Calendar: continuous. Advanced placement, accelerated degree program, independent study, distance learning, external degree program, adult/continuing education programs, graduate courses open to undergrads.

Entrance Requirements: Open admission. Option: deferred admission. Required: 1 recommendation. Required for some: high school transcript. Entrance: noncompetitive. Application deadline: Rolling.

Costs Per Year: Application fee: $110. Tuition: $11,850 full-time, $395 per credit part-time. Mandatory fees: $560 full-time.

Collegiate Environment: College housing not available. University Library with 444 books, 666 serials, an OPAC, and a Web page. System-wide operations spending for 2004 fiscal year: $3.2 million.

■ UNIVERSITY OF VICTORIA *M-11*

PO Box 1700 STN CSC

Victoria, BC, Canada V8W 2Y2

Tel: (250)721-7211

Admissions: (250)721-8131

Fax: (250)721-6225

Web Site: http://www.uvic.ca/

Description: Province-supported, university, coed. Awards bachelor's, master's, doctoral, and first professional degrees. Founded 1963. Setting: 380-acre suburban campus with easy access to Vancouver. Research spending for 2004 fiscal year: $59 million. Total enrollment: 18,955. Faculty: 750 (710 full-time, 40 part-time). Student-undergrad faculty ratio is 25:1. 7,648 applied, 72% were admitted. Full-time: 10,453 students, 59% women, 41% men. Part-time: 5,682 students, 61% women, 39% men. Students come from 13 provinces and territories, 92 other countries, 13% from out-of-province, 28% 25 or older, 16% live on campus, 11% transferred in. Calendar: Canadian standard year. Academic remediation for entering students, ESL program, services for LD students, advanced placement, self-designed majors, honors program, independent study, distance learning, double major, summer session for credit, part-time degree program, adult/continuing education programs, co-op programs and internships, graduate courses open to undergrads. Off campus study at Canadian University Student Exchange Consortium. Study abroad program.

Entrance Requirements: Options: electronic application, early admission, early action, deferred admission, international baccalaureate accepted. Required: high school transcript, minimum 2.5 high school GPA. Required for some: essay, minimum 3.0 high school GPA, interview, audition, portfolio. Entrance: moderately difficult. Application deadlines: 4/30, 2/28 for early action. Notification: continuous, 5/1 for early action.

Costs Per Year: Application fee: $100 Canadian dollars. Tuition, fee, and room and board charges are reported in Canadian dollars. Province resident tuition: $3574 full-time, $294 per unit part-time. Canadian resident tuition: $952 per unit part-time. Mandatory fees: $493 full-time, $493 per year part-time. College room and board: $5009. College room only: $3014. International student tuition: $11,562 full-time.

Collegiate Environment: Orientation program. Drama-theater group, choral group, student-run newspaper, radio station. Social organizations: 100 open to all. Major annual events: President's Welcome Barbecue, Alumni Homecoming Weekend, Week of Welcome. Student services: legal services, health clinic, personal-psychological counseling, women's center. Campus security: 24-hour emergency response devices and patrols, student patrols, late night transport-escort service. 2,400 college housing spaces available; all were occupied in 2003-04. Freshmen guaranteed college housing. Option: coed housing available. McPherson Library plus 4 others with 1.8 million books, 2.5 million microform titles, 14,000 serials, 17,200 audiovisual materials, an OPAC, and a Web page. Operations spending for 2004 fiscal year: $13 million. 400 computers available on campus for general student use. A campuswide network can be accessed from student residence rooms and from off campus. Staffed computer lab on campus.

Community Environment: The university is located in the suburban Gordon Head area of Greater Victoria. It is a 10-minute drive from downtown Victoria and is easily accessible by car, bus, and bicycle. Victoria, the capital of British Columbia, boasts magnificent legislative buildings and a downtown which has been developed to retain its turn-of-the-century architecture and historic landmarks. The city is a thriving center of artistic activity, offering the exceptional Royal British Columbia Museum, several art galleries, a symphony orchestra, an opera company and several professional theatre companies. Greater Victoria has a population of 270,000. The regional economy is based on government, tourism, the University, and growing service, high technology, and clean manufacturing sectors.

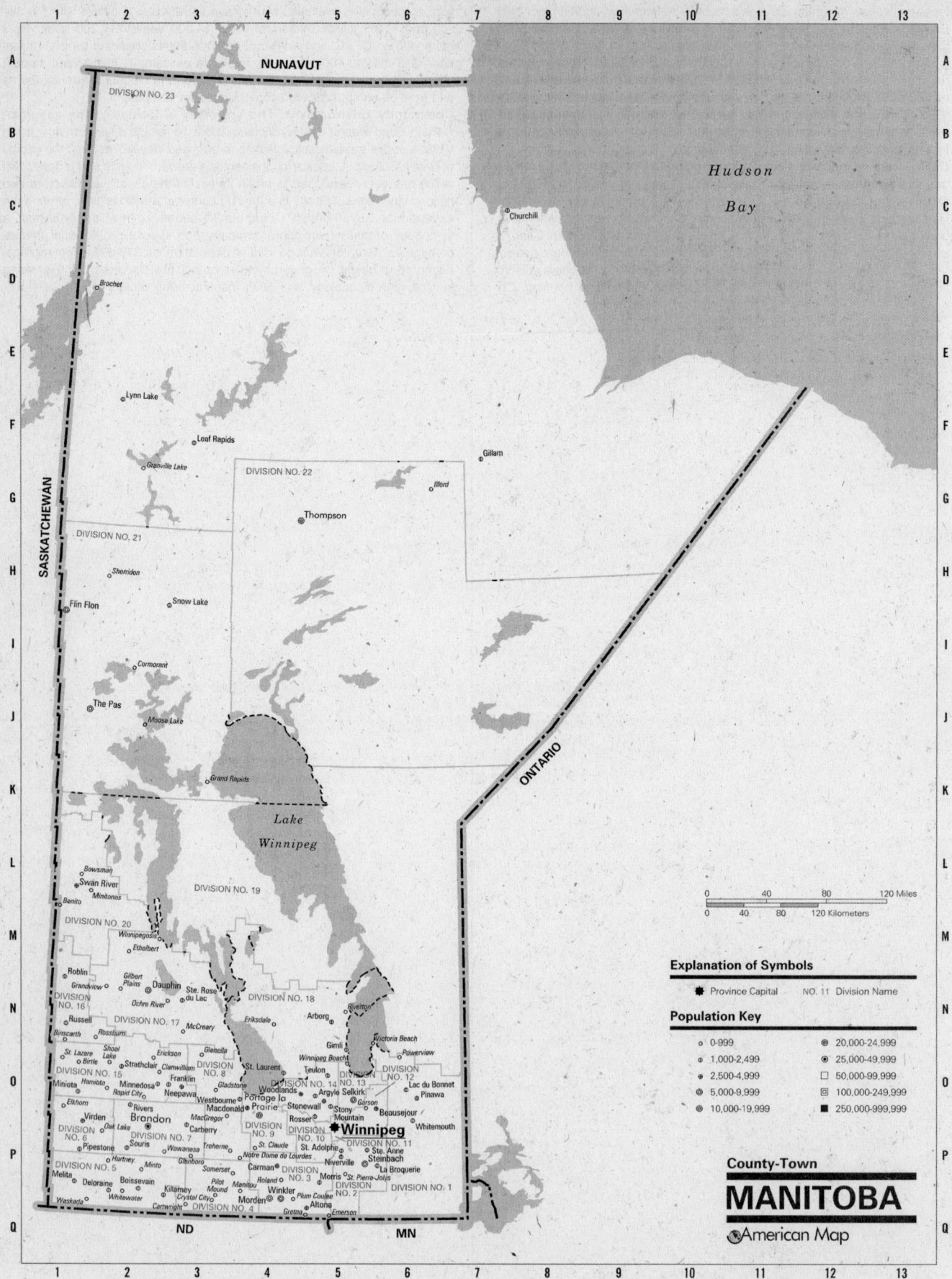

MANITOBA

■ **BRANDON UNIVERSITY** *P-2*
270 18th St.
Brandon, MB, Canada R7A 6A9
Tel: (204)728-9520
Admissions: (204)727-7352
E-mail: kerr@brandonu.ca
Web Site: http://www.brandonu.ca/
Description: Province-supported, comprehensive, coed. Awards bachelor's and master's degrees. Founded 1899. Setting: 30-acre small town campus. Endowment: $24 million. Research spending for 2004 fiscal year: $944,580. Total enrollment: 3,524. Faculty: 228 (215 full-time, 13 part-time). Student-undergrad faculty ratio is 11:1. 2,157 applied, 70% were admitted. Students come from 28 other countries, 18% from out-of-province, 36% 25 or older, 9% live on campus. Retention: 71% of full-time freshmen returned the following year. Core. Calendar: Canadian standard year. Academic remediation for entering students, ESL program, services for LD students, accelerated degree program, self-designed majors, honors program, distance learning, double major, summer session for credit, part-time degree program, graduate courses open to undergrads. Off campus study. Study abroad program.
Entrance Requirements: Open admission. Options: Common Application, electronic application, deferred admission. Required: high school transcript. Required for some: recommendations, criminal and child abuse registry checks. Entrance: noncompetitive. Application deadline: Rolling. Notification: continuous until 9/30.
Costs Per Year: Application fee: $60 Canadian dollars. Tuition, fee, and room and board charges are reported in Canadian dollars. Area resident tuition: $301.86 per credit part-time. Province resident tuition: $3,019 full-time, $301.68 per credit part-time. Canadian resident tuition: $3018 full-time. Mandatory fees: $345 full-time, $15.70 per credit hour part-time, $47.12. College room and board: $6270. College room only: $3614. International student tuition: $6,373 full-time. $637.26 per course for international students.
Collegiate Environment: Orientation program. Drama-theater group, choral group, student-run newspaper, radio station. Social organizations: 25 open to all. Most popular organizations: Psychology Club, Zoology Club, Inter-Varsity Christian Fellowship, International Students Club, Business Administration Club. Major annual events: Shinerama, Orientation, Multicultural Week. Student services: personal-psychological counseling. Campus security: 24-hour emergency response devices, controlled dormitory access, night residence hall security personnel. 460 college housing spaces available. Freshmen guaranteed college housing. Options: coed, men-only, women-only housing available. John E. Robbins Library with 238,816 books, 615,548 microform titles, 1,699 serials, 12,233 audiovisual materials, an OPAC, and a Web page. Operations spending for 2004 fiscal year: $636,522. 160 computers available on campus for general student use. A campuswide network can be accessed from student residence rooms. Staffed computer lab on campus.
Community Environment: Brandon, a city of 40,000, is located in the heart of the prairie land of Manitoba, on the Assiniboine River. The Manitoba Provincial Exhibition is held in Brandon every year. There are excellent recreational facilities in the nearby area, including camping, hunting, winter sports and fishing. Brandon is easily accessible by rail, road and air.

■ **CANADIAN MENNONITE UNIVERSITY** *P-5*
500 Shaftesbury Blvd.
Winnipeg, MB, Canada R3P 2N2
Tel: (204)487-3300; 877-231-4570
Fax: (204)487-3858
E-mail: abergen@cmu.ca
Web Site: http://www.cmu.ca/
Description: Independent Mennonite, comprehensive, coed. Awards bachelor's degrees. Founded 1943. Setting: 44-acre urban campus. Educational spending for 2005 fiscal year: $4650 per student. Total enrollment: 455. Student-undergrad faculty ratio is 15:1. 280 applied, 95% were admitted. Full-time: 349 students, 57% women, 43% men. Part-time: 83 students, 64% women, 36% men. Students come from 7 provinces and territories, 6 other countries, 30% from out-of-province, 5% 25 or older, 45% live on campus. Retention: 65% of full-time freshmen returned the following year. Academic areas with the most degrees conferred: liberal arts/general studies; interdisciplinary studies; psychology. Core. Calendar: semesters. Academic remediation for entering students, services for LD students, independent study, double major, part-time degree program, adult/continuing education programs, internships, graduate courses open to undergrads. Off campus study at University of Winnipeg. Study abroad program.
Entrance Requirements: Options: Common Application, electronic application, deferred admission. Required: high school transcript, minimum 2.0 high school GPA. Recommended: recommendations. Required for some: essay, recommendations. Entrance: moderately difficult. Application deadline: 8/28. Notification: continuous until 9/1.
Costs Per Year: Application fee: $35 Canadian dollars. Tuition, fee, and room and board charges are reported in Canadian dollars. Comprehensive fee: $9320 includes full-time tuition ($4650) and college room and board ($4670). College room only: $1612. Room and board charges vary according to board plan and housing facility. Part-time tuition: $465 per course. Part-time mandatory fees: $155 per credit hour. International student tuition: $8130 full-time.
Collegiate Environment: Orientation program. Drama-theater group, choral group, student-run newspaper. Social organizations: 10 open to all. Most popular organizations: Oratorio Choir, Fellowship Groups, Christian Emphasis Committee, Peace and Social Concerns, Witness and Service Committee. Major annual events: Opening Week, Community Festival Series, Winter Retreat. Student services: personal-psychological counseling. Campus security: student patrols, late night transport-escort service, controlled dormitory access, combination door locks to sections of the campus. 195 college housing spaces available; 175 were occupied in 2003-04. Freshmen given priority for college housing. Options: coed, men-only, women-only housing available. Canadian Mennonite University Library with 85,000 books, 125 serials, and an OPAC. Operations spending for 2004 fiscal year: $361,513. 40 computers available on campus for general student use. A campuswide network can be accessed from student residence rooms and from off campus. Staffed computer lab on campus.

■ **COLLÈGE UNIVERSITAIRE DE SAINT-BONIFACE**
200 Ave. de la Cathédrale
Saint-Boniface, MB, Canada R2H 0H7
Tel: (204)233-0210
Fax: (204)237-3240
Web Site: http://www.ustboniface.mb.ca/
Description: Independent religious, comprehensive.

■ **PROVIDENCE COLLEGE AND THEOLOGICAL SEMINARY**
10 College Crescent
Otterburne, MB, Canada R0A 1G0

Tel: (204)433-7488
Free: 800-668-7768
E-mail: mlittle@providence.mb.ca
Web Site: http://www.prov.ca/

Description: Independent interdenominational, comprehensive, coed. Awards bachelor's, master's, and doctoral degrees. Founded 1925. Setting: 100-acre rural campus with easy access to Winnipeg. Endowment: $715,028. Educational spending for 2005 fiscal year: $2427 per student. Total enrollment: 886. Students come from 16 provinces and territories, 17 other countries, 30% from out-of-province, 60% live on campus. Retention: 70% of full-time freshmen returned the following year. Core. Calendar: semesters. Academic remediation for entering students, ESL program, accelerated degree program, freshman honors college, independent study, distance learning, double major, part-time degree program, internships.

Entrance Requirements: Open admission. Option: deferred admission. Required: high school transcript, 4 recommendations. Entrance: noncompetitive. Application deadline: Rolling.

Costs Per Year: Application fee: $35 Canadian dollars. Tuition, fee, and room and board charges are reported in Canadian dollars. Comprehensive fee: $10,100 includes full-time tuition ($5400), mandatory fees ($500), and college room and board ($4200). Room and board charges vary according to board plan and housing facility. Part-time tuition: $192 per credit. Part-time mandatory fees: $25 per credit hour.

Collegiate Environment: Drama-theater group, choral group, student-run newspaper. Student services: health clinic, personal-psychological counseling. Campus security: student patrols, controlled dormitory access. 310 college housing spaces available; 298 were occupied in 2003-04. Freshmen guaranteed college housing. On-campus residence required in freshman year. Options: men-only, women-only housing available. 47,756 books and 635 serials. Operations spending for 2004 fiscal year: $204,000. 14 computers available on campus for general student use. A campuswide network can be accessed from off-campus. Staffed computer lab on campus.

■ **STEINBACH BIBLE COLLEGE** *P-5*

50 PTH 12N
Steinbach, MB, Canada R5G 1T4
Tel: (204)326-6451
Free: 800-230-8478
E-mail: thiebert@sbcollege.ca
Web Site: http://sbcollege.ca/

Description: Independent Mennonite, 4-year, coed. Awards bachelor's degrees. Founded 1936. Setting: 16-acre small-town campus with easy access to Winnipeg. Total enrollment: 190. Student-undergrad faculty ratio is 13:1. 54 applied, 83% were admitted. Calendar: semesters.

Entrance Requirements: Options: Common Application, electronic application. Entrance: minimally difficult.

Costs Per Year: Application fee: $35 Canadian dollars. Tuition, fee, and room and board charges are reported in Canadian dollars. Comprehensive fee: $9404 includes full-time tuition ($5376), mandatory fees ($107), and college room and board ($3921). Part-time tuition: $168 per credit hour. Part-time mandatory fees: $107 per year.

Collegiate Environment: 24 computers available on campus for general student use.

■ **UNIVERSITY OF MANITOBA** *P-5*

Winnipeg, MB, Canada R3T 2N2
Tel: (204)474-8880
Admissions: (204)474-6382
Web Site: http://www.umanitoba.ca/

Description: Province-supported, university, coed. Awards bachelor's, master's, and doctoral degrees. Founded 1877. Setting: 685-acre suburban campus. Total enrollment: 27,599. Faculty: 1,613. Full-time: 17,904 students, 54% women, 46% men. Part-time: 6,363 students, 62% women, 38% men. Academic areas with the most degrees conferred: liberal arts/general studies; education; business/marketing. Core. Calendar: 8-month academic year plus 6-week summer session. Academic remediation for entering students, honors program, summer session for credit, part-time degree program, external degree program, adult/continuing education programs, internships. Off campus study at University of Winnipeg, Red River Community College. ROTC: Army, Air Force.

Entrance Requirements: Required: high school transcript. Entrance: moderately difficult. Application deadline: 7/1. Notification: continuous. Preference given to province residents for some programs.

Costs Per Year: Application fee: $35.

Collegiate Environment: Orientation program. Drama-theater group, student-run newspaper. Social organizations: national fraternities, national sororities, local fraternities, local sororities. Student services: health clinic, personal-psychological counseling, women's center. Campus security: 24-hour emergency response devices, student patrols, late night transport-escort service. Option: coed housing available. Elizabeth Dafoe Library plus 12 others with 1.6 million books and 12,800 serials.

Community Environment: Winnipeg, despite its small size population, 652,350, and winter chill (zero to 30 degrees below Fahrenheit), offers students an extraordinary range of activities: opera, ballet, symphony orchestra, theatre, major league football and hockey, cosmopolitan restaurants, the only stone and fur trade fort still intact (Lower Fort Garry), and the 8,000-acre Oak Hammock Marsh wildlife preserve.

■ **THE UNIVERSITY OF WINNIPEG** *P-5*

515 Portage Ave.
Winnipeg, MB, Canada R3B 2E9
Tel: (204)786-7811
Admissions: (204)786-9740
E-mail: admissions@uwinnipeg.ca
Web Site: http://www.uwinnipeg.ca/

Description: Province-supported, comprehensive, coed. Awards bachelor's and master's degrees. Founded 1967. Setting: 8-acre urban campus. Endowment: $16.8 million. Research spending for 2004 fiscal year: $2.4 million. Educational spending for 2005 fiscal year: $3471 per student. Total enrollment: 8,397. Full-time: 5,747 students, 64% women, 36% men. Part-time: 2,650 students, 62% women, 38% men. Students come from 7 provinces and territories, 32 other countries, 27% 25 or older, 2% live on campus, 3% transferred in. Retention: 60% of full-time freshmen returned the following year. Core. Calendar: Canadian standard year. Academic remediation for entering students, ESL program, services for LD students, advanced placement, accelerated degree program, self-designed majors, honors program, summer session for credit, part-time degree program, adult/continuing education programs, co-op programs and internships. Off campus study at Red River Community College. Study abroad program.

Entrance Requirements: Options: early admission, deferred admission. Required: minimum 2 high school GPA. Required for some: high school transcript, interview. Entrance: moderately difficult. Application deadlines: 8/9, 7/15 for nonresidents. Notification: continuous, continuous for nonresidents.

Costs Per Year: Application fee: $35 Canadian dollars. Tuition, fee, and room and board charges are reported in Canadian dollars. Canadian resident tuition: $2786 full-time. Mandatory fees: $318 full-time. Full-time tuition and fees vary according to program. College room and board: $4296. College room only: $2800. International student tuition: $5108 full-time.

Collegiate Environment: Drama-theater group, choral group, student-run newspaper, radio station. Social organizations: 60 open to all; national fraternities, local fraternities; 25% of eligible men and 25% of eligible women are members. Most popular organizations: Woman's Centre, LGBT (Lesbian Gay Bisexual Transgender), radio station, International Resource Centre, Aboriginal Student Centre. Major annual event: Day of Action. Student services: health clinic, personal-psychological counseling, women's center. Campus security: 24-hour emergency response devices and patrols, student patrols, video controlled external access. 187 college housing spaces available; 185 were occupied in 2003-04. Freshmen given priority for college housing. Option: coed housing available. 442,614 books, 1,840 serials, an OPAC, and a Web page. Operations spending for 2004 fiscal year: $3.5 million. 175 computers available on campus for general student use. A campuswide network can be accessed from off-campus. Staffed computer lab on campus.

Community Environment: Winnipeg is the largest city (550,000) in Manitoba, its provincial capital, and the center of its cultural, political and social life. The city has the Winnipeg Art Gallery, Centennial Center with the Manitoba Museum of Man and Nature, Concert Hall and Theatre Center and many other cultural facilities and organizations, such as the Winnipeg Symphony and the Royal Winnipeg Ballet. Nearby Lake Winnipeg (which is larger than Lake Ontario) provides excellent recreation facilities. The city is the major east-west railroad junction and is accessible by all means of transportation. Industries include agriculture, meat packing and livestock, and manufacturing.

■ **WESTERN CHRISTIAN COLLEGE** *N-2*

220 Whitmore Ave. West
Box 5000

Dauphin, MB, Canada R7N 2V5
Tel: (204)638-8801
Fax: (204)638-7054
Web Site: http://www.westernchristian.ca/
Description: Independent, 4-year, coed, affiliated with Church of Christ. Founded 1957. Calendar: semesters.
Costs Per Year: Application fee: $50 Canadian dollars. Tuition, fee, and room and board charges are reported in Canadian dollars.

■ **WILLIAM AND CATHERINE BOOTH COLLEGE** *P-5*
447 Webb Place
Winnipeg, MB, Canada R3B 2P2
Tel: (204)947-6701
Free: 800-781-6044
Fax: (204)942-3856
Web Site: http://www.wcbc-sa.edu/

Description: Independent religious, 4-year, coed. Awards bachelor's degrees. Setting: urban campus. Total enrollment: 435. 40 applied, 90% were admitted. Students come from 6 provinces and territories, 5 other countries, 35% 25 or older. Calendar: semesters. Academic remediation for entering students, summer session for credit, external degree program, internships. Off campus study at University of Manitoba, University of Winnipeg, Concord College.
Entrance Requirements: Option: deferred admission. Required: high school transcript, recommendations. Recommended: interview. Required for some: SAT. Application deadline: 8/1.
Collegiate Environment: Orientation program. Drama-theater group, choral group. Student services: personal-psychological counseling. Campus security: 24-hour emergency response devices, late night transport-escort service. On-campus residence required through sophomore year. Option: coed housing available. 12 computers available on campus for general student use.

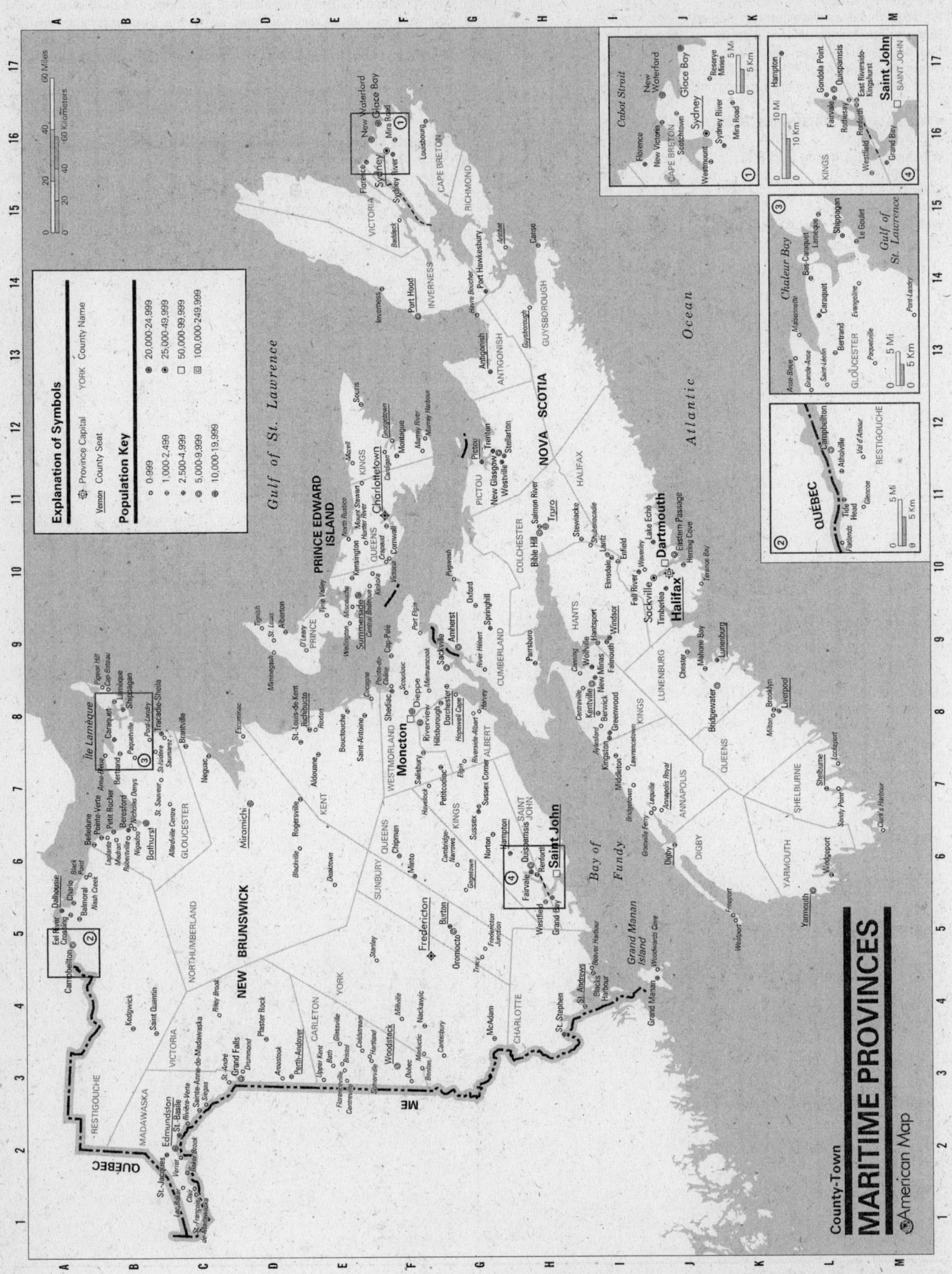

MARITIME PROVINCES

County-Town

American Map

Explanation of Symbols

⊕ Province Capital   YORK County Name

Ycnon County Seat

Population Key

○ 0-999
● 1,000-2,499
◉ 2,500-4,999
◎ 5,000-9,999
◉ 10,000-19,999
● 20,000-24,999
□ 25,000-49,999
□ 50,000-99,999
▣ 100,000-249,999

QUÉBEC

NEW BRUNSWICK

PRINCE EDWARD ISLAND

NOVA SCOTIA

CAPE BRETON

Gulf of St. Lawrence

Atlantic Ocean

Bay of Fundy

Grand Manan Island

Halifax

Dartmouth

Saint John

Moncton

Fredericton

Charlottetown

Sydney

Glace Bay

New Waterford

ME

New Brunswick

■ ATLANTIC BAPTIST UNIVERSITY *F-8*

Box 6004
Moncton, NB, Canada E1C 9L7
Tel: (506)858-8970; 888-YOU-N-ABU
Fax: (506)858-9694
Web Site: http://www.abu.nb.ca/
Description: Independent Baptist, 4-year, coed. Administratively affiliated with The Council of Christian Colleges and Universities. Awards bachelor's degrees. Founded 1949. Setting: 220-acre urban campus. Research spending for 2004 fiscal year: $20,000. Educational spending for 2005 fiscal year: $5320 per student. Total enrollment: 701. Students come from 12 provinces and territories, 5 other countries, 25% from out-of-province, 2% international, 18% 25 or older, 22% live on campus. Retention: 77% of full-time freshmen returned the following year. Core. Calendar: semesters. Accelerated degree program, honors program, double major, summer session for credit, part-time degree program, adult/continuing education programs, co-op programs and internships. Study abroad program.
Entrance Requirements: Options: Common Application, deferred admission, international baccalaureate accepted. Required: essay, high school transcript, minimum 2.60 high school GPA, 3 recommendations. Required for some: interview. Entrance: minimally difficult. Application deadline: Rolling. Notification: continuous until 9/15.
Collegiate Environment: Orientation program. Drama-theater group, choral group, student-run newspaper. Social organizations: 6 open to all. Most popular organizations: Student Association, drama, intramurals, debate team, choir. Major annual events: Christmas Banquet, Orientation week activities, Fall Foliage Day. Campus security: 24-hour emergency response devices, student patrols, controlled dormitory access. 140 college housing spaces available; 137 were occupied in 2003-04. Options: men-only, women-only housing available. George A. Rawlyk Library with 57,000 books, 3,000 microform titles, 185 serials, 350 audiovisual materials, and an OPAC. Operations spending for 2004 fiscal year: $230,000. 35 computers available on campus for general student use. A campuswide network can be accessed from student residence rooms. Staffed computer lab on campus.

■ BETHANY BIBLE COLLEGE *G-7*

26 Western St.
Sussex, NB, Canada E4E 1E6
Tel: (506)432-4400; 888-432-4422
Admissions: (506)432-4422
Fax: (506)432-4425
E-mail: shanksk@bethany-ca.edu
Web Site: http://www.bethany-ca.edu/
Description: Independent, 4-year, coed, affiliated with Wesleyan Church. Awards bachelor's degrees. Founded 1945. Setting: 55-acre small town campus. Endowment: $94,150. Total enrollment: 289. Student-undergrad faculty ratio is 19:1. Full-time: 270 students, 54% women, 46% men. Part-time: 19 students, 84% women, 16% men. Students come from 5 provinces and territories, 50% from out-of province, 1% Native American, 0.3% Hispanic, 2% black, 0% Asian Canadian, 0% international, 14% 25 or older, 77% live on campus, 3% transferred in. Retention: 72% of full-time freshmen returned the following year. Academic area with the most degrees conferred: theology and religious vocations. Core. Calendar: semesters. Academic

remediation for entering students, independent study, double major, summer session for credit, part-time degree program, internships.
Entrance Requirements: Options: Peterson's Universal Application, Common Application, electronic application. Required: high school transcript, 2 recommendations. Recommended: interview. Required for some: SAT or ACT. Entrance: moderately difficult. Application deadline: Rolling.
Costs Per Year: Application fee: $20 Canadian dollars. Tuition, fee, and room and board charges are reported in Canadian dollars. Comprehensive fee: $10,880 includes full-time tuition ($6330) and college room and board ($4550). Part-time tuition: $211 per credit hour.
Collegiate Environment: Orientation program. Drama-theater group, choral group. Most popular organizations: Ministerial Association, Athletic Association, Student Mission Fellowship, Social Committee, Drama Club. Major annual events: Missions Convention, High School Weekend, Spiritual Advancement Week. Student services: personal-psychological counseling. Campus security: controlled dormitory access. 259 college housing spaces available; all were occupied in 2003-04. On-campus residence required through senior year. Rogers Memorial Library with 27,319 books, 342 microform titles, 124 serials, 347 audiovisual materials, and an OPAC. Operations spending for 2004 fiscal year: $53,538. 23 computers available on campus for general student use. Staffed computer lab on campus.

■ MOUNT ALLISON UNIVERSITY *G-9*

65 York St.
Sackville, NB, Canada E4L 1E4
Tel: (506)364-2269
Admissions: (506)364-2166
Fax: (506)364-2272
Web Site: http://www.mta.ca/
Description: Province-supported, comprehensive, coed. Awards bachelor's and master's degrees. Founded 1839. Setting: 50-acre small town campus. Endowment: $65 million. Educational spending for 2005 fiscal year: $11,975 per student. Total enrollment: 2,369. Faculty: 164 (133 full-time, 31 part-time). Student-undergrad faculty ratio is 15:1. 1,872 applied, 61% were admitted. 59% from top 10% of their high school class, 81% from top quarter, 95% from top half. Full-time: 2,095 students, 60% women, 40% men. Part-time: 267 students, 55% women, 45% men. Students come from 13 provinces and territories, 39 other countries, 60% from out-of province, 4% 25 or older, 50% live on campus, 2% transferred in. Retention: 84% of full-time freshmen returned the following year. Academic areas with the most degrees conferred: psychology; biological/life sciences; business/marketing. Core. Calendar: Canadian standard year. Academic remediation for entering students, services for LD students, advanced placement, self-designed majors, honors program, independent study, distance learning, double major, summer session for credit, part-time degree program, adult/continuing education programs, internships. Off campus study at Moncton Campus, Miramichi Campus. Study abroad program.
Entrance Requirements: Options: electronic application, deferred admission, international baccalaureate accepted. Required: high school transcript, minimum 3.0 high school GPA. Recommended: 2 recommendations, SAT and SAT Subject Tests or ACT. Required for some: essay, interview. Entrance: moderately difficult. Application deadline: Rolling. Notification: continuous.
Costs Per Year: Application fee: $50 Canadian dollars. Tuition, fee, and room and board charges are reported in Canadian dollars. Province resident tuition: $6100 full-time. Mandatory fees: $242 full-time. Full-time tuition and

fees vary according to course load. College room and board: $6630. College room only: $3430. Room and board charges vary according to board plan. International student tuition: $12,200 full-time.

Collegiate Environment: Orientation program. Drama-theater group, choral group, student-run newspaper, radio station. Social organizations: 100 open to all. Most popular organizations: Commerce Society, Windsor Theatre, President's Leadership Development Certificate, Leadership Mount Allison, Garnet and Gold Society. Major annual events: homecoming, Winter Carnival, Orientation. Student services: health clinic, personal-psychological counseling. Campus security: 24-hour emergency response devices, late night transport-escort service. 1,112 college housing spaces available; 1,054 were occupied in 2003-04. Freshmen guaranteed college housing. Options: coed, women-only housing available. Ralph Pickard Bell Library plus 3 others with 400,000 books, 1,700 serials, an OPAC, and a Web page. Operations spending for 2004 fiscal year: $1.8 million. 100 computers available on campus for general student use. A campuswide network can be accessed from student residence rooms and from off campus. Staffed computer lab on campus.

■ **ST. THOMAS UNIVERSITY** *F-5*
51 Dineen Dr.
Fredericton, NB, Canada E3B 5G3
Tel: (506)452-0640
Admissions: (506)452-0532
Fax: (506)450-9615
E-mail: admissions@stthomasu.ca
Web Site: http://www.stu.ca/
Description: Independent Roman Catholic, 4-year, coed. Awards bachelor's and first professional degrees. Founded 1910. Setting: 16-acre small town campus. Endowment: $22.9 million. Research spending for 2004 fiscal year: $311,166. Educational spending for 2005 fiscal year: $3472 per student. Total enrollment: 3,167. Faculty: 265 (120 full-time, 145 part-time). Student-undergrad faculty ratio is 17:1. 1,587 applied, 75% were admitted. Full-time: 2,739 students, 69% women, 31% men. Part-time: 349 students, 61% women, 39% men. Students come from 11 provinces and territories, 38 other countries, 25% from out-of province, 10% 25 or older, 27% live on campus, 5% transferred in. Retention: 77% of full-time freshmen returned the following year. Academic areas with the most degrees conferred: social sciences; English; psychology. Core. Calendar: Canadian standard year. Academic remediation for entering students, ESL program, services for LD students, advanced placement, accelerated degree program, self-designed majors, honors program, independent study, distance learning, double major, summer session for credit, part-time degree program, co-op programs and internships. Off campus study at Miramichi At-Home Programme, a consortium of St. Thomas, Mount Allison University, and the University of New Brunswick.. Study abroad program.
Entrance Requirements: Options: electronic application, international baccalaureate accepted. Required: high school transcript, minimum 3.0 high school GPA. Required for some: essay. Entrance: moderately difficult. Application deadline: 3/31. Notification: continuous until 8/31.
Costs Per Year: Application fee: $35. Comprehensive fee: $10,526 includes full-time tuition ($4145), mandatory fees ($281), and college room and board ($6100). College room only: $3185. Full-time tuition and fees vary according to course load, degree level, and program. Room and board charges vary according to board plan, housing facility, and location. Part-time tuition: $467 per course. Part-time tuition varies according to course load. International student tuition: $8290 full-time.
Collegiate Environment: Orientation program. Drama-theater group, choral group, student-run newspaper, radio station. Social organizations: 25 open to all. Most popular organizations: Theatre St. Thomas, St. Thomas Student Union, Political Science Society, Economics Society, Student Help Centre. Major annual events: Fall Orientation Week, Dean's List Dinner, Music in the Box. Student services: health clinic, personal-psychological counseling. Campus security: 24-hour emergency response devices and patrols, late night transport-escort service, controlled dormitory access. 857 college housing spaces available; 796 were occupied in 2003-04. Freshmen guaranteed college housing. Options: coed, women-only housing available. Harriet Irving Library plus 2 others with 1.2 million books, 3.2 million microform titles, 13,535 serials, 4,375 audiovisual materials, an OPAC, and a Web page. Operations spending for 2004 fiscal year: $855,600. 200 computers available on campus for general student use. A campuswide network can be accessed from student residence rooms and from off campus. Staffed computer lab on campus.
Community Environment: New Brunswick's capital city has a population of about 45,000. The university's hillside campus overlooks the downtown and

the Saint John River Valley. Fredericton is home to the historic Legislative Assembly, a thriving artistic community, a professional theater troupe, one of Atlantic Canada's more impressive art galleries, tree-lined city streets and scores of elegant Victorian mansions. The city's per capita income is among the highest in the country.

■ **UNIVERSITÉ DE MONCTON** *F-8*
Moncton, NB, Canada E1A 3E9
Tel: (506)858-4000
Admissions: (506)858-4115
Fax: (506)858-4544
E-mail: gallanrm@umoncton.ca
Web Site: http://www.umoncton.ca/
Description: Province-supported, comprehensive, coed. Awards bachelor's, master's, doctoral, and first professional degrees (doctoral degree in French studies only). Founded 1963. Setting: 400-acre urban campus. Endowment: $19.8 million. Research spending for 2004 fiscal year: $5 million. Total enrollment: 6,002. 2,046 applied, 86% were admitted. Students come from 10 provinces and territories, 41 other countries, 11% from out-of province, 7% 25 or older, 15% live on campus. Retention: 83% of full-time freshmen returned the following year. Calendar: semesters. Academic remediation for entering students, ESL program, services for LD students, accelerated degree program, self-designed majors, honors program, distance learning, double major, summer session for credit, part-time degree program, external degree program, adult/continuing education programs, co-op programs and internships, graduate courses open to undergrads. Off campus study at other French colleges and universities in Canada. Study abroad program.
Entrance Requirements: Options: Common Application, deferred admission, international baccalaureate accepted. Required: high school transcript, French examination. Required for some: essay, minimum 2.0 high school GPA, 1 recommendation, interview. Entrance: moderately difficult. Application deadlines: 6/1, 2/1 for nonresidents. Notification: continuous until 9/1, continuous until 8/15 for nonresidents.
Collegiate Environment: Orientation program. Drama-theater group, choral group, student-run newspaper, radio station. Social organizations: 50 open to all. Most popular organizations: Amnesty International, student radio station, business clubs, Improvisational League, WSC. Major annual events: Homecoming, International Evening, Career Exposition. Student services: health clinic, personal-psychological counseling. Campus security: 24-hour emergency response devices and patrols, controlled dormitory access, student security attendants in residences 8 p.m. to 2 a.m. Options: coed, women-only housing available. Bibliotheque Champlain plus 2 others with 789,046 books, 588,927 microform titles, 2,059 serials, 28,818 audiovisual materials, an OPAC, and a Web page. Operations spending for 2004 fiscal year: $3.6 million. 900 computers available on campus for general student use. A campuswide network can be accessed from student residence rooms and from off campus. Staffed computer lab on campus.

■ **UNIVERSITY OF NEW BRUNSWICK FREDERICTON** *F-5*
PO Box 4400
Fredericton, NB, Canada E3B 5A3
Tel: (506)453-4666
Admissions: (506)453-4865
Fax: (506)453-5016
E-mail: unbfacts@unb.ca
Web Site: http://www.unb.ca/
Description: Province-supported, university, coed. Awards bachelor's, master's, and doctoral degrees. Founded 1785. Setting: 7,100-acre urban campus. Total enrollment: 9,498. Faculty: 645 (500 full-time, 145 part-time). Student-undergrad faculty ratio is 18:1. 2,618 applied, 79% were admitted. Students come from 12 provinces and territories, 65 other countries, 20% live on campus. Core. Calendar: Canadian standard year. ESL program, services for LD students, advanced placement, accelerated degree program, self-designed majors, honors program, independent study, distance learning, double major, summer session for credit, part-time degree program, external degree program, adult/continuing education programs, co-op programs and internships, graduate courses open to undergrads. Off campus study at University of Maine, Universite Laval, all forestry colleges in Canada. Study abroad program.
Entrance Requirements: Options: electronic application, early admission, deferred admission, international baccalaureate accepted. Required: high school transcript. Required for some: essay, 1 recommendation, interview, SAT. Entrance: moderately difficult. Application deadline: 3/31. Notification: continuous until 8/31.

Costs Per Year: Application fee: $45 Canadian dollars. Tuition, fee, and room and board charges are reported in Canadian dollars. Area resident tuition: $5008 full-time, $500 per term part-time. Mandatory fees: $613 full-time, $32 per term part-time. College room and board: $6768. Room and board charges vary according to board plan. International student tuition: $7573 full-time.

Collegiate Environment: Orientation program. Drama-theater group, choral group, student-run newspaper, radio station. Social organizations: 100 open to all. Student services: health clinic, personal-psychological counseling, women's center. Campus security: late night transport-escort service. 1,400 college housing spaces available. Freshmen guaranteed college housing. Options: coed, men-only, women-only housing available. Harriet Irving Library plus 3 others with 1.1 million books, 2.2 million microform titles, 4,817 serials, 65,000 audiovisual materials, an OPAC, and a Web page. 1,100 computers available on campus for general student use. A campuswide network can be accessed from student residence rooms and from off campus. Staffed computer lab on campus.

Community Environment: Fredericton, the capital of New Brunswick, has a population of 45,000. The city is located in the Saint John River Valley, about 55 miles from the city of Saint John. Major employers in Fredericton are service industries, university and government.

■ **UNIVERSITY OF NEW BRUNSWICK SAINT JOHN**
PO Box 5050
St. John, NB, Canada E2L 4L5
Tel: (506)648-5500
Free: 800-743-5691
Admissions: (506)648-5674
E-mail: apply@unbsj.ca
Web Site: http://www.unb.ca/

Description: Province-supported, comprehensive, coed. Awards bachelor's, master's, and doctoral degrees. Founded 1964. Setting: 250-acre urban campus. Research spending for 2004 fiscal year: $4.6 million. Educational spending for 2005 fiscal year: $4581 per student. Total enrollment: 2,791. 2,600 applied, 85% were admitted. Students come from 8 provinces and territories, 45 other countries, 6% from out-of province, 5% live on campus. Retention: 85% of full-time freshmen returned the following year. Core. Calendar: Canadian standard year. Academic remediation for entering students, ESL program, services for LD students, advanced placement, accelerated degree program, self-designed majors, honors program, independent study, distance learning, double major, summer session for credit, part-time degree program, adult/continuing education programs, co-op programs and internships. Off campus study at University of Maine. Study abroad program.

Entrance Requirements: Options: electronic application, early admission, deferred admission, international baccalaureate accepted. Required: high school transcript, SAT. Required for some: recommendations. Entrance: moderately difficult. Application deadlines: Rolling, 3/31 for nonresidents. Notification: continuous until 8/31, continuous for nonresidents.

Costs Per Year: Application fee: $35 Canadian dollars. Tuition, fee, and room and board charges are reported in Canadian dollars. Province resident tuition: $5008 full-time. Mandatory fees: $365 full-time, $535. College room and board: $5180. Room and board charges vary according to board plan and housing facility. International student tuition: $5130 full-time.

Collegiate Environment: Orientation program. Drama-theater group, choral group, student-run newspaper, radio station. Social organizations: 20 open to all. Most popular organizations: Business Administration Society, OPTAMUS, International Student Association, Chinese Cultural Association, Muslim Student Association. Major annual events: Orientation Week, Winter Carnival. Student services: personal-psychological counseling, women's center. Campus security: 24-hour emergency response devices and patrols, student patrols, late night transport-escort service, controlled dormitory access. 230 college housing spaces available; 71 were occupied in 2003-04. Option: coed housing available. Ward Chipman Library with 155,500 books, 700 serials, an OPAC, and a Web page. Operations spending for 2004 fiscal year: $270,000. 100 computers available on campus for general student use. A campuswide network can be accessed from student residence rooms and from off campus. Staffed computer lab on campus.

Nova Scotia

■ **ACADIA UNIVERSITY** *I-9*
Wolfville, NS, Canada B4P 2R6
Tel: (902)542-2201

Admissions: (902)585-1016
Fax: (902)585-1081
E-mail: admissions@acadiau.ca
Web Site: http://www.acadiau.ca/

Description: Province-supported, comprehensive, coed. Awards bachelor's and master's degrees. Founded 1838. Setting: 250-acre small town campus. Endowment: $42.4 million. Research spending for 2004 fiscal year: $1.4 million. Educational spending for 2005 fiscal year: $7362 per student. Total enrollment: 3,856. Faculty: 308 (200 full-time, 108 part-time). Student-undergrad faculty ratio is 12:1. 1,924 applied, 52% were admitted. Full-time: 3,446 students, 54% women, 46% men. Part-time: 113 students, 57% women, 43% men. Students come from 12 provinces and territories, 61 other countries, 36% from out-of province, 9% 25 or older, 40% live on campus, 5% transferred in. Retention: 82% of full-time freshmen returned the following year. Academic areas with the most degrees conferred: business/marketing; education; social sciences. Core. Calendar: Canadian standard year. Academic remediation for entering students, ESL program, advanced placement, honors program, distance learning, double major, summer session for credit, part-time degree program, co-op programs and internships. Off campus study at East Carolina University, Franklin College of Indiana, Bridgewater State College, New England/Nova Scotia Exchange Program. Study abroad program.

Entrance Requirements: Options: electronic application, deferred admission, international baccalaureate accepted. Required: high school transcript, minimum 2.5 high school GPA, SAT. Required for some: essay, recommendations, interview, SAT Subject Tests. Entrance: moderately difficult. Application deadlines: 7/1, 5/31 for nonresidents. Notification: continuous.

Costs Per Year: Application fee: $25. Canadian resident tuition: $6353 full-time, $719 per course part-time. Mandatory fees: $150 full-time, $4 per course part-time. College room and board: $5363. College room only: $2818. Room and board charges vary according to board plan and housing facility. International student tuition: $11,647 full-time.

Collegiate Environment: Orientation program. Drama-theater group, choral group, marching band, student-run newspaper, radio station. Social organizations: 57 open to all. Most popular organizations: Acadia Recreation Club, Acadia Ski Club, Education Society, Computer Science Club, Caricom. Major annual events: Winter Carnival, Frosh Week, Convocation. Student services: legal services, health clinic, personal-psychological counseling, women's center. Campus security: 24-hour emergency response devices and patrols, student patrols, late night transport-escort service, controlled dormitory access. 1,655 college housing spaces available; 1,564 were occupied in 2003-04. Options: coed, men-only, women-only housing available. Vaughan Memorial Library with 923,042 books, 438,583 microform titles, 16,314 serials, 5,283 audiovisual materials, an OPAC, and a Web page. Operations spending for 2004 fiscal year: $1.8 million. 3,700 computers available on campus for general student use. A campuswide network can be accessed from student residence rooms and from off campus. Staffed computer lab on campus.

Community Environment: Acadia University is located in the Annapolis Valley town of Wolfville, 100 kilometers northwest of Halifax. The main buildings are on a high terraced slope, facing the broad diked meadows of the Evangeline Country and the Minas Basin, the body of water in the northeastern part of the Bay of Fundy. Wolfville is a beautiful, residential town of 3,000 people, with four churches and good elementary and secondary schools.

■ **CAPE BRETON UNIVERSITY** *F-16*
Box 5300
1250 Grand Lake Rd.
Sydney, NS, Canada B1P 6L2
Tel: (902)539-5300; 888-959-9995
Admissions: (902)563-1198
Fax: (902)562-0119
E-mail: arlene_mullan@capebretonu.ca
Web Site: http://www.capebretonu.ca/

Description: Province-supported, comprehensive, coed. Awards bachelor's and master's degrees. Founded 1974. Setting: 57-hectare small town campus. Endowment: $15 million. Research spending for 2004 fiscal year: $5.4 million. Educational spending for 2005 fiscal year: $6384 per student. Total enrollment: 3,748. Faculty: 225 (172 full-time, 53 part-time). Student-undergrad faculty ratio is 16:1. 2,320 applied, 96% were admitted. Students come from 11 provinces and territories, 25 other countries, 9% from out-of province, 30% 25 or older, 5% live on campus. Retention: 63% of full-time freshmen returned the following year. Calendar: Canadian standard year.

Academic remediation for entering students, services for LD students, advanced placement, accelerated degree program, self-designed majors, honors program, distance learning, double major, summer session for credit, part-time degree program, co-op programs and internships. Study abroad program.

Entrance Requirements: Options: electronic application, international baccalaureate accepted. Required: high school transcript. Required for some: essay, 3 recommendations, interview. Entrance: moderately difficult. Application deadlines: 8/1, 3/31 for nonresidents. Notification: continuous.

Costs Per Year: Application fee: $35. Canadian resident tuition: $5450 full-time. Mandatory fees: $98 full-time. College room only: $2760. International student tuition: $10,095 full-time.

Collegiate Environment: Drama-theater group, student-run newspaper, radio station. Social organizations: 30 open to all. Most popular organizations: Marketing Society, International Students Society, Music Society, MacKenzie Residence Society, Nursing Society. Major annual events: Fresh Week, Sliderama (Muscular Dystrophy), Winter Carnival. Student services: legal services, health clinic, personal-psychological counseling, women's center. Campus security: 24-hour patrols, controlled dormitory access, security for social events, escort service. Option: coed housing available. University College Library with 451,271 books, 88,317 microform titles, 800 serials, 1,850 audiovisual materials, an OPAC, and a Web page. Operations spending for 2004 fiscal year: $769,000. 206 computers available on campus for general student use. A campuswide network can be accessed from off-campus. Staffed computer lab on campus.

Community Environment: Sydney, part of the Regional Municipality of Cape Breton, is on Cape Breton Island, which is at the northeast end of Nova Scotia. The island is connected to the mainland by a causeway. Sydney is an industrial city with a self-contained steel plant. It is also a port city. There are numerous historical sites and recreational facilities. A major restoration project being undertaken on Cape Breton Island is at the Fortress of Louisbourg National Historic Park.

■ **DALHOUSIE UNIVERSITY** *J-10*
Halifax, NS, Canada B3H 4R2
Tel: (902)494-2211
Admissions: (902)494-2148
Fax: (902)494-1630
E-mail: admissions@dal.ca
Web Site: http://www.dal.ca/

Description: Province-supported, university, coed. Awards bachelor's, master's, doctoral, and first professional degrees. Founded 1818. Setting: 80-acre urban campus. Endowment: $230.3 million. Research spending for 2004 fiscal year: $31.9 million. Total enrollment: 15,528. Faculty: 1,516. Student-undergrad faculty ratio is 14:1. 7,663 applied, 85% were admitted. Students come from 13 provinces and territories, 84 other countries, 0% from out-of province, 21% 25 or older, 14% live on campus. Retention: 82% of full-time freshmen returned the following year. Core. Calendar: semesters. Academic remediation for entering students, services for LD students, advanced placement, accelerated degree program, honors program, distance learning, double major, summer session for credit, part-time degree program, adult/continuing education programs, co-op programs. Off campus study at Saint Mary's University, Mount Saint Vincent University, Nova Scotia Agricultural College. Study abroad program.

Entrance Requirements: Options: Peterson's Universal Application, electronic application, early decision, deferred admission, international baccalaureate accepted. Required: high school transcript, minimum 3.0 high school GPA, SAT. Required for some: essay, 1 recommendation, interview, minimum 1100 comprehensive score on SAT for U.S. applicants. Entrance: moderately difficult. Application deadlines: 6/1, 3/15 for early decision. Notification: continuous.

Costs Per Year: Application fee: $45 Canadian dollars. Tuition, fee, and room and board charges are reported in Canadian dollars. Comprehensive fee: $13,952 includes full-time tuition ($5820), mandatory fees ($632), and college room and board ($7500). International student tuition: $11,460 full-time.

Collegiate Environment: Orientation program. Drama-theater group, choral group, student-run newspaper, radio station. Social organizations: 200 open to all; national fraternities, national sororities, local fraternities, local sororities. Most popular organizations: International Students Association, Arts Society, Science Society, Commerce Society, Dalhousie Outdoors Club. Major annual events: Frosh Week, Winter Carnival, Charity Ball. Student services: legal services, health clinic, personal-psychological counseling, women's center. Campus security: 24-hour emergency response devices and patrols, student patrols, late night transport-escort service, controlled dormitory access. 2,676 college housing spaces available. Freshmen given priority for college housing. Options: coed, men-only, women-only housing available. The Killam Memorial Library plus 4 others with 1.7 million books, 421,897 microform titles, 8,306 serials, 6,001 audiovisual materials, an OPAC, and a Web page. Operations spending for 2004 fiscal year: $7.6 million. 710 computers available on campus for general student use. Computer purchase/lease plans available. A campuswide network can be accessed from student residence rooms and from off campus. Staffed computer lab on campus.

■ **MOUNT SAINT VINCENT UNIVERSITY** *J-10*
166 Bedford Hwy.
Halifax, NS, Canada B3M 2J6
Tel: (902)457-6788
Admissions: (902)457-6117
Fax: (902)457-6455
E-mail: karl.turner@msvu.ca
Web Site: http://www.msvu.ca/

Description: Province-supported, comprehensive, coed. Awards bachelor's, master's, and first professional degrees. Founded 1873. Setting: 40-acre suburban campus. Endowment: $18.4 million. Research spending for 2004 fiscal year: $697,000. Educational spending for 2005 fiscal year: $4337 per student. Total enrollment: 4,385. Faculty: 279 (157 full-time, 122 part-time). Student-undergrad faculty ratio is 16:1. 1,058 applied, 74% were admitted. 25% from top 10% of their high school class, 70% from top quarter, 100% from top half. Students come from 13 provinces and territories, 41 other countries, 14% from out-of-province, 30% 25 or older, 6% live on campus. Retention: 67% of full-time freshmen returned the following year. Academic areas with the most degrees conferred: education; business/marketing; communications/journalism. Calendar: Canadian standard year. Academic remediation for entering students, ESL program, services for LD students, advanced placement, accelerated degree program, self-designed majors, honors program, independent study, distance learning, double major, summer session for credit, part-time degree program, external degree program, adult/continuing education programs, co-op programs and internships, graduate courses open to undergrads. Off campus study at Metro Halifax Universities Consortium, Acadia University. Study abroad program.

Entrance Requirements: Options: Common Application, electronic application, deferred admission, international baccalaureate accepted. Required: high school transcript, minimum 2.0 high school GPA, SAT and SAT Subject Tests or ACT. Required for some: essay, minimum 3.0 high school GPA, 2 recommendations, interview. Entrance: moderately difficult. Application deadlines: 3/15, 5/30 for nonresidents. Notification: continuous until 9/1, 6/1 for nonresidents.

Costs Per Year: Application fee: $30 Canadian dollars. Tuition, fee, and room and board charges are reported in Canadian dollars. Province resident tuition: $1068 per unit part-time. Canadian resident tuition: $5340 full-time, $1068 per unit part-time. Mandatory fees: $584 full-time, $47.84 per unit part-time, $10 per year part-time. Full-time tuition and fees vary according to course level, course load, degree level, location, program, reciprocity agreements, and student level. Part-time tuition and fees vary according to course level, course load, degree level, location, program, reciprocity agreements, and student level. College room and board: $6340. College room only: $4220. Room and board charges vary according to board plan and housing facility. International student tuition: $10,265 full-time.

Collegiate Environment: Orientation program. Choral group, student-run newspaper. Social organizations: 18 open to all. Most popular organizations: Business Society, Residence Society, Science Society, History Society, Queer/Straight Alliance. Major annual events: Frosh Week, Awards Banquet, Shinerama. Student services: health clinic, personal-psychological counseling, women's center. Campus security: 24-hour emergency response devices and patrols, late night transport-escort service, controlled dormitory access. 400 college housing spaces available; all were occupied in 2003-04. Freshmen given priority for college housing. Options: coed, men-only, women-only housing available. E. Margaret Fulton Communications Centre Library plus 3 others with 207,140 books, 379,076 microform titles, 3,570 serials, 1,243 audiovisual materials, an OPAC, and a Web page. Operations spending for 2004 fiscal year: $1.3 million. 150 computers available on campus for general student use. A campuswide network can be accessed from student residence rooms. Staffed computer lab on campus.

Community Environment: Mount Saint Vincent University is situated in Halifax, the capital of Nova Scotia. Overlooking the Bedford Basin, it offers scenic walkways and recreational facilities. Public transport and a good highway provide easy access both to the International Airport and to downtown Halifax, which offers cultural and intellectual opportunities, shopping, parks and entertainment.

■ **NOVA SCOTIA AGRICULTURAL COLLEGE** *H-11*
PO Box 550
Truro, NS, Canada B2N 5E3
Tel: (902)893-6600; 888-700-6722
Admissions: (902)893-6722
E-mail: wpaquet@nsac.ns.ca
Web Site: http://www.nsac.ns.ca/
Description: Province-supported, comprehensive, coed. Awards bachelor's and master's degrees. Founded 1905. Setting: 408-acre small town campus with easy access to Halifax. Total enrollment: 753. Faculty: 74 (60 full-time, 14 part-time). Student-undergrad faculty ratio is 9:1. 560 applied, 82% were admitted. Students come from 14 provinces and territories, 15 other countries, 30% from out-of province, 22% 25 or older. Retention: 85% of full-time freshmen returned the following year. Core. Calendar: semesters. Academic remediation for entering students, advanced placement, part-time degree program, adult/continuing education programs, co-op programs and internships, graduate courses open to undergrads. Off campus study at members of the Agricultural College Exchange Program.
Entrance Requirements: Option: Common Application. Required: high school transcript. Required for some: interview. Entrance: minimally difficult. Application deadline: 8/1.
Costs Per Year: Application fee: $25 Canadian dollars. Tuition, fee, and room and board charges are reported in Canadian dollars. Province resident tuition: $5290 full-time, $529 per course part-time. Mandatory fees: $394 full-time, $46 per course part-time. College room and board: $5634. International student tuition: $10,580 full-time.
Collegiate Environment: Orientation program. Student-run newspaper. Major annual events: Woodsmen Weekend, Harvestfest, College Royal. Student services: health clinic, personal-psychological counseling. Campus security: 24-hour patrols, student patrols. 350 college housing spaces available; 250 were occupied in 2003-04. Freshmen guaranteed college housing. Option: coed housing available. MacRae Library with 23,000 books and 800 serials. 110 computers available on campus for general student use. A campuswide network can be accessed. Staffed computer lab on campus.

■ **NSCAD UNIVERSITY** *J-10*
5163 Duke St.
Halifax, NS, Canada B3J 3J6
Tel: (902)422-7381
Admissions: (902)494-8129
Fax: (902)425-2420
E-mail: tbailey@nscad.ca
Web Site: http://www.nscad.ca/
Description: Province-supported, comprehensive, coed. Awards bachelor's and master's degrees. Founded 1887. Setting: 1-acre urban campus. Endowment: $1.1 million. Total enrollment: 1,011. Faculty: 113 (53 full-time, 60 part-time). Student-undergrad faculty ratio is 10:1. 412 applied. Full-time: 813 students, 68% women, 32% men. Part-time: 179 students, 79% women, 21% men. Students come from 11 provinces and territories, 17 other countries, 35% 25 or older, 10% transferred in. Academic area with the most degrees conferred: visual and performing arts. Core. Calendar: semesters. Services for LD students, self-designed majors, honors program, independent study, double major, summer session for credit, part-time degree program, external degree program, co-op programs and internships. Off campus study at AICAD Mobility Program, Independent Exchanges, 4 members of Canadian Art Colleges, New England/Nova Scotia Student Exchange (70+ institutions in total). Study abroad program.
Entrance Requirements: Options: deferred admission, international baccalaureate accepted. Required: essay, high school transcript, portfolio. Recommended: minimum 3.0 high school GPA. Required for some: 2 recommendations, interview. Entrance: very difficult. Application deadlines: 5/15, 3/15 for early decision. Notification: continuous until 6/30.
Costs Per Year: Application fee: $35. Province resident tuition: $5501 full-time, $230 per credit part-time. Canadian resident tuition: $5501 full-time, $230 per credit part-time. Mandatory fees: $32.51 per term part-time. College room and board: $8022. International student tuition: $12,125 full-time.
Collegiate Environment: Orientation program. Student services: personal-psychological counseling. Campus security: evening patrols by trained security personnel. College housing not available. Nova Scotia College of Art and Design Library with 32,000 books, 100 microform titles, 235 serials,

120,000 audiovisual materials, and an OPAC. Operations spending for 2004 fiscal year: $492,225. 60 computers available on campus for general student use. Staffed computer lab on campus.
Community Environment: The College is located in Halifax, the capital city of Nova Scotia, with a metropolitan population of 300,000. Halifax is the largest city in the Atlantic region. It is the home of a number of cultural institutions including the Atlantic Symphony Orchestra, the Neptune Theatre and the Nova Scotia Museum. In addition, there are a number of active art galleries, most notably the Art Gallery of Nova Scotia and the galleries connected with the city's three universities. The Arts Center at Dalhousie University provides, during the fall and winter months, a constant round of music concerts, plays, and other performances.

■ **ST. FRANCIS XAVIER UNIVERSITY** *G-13*
Box 5000
Antigonish, NS, Canada B2G 2W5
Tel: (902)863-3300; 877-867-STFX
Admissions: (902)867-2219
Fax: (902)867-2329
E-mail: mbarry@stfx.ca
Web Site: http://www.stfx.ca/
Description: Independent Roman Catholic, comprehensive, coed. Awards bachelor's and master's degrees. Founded 1853. Setting: 100-acre small town campus. Endowment: $34.9 million. Research spending for 2004 fiscal year: $3400. Educational spending for 2005 fiscal year: $5700 per student. Total enrollment: 4,969. Faculty: 265 (222 full-time, 43 part-time). Student-undergrad faculty ratio is 16:1. 2,281 applied, 42% were admitted. 25% from top 10% of their high school class, 50% from top quarter. Students come from 12 provinces and territories, 25 other countries, 41% from out-of province, 7% 25 or older, 43% live on campus. Retention: 88% of full-time freshmen returned the following year. Calendar: Canadian standard year. Academic remediation for entering students, ESL program, services for LD students, advanced placement, accelerated degree program, self-designed majors, honors program, independent study, distance learning, double major, summer session for credit, part-time degree program, adult/continuing education programs, co-op programs and internships. Off campus study at 18 colleges and universities in the New England states, St. Thomas Aquinas College. Study abroad program.
Entrance Requirements: Options: Peterson's Universal Application, Common Application, early decision, international baccalaureate accepted. Required: essay, high school transcript, 2 recommendations. Recommended: SAT or ACT, SAT Subject Tests. Required for some: SAT or ACT. Entrance: moderately difficult. Application deadline: Rolling. Notification: continuous until 8/15.
Costs Per Year: Application fee: $40 Canadian dollars. Tuition, fee, and room and board charges are reported in Canadian dollars. Comprehensive fee: $13,615 includes full-time tuition ($5975), mandatory fees ($1145), and college room and board ($6495). International student tuition: $10,875 full-time.
Collegiate Environment: Orientation program. Drama-theater group, choral group, student-run newspaper, radio station. Social organizations: 38 open to all. Most popular organizations: X-Project, Walkhome Program, orientation committee, Exekoi Tutoring, Off-Campus Society. Major annual events: Christmas Ball, Winter Carnival, X-Ring Ceremony. Student services: health clinic, personal-psychological counseling, women's center. Campus security: 24-hour emergency response devices and patrols, student patrols, late night transport-escort service, controlled dormitory access. 1,731 college housing spaces available. Freshmen guaranteed college housing. Options: coed, men-only, women-only housing available. Angus L. MacDonald Library plus 1 other with 632,575 books, 211,412 microform titles, 3,282 serials, 6,598 audiovisual materials, an OPAC, and a Web page. Operations spending for 2004 fiscal year: $2.4 million. 350 computers available on campus for general student use. A campuswide network can be accessed from student residence rooms and from off campus. Staffed computer lab on campus.
Community Environment: Pretty in its rural setting, Antigonish lies 140 miles from Halifax and each July hosts the Highland Games, a kind of Olympics of the Clans.

■ **SAINT MARY'S UNIVERSITY** *J-10*
Halifax, NS, Canada B3H 3C3
Tel: (902)420-5400
Admissions: (902)420-5415
Fax: (902)496-8100
E-mail: greg.ferguson@smu.ca

Web Site: http://www.stmarys.ca/

Description: Province-supported, comprehensive, coed. Awards bachelor's, master's, and doctoral degrees. Founded 1802. Setting: 30-acre urban campus. Total enrollment: 7,904. Full-time: 5,660 students, 53% women, 47% men. Part-time: 1,762 students, 55% women, 45% men. Students come from 12 provinces and territories, 55 other countries, 12% from out-of-province, 15% live on campus. Calendar: semesters. Academic remediation for entering students, ESL program, services for LD students, accelerated degree program, self-designed majors, honors program, independent study, distance learning, double major, summer session for credit, part-time degree program, adult/continuing education programs, co-op programs and internships. Off campus study. Study abroad program.

Entrance Requirements: Options: early action, international baccalaureate accepted. Required: high school transcript, minimum 2.0 high school GPA. Required for some: interview. Entrance: moderately difficult. Application deadlines: 7/1, 1/1 for early action. Notification: continuous, 4/1 for early action.

Collegiate Environment: Orientation program. Drama-theater group, student-run newspaper. Social organizations: 68 open to all. Most popular organizations: International Students Organization, Commerce Society, AIESEC, Journal Society, Political Science Society. Major annual events: Orientation, Homecoming. Student services: health clinic, personal-psychological counseling. Campus security: 24-hour emergency response devices and patrols, student patrols, late night transport-escort service, controlled dormitory access, electronic surveillance of labs and key areas. 1,038 college housing spaces available. No special consideration for freshman housing applicants. Options: coed, women-only housing available. Patrick Power Library with 366,267 books, 594,793 microform titles, 1,700 serials, an OPAC, and a Web page. 300 computers available on campus for general student use. A campuswide network can be accessed from student residence rooms and from off campus. Staffed computer lab on campus.

■ **UNIVERSITÉ SAINTE-ANNE**

Church Point, NS, Canada B0W 1M0
Tel: (902)769-2114
Fax: (902)769-2930
E-mail: admission@ustanne.ednet.ns.ca
Web Site: http://www.usainteanne.ca/

Description: Province-supported, 4-year, coed. Awards bachelor's degrees. Founded 1890. Setting: 115-acre rural campus. Endowment: $1.4 million. Research spending for 2004 fiscal year: $60,000. Educational spending for 2005 fiscal year: $3125 per student. Total enrollment: 286. 180 applied, 69% were admitted. 18% from top 10% of their high school class. Students come from 2 provinces and territories, 4 other countries, 35% from out-of-province, 8% 25 or older, 60% live on campus. Core. Calendar: semesters. Academic remediation for entering students, ESL program, accelerated degree program, self-designed majors, honors program, distance learning, double major, summer session for credit, part-time degree program, co-op programs and internships. Off campus study at Universite du Quebec, Acadia University, Universite de Moncton, Nova Scotia-New England Exchange Program.

Entrance Requirements: Options: Common Application, electronic application. Required: high school transcript. Required for some: essay, 3 recommendations. Entrance: minimally difficult. Application deadline: Rolling.

Collegiate Environment: Drama-theater group, choral group, student-run newspaper, radio station. Most popular organizations: Student Organization, Amnesty International, Club de Plein Air, Education Committee, Commerce Committee. Major annual events: Winter Carnival, Expo Commerce, Evening at the Theatre. Student services: health clinic, personal-psychological counseling, women's center. Campus security: student patrols, late night transport-escort service, 14-hour patrols by trained security personnel. Option: coed housing available. Louis R. Comeau Library plus 3 others with 84,000 books, 340 serials, and an OPAC. Operations spending for 2004 fiscal year: $185,000. 23 computers available on campus for general student use. A campuswide network can be accessed from student residence rooms and from off campus. Staffed computer lab on campus.

■ **UNIVERSITY OF KING'S COLLEGE** *J-10*

6350 Coburg Rd.
Halifax, NS, Canada B3H 2A1
Tel: (902)422-1271
Fax: (902)423-3357
E-mail: admissions@ukings.ns.ca
Web Site: http://www.ukings.ns.ca/

Description: Province-supported, 4-year, coed. Administratively affiliated with Dalhousie University. Awards bachelor's degrees. Founded 1789. Setting: 4-acre urban campus. Endowment: $30 million. Research spending for 2004 fiscal year: $33,000. Educational spending for 2005 fiscal year: $3900 per student. Total enrollment: 1,149. 1,050 applied, 74% were admitted. 55% from top 10% of their high school class, 90% from top quarter, 99% from top half. Full-time: 1,119 students, 60% women, 40% men. Part-time: 30 students, 53% women, 47% men. Students come from 10 provinces and territories, 12 other countries, 56% from out-of-province, 4% 25 or older, 26% live on campus, 1% transferred in. Retention: 64% of full-time freshmen returned the following year. Core. Calendar: Canadian standard year. Services for LD students, advanced placement, accelerated degree program, self-designed majors, honors program, independent study, double major, summer session for credit, part-time degree program, co-op programs and internships. Off campus study at Mount Saint Vincent University, Saint Mary's University, Nova Scotia College of Art and Design. Study abroad program.

Entrance Requirements: Option: international baccalaureate accepted. Required: high school transcript, minimum 3.0 high school GPA. Required for some: essay, writing sample, SAT. Entrance: moderately difficult. Application deadline: 3/1. Notification: 4/15.

Costs Per Year: Application fee: $45. Province resident tuition: $5820 full-time, $194 per credit hour part-time. Canadian resident tuition: $5820 full-time. Mandatory fees: $836 full-time, $810 per term part-time. Full-time tuition and fees vary according to course load and program. Part-time tuition and fees vary according to course load and program. College room and board: $7580. Room and board charges vary according to housing facility. International student tuition: $11,460 full-time.

Collegiate Environment: Drama-theater group, choral group, student-run newspaper, radio station. Social organizations: 28 open to all. Most popular organizations: King's Theatrical Society, student newspaper, King's College Dance Collective, St. Andrew's Missionary Society, King's Independent Film-Makers Society. Major annual events: Frosh Week, College Christmas, Young Alexandra Society Annual Ball. Student services: legal services, health clinic, personal-psychological counseling, women's center. Campus security: student patrols, late night transport-escort service. 274 college housing spaces available; all were occupied in 2003-04. Freshmen given priority for college housing. Options: coed, men-only, women-only housing available. University of King's College Library with 80,000 books, 612 microform titles, 201 serials, 123 audiovisual materials, and an OPAC. Operations spending for 2004 fiscal year: $289,000. 18 computers available on campus for general student use. Computer purchase/lease plans available. A campuswide network can be accessed from student residence rooms and from off campus. Staffed computer lab on campus.

Prince Edward Island

■ **UNIVERSITY OF PRINCE EDWARD ISLAND** *F-11*

550 University Ave.
Charlottetown, PE, Canada C1A 4P3
Tel: (902)566-0439
Admissions: (902)566-0361
Fax: (902)566-0795
Web Site: http://www.upei.ca/

Description: Province-supported, comprehensive, coed. Awards bachelor's, master's, doctoral, and first professional degrees. Founded 1834. Setting: 130-acre small town campus. Total enrollment: 3,912. Faculty: 208 (all full-time). Student-undergrad faculty ratio is 16:1. 1,224 applied, 67% were admitted. Students come from 11 provinces and territories, 25 other countries, 0% from out-of-province, 24% 25 or older, 10% live on campus. Retention: 68% of full-time freshmen returned the following year. Calendar: Canadian standard year. ESL program, services for LD students, honors program, distance learning, double major, summer session for credit, part-time degree program, co-op programs and internships. Study abroad program.

Entrance Requirements: Options: Common Application, electronic application, early admission, international baccalaureate accepted. Required: high school transcript, minimum 2.0 high school GPA. Required for some: 3 recommendations. Entrance: moderately difficult. Application deadlines: 8/15, 4/1 for nonresidents. Notification: continuous until 8/31, continuous until 6/30 for nonresidents.

Costs Per Year: Application fee: $50 Canadian dollars. Tuition, fee, and room and board charges are reported in Canadian dollars. Province resident tuition: $4620 full-time. Mandatory fees: $1060 full-time. Full-time tuition and fees vary according to course load and degree level. College room and board: $7490. College room only: $4300. Room and board charges vary according to board plan and housing facility. International student tuition: $8430 full-time.

Collegiate Environment: Orientation program. Drama-theater group, choral group, student-run newspaper. Social organizations: 20 open to all. Most popular organizations: Business Society, Biology Club, Music Society, intramurals, Theatre Society. Student services: health clinic, personal-psychological counseling, women's center. Campus security: 24-hour emergency response devices and patrols, late night transport-escort service, controlled dormitory access, late night residence hall security personnel. 300 college housing spaces available; all were occupied in 2003-04. Option: coed housing available. Robertson Library with 394,000 books, 92,000 microform titles, 1,700 serials, an OPAC, and a Web page. 120 computers available on campus for general student use. Computer purchase/lease plans available. A campuswide network can be accessed from student residence rooms and from off campus. Staffed computer lab on campus.

Community Environment: Charlottetown is the provincial capital and the largest community, approximately 30,000, on the island. It has an excellent harbor and is the center of the cultural and commercial activities of the island. Scenic attractions include Province House, St. Dunstan's Basilica, St. Peter's Anglican Cathedral, the Confederation Center and Government house.

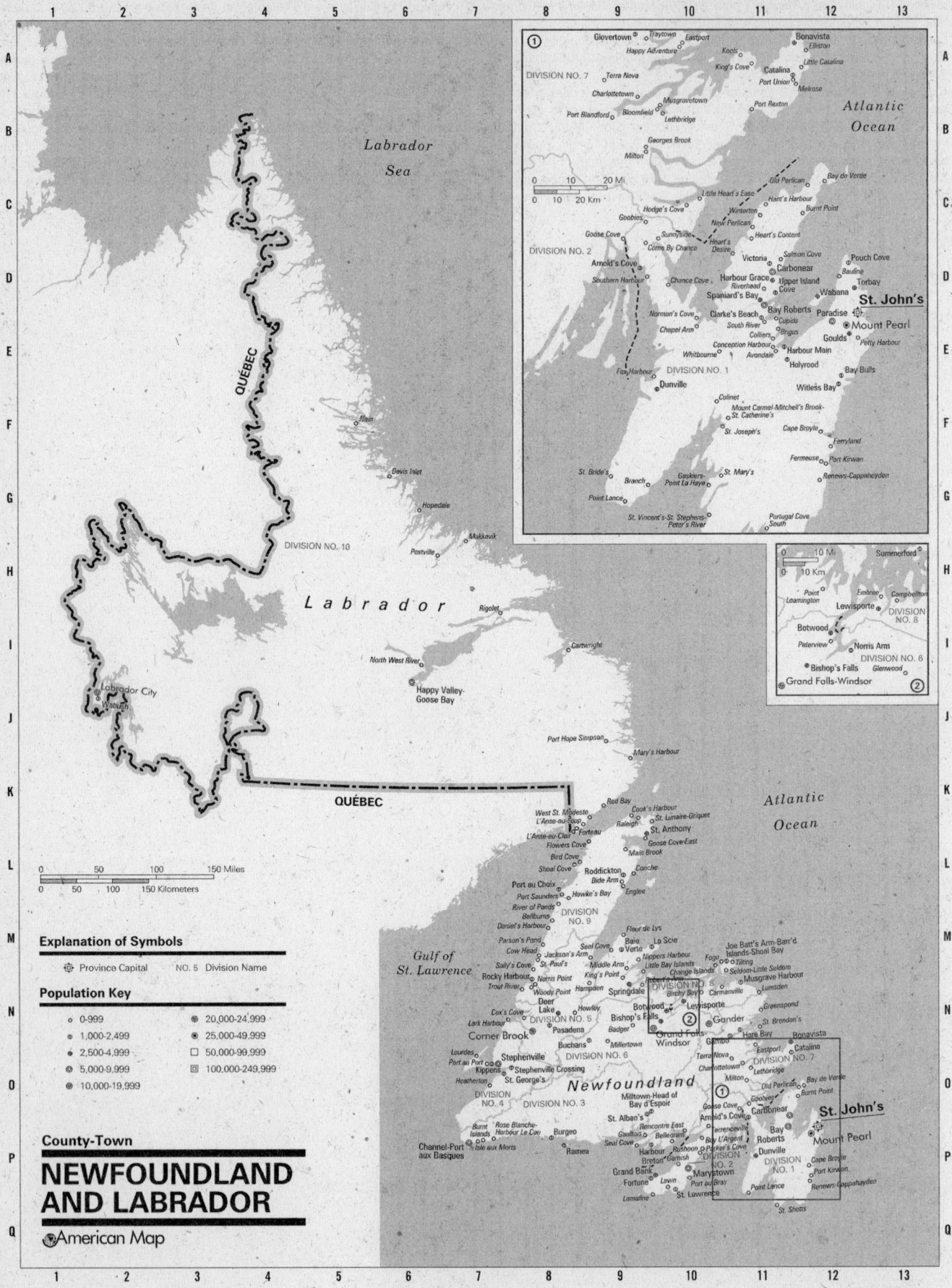

County-Town

NEWFOUNDLAND AND LABRADOR

American Map

Explanation of Symbols

Province Capital   NO.5 Division Name

Population Key

- 0-999
- 1,000-2,499
- 2,500-4,999
- 5,000-9,999
- 10,000-19,999
- 20,000-24,999
- 25,000-49,999
- 50,000-99,999
- 100,000-249,999

■ **MEMORIAL UNIVERSITY OF NEWFOUNDLAND** *P-12*
Elizabeth Ave.
St. John's, NL, Canada A1C 5S7
Tel: (709)737-8000
Admissions: (709)737-3705
Fax: (709)737-4569
E-mail: mabbott@morgan.ucs.mun.ca
Web Site: http://www.mun.ca/

Description: Province-supported, university, coed. Awards bachelor's, master's, and doctoral degrees. Founded 1925. Setting: 220-acre urban campus. Endowment: $53.8 million. Research spending for 2004 fiscal year: $73.9 million. Total enrollment: 17,567. Faculty: 1,108 (1,081 full-time, 27 part-time). Student-undergrad faculty ratio is 14:1. 3,793 applied, 78% were admitted. Full-time: 12,685 students, 61% women, 39% men. Part-time: 2,247 students, 60% women, 40% men. Students come from 12 provinces and territories, 77 other countries, 11% from out-of province, 14% 25 or older, 10% live on campus, 4% transferred in. Retention: 81% of full-time freshmen returned the following year. Calendar: trimesters. Academic remediation for entering students, ESL program, services for LD students, advanced placement, accelerated degree program, honors program, distance learning, double major, summer session for credit, part-time degree program, adult/continuing education programs, co-op programs and internships, graduate courses open to undergrads. Off campus study at University of New Brunswick, University of New Mexico. Study abroad program.

Entrance Requirements: Options: electronic application, early admission, early decision, deferred admission, international baccalaureate accepted. Required: high school transcript. Required for some: essay, 2 recommendations, interview, audition, portfolio. Entrance: moderately difficult. Application deadlines: Rolling, 3/1 for nonresidents.

Costs Per Year: Application fee: $40 Canadian dollars. Tuition, fee, and room and board charges are reported in Canadian dollars. Province resident tuition: $2550 full-time, $85 per credit hour part-time. Mandatory fees: $464 full-time. College room and board: $4878. College room only: $1820. International student tuition: $8800 full-time.

Collegiate Environment: Orientation program. Drama-theater group, choral group, student-run newspaper, radio station. Social organizations: 72 open to all. Most popular organizations: International Student Center, Students Older Than Average, Memorial's Organization for the Disabled, Biology Society, Student Parents at MUN. Major annual events: Winter Carnival, National University Week, Orientation. Student services: legal services, health clinic, personal-psychological counseling, women's center. Campus security: 24-hour emergency response devices and patrols, student patrols, late night transport-escort service. Options: coed, men-only, women-only housing available. Queen Elizabeth II Library plus 4 others with 1.7 million books, 2.8 million microform titles, 17,170 serials, 20,441 audiovisual materials, an OPAC, and a Web page. Operations spending for 2004 fiscal year: $12.2 million. 800 computers available on campus for general student use. A campuswide network can be accessed from student residence rooms and from off campus. Staffed computer lab on campus.

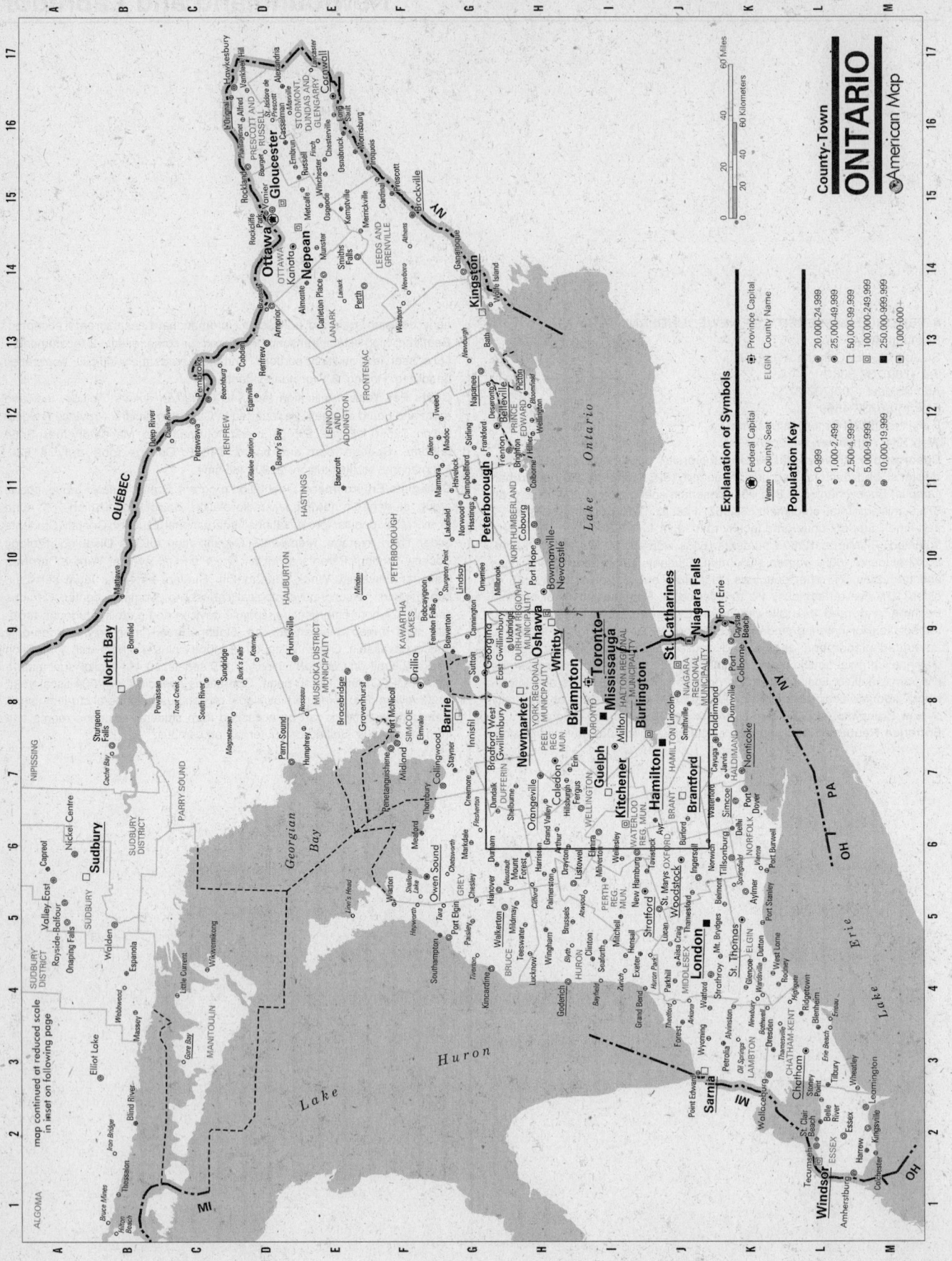

ONTARIO

County-Town

American Map

QUÉBEC

Explanation of Symbols

Federal Capital ⊛   Province Capital ⊛

Vernon   County Seat   ELGIN   County Name

Population Key

○ 0-999	◉ 20,000-24,999
○ 1,000-2,499	◉ 25,000-49,999
◌ 2,500-4,999	▢ 50,000-99,999
◍ 5,000-9,999	▣ 100,000-249,999
◉ 10,000-19,999	■ 250,000-999,999
	▨ 1,000,000+

60 Miles
60 Kilometers

map continued at reduced scale
in inset on following page

■ **BROCK UNIVERSITY**
500 Glenridge Ave.
St. Catharines, ON, Canada L2S 3A1
Tel: (905)688-5550
Fax: (905)988-5488
E-mail: mlea@brocku.ca
Web Site: http://www.brocku.ca/

Description: Province-supported, university, coed. Awards bachelor's, master's, and doctoral degrees. Founded 1964. Setting: 540-acre urban campus with easy access to Toronto. Research spending for 2004 fiscal year: $7.8 million. Total enrollment: 17,409. Faculty: 545 (all full-time). Student-undergrad faculty ratio is 30:1. 20,781 applied, 63% were admitted. Students come from 8 provinces and territories, 66 other countries, 16% live on campus. Core. Calendar: Canadian standard year. Academic remediation for entering students, ESL program, services for LD students, advanced placement, accelerated degree program, self-designed majors, honors program, double major, summer session for credit, part-time degree program, adult/continuing education programs, co-op programs and internships, graduate courses open to undergrads. Study abroad program.

Entrance Requirements: Options: Common Application, electronic application, international baccalaureate accepted. Required: high school transcript, minimum 3.0 high school GPA. Required for some: essay, interview, audition, portfolio. Entrance: moderately difficult. Application deadline: 4/1. Notification: continuous.

Costs Per Year: Application fee: $115 Canadian dollars. Tuition, fee, and room and board charges are reported in Canadian dollars. Canadian resident tuition: $4483 full-time, $896.53 per credit part-time. Mandatory fees: $528 full-time. College room and board: $7040. College room only: $3445. International student tuition: $11,378 full-time.

Collegiate Environment: Orientation program. Drama-theater group, choral group, student-run newspaper, radio station. Social organizations: 50 open to all. Most popular organizations: International Students Association, Brock University Student Association, Business Administration Association, Brock Christian Fellowship, Ace Brock. Major annual events: homecoming, Orientation Week. Student services: health clinic, personal-psychological counseling, women's center. Campus security: 24-hour emergency response devices and patrols, student patrols, late night transport-escort service, controlled dormitory access. 2,400 college housing spaces available; all were occupied in 2003-04. Freshmen given priority for college housing. Option: coed housing available. James A. Gibson Library plus 1 other with 1.6 million books, 660,598 microform titles, 856,587 serials, 26,765 audiovisual materials, an OPAC, and a Web page. 379 computers available on campus for general student use. Computer purchase/lease plans available. A campuswide network can be accessed from student residence rooms and from off campus. Staffed computer lab on campus.

■ **CARLETON UNIVERSITY** *D-15*
1125 Colonel By Dr.
Ottawa, ON, Canada K1S 5B6
Tel: (613)520-7400
Admissions: (613)520-3710
Fax: (613)520-7455
E-mail: liaison@admissions.carleton.ca
Web Site: http://www.carleton.ca/

Description: Province-supported, university, coed. Awards bachelor's, master's, and doctoral degrees. Founded 1942. Setting: 152-acre urban campus. Endowment: $135.2 million. Research spending for 2004 fiscal year: $53.2 million. Educational spending for 2005 fiscal year: $5157 per student. Total enrollment: 23,683. Faculty: 791 (783 full-time, 8 part-time). Student-undergrad faculty ratio is 26:1. 15,934 applied, 73% were admitted. Full-time: 16,509 students, 51% women, 49% men. Part-time: 4,237 students, 46% women, 54% men. Students come from 13 provinces and territories, 155 other countries, 8% from out-of province, 12% 25 or older, 15% live on campus, 4% transferred in. Retention: 87% of full-time freshmen returned the following year. Calendar: Canadian standard year. Academic remediation for entering students, ESL program, services for LD students, advanced placement, accelerated degree program, self-designed majors, honors program, independent study, distance learning, double major, summer session for credit, part-time degree program, adult/continuing education programs, co-op programs and internships, graduate courses open to undergrads. Off campus study at University of Ottawa, Algonquin College. Study abroad program.

Entrance Requirements: Options: Common Application, electronic application, deferred admission, international baccalaureate accepted. Required: high school transcript, minimum 3.0 high school GPA. Recommended: SAT. Required for some: essay, minimum 3.4 high school GPA, recommendations, interview, SAT and SAT Subject Tests or ACT. Entrance: moderately difficult. Application deadlines: 6/1, 4/1 for nonresidents. Notification: continuous, continuous for nonresidents.

Costs Per Year: Application fee: $85 Canadian dollars. Tuition, fee, and room and board charges are reported in Canadian dollars. Area resident tuition: $4691 full-time, $893 per credit part-time. Canadian resident tuition: $3031 per credit part-time. Mandatory fees: $74 per credit part-time. Full-time tuition varies according to course load, program, and reciprocity agreements. Part-time tuition and fees vary according to course load, program, and reciprocity agreements. College room and board: $7561. College room only: $5248. Room and board charges vary according to board plan and housing facility. International student tuition: $12,426 full-time.

Collegiate Environment: Orientation program. Drama-theater group, choral group, student-run newspaper, radio station. Social organizations: 100 open to all. Major annual events: Orientation, Prep Week, Charity Ball. Student services: health clinic, personal-psychological counseling, women's center. Campus security: 24-hour emergency response devices and patrols, student patrols, late night transport-escort service, controlled dormitory access. 2,623 college housing spaces available; 2,600 were occupied in 2003-04. Freshmen given priority for college housing. Options: coed, men-only, women-only housing available. MacOdrum Library with 1.9 million books, 1.4 million microform titles, 15,824 serials, 2,661 audiovisual materials, an OPAC, and a Web page. Operations spending for 2004 fiscal year: $12.4 million. 550 computers available on campus for general student use. Computer purchase/lease plans available. A campuswide network can be accessed from student residence rooms and from off campus. Staffed computer lab on campus.

Community Environment: As the site of the Parliament Buildings, the National Arts Center, and many of Canada's finest museums, Ottawa is a vibrant political and cultural center that provides Carleton's students with many unique opportunities. With its impressive network of trails, pathways, and waterways, Ottawa is an ideal location for jogging, skiing, and cycling enthusiasts. Outdoor recreation extends year-round, for Carleton is located beside the historic Rideau Canal, which in the winter becomes the world's longest skating rink, and the site of Ottawa's annual winter carnival.

■ COLLÈGE DOMINICAIN DE PHILOSOPHIE ET DE THÉOLOGIE
D-15

96, Ave. Empress
Ottawa, ON, Canada K1R 7G3
Tel: (613)233-5696
E-mail: registraire@collegedominicain.ca
Web Site: http://www.collegedominicain.ca/

Description: Independent Roman Catholic, comprehensive, coed. Awards bachelor's, master's, and doctoral degrees. Founded 1909. Setting: urban campus. Total enrollment: 231. Faculty: 40 (24 full-time, 16 part-time). 100% from top half of their high school class. Students come from 6 provinces and territories, 8 other countries, 0% from out-of province, 1% Hispanic, 1% black, 6% Asian Canadian, 2% international, 85% 25 or older. Retention: 72% of full-time freshmen returned the following year. Academic area with the most degrees conferred: theology and religious vocations. Core. Calendar: semesters. Accelerated degree program, summer session for credit, part-time degree program, graduate courses open to undergrads.

Entrance Requirements: Options: Common Application, electronic application. Required: high school transcript. Recommended: interview. Entrance: noncompetitive. Application deadline: 7/15.

Costs Per Year: Application fee: $30 Canadian dollars. Tuition, fee, and room and board charges are reported in Canadian dollars. Comprehensive fee: $8300 includes full-time tuition ($2900) and college room and board ($5400). Part-time tuition: $120 per credit.

Collegiate Environment: Most popular organization: Association Etudiant College Dominicain. Campus security: late night transport-escort service. 20 college housing spaces available; all were occupied in 2003-04. No special consideration for freshman housing applicants. Bibliotheque du College Dominicain with 125,000 books, 500 serials, and an OPAC. 4 computers available on campus for general student use. Staffed computer lab on campus.

■ EMMANUEL BIBLE COLLEGE *I-6*

100 Fergus Ave.
Kitchener, ON, Canada N2A 2H2
Tel: (519)894-8900
Fax: (519)894-9430
Web Site: http://www.ebcollege.on.ca/

Description: Independent, 4-year, coed, affiliated with Missionary Church. Awards bachelor's degrees. Founded 1940. Setting: 12-acre urban campus with easy access to Toronto. 82 applied, 83% were admitted. Students come from 3 provinces and territories, 8 other countries, 46% 25 or older. Core. Calendar: semesters. Academic remediation for entering students, accelerated degree program, summer session for credit, part-time degree program, internships.

Entrance Requirements: Option: deferred admission. Required: essay, high school transcript, 3 recommendations, interview, Christian testimony. Entrance: moderately difficult. Application deadline: Rolling.

Collegiate Environment: Orientation program. Drama-theater group, choral group, student-run newspaper. Student services: personal-psychological counseling. On-campus residence required through senior year. 19,250 books and 200 serials.

■ HERITAGE BAPTIST COLLEGE AND HERITAGE THEOLOGICAL SEMINARY *S-11*

175 Holiday Inn Dr.
Cambridge, ON, Canada N3C 3T2
Tel: (519)651-2869
E-mail: registrar@heritagecollege.net
Web Site: http://www.heritage-theo.edu/

Description: Independent Baptist, comprehensive, coed. Awards bachelor's and master's degrees (artist diploma). Founded 1993. Setting: 7-acre urban campus with easy access to Toronto. Endowment: $478.1 million. Educational spending for 2005 fiscal year: $24,330 per student. Total enrollment: 805. Faculty: 266 (114 full-time, 152 part-time). 2,523 applied, 5% were admitted. Full-time: 478 students, 48% women, 52% men. Students come from 4 provinces and territories, 2 other countries, 85% from out-of province, 0.4% Native American, 4% Hispanic, 12% black, 13% Asian Canadian, 20% international, 25% 25 or older, 3% transferred in. Retention: 94% of full-time freshmen returned the following year. Academic area with the most degrees conferred: visual and performing arts. Calendar: Canadian

standard year. Accelerated degree program, double major, summer session for credit, part-time degree program, internships.

Entrance Requirements: Open admission. Option: deferred admission. Required: essay, high school transcript, audition. Required for some: interview. Entrance: most difficult. Application deadline: 12/1. Notification: 4/1.

Costs Per Year: Application fee: $100. Comprehensive fee: $34,500 includes full-time tuition ($24,330), mandatory fees ($600), and college room and board ($9570).

Collegiate Environment: Orientation program. Drama-theater group, choral group, student-run newspaper. Major annual events: Missions Conference, Christmas and Graduation Banquets, Orientation. Student services: legal services, health clinic, personal-psychological counseling. Campus security: controlled dormitory access. Options: men-only, women-only housing available. Heritage Library with 40,430 books, 1,497 microform titles, 173 serials, 1,809 audiovisual materials, and an OPAC.

■ LAKEHEAD UNIVERSITY *T-3*

955 Oliver Rd.
Thunder Bay, ON, Canada P7B 5E1
Tel: (807)343-8110
Admissions: (807)343-8500
Fax: (807)343-8156
E-mail: admissions@lakeheadu.ca
Web Site: http://www.lakeheadu.ca/

Description: Province-supported, comprehensive, coed. Awards bachelor's, master's, and doctoral degrees. Founded 1965. Setting: 345-acre suburban campus. Research spending for 2004 fiscal year: $7.9 million. Total enrollment: 7,558. Faculty: (285 full-time). Student-undergrad faculty ratio is 27:1. 7,422 applied, 73% were admitted. Students come from 13 provinces and territories, 50 other countries, 32% 25 or older, 22% live on campus. Academic areas with the most degrees conferred: education; social sciences; engineering. Core. Calendar: Canadian standard year. Services for LD students, advanced placement, accelerated degree program, self-designed majors, honors program, independent study, distance learning, double major, summer session for credit, part-time degree program, external degree program, co-op programs and internships, graduate courses open to undergrads. Off campus study. Study abroad program.

Entrance Requirements: Options: Common Application, electronic application, early admission, international baccalaureate accepted. Required: Visual Arts Program requires a portfolio. Music Program requires an audition., SAT or ACT. Recommended: high school transcript, minimum 3 high school GPA. Required for some: essay, 3 recommendations. Entrance: moderately difficult. Application deadline: 9/19.

Costs Per Year: Application fee: $105. Province resident tuition: $828 per course part-time. Canadian resident tuition: $4140 full-time. Mandatory fees: $531 full-time, $81.35 per course part-time. College room and board: $6569. College room only: $4980. International student tuition: $10,000 full-time.

Collegiate Environment: Orientation program. Student-run newspaper, radio station. Social organizations: 140 open to all. Most popular organizations: Outdoor Recreation Students Association, Engineering Students Society, Business Association, ECHO/LUFROG, Educational Students Association. Major annual events: Orientation, Winter Carnival, Engineering Competitions. Student services: health clinic, personal-psychological counseling, women's center. Campus security: 24-hour emergency response devices and patrols, student patrols, late night transport-escort service, controlled dormitory access. 1,319 college housing spaces available; 1,019 were occupied in 2003-04. Freshmen guaranteed college housing. On-campus residence required through senior year. Option: coed housing available. Chancellor Norman M. Paterson Library plus 1 other with 780,974 books, 915,402 microform titles, 10,300 serials, 324 audiovisual materials, an OPAC, and a Web page. Operations spending for 2004 fiscal year: $3.2 million. 700 computers available on campus for general student use. A campuswide network can be accessed from student residence rooms and from off campus. Staffed computer lab on campus.

■ LAURENTIAN UNIVERSITY *B-6*

935 Ramsey Lake Rd.
Sudbury, ON, Canada P3E 2C6
Tel: (705)675-1151
Fax: (705)675-4840
E-mail: sjunkin@admin.laurentian.ca
Web Site: http://www.laurentian.ca/

Description: Province-supported, comprehensive, coed. Awards bachelor's, master's, and doctoral degrees. Founded 1960. Setting: 700-acre suburban campus. Endowment: $8.5 million. Research spending for 2004 fiscal year: $1.4 million. Total enrollment: 8,634. 6,938 applied. Students come from 9 provinces and territories, 41 other countries. Core. Calendar: Canadian standard year. Academic remediation for entering students, services for LD students, accelerated degree program, honors program, summer session for credit, part-time degree program, external degree program, adult/continuing education programs, co-op programs, graduate courses open to undergrads. Off campus study.

Entrance Requirements: Options: Common Application, early admission. Required: high school transcript. Required for some: essay, 2 recommendations, interview. Entrance: minimally difficult. Application deadline: 2/1.

Costs Per Year: Application fee: $50 Canadian dollars. Tuition, fee, and room only charges are reported in Canadian dollars. Tuition: $4184 full-time, $836.80 per course part-time. Mandatory fees: $332 full-time, $24.80 per term part-time. College room only: $2950. International student tuition: $10,087 full-time.

Collegiate Environment: Drama-theater group, student-run newspaper, radio station. Most popular organizations: Students General Association, Association des Etudiants Francophone, Association of Laurentian Part-time Students. Major annual events: Students General Association Winter Carnival, Alumni Rendez-vous. Student services: health clinic, personal-psychological counseling, women's center. Campus security: 24-hour emergency response devices and patrols, late night transport-escort service. Option: coed housing available. J. N. Desmarais Library plus 3 others with 696,838 books and a Web page. Operations spending for 2004 fiscal year: $3.4 million. 125 computers available on campus for general student use. Staffed computer lab on campus.

Community Environment: Sudbury is the largest city (population 90,000, region 160,100) in Northern Ontario. Thunder Bay is 300 miles to the West. Sudbury is 100 miles east of Sault Ste. Marie. The campus is on 750 acres of scenic countryside, surrounded by three lakes, just a 10-minute drive from the downtown area.

■ MASTER'S COLLEGE AND SEMINARY *I-8*

3080 Yonge St., Ste. 3040
Toronto, ON, Canada M4N 3N1
Tel: (416)482-2224
Free: 800-295-6368
Fax: (416)482-7004
E-mail: merv.anthony@mcs.edu
Web Site: http://www.mcs.edu/

Description: Independent Pentecostal, 4-year, coed. Awards bachelor's degrees. Founded 1939. Setting: urban campus. Total enrollment: 376. Student-undergrad faculty ratio is 11:1. 110 applied, 65% were admitted. Students come from 8 provinces and territories, 5 other countries, 20% from out-of-province. Retention: 42% of full-time freshmen returned the following year. Academic area with the most degrees conferred: theology and religious vocations. Core. Calendar: semesters. Academic remediation for entering students, services for LD students, accelerated degree program, independent study, distance learning, summer session for credit, part-time degree program, internships. Off campus study at Pan Africa Christian College in Nairobi, Kenya. Study abroad program.

Entrance Requirements: Option: deferred admission. Required: essay, high school transcript, 3 recommendations, Christian commitment. Recommended: minimum 2.0 high school GPA. Required for some: interview. Entrance: noncompetitive. Application deadline: 8/31.

Costs Per Year: Application fee: $75 Canadian dollars. Tuition and fee charges are reported in Canadian dollars. Tuition: $5600 full-time, $175 per credit hour part-time. Full-time tuition varies according to course load. Part-time tuition varies according to course load.

Collegiate Environment: Orientation program. Major annual event: Extravaganza. College housing not available. 46,438 books, 92 microform titles, 124 serials, 2,674 audiovisual materials, and an OPAC. 6 computers available on campus for general student use. A campuswide network can be accessed from off-campus. Staffed computer lab on campus.

■ MCMASTER UNIVERSITY *J-7*

1280 Main St. West
Hamilton, ON, Canada L8S 4M2
Tel: (905)525-9140
Fax: (905)527-1105
E-mail: macadmit@mcmaster.ca

Web Site: http://www.mcmaster.ca/

Description: Province-supported, university, coed. Awards bachelor's, master's, doctoral, and first professional degrees. Founded 1887. Setting: 300-acre suburban campus with easy access to Toronto. Total enrollment: 23,606. 31,018 applied, 67% were admitted. Students come from 12 provinces and territories, 79 other countries, 23% live on campus. Calendar: Canadian standard year. Academic remediation for entering students, services for LD students, accelerated degree program, self-designed majors, honors program, independent study, summer session for credit, part-time degree program, adult/continuing education programs, co-op programs and internships, graduate courses open to undergrads. Off campus study. Study abroad program.

Entrance Requirements: Options: early action, international baccalaureate accepted. Required: high school transcript. Required for some: essay, interview. Entrance: very difficult. Application deadlines: 7/15, 5/1 for nonresidents, 3/1 for early action. Notification: continuous until 9/1, 6/12 for early action.

Collegiate Environment: Orientation program. Drama-theater group, choral group, student-run newspaper, radio station. Social organizations: 120 open to all. Most popular organizations: Inter-Varsity Christian Fellowship Club, African-Caribbean Student Association, Chinese Students' Association, AIESEC (international leadership organization), Southeast Asian-American Society. Major annual events: Homecoming, Frosh Week, Alumni Weekend. Student services: legal services, health clinic, personal-psychological counseling, women's center. Campus security: 24-hour emergency response devices and patrols, student patrols, late night transport-escort service, controlled dormitory access. 3,366 college housing spaces available. Options: coed, men-only, women-only housing available. Mills Memorial Library plus 4 others with 1.7 million books, 11,976 serials, an OPAC, and a Web page. 400 computers available on campus for general student use. A campuswide network can be accessed from student residence rooms and from off campus. Staffed computer lab on campus.

Community Environment: Hamilton is the western point of the "Golden Triangle," Ontario's economic heartland. A major Great Lakes seaport, Hamilton's care for its past and present is reflected in the restored 36-room Regency Villa Dundurn Castle, and the 1,200-acre Coote's Paradise wildlife sanctuary.

■ NER ISRAEL YESHIVA COLLEGE OF TORONTO

8950 Bathurst St.
Thornhill, ON, Canada L4J 8A7
Tel: (905)731-1224

Description: Independent Jewish, comprehensive, men only. Awards bachelor's and master's degrees. Founded 1959. Setting: 14-acre campus. 50% from top 10% of their high school class, 100% from top half. Students come from 3 provinces and territories, 2 other countries, 80% 25 or older. Calendar: Canadian standard year. Summer session for credit.

Entrance Requirements: Required: high school transcript, 2 recommendations, interview. Entrance: very difficult. Application deadline: 8/15.

Collegiate Environment: Student services: personal-psychological counseling. On-campus residence required through senior year. 3,000 books.

■ NIPISSING UNIVERSITY *B-8*

100 College Dr., Box 5002
North Bay, ON, Canada P1B 8L7
Tel: (705)474-3461
Fax: (705)474-1947
Web Site: http://www.nipissingu.ca/

Description: Province-supported, comprehensive, coed. Awards bachelor's and master's degrees. Founded 1992. Setting: 290-hectare small town campus. Endowment: $4.4 million. Research spending for 2004 fiscal year: $565,000. Total enrollment: 6,265. 6,474 applied, 17% were admitted. Full-time: 2,201 students, 72% women, 28% men. Part-time: 628 students, 66% women, 34% men. Students come from 23 other countries, 35% 25 or older, 22% live on campus, 3% transferred in. Core. Calendar: semesters. Academic remediation for entering students, services for LD students, honors program, independent study, distance learning, double major, summer session for credit, part-time degree program, external degree program. Off campus study at Muskoka Campus, Wilfrid Laurier University. Study abroad program.

Entrance Requirements: Options: early admission, international baccalaureate accepted. Required: high school transcript. Entrance: minimally difficult. Application deadline: 6/1. Notification: continuous until 6/1.

Collegiate Environment: Orientation program. Drama-theater group, student-run newspaper. Social organizations: 15 open to all. Most popular organizations: BACCHUS, NUSAC (Nipissing University Student Athletic Counsel), Business Society, Drama Club Students on Stage, Literacy Club Frontier College. Major annual events: Winter Classic, Frosh Week, Shinerama (Cystic Fibrosis Foundation Fundraiser). Student services: health clinic, personal-psychological counseling, women's center. Campus security: 24-hour emergency response devices and patrols, student patrols, late night transport-escort service, controlled dormitory access. College housing designed to accommodate 788 students; 899 undergraduates lived in college housing during 2003-04. Freshmen guaranteed college housing. Option: coed housing available. Education Centre Library with 180,397 books, 324,471 microform titles, 5,680 serials, 2,689 audiovisual materials, an OPAC, and a Web page. Operations spending for 2004 fiscal year: $1.3 million. 163 computers available on campus for general student use. Computer purchase/lease plans available. A campuswide network can be accessed from student residence rooms and from off campus. Staffed computer lab on campus.

■ **QUEEN'S UNIVERSITY AT KINGSTON** *G-13*
Kingston, ON, Canada K7L 3N6
Tel: (613)533-2000
Admissions: (613)533-2218
Fax: (613)533-6300
Web Site: http://www.queensu.ca/
Description: Province-supported, university, coed. Awards bachelor's, master's, doctoral, and first professional degrees. Founded 1841. Setting: 160-acre urban campus. Endowment: $516.8 million. Research spending for 2004 fiscal year: $84.7 million. Total enrollment: 20,783. Faculty: 2,259 (1,049 full-time, 1,210 part-time). Student-undergrad faculty ratio is 12:1. Full-time: 13,291 students, 58% women, 42% men. Part-time: 3,147 students, 68% women, 32% men. Students come from 13 provinces and territories, 82 other countries, 16% from out-of-province, 7% 25 or older, 30% live on campus, 1% transferred in. Retention: 95% of full-time freshmen returned the following year. Academic areas with the most degrees conferred: education; social sciences; biological/life sciences. Calendar: Canadian standard year. ESL program, services for LD students, accelerated degree program, self-designed majors, honors program, distance learning, double major, summer session for credit, part-time degree program, adult/continuing education programs, co-op programs and internships. Study abroad program.
Entrance Requirements: Options: Common Application, deferred admission. Required: essay, high school transcript, minimum 2.3 high school GPA, SAT or ACT. Required for some: 1 recommendation. Entrance: most difficult. Application deadline: 2/25. Notification: continuous until 5/28.
Costs Per Year: Application fee: $90. Canadian resident tuition: $838 per credit part-time.
Collegiate Environment: Orientation program. Drama-theater group, choral group, marching band, student-run newspaper, radio station. Social organizations: 235 open to all. Most popular organizations: Arts and Sciences Undergraduate Society, Alma Mater Society, Engineering Society, Commerce Society, Dance Club. Major annual events: Orientation Week, Alumni Weekend. Student services: legal services, health clinic, personal-psychological counseling, women's center. Campus security: 24-hour emergency response devices and patrols, student patrols, late night transport-escort service, controlled dormitory access. 3,655 college housing spaces available; all were occupied in 2003-04. Freshmen guaranteed college housing. Options: coed, men-only, women-only housing available. Joseph S. Stauffer Library plus 4 others with 3.5 million books, 3.7 million microform titles, 16,109 serials, an OPAC, and a Web page. Operations spending for 2004 fiscal year: $10.9 million. 455 computers available on campus for general student use. A campuswide network can be accessed from student residence rooms and from off campus. Staffed computer lab on campus.

■ **REDEEMER UNIVERSITY COLLEGE** *T-12*
777 Garner Rd. East
Ancaster, ON, Canada L9K 1J4
Tel: (905)648-2131
Fax: (905)648-2134
E-mail: adm@redeemer.on.ca
Web Site: http://www.redeemer.on.ca/
Description: Independent interdenominational, 4-year, coed. Awards bachelor's degrees. Founded 1980. Setting: 78-acre small town campus with

easy access to Toronto. Endowment: $2.7 million. Research spending for 2004 fiscal year: $293,580. Educational spending for 2005 fiscal year: $18,337 per student. Total enrollment: 849. Student-undergrad faculty ratio is 17:1. 338 applied, 81% were admitted. Students come from 8 provinces and territories, 10 other countries, 9% 25 or older, 56% live on campus. Academic areas with the most degrees conferred: English; history; business/marketing. Core. Calendar: semesters. Academic remediation for entering students, services for LD students, honors program, independent study, double major, summer session for credit, part-time degree program, co-op programs and internships. Off campus study at University of Guelph, Ridgetown College, Redeemer in France. Study abroad program.
Entrance Requirements: Options: deferred admission, international baccalaureate accepted. Required: essay, high school transcript, minimum 2.0 high school GPA, 2 recommendations, personal reference. Required for some: interview, SAT or ACT. Entrance: moderately difficult. Application deadline: 5/31. Notification: continuous. Preference given to Christians.
Costs Per Year: Application fee: $35. Comprehensive fee: $16,591 includes full-time tuition ($11,082), mandatory fees ($393), and college room and board ($5116). Part-time tuition: $1110 per course. Part-time mandatory fees: $39 per course.
Collegiate Environment: Drama-theater group, choral group, student-run newspaper. Social organizations: 28 open to all. Most popular organizations: Church in the Box, mission trips, Bible study groups, choir, intramurals. Major annual events: Angels and Mortals, Mainstage Productions, Midnight Breakfast. Student services: health clinic, personal-psychological counseling. Campus security: 24-hour emergency response devices, student patrols, late night transport-escort service, controlled dormitory access, path lighting. 470 college housing spaces available; 452 were occupied in 2003-04. Freshmen guaranteed college housing. On-campus residence required through sophomore year. Options: men-only, women-only housing available. Redeemer College Library with 117,404 books, 350 serials, 2,153 audiovisual materials, an OPAC, and a Web page. Operations spending for 2004 fiscal year: $453,980. 35 computers available on campus for general student use. A campuswide network can be accessed from off-campus. Staffed computer lab on campus.
Community Environment: Redeemer University College is located just inside the southwestern corner of the town of Ancaster (population 16,542), Ontario, which is adjacent to Hamilton (population 307,690), on its southwest side. It is readily accessible by road or air transportation. The nearest international airport is at Toronto, 50 miles to the northeast. Ancaster is mainly a residential community for the large Hamilton industrial base, mainly the steel industry and related secondary industries. Hamilton is well provided with modern cultural and sport facilities.

■ **ROYAL MILITARY COLLEGE OF CANADA** *G-13*
PO Box 17000, Station Forces
Kingston, ON, Canada K7K 7B4
Tel: (613)541-6000
Fax: (613)542-3565
Web Site: http://www.rmc.ca/
Description: Federally supported, comprehensive, coed. Awards bachelor's, master's, and doctoral degrees. Founded 1876. Setting: 90-acre suburban campus. Total enrollment: 2,370. 1,500 applied, 50% were admitted. Students come from 11 provinces and territories, 60% from out-of-province, 50% 25 or older. Retention: 84% of full-time freshmen returned the following year. Core. Calendar: Canadian standard year. ESL program, honors program, distance learning, part-time degree program. Off campus study.
Entrance Requirements: Open admission for part-time students. Option: international baccalaureate accepted. Required: high school transcript, recommendations, interview, medical, aptitude and physical fitness testing for full-time students; Canadian residency. Entrance: most difficult. Application deadline: 3/12. Notification: 5/15.
Collegiate Environment: Drama-theater group, choral group, marching band, student-run newspaper. Social organizations: 30 open to all. Most popular organization: band. Major annual events: Ex-Cadet Weekend, Christmas Ball, Graduation Weekend. Student services: legal services, health clinic, personal-psychological counseling. Campus security: 24-hour emergency response devices and patrols. On-campus residence required through senior year. Option: coed housing available. Massey Library plus 1 other with 300,000 books, 18,000 microform titles, 1,100 serials, 2,510 audiovisual materials, an OPAC, and a Web page.
Community Environment: Kingston is situated at the confluence of Lake Ontario and the St. Lawrence River. Since 1673, when it was established as a trading post called Fort Frontenac, it has been of Canadian commercial

and geographic importance. Kingston's interest in preserving its historical flavor is exemplified in the restoration of Fort Henry, the key defense of the Kingston Naval Dockyard. Kingston is a very much a university town that enjoys the presence of RMC, Queen's and St. Lawrence Colleges.

■ RYERSON UNIVERSITY *I-8*

350 Victoria St.
Toronto, ON, Canada M5B 2K3
Tel: (416)979-5000
E-mail: chack@ryerson.ca
Web Site: http://www.ryerson.ca/

Description: Province-supported, comprehensive, coed. Awards bachelor's, master's, and doctoral degrees. Founded 1948. Setting: 20-acre urban campus. Endowment: $28 million. Total enrollment: 28,051. Faculty: 779 (594 full-time, 185 part-time). Student-undergrad faculty ratio is 20:1. 49,175 applied. Full-time: 13,795 students, 54% women, 46% men. Part-time: 13,626 students, 59% women, 41% men. Students come from 68 other countries, 6% from out-of-province, 6% live on campus. Retention: 89% of full-time freshmen returned the following year. Academic areas with the most degrees conferred: business/marketing; health professions and related sciences; engineering. Calendar: Canadian standard year or semesters depending on program. Academic remediation for entering students, ESL program, services for LD students, advanced placement, honors program, distance learning, double major, summer session for credit, part-time degree program, adult/continuing education programs, co-op programs and internships. Off campus study. Study abroad program.

Entrance Requirements: Options: electronic application, international baccalaureate accepted. Required: high school transcript. Required for some: essay, recommendations, interview, portfolio, audition, entrance examination. Entrance: moderately difficult. Application deadline: 3/1. Notification: continuous.

Costs Per Year: Application fee: $95 Canadian dollars. Tuition, fee, and room and board charges are reported in Canadian dollars. Area resident tuition: $426 per unit part-time. Province resident tuition: $4184 full-time. Mandatory fees: $527 full-time, $19 per unit part-time. Full-time tuition and fees vary according to course load, degree level, and program. Part-time tuition and fees vary according to course load, degree level, and program. College room and board: $7257. Room and board charges vary according to board plan and housing facility. International student tuition: $12,924 full-time.

Collegiate Environment: Orientation program. Drama-theater group, choral group, student-run newspaper, radio station. Social organizations: 55 open to all. Major annual events: Island Picnic, Winter Carnival, Cultural Caravan. Student services: health clinic, personal-psychological counseling, women's center. Campus security: 24-hour emergency response devices and patrols, late night transport-escort service, controlled dormitory access. 840 college housing spaces available; all were occupied in 2003-04. Freshmen given priority for college housing. Option: coed housing available. Ryerson Library with 606,603 books, 836,345 microform titles, 25,675 serials, 16,244 audiovisual materials, an OPAC, and a Web page. 1,400 computers available on campus for general student use. Computer purchase/lease plans available. A campuswide network can be accessed from student residence rooms and from off campus. Staffed computer lab on campus.

■ SAINT PAUL UNIVERSITY *D-15*

223 Main St.
Ottawa, ON, Canada K1S 1C4
Tel: (613)236-1393
Fax: (613)782-3033
Web Site: http://ustpaul.ca/

Description: Province-supported, university, coed. Administratively affiliated with University of Ottawa. Awards bachelor's, master's, and doctoral degrees. Founded 1848. Setting: 4-acre urban campus. Total enrollment: 757. Students come from 15 provinces and territories, 40 other countries. Calendar: Canadian standard year. ESL program, honors program, summer session for credit, part-time degree program, graduate courses open to undergrads.

Entrance Requirements: Options: Common Application, deferred admission, international baccalaureate accepted. Required: high school transcript. Recommended: SAT. Entrance: moderately difficult. Application deadline: 8/15. Notification: continuous until 9/4.

Collegiate Environment: Option: coed housing available. Saint Paul University Library with 400,000 books, 1,100 serials, and an OPAC. 30 computers available on campus for general student use. Staffed computer lab on campus.

■ TRENT UNIVERSITY *G-10*

1600 West Bank Dr.
Peterborough, ON, Canada K9J 7B8
Tel: (705)748-1011
Fax: (705)748-1629
E-mail: liaison@trentu.ca
Web Site: http://www.trentu.ca/

Description: Province-supported, university, coed. Awards bachelor's, master's, and doctoral degrees. Founded 1963. Setting: 1,400-acre suburban campus with easy access to Toronto. Endowment: $20 million. Research spending for 2004 fiscal year: $7.7 million. Educational spending for 2005 fiscal year: $9980 per student. Total enrollment: 8,170. Faculty: 445 (288 full-time, 157 part-time). Student-undergrad faculty ratio is 20:1. Full-time: 6,588 students, 67% women, 33% men. Part-time: 1,334 students, 68% women, 32% men. Students come from 21 provinces and territories, 106 other countries, 0% from out-of-province. Retention: 8% of full-time freshmen returned the following year. Calendar: Canadian standard year. Academic remediation for entering students, services for LD students, advanced placement, accelerated degree program, self-designed majors, honors program, double major, summer session for credit, part-time degree program, adult/continuing education programs. Off campus study at Sir Sandford Fleming College. Study abroad program.

Entrance Requirements: Options: deferred admission, international baccalaureate accepted. Required: high school transcript, minimum 2.8 high school GPA. Required for some: essay, recommendations, interview, SAT or ACT. Entrance: moderately difficult. Application deadline: 6/1.

Costs Per Year: Application fee: $95. Area resident tuition: $4184 full-time. College room and board: $7300. International student tuition: $10,725 full-time.

Collegiate Environment: Orientation program. Drama-theater group, choral group, student-run newspaper, radio station. Social organizations: 60 open to all. Most popular organizations: Trent Radio, Trent International Program, Trent Central Student Association, Arthur (student newspaper), Excalibur (yearbook). Major annual events: Head of Trent (Homecoming), Spring Music Festival, Elders Gathering. Student services: health clinic, personal-psychological counseling, women's center. Campus security: 24-hour emergency response devices and patrols, student patrols, late night transport-escort service. 1,200 college housing spaces available; all were occupied in 2003-04. Options: coed, women-only housing available. Thomas J. Bata Library plus 2 others with 579,557 books, 2,312 serials, an OPAC, and a Web page. Operations spending for 2004 fiscal year: $2.9 million. 250 computers available on campus for general student use. A campuswide network can be accessed from student residence rooms and from off campus. Staffed computer lab on campus.

Community Environment: The university is situated on the banks of the Otonabee River, three miles north of Peterborough, Ontario. Two other colleges are located in residential areas of downtown Peterborough, one of Ontario's oldest and loveliest cities.

■ TYNDALE UNIVERSITY COLLEGE & SEMINARY *I-8*

25 Ballyconnor Ct.
Toronto, ON, Canada M2M 4B3
Tel: (416)226-6380
Fax: (416)226-4210
E-mail: admissions@obcots.on.ca
Web Site: http://www.tyndale.ca/

Description: Independent interdenominational, comprehensive, coed. Awards bachelor's, master's, and first professional degrees. Founded 1894. Setting: 10-acre urban campus. Endowment: $2 million. Educational spending for 2005 fiscal year: $1678 per student. Total enrollment: 1,142. 368 applied, 53% were admitted. Full-time: 348 students, 47% women, 53% men. Part-time: 131 students, 50% women, 50% men. Students come from 7 provinces and territories, 12 other countries, 20% 25 or older, 30% live on campus. Retention: 49% of full-time freshmen returned the following year. Core. Calendar: semesters. Academic remediation for entering students, accelerated degree program, honors program, summer session for credit, part-time degree program, adult/continuing education programs. Off campus study at Seneca College.

Entrance Requirements: Options: deferred admission, international baccalaureate accepted. Required: essay, high school transcript, 2 recommendations, all post-secondary transcripts. Required for some: interview. Entrance: moderately difficult. Application deadline: 8/15. Notification: 9/19.

Costs Per Year: Application fee: $50 Canadian dollars. Tuition, fee, and room and board charges are reported in Canadian dollars. Comprehensive fee: $13,650 includes full-time tuition ($8910) and college room and board ($4740). Full-time tuition varies according to course load. Part-time tuition: $268 per credit hour. Part-time tuition varies according to course load.

Collegiate Environment: Orientation program. Drama-theater group, choral group, student-run newspaper. Social organizations: 5 open to all. Most popular organizations: choir, student government, Urban Ministry Team, 'Steadfast' drama team. Major annual events: Global Ministries Conference, Experience OBC. Student services: personal-psychological counseling. Campus security: student patrols, late night transport-escort service, controlled dormitory access. 220 college housing spaces available; 185 were occupied in 2003-04. Freshmen given priority for college housing. Option: coed housing available. J. William Horsey Library with 65,013 books, 1 microform title, 410 serials, and an OPAC. Operations spending for 2004 fiscal year: $440,000. 10 computers available on campus for general student use. A campuswide network can be accessed. Staffed computer lab on campus.

■ **UNIVERSITY OF GUELPH** *I-7*

Guelph, ON, Canada N1G 2W1

Tel: (519)824-4120

E-mail: internat@registrar.uoguelph.ca

Web Site: http://www.uoguelph.ca/

Description: Province-supported, university, coed. Awards bachelor's, master's, doctoral, and first professional degrees. Founded 1964. Setting: 817-acre urban campus with easy access to Toronto. Total enrollment: 18,616. Faculty: (830 full-time). Student-undergrad faculty ratio is 22:1. 18,852 applied, 73% were admitted. Students come from 12 provinces and territories, 85 other countries, 38% live on campus. Retention: 91% of full-time freshmen returned the following year. Core. Calendar: trimesters. Academic remediation for entering students, services for LD students, advanced placement, accelerated degree program, self-designed majors, freshman honors college, honors program, independent study, distance learning, double major, summer session for credit, part-time degree program, adult/continuing education programs, co-op programs, graduate courses open to undergrads. Study abroad program.

Entrance Requirements: Options: early admission, international baccalaureate accepted. Required: high school transcript, minimum 3.0 high school GPA, SAT or ACT. Required for some: essay, recommendations. Entrance: moderately difficult. Application deadline: 3/1. Notification: 4/20.

Costs Per Year: Application fee: $105. Province resident tuition: $4184 full-time. Canadian resident tuition: $418 per course part-time. Mandatory fees: $1,074 full-time, $16.96 per course part-time, $389.30 per term part-time. Full-time tuition and fees vary according to program. Part-time tuition and fees vary according to course load. College room and board: $7380. College room only: $3930. Room and board charges vary according to board plan and housing facility. International student tuition: $9730 full-time.

Collegiate Environment: Orientation program. Drama-theater group, choral group, student-run newspaper, radio station. Social organizations: 100 open to all. Major annual events: homecoming, College Royal Weekend, Community Bar-B-Que. Student services: legal services, health clinic, personal-psychological counseling, women's center. Campus security: 24-hour emergency response devices and patrols, late night transport-escort service, video camera surveillance in parking lots, alarms in women's locker room. 5,500 college housing spaces available. Freshmen guaranteed college housing. Options: coed, men-only, women-only housing available. McLaughlin Library plus 1 other with 2.1 million books, 1.5 million microform titles, 7,294 serials, 16,437 audiovisual materials, an OPAC, and a Web page. 1,200 computers available on campus for general student use. A campuswide network can be accessed from student residence rooms and from off campus. Staffed computer lab on campus.

Community Environment: Blending the sophistication of city life with the beautiful scenery of the countryside in the heart of southwestern Ontario, the city of Guelph is a lively, multicultural community of 100,000. Just a short walk from campus, students can enjoy sidewalk cafes, specialty boutiques and craft shops, and a wide variety of restaurants. An hour's drive west of Toronto, Guelph is easily accessible by bus or train. It is the home of the Guelph Spring Festival (May-June), the Guelph Jazz Festival (September), and the Hillside Folk Festival (July), as well as the site of the Guelph Center for the Performing Arts.

■ **UNIVERSITY OF OTTAWA** *D-15*

550 Cumberland St.

Ottawa, ON, Canada K1N 6N5

Tel: (613)562-5700

Admissions: (613)562-5800

E-mail: liaison@uottawa.ca

Web Site: http://www.uottawa.ca/

Description: Province-supported, university, coed. Awards bachelor's, master's, doctoral, and first professional degrees. Founded 1848. Setting: 70-acre urban campus. Endowment: $86.3 million. Educational spending for 2005 fiscal year: $6600 per student. Total enrollment: 33,576. Faculty: 1,873 (1,057 full-time, 816 part-time). Student-undergrad faculty ratio is 24:1. 31,975 applied, 62% were admitted. Students come from 13 provinces and territories, 164 other countries, 19% from out-of-province, 24% 25 or older. Retention: 89% of full-time freshmen returned the following year. Academic areas with the most degrees conferred: education; social sciences; health professions and related sciences. Core. Calendar: semesters. Academic remediation for entering students, ESL program, services for LD students, advanced placement, accelerated degree program, self-designed majors, honors program, distance learning, double major, summer session for credit, part-time degree program, external degree program, adult/continuing education programs, co-op programs and internships, graduate courses open to undergrads. Off campus study at Carleton University, Saint Paul University, Canadian Universities Student Exchange Consortium. Study abroad program.

Entrance Requirements: Options: electronic application, early admission, international baccalaureate accepted. Required: high school transcript, minimum 3.0 high school GPA, 1 recommendation. Required for some: interview. Entrance: moderately difficult. Application deadline: 6/1. Notification: continuous until 8/30.

Costs Per Year: Application fee: $165. Canadian resident tuition: $4163 full-time, $165 per credit part-time. Mandatory fees: $441 full-time, $92 per term part-time. Full-time tuition and fees vary according to program. Part-time tuition and fees vary according to program. College room and board: $5990. College room only: $3740. Room and board charges vary according to board plan and housing facility.

Collegiate Environment: Orientation program. Drama-theater group, choral group, student-run newspaper, radio station. Social organizations: national fraternities, national sororities, local fraternities, local sororities; 1% of eligible men and 1% of eligible women are members. Most popular organization: Student Federation of the University of Ottawa (SFUO). Major annual events: Welcome Week, Panda, Winter Carnival. Student services: legal services, health clinic, personal-psychological counseling, women's center. Campus security: 24-hour emergency response devices and patrols, student patrols, late night transport-escort service, controlled dormitory access. 2,848 college housing spaces available; all were occupied in 2003-04. Freshmen given priority for college housing. Option: coed housing available. Morisset Library plus 3 others with 2.6 million books, 1.8 million microform titles, 9,183 serials, an OPAC, and a Web page. Operations spending for 2004 fiscal year: $20.3 million. 1,500 computers available on campus for general student use. Computer purchase/lease plans available. A campuswide network can be accessed from student residence rooms and from off campus. Staffed computer lab on campus.

Community Environment: Ottawa, the capital of Canada, is a modern, cosmopolitan city with a population of nearly 1,000,000. This unique setting is renowned for its museums, its national festivities, and its year-round outdoor activities in a breathtaking and readily accessible natural environment. During the academic year, students can get acquainted with monuments, museums, art galleries, restaurants, theaters, and concert halls located downtown. Nature buffs will be thrilled with the multitude of green spaces and the extensive network of cycling paths. Come winter, the paths turn into cross-country ski trails and the Rideau Canal, alongside the campus, becomes the world's longest skating rink.

■ **UNIVERSITY OF TORONTO** *I-8*

Toronto, ON, Canada M5S 1A1

Tel: (416)978-2011

Admissions: (416)978-2190

E-mail: ask@adm.utoronto.ca

Web Site: http://www.utoronto.ca/uoft.html

Description: Province-supported, university, coed. Awards bachelor's, master's, doctoral, and first professional degrees. Founded 1827. Setting: 714-hectare urban campus. Endowment: $1.5 billion. Research spending for 2004 fiscal year: $236 million. Educational spending for 2005 fiscal year: $4250 per student. Total enrollment: 68,640. Faculty: 3,149 (2,787 full-time, 362 part-time). Student-undergrad faculty ratio is 26:1. 59,541 applied, 65% were admitted. Full-time: 39,400 students, 60% women, 40% men. Part-time: 6,114 students, 57% women, 43% men. Students come from 12 provinces and territories, 165 other countries, 2% from out-of province, 27% 25 or older, 15% live on campus. Retention: 95% of full-time freshmen returned the following year. Calendar: Canadian standard year. ESL program, services for LD students, double major, summer session for credit, part-time degree program, adult/continuing education programs, co-op programs, graduate courses open to undergrads. Off campus study at Sheridan Community College. Study abroad program.

Entrance Requirements: Option: deferred admission. Required: high school transcript, SAT and SAT Subject Tests or ACT. Required for some: interview. Entrance: very difficult. Application deadline: 3/1. Notification: continuous. Preference given to province residents for pharmacy program; Canadian residents for dentistry, physical and occupational therapy, rehabilitation medicine programs.

Costs Per Year: Application fee: $43 Canadian dollars. Tuition, fee, and room and board charges are reported in Canadian dollars. Province resident tuition: $850 per course part-time. Canadian resident tuition: $4250 full-time, $2800 per course part-time. Mandatory fees: $800 full-time. Full-time tuition and fees vary according to program. Part-time tuition varies according to course load. College room and board: $8000. College room only: $4500. Room and board charges vary according to board plan, housing facility, and location. International student tuition: $14,000 full-time.

Collegiate Environment: Orientation program. Drama-theater group, choral group, student-run newspaper, radio station. Social organizations: national fraternities, national sororities, local sororities. Student services: legal services, health clinic, personal-psychological counseling, women's center. Campus security: 24-hour emergency response devices and patrols, student patrols, late night transport-escort service. 6,670 college housing spaces available; all were occupied in 2003-04. Freshmen guaranteed college housing. Option: coed housing available. Robart's Library plus 43 others with 10.3 million books, 5 million microform titles, 53,547 serials, 1.2 million audiovisual materials, an OPAC, and a Web page. Operations spending for 2004 fiscal year: $41 million. 2,000 computers available on campus for general student use. A campuswide network can be accessed from student residence rooms and from off campus. Staffed computer lab on campus.

Community Environment: Toronto is the financial and industrial capital of Canada as well as Provincial capital of Ontario. It is often compared to New York and, in fact, was known as "York" (after the Duke of York) until 1834. The name "Toronto" was selected and is taken from an Indian word which means "meeting place" and it has become the meeting place or crossroads for nearly all Canadian activities. Cultural attractions abound and include the Art Gallery of Ontario, the Ontario Science Center, the Marine Museum of Upper Canada, Royal Ontario Museum and the Hummingbird Centre (which is home to the National Ballet of Canada, the Canadian Opera Company and scene of numerous plays). Toronto is one of two Canadian cities with baseball teams in the major leagues but more important to Canadians, it is the home of the Hockey Hall of Fame and of the Maple Leafs. The city also has many other sport and recreation facilities including the Skydome, a domed stadium. The city is one of the great inland ports of North America and is easily accessible by air, rail, bus and road. It has one of the best subway systems in the world and an excellent public bus system.

■ **UNIVERSITY OF WATERLOO** *R-10*
200 University Ave. West
Waterloo, ON, Canada N2L 3G1
Tel: (519)888-4567
Fax: (519)746-2882
E-mail: registrar@nhladm.uwaterloo.ca
Web Site: http://www.uwaterloo.ca/

Description: Province-supported, university, coed. Awards bachelor's, master's, doctoral, and first professional degrees. Founded 1957. Setting: 900-acre suburban campus with easy access to Toronto. Total enrollment: 25,900. Faculty: 1,577 (941 full-time, 636 part-time). Student-undergrad faculty ratio is 16:1. 31,741 applied, 66% were admitted. 100% from top half of their high school class. Full-time: 21,024 students, 45% women, 55% men. Part-time: 2,011 students, 66% women, 34% men. Students come from 12 provinces and territories, 122 other countries, 28% live on campus. Academic areas with the most degrees conferred: liberal arts/general studies; mathematics; engineering. Calendar: trimesters. Academic remediation for entering students, ESL program, services for LD students, accelerated degree program, self-designed majors, honors program, independent study, distance learning, double major, summer session for credit, part-time degree program, external degree program, adult/continuing education programs, co-op programs and internships, graduate courses open to undergrads. Off campus study at Wilfrid Laurier University, Brock University, Queen's

University at Kingston, University of Guelph, McMaster University, Conestoga College, Mohawk College, Canadian University Exchange Consortium, members of Regional Academic Mobility Program, members of The Group of Ten Exchange Program. Study abroad program.

Entrance Requirements: Options: electronic application, early admission, deferred admission, international baccalaureate accepted. Required: high school transcript, SAT or ACT. Required for some: essay, minimum 3.0 high school GPA, recommendations, interview, SAT or ACT, SAT Subject Tests. Entrance: moderately difficult. Application deadline: 3/31. Notification: continuous until 7/30.

Costs Per Year: Application fee: $115 Canadian dollars. Tuition, fee, and room and board charges are reported in Canadian dollars. Province resident tuition: $4362 full-time. Canadian resident tuition: $4362 full-time. College room and board: $7500. College room only: $4000. International student tuition: $16,092 full-time.

Collegiate Environment: Orientation program. Drama-theater group, choral group, marching band, student-run newspaper, radio station. Social organizations: national fraternities, national sororities; 1% of eligible men and 1% of eligible women are members. Major annual events: Oktoberfest, Canada Day, homecoming. Student services: legal services, health clinic, personal-psychological counseling, women's center. Campus security: 24-hour emergency response devices and patrols, student patrols, late night transport-escort service. 5,333 college housing spaces available. Freshmen guaranteed college housing. Options: coed, men-only, women-only housing available. Dana Porter Library plus 7 others with 3.8 million books, an OPAC, and a Web page. 6,000 computers available on campus for general student use. Computer purchase/lease plans available. A campuswide network can be accessed from student residence rooms and from off campus. Staffed computer lab on campus.

Community Environment: The University of Waterloo is located near Toronto in the heart of southern Ontario, Canada's most populous and highly developed province. The University's home community of Kitchener-Waterloo, population 260,000, is ethnically one of the most diverse in Canada. Residents enjoy a high standard of living, safe and clean neighborhoods, and may cultural and recreational attractions, as well as natural parks and protected wilderness areas.

■ **THE UNIVERSITY OF WESTERN ONTARIO** *J-5*
London, ON, Canada N6A 5B8
Tel: (519)661-2111
Admissions: (519)661-2116
E-mail: reguwo@uwoadmin.uwo.ca
Web Site: http://www.uwo.ca/

Description: Province-supported, university, coed. Awards bachelor's, master's, doctoral, and first professional degrees. Founded 1878. Setting: 420-acre suburban campus. Research spending for 2004 fiscal year: $164.9 million. Total enrollment: 33,448. Faculty: 2,449 (1,249 full-time, 1,200 part-time). Student-undergrad faculty ratio is 12:1. 27,652 applied, 59% were admitted. Full-time: 22,616 students, 59% women, 41% men. Part-time: 2,671 students, 62% women, 38% men. Students come from 13 provinces and territories, 5% from out-of-province, 13% live on campus. Retention: 91% of full-time freshmen returned the following year. Core. Calendar: Canadian standard year. Academic remediation for entering students, services for LD students, accelerated degree program, self-designed majors, honors program, distance learning, double major, summer session for credit, part-time degree program, adult/continuing education programs, co-op programs and internships, graduate courses open to undergrads. Off campus study at Universite Laval, University of Waterloo, Group of Ten Student Exchange Program. Study abroad program.

Entrance Requirements: Options: electronic application, deferred admission, international baccalaureate accepted. Required: high school transcript, minimum 3.5 high school GPA. Required for some: SAT. Entrance: very difficult. Application deadlines: 6/1, 5/15 for nonresidents.

Costs Per Year: Application fee: $100. Province resident tuition: $828 per course part-time. Canadian resident tuition: $4140 full-time, $2500 per course part-time. Mandatory fees: $863 full-time, $130.53 per course part-time. Full-time tuition and fees vary according to program. Part-time tuition and fees vary according to course load and program. College room and board: $6582. College room only: $4505. Room and board charges vary according to board plan and housing facility. International student tuition: $12,500 full-time.

Collegiate Environment: Orientation program. Drama-theater group, choral group, marching band, student-run newspaper, radio station. Social organizations: 121 open to all; national fraternities, national sororities. Major annual events: Orientation Week, Homecoming, Parents' Day. Student services: legal services, health clinic, personal-psychological counseling, women's center. Campus security: 24-hour emergency response devices and patrols, student patrols, late night transport-escort service. 4,160 college housing spaces available; 4,100 were occupied in 2003-04. Freshmen guaranteed college housing. Option: coed housing available. The University of Western Ontario Libraries plus 7 others with 3.1 million books, 3.9 million microform titles, 38,517 serials, 1.1 million audiovisual materials, an OPAC, and a Web page. Operations spending for 2004 fiscal year: $22.5 million. 351 computers available on campus for general student use. A campuswide network can be accessed from student residence rooms and from off campus. Staffed computer lab on campus.

Community Environment: The university is located on 155 hectares of land along the banks of the Thames River in London, Ontario, a thriving city of 331,000 people and is only 200 kilometers west of Toronto.

■ **UNIVERSITY OF WINDSOR** *L-2*
401 Sunset Ave.
Windsor, ON, Canada N9B 3P4
Tel: (519)253-3000
Fax: (519)973-7050
E-mail: liaison@uwindsor.ca
Web Site: http://www.uwindsor.ca/

Description: Province-supported, university, coed. Awards bachelor's, master's, and doctoral degrees. Founded 1857. Setting: 125-acre urban campus with easy access to Detroit. Endowment: $34.3 million. Research spending for 2004 fiscal year: $15.4 million. Educational spending for 2005 fiscal year: $5344 per student. Total enrollment: 16,765. Faculty: 744 (524 full-time, 220 part-time). Student-undergrad faculty ratio is 24:1. 13,763 applied, 64% were admitted. Full-time: 10,959 students, 56% women, 44% men. Part-time: 3,205 students, 52% women, 48% men. Students come from 12 provinces and territories, 88 other countries, 22% 25 or older, 13% live on campus, 5% transferred in. Retention: 85% of full-time freshmen returned the following year. Core. Calendar: semesters. Academic remediation for entering students, services for LD students, advanced placement, accelerated degree program, self-designed majors, honors program, distance learning, double major, summer session for credit, part-time degree program, external degree program, adult/continuing education programs, co-op programs and internships, graduate courses open to undergrads. Off campus study at Wayne State University, University of Akron, University of Massachusetts, Amherst. Study abroad program.

Entrance Requirements: Options: Common Application, electronic application, early admission, international baccalaureate accepted. Required: high school transcript, minimum 3.0 high school GPA. Required for some: essay, minimum 3.3 high school GPA, 1 recommendation, interview, SAT. Entrance: moderately difficult. Application deadlines: Rolling, 7/1 for nonresidents. Notification: continuous until 8/30.

Costs Per Year: Application fee: $60 Canadian dollars. Tuition, fee, and room and board charges are reported in Canadian dollars. Area resident tuition: $4990 full-time. Province resident tuition: $504 per course part-time. Canadian resident tuition: $1549 per course part-time. College room and board: $7124. International student tuition: $12,232 full-time.

Collegiate Environment: Orientation program. Drama-theater group, choral group, student-run newspaper, radio station. Social organizations: 80 open to all. Most popular organizations: University of Windsor Student Alliance, Environmental Awareness Association, Social Science Society, Commerce Society, Science Society. Major annual events: Health Fair, Headstart, Welcoming Convocation/Windsor Welcome Week. Student services: legal services, health clinic, personal-psychological counseling, women's center. Campus security: 24-hour emergency response devices and patrols, student patrols, late night transport-escort service, controlled dormitory access. 1,829 college housing spaces available; 1,406 were occupied in 2003-04. Freshmen guaranteed college housing. Options: coed, men-only, women-only housing available. Leddy Library plus 2 others with 2.8 million books, 1.1 million microform titles, 25,458 serials, 6,646 audiovisual materials, an OPAC, and a Web page. Operations spending for 2004 fiscal year: $7.4 million. 1,132 computers available on campus for general student use. Computer purchase/lease plans available. A campuswide network can be accessed from student residence rooms and from off campus. Staffed computer lab on campus.

Community Environment: The city of Windsor lies across the Detroit River from Detroit, Michigan, and its cultural, entertainment, athletic attractions. Yet by itself Windsor is an attraction as the hub of Canada's automotive industry, the City of Roses, the site of a three-story Art Gallery displaying

Canadian painting and sculpture from the eighteenth century on, home of the Windsor Symphony, and host of the International Freedom Festival.

■ **WILFRID LAURIER UNIVERSITY** *R-10*
75 University Ave. West
Waterloo, ON, Canada N2L 3C5
Tel: (519)884-1970
Admissions: (519)884-0710
Fax: (519)884-8826
E-mail: admissions@wlu.ca
Web Site: http://www.wlu.ca/

Description: Province-supported, comprehensive, coed. Awards bachelor's, master's, and doctoral degrees. Founded 1911. Setting: 40-acre urban campus with easy access to Toronto. Total enrollment: 12,296. 26,046 applied, 57% were admitted. Full-time: 9,569 students, 62% women, 38% men. Part-time: 1,684 students, 55% women, 45% men. Students come from 14 provinces and territories, 60 other countries, 7% 25 or older. Calendar: Canadian standard year. Services for LD students, accelerated degree program, honors program, summer session for credit, part-time degree program, adult/continuing education programs, co-op programs and internships. Off campus study at University of Waterloo. Study abroad program.

Entrance Requirements: Options: Common Application, international baccalaureate accepted. Required: high school transcript. Required for some: recommendations, interview, audition for music programs, SAT. Entrance: moderately difficult. Application deadline: 5/1. Notification: continuous.

Collegiate Environment: Orientation program. Drama-theater group, choral group, student-run newspaper, radio station. Social organizations: 62 open to all. Most popular organizations: Water Buffaloes, TAMIAE, Ski Club, Musicians' Network, Laurier Christian Fellowship. Major annual events: First-Year Students' Orientation, Boar's Head Dinner, Homecoming. Student services: legal services, health clinic, personal-psychological counseling, women's center. Campus security: 24-hour emergency response devices and patrols, student patrols, late night transport-escort service, controlled dormitory access. Option: coed housing available. Wilfrid Laurier University Library with 580,000 books and 4,500 serials. 450 computers available on campus for general student use. A campuswide network can be accessed from off-campus.

■ **YORK UNIVERSITY** *I-8*
4700 Keele St.
Toronto, ON, Canada M3J 1P3
Tel: (416)736-2100
Admissions: (416)736-5000
Fax: (416)736-5741
E-mail: intlenq@yorku.ca
Web Site: http://www.yorku.ca/

Description: Province-supported, university, coed. Awards bachelor's, master's, doctoral, and first professional degrees and post-master's certificates. Founded 1959. Setting: 650-acre urban campus. Total enrollment: 49,496. Faculty: 3,164. Student-undergrad faculty ratio is 23:1. Students come from 174 other countries, 2% from out-of province, 23% 25 or older, 6% live on campus. Core. Calendar: semesters. Academic remediation for entering students, ESL program, services for LD students, advanced placement, accelerated degree program, self-designed majors, honors program, independent study, distance learning, double major, summer session for credit, part-time degree program, adult/continuing education programs, internships. Off campus study at Centennial College, Humber College, Seneca College, Sheridan College, Georgian College, Durham College. Study abroad program.

Entrance Requirements: Options: electronic application, early admission, early action, deferred admission, international baccalaureate accepted. Required: high school transcript, minimum 3.0 high school GPA, audition/evaluation for fine arts program, supplemental applications for business and environmental studies, SAT or ACT. Required for some: essay, 1 recommendation, interview. Entrance: moderately difficult. Application deadlines: 2/1, 2/1 for early action. Notification: 6/1 for early action. Preference given to students with identified learning disabilities, extenuating circumstances.

Costs Per Year: Application fee: $90. Comprehensive fee: $10,981 includes full-time tuition ($4862) and college room and board ($6119). College room only: $3719. Full-time tuition varies according to course load, degree level, and program. Room and board charges vary according to board plan and housing facility. International student tuition: $14,862 full-time.

Collegiate Environment: Orientation program. Drama-theater group, choral group, student-run newspaper, radio station. Social organizations: 150 open

to all. Most popular organizations: college student councils, York Federation of Students, Jewish Student Association, First Nations and Aboriginal Student Association, International and Exchange Students Club. Major annual events: Homecoming, Orientation Week, Blue Bowl. Student services: legal services, health clinic, personal-psychological counseling, women's center. Campus security: 24-hour emergency response devices and patrols, student patrols, late night transport-escort service, controlled dormitory ac-

cess. 2,188 college housing spaces available. Freshmen given priority for college housing. Option: coed housing available. Scott Library plus 4 others with 6.1 million books, 540,000 serials, an OPAC, and a Web page. Operations spending for 2004 fiscal year: $18.4 million. 1,900 computers available on campus for general student use. A campuswide network can be accessed from student residence rooms and from off campus. Staffed computer lab on campus.

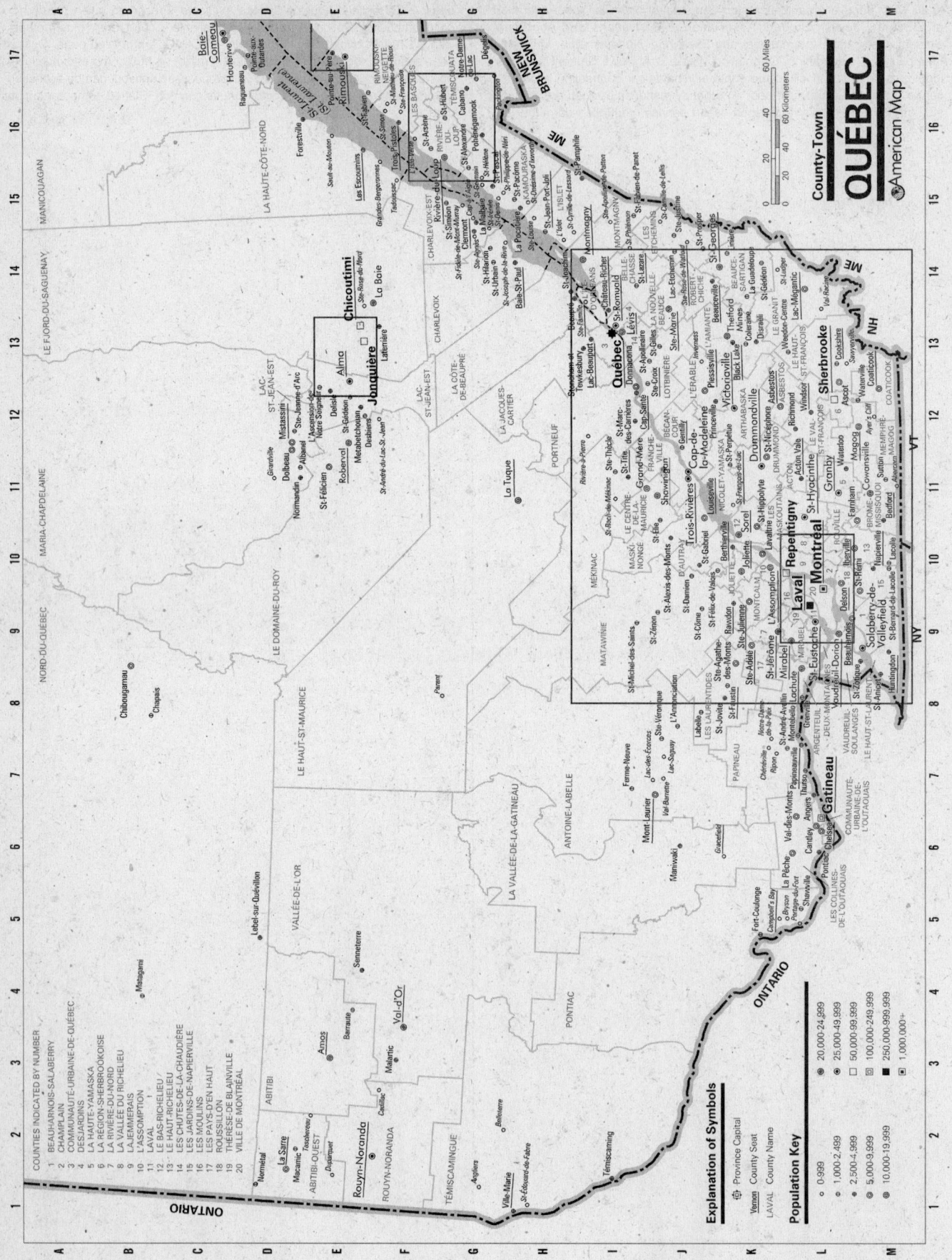

QUÉBEC

County-Town

American Map

Explanation of Symbols

⊕ Province Capital

Vernon County Seat

LAVAL County Name

Population Key

◉ 0-999
◉ 1,000-2,499
◎ 2,500-4,999
◉ 5,000-9,999
◉ 10,000-19,999
◉ 20,000-24,999
◻ 25,000-49,999
◻ 50,000-99,999
▣ 100,000-249,999
■ 250,000-999,999
▣ 1,000,000+

COUNTIES INDICATED BY NUMBER

1 BEAUHARNOIS-SALABERRY
2 CHAMPLAIN
3 COMMUNAUTÉ-URBAINE-DE-QUÉBEC
4 DESJARDINS
5 LA HAUTE-YAMASKA
6 LA RÉGION-SHERBROOKOISE
7 LA RIVIÈRE-DU-NORD
8 LA VALLÉE DU RICHELIEU
9 LAJEMMERAIS
10 L'ASSOMPTION
11 LAVAL
12 LE BAS-RICHELIEU
13 LE HAUT-RICHELIEU
14 LES CHUTES-DE-LA-CHAUDIÈRE
15 LES JARDINS-DE-NAPIERVILLE
16 LES MOULINS
17 LES PAYS-D'EN HAUT
18 ROUSSILLON
19 THÉRÈSE-DE BLAINVILLE
20 VILLE DE MONTRÉAL

■ BISHOP'S UNIVERSITY

Lennoxville, QC, Canada J1M 1Z7
Tel: (819)822-9600; 877-822-8200
Fax: (819)822-9661
E-mail: liaison@ubishops.ca
Web Site: http://www.ubishops.ca/

Description: Province-supported, comprehensive, coed. Awards bachelor's and master's degrees. Founded 1843. Setting: 500-acre small town campus. Endowment: $30 million. Research spending for 2004 fiscal year: $550,000. Educational spending for 2005 fiscal year: $7300 per student. Total enrollment: 2,721. Faculty: 177 (123 full-time, 54 part-time). Student-undergrad faculty ratio is 17:1. 1,403 applied, 85% were admitted. Students come from 10 provinces and territories, 37 other countries, 60% from out-of-province, 12% 25 or older, 31% live on campus. Retention: 82% of full-time freshmen returned the following year. Academic areas with the most degrees conferred: business/marketing; education; visual and performing arts. Calendar: Canadian standard year. Academic remediation for entering students, ESL program, services for LD students, advanced placement, accelerated degree program, self-designed majors, honors program, independent study, double major, summer session for credit, part-time degree program, adult/continuing education programs, co-op programs and internships. Off campus study at State Universities of California, New England Board of Higher Education, Quebec Inter-University Exchanges, University of New Mexico, University of North Dakota. Study abroad program.

Entrance Requirements: Options: Peterson's Universal Application, international baccalaureate accepted. Required: high school transcript, minimum 3.0 high school GPA, birth certificate, copy of student visa, SAT or ACT. Recommended: SAT Subject Tests. Required for some: essay, 1 recommendation. Entrance: moderately difficult. Application deadline: 3/1. Notification: continuous until 8/31.

Costs Per Year: Application fee: $55. Province resident tuition: $1668 full-time, $55.61 per credit part-time. Canadian resident tuition: $4518 full-time, $150.60 per credit part-time. Mandatory fees: $840 full-time. College room and board: $5320. College room only: $4440. International student tuition: $10,068 full-time.

Collegiate Environment: Orientation program. Drama-theater group, choral group, student-run newspaper, radio station. Social organizations: 65 open to all; national fraternities, national sororities; 3% of eligible men and 3% of eligible women are members. Most popular organizations: Big Buddies, The Campus, Psychology Club, Student Patrol, Inter-Varsity Christian Fellowship. Major annual events: Homecoming, Freshman Orientation Week, Winter Carnival. Student services: health clinic, personal-psychological counseling, women's center. Campus security: 24-hour emergency response devices and patrols, student patrols, late night transport-escort service, controlled dormitory access. 683 college housing spaces available; 675 were occupied in 2003-04. Freshmen guaranteed college housing. Options: coed, women-only housing available. John Bassett Memorial Library plus 1 other with 447,086 books, 118,415 microform titles, 5,662 serials, 24,232 audiovisual materials, an OPAC, and a Web page. Operations spending for 2004 fiscal year: $2 million. 200 computers available on campus for general student use. Computer purchase/lease plans available. A campuswide network can be accessed from student residence rooms and from off campus. Staffed computer lab on campus.

■ CONCORDIA UNIVERSITY *L-10*

1455 de Maisonneuve Blvd. West
Montreal, QC, Canada H3G 1M8
Tel: (514)848-2424
Fax: (514)848-2621
Web Site: http://www.concordia.ca/

Description: Province-supported, university, coed. Part of Province of Quebec University System. Awards bachelor's, master's, and doctoral degrees and post-master's certificates. Founded 1974. Setting: 110-acre urban campus. Endowment: $30.1 million. Research spending for 2004 fiscal year: $33 million. Total enrollment: 31,042. Faculty: 1,765 (831 full-time, 934 part-time). Student-undergrad faculty ratio is 35:1. 15,706 applied, 65% were admitted. Students come from 13 provinces and territories, 125 other countries, 1% live on campus. Retention: 76% of full-time freshmen returned the following year. Calendar: trimesters. Academic remediation for entering students, ESL program, services for LD students, advanced placement, accelerated degree program, self-designed majors, honors program, independent study, double major, summer session for credit, part-time degree program, external degree program, adult/continuing education programs, co-op programs and internships, graduate courses open to undergrads. Off campus study at Consortium of Quebec Universities (CREPUQ) Centre for International Academic Cooperation (CIAC). Study abroad program.

Entrance Requirements: Options: Peterson's Universal Application, Common Application, electronic application, international baccalaureate accepted. Required: high school transcript, minimum 2.76 high school GPA. Required for some: essay, 2 recommendations, interview. Entrance: moderately difficult. Application deadlines: 3/1, 2/1 for early action. Notification: continuous until 9/1. Preference given to graduates of Colleges d'Enseignement General et Professionnel (CEGEP).

Costs Per Year: Application fee: $50 Canadian dollars. Tuition, fee, and room and board charges are reported in Canadian dollars. Province resident tuition: $1668 full-time, $55.61 per credit part-time. Canadian resident tuition: $4651 full-time, $155.03 per credit part-time. Mandatory fees: $979 full-time, $177.96 per term part-time. Full-time tuition and fees vary according to program. Part-time tuition and fees vary according to program. College room and board: $6905. Room and board charges vary according to housing facility. International student tuition: $11,238 full-time.

Collegiate Environment: Orientation program. Drama-theater group, choral group, student-run newspaper, radio station. Social organizations: 160 open to all; national fraternities, national sororities, local fraternities, local sororities. Most popular organizations: ethnic clubs, student media, departmental clubs. Major annual events: Homecoming, Orientation, Concordia Shuffle. Student services: legal services, health clinic, personal-psychological counseling, women's center. Campus security: 24-hour emergency response devices and patrols, student patrols, late night transport-escort service, controlled dormitory access. 144 college housing spaces available; all were occupied in 2003-04. No special consideration for freshman housing applicants. Option: coed housing available. Webster Library plus 2 others with 3 million books, 5,900 serials, an OPAC, and a Web page. Operations spending for 2004 fiscal year: $11.7 million. 350 computers available on campus for general student use. Computer purchase/lease plans available.

A campuswide network can be accessed from student residence rooms and from off campus. Staffed computer lab on campus.

■ HEC MONTREAL L-10

3000, chemin de la Côte-Sainte-Catherine
Montréal, QC, Canada H3T 2A7
Tel: (514)340-6000
Admissions: (514)340-6991
Fax: (514)340-5640
Web Site: http://www.hec.ca/

Description: Province-supported, comprehensive, coed. Part of Universite de Montreal. Awards bachelor's, master's, and doctoral degrees. Founded 1910. Setting: 9-acre urban campus. Total enrollment: 11,784. Faculty: 611 (251 full-time, 360 part-time). Student-undergrad faculty ratio is 21:1. 2,466 applied, 72% were admitted. Full-time: 4,574 students, 46% women, 54% men. Part-time: 4,563 students, 53% women, 47% men. Students come from 4 provinces and territories, 41 other countries, 1% from out-of-province, 48% 25 or older. Retention: 79% of full-time freshmen returned the following year. Academic area with the most degrees conferred: business/marketing. Core. Calendar: trimesters. Academic remediation for entering students, ESL program, self-designed majors, honors program, independent study, summer session for credit, part-time degree program, adult/continuing education programs. Off campus study at all universities in Quebec. Study abroad program.

Entrance Requirements: Options: Common Application, deferred admission. Required: high school transcript. Required for some: cote de rendement collegial. Entrance: moderately difficult. Application deadlines: 3/1, 2/15 for nonresidents. Notification: 3/30, 4/30 for nonresidents.

Costs Per Year: Application fee: $60 Canadian dollars. Tuition, fee, and room only charges are reported in Canadian dollars. Province resident tuition: $1,668 full-time, $55.61 per credit part-time. Canadian resident tuition: $4,651 full-time, $155.03 per credit part-time. Mandatory fees: $622 full-time, $16.63 per credit part-time, $58.70 per term part-time. College room only: $2,927. International student tuition: $11,238 full-time. Nonresident alien program tuitions range from $9468 to $11240.

Collegiate Environment: Student-run newspaper, radio station. Student services: legal services, health clinic, personal-psychological counseling. Campus security: 24-hour emergency response devices and patrols. Myriam et J.-Robert Ouimet Library plus 1 other with 345,143 books, 16,757 microform titles, 5,557 serials, 2,313 audiovisual materials, an OPAC, and a Web page. 250 computers available on campus for general student use. A campuswide network can be accessed from off-campus. Staffed computer lab on campus.

■ MCGILL UNIVERSITY L-10

845 Sherbrooke St. West
Montréal, QC, Canada H3A 2T5
Tel: (514)398-4455
Admissions: (514)398-4193
Fax: (514)398-4193
E-mail: admissions@mcgill.ca
Web Site: http://www.mcgill.ca/

Description: Province-supported, university, coed. Awards bachelor's, master's, doctoral, and first professional degrees and post-master's certificates. Founded 1821. Setting: 80-acre urban campus. Endowment: $764.2 million. Research spending for 2004 fiscal year: $286.4 million. Educational spending for 2005 fiscal year: $27,617 per student. Total enrollment: 30,333. Faculty: 2,402 (1,597 full-time, 805 part-time). Student-undergrad faculty ratio is 16:1. 18,963 applied, 56% were admitted. Full-time: 17,972 students, 60% women, 40% men. Part-time: 3,363 students, 62% women, 38% men. Students come from 13 provinces and territories, 138 other countries, 32% from out-of-province, 11% 25 or older, 10% live on campus, 4% transferred in. Retention: 92% of full-time freshmen returned the following year. Academic areas with the most degrees conferred: social sciences; business/marketing; biological/life sciences. Calendar: semesters. ESL program, services for LD students, advanced placement, self-designed majors, honors program, independent study, distance learning, double major, summer session for credit, part-time degree program, adult/continuing education programs, co-op programs and internships, graduate courses open to undergrads. Off campus study at Canex, CREPUQ, CUSAP, Universitas 21. Study abroad program.

Entrance Requirements: Options: electronic application, deferred admission, international baccalaureate accepted. Required: high school transcript, minimum 3.3 high school GPA. Required for some: recommendations,

interview, audition for music program, portfolio for architecture program. Entrance: very difficult. Application deadline: 1/16. Notification: continuous.

Costs Per Year: Application fee: $60. Province resident tuition: $55.61 per credit part-time. Canadian resident tuition: $163.79 per credit part-time.

Collegiate Environment: Orientation program. Drama-theater group, choral group, student-run newspaper, radio station. Social organizations: 180 open to all. Most popular organizations: Debating Union, UNSAM (Model United Nations), Sexual Assault Centre, Walksafe, Queer McGill. Major annual events: Discover McGill, Orientation Week, Frosh Program. Student services: legal services, health clinic, personal-psychological counseling, disability services. Campus security: 24-hour emergency response devices and patrols, student patrols, late night transport-escort service, controlled dormitory access. 2,200 college housing spaces available; all were occupied in 2003-04. Freshmen guaranteed college housing. Options: coed, women-only housing available. McLennan Library plus 13 others with 4.2 million books, 1.8 million microform titles, 25,673 serials, 579,805 audiovisual materials, an OPAC, and a Web page. Operations spending for 2004 fiscal year: $24.6 million. 3,679 computers available on campus for general student use. A campuswide network can be accessed from student residence rooms and from off campus. Staffed computer lab on campus.

■ TÉLÉ-UNIVERSITÉ I-13

455, rue de l'Église
C.P. 4800, succ. Terminus
Québec, QC, Canada G1K 9H5
Tel: (418)657-2262
Fax: (418)657-2094
E-mail: info@teluq.uquebec.ca
Web Site: http://www.teluq.uquebec.ca/

Description: Province-supported, comprehensive, coed. Part of Universite du Quebec. Awards bachelor's and master's degrees (offers only distance learning degree programs). Founded 1972. 2,649 applied, 100% were admitted. Core. Calendar: trimesters. Services for LD students, accelerated degree program, summer session for credit, part-time degree program, adult/continuing education programs, internships. Off campus study at other units of the Universite du Quebec, other universities in the province of Quebec.

Entrance Requirements: Open admission. Option: Common Application. Required: Diploma of Collegiate Studies (and transcript) or equivalent. Entrance: noncompetitive. Application deadline: Rolling.

Collegiate Environment: College housing not available. 12,567 books and 277 serials.

■ UNIVERSITÉ LAVAL I-13

C.P. 2208, succursale Terminus
Québec, QC, Canada G1K 7P4
Tel: (418)656-3333; 877-785-2825
Admissions: (418)656-3080
Fax: (418)656-2809
E-mail: info@dap.ulaval.ca
Web Site: http://www.ulaval.ca/

Description: Independent, university, coed. Awards associate, bachelor's, master's, doctoral, and first professional degrees and first professional certificates. Founded 1852. Setting: 465-acre urban campus with easy access to Quebec City. Endowment: $410 million. Research spending for 2004 fiscal year: $96.2 million. Educational spending for 2005 fiscal year: $13,758 per student. Total enrollment: 38,376. Faculty: 1,456 (1,380 full-time, 76 part-time). Student-undergrad faculty ratio is 7:1. 10,847 applied, 66% were admitted. Students come from 7 provinces and territories, 91 other countries, 4% from out-of-province, 21% 25 or older, 7% live on campus. Retention: 95% of full-time freshmen returned the following year. Core. Calendar: trimesters. Academic remediation for entering students, ESL program, services for LD students, accelerated degree program, self-designed majors, honors program, distance learning, summer session for credit, part-time degree program, adult/continuing education programs, co-op programs and internships. Off campus study. Study abroad program.

Entrance Requirements: Options: Common Application, electronic application, international baccalaureate accepted. Required: high school transcript, general knowledge of French language. Required for some: essay, interview. Entrance: minimally difficult. Application deadlines: 3/1, 3/1 for nonresidents. Notification: 5/15.

Costs Per Year: Application fee: $30 Canadian dollars. Tuition, fee, and room and board charges are reported in Canadian dollars. Area resident tuition: $2076 full-time. Province resident tuition: $4809 full-time. Canadian resident tuition: $10,176 full-time. Mandatory fees: $900 full-time. College room and board: $9000. College room only: $3000.

Collegiate Environment: Drama-theater group, choral group, student-run newspaper, radio station. Social organizations: 88 open to all; national fraternities. Most popular organizations: Drama Club, Improvisation Ligue, Creation Litteraire, Chorale de L'universite Laval, Amnistie Internationale. Major annual events: Rendez-vous Laval, Carrefour de L'Emploi, Student Festival. Student services: health clinic, personal-psychological counseling. Campus security: 24-hour emergency response devices and patrols, student patrols, late night transport-escort service, controlled dormitory access, video cameras in most buildings, underground walkways. 2,400 college housing spaces available; 2,160 were occupied in 2003-04. No special consideration for freshman housing applicants. Options: coed, men-only, women-only housing available. Bibliotheque Generale plus 1 other with 3 million books, 55,507 microform titles, 13,928 serials, 20,094 audiovisual materials, an OPAC, and a Web page. Operations spending for 2004 fiscal year: $8.9 million. 2,200 computers available on campus for general student use. Computer purchase/lease plans available. A campuswide network can be accessed from student residence rooms and from off campus. Staffed computer lab on campus.

■ **UNIVERSITÉ DE MONTRÉAL** *L-10*
CP 6128, Succursale Centre-ville
Montréal, QC, Canada H3C 3J7
Tel: (514)343-6111
Admissions: (514)343-7076
Fax: (514)343-5788
E-mail: pierre.chenard@umontreal.ca
Web Site: http://www.umontreal.ca/

Description: Independent, university, coed. Administratively affiliated with L'Ecole Polytechnique de Montreal, HEC Montreal. Awards bachelor's, master's, and doctoral degrees. Founded 1920. Setting: 150-acre urban campus. Endowment: $837 million. Educational spending for 2005 fiscal year: $14,061 per student. Total enrollment: 55,150. Retention: 87% of full-time freshmen returned the following year. Core. Calendar: trimesters. ESL program, services for LD students, accelerated degree program, honors program, independent study, distance learning, summer session for credit, part-time degree program, adult/continuing education programs, internships. Off campus study at Quebec Interuniversity Exchange.

Entrance Requirements: Option: Common Application. Required: Diploma of Collegiate Studies (and transcript) or equivalent. Required for some: interview. Entrance: moderately difficult. Application deadline: 3/1. Notification: 5/15.

Costs Per Year: Application fee: $30 Canadian dollars. Tuition and fee charges are reported in Canadian dollars. Tuition: $55.61 per unit part-time. Canadian resident tuition: $335.61 per unit part-time.

Collegiate Environment: Drama-theater group, choral group, student-run newspaper, radio station. Social organizations: 50 open to all. Most popular organization: Federation des Associations Etudiantes du Campus. Major annual events: Winter Carnival, Multicultural Week, Inter-University Photograph Exhibition. Student services: legal services, health clinic, personal-psychological counseling. Campus security: 24-hour emergency response devices and patrols, student patrols, late night transport-escort service, controlled dormitory access, cameras, alarm systems, crime prevention programs. 1,122 college housing spaces available. Option: coed housing available. Bibliothique des lettres et sciences humaines plus 18 others with 1.7 million microform titles, 18,330 serials, 178,528 audiovisual materials, an OPAC, and a Web page. 1,500 computers available on campus for general student use. A campuswide network can be accessed from student residence rooms and from off campus. Staffed computer lab on campus.

■ **UNIVERSITÉ DU QUÉBEC EN ABITIBI-TÉMISCAMINGUE** *F-2*
445 Blvd. de l'Université
Rouyn-Noranda, QC, Canada J9X 5E4
Tel: (819)762-0971
Fax: (819)797-4727
Web Site: http://www.uqat.ca/

Description: Province-supported, comprehensive, coed. Part of Universite du Quebec. Awards bachelor's, master's, and doctoral degrees. Founded 1983. Setting: 5-acre small town campus. Total enrollment: 755. Students come from 8 other countries. Core. Calendar: trimesters. Services for LD students, accelerated degree program, summer session for credit, part-time degree program, adult/continuing education programs, internships. Off campus study at other units of the Universite du Quebec, other universities in the province of Quebec.

Entrance Requirements: Open admission except for some quota programs. Required: Diploma of Collegiate Studies (and transcript) or equivalent. Required for some: interview. Entrance: noncompetitive. Application deadline: Rolling. Notification: 5/15.

Collegiate Environment: Student-run newspaper. Student services: health clinic, personal-psychological counseling. Campus security: 24-hour patrols. College housing not available. 135,882 books, 302 serials, an OPAC, and a Web page. 85 computers available on campus for general student use. A campuswide network can be accessed from off-campus. Staffed computer lab on campus.

■ **UNIVERSITÉ DU QUÉBEC ÀCHICOUTIMI** *E-13*
555, Blvd. de L'Université
Chicoutimi, QC, Canada G7H 2B1
Tel: (418)545-5011
Admissions: (418)545-5005
Fax: (418)545-5012
E-mail: czoccast@uqac.uquebec.ca
Web Site: http://www.uqac.uquebec.ca/

Description: Province-supported, university, coed. Part of Universite du Quebec. Awards bachelor's, master's, and doctoral degrees. Founded 1969. Setting: 100-acre urban campus. Core. Calendar: trimesters. Services for LD students, accelerated degree program, summer session for credit, part-time degree program, adult/continuing education programs. Off campus study at other units of the Universite du Quebec, other universities in the province of Quebec.

Entrance Requirements: Open admission except for some quota programs. Required: Diploma of Collegiate Studies (and transcript) or equivalent. Required for some: interview. Entrance: noncompetitive. Application deadline: 3/1. Notification: 5/15.

Collegiate Environment: Student-run newspaper. Student services: health clinic, personal-psychological counseling. Campus security: 24-hour emergency response devices and patrols. Option: coed housing available. 689,214 books and 5,092 serials.

■ **UNIVERSITE DU QUEBEC, ECOLE DE TECHNOLOGIE SUPERIEURE** *L-10*
1100, rue Notre Dame Ouest
Montréal, QC, Canada H3C 1K3
Tel: (514)396-8800
Admissions: (514)396-8885
Fax: (514)289-8950
E-mail: admission@ets.mtl.ca
Web Site: http://www.etsmtl.ca/

Description: Province-supported, comprehensive, coed. Part of Universite du Quebec. Awards bachelor's, master's, and doctoral degrees. Founded 1974. Setting: urban campus. Total enrollment: 4,262. 1,541 applied, 88% were admitted. Full-time: 2,763 students, 8% women, 92% men. Part-time: 1,091 students, 16% women, 84% men. Core. Calendar: trimesters. Services for LD students, accelerated degree program, summer session for credit, part-time degree program, adult/continuing education programs, co-op programs. Off campus study at other units of the Universite du Quebec, other universities in the province of Quebec.

Entrance Requirements: Open admission. Required: Diploma of Collegiate Studies (and transcript) or equivalent. Entrance: noncompetitive. Application deadline: 3/1. Notification: 5/15.

Collegiate Environment: Student-run newspaper, radio station. Student services: health clinic, personal-psychological counseling. 400 college housing spaces available; all were occupied in 2003-04. 44,195 books, 630 serials, an OPAC, and a Web page.

■ **UNIVERSITÉ DU QUÉBEC ÀMONTRÉAL** *L-10*
CP 8888, Succursale Centre-ville
Montréal, QC, Canada H3C 3P8
Tel: (514)987-3000
Admissions: (514)987-7740
Fax: (514)987-7728
E-mail: admission@uqam.ca
Web Site: http://www.uqam.ca/

Description: Province-supported, university, coed. Part of Universite du Quebec. Awards bachelor's, master's, and doctoral degrees. Founded 1969. Setting: 286-acre urban campus. 42,208 applied. Students come from 10 provinces and territories, 102 other countries. Core. Calendar: trimesters. Services for LD students, accelerated degree program, summer session for credit, part-time degree program, adult/continuing education programs, internships. Off campus study at other units of the Universite du Quebec, other universities in the province of Quebec.

Entrance Requirements: Open admission except for some quota programs. Required: Diploma of Collegiate Studies (and transcript) or equivalent. Required for some: essay, recommendations, interview. Entrance: noncompetitive. Application deadline: 3/1. Notification: 5/15.

Collegiate Environment: Drama-theater group, choral group, student-run newspaper. Social organizations: 40 open to all. Most popular organizations: Centre D'Ecoute et de Reference Halt-Ami, Groupe de Recherche d'Interet, Public du Quebec A LUqam, Club Marketing Uqam, Association des Etudiants Africainses de LUqam. Major annual event: Salon Etudiant de la Rentre. Student services: legal services, health clinic, personal-psychological counseling. Campus security: 24-hour emergency response devices and patrols, late night transport-escort service. College housing not available. Bibliotheque Centrale plus 15 others with 2.3 million books, 10,819 serials, an OPAC, and a Web page. 889 computers available on campus for general student use. A campuswide network can be accessed from off-campus. Staffed computer lab on campus.

■ UNIVERSITÉ DU QUÉBEC EN OUTAOUAIS *L-6*
Case Postale 1250, Succursale Hull
Gatineau, QC, Canada J8X 3X7
Tel: (819)595-3900
Free: 800-567-1283
E-mail: luc.maurice@uqo.ca
Web Site: http://www.uqo.ca/

Description: Province-supported, university, coed. Part of Universite du Quebec. Awards bachelor's, master's, and doctoral degrees. Founded 1981. Setting: small town campus with easy access to Ottawa. Total enrollment: 5,510. Students come from 25 other countries, 0% from out-of province. Retention: 90% of full-time freshmen returned the following year. Core. Calendar: trimesters. Services for LD students, accelerated degree program, summer session for credit, part-time degree program, adult/continuing education programs, internships. Off campus study at other units of the Universite du Quebec, other universities in the province of Quebec. Study abroad program.

Entrance Requirements: Open admission except for some quota programs. Option: international baccalaureate accepted. Required: high school transcript, Diploma of Collegiate Studies (and transcript) or equivalent. Required for some: interview, Diploma of Collegiate Studies (and transcript) or equivalent. Entrance: noncompetitive. Application deadlines: 3/1, 3/1 for nonresidents. Notification: 5/15.

Costs Per Year: Application fee: $30. Tuition: $194.34 per credit part-time. Mandatory fees: $2099 full-time. International student tuition: $10,463 full-time. Area resident tuition: $2099 full-time. Canadian resident tuition: $474.34 per credit part-time. Mandatory fees: $2099 full-time. International student tuition: $10,463 full-time.

Collegiate Environment: Student-run newspaper, radio station. Most popular organizations: AGE, AIESEC, AEME, REMAA. Major annual events: Salon de l'Etudiant, Carnaval Etudiant, Jeux du Commerce. Student services: personal-psychological counseling. Campus security: 24-hour emergency response devices and patrols, late night transport-escort service. 200 college housing spaces available; all were occupied in 2003-04. No special consideration for freshman housing applicants. On-campus residence through senior year. Option: coed housing available. Brault Library plus 1 other with 230,910 books, 25,908 microform titles, 12,351 serials, 11,972 audiovisual materials, an OPAC, and a Web page. 141 computers available on campus for general student use. Computer purchase/lease plans available. A campuswide network can be accessed from off-campus. Staffed computer lab on campus.

■ UNIVERSITÉ DU QUÉBEC ÀRIMOUSKI *E-17*
300, Allee des Ursulines, CP 3300
Rimouski, QC, Canada G5L 3A1
Tel: (418)723-1986
Admissions: (418)724-1432
Fax: (418)724-1525
E-mail: raymond_cote@uqar.uquebec.ca
Web Site: http://www.uqar.qc.ca/

Description: Province-supported, comprehensive, coed. Part of Universite du Quebec. Awards bachelor's, master's, and doctoral degrees. Founded 1973. Setting: small town campus. 2,278 applied, 99% were admitted. Core. Calendar: trimesters. Services for LD students, accelerated degree program,

summer session for credit, part-time degree program, adult/continuing education programs, internships. Off campus study at other units of the Universite du Quebec, other universities in the province of Quebec.

Entrance Requirements: Open admission except for some quota programs. Required: Diploma of Collegiate Studies (and transcript) or equivalent. Required for some: interview. Entrance: noncompetitive. Application deadline: 3/1. Notification: 5/15.

Collegiate Environment: Student-run newspaper, radio station. Student services: legal services, health clinic, personal-psychological counseling. Campus security: 24-hour emergency response devices and patrols, security cameras. Option: coed housing available. 263,142 books and 3,951 serials.

■ UNIVERSITÉ DU QUÉBEC ÀTROIS-RIVIÈRES *J-11*
3351 blvd des Forges, Case post 500
Trois-Rivieres, QC, Canada G9A 5H7
Tel: (819)376-5011
Free: 800-365-0922
Admissions: (819)376-5045
Fax: (819)376-5210
Web Site: http://www.uqtr.ca/

Description: Province-supported, university, coed. Part of Universite du Quebec. Awards bachelor's, master's, and doctoral degrees. Founded 1969. Setting: urban campus with easy access to Montreal. Endowment: $3.3 million. Research spending for 2004 fiscal year: $579,866. Total enrollment: 9,618. Students come from 33 other countries. Core. Calendar: trimesters. Services for LD students, accelerated degree program, summer session for credit, part-time degree program, adult/continuing education programs. Off campus study at other units of the Universite du Quebec, other universities in the province of Quebec.

Entrance Requirements: Open admission except for some quota programs. Required: Diploma of Collegiate Studies (and transcript) or equivalent. Required for some: interview. Entrance: noncompetitive. Application deadline: 3/1. Notification: 6/1.

Collegiate Environment: Drama-theater group, choral group, student-run newspaper, radio station. Student services: health clinic, personal-psychological counseling. Campus security: 24-hour emergency response devices and patrols, late night transport-escort service, controlled dormitory access. Option: coed housing available. Main library plus 1 other with 464,338 books, an OPAC, and a Web page. Operations spending for 2004 fiscal year: $2.2 million. 200 computers available on campus for general student use. A campuswide network can be accessed from student residence rooms and from off campus. Staffed computer lab on campus.

■ UNIVERSITÉ DE SHERBROOKE *L-12*
Sherbrooke, QC, Canada J1K 2R1
Tel: (819)821-8000
Admissions: (819)821-7685
Fax: (819)821-7966
E-mail: information@usherbrooke.ca
Web Site: http://www.usherbrooke.ca/

Description: Independent, university, coed. Awards bachelor's, master's, doctoral, and first professional degrees. Founded 1954. Setting: 800-acre urban campus with easy access to Montreal. Total enrollment: 21,596. Faculty: 2,837 (1,014 full-time, 1,823 part-time). 8,467 applied, 74% were admitted. Full-time: 9,974 students, 55% women, 45% men. Part-time: 3,867 students, 59% women, 41% men. Students come from 3 provinces and territories, 62 other countries, 0% from out-of province. Calendar: Canadian standard year. ESL program, services for LD students, accelerated degree program, self-designed majors, summer session for credit, part-time degree program, adult/continuing education programs, co-op programs and internships, graduate courses open to undergrads. Off campus study at Consortium of Quebec Universities (CREPUQ). Study abroad program.

Entrance Requirements: Options: electronic application, early admission. Required: high school transcript. Required for some: recommendations, interview. Entrance: moderately difficult. Application deadline: 3/1. Notification: continuous until 5/15. Preference given to province residents.

Costs Per Year: Application fee: $50. Comprehensive fee: $8508 includes full-time tuition ($4650), mandatory fees ($362), and college room and board ($3496). College room only: $1760. Part-time tuition: $155.03 per credit. Part-time mandatory fees: $10.74 per credit, $30 per term. International student tuition: $9768 full-time.

Collegiate Environment: Drama-theater group, student-run newspaper, radio station. Social organizations: 20 open to all. Major annual events: homecoming, Winter Carnival. Student services: legal services, health clinic, personal-psychological counseling. Campus security: 24-hour emergency response devices and patrols. Option: coed housing available. Carrefour de l'Information plus 5 others with 1.2 million books, 5,937 serials, an OPAC, and a Web page. 300 computers available on campus for general student use. A campuswide network can be accessed from student residence rooms and from off campus. Staffed computer lab on campus.

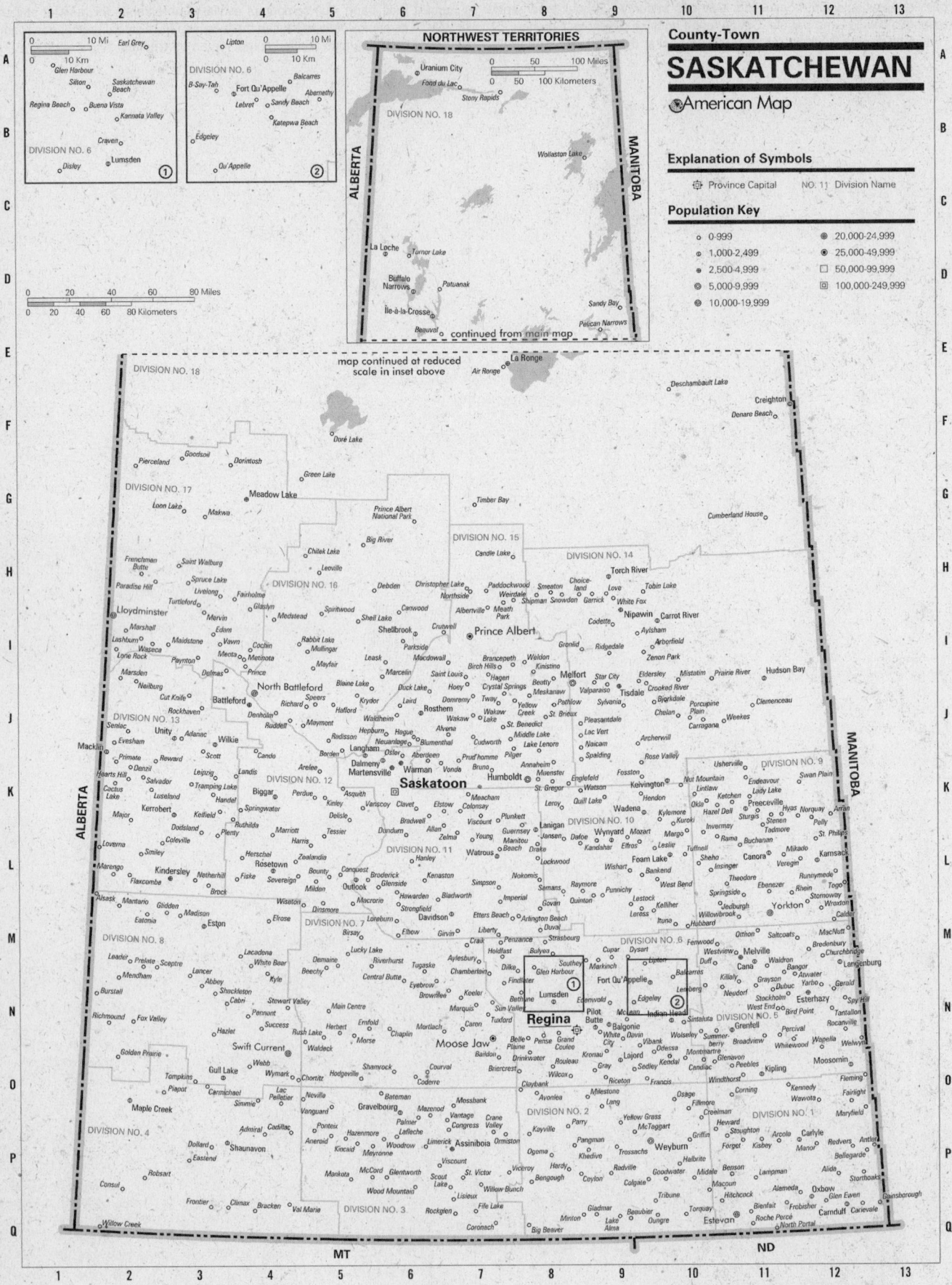

SASKATCHEWAN

County-Town

American Map

Explanation of Symbols

⊕ Province Capital NO. 11 Division Name

Population Key

○ 0-999 ⊛ 20,000-24,999
○ 1,000-2,499 ⊛ 25,000-49,999
○ 2,500-4,999 □ 50,000-99,999
⊙ 5,000-9,999 ⊡ 100,000-249,999
⊛ 10,000-19,999

personal-psychological counseling. Campus security: 24-hour emergency response devices and patrols. Option: coed housing available. Carrefour de l'Information plus 5 others with 1.2 million books, 5,937 serials, an OPAC, and a Web page. 300 computers available on campus for general student use. A campuswide network can be accessed from student residence rooms and from off campus. Staffed computer lab on campus.

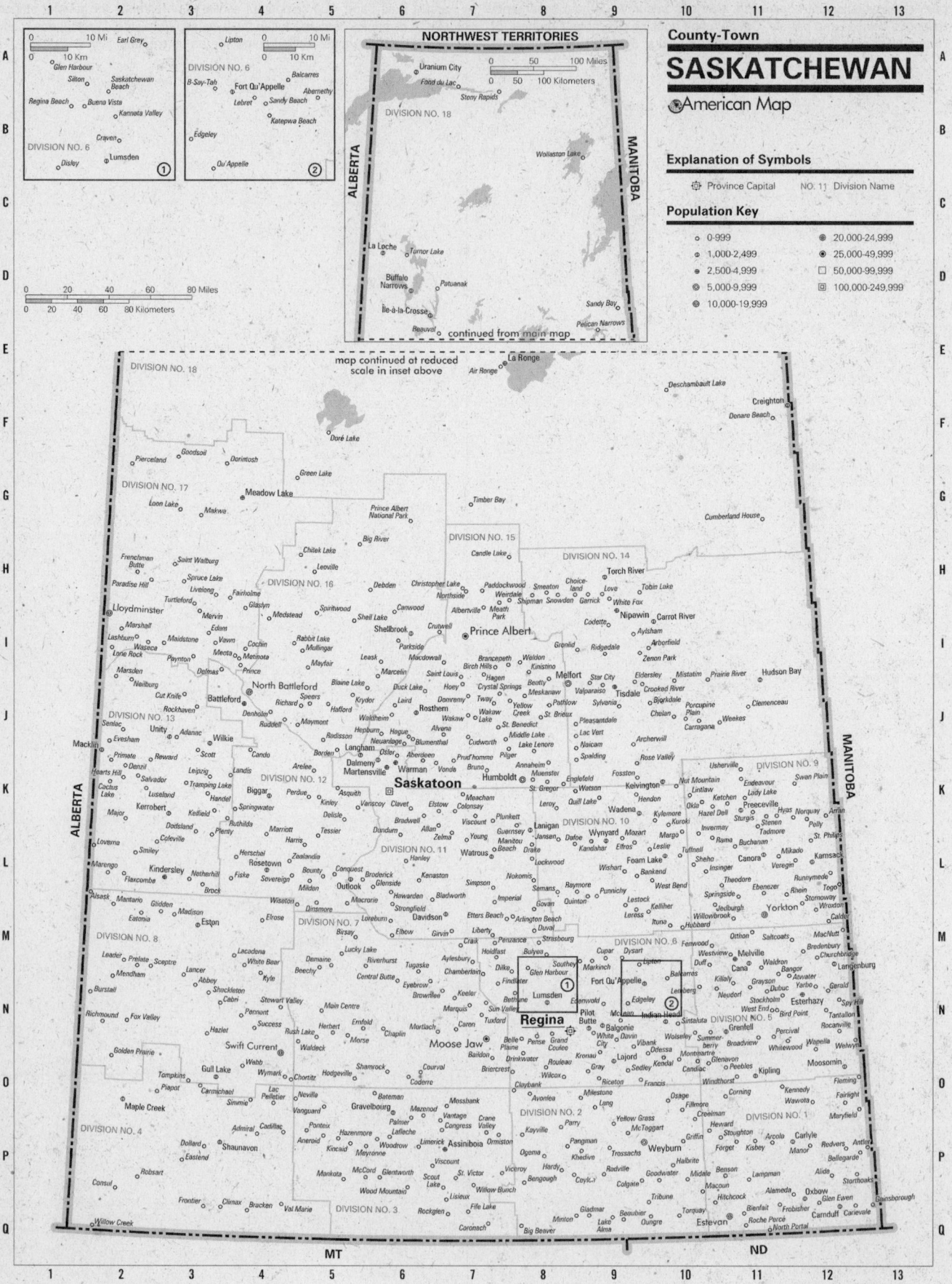

County-Town
SASKATCHEWAN
American Map

Explanation of Symbols

⊕ Province Capital   NO. 11 Division Name

Population Key

○ 0-999	⊛ 20,000-24,999
⊙ 1,000-2,499	⊕ 25,000-49,999
⊚ 2,500-4,999	☐ 50,000-99,999
⊚ 5,000-9,999	⊡ 100,000-249,999
⊚ 10,000-19,999	

■ BRIERCREST COLLEGE
510 College Dr.
Caronport, SK, Canada S0H 0S0
Tel: (306)756-3200
Fax: (306)756-5500
Web Site: http://www.briercrest.ca/
Description: Independent interdenominational, 4-year, coed. Part of Briercrest Family of Schools. Awards associate and bachelor's degrees. Founded 1935. Setting: 300-acre rural campus. Endowment: $950,000. Educational spending for 2005 fiscal year: $7800 per student. Total enrollment: 725. Student-undergrad faculty ratio is 16:1. 573 applied, 59% were admitted. Students come from 11 provinces and territories, 5 other countries, 76% from out-of-province, 14% 25 or older, 75% live on campus. Retention: 69% of full-time freshmen returned the following year. Core. Calendar: semesters. Academic remediation for entering students, accelerated degree program, independent study, distance learning, double major, summer session for credit, part-time degree program, external degree program, adult/continuing education programs, internships. Off campus study at Summit College.
Entrance Requirements: Open admission. Options: Common Application, electronic application, early admission, deferred admission, international baccalaureate accepted. Required: essay, high school transcript, 2 recommendations. Required for some: interview. Entrance: noncompetitive. Application deadline: 8/15. Notification: continuous until 9/1. Preference given to applicants interested in religious studies or ministries.
Costs Per Year: Application fee: $35. Comprehensive fee: $11,886 includes full-time tuition ($7086) and college room and board ($4800). College room only: $2719.
Collegiate Environment: Orientation program. Drama-theater group, choral group, student-run radio station. Social organizations: 20 open to all. Most popular organizations: Student Missions Fellowship, Student Families Association, yearbook committee, Weekend Activities Committee. Major annual events: Global Focus Conference, Christmas Musical, Youth Quake. Student services: legal services, health clinic, personal-psychological counseling. Campus security: 24-hour patrols. 625 college housing spaces available; 536 were occupied in 2003-04. Freshmen guaranteed college housing. On-campus residence required through senior year. Options: men-only, women-only housing available. Archibald Library with 76,000 books, 508,153 microform titles, 350 serials, 5,125 audiovisual materials, an OPAC, and a Web page. Operations spending for 2004 fiscal year: $264,475. 30 computers available on campus for general student use. A campuswide network can be accessed from off-campus. Staffed computer lab on campus.

■ CENTRAL PENTECOSTAL COLLEGE *K-6*
1303 Jackson Ave.
Saskatoon, SK, Canada S7H 2M9
Tel: (306)374-6655
Fax: (306)373-6968
E-mail: admissions@cpc-paoc.edu
Web Site: http://www.cpc-paoc.edu/
Description: Independent, 4-year, coed, affiliated with Pentecostal Assemblies of Canada. Administratively affiliated with University of Saskatchewan. Awards bachelor's degrees. Founded 1930. Setting: 5-acre urban campus. Educational spending for 2005 fiscal year: $4864 per student. Total enrollment: 61. Student-undergrad faculty ratio is 14:1. 24 applied, 96% were admitted. Full-time: 50 students, 48% women, 52% men.

Part-time: 11 students, 45% women, 55% men. Students come from 6 provinces and territories, 42% from out-of-province, 5% Native American, 5% Asian Canadian, 18% 25 or older, 27% live on campus, 2% transferred in. Retention: 85% of full-time freshmen returned the following year. Core. Calendar: semesters. Academic remediation for entering students, self-designed majors, independent study, distance learning, part-time degree program, internships. Study abroad program.
Entrance Requirements: Options: Common Application, electronic application, deferred admission, international baccalaureate accepted. Required: essay, high school transcript, 3 recommendations. Required for some: interview. Entrance: minimally difficult. Application deadline: 9/15.
Costs Per Year: Application fee: $45 Canadian dollars. Tuition, fee, and room and board charges are reported in Canadian dollars. Comprehensive fee: $9279 includes full-time tuition ($4864), mandatory fees ($415), and college room and board ($4000). Part-time tuition: $152 per credit hour.
Collegiate Environment: Orientation program. Drama-theater group, choral group. Major annual events: Christmas Banquet, Graduation Exercises, Graduation Banquet. Student services: personal-psychological counseling. Campus security: 24-hour emergency response devices, late night transport-escort service. 72 college housing spaces available; 28 were occupied in 2003-04. Freshmen guaranteed college housing. A. C. Schindel Library with 18,204 books, 5,892 microform titles, 4,161 serials, 362 audiovisual materials, an OPAC, and a Web page. Operations spending for 2004 fiscal year: $20,221. 30 computers available on campus for general student use. Computer purchase/lease plans available. A campuswide network can be accessed from student residence rooms and from off campus. Staffed computer lab on campus.

■ COLLEGE OF EMMANUEL AND ST. CHAD *K-6*
1337 College Dr.
Saskatoon, SK, Canada S7N 0W6
Tel: (306)975-3753
Admissions: (306)975-1558
Fax: (306)934-2683
Web Site: http://www.usask.ca/stu/emmanuel/
Description: Independent Episcopal, comprehensive, coed. Awards bachelor's and master's degrees. Founded 1879. Setting: urban campus. Endowment: $2.2 million. Educational spending for 2005 fiscal year: $4750 per student. Total enrollment: 23. Faculty: 3 (all full-time). Student-undergrad faculty ratio is 8:1. Students come from 4 provinces and territories, 4% from out-of-province, 100% 25 or older. Retention: 100% of full-time freshmen returned the following year. Academic area with the most degrees conferred: theology and religious vocations. Core. Calendar: Canadian standard year. Academic remediation for entering students, services for LD students, distance learning, summer session for credit, part-time degree program, adult/continuing education programs, co-op programs and internships, graduate courses open to undergrads. Off campus study at 3 members of the Saskatoon Theological Union.
Entrance Requirements: Open admission. Required: essay, high school transcript, 3 recommendations, interview. Entrance: noncompetitive. Application deadline: 6/30. Notification: 8/1. Preference given to Anglicans.
Costs Per Year: Application fee: $50. Tuition: $4750 full-time, $475 per course part-time. Mandatory fees: $515 full-time. Full-time tuition and fees vary according to course level and course load. Part-time tuition varies according to course level and course load.

Collegiate Environment: Orientation program. Major annual events: Color Night, Spring Festival. Campus security: 24-hour emergency response devices and patrols, late night transport-escort service. H. E. Sellers Library plus 11 others with 15,000 books and 93 serials. Operations spending for 2004 fiscal year: $15,797. 1 computer on campus for general student use.

■ UNIVERSITY OF REGINA *N-8*

3737 Wascana Parkway
Regina, SK, Canada S4S 0A2
Tel: (306)585-4111
Free: 800-664-4756
Admissions: (306)585-5166
Fax: (306)585-5203
E-mail: admissions.office@uregina.ca
Web Site: http://www.uregina.ca/

Description: Province-supported, university, coed. Awards bachelor's, master's, and doctoral degrees. Founded 1974. Setting: 930-hectare urban campus. Endowment: $20 million. Research spending for 2004 fiscal year: $12.5 million. Total enrollment: 12,670. Faculty: 425 (424 full-time, 1 part-time). Student-undergrad faculty ratio is 22:1. 1,663 applied, 91% were admitted. Full-time: 7,232 students, 61% women, 39% men. Part-time: 4,041 students, 62% women, 38% men. Students come from 11 provinces and territories, 76 other countries, 5% from out-of province, 30% 25 or older, 7% transferred in. Academic areas with the most degrees conferred: education; business/marketing; security and protective services. Calendar: semesters. Academic remediation for entering students, ESL program, services for LD students, advanced placement, self-designed majors, honors program, distance learning, double major, summer session for credit, part-time degree program, adult/continuing education programs, co-op programs and internships, graduate courses open to undergrads. Off campus study at Athol Murray College of Notre Dame, Gabriel Dumont Institute of Native Studies and Applied Research, Western Christian College, Canadian Theological Seminary, Canadian Bible College, Laval University. Study abroad program.

Entrance Requirements: Options: early admission, early action, deferred admission, international baccalaureate accepted. Required: high school transcript, minimum 2.3 high school GPA. Required for some: essay, recommendations, interview, SAT or ACT. Entrance: minimally difficult. Application deadlines: 7/1, 6/15 for early action. Preference given to province residents.

Costs Per Year: Application fee: $60 Canadian dollars. Tuition, fee, and room and board charges are reported in Canadian dollars. Province resident tuition: $136 per credit hour part-time. Canadian resident tuition: $4551 full-time, $136 per credit hour part-time. Mandatory fees: $412 full-time, $92 per term part-time. Full-time tuition and fees vary according to course load and program. Part-time tuition and fees vary according to course load and program. College room and board: $5767. College room only: $3960. Room and board charges vary according to board plan and housing facility. International student tuition: $8627 full-time.

Collegiate Environment: Orientation program. Drama-theater group, choral group, student-run newspaper. Social organizations: 35 open to all. Most popular organizations: Administration Students' Society, Education Students' Society, Engineering Students Society, Chinese Students and Scholars Association, Luther Student Association. Major annual events: May Convocation, October Convocation, Welcome Week. Student services: health clinic, personal-psychological counseling, women's center. Campus security: 24-hour emergency response devices and patrols, student patrols, late night transport-escort service, controlled dormitory access. 1,125 college housing spaces available; 644 were occupied in 2003-04. No special consideration for freshman housing applicants. Option: coed housing available. Dr. John Archer Library plus 3 others with 1.5 million books, 1.2 million microform titles, 10,772 serials, 39,791 audiovisual materials, an OPAC, and a Web page. Operations spending for 2004 fiscal year: $6.2 million. 300 computers available on campus for general student use. A campuswide network can be accessed from student residence rooms and from off campus. Staffed computer lab on campus.

Community Environment: Regina, population 185,000 is the capital city of Saskatchewan. Serving as a business and industrial center of the mainly agricultural province, Regina offers a wide range of cultural activities.

■ UNIVERSITY OF SASKATCHEWAN *K-6*

105 Administration Place
Saskatoon, SK, Canada S7N 5A2
Tel: (306)966-4343
Fax: (306)966-7026
Web Site: http://www.usask.ca/

Description: Province-supported, university, coed. Awards bachelor's, master's, and doctoral degrees. Founded 1907. Setting: 363-acre urban campus. Total enrollment: 19,639. 6,865 applied, 81% were admitted. Students come from 13 provinces and territories, 75 other countries, 0% from out-of province. Academic areas with the most degrees conferred: visual and performing arts; health professions and related sciences; education. Calendar: Canadian standard year. Academic remediation for entering students, ESL program, services for LD students, advanced placement, accelerated degree program, honors program, independent study, distance learning, double major, summer session for credit, part-time degree program, adult/continuing education programs, co-op programs and internships. Off campus study at Regional Colleges, SIAST Campuses. Study abroad program.

Entrance Requirements: Options: electronic application, early admission, early action, international baccalaureate accepted. Required: high school transcript. Required for some: essay, 3 recommendations, interview. Entrance: moderately difficult. Application deadline: 5/1. Notification: continuous. Preference given to province residents.

Costs Per Year: Application fee: $75 Canadian dollars. Tuition, fee, and room and board charges are reported in Canadian dollars. Area resident tuition: $4560 full-time, $152 per credit part-time. Province resident tuition: $395 per credit part-time. Mandatory fees: $448 full-time, $114 per year part-time. Full-time tuition and fees vary according to course load, degree level, location, and program. Part-time tuition and fees vary according to course load, degree level, location, and program. College room and board: $4894. College room only: $2226. Room and board charges vary according to board plan, housing facility, and location. International student tuition: $11,850 full-time.

Collegiate Environment: Orientation program. Drama-theater group, choral group, student-run newspaper, radio station. Most popular organizations: Ballroom Dancing Club, Ski Club, AIESEC. Major annual events: Welcome Week, December 6th Candlelight Vigil, Miracle Dance. Student services: health clinic, personal-psychological counseling, women's center. Campus security: 24-hour emergency response devices and patrols, late night transport-escort service. 2,070 college housing spaces available. No special consideration for freshman housing applicants. Options: coed, men-only, women-only housing available. University of Saskatchewan Main Library plus 7 others with 1.8 million books, 16,900 serials, an OPAC, and a Web page. 900 computers available on campus for general student use. A campuswide network can be accessed from off-campus. Staffed computer lab on campus.

Community Environment: Saskatoon (population 215,000), on the banks of the South Saskatchewan River, is known as the City of Bridges with its riverfront and many parks. It is the home of the Western Development Museum featuring Boomtown 1910, museums of Ukrainian arts and culture, the Mendel Art Gallery (Canadian, European, and Eskimo art), the Forestry Farm Park, and Saskatchewan Place (local and international sports, entertainment, and cultural events.)